Chilton's auto repair manual 1974

american cars
from 1967 to 1974

General Manager William D. Byrne
Editor-In-Chief John D. Kelly
Managing Editor John H. Weise, S.A.E.
Assistant Managing Editor Peter J. Meyer
Technical Editors Robert J. Brown
Phillip A. Canal
Stephen J. Davis
Kerry A. Freeman
David P. Gallucio
William J. Jones
John M. McGuigan
Ronald L. Sessions
N. Banks Spence Jr
William J. Wartman
Editor Paul J. Driscoll Jr.
Production Manager Warren Owens
Editorial Production Edna H. Jones, *Manager*
Carole L. DeCrescenzo
Byron P. Collins

CHILTON BOOK COMPANY Radnor, Pennsylvania

Published in Radnor by Chilton Book Company
Chilton Way, Radnor, Pa. 19089 215-687-8200
ISBN: 0-8019-5874-1 Library of Congress Catalog Card No. 54-17274

contents

Unit Repair Section

Although information in this manual is based on industry sources and is as complete as possible at the time of publication, the possibility exists that some car manufacturers made later changes which could not be included here. While striving for total accuracy, Chilton Book Company can not assume responsibility for any errors, changes, or omissions that may occur in the compilation of this data.

Car Section

Unit Repair Section

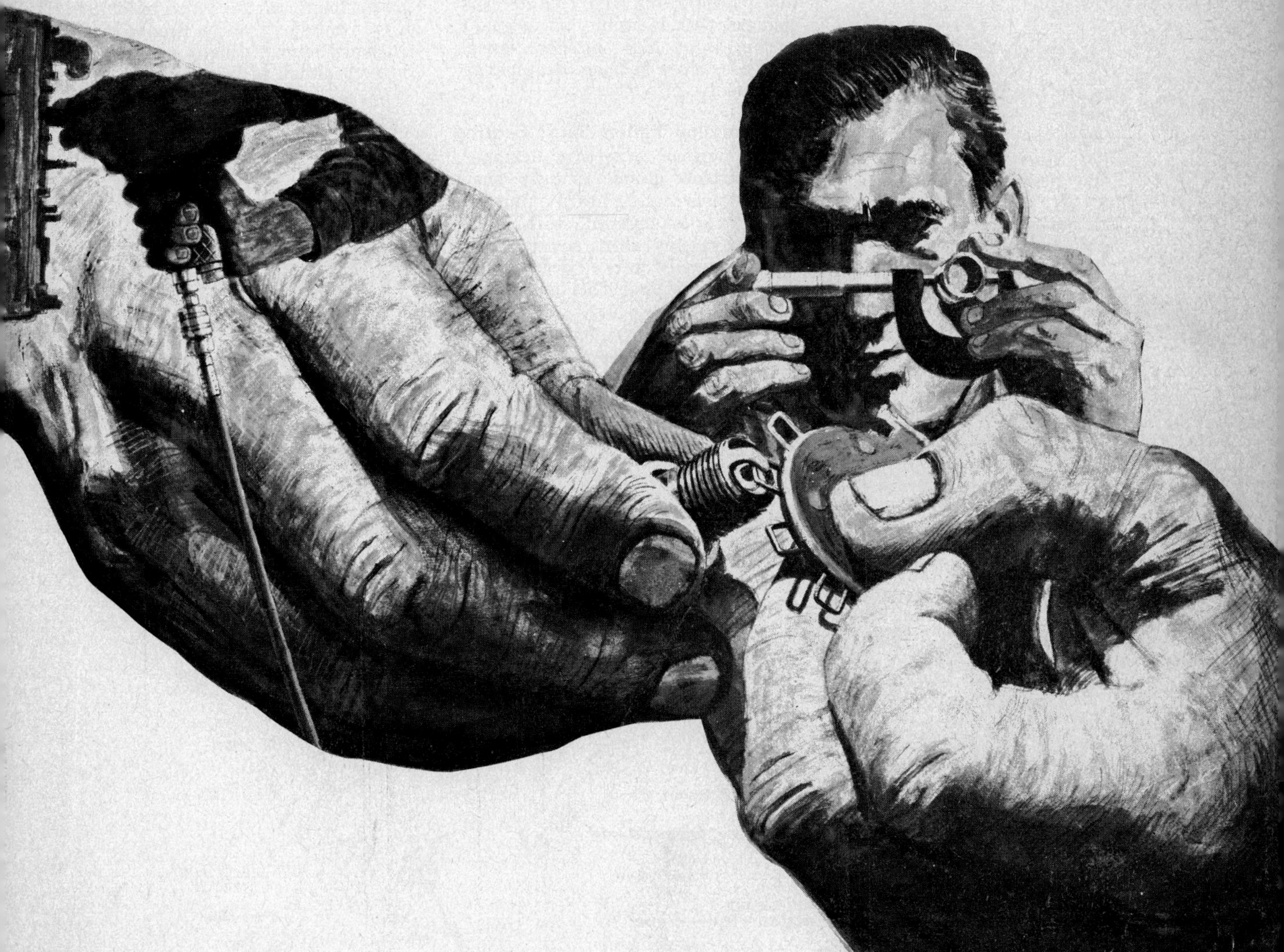

Clutch Problems

Problems and Solutions

When diagnosing problems in any area, there is no substitute for careful examination and experience. The following are some symptoms that may accompany clutch troubles.

1. Excessive noise.
2. Clutch chatter or grab.
3. Clutch slip.
4. Clutch drag or failure to release.
5. Pedal pulsation.
6. Low clutch facing life.
7. Gear lock up or hard shifting.
8. Hard pedal.

Excessive Noise

There are five common sources of clutch noise:

1. Release bearing.
2. Clutch shaft pilot bearing.
3. Transmission pinion shaft bearing.
4. Transmitted engine noises.
5. Clutch linkage noises.

Release Bearing

Release bearing noises vary with the degree of bearing failure. A dry or damaged bearing usually makes a shrill or scraping sound when depressing the clutch pedal to the point of release finger-to-bearing contact. This means that the noise should be audible at the lower end of clutch pedal free-play. Continued use of a car, with the release bearing in this condition, is damaging to the clutch release fingers.

Usual cause of release bearing failure is overwork—caused by riding the clutch. Other causes are not enough pedal free-play, lack of lubricant in the bearing, clutch release fingers worn or out of true.

Pilot Bearing

Clutch shaft pilot bearing noises can be heard only when the bearing is in operation. This is at any time crankshaft speed is different from that of the clutch shaft, (clutch disengaged with transmission in gear).

This is a high pitched squeal, caused by a dry bearing. Requires replacement.

Transmission Pinion Shaft Bearing

A rough, or otherwise damaged, transmission pinion (input) shaft bearing noise can be heard only when the clutch is engaged, with transmission in any shift position. The noise is usually quite noticeable with the gears in neutral. This noise should diminish and completely disappear as the transmission pinion gear slows down and stops after clutch release. This noise is easily distinguished from release bearing noise because of the opposite conditions of encounter.

Transmitted Engine Noises

Assuming that the clutch pedal has the required amount of free-play, there should be no objectionable amount of engine noise transmitted to the passenger area via the clutch. Some engine noises are transmitted through the positive pressure of the clutch release bearing and fingers to the clutch housing. Here they are amplified by the shape of the clutch housing and heard in the passenger compartment in the guise of clutch or transmission trouble. Engine noise transmission can usually be modified through clutch pedal manipulation.

Clutch Linkage Noise

Clutch linkage noise is usually a clicking or snapping sound that can be heard or felt in the pedal itself when moving it completely up or down. Locating the cause of trouble and correcting it is a matter of repositioning and lubrication. The trouble may be in the clutch assist spring, the retract spring, the release bearing lever, or even at the release bearing.

Clutch Chatter or Grab

Usually the cause of clutch chatter or grab can be located within the

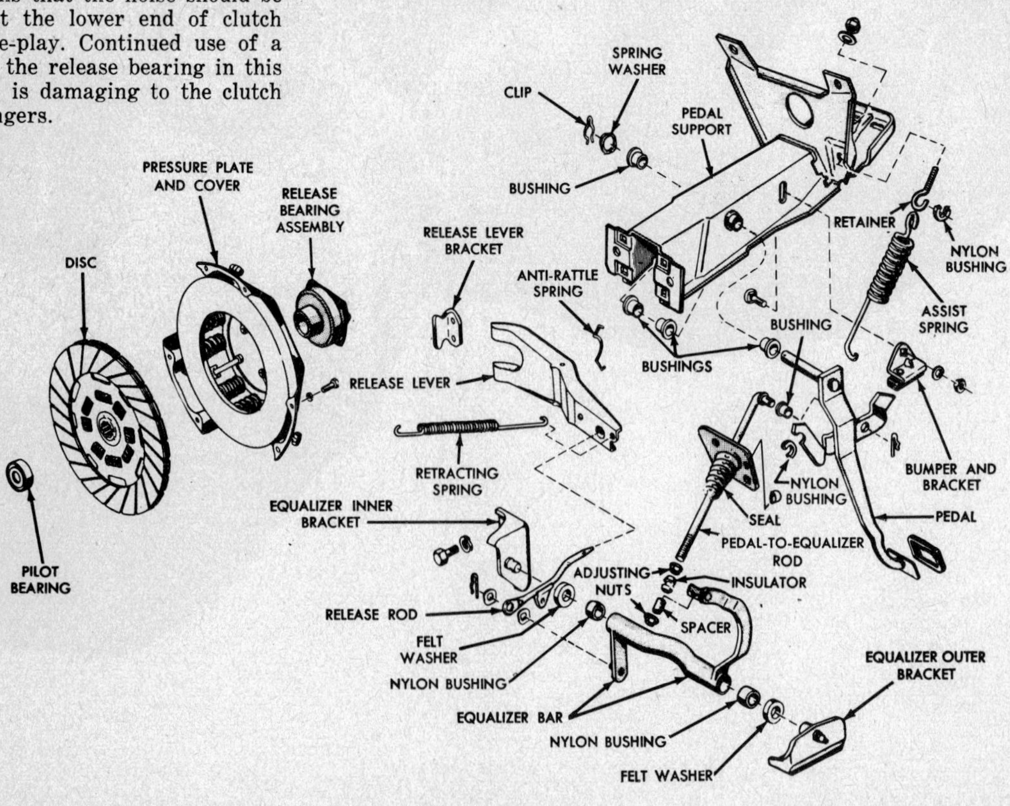

SPRING WASHER
CLIP
PEDAL SUPPORT
BUSHING
RETAINER
NYLON BUSHING
PRESSURE PLATE AND COVER
RELEASE BEARING ASSEMBLY
RELEASE LEVER BRACKET
ANTI-RATTLE SPRING
DISC
ASSIST SPRING
BUSHING
BUSHINGS
RELEASE LEVER
BUMPER AND BRACKET
RETRACTING SPRING
NYLON BUSHING
EQUALIZER INNER BRACKET
SEAL
PEDAL
PEDAL-TO-EQUALIZER ROD
PILOT BEARING
ADJUSTING NUTS
INSULATOR
RELEASE ROD
SPACER
FELT WASHER
EQUALIZER OUTER BRACKET
NYLON BUSHING
EQUALIZER BAR
NYLON BUSHING
FELT WASHER

Typical clutch linkage (© Ford Motor Co)

clutch assembly. To correct the trouble will require the removal of the clutch. However, symptoms resembling clutch trouble may be misleading and originate in other areas.

In order to isolate the cause of the problem, we suggest that the following items be checked in this order.

1. Be sure that the clutch linkage is in adjustment and not binding. If necessary, lubricate, align and adjust linkage.
2. Check for worn or loose engine or transmission mounts. If necessary, tighten or replace mounts.
3. Check for wear, looseness or misalignment of universal joints. Check attaching bolts on clutch pressure plate, transmission and clutch housing. Tighten, align or replace as necessary.
4. Check freedom of movement of the clutch release bearing on its sleeve. Free up or replace as necessary.
5. Check for oil or grease on the flywheel, friction disc or pressure plate.
6. Check for trueness of the friction disc, and that the disc hub is not binding on the splines of the transmission input shaft (clutch shaft).
7. Be sure that the disc or the pressure plate is not broken.
8. Examine clutch pressure plate and cover plate assembly for cracks or heat discoloration.
9. Check pressure plate and flywheel for warpage.

Clutch Slip

Clutch slippage is usually most noticeable when pulling away, and during acceleration from a standing start. A severe, but positive, test for slippage is to start the engine, set the parking brake and apply the service brakes; shift the transmission into high gear and release the clutch pedal while accelerating the engine. A clutch in good condition should hold and stall the engine. If the clutch slips, the cause may be one or more of the following:

1. Improper linkage adjustment (not enough free-play).
2. Broken or disconnected parts.
3. Clutch linkage or lever mechanism binding or broken, not allowing full pressure plate application.
4. Friction disc oil-saturated or excessively worn.
5. Pressure plate worn, springs weak from temper loss or failure (damaging heat will usually cause parts to appear blue).
6. Clutch plate not seated (after installation of a new plate).

Clutch Drag or Failure to Release

There are many reasons for clutch drag (spin) or failure to release. The following conditions, therefore, apply to unmodified versions of standard vehicles. Changing the driven plate mass (replacing the standard driven plate with a heavy duty unit), changing transmission oil viscosity, etc. may influence clutch spin-time. Three seconds is a good, typical, spin-time for the standard transmission and clutch, driven under normal conditions, in average temperate zone climates.

The friction disc and some of the transmission gears spin briefly after clutch disengagement, so normal clutch action should not be confused with a dragging clutch.

Clutch drag, failure to release or abnormal spin-time may be caused by one or more of the following:

1. Improper clutch linkage adjustment or release fork off pivot.
2. Clutch plate hub binding on the transmission input (pinion) shaft.
3. A warped or bent friction disc or pressure plate; or loose friction material on the driven disc.
4. The transmission input shaft may be binding or sticking in the pilot bearing.
5. Misalignment of transmission to the engine.
6. Transmission lubricant low or not heavy enough.

Pedal Pulsation

This condition can be felt by applying light foot pressure to the clutch pedal with the engine idling. It may be caused by any of the following:

1. Bent or uneven clutch release finger adjustment.
2. Excessive flywheel runout due to, bent wheel or crankshaft flange; or the flywheel may not be properly seated on the crankshaft flange.
3. Release bearing cocked on transmission bearing retainer.
4. Poor alignment of transmission with the engine.

Low Clutch Facing Life

This sort of complaint warrants a close study of the operator's driving habits. Poor clutch facing wear may be caused by any of the following:

1. Riding the clutch.
2. Drag strip type operation.
3. Continuous overloading, or the hauling of heavy trailers or other equipment.
4. Holding the car from drifting backward on a grade; by slipping the clutch instead of using the brakes.
5. Improper pedal linkage adjustment (free-play and pedal height).
6. Rough surface on flywheel or pressure plate.
7. Presence of oil or water on clutch facing.
8. Weak pressure plate springs, causing clutch creep or slip.

Gear Lock Up or Hard Shifting

This trouble is so closely related to Clutch Drag Or Failure To Release that diagnosis should be conducted in the same way as given under that heading. If, after checking the items listed and finding that the transmission still locks up or is hard to shift, the trouble probably lies in the transmission cover or shifter assembly, or in the transmission proper. In that case, transmission work is needed.

Hard Pedal

A stiff clutch pedal or a clutch release that requires abnormal pedal pressure may result from one or more of the following:

1. Dry and binding clutch linkage and levers.
2. Linkage out of alignment.
3. Improper (heavy) retracting spring.
4. Dry or binding release bearing sleeve or transmission bearing retainer.
5. Assist spring missing or improperly adjusted.
6. Wrong type clutch assembly (heavy duty) being used.

INDEX

Manual Transmissions

Make	Model	TYPE 3-spd	TYPE 4-spd
American Motors	1967-70 199-232 Six; 1971 232 Six	19	
	1967 287, 290 1967 Six HD 1968-72 232, 258, 290	18	
	304, 360	16	
	1967-69 290, 343 1968-70 390 1970-74 360; 1971-74 401		20
Apollo	1973-74	11	
Barracuda	1967-74		4
	1967-74 Six	3	
	1967-69	2	
	1970-74	1	
Buick	1970-71 LeSabre	6	
	1971 Centurion	6	
	1967-70 Wildcat	6	
	1967-68 LeSabre	11	
Buick Special	1967-74 1970-71 GS	11 10	 12
	1967-69	6	12
	1972-74 GS	11	12
Camaro	1967-74	11	12, 13
	1969-74	10	
	1967-68	17	
Challenger	1970-74 Six	3	
	1970-73	1	4
Chevelle	1967-74	11	12, 13
	1969-74	10	
	1967-68	17	
Chevrolet	1969-74	10, 11	
	1967-69		12, 13
	1967 396, 1968 427	17	
Chevy II, Nova	1969-72 1967-74	10 11	 12, 13
	1968	17	

Make	Model	TYPE 3-spd	TYPE 4-spd
Chrysler	1970-74	1	
	1967-69	2	
	1967		4
Comet	1967-70 V8		9
	1967, 1971-74	6	
Corvette	1967-74		12, 13
	1967-69	11	
Cougar	1967-74	6	9
Dart	1970-74	1	
	1967-74 Six	3	
	1967-74 V8		4
	1967-69	2	
Dodge	1970-74	1	
	1967-74 V8		4
	1967-74 Six	3	
	1967-69	2	
Fairlane	1967-74 V8		9
	1967-74 All	6	
Falcon	1967-70 All	6	
	1967-70 V8		10
	1967 Six	5	
Firebird	1970-74 HD	10	12
	1967-74	11	13
	1967-69 HD	6	
	1967 V8	17	
Ford	1967-71	6	
Maverick	1970-74	6	
Mercury	1967-71	6	12
Monte Carlo	1970-71		12
	1971-74	10	
Montego	1968-74	6	9
Mustang	1967-74		9, 21
	1967-74	6	
Oldsmobile Exc. 98 and Toronado	1967-71	6	

Type Numbers Refer to Sections in Text

Make	Model	TYPE 3-spd	4-spd
Oldsmobile	1970-71 4-4-2, F-85HD	10, 6	12
Omega	1973-74	11	
F-85	1967-73, 4-4-2 1972	11	12
Pinto	1971-74		7, 8
Plymouth	1970-74	1	
	1967-74		4
	1967-74 Six	3	
	1967-69	2	
Pontiac	1970-71 GP	10	
	1968-71 GP		13
	1967-74	6	

Make	Model	TYPE 3-spd	4-spd
Tempest	1970-74	10	12
	1967-74	11	13
	1967-69 HD	6	12
Torino	1971-74	6	9
Valiant	1970-72	1	
	1967-72		4
	1967-72 Six	3	
Vega	1971-72	14	15
	1973-74	11	13
Ventura II	1971-74	11	

Section Page Numbers

①1973 Vega 3-Speed see "Saginaw Fully Synchronized 3-Speed"
②1973 Vega 4-Speed see "Saginaw 4-Speed"

Manual Transmissions

Diagnosis

Jumping out of High Gear

1. Misalignment of transmission case or clutch housing.
2. Worn pilot bearing in crankshaft.
3. Bent transmission shaft.
4. Worn high speed sliding gear.
5. Worn teeth in clutch shaft.
6. Insufficient spring tension on shifter rail plunger.
7. Bent or loose shifter fork.
8. End-play in clutch shaft.
9. Gears not engaging completely.
10. Loose or worn bearings on clutch shaft or mainshaft.

Sticking in High Gear

1. Clutch not releasing fully.
2. Burred or battered teeth on clutch shaft.
3. Burred or battered transmission main-shaft.
4. Frozen synchronizing clutch.
5. Stuck shifter rail plunger.
6. Gearshift lever twisting and binding shifter rail.
7. Battered teeth on high speed sliding gear or on sleeve.
8. Lack of lubrication.
9. Improper lubrication.
10. Corroded transmission parts.
11. Defective mainshaft pilot bearing.

Jumping out of Second Gear

1. Insufficient spring tension on shifter rail plunger.
2. Bent or loose shifter fork.
3. Gears not engaging completely.
4. End-play in transmission mainshaft.
5. Loose transmission gear bearing.
6. Defective mainshaft pilot bearing.
7. Bent transmission shaft.
8. Worn teeth on second speed sliding gear or sleeve.
9. Loose or worn bearings on transmission mainshaft.
10. End-play in countershaft.

Sticking in Second Gear

1. Clutch not releasing fully.
2. Burred or battered teeth on sliding sleeve.
3. Burred or battered transmission main-shaft.
4. Frozen synchronizing clutch.
5. Stuck shifter rail plunger.
6. Gearshift lever twisting and binding shifter rail.
7. Lack of lubrication.
8. Second speed transmission gear bearings locked will give same effect as gears stuck in second.
9. Improper lubrication.
10. Corroded transmission parts.

Jumping out of Low Gear

1. Gears not engaging completely.
2. Bent or loose shifter fork.
3. End-play in transmission mainshaft.
4. End-play in countershaft.
5. Loose or worn bearings on transmission mainshaft.
6. Loose or worn bearings in countershaft.
7. Defective mainshaft pilot bearing.

Sticking in Low Gear

1. Clutch not releasing fully.
2. Burred or battered transmission main-shaft.
3. Stuck shifter rail plunger.
4. Gearshift lever twisting and binding shifter rail.
5. Lack of lubrication.
6. Improper lubrication.
7. Corroded transmission parts.

Jumping out of Reverse Gear

1. Insufficient spring tension on shifter rail plunger.
2. Bent or loose shifter fork.
3. Badly worn gear teeth.
4. Gears not engaging completely.
5. End-play in transmission mainshaft.
6. Idler gear bushings loose or worn.
7. Loose or worn bearings on transmission mainshaft.
8. Defective mainshaft pilot bearing.

Sticking in Reverse Gear

1. Clutch not releasing fully.
2. Burred or battered transmission main-shaft.
3. Stuck shifter rail plunger.
4. Gearshift lever twisting and binding shifter rail.
5. Lack of lubrication.
6. Improper lubrication.
7. Corroded transmission parts.

Failure of Gears to Synchronize

1. Binding pilot bearing on mainshaft, will synchronize in high gear only.
2. Clutch not releasing fully.
3. Detent springs weak or broken.
4. Weak or broken springs under balls in sliding gear sleeve.
5. Binding bearing on clutch shaft.
6. Binding countershaft.
7. Binding pilot bearing in crankshaft.
8. Badly worn gear teeth.
9. Scored or worn cones.
10. Improper lubrication.
11. Constant mesh gear not turning freely on transmission mainshaft. Will synchronize in that gear only.

Gears Spinning When Shifting into Gear from Neutral

1. Clutch not releasing fully.
2. In some cases an extremely light lubricant in transmission will cause gears to continue to spin for a short time after clutch is released.
3. Binding pilot bearing in crankshaft.

Caution Many manual transmissions produced after 1970 are equipped with transmission-controlled spark (TCS or TRS) switch. Do not remove the switch from the transmission unless it is being replaced.

Type-1 A-230 Fully Synchronized Chrysler 3-Speed

Application

Barracuda, 1970-73
Challenger, 1970-73
Charger, 1970-73
Chrysler, 1970-74
Dart, 1970-74
Dodge, 1970-74
Plymouth, 1970-74
Valiant, 1970-74

Disassembly

Shift Housing and Mechanism

1. Shift to second gear.
2. Unbolt and remove side cover with shift mechanism.

If shaft O-ring seals need replacement:

3. Pull shift forks out of shafts.
4. Remove nuts and operating levers from shafts.
5. Deburr shafts. Remove shafts.

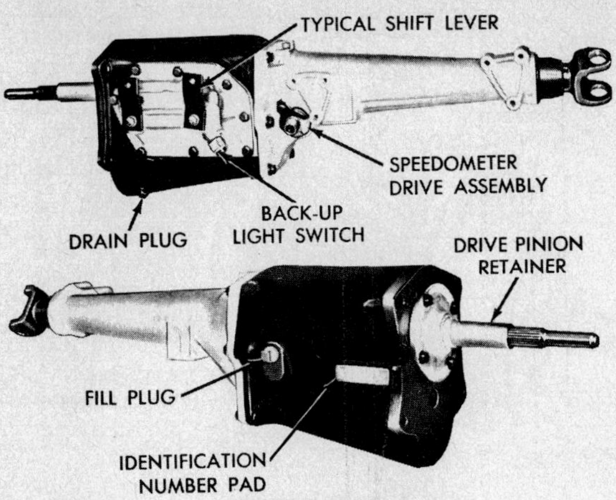
TYPICAL SHIFT LEVER
SPEEDOMETER
DRIVE ASSEMBLY
BACK-UP
LIGHT SWITCH
DRAIN PLUG
DRIVE PINION
RETAINER
FILL PLUG
IDENTIFICATION
NUMBER PAD

Side views of A-230 transmission
(© Chrysler Corp)

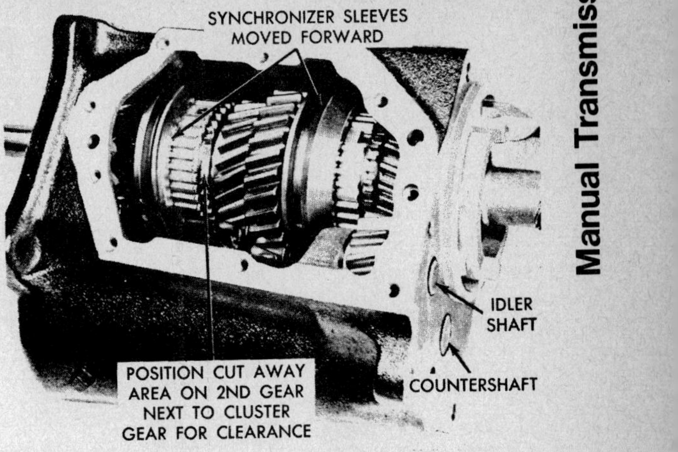
SYNCHRONIZER SLEEVES
MOVED FORWARD
IDLER
SHAFT
COUNTERSHAFT
POSITION CUT AWAY
AREA ON 2ND GEAR
NEXT TO CLUSTER
GEAR FOR CLEARANCE

Positioning second gear and shift sleeves for clearance
(© Chrysler Corp)

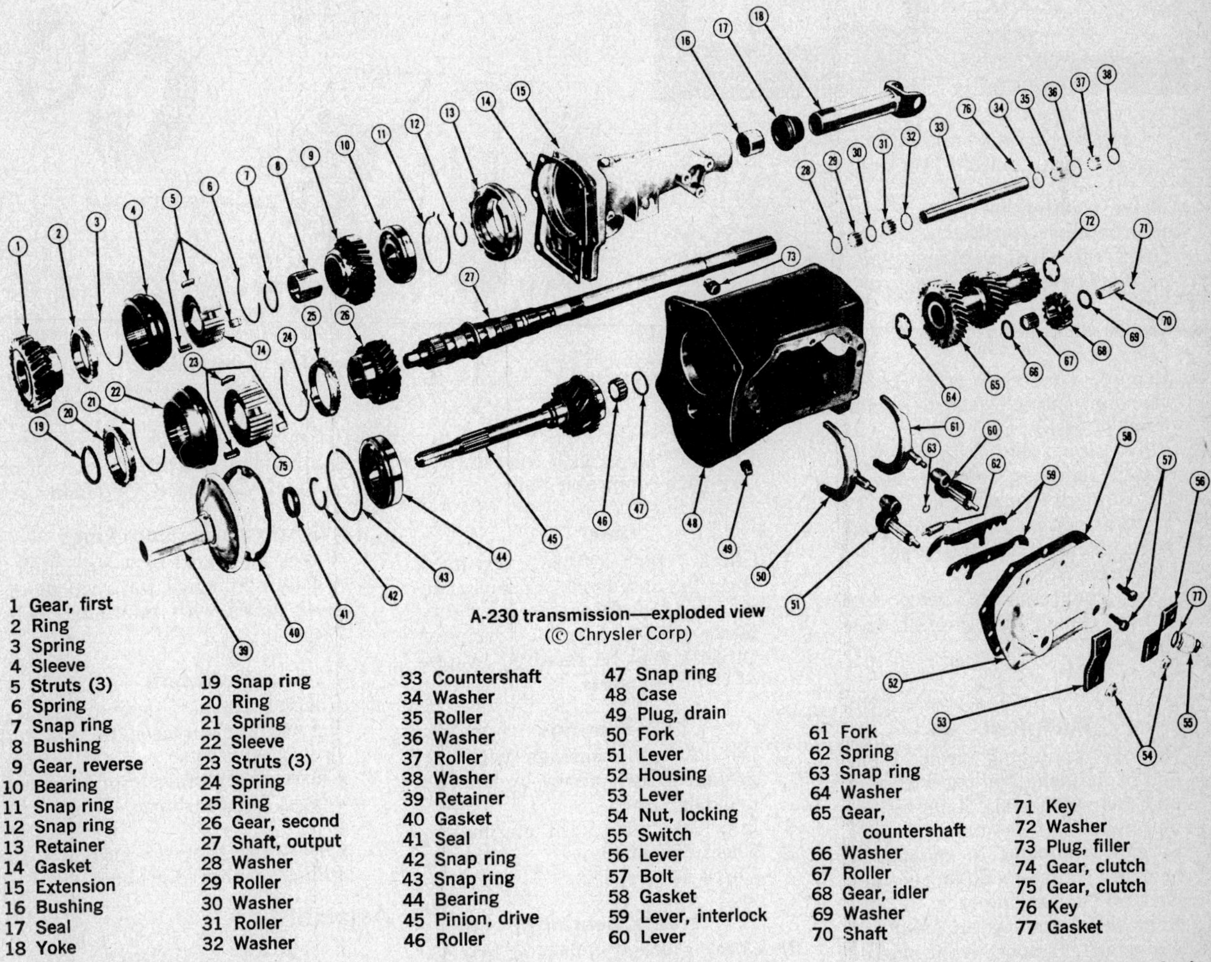

A-230 transmission—exploded view
(© Chrysler Corp)

1 Gear, first
2 Ring
3 Spring
4 Sleeve
5 Struts (3)
6 Spring
7 Snap ring
8 Bushing
9 Gear, reverse
10 Bearing
11 Snap ring
12 Snap ring
13 Retainer
14 Gasket
15 Extension
16 Bushing
17 Seal
18 Yoke
19 Snap ring
20 Ring
21 Spring
22 Sleeve
23 Struts (3)
24 Spring
25 Ring
26 Gear, second
27 Shaft, output
28 Washer
29 Roller
30 Washer
31 Roller
32 Washer
33 Countershaft
34 Washer
35 Roller
36 Washer
37 Roller
38 Washer
39 Retainer
40 Gasket
41 Seal
42 Snap ring
43 Snap ring
44 Bearing
45 Pinion, drive
46 Roller
47 Snap ring
48 Case
49 Plug, drain
50 Fork
51 Lever
52 Housing
53 Lever
54 Nut, locking
55 Switch
56 Lever
57 Bolt
58 Gasket
59 Lever, interlock
60 Lever
61 Fork
62 Spring
63 Snap ring
64 Washer
65 Gear, countershaft
66 Washer
67 Roller
68 Gear, idler
69 Washer
70 Shaft
71 Key
72 Washer
73 Plug, filler
74 Gear, clutch
75 Gear, clutch
76 Key
77 Gasket

Drive Pinion Retainer and Extension Housing

1. Unbolt pinion bearing retainer from front of transmission case. Remove retainer and gasket. Pry off retainer oil seal.

For clearance:

2. With a brass drift, tap drive pinion as far forward as possible. Rotate cut away part of second gear next to countershaft gear. Shift second-third synchronizer sleeve forward.
3. Remove speedometer pinion adapter retainer. Work adapter and pinion out of extension housing.
4. Unbolt extension housing. Break housing loose with plastic hammer and carefully remove.

Idler Gear and Mainshaft

1. Insert dummy shaft in case to push reverse idler shaft and key out of case.
2. Remove dummy shaft and idler gear together to prevent losing rollers.
3. Remove both tanged idler gear thrust washers.
4. Remove mainshaft assembly through rear of case.

Countershaft Gear and Drive Pinion

1. Using a mallet and dummy shaft, tap the countershaft rearward enough to remove key.

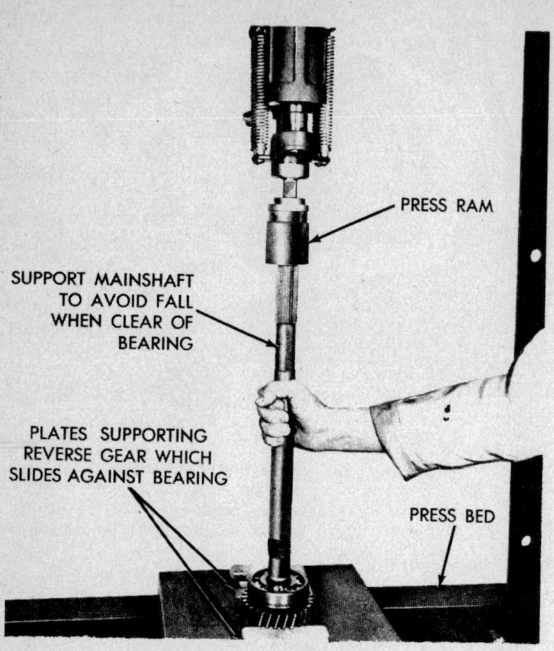
PRESS RAM
SUPPORT MAINSHAFT TO AVOID FALL WHEN CLEAR OF BEARING
PLATES SUPPORTING REVERSE GEAR WHICH SLIDES AGAINST BEARING
PRESS BED

Pressing off mainshaft bearing
(© Chrysler Corp)

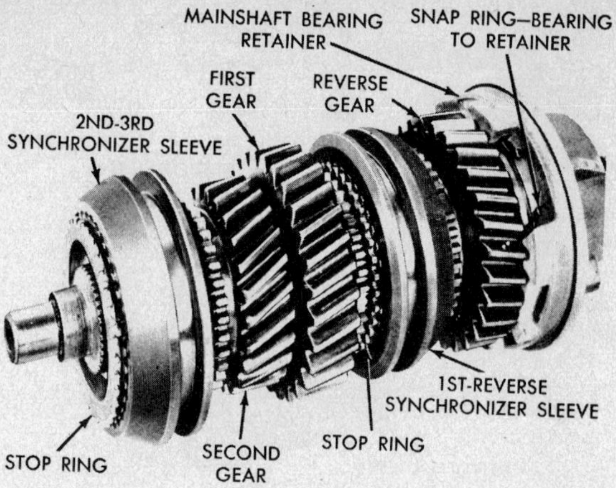
MAINSHAFT BEARING RETAINER
SNAP RING—BEARING TO RETAINER
FIRST GEAR
REVERSE GEAR
2ND-3RD SYNCHRONIZER SLEEVE
1ST-REVERSE SYNCHRONIZER SLEEVE
STOP RING
SECOND GEAR
STOP RING

Mainshaft assembly
(© Chrysler Corp)

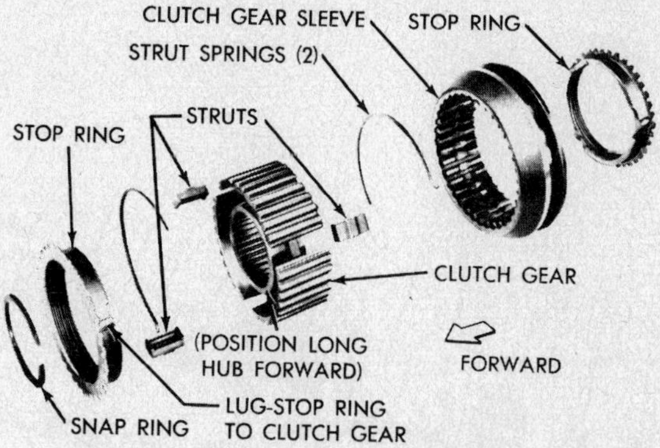
CLUTCH GEAR SLEEVE
STOP RING
STRUT SPRINGS (2)
STRUTS
STOP RING
CLUTCH GEAR
(POSITION LONG HUB FORWARD)
FORWARD
SNAP RING
LUG-STOP RING TO CLUTCH GEAR

Details of second-third synchronizer
(© Chrysler Corp)

Drive countershaft out of case, maintaining contact between countershaft and dummy shaft so that washers will not drop out.
2. Lower countershaft gear to bottom of case.
3. Remove snap-ring from pinion bearing outer race (outside front of case).
4. Drive pinion shaft into case with plastic hammer. Remove assembly through rear of case.
5. If bearing is to be replaced, remove snap-ring and press off bearing.
6. Lift countershaft gear and dummy shaft out through rear of case.

Mainshaft

1. Remove snap-ring from front end of mainshaft along with second gear stop ring. Remove second gear from mainshaft.
2. Spread snap-ring in mainshaft bearing retainer. Slide retainer back off the bearing race.
3. Remove snap-ring at rear of mainshaft. Support front side of reverse gear. Press bearing off mainshaft. Be careful not to let parts drop when bearing clears shaft.
4. Remove from press. Remove mainshaft bearing and reverse gear from shaft.
5. Remove snap-ring from rear of shaft. Slide first-reverse synchronizer assembly off splines and remove rearward. Remove stop-ring and first gear through the rear.

Inspection

1. Clean all parts with solvent.
2. Dry with compressed air.

Case

1. Check for cracks, stripped threads, and burrs or nicks on machined surfaces. Dress off any burrs with a fine file. Stripped threads may be repaired by use of Helicoil inserts.

Ball Bearings

1. Do not spin bearings with air pressure; turn slowly by hand to avoid damage.
2. Lubricate with light engine oil.
3. Check for pitting.
4. Check fit on shafts.

Needle Bearings

1. Check rollers for flats or brinelling.
2. Check roller spacers for wear or galling.

Gears

1. Check gear splines on synchronizer clutch gears and stop-rings for chipping or worn teeth.
2. Be sure the clutch sleeve slides easily on clutch gear.
3. Check countershaft gear and all gear teeth for chipping, broken teeth, or excessive wear. Stone off small nicks or burrs.
4. If oil seal contact area on drive pinion shaft is pitted, rusted, or scratched, replace the pinion.

Synchronizer Stop Rings

1. Check for cracks or wear.
2. Check new rings for good fit on gear cones with minimum wobble.

Mainshaft

1. Check mainshaft gear and bearing mating surfaces for galling or excessive wear.
2. Check snap-rings for burred edges. Remove burrs with a fine file.
3. Check synchronizer clutch gear splines on shaft for burrs.

Assembly

Countershaft Gear

1. Slide dummy shaft into countershaft gear.
2. Slide one roller thrust washer over dummy shaft and into gear, followed by 22 greased rollers.
3. Repeat Step 2, adding one roller thrust washer on end.
4. Repeat steps 2 and 3 at other end of countershaft gear. There is a total of 88 rollers and 6 thrust washers.
5. Place greased front thrust washer on dummy shaft against

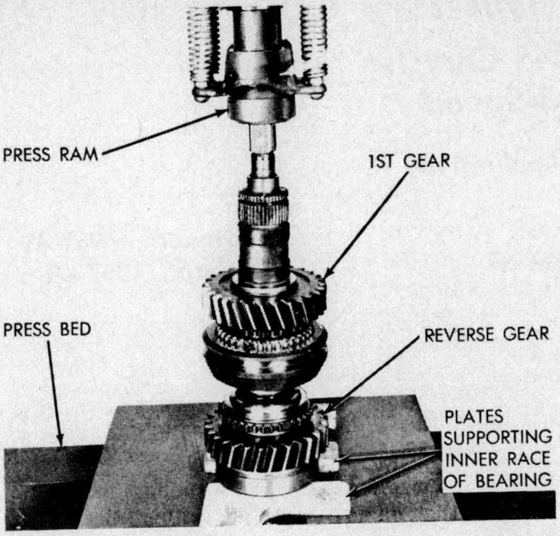
PRESS RAM
1ST GEAR
PRESS BED
REVERSE GEAR
PLATES SUPPORTING INNER RACE OF BEARING

Pressing on mainshaft bearing
(© Chrysler Corp)

gear with tangs forward.

6. Grease rear thrust washer and stick it in place in the case, with tangs rearward. Place countershaft gear assembly in bottom of transmission case until drive pinion is installed.

Pinion Gear

1. Press new bearing on pinion shaft with snap-ring groove forward. Install new snap-ring.
2. Install 15 rollers and retaining ring in drive pinion gear.
3. Install drive pinion and bearing assembly into case.
4. Install the countershaft gear assembly by positioning it and thrust washers so countershaft can be tapped into position. Be careful to keep the countershaft against the dummy shaft to keep parts from falling between them. Install key in countershaft.
5. Tap drive pinion forward for clearance.

Mainshaft

1. Place a stop-ring flat on the bench. Place a clutch gear and a sleeve on top. Drop the struts in their slots and snap in a strut spring placing the tang inside one strut. Turn the assembly over and install second strut spring, tang in a different strut.
2. Slide first gear and stop-ring over rear of mainshaft and against thrust flange between first and second gears on shaft.
3. Slide first-reverse synchronizer assembly over rear of mainshaft, indexing hub slots to first gear stop-ring lugs.
4. Install first-reverse synchronizer clutch gear snap-ring on mainshaft.
5. Slide reverse gear and mainshaft bearing into place. Press bearing on shaft, supporting inner race of bearing. Be sure snap-ring groove on outer race is forward.
6. Install bearing retaining snap-ring on mainshaft. Spread snap-ring in retainer groove and slide it over the bearing. Seat ring in groove.
7. Place second gear over front of mainshaft with thrust surface against flange.
8. Install stop-ring and second-third synchronizer assembly against second gear. Install second-third synchronizer clutch gear snap-ring on shaft.
9. Move second-third synchronizer sleeve forward as far as possible. Install front stop-ring, inside the sleeve with lugs indexed to struts. Coat the stop-ring with grease to hold it in position.
10. Rotate cut-out on second gear toward countershaft gear to provide clearance.
11. Insert mainshaft assembly into case. Tilt assembly to clear cluster gears and insert pilot rollers in drive pinion gear. If assembly is correct, the bearing retainer will bottom to the case without force. If not, check for a misplaced strut, pinion roller, or stop-ring.

Reverse Idler Gear

1. Place dummy shaft into idler gear. Insert 22 greased rollers.
2. Position reverse idler thrust washers in case with grease.
3. Position idler gear and dummy shaft in case. Install idler shaft and key.

Extension Housing

1. Remove extension housing yoke seal. Drive bushing out from inside housing.
2. Align oil hole in bushing with oil slot in housing. Drive bushing into place. Drive new seal into housing.
3. Install extension housing and gasket to hold mainshaft and bearing retainer in place.

Drive Pinion Bearing Retainer

1. Install outer snap-ring on drive pinion bearing. Tap assembly back until snap-ring contacts case.
2. Install a new seal in retainer bore.
3. Position main drive pinion bearing retainer and gasket on front of case. Coat threads with sealing compound, install bolts, torque to 30 ft. lbs.

Gearshift Mechanism and Housing

1. If removed, place two interlock levers on pivot pin with spring hangers offset toward each other, so that spring installs in a straight line. Place E-clip on pivot pin.
2. Grease and install new O-ring seals on both shift shafts. Grease housing bores. Push each shaft into its bore.
3. Install spring on interlock lever hangers.
4. Rotate each shift shaft fork bore to vertical position. Install shift forks through bores and under both interlock levers.
5. Position second-third synchronizer sleeve to rear, in second gear position. Position first-reverse synchronizer sleeve to middle of travel, in neutral position. Place shift forks in the same positions.
6. Install gasket and gearshift mechanism. The bolt with the extra long shoulder must be installed at the center rear of the case. Torque bolts to 15 ft. lbs.
7. Install speedometer drive pinion gear and adapter. Range number on adapter, which represents the number of teeth on the gear, should be in 6 o'clock position.

Exhaust Emission Control System Switch

Some models have a switch in the shift cover, adjacent to the 2-3 shift lever. It is actuated by a flat on the 2-3 shift lever, when in third gear. If vehicle is not equipped with Emission System, a plug is installed in the mounting hole. Torque the switch or plug to 15 ft. lbs.

Type-2
A-745 Chrysler
3-Speed

Application

Barracuda, 1967-69
Charger, 1967-69
Chrysler, 1967-69

Dart, 1967-69
Dodge, 1967-69

Plymouth, 1967-69
Valiant, 1967-69

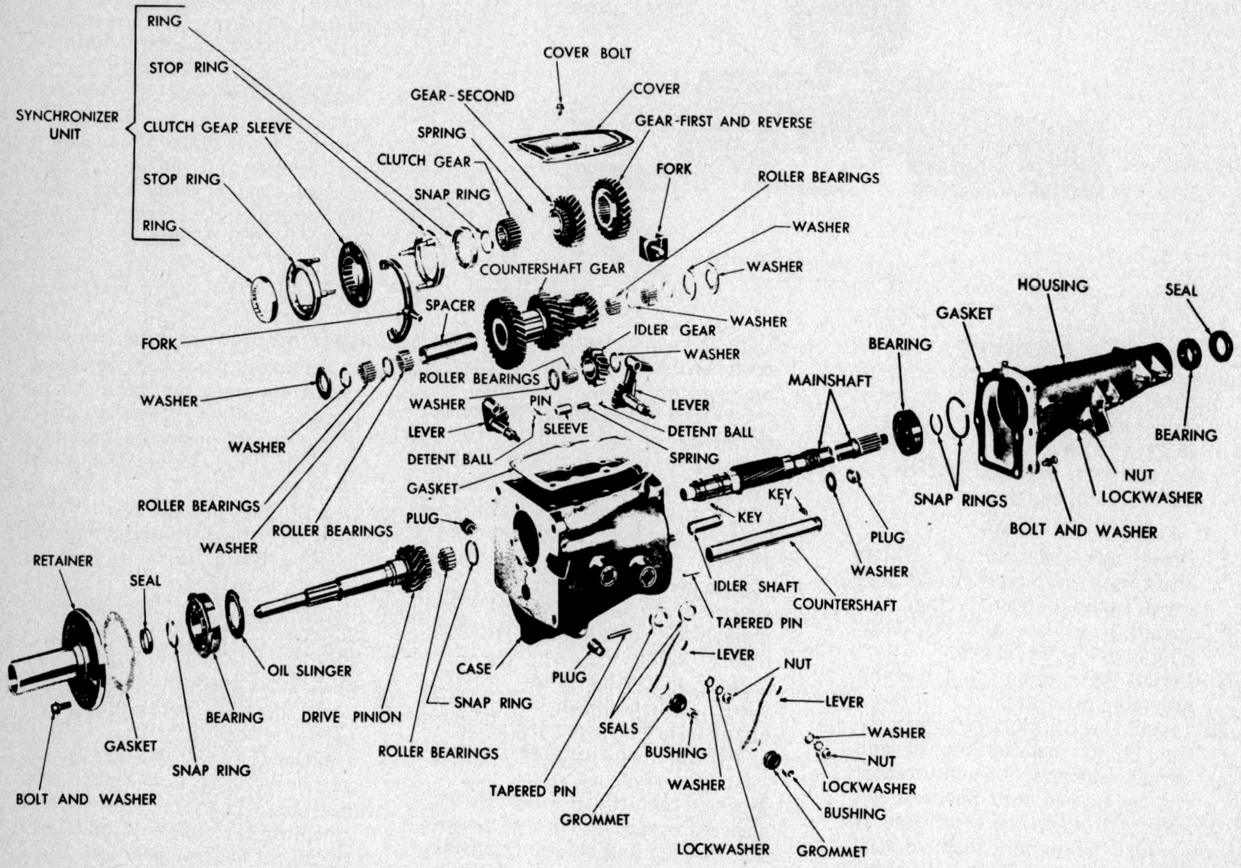

SYNCHRONIZER UNIT
RING
STOP RING
CLUTCH GEAR SLEEVE
STOP RING
RING
COVER BOLT
GEAR-SECOND
COVER
GEAR-FIRST AND REVERSE
SPRING
CLUTCH GEAR
FORK
SNAP RING
ROLLER BEARINGS
WASHER
WASHER
COUNTERSHAFT GEAR
HOUSING
SEAL
GASKET
SPACER
WASHER
FORK
IDLER GEAR
BEARING
WASHER
ROLLER BEARINGS
MAINSHAFT
WASHER
PIN
LEVER
LEVER
SLEEVE
DETENT BALL
BEARING
WASHER
DETENT BALL
SPRING
NUT
GASKET
KEY
SNAP RINGS
LOCKWASHER
KEY
ROLLER BEARINGS
PLUG
BOLT AND WASHER
PLUG
ROLLER BEARINGS
WASHER
WASHER
RETAINER
SEAL
IDLER SHAFT
COUNTERSHAFT
TAPERED PIN
LEVER
OIL SLINGER
CASE
NUT
PLUG
SNAP RING
LEVER
BEARING
DRIVE PINION
SEALS
WASHER
GASKET
NUT
ROLLER BEARINGS
BUSHING
SNAP RING
LOCKWASHER
TAPERED PIN
WASHER
BOLT AND WASHER
BUSHING
GROMMET
LOCKWASHER
GROMMET

A-745 Chrysler

Disassembly

1. Remove output flange nut, then the drum and flange assembly, if so equipped. Remove parking brake assembly, if so equipped.
2. Remove case cover. Measure synchronizer float with feeler gauges. This measurement is taken between the end of a synchronizer pin and the opposite synchronizer outer ring. A measurement from .050-.090 in. is acceptable for 1966-68 models. The measurement should be .060-.117 in. for 1969 models.
3. Remove five bolts and one nut attaching the extension housing to the transmission case.
4. Remove the extension housing.
5. Remove the mainshaft rear bearing, if it did not come off with the extension housing.
6. Remove transmission case cover and gasket.
7. Remove four bolts from the drive pinion bearing retainer, then remove the retainer.
8. When removing the drive pinion and bearing assembly from the transmission case, slide the front inner stop-ring from the short splines on the pinion as the assembly is being removed from the case.
9. Remove the snap-ring that holds the main drive pinion bearing onto the shaft.
10. Press bearing off pinion shaft and remove oil slinger.
11. Remove mainshaft pilot bearing snap-ring from the cavity of the pinion gear.
12. Remove the 15 pilot roller bearings.
13. Remove seal from pinion retainer.
14. Remove mainshaft rear bearing snap-ring from groove in mainshaft rear bearing bore in the case.
15. Slide the mainshaft and rear bearing assembly to the rear, until the rear bearing is out of the case.
16. Remove synchronizer assembly from case.
17. Remove second and third-speed shift fork.
18. Remove synchronizer clutch gear snap-ring.
19. Remove synchronizer clutch gear, second-speed gear, and first and reverse sliding gear from the mainshaft.
20. Withdraw mainshaft and bearing out through the rear of the case.

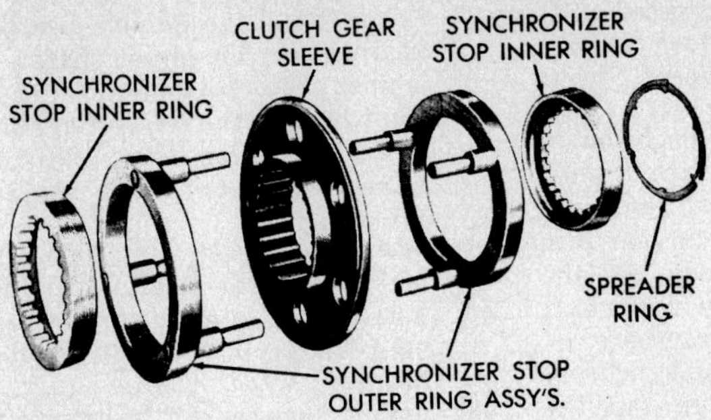
SYNCHRONIZER
STOP INNER RING
CLUTCH GEAR
SLEEVE
SYNCHRONIZER
STOP INNER RING
SPREADER
RING
SYNCHRONIZER STOP
OUTER RING ASSY'S.
Synchromesh assembly

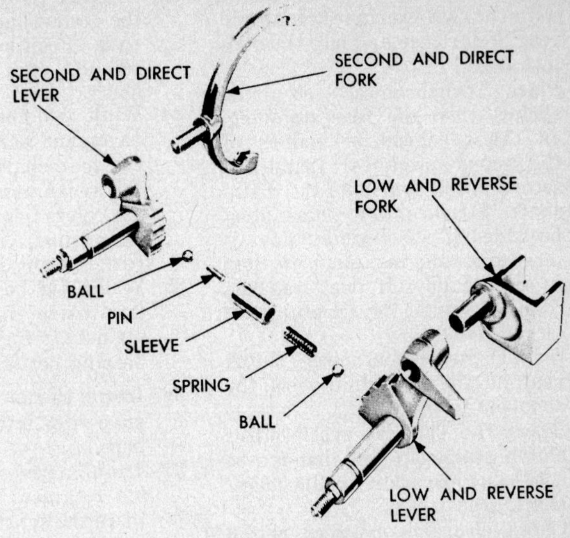
SECOND AND DIRECT
LEVER
SECOND AND DIRECT
FORK
LOW AND REVERSE
FORK
BALL
PIN
SLEEVE
SPRING
BALL
LOW AND REVERSE
LEVER
Shift forks and shafts

21. Remove the synchronizer clutch gear, second-speed gear, low and reverse sliding gear, and low and reverse shift fork from the case.
22. With a dummy shaft, drive the countershaft toward the rear of the case until the small key can be removed from the countershaft.
23. Drive the countershaft the remaining way out of the case.
24. Lift the cluster gear, the thrust washers and the dummy shaft assembly out of the case.
25. Remove the cluster gear (88 rollers, four spacer rings) and the center spacer from the cluster.
26. With a blunt drift, drive the reverse idler shaft toward the rear of the case far enough to remove the key from the shaft.
27. Completely remove the shaft from the case, then remove the idler gear.
28. Remove the thrust washers and 22 rollers.
29. With a small punch, remove low and reverse gear lever shaft tapered lockpin by driving it toward the top of the transmission case.
30. Remove the second and third gear lever shaft in the same manner.
31. Remove the lever shafts from the transmission case. Don't lose the spring-loaded detent balls.
32. Remove the interlock sleeve, spring, pin and detent balls.
33. Remove both lever shaft seals and discard same.

Assembly

1. Place oil slinger on the main drive pinion with the offset outer portion next to the drive pinion teeth.
2. Place the main drive pinion bearing on the pinion shaft with the outer snap-ring away from the pinion gear.
3. Press the bearing into position so it is seated firmly against the oil slinger and pinion gear.
4. Install the bearing retaining snap-ring on the pinion shaft. Be sure the snap-ring is seated in its groove.
5. Coat the 15 pilot bearing rollers with heavy grease and install them in the cavity at the rear of the main drive pinion.
6. Install the snap-ring.
7. Place the bearing spacer in the center of the bore in the cluster gear and use the dummy shaft to assist in assembling the roller bearings.
8. Install a row of 22 rollers next to one end of the spacer, using heavy grease to hold them.
9. Place one of the four bearing spacer rings next to the row of rollers, and install another row of 22 rollers next to the spacer ring.
10. Install another spacer ring at the outside end of the second row of bearing rollers.
11. At the opposite end of the cluster gear bore, install the remaining spacer rings and bearing rollers in the same sequence as listed in Steps 8, 9, and 10.
12. With a small amount of grease, install the front thrust washer on the dummy shaft at the front end of the cluster gear, with the tabs outward.
13. Install the tabbed rear thrust washer onto the dummy shaft against the rear of the cluster gear with the tabs positioned in the grooves provided in the cluster gear.
14. Install the remaining rear thrust washer plate onto the rear of the gear and dummy shaft with the step in the washer facing upward, as viewed from the rear.
15. Align tabs of the front thrust washer vertically to index with notches in the transmission case and with the step in the rear thrust washer positioned upward. Insert the cluster gear and dummy shaft in the transmission case.
16. Using the countershaft, drive the dummy shaft forward, out of the case. Countershaft end-play should be .0045-.028 in.
17. Position a dummy shaft in the reverse idler gear and, using heavy grease, install the 22 roller bearings into the gear.
18. Place the thrust washers at each end of the reverse idler gear, then position the assembly in the transmission case with the chamfered end of the gear teeth toward the front.
19. Insert the reverse idler shaft into the bore at the rear of the case, with the keyway to the rear, pushing the dummy shaft forward and out of the front of the transmission.
20. With the keyway in proper alignment, insert the key and continue driving the shaft forward until the key seats in the recess.
21. Install two new lever shaft seals in the transmission case.
22. Lubricate and install second and third-speed lever shaft in the bores of the case.
23. Install the second and third speed lever shaft lockpin in the hole in the case. Drive it in firmly, in a downward direction.
24. Place interlock parts in the case in the following order: ball, sleeve, spring, pin and ball.
25. Enter low and reverse lever shaft in the case bore, depress the detent ball against spring tension and push the lever shaft firmly into position, in order to prevent the ball from escaping.
26. Install low and reverse lever shaft lockpin in the case by driving it downward.
27. Place low and reverse fork in the lever shaft, with the offset toward the rear.
28. While holding the low and reverse sliding gear in position in the fork, with the hub extension to the rear, insert the mainshaft

with the rear bearing through the rear of the case and into the sliding gear.

29. Place synchronizer stop-ring spring, then the rear stop-ring, on the synchronizer splines of the second-speed gear. Install the second-speed gear onto the mainshaft. Synchronizer shims must be added if synchronizer float is more than the maximum in Step 2, disassembly. If float was less than minimum, the six pins must be shortened.
30. Install the synchronizer clutch gear on the mainshaft with the shoulder to the front.
31. Select the thickest synchronizer clutch gear snap-ring that can be used, and install it in the mainshaft groove.
32. Check clearance between clutch gear and second-speed gear. Clearance should be .004-.014 in.
33. Hold the synchronizer clutch gear sleeve and two outer rings together with pins properly entered into the holes in the clutch gear sleeve. The clutch gear sleeve should engage in the groove of the second- and third-speed shift fork. Position the fork in the second and third-speed lever shaft.
34. While holding the synchronizer parts and fork in position, slide the mainshaft forward, entering the synchronizer clutch gear into the clutch gear sleeve. At the same time, enter the mainshaft rear bearing in the case bore.
35. While still holding the synchronizer parts in position, tap the mainshaft forward until the rear bearing bottoms in the case bore.
36. Install the mainshaft rear bearing snap-ring into place in the case bore.
37. Install a new seal in the drive pinion retainer.
38. Place the synchronizer front inner ring in position in the front outer ring, and enter the main drive pinion through the case bore.
39. Engage the splines on the rear of the pinion with the inner stop ring, and tap the drive pinion into the case until the outer snap-ring on the pinion bearing is against the transmission case.
40. Place the drive pinion bearing retainer over the pinion shaft and against the transmission case. While holding the retainer against the transmission case, measure the clearance between the retainer and case.
41. Select a gasket .003-.005 in. thicker than the clearance found.
42. Install and tighten the front bearing retainer bolts to 30 ft. lbs. torque.
43. Install a new seal in the extension housing.
44. Install extension housing. Torque the attaching bolts and nuts to 50 ft. lbs.
45. Install the parking brake assembly, on vehicles so equipped.
46. Install the parking brake drum (if so equipped) and flange assembly. Install the washer and nut and torque to 175 ft. lbs.
47. Install the drain plug in the transmission case.
48. Install the gearshift operating levers, and torque to 12 ft. lbs.
49. Install the back-up light switch.
50. Install the speedometer cable and drive gear. Fill with transmission lubricant to the proper level.

Type-3
A-903 Chrysler 3-Speed

Application

Barracuda (6 Cyl.), 1967-74
Dart (6 Cyl.), 1967-74
Dodge (6 Cyl.), 1967-74
Charger (6 Cyl.), 1967-74
Challenger (6 Cyl.), 1970-74
Chrysler (6 Cyl.), 1971-74
Plymouth (6 Cyl.), 1967-72
Valiant (6 Cyl.), 1967-72

Disassembly

1. Remove output shaft yoke.
2. Remove the bolts that attach the extension housing to the transmission case. Remove the housing.
3. Remove extension housing oil seal.
4. Remove the transmission case cover. Measure synchronizer float with feeler gauges. This measurement is taken between the end of a synchronizer pin and the opposite synchronizer outer ring. A measurement from .050-.090 in. is acceptable for 1966-68 models. This measurement should be .060-.117 in. for 1969-72 models.
5. Remove the attaching bolts and remove the main drive pinion bearing retainer. Then grasp the pinion shaft and pull the assembly out of the case.

Caution Be careful not to bind the inner synchronizer ring on the drive pinion clutch teeth.

6. Remove the snap-ring that locks the main drive pinion bearing onto the pinion shaft. Remove the bearing washer, press the shaft out of the bearing and remove the oil slinger.
7. Remove the snap-ring from the pilot bearing in the end of the drive pinion and remove the 14 rollers.
8. With the transmission in reverse, remove the outer center bearing snap-ring, then partially remove the mainshaft.
9. Cock the mainshaft, then remove the clutch sleeve, the outer synchronizer rings, the front inner ring and the second-third shift box.
10. Remove clutch gear retaining snap ring and slide the clutch gear off the end of the mainshaft.
11. Slide the second-speed gear, stop-ring and synchronizer spring off the mainshaft.
12. Remove the low and reverse sliding gear and shift fork, as the mainshaft is completely withdrawn from the case.
13. Check cluster gear end-play. End-play should be .005-.022 in. This measurement will determine thrust washer value at reassembly.
14. Drive the countershaft rearward, removing key, and out of the case.
15. Lift the gear cluster and thrust washers out of the case. Remove the needle bearings, (22 each end) and spacer from the cluster.
16. Drive the reverse idler shaft toward the rear and out of the case. Remove key.
17. Lift the reverse idler gear, thrust washers and 22 needle bearings out of the case.
18. Remove gearshift operating levers from their respective shafts.
19. Drive out tapered retaining pin

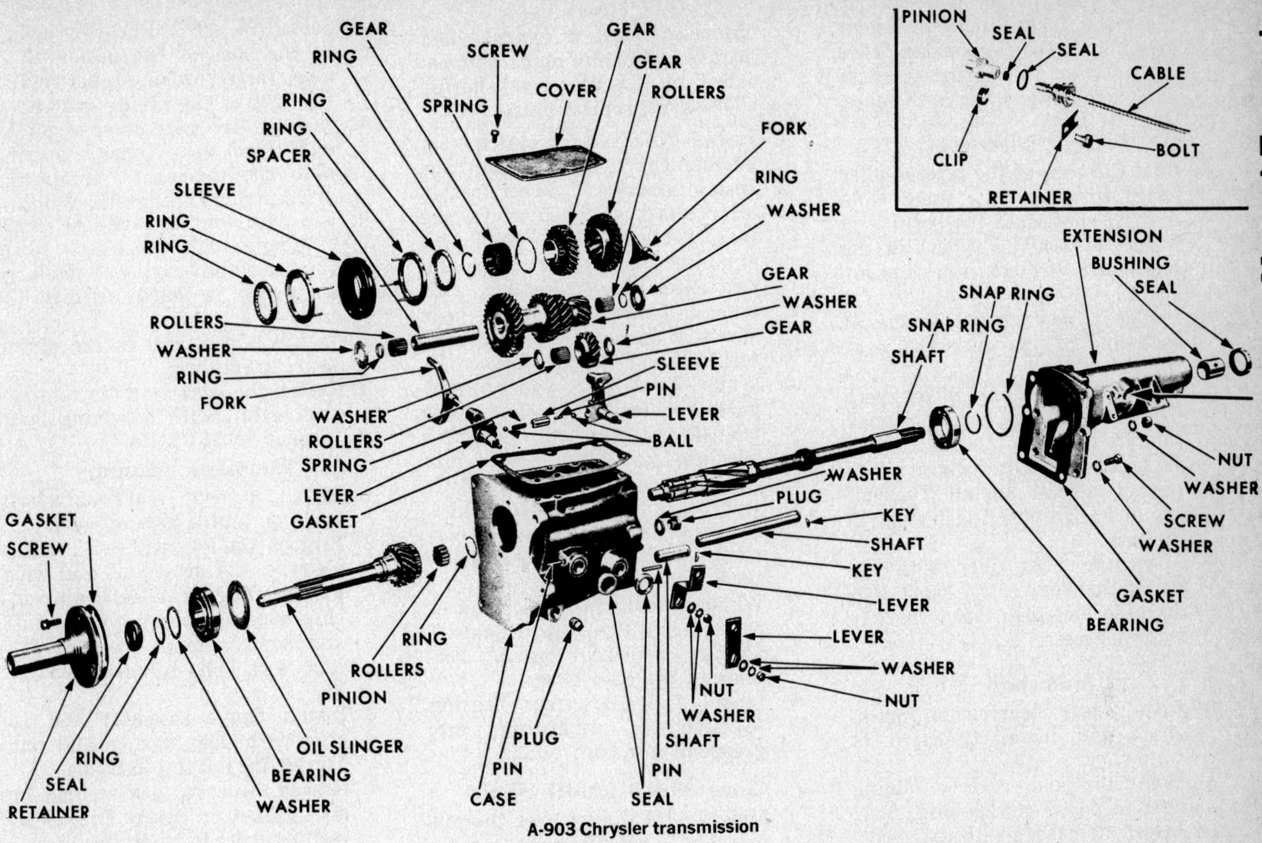
GEAR
RING
SCREW
GEAR
GEAR
ROLLERS
RING
SPRING
COVER
RING
SPACER
FORK
SLEEVE
RING
RING
RING
WASHER
GEAR
WASHER
GEAR
ROLLERS
WASHER
RING
FORK
SLEEVE
PIN
LEVER
BALL
WASHER
ROLLERS
SPRING
LEVER
GASKET
WASHER
PLUG
KEY
SHAFT
KEY
LEVER
LEVER
WASHER
NUT
GASKET
SCREW
RING
ROLLERS
PINION
OIL SLINGER
BEARING
WASHER
RING
SEAL
RETAINER
PLUG
PIN
CASE
NUT
WASHER
SHAFT
PIN
SEAL
PINION
SEAL
SEAL
CABLE
CLIP
BOLT
RETAINER
EXTENSION
BUSHING
SEAL
SNAP RING
SNAP RING
SHAFT
NUT
WASHER
SCREW
WASHER
GASKET
BEARING

A-903 Chrysler transmission

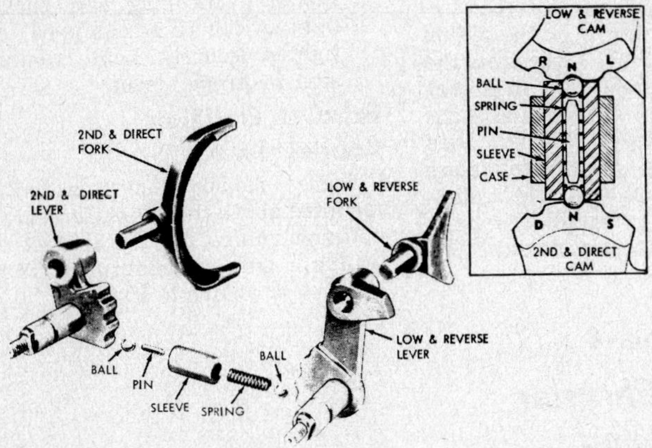
LOW & REVERSE CAM
R
N
L
BALL
SPRING
PIN
SLEEVE
CASE
D
N
S
2ND & DIRECT CAM
2ND & DIRECT FORK
2ND & DIRECT LEVER
LOW & REVERSE FORK
LOW & REVERSE LEVER
BALL
BALL
PIN
SLEEVE
SPRING

Shift forks and levers

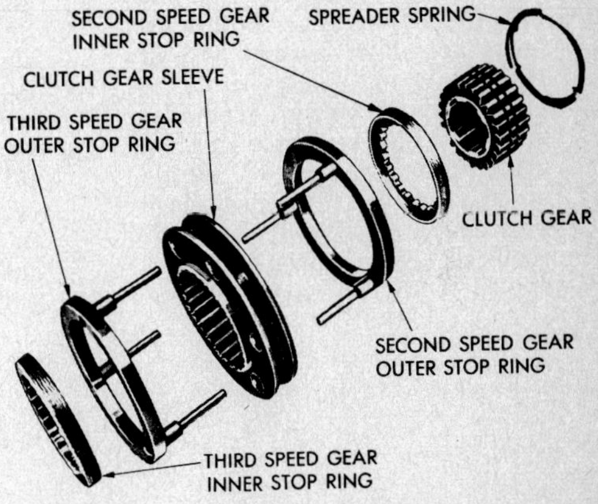
SECOND SPEED GEAR INNER STOP RING
SPREADER SPRING
CLUTCH GEAR SLEEVE
THIRD SPEED GEAR OUTER STOP RING
CLUTCH GEAR
SECOND SPEED GEAR OUTER STOP RING
THIRD SPEED GEAR INNER STOP RING

Synchronizer assembly

from either of the two lever shafts, then withdraw the shaft from inside the transmission case. (The detent balls are spring-loaded, as the shaft is being withdrawn, the balls will fall to the bottom of the case.)

20. Remove the interlock sleeve, spring, pin and both balls from the case. Drive out the remaining tapered pin, then slide the lever shaft out of the transmission.
21. Remove the lever shaft seals and discard them.

Assembly

1. Install two new shift lever shaft seals in the case.
2. Carefully insert low and reverse lever shaft into the rear of the case, through the seal and into position. Lock with a tapered pin. Turn lever until the center detent is in line with the interlock bore.
3. Slide the interlock sleeve in its bore in the case, followed by one of the interlock balls. Then, install interlock spring and pin.
4. Place the remaining interlock ball on top of the interlock spring.
5. Depress the interlock ball and at the same time install the second and high lever shaft into the fully seated position, with the center detent aligned with the detent ball. Secure the shaft with the remaining tapered pin.
6. Install the operating levers and secure to the shafts with nuts. Torque the nuts to 18 ft. lbs.

Countershaft (Cluster) Gear

1. Slide the dummy shaft and tubular spacer into the bore of the countergear.
2. Grease and install 22 bearing rollers into each end of the countergear bore in the area around the arbor. Install the bearing retaining rings at each end of the gear, covering the bearings. If countershaft gear end-play measured over .022 in. at disassembly, install new thrust washers.
3. Install a thrust washer at each end of the countergear and over

the arbor. Install the countergear assembly in the case, making sure the tabs on the thrust washers slide into the grooves in the case.

Reverse Idler Gear

1. Coat the bore of the reverse idler gear with grease, then slide dummy shaft into the bore, then install 22 bearing rollers in the bore and around the dummy shaft.
2. Install a new thrust washer at each end of the gear and over the arbor.
3. With the beveled end of the teeth forward, slide the gear into position in the case. Install the reverse idler shaft in its bore in the rear of the case. Install Woodruff key and align with the keyway in the case.
4. Align the idler gear with the shaft, then drive the shaft into the case and gear until the key seats in recess.

Mainshaft

1. Install rear bearing on mainshaft and install selective fit snap-ring.
2. Hold low and reverse sliding gear in position with shift fork. Insert mainshaft with rear bearing through rear of case and into the sliding gear. Both shift forks are offset toward rear of the case.
3. Place synchronizer spreader ring, and then rear stop ring, on synchronizer splines of second speed gear. Install second speed gear on mainshaft, with shims if required. Shims should be installed to correct excessive synchronizer float. If synchronizer float is below minimum, as measured on disassembly, shorten all six synchronizer pins.
4. Install synchronizer clutch gear on mainshaft. Install snap-ring.
5. Install second and direct fork in lever shaft with offset toward rear of transmission. Hold synchronizer clutch gear sleeve and two outer rings together, with pins in holes in clutch gear sleeve. Engage second and direct fork with clutch gear sleeve.
6. While holding synchronizer parts and fork in position, slide mainshaft forward, starting synchronizer clutch gear into clutch gear sleeve and mainshaft rear bearing into the case bore. Synchronizer parts must be correctly positioned before mainshaft is positioned.
7. While holding synchronizer parts in position, tap mainshaft forward until rear bearing bottoms in the case bore.
8. Install mainshaft rear bearing selective fit snap-ring into groove in case bore.

Drive Pinion (Clutch Shaft)

1. Slide the oil slinger over the pinion shaft and down against the gear.
2. Slide the bearing over the pinion shaft (ring groove away from the gear), then press to a firm seat against the oil slinger and gear.
3. Install the keyed washer, then the snap-ring. Four thicknesses of snap-ring are available to eliminate end-play. Install the large snap-ring onto the race of the ball bearing.
4. Install 14 greased bearing rollers in the bore of the pinion shaft gear. Install bearing roller retaining ring in the pinion gear bore.
5. Install third gear outer stop-ring and third gear inner stop-ring onto the mainshaft. Guide the drive pinion through the front of the case and engage the inner stop-ring with the clutch teeth, then seat the bearing so the large snap-ring is hard against the case.
6. Install a new seal in the pinion bearing retainer.
7. Install the gasket on the retainer and install with attaching bolts torqued to 30 ft. lbs.

Extension Housing

1. Install a new rear mainshaft bushing, and a new oil seal.
2. Protect the oil seal with thimble-type seal protector, and with gasket attached, slide the extension housing over the mainshaft and down against the case. Attach with bolts torqued to 50 ft. lbs.
3. Install flange assembly and secure with new washer and nut. Torque the nut to 140 ft. lbs.
4. Grease the cover gasket, and install gasket on cover. Torque attaching bolts to 12 ft. lbs.
5. Install drain plug and back-up light switch (if so equipped) and tighten securely. Refill transmission to proper level.

Exhaust Emission Control Switch

Some models have a switch mounted above the 2-3 shift lever, for emission control. In the absence of a switch a plug is substituted. Torque the plug or switch to 15 ft. lbs.

Type-4
A-833 Chrysler 4-Speed

Application

Barracuda, 1967-74
Challenger, 1970-74
Charger, 1967-74
Chrysler, 1967
Dart, 1967-74
Dodge, 1967-74
Plymouth, 1967-74
Valiant, 1967-74

This unit is used by Chrysler Corporation cars and varies somewhat with car application. However, illustrations and repair procedures may be considered as typical.

Disassembly

1. If available, mount transmission in a repair stand.
2. Disconnect gearshift control rods from the shift control levers and the transmission operating levers.
3. Remove the two gearshift control housing mounting bolts.
4. Remove gearshift control housing from the transmission extension housing or mounting bracket (if so equipped).
5. Remove the gearshift control housing mounting bracket bolts, then, remove the bracket (if so equipped).
6. Remove back-up light switch (if so equipped).
7. Remove output companion flange nut and washer, then pull the flange from the mainshaft (output shaft).
8. Remove gearshift housing-to-transmission case attaching bolts.
9. With all levers in the neutral detent position, pull housing out and away from the case.

NOTE: if first and second, or third and fourth shift forks remain in engagement with the synchronizer sleeves, work the sleeves and remove forks from the case.

10. Remove nuts, lock washers and flat washers that hold first-second, and third-fourth-speed shift operating levers to the shafts.
11. Disengage shift levers from the flats on the shafts and remove levers.

1 Bearing retainer
2 Bearing retainer gasket
3 Bearing retainer oil seal
4 Inner bearing snap-ring
5 Outer bearing snap-ring
6 Pinion bearing
7 Transmission case
8 Filler plug
9 2nd speed gear
10 Stop ring
11 Shift strut springs
12 Clutch gear
13 Shift struts (3)
14 Shift strut spring
15 Snap-ring
16 1st and 2nd clutch sleeve gear
17 Stop ring
18 1st speed gear
19 Bearing retainer ring
20 Rear bearing
21 Snap-ring
24 Baffle
25 Case to extension housing gasket
26 Lockwasher
27 Bolt
28 Extension housing
29 Mainshaft yoke bushing
30 Oil seal
31 Main drive pinion
33 Needle bearing rollers
34 Snap-ring
35 Stop ring
36 Snap-ring
37 Shift strut spring
38 Clutch gear
39 Shift strut spring
40 Clutch sleeve
41 Stop ring
42 3rd speed gear
43 Mainshaft (output)
44 Shift struts (3)
45 Woodruff key
46 Countershaft
47 Gear thrustwasher (1)
48 Needle roller bearing thrustwasher
49 Needle bearing rollers
50 Bearing spacer
51 Countershaft gear (cluster)

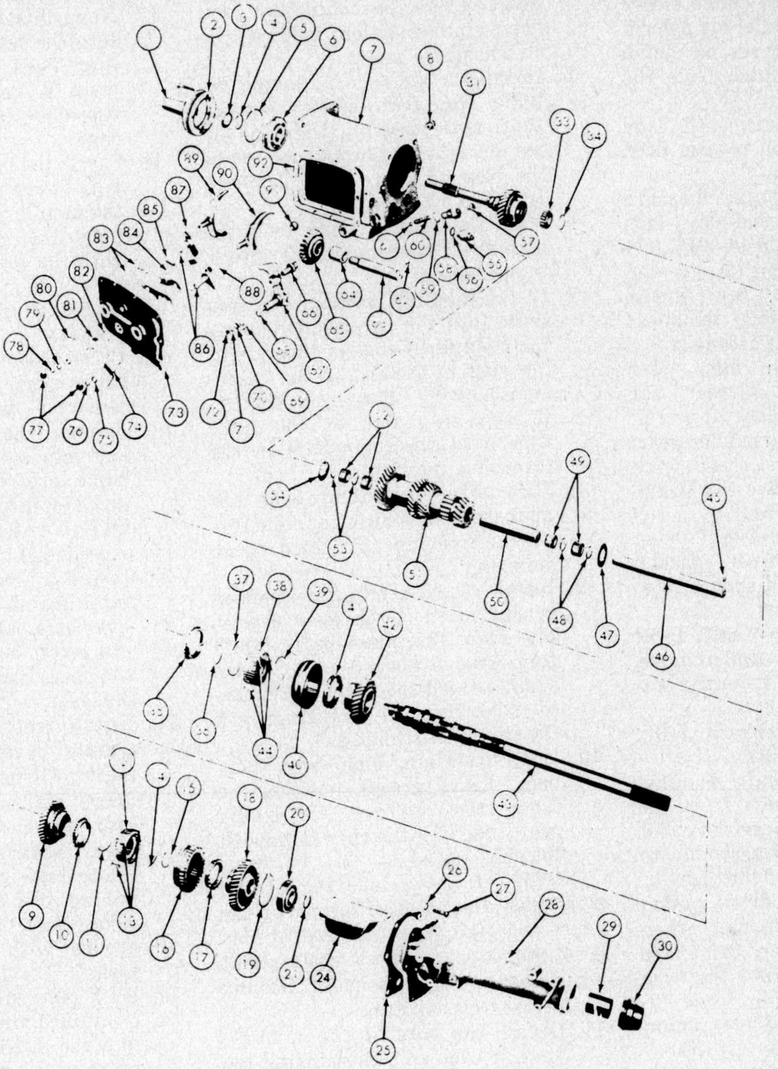

52 Needle bearing rollers
53 Needle roller bearing thrustwasher
54 Gear thrustwasher (1)
55 Backup light switch
56 Backup light switch gasket
57 Plug
58 Reverse detent ball spring retainer
59 Gasket
60 Reverse detent ball spring
61 Rerverse detent ball
62 Woodruff key
63 Reverse idler gear shaft
64 Reverse idler gear bushing
65 Reverse idler gear
66 Reverse shifter fork
67 Reverse lever
68 Reverse lever shaft oil seal
69 Reverse operating lever
70 Flatwasher
71 Lockwasher
72 Nut
73 Gearshift control housing
74 1st and 2nd operating lever
75 Flatwasher
76 Lockwasher lever
77 Lever nut
78 Lever lockwasher
79 Lever flatwasher
80 3rd and 4th operating lever
81 Switch
82 Gasket
83 Interlock lever (2)
84 E-ring
85 Spring
86 Oil seal (2)
87 3rd and 4th lever
88 Ist and 2nd lever
89 3rd and 4th speed fork
90 1st and 2nd speed fork
91 Drain plug
92 Shift control housing gasket

A-833 4-speed transmission

12. Remove gearshift lever shafts out of the housing, allowing detent balls to fall free. Remove seals and discard.
13. Slide interlock sleeve, interlock pin and spring from the housing.
14. Remove main drive pinion bearing retainer attaching bolts, then slide retainer and gasket from the main drive shaft. Remove the pinion oil seal.
15. Remove the attaching bolts that hold the tailshaft extension housing to the transmission case.
16. Slide the third-fourth synchronizer sleeve slightly forward, slide the reverse idler gear to the center of its shaft, then, using a soft hammer, tap rearward on the extension housing. Slide housing and mainshaft assembly out and away from the case.
17. Remove the snap-ring that holds the third-fourth synchronizer clutch gear and sleeve. Then, slide third-fourth synchronizer assembly from the end of the mainshaft.
18. Slide third speed gear and stop-ring from the mainshaft.

NOTE: do not separate third-fourth-speed synchronizer clutch gear, sleeve, shift plates or spring unless replacement is required.

19. With long-nose pliers, compress the snap-ring that retains the mainshaft center bearing in the extension housing.
20. With snap-ring compressed, pull the mainshaft assembly and bearing out of the extension housing.
21. Remove and discard extension housing rear oil seal.
22. Remove rear bearing from the mainshaft by inserting steel plates on the front side of first-speed gear, then, with an arbor press, force the rear bearing from the mainshaft.
23. Remove the snap-ring that holds the mainshaft bearing onto the shaft.
24. Remove mainshaft bearing, re-

tainer ring, first-speed gear, and first-speed stop-ring.

25. Remove the snap-ring that holds the first and second clutch sleeve gear and clutch to the mainshaft.
26. Slide the first and second clutch sleeve gear and clutch from the mainshaft.

NOTE: do not dismantle the clutch unless inspection reveals need for parts replacement.

27. With a feeler gauge, measure countershaft gear end-play. This measurement should be .015-.025 in. If measurement is greater than specified, a new thrust washer of desirable thickness must be installed at assembly.
28. Drive the reverse idler gear shaft, from front to rear, far enough out of the case to permit removal of the reverse idler gear.
29. Remove idler gear shaft from the case, then remove the Woodruff key from the shaft.
30. Remove reverse gearshift lever detent spring retainer, gasket, plug and detent ball spring from the rear of the case.
31. Push the reverse gearshift lever shaft into the case, and remove. Lift the detent ball from the bottom of the case.
32. Remove the shift fork from the shaft and detent plate.
33. Using a countershaft dummy, drive the countershaft from the gear and case, allowing the countergear and dummy assembly to rest on the bottom of the case.
34. Remove the main drive pinion bearing outer snap-ring, then with a soft hammer, drive the main drive pinion into the case and remove.
35. Remove the main drive pinion bearing outer snap-ring, then, with an arbor press, remove the bearing from the main drive pinion. Remove the oil slinger.
36. Lift the countergear cluster from the bottom of the case.
37. Remove the countergear dummy shaft, 76 bearing rollers, thrust washers and tubular spacer from the center of the countergear.

Assembly

1. Slide the second-speed gear over the mainshaft (synchronizer cone toward rear) and down into position against the shoulder on the shaft.
2. Slide first and second clutch sleeve gear assembly (including second gear stop-ring) over the mainshaft. Be sure shift fork groove is toward the front and down into position against second-speed gear, (stop-ring must be indexed with the shift plates). Install a new snap-ring to secure.
3. Slide low gear stop-ring over the shaft and down into position and index with the shift plates.
4. Slide first-speed gear, (synchronizer cone toward clutch sleeve gear) over the mainshaft and down into position against the clutch sleeve gear.
5. Install the mainshaft bearing retainer ring, followed by the mainshaft center bearing. Using an arbor or other suitable tool, press the bearing down into position. Install new snap-ring.
6. Slide the rear bearing over the mainshaft and drive, or press, into position.
7. Install partially assembled mainshaft into the extension housing far enough to engage the retaining ring in the slot in the extension housing. Compress the retaining ring and, at the same time, seat the mainshaft in the extension housing.
8. Slide third-speed gear over the mainshaft, synchronizer cone forward, followed by third gear stop-ring.
9. Install third and fourth-speed synchronizer clutch gear assembly onto the mainshaft (shift fork groove toward rear) down against third-speed gear. Be sure to index the rear stop-ring with the clutch shift plates.
10. Install retaining snap-ring, then, using heavy grease, position the front stop-ring over the clutch gear, indexing the ring slots with the shift plates.

NOTE: if above indexing of the stop-rings and the positioning of the gears and clutches is ignored at this point, damage will most likely result when mating the extension housing to the transmission case.

11. Grease the bore of the countergear at each end, then install the roller bearing tubular spacer (centered). Insert the countergear dummy shaft.
12. Grease each bearing roller, then install 19 bearing rollers at each end of the gear. Now, install a flat spacer onto each end of the dummy shaft and into the gear, followed by 19 more bearing rollers and a spacer ring into each end of the countergear.
13. Grease the tanged thrust washers and install them, one over each end of the dummy shaft, with the tangs toward the case (away from the gear).
14. Lay the countergear assembly into the bottom of the case.
15. To install the main drive pinion, slide the bearing oil slinger over the main drive pinion shaft, then, press the main drive pinion bearing on the pinion shaft. (Be sure the outer snap-ring groove is toward the front). Seat bearing all the way, against shoulder on gear.
16. Install a new inner snap-ring into the bearing retainer groove of the shaft.
17. Now, install the outer snap-ring into the main drive pinion bearing. Then, insert and tap the main drive pinion and bearing assembly into the front of the case.
18. Start the countershaft into its bore at the rear of the case. Raise the countergear cluster assembly until the gear bore is aligned with the countershaft bore in the case. (Be sure the thrust washer tangs are in place in the case recesses.)
19. Press the countershaft into the countergear, washer and bearings assembly while displacing the dummy shaft. Install Woodruff key into countershaft, then continue pressing the countershaft and key into its bore and recess.

NOTE: countergear end-play should not exceed .029 in.

20. Install a new oil seal onto the reverse gearshift lever shaft.
21. Lubricate and carefully install the lever shaft into the bore in the case. Insert reverse fork into the lever.
22. Install reverse shift detent ball and spring retainer gasket and retainer. Tighten securely.
23. Start reverse idler gear shaft into the end of the case, and press in far enough to position the reverse idler gear on the protruding end of the shaft. At the same time, engage the shifter groove with the reverse shift fork.
24. With reverse idler gear properly positioned, install Woodruff key into the sliding gear shaft, then finish seating the shaft and key flush with the end of the case.
25. Grease, then position a new gasket on the end of the extension housing.
26. Center reverse sliding gear on its shaft, then carefully insert the mainshaft assembly into the case. (Be sure of the indexing of third and fourth-speed stop-rings and shifter plates.)
27. Move third and fourth - speed clutch sleeve slightly toward the front, and, at the same time, align the end of the mainshaft with the main drive pinion. Push in on the extension housing assembly until it is entirely seated against the rear of the case.
28. Install extension-to-case attaching bolts and torque to 50 ft. lbs.
29. Install back-up light switch (if so equipped).
30. Move reverse sliding gear ahead to neutral position.
31. Slide interlock sleeve into position in the gearshift housing. Lubricate and slide a new seal

over a shifter shaft and down into its groove.

32. Install the gearshift lever shaft into position in the housing, then install the gearshift operating lever onto the flats of the shaft, (lever pointing up). Install flat washer, lockwasher and nut. Tighten securely.
33. Place a detent ball in the sleeve, followed by the poppet spring and interlock pin.
34. Lubricate and slide a new seal over the other shifter shaft and down into its groove.
35. As with the first gearshift lever shaft, push the shaft into position in the housing, then install the operating lever onto the flats of the shaft (lever pointing up). Install flat washer, lockwasher and nut and tighten securely.
36. Place remaining detent ball on the poppet spring, compress the ball and spring with a small screwdriver, then, push the shafts in until seated. Turn the shafts until the balls drop into the neutral position detent.
37. Place transmission on its side, gearshift cover opening up.
38. Install a shift fork onto each synchronizer sleeve collar, and, with both sleeves in neutral position, install the shift housing and new gasket.
39. Install attaching bolts and tighten to 12 ft. lbs. (The center bolt on each side of the cover is a pilot bolt and should be installed first.)
40. Lubricate and install a new oil seal in the main drive pinion retainer bore, then install the retainer and gasket. Install attaching bolts, torqued to 15-20 ft. lbs.
41. Install gearshift control and rod assembly on the extension housing, then, secure rods with washers and clips.
42. Install output companion flange, washer and nut. Torque to 175 ft. lbs.

Type-5
2.77 Ford 3-Speed

Application

Falcon (6 Cyl.), 1967

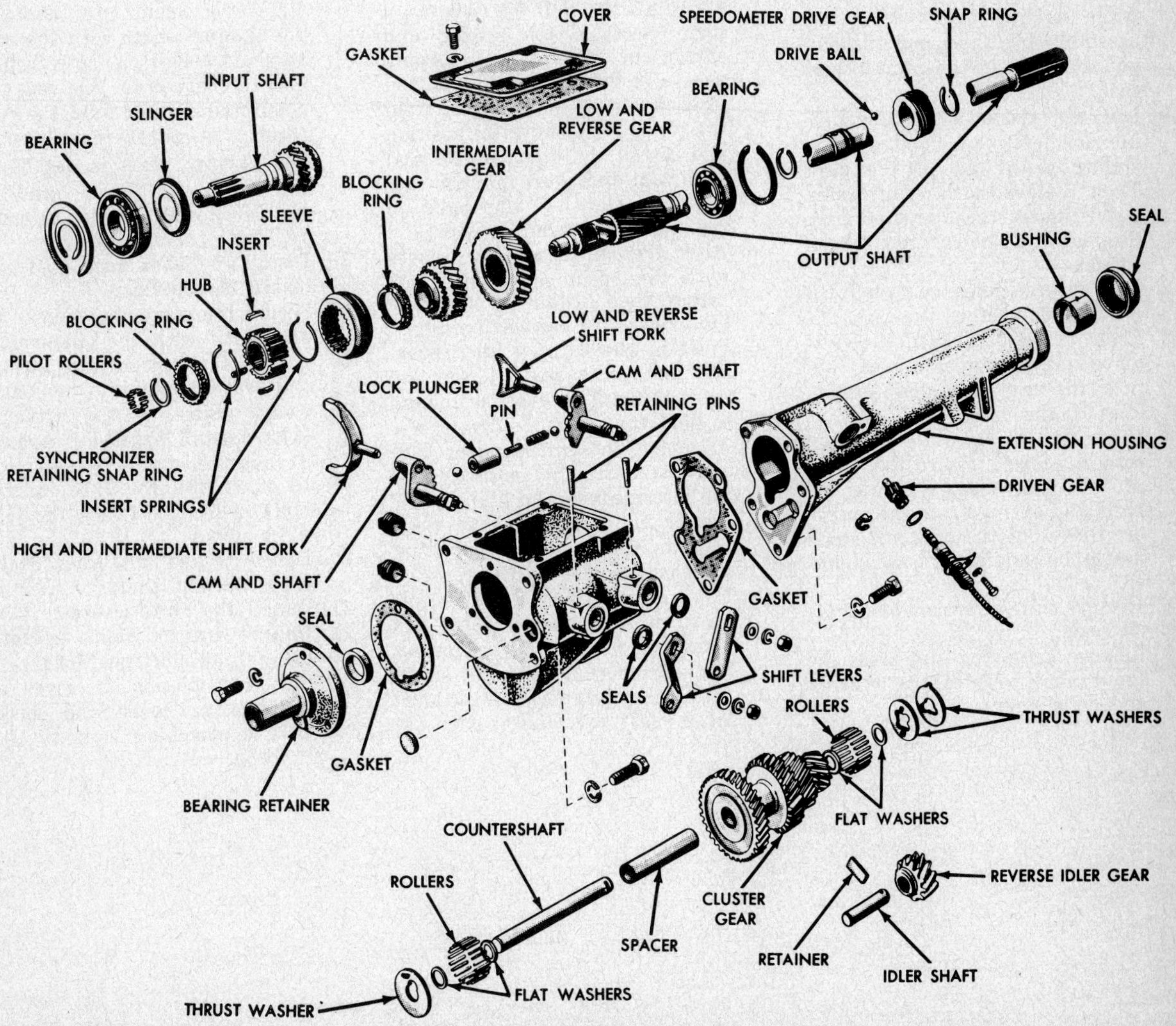
COVER
SPEEDOMETER DRIVE GEAR
SNAP RING
GASKET
DRIVE BALL
INPUT SHAFT
BEARING
SLINGER
LOW AND REVERSE GEAR
BEARING
INTERMEDIATE GEAR
BLOCKING RING
SLEEVE
SEAL
INSERT
OUTPUT SHAFT
BUSHING
HUB
BLOCKING RING
LOW AND REVERSE SHIFT FORK
PILOT ROLLERS
LOCK PLUNGER
CAM AND SHAFT
PIN
RETAINING PINS
EXTENSION HOUSING
SYNCHRONIZER RETAINING SNAP RING
DRIVEN GEAR
INSERT SPRINGS
HIGH AND INTERMEDIATE SHIFT FORK
CAM AND SHAFT
GASKET
SEAL
SHIFT LEVERS
SEALS
ROLLERS
THRUST WASHERS
GASKET
BEARING RETAINER
FLAT WASHERS
COUNTERSHAFT
REVERSE IDLER GEAR
ROLLERS
CLUSTER GEAR
SPACER
RETAINER
IDLER SHAFT
FLAT WASHERS
THRUST WASHER

2.77 Ford 3-speed transmission (© Ford Motor Co)

Disassembly

1. Drain the unit and remove transmission cover and gasket.
2. Remove outer shift levers and the interlock linkage.
3. Remove extension housing attaching bolts and remove the engine rear support bracket and the extension housing and gasket. Tap the end of the output shaft with a soft hammer and withdraw extension housing.
4. Remove speedometer drive gear snap-ring. Then, remove the drive gear and drive ball from the output shaft.
5. Remove idler and countershaft retainer.
6. With a dummy shaft, drive the shaft out of the cluster gear and case. Leave the dummy shaft in the cluster, at rest, in the bottom of the case.
7. Remove input shaft bearing retainer and gasket.
8. Remove input shaft assembly and front synchronizer blocking ring from the case.
9. Remove synchronizer snap-ring from the output shaft. Then, while holding the synchronizer assembly together, pull the output shaft out of the transmission case.
10. Lift the synchronizer assembly, intermediate, low and reverse sliding gears out of the case. Then, remove the two shift forks.
11. Drive the reverse idler shaft from the gear and remove from rear of the case.
12. Lift reverse idler gear and the cluster gear out of the case.
13. From the underside of the case, drive out the tapered pins that hold the cam and shaft assemblies in the case.
14. Drive the intermediate and high cam and shaft toward the inside of the case, then, separate the balls and spring from the plunger. Drive out the cam and shaft assemblies and remove the plunger.
15. Remove shift lever cam and shaft oil seals.
16. Remove snap-ring and press the input shaft out of the bearing and oil slinger.
17. Remove snap-ring, and remove the bearing from the output shaft.
18. Dismantle the components, such as synchronizer, countershaft cluster, etc., then clean and inspect parts.

Assembly

1. Press the input shaft bearing and oil slinger onto the input shaft, then install the snap-ring onto the shaft.
2. Press the output shaft bearing onto the output shaft, install snap-ring on the shaft.
3. Insert the tubular spacer and dummy shaft into the cluster gear assembly. Position one flat washer at each end of the spacer. Apply grease to the needle bearings and assemble the needle rollers around the dummy shaft at each end of the gear. Apply grease to the other two flat washers and thrust washers and assemble at each end of the cluster gear. Position the gear cluster assembly in the bottom of the transmission case.
4. Install reverse and low shift cam and shaft through the case opening. Assemble the spacer and spring in the plunger. Apply grease to each ball and position in each end of the plunger. Hold the plunger assembly in position and install the intermediate and high cam and shaft into the case opening, allowing the balls to register in the cam detents.
5. Align the cam and shaft grooves with the openings in the shaft bosses, then install the retaining pins. Check the cam action.
6. Position the reverse idler gear, and insert the shaft (from the rear) through the case far enough to hold the gear.
7. Assemble the synchronizer hub and insert the hub assembly into the intermediate and high sleeve. Install one of the blocking rings into the rear side of the hub. Coat the blocking rings with grease.
8. Using grease, assemble the needle bearings in the input shaft and install the front synchronizer blocking ring on the input shaft.
9. Install the shift forks in the shift lever shaft assemblies, with the large fork in the intermediate and high shaft assembly. The web of the low and reverse fork must be to the rear of the shaft center.
10. Start the output shaft through the rear opening of the transmission case. Place the low and reverse gear on the shaft, followed by the intermediate gear. Tilt the output shaft enough to allow the rear shift fork to engage the sliding gear groove.
11. With the longer hub forward, slide the synchronizer assembly onto the output shaft and engage the synchronizer sleeve in the intermediate and high shift fork.
12. Install the synchronizer hub snap ring.
13. Position the input shaft and front synchronizer blocking ring.
14. Place a new gasket on the input shaft bearing retainer. Install bearing retainer oil seal, then install the bearing retainer. Line up the drain groove in the retainer with the oil hole in the case, then with sealer on the retainer attaching screws, torque them to 12-15 ft. lbs.
15. Raise the cluster gear and align the dummy shaft with the countershaft hole in the case. Tap the countershaft into the case and countershaft gear until the countershaft is entirely in position and the dummy shaft is out of the case. Cluster gear end-play should be .004-.018 in. Adjust by replacing thrust washers.
16. Install the idler gear shaft and install the retainer.
17. Secure the speedometer gear and drive ball with the snap-ring.
18. If necessary, install new bushing and seal in extension housing.
19. Using sealer on the attaching bolts, install extension housing. Torque the attaching bolts to 37 to 42 ft. lbs. for 7/16 in. x 14 bolts or 28 to 38 ft. lbs. for 3/8 in. x 16 bolts.
20. Lubricate and install new seal on each cam and shaft.
21. Install the shift levers.
22. Check transmission operation through all shift positions.
23. Fill transmission to level and install case cover and gasket. Torque attaching bolts to 10-13 ft. lbs.

Type-6
3.03 Fully Synchronized Ford 3-Speed

Application

Buick LeSabre, 1970-71,
Centurion, 1971
Buick Wildcat, 1967-70
Buick Special, 1967-69 (GS),
1967-69 (V8)
Comet, 1967 (V8),
1967 (All), 1971-74
Cougar, 1967-74

Fairlane, 1967 (V8),
1967-74 (All)
Firebird (V8), 1968-69
Ford, 1967-71
Maverick, 1970-74
Mercury, 1967-71
Montego, 1968-74

Mustang, 1967 (V8),
1967-72 (All)
Oldsmobile, 1967-71
Olds F-85 (V8), 1967-69
Tempest (V8), 1967-69
Torino, 1971-74
Pontiac, 1967-71

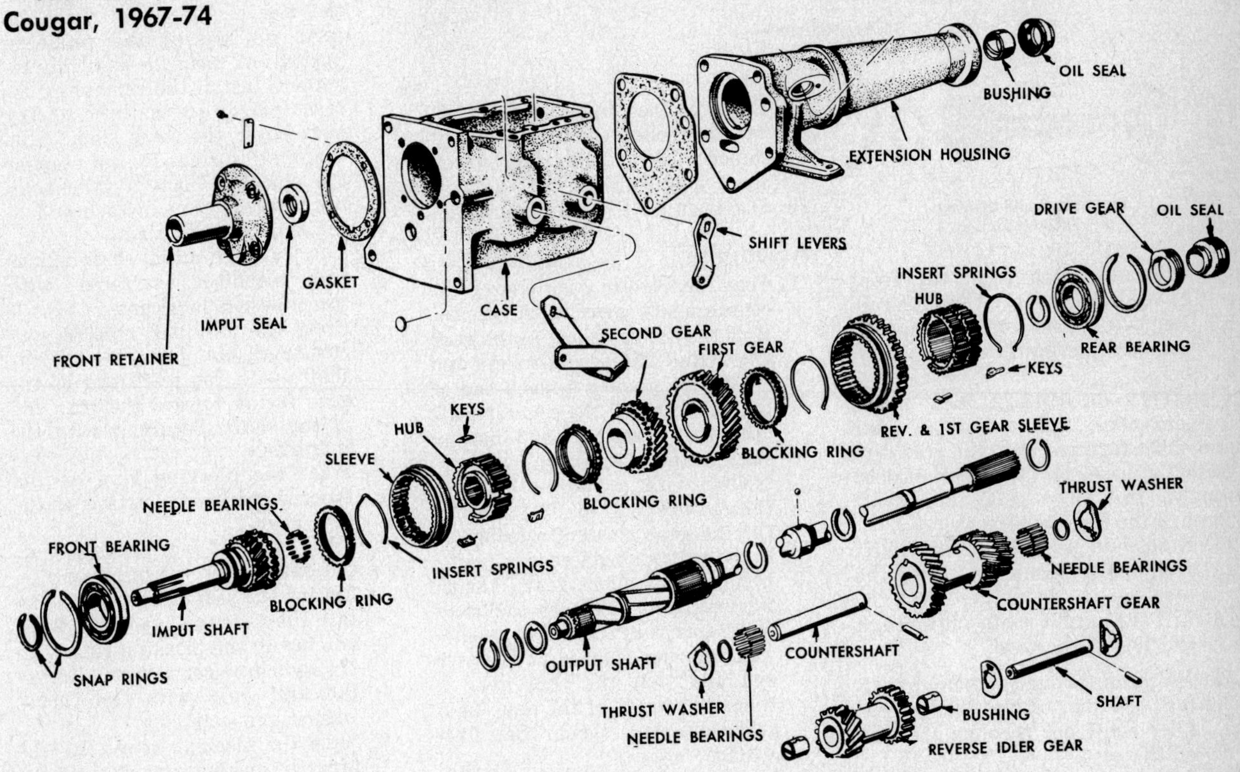
OIL SEAL
BUSHING
EXTENSION HOUSING
SHIFT LEVERS
GASKET
CASE
IMPUT SEAL
FRONT RETAINER
DRIVE GEAR
OIL SEAL
INSERT SPRINGS
HUB
REAR BEARING
KEYS
SECOND GEAR
FIRST GEAR
REV. & 1ST GEAR SLEEVE
BLOCKING RING
KEYS
HUB
SLEEVE
BLOCKING RING
NEEDLE BEARINGS
THRUST WASHER
FRONT BEARING
INSERT SPRINGS
NEEDLE BEARINGS
COUNTERSHAFT GEAR
BLOCKING RING
IMPUT SHAFT
SNAP RINGS
OUTPUT SHAFT
COUNTERSHAFT
THRUST WASHER
NEEDLE BEARINGS
BUSHING
SHAFT
REVERSE IDLER GEAR

3.03 Ford 3-speed transmission (© Ford Motor Co)

Disassembly

1. Drain the lubricant, then remove the cover bolts and the case cover.
2. Remove the five attaching screws, then remove the extension housing from the transmission case. Remove a long spring which retains the detent plug in the case. Remove the detent plug with a small magnet.
3. Remove the four attaching screws, then remove the front bearing retainer from the case.
4. Remove the filler plug. Working through the filler plug hole, drive the roll pin out of the case and countershaft with a small punch.
5. With a dummy shaft, push the countershaft out of the rear of the case until the countershaft cluster gear can be lowered to the bottom of the case. Remove the countershaft from the rear of the case.
6. Remove the snap-ring. Lift the input gear and shaft from the front of the case. Press the shaft out of the bearing.
7. Remove the snap-ring that holds the speedometer gear onto the shaft. Slide the speedometer gear off the output shaft. Remove the speedometer gear lockball.
8. Remove the snap-ring that holds the output shaft bearing on the shaft. With a puller, remove the bearing from both the case and shaft.
9. Place both shaft levers in the neutral position.
10. Remove the set screw that holds the detent springs and plugs in the case. Remove a detent spring and plug from the case.
11. Remove the set screw that holds the first and reverse shift fork to the shift rail. Slide first and reverse shift rail out through the rear of the case.
12. Rotate the first and reverse shift fork upward, then lift it from the case.
13. Remove the set screw that holds the second and third shift fork to the shift rail. Rotate the shift rail 90°.
14. With a magnet, lift the interlock plug from the case.
15. Tap on the inner end of the second and third shift rail to remove the

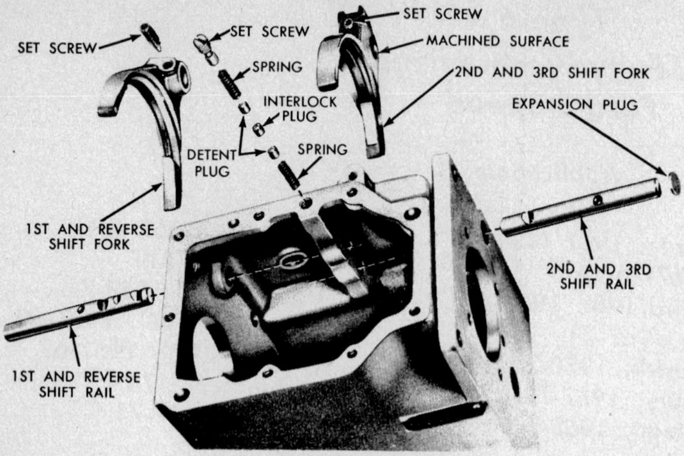
SET SCREW
SET SCREW
SET SCREW
MACHINED SURFACE
SPRING
2ND AND 3RD SHIFT FORK
INTERLOCK PLUG
EXPANSION PLUG
DETENT PLUG
SPRING
1ST AND REVERSE SHIFT FORK
2ND AND 3RD SHIFT RAIL
1ST AND REVERSE SHIFT RAIL

Shift rail and forks

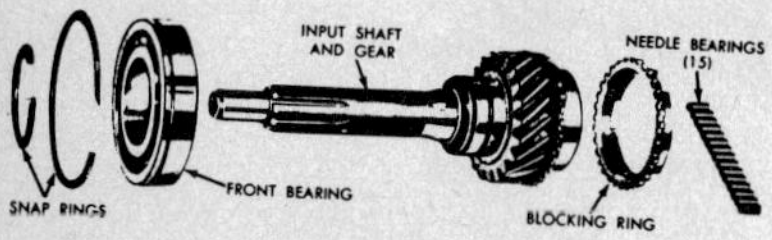
INPUT SHAFT AND GEAR
NEEDLE BEARINGS (15)
SNAP RINGS
FRONT BEARING
BLOCKING RING

Input shaft and bearing
(© Ford Motor Co)

expansion plug from the front of the case. Remove the shift rail.

16. Remove second and third detent plug and spring from the detent bore.

NOTE: on 1971-72 RAT model transmissions, pull the input gear and shaft forward until the gear contacts the case. On all other models, remove the input gear and shaft through the front of the case.

17. Rotate the second and third shift fork upward, then lift it from the case.
18. Lift the output shaft out through the top of the case.
19. Working through the front bearing opening, drive the reverse idler shaft out through the rear of the case.
20. Lift the reverse idler gear and two thrust washers from the case.
21. Lift the countershaft gear and thrust washers from the case.
22. Remove the countershaft-to-case retaining pin and any needle bearings which may have fallen into the case.
23. Remove the shift levers and shafts from the case. Discard the O-rings.
24. Remove the snap-ring from the front of the output shaft, then slide the synchronizer and the second-speed gear from the shaft.
25. Remove the next snap-ring and thrust washer from the output shaft, then slide the first gear and blocking ring off the shaft.
26. Remove the next snap-ring from the output shaft, then press off the first-reverse synchronizer hub from the shaft.
27. Remove the dummy shaft, 50 bearing rollers and the two retainer washers from the countershaft gear.
28. Disassemble the synchronizers.

Assembly

1. Coat the bore in each end of the countershaft gear with grease. Hold the dummy shaft in the gear and install 25 bearing rollers and a retainer washer in each end of the gear. Install the countershaft gear, thrust washers and dummy shaft in the case. End-play is controlled with variable thickness thrust washers to .004-.018 in. Let the gear cluster assembly lie in the bottom of the case.
2. Install the idler gear, thrust washers and shaft in the case. Make sure that the thrust washer with the flat side, is at the web end and that the spur gear is toward the rear of the case. Idler gear end-play should be .004-.018 in.
3. Install an insert spring into the groove of the first and reverse synchronizer hub. Be sure that the spring covers all insert grooves. Start the hub in the sleeve, being sure the alignment marks are properly indexed. Position the three inserts in the hub and be sure the small end is over the spring and that the shoulder is on the inside of the hub. Slide the sleeve and reverse gear onto the hub until the detent is engaged. Install the other insert

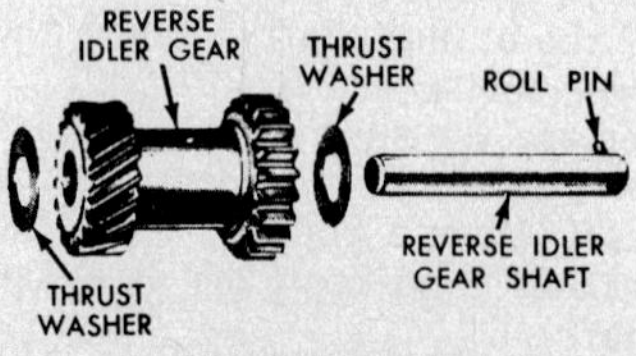
REVERSE IDLER GEAR
THRUST WASHER
ROLL PIN
REVERSE IDLER GEAR SHAFT
THRUST WASHER

Reverse idler shaft
(© Ford Motor Co)

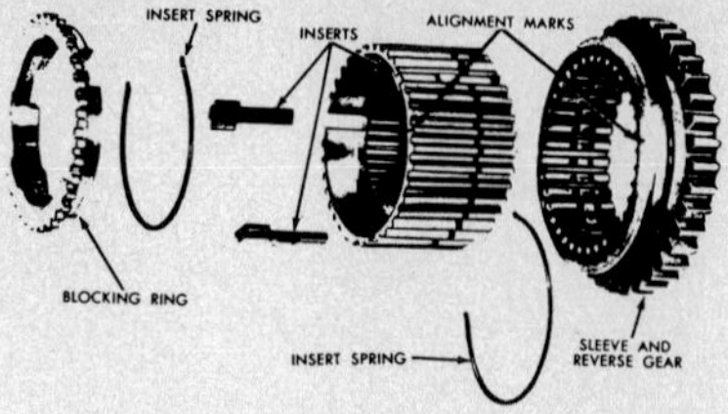
INSERT SPRING
INSERTS
ALIGNMENT MARKS
BLOCKING RING
INSERT SPRING
SLEEVE AND REVERSE GEAR

First and reverse synchronizer
(© Ford Motor Co)

spring in the front of the hub to hold the inserts against it.

4. Install one insert spring into a groove of the second-third synchronizer hub. With the alignment marks on the hub and sleeve aligned, start the hub into the sleeve. Place the three inserts on top of the retaining spring and push the assembly together. Install the remaining insert spring, so that the spring ends cover the same slots as do the other spring. Do not stagger the springs. Place a synchronizer blocking ring in each end of the synchronizer sleeve.
5. Lubricate the output shaft splines and machined surfaces with transmission lubricant.
6. Press the first and reverse synchronizer hub onto the output shaft, with the teeth end of the gear facing toward the rear end of the shaft. Secure it with the snap-ring.
7. Place the blocking ring on the tapered machined surface of the first gear.
8. Slide the first gear onto the output shaft, with the blocking ring toward the rear of the shaft. Rotate the gear to engage the three notches in the blocking ring with the synchronizer inserts. Secure the first gear with the thrust washer and snap-ring.
9. Slide the blocking ring onto the tapered, machined surface of the second gear. Slide the second gear, with blocking ring and the second and third gear synchronizer, onto the mainshaft. The tapered machined surface of the second gear must be toward the front of the shaft. Secure the synchronizer with a snap-ring.
10. Install new O-rings onto the two shift lever shafts. Lubricate the shafts with transmission fluid and install them into the case. Secure each shift lever onto its shaft.
11. Coat the bore of the input shaft with a light coat of grease. Install the 15 bearing rollers into the bore.

NOTE: on RAT models (1971-72) install the input gear and bearing through the top of the case. On other models the input shaft is installed through the front of the transmission.

12. Position the output shaft assembly in the case.
13. Place a detent plug spring and a plug in the case. Place a second and third-speed shift fork in the synchronizer groove. Rotate the fork into position and install the second and third-speed shift rail. Move the rail inward until the detent plug engages the forward notch (second). Secure the fork to the shaft with a set screw. Move the synchronizer to the neutral position.
14. Install the interlock plug in the case.
15. Place first and reverse shift fork in the groove of the first and reverse synchronizer. Rotate the fork into position and install the first and reverse shift rail. Move the rail inward until the center notch is aligned with the detent bore. Secure the fork to the shaft with a set screw. Install the remaining detent plug and spring. Secure the detent spring with the slotted head set screw. Tighten set screw until the head is flush with the case.
16. Install a new expansion plug in the case front.
17. Install the input shaft and gear in the front of the case.
18. Place front bearing retainer (with new gasket in place) on the case with the oil return groove at the bottom. Torque attaching screws to 30 ft. lbs.
19. Install the large snap-ring on the rear bearing. Place the bearing on the output shaft, with the snap-ring end toward the rear of the shaft. Press bearing into place and secure with a snap-ring.
20. Hold the speedometer drive gear lock ball in the detent and slide the speedometer gear into place. Secure the gear with a snap-ring.
21. Lift the countershaft gear cluster up into place, and, by entering the countershaft at the rear of the case, push the dummy shaft out of the gear and transmission case. Before the countershaft is completely in place, align the roll pin hole in the shaft with the hole in the case.

NOTE: on all eight-cylinder vehicles and Ford six-cylinder models the countershaft is a press fit in the case. On Ford six-cylinder models with RAN transmissions, there is a radial clearance of .020 in. at front bore and .010 in. at rear.

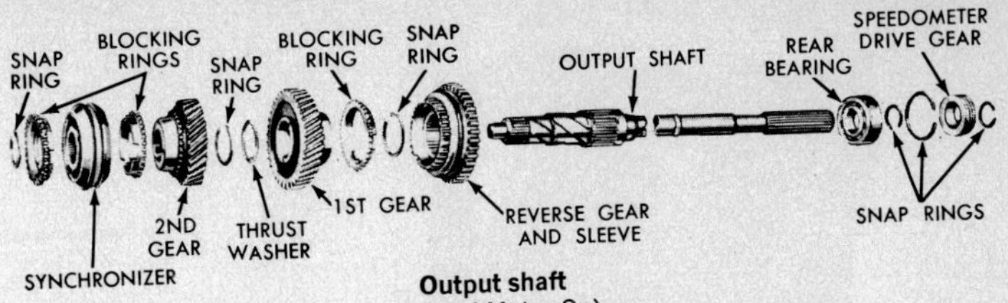
SNAP RING
BLOCKING RINGS
SNAP RING
BLOCKING RING
SNAP RING
OUTPUT SHAFT
REAR BEARING
SPEEDOMETER DRIVE GEAR
SNAP RINGS
REVERSE GEAR AND SLEEVE
1ST GEAR
THRUST WASHER
2ND GEAR
SYNCHRONIZER
Output shaft
(© Ford Motor Co)

22. Working through the filler hole, install a roll pin into the case and countershaft.
23. Install filler and drain plugs in the case.
24. Coat a new extension housing gasket with sealer and install it on the case.
25. Apply sealer to attaching screws and secure extension housing to the case by torqueing the screws to 42 to 50 ft. lbs.
26. With transmission in gear, pour lubricant over the entire gear train while rotating the input or output shaft.
27. Install the transmission cover, with a new sealer-coated gasket in place, and torque the nine attaching screws to 14-19 ft. lbs.
28. Check operation of transmission in all of the gear positions.

Type-7

Ford (Pinto 1600 and 2000) 4-Speed

Application Pinto, 1971-74

NOTE: cars equipped with this transmission are identified by a transmission code of "5" on the vehicle identification plate.

Transmission Disassembly

1. Remove the clutch release bearing and detach the clutch housing.
2. Drain the lubricant and remove the cover and gasket from the case.
3. Remove the threaded plug, spring and shift rail detent plunger from the front of the case.
4. Drive the access plug from the rear of the case. Drive the interlock retaining pin from the case and remove the interlock plate.
5. Remove the roll pin from the selector lever arm.
6. Tap the front end of the shift rail, to displace the plug at the rear of the extension housing.
7. Remove the selector arm and shift fork from the case.
8. Loosen the extension housing and rotate the housing to align the countershaft with the cutaway in the extension housing flange.
9. Drive the countershaft rearward until the shaft clears the front of the case. Install a dummy shaft in the case and gear until the countershaft gear can be lowered to the bottom of the case. Remove the countershaft.
10. Lift the extension housing and mainshaft from the case as an assembly.
11. Remove the input shaft and bearing retainer from the case as an assembly.
12. Remove the reverse idler gear and shaft from the rear of the case.
13. Remove the bearing retainers, bearings (19 each end), dummy shaft and spacer from the countershaft gear.
14. Remove the pilot bearing and bearing retainer from the input shaft gear.
15. Do not remove the ball bearing from the input shaft unless replacement is necessary.
16. Pry the input shaft seal out of the bearing retainer.
17. Lift the fourth gear blocker ring from the front of the output shaft.
18. Remove the snap-ring from the forward end of the output shaft.
19. Support third gear on press plates and place the output shaft and extension housing in a press. Press the output shaft out of the third-fourth speed synchronizer and third gear, while supporting the extension housing and output shaft from beneath. Remove the snap-ring and washer and remove second gear and the blocker ring from the output shaft.
20. Disassemble the synchronizer assembly by pulling the sleeve from the hub and removing the inserts and spring.
21. Remove the snap-ring which retains the output shaft bearing to the extension housing.
22. Use a plastic hammer and tap the output shaft assembly from the extension housing.
23. Position press plates behind first gear and place the assembly in a press. The first and second speed

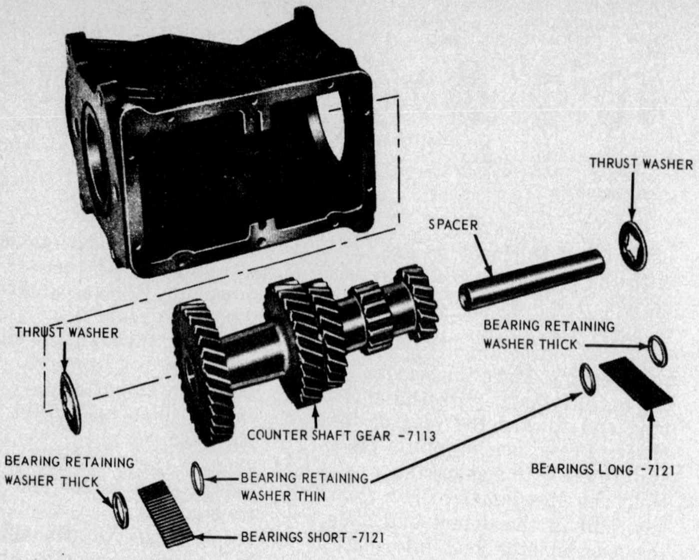
THRUST WASHER
SPACER
THRUST WASHER
BEARING RETAINING
WASHER THICK
COUNTER SHAFT GEAR -7113
BEARING RETAINING
WASHER THICK
BEARING RETAINING
WASHER THIN
BEARINGS LONG -7121
BEARINGS SHORT -7121

Countershaft gear disassembled (© Ford Motor Co)

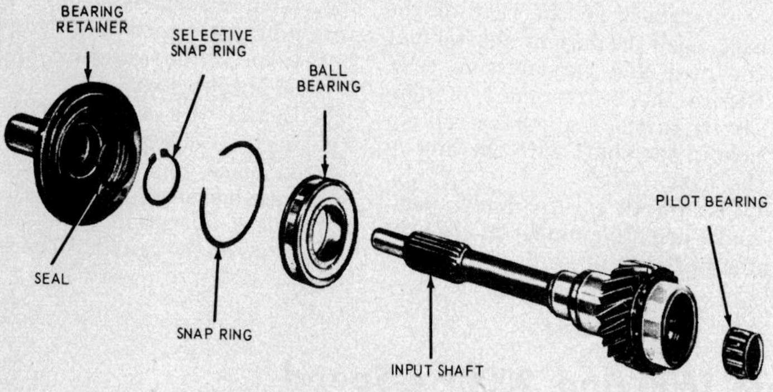
BEARING
RETAINER
SELECTIVE
SNAP RING
BALL
BEARING
PILOT BEARING
SEAL
SNAP RING
INPUT SHAFT

Input shaft disassembled (© Ford Motor Co)

synchronizer are serviced as an assembly. No attempt should be made to separate the hub from the shaft. The only serviceable parts are the springs and inserts. If the hub or sleeve is worn, the shaft and synchronizer must be replaced as an assembly.

24. Drive the shift rail bushing from the rear of the extension housing, using a 9/16 in. socket. Do not remove serviceable bushings.
25. Pry the shift rail seal from the rear of the case.
26. Remove the remaining shaft linkage from the case.

Transmission Assembly

1. Install a new shift rail seal in the rear of the case.
2. If the shift rail bushing was removed, drive a new one into position with a 9/16 in. socket.
3. Slide the synchronizer hub over the shaft, making sure that the shift fork groove is toward the front of the shaft. The sleeve and hub are select fit and must be assembled with the etch marks in the same relative locations. Locate an insert in each of three slots in the hub. Oil all parts, and install an insert spring inside the sleeve. The spring tab must locate in a section of an insert. Fit the other spring to the opposite face, making sure that the tab locates in the same insert. Both springs should be in the same rotational direction. The tab end of one spring should be aligned with the tab of the spring on the opposite side.
4. Assemble a blocker ring on the first gear side of the first-second synchronizer. Lubricate the cone surface of first gear and slide the cone onto the output shaft, so that the cone surface engages the blocker ring.
5. Position the spacer on the output shaft, larger diameter rearward.
6. Install a snap-ring (selected from the chart) which will come closest to removing all end-play from the output shaft bearing. Position the output shaft bearing on the shaft and press the bearing into place. Secure the bearing with the thickest snap-ring that will fit the groove.

Part No.	*Thickness*	*Identification*
D1FZ-7030-A	0.0679-	Color Coded—Copper
D1FZ-7030-B	0.0689-	Letter—W
D1FZ-7030-C	0.0699-	Letter-V
D1FZ-7030-D	0.0709-	Letter—U
D1FZ-7030-E	0.0719-	None
D1FZ-7030-F	0.0728-	Color Coded—Blue
D1FZ-7030-G	0.0738-	Color Coded—Black
D1FZ-7030-H	0.0748-	Color Coded—Brown

7. Slide the synchronizer over the hub and locate an insert in each of three slots in the sleeve. The sleeve and hub must be assembled with the etch marks in the same relative locations. Lightly oil all parts. Complete assembly

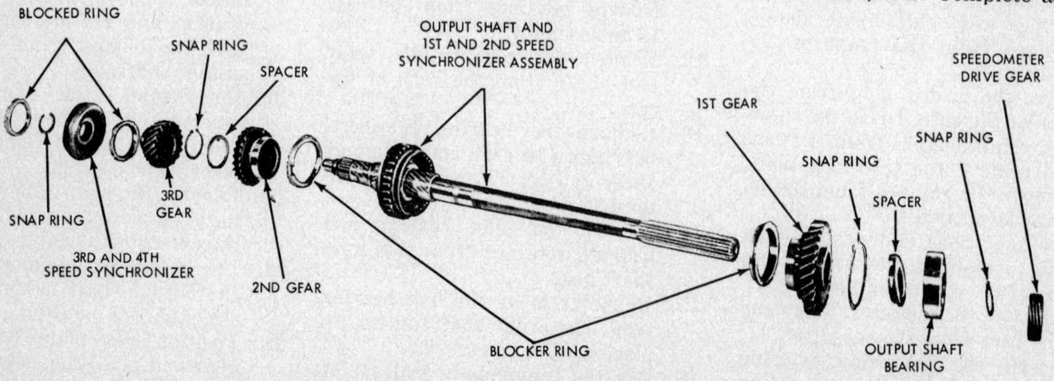
BLOCKED RING
SNAP RING
SPACER
OUTPUT SHAFT AND
1ST AND 2ND SPEED
SYNCHRONIZER ASSEMBLY
1ST GEAR
SPEEDOMETER
DRIVE GEAR
SNAP RING
SNAP RING
SPACER
SNAP RING
3RD
GEAR
3RD AND 4TH
SPEED SYNCHRONIZER
2ND GEAR
BLOCKER RING
OUTPUT SHAFT
BEARING

Output shaft disassembled (© Ford Motor Co)

of the synchronizer by following directions in previous Step 3.

8. Position second gear and the blocker ring on the output shaft, dog teeth facing rearward. Install the washer and snap-ring. Position third gear on the output shaft, dog teeth forward. Lubricate the gear cones and assemble a blocker ring on third gear cone.
9. Position the third-fourth synchronizer assembly on the output shaft, hub boss facing forward.
10. Install press plates against the boss on the synchronizer hub.
11. Place the entire unit in a press, extension end up, and press the synchronizer assembly onto the output shaft as far as possible.
12. Retain the third-fourth synchronizer assembly to the output shaft with a snap-ring. Pull up on the synchronizer so that the snap-ring is tight in the groove.
13. Lubricate the gear cone and place the blocker ring on the input shaft gear cone.
14. Using Tool T71P-17271-A, press the speedometer drive gear onto the shaft until the dowels of the tool just contact the bearing outer race.
15. Lubricate the bearing bore of the extension housing. Install the output shaft in the housing. It may be necessary to tap the shaft while holding the synchronizer sleeves firmly. Secure the shaft to the housing with the snap-ring previously installed.
16. Press the bearing on the input shaft. The snap-ring groove must be toward the front of the shaft. Use the thickest snap-ring that will fit.
17. Slide the spacer and dummy shaft into the countershaft gear. Position a thin bearing retaining washer on each end of the dummy shaft. Lubricate the roller bearings and load 19 long bearings in the small end of the gear and 19 short bearings in the long end of the gear. Place a thick retaining washer over each end of the dummy shaft. Grease the thrust washers and place one on each end of the dummy shaft. The tabs must be in the same relative position to engage the slots in the case when the gear is lowered. Loop a piece of rope around each end of the gear and carefully install the gear and rope through the rear of the case. Lower the gear in place.
18. Lubricate the reverse idler gear shaft. Position the selector lever relay on the pivot pin. Secure with a spring clip. Hold the gear in the lever, long hub toward the rear of the case, and slide the reverse idler shaft into place. Seat the shaft in the case with a brass hammer.
19. Install a new seal in the input shaft bearing retainer. Install the input shaft in the case with a new bearing retainer O-ring. Tap on the outer race of the bearing to seat the outer snap-ring.

Caution Use a soft hammer and do not tap on the input shaft itself.

20. Carefully slide third-fourth synchronizer sleeve into fourth speed position.
21. Place a new gasket on the extension housing.
22. Lubricate and install the input shaft pilot bearing on the shaft. Slide the extension housing and output shaft into place, being careful not to disturb the fourth speed synchronizer.
23. Align the cutaway in the extension housing flange with the countershaft bore in the rear of the case.
24. Lift the countershaft gear into place and install the countershaft, making sure that the thrust washers remain in place. The flat on the countershaft should be parallel to the top of the case. Tap the shaft with a brass hammer until the front of the shaft is flush with the case.
25. Place the shift forks in the synchronizer sleeves. Install the interlock lever and new retaining pin. Lubricate the shift rail oil seal and slide the shift rail through the extension housing, case and second and first speed shift forks. Position the selector arm on the rail and slide the rail through third and fourth speed shift fork. Slide the shift rail through the front of the case until the center detent bore is aligned with the detent plunger bore. Install a new retaining pin in the selector arm.
26. Install the detent plunger, spring and plug.
27. Install a new access plug in the rear of the case.
28. Align the extension housing and install the bolts finger-tight. Be sure the shift rail slides freely. Tighten the bolts.
29. Position a new oil seal with tension spring and lip facing in the direction of the case.
30. Drive the seal in until it bottoms.
31. Position a new O-ring in the groove in the case. Position the input shaft bearing retainer with the groove in the retainer aligned with the oil passage in the case. Install the retaining bolts finger-tight.
32. Install the flywheel housing and tighten the retaining bolts and the front bearing retainer attaching bolts.
33. Install the clutch release arm and bearing.
34. Install a new extension housing plug.
35. Install a new cover gasket and cover.

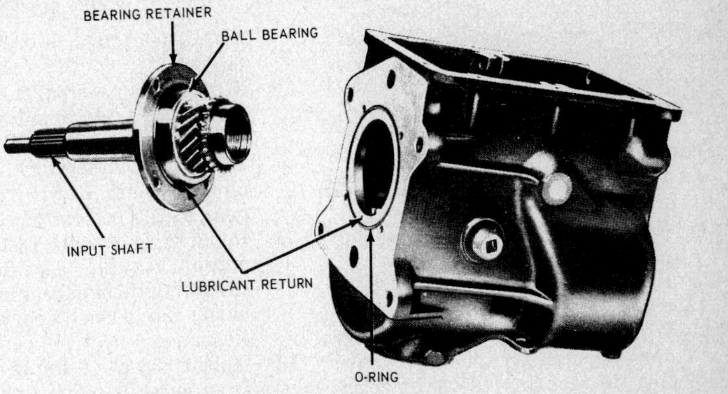
BEARING RETAINER
BALL BEARING
INPUT SHAFT
LUBRICANT RETURN
O-RING
Installing input shaft gear (© Ford Motor Co)

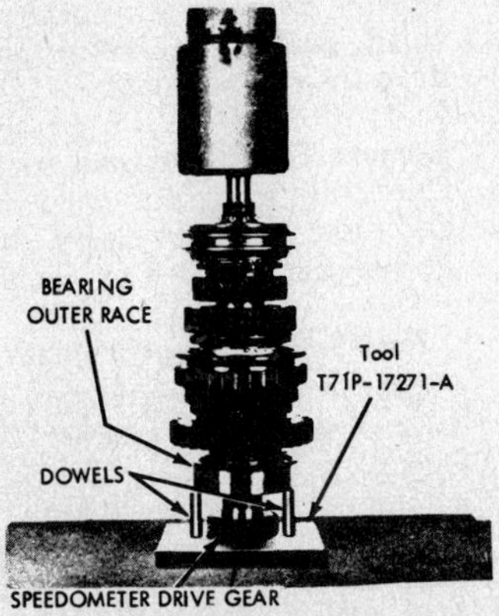
BEARING OUTER RACE
Tool T71P-17271-A
DOWELS
SPEEDOMETER DRIVE GEAR
Installing speedometer driven gear (© Ford Motor Co)

Type 8
Ford (Pinto 1600)
4-Speed

Application
Pinto, 1971-73

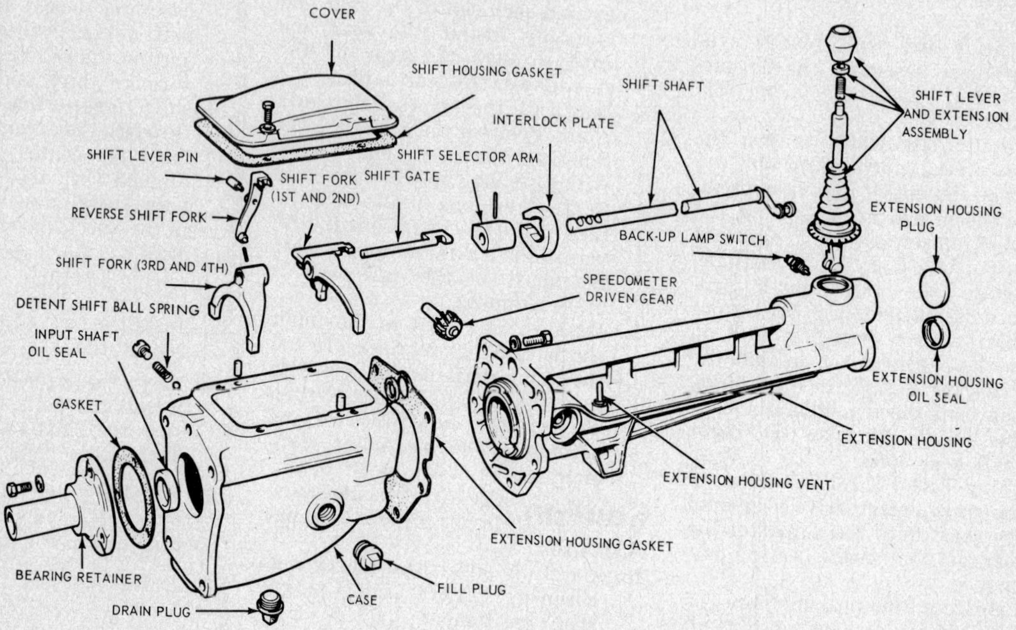
COVER
SHIFT HOUSING GASKET
SHIFT SHAFT
SHIFT LEVER AND EXTENSION ASSEMBLY
INTERLOCK PLATE
SHIFT SELECTOR ARM
SHIFT LEVER PIN
SHIFT FORK (1ST AND 2ND)
SHIFT GATE
REVERSE SHIFT FORK
BACK-UP LAMP SWITCH
EXTENSION HOUSING PLUG
SHIFT FORK (3RD AND 4TH)
SPEEDOMETER DRIVEN GEAR
DETENT SHIFT BALL SPRING
INPUT SHAFT OIL SEAL
EXTENSION HOUSING OIL SEAL
GASKET
EXTENSION HOUSING
EXTENSION HOUSING VENT
EXTENSION HOUSING GASKET
BEARING RETAINER
FILL PLUG
CASE
DRAIN PLUG

British 4 speed transmission

NOTE: cars equipped with this transmission are identified by a transmission code of "E" on the vehicle identification plate.

Transmission Disassembly

1. Remove four bolts and top cover plate.
2. Pry plug from rear of extension housing.
3. Remove plunger screw from right side of case.
4. Working through the top cover opening, use a punch to remove the pin securing the shift selector arm to the shift shaft.
5. Pull the shift shaft rearward, being careful not to drop the shift selector arm and the interlock plate.
6. Move the first-second and third-fourth gear synchronizer hubs toward the input shaft bearing.
7. If necessary, remove the shift shaft plunger spring from the case. The plunger screw was removed in Step 3.
8. Remove the pin from the third-fourth shift fork. Remove the fork.
9. Unbolt extension housing from case. With a plastic hammer, tap the extension housing slightly rearward. Rotate the housing until the countershaft lines up with the notch in the housing flange.
10. Tap the countershaft rearward with a brass drift until it is just clear of the front of the case. Push the countershaft out with a dummy shaft. Lower the cluster gear to the bottom of the case.
11. Remove extension housing and output shaft assembly. The third-fourth synchronizer sleeve must be pushed forward for clearance.
12. Unbolt front bearing retainer from case. Remove retainer and gasket.
13. Remove input shaft oil seal.
14. Remove the snap ring around the input shaft bearing. Tap the input shaft gear and bearing assembly out of the transmission with a brass drift. Remove the needle roller bearing from the recess in the end of the input shaft gear.
15. Remove the cluster gear, two thrust washers, and the dummy shaft from the case. Remove 20 needle rollers and a retaining washer from each end of the cluster gear.
16. Assemble a nut, a flat washer, and a sleeve on a 5/16 in. x 24 UNF threaded bolt. Screw the bolt into the reverse idler shaft and tighten to pull out the shaft.
17. Remove the low-reverse shift fork from the lever pin inside the case. Do not remove the pin.

Component Disassembly

Third-Fourth Synchronizer

1. Remove fourth gear blocking ring from input shaft gear side of assembly.
2. Remove synchronizer hub snap-ring from forward end of output shaft and discard.
3. Support third gear. Press the output shaft out of the third-fourth gear synchronizer and third gear. Be careful not to drop the output shaft.
4. Pull the sleeve off the hub. Remove the inserts and springs.
5. Check all parts for wear. Synchronizer hub and sleeve should be replaced if worn or damaged.

First-Second Synchronizer

1. Remove plug in extension housing. Remove speedometer driven gear.
2. Remove snap-ring holding output shaft bearing to extension housing. With a plastic hammer, tap output shaft assembly out of housing.
3. Remove snap-ring holding speed-

Press Ram

Removing low-reverse sliding gear, spacer and output shaft bearing
(© Ford Motor Co)

ometer drive gear. Pull off gear. Remove snap-ring holding output shaft bearing.

4. Support low and reverse sliding gear. Press low and reverse sliding gear, spacer, and output shaft bearing from the output shaft.
5. Remove snap-ring holding first-second synchronizer assembly to output shaft.
6. Support second gear. Press second gear and first-second synchronizer assembly from output shaft.
7. Dismantle synchronizer assembly. Replace synchronizer hub or sleeve if worn or damaged. The output shaft bearing must be replaced.

Input Shaft and Gear

1. Remove and discard input shaft snap-ring.
2. Press off input shaft bearing.

Component Assembly

Third-Fourth Synchronizer

1. Slide gear over hub. Locate an insert in each slot.
2. Install a synchronizer spring inside the sleeve beneath the inserts; the spring tang should fit into an insert. Install the other spring on the opposite side, fitting the tang into the same insert. When viewed from the edge, the springs should run in opposite directions.
3. Place the third gear on the output shaft with the dog teeth forward. Assemble the blocking ring on the third gear cone.
4. Place the synchronizer assembly on the output shaft with the boss forward.
5. Support the hub. Press the hub on the output shaft and install a new snap-ring.

First-Second Synchronizer

1. Install the second gear on the output shaft with the cone and dog teeth to the rear.
2. Slide the synchronizer sleeve over the hub. Place an insert in each of the three slots.
3. Install synchronizer springs as for third-fourth synchronizer assembly.
4. Install a blocking ring to cone on second gear.
5. Install synchronizer assembly on output shaft with the gear teeth on the periphery of the synchronizer sleeve forward. Slide low and reverse sliding gear to the rear of the synchronizer hub.
6. Support the sliding gear. Press synchronizer assembly onto output shaft as far as possible.
7. Secure the synchronizer assembly with snap-ring.
8. Place a blocking ring on first gear side of first-second synchronizer assembly on output shaft. Install first gear, cone side forward.
9. Place the spacer with the larger

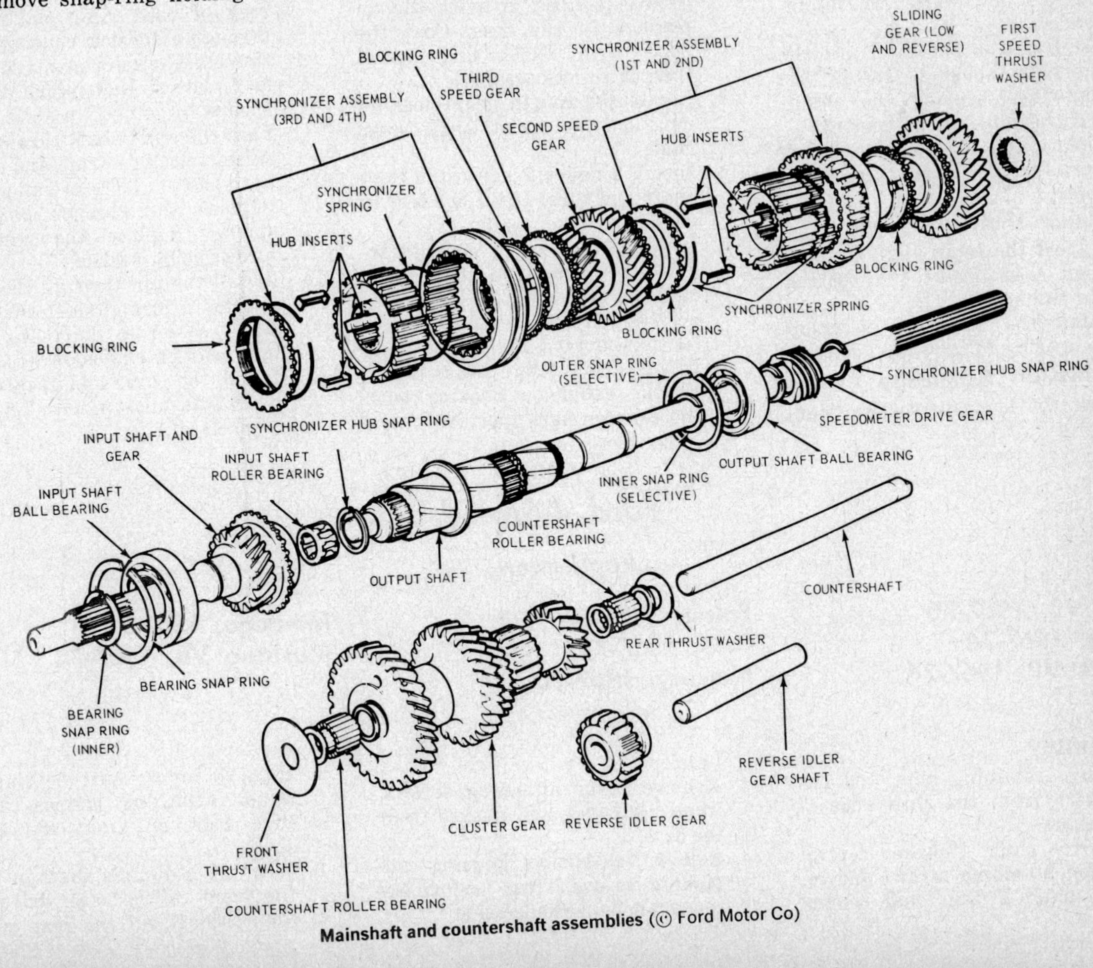
BLOCKING RING
SYNCHRONIZER ASSEMBLY (3RD AND 4TH)
THIRD SPEED GEAR
SYNCHRONIZER ASSEMBLY (1ST AND 2ND)
SLIDING GEAR (LOW AND REVERSE)
FIRST SPEED THRUST WASHER
SECOND SPEED GEAR
HUB INSERTS
SYNCHRONIZER SPRING
HUB INSERTS
BLOCKING RING
SYNCHRONIZER SPRING
BLOCKING RING
BLOCKING RING
OUTER SNAP RING (SELECTIVE)
SYNCHRONIZER HUB SNAP RING
SPEEDOMETER DRIVE GEAR
SYNCHRONIZER HUB SNAP RING
INPUT SHAFT AND GEAR
INPUT SHAFT ROLLER BEARING
OUTPUT SHAFT BALL BEARING
INNER SNAP RING (SELECTIVE)
INPUT SHAFT BALL BEARING
COUNTERSHAFT ROLLER BEARING
OUTPUT SHAFT
COUNTERSHAFT
REAR THRUST WASHER
BEARING SNAP RING
BEARING SNAP RING (INNER)
REVERSE IDLER GEAR SHAFT
CLUSTER GEAR
REVERSE IDLER GEAR
FRONT THRUST WASHER
COUNTERSHAFT ROLLER BEARING

Mainshaft and countershaft assemblies (© Ford Motor Co)

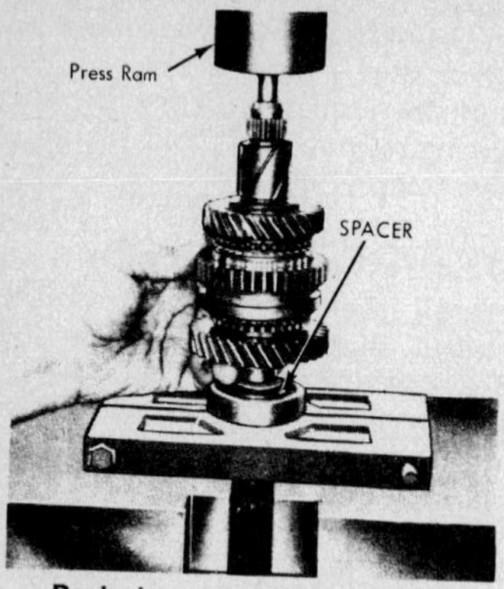
Press Ram
SPACER

Replacing output shaft bearing
(© Ford Motor Co)

diameter adjacent to first gear.

10. Select a snap-ring of the proper size to hold the output shaft bearing into the bearing recess with no end float.
11. Position the selected snap-ring loosely on the output shaft next to the spacer.
12. Support the bearing inner race. Press the bearing onto the shaft.
13. Select the thickest snap-ring that fits the groove to hold the bearing to the output shaft.
14. Locate output shaft ball bearing in shaft indent, push speedometer drive gear onto output shaft. Install new snap-ring.
15. Heat the end of the extension housing. Do not use a torch. A pan of hot water is recommended.
16. Install the output shaft into the extension housing. Install the snap-ring securing the output shaft bearing to the housing.
17. Replace the speedometer driven gear. Install a new plug, using sealer.

Input Shaft and Gear

1. Support the input shaft bearing inner race. Press the bearing onto the shaft.
2. Install the snap-ring securing the bearing to the input shaft.

Transmission Assembly

1. Slide the low-reverse lever onto the lever pin inside the case.
2. Push the idler shaft into the case. Place the reverse idler gear on the shaft. Locate the low-reverse lever in the gear groove. Tap the reverse idler shaft into position with a soft hammer.
3. Slide a dummy shaft into the cluster gear. Push a retainer washer into the gear bore. Grease and install 20 needle rollers and the second retaining washer. Install the washers and rollers at the other end of the gear. Grease and install the thrust washers with their convex side into the gear recess.
4. Place the cluster gear in the bottom of the case. Position the thrust washers with the flat upward.
5. Place the input shaft and gear in the case. Using a brass drift, tap bearing outer race into place. Be careful not to damage the dog teeth on the input shaft gear with the cluster gear. Install the bearing snap-ring.
6. Place the input shaft needle bearing in the input shaft gear recess.
7. Drive a new oil seal into the input shaft retainer. Cover the input shaft splines. Install a new gasket on the transmission front face. Check that the retainer oil groove is lined up with the oil passage in the case. Coat the bolts with sealer and install them with lock-washers.
8. Locate the fourth gear blocking ring on the input shaft gear cone.
9. Install a new oil seal in the shift shaft aperture. Drive the seal in with a socket.
10. Install a new sealer coated gasket to the extension housing.
11. Pull the third-fourth synchronizer sleeve forward. Slide the extension housing and output shaft into position. Align the cutaway on the extension housing with the countershaft aperture in the rear face of the case.

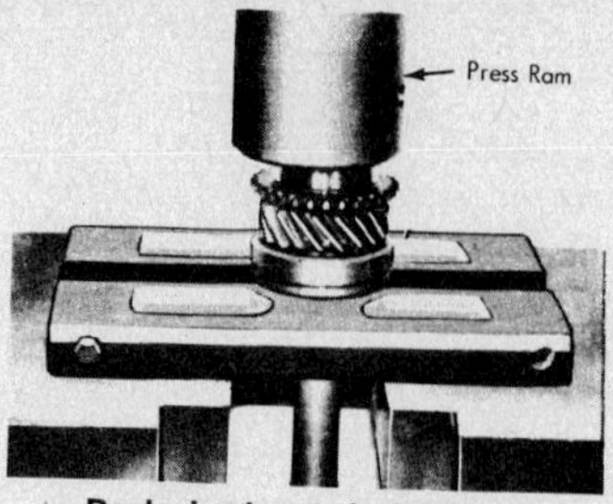
Press Ram

Replacing input shaft bearing
(© Ford Motor Co)

12. Using loops of cord, lift the cluster gear into mesh with the output and input shaft gears. Take care not to drop the countershaft thrust washers.
13. Tap the countershaft into place, driving out the dummy shaft, ensuring that the lug on the rear of the countershaft fits into the recess on the extension housing flange.
14. Push the extension housing onto the transmission case. Apply sealer to bolts. Torque to 30-35 ft. lbs.
15. Replace both shift forks. Secure third-fourth fork with a new pin.
16. Position shift forks to synchronizer sleeves. Move synchronizer hubs into neutral positions.
17. Grease shift shaft oil seal in rear of case. Slide shift shaft through extension housing. Position shift selector arm and interlock plate so that interlock plate locates in cutouts in shift forks. Pass the shift shaft through the shift selector arm and forks until the pin holes are aligned.
18. Replace the plunger ball and spring. Replace the retaining screw, using sealer.
19. Install the pin through the shift selector arm and shift shaft.
20. Apply sealer to plug. Tap plug into rear of extension housing.
21. Install top cover and gasket.
22. Refill transmission with 2.8 pints SAE 80 oil.

Type 9
Ford 4-Speed

Application

Comet V8, 1967-70
Cougar, 1967-74
Fairlane V8, 1967-74
Falcon V8, 1967-70
Ford, 1967-71
Mercury, 1967-70
Montego, 1968-74
Mustang V8, 1967-74

Disassembly

1. Remove retaining clips and flat washers from the shift rods at the levers.
2. Remove shift linkage control bracket attaching screws and remove shift linkage and control bracket.
3. Remove cover attaching screws. Then lift cover and gasket from the case.
4. Remove extension housing attaching screws. Then, remove extension housing and gasket.
5. Remove input shaft bearing retainer attaching screws. Then, slide retainer from the input shaft.
6. Working a dummy shaft in from the front of the case, drive the countershaft out the rear of the

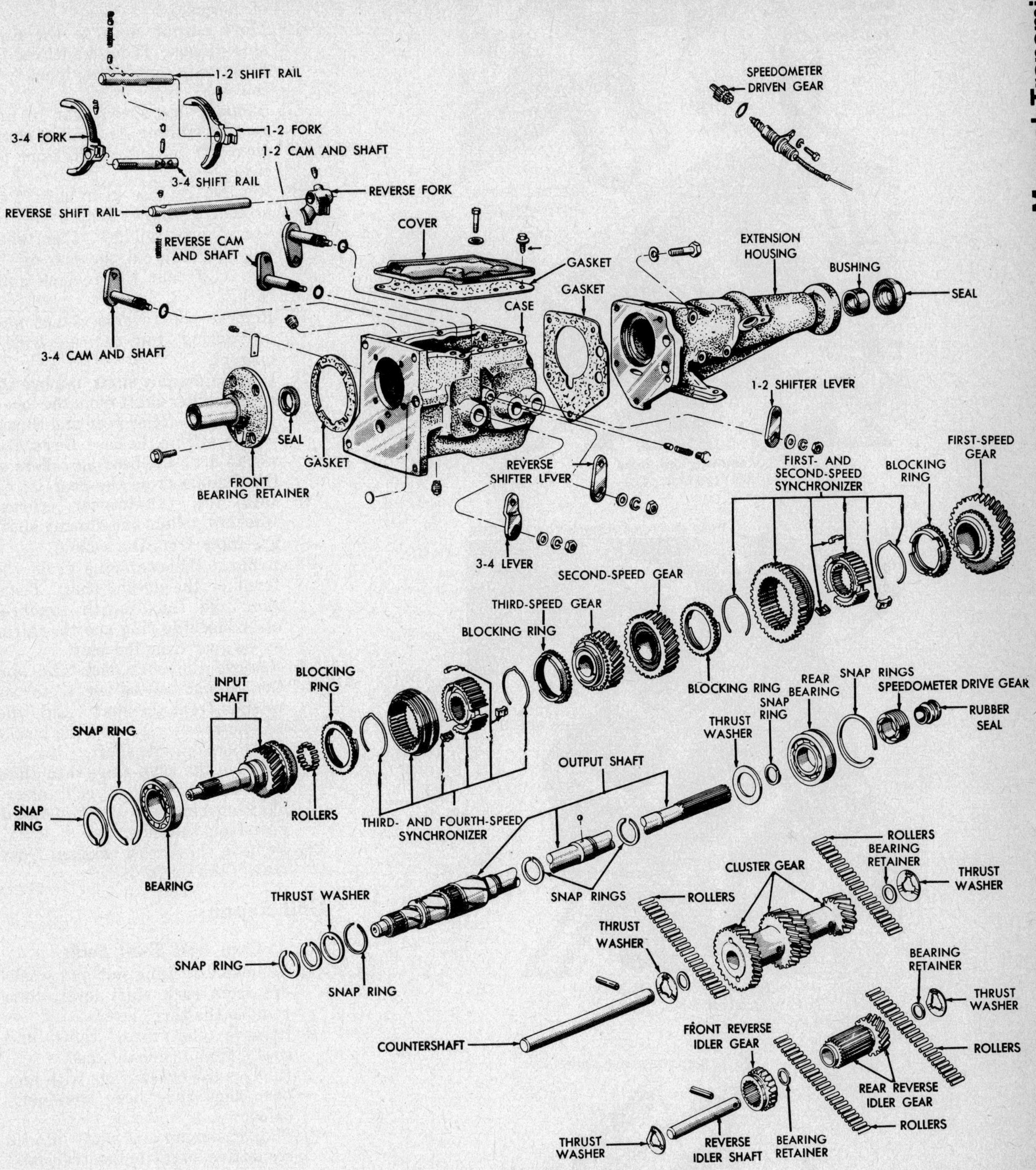
1-2 SHIFT RAIL
3-4 FORK
1-2 FORK
1-2 CAM AND SHAFT
3-4 SHIFT RAIL
REVERSE FORK
REVERSE SHIFT RAIL
COVER
REVERSE CAM AND SHAFT
GASKET
SPEEDOMETER DRIVEN GEAR
EXTENSION HOUSING
BUSHING
SEAL
GASKET
CASE
3-4 CAM AND SHAFT
1-2 SHIFTER LEVER
SEAL
GASKET
FRONT BEARING RETAINER
REVERSE SHIFTER LEVER
FIRST-SPEED GEAR
FIRST- AND SECOND-SPEED SYNCHRONIZER
BLOCKING RING
3-4 LEVER
SECOND-SPEED GEAR
THIRD-SPEED GEAR
BLOCKING RING
INPUT SHAFT
BLOCKING RING
BLOCKING RING
REAR BEARING
SNAP RINGS
SPEEDOMETER DRIVE GEAR
RUBBER SEAL
SNAP RING
THRUST WASHER
SNAP RING
OUTPUT SHAFT
SNAP RING
ROLLERS
THIRD- AND FOURTH-SPEED SYNCHRONIZER
BEARING
ROLLERS
BEARING RETAINER
CLUSTER GEAR
THRUST WASHER
THRUST WASHER
SNAP RINGS
ROLLERS
THRUST WASHER
SNAP RING
SNAP RING
BEARING RETAINER
THRUST WASHER
COUNTERSHAFT
FRONT REVERSE IDLER GEAR
ROLLERS
REAR REVERSE IDLER GEAR
ROLLERS
THRUST WASHER
REVERSE IDLER SHAFT
BEARING RETAINER

Ford 4-speed transmission (© Ford Motor Co)

case. Let the countergear assembly lie in the bottom of the case.

7. Locate first - second - speed gear shift lever in neutral. Locate third fourth-speed gear shift lever in third-speed position.
8. Remove the lockbolt that holds the third-fourth-speed shift rail detent spring and plug the left side of the case. Remove spring and plug with a magnet.
9. Remove the detent mechanism set screw from top of case. Then, remove the detent spring and plug with a small magnet.
10. Remove attaching screw from the third-fourth-speed shift fork. Tap lightly on the inner end of the shift rail to remove the expansion plug from front of case. Then, withdraw the third-fourth-speed shift rail from the front. (Do not lose the interlock pin from rail.)
11. Remove attaching screw from the first and second-speed shift fork. Slide the first-second shift rail from the rear of case.
12. Remove the interlock and detent plugs from the top of the case with a magnet.
13. Remove the snap-ring or disengage retainer that holds the speedometer drive gear to the output shaft. Slide the gear from the shaft, then remove speedometer gear drive ball.
14. Remove the snap-ring used to hold the output shaft bearing to the shaft. Remove output shaft bearing.
15. Remove the input shaft bearing and blocking ring from the front

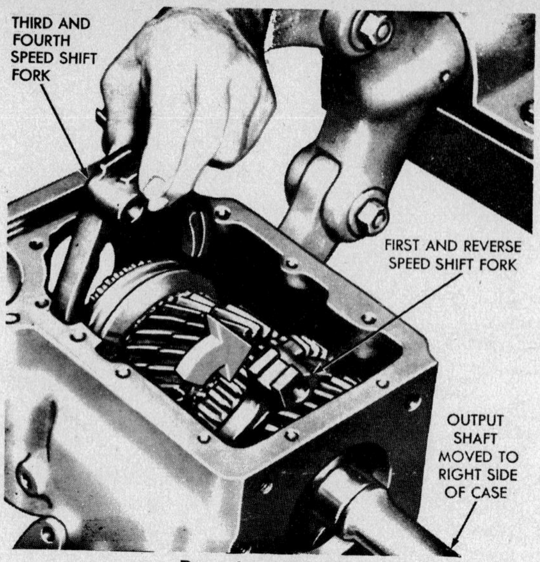
THIRD AND FOURTH SPEED SHIFT FORK
FIRST AND REVERSE SPEED SHIFT FORK
OUTPUT SHAFT MOVED TO RIGHT SIDE OF CASE

Removing shift forks
(© Ford Motor Co)

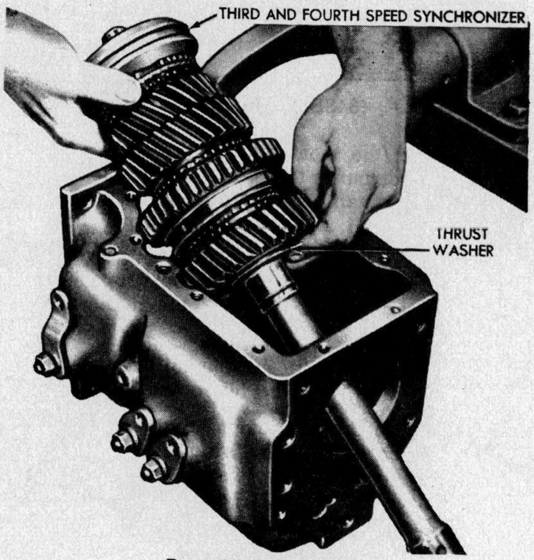
THIRD AND FOURTH SPEED SYNCHRONIZER
THRUST WASHER

Removing output shaft
(© Ford Motor Co)

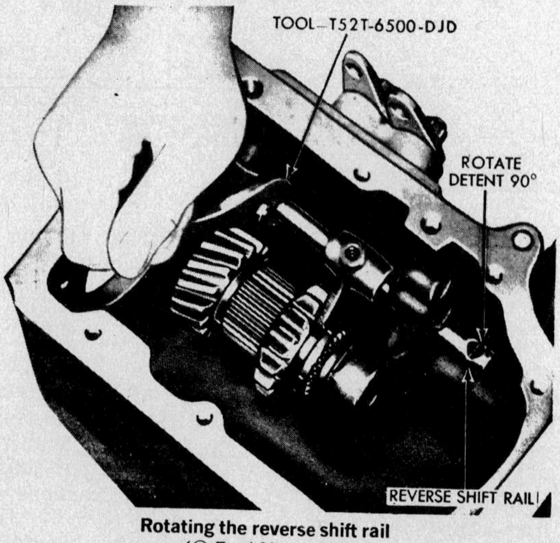
TOOL—T52T-6500-DJD
ROTATE DETENT 90°
REVERSE SHIFT RAIL

Rotating the reverse shift rail
(© Ford Motor Co)

of the case.

16. Move output shaft to the right side of case. Then, maneuver the forks to permit lifting them from the case.
17. Support first-speed gear to prevent it sliding from the shaft, then lift output shaft from the case.
18. Remove reverse gear shift fork attaching screw. Rotate the reverse shift rail 90°, then, slide the shift rail out the rear of the case. Lift out the reverse shift fork.
19. Remove the reverse detent plug and spring from the case with a magnet.
20. Using a dummy shaft, remove the reverse idler shaft from the case.
21. Lift reverse idler gear and thrust washers from the case. Be careful not to drop the bearing rollers or the dummy from the gear.
22. Lift the countergear, thrust washers, rollers and dummy shaft assembly from the case.
23. Remove the snap-ring from the front of the output shaft. Then, slide the third-fourth synchronizer blocking ring and the third-speed gear from the shaft.
24. Remove the next snap-ring and the second - speed gear thrust washer from the shaft. Slide the second-speed gear and the blocking ring from the shaft.
25. Remove the snap-ring, then slide the first - second synchronizer, blocking ring and the first-speed gear from the shaft.
26. Remove the thrust washer from rear of the shaft.

Unit Repairs

Cam and Shaft Seals

1. Remove attaching nut and washers from each shift lever, then remove the three levers.
2. Remove the three cams and shafts from inside the case.
3. Replace the old O-rings with new ones that have been well-lubricated.
4. Slide each cam and shaft into its respective bore in the transmission.
5. Install the levers and secure them with their respective washers and nuts.

Input Shaft Bearing

1. Remove the snap-ring that holds the bearing to the shaft.
2. Press the shaft gear from the bearing.
3. Press a new bearing onto the input shaft.
4. Secure the bearing with a snap-ring.

Synchronizers

1. Push the synchronizer hub from

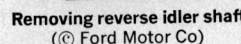

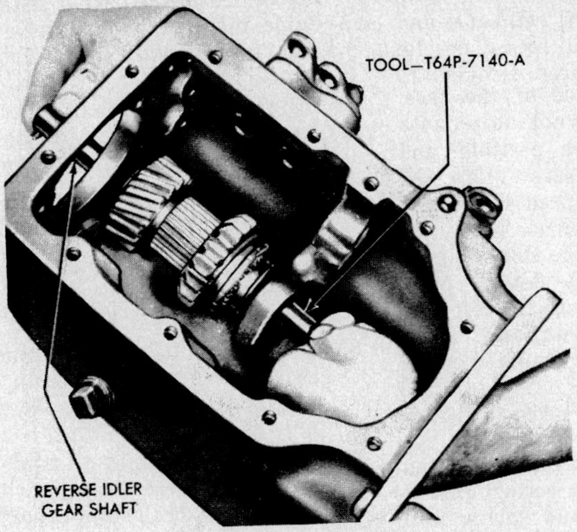
TOOL–T64P-7140-A
REVERSE IDLER
GEAR SHAFT
Removing reverse idler shaft
(© Ford Motor Co)

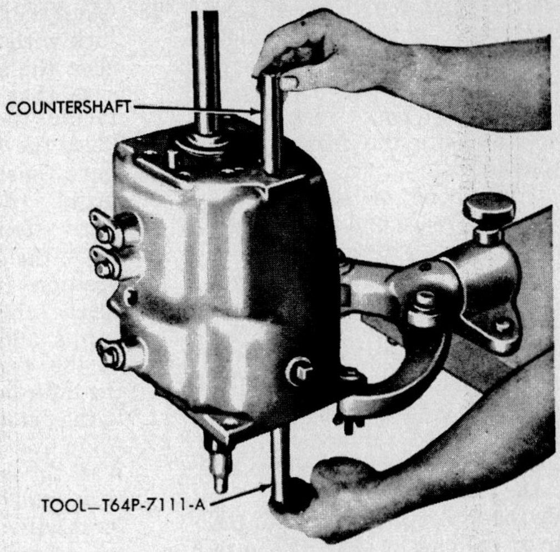
COUNTERSHAFT
TOOL–T64P-7111-A
Installing countershaft
(© Ford Motor Co)

each synchronizer sleeve.

2. Separate the inserts and springs from the hubs. Do not mix parts of the first-second with parts of third-fourth synchronizers.
3. To assemble, position the hub in the sleeve. Be sure the alignment marks are properly indexed.
4. Place the three inserts into place on the hub. Install the insert springs so that the irregular surface (hump) is seated in one of the inserts. Do not stagger the springs.

Countershaft Gear

1. Dismantle the countershaft gear assembly.
2. Assemble the gear by coating each end of the countershaft gear bore with grease.
3. Install dummy shaft in the gear. Then install 21 bearing rollers and a retainer washer in each end of the gear.

Reverse Idler Gear

1. Dismantle reverse idler gear.
2. Assemble reverse idler gear by coating the bore in each end of reverse idler gear with grease.
3. Hold the dummy shaft in the gear and install the 22 bearing rollers and the retainer washer into each end of the gear.
4. Install the reverse idler sliding gear on the splines of the reverse idler gear. Be sure the shift fork groove is toward the front.

Input Shaft Seal

1. Remove the seal from the input shaft bearing retainer.
2. Coat the sealing surface of a new seal with lubricant, then press the new seal into the input shaft bearing retainer.

Assembly

1. Grease the countershaft gear thrust surfaces in the case. Then, position a thrust washer at each end of the case.
2. Position the countershaft gear, dummy shaft, and roller bearings in the case.
3. Align the gear bore and thrust washers with the bores in the case. Install the countershaft.
4. With the case in a horizontal position, countershaft gear end-play should be from .004-.018 in. Use thrust washers to obtain play within these limits.
5. After establishing correct end-play, place the dummy shaft in the countershaft gear and allow the gear assembly to remain on the bottom of the case.
6. Grease the reverse idler gear thrust surfaces in the case, and position the two thrust washers.
7. Position the reverse idler gear, sliding gear, dummy, etc. in place. Make sure that the shift fork groove in the sliding gear is toward the front.
8. Align the gear bore and thrust washers with the case bores and install the reverse idler shaft.
9. Reverse idler gear end - play should be .004-.018 in. Use selective thrust washers to obtain play within these limits.
10. Position reverse gear shift rail detent spring and detent plug in the case. Hold the reverse shift fork in place on the reverse idler sliding gear and install the shift rail from the rear of the case. Lock the fork to the rail with the Allen head set screws.
11. Install the first-second synchronizer onto the output shaft. The first and reverse synchronizer hub are a press fit and should be installed with gear teeth facing the rear of the shaft.
12. Slide second-speed gear onto the front of the shaft with the synchronizer coned surface toward the rear.
13. Install the second-speed gear thrust washer and snap-ring.
14. Slide the third-speed gear onto the shaft with the synchronizer coned surface front.
15. Coat the cone of third-speed gear with grease. Place a blocking ring on the third-speed gear.

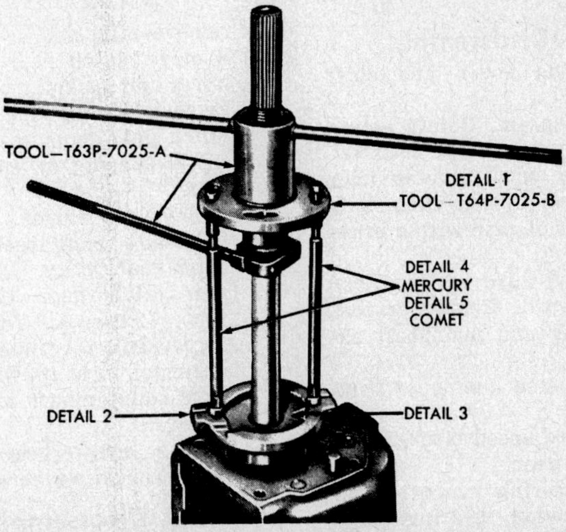
TOOL–T63P-7025-A
DETAIL 1
TOOL–T64P-7025-B
DETAIL 4
MERCURY
DETAIL 5
COMET
DETAIL 2
DETAIL 3
Installing output shaft bearing
(© Ford Motor Co)

16. Slide the third-fourth speed gear synchronizer onto the shaft. Be sure that the inserts in the synchronizer engage the notches in the blocking ring. Install the snap-ring onto the front of the output shaft.
17. Coat the cone of second-speed gear with grease and position the blocking ring on the gear.
18. Slide the first-second speed synchronizer onto the rear of the output shaft. Be sure that the inserts engage the notches in the blocking ring and that the shift fork groove is toward the rear.
19. Coat the coned surface of first-speed gear with grease and position the blocking ring on it.
20. Slide the first-speed gear onto the rear of the output shaft. Be sure that the notches in the blocker ring engage the synchronizer inserts.
21. Install heavy thrust washer onto the rear of the output shaft.
22. Lower the output shaft assembly into the case.
23. Position the first-second speed shift fork and the third-fourth-speed shift fork in place on their respective gears. Rotate them into place.
24. Place a detent plug in the detent bore. Place the reverse shift rail into neutral position.
25. Coat the third-fourth-speed shift rail interlock pin with grease, then position it in the shift rail.
26. Align the third-fourth-speed shift fork with the shift rail bores and slide the shift rail into place. Be sure that the three detents are facing the outside of the case. Place the front synchronizer into third-fourth-speed position and install the set screw into the third - fourth - speed shift fork. Move the synchronizer to neutral position. Install the third-fourth-speed shift rail detent plug, spring and bolt into the left side of the transmission case. Place the interlock plug (tapered ends) in the detent bore.
27. Align first-second-speed shift fork with the case bores and slide the shift rail into place. Lock the fork with the set screw. Install the detent plug and spring into the detent bore. Thread the set screw into the case until the head is flush with the case.
28. Coat the input gear bore with a small amount of grease. Then install the 15 bearing rollers.
29. Place the input shaft gear in the case. Be sure that the output shaft pilot enters the roller bearing of the input shaft gear.
30. With a new gasket on the input bearing retainer, dip attaching bolts in sealer, install bolts and torque to 30-36 ft. lbs.
31. Install the output shaft bearing, then install the snap-ring to hold the bearing.
32. Position the speedometer gear drive ball in the output shaft and slide the speedometer drive gear into place. Secure gear with snap-ring.
33. Align the countershaft gear bore and thrust washers with the bore in the case. Install the countershaft.
34. With a new gasket in place, install and secure the extension housing. Dip the extension housing screws in sealer, then torque screws to 42-50 ft. lbs.
35. Install the filler plug (torque 10-20 ft. lbs.) and the drain plug (torque 20-30 ft. lbs.), the drain plug is magnetic.
36. Pour in four pints of mild E.P. gear oil over the entire gear train while rotating the input shaft.
37. Place each shift fork in all positions to make sure they function properly.
38. With a new cover gasket in place, install the cover. Dip attaching screws in sealer, then torque screws to 14-19 ft. lbs.
39. Coat the third-fourth speed shift rail plug bore with sealer. Install a new plug.
40. Secure each shift rod to its respective lever with a spring washer, flat washer and retaining pin.
41. Position the shift linkage control bracket to the extension housing. Install and torque the attaching screws to 12-15 ft. lbs.

Type-10 Muncie Fully Synchronized 3-Speed

Application

Camaro, 1969-74
Chevelle, 1969-74
Chevrolet, 1969-74
Chevy II, 1969-74
Firebird, 1970-74
GTO, 1970-74
Monte Carlo, 1970-74
Olds F-85, 4-4-2, 1970-71
Pontiac Grand Prix, 1970-74
Tempest, 1970-71

Transmission Disassembly

1. Remove side cover and shift forks.
2. Unbolt extension. Rotate extension to line up groove in extension flange with reverse idler shaft. Drive reverse idler shaft and key out of case with a brass drift.
3. Move second-third synchronizer sleeve forward. Remove extension housing and mainshaft assembly.
4. Remove reverse idler gear from case.
5. Remove third speed blocker ring from clutch gear.
6. Expand snap-ring which retains mainshaft rear bearing. Tap gently on end of mainshaft to remove extension.
7. Remove clutch gear bearing retainer and gasket.
8. Remove snap-ring. Remove clutch gear from inside case by gently tapping on end of clutch gear.
9. Remove oil slinger. Remove 16 mainshaft pilot bearings from clutch gear cavity.
10. Slip clutch gear bearing out front of case. Aid removal with a screwdriver between case and bearing outer snap-ring.
11. Drive countershaft and key out to rear.
12. Remove countergear and two tanged thrust washers.

Mainshaft Disassembly

1. Depress speedometer drive gear retaining clip. Slide off gear. Some speedometer drive gears, made of metal, must be pulled off.
2. Remove rear bearing snap-ring.
3. Support reverse gear and press on rear of mainshaft to remove reverse gear, thrust washer, and rear bearing. Be careful not to cock the bearing on the shaft.
4. Remove first and reverse sliding clutch hub snap-ring.
5. Support first gear. Press on rear of mainshaft to remove clutch assembly, blocker ring, and first gear.
6. Remove second and third speed sliding clutch hub snap-ring.
7. Support second gear. Press on front of mainshaft to remove clutch assembly, second speed

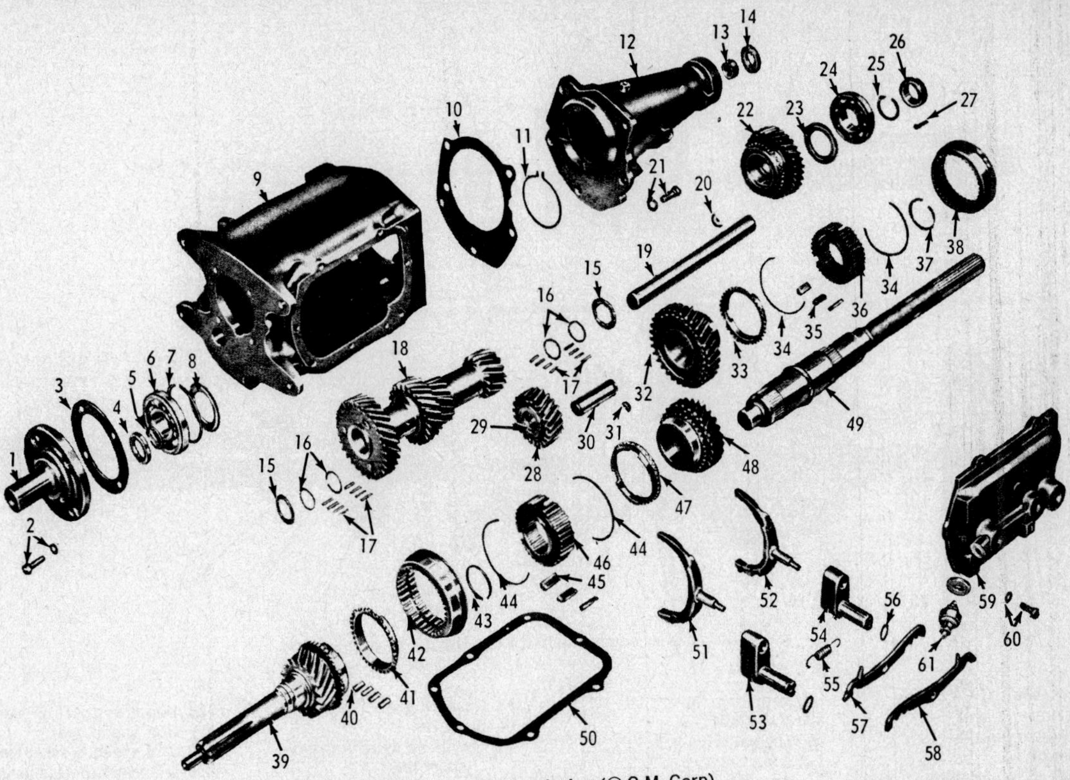

Muncie 3-speed transmission (© G.M. Corp)

1 Bearing retainer
2 Bolt and lock washer
3 Gasket
4 Oil seal
5 Snap ring (bearing-to-main drive gear)
6 Main drive gear bearing
7 Snap ring bearing
8 Oil slinger
9 Case
10 Gasket
11 Snap ring (rear bearing-to-extension)
12 Extension
13 Extension bushing
14 Oil seal
15 Thrust washer
16 Bearing washer
17 Needle bearings
18 Countergear
19 Countershaft
20 Woodruff key
21 Bolt (extension-to-case)
22 Reverse gear
23 Thrust washer
24 Rear bearing
25 Snap ring
26 Speedometer drive gear
27 Retainer clip
28 Reverse idler gear
29 Reverse idler bushing
30 Reverse idler shaft
31 Woodruff key
32 1st speed gear
33 1st speed blocker ring
34 Synchronizer key spring
35 Synchronizer keys
36 1st and reverse synchronizer hub assembly
37 Snap ring
38 1st and reverse synchronizer collar
39 Main drive gear
40 Pilot bearings
41 3rd speed blocker ring
42 2nd and 3rd synchronizer collar
43 Snap ring
44 Synchronizer key spring
45 Synchronizer keys
46 2nd and 3rd synchronizer hub
47 2nd speed blocker ring
48 2nd speed gear
49 Mainshaft
50 Gasket
51 2nd and 3rd shifter fork
52 1st and reverse shifter fork
53 2-3 shifter shaft assembly
54 1st and reverse shifter shaft assembly
55 Spring
56 O-ring seal
57 1st and reverse detent cam
58 2nd and 3rd detent cam
59 Side cover
60 Bolt and lock washer

blocker ring, and second gear from shaft.

Inspection

1. Wash all parts in solvent.
2. Air dry.

Case

1. Check for cracks.
2. Check faces for burrs. Remove with a fine file.
3. Check bearing bores for damage. If they are damaged, replace case.

Front and Rear Bearings

1. Do not spin bearings with air pressure; turn them slowly by hand.
2. Lubricate bearings with light oil. Turn slowly to check for roughness.

Bearing Rollers

1. Check for wear; replace if worn.
2. Check countershaft and reverse idler shaft.
3. Replace all worn washers.

Gears

1. Check for wear, chips, or cracks.
2. If reverse gear bushing is worn or damaged, replace entire gear.
3. Check to see that both clutch sleeves slide freely on their hubs.

Reverse Idler Gear Bushing

This bushing may not be serviced separately. If the bushing requires replacement, replace the gear.

Countergear Anti-Lash Plate

1. Check the plate teeth for wear or damage.
2. Do not disassemble.

Repair

Clutch Keys and Springs

Keys and springs may be replaced if worn or broken, but the hubs and sleeves must be kept together as originally assembled.

1. Mark hub and sleeve for reassembly.
2. Push hub from sleeve. Remove keys and springs.
3. Place three keys and two springs, one on each side of hub, so all three keys are engaged by both springs. The tanged end of the springs should not be installed into the same key.
4. Slide the sleeve onto the hub, aligning the marks.

Extension Oil Seal and Bushing

1. Remove seal.
2. Using bushing remover and installer, or other suitable tool, drive bushing into extension housing.
3. Drive new bushing in from rear. Lubricate inside of bushing and seal. Install new oil seal with extension seal installer or suitable tool.

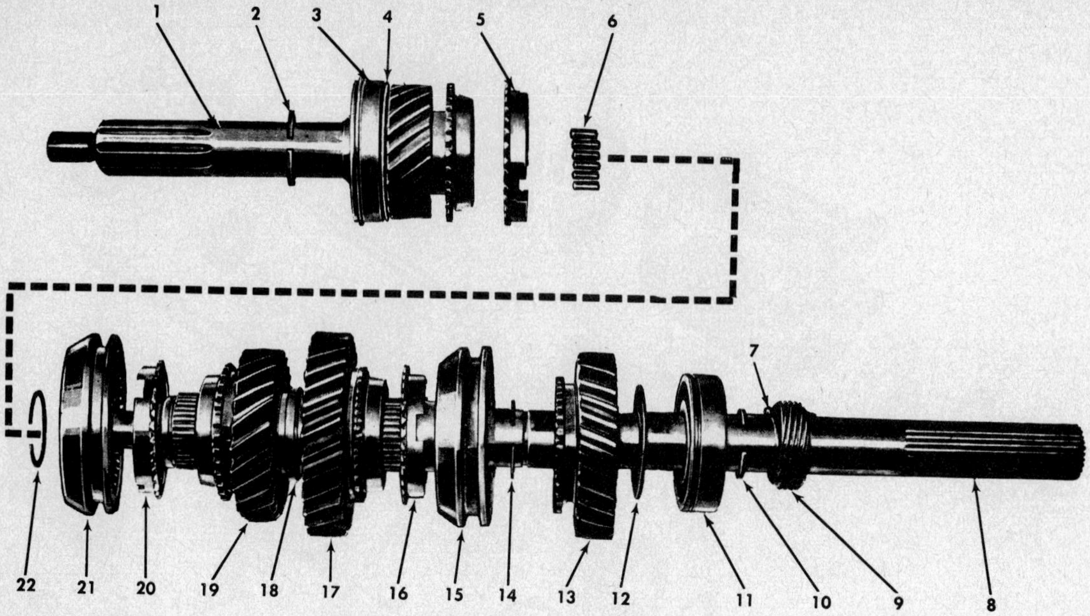
1
2
3
4
5
6
7
22
21
20
19
18
17
16
15
14
13
12
11
10
9
8

Clutch gear and mainshaft assembly (© G.M. Corp)

1 Clutch gear
2 Snap ring
3 Clutch gear bearing
4 Oil slinger
5 3rd speed blocker ring
6 Mainshaft pilot bearings (16)
7 Retaining clip
8 Mainshaft
9 Speedo drive gear
10 Snap ring
11 Rear bearing
12 Reverse gear thrust washer
13 Reverse gear
14 Snap ring
15 1st speed synchronizer assembly
16 1st speed blocker ring
17 1st speed gear
18 Shoulder (part of mainshaft)
19 2nd speed gear
20 2nd speed blocker ring
21 2-3 synchronizer assembly
22 Snap ring

Clutch Bearing Retainer Oil Seal

1. Pry old seal out.
2. Install new seal using seal installer or suitable tool. Seat seal in bore.

Mainshaft Assembly

1. Turn front of mainshaft up.
2. Install second gear with clutching teeth up; the rear face of the gear butts against the flange on the mainshaft.
3. Install a blocking ring with clutching teeth downward. All three blocking rings are the same.
4. Install second and third synchronizer assembly with fork slot down. Press it onto mainshaft splines. Both synchronizer assemblies are identical but are assembled differently. The second-third speed hub and sleeve is assembled with the sleeve fork slot toward the thrust face of the hub; the first-reverse hub and sleeve, with the fork slot opposite the thrust face. Be sure that the blocker ring notches align with the synchronizer assembly keys.
5. Install synchronizer snap-ring. Both synchronizer snap-rings are the same.
6. Turn rear of shaft up.
7. Install first gear with clutching teeth upward; the front face of the gear butts against the flange on the mainshaft.
8. Install a blocker ring with clutching teeth down.
9. Install first and reverse synchronizer assembly with fork slot up. Press it onto mainshaft splines. Be sure blocker ring notches align with synchronizer assembly keys and both synchronizer sleeves face front of mainshaft.
10. Install snap-ring.
11. Install reverse gear with clutching teeth down.
12. Install steel reverse gear thrust washer with flats aligned.
13. Press rear ball bearing onto shaft with snap-ring slot down.
14. Install snap-ring.
15. Install speedometer drive gear and retaining clip.

Transmission Assembly

1. Place a row of 29 roller bearings, a bearing washer, a second row of 29 bearings, and a second bearing washer at each end of the countergear. Hold in place with grease.
2. Place countergear assembly through rear case opening with a tanged thrust washer, tang away from gear, at each end. Install countershaft and key from rear of case. Be sure that thrust washer tangs are aligned with notches in case.
3. Place reverse idler gear in case. Do not install reverse idler shaft yet.
4. Expand snap-ring in extension. Assemble extension over mainshaft and onto rear bearing. Seat snap-ring.
5. Load 16 mainshaft pilot bearings into clutch gear cavity. Assemble third speed blocker ring onto clutch gear clutching surface with teeth toward gear.
6. Place clutch gear assembly, without front bearing, over front of mainshaft. Make sure that blocker ring notches align with keys in second-third synchronizer assembly.
7. Stick gasket onto extension housing with grease. Assemble clutch gear, mainshaft, and extension to case together. Make sure that clutch gear teeth engage teeth of countergear antilash plate.
8. Rotate extension housing. Install reverse idler shaft and key.
9. Torque extension bolts to 45 ft. lbs.
10. Install oil slinger with inner lip facing forward. Install front bearing outer snap-ring to bearing. Slide bearing into case bore.
11. Install snap-ring to clutch gear stem. Install bearing retainer and gasket. Torque bolts to 20 ft. lbs. Retainer oil return hole must be at 6 o'clock.
12. Shift both synchronizer sleeves to neutral positions. Install side cover, aligning shifter forks with synchronizer sleeve grooves.
13. Torque side cover bolts to 20 ft. lbs.

Type-11 Saginaw Fully Synchronized 3-Speed

Application

Apollo, 1973-74
Buick LeSabre, 1967-68
Buick Special, 1967-74
Camaro, 1967-74
Chevelle, 1967-74
Chevrolet, 1967-74
Chevy II, 1967-74
Corvette, 1967-69
Firebird, 1967-74
Olds F-85, 1967-74
Olds 442, 1972
Omega, 1973-74
Tempest, 1967-74
Ventura II, 1971-74
Vega, 1973-74

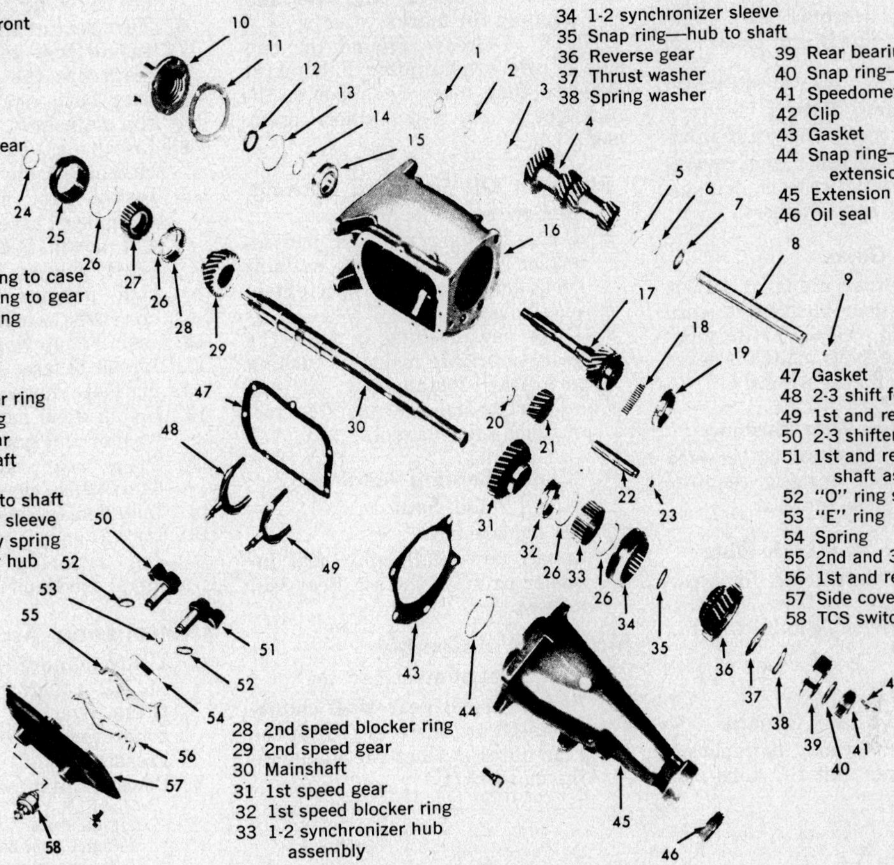

1 Thrust washer—front
2 Bearing washer
3 Needle bearings
4 Countergear
5 Needle bearings
6 Bearing washer
7 Thrust washer—rear
8 Counter shaft
9 Woodruff key
10 Bearing retainer
11 Gasket
12 Oil seal
13 Snap ring—bearing to case
14 Snap ring—bearing to gear
15 Clutch gear bearing
16 Case
17 Clutch gear
18 Pilot bearings
19 3rd speed blocker ring
20 Retainer "E" ring
21 Reverse idler gear
22 Reverse idler shaft
23 Woodruff key
24 Snap ring—hub to shaft
25 2-3 synchronizer sleeve
26 Synchronizer key spring
27 2-3 synchronizer hub assembly
28 2nd speed blocker ring
29 2nd speed gear
30 Mainshaft
31 1st speed gear
32 1st speed blocker ring
33 1-2 synchronizer hub assembly
34 1-2 synchronizer sleeve
35 Snap ring—hub to shaft
36 Reverse gear
37 Thrust washer
38 Spring washer
39 Rear bearing
40 Snap ring—bearing to shaft
41 Speedometer drive gear
42 Clip
43 Gasket
44 Snap ring—rear bearing to extension
45 Extension
46 Oil seal
47 Gasket
48 2-3 shift fork
49 1st and reverse shift fork
50 2-3 shifter shaft assembly
51 1st and reverse shifter shaft assembly
52 "O" ring seal
53 "E" ring
54 Spring
55 2nd and 3rd detent cam
56 1st and reverse detent cam
57 Side cover
58 TCS switch

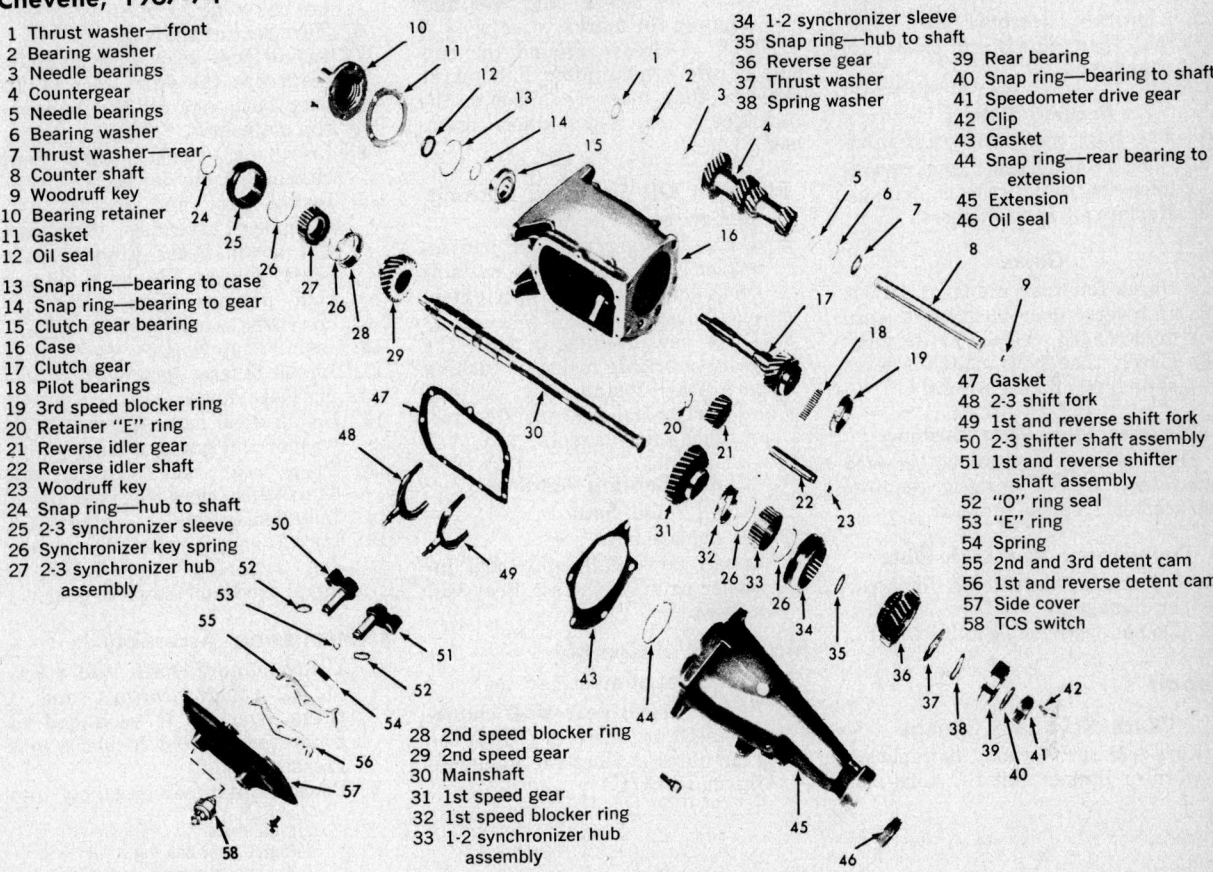

Saginaw transmission—exploded view (© G.M. Corp)

Transmission Disassembly

1. Remove side cover assembly and shift forks.
2. Remove clutch gear bearing retainer.
3. Remove clutch gear bearing to gear stem snap-ring. Pull clutch gear outward until a screwdriver can be inserted between bearing and case. Remove clutch gear bearing.
4. Remove speedometer driven gear and extension bolts.
5. Remove reverse idler shaft snap-ring. Slide reverse idler gear forward on shaft.
6. Remove mainshaft and extension assembly.
7. Remove clutch gear and third speed blocker ring from inside case. Remove 14 roller bearings from clutch gear.
8. Expand the snap-ring which retains the mainshaft rear bearing. Remove the extension.
9. Using a dummy shaft, drive the countershaft and key out the rear of the case. Remove the gear, two tanged thrust washers, and dummy shaft. Remove bearing washer and 27 roller bearings from each end of countergear.
10. Use a long drift to drive the reverse idler shaft and key through the rear of the case.
11. Remove reverse idler gear and tanged steel thrust washer.

Mainshaft Disassembly

1. Remove second and third speed sliding clutch hub snap-ring from mainshaft. Remove clutch assembly, second speed blocker ring, and second gear from front of mainshaft.
2. Depress speedometer drive gear retaining clip. Remove gear. Some units have a metal speedometer drive gear which must be pulled off.
3. Remove rear bearing snap-ring.
4. Support reverse gear. Press on rear of mainshaft. Remove reverse gear, thrust washer, spring washer, rear bearing, and snap-ring. When pressing off the rear bearing, be careful not to cock the bearing on the shaft.
5. Remove first and reverse sliding clutch hub snap-ring. Remove clutch assembly, first speed blocker ring, and first gear.

Inspection

1. Wash all parts in solvent.

2. Air dry.

Case

1. Check for cracks.
2. Check faces for burrs. Remove with a fine file.
3. Check bearing bores for damage. If they are damaged, replace case.

Front and Rear Bearings

1. Do not spin bearings with air pressure; turn them slowly by hand.
2. Lubricate bearings with light oil. Turn slowly to check for roughness.

Bearing Rollers

1. Check for wear; replace if worn.
2. Check countershaft and reverse idler shaft for wear or damage.
3. Replace all worn washers.

Gears

1. Check for wear, chips, or cracks.
2. If reverse gear bushing is worn or damaged, replace entire gear.
3. Check that both clutch sleeves slide freely on their hubs.

Reverse Idler Gear Bushing

This bushing may not be serviced separately. If the bushing requires replacement, replace the gear.

Countergear Anti-Lash Plate

1. Check the plate teeth for wear or damage.
2. Do not disassemble unit.

Repair

Clutch Keys and Springs

Keys and springs may be replaced if worn or broken, but the hubs and sleeves are matched pairs and must be kept together.

1. Mark hub and sleeve for reassembly.
2. Push hub from sleeve. Remove keys and springs.
3. Place three keys and two springs, one on each side of hub, in position, so all three keys are engaged by both springs. The tanged end of the springs should not be installed into the same key.
4. Slide the sleeve onto the hub, aligning the marks.

NOTE: a groove around the outside of the synchronizer hub marks the end that must be opposite the fork slot in the sleeve when assembled.

Extension Oil Seal and Bushing

1. Remove seal.
2. Using bushing remover and installer tool, or other suitable tool, drive bushing into extension housing.
3. Drive new bushing in from the rear. Lubricate inside of bushing and seal. Install new oil seal with extension seal installer tool or other suitable tool.

Clutch Bearing Retainer Oil Seal

1. Pry old seal out.
2. Install new seal using seal installer or suitable tool. Seat seal in bore.

Mainshaft Assembly

1. Turn front of mainshaft up.
2. Install second gear with clutching teeth up; the rear face of the gear butts against the flange on the mainshaft.
3. Install a blocker ring with clutching teeth down. All three blocker rings are the same.
4. Install second and third speed synchronizer assembly with fork slot down. Press it onto mainshaft splines. Both synchronizer assemblies are the same. Be sure that blocker ring notches align with synchronizer assembly keys.
5. Install synchronizer snap-ring. Both synchronizer snap-rings are the same.
6. Turn rear of shaft up.
7. Install first gear with clutching teeth up; the front face of the gear butts against the flange on the mainshaft.
8. Install a blocker ring with clutching teeth down.
9. Install first and reverse synchronizer assembly with fork slot down. Press it onto mainshaft splines. Be sure blocker ring notches align with synchronizer assembly keys.
10. Install snap-ring.
11. Install reverse gear with clutching teeth down.
12. Install steel reverse gear thrust washer and spring washer.
13. Press rear ball bearing onto shaft with snap-ring slot down.
14. Install snap-ring.
15. Install speedometer drive gear and retaining clip. Press on metal speedometer drive gear.

Transmission Assembly

1. Using dummy shaft, load a row of 27 roller bearings and a thrust washer at each end of countergear. Hold in place with grease.
2. Place countergear assembly into

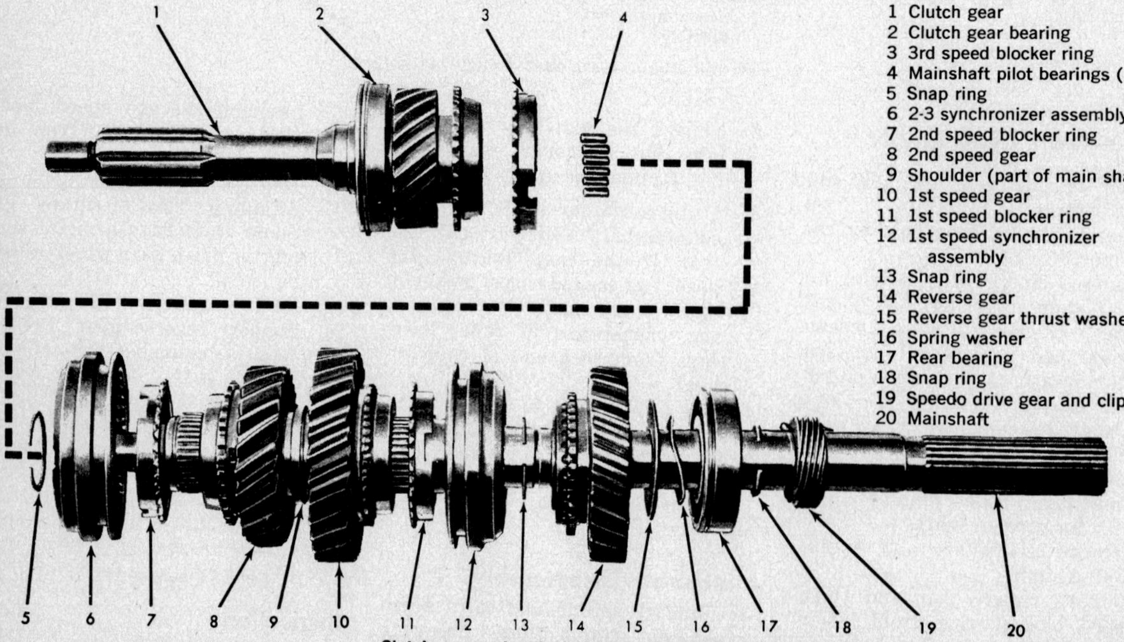

1
2
3
4
5
6
7
8
9
10
11
12
13
14
15
16
17
18
19
20

1 Clutch gear
2 Clutch gear bearing
3 3rd speed blocker ring
4 Mainshaft pilot bearings (14)
5 Snap ring
6 2-3 synchronizer assembly
7 2nd speed blocker ring
8 2nd speed gear
9 Shoulder (part of main shaft)
10 1st speed gear
11 1st speed blocker ring
12 1st speed synchronizer assembly
13 Snap ring
14 Reverse gear
15 Reverse gear thrust washer
16 Spring washer
17 Rear bearing
18 Snap ring
19 Speedo drive gear and clip
20 Mainshaft

Clutch gear and mainshaft assembly (© G.M. Corp)

case through rear. Place a tanged thrust washer, tang away from gear, at each end. Install countershaft and key, making sure that tangs align with notches in case.

3. Install reverse idler gear thrust washer, gear, and shaft with key from rear of case. Be sure thrust washer is between gear and rear of case with tang toward notch in case.
4. Expand snap-ring in extension. Assemble extension over rear of mainshaft and onto rear bearing. Seat snap-ring in rear bearing groove.
5. Install 14 mainshaft pilot bearings into clutch gear cavity. Assemble third speed blocker ring onto clutch gear clutching surface with teeth toward gear.
6. Place clutch gear, pilot bearings, and third speed blocker ring assembly over front of mainshaft assembly. Be sure blocker rings align with keys in second-third synchronizer assembly.
7. Stick extension gasket to case with grease. Install clutch gear, mainshaft, and extension together. Be sure clutch gear engages teeth of countergear anti-lash plate. Torque extension bolts to 45 ft. lbs.
8. Place bearing over stem of clutch gear and into front case bore. Install front bearing to clutch gear snap-ring.
9. Install clutch gear bearing retainer and gasket. The retainer oil return hole must be at the bottom. Torque retainer bolts to 10 ft. lbs.
10. Install reverse idler gear shaft E-ring.
11. Shift synchronizer sleeves to neutral positions. Install cover, gasket, and forks, aligning forks with synchronizer sleeve grooves. Torque side cover bolts to 10 ft. lbs.
12. Install speedometer driven gear.

Type-12
Muncie 4-Speed
Application

Buick Special (GS), 1967-74
Camaro, 1967-74
Chevelle, 1967-74
Chevrolet, 1967-69
Chevy II, 1967-74
Corvette, 1967-74
Firebird, 1967-74
GTO, 1971-74
Monte Carlo, 1970-71
Olds F-85, 1967-74
Olds Cutlass, 442, 1971-74
Pontiac, 1968-69
Pontiac (GP), 1968-71
Tempest, 1967-74

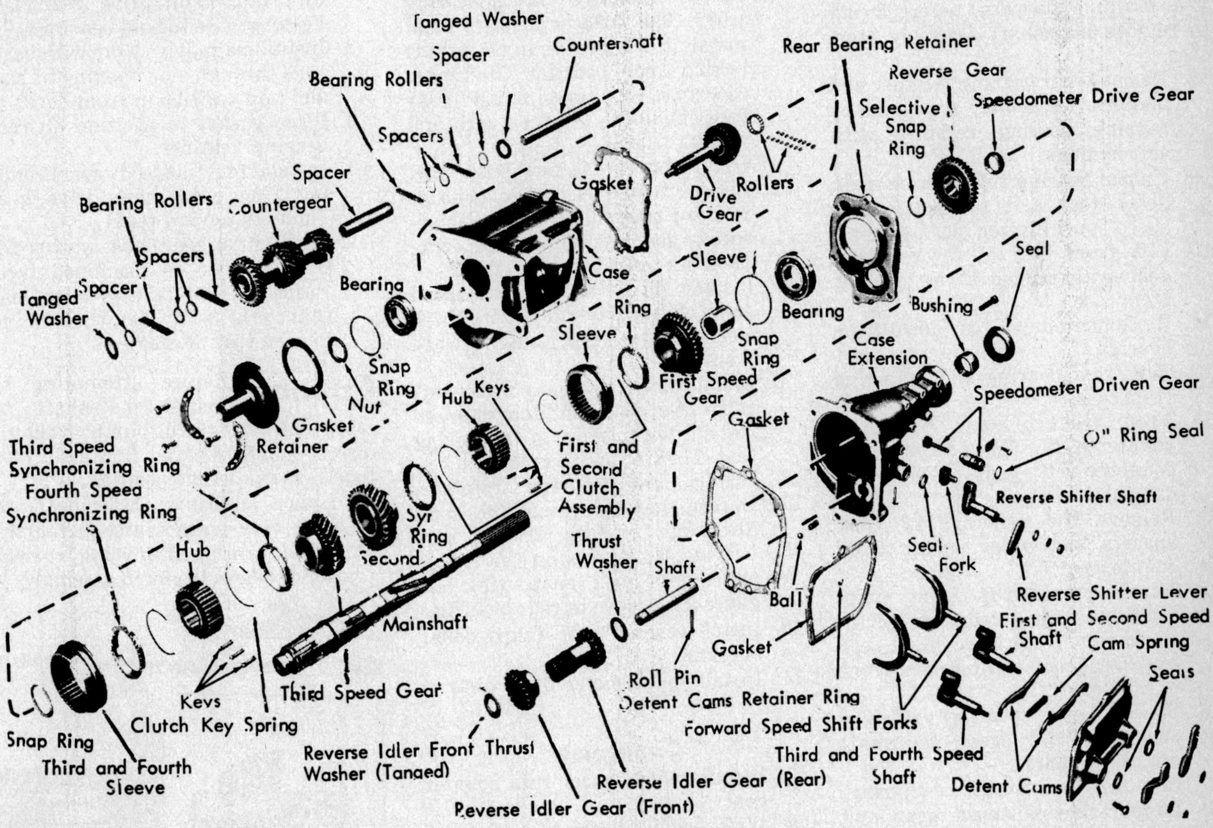
Tanged Washer
Spacer
Countershaft
Bearing Rollers
Spacers
Spacer
Bearing Rollers
Countergear
Spacers
Tanged Washer
Spacer
Bearing
Gasket
Case
Drive Gear
Rollers
Rear Bearing Retainer
Reverse Gear
Selective Snap Ring
Speedometer Drive Gear
Sleeve
Ring
Bearing
Seal
Bushing
Snap Ring
Nut
Gasket
Retainer
Hub
Keys
Sleeve
Snap Ring
First Speed Gear
Case Extension
Speedometer Driven Gear
"O" Ring Seal
Third Speed Synchronizing Ring
Fourth Speed Synchronizing Ring
First and Second Clutch Assembly
Gasket
Reverse Shifter Shaft
Syn Ring
Second
Thrust Washer
Shaft
Seal
Fork
Hub
Reverse Shifter Lever
Ball
First and Second Speed Shaft
Cam Spring
Mainshaft
Gasket
Seals
Keys
Third Speed Gear
Roll Pin
Detent Cams Retainer Ring
Clutch Key Spring
Forward Speed Shift Forks
Snap Ring
Third and Fourth Sleeve
Reverse Idler Front Thrust Washer (Tanged)
Third and Fourth Speed Shaft
Reverse Idler Gear (Rear)
Detent Cams
Reverse Idler Gear (Front)

Muncie 4-speed transmission

Disassembly

1. Remove side cover and shift controls after draining.
2. Remove bolts and bolt lock strips from front bearing retainer and remove retainer and gasket.
3. Lock up transmission by shifting into two gears and remove main drive gear retaining nut.

NOTE: this nut may have left-hand threads.

4. Return gears to neutral and remove lock pin from reverse shifter lever boss and pull shaft out about 1/8 in. This will disengage reverse shift fork from reverse gear.
5. Remove extension case attaching

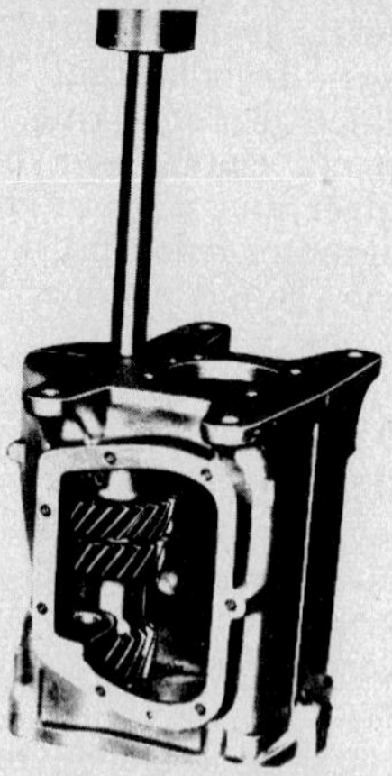

Removing countershaft
(© G.M. Corp)

bolts. Tap extension with soft hammer toward rear. When idler shaft is out as far as it will go, move extension to left so reverse fork clears gear and remove extension and gasket.

6. Remove reverse idler gear, flat washer, shaft and roll spring pin.
7. Remove speedometer and reverse gears.

NOTE: slide third-fourth synchronizer clutch sleeve to fourth-speed gear position (forward) before trying to remove mainshaft assembly from case.

8. Remove rear bearing retainer and mainshaft assembly from case by tapping bearing retainer with soft hammer.
9. Unload bearing rollers from main drive gear and remove fourth-speed synchronizer blocking ring.
10. Lift front half of reverse idler gear with tanged thrust washer from case.
11. Press main drive gear down from bearing.
12. Tap front bearing and snap-ring from case.
13. From front of case, press out countershaft. Then, remove the countershaft gear and both tanged washers.
14. Remove the rollers (112), six spacers and roller spacer from countergear.
15. Remove mainshaft front snap-ring and slide third and fourth-speed clutch and third-speed gear and synchronizer ring from front of mainshaft.
16. Spread rear bearing retainer snap-ring and press mainshaft out of retainer.
17. Remove mainshaft snap-ring. Support second-speed gear and press on rear of mainshaft to remove rear bearing, first-speed gear and sleeve, first-speed synchronizing ring, first-second-speed synchronizer clutch, second-speed synchronizer ring and second-speed gear.

After thoroughly cleaning case and all parts, make thorough inspection and replace required parts. In checking bearings do not spin at high speeds, but rather clean and rotate by hand to detect roughness and unevenness. Spinning can damage balls and races.

Assembly

Mainshaft

1. From rear of shaft, assemble second-speed gear (hub of gear toward rear of shaft).
2. Install first-second synchronizer clutch assembly onto mainshaft (sleeve taper toward rear, hub to front); together with a synchronizer ring on each side of clutch assembly so that keyways line up with clutch keys.
3. Press first-speed sleeve onto mainshaft. (A 1¾ in. or 1⅝ in. ID pipe cut to convenient length makes a suitable tool).
4. Install first-speed gear (hub toward front) and press onto the rear bearing with snap-ring grooves toward front of transmission. Be sure bearing is firmly seated.
5. Choose selective fit snap-ring (.087, .090, .093 or .096 in.) and install it into groove in mainshaft behind rear bearing. Maximum clearance of snap-ring and rear face should be between zero and .005 in.

NOTE: always use new snap-ring.

6. Install third-speed gear (hub to front of transmission) and third-speed gear synchronizing ring (notches to front).
7. Install third and fourth-speed gear clutch assembly with both sleeve taper and hub toward front.
8. Install snap-ring onto mainshaft in front of third and fourth-speed clutch, with ends of snap-ring seated behind spline teeth.
9. Install rear bearing retainer. Spread snap-ring in plate, to allow ring to drop around rear bearing, and press on the end of mainshaft until snap-ring engages the groove in rear bearing.
10. Install reverse gear (shift collar to rear).
11. Install speedometer drive gear.

Countergear

1. Install roller spacer into counter gear.
2. With heavy grease to assist, install a spacer in either end of countergear, 28 roller bearings, then a spacer and 28 more rollers. Then, install another spacer. In the other end of the countergear, do the same.
3. Insert dummy shaft into counter gear.

Transmission

1. Rest case on side with cover opening toward mechanic. Install countergear tanged thrust washers in place, holding with heavy grease. Make sure tangs are in proper notches.
2. Set countergear in place. Use care not to disturb tanged washers.
3. Position transmission case so that it rests on front face.
4. Lubricate and insert countershaft in rear. Turn countershaft so flat on end of shaft is horizontal and facing bottom of case.

NOTE: the flat of shaft must be horizontal and toward bottom to mate with rear bearing retainer when installed.

5. Align countergear with shaft in rear and hole in front of case (pushing dummy shaft out front of case) until flat of shaft is flush with rear of case. Be sure thrust washers remain in place.
6. Check end-play in countergear (dial indicator should be used). If end-play is more than .025 in. install new thrust washer.
7. Install cage and 17 roller bearings into main drive gear. Use heavy grease to hold bearings.
8. Install main drive gear with bearings through side opening of case and into position in front bore.
9. Place gasket in position on rear bearing retainer.
10. Install fourth-speed synchronizing ring onto main drive gear (notches toward rear).
11. Position tanged thrust washer for reverse idler on machined face. Position front reverse idler gear next to thrust washer (hub facing toward rear of case).

Caution Before attempting to install mainshaft to case, slide the third-fourth synchronizer clutch sleeve forward into fourth-speed detent position.

12. Lower mainshaft assembly into case. Be sure notches on fourth-speed synchronizer ring correspond to keys in clutch assembly.

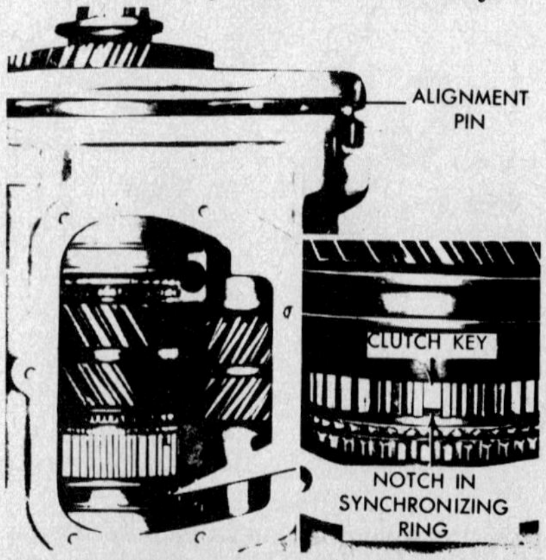
ALIGNMENT PIN
CLUTCH KEY
NOTCH IN SYNCHRONIZING RING

Installing mainshaft assembly
(© G.M. Corp)

13. With guide pin in rear bearing retainer aligned with hole in rear of case, tap rear bearing retainer into position with soft hammer.
14. From rear of case, insert reverse idler gear, engaging splines with portion of front gear in case.
15. Place gasket in position on rear face of bearing retainer.
16. Install remaining flat washer on reverse idler shaft.
17. Install reverse idler shaft, roll pin, and thrust washer into gears and front boss of case. Make sure to pick up front tanged thrust washer.
18. Pull reverse shifter shaft to left side of extension and rotate shaft to bring reverse shift fork forward in extension (reverse detent position). Start extension onto transmission case, while slowly pushing in on shifter shaft to engage the shift fork with the reverse gear shift collar. Then, pilot the reverse idler shaft into the extension housing, permitting the extension to slide into the transmission case.
19. Install extension and retainer-to-case attaching bolts.
20. Push or pull reverse shifter shaft to line up grooves in the shaft with the holes in the boss and drive in the lockpin. Install shift lever.
21. Press bearing onto main drive gear (snap-ring groove in front), and into case until several main drive gear retaining nut threads are exposed.
22. Lock transmission by shifting into two gears. Install main drive gear retaining nut onto the gear shaft and draw it up tight. Be sure bearing is completely seated against shoulder. Torque retaining nut to 40 ft. lbs. and lock in place by staking into main drive gear shaft hole with punch. Do not damage shaft threads.
23. Install main drive gear bearing retainer, gasket attaching bolts and boltlock retainers. Use a suitable seal on bolts. Tighten to 20 ft. lbs.
24. Shift mainshaft third-fourth sliding clutch sleeve into neutral position and first-second sliding clutch into second gear (forward) detent position. Shift side cover third-fourth shift lever into neutral detent and first-second shift lever into second gear detent position.
25. Install side cover, with gasket, and carefully position in place. A dowel pin provides proper alignment position. Install bolts and tighten evenly to avoid distortion. Torque to 20 ft. lbs.

Type-13
Saginaw 4-Speed

Application

Camaro, 1967-74
Chevy II, 1967-74
Chevelle, 1967-74
Chevrolet, 1967-69
Corvette, 1967-74
Tempest, 1967-74
Firebird, 1969 (6 Cyl.)
Vega, 1973-74

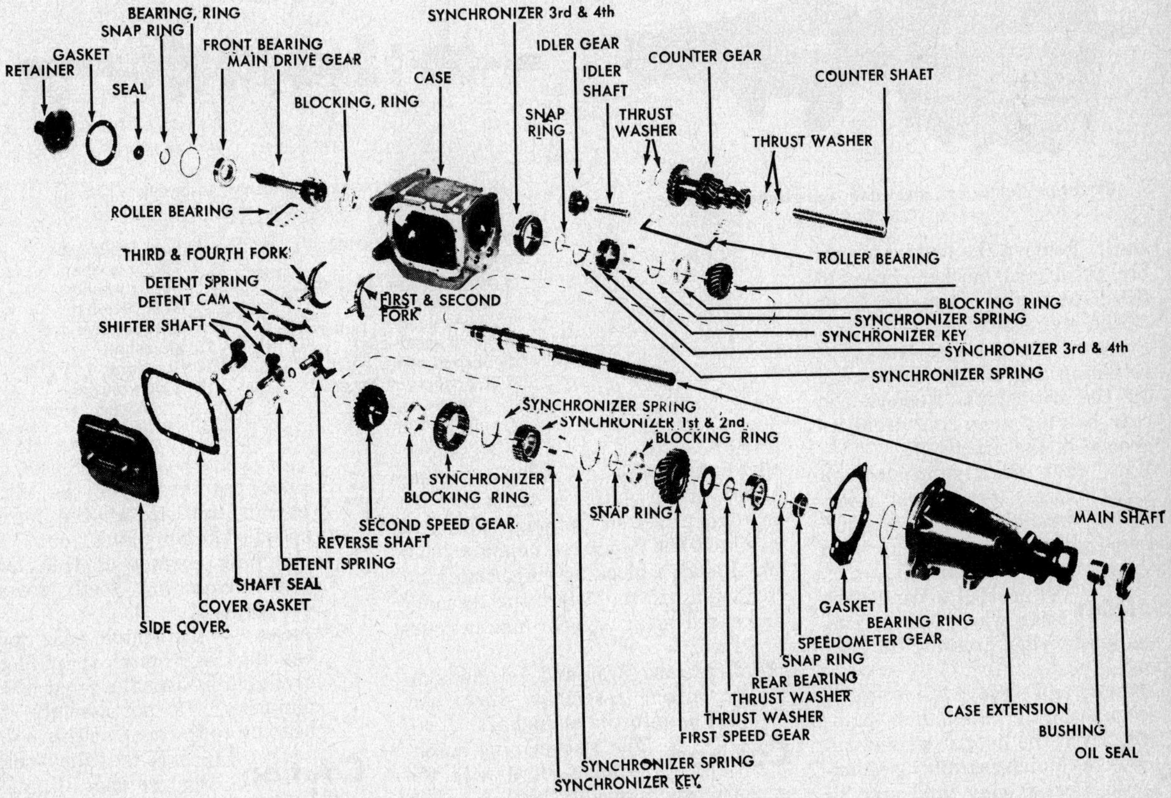
BEARING, RING
SNAP RING
GASKET
RETAINER
SEAL
FRONT BEARING
MAIN DRIVE GEAR
BLOCKING, RING
CASE
SYNCHRONIZER 3rd & 4th
IDLER GEAR
IDLER SHAFT
SNAP RING
THRUST WASHER
COUNTER GEAR
COUNTER SHAFT
THRUST WASHER
ROLLER BEARING
THIRD & FOURTH FORK
DETENT SPRING
DETENT CAM
SHIFTER SHAFT
FIRST & SECOND FORK
ROLLER BEARING
BLOCKING RING
SYNCHRONIZER SPRING
SYNCHRONIZER KEY
SYNCHRONIZER 3rd & 4th
SYNCHRONIZER SPRING
SYNCHRONIZER SPRING
SYNCHRONIZER 1st & 2nd.
BLOCKING RING
SYNCHRONIZER
BLOCKING RING
SNAP RING
SECOND SPEED GEAR
REVERSE SHAFT
DETENT SPRING
SHAFT SEAL
COVER GASKET
SIDE COVER
MAIN SHAFT
GASKET
BEARING RING
SPEEDOMETER GEAR
SNAP RING
REAR BEARING
THRUST WASHER
THRUST WASHER
FIRST SPEED GEAR
CASE EXTENSION
BUSHING
OIL SEAL
SYNCHRONIZER SPRING
SYNCHRONIZER KEY

Saginaw 4-speed transmission

Disassembly

1. Remove the side cover and shift forks after draining the transmission.
2. Remove the clutch gear bearing retainer. Remove the bearing-to-gear stem snap-ring and pull out on the clutch gear until a screwdriver can be inserted between the bearing, large snap-ring, and case to pry the bearing off.

NOTE: the clutch gear bearing is a slip-fit on the gear and in the case. Removal of the bearing will provide clearance for clutch gear and mainshaft removal.

3. Remove the rear extension attaching bolts and remove the clutch gear, mainshaft, and extension as an assembly.
4. Spread the snap-ring which holds the mainshaft rear bearing and remove the extension case.
5. Remove the countershaft and its woodruff key by driving out of the rear of the case with a pipe or an old countershaft. Remove the countergear assembly and bearings.
6. Using a long drift, drive the reverse idler shaft and woodruff key through the rear of the case.
7. Expand and remove the third and fourth-speed sliding clutch hub snap-ring from the mainshaft. Remove the clutch assembly, third gear blocker ring, and third-speed gear from the front of the mainshaft.

Removing clutch gear, mainshaft, and extension housing
(© G.M. Corp)

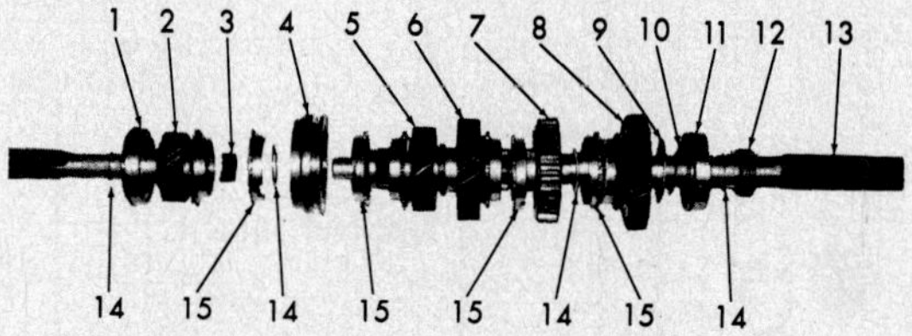
1 2 3 4 5 6 7 8 9 10 11 12 13
14 15 14 15 15 14 15 14

Clutch gear and mainshaft assembly
(© G.M. Corp)

1 Clutch gear bearing
2 Clutch gear
3 Mainshaft pilot bearings
4 3-4 synchronizer assembly
5 Third speed gear
6 Second speed gear
7 1-2 synchronizer and reverse gear assembly
8 First speed gear
9 Thrust washer
10 Spring washer
11 Rear bearing
12 Speedo drive gear
13 Mainshaft
14 Snap-ring
15 Synchronizing "blocker" ring

8. Press in the speedometer gear retaining clip and slide the gear off the mainshaft. Remove the rear bearing snap-ring from its groove in the mainshaft.
9. With first gear supported on press plates, press first gear, thrust washer, spring washer, rear bearing, and snap-ring from the rear of the mainshaft.

Caution Be careful to center the gear, washers, bearings, and snap-ring when pressing the rear bearing.

10. Expand and remove the first and second sliding clutch hub snap-ring from the mainshaft and remove the clutch assembly, second-speed blocker ring, and second-speed gear from the rear of the mainshaft.

After thoroughly cleaning all parts and the transmission case, inspect and replace all damaged or worn parts. When checking the bearings, do not spin them at high speeds. Clean and rotate the bearings by hand to detect roughness and uneveness. Spinning can damage balls and races.

Assembly

Mainshaft

Install the following parts with the front of the mainshaft facing up:

1. Install the third-speed gear with the clutching teeth up; the rear face of the gear will abut with the mainshaft flange.
2. Install a blocking ring, clutching teeth down, over the third-speed gear synchronizing surface.

NOTE: all four blocker rings are the same.

3. Press the third and fourth synchronizer assembly, fork slot down, onto the mainshaft splines until it bottoms.

Caution The blocker ring notches must align with the synchronizer assembly keys.

4. Install the synchronizer hub-to-mainshaft snap-ring. (Both synchronizer snap-rings are the same.)

Install the following parts with the rear of the mainshaft up.

5. Install the second-speed gear with the clutching teeth up; the front face of the gear will abut with the flange on the mainshaft.
6. Install a blocking ring, clutching teeth down, over the second-speed gear synchronizing surface.
7. Press the first and second synchronizer assembly, fork slot down, onto the mainshaft.

Caution The blocker ring notches must align with the synchronizer assembly keys.

8. Install the synchronizer hub-to-mainshaft snap-ring.
9. Install a blocker ring with the notches down so they align with the first/second synchronizer assembly keys.
10. Install first gear with the clutching teeth down. Install the first gear thrust washer and spring washer.
11. Press the rear ball bearing and snap-ring, slot down, onto the mainshaft. Install the snap-ring. Install the speedometer gear and clip.

Transmission

1. Using a dummy countergear shaft, load a row of roller bearings (27) and bearing thrust washers at each end of the countergear. Grease can be used to hold the bearings in place.
2. Position the countergear assembly into the case through the rear opening. Place a tanged thrust washer at each end of the countergear.
3. Install the countergear shaft and woodruff key from the rear of the case. Make sure that the shaft engages both thrust washers and that the tangs align with their notches in the case.
4. Install the reverse idler gear and shaft and the woodruff key. Install the extension-to-rear bearing snap-ring.
5. Install the fourteen mainshaft pilot bearings into the clutch opening and install the fourth-speed blocker ring onto the clutching surface of the clutch gear (clutching teeth toward the gear.)
6. Assemble the clutch gear, pilot bearings, and fourth-speed blocker ring unit over the front of the mainshaft. Do not assemble the bearing to the gear at this point.

Caution Be sure that the blocker ring notches line up with third/fourth synchronizer assembly keys.

7. Install the extension-to-case gasket and secure it with grease. In-

sert the clutch gear, mainshaft, and extension into the case as a unit. Install the extension-to-case bolts (apply sealer to the bottom bolt) and torque to 45 ft lbs.

8. Install the outer snap-ring on the front bearing and place the bearing over the stem of the clutch gear and into the case bore.

9. Install the snap-ring to the clutch gear stem. Install the clutch gear bearing retainer and gasket to the case, with the retainer oil return hole at the bottom.

10. Place the synchronizer sleeves into neutral positions and install the cover, gasket, and fork assemblies to the case. Be sure the forks align with their synchronizer sleeve grooves. Torque the cover bolts to 22 ft lbs.

Type-14

Vega 3-Speed

Application

Vega, 1971-72

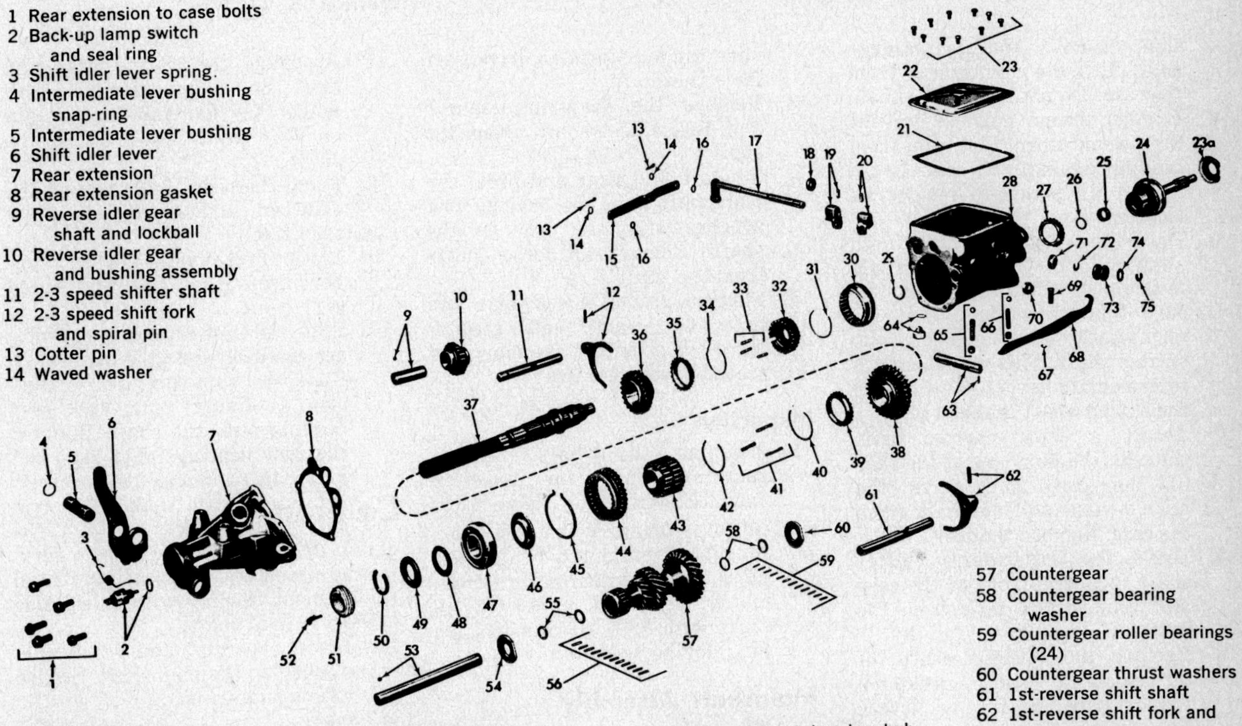

1 Rear extension to case bolts
2 Back-up lamp switch and seal ring
3 Shift idler lever spring.
4 Intermediate lever bushing snap-ring
5 Intermediate lever bushing
6 Shift idler lever
7 Rear extension
8 Rear extension gasket
9 Reverse idler gear shaft and lockball
10 Reverse idler gear and bushing assembly
11 2-3 speed shifter shaft
12 2-3 speed shift fork and spiral pin
13 Cotter pin
14 Waved washer
15 Shift selector rod
16 Washer
17 Selector shaft
18 Selector shaft seal
19 2-3 intermediate shift lever and spiral pin
20 Ist-reverse intermediate shift lever and spiral pin
21 Cover gasket
22 Cover assembly
23 Cover-to-case screws
23a Clutch drive gear seal
24 Clutch drive gear assembly
25 Mainshaft pilot bearing assembly
26 Pilot bearing spacer ring
27 3rd gear synchronizer ring
28 Transmission case
29 2-3 speed synchronizer assembly retaining ring
30 2-3 speed synchronizer sleeve
31 Synchronizer spring
32 2-3 synchronizer hub
33 2-3 synchronizer keys
34 Synchronizer spring
35 2nd gear synchronizer ring
36 2nd speed gear
37 Mainshaft
38 1st speed gear
39 1st speed gear synchronizer ring
40. Synchronizer spring
41 1st-reverse synchronizer keys
42 Synchronizer spring
43 1st-reverse synchronizer hub
44 1st-reverse synchronizer sleeve
45 Rear bearing to extension locking ring
46 1st-reverse key stop-ring
47 Mainshaft rear bearing
48 Rear bearing spacer
49 Belleville washer
50 Rear bearing retaining ring
51 Speedo drive gear
52 Speedo drive clip
53 Countergear shaft and lockball
54 Countergear thrust washer
55 Countergear bearing washer
56 Countergear roller bearings (24)
57 Countergear
58 Countergear bearing washer
59 Countergear roller bearings (24)
60 Countergear thrust washers
61 1st-reverse shift shaft
62 1st-reverse shift fork and spiral pin
63 Intermediate lever shaft and pin
64 TCS switch and gasket
65 2-3 shift detent ball, spring and hole plug
66 1st-reverse shift detent ball, spring and hole plug
67 Pivot pin lockring
68 Shift selector rod
69 Selector lever pivot pin
70 Oil filler plug
71 Selector shaft oil seal
72 Selector shaft lockring
73 Selector shaft ring
74 Belleville washer
75 Selector shaft lockring

Exploded view (inverted) of Vega 3-speed transmission
(© Chevrolet Div., G.M. Corp)

Transmission Disassembly

1. Remove the shift lever boot. Remove the TCS switch and back-up light switch.
2. Remove the cotter pins from each end of the shift control rod. Remove washers and shift control rod.
3. Remove retaining rings, wave rings, and selector ring from selector shaft. Slide the selector lever and shift idler lever shaft from the intermediate shift lever assembly while simultaneously removing the selector ring.
4. Remove the transmission case cover and gasket.
5. Invert the transmission to drain the oil.
6. Remove the rear extension attaching bolts and rotate the extension until the countergear shaft is exposed.
7. From the front of the transmis-

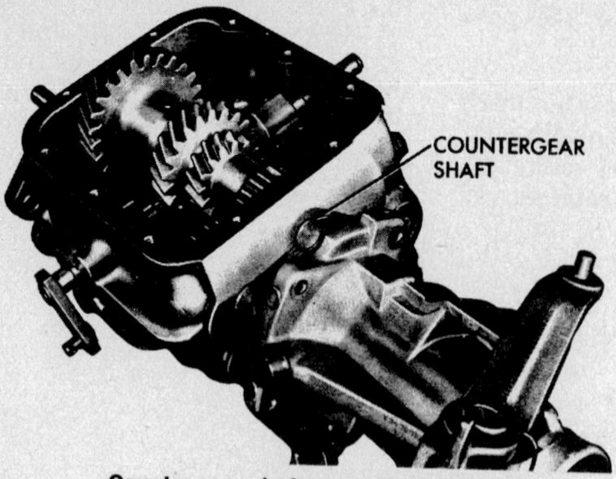
COUNTERGEAR
SHAFT

Counter gear shaft exposed for removal
(© Chevrolet Div., G.M. Corp)

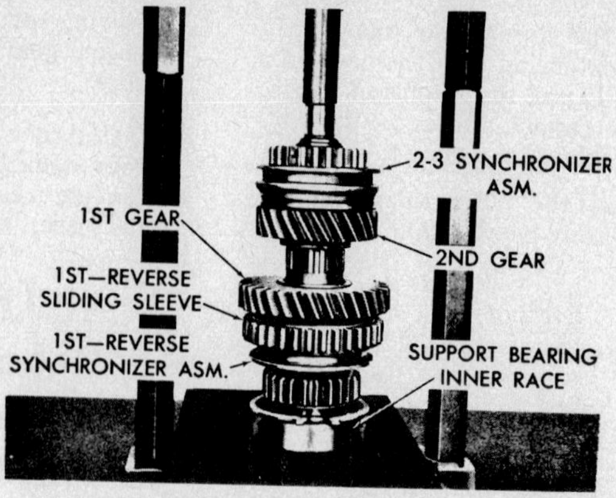
2-3 SYNCHRONIZER
ASM.
1ST GEAR
2ND GEAR
1ST—REVERSE
SLIDING SLEEVE
1ST—REVERSE
SYNCHRONIZER ASM.
SUPPORT BEARING
INNER RACE

Assembling mainshaft components
(© Chevrolet Div., G.M. Corp)

sion, remove the countergear shaft. Lift the countergear from the case. Do not lose the lockball.

8. Engage second gear to prevent the second-third fork pin from binding against the case. Use a ⅛ in. pin punch to remove all lockpins.
9. Drive the lockpins from both shifter forks. Place the transmission in third gear and be sure that the second-third intermediate lever engages the shifter shaft. This will allow the intermediate levers to pivot as the shifter shaft is removed.
10. Insert a long narrow drift through the bolt hole at the rear of the case and drive the second-third shifter shaft from the case. Remove the fork.
11. Drive the first-reverse shifter shaft from the front of the case and remove the fork from the case.
12. Remove the selector shaft intermediate lever lockpins. Remove the shaft and levers from the case.
13. Remove the snap-ring from the rear bearing retainer groove and slide the rear extension from the mainshaft assembly.
14. Remove the clutch drive gear from the case.
15. Position first-reverse sliding gear to the rear of the hub shaft and remove the mainshaft assembly from the case. Remove the lockpins and detent balls from the bottom of the case.
16. Drive the plugs and springs from the shift rail detent holes.
17. Remove the reverse idler gear and shaft from the case.

Mainshaft Disassembly

NOTE: the synchronizer hubs and sliding sleeves are a select assembly and kept together as originally assembled. Keys and springs may be replaced.

1. Remove the snap-ring from in front of the clutch hub.
2. Depress the retaining clip and slide the speedometer drive gear from the shaft.
3. Remove the snap-ring, spacer and Belleville washer from the shaft.
4. Support first gear and press the mainshaft until the bearing and synchronizers are free on the shaft. Remove all loose parts from the shaft.
5. Support second speed gear and press and shaft until second-third synchronizer assembly and second speed gear are free.

Inspection

1. Examine the shaft, bearing gear and hubs for excessive wear. Examine for chips, nicking or scoring. Wash ball bearings in solvent and blow dry. Replace worn synchronizer rings, clutch keys and hubs. Oil all parts with SAE 90 transmission fluid during assembly.

Mainshaft Assembly

1. From the front of the mainshaft, install the second speed gear. The gear must turn freely on the shaft.
2. Install the second-third synchronizer onto second speed gear cone.
3. Install front and rear synchronizer key springs into second-third speed synchronizer hubs, so that hooked spring ends are in the same slot and raised ends are against the blocker rings.
4. Install sliding sleeve and keys on clutch hub. Arrows must point to front of shaft.
5. Press second-third speed synchronizer hub onto the mainshaft. Secure with a snap-ring.
6. Install both clutch key springs into first-reverse speed synchronizer hub. Hooks of both springs must rest in the same hub slot and raised spring ends should be positioned opposite each other against the blocker rings.
7. Assemble the sliding gear and keys on hub assembly with longer key flat and fork groove on gear toward the rear of the shaft.
8. From the rear of the mainshaft, slide on first gear. Gear must turn freely.
9. Place first-reverse speed synchronizer ring onto first speed gear cone.
10. Slide the first-reverse synchronizer assembly onto the mainshaft. Slide the stop-ring, rear extension retaining ring and rear bearing onto the shaft. Support the rear bearing inner race and press the components together.

Caution Align slots with synchronizer keys. The clutch drive bearing is used to service the mainshaft rear bearing. Install replacement bearing with shield side toward rear of shaft.

11. Place spacer and Belleville washer on the mainshaft. Secure with a snap-ring.
12. Position the speedometer drive gear retaining clip on shaft and install the speedometer drive gear.
13. Install the mainshaft into the extension housing up to the stop. Secure with a retaining ring.

Transmission Assembly

1. Install a new gasket on the rear extension and slide mainshaft assembly into the case. Install one or two bolts to keep the extension from rotating.
2. Coat the pilot roller bearing with grease. From the front, slide the lockring and pilot roller bearing onto the mainshaft.
3. Install the blocker ring on clutch drive gear, and install the gear into the transmission case, up to the snap-ring stop.
4. Insert the first-reverse speed shifter shaft at the front of the case with the notches down, pushing it through the shifter

fork. Position the fork shoulder toward the front of the case. Drive the lockpin in place.

NOTE: all lockpins should be installed protruding 1/16 in. to 5/16 in. above the fork or lever.

5. Insert the second-third speed shifter shaft, from the front of the case, with the notches down, pushing it through the shifter fork shoulder toward the front. Install the lockpin.
6. Install the selector shaft in the case. Push it through the second-third speed intermediate lever and the first-reverse lever. Install lockpins.
7. Install both lockballs and springs into the bores in the case and drive in the plugs.
8. Remove the rear extension bolt(s), pull back on the extension and rotate the extension until the bore for the reverse idler gear is exposed.
9. Install the lockball into the shaft

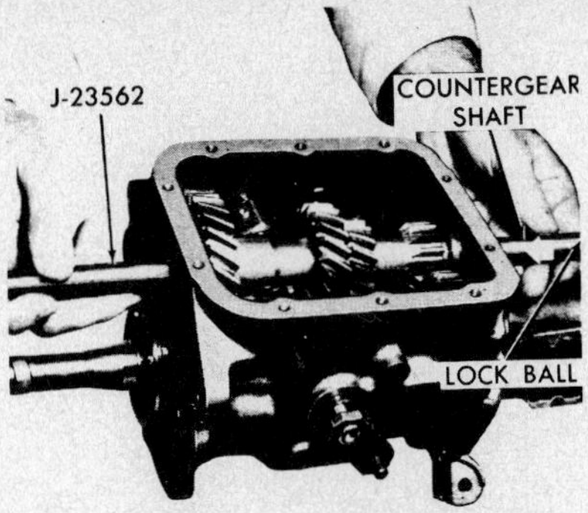
J-23562
COUNTERGEAR SHAFT
LOCK BALL
Installing countergear shaft
(© Chevrolet Div., G.M. Corp)

from the rear of the case and install the shaft into the gear. Drive the shaft into place.

10. Using a dummy shaft, install a spacer at each end of the countergear. Hold them in place with heavy grease.
11. Coat the thrust washer with grease and stick it to the case. The lugs of the thrust washers must engage the slots in the case.
12. Turn the case extension until the countergear bore is exposed.
13. Place the lockball in the shaft. From the rear of the transmission, insert the shaft so that the thrust washer is held in position. Hold the opposite thrust washer in position with a short drift.
14. Insert the countergear into the case.
15. Insert the shaft into the countergear and push out the dummy shaft. Align the lockball with the groove in the case and tap the shaft into the case.
16. Align the rear bearing retainer and tighten the bolts.
17. Install the case cover gasket, cover and screws.
18. Install the gearshift linkages in reverse sequence to removal.

NOTE: start the idler lever shaft into the shift control simultaneously when installing selector ring.

Type-15

Vega 4-Speed

Application

Vega, 1971-72

Transmission Disassembly

1. Follow Steps 1-7 under Vega 3-Speed (Type-15) for removal of gearshift linkage, case cover and countergear shaft and countergear.
2. Drive out intermediate shift lever pin and remove intermediate lever. Use a 1/8 in. pin punch to drive out all pins.
3. Slide the reverse shaft to rear of the case so that the scallop in the selector shaft will clear the reverse shaft.
4. Shift transmission to neutral. Push in on the selector shaft and turn so that the lockpins are in the vertical position. Drive the lockpin out of the third-fourth speed intermediate lever cam and then from the first-second speed intermediate lever cam. Remove the selector shaft.
5. Pry the selector shaft seal rings out of the case.
6. Remove the lockball plugs with a slide hammer. Remove the thrust springs and balls.
7. Place the transmission in first gear and drive the lockpins out of the shifter forks and selector levers. Remove the first-second lever pin first.
8. From the rear of the transmission drive out the first-second shifter shaft with a brass drift. Remove the fork from the sliding sleeve.
9. Tap the third-fourth shifter shaft rearward until the fork can be removed from the shaft, then drive out the third-fourth shifter shaft through the front of the case.
10. Remove the clutch drive gear from the case.
11. Remove the rear extension and mainshaft from the case.
12. Push the reverse idler gear shaft toward the rear. Be sure that the lockball is not lost, and remove the reverse idler gear and shaft from the case.
13. From the front of the transmission, drive out the reverse shifter shaft with a brass drift. Remove the shifter fork from the case.

Mainshaft Disassembly

1. Remove the snap-ring from the rear bearing retainer groove and remove the mainshaft assembly from the rear bearing retainer.
2. Depress the retaining clip and remove the speedometer driven gear.
3. Remove needle bearing, spacer ring and synchronizer ring. The sliding sleeve, keys and clutch keys can also be removed.

NOTE: the synchronizer hubs and sliding sleeves are a select assembly and should be kept together as originally assembled.

4. Remove the snap-ring from in front of the synchronizer hub.
5. Remove the snap-ring, spacer and Belleville washer from the shaft.
6. Support second gear and press the mainshaft until the bearing and synchronizers are free on the shaft. Remove all loose parts.
7. Remove third speed synchronizer hub snap-ring. Support third gear and press the mainshaft until the synchronizer and third gear are free.

Inspection

1. See inspection of components under Vega 3-Speed (Type-15) transmission.

Mainshaft Assembly

1. From the front of the mainshaft, install the third speed gear. Gear must turn freely.
2. Install the third speed synchronizer ring onto the third speed gear cone.
3. Install the rear clutch key spring into the third-fourth speed synchronizer hub so that the hooked spring rests in one of the slots and the raised end is toward the blocker ring.
4. Press the third-fourth speed clutch hub onto the mainshaft.
5. Secure the third-fourth synchronizer hub with a snap-ring.
6. From the rear of the mainshaft slide on the second speed gear. Gear must turn freely.
7. Place the second speed synchro-

1 Intermediate lever bushing snap-ring
2 Cotter pin
3 Shift idler lever and spring
4 Intermediate lever bushing
5 Rear extension and retaining bolts
6 Rear extension gasket
7 Reverse idler gear shaft and lockball
8 Reverse idler gear and bushing assembly

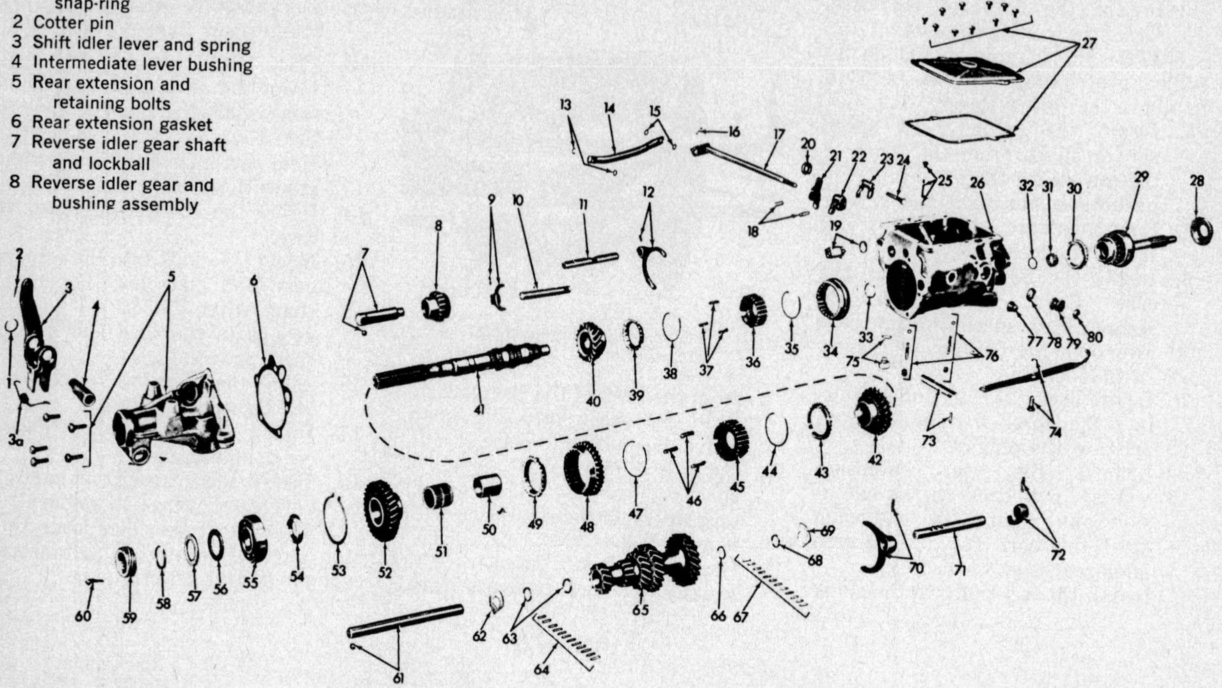

9 Reverse idler gear shift fork and spiral pin
10 Reverse idler gear shifter shaft
11 3-4 speed shifter shaft
12 3-4 speed shift fork and spiral pin
13 Washers
14 Shift control rod
15 Washers
16 Cotter pin
17 Selector shaft
18 Spiral pins
19 Back-up lamp switch and seal ring
20 Selector shaft oil seal
21 3rd-4th speed intermediate shifter lever
22 1st-2nd intermediate shift lever
23 Reverse intermediate lever
24 Reverse intermediate lever pin
25 Reverse shifter shaft detent ball, spring and cap
26 Transmission case
27 Cover gasket, cover, and screws
28 Clutch drive gear to housing seal
29 Clutch drive gear assembly
30 4th gear synchronizer ring
31 Mainshaft pilot bearing assembly
32 Pilot bearing spacer ring
33 3-4 speed synchronizer assembly retaining ring
34 3-4 speed synchronizer sleeve
35 Synchronizer spring
36 3-4 synchronizer hub
37 3-4 synchronizer keys
38 Synchronizer spring
39 3rd speed gear synchronizer ring
40 3rd speed gear
41 Mainshaft
42 2nd speed gear
43 2nd speed synchronizer ring
44 Synchronizer spring
45 1st-2nd synchronizer hub
46 1st-2nd synchronizer keys
47 Synchronizer spring
48 1st-2nd synchronizer sleeve
49 1st speed synchronizer ring
50 1st speed gear bushing
51 1st gear needle bearing assembly
52 1st speed gear
53 Rear bearing to extension locking ring
54 Rear bearing spacer ring (front)
55 Mainshaft rear bearing
56 Rear bearing spacer (rear)
57 Belleville washer
58 Rear bearing retaining ring (brg.-to-mainshaft)
59 Speedo drive gear
60 Speedo drive clip
61 Countergear shaft and lockball
62 Countergear thrust washer
63 Countergear bearing washers
64 Countergear roller bearings (24)
65 Countergear
66 Countergear bearing washer
67 Countergear roller bearings (24)
68 Countergear bearing washer
69 Countergear thrust washer
70 1st-2nd shift fork and spiral pin
71 1st-2nd shift shaft
72 1st-2nd selector lever cam and spiral pin
73 Intermediate lever shaft and pin
74 Shift selector rod, pivot pin and lock ring
75 TCS switch and gasket
76 Shifter shaft detent balls, springs and hole plugs
77 Oil filler plug
78 Selector shaft oil seal
79 Selector shaft adjusting ring
80 Selector shaft locknut

Exploded view (inverted) of Vega 4-speed transmission (© Chevrolet Div., G.M. Corp)

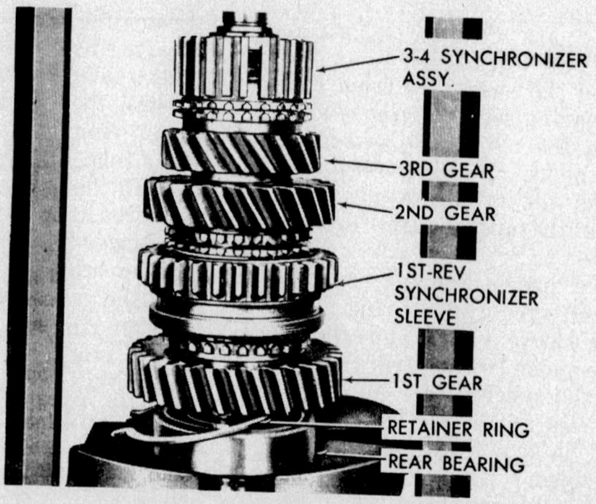
3-4 SYNCHRONIZER ASSY.
3RD GEAR
2ND GEAR
1ST-REV SYNCHRONIZER SLEEVE
1ST GEAR
RETAINER RING
REAR BEARING

Assembling mainshaft components
(© Chevrolet Div., G.M. Corp)

nizer ring on the second speed gear cone.

8. Install both synchronizer key springs into the first-second speed synchronizer hub, so that the spring hooks rest in the same hub slot and the other spring ends are positioned opposite each other and toward the blocker rings. Install the sliding gear and keys on the hub.
9. Slide the first-second speed synchronizer hub, needle bearing and inner sleeve onto the mainshaft. Slide the spacer, rear extension retaining ring and rear bearing onto the shaft.
10. Support the rear bearing inner race and press the components together.

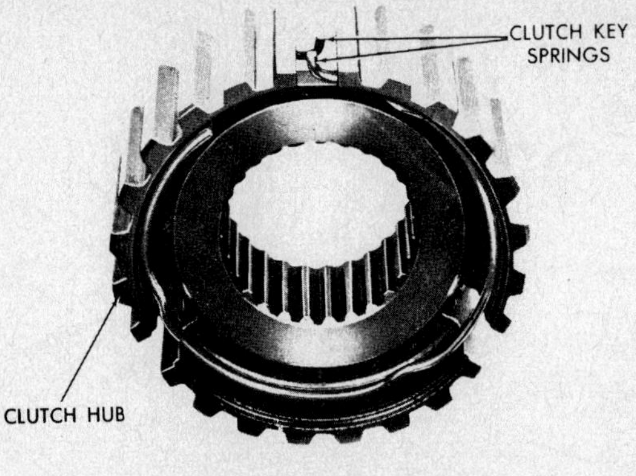
CLUTCH KEY
SPRINGS
CLUTCH HUB

Installing synchronizer key springs
(© Chevrolet Div., G.M. Corp)

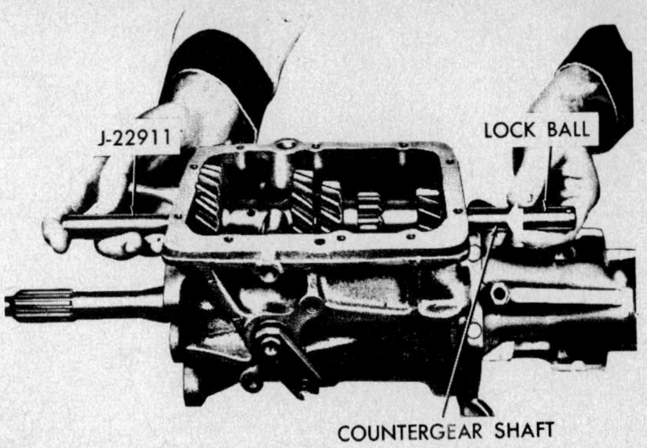
J-22911
LOCK BALL
COUNTERGEAR SHAFT

Installing counter gear shaft
(© Chevrolet Div., G.M. Corp)

NOTE: align the slots in the synchronizer rings with the synchronizer keys.

11. Install the spacer and Belleville washer on the mainshaft and secure with snap-ring.

NOTE: the concave side of the Belleville washer should face the bearing.

12. Position the speedometer gear retaining clip on the shaft and install the gear.
13. Place the mainshaft assembly into the rear bearing retainer up to the stop. Secure with a snap-ring.
14. Assemble the third-fourth speed synchronizer assembly on hub with the raised end of the key springs toward the blocker ring.

NOTE: arrows on the keys point toward the shifter fork groove.

Transmission Assembly

1. Install a new gasket onto the rear extension.
2. Slide the mainshaft assembly into the transmission case.
3. From the front, slide the spacer ring and needle bearing onto the mainshaft. Coat the needle bearing and roller with grease.
4. Install the synchronizer blocker ring on the clutch drive gear and install the gear into the case up to the stop.
5. Insert the first-second shifter shaft at the front of the case with the notches down, pushing it first through the L shaped selector dog. Push the first-second speed selector shaft through the shifter fork, positioning the shoulder toward the front of the case. Drive the lockpins in. Install selector dog pin first.

NOTE: all lockpins should protrude 1/16 in. to 5/64 in.

6. Insert the third-fourth speed shifter shaft from the front of the case. The notches should be down and it is pushed through the third-fourth speed shifter fork, positioning the shoulder toward the front. Install lockpin.
7. Install the reverse shifter shaft from the rear of the case with the notches up. Push it through the reverse shifter fork and install the lockpin. Position the shoulder of the shift fork toward the front of the case.
8. Insert the selector shaft into the case, through the third-fourth speed intermediate lever and through the first-second speed intermediate lever. Install lockpins.
9. Place the transmission in neutral and rotate the selector shaft to engage the levers with the shifter shafts.
10. Engage reverse speed intermediate levers with third-fourth speed intermediate lever and install pivot pin. Reverse speed intermediate lever end-play on the pin should be .004-.012 in.
11. Insert both lockballs and springs into their bores. Drive in plugs.
12. Turn the transmission case extension until the bore for the reverse idler gear shaft is exposed.
13. Place the lockball into the shaft and from the rear of the case, install the shaft into the gear.
14. Simultaneously, position the reverse idler gear and reverse shifter fork. The shifter fork groove of the reverse idler gear and the shoulder of the shifter fork should be toward the front of the mainshaft.
15. Follow Steps 10-18 under Transmission Assembly for Vega 3-Speed (Type-15).

Type-16
Warner T-14, T-15 Fully Synchronized 3-Speed

T-14 Application
American Motors (232), 1968-74
American Motors, (258), 1971-74

T-15 Application
American Motors (232, 290, 304, 360), 1968-70
American Motors, (304, 360), 1971-74

Transmission Disassembly

1. Remove cover, front bearing cap, gasket, and two front bearing snap rings.
2. Align notch in clutch shaft third gear with countergear. Remove clutch shaft and front bearing. A puller may be needed.
3. Pull off front bearing.
4. Remove extension housing and gasket. Using oil seal remover and slide hammer, remove extension housing oil seal. Remove extension housing bushing. Install new bushing, aligning oil groove with housing slot.
5. Remove snap-ring, speedometer drive gear, and locating ball.

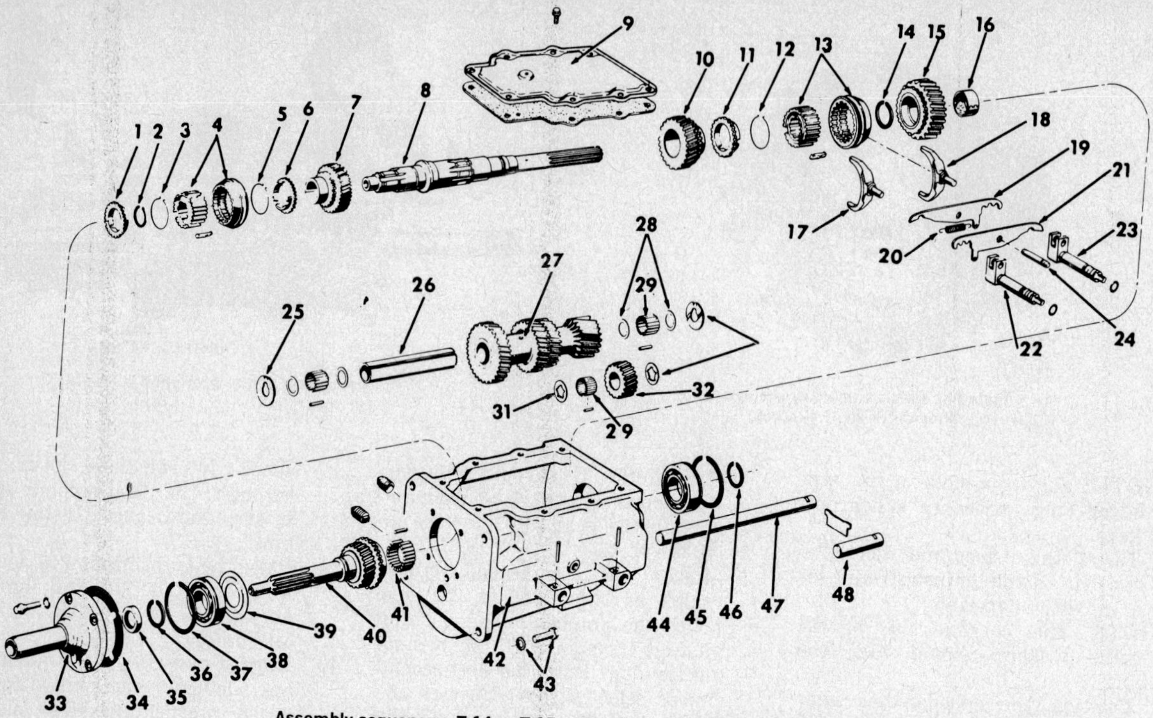

1
2
3
4
5
6
7
8
9
10
11
12
13
14
15
16
17
18
19
20
21
22
23
24
25
26
27
28
29
29
31
32
33
34
35
36
37
38
39
40
41
42
43
44
45
46
47
48

Assembly sequence—T-14 or T-15 transmission—exploded view (© American Motors Corp)

1 Synchro ring
2 Snap-ring
3 Retaining ring
4 2-3 synchro assy
5 Retaining ring
6 Synchro ring
7 2nd gear
8 Mainshaft
9 Cover
10 1st gear
11 Synchro ring
12 Retaining ring
13 1st-rev. synchro assy
14 Snap-ring
15 Reverse gear
16 Bushing
17 2nd-3rd fork
18 1st-rev. fork
19 1st-rev. lever
20 Interlock spring
21 2nd-3rd lever
22 2nd-3rd shaft
23 1st-rev. shaft
24 Interlock pin
25 Thrust washer
26 Spacer
27 Countergear
28 Washer
29 Rollers
30 Washer
31 Washer
32 Idler gear
33 Bearing cap
34 Gasket
35 Front seal
36 Snap ring
37 Lock ring
38 Front bearing
39 Washer
40 Clutch shaft
41 Rollers
42 Case
43 Case-to-bellhousing bolt (4)
44 Rear bearing
45 Snap-ring
46 Snap-ring
47 Countershaft
48 Idler shaft

6. Remove two rear bearing snap-rings and pull off rear bearing.
7. Move mainshaft aside. Remove both shift forks.
8. Push front synchronizer toward rear. Tilt front of mainshaft up and out through top of case.
9. If necessary, remove the transmission controlled spark switch assembly.
10. Drive out roll pins. Push shift shafts into case. Remove shift shafts and detent assembly.
11. Tap reverse idler shaft and countershaft rearward. Remove shaft lockplate. Drive reverse idler shaft from case. Use dummy shaft to drive out countershaft.

Mainshaft Disassembly

1. From front of shaft, remove front snap-ring, second-third synchro-clutch assembly, and second gear.
2. From rear of shaft, remove reverse gear, rear snap-ring, rear synchro-clutch assembly, and low gear.

Inspection

1. Check gears for worn, chipped, or cracked teeth. Check fit to mainshaft.
2. Check bearings for smoothness and excessive play.
3. Check roller bearings for wear or damage.
4. Slide synchro-clutch and friction rings on gear cones and clutch shaft. Replace rings if taper is worn or pitted. There should be no play between hub and shaft splines.
5. Check case for cracks or damaged bearing bores.

Mainshaft Assembly

1. Install low gear and friction ring; friction ring hub to the rear.
2. Install low synchro-gear into synchro-collar so deep end of gear faces low gear. Install synchro-plates (dogs) and retainer ring with large end of plates toward low gear.
3. Place synchro-clutch assembly on mainshaft with synchro-collar groove toward low gear. Install the thickest snap-ring that will fit in groove.
4. Measure clearance between first gear and collar on mainshaft. The clearance should be .003-.012 in. for the T-14; .003-.014 in. for the T-15.
5. Place second gear and the friction ring on the front of the mainshaft with the gear hub and ring forward. Place second synchro-gear into synchro-collar with deep end of gear facing rear of shaft.
6. Hold synchro-clutch assembly with one synchro-plate, or dog, in 12 o'clock position. Install tang of retainer ring into the dog at 12 o'clock and install ring clockwise. On opposite side, start with the same dog and install ring clockwise.
7. Place second synchro assembly on shaft with deep end to rear. Install the thickest snap-ring that will fit into the groove.
8. Measure clearance between second gear and collar on mainshaft. It must be .003-.018 in.
9. Install reverse gear on rear of mainshaft.

Transmission Assembly

1. Install dummy shaft in counter-

gear. Install spacer washers and roller bearings.

2. Place countergear in case. Align thrust washers at each end. Insert countershaft.
3. Install rollers in reverse idler gear. Hold rollers with petroleum jelly. Place gear in case. Position thrust washers. Insert shaft. Install shaft lockplate.
4. Insert shifter shafts in case. Position low-reverse lever to inside of case. Locate notches on top of levers to rear of case stud. Align shift detent assembly with shifter shafts and case stud. Push detent assembly and shifter shafts into place. Install shaft roll pins.
5. If removed, install the transmission controlled spark switch.
6. Place front synchronizer in second shift position. Place mainshaft assembly in case to one side.
7. Pull detent levers up. Place shift forks in shifting assembly.
8. Install mainshaft pilot end support in case. Install front bearing cap. Drive rear bearing on thickest rear bearing snap-ring with a 1¼ x 17 in. pipe. Install support and bearing cap.
9. Install locating ball, speedometer drive gear, and snap-ring.
10. Press front bearing onto clutch shaft.
11. Place rollers in clutch shaft. Hold with petroleum jelly.
12. Place friction ring on mainshaft. Slide clutch shaft into position from front.
13. Install thickest front bearing snap-ring that will fit in groove, gasket and cap. Align cap lubrication hole with hole in case.
14. Install extension housing. Install oil seal. Install shift lever, gaskets, and cover.

Type-17 Warner T-16 Fully Synchronized 3-Speed

Application

Camaro, 1967-68
Chevelle, 1967-68

Chevrolet, 1967, (396-427), 1968

Chevy II, 1968
Firebird, 1967 (V8)

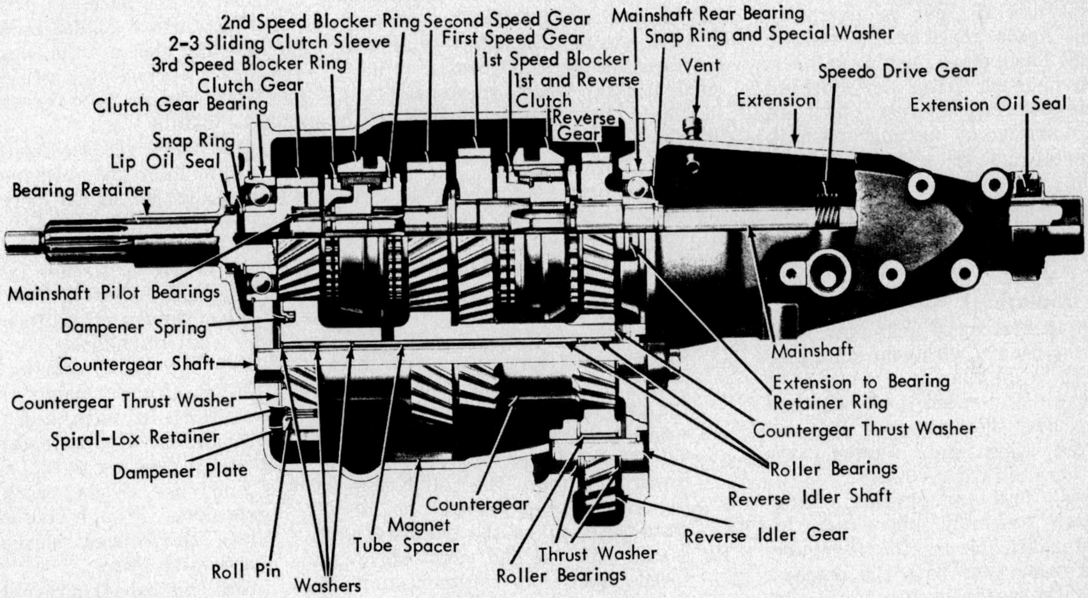
2nd Speed Blocker Ring
Second Speed Gear
Mainshaft Rear Bearing
2-3 Sliding Clutch Sleeve
First Speed Gear
Snap Ring and Special Washer
3rd Speed Blocker Ring
1st Speed Blocker
Vent
Speedo Drive Gear
Clutch Gear
1st and Reverse Clutch
Clutch Gear Bearing
Reverse Gear
Extension
Extension Oil Seal
Snap Ring
Lip Oil Seal
Bearing Retainer
Mainshaft Pilot Bearings
Dampener Spring
Countergear Shaft
Countergear Thrust Washer
Spiral-Lox Retainer
Dampener Plate
Mainshaft
Extension to Bearing Retainer Ring
Countergear Thrust Washer
Roller Bearings
Reverse Idler Shaft
Reverse Idler Gear
Countergear
Magnet
Tube Spacer
Thrust Washer
Roller Bearings
Roll Pin
Washers

Warner T-16 transmission

Disassembly of Unit

1. Clean outside of transmission to keep foreign matter from entering the case and to improve working conditions.
2. Remove side cover assembly and shift forks.
3. Remove extension housing attaching screws. Rotate extension clockwise to expose reverse idler gear shaft.
4. With a long drift through the side cover opening, drive the reverse idler shaft and Woodruff key through the rear of the case.
5. Rotate the extension counterclockwise to expose countergear shaft and, with a brass drift, drive shaft and Woodruff key out the rear of case.
6. With the countergear dropped to the bottom of case, remove the mainshaft and extension assembly through the rear of the case, remove the mainshaft pilot roller bearings from the clutch gear.
7. Remove snap-ring which retains mainshaft rear bearing and remove the extension from the rear bearing and mainshaft by tapping on end.
8. Remove the clutch gear bearing retainer and clutch gear bearing snap-ring and washer from the mainshaft.
9. Drive the clutch gear through its bearing into the case and remove the bearing by tapping from inside the case.
10. Remove countergear and roller bearings, both countergear thrust washers, reverse idler gear and 25 roller bearings, and both idler gear thrust washers from the case.

Mainshaft Disassembly

1. With snap-ring pliers, remove second and third-speed sliding clutch hub snap-ring from mainshaft. Then remove clutch assembly, second-speed blocker ring and second-speed gear from front of mainshaft.
2. Remove rear bearing snap-ring

from mainshaft groove.

3. With reverse gear supported on press plates, apply pressure to the rear of the mainshaft to remove reverse gear, rear bearing, special washer, snap-ring and the speedometer drive gear from rear of mainshaft.
4. Remove first and reverse sliding clutch hub snap-ring from the mainshaft and remove clutch assembly, first-speed blocker ring and first-speed gear from rear of mainshaft.

Cleaning and Inspection

Clean and inspect all parts for wear or other damage. Replace if necessary.

The countergear anti-rattle plate is spring-loaded. If weak or broken, remove plate and/or spring. Replace as necessary.

Synchronizer clutch hubs and sliding sleeves are selected assemblies and should be kept together as in the original assembly. The keys and springs, however, may be replaced if worn or broken.

If bushing in rear of extension housing needs replacement, remove the seal. Then, drive bushing into extension housing. Drive new bushing into the case from the rear. Lubricate inside diameter of bushing and seal, then install new oil seal with driver.

If the lip seal in the clutch bearing retainer needs replacing, pry out the old seal. Then, drive a new seal into place until seal bottoms in its bore.

Mainshaft Assembly

1. Install first-speed gear onto rear of mainshaft, with gear clutching teeth to the rear.
2. Install first-speed gear blocker ring over the first-speed gear tapered cone end (clutch key notches toward the rear).
3. Install first and reverse sliding clutch assembly over rear of mainshaft (be careful to engage the three keys with the notches of first-speed blocker ring). If properly installed, the straightest side of the clutch hub and the taper of the sliding sleeve will both be toward the rear of the mainshaft.
4. Install the first and reverse clutch hub snap-ring into the mainshaft groove.

NOTE: snap-rings are available in three thicknesses. Use thickest snap-

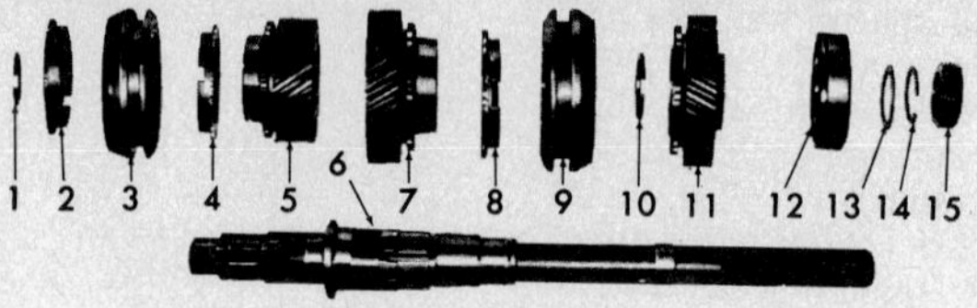
1
2
3
4
5
6
7
8
9
10
11
12
13
14
15

Mainshaft assembly
(© G.M. Corp)

1 Snap ring
2 3rd speed blocker ring
3 2-3 clutch assembly
4 2nd speed blocker ring
5 2nd speed gear
6 Mainshaft
7 1st speed gear
8 1st speed blocker ring
9 1st reverse clutch assembly
10 Snap ring
11 Reverse gear
12 Rear bearing
13 Special washer
14 Snap ring
15 Speedo drive gear

ring that will assemble with all parts stacked tightly, endwise.

5. Install reverse gear over rear of mainshaft, with the gear clutching teeth toward the front.
6. Press mainshaft rear bearing over rear of mainshaft, with its outer race snap-ring groove closest to reverse gear.
7. Install rear bearing special washer and snap-ring onto mainshaft.
8. Press the speedometer gear onto the rear of mainshaft until centered on the shaft boss.
9. Install the second-speed gear over the front of the mainshaft, with the gear clutching teeth toward the front.
10. Install the second-speed gear blocker ring over the second-speed gear tapered cone end (clutch key notches toward the front).
11. Install the second and third sliding clutch assembly over the front of the mainshaft, engaging the clutch keys with the notches of the second-speed blocker ring. If properly installed, the straightest side of the clutch hub should be toward the rear. The clutch sliding sleeve taper should be toward the front of the mainshaft.
12. Install the second and third-speed clutch hub retainer snap-ring onto the mainshaft

NOTE: snap-rings are available in four thicknesses. Use thickest snap-ring that will assemble with all parts stacked tightly, endwise.

Assembly of Unit

1. Insert tube spacer in countergear. Install a spacer, 20 rollers, another spacer, 20 more rollers, then another spacer at each end of countergear. Use heavy grease and the dummy shaft to hold them in place.
2. Insert countergear assembly through case rear opening along with a tanged countergear thrust washer (tang away from the gear) at each end (large washer at front) and install countergear shaft and Woodruff key from the rear of the case.

NOTE: attach a dial indicator to the case and measure the countergear end-play. If end-play greater than 0.025 in. is shown, new thrust washer must be installed.

3. With heavy grease, insert the 25 reverse idler gear bearing rollers into position in the bore of the reverse gear. Place gear and bearing assembly, along with a thrust washer on each end, into position inside the case. The beveled edge of the gear teeth face toward the front of the case.
4. Load the pilot bearing rollers into clutch gear, using grease to hold them in place, and position gear in case. Do not install clutch gear ball bearing at this time.
5. Stand case on end with clutch gear down through hole in bench. Place third-speed blocker ring over clutch gear.
6. Install mainshaft assembly from the rear of the case, picking up the spacers, pilot bearing and third-speed blocker rings.
7. Install reverse idler shaft and Woodruff key.
8. Install extension housing gasket to rear of case. Then, using snap-ring pliers, expand the extension-to-bearing snap-ring and install extension over mainshaft and rear bearing. Be sure the snap-ring has started over the rear bearing. Install and tighten extension attaching bolts to 35-45 ft. lbs. Use graphite sealer on the two lower attaching bolts.
9. Tap on the front of clutch gear shaft to force rear bearing-to-extension snap-ring to seat in its groove.
10. With driving sleeve, drive the

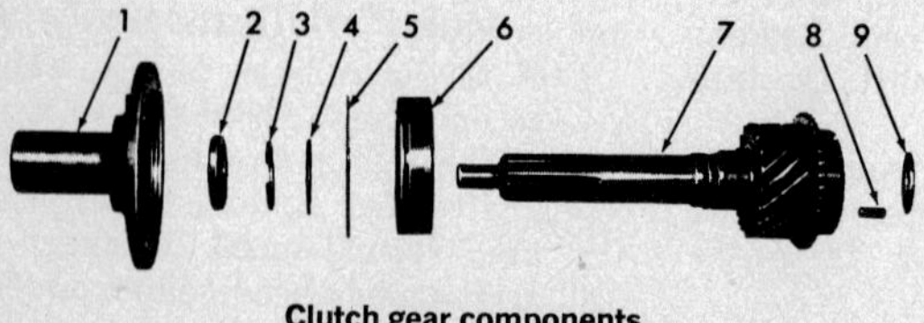
1
2
3
4
5
6
7
8
9

Clutch gear components
(© G.M. Corp)

1 Retainer
2 Lip seal
3 Snap ring
4 Special washer
5 Snap ring
6 Clutch gear bearing
7 Clutch gear
8 Mainshaft pilot bearings
9 Bearing spacer

clutch gear ball bearing onto the clutch gear and into the case. Install washer and snap-ring onto input shaft.

NOTE: this snap-ring is available in five thicknesses. Use thickest snap-ring that will assemble with all parts stacked tightly, endwise.

Install snap-ring to outer race of clutch gear bearing. If bearing snap-ring groove is partially inside case opening, tap on inside bearing outer race with a long drift through side cover opening.

NOTE: if mainshaft does not turn freely, check clutch sliding sleeves for neutral positions and that the blocker rings are free on their gear cone surfaces.

11. Install gaskets, clutch gear bearing retainer and lip seal assembly with oil drain passages at bottom. Then, tighten attaching screws to 15-20 ft. lbs. Use graphite sealer on threads of retainer bolts.

NOTE: install two retainer-to-case gaskets (.010 and .015 in. thick) instead of the one .025 in. production gasket removed.

12. Place the shift forks in the clutch sleeve grooves with the first and reverse fork hump toward the bottom.
13. Install side cover and gasket. Torque retaining bolts to 15-20 ft. lbs.

NOTE: the two side cover-to-case retaining bolts have special oil sealing splines and must be used at these two through locations.

Type-18 Warner T-90, T-86 3-Speed

T-90 Application

American Motors (6 Cyl. HD), 1967

T-86 Application

American Motors (287, 290), 1967

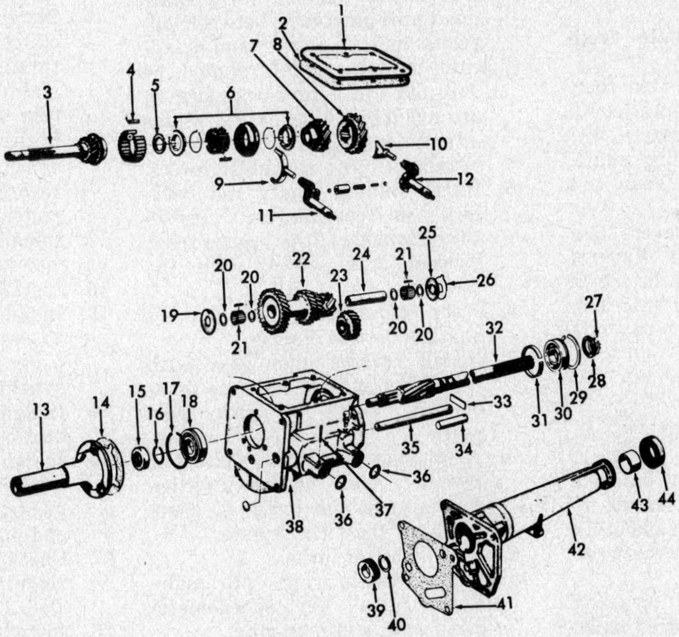

1 Top cover
2 Cover gasket
3 Clutch shaft
4 Bearing rollers
5 Snap-ring
6 Synchronizer assembly
7 Second gear
8 First and reverse gear
9 Second and third fork
10 First and reverse fork
11 Second and third shaft
12 First and reverse shaft
13 Bearing cap
14 Gasket
15 Front seal
16 Snap-ring
17 Snap-ring
18 Bearing
19 Thrust washer
20 Washer
21 Bearing rollers
22 Countershaft gear
23 Reverse idler gear
24 Spacer
25 Thrust washer
26 Thrust washer
27 Snap-ring
28 Spacer
29 Snap-ring
30 Bearing
31 Ring
32 Mainshaft
33 Plate
34 Reverse idler shaft
35 Countershaft
36 Seal
37 Pin
38 Case
39 Speedometer gear
40 Snap-ring
41 Gasket
42 Extension housing
43 Bushing
44 Seal

T-90 or T-86 transmission—exploded view (© American Motors Corp)

Disassembly

1. Remove cover.
2. Remove front bearing cap, clutch shaft snap-ring and bearing lock-ring.
3. Remove the front bearing, using a bearing puller and a thrust yoke to prevent damaging synchronizer clutches.
4. Remove extension housing. Drive out seal from inside housing with oil seal remover and installer tool. Use bushing remover and installer tool to replace bushing.
5. Move mainshaft assembly back about ¾ in. Lower front end of clutch shaft, move mainshaft assembly over countergear and out of shift forks. Remove clutch shaft from front of case.
6. Check roller bearings inside rear of clutch shaft for wear or damage.
7. Remove snap-ring, speedometer drive gear, and key.
8. Remove snap-ring, synchro-clutch assembly, second gear, friction ring, and low-reverse sliding gear. Press off rear bearing.
9. Remove shifter forks.
10. Remove shaft lockplate from rear of case.
11. Drive countershaft out to rear, using dummy shaft. Lower countergear to bottom of case.
12. Drive out reverse idler shaft. Remove reverse idler gear and countergear.
13. Remove outer shift levers and shifter shaft lockpins. Remove shifter shafts and two interlock ball bearings. Remove interlock sleeve and spring. Remove shaft oil seals from case.

Inspection

1. Wash all parts in solvent.
2. Air dry.
3. Check gears for worn, cracked, or chipped teeth. Check fit to shaft. Gears should fit smoothly without excessive play between splines.
4. Check bearings for cracked races, and worn or scored balls.

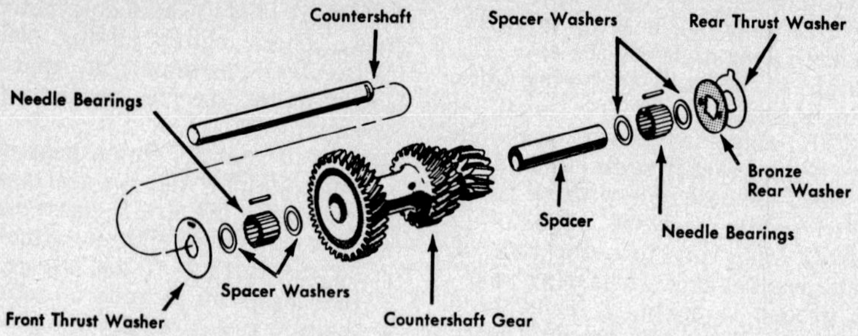
Countershaft
Spacer Washers
Rear Thrust Washer
Needle Bearings
Bronze
Rear Washer
Spacer
Needle Bearings
Spacer Washers
Front Thrust Washer
Countershaft Gear
Countershaft assembly sequence (© American Motors Corp)

5. Slide synchronizer rings on cones of second gear and clutch shaft. Replace rings if there is excessive wear or pits on the taper.
6. Check case bearing recesses for wear or scoring. Check case for cracks.

Assembly

1. Install new shift shaft oil seals.
2. Install low-reverse shift shaft, interlock sleeve, ball bearing, pin, and spring. Install second-third shift shaft and second ball bearing.
3. Shift mechanism into any gear position. With one end of interlock sleeve against shift shaft quadrant, clearance between opposite end of sleeve and quadrant on other shaft should be .001-.007 in. Interlock sleeves are available in several sizes for adjustment.
4. Install lockpins and shift levers.
5. Install dummy shaft and bearings in countergear. Install thrust washers; the bronze front washer must index with the case.
6. Place countergear and dummy shaft in bottom of case.
7. Install reverse idler gear with chamfered side of teeth to front of case. Drive in shaft from rear.
8. Align slots in countershaft and reverse idler shaft. Position countergear and drive in countershaft. Install lockplate.
9. Install shifter forks.
10. Press rear bearing onto mainshaft. Install key, speedometer drive gear, and snap-ring.
11. Install low-reverse sliding gear on mainshaft with sliding collar to front. Gear should slide easily. Install second gear with tapered cone to front.
12. Install rear bearing snap-ring. Install the thickest mainshaft rear snap-ring that will fit into groove.
13. Install synchro-clutch assembly and thickest mainshaft front snap-ring that will fit in groove.
14. When synchro-clutch hub is pressed against snap-ring, there should be .003-.010 in. clearance between second gear and shoulder on mainshaft.
15. Install 14 rollers in clutch shaft. Retain with light grease.
16. Install front friction ring on clutch shaft. Insert clutch shaft through top of case. Install mainshaft assembly through rear of case, moving to right to engage shifter forks in synchro-clutch collar and low-reverse sliding gear. Guide clutch shaft onto mainshaft.
17. Install a new oil seal in extension housing.
18. Install extension housing.
19. Install oil slinger, concave side to rear. Drive in front bearing using thrust yoke to prevent synchronizer damage.
20. Install thickest clutch shaft snap-ring that will fit in groove.
21. Install front bearing cap with new gasket. Choose thickness of gasket to give zero clutch shaft end-play.
22. Check clearance of friction rings. The clearance should be .056-.145 in.
23. Install cover and gasket.

Type-19
Warner T-96 3-Speed

Application

American Motors, 1967-74
(199, 232 6 Cyl.)

Disassembly

1. Remove top cover.
2. Remove front bearing cap, clutch shaft snap-ring, and bearing lockring.
3. Use a bearing puller and a thrust yoke to remove front bearing.
4. Remove oil slinger.
5. Remove extension housing. Replace rear bearing oil seal and extension housing bushing if necessary.
6. Remove speedometer drive gear snap-ring, drive gear, and retaining ball.
7. Move mainshaft assembly to

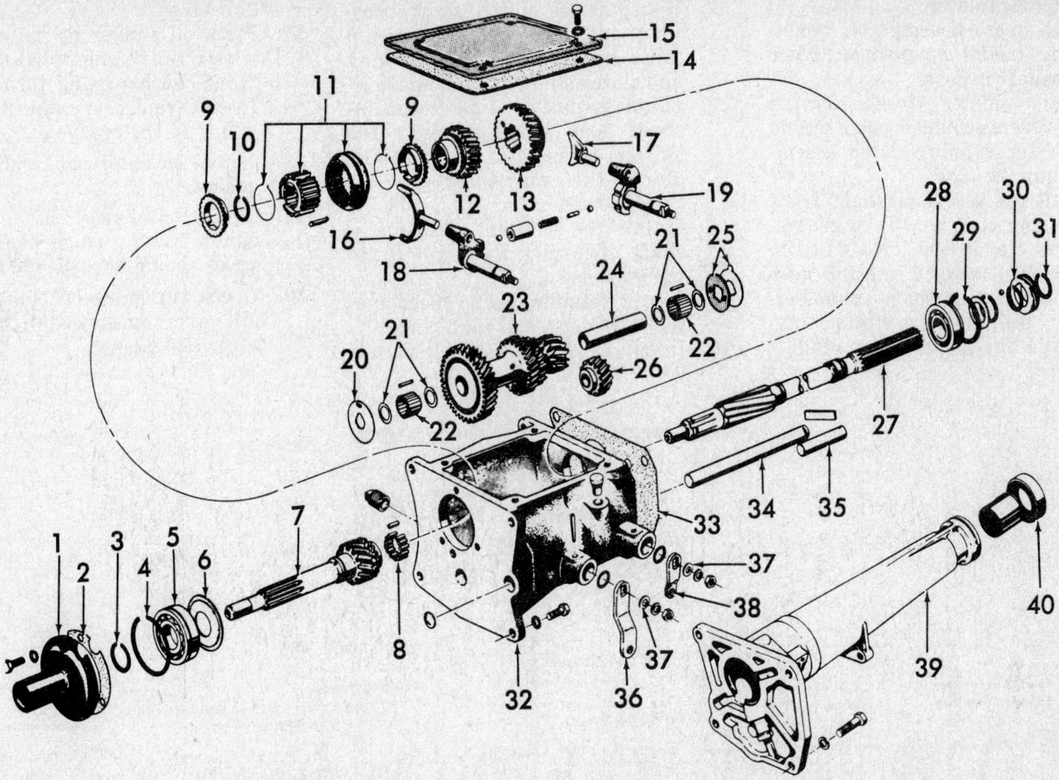
15
14
11
9
10
9
17
12
13
19
16
18
28
30
29
31
21
25
24
23
22
21
20
26
22
27
7
1
3
5
2
4
6
33
34
35
37
38
40
8
37
39
32
36

T-96 transmission—exploded view (© American Motors Corp)

1 Bearing cap
2 Gasket
3 Snap-ring
4 Lock ring
5 Bearing
6 Retaining washer
7 Clutch shaft
8 Bearing rollers
9 Friction ring set
10 Snap-ring
11 Synchronizer
12 Second gear
13 First and reverse gear
14 Cover gasket
15 Cover
16 Second and third fork
17 First and reverse fork
18 Second and third shaft
19 First and reverse shaft
20 Thrust washer
21 Bearing washers
22 Bearing rollers
23 Countershaft gear
24 Countershaft spacer
25 Thrust washer
26 Reverse idler gear
27 Mainshaft
28 Rear bearing
29 Lock ring
30 Speedometer drive gear
31 Snap-ring
32 Case
33 Extension gasket
34 Countershaft
35 Reverse idler shaft
36 Second and third lever
37 Shift lever seal
38 First and reverse lever
39 Extension
40 Extension seal

rear ½ in. Lower front of clutch shaft and raise rear of countergear. Remove clutch shaft.

8. Check 21 roller bearings inside rear of clutch shaft for wear, pitting, or scoring.
9. Remove second-third shifter fork. Tilt mainshaft to remove synchro-clutch snap-ring.
10. Remove synchro-clutch. second gear, and low and reverse gear.
11. Remove low-reverse shifter fork.
12. Remove mainshaft and rear bearing from rear of case. Press rear bearing from shaft.
13. Remove reverse idler shaft and countershaft lockplate.
14. Drive countershaft out to rear with a dummy shaft. Lower dummy shaft and countergear to bottom of case.
15. Drive reverse idler shaft out to rear. Remove gear. Remove countergear.
16. Note position of reverse idler shaft thrust washers; check for wear or damage.
17. Remove outer shift levers and shifter shaft lockpin. Remove shifter shafts from inside case. Remove two interlock ball bearings. Remove interlock sleeve, pin, and spring. Remove shifter shaft O-rings.

Inspection

1. Wash all parts in solvent.
2. Air dry.

Gears and Mainshaft

1. Check for worn, cracked, or chipped teeth.
2. Check fit of gears to mainshaft. If gears are replaced, also replace the gear with which they mesh.

Bearings

1. Check for cracked races.
2. Check for worn or scored balls.

Synchro-Clutch and Friction Rings

1. Slide rings on cones of second gear and clutch shaft.
2. Replace rings if there is excessive wear or a pitted condition on the taper.

Case

1. Check for evidence of bearings turning in their bores.
2. Check for cracks.

Assembly

1. Install new shift shaft O-rings.
2. Install low-reverse shift shaft interlock sleeve, ball bearing, and spring.
3. Install second-third shift shaft. Place second ball bearing in position.
4. Place shifter mechanism in any gear. With one end of interlock sleeve against shifter shaft quadrant, measure clearance between opposite end of sleeve and the other quadrant. Clearance should be .001-.007 in. Selective lengths of interlock sleeves are available for adjustment. Install lockpins and shift levers.
5. Install dummy shaft in countergear. Install needle bearings, spacer, and washers. Install thrust washers. The bronze front washer must index with the case. Install countergear assembly in bottom of case.
6. Install reverse idler gear with chamfered side of teeth to front. Drive reverse idler shaft in from rear.
7. Drive countershaft into place.

Install lockplate.

8. Press rear bearing on mainshaft. Install snap-rings. Place mainshaft in case.
9. Install shifter forks. Install first-reverse sliding gear, second gear, and synchro-clutch assembly, hub forward.
10. Install thickest mainshaft front snap-ring that will fit in groove.
11. There should be .003-.010 in. clearance between second gear and the mainshaft shoulder, with the synchro-clutch hub pressed against the snap-ring.
12. Hold the 21 clutch shaft bearings in place with petroleum jelly. Install front friction ring and clutch shaft on mainshaft.
13. Simultaneously install the mainshaft rear bearing, align the shifter forks and gears, and guide the mainshaft into the clutch shaft.
14. Install the thickest rear mainshaft snap-ring that will fit in the groove.
15. Install retaining ball, speedometer drive gear, and snap-ring.
16. Install extension housing with a new oil seal.
17. Place oil slinger on clutch shaft with concave side to rear. Install front bearing using thrust yoke. Install thickest snap-ring that will fit in the groove.
18. Install bearing cap and a new gasket.
19. Check clearance of synchro-clutch friction rings. Both clearances should be .036-.100 in.
20. Check transmission operation in all gears; then install the case cover and gasket.

Type-20
Warner T-10 4-Speed
Application

American Motors, 1967-69 (290, 343), 1968-70 (390), 1970-74 (360), 1971-74 (401)

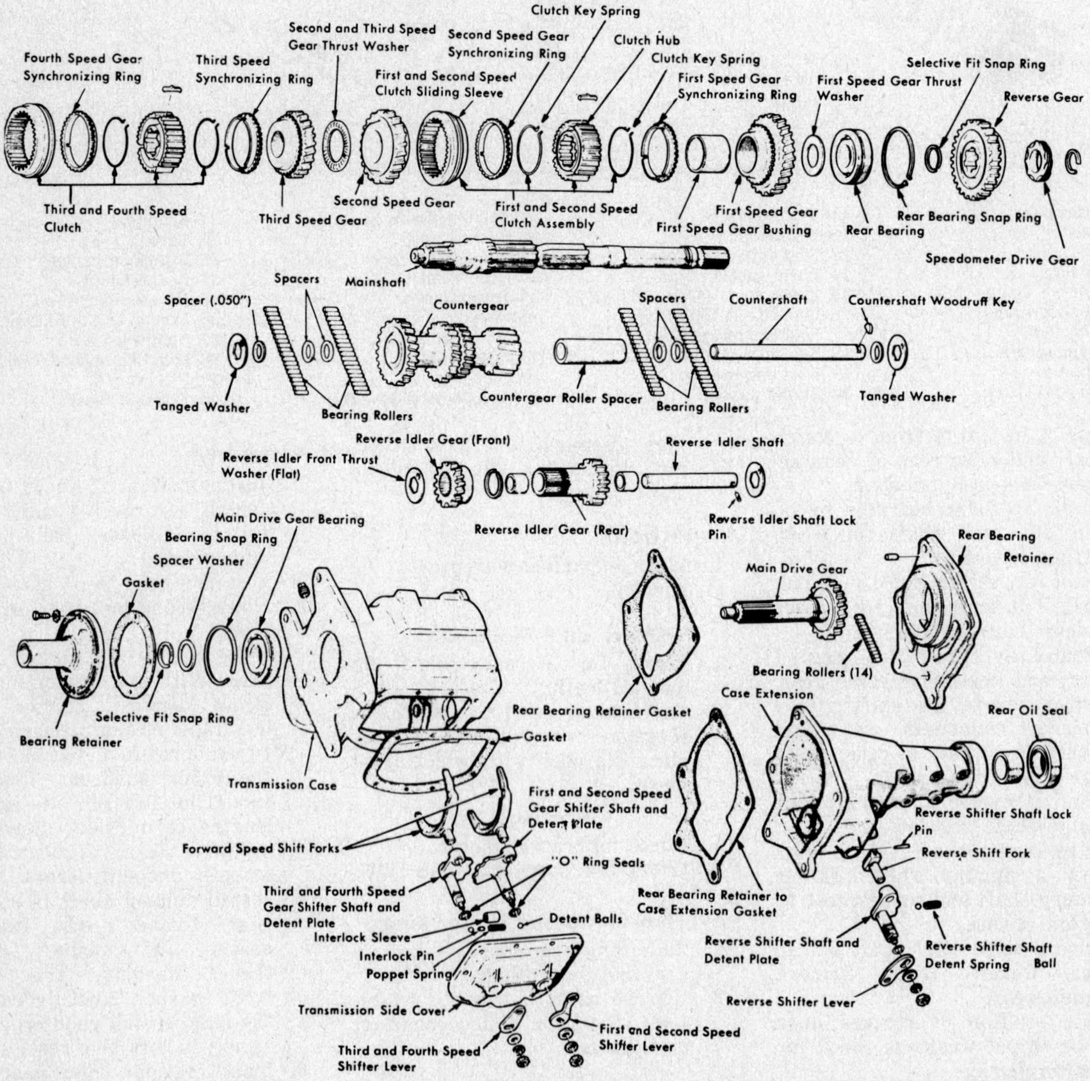

Clutch Key Spring
Second and Third Speed Gear Thrust Washer
Second Speed Gear Synchronizing Ring
Clutch Hub
Fourth Speed Gear Synchronizing Ring
Third Speed Synchronizing Ring
First and Second Speed Clutch Sliding Sleeve
Clutch Key Spring
First Speed Gear Synchronizing Ring
First Speed Gear Thrust Washer
Selective Fit Snap Ring
Reverse Gear
Third and Fourth Speed Clutch
Third Speed Gear
Second Speed Gear
First and Second Speed Clutch Assembly
First Speed Gear
First Speed Gear Bushing
Rear Bearing
Rear Bearing Snap Ring
Speedometer Drive Gear
Mainshaft
Spacers
Spacer (.050")
Countergear
Spacers
Countershaft
Countershaft Woodruff Key
Tanged Washer
Bearing Rollers
Countergear Roller Spacer
Bearing Rollers
Tanged Washer
Reverse Idler Gear (Front)
Reverse Idler Shaft
Reverse Idler Front Thrust Washer (Flat)
Reverse Idler Gear (Rear)
Reverse Idler Shaft Lock Pin
Main Drive Gear Bearing
Bearing Snap Ring
Spacer Washer
Gasket
Rear Bearing Retainer
Main Drive Gear
Bearing Rollers (14)
Case Extension
Selective Fit Snap Ring
Bearing Retainer
Rear Bearing Retainer Gasket
Rear Oil Seal
Gasket
Transmission Case
First and Second Speed Gear Shifter Shaft and Detent Plate
Reverse Shifter Shaft Lock Pin
Reverse Shift Fork
Forward Speed Shift Forks
"O" Ring Seals
Third and Fourth Speed Gear Shifter Shaft and Detent Plate
Rear Bearing Retainer to Case Extension Gasket
Detent Balls
Interlock Sleeve
Interlock Pin
Poppet Spring
Reverse Shifter Shaft and Detent Plate
Reverse Shifter Shaft Detent Spring
Ball
Reverse Shifter Lever
Transmission Side Cover
First and Second Speed Shifter Lever
Third and Fourth Speed Shifter Lever

Warner T-10 transmission (General Motors application) (© Buick Div., G.M. Corp)

Disassembly

1. Drain transmission, mount in adequate stand. Then remove the side cover and shift controls.
2. Remove four bolts from front bearing retainer, then remove retainer and gasket.
3. Remove output shaft companion flange.
4. Drive lockpin up from reverse shifter lever boss, then pull shiftshaft out about ⅛ in. to disengage shifter fork from reverse gear.
5. Remove five bolts from the case extension and tap the extension (with soft hammer) rearward. When idler gear shaft is out as far as it will go, move extension to the left so the reverse fork clears the reverse gear. Remove extension and gasket.
6. Remove rear bearing snap-ring from mainshaft.
7. Remove case extension oil seal.
8. Remove speedometer drive gear with puller.
9. Remove the reverse gear, reverse idler gear and tanged thrust washer.
10. Remove self-locking bolt holding the rear bearing retainer to transmission case.
11. Remove the entire mainshaft assembly.
12. Unload bearing rollers from main drive gear and remove fourth-speed synchronizer blocking ring.
13. Lift the front half of reverse idler gear and its thrust washer from the case.
14. Remove the main drive gear snap-ring and remove spacer washer.
15. With soft hammer, tap main drive gear toward rear and out of front bearing.
16. From inside the case, tap out front bearing and snap-ring.
17. From the front of the case, tap out the countershaft, using dummy shaft.
18. Then lift out the countergear assembly with both tanged washers.
19. Dismantle the countergear, consisting of 80 rollers, six .050 in. spacers and a roller tubular spacer.
20. Remove mainshaft front snap-ring and slide third and fourth-speed clutch assembly, third-speed gear and synchronizer ring, second and third-speed gear thrust bearing, second-speed gear and second-speed synchronizer ring from front of mainshaft.
21. Spread rear bearing retainer snap-ring and press mainshaft out of retainer.
22. Remove the mainshaft rear snap-ring.
23. Support first and second-speed clutch assembly and press on rear of mainshaft to remove shaft from rear bearing, first-speed gear, and synchromesh ring, first

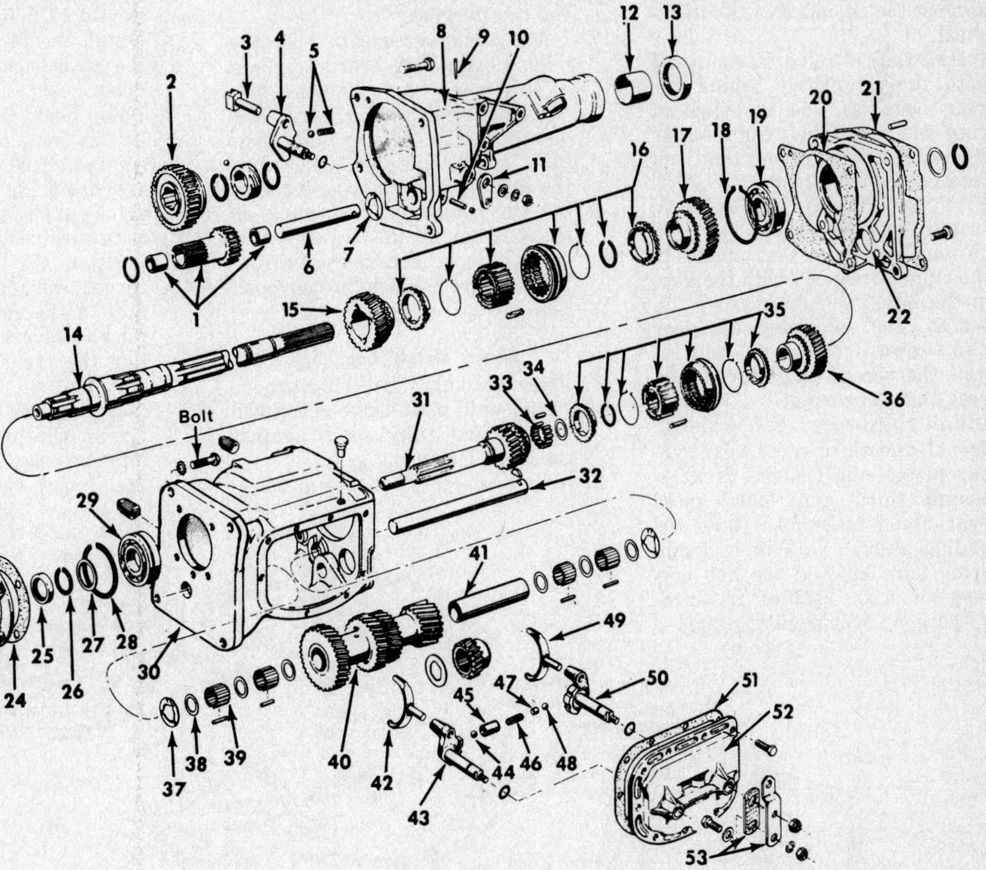
1
2
3
4
5
6
7
8
9
10
11
12
13
14
15
16
17
18
19
20
21
22
23
24
25
26
27
28
29
30
31
32
33
34
35
36
37
38
39
40
41
42
43
44
45
46
47
48
49
50
51
52
53
Bolt

Warner T-10 transmission (American Motors application)

1 Reverse idler gear
2 Reverse gear
3 Reverse fork
4 Reverse shaft
5 Poppet ball and spring
6 Idler shaft
7 Thrust washer
8 Reverse housing
9 Reverse pin
10 Lock pin
11 Reverse lever
12 Bushing
13 Seal
14 Mainshaft
15 2nd gear
16 Synchro assy
17 1st gear
18 Snap-ring
19 Adapter bearing
20 Adapter
21 Gasket
22 Adapter
23 Front bearing cap
24 Gasket
25 Seal
26 Snap-ring
27 Washer
28 Lock ring
29 Front bearing
30 Case
31 Clutch shaft
32 Countershaft
33 Rollers
34 Roller spacer
35 Synchro assy
36 3rd gear
37 Countergear washer
38 Roller bearing washer
39 Rollers
40 Countergear
41 Spacer
42 3rd-4th fork
43 3rd-4th shaft
44 Poppet ball
45 Interlock sleeve
46 Poppet spring
47 Interlock
48 Poppet ball
49 1st-2nd fork
50 1st-2nd shaft
51 Cover gasket
52 Cover
53 Shift levers

and second-speed clutch sliding sleeve and first-speed gear bushing.

Assembly

Mainshaft

1. From the rear of the mainshaft, assemble first and second-speed clutch assembly to mainshaft (sliding clutch sleeve taper toward the rear, hub to the front) and press the first-speed gear bushing onto the shaft.
2. Install first-speed gear synchronizing ring so notches in ring align with keys in hub.
3. Install first-speed gear (hub toward front) and the first-speed gear thrust washer. Be sure the grooves in the washer are facing first-speed gear.
4. Press on the rear bearing, with the snap-ring groove toward the front of the transmission. Be sure the bearing is firmly seated against the shoulder on the mainshaft.
5. Install the selective fit snap-ring onto the mainshaft behind the rear bearing. Use the thickest ring that will fit between the rear face of the bearing and the front face of the snap-ring.
6. From the front of the mainshaft, install the second-speed gear synchronizing ring so that notches in the ring correspond with the keys in the hub.
7. Install the second-speed gear (hub toward the back) and install the second and third-speed gear thrust bearing.
8. Install third-speed gear (hub to front) and third-speed gear synchronizing ring (notches front).
9. Install third and fourth-speed gear clutch assembly (hub and sliding sleeve) with taper front, being sure keys in the hub correspond with notches in third-speed gear synchronizing ring.
10. Install snap-ring (.086-.088 in. thickness) into groove in mainshaft, in front of the third and fourth-speed clutch assembly.
11. Install rear bearing retainer plate. Spread the snap-ring on the plate to allow the snap-ring to drop around the rear bearing and press on the end of the mainshaft until the snap-ring engages the groove in the rear bearing.
12. Install reverse gear (shift collar to the rear).
13. Press speedometer drive gear onto the mainshaft. Position the speedometer gear to get a measurement of 4½ in. from the center of the gear to the flat surface of the rear bearing retainer.
14. Install special snap-ring into the groove at the rear of the mainshaft.

Countergear

1. Install countergear dummy and tubular roller bearing spacer into the countergear.
2. Using heavy grease to hold the rollers, install 20 bearing rollers in either end of the countergear, two spacers, 20 more rollers, then one spacer. Install the same combination of rollers and spacers in the other end of the countergear.
3. Set the countergear assembly in the bottom of the transmission case, be sure the tanged thrust washers are in their proper position.

Main Drive Gear

1. Press bearing (snap-ring groove front) onto main drive gear until the bearing fully seats against the shoulder on the gear.
2. Install spacer washer and selective fit snap-ring in the groove in the main drive gear shaft.

NOTE: variable thickness snap-rings are available to obtain a prescribed clearance of .000-.005 in. between the rear face of the snap ring and the front face of the spacer washer.

Transmission

1. Install main drive gear and bearing assembly through the side cover opening and into position in the transmission front bore. After assembly is in place, install snap-ring into groove in front bearing.
2. Lift countergear and thrust washers into place. Install Woodruff key into end of countershaft, then from the rear of the case, press the countershaft in until the end of the shaft is flush with rear of transmission case and the dummy shaft is displaced. End-play in the countergear must not exceed .025 in.
3. Install the 14 bearing rollers into the grease-coated end of the main drive gear.
4. Using heavy grease, position gasket on front face of rear bearing retainer. Install the fourth-speed synchronizing ring onto main drive gear with clutch key notches toward rear of transmission.
5. Position the reverse idler gear thrust washer on the machined face of the gear cast in the case for the reverse idler shaft. Position the front reverse idler gear on top of the thrust washer, hub facing toward rear of case.
6. Lower the mainshaft assembly into the case, with the notches of the fourth-speed synchronizing

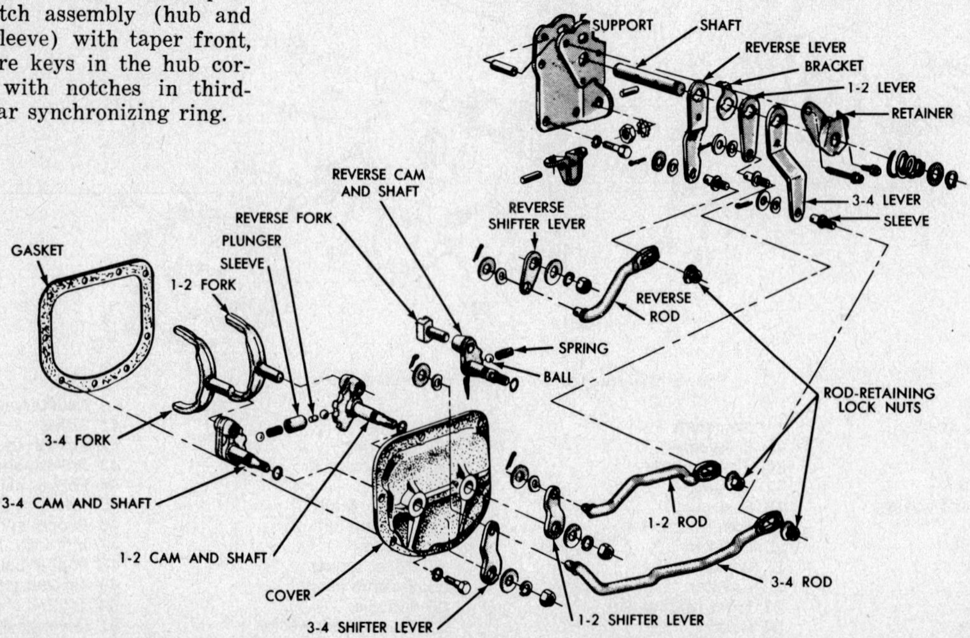

SUPPORT
SHAFT
REVERSE LEVER
BRACKET
1-2 LEVER
RETAINER
3-4 LEVER
SLEEVE
REVERSE CAM AND SHAFT
REVERSE FORK
PLUNGER
SLEEVE
GASKET
1-2 FORK
REVERSE SHIFTER LEVER
REVERSE ROD
SPRING
BALL
ROD-RETAINING LOCK NUTS
3-4 FORK
3-4 CAM AND SHAFT
1-2 CAM AND SHAFT
1-2 ROD
3-4 ROD
COVER
3-4 SHIFTER LEVER
1-2 SHIFTER LEVER

Linkage and cover

ring corresponding to the keys in the clutch assembly.

7. Install self-locking bolt, holding the rear bearing retainer to the transmission case. Torque to 20-30 ft. lbs.
8. From the rear of the case, insert the rear reverse idler gear, engaging the splines with the portion of the gear within the case.
9. Grease gasket, and place in position on the rear face of the rear bearing retainer.
10. Install remaining tanged thrust washer into place on reverse idler shaft, being sure the tang on the thrust washer is in the notch in the idler thrust face of the extension.
11. Place the two clutches in neutral position.
12. Pull reverse shifter shaft to left side of extension and rotate shaft to bring reverse fork to extreme forward position in extension. Line up forward and reverse idler gears.
13. Start the extension onto the transmission case by inserting reverse idler shaft through reverse idler gears. Push in on shifter until shift fork engages reverse gear shift collar. When the fork engages, rotate the shifter shaft to move reverse gear rearward. This will allow the extension to slide onto the transmission case.
14. Install three extension and retainer to case attaching bolts and torque to 35-45 ft. lbs. Install two extension to retainer attaching bolts and torque to 20-30 ft. lbs. Use sealer on the lower, right attaching bolt.
15. Adjust reverse shift shaft so that groove in shaft lines up with hole in boss. Drive in lockpin from top of boss.
16. Install the main drive gear bearing retainer and gasket, being sure the oil well lines up with the oil outlet hole. Install four sealer-coated attaching bolts and torque to 15-20 ft. lbs.
17. Install a shift fork into each clutch sleeve.
18. With both clutches in neutral, install side cover gasket and lower side cover into place.
19. Install attaching bolts and torque to 10-20 ft. lbs. Use sealer on the lower right bolt.
20. Install first and second, and third and fourth shift levers, lockwashers and nuts.

Hurst Shift Linkage

Syncro/Loc®
Three-Speed Transmission Floor Shift Linkage Adjustment

NOTE: factory-installed Hurst shifters are adjusted in the same manner as the aftermarket shifter, with the exception of adjusting the shifter stop-bolts which are not fitted to the factory-installed shifters. GM cars substitute adjustable trunnions for the swivel buttons, but the adjustment is the same.

The floor-mounted three-speed transmission linkage uses two shift rods and levers. Adjustment can be made with the aid of a neutral alignment rod, supplied with the floor shift linkage kit, or a 1/4 in. diameter rod.

Adjustment Procedure

1. Place shifter unit in the neutral position.
2. Back both shifter stop bolts out of shifter frame until only a few threads remain engaged.
3. Remove both shifting rods and rod adjusting buttons from the shifter unit.
4. Place neutral alignment rod through alignment holes in shifter unit and levers.
5. Making doubly sure that both transmission levers are in the neutral position, adjust the rod adjusting buttons to permit easy slip-in fit of button into nylon bushing in proper lever.
6. Fasten buttons in lever with spring clips and remove neutral alignment rod.
7. Push stick firmly into second gear and hold. Screw second gear stop bolt in until contact is felt. Back bolt out one full turn and tighten locknut. Pull stick firmly back into third gear, screw third gear stop bolt in until contact is made, then back stop bolt out one full turn and tighten locknut.

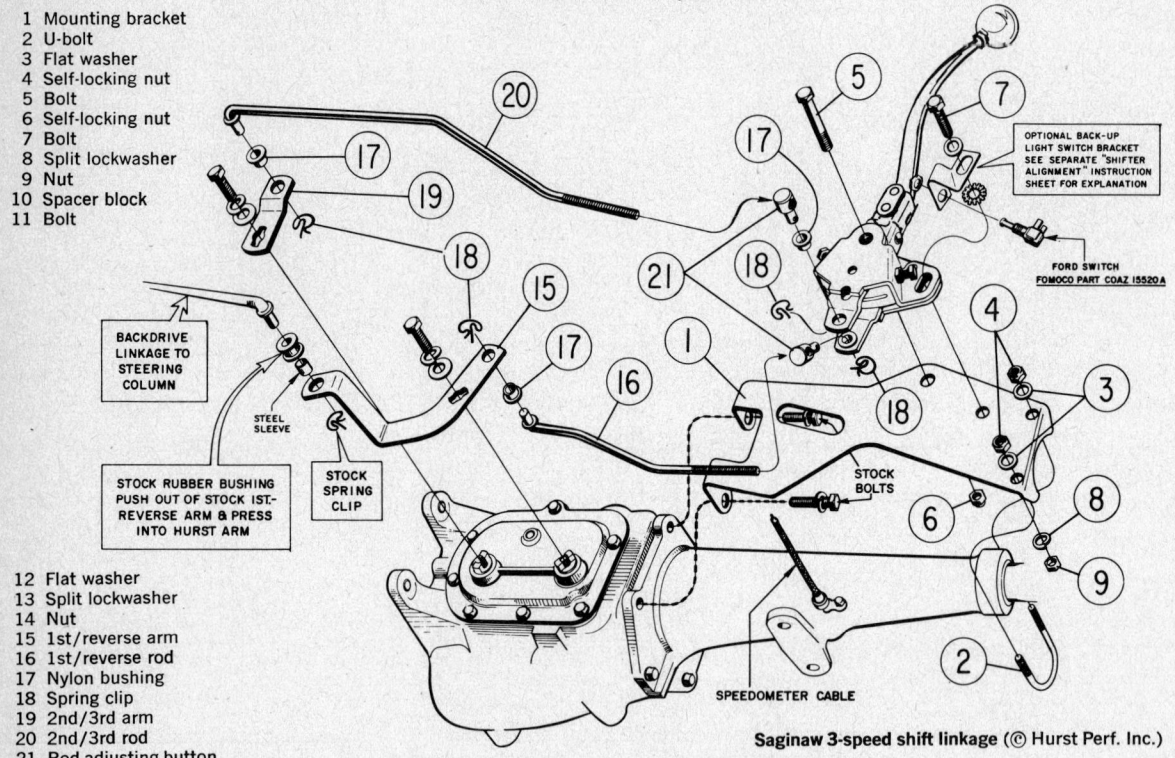

1 Mounting bracket
2 U-bolt
3 Flat washer
4 Self-locking nut
5 Bolt
6 Self-locking nut
7 Bolt
8 Split lockwasher
9 Nut
10 Spacer block
11 Bolt
12 Flat washer
13 Split lockwasher
14 Nut
15 1st/reverse arm
16 1st/reverse rod
17 Nylon bushing
18 Spring clip
19 2nd/3rd arm
20 2nd/3rd rod
21 Rod adjusting button

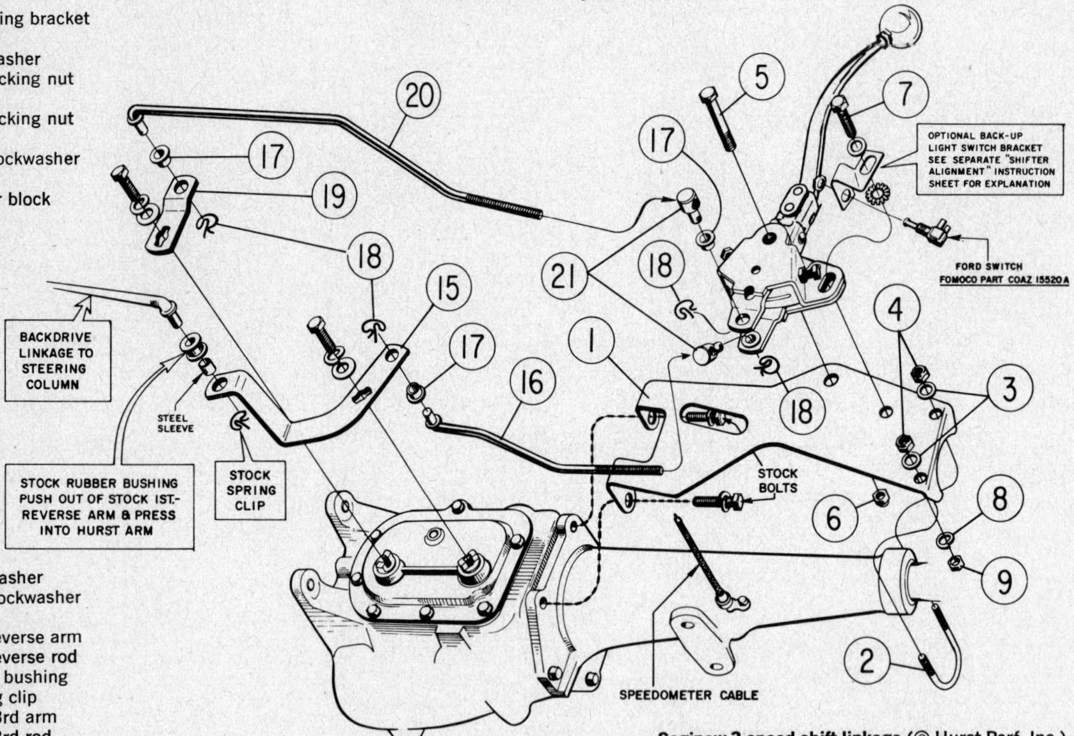
OPTIONAL BACK-UP LIGHT SWITCH BRACKET SEE SEPARATE "SHIFTER ALIGNMENT" INSTRUCTION SHEET FOR EXPLANATION
FORD SWITCH FOMOCO PART COAZ 15520A
BACKDRIVE LINKAGE TO STEERING COLUMN
STEEL SLEEVE
STOCK RUBBER BUSHING PUSH OUT OF STOCK 1ST.-REVERSE ARM & PRESS INTO HURST ARM
STOCK SPRING CLIP
STOCK BOLTS
SPEEDOMETER CABLE

Saginaw 3-speed shift linkage (© Hurst Perf. Inc.)

Competition Plus®
Four-Speed Transmission Linkage Adjustment

NOTE: with the exception of American Motors products, factory-installed Hurst shifters are adjusted in the same manner as the aftermarket shifter. Factory-installed shifters do not have the stop-bolt feature, however, so this step can be skipped. GM cars use adjustable trunnions in place of the swivel buttons, but the adjustment procedure is the same.

The four-speed transmission gearshift linkage uses three shift rods and levers. The adjustment can be made with the aid of a neutral alignment rod, supplied with the floor shift linkage kit, or a 1/4 in. diameter rod.

Adjustment Procedure

1. Place shifter unit in the neutral position.
2. Back both shifter stop bolts out of shifter frame until only a few threads remain engaged.
3. Remove shifting rods and rod adjusting buttons from the shifter unit.
4. Align levers with shifter frame and insert neutral alignment rod through notches in frame and holes in levers.
5. Rotate transmission arms backward and forward. The neutral position for each arm can be felt at the mid-position of full travel. Reverse arm must be moved to

the end of its travel toward the front (disengaged position).

6. Adjust positions of buttons on each rod to permit easy slip-in fit of button into nylon bushing in proper lever.

NOTE: transmission arms must remain in neutral positions while alignment is accomplished. Fasten buttons in levers with spring clips.

7. Remove neutral alignment rod. Test shifter. Stick should move freely from side to side in neutral. If shifter functions properly, proceed to Step 10.

8. If the stick cannot be moved freely between first-second, third-fourth or reverse path, one or more of the rod button adjustments must be corrected. Move stick forward to third gear, then back to fourth, then into neutral. Insert neutral alignment rod. If rod cannot be inserted freely, the third-fourth rod button is incorrectly adjusted. Similar testing of first-second shift will prove alignment of first-second adjustment.

9. To check reverse rod button adjustment, place stick at neutral. Disconnect reverse rod adjusting button from reverse lever. Grasp rod and push toward front of car. (Reverse arm is disengaged when at end of forward travel). Adjust rod button for easy slip-in fit in bushing. Reassemble and fasten with spring clip.

10. Push stick firmly into third gear and hold. Screw third gear stop bolt in until contact is felt. Back bolt out one full turn and tighten locknut. Pull stick firmly back into fourth gear, screw fourth gear stop bolt in until contact is felt, then back stop bolt out one full turn and tighten locknut.

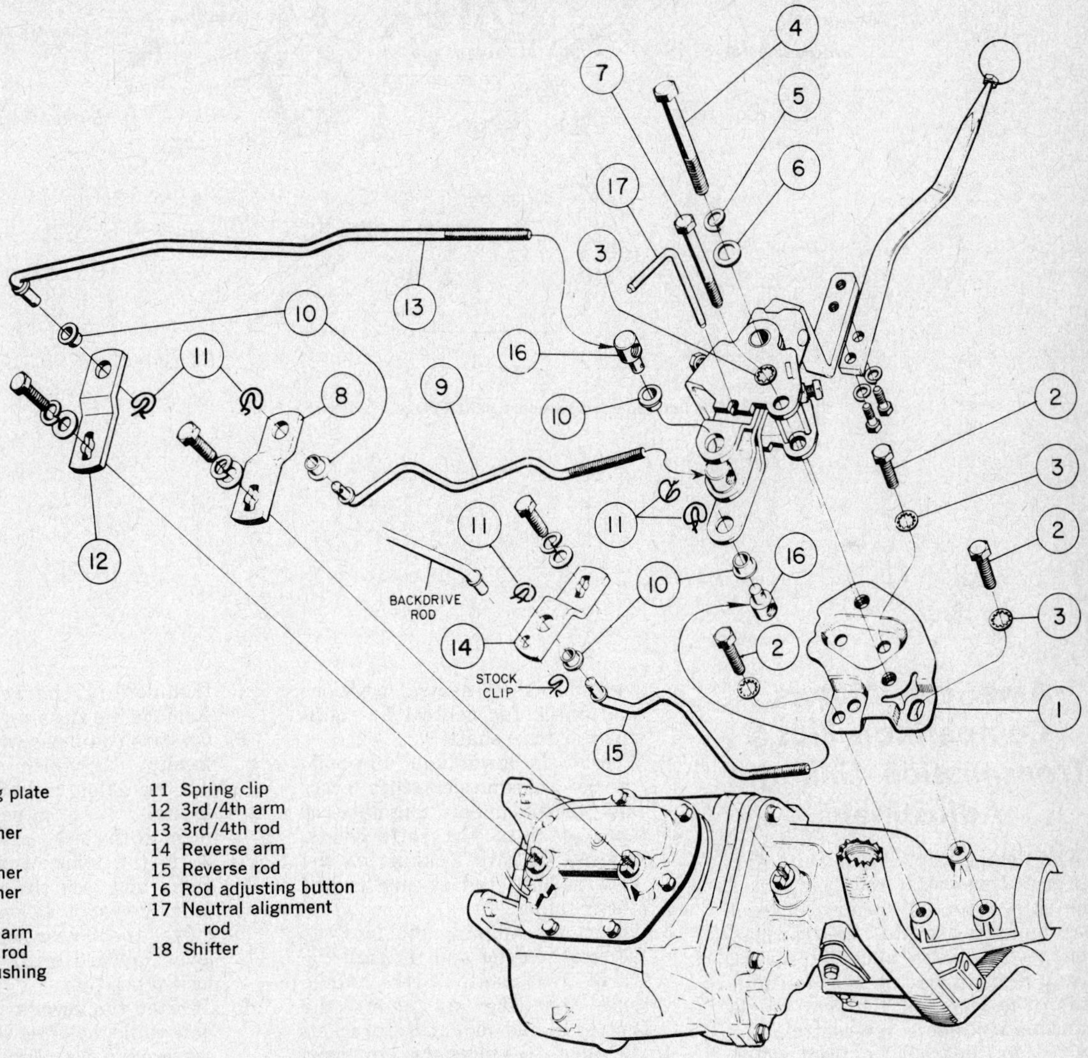
4
7
5
17
6
3
13
10
16
11
8
9
10
2
3
11
11
12
16
10
BACKDRIVE ROD
2
3
14
2
STOCK CLIP
1
15

1 Mounting plate
2 Bolt
3 Lockwasher
4 Bolt
5 Lockwasher
6 Flat washer
7 Bolt
8 1st/2nd arm
9 1st/2nd rod
10 Nylon bushing
11 Spring clip
12 3rd/4th arm
13 3rd/4th rod
14 Reverse arm
15 Reverse rod
16 Rod adjusting button
17 Neutral alignment rod
18 Shifter

Muncie 4-speed shift linkage (© Hurst Perf. Inc.)

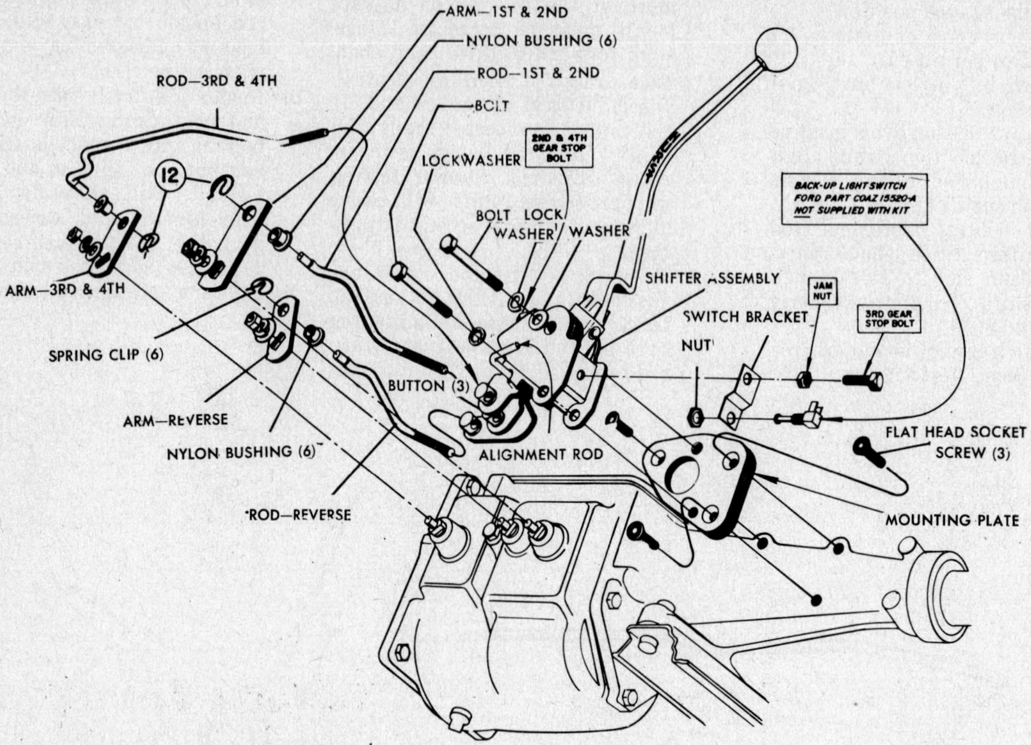
ARM—1ST & 2ND
NYLON BUSHING (6)
ROD—1ST & 2ND
BOLT
ROD—3RD & 4TH
2ND & 4TH GEAR STOP BOLT
LOCKWASHER
12
BACK-UP LIGHT SWITCH FORD PART COAZ 15520-A NOT SUPPLIED WITH KIT
BOLT LOCK WASHER WASHER
ARM—3RD & 4TH
SHIFTER ASSEMBLY
JAM NUT
SWITCH BRACKET
3RD GEAR STOP BOLT
NUT
SPRING CLIP (6)
BUTTON (3)
ARM—REVERSE
FLAT HEAD SOCKET SCREW (3)
NYLON BUSHING (6)
ALIGNMENT ROD
ROD—REVERSE
MOUNTING PLATE

Ford (ten bolt top cover) 4-speed shift linkage (© Hurst Perf. Inc.)

American Motors Competition Plus® Transmission Linkage Adjustment

The Competition Plus® shift linkage uses three shift rods and levers. The shift lever on the transmission rear housing operates the transmission reverse gear and the reverse lockup mechanism (on cars so equipped). The lever on the rear of the transmission side cover controls first and second gears. The front transmision lever controls third and fourth gears. A spring load of 21-28 lbs. must be overcome to move the shift lever to the extreme left for a shift into reverse. Adjustment of the shifter can be made with the aid of a neutral alignment rod or a short ¼ in. diameter pin.

Adjustment Procedure

1. Place the transmission shift levers into their neutral positions and check for neutral by rotating the drive shaft.
2. Loosen the lower nuts and bolts on the transmission shift levers and the two upper "hug nuts" at the center of the shift levers. Loosen the two locknuts on the reverse shift rod at each end of the trunnion.
3. Insert the aligning pin into the shifter housing and through the three rear shift levers. Make sure that the pin enters the notch in the mounting bracket.
4. Remove the aligning pin completely and reinsert the pin. The shifter is aligned correctly in neutral if the aligning pin freely enters the housing and the holes in the levers.
5. Tighten the lower bolts and nuts at the forward shift levers, then tighten the upper "hug nuts" to 10 ft. lbs. Tighten the trunnion nuts to lock the trunnion in position, taking care not to bind the trunnion in the reverse lever. Remove the aligning pin.
6. On cars equipped with a reverse lockup mechanism the lockup rod trunnion locknuts must be loosened ½ in. to permit adjustment of the lock.
7. Shift the transmission into reverse and lock the steering column. It may be necessary to move the lower column shift lever upward until it is in the locked position.
8. Tighten the lower trunnion locknut while holding the trunnion centered in the column lever.
9. Unlock the steering column and check for proper engagement of all gears, including reverse. The steering must lock without any binding when reverse is engaged.
10. On cars equipped with a backup light switch actuated by the shift linkage check for correct operation of lights.

Hurst Shift Linkage

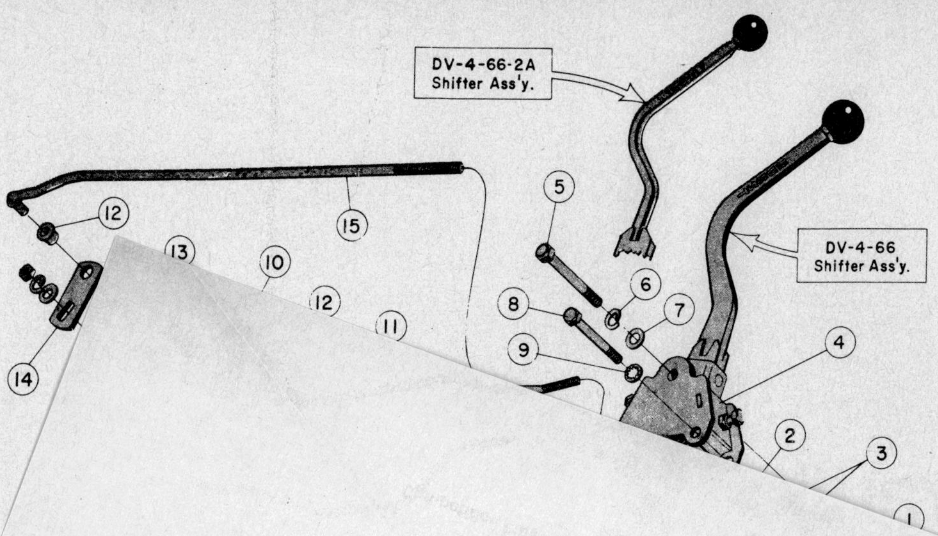

DV-4-66-2A
Shifter Ass'y.
DV-4-66
Shifter Ass'y.
1
2
3
4
5
6
7
8
9
10
11
12
13
14
15

1 Mounting plate
2 Flat head socket screw
3 Flat head socket screw
4 Shifter assembly
5 Bolt
6 Lockwasher
7 Flat washer
8 Bolt
9 Lockwasher
10 1st/2nd arm
11 1st/2nd rod
12 Nylon bushing
13 Spring clip
14 3rd/4th arm
15 3rd/4th rod
16 Reverse arm
17 Reverse rod
18 Rod adjusting button

U58

FORD MOTOR CO.
1967–74 all models
GENERAL MOTORS CORP.
1967–74 all models except Vega
1971–74 Vega

Bendix Duo-Servo
Bendix Duo-Servo
Bendix Duo-Servo
Bendix Duo-Servo
Bendix Duo-Servo

Star & Screw
Star & Screw
Star & Screw
Star & Screw
Star & Screw
Expanding Strut

INDEX

Hydraulic Brakes

DRUM BRAKE APPLICATION CHART

Car and Years	Brake Type	Self-Adjuster Type
AMERICAN MOTORS		
1967–68 all models with 4 wheel drum brakes except 6 cyl American and Rebel Sedan	Bendix Duo-Servo	Star & Screw
1967–68 all models with front disc brakes	Bendix Non-Servo	Star & Screw
1967–69 6 cyl Rebel Sedan	Wagner Compound	Star & Screw
1969 all models except 6 cyl Rebel Sedan	Bendix Duo-Servo	
1970–74 all models		
CHRYSLER CORP		

1 Mounting plate
2 Flat head socket screw
3 Flat head socket screw
4 Shifter assembly
5 Bolt
6 Lockwasher
7 Flat washer
8 Bolt
9 Lockwasher
10 1st/2nd arm
11 1st/2nd rod
12 Nylon bushing
13 Spring clip
14 3rd/4th arm
15 3rd/4th rod
16 Reverse arm
17 Reverse rod
18 Rod adjusting button

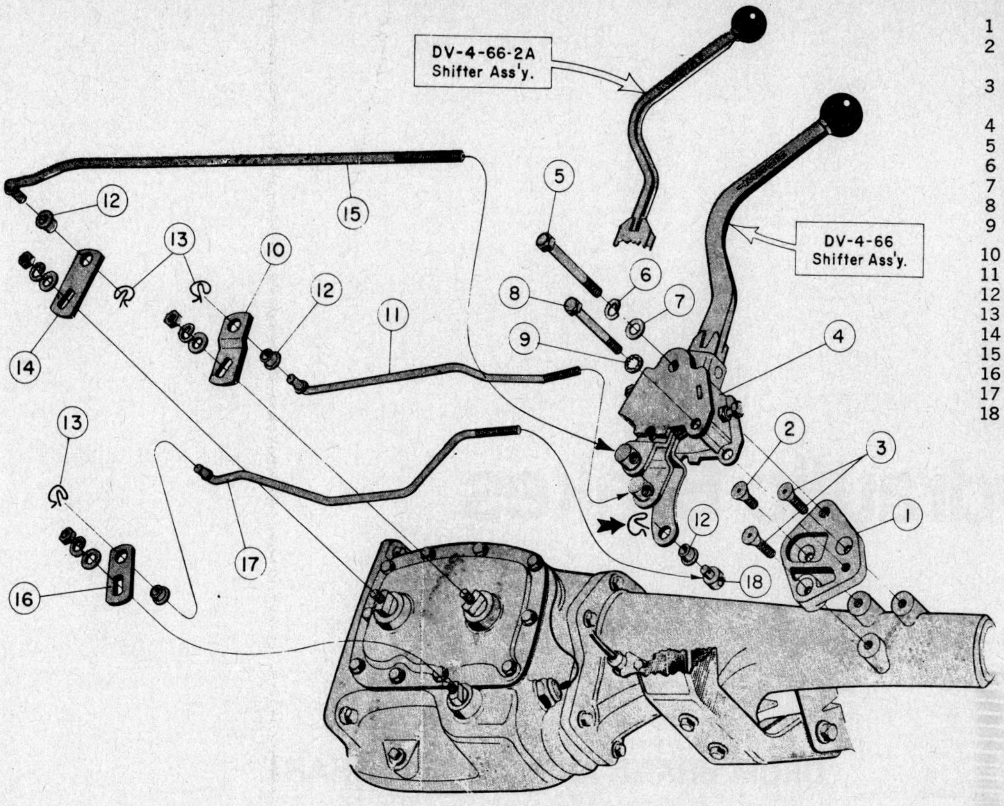
DV-4-66-2A
Shifter Ass'y.
DV-4-66
Shifter Ass'y.

Chrysler New Process 4-speed shift linkage (© Hurst Perf. Inc.)

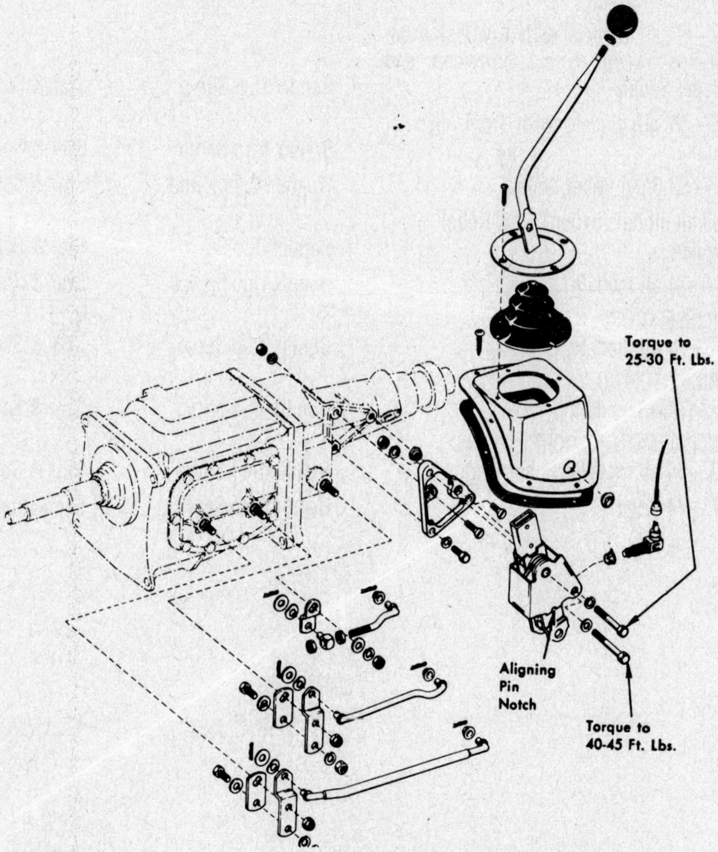
Torque to
25-30 Ft. Lbs.
Aligning
Pin
Notch
Torque to
40-45 Ft. Lbs.

Competition Plus® linkage as used on Borg Warner T10 (© American Motors Corp)

INDEX

Hydraulic Brakes

DRUM BRAKE APPLICATION CHART

Car and Years	Brake Type	Self-Adjuster Type
AMERICAN MOTORS		
1967–68 all models with 4 wheel drum brakes except 6 cyl American and Rebel Sedan	Bendix Duo-Servo	Star & Screw
1967–68 all models with front disc brakes	Bendix Non-Servo	Star & Screw
1967–69 6 cyl Rebel Sedan	Wagner Compound	Star & Screw
1969 all models except 6 cyl Rebel Sedan	Bendix Duo-Servo	Star & Screw
1970–74 all models	Bendix Duo-Servo	Star & Screw
CHRYSLER CORP.		
1967–74 all models	Bendix Duo-Servo	Star & Screw
FORD MOTOR CO.		
1967–74 all models	Bendix Duo-Servo	Star & Screw
GENERAL MOTORS CORP.		
1967–74 all models except Vega	Bendix Duo-Servo	Star & Screw
1971–74 Vega	Bendix Duo-Servo	Expanding Strut

Hydraulic Brakes

Brake Diagnosis Chart

Condition	*Mechanical*	*Hydraulic*	*Vacuum (Power Unit)*
Low pedal (Excessive pedal travel to apply brakes)	FGIMfg	T	k
Spongy Pedal (A springy sensation of pedal upon application)	I	PQU	
Hard Pedal (Excessive pedal pressure needed to stop vehicle)	AFGKVaf	RTUW	cehk
Fading Pedal (A falling away of pedal under steady foot pressure)	I	PQSTW	
Grabbing or Pulling	ADEGHIKL NVXYZa	RW	k
Noise (Squealing, clicking or scraping noise)	FGHILMN		
Chatter or Shudder (May be accompanied by brake roughness or pedal pumping)	DGILNO		
Dragging Brakes (Slow or incomplete release of brakes)	ABCFGHK LVafg	RUTW	k

A. Pedal linkage binding. (Check by bleeding one wheel cylinder using light pedal effort. Observe for smooth full travel of pedal)
B. Parking brake cables and linkage sticking, dirty or corroded.
C. Parking brake improperly adjusted (too loose or too tight).
D. Wheel bearings loose.
E. Front wheel alignment or uneven tire tread.
F. Brake shoes improperly adjusted. Automatic adjuster parts corroded, distorted or broken.
G. Brake linings or disc pads worn, contaminated or distorted.
H. Shoe return spring weak, broken, improperly installed.
I. Drums cracked, thin (beyond 0.060" of original specifications), scored, hard spotted, or out of round.
K. Brake support plate ledges rusted or grooved.
L. Support plate loose, worn, or distorted.
M. Disc brake pad "knock back" (loose or worn wheel bearings or steering parts).
N. Caliper not aligned with disc or loose.
O. Disc has excessive lateral runout. Excessively out of parallel.
P. Hydraulic system fluid has air in it, improper quality (low boiling point).
Q. Hoses and lines soft or weak (expanding under pressure).
R. Hose sand lines kinked, collapsed, dented, or clogged.
S. Hoses and lines loosely connected, ruptured, or damaged (causing leakage).
T. Master cylinder primary cup worn or damaged, bore worn, rough, corroded.
U. Master cylinder check valve faulty, or compensator port blocked.
V. Wheel or caliper cylinder pistons frozen or seized.
W. Wheel or caliper cylinder cups swollen, worn or damaged seals; bores rough or corroded.
X. Wheel or caliper cylinders mismatched (size).
Y. Check tire pressure.
Z. Rear wheels (both) grabbing. Rear brake line proportioning valve defective—replace.
a. Power unit valve rod linkage binding.
c. Vacuum lines loose, broken, collapsed. Engine vacuum low.
e. Vacuum check valve defective or sticking.
f. Power unit hydraulic pushrod improperly adjusted.
g. Air trapped in hub cavity of master cylinder. Inspect and remove master cylinder boot if installed.
h. Air filter dirty, clogged.
k. Corrosion or lack of lubrication in power cylinder. Control valve, power cylinder, piston or diaphragm defective.

Servicing Self-Adjusting Brakes

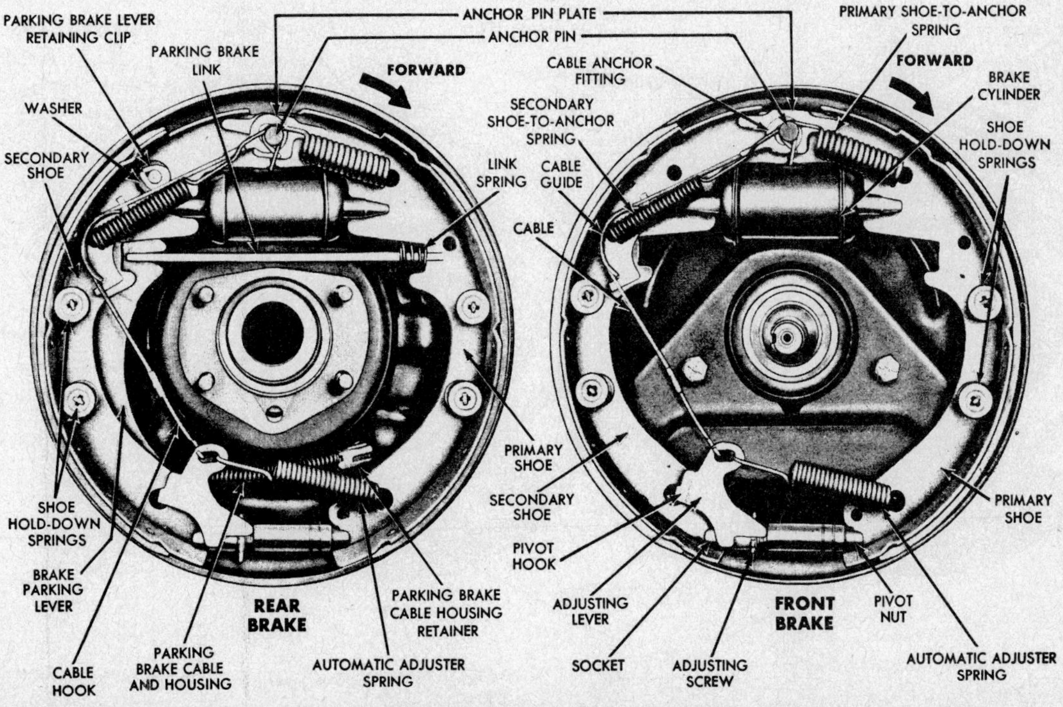
PARKING BRAKE LEVER RETAINING CLIP
PARKING BRAKE LINK
ANCHOR PIN PLATE
ANCHOR PIN
PRIMARY SHOE-TO-ANCHOR SPRING
FORWARD
FORWARD
WASHER
CABLE ANCHOR FITTING
BRAKE CYLINDER
SECONDARY SHOE-TO-ANCHOR SPRING
SECONDARY SHOE
SHOE HOLD-DOWN SPRINGS
LINK SPRING
CABLE GUIDE
CABLE
PRIMARY SHOE
SECONDARY SHOE
PRIMARY SHOE
SHOE HOLD-DOWN SPRINGS
PIVOT HOOK
BRAKE PARKING LEVER
ADJUSTING LEVER
FRONT BRAKE
PIVOT NUT
REAR BRAKE
PARKING BRAKE CABLE HOUSING RETAINER
CABLE HOOK
PARKING BRAKE CABLE AND HOUSING
AUTOMATIC ADJUSTER SPRING
SOCKET
ADJUSTING SCREW
AUTOMATIC ADJUSTER SPRING

Bendix duo-servo self-adjusting brakes

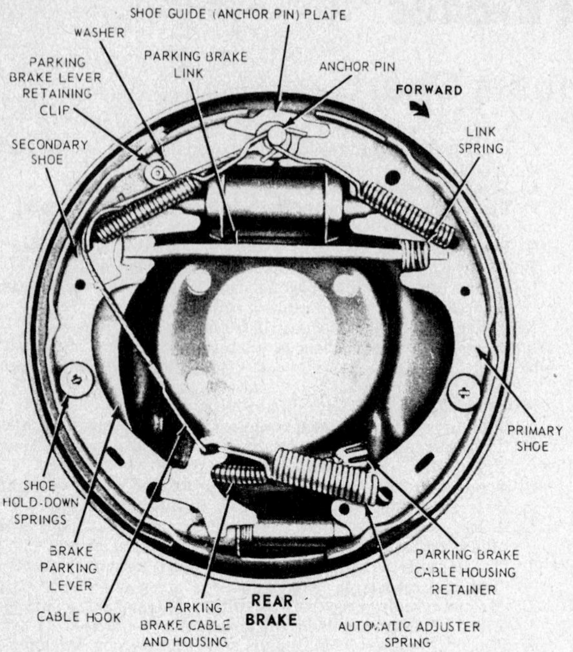
SHOE GUIDE (ANCHOR PIN) PLATE
WASHER
PARKING BRAKE LEVER RETAINING CLIP
PARKING BRAKE LINK
ANCHOR PIN
FORWARD
LINK SPRING
SECONDARY SHOE
PRIMARY SHOE
SHOE HOLD-DOWN SPRINGS
BRAKE PARKING LEVER
PARKING BRAKE CABLE HOUSING RETAINER
CABLE HOOK
PARKING BRAKE CABLE AND HOUSING
REAR BRAKE
AUTOMATIC ADJUSTER SPRING

Bendix duo-servo self-adjusting brake—Ford type

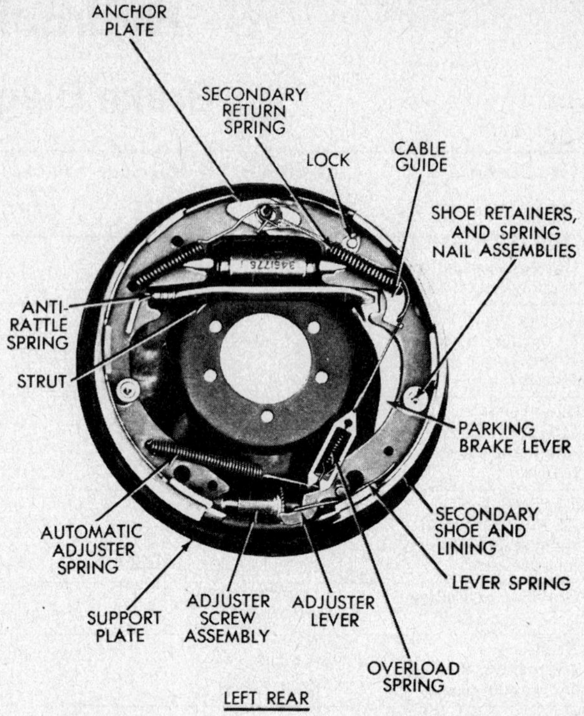
ANCHOR PLATE
SECONDARY RETURN SPRING
LOCK
CABLE GUIDE
SHOE RETAINERS, AND SPRING NAIL ASSEMBLIES
ANTI-RATTLE SPRING
STRUT
PARKING BRAKE LEVER
AUTOMATIC ADJUSTER SPRING
SECONDARY SHOE AND LINING
LEVER SPRING
SUPPORT PLATE
ADJUSTER SCREW ASSEMBLY
ADJUSTER LEVER
OVERLOAD SPRING
LEFT REAR

Bendix duo-servo self-adjusting brake—Chrysler Corp. 11 in. type

Bendix Duo-Servo Brake

Star and Screw Type

The Bendix duo-servo brake, with star and screw type self-adjusters, is by far the most common brake used on late-model American cars. The same basic brake unit has been used on all cars (except Vega) since 1970, and on most cars from 1966. General Motors cars use a rod-operated lever to turn the starwheel, while all others use a cable-operated lever. This is the only difference, other than size, between units used on different models.

Adjustment

1. Remove the access slot plug from the backing plate or front of drum on GM cars. On some late-model cars, there is no access slot in the backing plate or in the front of the drums on GM cars. It has been filled in and must be punched out to gain access to the adjuster. Complete the adjustment and cover the hole with the plug to prevent entrance of dirt and water.
2. Using a brake adjusting spoon or screwdriver, pry downward on the end of the tool (starwheel teeth moving up) to tighten the brakes, or upward on the end of

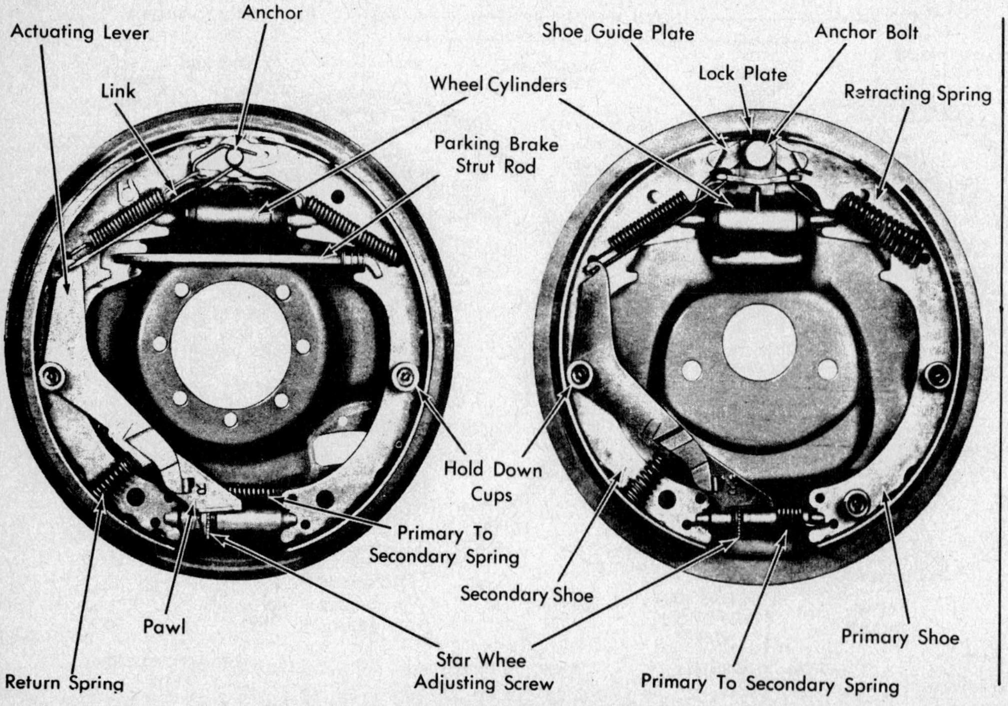
Actuating Lever
Anchor
Link
Wheel Cylinders
Parking Brake Strut Rod
Shoe Guide Plate
Lock Plate
Anchor Bolt
Retracting Spring
Hold Down Cups
Primary To Secondary Spring
Secondary Shoe
Pawl
Return Spring
Star Whee Adjusting Screw
Primary To Secondary Spring
Primary Shoe

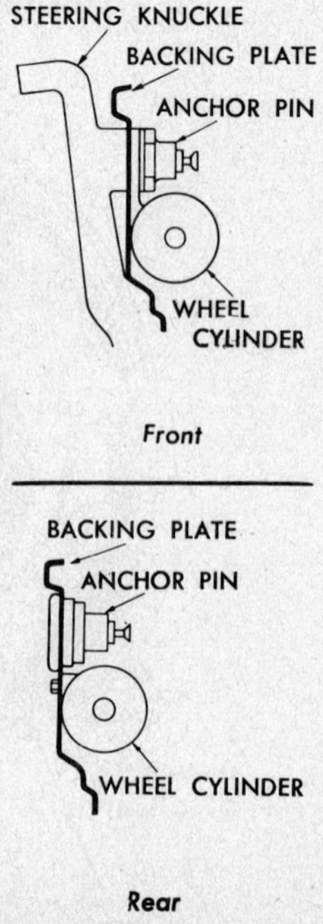
STEERING KNUCKLE
BACKING PLATE
ANCHOR PIN
WHEEL CYLINDER
Front
BACKING PLATE
ANCHOR PIN
WHEEL CYLINDER
Rear

Bendix duo-servo self-adjusting brake—G.M. type

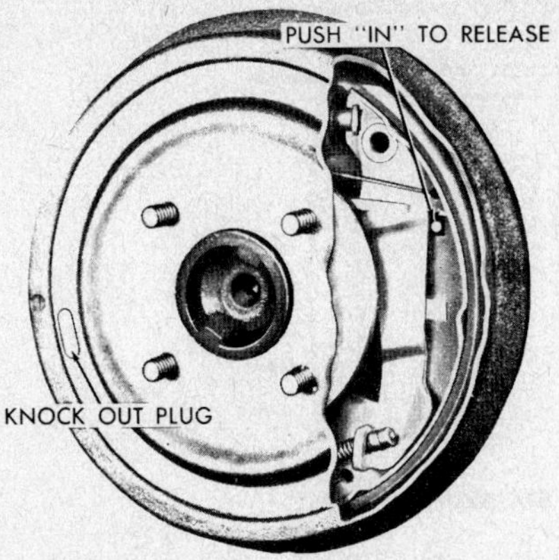
PUSH "IN" TO RELEASE
KNOCK OUT PLUG

Release adjuster (Vega) to remove drum
(© Chevrolet Div., G.M. Corp)

the tool (starwheel teeth moving down) to loosen the brakes.

NOTE: it will be necessary to use a small screwdriver to hold the adjusting lever away from the starwheel. Be careful not to bend the adjusting lever.

3. When the brakes are tight almost to the point of being locked, back off on the starwheel until the wheel is able to rotate freely. The starwheel on each set of brakes (front or rear) must be backed off the same number of turns to prevent brake pull from side to side.
4. When all four brakes are adjusted, check brake pedal travel and then make several stops, while backing the car up, to equalize all the wheels.

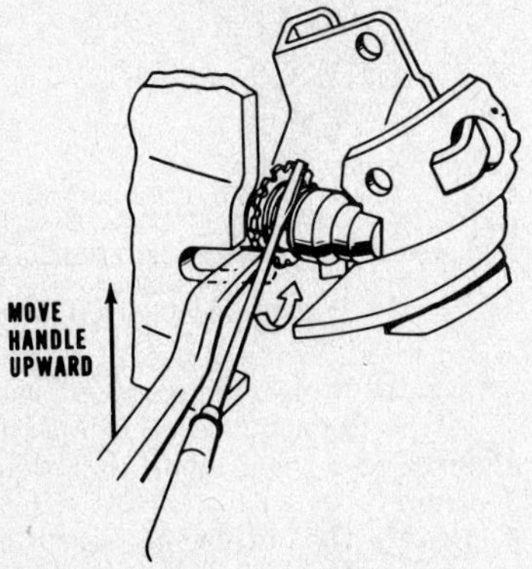
MOVE HANDLE UPWARD

Self-adjuster method. Push the self-adjusting lever out of the way with a small screwdriver or ice pick to back off star wheel.

Testing Adjuster

1. Raise the vehicle on a hoist, with a helper in the car, to apply the brakes.
2. Loosen the brakes by holding the adjuster lever away from the starwheel and backing off the starwheel approximately 30 notches.
3. Spin the wheel and brake drum in reverse and apply the brakes. The movement of the secondary shoe should pull the adjuster lever up, and when the brakes are released the lever should snap down and turn the starwheel.
4. If the automatic adjuster doesn't work, the drum must be removed and the adjuster components inspected carefully for breakage, wear, or improper installation.

1 Shoe guide plate
2 Cable anchor fitting
3 Cable guide
4 Cable
5 Cable hook
6 Lever
7 Pivot hook
8 Socket
9 Spring—automatic adjuster
10 Pivot nut
11 Adjusting screw

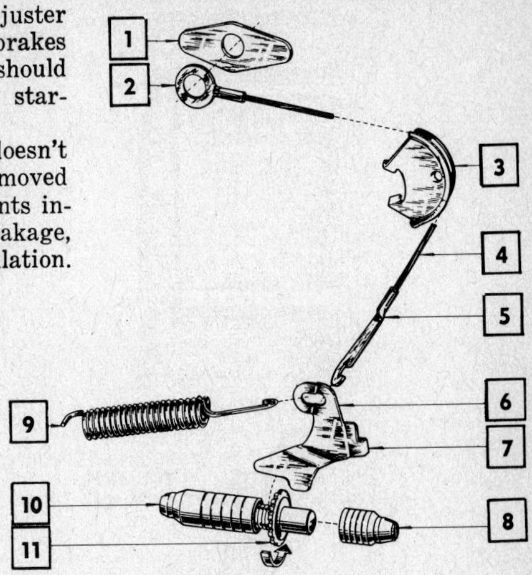
1
2
3
4
5
6
7
8
9
10
11

Self-adjusting brake components

Brake Shoe Removal

NOTE: if you are not thoroughly familiar with the procedures involved in brake replacement, disassemble and assemble one side at a time, leaving the other wheel intact, as a reference.

1. Remove the brake drum.
2. Place the hollow end of a brake spring service tool on the brake shoe anchor pin and twist it to disengage one of the brake retaining springs. Repeat this operation to remove the other spring. On GM cars, grasp the secondary shoe return spring with a pair of pliers and lift upward on the spring to disengage it from the automatic adjuster link.

Caution Be careful that the springs do not slip off the tool during removal, as the springs could break loose and cause personal injury.

3. Reach behind the brake backing plate and place a finger on the end of one of the brake hold-down mounting pins. Using a pair of pliers, grasp the washer on the top of the hold-down spring that corresponds to the pin that you are holding. Push down on the pliers and turn them 90° to align the slot in the washer with the head on the spring mounting pin. Remove the spring and washer and repeat this operation on the hold-down spring of the other brake shoe.
4. Step 4 varies according to manufacturer:

   On Ford and American Motors cars, place the tip of a screwdriver on the top of the brake adjusting screw and move the screwdriver upward to lift up on the brake adjusting lever. When there is enough slack in the automatic adjuster cable, disconnect the loop on the top of the cable from the anchor. Grasp the top of each brake shoe and move them outward to disengage from the wheel cylinder and parking brake link (if working on rear wheels). When the brake shoes are clear, lift them from the backing plate. Twist the shoes slightly and the automatic adjuster assembly will disassemble itself.

   On GM cars, remove the automatic adjuster link. Remove the automatic adjuster lever, pivot, and override spring from the secondary spring as an assembly. Move the top of each brake shoe outward to clear the wheel cylinder pins and parking brake link (rear brakes). Lift the brakes from the backing plate and remove the adjusting screw.

   On Chrysler cars, slide the automatic adjuster cable from the anchor pin and disengage it from the adjusting lever. Remove the cable, overload spring, and cable guide. Disconnect the automatic adjuster lever return spring and remove the spring and lever. Move the top of the brake shoes outward to clear the wheel cylinder pins and parking brake link (rear brakes). Lift the brakes from the backing plate and remove the adjusting screw.
5. If you are working on rear brakes, grasp the end of the brake cable spring with a pair of pliers and, using the brake lever as a fulcrum, pull the end of the spring away from the lever. Disengage the cable from the brake lever.

Brake Shoe Installation

1. If you are working on rear

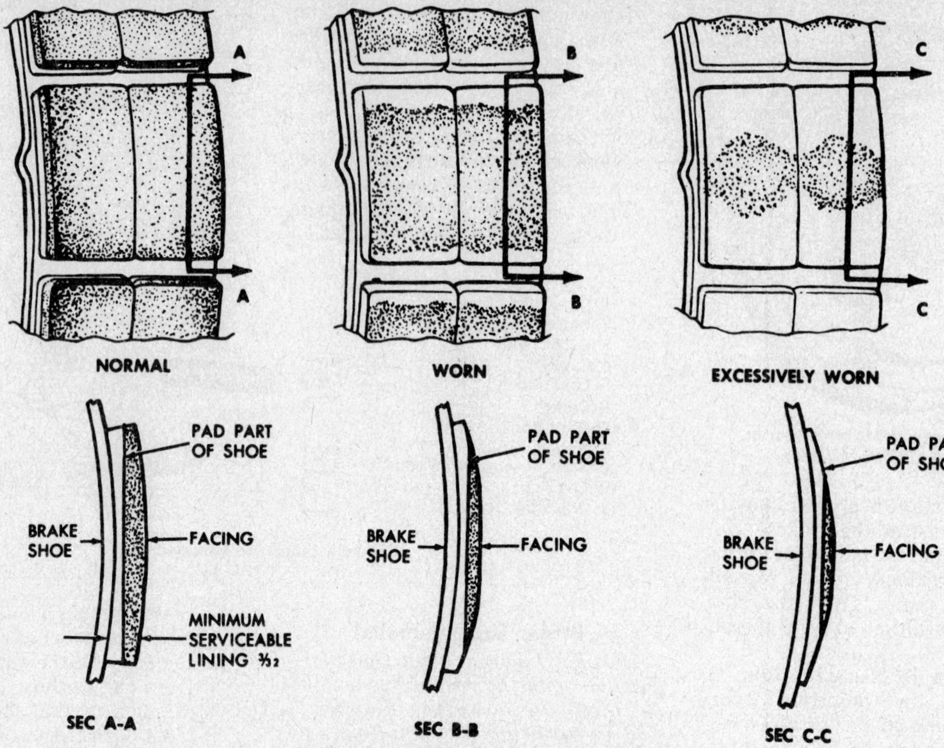
A
A
B
B
C
C
NORMAL
WORN
EXCESSIVELY WORN
PAD PART OF SHOE
BRAKE SHOE
FACING
MINIMUM SERVICEABLE LINING 3/32
SEC A-A
PAD PART OF SHOE
BRAKE SHOE
FACING
SEC B-B
PAD PART OF SHOE
BRAKE SHOE
FACING
SEC C-C
Metallic brake linings—Pontiac and Chevrolet

brakes, the brake cable must be connected to the secondary brake shoe before the shoe is installed on the backing plate. To do this, transfer the parking brake lever from the old secondary shoe to the new one. This is accomplished by spreading the bottom of the horseshoe clip and disengaging the lever. Position the lever on the new secondary shoe and install the spring washer and the horseshoe clip. Close the bottom of the clip after installing it. Grasp the metal tip of the parking brake cable with a pair of pliers. Position a pair of side cutters on the end of the cable coil spring and, using the pliers as a fulcrum, pull the coil spring back with the side cutters. Position the cable in the parking brake lever.

2. Apply a light coating of high-temperature grease to the brake shoe contact points on the backing plate. Position the primary brake shoe on the front of the backing plate and install the hold-down spring and washer over the mounting pin. Install the secondary shoe on the rear of the backing plate.
3. If working on rear brakes, install the parking brake link between the primary brake shoe and the secondary brake shoe.
4. Step 4 varies according to manufacturer:

   On Ford and American Motors cars, install the automatic adjuster cable loop end on the anchor pin. Make sure that the crimped side of the loop faces the backing plate.

   On GM cars, assemble the automatic adjuster lever, pivot, and override spring and install to the secondary spring as an assembly.

   On Chrysler, install the automatic adjuster lever and return spring. Install the adjuster overload spring and cable. One end of the cable engages with the adjusting lever while the other slips over the anchor pin underneath the primary and secondary return springs.
5. Install the return spring in the primary brake shoe and, using the tapered end of a brake spring service tool, slide the top of the spring onto the anchor pin.

Caution Be careful to make sure that the spring does not slip off the tool during installation, as the spring could break loose and cause personal injury.

6. Install the automatic adjuster cable guide in the secondary brake shoe, making sure that the flared hole in the cable guide is inside the hole in the brake shoe. Fit the cable into the groove in the top of the cable guide.
7. Install the secondary shoe return spring through the hole in the cable guide and the brake shoe. Using the brake spring tool, slide the top of the spring onto the anchor pin.
8. Clean the threads on the adjusting screw and apply a *light* coating of high-temperature grease to the threads. Screw the adjuster closed, then open it one-half turn.

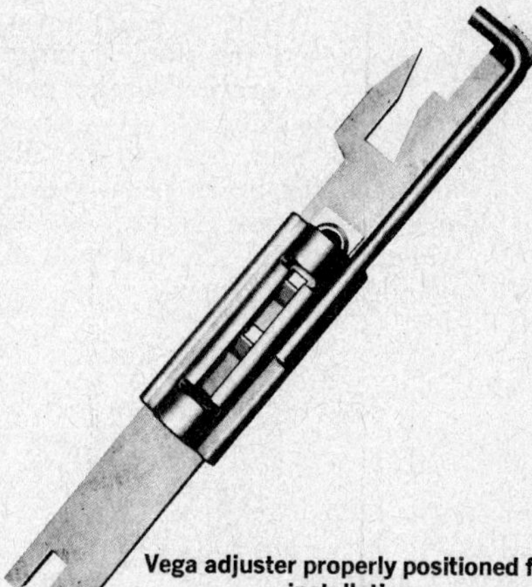
Vega adjuster properly positioned for installation
(© Chevrolet Div., G.M. Corp)

9. Install the adjusting screw between the brake shoes with the star wheel nearest to the secondary shoe. Make sure that the star wheel is in a position that is accessible from the adjusting slot in the backing plate.
10. Install the short, hooked end of the automatic adjuster spring in the proper hole in the primary brake shoe.
11. Connect the hooked end of the automatic adjuster cable and the free end of the automatic adjuster spring in the slot in the top of the automatic adjuster lever.
12. Pull the automatic adjuster lever (the lever will pull the cable and

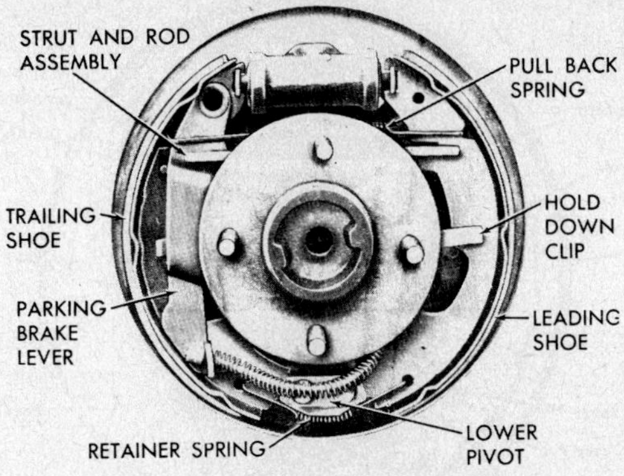
STRUT AND ROD ASSEMBLY
PULL BACK SPRING
TRAILING SHOE
HOLD DOWN CLIP
PARKING BRAKE LEVER
LEADING SHOE
RETAINER SPRING
LOWER PIVOT

Bendix duo-servo self-adjusting brake—Vega
(© Chevrolet Div., G.M. Corp)

spring with it) downward and to the left, and engage the pivot hook of the lever in the hole in the secondary brake shoe.

13. Check the entire brake assembly to make sure everything is installed properly. Make sure that the shoes engage the wheel cylinder properly and are flush on the anchor pin. Make sure that the automatic adjuster cable is flush on the anchor pin and in the slot on the back of cable guide. Make sure that the adjusting lever rests on the adjusting screw star wheel. Pull upward on the adjusting cable until the adjusting lever is free of the star wheel, then release the cable. The adjusting lever should snap back into place on the adjusting screw star wheel and turn the wheel one tooth.
14. Expand the brake adjusting screw until the brake drum will just fit over the brake shoes.
15. Install the wheel and drum and adjust the brakes. (See "Brake Adjustment.")

Expanding Strut Type

Bendix duo-servo brakes with expanding strut adjusters are used exclusively on the Vega.

Adjuster Assembly Disassembly

1. Remove the adjuster assembly from the wheel.
2. Separate the rod assembly from the adjuster locks.
3. Slide the rod off from the strut.

Assembly

1. Assemble the adjuster lock to the strut, making sure that the index hole in the lock is lined up and seated with the hole in the strut.
2. Slide the rod assembly onto the strut and over the adjuster locks. When properly installed, ½ of the index hole in the adjuster lock should be covered by the rod assembly.

Shoe Replacement

1. If the drum does not slip off easily, it will be necessary to knock out the metal plug in the drum and push in on the adjuster rod so that the spring will pull the shoes away from the drum. Remove the drum. The adjuster rod is at the 2 o'clock position on the left wheel and at the 10 o'clock position on the right wheel.
2. Release all tension from the parking brake equalizer.
3. Remove the parking brake cable from the lever next to the shoe. Allowing the lever to swing forward will engage the adjuster rod and change the adjustment position.
4. Remove the pull-back spring.
5. Remove the shoes from under the clips and lift out with the strut and adjuster assembly attached.
6. Separate the shoes, and remove the strut and adjuster assembly.
7. Remove the parking brake lever.
8. Remove the shoe hold-down clips only if they are broken or worn.
9. Using white grease, lubricate the six contact surfaces on the backing plate. Do not allow any grease to contact the brake linings.
10. Install the parking brake lever to the rear brake shoe and install the parking brake strut and adjuster. The rear shoe can be identified as having a hole for the parking brake lever and one for the adjusting rod.
11. Connect both shoes with the lower spring.
12. Install both shoes with the spring onto the backing plate, placing the spring under the shoe anchor. Position the lever and adjuster assembly.
13. Engage the wheel cylinder links with the shoes.
14. Engage the parking brake strut to the leading shoe and install the pull-back spring.
15. Connect the parking brake cable to its lever, being careful not to activate the adjuster.
16. Install the drums and wheels, and adjust the parking brake equalizer. Lower the vehicle to the floor.
17. Adjust the parking brake and service brake by pulling and releasing the handle several times.
18. Seal the adjuster hole in the drum with a rubber or plastic replacement plug.

Wagner Compound Shoe Brake

Servicing and Adjustment

This brake unit is very similar to

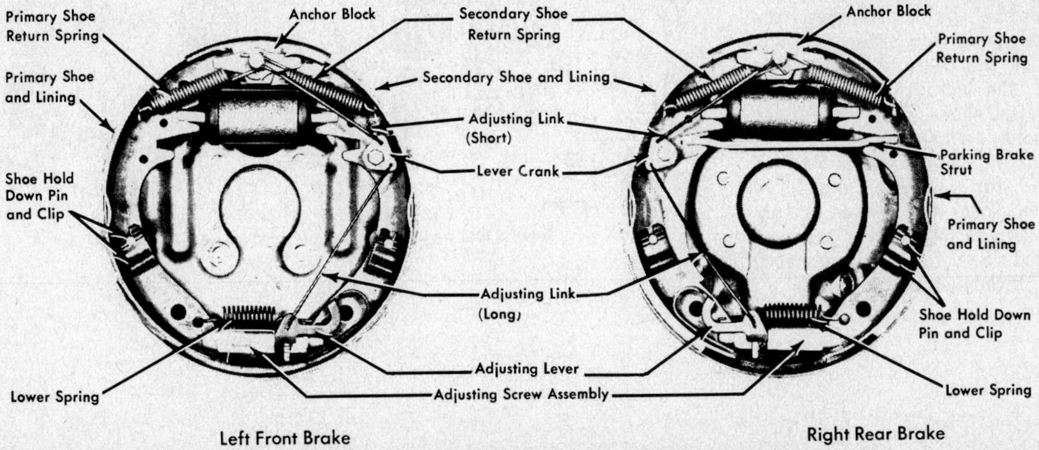
Primary Shoe Return Spring
Anchor Block
Secondary Shoe Return Spring
Primary Shoe and Lining
Secondary Shoe and Lining
Adjusting Link (Short)
Lever Crank
Shoe Hold Down Pin and Clip
Adjusting Link (Long)
Adjusting Lever
Adjusting Screw Assembly
Lower Spring
Anchor Block
Primary Shoe Return Spring
Parking Brake Strut
Primary Shoe and Lining
Shoe Hold Down Pin and Clip
Lower Spring
Left Front Brake
Right Rear Brake

Wagner compound shoe self-adjusting brake (© Chevrolet Div., G.M. Corp)

the Bendix duo-servo type with star and screw self-adjusters. Servicing and adjusting procedures are virtually the same, with these exceptions:

1. Do not lift the adjusting lever off the starwheel when adjusting the brakes manually. The adjuster levers are painted red for right-side brakes and blue for left-side brakes. The lever crank (fits into the secondary shoe) is marked with a "R" (right) or "L" (left), depending upon the wheel in which it is used.
2. The lower brake spring should be installed with the long hook end in the secondary shoe and the hook facing out to prevent interference with the starwheel or the lever.
3. If the shoes have been removed for any reason, an initial adjustment must be made before drum installation. Adjust the screw assemblies so that approximately 1/4 in. of threads are exposed between the starwheel and starwheel nut.
4. The anchor block must be installed with the arrow pointing in the direction of forward rotation.

NOTE: do not interchange the right-side adjuster assembly with the left-side assembly. Interchanging them will cause the shoe to retract rather than expand.

Bendix Non-Servo Brake

This brake is used only on the rear of 1967-68 American Motors models that are equipped with front disc brakes. Adjustment is automatically made through brake applications.

Shoe Replacement

1. Insert a screwdriver through the access hole in the backing plate and push down on the adjuster latch to allow the shoes to retract.
2. Remove the adjuster spring from the strut. Remove the upper and lower brake springs.
3. Unhook the parking brake cable from the actuation lever and slide the shoes out from under the hold down springs.
4. To install, follow steps 6-10 as given for Bendix duo-servo brakes. When the brakes are assembled the latch lever must be pressed down to engage its teeth with the adjuster lever.

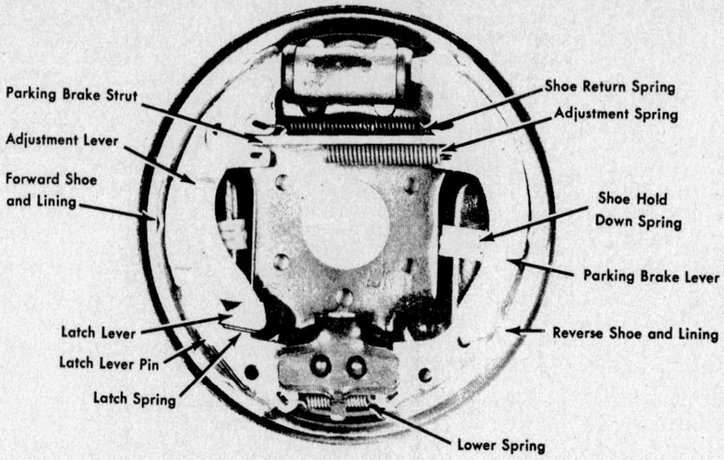
Parking Brake Strut
Adjustment Lever
Forward Shoe and Lining
Latch Lever
Latch Lever Pin
Latch Spring
Shoe Return Spring
Adjustment Spring
Shoe Hold Down Spring
Parking Brake Lever
Reverse Shoe and Lining
Lower Spring
Bendix non-servo self-adjusting brake (© American Motors Corp)

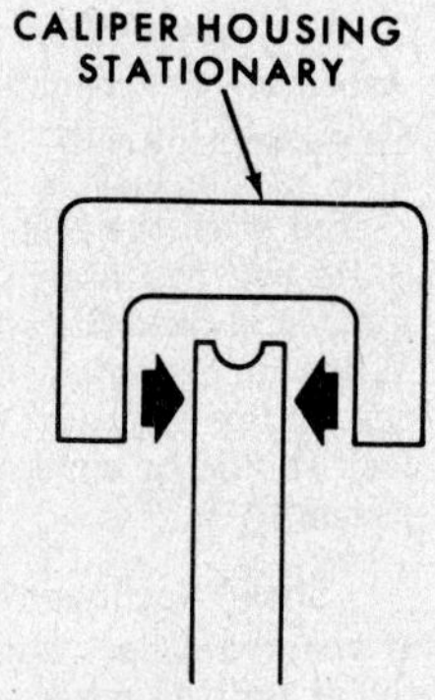
CALIPER HOUSING STATIONARY
Fixed caliper disc brake operation

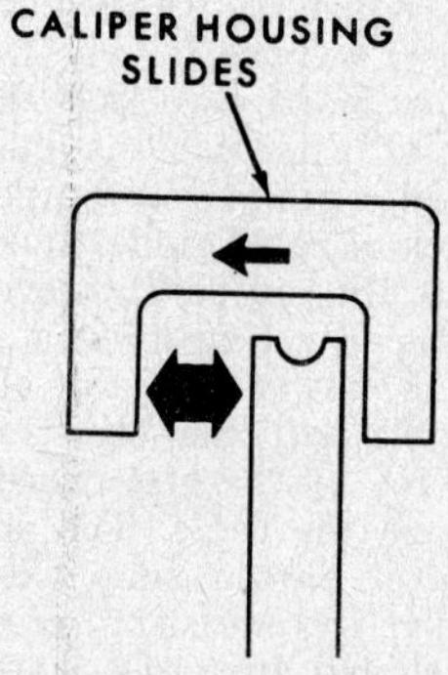
CALIPER HOUSING SLIDES
Floating caliper disc brake operation

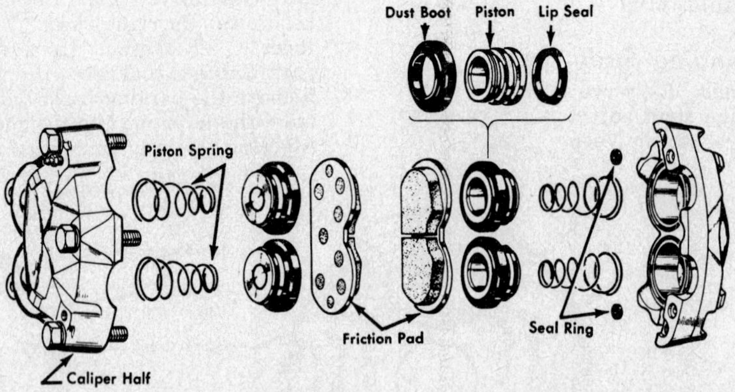
Dust Boot
Piston
Lip Seal
Piston Spring
Friction Pad
Seal Ring
Caliper Half
Bendix four piston disc brake (© American Motors Corp)

Disc Brake Specifications

Manufacturer/Model	Year	Fixed Caliper Four Piston	Floating or Sliding Caliper Single Piston	Mounting Bolts Torque ft lbs	Bridge Bolts Torque ft lbs	Proportioning Valve	Metering Valve	Original Thickness (in.)	Resurfacing Min. Thickness (in.)	Parallel Variation (in.)	Runout Maximum (in.)
		CALIPER SPECIFICATIONS				HYDRAULIC CONTROLS		DISC SPECIFICATIONS			
AMERICAN MOTORS											
All	1971-74		Kelsey-Hayes	upper: 105/lower: 85	30-35(2)	yes	yes	1.000	.940	.0005	.005
All	1966-70	Bendix		75-80 (85 for 68-70)	100-110	yes 68-70	no	.500	.450	.0005	.005
CHRYSLER CORPORATION											
Imperial Full Size Models	1973-74 1973-74		Kelsey-Hayes sliding			yes(10)	yes	1.250	(11)	.0005	.0025
Intermediates Barracuda	1973-74 1973-74		Kelsey-Hayes sliding			yes(10)	yes	1.000	(11)	.0005	.0025
Valiant Dart	1973 1973		Kelsey-Hayes sliding			yes	no	1.000	(11)	.0005	.0025
Imperial Full Size Models	1970-72 1969-72		Kelsey-Hayes	75-100	30-35(2)	no(5)	yes	1.250	1.200(6)	.0005	.0025
Intermediates Barracuda	1970-72 1970-72		Kelsey-Hayes	75-100	35	yes	yes	1.000-1.010	.980(6)	.0005	.0025
Valiant, Dart Barracuda	1966-72 1966-69	Kelsey-Hayes		50-80 (68-72), 45-60 (66-67)	70-80	yes	no (66-67) yes (68-72)	.810	.780	.0005(3)	.0025
Imperial Full Size Models	1967-69 1966-68	Budd		70-80(4)	7/16 in. 50-60 5/8 in. 140-160	no	yes	.8725-.8775	.829	.0005	.005
Intermediates	1967-69	Bendix		85-90(7)	120-140	yes	no	.886-.878	.816	.0005	.005
FORD MOTOR COMPANY											
Lincoln Full Size Models	1970-72 1968-72(1)		Kelsey-Hayes	upper: 125/lower: 105	25-35(2)	yes	yes	1.180	1.120	.0007	.003
All but Full Size	1968-72(1)		Kelsey-Hayes	upper: 120/lower: 70	25-35	yes	no	.935-.810 (68)	.875	.0007	.002
Lincoln Full Size Models	1966-69 1966-67	Kelsey-Hayes		1966: 100 1967-on: 125(9)	1966: 70 1967-on: 90	yes	no (Lincoln yes)	1.250	1.215	.0007	.002
All but Full Size	1966-67			45-60	75-105(8)	yes	no	.810	.780	.0007	.002
Pinto	1971-72		Ford sliding			yes	no	.750	.685	.0007	.003
Mark IV,	1972		Ford sliding			yes	yes	1.180	1.120	.0005	.003
Thunderbird,	1972		Ford sliding			yes	yes	1.180	1.120	.0005	.003
Montego, Torino	1972		Ford sliding			yes	yes	1.180	1.120	.0005	.003
All Models	1973-74		Ford sliding			yes	yes	1.180	1.120	.0005	.003
GENERAL MOTORS											
Buick (Full Size)	1970-74		Delco-Moraine		35	yes (no 1970)	yes	1.290	1.230 1.215 (73-74)	.0005	.005
Buick Special	1969-74		Delco-Moraine	125	35	no	yes	1.040	.965	.0005	.004
Buick (Full Size)	1967-69	Bendix		70	125	no	yes	1.000	.965	.0005	.005
Buick Special	1967-68	Delco-Moraine		75	130	no	yes	1.000	.965	.0005	.004
Cadillac Eldorado	1969-74		Delco-Moraine	95	30	yes	yes	1.210	1.195	.0005	.008 (on hub)
Cadillac	1968-74		Delco-Moraine		35	yes (68-70 no)	yes	1.250	1.230	.0005	.0025 .005 (73)
Cadillac Eldorado	1967-68	Kelsey-Hayes		95	75-105	yes	yes	1.250	1.215	.0007	.002
Chevrolet (Full Size)	1969-74		Delco-Moraine	60-90	35	yes (69-70 no)	yes	1.250 (69-70) 1.285 (71-72)	1.215 (69-72) 1.230 (71-74)	.0005 .003 (73)	.002 .005 (73)
Corvette	1967-74	Delco-Moraine		60-90	F/130 R/60	yes (HD)	no	1.250	1.215	.0005 .003 (73)	.002 .005 (73)

Disc Brake Specifications

Chevelle, Nova Camaro	1969-74	Delco-Moraine	125	1969-70: 35 1971-72: 85	yes	yes	1969-70: 1.00 1971-72: 1.035	1969-70: .965 1971-74: .980	.0005 .003 (73)	.002 .005 (73)
Chev. (Full Size)	1967-68	Delco-Moraine	60-90	130	no	yes	1.250	1.215	.0005	.002
Chevelle, Camaro, Chevy II	1967-68	Delco-Moraine	60-90	130	yes	yes	1.000	.965	.0005	.002
Olds Toronado	1969-72	Delco-Moraine	55	40	yes	yes	1.205	1.185	.0005	.002
Olds 88 & 98	1969-74	Delco-Moraine		40	yes	yes	1.250 (69-70) 1.280 (71-72)	1.215 (69-70) 1.230 (71-72)	.0005 .0005	.004 .005
Olds F85	1969-74	Delco-Moraine	70	35	no	yes	1.035	.980	.0005	.004
Olds Toronado	1967-68	Kelsey-Hayes	54	85	yes	yes	1.250	1.215	.0007	.002
Olds 88 & 98	1967-68	Delco-Moraine	70	130	yes	yes	1.250	1.215	.0005	.004
Olds F85	1967-68	Delco-Moraine	70	130	no	yes	1.000	.965	.0005	.004
Pontiac (Full Size)	1969-74	Delco-Moraine		35	yes (no 69-70)	yes	1.250 (71-72) 1.285 (73) 1.230 (69-70)	1.230 (71-72) 1.215 (73) 1.195 (69-70)	.0005	.002 .004 (73)
Tempest, LeMans, Firebird, G.P.	1969-74	Delco-Moraine		35	yes	yes	1.005 1.035 (73)	.960	.0007	.004
Pontiac (Full Size)	1967-68	Delco-Moraine	60	130	no	yes	1.250	1.215	.0005	.004
Tempest, LeMans, Firebird, G.P.	1967-68	Delco-Moraine	60	130	yes	yes	1.000	.965	.0005	.004
Vega	1971-74	Delco-Moraine			yes	no	.500	.470	.0005	.005
Ventura II (see Pontiac)	1971-74									

① Except 1972 Montego, Thunderbird, Torino, and Mark IV.
② Caliper guide pin torque.
③ 0.001 in. for 1966
④ 80-90 for 1968-69 models
⑤ Yes for 1972 Fury, Chrysler (except wagon), Imperial, Polara, and Monaco (except wagon).
⑥ 1971-72 Chrysler, Imperial, and full-size Dodge and Plymouth minimum thickness is 1.180 in.
1971-72 Intermediates and Barracuda minimum thickness is 0.940 in.
⑦ 1969 models 75-105.
⑧ 1966 models 65-75
⑨ 1966 Ford and Mercury 45-60, 1966 Thunderbird 100.
⑩ No proportioning valve on station wagons (exc. Chrysler).
⑪ Resurfacing minimum thickness is cast on the disc.

Servicing Disc Brakes

General Description and Inspection

Caliper disc brakes can be divided into three types: the four-piston, fixed-caliper type; the single-piston, floating-caliper type, and the single-piston sliding-caliper type.

In the four piston type (two in each side of the caliper) braking effect is achieved by hydraulically pushing both shoes against the disc sides. With the single piston type the inboard shoe is pushed hydraulically into contact with the disc, while the reaction force thus generated is used to pull the outboard shoe into frictional contact (made possible by letting the caliper move slightly along the axle centerline).

The sliding caliper (single piston) was used by Ford on the 1971 Pinto and many of its 1972 models. All 1973 Ford and Chrysler models, that are equipped with disc brakes, use the sliding caliper design. The caliper assembly slides along the machined surfaces of the anchor plate. A steel key located between the machined surfaces of the caliper and the machined surfaces of the anchor plate is held in place with either a retaining screw or two cotter pins. The caliper is held in place against the anchor plate with one or two support springs.

To properly inspect disc pad wear it may be necessary to remove the pads. On some systems, it is necessary to remove the caliper to accomplish this. Disc pads (lining and shoe assemblies) should be replaced in axle sets (both wheels) when the lining on any pad is worn to 1/8 in. at any point. *If lining is allowed to wear past 1/16 in. minimum thickness severe damage to disc may result.* Note that disc pads in floating caliper type brakes may wear at an angle, and measurement should be made at the narrow end of the taper. Tapered linings should be replaced if the taper exceeds 1/8 in. from end to end (the difference betweeen the thickest and thinest points).

Caution To prevent costly paint damage, remove some brake fluid (don't re-use) from the reservoir and install the reservoir cover before replacing the disc pads. When replacing the pads, the piston is depressed and fluid is forced back through the lines to squirt out of the fluid reservoir.

When the caliper is unbolted from the hub do not let it dangle by the brake hose; it can be rested on a suspension member or wired onto the frame. All disc brake systems are inherently self-adjusting and have no provision for manual adjustment.

Bendix 4 Piston Brake

Disc Pad Replacement

1. Raise the vehicle on a hoist and remove the front wheels.

See CAUTION under Delco-Moraine 4 Piston Brake.

2. Working on one side at a time only, remove the caliper mounting bolts and slide the caliper off of the disc.

NOTE: on American Motors cars the shims under the mounting bolts must be replaced exactly as removed. Remove the lower bolt, shake out the shims, and tag them as "lower." Remove the upper shims and tag them as "upper."

3. Remove the disc pads and inspect the caliper for damaged or leaking seals and casting cracks.
4. To install new pads insert the curved edge first (tabs, if any, should be up) and position the steel plate against the pistons.
5. Spread the pads apart until the pistons are bottomed in their bores and slide the caliper assembly over the disc.
6. Align the mounting holes and install shims (if used) and mounting bolts. Torque to specifications.
7. Check brake fluid level and pump the brake pedal to seat the linings against the disc. Replace the wheels and road test the vehicle.

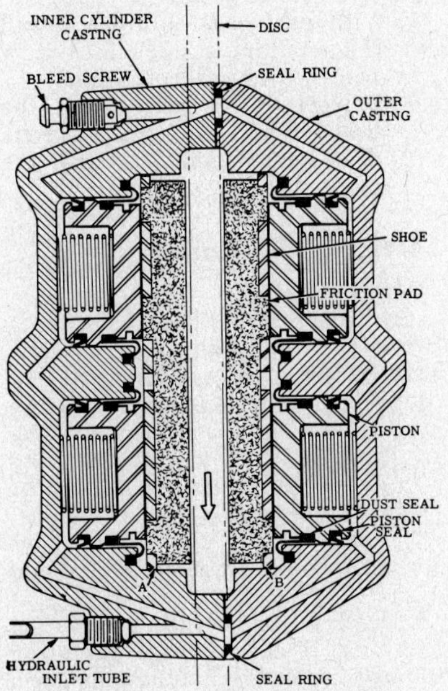
INNER CYLINDER CASTING
DISC
BLEED SCREW
SEAL RING
OUTER CASTING
SHOE
FRICTION PAD
PISTON
DUST SEAL
PISTON SEAL
A
B
HYDRAULIC INLET TUBE
SEAL RING
Cross-section—caliper and passages

Servicing the Caliper Assembly

1. Raise the vehicle on a hoist and remove the front wheels.
2. Working on one side at a time only, disconnect the hydraulic inlet line from the caliper and plug the end. Remove the caliper mounting bolts and shims (if used) and slide the caliper off of the disc.
3. Remove the disc pads from the caliper. If the old ones are to be reused, mark them so that they can be reinstalled in their original positions.
4. Open the caliper bleed screw and drain the fluid. Clean the outside of the caliper and mount it in a vise with padded jaws.

Caution When cleaning any brake components, use only brake fluid or denatured alcohol. Never use a mineral-based solvent, such as gasoline or paint thinner, since it will swell and quickly deteriorate rubber parts.

5. Remove the bridge bolts, separate the caliper halves, and remove the two O-ring seals from the transfer holes.
6. Pry the lip on each piston dust boot from its groove and remove the piston assemblies and springs from the bores. If necessary, air pressure may be used to force the pistons out of the bores, using care to prevent them from popping out of control.
7. Remove the boots and seals from the pistons and clean the pistons in brake fluid. Blow out the caliper passages with an air hose.
8. Inspect the cylinder bores for scoring, pitting, or corrosion. Corrosion is a pitted or rough condition not to be confused with staining. Light rough spots may be removed by rotating crocus cloth, using finger pressure, in the bores. Do not polish with an in and out motion or use any other abrasive.
9. If the pistons are pitted, scored, or worn, they must be replaced. A corroded or deeply scored caliper should also be replaced.
10. Check the clearance of the pistons in the bores using a feeler gauge. Clearance should be 0.002-0.006 in. If there is excessive clearance the caliper must be replaced.
11. Replace all rubber parts and lubricate with brake fluid. Install the seals and boots in the grooves in each piston. The seal should be installed in the groove closest to the closed end of the piston with the seal lips facing the closed end. The lip on the boot should be facing the seal.
12. Lubricate the piston and bore with brake fluid. Position the piston return spring, large coil first, in the piston bore.
13. Install the piston in the bore, taking great care to avoid damaging the seal lip as it passes the edge of the cylinder bore.
14. Compress the lip on the dust boot into the groove in the caliper. Be sure the boot is fully seated in the groove, as poor sealing will allow contaminants to ruin the bore.
15. Position the O-rings in the cavities around the caliper transfer holes, and fit the caliper halves together. Install the bridge bolts (lubricated with brake fluid) and be sure to torque to specification.
16. Install the disc pads in the caliper and remount the caliper on the hub (see Disc Pad Replacement). Connect the brake line to the caliper and bleed the brakes (see Brake Bleeding). Replace the wheels. Recheck the brake fluid level, check the brake pedal travel, and road test the vehicle.

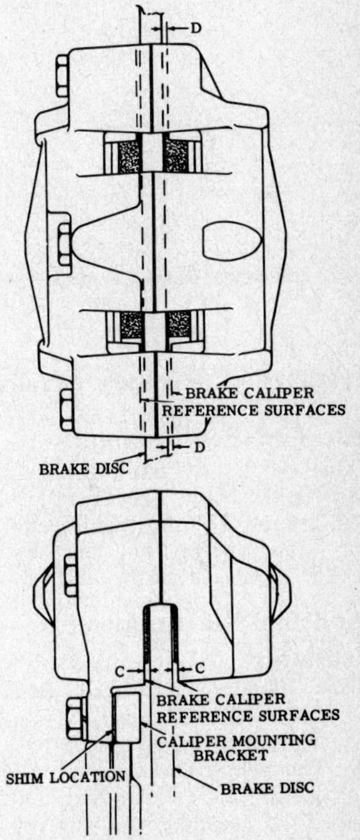
D
BRAKE CALIPER REFERENCE SURFACES
D
BRAKE DISC
C
C
BRAKE CALIPER REFERENCE SURFACES
CALIPER MOUNTING BRACKET
SHIM LOCATION
BRAKE DISC
Alignment of caliper to disc—American Motors Cars

Caliper Alignment Procedure for American Motors Cars

1. Check dimension "C" on either side of the disc (rotor). Both measurements should be within 0.010 in. of each other.
2. Check dimension "D" at both ends of the caliper. The measurements between the caliper reference surface and disc at both ends of the caliper should be within 0.005 in. of each other.
3. Add or remove shims as required to bring the dimensions to within the tolerance limits.

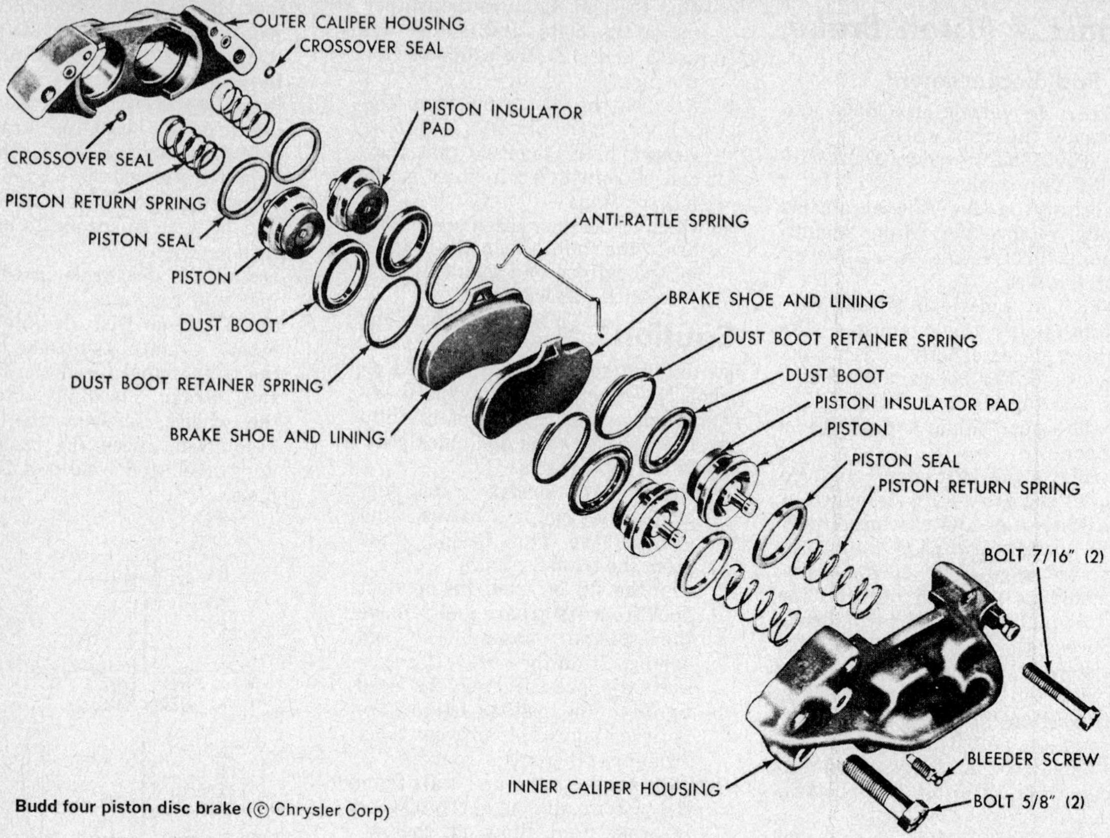
OUTER CALIPER HOUSING
CROSSOVER SEAL
PISTON INSULATOR PAD
CROSSOVER SEAL
PISTON RETURN SPRING
PISTON SEAL
PISTON
ANTI-RATTLE SPRING
DUST BOOT
BRAKE SHOE AND LINING
DUST BOOT RETAINER SPRING
DUST BOOT RETAINER SPRING
DUST BOOT
BRAKE SHOE AND LINING
PISTON INSULATOR PAD
PISTON
PISTON SEAL
PISTON RETURN SPRING
BOLT 7/16" (2)
BLEEDER SCREW
INNER CALIPER HOUSING
BOLT 5/8" (2)

Budd four piston disc brake (© Chrysler Corp)

Budd 4 Piston Brake

Disc Pad Replacement

See Bendix 4 Piston Brake—Disc Pad Replacement. Procedure is identical except that the Budd brake has a retainer spring that must be unhooked to release the disc pads.

Servicing the Caliper Assembly

See Bendix 4 Piston Brake—Servicing the Caliper Assembly. Prodecure is identical except that:

1. The piston boot has a retaining spring. It can be removed and installed with a small screwdriver, and should be fully seated in its groove upon assembly of the caliper.
2. The piston dust boot should be installed so that the lip of the boot is toward the piston insulator pad.
3. The piston seal does not need to be installed in its groove in any special manner.

Delco-Moraine 4 Piston Brake

Disc Pad Replacement

1. Raise the car and remove the front wheels.

Caution To prevent paint damage from brake fluid, be sure to remove part of brake fluid (don't re-use) from master cylinder and to keep the master cylinder covered. Do not allow cylinder to drain too low or air will be pumped into system.

2. Remove and discard the cotter pin from the end of the pad retaining pin. Remove the retaining pin or pins. If old pads are to be re-used, mark them so that they can be returned to their original positions.
3. Push one pad back so that it is as far away from the disc as possible. Remove that pad and replace it with a new one. Replace the second pad in the same manner. Pistons are spring loaded so it will be difficult to insert the new pad. To facilitate this job, use a stiff, long-bladed putty knife to hold back the pistons while inserting the new pad. If this fails to work, it may be necessary to release some of the fluid pressure by loosening the bleeder screw. This will require bleeding air from the system later.

NOTE: pads are interchangeable from inboard to outboard and right to left on all cars except the Corvette. Disc pads for the Corvette have more metal showing (in relation to the lining centerline) at one end of the pad, and this end must be towards the front of the car. To remove Corvette pads lift straight out, to remove all others swivel one end up and lift out. Shims (if any) between the pads and pistons should be replaced in the exact position as removed.

4 With new pads in place install the retaining pin and lock it in place with a new cotter pin.
5. Replace the wheels, check the brake fluid level, check brake pedal travel, and road test the car.

Servicing the Caliper Assembly

See Bendix 4 Piston Brake—Servicing the Caliper Assembly. Procedure is identical except that:

1. When the pistons are installed in the caliper, a small screwdriver must be used to "tuck" the lip of the piston seal into the caliper bore (Step 13).
2. Corvette rear disc brakes have only one transfer hole and O-ring (Step 5).
3. Each piston boot has a retaining ring. It can be pried out using the piston as a fulcrum. When installing the ring in the piston bore make sure it is seated evenly flush or below the machined face of the caliper (Steps 6 & 13).
4. Piston to bore clearance should be from 0.0045-0.010 in. (except Corvette rear which is 0.0035-0.009 in. (Step 10).
5. The piston seal lip faces toward

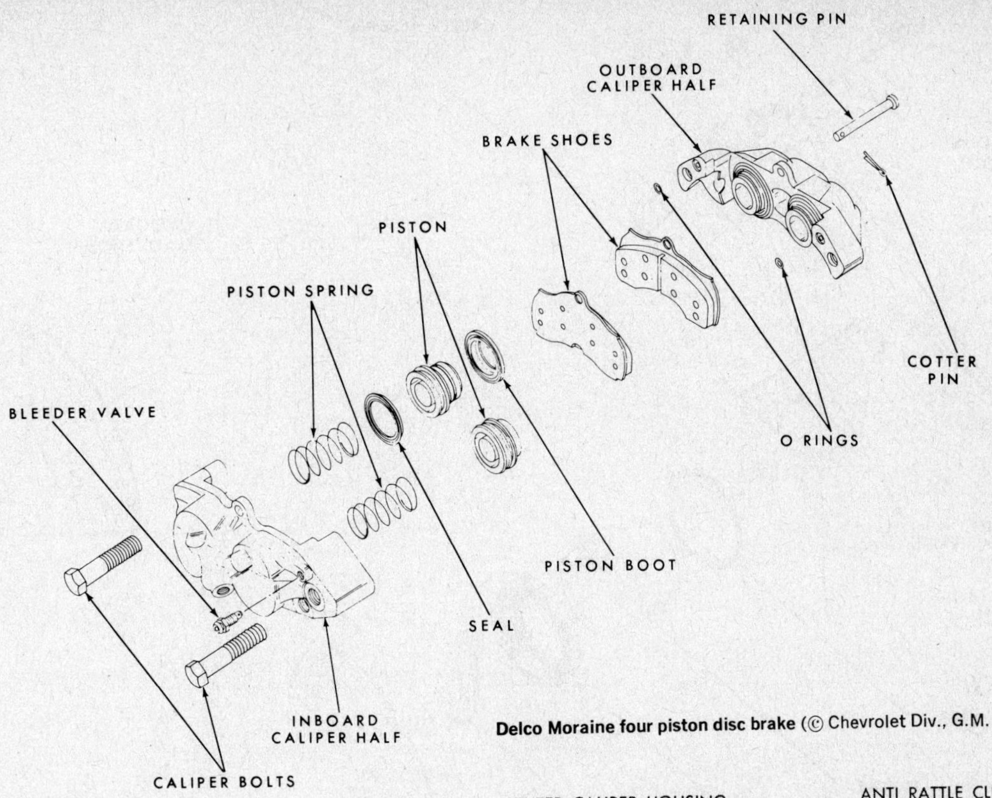
RETAINING PIN
OUTBOARD CALIPER HALF
BRAKE SHOES
PISTON
PISTON SPRING
COTTER PIN
BLEEDER VALVE
O RINGS
PISTON BOOT
SEAL
INBOARD CALIPER HALF
CALIPER BOLTS

Delco Moraine four piston disc brake (© Chevrolet Div., G.M. Corp)

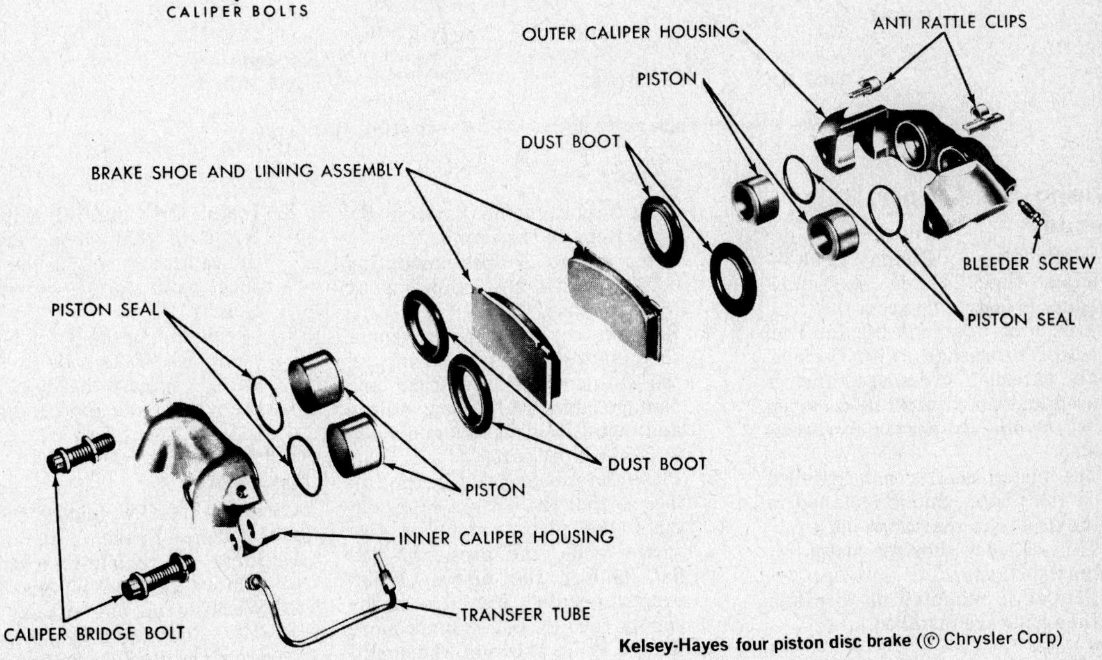
OUTER CALIPER HOUSING
ANTI RATTLE CLIPS
PISTON
DUST BOOT
BRAKE SHOE AND LINING ASSEMBLY
BLEEDER SCREW
PISTON SEAL
PISTON SEAL
DUST BOOT
PISTON
INNER CALIPER HOUSING
TRANSFER TUBE
CALIPER BRIDGE BOLT

Kelsey-Hayes four piston disc brake (© Chrysler Corp)

the spring end of the piston, and the fold in the piston boot faces toward the seal (Step 14).

6. Slide the caliper over the disc. A putty knife can be used to hold back the pistons so that the caliper can be completely lowered into position. The caliper should be positioned carefully to avoid tearing the rubber boot on the edge of the disc. Secure the caliper to the mounting bracket and torque to specifications. Install the pads as instructed earlier (Step 16).
7. When the brake hose is connected it should not be twisted or touch other parts at any time during suspension or steering travel (Step 16).

Kelsey-Hayes 4 Piston Brake

Disc Pad Replacement

See CAUTION under Delco-Moraine 4 Piston Brake.

1. Raise the car and remove the front wheels.
2. Remove the retainer bolts and the retainer(s).
3. Using two pairs of pliers, grasp the outer ends of one of the pads and pull straight out. Push the two pistons into their bores using a flat metal bar and install a new disc pad. Repeat for the second pad.
4. Install the retainer(s) and bolts.
5. Replace the wheels, check the brake fluid level, check brake pedal travel, and road test the car.

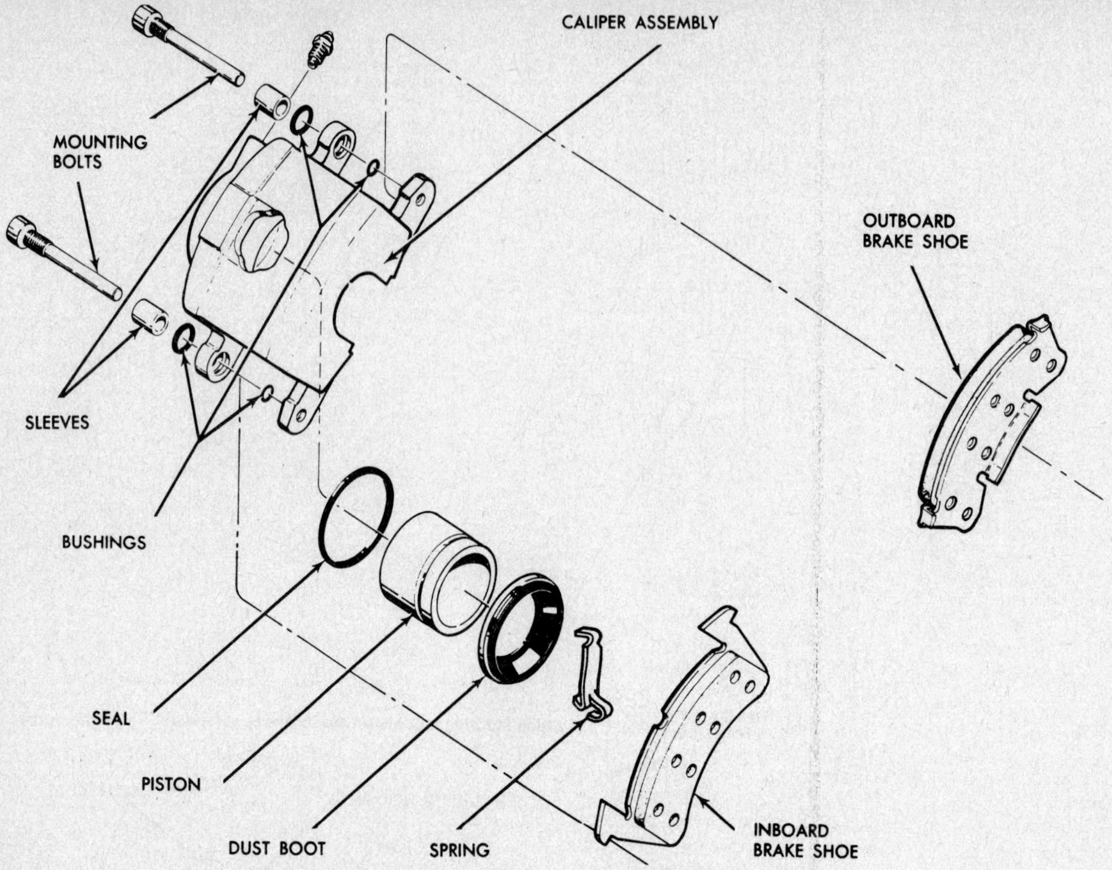
CALIPER ASSEMBLY
MOUNTING BOLTS
OUTBOARD BRAKE SHOE
SLEEVES
BUSHINGS
SEAL
PISTON
DUST BOOT
SPRING
INBOARD BRAKE SHOE

Delco-Moraine single piston disc brake (© Chevrolet Div., G.M. Corp)

Servicing the Caliper Assembly

See Bendix 4 Piston Brake—Servicing the Caliper Assembly. Procedure is identical except that:

1. This unit does not use internal transfer passages with O-rings, an external crossover line is used instead. It must be removed before the caliper is disassembled.
2. The piston seal is not installed on the piston, but is installed in the groove in the piston bore.
3. This unit does not use piston return springs.
4. Caliper is mounted on disc and then pads are installed.

Delco-Moraine Single Piston Brake

Disc Pad Replacement

See CAUTION under Delco-Moraine 4 Piston Brake.

1. Raise the vehicle on a hoist and remove the front wheels.
2. Place a "C" clamp on the caliper so that the solid side of the clamp rests against the back of the caliper and the screw end rests against the metal part of the outboard shoe. Tighten the clamp until the caliper moves enough to bottom the piston in the bore. Remove the clamp.
3. Remove the caliper mounting bolts and lift the caliper away from the disc.
4. Remove the disc pads (mark them as to location) and inspect the caliper for fluid leaks and damage. Lubricate with silicon and install new sleeves and bushings in caliper ears.
5. Place the inboard pad in the caliper so that the bottom edge contacts the piston and the two spring ends, and press the pad flat against the piston. When properly seated, the ends of the spring should not extend more than 0.10 in. beyond the metal part of the pad.

NOTE: most 1970 and later cars use a different type of spring to locate the pad. The clip-type spring must be assembled onto the pad before the pad is placed over the piston.

6. Place the outboard pad in the caliper so that the two ears on the pad fit over the ears on the caliper. Squeeze the ears on the pad tight around the caliper ears with a pair of pliers.
7. Position the caliper assembly onto the disc, align the mounting holes, and make sure that the brake line isn't twisted.
8. Install the mounting bolts (making sure that they pass under the retaining ears on the inboard shoe) and torque to specification.
9. Check the brake fluid level and pump the brake pedal to seat the linings against the disc. Replace the wheels and road test the car.

Servicing the Caliper Assembly

See CAUTION under Delco-Moraine 4 Piston Brake.

1. Raise the vehicle on a hoist and remove the front wheels.
2. Working on one side at a time only, disconnect the brake hose from the steel brake line and cap the fittings. Remove the U-shaped retainer from the hose fitting (if applicable).
3. Remove the caliper mounting bolts (locating pins) and lift the caliper away from the disc.
4. Clean the holes and the bushing grooves in the caliper ears, and wipe all dirt from the mounting bolts. If the bolts are corroded or damaged they should be replaced.
5. Remove the shoe support springs (if applicable) from the piston.
6. Remove the sleeves from the ears of the caliper with a suit-

able drift pin. Remove the rubber bushings from the grooves in the caliper ears.

7. Remove the brake hose, drain the brake fluid, and clean the outside of the caliper.
8. Pad the inside of the caliper with towels and direct compressed air into the brake fluid inlet hole to remove the piston.

Caution To prevent damage to the piston use just enough air pressure to ease it out of the bore. Do not attempt to catch or protect the piston with the hand since this may cause serious injury.

9. Use a screwdriver to pry the boot out of the caliper. Avoid scratching the bore.
10. Remove the piston seal from its groove in the caliper bore. *Do not use a metal tool of any type for this operation.*
11. Blow out all passages in the caliper and bleeder valve. Clean the piston and piston bore with fresh brake fluid.
12. Examine the piston for scoring, scratches, or corrosion. If any of these conditions exist the piston must be replaced, as it is plated and cannot be refinished.
13. Examine the bore for the same defects. Light rough spots may be removed by rotating crocus cloth, using finger pressure, in the bore. Do not polish with an in and out motion or use any other abrasive.
14. Lubricate the piston bore and the new rubber parts with fresh brake fluid. Position the seal in the piston bore groove.
15. Lubricate the piston with brake fluid and assemble the boot into the piston groove so that the fold faces the open end of the piston.
16. Insert the piston into the bore, taking care not to unseat the seal.
17. Force the piston to the bottom of the bore. (This will require a force of 50-100 lbs.). Seat the boot lip around the caliper counterbore. Proper seating of the boot is very important for sealing out contaminants.
18. Install the brake hose into the caliper using a new copper gasket.
19. Lubricate the new sleeves and rubber bushings. Install the bushings in the caliper ears. Install the sleeves so that the end toward the disc pad is flush with the machined surface.

NOTE: lubrication of the sleeves and bushings is essential to ensure the proper operation of the sliding caliper design.

20. Install the shoe support spring (if applicable) in the piston.
21. Install the disc pads in the caliper and remount the caliper on the hub (see Disc Pad Replacement).
22. Reconnect the brake hose to the steel brake line. Install the retainer clip. Bleed the brakes (see Brake Bleeding).
23. Replace the wheels, check the brake fluid level, check the brake pedal travel, and road test the vehicle.

Kelsey-Hayes Single Piston Brake (Chrysler and American Motors)

See CAUTION under Delco-Moraine 4 Piston Brake.

Disc Pad Replacement

1. Raise the vehicle on a hoist and remove front wheels.
2. Working on only one brake at a time, remove the caliper guide pins and positioners which attach caliper to adapter. Lift the caliper away from the disc.
3. Remove (and discard) the positioners and inner bushings from the guide pins, and the outboard bushings from the caliper.
4. Slide the disc pads out of the caliper, and carefully push the piston back into the bore.
5. Lubricate new outboard bushings and work them into position from the ouboard side of the caliper.
6. Slide the new disc pads into position (outboard pad in the retaining spring) and carefully slide the caliper assembly over the rotor.
7. Lubricate and install new inner bushings in the caliper. Install new positioners on the guide pins with the open ends toward the outside.
8. Install the assembled guide pins from the inboard side and press in while threading pin into adapter. *Use extreme care to avoid crossing threads.* Tighten to specifications. Be sure the tabs

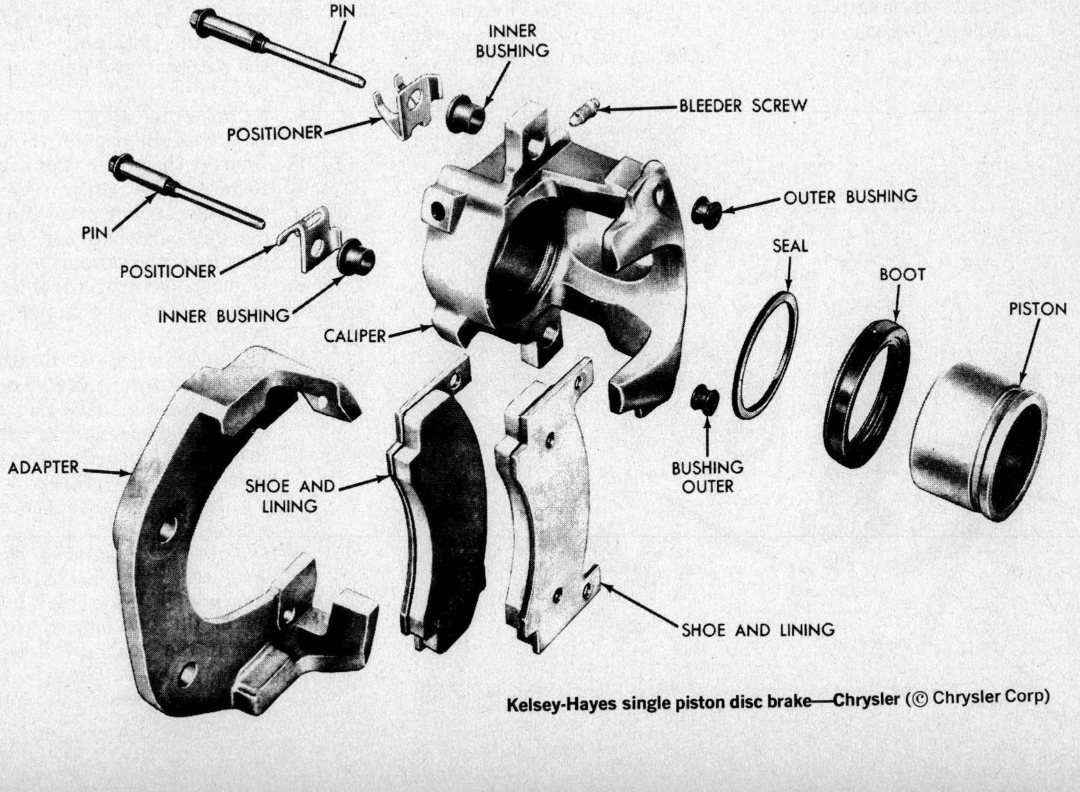
PIN
INNER BUSHING
BLEEDER SCREW
POSITIONER
OUTER BUSHING
PIN
SEAL
POSITIONER
BOOT
PISTON
INNER BUSHING
CALIPER
ADAPTER
SHOE AND LINING
BUSHING OUTER
SHOE AND LINING

Kelsey-Hayes single piston disc brake—Chrysler (© Chrysler Corp) of the positioners are over the machined surfaces of the caliper.

9. Check the brake fluid level and pump the brake pedal to seat the linings against the disc. Replace the wheels and road test the car.

Servicing the Caliper Assembly

See Delco-Moraine Single Piston Brake—Servicing the Caliper Assembly. Procedure is identical, except that:

1. The Kelsey-Hayes brake has no removable sleeves in the guide pin holes.
2. The retaining (support) springs are of a different shape.
3. Piston to bore clearance should be 0.002-0.006 in.
4. The guide pin positioners must be correctly installed on the guide pins (see Disc Pad Replacement).

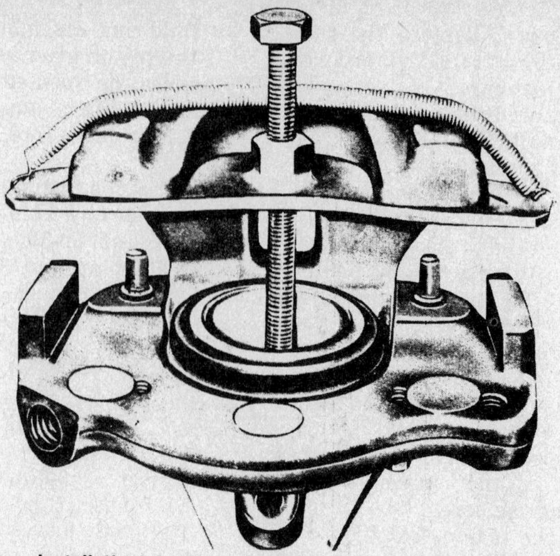

Installation of piston retracting rod (© Ford Motor Co)

Kelsey-Hayes Single Piston Brake (Ford)

Disc Pad Replacement—Floating Caliper

1968-69 (All Models)

1. Raise the vehicle on a hoist and remove the front wheels. Disconnect the brake line from the caliper and cap the end to prevent leakage.

See CAUTION under Delco-Moraine 4 Piston Brake.

2. Remove the lockwires from the two mounting bolts and lift the caliper away from the rotor.
3. Remove the retaining clips with a screwdriver and slide the outboard pad and retaining pins out of the caliper. Remove the inboard pad. Loosen the bleed screw and drain fluid.
4. Slide the new inboard pad into the caliper so that the tabs are between the retaining clips and anchor plate and the backing plate lies flush against the piston.
5. Insert the outboard pad retaining pins into the outboard pad and position in caliper.

NOTE: stabilizer, insulators, pad clips and pins should always be replaced when disc pads are replaced.

6. Hold the retaining pins in place (one at a time) with a short drift pin or dowel and install the retaining clips.
7. Slide the caliper assembly over the disc and align the mounting bolt holes.
8. Install the lower bolt finger-tight. Install the upper bolt and torque to specification. Torque the lower bolt to specification. Safety wire both bolts.

Caution Do not deviate from this procedure. The alignment of the anchor plate depends on the proper sequence of bolt installation.

9. Check the brake fluid level and pump the brake pedal to seat the linings against the disc. Replace the wheels and road test the car.

1970-71 Thunderbird, Continental Mark III
1970-72 Ford, Mercury, Lincoln

1. Check brake fluid level in the large (primary) reservoir of the master cylinder. Remove enough fluid so that this reservoir is only half full. Do not re-use this fluid, throw it away.
2. Remove the wheel and tire assembly.
3. Remove the inboard pad hold down clips.
4. Using a small screwdriver, remove the retaining clips from the outboard pad and remove the pad.
5. Remove the caliper locating pins (2) from the back of the caliper.
6. Remove the upper stabilizer.
7. Remove the caliper assembly from the anchor plate and detach the outboard pad and retaining pins from the caliper.
8. Using a piece of wire, hang the caliper from the upper control arm.
9. Remove the caliper locating pin insulators from the anchor plate.
10. Remove the inboard pad and inspect the disc surfaces for wear.
11. Install the inboard pad to the anchor plate. Insert new locating pin insulators into the anchor plate.

NOTE: when replacing pads, install new stabilizer, insulators, shoe clips and pins. It may help to wet insulators with water before installing.

12. Install the inboard pad hold down clips and tighten bolts.
13. The piston must be fully re-

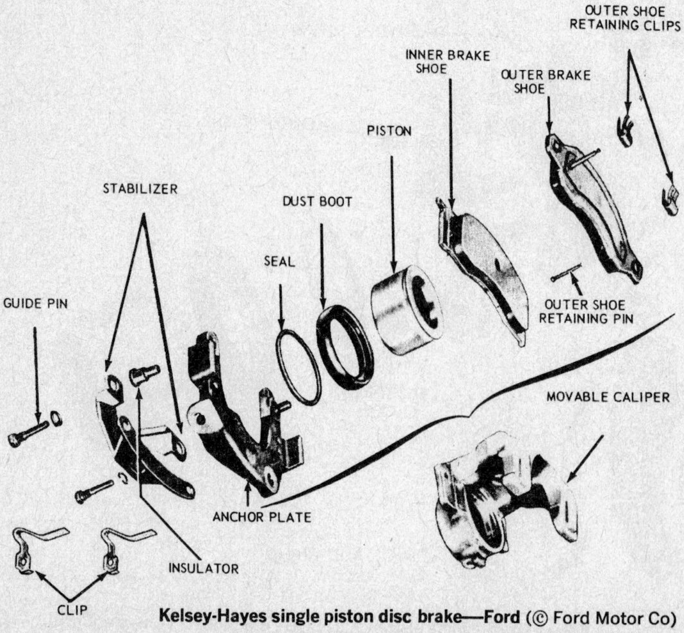
OUTER SHOE RETAINING CLIPS
INNER BRAKE SHOE
OUTER BRAKE SHOE
PISTON
STABILIZER
DUST BOOT
SEAL
GUIDE PIN
OUTER SHOE RETAINING PIN
MOVABLE CALIPER
ANCHOR PLATE
INSULATOR
CLIP

Kelsey-Hayes single piston disc brake—Ford (© Ford Motor Co)

tracted into the cylinder before the caliper and pad assembly will fit over the disc. Retracting the piston can be made easier by fabricating a retracting tool using a bolt, a nut, a used outer brake pad and a retaining spring.

14. Position the tool onto the caliper holding it in place with the retaining spring. Gradually turn in on the bolt pausing to allow the piston to pull in the seal. Make sure the piston is fully bottomed in the cylinder to create proper clearance between the pads. Inspect piston dust boot and replace if cracked. See Servicing the Caliper Assembly for replacement procedures.
15. Install the outer brake pad, retaining pins and new retainer clips.
16. Join the caliper assembly to the anchor plate.
17. Install the stabilizers to caliper.
18. Check the brake fluid level and pump the brake pedal to seat the pads against the disc. Install the wheels and road test the car.

1970 Fairlane
1971 Torino, 1970-71 Montego
1970-74 Mustang and Cougar

1. Make sure large master cylinder reservoir is only half full.
2. Remove the front wheel and tire.
3. Disconnect and plug the brake line if necessary.
4. Remove the caliper locating pins and stabilizer bolts.
5. Lift caliper off disc. If working on both wheels, mark calipers right or left.
6. Remove the inboard pad hold down clips and the pin insulators from the anchor plate.
7. Remove the inboard pad.
8. Using a small screwdriver, lift the outer pad retaining clips off the retaining pins. Remove the outer pad.
9. Insert new caliper locating pin insulators in the anchor plate.
10. Install the inboard pad retaining clips.
11. Using a piston retracting tool (see steps 13 & 14 of Disc Pad Replacement for Ford, Mercury, etc.), push the piston completely into its cylinder.
12. Install outer pad and retaining clips.
13. Install the caliper onto the disc being careful not to pinch the piston boot between the inner pad and the piston.
14. Attach a new stabilizer to the caliper with clean locating pins.
15. Attach the stabilizer to the anchor plate.
16. Connect brake hose (if previously disconnected) using new copper washers, one on each side of the hose fitting. Bleed brakes.
17. Check the brake fluid level and pump the brake pedal to seat the pads against the disc. Install the wheels and road test the car.

DUST SHIELD
ANCHOR PLATE
CALIPER ASSEMBLY
KEY RETAINER SCREW
KEY
CALIPER SUPPORT SPRING
OUTER BRAKE SHOE AND LINING ASSEMBLY
HUB AND ROTOR ASSEMBLY

Sliding caliper disc brake—1972-74 Mark IV, Thunderbird, Montego, Torino
(© Ford Motor Co)

Disc Pad Replacement—Sliding Caliper

1972-74 Continental Mark IV
1972-74 Thunderbird
1972-74 Montego
1972-74 Torino
1973-74 Continental
1973-74 Ford
1973-74 Mercury
1973-74 Meteor

1. Raise the car, safely support it and remove the tire and wheel assembly.
2. Remove the retaining screw from the caliper retaining key.
3. Using a hammer and drift, remove the caliper retaining key and support spring from the anchor plate. Be careful not to damage key.
4. Push the caliper down against the anchor plate and rotate the upper end off the anchor plate.
5. Remove the inboard pad from the anchor plate. Do not lose the anti-rattle clip. Tap lightly on the outer pad to free it from the caliper. If the original pads are to be reused, mark them as to location for correct installation.
6. Clean all components and inspect for damage, leakage and excessive wear.

NOTE: if the pads on one wheel are replaced it is necessary to replace those on the other wheel to maintain equal braking action.

7. When installing new pads, use a 4 in. c-clamp and a block of wood measuring 1-¾ in. x 1 in. x ¾ in. thick. This will aid in seating the piston in its cylinder so that the caliper will fit over the new pads when installed.
8. Install the anti-rattle clip on the lower inboard pad support located on the anchor plate. The pigtail of the clip must be toward the inside of the plate. Place the inner pad on the anchor plate.
9. Install the outer pad with the upper flanges over the shoulders on the caliper legs. If the old pads are reused, be certain they are installed in their original positions.
10. If previously used, remove the C-clamp from the caliper since the piston will remain seated in its cylinder.
11. Position the caliper assembly lower V-groove on the anchor plate lower abutment surface.
12. Pivot the caliper housing upward toward the disc until the outer edge of the piston dust boot is about ¼ in. from the upper edge of inboard pad.
13. Place a piece of thin cardboard between the inboard pad and the lower half of the piston dust boot to prevent pinching of the boot when rotating the caliper onto the disc.
14. Continue to rotate the caliper onto the disc until a slight resistance is felt.
15. Gradually remove the cardboard as the caliper rotates onto the disc. Complete the rotation onto the disc and completely remove the cardboard.
16. Slide the caliper up against the upper anchor plate abutment and center it over the lower anchor plate abutment.

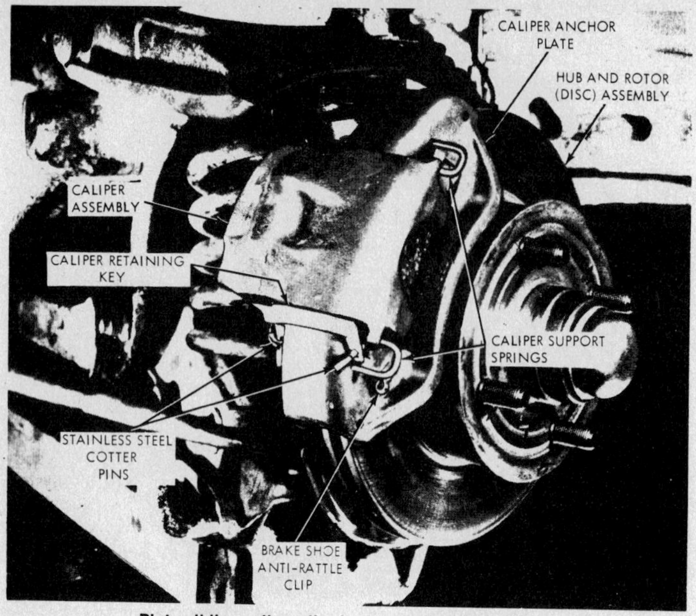
CALIPER ANCHOR PLATE
HUB AND ROTOR (DISC) ASSEMBLY
CALIPER ASSEMBLY
CALIPER RETAINING KEY
CALIPER SUPPORT SPRINGS
STAINLESS STEEL COTTER PINS
BRAKE SHOE ANTI-RATTLE CLIP

Pinto sliding caliper disc brake (© Ford Motor Co)

17. Install the caliper support spring and key into the opening between the lower end of the caliper and the lower anchor plate abutment. The hole in the slot must be centered over the threaded hole in the anchor plate.
18. Install the key retaining screw and torque to 12-16 ft. lbs.
19. Check the brake fluid level and pump the brake pedal to seat the pads against the disc. Install the wheels and road test the car.

1971-74 Pinto

1. Raise car and support safely. Remove wheel and tire assembly.
2. Remove the two cotter pins from the retaining key.
3. Using a hammer and drift, carefully remove the key.
4. Push in on the caliper assembly and lift it away from the anchor plate.

NOTE: do not stretch or twist the brake hose.

5. Using wire, temporarily suspend the caliper assembly from the upper suspension arms.
6. If brake pads are to be reused, mark them as to correct location.
7. Remove the pads from the anchor plate.
8. Clean the caliper, anchor plate and disc and inspect them for leakage, damage or excessive wear.

NOTE: if the shoes are replaced on one wheel they must also be replaced on the other wheel to maintain balanced brake action.

9. When installing new pads, it is necessary to compress the piston in its cylinder to provide enough clearance for the caliper to fit over the pads. To perform this, place a block of wood (1-¾" x 1" x ¾" thick) on the piston and clamp down on it with a 4 in. C-clamp.
10. Place pads and anti-rattle clips in anchor plate.
11. Remove the C-clamp from the piston and remove the wire holding the caliper to the suspension arm.
12. Place the caliper on the anchor plate so that the lower edge of the caliper is on top of the rear caliper support spring.
13. Pivot the caliper over the pads until the upper edge of the caliper can be pushed over the forward caliper support spring.
14. Using a heavy screwdriver, hold the caliper over the upper support spring and against the anchor plate. Insert the retaining key.
15. Install two new stainless steel cotter pins in the key.
16. Check the brake fluid level and pump the brake pedal to seat the pads against the disc. Install the wheels and road test the car.

Servicing the Caliper Assembly—Floating Caliper

1968-71 All Models Except Pinto 1972 All Models Except Pinto, Continental Mark IV, Thunderbird, Montego, and Torino 1973-74 Mustang and Cougar

1. Raise the vehicle on a hoist and remove the front wheels.
2. Disconnect and plug the brake line.
3. Remove the lockwires from the two caliper mounting bolts and remove the bolt. Lift the caliper off the disc.
4. Remove and discard the locating pin insulators. Replace all rubber parts at reassembly.
5. Remove the retaining clips with a screwdriver and slide the outboard pad and retaining pins out of the caliper. Remove the inboard pad. Loosen the bleed screw and drain the brake fluid.
6. Remove the two small bolts and caliper stabilizers.
7. Remove the inboard pad retaining clips and bolts.
8. Clean and inspect all parts, and reinstall on anchor plate. Do not tighten stabilizer bolts at this time.
9. Remove the piston by applying compressed air to the fluid inlet hole. Use care to prevent the piston from popping out of control.

Caution Do not attempt to catch the piston with the hand. Use folded towels to cushion it.

10. Remove the piston boot. Inspect the piston for scoring, pitting, or corrosion. The piston must be replaced if there is any visible damage or wear.
11. Remove the piston seal from the cylinder bore. *Do not use any metal tools for this operation.*
12. Clean the caliper with fresh brake fluid. Inspect the cylinder bore for damage or wear. Light defects can be removed by rotating crocus cloth around the bore. Do not use any other type of abrasive.
13. Lubricate all new rubber parts in brake fluid. Install the piston seal in the cylinder groove. Install the boot into its piston groove.
14. Install the piston, open end out, into the bore while working the boot around the outside of the piston. Make sure boot lip is seated in the piston groove.
15. Slide the anchor plate assembly onto the caliper housing and reinstall the locating pins. Tighten pins to specification. Tighten stabilizer anchor plate bolts. Perform Steps 4-8 of Disc Pad Replacement.
16. Connect the brake line and bleed the brakes (see Brake Bleeding).
17. Install the front wheels, recheck the brake fluid level, and road test the car.

Servicing the Caliper Assembly—Sliding Caliper

1972-74 Lincoln-Continental, Continental Mark IV, Thunderbird, Montego, Pinto, Torino, Ford, Mercury, Meteor

To service the caliper on these models, follow the instructions listed for the same models under Disc Pad Replacement—Sliding Caliper. The instructions are identical with one exception—caliper service requires you to disconnect and connect the brake hose from the caliper and bleed the brakes. If it is necessary to remove and install piston, follow steps 6-12 of 1971-74 Pinto.

1971-74 Pinto

1. Raise the car and support safely. Remove the wheel and tire assembly.
2. Disconnect the brake hose from the caliper.
3. Remove the two cotter pins from the retaining key.
4. Using a drift and hammer, remove the retaining key.
5. Press inward on the caliper assembly and lift it away from the anchor plate.
6. Remove the piston by applying air pressure to the caliper fluid port.

IMPORTANT: to prevent piston damage and possible personal injury, place a cloth over the piston before applying air pressure.

7. If the piston is seized in its cylinder, tap lightly around the piston while applying air pressure.
8. Remove and discard the piston dust boot and seal.
9. Clean (using alcohol) and inspect all parts for damage or excessive wear. Replace the piston if pitted or scored or if the chrome plating is worn off.
10. Lightly coat a new piston seal with clean brake fluid and seat it in the piston groove.
11. Install a new dust boot with its flange in the outer groove of the cylinder.
12. Coat the piston with fluid and install in the cylinder. Spread the dust boot over the piston while inserting it in cylinder and seat it in the piston groove.
13. Place the caliper on the anchor plate so that the lower edge of the caliper can be pushed over the forward caliper support spring.
14. Using a heavy screwdriver, hold the caliper over the upper support spring and against the anchor plate. Insert the retaining key.
15. Install two new stainless steel cotter pins in the key.
16. Connect the brake hose and bleed the brakes.
17. Check the brake fluid level and pump the brake pedal to seat the pads against the disc. Install the wheels and road test the car.

Servicing the Disc

Disc Replacement

1. Raise the vehicle on a hoist and remove the wheel.
2. Remove the caliper mounting bolts. Slide the caliper away from the disc and suspend it using a wire loop. On some cars, it is advisable to install a cardboard spacer between the pads to prevent the piston from coming out of its cylinder.
3. Remove the wheel bearing nut from the spindle and remove the outer wheel bearing roller assembly from the hub.

   On Ford sliding caliper brakes, remove the wheel bearing adjusting nut and pull the hub and disc assembly outward enough to loosen the washer and outer wheel bearing. Push the assembly back onto the spindle and remove the washer and outer wheel bearing from the spindle.
4. Remove the hub and disc assembly from the spindle.
5. Installation of hub and disc is in reverse order of removal.

Caution Alignment of the caliper assembly depends on proper sequence of bolt installations on some cars. Check caliper installation procedure under Disc Pad Replacement of proper brake type.

NOTE: the disc is removable from the hub on the Eldorado, Toronado, and Corvette (rear only).

To separate the rear disc and hub on a Corvette the three hub-to-disc attaching rivets must be drilled out. This can be done with the hub and rotor mounted on the car. It is not necessary to install new rivets when the disc is installed.

Lateral Runout

Lateral runout is the movement of the disc from side to side (wobble) as it rotates. Excessive runout will result in brake chatter, pedal pumping, excessive pedal travel, or vibration during braking.

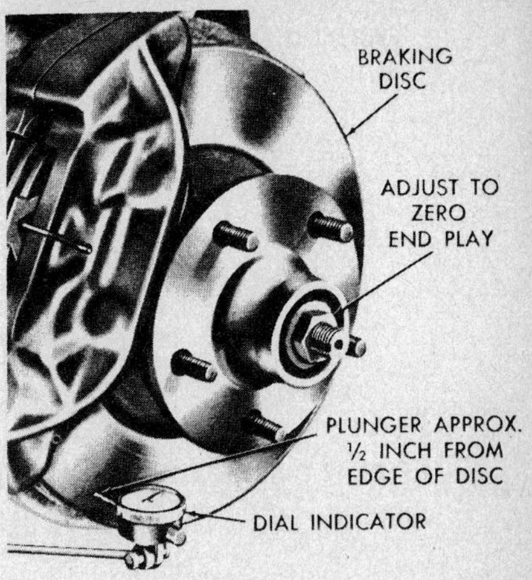
BRAKING DISC
ADJUST TO ZERO END PLAY
PLUNGER APPROX. ½ INCH FROM EDGE OF DISC
DIAL INDICATOR

Checking disc runout
(© Chrysler Corp)

To check lateral runout:

1. Tighten the spindle nut until there is no end-play in the bearings, just loose enough to allow wheel to turn.
2. Fasten a dial indicator to the suspension so that the point contacts the disc face about ½ in. from the outer edge.
3. Set the dial to zero. Turn the disc through one complete revolution and check the indicator as the disc moves.

If the runout is more than the allowable maximum the disc and hub assembly should be replaced. Be sure to readjust the spindle nut if its setting was changed while checking the disc.

Parallelism

Parallelism refers to the variations in thickness of the disc. Excessive variation can cause pedal vibration and front end vibration during braking. Parallelism can be checked by measuring thickness at four or more equally spaced points around the braking surface of the disc. All measurements must be made at the same distance from the outer edge of the disc. The disc and hub should be replaced if variations in thickness exceed specification. Do not forget to adjust the spindle nut to specification if its setting was changed while checking the disc.

Hydraulic Cylinders and Valves

Master Cylinders

Dual master cylinders, commonly in use since 1967, are actually two single master cylinders operating in the same bore. They are designed so that the front and rear brakes have separate hydraulic systems. Malfunction in either system has no effect on the other system but is immediately evident to the driver because of the additional pedal travel required to actuate the remaining half of the brake system. Service procedure for single master cylinders is identical, except that there is only one piston assembly and no stop screw. Some master cylinders have bleed screws on the outlet flanges and may be bled without disturbing the wheel cylinders.

Servicing Master Cylinders

1. Remove the cylinder from the car and drain the brake fluid.

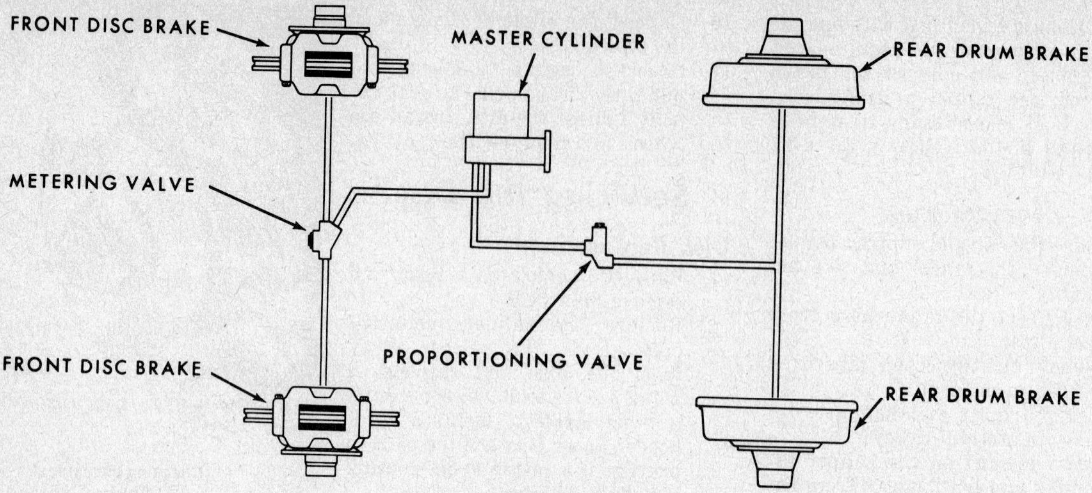
FRONT DISC BRAKE
MASTER CYLINDER
REAR DRUM BRAKE
METERING VALVE
PROPORTIONING VALVE
FRONT DISC BRAKE
REAR DRUM BRAKE

Disc brake hydraulic system

2. Mount the cylinder in a vise so that the outlets are up and remove the seal from the hub.
3. Remove the stop screw from the bottom of the front reservoir.
4. Remove the snap-ring from the front of the bore and remove the primary piston assembly.
5. Remove the secondary piston assembly using compressed air or a piece of wire. Cover the bore opening with a cloth to prevent damage to the piston.
6. Clean metal parts in brake fluid and discard rubber parts.
7. Inspect the bore for damage or wear, and check pistons for damage and proper clearance in the bore.
8. If the bore is only slightly scored or pitted it may be honed. Always use hones that are in good condition and completely clean the cylinder with brake fluid when honing is completed. If any evidence of contamination exists in the master cylinder the entire hydraulic system should be flushed and refilled with clean brake fluid. Blow out passages with compressed air.
9. Install new secondary seals in the two grooves in the flat end of the front piston. The lips of the seals will be facing away from each other.
10. Install a new primary seal and the seal protector on opposite end of the front piston with the lips of the seal facing outward.
11. Coat the seals with brake fluid. Install the spring on the front piston with the spring retainer in the primary seal.
12. Insert the piston assembly, spring end first, into the bore and use a wooden rod to seat it.
13. Coat the rear piston seals with brake fluid and install them into the piston grooves with the lips facing the spring end.
14. Assemble the spring onto the piston and install the assembly into the bore spring first. Install the snap-ring.
15. Hold the piston train at the bottom of the bore and install the stop screw. Install a new seal on the hub. Bench-bleed the cylinder or install and bleed the cylinder on the car.

Wheel Cylinders

Servicing Wheel Cylinders

1. Raise the vehicle on a hoist and remove the wheel and drum from the brake to be serviced.
2. Remove the brake shoes and clean the backing plate and wheel cylinder.
3. Disconnect the brake line from the brake hose. Remove the brake hose retainer clip at the frame bracket and remove the hose from the wheel cylinder. (On rear brakes it will only be necessary to remove the line from the cylinder.)
4. Remove the cylinder mounting bolts and remove the cylinder.
5. Remove the boots from the cylinder ends and discard. Remove the pistons, remove and discard the seal cups, and remove the ex-

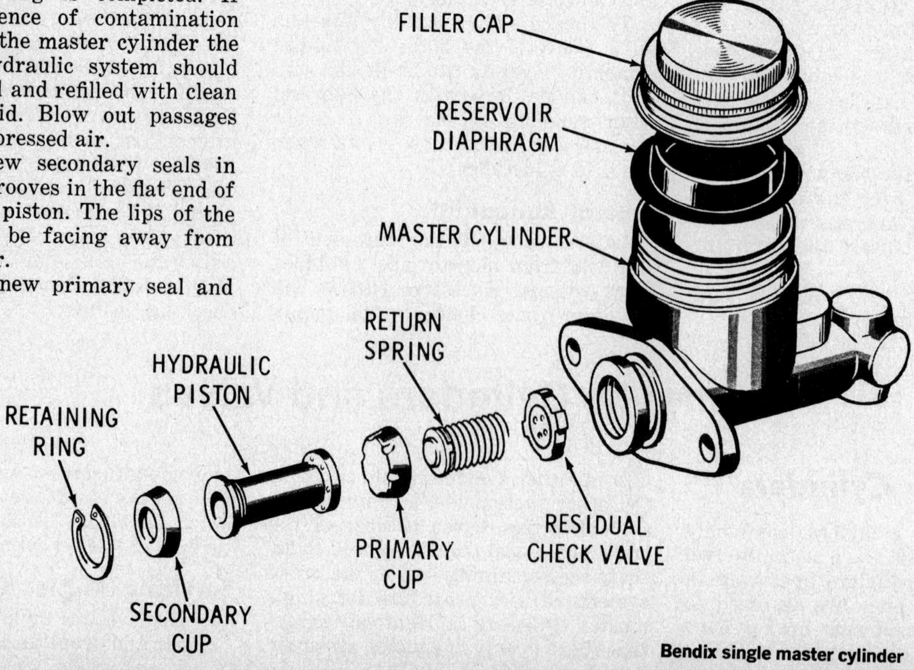
FILLER CAP
RESERVOIR DIAPHRAGM
MASTER CYLINDER
RETURN SPRING
HYDRAULIC PISTON
RETAINING RING
RESIDUAL CHECK VALVE
PRIMARY CUP
SECONDARY CUP

Bendix single master cylinder

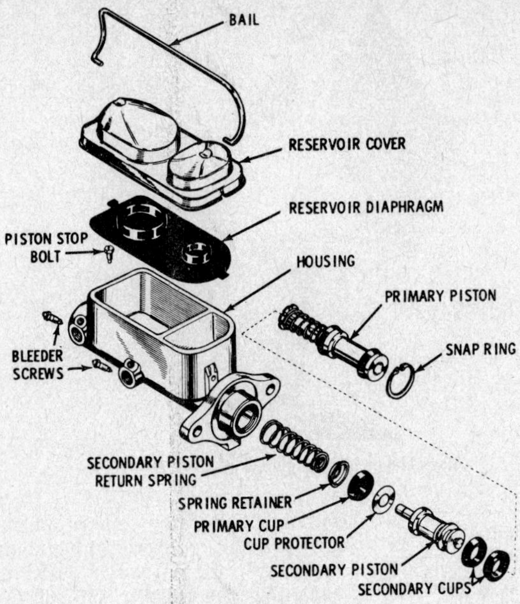
BAIL
RESERVOIR COVER
RESERVOIR DIAPHRAGM
PISTON STOP BOLT
HOUSING
PRIMARY PISTON
SNAP RING
BLEEDER SCREWS
SECONDARY PISTON RETURN SPRING
SPRING RETAINER
PRIMARY CUP
CUP PROTECTOR
SECONDARY PISTON
SECONDARY CUPS

Bendix dual master cylinder
(© Oldsmobile Div., G.M. Corp)

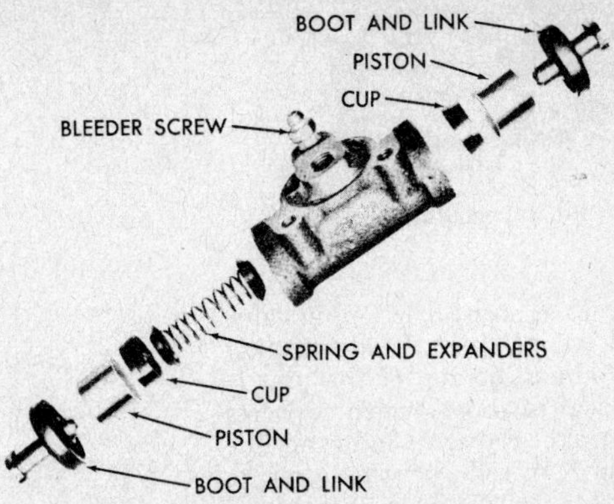
BOOT AND LINK
PISTON
CUP
BLEEDER SCREW
SPRING AND EXPANDERS
CUP
PISTON
BOOT AND LINK

Wheel cylinder
(© Chevrolet Div., G.M. Corp)

panders and spring.

6. Inspect the bore and pistons for damage or wear. Damaged pistons should be discarded, as they cannot be reconditioned. Slight bore roughness can be removed using a brake cylinder hone or crocus cloth. (Cloth should be rotated in the bore under finger pressure. Do not slide lengthwise). Use only lint-free cloth for cleaning.
7. Clean the cylinder and internal parts *using only brake fluid or denatured alcohol.*
8. Insert the spring expander assembly. Lubricate all rubber parts using only fresh brake fluid.
9. Install new cups with the seal lips facing inwards.
10. Install the pistons and rubber boots. Install the cylinder on the car in reverse order of removal. Bleed the cylinder (see Brake Bleeding).

Proportioning Valves

On vehicles equipped with front disc and rear drum brakes a proportioning valve is an important part of the system. It is installed in the hydraulic line to the rear brakes. Its function is to maintain the correct proportion between line pressures to the front and rear brakes. It prevents early lock-up of rear brakes and provides balanced braking during hard stops. *No attempt at adjustment of this valve should be made, as adjustment is pre-set and tampering will result in uneven braking action.*

To assure correct installation when replacing the valve, the outlet to the rear brakes is stamped with the letter "R". Replacement is a simple job requiring no special instructions.

Beginning with 1971 models, General Motors and American Motors installed a combination valve on their front disc (rear drum) brake cars. This valve combines in one unit, a

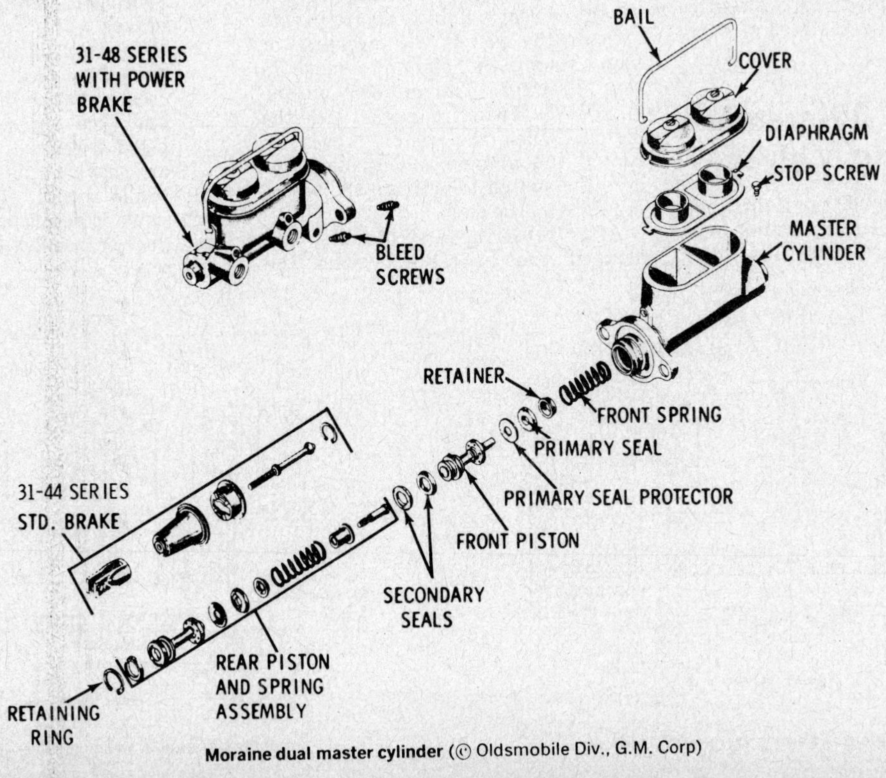
31-48 SERIES WITH POWER BRAKE
BLEED SCREWS
BAIL
COVER
DIAPHRAGM
STOP SCREW
MASTER CYLINDER
RETAINER
FRONT SPRING
PRIMARY SEAL
PRIMARY SEAL PROTECTOR
FRONT PISTON
31-44 SERIES STD. BRAKE
SECONDARY SEALS
REAR PISTON AND SPRING ASSEMBLY
RETAINING RING

Moraine dual master cylinder (© Oldsmobile Div., G.M. Corp)

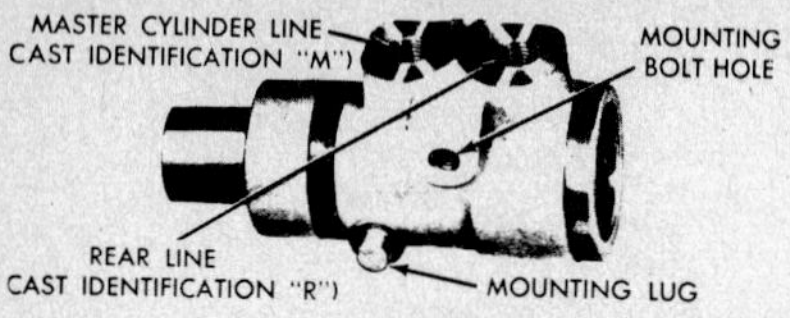
MASTER CYLINDER LINE
CAST IDENTIFICATION "M"
MOUNTING
BOLT HOLE
REAR LINE
CAST IDENTIFICATION "R"
MOUNTING LUG
Proportioning valve

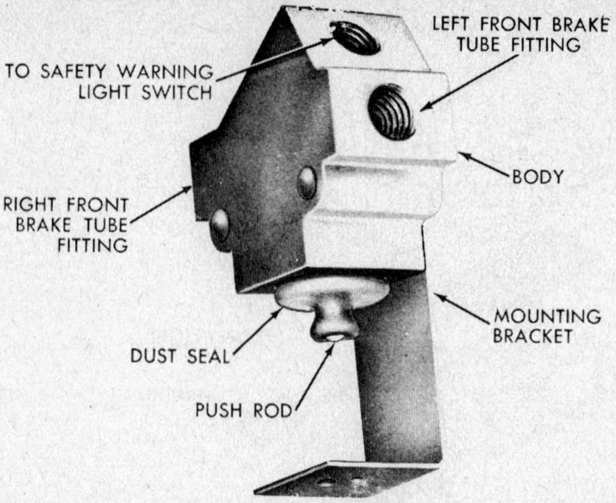
TO SAFETY WARNING
LIGHT SWITCH
LEFT FRONT BRAKE
TUBE FITTING
BODY
RIGHT FRONT
BRAKE TUBE
FITTING
MOUNTING
BRACKET
DUST SEAL
PUSH ROD
Kelsey-Hayes metering valve

metering valve, a proportioning valve and a pressure differential warning valve. Mounted on top of the unit is an electrical terminal which connects to the brake warning light on the dash. Ford introduced this unit to their cars in 1972. This unit is not serviceable and must be replaced if faulty.

Metering Valves

On some vehicles equipped with front disc brakes a metering valve is used. This valve is installed in the hydraulic line to the front brakes, and functions to delay pressure buildup to the front brakes on application. It provides balanced braking during mild stops. Its purpose is to reduce front brake pressure until rear brake pressure builds up adequately to overcome the rear brake shoe return springs. In this way disc brake pad life is extended because it prevents the front disc brakes from carrying all or most of the braking load at low operating line pressures.

The metering valve can be checked very simply. With the car stopped, gently apply the brakes. At about one inch of travel a very small change in pedal effort (like a small bump) will be felt if the valve is operating properly. Metering valves are not serviceable, and must be replaced if defective.

Pressure Differential Warning Valves

Since the introduction of dual master cylinders to the hydraulic brake system, a pressure differential warning signal has been added. This signal consists of a warning light on the dashboard activated by a differential pressure switch located below the master cylinder. The signal indicates a loss of fluid pressure in either the front or rear brakes, and should warn the driver that a hydraulic failure has occurred.

The pressure differential warning valve is a housing with the brake warning light switch mounted centrally on top. Directly below the switch is a bore containing a piston assembly. The piston assembly is located in the center of the bore and kept in that position by equal fluid pressure on either side. Fluid pressure is provided by two brake lines, one coming from the rear brake system and one from the front brakes. If a leak develops in either system (front or rear), fluid pressure to that side of the piston will decrease or stop causing the piston to move in that direction. The plunger on the end of the switch engages with the piston. When the piston moves off center, the plunger moves and triggers the switch to activate the warning light on the dash.

After repairing and bleeding any part of the hydraulic system the warning light may remain on due to the pressure differential valve remaining in the off-center position. To centralize the valve in 1967-69 Fords, a pressure difference (a leak) must be created in the opposite (rear or front) branch of the hydraulic system that was repaired or bled last. 1970-1973 Ford products, General Motors cars, Chrysler products and 1971-73 American Motors cars (disc brakes) have a self-centering valve. After repairs or bleeding have been performed, center the valve by applying moderate pressure on the brake pedal. This will turn out the light.

NOTE: front wheel balancing of cars equipped with disc brakes may also cause a pressure differential in the front branch of the system.

To centralize the valve on 1967-69 Fords:

1. Switch the ignition on and bleed brakes.
2. If the front brake system was repaired or bled, a leak must be created in the rear brake system and vice versa. Just open the bleed screw at one rear brake and have an assistant press the brake pedal slowly until the valve is centralized and the light goes out. Quickly close the bleed screw.

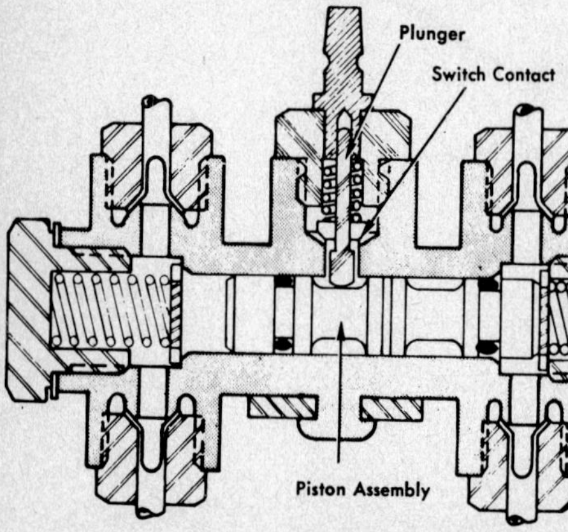
Plunger
Switch Contact
Piston Assembly
Pressure differential warning valve—ON position

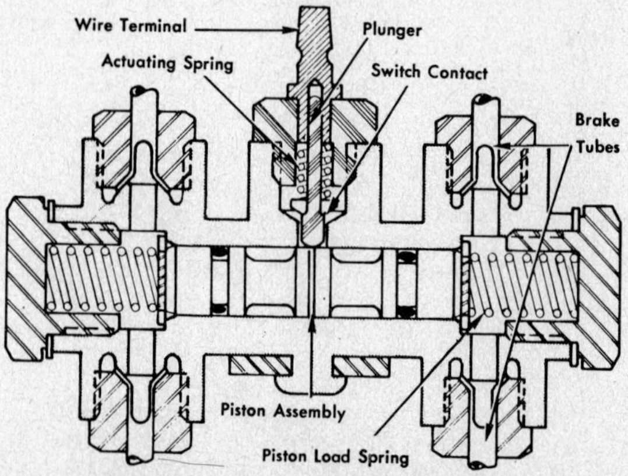
Wire Terminal
Plunger
Actuating Spring
Switch Contact
Brake
Tubes
Piston Assembly
Piston Load Spring
Pressure differential warning valve—OFF position

3. Check brake fluid level and brake pedal height and firmness. Road test the car.

To centralize the valve on 1967-1970 (drum and disc) and 1971-1973 (drum only) American Motors cars, perform the following procedure:

1. Before repairing or bleeding the brakes, disconnect the switch terminal wire and remove the nylon switch terminal, contact plunger spring, and nylon plunger with contact.
2. If the light had come on and actuated the valve, spring pressure may hold the plunger. To release the plunger, apply a small amount of brake pedal pressure.

NOTE: location of the leak can be determined by the position of the plunger in its bore. The top of the plunger will lean to the side (front or rear) which has the low pressure.

3. Make the repair and bleed the brakes. Install the spring and plunger in the valve with the contact down.
4. Install the nylon terminal and connect the warning light wire to the terminal.
5. Replace the valve assembly if any fluid leaks from the center terminal opening while removing the terminal.

IMPORTANT: the switch assembly is non-serviceable, replace if faulty.

Brake Bleeding

The purpose of bleeding brakes is to expel air trapped in the hydraulic system, and there are two methods of accomplishing this. The quickest and easiest of the two is pressure bleeding, but special pressure equipment is needed to externally pressurize the hydraulic system. The other, more commonly used method is gravity bleeding.

Gravity Bleeding Procedure

NOTE: when bleeding brakes on American Motors cars (1967-70 drum and disc, 1971-72 drum only), it is necessary to remove warning light switch terminal and plunger. For details, see Pressure Differential Warning Valves.

1. Clean the bleed screw at each wheel.
2. Attach a small rubber hose to one of the bleed screws and place the end in a container of brake fluid.
3. Top up the master cylinder with brake fluid. (Check often during bleeding). Pump up the brake pedal and hold.
4. Open the bleed screw about one-quarter turn, press the brake pedal to the floor, close the bleed screw and slowly release the pedal. Continue until no more air bubbles are forced from the cylinder on application of the brake pedal.
5. Repeat procedure on remaining wheel cylinders.

Master cylinders equipped with bleed screws may be bled independently. When bleeding the Bendix-type dual master cylinder it is necessary to solidly cap one reservoir section while bleeding the other to prevent pressure loss through the cap vent hole.

Disc brakes may be bled in the same manner as drum brakes, except that:

1. It usually requires a longer time to bleed a disc brake thoroughly.
2. The disc should be rotated to make sure that the piston has returned to the unapplied position when bleeding is completed and the bleed screw closed.

Pressure Bleeding Disc Brakes

NOTE: see NOTE under Gravity Bleeding Procedure.

Pressure bleeding disc brakes will close the metering valve and the front brakes will not bleed. For this reason it is necessary to manually hold the metering valve open during pressure bleeding. Never use a block or clamp to hold the valve open, and never force the valve stem beyond its normal position. Two different types of valves are used. The most common type requires the valve stem to be held in while bleeding the brakes, while the second type requires the valve stem to be held out (.060 in. minimum travel). Determine the type by visual inspection.

Power Brakes

The following items are in addition to those listed under non-power brakes. Check those items first.

Dragging Brakes

(Refer to non-power brakes first)

1. Excessive hydraulic seal friction or binding.
2. Compensator port plugged.
3. Sticking valve plunger.
4. Improper booster pushrod length.
5. Fluid return lines blocked.
6. Valve sleeve not properly positioned or staked.

Grabbing Brakes

(Refer to non-power brakes first)

1. Sticking actuating valve.
2. Broken plunger stem.

Hard Pedal

(Refer to non-power brakes first)

1. Faulty vacuum check valve.
2. Collapsed or leaking vacuum hose.
3. Plugged vacuum fittings.
4. Leaking vacuum chamber.
5. Diaphragm assembly out of place.
6. Vacuum leak in forward vacuum housing.

Pedal Goes to Floor (or Excessively Low)

(Refer to non-power brakes first)

1. Shoe (s) hanging at backing plate.
2. Broken plunger stem.
3. Self-adjusters not operating.

Overhaul

Due to complex repair procedure and the need for special tools, it is suggested that the unit be replaced with a new or rebuilt unit or be taken to a shop with adequate facilities.

INDEX

Manual Steering

GEAR APPLICATION INDEX

Listed below are the five different types of steering gears and the make of car each is used in. Section numbers refer to the text sections that cover that particular type of steering gear.

Gear Type	Section	Make	Year
A	2	American Motors Corp., American	1967
B	3	Ford Motor Co. and Lincoln-Mercury Division All models except Pinto, Lincoln Continental, Continental Mark III, Thunderbird.	1967–74
C	4	General Motors Corp., All models	1967–74
		American Motors Corp., All models except American	1967–74
D	5	Chrysler Corp., All models	1967–74
E	6	Ford Motor Co., Pinto	1971–74

Gear Types

A Gemmer worm and double roller tooth with screw adjusted mesh
B Ford steering gear, recirculating ball
C Saginaw steering gear, recirculating ball
D Chrysler steering gear, recirculating ball
E Rack and pinion steering gear

Section Page Numbers

Manual Steering

Manual Steering Diagnosis

Condition	Possible Cause	Correction
Hard steering	(a) Low or uneven tire pressure.	(a) Inflate tires to recommended pressures.
	(b) Insufficient lubricant in the steering gear housing or in steering linkage.	(b) Lubricate as necessary.
	(c) Steering gear shaft adjusted too tight.	(c) Adjust according to instructions.
	(d) Front wheels out of line.	(d) Align the wheels. See the Front Suspension Section.
	(e) Steering column misaligned.	(e) See the Car Section for alignment procedures.
Excessive play or looseness in the steering wheel	(a) Steering gear shaft adjusted too loose or badly worn.	(a) Replace worn parts and adjust according to instructions.
	(b) Steering linkage loose or worn.	(b) Replace worn parts. See the Front Wheel Alignment Section.
	(c) Front wheel bearings improperly adjusted.	(c) Adjust according to instructions.
	(d) Steering arm loose on steering gear shaft.	(d) Inspect for damage to the gear shaft and steering arm, replace parts as necessary.
	(e) Steering gear housing attaching bolts loose.	(e) Tighten attaching bolts to specifications.
	(f) Steering arms loose at steering knuckles.	(f) Tighten according to specifications.
	(g) Worn ball joints.	(g) Replace the ball joints as necessary. See the Front Suspension Section.
	(h) Worm shaft bearing adjustment too loose.	(h) Adjust worm bearing preload according to instructions.

Section 1
Steering Gear Alignment

Before any steering gear adjustments are made, it is recommended that the front end of the car be raised and a thorough inspection be made for stiffness or lost motion in the steering gear, steering linkage and front suspension. Worn or damaged parts should be replaced, since a satisfactory adjustment of the steering gear cannot be obtained if bent or badly worn parts exist.

It is also very important that the steering gear be properly aligned in the car. Misalignment of the gear places a stress on the steering worm shaft, therefore a proper adjustment is impossible. To align the steering gear, loosen the mounting bolts to permit the gear to align itself. Check the steering gear mounting seat, and if there is a gap at any of the mounting bolts, proper alignment may be obtained by placing shims where excessive gap appears. Tighten the steering gear bolts. Alignment of the gear in the car is very important and should be done carefully so that a satisfactory, trouble-free gear adjustment may be obtained.

Section 2
Gemmer Worm and Double Roller Tooth Type With Screw Adjusted Mesh

The steering gear is of the worm and roller type with a 24 to 1 gear ratio. The cross-shaft is straddle mounted with a bearing surface at the top and bottom points of the shaft mounting areas. The three tooth cross-shaft roller is mounted in ball bearings. The proper lubricant used in the gear box is S.A.E. 90 Extreme Pressure Lubricant.

The external adjustments given below will remove all play from the steering gear. Before doing these adjustments, refer to Section 1 to insure that the steering gear requires adjustment.

Worm Bearing Adjustment

1. Turn the steering wheel about one full turn from straight ahead and secure it so it doesn't move.
2. Determine if there is any worm gear end-play by shaking the front wheel sideways and noting if there is any end movement that may be felt between the steering wheel hub and the steering jacket tube. *Be sure any movement noted is not looseness in the steering jacket tube.*
3. If end-play is present, adjust the worm bearings by loosening the four cover cap screws about 1/8 in. Separate the top shim, using a knife blade, and remove it. Do not damage the remaining shims or gaskets.
4. Replace the cover and recheck the end-play again. If necessary, repeat steps 2 and 3 until the end-play movement is as small as possible without tightening the steering gear too much.

NOTE: adjustment may be done with the pitman arm disconnected. With the steering wheel turned about one full turn from straight ahead, using the Spring Scale, adjust with the shims as given above until the spring scale pull is between 1/4 and 5/8 lbs.

NOTE: torque wrench calibrated in in. lbs. may be used instead of spring scale.

Cross-Shaft Roller and Worm Mesh Adjustment

1. Turn the steering wheel to the middle of its turning limits with

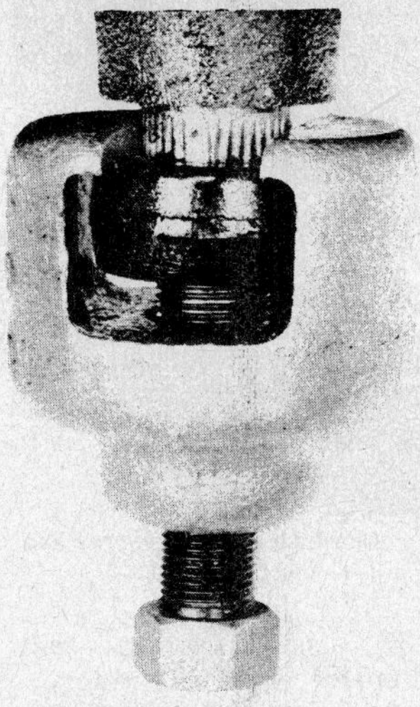

Removing pitman arm
(© American Motors Corp)

the pitman arm disconnected. The steering gear roller should be on the worm high spot.

2. Shake the pitman arm sideways to determine the amount of clearance between the worm cross-shaft roller. Movement of more than 1/32 in. indicates the roller and worm mesh must be adjusted.
3. Loosen the adjusting screw lock nut and tighten the external cross-shaft adjusting screw a small amount. Recheck the clearance by shaking the pitman arm. Repeat until the clearance is correct. *Do not overtighten.*

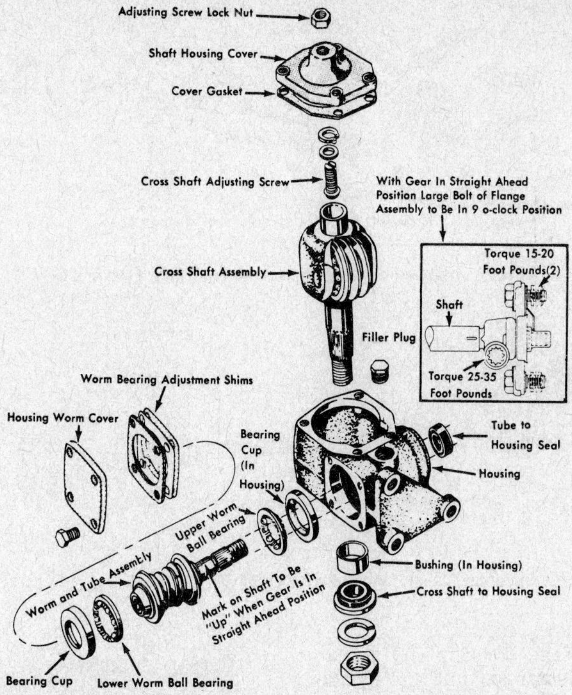
Adjusting Screw Lock Nut
Shaft Housing Cover
Cover Gasket
Cross Shaft Adjusting Screw
With Gear In Straight Ahead Position Large Bolt of Flange Assembly to Be In 9 o-clock Position
Torque 15-20 Foot Pounds(2)
Shaft
Torque 25-35 Foot Pounds
Cross Shaft Assembly
Filler Plug
Worm Bearing Adjustment Shims
Housing Worm Cover
Bearing Cup (In Housing)
Tube to Housing Seal
Housing
Upper Worm Ball Bearing
Worm and Tube Assembly
Mark on Shaft To Be "Up" When Gear Is In Straight Ahead Position
Bushing (In Housing)
Cross Shaft to Housing Seal
Bearing Cup
Lower Worm Ball Bearing

Gemmer worm and double roller tooth type steering gear
(© American Motors Corp)

NOTE: the cross-shaft roller and worm mesh adjustment may be done, using Spring Scale, by measuring the amount of wheel pull as the external cross-shaft adjusting screw is tightened. When the spring scale pull is between 7/8 and 1 1/8 lbs. through the high spot the adjustment is correct.

4. Tighten the pitman arm attaching nut to 100-125 ft. lbs. and center punch at threads to insure retention. The steering wheel nut (if loosened) should be tightened to 15-20 ft. lbs.

Section 3
Ford Steering Gear—Recirculating Ball Type

Steering Worm and Sector Gear Adjustments

The ball nut assembly and the sector gear must be adjusted properly to maintain a minimum amount of steering shaft end-play and a minimum amount of backlash between the sector gear and the ball nut. There are only two adjustments that may be done on this steering gear and they should be done as given below:

1. Disconnect the pitman arm from the steering pitman-to-idler arm rod.
2. Loosen the locknut on the sector shaft adjustment screw and turn the adjusting screw counterclockwise.
3. Measure the worm bearing preload by attaching an in. lbs. torque wrench to the steering wheel nut. With the steering wheel off center, note the reading required to rotate input shaft about 1 1/2 turns either side of center. If the torque reading is not about 4-5 in. lbs., adjust the gear as given

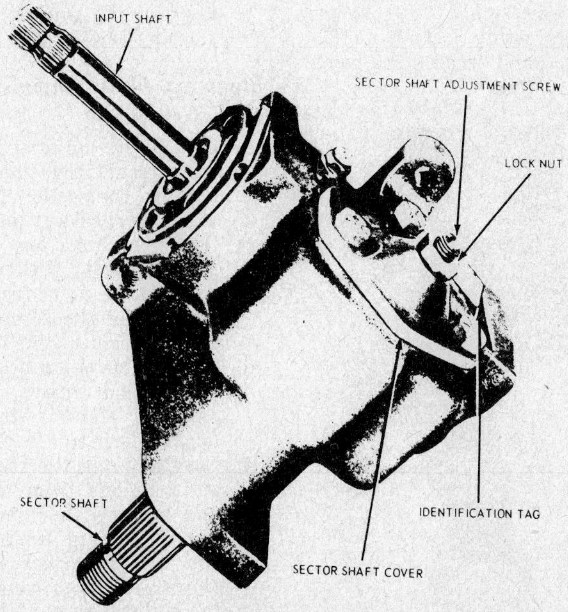
INPUT SHAFT
SECTOR SHAFT ADJUSTMENT SCREW
LOCK NUT
SECTOR SHAFT
IDENTIFICATION TAG
SECTOR SHAFT COVER

Ford manual steering gear, recirculating ball type
(© Ford Motor Co)

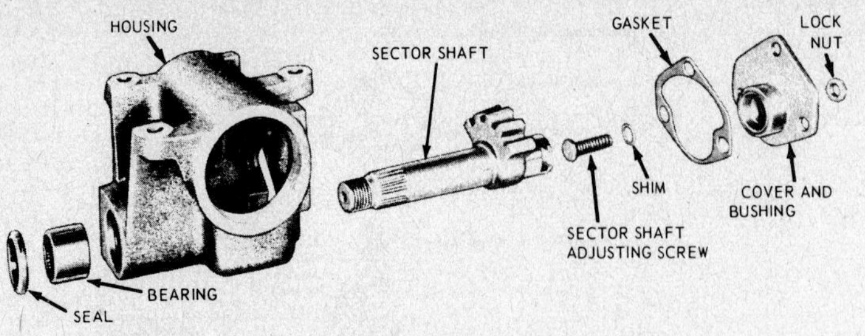
HOUSING
SECTOR SHAFT
GASKET
LOCK NUT
SHIM
COVER AND BUSHING
SECTOR SHAFT ADJUSTING SCREW
BEARING
SEAL

Sector shaft and housing disassembled (© Ford Motor Co)

Inch-Pound Torque Wrench

Checking steering gear preload
(© Ford Motor Co)

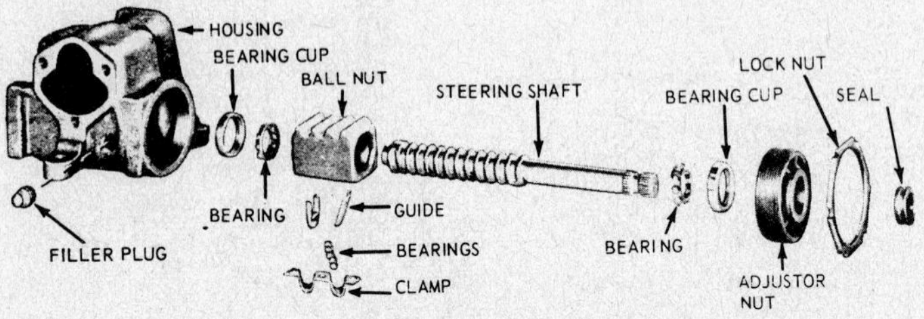
HOUSING
BEARING CUP
BALL NUT
STEERING SHAFT
LOCK NUT
BEARING CUP
SEAL
BEARING
GUIDE
BEARINGS
CLAMP
BEARING
ADJUSTOR NUT
FILLER PLUG

Steering shaft, ball nut, and bearings disassembled (© Ford Motor Co)

in the next step.

4. Loosen the steering shaft bearing adjuster locknut and tighten or back off the bearing adjusting screw until the preload is within the specified limits.
5. Tighten the steering shaft bearing adjuster locknut, and recheck the preload torque.
6. Turn the steering wheel slowly to either stop. Turn *gently* against the stop to avoid possible damage to the ball return guides. Then rotate the wheel 2¾ turns to center the ball nut.
7. Turn the sector adjusting screw clockwise until the proper torque (9-10 in. lbs.) is obtained that is necessary to rotate the worm gear past its center (high spot).
8. While holding the sector adjusting screw, tighten the sector screw adjusting locknut to 32-40 ft. lbs. and recheck the backlash adjustment.

Removing pitman arm
(© Ford Motor Co)

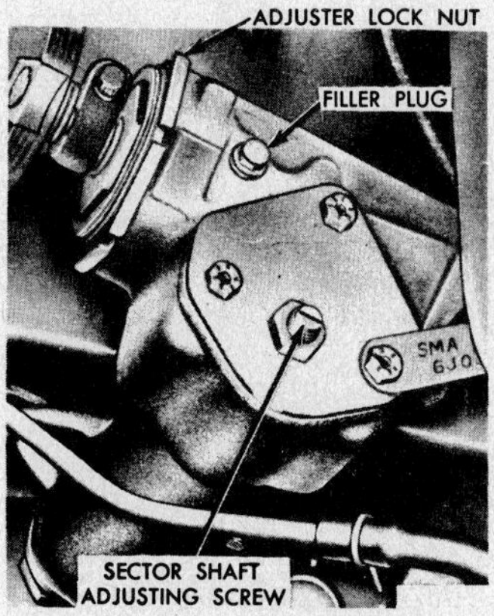
ADJUSTER LOCK NUT
FILLER PLUG
SECTOR SHAFT ADJUSTING SCREW

Steering gear adjustments
(© Ford Motor Co)

9. Connect the pitman arm to the steering arm-to-idler arm rod.

Steering Gear Disassembly and Assembly

1. Rotate the steering shaft three turns from either stop.
2. Remove the sector shaft adjusting screw locknut and the housing cover bolts and remove the sector shaft with the cover. Remove the cover from the shaft by turning the screw clockwise. *Keep the shim with the screw.*
3. Loosen the worm bearing adjuster nut and remove the adjuster assembly and the steering shaft upper bearing.
4. Carefully pull the steering shaft and ball nut from the housing, and remove the steering shaft lower bearing. *Do not run the ball nut to either end of the worm gear to prevent damaging the ball return guides. Disassemble the ball nut only if there are signs of binding or tightness.*
5. To disassemble the ball nut, remove the ball return guide clamp and the ball return guides from the ball nut. *Keep ball nut clamp side up until ready to remove the ball bearings.*
6. Turn the ball nut over and rotate the worm shaft from side to side until all the balls have dropped out into a clean pan. With all balls removed, the ball nut will slide off the wormshaft.
7. Remove the upper bearing cup from the bearing adjuster and the lower cup from the housing. It may be necessary to tap the housing or the adjuster on a wooden block to jar the bearing cups loose.
8. If the inspection shows bearing damage, the sector shaft bearing and the oil seal should be pressed out.
9. If the sector shaft bearing and oil seal have been removed, press a new bearing and oil seal into the housing. Do not clean, wash, or soak seals in cleaning solvent. Apply the recommended steering gear lubricant to the housing and seals.
10. Install a bearing cup in the lower end of the housing and in the adjuster. This is a clearance fit not a press fit.
11. Install a new seal in the bearing

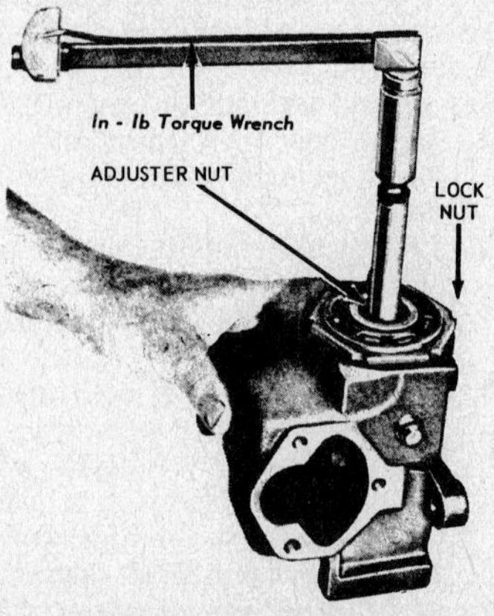
In - lb Torque Wrench
ADJUSTER NUT
LOCK NUT

Checking steering shaft bearing preload
(© Ford Motor Co)

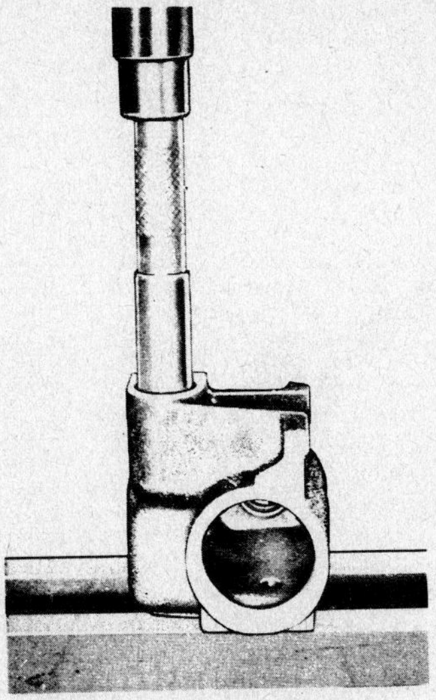

Removing oil seal and bearing
(© Ford Motor Co)

adjuster if the old seal was removed.

12. Insert the ball guides into the holes in the ball nut, lightly tapping them if necessary to seat them.
13. Insert half of the balls into the hole in the top of each ball guide. If necessary, rotate the shaft slightly to distribute the balls evenly in the circuit.
14. Install the ball guide clamp, tightening the screws to 42 in. lbs. Check that the worm shaft rotates freely.
15. Coat the threads of the steering shaft bearing adjuster, the housing cover bolts, and the sector adjusting screw with a suitable oil-resistant sealing compound. Do not apply sealer to female threads. *Do not get sealer on the steering shaft bearings.*
16. Coat the worm bearings, sector shaft bearings, and gear teeth with steering gear lubricant.
17. Clamp the housing in a vise, with the sector shaft axis horizontal, and place the steering shaft lower bearing in its cup. Place the steering shaft and ball nut assemblies in the housing.
18. Position the steering shaft upper bearing on top of the worm gear and install the steering shaft bearing adjuster, adjuster nut, and the bearing cup. Leave the nut loose.
19. Adjust the worm bearing preload according to the instructions given earlier.
20. Position the sector adjusting screw and adjuster shim, and check for a clearance of not more than 0.002 in. between the screw head and the end of the sector shaft. If the clearance exceeds 0.002 in., add enough shims to reduce the clearance to under 0.002 in. clearance.
21. Start the sector shaft adjusting screw into the housing cover. Install a new gasket on the cover.
22. Rotate the steering shaft until the ball nut teeth mesh with the sector gear teeth, tilting the housing so the ball will tip toward the housing cover opening.
23. Lubricate the sector shaft journal and install the sector shaft and cover. With the cover moved to one side, fill the gear with steering gear lubricant (0.90 lb.). Push the cover and the sector shaft into place, and install the two top housing bolts. Do not tighten the bolts until checking to see that there is some lash between the ball nut and the sector gear teeth. Hold or push the cover away from the ball nut and tighten the bolts to 30-40 ft-lbs.
24. Loosely install the sector shaft adjusting screw locknut and adjust the sector shaft mesh load as given earlier. Tighten the adjusting screw locknut.

Section 4
Saginaw Recirculating Ball Type

The steering gear is of the recirculating ball nut type. The ball nut, mounted on the worm gear, is driven by means of steel balls which circulate in helical grooves in both the worm and nut. Ball return guides attached to the nut serve to recirculate the two sets of balls in the grooves. As the steering wheel is turned to the right, the ball nut moves upward. When the wheel is turned to the left, the ball nut moves downward.

The sector teeth on the pinion shaft and the ball nut are designed so that they fit the tightest when the steering wheel is straight ahead. This mesh action is adjusted by an adjusting screw which moves the pinion shaft endwise until the teeth mesh properly. The worm bearing adjuster provides proper preloading of the upper and lower bearings.

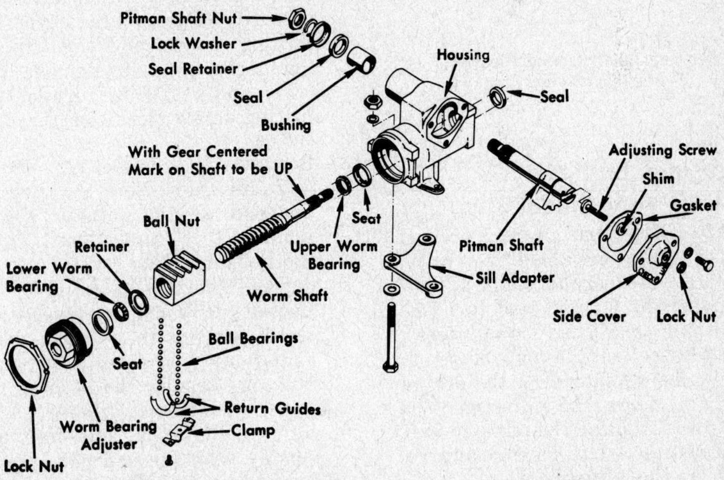
Pitman Shaft Nut
Lock Washer
Seal Retainer
Seal
Bushing
Housing
Seal
With Gear Centered
Mark on Shaft to be UP
Adjusting Screw
Shim
Gasket
Seat
Ball Nut
Retainer
Lower Worm
Bearing
Upper Worm
Bearing
Pitman Shaft
Sill Adapter
Worm Shaft
Side Cover
Lock Nut
Ball Bearings
Seat
Return Guides
Clamp
Worm Bearing
Adjuster
Lock Nut

Saginaw steering gear, recirculating ball type (© American Motors Corp)

Before doing the adjustment procedures given below, refer to Section 1 to ensure that the steering problem is not caused by faulty suspension components, bad front end alignment, etc. Then, proceed with the following adjustments.

Worm Bearing Preload Adjustment

Caution Do not turn steering wheel hard against stops as damage to ball nut assembly may result.

1. Disconnect the ball stud from the pitman arm, and retighten the pitman arm nut.
2. Loosen the pitman shaft adjusting screw locknut and back off adjusting screw a few turns.
3. Attach Spring Scale to the steering wheel and measure the pull needed to move the steering wheel when off the high point. The pull should be between 1/8 and 3/8 lb.
4. To adjust the worm bearing, loosen the worm bearing adjuster locknut with a brass drift and turn the adjuster screw until the proper pull is obtained. When adjustment is correct, tighten the adjuster locknut, and recheck with the spring scale again.

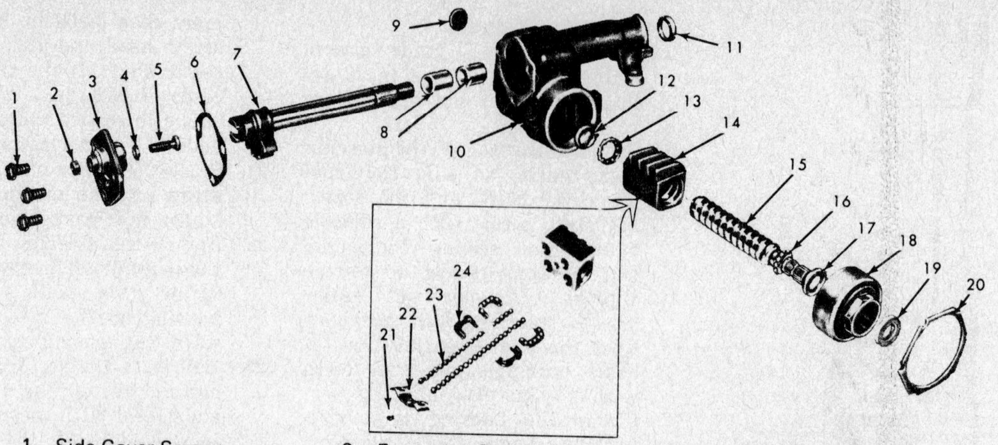
1
2
3
4
5
6
7
8
9
10
11
12
13
14
15
16
17
18
19
20
21
22
23
24

1. Side Cover Screws
2. Lash Adjuster Locknut
3. Side Cover and Bushing
4. Lash Adjuster Shim
5. Lash Adjuster Screw
6. Side Cover Gasket
7. Pitman Shaft
8. Pitman Shaft Bushings
9. Expansion Plug
10. Steering Gear Housing
11. Pitman Shaft Seal
12. Worm Bearing Race—Lower
13. Worm Bearing—Lower
14. Ball Nut
15. Wormshaft
16. Worm Bearing—Upper
17. Worm Bearing Race—Upper
18. Adjuster Plug
19. Wormshaft Seal
20. Adjuster Plug Locknut
21. Clamp Screw
22. Ball Guide Clamp
23. Balls
24 Ball Guides

Corvette steering gear, recirculating ball type (© G.M. Corp)

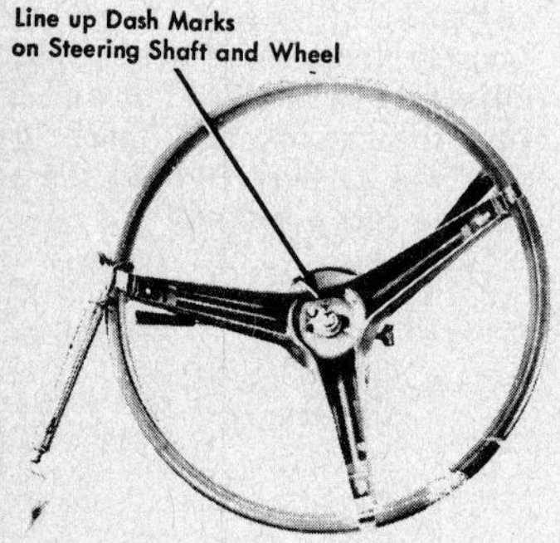
Line up Dash Marks
on Steering Shaft and Wheel

Checking pull at steering wheel rim
(© American Motors Corp)

Sector and Ball Nut Backlash Adjustment

1. After the worm bearing preload has been adjusted correctly, loosen the pitman shaft adjusting screw locknut and turn the pitman shaft adjusting screw clockwise until a pull of 3/4 to 1 1/8 lbs. is shown on the spring scale. When the adjustment is correct, tighten the pitman shaft adjusting screw locknut and recheck the adjustment.

NOTE: a torque wrench calibrated in in. lbs. may be substituted for the spring scale in adjusting steering gear.

2. Turn the steering wheel to the center of its turning limits (pitman arm disconnected). If the steering wheel is removed, the mark on the steering shaft should be at top center.
3. Connect the ball stud to the pitman arm, tightening the attaching nut to 115 ft. lbs. (Vega—93 ft. lbs.).

Steering Gear Disassembly and Assembly

1. After removing the steering gear from the car, place the steering gear assembly in a bench vise.

NOTE: worm seal may be replaced without disassembling gear. Be careful not to damage shaft or housing when removing seal.

2. Rotate the worm shaft until it is centered with the mark facing upward. Remove three cover attaching screws and the adjusting screw locknut. Remove the cover and gasket by turning adjusting screw clockwise through the cover.
3. Remove the adjusting screw with its shim from the slot in the end of the pitman shaft. Remove the pitman shaft from the housing being careful not to damage the seal in the housing.
4. Loosen the worm bearing adjuster locknut with a brass drift and remove the adjuster and bearing. Remove the bearing retainer with a screwdriver.
5. Remove the worm and shaft assembly with the ball nut assembly and bearing. Remove the ball nut return guide clamp by removing screws. Remove the guides, turn ball nut over, and remove the steel balls by rotating the shaft from side to side. After all steel balls have been removed, take the ball nut off the worm shaft.
6. Clean all parts in solvent. Inspect all bearings, bearing cups, bushings, seals, worm groove, and gear teeth for signs of wear, scoring, pitting, etc. If the pitman shaft bushings or seal, steering shaft seal, or upper and lower bearing cups need replacement, see the replacement procedures given below.
7. Remove the pitman shaft seal with a screwdriver or punch. If there is leakage around the threads of the bearing adjuster, apply a non-hardening sealer.
8. Remove faulty bushings from the pitman shaft with Puller and Slide Hammer. Install new bushings, seating the inner end of the bushing flush with the inside surface of the housing.
9. Remove the steering shaft seal with a punch or screwdriver. Tap new seal in place, using a section of tubing to seat the seal.
10. Remove the upper or lower bearing cup from the worm bearing adjuster or steering gear housing using Puller and Slide Hammer. Install the new bearing cups.
11. Lubricate all seals, bushings, and bearings before installing into the steering gear assembly.
12. Position the ball nut on the worm shaft. Install the steel balls in the return guides and the ball nut, placing an equal number in each circuit of the ball nut. Install the return guide clamp and screws.

Caution do not rotate the worm shaft while installing

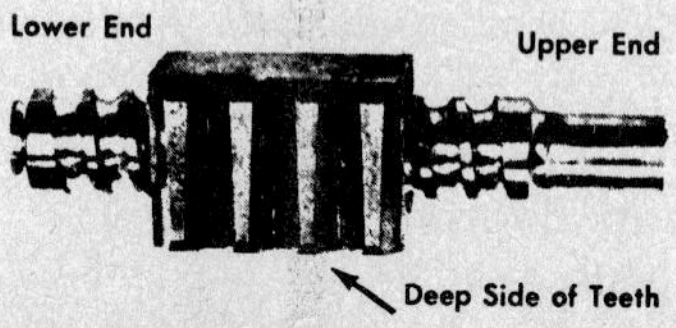
Lower End
Upper End
Deep Side of Teeth

Ball nut properly installed on worm shaft
(© American Motors Corp)

the steel balls since the balls may enter the crossover passage between the circuits, causing incorrect operation of the ball nut.

13. Place bearing on shaft above the worm gear, center ball nut on worm gear; then, slide the steering shaft, bearing, and ball nut into the housing. *Do not damage the steering shaft seal in the housing.*
14. Place the bearing in the worm adjuster, install the bearing retainer, and install the adjuster and locknut on the housing, tightening it just enough to hold the bearing in place.
15. Install the pitman shaft adjusting screw and selective shim in the pitman shaft. Be sure there is no more than 0.002 in. of end play of the screw in the slot. If the end-play is more than 0.002 in., install a new selective shim to get the proper clearance. Shims are available in four thicknesses: 0.063 in., 0.065 in.,

Ball Nut
Pitman Shaft Gear
Shim
Adjusting Screw

Positioning the pitman shaft and ball nut in housing
(© American Motors Corp)

0.067 in., and 0.069 in.

16. Install the pitman shaft and adjusting screw with the sector and ball nut positioned as shown.
17. Install the cover and gasket on the adjusting screw, turning screw counterclockwise until it extends through the cover from 5/8 to 3/4 in. Install the cover attaching screws and torque to 35 ft. lbs. (Vega—18 ft. lbs.).
18. Tighten the pitman shaft adjusting screw so that the teeth on the shaft and the ball nut engage but do not bind. Final adjustment must be made later.
19. Wrap the pitman shaft splines with tape to protect the seal and install the seal.
20. Fill steering gear with a good quality steering gear lubricant. Turn the steering gear from one extreme to the other to make sure it does not bind. *Do not allow the ball nut to strike the ends of the ball races on the worm gear to avoid damaging the ball return guides.*
21. Install the steering gear as described previously. Perform the final adjustments on the worm bearing preload and the sector and ball nut backlash adjustments.

Section 5
Chrysler Recirculating Ball Type Steering Gear

This steering gear is quite similar to the Saginaw recirculating ball design. The main differences are adjustment and torque specifications. Refer to the introduction in Section 4 before proceeding with the adjustments below.

Worm Bearing Pre-load Adjustment

1. Remove the steering gear arm and lockwasher, using a suitable gear puller.
2. Remove the horn button or horn ring.
3. Loosen the cross-shaft adjusting screw locknut, and back out the adjusting screw about two turns.
4. Turn the steering wheel two complete turns from the straight ahead position, and place torque wrench on the steering shaft nut.
5. Rotate the steering shaft at least one turn toward the straight ahead position while measuring the torque on the torque wrench. The torque should be between $1\frac{1}{2}$ and $4\frac{1}{2}$ in. lbs. to move the steering wheel. If torque is not

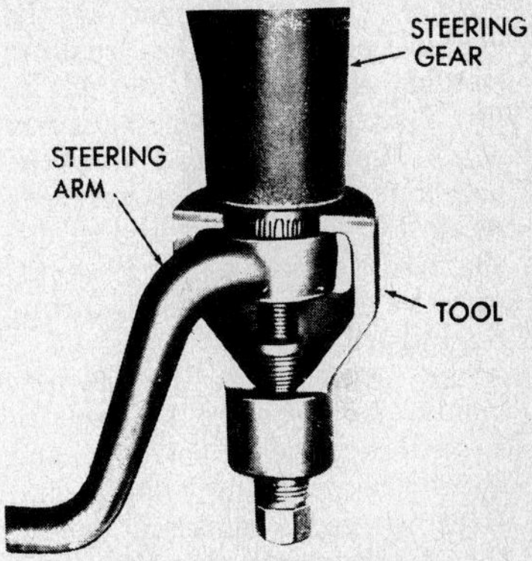
STEERING GEAR
STEERING ARM
TOOL

Removing steering gear arm
(© Chrysler Corp)

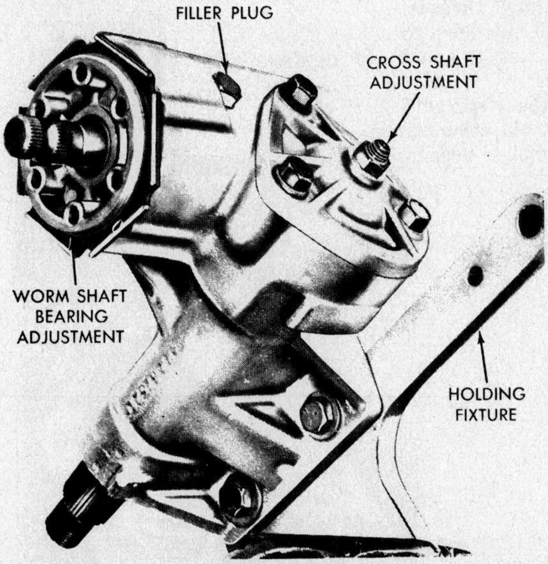
FILLER PLUG
CROSS SHAFT ADJUSTMENT
WORM SHAFT BEARING ADJUSTMENT
HOLDING FIXTURE

Steering gear adjustment locations
(© Chrysler Corp)

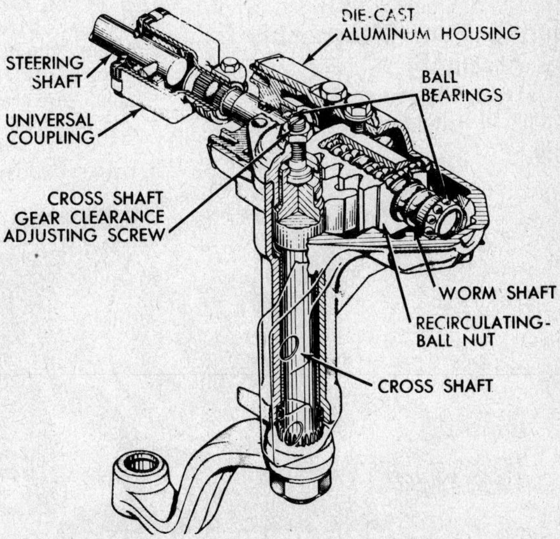
DIE-CAST ALUMINUM HOUSING
STEERING SHAFT
BALL BEARINGS
UNIVERSAL COUPLING
CROSS SHAFT GEAR CLEARANCE ADJUSTING SCREW
WORM SHAFT
RECIRCULATING-BALL NUT
CROSS SHAFT

Chrysler steering gear, recirculating ball type
(© Chrysler Corp)

within these limits, loosen the worm shaft bearing adjuster locknut and turn the adjuster clockwise to increase the preload or counterclockwise to decrease the preload. When the preload is correct, hold the adjuster screw steady and tighten the locknut. Recheck preload.

TOOL
CROSS SHAFT

Removing the cross shaft
(© Chrysler Corp)

Ball Nut Rack and Sector Mesh Adjustment

NOTE: this adjustment can be accurately made only after proper preloading of worm bearing.

1. Turn steering wheel gently from one stop to the other. counting the number of turns. Turn the steering wheel back exactly half way, to the center position.
2. Turn the cross-shaft adjusting screw clockwise to remove all lash between ball nut rack and the sector gear teeth, then tighten adjusting screw locknut to 35 ft. lbs.
3. Turn the steering wheel about ¼ turn away from the center or high spot position. With the torque wrench on the steering wheel nut measure the torque required to turn the steering wheel through the high spot at the center position. The reading should be between 8 and 11 in. lbs. This is the total of the worm shaft bearing preload and the ball nut rack and sector gear mesh load. Readjust the cross-shaft adjustment screw if necessary to obtain a correct torque reading.
4. After completing the adjustments, place the front wheels in a straight ahead position, and with the steering wheel and steering gear centered, install the steering arm on cross-shaft. Tighten the steering arm retaining nut to 180 ft. lbs.

Steering Gear Disassembly and Assembly

1. Attach the steering gear assembly to a holding fixture and put the holding fixture in a bench vise. Thoroughly clean the outside surface before disassembly.
2. Loosen the cross-shaft adjusting screw locknut, and back out the adjusting screw about two turns to relieve the mesh load between the ball nut rack and the sector gear teeth. Remove the cross-shaft seal as given in the procedure for cross-shaft seal replacement.
3. Position the steering gear worm shaft in a straight ahead position.
4. Remove the attaching bolts from the cross-shaft cover and slowly remove the cross-shaft while sliding arbor tool into the housing. Remove the locknut from the adjusting screw and remove the screw from the cover by turning it clockwise. Slide the adjustment screw and its shim out of the slot in the end of the cross-shaft.
5. Loosen the worm shaft bearing adjuster locknut with a brass drift (punch) and remove the locknut. Hold the worm shaft steady while unscrewing the adjuster. Slide the worm adjuster off the shaft.

Caution Handle the adjuster carefully to avoid damaging the aluminum threads. Also, do not run the ball nut down to either end of the worm shaft to avoid damaging the ball guides.

6. Carefully remove the worm and ball nut assembly. This assembly is serviced as a complete assembly only and is not to be disassembled or the ball return guides removed or disturbed.
7. Remove the cross-shaft needle bearing by placing the gear housing in an arbor press; insert a tool in the lower end of the housing and press both bearings through the housing.
   The cross-shaft cover assembly, including a needle bearing or bushing, is serviced as an assembly.
8. Remove the worm shaft oil seal from the worm shaft bearing adjuster by inserting a blunt punch behind the seal and tapping alternately on each side of the seal until it is driven out of the adjuster.
9. Remove the worm shaft in the same manner as that given in step 8. *Be careful not to cock the bearing cup and distort the adjuster counter bore.*
10. Remove the lower cup if necessary by placing the locking head jaws of remover tool C-3868 behind the bearing cup and expanding the remover head by pressing down on the center plunger of the tool. Pull the bearing cup out by turning the

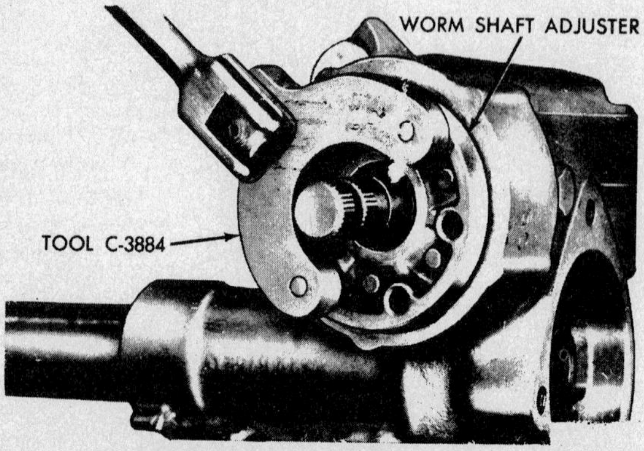
WORM SHAFT ADJUSTER
TOOL C-3884

Removing the worm shaft adjuster
(© Chrysler Corp)

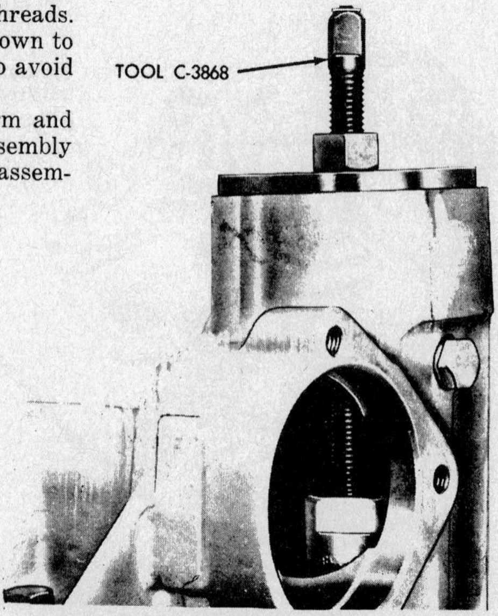
TOOL C-3868

Removing the lower bearing cup
(© Chrysler Corp)

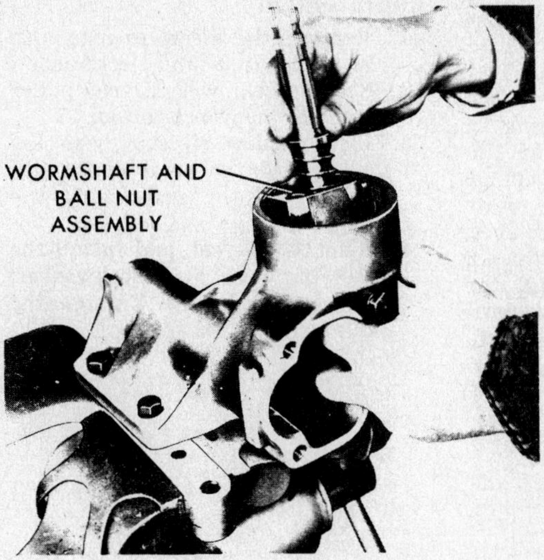
WORMSHAFT AND
BALL NUT
ASSEMBLY

Removing the worm shaft and ball nut assembly
(© Chrysler Corp)

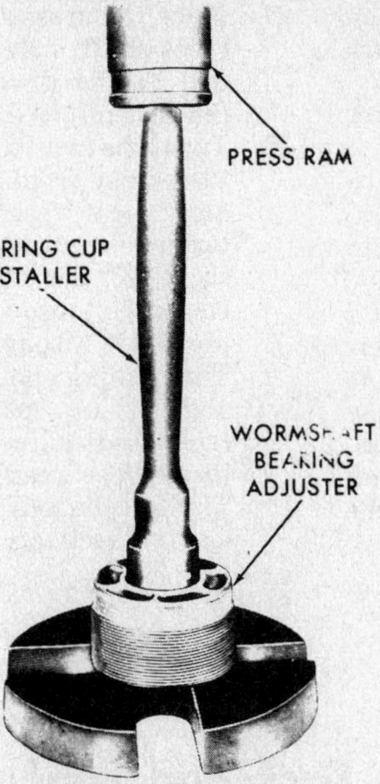
PRESS RAM
BEARING CUP
INSTALLER
WORMSHAFT
BEARING
ADJUSTER

Installing the worm shaft upper bearing cup
(© Chrysler Corp)

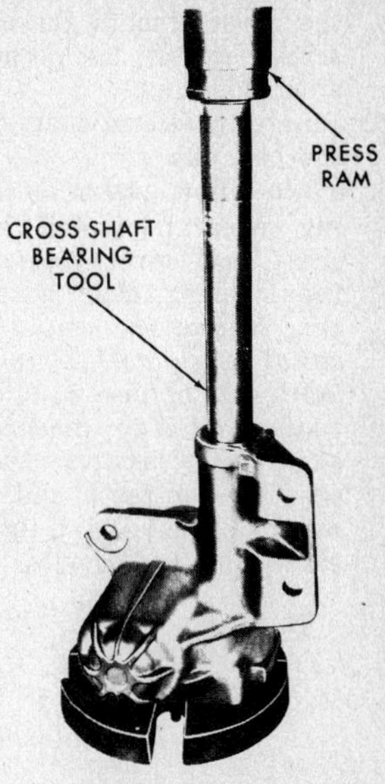
PRESS
RAM
CROSS SHAFT
BEARING
TOOL

Removing the cross shaft inner and outer bearings
(© Chrysler Corp)

remover screw clockwise while holding the center screw steady.

11. Wash all parts in clean solvent and dry thoroughly. Inspect all parts for wear, scoring, pitting, etc. Test operation of the worm shaft and ball nut assembly. If ball nut does not travel smoothly and freely on the worm shaft or if there is binding, replace the assembly.

NOTE: extreme care must be taken when handling the aluminum worm bearing adjuster to avoid thread damage. Also, be careful not to damage the threads in the gear housing. Always lubricate the worm bearing adjuster before screwing it into the housing.

12. Inspect the cross-shaft for wear and check the fit of the shaft in the housing bearings. Inspect the fit of the shaft pilot bearing in the housing. Be sure the worm shaft is not bent or damaged.
13. Install the cross-shaft outer needle bearing. Press the bearing into the housing about ½ in. below the end of the bore to leave space for the new oil seal.
14. Install the inner needle bearing in the same manner and press it into the inside end of the housing bore flush with the inside end of the bore surface.
15. Install the worm shaft bearing cups (upper and lower) by placing them and their spacers in the adjuster nut and press them into place.
16. Install the worm shaft oil seal by placing the seal in the worm shaft adjuster with the metal seal retainer up. Drive the seal into place with a suitable sleeve until it is just below the end of the bore in the adjuster.

NOTE: apply a coating of steering gear lubricant to all moving parts during assembly. Also, put lubricant on and around oil seal lips.

17. Clamp the holding fixture and housing in a bench vise with the bearing adjuster opening upward. Place a thrust bearing in the lower cup in the housing.
18. Hold the ball nut from turning and insert the worm shaft and ball nut assembly into the housing with the end of the worm shaft resting in the thrust bearing. Place the upper thrust bearing on the worm shaft. Thoroughly lubricate the threads on the adjuster and the threads in the housing.
19. Place a protective sleeve of tape over the splines on the worm shaft to avoid damaging the seal. Slide the adjuster assembly over the shaft.
20. Thread the adjuster into the housing and, with Tool wrench C-3884 and the splined nut set, tighten the adjuster to 50 ft. lbs. while rotating the worm shaft to seat the bearings.
21. Loosen the adjuster so no bearing preload exists. Tighten the adjuster for a worm shaft bearing preload of 1⅛ to 4½ in. lbs. Tighten the bearing adjuster locknut and recheck the preload.
22. Before installing the cross-shaft, pack the worm shaft cavities in the housing above and below the ball nut with steering gear lubricant. A good grade of multi-purpose lubricant may be used if steering gear lubricant is not available. *Do not use gear oil.* Pack enough lubricant into the worm cavities to cover the worm.
23. Slide the cross-shaft adjusting screw and shim into the slot in the end of the shaft. Check the end clearance for no more than 0.004 in. clearance. If the clearance is not within the limit, remove old shim and install a new shim, available in three different thicknesses, to get the proper clearance.
24. Start the cross-shaft and adjuster screw into the bearing in the housing cover. Using a screwdriver through the hole in the cover, turn the screw counterclockwise to pull the shaft into

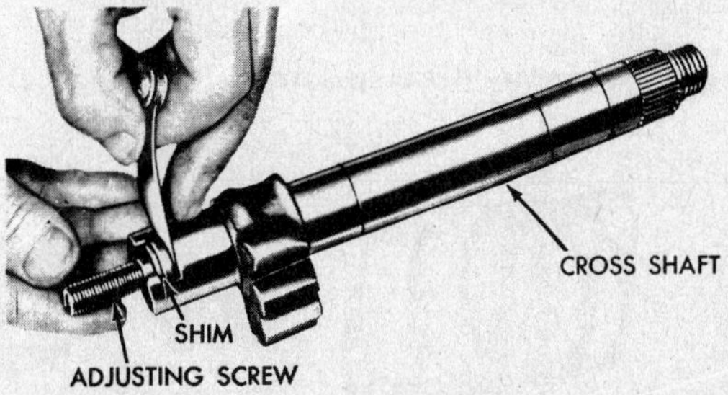
CROSS SHAFT
SHIM
ADJUSTING SCREW

Measuring cross shaft adjusting screw end clearance
(© Chrysler Corp)

the cover. Install the adjusting screw locknut, but do not tighten at this time.

25. Rotate the worm shaft to center the ball nut.
26. Place a new gasket on the housing cover and install the cross-shaft and cover assembly into the steering gear housing. *Be sure to coat the cross-shaft and sector teeth with steering gear lubricant before installing the cross-shaft in the housing.* Allow some lash between the cross-shaft sector teeth and the ball nut rack. Install and tighten the cover bolts to 25 ft. lbs.
27. Place the cross-shaft seal on the cross-shaft with the lip of the seal facing the housing. Press the seal in place.
28. Turn the worm shaft about 1/4 turn away from the center of the high spot position. Using a torque wrench and a 3/4 in. socket on the worm shaft spline, check the torque needed to rotate the shaft through the high spot. The reading should be between 8 and 11 in. lbs. Readjust the cross-shaft adjusting screw until the proper reading is obtained. Tighten the locknut to 35 ft. lbs. and recheck cross-shaft torque.

Cross-Shaft Oil Seal Replacement

1. Remove the steering gear arm retaining nut and lockwasher.
2. Remove seal with a seal puller or other appropriate tool.
3. Place a new oil seal onto the splines of the cross-shaft with the lip of the seal facing the housing.
4. Remove the tool, and install the steering gear arm, lockwasher, and retaining nut. Tighten the nut to 180 ft. lbs. torque.

Section 6
Rack and Pinion Gear Type

The steering gear input shaft is connected to the steering shaft. A pinion gear is machined on the input shaft and engages the rack. Rotation of the input shaft pinion causes the rack to move from side to side.

A tie rod is attached at both ends of the rack by a moveable joint. The unit is sealed at each end with a rubber bellows. The steering gear is filled with five ounces of SAE-90 oil at initial assembly and checking or refilling is not required unless leakage is evident.

Replacement of the inner tie rods, rack, housing, or upper pinion bearing, necessitates installation of new steering gear assembly.

It is important to remember that when the front wheels are off the ground, the steering wheel should not be moved quickly or forcefully from lock to lock. This could cause a build-up of hydraulic pressure within the assembly which could damage or blow off the bellows.

With the front suspension and linkage in good condition and gear in proper adjustment, there should be no more than 3/8 in. free-play measured at the rim of the steering wheel.

When turning the steering wheel from one stop to the other in a stationary vehicle, there should be no knock produced by the steering gear.

All repair and adjustment procedures require the removal of the rack and pinion gear from the vehicle.

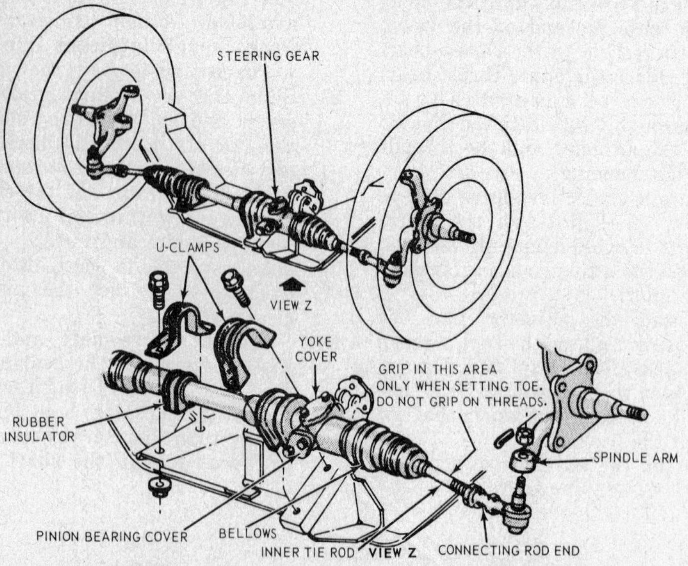
STEERING GEAR
U-CLAMPS
VIEW Z
YOKE COVER
GRIP IN THIS AREA ONLY WHEN SETTING TOE. DO NOT GRIP ON THREADS.
RUBBER INSULATOR
SPINDLE ARM
PINION BEARING COVER
BELLOWS
INNER TIE ROD
VIEW Z
CONNECTING ROD END

Steering gear assembly, rack and pinion type (© Ford Motor Co)

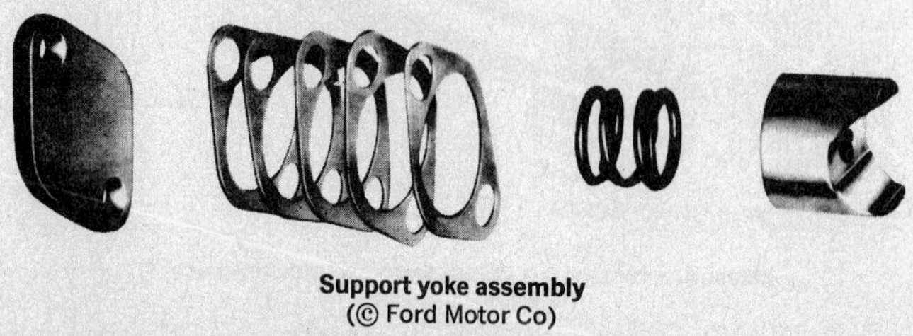

Support yoke assembly (© Ford Motor Co)

Support Yoke to Rack Adjustment

1. Clean the exterior of the gear thoroughly and place it, using the mounting pads, in a soft-jawed vice, with the yoke cover up.
2. Remove the yoke cover, gasket, shims, and yoke spring.
3. Clean the cover and housing flange areas thoroughly.
4. Reinstall the yoke and cover, omitting the gasket, shims, and spring. Tighten the cover bolts lightly, until the cover just touches the yoke.
5. Measure the gap between the cover and the housing flange with a feeler gauge. With the gasket, add selected shims to give a combined pack thickness of 0.005-0.006 in. gap.
6. Remove the cover.
7. Assemble the gasket next to the housing flange and then assemble the selected shims, spring, and cover.
8. Add a sealant to cover the bolt threads and torque to 6.5-10 ft. lbs.

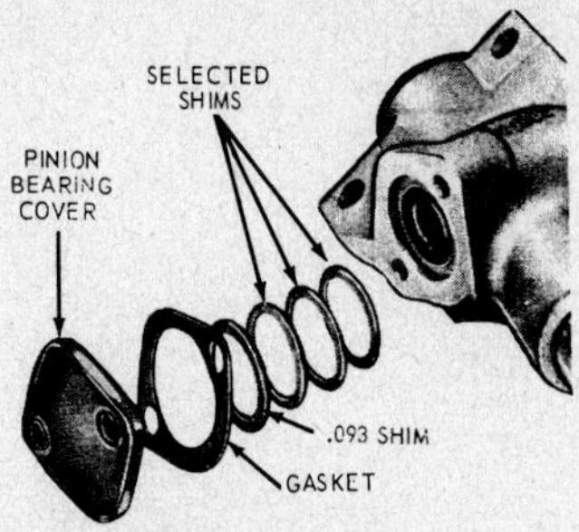
SELECTED SHIMS
PINION BEARING COVER
.093 SHIM
GASKET

Pinion bearing preload cover and shims
(© Ford Motor Co)

9. Check to see that gear operates smoothly without binding or slackness.

Pinion Bearing Preload Adjustment

1. Loosen the attaching bolts of the yoke cover to relieve spring pressure on the rack.
2. Remove the pinion cover and clean area thoroughly.
3. Remove gasket and shims.
4. Install a new gasket and fit shims until shim pack is flush with the gasket. Check with a straight-edge using light pressure. Install the thinnest of the selected shims first, then the 0.093 in. shim and cover.
5. Add one 0.005 in. shim to the pack in order to preload the bearing.
6. Add sealant to the bolt threads and install. Torque to 15-20 ft. lbs.
7. Torque yoke cover bolts to 6.5-10 ft. lbs.

Input Shaft Seal Replacement

1. Clean the area around the input shaft end-seal. Do not scratch or damage the pinion shaft.
2. Pry the pinion seal from its bore.
3. Lubricate the new pinion seal and install it over the shaft.
4. Use a piece of tubing to engage the outer flange of the seal and press or tap the seal into place so it is flush with shoulder of the bore.

INDEX

Power Steering

APPLICATION INDEX

Section Numbers Refer to Sections in Text

Make	Year	Gear Type	Sections
American Motors			
All	1967–74	D	2,6
Chrysler Corporation			
All	1967–74	C	2,7
Ford Motor Company			
Maverick-Comet	1970–74	A	2,4
Falcon	1967–70	A	2,4
Mustang-Cougar	1967–70	A	2,4
	1971–74	D	2,6
Fairlane	1967	A	2,4
Fairlane-Torino-Montego	1967	A	2,4
Torino-Montego	1972–74	E	2,8
Ford-Mercury	1967–74	E	2,8
Ford-Mercury	1967–68	D	2,6
Ford	1969	D	2,6
Thunderbird	1967–74	E	2,8
Lincoln, Mark III Mark IV	1967–74	E	2,8

Gear Type

A—Bendix linkage
B—Saginaw linkage
C—Chrysler constant control
D—Saginaw rotary
E—Ford torsion bar

Make	Year	Gear Type	Sections
General Motors			
Chevrolet	1967–74	D	2,6
Chevelle	1967–74	D	2,6
Chevy II	1967–68	B	2,5
Nova	1967–74	D	2,6
Camaro	1967–74	D	2,6
Corvette	1967–74	B	2,5
Vega	1971–74	D	2,6
Pontiac	1967–74	D	2,6
Oldsmobile	1967–74	D	2,6
Buick	1967–74	D	2,6
Cadillac	1967–74	D	2,6

Section Page Numbers

Power Steering

Preliminary

Before investigating any power steering system, first be sure of the general condition of the systems around it. Simple items such as tire pressure, loose belts, or faulty front end parts can have great effect on the function of the power steering system. After a common-sense general inspection has been made, consult Section 1 and proceed from there. Specific listings of make, model and year will be found in the Application Index.

Section 1
General Diagnosis

Hard Steering

1. Improper tire pressure.
2. Loose pump drive belt.
3. Low or incorrect hydraulic fluid.
4. Loose, bent or poorly lubricated front end parts.
5. Improper front end alignment, especially caster.
6. Bind in steering column or mechanism.
7. Air in hydraulic system.
8. Low pump output or leaks in system.
9. Obstruction in lines.
10. Pump valves sticking or out of adjustment.

Loose Steering

1. Loose wheel bearings.
2. Faulty shocks.
3. Worn Pitman arm or front end components.
4. Loose steering gear mountings or linkage points.
5. Steering mechanism worn or improperly adjusted.
6. Valve spool improperly adjusted.

Veer or Wander

1. Improper tire pressure.
2. Improper front end alignment.
3. Dragging brakes.
4. Bent frame.
5. Improper rear end alignment.
6. Faulty shocks or springs.
7. Loose or bent front end components.
8. Play in Pitman arm.
9. Loose wheel bearings.
10. Binding Pitman arm.
11. Spool valve sticking or improperly adjusted.

Wheel Oscillation

1. Improper tire pressure.
2. Loose wheel bearings.
3. Improper front end alignment.
4. Bent spindle.
5. Worn, bent or broken front end components.
6. Tires out of round or imbalanced.

Noises

1. Loose belts.
2. Low fluid, air in system.
3. Foreign matter in system.
4. Improper lubrication.
5. Interference or chafing in front end.
6. Steering gear mountings loose.
7. Incorrect adjustment or wear in mechanism.
8. Faulty valves or wear in pump.

Section 2
Preliminary Tests

Turning Effort

Check the effort required to turn the steering wheel after aligning the front wheels and inflating the tires to the proper pressure.

1. With the vehicle on dry pavement and the front wheels straight ahead, set the parking brake and turn the engine on.
2. After a short warm-up period turn the steering wheel back and forth several times to warm the steering fluid.
3. Attach a spring scale to the steering wheel rim and measure the pull required to turn the steering wheel one complete revolution in each direction. The effort needed to turn the steering wheel should not exceed the limits given in the specifications.

NOTE: this test may be done with torque wrench on the steering wheel nut. See the section on Manual Steering for a discussion of this test.

Power Steering Pump Flow

Since the power steering pump provides all the power assist in a power steering system, the pump must operate properly at all times. After performing all the checks given above, the power steering pump may be tested for proper flow by the following procedure:

1. Disconnect the pressure and return lines at the power steering pump and connect the test pressure and return lines to the pump. The test pressure and return lines are connected to a pressure gauge and two manual valves.
2. Open the two manual valves, connect a tachometer to the engine, and start the engine. Run the engine at idle speed until the reservoir fluid temperature reaches 165-175°F. *This temperature must be maintained during the test.* Manual valve B may be partially closed to create a back pressure of no more than 350 psi to aid the temperature rise. Reservoir fluid must be at the proper level.
3. After the engine and the reservoir fluid are sufficiently warmed up, close valve B. Note the pressure gauge reading. It must be a minimum of 620 psi.
4. If the pressure reading is below the minimum acceptable pressure, the pump is defective and must be repaired. If the pressure reading is at or above the minimum value, the pump is normal. Open manual valve B and proceed to the pump fluid pressure test.

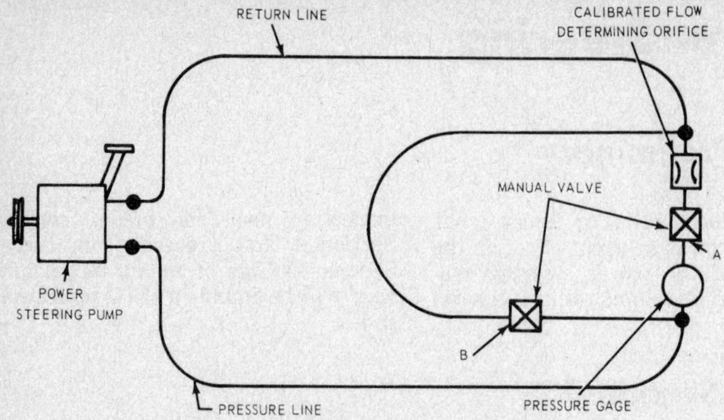
RETURN LINE
CALIBRATED FLOW DETERMINING ORIFICE
MANUAL VALVE
A
B
POWER STEERING PUMP
PRESSURE LINE
PRESSURE GAGE

Power steering pump test circuit diagram (© Ford Motor Co)

Power Steering Pump Fluid Pressure Test

1. Keep the lines and pressure gauge connected as in the Pump Flow Test.
2. With manual valves A and B opened fully, run the engine at the proper idle speed. Then, close valve A and valve B, in that order. *Do not keep both valves closed for more than 5 seconds since the fluid temperature will increase causing severe pump wear.*
3. With both manual valves closed, the pressure reading should be as given in the specifications. If the pressure reading is below the minimum reading, the pump is defective and must be repaired. If the pressure reading is at or above the minimum reading, the pump is normal and the power steering gear or power assist control valve must be checked.

Checking the Oil Flow and Pressure Relief Valve in the Pump Assembly

When the wheels are turned hard right or hard left, against the stops, the oil flow and pressure relief valves come into action. If these valves are working, there should be a slight buzzing noise. Do not hold the wheels in the extreme position for over three or four seconds because, if the pressure relief valve is not working, the pressure could get high enough to damage the system.

Section 3 Power Steering Oil Pumps

The power steering oil pump supplies all the power assist used in power steering systems of all designs. There are various designs of oil pumps used by the automobile manufacturers but all pumps supply power to operate the steering systems with the least effort. All power steering pumps have a reservoir tank built onto the oil pump. These pumps are driven by belts turned by pulleys on the front of the crankshaft.

With the engine at idle speed, the pump supplies high fluid pressure. When the car is moving straight ahead, less pressure is needed and the excess is relieved through a pressure relief and flow control valve. The pressure relief part of the valve is inside the flow control part and is basically the same for all pumps. The flow control valve regulates the constant flow of fluid from the pump to meet the demands of the steering gear. The pressure relief valve limits the hydraulic pressure built up when the steering gear is turned against its stops.

During all pump disassembly work, make sure all work is done on a clean work surface. Clean the outside of the pump thoroughly and do not allow dirt of any kind to get in-

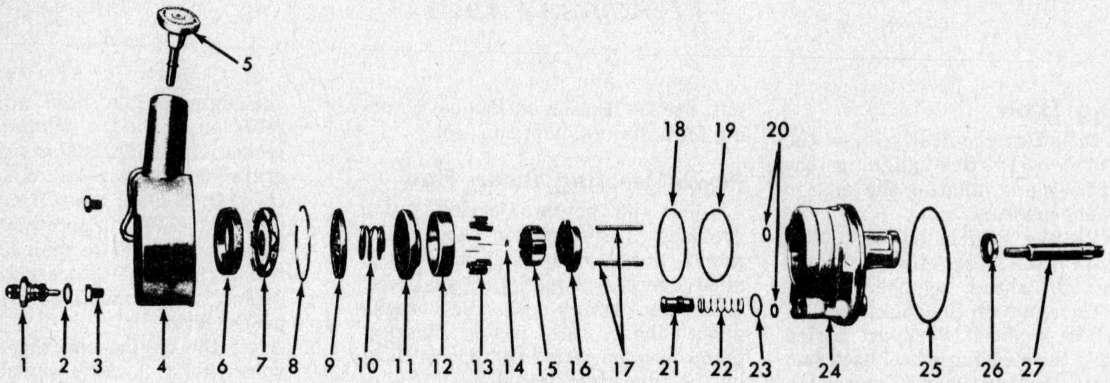
1
2
3
4
5
6
7
8
9
10
11
12
13
14
15
16
17
18
19
20
21
22
23
24
25
26
27

Vane type pump, exploded view (© Chevrolet Motor Div., G.M. Corp)

1 Union
2 Seal
3 Mounting studs
4 Reservoir
5 Dip stick and cover
6 Element (Chevy II and Corvette)
7 Filter assembly (Chevy II and Corvette)
8 End plate retaining ring
9 End plate
10 Spring
11 Pressure plate
12 Pump ring
13 Vanes
14 Drive shaft retaining ring
15 Rotor
16 Thrust plate
17 Dowel pins
18 End plate O-ring
19 Pressure plate O-ring
20 Mounting stud O-ring seals
21 Flow control valve
22 Flow control valve spring
23 Flow control valve O-ring seal
24 Pump housing
25 Reservoir O-ring seal
26 Shaft seal
27 Shaft

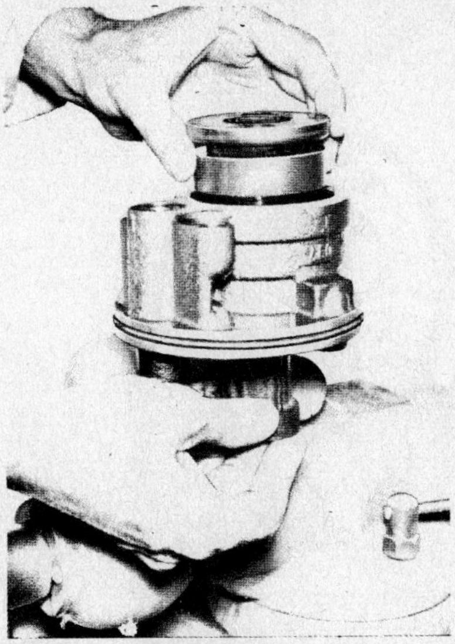

Removing impeller unit
(© Chevrolet Motor Div., G.M. Corp)

Removing end plate ring
(© Chevrolet Motor Div., G.M. Corp)

side the pump. Do not immerse the shaft oil seal in solvent.

When replacing the rotor shaft seal, be extremely careful not to scratch sealing surfaces.

Vane Type Power Steering Pump Overhaul

The vane type power steering pump is used in Saginaw steering systems. The operation is basically the same as that of the roller type pumps. Centrifugal force moves a number of vanes outward against the pump ring, pumping the fluid to the control valve.

Disassembly

1. Clean the outside of the pump in a non-toxic solvent before disassembling, and remove it from the engine.
2. Mount the pump in a vise, being careful not to distort the front hub of the pump. Remove pulley retaining nut and remove pulley.
3. Remove the union and seal.
4. Remove the reservoir retaining studs and separate the reservoir from the housing.
5. Remove the mounting bolt O-rings and the union O-rings.
6. Remove the filter and filter cage; discard the filter element.
7. Remove the end plate retaining ring by compressing the retaining ring and then prying it out with a screwdriver. The retaining ring may be compressed by inserting a small punch in the 1/8 in. diameter hole in the housing and pushing in until the ring clears the groove.
8. Remove the end plate. The end plate is spring-loaded and should rise above the housing level. If it is stuck inside the housing, gentle tapping should free the plate.
9. Remove the shaft Woodruff key and tap the end of the shaft gently to free the pressure plate, pump ring, rotor assembly, and thrust plate. Remove these parts as one unit.
10. Remove the end plate O-ring. Separate the pressure plate, pump ring, rotor assembly, and thrust plate.

Inspection

Clean all metal parts in a non-toxic solvent and inspect them as noted below:

1. Check the flow control valve for free movement in the housing bore. If the valve is sticking, see if there is dirt or roughness in the bore.
2. Check the cap screw in the end of the flow control valve for looseness. Tighten if necessary, being careful not to damage the machined surfaces.
3. Inspect the pressure plate and pump plate surfaces for flatness, cracks, or scores. Do not mistake the normal wear marks for scoring.
4. Check the vanes in the rotor assembly for free movement. See that they were installed with the radiused edge toward the pump ring.
5. If the flow control valve plunger is defective, install a new part. It is factory calibrated and supplied as a unit.
6. Check the driveshaft for worn splines, cracks, bushing material pick-up, etc.
7. Check the reservoir, studs, casting, etc. for burrs and other defects that would impair operation.
8. Use new O-rings when assembling.

Assembly

1. Install a new shaft seal in the housing and insert the shaft at the hub end of housing, splined end entering mounting face side.
2. Install the thrust plate on the dowel pins with the ported side facing the rear of the pump housing.
3. Install the rotor on the shaft, making sure it moves freely on the splines. Countersunk side must be toward the pulley.
4. Install the shaft retaining ring. Install the pump ring on the dowel pins with the direction of rotation arrow to the rear of the pump housing. Rotation is clockwise as seen from the pulley.
5. Install the vanes in the rotor slots with the radius edge towards the outside.
6. Lubricate the outside diameter and chamfer of the pressure plate with petroleum jelly so as not to damage the O-ring and install the plate on the dowel pins with the ported face toward the pump ring. Seat the pressure plate by placing a large socket on top of the plate and pushing down with hand.
7. Install the pressure plate spring in the center groove of the plate.
8. Install the end plate O-ring. Lubricate the outside diameter and chamfer of the end plate with petroleum jelly so as not to damage the O-ring and install the end plate in the housing using an arbor press. Install the end plate retaining ring while pump is in the arbor press. Be sure the ring is in the groove and the ring gap is positioned properly.
9. Install the flow control spring and plunger, hex head screw end in bore first. Install the filter cage, new filter stud seals and union seal.
10. Place the reservoir in the normal position and press down until the reservoir seats on the housing. Check the position of the stud seals and the union seal.
11. Install the studs, union, and driveshaft Woodruff key. Support the shaft on the opposite side of the key when tapping the key into place.

Roller Type Power Steering Pump Overhaul

The roller type power steering pump is similar to other constant flow centrifugal force pumps. A star-shaped rotor forces 12 steel rollers against the inside surface of a cam ring. As the rollers follow the eccentric pattern of the cam ring, oil is drawn into the inlet ports and exhausted through the discharge ports

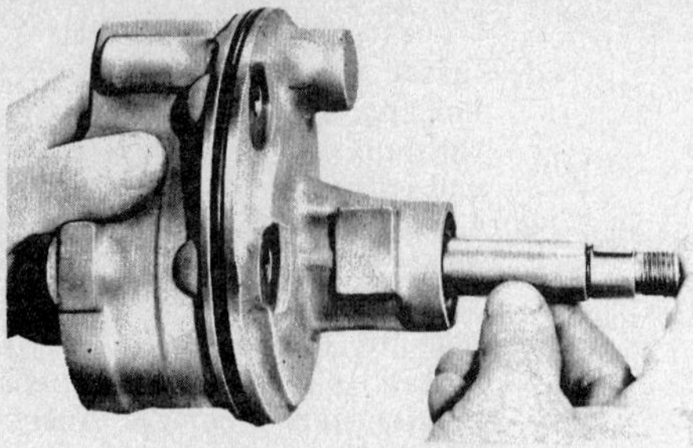

Shaft installation
(© Chevrolet Motor Div., G.M. Corp)

Installing thrust plate
(© Chevrolet Motor Div., G.M. Corp)

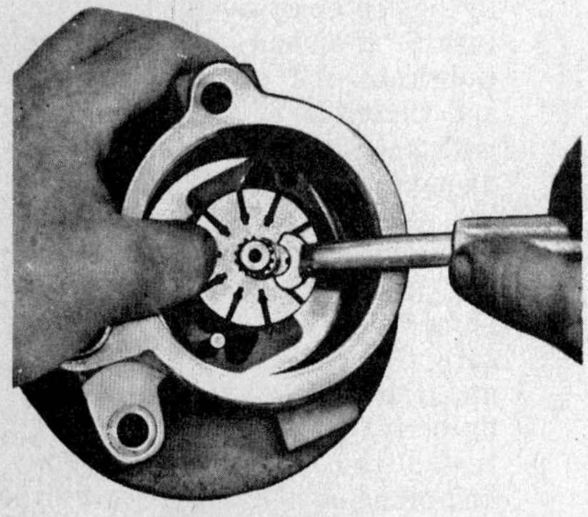

Installing shaft snap ring
(© Chevrolet Motor Div., G.M. Corp)

while the rollers are forced into vee shaped cavities of the rotor, forcing oil into the high pressure circuit. A flow control valve permits a regulated amount of oil to return to the intake side of the pump when excess output is produced during high speed operation. This reduces the power needed to drive the pump and minimizes temperature build-up.

Under high pressure demand (such as turning the wheels against the stops), the pressure built up in the steering gear exerts force on the spring end of the flow control valve. This end of the valve contains the pressure relief valve. High pressure lifts the relief valve ball from its seat, allowing oil to flow through a trigger orifice located in the front land of the flow control valve. This reduces pressure on the spring end of

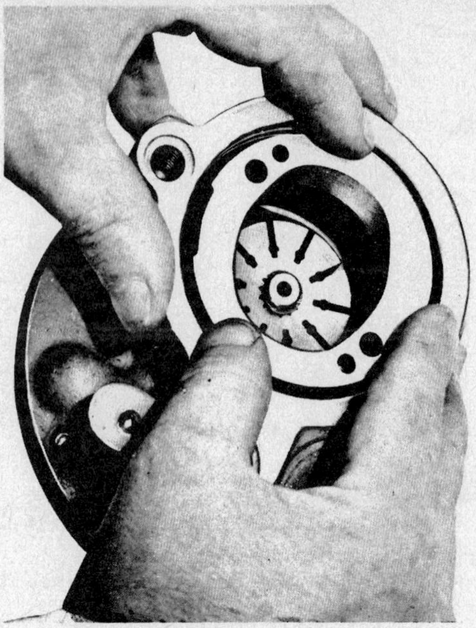

Installing pump ring
(© Chevrolet Motor Div., G.M. Corp)

Installing vanes
(© Chevrolet Motor Div., G.M. Corp)

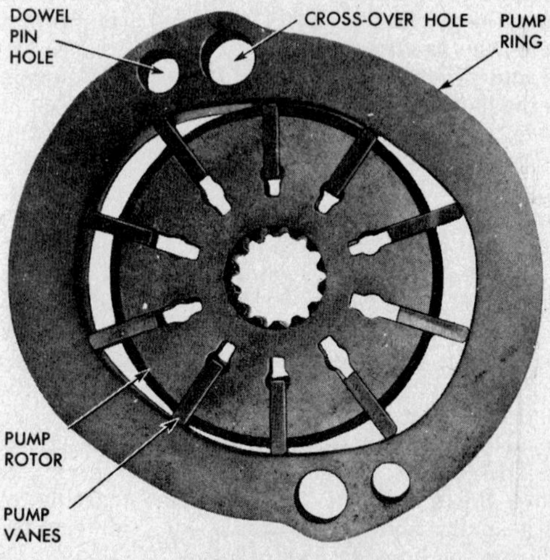
DOWEL PIN HOLE
CROSS-OVER HOLE
PUMP RING
PUMP ROTOR
PUMP VANES

Correct vane assembly
(© Chevrolet Motor Div., G.M. Corp)

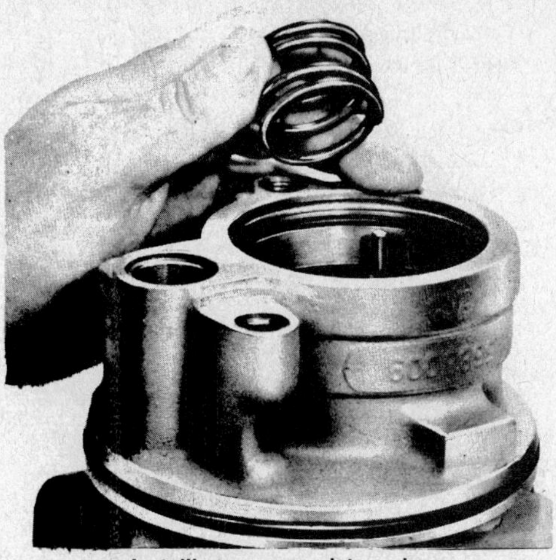

Installing pressure plate spring
(© Chevrolet Motor Div., G.M. Corp)

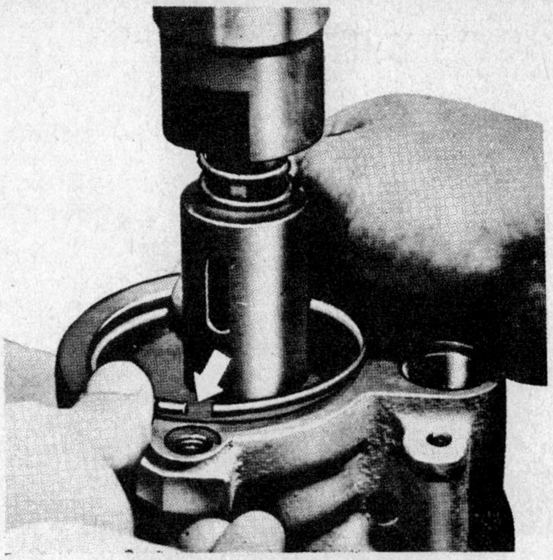

Installing end plate retaining ring
(© Chevrolet Motor Div., G.M. Corp)

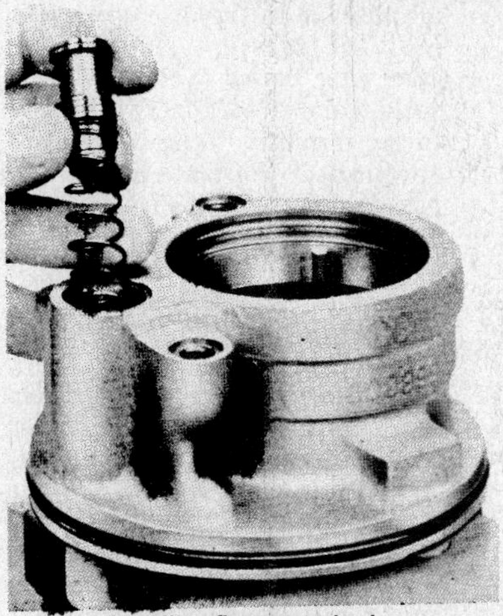

Installing flow control valve
(© Chevrolet Motor Div., G.M. Corp)

the valve which then opens and allows the oil to return to the intake side of the pump. This action limits the maximum pressure output of the pump to a safe level.

Disassembly

1. Remove pump from engine, drain reservoir, and clean outside of pump. Clamp the pump in a vise at the mounting bracket.
2. Remove the drive pulley.
3. Remove the shaft seal.
4. Remove the pump from the vise and remove the bracket mounting bolts. Remove the bracket.
5. Remove the reservoir and place the pump in a soft-faced vise with the shaft down. Discard the mounting bolt and the reservoir O-rings.
6. Move the end cover retaining ring around until one end of the ring lines up with the hole in the pump body. Insert a small punch in the hole and push it in far enough to bend the ring so a screwdriver can be inserted to pry the ring loose.
7. Remove the end cover and spring from the housing. It may be necessary to tap the cover gently to loosen it.
8. Remove the pump from the vise and turn the pump over so the rotating group may come out of the housing. Tap the end of the driveshaft to loosen these parts. Lift the pump body off the rotating group. Check that the seal plate is removed from the bottom of the housing bore.
9. Discard the O-rings from the pressure plate and end cover.
10. Remove the snap ring, bore plug, flow control valve and spring from the housing. Discard the O-ring. If necessary to disassemble the flow control valve for cleaning, see the procedure for disassembly.

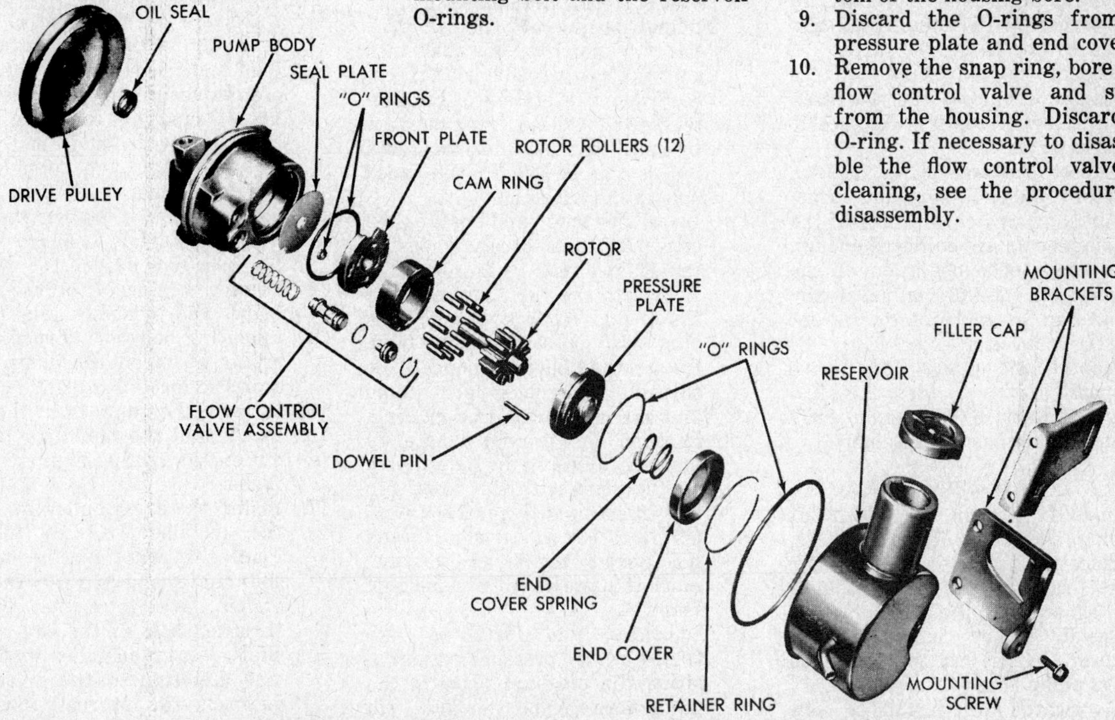
OIL SEAL
PUMP BODY
SEAL PLATE
"O" RINGS
FRONT PLATE
ROTOR ROLLERS (12)
CAM RING
DRIVE PULLEY
ROTOR
PRESSURE PLATE
MOUNTING BRACKETS
FILLER CAP
"O" RINGS
RESERVOIR
FLOW CONTROL VALVE ASSEMBLY
DOWEL PIN
END COVER SPRING
END COVER
RETAINER RING
MOUNTING SCREW

Chrysler 1.06 power steering pump, disassembled view (© Chrysler Corp)

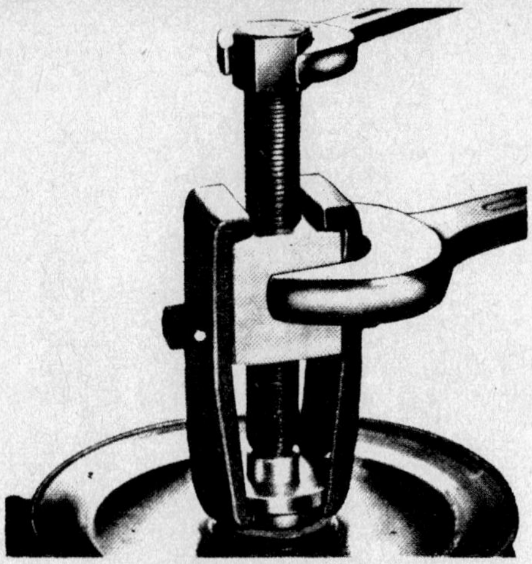

Removing drive pulley
(© Chrysler Corp)

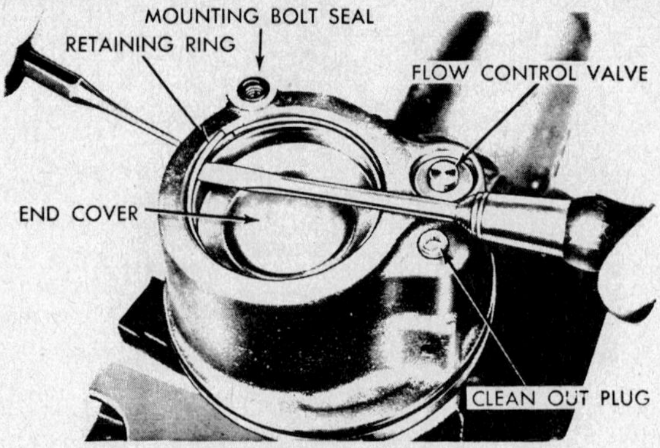
MOUNTING BOLT SEAL
RETAINING RING
FLOW CONTROL VALVE
END COVER
CLEAN OUT PLUG

Removing end cover retaining ring
(© Chrysler Corp)

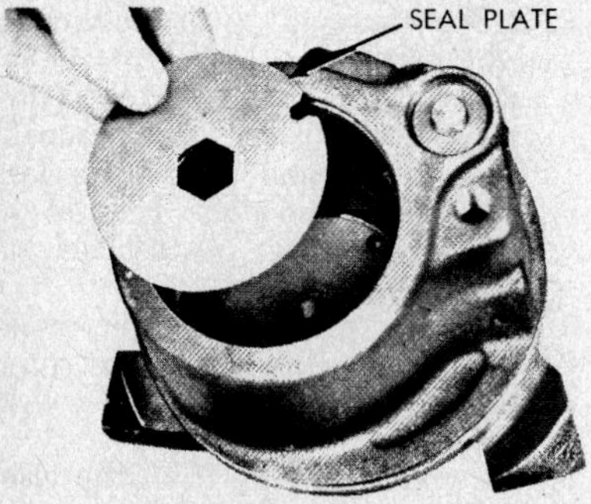
SEAL PLATE

Installing seal plate
(© Chrysler Corp)

Inspection

1. Remove the clean out plug with an Allen wrench.
2. Wash all metal parts in clean, non-toxic solvent. Blow out all passages with compressed air and air dry all cleaned parts.
3. Inspect the driveshaft for excessive wear and the seal area for nicks or scoring. Replace if necessary.
4. Inspect the end plates, rollers, rotor and cam ring for nicks, burrs, or scratches. If any of the components are damaged enough to cause poor operation of the pump, all the internal parts may have to be replaced to prevent later failures.
5. Inspect the pump body drive shaft bushing for excessive wear. Replace the pump body and bushing as one assembly.

Assembly

1. Install the ⅛ in. pipe clean out plug, tightening it to 80 in. lbs.
2. Place the pump body on a clean flat surface and drive a new shaft seal into the bore.
3. Install a new lubricated end cover O-ring into the groove in the pump bore.
4. Lubricate and install a new O-ring on the pump body to reservoir joint.
5. Install a new fiber gasket and brass seal plate on bottom of housing floor, taking care to align correctly. Align the notch in the seal plate with the dowel pin hole in the housing.
6. Carefully install the front plate with the chamfered edge down in the pump bore. Align the index notch in the plate with the dowel pin hole in the housing.

Caution Be extremely careful to align the dowel pin properly. Pump can be completely assembled with the dowel pin improperly seated in the housing and positioned improperly in the end plates.

7. Place the dowel pin in the cam ring and position the cam ring inside the pump bore. Notch in the cam ring must be facing up (away from the pulley end of pump housing). If the cam ring has two notches, one machined and one cast, install with machined notch up. If dowel pin protrudes above cam ring surface by more than 3/16 in., the dowel pin is not seated in the index hole in the housing.
8. Install the rotor and shaft in the cam ring and carefully install the 12 steel rollers in the rotor. Lubricate the rotor, rollers, and the inside surface of the cam ring with power steering fluid. Rotate the shaft by hand to be sure all the rollers are seated and are not sticking or binding.
9. Position the pressure plate by carefully aligning the index notch on the plate with the dowel pin and inserting a clean drill (number 13 to 16) in the cam ring oil hole next to the dowel pin notch until it bottoms on the housing floor.
10. Lubricate and install a new O-ring on the pressure plate. Position the pressure plate in the pump bore so that the dowel pin is in the index notch on the plate and the drill extends through the oil passage in the pressure plate. Seat the pressure plate on the cam ring using a clean 1⅛ in. socket and a soft-faced hammer to tap it gently. Remove the drill and inspect the plate at both oil passage slots to be sure that the plate is squarely seated on the cam ring.
11. Place the large coil spring over the raised portion of the installed pressure plate.
12. Place the end cover, lip edge facing up, over the spring. Press the end cover down below the retaining ring groove. Install the retaining ring in the groove. Be sure the end cover chamfer is squarely seated against the snap-ring.
13. Replace the reservoir mounting bolt seal.
14. Lubricate the flow control valve assembly with power steering fluid and insert the valve spring and valve in the bore. Install a new O-ring on the bore plug, lubricate with fluid, and carefully install in the bore. Install the snap ring with the sharp edge up. *Do not depress the bore plug more than 1/16 in. below the snap-ring groove.*
15. Place the reservoir on the pump body and visually align the mounting bolt hole. Tap the reservoir down on the pump with a plastic-faced hammer.
16. Remove the pump from the vise and install the mounting brackets on the pump. Tighten to 18 ft. lbs.
17. Install the drive pulley by using the installer tool as follows. Place the pulley on the end of the shaft and thread the installer tool into the ⅜ in. threaded hole in the end of the shaft. Put the installer shaft in a vise and tighten the drive nut against the thrust bearing, pressing the pulley on the shaft until it is flush with the end of

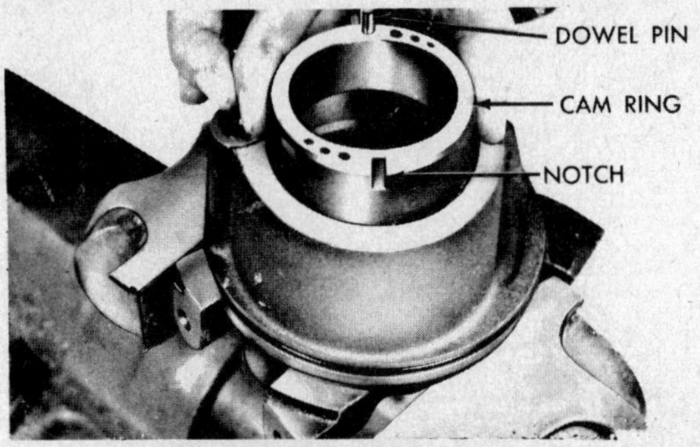
DOWEL PIN
CAM RING
NOTCH
Installing cam ring (© Chrysler Corp)

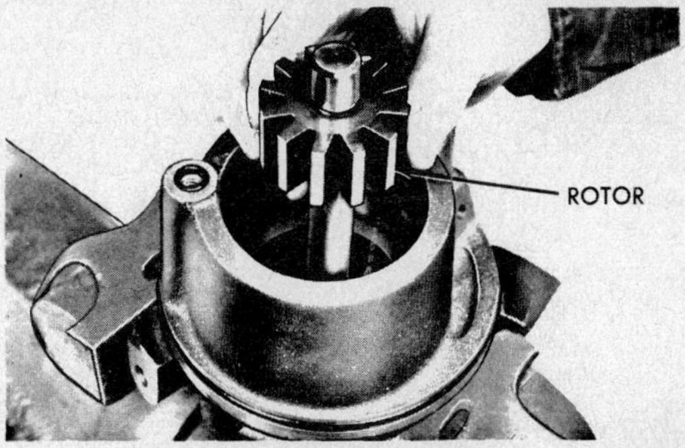
ROTOR
Installing rotor (© Chrysler Corp)

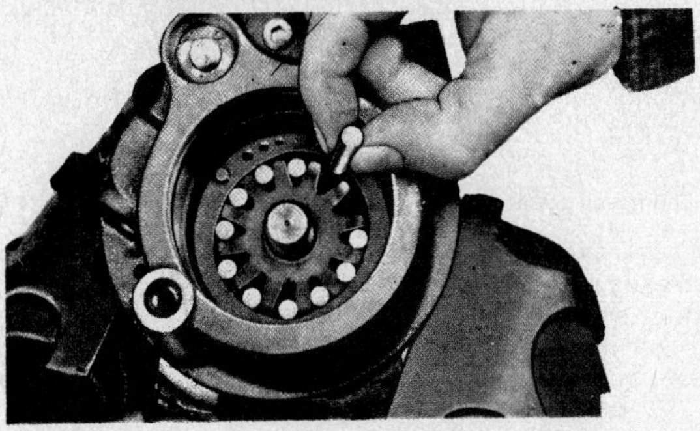
Installing rollers in rotor
(© Chrysler Corp)

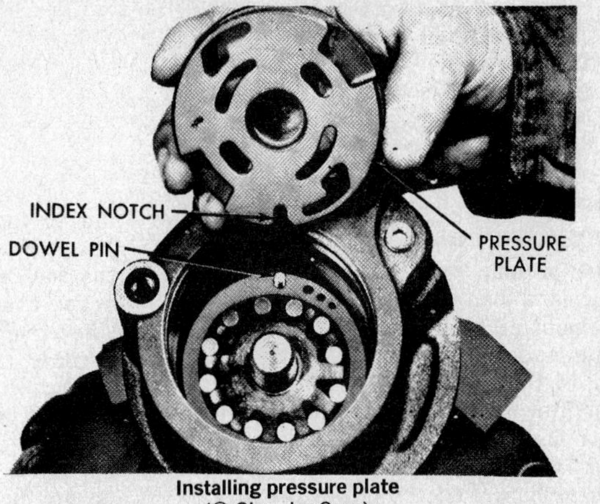
INDEX NOTCH
DOWEL PIN
PRESSURE PLATE
Installing pressure plate
(© Chrysler Corp)

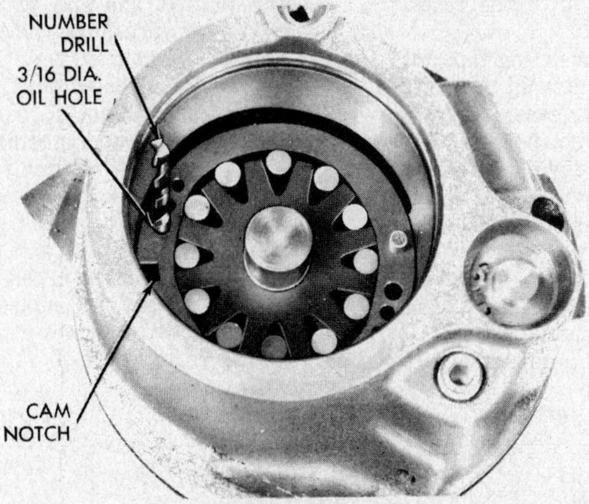
NUMBER DRILL
3/16 DIA. OIL HOLE
CAM NOTCH
Aligning oil holes
(© Chrysler Corp)

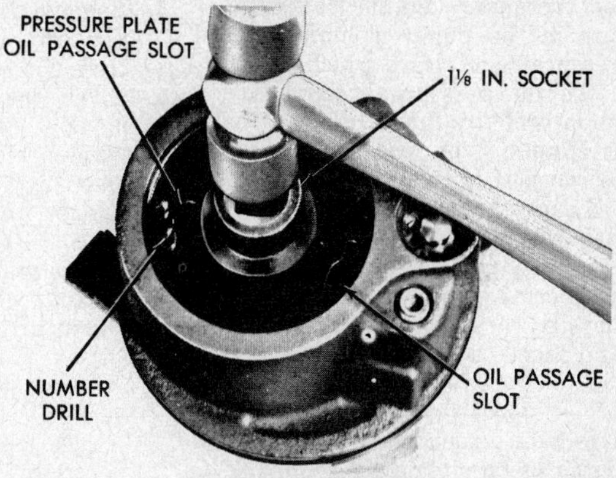
PRESSURE PLATE OIL PASSAGE SLOT
1⅛ IN. SOCKET
NUMBER DRILL
OIL PASSAGE SLOT
Seating pressure plate
(© Chrysler Corp)

the shaft. *Do not try to press the pulley on the shaft without the special installer tool since the pump will be damaged by any other installation procedure.* A small amount of driveshaft end-play will be seen when the pulley is installed. This end-play is necessary and will be minimized by a thin coat of oil between the rotor and the end plates when the pump is operating.

18. Install the pump assembly on the engine, install the drive belt and hoses (use new O-ring on pressure hose), and check for leaks.

Flow Control Valve Disassembly

1. After removing the pump from the engine and the reservoir from the pump, remove the snap-ring and plug from the flow bore. Discard the O-ring.
2. Depress the control valve against the spring pressure and allow the valve to spring out of the bore. If the valve is stuck in the bore or it did not come out far enough, it may be necessary to tap the housing lightly.
3. If the valve has dirt or foreign particles on it or in its bore, the rest of the pump needs cleaning. The hoses should be flushed and the steering gear valve body reconditioned. If the valve bore is badly scored, replace the pump body and the flow control valve.
4. Remove any nicks or burrs by gently rubbing the valve with crocus cloth. Clamp the valve land in a soft-jawed vise and remove the hex head ball seat and shims. Note the number and gauge (thickness) of the shims on the ball seat. They must be re-installed at the same shim thickness to keep the same value of relief pressure.
5. Remove the valve from the vise and remove the pressure relief ball, guide, and spring.

Flow Control Valve Assembly

1. Insert the spring, guide and pressure relief ball in the end of the flow control valve.
2. Install the hex head plug using the same number and thickness shims that were removed. Tighten the plug to 80 in. lbs.
3. Lubricate the valve with power steering fluid and insert the flow

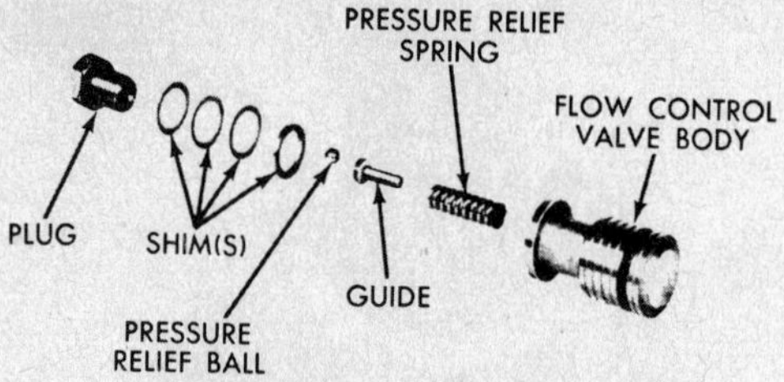
PRESSURE RELIEF SPRING
FLOW CONTROL VALVE BODY
PLUG
SHIM(S)
GUIDE
PRESSURE RELIEF BALL

Flow control valve, disassembled view
(© Chrysler Corp)

control valve spring and valve in the housing bore. Install a new O-ring on the bore plug, lubricate with fluid and carefully install into the bore. Install the snap ring. *Do not depress the bore plug more than 1/16 in. beyond the snap-ring groove.*

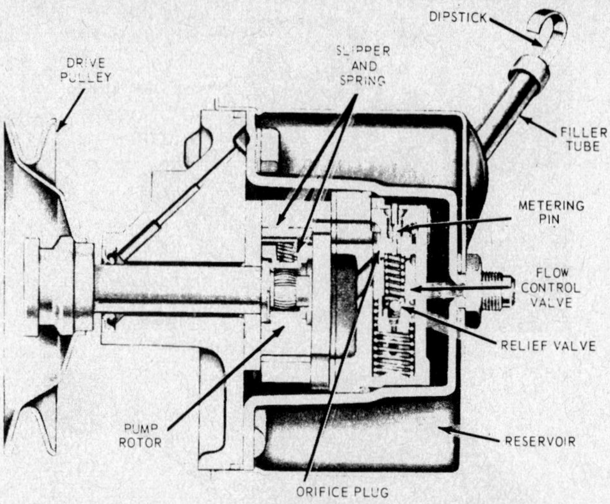
DIPSTICK
DRIVE PULLEY
SLIPPER AND SPRING
FILLER TUBE
METERING PIN
FLOW CONTROL VALVE
RELIEF VALVE
PUMP ROTOR
RESERVOIR
ORIFICE PLUG

Ford-Thompson power steering pump, sectional view (© Ford Motor Co)

Slipper Type Power Steering Pump Overhaul

The slipper type power steering pump is a belt-driven constant displacement unit that uses a number of spring-loaded slippers in the pump rotor to force oil from the inlet side to the flow control valve. Openings in the metering pin allow a flow of about two gpm. of fluid to the steering gear before the flow control valve directs the excess fluid to the inlet side of the pump again. Maximum pressure in the pump is limited by the pressure relief valve which opens when the oil pressure exceeds the maximum pressure limits.

The slipper type power steering pump discussed in this section is used in Ford cars except the Lincoln Continental and Continental Mark III and is called the Ford-Thompson power steering pump. It is also used in Chrysler cars, such as the Imperial, and called the 1.2 pump.

Disassembly

1. Drain as much fluid from the pump as possible after removing the pump from the car.
2. Install a 3/8-16 in. capscrew in the end of the pump shaft to avoid damaging the shaft. Install the pulley remover tool on the pulley hub and place the pump and remover tool in a vise as shown. Hold the pump steady and turn the tool nut counterclockwise to draw the pulley off the shaft. *The pulley must be removed without in and out pressure on the pump shaft to avoid damaging the internal thrust washers.*
3. Remove the pump reservoir by installing the pump in a holding fixture in a vise with the reservoir facing up.
4. Remove the outlet fitting hex nut and any other attaching parts from the reservoir case.
5. Invert the pump so the reservoir is now facing down. Using a wooden block, remove the reservoir by tapping around the flange until the reservoir is loose. Remove the reservoir O-ring seal and the outlet fitting gasket from the pump.
6. Again invert the pump assembly in the vise, remove the pump housing holding bolts, and the pump housing.
7. Remove the housing cover, the O-ring seal, and the pressure springs from inside the pump housing. Remove the pump cover gasket and discard it.
8. Remove the retainer end plate and upper pressure plate. In some pumps, the end plate and the upper pressure plate are one unit.
9. Remove the loose-fitting dowel pin. Be careful not to bend the fixed dowel pin which remains in the housing plate assembly.
10. Remove the rotor assembly, being careful not to let the slippers and springs fall out of the rotor. It may not be necessary to disassemble the rotor assembly unless the lower pressure plate, housing plate, rotor shaft and/or

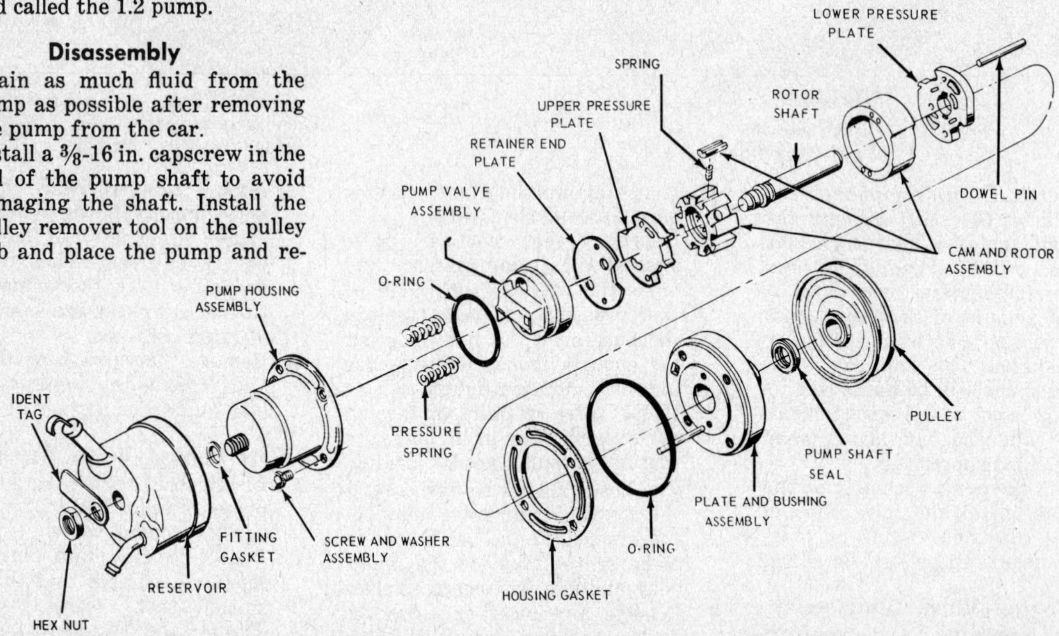
LOWER PRESSURE PLATE
SPRING
ROTOR SHAFT
UPPER PRESSURE PLATE
RETAINER END PLATE
PUMP VALVE ASSEMBLY
DOWEL PIN
CAM AND ROTOR ASSEMBLY
O-RING
PUMP HOUSING ASSEMBLY
IDENT TAG
PRESSURE SPRING
PULLEY
PUMP SHAFT SEAL
PLATE AND BUSHING ASSEMBLY
FITTING GASKET
SCREW AND WASHER ASSEMBLY
O-RING
RESERVOIR
HOUSING GASKET
HEX NUT

Ford-Thompson power steering pump, disassembled view (© Ford Motor Co)

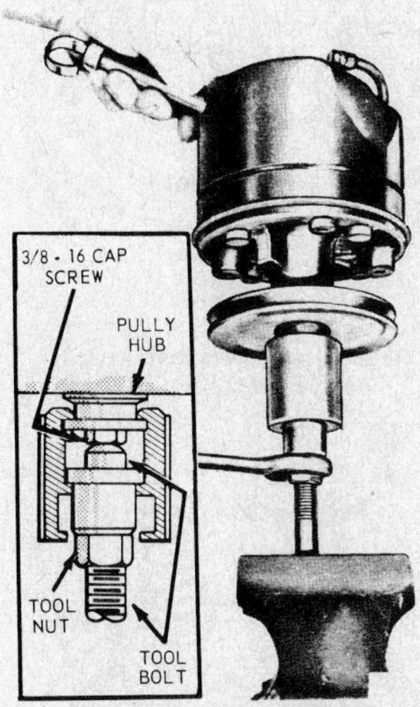
3/8 - 16 CAP SCREW
PULLY HUB
TOOL NUT
TOOL BOLT
Removing drive pulley
(© Ford Motor Co)

OUTLET FITTING GASKET
O-RING SEAL
Pump gasket locations
(© Ford Motor Co)

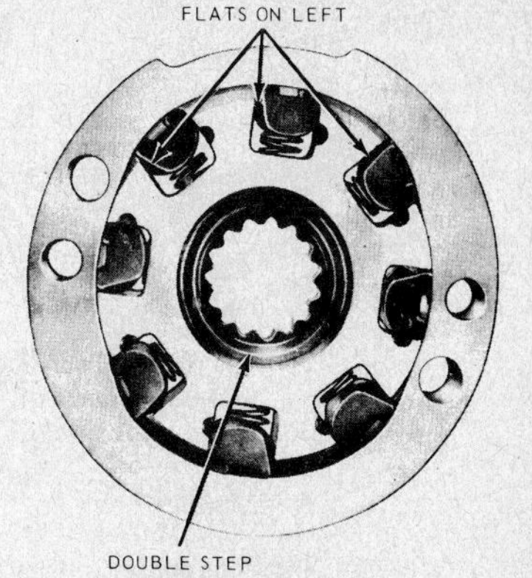
FLATS ON LEFT
DOUBLE STEP
Correct slipper installation, Ford-Thompson power steering pump
(© Ford Motor Co)

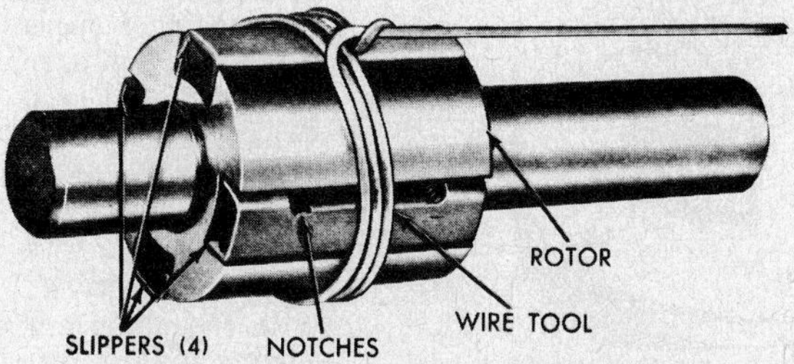
ROTOR
WIRE TOOL
SLIPPERS (4)
NOTCHES
Slippers installed in rotor (© Chrysler Corp)

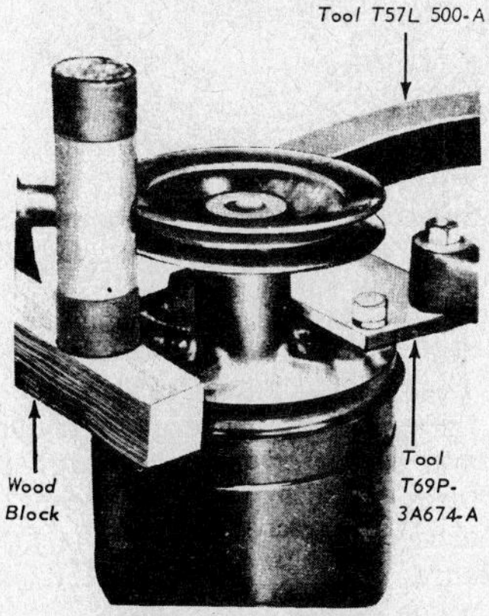
Tool T57L 500-A
Wood Block
Tool T69P-3A674-A
Removing pump reservoir
(© Ford Motor Co)

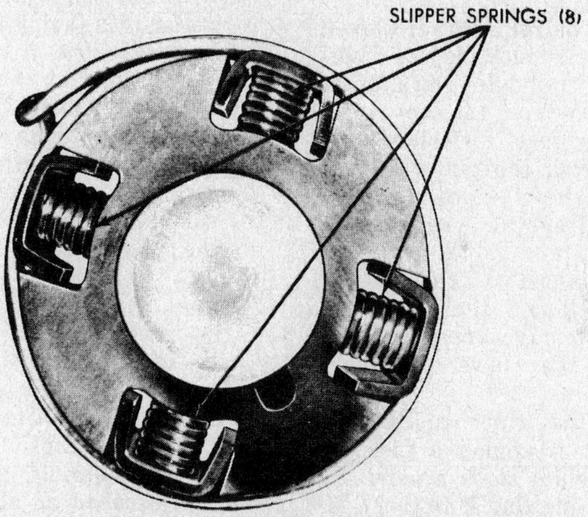
SLIPPER SPRINGS (8)
Correct slipper installation, Chrysler 1.2 power steering pump
(© Chrysler Corp)

FIXED DOWEL
DOUBLE STEP
ARROW POINTING DOWN
Cam and rotor installation
(© Ford Motor Co)

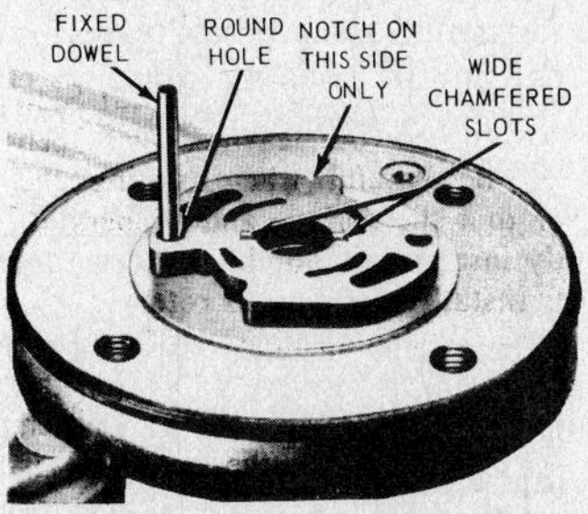
FIXED DOWEL
ROUND HOLE
NOTCH ON THIS SIDE ONLY
WIDE CHAMFERED SLOTS
Low pressure plate installed
(© Ford Motor Co)

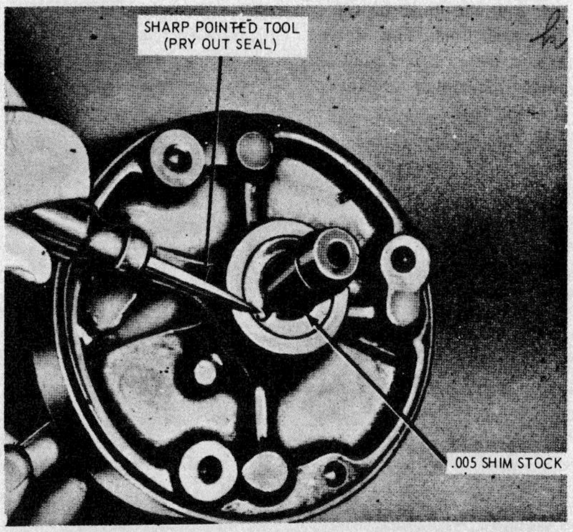
SHARP POINTED TOOL (PRY OUT SEAL)
.005 SHIM STOCK
Rotor shaft seal removal (© Ford Motor Co)

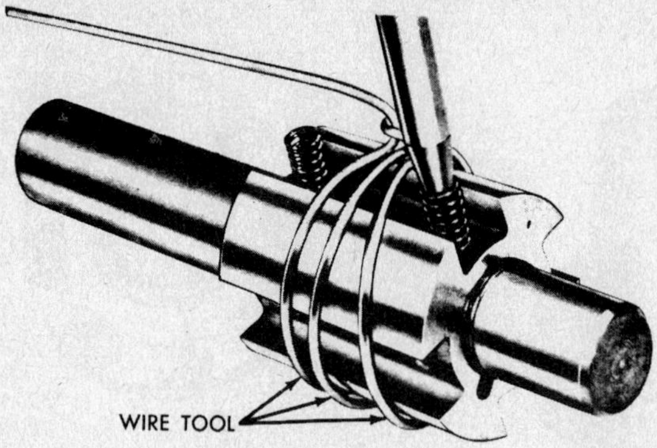
WIRE TOOL

Installing slipper springs (© Chrysler Corp)

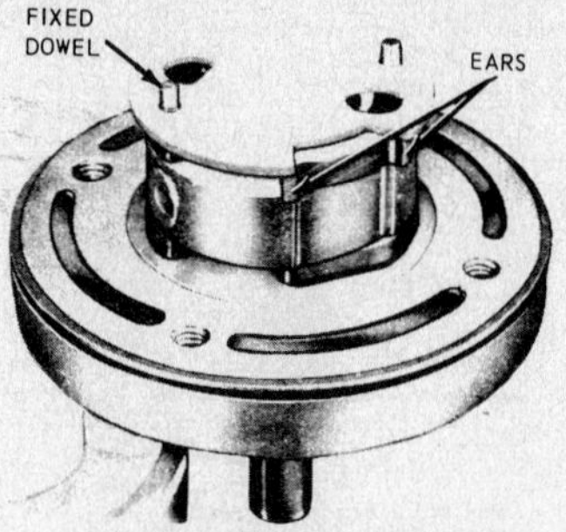
FIXED
DOWEL
EARS

Retainer end plate installation
(© Ford Motor Co)

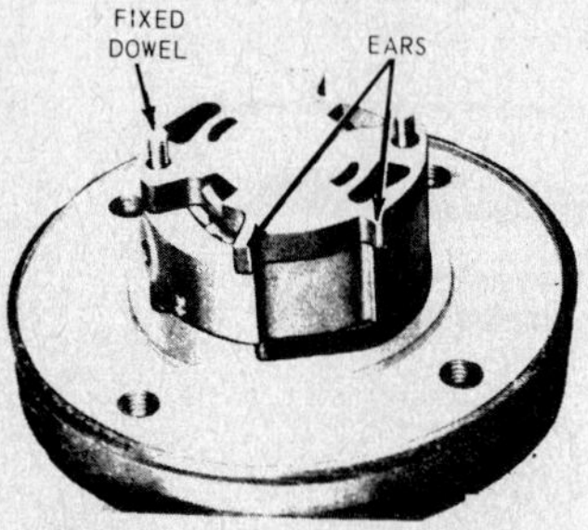
FIXED
DOWEL
EARS

Upper pressure plate installation
(© Ford Motor Co)

seal is to be replaced. However, the rotor assembly may be disassembled by removing the slippers and springs from the cam ring.

11. Clean any rust, dirt, burrs, or scoring from the pulley end of the rotor shaft before removing the shaft from the housing plate. The shaft must come out without restrictions to avoid scoring or damaging the bushing. Remove the pump rotor shaft.
12. Remove the lower pressure plate.
13. Remove the rotor shaft seal after first wrapping a piece of 0.005 in. shim stock around the shaft and pushing it into the inside of the seal until it touches the bushing. With a sharp tool, pierce the seal body and pry the seal out. *Do not damage the bushing, housing, or the shaft.* Install a new seal using the tool shown and a soft-faced hammer.
14. If the pump has a flow control valve, disassemble according to instructions given in the section on the roller type power steering pump.

Inspection

1. Wash all metal parts in clean, non-toxic solvent. Blow out all oil passages with compressed air and air dry all cleaned parts.
2. Inspect the driveshaft for excessive wear and the seal area for nicks or scoring. Replace if necessary.
3. Inspect the pressure plates, slippers, rotor, and cam ring for nicks, burrs, or scratches. If any of the parts are damaged enough to cause poor operation or binding of the pump, replace the defective part.
4. Inspect the driveshaft bushing in the pump body for excessive wear. Replace if necessary.

Assembly

1. With the pump assembly in the holding fixture, install the lower pressure plate on the anchor pin with the chamfered slots at the center hole facing up.
2. Lubricate the rotor shaft with power steering fluid and insert the shaft into the lower pressure plate and housing plate.
3. Assemble the rotor, slippers, and springs by wrapping a piece of wire around the rotor, installing the springs, and sliding a slipper into each groove of the rotor over the springs. Then, insert the assembly into the cam ring. Be sure the flat side of the slippers are toward the left side as shown. (Ford-Thompson power steering pump). The Chrysler power steering pump slippers are installed as shown. Be sure that the springs are installed straight and are not cocked to one side under the slippers.
4. Install the cam ring and rotor assembly on the driveshaft with the fixed dowel passing through the first hole to the left of the cam notch when the arrow on the cam outside diameter is pointing toward the lower pressure plate. If the cam and rotor assembly does not seat properly, turn the rotor shaft slightly until the spline teeth mesh, allowing the cam and rotor to drop into position.
5. Insert the loose-fitting dowel through the cam insert and lower pressure plate into the hole in the housing plate assembly. When both dowels are installed properly, they will be the same height.
6. Install the upper pressure plate so the tapered notch is facing down against the cam insert. The fixed dowel should pass through the round dowel hole and the loose dowel through the long hole. The slot between the ears on the outside of the pressure plate should match the notch on the cam insert.

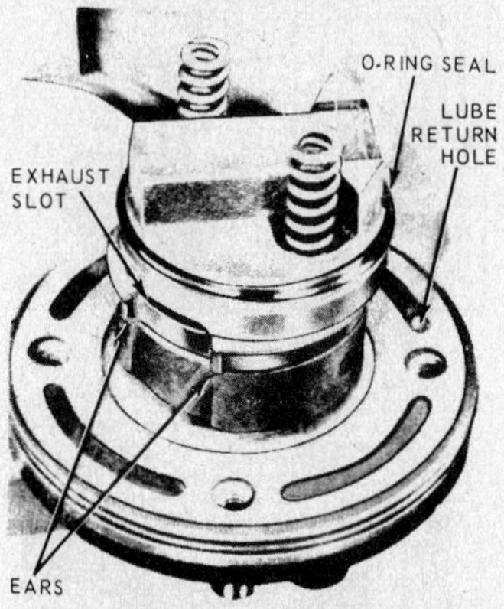
O-RING SEAL
LUBE
RETURN
HOLE
EXHAUST
SLOT
EARS

Valve and pressure spring installation
(© Ford Motor Co)

7. Install the retainer end plate so the slot on the end plate matches the notches on the upper pressure plate and the cam insert.
8. Install the pump valve assembly O-ring seal on the pump valve assembly. *Do not twist the seal.*
9. Place the pump valve assembly on top of the retainer end plate with the large exhaust slot on the pump valve in line with the outside notches of the cam, upper pressure plate, and retainer end plate. All parts must be fully seated. If correctly installed, the relief valve stem will be in line with the lube return hole in the pump housing plate.
10. Put small amounts of vaseline on the pump housing plate to hold the cover gasket in place. Install the cover gasket.
11. Insert the pressure plate springs into the pockets in the pump valve assembly.
12. Block the intake hole in the housing.
13. Lubricate the inside of the housing and the housing cover seal with power steering fluid. Make and install two studs for use as

positioning guides, one in the bolt hole nearest the drain hole and the other in the bolt hole on the opposite side of the housing plate.
14. Align the small lube hole in the housing rim and the lube hole in the housing plate. Install the housing, using a steady, even, downward pressure. *Do not jar the pressure spring out of position.* Remove the guide studs and loosely install the housing retaining bolts finger tight. Remove the block from the intake hole.
15. Tighten the retaining bolts evenly to 28-32 ft. lbs. until the housing flange contacts the gasket.
16. Install a 3/8-16 hex head screw into the end of the rotor shaft. Check the amount of torque needed to rotate the shaft. If the torque is more than 15 in. lbs., loosen the retaining bolts slightly and rotate the rotor shaft. Then, retighten the retaining bolts evenly. *Do not use the pump if the shaft torque exceeds 15 in. lbs.*
17. Remove pump from the bench holding fixture and shake the assembly back and forth. If there is a rattle, the pressure springs have fallen out of their seats and must be reinstalled.
18. Install the reservoir O-ring seal on the housing plate without twisting it. Lubricate the seal and install the reservoir, aligning the notch in the reservoir flange with the notch in the outside edge of the pump housing plate and bushing assembly. Using a soft-faced hammer, tap at the rear outer corners of the reservoir. Inspect the assembly to be sure the reservoir is fully seated on the housing plate.
19. Install the identification tag (if any) on the outlet valve fitting. Install the outlet valve fitting nut and tighten to 43-45 ft. lbs.
20. Turn the pump assembly over and install the pulley with the tool used to remove it. Draw the pulley onto the shaft until it is flush with the shaft end. *Do not exert inward and outward pressures on the shaft to avoid damaging the internal thrust areas.*

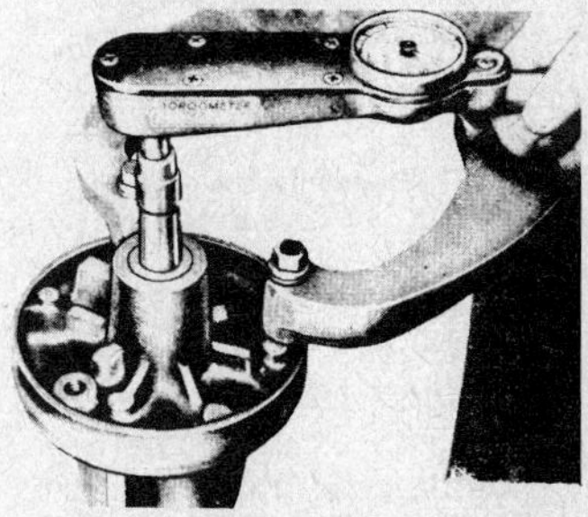

Checking pump rotational torque
(© Ford Motor Co)

Section 4
Bendix Linkage-Type Power Steering System

The Bendix linkage-type power steering system is a hydraulically controlled linkage-type system composed of an integral pump and fluid reservoir, a control valve, a power cylinder, connecting fluid lines, and the steering linkage. The hydraulic pump, which is driven by a belt turned by the engine, draws fluid from the reservoir and provides fluid pressure through hoses to the control valve and the power cylinder. There is a pressure relief valve to limit the pressures within the steering system to a safe level. After the fluid has passed from the pump to the control valve and the power cylinder, it returns to the reservoir.

The Bendix linkage-type steering system when used in Ford-built cars is called the Ford Non-Integral Power Steering System.

Control Valve Disassembly and Assembly

1. Clean the outside of the control valve of dirt and fluid.
2. Remove the centering spring cap from the valve housing. The control valve should be put in a soft-faced bench vise during disassembly. Clamp the control valve around the sleeve flange only, to avoid damaging the housing, spool, or sleeve.
3. Remove the nut from the end of the valve spool bolt. Remove the washers, spacer, centering spring, adapter, and the bushing from the bolt and valve housing.
4. Remove the two bolts holding the valve housing and the sleeve together. Separate the valve housing and the sleeve.
5. Remove the plug from the sleeve. Push the valve spool out of the centering spring end of the valve housing, and remove the seal from the spool.
6. Remove the spacer, bushing, and seal from the sleeve end.
7. Drive the stop-pin out of the travel regulator stop with a punch and hammer. *Pull the head of the valve spool bolt tightly against the travel regulator stop before driving out the pin.*
8. Turn the travel regulator stop counterclockwise in the valve sleeve to remove the stop from the sleeve.
9. Remove the valve spool bolt, spacer, and rubber washer from the stop.
10. Remove the rubber boot and clamp from the valve sleeve. Slide the bumper, spring, and ball stud seat out of the valve sleeve, and remove the ball stud socket from the sleeve.
11. Remove the return port hose seat and the return port relief valve.
12. Remove the spring plug and O-ring. Then, remove the reaction limiting valve.
13. Replace all worn or damaged hose seats by using an Easy-Out screw extractor or a bolt of proper size as a puller. Tap the existing hole in the hose seat, using a starting tap of the correct size. *Remove all metal chips from the hose seat after tapping.* Place a nut and washer on a bolt of the same size as the tapped hole. The washer must be large enough to cover the hose seat port. Insert the bolt in the tapped hole and remove the hose seat by turning the nut clockwise and drawing the bolt out. Install a new hose seal in the port, and thread a bolt of the correct size in the port. Tighten the bolt enough to bottom the seal in the port.
14. Coat all parts of the control valve assembly, except the seals, with power steering fluid. Use grease on the seals.
15. Install the reaction limiting valve, spring, and plug. Install the return port relief valve and the hose seat.
16. Insert one of the ball stud seats (flat end first) into the ball stud socket, and insert the threaded end of the ball stud into the socket.
17. Place the socket in the control valve sleeve so that the threaded end of the ball stud can be pulled out through the slot in the

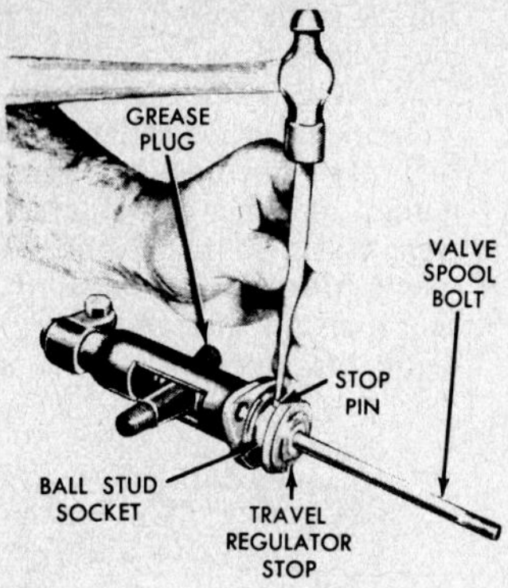
GREASE
PLUG
VALVE
SPOOL
BOLT
STOP
PIN
BALL STUD
SOCKET
TRAVEL
REGULATOR
STOP

Removing the stop pin
(© Ford Motor Co)

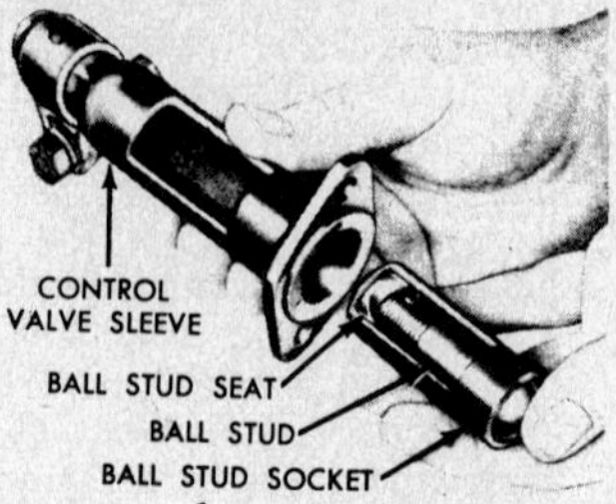
CONTROL
VALVE SLEEVE
BALL STUD SEAT
BALL STUD
BALL STUD SOCKET

Installing ball socket, seal, and bracket
(© Ford Motor Co)

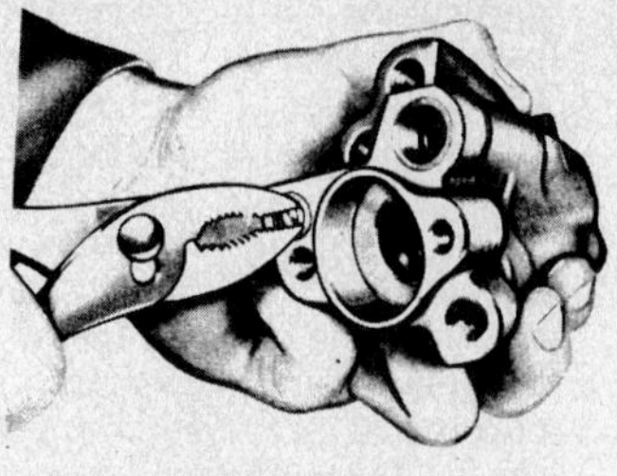

Removing the reaction valve plug
(© Ford Motor Co)

sleeve.

18. Place the other ball stud seat, spring, and bumper in the socket. Install and securely tighten the travel regulator stop.
19. Loosen the stop just enough to align the nearest hole in the stop with the slot in the ball stud socket, and install the stop pin in the ball stud socket, travel regulator stop, and valve spool bolt.
20. Install the rubber boot, clamp, and the plug on the control valve sleeve. Be sure the lubrication fitting is turned on tightly and does not bind on the ball stud socket.
21. Insert the valve spool in the valve housing, rotating it while installing.
22. Move the spool toward the centering spring end of the housing, and place the small seal, bushing, and spacer in the sleeve end of the housing.
23. Press the valve spool against the inner lip of the seal and, at the same time, guide the lip of the seal over the spool with a small screwdriver. *Do not nick or scratch the seal or spool during installation.*
24. Place the sleeve end of the housing on a flat surface so that the seal, bushing, and spacer are at the bottom end, and push down the valve spool until it stops.
25. Carefully install the spool seal and bushing in the centering spring end of the housing. Press

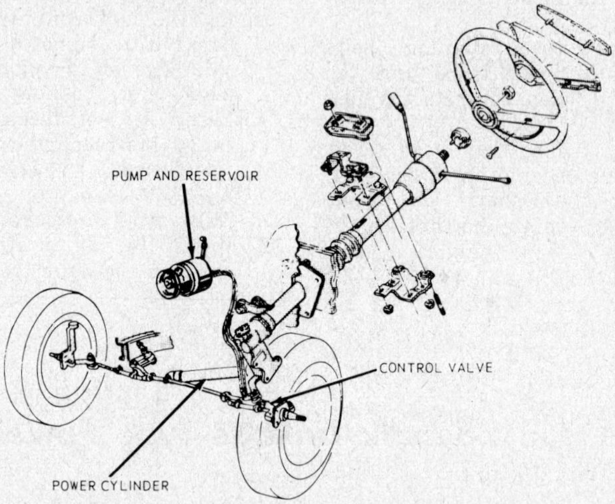
PUMP AND RESERVOIR
CONTROL VALVE
POWER CYLINDER

Bendix linkage-type power steering system (© Ford Motor Co)

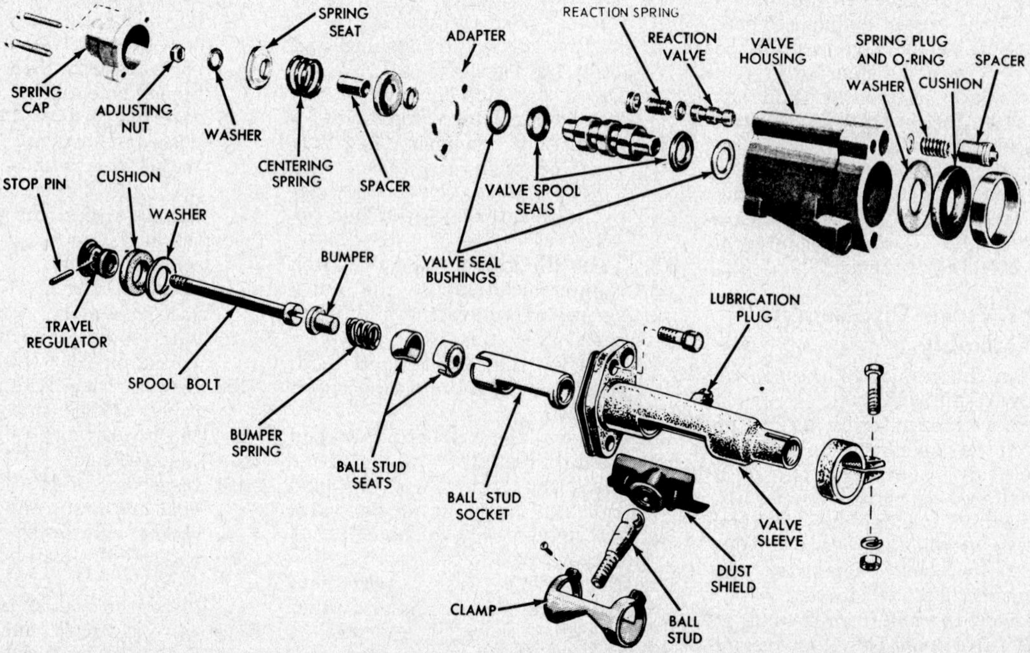
SPRING
SEAT
REACTION SPRING
ADAPTER
REACTION
VALVE
VALVE
HOUSING
SPRING PLUG
AND O-RING
SPACER
WASHER
CUSHION
SPRING
CAP
ADJUSTING
NUT
WASHER
CENTERING
SPRING
SPACER
VALVE SPOOL
SEALS
STOP PIN
CUSHION
WASHER
BUMPER
VALVE SEAL
BUSHINGS
TRAVEL
REGULATOR
SPOOL BOLT
LUBRICATION
PLUG
BUMPER
SPRING
BALL STUD
SEATS
BALL STUD
SOCKET
VALVE
SLEEVE
DUST
SHIELD
CLAMP
BALL
STUD

Control valve, disassembled view (© Ford Motor Co)

the seal against the end of the spool, guiding the seal over the spool with a small screwdriver. *Do not nick or scratch the seal or the spool during installation.*
26. Pick up the housing, and slide the spool back and forth to check for free movement.
27. Place the body gasket and valve sleeve on the housing so that the ball stud is on the same side of the housing as the ports for the two power cylinder lines. Install the two bolts in the sleeve, and torque them to the proper specification.
28. Place the adapter on the centering spring end of the housing, and install the bushing, washers, spacers, and centering spring on the valve spool bolt.
29. Compress the centering spring, and install the nut on the bolt. Tighten the nut snug (90-100 in. lbs.) ; then, loosen it not more than 1/4 turn. *Do not overtighten, to avoid breaking the stop-pin at the travel regulator stop.*
30. Move the ball stud back and forth to check for free movement.
31. Lubricate the two cap attaching bolts. Install the centering spring cap on the valve housing, and tighten the two cap bolts to the proper torque.
32. Install the nut on the ball stud so that the valve can be put in a vise. Then, push forward on the cap end of the valve to check the valve spool for free movement.
33. Turn the valve around in the vise, and push forward on the sleeve end to check for free movement.

Power Cylinder Seal Removal and Installation

1. Clamp the power cylinder in a vise, and remove the snap-ring from the end of the cylinder. *Do not distort or crack the cylinder in the vise.*
2. Pull the piston rod out all the way to remove the scraper, bushing, and seals. If the seals cannot be removed in this manner, remove them by carefully prying them out of the cylinder with a sharp pick. *Do not damage the shaft or seal seat.*
3. Coat the new seals with power steering fluid and place the parts on the piston rod, which should be lubricated.
4. Push the rod in all the way, and install the parts in the cylinder with a deep socket slightly smaller than the cylinder opening.

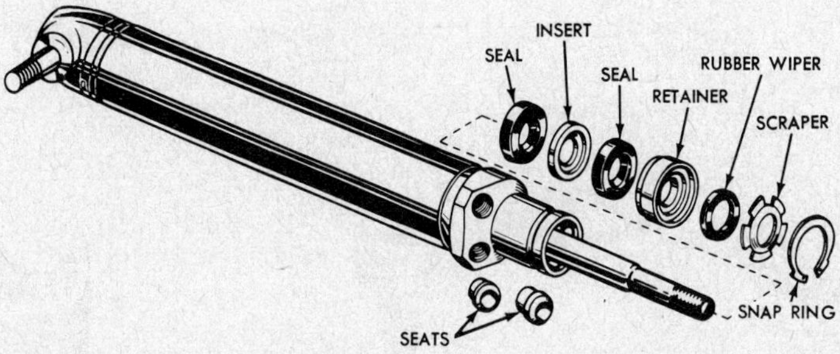
INSERT
SEAL
SEAL
RUBBER WIPER
RETAINER
SCRAPER
SNAP RING
SEATS

Power cylinder, disassembled view (© Ford Motor Co)

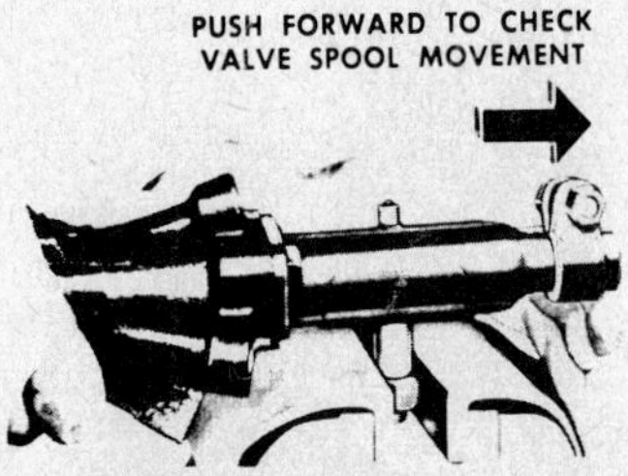
PUSH FORWARD TO CHECK VALVE SPOOL MOVEMENT

Inspecting valve spool movement
(© Ford Motor Co)

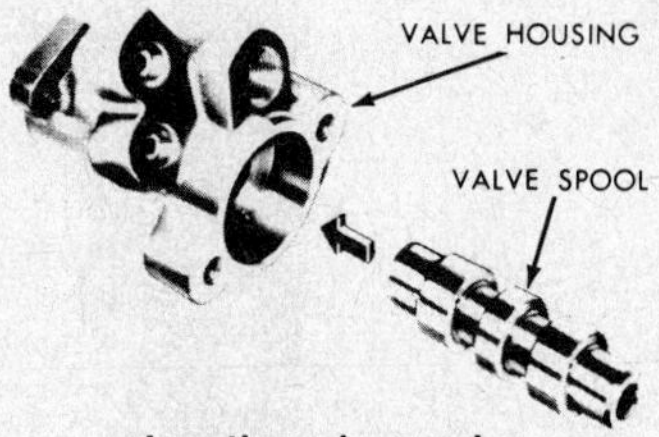
VALVE HOUSING
VALVE SPOOL

Inserting valve spool
(© Ford Motor Co)

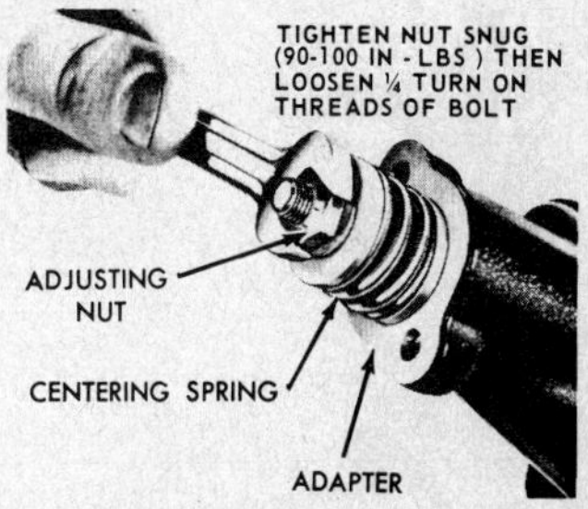
TIGHTEN NUT SNUG (90-100 IN - LBS) THEN LOOSEN ¼ TURN ON THREADS OF BOLT
ADJUSTING NUT
CENTERING SPRING
ADAPTER

Adjusting centering spring
(© Ford Motor Co)

Section 5
Saginaw Linkage-Type Power Steering System

Control Valve

Disassembly

1. Place valve assembly in vise with dust cap end up and remove dust cap.
2. Remove adjusting nut.
3 Remove valve-to-adapter bolts and remove valve housing and spool from adapter.
4. Remove spool from housing.
5. Remove spring, reaction spool, washer, reaction spring, and seal. O-ring may now be removed from reaction spool.
6. Remove annulus spacer, valve shaft washer, and plug-to-sleeve key. Remove the ball stud seal and ball stud seal clamp.
7. Carefully turn adjuster plug out of sleeve. Use care not to nick the top surface.
8. If necessary to replace a connector seat, tap threads in center hole using a 5/16-18 tap. Thread a bolt with a nut and a flat washer into the tapped hole so the washer is against the face of the port boss and the nut is against the washer. Hold the bolt from turning while backing the nut off the bolt. This will force the washer against the port boss face and back out the bolt, drawing the connector seat from the top cover housing. Discard the old connector seat and clean the housing out thoroughly to remove any metal chips. Drive a new connector seat against the housing seat, being careful not to damage either the connector seat or the housing seat.
9. Remove adapter from vise and turn over to allow spring and

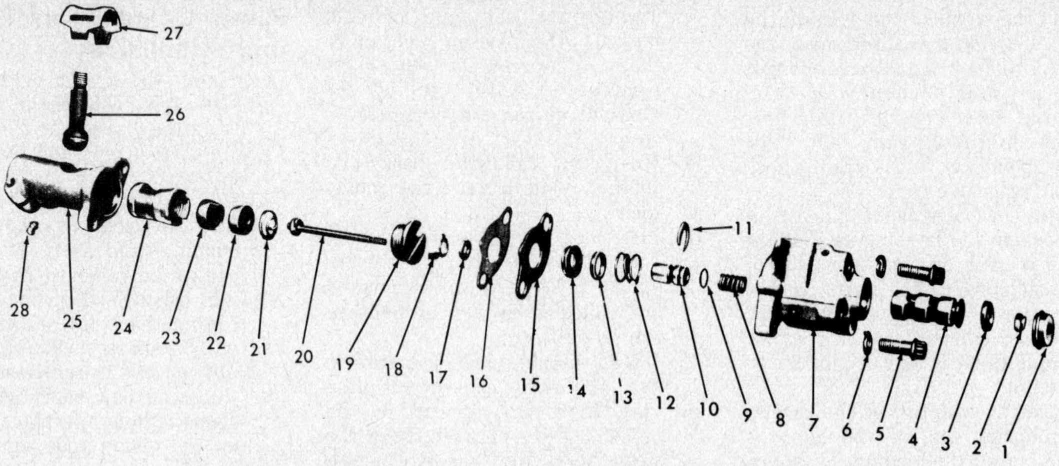
27
26
11
28
25
24
23
22
21
20
19
18
17
16
15
14
13
12
10
9
8
7
6
5
4
3
2
1

Control valve, disassembled view (© Chevrolet Motor Div., G.M. Corp)

1 Dust cover
2 Adjusting nut
3 Vee block seal
4 Valve spool
5 Valve mounting bolts
6 Lock washer
7 Valve housing
8 Valve adjustment spring
9 "O" ring seal
10 Valve reaction spool
11 Spring thrust washer
12 Valve spring
13 Spring retainer
14 Annulus seal
15 Annulus spacer
16 Gasket
17 Valve shaft washer
18 Plug to sleeve key
19 Ball adjuster nut
20 Valve shaft
21 Ball seat spring
22 Ball seat
23 Ball seat
24 Sleeve bearing
25 Adapter housing
26 Ball stud
27 Dust shield
28 Lubrication fitting

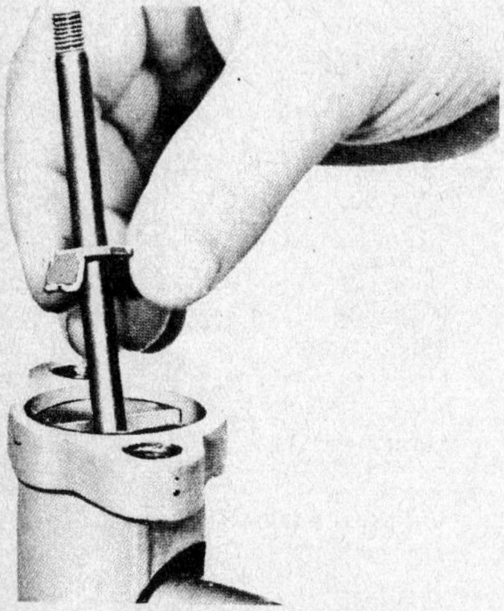

Removing plug-to-sleeve key
(© Chevrolet Motor Div., G.M. Corp)

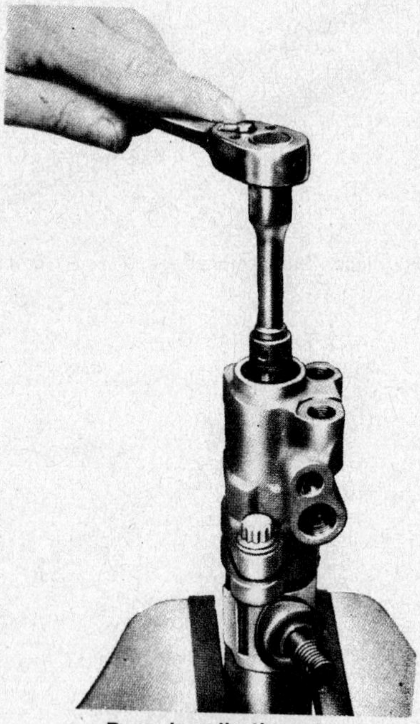

Removing adjusting nut
(© Chevrolet Motor Div., G.M. Corp)

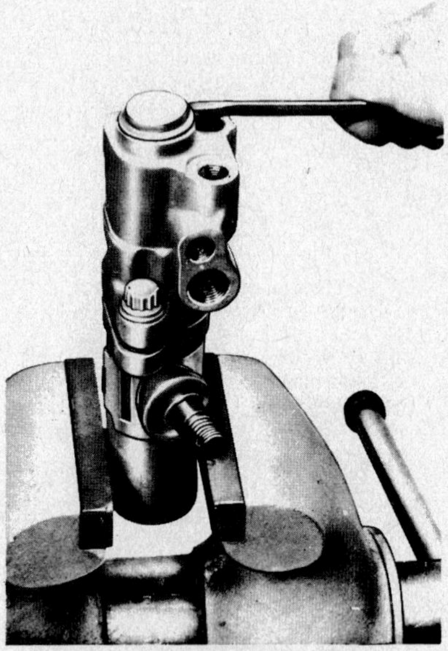

Dust cap removal
(© Chevrolet Motor Div., G.M. Corp)

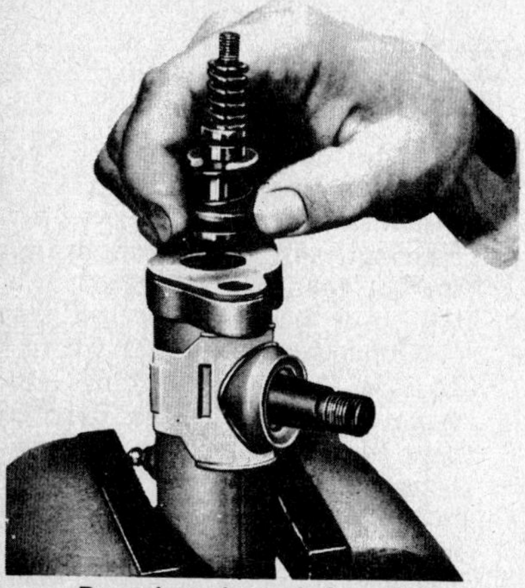

Removing valve parts from shaft
(© Chevrolet Motor Div., G.M. Corp)

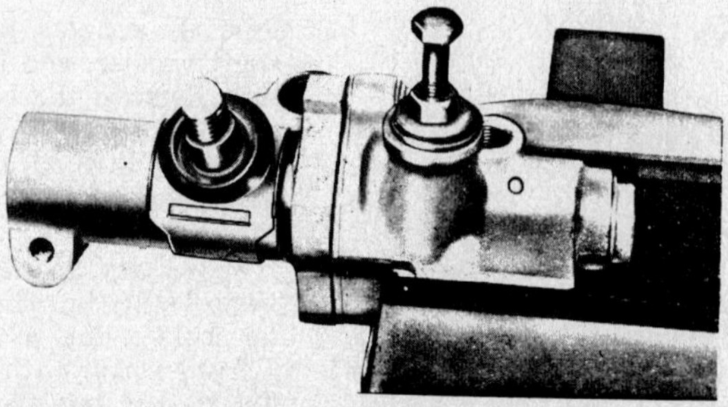

Removing connector seat
(© Chevrolet Motor Div., G.M. Corp)

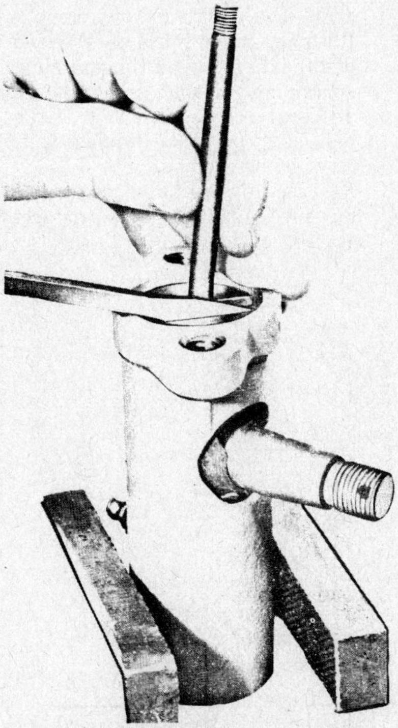

Turning adjuster plug out of sleeve
(© Chevrolet Motor Div., G.M. Corp)

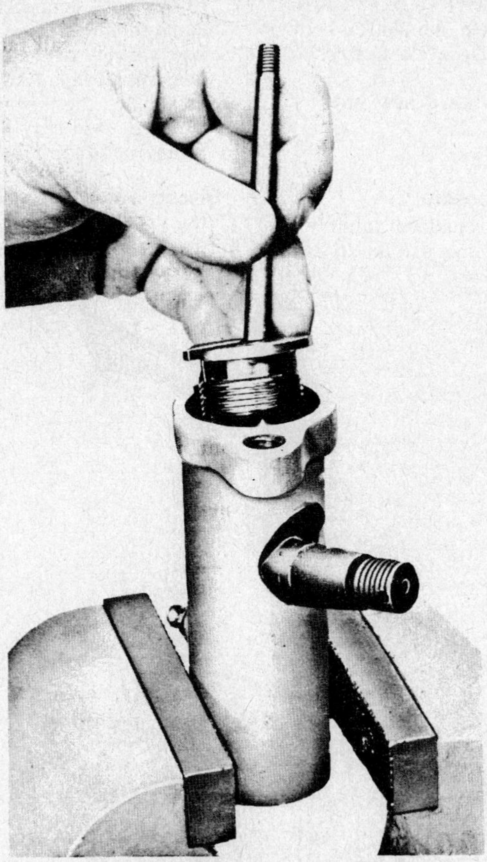

Replacing adjuster plug and shaft
(© Chevrolet Motor Div., G.M. Corp)

Removing spool from housing
(© Chevrolet Motor Div., G.M. Corp)

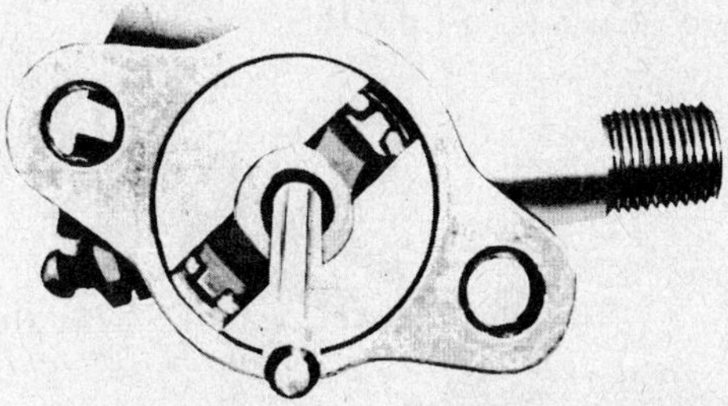

Proper key installation
(© Chevrolet Motor Div., G.M. Corp)

one of the two ball seats to drop out.

10. Remove ball stud with other ball seat and allow sleeve to fall free.

Inspection

1. Wash all parts in clean, non-toxic solvent and blow dry with air.
2. Inspect all parts for scratches, burrs, distortion, or excessive wear and replace worn or damaged parts.
3. Replace all seals and gaskets.

NOTE: Corvette valves incorporate a 55 pound centering spring which might be interchanged with Chevrolet, Chevelle and Chevy II springs. They should not be interchanged as the other springs are only 30 pounds. Corvette valves are stamped with an X on the dust cover.

Assembly

1. Replace sleeve and ball seat in adapter, then the ball stud and then the other ball seat and spring. (small end down)
2. Place adapter in vise. Put the shaft through the seat in the adjuster plug and screw adjuster plug into sleeve.
3. Turn plug in until tight, then back off until slot lines up with notches in sleeve.
4. Insert key. Be sure small tangs on end of key fit into notches in sleeve.
5. Install valve shaft washer, annulus spacer, and reaction seal (lip up), spring retainer, reaction spring and spool, then washer and adjustment spring. Install O-ring seal on reaction spool before installing spool on shaft. Install washer with chamfer up.
6. Install seal on valve spool with lip down. Then install spool, being careful not to jam spool in housing.
7. Install housing with spool onto adapter. The side ports should be on the same side as the ball stud. Bolt the housing to the adapter.

8. Depress the valve spool and turn the locknut into the shaft about four turns. Use a clean wrench or socket.

NOTE: always use a new nut.

Power Cylinder

Inspection

1. Check seals for leaks around cylinder rod. If leaks are found, replace seals.
2. Check hose connection seats for damage and replace if necessary.
3. For service other than seat or seal replacement, it is necessary to replace the power cylinder.
4. The ball stud may be replaced by removing snap-ring.

Disassembly and Reassembly

1. To remove piston rod seal, remove snap-ring and pull out on rod. Remove back-up washer, piston rod scraper, and piston rod seal from rod.
2. To remove the ball stud, depress the end plug and remove the snap ring. Push on the end of the ball stud and the end plug, spring, spring seat, and ball stud and seal may be removed. If the ball seat is to be replaced, it must be pressed out.
3. Reverse disassembly procedure. Be sure snap-ring is properly seated.

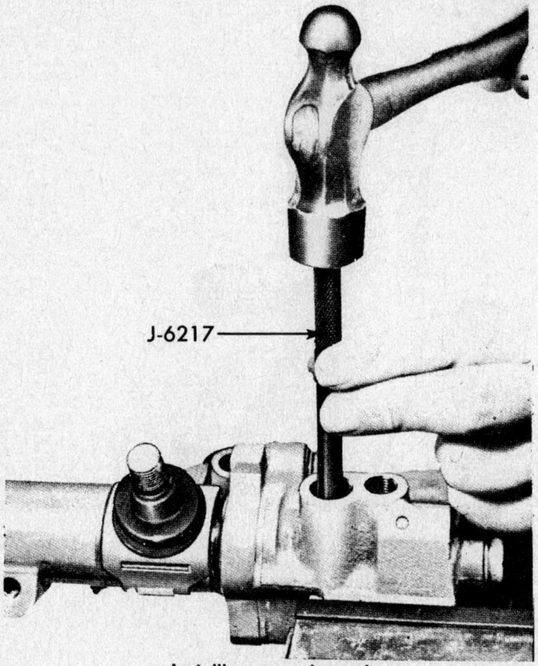
J-6217

Installing connector seat
(© Chevrolet Motor Div., G.M. Corp)

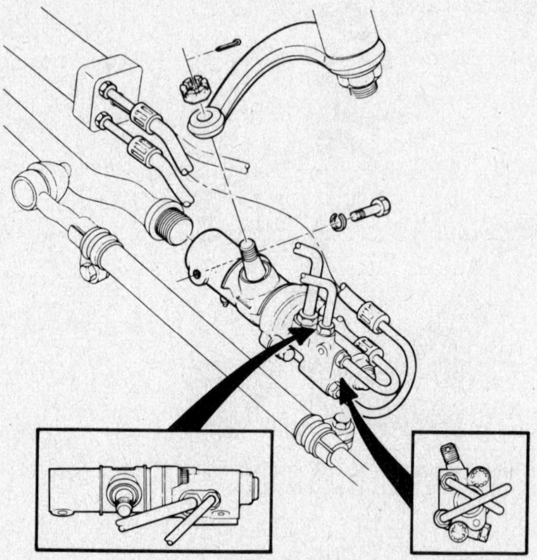

Power steering hose installation
(© Chevrolet Motor Div., G.M. Corp)

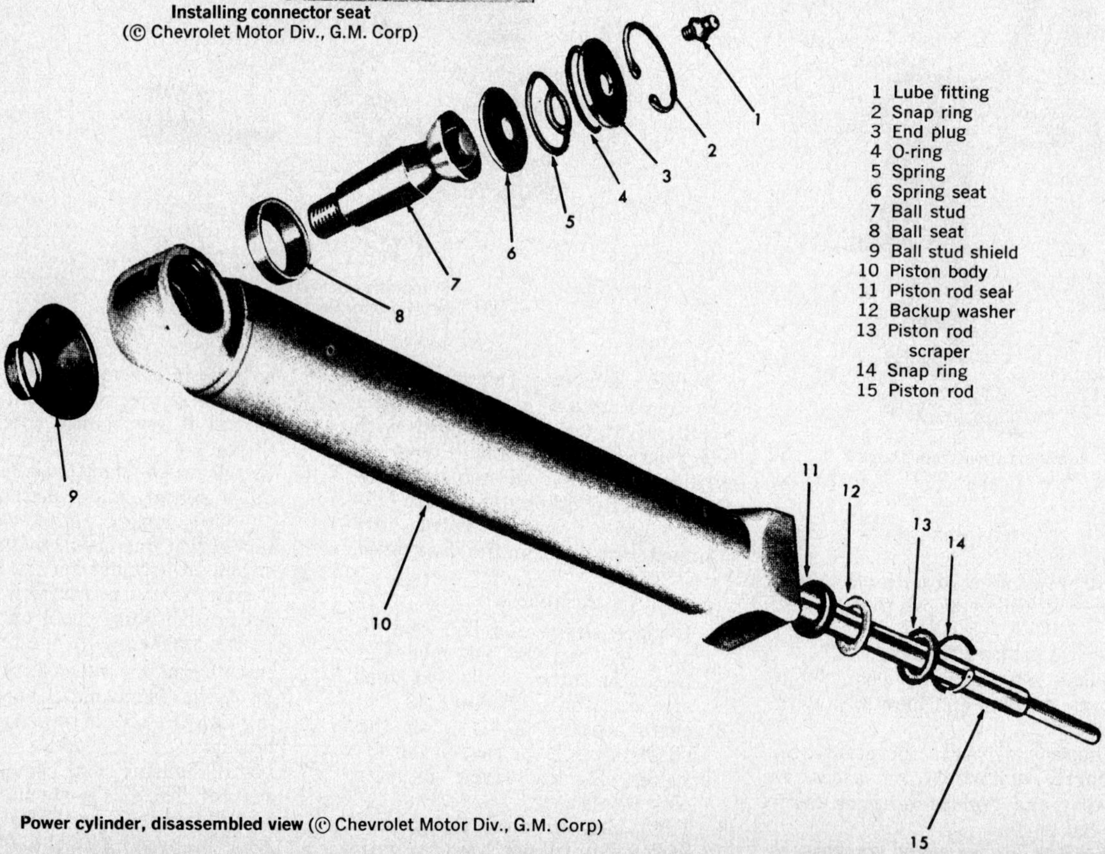
1
2
3
4
5
6
7
8
9
10
11
12
13
14
15
1 Lube fitting
2 Snap ring
3 End plug
4 O-ring
5 Spring
6 Spring seat
7 Ball stud
8 Ball seat
9 Ball stud shield
10 Piston body
11 Piston rod seal
12 Backup washer
13 Piston rod scraper
14 Snap ring
15 Piston rod

Power cylinder, disassembled view (© Chevrolet Motor Div., G.M. Corp)

Section 6
Saginaw Rotary-Type Power Steering

The rotary type power steering gear is designed with all components in one housing.

The power cylinder is an integral part of the gear housing. A double-acting piston allows oil pressure to be applied to either side of the piston. The one-piece piston and power rack is meshed to the sector shaft.

The hydraulic control valve is composed of a sleeve and valve spool. The spool is held in the neutral position by the torsion bar and spool actuator. Twisting of the torsion bar moves the valve spool, allowing oil pressure to be directed to either side of the power piston, depending on the directional rotation of the steering wheel, to give power assist.

On many General Motors cars a modified version of the system provides variable ratio steering for easier and safer control. The steering gear ratio will vary from a high ratio of about 16:1 while steering straight ahead to a lower gear ratio of about 12.4:1 while making a full turn to either side. See the specifications for the exact gear ratios.

Power Steering Unit

Checking Steering Effort

Run the engine to attain normal operating temperatures. With the wheels on a dry floor, hook a pull scale to the spoke of the steering wheel at the outer edge. The effort required to turn the steering wheel should be 3½-5 lbs. If the pull is not within these limits, check the hydraulic pressure.

Pressure Test

To check the hydraulic pressure, disconnect the pressure hose from the gear. Now connect the pressure gauge between the pressure hose from the pump and the steering gear housing. Run the engine to attain normal operating temperatures, then turn the wheel to a full right and a full left turn to the wheel stops.

Hold the wheel in this position only long enough to obtain an accurate reading.

The pressure gauge reading should be within the limits specified. If the pressure reading is less than the minimum pressure needed for proper operation, close the valve at the gauge and see if the reading increases. If the pressure is still low, the pump is defective and needs repair. If the

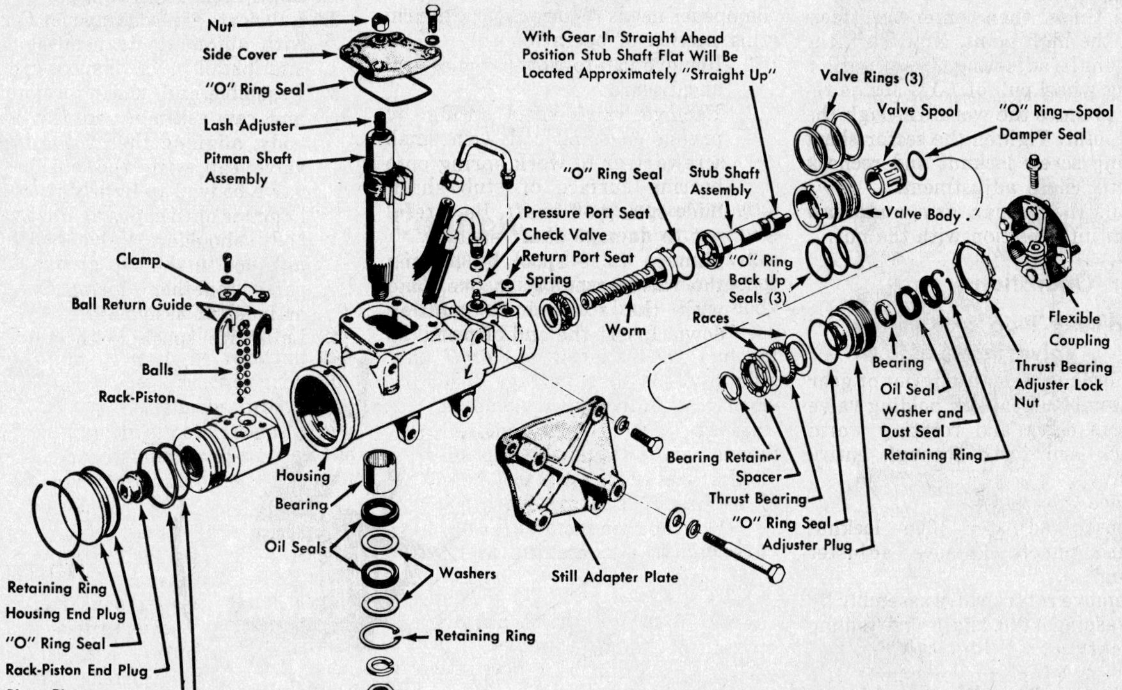
Nut
Side Cover
"O" Ring Seal
Lash Adjuster
Pitman Shaft Assembly
With Gear In Straight Ahead Position Stub Shaft Flat Will Be Located Approximately "Straight Up"
Valve Rings (3)
Valve Spool
"O" Ring—Spool Damper Seal
"O" Ring Seal
Stub Shaft Assembly
Valve Body
Pressure Port Seat
Check Valve
Return Port Seat
Spring
"O" Ring Back Up Seals (3)
Clamp
Ball Return Guide
Worm
Races
Flexible Coupling
Balls
Rack-Piston
Bearing
Thrust Bearing Adjuster Lock Nut
Oil Seal
Washer and Dust Seal
Retaining Ring
Bearing Retainer
Spacer
Thrust Bearing
"O" Ring Seal
Adjuster Plug
Housing
Bearing
Oil Seals
Washers
Still Adapter Plate
Retaining Ring
Retaining Ring
Housing End Plug
"O" Ring Seal
Rack-Piston End Plug
Piston Ring
Back-Up "O" Ring

Saginaw rotary gear, exploded view (© American Motors Corp)

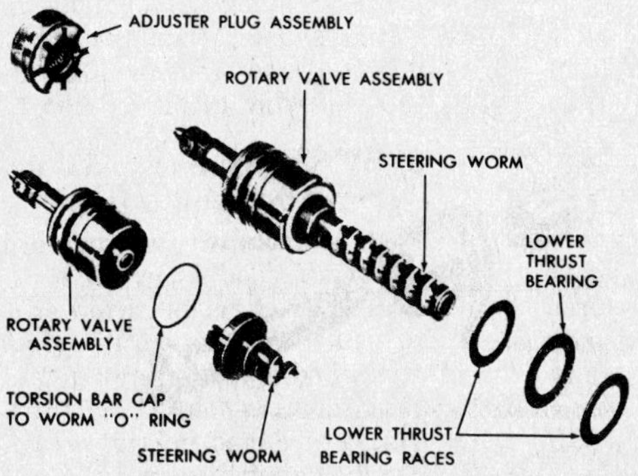
ADJUSTER PLUG ASSEMBLY
ROTARY VALVE ASSEMBLY
STEERING WORM
LOWER THRUST BEARING
ROTARY VALVE ASSEMBLY
TORSION BAR CAP TO WORM "O" RING
STEERING WORM
LOWER THRUST BEARING RACES

Adjuster plug and O-ring removal
(© Pontiac Div., G.M. Corp)

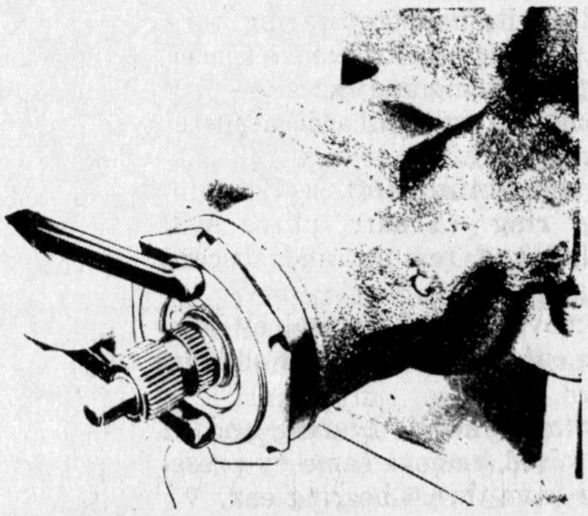

Removing adjuster plug assembly
(© Pontiac Div., G.M. Corp)

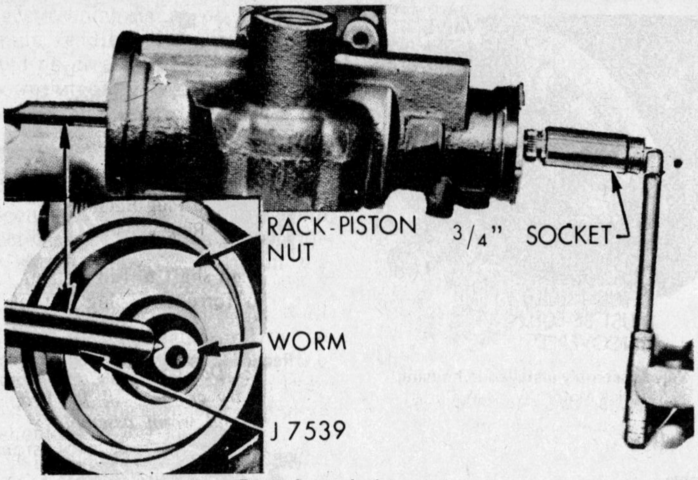
RACK-PISTON NUT
3/4" SOCKET
WORM
J 7539

Removing rack-piston nut
(© Buick Motor Div., G.M. Corp)

TORQUE END PLUG TO 50 LB. FT.

Torquing rack-piston nut end plug
(© Buick Motor Div., G.M. Corp)

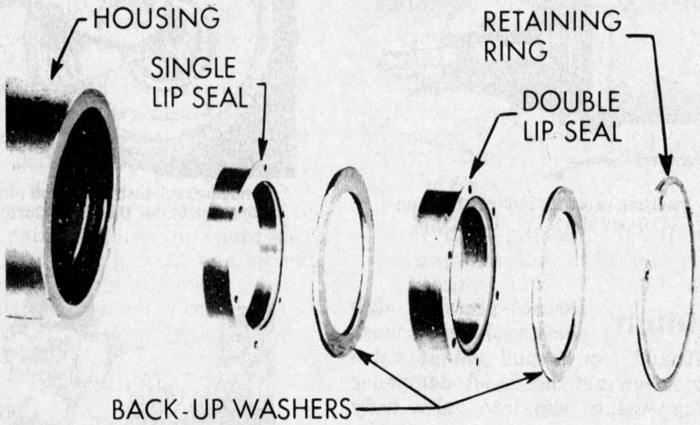
HOUSING
SINGLE LIP SEAL
RETAINING RING
DOUBLE LIP SEAL
BACK-UP WASHERS

Pitman shaft seals
(© Buick Motor Div., G.M. Corp)

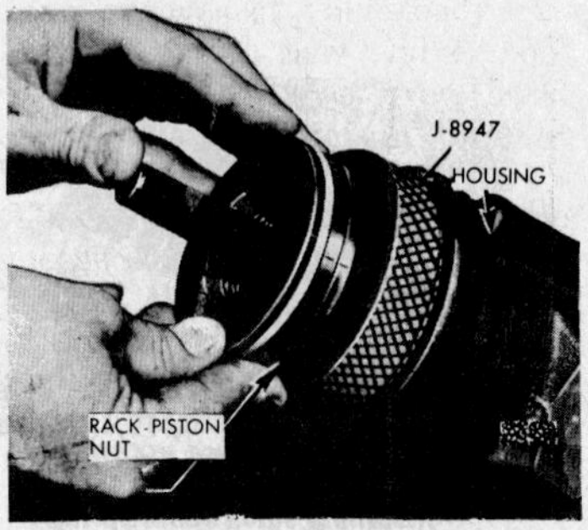
J-8947
HOUSING
RACK-PISTON NUT

Installing rack-piston nut—43, 44, 45000 series
(© Buick Motor Div., G.M. Corp)

rack-piston nut from gear housing.

8. Remove adjuster plug and rotary valve assemblies as previously described.
9. Remove worm and lower thrust bearing and races.
10. Remove cap-to-O-ring seal and discard.

Rack-Piston Nut and Worm Disassembly and Reassembly

1. Remove and discard piston ring and back-up O-ring on rack-piston nut.
2. Remove ball guide clamp and return guide.
3. Place nut on clean cloth and remove ball retaining tool. Make sure all balls are removed.
4. Inspect all parts for wear, nicks, scoring or burrs. If worm or rack-piston nut need replacing, both must be replaced as a matched pair.
5. In assembling, reverse the above.

NOTE: when assembling, alternate black and white balls, and install guide and clamp. Packing with grease helps in holding during assembly.

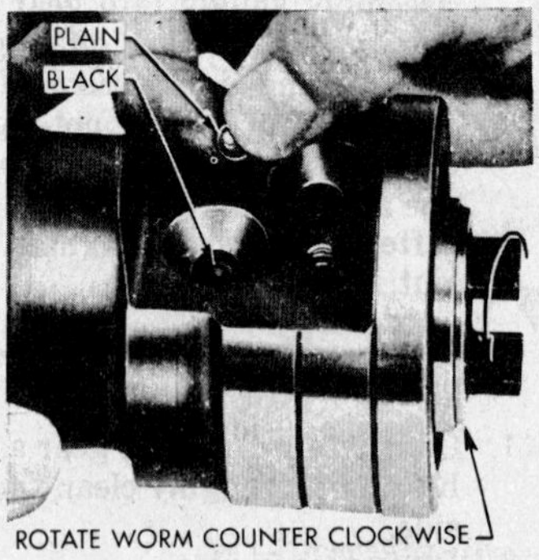
PLAIN
BLACK
ROTATE WORM COUNTER CLOCKWISE

Loading balls in rack-piston nut
(© Buick Motor Div., G.M. Corp)

When new balls are used, various sizes are available and a selection must be made to secure proper torque when making the high point adjustment.

Rack-Piston Nut and Worm Assembly Installation

1. Install in reverse of removal procedure.
2. In all cases use new O-ring seals.
3. Make adjustments as described in that section.

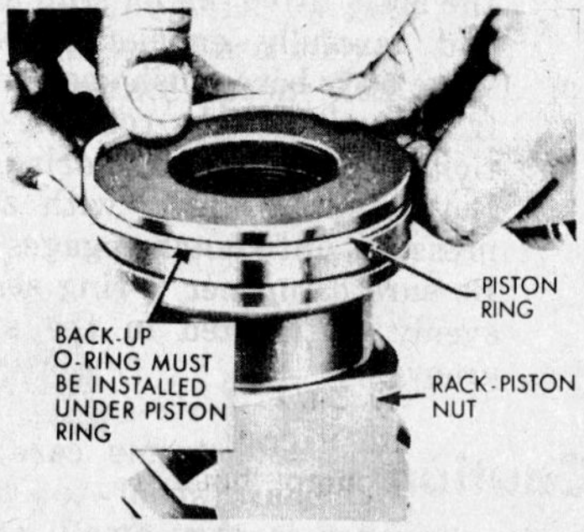
PISTON RING
BACK-UP O-RING MUST BE INSTALLED UNDER PISTON RING
RACK-PISTON NUT

Installing rack-piston ring on rack-piston nut
(© Buick Motor Div., G.M. Corp)

RACK-PISTON NUT
HOUSING

Installing rack-piston nut—46, 48, 49000 series
(© Buick Motor Div., G.M. Corp)

Section 6
Saginaw Rotary-Type Power Steering

The rotary type power steering gear is designed with all components in one housing.

The power cylinder is an integral part of the gear housing. A double-acting piston allows oil pressure to be applied to either side of the piston. The one-piece piston and power rack is meshed to the sector shaft.

The hydraulic control valve is composed of a sleeve and valve spool. The spool is held in the neutral position by the torsion bar and spool actuator. Twisting of the torsion bar moves the valve spool, allowing oil pressure to be directed to either side of the power piston, depending on the directional rotation of the steering wheel, to give power assist.

On many General Motors cars a modified version of the system provides variable ratio steering for easier and safer control. The steering gear ratio will vary from a high ratio of about 16:1 while steering straight ahead to a lower gear ratio of about 12.4:1 while making a full turn to either side. See the specifications for the exact gear ratios.

Power Steering Unit

Checking Steering Effort

Run the engine to attain normal operating temperatures. With the wheels on a dry floor, hook a pull scale to the spoke of the steering wheel at the outer edge. The effort required to turn the steering wheel should be 3½-5 lbs. If the pull is not within these limits, check the hydraulic pressure.

Pressure Test

To check the hydraulic pressure, disconnect the pressure hose from the gear. Now connect the pressure gauge between the pressure hose from the pump and the steering gear housing. Run the engine to attain normal operating temperatures, then turn the wheel to a full right and a full left turn to the wheel stops.

Hold the wheel in this position only long enough to obtain an accurate reading.

The pressure gauge reading should be within the limits specified. If the pressure reading is less than the minimum pressure needed for proper operation, close the valve at the gauge and see if the reading increases. If the pressure is still low, the pump is defective and needs repair. If the

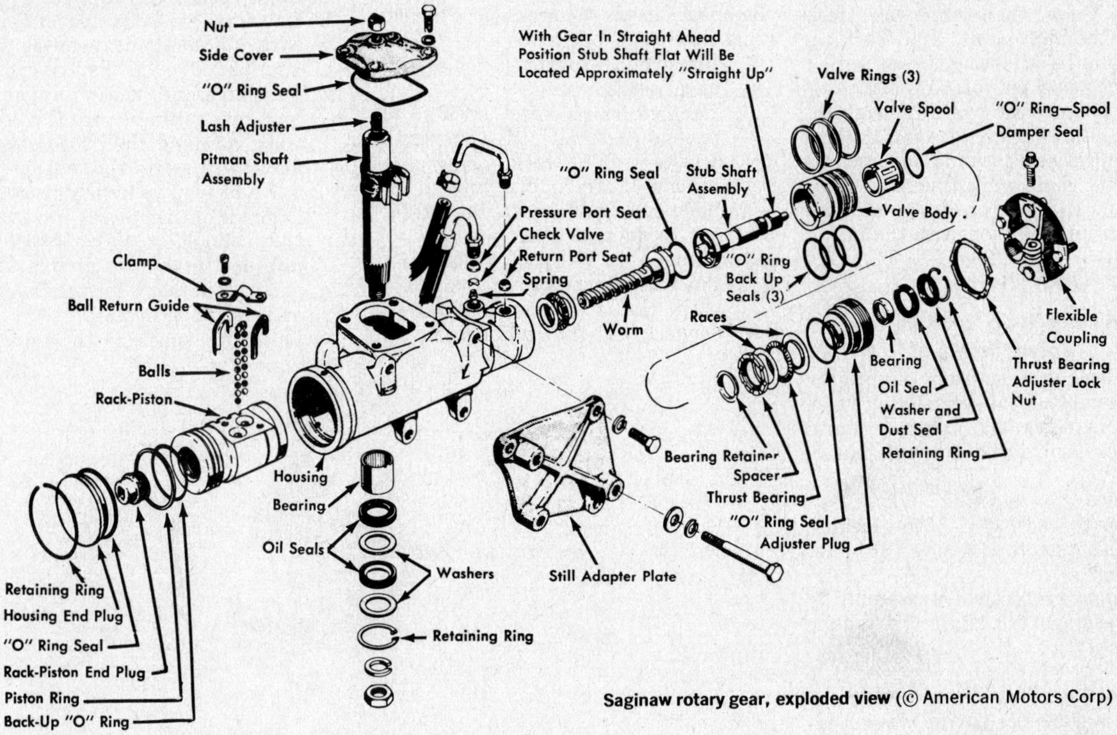
Nut
Side Cover
"O" Ring Seal
Lash Adjuster
Pitman Shaft Assembly
With Gear In Straight Ahead Position Stub Shaft Flat Will Be Located Approximately "Straight Up"
Valve Rings (3)
Valve Spool
"O" Ring—Spool Damper Seal
"O" Ring Seal
Stub Shaft Assembly
Valve Body
Pressure Port Seat
Check Valve
Return Port Seat
Spring
Worm
"O" Ring Back Up Seals (3)
Clamp
Ball Return Guide
Balls
Rack-Piston
Races
Bearing
Oil Seal
Washer and Dust Seal
Retaining Ring
Flexible Coupling
Thrust Bearing Adjuster Lock Nut
Housing
Bearing
Oil Seals
Washers
Still Adapter Plate
Bearing Retainer
Spacer
Thrust Bearing
"O" Ring Seal
Adjuster Plug
Retaining Ring
Housing End Plug
"O" Ring Seal
Rack-Piston End Plug
Piston Ring
Back-Up "O" Ring
Retaining Ring
Saginaw rotary gear, exploded view (© American Motors Corp)

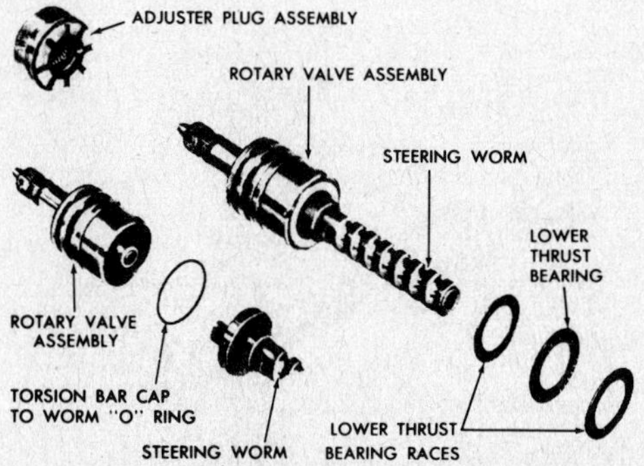
ADJUSTER PLUG ASSEMBLY
ROTARY VALVE ASSEMBLY
STEERING WORM
LOWER THRUST BEARING
ROTARY VALVE ASSEMBLY
TORSION BAR CAP TO WORM "O" RING
STEERING WORM
LOWER THRUST BEARING RACES
Adjuster plug and O-ring removal (© Pontiac Div., G.M. Corp)

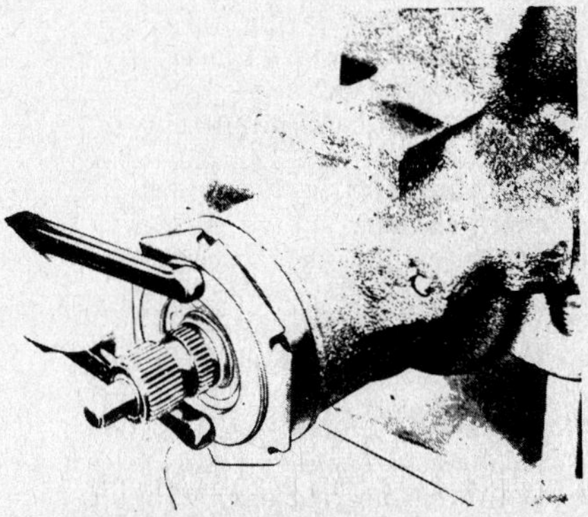
Removing adjuster plug assembly (© Pontiac Div., G.M. Corp)

pressure reading is at or near the minimum reading, the pump is normal and needs only an adjustment of the power steering gear or power assist control valve.

Worm Bearing Preload and Sector Mesh Adjustments

Disconnect the Pitman arm from the sector shaft, then back off on the sector shaft adjusting screw on the sector shaft cover.

Center the steering on the high point, then attach a pull scale to the spoke of the steering wheel at the outer edge. The pull required to keep the wheel moving for one complete turn should be ½-⅔ lbs.

If the pull is not within these limits, loosen the thrust bearing locknut and tighten or back off on the valve sleeve adjuster locknut to bring the preload within limits. Tighten the thrust bearing locknut and recheck the preload.

Slowly rotate the steering wheel several times, then center the steering on the high point. Now, turn the sector shaft adjusting screw until a steering wheel pull of 1-1½ lbs. is required to move the worm through the center point. Tighten the sector shaft adjusting screw locknut and recheck the sector mesh adjustment.

Install the pitman arm and draw the arm into position with the nut.

Repair Operations

Adjuster Plug and Rotary Valve Removal

1. Thoroughly clean exterior of gear assembly. Drain by holding valve ports down and rotating worm back and forth through entire travel.
2. Place gear in vise.
3. Loosen adjuster plug locknut with punch. Remove adjuster plug.
4. Remove rotary valve assembly by grasping stub shaft and pulling it out.

Adjuster Plug Disassembly

1. Remove upper thrust bearing retainer with screwdriver. Be careful not to damage bearing bore. Discard retainer. Remove spacer, upper bearing and races.
2. Remove and discard adjuster plug O-ring.
3. Remove stub shaft seal retaining ring (Truarc pliers will help) and remove and discard dust seal.
4. Remove stub shaft seal by prying out with screwdriver and discard.
5. Examine needle bearing and, if required, remove same by pressing from thrust bearing end.
6. Inspect thrust bearing spacer, bearing rollers and races.

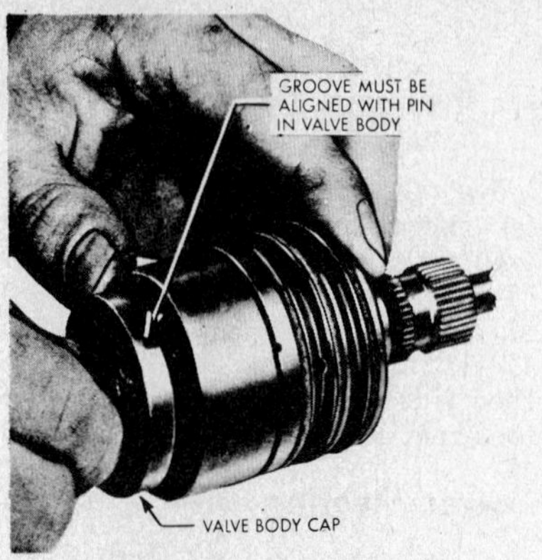
GROOVE MUST BE ALIGNED WITH PIN IN VALVE BODY
VALVE BODY CAP

Assembling stub shaft, torsion bar, and cap assembly
(© Buick Motor Div., G.M. Corp)

7. Reassemble in reverse of above.

Rotary Valve Disassembly

Repairs are seldom needed. Do not disassemble unless absolutely necessary. If the O-ring seal on valve spool dampener needs replacement, perform this portion of operation only.

1. Remove cap-to-worm O-ring seal and discard.
2. Remove valve spool spring by prying on small coil with small screwdriver to work spring onto bearing surface of stub shaft. Slide spring off shaft. Be careful not to damage shaft surface.
3. Remove valve spool by holding the valve assembly in one hand with the stub shaft pointing down. Insert the end of pencil or wood rod through opening in valve body cap and push spool until it is out far enough to be removed. In this procedure, rotate to prevent jamming. If spool becomes jammed it may be necessary to remove stub shaft, torsion bar and cap assembly.

Rotary Valve Reassembly

Caution All parts must be free of dirt, chips, etc., before assembly and must be protected after assembly.

1. Lubricate three new back-up O-ring seals with automatic transmission oil and reassemble in the ring grooves of valve body. Assemble three new valve body rings in the grooves over the O-ring seals by carefully slipping over the valve body.

NOTE: if the valve body rings seem loose or twisted in the grooves, the heat of the oil during operation will cause them to straighten.

2. Lubricate a new dampener O-ring with automatic transmission oil and install in valve spool groove.
3. Assemble stub shaft torsion bar and cap assembly in the valve body, aligning the groove in the valve cap with the pin in the valve body. Tap lightly with soft hammer until cap is against valve body shoulder. Valve body pin must be in the cap groove. Hold parts together during the remainder of assembly.
4. Lubricate spool. With notch in

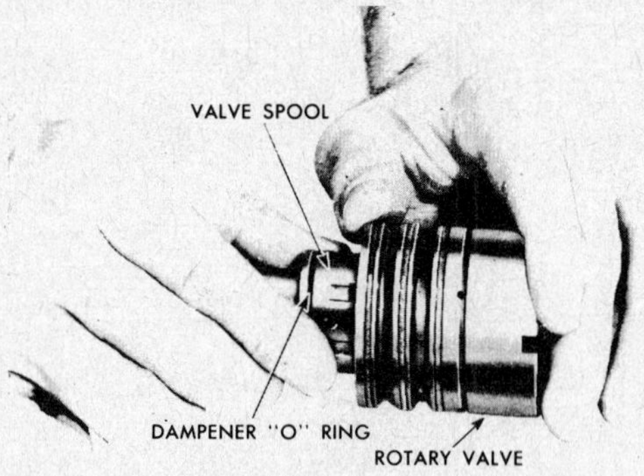
VALVE SPOOL
DAMPENER "O" RING
ROTARY VALVE

Removing valve spool from rotary valve
(© Pontiac Div., G.M. Corp)

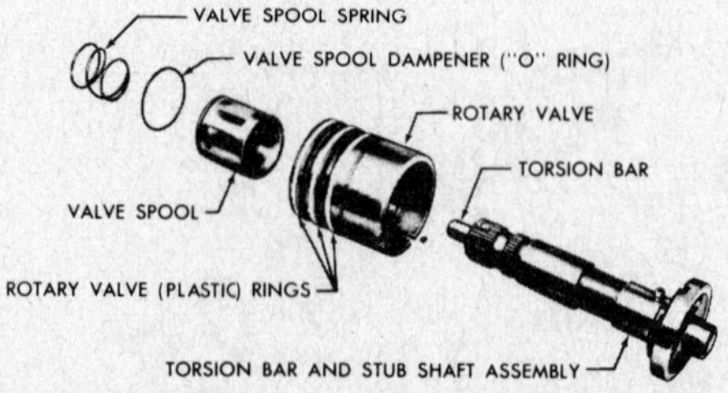
VALVE SPOOL SPRING
VALVE SPOOL DAMPENER ("O" RING)
ROTARY VALVE
TORSION BAR
VALVE SPOOL
ROTARY VALVE (PLASTIC) RINGS
TORSION BAR AND STUB SHAFT ASSEMBLY

Rotary valve, disassembled view
(© Pontiac Div., G.M. Corp)

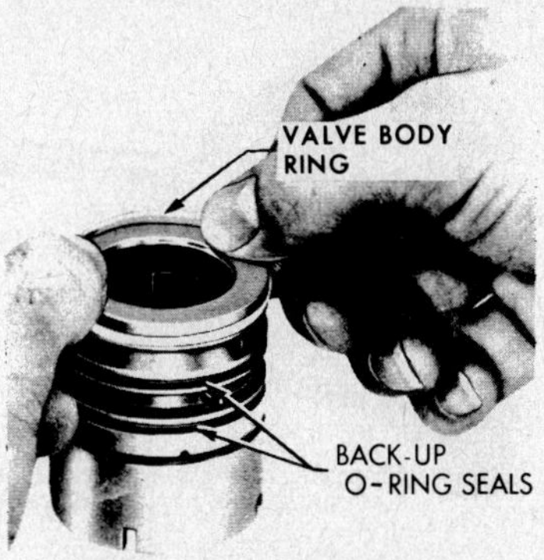
VALVE BODY RING
BACK-UP O-RING SEALS
Installing valve body rings
(© Buick Motor Div., G.M. Corp)

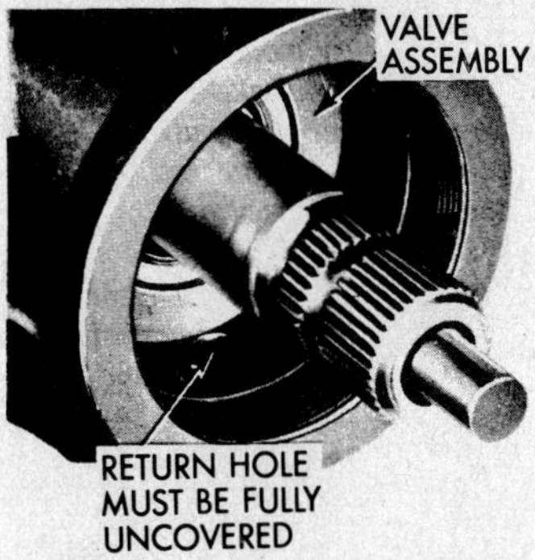
VALVE ASSEMBLY
RETURN HOLE MUST BE FULLY UNCOVERED
Valve assembly installed in housing
(© Buick Motor Div., G.M. Corp)

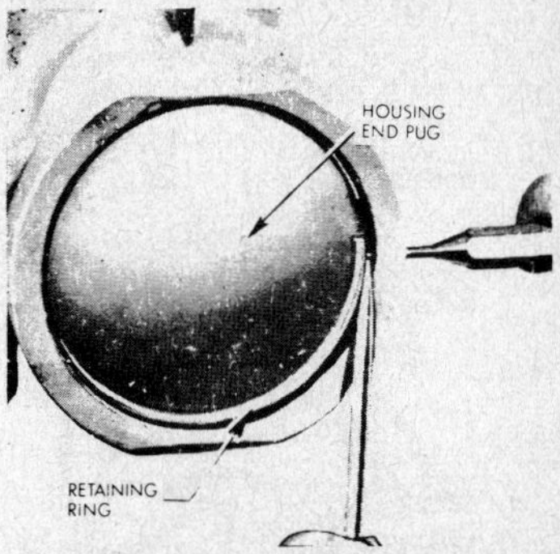
HOUSING END PUG
RETAINING RING
Removing housing end plug retaining ring
(© Buick Motor Div., G.M. Corp)

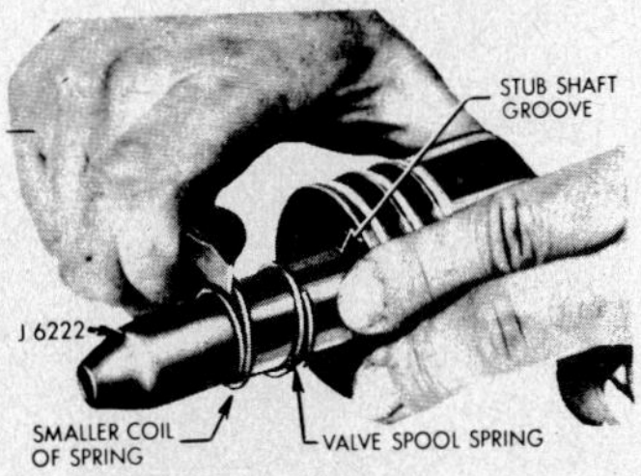
STUB SHAFT GROOVE
J 6222
SMALLER COIL OF SPRING
VALVE SPOOL SPRING
Installing valve spool spring
(© Buick Motor Div., G.M. Corp)

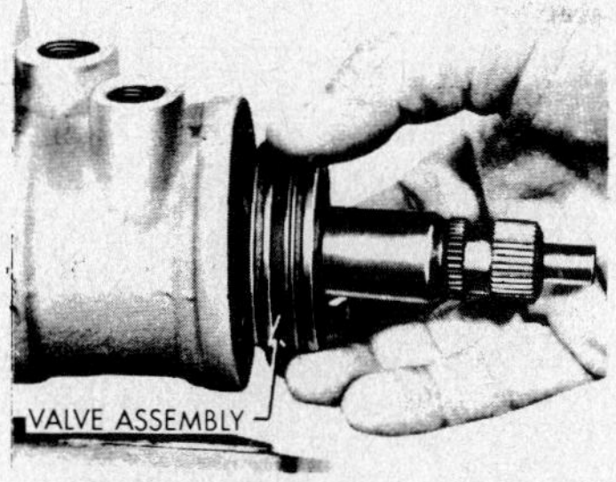
VALVE ASSEMBLY
Inserting valve assembly in housing
(© Buick Motor Div., G.M. Corp)

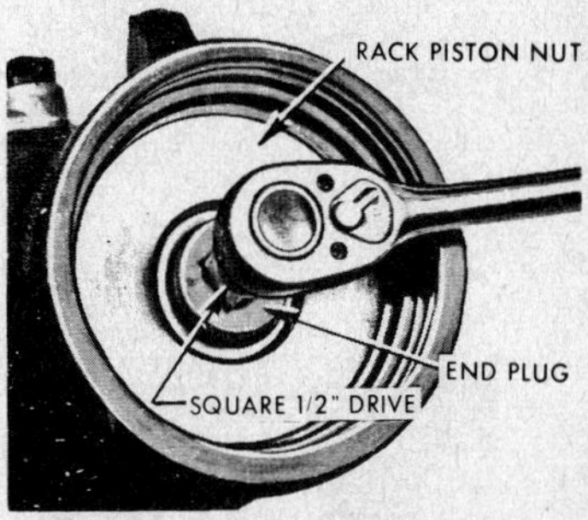
RACK PISTON NUT
END PLUG
SQUARE 1/2" DRIVE
Removing rack-piston nut end plug
(© Buick Motor Div., G.M. Corp)

spool toward valve body, slide the spool over the stub shaft. Align the notch on the spool with the spool drive pin on stub shaft and carefully engage spool in valve body bore. Push spool evenly and with slight rotating motion until spool reaches drive pin. Rotate spool slowly, with some pressure, until notch engages pin. Be sure dampener O-ring seal is evenly distributed in the spool groove.

Caution Use extreme care because spool-to-valve body clearance is very small. Damage is easily caused.

5. With seal protector tool over stub shaft, slide valve spool spring over stub shaft, with small diameter of spring going over shaft last. Work spring onto shaft until small coil is located in stubshaft groove.
6. Lubricate a new cap-to-O-ring seal and install in valve body.

Adjuster Plug and Rotary Valve Installation

1. Align narrow pin slot on valve body with valve body drive pin on the worm. Insert the valve assembly into gear housing by pressing against valve body with finger tips. Do not press on stub shaft or torsion bar. The return hole in the gear housing should be fully visible when properly assembled.

Caution Do not press on stub shaft as this may cause shaft and cap to pull out of valve body, allowing the spool dampener O-ring seal to slip into valve body oil grooves.

2. With protector over end of stub shaft, install adjuster plug assembly snugly into gear housing then back plug off approximately one-eighth turn. Install plug locknut but do not tighten. Adjust preload as described in the adjustment section.
3. After adjustment, tighten locknut.

Pitman Shaft Removal and Installation

1. Completely drain the gear assembly and thoroughly clean the outside.
2. Place gear in vise.
3. Rotate stub shaft until pitman shaft gear is in center position. Remove side cover retaining bolts.
4. Tap end of pitman shaft with soft hammer and slide shaft out of housing.
5. Remove and discard side cover O-ring seal.
6. The seals, washers, retainers and bearings may now be removed and examined.
7. Examine all parts for wear or damage and replace as required.
8. Install in reverse of above. Make proper adjustment as described in adjustment section.

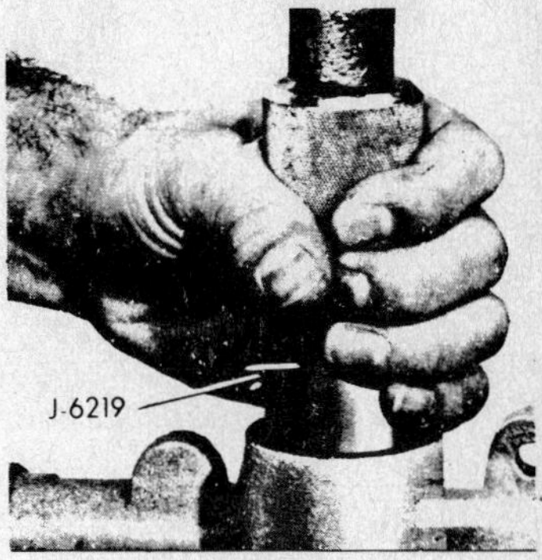
J-6219
Installing pitman shaft seals
(© Buick Motor Div., G.M. Corp)

Rack-Piston Nut and Worm Assembly Removal

1. Completely drain the gear assembly and thoroughly clean the outside.
2. Remove pitman shaft assembly, previously described.
3. Rotate housing end plug retaining ring so that one end of ring is over hole in gear housing. Spring one end of ring so screwdriver can be inserted to lift out ring.
4. Rotate stub shaft to full left turn position to force end plug out of housing.
5. Remove and discard housing end plug O-ring seal.
6. Remove rack-piston nut end plug with ½ in. square drive.
7. Insert tool in end of worm. Turn stub shaft so that rack-piston nut will go into tool and remove

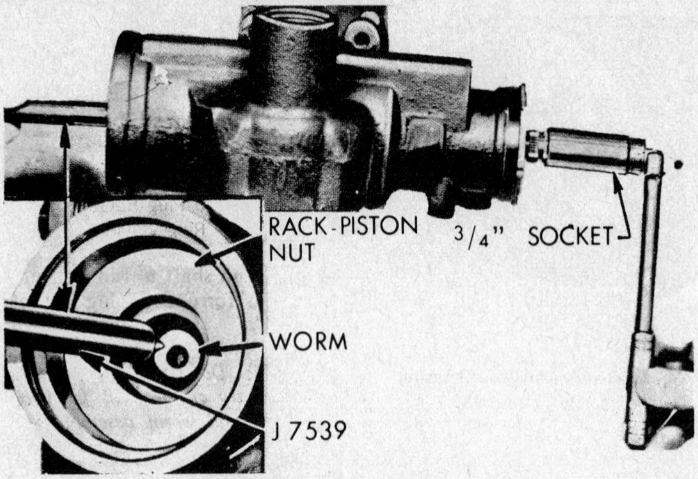
RACK-PISTON NUT
3/4" SOCKET
WORM
J 7539
Removing rack-piston nut
(© Buick Motor Div., G.M. Corp)

TORQUE END PLUG TO 50 LB. FT.
Torquing rack-piston nut end plug
(© Buick Motor Div., G.M. Corp)

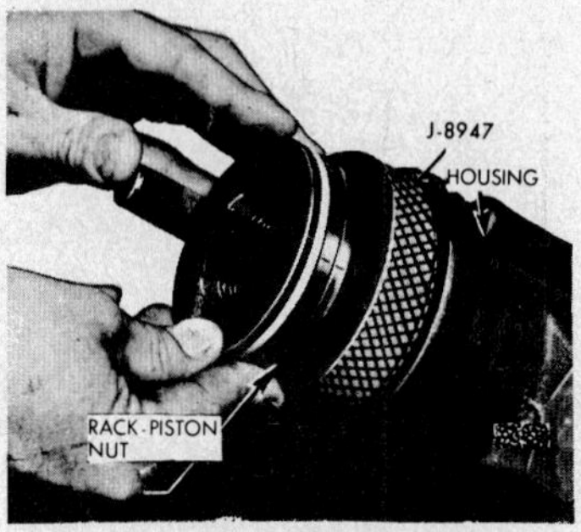
J-8947
HOUSING
RACK-PISTON NUT
Installing rack-piston nut—43, 44, 45000 series
(© Buick Motor Div., G.M. Corp)

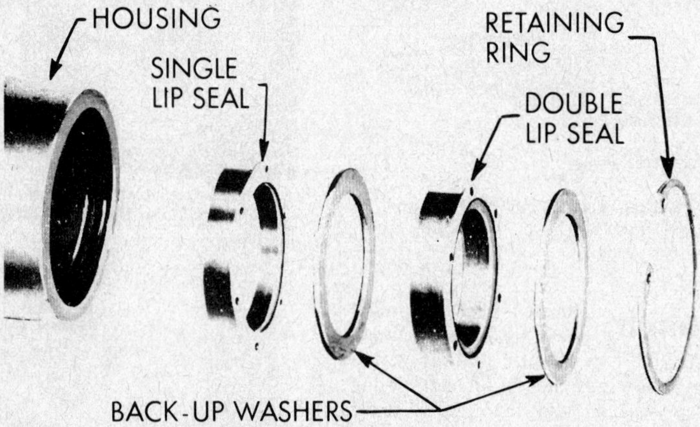
HOUSING
SINGLE LIP SEAL
RETAINING RING
DOUBLE LIP SEAL
BACK-UP WASHERS
Pitman shaft seals
(© Buick Motor Div., G.M. Corp)

rack-piston nut from gear housing.

8. Remove adjuster plug and rotary valve assemblies as previously described.
9. Remove worm and lower thrust bearing and races.
10. Remove cap-to-O-ring seal and discard.

Rack-Piston Nut and Worm Disassembly and Reassembly

1. Remove and discard piston ring and back-up O-ring on rack-piston nut.
2. Remove ball guide clamp and return guide.
3. Place nut on clean cloth and remove ball retaining tool. Make sure all balls are removed.
4. Inspect all parts for wear, nicks, scoring or burrs. If worm or rack-piston nut need replacing, both must be replaced as a matched pair.
5. In assembling, reverse the above.

NOTE: when assembling, alternate black and white balls, and install guide and clamp. Packing with grease helps in holding during assembly.

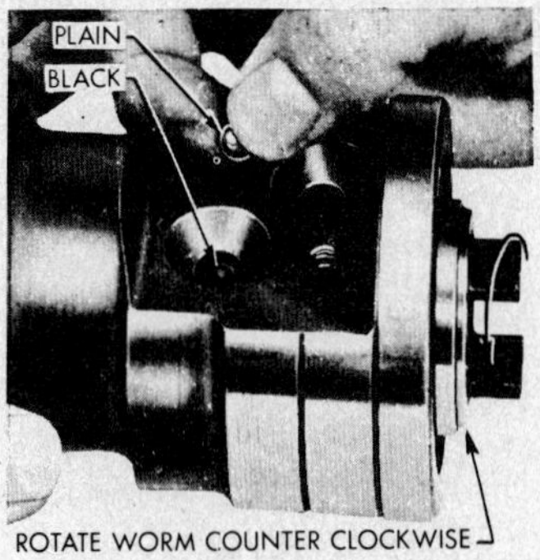
PLAIN
BLACK
ROTATE WORM COUNTER CLOCKWISE
Loading balls in rack-piston nut
(© Buick Motor Div., G.M. Corp)

When new balls are used, various sizes are available and a selection must be made to secure proper torque when making the high point adjustment.

Rack-Piston Nut and Worm Assembly Installation

1. Install in reverse of removal procedure.
2. In all cases use new O-ring seals.
3. Make adjustments as described in that section.

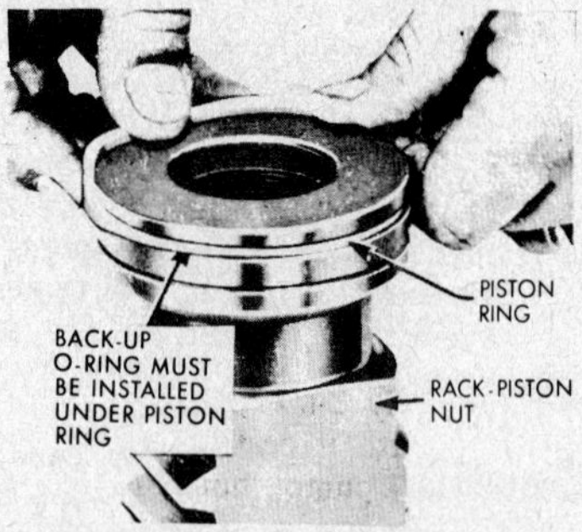
PISTON RING
BACK-UP O-RING MUST BE INSTALLED UNDER PISTON RING
RACK-PISTON NUT
Installing rack-piston ring on rack-piston nut
(© Buick Motor Div., G.M. Corp)

RACK-PISTON NUT
HOUSING
Installing rack-piston nut—46, 48, 49000 series
(© Buick Motor Div., G.M. Corp)

Section 7
Chrysler Full-Time Power Steering (Constant Control Type)

The power steering gear system for Chrysler Corporation cars is called the Constant Control type. This system consists of a hydraulic pressure pump, a power steering gear and connecting hoses.

The power steering gear housing contains a gear shaft and sector gear, a power piston with gear teeth milled into the side of the piston which is in constant mesh with the gear shaft sector teeth, a worm shaft which connects the steering wheel to the power piston through a coupling. The worm shaft is geared to the piston through recirculating ball contact.

A pivot lever is fitted into the spool valve at the upper end and into a drilled hole in the center thrust bearing race at the lower end. The center thrust bearing race is held firmly against the shoulder of the worm shaft by two thrust bearings, bearing races and an adjusting nut. The pivot lever pivots in the spacer which is held in place by the pressure plate.

When the steering wheel is turned to the left the worm shaft moves out of the power piston a few thousandths of an inch, the center thrust bearing race moves the same distance since it is clamped to the worm shaft. The race thus tips the pivot lever and moves the spool valve down, allowing oil under pressure to flow into the left-turn power chamber and force the power piston down. As the power piston moves, it rotates the cross-shaft sector gear and, through the steering linkage, turns the front wheels.

On a right turn the worm shaft moves into the power piston, the center thrust bearing race thus tips the pivot lever and moves the spool valve up, allowing oil under pressure to flow into the right power chamber and force the power piston up.

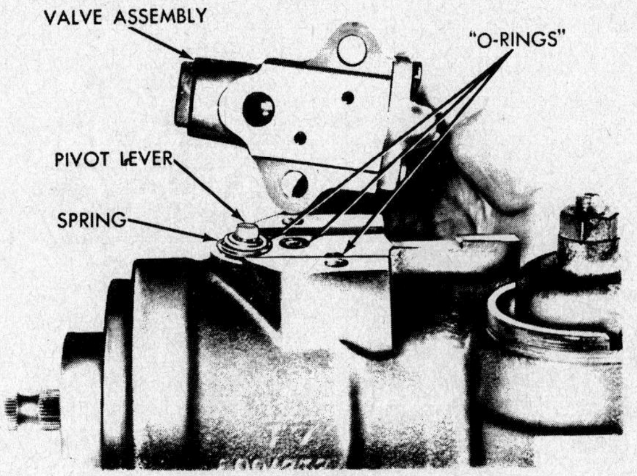
VALVE ASSEMBLY
"O-RINGS"
PIVOT LEVER
SPRING
Removing valve body assembly
(© Chrysler Corp)

Pressure Test

Connect the pressure test hoses with the pressure gauge installed between the pump and steering gear.

Now, fill the reservoir to the level mark, then start the engine and bleed the system. Allow the engine to idle until the fluid in the reservoir is between 150° F. and 170° F. Now turn the steering wheel to the extreme right and check the pressure reading, then turn to the extreme left and check the reading again. The gauge reading should be equal in each direction. If not, it indicates excessive internal leakage in the unit.

The pressure should agree with the specifications in Pump Section for satisfactory power steering operation.

Repair Operations

Reconditioning

1. Drain gear by turning worm shaft from limit to limit with oil connections held downward. Thoroughly clean outside.
2. Remove valve body attaching screws, body and three O-rings.
3. Remove pivot lever and spring. Pry under spherical head with a screwdriver.

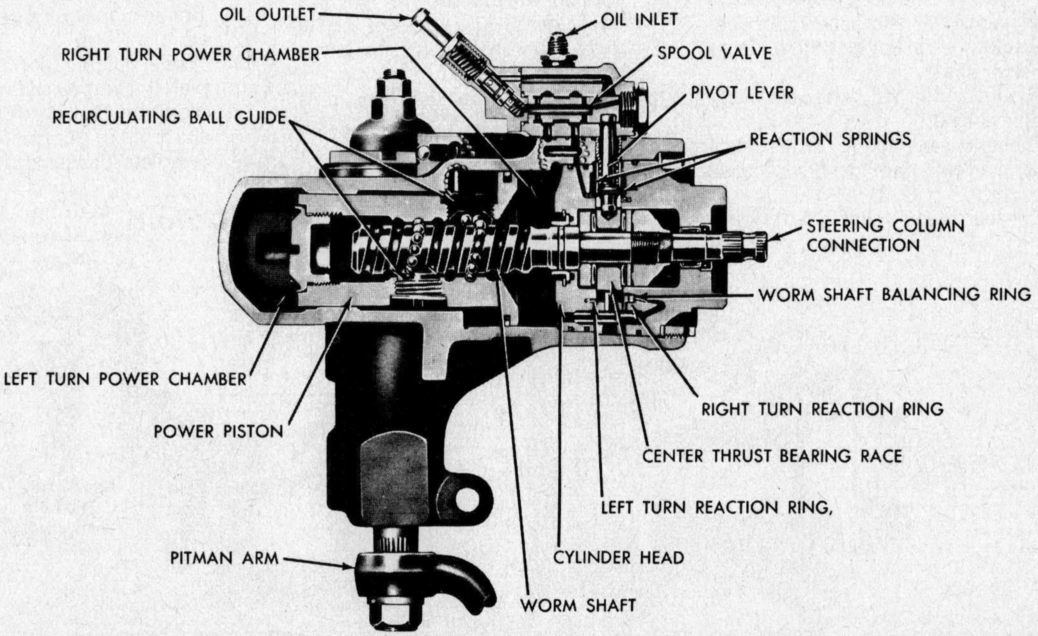
OIL OUTLET
OIL INLET
RIGHT TURN POWER CHAMBER
SPOOL VALVE
PIVOT LEVER
RECIRCULATING BALL GUIDE
REACTION SPRINGS
STEERING COLUMN CONNECTION
WORM SHAFT BALANCING RING
LEFT TURN POWER CHAMBER
RIGHT TURN REACTION RING
POWER PISTON
CENTER THRUST BEARING RACE
LEFT TURN REACTION RING,
PITMAN ARM
CYLINDER HEAD
WORM SHAFT
Chrysler power steering gear (© Chrysler Corp)

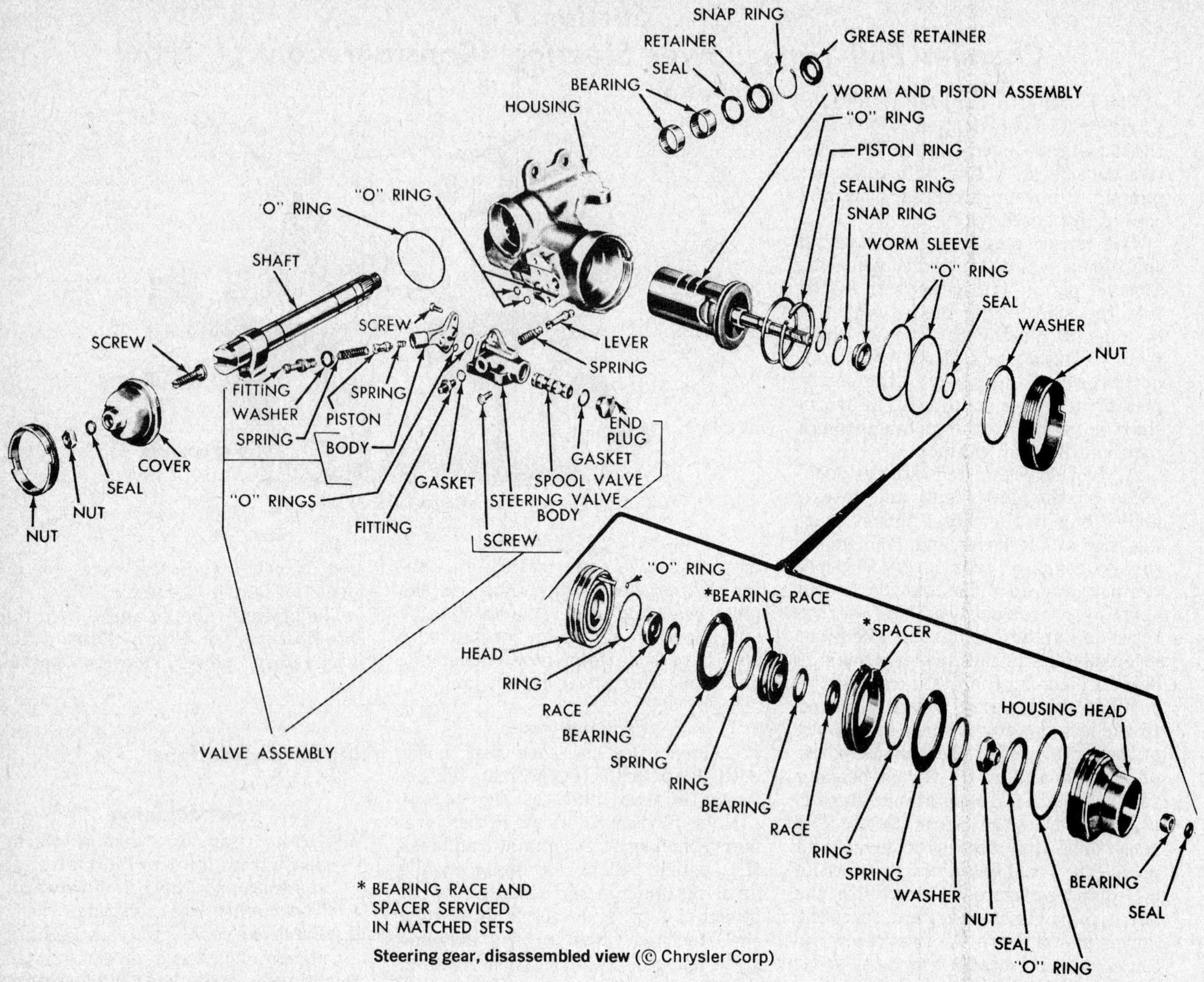

SNAP RING
RETAINER
GREASE RETAINER
SEAL
BEARING
WORM AND PISTON ASSEMBLY
HOUSING
"O" RING
PISTON RING
SEALING RING
SNAP RING
WORM SLEEVE
"O" RING
SEAL
WASHER
NUT
SHAFT
SCREW
LEVER
SPRING
FITTING
WASHER
SPRING
PISTON
BODY
COVER
SEAL
NUT
NUT
END PLUG
GASKET
SPOOL VALVE
STEERING VALVE BODY
GASKET
"O" RINGS
FITTING
SCREW
HEAD
RING
RACE
BEARING
SPRING
RING
BEARING
*BEARING RACE
*SPACER
RACE
RING
SPRING
WASHER
NUT
SEAL
"O" RING
HOUSING HEAD
BEARING
SEAL
VALVE ASSEMBLY
* BEARING RACE AND SPACER SERVICED IN MATCHED SETS

Steering gear, disassembled view (© Chrysler Corp)

Caution Use care not to collapse slotted end of valve lever as this will destroy bearing tolerances of the spherical head.

4. Remove steering gear arm from sector shaft.
5. Remove snap-ring and seal back-up washer.
6. Remove seal, using proper tool to prevent damage to relative parts.
7. Loosen gear shaft adjusting screw locknut and remove gear shaft cover nut.
8. Rotate wormshaft to position sector teeth at center of piston travel. Loosen power train retaining nut.
9. Insert tools into housing until both tool and shaft are engaged with bearings.
10. Turn worm shaft either to full left or full right (depending on car application) to compress power train parts. Then remove power train retaining nut as mentioned above.
11. Remove housing head tang washer.
12. While holding power train completely compressed, pry on piston teeth with screwdriver, using shaft as a fulcrum, and remove complete power train.

Caution Maintain close contact between cylinder head,

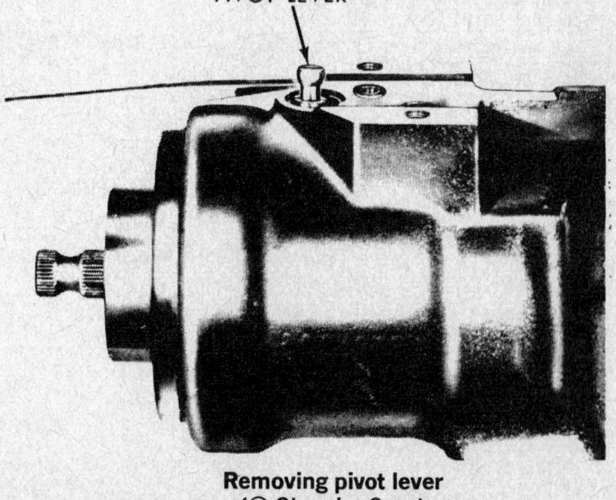

PIVOT LEVER

Removing pivot lever
(© Chrysler Corp)

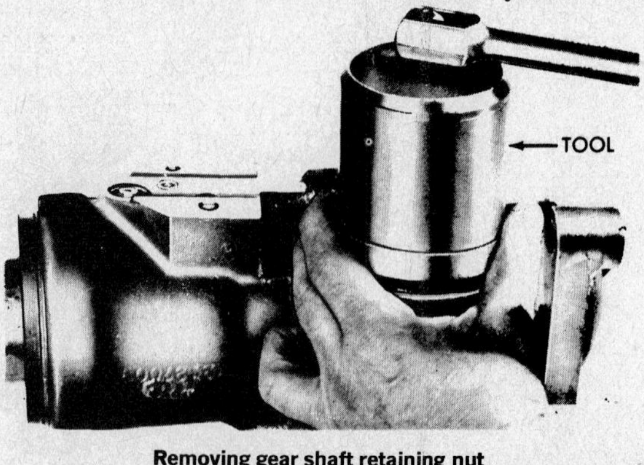

TOOL

Removing gear shaft retaining nut
(© Chrysler Corp)

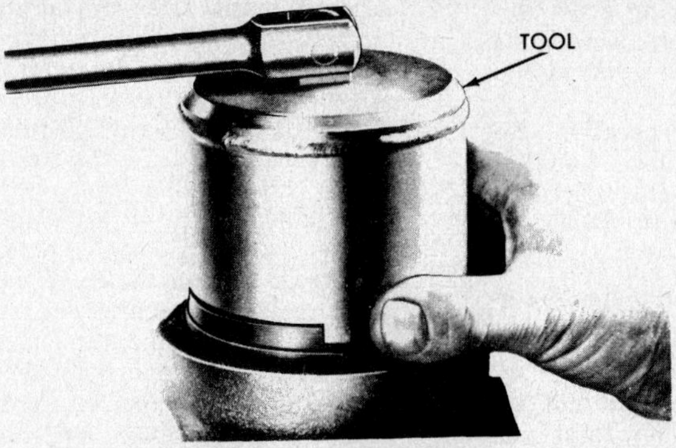
TOOL
Removing power train retaining nut
(© Chrysler Corp)

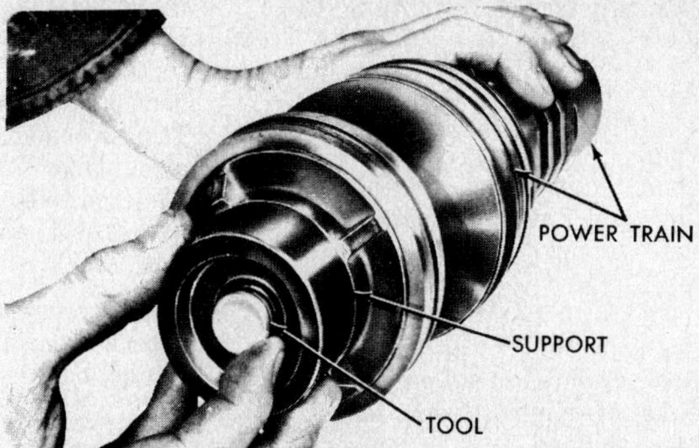
POWER TRAIN
SUPPORT
TOOL
Retaining bearing rollers with arbor tool
(© Chrysler Corp)

center race and spacer assembly and the housing head. This will eliminate the possibility of reactor rings becoming disengaged from their grooves in cylinder and housing head. It will prohibit center spacer from separating from center race and cocking in the housing. This could make it impossible to remove the power train without damaging involved parts.

13. Place power train in soft-jawed vise in vertical position. The worm bearing rollers will fall out. Use of arbor tool will hold roller when the housing is removed.
14. Raise housing head until wormshaft oil shaft just clears the top of wormshaft and position arbor tool on top of shaft and into seal. With arbor in position, pull up on housing head until arbor is positioned in bearing. Remove when the housing is removed.
15. Remove large O-ring from housing head groove.
16. Remove reaction seal from groove in face of head with air pressure directed into ferrule chamber.
17. Remove reactor spring, reactor ring, worm balancing ring and spacer.
18. While holding wormshaft from turning, turn nut with enough force to release staked portions from knurled section and remove nut.

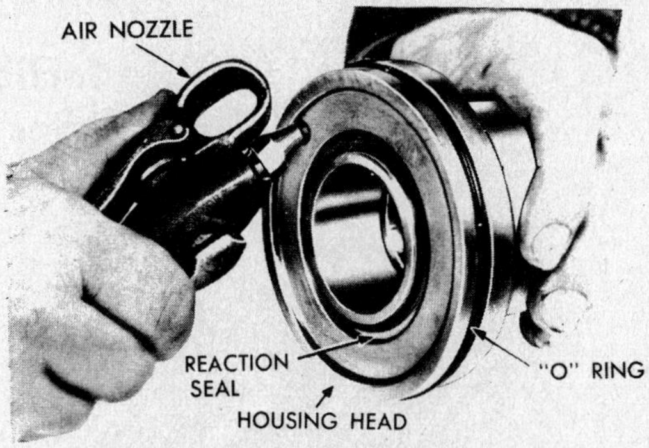
AIR NOZZLE
REACTION SEAL
"O" RING
HOUSING HEAD
Removing reaction seal from wormshaft support
(© Chrysler Corp)

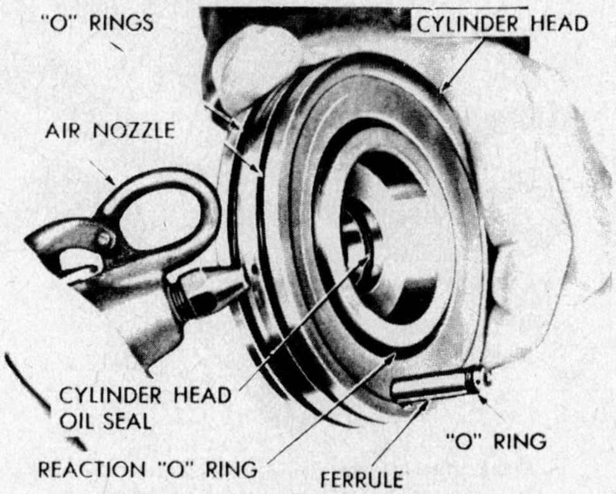
"O" RINGS
CYLINDER HEAD
AIR NOZZLE
CYLINDER HEAD OIL SEAL
"O" RING
REACTION "O" RING
FERRULE
Removing reaction seal from cylinder head
(© Chrysler Corp)

ARBOR
POWER TRAIN ASSEMBLY
CROSS SHAFT
Removing power train
(© Chrysler Corp)

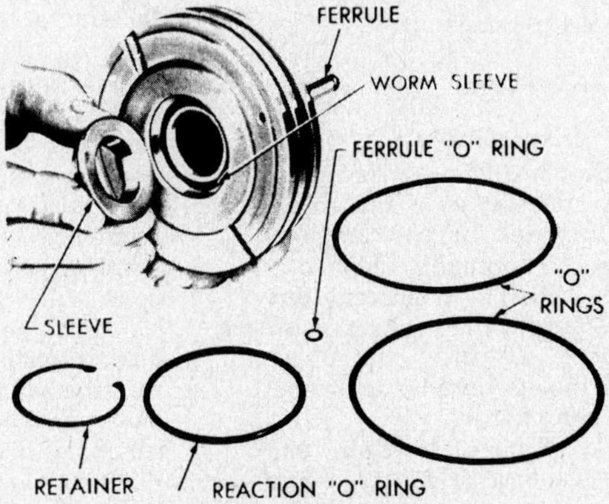
FERRULE
WORM SLEEVE
FERRULE "O" RING
"O" RINGS
SLEEVE
RETAINER
REACTION "O" RING
Removing cylinder head oil seal
(© Chrysler Corp)

NOTE: pay strict attention to cleanliness.

19. Remove upper thrust bearing race (thin) and upper thrust bearing.
20. Remove center bearing race.
21. Remove lower thrust bearing and lower thrust bearing race (thick).
22. Remove lower reaction ring and reaction spring.
23. Remove cylinder head assembly.
24. Remove O-rings from outer grooves in head.
25. Remove reaction O-ring from groove in face of cylinder head. Use air pressure in oil hole located between O-ring grooves.
26. Remove snap-ring, sleeve and rectangular oil seal from cylinder head counterbore.
27. Test wormshaft operation. Not more than 2 in. lbs. should be required to turn it through its entire travel, and with a 15 ft. lb. side load.

NOTE: the worm and piston is serviced as a complete assembly and should not be disassembled.

28. Shaft side play should not exceed 0.008 in. under light pull applied 2 5/16 in. from piston flange.
29. Assemble in reverse of above, noting proper adjustments and preload requirements following.
30. When cover nut in installed, tighten to 20 ft-lbs. torque.
31. Valve mounting screws should be tightened to 200 in.-lbs. torque.
32. With hoses connected, system bled, and engine idling roughly, center valve unit until not self-steering. Tap on head of valve body attaching screws to move valve body up, and tap on end plug to move valve body down.
33. With steering gear on center, tighten gear shaft adjusting screw until lash just disappears.
34. Continue to tighten 3/8 to 1/2 turn and tighten locknut to 50 ft. lbs.

Section 8
Ford Torsion Bar Power Steering

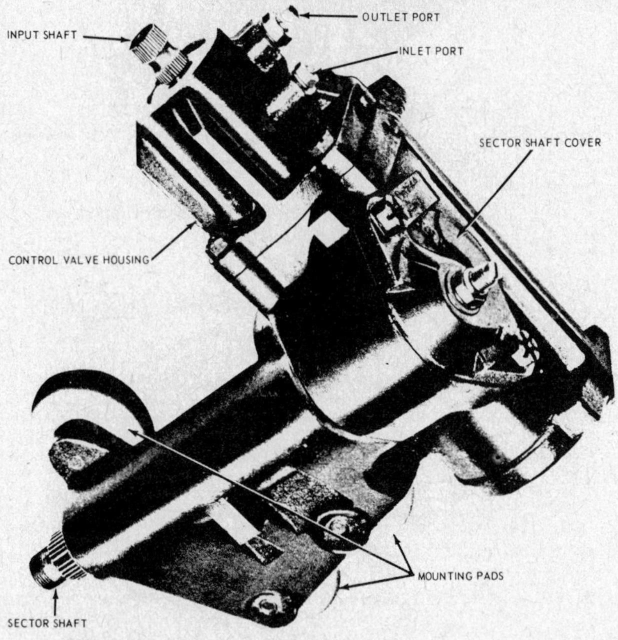
INPUT SHAFT
OUTLET PORT
INLET PORT
SECTOR SHAFT COVER
CONTROL VALVE HOUSING
MOUNTING PADS
SECTOR SHAFT
Power steering gear (© Lincoln-Mercury Div., Ford Motor Co)

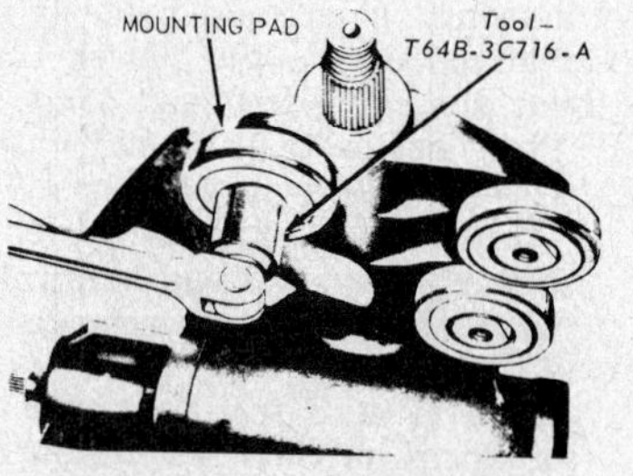
MOUNTING PAD
Tool–
T64B-3C716-A
Removing or installing steering gear mounting pads
(© Lincoln-Mercury Div., Ford Motor Co)

This is an integral type with steering gear, power unit and control valve combined as one unit.

Repair Operations

Disassembly

1. Remove housing mounting pads.
2. Invert steering gear and rotate shaft back and forth to completely drain. Thoroughly clean outside of housing to prevent dirt interference while working on assembly.
3. Mount in soft-jawed vise or special holding fixture.
4. Remove Teflon locknut and brass washer from adjusting screw.
5. Turn input shaft to either lock then back 1¾ turns to center the gear.
6. Remove sector shaft cover attaching screws and identifying tag.
7. Tap lower end of sector shaft with soft hammer to loosen it, then lift cover and shaft from housing as a unit. Discard O-ring.
8. Turn cover counterclockwise and remove from adjusting screw.
9. Remove valve housing attaching bolts. Lift valve housing from steering gear housing, while holding piston to prevent it from rotating off the worm shaft. Remove housing and passage O-rings and discard.
10. With valve body and piston on end (piston end down), rotate input shaft counterclockwise out of piston. Allow ball bearings to drop into piston.
11. With cloth over open end of piston, invert to remove balls.
12. Remove ball guide clamp and guides.
13. Install valve body in holding fixture. Do not use vise. Remove locknut and retaining nut.
14. Slide worm and valve assembly out of valve housing.
15. Remove shim from valve housing bore.

Valve Housing R & R

1. Remove dust seal from rear of housing.
2. Remove snap-ring from housing.
3. Turn fixture to invert valve housing.

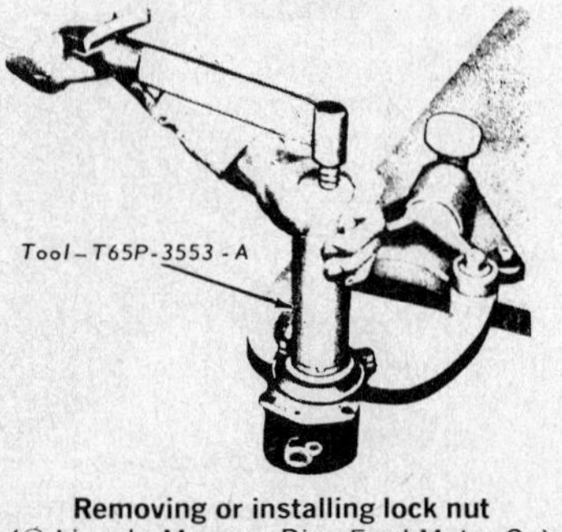
Tool–T65P-3553-A
Removing or installing lock nut
(© Lincoln-Mercury Div., Ford Motor Co)

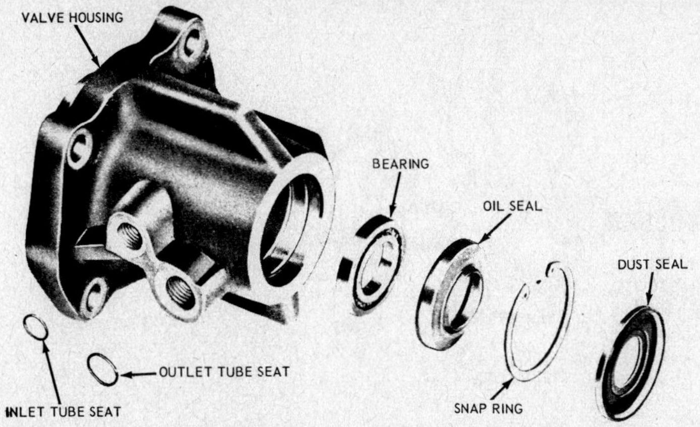
VALVE HOUSING
BEARING
OIL SEAL
DUST SEAL
OUTLET TUBE SEAT
INLET TUBE SEAT
SNAP RING

Valve housing, disassembled view (© Lincoln-Mercury Div., Ford Motor Co)

4. From opposite the seal end, gently tap bearing and seal from housing. Discard seal. Use care not to mar or damage the bore in housing.
5. Remove inlet and outlet seats if damaged. Use an Easy-out.
6. If installing new seats, coat with vaseline and position them in housing. Install and tighten tube nuts to press seats into proper position.
7. Coat bearing and seal surfaces with vaseline.
8. Position bearing in housing and, with proper tool, see that it is thoroughly seated.
9. Lubricate new seal with gear lubricant and place in housing with metal side of seal facing outward. Drive seal into housing until outer edge of seal does not quite clear the snap-ring groove.
10. Place snap-ring in housing and gently drive ring in until it seats in its groove. This will properly locate the seal.
11. Place dust seal in housing with rubber side out and drive into place. The seal must be located behind the undercut.

Worm and Valve R & R

1. Remove snap-ring from end of actuator.

NOTE: in 1971 Ford, Mercury, Thunderbird, Lincoln, Mark III and 1972 Torino and Montego, a Belleville spring is added to the actuator assembly. The addition of this spring eliminates the necessity for selective snap rings, so that only the (.048-.050) snap ring is needed. The Belleville spring is assembled beneath the tapered snap-ring with the convex side (color coded) away from the spool.

2. Slide control valve spool off of actuator.
3. Install valve spool evenly and slowly with slight oscillating motion into flanged end of housing with identification groove between the valve spool lands facing outward. Check for freedom of valve movement within working area. Spool should enter housing freely and fall by its own weight.
4. If spool is not free, check for burrs and remove with a hard stone.
5. Check valve for burrs and if burrs are found, stone valve in a radial direction only. Be sure valve is entirely free.
6. Remove spool from housing.
7. Slide spool into actuator, making sure groove in spool annulus is toward worm.
8. Install snap-ring to retain spool.
9. Check clearance between spool and snap-ring. It should be 0.0005-0.0035 in. If not within these limits, select snap-ring that will produce 0.002 in clearance.

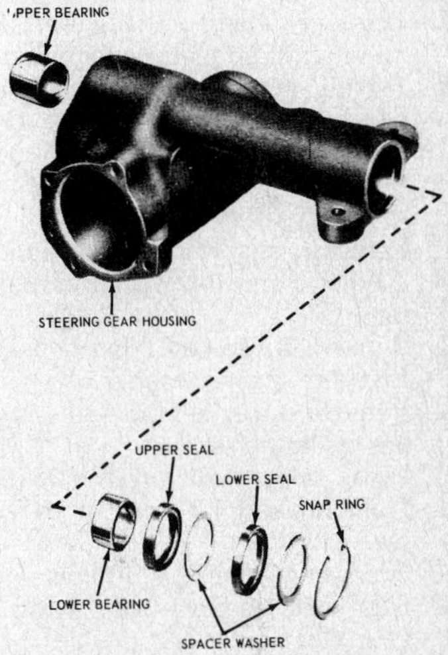
UPPER BEARING
STEERING GEAR HOUSING
UPPER SEAL
LOWER SEAL
SNAP RING
LOWER BEARING
SPACER WASHER

Steering gear housing, disassembled view (© Lincoln-Mercury Div., Ford Motor Co)

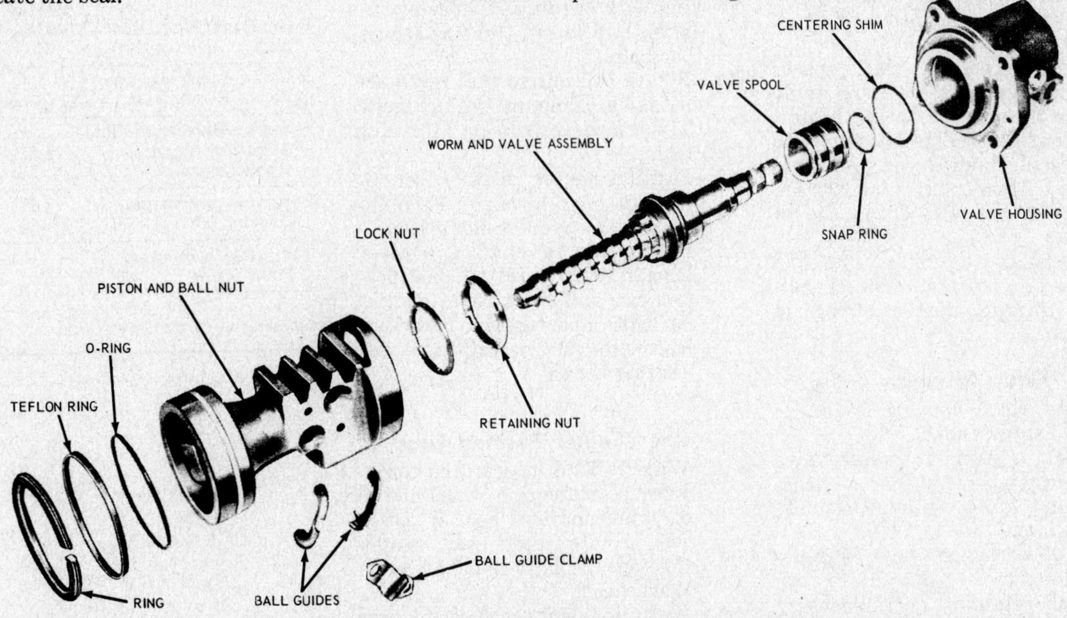
CENTERING SHIM
VALVE SPOOL
WORM AND VALVE ASSEMBLY
VALVE HOUSING
SNAP RING
LOCK NUT
PISTON AND BALL NUT
O-RING
TEFLON RING
RETAINING NUT
BALL GUIDE CLAMP
RING
BALL GUIDES

Ball nut and valve housing, disassembled view (© Lincoln-Mercury Div., Ford Motor Co)

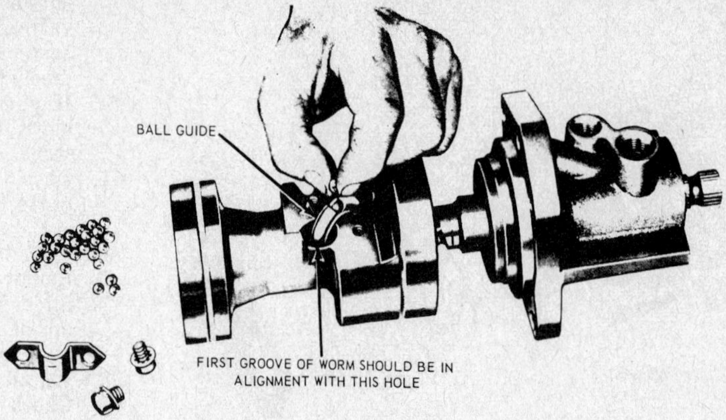
BALL GUIDE
FIRST GROOVE OF WORM SHOULD BE IN
ALIGNMENT WITH THIS HOLE

Assembling piston on wormshaft (© Lincoln-Mercury Div., Ford Motor Co)

Piston and Ball Nut R & R

1. Remove the Teflon ring and O-ring from piston and ball nut.
2. Dip new O-ring in gear lubricant and install on piston and ball nut.
3. Install new Teflon ring, using care not to stretch more than necessary.

Gear Housing R & R

1. Remove snap-ring and spacer washer from lower end of housing.
2. Remove outer seal from housing. Lift out spacer washer.
3. Remove upper seal in same manner as lower seal.
4. Press upper and lower bushings from housing if worn or defective.
5. Press new bushings into place.
6. Dip both sector shaft seals in gear lubricant.
7. Apply lubricant to sector shaft seal bore of housing and position sector shaft inner seal in housing with lip facing inward. Press into place.
8. Place a 0.090 in. thick spacer washer on top of seal and apply more lubricant to housing bore.
9. Place outer seal in housing with lip facing inward and press into place. Then place a 0.090 in. thick spacer washer on top of seal.
10. Place snap-ring in housing and press into position to locate seals and engage the snap-ring in groove.

Gear Assembly

1. Mount valve housing in fixture with flanged end up.
2. Place the same thickness valve spool centering shim in the housing as was removed. Use only one shim.
3. Install worm and valve in housing.
4. Install retaining nut in housing and torque to 55-65 ft. lbs.
5. Install locknut and tighten to 20-30 ft. lbs.
6. Place piston on bench with ball guide holes facing up. Insert worm shaft into piston so that first groove is in alignment with hole nearest to center of piston.
7. Place ball guide in position and feed balls into guide, turning worm clockwise. If all balls have not been fed into guide upon reaching stop, rotate shaft back and forth while installing balance of balls.
8. Secure guides in ball nut with the clamp.
9. Position new lube passage O-ring in counterbore of housing.
10. Apply vaseline to Teflon seal on piston.
11. Place new O-ring on valve housing.
12. Position housing spacer ring in housing and slide piston and valve into gear housing. Do not damage Teflon seal.
13. Align lube passage in valve housing with one in gear housing. Install, but do not tighten, attaching bolts.
14. Rotate ball nut so that teeth are in same plane as sector teeth. Tighten valve housing attaching bolts.
15. Position sector shaft cover O-ring in gear housing. Turn input shaft to center the piston.
16. Position sector shaft and cover in gear housing. Install identification tag and shaft cover attaching bolts and tighten. Make adjustments as described under "Adjustments."

Over Center Position Load

1. With no fluid in gear and torque wrench on steering wheel nut, or on input shaft of gear if out of car, rotate the gear slowly through the high point of sector shaft mesh.
2. With no load required to turn through this position and with adjuster locknut loose, gradually turn the adjuster screw to produce 11-12 in. lbs. more than required to turn when mesh is at no contact. Tighten locknut and recheck the torque.

Steering Wheel Turning Effort

Vehicle Model	*Lbs. Effort*
Ford, Mercury	5.0
Cougar, Fairlane, Falcon, Montego, Mustang, Maverick, Comet	6.5
Lincoln Continental, Mark III, Thunderbird	3.75

Power Steering Pump Service Specifications

Description	*Ford—Thompson*	*Eaton*
Pump Rotor Shaft End Play	.017 in. Max.—.003 in. Min.	
Max. Torque Allowed to Rotate Rotor Shaft	15 In-Lb.	
Stamped Housing-to-Plate Assy. Screw and Washer Assy.	28-32 Ft.-Lb.	
Reservoir-to-Stamped Housing Nut	43-47 Ft.-Lb.	
Cam Ring-to-Pressure Plate Screw		20 In-Lb.
Housing-to-Cover Screw		15-20 Ft.-Lb.

Steering Gear Torque Limits (Ft. Lbs.)

Description	*Manual and Power Assist* Fairlane, Falcon, Montego, Maverick, Comet	Mustang Cougar	Ford (XR-50) Power Steering	Saginaw Power Steering
Sector shaft cover bolts	17-25	15-22	55-70	30-35
Mesh load adjusting screw lock nut	32-40	32-40	25-35	20-30
Ball return guide clamp screw	42-60 ④	18-42 ④	60-120 ④	3-6
Preload adjuster lock nut	60-80	45-60		50-110
Valve housing to gear housing screw			35-45	
Race retaining inner nut			①	
Race lock nut			②	
Piston end cap			50-75	50-100
Set screw-rack adjustment				
Lubricant fill plug and vent	3-9 ③	3-9 ③		

① With tool T66P-3553-B - compute the torque as follows:

$$\text{Torque} = \frac{\text{Length of Torque Wrench} \times 60 \text{ Lb. Ft.}}{\text{Length of Torque Wrench} + 5.5 \text{ Inches}}$$

Example: With 13 inch torque wrench

$$\frac{13 \text{ In.} \times 60 \text{ Lb. Ft.}}{13 \text{ In.} + 5.5 \text{ In.}} = \frac{13 \times 60 \text{ Lb. Ft.}}{18.5} = 0.703 \times 60 = 42 \text{ (Lb. Ft.)}$$

② With tool T66P-3553-B - compute the torque as follows:

$$\text{Torque} = \frac{\text{Length of torque wrench} \times 25 \text{ Lb. Ft.}}{\text{Length of torque wrench} + 5.5 \text{ Inches}}$$

③ Minimum of one thread must remain exposed when installed.
④ In. Lbs.

Steering Gear and Column Torque Limits—Lincoln-Continental

Description	*Ft. Lbs.*
Meshload adjusting screw locknut	25—35
Ball return guide clamp screw (in. lbs.)	42—70
Gear cover to gear housing —power steering	55—65
Valve housing to gear housing—power steering	35—45
Race retaining inner nut—power steering	①
Race lock nut—power steering	②
Piston end cap—power steering	50—75

① With Tool T65P-3553-A—Torque to 55—65 Ft. Lbs.
With Tool T66P-3553-B, Compute the Torque as Follows:

$$\text{Torque} = \frac{\text{Length of Torque Wrench} + 5.5''}{\text{Length of Torque x 60 Ft. Lbs.}}$$

Example—With 13 in. Torque Wrench

$$\frac{13 \text{ in x } 60 \text{ Ft. Lbs.} \quad 13 \text{ x } 60 \text{ Ft. Lbs.}}{13'' \text{ x } 5.5''} \text{—}0.704 \text{ x } 60 \text{ —}42 \text{ Ft. Lbs.}$$

② With Tool T65P-3553-A — Torque to 20—30 Ft. Lbs.
With Tool T66P-3553-B, Compute the Torque as Follows:

$$\text{Torque} = \frac{\text{Length of Torque Wrench x 25 Ft. Lbs.}}{\text{Length of Torque Wrench} + 5.5 \text{ in.}}$$

Integral Power Steering Gear Specifications

Description	*Ford Design (XR—50)*	*Saginaw Design*
Type	Recirculating ball torsion bar	
Ratio	17:1	17.5:1
Turns of steering wheel (lock to lock-linkage disconnected)	4	4⅛
Fluid specifications	M—2C33—F	
Fluid capacity (included in pump reservoir fill)	1.6 Pints (Approx.)	
Phosphorescent Dye Additive (for leak detection)	M99B103—A (4 Oz. per quart)	
Sector shaft end play—linkage disconnected	None	.002″ Max.
Sector shaft mesh load. Total over mechanical center position. Must be①greater than worm Bearing preload torque, shown below	14 In. Lb. (Max) (Exc. Lincoln) 17 In. Lb. (Max.) (Lincoln)	14 In. Lb. (Max)
Worm bearing preload	2-7 In. Lb.	4-7 In. Lb. ②
Clearance between valve spool & retaining ring	.0035—.0005″ Preferable .002″	—
Pressure variation between right & left turn (at 250 P.S.I.)— Check efforts each side of center	4 In. Lb. Max. Variation	—
Clearance between inner sector seal and housing	.025″	—

① 8-9 in lb (XR—50 exc. Lincoln) 11-12 in lb for Lincoln, 4—8 in lb for Saginaw Gear.
② 3 in lb in excess of valve assy. Drag total worm bearing preload and seal drag not to exceed 8 in lb.

Steering Gear Adjustments

Description	
Sector shaft mesh load total over mechanical center position —must be 11—12 in-lbs greater than the off-center torque of 2 to 7 in-lbs	14 in. lbs. maximum ②
Clearance between valve spool and retaining ring	.002—.005 in Preferable 0.003 in
Pressure variation between right and left turns (at 250 lbs pressure)—Check efforts each side of center	4 in. lbs. Maximum Variation
Clearance between inner sector seal and housing	0.025

Power Steering Gear—Chrysler

Type	Constant control full time power
Ratio	15.7 to 1
Wheel turns—stop to stop	3 ½
Cross shaft bearings	1 needle bearing and 1 direct bearing on grey iron cover
Worm shaft thrust bearing pre-load	16-24 ozs.
Cross shaft adjustment	Tighten adjusting screw ⅜ to ½ turn past zero back lash (center of high spot)
Fluid capacity of hydraulic system	4 pts. (3¾ imperial pts.)
Type of fluid	Power steering fluid part No. 2084329 or equivalent

Pump

Type	Constant displacement—1.06 cu. in. per revolution	Constant displacement—.94 cu. in per revolution
Maximum pressure	1200 to 1300 PSI	950 to 1075 PSI
Pump output		
High level	2.5 to 3.0 gpm	2.1 to 2.6 gpm
Low level	1.4 to 1.8 gpm	
Type of fluid	Power steering—Part No. 2084329 or equivalent. Do not use Type "A" Transmission fluid	Power steering—Part No. 2084329 or equivalent Do not use Type "A" Transmission fluid

Power Steering Gear Torques

	Ft. Lbs.		*Pounds Foot*	*Pounds Inch*
Gear housing to frame bolt	100	Steering column support nut		140
Gear shaft adjusting screw lock nut	25-35	Steering shaft coupling bolts		200
Gear shaft cover nut	50	Valve body attaching bolts		200
Pump inlet fitting	30	Valve body end plug	30-40	
Steering arm nut	120	Steering wheel nut	27	

Chevrolet Adjustment Specifications—Power Steering

	Monte Carlo, Nova and Vega
Ball drag	3 in. lb. max.
Thrust bearing preload	½ - 2 in. lb. in excess of valve assy. drag
Over center preload	3 - 6 in. lb. in excess of above
Total steering gear preload	14 in. lb. max.
	Corvette
Worm bearing preload	4 to 7 in. lb.
Sector lash adjustment	4 to 10 in. lb. excess of above
Total steering gear preload	14 in. lb. max.

Chevrolet Power Steering—Pump Pressure

Vehicle	*Constant Ratio Steering*	*Variable Ratio Steering*
Chevrolet		1350-1450
Chevelle		1200-1300 (L-6) 1350-1450 (V-8)
Station Wagon and Vega	900-1000	
Monte Carlo		1350-1450
Nova		1200-1300 (L-6) 1350-1450 (V-8)
Corvette	870-1000	

Steering-Gear—Lincoln-Continental

Model	*XR-50*
Type	Recirculating ball torsion bar
Ratio	17:1
Turns of steering wheel (lock to lock) ①	3.6
Lube type ②	C1AZ-19582-A
Lube capacity—Lbs	1.6 Pints (Approx)

① Gear only—not attached to Pitman arm
② Phosphorescent dye additive for leak detection 4 oz per quart of fluid

Pump Torques

Location	*Ft. Lbs.*
High pressure hose fittings	13
Pump bracket bolts	23
Flow control valve plug	7
Bracket mounting bolts	30
⅛ in. pipe clean out plug	7

Front End Alignment

SERVICE PROCEDURE INDEX

Numbers refer to section numbers in text

Car	Year	Caster, Camber, and Toe-in
American Motors (except Rambler American)	1967	4
	1968–74	3
Buick (all)	1967–74	1
Cadillac	1967–74	2
Cadillac Eldorado	1967–74	See Car Section
Camaro	1967–74	1
Chevelle and Monte Carlo	1967–74	1
Chevrolet	1967–70	3
	1971–74	1
Chevy II and Nova	1967	3
	1968–74	1
Chrysler and Imperial	1967–74	4
Comet	1967	3
	1971–74	3
Corvette	1967–74	1
Cougar	1967–73	3
	1974	7
Dodge Coronet and Charger	1967–72	4
	1973–74	5
Dodge Polara and Challenger	1967–74	4
Fairlane, Montego, and Torino	1967–71	3
	1972–74	7
Falcon	1967–70	3
Ford and Mercury	1967–74	7
Lincoln Continental (except Mark III & IV)	1967–69	6
	1970–74	7
Lincoln Mark III & IV	1969–74	7
Maverick	1970–74	3
Mustang	1967–73	3
	1974	8
Oldsmobile, F-85, Cutlass, 4-4-2	1967–74	1
Oldsmobile Toronado	1967–74	See Car Section
Pinto	1971–74	8
Plymouth Belvedere, Road Runner, GTX and Satellite	1967–72	4
	1973–74	5
Plymouth Fury and Barracuda	1967–74	4
Pontiac (all)	1967–74	1
Rambler American	1967–69	3
Thunderbird	1967–73	7
Valiant, Dart, Duster, Demon	1967–74	4
Vega	1971–74	9

Section Page Numbers

1	U123	4	U124	7	U125
2	U124	5	U125	8	U125
3	U124	6	U125	9	U126

Wheel Alignment

Front wheel alignment is the position of the front wheels relative to each other and to the vehicle. It is determined, and must be maintained to provide safe, accurate steering, directional stability, and minimum tire wear. Many factors are involved in wheel alignment, and adjustments are provided to return those that might change due to normal wear to their original value. The factors which determine wheel alignment are dependent on one another; therefore, when one of the factors is adjusted, the others must be adjusted to compensate.

Descriptions of these factors and their effects on the car are provided below. Adjustment specifications for each model year are given at the beginning of each Car Section.

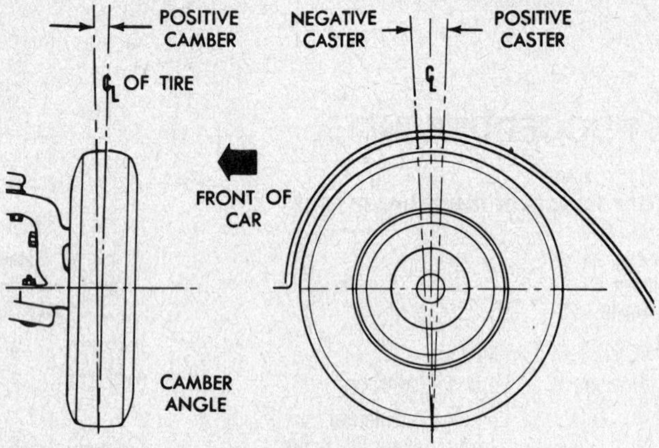

POSITIVE CAMBER
NEGATIVE CASTER
POSITIVE CASTER
℄ OF TIRE
℄
FRONT OF CAR
CAMBER ANGLE

Caster and camber angles

Camber

Camber angle is the number of degrees that the centerline of the wheel is inclined from the vertical when viewed from the front. A small degree of positive camber reduces loading of the outer wheel bearing, and allows for easier steering.

Caster

Caster angle is the number of degrees that a line drawn through the steering knuckle pivots is inclined from the vertical, toward the front or rear of the car. A small degree of positive caster improves directional stability and decreases susceptibility to crosswinds or road surface deviations.

Steering Axis Inclination

Steering axis inclination is the number of degrees that a line drawn through the steering knuckle pivots is inclined to the vertical, when viewed from the front of the car. This, in combination with caster, is responsible for directional stability and self-centering of the steering. As the steering knuckle swings from lock to lock, the spindle generates an arc (see illustration), the high point being the straight ahead position of the wheel. Due to this arc, as the wheel turns, the front of the car is raised. The weight of the car acts against this lift, and attempts to return the spindle to the high point of the arc, resulting in self-centering when the steering wheel is released, and straight line stability.

Included Angle

Included angle is the sum of the camber angle and the steering axis inclination. This angle is determined by the design of the steering knuckle forging and must remain constant. Therefore, if a different camber angle is necessary to make the included angle on both sides identical, a bent spindle or steering knuckle is indicated. When indicated, the damaged suspension member must be replaced, to permit accurate front wheel alignment. Since steering knuckle damage is most commonly due to impact on the lower portion of the wheel (i.e., hitting curb), the side with the greater included angle (camber angle same on each side) will often be found to have a bent spindle.

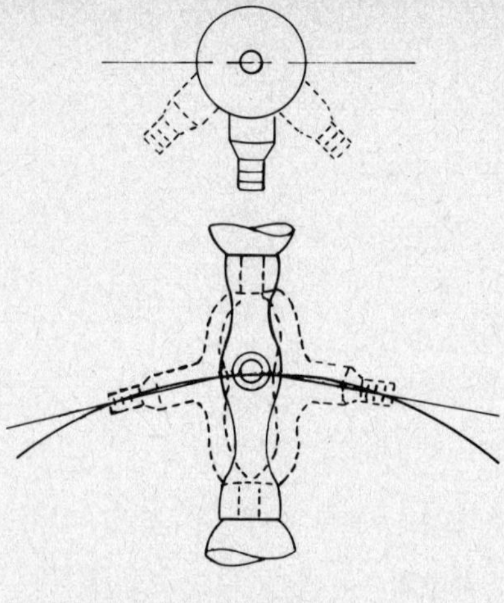
Arc generated by the spindle as the steering knuckle turns

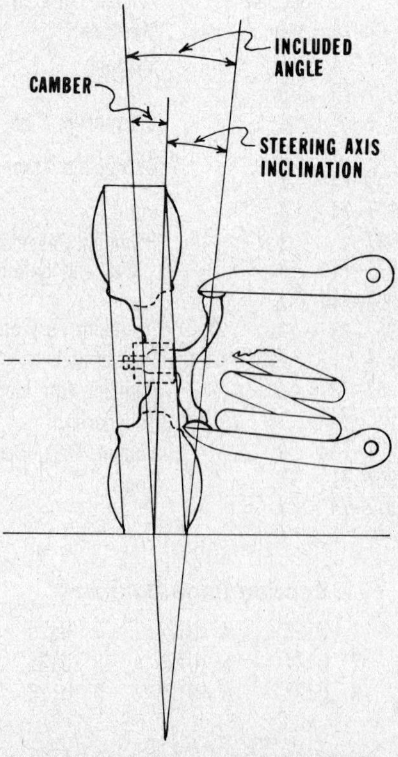

INCLUDED ANGLE
CAMBER
STEERING AXIS INCLINATION

Camber, steering axis, and included angle

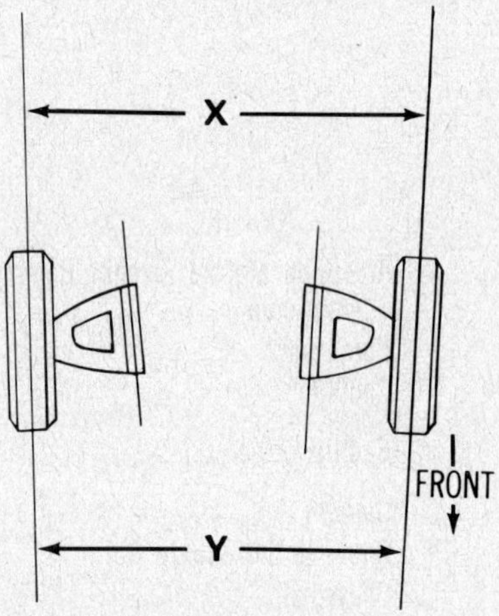

X
Y
FRONT

X-Y=Toe-in

Toe-In

Toe-in is the difference of the distance between the centers of the front and rear of the front wheels measured at spindle height. It is most commonly measured in inches, but is occasionally referred to as an angle between the wheels. Toe-in is necessary to compensate for the tendency of the wheels to deflect rearward while in motion. Due to this tendency, the wheels of a vehicle with properly adjusted toe-in are traveling straight forward when the vehicle itself is traveling straight forward, resulting in directional stability and minimum tire wear.

Steering wheel spoke misalignment is often an indication of incorrect front end alignment. Care should be exercised when aligning the front end to maintain steering wheel spoke position. When adjusting the tie rod ends, adjust each an equal amount (in the opposite direction) to increase or decrease toe-in. If, follow-

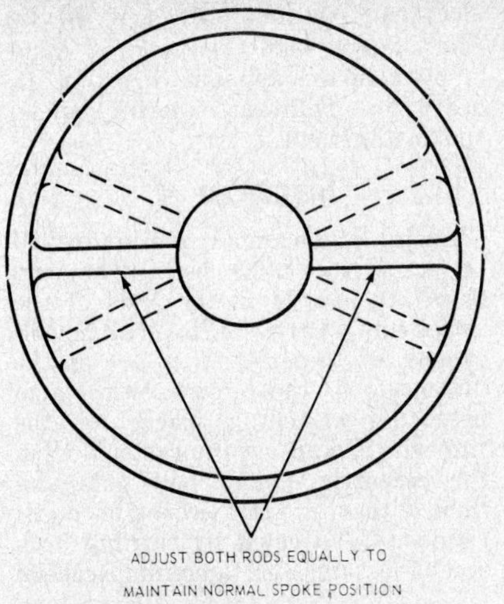
ADJUST BOTH RODS EQUALLY TO
MAINTAIN NORMAL SPOKE POSITION

Steering wheel spoke alignment

ing toe-in adjustment, further adjustments are necessary to center the steering wheel spokes, adjust the tie rod ends an equal amount in the same direction.

Steering Radius

When a car is negotiating a turn, the outer wheel follows the path of a circle of a larger radius than the inner wheel (see illustration). For this reason, the inner wheel must be steered to a somewhat larger angle than the outer wheel. This value (known as the Ackerman effect) is designed into the steering linkage; therefore, if alignment is adjusted properly, and the steering radius (or toe-out on turns) appears to be incorrect, it is indicated that the steering arms or the linkage is bent.

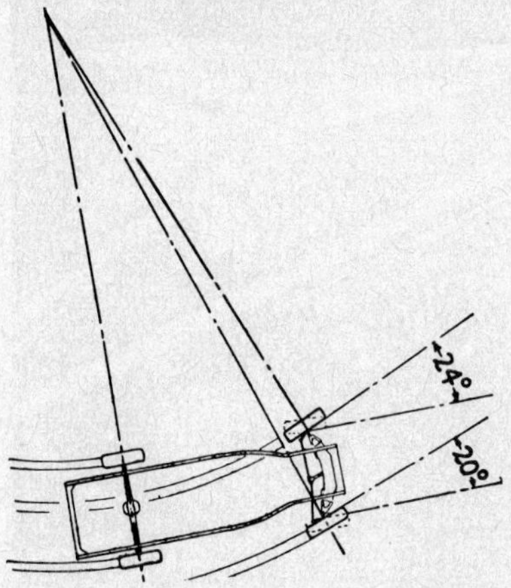
24°
20°

Toe-out. Inside wheel turns a greater number of degrees

Tracking

Tracking is the relationship between the paths traveled by the front and rear wheels when the vehicle is traveling in a straight line. When a car is tracking correctly, the path of the rear wheels will duplicate, or evenly straddle the path of the front wheels. Observing the car from the rear as it is driven away in a straight line will often make incorrect tracking evident.

If incorrect tracking is indicated, check as follows: Drop a plumb line from each lower ball joint, and from a point at each end of the rear axle, and mark the points on the ground with chalk. Measure these points from front to rear and diagonally. If the diagonal measurements are different (a tolerance of +¼″ is acceptable), but the longitudinal measurements are the same, the frame is swayed (diamond shaped). If the diagonal and longitudinal measurements are both different, the rear axle is misaligned. If both diagonal and longitudinal measurements are different, but the car does not appear to be tracking incorrectly, a kneeback condition is indicated. Kneeback implies that one side of the front suspension is bent or pushed back. It is possible to align the front end to specifications, and, if kneeback exists, have very poor handling characteristics.

Diagnosis

Hard Ride

1. Excessive tire pressure
2. Shock absorbers malfunctioning
3. Broken spring
4. Worn suspension bushings

Soft Ride

1. Insufficient tire pressure
2. Worn shock absorbers
3. Collapsed or weak spring

Car Veers to One Side

1. Unequal tire pressures
2. Incorrect caster, camber or toe-in
3. Unequal spring rates
4. Unequal shock absorber control
5. Incorrect steering axis inclination (bent spindle)
6. Damaged suspension components or bushings
7. Incorrect tracking
8. Dragging brake
9. Grease on brake lining

Wander

1. Incorrect or unequal tire pressures
2. Incorrect caster or toe-in
3. Excessively worn or damaged suspension components

Hard or Erratic Steering

1. Insufficient tire pressure
2. Lack of lubrication
3. Binding or damaged steering column, steering gear, or linkage
4. Loose power steering pump belt, or poor pump operation
5. Worn or damaged suspension components

Tires Wear in Center

1. Excessive tire pressure

Tires Wear on Both Edges

1. Insufficient tire pressure

Tires Wear Evenly on One Edge

1. Incorrect camber or toe-in
2. Bent or damaged suspension components

Tires Wear Unevenly on One Edge

1. Insufficient tire pressure
2. Incorrect camber or toe-in
3. Out of round wheel and/or tire
4. Loose steering linkage
5. Severe cornering

Tires Wear Unequally

1. Unequal tire pressure
2. Unequal tire size
3. Incorrect toe-in or camber
4. Loose or bent steering linkage

Squeal on Cornering

1. Insufficient tire pressure
2. Incorrect toe-in or camber
3. Severe cornering

Caster, Camber and Toe-in Adjustment

Section 1

Caster and Camber are controlled by shims between the frame bracket

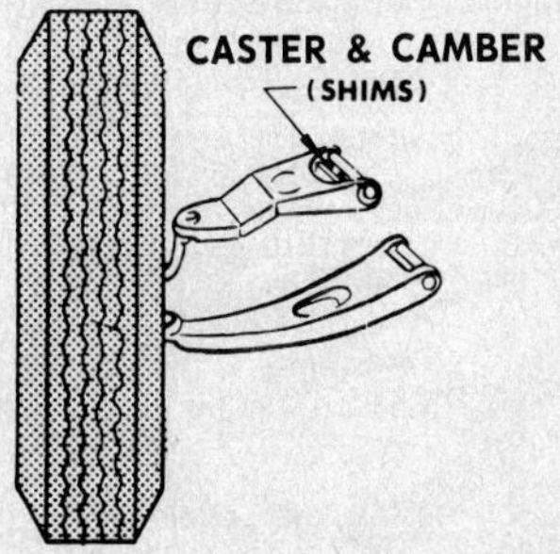
CASTER & CAMBER
(SHIMS)

Location of caster and camber adjustments for type 1
(© Snap-On Tools Corp)

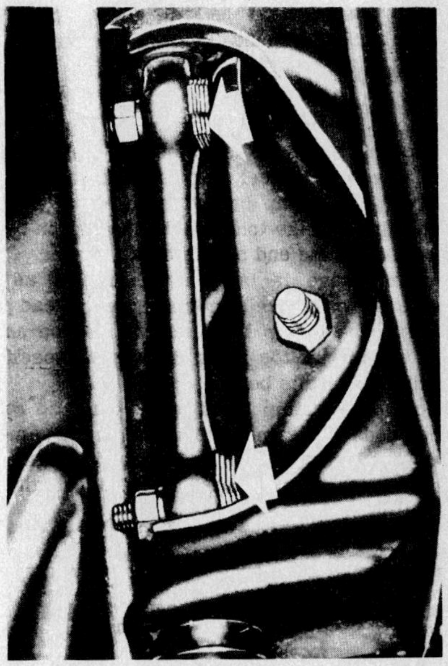

Typical type 1 caster and camber adjusting shim location
(© Chevrolet Div, G.M. Corp)

and the upper suspension arm pivot shaft.

To adjust caster, remove shims from the front bolt and replace them at the rear bolt, or vice versa. To adjust camber, add or remove the same number of shims from each bolt.

Keep in mind when loosening the bolts that the upper suspension arm is supporting the weight of the vehicle. Loosen the bolts only a sufficient amount to remove the shims.

Adjust toe-in by loosening the clamps on the sleeves at the outer ends of the tie-rod, and turning the sleeves an equal amount in the opposite direction, to maintain steering wheel spoke alignment while adjusting toe-in.

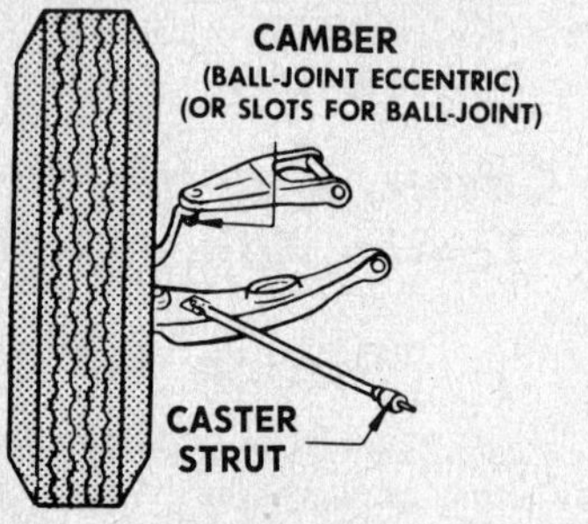

CAMBER
(BALL-JOINT ECCENTRIC)
(OR SLOTS FOR BALL-JOINT)
CASTER
STRUT

Location of caster and camber adjustments for type 2
(© Snap-On Tools Corp)

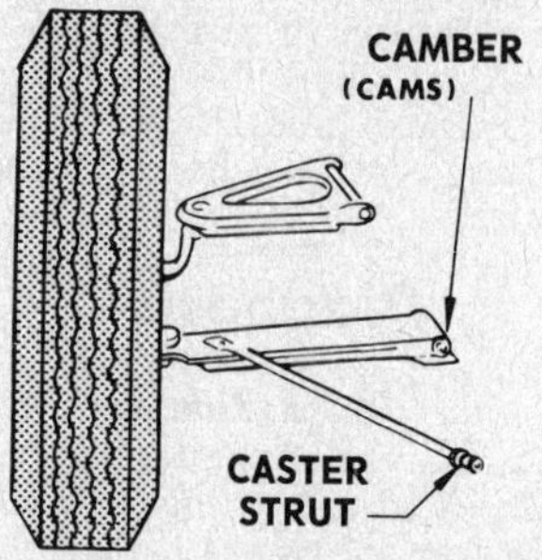

CAMBER
(CAMS)
CASTER
STRUT

Location of caster and camber adjustments for type 3
(© Snap-On Tools Corp)

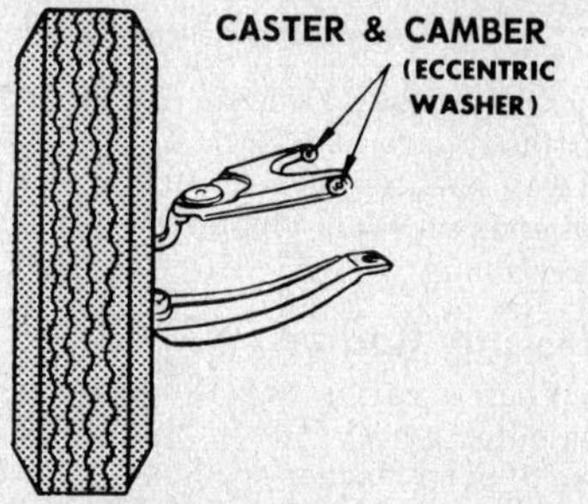

CASTER & CAMBER
(ECCENTRIC
WASHER)

Location of caster and camber adjustment for type 4 (except Imperial)
(© Snap-On Tools Corp)

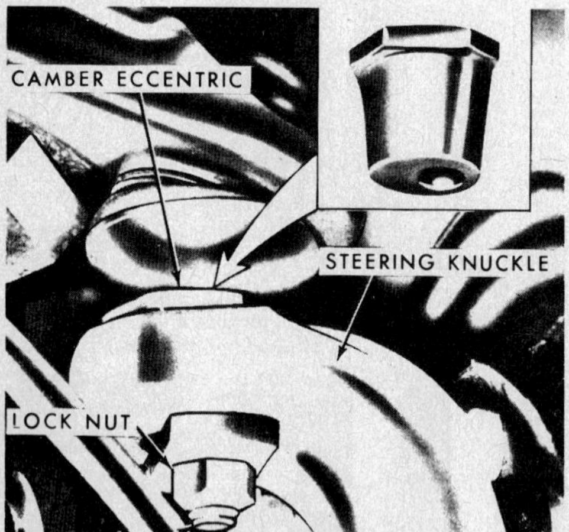

CAMBER ECCENTRIC
STEERING KNUCKLE
LOCK NUT
JOINT STUD

Details of type 2 camber adjustment
(© Cadillac Div, G.M. Corp)

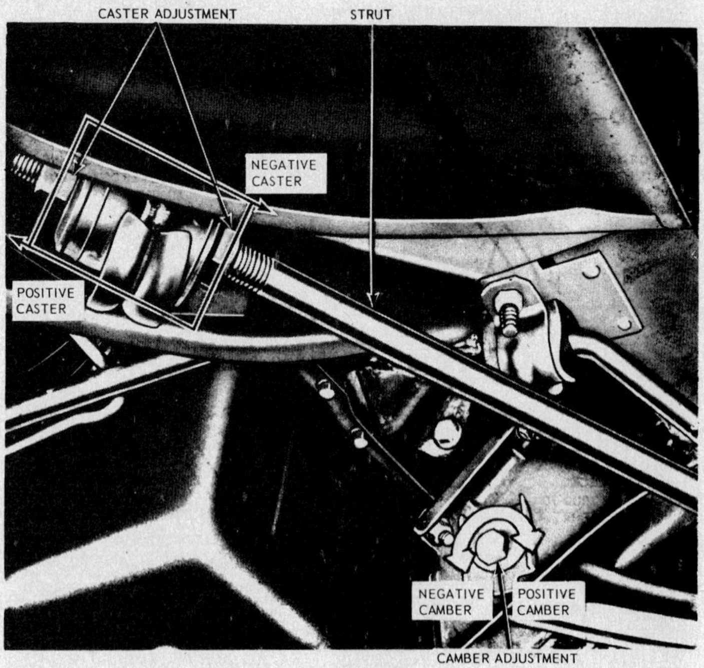

CASTER ADJUSTMENT
STRUT
NEGATIVE
CASTER
POSITIVE
CASTER
NEGATIVE
CAMBER
POSITIVE
CAMBER
CAMBER ADJUSTMENT

Type 3 caster and camber adjustment points

Section 2

Caster is adjusted by lengthening or shortening the struts at the frame crossmember. To adjust, turn both nuts an equal number of turns in the same direction. Lengthening the strut increases negative caster. One turn of the nuts changes caster approximately $\frac{1}{2}°$.

Camber is adjusted by turning the camber eccentric located in the steering knuckle upper support. Turning the eccentric changes the camber by moving the steering knuckle in or out. Loosen the ball joint stud locknut and tap the knuckle to free the eccentric, being careful not to strike the brake line or ball joint seal. Turn the eccentric until camber is within specifications. The stud must be positioned to the rear of the eccentric in order to maintain correct steering geometry. Tighten the ball joint stud nut to 60 ft. lbs.

Adjust toe-in by loosening the clamp bolts, and turning the adjuster sleeves at the outer ends of the tie rod. Turn each sleeve an equal amount in the opposite direction, in order to maintain steering wheel spoke alignment.

Section 3

Caster is adjusted by lengthening or shortening the struts at the frame crossmember. To adjust, turn both nuts an equal number of turns in the same direction. Caster adjustments should be within $\frac{1}{4}°$ of the opposing side of the car.

To adjust camber, loosen the lower control arm pivot bolt and rotate the eccentrics.

Adjust toe-in by loosening the clamp bolts, and turning the adjuster sleeves at the outer ends of the tie rod. Turn each sleeve an equal amount in the opposite direction, in order to maintain steering wheel spoke alignment.

Section 4

Caster and camber are controlled by eccentric (cam) bolts. The cam bolts are located at the ends of the upper control arm shafts on all models except the Imperial. They are on the underside of the upper control arm pivot bar attaching bracket on the Imperial. To adjust the caster, loosen the eccentric (cam) bolt nuts and turn either of the eccentric bolts. Camber is adjusted by turning both eccentrics an equal amount. Recheck caster after setting camber. Torque the eccentric (cam) bolts to 50–55 ft lbs (1967 American Motors), 65–70 ft lbs (all Chrysler Corp. except Imperial), and 160 ft lbs (Imperial).

To adjust toe-in, loosen the tie rod clamp bolts and turn the adjuster sleeves at the outer ends of the tie-rod an equal amount in opposite directions so that steering wheel spoke alignment is maintained.

Section 5

Caster and camber are controlled by the positioning of the upper control arm pivot bar adjusting bolts. To adjust caster, loosen one of the pivot bar adjusting bolt nuts and slide one end of the bar either inboard or outboard in its elongated mounting hole in the cross-member. Camber is adjusted by loosening both the pivot bar adjusting bolt nuts and sliding both ends of the bar an equal amount.

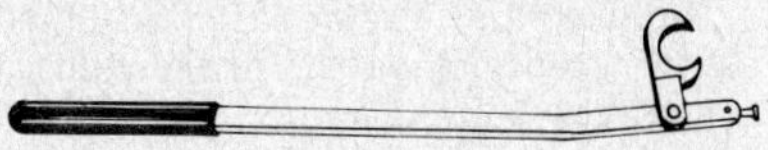

Type 5 caster and camber adjusting pry bar
(© Chrysler Corp)

NOTE: Plymouth recommends the use of a special pry bar no. C-4196 for the adjusting operation on the Satellite.

Recheck caster after setting camber. Torque the pivot bar adjusting bolt nuts to 160 ft lbs.

To adjust toe-in, loosen the tie rod clamp bolts and turn the adjuster sleeves at the outer ends of the tie rod an equal amount in opposite directions, so that steering wheel spoke alignment is maintained.

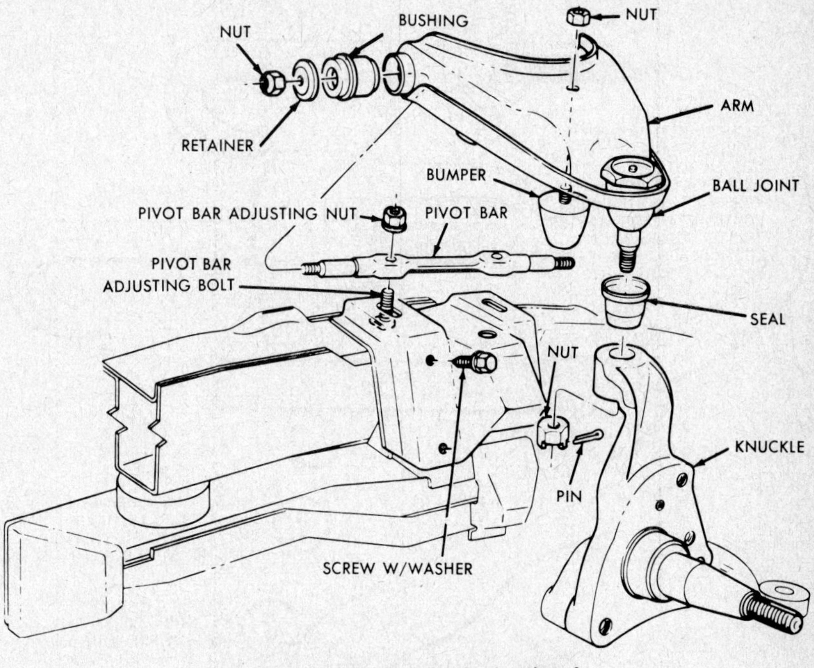
NUT
BUSHING
NUT
RETAINER
ARM
BUMPER
BALL JOINT
PIVOT BAR ADJUSTING NUT
PIVOT BAR
PIVOT BAR
ADJUSTING BOLT
SEAL
NUT
KNUCKLE
PIN
SCREW W/WASHER

Type 5 upper control arm showing location of pivot bar and pivot bar adjusting nut and bolt
(© Chrysler Corp)

Section 6

With the car positioned to adjust alignment, mark the position of the upper control arm pivot shaft, and loosen the pivot shaft retaining bolts. Lift the front end of the car and allow it to drop, to break the shaft loose from the frame. Using a pry bar, return the shaft to the index marks, and tighten the retaining bolts only enough to hold the shaft in position (loose enough to permit movement with the pry bar).

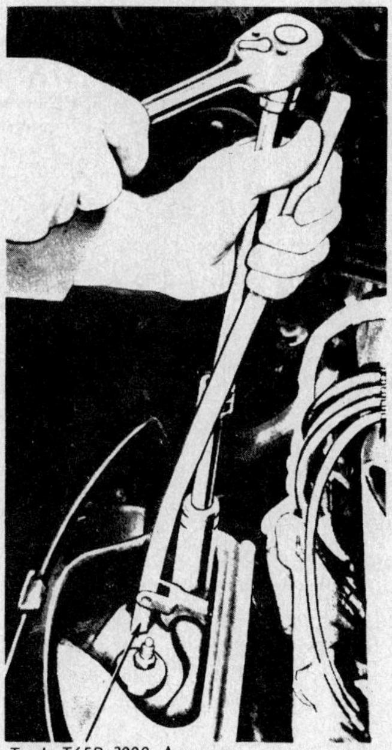
Tool—T65P-3000-A

Type 6 caster and camber adjustment using pry bar
(© Ford Motor Co)

To adjust caster, move either end of the pivot shaft in or out, using the pry bar. A movement of 3/32 in. at either bolt location will change caster approximately ½°. Camber is adjusted in a similar manner, by moving both ends of the shaft an equal distance. Moving the entire shaft 3/32 in. will change camber approximately ½°. After adjusting camber, tighten the retaining bolts to specifications and recheck caster.

To adjust toe-in, loosen the sleeve clamp bolts, and turn the adjuster sleeves at the outer ends of the tie-rod an equal amount in the opposite direction, to maintain steering wheel spoke alignment.

Section 7

Install Ford tool T65P-3000D or its equivalent on the frame rail, position the hooks around the upper control arm pivot shaft, and tighten the adjusting nuts of the tool slightly. Loosen the pivot shaft retaining bolts to permit adjustment.

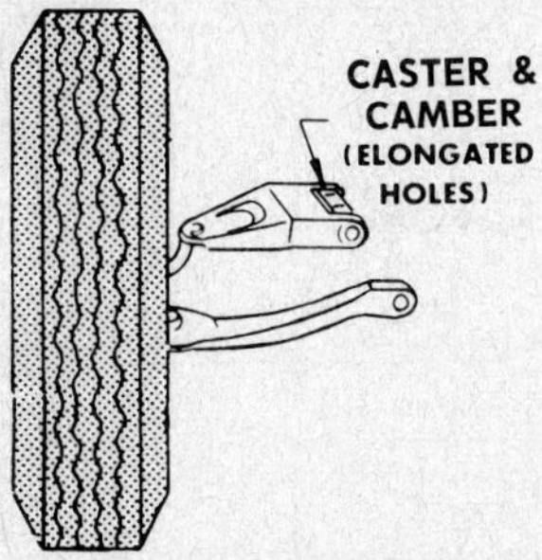
CASTER &
CAMBER
(ELONGATED
HOLES)

Location of caster and camber adjustments for type 7
(© Snap-On Tools Corp)

To adjust caster, loosen or tighten either the front or rear adjusting nut. After adjusting caster, adjust camber by loosening or tightening both nuts an equal amount. Tighten the shaft retaining bolts to specifications, remove the tool, and recheck the adjustments.

Adjust toe-in by loosening the clamp bolts, and turning the adjuster sleeves at the outer ends of the tie-rod. Turn the sleeves an equal amount in the opposite direction, to maintain steering wheel spoke alignment.

Section 8

Position one Ford tool T71P-3000-A at each end of the upper control arm, pivot shaft with the leg of the tools through the holes in the sheet metal (see illustration). Turn the adjusting bolts until they are solidly contacting sheet metal, and loosen the pivot shaft retaining bolts.

Caster is adjusted by turning the front and rear adjusting bolts in the opposite direction. Camber is adjusted by turning both bolts an equal amount in the same direction. Following the adjustments, tighten the pivot shaft retaining bolts, remove the adjusting tools, and recheck caster and camber.

Prior to adjusting toe-in, align the straight ahead marks at the base of the steering wheel and the head of the steering column. Loosen both the

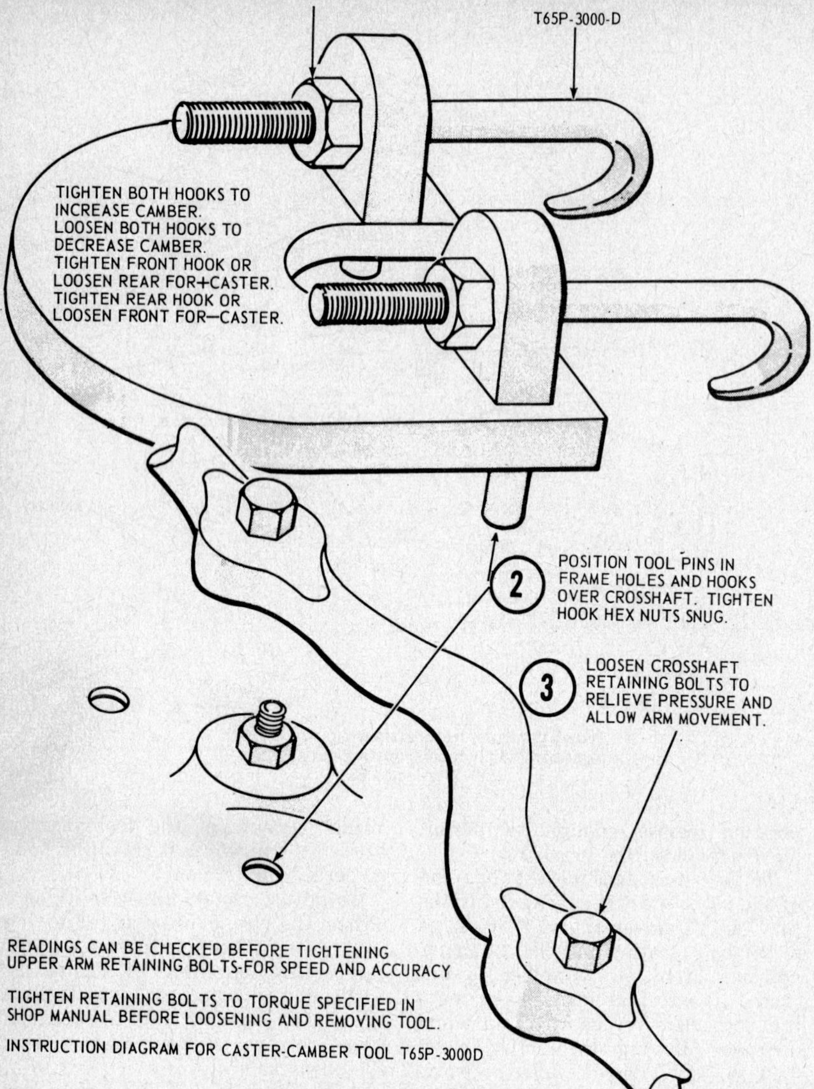
T65P-3000-D
TIGHTEN BOTH HOOKS TO INCREASE CAMBER.
LOOSEN BOTH HOOKS TO DECREASE CAMBER.
TIGHTEN FRONT HOOK OR LOOSEN REAR FOR+CASTER.
TIGHTEN REAR HOOK OR LOOSEN FRONT FOR—CASTER.
2
POSITION TOOL PINS IN FRAME HOLES AND HOOKS OVER CROSSHAFT. TIGHTEN HOOK HEX NUTS SNUG.
3
LOOSEN CROSSHAFT RETAINING BOLTS TO RELIEVE PRESSURE AND ALLOW ARM MOVEMENT.
READINGS CAN BE CHECKED BEFORE TIGHTENING UPPER ARM RETAINING BOLTS-FOR SPEED AND ACCURACY
TIGHTEN RETAINING BOLTS TO TORQUE SPECIFIED IN SHOP MANUAL BEFORE LOOSENING AND REMOVING TOOL.
INSTRUCTION DIAGRAM FOR CASTER-CAMBER TOOL T65P-3000D

Caster and camber adjusting tool for type 7

clamp at the outer end of the rack bellows and the tie rod jam nuts. Using suitable pliers (i.e. Vise-Grips), turn the inner tie rod shafts to adjust toe-in. Turn the shafts an equal amount in the opposite direction, to maintain steering wheel spoke alignment. Following the adjustment, hold the inner shafts with pliers, and tighten the jam nuts.

Section 9

Camber and caster are adjusted using eccentrics on the lower control arm pivot bolts. Camber is adjusted first, by loosening the front pivot nut and rotating the eccentric. Tighten the front, and loosen the rear pivot nuts. Adjust caster by rotating the rear eccentric, and tighten the rear pivot nut while holding the bolt in position. Recheck camber and caster.

To adjust toe-in, loosen the clamps on the adjusting sleeves at the outer ends of the tie rod, and turn each sleeve an equal amount in the opposite direction, to maintain steering wheel spoke alignment while adjusting toe-in.

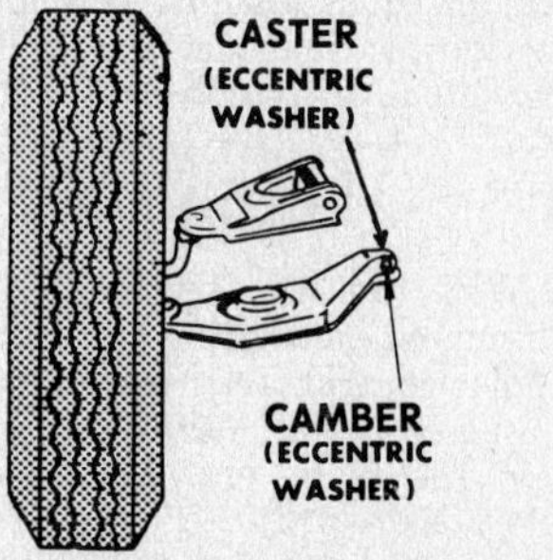
CASTER
(ECCENTRIC WASHER)
CAMBER
(ECCENTRIC WASHER)

Location of caster and camber adjustments for type 9
(© Snap-On Tools Corp)

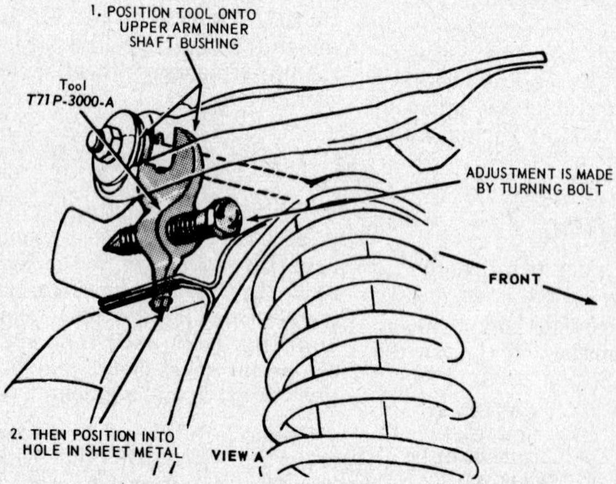
1. POSITION TOOL ONTO UPPER ARM INNER SHAFT BUSHING
Tool
T71P-3000-A
ADJUSTMENT IS MADE BY TURNING BOLT
FRONT
2. THEN POSITION INTO HOLE IN SHEET METAL
VIEW A

Type 8 caster and camber adjusting tool installation
(© Ford Motor Co)

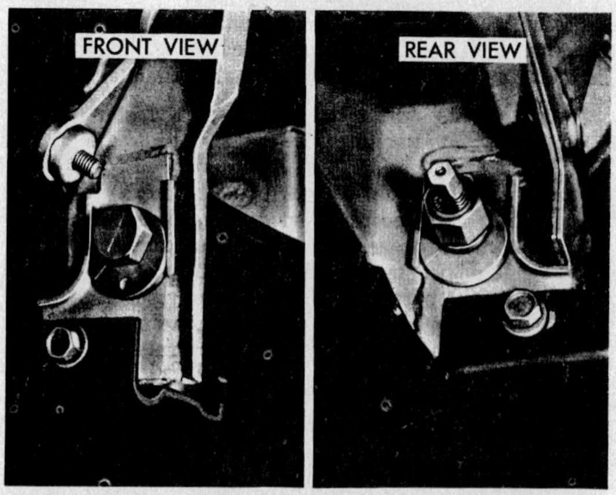
FRONT VIEW
REAR VIEW

Type 9 camber (left) and caster (right) adjustments
(© Chevrolet Div, G.M. Corp)

Charging · Starting Systems

Testing the Battery

Selection of Battery

The modern car battery (with very few exceptions) is a 12-volt lead-acid unit having a particular ampere hours capacity, depending upon the required work load (radio, air conditioning, electric windows, tail gate, telephone, etc.).

Batteries come in different forms as specified and designed by the car manufacturer and are matched to the car's electrical needs.

The prime purpose of the battery is to supply a source of energy for cranking the car engine. It also provides the necessary power for the ignition system. A battery can, for a limited time, supply adequate current to satisfy electrical demands during periods when requirements exceed generator output.

Replacing a Battery

The most convenient and popular way to store new batteries is in a dry state. They are charged (with special equipment) at the time of manufacture. A dry charged unit will hold this charge almost indefinitely, in the absence of moisture.

Before deciding on a particular battery, consider some of the essentials that may put the replacement battery in a different category from that of the unit originally supplied with the vehicle. When the original battery wears out, resistance in the wiring circuits is probably much increased, and the starter may be less efficient, along with the ignition system. There is also the likelihood that electrical accessories have been added.

All of the above reasons are justification for choosing a battery of greater capacity than the one supplied by the manufacturer.

Preparation

After the electrical needs have been considered, and a selection made, place the new battery on a bench or work table. Never activate a battery installed in the car. Remove vent caps from all the cells.

Fill each cell carefully, using sulfuric acid and distilled water (electrolyte) at a strength of 1.250-1.265 specific gravity to about 3/8 in. above the top of the separators, or to indicated level mark.

Place a battery type thermometer in one of the center cells. Check specific gravity of the electrolyte with a battery hydrometer. The battery temperature must be above 80°F. and specific gravity must be above 1.250 prior to installing the battery.

In charging 12-volt batteries, set charging rate at 35 amperes (6-volt batteries at 70 amperes) until electrolyte has reached 80° F. and electrolyte gravity is 1.250 or higher. Lower charging rates also may be used to obtain 80° F. and 1.250 specific gravity. When charging, do not allow electrolyte temperature to exceed 125° F. Normally, 10-15 minutes charging will be sufficient; however, in colder climates a little longer is O.K.

When the battery is removed from the charger, top up if necessary, with electrolyte, and replace the vent plugs.

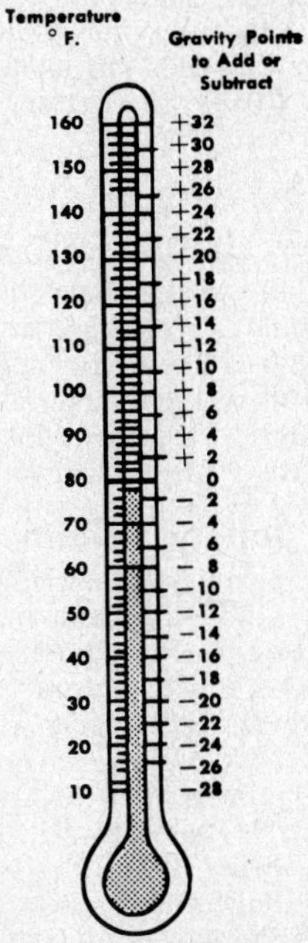
Temperature °F.
Gravity Points to Add or Subtract
160
150
140
130
120
110
100
90
80
70
60
50
40
30
20
10
+32
+30
+28
+26
+24
+22
+20
+18
+16
+14
+12
+10
+8
+6
+4
+2
0
−2
−4
−6
−8
−10
−12
−14
−16
−18
−20
−22
−24
−26
−28

Hydrometer temperature correction chart
(© Chrysler Corp)

When installing, make sure that both ends of the battery cables are clean and securely tightened, observing correct polarity.

Start engine and make sure that the generator is charging with lights and all accessories on.

Caution Be careful not to install or charge the battery with cables reversed. Damage to battery and generator can result, especially if the car is equipped with an alternator or transistorized radio.

Caution Because electrolyte is extremely corrosive to metals and many other materials, do not pour into sinks or drains. If battery acid is spilled on battery during filling or charging, or on bench or clothing, immediately flush it off with generous amounts of water and baking soda or ammonia.

Battery Troubles—Causes

1. Battery too small for the job (accessories, etc.).
2. Tired battery (worn out).
3. Corroded battery connections.
4. Generator not charging.
5. Generator charging rate too low.
6. Regulator defective.
7. Regulator out of adjustment.
8. Regulator has poor ground.
9. Alternator inoperative.
10. Loose generator or alternator drive belt.
11. Constant drain of current due to short circuit.

Battery Troubles—Corrections

1. Battery capacity may be less than requirements demand. Additional accessories, too frequent use of starter, low operational speeds, require a greater source of electrical supply. Install a larger capacity battery.
2. Either age or abuse is the usual cause of a tired battery. No amount of charging will offer more than temporary relief. Install a new battery of proper capacity if plates are sulfated.
3. Corroded battery posts and connections result from the chemical reaction between dissimilar metals and battery electrolyte. Excessive corrosion at a battery post is usually an indication of the failure of a seal between the post and the battery cover. Clean post and cable clamp, seal post-to-battery cover with rubber cement or other plastic material, then coat post with petroleum jelly, install cable clamp and tighten.
4. Generator not charging can be caused by a defective generator or other system component. Check entire charging system and correct the fault.
5. Low generator charging rate may be caused by a loose drive belt, loose or poor battery post connections, high resistance in charging circuit or a poor or improperly adjusted regulator.
6. Regulator may be defective because of burned points in the regulator or any open circuit in the control system.
7. Regulator out of adjustment.
8. A possible cause of trouble in DC systems is a poor regulator ground in any of the externally grounded (Type A) field circuit or, in heavy-duty (Type B) circuits, the internally grounded field within the generator.
9. The alternator may be inoperative because of damaged diodes, poor internal connections, open, grounded, or shorted field circuit, grounded or shorted stator windings.
10. A loose generator drive belt will cause low, or partial charging. Correct by adjusting drive belt.
11. **A constant drain of current from the battery may be caused by frayed insulation on any live wire in the electrical system. This can cause a short circuit. There is also the possibility of a light (in the trunk, glove box, under the hood. etc.) or other**

electric accessory remaining on after the ignition is turned off. To correct the situation:

First, with a sensitive ammeter, determine whether or not there is a current drain by opening the circuit at either battery post connection, hooking the ammeter in series, and checking for current drain.

Second, if the meter registers a drain, isolate the leak by reconnecting the battery, then, one by one, check each circuit at the fuse block. This is a tedious but unavoidable procedure and consists of removing each fuse and testing that circuit with the prods of an ammeter (in series). The circuit which activates the meter is the guilty one; identify the trouble spot by elimination. Correct the trouble by correcting the short or replacing the switch or other electrical component.

In the event that the fuse block test does not indicate the trouble, check the circuits which are protected with circuit breakers, (headlamps, parking lamps, seat and window controls, etc.).

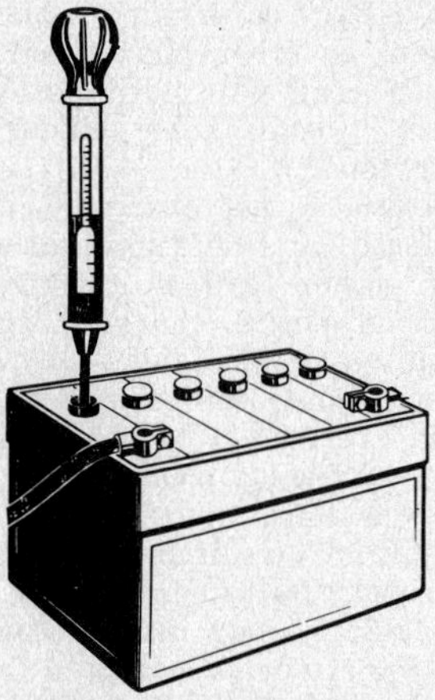

Testing battery specific gravity

Specific Gravity Test—Hydrometer

Before attempting any electrical checks, it is important to check the condition of the battery.

While not technically exact, a practical measurement of the chemical condition of the battery is indicated by measuring the specific gravity of the acid (electrolyte) contained in each cell. The electrolyte in a fully charged battery is usually between 1.260 and 1.280 times as heavy as pure water at the same temperature (80°F.). Variations in the specific gravity readings for a fully charged battery may differ. Therefore, it is most important that all battery cells produce an equal reading.

As a battery discharges, a chemical change takes place within each cell. The sulfate factor of the electrolyte combines chemically with the battery plates, reducing the weight of the electrolyte. A reading of the specific gravity of the acid, or electrolyte, of any partially charged battery, will therefore be less than that taken in a fully charged one.

The hydrometer is the instrument in general use for determining the specific gravity of liquids. The battery hydrometer is readily available from many sources, including local auto replacement parts stores. The following chart gives an indication of specific gravity value, related to battery charge condition. If, after charging, the specific gravity between any two cells varies more than 50 points (.050), the battery is probably bad.

Specific Gravity Reading	*Charged Condition*
1.260-1.280	Fully charged
1.230-1.250	Three-quarter charged
1.200-1.220	One-half charged
1.170-1.190	One-quarter charged
1.140-1.160	Just about flat
1.110-1.130	All the way down

Testing Battery Polarity

Battery polarity is very important, especially since the introduction of AC generators. Permanent damage to the diodes of alternators (AC generators) will result from reversing polarity.

To determine battery polarity, turn the voltmeter selector to the high reading scale. Connect voltmeter leads to the battery posts. If the gauge needle moves in the correct direction, the positive lead of the meter is on the positive (+) post of the battery. If the gauge needle moves in the wrong direction, polarity is reversed.

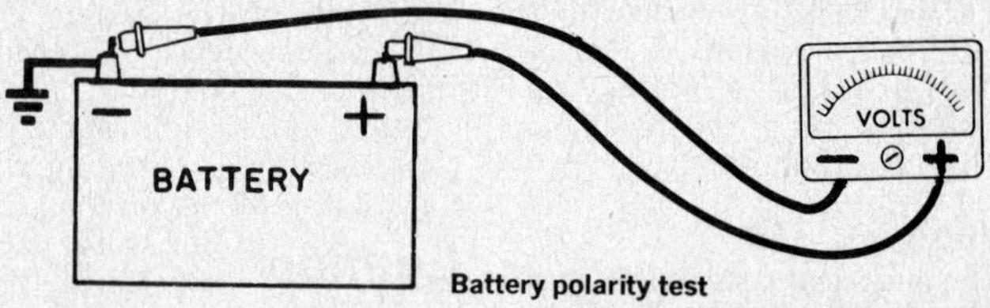

BATTERY
VOLTS

Battery polarity test

Know Your Instruments

Ohmmeter

An ohmmeter is used to measure electrical resistance in a unit or circuit. The ohmmeter has a self-contained power supply. In use, it is connected across (or in parallel with) the terminals of the unit being tested.

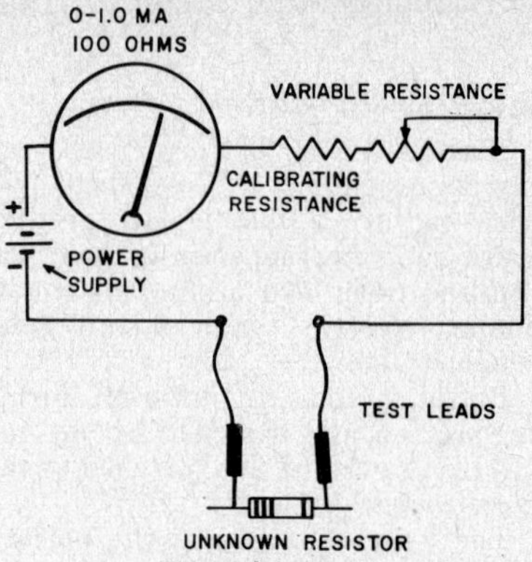

0-1.0 MA
100 OHMS
VARIABLE RESISTANCE
CALIBRATING RESISTANCE
POWER SUPPLY
TEST LEADS
UNKNOWN RESISTOR

Ohmmeter circuit

Ammeter

An ammeter is used to measure current (amount of electricity) flowing through a unit, or circuit. Ammeters are always connected in the line (in series) with the unit or circuit being tested.

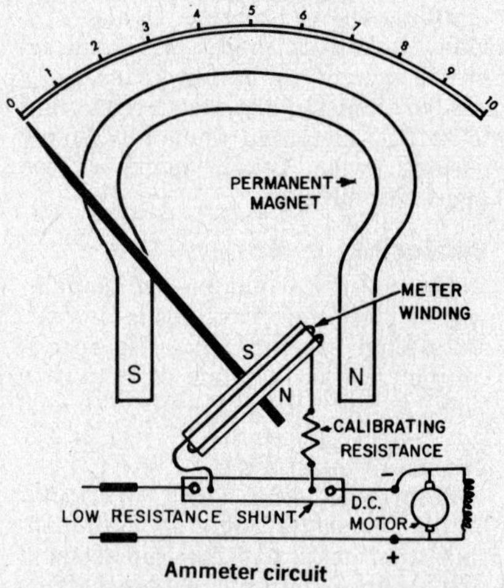

PERMANENT MAGNET
METER WINDING
CALIBRATING RESISTANCE
LOW RESISTANCE SHUNT
D.C. MOTOR

Ammeter circuit

Voltmeter

A voltmeter is used to measure voltage (electrical pressure) pushing the current through a unit, or circuit. The meter is connected across the terminals of the unit being tested. The meter reading will be the difference in pressure (voltage drop) between the two sides of the unit.

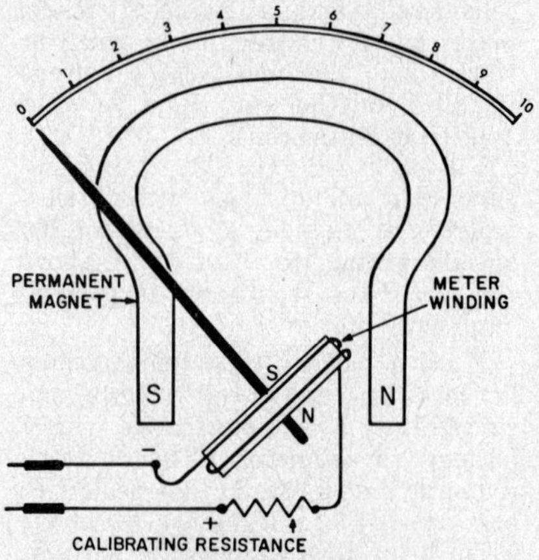

PERMANENT MAGNET
METER WINDING
CALIBRATING RESISTANCE

Voltmeter circuit

Boost Charging Rates

12-volt Battery: 1,000 ampere/minutes (50 amps. x 20 min.)

6-volt Battery: 1,800 ampere/minutes (60 amps. x 30 min.)

Testing the Starting Motor

Testing the Starter Circuit

The starter circuit should be divided and tested in four separate phases:

1. Cranking voltage check.
2. Amperage draw.
3. Voltage drop—grounded side.
4. Voltage drop—battery side.

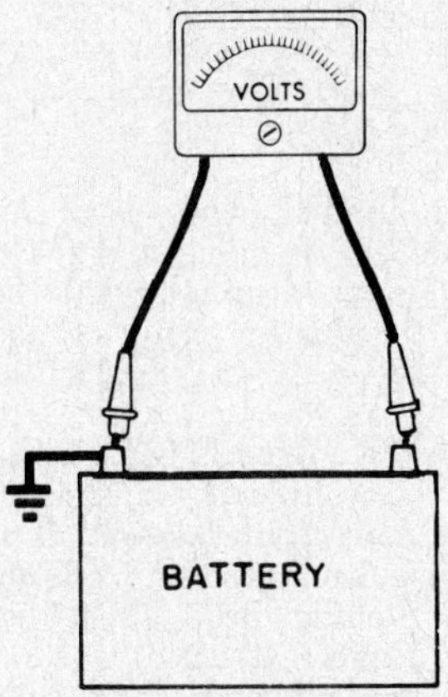
VOLTS
BATTERY
Cranking voltage test

NOTE: The battery must be in good condition for this test to have significance. To accurately check battery condition, use equipment designed to measure its capacity under a load. Instructions accompanying the equipment should be followed.

Cranking Voltage

Turn voltmeter selector to 8-10 volt scale for cars equipped with 6-volt systems, and to the 16-20 volt scale for cars equipped with 12-volt systems.

Connect voltmeter leads to prods tapped into the battery posts (observe polarity and reverse meter leads if necessary). Remove the high tension wire from the distributor cap and ground it to prevent starting. Now, turn the key. Observe both voltmeter reading and cranking speed. The cranking speed should be even, and at a satisfactory rate of speed, with a voltmeter reading of 4.8 volts or more for 6-volt systems, and at least 9.6 volts for 12-volt systems.

Amperage Draw

The amount of current the starter motor draws is usually (but not always) associated with the mechanical problems involved in cranking the engine. (Mechanical trouble in the engine, frozen or worn starter parts, misaligned starter or starter components, etc.) Because starter motor amperage draw is directly influenced by anything restricting the free turning of the engine, or starter, it is important that the engine and all components be at operating temperatures.

To measure starter current draw, remove the high tension wire from the center of the distributor cap and ground it. A very simple and inexpensive starter current indicator is available at auto stores. This indicator is an induction type gauge and shows, without disconnecting any wires, starter current draw.

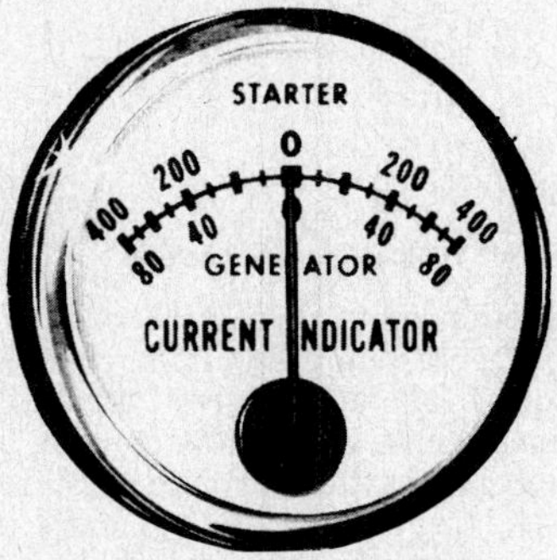
STARTER
0
200 200
400 400
40 40
80 80
CURRENT
Starter current indicator

Place the yoke of the meter directly over the insulated starter supply cable (cable must be straight for a minimum of 2 in.). Close the starter switch for about 20 seconds, watch the meter dial and record the average reading. If the indicator swings in the wrong direction, reverse the position of the meter. On 6-volt systems, normal draw for small to medium size engines is 150 to 225 amperes. Larger and high compression engines may draw as much as 400 amperes. On 12-volt systems, the current draw should be about one-half the amount registered for the 6-volt system.

More accurate but complex equipment is available from many name brand manufacturers. This equipment consists of a combination voltmeter, ammeter, and carbon pile rheostat. When using this equipment, follow the equipment manufacturer's procedures and recommendations.

High amperage and lazy performance would suggest an excessively tight engine, friction in the starter or starter drive, grounded starter field or armature.

Normal amperage and lazy per-

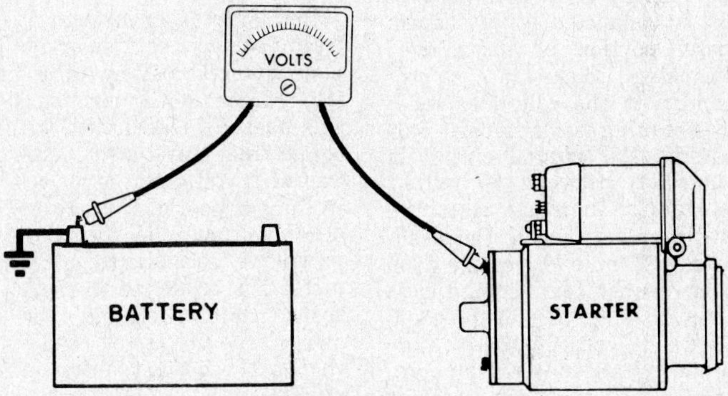
VOLTS
BATTERY
STARTER

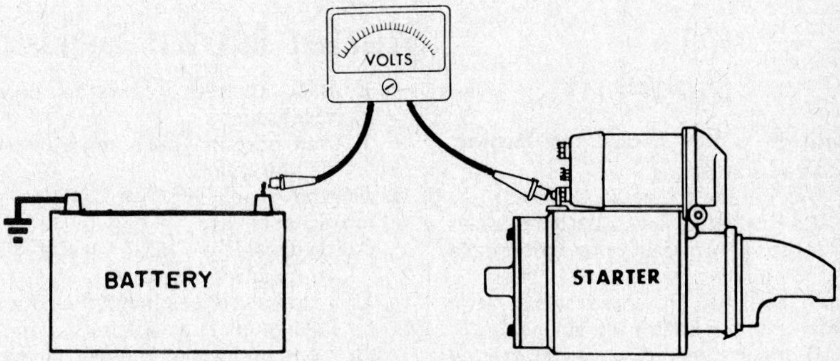
VOLTS
BATTERY
STARTER

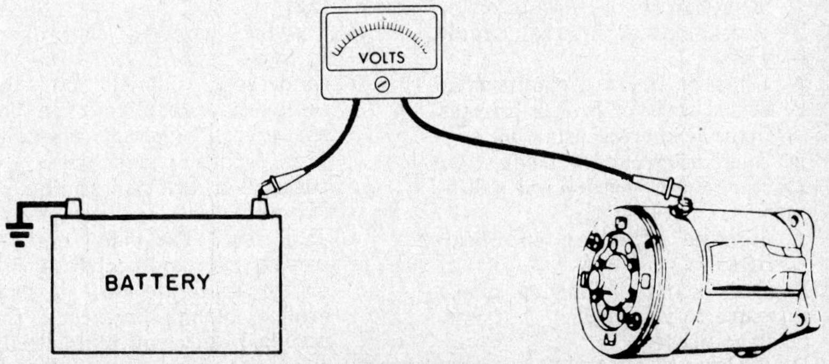
VOLTS
BATTERY
Typical Ford hook-up

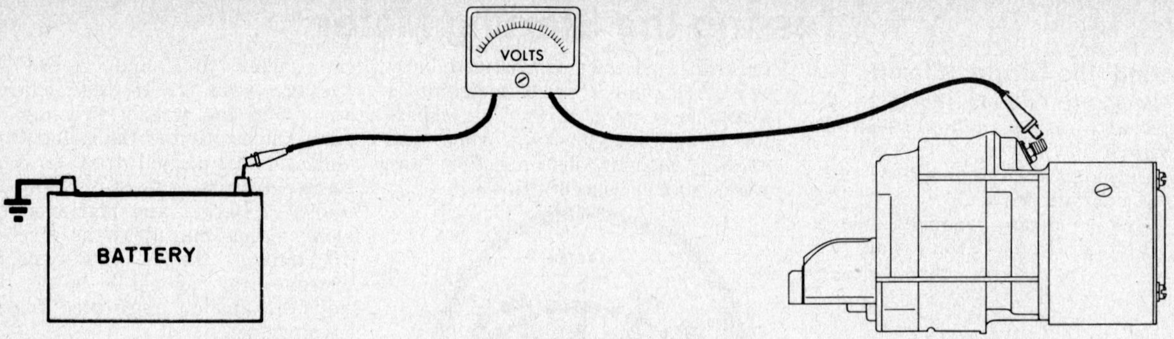
VOLTS
BATTERY

Typical Chrysler hook-up

formance suggest high resistance, or possibly poor connections somewhere in the starter circuit.

Low amperage and lazy or no performance suggest battery condition poor, bad cables or connections along the line.

Voltage Drop—Grounded Side

With a voltmeter on the 3-volt scale, without disconnecting any wires, connect negative test lead of the voltmeter to a prod secured in the grounded battery post. The positive test lead is connected to a cleaned, bare metal portion of the starter motor housing. Close the starter switch and note the voltmeter reading. If the reading is the same as battery reading, the ground circuit is open somewhere between the battery and the starter. In many cases the reading will be very small. The reading shown will indicate voltage drop (loss) between battery ground post and starter housing. The drop should not exceed 0.2 volt. If the voltage drop is above the specified amount, the next step is to isolate and correct the cause. It can be a bad cable or connection anywhere in the battery-to-starter ground circuit. A check of this type should progress along the various points of possible trouble, between the battery ground post and the starter motor housing, until the trouble spot has been located.

NOTE: due to the design of the Chrysler reduction gear starter, testing is limited to measuring voltage drop to starter cable connection.

Voltage Drop—Battery Side

Bad starter cranking may result from poor connections or faulty components of the battery or hot phase of the starter motor circuit. To check this phase of the circuit, without disconnecting any wires, connect one lead of a voltmeter to a prod secured in the hot post of the battery and the other voltmeter lead to the field terminal of the starting motor. The meter should be set to the 16-20 volt scale. Before closing the starter switch, the voltmeter reading will be that of the battery. After closing the starter switch, change the selector on the voltmeter to the 3-volt scale. With a jumper wire between the relay battery terminal and the relay starter switch terminal, crank the engine. If the starting motor cranks the engine, the relay (solenoid) is operating.

While the engine is being cranked, watch the voltmeter. It should not register more than 0.5 volt. If more than this, check each part of the circuit for voltage drop to isolate the trouble, (high resistance).

Without disturbing the voltmeter-to-battery hook-up, move the free voltmeter lead to the battery terminal of the relay (solenoid), and crank the engine. The voltmeter should show no more than 0.1 volt.

If this reading is correct, move the same voltmeter lead to the starting motor terminal of the relay (solenoid). While the engine is being cranked, the voltmeter should show no more than 0.3 volt. If it does, the trouble lies in the relay.

If the reading is correct, the trouble is in the cable or connections between the relay and the starting motor.

Starter Motor Service

Diagnosis

Starter Won't Crank the Engine

1. Dead battery.
2. Open starter circuit, such as:
   A. Broken or loose battery cables.
   B. Inoperative starter motor solenoid.
   C. Broken or loose wire from starter switch to solenoid.
   D. Poor solenoid or starter ground.
   E. Bad starter switch, (ignition, dash button or carburetor).
3. Defective starter internal circuit, such as:
   A. Dirty or burnt commutator.
   B. Stuck, worn or broken brushes.
   C. Open or shorted armature.
   D. Open or grounded fields.
4. Starter motor mechanical faults, such as:
   A. Jammed armature end bearings.
   B. Bad bearing, allowing armature to rub fields.
   C. Bent shaft.
   D. Broken starter housing.
   E. Bad starter worm or drive mechanism.
   F. Bad starter drive or flywheel driven gear.
5. Engine hard or impossible to crank, such as:
   A. Hydrostatic lock, water in combustion chamber.
   B. Crankshaft seizing in bearings.
   C. Piston or ring seizing.
   D. Bent or broken connecting rod.
   E. Seizing of connecting rod bearing.
   F. Flywheel jammed or broken.
   G. In some remote cases, an incandescent particle in the combustion chamber of a hot engine will prevent starting. This condition acts like a low battery or ignition timing so far advanced that the engine kicks back. The piston refuses to pass over top center. A two or three minute wait is generally enough to cool the troubled spot and temporarily clear the fault.

Starter Spins Free, Won't Engage

1. Sticking or broken drive mechanism.

Magnetic Switches

Magnetic switches serve only to make contact for the starter motor. Usually, such switches are located on the inner fender panel, although they are found mounted on the starter in a few cases.

Magnetic Switches with Two Control Terminals

On this type of magnetic switch current is supplied from the ignition switch or transmission neutral button to one of the magnetic switch control terminals. The other control terminal is connected to the transmission neutral safety switch (on the transmission) where it is grounded.

Magnetic Switches with Ignition Resistor By-Pass Terminals

Used with 12-volt systems. All

normally use a magnetic switch with a single control terminal. The second terminal is an ignition resistor by-pass terminal.

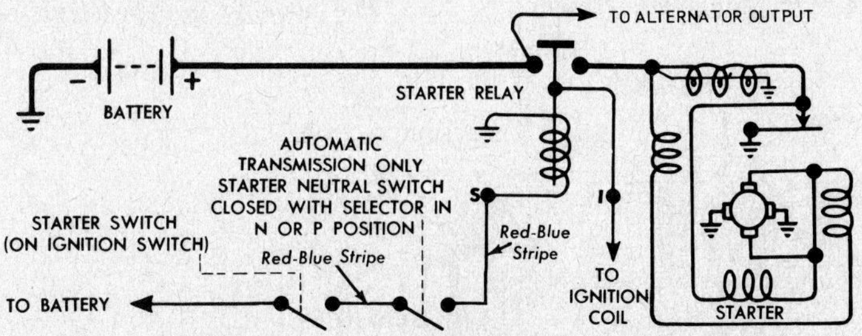
TO ALTERNATOR OUTPUT
BATTERY
STARTER RELAY
AUTOMATIC TRANSMISSION ONLY
STARTER NEUTRAL SWITCH CLOSED WITH SELECTOR IN N OR P POSITION
STARTER SWITCH (ON IGNITION SWITCH)
Red-Blue Stripe
Red-Blue Stripe
S
I
TO IGNITION COIL
STARTER
TO BATTERY

Ford positive engagement starter circuit (© Ford Motor Co)

Solenoids Without Relays

This type of starter solenoid is always mounted on the starter. Makes electrical contact for the starter and pulls the starter and drive clutch into mesh with the flywheel. The Chrysler reduction gear starter has this solenoid embodied in the starter housing. (See illustration.)

There is only one control terminal on the solenoid.

The ignition by-pass terminal is usually marked R or IGN, if it is used.

Solenoids With Separate Relays

The solenoid itself is always mounted on the starter. In addition to making contact for the starter, it also pulls the starter drive clutch gear into mesh with the flywheel. A single control terminal is used on the solenoid itself. The relay is usually found mounted to the inner fender panel or on the firewall.

Solenoids With Built-In Relays

These units are always mounted on the starter and are connected, through linkage, to the starter drive clutch. The relay portion is a square box built into and integral with the front end of the solenoid assembly.

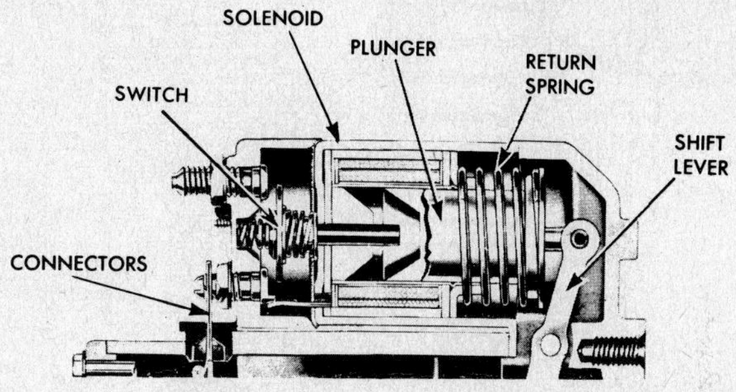
SOLENOID
PLUNGER
RETURN SPRING
SWITCH
SHIFT LEVER
CONNECTORS

Starter solenoid mounted on starter motor

Neutral Safety Switches

The purpose of the neutral safety switch is to prevent the starter from cranking the engine except when the transmission is in neutral or park.

On some cars, the neutral safety switch is located on the transmission. It serves to ground the solenoid or magnetic switch, whichever is used.

On other cars the neutral safety switch is located either at the bottom of the steering column, where it contacts the shift mechanism, on the steering column, underneath the dash, or on the shift linkage (console).

On most cars, the neutral safety switch and the back-up light switch are combined into a single switch mechanism.

See the car sections for specific details.

Troubleshooting Neutral Safety Switches—Quick Test

If the starter fails to function and the neutral safety switch is to be checked, a jumper can be placed across its terminals. If the starter then functions the safety switch is defective.

In the case of neutral safety switches with one wire, this wire must be grounded for testing purposes. If the starter works with the wire grounded, the switch is defective.

Neutral Safety Switch—Back-Up Light Switch

When the neutral safety switch is built in combination with the back-up light switch, the easiest way to tell which terminals are for the back-up

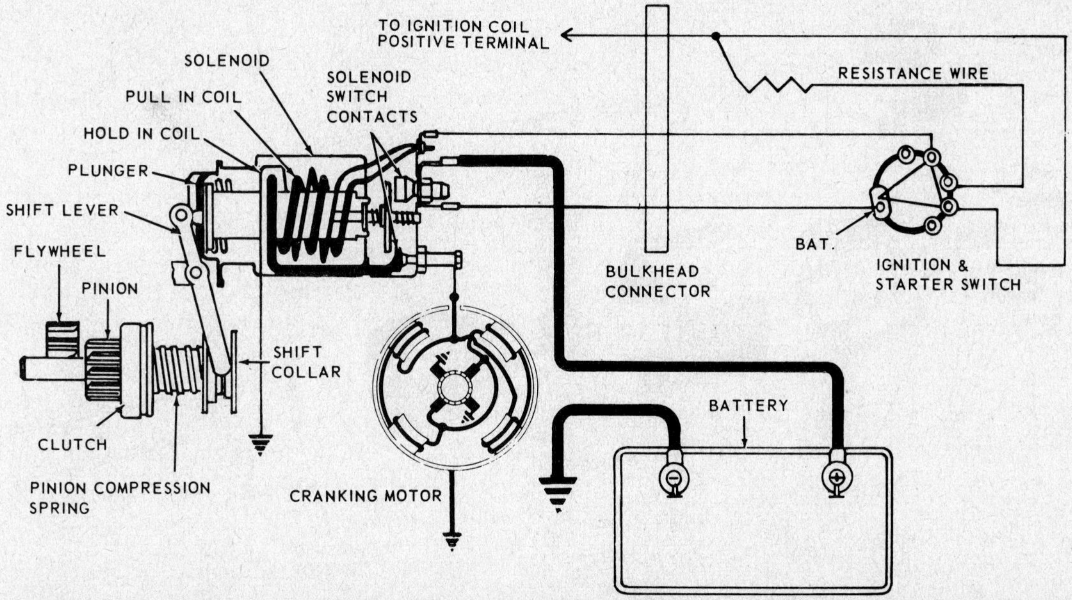
TO IGNITION COIL POSITIVE TERMINAL
RESISTANCE WIRE
SOLENOID
PULL IN COIL
SOLENOID SWITCH CONTACTS
HOLD IN COIL
PLUNGER
SHIFT LEVER
FLYWHEEL
PINION
SHIFT COLLAR
CLUTCH
PINION COMPRESSION SPRING
CRANKING MOTOR
BAT.
IGNITION & STARTER SWITCH
BULKHEAD CONNECTOR
BATTERY

G.M. starter circuit (© G.M. Corp)

lights is to take a jumper and cross every pair of wires. The pair of wires which light the back-up lamps should be ignored when testing the neutral safety switch. Once the back-up light wires have been located, jump the other pair of wires to test the neutral safety switch. If the starter functions only when the jumper is placed across these two wires, the neutral safety switch is defective or requires adjustment.

Reduction-Gear Starter Motor

(Chrysler Corporation)

The housing is die-cast aluminum.

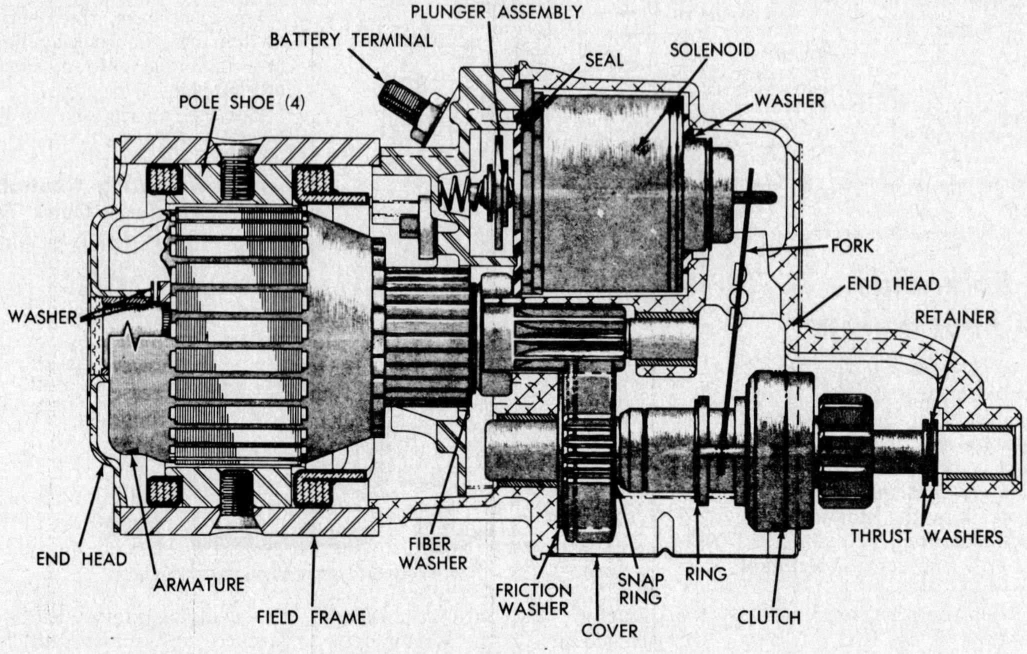
PLUNGER ASSEMBLY
BATTERY TERMINAL
SEAL
SOLENOID
POLE SHOE (4)
WASHER
FORK
END HEAD
RETAINER
WASHER
THRUST WASHERS
END HEAD
ARMATURE
FIELD FRAME
FIBER WASHER
FRICTION WASHER
COVER
SNAP RING
RING
CLUTCH

Reduction gear starter motor (© Chrysler Corp)

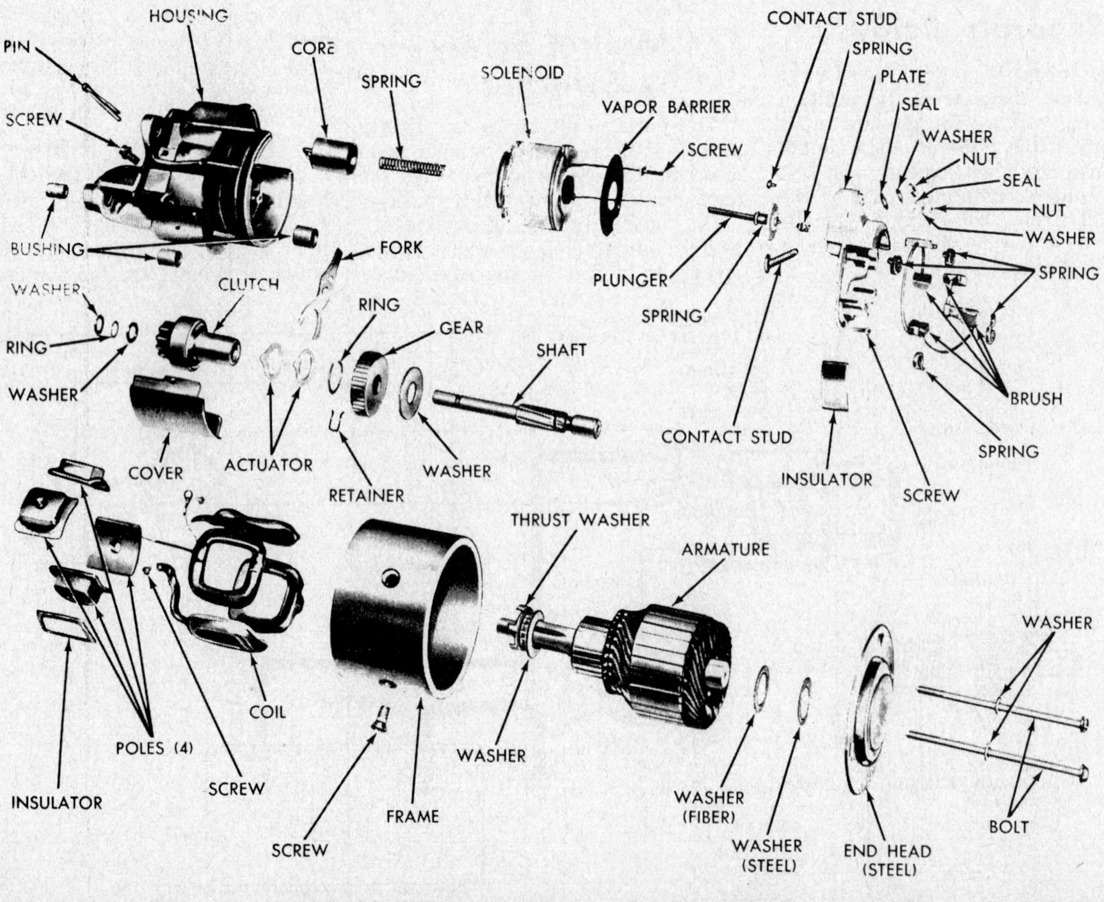
HOUSING
PIN
CORE
SPRING
SOLENOID
VAPOR BARRIER
SCREW
CONTACT STUD
SPRING
PLATE
SEAL
WASHER
NUT
SEAL
NUT
WASHER
SPRING
SCREW
BUSHING
FORK
PLUNGER
WASHER
CLUTCH
RING
GEAR
SPRING
RING
SHAFT
WASHER
BRUSH
COVER
ACTUATOR
RETAINER
WASHER
CONTACT STUD
INSULATOR
SCREW
SPRING
THRUST WASHER
ARMATURE
WASHER
COIL
POLES (4)
WASHER
INSULATOR
SCREW
FRAME
SCREW
WASHER (FIBER)
WASHER (STEEL)
END HEAD (STEEL)
BOLT

Reduction gear motor—exploded view (© Chrysler Corp)

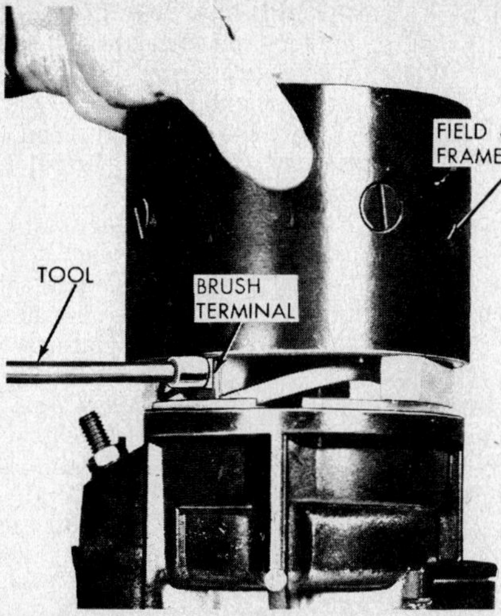
FIELD &
FRAME ASSEMBLY
TOOL
BRUSH
TERMINAL
Removing terminal screw—reduction gear motor
(© Chrysler Corp)

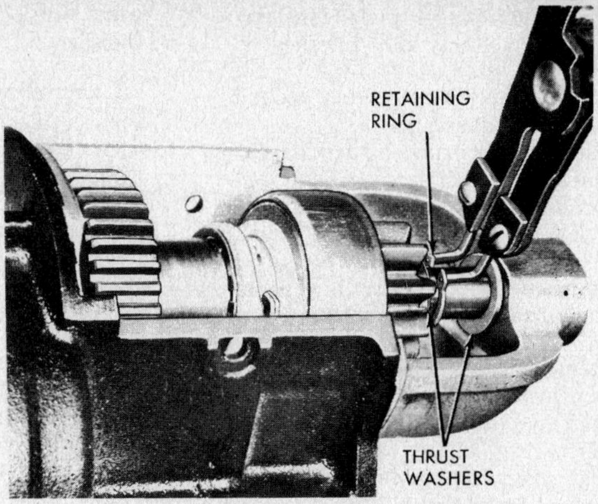
RETAINING
RING
THRUST
WASHERS
Removing retainer ring—reduction gear motor
(© Chrysler Corp)

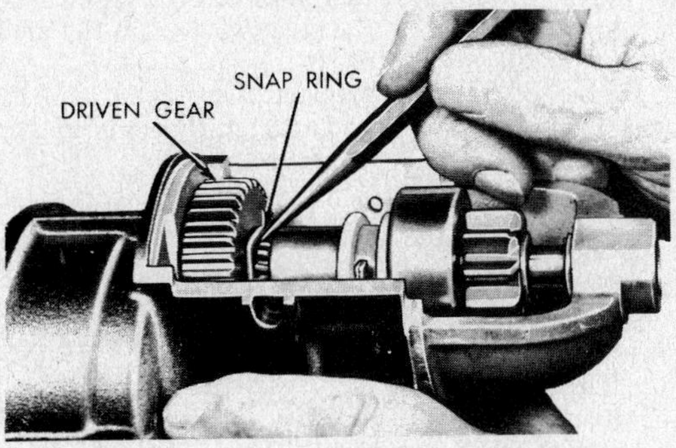
SNAP RING
DRIVEN GEAR
Removing drive gear snap-ring—reduction gear motor
(© Chrysler Corp)

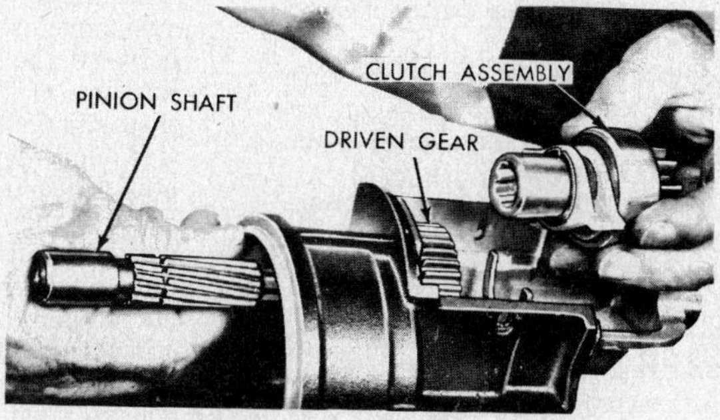
CLUTCH ASSEMBLY
PINION SHAFT
DRIVEN GEAR
Removing clutch assembly—reduction gear motor
(© Chrysler Corp)

A 3.5 to 1 reduction, combined with the starter to ring gear ratio, results in a total gear reduction of about 45 to 1.

NOTE: the high-pitched sound is caused by the higher starter speed.

The positive shift solenoid is enclosed in the starter housing and is energized through the ignition switch. When ignition switch is turned to start, the solenoid plunger engages drive gear through a shifting fork. At the completion of travel, the plunger closes a switch to revolve the starter.

The tension of the spring-type shifting prevents a butt-tooth lock up and motor will not start before total shift.

An overrunning clutch prevents motor damage if key is held on after engine starts.

No lubrication is required due to Oilite bearings.

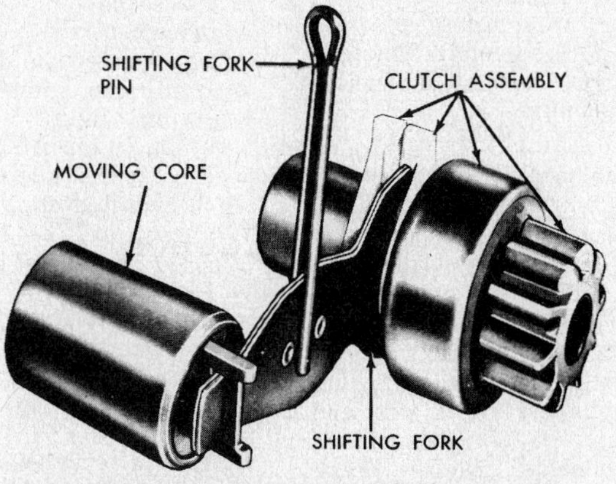
SHIFTING FORK
PIN
CLUTCH ASSEMBLY
MOVING CORE
SHIFTING FORK
Shift fork and clutch arrangement—reduction gear motor
(© Chrysler Corp)

Disassembly

1. Support assembly in a vise equipped with soft jaws. Do not clamp. Care must be used not to distort or damage the die cast aluminum.
2. Remove the thru-bolts and the end housing.
3. Carefully pull the armature up and out of the gear housing, and the starter frame and field assembly. Remove the steel and fiber thrust washer.

NOTE: on eight cylinder engines the starting motors have the wire of the shunt field coil soldered to the brush terminal. Six cylinder engines have the four coils in series and do not have a wire soldered to the brush terminal. One pair of brushes is connected to this terminal. The other pair of brushes is attached to the series field coils by means of a terminal screw. Carefully pull the frame and field assembly up just enough to expose the terminal screw and the solder connection of the shunt field at the brush terminal. Place two wood blocks between the starter frame and starter gear housing to facilitate removal of the terminal screw and unsoldering of the shunt field wire at the brush terminal.

4. Support the brush terminal with a finger behind terminal and remove screw.
5. On eight cylinder engine starters unsolder the shunt field coil lead from the brush terminal and housing.

6. The brush holder plate with terminal, contact and brushes is serviced as an assembly.
7. Clean all old sealer from around plate and housing.
8. Remove the brush holder attaching screw.
9. On the shunt type, unsolder the solenoid winding from the brush terminal.
10. Remove 11/32 in. nut, washer and insulator from solenoid terminal.
11. Remove brush holder plate with brushes as an assembly.
12. Remove gear housing ground screw.
13. The solenoid assembly can be removed from the well.
14. Remove nut, washer and seal from starter battery terminal and remove terminal from plate.
15. Remove solenoid contact and plunger from solenoid and remove the coil sleeve.
16. Remove the solenoid return spring, coil retaining washer, retainer and the dust cover from the gear housing.
17. Release the snap-ring that locates the driven gear on pinion shaft.
18. Release front retaining ring.
19. Push pinion shaft toward the rear and remove snap-ring, thrust washers, clutch and pinion, and two shift fork nylon actuators.
20. Remove driven gear and friction washer.
21. Pull shifting fork forward and remove moving core.
22. Remove fork retainer pin and shifting fork assembly. The gear housing with bushings is serviced as an assembly.

Replacement of Brushes

1. Brushes that are worn more than one-half the length of new brushes, or are oil-soaked, should be replaced.
2. When resoldering the shunt field and solenoid lead, make a strong, low-resistance connection using a high-temperature solder and resin flux. Do not use acid or acid-core solder. Do not break the shunt field wire units when removing and installing the brushes.

Starter Clutch and Pinion Gear Inspection

1. Do not immerse the starter clutch unit in a cleaning solvent. The outside of the clutch and pinion must be cleaned with a cloth so as not to wash the lubricant from the inside of the clutch.
2. Rotate the pinion. The pinion gear should rotate smoothly and in one direction only. If the starter clutch unit does not function properly, or if the pinion is worn, chipped, or burred, replace the starter clutch unit.

Commutator Inspection

1. Inspect the commutator and the surface contacted by the brushes when the starter is assembled, for flat spots, out-of-roundness, or excessive wear.
2. Reface the commutator if necessary, removing only a sufficient amount of metal to provide a smooth, even surface.
3. Using light pressure, clean the grooves of the face of the commutator with a pointed tool. Neither remove any metal or widen the grooves.

Assembly

1. The shifter fork consists of two spring steel plates held together by two rivets. Before assembling the starter, check the plates for side movement. After lubricating between the plates with a small amount of SAE 10 engine oil, they should have about 1/16 in. side movement to insure proper pinion gear engagement.
2. Position the shift fork in the drive housing and install the shifting fork retainer pin. One tip of the pin should be straight and the other bent at a 15 degree angle away from the housing. The fork and retainer pin should operate freely after bending the tip of the pin.
3. Install the solenoid moving core and engage the shifting fork.
4. Place the pinion shaft into the drive housing and install the friction washer and drive gear.
5. Install the clutch and pinion assembly, thrust washer, and retaining washer.
6. Engage the shifting fork with the clutch actuators.

Caution The friction washer must be positioned on the shoulder of the splines of the pinion shaft before the driven gear is positioned.

7. Install the driven gear snap ring.
8. Install the pinion shaft retaining ring.
9. The starter solenoid return spring can now be inserted in the moveable core.
10. Install the solenoid contact plunger assembly into the solenoid and reform the double wires so they can be curved around the contactor. This will allow the terminal stud to enter the brush holder properly.

Caution The contactor must not touch these double wires after assembly is complete.

11. Assemble the battery terminal stud in the brush holder.
12. Position the seal on the brush holder plate.
13. Run the solenoid lead wire through the hole in the brush holder and attach the solenoid stud, insulating washer, flat washer, and nut.
14. Wrap the solenoid lead wire tightly around the brush terminal post and solder it.
15. Fix the brush holder to the solenoid attaching screws.
16. Gently lower the solenoid coil and brush plate into the gear housing.
17. Position the brush plate assembly into the starter gear housing, install the nuts, and tighten.
18. Solder the shunt coil lead wire to the starter brush terminal.
19. Install the brush terminal screw.
20. Position the field frame on the gear housing and start the armature into the housing, carefully engaging the splines on the shaft with the reduction gear by rotating the armature.
21. Install the fiber thrust washer and the steel washer on the armature shaft.
22. Replace the starter end housing and starter through bolts; tighten securely.

Direct Drive Starter Motor

(Chrysler Corporation)

Disassembly

1. Remove through bolts and tap commutator end head from frame.
2. Remove thrust washers from armature shaft.
3. Lift brush holder springs and remove brushes from holders.
4. Remove brush holder plate.
5. Disconnect the field coil wires at the solenoid connector, and remove the solenoid screws.
6. Remove solenoid and boot.
7. Drive out shift fork pivot pin.
8. Remove drive end pinion housing and spacer washer.
9. Remove shift fork from starter drive.
10. Slide overrunning clutch pinion gear toward commutator, drive stop retainer toward clutch pinion gear and remove the now-exposed snap-ring.
11. Remove overrunning clutch drive from armature shaft.
12. If field coils are good, stop disassembly at this point. If field coils must be replaced, remove ground brushes terminal screw and remove brushes, terminal and shunt wire. Remove pole shoe screws, using a ratchet-type impact driver and special wide screwdriver blade, then remove field coils.
13. Replacement of the brushes, inspection of the starter clutch and pinion, and inspection of the commutator procedures are the same as the reduction-gear starter procedures.

Assembly

1. Install field coils into frame, if removed.
2. Lubricate armature shaft and splines with engine oil.
3. Install starter drive, stop retainer, lock ring and spacer washer.
4. Install shift fork, with *narrow* leg of fork toward commutator.
5. Install pinion housing onto armature shaft, indexing shift fork with slot in housing.
6. Install shift fork pivot pin.
7. With clutch drive, shift fork, and pinion housing assembled onto the armature, slide armature into frame until pinion housing indexes with slot.
8. Install solenoid and boot, tightening bolts to 60-70 in. lbs.
9. Connect field coil wires to solenoid connector, making sure they do not touch frame.
10. Install brush holder plate, indexing tang in frame hole.
11. Place brushes in holders, making sure field coil wires do not interfere.
12. Install thrust washers on commutator end of armature shaft to obtain a maximum of 0.010 in. end-play.
13. Install commutator end head and through bolts. Tighten bolts to 40-50 in. lbs.
14. Measure drive gear pinion clearance; it should be ⅛ in. Adjust by moving solenoid fore and aft as required.

Autolite Positive Engagement Starter Motor

(Ford Motor Co.)

This starting motor is a series-parallel wound, four pole, four brush unit. It is equipped with an over-running clutch drive pinion, which is engaged with the flywheel ring gear by an actuating lever, operated by a movable pole piece. This pole piece is hinged to the starter frame and can drop into position through an opening in the frame.

Three conventional field coils are located at three pole piece positions. The fourth field coil is designed to serve also as an engaging coil and a hold-in coil for the operation of the drive pinion.

When the ignition switch is turned to the start position, the starter relay is energized and current flows from the battery to the starter motor terminal. This prime surge of current first flows through the starter engaging coil, creating a very strong magnetic field. This magnetism draws the movable pole piece down toward the starter frame, which then causes the lever attached to it to move the starter pinion into engagement with the flywheel ring gear.

When the movable pole shoe is fully seated, it opens the field coil, grounding contacts, and the starter is then in normal operation. A holding coil is used to hold the movable pole shoe in the fully seated position during the engine cranking operation.

Cars equipped with automatic transmissions have a starter neutral switch circuit control. This is to prevent operation of the starter if the selector lever is not in Neutral or Park.

This type starter is used on both Ford and late-model American Motors products.

Disassembly

1. Remove brush cover band and starter drive gear actuating lever cover. Observe the brush lead locations for reassembly, then remove the brushes from their holders.

NOTE: factory brush length is ½ in.; wear limit is ¼ in.

2. Remove the through bolts, starter drive gear housing and the drive gear actuating lever return spring.
3. Remove the pivot pin retaining the starter gear actuating lever and remove the lever and the armature.
4. Remove the stop ring retainer. Remove and discard the stop ring holding the drive gear to the armature shaft; then remove the drive gear assembly.
5. Remove the brush end plate.
6. Remove the two screws holding the ground brushes to the frame.
7. On the field coil that operates the starter drive gear actuating lever, bend the tab up on the field retainer and remove the field coil retainer.
8. Remove the three coil retaining screws. Unsolder the field coil leads from the terminal screw, then remove the pole shoes and coils from the frame (use a 300 watt iron).
9. Remove the starter terminal nut, washer, insulator and terminal from the starter frame.
10. Check the commutator for run-out. If the commutator is rough, has flat spots, or is more than 0.005 in. out of round, reface the commutator. Clean the grooves in the commutator face.
11. Inspect the armature shaft and the two bearings for scoring and excessive wear. Replace if necessary.
12. Inspect the starter drive. If the gear teeth are pitted, broken, or excessively worn, replace the starter drive.

Assembly

1. Install starter terminal, insulator, washers and retaining nut in the frame. (Be sure to position the slot in the screw perpendicular to the frame end surface.)
2. Position coils and pole pieces, with the coil leads in the terminal screw slot, then install the retaining screws. As the pole screws are tightened, strike the frame several sharp hammer blows to align the pole shoes. Tighten, then stake the screws.
3. Install solenoid coil and retainer and bend the tabs to hold the coils to the frame.
4. Solder the field coils and solenoid wire to the starter terminal, using rosin-core solder and a 300 watt iron.
5. Check for continuity and ground connections in the assembled coils.
6. Position the solenoid coil ground terminal over the nearest ground screw hole.
7. Position the ground brushes to the starter frame and install retaining screws.
8. Position the brush end plate to the frame, with the end plate boss in the frame slot.
9. Lightly Lubriplate the armature shaft splines and install the starter drive gear assembly on the shaft. Install a new retaining stop ring and stop ring retainer.
10. Position the fiber thrust washer on the commutator end of the armature shaft, then position the armature in the starter frame.
11. Position the starter drive gear actuating lever to the frame and starter drive assembly, and install the pivot pin.

NOTE: fill drive gear housing bore ¼ full of grease.

12. Position the drive actuating lever return spring and the drive gear housing to the frame, then install and tighten the through bolts. Do not pinch brush leads between brush plate and frame. Be sure that the stop ring retainer is properly seated in the drive housing.
13. Install the brushes in the brush holders and center the brush springs on the brushes.
14. Position the drive gear actuating lever cover on the starter and install the brush cover band with a new gasket.
15. Check starter no-load amperage draw.

Autolite Solenoid Actuated Starter Motor

(Ford Motor Co.)

This starter motor, usually used with late-model 429 and 460 engines, is a four-brush, four-field, four-pole wound unit. The frame encloses a wound armature, which is supported

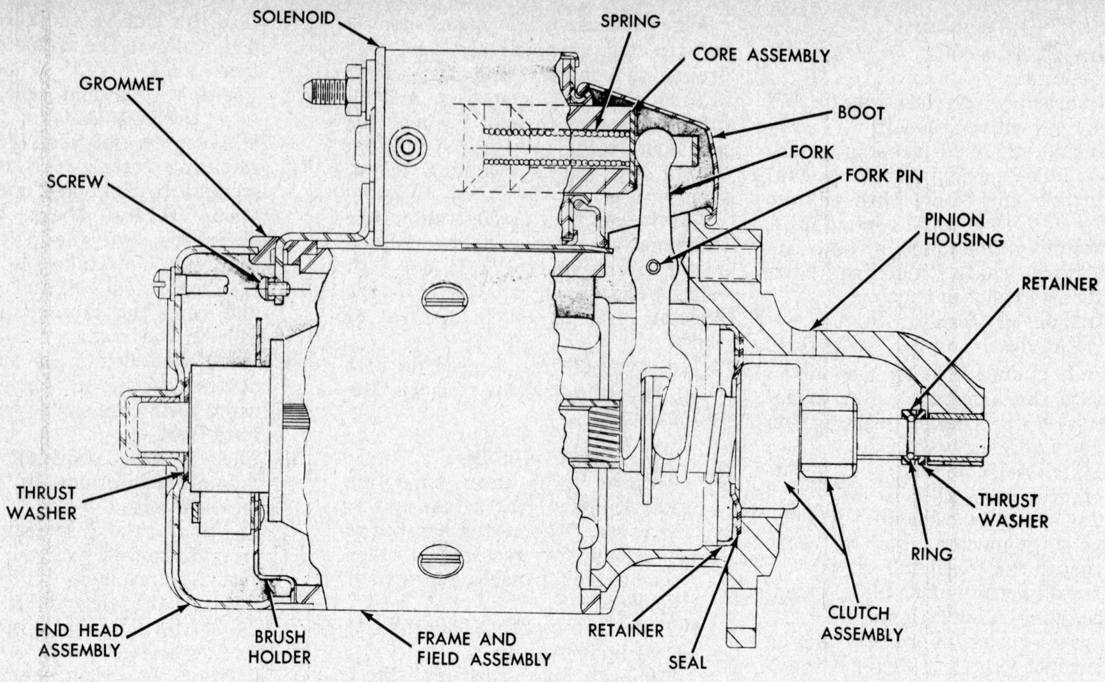
SOLENOID
SPRING
CORE ASSEMBLY
GROMMET
BOOT
FORK
SCREW
FORK PIN
PINION
HOUSING
RETAINER
THRUST
WASHER
THRUST
WASHER
RING
END HEAD
ASSEMBLY
BRUSH
HOLDER
FRAME AND
FIELD ASSEMBLY
RETAINER
SEAL
CLUTCH
ASSEMBLY

Chrysler direct drive starter motor (© Chrysler Corp)

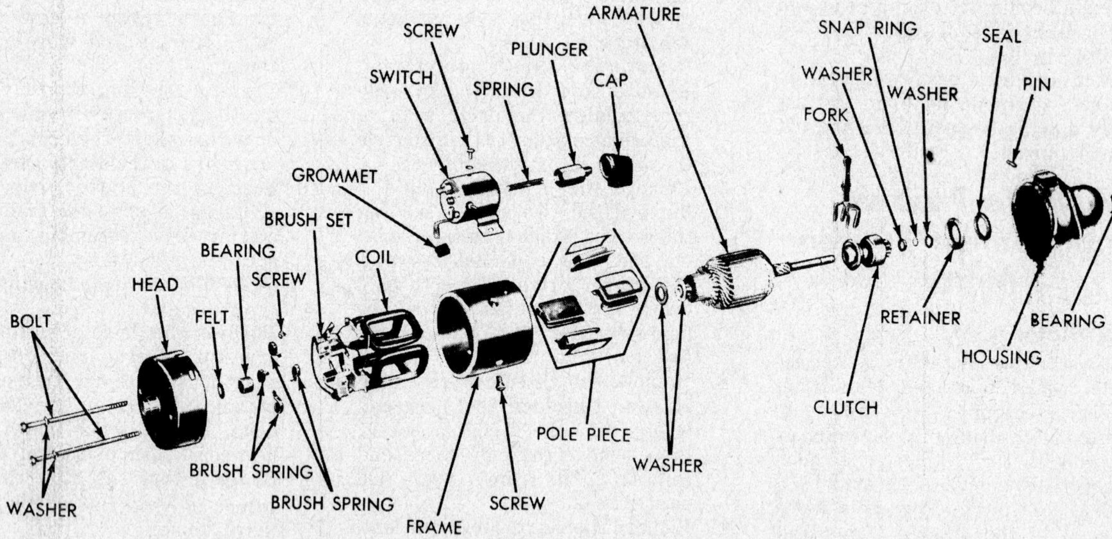
ARMATURE
SCREW
PLUNGER
SWITCH
SPRING
CAP
SNAP RING
WASHER
WASHER
SEAL
PIN
FORK
GROMMET
BRUSH SET
BEARING
COIL
SCREW
HEAD
FELT
BOLT
RETAINER
BEARING
HOUSING
CLUTCH
POLE PIECE
WASHER
BRUSH SPRING
BRUSH SPRING
WASHER
FRAME
SCREW

Chrysler direct drive motor—exploded view (© Chrysler Corp)

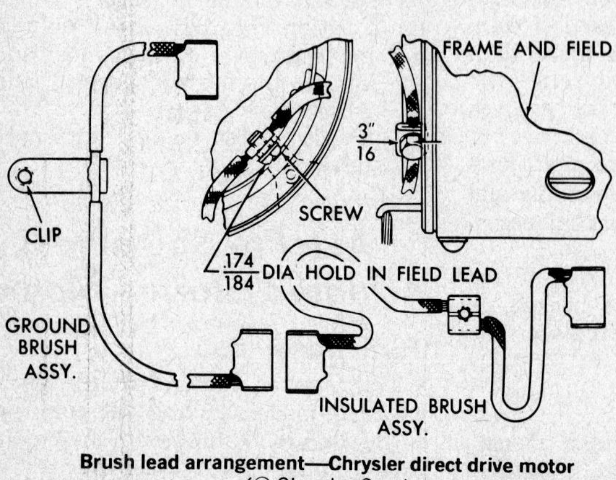
FRAME AND FIELD
3"
16
CLIP
SCREW
.174
.184
DIA HOLD IN FIELD LEAD
GROUND
BRUSH
ASSY.
INSULATED BRUSH
ASSY.

Brush lead arrangement—Chrysler direct drive motor
(© Chrysler Corp)

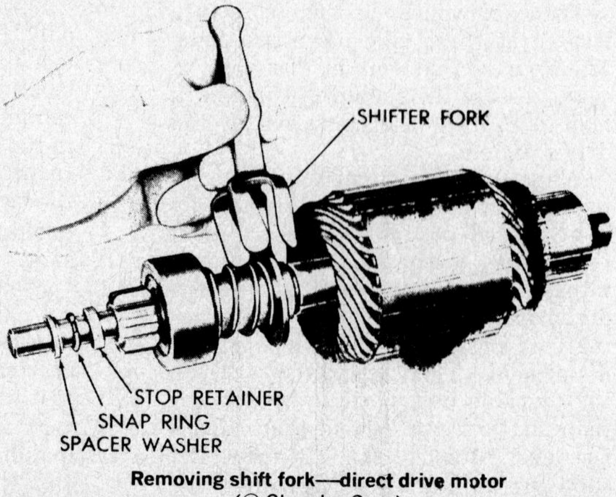
SHIFTER FORK
STOP RETAINER
SNAP RING
SPACER WASHER

Removing shift fork—direct drive motor
(© Chrysler Corp)

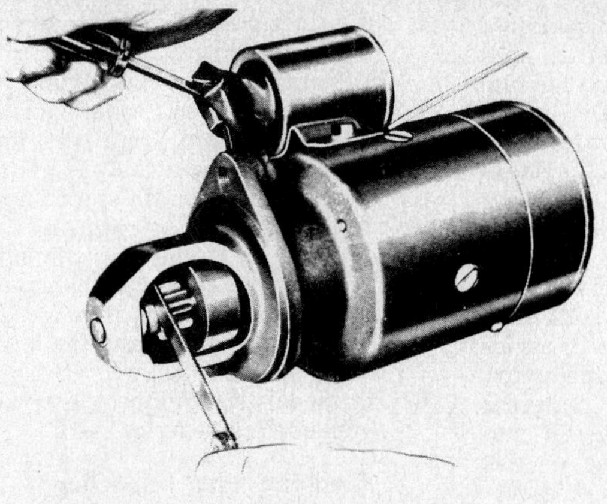

Checking drive pinion clearance—direct drive motor (© Chrysler Corp)

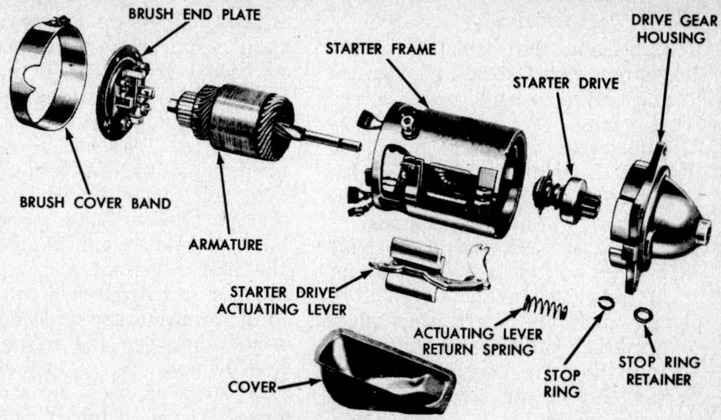
BRUSH END PLATE
DRIVE GEAR HOUSING
STARTER FRAME
STARTER DRIVE
BRUSH COVER BAND
ARMATURE
STARTER DRIVE ACTUATING LEVER
ACTUATING LEVER RETURN SPRING
STOP RING
STOP RING RETAINER
COVER

Autolite starter motor

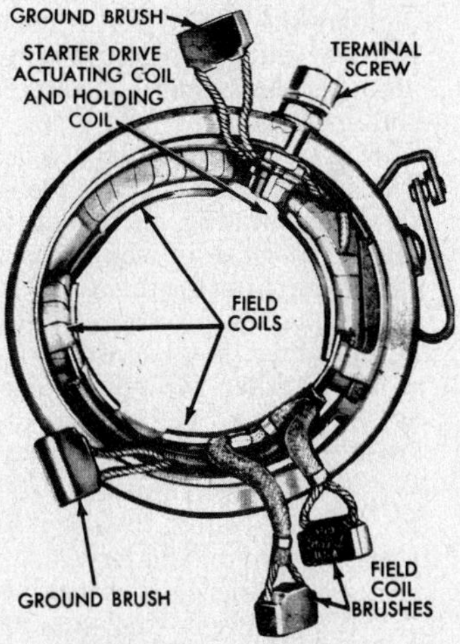
GROUND BRUSH
STARTER DRIVE ACTUATING COIL AND HOLDING COIL
TERMINAL SCREW
FIELD COILS
GROUND BRUSH
FIELD COIL BRUSHES

Autolite field coil assembly

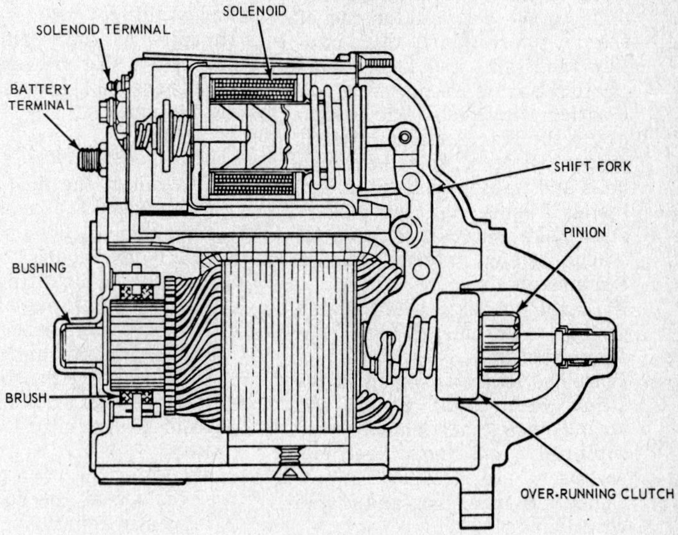
SOLENOID
SOLENOID TERMINAL
BATTERY TERMINAL
SHIFT FORK
PINION
BUSHING
BRUSH
OVER-RUNNING CLUTCH

Ford solenoid actuated starter motor (© Ford Motor Co)

at the drive end by caged needle bearings and at the commutator end by a sintered copper bushing. The four pole shoes are retained to the frame by one pole screw apiece, and on each pole shoe is wound a ribbon-type field coil connected in series-parallel.

The solenoid is mounted to a flange on the starter drive housing, which encloses the entire shift mechanism and solenoid plunger. The solenoid, following standard industry practice, utilizes two windings—a pull-in winding and a hold-in winding.

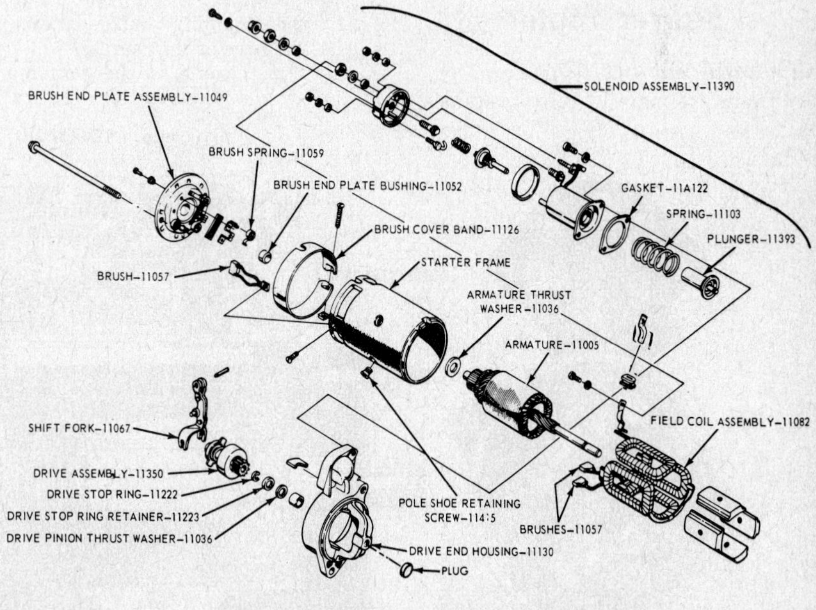
SOLENOID ASSEMBLY–11390
BRUSH END PLATE ASSEMBLY–11049
BRUSH SPRING–11059
BRUSH END PLATE BUSHING–11052
GASKET–11A122
SPRING–11103
PLUNGER–11393
BRUSH COVER BAND–11126
STARTER FRAME
BRUSH–11057
ARMATURE THRUST WASHER–11036
ARMATURE–11005
FIELD COIL ASSEMBLY–11082
SHIFT FORK–11067
DRIVE ASSEMBLY–11350
DRIVE STOP RING–11222
DRIVE STOP RING RETAINER–11223
DRIVE PINION THRUST WASHER–11036
POLE SHOE RETAINING SCREW–114:5
BRUSHES–11057
DRIVE END HOUSING–11130
PLUG

Ford solenoid actuated starter motor (© Ford Motor Co)

Disassembly

1. Disconnect the copper strap from the solenoid starter terminal, remove the remaining screws and remove the solenoid.
2. Loosen the retaining screw and slide the brush cover band back far enough to gain access to the brushes.
3. Remove the brushes from their holders, then remove the through bolts and separate the drive end housing from the frame and brush end plate.

NOTE: factory brush length is ½ in., wear limit ¼ in.

4. Remove the solenoid plunger and shift fork. These two items can be separated from each other by removing the roll pin.
5. Remove the armature and drive assembly from the frame. Remove the drive stop ring and slide the drive off the armature shaft.
6. Remove the drive stop ring retainer from the drive housing.
7. Inspection of the commutator, armature and bearings, and pinion gear procedures is the same as the positive engagement starter procedures.

Assembly

1. Lubricate the armature shaft splines with Lubriplate, then install drive assembly and a new stop ring.
2. Lubricate shift lever pivot pin with Lubriplate, then position solenoid plunger and shift lever assembly in the drive housing.
3. Place a new retainer in the drive housing. Apply a small amount of Lubriplate to the drive end of the armature shaft, then place armature and drive assembly into the drive housing, indexing the shift lever tangs with the drive assembly.
4. Apply a small amount of Lubriplate to the commutator end of the armature shaft, then position the frame and field assembly to the drive housing.
5. Position the brush plate assembly to the frame, making sure it properly indexes. Install through bolts and tighten to 45-85 in. lbs.
6. Install brushes into their holders and make sure leads are not touching any interior starter components.
7. Place the rubber gasket between the solenoid mount and the frame surface.
8. Place the starter solenoid in position with metal gasket and spring, install heat shield (if so equipped) and install solenoid screws.
9. Connect copper strap and install cover band.

Delco-Remy Starter Motor

(General Motors Corp.)

There are many different versions of the Delco-Remy starter, depending upon application. In general, six-cylinder engines use a unit having four field coils in series between the terminal and armature. Standard V8 engines use, depending on displacement, one of three types: one has two field coils in series with the armature and parallel to each other; another has two field coils in parallel between the field terminal and ground, and another has three field coils in series with the armature and one field connected between the motor terminal and ground. Heavy-duty starter motors, such as used on some of the largest G.M. high-output engines (over 400 cu. in.) have series compound windings.

In spite of these differences, all Delco-Remy starters are disassembled and assembled in essentially the same manner.

Disassembly

1. Disconnect the field coil connectors from the motor solenoid terminal.

NOTE: on models so equipped, remove solenoid mounting screws.

2. Remove the through bolts.
3. Remove commutator end frame, field frame and armature assembly from drive housing.
4. Remove the overrunning clutch from the armature shaft as follows:
   a. Slide the two-piece thrust collar off the end of the armature shaft.
   b. Slide a standard ½ in. pipe coupling or other spacer onto the shaft so that the end of the coupling butts against the edge of the retainer.
   c. Tap the end of the coupling with a hammer, driving retainer towards armature end of snap-ring.
   d. Remove snap-ring from its groove in the shaft using pliers. Slide retainer and clutch from armature shaft.
5. Disassemble brush assembly from field frame by releasing the V-spring and removing the support pin. The brush holders, brushes and springs now can be pulled out as a unit and the leads disconnected.
6. On models so equipped, separate solenoid from lever housing.

Cleaning and Inspection

1. Clean parts with a rag, but do not immerse the parts in a solvent. Immersion in a solvent will dissolve the grease that is packed in the clutch mechanism and damage the armature and field coil insulation.
2. Test overrunning clutch action. The pinion should turn freely in the overrunning direction and must not slip in the cranking direction. Check pinion teeth to see that they have not been chipped, cracked, or excessively worn. Replace the unit if necessary.
3. Inspect the armature commutator. If the commutator is rough or out of round, it should be turned down and undercut.

Caution Undercut the insulation between the commatator bars by 1/32 in.

This undercut must be the full width of the insulation and flat at the bottom; a triangular groove will not be satisfactory. Some starter motor models use a molded armature commutator design and no attempt to undercut the insulation should be made

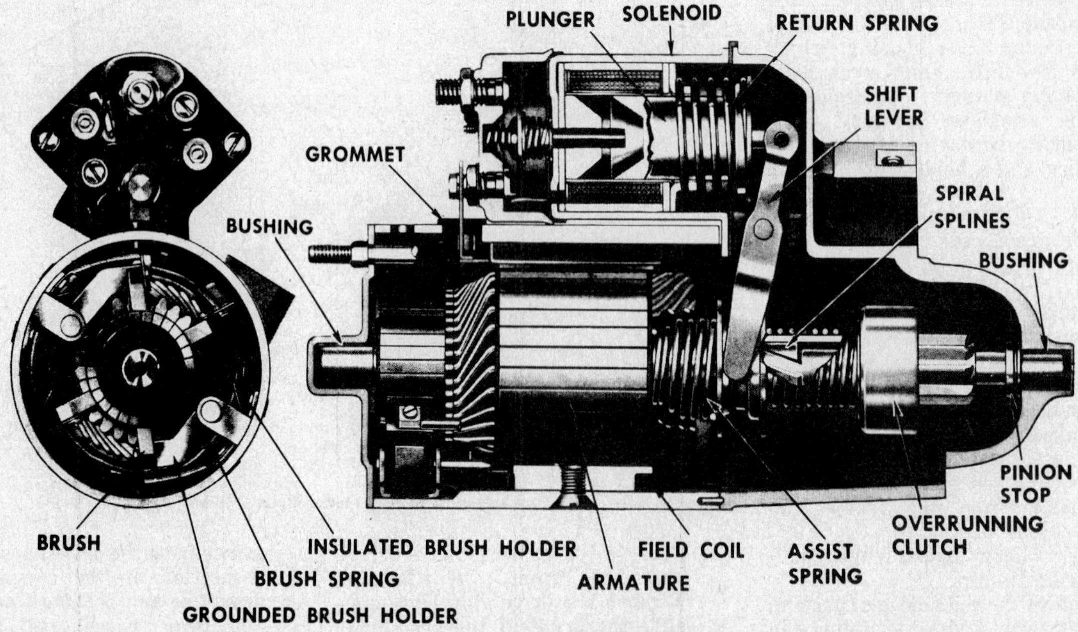
PLUNGER
SOLENOID
RETURN SPRING
SHIFT LEVER
GROMMET
SPIRAL SPLINES
BUSHING
BUSHING
PINION STOP
OVERRUNNING CLUTCH
BRUSH
INSULATED BRUSH HOLDER
FIELD COIL
ASSIST SPRING
BRUSH SPRING
ARMATURE
GROUNDED BRUSH HOLDER

Typical Delco-Remy starter motor using an assist spring—light duty Chevrolet illustrated
(© Chevrolet Div., G.M. Corp)

or serious damage may result to the commutator.

Assembly

1. Install brushes into holders. Install solenoid, if so equipped.
2. Assemble insulated and grounded brush holder together using the V-spring and position the assembled unit on the support pin. Push holders and spring to bottom of support and rotate spring to engage the slot in support. Attach ground wire to grounded brush and field lead wire to insulated brush, then repeat for other brush sets.
3. Assemble overrunning clutch to armature shaft as follows:
   a. Lubricate drive end of shaft with silicone lubricant.
   b. Slide clutch assembly onto shaft with pinion outward.
   c. Slide retainer onto shaft with cupped surface facing away from pinion.
   d. Stand armature up on a wood surface, commutator downwards. Position snap-ring on upper end of shaft and drive it onto shaft with a small block of wood and a hammer. Slide snap-ring into groove.
   e. Install thrust collar onto shaft with shoulder next to snap-ring.
   f. With retainer on one side of snap-ring and thrust collar on the other side, squeeze together with two sets of pliers until ring seats in retainer. On models without thrust collar, use a washer. Remember to remove washer before continuing.
4. Lubricate drive end bushing with silicone lubricant, then slide armature and clutch assembly into place, at the same time engaging shift lever with clutch.

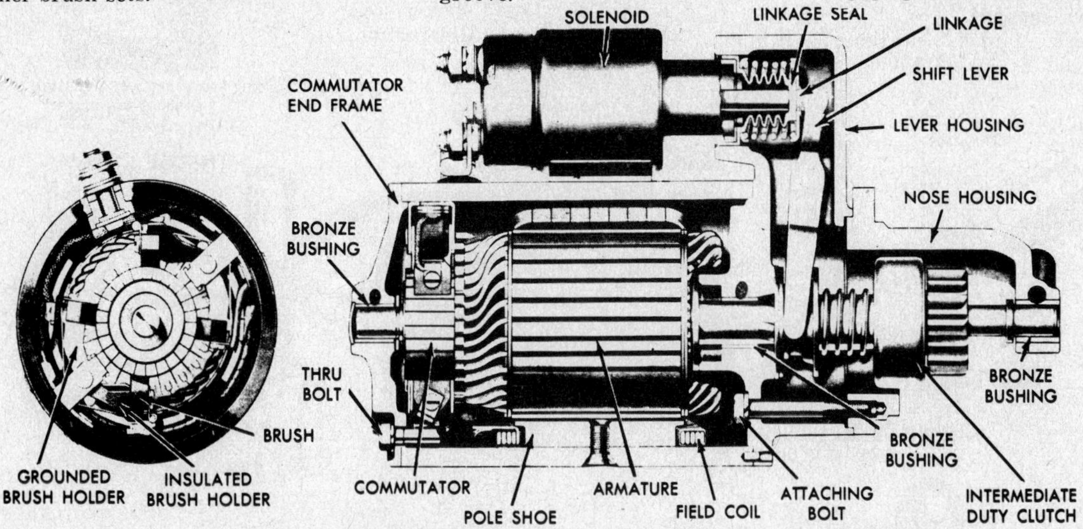
SOLENOID
LINKAGE SEAL
LINKAGE
SHIFT LEVER
LEVER HOUSING
COMMUTATOR END FRAME
NOSE HOUSING
BRONZE BUSHING
THRU BOLT
BRUSH
BRONZE BUSHING
BRONZE BUSHING
GROUNDED BRUSH HOLDER
INSULATED BRUSH HOLDER
COMMUTATOR
ARMATURE
ATTACHING BOLT
INTERMEDIATE DUTY CLUTCH
POLE SHOE
FIELD COIL

Typical Delco-Remy starter motor as used on intermediate models—Chevrolet application illustrated (© Chevrolet Div., G.M. Corp)

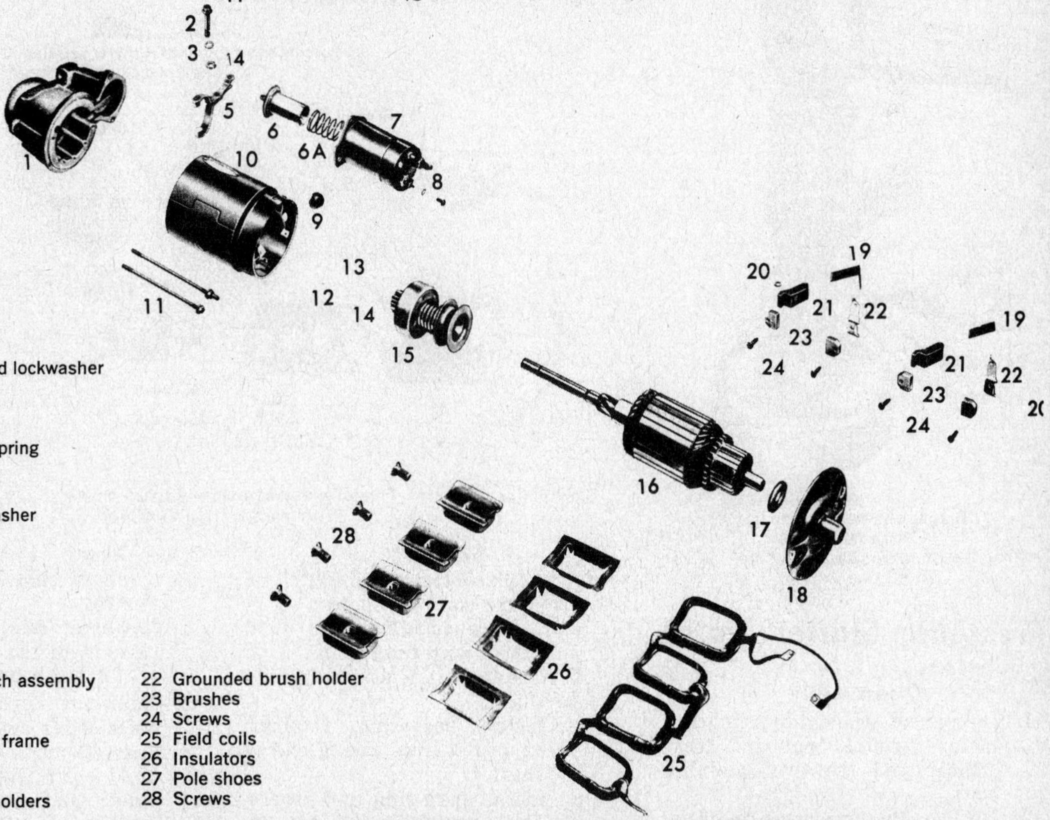

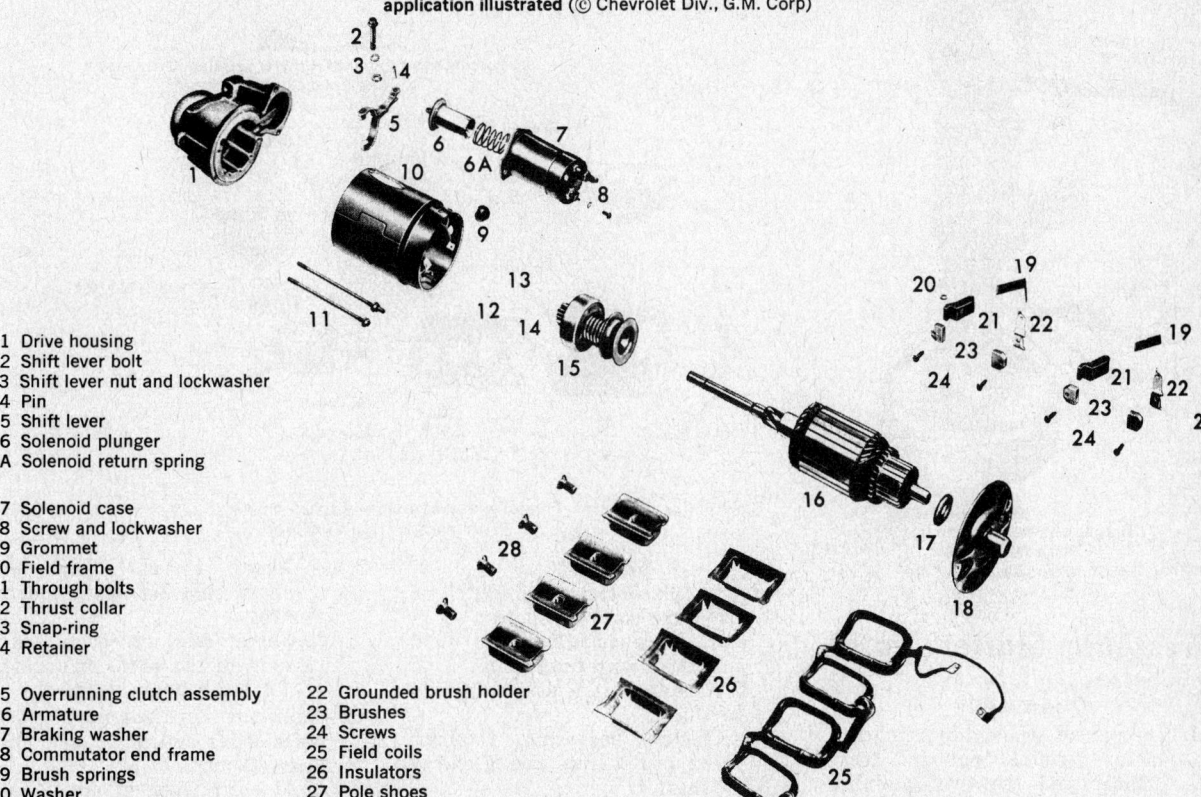

1 Drive housing
2 Shift lever bolt
3 Shift lever nut and lockwasher
4 Pin
5 Shift lever
6 Solenoid plunger
6A Solenoid return spring
7 Solenoid case
8 Screw and lockwasher
9 Grommet
10 Field frame
11 Through bolts
12 Thrust collar
13 Snap-ring
14 Retainer
15 Overrunning clutch assembly
16 Armature
17 Braking washer
18 Commutator end frame
19 Brush springs
20 Washer
21 Insulated brush holders
22 Grounded brush holder
23 Brushes
24 Screws
25 Field coils
26 Insulators
27 Pole shoes
28 Screws

Typical Delco-Remy starter motor exploded view—light duty Chevrolet illustrated (© Chevrolet Div., G.M. Corp)

5. Position field frame over armature and apply sealer (silicone) between frame and solenoid case. Position frame against drive housing, making sure brushes are not damaged in the process.
6. Lubricate commutator end bushing with silicone lubricant, place a leather brake washer on the armature shaft and slide commutator end frame onto shaft. Install through bolts and tighten to 65 in. lbs.
7. Reconnect field coil connector/s to the solenoid motor terminal. Install solenoid mounting screws, if so equipped.
8. Check pinion clearance; it should be 0.010-0.140 in. on all models.

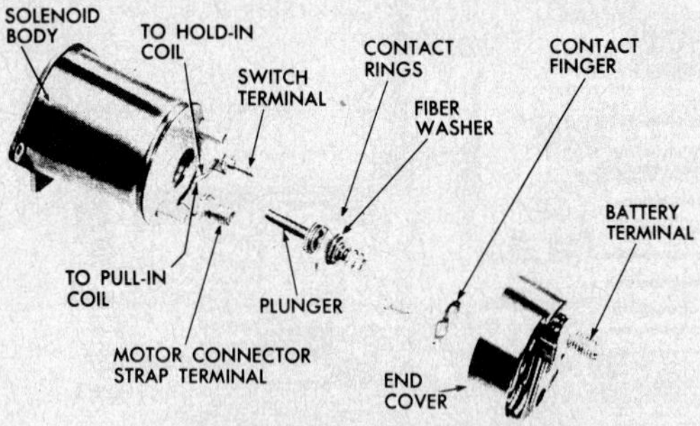
SOLENOID BODY
TO HOLD-IN COIL
SWITCH TERMINAL
CONTACT RINGS
FIBER WASHER
CONTACT FINGER
BATTERY TERMINAL
TO PULL-IN COIL
PLUNGER
MOTOR CONNECTOR STRAP TERMINAL
END COVER

Delco-Remy starter solenoid
(© Chevrolet Div., G.M. Corp)

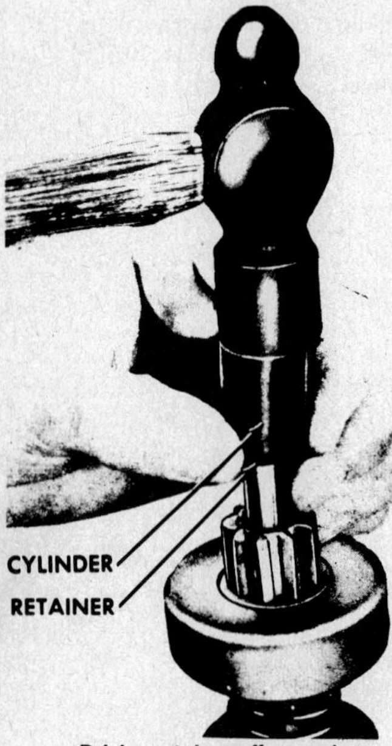
CYLINDER
RETAINER

Driving retainer off snap ring
—Delco-Remy motor
(© Chevrolet Div., G.M. Corp)

Prestolite Starter Motor

Disassembly

1. Disconnect solenoid by removing motor terminal nut and lockwasher and the two retaining bolts.
2. Remove link cover boot and solenoid.
3. Remove starter through bolts, then remove commutator end head and frame.
4. Remove shift lever pin retainer, boot and pivot pin.
5. Remove armature, drive and shift lever from pinion housing.
6. Remove drive assembly as follows:
   a. Slide thrust collar off armature shaft.
   b. Using a standard ½ in. pipe connector, drive snap-ring retainer off shaft.
   c. Remove snap-ring from groove, then remove drive assembly.
7. See the Delco-Remy starter section for cleaning and inspection procedures.

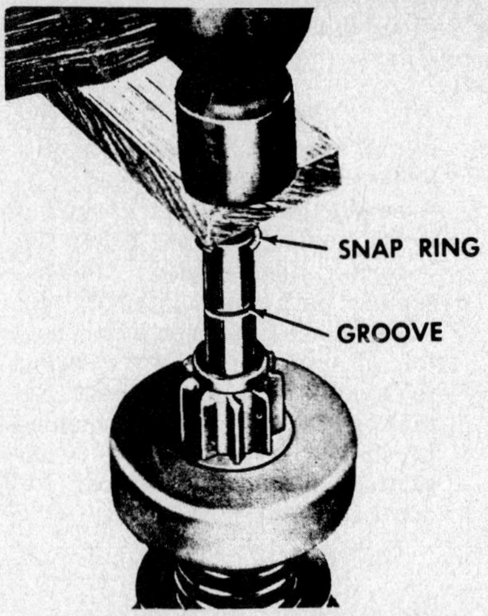
SNAP RING
GROOVE

Forcing snap ring over armature shaft—
Delco-Remy motor
(© Chevrolet Div., G.M. Corp)

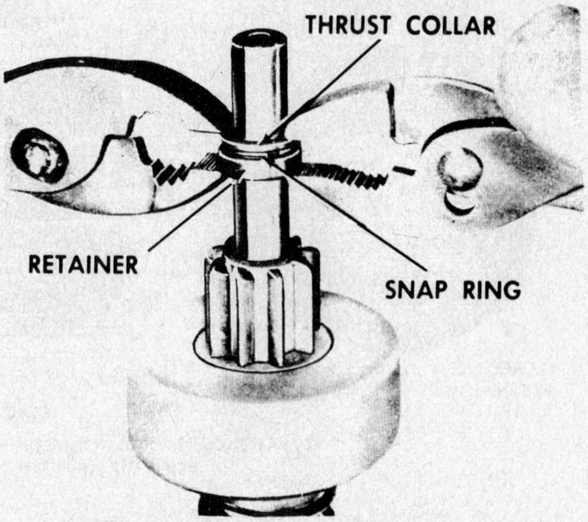
THRUST COLLAR
RETAINER
SNAP RING

Forcing snap ring into retainer—Delco-Remy motor
(© Chevrolet Div., G.M. Corp)

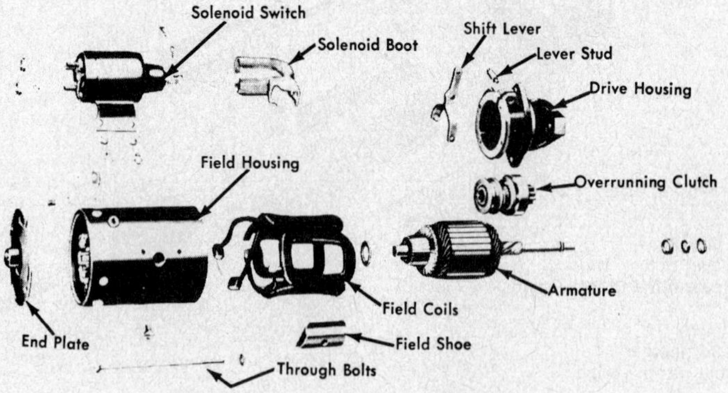
Solenoid Switch
Solenoid Boot
Shift Lever
Lever Stud
Drive Housing
Field Housing
Overrunning Clutch
Armature
Field Coils
End Plate
Field Shoe
Through Bolts

Prestolite starter motor—exploded view
(© American Motors Corp)

Assembly

1. Assemble overrunning clutch to armature shaft as follows:
   a. Lubricate drive end and splines with Lubriplate.
   b. Install clutch assembly onto shaft.
   c. Install snap-ring retainer, cupped surface facing end of shaft.
   d. Install snap-ring into groove. Use a new snap-ring if necessary.
   e. Install thrust collar onto shaft, shoulder against snap-ring.
   f. Force retainer over snap-ring in the same manner as for Delco-Remy starters.
2. Lubricate overrunning clutch shift collar and drive end bushing with engine oil.
3. Hold shift lever in position on collar and assemble armature, drive and shift lever into housing.

4. Install shift lever pivot pin, boot and retainer.
5. Install frame and field coil assembly, making sure brushes are not damaged in the process.
6. Saturate felt washer (commutator head) with engine oil, drain excess and install washer.
7. Install through bolts and tighten to 65 in. lbs.
8. Check armature end-play; it should be 0.005-0.030 in. Adjust, if necessary, by adding or removing thrust washers at commutator end of shaft.
9. Check pinion clearance; it should be 0.010-0.140 in.

AC Generators

Preliminary Charging System Inspection

NOTE: before performing any tests on the charging systems, these precautions should be taken to ensure the accuracy of the tests in this section.

1. Check the condition of the alternator belt and tighten it if necessary.
2. Clean the battery cable connections at the battery. Make sure that the connections between the battery wires and the battery clamps are good. Reconnect the negative terminal only, and proceed to the next step.
3. With the key off, insert a test light between the positive terminal on the battery and the disconnected positive battery terminal clamp. If the test light comes on, there is a short in the electrical system of the car. The short has to be repaired before proceeding. If the light fails to glow, reconnect the clamp and proceed to the next step.

NOTE: alternators with transistorized regulators sometimes draw a slight current even when the key is turned off. To properly check these systems for a short, the regulator must be disconnected. Also, on cars equipped with an electric clock, disconnect the lead wire from the clock.

4. Check the charging system wiring for breaks or shorts.
5. Check the battery to make sure that it is fully charged and in good condition.

Chrysler Isolated Field Alternator (Electronic Regulator)

The Chrysler isolated field alternator replaced the grounded brush alternator in 1970 and derived its name from its construction. Both of the brushes are insulated from ground and there is no heat sink connection, thereby isolating the internal field.

Troubleshooting

NOTE: see the "Preliminary Charging System Inspection" section before proceeding further. Make sure that the continuous running blower, if equipped, is disconnected. This blower will run with the key turned on even if the blower controls are off unless disconnected.

Fusible Links

Chrysler Corporation cars have a single fusible link which is connected between the starter relay and the junction block. Failure of this link will cause all electrical systems to stop functioning.

Charging System Operation

NOTE: if the current indicator is to give an accurate reading, the battery cables must be of the same gauge and length as the original equipment.

1. With the engine running and all electrical systems off, place a current indicator over the positive battery cable.
2. If a charge of about 5 amps is recorded, the charging system is working. If a draw of about 5 amps is recorded the system is not working. The needle moves toward the battery when a charge condition is indicated and away from the battery when a draw condition is indicated. If a draw is indicated, proceed to the next testing procedure. If an overcharge of 10-15 amps is indicated, check for a faulty regulator.

Ignition Switch-to-Regulator Circuit Check

1. Disconnect the regulator wires at the regulator.
2. Turn the key on but do not start the engine.
3. Using a voltmeter or test light, check for voltage across the I and F terminals. If there is current present, the circuit is good. If there is no current, check for bad connections, a bad ballast resistor, a bad ammeter, broken wires, or bad ground at the alternator or voltage regulator. Also, check for voltage from the I wire to ground; current should be present. Check for voltage from the F terminal to ground; current should not be present.

Isolation Test

This test determines whether the regulator or alternator is bad if everything else in the circuit was OK.

1. Disconnect, at the alternator, the wire that runs between one of the alternator field connections and the voltage regulator.
2. Run a jumper wire from the disconnected alternator terminal to ground.
3. Connect a voltmeter to the battery. The positive voltmeter lead connects to the positive battery terminal, and the negative lead goes to the negative terminal. Record the reading.
4. Make sure that all electrical systems are turned off. Start the engine. Do not race the engine.
5. Gradually raise engine speed to 1500–2000 rpm. There should be an increase of one to two volts on the voltmeter. If this is true, the alternator is good and the voltage regulator should be repaired. If there is no voltage increase, the alternator is faulty.

NOTE: the following tests require the use of a carbon pile and an ammeter.

Current Output Test—1970-74

1. The ammeter and carbon pile hookup should remain the same as for the circuit resistance test.
2. Connect the voltmeter negative lead to the battery negative post.
3. Move the positive voltmeter lead to the alternator "BATT" post.
4. Start the engine and adjust speed to 1250 rpm.
5. Note voltmeter and ammeter readings. Maintain a 15 volt reading by adjusting the carbon pile control.
6. Compare ammeter reading with manufacturer's specifications. The reading should be no less than specified, 3 amps.
7. If below specifications, internal trouble is indicated. Remove the alternator for further testing.

Electronic Voltage Regulator Test—1970-74

1. Make sure battery terminals are clean and battery is charged.
2. Connect the positive lead of a test voltmeter to ignition Terminal No. 1 of the ballast resistor.
3. Connect the negative voltmeter lead to a good *body* ground.
4. Start engine and allow it to idle at 1250 rpm, all lights and accessories turned off. Voltage should be as follows:

Ambient Temp. ¼ in. from Regulator	*Voltage*
-20°F.	14.3-15.3
80°F.	13.8-14.4
140°F.	13.3-14.0

5. If the voltage is *below* specifications, check the following:
   a. Voltage regulator ground—check voltage drop between regulator cover and ground.

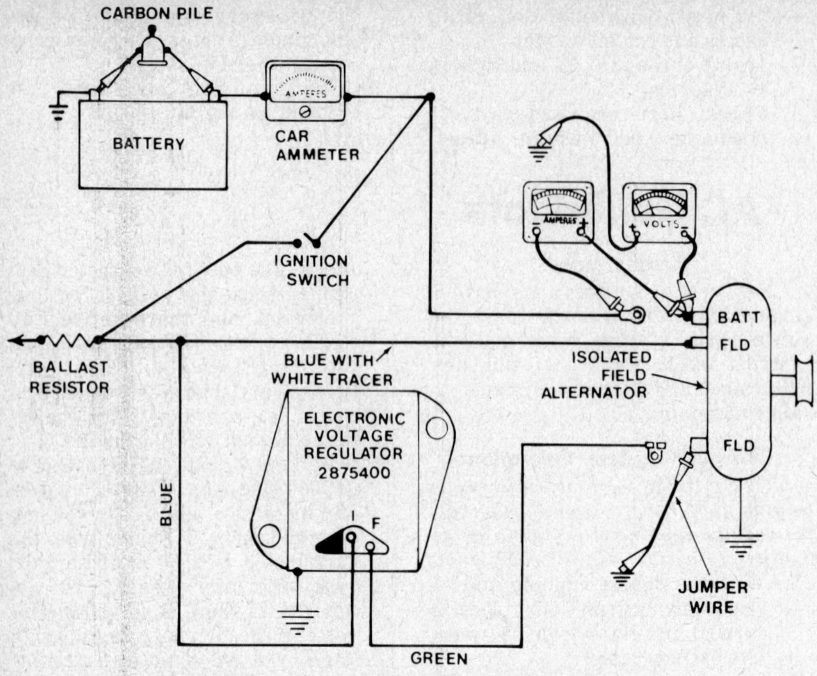

CARBON PILE
AMPERES
BATTERY
CAR
AMMETER
AMPERES
VOLTS
IGNITION
SWITCH
BATT
FLD
BALLAST
RESISTOR
BLUE WITH
WHITE TRACER
ISOLATED
FIELD
ALTERNATOR
ELECTRONIC
VOLTAGE
REGULATOR
2875400
FLD
BLUE
I
F
JUMPER
WIRE
GREEN

Current output test hook-up—Chrysler isolated field alternator

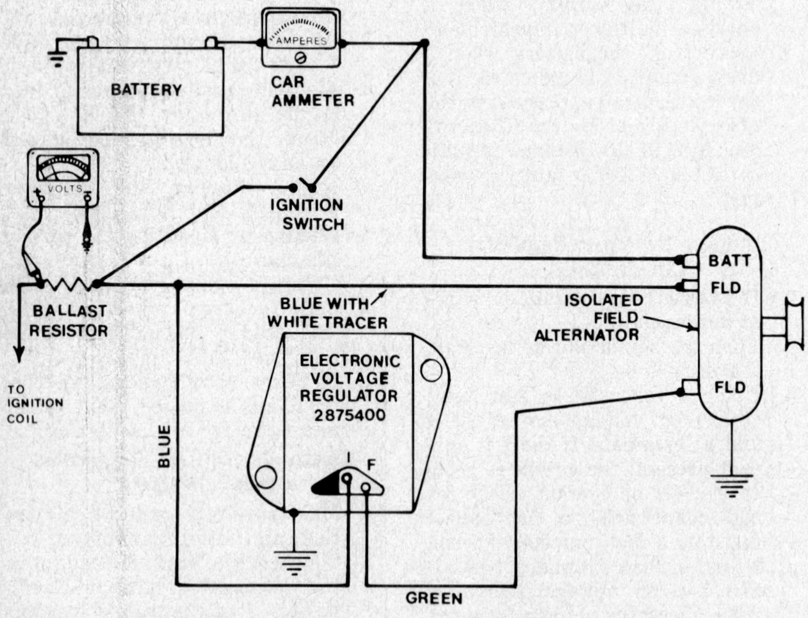

AMPERES
BATTERY
CAR
AMMETER
VOLTS
IGNITION
SWITCH
BATT
FLD
BALLAST
RESISTOR
BLUE WITH
WHITE TRACER
ISOLATED
FIELD
ALTERNATOR
TO
IGNITION
COIL
ELECTRONIC
VOLTAGE
REGULATOR
2875400
FLD
BLUE
I
F
GREEN

Voltage regulator test hook-up—Chrysler isolated field alternator

b. Harness wiring—disconnect regulator plug (ign. switch off), then turn on ign. switch and check for battery voltage at the terminal having the blue and green leads. *Wiring harness must be disconnected from the regulator when checking individual leads.* If no voltage is present in either lead, the problem is in the car wiring or alternator field.

6. If Step 5 tests showed no malfunctions, install a new regulator and repeat Step 4.
7. If voltage is *above* specifications (Step 4), or fluctuates, check the following:
   a. Ground between regulator and body, and between body and engine.
   b. Ignition switch circuit between switch and regulator.
8. If voltage is still more than ½ volt above specifications, install a new regulator and repeat Step 4.

Chrysler Alternator (Electro-Mechanical Regulator)

The alternator that was used until 1969 was the grounded brush alternator with an electro-mechanical voltage regulator. This alternator has one brush connected to the single field terminal and the other brush grounded to the housing. In this system, the field circuit is grounded at the alternator through the ground brush.

Troubleshooting

NOTE: before performing any tests, see the "Preliminary System Inspection" section. This will help ensure the accuracy of the tests. Make sure the continuous running blower, if equipped, is disconnected.

Fusible Link

1. Check the condition of the fusible link as described in the "Isolated Field Alternator" section.

Charging System Operation

1. Check the operation of the system as described in the "Isolated Field Alternator" section.

Check Ignition Switch-to-Regulator Circuit

1. Disconnect the ignition wire from its voltage regulator terminal.
2. Turn on the ignition switch but do not start the engine.
3. Using a voltmeter or a test light, check for voltage between the ignition wire and ground. If no voltage is found, trace the wire back, checking for a break or short in the wire, a bad indicator bulb, resistor wire, or ammeter.

Isolation Test

This test determines whether the regulator or the alternator is bad, if the rest of the circuit is OK.

1. Disconnect the regulator field terminal at the alternator.
2. With a jumper wire, connect the alternator field terminal to the alternator battery terminal.
3. Connect the positive lead from a voltmeter to the positive terminal of the battery, and connect the negative lead to the negative terminal. Record the reading on the voltmeter.
4. Connect the red lead of a tachometer to the distributor terminal on the coil and the black lead to ground.
5. Start the engine, making sure all electrical systems are turned off. Do not race the engine upon starting.
6. Gradually increase engine speed to 1500–2000 rpm. The voltmeter reading should increase above

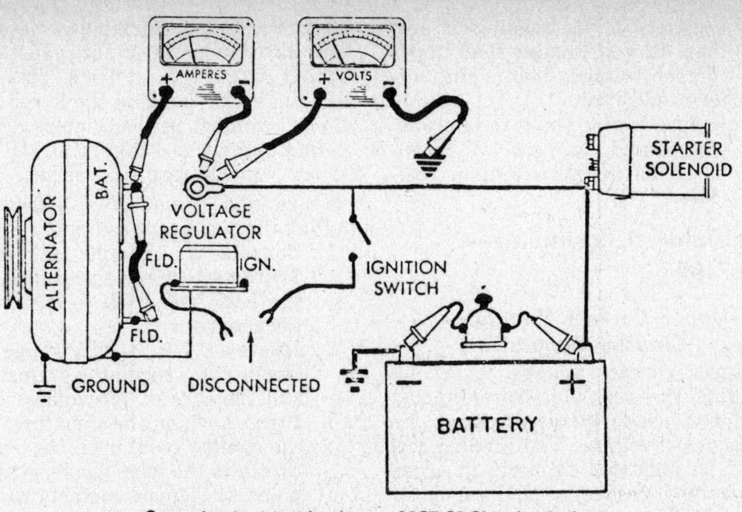
AMPERES
VOLTS
STARTER
SOLENOID
ALTERNATOR
BAT.
VOLTAGE
REGULATOR
FLD.
IGN.
IGNITION
SWITCH
FLD.
GROUND
DISCONNECTED
BATTERY

Current output test hook-up—1967-69 Chrysler design

the previously recorded battery voltage reading by at least one to two volts. If there is no increase, the alternator is not working correctly. If there is an increase, the voltage regulator needs to be repaired.

NOTE: the following tests require the use of a carbon pile and an ammeter.

Current Output Test—1967-69

1. Disconnect battery ground cable.
2. Disconnect the BATT. lead from the alternator BATT. terminal.
3. Connect a test ammeter in series between the alternator BATT. terminal and the lead just disconnected from it.
4. Connect the positive lead of a test voltmeter to the BATT. lead and the negative voltmeter test lead to ground.
5. Disconnect the FLD. lead from the alternator and the ignition lead from the regulator IGN. terminal.
6. Connect a jumper wire between the alternator FLD. terminal and the alternator BATT. terminal.
7. Connect a tachometer to the engine and reconnect the negative battery cable.
8. Connect a carbon pile rheostat between the two battery terminals.
9. Start engine and allow it to idle. Adjust carbon pile and engine speed until 1250 rpm and 15 volts are attained. *Do not exceed* 16 volts.
10. The ammeter should now read specified output for the particular alternator. A reading 5-7 amps. less than specified may indicate an open rectifier; a considerably less than normal reading could mean a shorted rectifier.
11. If reading is within limits, remove test gear and reconnect all leads to original terminals. If reading is outside of limits, remove alternator for bench tests.

Voltage Regulator Test

Upper Contacts

1. With the battery ground cable disconnected at the battery and the BATT. lead disconnected from the alternator output terminal, hook up an ammeter as follows:
   a. Connect the ammeter positive lead to the alternator output terminal.
   b. Connect the ammeter negative lead to the lead just disconnected from the alternator output terminal.
2. Hook up a voltmeter as follows:
   a. Disconnect the ignition wire

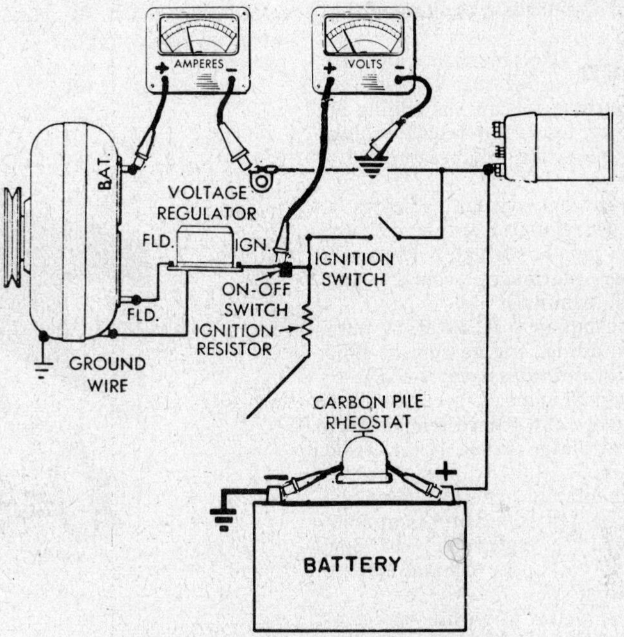
AMPERES
VOLTS
BAT.
VOLTAGE
REGULATOR
FLD.
IGN.
IGNITION
SWITCH
ON-OFF
SWITCH
FLD.
IGNITION
RESISTOR
GROUND
WIRE
CARBON PILE
RHEOSTAT
BATTERY

Voltage regulator test hook-up—1967-69 Chrysler electro-mechanical regulator

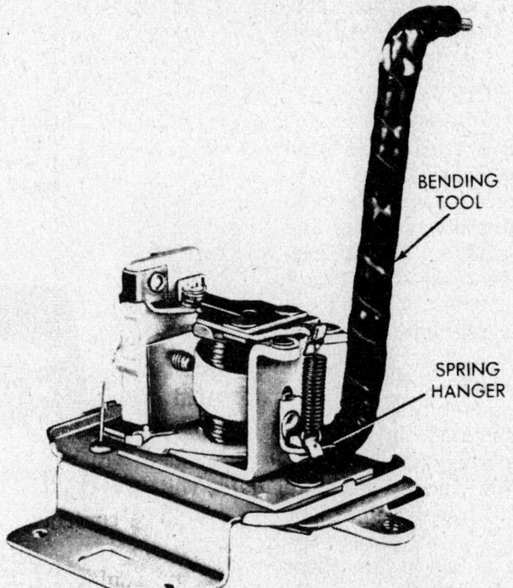
BENDING
TOOL
SPRING
HANGER

Adjusting upper contact voltage—Chrysler built regulator to 1969
(© Chrysler Corp)

at the IGN. terminal of the regulator. Install a pushbutton switch in series with the IGN. terminal and the wire just disconnected.

b. Connect the negative voltmeter lead to ground.

c. Connect the positive voltmeter lead to the IGN. terminal of the regulator or to the regulator side of the test switch.

3. Connect a tachometer to the engine.
4. Hook up the ground cable to the battery.
5. Hook up a carbon pile (load control turned to the off position) between the battery posts.
6. With engine operating at 1250 rpm, adjust carbon pile and/or turn on headlights; watch the voltmeter and ammeter. A 15 amp. output must be obtained.

Caution Voltmeter reading must not exceed 15 volts. Continue to run the engine at this setting until the regulator has reached operating temperature (15 min.)

7. No current output indicates a low set regulator or a blown fuse wire inside regulator (between upper stationary contact and IGN. terminal).
8. If output is O.K. after 15 minutes, adjust engine rpm to 1250 again and adjust carbon pile to obtain 15 amps.
9. Measure and record temperature of regulator about 1/4 in. from cover.
10. Momentarily open and close the test switch several times and observe the voltmeter; it now reads the upper contact setting (see chart).
11. If regulator is within specifications, proceed to the *Lower Contacts* test. If not, remove regulator cover and adjust upper contacts (see *Regulator Adjustments*).

Lower Contacts

1. Keep the same hook-up as used for upper contact test.
2. Increase engine speed to 2200 rpm, then turn off all lights and accessories and/or adjust carbon pile to decrease output to 7 amps.
3. Again take a regulator temperature reading and turn the test switch on and off a few times.
4. The test voltmeter now will register an increase in voltage over that recorded for the upper contacts. This increase should not be less than 0.2 volt, or greater than 0.7 volt. If the voltage increase is not within these limits, it indicates that the air gap/contact clearance must be adjusted (see *Regulator Adjustments*). If the reading is less than 0.2 volt greater than upper contact voltage, charge the battery and retest.
5. Reduce engine speed to idle, stop engine and reconnect all terminal leads to their original positions.

Regulator Adjustments—1967-69

Upper Contact Voltage—Chrysler Regulator

Upper contact voltage is set by bending the regulator lower spring hanger *down* to increase voltage, *up* to decrease voltage. The bending tool must be insulated properly in order to prevent grounding and regulator damage. The regulator must be installed, correctly connected and retested after each adjustment of the lower spring hanger. *Cover must be on.*

Lower Contact Voltage—Chrysler Regulator

If the adjustment of the upper contact voltage does not bring the regulator within specifications, measure the lower contact point gap. Gap should be 0.014 in. ± 0.002. This gap is adjusted by bending the lower *stationary* contact bracket, making sure points remain in alignment. If the lower contact gap is correct, and voltage still is out of specification, adjust the air gap, as follows:

1. Connect a 1½-volt test light (with battery) in series between the IGN. and FLD terminals of the regulator.
2. Insert a 0.048 in. wire gauge between the regulator armature and the core of the voltage coil.
3. Press down on the armature, not the contact reed, until the armature hits the wire gauge. At this point, the upper contacts should just open and the test light should be dim.
4. Insert a 0.052 in. wire gauge between the armature and voltage coil coil, next to the armature stop pin. (After removing 0.048 in. gauge).
5. Press down on the armature until it hits the wire gauge. The

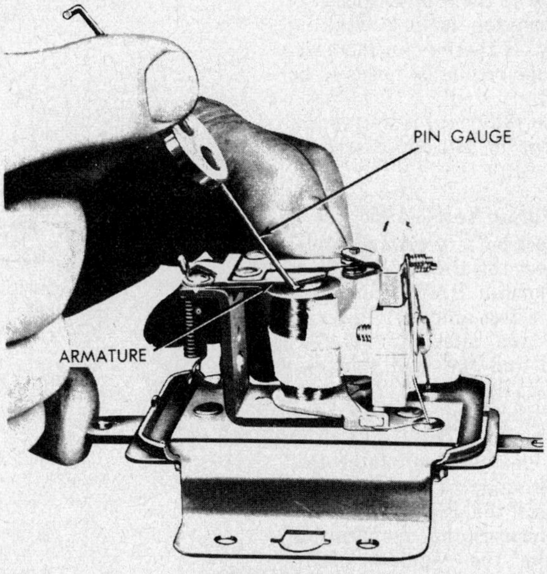
PIN GAUGE
ARMATURE

Checking air gap on Chrysler regulator to 1969
(© Chrysler Corp)

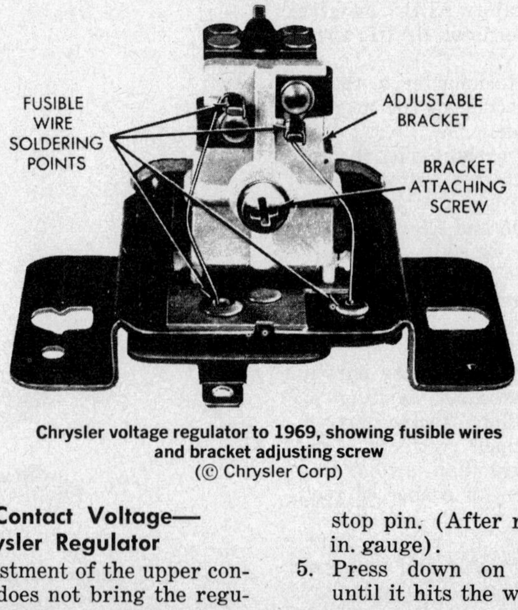
FUSIBLE WIRE SOLDERING POINTS
ADJUSTABLE BRACKET
BRACKET ATTACHING SCREW

Chrysler voltage regulator to 1969, showing fusible wires and bracket adjusting screw
(© Chrysler Corp)

upper contacts should remain closed and the test light should be bright.

6. If an adjustment is required, loosen the stationary contact bracket screw and move bracket up and down as necessary to obtain the proper air gap. Following are guidelines for this adjustment:

Voltage Difference	*Air. Gap Min.**	*Air Gap Max.#*
0.7 volt	0.045	0.048
0.2 volt	0.052	0.055

* Contacts open, test light dim.
\# Contacts closed, test light bright.

Lower Contact Voltage— Essex Wire Regulator

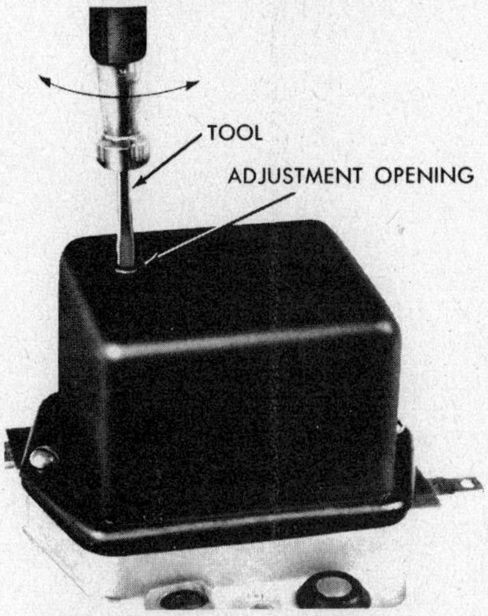
TOOL
ADJUSTMENT OPENING

Lower contact voltage adjustment— Essex Wire-built regulator
(© Chrysler Corp.)

Lower contact voltage is adjusted by turning the adjustment screw, accessible through the cover opening. Turning clockwise increases voltage, turning counterclockwise decreases voltage.

Upper Contact Point Gap— Essex Wire Regulator

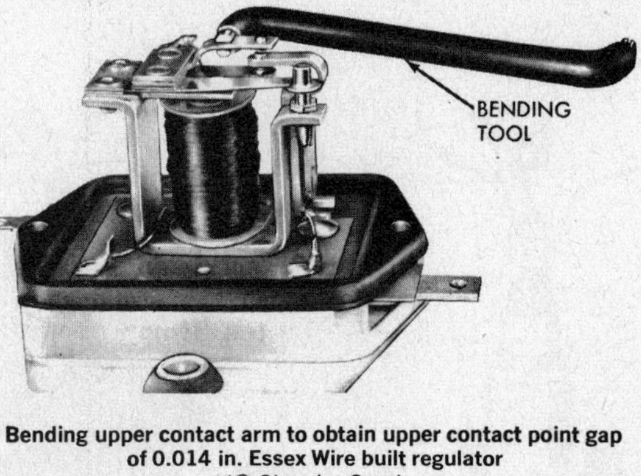
BENDING
TOOL

Bending upper contact arm to obtain upper contact point gap of 0.014 in. Essex Wire built regulator
(© Chrysler Corp)

Measure the upper contact point gap; it should be 0.014 in. ± 0.004. Adjust gap by bending armature upper contact bracket with an insulated tool, making sure contacts remain in alignment. If upper contact gap is correct, and voltage still is out of specifications, adjust air gap, as follows:

1. Connect a 1½-volt test light (with battery) in series between the IGN. and FLD. terminals of the regulator.
2. Insert a 0.032 in. wire gauge between the regulator armature and voltage core coil.
3. Press down on armature until it hits the gauge. At this point, lower contacts should just open and test light should be dim.

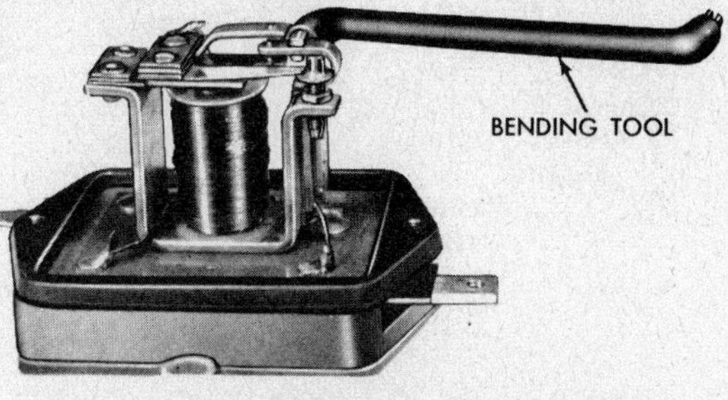
BENDING TOOL

Bending stationary contact arm to obtain proper air gap —Essex Wire built regulator
(© Chrysler Corp)

4. Check that a 0.042 in. gauge cannot be inserted between the armature and voltage core. This must not be possible, or air gap must be readjusted.

NOTE: if voltage difference is greater than 0.7 volt, reduce air gap; if less than 0.2 volt, increase air gap.

Chrysler Overhaul and Internal Testing

Alternator disassembly, repair and assembly procedures are basically the same for all Chrysler alternators, including the Isolated Field type used for the first time in 1970. Certain variations in design, or in-production modifications, could require slightly different procedures that should be obvious upon inspection of the unit being serviced. An example of this is the new isolated field alternator, which has two FLD. terminals.

Disassembly

To prevent damage to the brush assemblies they should be removed before proceeding with the disassembly of the alternator. The insulated brush is mounted in a plastic holder that positions the brush vertically against one of the slip rings.

1. Remove the retaining screw, flat washer, nylon washer and field terminal and carefully lift the plastic holder containing the spring and brush assembly from the end housing.
2. The ground brush is positioned horizontally against the remaining slip ring and is retained in the holder that is integral with the end housing. Remove the retaining screw and lift the clip, spring and brush assembly from the end housing.

Caution The stator is laminated, don't burr the stator or end housings.

3. Remove the through bolts and pry between the stator and drive end housing with a thin blade screwdriver. Carefully separate the drive end housing, pulley and rotor assembly from the stator and rectifier housing assembly.
4. The pulley is an interference fit on the rotor shaft. Remove with a puller and special adapters.
5. Remove the three nuts and washers and, while supporting the end frame, tap the rotor shaft with a plastic hammer and separate the rotor and end housing.
6. The drive end ball bearing is an interference fit with the rotor shaft. Remove the bearing with puller and adapters.

NOTE: further dismantling of the rotor is not advisable, as the remainder of the rotor assembly is not serviced separately.

7. Remove the DC output terminal nuts and washers and remove terminal screw and inside capacitor (on units so equipped).

NOTE: the heat sink is also held in place by the terminal screw.

8. Remove the insulator.

NOTE: three positive rectifiers are pressed into the heat sink and three negative rectifiers in the end housing. When removing the rectifiers, it is

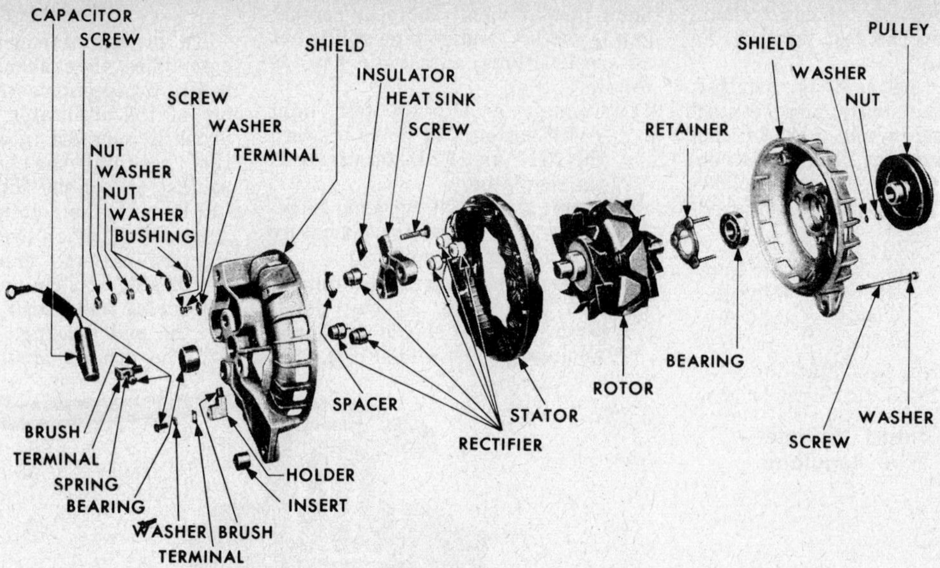
CAPACITOR
SCREW
SHIELD
INSULATOR
HEAT SINK
SCREW
SCREW
WASHER
TERMINAL
NUT
WASHER
NUT
WASHER
BUSHING
RETAINER
SHIELD
WASHER
NUT
PULLEY
BEARING
ROTOR
STATOR
RECTIFIER
SPACER
BRUSH
TERMINAL
SPRING
BEARING
WASHER
BRUSH
TERMINAL
HOLDER
INSERT
WASHER
SCREW

Alternator—typical 1967-69 Chrysler

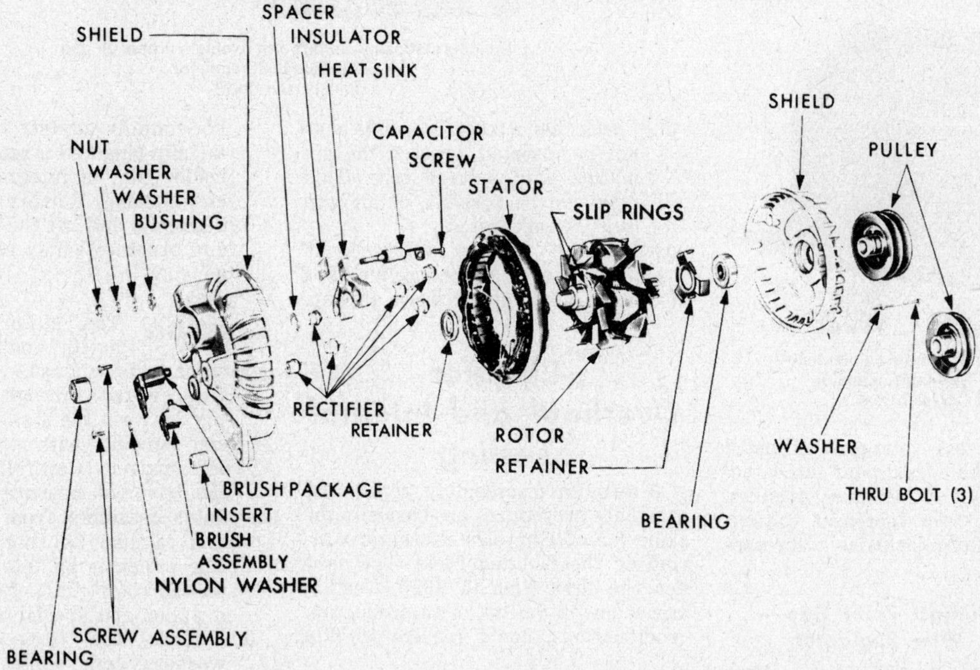
SHIELD
SPACER
INSULATOR
HEAT SINK
CAPACITOR
SCREW
STATOR
SLIP RINGS
SHIELD
PULLEY
NUT
WASHER
WASHER
BUSHING
RECTIFIER
RETAINER
ROTOR
RETAINER
BEARING
WASHER
THRU BOLT (3)
BRUSH PACKAGE
INSERT
BRUSH
ASSEMBLY
NYLON WASHER
SCREW ASSEMBLY
BEARING

Chrysler isolated field alternator—1970-72 (© Chrysler Corp)

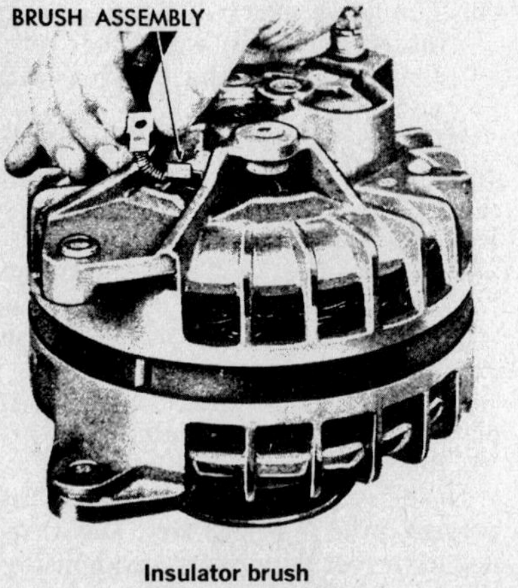
BRUSH ASSEMBLY

Insulator brush
(© Chrysler Corp)

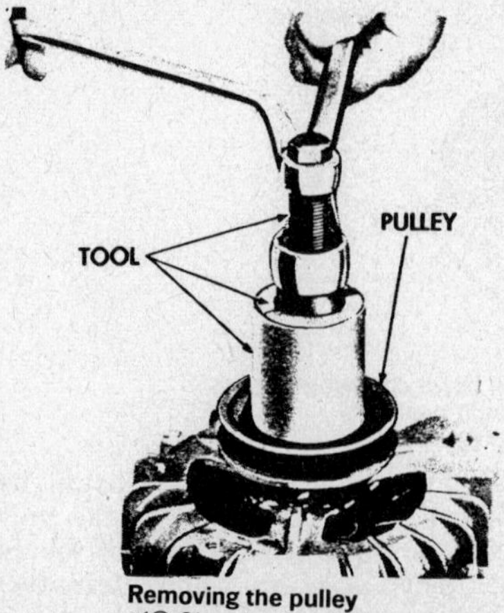
TOOL
PULLEY

Removing the pulley
(© Chrysler Corp)

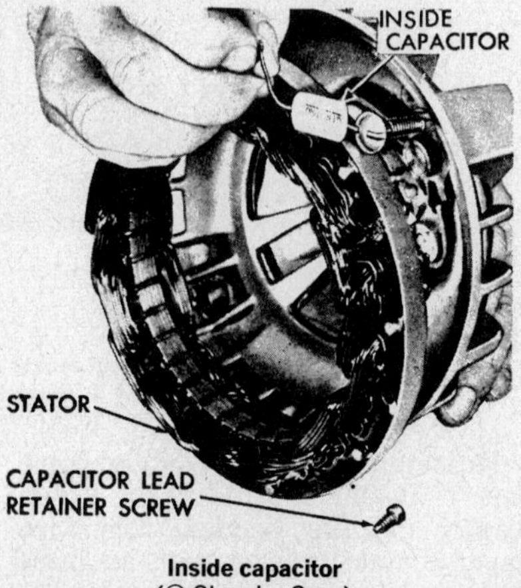
INSIDE
CAPACITOR
STATOR
CAPACITOR LEAD
RETAINER SCREW

Inside capacitor
(© Chrysler Corp)

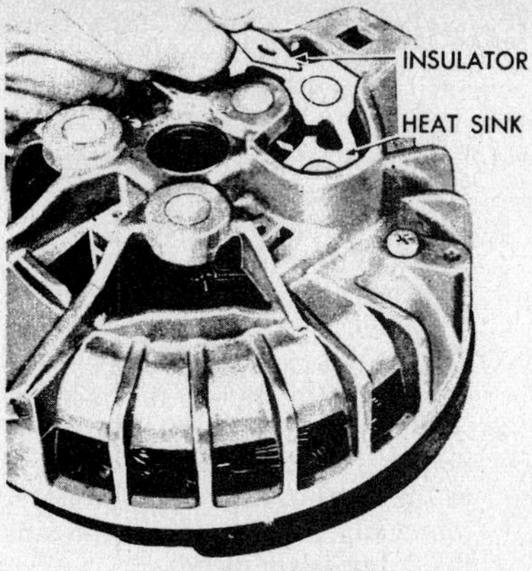
INSULATOR
HEAT SINK
Heat sink and insulator
(© Chrysler Corp)

necessary to support the end housing and or heat sink to prevent damage to these castings. Another caution is in order relative to the diode rectifiers. Don't subject them to unnecessary jolting. Heavy vibration or shock may ruin them.

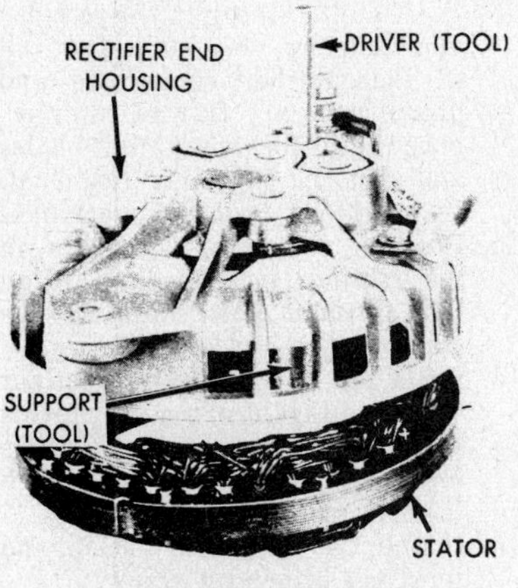
RECTIFIER END HOUSING
DRIVER (TOOL)
SUPPORT (TOOL)
STATOR
Removing a rectifier
(© Chrysler Corp)

A. Cut rectifiier wire at point of crimp.
B. Support rectifier housing.

NOTE: the factory tool is cut away and slotted to fit over the wires and around the bosses in the housing. Be sure that the bore of the tool completely surrounds the rectifier, then press the rectifier out of the housing.

NOTE: the roller bearing in the rectifier end frame is a press fit. To protect the end housing it is necessary to support the housing with a tool when pressing out the bearing.

Bench Tests

Testing Silicon Diode Rectifiers With Ohmmeter

Preferred method—rectifiers open in all three phases.

Disassemble the alternator and separate the wires at the Y-connection of the stator.

There are six diode rectifiers mounted in the back of the alternator. Three of them are marked with a plus (+), and three are marked with a minus (—). These marks indicate diode case polarity.

To test, set ohmmeter to its lowest range. If case is marked positive (+), place positive meter probe to case and negative probe to the diode lead. Meter should read between 4 and 10 ohms. Now, reverse leads of ohmmeter, connecting negative meter probe to positive case and positive meter probe to wire of rectifier. Set meter on a high range. Meter needle should move very little, if any (infinite reading). Do this to all three positive diode rectifiers.

The three with minus (—) marks on their cases are checked the same way as above. Only now the negative ohmmeter probe is connected to the case for a reading of 4 to 10 ohms. Reverse leads as above for the other part to test.

If a reading of 4 to 10 ohms is obtained in one direction and no reading (infinity) is read on the ohmmeter in the other direction, diode rectifiers are good. If either infinity or a low resistance is obtained in both directions on a rectifier, it must be replaced.

If meter reads more than 10 ohms when ohmmeter positive probe is connected to positive on diode, and negative probe to negative, replace diode rectifier.

NOTE: with this test, it is necessary to determine the polarity of the ohmmeter probes. This can be done by connecting the ohmmeter to a DC voltmeter. The voltmeter will read up-scale when the positive probe of the ohmmeter is connected to the positive side of the voltmeter and the negative probe of the ohmmeter is connected to the negative side of the voltmeter.

Alternate method—test light.

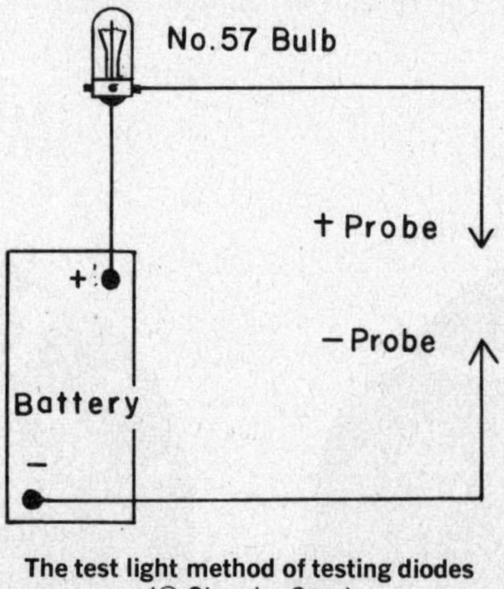
No.57 Bulb
+ Probe
− Probe
+
Battery
−
The test light method of testing diodes
(© Chrysler Corp)

Make up a tester as shown in the sketch. Be sure that the lead from the center of the diode rectifiers is disconnected.

To test rectifiers with plus (+) case, touch positive probe of tester to case and minus (—) probe to lead wire of rectifier. Bulb should light if rectifier is good. If bulb does not light, replace rectifier.

Now reverse tester probe connections to rectifier. Bulb should not light. If bulb does light, replace rectifier.

For testing minus (—) marked cases, follow above procedure, except that now bulb should light with negative probe of tester touching rectifier case and positive probe touching lead wire.

Rectifier is good if the bulb lights when tester probes are connected one way, and does not light when tester connections are reversed.

Rectifier must be replaced if the bulb does not light either way. Also, replace rectifier if bulb lights both ways.

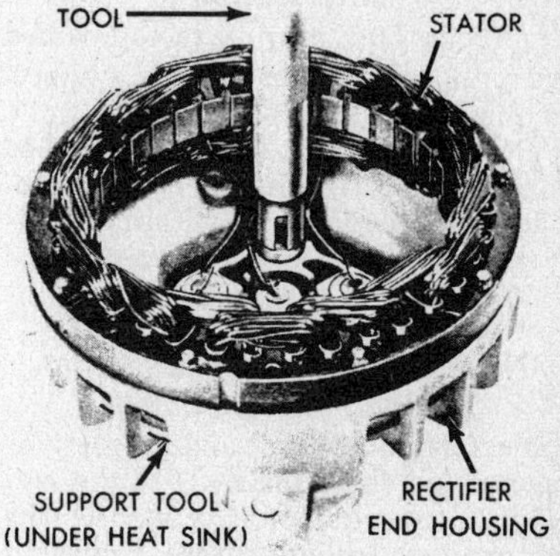
TOOL
STATOR
SUPPORT TOOL (UNDER HEAT SINK)
RECTIFIER END HOUSING
Installing diode rectifier
(© Chrysler Corp)

NOTE: the usual cause of an open or blown diode or rectifier is a defective capacitor or a battery that has been installed in reverse polarity. If the battery is installed properly and the diodes are open, test the capacitor.

Capacitor capacity:
(int. installed)
. . . . .158 microfarad, min.
(ext. installed) . . . . .5 microfarad

Alternator Bench Tests

Field Coil Draw

1. Connect a jumper between one FLD terminal and the positive terminal of a fully charged 12 volt battery.
2. Connect the positive lead of a test ammeter to the other field (FLD) terminal and the negative test lead to the negative battery terminal.
3. Slowly rotate the rotor by hand and observe the ammeter. The proper field coil draw is 2.3–2.7 amps at 12 volts.

Field Circuit Ground Test

1. Touch one test lead of a 110 volt AC test bulb to one of the alternator brush (field) terminals and the other test lead to the end shield.
2. If the lamp lights, remove the field brush assemblies and separate the end housing by removing the three thru-bolts.
3. Place one test lead on a slip ring and the other on the end shield.

4. If the lamp lights, the rotor assembly is grounded internally and must be replaced.
5. If the lamp does not light, the cause of the problem was a grounded brush.

Grounded Stator

1. Disconnect the diode rectifiers from the stator leads.
2. Test from stator leads to stator core, using a 110-volt test lamp. Test lamp should not light. If it does, stator is grounded and must be replaced.

Low Output

(About 50% output accompanied with a growl-hum caused by a shorted phase or a shorted rectifier.)

Perform Steps 1, 2 and 3 (rectifier open in all three phases). If the rectifiers are found to be within specifications, replace the stator assembly.

Current Output Too High (No Control) Caused by Open Rectifier or Open Phase

Perform Steps 1, 2 and 3 (rectifier open in all three phases). If the rectifier tests satisfactorily, inspect the stator connections before replacing the stator.

Assembly

1. Support the heat sink or rectifier end housing on circular plate.
2. Check rectifier identification to be sure the correct rectifier is being used. The part numbers are stamped on the case of the rectifier. They are also marked, red for positive and black for negative.
3. Start the new rectifier into the casting and press it in squarely.

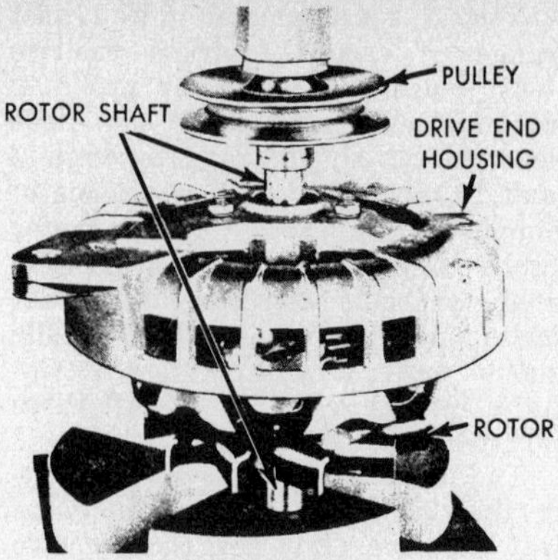
PULLEY
ROTOR SHAFT
DRIVE END HOUSING
ROTOR

Installing the pulley (© Chrysler Corp)

Caution Do not start rectifier with a hammer or it will be ruined.

4. Crimp the new rectifier wire to the wires disconnected at removal, or solder (using a heat sink with rosin core solder).
5. Support the end housing on tool so that the notch in the support tool will clear the raised section of the heat sink, then press the bearing into position with tool SP-3381, or equivalent.

NOTE: new bearings are pre-lubricated, additional lubrication is not required.

6. Insert the drive end bearing in the drive end housing and install the bearing plate, washers and nuts to hold the bearing in place.
7. Position the bearing and drive end housing on the rotor shaft and, while supporting the base of the rotor shaft, press the bearing and housing in position on the rotor shaft with an arbor press and arbor tool.

Caution Be careful that there is no cocking of the bearing at installation; or damage will result. Press the bearing on the rotor shaft until the bearing contacts the shoulder on the rotor shaft.

8. Install pulley on rotor shaft. Shaft of rotor must be supported so that all pressing force is on the pulley hub and rotor shaft.

NOTE: Do not exceed 6,800 lbs. pressure. Pulley hub should just contact bearing inner race.

9. Some alternators will be found to have the capacitor mounted internally. Be sure the heat sink insulator is in place.
10. Install the output terminal screw with the capacitor attached through the heat sink and end housing.
11. Install insulating washers, lockwashers and locknuts.
12. Make sure the heat sink and insulator are in place and tighten the locknut.
13. Position the stator on the rectifier end housing. Be sure that all of the rectifier connectors and phase leads are free of interference with the rotor fan blades and that the capacitor (internally mounted) lead has clearance.
14. Position the rotor assembly in the rectifier end housing. Align the through bolt holes in the stator with both end housings.
15. Enter stator shaft in the rectifier end housing bearing, compress stator and both end housings manually and install through bolts, washers and nuts.
16. Install the insulated brush and terminal attaching screw.
17. Install the ground screw and attaching screw.

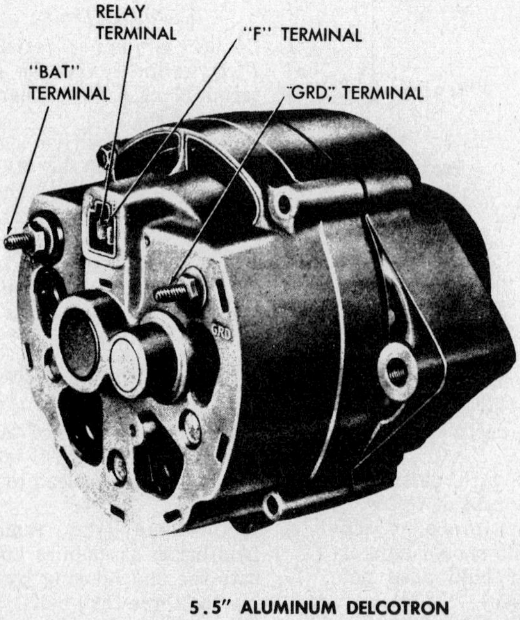
RELAY TERMINAL
"F" TERMINAL
"BAT" TERMINAL
"GRD" TERMINAL

5.5" ALUMINUM DELCOTRON

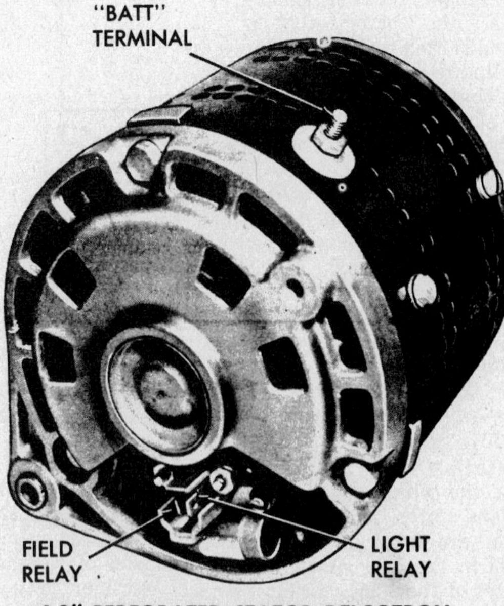
"BATT" TERMINAL
FIELD RELAY
LIGHT RELAY

6.2" PERFORATED STATOR DELCOTRON

5.5 and 6.2 Delcotron models (© Chevrolet Div., G.M. Corp)

18. Rotate pulley slowly to be sure the rotor fan blades do not hit the rectifier and stator connectors.

Delcotron 5.5 Series 1D and 6.2 Series 2D (General Motors Corporation)

Description

The Delcotron continuous output AC generator consists of two major parts—the stator and the rotor. The stator is composed of many turns of wire on the inside of a laminated core that is attached to the generator frame. The rotor is mounted on bearings at each end. Two brushes carry current through slip rings to the field coils, which are wound on the rotor shaft.

The 5.5 Series 1D Delcotron is similar in operation to the 6.2 Series 2D perforated Stator Delcotron. Where differences exist, the two units are mentioned separately.

Six diodes, mounted on internal heat sinks, change the AC current output into DC current. This current is controlled by the regulator. The regulator is a double-contact unit combined with a field relay or a triple-contact unit containing an indicator lamp relay as well as the field relay and voltage relay. Transistor regulators were also used in production intermittently.

On high-output Delcotron units, the regulator incorporates a field discharge diode.

Troubleshooting

NOTE: see the "Preliminary Charging System Inspection" section before proceeding further. Make sure that the continuous running blower, if equipped, is disconnected. This blower will run with the key on and even if the blower control is off, it is not disconnected.

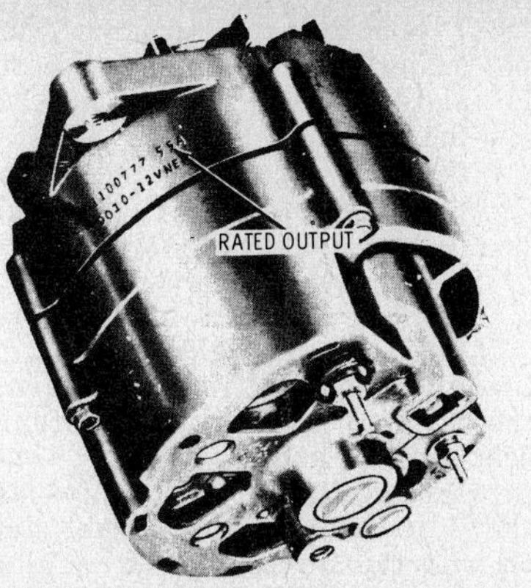
RATED OUTPUT
Delcotron rated output is stamped on the case
(© Oldsmobile Div., G.M. Corp)

Fusible Links

There are four fusible links on all GM cars.

1. The 14 gauge wire that runs from the junction block to the positive battery terminal serves as a fusible link.
2. There is a second link in the circuit between the horn relay and the ignition switch.
3. A third link is in the wire running to the No. 3 voltage regulator terminal. It's purpose is to protect the regulator contacts and the alternator field circuit.
4. The fourth link is connected between the main junction block and the horn relay.

These links must be inspected before proceeding with troubleshooting.

Charging System Operation

NOTE: if the current indicator is to give an accurate reading, the battery cables must be the same gauge and length as the original equipment.

1. With the engine running and all electrical systems turned off, place a current indicator over the positive battery cable.
2. If a charge of about 5 amps is recorded, the charging system is working. If a draw of about 5 amps is recorded, the system is not working. The needle moves toward the battery when a charge condition is indicated, and away from the battery when a draw condition is indicated. If a draw is indicated, proceed with further testing. If an excessive charge (10–15 amps) is indicated, check for an overcharge, caused by a faulty regulator.

Indicator Light Circuit Testing

The indicator light is important in AC charging systems, for it provides

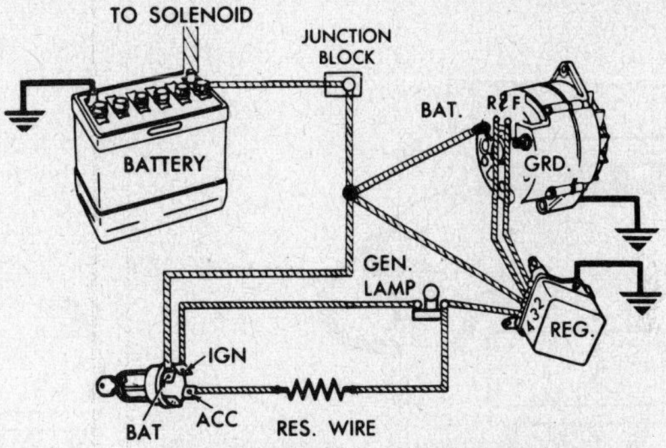
TO SOLENOID
JUNCTION BLOCK
BAT.
R
F
GRD.
BATTERY
GEN. LAMP
REG.
IGN
BAT
ACC
RES. WIRE
Typical Delcotron circuit diagram
(© Chevrolet Div., G.M. Corp)

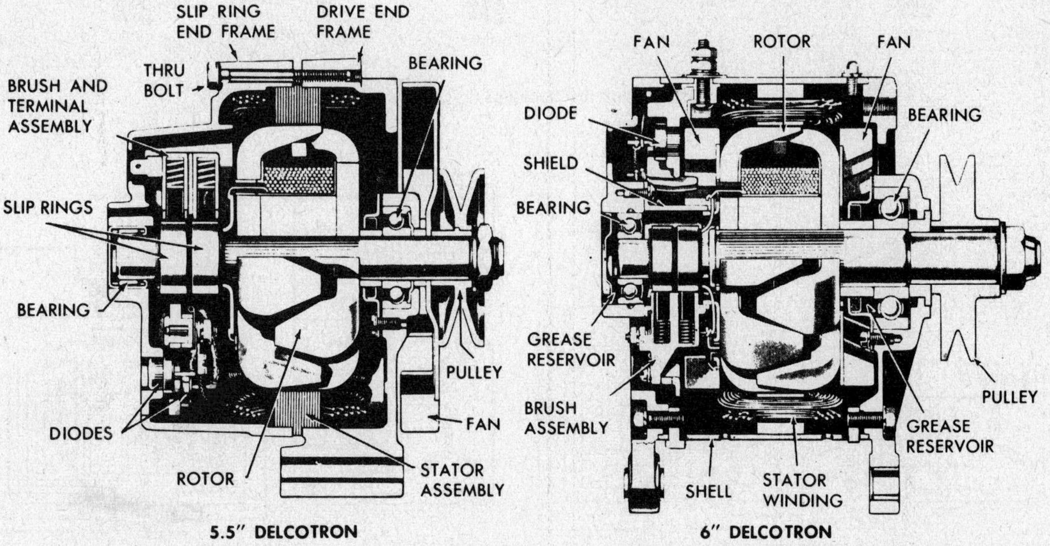
SLIP RING END FRAME
DRIVE END FRAME
THRU BOLT
BEARING
BRUSH AND TERMINAL ASSEMBLY
SLIP RINGS
BEARING
PULLEY
FAN
DIODES
ROTOR
STATOR ASSEMBLY
5.5" DELCOTRON
FAN
ROTOR
FAN
DIODE
BEARING
SHIELD
BEARING
GREASE RESERVOIR
BRUSH ASSEMBLY
PULLEY
GREASE RESERVOIR
SHELL
STATOR WINDING
6" DELCOTRON
5.5 and 6.2 Delcotron models—cross sectional views (© Chevrolet Div., G.M. Corp)

initial field excitation current to the alternator. The light goes out when the field relay closes, which applies battery current to both sides of the bulb. If the light does not go on when key is turned, the bulb could be faulty, there could be an open circuit in the wiring or a positive diode in the alternator could be shorted to ground.

1. Disconnect plug from regulator and connect a test light between terminal No. 4 (in plug) and ground. Turn on ignition switch and observe the light. If light does not go on, check bulb, socket or wiring between switch and regulator plug. If light goes on, check regulator, wiring between regulator F terminal and alternator, or Delcotron itself.
2. Disconnect jumper wire at ground end and reconnect to F terminal in plug. Turn on ignition for a second and note light. If light goes on, problem is in regulator. If light does not go on, problem is in wire between F terminals (regulator and alternator).
3. Disconnect light at plug F terminal and reconnect the free end to F terminal at alternator. Turn on ignition switch for a second and note light. If light goes on, the problem is an open circuit in the wire connecting the regulator and alternator F terminals. If light does not go on, the alternator field windings are defective.

If the indicator light does not extinguish when engine is started, check for a loose drive belt, faulty field relay, faulty alternator, open parallel resistance wire (usually shows up at idle). If the light stays on with the key turned off, an alternator positive diode is shorted to ground.

Isolation Test

1. Disconnect the wiring harness from the voltage regulator. With a jumper wire connect the F wire to the no. 3 wire in the wire harness plug.
2. Connect a voltmeter across the battery terminals, the positive voltmeter lead to the positive battery terminal, and the negative lead to the negative terminal. Record the reading.
3. Start the engine. Do not race the engine.
4. Gradually raise engine speed to 1500-2000 rpm. The reading on the voltmeter should increase one to two volts over the initial reading. If there is no increase in the reading, repair the alternator. If there is an increase in the voltmeter reading, replace the regulator.

Field Relay Test

1. Connect a voltmeter between the No. 2 terminal and the ground on the regulator.
2. Turn ignition switch on; do not start the engine. Voltmeter should read battery voltage.
3. If voltmeter reads zero, check circuit connecting regulator terminal No. 2 and Delcotron R terminal.
4. Start engine and run at 1,500-2,000 rpm. If voltage exceeds closing voltage (field relay), and light remains on, field relay is faulty and must be checked.

Field Relay Adjustment

1. Connect a voltmeter between No.

REGULATOR
F 2 3 4
STEP I
F 2 3 4
STEP II
F 2 3 4
STEP III

Initial field excitation circuit test hook-ups (© Chevrolet Div., G.M. Corp)

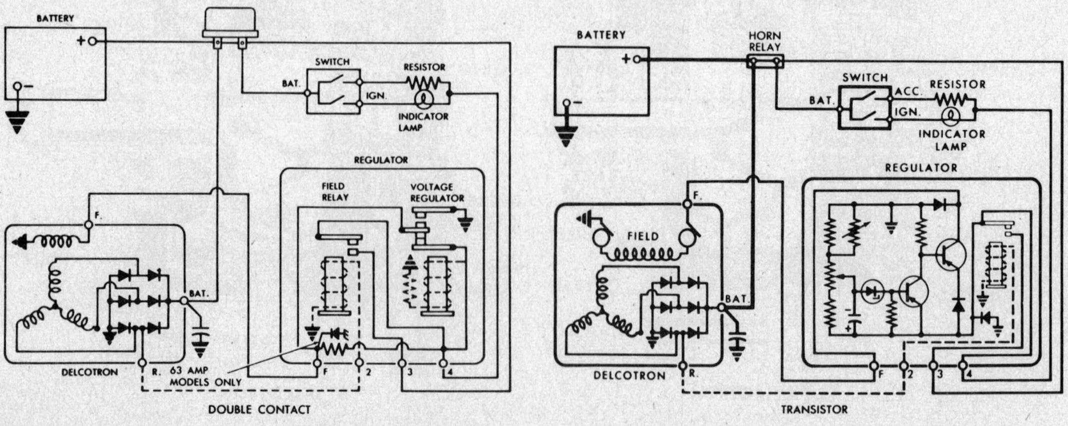
BATTERY
SWITCH
BAT.
IGN.
RESISTOR
INDICATOR LAMP
REGULATOR
FIELD RELAY
VOLTAGE REGULATOR
F.
BAT.
DELCOTRON
R.
63 AMP MODELS ONLY
F 2 3 4
DOUBLE CONTACT
BATTERY
HORN RELAY
SWITCH
BAT.
ACC.
IGN.
RESISTOR
INDICATOR LAMP
REGULATOR
FIELD
F.
BAT.
DELCOTRON
R.
F 2 3 4
TRANSISTOR

Voltage regulator circuit diagrams (© Chevrolet Div., G.M. Corp)

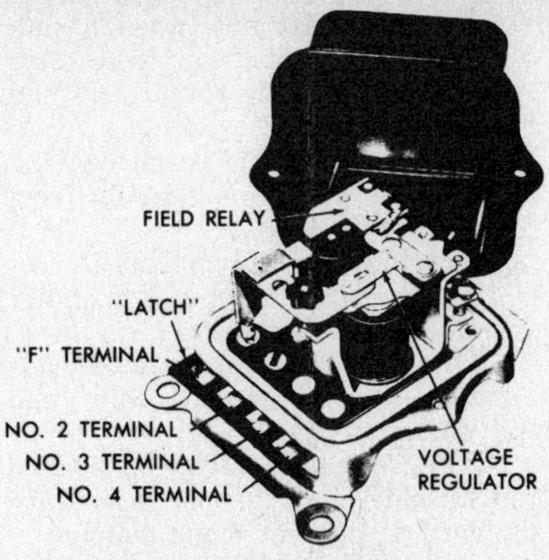
FIELD RELAY
"LATCH"
"F" TERMINAL
NO. 2 TERMINAL
NO. 3 TERMINAL
NO. 4 TERMINAL
VOLTAGE REGULATOR

Mechanical voltage regulator
(© Chevrolet Div., G.M. Corp)

2 regulator terminal and ground.

2. To adjust, connect a 50 ohm rheostat between wiring harness terminal No. 3 and regulator terminal No. 2, after disconnecting the spade lug on the end of the No. 2 regulator terminal wire. Connect a voltmeter between regulator terminal No. 2 and ground, then turn the resistor to "open" position, turn off ignition switch and slowly decrease resistance until relay closes (noting voltage at this point). Voltage can be adjusted by bending heel iron as illustrated.

Field Circuit Resistance Testing

The resistance wire is an integral part of the ignition wiring harness. The wire cannot be soldered; any connections must be made using crimp-type connectors. Resistance is 10 ohms, 6¼ watts.

1. Connect a voltmeter between the wiring harness terminal No. 4 and ground.
2. Turn on ignition switch, needle must indicate or resistor is open.

Delcotron Current Output Test

NOTE: disconnect battery ground cable while making test connections,

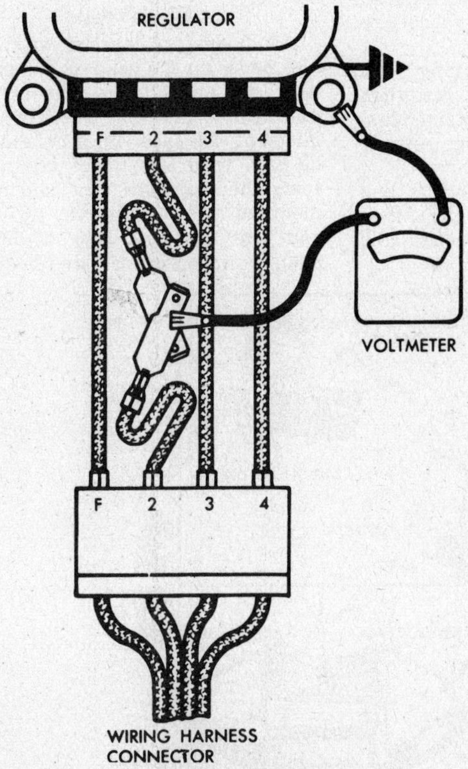
REGULATOR
F 2 3 4
VOLTMETER
F 2 3 4
WIRING HARNESS CONNECTOR

Testing field relay
(© Chevrolet Div., G.M. Corp)

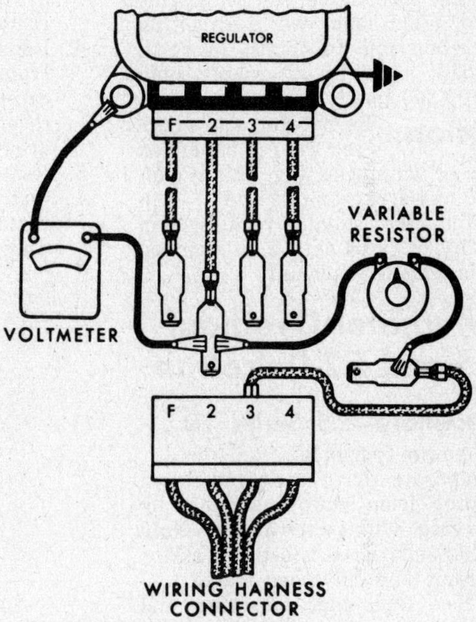
REGULATOR
F 2 3 4
VARIABLE RESISTOR
VOLTMETER
F 2 3 4
WIRING HARNESS CONNECTOR

Testing field relay closing voltage
(© Chevrolet Div., G.M. Corp)

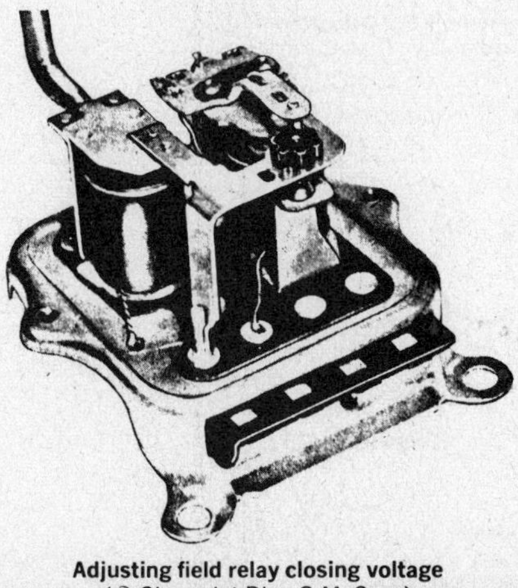

Adjusting field relay closing voltage
(© Chevrolet Div., G.M. Corp)

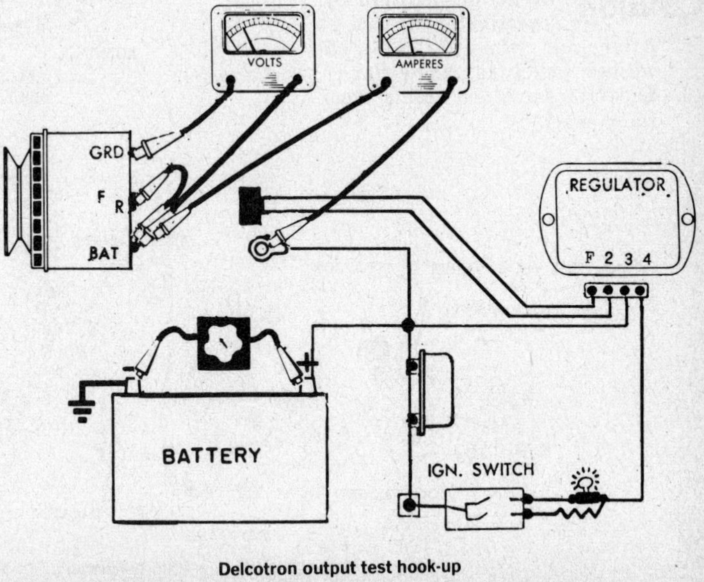
VOLTS
AMPERES
GRD
F
R
BAT
REGULATOR
F 2 3 4
BATTERY
IGN. SWITCH

Delcotron output test hook-up

then reconnect cable after completing Step 5. Disconnect battery ground cable again before removing test set-up. This test yields the same information as the isolation test but requires the use of an ammeter and a carbon pile.

1. Disconnect lead from BAT. terminal of Delcotron.
2. Hook an ammeter to the lead just disconnected, and to the BAT. terminal of the Delcotron.
3. Hook up the voltmeter leads to the BAT. terminal and a good ground on the alternator.
4. Disconnect the lead from the FR. terminal of the Delcotron.
5. Hook up a jumper wire between BAT. and F terminals of the Delcotron.
6. With a carbon pile load control hooked up to the battery posts, start the engine and set engine to 1,500 rpm, while adjusting carbon pile to obtain 14 volts. With a 6.2 in. alternator, only 600-800 rpm is required.

Caution Be careful not to exceed the recommended regulator voltage setting. This is controlled by the carbon pile load.

7. Ammeter should read within 10% of rated output, as stamped on frame of each unit.

Alternator Overhaul (5.5 and 6.2 Delcotron

Disassembly—5.5 Series 1D

1. Remove four bolts.
2. Separate drive end frame and rotor from stator assembly by prying with screwdriver. Note that separation is between stator frame and drive end frame.
3. Place tape over slip ring end frame bearing to seal dirt.
4. Lightly clamp rotor in vise to remove shaft nut.

Caution Do not distort rotor by overtightening vise.

5. After nut removal, take off washer, pulley, fan and collar.
6. Separate drive end frame from rotor shaft.
7. Remove three stator lead attaching nuts and separate stator from end frame.
8. Remove screws, brushes and holder assembly.
9. Remove BAT., GND., and attaching screw terminals, then remove heat sink.

Disassembly—6.2 Series 2D

1. Clamp drive end mounting flange in a vise, remove the two screws that secure the cover to the brush holder and remove the cover.
2. Remove the nut that holds the indicator light wire to the blade connector post; disconnect wire lead from post.
3. Remove the two screws that hold the condenser and brush holder to rear end frame, then remove brush holder. Allow condenser to remain with alternator.
4. Remove three slip ring end frame bolts and tab nuts, then carefully pry end frame and case apart, working evenly around the circumference.
5. Remove the three drive end frame bolts and tab nuts, then remove end frame, rotor and pulley as an assembly.
6. Remove shaft nut, washer, pulley and Woodruff key from rotor shaft, then slide rotor from end frame.
7. Remove drive end frame bearing retainer plate and bearing from end frame.
8. Bearing can be removed, if necessary, at this time. Use puller to prevent damage.
9. Disconnect the three stator leads by cutting between coils and diodes.

NOTE: diode leads can be cleaned and unsoldered, *if* proper heat sinks are used to prevent diode damage.

10. Remove heat sink-to-case retaining screws, then remove heat sinks. Insulated heat sink (BATT. terminal) holds positive diode.

Diode Tests

All diodes are marked with either a + or — on the head or are marked with *red* paint for + diodes, *black* paint for — diodes to identify the polarity of the case. On a generator to be used with a negative ground system, the negative case diodes are mounted into the slip ring end frame and the positive case diodes are mounted into the insulated heat sink.

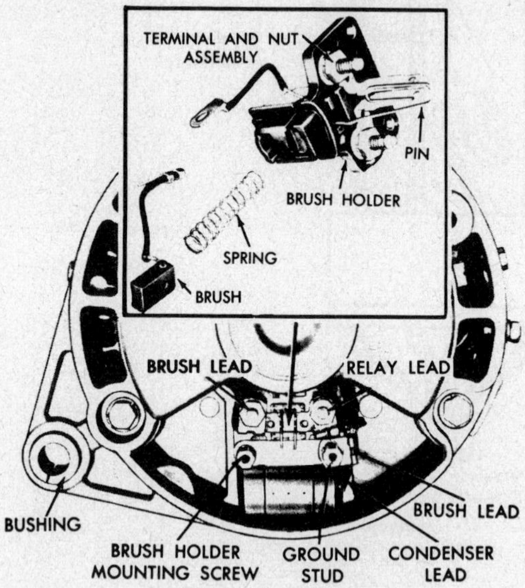
TERMINAL AND NUT ASSEMBLY
PIN
BRUSH HOLDER
SPRING
BRUSH
BRUSH LEAD
RELAY LEAD
BRUSH LEAD
BUSHING
BRUSH HOLDER MOUNTING SCREW
GROUND STUD
CONDENSER LEAD

Brush assembly 6.2 Delcotron (© Chevrolet Div., G.M. Corp)

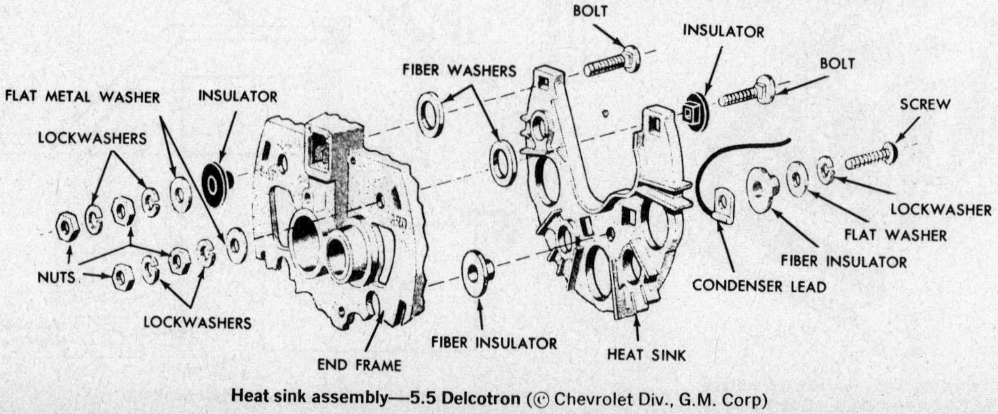
BOLT
INSULATOR
BOLT
FIBER WASHERS
SCREW
FLAT METAL WASHER
INSULATOR
LOCKWASHERS
LOCKWASHER
FLAT WASHER
FIBER INSULATOR
CONDENSER LEAD
NUTS
LOCKWASHERS
FIBER INSULATOR
HEAT SINK
END FRAME

Heat sink assembly—5.5 Delcotron (© Chevrolet Div., G.M. Corp)

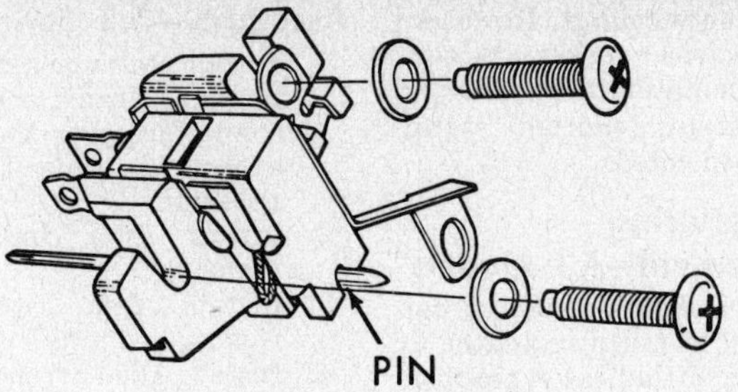
PIN

Brush assembly—5.5 Delcotron
(© Chevrolet Div., G.M. Corp)

Diodes with a negative case have positive polarity leads, whereas positive case diodes have negative polarity leads.

Diodes can be checked for shorts or opens with an ohmmeter.

With the stator leads disconnected, connect one ohmmeter test prod to the diode lead and the other test prod to the heat sink. Reverse the test prods and note the ohmmeter readings. The meter should read high ohms in one direction, low ohms in the other. If both readings are the same, either both high or both low, the diode is faulty and must be replaced. A 1½ volt test light also will indicate a faulty diode. It will light in one direction and not in the other if the diode is good. If it lights in both directions, or in neither direction, the diode is bad.

Diode Replacement

Early Delcotrons had screwed-in diodes, as does the extremely heavy-duty 6.6 Series 4D Delcotron. Models covered here use pressed-in diodes exclusively. If there is any doubt about the year and model of the Delcotron being serviced, note the diode construction—screwed-in diodes have hexagonal heads and the later, pressed-in, units have straight sides with no hex head. Old-style, screwed-in diodes have both right- and left-hand threads. Plus (+) diodes have left-hand and minus (—) have right-hand threads.

5.5 Series 1D

1. Support end frame on a deep socket with a larger inside diameter than the diode outside diameter.
2. Carefully *press* out the diode with a brass drift and an arbor press, or a large bench vise. Be extremely careful so as not to distort the end frame.
3. Select a new diode (red or black), noting that the red (+) diodes go into the heat sink and the black (—) diodes into the end frame.
4. Support end frame on a flat, smooth surface around diode hole and carefully *press* the new diode into position. Diode must be square when starting or both diode and frame will be ruined.

6.2 Series 2D

1. Cut leads connected to diode stem as close as possible to stem, then support end frame as for 5.5 Delcotron and press out diode.
2. Select diode with proper color marking (same as for 5.5 Delcotron), then press new diode into position.
3. Scrape enough insulation from diode stem and leads to ensure good contact, then install a sleeve over diode and place the T-clip from diode package over diode stem.
4. Place the flexible lead and stator lead (if applicable) into the T-clip, crimp clip and solder with rosin core solder only, using heat sinks (pliers) to avoid destroying diode.
5. Tape the leads together to prevent vibration damage.

Rotor Checks—All Models

The rotor may be checked electrically for grounded, open, or shorted field coils.

To check for grounds, connect a 110-volt test light from either slip ring to the rotor shaft or to the laminations. If the lamp lights, the field windings are grounded.

To check for opens, connect the leads of a 110-volt test light to each slip ring. If the lamp fails to light, the windings are open.

The windings are checked for short-circuits by connecting a battery and ammeter in series with the two slip rings. Note the ammeter reading.

An ammeter reading greater than

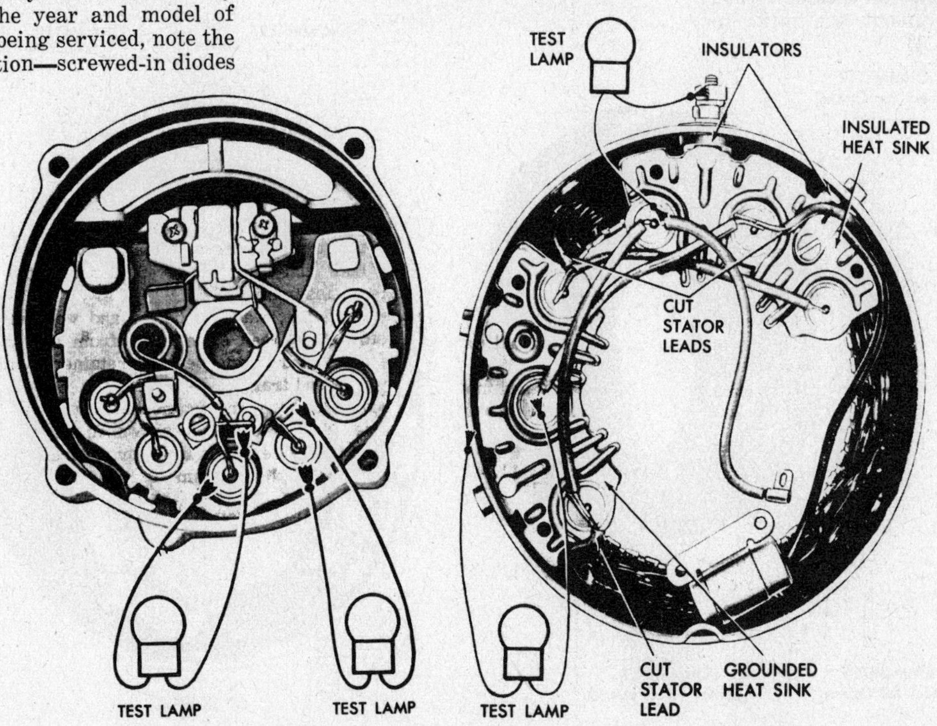
TEST LAMP
INSULATORS
INSULATED HEAT SINK
CUT STATOR LEADS
TEST LAMP
TEST LAMP
TEST LAMP
CUT STATOR LEAD
GROUNDED HEAT SINK
5.5" DELCOTRON
6" DELCOTRON

Testing diodes (© Chevrolet Div., G.M. Corp)

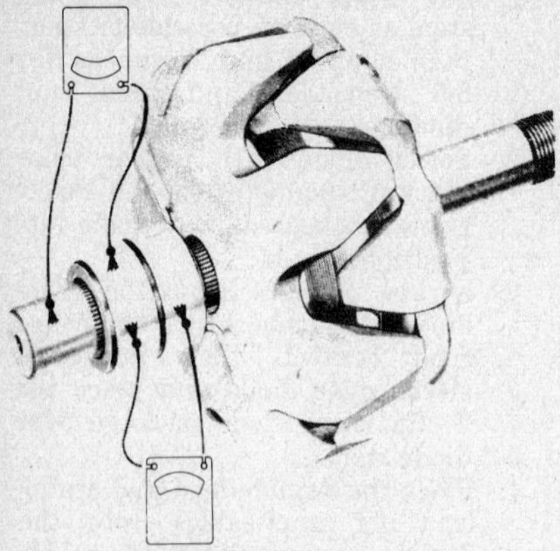
(CHECK FOR GROUNDS)
OHMMETER
OHMMETER
(CHECK FOR SHORTS AND OPENS)

Checking rotor for grounds or opens—all Delcotron models
(© Chev. Div., G.M. Corp.)

that specified in the charts preceding each car section of this manual indicates shorted windings.

Since the field windings are not serviced separately, the rotor assembly must be replaced if the windings are defective.

Stator Checks—All Models

Stator windings may be checked for grounded, open, or shorted windings. If a 110-volt test lamp lights when connected from any stator lead to the stator frame, the windings are grounded. If the lamp fails to light when successively connected between each pair of stator leads, the windings are open.

A short circuit in the stator windings is difficult to locate without laboratory equipment, due to the low resistance of the windings. However, if all other electrical checks are normal and the generator fails to supply the rated output, shorted stator windings are indicated.

Slip Ring Servicing and Replacement—All Models

Slip rings which are rough or out of round should be trued in a lathe to .001 in. maximum indicator reading. Remove only enough material to make the rings smooth and round. Finish with 400 grit or finer polishing cloth and blow away all dust.

Slip rings which must be replaced can be removed from the shaft with a gear puller, after the leads have been unsoldered. The new assembly should be pressed on with a sleeve which just fits over the shaft; this will apply all the pressure to the inner slip ring collar and prevent damage to the outer slip ring. Only pure tin solder should be used when reconnecting field leads.

Brush Replacement—All Models

The extent of brush wear can be determined by comparison with a new brush. If brushes are one-half worn, they should be replaced.

1. Remove brush holder assembly from end frame by removing two holder assembly screws.
2. Place springs and brushes in the holder and insert straight wire or pin into holes at bottom of holder to retain brushes.
3. Attach holder assembly onto end frame.

Assembly—5.5 Series 1D

1. Install stator assembly into slip ring end frame and locate diode connectors over the relay, diode and stator leads. Tighten terminal nuts.
2. Install rotor into drive end frame.
3. Install fan, spacer, pulley washer and nut.
4. Install Allen wrench (5/16 in.) into end of shaft to hold drive shaft, then tighten pulley nut to 40-50 ft. lbs. using a crowsfoot wrench (15/16 in.) and torque wrench.
5. Assemble slip ring end frame and stator assembly to drive end frame and rotor.
6. Install four through bolts and tighten securely.

Assembly—6.2 Series 2D

1. Install stator assembly into slip ring end frame and locate diode connectors over the relay, diode and stator leads. Tighten terminal nuts.
2. Install the front frame over the rotor.
3. Install fan, spacer, Woodruff key, pulley, washer and nut.
4. Clamp pulley in a padded-jaw vise and tighten shaft nut to 50-60 ft. lbs.

Caution Do not clamp rotor, or segments will be distorted.

5. Position rotor and drive end frame assembly into slip ring end frame and stator. Install through bolts and tighten securely.

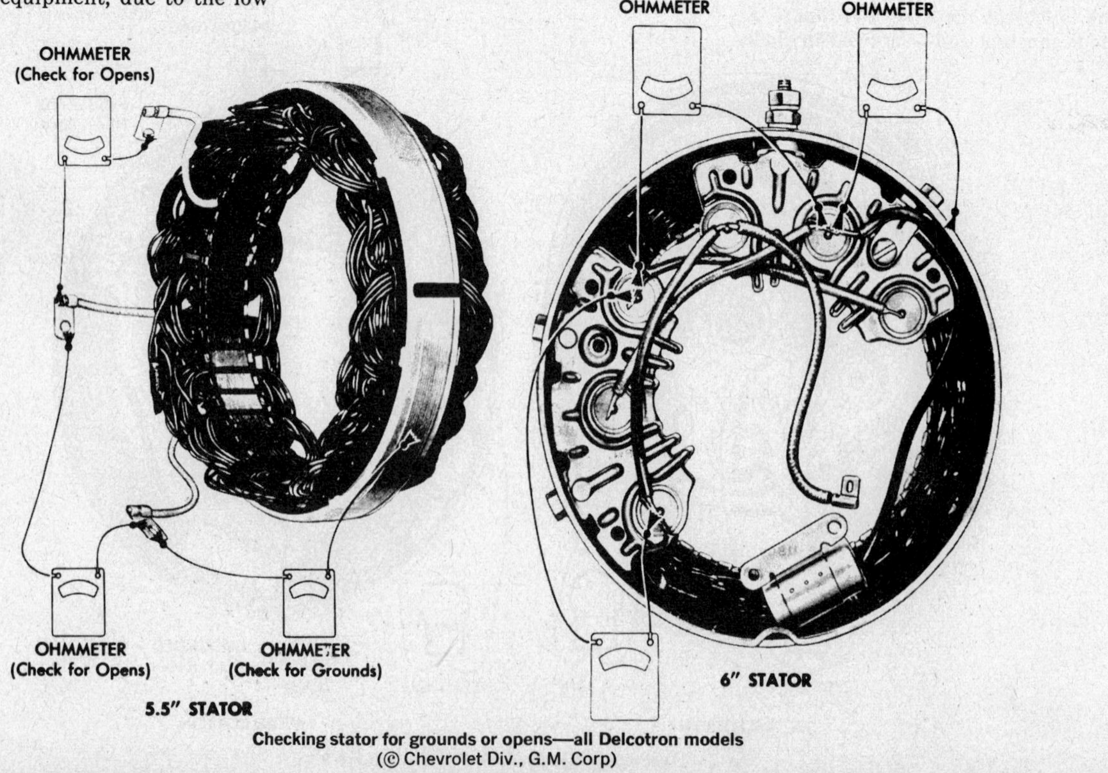
OHMMETER
(Check for Opens)
OHMMETER
(Check for Opens)
OHMMETER
(Check for Grounds)
5.5" STATOR
OHMMETER
OHMMETER
6" STATOR

Checking stator for grounds or opens—all Delcotron models
(© Chevrolet Div., G.M. Corp)

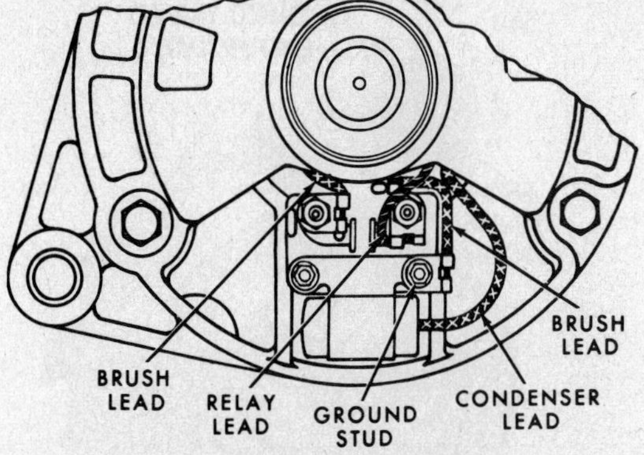
BRUSH LEAD
RELAY LEAD
GROUND STUD
CONDENSER LEAD
BRUSH LEAD

Brush lead arrangement after assembly—6.2 Delcotron
(© Chevrolet Div., G.M. Corp)

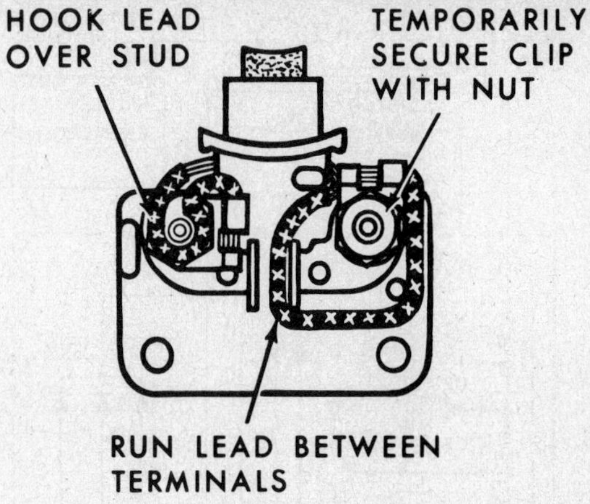
HOOK LEAD OVER STUD
TEMPORARILY SECURE CLIP WITH NUT
RUN LEAD BETWEEN TERMINALS

Brush lead arrangement during assembly—6.2 Delcotron
(© Chevrolet Div., G.M. Corp)

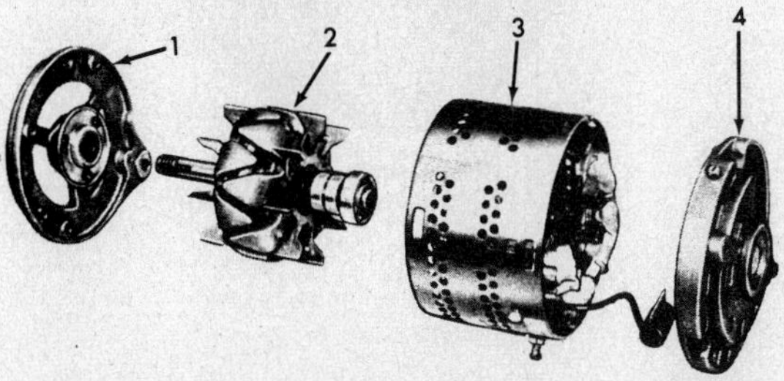
1
2
3
4

6.2 Delcotron assembly sequence: 1) drive end frame 2) rotor 3) stator 4) end frame
(© Chevrolet Div., G.M. Corp)

6. Push the brushes into the holder and secure the leads.
7. Attach brush assembly and condenser to the end frame with left-hand hex stud only.
8. Arrange the leads with the right-hand brush lead connected under the right-hand hex stud.
9. Attach terminal cover with two screws, making sure not to pinch the leads.

Delcotron 10-SI Series 100 (General Motors Corp.)

This system is an integrated AC generating system containing a built-in voltage regulator. Removal and replacement is essentially the same as for the standard AC generator.

The regulator is mounted inside the slip ring end frame. All regulator components are enclosed in an epoxy molding, and the regulator cannot be adjusted. Rotor and stator tests are the same as for the 5.5 Delcotron, covered previously.

Troubleshooting

NOTE: see the "Preliminary Charging System Inspection" section before proceeding further. Make sure that the continuous running blower, if equipped, is disconnected. This blower will run with the key on even if the blower control is off, unless disconnected.

Charging System Test—Low Charging Rate

1. After battery condition, drive belt tension, and wiring terminals and connections have been checked, charge the battery fully and perform the following test:
2. Connect a test voltmeter between the alternator BAT. terminal and ground, ignition switch on. Connect the voltmeter in turn to alternator terminals No. 1 and No. 2, the other voltmeter lead being grounded as before. A zero reading indicates an open circuit between the battery and each connection at the alternator. If this test discloses no faults in the wiring, proceed to Step 3.
3. Connect the test voltmeter to the alternator BAT. terminal (the other test lead to ground), start the engine and run at 1,500-2,000 rpm with all lights and electrical accessories turned on. If the voltmeter reads 12.8 volts or greater, the alternator is good and no further checks need be made. If the voltmeter reads less than 12.8 volts, ground the field winding by inserting a screwdriver into the test hole in the end frame.

Caution Do not force tab more than ¾ in. into end frame.

a. If voltage increases to 13 volts or more, the regulator unit is defective.
b. If voltage does not increase significantly, generator is defective.

Alternator Output Test

1. Connect a test voltmeter, ammeter and 10 ohm 6 watt resistor into the charging circuit. Do not connect the carbon pile to the battery posts at this time.
2. Increase alternator speed and observe voltmeter—if voltage is uncontrolled with speed and increases to 16 volts or more, check for a grounded brush lead clip as covered previously. If brush lead clip is not grounded, the voltage regulator is faulty and must be replaced.
3. Connect the carbon pile load to the battery terminals.
4. Operate the alternator at moderate speed and adjust the carbon pile to obtain maximum alternator output as indicated on the ammeter. If output is within 10% of rated output as stamped on the alternator frame, alternator is O.K. If output is not within specifications, ground the alternator field by inserting a screwdriver into the test hole in the end frame. If output now is within 10% of rating, replace the voltage regulator; if still not within specifications, check field winding, diode trio, rectifier bridge and stator, as described later. Dissasembly of alternator up to and including Step 6 is necessary.

Disassembly and Assembly

1. Place alternator in a vise, clamped by the mounting flange only.
2. Remove the four through bolts and separate the slip ring end frame and stator assembly from the drive end and rotor assembly, using a screwdriver to pry the two sections apart. Use the slots provided for the purpose.
3. Place a piece of tape over the slip ring end frame bearing to prevent entry of dirt; also tape shaft at slip ring end to prevent scratches.

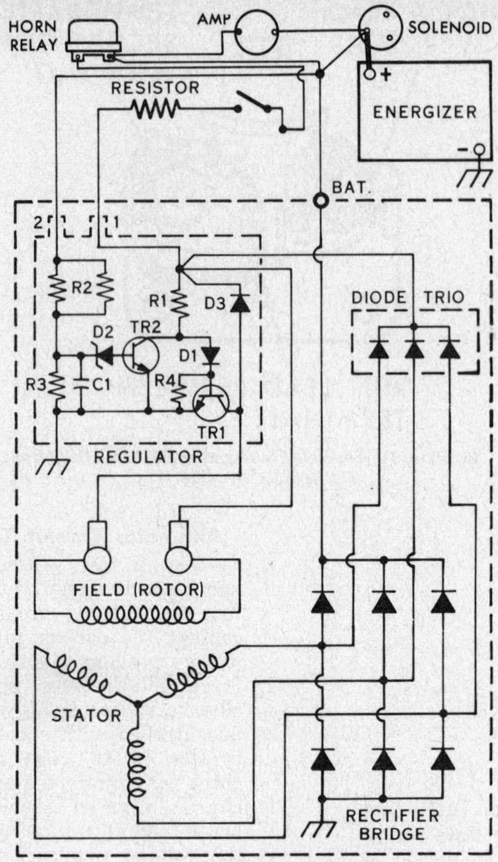
HORN
RELAY
AMP
SOLENOID
RESISTOR
ENERGIZER
BAT.
2
1
R2
R1
D3
DIODE TRIO
D2
TR2
D1
R3
C1
R4
TR1
REGULATOR
FIELD (ROTOR)
STATOR
RECTIFIER
BRIDGE

10-S1 charging circuit schematic
(© Chevrolet Div., G.M. Corp)

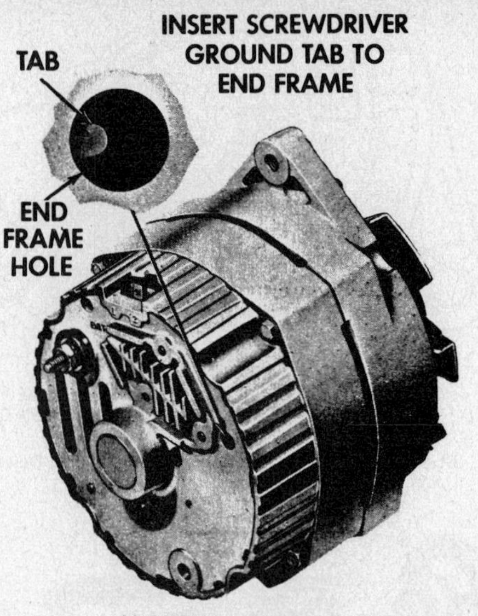
INSERT SCREWDRIVER
GROUND TAB TO
END FRAME
TAB
END
FRAME
HOLE

10-S1 Delcotron end view
(© Chevrolet Div., G.M. Corp)

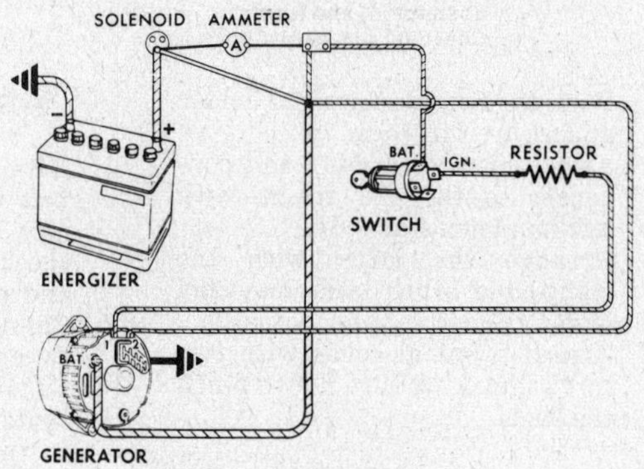
SOLENOID
AMMETER
BAT.
IGN.
RESISTOR
SWITCH
ENERGIZER
GENERATOR

10-S1 basic wiring diagram
(© Chevrolet Div., G.M. Corp)

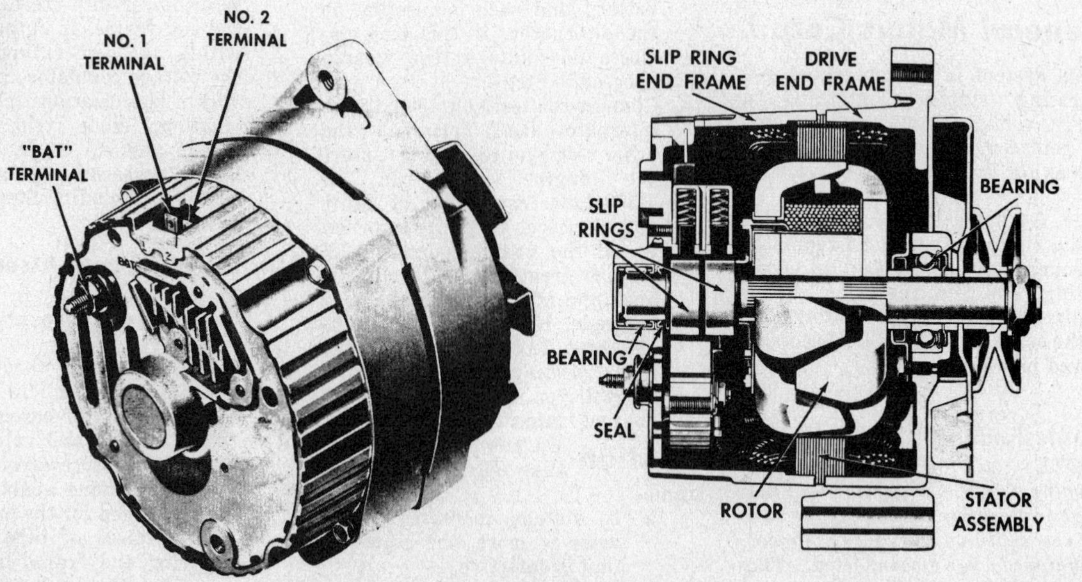
NO. 1
TERMINAL
NO. 2
TERMINAL
"BAT"
TERMINAL
SLIP RING
END FRAME
DRIVE
END FRAME
BEARING
SLIP
RINGS
BEARING
SEAL
ROTOR
STATOR
ASSEMBLY

10-S1 Delcotron
(© Chevrolet Div., G.M. Corp)

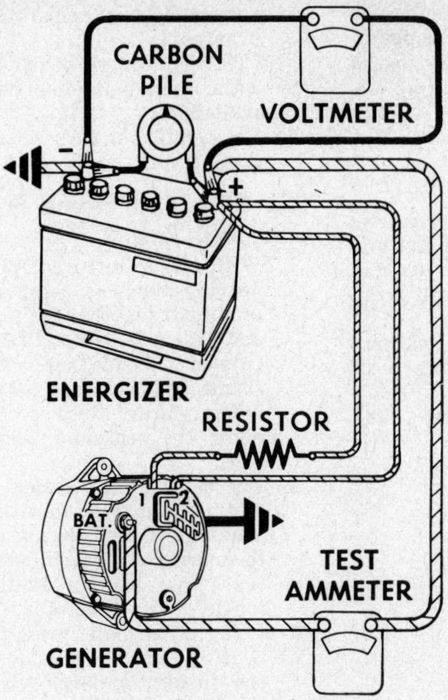
CARBON PILE
VOLTMETER
ENERGIZER
RESISTOR
BAT.
1
2
TEST AMMETER
GENERATOR

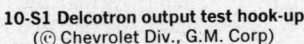

10-S1 Delcotron output test hook-up
(© Chevrolet Div., G.M. Corp)

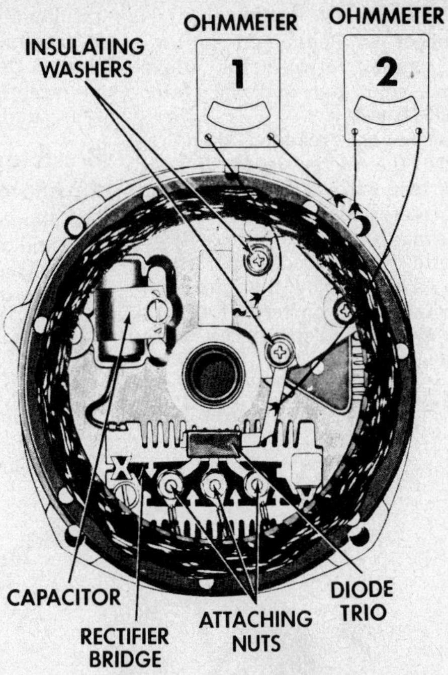
OHMMETER
OHMMETER
INSULATING WASHERS
1
2
CAPACITOR
RECTIFIER BRIDGE
ATTACHING NUTS
DIODE TRIO

Brush lead clip ground test—
10-S1 Delcotron
(© Chevrolet Div., G.M. Corp)

4. Clean brushes, if they are to be reused, with trichloroethylene or carbon tetrachloride solvent. Use these solvents only in an adequately ventilated area.
5. Remove the stator lead nuts and separate the stator from the end frame.
6. Remove the screw that secures the diode trio and remove diode trio.

NOTE: at this point, test the rotor, rectifier bridge, stator and diode trio if these tests are necessary.

7. Remove the rectifier bridge hold-down screw and the BAT. terminal screw, then disconnect condenser lead. Remove rectifier bridge from end frame.
8. Remove the two securing screws and brush holder and regulator assemblies. Note the insulating sleeves over the screws.
9. Remove the retaining screw and condenser from the end frame.
10. Remove the slip ring end frame bearing, if it is to be replaced, using the procedure given later in this section.
11. Remove the pulley nut, washer, pulley, fan and spacer from the rotor shaft, using a 5/16 in. Allen key to hold the shaft while loosening the nut.
12. Remove rotor and spacers from drive end frame assembly.
13. Remove drive end frame bearing retainer plate, screws, plate, bearing, and slinger from end frame, if necessary.
14. To assemble, reverse order of disassembly. Pulley nut must be tightened to 40-50 ft. lbs.

Cleaning and Inspection

1. Clean all metal parts, except stator and rotor assemblies, in solvent.
2. Wipe off bearings and inspect them for pitting or roughness.
3. Inspect rotor slip rings for scoring. They may be cleaned with 400 grit sandpaper (not emery), rotating the rotor to make the rings concentric. Maximum out-of-true is 0.001 in. If slip rings are deeply scored, the entire rotor must be replaced as a unit.
4. Inspect brushes for wear; minimum length is ¼ in.

Charging System Test—High Charging Rate

1. With the battery fully charged, connect a voltmeter between alternator terminal no. 2 and ground. If the reading is zero, no. 2 circuit from the battery is open.
2. If no. 2 circuit is OK, but an obvious overcharging condition still exists, proceed as follows:
   a. Remove the alternator and separate the end frames.
   b. Connect a low-range ohmmeter between the brush lead clip and the end frame, as illustrated (test no. 1), then reverse the lead connections. If both readings are zero, either the brush lead clip is grounded or the regulator is defective. A grounded brush lead clip can be due to a damaged insulating sleeve or omission of the insulating washer.

Diode Trio Initial Testing

1. Before removing this unit, connect an ohmmeter between the brush lead clip and the end frame. The lowest reading scale should be used for this test.
2. After taking a reading, reverse the lead connections. If the meter reads zero, the brush lead clip is probably grounded, due to omission of the insulating sleeve or insulating washer.

Diode Trio Removal

1. Remove the three nuts which secure the stator.
2. Remove stator.
3. Remove the screw which secures the diode trio lead clip, then remove diode trio.

NOTE: The position of the insulating washer on the screw is critical; make sure it is returned to the same position on reassembly.

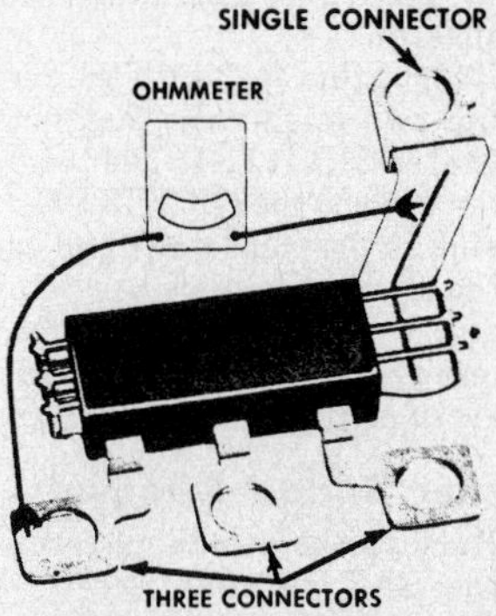
SINGLE CONNECTOR
OHMMETER
THREE CONNECTORS

Testing diode trio—10-S1 AC generator
(© Pontiac Motor Div., G.M. Corp)

Diode Trio Testing

1. Connect an ohmmeter, on lowest range, between the single brush connector and one stator lead connector.
2. Observe the reading, then reverse the meter leads. Repeat this test with each of the other two stator lead connectors. The readings on each of these tests should NOT be identical, there should be one low and one high reading for each test. If this is not the case, replace the diode trio.

Caution Do not use high voltage on the diode trio.

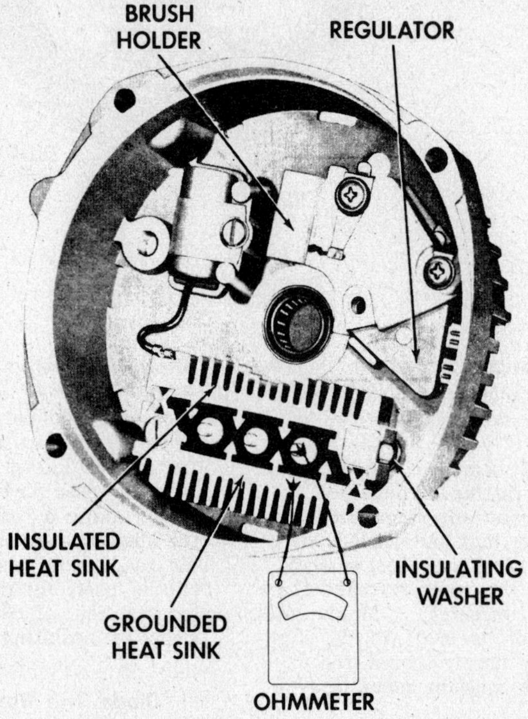
BRUSH HOLDER
REGULATOR
INSULATED HEAT SINK
INSULATING WASHER
GROUNDED HEAT SINK
OHMMETER

Rectifier bridge testing—10-S1 Delcotron
(© Chevrolet Div., G.M. Corp)

Rectifier Bridge Testing

1. Connect an ohmmeter between the heat sink (ground) and the base of one of the three terminals. Then, reverse the meter leads and take a reading. If both readings are identical, the bridge is defective and must be replaced.
2. Repeat this test with the remaining two terminals, then between the INSULATED heat sink (as opposed to the GROUNDED heat sink in previous test) and each of the three terminals. As before, if any two readings are identical, on reversing the meter leads, the rectifier bridge must be replaced.

Rectifier Bridge Removal

1. Remove the attaching screw and the BAT. terminal screw.
2. Disconnect the condenser lead.
3. Remove the rectifier bridge.

NOTE: The insulator between the insulated heat sink and the end frame is extremely important to the operation of the unit. It must be replaced in exactly the same position on reassembly.

Brush and/or Voltage Regulator R & R

1. Remove two brush holder screws and stator lead to strap nut and washer, brush holder screws and one of the diode trio lead strap attaching screws.

NOTE: The insulating washers must be replaced in the same position on reassembly.

2. Remove brush holder and

Brush holder—10-S1 generator
(© Pontiac Motor Div., G.M. Corp)

brushes. The voltage regulator may also be removed at this time, if desired.
3. Brushes and brush springs must be free of corrosion and must be undamaged and completely free of oil or grease.
4. Insert spring and brushes into holder, noting whether they slide freely without binding. Insert wooden or plastic toothpick into bottom hole in holder to retain brushes.

NOTE: The brush holder is serviced as a unit; individual parts are not available.

5. Reassemble in reverse order of disassembly.

Slip Ring End Frame Bearing and Seal R & R

1. With stator removed, press out bearing and seal, using a socket or similar tool that fits inside the end frame housing. Press from outside to inside, supporting the frame inside with a hollow cylinder (large, deep socket) to allow the seal and bearing to pass.
2. The bearings are sealed for life and permanently lubricated. If a bearing is dry, do not attempt to repack it, as it will throw off the grease and contaminate the inside of the generator.
3. Using a flat plate, press the new bearing from the outside toward the inside. A large vise is a handy press, but care must be exercised so that end frame is not distorted or cracked. Again, use a deep socket to support the inside of the end frame.
4. From inside the end frame, insert seal and press flush with housing.
5. Install stator and reconnect leads.

Ford-Autolite (Ford Motor Co.) with Electro-Mechanical Regulator

The Ford-Autolite charging system is a negative ground system. It includes an alternator, an electro-mechanical regulator, a charge indicator, and a storage battery.

Troubleshooting

NOTE: See the "Preliminary Charging System Inspection" section before proceeding further.

Fusible Links

1. Check the fusible link located between the starter relay and the alternator. Replace the link if it is burned or open.

Charging System Operation

NOTE: if the current indicator is to give an accurate reading, the battery cables must be of the same gauge and length as the original equipment.

1. With the engine running, and all electrical systems turned off, place a current indicator over the positive battery cable.
2. If a charge of about 5 amps is recorded, the charging system is working. If a draw of about 5 amps is recorded, the system is

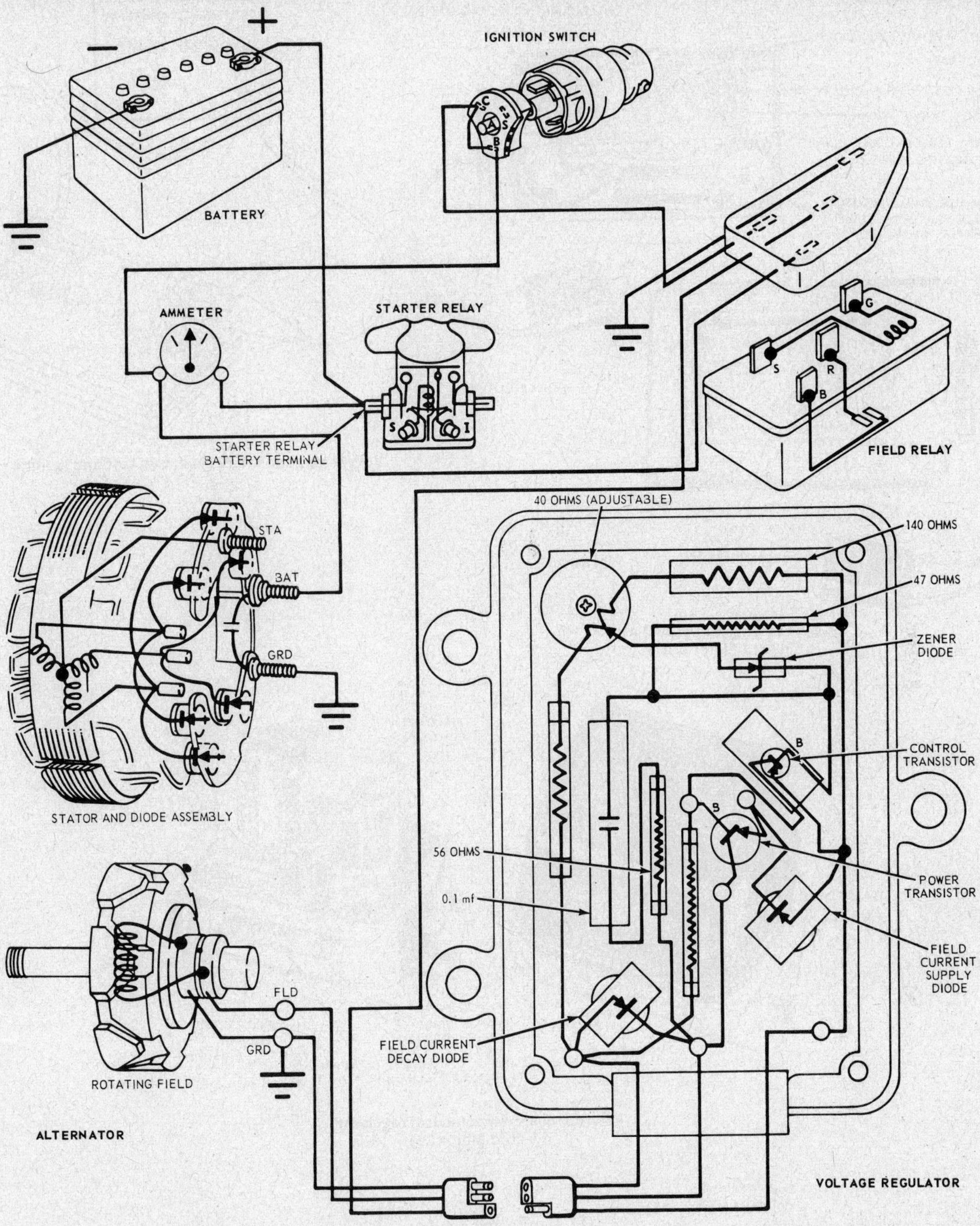
IGNITION SWITCH
BATTERY
AMMETER
STARTER RELAY
STARTER RELAY
BATTERY TERMINAL
FIELD RELAY
STA
BAT
GRD
STATOR AND DIODE ASSEMBLY
40 OHMS (ADJUSTABLE)
140 OHMS
47 OHMS
ZENER
DIODE
CONTROL
TRANSISTOR
56 OHMS
0.1 mf
POWER
TRANSISTOR
FIELD
CURRENT
SUPPLY
DIODE
FLD
GRD
FIELD CURRENT
DECAY DIODE
ROTATING FIELD
ALTERNATOR
VOLTAGE REGULATOR

Charging system schematic with transistor regulator and ammeter (© Ford Motor Co)

not working. The needle moves toward the battery when a charge condition is indicated, and away from the battery when a draw condition is indicated. If a draw is indicated, continue to the next testing procedure. If an overcharge of 10-15 amps is indicated, check for a faulty regulator or a bad ground at the regulator or the alternator.

Testing the Ignition Switch to Regulator Circuit

1. Disconnect the regulator wiring harness from the regulator.
2. Turn on the key. Using a test light or voltmeter, check for voltage between the I wire and ground. Check for voltage between the A wire and ground. If voltage is present at this part of the system, the circuit is OK. If there is no voltage at the I wire, check for a burned-out charge indicator bulb, a burned-out resistor, or a break or short in the wiring. If there is no voltage present at the A wire, check for a bad connection at the starter relay or a break or short in the wire.

Isolation Test

This test determines whether the regulator or the alternator is faulty, after the rest of the circuit is found to be in good working order.

1. Disconnect the regulator wiring harness from the regulator.
2. Connect a jumper wire from the A wire to the F wire in the wiring harness plug.
3. Connect a voltmeter to the battery. The positive voltmeter lead goes to the positive terminal and the negative lead to the negative terminal. Record the reading on the voltmeter.
4. Turn off all of the electrical systems and start the engine. Do not race the engine.
5. Gradually increase engine speed to 1500-2000 rpm. The voltmeter reading should increase above the previously recorded battery voltage reading by at least one to

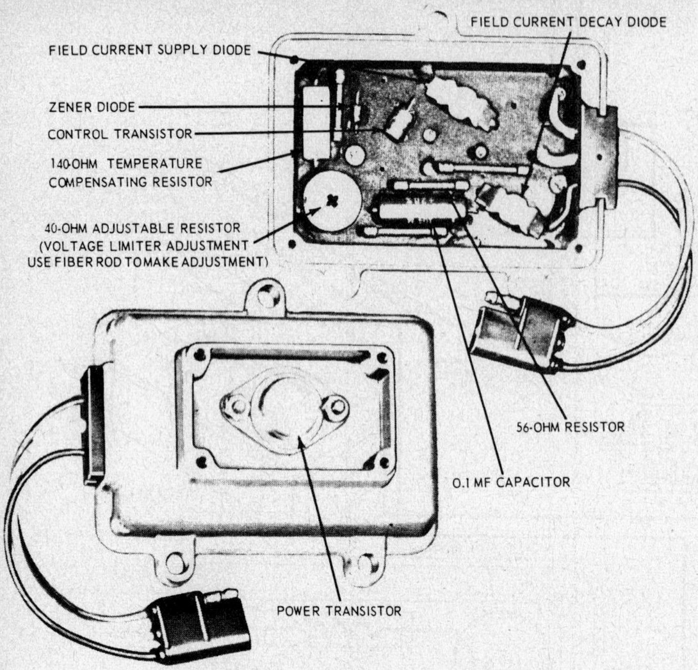
FIELD CURRENT DECAY DIODE
FIELD CURRENT SUPPLY DIODE
ZENER DIODE
CONTROL TRANSISTOR
140-OHM TEMPERATURE COMPENSATING RESISTOR
40-OHM ADJUSTABLE RESISTOR (VOLTAGE LIMITER ADJUSTMENT USE FIBER ROD TO MAKE ADJUSTMENT)
56-OHM RESISTOR
0.1 MF CAPACITOR
POWER TRANSISTOR

External transistor regulator
(© Ford Motor Co)

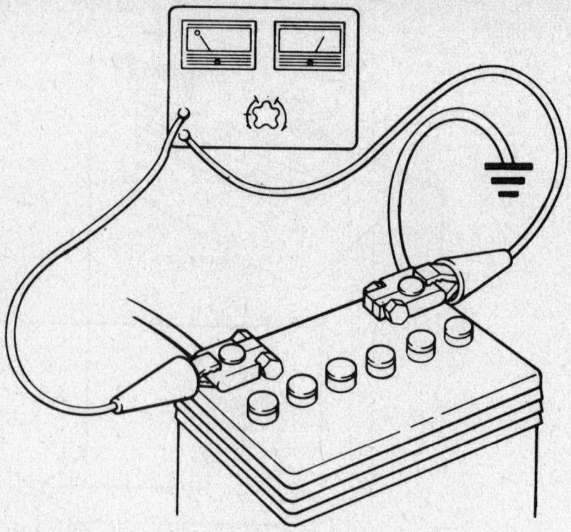

Voltmeter connections isolation test and ignition circuit test
(© Ford Motor Co)

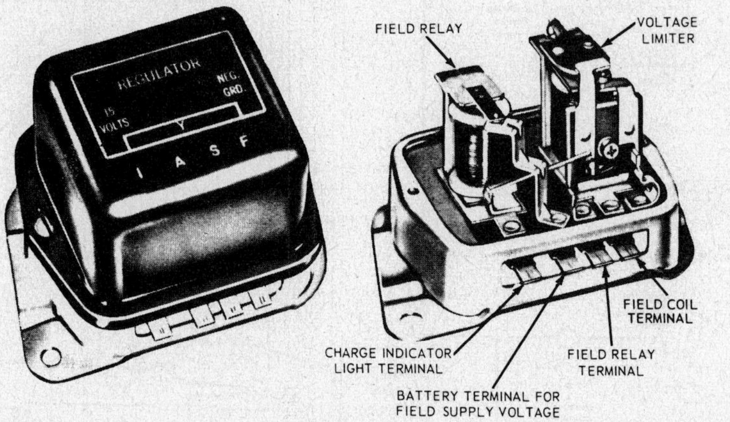
REGULATOR
15 VOLTS
NEG. GRD.
I A S F
FIELD RELAY
VOLTAGE LIMITER
FIELD COIL TERMINAL
CHARGE INDICATOR LIGHT TERMINAL
FIELD RELAY TERMINAL
BATTERY TERMINAL FOR FIELD SUPPLY VOLTAGE

External electro-mechanical regulator
(© Ford Motor Co)

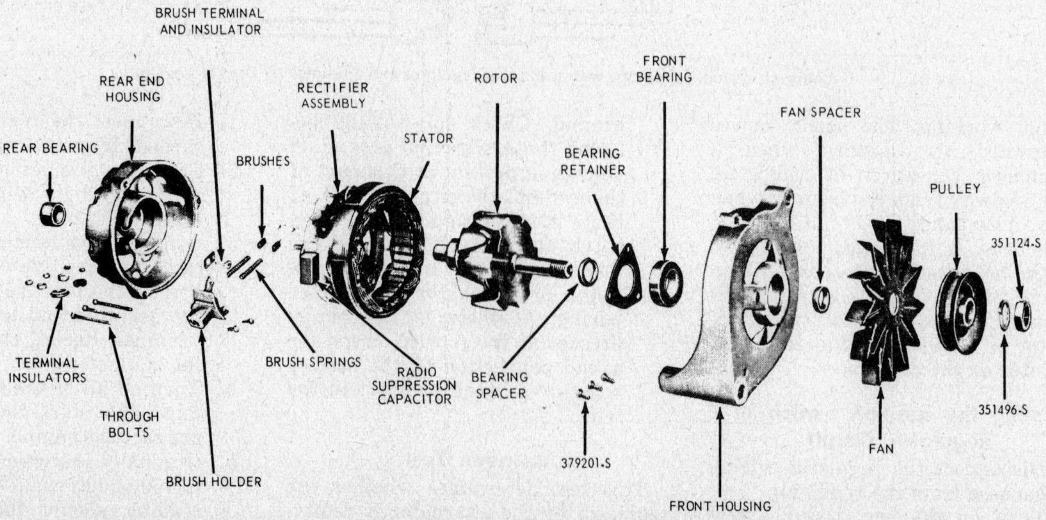
BRUSH TERMINAL AND INSULATOR
REAR END HOUSING
REAR BEARING
RECTIFIER ASSEMBLY
ROTOR
FRONT BEARING
FAN SPACER
STATOR
BRUSHES
BEARING RETAINER
PULLEY
351124-S
TERMINAL INSULATORS
BRUSH SPRINGS
RADIO SUPPRESSION CAPACITOR
BEARING SPACER
351496-S
THROUGH BOLTS
379201-S
FAN
BRUSH HOLDER
FRONT HOUSING

Typical disassembled Autolite alternator—except 65 amp unit (© Ford Motor Co)

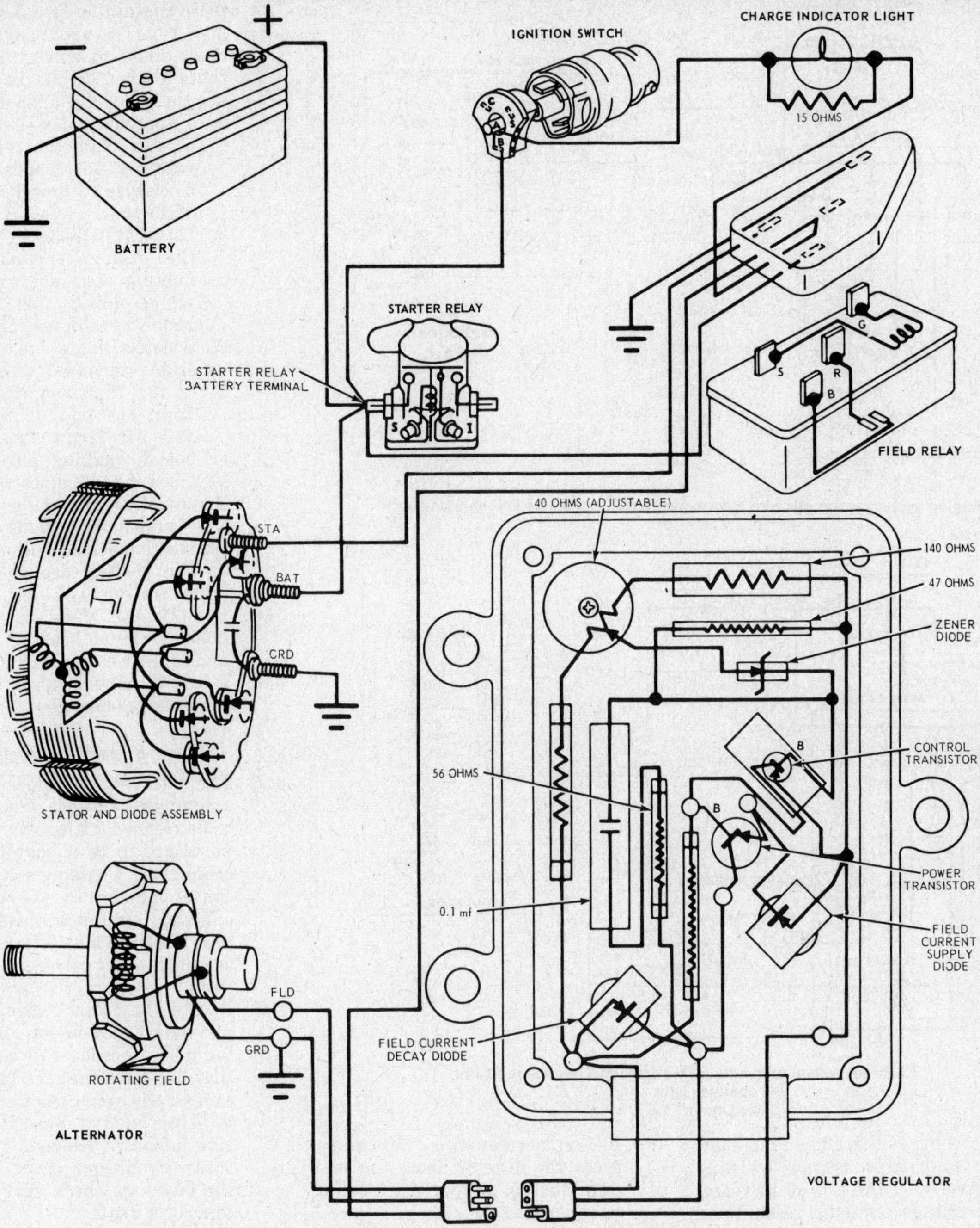
BATTERY
IGNITION SWITCH
CHARGE INDICATOR LIGHT
15 OHMS
STARTER RELAY
STARTER RELAY BATTERY TERMINAL
FIELD RELAY
STA
BAT
GRD
STATOR AND DIODE ASSEMBLY
40 OHMS (ADJUSTABLE)
140 OHMS
47 OHMS
ZENER DIODE
CONTROL TRANSISTOR
56 OHMS
POWER TRANSISTOR
0.1 mf
FIELD CURRENT SUPPLY DIODE
FLD
GRD
FIELD CURRENT DECAY DIODE
ROTATING FIELD
ALTERNATOR
VOLTAGE REGULATOR

Charging system schematic with transistor regulator and charging light (© Ford Motor Co)

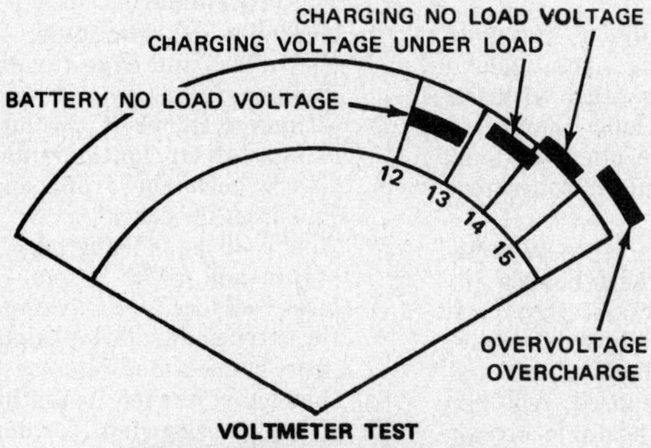
CHARGING NO LOAD VOLTAGE
CHARGING VOLTAGE UNDER LOAD
BATTERY NO LOAD VOLTAGE
12
13
14
15
OVERVOLTAGE
OVERCHARGE
VOLTMETER TEST
TYPICAL VOLTAGE BANDS SHOWN

Voltmeter readings isolation test
(© Ford Motor Co)

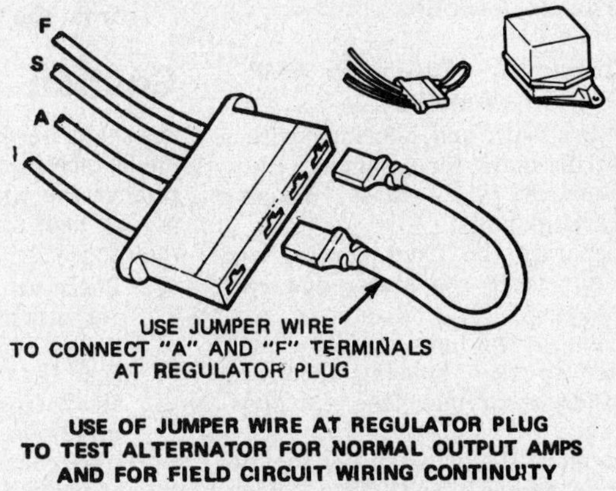
F
S
A
I
USE JUMPER WIRE
TO CONNECT "A" AND "F" TERMINALS
AT REGULATOR PLUG
USE OF JUMPER WIRE AT REGULATOR PLUG
TO TEST ALTERNATOR FOR NORMAL OUTPUT AMPS
AND FOR FIELD CIRCUIT WIRING CONTINUITY

Isolation test jumper wire
(© Ford Motor Co)

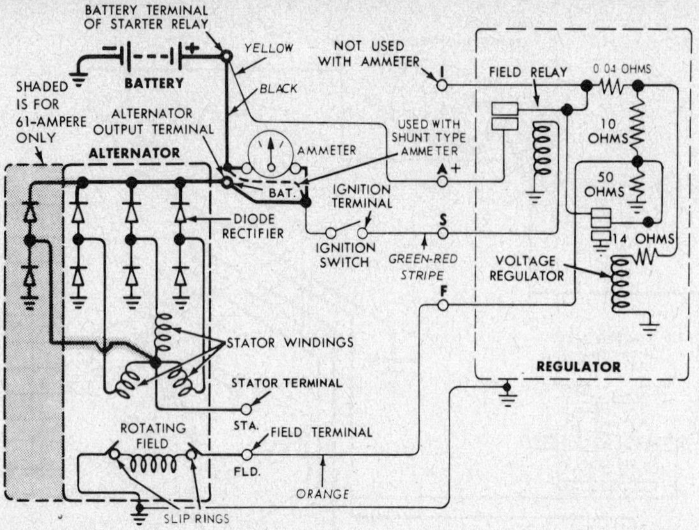

BATTERY TERMINAL OF STARTER RELAY
YELLOW
NOT USED WITH AMMETER
BATTERY
BLACK
SHADED IS FOR 61-AMPERE ONLY
ALTERNATOR OUTPUT TERMINAL
ALTERNATOR
AMMETER
USED WITH SHUNT TYPE AMMETER
BAT.
IGNITION TERMINAL
DIODE RECTIFIER
IGNITION SWITCH
GREEN-RED STRIPE
FIELD RELAY
0.04 OHMS
10 OHMS
50 OHMS
14 OHMS
VOLTAGE REGULATOR
REGULATOR
STATOR WINDINGS
STATOR TERMINAL
STA.
ROTATING FIELD
FIELD TERMINAL
FLD.
ORANGE
SLIP RINGS
I
A+
S
F

Charging system schematic with electro-mechanical regulator and charging light
(© Ford Motor Co)

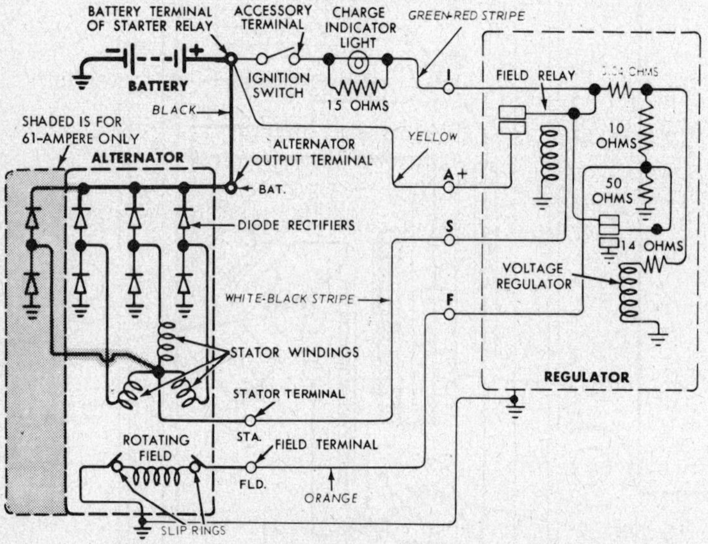

BATTERY TERMINAL OF STARTER RELAY
ACCESSORY TERMINAL
CHARGE INDICATOR LIGHT
GREEN-RED STRIPE
BATTERY
IGNITION SWITCH
15 OHMS
BLACK
SHADED IS FOR 61-AMPERE ONLY
ALTERNATOR OUTPUT TERMINAL
YELLOW
ALTERNATOR
BAT.
FIELD RELAY
10 OHMS
50 OHMS
14 OHMS
DIODE RECTIFIERS
VOLTAGE REGULATOR
WHITE-BLACK STRIPE
STATOR WINDINGS
REGULATOR
STATOR TERMINAL
STA.
ROTATING FIELD
FIELD TERMINAL
FLD.
ORANGE
SLIP RINGS
I
A+
S
F

Charging system schematic with electro-mechanical regulator and charging light
(© Ford Motor Co)

two volts. If there is no increase, the alternator is not working correctly. If there is an increase, the voltage regulator needs to be replaced.

Overhaul—Autolite

Disassembly—Except 65 AMP Autolite

1. Mark both end housings with a scribe mark for assembly.
2. Remove the three housing through bolts.
3. Separate the front housing and rotor from the stator and rear housing.
4. Remove the nuts from the rectifier to rear housing mounting studs, and remove the rear housing.
5. Remove the brush holder mounting screws and the holder, brushes, springs, insulator, and terminal.
6. If replacement is necessary, press the bearing from the rear end housing, supporting housing on inner boss.
7. If rectifiers are to be replaced, carefully unsolder the leads from the terminals.

Caution Use only a 100-watt soldering iron. Leave the soldering iron in contact with the diode terminals only long enough to remove the wires. Use pliers as temporary heat sinks in order to protect the diodes.

8. There are various types of rectifier assembly circuit boards installed in production. One type has the circuit board spaced away from the diode plates and the diodes are exposed. Another type consists of a single circuit board with integral diodes; and still another has integral diodes with an additional booster diode plate containing two diodes. This last type is used only on the eight-diode, 61-amp. 1971-72 Autolite alternator. To disassemble, use the following procedures:
   a. Exposed Diodes—remove the screws from the rectifier by rotating bolt heads ¼ turn clockwise to unlock, then unscrewing.
   b. Integral Diodes—press out the stator terminal screw, making sure not to twist it while doing this. Do not remove grounded screw.
   c. Booster Diodes—press out the stator terminal screw about ¼ in., then remove the nut from the end of the screw and lift screw from circuit board, making sure not to twist it as it comes out.
9. Remove the drive pulley and fan. On alternator pulleys with threaded holes in the outer end of the pulley, use a standard puller for removal.
10. Remove the three screws that hold the front bearing retainer, and remove the front housing.
11. If the bearing is to be replaced, press from housing.

Cleaning and Inspection

1. The rotor, stator, diode rectifier assemblies, and bearings are not to be cleaned with solvent. These parts are to be wiped off with a clean cloth. Cleaning solvent may cause damage to the electrical parts or contaminate the bearing internal lubricant. Wash all other parts in solvent and dry them.
2. Rotate the front bearing on the driveshaft. Check for any scraping noise, looseness or roughness that indicates that the bearing is excessively worn. As the bearing is being rotated, look for excessive lubricant leakage. If any of these conditions exist, replace the bearing. Check rear bearing and rotor shaft.
3. Place the rear end housing on the slip ring end of the shaft and rotate the bearing on the shaft. Make a similar check for noise, looseness or roughness. Inspect the rollers and cage for damage. Replace the bearing if these conditions exist, or if the lubricant is missing or contaminated.
4. Check both the front and rear housings for cracks.
5. Check all wire leads on both the stator and rotor assemblies for loose soldered connections, and for burned insulation. Solder all poor connections. Replace parts that show burned insulation.
6. Check the slip rings for damaged insulation and runout. If the slip rings are more than 0.0005 in. out of round, take a light

cut (minimum diameter limit 1.22 in.) from the face of the rings to true them. If the slip rings are badly damaged, the entire rotor will have to be replaced, as they are serviced as a complete assembly.

7. Replace any parts that are burned or cracked. Replace brushes that are worn to less than 5/16 in. in length. Replace the brush spring if it has less than 7-12 oz. tension.

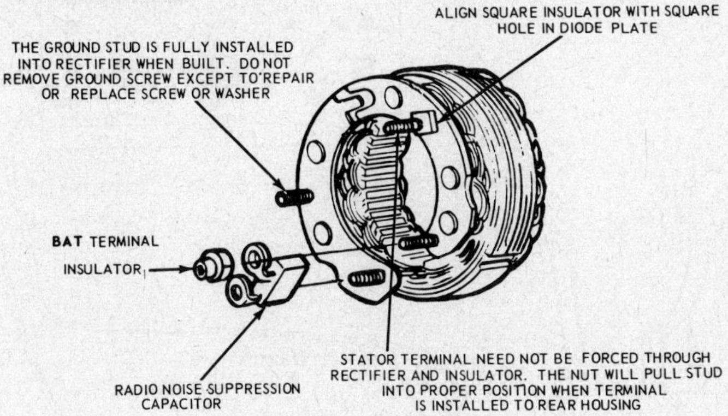
ALIGN SQUARE INSULATOR WITH SQUARE HOLE IN DIODE PLATE
THE GROUND STUD IS FULLY INSTALLED INTO RECTIFIER WHEN BUILT. DO NOT REMOVE GROUND SCREW EXCEPT TO REPAIR OR REPLACE SCREW OR WASHER
BAT TERMINAL
INSULATOR
RADIO NOISE SUPPRESSION CAPACITOR
STATOR TERMINAL NEED NOT BE FORCED THROUGH RECTIFIER AND INSULATOR. THE NUT WILL PULL STUD INTO PROPER POSITION WHEN TERMINAL IS INSTALLED TO REAR HOUSING
Terminal insulators—fiber circuit board
(© Ford Motor Co)

Field Current Draw Test

NOTE: alternator must be removed from the car.

1. Connect a test ammeter between the alternator frame and the positive post of a 12-volt test battery.
2. Connect a jumper wire between the negative test battery post and the alternator field terminal.
3. Observe the ammeter:
   a. Little or no current flow indicates high brush resistance, open field windings, or high winding resistance.
   b. Current in excess of specifications (approximately 2.9 amps. for most models) indicates shorted or grounded field windings, or brush leads touching.

NOTE: sometimes the alternator produces current output at low engine speeds, but ceases to put out at higher speeds. This can be caused by certrifugal force expanding the rotor windings to the point where they short to ground. Place in a test stand and check field current draw while spinning alternator.

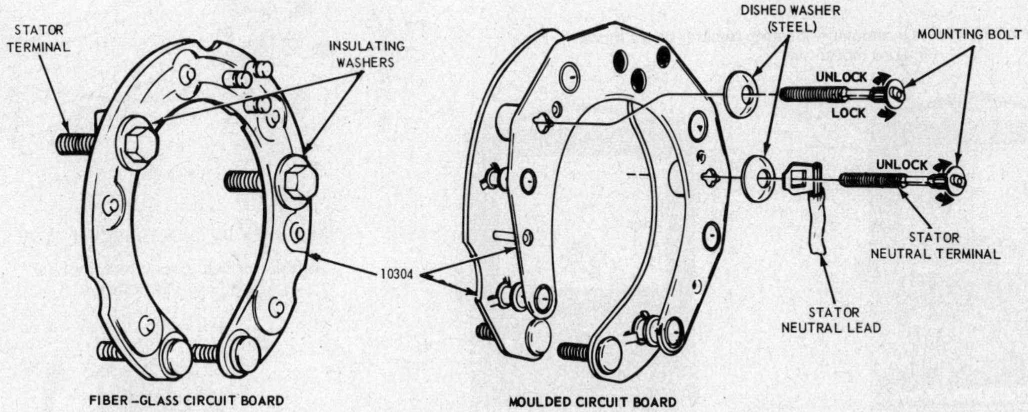
STATOR TERMINAL
INSULATING WASHERS
10304
FIBER-GLASS CIRCUIT BOARD
DISHED WASHER (STEEL)
MOUNTING BOLT
UNLOCK
LOCK
UNLOCK
STATOR NEUTRAL TERMINAL
STATOR NEUTRAL LEAD
MOULDED CIRCUIT BOARD
Rectifier assembly (© Ford Motor Co)

Diode Tests

Disassemble the alternator. Disconnect diode assembly from stator and make tests as illustrated. To test one set of diodes, contact one ohmmeter probe to the diode plate and contact each of the three stator lead termi-

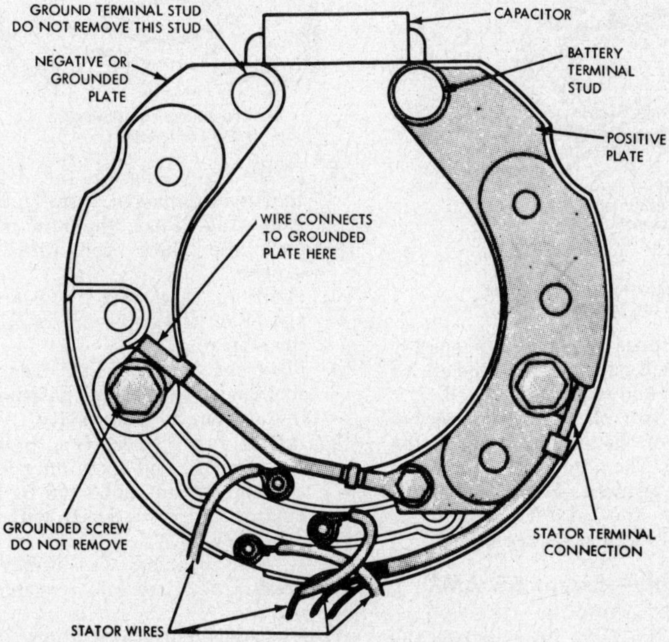
GROUND TERMINAL STUD DO NOT REMOVE THIS STUD
CAPACITOR
NEGATIVE OR GROUNDED PLATE
BATTERY TERMINAL STUD
POSITIVE PLATE
WIRE CONNECTS TO GROUNDED PLATE HERE
GROUNDED SCREW DO NOT REMOVE
STATOR TERMINAL CONNECTION
STATOR WIRES
Rectifier terminal locations—61 amp booster diode model
(© Ford Motor Co)

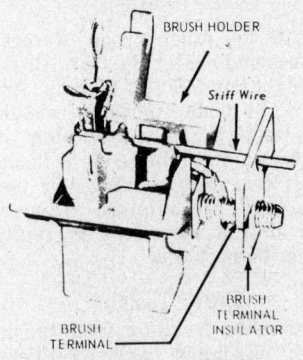

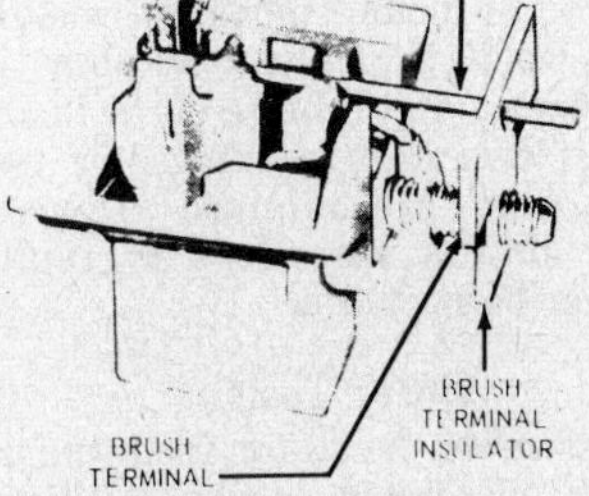
BRUSH HOLDER
Stiff Wire
BRUSH TERMINAL INSULATOR
BRUSH TERMINAL
Autolite brush holder assembly
(© Ford Motor Co)

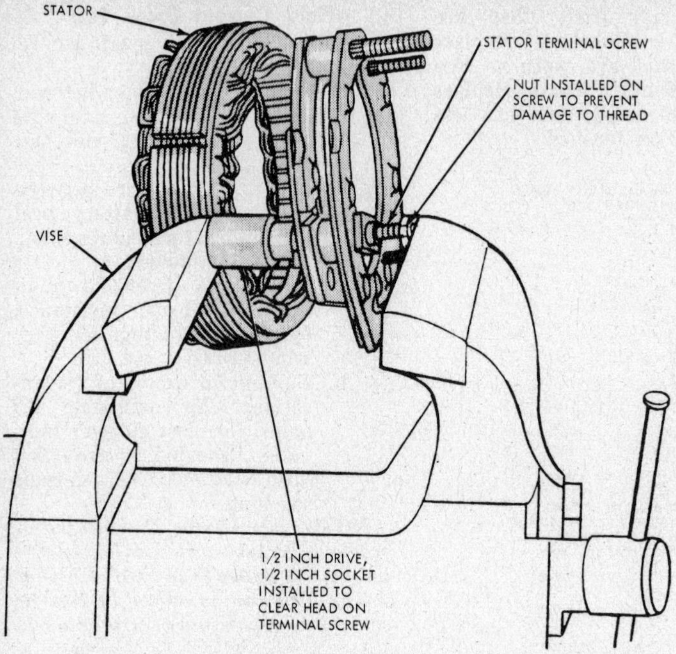
STATOR
STATOR TERMINAL SCREW
NUT INSTALLED ON SCREW TO PREVENT DAMAGE TO THREAD
VISE
1/2 INCH DRIVE, 1/2 INCH SOCKET INSTALLED TO CLEAR HEAD ON TERMINAL SCREW

Stator terminal screw removal—61 amp booster diode model
(© Ford Motor Co)

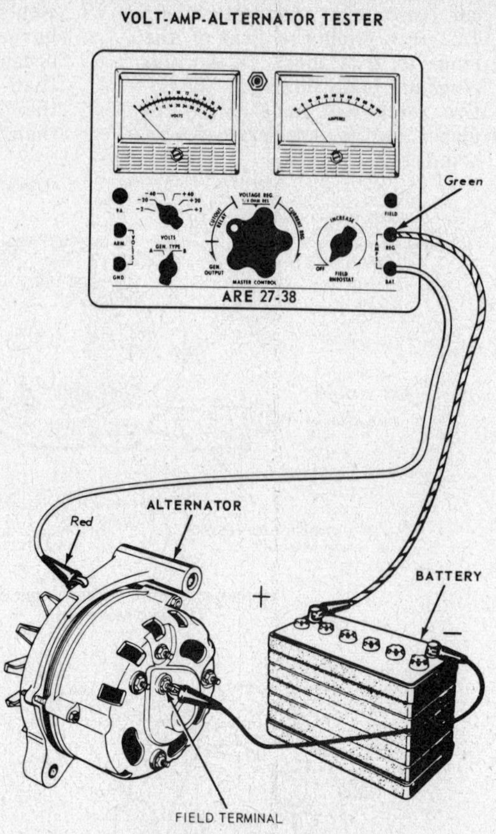
VOLT-AMP-ALTERNATOR TESTER
ARE 27-38
Green
Red
ALTERNATOR
BATTERY
+
−
FIELD TERMINAL

FIELD OPEN OR SHORT CIRCUIT TEST
Alternator field circuit test hook-up
(© Ford Motor Co)

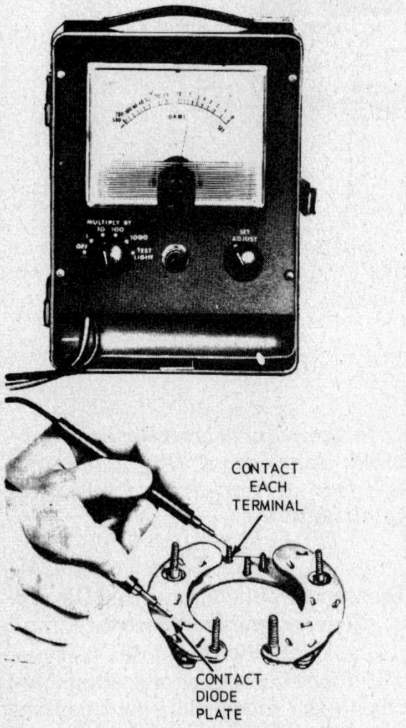
CONTACT EACH TERMINAL
CONTACT DIODE PLATE

Testing diodes—all except 65 Amp Autolite
(© Ford Motor Co)

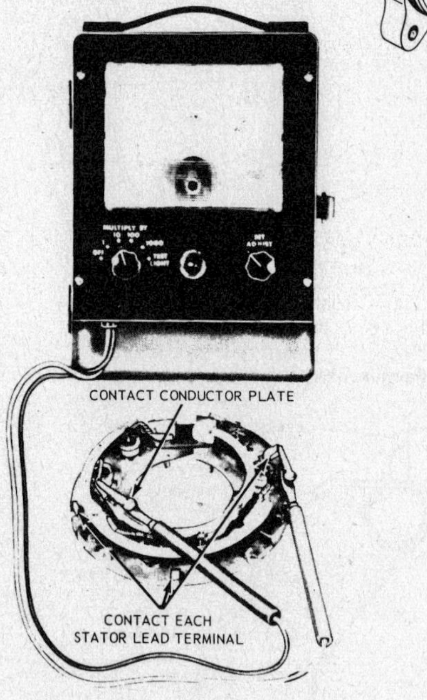
CONTACT CONDUCTOR PLATE
CONTACT EACH STATOR LEAD TERMINAL

Testing diodes—65 amp Autolite
(© Ford Motor Co)

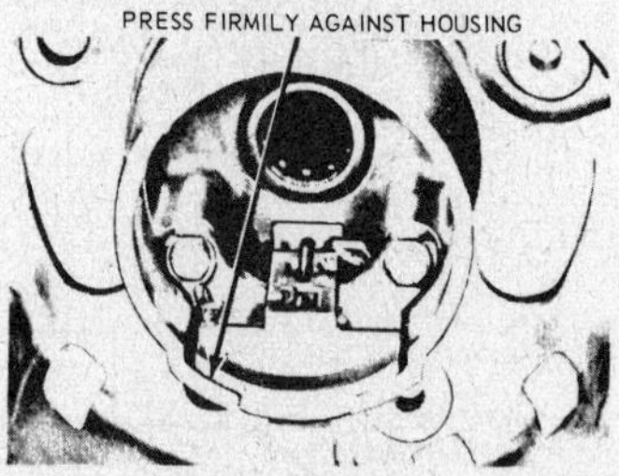
PRESS FIRMILY AGAINST HOUSING

Brush lead positioning
(© Ford Motor Co)

nals with the other probe. Reverse the probes and repeat the test. All six tests (eight for 1971-72 61 amp. Autolite eight-diode models) should show a reading of about 60 ohms in one direction and infinite ohms in the other. If two high readings, or two low readings, are obtained after reversing probes the diode is faulty and must be replaced.

Stator Tests

Disassemble the stator from the alternator assembly and rectifiers. Connect test ohmmeter probes between each pair of stator leads. If the ohmmeter does not indicate equally between each pair of leads, the stator coil is open and must be replaced.

Connect test ohmmeter probes between one of the stator leads and the stator core. The ohmmeter should not show any reading. If it does show continuity, the stator winding is grounded and must be replaced.

Assembly—Except 65 AMP Autolite

1. Press the front bearing into the front housing boss, putting pressure on outer race only. Install bearing retainer.
2. If the stop ring on the driveshaft was damaged, install a new stop ring. Push the new ring onto the shaft and into the groove.
3. Position the front bearing spacer on the driveshaft against the stop ring.
4. Place the front housing over the shaft, with the bearing positioned in the front housing cavity.
5. Install fan spacer, fan, pulley, lockwasher and retaining nut and tighten nut to 60-100 ft. lbs. holding the drive shaft with an Allen key.
6. If rear bearing was removed, press a new one into rear housing.
7. Assemble brushes, springs, terminal and insulator in the brush holder, retract the brushes and insert a short length of ⅛ in.

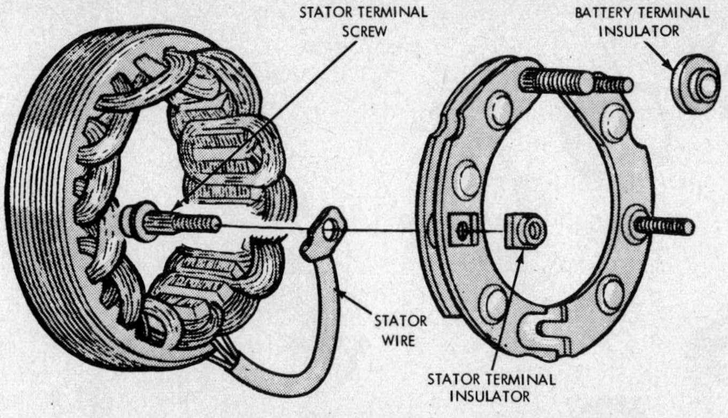
STATOR TERMINAL SCREW
BATTERY TERMINAL INSULATOR
STATOR WIRE
STATOR TERMINAL INSULATOR

Stator and rectifier assembly—61 amp booster diode model
(© Ford Motor Co)

rod or stiff wire through the hole in the holder to hold the brushes in the retracted position.

8. Position the brush holder assembly in the rear housing and install mounting screws. Position brush leads as illustrated to prevent shorting.
9. Wrap the three stator winding leads around the circuit board terminals and solder them using only rosin core solder and a 100-watt iron. Position the stator neutral lead eyelet on the stator terminal screw and install the screw in the rectifier assembly.
10. A. Exposed Diodes—insert the special screws through the wire lug, dished washers and circuit board. Turn ¼ turn counterclockwise to lock in place.

    B. Integral Diodes—insert the screws straight through the holes.

NOTE: the dished washers are to be used on *molded* circuit boards only. Using these washers on a *fiber* board will result in a serious short circuit, as only a flat insulating washer between the stator terminal and the board is used on fiber circuit boards.

    C. Booster Diodes—position the stator wire terminal on the stator terminal screw, then position screw on rectifier. Position square insulator over the screw and into the square hole in the rectifier, rotate terminal screw until it locks, then press it in finger-tight. Position the stator wire, then press the terminal screw into the rectifier and insulator with a vise.

11. Place the radio noise suppression condenser on the rectifier terminals. With molded circuit board, install the STA and BAT terminal insulators. With fiber circuit board, place the square stator terminal insulator in the square hole in the sectifier assembly, then position BAT terminal insulator.

    Position the stator and rectifier assembly in the rear housing, making sure that all terminal insulators are seated properly in the recesses. Position STA, BAT and FLD insulators on terminal bolts; install nuts.

12. Clean the rear bearing surface of the rotor shaft with a rag, then position rear housing and stator assembly over rotor. Align matchmarks made during disassembly and install through bolts. *Remove brush retracting wire and place a dab of silicone sealer over the hole.*

Disassembly—65 AMP. Autolite

1. Remove the brush holder and cover assembly from the rear housing.
2. Mark both end housings and the stator.
3. Remove the three housing through bolts.
4. Separate the front housing and rotor from the stator and rear housing.
5. Remove the drive pulley nut, lockwasher, flat washer, pulley, fan, fan spacer and rotor from the front housing.
6. Remove the three screws that hold the front bearing retainer and remove the retainer. If the bearing is damaged or has lost its lubricant, support the housing close to the bearing boss and press out the bearing.
7. Remove all the nut and washer assemblies and insulators from the rear housing and remove the rear housing from the stator and rectifier assembly.
8. If necessary, press the rear bearing from the housing, supporting the housing on the inner boss.
9. Unsolder the three stator leads from the rectifier assembly, and separate the stator from the assembly. Use a 200-watt soldering iron.
10. Perform a diode test and an open and grounded stator coil test.

Cleaning and Inspection

Nicks and scratches may be removed from the rotor slip rings by turning down the slip rings. Do not go beyond the minimum diameter limit of 1.22 in. If the slip rings are badly damaged, the entire rotor must be replaced. The rectifier also is serviced as an assembly. See Lower Ampere Alternator Section for test procedures.

Assembly—65 AMP. Autolite

1. If the front bearing is being replaced, press the new bearing into the bearing boss, putting pressure on the outer race only. Install the bearing retainer and tighten the retainer screws until the tips of the retainer touch the housing.
2. Position the rectifier assembly to the stator, wrap the three stator leads around the diode plate terminals and solder them using a 200-watt soldering iron.
3. If the rear housing bearing was removed, press in a new bearing from the inside of the housing, putting pressure on the outer race only.
4. Install the BAT-GRD insulator, and position the stator and rectifier assembly in the rear housing.
5. Install the STA (purple) and BAT (red) terminal insulators on the terminal bolts and install the nut and washer assemblies. *Make certain that the shoulders on all insulators, both inside and outside of the housing, are seated properly before tightening the nuts.*
6. Position the front housing over the rotor and install the fan spacer, fan, pulley, flat and lockwashers and nut on the rotor shaft.
7. Wipe the rear bearing surface of the rotor shaft with a clean rag.
8. Position the rotor with the front housing into the stator and rear housing assembly, and align the matchmarks made during disassembly. Seat the machined portion of the stator core into the step in both housings and install the through bolts.
9. If the field brushes have worn to less than ⅜ in., replace both brushes. Hold the brushes in position by inserting a stiff wire into the brush holder.
10. Position the brush holder assembly into the rear housing and install the three mounting screws. Remove the brush retracting wire and put a dab of silicone cement over the hole.

Brush Replacement—65 AMP Autolite

1. Remove the brush holder and cover assembly from the rear housing.

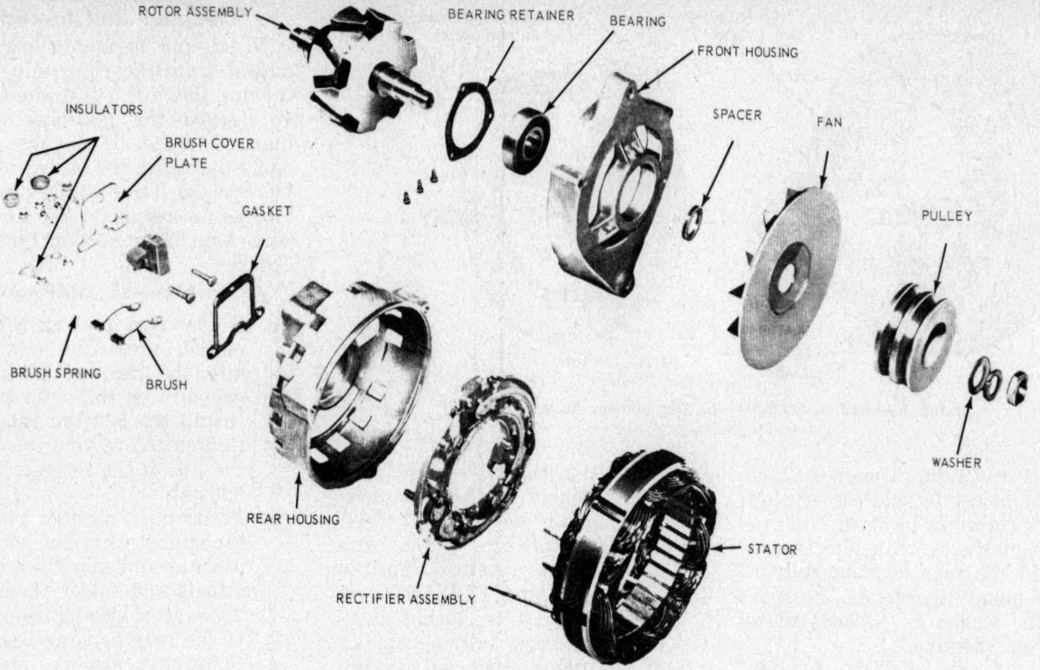
ROTOR ASSEMBLY
BEARING RETAINER
BEARING
FRONT HOUSING
INSULATORS
BRUSH COVER PLATE
SPACER
FAN
GASKET
PULLEY
BRUSH SPRING
BRUSH
WASHER
REAR HOUSING
STATOR
RECTIFIER ASSEMBLY

Disassembled view of 65 amp Autolite alternator (© Ford Motor Co)

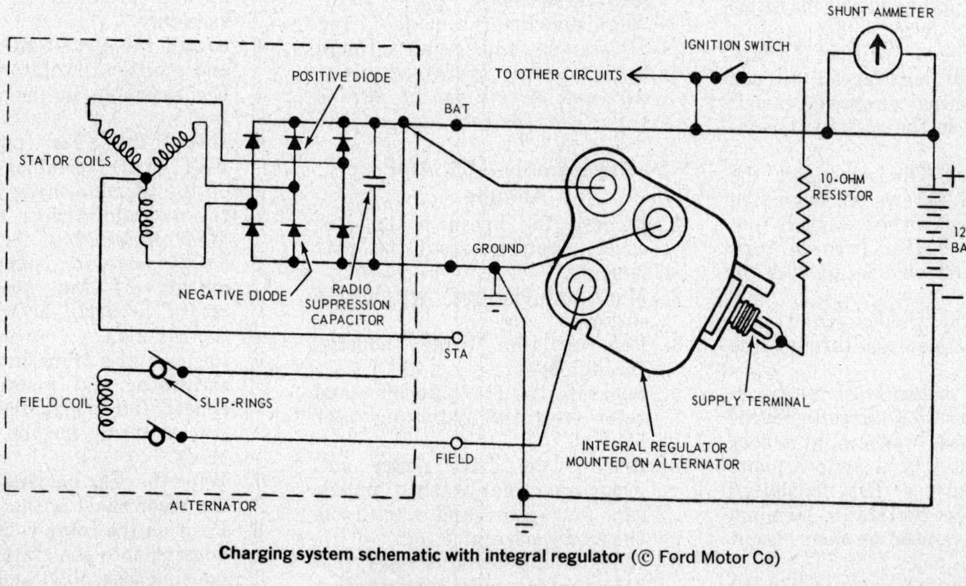
SHUNT AMMETER
IGNITION SWITCH
TO OTHER CIRCUITS
POSITIVE DIODE
BAT
STATOR COILS
10-OHM RESISTOR
12-VOLT BATTERY
GROUND
NEGATIVE DIODE
RADIO SUPPRESSION CAPACITOR
STA
FIELD COIL
SLIP-RINGS
SUPPLY TERMINAL
FIELD
INTEGRAL REGULATOR MOUNTED ON ALTERNATOR
ALTERNATOR

Charging system schematic with integral regulator (© Ford Motor Co)

2. Remove the terminal bolts from the brush holder and cover assembly, then remove the brush assemblies.
3. Position the new brush terminals on the terminal bolts and assemble the terminals, bolts, brush holder washers and nuts. The insulating washer mounts under the FLD terminal nut. The entire brush and cover assembly also is available for service.
4. Depress the brush springs in the brush holder cavities and insert the brushes on top of the springs. Hold the brushes in position by inserting a stiff wire in the brush holder as shown. Position the brush leads as shown.
5. Install the brush holder and cover assembly into the rear housing. Remove the brush retracting wire and put a dab of silicone cement over the hole.

Autolite Alternator with Integral Regulator

Description

Starting in 1969, some vehicles are equipped with an Autolite alternator having an integral regulator mounted to the rear end housing. The regulator is a hybrid unit featuring use of solid state integrated circuits. These circuits may consist of transistors, diodes and resistors. The unusual feature of this type of microelectronic circuit is that the entire circuit is within a silicone crystal approximately ⅛ in. square. Because of the small size of the circuit, it is not repairable or adjustable and must be replaced as a unit if found to be defective. It should be noted that the size of the regulator housing is dictated only by the fact that some means of connecting the regulator to the alternator is necessary. Overhaul is the same as for other Autolite alternators.

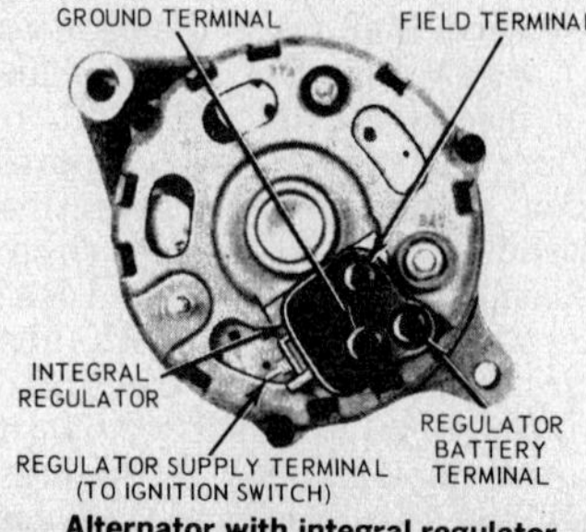
GROUND TERMINAL
FIELD TERMINAL
INTEGRAL REGULATOR
REGULATOR BATTERY TERMINAL
REGULATOR SUPPLY TERMINAL (TO IGNITION SWITCH)

Alternator with integral regulator (© Ford Motor Co)

Troubleshooting

NOTE: see the "Preliminary Charging System Inspection" section before proceeding further.

Fusible Links

1. Check the fusible link located between the starter relay and the alternator. Replace the link if it is burned or open.

Output Test

1. Place transmission in Neutral or Park.
2. Remove the positive battery cable and install a battery adapter switch in the line.
3. Attach one lead of a test voltmeter to the negative battery post and the other test lead to the circuit side of the adapter switch.
4. Connect a test ammeter to each side of the adapter switch, so that charging current will go through the ammeter when the switch is opened.
5. Connect a jumper wire between the alternator frame and the integral regulator field terminal (cover plug removed).
6. Close adapter switch, start engine and open adapter switch.
7. Running engine at 2,000 rpm, observe voltmeter and ammeter. At 15 volts indicated, the ammeter should read 50-57 amps. If so, and there is still a no-charge condition, the regulator is probably faulty and must be replaced. An output 2-8 amps. below 50 amps. usually indicates an open diode rectifier, while an output 10-15 amps. below minimum specifications usually indicates a shorted diode. An alternator with a shorted diode usually will whine at idle speed.

Field Test (Voltmeter)

1. Turn ignition switch to OFF position.
2. Remove wire from regulator supply terminal.
3. Remove cover plug from regulator field terminal and connect one test voltmeter lead to this terminal. A 1/4 ohm resistor should be in the circuit.
4. Connect the other test voltmeter lead to a good engine ground.
5. The voltmeter should read 12 volts. If *no* voltage is present, the field circuit is open or grounded.
6. If voltmeter reads more than 1 volt, but still less than battery voltage, there is probably a partial ground in the alternator field circuit and the circuit should be checked with an ohmmeter.

Field Test (Ohmmeter)

1. Disconnect battery ground cable; remove alternator from car.
2. Remove the regulator from the alternator (covered later).
3. Make the ohmmeter tests as illustrated. If any of the tests indicates a field circuit problem, disassemble the alternator to further isolate the trouble.
   a. Contact each ohmmeter probe to a slip ring. Resistance should be 4-5 ohms. A higher reading indicates a damaged slip ring soldered connection or a broken wire. A lower reading indicates a shorted wire or slip ring assembly.
   b. Contact one ohmmeter probe to a slip ring and the other probe to the rotor shaft. Any reading other than infinite ohms indicates a short to ground. If neither of these tests (A and B) isolates the trouble, the brushes or brush assembly are the probable cause.

Voltage Limiter Test

1. Check the battery specific gravity. If it is not at least 1.230, charge the battery or install a charged battery for the test.
2. Make sure all lights and accessories are turned off, including such items as dome lights and radio.
3. Make the test connections as illustrated.
4. Place transmission in Neutral or Park, close battery adapter switch and start the engine.
5. Open the battery adapter switch and operate engine at 2,000 rpm for 5 minutes. The voltmeter should read 13.3-15.3 volts.
6. If voltage does not rise above 12 volts, perform a regulator supply voltage test to determine whether or not the regulator is getting voltage from the battery. Before replacing a regulator, check the wiring of the entire

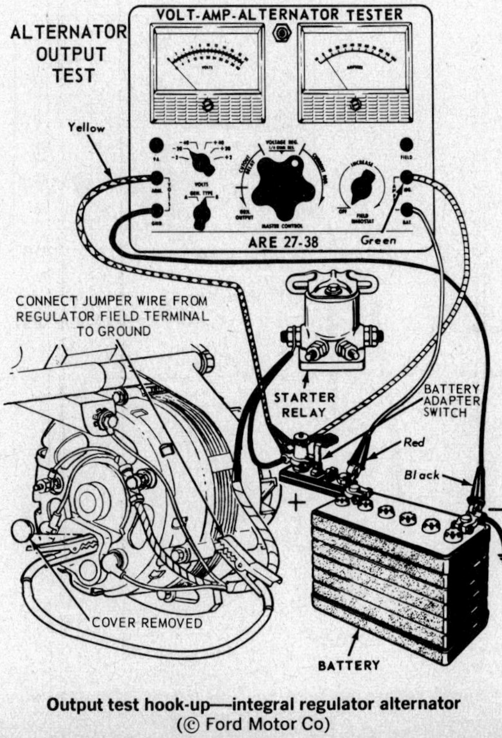
ALTERNATOR OUTPUT TEST
VOLT-AMP-ALTERNATOR TESTER
ARE 27-38
Yellow
Green
CONNECT JUMPER WIRE FROM REGULATOR FIELD TERMINAL TO GROUND
STARTER RELAY
BATTERY ADAPTER SWITCH
Red
Black
+
−
COVER REMOVED
BATTERY

Output test hook-up—integral regulator alternator
(© Ford Motor Co)

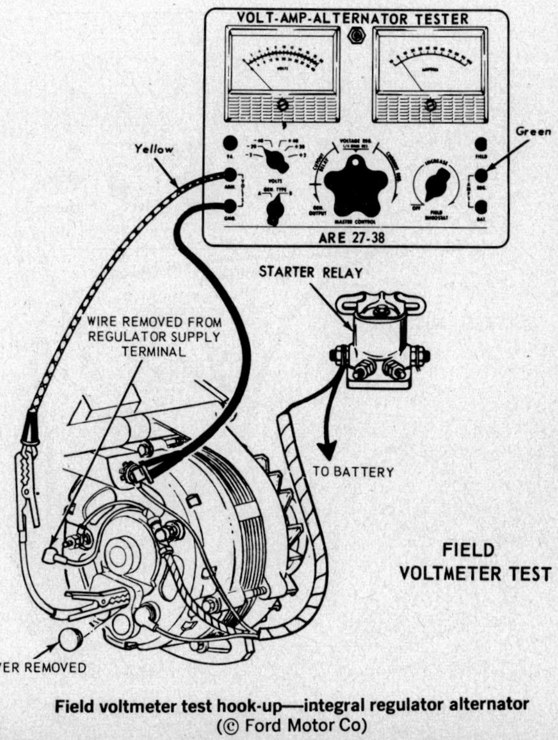
VOLT-AMP-ALTERNATOR TESTER
ARE 27-38
Yellow
Green
STARTER RELAY
WIRE REMOVED FROM REGULATOR SUPPLY TERMINAL
TO BATTERY
FIELD VOLTMETER TEST
COVER REMOVED

Field voltmeter test hook-up—integral regulator alternator
(© Ford Motor Co)

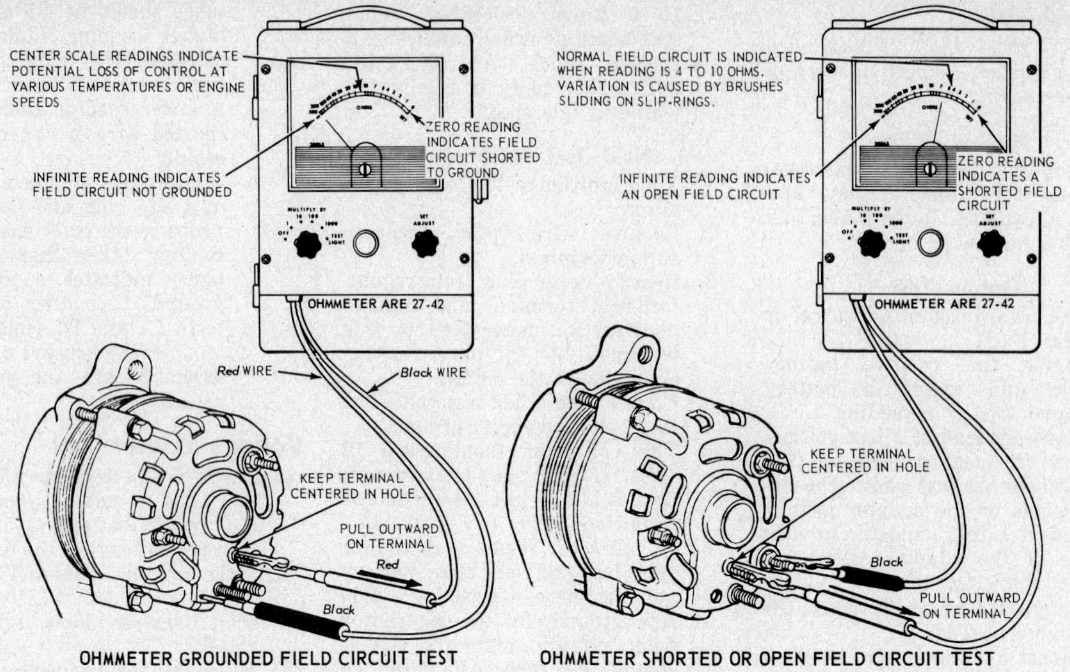

CENTER SCALE READINGS INDICATE POTENTIAL LOSS OF CONTROL AT VARIOUS TEMPERATURES OR ENGINE SPEEDS
ZERO READING INDICATES FIELD CIRCUIT SHORTED TO GROUND
INFINITE READING INDICATES FIELD CIRCUIT NOT GROUNDED
OHMMETER ARE 27-42
Red WIRE
Black WIRE
KEEP TERMINAL CENTERED IN HOLE
PULL OUTWARD ON TERMINAL
Red
Black
OHMMETER GROUNDED FIELD CIRCUIT TEST
NORMAL FIELD CIRCUIT IS INDICATED WHEN READING IS 4 TO 10 OHMS. VARIATION IS CAUSED BY BRUSHES SLIDING ON SLIP-RINGS.
INFINITE READING INDICATES AN OPEN FIELD CIRCUIT
ZERO READING INDICATES A SHORTED FIELD CIRCUIT
OHMMETER ARE 27-42
KEEP TERMINAL CENTERED IN HOLE
Black
PULL OUTWARD ON TERMINAL
OHMMETER SHORTED OR OPEN FIELD CIRCUIT TEST

Field circuit test hook-ups with ohmmeter—integral regulator alternator (© Ford Motor Co)

charging system for shorts, opens, or high resistance connections.

Regulator Supply Voltage Test

The regulator is "turned on" by the application of battery voltage through a 10 ohm resistor wire. If the supply circuit is defective, the regulator will not function and the alternator will not put out current.

1. Connect a 12-volt test light or voltmeter between the regulator supply lead and ground.
2. Turn on the ignition switch. The test light should glow or the volmeter indicate. If not, the supply circuit should be checked back to the battery, especially the resistance wire.

Overhaul

The overhaul procedures for the alternator are the same as for the Ford Autolite electro-mechanical alternator.

The Motorola System

The Motorola alternator is designed to pass all the DC current through an isolation diode, or diodes, mounted in an external aluminum heat sink.

Due to the nature of the alternator, residual magnetism is at near zero when the unit is at rest. It is, therefore, necessary to provide some small current to excite the field prior to generating current. With Motorola, this priming current is supplied by

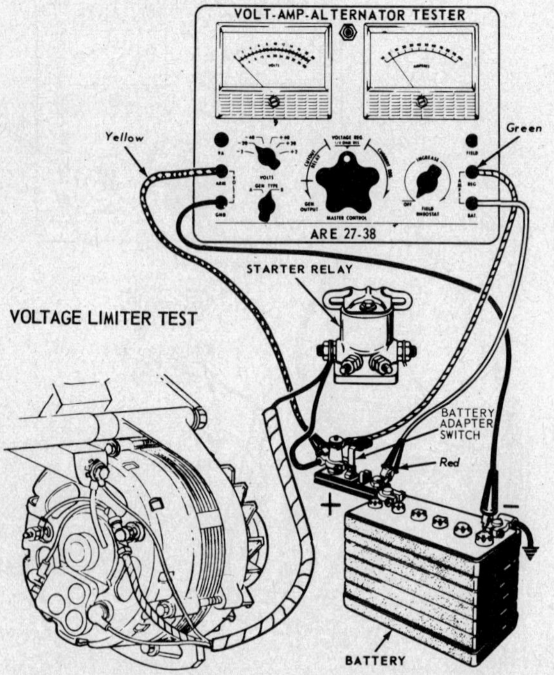

VOLT-AMP-ALTERNATOR TESTER
ARE 27-38
Yellow
Green
STARTER RELAY
VOLTAGE LIMITER TEST
BATTERY ADAPTER SWITCH
Red
+
−
BATTERY

Voltage limiter test hook-up—integral regulator alternator
(© Ford Motor Co)

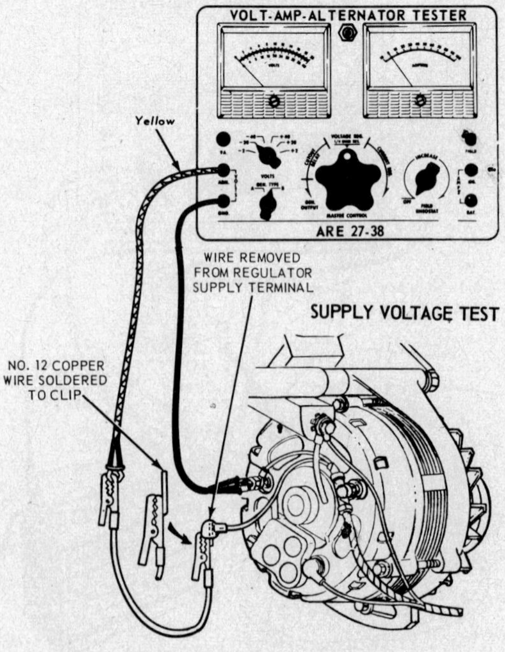

VOLT-AMP-ALTERNATOR TESTER
ARE 27-38
Yellow
WIRE REMOVED FROM REGULATOR SUPPLY TERMINAL
SUPPLY VOLTAGE TEST
NO. 12 COPPER WIRE SOLDERED TO CLIP

Supply voltage test hook-up—integral regulator alternator
(© Ford Motor Co)

means of a 75 ohm resistance unit between the ignition coil and the alternator (inside the regulator). It is quite important that this resistance unit be checked and found satisfactory before proceeding with subsequent tests.

The charge indicator light on some cars operates in the same way as this resistor by furnishing the necessary initial field starting current. If this resistor circuit is open (a burned out indicator lamp) on some models, the alternator will not function. On later models, a resistor is placed in parallel with the bulb to provide excitation current if the bulb burns out.

The regulator is a sealed unit and should require no adjustment. It is therefore, recommended that nonfunctioning regulators be replaced.

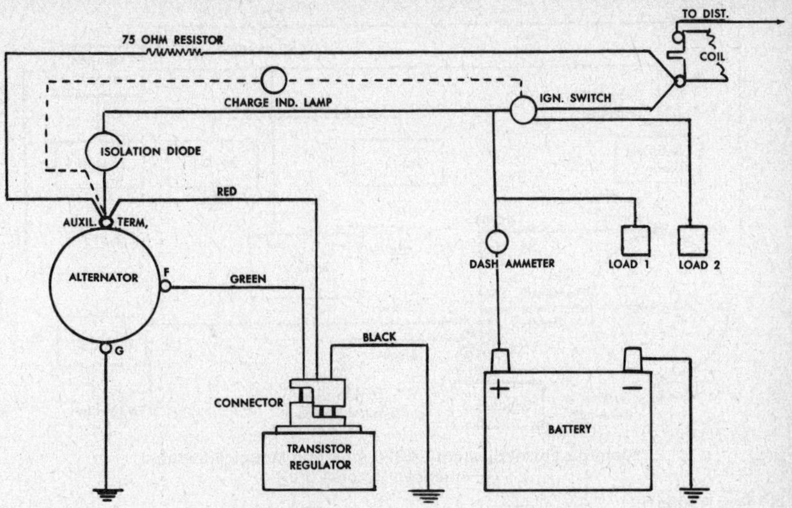
TO DIST.
75 OHM RESISTOR
COIL
CHARGE IND. LAMP
IGN. SWITCH
ISOLATION DIODE
RED
AUXIL. TERM.
ALTERNATOR
F
GREEN
DASH AMMETER
LOAD 1
LOAD 2
G
BLACK
CONNECTOR
TRANSISTOR REGULATOR
BATTERY
+
−
Typical Motorola alternator system charging circuit
(© American Motors Corp)

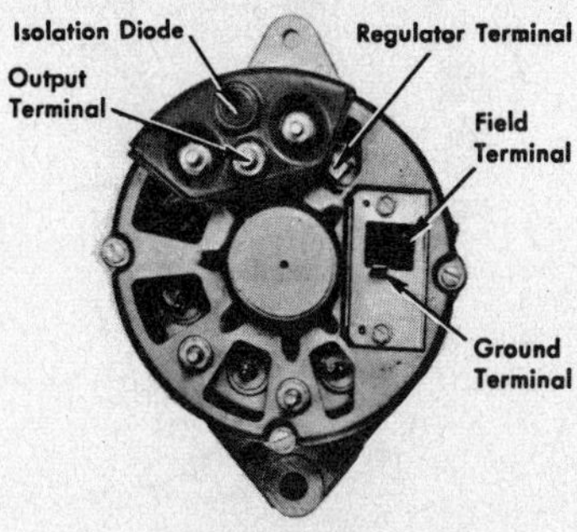
Isolation Diode
Regulator Terminal
Output Terminal
Field Terminal
Ground Terminal
35 amp alternator—Motorola
(© American Motors Corp)

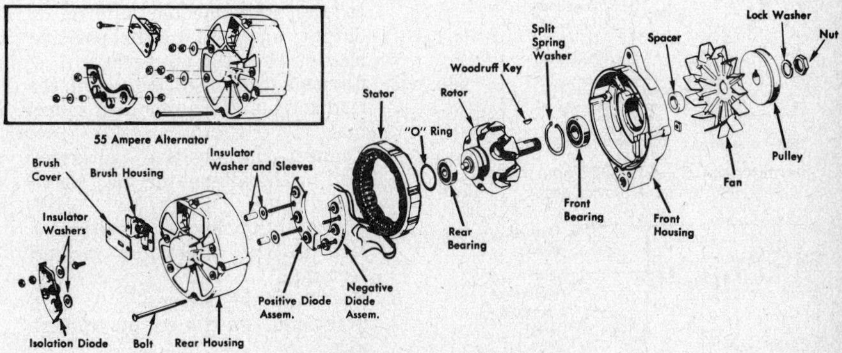
55 Ampere Alternator
Lock Washer
Nut
Split Spring Washer
Spacer
Woodruff Key
Stator
Rotor
"O" Ring
Pulley
Fan
Front Bearing
Front Housing
Rear Bearing
Brush Cover
Brush Housing
Insulator Washer and Sleeves
Insulator Washers
Positive Diode Assem.
Negative Diode Assem.
Isolation Diode
Bolt
Rear Housing
Motorola alternator—exploded view
(© American Motors Corp)

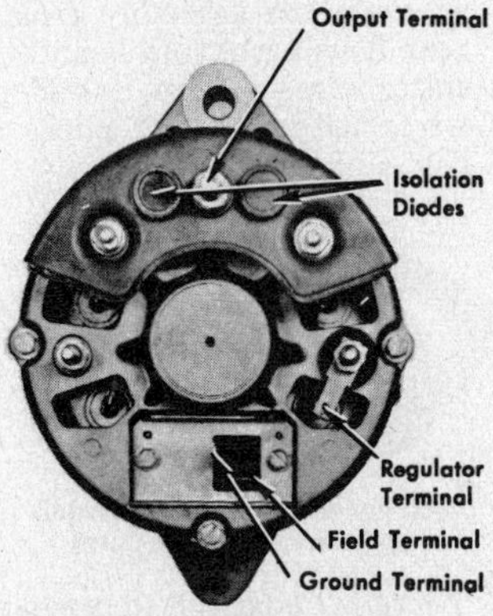
Output Terminal
Isolation Diodes
Regulator Terminal
Field Terminal
Ground Terminal
55 amp alternator—Motorola
(© American Motors Corp)

Troubleshooting

NOTE: see the "Preliminary Charging System Inspection" section before proceeding further.

Fusible Link Test

There are many fuse links in the car, however, the fuse link located in the wiring between the battery terminal of the horn relay to the main wire harness is the only one that concerns the charging system. This link protects the entire wiring harness. If it fails, all the electrical systems will fail to function.

Charging System Operation

NOTE: if the current indicator is to give an accurate reading, the battery cables must be of the same gauge and length as the original equipment.

1. With the engine running and all electrical systems off, place a current indicator over the positive battery cable.
2. If a charge of about 5 amps is recorded, the charging system is working. If a draw of about 5 amps is recorded, the system is not working. The needle moves toward the battery when a charge condition is indicated, and away from the battery when a draw condition is indicated. If a draw is indicated, continue to the next testing procedure. If an overcharge of 10-15 amps is indicated, check for a faulty regulator, or a bad ground at the regulator or the alternator.

Testing the Ignition Switch to Regulator Circuit

1. Disconnect the regulator wires from the regulator.
2. Turn on the key. Using a test light or voltmeter, check for current between the voltage supply wire and ground. This wire is usually orange and has another wire connected to it, usually blue or orange with a tracer.
3. If current is present, this part of the system is OK. If no voltage is present, check for broken or shorted wiring, a bad indicator bulb, a bad fuse in the fuse panel, or a bad connection at the ignition switch or on the battery side of the starter relay.

Isolation Test

This test determines whether the regulator or the alternator is faulty, after the rest of the circuit is found to be in good working order.

1. Disconnect the regulator wiring harness from the regulator.
2. Connect a jumper wire from the voltage supply wire from the battery, orange, to the field wire for the alternator, green.
3. Connect a voltmeter to the battery. The positive voltmeter lead goes to the positive terminal and the negative lead to the negative terminal. Record the reading on the voltmeter.
4. Turn off all of the electrical systems and start the engine. Do not race the engine.
5. Gradually increase engine speed

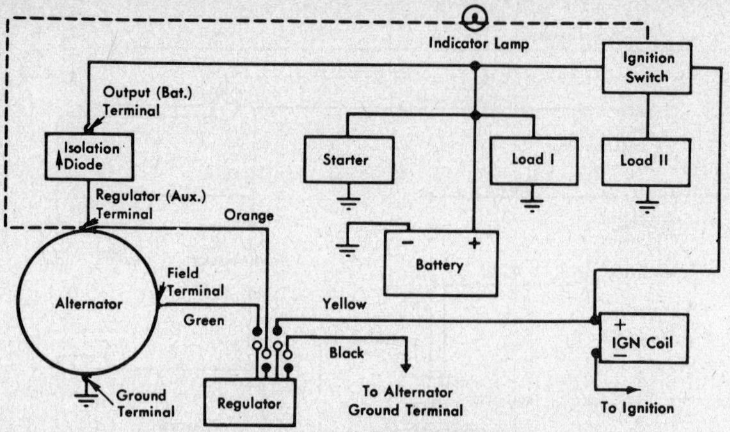
Indicator Lamp
Ignition Switch
Output (Bat.) Terminal
Isolation Diode
Starter
Load I
Load II
Regulator (Aux.) Terminal
Orange
Battery
Field Terminal
Alternator
Yellow
Green
IGN Coil
Black
Ground Terminal
Regulator
To Alternator Ground Terminal
To Ignition

Motorola circuit diagram—1970 American Motors illustrated
(© American Motors Corp)

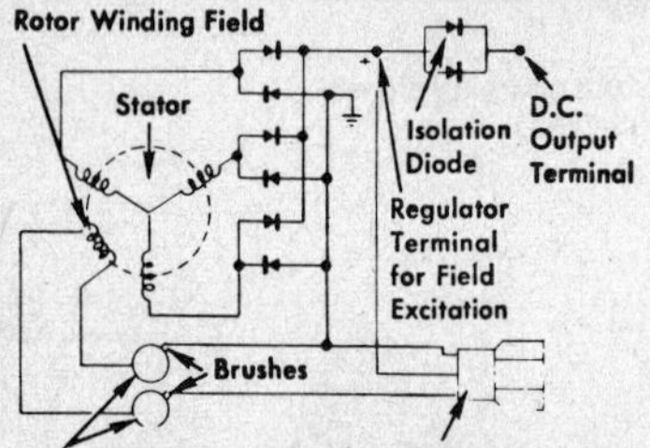
Rotor Winding Field
Stator
Isolation Diode
D.C. Output Terminal
Regulator Terminal for Field Excitation
Brushes
Rotor Slip Rings
Regulator Connector

Alternator circuit—40 and 55 amp models
(© American Motors Corp)

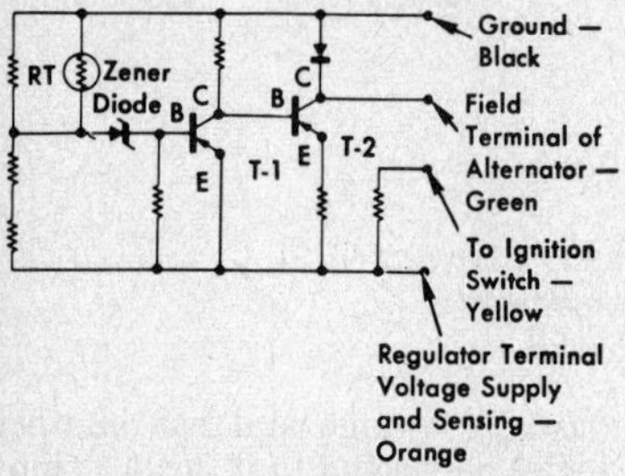
RT
Zener Diode
B
C
E
T-1
T-2
Ground — Black
Field Terminal of Alternator — Green
To Ignition Switch — Yellow
Regulator Terminal Voltage Supply and Sensing — Orange

Voltage regulator circuit. RT is a thermistor that regulates voltage according to temperature
(© American Motors Corp)

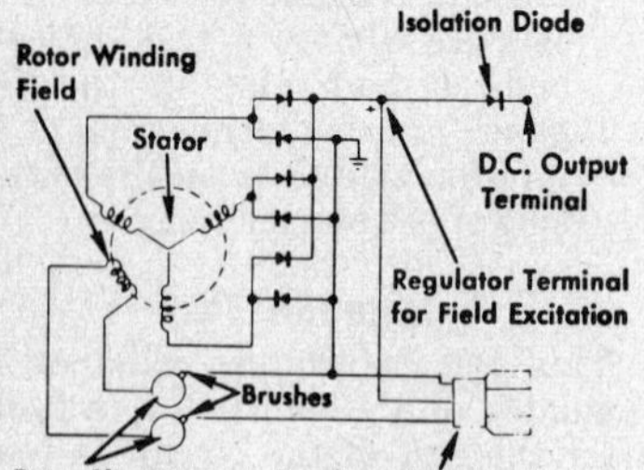
Isolation Diode
Rotor Winding Field
Stator
D.C. Output Terminal
Regulator Terminal for Field Excitation
Brushes
Rotor Slip Rings
Regulator Connector

Alternator circuit—35 amp models
(© American Motors Corp)

to 1500-2000 rpm. The voltmeter reading should increase above the previously recorded battery voltage reading by at least one to two volts. If there is no increase, the alternator is not working correctly. If there is an increase the voltage regulator needs to be replaced.

Field Current Draw Test

1. With battery disconnected, disconnect the wires from the alternator output terminal and the alternator field terminal.
2. With a field rheostat in the open position, connect its leads to the disconnected alternator output wire and to the positive lead of the test ammeter.
3. Connect the negative ammeter lead to the alternator field terminal.
4. Connect the positive voltmeter lead to the alternator field terminal.
5. Connect the negative voltmeter lead to the alternator ground terminal.
6. Reconnect the battery.
7. Start and run the engine at fast idle.
8. Adjust field rheostat to closed position, then note the voltmeter and ammeter readings.
9. Adjust field rheostat control to the open position.
10. Compare the readings obtained in Step 8 with manufacturers' specifications.
11. If readings are zero, there is an indication of trouble in the field coil, or the connections between field coil and slip ring.
12. If readings are low, there is probable trouble in the slip rings or brushes.
13. If readings are high, the field coil is probably shorted.
14. If readings are normal, on an alternator which failed to produce its rated output, the probable cause lies in the stator or diodes. Replace the alternator in this case.

Alternator Disassembly

1. Remove the two self-tapping screws and the cover. Pull the brush assembly straight up to clear the locating pins, then lift out the brush assembly.
2. Remove the two locknuts and remove the isolation diode assembly from the rear housing.
3. Scribe a matchmark across the front housing, stator, and rear housing. Remove the four thru-bolts and nuts, then carefully separate the rear housing and strator from the front housing using two screwdrivers in the slots provided.

Caution Do not insert screwdrivers deeper than 1/16 in., to avoid damaging stator winding.

4. Remove the four locknuts and insulating washers that hold the stator and diode assembly, then separate the assembly from the rear housing. Avoid bending the stator wires—do not unsolder the wires without using pliers as a heat sink.

Separating Motorola alternator housing
(© American Motors Corp)

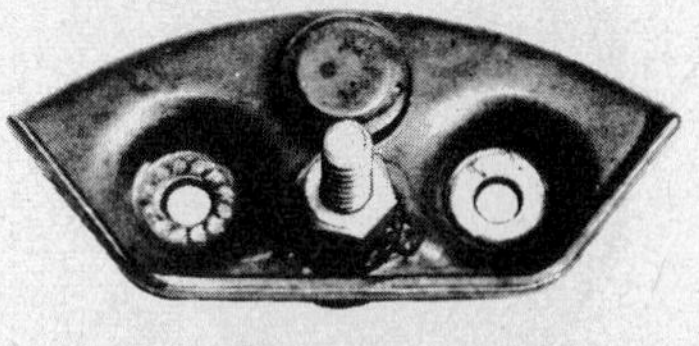

Isolation diode—35 amp models
(© American Motors Corp)

5. There is no reason to remove the rotor from the front housing unless there is a defect in the field coil or front bearing. Front and rear bearings are lubricated for life and sealed and, as a rule, do not go bad unless the drive belt has been adjusted with too much tension. If the rotor must be removed, use a puller to remove the front drive pulley, then unseat the split-ring washer using long-nose pliers through the front housing to compress the washer while pulling on the rotor. Tap the rotor shaft lightly to remove the rotor and front bearing, then reach in and remove the split-ring washer. Bearings must be removed using a puller and new bearings must be pressed into place.

Bench Tests

Isolation Diode Circuit Test

Excessive leakage through the isolation diode will discharge the battery. The rate of discharge depends upon the degree of leakage. Normal and tolerable leakage is less than .001 amperes.

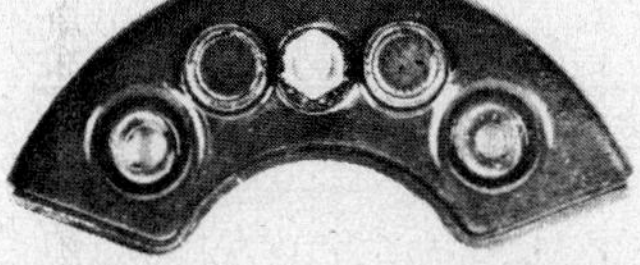

Isolation diodes—55 amp models
(© American Motors Corp)

1. To check isolation diode leakage, connect the regulator to the battery. Do not operate the alternator.
2. Measure the voltage from auxiliary terminal F to ground terminal G. The voltage appearing at the auxiliary terminal should not exceed 0.1 volt. Voltage greater than this indicates leakage through the isolation diode. Check the isolation diode with a commercial diode tester, or with a 12-volt DC test lamp.

Rotor Open Circuit Test

An ohmmeter may be used to check continuity of the rotor. Connect ohmmeter probes to field terminal and ground terminal (test points B and G). Resistance should be about 6 ohms. If resistance is high, field coil is open.

Isolation Diode Test

If a commercial diode tester is not available, use a 12-volt DC test lamp only, otherwise diodes can be damaged.

1. Connect the test lamp to output terminal and auxiliary terminal. Then reverse the test probes. Test lamp should light in one direction only. If test light lights in both directions, the isolation diode is shorted. If lamp won't light in either direction, the diode is open.

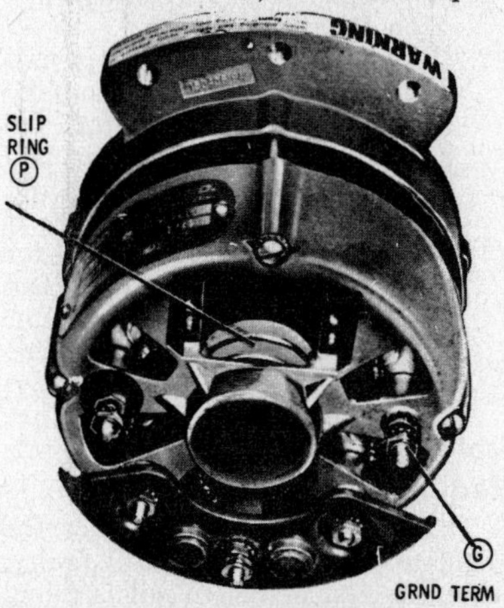
WARNING
SLIP RING
P
G
GRND TERM

Rotor leakage test points

Rotor Leakage Test

This is a check of the field coil for leakage or shorts to rotor poles. An ohmmeter or test lamp (12V or 120V) may be used.

1. Remove the brush assembly to gain access to rotor slip rings.
2. Connect ohmmeter or test lamp probes to one of the slip rings and the ground terminal, points G and P.

Ohmmeter resistance should be infinite or test lamp should not light. If condition is contrary, leakage or a short exists between field coil and rotor.

Repeat test after rotor has been removed from the alternator to pinpoint findings.

Out-of-Circuit Stator Leak Test

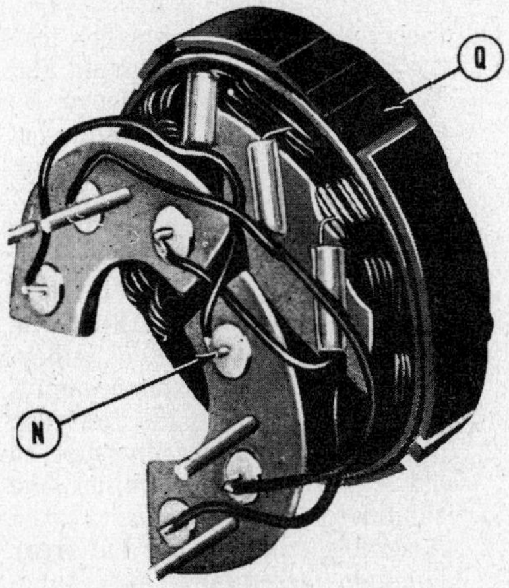
Q
N

Stator leakage test points

Disassemble alternator and remove the rectifier-diode plates and stator as an assembly.

An ohmmeter or 12-volt DC test lamp may be used.

1. Connect ohmmeter or test lamp probes to one of the rectifier diode terminals and to the stator test points N and Q.
   Resistance reading should be infinite (or the test light should not light). If result is contrary, high leakage or a short exists between stator winding and stator. In either case, stator should be replaced.

Stator Coil Leak and Continuity Test

This check is for shorts or leakage between stator coil windings. The 30 and 40 amp. alternators use a Wye-Type winding. 45 ampere models use a Delta type winding.

Wye Type (30 and 40 Amp. Models)

1. Separate winding ends. An ohmmeter or 12-volt DC test lamp may be used.
2. Connect one lead of the ohmmeter or test lamp to point 1. Connect the other test lead to point 2 and then to point 3.

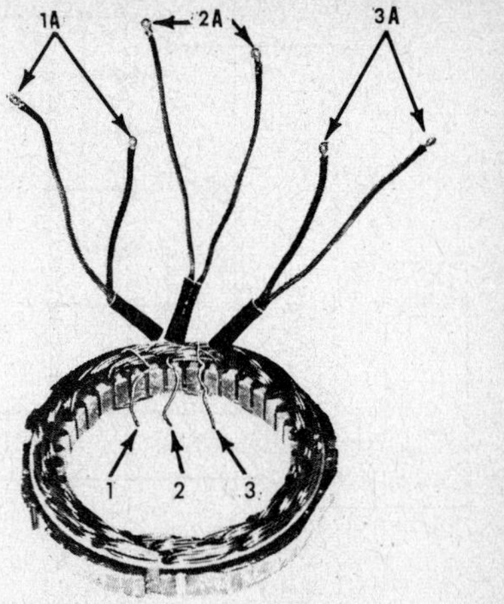
1A
2A
3A
1
2
3

Stator coil test points (Wye type)

   Ohmmeter reading should be infinite or the test lamp should not light.
3. Connect test leads to points 2 and 3. Ohmmeter reading should be infinite, or the test lamp should not light.

In test 2 or test 3, if the test results are contrary, excess leakage or a short exists between stator windings; replace the stator.

4. Check continuity by measuring the resistance of each winding in the stator with an ohmmeter, between test points, 1 to 1A, 2 to 2A and 3 to 3A.
   Resistance should be very low (about 0.1 ohm).

Never replace stator until all other components have been checked and proven satisfactory.

Delta Type (45 Amp. Models)

1. Separate stator winding ends. An ohmmeter or 12-volt DC test lamp may be used.
2. Connect one lead of the ohmmeter or test lamp to point 4. Connect the other test lead to point 5 and then to point 6. Ohmmeter reading should be infinite or the test lamp should not light.
3. Connect test leads to test points 5 and 6. Ohmmeter reading should be infinite, or the test lamp should not light.

In test 2 or test 3, if the test results are contrary, excess leakage or a short exists between stator windings; replace the stator.

4. Check continuity by measuring the resistance of each winding in the stator with an ohmmeter placed between test points 4 to 4A, 5 to 5A and 6 to 6A.
   Resistance should be very low (about 0.1 ohm).

Never replace stator until all other components have been checked and proven satisfactory.

Out-of-Circuit Rectifier Diode Test

If a commercial diode tester is not available, check the diodes with a 12-volt DC test lamp only.

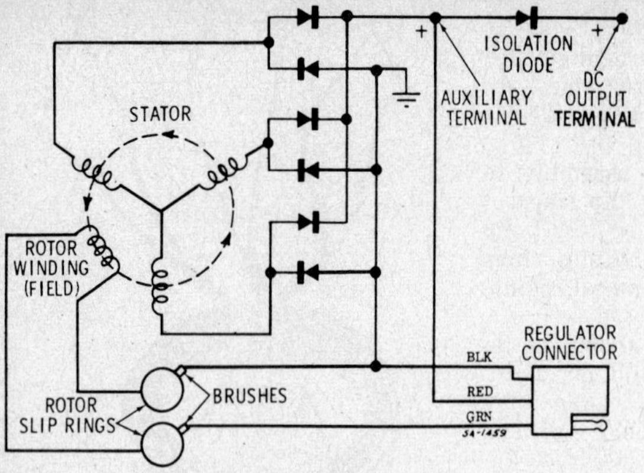
ISOLATION
DIODE
AUXILIARY
TERMINAL
DC
OUTPUT
TERMINAL
STATOR
ROTOR
WINDING
(FIELD)
REGULATOR
CONNECTOR
BLK
RED
GRN
BRUSHES
ROTOR
SLIP RINGS

Wye-type circuit

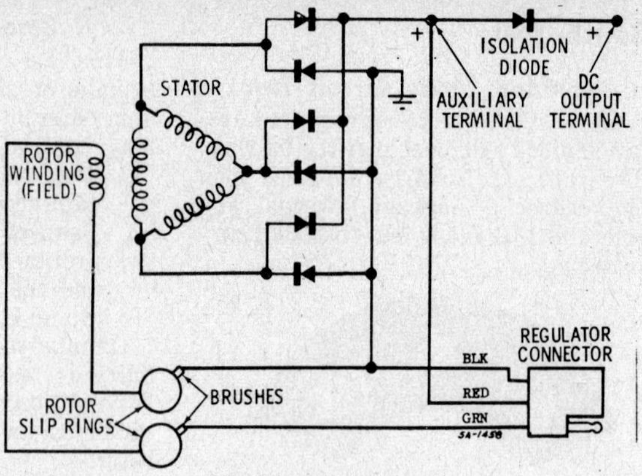
ISOLATION
DIODE
AUXILIARY
TERMINAL
DC
OUTPUT
TERMINAL
STATOR
ROTOR
WINDING
(FIELD)
REGULATOR
CONNECTOR
BLK
RED
GRN
BRUSHES
ROTOR
SLIP RINGS

Delta type circuit

Caution When unsoldering the stator wires from the rectifier diode assembly, provide a heat sink to the diode terminal with a pair of longnosed pliers.

1. Connect test lamp probes to diode terminal and diode plate stud, then reverse test lamp probes. The test light should light in one direction but not in the other.

   If the test lamp lights in both directions, the diode is shorted. If test lamp does not light in either direction, the diode is open.

   Test the remaining diodes of the assembly in the same manner. Replace entire assembly if one of the diodes is found to be bad.

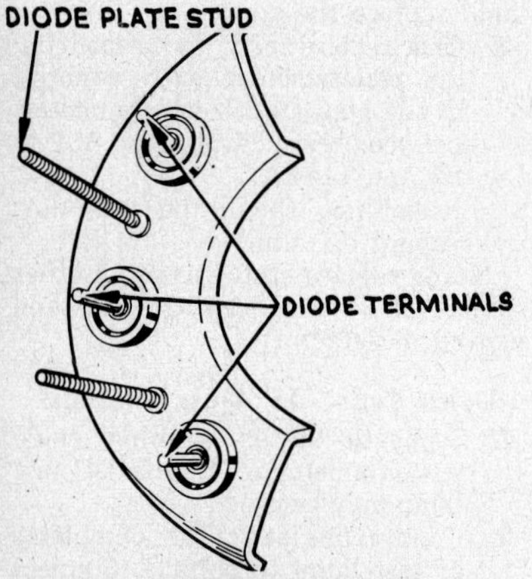
DIODE PLATE STUD
DIODE TERMINALS

Rectifier diode test points (positive or negative)

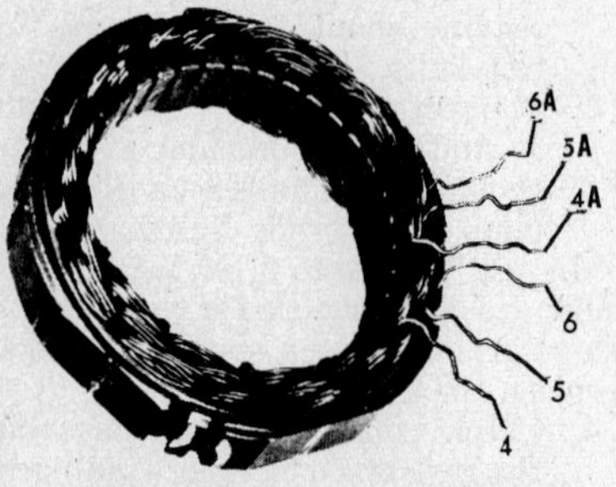
6A
5A
4A
6
5
4

Stator coil test points (delta type)

Alternator Assembly

1. Clean the bearing and the inside of the bearing hub in the front housing, then gently seat the bearing using a socket of appropriate size and a small hammer.
2. Insert the split-ring washer into the hub of the front housing and seat the washer in its groove. Be extremely careful doing this, because the bearing seal is easily damaged.
3. The front bearing now must be seated against the shoulder on the rotor shaft. Install the fan and pulley spacer, then the Woodruff key, fan and pulley. Using a 7/16 in. socket or equivalent tool to fit inside the rear bearing race, apply pressure to drive the bearing against the shoulder of the rotor shaft.
4. Assemble the front and rear housing assemblies by hand, making certain that the rear bearing is properly seated in the rear housing hub and that the diode wires are not touching the rotor at any point.
5. Align the matchmarks made during disassembly, then spin the rotor to make sure sufficient clearance exists between it and the diode wires. Install the through bolts and tighten them evenly, using only a hand wrench. Continue assembly in reverse of disassembly.

The Prestolite System

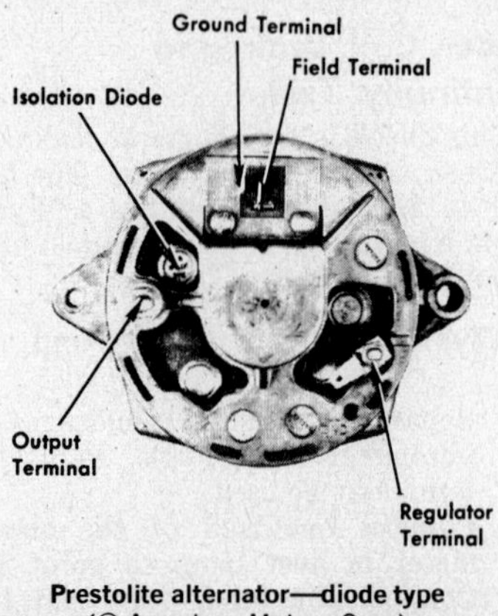
Ground Terminal
Field Terminal
Isolation Diode
Output
Terminal
Regulator
Terminal

Prestolite alternator—diode type
(© American Motors Corp)

The Prestolite AC generator regulator with a circuit breaker (C. B. type) incorporates a polarity sensing feature for the purpose of isolating generator output from battery potential when the system is out of operation. This feature prevents damage to the components of the charging system in the event of battery polarity reversal.

Late model Prestolite alternators incorporate an *isolation diode,* mounted as a component part of the internal positive heat sink assembly. Such alternators are almost identical to late model Motorola units in operation. Test procedures for the Motorola alternator also apply to the diode-equipped Prestolite.

Troubleshooting

NOTE: see the "Preliminary Charging System Inspection" section before proceeding further.

Fusible Link Test

See the Motorola system section for the fuse link test.

Charging System Operation

See the Motorola system section for the "Charging System Operation" tests.

Testing the Ignition Switch-to-Regulator Circuit

1. Disconnect the regulator wires from the regulator.
2. Turn on the key. Using a test light or voltmeter, check for current between the I terminal and ground and the L terminal ground. If voltage is present, this part of the system is OK. If no voltage is present, check for broken or shorted wires, a bad indicator bulb, a bad ammeter (if so equipped), or bad connections.

Isolation Test—2 Unit Regulator

This test determines whether the regulator or the alternator is faulty, after the rest of the circuit is found to be in good working order.

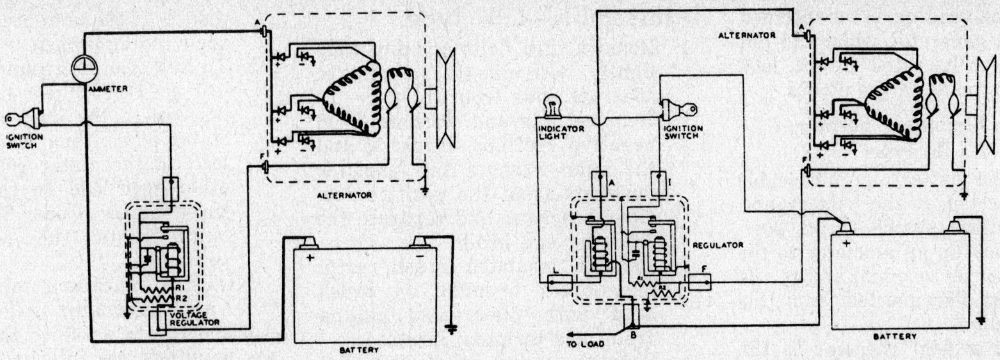
AMMETER
IGNITION SWITCH
ALTERNATOR
VOLTAGE REGULATOR
BATTERY
INDICATOR LIGHT
IGNITION SWITCH
REGULATOR
TO LOAD

Single and two unit Prestolite C.B. circuits

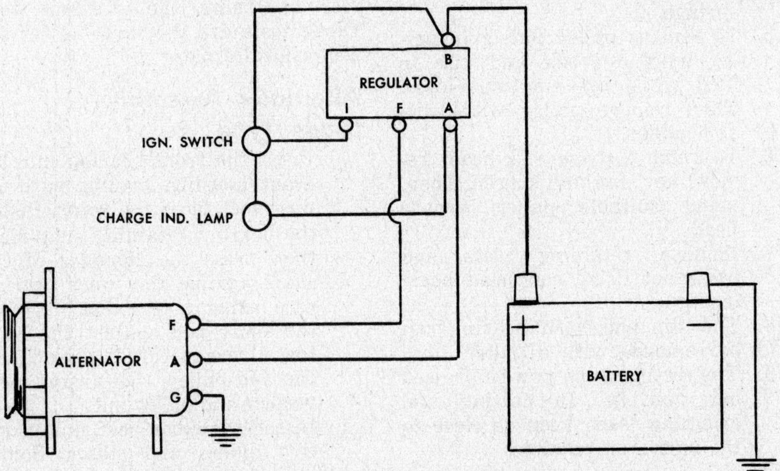
REGULATOR
B
I
F
A
IGN. SWITCH
CHARGE IND. LAMP
ALTERNATOR
G
BATTERY

Typical wiring circuit diagram, Prestolite C.B. alternator system

1. Disconnect the regulator wiring harness from the regulator.
2. Connect a jumper wire from the A wire to the F wire.
3. Connect a voltmeter to the battery. The positive voltmeter lead goes to the positive terminal and the negative lead to the negative terminal. Record the reading.
4. Turn off all of the electrical system and start the engine. Do not race the engine.
5. Gradually increase engine speed to 1500-2000 rpm. The voltmeter reading should increase by at least one to two volts. If there is no increase, the alternator is not working correctly. If there is an increase, the voltage regulator needs to be replaced.

Isolation Test—Single Unit Regulator

1. Disconnect the field wire from the alternator. Do not allow the wire to touch ground.
2. Connect a jumper wire from the alternator A terminal to the alternator F terminal.
3. Connect a voltmeter to the battery. The positive voltmeter lead goes to the positive terminal and the negative lead goes to the negative terminal. Record the reading on the voltmeter.
4. Turn off all of the electrical systems and start the engine. Do not race the engine.
5. Gradually increase engine speed to 1500-2000 rpm. The voltmeter reading should increase above the previously recorded battery voltage reading by at least one to two volts. If there is no increase, the alternator is not working correctly. If there is an increase, the voltage regulator needs to be replaced.

Field Current Draw Test—C. B. Type

1. Disconnect the generator F terminal and insulate the lead to prevent accidental grounding.
2. Connect an ammeter and a field rheostat in series, between the generator F terminal and the generator A terminal in the following manner:
   A. With a field rheostat set in the open position, connect one of its leads to the generator A terminal and the other lead to the test ammeter.
   B. Connect the other test ammeter lead to the generator F terminal.
3. Hook up a voltmeter by connecting one voltmeter lead to the generator F terminal and the other lead to the generator frame.
4. Reconnect the battery ground cable.
5. Turn ignition switch on.

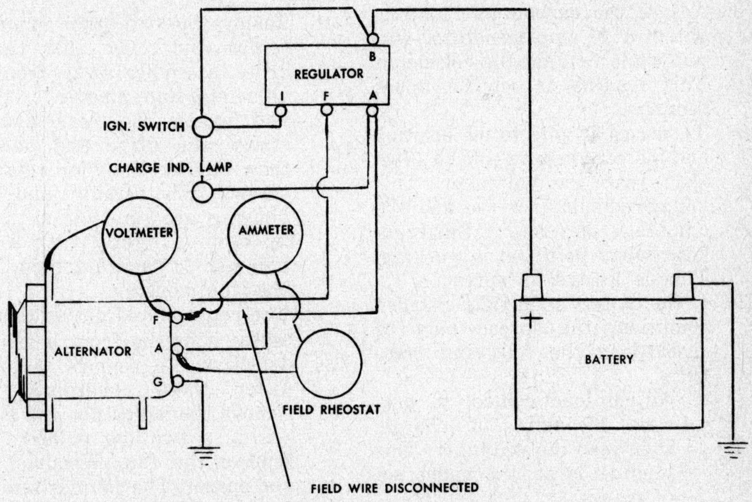
REGULATOR
B
I
F
A
IGN. SWITCH
CHARGE IND. LAMP
VOLTMETER
AMMETER
ALTERNATOR
G
FIELD RHEOSTAT
BATTERY
FIELD WIRE DISCONNECTED

Plan to make field current draw test—C.B. type

6. Adjust the field rheostat to obtain recommended voltage.
7. Now, read the ammeter. This represents the rotor field current draw.
8. Adjust field rheostat to open position, and turn ignition switch off.
9. Compare the reading with manufacturers' specifications.
   A. If the reading is too low, it indicates trouble, probably slip rings or brushes.
   B. If the reading is too high, it indicates a short in the field winding.

C. If the reading is as specified on a generator which did not deliver its rated output, look for trouble in the diodes.

Voltage Regulator Setting—C. B. Type

1. With the battery ground cable disconnected at the battery and the ignition switch in off position, hook up an ammeter to the generator A terminal and to the lead just disconnected from this A terminal.
2. Connect a field rheostat to the generator F terminal and to the lead just disconnected from this F terminal. Adjust rheostat to open position.
3. Connect a voltmeter to the regulator B terminal and a good ground on the frame of the regulator.
4. Connect the battery ground cable.
5. Hook up a carbon pile (load control turned to the off position) between the battery posts.
6. Start the engine and while operating at 850 rpm, adjust the field rheostat to obtain a 10 amp. charge. Be careful not to exceed factory voltage recommendation. Run engine long enough to develop normal regulator operating temperature.
7. Open, then fully close the field rheostat to cycle the system.
8. Adjust the carbon pile load to obtain a 10 amp. generator output while reading the voltmeter. This reading is on the upper contacts.
9. Turn carbon pile to off position and increase engine rpm to 1750, then read the voltmeter. This voltage should increase and the amperage decrease if the regulator lower point set is working. This is known as spread.
10. If the battery is in fully charged condition, the spread may be checked in the following manner.
    A. Adjust load control to produce 15 amps. of charge, then read the voltmeter. This reading is on the upper set of points.
    B. Adjust load control to off position, wait about one-half minute, then read the voltmeter. This reading is on the lower set of points. The difference between the two readings is spread.
    C. Spread should be 0.2 to 0.5 volts higher when operating on lower grounding contact. Operation on lower contacts must not exceed 14.7 volts. If necessary, adjust regulator so as not to exceed 14.7 volts.
11. If regulator does not operate within specifications, renew the regulator.

Disassembly—C.B. Type

1. Remove thru bolts and tap ends lightly with plastic hammer to separate ends from rotor.
2. Remove nuts and washers from negative rectifier brackets, and the nuts, washers and insulator bushings from the positive rectifier brackets, and separate the slip ring end head.
3. Remove insulated brush, gripping brass terminal on brush head with pliers and pulling from field terminal insulator.
4. Remove screw that attaches ground brush. Do not lose brush springs.
5. To remove pulley nut, grip pulley with fan belt and vise to hold while breaking nut loose. Then remove pulley with suitable puller.
6. To remove drive end head, remove key, fan and spacer. Then, using suitable puller remove head.
7. Remove retaining plate and press out drive end head bearing.
8. The slip end head bearing can be removed with a puller.
9. The rectifiers can now be pressed out and in. In cutting and crimping leads keep as close to the sleeve as possible.

Alternator Disassembly—Diode Type

1. Remove the two brush mounting screws and cover, then tip the brush assembly away from the alternator and remove.
2. Matchmark the rear housing, stator and drive end housing, then remove the four retaining screws. The stator and rear housing are removed as a unit by tapping lightly with a fiber hammer to separate them from the front housing.
3. The rotor should not be removed unless it or the front bearing is defective. To remove the rotor under these conditions, first remove the pulley nut and pulley (using a two-jaw puller), then remove the fan, Woodruff key and spacer. The rotor is removed from the front housing using a three-jaw puller. (Such a puller is made by Snap-On Tool Corp. — part No. CG 253).
4. The front bearing is easily removed, after taking out the retaining ring, by pressing it out in a large vise using sockets to support the housing from the rear.

Stator Coil Test—Diode Type

1. Using a No. 57 bulb, connected in series with a 12-volt battery, as a test light, touch one test lead to the connection of the three stator windings and the other test lead to each stator lead that is connected to the diodes. If the bulb does not light, the winding is open.
2. To test for a grounded stator, use a 110-volt test lamp. First disconnect the diodes from the stator leads, then touch one test lead to the stator core and the other test lead to each of the three stator leads. If the test lamp lights, the winding is grounded.

NOTE: if all other components are O.K. and alternator still does not work, it can be assumed that the stator windings are internally shorted. This type of short is impossible to detect by using the previous test. Diode tests are the same as for the Motorola alternator.

Alternator Assembly—Diode Type

1. Press the front bearing into the front housing, making sure the dust seal faces the rotor. Install the bearing retaining snap-ring, then press the shoulder of the shaft against the inner bearing race using a tool that fits over the shaft and against the race. Install the spacer, Woodruff key, fan and pulley, then install lockwasher and pulley nut.
2. Install the diode heat sink, negative diodes and stator. Solder any stator to diode connections that were unsoldered, using pliers as a heat sink to prevent overheating.
3. Install the rotor and front drive housing to stator and rear housing, aligning matchmarks made during disassembly. Install the four retaining screws, then the brush holder assembly and retaining screws.
4. Make sure the stator leads and brush holder assembly clear the rotor and that the rotor can be spun by hand without binding.

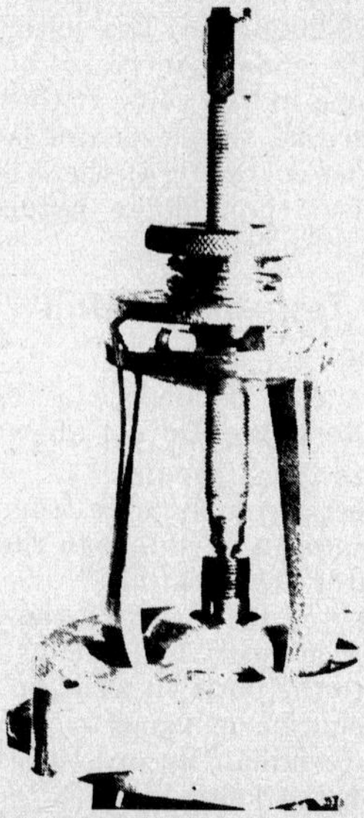

Removing rotor from front end housing —Prestolite
(© American Motors Corp)

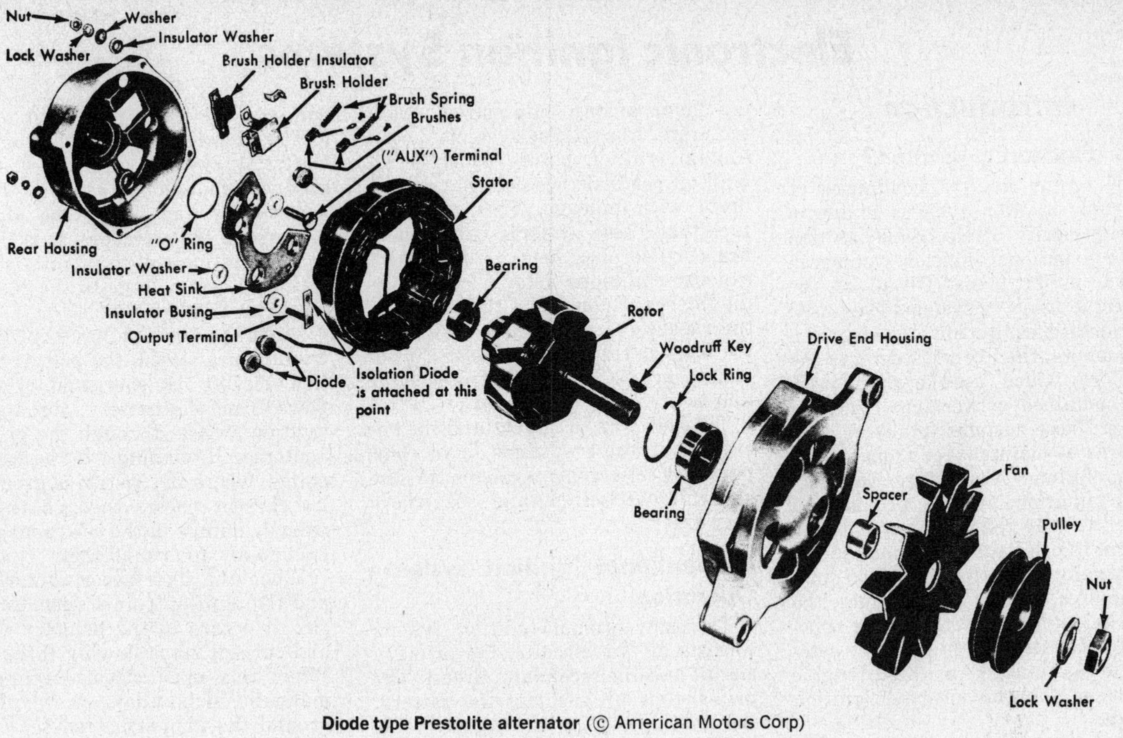
Nut
Washer
Insulator Washer
Lock Washer
Brush Holder Insulator
Brush Holder
Brush Spring
Brushes
("AUX") Terminal
Stator
Rear Housing
"O" Ring
Insulator Washer
Heat Sink
Insulator Busing
Output Terminal
Diode
Isolation Diode is attached at this point
Bearing
Rotor
Woodruff Key
Lock Ring
Drive End Housing
Bearing
Spacer
Fan
Pulley
Nut
Lock Washer

Diode type Prestolite alternator (© American Motors Corp)

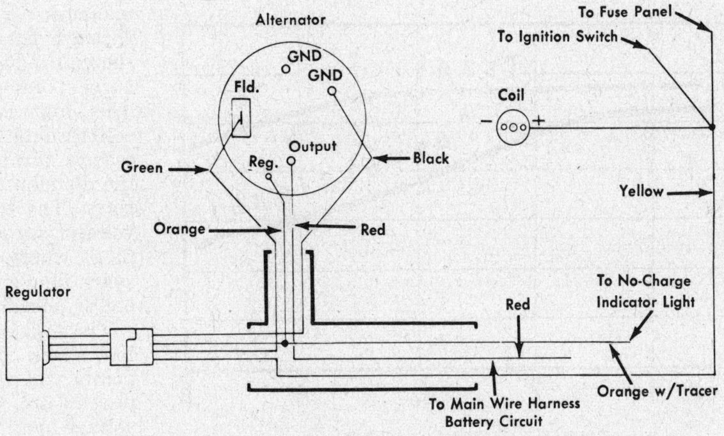
Alternator
GND
GND
Fld.
Output
Reg.
Green
Black
Orange
Red
Coil
To Fuse Panel
To Ignition Switch
Yellow
Regulator
Red
To No-Charge Indicator Light
Orange w/Tracer
To Main Wire Harness Battery Circuit

Prestolite wiring diagram

Electronic Ignition Systems

Introduction

Why Electronic Ignition?

The recent rise to prominence of electronic ignition systems is due to the superiority of electronic ignition over conventional ignition systems in several major areas. Of all of the electronic ignition systems ever used as standard equipment on American automobiles, the Ford system was the only one which used a distributor that contained conventional ignition points. These systems totally remove one area of maintenance from the ignition system. Also, since the electronic ignition system produces a higher voltage than the conventional system, the electronic ignition system can usually fire a fouled spark plug. In the area of high performance, the electronic ignition system is far superior in that its voltage does not deteriorate as quickly at high engine speeds as the conventional ignition system.

As automotive antipollution laws become stricter, the maintenance-free electronic ignition systems are gaining favor among automotive manufacturers. Since these systems do not contain ignition points which wear, ignition performance does not deteriorate with mileage. This, plus the fact that these systems can usually fire a fouled plug, helps to keep down exhaust emissions after a car leaves the factory. Evidence of the manufacturer's acceptance of these systems is the fact that all 1973 Chrysler Corporation cars will have electronic ignition as standard equipment.

The best way to understand the operation of these systems is to compare the electronic systems to the conventional system and see where they differ.

Conventional Ignition System Operation

The conventional ignition system consists of two circuits, the primary circuit and the secondary circuit. The primary circuit includes the battery, the ignition switch, the primary side of the coil, and the ignition points and condenser. The secondary circuit consists of the secondary side of the coil, and the spark plugs and wires.

The 12 volts (v) of the automotive electrical system cannot, by itself, produce enough current to fire a spark plug and ignite the air/fuel mixture in the cylinders. It is the job of the ignition coil to increase the ignition system voltage to the required level (10,000-20,000v).

When the ignition points in the distributor are closed, the primary ignition circuit is energized. Current flows from the battery, through the ignition switch, through the primary (outer) coil windings, to the ignition points, where the system is grounded. As current passes through the primary windings in the coil, a magnetic field builds up around these windings.

When the distributor cam rotates and the ignition points open, an open circuit occurs in the primary circuit and current stops flowing through it. When this open circuit occurs, the magnetic field that was built up around the primary windings in the coil collapses and the magnetic lines of force cut through the secondary (inner) windings in the coil. These magnetic lines of force cutting through the secondary windings in the coil induce a very high electrical current into the secondary circuit. This high-voltage surge leaves the coil through the large coil wire and travels through the center tower in the distributor cap to the distributor rotor. The turning rotor directs the voltage surge to the proper spark-plug, where the voltage jumps the spark plug gap and completes the secondary circuit.

The higher the voltage supplied to the spark plug (up to a certain point), the better the ability of the plug to fire. One way to increase the voltage available to the plugs is to increase the amount of current in the primary circuit of the ignition system. It is very logical that the higher the current in the primary circuit, the higher the voltage in the secondary circuit will be when the primary circuit collapses. However, the more voltage that is used in the primary circuit, the quicker the points will pit and burn as they open. In fact, the points are so sensitive to high current that full battery current (12 v) is only applied to the points during starting. The remainder of the time that the engine is running, the current from the ignition switch to the primary side of the coil passes through resistance wire which limits the amount of current supplied to the ignition points. While the ignition condenser serves to limit the amount of arcing between the points when they open, it cannot handle high current loads. When the ignition points

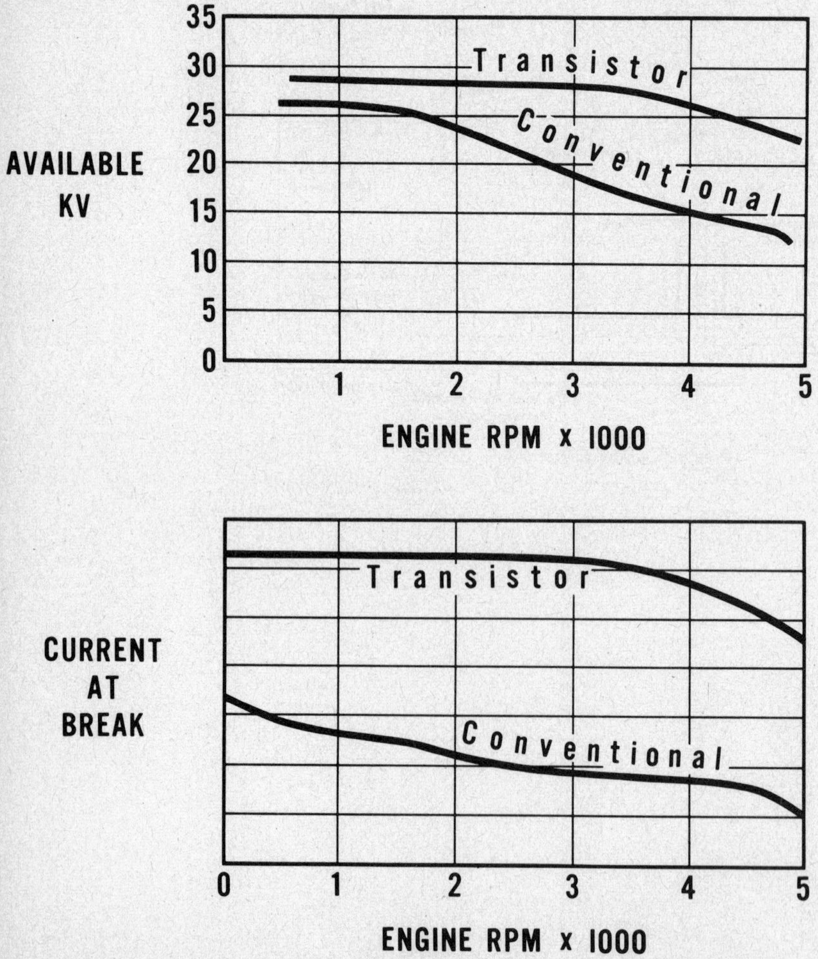
AVAILABLE KV
35
30
25
20
15
10
5
0
1
2
3
4
5
Transistor
Conventional
ENGINE RPM x 1000
CURRENT AT BREAK
Transistor
Conventional
0
1
2
3
4
5
ENGINE RPM x 1000

Comparison of conventional and transistor ignition system coil output and break current (© Ford Motor Co)

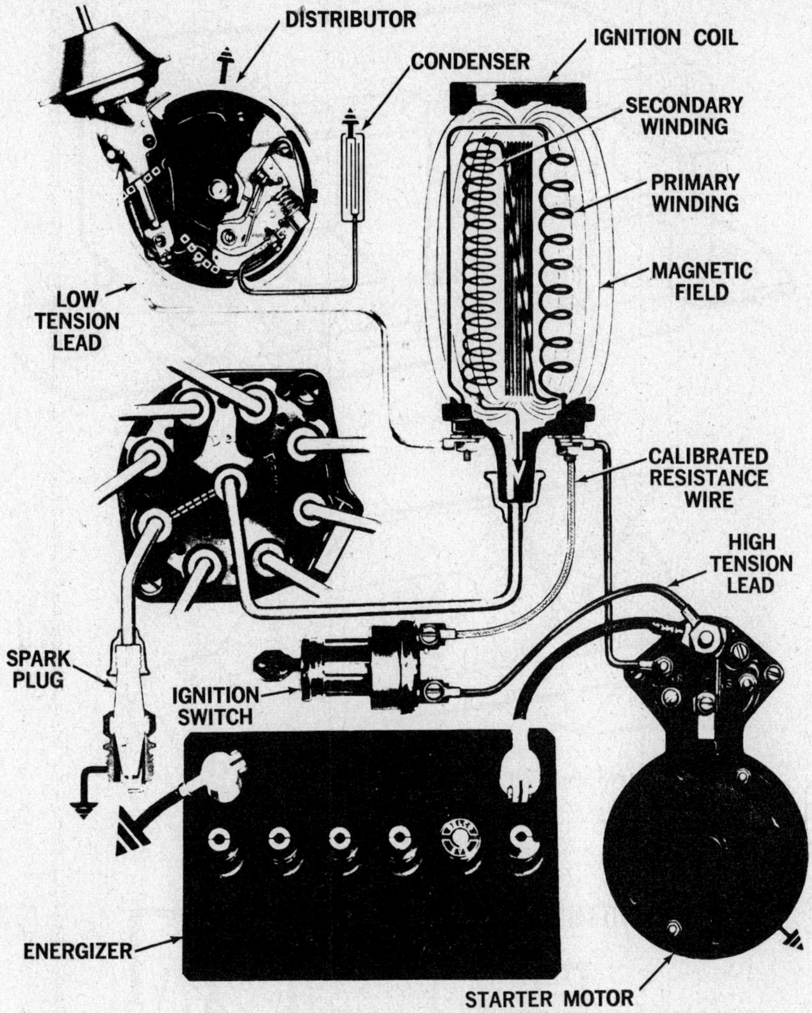
DISTRIBUTOR
IGNITION COIL
CONDENSER
SECONDARY WINDING
PRIMARY WINDING
MAGNETIC FIELD
LOW TENSION LEAD
CALIBRATED RESISTANCE WIRE
HIGH TENSION LEAD
SPARK PLUG
IGNITION SWITCH
ENERGIZER
STARTER MOTOR

Typical conventional ignition system

become pitted or burned, two things happen: it becomes very difficult for current to pass from one contact to the other when the points are closed, and the gap between the open points (which determines how long the magnetic field from the collapsed primary circuit will have to cut into the coil secondary windings) gradually diminishes.

Since the ignition points open and close 16,000 times each minute at 4,000 rpm (8 cylinder, 4 cycle engine), any weak links in the system become very critical.

In the following pages you will find explanations of how American auto manufacturers have designed electronic ignition systems which minimize or eliminate the weak spots in the ignition system.

Ford-Autolite Breaker Point System

This transistorized system uses conventional breaker points, but does not use a condenser. The only external components that serve to distinguish this system from a conventional ignition are an external ballast resistor, a tachometer connecting block, a cold-start relay and an amplifier (transistor switching device).

As was mentioned in the earlier discussion of conventional ignition systems, the major hurdle to increasing primary ignition circuit voltage is that the points burn very easily. This system uses a transistor to bypass that weakness.

The design of the main transistor in this system allows it to conduct current from the wire running into it

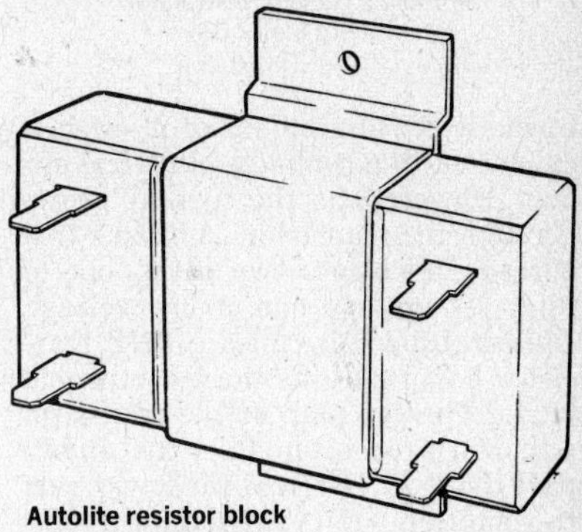

Autolite resistor block
(© Ford Motor Co)

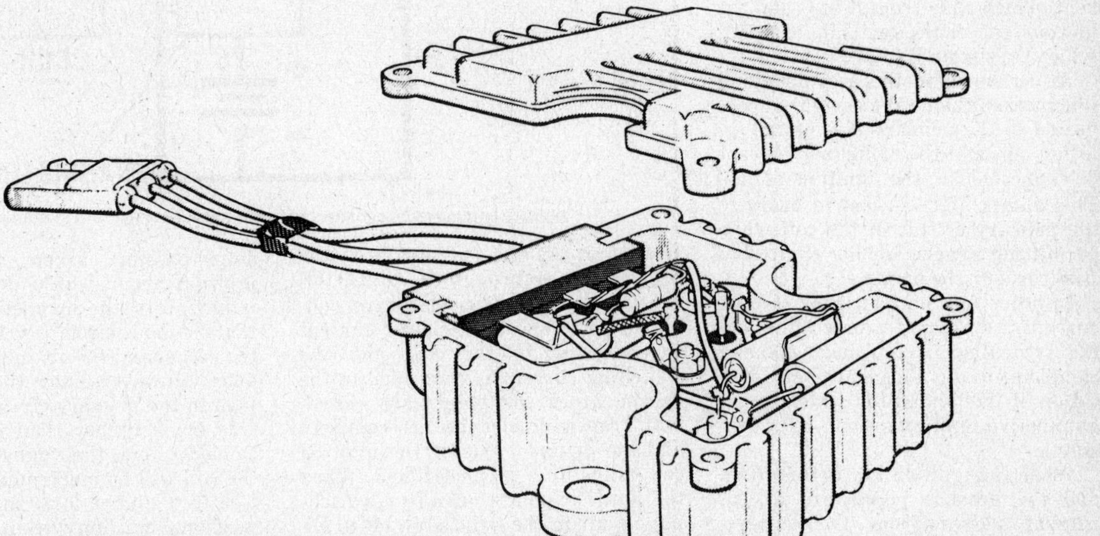

Autolite amplifier assembly (© Ford Motor Co)

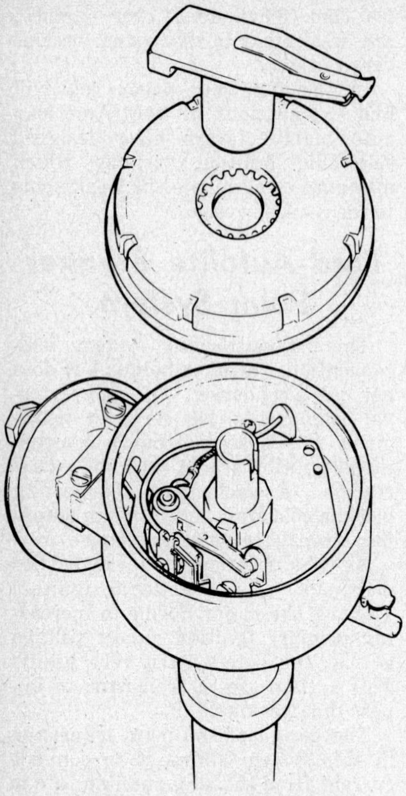

Autolite transistor distributor
(© Ford Motor Co)

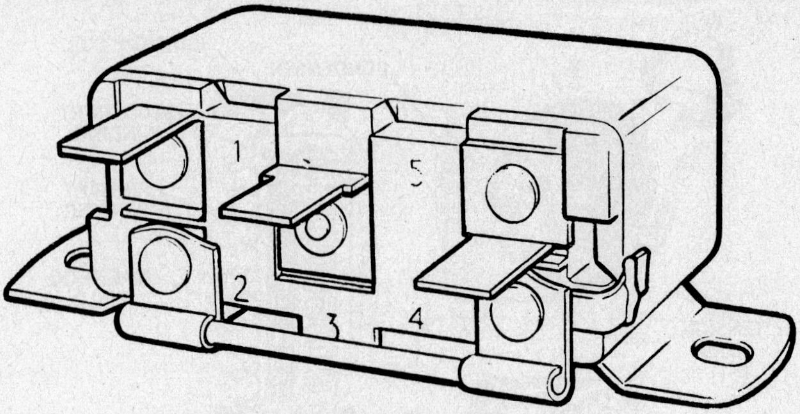
1
5
2
3
4

Autolite cold start relay (© Ford Motor Co)

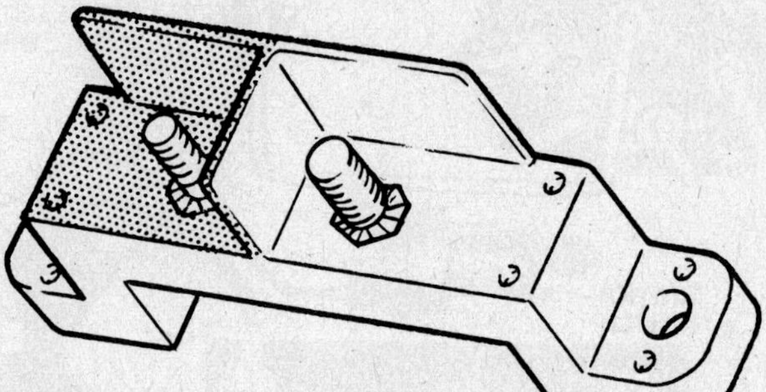

Autolite tach block (© Ford Motor Co)

to the wire running out of it—if it is connected to a complete electrical circuit. However, as the current passes through the transistor, it breaks that current down into two paths, one of high voltage and one of low voltage. This transistor is called a PNP transistor because of it's three component parts. The top part of the transistor is called a collector (C), the middle part the base (B), and the lower part the emitter (E). The two currents that form inside the transistor are the high current one, or power current, which runs from E to C and the low current, or the switching current, which runs from B to E.

As is shown in the accompanying illustration, the power current is connected to the primary side of the ignition coil and the switching current is connected to the ignition points. This allows high current to energize the primary circuit in the coil while permitting a much smaller current to pass through the points.

In order for the transistor to pass current, both the power circuit and the switching circuit must make a complete circuit. This has made adaptation of this transistor system to an automotive ignition system relatively simple.

When the ignition key is turned on and the breaker points are closed, current passes from the battery, through the ignition switch, to the amplifier which contains the PNP

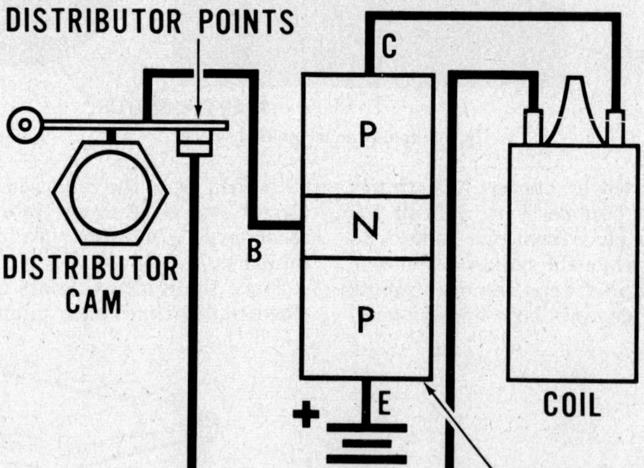
DISTRIBUTOR POINTS
C
P
N
P
B
DISTRIBUTOR CAM
E
+
-
COIL
TRANSISTOR

Primary ignition circuit connected to PNP transistor (© Ford Motor Co)

transistor. As the current from the battery passes through the transistor, the two transistor circuits are connected as follows: the power current is connected to the coil, and the switching current is connected to the points. Since the points are closed, both transistor circuits are complete and the primary side of the ignition coil builds up a magnetic field. When the ignition points open, the switching circuit in the transistor (B to E) opens causing the transistor to stop passing current. When the transistor stops passing current, the primary ignition circuit breaks down, and the induction of the magnetic field from the primary circuit in the coil into the secondary circuit in the coil takes place. However, since the initial voltage in the primary circuit in the coil was much higher than in a conventional system, the voltage buildup in the coil will be much quicker and will rise to a higher level than in a conventional ignition system.

The other components of the system, all of which are contained in the

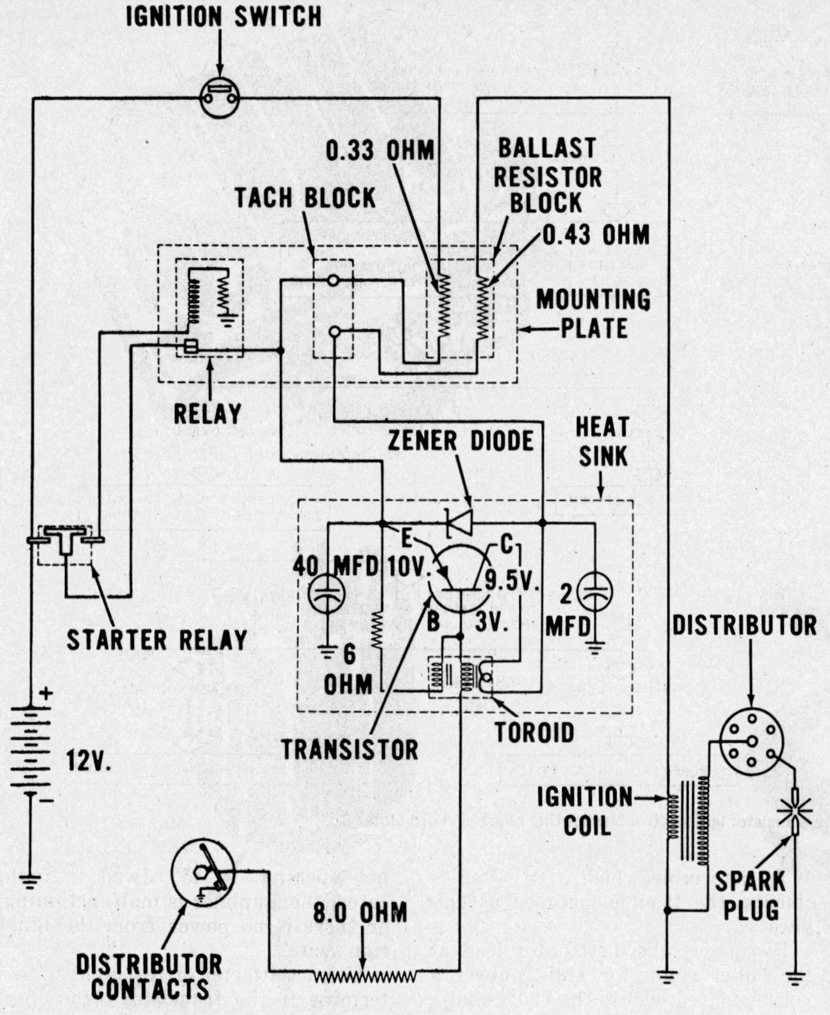
IGNITION SWITCH
0.33 OHM
BALLAST
RESISTOR
BLOCK
TACH BLOCK
0.43 OHM
MOUNTING
PLATE
RELAY
ZENER DIODE
HEAT
SINK
E
C
40 MFD
10V.
9.5V.
2
MFD
B
3V.
6
OHM
STARTER RELAY
DISTRIBUTOR
TOROID
TRANSISTOR
12V.
IGNITION
COIL
SPARK
PLUG
8.0 OHM
DISTRIBUTOR
CONTACTS

Ford-Autolite transistor ignition schematic (© Ford Motor Co)

amplifier housing with the PNP transistor, are a condenser, a zener diode, a toroid, a base-to-emitter resistor, and a collector resistor.

The base resistor is similar to the conventional ignition resistor wire and is located between the distributor and the transistor (heat sink). It provides an 8.0 ohm resistance which is necessary for current limitation and it should not be replaced with any other wire, resistance or otherwise. To do so would result in immediate transistor destruction.

The collector and emitter resistors both are located in a ballast resistor block made of white ceramic for electrical and thermal insulation. Both resistors serve the same purpose —limiting system current and control of voltages within their respective circuits. The two resistors are in series in the collector-emitter circuit, together with the ignition coil, toroid and transistor. The emitter resistor also is in series with the base resistor, the toroid, and the transistor, in the base-emitter circuit. The transistor and emitter resistance therefore are common to both circuits. The combined resistances in each circuit permit a base current of approximately 1.0 amp. and a collector current of approximately 12 amps.

A tach block is included in the circuit for attaching tachometer and dwellmeter leads. In the conventional system, these leads are connected to the distributor primary lead and ground, but in the transistorized circuit, the connection of the leads in this manner would jump the contact gap, contributing to a current buildup in the base circuit and in the collector circuit which would overheat and burn out the transistor. The area surrounding the collector terminal is colored *red* for the meter red lead while the area surrounding the emitter terminal is colored *black* for the meter black lead.

A cold start relay is incorporated into the circuit at the starter relay, interrupting the conventional battery-to-coil lead. The purpose of this is to furnish additional current to the coil primary windings during situations when the starter draw is excessive. The cold start relay contacts normally are closed; only opening during the cranking cycle. However, when the available battery voltage drops below a predetermined value during the cranking cycle, they again close, bypassing the ignition resistor and furnishing full battery current to the system.

The distributor differs from the conventional distributor only in the absence of the condenser and in the highly polished breaker cam. Because one of the big advantages of the transistor ignition is long breaker point life, wear on the rubbing block must be reduced to a minimum. Because the current at the breaker points is so small, the amount of pitting that occurs during normal operation is hardly measurable and point life should be indefinite. The points should be set to .020" gap and Chevron O.H.T. grease used for cam lubrication.

When testing the transistor ignition distributor in a test machine, incorporate a condenser into the primary-to-ground circuit using a jumper wire. This will prevent point pitting or oxidation during testing.

Caution When connecting an in-car tachometer to the Ford System, always shunt the tachometer leads that go to the coil IGN terminal and ignition switch with a 10 in. length of Ford ignition resistor wire, part No. COLF-12250-A, to prevent tachometer damage. The higher current draw of the transistor system can ruin a tach if this precaution is not taken.

Troubleshooting

Ignition problems are caused by a failure in the primary or secondary circuit, or incorrect ignition timing. Isolate the trouble as follows:

1. Remove the coil high tension lead from the distributor cap.
2. Disconnect the brown wire from the starter relay "I" terminal and the red and blue wire from the starter relay "S" terminal.
3. Turn the ignition switch on.
4. While holding the high tension lead approximately ¼ in. from the engine block, crank the engine by using remote starter switch between the starter relay "S" and battery terminals.

If the spark is good, the trouble lies in the secondary (high voltage) circuit. If there is no spark or a weak spark, the trouble is in the primary (low voltage) circuit.

A breakdown or energy loss in the primary circuit can be caused by:

1. Defective primary wiring.
2. Improperly adjusted, contaminated or defective distributor points.
3. Defective amplifier assembly.

The trouble can be isolated by performing a primary circuit test.

A breakdown or energy loss in the secondary circuit can be caused by:

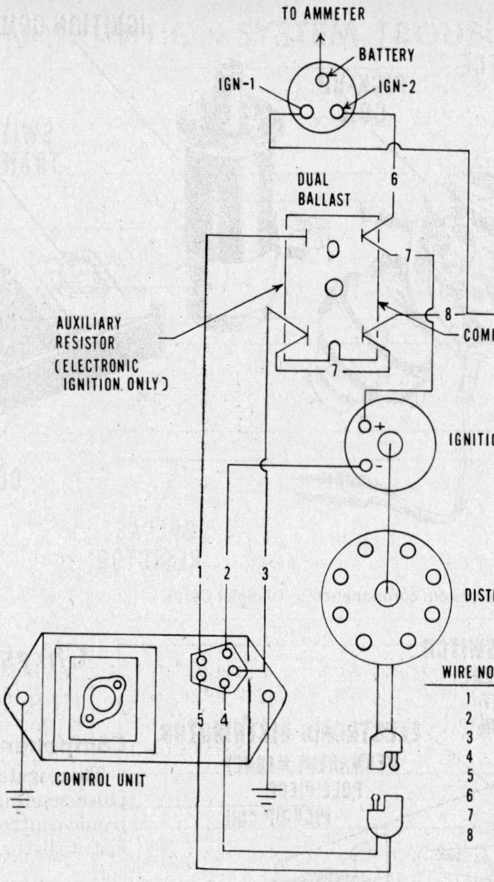
TO AMMETER
BATTERY
IGN-1
IGN-2
DUAL BALLAST
6
7
TO VOLTAGE REGULATOR AND ALTENATOR FIELD
8
COMPENSATING RESISTOR
AUXILIARY RESISTOR (ELECTRONIC IGNITION ONLY)
7
IGNITION COIL
1 2 3
DISTRIBUTOR
5 4
CONTROL UNIT

WIRE NO.	COLOR CODED
1	DARK GREEN w/ RED TRACER
2	BLACK w/YELLOW TRACER
3	DARK BLUE w/ YELLOW TRACER
4	GREY w/ WHITE TRACER
5	BROWN w/ WHITE TRACER
6	BROWN
7	BLACK
8	DARK BLUE

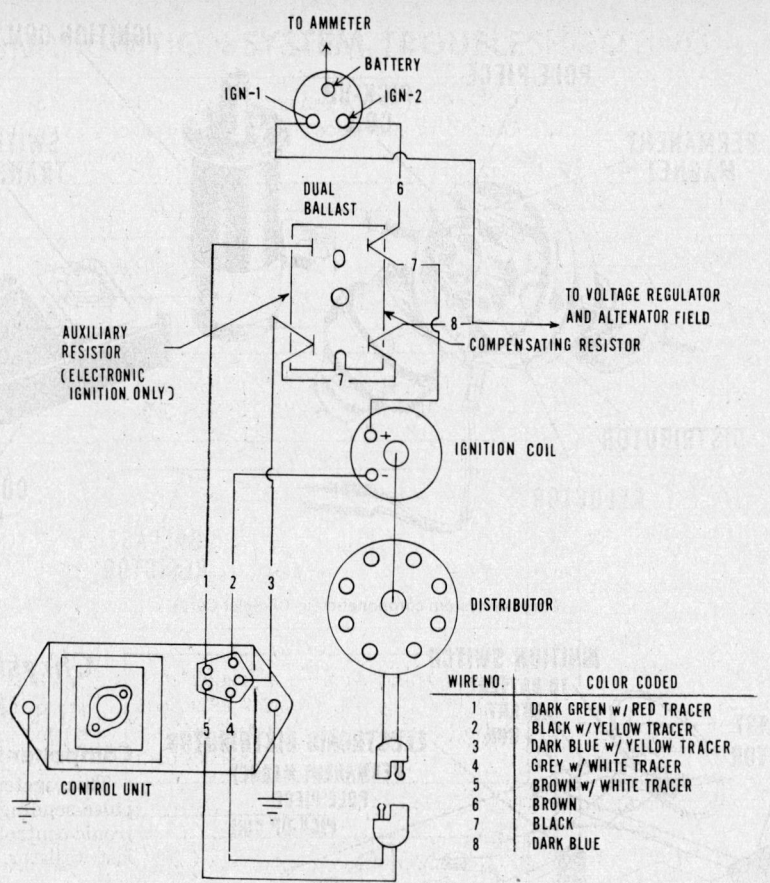

Chrysler system schematic

ondary side of the coil, the coil wire to the distributor, the rotor, the spark plug wires, and the spark plugs.

The magnetic pulse distributor is also connected to the control unit. As the distributor shaft rotates, the distributor reluctor turns past the pick-up unit. As the reluctor turns past the pick-up unit, each of the eight teeth on the reluctor pass near the pick-up unit once during each distributor revolution (two crankshaft revolutions since the distributor runs at one-half crankshaft speed). As the reluctor teeth move close to the pick-up unit, the magnetic rotating reluctor induces voltage into the magnetic pick-up unit. This voltage pulse is sent to the ignition control unit from the magnetic pick-up unit. When the pulse enters the control unit, it signals the control unit to interrupt the ignition primary circuit. This causes the primary circuit to collapse and begins the induction of the magnetic lines of force from the primary side of the coil into the secondary side of the coil. This induction provides the required voltage to fire the spark plugs.

The advantages of this system are that the transistors in the control unit can make and break the primary ignition circuit much faster than conventional ignition points can, and higher primary voltage can be utilized, since this system can be made to handle higher voltage without adverse effects, whereas ignition breaker points cannot. The quicker switching time of this system allows longer coil primary circuit saturation time and longer induction time when the primary circuit collapses. This increased time allows the primary circuit to build up more current and the secondary circuit to discharge more current.

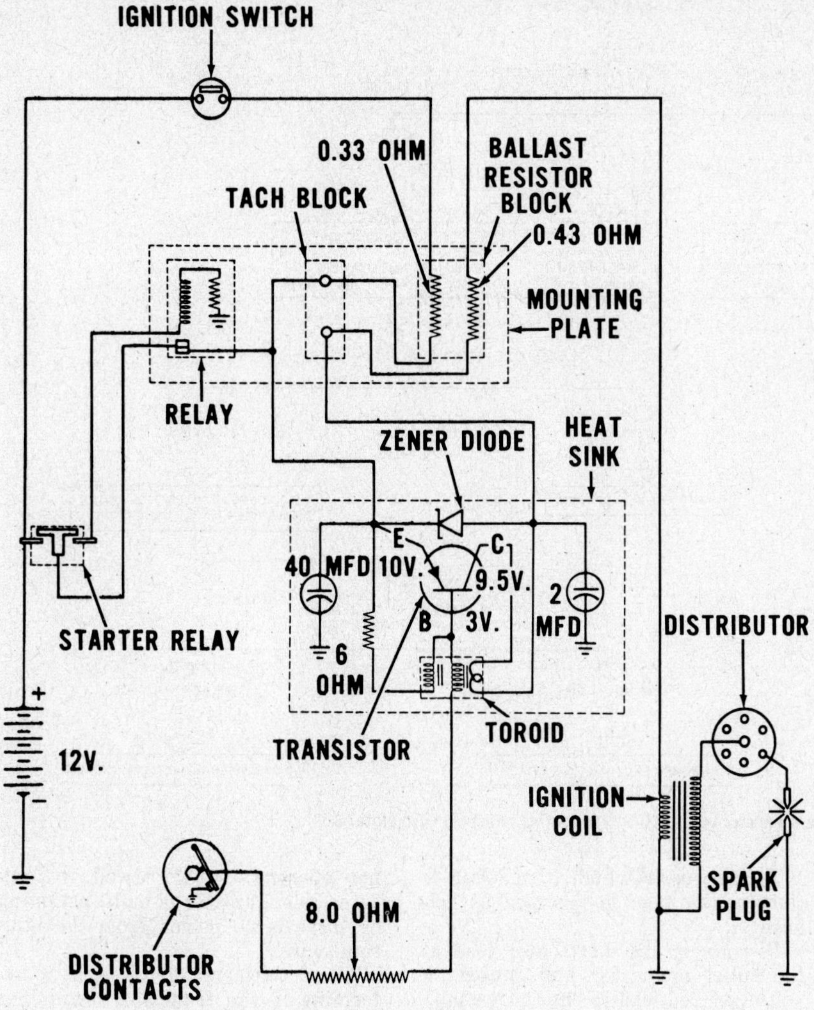
IGNITION SWITCH
0.33 OHM
BALLAST RESISTOR BLOCK
TACH BLOCK
0.43 OHM
MOUNTING PLATE
RELAY
ZENER DIODE
HEAT SINK
E
C
40 MFD
10V.
9.5V.
2 MFD
B
3V.
6 OHM
STARTER RELAY
TOROID
TRANSISTOR
12V.
DISTRIBUTOR
IGNITION COIL
SPARK PLUG
8.0 OHM
DISTRIBUTOR CONTACTS

Ford-Autolite transistor ignition schematic (© Ford Motor Co)

amplifier housing with the PNP transistor, are a condenser, a zener diode, a toroid, a base-to-emitter resistor, and a collector resistor.

The base resistor is similar to the conventional ignition resistor wire and is located between the distributor and the transistor (heat sink). It provides an 8.0 ohm resistance which is necessary for current limitation and it should not be replaced with any other wire, resistance or otherwise. To do so would result in immediate transistor destruction.

The collector and emitter resistors both are located in a ballast resistor block made of white ceramic for electrical and thermal insulation. Both resistors serve the same purpose —limiting system current and control of voltages within their respective circuits. The two resistors are in series in the collector-emitter circuit, together with the ignition coil, toroid and transistor. The emitter resistor also is in series with the base resistor, the toroid, and the transistor, in the base-emitter circuit. The transistor and emitter resistance therefore are common to both circuits. The combined resistances in each circuit permit a base current of approximately 1.0 amp. and a collector current of approximately 12 amps.

A tach block is included in the circuit for attaching tachometer and dwellmeter leads. In the conventional system, these leads are connected to the distributor primary lead and ground, but in the transistorized circuit, the connection of the leads in this manner would jump the contact gap, contributing to a current buildup in the base circuit and in the collector circuit which would overheat and burn out the transistor. The area surrounding the collector terminal is colored *red* for the meter red lead while the area surrounding the emitter terminal is colored *black* for the meter black lead.

A cold start relay is incorporated into the circuit at the starter relay, interrupting the conventional battery-to-coil lead. The purpose of this is to furnish additional current to the coil primary windings during situations when the starter draw is excessive. The cold start relay contacts normally are closed; only opening during the cranking cycle. However, when the available battery voltage drops below a predetermined value during the cranking cycle, they again close, bypassing the ignition resistor and furnishing full battery current to the system.

The distributor differs from the conventional distributor only in the absence of the condenser and in the highly polished breaker cam. Because one of the big advantages of the transistor ignition is long breaker point life, wear on the rubbing block must be reduced to a minimum. Because the current at the breaker points is so small, the amount of pitting that occurs during normal operation is hardly measurable and point life should be indefinite. The points should be set to .020" gap and Chevron O.H.T. grease used for cam lubrication.

When testing the transistor ignition distributor in a test machine, incorporate a condenser into the primary-to-ground circuit using a jumper wire. This will prevent point pitting or oxidation during testing.

Caution When connecting an in-car tachometer to the Ford System, always shunt the tachometer leads that go to the coil IGN terminal and ignition switch with a 10 in. length of Ford ignition resistor wire, part No. COLF-12250-A, to prevent tachometer damage. The higher current draw of the transistor system can ruin a tach if this precaution is not taken.

Troubleshooting

Ignition problems are caused by a failure in the primary or secondary circuit, or incorrect ignition timing. Isolate the trouble as follows:

1. Remove the coil high tension lead from the distributor cap.
2. Disconnect the brown wire from the starter relay "I" terminal and the red and blue wire from the starter relay "S" terminal.
3. Turn the ignition switch on.
4. While holding the high tension lead approximately 1/4 in. from the engine block, crank the engine by using remote starter switch between the starter relay "S" and battery terminals.

If the spark is good, the trouble lies in the secondary (high voltage) circuit. If there is no spark or a weak spark, the trouble is in the primary (low voltage) circuit.

A breakdown or energy loss in the primary circuit can be caused by:

1. Defective primary wiring.
2. Improperly adjusted, contaminated or defective distributor points.
3. Defective amplifier assembly.

The trouble can be isolated by performing a primary circuit test.

A breakdown or energy loss in the secondary circuit can be caused by:

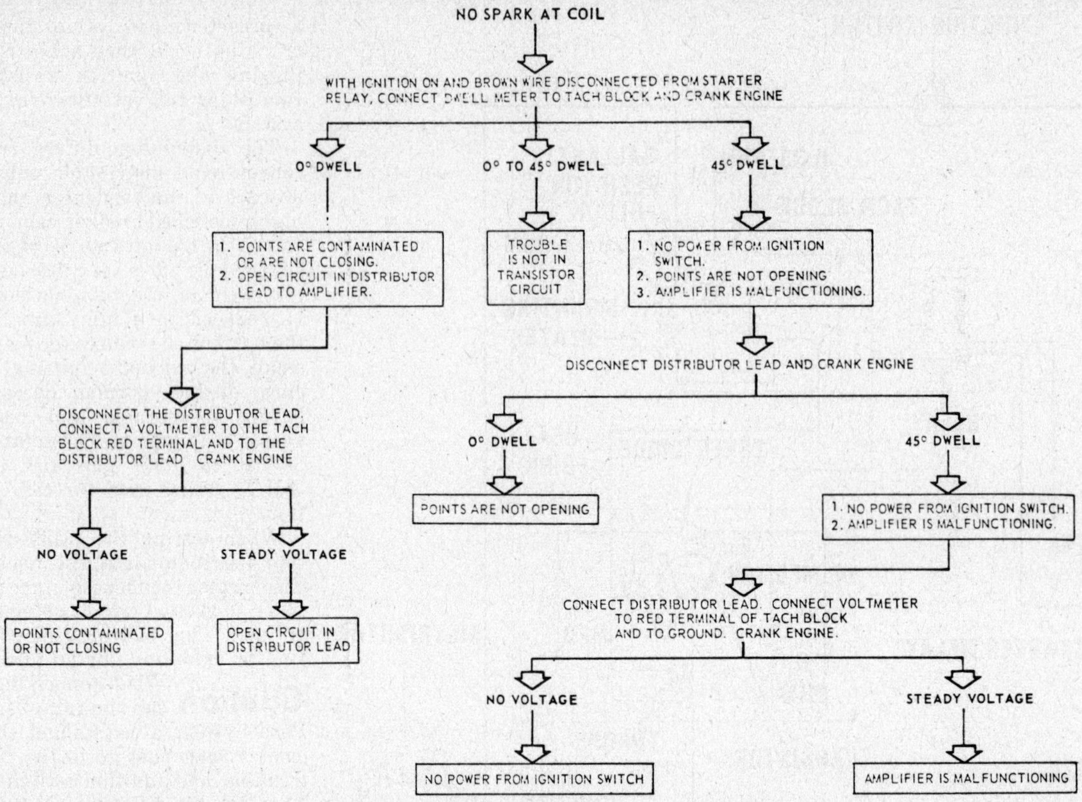
NO SPARK AT COIL
WITH IGNITION ON AND BROWN WIRE DISCONNECTED FROM STARTER RELAY, CONNECT DWELL METER TO TACH BLOCK AND CRANK ENGINE
0° DWELL
0° TO 45° DWELL
45° DWELL
1. POINTS ARE CONTAMINATED OR ARE NOT CLOSING.
2. OPEN CIRCUIT IN DISTRIBUTOR LEAD TO AMPLIFIER.
TROUBLE IS NOT IN TRANSISTOR CIRCUIT
1. NO POWER FROM IGNITION SWITCH.
2. POINTS ARE NOT OPENING
3. AMPLIFIER IS MALFUNCTIONING.
DISCONNECT DISTRIBUTOR LEAD AND CRANK ENGINE
DISCONNECT THE DISTRIBUTOR LEAD. CONNECT A VOLTMETER TO THE TACH BLOCK RED TERMINAL AND TO THE DISTRIBUTOR LEAD CRANK ENGINE
0° DWELL
45° DWELL
POINTS ARE NOT OPENING
1. NO POWER FROM IGNITION SWITCH.
2. AMPLIFIER IS MALFUNCTIONING.
NO VOLTAGE
STEADY VOLTAGE
POINTS CONTAMINATED OR NOT CLOSING
OPEN CIRCUIT IN DISTRIBUTOR LEAD
CONNECT DISTRIBUTOR LEAD. CONNECT VOLTMETER TO RED TERMINAL OF TACH BLOCK AND TO GROUND. CRANK ENGINE.
NO VOLTAGE
STEADY VOLTAGE
NO POWER FROM IGNITION SWITCH
AMPLIFIER IS MALFUNCTIONING

Autolite transistor ignition troubleshooting chart (© Ford Motor Co)

1. Fouled or improperly adjusted spark plugs.
2. Defective high voltage wiring.
3. High voltage leakage across the coil distributor cap or rotor.

To isolate a problem in the secondary circuit, turn the ignition switch off, remove the remote starter switch from the starter relay, install the coil high tension lead in the distributor cap, the red and blue wire to the starter relay (this goes on the "S" terminal) and the brown wire to the starter relay (this goes on the "I" terminal) and perform a secondary circuit test.

Primary Circuit Tests

Caution Do not use any other procedure, conventional short-cut, or connect test equipment in any other manner than described, or extensive damage can be caused to the transistor ignition system.

Connect a dwell meter to the tachometer block. Connect the black lead to the black (large) terminal and the red lead to the red (small) terminal.

With the remote starter switch installed and the ignition switch on, ground the coil high tension wire and crank the engine and observe the dwell reading.

0° Dwell

1. The distributor points are contaminated or are not closing.
2. An open circuit in the distributor lead to the amplifier.

To determine which item listed is causing the trouble, proceed as follows:

Disconnect the distributor lead at the bullet connector and connect a voltmeter red lead to the red (small) tach block terminal and the voltmeter black lead to the distributor lead from the distributor. *Do not connect the voltmeter to the lead from the amplifier.* Crank the engine and note the voltmeter reading.

If a steady indication of voltage is obtained, the trouble is in the distributor lead to the amplifier. Absence of any voltage indication on the voltmeter shows that there is an open circuit between the distributor lead and the breaker point ground.

0-45° Dwell

1. The transistor and the primary circuit are functioning properly.
2. The trouble could be in the secondary circuit.

45° Dwell

1. No power from the ignition switch.
2. The distributor points are closed and not opening.
3. Defective amplifier assembly.

To determine which of the three items listed is causing the trouble, proceed as follows:

Disconnect the distributor lead at the bullet connector, and crank the engine. If the dwellmeter indicates 0° dwell, the distributor points are not opening. If 45° dwell is indicated, the amplifier is malfunctioning or there is no power from the ignition switch.

Use a voltmeter or test light to determine if the transistor (amplifier assembly) is at fault. Connect the voltmeter to the red-green lead terminal of the ballast resistor and to ground. Crank the engine.

Absence of any voltage indication on the voltmeter shows there is an open circuit, or no power between the ignition switch and the amplifier. The ballast resistor could be defective. Replace it with a good ballast resistor, and repeat the test.

A steady indication of voltage on the voltmeter indicates either a defective amplifier or the coil to amplifier lead is defective or improperly connected to the ballast resistor. Proceed as follows:

1. Disconnect the amplifier at the quick disconnect.
2. Connect an ohmmeter across the outside terminals of the amplifier side of the quick disconnect.
3. Reverse the ohmmeter leads.

If a very high resistance is obtained one way and a very low or *zero* resistance is obtained the other way, the amplifier is not defective. Check the coil to amplifier wiring for a loose connection or defective wiring.

After a repair has been made, run through the test again to check for any other malfunctions.

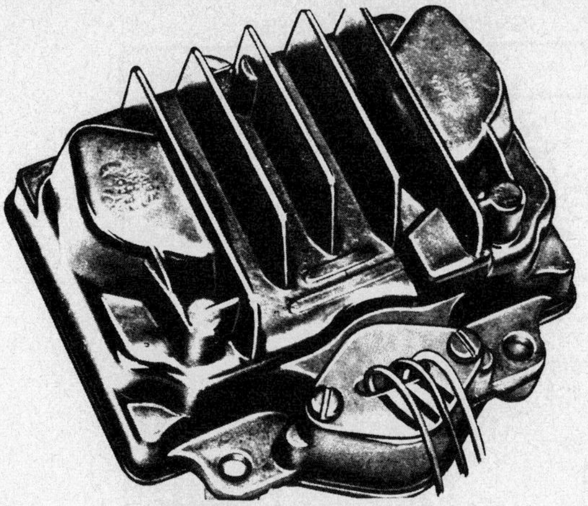

Delco-Remy amplifier unit
(© Chevrolet Div., G.M. Corp)

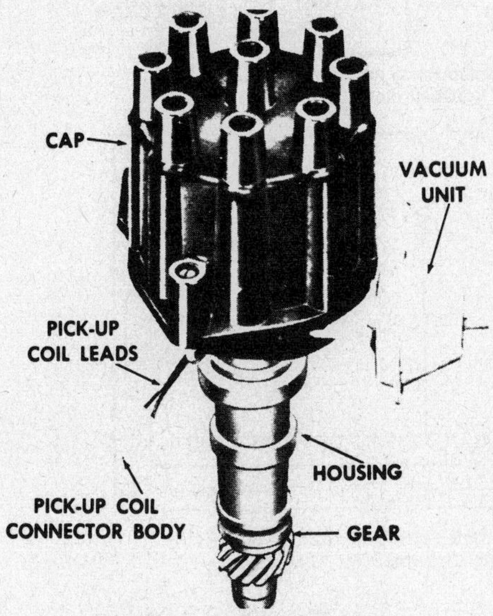
CAP
VACUUM UNIT
PICK-UP COIL LEADS
HOUSING
PICK-UP COIL CONNECTOR BODY
GEAR

Delco-Remy magnetic pulse distributor
(© Chevrolet Div., G.M. Corp)

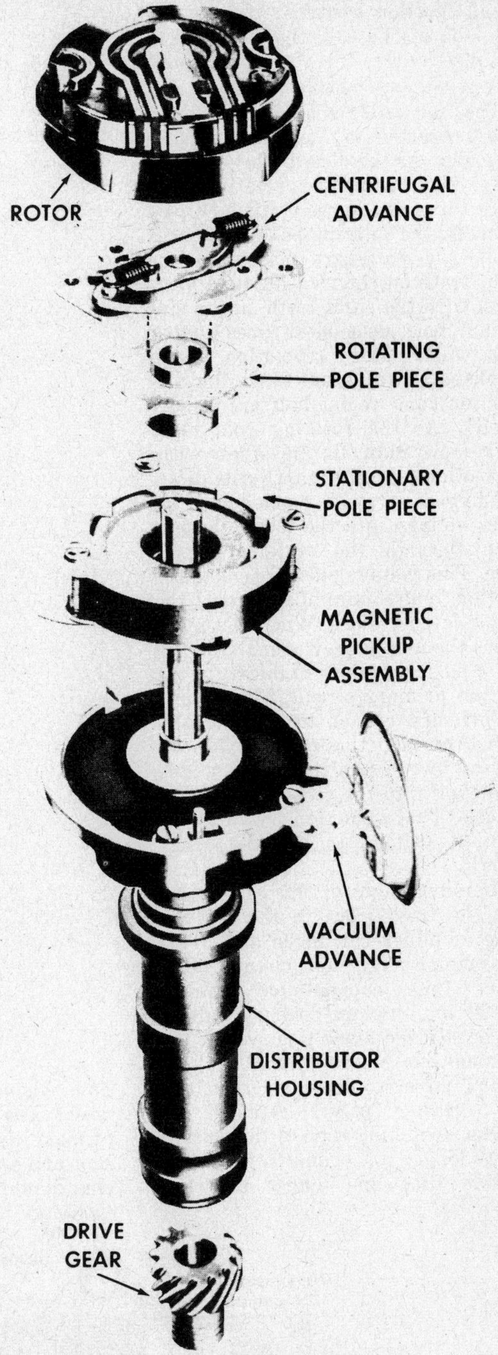
ROTOR
CENTRIFUGAL ADVANCE
ROTATING POLE PIECE
STATIONARY POLE PIECE
MAGNETIC PICKUP ASSEMBLY
VACUUM ADVANCE
DISTRIBUTOR HOUSING
DRIVE GEAR

Delco-Remy pulse distributor exploded view
(© Chevrolet Div., G.M. Corp)

Secondary Circuit Tests

Use conventional system test procedures.

Delco-Remy Magnetic Pulse System

Components

The Delco-Remy magnetic pulse, fully transistorized ignition system uses a magnetic pulse distributor having no breaker points. This system switches power electronically rather than with ignition contact points. Instead of the familiar cam and breaker plate assembly, this distributor uses a rotating iron timer core and a magnetic pickup assembly. The magnetic pickup assembly consists of a bearing plate on which are sandwiched a ceramic ring-type permanent magnet, two pole pieces and a pick-up coil. The pole pieces are doughnut shaped steel plates with accurately spaced internal teeth, one tooth for each cylinder of the engine.

A critically important part is the iron timer core. It has a number of equally spaced projections or vanes and is attached to, and rotates with, the distributor shaft.

The transistor control unit, the switchbox of the system, is mounted in an aluminum case and contains three transistors, a zener diode, a condenser and five small resistors. The zener diode is a circuit protection device. Remaining components control and switch ignition-coil current electronically; there are no moving parts in the control unit.

The ignition coil is of standard design except for a special winding. The external primary resistor is a ceramic type, similar to those used on various conventional systems.

Operation

The ignition primary circuit is connected from the battery, through the ignition switch, through the ignition pulse amplifier assembly, through the primary side of the ignition coil, and back to the amplifier housing where it is grounded externally. The secondary circuit is the same as in conventional ignition systems: the secondary side of the coil, the coil wire to the distributor, the rotor, the spark plug wires and the spark plugs.

The magnetic pulse distributor is also connected to the ignition pulse amplifier. As the distributor shaft rotates, the distributor rotating pole piece turns inside the stationary pole piece. As the rotating pole piece turns inside the stationary pole piece, the eight teeth on the rotating pole piece align with the eight teeth on the stationary pole piece eight times during each distributor revolution (two crankshaft revolutions since the distributor runs at one-half crankshaft speed). As the rotating pole piece teeth move close to, and align with, the teeth on the stationary pole piece, the magnetic rotating pole piece induces voltage into the magnetic pole piece through the stationary pole piece. This voltage pulse is sent to the ignition pulse amplifier from the magnetic pole piece. When the pulse enters the amplifier, it signals the ignition pulse amplifier to interrupt the ignition primary circuit. This causes the primary circuit to collapse and begins the induction of the magnetic lines of force from the primary side of the coil into the secondary side of the coil. This induction provides the required voltage to fire the spark plugs.

The advantages of this system are that the transistors in the ignition pulse amplifier can make and break the primary ignition circuit much faster than conventional ignition points, and higher primary voltage can be utilized since this system can be made to handle higher voltage without adverse effects, whereas ignition breaker points cannot. The shorter switching time of this system allows longer coil primary circuit saturation time and longer induction time when the primary circuit collapses. This increased time allows the primary circuit to build up more current and the secondary circuit to discharge more current.

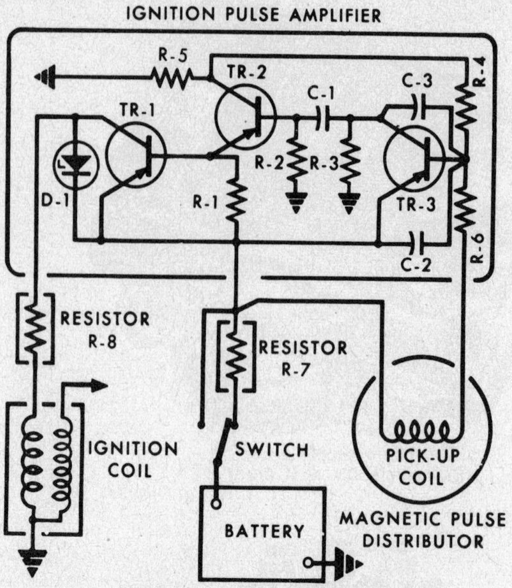
IGNITION PULSE AMPLIFIER
R-5
TR-2
TR-1
C-1
C-3
R-4
R-2
R-3
D-1
R-1
TR-3
C-2
R-6
RESISTOR R-8
RESISTOR R-7
IGNITION COIL
SWITCH
PICK-UP COIL
BATTERY
MAGNETIC PULSE DISTRIBUTOR

Delco-Remy amplifier schematic
(© Chevrolet Div., G.M. Corp)

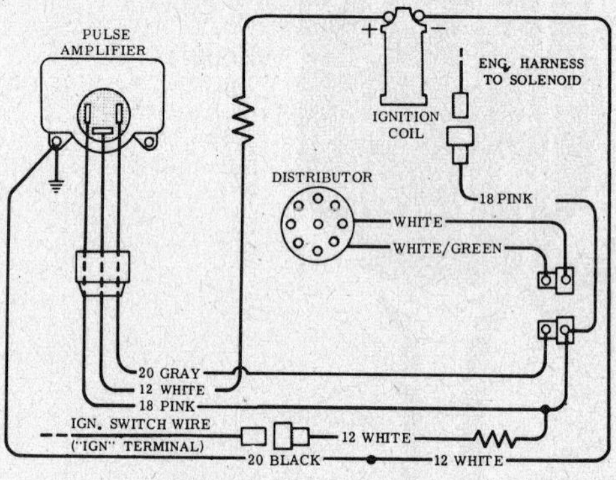
PULSE AMPLIFIER
IGNITION COIL
ENG. HARNESS TO SOLENOID
DISTRIBUTOR
18 PINK
WHITE
WHITE/GREEN
20 GRAY
12 WHITE
18 PINK
IGN. SWITCH WIRE
("IGN" TERMINAL)
12 WHITE
20 BLACK
12 WHITE

Delco-Remy circuit diagram
(© Chevrolet Div., G.M. Corp)

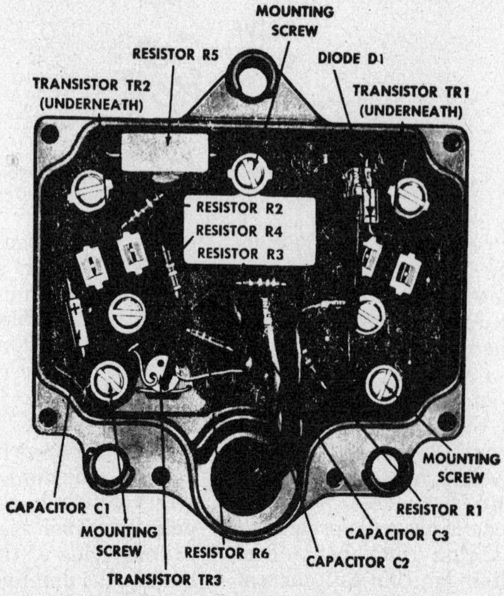
MOUNTING SCREW
RESISTOR R5
DIODE D1
TRANSISTOR TR2 (UNDERNEATH)
TRANSISTOR TR1 (UNDERNEATH)
RESISTOR R2
RESISTOR R4
RESISTOR R3
MOUNTING SCREW
RESISTOR R1
CAPACITOR C1
MOUNTING SCREW
CAPACITOR C3
RESISTOR R6
CAPACITOR C2
TRANSISTOR TR3

Delco-Remy amplifier panel board components
(© Chevrolet Div., G.M. Corp)

Troubleshooting

Cautions

1. Don't use 18 volts or 24 volts for emergency starting.
2. Never crank engine with coil high-tension lead or more than three spark plug leads disconnected.
3. Don't short circuit between coil positive terminal and ground.
4. On any repair that necessitates replacement of control unit or ignition resistor, perform complete charging system check before releasing the unit. Basic cause of trouble may be high or uncontrolled charging rate.

Engine Surge or Intermittent Miss

Since there are so many possible causes for this problem, all other possible defects must be ruled out before the specialized components of the electronic ignition system are judged defective.

As a general rule, a miss or surge that is caused by an ignition problem will be much more pronounced than a similiar problem that is caused by carburetion. Also, carburetion is usually affected by temperature more than the ignition system is. A carburetor or intake manifold vacuum leak is often compensated for by the choke when the engine is cold. When the engine warms up and the choke is released, the engine surge will show up.

If the ignition system is found to be the source of the problem, first check all connections in the system to make sure that they are *clean and tight.* Check the coil and spark plug high-tension wires with an ohmmeter to be sure they have the correct resistance. Check the inside and outside of the distributor cap and the tower on the ignition coil for cracks which would allow the high voltage intended for the spark plugs to short to ground.

If none of the above checks uncovers a defective component, the distributor pick-up coil leads may be reversed in the connector, or the pick-up coil itself may have an intermittent open.

Engine Will Not Start or Is Hard to Start

1. Disconnect a spark plug wire from one spark plug and hold the wire 1/4 in. from a good ground with a pair of insulated pliers.
2. Crank the engine over and observe whether a spark jumps from the plug wire to ground.
3. *If spark occurs,* the problem is not in the ignition system.
4. *If spark does not occur,* reconnect the spark plug wire that was disconnected and connect a tachometer between the positive (+) coil primary terminal and the pink wire in the three-wire connector to the ignition pulse amplifier.
5. Crank the engine over and observe the tachometer.
6. *If the tachometer needle deflects* while cranking the engine, perform "Ignition Distributor Test" to locate the problem.
7. *If the tachometer needle does not deflect* while cranking the engine, perform "Circuit Resistance Test" to pinpoint the problem.

Ignition Distributor Check

1. Disconnect the distributor leads from the engine wiring harness.
2. Connect the two leads of an ohmmeter to the distributor leads at the connector.
3. Rotate the magnetic pick-up assembly in the distributor through full vacuum advance travel and read the ohmmeter. If the reading is not within a range of 500-700 ohms, replace the magnetic pick-up assembly.
4. If the reading is within the 500-700 ohms range, disconnect one ohmmeter lead from the distributor connector and connect it to a good ground. If the reading is less than infinity (needle moves to end of scale), replace the magnetic pick-up assembly.
5. If the reading is infinite, and there was no spark when the spark plug wire was disconnected from the plug, the amplifier is defective.

Delcotronic Capacitor Discharge System

Components

The capacitive discharge ignition system consists of a magnetic pulse distributor, an ignition pulse amplifier, and a special ignition coil and distributor cap. The coil and distributor cap are red to distinguish them from standard coils and distributor caps. The ignition pulse amplifier contains transistors, diodes, resistors, capacitors, a thyristor, and a transformer. These components are mounted on a printed circuit board in the amplifier housing.

System Operation

The magnetic pulse distributor used in this system is similar to the one used in the previously described Delco-Remy Magnetic Pulse Ignition

Circuit Resistance Test

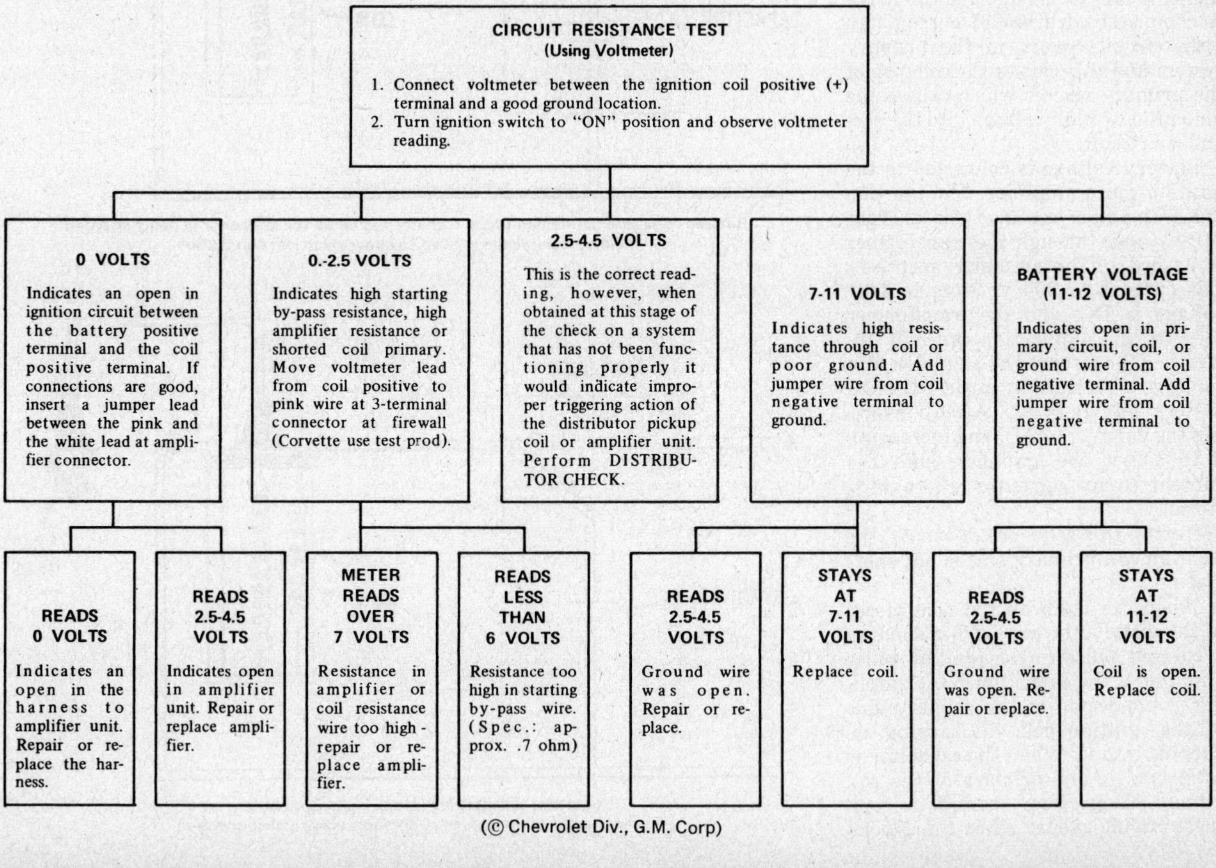
CIRCUIT RESISTANCE TEST
(Using Voltmeter)
1. Connect voltmeter between the ignition coil positive (+) terminal and a good ground location.
2. Turn ignition switch to "ON" position and observe voltmeter reading.
0 VOLTS
Indicates an open in ignition circuit between the battery positive terminal and the coil positive terminal. If connections are good, insert a jumper lead between the pink and the white lead at amplifier connector.
0.-2.5 VOLTS
Indicates high starting by-pass resistance, high amplifier resistance or shorted coil primary. Move voltmeter lead from coil positive to pink wire at 3-terminal connector at firewall (Corvette use test prod).
2.5-4.5 VOLTS
This is the correct reading, however, when obtained at this stage of the check on a system that has not been functioning properly it would indicate improper triggering action of the distributor pickup coil or amplifier unit. Perform DISTRIBUTOR CHECK.
7-11 VOLTS
Indicates high resistance through coil or poor ground. Add jumper wire from coil negative terminal to ground.
BATTERY VOLTAGE (11-12 VOLTS)
Indicates open in primary circuit, coil, or ground wire from coil negative terminal. Add jumper wire from coil negative terminal to ground.
READS 0 VOLTS
Indicates an open in the harness to amplifier unit. Repair or replace the harness.
READS 2.5-4.5 VOLTS
Indicates open in amplifier unit. Repair or replace amplifier.
METER READS OVER 7 VOLTS
Resistance in amplifier or coil resistance wire too high - repair or replace amplifier.
READS LESS THAN 6 VOLTS
Resistance too high in starting by-pass wire. (Spec.: approx. .7 ohm)
READS 2.5-4.5 VOLTS
Ground wire was open. Repair or replace.
STAYS AT 7-11 VOLTS
Replace coil.
READS 2.5-4.5 VOLTS
Ground wire was open. Repair or replace.
STAYS AT 11-12 VOLTS
Coil is open. Replace coil.

(© Chevrolet Div., G.M. Corp)

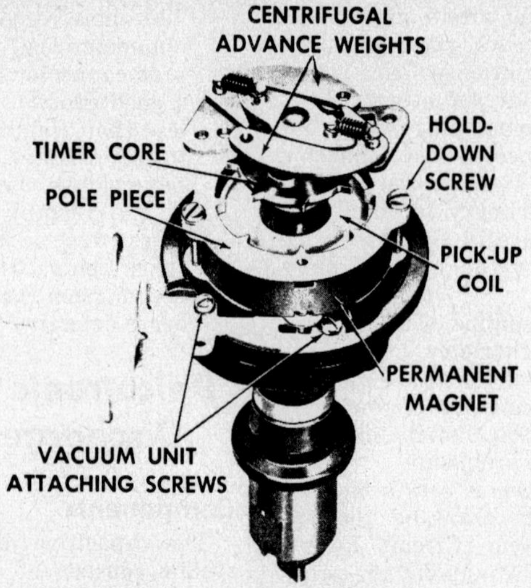
CENTRIFUGAL
ADVANCE WEIGHTS
TIMER CORE
HOLD-
DOWN
SCREW
POLE PIECE
PICK-UP
COIL
PERMANENT
MAGNET
VACUUM UNIT
ATTACHING SCREWS

C-D distributor—Delcotronic System
(© Oldsmobile Div., G.M. Corp)

system. The system functions in a much different way, however. In the Magnetic Pulse Distributor System, the ignition primary circuit is connected through the ignition pulse amplifier and, upon receiving a signal from the distributor, the primary circuit is broken and the induction of high voltage into the secondary circuit takes place. In the capacitive discharge system, the ignition primary circuit is energized when the distributor signals the ignition pulse amplifier to discharge 300 v that the amplifier has been storing in its capacitor. When this voltage is discharged into the primary circuit and the capacitor is completely drained of current, an open circuit occurs in the primary system and this causes the collapse of the primary circuit which causes the induction of high voltage into the secondary circuit.

Battery voltage is connected to the ignition pulse amplifier. The ignition pulse amplifier receives this current (12 v) and, through the transformer contained in the amplifier, increases this current to 300 v. Since battery voltage is DC, and the transformer used in this application can only increase AC current; the amplifier also contains a rectifier to convert the DC battery voltage to AC. After converting the current to AC, and increasing it to 300 v, the amplifier sends the current to its capacitor where it is stored.

During this sequence of events, the ignition coil primary side is not energized.

When the teeth on the pole pieces in the distributor align (thus sending a current pulse to the ignition pulse amplifier), the capacitor in the amplifier is connected to the primary side of the ignition coil, discharging its current into it. When the capacitor is connected to the primary of the coil and is discharging current, a complete circuit exists. When the capacitor is completely drained of current, however, it causes an open circuit in the ignition primary. This open circuit causes the ignition primary circuit to collapse, which brings about the induction of the magnetic lines of force from the primary side of the coil across the ignition coil secondary windings. This causes high voltage to be induced into the secondary circuit which fires the spark plugs.

This system has all of the advantages of the Magnetic Pulse Distributor System, plus the extra advantage of containing a transformer. The use of a transformer permits the system to operate on a minimum current drain on the battery. This is due to the transformer's ability to greatly increase the current that is supplied to it. Thus, ignition primary current can be increased (which means higher secondary current) without imposing the extra load on the battery that the Magnetic Pulse System does.

Amplifier Operation

Transistor Q2 and accompanying circuitry momentarily supplies voltage through the primary of transformer T1. This voltage is increased through transformer action and a much higher voltage is induced in the

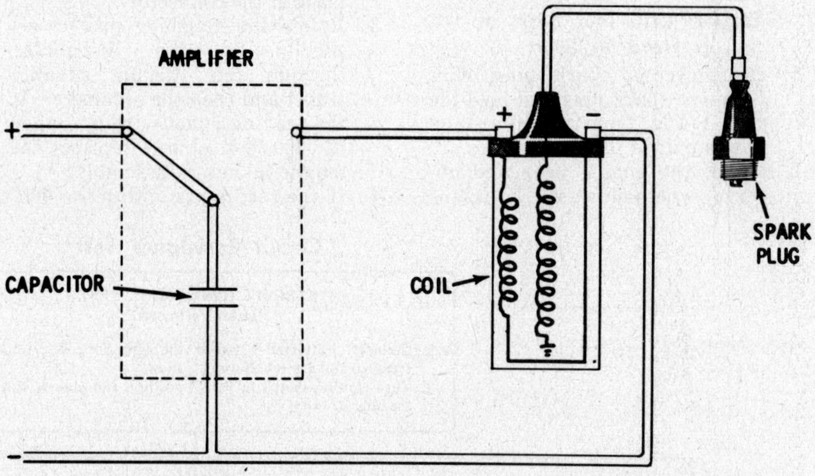
AMPLIFIER
+
-
CAPACITOR
COIL
SPARK
PLUG

Battery voltage is connected to the transformer while the capacitor is being charged mechanical linkage is used to show electrical connection

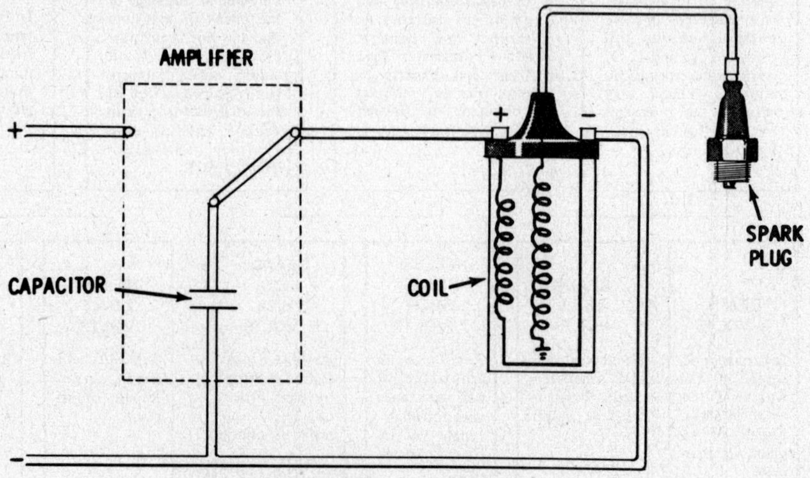
AMPLIFIER
+
-
CAPACITOR
COIL
SPARK
PLUG

Capacitor discharging into primary ignition circuit mechanical linkage is used to show electrical connection

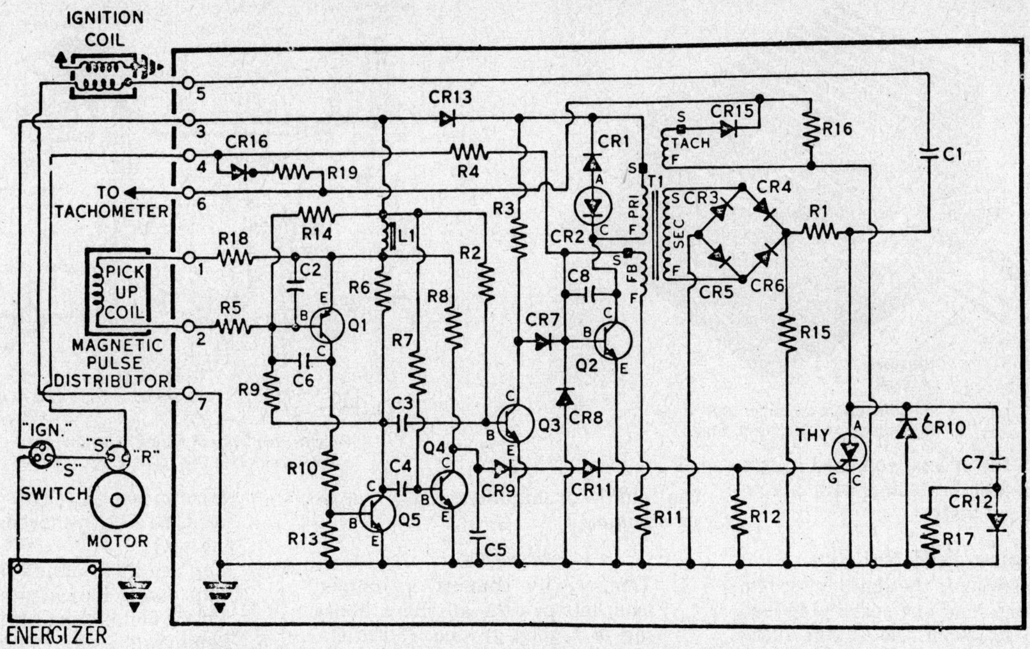
IGNITION COIL
TO TACHOMETER
PICK UP COIL
MAGNETIC PULSE DISTRIBUTOR
"IGN."
"S"
"R"
SWITCH
MOTOR
ENERGIZER
CR13
CR16
R19
R4
R14
R18
R5
C2
L1
R6
Q1
C6
R9
R7
R8
R2
R3
CR1
CR2
C8
T1
PRI
SEC
FB
TACH
CR15
R16
C1
CR3
CR4
CR5
CR6
R1
R15
CR7
Q2
CR8
C3
Q3
Q4
C4
R10
R13
Q5
CR9
C5
CR11
R11
R12
THY
CR10
C7
CR12
R17

Delcotronic Capacitor Discharge System schematic (© Oldsmobile Div., G.M. Corp)

secondary. The four diodes, CR3, 4, 5 and 6 form a full wave rectifier which has the capability of delivering maximum DC voltage from the transformer T1 secondary. It is this voltage that charges the capacitor C1.

The following is a list of the parts, and their function, used in the amplifier as illustrated in the schematic.

Transistor

- Q1 Initiates turn-on and turn-off of Q5.
- Q2 Turns T1 primary on and off.
- Q3 Turns Q2 on and off with engine running.
- Q4 Triggers Thyristor THY.
- Q5 When on, it turns off Q3 and Q4.

Diode

- CR1 Blocks 3 line current through CR2.
- CR2 (Zener) Clips T1 primary voltage to limit secondary output to approximately 300 volts across C1.
- CR3,CR4 CR5,CR6 Provide full wave rectification of T1 secondary voltage.
- CR7 Provides proper bias to Q2.
- CR8 Clips FB voltage of T1 to limit reverse voltage across E-B of Q2.
- CR9 Provides proper biasing of THY.
- CR10 Eliminates reverse voltage across THY, allows ignition coil primary to partially recharge C1.
- CR12 Provides proper biasing of THY.
- CR13 With C7 and R17 reduces rate of voltage increases across THY. Protects amplifier in case of battery reverse polarity, or lead reversal.
- CR15 Half wave rectified T1 tachometer winding voltages for proper tachometer operation.
- CR16 With R19 prevents erroneous tachometer reading during cranking.

Resistor

- R1 Prevents T1 secondary rectified voltage from being shorted to ground when THY is on.
- R2 Provides proper biasing of Q3.
- R3 Limits current through Q3.
- R4 Provides proper biasing of Q2.
- R5 Prevents damage to amplifier if #2 lead is grounded.
- R6 Limits current through Q5.
- R7 Provides proper biasing of Q4.
- R8 Limits current through Q4.
- R9 Provides feed back for Q1, holds Q1 on after pick up coil voltage has ceased.
- R10 Provides signal to Q5 when Q1 turns on.
- R11 Limits current through Q2 from winding of T1.
- R12 Provides bias to THY.
- R13 Biases B-E of Q5.
- R14 Biases E-B of Q1.
- R15 Allows C1 to bleed off during shut-down.
- R16 Provides proper voltage to tachometer.
- R17 Reduces rate of voltage change imposed on THY when C7 discharges.
- R18 Prevents damage to amplifier if #1 lead is grounded.
- R19 With CR16 prevents erroneous tachometer reading during cranking.

Capacitor

- C1 Stores charge from T1 to energize ignition coil primary.
- C2 Protects Q1 from transient voltages.
- C3 Turns Q3 off.
- C4 Turns Q4 off.
- C5 Protects Q4 from transient voltages.
- C6 Protects Q1 from transient voltages.
- C7 With CR12 and R17 reduces rate of voltage increase across THY.
- C8 Reduces radio noise.

Transformer

- T1 Steps up voltage to charge C1; provides voltage to operate tachometer; provides feed back voltage to operate Q2.

Thyristor

- THY Discharges C1 through primary of ignition coil.

Troubleshooting

Faulty engine performance will be evidenced by one of the following conditions:

a. Engine will not run.
b. Engine will start but not run.
c. Engine will miss or surge.

When troubleshooting the system, use care to avoid accidental shorts and grounds, which may cause instant damage to the amplifier and wiring.

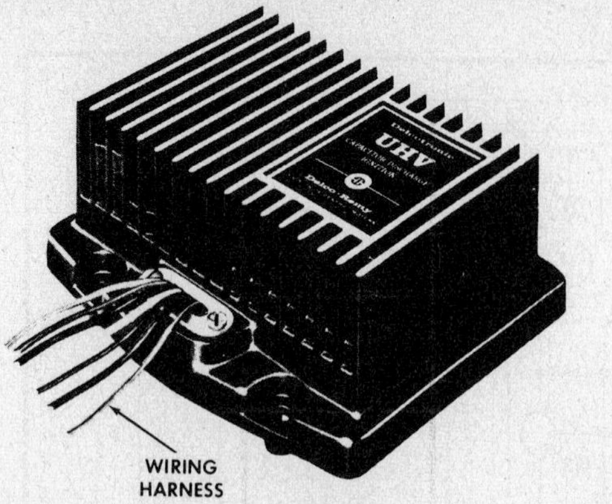
WIRING
HARNESS
Delcotronic amplifier unit
(© Oldsmobile Div., G.M. Corp)

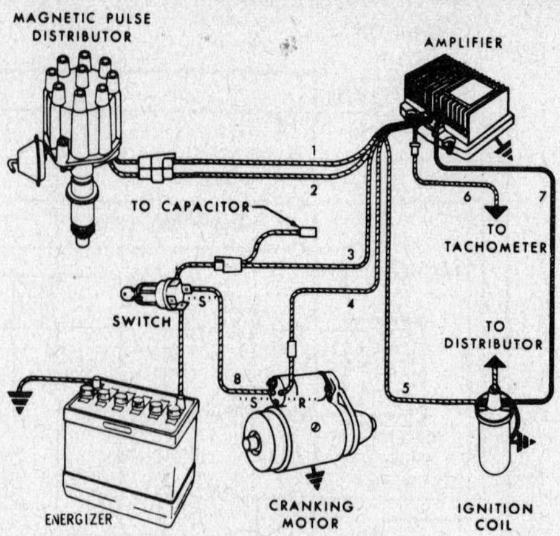
MAGNETIC PULSE
DISTRIBUTOR
AMPLIFIER
TO CAPACITOR
TO
TACHOMETER
SWITCH
TO
DISTRIBUTOR
ENERGIZER
CRANKING
MOTOR
IGNITION
COIL
Delcotronic System wiring diagram
(© Oldsmobile Div., G.M. Corp)

NOTE: the special coil used in this system cannot be tested with a conventional coil tester.

Engine Will Not Run

To determine if the ignition system is operating, hold one spark plug lead about 1/4 in. from the engine block and crank the engine. If sparking occurs, the trouble most likely is not ignition. If sparking does not occur, and the vehicle fuel system is satisfactory, check the ignition system. The spark plugs, wiring, distributor cap and rotor can be checked in the conventional manner. Only the coil requires a different procedure. The ignition coil can be checked for primary and secondary winding continuity with an ohmmeter as follows: with leads disconnected from coil, connect ohmmeter across primary terminals. If reading is infinite, winding is open. To check secondary, connect ohmmeter to high voltage (center tower) and coil case. An infinite reading means coil secondary is open.

NOTE: when checking secondary, use middle or high resistance range on ohmmeter.

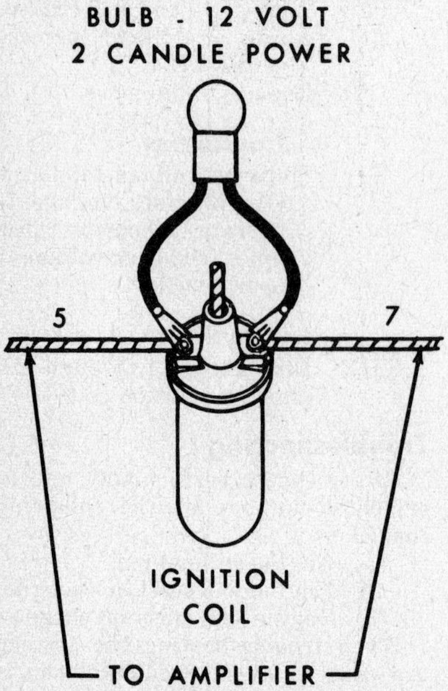
BULB - 12 VOLT
2 CANDLE POWER
5
7
IGNITION
COIL
TO AMPLIFIER
Amplifier test hook-up
(© Oldsmobile Div., G.M. Corp)

Amplifier

1. Temporarily connect a jumper lead between the amplifier housing to a good ground. If the engine will not start and run, the amplifier is not properly grounded. Correct as required.
2. Connect a 12-volt, 2-candlepower bulb to the primary terminals of the ignition coil.
3. Crank the engine.
   a. If the bulb flickers on and off, the amplifier is operating properly. In this case, recheck the secondary system for the cause of the "no run" condition.
   b. If the bulb does not flicker on and off, proceed to next test.

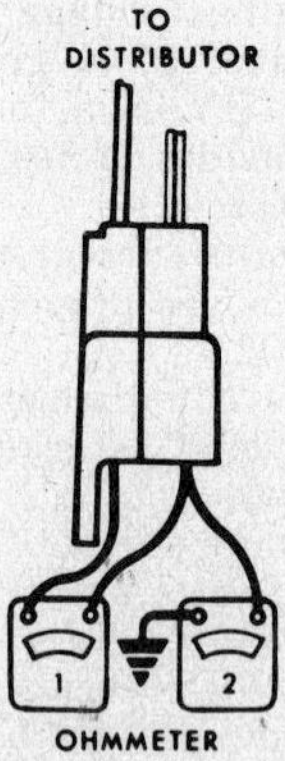
TO
DISTRIBUTOR
1
2
OHMMETER
Distributor test hook-up
(© Oldsmobile Div., G.M. Corp)

Distributor

1. Insure that the two distributor leads are connected to the distributor connector body as illustrated.
2. With the distributor connector disconnected from the harness connector, connect an ohmmeter (1) to the two terminals of the distributor connector as shown.
3. Connect a vacuum source to the distributor, and observe the ohmmeter reading throughout the vacuum range. (The distributor need not be removed from the engine.)
4. Any reading outside the 550-750 ohm range indicates a defective pickup coil in the distributor.
5. Remove one ohmmeter (2) lead from the connector body and connect to ground.
6. Observe the ohmmeter reading throughout the vacuum range.
7. Any reading less than infinite indicates a defective pickup coil.
8. Reconnect the harness connector to the distributor connector.

Continuity

Carefully inspect all wiring connections to ensure that they are clean and tight. If satisfactory, disconnect the amplifier No. 3 and No. 4 leads from the two connectors. Proceed as follows:

1. Connect a voltmeter from ground to the No. 4 connector lead.
2. Turn switch to "Start" position.
3. If reading is zero, circuit is open between connector body and battery.
4. If reading is obtained, connect voltmeter from ground to the No. 3 connector lead.
5. Turn switch to the run position.
6. If reading is zero, circuit is open between connector body and switch.
7. If reading is obtained, replace amplifier.

Engine Will Start But Not Run

If the engine starts, but then stops when the switch is returned to the run position, check as follows:

1. Ensure that the leads are properly connected in the No. 3 lead connector body.
2. If satisfactory, connect a voltmeter from ground to the terminal connection inside the connector.
3. Turn switch to run position.
4. If reading is zero, lead between connector and ignition switch is open.

5. If reading is obtained, replace amplifier.

Engine Miss or Surge

The vehicle fuel system should be checked in the usual manner. If satisfactory, check the ignition system as follows:

Timing, Spark Plugs, Wiring, Distributor Cap and Ignition Coil

Checks in these areas should be made in the same manner as for a conventional ignition system. In particular, the spark plugs should be checked in the usual manner. Plugs should be gapped to 0.045 in. Also the timing, the high-voltage wiring, the ignition coil tower, and the distributor cap inside and out should be inspected for evidence of arcing or leakage to ground. The ignition coil can be checked for primary and secondary winding continuity with an ohmmeter, as follows: disconnect coil leads and connect ohmmeter across primary terminals. If reading is infinite (no reading) winding is open. To check secondary, connect ohmmeter to high voltage (center tower) and coil case. An infinite reading means coil secondary is open.

NOTE: when checking secondary, use middle or high resistance range on ohmmeter.

Amplifier

A poorly grounded amplifier can cause an engine miss or surge. To check, temporarily connect a jumper lead from the amplifier housing to a good ground. If the engine performance improves, the amplifier is poorly grounded. Correct as required.

If no defects up to this point have been found, and the secondary system (plugs, wiring, distributor cap and coil) have been thoroughly checked, the most likely cause of the engine condition is a defective amplifier.

C-D Distributor Removal

1. Disconnect the harness connector.
2. Remove distributor cap.

NOTE: if necessary to remove secondary wires from cap, mark position on cap tower for lead to No. 1 cylinder. This will aid in reinstalling of leads.

3. Remove vacuum hose line from vacuum advance unit.
4. Remove distributor clamp.
5. Note position of rotor, then pull distributor up until rotor just stops turning counterclockwise and again note position of rotor.
6. To install, reverse removal procedure.

NOTE: to ensure correct timing of the distributor, the distributor must be installed with the rotor correctly positioned as noted in Step 5.

7. If the engine has been turned after the distributor was removed, it will be necessary to crank the engine until the slot on the harmonic balancer indexes with the 0° timing mark on the engine front cover. If both valves of the No. 1 cylinder are closed, the piston will be on top dead center of the firing stroke.

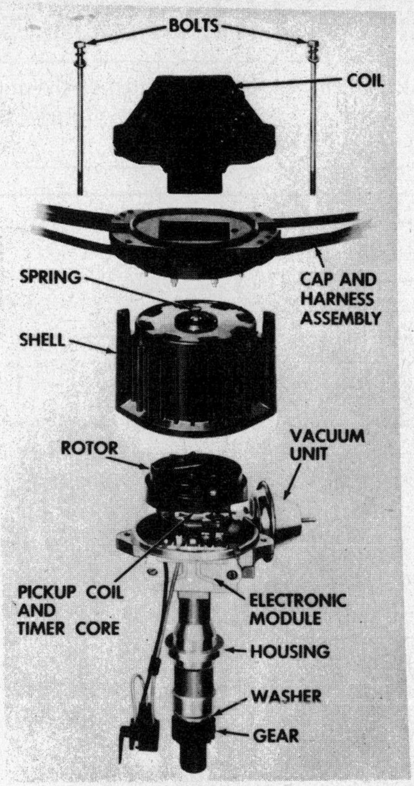
BOLTS
COIL
SPRING
CAP AND HARNESS ASSEMBLY
SHELL
ROTOR
VACUUM UNIT
PICKUP COIL AND TIMER CORE
ELECTRONIC MODULE
HOUSING
WASHER
GEAR

Unit Ignition System components
(© Pontiac Div., G.M. Corp)

Distributor Disassembly

1. Remove screws securing rotor; remove rotor.
2. Remove centrifugal weight springs, if necessary.
3. Remove centrifugal weights.
4. Remove roll pin.
5. Remove drive gear and washer.
6. Remove drive shaft.
7. Remove weight support and timer core from drive shaft.
8. Remove screws securing magnetic core assembly; remove assembly.
9. Remove connector from primary lead by disengaging leads from connector.
10. Remove coil assembly.
11. Remove retaining ring which secures magnetic core support plate and remove plate.
12. Remove brass washer and felt.
13. Remove vacuum advance unit.
14. To assemble, reverse disassembly procedure.

C-D Amplifier Removal

1. Disconnect negative battery cable.
2. Disconnect the following leads from the amplifier harness assembly:
   a. Tachometer pickup
   b. Harness ground
   c. Coil wires
   d. Distributor connector
   e. Connectors at fuse panel
   f. Connector at junction block
3. Remove three retaining nuts from amplifier assembly and remove amplifier.
4. To install, reverse removal procedure.

No adjustments can be made to the C-D ignition system, and no periodic maintenance is required.

Delco-Remy Unit Ignition System

This system is almost identical to the Delco-Remy Magnetic Pulse System. The ignition primary circuit passes through the electronic module (called the ignition pulse amplifier in Delco-Remy system) and is interrupted when a signal is sent to the control module from the distributor. The main difference between the two systems is that, in the Unitized System, the ignition coil and control module are attached to the distributor body, making a compact, one-piece ignition system.

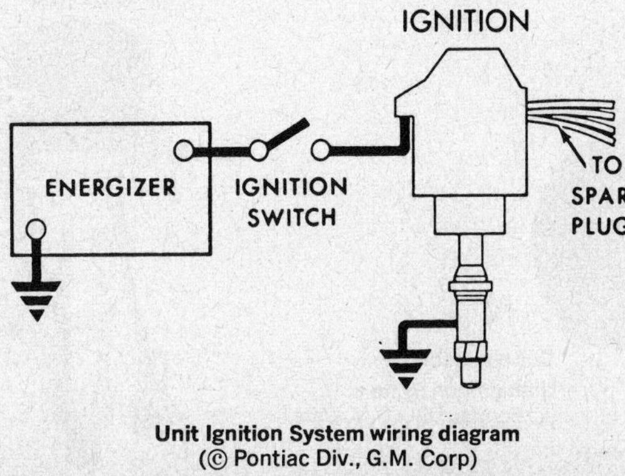
UNIT IGNITION
ENERGIZER
IGNITION SWITCH
TO SPARK PLUGS

Unit Ignition System wiring diagram
(© Pontiac Div., G.M. Corp)

UNIT IGNITION SYSTEM TROUBLESHOOTING

Insure that black and pink leads are connected as shown in Fig. 1. Tighten both bolts, Fig. 1. Loose bolts may cause poor performance and radio interference.

ON THE VEHICLE

ENGINE WILL NOT RUN

1. Check ignition switch connector, Fig. 1.
2. Connect voltmeter from ignition switch connector to ground.
3. Turn on ignition switch.
4. If reading is zero, circuit is open between connector and ignition switch. Repair if needed.
5. If reading is battery voltage, hold one spark lead with insulating pliers about 1/4 in. from dry area of engine block while cranking engine.

If sparking occurs, trouble most likely is not ignition. Check fuel system.

If no spark, follow procedure under "On the Bench," with Unit Ignition System initially either on or off the engine.

ENGINE WILL START BUT NOT RUN, AND ENGINE MISS OR SURGE.

1. Insure that fuel system is satisfactory.
2. Check spark plug leads for arcing or leakage to ground.
3. Check spark plugs.

If no defects are found, follow procedure under "On the Bench" with Unit Ignition System initially either on or off the vehicle.

ON THE BENCH

1. Disassemble unit (Fig. 2).
2. Inspect coil, eight inserts, shell and rotor for arc-over or leakage.

---

1. Connect ohmmeter, Fig. 3.
2. Parts A and B each should be practically zero. If infinite on either reading, replace coil.
3. Part C should be 6000-9000 ohms. If outside range, replace coil.
4. Part D should be infinite. If not, replace coil.

---

1. Connect test stand vacuum source to vacuum unit.
2. Connect ohmmeter Parts A and B, Fig. 4.
3. Observe ohmmeter throughout vacuum range.
4. If Part A reads less than 650 ohms, or more than 850 ohms at any time, replace pickup coil, per Step 7 below.
5. If Part B reads other than infinite at any time, replace pickup coil, per step 7 below.
6. If vacuum unit is inoperative, replace per Step 7 below.
7. Remove unit from engine, drive pin from gear, remove rotor and shaft assembly from housing, remove shim and then "C" washer to replace pickup coil or vacuum unit (Fig. 5).

If no defects have been found, remove two attaching screws and replace module.

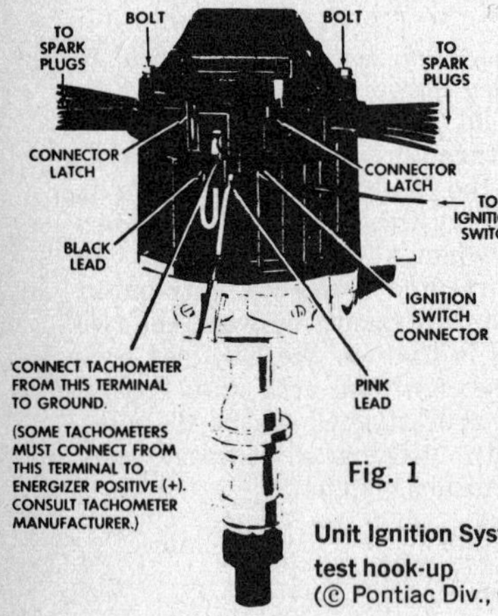
BOLT
BOLT
TO SPARK PLUGS
TO SPARK PLUGS
CONNECTOR LATCH
CONNECTOR LATCH
TO IGNITION SWITCH
BLACK LEAD
IGNITION SWITCH CONNECTOR
CONNECT TACHOMETER FROM THIS TERMINAL TO GROUND.
(SOME TACHOMETERS MUST CONNECT FROM THIS TERMINAL TO ENERGIZER POSITIVE (+). CONSULT TACHOMETER MANUFACTURER.)
PINK LEAD

Fig. 1

Unit Ignition System test hook-up
(© Pontiac Div., G.M. Corp)

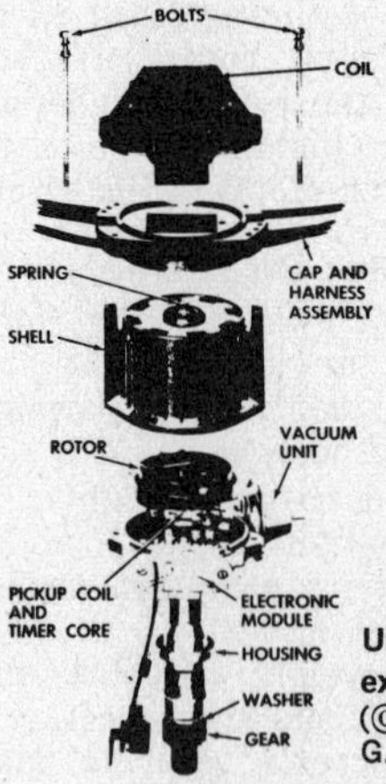
BOLTS
COIL
SPRING
CAP AND HARNESS ASSEMBLY
SHELL
ROTOR
VACUUM UNIT
PICKUP COIL AND TIMER CORE
ELECTRONIC MODULE
HOUSING
WASHER
GEAR

Fig. 2

Unit Ignition System exploded view
(© Pontiac Div., G.M. Corp)

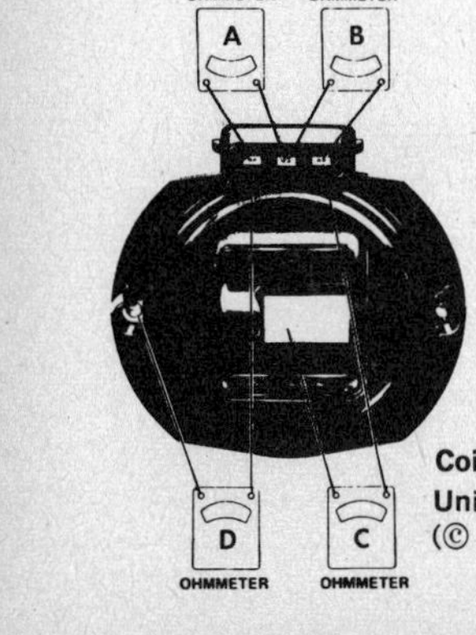
OHMMETER
OHMMETER
A
B
D
C
OHMMETER
OHMMETER

Fig. 3

Coil test hook-up—Unit Ignition System
(© Pontiac Div., G.M. Corp)

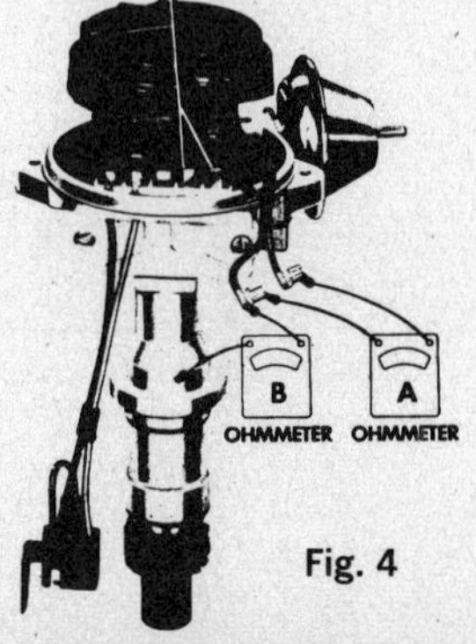
DETACH LEADS
B
A
OHMMETER
OHMMETER

Fig. 4

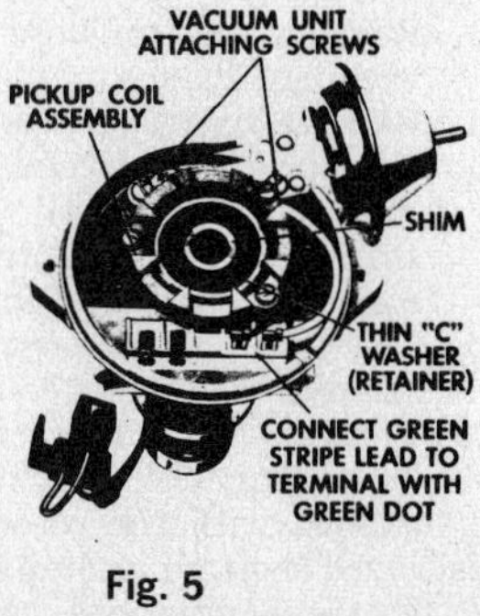
VACUUM UNIT ATTACHING SCREWS
PICKUP COIL ASSEMBLY
SHIM
THIN "C" WASHER (RETAINER)
CONNECT GREEN STRIPE LEAD TO TERMINAL WITH GREEN DOT

Fig. 5

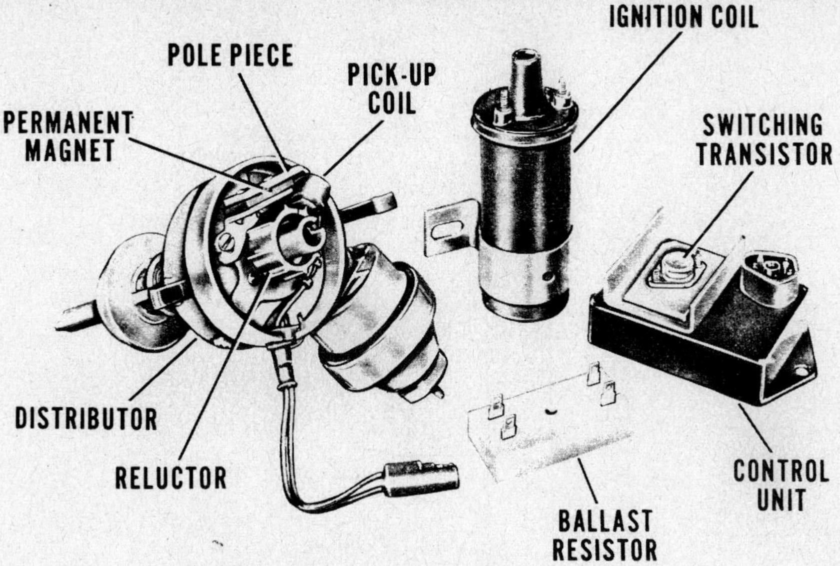
IGNITION COIL
POLE PIECE
PICK-UP
COIL
PERMANENT
MAGNET
SWITCHING
TRANSISTOR
DISTRIBUTOR
RELUCTOR
CONTROL
UNIT
BALLAST
RESISTOR

Chrysler system components (© Chrysler Corp)

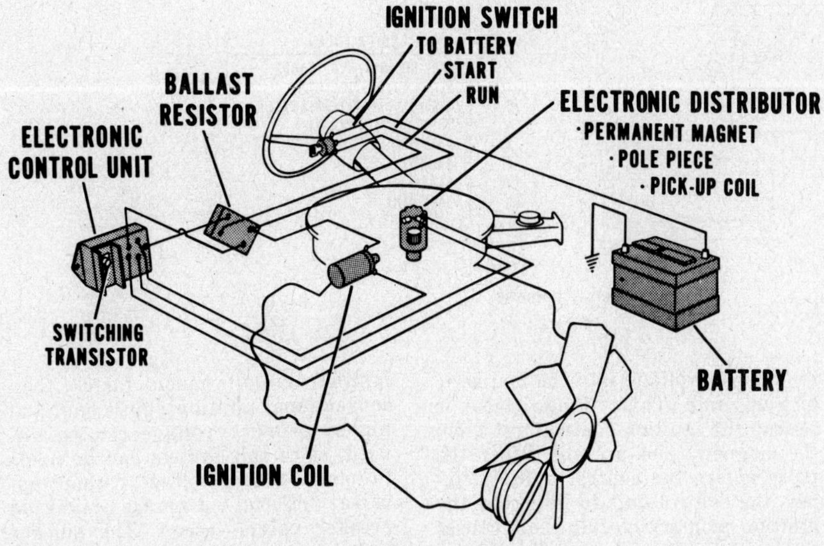
IGNITION SWITCH
TO BATTERY
START
RUN
BALLAST
RESISTOR
ELECTRONIC DISTRIBUTOR
·PERMANENT MAGNET
·POLE PIECE
·PICK-UP COIL
ELECTRONIC
CONTROL UNIT
SWITCHING
TRANSISTOR
BATTERY
IGNITION COIL

Chrysler system wiring diagram (© Chrysler Corp)

Chrysler Electronic Ignition

Components

This system consists of a special pulse-sending distributor, an electronic control unit, a two-element ballast resistor, and a special ignition coil.

The distributor does not contain breaker points or a condenser, these parts being replaced by a distributor reluctor and a pick-up unit.

Operation

The ignition primary circuit is connected from the battery, through the ignition switch, through the primary side of the ignition coil, to the control unit where it is grounded. The secondary circuit is the same as in conventional ignition systems: the sec-

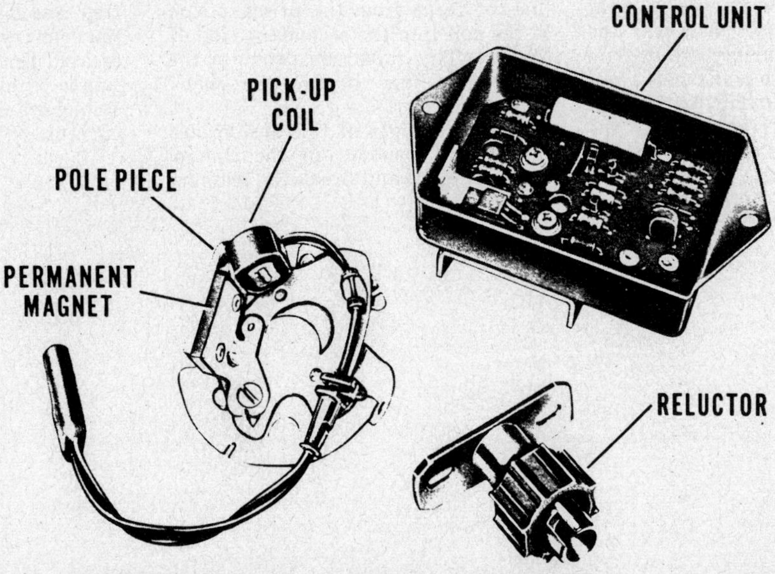
CONTROL UNIT
PICK-UP
COIL
POLE PIECE
PERMANENT
MAGNET
RELUCTOR

Distributor pickup and control unit components (© Chrysler Corp)

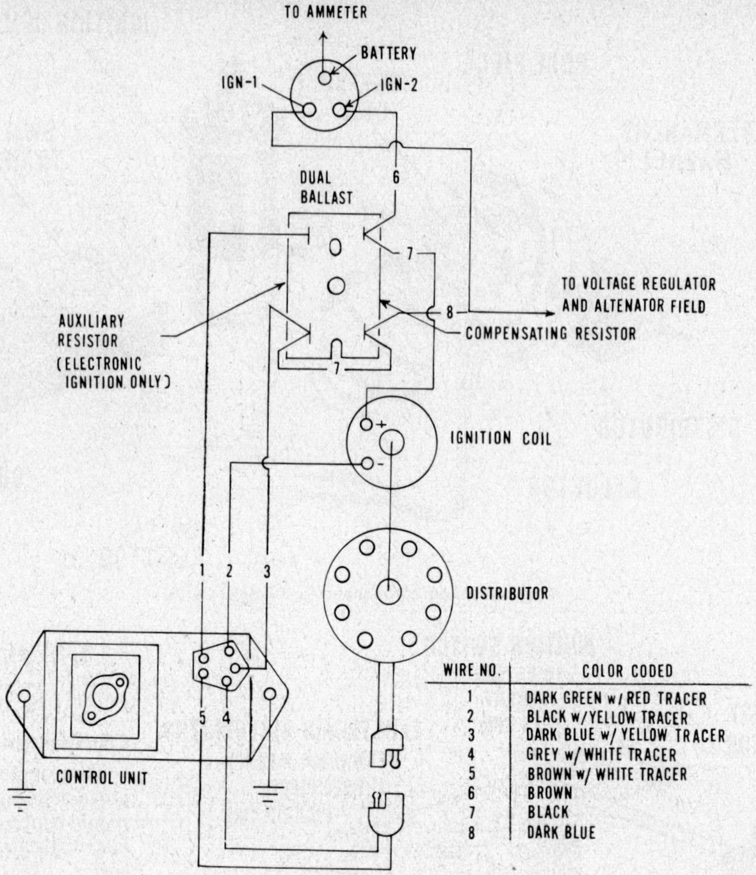
TO AMMETER
BATTERY
IGN-1
IGN-2
DUAL
BALLAST
6
7
TO VOLTAGE REGULATOR
AND ALTENATOR FIELD
8
AUXILIARY
RESISTOR
(ELECTRONIC
IGNITION ONLY)
COMPENSATING RESISTOR
7
IGNITION COIL
1 2 3
DISTRIBUTOR
5 4
CONTROL UNIT

WIRE NO.	COLOR CODED
1	DARK GREEN w/ RED TRACER
2	BLACK w/ YELLOW TRACER
3	DARK BLUE w/ YELLOW TRACER
4	GREY w/ WHITE TRACER
5	BROWN w/ WHITE TRACER
6	BROWN
7	BLACK
8	DARK BLUE

Chrysler system schematic

ondary side of the coil, the coil wire to the distributor, the rotor, the spark plug wires, and the spark plugs.

The magnetic pulse distributor is also connected to the control unit. As the distributor shaft rotates, the distributor reluctor turns past the pick-up unit. As the reluctor turns past the pick-up unit, each of the eight teeth on the reluctor pass near the pick-up unit once during each distributor revolution (two crankshaft revolutions since the distributor runs at one-half crankshaft speed). As the reluctor teeth move close to the pick-up unit, the magnetic rotating reluctor induces voltage into the magnetic pick-up unit. This voltage pulse is sent to the ignition control unit from the magnetic pick-up unit. When the pulse enters the control unit, it signals the control unit to interrupt the ignition primary circuit. This causes the primary circuit to collapse and begins the induction of the magnetic lines of force from the primary side of the coil into the secondary side of the coil. This induction provides the required voltage to fire the spark plugs.

The advantages of this system are that the transistors in the control unit can make and break the primary ignition circuit much faster than conventional ignition points can, and higher primary voltage can be utilized, since this system can be made to handle higher voltage without adverse effects, whereas ignition breaker points cannot. The quicker switching time of this system allows longer coil primary circuit saturation time and longer induction time when the primary circuit collapses. This increased time allows the primary circuit to build up more current and the secondary circuit to discharge more current.

TROUBLESHOOTING CHRYSLER ELECTRONIC IGNITION

Condition	*Possible Cause*	*Correction*
ENGINE WILL NOT START (Fuel and Carburetion Known to be OK)	a) Dual Ballast	Check resistance of each section: Compensating resistance: .50-.60 ohms @ 70°-80°F Auxiliary Ballast: 4.75-5.75 ohms Replace if faulty. Check wire positions.
	b) Faulty Ignition Coil	Check for carbonized tower. Check primary and secondary resistances: Primary: 1.41-1.79 ohms @ 70°-80°F Secondary: 9,200-11,700 ohms @ 70°-80°F Check in coil tester.
	c) Faulty Pickup or Improper Pickup Air Gap	Check pickup coil resistance: 400-600 ohms Check pickup gap: .010 in. feeler gauge should not slip between pickup coil core and an aligned reluctor blade. No evidence of pickup core striking reluctor blades should be visible. To reset gap, tighten pickup adjustment screw with a .008 in. feeler gauge held between pickup core and an aligned reluctor blade. After resetting gap, run distributor on test stand and apply vacuum advance, making sure that the pickup core does not strike the reluctor blades.
	d) Faulty Wiring	Visually inspect wiring for brittle insulation. Inspect connectors. Molded connectors should be inspected for rubber inside female terminals.
	e) Faulty Control Unit	Replace if all of the above checks are negative. Whenever the control unit or dual ballast is replaced, make sure the dual ballast wires are correctly inserted in the keyed molded connector.
ENGINE SURGES	a) Wiring	Inspect for loose connection and/or broken conductors in harness.
SEVERELY (Not Lean	b) Faulty Pickup Leads	Disconnect vacuum advance. If surging stops, replace pickup.
Carburetor)	c) Ignition Coil	Check for intermittent primary.
ENGINE MISSES (Carburetion OK)	a) Spark Plugs	Check plugs. Clean and regap if necessary.
	b) Secondary Cable	Check cables with an ohmmeter, or observe secondary circuit performance with an oscilloscope.
	c) Ignition Coil	Check for cabonized tower. Check in coil tester.
	d) Wiring	Check for loose or dirty connections.
	e) Faulty Pickup Lead	Disconnect vacuum advance. If miss stops, replace pickup.
	f) Control Unit	Replace if the above checks are negative.

INDEX

Carburetors

Carburetor Functions, Principles, and Circuits

Functions

Gasoline is the source of fuel for power in the automobile engine and the carburetor is the mechanism which automatically mixes liquid fuel with air in the correct proportions to provide the desired power output from the engine. The carburetor performs this function by metering, atomizing, and mixing fuel with air flowing through the engine.

A carburetor also regulates the proportion of air-to-fuel which enters the engine. It is the carburetor's regulation of the mixture flow which gives the operator control of the engine speed.

Metering

The automotive internal combustion engine operates efficiently within a relatively small range of air-to-fuel ratios. It is the function of the carburetor to meter the fuel in exact proportions to the air flowing into the engine, so that the optimum ratio of air-to-fuel is maintained under all operating conditions. Regulations governing exhaust gas emissions have made the proper metering of fuel by the carburetor an increasingly important factor. Too rich a mixture will result in poor economy and increased emissions, while too lean a mixture will result in loss of power and generally poor performance.

Carburetors are matched to engines so that metering can be accomplished by using carefully calibrated metering jets which allow fuel to enter the engine at a rate proportional to the engine's ability to draw air.

Atomization

The liquid fuel must be broken up into small particles so that it will more readily mix with air and vaporize. The more contact the fuel has with the air, the better the vaporization. Atomization can be accomplished in two ways: air may be drawn into a stream of fuel which will cause a turbulence and break the solid stream of fuel into smaller particles; or a nozzle can be positioned at the point of highest air velocity in the carburetor and the fuel will be torn into a fine spray as it enters the air stream.

Distribution

The carburetor is the primary device involved in the distribution of fuel to the engine. The more efficiently fuel and air are combined in the carburetor, the smoother the flow of vaporized mixture through the intake manifold to each combustion chamber. Hence, the importance of the carburetor in fuel distribution.

Principles

Vacuum

All carburetors operate on the basic principle of pressure difference. Any pressure less than atmospheric pressure is considered vacuum or a low pressure area. In the engine, as the piston moves down on the intake stroke with the intake valve open, a partial vacuum is created in the intake manifold. The farther the piston travels downward, the greater the vacuum created in the manifold. As the pressure drops in the manifold, a difference in pressure occurs between the carburetor and combustion cylinder above and below the manifold. The carburetor is positioned in such a way that the high pressure above it, and the vacuum or low pressure beneath it, causes air to be drawn through it. Fuel and air always move from high to low pressure areas.

Venturi Principle

To obtain greater pressure drop at the tip of the fuel nozzle so that fuel will flow, the principle of increasing the air velocity to create a low pressure area is used. The device used to increase the velocity of the air flowing through the carburetor is called a venturi. A venturi is a specially designed restriction placed in the air flow. In order for the air to pass through the restriction, it must accelerate causing a pressure drop or vacuum as it passes.

Carburetor Circuits

Float Circuit

The float circuit includes the float, float bowl, and a needle valve and seat. This circuit controls the amount of gas allowed to flow into the carburetor.

As the fuel level rises, it causes the float to rise which pushes the needle valve into its seat. As soon as the valve and seat make contact, the flow of gas is cut off from the fuel inlet. When the level of fuel drops, the float sinks and releases the needle valve from its seat which allows the gas to flow in. In actual operation, the fuel is maintained at practically a constant level. The float tends to hold the needle valve partly closed so that the incoming fuel just balances the fuel being withdrawn.

Idle and Low Speed Circuit

When the throttle is closed or only slightly opened, the air speed is low and practically no vacuum develops in the venturi. This means that the fuel nozzle will not feed. Thus, the carburetor must have another circuit to supply fuel during operation with a closed or slightly opened throttle.

This circuit is called the idle and low speed circuit. It consists of passages in which air and gas can flow beneath the throttle plate. With the throttle plate closed, there is high vacuum from the intake manifold. Atmospheric pressure pushes the

Float circuit
(© United Delco Div., G.M. Corp)

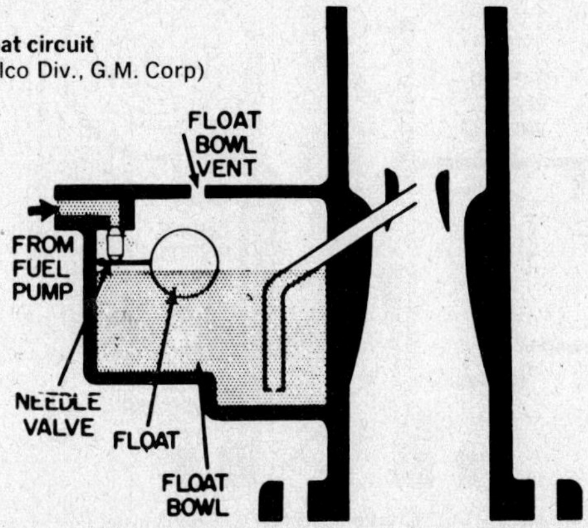
FLOAT
BOWL
VENT
FROM
FUEL
PUMP
NEEDLE
VALVE
FLOAT
FLOAT
BOWL

Idle and low speed circuit
(© United Delco Div., G.M. Corp)

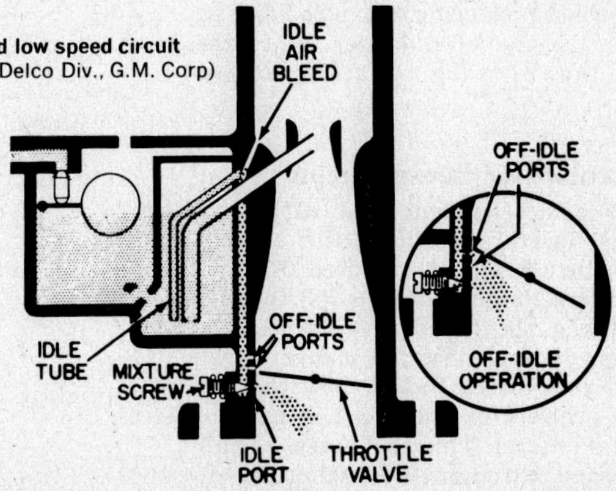
IDLE
AIR
BLEED
OFF-IDLE
PORTS
OFF-IDLE
PORTS
OFF-IDLE
OPERATION
IDLE
TUBE
MIXTURE
SCREW
IDLE
PORT
THROTTLE
VALVE

air/fuel mixture through the passages of the idle and low speed circuit and past the tapered point of the idle adjustment screw, which regulates engine idle speed.

High Speed Partial Load Circuit

When the throttle plate is opened sufficiently, there is little difference in vacuum between the upper and lower part of the air horn. Thus, little air/fuel mixture will discharge from the low speed and idle circuit. However, under this condition enough air is moving through the air horn to produce vacuum in the venturi to cause the main nozzle or high speed nozzle to discharge fuel. The circuit from the float bowl to the main nozzle is called the high speed partial load circuit. A nearly constant air/fuel ratio is maintained by this circuit from part to full-throttle.

High Speed Full Power Circuit

For high-speed, full-power, wide-open throttle operation, the air/fuel mixture must be enriched; this is done either mechanically or by intake manifold vacuum.

Full Power Circuit (Mechanical)

This circuit includes a metering rod jet and a metering rod. The rod has two steps of different diameters and is attached to the throttle linkage.

When the throttle is wide open, the metering rod is lifted which brings the smaller diameters of the rod into the jet. When the throttle is partly closed, the larger diameter of the metering rod is in the jet. This restricts fuel flow to the main nozzle but adequate amounts of fuel do flow for part-throttle operation.

Full Power Circuit (Vacuum)

This circuit is operated by intake manifold vacuum. It includes a vacuum diaphragm linked to a valve on a metering rod.

When the throttle is opened so that intake manifold vacuum is reduced, the spring raises the diaphragm. This allows the metering rod to be lifted so that its smaller diameter clears the jet, thus allowing more fuel to flow in.

Accelerator Pump Circuit

For acceleration, the carburetor must deliver additional fuel. A sudden inrush of air is caused by rapid acceleration or applying full throttle.

When the throttle is opened, the pump lever pushes the plunger down and this forces fuel to flow through the accelerator pump circuit and out the pump jet. This fuel enters the air passage through the carburetor to supply additional fuel demands.

Choke

When starting an engine, it is necessary to increase the amount of fuel delivered to the intake manifold. This increase is controlled by the choke.

The choke consists of a valve in the top of the air horn controlled mechanically by an automatic device. When the choke valve is closed, only a small amount of air can get past it.

When the engine is cranked, a fairly high vacuum develops in the air horn. This vacuum causes the main nozzle to discharge a heavy stream of fuel. The quantity delivered is sufficient to produce the correct air/fuel mixture needed for starting the engine. The choke is released either manually or by heat from the engine.

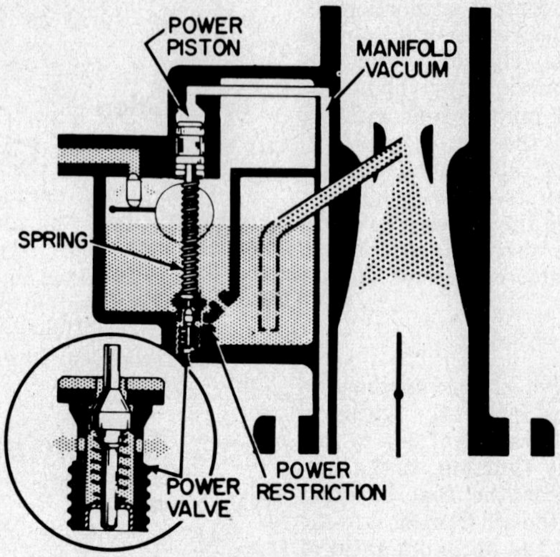
POWER PISTON
MANIFOLD VACUUM
SPRING
POWER VALVE
POWER RESTRICTION

Power circuit
(© United Delco Div., G.M. Corp)

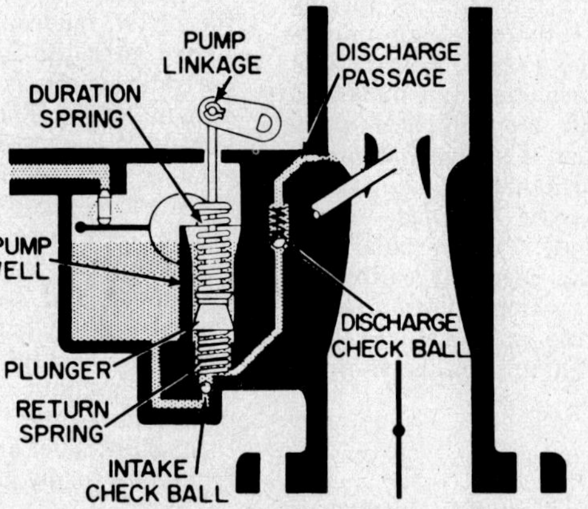
PUMP LINKAGE
DISCHARGE PASSAGE
DURATION SPRING
PUMP WELL
DISCHARGE CHECK BALL
PLUNGER
RETURN SPRING
INTAKE CHECK BALL

Accelerator pump circuit
(© United Delco Div., G.M. Corp)

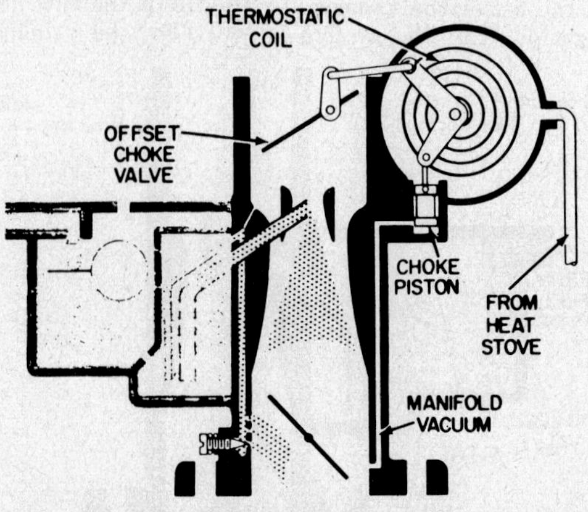
THERMOSTATIC COIL
OFFSET CHOKE VALVE
CHOKE PISTON
FROM HEAT STOVE
MANIFOLD VACUUM

Choke system
(© United Delco Div., G.M. Corp)

TROUBLESHOOTING

NOTE: Carburetor problems cannot be isolated effectively unless all other engine systems are functioning correctly and the engine is properly tuned.

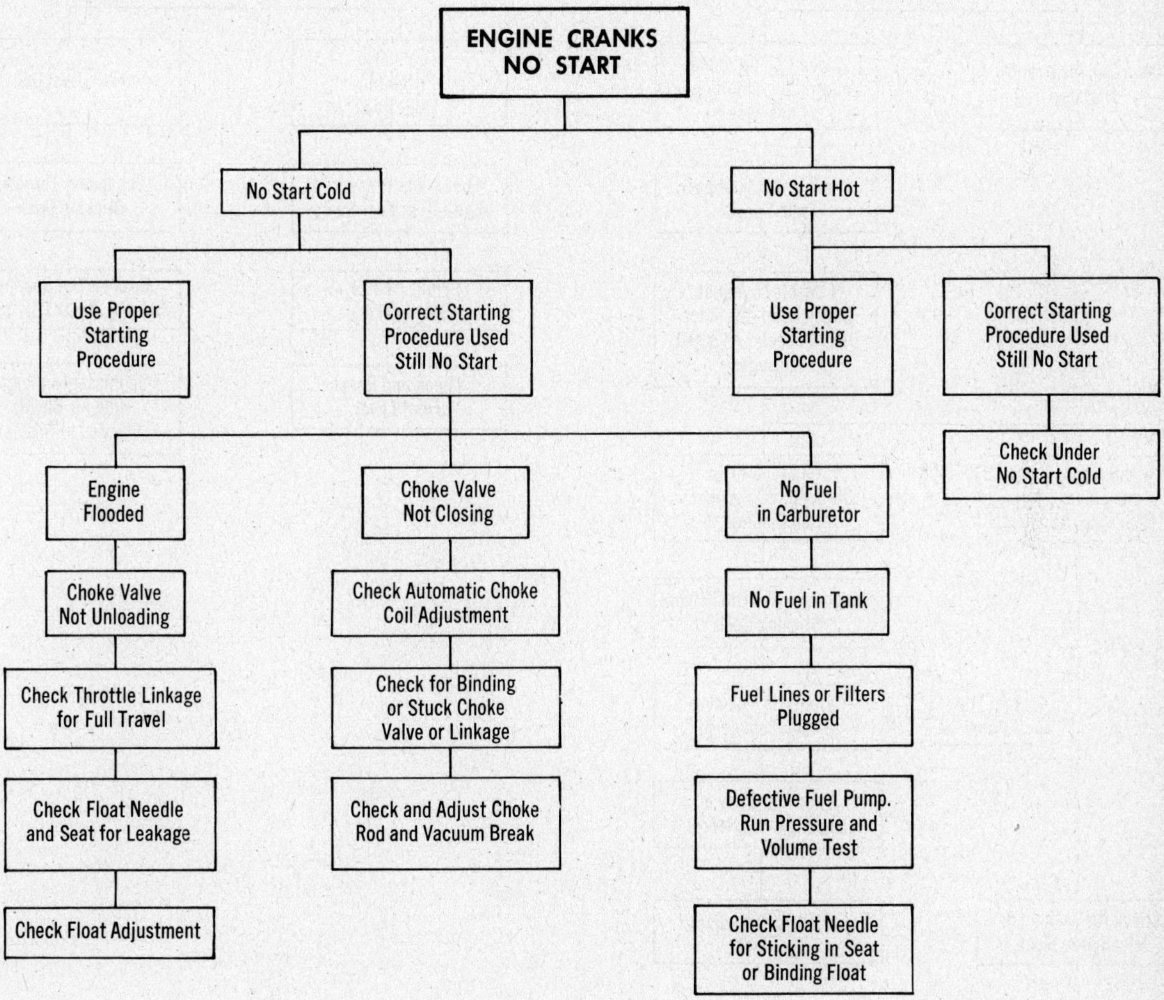
ENGINE CRANKS NO START
No Start Cold
No Start Hot
Use Proper Starting Procedure
Correct Starting Procedure Used Still No Start
Use Proper Starting Procedure
Correct Starting Procedure Used Still No Start
Check Under No Start Cold
Engine Flooded
Choke Valve Not Closing
No Fuel in Carburetor
Choke Valve Not Unloading
Check Automatic Choke Coil Adjustment
No Fuel in Tank
Check Throttle Linkage for Full Travel
Check for Binding or Stuck Choke Valve or Linkage
Fuel Lines or Filters Plugged
Check Float Needle and Seat for Leakage
Check and Adjust Choke Rod and Vacuum Break
Defective Fuel Pump. Run Pressure and Volume Test
Check Float Adjustment
Check Float Needle for Sticking in Seat or Binding Float

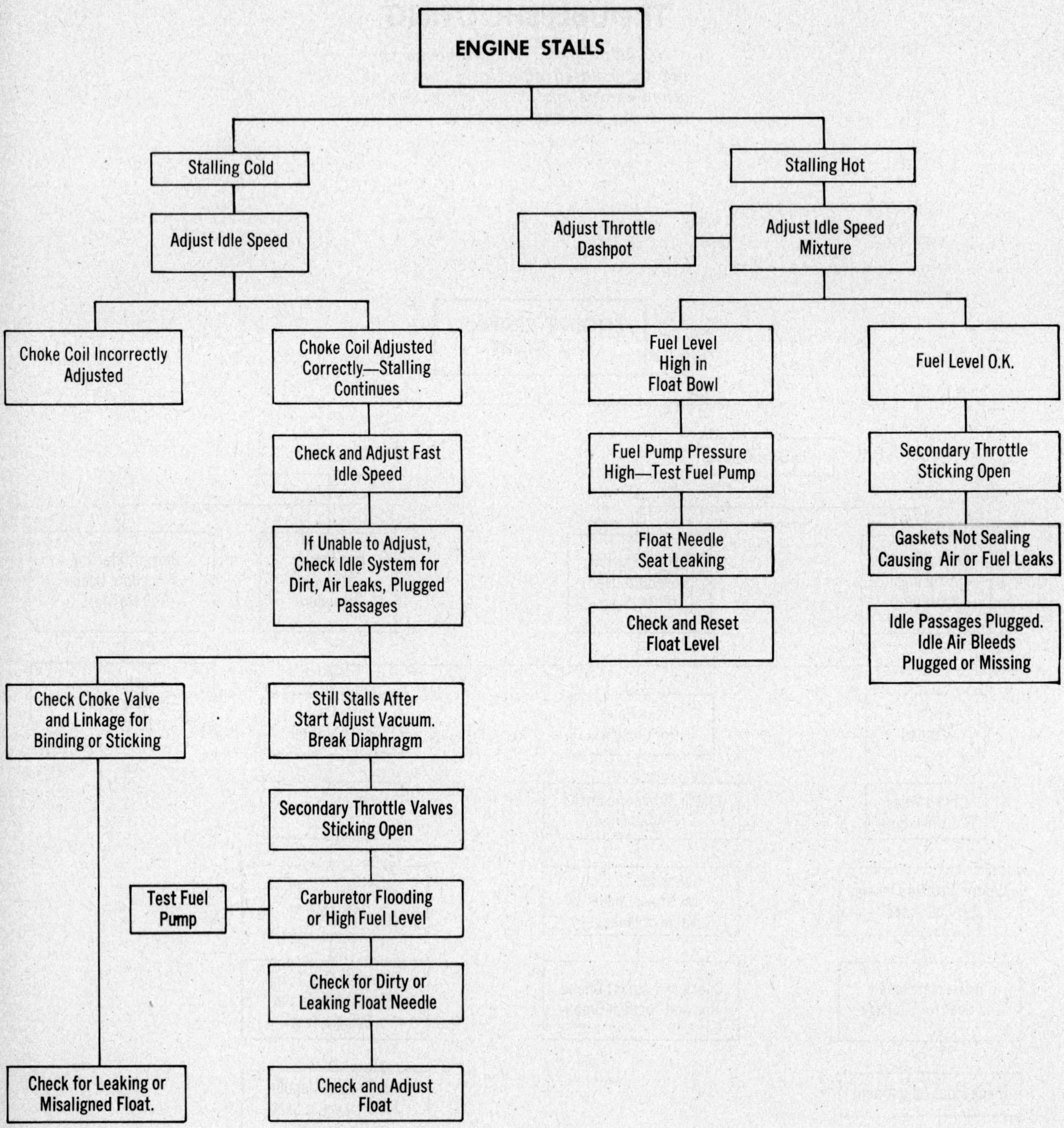
ENGINE STALLS
Stalling Cold
Adjust Idle Speed
Choke Coil Incorrectly Adjusted
Choke Coil Adjusted Correctly—Stalling Continues
Check and Adjust Fast Idle Speed
If Unable to Adjust, Check Idle System for Dirt, Air Leaks, Plugged Passages
Check Choke Valve and Linkage for Binding or Sticking
Still Stalls After Start Adjust Vacuum. Break Diaphragm
Secondary Throttle Valves Sticking Open
Test Fuel Pump
Carburetor Flooding or High Fuel Level
Check for Dirty or Leaking Float Needle
Check for Leaking or Misaligned Float.
Check and Adjust Float
Stalling Hot
Adjust Throttle Dashpot
Adjust Idle Speed Mixture
Fuel Level High in Float Bowl
Fuel Pump Pressure High—Test Fuel Pump
Float Needle Seat Leaking
Check and Reset Float Level
Fuel Level O.K.
Secondary Throttle Sticking Open
Gaskets Not Sealing Causing Air or Fuel Leaks
Idle Passages Plugged. Idle Air Bleeds Plugged or Missing

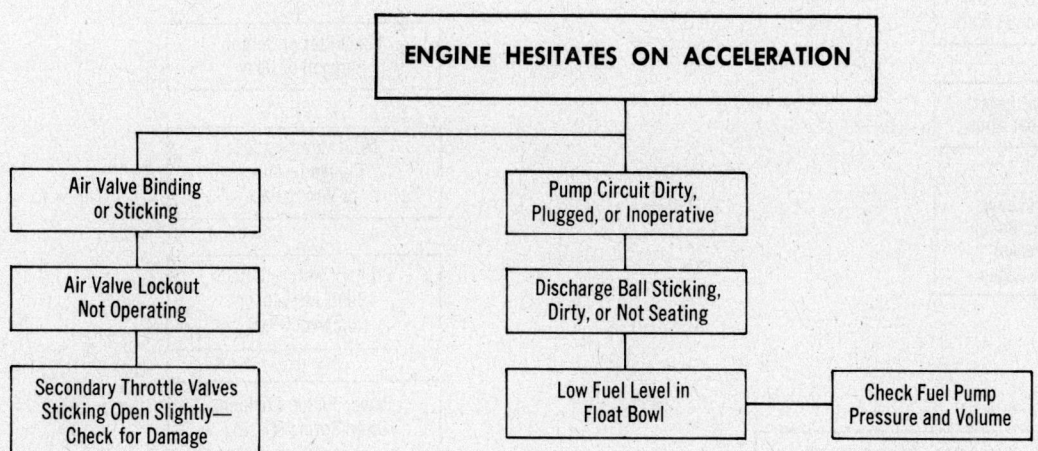

ENGINE HESITATES ON ACCELERATION

- Air Valve Binding or Sticking
  - Air Valve Lockout Not Operating
    - Secondary Throttle Valves Sticking Open Slightly—Check for Damage
- Pump Circuit Dirty, Plugged, or Inoperative
  - Discharge Ball Sticking, Dirty, or Not Seating
    - Low Fuel Level in Float Bowl — Check Fuel Pump Pressure and Volume

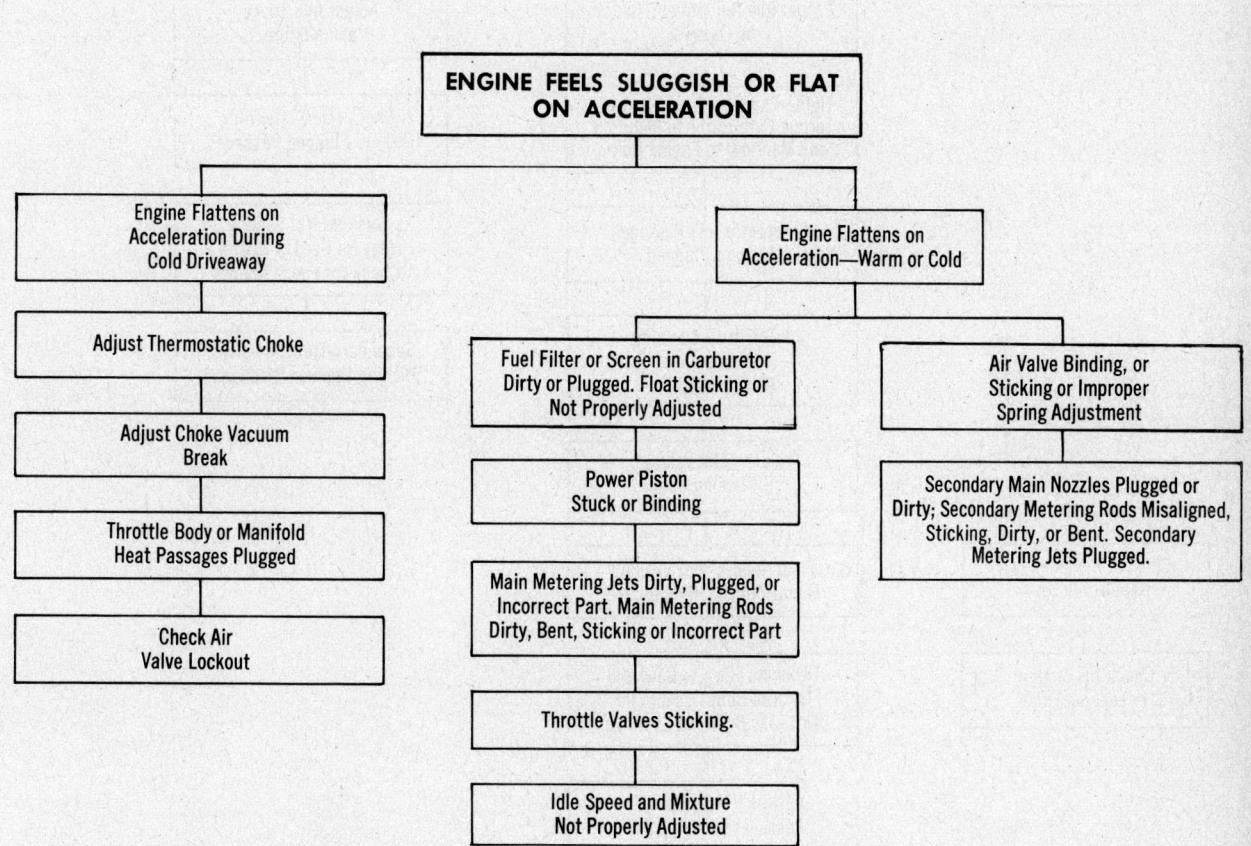

ENGINE FEELS SLUGGISH OR FLAT ON ACCELERATION

- Engine Flattens on Acceleration During Cold Driveaway
  - Adjust Thermostatic Choke
  - Adjust Choke Vacuum Break
  - Throttle Body or Manifold Heat Passages Plugged
  - Check Air Valve Lockout
- Engine Flattens on Acceleration—Warm or Cold
  - Fuel Filter or Screen in Carburetor Dirty or Plugged. Float Sticking or Not Properly Adjusted
    - Power Piston Stuck or Binding
    - Main Metering Jets Dirty, Plugged, or Incorrect Part. Main Metering Rods Dirty, Bent, Sticking or Incorrect Part
    - Throttle Valves Sticking.
    - Idle Speed and Mixture Not Properly Adjusted
  - Air Valve Binding, or Sticking or Improper Spring Adjustment
    - Secondary Main Nozzles Plugged or Dirty; Secondary Metering Rods Misaligned, Sticking, Dirty, or Bent. Secondary Metering Jets Plugged.

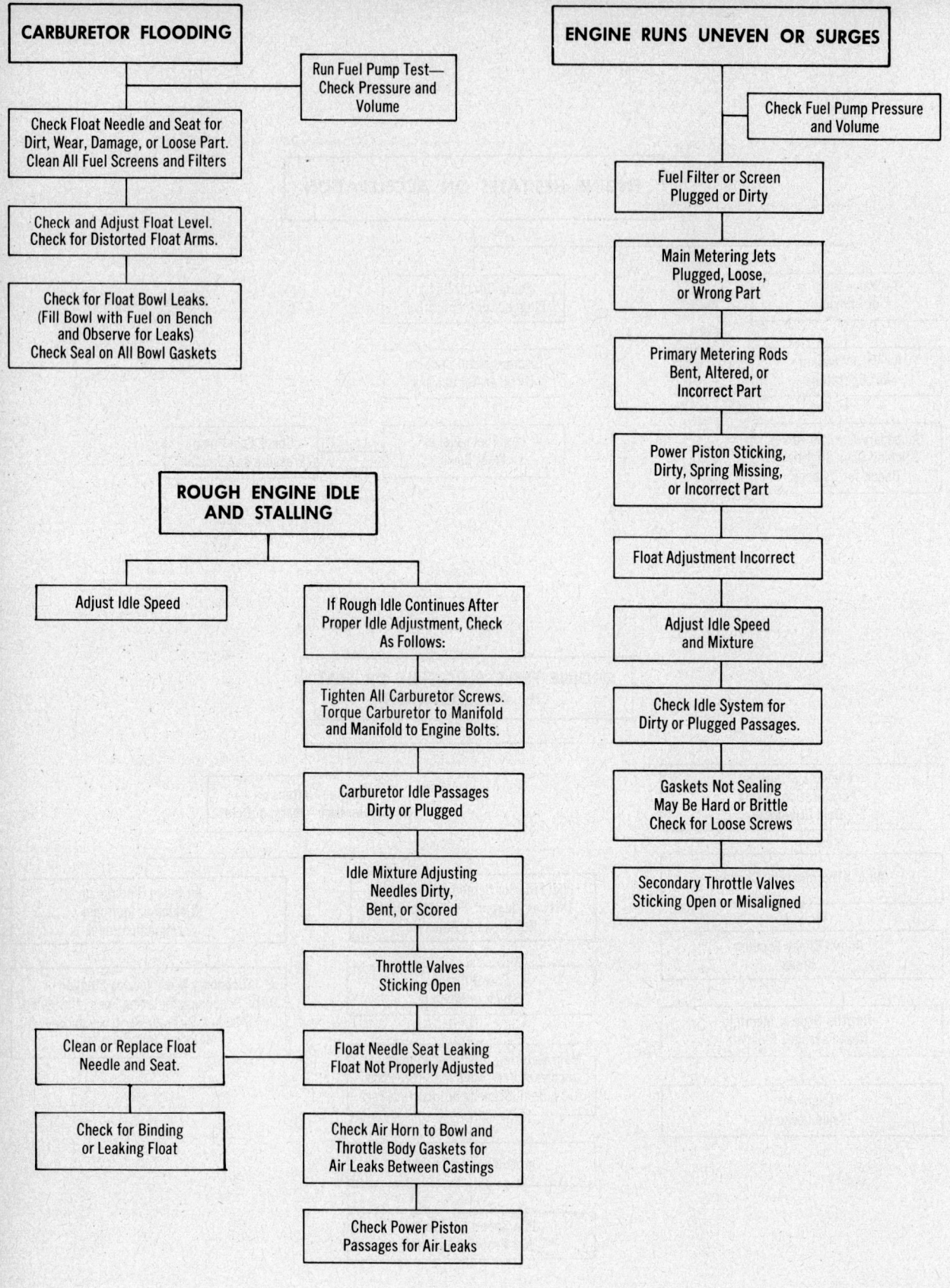

CARBURETOR FLOODING

- Run Fuel Pump Test—Check Pressure and Volume
- Check Float Needle and Seat for Dirt, Wear, Damage, or Loose Part. Clean All Fuel Screens and Filters
- Check and Adjust Float Level. Check for Distorted Float Arms.
- Check for Float Bowl Leaks. (Fill Bowl with Fuel on Bench and Observe for Leaks) Check Seal on All Bowl Gaskets

ENGINE RUNS UNEVEN OR SURGES

- Check Fuel Pump Pressure and Volume
- Fuel Filter or Screen Plugged or Dirty
- Main Metering Jets Plugged, Loose, or Wrong Part
- Primary Metering Rods Bent, Altered, or Incorrect Part
- Power Piston Sticking, Dirty, Spring Missing, or Incorrect Part
- Float Adjustment Incorrect
- Adjust Idle Speed and Mixture
- Check Idle System for Dirty or Plugged Passages.
- Gaskets Not Sealing May Be Hard or Brittle Check for Loose Screws
- Secondary Throttle Valves Sticking Open or Misaligned

ROUGH ENGINE IDLE AND STALLING

- Adjust Idle Speed
- If Rough Idle Continues After Proper Idle Adjustment, Check As Follows:
  - Tighten All Carburetor Screws. Torque Carburetor to Manifold and Manifold to Engine Bolts.
  - Carburetor Idle Passages Dirty or Plugged
  - Idle Mixture Adjusting Needles Dirty, Bent, or Scored
  - Throttle Valves Sticking Open
  - Float Needle Seat Leaking Float Not Properly Adjusted
    - Clean or Replace Float Needle and Seat.
    - Check for Binding or Leaking Float
  - Check Air Horn to Bowl and Throttle Body Gaskets for Air Leaks Between Castings
  - Check Power Piston Passages for Air Leaks

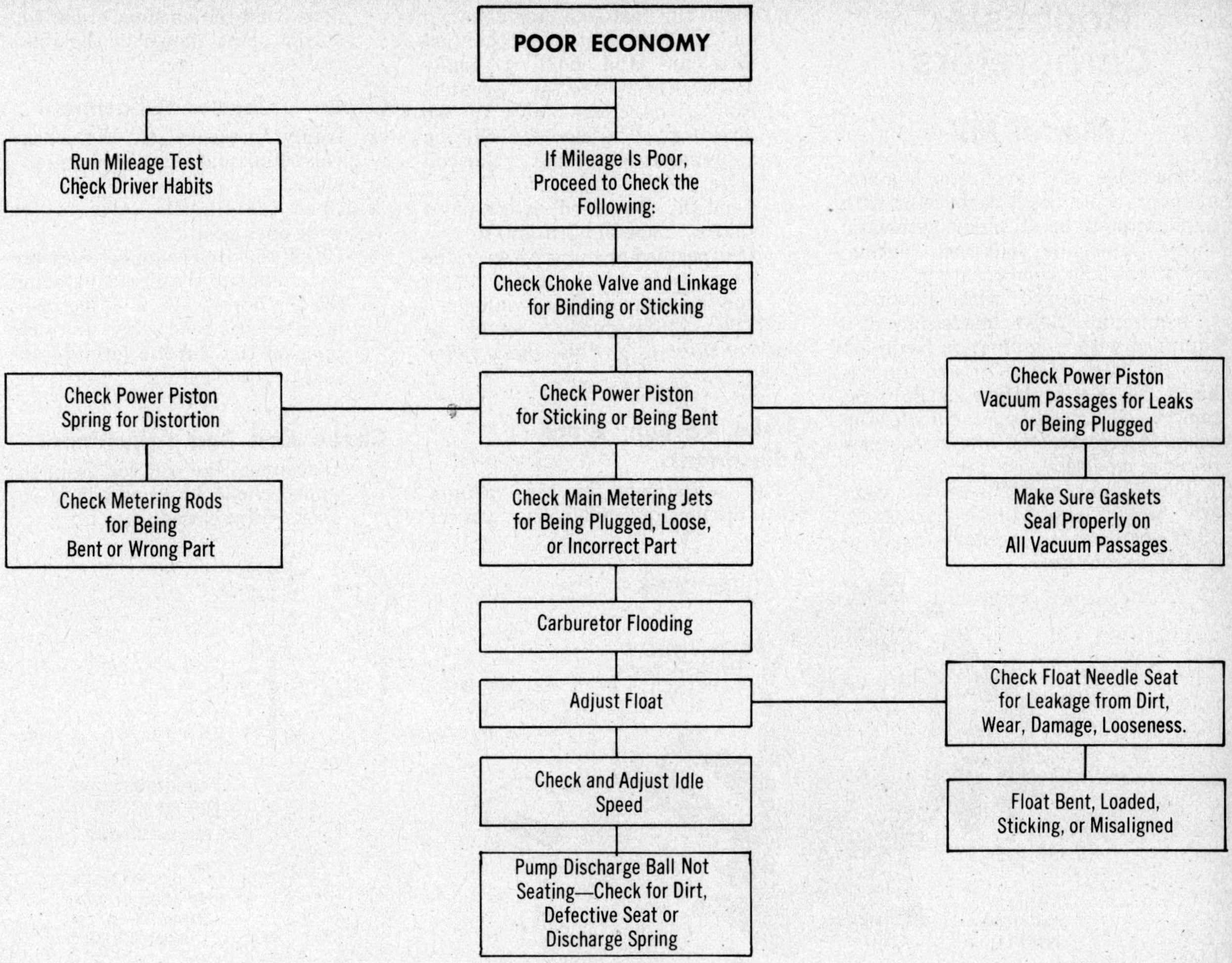
POOR ECONOMY
Run Mileage Test
Check Driver Habits
If Mileage Is Poor, Proceed to Check the Following:
Check Choke Valve and Linkage for Binding or Sticking
Check Power Piston Spring for Distortion
Check Power Piston for Sticking or Being Bent
Check Power Piston Vacuum Passages for Leaks or Being Plugged
Check Metering Rods for Being Bent or Wrong Part
Check Main Metering Jets for Being Plugged, Loose, or Incorrect Part
Make Sure Gaskets Seal Properly on All Vacuum Passages
Carburetor Flooding
Adjust Float
Check Float Needle Seat for Leakage from Dirt, Wear, Damage, Looseness.
Check and Adjust Idle Speed
Float Bent, Loaded, Sticking, or Misaligned
Pump Discharge Ball Not Seating—Check for Dirt, Defective Seat or Discharge Spring

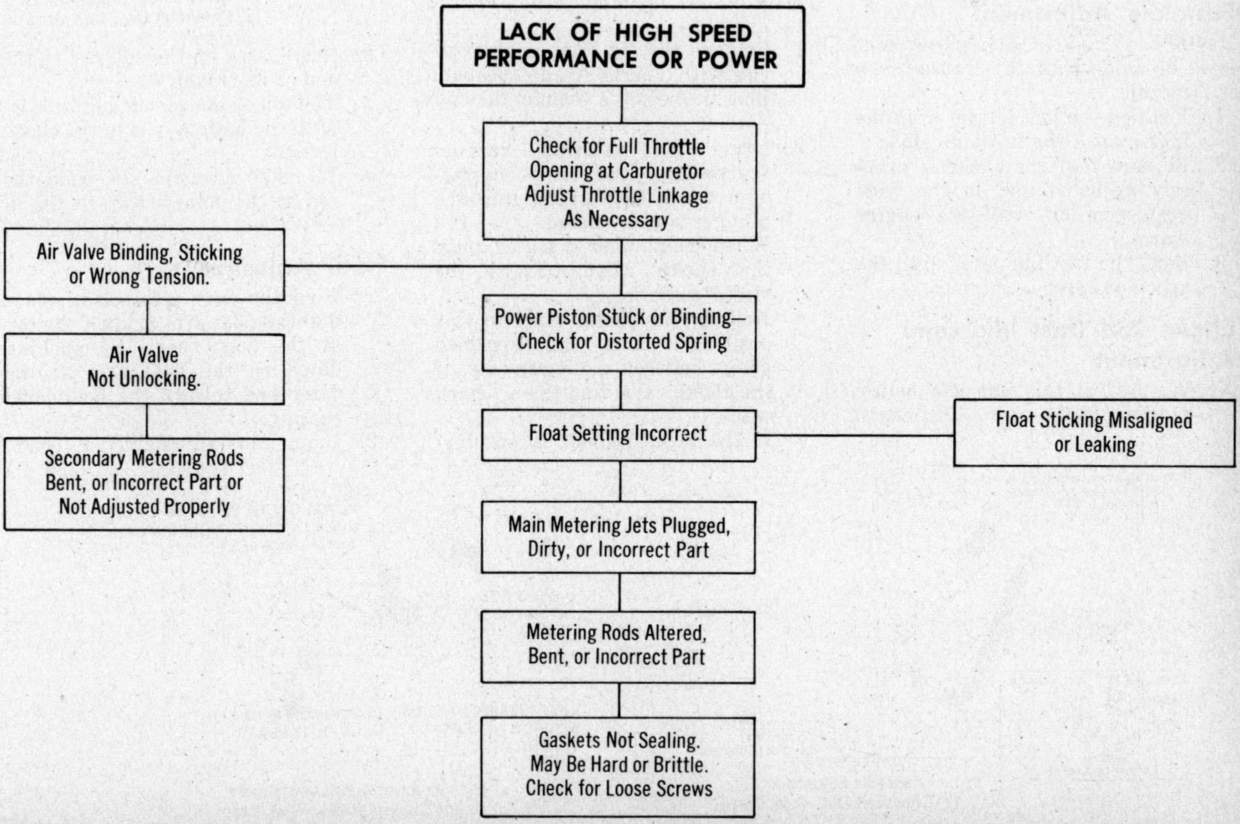
LACK OF HIGH SPEED PERFORMANCE OR POWER
Check for Full Throttle Opening at Carburetor Adjust Throttle Linkage As Necessary
Air Valve Binding, Sticking or Wrong Tension.
Power Piston Stuck or Binding—Check for Distorted Spring
Air Valve Not Unlocking.
Float Setting Incorrect
Float Sticking Misaligned or Leaking
Secondary Metering Rods Bent, or Incorrect Part or Not Adjusted Properly
Main Metering Jets Plugged, Dirty, or Incorrect Part
Metering Rods Altered, Bent, or Incorrect Part
Gaskets Not Sealing. May Be Hard or Brittle. Check for Loose Screws

Rochester Carburetors

Model MV

The model MV carburetor is a single bore, down-draft carburetor with an aluminum throttle body, automatic choke, internally balanced venting, and a hot idle compensating system for cars equipped with automatic transmissions. Newer models are also equipped with Combination Emission Control valves (C.E.C.) and an Exhaust Gas Recirculation (EGR) system. An electrically operated idle stop solenoid replaces the idle stop screw of older models.

The MV carburetor is used on General Motors six cylinder cars from 1968 and service procedures apply to all MV carburetors.

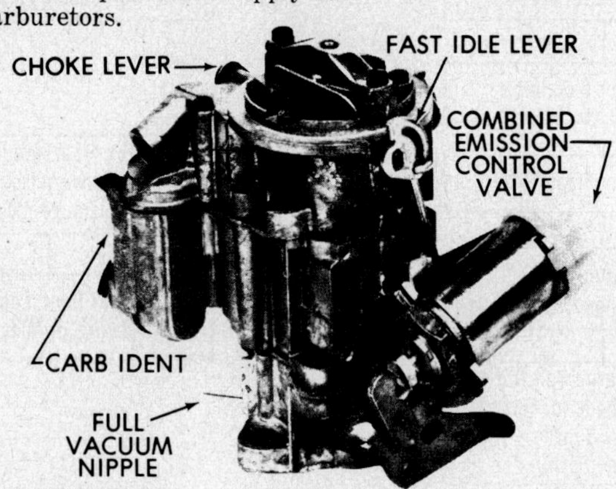
CHOKE LEVER
FAST IDLE LEVER
COMBINED EMISSION CONTROL VALVE
CARB IDENT
FULL VACUUM NIPPLE

Rochester Monojet Carburetor
(© Buick Div., G.M. Corp)

Fast Idle Adjustment

NOTE: The fast idle adjustment must be made with the transmission in Neutral.

1. Position the fast idle lever on the high step of the fast idle cam.
2. Be sure that the choke is properly adjusted and in the wide open position with the engine warm.
3. Bend the fast idle lever until the specified speed is obtained.

Choke Rod (fast idle cam) Adjustment

NOTE: Adjust the fast idle before making choke rod adjustments.

1. Place the fast idle cam follower on the second step of the fast idle cam and hold it firmly against the rise to the high step.
2. Rotate the choke valve in the direction of a closed choke by applying force to the choke coil lever.
3. Bend the choke rod, at the point shown in the illustration, to give the specified opening between the lower edge of the choke valve and the inside air horn wall.

NOTE: Measurement must be made at the center of the choke valve.

Choke Vacuum Break Adjustments

The adjustment of the vacuum break diaphragm unit insures correct choke valve opening after engine starting.

1. Remove the air cleaner on vehicles with Therm AC air cleaner; plug the sensor's vacuum take off port.
2. Using an external vacuum source, apply vacuum to the vacuum break diaphragm until the plunger is fully seated.
3. When the plunger is seated, push the choke valve toward the closed position.
4. Holding the choke valve in this position, place the specified gauge between the lower edge of the choke valve and the air horn wall.
5. If the measurement is not correct, bend the vacuum break rod at the point shown in the illustration.

Choke Unloader Adjustment

1. Apply pressure to the choke valve and hold it in the closed position.
2. Open the throttle valve to the wide open position.
3. Check the dimension between the lower edge of the choke plate and the air horn wall; if adjustment is needed, bend the unloader tang on the throttle lever to adjust to specification.

Choke Coil Rod Adjustment

1. Disconnect the coil rod from the upper choke lever and hold the choke valve closed.

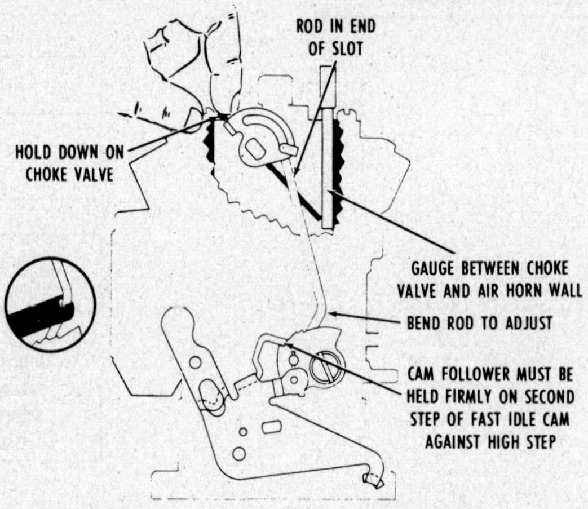
ROD IN END OF SLOT
HOLD DOWN ON CHOKE VALVE
GAUGE BETWEEN CHOKE VALVE AND AIR HORN WALL
BEND ROD TO ADJUST
CAM FOLLOWER MUST BE HELD FIRMLY ON SECOND STEP OF FAST IDLE CAM AGAINST HIGH STEP

Fast Idle Cam Adjustment
(© Chevrolet Div., G.M. Corp)

2. Push down on the coil rod to the end of its travel.
3. The top of the rod should be even with the bottom hole in the choke lever.
4. To make adjustments, bend the rod at the point shown in the illustration.

Float Adjustment

1. Hold the float retainer in place and the float arm against the top of the float needle by pushing down on the float arm at the outer end toward the float bowl casting.
2. Using an adjustable T scale,

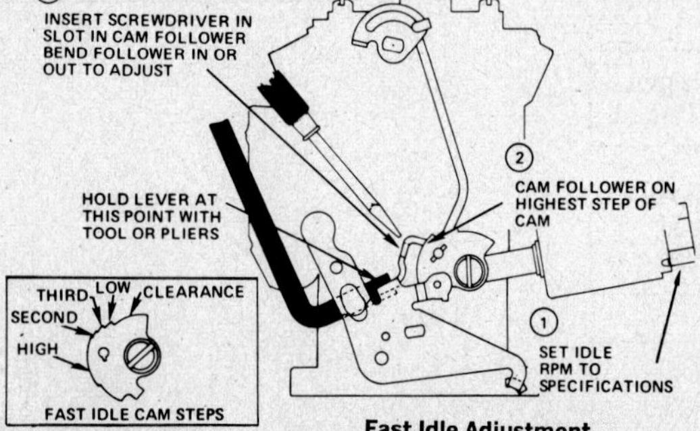
③
INSERT SCREWDRIVER IN SLOT IN CAM FOLLOWER BEND FOLLOWER IN OR OUT TO ADJUST
HOLD LEVER AT THIS POINT WITH TOOL OR PLIERS
② CAM FOLLOWER ON HIGHEST STEP OF CAM
① SET IDLE RPM TO SPECIFICATIONS
THIRD
LOW
CLEARANCE
SECOND
HIGH
FAST IDLE CAM STEPS

Fast Idle Adjustment
(© Chevrolet Div., G.M. Corp)

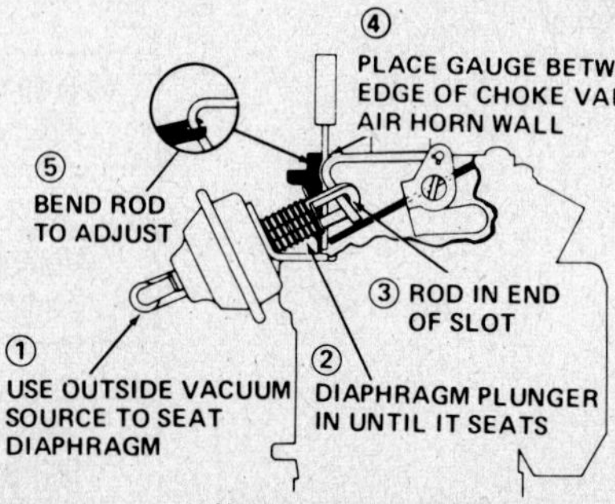
④ PLACE GAUGE BETWEEN LOWER EDGE OF CHOKE VALVE AND AIR HORN WALL
⑤ BEND ROD TO ADJUST
③ ROD IN END OF SLOT
① USE OUTSIDE VACUUM SOURCE TO SEAT DIAPHRAGM
② DIAPHRAGM PLUNGER IN UNTIL IT SEATS

Vacuum Break Adjustment
(© Chevrolet Div., G.M. Corp)

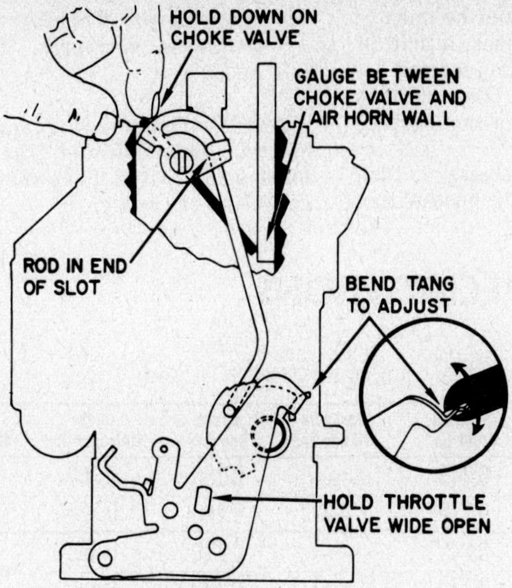
HOLD DOWN ON
CHOKE VALVE
GAUGE BETWEEN
CHOKE VALVE AND
AIR HORN WALL
ROD IN END
OF SLOT
BEND TANG
TO ADJUST
HOLD THROTTLE
VALVE WIDE OPEN
Adjusting Choke Unloader
(© Chevrolet Div., G.M. Corp)

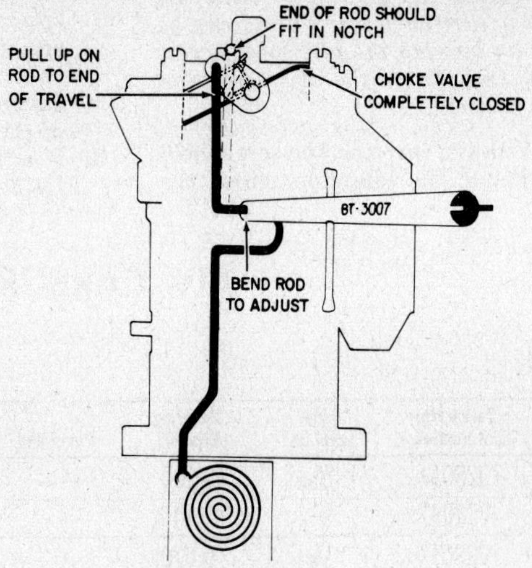
END OF ROD SHOULD
FIT IN NOTCH
PULL UP ON
ROD TO END
OF TRAVEL
CHOKE VALVE
COMPLETELY CLOSED
BT-3007
BEND ROD
TO ADJUST
Choke Coil Rod Adjustment
(© Pontiac Div., G.M. Corp)

measure the distance from the toe of the float to the float bowl gasket surface.

NOTE: The float bowl gasket should be removed and the gauge held on the index point on the float for accurate measurement.

3. Adjust the float level by bending the float arm up or down at the float arm junction.

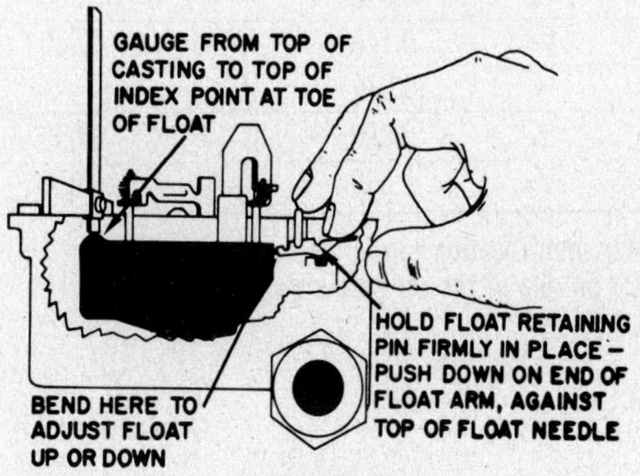
GAUGE FROM TOP OF
CASTING TO TOP OF
INDEX POINT AT TOE
OF FLOAT
HOLD FLOAT RETAINING
PIN FIRMLY IN PLACE –
PUSH DOWN ON END OF
FLOAT ARM, AGAINST
TOP OF FLOAT NEEDLE
BEND HERE TO
ADJUST FLOAT
UP OR DOWN
Float Level
(© Pontiac Div., G.M. Corp)

Metering Rod Adjustments

1. Hold the throttle valve wide open and push down on the metering rod against spring tension, then remove the rod from the main metering jet.
2. In order to check adjustment, the slow idle screw must be backed out and the fast idle cam rotated so that the fast idle cam follower does not contact the steps on the cam.
3. With the throttle valve closed, push down on the power piston until it contacts its stop.
4. With the power piston depressed, swing the metering rod holder over the flat surface of the bowl casting next to the carburetor bore.
5. Insert a specified size drill between the bowl casting sealing bead and the lower surface of the metering rod holder. The drill should slide smoothly between both surfaces.
6. If adjustment is needed, carefully bend the metering rod holder up or down at the point shown. After adjustment, reinstall the metering rod.

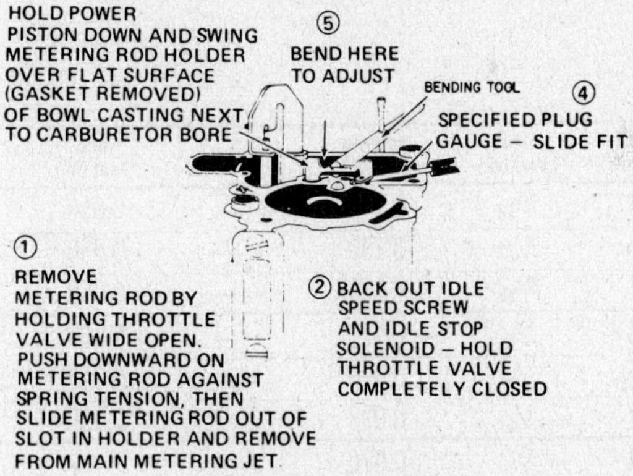
HOLD POWER
PISTON DOWN AND SWING
METERING ROD HOLDER
OVER FLAT SURFACE
(GASKET REMOVED)
OF BOWL CASTING NEXT
TO CARBURETOR BORE
⑤
BEND HERE
TO ADJUST
BENDING TOOL
④
SPECIFIED PLUG
GAUGE – SLIDE FIT
①
REMOVE
METERING ROD BY
HOLDING THROTTLE
VALVE WIDE OPEN.
PUSH DOWNWARD ON
METERING ROD AGAINST
SPRING TENSION, THEN
SLIDE METERING ROD OUT OF
SLOT IN HOLDER AND REMOVE
FROM MAIN METERING JET
② BACK OUT IDLE
SPEED SCREW
AND IDLE STOP
SOLENOID – HOLD
THROTTLE VALVE
COMPLETELY CLOSED
Metering Rod Adjustment
(© Chevrolet Div., G.M. Corp)

Idle Vent Adjustment

1. The engine idle must be set at the specified RPM and the choke valve held wide open so that the fast idle cam follower is not contacting the cam.

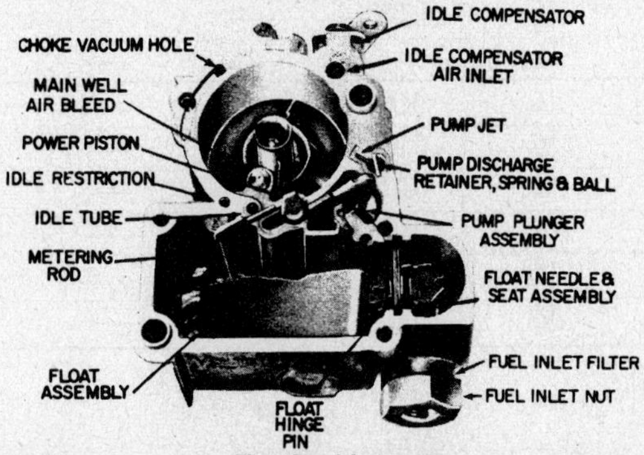
IDLE COMPENSATOR
CHOKE VACUUM HOLE
IDLE COMPENSATOR
AIR INLET
MAIN WELL
AIR BLEED
PUMP JET
POWER PISTON
PUMP DISCHARGE
RETAINER, SPRING & BALL
IDLE RESTRICTION
IDLE TUBE
PUMP PLUNGER
ASSEMBLY
METERING
ROD
FLOAT NEEDLE &
SEAT ASSEMBLY
FUEL INLET FILTER
FLOAT
ASSEMBLY
FUEL INLET NUT
FLOAT
HINGE
PIN
Float Bowl Assembly
(© Oldsmobile Div., G.M. Corp)

NOTE: If the carburetor is off the car, a preliminary idle setting can be made by turning the idle speed screw in 1 1/2 turns from the closed throttle valve position.

2. With the throttle stop screw held against the idle stop screw, the idle vent valve should be open to specification. To check, a drill of specified size may be inserted between the top of the air horn casting and the bottom surface of the valve.
3. If adjustment is necessary, turn the slotted vent valve head with a screwdriver. Turning the head clockwise *increases* the clearance.

NOTE: On models equipped with an idle stop solenoid, the solenoid must be activated when checking and adjusting the valve.

MV CARBURETOR SPECIFICATIONS

BUICK

Year	Carburetor Identification①	Float Level (in.)	Metering Rod (in.)	Pump Rod	Idle Vent (in.)	Vacuum Break (in.)	Fast Idle Off Car (in.)	Choke Rod (in.)	Choke Unloader (in.)	Fast Idle Speed (rpm)
1968	7028014	9/32	0.100	—	0.050	0.245	—	0.180	0.350	—
	7028047	5/16	0.140	—	0.020	0.275	—	0.190	0.325	—
1969	7029014	1/4	0.070	—	0.050	0.245	—	0.170	0.350	620
	7029047	9/32	0.140	—	0.020	0.275	—	0.190	0.350	720
1970	7040014	1/4	0.070	—	0.050	0.245	—	0.170	0.350	650
	7040015	1/4	0.140	—	0.050	0.275	—	0.200	0.350	900
	7040017	1/4	0.070	—	—	0.230	0.100	0.190	0.350	900
1971	7041014	1/4	0.080	—	0.050	0.225	—	0.160	0.500	500
	7041017	1/4	0.080	—	0.050	0.225	—	0.180	0.350	550

① The Carburetor identification tag is located at the rear of the carburetor on one of the air horn screws.

CHEVROLET

Year	Carburetor Identification①	Float Level (in.)	Metering Rod (in.)	Pump Rod	Idle Vent (in.)	Vacuum Break (in.)	Fast Idle Off Car (in.)	Choke Rod (in.)	Choke Unloader (in.)	Fast Idle Speed (rpm)
1968	7028014	9/32	0.120	—	0.050	0.245	1 1/2	0.150	0.350	2400②
	7028015	9/32	0.130	—	0.050	0.275	1 1/2	0.150	0.350	2400②
	7028017	9/32	0.130	—	0.050	0.275	1 1/2	0.150	0.350	2400②
1969	7029014	1/4	0.070	—	0.050	0.245	0.100	0.170	0.350	2400②
	7029015	1/4	0.090	—	0.050	0.275	0.100	0.200	0.350	2400②
	7029017	1/4	0.090	—	0.050	0.275	0.100	0.200	0.350	2400②
1970	7040014	1/4	0.070	—	—	0.200	0.110	0.170	0.350	2400②
	7040017	1/4	0.090	—	—	0.160	0.100	0.190	0.350	2400②
1971	7041014	1/4	0.080	—	—	0.200	0.100	0.160	0.350	—
	7041017	1/4	0.080	—	—	0.230	0.100	0.180	0.350	—
	7041023	1/16	—	—	—	0.200	0.110	0.120	0.350	—
1972	7042014	1/4	0.080	—	—	0.190	—	0.125	0.500	2400②
	7042017	1/4	0.078	—	—	0.225	—	0.150	0.500	2400②
	7042984	1/4	0.078	—	—	0.190	—	0.125	0.500	2400②
	7042987	1/4	0.076	—	—	0.225	—	0.150	0.500	2400②
1973	7043014	1/4	0.080	—	—	0.300	—	0.245	0.500	1800②
	7043017	1/4	0.080	—	—	0.350	—	0.275	0.500	1800②

② High step of cam

OLDSMOBILE

Year	Carburetor Identification①	Float Level (in.)	Metering Rod (in.)	Pump Rod	Idle Vent (in.)	Vacuum Break (in.)	Fast Idle Off Car (in.)	Choke Rod (in.)	Choke Unloader (in.)	Fast Idle Speed (rpm)
1968	7028014	9/32	0.120	—	0.050	0.245	—	0.180	0.350	650③
	7028057	11/32	0.120	—	0.050	0.275	—	0.190	0.350	650③
1969	7029014	1/4	0.070	—	0.050	0.245	—	0.170	0.350	750③
	7029057	5/16	0.120	—	0.030	0.260	—	0.180	0.350	750③
1970	7040014	1/4	0.070	—	—	0.200	—	0.170	0.350	900③
	7040017	1/4	0.070	—	—	0.225	—	0.190	0.350	750③
1971	7041014	1/4	0.070	—	—	0.200	—	0.160	0.350	900③
	7041019	1/4	0.070	—	—	0.225	—	0.180	0.350	750③

③ Low step of cam

PONTIAC

Year	Carburetor Identification①	Float Level (in.)	Metering Rod (in.)	Pump Rod	Idle Vent (in.)	Vacuum Break (in.)	Fast Idle Off Car (in.)	Choke Rod (in.)	Choke Unloader (in.)	Fast Idle Speed (rpm)
1968	7028067	5/16	0.085	—	0.040	0.300	0.090	0.200	0.245	2400②
	7028075	5/16	0.085	—	0.040	0.290	—	0.200	0.245	2400②
	7028065	5/16	0.075	—	0.040	0.300	0.090	0.200	0.245	2400②
1969	7029165	9/32	0.085	—	0.040	0.275	0.120	0.200	0.450	2400②
	7029166	9/32	0.085	—	0.040	0.260	0.130	0.180	0.450	2800②
	7029167	9/32	0.085	—	0.040	0.275	0.120	0.200	0.450	2600②
	7029168	9/32	0.085	—	0.040	0.260	0.130	0.180	0.450	2800②
1970	7040014	1/4	0.100	—	—	0.200	—	0.170	0.350	—
	7040017	1/4	0.100	—	—	0.230	—	0.190	0.350	—
1971	7041014	1/4	0.080	—	—	0.200	—	0.160	0.350	—
	7041017	1/4	0.078	—	—	0.225	—	0.180	0.350	—
1972	7042014	1/4	0.080	—	—	0.200	—	0.160	0.500	2400②
	7042017	1/4	0.080	—	—	0.230	—	0.180	0.500	2400②
	7042984	1/4	0.080	—	—	0.200	—	0.160	0.500	2400②
	7042987	1/4	0.080	—	—	0.230	—	0.180	0.500	2400②
1973	7043014	1/4	0.080	—	—	0.300	—	0.245	0.500	2400②
	7043017	3/4	0.080	—	—	0.350	—	0.275	0.500	2400②

Model 2GC, 2GV— 1¼, 1½

This two barrel downdraft carburetor comes in two bore sizes to provide a wide variety of usage. The newer carburetors use a plastic float and a longer needle and seat to provide better fuel control.

The carburetor is used on General Motors cars and on some 1971 Chrysler Corp vehicles.

Fast Idle Adjustment

1. On 2GC and 2GV models, except on Oldsmobile and Chrysler Corp cars, the fast idle is set automatically when the curb idle and mixture is set.
2. Oldsmobile 2GC carburetors have a screw to adjust the fast idle. (See illustration)
3. On Chrysler Corp cars, follow this procedure: with engine off and the transmission in Neutral, open the throttle slightly. Close the choke valve until the fast idle screw can be positioned on the second step of the fast idle cam. Start the engine to determine speed. Turn the fast idle screw to obtain the specified RPM.

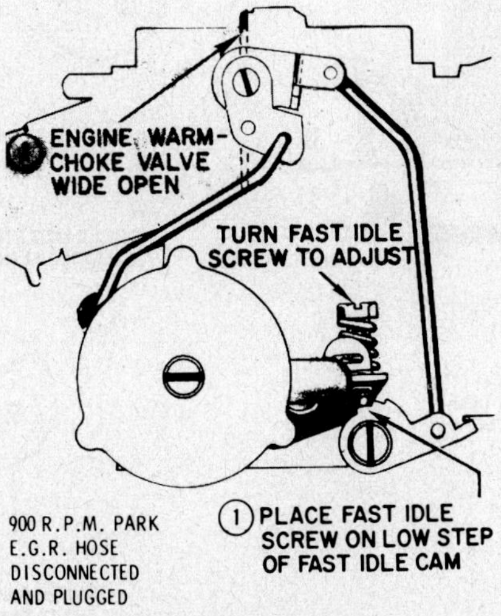
ENGINE WARM-CHOKE VALVE WIDE OPEN
TURN FAST IDLE SCREW TO ADJUST
900 R.P.M. PARK E.G.R. HOSE DISCONNECTED AND PLUGGED
1 PLACE FAST IDLE SCREW ON LOW STEP OF FAST IDLE CAM

Fast Idle Speed Setting
(© Oldsmobile Div., G.M. Corp)

Choke Rod (fast idle cam)

1. Turn in the idle cam stop screw until it just contacts the bottom step of the fast idle cam. Then turn the screw one full turn.
2. Place the idle screw on the second step of the fast idle cam against the shoulder of the high step.
3. Hold the choke valve closed and check the clearance between the upper edge of the choke valve and the air horn wall.
4. Adjust the clearance by bending the tang on the choke lever.

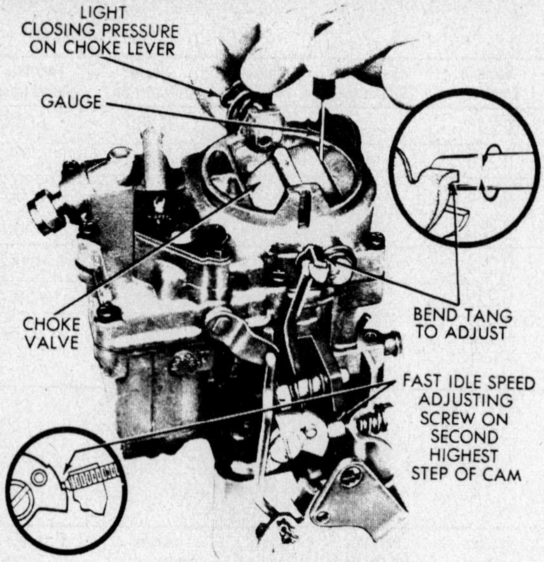
LIGHT
CLOSING PRESSURE
ON CHOKE LEVER
GAUGE
CHOKE
VALVE
BEND TANG
TO ADJUST
FAST IDLE SPEED
ADJUSTING
SCREW ON
SECOND
HIGHEST
STEP OF CAM

Fast Idle Cam Setting
(© Dodge Div., Chrysler Corp)

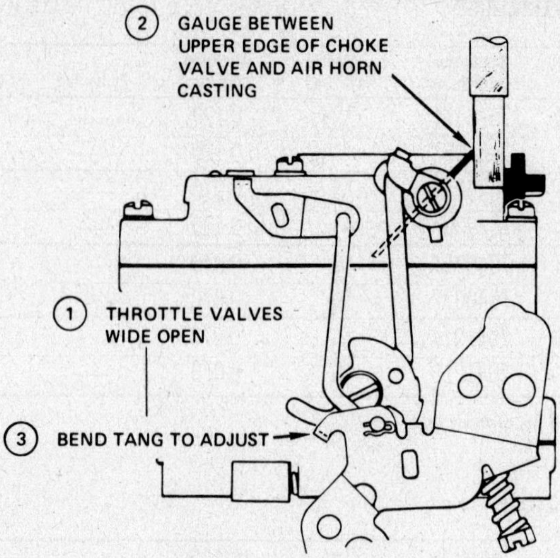
2 GAUGE BETWEEN
UPPER EDGE OF CHOKE
VALVE AND AIR HORN
CASTING
1 THROTTLE VALVES
WIDE OPEN
3 BEND TANG TO ADJUST

Choke Unloader Adjustment
(© Chevrolet Div., G.M. Corp)

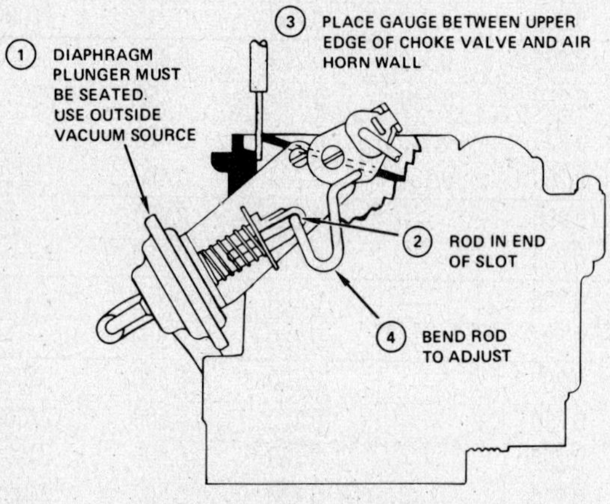
1 DIAPHRAGM
PLUNGER MUST
BE SEATED.
USE OUTSIDE
VACUUM SOURCE
3 PLACE GAUGE BETWEEN UPPER
EDGE OF CHOKE VALVE AND AIR
HORN WALL
2 ROD IN END
OF SLOT
4 BEND ROD
TO ADJUST

Vacuum Break Adjustment
(© Chevrolet Div., G.M. Corp)

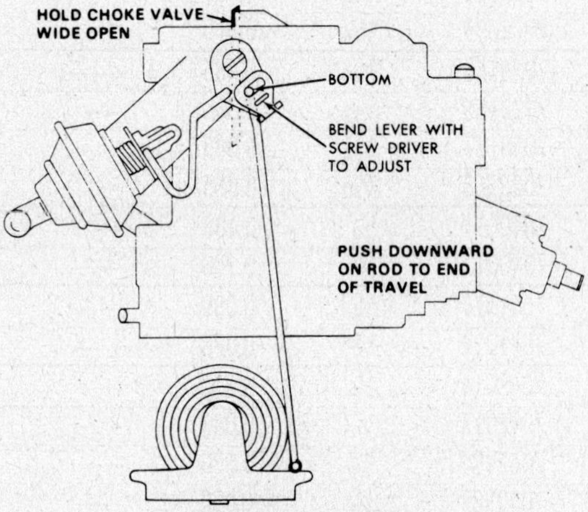
HOLD CHOKE VALVE
WIDE OPEN
BOTTOM
BEND LEVER WITH
SCREW DRIVER
TO ADJUST
PUSH DOWNWARD
ON ROD TO END
OF TRAVEL

Choke Coil Rod Adjustment
(© Chevrolet Div., G.M. Corp)

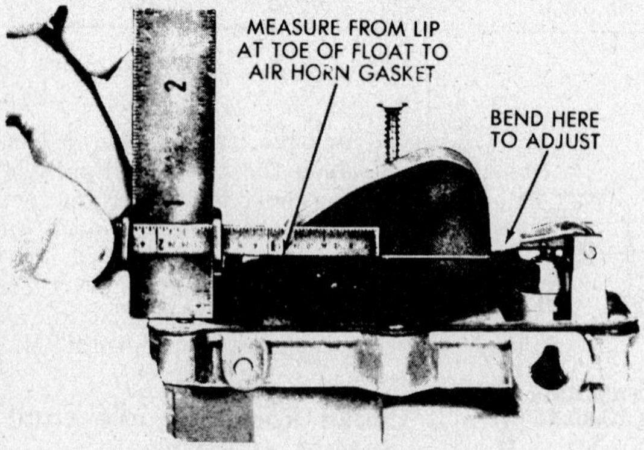
MEASURE FROM LIP
AT TOE OF FLOAT TO
AIR HORN GASKET
BEND HERE
TO ADJUST

Float Level Measurement, Plastic Float
(© Dodge Div., Chrysler Corp)

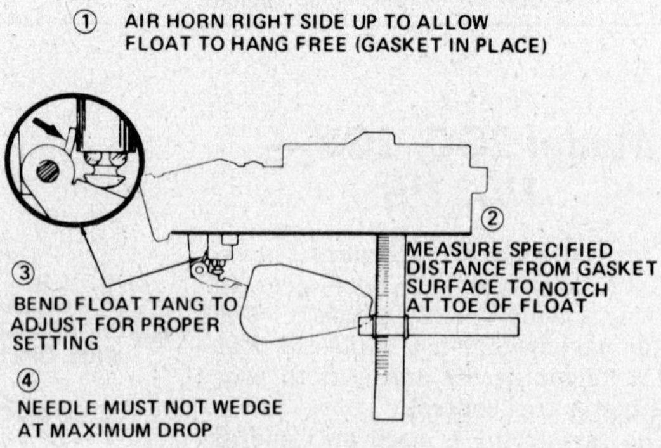
1 AIR HORN RIGHT SIDE UP TO ALLOW
FLOAT TO HANG FREE (GASKET IN PLACE)
2 MEASURE SPECIFIED
DISTANCE FROM GASKET
SURFACE TO NOTCH
AT TOE OF FLOAT
3 BEND FLOAT TANG TO
ADJUST FOR PROPER
SETTING
4 NEEDLE MUST NOT WEDGE
AT MAXIMUM DROP

Float Drop, Plastic Float

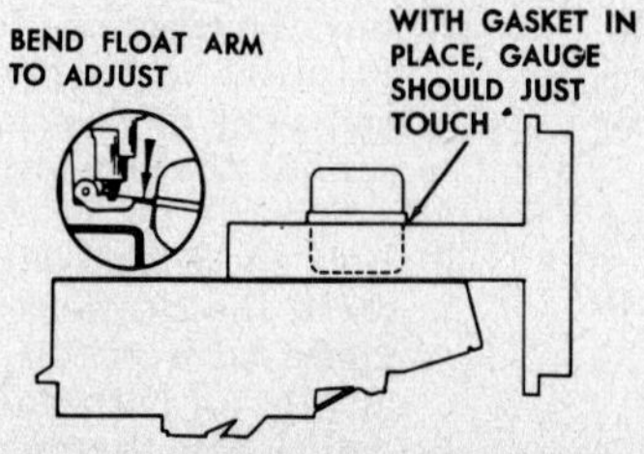
BEND FLOAT ARM
TO ADJUST
WITH GASKET IN
PLACE, GAUGE
SHOULD JUST
TOUCH

Float Level Measurement, Metal Float

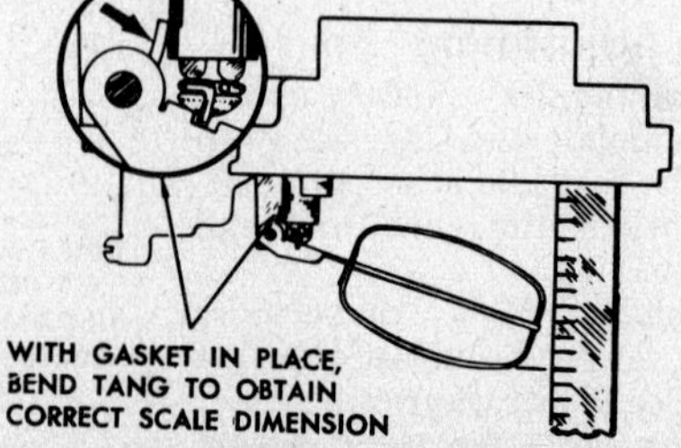
WITH GASKET IN PLACE,
BEND TANG TO OBTAIN
CORRECT SCALE DIMENSION

Float Drop, Metal Float

Vacuum Break Adjustment

1. Remove the air cleaner. Vehicles with a Therm AC air cleaner should have the sensor's vacuum take-off port plugged.
2. Using an external vacuum source, apply vacuum to the vacuum break diaphragm until the plunger is fully seated.
3. When the plunger is seated, push the choke valve toward the closed position.
4. Holding the choke valve in this position, place the specified size gauge between the lower edge of the choke valve and the air horn wall.
5. If the measurement is not correct, bend the vacuum break rod at the point shown in the illustration.

Choke Unloader Adjustment

1. Hold the throttle valves wide open.
2. Close the choke valve.
3. Bend the unloader tang to obtain the proper clearance between the upper edge of the choke valve and air horn wall.

Choke Coil Rod Adjustment

1. Hold the choke valve completely open.
2. Disconnect the coil rod from the upper lever and push down on the rod to the end of its travel.
3. When the rod is all the way down, it should line up with the bottom of the slotted hole on the choke valve linkage.
4. Adjust by bending the lever at the point shown in illustration.

Float Level

With the air horn assembly upside down, measure the distance from the air horn gasket to the lip at the toe of the float. Bend the float arm to adjust to specifications.

Float Drop

Holding the air horn assembly upright, measure the distance from the gasket to the lip at the toe of the float. If correction is necessary, bend the float tang at the rear, next to the needle and seat.

Accelerator Pump Rod

1. Back out the idle speed screw and completely close the throttle valves.
2. Place the pump gauge across the air cleaner mounting surface.
3. With the T-scale set to the specified height, the lower leg of the gauge should just touch the top of the accelerator pump rod.
4. Bend the pump rod to adjust.

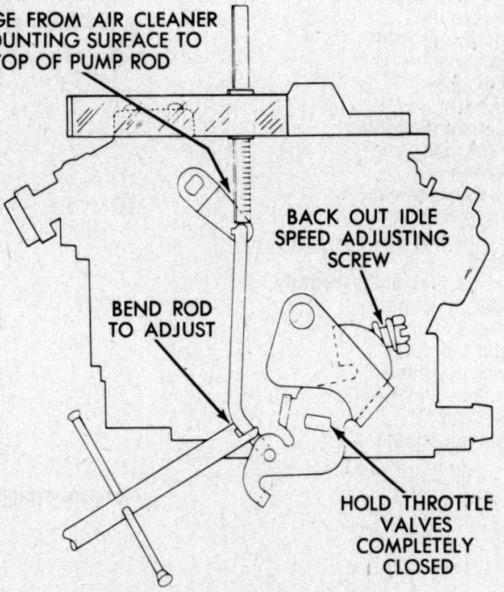
GAUGE FROM AIR CLEANER MOUNTING SURFACE TO TOP OF PUMP ROD
BACK OUT IDLE SPEED ADJUSTING SCREW
BEND ROD TO ADJUST
HOLD THROTTLE VALVES COMPLETELY CLOSED

Accelerator Pump Rod
(© Dodge Div., Chrysler Corp)

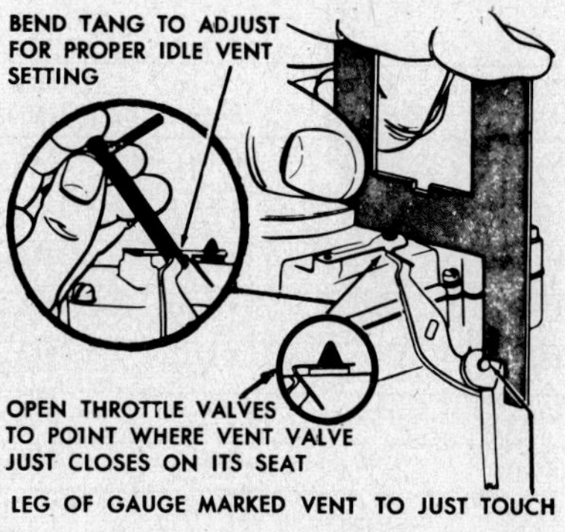
BEND TANG TO ADJUST FOR PROPER IDLE VENT SETTING
OPEN THROTTLE VALVES TO POINT WHERE VENT VALVE JUST CLOSES ON ITS SEAT
LEG OF GAUGE MARKED VENT TO JUST TOUCH

Idle Vent Adjustment

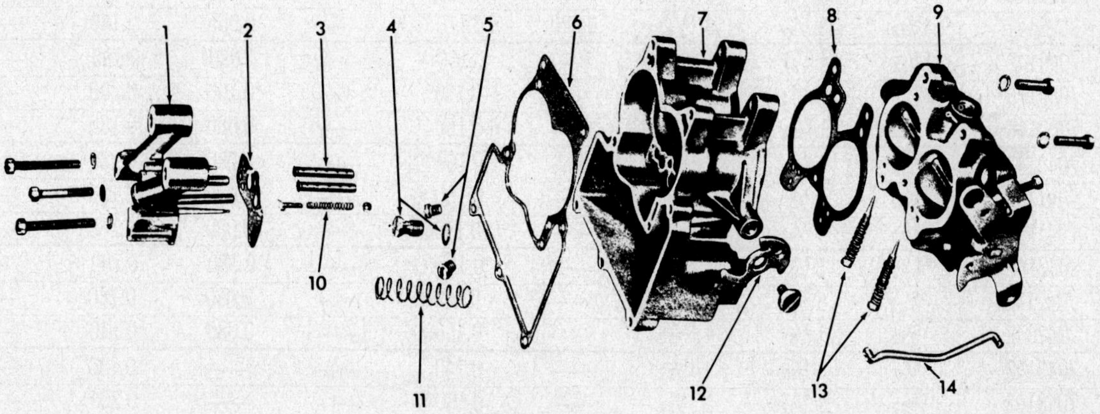
1
2
3
4
5
6
7
8
9
10
11
12
13
14

Float Bowl, Exploded View

1. Cluster assembly
2. Gasket
3. Splash shield—main well
4. Power valve assembly
5. Main jets
6. Air horn gasket
7. Bowl assembly
8. Throttle body-to-bowl gasket
9. Throttle body assembly
10. Pump discharge check assembly
11. Accelerator pump spring
12. Fast idle cam
13. Idle mixture screws
14. Choke rod

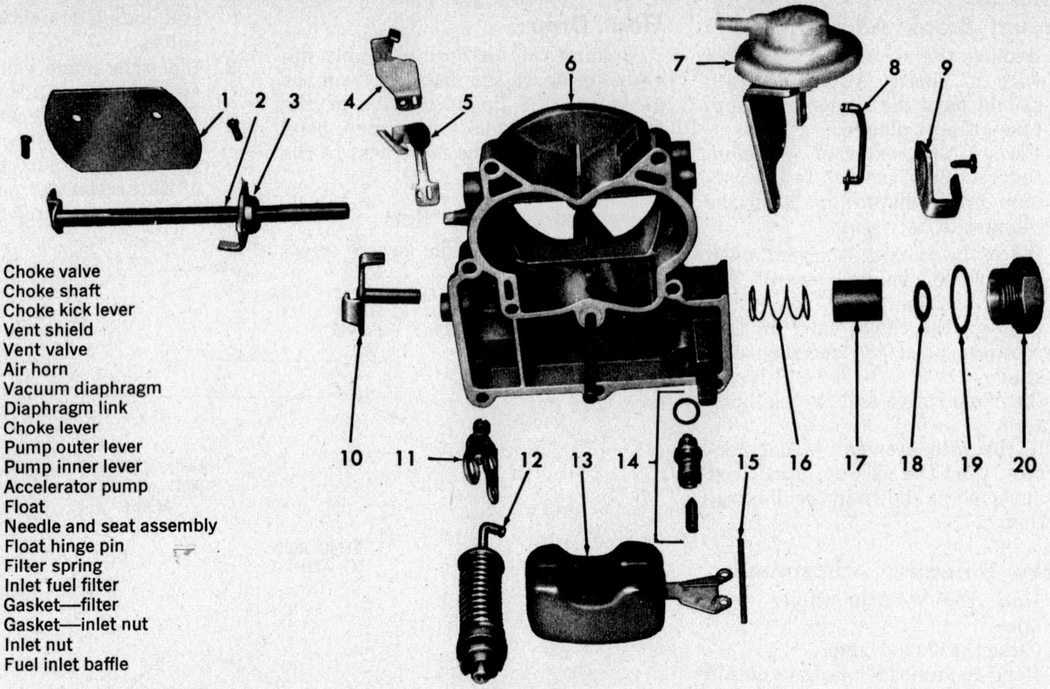
1
2
3
4
5
6
7
8
9
10
11
12
13
14
15
16
17
18
19
20

1. Choke valve
2. Choke shaft
3. Choke kick lever
4. Vent shield
5. Vent valve
6. Air horn
7. Vacuum diaphragm
8. Diaphragm link
9. Choke lever
10. Pump outer lever
11. Pump inner lever
12. Accelerator pump
13. Float
14. Needle and seat assembly
15. Float hinge pin
16. Filter spring
17. Inlet fuel filter
18. Gasket—filter
19. Gasket—inlet nut
20. Inlet nut
21. Fuel inlet baffle

Air horn, exploded view, 2GC, 2GV

2GC, 2GV CARBURETOR SPECIFICATIONS

BUICK

Year	Carburetor Identification①	Float Level (in.)	Float Drop (in.)	Pump Rod (in.)	Idle Vent (in.)	Vacuum Break (in.)	Automatic Choke	Choke Rod (in.)	Choke Unloader (in.)	Fast Idle Speed
1967	7027040	1/2	1 9/32	1 1/16	31/32	—	index	0.055	0.140	—
	7027041	1/2	1 9/32	1 1/16	31/32	—	index	0.055	0.140	—
	7027042	1/2	1 9/32	1 5/32	31/32	—	index	0.055	0.140	—
	7027044	15/32	1 9/16	1 5/32	31/32	—	index	0.055	0.140	—
	7027045	15/32	1 9/16	1 5/32	31/32	—	index	0.055	0.140	—
	7027046	15/32	1 9/16	1 5/32	31/32	—	index	0.055	0.140	—
	7027049	15/32	1 9/16	1 5/32	31/32	—	index	0.055	0.140	—
1968	7028140	15/32	1 9/32	1 11/32	0.025	0.120	lower hole	0.050	0.140	—
	7028141	15/32	1 9/32	1 11/32	0.025	0.120	lower hole	0.050	0.140	—
1969	7029140	15/32	1 7/32	1 11/32	0.020	0.110	—	0.055	0.140	—
	7029141	15/32	1 7/32	1 11/32	0.020	0.110	—	0.055	0.140	—
1970	7040142	15/32	1 7/32	1 13/32	—	0.150	—	0.080	0.180	—
	7040143	15/32	1 7/32	1 15/32	—	0.190	—	0.100	0.200	—
	7040446	15/32	1 7/32	1 13/32	—	0.150	—	0.080	0.180	—
1971	7040143	15/32	1 7/8	1 15/32	—	0.160②	—	0.080	0.180	—
	7041142	15/32	1 7/8	1 15/32	—	0.150②	—	0.080	0.180	—
	7041442	15/32	1 7/8	1 15/32	—	0.150②	—	0.080	0.180	—
1972	7042142	15/32	1 7/8	1 15/32	—	0.150②	—	0.080	0.180	—
	7042143	15/32	1 7/8	1 15/32	—	0.160②	—	0.080	0.180	—
	7042842	15/32	1 7/8	1 15/32	—	0.150②	—	0.080	0.180	—
1973	7043142	15/32	1 9/32	1 15/32	—	0.140③	—	—	0.180	—
	7043143	15/32	1 9/32	1 15/32	—	0.150③	—	—	0.200	—

① The carburetor identification tag is located at the rear of the carburetor on one of the air horn screws.
② Secondary adjustment—0.140
③ Secondary adjustment—0.120

CHEVROLET

Year	Carburetor Identification①	Float Level (in.)	Float Drop (in.)	Pump Rod (in.)	Idle Vent (in.)	Vacuum Break (in.)	Automatic Choke	Choke Rod (in.)	Choke Unloader (in.)	Fast Idle Speed
1967	7027101	3/4	1 3/4	1 1/8	1.000	0.120	—	0.060	0.215	—
	7027103	3/4	1 3/4	1 1/8	1.000	0.120	—	0.060	0.215	—
	7027110	3/4	1 3/4	1 1/8	1.000	0.110	—	0.060	0.215	—
	7027112	3/4	1 3/4	1 1/8	1.000	0.110	—	0.060	0.215	—
	7037101	3/4	1 3/4	1 1/8	1.000	0.130	—	0.060	0.215	—
	7037103	3/4	1 3/4	1 1/8	1.000	0.130	—	0.060	0.215	—
	7037110	3/4	1 3/4	1 1/8	1.000	0.110	—	0.060	0.215	—
	7037112	3/4	1 3/4	1 1/8	1.000	0.110	—	0.060	0.215	—
1968	7028110	3/4	1 3/4	1 1/8	1.000	0.100	—	0.060	0.200	—
	7028101	3/4	1 3/4	1 1/8	1.000	0.100	—	0.060	0.200	—
	7028112	3/4	1 3/4	1 1/8	1.000	0.100	—	0.060	0.200	—
	7028103	3/4	1 3/4	1 1/8	1.000	0.100	—	0.060	0.200	—
1969	7029101	27/32	1 3/4	1 1/8	0.020	0.100	—	0.060	0.215	—
	7029103	27/32	1 3/4	1 1/8	0.020	0.100	—	0.060	0.215	—
	7029110	27/32	1 3/4	1 1/8	0.020	0.100	—	0.060	0.215	—
	7029112	27/32	1 3/4	1 1/8	0.020	0.100	—	0.060	0.215	—
	7029102	3/4	1 3/4	1 13/32	0.020	0.215	—	0.085	0.275	—
	7029104	3/4	1 3/4	1 13/32	0.020	0.215	—	0.085	0.275	—
	7029127	3/4	1 3/4	1 13/32	0.020	0.215	—	0.085	0.275	—
	7029129	3/4	1 3/4	1 13/32	0.020	0.215	—	0.085	0.275	—
	7029117	3/4	1 3/4	1 13/32	0.020	0.215	—	0.085	0.275	—
	7029118	3/4	1 3/4	1 13/32	0.020	0.215	—	0.085	0.275	—
	7029119	5/8	1 3/4	1 13/32	0.020	0.215	—	0.085	0.275	—
	7029120	5/8	1 3/4	1 13/32	0.020	0.215	—	0.085	0.275	—
1970	7040110	27/32	1 3/4	1 1/8	0.020	0.100	—	0.060	0.215	—
	7040112	27/32	1 3/4	1 1/8	0.020	0.100	—	0.060	0.215	—
	7040101	27/32	1 3/4	1 1/8	0.020	0.125	—	0.060	0.160	—
	7040103	27/32	1 3/4	1 1/8	0.020	0.125	—	0.060	0.225	—
	7040114	23/32	1 3/8	1 17/32	0.020	0.200	—	0.085	0.325	—
	7040116	23/32	1 3/8	1 17/32	0.020	0.200	—	0.085	0.325	—
1970	7040113	23/32	1 3/8	1 17/32	0.020	0.215	—	0.085	0.275	—
	7040115	23/32	1 3/8	1 17/32	0.020	0.215	—	0.085	0.275	—
	7040118	23/32	1 3/8	1 17/32	0.020	0.215	—	0.085	0.325	—
	7040120	23/32	1 3/8	1 17/32	0.020	0.215	—	0.085	0.325	—
	7040117	23/32	1 3/8	1 17/32	0.020	0.215	—	0.085	0.325	—
	7040119	23/32	1 3/8	1 17/32	0.020	0.215	—	0.085	0.325	—
1971	7041024	1/16	—	—	—	0.140	—	0.080	0.350	—
	7041101	13/16	1 3/4	1 3/64	—	0.110	—	0.075	0.215	—
	7041110	13/16	1 3/4	1 3/64	—	0.080	—	0.040	0.215	—
	7041102	25/32	1 3/8	1 5/32	—	0.170	—	0.100	0.325	—
	7041114	25/32	1 3/8	1 5/32	—	0.170	—	0.100	0.325	—
	7041113	23/32	1 3/8	1 5/32	—	0.180	—	0.100	0.325	—
	7041127	23/32	1 3/8	1 5/32	—	0.180	—	0.100	0.325	—
	7041117	23/32	1 3/8	1 5/32	—	0.170	—	0.100	0.325	—
	7041118	23/32	1 3/8	1 5/32	—	0.170	—	0.100	0.325	—
	7041181	5/8	1 3/4	1 3/8	—	0.120	—	0.080	0.180	—
	7041182	5/8	1 3/4	1 3/8	—	0.120	—	0.080	0.180	—

U210

CHEVROLET

Year	Carburetor Identification①	Float Level (in.)	Float Drop (in.)	Pump Rod (in.)	Idle Vent (in.)	Vacuum Break (in.)	Automatic Choke	Choke Rod (in.)	Choke Unloader (in.)	Fast Idle Speed
1972	7042111	23/32	1 9/32	1 1/2	—	0.180	—	0.100	0.325	—
	7042113	23/32	1 9/32	1 1/2	—	0.180	—	0.100	0.325	—
	7042831	23/32	1 9/32	1 1/2	—	0.180	—	0.100	0.325	—
	7042833	23/32	1 9/32	1 1/2	—	0.180	—	0.100	0.325	—
	7042112	23/32	1 9/32	1 1/2	—	0.170	—	0.100	0.325	—
	7042114	23/32	1 9/32	1 1/2	—	0.170	—	0.100	0.325	—
	7042118	23/32	1 9/32	1 1/2	—	0.190	—	0.100	0.325	—
	7042832	23/32	1 9/32	1 1/2	—	0.170	—	0.100	0.325	—
	7042834	23/32	1 9/32	1 1/2	—	0.170	—	0.100	0.325	—
	7042838	23/32	1 9/32	1 1/2	—	0.190	—	0.100	0.325	—
	7042100	25/32	1 31/32	1 5/16	—	0.080	—	0.040	0.215	—
	7042820	25/32	1 31/32	1 5/16	—	0.080	—	0.040	0.215	—
	7042101	25/32	1 31/32	1 5/16	—	0.110	—	0.075	0.215	—
	7042821	25/32	1 31/32	1 5/16	—	0.110	—	0.075	0.215	—
1973	7043100	21/32	1 9/32	1 5/16	—	0.080	—	0.150	0.215	—
	7043101	21/32	1 9/32	1 5/16	—	0.080	—	0.150	0.215	—
	7043120	21/32	1 9/32	1 5/16	—	0.080	—	0.150	0.215	—
	7043105	21/32	1 9/32	1 5/16	—	0.080	—	0.150	0.215	—
	7043114	19/32	1 9/32	1 7/16	—	0.130	—	0.245	0.325	—
	7043113	19/32	1 9/32	1 7/16	—	0.140	—	0.200	0.250	—
	7043112	19/32	1 9/32	1 7/16	—	0.130	—	0.245	0.325	—
	7043111	19/32	1 9/32	1 7/16	—	0.140	—	0.200	0.250	—
	7043118	19/32	1 9/32	1 7/16	—	0.130	—	0.245	0.325	—

CHRYSLER

Year	Carburetor Identification①	Float Level (in.)	Float Drop (in.)	Pump Rod (in.)	Idle Vent (in.)	Vacuum Break (in.)	Automatic Choke	Choke Rod (in.)	Choke Unloader (in.)	Fast Idle Speed
1971	7041180	21/32	1 3/4	1 5/64	—	41 drill	—	—	29 drill	1800

OLDSMOBILE

Year	Carburetor Identification①	Float Level (in.)	Float Drop (in.)	Pump Rod (in.)	Idle Vent (in.)	Vacuum Break (in.)	Automatic Choke	Choke Rod (in.)	Choke Unloader (in.)	Fast Idle Speed
1967	7027033	19/32	1 3/8	1 7/16	1 5/16	Flush	Index	0.150	0.160	—
	7027035	19/32	1 3/8	1 7/16	1 5/16	1st groove	Index	0.150	0.160	—
	7027133	19/32	1 3/8	1 7/16	1 5/16	1st groove	Index	0.150	0.160	—
	7027136	19/32	1 3/8	1 7/16	1 5/16	1st groove	Index	0.150	0.160	—
	7027139	9/16	1 3/8	1 7/16	1 5/16	Flush	Index	0.150	0.160	—
	7037050	19/32	1 3/8	1 7/16	1 5/16	1st groove	Index	0.150	0.160	—
	7037051	19/32	1 3/8	1 7/16	1 5/16	1st groove	Index	0.150	0.160	—
	7037052	19/32	1 3/8	1 7/16	1 5/16	1st groove	Index	0.150	0.160	—
	7037053	19/32	1 3/8	1 7/16	1 5/16	1st groove	Index	0.150	0.160	—
	7037054	19/32	1 3/8	1 7/16	1 5/16	Flush	Index	0.150	0.160	—
	7037055	19/32	1 3/8	1 7/16	1 5/16	Flush	Index	0.150	0.160	—
	7037056	1/2	1 3/8	1 7/16	1 5/16	Flush	Index	0.150	0.160	—
	7037057	1/2	1 3/8	1 7/16	1 5/16	Flush	Index	0.150	0.160	—
	7037058	19/32	1 3/8	1 7/16	1 5/16	Flush	1 Lean	0.150	0.160	—
1968	7028154	9/16	1 3/8	1 7/16	0.025	1st groove	Index	0.150	0.160	—
	7028155	9/16	1 3/8	1 7/16	0.025	Flush	1 Lean	0.150	0.160	—
	7028156	9/16	1 3/8	1 7/16	0.025	1st groove	Index	0.150	0.160	—
	7028157	9/16	1 3/8	1 7/16	0.025	1st groove	Index	0.150	0.160	—
	7028158	9/16	1 3/8	1 7/16	0.025	Flush	Index	0.150	0.160	—
	7028159	9/16	1 3/8	1 7/16	0.025	Flush	1 Lean	0.150	0.160	—

OLDSMOBILE

Year	Carburetor Identification①	Float Level (in.)	Float Drop (in.)	Pump Rod (in.)	Idle Vent (in.)	Vacuum Break (in.)	Automatic Choke	Choke Rod (in.)	Choke Unloader (in.)	Fast Idle Speed
1969	7029155	9/16	1 3/8	1 7/16	0.025	0.180	1 Lean	0.140	0.170	—
	7029156	9/16	1 3/8	1 7/16	0.025	0.180	Index	0.140	0.170	—
	7029158	9/16	1 3/8	1 7/16	0.025	0.180	Index	0.140	0.170	—
	7029159	9/16	1 3/8	1 7/16	0.025	0.180	Index	0.140	0.170	—
1970	7040154	9/16	1 3/8	1 11/32	—	0.160	Index	0.140	0.170	—
	7040155	9/16	1 3/8	1 11/32	—	0.160	1 Lean	0.140	0.170	—
	7040156	9/16	1 3/8	1 11/32	—	0.160	Index	0.140	0.170	—
	7040158	9/16	1 3/8	1 11/32	—	0.160	Index	0.140	0.170	—
	7040159	9/16	1 3/8	1 11/32	—	0.160	Index	0.140	0.170	—
1971	7041155	9/16	1 3/8	1 11/32	—	0.200	1 Lean	0.140	0.170	—
	7041156	9/16	1 3/8	1 11/32	—	0.200	Index	0.140	0.170	—
	7041159	9/16	1 3/8	1 11/32	—	0.215	Index	0.140	0.170	—
1972	7042155	17/32	1 3/8	1 3/8	—	0.200	1 Lean	0.160	0.170	—
	7042156	17/32	1 3/8	1 3/8	—	0.200	Index	0.160	0.170	—
1973	All	15/32	1 9/32	1 11/32	—	0.200	Index	0.160	0.250	—

PONTIAC

Year	Carburetor Identification①	Float Level (in.)	Float Drop (in.)	Pump Rod (in.)	Idle Vent (in.)	Vacuum Break (in.)	Automatic Choke	Choke Rod (in.)	Choke Unloader (in.)	Fast Idle Speed
1967	7027060	9/16	1 9/16	1 11/32	1 9/16	—	Index	0.085	0.160	—
	7027061	9/16	1 9/16	1 11/32	1 9/32	—	Index	0.085	0.160	—
	7027062	9/16	1 9/16	1 11/32	1 9/32	—	Index	0.085	0.160	—
	7027066	9/16	1 9/16	1 11/32	1 9/32	—	Index	0.085	0.160	—
	7027071	9/16	1 9/16	1 11/32	1 9/32	—	Index	0.085	0.160	—
	7037061	9/16	1 9/16	1 11/32	1 9/32	—	Index	0.085	0.160	—
	7037062	9/16	1 9/16	1 11/32	1 9/32	—	Index	0.085	0.160	—
	7037066	9/16	1 9/16	1 11/32	1 9/32	—	Index	0.085	0.160	—
	7037071	9/16	1 9/16	1 11/32	1 9/32	—	Index	0.085	0.160	—
	7037162	9/16	1 9/16	1 11/32	1 9/32	—	Index	0.085	0.160	—
1968	7028060	9/16	1 3/4	1 11/32	—	0.150	—	0.085	0.180	—
	7028062	9/16	1 3/4	1 11/32	—	0.150	—	0.085	0.180	—
	7028066	9/16	1 3/4	1 11/32	—	0.170	—	0.085	0.180	—
	7028071	9/16	1 3/4	1 11/32	—	0.160	—	0.085	0.180	—
1969	7028066	9/16	1 3/4	1 11/32	—	0.170	—	0.085	0.180	—
	7028071	9/16	1 3/4	1 11/32	—	0.160	—	0.085	0.180	—
	7029060	9/16	1 3/4	1 11/32	—	0.150	—	0.085	0.180	—
	7029062	9/16	1 3/4	1 11/32	—	0.150	—	0.085	0.180	—
1970	7040060	11/16	1 3/4	1 11/32	—	0.180	—	0.085	0.180	—
	7040062	9/16	1 3/4	1 11/32	—	0.150	—	0.085	0.180	—
	7040064	11/16	1 3/4	1 11/32	—	0.150	—	0.085	0.180	—
	7040066	11/16	1 3/4	1 11/32	—	0.170	—	0.085	0.180	—
	7040071	9/16	1 3/4	1 11/32	—	0.160	—	0.085	0.180	—
	7040072	9/16	1 3/4	1 11/32	—	0.150	—	0.085	0.180	—
	7040460	11/16	1 3/4	1 11/32	—	0.150	—	0.085	0.180	—
	7040461	11/16	1 3/4	1 11/32	—	0.150	—	0.085	0.180	—
	7040462	9/16	1 3/4	1 11/32	—	0.150	—	0.085	0.180	—
	7040463	9/16	1 3/4	1 11/32	—	0.150	—	0.085	0.180	—
	7040466	11/16	1 3/4	1 11/32	—	0.170	—	0.085	0.180	—
	7040471	9/16	1 3/4	1 11/32	—	0.160	—	0.085	0.180	—

PONTIAC

Year	Carburetor Identification①	Float Level (in.)	Float Drop (in.)	Pump Rod (in.)	Idle Vent (in.)	Vacuum Break (in.)	Automatic Choke	Choke Rod (in.)	Choke Unloader (in.)	Fast Idle Speed
1971	7041060	11/16	1 3/4	1 11/32	—	0.125	—	0.085	0.180	—
	7041061	11/16	1 3/4	1 11/32	—	0.125	—	0.085	0.180	—
	7041062	9/16	1 3/4	1 11/32	—	0.105	—	0.085	0.180	—
	7041063	9/16	1 3/4	1 11/32	—	0.105	—	0.085	0.180	—
	7041064	11/16	1 3/4	1 11/32	—	0.130	—	0.085	0.180	—
	7041070	11/16	1 3/4	1 11/32	—	0.125	—	0.085	0.180	—
	7041072	9/16	1 3/4	1 11/32	—	0.105	—	0.085	0.180	—
	7041074	11/16	1 3/4	1 11/32	—	0.130	—	0.085	0.180	—
	7041171	9/16	1 3/4	1 11/32	—	0.140	—	0.085	0.180	—
1972	7042060	5/8	1 9/32	1 11/32	—	0.122	—	0.085	0.180	—
	7042061	5/8	1 9/32	1 11/32	—	0.122	—	0.085	0.180	—
	7042062	9/16	1 9/32	1 11/32	—	0.105	—	0.085	0.180	—
	7042064	5/8	1 9/32	1 11/32	—	0.150	—	0.085	0.180	—
	7042100	25/32	1 31/32	1 5/16	—	0.080	—	0.040	0.215	—
	7042101	25/32	1 31/32	1 5/16	—	0.100	—	0.075	0.215	—
1973	7043062	21/32	1 9/32	1 5/16	—	0.167	—	0.085	0.180	—
	7043063	21/32	1 9/32	1 5/16	—	0.167	—	0.085	0.180	—
	7043071	23/32	1 9/32	1 5/16	—	0.195	—	0.085	0.180	—
	7043072	23/32	1 9/32	1 5/16	—	0.167	—	0.085	0.180	—
	7043060	21/32	1 9/32	1 5/16	—	0.157	—	0.085	0.180	—
	7043061	21/32	1 9/32	1 5/16	—	0.157	—	0.085	0.180	—
	7043066	21/32	1 9/32	1 5/16	—	0.180	—	0.085	0.180	—
	7043067	21/32	1 9/32	1 5/16	—	0.180	—	0.085	0.180	—
	7043070	23/32	1 9/32	1 5/16	—	0.157	—	0.085	0.180	—

Model 4MC, 4MV

The Rochester Quadrajet carburetor is a two stage, four-barrel downdraft carburetor. The designation MC or MV refers to the type of choke system the carburetor is designed for. The MV model is equipped with a manifold mounted thermostatic choke coil. The MC model has a choke housing and coil mounted on the side of the float bowl.

The primary side of the carburetor is equipped with 1⅜ diameter bores and a triple venturi with plain tube nozzles. During off idle and part throttle operation, the fuel is metered through tapered metering rods operating in specially designed jets positioned by a manifold vacuum responsive piston.

The secondary side of the carburetor contains two 2¼ bores. An air valve is used on the secondary side for metering control and supplements the primary bores.

The secondary air valve operates tapered metering rods which regulate the fuel in constant proportion to the air being supplied.

Fast Idle

1. Position the fast idle lever on the high step of the fast idle cam.
2. Be sure that the choke is wide open and the engine warm.
3. Turn the fast idle screw to gain the proper fast idle rpm.

Choke Rod (Fast idle cam)

1. Place the cam follower on the second step of the fast idle cam.
2. Close the choke valve by exerting counterclockwise pressure on the external choke lever.
3. Insert a gauge of the proper size between the lower edge of the choke valve and the inside air horn wall.
4. To adjust, bend the choke rod.

Vacuum Break

1. Fully seat the vacuum break diaphragm using an outside vacuum source.
2. Open the throttle valve enough to allow the fast idle cam follower to clear the fast idle cam.
3. The end of the vacuum break rod should be at the outer end of the slot in the vacuum break diaphragm plunger.

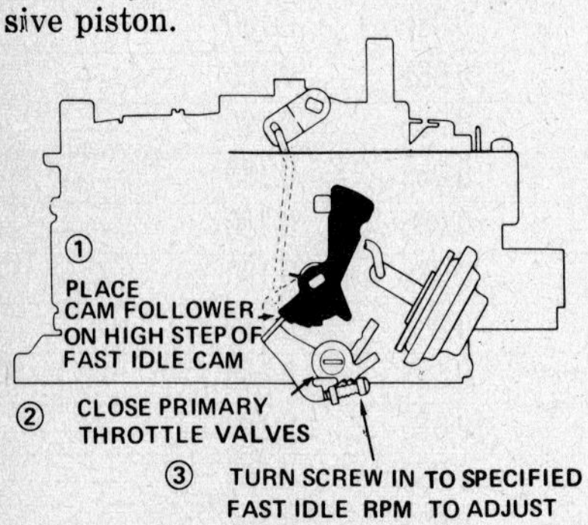

① PLACE CAM FOLLOWER ON HIGH STEP OF FAST IDLE CAM
② CLOSE PRIMARY THROTTLE VALVES
③ TURN SCREW IN TO SPECIFIED FAST IDLE RPM TO ADJUST

Fast Idle Adjustment
(© Chevrolet Div., G.M. Corp)

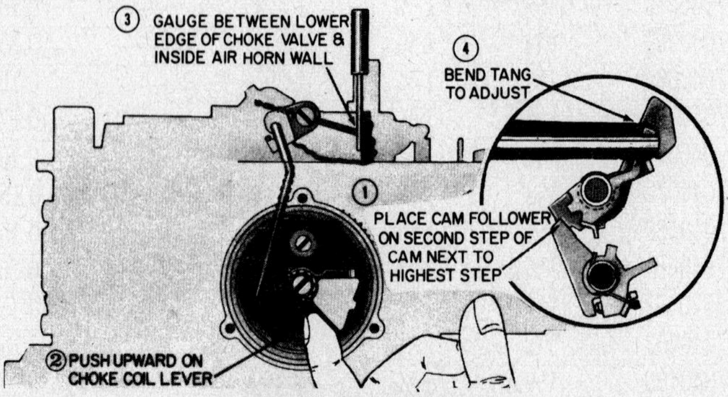

③ GAUGE BETWEEN LOWER EDGE OF CHOKE VALVE & INSIDE AIR HORN WALL
④ BEND TANG TO ADJUST
① PLACE CAM FOLLOWER ON SECOND STEP OF CAM NEXT TO HIGHEST STEP
② PUSH UPWARD ON CHOKE COIL LEVER

Fast Idle Cam Adjustment
(© Oldsmobile Div., G.M. Corp)

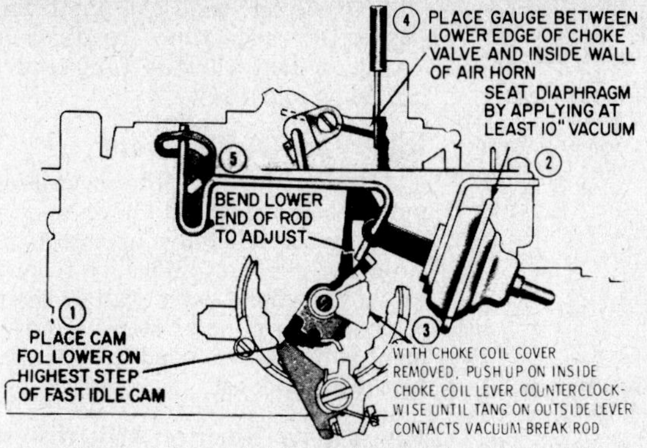
4 PLACE GAUGE BETWEEN LOWER EDGE OF CHOKE VALVE AND INSIDE WALL OF AIR HORN
SEAT DIAPHRAGM BY APPLYING AT LEAST 10" VACUUM
2
5
BEND LOWER END OF ROD TO ADJUST
1 PLACE CAM FOLLOWER ON HIGHEST STEP OF FAST IDLE CAM
3 WITH CHOKE COIL COVER REMOVED, PUSH UP ON INSIDE CHOKE COIL LEVER COUNTERCLOCKWISE UNTIL TANG ON OUTSIDE LEVER CONTACTS VACUUM BREAK ROD

Vacuum Break Adjustment
(© Oldsmobile Div., G.M. Corp)

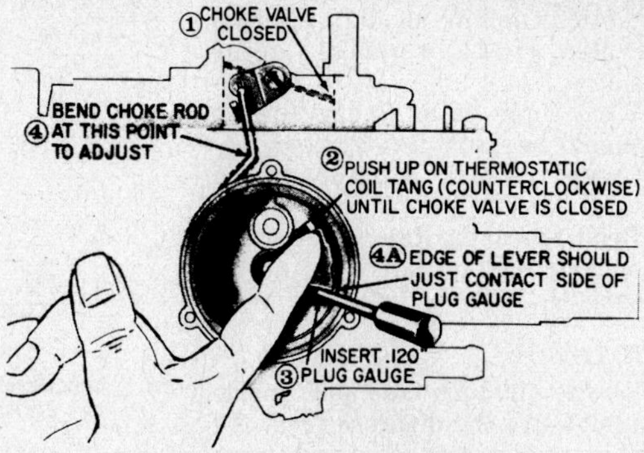
1 CHOKE VALVE CLOSED
4 BEND CHOKE ROD AT THIS POINT TO ADJUST
2 PUSH UP ON THERMOSTATIC COIL TANG (COUNTERCLOCKWISE) UNTIL CHOKE VALVE IS CLOSED
4A EDGE OF LEVER SHOULD JUST CONTACT SIDE OF PLUG GAUGE
INSERT .120"
3 PLUG GAUGE

Choke Coil Rod Adjustment
(© Oldsmobile Div., G.M. Corp)

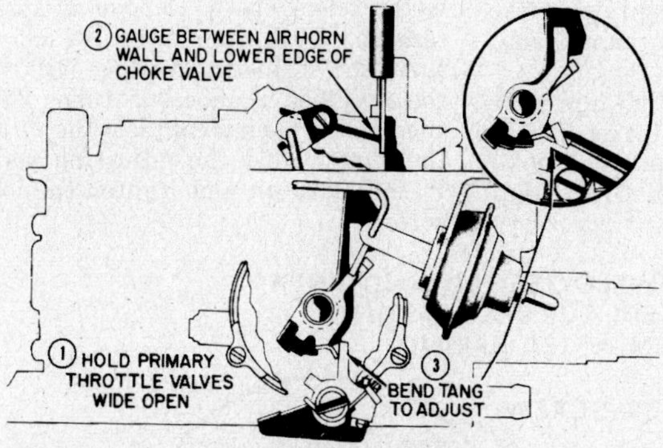
2 GAUGE BETWEEN AIR HORN WALL AND LOWER EDGE OF CHOKE VALVE
1 HOLD PRIMARY THROTTLE VALVES WIDE OPEN
3 BEND TANG TO ADJUST

Choke Unloader Adjustment
(© Oldsmobile Div., G.M. Corp)

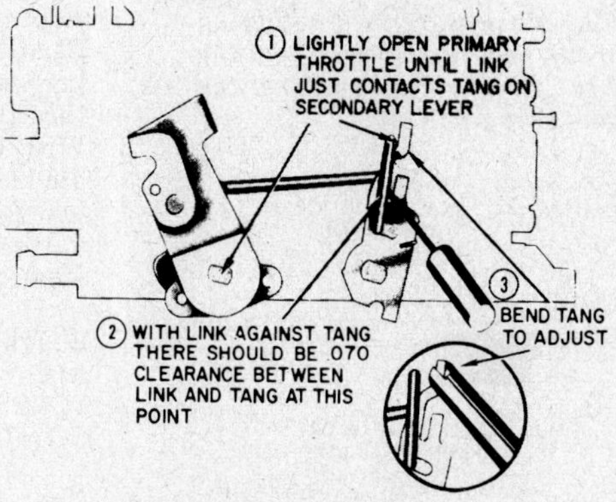
1 LIGHTLY OPEN PRIMARY THROTTLE UNTIL LINK JUST CONTACTS TANG ON SECONDARY LEVER
2 WITH LINK AGAINST TANG THERE SHOULD BE .070 CLEARANCE BETWEEN LINK AND TANG AT THIS POINT
3 BEND TANG TO ADJUST

Secondary Opening Adjustments
(© Oldsmobile Div., G.M. Corp)

4. The specified clearance should register from the lower end of the choke valve to the inside air horn wall.
5. If the clearance is not correct, bend the vacuum break link at the point shown in the illustration.

Secondary Vacuum Break

1. Using an outside vacuum source, seat the auxiliary vacuum break diaphragm plunger.
2. Rotate the choke lever in the closed position until the spring loaded diaphragm plunger is fully extended.
3. Holding the choke valve closed, check the distance between the lower edge of the choke valve and the air horn wall.
4. To adjust to specifications, bend the vacuum break link.

Choke Unloader

1. Push up on the vacuum break lever and fully open the throttle valves.
2. Measure the distance from the lower edge of the choke valve to the air horn wall.
3. To adjust, bend the tang on the fast idle lever.

Choke Coil Rod

1. Close the choke valve by rotating the choke coil lever counterclockwise.
2. Disconnect the thermostatic coil rod from the upper lever.
3. Push down on the rod until it contacts the bracket of the coil.
4. The rod must fit in the notch of the upper lever.
5. If it does not, it must be bent on the curved portion just below the upper lever.

Secondary Closing Adjustment

This adjustment assures proper closing of the secondary throttle plates.

1. Set the slow idle as per instructions in the appropriate car section. Make sure that the fast idle cam follower is not resting on the fast idle cam.
2. There should be 0.020 in. clearance between the secondary throttle actuating rod and the front of the slot on the secondary throttle lever with the closing tang on the throttle lever resting against the actuating lever.
3. Bend the tang on the primary throttle actuating rod to adjust.

Secondary Opening Adjustment

1. Open the primary throttle valves until the actuating link contacts the upper tang on the secondary lever.

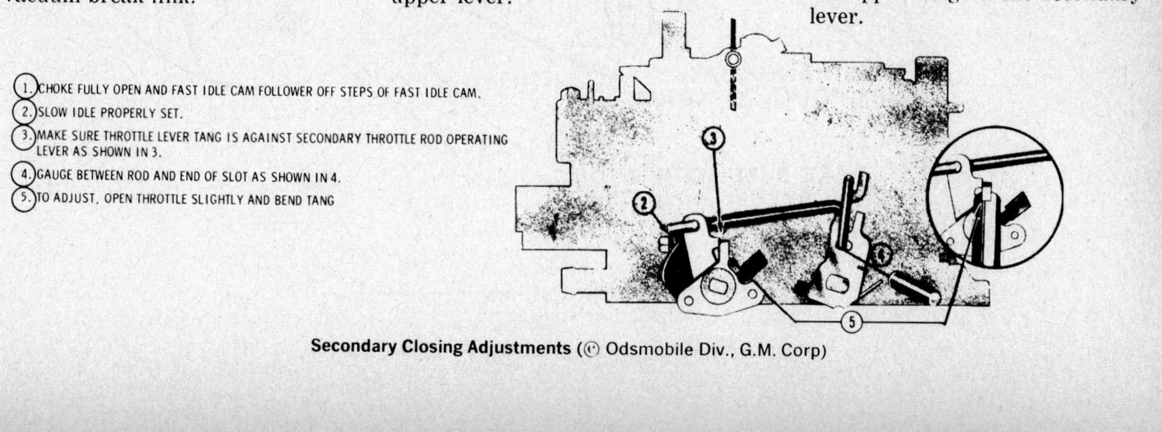
1. CHOKE FULLY OPEN AND FAST IDLE CAM FOLLOWER OFF STEPS OF FAST IDLE CAM.
2. SLOW IDLE PROPERLY SET.
3. MAKE SURE THROTTLE LEVER TANG IS AGAINST SECONDARY THROTTLE ROD OPERATING LEVER AS SHOWN IN 3.
4. GAUGE BETWEEN ROD AND END OF SLOT AS SHOWN IN 4.
5. TO ADJUST, OPEN THROTTLE SLIGHTLY AND BEND TANG
3
2
4
5

Secondary Closing Adjustments (© Odsmobile Div., G.M. Corp)

2. With two point linkage, the bottom of the link should be in the center of the secondary lever slot.
3. With three point linkage, there should be 0.070 in. clearance between the link and the middle tang.
4. Bend the upper tang on the secondary lever to adjust as necessary.

Float Level

With the air horn assembly upside down, measure the distance from the air horn gasket surface (gasket removed) to the top of the float at the toe.

NOTE: Make sure the retaining pin is firmly held in place and that the tang of the float is firmly against the needle and seat assembly.

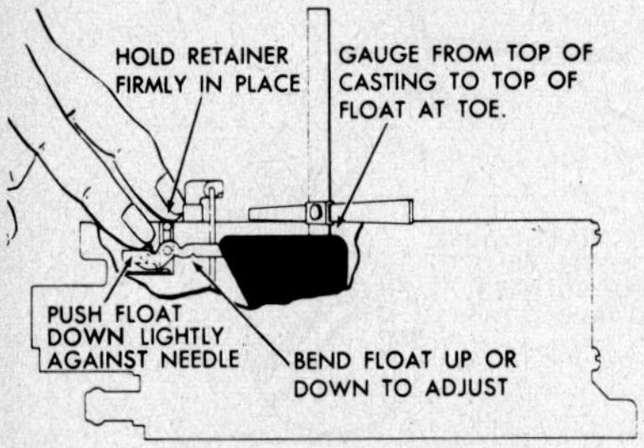
HOLD RETAINER FIRMLY IN PLACE
GAUGE FROM TOP OF CASTING TO TOP OF FLOAT AT TOE.
PUSH FLOAT DOWN LIGHTLY AGAINST NEEDLE
BEND FLOAT UP OR DOWN TO ADJUST

Adjusting Float Level
(© Pontiac Div., G.M. Corp)

Secondary Metering Rod Adjustment

1. Measure from the top of each metering rod to the top of the air horn casting.
2. The measurement should be 53/64 in.; if not, correct by bending the metering rod hanger. Make sure both rods are adjusted correctly.

Accelerator Pump

1. Close the primary throttle valves by backing out the slow idle screw and making sure that the fast idle cam follower is off the steps of the fast idle cam.
2. Bend the secondary throttle closing tang away from the primary throttle lever.
3. With the pump in the appropriate hole in the pump lever, measure from the top of the choke valve wall to the top of the pump stem.

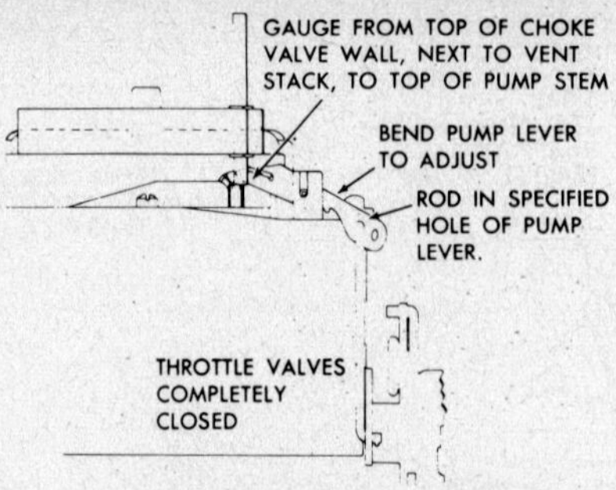
GAUGE FROM TOP OF CHOKE VALVE WALL, NEXT TO VENT STACK, TO TOP OF PUMP STEM
BEND PUMP LEVER TO ADJUST
ROD IN SPECIFIED HOLE OF PUMP LEVER.
THROTTLE VALVES COMPLETELY CLOSED

Accelerator Pump Rod Adjustment
(© Pontiac Div., G.M. Corp)

4. To adjust, bend the pump lever.
5. After adjusting, readjust the secondary throttle tang and the slow idle screw.

Idle Vent Adjustment

After adjusting the accelerator pump rod as specified above, open the primary throttle valve enough to just close the idle vent. Measure from the top of the choke valve wall to the top of the pump plunger stem. If adjustment is necessary, bend the wire tang on the pump lever.

Air Valve Spring Adjustment

To adjust the air valve spring windup, loosen the Allen head lockscrew and turn the adjusting screw counterclockwise to remove all spring tension. With the air valve closed, turn the adjusting screw clockwise the specified number of turns after the torsion spring contacts the pin on the shaft. Hold the adjusting screw in this position and tighten the lockscrew.

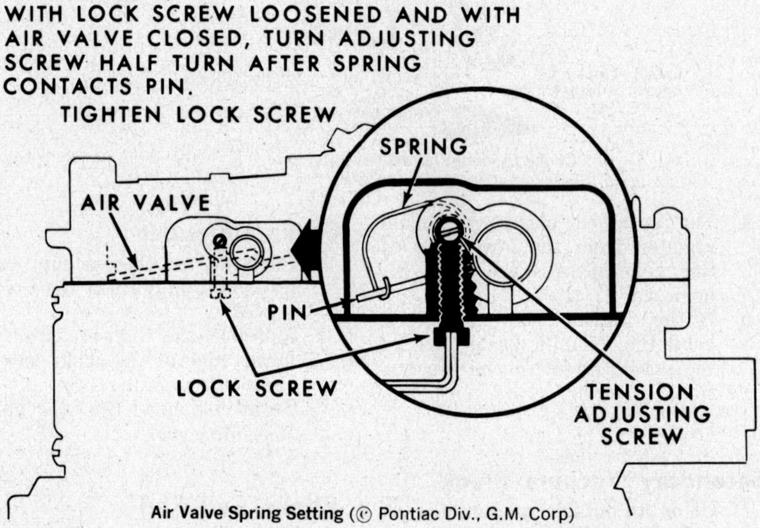
WITH LOCK SCREW LOOSENED AND WITH AIR VALVE CLOSED, TURN ADJUSTING SCREW HALF TURN AFTER SPRING CONTACTS PIN.
TIGHTEN LOCK SCREW
SPRING
AIR VALVE
PIN
LOCK SCREW
TENSION ADJUSTING SCREW

Air Valve Spring Setting (© Pontiac Div., G.M. Corp)

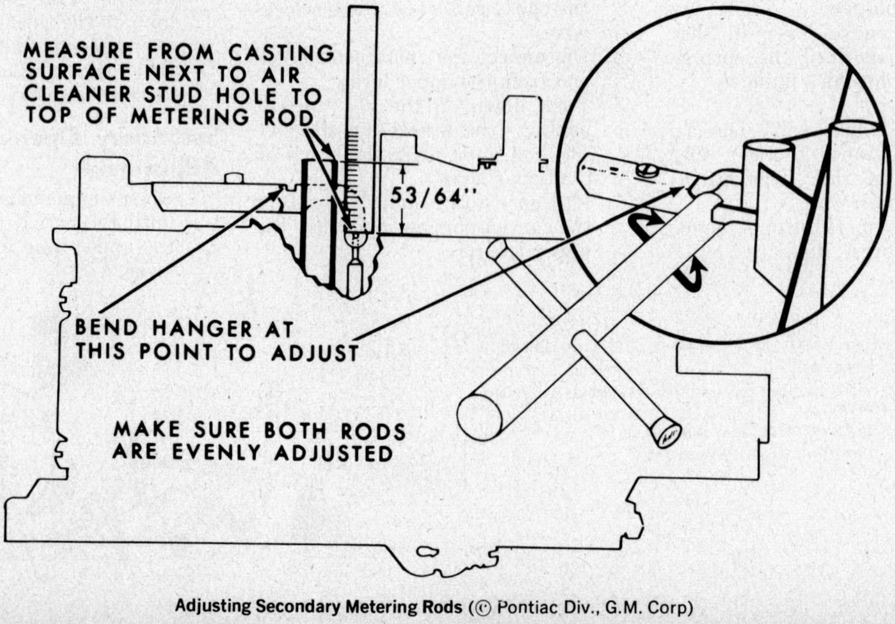
MEASURE FROM CASTING SURFACE NEXT TO AIR CLEANER STUD HOLE TO TOP OF METERING ROD
53/64"
BEND HANGER AT THIS POINT TO ADJUST
MAKE SURE BOTH RODS ARE EVENLY ADJUSTED

Adjusting Secondary Metering Rods (© Pontiac Div., G.M. Corp)

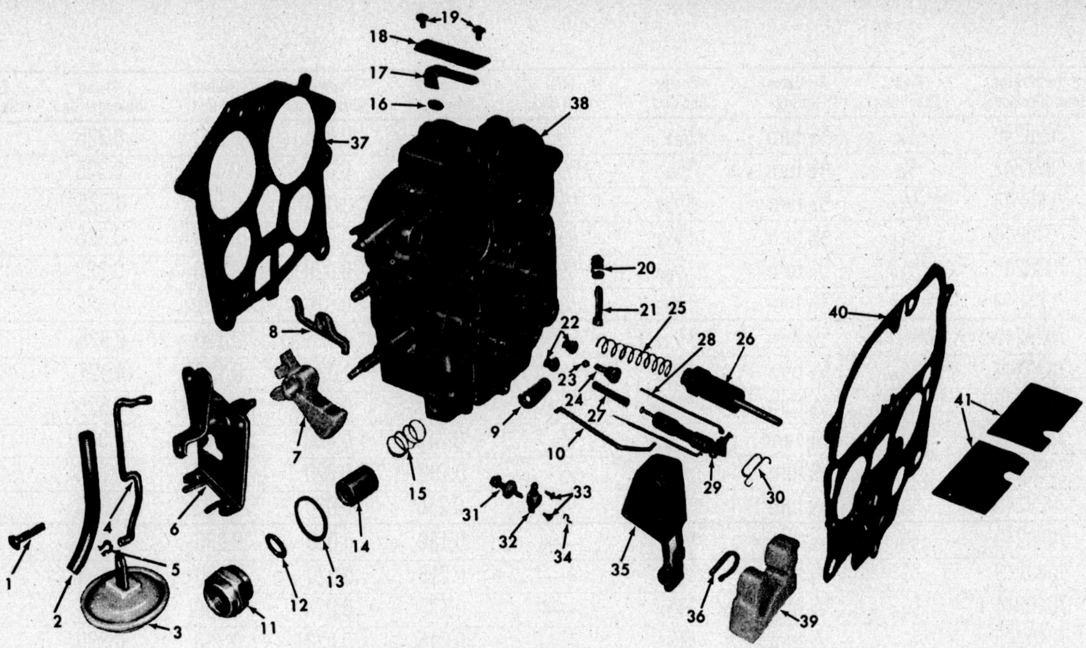

Exploded View 4MV Float Bowl (© Chevrolet Div., G.M. Corp)

1. Screw—choke control
2. Hose—vacuum break
3. Vacuum break
4. Link—vacuum break
5. Clip—vacuum break rod
6. Bracket assembly—choke control
7. Cam—fast idle
8. Lever—secondary lock out
9. Lever—choke intermediate
10. Rod—choke
11. Nut—fuel inlet
12. Gasket—fuel filter
13. Gasket—fuel inlet nut
14. Filter—fuel inlet
15. Spring—fuel filter
16. Gasket—idle compensator
17. Idle compensator assembly
18. Cover—idle compensator
19. Screw—idle compensator cover
20. Spring—idle speed screw
21. Screw—idle speed
22. Jet—primary
23. Ball—pump discharge
24. Retainer—pump discharge ball
25. Spring—pump return
26. Pump assembly
27. Spring—power piston
28. Metering rod—primary
29. Power piston assembly—primary
30. Spring—metering rod primary
31. Float needle and diaphragm assembly
32. Retainer—float needle assembly
33. Screw—float needle retainer
34. Pull clip—float needle
35. Float assembly
36. Hinge pin—float assembly
37. Gasket—throttle body
38. Float bowl assembly
39. Insert—float bowl
40. Gasket—air horn
41. Baffle—float bowl

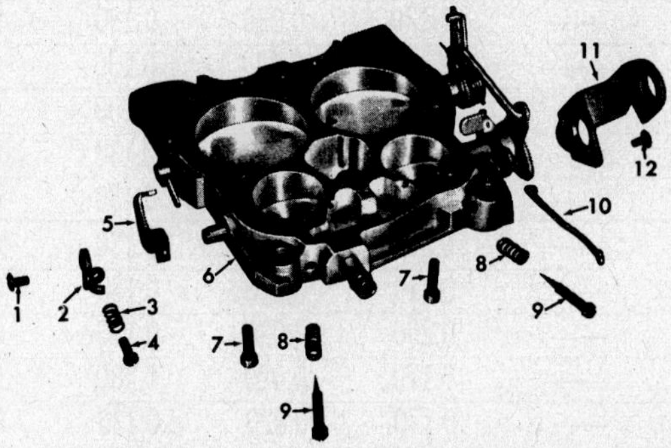

1. Screw—cam and fast idle levers
2. Fast idle lever
3. Spring—fast idle screw
4. Screw—fast idle adjusting
5. Cam lever
6. Throttle body assembly
7. Screw—throttle body
8. Spring—idle needle
9. Idle needle
10. Rod—accelerator pump
11. Throttle lever
12. Screw—throttle lever

Throttle Body 4MV, Exploded View
(© Chevrolet Div., G.M. Corp)

4MC, 4MV CARBURETOR SPECIFICATIONS

BUICK

Year	Carburetor Identification①	Float Level (in.)	Air Valve Spring	Pump Rod (in.)	Idle Vent (in.)	Vacuum Break (in.)	Secondary Closing (in.)	Choke Rod (in.)	Choke Unloader (in.)	Fast Idle Speed (rpm)
1967	7027140	9/32	5/8 turn	9/32	7/16	0.200	0.020	0.130	0.325	600
	7027140	9/32	5/8 turn	13/32	7/16	0.200	0.020	0.130	0.325	600
	7027146	7/32	5/8 turn	9/32	1/2	0.200	0.020	0.130	0.325	600
	7027147	7/32	5/8 turn	13/32	1/2	0.200	0.020	0.130	0.325	600
	7027148	7/32	5/8 turn	9/32	3/8	0.215	0.020	0.130	0.325	600
	7027149	7/32	5/8 turn	9/32	3/8	0.215	0.020	0.130	0.325	600
	7027240	9/32	5/8 turn	9/32	7/16	0.200	0.020	0.130	0.325	600
	7027241	9/32	5/8 turn	13/32	7/16	0.200	0.020	0.130	0.325	600
	7027244	1/4	5/8 turn	13/32	1/2	0.200	0.020	0.130	0.325	600
	7027246	1/4	5/8 turn	9/32	3/8	0.215	0.020	0.120	0.325	600
	7027248	5/16	5/8 turn	9/32	7/16	0.200	0.020	0.120	0.325	600

BUICK

Year	Carburetor Identification①	Float Level (in.)	Air Valve Spring	Pump Rod (in.)	Idle Vent (in.)	Vacuum Break (in.)	Secondary Closing (in.)	Choke Rod (in.)	Choke Unloader (in.)	Fast Idle Speed (rpm)
1968	7028240	3/8	5/8 turn	9/32	1/2	0.200	0.020	0.130	0.325	600
	7028242	3/8	5/8 turn	9/32	1/2	0.180	0.020	0.130	0.325	600
	7028243	7/16	5/8 turn	11/32	1/2	0.215	0.020	0.140	0.325	600
	7028244	5/16	5/8 turn	13/32	1/2	0.200	0.020	0.130	0.325	600
	7028245	5/16	5/8 turn	13/32	1/2	0.215	0.020	0.130	0.325	600
	7028248	9/32	5/8 turn	13/32	1/2	0.180	0.020	0.130	0.325	600
1969	7029240	3/8	5/8 turn	13/32	1/2	0.180	0.020	0.130	0.325	600
	7029241	5/16	5/8 turn	13/32	1/2	0.180	0.020	0.130	0.325	600
	7029242	3/8	5/8 turn	13/32	1/2	0.180	0.020	0.130	0.325	600
	7029243	3/8	5/8 turn	13/32	1/2	0.215	0.020	0.140	0.325	600
	7029244	5/16	5/8 turn	13/32	1/2	0.190	0.020	0.130	0.325	600
	7029245	5/16	5/8 turn	13/32	1/2	0.215	0.020	0.130	0.325	600
1970	7040240	3/8	1/2 turn	9/32	—	0.180	0.020	0.130	0.335	720
	7040243	3/8	1/2 turn	9/32	—	0.215	0.020	0.130	0.335	650
	7040244	5/16	1/2 turn	13/32	—	0.170	0.020	0.130	0.335	720
	7040245	5/16	1/2 turn	13/32	—	0.215	0.020	0.130	0.335	650
	7040246	5/16	1/2 turn	9/32	—	0.200	0.020	0.130	0.335	650
	7040247	3/8	1/2 turn	9/32	—	0.160	0.020	0.130	0.335	650
1971	7041242	3/8	1/2 turn	1/4	—	0.200	0.020	0.130	0.335	800
	7041243	13/32	1/2 turn	1/4	—	0.215	0.020	0.130	0.335	600
	7041245	15/32	1/2 turn	9/32	—	0.170	0.020	0.130	0.335	700
	7041540	3/8	1/2 turn	1/4	—	0.180	0.020	0.130	0.335	600
	7041544	15/32	1/2 turn	9/32	—	0.170	0.020	0.130	0.335	600
1972	7042240	3/8	1/2 turn	1/4	—	0.180	0.020	0.130	0.335	820
	7042242	3/8	1/2 turn	1/4	—	0.200	0.020	0.130	0.335	700
	7042243	13/32	1/2 turn	1/4	—	0.215	0.020	0.130	0.335	920
	7042244	15/32	1/2 turn	9/32	—	0.170	0.020	0.130	0.335	700
	7042245	15/32	1/2 turn	9/32	—	0.170	0.020	0.130	0.335	920
	7042940	3/8	1/2 turn	1/4	—	0.180	0.020	0.130	0.335	700
	7042942	3/8	1/2 turn	1/4	—	0.200	0.020	0.130	0.335	700
	7042944	15/32	1/2 turn	9/32	—	0.170	0.020	0.130	0.335	700
1973	7043240	13/32	7/16 turn	7/16	—	0.215	0.020	0.130	0.335	900
	7043243	13/32	7/16 turn	7/16	—	0.215	0.020	0.130	0.335	900
	7043242	13/32	7/16 turn	7/16	—	0.200	0.020	0.130	0.335	900
	7043244	15/32	11/16 turn	0.306	—	0.170	0.020	0.130	0.335	900
	7043245	15/32	11/16 turn	0.410	—	0.170	0.020	0.130	0.335	900

① The carburetor identification tag is located at the rear of the carburetor on one of the air horn screws.

② Third step of cam

③ Second step of cam

CADILLAC

Year	Carburetor Identification①	Float Level (in.)	Air Valve Spring	Pump Rod (in.)	Idle Vent (in.)	Vacuum Break (in.)	Secondary Closing (in.)	Choke Rod (in.)	Choke Unloader (in.)	Fast Idle Speed (rpm)
1967	7027230	1/4	1/4 turn	11/16	—	0.180	0.020	0.090	0.300	—
	7027231	1/4	1/4 turn	11/16	—	0.180	0.020	0.090	0.300	—
	7027233	1/4	1/4 turn	11/16	—	0.180	0.020	0.090	0.300	—
	7027234	1/4	1/4 turn	11/16	—	0.180	0.020	0.090	0.300	—
	7027235	1/4	1/4 turn	11/16	—	0.180	0.020	0.090	0.300	—
	7037230	1/4	1/4 turn	11/32	—	0.180	0.020	0.090	0.300	—
	7037231	1/4	1/4 turn	11/32	—	0.180	0.020	0.090	0.300	—
	7037234	1/4	1/4 turn	11/32	—	0.180	0.020	0.090	0.300	—
	7037235	1/4	1/4 turn	11/32	—	0.180	0.020	0.090	0.300	—

CADILLAC

Year	Carburetor Identification①	Float Level (in.)	Air Valve Spring	Pump Rod (in.)	Idle Vent (in.)	Vacuum Break (in.)	Secondary Closing (in.)	Choke Rod (in.)	Choke Unloader (in.)	Fast Idle Speed (rpm)
1968	7028230	1/4	1/2 turn	11/32	—	0.180	0.020	0.090	0.300	—
	7028231	1/4	1/2 turn	11/32	—	0.180	0.020	0.090	0.300	—
	7028234	11/32	1/2 turn	11/32	—	0.180	0.020	0.090	0.300	—
	7028235	11/32	1/2 turn	11/32	—	0.180	0.020	0.090	0.300	—
	7028236	1/4	1/2 turn	11/32	—	0.215	0.020	0.090	0.300	—
	7028237	1/4	1/2 turn	11/32	—	0.215	0.020	0.090	0.300	—
	7028238	11/32	1/2 turn	11/32	—	0.215	0.020	0.090	0.300	—
	7028239	11/32	1/2 turn	11/32	—	0.215	0.020	0.090	0.300	—
1969	7029230	1/4	1/2 turn	11/32	—	0.230	0.020	0.090	0.300	—
	7029231	1/4	1/2 turn	11/32	—	0.230	0.020	0.090	0.300	—
1970	7047030	1/4	1/2 turn	11/32	—	0.230	0.020	0.090	0.300	—
1971	7041766	1/4	1/2 turn	11/32	—	0.300	0.020	0.090	0.310	—
	7041777	23/64	1/2 turn	11/32	—	0.300	0.020	0.090	0.310	—
1972	7047231	15/64	1/2 turn	11/32	—	0.140	0.020	0.090	0.312	—
	7047232	23/64	1/2 turn	11/32	—	0.140	0.020	0.090	0.312	—
1973	7047331	1/4	1/2 turn	11/32	—	0.200	0.020	0.090	0.015	—
	7047332	23/64	1/2 turn	11/32	—	0.205	0.020	0.090	0.015	—

CHEVROLET

Year	Carburetor Identification①	Float Level (in.)	Air Valve Spring	Pump Rod (in.)	Idle Vent (in.)	Vacuum Break (in.)	Secondary Closing (in.)	Choke Rod (in.)	Choke Unloader (in.)	Fast Idle Speed (rpm)
1967	7027202	9/32	7/8 turn	13/32	3/8	0.160	0.015	0.100	0.260	—
	7027203	9/32	7/8 turn	13/32	3/8	0.200	0.015	0.100	0.300	—
	7027200	9/32	7/8 turn	13/32	3/8	0.160	0.015	0.100	0.300	—
	7027201	9/32	7/8 turn	13/32	3/8	0.240	0.015	0.100	0.300	—
	7027202	9/32	7/8 turn	13/32	3/8	0.160	0.015	0.100	0.260	—
	7027203	9/32	7/8 turn	13/32	3/8	0.200	0.015	0.100	0.300	—
	7037200	9/32	7/8 turn	13/32	3/8	0.160	0.015	0.100	0.300	—
	7037201	9/32	7/8 turn	13/32	3/8	0.240	0.015	0.100	0.300	—
1968	7028212	9/32	3/8 turn	9/32	3/8	0.160	0.010	0.100	0.260	—
	7028213	9/32	3/8 turn	9/32	3/8	0.245	0.010	0.100	0.300	—
	7028229	9/32	7/8 turn	9/32	3/8	0.245	0.010	0.100	0.300	—
	7028208	9/32	3/8 turn	9/32	3/8	0.160	0.010	0.100	0.260	—
	7028207	9/32	3/8 turn	9/32	3/8	0.245	0.010	0.100	0.300	—
	7028219	9/32	7/8 turn	9/32	3/8	0.245	0.010	0.100	0.300	—
	7028218	3/16	7/8 turn	9/32	3/8	0.160	0.010	0.100	0.300	—
	7028217	3/16	7/8 turn	9/32	3/8	0.245	0.010	0.100	0.300	—
	7028210	3/16	7/8 turn	9/32	3/8	0.160	0.010	0.100	0.300	—
	7028211	3/16	7/8 turn	9/32	3/8	0.245	0.010	0.100	0.300	—
	7028216	3/16	7/8 turn	9/32	3/8	0.160	0.010	0.100	0.300	—
	7028209	3/16	7/8 turn	9/32	3/8	0.245	0.010	0.100	0.300	—
1969	7029203	7/32	7/16 turn	5/16	3/8	0.245	0.015	0.100	0.450	—
	7029202	7/32	7/16 turn	5/16	3/8	0.180	0.015	0.100	0.450	—
	7029207	3/16	13/16 turn	5/16	3/8	0.245	0.015	0.100	0.450	—
	7029215	1/4	13/16 turn	5/16	3/8	0.245	0.015	0.100	0.450	—
	7029204	1/4	13/16 turn	5/16	3/8	0.180	0.015	0.100	0.450	—

CHEVROLET

Year	Carburetor Identification①	Float Level (in.)	Air Valve Spring	Pump Rod (in.)	Idle Vent (in.)	Vacuum Break (in.)	Secondary Closing (in.)	Choke Rod (in.)	Choke Unloader (in.)	Fast Idle Speed (rpm)
1970	7040202	1/4	7/16 turn	5/16	—	0.245	—	0.100	0.450	—
	7040203	1/4	7/16 turn	5/16	—	0.275	—	0.100	0.450	—
	7040207	1/4	13/16 turn	5/16	—	0.275	—	0.100	0.450	—
	7040200	1/4	13/16 turn	5/16	—	0.245	—	0.100	0.450	—
	7040201	1/4	13/16 turn	5/16	—	0.275	—	0.100	0.450	—
	7040204	1/4	13/16 turn	5/16	—	0.245	—	0.100	0.450	—
	7040205	1/4	13/16 turn	5/16	—	0.275	—	0.100	0.450	—
1971	7041200	1/4	7/16 turn	—	—	0.260	—	0.100	—	—
	7041202	1/4	7/16 turn	—	—	0.260	—	0.100	—	—
	7041204	1/4	7/16 turn	—	—	0.260	—	0.100	—	—
	7041212	1/4	7/16 turn	—	—	0.260	—	0.100	—	—
	7041201	1/4	7/16 turn	—	—	0.275	—	0.100	—	—
	7041203	1/4	7/16 turn	—	—	0.275	—	0.100	—	—
	7041205	1/4	7/16 turn	—	—	0.275	—	0.100	—	—
	7041213	1/4	7/16 turn	—	—	0.275	—	0.100	—	—
1972	7042220	1/4	7/16 turn	3/8	—	0.250	—	0.100	0.450	—
	7042216	1/4	7/16 turn	3/8	—	0.250	—	0.100	0.450	—
	7042215	1/4	7/16 turn	3/8	—	0.250	—	0.100	0.450	—
	7042217	1/4	7/16 turn	3/8	—	0.250	—	0.100	0.450	—
	7042202	1/4	1/2 turn	3/8	—	0.215	—	0.100	0.450	—
	7042203	1/4	1/2 turn	3/8	—	0.215	—	0.100	0.450	—
	7042902	1/4	1/2 turn	3/8	—	0.215	—	0.100	0.450	—
	7042903	1/4	1/2 turn	3/8	—	0.215	—	0.100	0.450	—
1973	7043202	7/32	1/2 turn	13/32	—	0.250	—	0.430	0.450	—
	7043203	7/32	1/2 turn	13/32	—	0.250	—	0.430	0.450	—
	7043212	7/32	1 turn	13/32	—	0.250	—	0.430	0.450	—
	7043213	7/32	1 turn	13/32	—	0.250	—	0.430	0.450	—
	7043200	1/4	11/16 turn	13/32	—	0.250	—	0.430	0.450	—
	7043201	1/4	11/16 turn	13/32	—	0.250	—	0.430	0.450	—

FORD

Year	Carburetor Identification①	Float Level (in.)	Air Valve Spring	Pump Rod (in.)	Idle Vent (in.)	Vacuum Break (in.)	Secondary Closing (in.)	Choke Rod (in.)	Choke Unloader (in.)	Fast Idle Speed (rpm)
1970	DOOF-A	5/8	0.030	5/16	—	0.140	—	0.130	0.300	750②
	DOOF-B	5/8	0.030	5/16	—	0.190	—	0.166	0.300	1850③
	DOOF-E	5/8	0.030	5/16	—	0.190	—	0.166	0.300	1850③
	DOOF-F	5/8	0.030	5/16	—	0.140	—	0.130	0.300	750②
1971	DOOF-A	11/32	0.030	5/16	—	0.140	—	0.130	0.300	1800③
	DOOF-E	11/32	0.030	5/16	—	0.190	—	0.166	0.300	2000③

OLDSMOBILE

Year	Carburetor Identification①	Float Level (in.)	Air Valve Spring	Pump Rod (in.)	Idle Vent (in.)	Vacuum Break (in.)	Secondary Closing (in.)	Choke Rod (in.)	Choke Unloader (in.)	Fast Idle Speed (rpm)
1967	7027032	1/4	1/2 turn	5/16	3/8	0.200	—	0.140	0.325	—
	7027036	1/4	1/2 turn	5/16	3/8	0.200	—	0.140	0.325	—
	7027130	1/4	1/2 turn	5/16	3/8	0.200	—	0.140	0.325	—
	7027131	1/4	1/2 turn	5/16	3/8	0.200	—	0.140	0.325	—
	7027132	1/4	1/2 turn	5/16	3/8	0.200	—	0.140	0.325	—
	7027135	1/4	1/2 turn	5/16	3/8	0.200	—	0.140	0.325	—
	7027153	1/4	1/2 turn	5/16	3/8	0.200	—	0.140	0.325	—
	7027156	1/4	3/4 turn	5/16	3/8	0.200	—	0.140	0.325	—
	7027157	1/4	3/4 turn	5/16	3/8	0.200	—	0.140	0.325	—

OLDSMOBILE

Year	Carburetor Identification①	Float Level (in.)	Air Valve Spring	Pump Rod (in.)	Idle Vent (in.)	Vacuum Break (in.)	Secondary Closing (in.)	Choke Rod (in.)	Choke Unloader (in.)	Fast Idle Speed (rpm)
1968	7028250	1/4	1/2 turn	5/16	—	0.180	—	0.140	0.200	—
	7028251	1/4	3/4 turn	5/16	—	0.180	—	0.140	0.200	—
	7028252	1/4	3/4 turn	5/16	—	0.180	—	0.140	0.200	—
1969	7029250	1/4	1/2 turn	5/16	—	—	—	0.140	0.200	—
	7029251	1/4	3/4 turn	5/16	—	—	—	0.140	0.200	—
	7029252	1/4	3/4 turn	5/16	—	—	—	0.140	0.200	—
	7029253	1/4	3/4 turn	5/16	—	—	—	0.120	0.200	—
	7029254	1/4	3/4 turn	5/16	—	—	—	0.140	0.200	—
	7029255	1/4	3/4 turn	5/16	—	—	—	0.090	0.200	—
1970	7040250	1/4	1/2 turn	3/8	—	0.200	—	0.120	0.200	—
	7040251	1/4	3/4 turn	3/8	—	0.200	—	0.120	0.200	—
	7040252	1/4	3/4 turn	3/8	—	0.200	—	0.120	0.200	—
	7040253	1/4	3/4 turn	3/8	—	0.275	—	0.120	0.200	—
	7040255	1/4	3/4 turn	3/8	—	0.325	—	0.120	0.200	—
	7040256	1/4	3/4 turn	3/8	—	0.325	—	0.120	0.200	—
	7040257	1/4	3/4 turn	3/8	—	0.200	—	0.120	0.200	—
	7040258	1/4	3/4 turn	3/8	—	0.200	—	0.120	0.200	—
1971	7041250	1/4	1/2 turn	3/8	—	0.200	—	0.120	0.200	—
	7041251	1/4	3/4 turn	3/8	—	0.200	—	0.120	0.200	—
	7041252	1/4	3/4 turn	3/8	—	0.200	—	0.120	0.200	—
	7041253	1/4	3/4 turn	3/8	—	0.200	—	0.120	0.200	—
	7041257	1/4	3/4 turn	3/8	—	0.200	—	0.120	0.200	—
1972	7042250	1/4	1/2 turn	3/8	—	0.230	—	0.120	0.200	—
	7042251	1/4	3/4 turn	3/8	—	0.215	—	0.120	0.200	—
	7042252	1/4	3/4 turn	3/8	—	0.215	—	0.120	0.200	—
	7042953	1/4	3/4 turn	3/8	—	0.275	—	0.120	0.200	—
1973	7043256	1/4	3/4 turn	—	—	0.200	—	0.120	0.300	—
	7043257	1/4	1/2 turn	—	—	0.200	—	0.120	0.300	—
	7043255	1/4	3/4 turn	—	—	0.200	—	0.120	0.300	—
	7043251	1/4	3/4 turn	—	—	0.200	—	0.120	0.300	—
	7043253	1/4	3/4 turn	—	—	0.275	—	0.120	0.300	—
	7043252	1/4	3/4 turn	—	—	0.200	—	0.120	0.300	—
	7043259	1/4	3/4 turn	—	—	0.215	—	0.120	0.300	—

PONTIAC

Year	Carburetor Identification①	Float Level (in.)	Air Valve Spring	Pump Rod (in.)	Idle Vent (in.)	Vacuum Break (in.)	Secondary Closing (in.)	Choke Rod (in.)	Choke Unloader (in.)	Fast Idle Speed (rpm)
1967	7027260	7/32	1/2 turn	9/32	3/8	0.130	—	0.085	0.325	—
	7027261	7/32	1/2 turn	9/32	3/8	0.130	—	0.085	0.325	—
	7027262	3/16	1/2 turn	9/32	3/8	0.180	—	0.040	0.325	—
	7027263	3/16	1/2 turn	9/32	3/8	0.230	—	0.090	0.325	—
	7037260	7/32	1/2 turn	9/32	3/8	0.130	—	0.085	0.325	—
	7037261	7/32	1/2 turn	9/32	3/8	0.130	—	0.085	0.325	—
	7037262	3/16	1/2 turn	9/32	3/8	0.180	—	0.040	0.325	—
	7037263	3/16	1/2 turn	9/32	3/8	0.230	—	0.090	0.325	—

PONTIAC

Year	Carburetor Identification①	Float Level (in.)	Air Valve Spring	Pump Rod (in.)	Idle Vent (in.)	Vacuum Break (in.)	Secondary Closing (in.)	Choke Rod (in.)	Choke Unloader (in.)	Fast Idle Speed (rpm)
1968	7028260	5/16	1/2 turn	9/32	3/8	0.245	—	0.085	0.300	—
	7028261	5/16	1/2 turn	9/32	3/8	0.245	—	0.085	0.300	—
	7028262	1/4	1/2 turn	9/32	3/8	0.230	—	0.100	0.300	—
	7028263	1/4	1/2 turn	9/32	3/8	0.245	—	0.100	0.300	—
	7028264	1/4	1/2 turn	9/32	3/8	0.230	—	0.100	0.300	—
	7028265	1/4	1/2 turn	9/32	3/8	0.245	—	0.100	0.300	—
	7028266	1/4	1/2 turn	9/32	3/8	0.230	—	0.100	0.300	—
	7028267	1/4	1/2 turn	9/32	3/8	0.245	—	0.100	0.300	—
	7028268	1/4	1/2 turn	9/32	3/8	0.230	—	0.100	0.300	—
	7028269	1/4	1/2 turn	9/32	3/8	0.245	—	0.100	0.300	—
	7028271	1/4	1/2 turn	9/32	3/8	0.245	—	0.100	0.300	—
	7028274	1/4	1/2 turn	9/32	3/8	0.230	—	0.100	0.300	—
	7028275	1/4	1/2 turn	9/32	3/8	0.245	—	0.100	0.300	—
	7028276	1/4	1/2 turn	9/32	3/8	0.230	—	0.100	0.300	—
	7028277	1/4	1/2 turn	9/32	3/8	0.245	—	0.100	0.300	—
1969	7029260	3/16	1/2 turn	9/32	3/8	0.150	—	0.100	0.300	—
	7029261	3/16	1/2 turn	9/32	3/8	0.180	—	0.100	0.300	—
	7029262	9/32	1/2 turn	9/32	3/8	0.245	—	0.100	0.300	—
	7029263	9/32	1/2 turn	9/32	3/8	0.245	—	0.100	0.300	—
	7029268	9/32	1/2 turn	9/32	3/8	0.245	—	0.100	0.300	—
	7029270	9/32	1/2 turn	1/4	3/8	0.245	—	0.100	0.300	—
	7029273	9/32	1/2 turn	1/4	3/8	0.245	—	0.100	0.300	—
	7028270	1/4	1/2 turn	9/32	3/8	0.245	—	0.100	0.300	—
1970	7040262	9/32	7/16 turn	—	—	0.400	—	0.100	—	—
	7040263	9/32	7/16 turn	—	—	0.400	—	0.100	—	—
	7040264	9/32	7/16 turn	—	—	0.400	—	0.100	—	—
	7040267	9/32	7/16 turn	—	—	0.400	—	0.100	—	—
	7040268	9/32	7/16 turn	—	—	0.400	—	0.100	—	—
	7040270	9/32	7/16 turn	—	—	0.245	—	0.100	—	—
	7040273	9/32	7/16 turn	—	—	0.245	—	0.100	—	—
	7040274	9/32	7/16 turn	—	—	0.400	—	0.100	—	—
1971	7041262	9/32	7/16 turn	—	—	0.240	—	0.100	—	—
	7041263	9/32	7/16 turn	—	—	0.240	—	0.100	—	—
	7041264	9/32	7/16 turn	—	—	0.240	—	0.100	—	—
	7041267	9/32	1/2 turn	—	—	0.370	—	0.100	—	—
	7041268	9/32	1/2 turn	—	—	0.430	—	0.100	—	—
	7041270	9/32	1/2 turn	—	—	0.430	—	0.100	—	—
	7041271	9/32	7/16 turn	—	—	0.240	—	0.100	—	—
	7041273	9/32	1/2 turn	—	—	0.370	—	0.100	—	—
1972	7042262	1/4	7/16 turn	13/32	—	0.290	—	0.100	—	—
	7042263	1/4	11/16 turn	13/32	—	0.290	—	0.100	—	—
	7042264	1/4	5/8 turn	13/32	—	0.290	—	0.100	—	—
	7042270	1/4	7/16 turn	7/16	—	0.290	—	0.100	—	—
	7042273	1/4	7/16 turn	7/16	—	0.290	—	0.100	—	—
1973	7043263	13/32	5/8 turn	13/32	—	0.290	—	0.100	—	—
	7043264	13/32	1/2 turn	13/32	—	0.290	—	0.100	—	—
	7043274	13/32	9/16 turn	13/32	—	0.290	—	0.100	—	—
	7043262	13/32	3/8 turn	13/32	—	0.290	—	0.100	—	—
	7043265	13/32	9/16 turn	13/32	—	0.290	—	0.100	—	—
	7043272	13/32	3/8 turn	13/32	—	0.290	—	0.100	—	—

Holley Carburetors

Model 1920

On these units, the choke valve in the carburetor bore is connected to a well-type automatic choke.

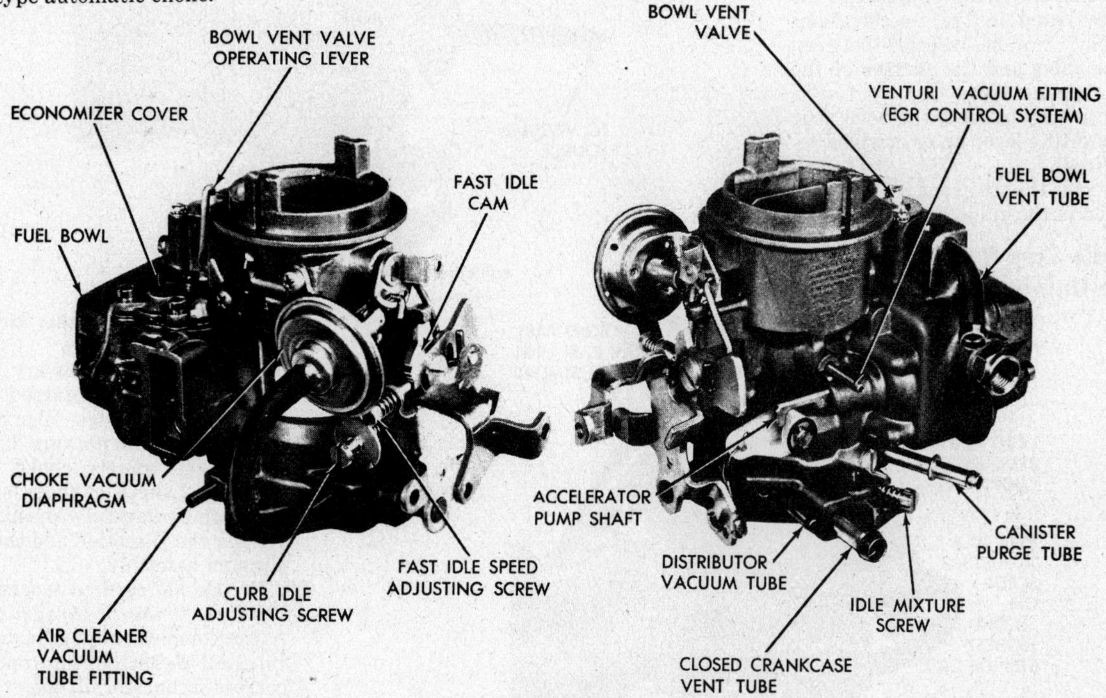
BOWL VENT VALVE
OPERATING LEVER
ECONOMIZER COVER
FUEL BOWL
FAST IDLE
CAM
CHOKE VACUUM
DIAPHRAGM
AIR CLEANER
VACUUM
TUBE FITTING
CURB IDLE
ADJUSTING SCREW
FAST IDLE SPEED
ADJUSTING SCREW
BOWL VENT
VALVE
VENTURI VACUUM FITTING
(EGR CONTROL SYSTEM)
FUEL BOWL
VENT TUBE
ACCELERATOR
PUMP SHAFT
CANISTER
PURGE TUBE
DISTRIBUTOR
VACUUM TUBE
IDLE MIXTURE
SCREW
CLOSED CRANKCASE
VENT TUBE
Carburetor assembly—Holley 1920

Some models are equipped with a spring-staged choke, which is a device incorporated in the choke mechanism to limit choke valve closing torque when cranking the engine at temperatures below zero. The spring-staging of the choke is suited for starting mixture requirements at both low and moderate temperatures.

The accelerator pump is a diaphragm, spring-driven type operated by a lever connected to the throttle shaft.

A two-stage power valve, mounted in the metering body and actuated by manifold vacuum, delivers additional fuel for full power and high speed operation.

Float Level Adjustment

NOTE: Do not allow the float tab to contact the float needle head during the adjustment procedure as the rubber tip of the needle can be compressed, giving a false reading.

1967-72 Units

1. With the carburetor inverted, slide the float gauge into position and test the setting on the "touch" leg of the gauge. The float should just touch the gauge.
2. Reverse the gauge and test the "no touch" leg. The float should just clear the gauge.
3. To adjust, bend the float tab which touches the head of the fuel inlet needle, using needle nose pliers.

1973 Units

1. With the carburetor inverted, measure from the top of the float to the upper wall of the main body with the gauge against the cast rib, approximately 2 in. from the float hinge pin.
2. Be sure that the gauge is parallel with the top of the float. Refer to the Specifications Chart for the proper dry float setting.
3. Adjust by bending the float tab

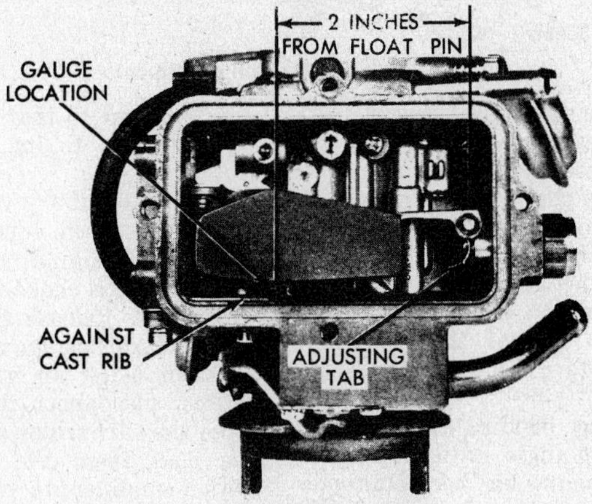
2 INCHES
FROM FLOAT PIN
GAUGE
LOCATION
AGAINST
CAST RIB
ADJUSTING
TAB

FLOAT
GAUGE
Adjusting the float level

which touches the head of the fuel needles using needle nosed pliers.

Float Bowl Vent Valve Adjustment

1. With the throttle valve closed, the bowl vent should be adjusted so that the shank of a drill of the size listed in the Specifications Chart can be inserted between the valve and the surface of the carburetor body.
2. Adjust by bending the bowl vent operating lever up or down as required.
3. Be sure that the vent rod does not bind in the guide after adjusting.

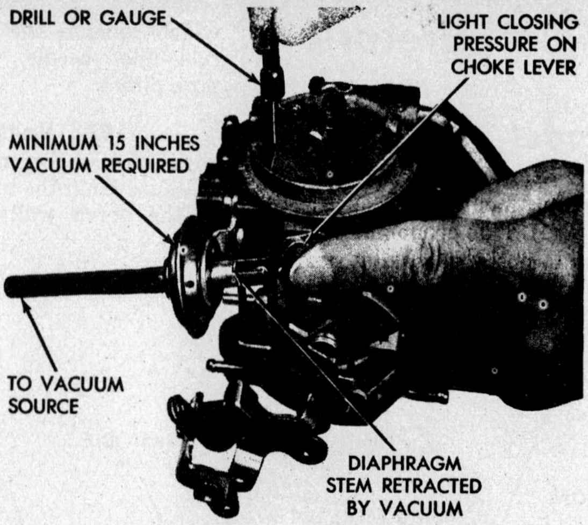
DRILL OR GAUGE
LIGHT CLOSING PRESSURE ON CHOKE LEVER
MINIMUM 15 INCHES VACUUM REQUIRED
TO VACUUM SOURCE
DIAPHRAGM STEM RETRACTED BY VACUUM

Adjusting the choke vacuum kick

Fast Idle Cam Position and Choke Unloader Adjustment

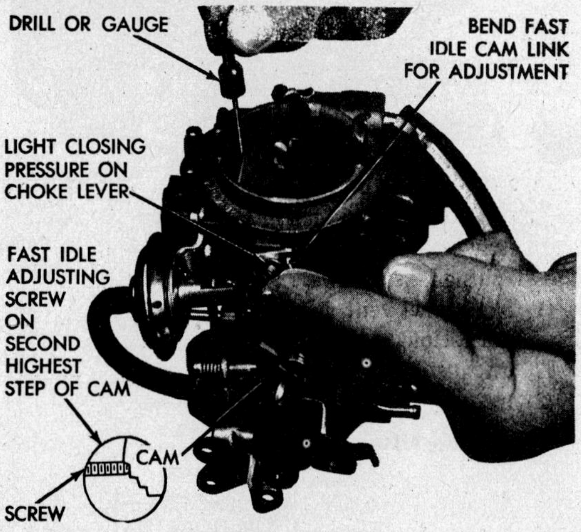
DRILL OR GAUGE
BEND FAST IDLE CAM LINK FOR ADJUSTMENT
LIGHT CLOSING PRESSURE ON CHOKE LEVER
FAST IDLE ADJUSTING SCREW ON SECOND HIGHEST STEP OF CAM
CAM
SCREW

Fast idle cam position adjustment

1. With the fast idle speed adjusting screw contacting the second highest step on the fast idle cam, move the choke valve toward the closed position with light pressure on the choke shaft lever.
2. Insert the specified gauge between the top of the choke valve and the wall of the air horn. Refer to the Specifications Chart.
3. Adjust by bending the fast idle link at an angle, until the correct valve opening has been obtained.

NOTE: When the correct fast idle cam position adjustment has been made, the choke unloader (wide open kick) adjustment has also been obtained. No further adjustment is required.

Choke Vacuum Kick

NOTE: The test can be made on or off the vehicle.

1. If adjustments are to be made with the engine running, back off the fast idle speed screw until the choke can be closed to the kick position with the engine at curb idle.
2. Note the number of screw turns required so that fast idle can be returned to its original adjustment.
3. If an auxiliary vacuum source is to be used, open the throttle valve (engine not running) and move the choke to the closed position. Release the throttle first, then release the choke.

When using an auxiliary vacuum source, disconnect the vacuum hose from the carburetor and connect it to the hose from the vacuum supply with a small length of tube to act as a fitting. Removal of the hose from the diaphragm may damage the system. Apply a vacuum of 15 or more in. of mercury.

4. Insert the gauge between the top of the choke valve and the wall of the air horn. Refer to the Specifications Chart.
5. Apply sufficient closing pressure on the lever to which the choke rod attaches to provide a minimum choke valve opening without distortion of the diaphragm link.

NOTE: The cylindrical stem of the diaphragm extends as the internal spring is compressed. This spring must be fully compressed for proper measurement of the vacuum kick adjustment.

6. Adjustment is necessary if a slight drag is not obtained when removing the gauge. Shorten or lengthen the diaphragm link to obtain the correct choke valve opening. Length changes should be made by carefully opening or closing the U-section and the diaphragm assembly.

NOTE: Do not apply a twisting or bending force to the diaphragm.

7. After completion of adjustment, reinstall the vacuum hose onto the correct carburetor fitting.
8. Return the fast idle screw to its original location if disturbed. Make the following check. With no vacuum applied to the diaphragm, the choke valve should move freely between the open and closed positions. If the movement is not free, examine the linkage for misalignment or interferences caused by the bending operation.

Well-Type Automatic Choke

1. To function properly, it is important that all parts be clean and move freely. Other than an occasional cleaning, the choke requires no attention. However, it is important that the choke control unit work freely in the well and at the choke shaft.
2. Move the choke rod up and down to check for free movement on the pivot. If the unit binds, a new choke unit should be installed.

NOTE: This type of choke is serviced only as a unit. Do not attempt to repair or change the setting.

When installing the choke unit, be certain that the coil housing does not contact the sides of the well in the exhaust manifold. Any contact at this point will affect choke operation. Do not lubricate any parts of the choke or the control unit. This causes an accumulation of dirt which will result in binding of the mechanism.

Spring Staged Choke Adjustment

1. To test the adjustment on carburetors equipped with this feature, press against the choke lever firmly.
2. Measure the clearance between the hub lever and the shaft lever.
3. If the clearance is not within 0.010 in. and 0.025 in., bend the fast idle rod slightly until the normal clearance is obtained.

Model 1931

This carburetor has a one-piece main body and throttle body casting, together with a large capacity fuel bowl cover, to maintain a stable fuel level for the best performance on turns. The large capacity fuel bowl is designed to efficiently handle vapor loaded fuels and fuel vapors.

The automatic choke is mounted in a heat sink on the exhaust manifold and is connected to the carburetor by a choke rod.

Float Adjustment

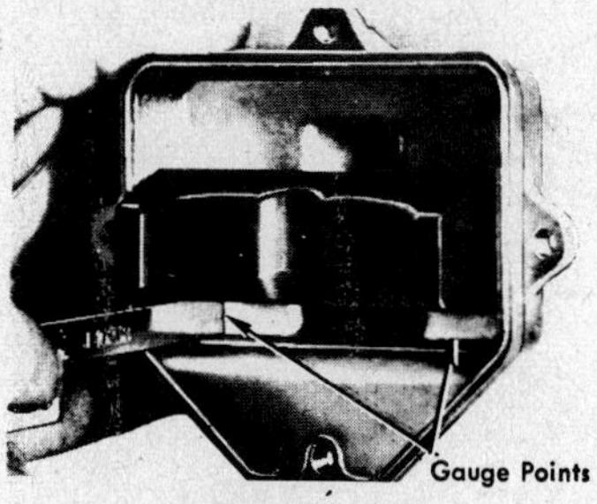
Gauge Points

Float adjustment

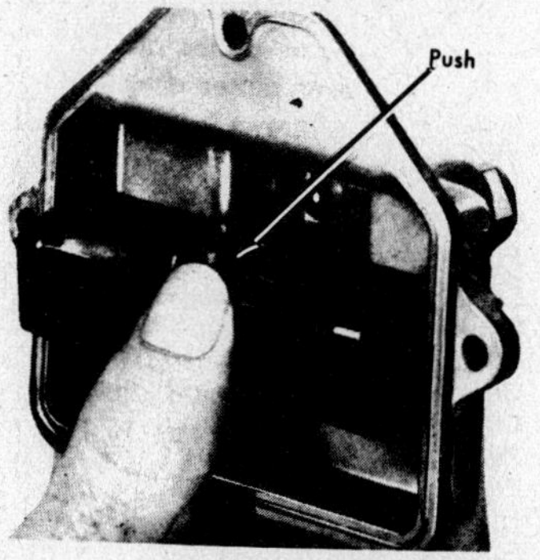
Push

Raising the float

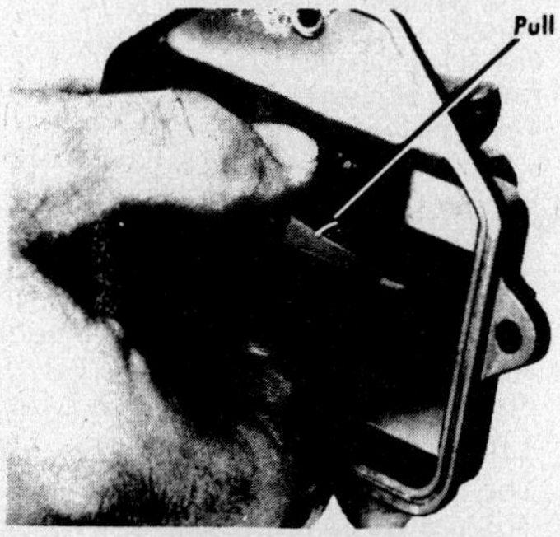
Pull

Lowering the float

1. Invert the carburetor fuel bowl cover and check the float setting at both ends.
2. If float adjustment is necessary, the float may be raised by pushing on the center of the float.

Caution During float adjustment, do not allow the float tab to contact the fuel inlet needle as the resilient tip of the needle can be damaged or compressed, resulting in an improper float setting and a leaky needle and seat.

If the proper gauge is not available, measure the distance between the roof of the float cover and the top of the float. If the setting is not as listed in the Specifications Chart, adjust as required.

Fast Idle Adjustment

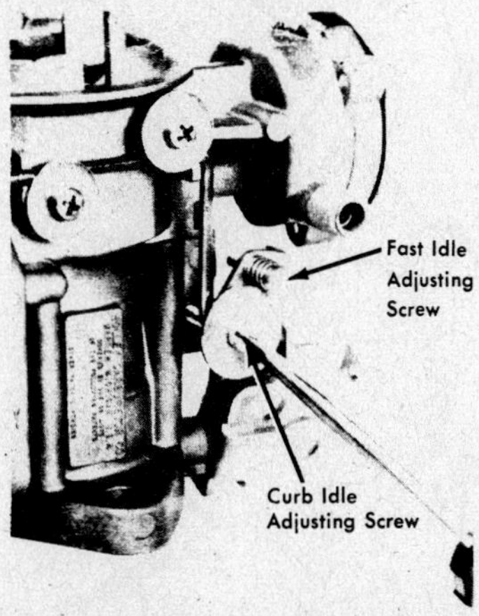
Fast Idle
Adjusting
Screw
Curb Idle
Adjusting Screw

Fast and curb idle speed adjusting screws

1. With the fast idle screw resting on the second step of the fast idle cam and the engine at normal operating temperature, screw it in clockwise.
2. Adjust by bending the tab on the throttle lever.

Choke Unloader Adjustment

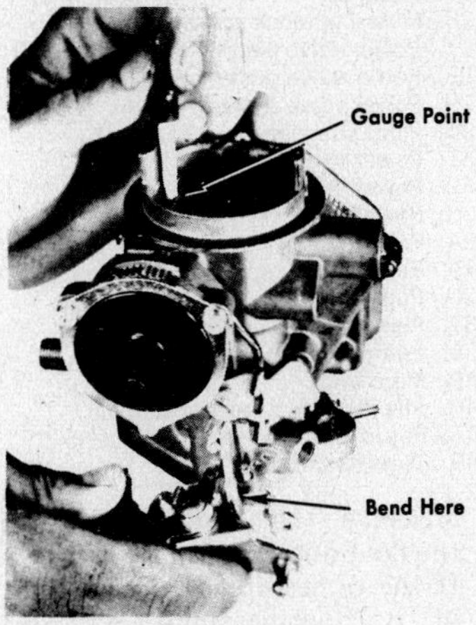
Gauge Point
Bend Here

Unloader adjustment

1. With the throttle valve held in the wide open position and the choke plate rotated toward the closed position, the distance between the top edge of the choke plate and the flat portion of the air horn can be referred to in the Specifications Chart.
2. Adjust by bending the tab on the throttle lever.

Choke Piston Stop Adjustment

1. Hold the choke piston against the stop screw with a wire inserted in the slot above the choke piston link.
2. Rotate the choke plate toward the closed position until the link is firm. The distance between the top edge of the choke plate and the flat portion of the air horn should be 3/16 in.
3. Adjust by turning the piston stop screw in or out as required.

Automatic Choke Adjustment

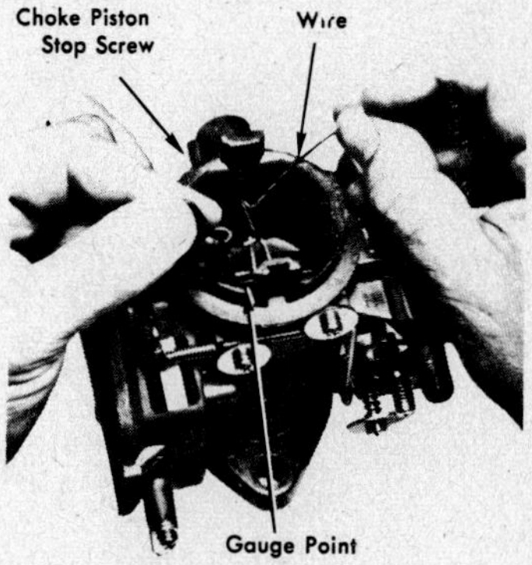
Choke Piston
Stop Screw
Wire
Gauge Point

Automatic choke adjustment

1. The adjustment is made by loosening the choke cover screws and rotating the cover in the desired direction as indicated by an arrow on the cover.
2. The choke should be set to the mark specified in the Specifications Chart for all normal driving.
3. Never set the choke more than two graduations in either direction of the specified setting.

Bowl Vent Adjustment

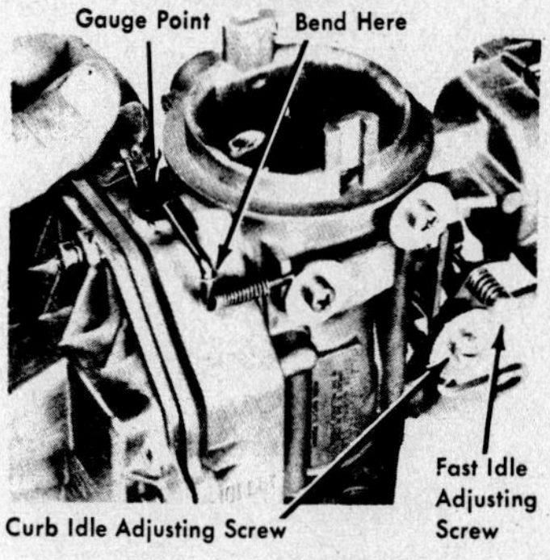
Gauge Point
Bend Here
Fast Idle
Adjusting
Screw
Curb Idle Adjusting Screw

Bowl vent adjustment

1. With the throttle set at curb idle, the clearance between the vent valve and the seat should be as listed in the Specifications Chart.
2. If an adjustment is necessary, bend the vent rod at the horizontal portion above the fuel bowl.

Check the operation of the vent rod for binding.

Accelerator Pump Adjustment

1. The accelerator link is set in the middle hole in the throttle lever for normal driving conditions.
2. If a richer pump discharge is required, place the pump link in the outer hole of the throttle lever. For a leaner pump discharge, place the pump link in the inner hole of the throttle lever.

Float Level Adjustment

1. Check the float setting with float dry and the air horn inverted.

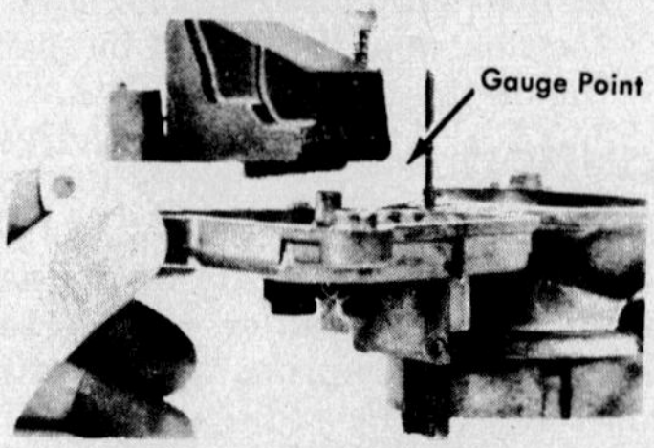
Gauge Point

Float level adjustment

should be parallel with the air horn, as shown.

2. Adjust by bending the float drop tab.

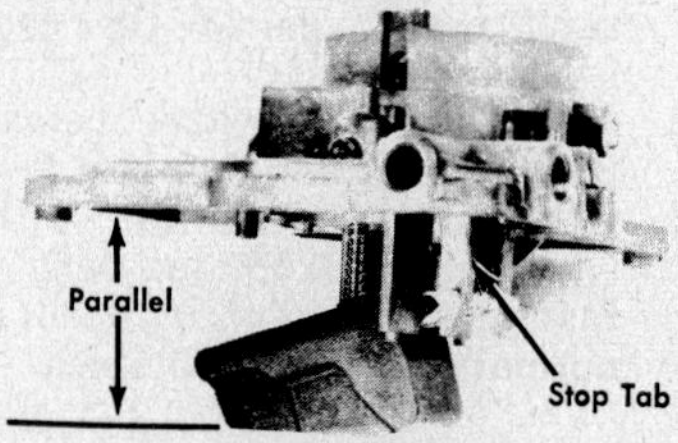
Parallel
Stop Tab

Checking the float drop

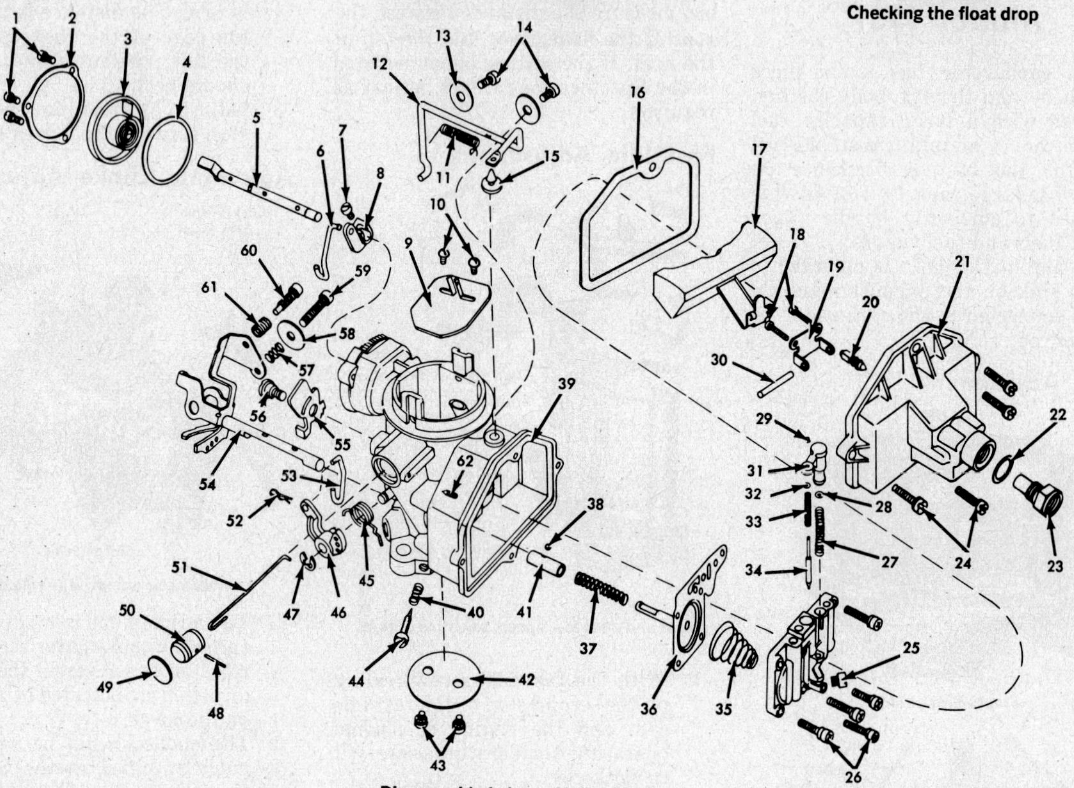

Disassembled view—Holley 1931

1. Choke thermostat cover screw
2. Choke thermostat cover retainer
3. Choke thermostat cover assembly
4. Choke thermostat cover gasket
5. Choke shaft assembly
6. Fast idle connector rod
7. Choke lever screw
8. Choke lever
9. Choke plate
10. Choke plate screws
11. Bowl vent rod spring
12. Bowl vent rod
13. Vent rod retainer washer
14. Vent rod retainer screws
15. Bowl vent valve
16. Fuel bowl gasket
17. Foat assembly
18. Float shaft bracket screws
19. Float shaft retaining bracket
20. Fuel inlet needle
21. Float bowl
22. Fuel inlet fitting gasket
23. Fuel inlet fitting
24. Float bowl screws
25. Main jet
26. Metering block screws
27. Power valve piston spring
28. Power valve piston spring washer
29. Power valve retainer
30. Float shaft pin
31. Power valve piston
32. Power valve spring washer
33. Power valve spring
34. Power valve
35. Pump return spring
36. Pump diaphragm assembly
37. Pump override spring
38. Pump push rod sleeve ball
39. Main body
40. Idle mixture needle spring
41. Pump push rod sleeve
42. Throttle plate
43. Throttle plate screws
44. Idle mixture adjustment needle
45. Pump return spring
46. Pump operating cam lever
47. Pump operating cam lever retainer
48. Choke piston pin
49. Choke piston plug
50. Choke piston
51. Choke piston link
52. Pump link retainer
53. Pump link
54. Throttle shaft assembly
55. Fast idle cam
56. Fast idle cam screw
57. Throttle stop screw spring
58. Vent rod operating washer
59. Throttle stop screw
60. Fast idle adjusting screw
61. Fast idle adjusting screw spring
62. Choke piston stop screw

Model 2209

This carburetor has a large capacity side inlet fuel bowl with a separate throttle body and gasket to create a thermal barrier which reduces heat transfer to the fuel. The automatic choke is part of the throttle body and is connected to the choke plate by a choke rod.

2. Measure the distance between the float and the air horn.
3. If the dimension is not as listed in the Specifications Chart, adjust by bending the float tab as required.

Checking Float Drop

1. With the air horn held upright, the bottom surface of the float

Choke Unloader Adjustment

1. With the throttle held in the wide open position, there should be the clearance listed in the Specifications Chart between the top edge of the choke plate and the air horn wall as shown.
2. Adjust by bending the tab on the fast idle cam.

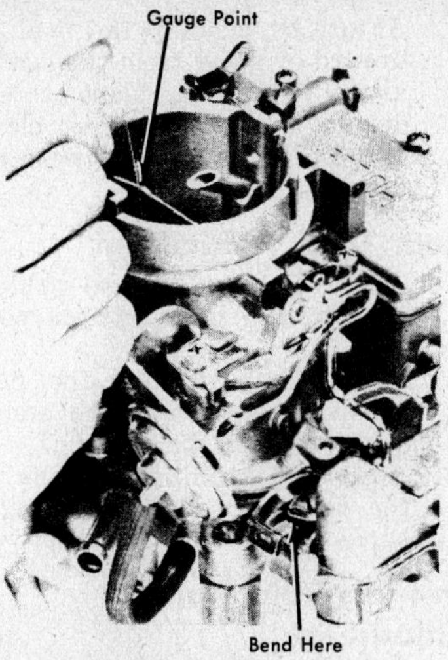
Gauge Point
Bend Here

Choke unloader adjustment

Choke Adjustment

Index Mark

Choke adjustment

1. Set the automatic choke on the index mark for all normal driving.
2. If a richer or leaner mixture is desired during the warm-up period, the choke can be reset by rotating the choke thermostat shaft clockwise for a richer mixture and counterclockwise for a leaner mixture.
3. Never set the choke more than two graduations in either direction from the specified mark listed in the Specifications Chart.

Fast Idle Adjustment

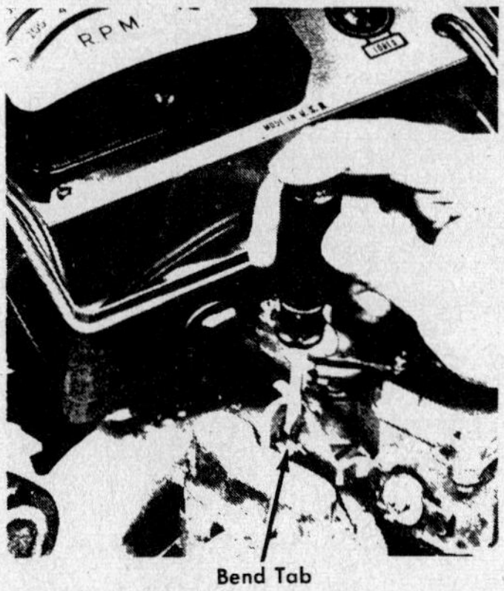
RPM
Bend Tab

Fast idle adjustment

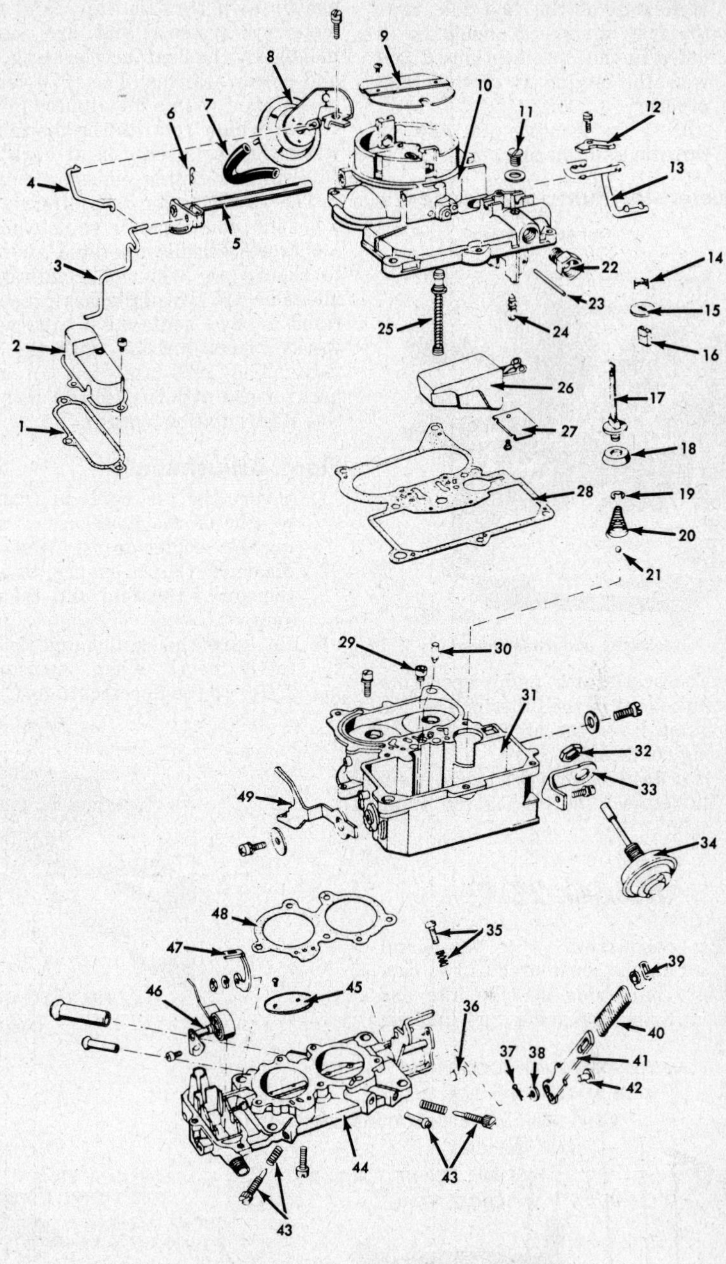

Disassembled view—Holley 2209 Carburetor

1. Thermostat housing cover gasket
2. Thermostat cover and guide assembly
3. Choke rod
4. Choke diaphragm rod
5. Choke shaft and lever assembly
6. Choke rod retainer
7. Vacuum hose
8. Choke diaphragm
9. Choke plate
10. Air horn assembly
11. Screw plug
12. Pump rod clamp
13. Pump rod
14. Bowl vent spring
15. Bowl vent washer
16. Bowl vent adjustment clip
17. Accelerator pump shaft
18. Pump cup
19. Pump cup retainer
20. Pump return spring
21. Pump inlet check valve (ball)
22. Fuel inlet fitting
23. Float hinge pin
24. Fuel inlet needle
25. Power valve piston assembly
26. Float assembly
27. Fuel bowl baffle
28. Main body gasket
29. Main jet
30. Pump discharge check needle
31. Main body
32. Dashpot locknut
33. Dashpot bracket
34. Dashpot
35. Throttle stop screw and spring
36. Throttle shaft bearing
37. Pump link retainer
38. Pump link washer
39. Nylon slide
40. Pump override spring
41. Pump link
42. Pump link pin
43. Idle mixture adjusting needle and spring
44. Throttle body
45. Throttle plate
46. Choke thermostat assembly
47. Choke unloader lever
48. Throttle body gasket
49. Fast idle cam

1. With the throttle stopped on the high step of the fast idle cam, the fast idle speed should be as listed in the Specifications Chart with the engine at normal temperature.
2. Adjust by bendng the tab on throttle lever, as shown.

Accelerator Pump Adjustment

Vent Adjustment Clip
Stop Screw

Accelerator pump adjustment

1. The accelerator pump operating link is set in the inner hole of the pump lever for all normal driving conditions.
2. If a leaner pump discharge is required, set the link in the outer hole.

Model 2210

This carburetor is a two-barrel unit but can be considered as two carburetors built side by side into one unit, utilizing the same fuel and air inlets. Each throat of the carburetor has its own throttle valve and main metering systems and are supplemented by the float, accelerating, idle, and power systems. The 1970 version is equipped with a distributor ground switch which retards the distributor when the carburetor is at curb idle, resulting in better emission control.

The 1971 version is equipped with a hot idle compensator valve which is a thermostatically operated air bleed to relieve an over-rich condition at idle. The 1971-73 units have incorporated a bowl vent valve tube which works in conjunction with the vent valve. The 1973 unit has an extra port for use with the (EGR) Exhaust Gas Recirculation system.

Float Adjustment

1. Invert the air horn so that the weight of the float only is forcing the needle against the seat.
2. Measure the clearance between the top of the float and the float stop.
3. Be sure the drill gauge is perfectly level when measuring. Refer to the Specifications Chart.

Adjust by bending the float lip toward or away from the needle, using a narrow blade screwdriver, until the correct clearance of the setting has been obtained.

Float Drop Adjustment

1. Check the float drop by holding the air horn in an upright position.
2. The bottom edge of the float should be parallel to the underside surface of the air horn.
3. Adjust by bending the tang on the float arm until the parallel surfaces have been obtained.

Fast Idle Cam Position Adjustment

1. With the fast idle speed adjusting screw contacting the second highest step on the fast idle cam, move the choke valve toward the closed position with light pressure on the choke shaft lever.
2. Insert the specified gauge between the top of the choke valve and the wall of the air horn. Refer to the Specifications Chart.

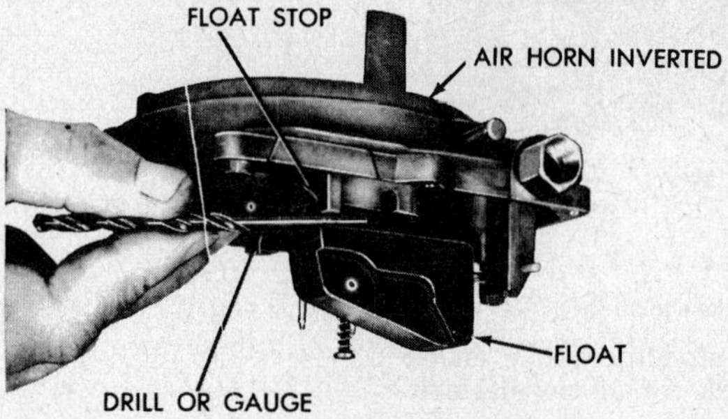
FLOAT STOP
AIR HORN INVERTED
FLOAT
DRILL OR GAUGE

Checking the float adjustment

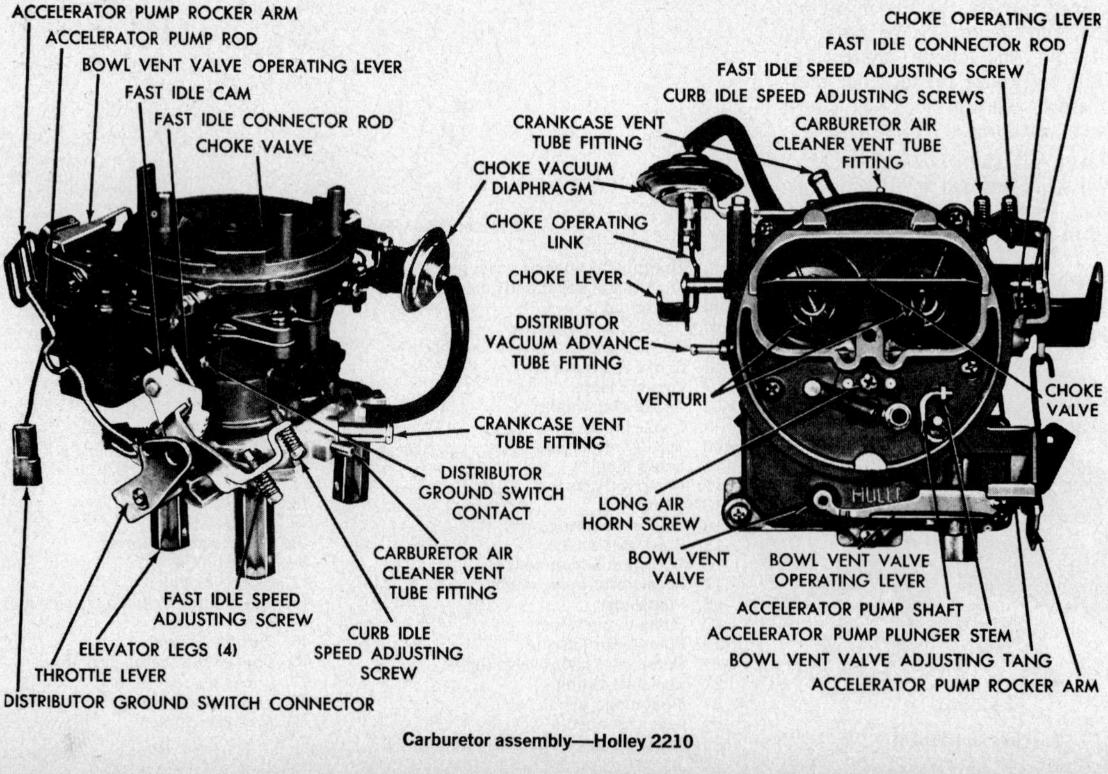
ACCELERATOR PUMP ROCKER ARM
ACCELERATOR PUMP ROD
BOWL VENT VALVE OPERATING LEVER
FAST IDLE CAM
FAST IDLE CONNECTOR ROD
CHOKE VALVE
CRANKCASE VENT TUBE FITTING
DISTRIBUTOR GROUND SWITCH CONTACT
CARBURETOR AIR CLEANER VENT TUBE FITTING
FAST IDLE SPEED ADJUSTING SCREW
CURB IDLE SPEED ADJUSTING SCREW
ELEVATOR LEGS (4)
THROTTLE LEVER
DISTRIBUTOR GROUND SWITCH CONNECTOR
CHOKE OPERATING LEVER
FAST IDLE CONNECTOR ROD
FAST IDLE SPEED ADJUSTING SCREW
CURB IDLE SPEED ADJUSTING SCREWS
CRANKCASE VENT TUBE FITTING
CARBURETOR AIR CLEANER VENT TUBE FITTING
CHOKE VACUUM DIAPHRAGM
CHOKE OPERATING LINK
CHOKE LEVER
DISTRIBUTOR VACUUM ADVANCE TUBE FITTING
VENTURI
CHOKE VALVE
LONG AIR HORN SCREW
BOWL VENT VALVE
BOWL VENT VALVE OPERATING LEVER
ACCELERATOR PUMP SHAFT
ACCELERATOR PUMP PLUNGER STEM
BOWL VENT VALVE ADJUSTING TANG
ACCELERATOR PUMP ROCKER ARM

Carburetor assembly—Holley 2210

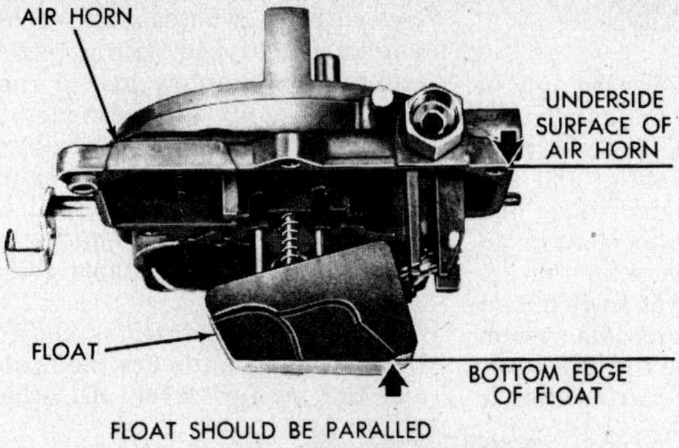
AIR HORN
UNDERSIDE SURFACE OF AIR HORN
FLOAT
BOTTOM EDGE OF FLOAT
FLOAT SHOULD BE PARALLED
Checking the float drop

3. An adjustment will be necessary if a slight drag is not obtained as the drill shank is being removed.
4. Adjust by bending the fast idle link at an angle, until the correct valve opening has been obtained.

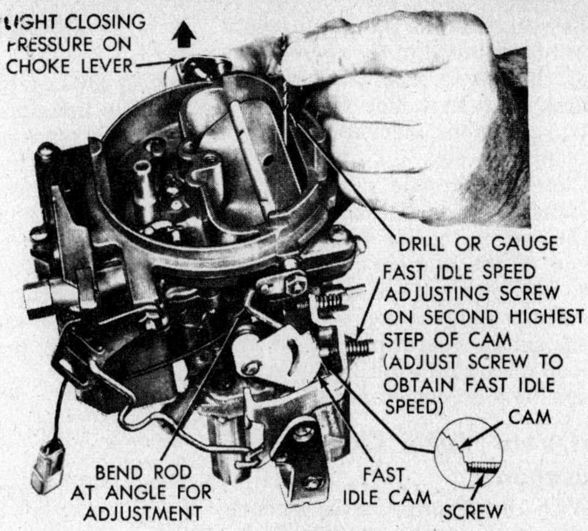
LIGHT CLOSING PRESSURE ON CHOKE LEVER
DRILL OR GAUGE
FAST IDLE SPEED ADJUSTING SCREW ON SECOND HIGHEST STEP OF CAM (ADJUST SCREW TO OBTAIN FAST IDLE SPEED)
CAM
BEND ROD AT ANGLE FOR ADJUSTMENT
FAST IDLE CAM
SCREW
Fast idle cam position adjustment

Choke Vacuum Kick Adjustment

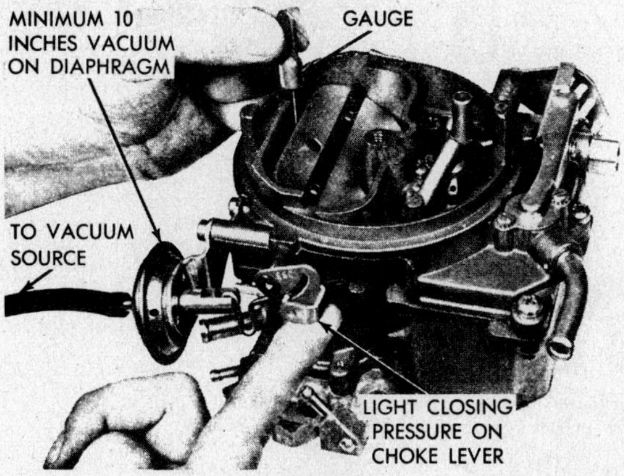
MINIMUM 10 INCHES VACUUM ON DIAPHRAGM
GAUGE
TO VACUUM SOURCE
LIGHT CLOSING PRESSURE ON CHOKE LEVER
Vacuum kick adjustment

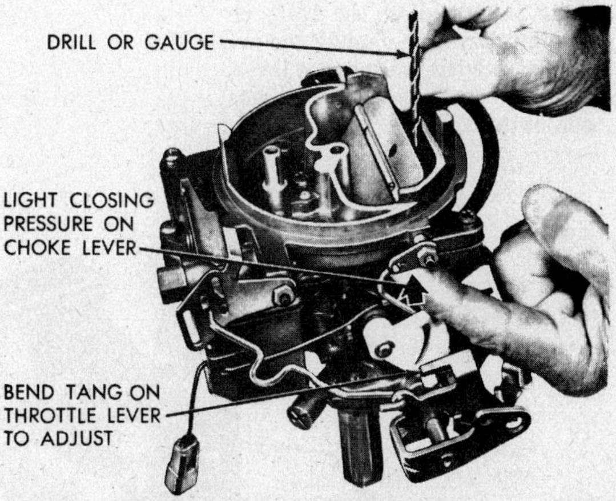
DRILL OR GAUGE
LIGHT CLOSING PRESSURE ON CHOKE LEVER
BEND TANG ON THROTTLE LEVER TO ADJUST
Choke unloader adjustment

NOTE: The test can be made on or off the vehicle.

1. If the adjustment is to be made with the engine running, back off the fast idle speed screw until the choke can be closed to the kick position with the engine at curb idle. (Note the number of screw turns required so that the fast idle can be returned to the original adjustment.)
2. If an auxiliary vacuum source is to be used, open the throttle valve (engine not running) and move the choke to the closed position. Release the throttle first, then release the choke.

When using an auxiliary vacuum source, disconnect the vacuum hose from the carburetor and connect it to the hose from the vacuum supply with a small length of tube to act as a fitting. Removal of the hose from the diaphragm may damage the system. Apply a vacuum of 15 or more in. of mercury.

3. Insert the gauge between the top of the choke valve and the wall of the air horn. Refer to the Specifications Chart.
4. Apply sufficient closing pressure on the lever to which the choke rod attaches, to provide a minimum choke valve opening without distortion of the diaphragm link.

NOTE: The cylindrical stem of the diaphragm extends as the internal spring is compressed. This spring must be fully compressed for proper measurement of the vacuum kick adjustment.

5. Adjustment is necessary if a slight drag is not obtained when removing the gauge. Shorten or lengthen the diaphragm link to obtain the correct choke valve opening. Length changes should be made by carefully opening or closing the U-bend provided in the link. Improper bending causes contact between the U-section and the diaphragm assembly.

NOTE: Do not apply a twisting or bending force to diaphragm.

6. After completing adjustments, reinstall the vacuum hose on the correct carburetor fitting.
7. Return the fast idle screw to its original location if it was disturbed. Make the following check. With no vacuum applied to the diaphragm, the choke valve should move freely between the open and closed positions. If the movement is not free, examine the linkage for misalignment or interferences caused by the bending operation.

Choke Unloader (Wide Open Kick) Adjustment

1. With the throttle valve in the wide open position, insert a drill gauge between the upper edge of the choke valve and the inner wall of the air horn. Refer to the Specifications Chart.
2. With a finger lightly pressing against the shaft lever, a slight drag should be felt as the drill is being withdrawn.
3. Adjust by bending the unloader tang on the throttle lever until the correct opening has been obtained.

Accelerator Pump Adjustment

1. Back off the curb idle speed adjusting screw.
2. Open the choke valve so that the fast idle cam allows the throttle valves to be completely seated in the bores.

3. Be sure that the pump connector rod is installed in the correct slot of the accelerator pump rocker arm. The first slot for manual transmissions is next to the attaching screw.
4. Close the throttle valves tightly. Measure the distance between the top of the air horn and the end of the plunger shaft. Refer to the Specifications Chart.
5. Adjust pump travel by bending the pump operating rod at the loop of the rod, until the correct setting has been obtained.

Bowl Vent Valve Clearance Adjustment

1. With the throttle valves at curb idle, it should be possible to insert an inch gauge between the bowl vent valve plunger stem and the operating rod. Refer to the Specifications Chart.
2. Adjust by bending the tang on the pump lever to change the arc of contact with the throttle lever, until the correct clearance has been obtained.

Model 2300

The 2300 carburetor is used only in a triple installation. This sytem utilizes two types of Holley two-barrels, one mounted in the center and the two secondaries mounted fore and aft. The secondary units contain all the regulatory systems with the exception of chokes, power enrichment valve, accelerating pump, idle system and spark advance. The throttle operation of the primary carburetor is conventional whereas the secondary units are equipped with throttle control vacuum diaphragms for the purpose of opening the secondary throttles which close mechanically. The choke used only on the primary unit is controlled by a temperature sensing choke coil mounted on the intake manifold, over the exhaust crossover passage.

The only adjustments required on the secondary units are the float level and the jet fuel lever. All other ad-

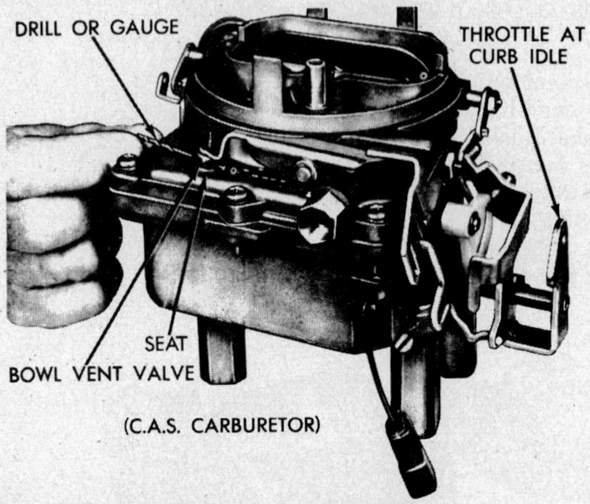
DRILL OR GAUGE
THROTTLE AT CURB IDLE
SEAT
BOWL VENT VALVE
(C.A.S. CARBURETOR)
Bowl vent valve adjustment

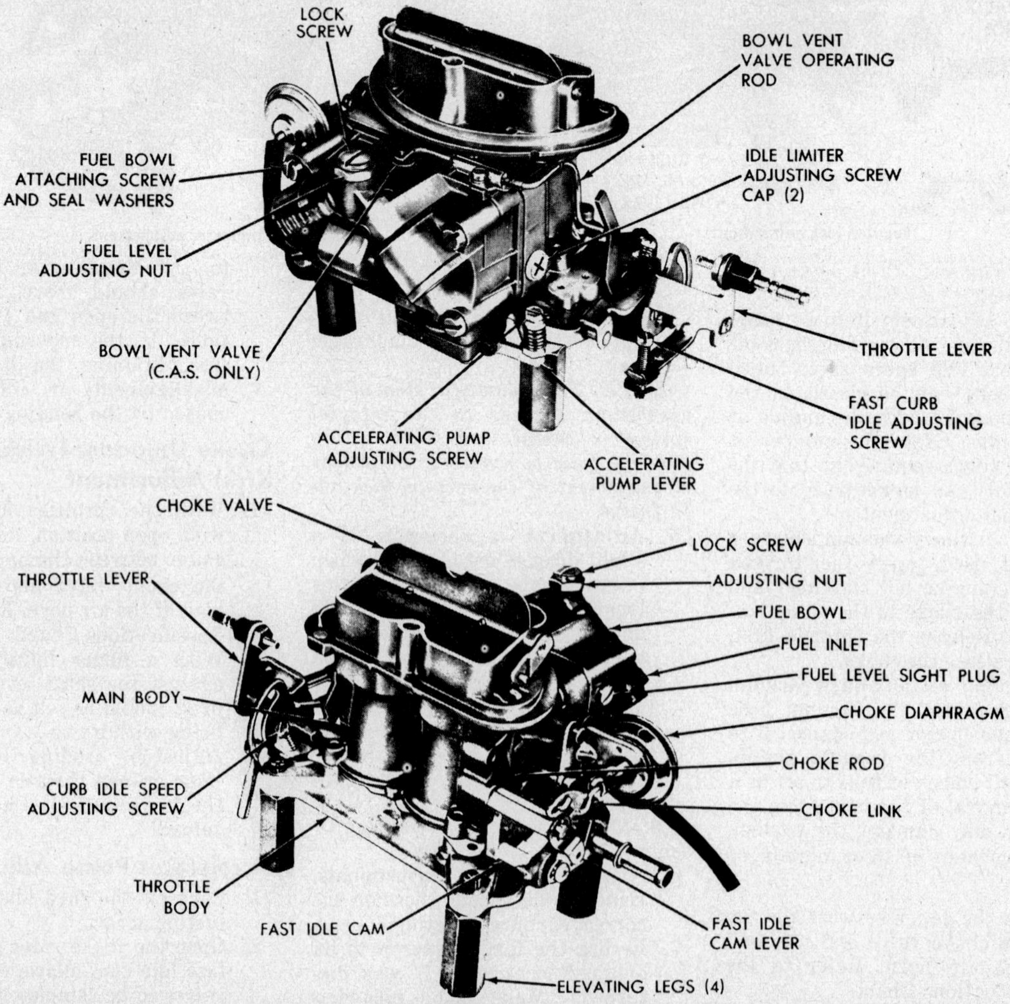
LOCK SCREW
BOWL VENT VALVE OPERATING ROD
FUEL BOWL ATTACHING SCREW AND SEAL WASHERS
IDLE LIMITER ADJUSTING SCREW CAP (2)
FUEL LEVEL ADJUSTING NUT
THROTTLE LEVER
BOWL VENT VALVE (C.A.S. ONLY)
FAST CURB IDLE ADJUSTING SCREW
ACCELERATING PUMP ADJUSTING SCREW
ACCELERATING PUMP LEVER
CHOKE VALVE
LOCK SCREW
THROTTLE LEVER
ADJUSTING NUT
FUEL BOWL
FUEL INLET
FUEL LEVEL SIGHT PLUG
MAIN BODY
CHOKE DIAPHRAGM
CHOKE ROD
CURB IDLE SPEED ADJUSTING SCREW
CHOKE LINK
THROTTLE BODY
FAST IDLE CAM
FAST IDLE CAM LEVER
ELEVATING LEGS (4)
Carburetor assembly—Holley 2300

justments are made on the primary unit.

Float Adjustment

1. Make a preliminary float adjustment by inverting the fuel bowl and turning the adjustable needle and seat until the top of the float is the specified distance from the top of the fuel bowl. Refer to the Specifications Chart.
2. Do not fully tighten the lock screw. Snug the screw to temporarily retain adjustment.

NOTE: Final adjustment of the float is made on the vehicle.

Wet Fuel Level

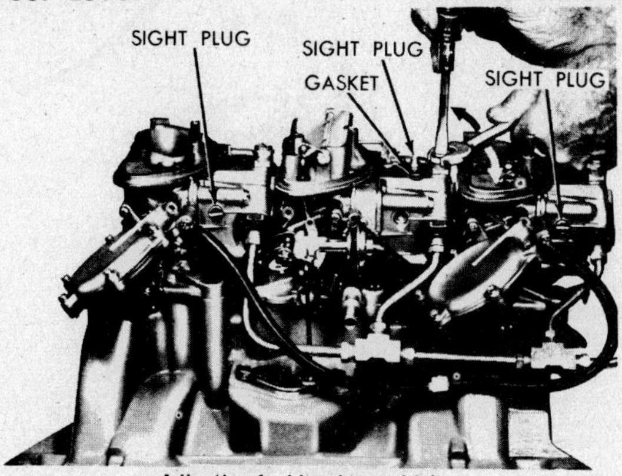
SIGHT PLUG
SIGHT PLUG
GASKET
SIGHT PLUG

Adjusting fuel level on vehicle

1. With the car level and the engine idling, remove the sight plug from the fuel bowl.
2. The fuel level should be in line with the threads at the bottom of the sight plug hole.
3. To adjust, loosen the lock screw and turn the adjusting nut as required to raise or lower the fuel level.

Automatic Choke Control Lever Setting

Adjustment of the choke control lever is necessary to provide the correct relationship between the choke valve, the thermostatic coil spring, and the fast idle cam. It should be checked and adjusted (if necessary), as preparation of the choke system linkage before making the Vacuum Kick, Cam Position, or Unloader adjustment. These three adjustments must be made after qualification of the choke control lever.

NOTE: Improper bending of the choke rod will result in binding.

Chevrolet

1. Close the choke rod by applying slight pressure on the choke control lever; the thermostatic choke rod should be even with the top of the choke rod hole.
2. Adjust by bending the choke rod at the upper angle.

Chrysler

1. Open the throttle to mid-position; close the choke valve by applying slight pressure on the choke control lever.
2. The top of choke rod hole in the control lever should be 3 49/64 in. above the choke pad with the carburetor on the engine, or 1 23/32 in. above the carburetor base with the carburetor on a bench.
3. Adjust by bending the choke shaft rod at the indicated point.

Fast Idle Cam Position Adjustment

Chevrolet

1. With the throttle slightly open, close the choke plate positioning fast idle lever against the top step of the fast idle cam.
2. Adjust the fast idle screw to obtain the clearance listed in the Specifications Chart between the throttle valve and the bore on the idle transfer slot side of the carburetor.
3. Adjust by bending the idle lever.

Chrysler

1. With the fast idle speed adjusting screw contacting the second highest step on the fast idle cam, move the choke valve toward the closed position with light pressure on the choke shaft lever.
2. Insert the specified gauge between the top of the choke valve

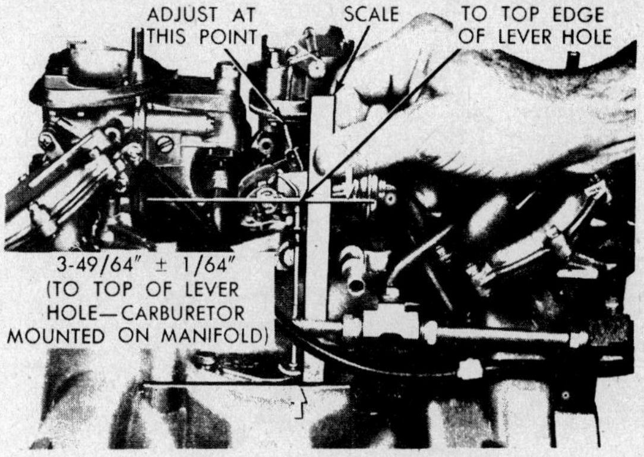
ADJUST AT THIS POINT
SCALE
TO TOP EDGE OF LEVER HOLE
3-49/64" ± 1/64" (TO TOP OF LEVER HOLE—CARBURETOR MOUNTED ON MANIFOLD)

Adjusting the choke control lever

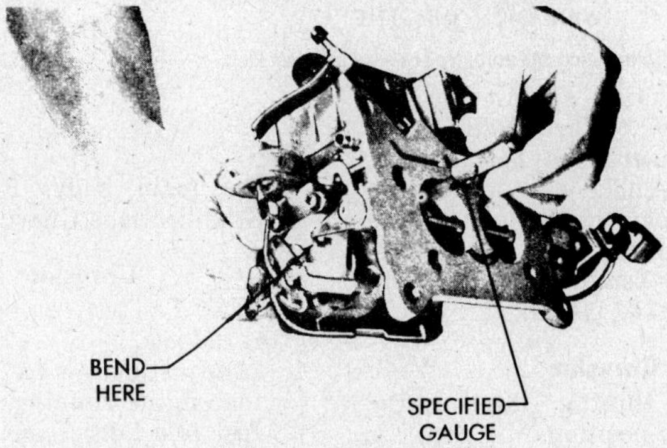
BEND HERE
SPECIFIED GAUGE

Fast idle cam adjustment

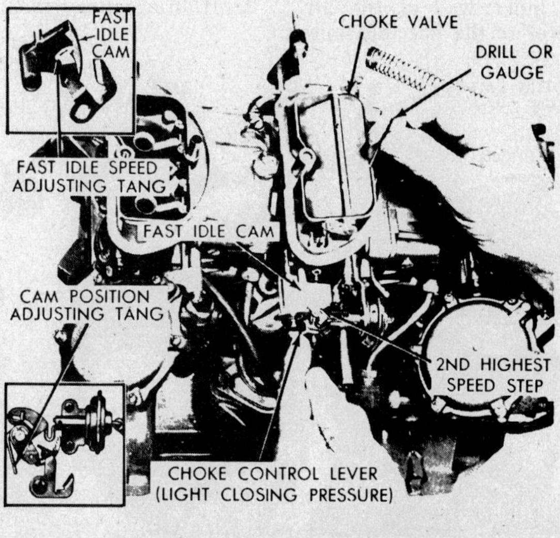
FAST IDLE CAM
CHOKE VALVE
DRILL OR GAUGE
FAST IDLE SPEED ADJUSTING TANG
FAST IDLE CAM
CAM POSITION ADJUSTING TANG
2ND HIGHEST SPEED STEP
CHOKE CONTROL LEVER (LIGHT CLOSING PRESSURE)

Fast idle cam position adjustment

and the wall of the air horn. Refer to the Specifications Chart.

3. An adjustment will be necessary if a slight drag is not obtained as the drill shank is being removed.
4. Adjust by bending the cam position adjusting tang.

Choke Unloader Adjustment (Wide Open Kick)

Chevrolet

1. Hold the throttle lever in the wide open throttle position with a rubber band.
2. Hold the choke valve toward the

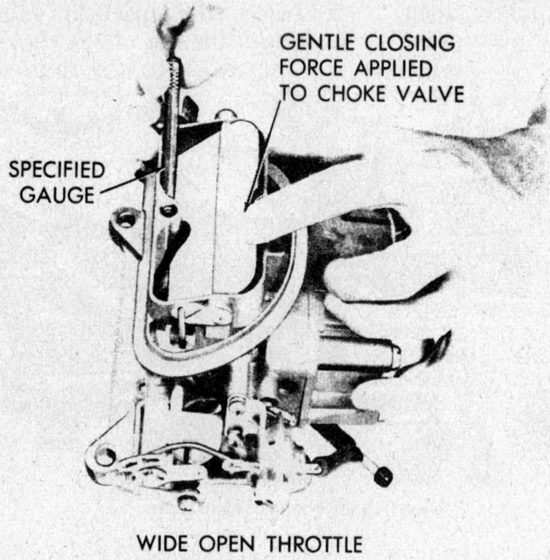
GENTLE CLOSING
FORCE APPLIED
TO CHOKE VALVE
SPECIFIED
GAUGE
WIDE OPEN THROTTLE

Choke unloader adjustment—wide open kick

closed position against the unloader tang of the throttle shaft, then measure the opening between the choke valve lower edge and the main body. Refer to the Specifications Chart.

3. Adjust by bending the choke rod (at the off-set bend).

Chrysler

1. Hold the throttle valves in the wide-open position.
2. Insert the specified drill between the upper edge of the choke valve and the inner wall of the air horn. Refer to the Specifications Chart.
3. With a finger lightly pressing against the choke control lever, a slight drag should be felt as the drill is being withdrawn.
4. Adjust by bending the indicated tang until the correct opening has been obtained.

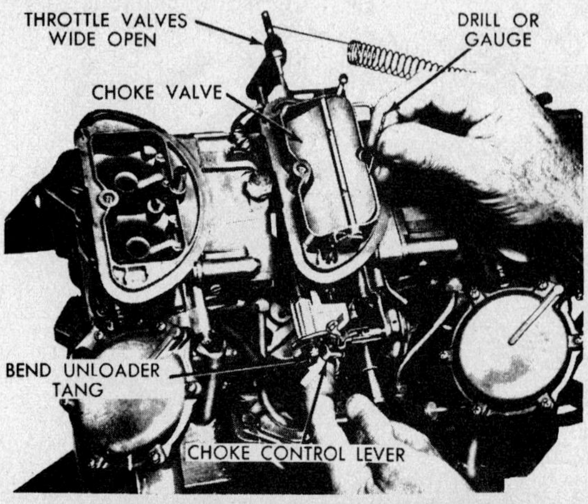
THROTTLE VALVES
WIDE OPEN
DRILL OR
GAUGE
CHOKE VALVE
BEND UNLOADER
TANG
CHOKE CONTROL LEVER

Choke unloader adjustment—wide open kick

Choke Vacuum Kick Adjustment

Chevrolet

1. With the choke valve closed, hold the vacuum break against the stop.
2. Measure the distance between the choke valve lower edge and

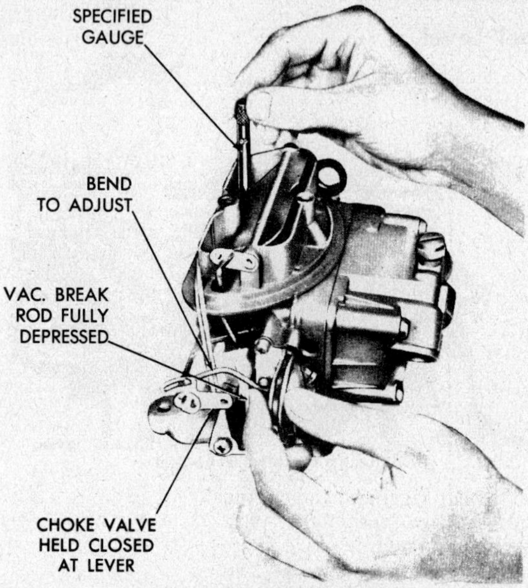
SPECIFIED
GAUGE
BEND
TO ADJUST
VAC. BREAK
ROD FULLY
DEPRESSED
CHOKE VALVE
HELD CLOSED
AT LEVER

Choke vacuum kick adjustment

the main body. Refer to the Specifications Chart.

Chrysler

NOTE: The test can be made on or off the vehicle.

1. If adjustment is to be made with the engine running, position the fast idle tang (cam position adjustment) to allow the choke to close to the kick position.
2. If an auxiliary vacuum source is to be used, open the throttle valve (engine not running) and move the choke to the closed position. Release the throttle first, then release the choke.

When using an auxiliary vacuum source, disconnect the vacuum hose from the carburetor and connect it to the hose from the vacuum supply with a small length of tube to act as a fitting. Removal of the hose from the diaphragm may require forces which damage the system. Apply a vacuum of 10 or more in. of mercury.

3. Insert the gauge between the top of the choke valve and the wall of the air horn. Refer to the Specifications Chart.
4. Apply sufficient closing pressure on the lever to which the choke rod attaches to provide a minimum choke valve opening without distortion of the diaphragm link.

NOTE: The cylindrical stem of the diaphragm extends as the internal spring is compressed for proper measurement of the vacuum kick adjustment.

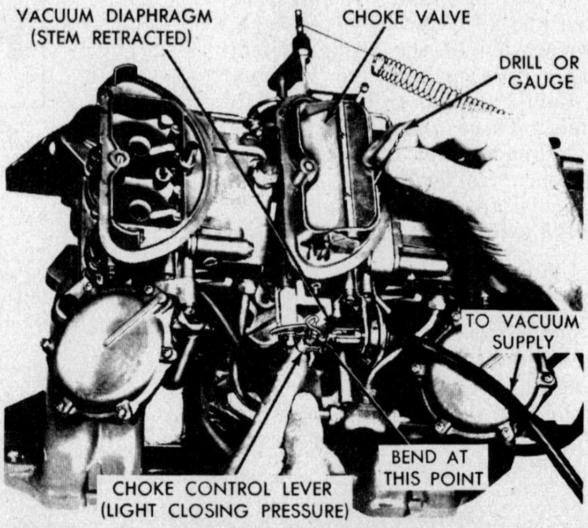
VACUUM DIAPHRAGM
(STEM RETRACTED)
CHOKE VALVE
DRILL OR
GAUGE
TO VACUUM
SUPPLY
BEND AT
THIS POINT
CHOKE CONTROL LEVER
(LIGHT CLOSING PRESSURE)

Choke vacuum kick adjustment

5. Adjustment is necessary if a slight drag is not obtained when removing the gauge. Shorten or lengthen the diaphragm link to obtain the correct choke valve opening. Length changes should be made by carefully opening or closing the U-bend provided in the link. Improper bending causes contact between the U-section and the diaphragm assembly.

NOTE: Do not apply a twisting or bending force to the diaphragm.

6. After completion of adjustment, reinstall the vacuum hose onto the correct carburetor fitting.
7. Return the fast idle screw to its original location if it was disturbed. Make the following check. With no vacuum applied to the diaphragm, the choke valve should move freely between the open and closed positions. If the movement is not free, examine the linkage for misalignment or interferences caused by the bending operation.

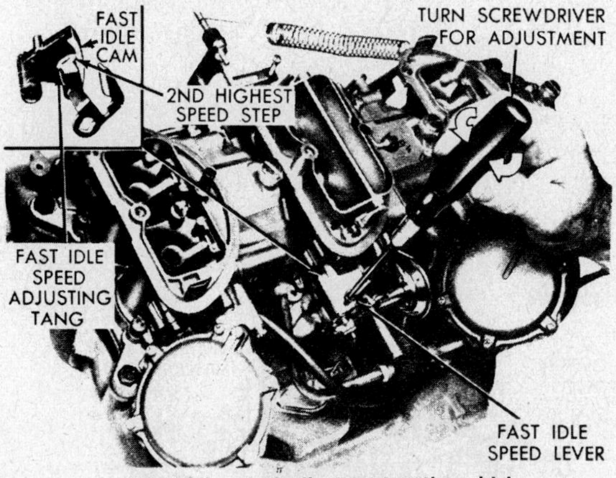
FAST IDLE CAM
2ND HIGHEST SPEED STEP
TURN SCREWDRIVER FOR ADJUSTMENT
FAST IDLE SPEED ADJUSTING TANG
FAST IDLE SPEED LEVER

Fast idle speed adjustment on the vehicle

Fast Idle Cam Adjustment (On Vehicle)

Chrysler

1. Close the choke valve until the fast idle screw tang can be positioned on the second highest-speed step of the fast idle cam.
2. Start the engine and determine the stabilized speed.
3. Bend the fast idle tang by use of a screwdriver placed in the tang slot to secure the specified speed. Refer to the Specifications Chart.

NOTE: Bend it only in a direction perpendicular to the contact surface of the cam. Movement in any other direction changes the cam position adjustment. Bend it only when the tang is clear of the cam. Stopping the engine between adjustments is not necessary. However, reposition the fast idle tang on the cam after each speed adjustment to provide correct throttle closing torque.

Accelerator Pump Adjustment

1. With the throttle lever in the wide open position and the pump lever fully compressed (down), measure the clearance between the spring adjusting nut and the arm of the pump lever. Refer to Specifications Chart.
2. Adjust by turning the nut or screw as required while holding the opposite end. (The pump operating lever is not threaded.) There should be no free movement of the pump lever when the throttle is at curb idle.

Bowl Vent Valve Adjustment

1. With the throttle valves at fast curb idle, insert the drill gauge between the bowl vent valve and the bowl vent rod with the fast curb idle speed properly set. Refer to the Specifications Chart.
2. Adjust by bending the rod to change the arc of contact with the throttle lever, until the correct clearance has been obtained.

Refer to pages U234-36 for one and two barrel specifications.

Model 4150, 4160

The 4150 and 4160 are four barrel carburetors which contain all the basic systems in the primary sides. The secondary sides of these units contain a fuel transfer and bypass system which richens the mixture when needed.

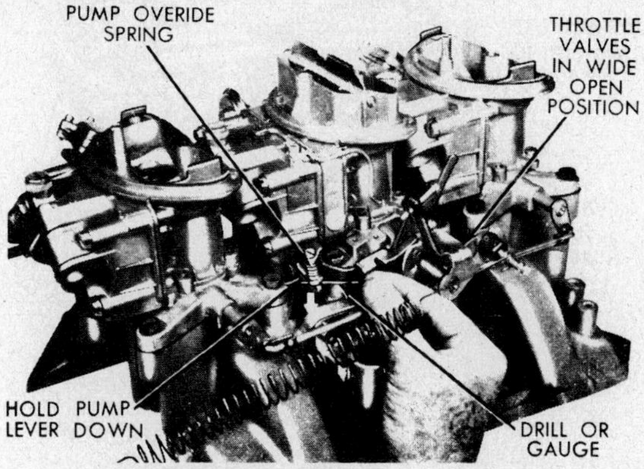
PUMP OVERIDE SPRING
THROTTLE VALVES IN WIDE OPEN POSITION
HOLD PUMP LEVER DOWN
DRILL OR GAUGE

Checking the accelerator pump lever adjustment

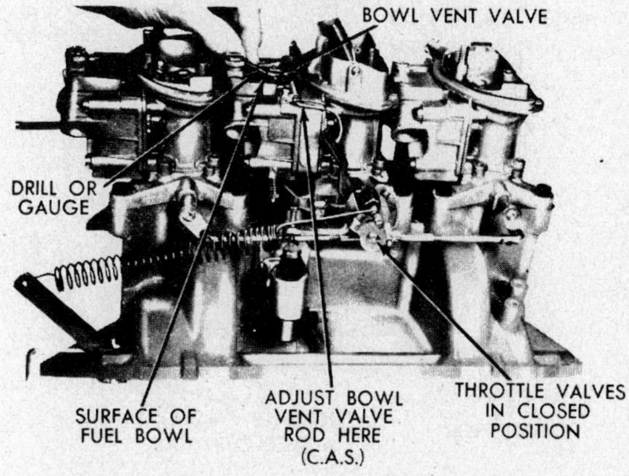
BOWL VENT VALVE
DRILL OR GAUGE
SURFACE OF FUEL BOWL
ADJUST BOWL VENT VALVE ROD HERE (C.A.S.)
THROTTLE VALVES IN CLOSED POSITION

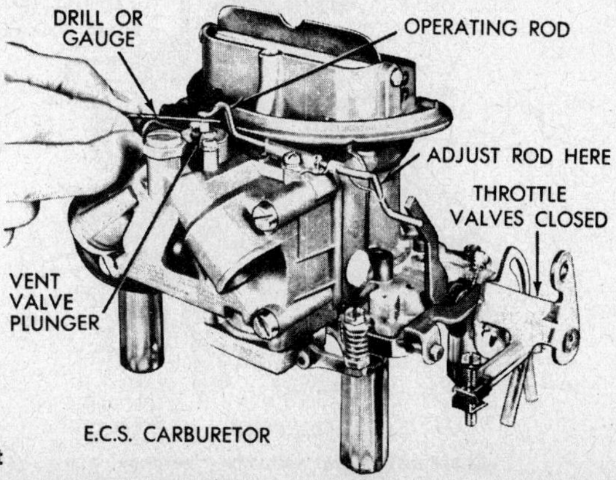
DRILL OR GAUGE
OPERATING ROD
ADJUST ROD HERE
THROTTLE VALVES CLOSED
VENT VALVE PLUNGER
E.C.S. CARBURETOR

Checking the bowl vent valve adjustment

Some 4150 models have a central fuel inlet whereas other units have a side inlet.

Model 4150, 4160 Adjustments (Chrysler Products)

Vent Valve Adjustment

1. With the throttle valves at curb idle, it should be possible to insert a 0.015 in. gauge between the bowl vent valve plunger stem and the operating rod.
2. If an adjustment is necessary, bend the rod to change the arc of contact with the throttle lever until the correct clearance has been obtained.

Accelerator Pump Adjustment

1. With the throttle valves open wide and the pump lever held down, it should be possible to insert a 0.015 in. feeler gauge between the adjusting nut and the lever.

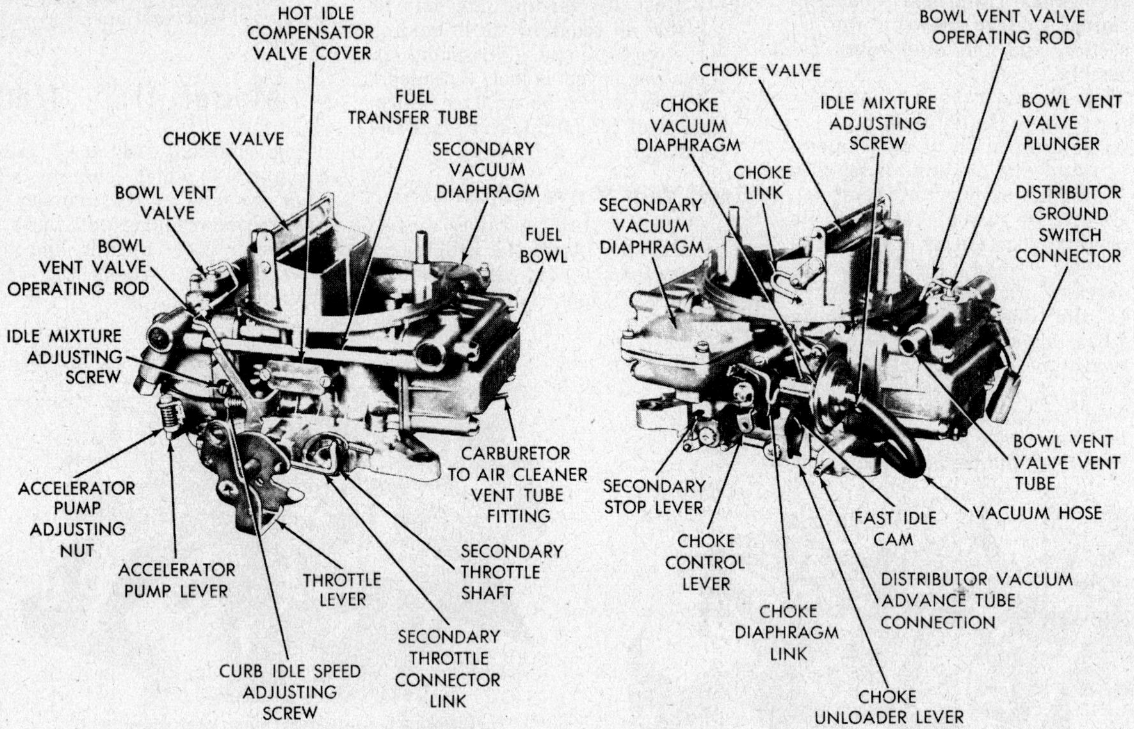
HOT IDLE
COMPENSATOR
VALVE COVER
FUEL
TRANSFER TUBE
CHOKE VALVE
SECONDARY
VACUUM
DIAPHRAGM
BOWL VENT
VALVE
FUEL
BOWL
BOWL
VENT VALVE
OPERATING ROD
IDLE MIXTURE
ADJUSTING
SCREW
CARBURETOR
TO AIR CLEANER
VENT TUBE
FITTING
ACCELERATOR
PUMP
ADJUSTING
NUT
SECONDARY
THROTTLE
SHAFT
ACCELERATOR
PUMP LEVER
THROTTLE
LEVER
SECONDARY
THROTTLE
CONNECTOR
LINK
CURB IDLE SPEED
ADJUSTING
SCREW
BOWL VENT VALVE
OPERATING ROD
CHOKE VALVE
CHOKE
VACUUM
DIAPHRAGM
IDLE MIXTURE
ADJUSTING
SCREW
BOWL VENT
VALVE
PLUNGER
CHOKE
LINK
SECONDARY
VACUUM
DIAPHRAGM
DISTRIBUTOR
GROUND
SWITCH
CONNECTOR
BOWL VENT
VALVE VENT
TUBE
SECONDARY
STOP LEVER
FAST IDLE
CAM
VACUUM HOSE
CHOKE
CONTROL
LEVER
DISTRIBUTOR VACUUM
ADVANCE TUBE
CONNECTION
CHOKE
DIAPHRAGM
LINK
CHOKE
UNLOADER LEVER

Carburetor assembly—Holley 4160

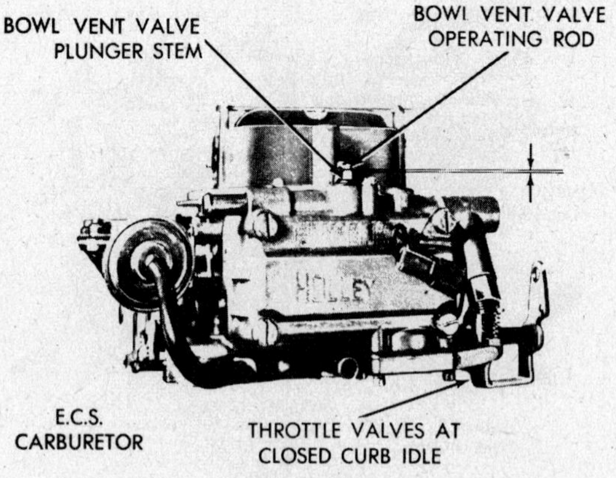
BOWL VENT VALVE
PLUNGER STEM
BOWL VENT VALVE
OPERATING ROD
E.C.S.
CARBURETOR
THROTTLE VALVES AT
CLOSED CURB IDLE

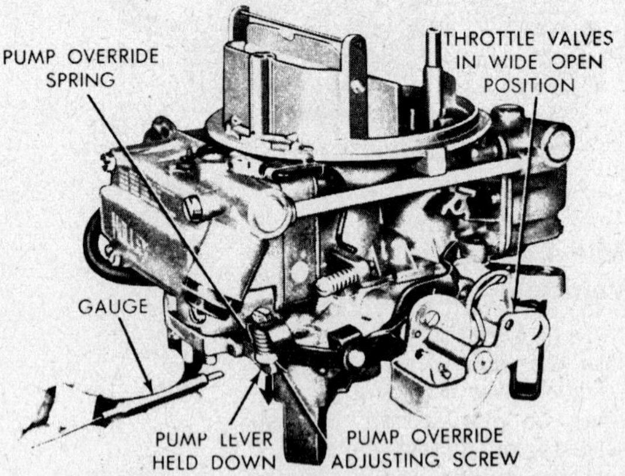
PUMP OVERRIDE
SPRING
THROTTLE VALVES
IN WIDE OPEN
POSITION
GAUGE
PUMP LEVER
HELD DOWN
PUMP OVERRIDE
ADJUSTING SCREW

Checking accelerator pump lever clearance

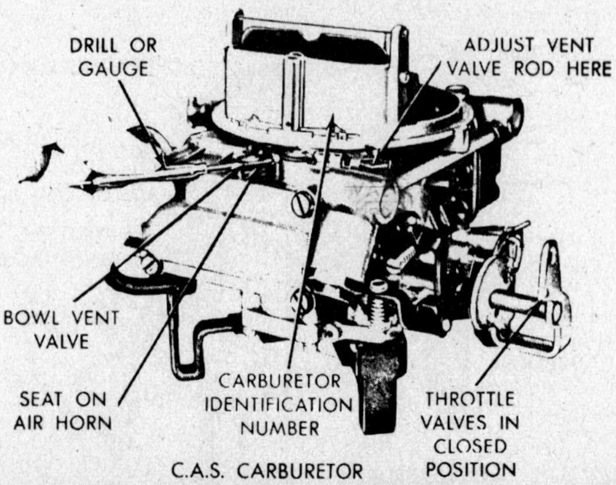
DRILL OR
GAUGE
ADJUST VENT
VALVE ROD HERE
BOWL VENT
VALVE
SEAT ON
AIR HORN
CARBURETOR
IDENTIFICATION
NUMBER
THROTTLE
VALVES IN
CLOSED
POSITION
C.A.S. CARBURETOR

Checking the bowl vent valve clearance

2. If an adjustment is necessary, adjust the pump override screw until the correct clearance has been obtained.
3. There must be no free movement of the pump lever when the throttle is at curb idle.

Choke Lever Adjustment

1. Open the throttle to the mid position.
2. Close the choke valve by exerting slight pressure on the choke control lever.

3. The top of the choke rod hole in the control lever should be 2¾ in. above the choke assembly with the carburetor on the engine. With the carburetor on the bench, the measurement should be 1-9/16 in. above the carburetor base.
4. To adjust, bend the choke shaft rod at the point indicated.

Caution Improper bending will cause binding of the rod. Check for free movement between the open and closed position.

Choke Unloader Adjustment (Wide Open Kick)

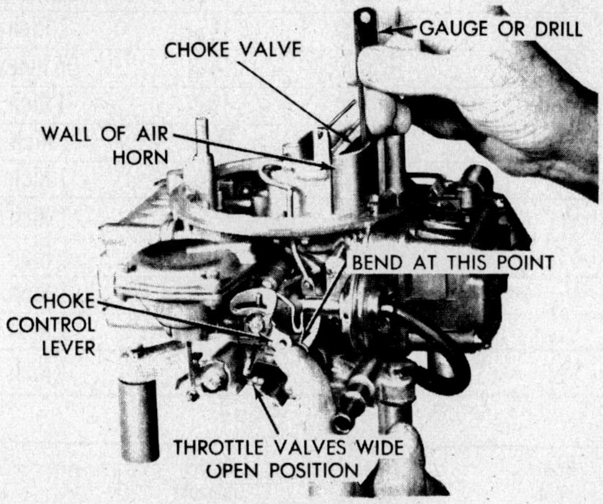
GAUGE OR DRILL
CHOKE VALVE
WALL OF AIR HORN
BEND AT THIS POINT
CHOKE CONTROL LEVER
THROTTLE VALVES WIDE OPEN POSITION

Choke unloader adjustment

1. Adjust the choke control lever.
2. Hold the throttle valves in the wide-open position. Insert the specified drill between the upper edge of the choke valve and the inner wall of the air horn.
3. With a finger pressed against the choke control lever, a slight drag should be felt as the drill is being withdrawn. If an adjustment is to be made, bend the flat tang that contacts the bottom of the fast idle cam until the correct opening has been obtained.

Fast Idle Speed Adjustment

1. With the engine off and the transmission in Neutral, open the throttle slightly.
2. Close the choke valve until the fast idle screw tang can be positioned on the second highest step of the fast idle cam.
3. Start the engine and determine the stabilized speed. Bend the fast idle tang by use of a screwdriver placed in the tang slot to secure the specified speed.

Caution Bend only in a direction perpendicular to the contact surface of the cam. Movement in any other direction will change the cam position adjustment described earlier.

4. Reposition the fast idle tang on the cam after each speed adjustment, to provide the correct throttle torque.

Fast Idle Cam Position Adjustment

1. Adjust the choke control lever.
2. With the fast idle speed adjusting screw contacting the second highest speed step on the fast idle cam, move the choke valve toward the closed position with light pressure on the choke control lever.
3. Insert the No. 53 drill between the choke valve and the wall of the air horn. An adjustment will be necessary if a slight drag is not obtained as the drill is being removed.

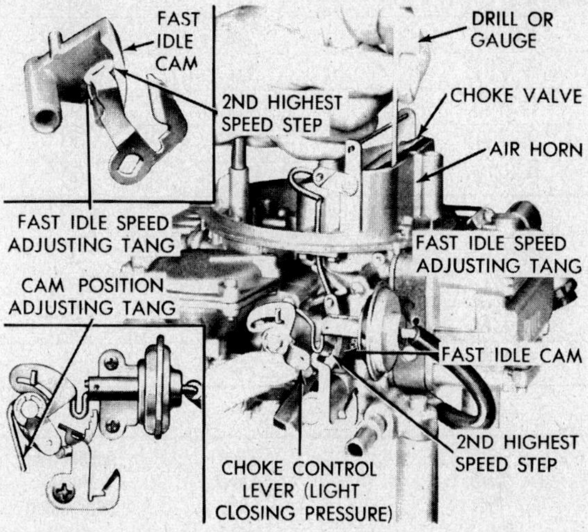
FAST IDLE CAM
DRILL OR GAUGE
2ND HIGHEST SPEED STEP
CHOKE VALVE
AIR HORN
FAST IDLE SPEED ADJUSTING TANG
FAST IDLE SPEED ADJUSTING TANG
CAM POSITION ADJUSTING TANG
FAST IDLE CAM
2ND HIGHEST SPEED STEP
CHOKE CONTROL LEVER (LIGHT CLOSING PRESSURE)

Fast idle cam position adjustment

4. To adjust, bend the indicated tang until the correct choke valve opening has been obtained.

Vacuum Kick Adjustment

1. Start the engine and position the fast idle tang to allow the choke closure to the kick position.
2. Insert the specified drill between the choke valve and the wall of the air horn. Apply sufficient closing pressure on the lever to which the choke rod attaches to provide a minimum choke valve opening without distortion of the diaphragm link.

NOTE: The cylindrical stem of the diaphragm will extend as an internal spring is compressed. This spring must be fully compressed for proper measurement of the vacuum link adjustment.

4. An adjustment will be necessary if a slight drag is not obtained as the drill is being removed. Shorten or lengthen the diaphragm link to obtain the correct choke opening. Length changes should be made by carefully opening or closing the bend provided in the diaphragm link.

Caution Do not apply twisting or bending force to the diaphragm.

5. With no vacuum applied to the diaphragm, the choke valve should move freely between the open and closed positions. If the movement is not free, examine the linkage for misalignment or interferences caused by the bending operation. Repeat the adjustment if necessary to provide the proper link operation.

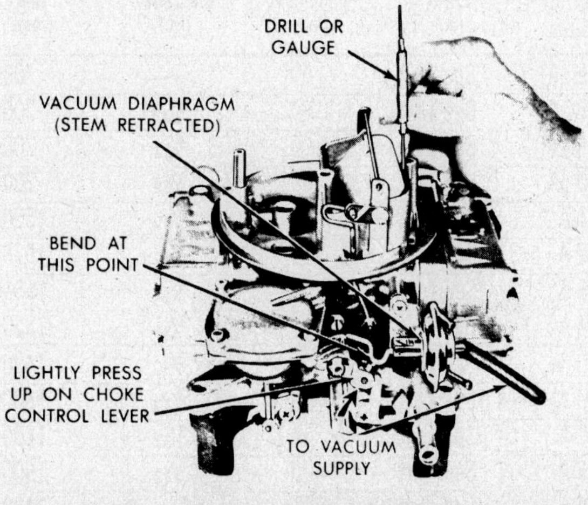
DRILL OR GAUGE
VACUUM DIAPHRAGM (STEM RETRACTED)
BEND AT THIS POINT
LIGHTLY PRESS UP ON CHOKE CONTROL LEVER
TO VACUUM SUPPLY

Vacuum kick adjustment

HOLLEY ONE AND TWO BARREL SPECIFICATIONS

Year	Carb. Part No. ⑦	Float Level Dry (in.)	Accelerator Pump Adjustment (in.)	Bowl Vent Clearance (in.)	Fast Idle On Car (rpm)	Choke Unloader Clearance (in.)	Choke
AMERICAN MOTORS							
1967	R-3253	5/16	⑥	1/16	1400⑧	15/64	1 Lean
	R-3307-1	11/32	⑥	5/64	1650⑧	3/16	1 Lean
	R-3308-1	11/32	⑥	5/64	1650⑧	3/16	1 Lean
	R-3483-1	11/32	⑥	5/64	1600⑧	3/16	1 Lean
	R-3484-1	11/32	⑥	5/64	1400⑧	3/16	1 Rich
	R-3704	5/16	⑥	1/16	1400⑧	15/64	On Index
	R-3705	5/16	⑥	1/16	1400⑧	15/64	On Index
	R-3706	5/16	⑥	1/16	1550⑧	15/64	1 Rich
	R-3707	5/16	⑥	1/16	1600⑧	15/64	On Index
	R-3708	5/16	⑥	1/16	1400⑧	15/46	1 Rich
	R-3709	5/16	⑥	1/16	1400⑧	15/64	1 Rich
	R-3978	5/16	⑥	1/16	1550②	15/64	1 Rich
1968	3966A	5/16	⑥	1/16	1600⑧	15/64	1 Rich
	3967A	5/16	⑥	1/16	1600⑧	15/64	1 Rich
	3968A	5/16	⑥	1/16	1600⑧	15/64	1 Rich
	4102A	5/16	⑥	1/16	1600⑧	15/64	1 Rich
1969	4294A	5/16	⑥	1/16	1600⑧	15/64	1 Rich

Year	Carb. Part No. ⑦	Float Level Dry (in.)	Accelerator Pump Adjustment (in.)	Bowl Vent Clearance (in.)	Fast Idle On Car (rpm)	Choke Unloader Clearance (in.)	Choke
CHEVROLET							
1967	R3659-A	0.350	—	—	—	—	—
	R3660-A	0.350	0.015	—	2200	0.275	⑥
	R3888-A	0.350	0.015	—	2200	0.275	⑥
1968-70	R4055-A	0.350	0.015	0.085	2200	0.250	⑥
	R4056-A	0.350	0.015	0.085	2200	0.250	⑥
	A3659-A	0.350	—	—	—	—	—

CHRYSLER PRODUCTS

Year	Carb. Part No. ⑦	Float Level (in.)	Accelerator Pump Adjustment (in.)	Bowl Vent Clearance (in.)	Fast Idle (rpm)	Choke Unloader Clearance (in.)	Vacuum Kick Drill Size (in.)	Cam Position Drill Size (in.)	Choke
1967	R-3275-1A	See Text	⑥	—	700①	④	#30	#52	2 Rich
	R-3276-1A	See Text	⑥	3/32	700①	④	#43	#52	2 Rich
	R-3279-1A	See Text	⑥	3/32	700①	④	#30	#52	2 Rich
	R-3280-1A	See Text	⑥	3/32	700①	④	#43	#52	2 Rich
	R-3671-A	See Text	⑥	3/32	1550②	④	#28	#41	—
	R-3672-A	See Text	⑥	3/32	1550②	④	#38	#52	2 Rich
	R-3673-A	See Text	⑥	3/32	1550②	④	#28	#41	2 Rich
	R-3674-A	See Text	⑥	3/32	1550②	④	#38	#52	—
1968	R-3919-A	See Text	⑥	3/32	1400②	④	#30	#41	2 Rich
	R-3920-A	See Text	⑥	3/32	1600②	④	#38	#52	2 Rich
	R-3921-A	See Text	⑥	3/32	1400②	④	#30	#41	2 Rich
	R-3922-A	See Text	⑥	3/32	1600②	④	#38	#52	—
	R-3924-A	See Text	⑥	3/32	1400②	④	#38	#52	—

CHRYSLER PRODUCTS

Year	Carb. Part No. ⑦	Float Level (in.)	Accelerator Pump Adjustment (in.)	Bowl Vent Clearance (in.)	Fast Idle (rpm)	Choke Unloader Clearance (in.)	Vacuum Kick Drill Size (in.)	Cam Position Drill Size (in.)	Choke
1969	R-4161-A	See Text	⑥	3/32	1600②	9/32⑮	#39	#52	2 Rich
	R-4162-A	See Text	⑥	3/32	1800②	9/32⑮	#50	#52	2 Rich
	R-4163-A	See Text	⑥	3/32	1600②	9/32⑮	#39	#52	2 Rich
	R-4164-A	See Text	⑥	3/32	1800②	9/32⑮	#50	#52	2 Rich
	R-4165-A	See Text	⑥	3/32	1700②	9/32⑮	#39	#52	—
	R-4391-A	9/16	0.015	0.080-0.125	2200	5/32	—	—	See Text
	R-4392-A	9/16	0.015	0.080-0.125	1800	5/32	—	—	See Text
	R-4393-A	3/4	—	—	—	—	—	—	—
	R-4394-A	3/4	—	—	—	—	—	—	—
1970	R-4351-A	See Text	⑥	3/32	1600②	⑤	#39	#52	2 Rich
	R-4352-A	See Text	⑥	3/32	1800②	⑤	#50	#52	2 Rich
	R-4353-A	See Text	⑥	3/32	1600②	⑤	#39	#52	2 Rich
	R-4354-A	See Text	⑥	3/32	1800②	⑤	#50	#52	2 Rich
	R-4355-A	See Text	⑥	3/32	1700②	⑤	#39	#52	2 Rich
	R-4363-A	See Text	⑥	3/32	1700②	⑤	#39	#52	2 Rich
	R-4371-A	0.200	—	5/64	1700②	11/64	#28	#35	2 Rich
	R-4175-AF	③	—	—	—	—	—	—	—
	R-4144-A	③	0.015	0.101	1800	5/32	#50	#53	2 Rich
	R-4365-AR	③	—	—	—	—	—	—	—
	R-4374-A	③	0.015	0.101	2200	5/32	#28	#53	2 Rich
	R-4375-A	③	0.015	0.101	2200	5/32	#28	#53	2 Rich
	R-4376-A	③	0.015	0.101	1800	5/32	#50	#53	2 Rich
	R-4382-AF	③	—	—	—	—	—	—	—
	R-4383-AR	③	—	—	—	—	—	—	—
1971	R-4655-A	See Text	—	1/32	1600	9/32	#39	#52	2 Rich
	R-4656-A	See Text	—	1/32	1900	5/32	#39	#52	2 Rich
	R-4659-A	See Text	—	1/32	1800	9/32	#39	#52	2 Rich
	R-6363-A	See Text	—	1/64	2000	9/32	—	—	2 Rich
	R-6364-A	See Text	—	1/64	1900	9/32	—	—	2 Rich
	R-4373-A	0.200	9/16	5/64	1700	11/64	—	—	2 Rich
	R-4665-A	0.200	9/16	0.015	1800	1/4	#28	#35	2 Rich
	R-4666-A	0.200	9/16	0.015	1800	1/4	#30	#35	2 Rich
	R-4669-A	③	0.015	0.101	1800	5/32	—	—	2 Rich
	R-4670-A	③	0.015	0.101	1800	5/32	—	—	2 Rich
	R-4671-A	③	—	—	—	—	—	—	—
	R-4672-A	③	—	—	—	—	—	—	—
	R-4789-A	③	—	—	—	—	—	—	—
	R-4790-A	③	—	—	—	—	—	—	—
	R-4791-A	③	0.015	0.101	2600	5/32	#28	#53	On Index
	R-4792-A	③	0.015	0.101	2800	5/32	#39	#53	On Index
1972	R-6153-A	See Text	—	0.015	2000	⑤	0.100	0.064	Fixed
	R-6154-A	See Text	—	0.015	2000	⑤	0.100	0.064	Fixed
	R-6155-A	See Text	—	0.015	2000	⑤	0.100	0.064	Fixed
	R-6156-A	See Text	—	0.015	2000	⑤	0.100	0.064	Fixed
	R-6159-A	See Text	—	0.015	1900	⑤	0.100	0.064	Fixed
	R-6363-A	See Text	—	0.015	2000	⑤	0.100	0.064	Fixed
	R-6364-A	See Text	—	0.015	1900	⑤	0.100	0.064	Fixed
	R-6365-A	See Text	—	0.015	2000	⑤	0.100	0.064	Fixed
	R-6366-A	See Text	—	0.015	2000	⑤	0.100	0.064	Fixed

Year	Carb. Part No. ⑦	Float Level (in.)	Accelerator Pump Adjustment (in.)	Bowl Vent Clearance (in.)	Fast Idle (rpm)	Choke Unloader Clearance (in.)	Vacuum Kick Drill Size (in.)	Cam Position Drill Size (in.)	Choke
1972	R-6162-A	0.180	0.285	0.015	1900	0.170	0.100	0.064	Fixed
	R-6164-A	0.180	0.250	0.015	2000	0.170	0.100	0.064	Fixed
	R-6368-A	0.180	0.285	0.015	1900	0.170	0.100	0.064	Fixed
	R-6370-A	0.180	0.285	0.015	2000	0.170	0.100	0.064	Fixed
	R-6404-A	③	0.015	0.015	1800	0.150	0.130	0.110	Fixed
	R-6405-A	—	—	—	—	—	0.130	0.110	—
	R-6406-A	—	—	—	—	—	0.130	0.110	—
1973	R-6447-A	0.260	—	0.015	2000	⑤	0.100	0.065	Fixed
	R-6448-A	0.260	—	0.015	1700	⑤	0.080	0.045	Fixed
	R-6593-A	0.260	—	0.015	2000	⑤	0.100	0.065	Fixed
	R-6594-A	0.260	—	0.015	1700	⑤	0.100	0.065	Fixed
	R-6595-A	0.260	—	0.015	2000	⑤	0.100	0.065	Fixed
	R-6596-A	0.260	—	0.015	1700	⑤	0.100	0.065	Fixed
	R-6452-A	0.180	0.250	0.015	1900	0.170	0.150	0.110	Fixed
	R-6454-A	0.180	0.250	0.015	1800	0.170	0.150	0.110	Fixed
	R-6472-A	0.180	0.250	0.015	1800	0.170	0.150	0.110	Fixed
	R-6575-A	0.180	0.250	0.015	1900	0.170	0.150	0.110	Fixed

① Engine hot and screw on the lowest step of the cam
② Engine hot and on the highest step of the cam
③ Center the float in the bowl with the bowl inverted
④ See the fast idle index in the text
⑤ Unloader automatically set when the fast idle cam is adjusted
⑥ Seasonal setting, the long stroke hole for winter, the short stroke hole for summer
⑦ Located on the tag attached to the carburetor or on the casting
⑧ Engine hot and screw on the second step of the cam

Model 4150, 4160 Adjustments (General Motors)

Float Adjustment

1. A preliminary float adjustment can be made by inverting the primary fuel bowl and turning the adjustable needle seat until the top of the float is the specified distance from the top of the fuel bowl.
2. Repeat Step 1 for the secondary float.

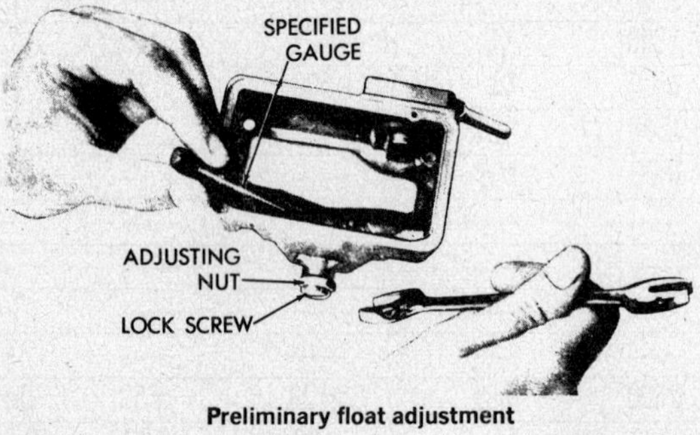
SPECIFIED GAUGE
ADJUSTING NUT
LOCK SCREW

Preliminary float adjustment

Secondary Throttle Valve Stop Screw

1. Back off the adjustment screw until the throttle plates are fully closed.
2. Turn the adjustment screw until it just touches the throttle lever and then make ½ turn more to position the valves.

Air Vent Valve Adjustment

1. Back off the idle speed screw until the throttle valves are fully closed.
2. Check the clearance between the choke valve and the seat.
3. Bend the air valve rod to adjust.
4. Turn the idle screw in until contact is made with the throttle lever, then turn the screw in 1½ additional turns for preliminary idle speed adjustments.

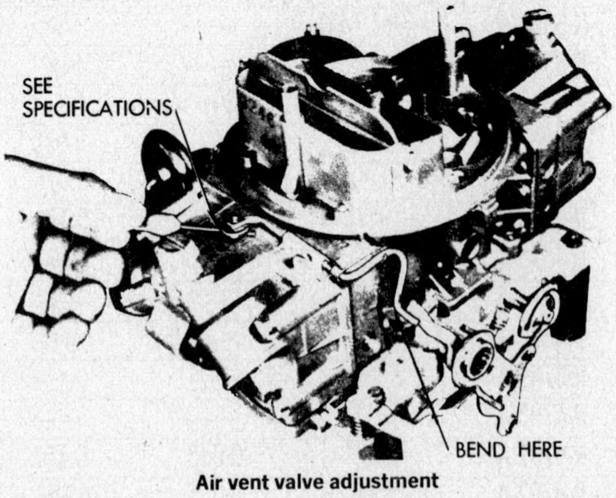
SEE SPECIFICATIONS
BEND HERE

Air vent valve adjustment

Fast Idle Cam Adjustment

1. Open the throttle slightly, close the choke plate, and position the fast idle lever against the top step of the fast idle cam.
2. Adjust the fast idle to give the 0.025 in. opening on the throttle plates on the idle transfer slot side of the carburetor.
3. Bend the fast idle lever to adjust.

Accelerator Pump Adjustment

1. Hold the throttle lever in the wide-open position with a rubber band; hold the pump lever fully compressed down; then measure the clearance between the spring adjusting nut and the arm of the pump lever.
2. Clearance should be 0.015 in.; adjust by turning the nut or

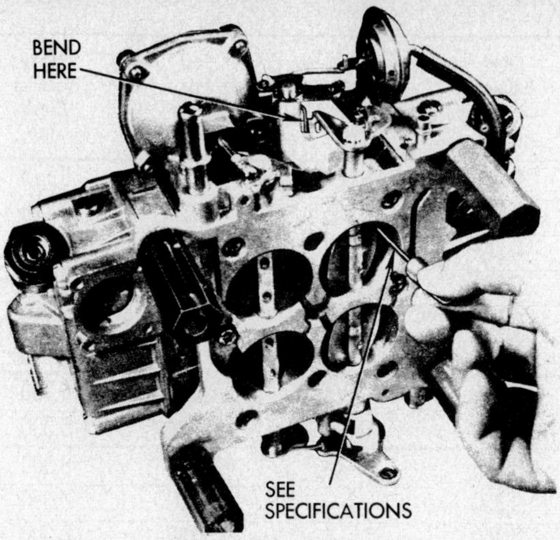
BEND
HERE
SEE
SPECIFICATIONS
Fast idle cam adjustment

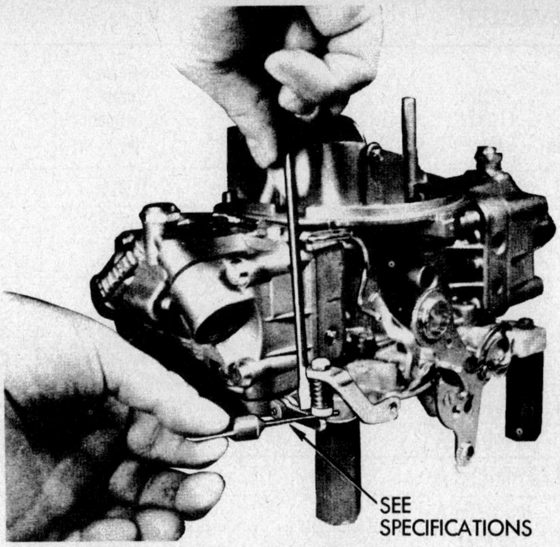
SEE
SPECIFICATIONS
Accelerator pump adjustment

screw as required while holding the opposite end.

3. After the adjustment is made, rotate the throttle lever to fully closed and partly open again. Any movement of the throttle lever should be noticed at the operating lever spring end, indicating the correct pump tip-in.

Choke Unloader Adjustment

1. Hold the throttle lever in the wide-open position with a rubber band.
2. Hold the choke valve toward the closed position against the unloader tang of the throttle shaft, then measure the opening between the choke valve lower edge and the main body.
3. To adjust, bend the choke rod at the offset end. Recheck after adjusting.

Vacuum Break Adjustment

1. Hold the choke valve closed with a rubber band attached to the linkage.
2. Hold the vacuum break in against the stop.
3. Measure the distance between the choke valve lower edge and the main body.
4. Bend the vacuum break link to adjust.

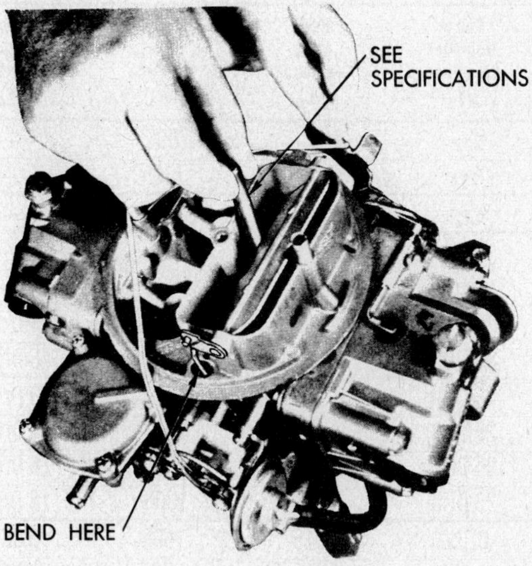
SEE
SPECIFICATIONS
BEND HERE
Choke unloader adjustment

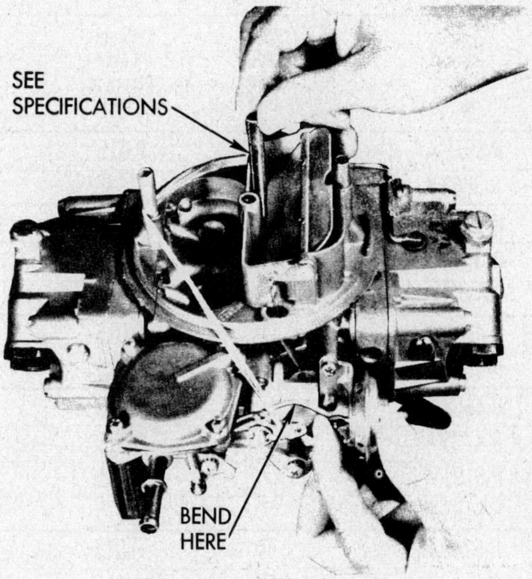
SEE
SPECIFICATIONS
BEND
HERE
Vacuum break adjustment

HOLLEY 4150 and 4160 SPECIFICATIONS

CHEVROLET

Year	Carb. Part No. ①	Float Level (Dry) (in.)	Accelerator Pump Adjustment (in.)	Choke (in.)	Choke Unloader Clearance (in.)	Bowl Vent Clearance (in.)	Fast Idle On Car (rpm)	Choke Vacuum Break (in.)
1967	R3418-A	③	0.015	See Text	0.350	0.065	2200	0.350
	R3806-A	②	0.015	See Text	0.265	0.065	2200	0.190
	R3807-A	②	0.015	See Text	0.265	0.065	2200	0.190
	R3810-A	②	0.015	See Text	0.265	0.065	2200	0.190
	R3811-A	②	0.015	See Text	0.265	0.065	2200	0.175

CHEVROLET

Year	Carb. Part No. ①	Float Level (Dry) (in.)	Accelerator Pump Adjustment (in.)	Choke (in.)	Choke Unloader Clearance (in.)	Bowl Vent Clearance (in.)	Fast Idle On Car (rpm)	Choke Vacuum Break (in.)
1967	R3814-A	②	0.015	See Text	0.265	0.065	2200	0.175
	R3815-A	②	0.015	See Text	0.265	0.065	2200	0.175
	R3836-A	②	0.015	See Text	0.265	0.065	2200	0.175
	R3837-A	②	0.015	See Text	0.265	0.065	2200	0.175
	R3838-A	②	0.015	See Text	0.265	0.065	2200	0.175
	R3839-A	②	0.015	See Text	0.265	0.065	2200	0.175
1968	R4053-A	⑥	0.015	See Text	0.350	0.065	2200	0.300
	R4054-A	⑥	0.015	See Text	0.350	0.065	2200	0.300
1969-70	R4053-A	⑥	0.015	⑧	0.350	—	2200	0.300
	R4296-A	⑥	0.015	⑧	0.350	—	2200	0.350
	R4346	⑥	0.015	⑧	0.350	—	2200	0.300
	R4492-A	⑥	0.015	⑧	0.350	—	2200	0.350
	R4557-A	⑥	0.015	⑧	0.350	—	2200	0.350
1971	R4800-A	⑩	0.015	1.320⑪	0.350	—	2200	0.350
	R4801-A	⑩	0.015	1.320⑪	0.350	—	2200	0.350
	R4802-A	⑩	0.015	1.320⑪	0.350	—	2200	0.350
	R4803-A	⑩	0.015	1.320⑪	0.350	—	2200	0.350
1972	R6238-A	⑩	0.015	1.320⑪	0.350	—	2350	0.350
	R6239-A	⑩	0.015	1.320⑪	0.350	—	2350	0.350

CHRYSLER PRODUCTS

Year	Carb. Part No. ①	Float Level (Dry) (in.)	Pump Lever Clearance (in.)	Choke Setting	Choke Unloader Clearance (in.)	Bowl Vent Clearance (in.)	Fast Idle On Car (rpm)	Choke Vacuum Break (in.)
1967	R-3575-A	④	0.015	—	5/32	3/32	700⑤	—
	R-3667-A	④	0.015	—	5/32	3/32	700⑤	—
1968	R-3918-A	⑦	0.015	See Text	5/32	50 Drill	1400⑨	—
1969	R-4166-A	⑦	0.015	See Text	5/32	5/64	1400⑤	—
	R-4440-A	⑦	0.015	See Text	5/32	5/64	1500⑨	—
1970-71	R-4360-A	⑦	0.015	2 Rich	25 Drill	72 Drill	1600	46 Drill
	R-4366-A	⑦	0.015	2 Rich	25 Drill	5/64	1600	46 Drill
1971	R-4668-A	⑦	0.015	2 Rich	25 Drill	0.015	1700	46 Drill
	R-4735-A	⑦	0.015	2 Rich	25 Drill	0.015	1700	46 Drill
	R-6191-A	⑦	0.015	2 Rich	25 Drill	0.015	1800	18 Drill
	R-6193-A	⑦	0.015	2 Rich	25 Drill	0.015	1800	18 Drill
1972	R-6160-A	⑫	0.015	Fixed	0.150	0.015	1600	0.080
	R-6252-A	⑫	0.015	Fixed	0.150	0.015	1800	0.140
	R-6253-A	⑫	0.015	Fixed	0.150	0.015	1600	0.080
	R-6254-A	⑫	0.015	Fixed	0.150	0.015	1800	0.140
	R-6255-A	⑫	0.015	Fixed	0.150	0.015	1600	0.080
	R-6256-A	⑫	0.015	Fixed	0.150	0.015	2000	0.140
	R-6257-A	⑫	0.015	Fixed	0.150	0.015	1800	0.080
	R-6290-A	⑫	0.015	Fixed	0.150	0.015	1500	0.080

① Located on tag attached to carburetor, or on the casting or choke plate
② Primary 0.170 in., secondary 0.300 in.
③ Primary 0.350 in., secondary 0.450 in.
④ Primary 7/64 in., secondary 15/64 in.
⑤ No. 5 Step on cam
⑥ Primary 0.350 in., secondary 0.500 in.
⑦ Primary 15/64 in., secondary 17/64 in.
⑧ Top of rod even with bottom of hole
⑨ No. 2 Step on cam
⑩ Float centered in bowl
⑪ Bottom of throttle body to center of hole in operating lever
⑫ Primary 0.110 in., secondary 0.204 in.

Model 5210

The Holley 5210 is a two barrel carburetor with a new automatic choke system which is activated by a water heated thermostatic coil. It also has an exhaust gas recirculation system with the valve located in the intake manifold.

Fast Idle Cam Adjustments

1. Place the fast idle screw on the second step of the fast idle cam and against the shoulder of the first step.
2. Place a 0.140 drill or gauge on the downstream side of the choke plate.
3. To adjust, bend the choke lever tang.

Choke Plate Pulldown Adjustment

1. Remove the three hex headed screws and ring which retain the choke cover.

Caution Do not remove the choke water housing screw if adjusting on the car. Pull the choke water housing and bimetal cover assembly back out of the way.

Dechoke (Unloader) Adjustment

The dechoke adjustment is automatically set when the fast idle cam index is adjusted.

Fast Idle Adjustment

1. Engine temperature must be normal.
2. Position the fast idle screw on the top step of the fast idle cam.
3. Adjust the fast idle to specifications.
4. Adjustments are made by turning the fast idle screw in or out.

Idle Adjustments

There are four idle adjustments.

1. Fast idle
2. Low idle
3. Curb idle
4. Idle mixture.

See the illustration for the location of the adjustment screws.

NOTE: A limiter screw cap is installed on the idle mixture screw to limit maximum idle richness.

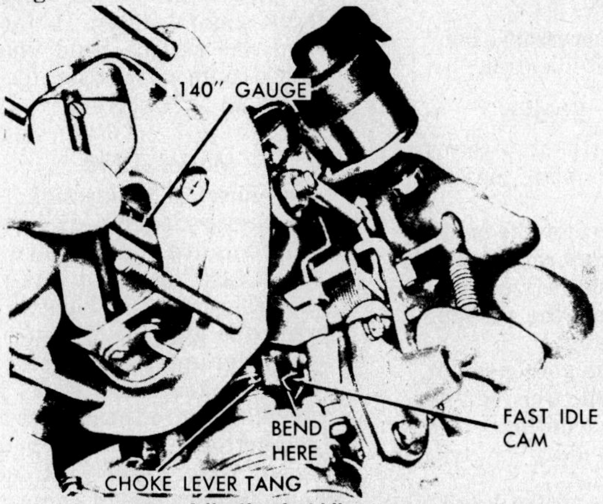
.140" GAUGE
BEND HERE
FAST IDLE CAM
CHOKE LEVER TANG
Adjusting fast idle cam

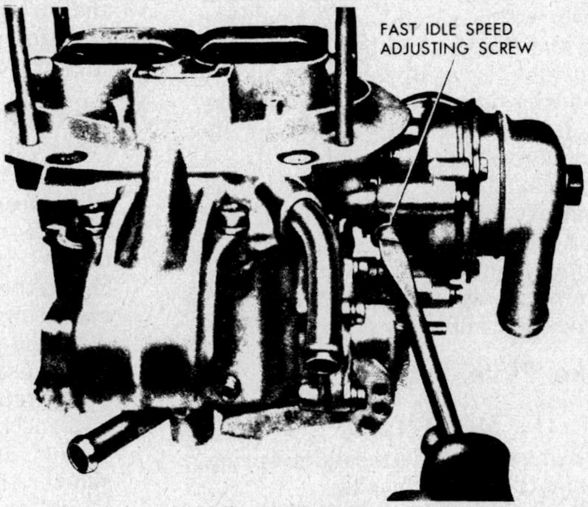
FAST IDLE SPEED ADJUSTING SCREW
Adjusting fast idle

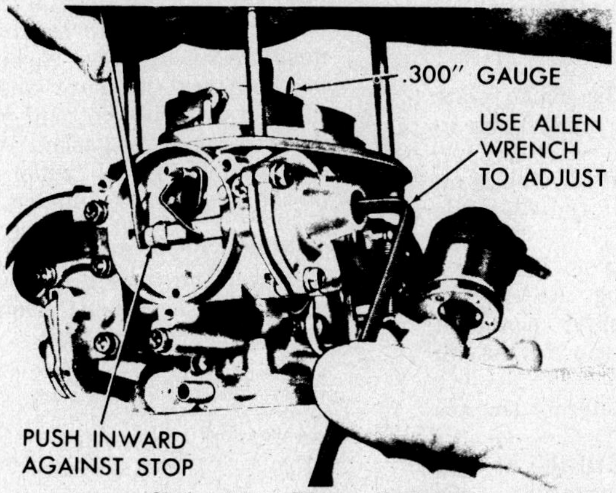
.300" GAUGE
USE ALLEN WRENCH TO ADJUST
PUSH INWARD AGAINST STOP
Choke plate pulldown adjustment

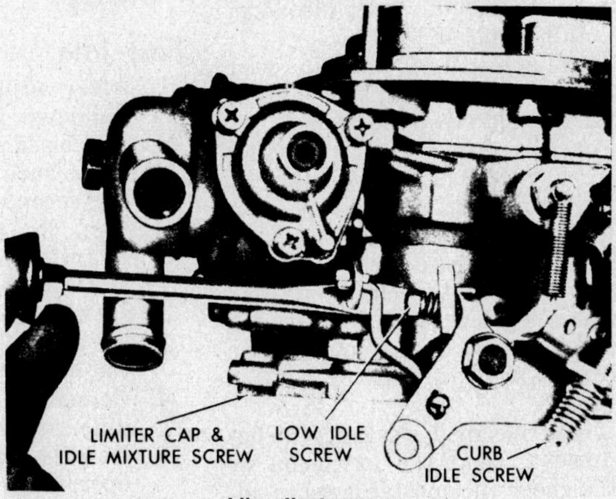
LIMITER CAP & IDLE MIXTURE SCREW
LOW IDLE SCREW
CURB IDLE SCREW
Idle adjustment

HOLLEY 5210 SPECIFICATIONS

CHEVROLET

Year	Carb. Part No. ①	Float Level (Dry) (in.)	Float Drop (in.)	Pump Position	Fast Idle Cam Index (in.)	Vacuum Plate Pulldown (in.)	Fast Idle Setting (rpm)	Choke Setting
1973	R-6477A	0.420	1	#3	0.140	0.300	2000	1 Rich
	R-6478-A	0.420	1	#2	0.140	0.300	2200	2 Rich
	R-6580A	0.420	1	#2	0.140	0.300	2200	2 Rich
	R-6581A	0.420	1	#3	0.140	0.300	2000	1 Rich

① Located on tag attached to the carburetor, or on the casting or on the choke plate

Ford, Autolite, Motorcraft Carburetors

Models 1100, 1101, and 1250

These carburetors are essentially the same as far as adjustments are concerned and, therefore, will be grouped together for easier reference.

The Model 1100 carburetor is used on Ford six cylinder cars and is essentially the same as the Model 1101 carburetor. Both carburetors consist of two major assemblies, the upper body and the throttle body. The 1100 carburetor is equipped with a hydraulically operated dashpot, and the 1101 is equipped with an externally mounted pneumatic dashpot.

The model 1250 is a single barrel downdraft carburetor designed for use on the 1600 cc Pinto engine. It is equipped with a diaphragm type accelerator pump and a water heated thermostatic choke.

Choke Plate Pulldown

Model 1250

1. Remove the thermostatic spring and the water housing.
2. Push in on the vacuum piston until the vacuum inner bleed slot is fully exposed.
3. Take a length of 0.040 in. wire and insert it into this slot. Raise the piston to trap the wire.
4. Partially open the throttle valve so that the choke plate may be moved toward the closed position.
5. Close the choke plate until its movement is stopped.
6. Check the clearance between the bottom of the choke plate and the inside wall of the carburetor body.
7. If the specified clearance is not present, bend the extension of the choke thermostat lever to adjust it.

Models 1100 and 1101

1. Position the fast idle adjusting screw on the highest step of the fast idle cam.
2. Insert a gauge of the proper dimension between the lower edge of the choke plate and the air horn wall.
3. If needed, adjust by turning the plastic nut on the choke plate pulldown rod until it contacts the swivel on the choke lever assembly.

Dechoke (Unloader)

1. Open the throttle valve fully and measure the clearance between the bottom of the choke plate and the carburetor body.
2. If adjustment is necessary, bend the tang on the fast idle cam.

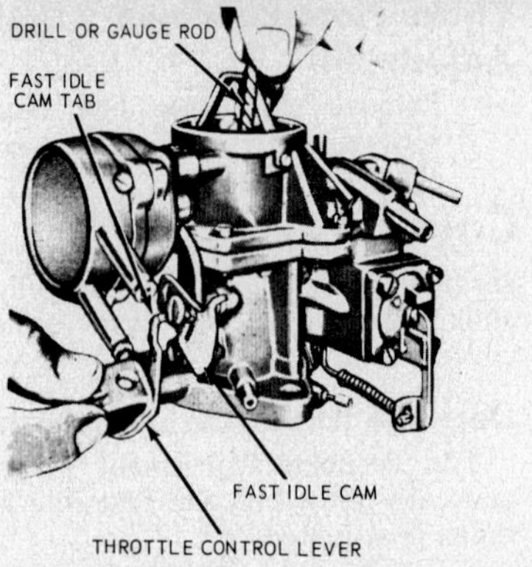
DRILL OR GAUGE ROD
FAST IDLE CAM TAB
FAST IDLE CAM
THROTTLE CONTROL LEVER
Dechoke adjustment—Autolite 1 barrel
(© Ford Motor Co)

Accelerator Pump Stroke

1. Back out the throttle stop screw so that the throttle plate may be fully closed.
2. Depress the plunger of the accelerator pump diaphragm and check the clearance between the operating lever and the plunger with the proper gauge.
3. To adjust, bend the gooseneck of the pump push rod. Closing the gooseneck will lengthen the stroke and expanding it will shorten the stroke.
4. Reset the throttle valve stop screw.

Fast Idle

1. After adjusting the choke plate pulldown, hold the choke valve in the closed position.
2. Make sure the fast idle tab is on the second step of the fast idle cam.
3. Install the thermostatic spring and water housing. Locate the spring in the center slot and accurately align the marks on the housing.
4. Connect a tachometer to the engine.
5. Run the engine until the normal operating temperature is reached.
6. Put the fast idle tab on the second step of the fast idle cam and check engine speed. If adjustment is needed, bend the tab which contacts the fast idle cam.

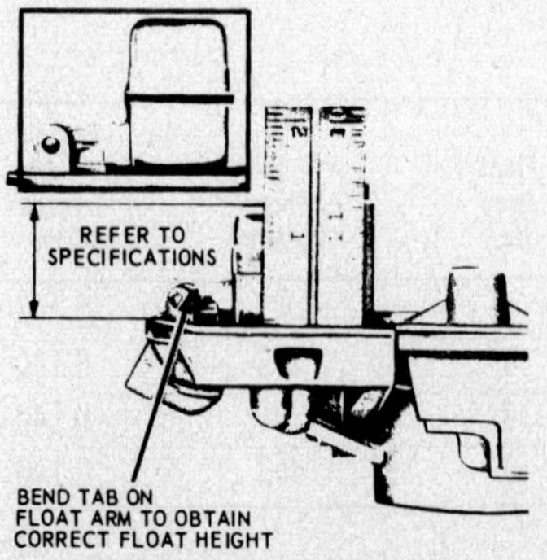
REFER TO SPECIFICATIONS
BEND TAB ON FLOAT ARM TO OBTAIN CORRECT FLOAT HEIGHT
Float level adjustment—Autolite 1100, 1101
(© Ford Motor Co)

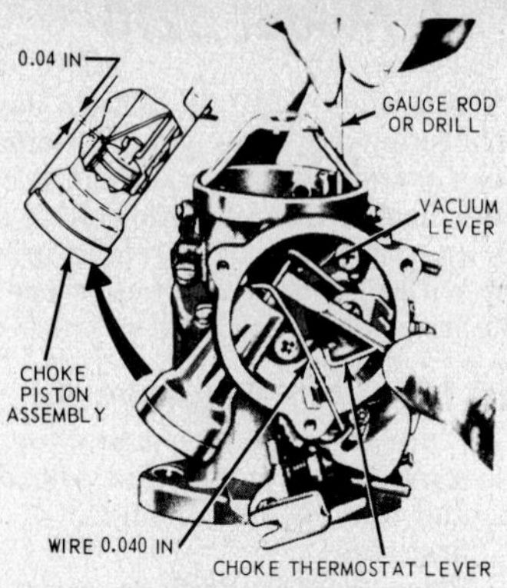
0.04 IN
GAUGE ROD OR DRILL
VACUUM LEVER
CHOKE PISTON ASSEMBLY
WIRE 0.040 IN
CHOKE THERMOSTAT LEVER
Choke plate pulldown adjustment
(© Ford Motor Co)

Float Level

Model 1250

1. Disconnect all connections to the carburetor upper body including the fuel line, decel valve hose, choke fast idle pivot screw, and the thermostatic housing. Remove the upper carburetor body.
2. With the upper carburetor body held so that the float hangs down, measure the distance from the bottom of the float to the upper body gasket. To adjust, bend the tab which contacts the needle valve and seat assembly.
3. Invert the carburetor so that the float rests on the carburetor body. Again measure the distance from the bottom of the float to the body gasket. Adjust by bending the tab which rests on the needle valve housing.

Models 1100 and 1101

1. Remove the upper carburetor body and the gasket from the lower carburetor section.

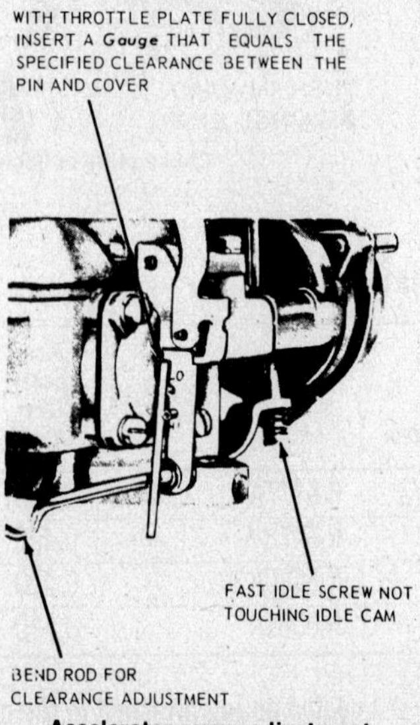
WITH THROTTLE PLATE FULLY CLOSED, INSERT A Gauge THAT EQUALS THE SPECIFIED CLEARANCE BETWEEN THE PIN AND COVER
FAST IDLE SCREW NOT TOUCHING IDLE CAM
BEND ROD FOR CLEARANCE ADJUSTMENT
Accelerator pump adjustment
(© Ford Motor Co)

2. Measure the distance from the upper body gasket surface to the top of the float. This should be done with the carburetor sitting on the air cleaner gasket surface.
3. Adjust by bending the float arm tab.

Caution Do not apply pressure to the fuel inlet needle as this will damage the Viton® tip of the needle.

Vent Valve Adjustment

1. Adjust the vent valve only after the accelerator pump has been properly adjusted.
2. Set the linkage in the hot idle position.
3. The groove in the vent valve should now be even with the open end of the vent.
4. Bend the arm on the vent valve actuating lever to align the groove with the edge of the bore.

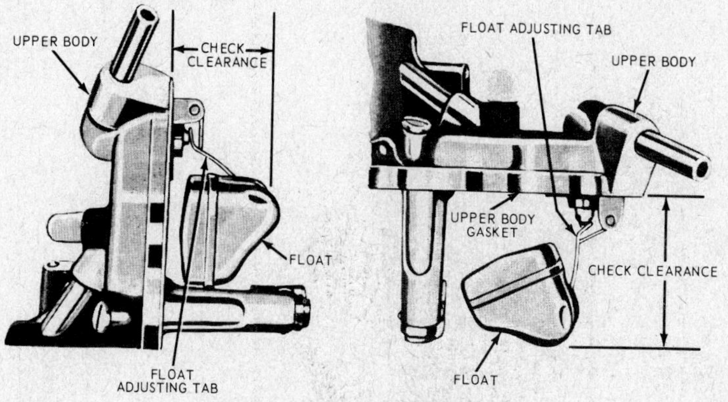
UPPER BODY
CHECK CLEARANCE
FLOAT
FLOAT ADJUSTING TAB
FLOAT ADJUSTING TAB
UPPER BODY
UPPER BODY GASKET
CHECK CLEARANCE
FLOAT

Adjusting float level—Model 1250
(© Ford Motor Co)

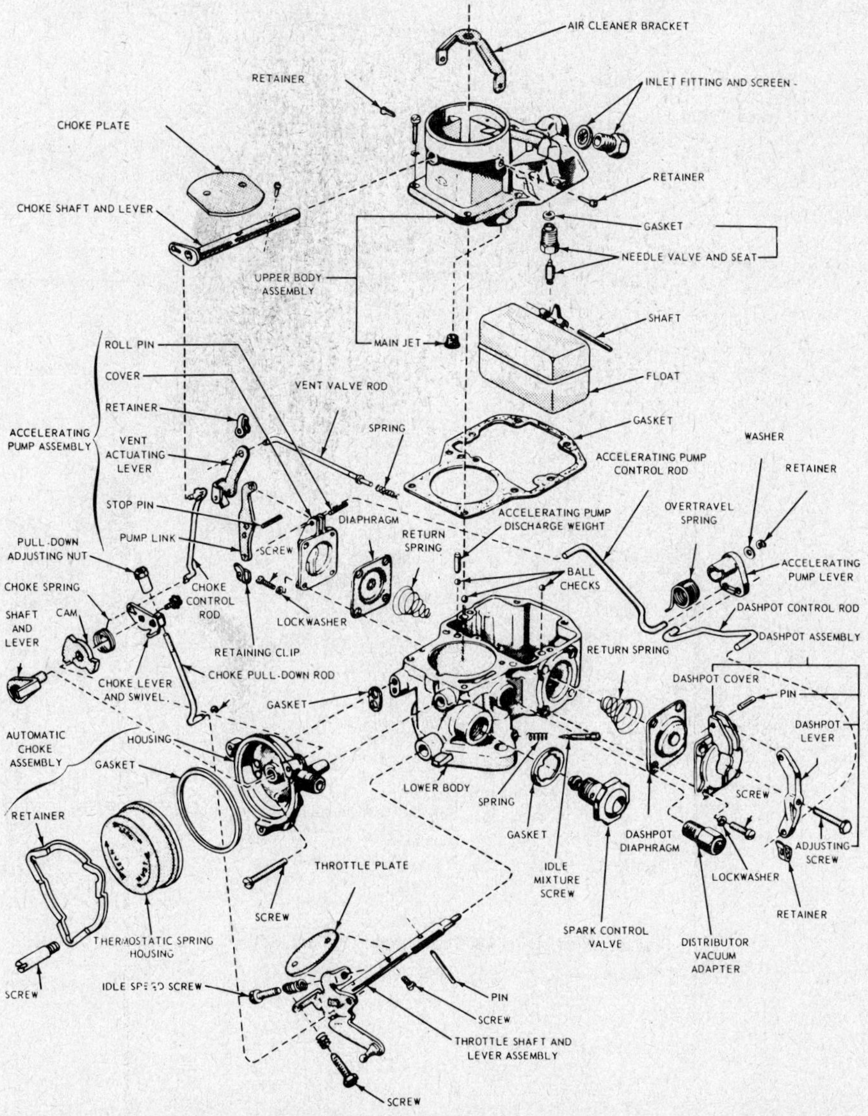
AIR CLEANER BRACKET
RETAINER
INLET FITTING AND SCREEN
CHOKE PLATE
RETAINER
CHOKE SHAFT AND LEVER
GASKET
NEEDLE VALVE AND SEAT
UPPER BODY ASSEMBLY
SHAFT
ROLL PIN
MAIN JET
COVER
FLOAT
VENT VALVE ROD
RETAINER
GASKET
SPRING
WASHER
ACCELERATING PUMP ASSEMBLY
VENT ACTUATING LEVER
ACCELERATING PUMP CONTROL ROD
RETAINER
STOP PIN
DIAPHRAGM
ACCELERATING PUMP DISCHARGE WEIGHT
OVERTRAVEL SPRING
PULL-DOWN ADJUSTING NUT
PUMP LINK
SCREW
RETURN SPRING
ACCELERATING PUMP LEVER
BALL CHECKS
CHOKE SPRING
CHOKE CONTROL ROD
LOCKWASHER
DASHPOT CONTROL ROD
SHAFT AND LEVER
CAM
DASHPOT ASSEMBLY
RETAINING CLIP
RETURN SPRING
CHOKE PULL-DOWN ROD
DASHPOT COVER
CHOKE LEVER AND SWIVEL
PIN
GASKET
DASHPOT LEVER
AUTOMATIC CHOKE ASSEMBLY
HOUSING
GASKET
LOWER BODY
SCREW
SPRING
RETAINER
GASKET
DASHPOT DIAPHRAGM
ADJUSTING SCREW
THROTTLE PLATE
IDLE MIXTURE SCREW
LOCKWASHER
SCREW
RETAINER
SPARK CONTROL VALVE
DISTRIBUTOR VACUUM ADAPTER
THERMOSTATIC SPRING HOUSING
SCREW
PIN
SCREW
THROTTLE SHAFT AND LEVER ASSEMBLY
SCREW

Exploded view—Model 1100 (© Ford Motor Co)

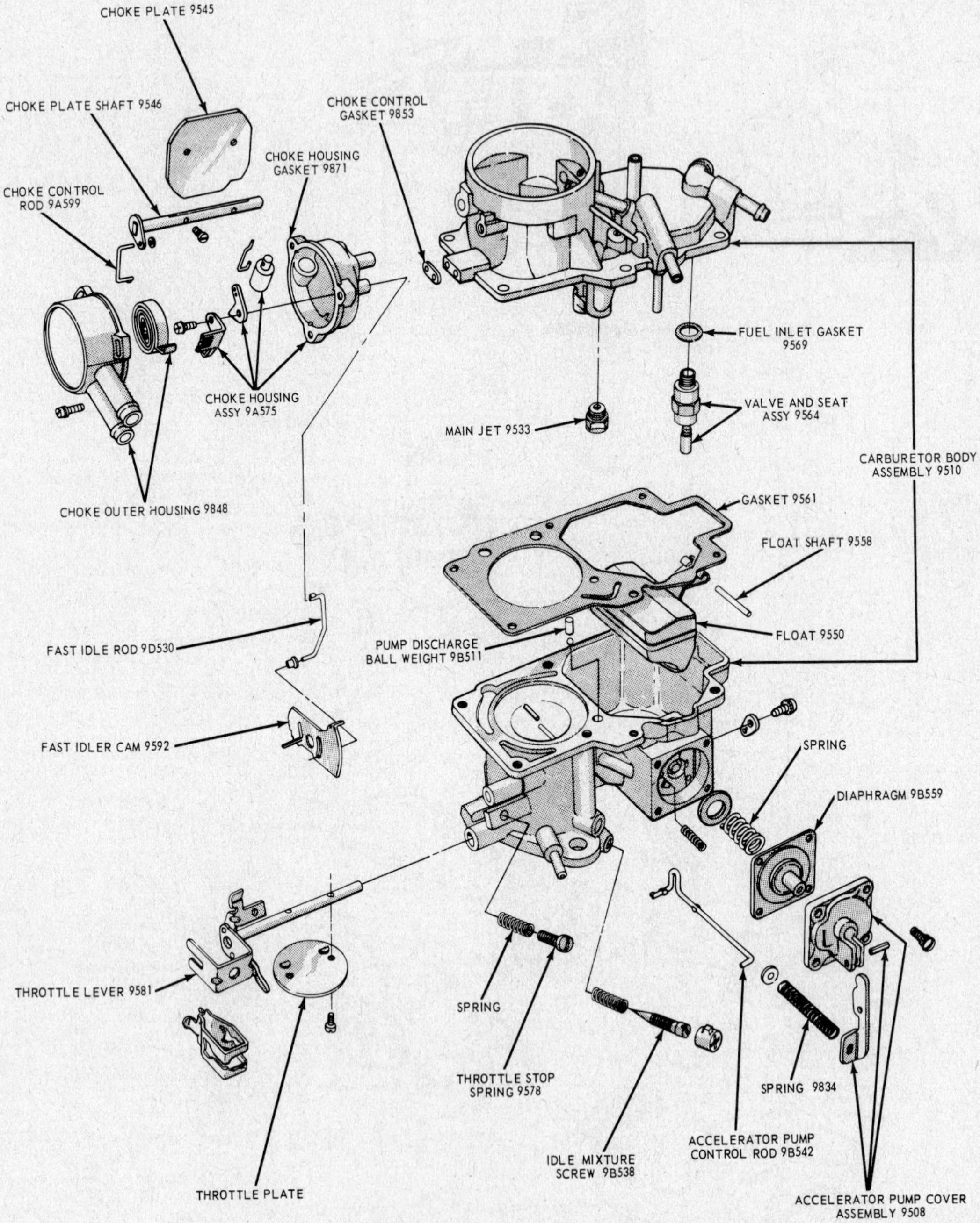
CHOKE PLATE 9545
CHOKE PLATE SHAFT 9546
CHOKE CONTROL ROD 9A599
CHOKE CONTROL GASKET 9853
CHOKE HOUSING GASKET 9871
CHOKE HOUSING ASSY 9A575
CHOKE OUTER HOUSING 9848
FUEL INLET GASKET 9569
VALVE AND SEAT ASSY 9564
MAIN JET 9533
CARBURETOR BODY ASSEMBLY 9510
GASKET 9561
FLOAT SHAFT 9558
FAST IDLE ROD 9D530
PUMP DISCHARGE BALL WEIGHT 9B511
FLOAT 9550
FAST IDLER CAM 9592
SPRING
DIAPHRAGM 9B559
THROTTLE LEVER 9581
SPRING
THROTTLE STOP SPRING 9578
SPRING 9834
ACCELERATOR PUMP CONTROL ROD 9B542
IDLE MIXTURE SCREW 9B538
THROTTLE PLATE
ACCELERATOR PUMP COVER ASSEMBLY 9508

Disassembled Model 1250 carburetor (© Ford Motor Co)

FORD, AUTOLITE, MOTORCRAFT MODEL 1100,1101, SPECIFICATIONS

Ford and Mercury

Year	(9510)* Carburetor Identification	Float Level (in.)	Pump (in.)①	Fast Idle (rpm)	Choke Plate Pulldown (in.)②	Dechoke (in.)③	Choke Setting
1967	C6DF-R	1 3/32	0.190	1500	0.150	1/16	Index
	C6DF-S	1 3/32	0.190	1300	0.110	1/16	2 Lean
	C6OF-AB	1 3/32	0.190	1300	0.140	1/16	1 Lean
	C6OF-AC	1 3/32	0.190	1500	0.150	1/16	Index
	C6OF-AD	1 3/32	0.190	1300	0.140	1/16	1 Lean
	C7DF J	1 3/32	0.190	1400	0.110	1/16	2 Lean
	C7DF-K	1 3/32	0.190	1500	0.150	1/16	Index
	C7OF-N	1 3/32	0.190	1400	0.110	1/16	2 Lean
	C7OF-R	1 3/32	0.190	1500	0.150	1/16	Index
1968	C8OF-A	1 3/32	0.090	1400	0.150	15/64	2 Lean
	C8OF-B	1 3/32	—	1500	0.130	15/64	1 Lean
1969	C8OF-B	1 3/32	0.190	1500	0.130	1/4	1 Lean
	C9DF-B	1 3/32	0.150	1500	0.150	1/4	3 Lean
	C8AF-E	1 3/32	0.190	1500	0.200	0.160	3 Lean
	C9OF-A	1 3/32	0.190	1500	0.200	0.160	3 Lean
	C9OF-B	1 3/32	0.190	1500	0.200	0.160	1 Lean
	C9OF-J	1 3/32	0.190	1500	0.200	0.160	1 Lean
	C9OF-K	1 3/32	0.190	1500	0.200	0.160	3 Lean

* Basic carburetor number
① Given in inches with pin in high position and throttle valve fully seated
② ± 0.010
③ Minimum clearance between choke valve and air horn wall with throttle valve wide open

FORD, AUTOLITE, MOTORCRAFT MODEL 1250 SPECIFICATIONS

Pinto

Year	(9510)* Carburetor Identification	Float Level (in.)	Pump (in.)	Fast Idle (rpm)	Choke Plate Pulldown (in.)	Dechoke (in.)	Choke Setting
1971	711-BDA	①	0.085	1700	0.120	0.210	Index
	711-BDB	①	0.070	1700	0.075	0.210	Index
1972	721F-KFA	②	0.070	1700	0.075	0.210	Index
1973	731F-KAA	②	0.085	—	0.075	—	Index

* Basic carburetor number
① Body vertical—1.160-1.200
Body horizontal—1.350-1.370
② Body vertical—1.200

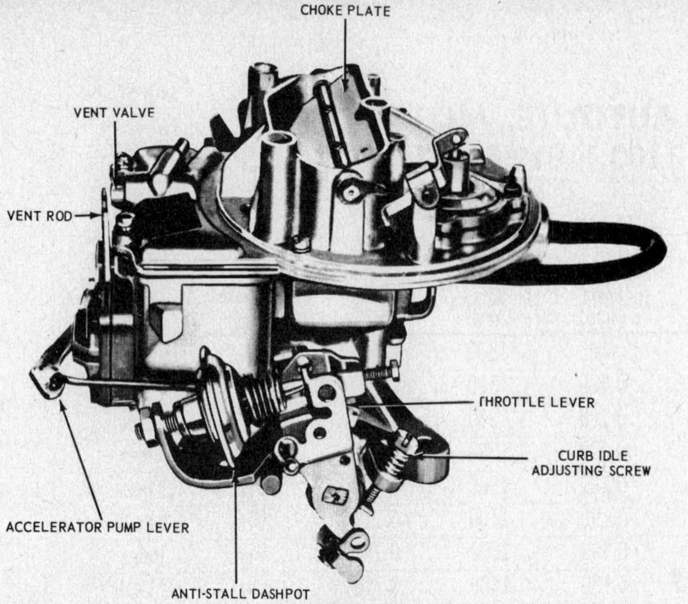
CHOKE PLATE
VENT VALVE
VENT ROD
THROTTLE LEVER
CURB IDLE ADJUSTING SCREW
ACCELERATOR PUMP LEVER
ANTI-STALL DASHPOT

Model 2100 two barrel carburetor
(© Ford Motor Co)

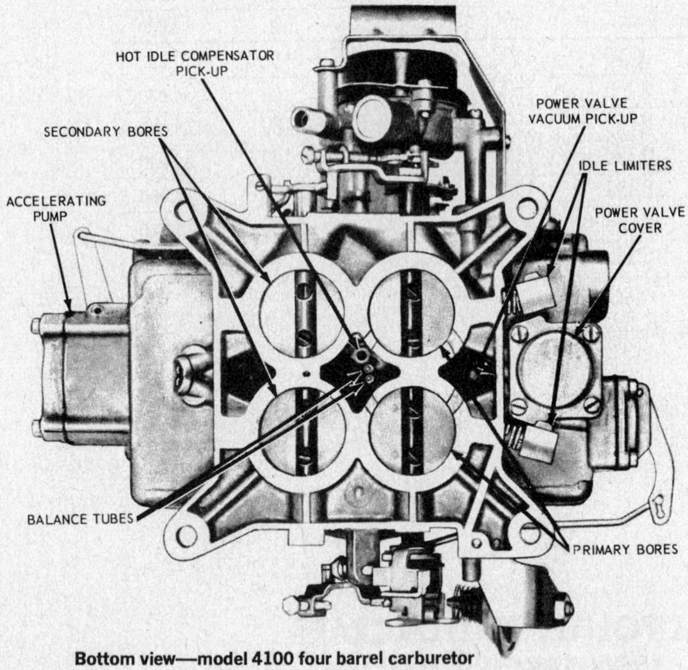
HOT IDLE COMPENSATOR PICK-UP
SECONDARY BORES
POWER VALVE VACUUM PICK-UP
IDLE LIMITERS
ACCELERATING PUMP
POWER VALVE COVER
BALANCE TUBES
PRIMARY BORES

Bottom view—model 4100 four barrel carburetor
(© Ford Motor Co)

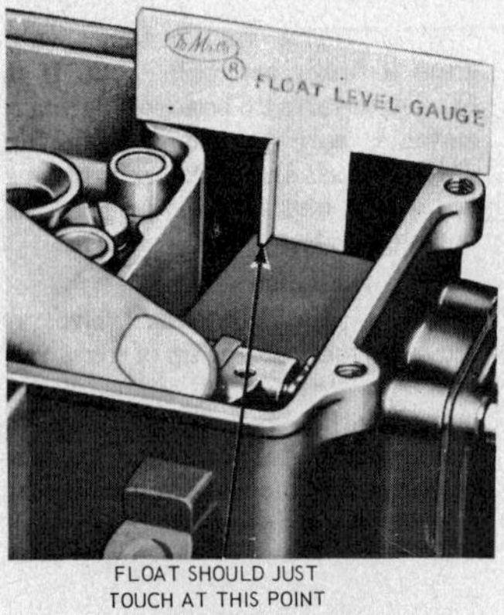
FLOAT LEVEL GAUGE
FLOAT SHOULD JUST TOUCH AT THIS POINT

Checking float level (dry)
(© Ford Motor Co)

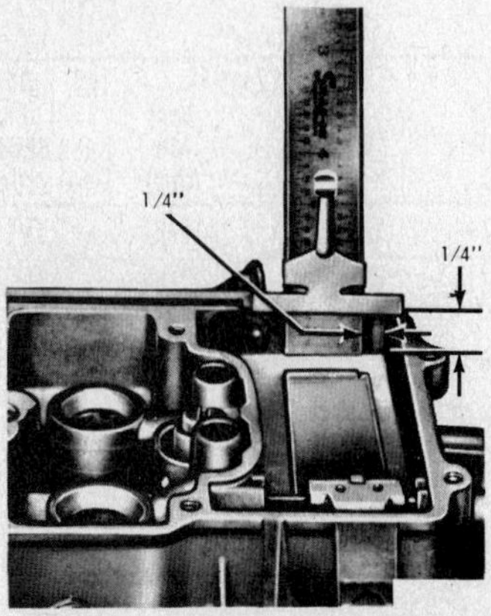
1/4"
1/4"

Fuel level measurement (wet)
(© Ford Motor Co)

Models 2100, 4100

The Model 2100 two barrel carburetor and the 4100 four barrel carburetor are basically the same in construction. Adjustments are performed in the same manner for both carburetors.

The air horn assembly covers the main body and houses the choke plate and the internal fuel bowl vents. The throttle plate, accelerator pump assembly, power valve assembly, and fuel bowl are contained in the main body. The automatic choke is also attached to the main body. On the 2100 two barrel, each bore contains a main and booster venturi, a main fuel discharge, an accelerating pump discharge, an idle fuel discharge, and a throttle plate. The four barrel 4100 model has vacuum operated throttle plates and a main fuel discharge in each secondary bore.

Float Level (Dry)

The dry float level measurement is a preliminary check and must be followed by a wet float level measurement with the carburetor mounted on the engine.

1. With the air horn removed and the fuel inlet needle seated lightly, gently raise the float and measure the distance between the main body gasket surface (gasket removed) and the top of the float.
2. If necessary, bend the float tab to obtain the correct level.

Float Level (Wet)

1. Remove the screws that hold the air horn to the main body and break the seal between the air horn and main body. Leave the air horn and gasket loosely in place on top of the main body.
2. Start the engine and allow it to idle for at least three minutes.
3. After the engine has idled long enough to stabilize the fuel level, remove the air horn assembly.
4. With the engine idling, use a T-scale to measure the distance from the top of the fuel bowl machined surface to the surface of the fuel. The scale must be held at least 1/4 in. away from any vertical surface to ensure proper measurement.
5. If any adjustment is required, stop the engine to avoid a fire from fuel spraying on the engine.
6. Bend the float tab upward to raise the level and downward to lower the level.

Caution Be sure to hold the fuel inlet needle off its seat when bending the float tab so as not to damage the Viton® tip.

7. Each time the float level is changed, the air horn must be temporarily positioned and the

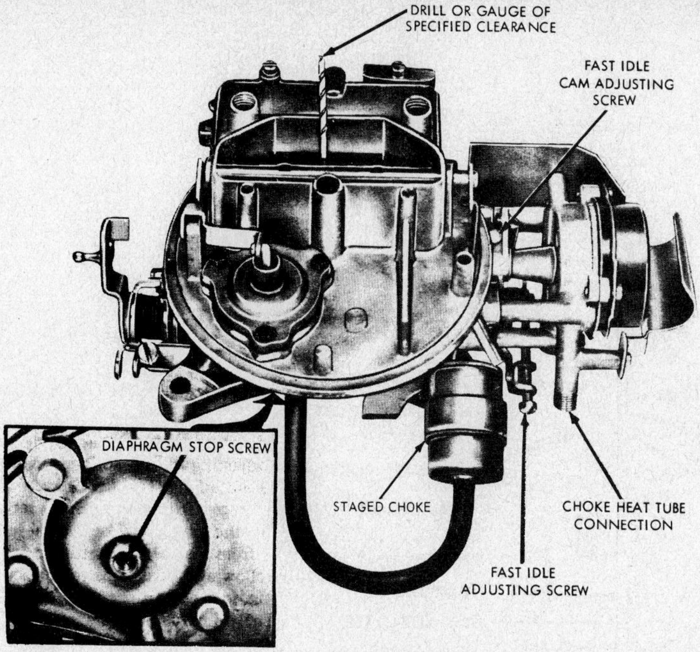

DRILL OR GAUGE OF SPECIFIED CLEARANCE
FAST IDLE CAM ADJUSTING SCREW
DIAPHRAGM STOP SCREW
STAGED CHOKE
CHOKE HEAT TUBE CONNECTION
FAST IDLE ADJUSTING SCREW

Adjusting choke plate pulldown
(© Ford Motor Co)

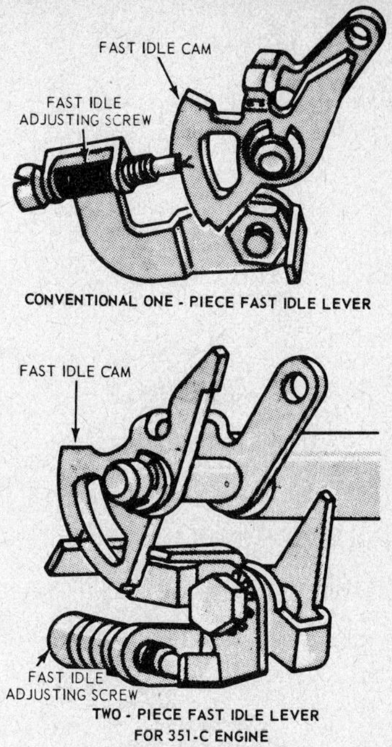

FAST IDLE CAM
FAST IDLE ADJUSTING SCREW
CONVENTIONAL ONE - PIECE FAST IDLE LEVER
FAST IDLE CAM
FAST IDLE ADJUSTING SCREW
TWO - PIECE FAST IDLE LEVER FOR 351-C ENGINE

Fast idle adjustment
(© Ford Motor Co)

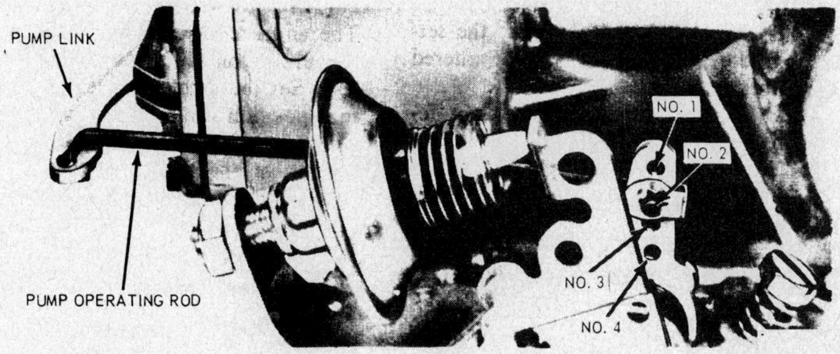

PUMP LINK
PUMP OPERATING ROD
NO. 1
NO. 2
NO. 3
NO. 4

Accelerator pump stroke adjustment
(© Ford Motor Co)

engine started to stabilize the fuel level before again checking it.

Choke Plate Pulldown

1. Loosen the screws on the choke cover and rotate the cover 1/4 turn clockwise (rich), then tighten the screws.
2. Operate the throttle to allow full closing of the choke valve.
3. Press down on the choke modulator arm until the choke modulator diaphragm is bottomed and then measure the distance from the lower edge of the choke valve to the inside air horn wall.
4. Adjustment is achieved by turning the diaphragm stop screw on the underside of the air horn.
5. Turn the screw clockwise to decrease clearance and counterclockwise to increase clearance.

NOTE: Do not reset the choke cover until the fast idle cam adjustment is made.

Fast Idle Cam

1. Push down on the fast idle cam lever until the fast idle screw is in contact with the second step of the fast idle cam and against the shoulder of the high step.
2. The specified clearance should be present between the lower edge of the choke valve and the air horn wall.
3. The adjustment is made by turning the fast idle cam lever screw.
4. The choke cover may now be replaced and indexed according to specification.

Choke Unloader (Dechoke)

1. With the throttle held completely open, move the choke valve to the closed position.
2. Measure the distance between the lower edge of the choke valve and the air horn wall.
3. Adjust by bending the tang on the fast idle speed lever which is located on the throttle shaft.

NOTE: Final unloader adjustment must be performed on the car and the throttle should be opened by using the accelerator pedal of the car. This is to be sure that full throttle operation is achieved.

Accelerator Pump

The accelerator pump operating rod must be positioned in the proper holes of the accelerator pump lever and the throttle over-travel lever to assure correct pump travel. If adjusting is required, additional holes are provided in the throttle over-travel lever.

Dashpot Adjustment

With the throttle set at the curb idle position, fully depress the dashpot stem and measure the distance between the stem and the throttle lever. Adjust by loosening the locknut and turning the dashpot.

Fast Idle

Adjust the fast idle setting with the engine at operating temperature. The fast idle screw should be resting against the second step of the fast idle cam. Adjust by turning the fast idle screw.

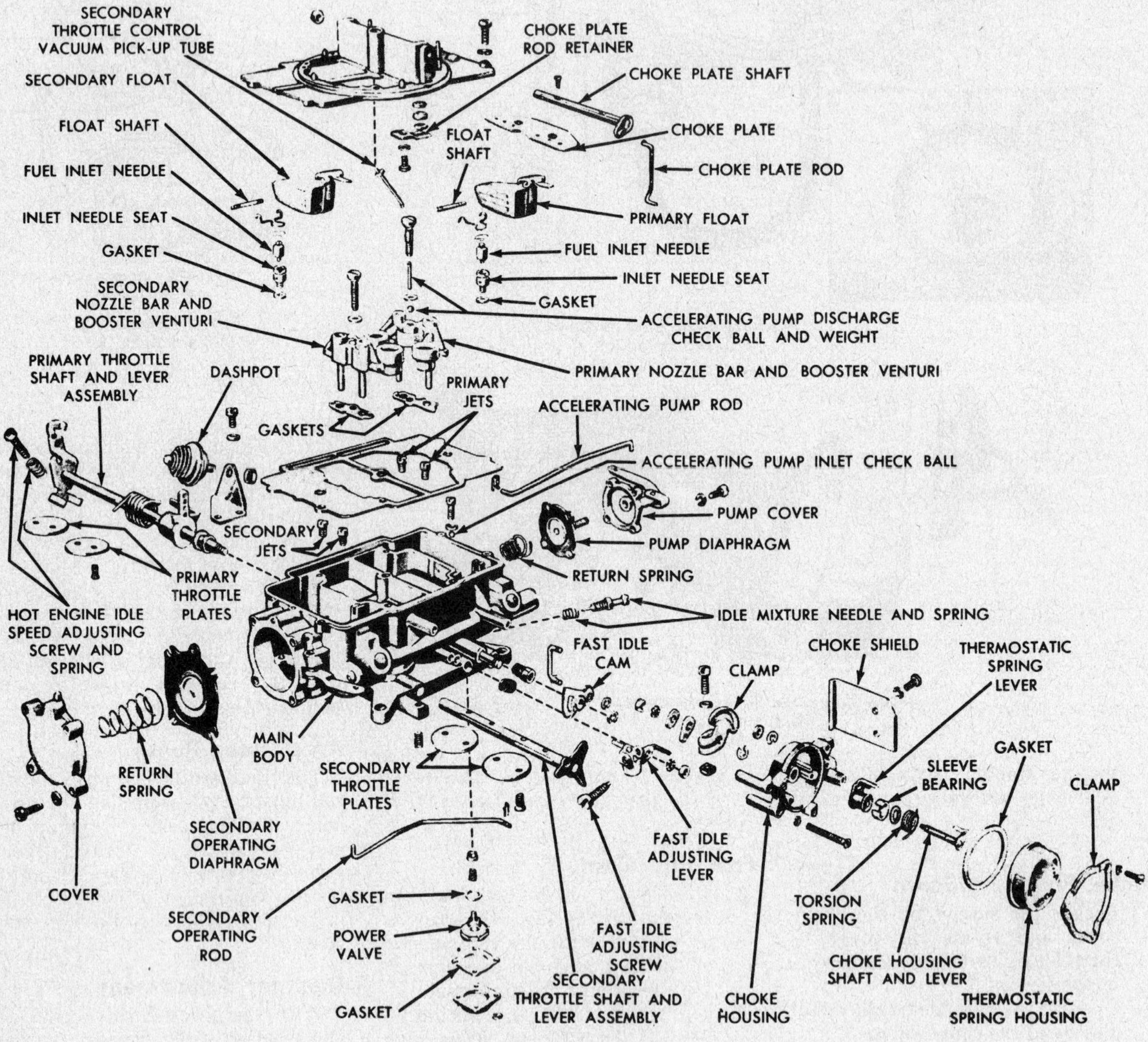
SECONDARY THROTTLE CONTROL VACUUM PICK-UP TUBE
SECONDARY FLOAT
FLOAT SHAFT
FUEL INLET NEEDLE
INLET NEEDLE SEAT
GASKET
SECONDARY NOZZLE BAR AND BOOSTER VENTURI
PRIMARY THROTTLE SHAFT AND LEVER ASSEMBLY
DASHPOT
GASKETS
PRIMARY JETS
SECONDARY JETS
PRIMARY THROTTLE PLATES
HOT ENGINE IDLE SPEED ADJUSTING SCREW AND SPRING
MAIN BODY
RETURN SPRING
SECONDARY OPERATING DIAPHRAGM
COVER
SECONDARY THROTTLE PLATES
SECONDARY OPERATING ROD
GASKET
POWER VALVE
GASKET
SECONDARY THROTTLE SHAFT AND LEVER ASSEMBLY
FAST IDLE ADJUSTING SCREW
FAST IDLE ADJUSTING LEVER
CHOKE HOUSING
TORSION SPRING
CHOKE HOUSING SHAFT AND LEVER
THERMOSTATIC SPRING HOUSING
CLAMP
GASKET
SLEEVE BEARING
THERMOSTATIC SPRING LEVER
CHOKE SHIELD
CLAMP
FAST IDLE CAM
IDLE MIXTURE NEEDLE AND SPRING
RETURN SPRING
PUMP DIAPHRAGM
PUMP COVER
ACCELERATING PUMP INLET CHECK BALL
ACCELERATING PUMP ROD
PRIMARY NOZZLE BAR AND BOOSTER VENTURI
ACCELERATING PUMP DISCHARGE CHECK BALL AND WEIGHT
GASKET
INLET NEEDLE SEAT
FUEL INLET NEEDLE
PRIMARY FLOAT
CHOKE PLATE ROD
CHOKE PLATE
FLOAT SHAFT
CHOKE PLATE SHAFT
CHOKE PLATE ROD RETAINER

Model 4100 carburetor (© Ford Motor Co)

FORD, AUTOLITE, MOTORCRAFT MODEL 2100 SPECIFICATIONS

American Motors

Year	(9510)* Carburetor Identification	Dry Float Level (in.)	Wet Float Level (in.)	Pump Setting Hole #①	Choke Plate Pulldown (in.)	Fast Idle Cam Linkage Clearance (in.)	Fast Idle (rpm)	Dechoke (in)	Choke Setting	Dashpot (in.)
1968	8HM2	3/8	3/4	3	0.125	0.120	1600	0.080	Index	—
	8HA2	3/8	3/4	3	0.140	0.120	1600	0.080	Index	0.095
	8ZA2	3/8	3/4	3	0.140	0.120	1600	0.080	Index	0.095
1969	9HM2	1/2	13/16	3	0.125	0.120	1600	0.080	Index	0.140
	9HA2	1/2	13/16	3	0.140	0.120	1600	0.080	Index	0.140
	9ZA2	1/2	13/16	3	0.140	0.120	1600	0.080	Index	0.140
1970	0DA2	3/8	13/16	3	0.300	0.170	1600	0.200	2 Rich	1/8
	0DM2	3/8	13/16	3	0.260	0.170	1600	0.200	Index	1/8
	0RA2	3/8	13/16	3	0.350	0.170	1600	0.200	1 Rich	1/8
1971	1DA2	3/8	13/16	3	0.190	0.170	1600	0.200	2 Rich	1/8
	1DM2	3/8	13/16	3	0.190	0.170	1600	0.200	1 Rich	1/8
	1RA2	3/8	13/16	3	0.190	0.170	1600	0.200	2 Rich	1/8
1972	2DA2	3/8	3/4	3A	0.130	0.120	1600	0.200	2 Rich	9/64
	2DM2	3/8	3/4	3A	0.140	0.130	1600	0.200	1 Rich	7/64
	2RA2	3/8	3/4	3A	0.130	0.120	1600	0.200	2 Rich	—
1973	3DA2	3/8	3/4	3A	0.120	0.110	1600	0.250	2 Rich	—
	3DM2	3/8	3/4	3A	0.130	0.130	1600	0.250	1 Rich	9/64
	3RA2	3/8	3/4	3A	0.120	0.110	1600	0.250	2 Rich	—

Ford and Mercury

Year	(9510)* Carburetor Identification	Dry Float Level (in.)	Wet Float Level (in.)	Pump Setting Hole #①	Choke Plate Pulldown (in.)	Fast Idle Cam Linkage Clearance (in.)	Fast Idle (rpm)	Dechoke (in)	Choke Setting	Dashpot (in.)
1967	C7AF-N	0.484	0.875	4	0.140	0.130	1400	1/16	Index	—
	C7AF-R	0.484	0.875	3	0.120	0.110	1600	1/16	2 Rich	—
	C7AF-S	0.531	0.905	3	0.120	0.110	1400	1/16	Index	1/8
	C7AF-T	0.531	0.905	3	0.120	0.110	1600	1/16	2 Rich	1/8
	C7AF-U	0.484	0.875	3	0.200	0.160	1300	1/16	Index	—
	C7AF-V	0.375	0.750	3	0.180	0.150	1400	1/16	2 Rich	—
	C7AF-Y	0.531	0.905	3	0.200	0.170	1300	1/16	Index	0.090
	C7AF-Z	0.531	0.905	4	0.180	0.150	1500	1/16	Index	0.090
	C7AF-AK	0.406	0.781	3	0.120	0.100	1400	1/16	Index	1/8
	C7AF-BE	0.406	0.781	3	0.120	0.100	1500	1/16	Index	—
	C7AF-BF	0.406	0.781	3	0.180	0.160	1300	1/16	Index	—
	C7AF-BG	0.406	0.781	3	0.200	0.160	1300	1/16	Index	1/8
	C7AF-BN	0.375	0.750	3	0.120	0.110	1600	1/16	2 Rich	1/8
	C7AF-BR	0.406	0.781	3	0.120	0.110	1400	1/16	Index	1/8
	C7AF-BS	0.406	0.781	3	0.120	0.100	1500	1/16	Index	—
1968	C8AF-L	3/8	3/4	2	0.140	0.120	1400	0.060	1 Lean	0.125
	C8AF-M	31/64	7/8	3	0.210	0.170	1300	0.060	Index	—
	C8AF-N	31/64	7/8	3	0.120	0.100	1500	0.060	Index	0.125
	C8AF-AK	3/8	3/4	2	0.120	0.110	1200	0.060	Index	—
	C8AF-AN	31/64	7/8	3	0.120	0.100	1500	0.060	Index	0.125

U248

Ford and Mercury

Year	(9510)* Carburetor Identification	Dry Float Level (in.)	Wet Float Level (in.)	Pump Setting Hole #①	Choke Plate Pulldown (in.)	Fast Idle Cam Linkage Clearance (in.)	Fast Idle (rpm)	Dechoke (in)	Choke Setting	Dashpot (in.)
1969	C8AF-BD	3/8	3/4	2	0.130	0.110	1400	0.060	2 Rich	0.125
	C9AF-A	3/8	3/4	3	0.120	0.110	1400	0.060	Index	0.125
	C9OF-C	31/64	7/8	3	0.120	0.100	1600	0.060	2 Rich	—
	C9ZF-A	9/16	15/16	3	0.150	0.130	1300	0.060	1 Rich	7/64
	C9AF-B	31/64	7/8	2	0.210	0.170	1300	0.060	1 Rich	1/8
	C9AF-C	31/64	7/8	3	0.130	0.100	1500	0.060	2 Rich	1/8
	C9MF-A	31/64	7/8	3	0.150	0.120	1500	0.060	2 Rich	1/8
	C9AF-J	31/64	7/8	3	0.130	0.100	1500	0.060	2 Rich	1/8
1970	D0AF-C	7/16	13/16	3	0.150	0.130	1400	0.060	1 Rich	—
	D0AF-D	7/16	13/16	3	0.150	0.130	1500	0.060	1 Rich	1/8
	D0AF-U	7/16	13/16	3	0.150	0.130	1500	0.060	1 Rich	—
	D0AF-E	7/16	13/16	3	0.230	0.190	1300	0.190	2 Lean	—
	D0AF-F	7/16	13/16	3	0.200	0.170	1600	0.170	2 Lean	1/8
	D0AF-V	7/16	13/16	3	0.200	0.170	1600	0.170	2 Lean	—
	D0OF-K	7/16	13/16	3	0.220	0.190	1500	0.190	Index	—
	D0OF-L	7/16	13/16	3	0.190	0.130	1500	0.130	1 Rich	1/8
	D0OF-M	7/16	13/16	3	0.190	0.130	1500	0.130	1 Rich	—
1971	D1YF-DA	7/16	13/16	3	0.200	0.160	1500	0.060	Index	—
	D1MF-JA	7/16	13/16	3	0.190	0.160	1500	0.060	1 Rich	1/8
	D1MF-FA	7/16	13/16	3	0.200	0.160	1500	0.060	1 Rich	1/8
1972	D2AF-FB	7/16	13/16	3	0.140	0.130	1500	0.030	Index	1/8
	D2AF-GB	7/16	13/16	3	0.140	0.130	1500	0.030	Index	1/8
	D2AF-HA	7/16	13/16	2	0.150	0.130	1400	0.060	1 Rich	1/8
	D2GF-AA	7/16	13/16	2	0.150	0.130	1400	0.060	1 Rich	1/8
	D2GF-BA	7/16	13/16	2	0.150	0.130	1400	0.060	1 Rich	—
	D2MF-FB	7/16	13/16	4	0.180	0.150	1500	0.060	1 Rich	—
	D2OF-KA	7/16	13/16	2	0.150	0.130	1400	0.060	1 Rich	—
	D2OF-VB	7/16	13/16	3	0.190	0.160	1400	0.030	2 Rich	—
	D2WF-CA	7/16	13/16	3	0.190	0.160	1400	0.030	2 Rich	—
	D2ZF-FA	7/16	13/16	2	0.150	0.130	1400	0.060	1 Rich	—
	D2ZF-LA	7/16	13/16	3	0.240	0.210	1500	0.030	1 Rich	—
1973	D3AF-CE	7/16	13/16	3A	②	②	1500	②	1 Rich	—
	D3AF-DC	7/16	13/16	3A	②	②	1500	②	3 Rich	—
	D3GF-AF	7/16	13/16	2A	②	②	1400	②	3 Rich	—
	D3GF-BB	7/16	13/16	2A	②	②	1250	②	3 Rich	—
	D3ZF-EA	7/16	13/16	2A	②	②	1400	②	1 Rich	—

* Basic carburetor number
① With link in inboard hole of pump lever
② Electric choke

FORD, AUTOLITE, MOTORCRAFT MODEL 4100 SPECIFICATIONS

Ford and Mercury

Year	(9510)* Carburetor Identification	Dry Float Level (in.) Pri.	Dry Float Level (in.) Sec.	Wet Float Level (in.) Pri.	Wet Float Level (in.) Sec.	Pump Setting Hole	Choke Plate Pulldown (in.)	Fast Idle Cam Linkage (in.)	Fast Idle (rpm)	Dechoke (in.)	Choke Setting	Dashpot (in.)
1967	C6ZF-C	0.491	0.621	0.875	1.00	3	0.230	—	—	1/16	—	—
	C7AF-AL	0.531	0.687	0.906	1.062	3	0.160	0.130	1200	1/16	Index	—
	C7AF-AM	0.531	0.687	0.906	1.062	3	0.140	0.120	1300	1/16	Index	—
	C7AF-AN	0.531	0.687	0.906	1.062	3	0.160	0.130	1300	1/16	Index	1/8
	C7AF-AR	0.531	0.687	0.906	1.062	3	0.140	0.120	1500	1/16	1 Rich	1/8
1968	C8AF-AE	17/32	1 1/16	29/32	1 1/16	3	0.140	0.120	—	1/16	—	—
1969	C8AF-AE	17/32	1 1/16	29/32	1 1/16	3	0.140	0.120	1350	1/16	2 Rich	7/64

* Basic carburetor number

Model 5200

The 5200 carburetor is a two-stage, two-venturi carburetor in which the secondary venturi is the larger. The secondary system is mechanically operated.

Fast Idle Cam

1. Insert a 5/32 in. drill between the lower edge of the choke plate and the air horn wall.
2. With the fast idle screw held on the second step of the fast idle cam, measure the clearance between the tang of the choke lever and the arm on the fast idle cam.
3. Bend the choke lever tang to adjust it if it is not up to specification.

Choke Plate Pulldown

1. Remove the choke thermostatic spring cover.
2. Pull the water cover and the thermostatic spring cover assembly out of the way.
3. Set the fast idle cam on the high step.
4. Push the diaphragm stem against its stop and insert the specified gauge between the lower edge of the choke valve and the air horn wall.
5. Apply sufficient pressure to the upper edge of the choke valve to take up any slack in the choke linkage.
6. Turn the adjusting screw in or out to adjust the choke plate-to-air horn clearance.

Dechoke (Unloader) Adjustment

1. Hold the throttle in the wide open position.
2. Remove any slack from the choke linkage by applying pressure to the upper edge of the choke valve.

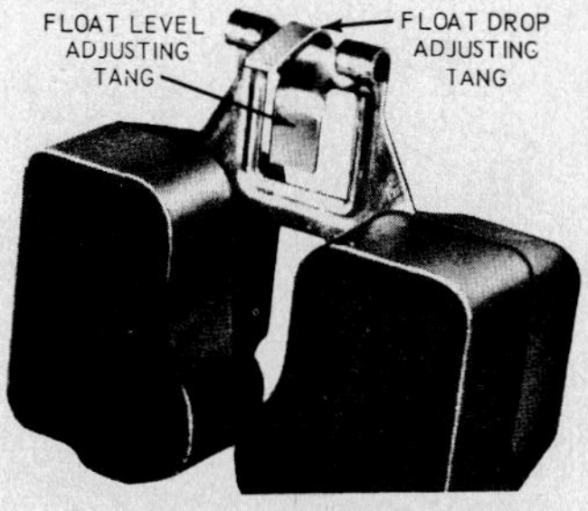
FLOAT LEVEL ADJUSTING TANG
FLOAT DROP ADJUSTING TANG
Float adjustment
(© Ford Motor Co)

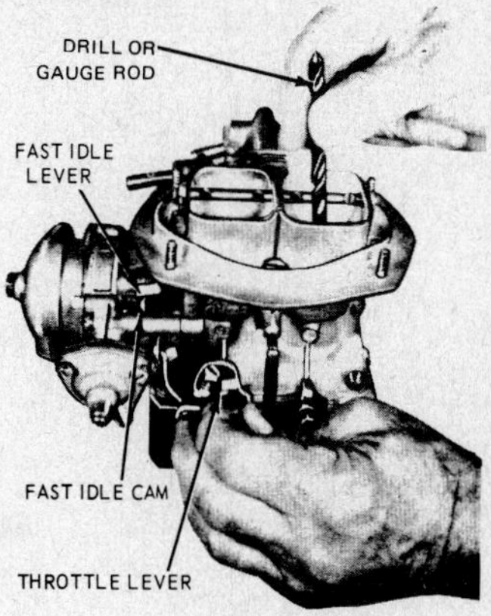
DRILL OR GAUGE ROD
FAST IDLE LEVER
FAST IDLE CAM
THROTTLE LEVER
Dechoke adjustment
(© Ford Motor Co)

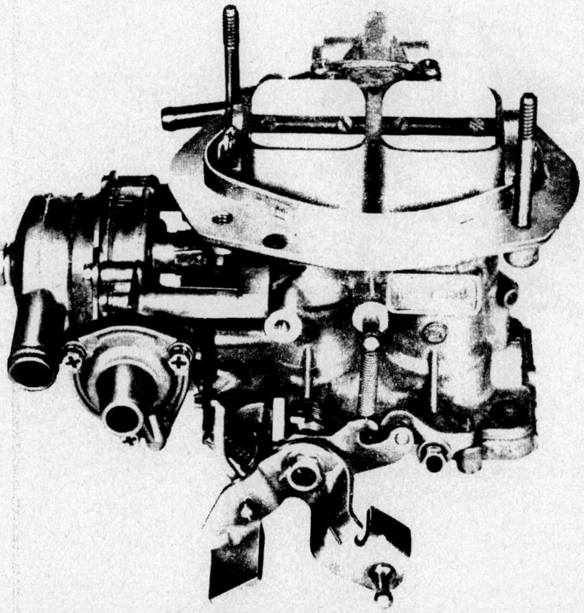
Model 5200 carburetor
(© Ford Motor Co)

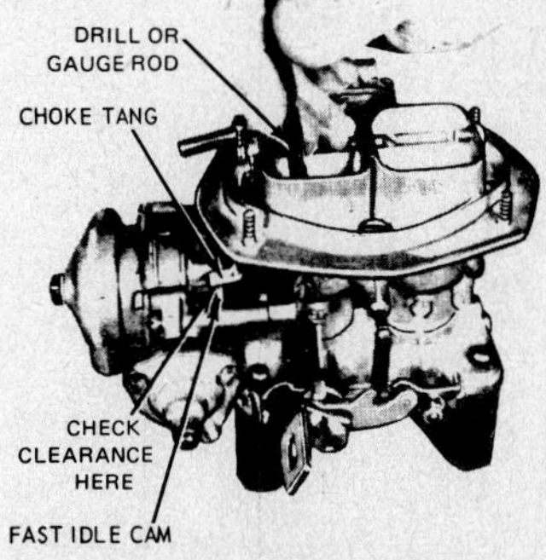
DRILL OR GAUGE ROD
CHOKE TANG
CHECK CLEARANCE HERE
FAST IDLE CAM
Fast idle cam adjustment
(© Ford Motor Co)

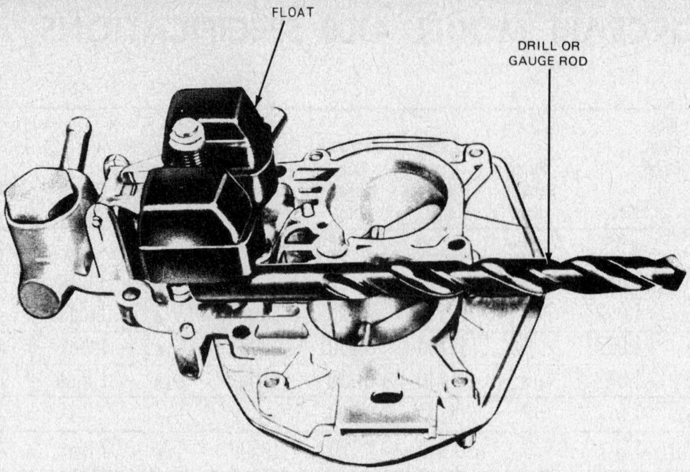
FLOAT
DRILL OR
GAUGE ROD

Checking float level
(© Ford Motor Co)

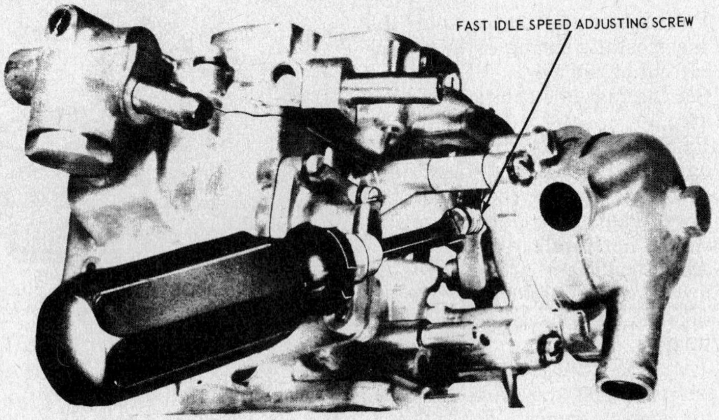
FAST IDLE SPEED ADJUSTING SCREW

Fast idle adjustment
(© Ford Motor Co)

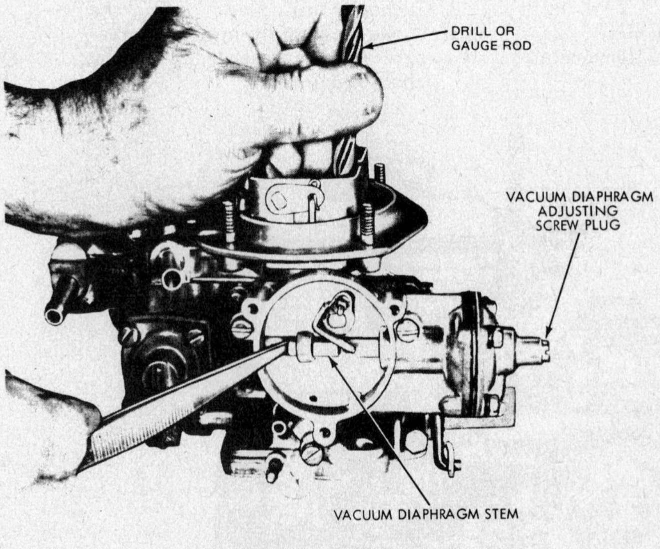
DRILL OR
GAUGE ROD
VACUUM DIAPHRAGM
ADJUSTING
SCREW PLUG
VACUUM DIAPHRAGM STEM

Choke plate pulldown adjustment
(© Ford Motor Co)

3. Measure the distance from the lower edge of the choke valve to the air horn wall.
4. Make adjustments by bending the tab on the fast idle lever where it touches the fast idle cam.

Fast Idle

Set the fast idle speed with the fast idle screw positioned on the second step of the fast idle cam and with the engine at operating temperature.

Float Level Adjustment

With the bowl cover held upside down and the float tang resting lightly on the spring loaded fuel inlet needle, measure the clearance between the edge of the float and the bowl cover. To adjust the level, bend the float tang up or down as required. Adjust both floats equally.

Secondary Throttle Stop Screw

1. Turn the secondary throttle stop screw counterclockwise until the secondary throttle plate seats in its bore.
2. Turn the screw clockwise until it touches the tab on the secondary throttle lever.
3. Add ¼ turn clockwise and the stop is adjusted.

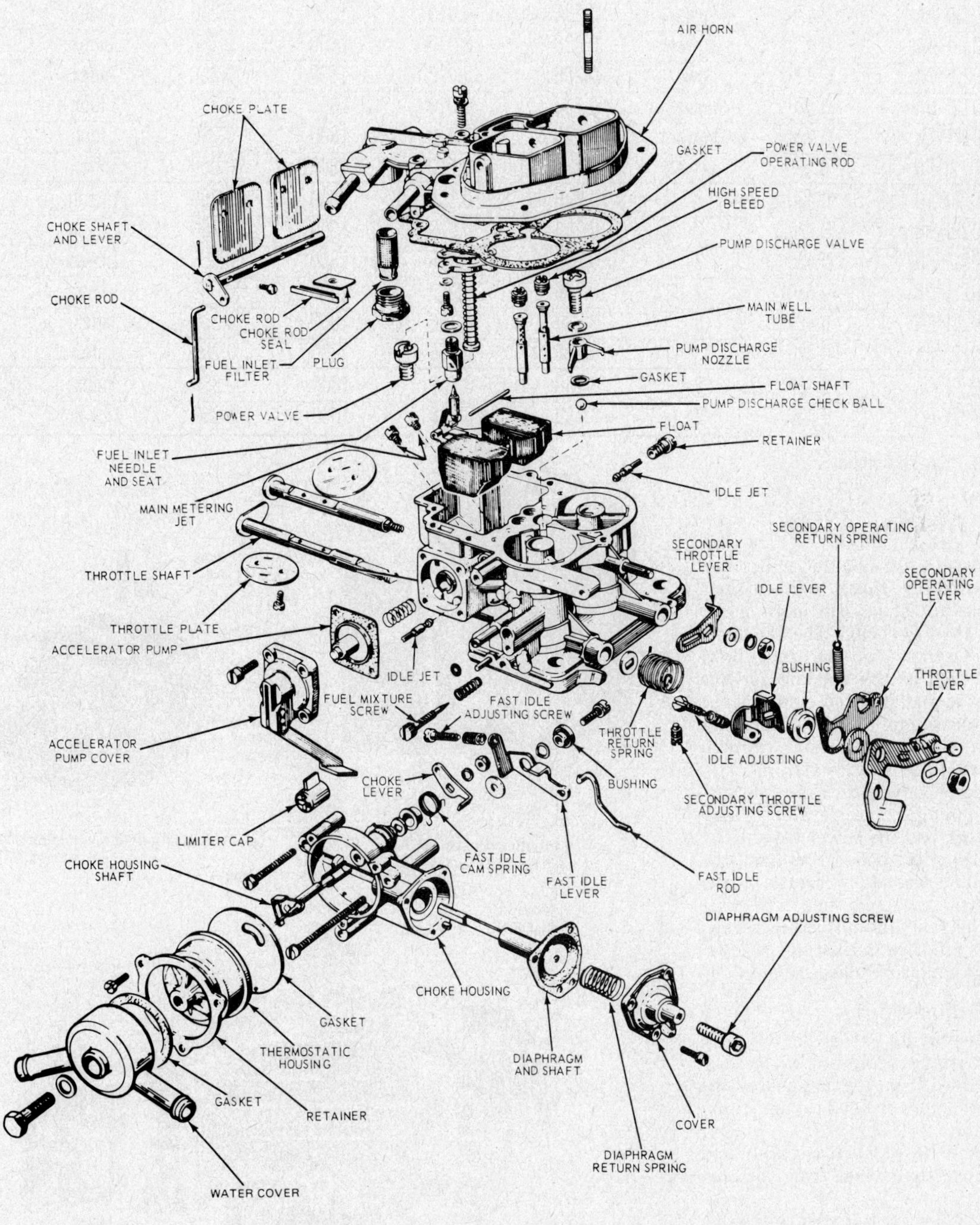
AIR HORN
CHOKE PLATE
GASKET
POWER VALVE OPERATING ROD
HIGH SPEED BLEED
PUMP DISCHARGE VALVE
CHOKE SHAFT AND LEVER
CHOKE ROD
MAIN WELL TUBE
CHOKE ROD
CHOKE ROD SEAL
PUMP DISCHARGE NOZZLE
FUEL INLET FILTER
PLUG
GASKET
FLOAT SHAFT
POWER VALVE
PUMP DISCHARGE CHECK BALL
FLOAT
FUEL INLET NEEDLE AND SEAT
RETAINER
IDLE JET
MAIN METERING JET
SECONDARY OPERATING RETURN SPRING
SECONDARY THROTTLE LEVER
THROTTLE SHAFT
IDLE LEVER
SECONDARY OPERATING LEVER
THROTTLE PLATE
ACCELERATOR PUMP
BUSHING
THROTTLE LEVER
IDLE JET
FUEL MIXTURE SCREW
FAST IDLE ADJUSTING SCREW
THROTTLE RETURN SPRING
ACCELERATOR PUMP COVER
IDLE ADJUSTING
CHOKE LEVER
BUSHING
SECONDARY THROTTLE ADJUSTING SCREW
LIMITER CAP
FAST IDLE CAM SPRING
CHOKE HOUSING SHAFT
FAST IDLE LEVER
FAST IDLE ROD
DIAPHRAGM ADJUSTING SCREW
CHOKE HOUSING
GASKET
THERMOSTATIC HOUSING
DIAPHRAGM AND SHAFT
GASKET
RETAINER
COVER
DIAPHRAGM RETURN SPRING
WATER COVER

Model 5200 carburetor—exploded view (© Ford Motor Co)

FORD, AUTOLITE, MOTORCRAFT MODEL 5200 SPECIFICATIONS

Year	(9510)* Carburetor Identification	Dry Float Level (in.)	Pump Hole Setting	Choke Plate Pulldown (in.)	Fast Idle Cam Linkage (in.)	Fast Idle (rpm)	Dechoke (in.)	Choke Setting	Dashpot
1971	D12F-AA	0.420	Lower	0.236	0.010	1800	0.256	Index	—
	D12F-BA	0.420	Lower	0.236	0.010	1600	0.256	Index	—
	D12F-CA	0.420	Lower	0.236	0.010	1800	0.256	Index	—
	D12F-DA	0.420	Lower	0.236	0.010	1800	0.256	1 Rich	—
	D12F-EA	0.420	Lower	0.236	0.010	1600	0.256	1 Rich	—
	D12F-FA	0.420	Lower	0.236	0.010	1800	0.256	1 Rich	—
1972	D22F-AB	0.420	3	0.236	0.156	1800	0.256	1 Lean	—
	D22F-BB	0.420	2	0.236	0.079	1600	0.256	1 Lean	—
	D22F-CB	0.420	3	0.236	0.156	1800	0.256	1 Lean	—
	D22F-DB	0.420	2	0.236	0.079	1600	0.256	1 Lean	—
	D22F-EA	0.420	3	0.236	0.156	1800	0.256	Index	—
	D22F-GA	0.420	3	0.236	0.156	1800	0.256	Index	—
1973	D32F-CA	0.420	2	0.158	0.158	1800	0.256	Index	—
	D32F-BD	0.420	2	0.158	0.118	1600	0.256	1 Lean	—

* Basic carburetor number

Model 4300

The model 4300 4 barrel carburetor is composed of three main assemblies: the air horn, the main body, and the throttle body. The air horn assembly serves as the fuel bowl cover as well as the housing for the choke valve and shaft. It contains the accelerator pump linkage, fuel inlet seat, float and lever, booster venturi, and internal fuel bowl vents.

The main body houses the fuel metering passages, accelerator pump mechanism, and the power valve.

The throttle body contains the primary and secondary throttle valves and shafts, the curb idle adjusting screw, the fast idle adjusting screw, the idle mixture adjusting screws, and the automatic choke assembly.

Float Adjustment

1. Adjustments to the fuel level are best made with the carburetor removed from the engine and the carburetor cleaned upon disassembly.
2. Invert the air horn assembly and remove the gasket from the surface.
3. Use a T-scale to measure the distance from the floats to the air horn casting. Position the scale horizontally over the flat surface of both floats at the free ends and parallel to the air horn casting. Hold the lower end of the vertical scale in full contact with the smooth surface of the air horn.

Caution The end of the vertical scale must not come into contact with any gasket sealing ridges while measuring the float level.

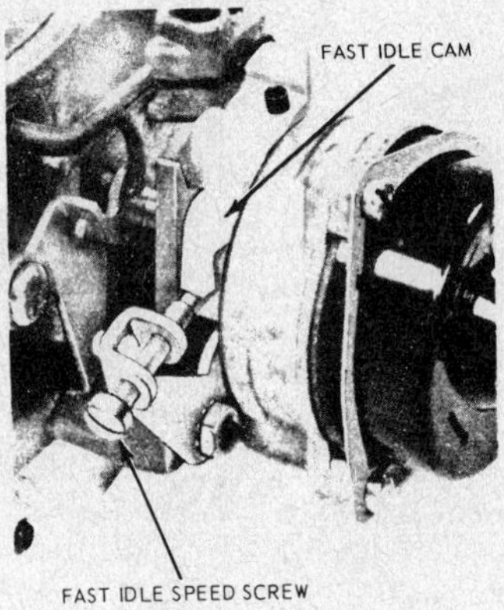
FAST IDLE CAM
FAST IDLE SPEED SCREW
Fast idle adjustment
(© Ford Motor Co)

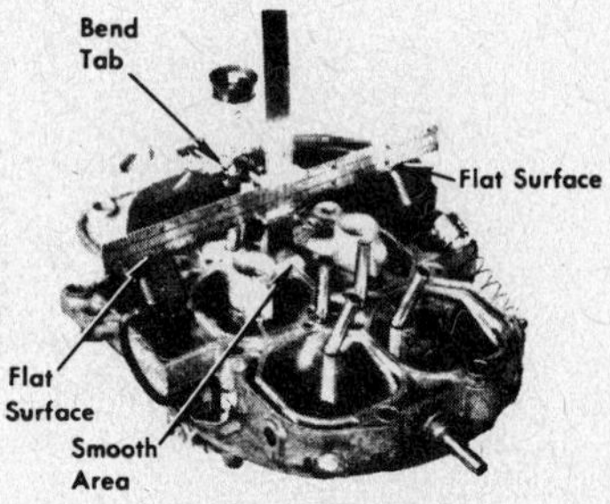
Bend Tab
Flat Surface
Flat Surface
Smooth Area
Checking float level using a T-scale
(© American Motors Co)

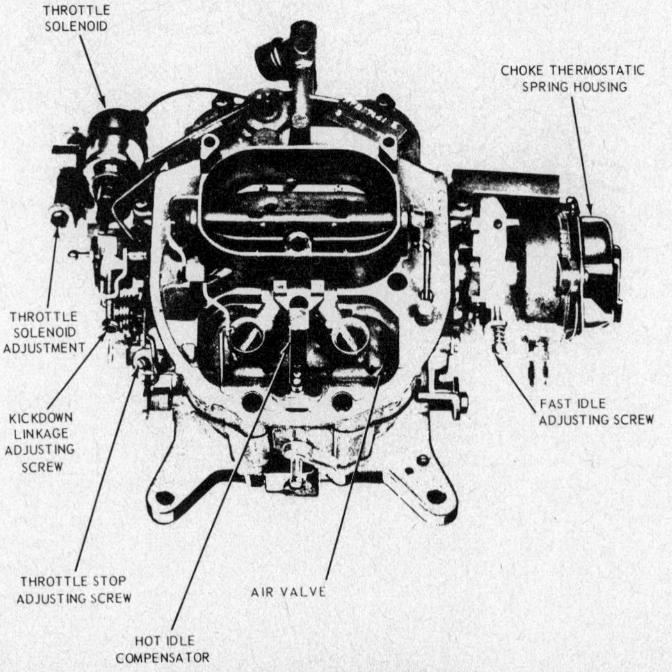
THROTTLE SOLENOID
CHOKE THERMOSTATIC SPRING HOUSING
THROTTLE SOLENOID ADJUSTMENT
KICKDOWN LINKAGE ADJUSTING SCREW
FAST IDLE ADJUSTING SCREW
THROTTLE STOP ADJUSTING SCREW
AIR VALVE
HOT IDLE COMPENSATOR
Top view—Model 4300 carburetor
(© Ford Motor Co)

4. The free end of each float should just touch the horizontal scale, if one float is lower than the other; twist the float and lever assembly slightly to correct.
5. Adjust the float level by bending the tab which contacts the needle and seat assembly.

NOTE: The illustrations in this section show an alternate method of adjusting the floats on the model 4300 carburetor.

The procedure includes the fabrication of a gauge and a bending device. After fabricating the gauge, it is possible to adjust it to the specified dimensions and insert it into the air horn outboard holes. Both pontoons should just touch the gauge.

A float tab bending tool is also shown and may be used in the following manner.

To raise the float: insert the open end of the bending tool to the RIGHT side of the float lever tab and between the needle and float hinge. Raise the float lever off of the needle and bend the tab downward.

To lower the float: insert the bending tool to the LEFT side of the float lever tab between the needle and float hinge, support the float lever, and bend the tab upward.

Choke Plate Pulldown

1. Remove the choke thermostatic spring housing.
2. Bend a wire gauge (0.036 in. diameter) at a 90 degree angle about 1/8 in. from one end.
3. Block the throttle open so that the fast idle screw does not contact the fast idle cam.
4. Insert the bent end of the wire gauge between the lower edge of the piston slot and the upper edge of the right hand slot in the choke housing.
5. Pull the choke piston lever counterclockwise until the gauge is snug in the piston slot. Hold the wire in place by exerting light pressure in a rearward direction on the choke piston lever. Check the distance from the lower edge of the choke valve to the air horn wall.
6. Adjustment is done by loosening the hex head screw (left-hand thread) on the choke valve shaft and prying the link away from the shaft. Use a drill gauge 0.010 in. under the specified clearance between the lower edge of the choke valve and the air horn wall. Hold the choke valve against the gauge and maintain a light rearward pressure on the choke lever.
7. With the choke piston snug against the 0.036 in. wire and the choke valve against the drill, tighten the hex screw on the choke valve shaft. The use of a gauge 0.010 in. undersize compensates for tolerance in the linkage.
8. Use the correct size gauge for final measurement.
9. Replace the housing on the thermostatic spring.

Fast Idle Cam Adjustment

1. Loosen the screws on the choke thermostatic spring cover and rotate the housing 1/4 turn clockwise. Tighten the screws.
2. Open the throttle and allow the choke valve to close completely.
3. Push down on the fast idle cam counterweight until the fast idle screw is in contact with the second step of the cam and against the high step.
4. Measure the clearance between the lower edge of the choke valve and the air horn wall.
5. Adjust by turning the fast idle cam adjusting screw.
6. Return the housing on the thermostatic spring to its original position.

Choke Unloader (Dechoke) Adjustment

1. Open the throttle fully and hold it in this position.
2. Rotate the choke valve toward the closed position until the pawl on the fast idle speed lever contacts the fast idle cam.
3. Check the clearance between the lower edge of the choke valve and the air horn wall.
4. Adjust by bending the pawl on the fast idle speed lever forward to increase the clearance and backward to decrease the clearance.

Accelerator Pump Stroke Adjustment

The accelerator pump should not need adjustment as its stroke is preset in compliance with exhaust emission control standards. If for any reason the stroke must be altered, it may

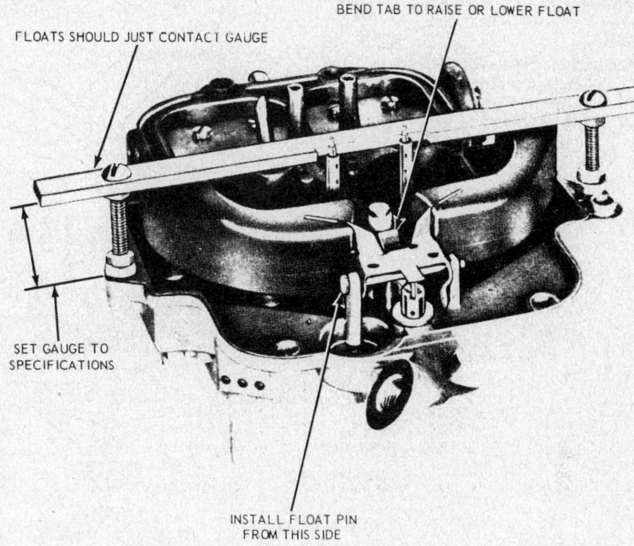
BEND TAB TO RAISE OR LOWER FLOAT
FLOATS SHOULD JUST CONTACT GAUGE
SET GAUGE TO SPECIFICATIONS
INSTALL FLOAT PIN FROM THIS SIDE

Measuring float level
(© Ford Motor Co)

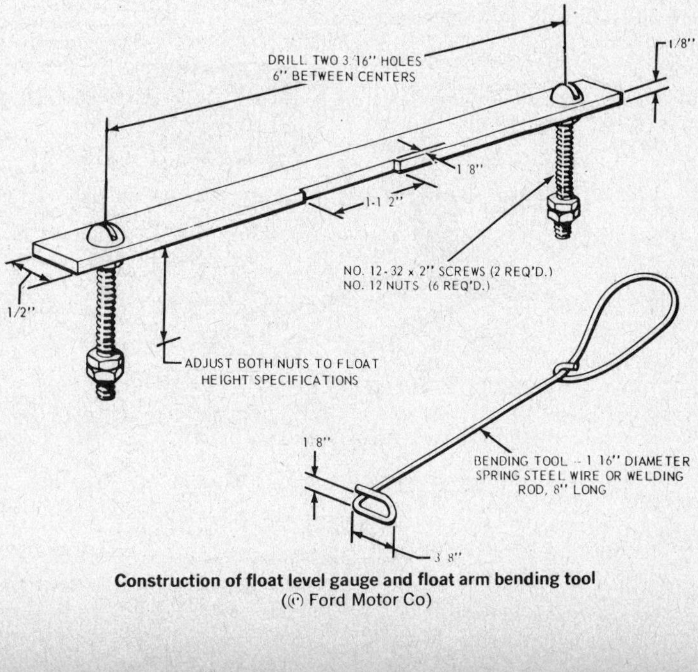
DRILL TWO 3 16" HOLES 6" BETWEEN CENTERS
1/8"
1 8"
1-1 2"
NO. 12-32 x 2" SCREWS (2 REQ'D.) NO. 12 NUTS (6 REQ'D.)
1/2"
ADJUST BOTH NUTS TO FLOAT HEIGHT SPECIFICATIONS
1 8"
BENDING TOOL – 1 16" DIAMETER SPRING STEEL WIRE OR WELDING ROD, 8" LONG
3 8"

Construction of float level gauge and float arm bending tool
(© Ford Motor Co)

be done by repositioning the link in the desired holes.

Fast Idle Speed

The fast idle speed is adjusted with the engine at operating temperature and the fast idle screw on the second step of the fast idle cam. Adjust by turning the fast idle screw in or out as required.

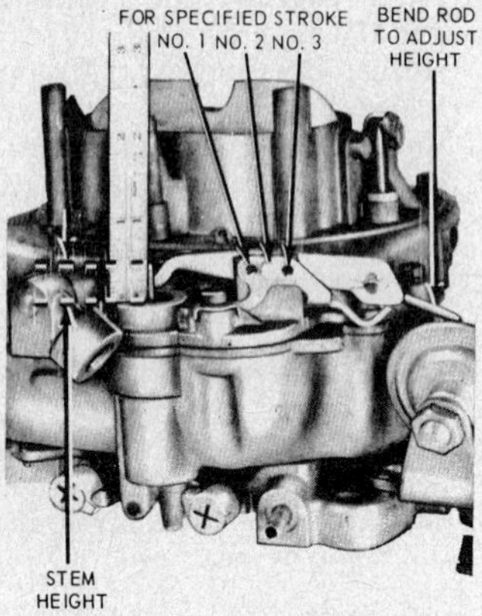
FOR SPECIFIED STROKE
NO. 1 NO. 2 NO. 3
BEND ROD TO ADJUST HEIGHT
STEM HEIGHT

Accelerator pump adjustment
(© Ford Motor Co)

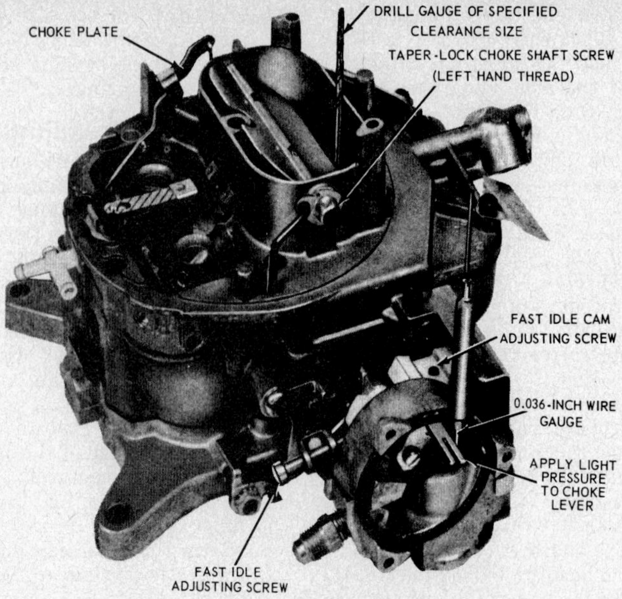
CHOKE PLATE
DRILL GAUGE OF SPECIFIED CLEARANCE SIZE
TAPER-LOCK CHOKE SHAFT SCREW (LEFT HAND THREAD)
FAST IDLE CAM ADJUSTING SCREW
0.036-INCH WIRE GAUGE
APPLY LIGHT PRESSURE TO CHOKE LEVER
FAST IDLE ADJUSTING SCREW

Choke plate pulldown and fast idle cam adjustment
(© Ford Motor Co)

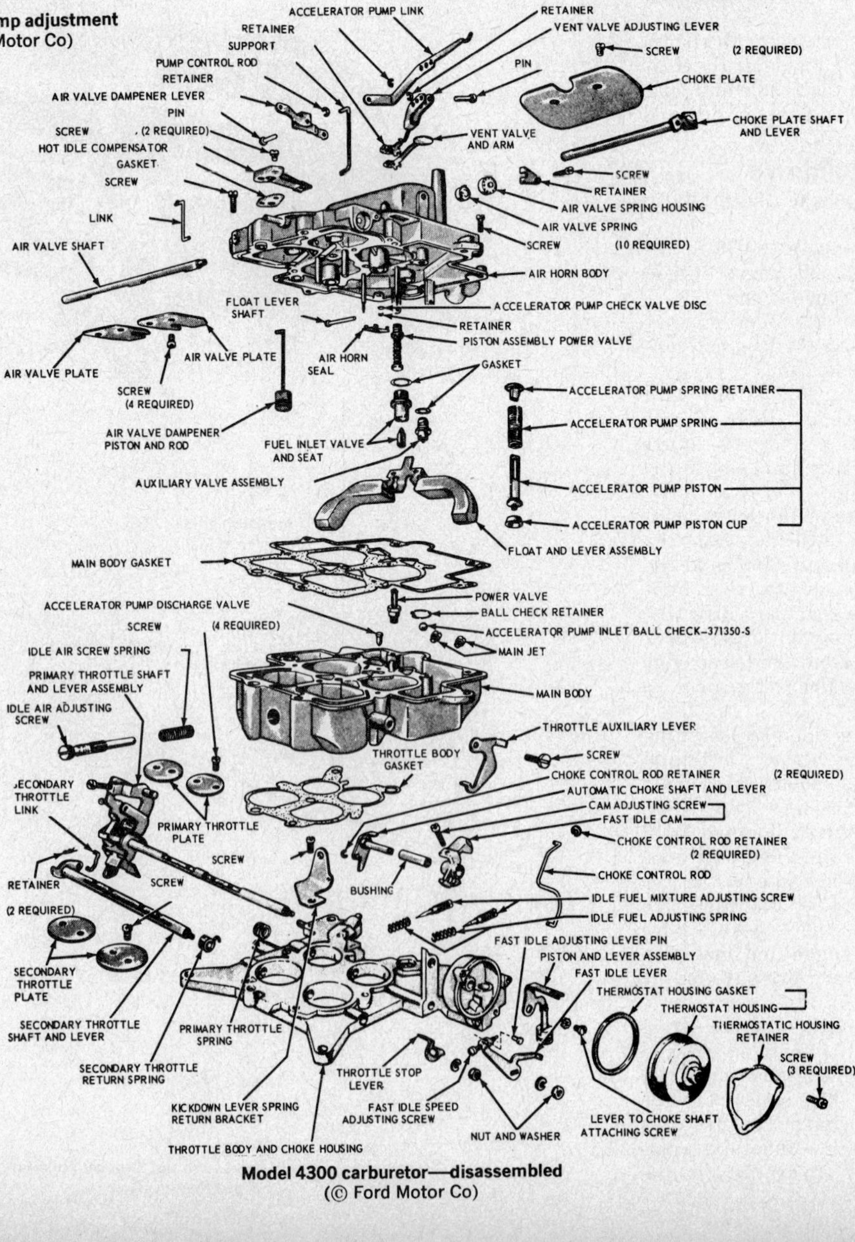
ACCELERATOR PUMP LINK
RETAINER
VENT VALVE ADJUSTING LEVER
RETAINER
SUPPORT
PUMP CONTROL ROD
RETAINER
SCREW
(2 REQUIRED)
PIN
CHOKE PLATE
AIR VALVE DAMPENER LEVER
PIN
SCREW
(2 REQUIRED)
CHOKE PLATE SHAFT AND LEVER
VENT VALVE AND ARM
HOT IDLE COMPENSATOR
GASKET
SCREW
SCREW
RETAINER
AIR VALVE SPRING HOUSING
LINK
AIR VALVE SPRING
SCREW
(10 REQUIRED)
AIR VALVE SHAFT
AIR HORN BODY
FLOAT LEVER SHAFT
ACCELERATOR PUMP CHECK VALVE DISC
RETAINER
PISTON ASSEMBLY POWER VALVE
AIR VALVE PLATE
AIR HORN SEAL
AIR VALVE PLATE
GASKET
SCREW (4 REQUIRED)
ACCELERATOR PUMP SPRING RETAINER
ACCELERATOR PUMP SPRING
AIR VALVE DAMPENER PISTON AND ROD
FUEL INLET VALVE AND SEAT
AUXILIARY VALVE ASSEMBLY
ACCELERATOR PUMP PISTON
ACCELERATOR PUMP PISTON CUP
FLOAT AND LEVER ASSEMBLY
MAIN BODY GASKET
ACCELERATOR PUMP DISCHARGE VALVE
POWER VALVE
BALL CHECK RETAINER
SCREW
(4 REQUIRED)
ACCELERATOR PUMP INLET BALL CHECK-371350-S
MAIN JET
IDLE AIR SCREW SPRING
PRIMARY THROTTLE SHAFT AND LEVER ASSEMBLY
MAIN BODY
IDLE AIR ADJUSTING SCREW
THROTTLE AUXILIARY LEVER
SCREW
THROTTLE BODY GASKET
CHOKE CONTROL ROD RETAINER
(2 REQUIRED)
SECONDARY THROTTLE LINK
AUTOMATIC CHOKE SHAFT AND LEVER
CAM ADJUSTING SCREW
FAST IDLE CAM
PRIMARY THROTTLE PLATE
CHOKE CONTROL ROD RETAINER
(2 REQUIRED)
SCREW
RETAINER
(2 REQUIRED)
SCREW
BUSHING
CHOKE CONTROL ROD
IDLE FUEL MIXTURE ADJUSTING SCREW
IDLE FUEL ADJUSTING SPRING
FAST IDLE ADJUSTING LEVER PIN
PISTON AND LEVER ASSEMBLY
SECONDARY THROTTLE PLATE
FAST IDLE LEVER
THERMOSTAT HOUSING GASKET
THERMOSTAT HOUSING
THERMOSTATIC HOUSING RETAINER
SECONDARY THROTTLE SHAFT AND LEVER
PRIMARY THROTTLE SPRING
SCREW
(3 REQUIRED)
SECONDARY THROTTLE RETURN SPRING
THROTTLE STOP LEVER
KICKDOWN LEVER SPRING RETURN BRACKET
FAST IDLE SPEED ADJUSTING SCREW
NUT AND WASHER
LEVER TO CHOKE SHAFT ATTACHING SCREW
THROTTLE BODY AND CHOKE HOUSING

Model 4300 carburetor—disassembled
(© Ford Motor Co)

FORD, AUTOLITE, MOTORCRAFT MODEL 4300 SPECIFICATIONS

American Motors

Year	(9510)* Carburetor Identification①	Dry Float Level (in.)	Pump Setting Hole	Choke Plate Pulldown (in.)	Fast Idle Cam Linkage (in.)	Fast Idle (rpm)	Dechoke (in.)	Choke Setting	Dashpot (in.)
1970	0WA4	13/16	Center	0.170	0.190	1600	0.300	2 Rich	1/8
	0WM4	13/16	Center	0.190	0.200	1600	0.300	2 Rich	1/16
1971	1TA4	13/16	Center	0.190	0.200	1600	0.300	Index	1/8
	1TM4	13/16	Center	0.170	0.190	1600	0.300	Index	1/16
1972	2RA4	13/16	Center	0.190	0.190	1600	0.300	1 Rich	9/64
	2TA4	13/16	Center	0.190	0.190	1600	0.300	1 Rich	9/64
	2TM4	13/16	Center	0.190	0.190	1600	0.300	1 Rich	9/64
1973	3TA4	13/16	Center	0.190	0.160	1600	0.275	2 Rich	9/64
	3TA4 (Police)	15/16	Center	0.190	0.160	1600	0.275	2 Rich	9/64
	3TM4	13/16	Center	0.190	0.160	1600	0.275	2 Rich	9/64

* Basic carburetor number
① The identification tag is located on the bowl cover

② 8 cyl. 390—Imco 2 Rich
Thermactor 1 Rich
8 cyl. 428—Imco Index
Thermactor 1 Rich

Ford and Mercury

Year	(9510)* Carburetor Identification①	Dry Float Level (in.)	Pump Setting Hole	Choke Plate Pulldown (in.)	Fast Idle Cam Linkage (in.)	Fast Idle (rpm)	Dechoke (in.)	Choke Setting	Dashpot (in.)
1967	C7AF-F	25/32	2	0.200	0.100	1400	1/16	Index	—
	C7AF-L	25/32	2	0.210	0.100	1300	1/16	Index	1/8
	C7AF-M	25/32	2	0.200	0.100	1500	1/16	Index	1/8
	C7AF-AC	25/32	1	0.200	0.100	1200	1/16	Index	—
	C7AF-AD	25/32	2	0.110	0.090	1200	1/16	Index	—
	C7AF-AE	25/32	2	0.210	0.100	1200	1/16	Index	—
	C7AF-AF	25/32	2	0.120	0.090	1200	1/16	Index	—
	C7AF-AG	25/32	1	0.200	0.100	1300	1/16	Index	1/8
	C7AF-AH	25/32	3	0.100	0.080	1200	1/16	Index	—
1968	C8AF-A	25/32	3	0.300	0.100	1300	—	②	0.093
	C8AF-B	25/32	3	0.300	0.100	1400	—	②	0.093
	C8SF-E	25/32	2	0.230	0.160	1500	0.300	1 Rich	3/32
	C8VF-F	25/32	1	0.230	0.160	1500	0.300	1 Rich	3/32
	C8VF-H	25/32	2	0.230	0.160	1300	0.300	1 Rich	3/32
	C8ZF-C	13/16	2	0.120	0.090	1900	0.300	—	0.100
	C8ZF-D	13/16	1	0.140	0.100	2100	0.300	—	0.100
1969	C8SF-H	25/32	2	0.230	0.160	1300	0.300	—	3/32
	C8VF-J	25/32	2	0.230	0.160	1300	0.300	—	3/32
	C9AF-G	25/32	2	0.270	0.220	1200	0.300	—	3/32
	C9AF-R	25/32	2	0.230	0.160	1300	0.300	—	—
	C9OF-D	13/16	2	0.160	0.100	1400	0.300	—	—
	C9OF-E	13/16	3	0.250	0.230	1400	0.300	—	—
	C9ZF-C	13/16	2	0.170	0.130	1250	0.300	—	3/32
	C9ZF-D	13/16	2	0.160	0.100	1400	0.300	—	—
	C9ZF-E	13/16	3	0.230	0.210	1300	0.300	—	1/8
	C9ZF-F	13/16	3	0.250	0.230	1400	0.300	—	—

Year	(9510)* Carburetor Identification①	Dry Float Level (in.)	Pump Setting Hole	Choke Plate Pulldown (in.)	Fast Idle Cam Linkage (in.)	Fast Idle (rpm)	Dechoke (in.)	Choke Setting	Dashpot (in.)
1970	D0AF-K	49/64	2	0.220	0.170	1300	0.300	Index	0.070
	D0AF-L	25/32	2	0.250	0.220	1400	0.300	Index	0.070
	D0AF-M	1.00	3	0.160	0.120	1600	0.300	2 Rich	0.080
	D0AF-R	1.00	3	0.160	0.120	1600	0.300	2 Rich	—
	D0AF-AD	1.00	3	0.160	0.120	1600	0.300	2 Rich	0.080
	D0AF-AJ	1.00	3	0.160	0.120	1600	0.300	2 Rich	0.080
	D0AF-AE	1.00	3	0.160	0.120	1600	0.300	2 Rich	—
	D0AF-AK	1.00	3	0.160	0.120	1600	0.300	2 Rich	—
	D0AF-AB	25/32	2	0.250	0.220	1400	0.300	Index	0.070
	D0AF-AL	25/32	2	0.250	0.220	1400	0.300	Index	0.070
	D0AF-AG	25/32	2	0.220	0.170	1300	0.300	Index	0.070
	D0AF-AM	25/32	2	0.220	0.170	1300	0.300	Index	0.070
	D0AF-AN	49/64	2	0.225	0.170	1350	0.300	Index	0.070
	D0OF-B	13/16	2	0.180	0.160	1250	0.300	Index	—
	D0OF-C	13/16	2	0.200	0.180	1400	0.300	Index	0.080
	D0OF-D	13/16	2	0.180	0.160	1250	0.300	Index	—
	D0OF-H	13/16	2	0.200	0.180	1400	0.300	Index	—
	D0OF-Y	13/16	2	0.180	0.160	1250	0.300	Index	—
	D0OF-Z	13/16	2	0.180	0.160	1250	0.300	Index	—
	D0OF-AA	13/16	2	0.200	0.180	1400	0.300	Index	—
	D0OF-AB	13/16	2	0.180	0.160	1250	0.300	Index	—
	D0OF-AC	13/16	2	0.200	0.180	1400	0.300	Index	0.080
	D0OF-AD	13/16	2	0.200	0.180	1400	0.300	Index	—
	D0OF-AE	13/16	2	0.180	0.160	1250	0.300	Index	—
	D0SF-A	25/32	2	0.220	0.170	1300	0.300	Index	0.070
	D0SF-D	25/32	2	0.220	0.170	1300	0.300	Index	0.070
	D0SF-E	25/32	2	0.220	0.170	1300	0.300	Index	0.070
	D0VF-A	25/32	2	0.230	0.170	1250	0.300	Index	0.100
1971	D1AF-MA	49/64	2	0.220	—	1350	—	Index	1/16
	D1OF-EA	13/16	2	0.180	0.160	1250	—	Index	—
	D1OF-AAA	13/16	2	0.200	0.180	1400	—	Index	—
	D1SF-AA	49/64	2	0.220	—	1350	—	Index	1/16
	D1VF-AA	49/64	2	0.220	0.170	1250	—	1 Rich	0.100
1972	D2AF-AA	49/64	1	0.220	0.200	1350	—	2 Rich	—
	D2AF-LA	49/64	1	0.215	0.190	1900	—	2 Rich	—
	D2SF-AA	49/64	1	0.220	0.200	1350	—	2 Rich	—
	D2SF-BA	49/64	1	0.220	0.200	1350	—	2 Rich	—
	D2VF-AA	49/64	1	0.230	0.200	1250	—	Index	—
	D2VF-BA	49/64	1	0.230	0.200	1250	—	Index	—
	D2ZF-AA	13/16	1	0.200	0.180	1200	—	Index	—
	D2ZF-BB	13/16	1	0.200	0.200	1200	—	Index	—
	D2ZF-DA	13/16	1	0.200	0.200	1200	—	Index	—
	D2ZF-GA	13/16	1	0.200	0.180	1200	—	Index	—
1973	D3VF-DA	0.76	1	0.210	0.190	1350	—	Index	—

Carter Carburetors

Model BBS

Introduction

The BBS series carburetor is a standard Ball and Ball single throat model. It uses a CAP (Cleaner Air Package), CAS (Cleaner Air System), and ECS (Evaporation Control System) on its newer models. It also uses a spring staged choke which is a device incorporated into the choke mechanism which limits the choke blade closing torque when cranking the engine at temperatures below zero. Thus, the spring staging of the choke is a better match for the engine's starting requirements at low temperatures.

Float Level Adjustments

1. Invert the main body so that the weight of each float is forcing the needle against the seat.
2. If the proper gauge is not available, measure from the surface of the bowl to the crown of each float at the center.
3. Adjustment is listed in the specifications chart.
4. To adjust, bend the lip of the float lever in or out until adjustment is correct.

NOTE: On the ECS BBS carburetor, it is necessary to check or set the accelerator pump travel before checking the bowl vent valve opening.

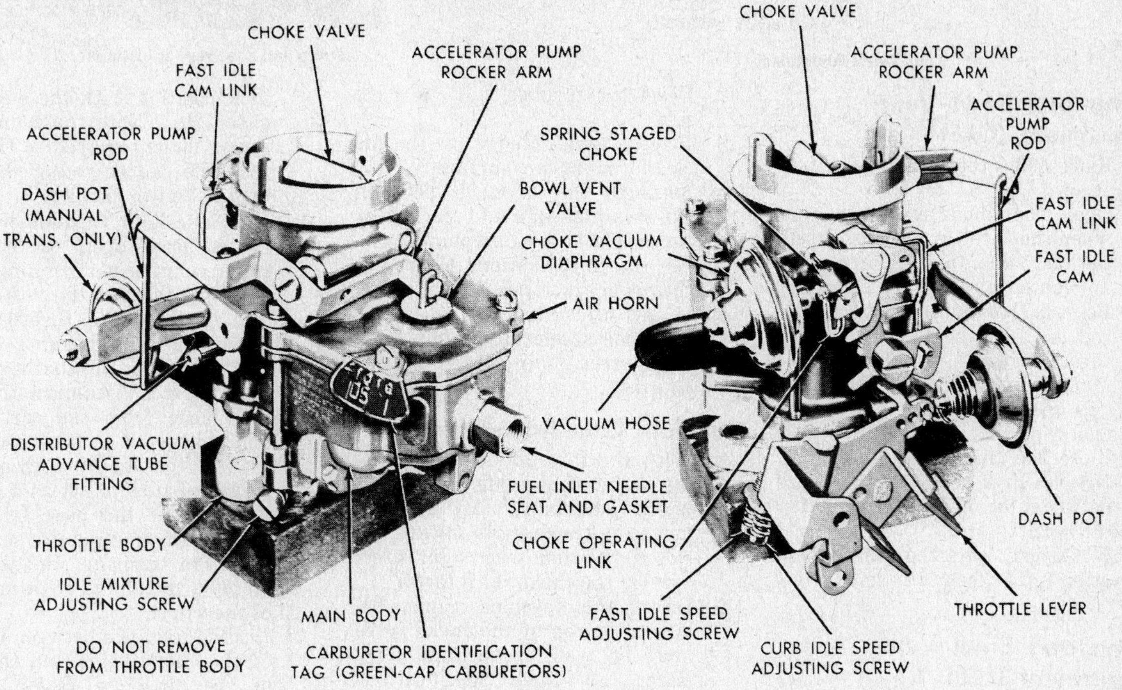
CHOKE VALVE
FAST IDLE CAM LINK
ACCELERATOR PUMP ROCKER ARM
ACCELERATOR PUMP ROD
DASH POT (MANUAL TRANS. ONLY)
BOWL VENT VALVE
AIR HORN
DISTRIBUTOR VACUUM ADVANCE TUBE FITTING
THROTTLE BODY
IDLE MIXTURE ADJUSTING SCREW
DO NOT REMOVE FROM THROTTLE BODY
MAIN BODY
CARBURETOR IDENTIFICATION TAG (GREEN-CAP CARBURETORS)
FUEL INLET NEEDLE SEAT AND GASKET
CHOKE VALVE
ACCELERATOR PUMP ROCKER ARM
ACCELERATOR PUMP ROD
SPRING STAGED CHOKE
FAST IDLE CAM LINK
CHOKE VACUUM DIAPHRAGM
FAST IDLE CAM
VACUUM HOSE
CHOKE OPERATING LINK
DASH POT
FAST IDLE SPEED ADJUSTING SCREW
CURB IDLE SPEED ADJUSTING SCREW
THROTTLE LEVER

Carburetor assembly BBS

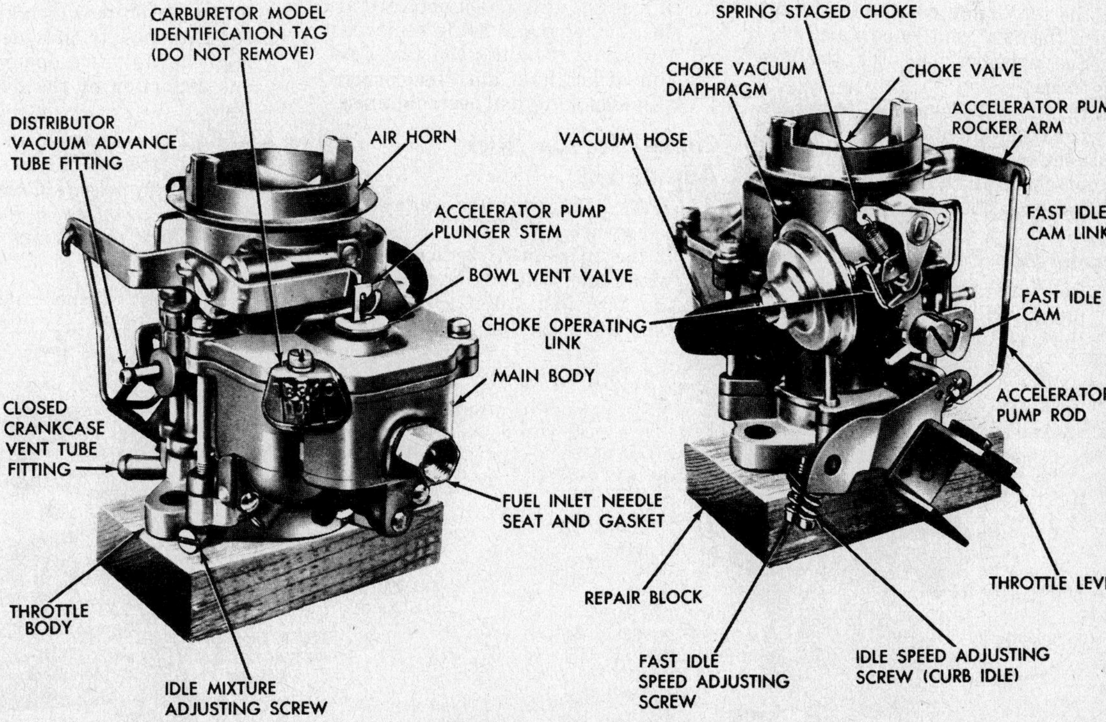
CARBURETOR MODEL IDENTIFICATION TAG (DO NOT REMOVE)
DISTRIBUTOR VACUUM ADVANCE TUBE FITTING
AIR HORN
ACCELERATOR PUMP PLUNGER STEM
BOWL VENT VALVE
CHOKE OPERATING LINK
MAIN BODY
CLOSED CRANKCASE VENT TUBE FITTING
FUEL INLET NEEDLE SEAT AND GASKET
THROTTLE BODY
IDLE MIXTURE ADJUSTING SCREW
SPRING STAGED CHOKE
CHOKE VACUUM DIAPHRAGM
CHOKE VALVE
VACUUM HOSE
ACCELERATOR PUMP ROCKER ARM
FAST IDLE CAM LINK
FAST IDLE CAM
ACCELERATOR PUMP ROD
REPAIR BLOCK
THROTTLE LEVER
FAST IDLE SPEED ADJUSTING SCREW
IDLE SPEED ADJUSTING SCREW (CURB IDLE)

Carburetor assembly BBS

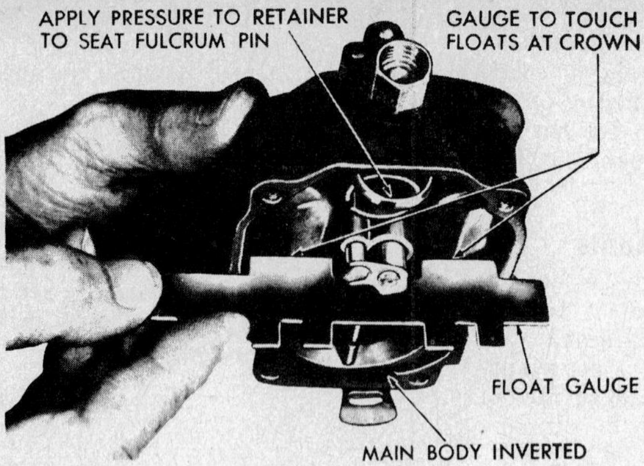
APPLY PRESSURE TO RETAINER TO SEAT FULCRUM PIN
GAUGE TO TOUCH FLOATS AT CROWN
FLOAT GAUGE
MAIN BODY INVERTED

Float level adjustment

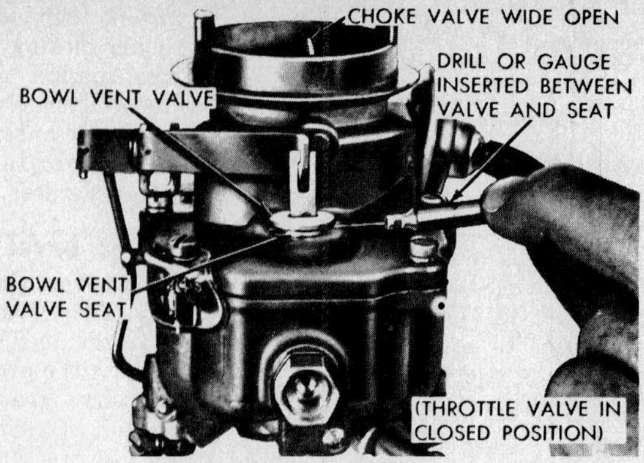
CHOKE VALVE WIDE OPEN
DRILL OR GAUGE INSERTED BETWEEN VALVE AND SEAT
BOWL VENT VALVE
BOWL VENT VALVE SEAT
(THROTTLE VALVE IN CLOSED POSITION)

Pump and bowl vent adjustment

Pump and Bowl Vent Adjustment (CAS)

1. Back off the idle adjusting screw.
2. Open the choke valve so that when the throttle valve is closed, the fast idle adjusting screw will not contact the fast idle cam.
3. Be sure that the pump operating rod is in the center hole in the throttle lever.
4. Make sure that the bowl vent clip on the pump stem is in the center groove.
5. Close the throttle valve tightly.
6. Insert a drill of the specified size between the bowl vent and the air horn.
7. To adjust, bend the pump operating rod at the lower angle.

Pump and Bowl Vent Adjustment (ECS)

1. With the throttle valve at curb idle, measure the distance from the top of the casting to the top of the bowl vent valve stem.
2. See specifications for the distance.
3. If an adjustment is necessary, bend the lower tang on the bowl vent valve operating lever at the pivot until the correct opening has been obtained.

Accelerator Pump Adjustment

1. Be sure that the accelerator pump rod is in the outer hole of the throttle lever.
2. Close the throttle valve to curb idle.
3. Place a straightedge on the air cleaner mounting surface.
4. Measure the distance between the straight edge and the top of the accelerator pump plunger.
5. See the Specifications Chart for the proper distance.
6. If an adjustment is necessary, bend the accelerator pump until the correct pump angle has been obtained.

Fast Idle Cam Adjustment

1. With the fast idle speed adjusting screw contacting the second highest step on the fast idle cam, move the choke valve toward the closed position with light pressure on the choke shaft lever.
2. Insert the specified gauge between the top of the choke valve and the wall of the air horn. Refer to the Specifications Chart.
3. An adjustment will be necessary if a slight drag is not obtained as the drill shank is being removed.
4. Adjust by bending the fast idle link at an angle, until the correct valve opening has been obtained.

Choke Vacuum Kick Adjustment

NOTE: The test can be made on or off the vehicle.

1. If the adjustment is to be made with the engine running, back off the fast idle speed screw until the choke can be closed to the kick position with the engine at curb idle. (Note the number of screw turns required so that the fast idle can be returned to the original adjustment.)
2. If an auxiliary vacuum source is to be used, open the throttle valve (engine not running) and move the choke to the closed position. Release the throttle first, then release the choke.

   When using an auxiliary vacuum source, disconnect the vacuum hose from the carburetor and connect it to the hose from the vacuum supply with a small length of tube to act as a fitting. Removal of the hose from the diaphragm may require sufficient force to damage the system. Apply a vacuum of 15 or more in. of mercury.
3. Insert the gauge between the top of the choke valve and the wall of the air horn. Refer to the Specifications Chart.
4. Apply sufficient closing pressure on the lever to which the choke rod attaches, to provide a minimum choke valve opening without distortion of the diaphragm link.

NOTE: The cylindrical stem of the diaphragm extends as the internal spring is compressed. This spring must be fully compressed for proper measurement of the vacuum kick adjustment.

5. Adjustment is necessary if a

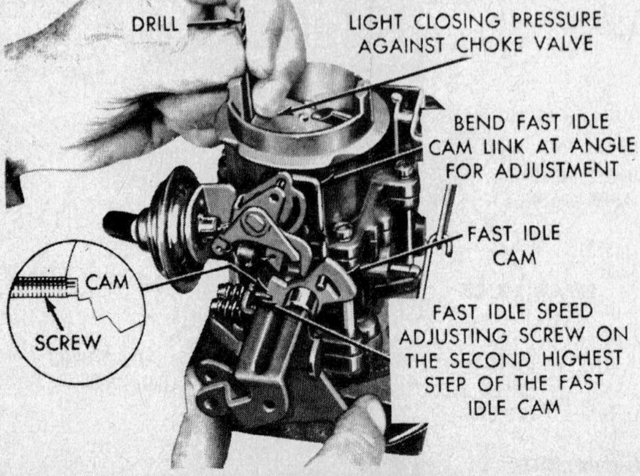
DRILL
LIGHT CLOSING PRESSURE AGAINST CHOKE VALVE
BEND FAST IDLE CAM LINK AT ANGLE FOR ADJUSTMENT
FAST IDLE CAM
CAM
SCREW
FAST IDLE SPEED ADJUSTING SCREW ON THE SECOND HIGHEST STEP OF THE FAST IDLE CAM

Fast idle cam adjustment

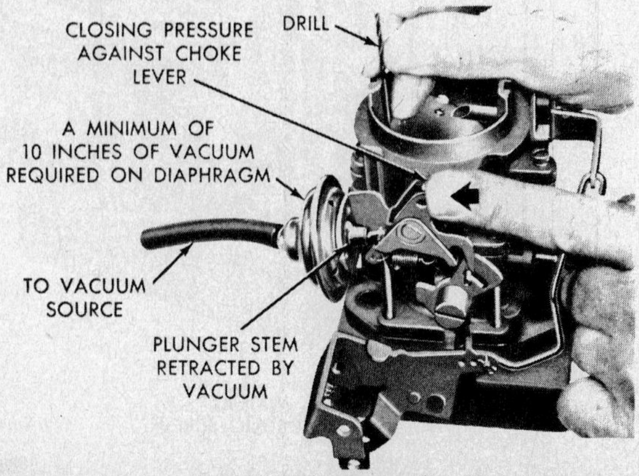
CLOSING PRESSURE AGAINST CHOKE LEVER
DRILL
A MINIMUM OF 10 INCHES OF VACUUM REQUIRED ON DIAPHRAGM
TO VACUUM SOURCE
PLUNGER STEM RETRACTED BY VACUUM

Vacuum kick adjustment

slight drag is not obtained when removing the gauge. Shorten or lengthen the diaphragm link to obtain the correct choke valve opening. Length changes should be made by carefully opening or closing the U-bend provided in the link. Improper bending causes contact between the U-section and the diaphragm assembly.

NOTE: Do not apply a twisting or bending force to diaphragm.

6. After completing adjustments, reinstall the vacuum hose on the correct carburetor fitting.
7. Return the fast idle screw to its original location if it was disturbed. Make the following check. With no vacuum applied to the diaphragm, the choke valve should move freely between the open and closed positions. If the movement is not free, examine the linkage for misalignment or interferences caused by the bending operation.

Choke Unloader (Wide Open Kick) Adjustment

1. With the throttle valve in the wide open position, insert a drill gauge between the upper edge of the choke valve and the inner wall of the air horn. Refer to the Specifications Chart.
2. With a finger lightly pressing against the shaft lever, a slight drag should be felt as the drill is being withdrawn.
3. Adjust by bending the unloader tang on the throttle lever until the correct opening has been obtained.

Fast Idle Speed Adjustment (On the Vehicle)

1. With the engine off and transmission in Neutral, open the throttle slightly.
2. On standard carburetors, close the choke valve about 20 degrees, then allow the throttle to close. The fast idle speed screw should be turned in or out to secure the specified speed.
3. On the CAP carburetors, close the choke valve until the fast idle screw can be positioned on the second highest speed step of the fast idle cam.
4. Start engine and let the idle speed stabilize. Turn the fast idle speed screw in or out to obtain a fast idle of 1800 RPM.
5. To provide the correct throttle closing torque, reposition the fast idle speed screw on the cam after each adjustment.

Spring Staged Choke Adjustment

1. Push the hub lever to the closed choke position.
2. There should be between 0.010-0.040 in. distance between the shaft and the hub levers.
3. If an adjustment is necessary, bend the hub lever tang until the correct opening has been obtained.

Choke Adjustment

1. Loosen the mounting post locknut.
2. Turn the mounting post with a screwdriver until the index mark on the disc is positioned as listed in the specifications chart.
3. Hold in this position with a screwdriver and tighten with the locknut.

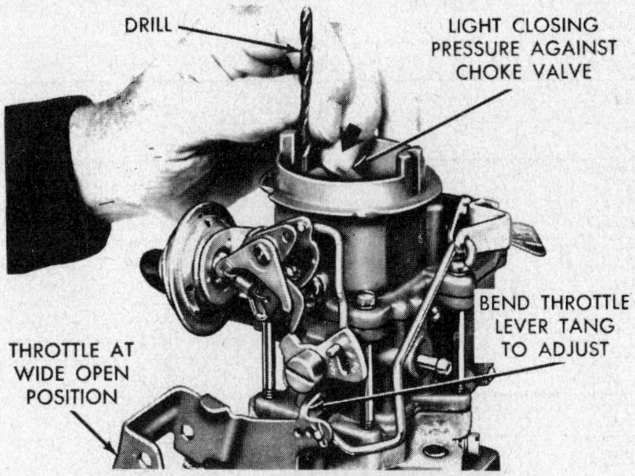
DRILL
LIGHT CLOSING PRESSURE AGAINST CHOKE VALVE
BEND THROTTLE LEVER TANG TO ADJUST
THROTTLE AT WIDE OPEN POSITION
Choke unloader adjustment wide open kick

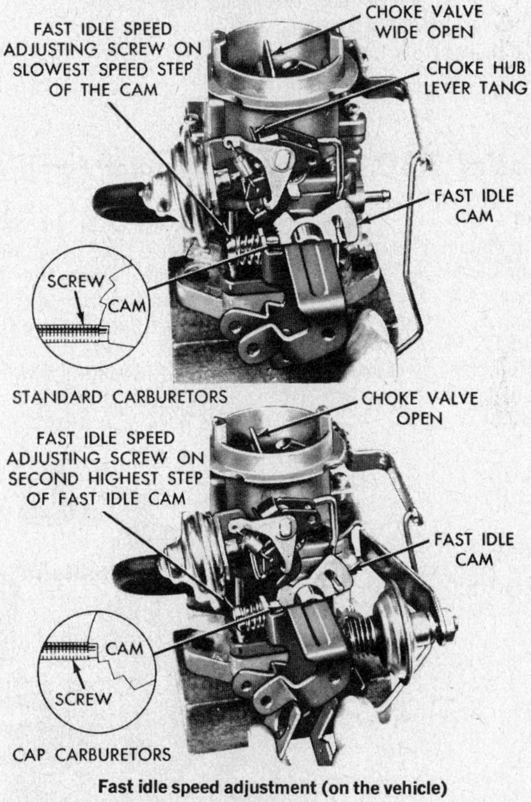
FAST IDLE SPEED ADJUSTING SCREW ON SLOWEST SPEED STEP OF THE CAM
CHOKE VALVE WIDE OPEN
CHOKE HUB LEVER TANG
FAST IDLE CAM
SCREW
CAM
STANDARD CARBURETORS
CHOKE VALVE OPEN
FAST IDLE SPEED ADJUSTING SCREW ON SECOND HIGHEST STEP OF FAST IDLE CAM
FAST IDLE CAM
CAM
SCREW
CAP CARBURETORS
Fast idle speed adjustment (on the vehicle)

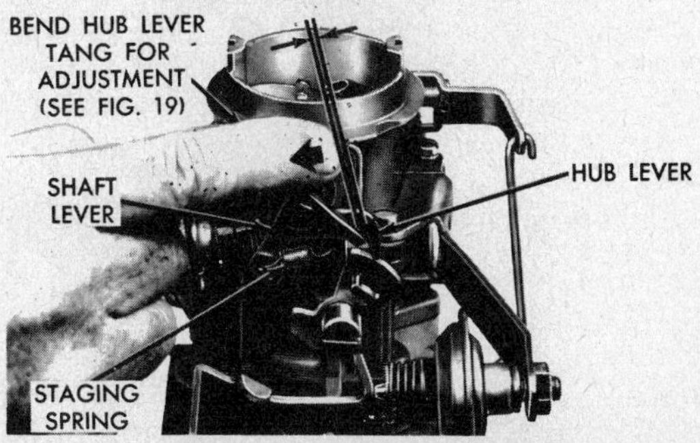
BEND HUB LEVER TANG FOR ADJUSTMENT (SEE FIG. 19)
HUB LEVER
SHAFT LEVER
STAGING SPRING
Spring staged choke adjustment

CARTER BBS SPECIFICATIONS

DODGE AND PLYMOUTH

Year	Model ②	Float Level (in.)	Accelerator Pump Travel (in.)	Bowl Vent (in.)	Choke Unloader (in.)	Fast Idle Cam Position ①	Choke Vacuum Kick ①
1967	4286S	1/4	—	1/16	3/16	48	20
	4287S	1/4	—	1/16	3/16	48	41
	4302S	1/4	—	1/16	3/16	48	20
	4303S	1/4	—	1/16	3/16	48	28
1968	4414S	1/4	—	1/16	3/16	48	20
	4415S	1/4	—	1/16	3/16	48	35
1969	4601S	1/4	—	1/16	3/16	48	35
	4602S	1/4	—	1/16	3/16	48	35
1970	4715S	1/4	—	1/32	3/16	48	35
	4716S	1/4	—	1/32	3/16	48	48
	4717S	1/4	5/16	9/32	3/16	48	35
	4718S	1/4	5/16	9/32	3/16	48	48
1971	4955S	1/4	5/16	17/64	3/16	48	35
	4956S	1/4	5/16	17/64	3/16	48	35

① Indicates the drill bit number. See "Mechanics Data"
② Model numbers located on tag or casting
Note: Automatic choke setting 2 Rich for all BBS

Model BBD

Introduction

The BBD carburetor is a two barrel unit. It has been equipped with CAP (Cleaner Air Package) and CAS (Cleaner Air System) packages and now uses ECS (Evaporation Control System) on the newer models. It is also equipped with a dashpot on some applications.

Accelerator Pump Adjustment

Except 1 1/4 in. Bore Units

1. Back off the idle adjusting screw. Open the choke valve so that the fast idle cam allows the throttle valves to finally close. Be sure that the pump connector rod is installed in the center hole of the throttle lever.
2. With the throttle valves closed tightly, measure the distance between the top of the air horn and the end pump plunger shaft. If the dimension is not as specified, bend the pump connector rod at an angle on the rod until the correct setting is obtained.

Fast Idle Cam Position Adjustment

1. With the fast idle speed adjust-

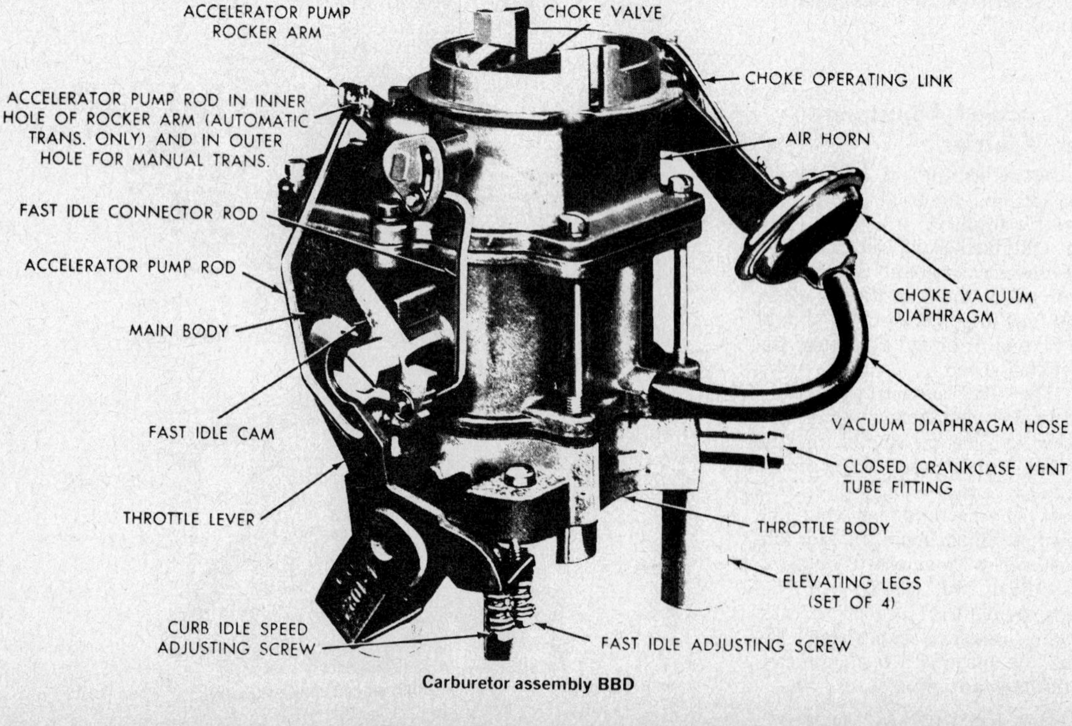
ACCELERATOR PUMP ROCKER ARM
CHOKE VALVE
ACCELERATOR PUMP ROD IN INNER HOLE OF ROCKER ARM (AUTOMATIC TRANS. ONLY) AND IN OUTER HOLE FOR MANUAL TRANS.
CHOKE OPERATING LINK
AIR HORN
FAST IDLE CONNECTOR ROD
ACCELERATOR PUMP ROD
CHOKE VACUUM DIAPHRAGM
MAIN BODY
FAST IDLE CAM
VACUUM DIAPHRAGM HOSE
CLOSED CRANKCASE VENT TUBE FITTING
THROTTLE LEVER
THROTTLE BODY
ELEVATING LEGS (SET OF 4)
CURB IDLE SPEED ADJUSTING SCREW
FAST IDLE ADJUSTING SCREW

Carburetor assembly BBD

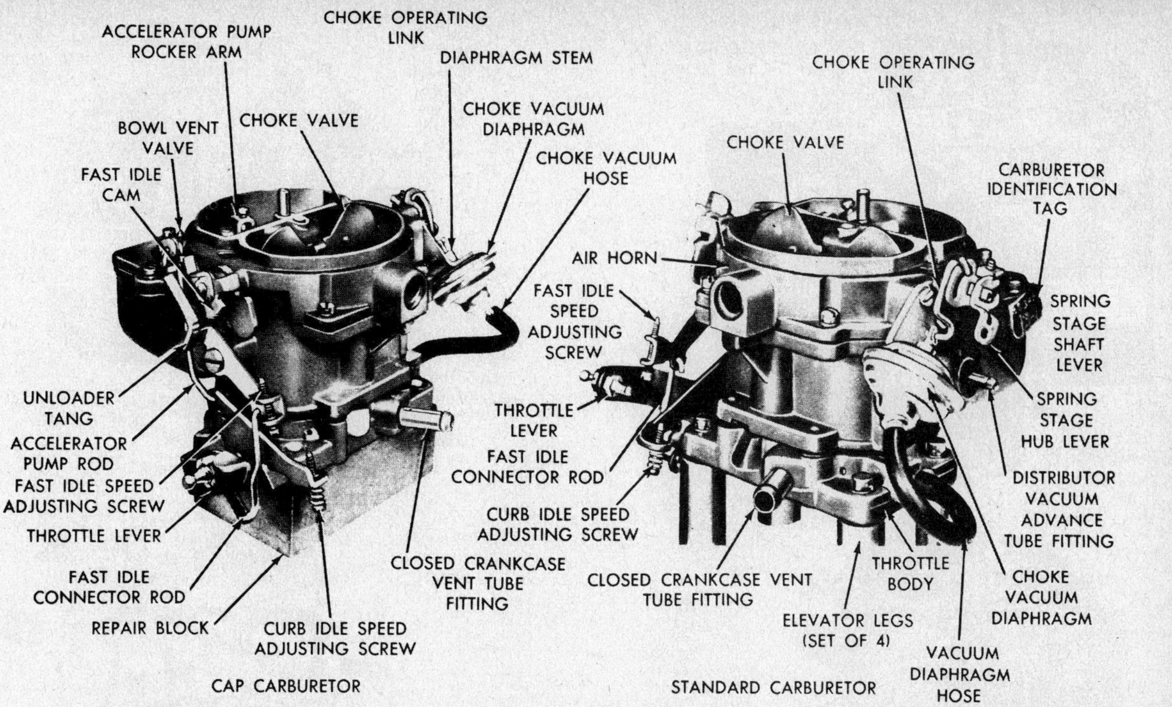
ACCELERATOR PUMP ROCKER ARM
CHOKE OPERATING LINK
DIAPHRAGM STEM
BOWL VENT VALVE
CHOKE VALVE
CHOKE VACUUM DIAPHRAGM
FAST IDLE CAM
CHOKE VACUUM HOSE
UNLOADER TANG
ACCELERATOR PUMP ROD
FAST IDLE SPEED ADJUSTING SCREW
THROTTLE LEVER
FAST IDLE CONNECTOR ROD
REPAIR BLOCK
CURB IDLE SPEED ADJUSTING SCREW
CLOSED CRANKCASE VENT TUBE FITTING
CAP CARBURETOR
CHOKE OPERATING LINK
CHOKE VALVE
CARBURETOR IDENTIFICATION TAG
AIR HORN
FAST IDLE SPEED ADJUSTING SCREW
SPRING STAGE SHAFT LEVER
THROTTLE LEVER
SPRING STAGE HUB LEVER
FAST IDLE CONNECTOR ROD
DISTRIBUTOR VACUUM ADVANCE TUBE FITTING
CURB IDLE SPEED ADJUSTING SCREW
THROTTLE BODY
CHOKE VACUUM DIAPHRAGM
CLOSED CRANKCASE VENT TUBE FITTING
ELEVATOR LEGS (SET OF 4)
VACUUM DIAPHRAGM HOSE
STANDARD CARBURETOR

Carburetor assembly BBD

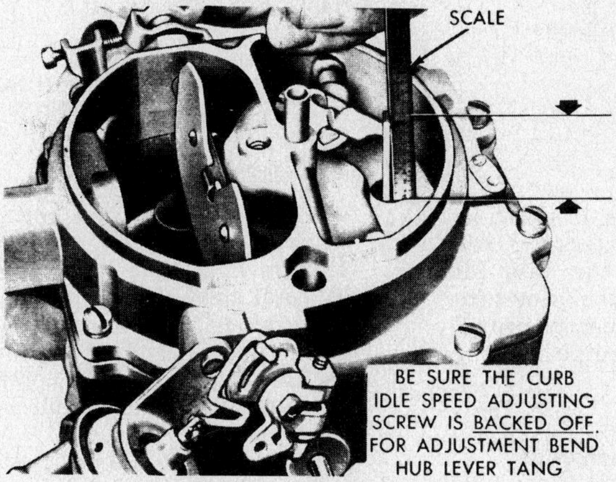
SCALE
BE SURE THE CURB IDLE SPEED ADJUSTING SCREW IS BACKED OFF. FOR ADJUSTMENT BEND HUB LEVER TANG

Accelerator pump adjustment

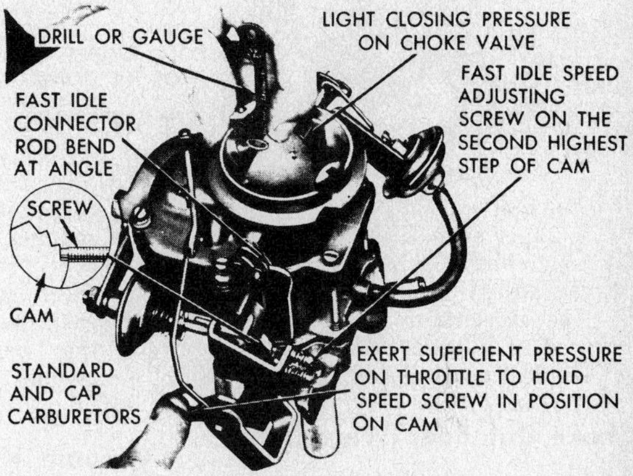
DRILL OR GAUGE
LIGHT CLOSING PRESSURE ON CHOKE VALVE
FAST IDLE SPEED ADJUSTING SCREW ON THE SECOND HIGHEST STEP OF CAM
FAST IDLE CONNECTOR ROD BEND AT ANGLE
SCREW
CAM
STANDARD AND CAP CARBURETORS
EXERT SUFFICIENT PRESSURE ON THROTTLE TO HOLD SPEED SCREW IN POSITION ON CAM

Fast idle cam position adjustment

ing screw contacting the second highest speed step on the fast idle cam, move the choke valve toward the closed position with light pressure on the choke shaft lever.

2. Insert the specified drill (refer to Specifications), between the choke valve and the wall of the air horn. An adjustment will be necessary if a slight drag is not obtained as the drill is being removed.
3. If an adjustment is required, bend the fast idle connector rod at the lower angle. On 1967-69 units, bend the stop on the choke shaft.

Accelerator Pump & Bowl Vent (ECS)

1 ¼ in. bore units

1. Back off the idle speed adjusting screw to completely close the throttle valves. Open the choke valve so that the fast idle cam allows the throttle valves to seat in the bores.
2. Be sure that the accelerator pump operating rod is in the medium stroke hole in the throttle lever.
3. Close the throttle valves tightly. Measure the distance between the top of the vent valve plastic

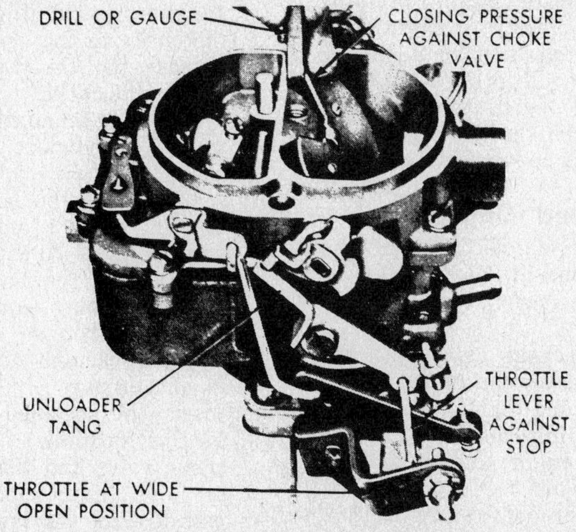
DRILL OR GAUGE
CLOSING PRESSURE AGAINST CHOKE VALVE
UNLOADER TANG
THROTTLE LEVER AGAINST STOP
THROTTLE AT WIDE OPEN POSITION

Choke unloader adjustment wide open kick

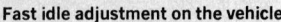

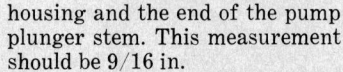

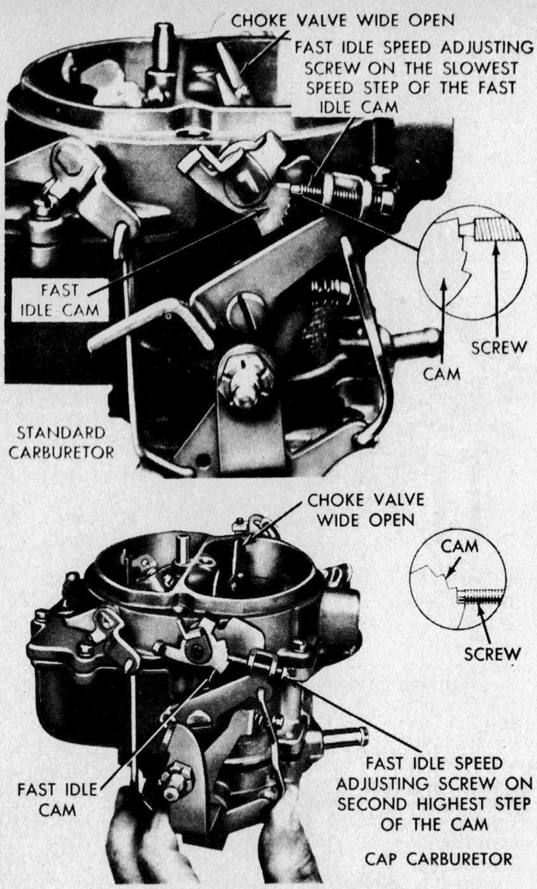
CHOKE VALVE WIDE OPEN
FAST IDLE SPEED ADJUSTING SCREW ON THE SLOWEST SPEED STEP OF THE FAST IDLE CAM
FAST IDLE CAM
SCREW
CAM
STANDARD CARBURETOR
CHOKE VALVE WIDE OPEN
CAM
SCREW
FAST IDLE CAM
FAST IDLE SPEED ADJUSTING SCREW ON SECOND HIGHEST STEP OF THE CAM
CAP CARBURETOR

Fast idle adjustment on the vehicle

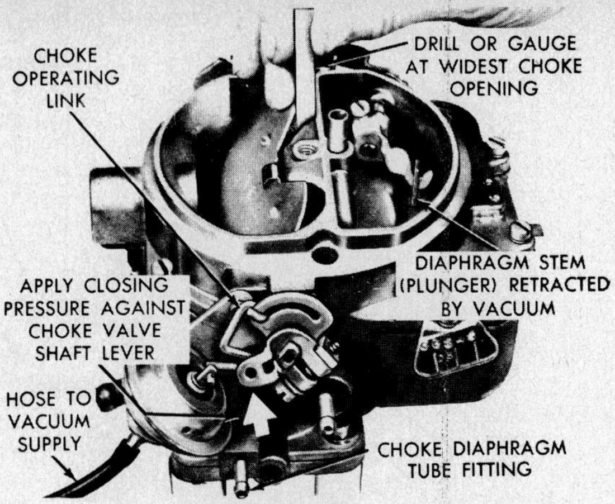
CHOKE OPERATING LINK
DRILL OR GAUGE AT WIDEST CHOKE OPENING
APPLY CLOSING PRESSURE AGAINST CHOKE VALVE SHAFT LEVER
DIAPHRAGM STEM (PLUNGER) RETRACTED BY VACUUM
HOSE TO VACUUM SUPPLY
CHOKE DIAPHRAGM TUBE FITTING

Vacuum kick adjustment

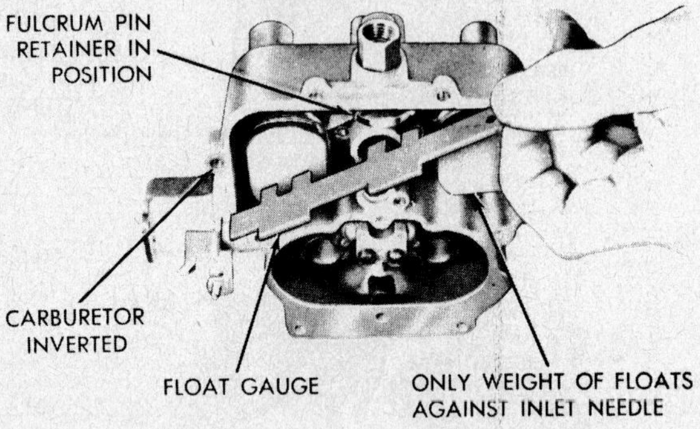
FULCRUM PIN RETAINER IN POSITION
CARBURETOR INVERTED
FLOAT GAUGE
ONLY WEIGHT OF FLOATS AGAINST INLET NEEDLE

Float level adjustment

housing and the end of the pump plunger stem. This measurement should be 9/16 in.

4. To adjust the pump travel, bend the accelerator pump operating rod at a lower angle, until the correct pump travel has been obtained.

Choke Unloader (Wide Open Kick)

1. Hold the throttle valves in the wide open position. Insert the specified drill (see Specifications) between the upper edge of the choke valve and the inner wall of the air horn.
2. With a finger lightly pressing against the valve, a slight drag should be felt as the drill is being withdrawn. If an adjustment is necessary, bend the unloader tang on the throttle lever until the correct opening has been obtained.

Fast Idle Speed (On Vehicle)

1. With the engine off and the transmission in Park or Neutral position, open the throttle slightly.
2. Close the choke valve until the fast idle screw can be positioned on the second highest speed step of the fast idle cam.
3. Start the engine and let the idle stabilize. Turn the fast idle speed screw in or out to obtain 1800 rpm.
4. Stopping the engine between adjustments is not necessary. However, reposition the fast idle speed screw on the cam after each speed adjustment to provide the correct throttle closing torque.

Vacuum Kick Adjustment

1. If the adjustment is to be made with the engine running, disconnect the fast idle linkage to allow the choke to close to the kick position with engine at curb idle. If an auxiliary vacuum source is to be used, open the throttle valves (engine not running) and move the choke to the closed position. Release the throttle first, then release the choke.
2. When using an auxiliary vacuum source, disconnect the vacuum hose from the carburetor and connect it to the hose from the vacuum supply with a small length of tube to act as a fitting. Removal of the hose from the diaphragm may require sufficient force to damage the system. Apply a vacuum of 10 or more in. of mercury.
3. Insert the specified drill (refer to Specifications) between the choke valve and the wall of the air horn. Apply sufficient closing pressure on the lever to which the choke rod attaches to provide a minimum choke valve opening without distortion of the diaphragm link. Note that the cylindrical stem of the diaphragm will extend as the internal spring is compressed. This spring must be fully compressed for proper measurement of the vacuum kick of adjustment.
4. An adjustment will be necessary if a slight drag is not obtained as the drill is being removed. Shorten or lengthen the diaphragm link to obtain the correct choke opening. Length changes should be made carefully by bending (opening or closing) the bend provided in the diaphragm link.

Caution Do not apply twisting or bending force to the diaphragm.

5. Reinstall the vacuum hose on the correct carburetor fitting. Return the fast idle linkage to its original condition if it was disturbed, as suggested in Step 1.
6. Make the following check: With no vacuum applied to the diaphragm, the choke valve should move freely between the open and closed positions. If its movement is not free, examine the linkage for misalignment or interference caused by the bending operation. Repeat the adjustment if necessary to provide proper link operation.

Float Level

1. Invert the carburetor so that the weight of the floats is the only force on the needle and seat.
2. Use a T-scale to check the float level. Measure the area from the surface of the fuel bowl to the crown of each float at center.
3. To adjust, hold the floats on the bottom of the bowl and bend the float lip to give the specified dimension.

Bowl Vent Adjustment

1 ½ in. bore units

1. Open the choke valve so that the fast idle cam allows the valves to close to curb idle.
2. Be sure that the pump operating rod is in the long stroke hole in the throttle lever. Remove the bowl vent valve cover if it was not previously done.
3. On ECS units, close the throttle valves tightly. Using a narrow ruler, measure the distance from the top of the bowl vent valve to the top of the air horn casting.

On CAS units, with the throttle valves closed (curb idle), there should be the specified clearance between the bowl vent valve and the seat on the air horn. Measure at the outermost or the longest dimension.

4. To adjust, bend the lift arm until the correct clearance has been obtained.

CARTER BBD SPECIFICATIONS

CHRYSLER, DODGE AND PLYMOUTH

Year	Model ④	Float Level (in.)	Accelerator Pump Travel (in.)	Bowl Vent (in.)	Choke Unloader (in.)	Choke Vacuum Kick ①	Fast Idle Cam Position ①	Automatic Choke Adjustment
1967	4113SA	1/4	—	1/16	1/4	15	41	2 Rich
	4114SA	1/4	—	1/16	1/4	1/8	41	2 Rich
	4115SA	1/4	1 1/16	—	1/4	15	41	Index
	4116SA	1/4	1 1/16	—	1/4	1/8	41	Index
	4296S	5/16	29/32	1/16	1/4	20	42	2 Rich
	4297S	5/16	29/32	1/16	1/4	42	42	2 Rich
	4306S	5/16	1	3/64	1/4	20	42	2 Rich
	4307S	5/16	1	3/64	1/4	30	42	2 Rich
	4463S	1/4	—	1/16	1/4	28	41	2 Rich
1968	441S	1/4	—	1/16	1/4	4	50	2 Rich
	4417S	1/4	—	1/16	1/4	41	50	2 Rich
	4420S	1/4	—	1/16	1/4	4	41	2 Rich
	4421S	1/4	—	1/16	1/4	28	41	2 Rich
	4422S	5/16	29/32	3/64	1/4	1	30	2 Rich
	4423S	5/16	29/32	3/64	1/4	16	30	2 Rich
	4578S	11/32	1	3/64	1/4	11/64	30	2 Rich
1969	4605S	1/4	—	1/16	1/4	20	41	Index
	4606S	1/4	—	1/16	1/4	41	41	Index
	4607S	1/4	—	1/16	1/4	20	41	Index
	4608S	1/4	—	1/16	1/4	28	41	Index
	4613S	5/16	1	1/16	1/4	20	30	2 Rich
	4614S	5/16	1	1/16	1/4	20	30	2 Rich
	4474S	5/16	1	1/16	1/4	20	30	2 Rich
1970	4721S	1/4	—	1/32	1/4	20	41	Index
	4722S	1/4	—	1/32	1/4	20	41	Index
	4723S	1/4	—	15/64	1/4	20	41	Index
	4724S	1/4	—	15/64	1/4	20	41	Index
	4725S	11/32	1	1/32	1/4	20	28	2 Rich
	4726S	11/32	1	1/32	1/4	28	28	2 Rich
	4727S	11/32	1	1/8	1/4	20	28	2 Rich
	4728S	11/32	1	3/16	1/4	28	28	2 Rich
	4894S	11/32	1	1/32	1/4	28	28	2 Rich
	4895S	1/4	1	1/32	1/4	20	41	Index

Year	Model ④	Float Level (in.)	Accelerator Pump Travel (in.)	Bowl Vent (in.)	Choke Unloader (in.)	Choke Vacuum Kick ①	Fast Idle Cam Position ①	Automatic Choke Adjustment
1971	4957S	1/4	0.200②	13/64	1/4	20	41	Index
	4958S	1/4	0.200②	13/64	1/4	20	41	Index
	4961S	5/16	1	3/16	1/4	20	20	2 Rich
	4962S	5/16	1	3/16	1/4	28	28	2 Rich
1972	6149S	1/4	0.225③	15/64	1/4	25	41	Fixed
	6150S	1/4	0.225③	15/64	1/4	25	41	Fixed
	6151S	1/4	0.225③	15/64	1/4	25	41	Fixed
	6152S	1/4	0.225③	15/64	1/4	25	41	Fixed
1973	6316SA	1/4	0.242③	—	1/4	24	41	Fixed
	6317SA	1/4	0.242③	—	1/4	30	41	Fixed
	6343SA	1/4	0.242③	—	1/4	24	41	Fixed
	6344SA	1/4	0.242③	—	1/4	24	41	Fixed

① Indicates the drill bit number. See "Mechanics Data"
② Throttle closed
③ At idle
④ Model numbers located on the tag or casting

Model YF

Introduction

The YF carburetor is a single barrel downdraft carburetor with a diaphragm typc accelerator pump and diaphragm operated metering rods.

Float Adjustment

1. Invert the air horn assembly and check the clearance from the top of the float to the surface of the air horn with a T-scale. The air horn should be held at eye level when gauging and the float arm should be resting on the needle pin.
2. Do not exert pressure on the needle valve when measuring or adjusting the float. Bend the float arm as necessary to adjust the float level.

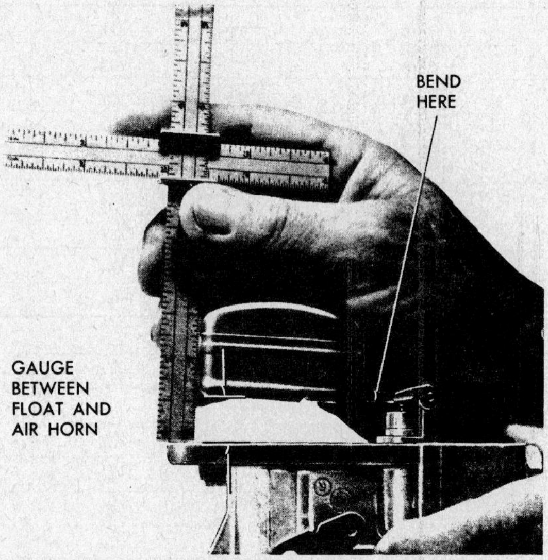
BEND
HERE
GAUGE
BETWEEN
FLOAT AND
AIR HORN

Float level adjustment

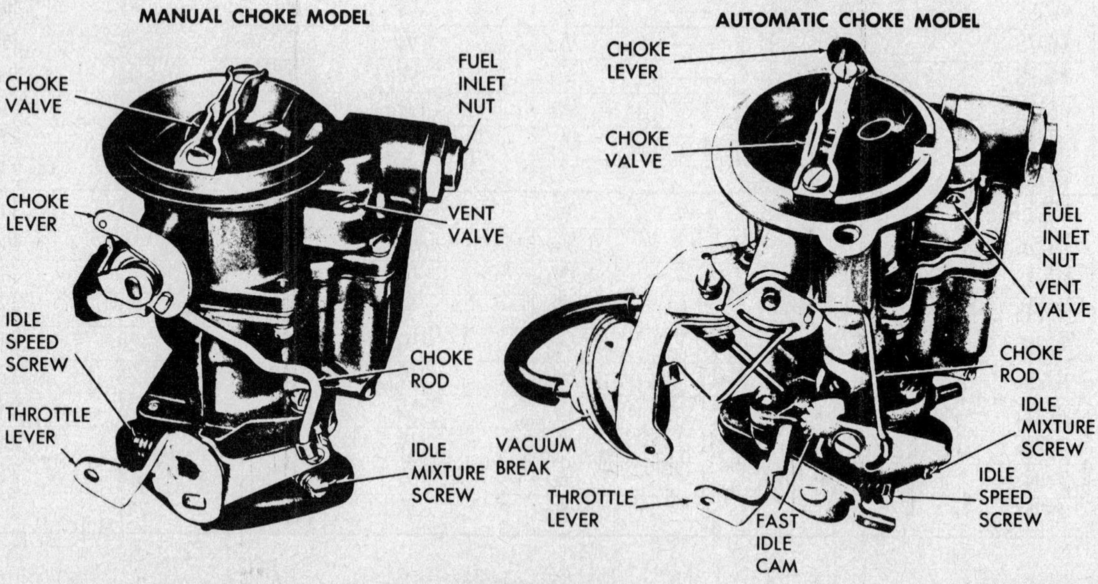
MANUAL CHOKE MODEL
CHOKE VALVE
FUEL INLET NUT
CHOKE LEVER
VENT VALVE
IDLE SPEED SCREW
CHOKE ROD
THROTTLE LEVER
IDLE MIXTURE SCREW
AUTOMATIC CHOKE MODEL
CHOKE LEVER
CHOKE VALVE
FUEL INLET NUT
VENT VALVE
CHOKE ROD
IDLE MIXTURE SCREW
VACUUM BREAK
IDLE SPEED SCREW
THROTTLE LEVER
FAST IDLE CAM

Carter YF carburetor

Caution Do not bend the tab at the end of the float arm as it prevents the float from striking the bottom of the fuel bowl when empty.

Accelerator Pump Adjustment

1. Seat the throttle valve in the bore of the carburetor.
2. Press down on the upper end of the diaphragm shaft until it bottoms.
3. The metering rod arm should now contact the pump lifter link at the outer end nearest the springs.
4. To make the adjustment, bend the pump connector link at its lower angle.

Metering Rod Adjustment

1. Back out the idle speed adjusting screw until the throttle plate is seated fully in its bore.
2. Press down on the upper end of the diaphragm shaft until the diaphragm bottoms in the vacuum chamber.
3. The metering rod should contact the bottom of the metering rod well and lifter link at the outer end nearest the springs and at the supporting link.
4. On models not equipped with an adjusting screw, adjust by bending the lip of the metering rod arm to which the metering rod is attached.
5. On models with an adjusting screw, turn the screw until the metering rod just bottoms in the body casting. For final adjustment, turn the screw one additional turn clockwise.

Idle Vent Adjustment

1. This adjustment should not be made until the accelerator pump and metering rod adjustments have been completed. Install the bowl cover and air horn assembly.
2. With the throttle valve tightly closed, the specified clearance should exist between the idle vent valve and the inside of the bowl cover.
3. Adjust the idle vent screw as required.

Fast Idle Cam Adjustment

1. Open the throttle wide enough to allow full closing of the choke valve. Be sure that the fast idle screw is not contacting the fast idle cam.
2. Close the throttle valve and the fast idle cam should revolve to the fast idle position.
3. On 1967-70 Fords, the clearance is measured between the throttle valve and the throttle bore on the side opposite the idle port.
4. On 1971-72 Ford models, the clearance is measured between the lower edge of the choke valve and the air horn wall.
5. On models other than Ford with automatic choke, the index mark on the fast idle cam should line up with the upper edge of the tang on the throttle lever. If adjustment is necessary, bend the fast idle tang to achieve correct alignment.

Choke Unloader Adjustment

1. With the throttle valve held wide open and the choke valve held in the closed position, bend the unloader tang on the throttle lever to obtain the specified clearance between the lower edge of the choke valve and the air horn wall.

Automatic Choke Adjustment

1. Loosen the choke cover retaining screws.
2. Turn the choke over so that the index mark on the cover lines up with the specified mark on the choke housing.

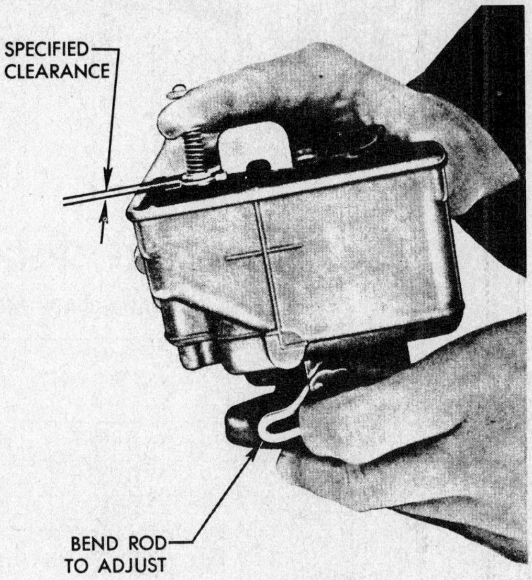
SPECIFIED CLEARANCE
BEND ROD TO ADJUST

Accelerator pump adjustment

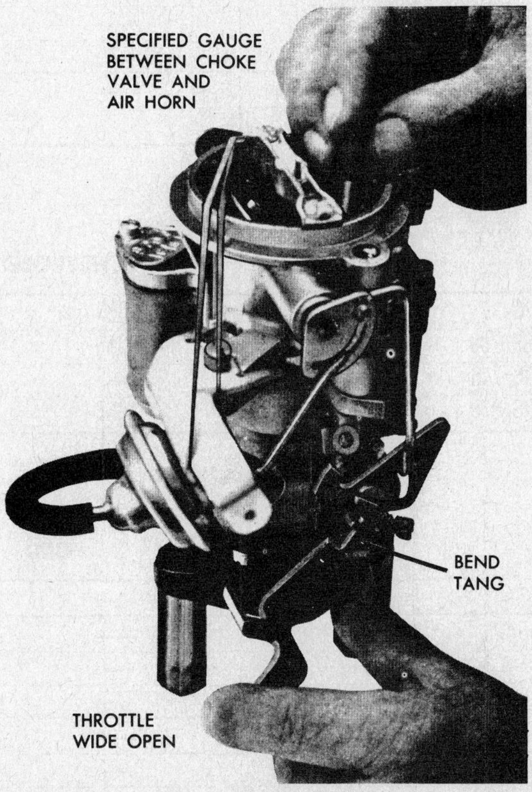
SPECIFIED GAUGE BETWEEN CHOKE VALVE AND AIR HORN
BEND TANG
THROTTLE WIDE OPEN

Choke unloader adjustment

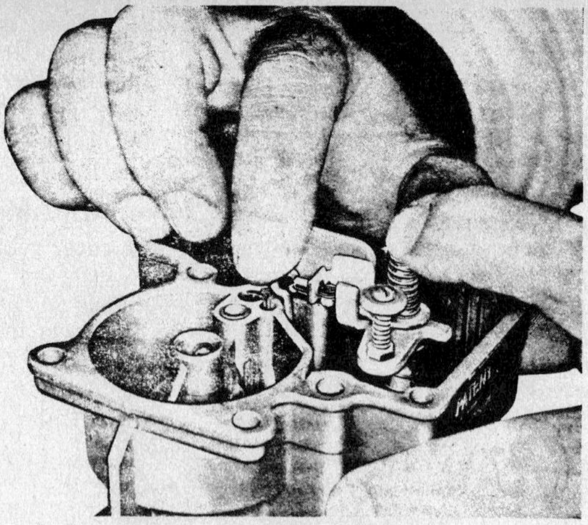

Metering rod adjustment

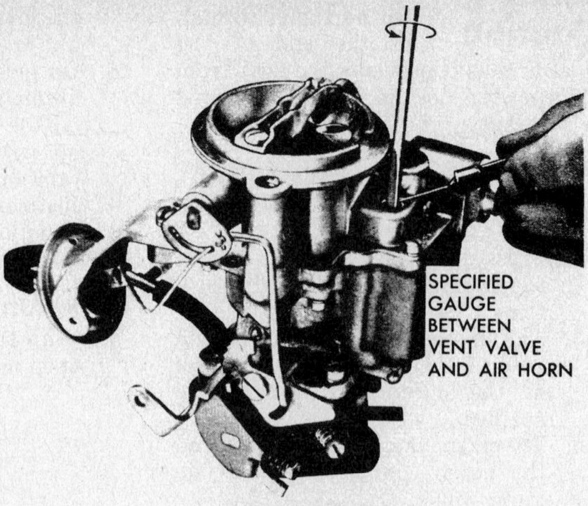
SPECIFIED
GAUGE
BETWEEN
VENT VALVE
AND AIR HORN

Idle vent adjustment

CARTER YF SPECIFICATIONS

AMERICAN MOTORS

Year	Model ①	Float Level (in.)	Idle Vent (in.)	Fast Idle Cam (in.)	Unloader (in.)	Choke
1970	4767S	29/64	0.052	2300 RPM	0.300	Index
	4768S	29/64	0.052	2300 RPM	0.325	Index
	4769S	29/64	0.055	2300 RPM	0.300	Index
	4770S	29/64	0.055	2300 RPM	0.300	Index
	4978S	29/64	0.055	2300 RPM	0.300	1 Rich
1971	6038S	29/64	—	2300 RPM	0.300	Index
	6093S	29/64	—	2300 RPM	0.300	Index
	6094S	29/64	—	2300 RPM	0.300	1 Rich
	6095S	29/64	—	2300 RPM	0.300	Index
	6096S	29/64	—	2300 RPM	0.300	1 Rich
1972	6199S	29/64	—	1600 RPM	0.300	Index
	6200S	29/64	—	1600 RPM	0.300	Index

CHEVROLET

Year	Model ①	Float Level (in.)	Idle Vent (in.)	Fast Idle Cam (in.)	Unloader (in.)	Choke
1967	4367S	7/32	0.065	0.015	0.250	Index
	4368S, 78S	7/32	0.065	0.015	0.250	Index
	4373S, 74S	7/32	—	0.015	0.250	Index
	4377S, 87S	7/32	0.065	0.015	0.250	Index

FORD

Year	Model ①	Float Level (in.)	Idle Vent (in.)	Fast Idle Cam (in.)	Unloader (in.)	Choke
1967	C7ZF-A	7/32	—	0.065	0.250	1 Rich
1968	C8DF-A	7/32	—	0.035	0.280	Index
	C8DF-B	7/32	—	0.046	0.280	1 Lean
	C8AF-V	7/32	—	0.035	0.280	Index
1969	C8AF-BF	7/32	—	0.035	0.280	Index
	C8DF-G	7/32	—	0.046	0.280	Index
	C8DF-H	7/32	—	0.040	0.280	1 Lean

Year	Model ①	Float Level (in.)	Idle Vent (in.)	Fast Idle Cam (in.)	Unloader (in.)	Choke
1970	D0AF-A	3/8	—	0.029	0.250	Index
	D0AF-B	3/8	—	0.025	0.250	1 Lean
	D0DF-L	3/8	—	0.036	0.250	Index
	D0DF-M	3/8	—	0.031	0.250	Index
	D0DF-N	7/32	—	0.035	0.280	Index
	D0DF-R	7/32	—	0.036	0.280	1 Rich
	D0DF-S	7/32	—	0.035	0.280	Index
	D0DF-T	3/8	—	0.031	0.250	Index
	D0DF-U	7/32	—	0.036	0.280	1 Rich
	D0DF-V	3/8	—	0.036	0.250	Index
1971	D1DF-EA	3/8	—	0.105	0.250	Index
	D1DF-GA, HA	3/8	—	0.170	0.250	Index
	D1DF-JA, LA	3/8	—	0.140	0.250	Index
	D1DF-KA, MA	3/8	—	0.140	0.250	Index
	D1DF-PA	3/8	—	0.190	0.250	Index
	D1DF-RA	3/8	—	0.220	0.250	Index
1972	D2DF-AA	3/8	—	0.105	0.280	Index
	D2DF-BA	3/8	—	0.170	0.250	Index
	D2DF-CA	3/8	—	0.170	0.250	Index
	D2DF-DA	3/8	—	0.140	0.250	1 Rich
	D2DF-EA	3/8	—	0.140	0.250	1 Rich
	D2AF-JA	3/8	—	0.220	0.250	1 Lean
1973	D3DF-AA	3/8	—	0.170	0.250	Index
	D3DF-CA	3/8	—	0.140	0.250	1 Rich
			OLDSMOBILE			
1967	4072SA	7/32	0.060	0.015	1/4	Index
	4367S	7/32	0.060	0.015	1/4	Index

① Model number located on the tag or casting

Model RBS

Introduction

The Carter RBS is a single barrel carburetor made from aluminum casting. It is equipped with a vacuum piston automatic choke. The 1973 model uses an EGR (Exhaust Gas Recirculation) system.

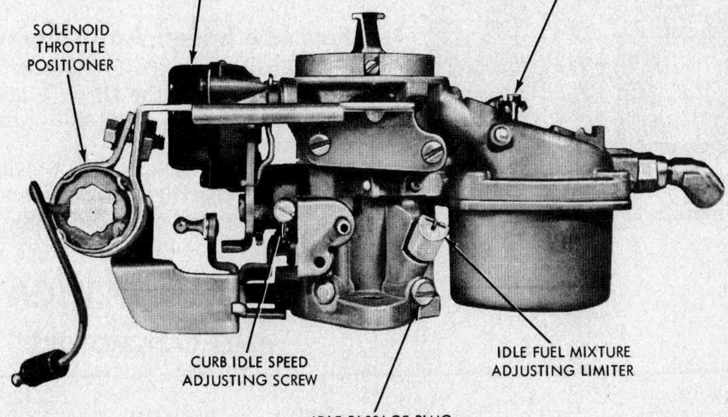
AUTOMATIC CHOKE
ACCELERATING PUMP
SOLENOID THROTTLE POSITIONER
CURB IDLE SPEED ADJUSTING SCREW
IDLE FUEL MIXTURE ADJUSTING LIMITER
IDLE PASSAGE PLUG (DO NOT TURN)

Carburetor assembly RBS

Float Level Adjustment

1. After removing the bowl and the bowl gasket, invert the carburetor so that only the weight of the float is pressing down on the needle and seat assembly.
2. Measure the vertical distance from the casting to the projections at the outer ends of the float.
3. Measure both ends of the float and, if adjustment is necessary, it can be done by holding the lip end of the float bracket with needle nose pliers and bending the float bracket at its narrowest point.

Float Drop Adjustment

With the air horn upright and the float hanging free, measure the vertical distance from the main body casting surface of the fuel bowl to the outer ends of the float on the top side. Adjust by bending the tab at the end of the float arm. The proper setting is 1.250 in.

Accelerator Pump Adjustment

NOTE: The accelerator pump adjustment must be made before adjusting the bowl vent or the choke unloader.

Back out the curb idle adjusting screw and hold the choke valve wide open so that the throttle valve is completely closed. Turn the pump adjust-

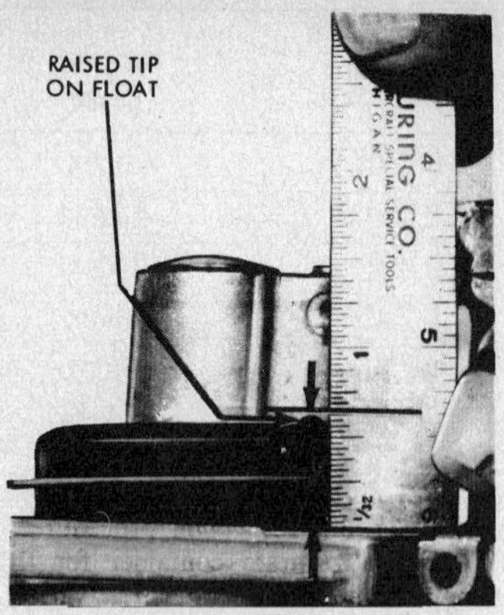
RAISED TIP
ON FLOAT

Float level adjustment

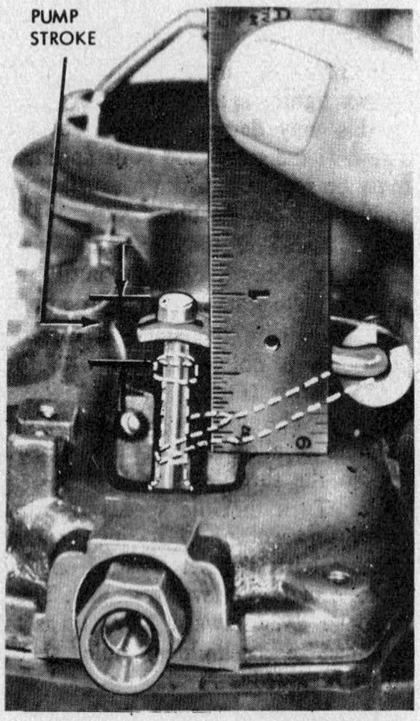
PUMP
STROKE

Accelerator pump adjustment

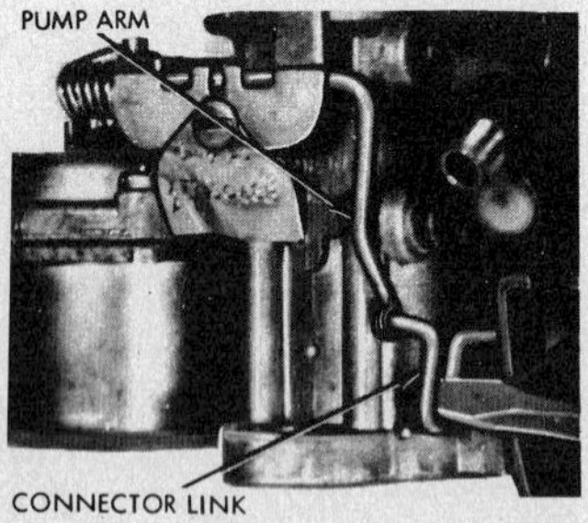
PUMP ARM
CONNECTOR LINK

Accelerator pump adjustment 1970-1973

ing nut until the specified clearance is obtained between the shoulder on the pump shaft and the pump arm. This procedure may be used through 1969.

On later models 1970 and up, the pump stroke is measured as the difference in height between the measured height with the throttle valve fully closed and fully open. To adjust, open or close the pump connector link at the offset portion.

Bowl Vent Adjustment

After adjusting the accelerator pump stroke, close the throttle valve completely and measure the distance between the vent valve and the carburetor casting. To adjust, bend the connector rod at the accelerator pump end.

Fast Idle Cam Adjustment

1967-70

With the choke valve tightly closed and the choke connector rod in the upper end of the slot in the cam, align the cam index with the center of the fast idle tang. Adjust by bending the choke connector rod at the offset portion.

1971-73

Place the fast idle screw on the second step of the fast idle cam and against the shoulder of the high step. Specified clearance should exist between the lower edge of the choke valve and the air horn wall. If adjustment is needed, bend the choke plate connecting rod.

Choke Unloader Adjustment

With the throttle valve wide open, the clearance between the upper edge of the valve and the inner air horn wall should be to specification. If it is not, adjust by bending the tang on the throttle lever.

Fast Idle Speed Adjustment

1. Revolve the fast idle cam until the tang on the throttle lever is aligned with the mark on the cam.
2. Proper clearance should exist between the throttle valve and the carburetor bore on the idle port side.

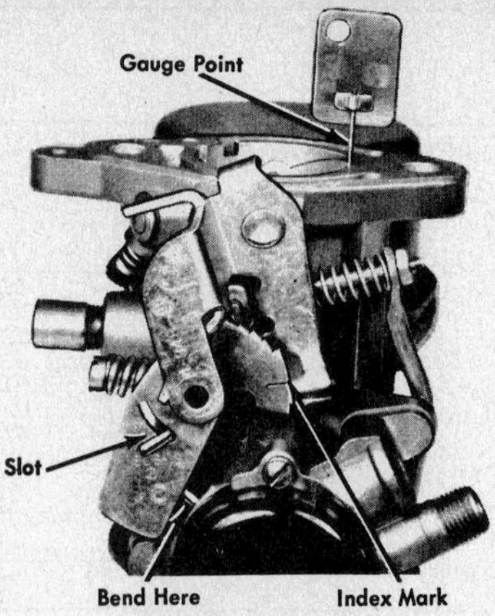
Gauge Point
Slot
Bend Here
Index Mark

Fast idle cam adjustment

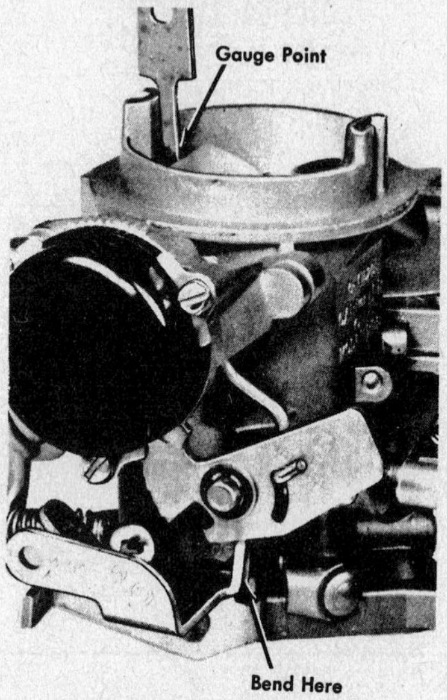
Gauge Point
Bend Here

Choke unloader adjustment

3. If adjustment is required, close the choke valve fully and put the fast idle connector rod against the end of the slot in the cam. Bend the connector rod at the offset portion to align the marks.

Automatic Choke Adjustment

1. Loosen the choke cover retaining screws.
2. Turn the choke cover so that the index mark on the cover lines up with the specified mark on the choke housing.

CARTER RBS SPECIFICATIONS

AMERICAN MOTORS

Year	Model ①	Float Level (in.)	Bowl Vent (in.)	Accelerator Pump (in.)	Fast Idle (rpm)	Fast Idle Throttle Plate (in.)	Choke Unloader (in.)	Choke
1967	3882S	15/32	1/16	—	2000	0.033	1/8	1 Rich
	4470S	9/16	5/64	1/64	2000	0.035	1/8	2 Rich
1968	4626S	9/16	5/64	1/64	2000	0.035	1/8	2 Rich
	4631S	9/16	5/64	1/64	2000	0.035	1/8	Index
	4633S	9/16	5/64	1/64	2000	0.035	3/16	Index
1969	4634S	9/16	5/64	1/64	2000	0.035	3/16	2 Rich
	4666S	9/16	5/64	1/64	2000	0.035	1/8	2 Rich

FORD MOTOR CO.

Year	Model ①	Float Level (in.)	Bowl Vent (in.)	Accelerator Pump (in.)	Fast Idle (rpm)	Fast Idle Throttle Plate (in.)	Choke Unloader (in.)	Choke
1970	D0ZF-C	9/16	—	0.400③	See Text	0.040	0.250	Index
	D0ZF-D	9/16	—	0.400③	See Text	0.046	0.252	1 Rich
	D0ZF-F	9/16	—	0.400③	See Text	—	0.252	1 Rich
1971	D1ZF-HA, LA	9/16	—	0.400③	0.115②	—	0.250	Index
	D1ZF-NA, KA	9/16	—	0.400③	0.115②	—	0.250	1 Rich
1972	D2OF-LA	9/16	—	0.400③	0.115②	—	0.250	Index
	D2OF-MA	9/16	—	0.400③	0.115②	—	0.250	1 Rich
	D2OF-SA	9/16	—	0.400③	0.115②	—	0.250	1 Rich
1973	D3OF-BA	9/16	—	0.420③	0.115②	—	0.250	Index
	D3OF-CA	9/16	—	0.400③	0.115②	—	0.250	Index

① Model numbers located on a tag or on the casting
② At kickdown
③ Closed throttle.

Model WCD

Introduction

This is a two barrel carburetor using a single needle valve even though two floats are provided. On several of these units, the floats operate independently of each other so that the highest float always controls the fuel level. This is necessary when the carburetor is mounted with the float centerline parallel to the centerline of the engine.

Float Adjustment

(Lateral)

1. Invert the bowl cover.
2. Remove the bowl cover gasket.
3. Place the float gauge directly under the floats with the notched portions of the gauge fitted over the edges of the casting.

Gauge Point

Float level adjustment

4. The sides of the float should barely touch the vertical uprights of the float gauge. A gauge is normally included in a rebuilding kit.
5. Adjustment is made by bending the arms of the floats.

(Vertical)

1. With the float gauge in the same position as for the lateral adjustment, the floats should just clear the horizontal portion of the gauge.
2. The vertical distance between the top center of the float and the machined surface of the casting must be 7/32 in.
3. Adjust by bending the float arms as required.
4. To install the bowl cover gasket, remove the floats, install the gasket, and reinstall the floats.

Pump adjustment

Pump Adjustment

1. Install the pump connector link in the outer hole (long stroke) of the pump arm with the ends extending away from the countershaft arm.
2. Back out the throttle lever set screw until the throttle valves seat in the carburetor bores.
3. Be sure that the fast idle adjustment screw does not hold the throttle open.
4. Hold a straightedge across the top of the dust cover boss at the pump arm.
5. The flat on top of the pump arm should be parallel to the straightedge.
6. Adjust by bending the throttle connector rod to the upper angle.

Metering Rod Adjustment

1. Complete the pump adjustment.
2. Back out the throttle lever set screw to allow the valves (throttle) to seat in the bores of the carburetor.

Metering rod adjustment

3. Loosen the metering rod clamp screw.
4. With the metering rod in place, press down on the vacumeter link until the metering rods bottom in the carburetor body casting.
5. While holding the rods in a downward position, revolve the metering rod arm until the finger on the arm contacts the lip of the vacumeter link.
6. Hold in place and carefully tighten the clamp screw.

Fast Idle Cam Adjustment

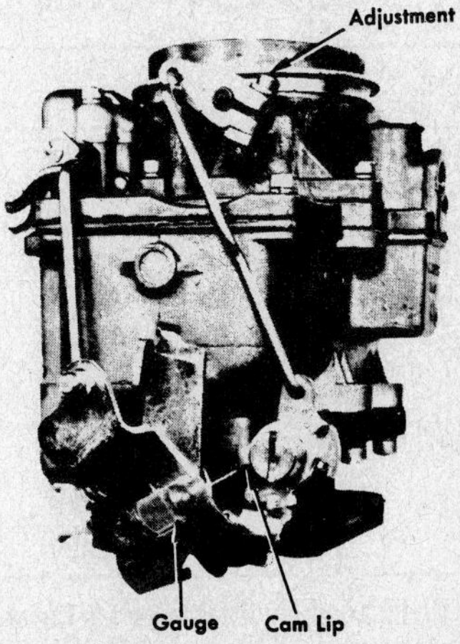
Adjustment
Gauge
Cam Lip

Fast idle cam adjustment

1. Loosen the choke lever clamp screw on the choke shaft.
2. Insert a 0.010 in. feeler gauge between the lip of the fast idle cam and the boss of the flange casting.
3. Hold the choke valve tightly closed and take the slack out of the linkage by pressing the choke lever toward the closed position.
4. With the choke valve in the closed position, tighten the fast idle adjusting screw to obtain the specified clearance.
5. Be sure that the fast idle adjusting screw is on the high step of the cam or index mark while making this adjustment.

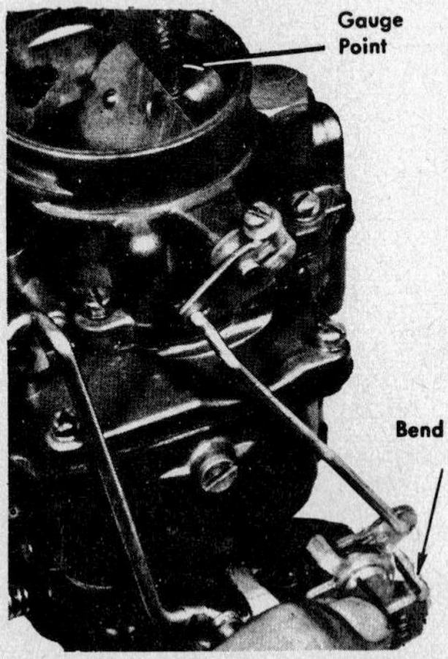
Gauge Point
Bend
Choke unloader adjustment

Automatic Choke Adjustment

1. Loosen the choke cover retaining screws.
2. Turn the cover so that the index mark on the cover lines up with the specified mark on the choke housing.
3. See the Specifications Chart for the proper mark alignment.

WCD AUTOMATIC CHOKE SPECIFICATIONS

Year	Model ①	Choke
1967	3888S	Index
	4365S	2 Rich
1968	4410S	Index
	4537S	Index
1969	4667S	Index
	4668S	Index
1970	4816S	Index
	4817S	Index
	4950S	Index

① Model numbers located on the tag or the casting

Choke Unloader Adjustment

1. With the throttle valves wide open, there should be clearance between the upper edge of the choke valve and the inner wall of the air horn.
2. Adjust by bending the unloader lip on the throttle shaft lever.
3. Adjustment is 3/16 in.

Model WGD

Introduction

The WGD carburetor is the same basic carburetor as the WCD, the only difference being that the WGD has only one float. The choke is operated by a thermostatic coil. This carburetor is used mainly on 1972 Pontiacs. It carries model number 6311S.

Float Adjustment

1. With the air horn inverted, check to see that the float is parallel with the outer edge of the air horn casting.
2. Adjust by bending the float arm. Next, place the gauge between the air horn and the center of the float. The distance should be 5/16 in.
3. Adjust the float level by bending the float arm until the float touches the gauge. The float should not have excessive clearance at the hinge pin and must operate freely.

NOTE: When adjusting the float, care must be exercised to avoid pressing the flared tip needle into the needle seats as a false setting will result. Allow only the float weight to seat the needle when gauging.

Pump Adjustment

1. Back out the throttle stop screw.
2. Turn the fast idle cam to "hot" position and fully close the throttle valves.
3. Place a 1/4 in. gauge or a similar straightedge across the dust cover boss. The dust cover boss

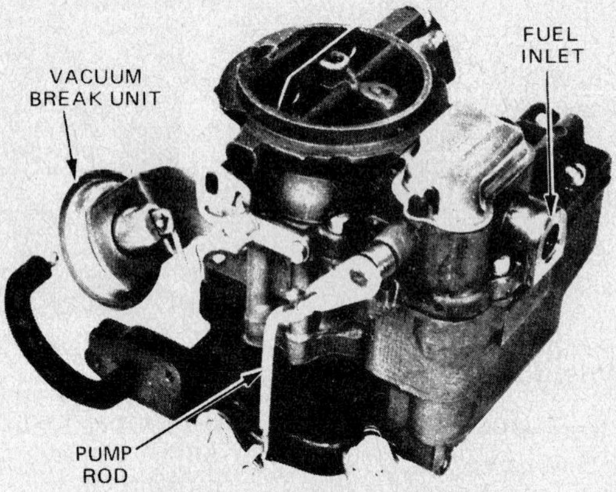
VACUUM BREAK UNIT
FUEL INLET
PUMP ROD
Carburetor assembly WGD

GAUGE FROM CENTER – OF FLOAT TO GASKET SURFACE
5/16" GAUGE
Float level adjustment

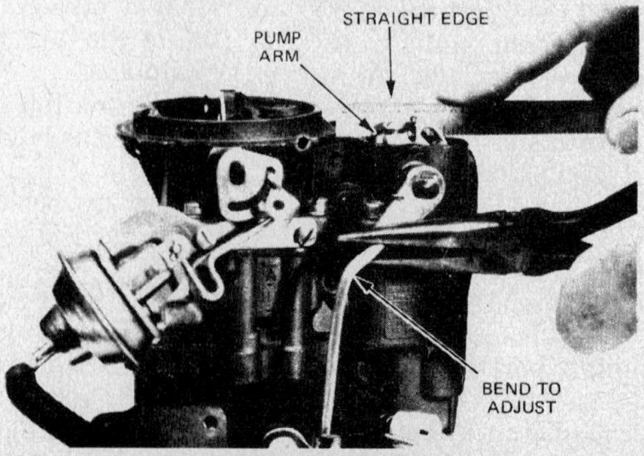
PUMP ARM
STRAIGHT EDGE
BEND TO ADJUST
Pump adjustment

should be parallel with the top surface of the pump arm.
4. Adjust by bending the pump rod at the offset.

Metering Rod Adjustment

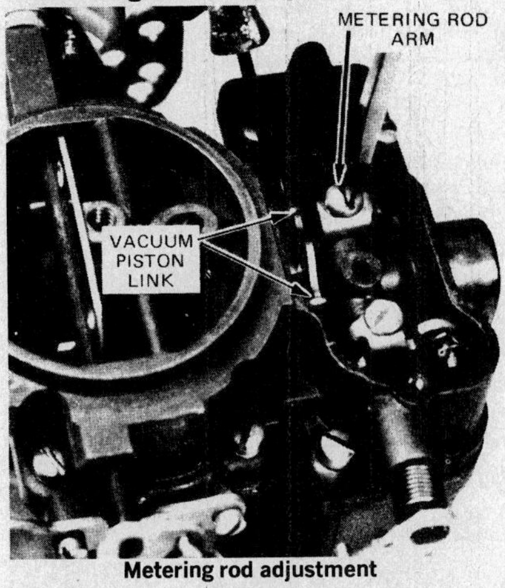
METERING ROD ARM
VACUUM PISTON LINK
Metering rod adjustment

NOTE: This adjustment should be made after the pump adjustment. No metering rod gauges are necessary.

1. Back out the throttle screw and fully close the throttle valves. Press down on the vacuum piston link until the metering rods bottom.
2. While holding the rods down and the metering arm tongue against the lip of the vacuum piston link, carefully tighten the metering arm set screw.

Fast Idle Cam Adjustment

.005" MINIMUM CLEARANCE BETWEEN INNER AND OUTER LEVERS
CHOKE HELD FULLY CLOSED
Fast idle cam adjustment

1. Open the throttle to clear the fast idle cam and close the choke valve.
2. With the choke valve held fully closed and the stop on the fast idle cam against the casting, there should be 0.005 in. minimum clearance between the inner and outer choke levers.
3. Adjust by bending the outer lever lug as required.

NOTE: With the choke fully closed, the tang on the fast idle cam must clear the stop on the throttle body flange.

Unloader Adjustment

1. Hold the choke closed lightly.
2. Fully open the throttle, forcing the choke valve open.
3. Check the clearance between the upper edge of the choke valve and the wall of the air horn. The clearance should be 3/16 in.
4. Adjust by bending the unloader arm as required.

3/16" GAUGE
UNLOADER ARM
BEND UNLOADER ARM
Choke unloader adjustment

Fast Idle Speed Adjustment

CHOKE HELD CLOSED
FAST IDLE TANG
Fast idle speed adjustment

1. With the carburetor on the engine, rotate the fast idle cam until the fast idle tang contacts the cam's high step.
2. With the engine at normal operating temperature, adjust the fast idle tang to obtain an engine speed of 1500 rpm.

Model AVS

Introduction

The AVS carburetor is very similar to the AFB carburetor. AVS means Air Valve Secondary. It employs a spring loaded air valve located above the secondary fuel nozzles. This system gives smooth response whenever the secondaries are opened. Venturi clusters are used in the primary side for fuel control in the idle and economy ranges.

Float Alignment

1. The sides of the float should be parallel to the edge of the casting with minimum clearance between the lever and the air horn lugs without binding.
2. To adjust, bend the float arm lever.

Float Level Adjustment

1. With the air horn inverted, the air horn gasket in place, and the float needle seated, slide the float gauge between the top of the float, at the outer edge, and the air horn gasket. Refer to the Specifications Chart.
2. Check the other float in the same manner.
3. Adjust by bending the float arm. After bending the arm, recheck the float alignment.

Float Drop Adjustment

1. The dimension listed in the Specifications Chart should exist between the tops of the floats, at the outer end, and the air horn gasket.
2. To adjust, bend the stop tabs on the float brackets.

Pump Adjustment

1. With the throttle valves closed tightly, the dimension listed in the Specifications Chart should be from the top of the air horn to the top of the pump plunger shaft with the throttle connector rod in the inner hole of the pump arm.
2. To adjust, bend the throttle connector rod at an angle.

Fast Idle Cam Adjustment

1. With the fast idle speed adjusting screw contacting the second highest speed step on the fast idle cam, move the choke valve toward the closed position with light pressure on the choke shaft lever.
2. Insert the drill gauge between the choke valve and the wall of the air horn. Refer to the Specifications Chart.
3. An adjustment will be necessary if a slight drag is not obtained as the drill is beginning to be removed.
4. Adjust by bending the fast idle connector rod at an angle.

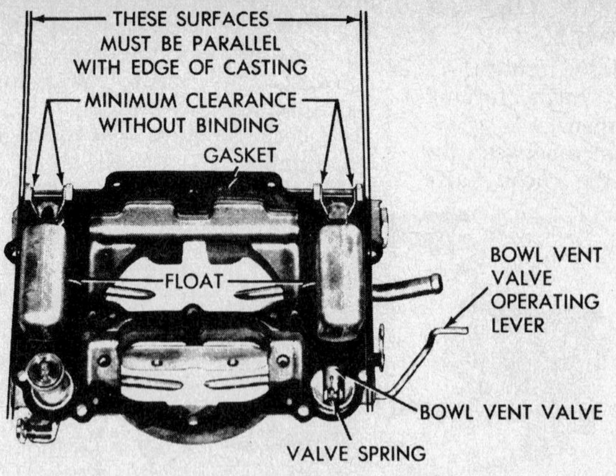
THESE SURFACES
MUST BE PARALLEL
WITH EDGE OF CASTING
MINIMUM CLEARANCE
WITHOUT BINDING
GASKET
FLOAT
BOWL VENT
VALVE
OPERATING
LEVER
BOWL VENT VALVE
VALVE SPRING

Float alignment

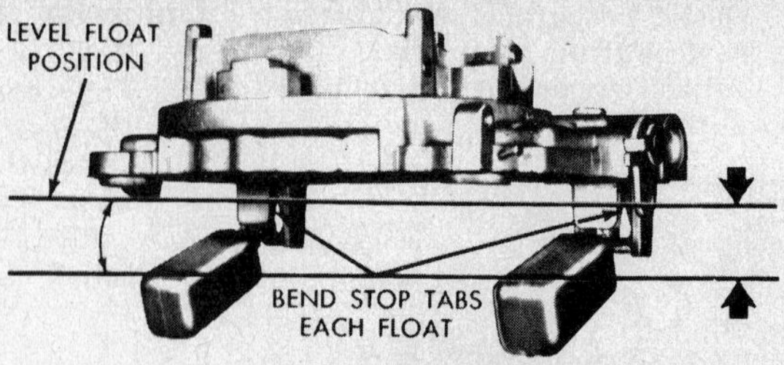
LEVEL FLOAT
POSITION
BEND STOP TABS
EACH FLOAT

Float drop adjustment

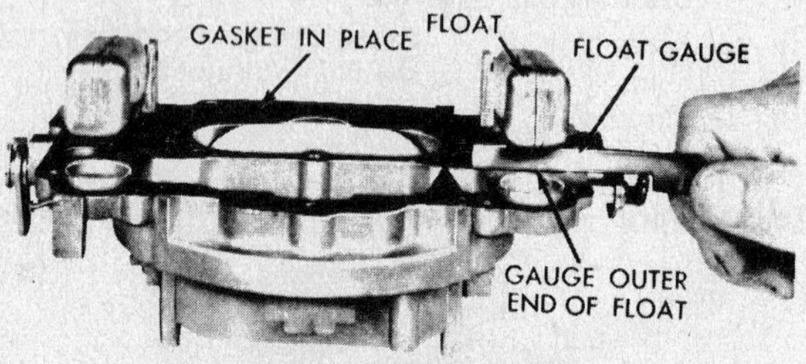
GASKET IN PLACE
FLOAT
FLOAT GAUGE
GAUGE OUTER
END OF FLOAT

Float level adjustment

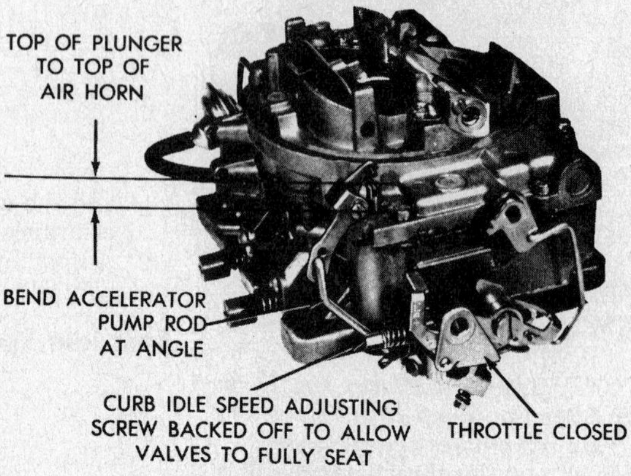
TOP OF PLUNGER
TO TOP OF
AIR HORN
BEND ACCELERATOR
PUMP ROD
AT ANGLE
CURB IDLE SPEED ADJUSTING
SCREW BACKED OFF TO ALLOW
VALVES TO FULLY SEAT
THROTTLE CLOSED

Pump adjustment

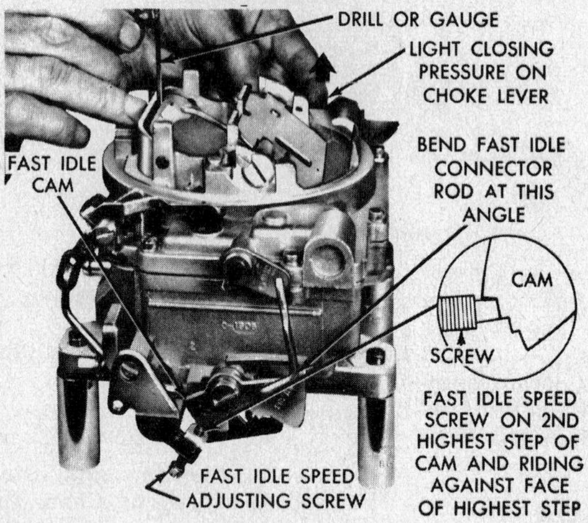
DRILL OR GAUGE
LIGHT CLOSING
PRESSURE ON
CHOKE LEVER
FAST IDLE
CAM
BEND FAST IDLE
CONNECTOR
ROD AT THIS
ANGLE
CAM
SCREW
FAST IDLE SPEED
SCREW ON 2ND
HIGHEST STEP OF
CAM AND RIDING
AGAINST FACE
OF HIGHEST STEP
FAST IDLE SPEED
ADJUSTING SCREW

Fast idle cam adjustment

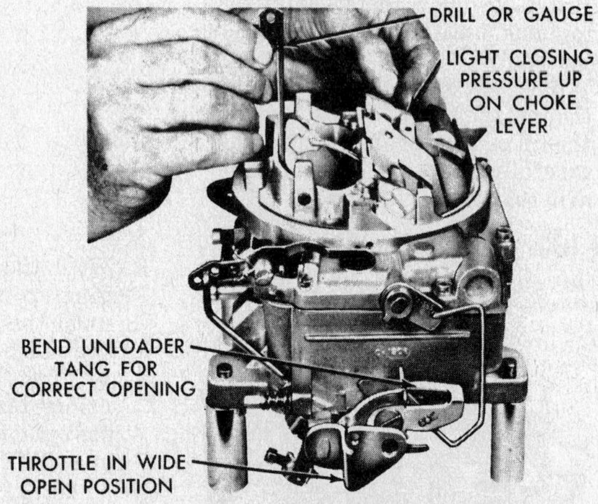
DRILL OR GAUGE
LIGHT CLOSING
PRESSURE UP
ON CHOKE
LEVER
BEND UNLOADER
TANG FOR
CORRECT OPENING
THROTTLE IN WIDE
OPEN POSITION

Choke unloader adjustment

Choke Unloader Adjustment

1. With the throttle valves wide open there should be 1/4 in. clearance between the upper edge of the choke valve and the inner wall of the air horn.
2. To adjust, bend the unloader tang on the fast idle cam.

Bowl Vent Adjustment

CAS Equipped

1. With the throttle valves tightly closed, insert a drill gauge between the air horn and the valve at the smallest opening. Refer to the Specifications Chart.
2. Adjust by bending the tang on the pivot end of the lever.

ECS Equipped

1. Remove the bowl vent valve and check the hole plug in the air horn.

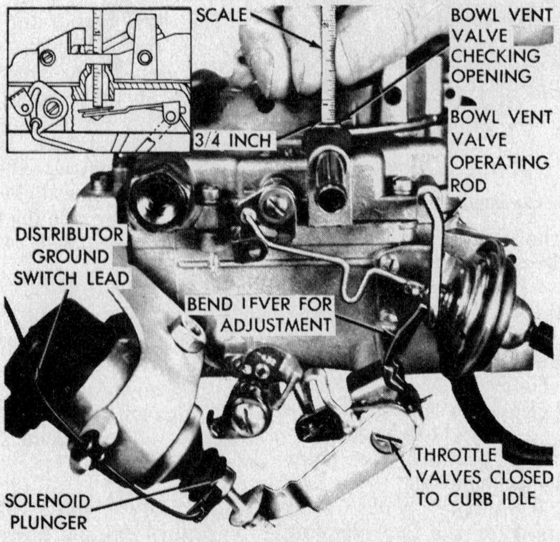
SCALE
3/4 INCH
BOWL VENT
VALVE
CHECKING
OPENING
BOWL VENT
VALVE
OPERATING
ROD
DISTRIBUTOR
GROUND
SWITCH LEAD
BEND LEVER FOR
ADJUSTMENT
THROTTLE
VALVES CLOSED
TO CURB IDLE
SOLENOID
PLUNGER

Bowl vent adjustment

2. With the throttle valves at closed curb idle position, insert a narrow ruler down through the hole. Allow the ruler to rest lightly on top of the valve.
3. Measure from the top of the valve to the top of the air horn casting at the opening. Refer to the Specifications Chart.
4. Adjust by bending the bowl vent operating lever.
5. Install the plug and rap lightly on the seat, using a hammer.

Secondary Air Valve Adjustment

1. Loosen the lock screw and allow the air valve to position itself at the wide open position.
2. From the wide open position, turn the slotted sleeve 2½ turns counterclockwise.
3. Hold the sleeve in this position with your fingers, then tighten the lock screw securely.
4. Check the valve for freedom of movement.

Secondary Throttle Lever Adjustment

1. Block the choke valve in the wide open position and invert the carburetor.
2. Slowly open the primary throttle valves until the specified measurement is obtained between the lower edge of the primary valve and the bore opposite the idle port. Refer to the Specifications Chart.
3. At this measurement, the secondary valves should just start to open.
4. Adjust by bending the secondary throttle operating rod at the angle.

Closing Shoe Adjustment

1. With the primary and secondary throttle valves closed, bend the secondary closing shoe to obtain 0.020 in. clearance between the positive closing shoes on the primary and secondary throttle levers.
2. To adjust, bend the shoe on the secondary lever.

Secondary Throttle Lockout

1. Crack the throttle valves and manually open and close the choke valve. The tang on the secondary throttle lever should freely engage in the notch of the lockout dog.
2. To adjust, bend the tang on the secondary throttle lever.

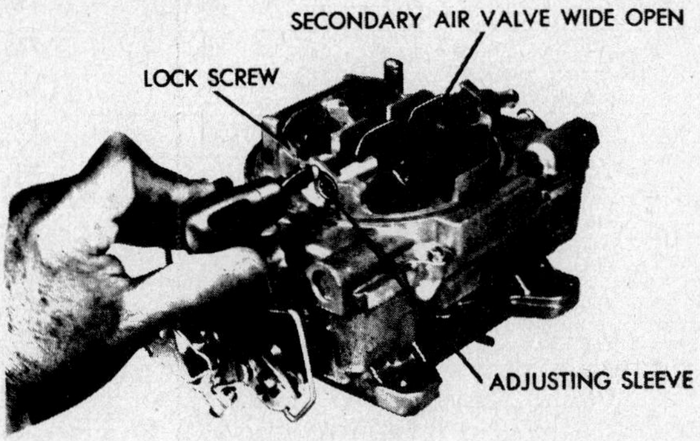
SECONDARY AIR VALVE WIDE OPEN
LOCK SCREW
ADJUSTING SLEEVE

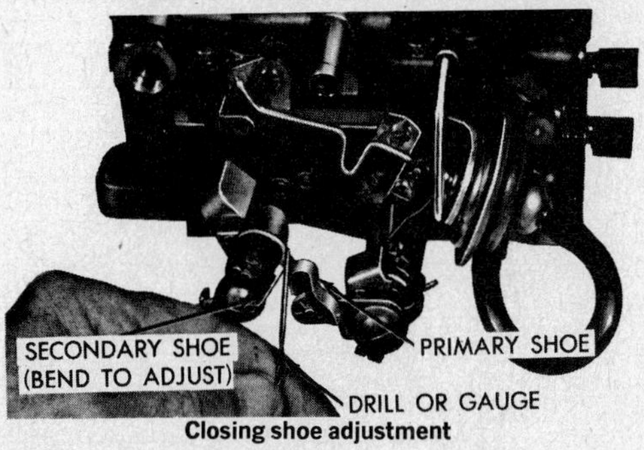
SECONDARY SHOE
(BEND TO ADJUST)
PRIMARY SHOE
DRILL OR GAUGE

Closing shoe adjustment

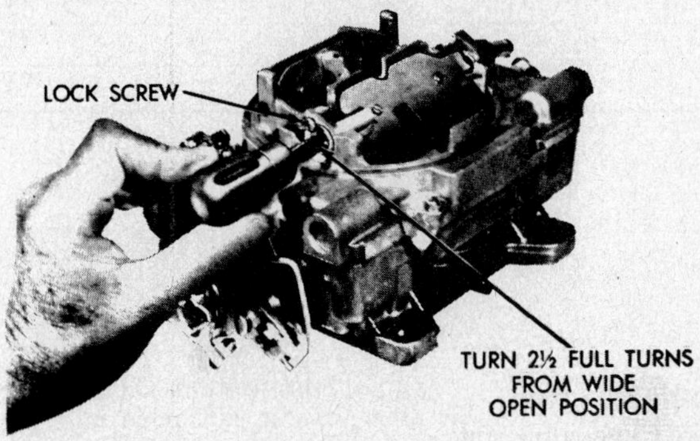
LOCK SCREW
TURN 2½ FULL TURNS
FROM WIDE
OPEN POSITION

Secondary air valve adjustment

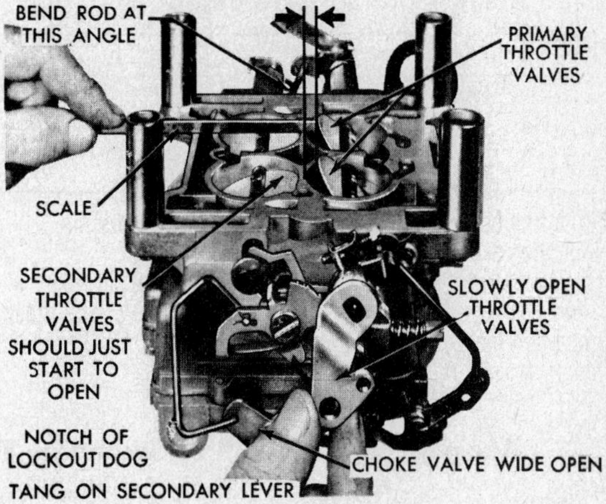
BEND ROD AT
THIS ANGLE
PRIMARY
THROTTLE
VALVES
SCALE
SECONDARY
THROTTLE
VALVES
SHOULD JUST
START TO
OPEN
SLOWLY OPEN
THROTTLE
VALVES
NOTCH OF
LOCKOUT DOG
CHOKE VALVE WIDE OPEN
TANG ON SECONDARY LEVER

Secondary throttle lockout

CARTER AVS SPECIFICATIONS

CHRYSLER, DODGE, PLYMOUTH, AND IMPERIAL

Year	Carb. Model ①	Float Level (in.)	Float Drop (in.)	Accelerator Pump (in.)	Bowl Vent (in.)	Fast Idle Cam (in.) ②	Secondary Throttle Lever (in.)
1968	4401S	5/16	23/32	7/16	1/8	78	21/64
	4424S	7/32	23/32	7/16	1/8	79	21/64
	4425S	7/32	23/32	7/16	1/8	0.012	21/64
	4426S	5/16	23/32	7/16	1/8	0.012	21/64
	4428S	7/32	23/32	7/16	1/8	80	21/64
	4429S	7/32	23/32	7/16	1/8	80	21/64

Year	Carb. Model ①	Float Level (in.)	Float Drop (in.)	Accelerator Pump (in.)	Bowl Vent (in.)	Fast Idle Cam (in.) ②	Secondary Throttle Lever (in.)
1969	4611S	7/32	1/2	7/16	1/8	50	21/64
	4612S	7/32	1/2	7/16	1/8	50	21/64
	4615S	5/16	1/2	7/16	1/8	50	21/64
	4616S	5/16	1/2	7/16	1/8	50	21/64
	4617S	7/32	1/2	7/16	1/8	50	11/32
	4618S	7/32	1/2	7/16	1/8	50	3/8
	4638S	5/16	1/2	7/16	1/8	50	21/64
	4639S	7/32	1/2	7/16	1/8	50	21/64
	4640S	7/32	1/2	7/16	1/8	50	1/8
	4682S	5/16	1/2	7/16	1/8	50	21/64
	4711S	5/16	1/2	7/16	1/8	50	21/64
1970	4732S*	5/16	1/2	7/16	3/64	50	19/64
	4734S*	5/16	1/2	7/16	3/64	50	19/64
	4736S*	5/16	1/2	7/16	3/64	50	19/64
	4737S*	7/32	1/2	7/16	3/64	50	23/64
	4738S	7/32	1/2	7/16	3/64	50	23/64
	4739S	7/32	1/2	7/16	3/64	50	23/64
	4740S	7/32	1/2	7/16	3/64	50	23/64
	4741S	7/32	1/2	7/16	3/64	50	23/64
	4933S	7/32	1/2	7/16	3/64	50	19/64
	4934S	7/32	1/2	7/16	1/8	50	19/64
	4935S	7/32	1/2	7/16	1/8	50	19/64
	4936S	7/32	1/2	7/16	3/4	50	19/64
	4937S	7/32	1/2	7/16	3/4	50	19/64
1971	4966S	7/32	1/2	7/16	3/4	50	23/64
	4967S	7/32	1/2	7/16	3/4	50	23/64
	4968S	7/32	1/2	7/16	3/4	50	23/64
	6125S	7/32	1/2	7/16	3/4	50	23/64

① Model numbers are located on a tag or on the casting
② Indicates drill bit number. See Mechanic's Data
NOTE: Accelerator pump adjustment is 7/16 in. for all AVS carburetors. Choke setting on all models from 1968-70 on the index except when marked (*) which are 2 notches rich. 1972 models 2 rich

Model TQ

Introduction

The TQ (Thermo Quad) has a fuel bowl made of phenolic resin. This acts as a heat insulator. Fuel is kept 20 degrees cooler than in metal carburetors. It also has a suspended design metering system which aids in cooling. All the calibration points are in the upper aluminum casting or air horn and are in effect suspended in the cavities in the main body.

Float Adjustment

1. With the bowl cover inverted, the gasket installed, and the floats resting on the seated needle, the dimension of each float from the bowl cover gasket to the bottom side of the float should be as shown in the specifications chart.

Secondary Throttle Linkage

1. Block the choke valve in the wide open position and invert the carburetor.
2. Slowly open the primary throttle valves until it is possible to measure between the lower edge of the primary valve and its bore.
3. If it is necessary to adjust, bend the rod until the correct dimension is obtained.

Secondary Air Valve Opening

1. With the air valve in the closed position, the opening along the air valve at its long side must be at its maximum and parallel with the air horn gasket surface.
2. With the air valve wide open, the opening of the air valve at the short side and the air horn must match the dimensions in the Specifications Charts. The corner of the air valve is notched for adjustment. Bend the corner with a pair of pliers to give proper opening.

Accelerator Pump Adjustment

1. Move the choke valve wide open to release the fast idle cam.
2. Back off the idle speed adjusting screw until the throttle valves are seated in the bores.
3. Be sure that the throttle connector rod is in the center hole of the pump arm.
4. Close the throttle valve tightly and measure the distance between the top of the bowl cover and the end of the plunger shaft. The dimension should be as shown in the Specifications Chart.
5. Bend the throttle connector rod at the lower angle to adjust.

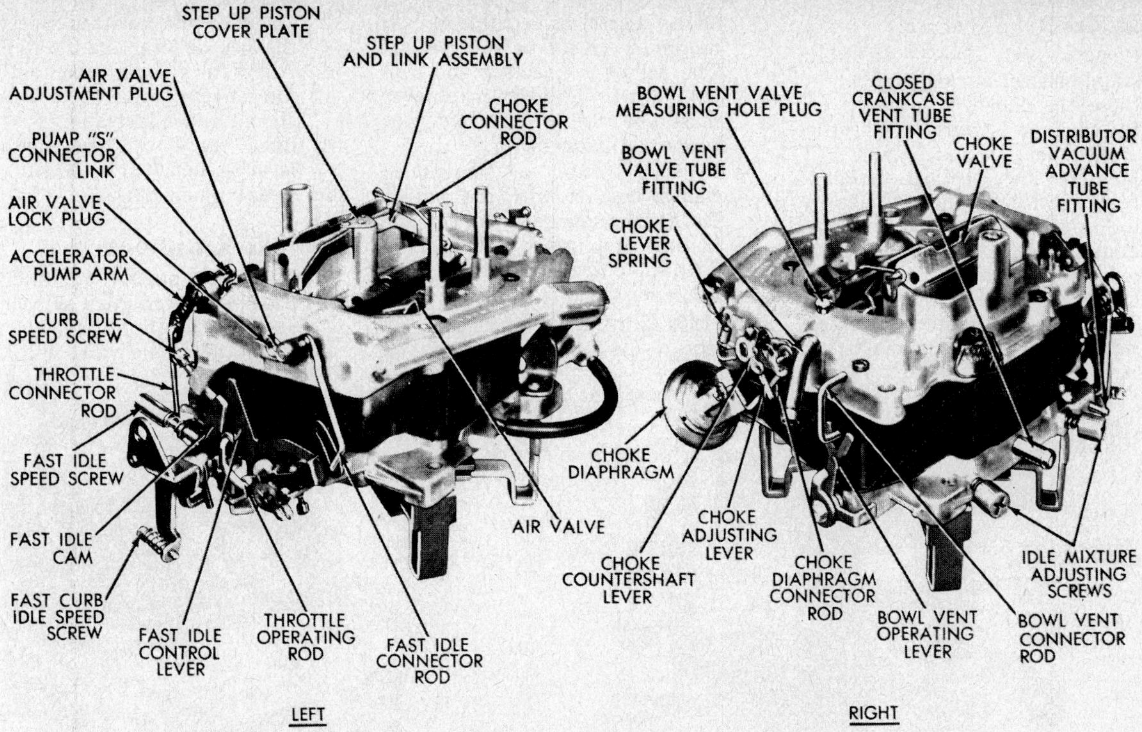
STEP UP PISTON COVER PLATE
STEP UP PISTON AND LINK ASSEMBLY
AIR VALVE ADJUSTMENT PLUG
CHOKE CONNECTOR ROD
PUMP "S" CONNECTOR LINK
AIR VALVE LOCK PLUG
ACCELERATOR PUMP ARM
CURB IDLE SPEED SCREW
THROTTLE CONNECTOR ROD
FAST IDLE SPEED SCREW
FAST IDLE CAM
FAST CURB IDLE SPEED SCREW
FAST IDLE CONTROL LEVER
THROTTLE OPERATING ROD
FAST IDLE CONNECTOR ROD
AIR VALVE
BOWL VENT VALVE MEASURING HOLE PLUG
CLOSED CRANKCASE VENT TUBE FITTING
BOWL VENT VALVE TUBE FITTING
CHOKE VALVE
DISTRIBUTOR VACUUM ADVANCE TUBE FITTING
CHOKE LEVER SPRING
CHOKE DIAPHRAGM
CHOKE ADJUSTING LEVER
CHOKE COUNTERSHAFT LEVER
CHOKE DIAPHRAGM CONNECTOR ROD
BOWL VENT OPERATING LEVER
BOWL VENT CONNECTOR ROD
IDLE MIXTURE ADJUSTING SCREWS
LEFT
RIGHT

Carburetor assembly TQ

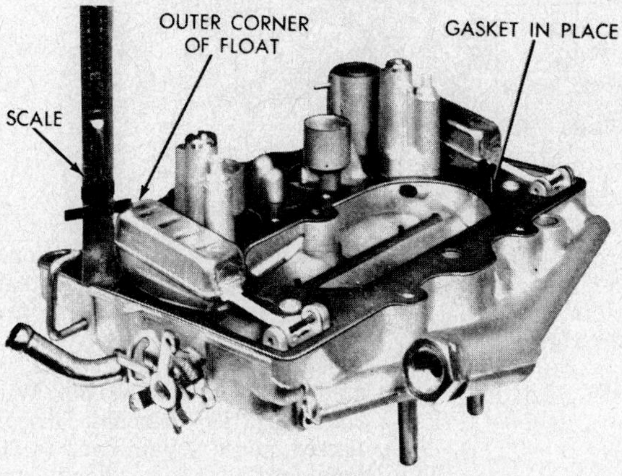
OUTER CORNER OF FLOAT
GASKET IN PLACE
SCALE

Float adjustment

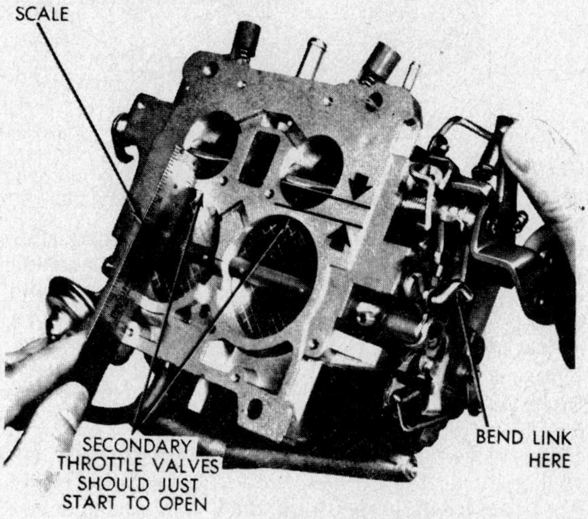
SCALE
SECONDARY THROTTLE VALVES SHOULD JUST START TO OPEN
BEND LINK HERE

Secondary throttle adjustment

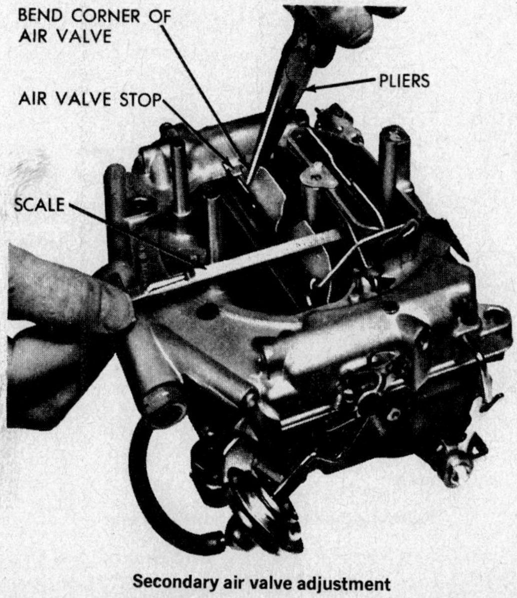
BEND CORNER OF AIR VALVE
PLIERS
AIR VALVE STOP
SCALE

Secondary air valve adjustment

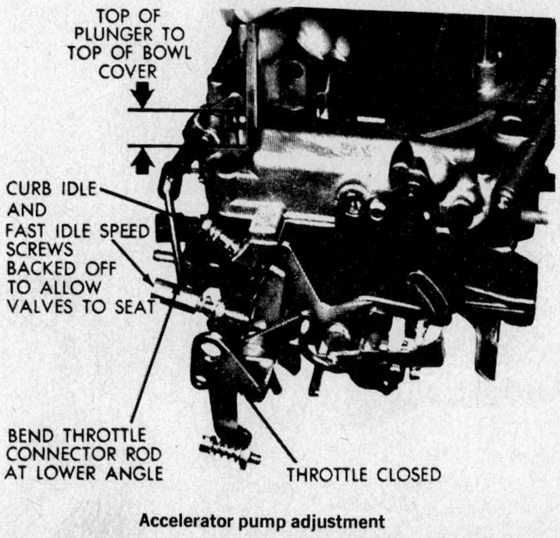
TOP OF PLUNGER TO TOP OF BOWL COVER
CURB IDLE AND FAST IDLE SPEED SCREWS BACKED OFF TO ALLOW VALVES TO SEAT
BEND THROTTLE CONNECTOR ROD AT LOWER ANGLE
THROTTLE CLOSED

Accelerator pump adjustment

Choke Control Lever

1. Remove the choke assembly stainless steel cup and gasket.
2. Close the choke by pushing on the choke lever with the throttle partly open.
3. Measure the vertical distance from the top of the rod hole in the control lever down to the clean choke rod surface. The dimensions should be as shown in the Specifications Chart.
4. To adjust, bend the link which connects the two choke shafts.

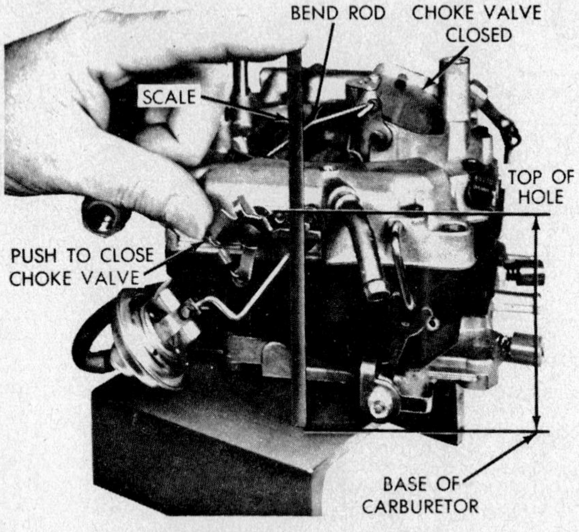
BEND ROD
CHOKE VALVE CLOSED
SCALE
TOP OF HOLE
PUSH TO CLOSE CHOKE VALVE
BASE OF CARBURETOR
Choke control lever

Vacuum Kick Adjustment

1. With the engine running, back off the fast idle speed screw until the choke can be closed to the kick position at idle.
2. Count the number of screw turns so that the fast idle can be turned back to the original adjustment.
3. Insert a #35 drill between the long side, lower edge, of the choke valve and the air horn wall.
4. Apply sufficient pressure on the choke control lever to provide a minimum choke valve opening. The spring connecting the control lever to the adjustment lever must be fully extended for proper adjustment.
5. Bend the tang as shown to change contact with the end of the diaphragm rod. Do not adjust the diaphragm rod. A slight drag should be felt as the drill is being removed.

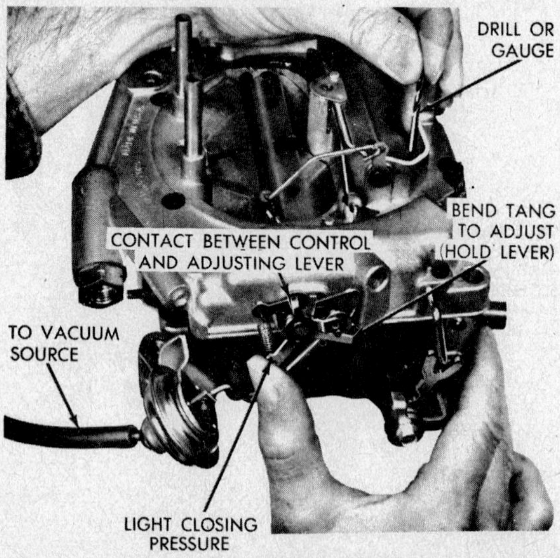
DRILL OR GAUGE
BEND TANG TO ADJUST (HOLD LEVER)
CONTACT BETWEEN CONTROL AND ADJUSTING LEVER
TO VACUUM SOURCE
LIGHT CLOSING PRESSURE
Vacuum kick adjustment

Fast Idle Cam and Linkage

1. With the fast idle screw on the second step of the cam against the shoulder of the first step, there should be 0.110 in. between the air horn wall and edge of the choke valve.
2. To adjust, bend the fast idle connector rod.

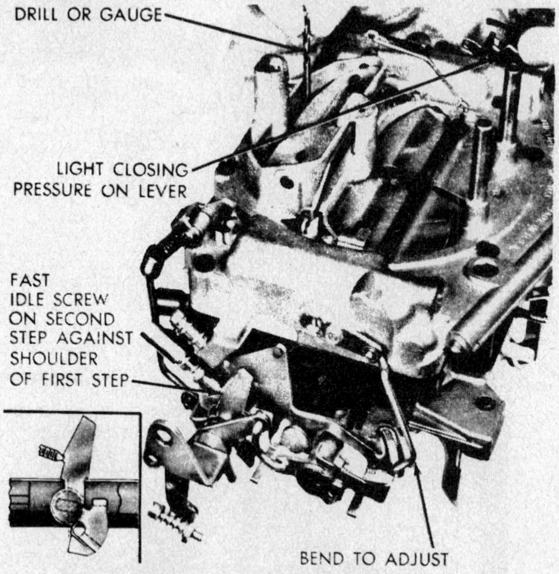
DRILL OR GAUGE
LIGHT CLOSING PRESSURE ON LEVER
FAST IDLE SCREW ON SECOND STEP AGAINST SHOULDER OF FIRST STEP
BEND TO ADJUST
Adjusting fast idle cam and linkage

Secondary Throttle Lockout

1. Move the choke control lever to the open choke position.
2. Measure the clearance between the lockout lever and the stop.
3. Allow the ruler to rest lightly on top of the valve. The reading should be as illustrated.
4. Bend the bowl vent operating lever at the notch to adjust.
5. Install a new plug.

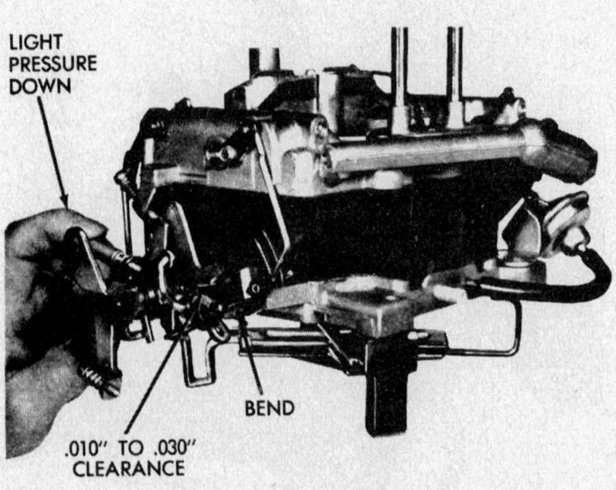
LIGHT PRESSURE DOWN
BEND
.010" TO .030" CLEARANCE
Adjusting the secondary throttle locknut

Fast Idle Speed Cam

1. With the engine off and the transmission in Park or Neutral, open the throttle slightly.
2. Close the choke valve until the fast idle screw can be positioned on the second step of the cam against the shoulder of the first step.
3. Start the engine and adjust the screw to secure 1800 rpm. With the throttle solenoid disconnected, speed should drop to 900 rpm.

Choke Unloader Adjustment

1. Hold the throttle valves in the

wide open position and insert the specified drill between the long side of the choke valve and inner wall of the air horn.

2. With a finger pressing lightly against the choke control lever, a slight drag should be felt as the drill is being withdrawn.
3. To adjust, bend the tang on the fast idle control lever.

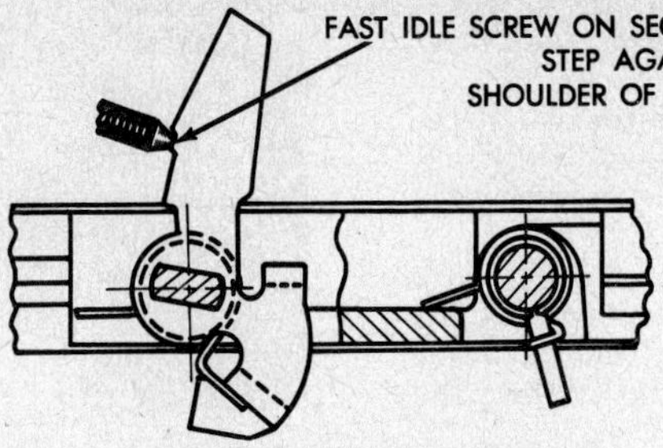
FAST IDLE SCREW ON SECOND STEP AGAINST SHOULDER OF FIRST STEP

Fast idle cam adjustment

CARTER TQ SPECIFICATIONS

CHRYSLER, DODGE, PLYMOUTH, IMPERIAL

Year	Model ①	Float Setting (in.)	Secondary Throttle Linkage (in.)	Secondary Air Valve Opening (in.)	Secondary Air Valve Spring (turns)	Accelerator Pump (in.)	Choke Control Lever (in.)	Choke Unloader (in.)
1971	4972S	1	11/32	31/64	1 1/4	31/64	5 41/64	0.190
	4973S	1	11/32	31/64	1 1/4	31/64	5 41/64	0.190
1972	6090S	1	②	31/64	1	31/64	3 3/8	0.190
	6138S	1	②	29/64	1	9/16	3 3/8	0.190
	6139S	1	②	29/64	1	31/64	3 3/8	0.190
	6140S	1	②	31/64	1	9/16	3 3/8	0.190
	6165S	1	②	31/64	1	9/16	3 3/8	0.190
	6166S	1	②	31/64	1	31/64	3 3/8	0.190
1973	6318S	1 1/16	②	29/64	1 1/4	35/64	3 3/8	0.190
	6319S	1 1/16	②	29/64	1 1/4	31/64	3 3/8	0.190
	6320S	1 1/16	②	31/64	1 1/4	35/64	3 3/8	0.190
	6321S	1 1/16	②	31/64	1 1/4	31/64	3 3/8	0.190
	6322S	1 1/16	②	31/64	1 1/4	31/64	3 3/8	0.190
	6324S	1 1/16	②	31/64	1 1/4	31/64	3 3/8	0.190
	6339S	1 1/16	②	29/64	1 1/4	35/64	3 3/8	0.190
	6340S	1 1/16	②	29/64	1 1/4	31/64	3 3/8	0.190
	6341S	1 1/16	②	29/64	1 1/4	35/64	3 3/8	0.190
	6342S	1 1/16	②	29/64	1 1/4	31/64	3 3/8	0.190
	6410S	1 1/16	②	31/64	1 1/4	31/64	3 3/8	0.190
	6411S	1 1/16	②	31/64	1 1/4	31/64	3 3/8	0.190

① Model numbers located on the tag or on the casting
② Adjust link so primary and secondary stops both contact at same time
NOTE: All choke settings fixed except 1971 which is 2 notches rich

Model AFB

Introduction

The Carter AFB carburetor has four barrels. All the major castings are of aluminum and the venturi assemblies are replaceable. For better performance in cornering and stopping, one fuel bowl feeds the primary and secondary on the left. The other bowl feeds the primary and secondary on the right. Thermostatic spring coil chokes are used on most models.

Float Alignment

1. Sight down the side of the float to determine if it is parallel to the outer edge of the air horn casting.

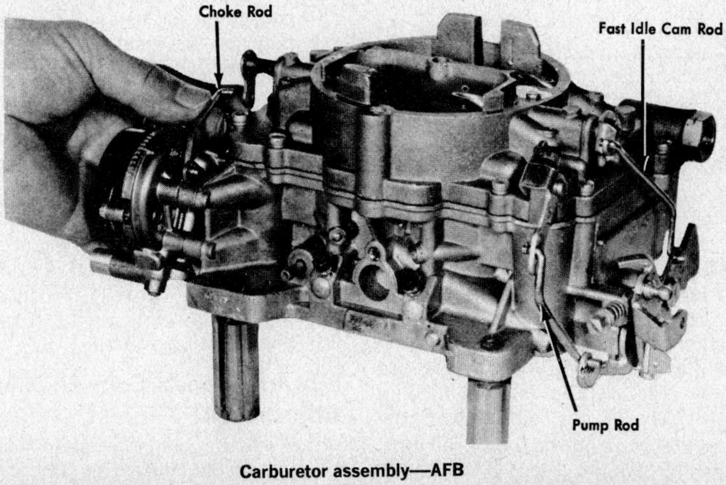
Choke Rod
Fast Idle Cam Rod
Pump Rod

Carburetor assembly—AFB

2. To adjust, bend the float lever accordingly.
3. Apply pressure on the end of the float with your fingers while supporting the float lever with your thumb.
4. After aligning the float, remove as much clearance as possible between the arms of the float lever and the lugs on the air horn by bending the float lever.
5. The arms of the float lever should be parallel to the inner surfaces of the lugs on the air horn. The floats must operate freely without excess clearance on the hinge pin.

Float Level Adjustment

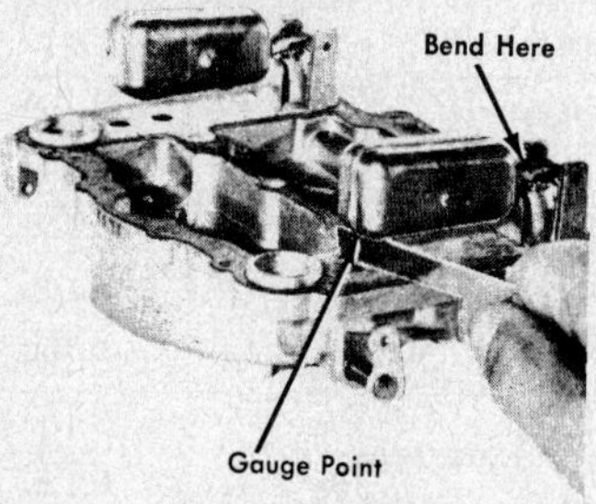
Bend Here
Gauge Point

Float level adjustment

1. With the air horn inverted, the bowl cover in place, and the needle seated, clearance between the top of the float (at outer edge) and the air horn gasket should be as listed in the Specifications Chart.
2. To adjust, bend the float arm. Adjust both floats and recheck the float alignment.

Float Drop Adjustment

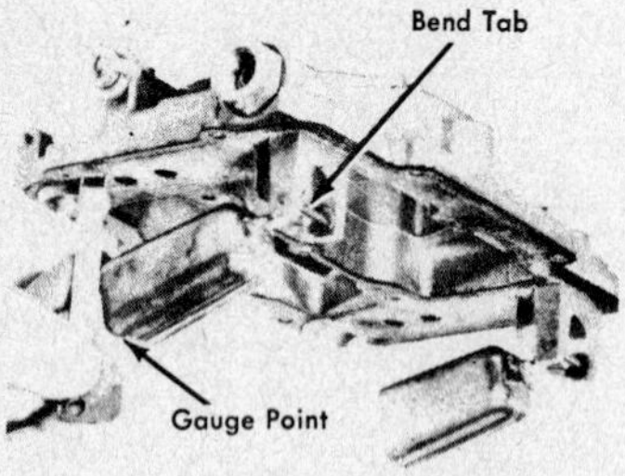
Bend Tab
Gauge Point

Float drop adjustment

1. With the bowl cover held in the upright position, measure between the outer end of each float, the distance between the top of the floats and the bowl cover gasket as listed in the Specifications Chart.
2. To adjust, bend the tabs on the float brackets.

Pump Adjustment

1. Back out the idle speed screw until the throttle valve seats in the carburetor bores.
2. With the throttle connector rod in the center hole (medium stroke) of the pump arm, the distance from the top of the bowl cover to the top of the pump

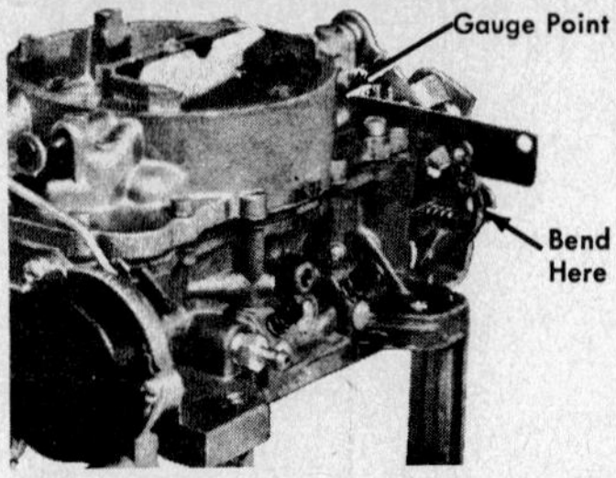
Gauge Point
Bend
Here

Pump adjustment

plunger shaft should be as listed in the Specifications Chart.

To adjust, bend the throttle connector rod at its offset angle.

NOTE: Some models require the throttle connector rod to be placed in the inner hole (long stroke) or the outer hole (short stroke). In such cases the chart will indicate the proper hole connection.

Fast Idle Linkage Adjustment

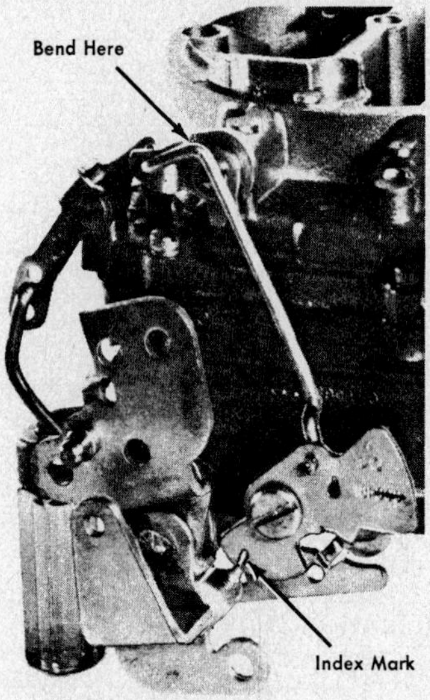
Bend Here
Index Mark

Fast idle linkage adjustment

1. With the choke valve tightly closed and the lug on the outer choke shaft lever contacting the stop on the inner choke shaft lever, align the center of the fast idle screw with the index mark on the cam.
2. To adjust, bend the fast idle connector rod. On some models it may be necessary to bend the stop lug on the fast idle cam.

Fast Idle Throttle Valve Clearance

1. Close the choke valve.
2. Tighten the fast idle and adjusting screw on the index mark on the cam until the clearance between the throttle valve and the carburetor bore (side opposite the idle port) is as listed in the Specifications Chart.

Fast Idle Speed Cam Position Adjustment

1. With the fast idle speed adjusting screw contacting the second highest speed step on the fast idle cam, move the choke valve toward the closed position with light pressure on the choke shaft lever.
2. Insert a drill gauge between the choke valve and the wall of the air horn. Refer to the Specifications Chart.
3. Adjustment is necessary if a slight drag is not obtained as the drill is being removed.
4. Adjust by bending the fast idle connector rod at the angle.

Choke Unloader Adjustment

1. With the throttle wide open, the clearance between the upper edge of the choke valve and the inner wall of the air horn should be as listed in the Specifications Chart.
2. To adjust, bend the unloader tang on the throttle shaft lever.

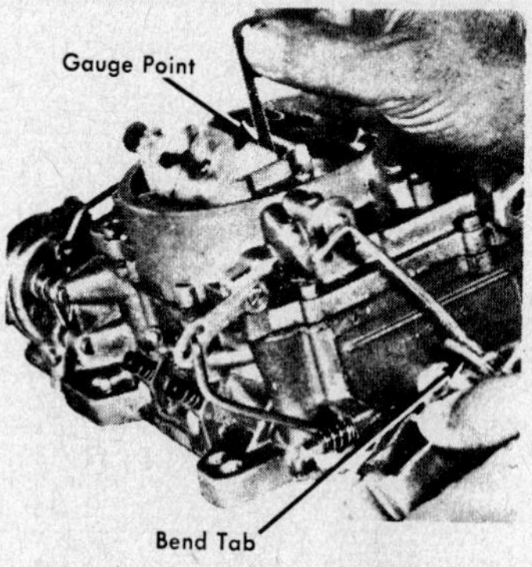
Gauge Point
Bend Tab

Choke unloader adjustment

Secondary Throttle Lever Adjustment

1. Block the choke valve wide open. The secondary throttle valves should just start to open when the primary throttle valves are opened to the clearance (listed in the Specifications Chart) between the lower edge of the throttle valve and the carburetor bore.
2. To adjust, bend the throttle connecting rod.

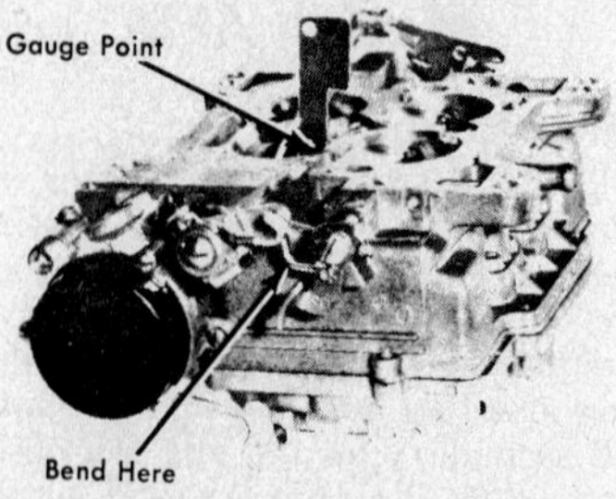
Gauge Point
Bend Here

Secondary throttle lever adjustment

Secondary Throttle Lockout

1. Crack the throttle valves and manually open and close the choke valve.
2. The tang on the secondary throt-

tle lever should freely engage in the notch of the lockout dog.

3. To adjust, bend the tang on the throttle lever. Refer to the Specifications Chart.

Bowl Vent Valve Adjustment

1. With the throttle valves tightly closed, insert the drill gauge between the air horn and the valve at the smallest opening. Refer to the Specifications Chart.
2. Adjust by bending the adjusting tang on the pivot end of the lever.

ECS Equipped

1. Remove the bowl vent valve and checking the hole plug in the air horn.
2. With the throttle valves in the closed curb idle position, insert a narrow ruler down through the hole.
3. Allow the ruler to rest lightly on top of the valve.
4. Measure from the top of the valve to the top of the air horn casting at the opening. Refer to the Specifications Chart.
5. Adjust by bending the bowl vent valve operating lever.
6. Install a new plug and rap lightly to seat it, using a hammer.

Automatic Choke Adjustment

1. Loosen the choke cover retaining screws.
2. Turn the choke cover so that the index mark on the cover lines up with the specified mark on the choke housing.

CARTER AFB SPECIFICATIONS

BUICK

Year	Carb. Model ⑥	Float Level (in.)	Float Drop (in.)	Accelerator Pump Travel (in.)	Fast Idle ④	Choke Unloader (in.)	Secondary Throttle Lever (in.)	Secondary Throttle Lockout (in.)	Bowl Vent (in.)	Choke
1967	4331S	1 13/32	3/4	7/16①	66	0.160	21/64	0.020	—	1 Rich
	4332S	1 13/32	3/4	7/16①	71	0.160	21/64	0.020	—	Index
	4344S	1 13/32	3/4	17/32①	66	0.160	21/64	0.020	—	2 Rich

DODGE, PLYMOUTH, CHRYSLER, AND IMPERIAL

Year	Carb. Model ⑥	Float Level (in.)	Float Drop (in.)	Accelerator Pump Travel (in.)	Fast Idle ④	Choke Unloader (in.)	Secondary Throttle Lever (in.)	Secondary Throttle Lockout (in.)	Bowl Vent (in.)	Choke
1967	4139S	①	23/32	7/16	—	—	21/64	—	—	—
	4294S	7/32	3/4	7/16	50	7/32	21/64	0.020	5/32	2 Rich
	4295S	7/32	3/4	7/16	50	7/32	21/64	0.020	5/32	2 Rich
	4298S	7/32	3/4	7/16	50	3/8	21/64	0.020	—	2 Rich
	4299S	7/32	3/4	7/16	50	3/8	21/64	0.020	—	2 Rich
	4304S	5/16	3/4	7/16	50	7/32	21/64	0.020	5/32	Index
	4305S	5/16	3/4	7/16	50	7/32	21/64	0.020	5/32	Index
	4309S	5/16	3/4	7/16	50	5/16	21/64	0.020	5/32	Index
	4310S	5/16	3/4	7/16	50	5/16	21/64	0.020	5/32	Index
	4311S	5/16	3/4	7/16	50	5/16	21/64	0.020	5/32	Index
	4312S	5/16	3/4	7/16	50	5/16	21/64	0.020	—	Index
	4324S	5/16	3/4	7/16	—	—	17/64	0.020	5/32	—
	4325S	7/32	3/4	7/16	50	1/4	17/64	0.020	5/32	1 Rich
	4326S	7/32	3/4	7/16	50	3/8	21/64	0.020	5/32	Index
	4327S	7/32	3/4	7/16	50	3/8	21/64	0.020	5/32	Index
	4328S	5/16	3/4	7/16	50	3/8	17/64	0.020	5/32	Index
	4329S	5/16	3/4	7/16	50	3/8	17/64	0.020	5/32	Index
	4343S	7/32	3/4	7/16	50	3/8	17/64	0.020	5/32	1 Rich
1968	4430S	7/32	3/4	7/16	—	—	17/64	0.020	—	—
	4431S	7/32	3/4	7/16	50	1/4	17/64	0.020	5/32	2 Rich
	4432S	7/32	3/4	7/16	50	1/4	17/64	0.020	5/32	2 Rich
1969	4619S	7/32	3/4	7/16	—	—	17/64	0.020	—	—
	4620S	7/32	3/4	7/16	50	1/4	17/64	0.020	5/32	2 Rich
	4621S	7/32	3/4	7/16	50	1/4	17/64	0.020	5/32	2 Rich
1970	4742S	7/32	3/4	7/16	—	—	17/64	0.020	—	—
	4745S	7/32	3/4	7/16	50	1/4	17/64	0.020	3/4③	2 Rich
	4746S	7/32	3/4	7/16	50	1/4	17/64	0.020	3/4③	2 Rich
1971	4969S	7/32	3/4	31/64	—	1/4	17/64	0.020	3/4③	—
	4970S	7/32	3/4	31/64	50	1/4	17/64	0.020	3/4③	—
	4971S	7/32	3/4	31/64	50	—	17/64	0.020	—	—

Year	Carb. Model ⑥	Float Level (in.)	Float Drop (in.)	Accelerator Pump Travel (in.)	Fast Idle ④	Choke Unloader (in.)	Secondary Throttle Lever (in.)	Secondary Throttle Lockout (in.)	Bowl Vent (in.)	Choke
					LINCOLN					
1967	C7VF-A	3/16	23/32	⑤	71	—	17/64	0.020	0.070	1 Rich
	C7VF-B	3/16	23/32	⑤	71	0.096	17/64	0.020	0.070	1 Rich
	C7VF-C	3/16	23/32	⑤	71	0.096	17/64	0.020	0.070	1 Rich
	C7VF-D	3/16	23/32	⑤	71	0.096	17/64	0.020	0.070	1 Rich
1968	C8VF-E	3/16	23/32	⑤	71	0.096	17/64	0.020	0.070	Index
					AMERICAN MOTORS					
1967	4216S	5/16	2	3/8	77	9/32	7/16	0.020	—	2 Rich
	4258S	5/16	2	3/8	77	5/32	7/16	0.020	—	1 Rich
	4352S	5/16	2	3/8	77	9/64	7/16	0.020	—	Index
	4353S	5/16	2	3/8	77	9/64	7/16	0.020	—	2 Rich
	4354S	5/16	2	3/8	77	9/32	7/16	0.020	—	2 Rich
	4358S	5/16	2	3/8	77	5/32	7/16	0.020	—	Index
1968	4467S	11/32	23/32	13/32	80	5/32	7/16	0.020	—	2 Rich
	4468S	11/32	23/32	7/16	77	5/32	7/16	0.020	—	1 Rich
	4469S	11/32	23/32	7/16	77	5/32	7/16	0.020	—	2 Rich
	4583S	11/32	23/32	13/32	76	5/32	7/16	0.020	—	2 Rich
	4584S	11/32	23/32	7/16	76	5/32	7/16	0.020	—	1 Rich
	4585S	11/32	23/32	7/16	73	5/32	7/16	0.020	—	1 Rich
	4622S	11/32	23/32	13/32	80	5/32	7/16	0.020	—	2 Rich
	4623S	11/32	23/32	7/16	77	5/32	7/16	0.020	—	1 Rich
	4624S	11/32	23/32	7/16	77	5/32	7/16	0.020	—	2 Rich
1969	4660S	11/32	2	21/64	—	5/32	7/16	0.015	—	2 Rich
	4661S	11/32	2	21/64	—	5/32	7/16	0.015	—	Index
	4662S	11/32	2	21/64	—	5/32	7/16	0.015	—	Index
	4663S	11/32	2	21/64	—	5/32	7/16	0.015	—	Index
	4664S	11/32	2	21/64	—	5/32	7/16	0.015	—	Index
	4665S	11/32	2	21/64	—	5/32	7/16	0.015	—	Index

① The center hole
② The top hole
③ At curb idle
④ Indicates drill bit number. See Mechanic's Data
⑤ Place the connector rod in the inner hole
⑥ Model numbers are located on a tag or on the casting

Dash Gauges and Indicators

There are various systems used to indicate values of heat, pressure, current flow and fuel supply. The following are the more popular systems used.

Bourdon Tube

This gauge consists of a flattened tube that is bent to form a curve. The curve tends to straighten under internal pressure caused by engine oil pressure. The curved tube is geared or linked to an indicator needle which may be read on a calibrated scale.

Bourdon tube oil pressure gauges are used on Corvettes and the optional instrument panels on some Chevrolet sport models. This type of gauge may be easily distinguished from the electrical type by the small copper or nylon tube running from the gauge to the engine.

Bi-Metallic or Thermal

This gauge is activated by the difference in the expansion factors of a bi-metal bar. A sending unit, consisting of a variable resistance conductor, influences current flow to a voltage limiter, or directly to a heating element coiled around a bi-metal bar in the gauge. A bi-metallic gauge pointer will move slowly to its gauging position.

Magnetic

In this system, the indicator needle is moved by changing the balance between the magnetic pull of two coils built in the gauge. When the ignition switch is in the "off" position, the pointer may rest any place on the gauge dial. Balance is controlled by the action of a sending unit or a tank unit containing a rheostat, the value of which varies with temperature, pressure or movement of a float arm. A magnetic gauge will snap to its position when turned on.

Warning Lights

This system is quite popular and may be used to indicate heat, low pressure or as a battery discharge indicator. General Motors uses a two-light temperature indicator version of this unit in some models.

Section 1
Bourdon Tube

Oil Pressure

The gauge is the pressure expansion type and is activated by oil pressure developed by the oil pump, acting directly on the mechanism of the gauge. The gauge is connected by a small tube to the main oil passage in the engine oiling system. This design

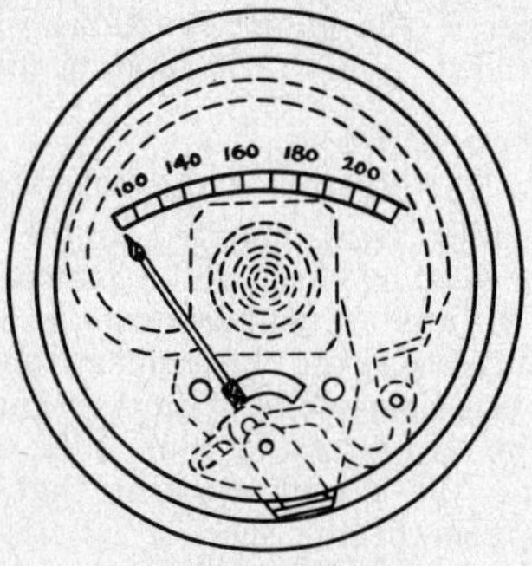

100
140
160
180
200

Bourdon tube gauge

registers the full pressure of the oil pump.

Testing

A gauge pointer that flutters is usually an indication that oil has entered the gauge tube. The tube should contain trapped air to cushion the pulsations of the oil pump and relief valve. Oil can work up into the gauge line as a result of a gauge or tube leak or improper installation. To correct this condition, renew the unit or correct the leak; then, with the gauge line disconnected at both ends, blow the line clear. Connect line at gauge first and then at the engine.

If the gauge reads too low or reads no pressure, test for a possible obstruction by disconnecting the line at the gauge. Hold the end of the line over an empty container, then start the engine. After a few bubbles, oil should flow steadily.

If oil does not flow satisfactorily, first make sure that the oil level is correct and that the oil pump is functioning. Should the engine oil system be operating correctly, the problem is either with the gauge or the line. Check the line for kinks, leaks, or blockage which would prevent oil from reaching the gauge. If the line is unobstructed, remove the gauge unit from the instrument panel. Check to make sure that the hole leading to the Bourdon tube is clear and be sure that the lever linkage and pointer gears operate freely. If none of these points is at fault, the Bourdon tube itself is defective and the gauge must be replaced.

Caution Do not distort the gauge during installation, or the Bourdon tube may be damaged.

Section 2
Bi-Metal

Fuel

Bi-metal or thermal type gauges operate on the principle of constant applied voltage and are sensitive only to changes originating at the sending unit.

The fuel gauge system consists of a sending unit, located in the fuel tank, and a registering unit mounted in the instrument cluster. The sending unit is a rheostat that varies its resistance depending on the amount of fuel in the tank.

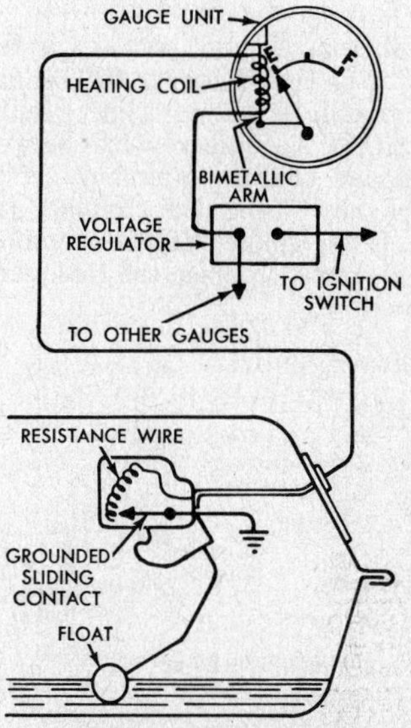

GAUGE UNIT
HEATING COIL
E
F
BIMETALLIC ARM
VOLTAGE REGULATOR
TO IGNITION SWITCH
TO OTHER GAUGES
RESISTANCE WIRE
GROUNDED SLIDING CONTACT
FLOAT

Bi-metallic fuel gauge system

Testing the Dash Gauge

Caution Gauge systems using constant voltage regulators should not be grounded while testing. An excess of 5 volts is likely to burn out the unit.

To safely test this type of voltage regulated system:

1. Have the ignition switch in the "off" position.
2. Connect the terminals of four, series-connected, D-type flashlight batteries (total of six volts) to the terminals of the gauge to be tested. Three volts should cause the gauge to read approximately half-scale.

If the gauge reads half-full and was not working properly before, the sending unit in the tank is probably defective.

If the gauge is inaccurate or does not register, replace it.

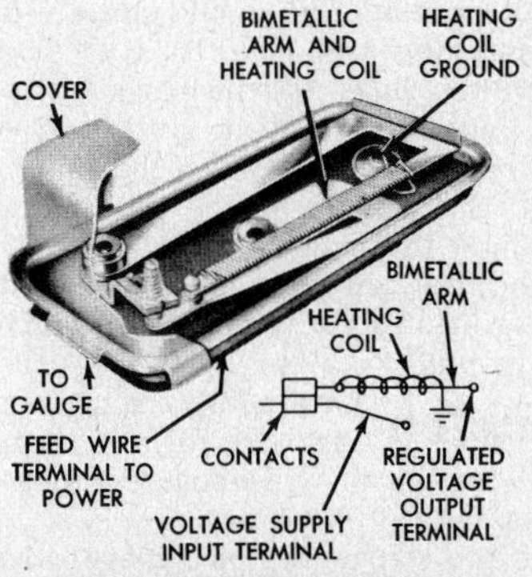

BIMETALLIC ARM AND HEATING COIL
HEATING COIL GROUND
COVER
BIMETALLIC ARM
HEATING COIL
TO GAUGE
FEED WIRE TERMINAL TO POWER
CONTACTS
REGULATED VOLTAGE OUTPUT TERMINAL
VOLTAGE SUPPLY INPUT TERMINAL

Constant voltage regulator

If both the fuel gauge and temperature gauge are in error, in the same manner, the constant voltage regulator is probably at fault.

While working under the dash, be careful not to ground any of the gauges. A full flow of current through the regulator to ground is likely to burn out the regulator.

Testing the Sending Unit

If the dash gauge test shows that unit to be satisfactory, the sending unit or gauge system wiring is faulty. Substitute a jumper wire between the gauge and the tank unit. If the gauge now functions, replace the wire. If the gauge still does not function correctly, replace the tank sending unit.

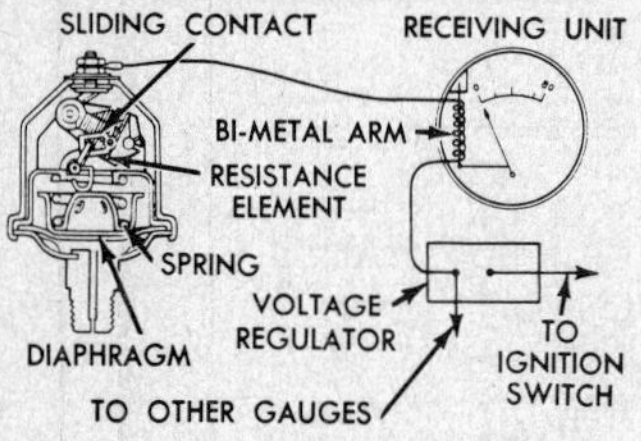
SLIDING CONTACT
RECEIVING UNIT
BI-METAL ARM
RESISTANCE ELEMENT
SPRING
VOLTAGE REGULATOR
DIAPHRAGM
TO IGNITION SWITCH
TO OTHER GAUGES

Bi-metallic oil gauge circuit

Oil Pressure

Oil pressure gauges of the bi-metal type operate on the same principle as gas gauges. They are activated by temperature and the difference in the expansion factors of a bi-metal bar.

The pressure sending unit consists of a pressure-activated variable resistor. This sealed unit is usually screwed into the engine oil pressure circuit. As pressure is applied to one side of a diaphragm, linkage advances a contact arm across the coils of a resistor. This action reduces resistance in the gauge circuit, thus increasing current flow and heat to the bi-metal arm in the gauge. The gauge is calibrated to read oil pressure in psi.

Run the engine and have an assistant watch the dash gauge. If the gauge reads zero, turn off the engine and remove the sending unit from the engine block. Restart the engine and allow it to idle for a minute. If there is oil pressure, oil should surge from the sending unit hole. If no oil flows from the hole, the problem is with the engine lubricating system. If oil flows, the fault lies with the sending unit, the wiring, or the dash gauge.

Check the gauge by grounding the connecting wire for an instant with the ignition switch turned on. A good gauge will go to the top of its scale.

Caution Grounding the connecting wire for any longer than a moment will damage the dash units.

If the gauge did not move when grounded, check the wiring to the dash unit for continuity. If the wiring is not faulty and the gauge doesn't register when grounded, replace the gauge. If the gauge functions when grounded, replace the sending unit.

Temperature

The temperature gauge consists of a sending unit, mounted in the cylinder head or block, and a remote resistor unit (temperature gauge) mounted on the instrument panel. The principle of operation is essentially the same as the bi-metallic fuel gauge, the exception being that the resistance of the sending unit is influenced by engine temperature instead of tank fuel level, as with the fuel gauge.

The temperature sending unit is constructed with a coil spring and sensing disc. Current passing through this coil encounters increased resistance, proportional to an increase in temperature. The gauge registers this resistance change and is calibrated to indicate the temperature.

Testing the Dash Gauge

Connect four D-cells (total of 6 volts) in series with the dash gauge, with the ignition switched off. A good gauge will register ½ on the scale. Replace the gauge if it does not move.

Testing the Sending Unit

Bring the engine to normal operating temperature (check with a thermometer). If the gauge doesn't register, disconnect the connecting wire from the engine sending unit and ground the connecting wire for an instant and have an assistant observe the gauge.

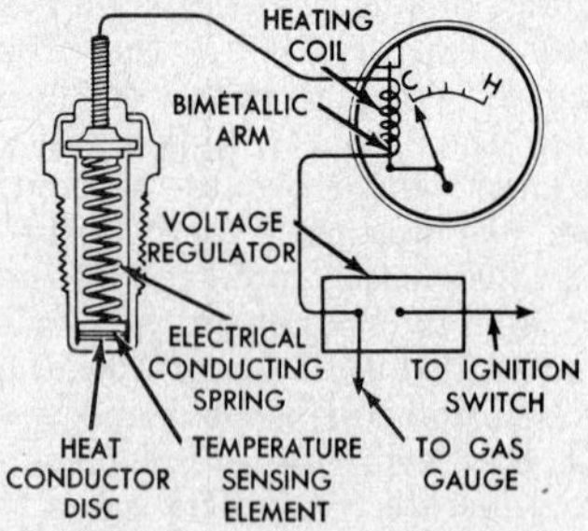
HEATING COIL
BIMETALLIC ARM
VOLTAGE REGULATOR
ELECTRICAL CONDUCTING SPRING
TO IGNITION SWITCH
HEAT CONDUCTOR DISC
TEMPERATURE SENSING ELEMENT
TO GAS GAUGE

Bi-metallic temperature gauge

Caution Grounding the wire for any longer than a moment will damage the dash units.

If the gauge shows no reading, replace the connecting wire. If the gauge registers when grounded, replace the sending unit.

Section 3
Magnetic

Fuel

The magnetic fuel gauge consists of two units, the dash unit and the sending unit in the fuel tank. One terminal of the dash unit is connected to the ignition switch so that the system is active only when the ignition is on. With the ignition off, the pointer may come to rest at any position on the dial.

The gauge pointer is moved by varying the magnetic pull of two coils in the unit. The magnetic pull is controlled by the action of the tank unit which contains a variable rheostat, the value of which varies with movement of a float and arm.

When the ignition switch is on and the tank unit arm is in the full position, the current flow to ground is through the resistor, battery coil and the ground coil. Because the ground coil has more windings than the battery coil, it builds up a stronger magnetic field and the pointer is pulled to the full position.

When the tank unit arm is in the empty position, the current flow is through the resistor, the battery coil and the wire to ground at the tank unit. The pointer is thus pulled to the empty position. The resistor in series with the battery coil balances resistance between the two coils in the dash unit.

Testing the Dash Gauge

Disconnect the wire from the tank unit. Using a tank unit of known accuracy, clip a test wire from the body of the test unit to ground. Clip another test wire from the connector of the test unit to the tank unit wire. With the ignition on, moving the float arm through its entire range should cause the gauge to respond proportionally. If the dash gauge does not correspond to the movement of the test unit and the wiring to the gauge is OK, the dash unit is bad.

Testing the Tank Unit

If tests indicate that the trouble lies in the tank unit, remove the unit and check for mechanical failure. The unit may have either a fuel logged or binding float.

An electrical check for circuit continuity may be made throughout the unit's range.

Temperature

The temperature gauge system consists of a magnetic dash unit and a resistance-type sending unit screwed into the water jacket of the cylinder head or the engine block.

The dash unit has two magnetic poles. One of the windings is connected to the ignition switch and ground. This electromagnet exerts a steady pull to hold the gauge pointer to the left or "cold" position when the ignition is on.

The other winding in the dash unit connects to a ground through the engine sending unit. This electromag-

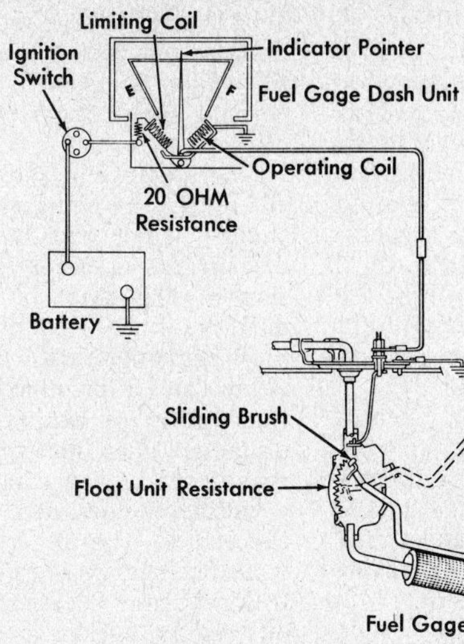
Limiting Coil
Ignition Switch
Indicator Pointer
Fuel Gage Dash Unit
E
F
Operating Coil
20 OHM Resistance
Battery
Sliding Brush
Float Unit Resistance
Float
Filter
Fuel Gage Tank Unit

Magnetic fuel gauge circuit

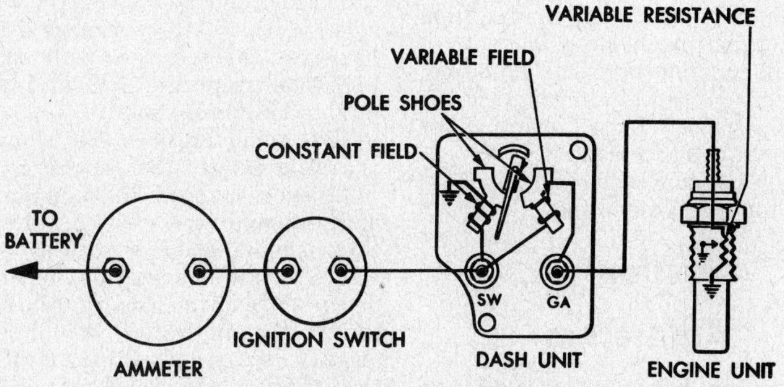
VARIABLE RESISTANCE
VARIABLE FIELD
POLE SHOES
CONSTANT FIELD
TO BATTERY
SW
GA
AMMETER
IGNITION SWITCH
DASH UNIT
ENGINE UNIT

Magnetic temperature gauge

net exerts a steady pull on the gauge pointer toward the right, or "hot" side of the gauge. The strength of this pull is dependent upon the current allowed to pass through the engine unit (sending unit) resistor.

The sending unit, located in the engine cooling system, contains a flat disc (thermistor) that changes resistance as its temperature varies.

NOTE: this sending unit, while similar in appearance, is different and is not interchangeable with the unit used in systems using bi-metal or thermal dash gauges. The resistance of the thermistor disc is maximum when the temperature is cold and minimum when hot. The decrease in resistance allows more current to flow through the electromagnet connected to the engine unit. The resulting increase in magnetic pull causes the gauge pointer to move to the right, or "hot" side.

Tests

1. Disconnect the wire at the sending unit and turn on the ignition switch. The gauge hand should stay against the cold side stop pin.
2. Ground the wire disconnected from the sending unit. With the ignition switch still on, the gauge hand should swing across the dial to the hot stop pin.

Corrective Measures

If the gauge hand does not stay to the left, either the wire is grounded between the dash unit and the engine unit or the dash unit is defective.

Test further by disconnecting the sending unit wire at the gauge. Turn on the ignition. If the gauge hand stays on the left-hand stop pin, replace the disconnected wire. If the gauge still moves, replace the gauge.

If the gauge hand does not swing across the dial, there is an open circuit in the wire between the sending unit and gauge, the gauge is defective, or current is not reaching the dash gauge.

Test further by grounding the sending unit terminal of the dash gauge and turning on the ignition. If the gauge hand now moves, replace the disconnected wire. If the gauge hand does not move, connect a test lamp into the circuit. If the test lamp does not light, test the wire between the ignition switch and the dash unit by connecting the lamp to the accessory terminal at the ignition switch and ground. The test lamp should light.

If the gauge hand operates correctly, but the gauge does not indicate temperature correctly, either the sending unit is defective or the dash gauge is out of calibration. Replace sending unit with one of known accuracy. If gauge reading is still incorrect, replace the gauge.

If the gauge hand is at maximum at all times, and tests 1 and 2 indicate that the wiring and the dash unit are good, the sending unit must be replaced.

If the gauge hand will not move, the dash unit is bad, or incorrectly installed. Correct the installation or replace the gauge.

Section 4
Warning Lights

Oil Pressure

The warning or indicator light system supplies the driver with a visual signal of low engine oil pressure. The light usually lights at pressures below 5 psi.

The low pressure warning light is wired in series with an oil pressure sending unit. The sending unit is tapped into the main oil gallery and is sensitive to oil pressure. The unit contains a diaphragm, spring linkage and electrical contacts. When the ignition switch is on, the warning light circuit is energized and the circuit is completed through the closed contacts in the sending unit. When the engine starts, oil pressure will compress the diaphragm, opening the contact points and breaking the circuit.

Tests

The light should light when the engine is not running and the ignition switch is turned on. If the light does not go on, first substitute a new bulb. If there is still no light, check the wire from the light to the switch. If the wire is not at fault, disconnect the wire at the sending unit and ground it. Replace the sending unit if the light now lights.

Temperature

This system employs a heat sending unit with either one or two sets of contacts. Some systems use a green light to indicate subnormal, and a red light to warn of abnormal heat. The more common system, however, uses a simple make-and-break heat-sensitive sending unit screwed into the engine cooling system, and wired in series with the hot indicator light in the instrument panel.

The two-light system uses a bi-metal element mounted between two signal circuits. Normal operating temperature (somewhere between 120°F. and 250°F.) will cause the bi-metal bar to assume a position of no contact between the low and the high temperature circuit. When the igni-

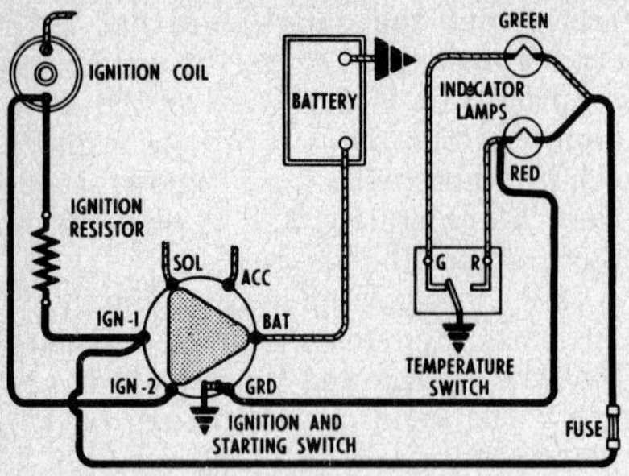
GREEN
IGNITION COIL
BATTERY
INDICATOR LAMPS
RED
IGNITION RESISTOR
SOL
ACC
IGN-1
BAT
G R
TEMPERATURE SWITCH
IGN-2
GRD
IGNITION AND STARTING SWITCH
FUSE

Cold and hot temperature indicator circuit

tion switch is turned on, with a cold engine, the cold (green) circuit is complete. If the engine becomes hot enough to move the bi-metal bar so that it touches the contacts of the hot circuit, the hot (red) light comes on. This hot signal indicates that temperatures are in the area of 250°F. in the sealed cooling system.

Tests

Use the same testing procedure given for oil pressure.

Charge Indicator

A light is used to indicate general charging system operation. When output is below battery potential, a red light is shown. When output is above battery potential, other factors (wiring, voltage regulator, etc.) being normal, the light is out.

The charge indicator bulb is connected to the charging circuit, obtaining its ground through the voltage regulator. When the output rises above battery potential, the current flow causes the light to go out.

When an alternator is used, it is necessary to supply a small amount of excitation current to the alternator field, due to the small amount of residual magnetism. Current can be supplied from the battery, through the indicator light, and to the regulator terminal on the alternator. This current has a value of about 12 volts at .25 amperes and will cause the indicator light to come on when the ignition switch is turned on.

When the alternator starts to generate, an output voltage is developed at the regulator terminal. When this voltage exceeds the battery voltage, current will pass from the alternator to the battery and to the system. This current is flowing in the reverse direction of the voltage supplied by the battery. The current flow coming from the alternator exceeds the battery current by a regulated 1 or 2 volts. This is not enough to light the indicator light, therefore, the light will go out when the alternator is supplying sufficient current.

If the alternator output current should drop below battery voltage, current will begin to flow in the opposite direction. If it exceeds 2 or 3 volts, the light will glow indicating that the alternator is not operating properly.

Caution In some instances, a glow of the indicator light will be noticed at night while cruising. This can exist in a system that is operating normally and with a fully charged battery. The condition, while of no great importance, is probably caused by an overload of equipment and accessories.

See "Charging and Starting Systems" for troubleshooting.

Section 5

Ammeters

The automotive ammeter is a gauge or meter used to indicate direction and relative value of current flow. This type of charge indicator is usually equipped with a dampening device to reduce pointer fluctuation during current surge from the voltage regulator.

The meter will show charge when the battery is being charged and discharge when the battery is being discharged. It merely gives an indication of the state of charge of the battery, since it shows a relatively high charging rate when the battery is low, and a low charging rate when the battery is near full charge. An ammeter does not give a complete report of battery condition, whereas a voltmeter does. Just after cranking the engine, the meter will swing toward the charge side for a short time, if lights and accessories are turned off. As the energy spent in cranking is restored to the battery, the pointer will gradually move back toward center but should stay on the charge side. If the battery charge is low, however, the indicator will show a high charging rate for an indeterminate length of time.

The ammeter does not show the charging rate of the generator.

At speeds above 30-35 mph, with all lights and accessories on, the indicator should show a reading somewhere on the charge side, depending on the state of the battery. Above this speed, the indicator should never show a discharge reading; if it does, the generator and regulator should be tested. See "Charging and Starting Systems" for troubleshooting.

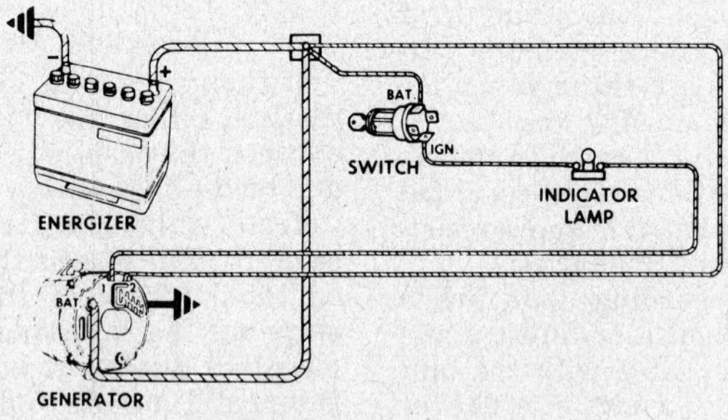
BAT
SWITCH
IGN.
INDICATOR LAMP
ENERGIZER
BAT
GENERATOR

Charging indicator light circuit

INDEX

Emission Control Systems

Section Contents

General Introduction

With emission level maintenance standards getting stricter on both the State and Federal levels, proper testing and adjustment of emission control systems are becoming increasingly important. Much confusion results from the many types and combinations of emission control systems currently in use.

To ease some of the confusion, the emission control systems section in this book has been divided into two parts. The first part is found in each of the individual car sections. It explains which system and components each make and model uses. Component R&R is also given where it is available.

The second part, below, covers testing and adjustment of the emission control systems and their individual components. Many of the components are similar (or the same) from one manufacturer to another and therefore the testing procedures are the same. Thus, one test may be used for several different manufacturers or models. Where components, although similar, differ significantly the tests are different.

For the sake of added clarity, a general description of the various types of emission control systems follows.

Positive Crankcase Ventilation (PCV) Systems

A simple valve, operated by intake manifold vacuum, is used to meter the flow of air and vapors through the crankcase. Air is drawn in through either the breather cap, on pre-1968 cars (open system), or, on cars made after 1968, through the carburetor air cleaner (closed system). When the car is decelerating or the engine is idling, high manifold vacuum closes the valve; this restricts the flow of crankcase vapor into the intake manifold. During acceleration or at a constant speed, the intake manifold vacuum drops, the valve spring forces the valve open and more vapors flow into the intake manifold from the crankcase. If a backfire occurs the valve closes, preventing the vapor in the crankcase from being ignited. If the vapor is ignited, an explosion will result.

Air Injection System

A belt-driven air pump supplies air to an injection manifold which has a nozzle positioned behind each exhaust valve. Injection of air at this point causes combustion of any unburned hydrocarbons in the exhaust manifold rather than allowing them to escape into the atmosphere. An antibackfire valve controls the flow of air from the pump to prevent backfires resulting from an overly rich mixture under closed throttle conditions. A check valve, sometimes an integral part of the air injection manifold, functions to prevent hot exhaust gas backflow into the pump and hoses in case of pump failure or when the antibackfire valve is working.

Thermostatically Controlled Air Cleaner

Thermostatically controlled air cleaners are used to improve operation of the engine and to prevent carburetor icing during warm-up in cold weather.

A movable door in the air cleaner snorkle allows air to be drawn in from either a manifold heat stove (cold operation) or from under the hood (normal operation). The door may be operated by a bimetallic spring or a vacuum motor. Doors of both types may use a vacuum override to provide cold air intake during periods of hard acceleration when stove-heated air is normally being supplied.

Distributor Controls

There are three basic types of distributor controls:

1. Engine vacuum controls
2. Transmission-controlled spark —transmission gear selected and/or temperature.
3. Speed-controlled spark—vehicles speed and/or temperature.

It is easier to consider these three types separately, although some of them perform similar functions and may be used in conjunction with one another.

Engine Vacuum Controls

Many small valves and solenoids fall into this class of emission controls. Some distributors are equipped with a dual-diaphragm vacuum unit which retards the spark during closed throttle deceleration and idle. On some distributors, solenoids may be used to either advance or retard the timing under predetermined conditions.

A deceleration valve may be used to provide maximum vacuum advance when the car is slowing down, by sending intake manifold vacuum to the distributor vacuum unit. By doing this, emissions may be better controlled during deceleration.

Because emission-controlled engines run hotter, it is often necessary to use a coolant temperature vacuum valve to provide additional vacuum advance when the engine is overheated. The valve is threaded into an engine coolant passage. If the engine overheats, the additional vacuum advance causes the engine speed to increase; allowing it to cool down quite rapidly. A similar valve may also be used to determine the temperature at which a TCS, SCS, or EGR system operates (see below).

A spark delay valve is installed on some engines to prevent the vacuum advance from working immediately under heavy acceleration.

Transmission-Controlled Spark (TCS) System

Many variations of transmission-controlled spark (TCS) systems are used to control vehicle emissions. The basic components of these systems are: a transmission switch, which is operated either by oil pressure (automatic transmissions) or by the gear selected (manual transmission); and a vacuum solenoid. The solenoid allows vacuum to be supplied to the distributor vacuum unit or ports it into the atmosphere. Usually vacuum is supplied only in high gear and is ported in the lower gears. However, few TCS systems are quite this simple.

For example, most TCS systems use some type of temperature switch to control their operation, i.e., the system will not function below a specified air or engine temperature. In some cases it will not work above a specified temperature either. Some cars use a coolant temperature-operated vacuum valve in conjuction with the TCS system.

Various reversing and time delay relays may also be used, depending upon the needs of the engine and transmission.

Speed-Controlled Spark (SCS) Systems

Speed-controlled spark (SCS) systems perform a similar function to the transmission-controlled systems above. Many of the components are the same and used in similar way in both of the systems. The major difference lies in the switch which is activated by the speed, rather than the gear.

In its simplest form, this switch is nothing more than a centrifugal switch, connected to the speedometer drive, which completes the SCS circuit at or above a predetermined speed. A more complicated type of switch uses a small speedometer gear (or speedometer cable) driven pulse generator to send a signal to an amplifier, which, in turn, completes the SCS system circuit at predetermined speed.

Once the circuit has been completed, vacuum is allowed to flow to the distributor vacuum unit. When the circuit is not energized, vacuum is ported into the atmosphere.

Like the transmission-controlled spark systems, SCS systems use temperature switches and various relays.

Carburetor Controls

Because of the increase in engine speed necessary to control emissions at idle, dieseling has become a problem. As a result, many carburetors use a solenoid to allow the throttle to close when the ingition is shut off, thus reducing engine speed which, in turn, prevents dieseling.

To prevent dieseling on some air-conditioned cars, a signal from an amplifier engages the A/C compressor clutch momentarily when the engine is shut off. This puts a load on the engine, thus slowing it down.

Evaporative Emission Control Systems

To control emissions resulting from fuel evaporation, all cars made after 1971 use a closed fuel supply system. Instead of fuel vapor being vented into the atmosphere, it goes into a vapor/liquid separator and is routed from there, either directly through a charcoal storage canister, or into the crankcase. To prevent vapor loss at other points, the carburetor has controlled vents and a PCV system (see above) is used along with the evaporative emission control system.

Exhaust Gas Recirculation (EGR)

Exhaust gas recirculation (EGR) systems are used to reduce NO_x emissions by lowering peak flame temperature during combustion. Exhaust gases are routed into the intake manifold via floor jets, intake manifold passages, and/or an EGR control valve. This valve may be located either on the intake manifold or on a special carburetor spacer.

Some EGR systems use coolant temperature-operated vacuum valves or air temperature-operated valves to determine when they function. In addition, a vacuum amplifier (mechanical) may be provided if a weak vacuum signal is being supplied to the EGR valve.

Troubleshooting

NOTE: For model usage, a description of, as well as, available removal and installation procedures for the components of emission control systems, consult the individual car repair sections. This section covers tests and adjustments only. Tests and adjustments for 1974 models may be found in the individual car sections.

Positive Crankcase Ventilation (PCV) System

Valve Tests

1. See if any deposits are present in the carburetor passages, the oil filler cap, or the hoses. Clean these as required.
2. Connect a tachometer, as instructed by its manufacturer, to the engine.
3. With the engine idling, do one of the following:
   a. Remove the PCV valve hose from the crankcase or the oil filler connection.
   b. On cars with the PCV valve located in a grommet on the valve cover, remove both the valve and the grommet.

NOTE: If the valve and the hoses are not clogged-up, a hissing sound should be present.

4. Check the tachometer reading. Place a finger over the valve or hose opening (a suction should be felt).
5. Check the tachometer again. The engine speed should have dropped at least 50 rpm. It should return to normal when the finger is removed from the opening.
6. If the engine does not change speed or if the change is less than 50 rpm, the hose is clogged or the valve is defective. Check the hose first. If the hose is not clogged replace, do not attempt to repair, the PCV valve.
7. Test the new valve in the above manner, to make sure that it is operating properly.

NOTE: There are several commercial PCV valve testers available. Be sure that the one used is suitable for the valve to be tested, as the testers are not universal. Follow the manufacturer's instructions.

Air Injection Systems

Air Pump Tests

Caution Do not hammer on, pry, or bend the pump housing while tightening the drive belt or testing the pump.

Belt Tension and Air Leaks

1. Before proceeding with the tests, check the pump drive belt tension to see if it is within specifications.
2. Turn the pump by hand. If it has seized, the belt will slip, producing noise. Disregard any chirping, squealing, or rolling sounds from inside the pump; these are normal when it is turned by hand.
3. Check the hoses and connections for leaks. Hissing or a blast of air is indicative of a leak. Soapy water, applied lightly around the area in question, is a good method for detecting leaks.

Air Output Tests

1. Disconnect the air supply hose at the antibackfire valve.
2. Connect a vacuum gauge, using a suitable adaptor, to the air supply hose.

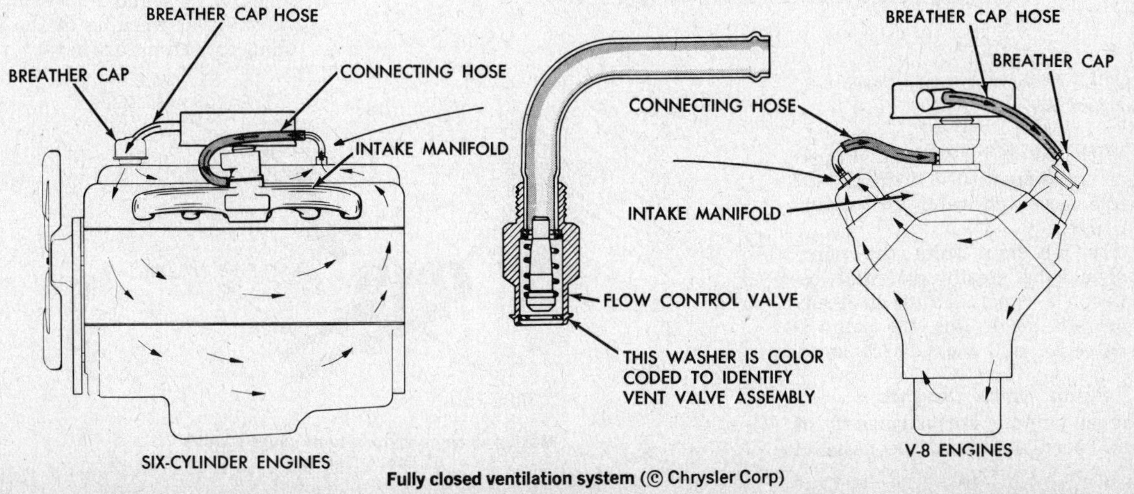
BREATHER CAP HOSE
BREATHER CAP
CONNECTING HOSE
INTAKE MANIFOLD
SIX-CYLINDER ENGINES
FLOW CONTROL VALVE
THIS WASHER IS COLOR CODED TO IDENTIFY VENT VALVE ASSEMBLY
BREATHER CAP HOSE
BREATHER CAP
CONNECTING HOSE
INTAKE MANIFOLD
V-8 ENGINES

Fully closed ventilation system (© Chrysler Corp)

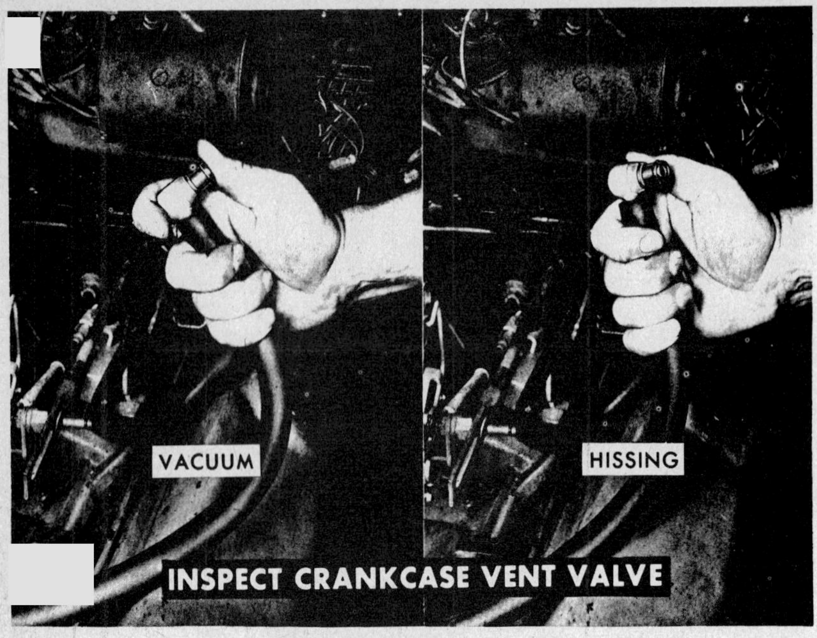
VACUUM
HISSING
INSPECT CRANKCASE VENT VALVE

Testing PCV valve (© Chrysler Corp)

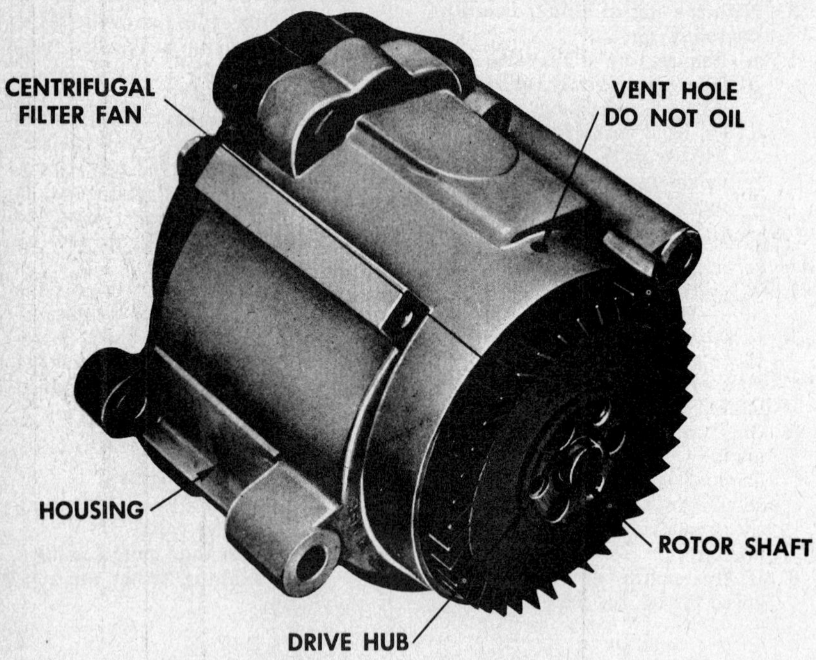
CENTRIFUGAL FILTER FAN
VENT HOLE DO NOT OIL
HOUSING
ROTOR SHAFT
DRIVE HUB

Identifying the external parts of an air pump (© G.M. Corp)

NOTE: If there are two hoses plug the second one up.

3. With the engine at normal operating temperature, increase the idle speed and watch the vacuum gauge.
4. The air flow from the pump should be steady and fall between 2–6 psi. If it is unsteady or falls below this, the pump is defective and must be replaced.

Pump Noise Diagnosis

The air pump is normally noisy; as engine speed increases, the noise of the pump will rise in pitch. The rolling sound the pump bearings make is normal, however if this sound becomes objectionable at certain speeds, the pump is defective and will have to be replaced.

A continual hissing sound from the air pump pressure relief valve at idle, indicates a defective valve. Replace the relief valve.

If the pump rear bearing fails, a continual knocking sound will be heard. Since the rear bearing is not separately replaceable, the pump will have to be replaced as an assembly.

Antibackfire Valve Tests

There are two different types of antibackfire valves used with air injection systems. A by-pass (diverter) valve is used on most current engines, while most older engines use a gulp type antibackfire valve. Test procedures for both types are given below.

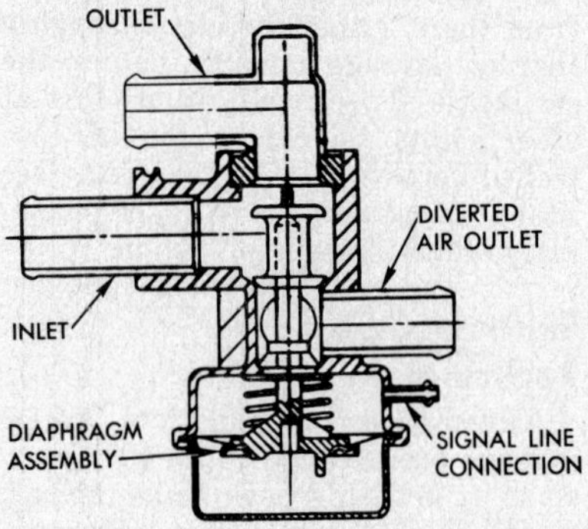
OUTLET
DIVERTED AIR OUTLET
INLET
DIAPHRAGM ASSEMBLY
SIGNAL LINE CONNECTION

VALVE IN OPEN POSITION

GM type air by-pass (diverter) valve

Gulp Valve

1. Detach the air supply hose which runs between the pump and the gulp valve.
2. Connect a tachometer and run the engine between 1,500–2,000 rpm.
3. Allow the throttle to snap closed. This should produce a loud sucking sound from the gulp valve.
4. Repeat this operation several times. If no sound is present, the valve is not working or the vacuum connections are loose.

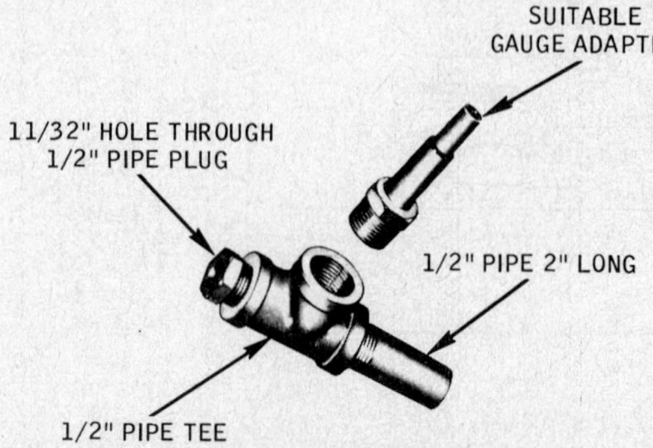
SUITABLE GAUGE ADAPTER
11/32" HOLE THROUGH 1/2" PIPE PLUG
1/2" PIPE 2" LONG
1/2" PIPE TEE

Making an air pump-to-vacuum gauge adaptor (© Ford Motor Co)

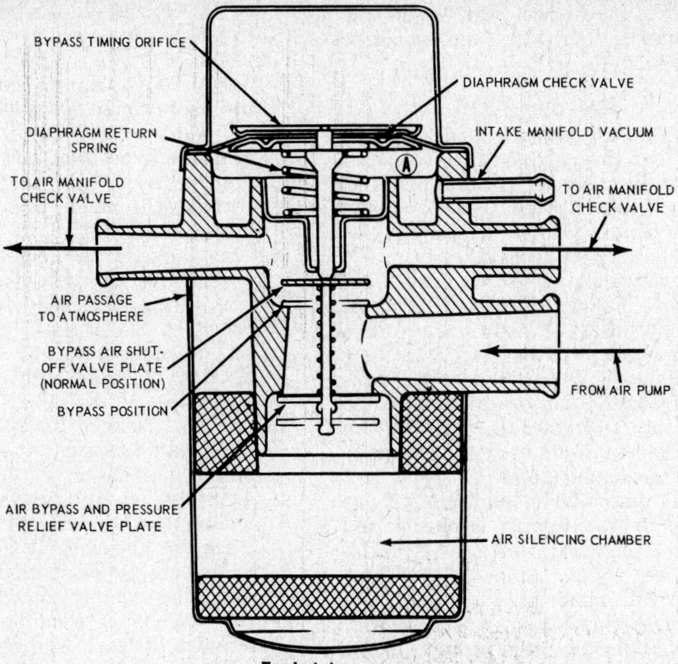
BYPASS TIMING ORIFICE
DIAPHRAGM CHECK VALVE
DIAPHRAGM RETURN SPRING
INTAKE MANIFOLD VACUUM
TO AIR MANIFOLD CHECK VALVE
TO AIR MANIFOLD CHECK VALVE
A
AIR PASSAGE TO ATMOSPHERE
BYPASS AIR SHUT-OFF VALVE PLATE (NORMAL POSITION)
BYPASS POSITION
FROM AIR PUMP
AIR BYPASS AND PRESSURE RELIEF VALVE PLATE
AIR SILENCING CHAMBER

Ford air by-pass valve

5. Check the vacuum connections. If they are secure, replace the gulp valve.

By-pass (Diverter) Valve

1. Detach the hose, which runs from the by-pass valve to the check valve, at the by-pass valve hose connection.
2. Connect a tachometer to the engine. With the engine running at normal idle speed, check to see that air is flowing from the by-pass valve hose connection.
3. Speed the engine up, so that it is running at 1,500–2,000 rpm. Allow the throttle to snap shut. The flow of air from the by-pass valve at the check valve hose connection should stop momentarily and air should then flow from the exhaust port on the valve body or the silencer assembly.
4. Repeat step three several times. If the flow of air is not diverted into the atmosphere from the valve exhaust port or if it fails to stop flowing from the hose connection, check the vacuum lines and connections. If these are tight, the valve is defective and requires replacement.
5. A leaking diaphragm will cause the air to flow out both the hose connection and the exhaust port at the same time. If this happens, replace the valve.

Check Valve Test

1. Before starting the test, check all of the hoses and connections for leaks.
2. Detach the air supply hose(s) from the check valve(s).
3. Insert a suitable probe into the check valve and depress the plate. Release it; the plate should return to its original position against the valve seat. If binding is evident, replace the valve.
4. Repeat step three if two valves are used.
5. With the engine running at normal operating temperature, gradually increase its speed to 1,500 rpm. Check for exhaust gas leakage. If any is present, replace the valve assembly.

NOTE: Vibration and flutter of the check valve at idle speed is a normal condition and does not mean that the valve should be replaced.

Thermostatically Controlled Air Cleaner

Air Door Tests

Non-Vacuum-Operated and Ford Vacuum-Operated

1. Unfasten the temperature sensing valve and snorkle assembly from the air cleaner. Place it in a container of cold water. Make sure that the thermostat is completely covered with water.
2. Place a thermometer, of known accuracy, in the water. Heat the water slowly and watch the temperature.
3. At 105° F, or less, the door should be closed (manifold heat position).
4. Continue heating the water until it reaches 130° F. The door should be fully open to the outside air position.

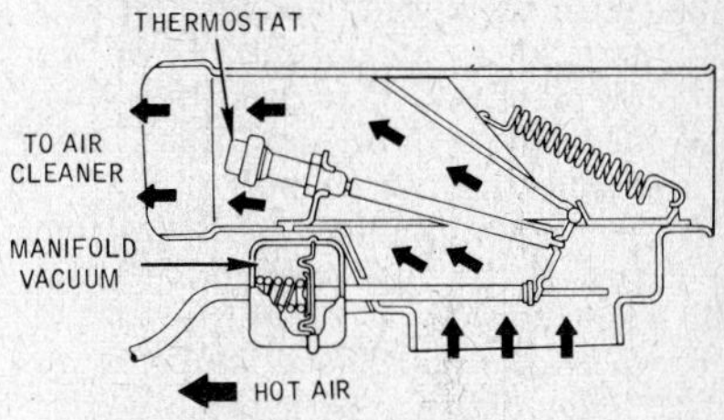
THERMOSTAT
TO AIR CLEANER
MANIFOLD VACUUM
HOT AIR

Duct and valve assembly in "heat on" position — warm-up

5. If the door does not open at or near this temperature, check it for binding or a detached spring. If neither of this situations exist, the sensor is defective and must be replaced.

NOTE: This usually means that the entire snorkle assembly must be replaced.

Vacuum-Operated Door—Except Ford

1. Either start with a cold engine or remove the air cleaner from the engine for at least half an hour. While cooling the air cleaner, leave the engine compartment hood open.
2. Tape a thermometer, of known accuracy, to the inside of the air cleaner so that it is near the temperature sensor unit. Install the air cleaner on the engine but do not fasten its securing nut.
3. Start the engine. With the engine cold and the outside temperature less than 90°F., the door should be in the "heat on" position (closed to outside air).

AIR INJECTION SYSTEM DIAGNOSIS CHART

Problem	*Cause*	*Cure*
1. Noisy drive belt	1a Loose belt 1b Seized pump	1a Tighten belt 1b Replace
2. Noisy pump	2a Leaking hose 2b Loose hose 2c Hose contacting other parts 2d Diverter or check valve failure 2e Pump mounting loose 2g Defective pump	2a Trace and fix leak 2b Tighten hose clamp 2c Reposition hose 2d Replace 2e Tighten securing bolts 2g Replace
3. No air supply	3a Loose belt 3b Leak in hose or at fitting 3c Defective anti-backfire valve 3d Defective check valve 3e Defective pump	3a Tighten belt 3b Trace and fix leak 3c Replace 3d Replace 3e Replace
4. Exhaust backfire	4a Vacuum or air leaks 4b Defective anti-backfire valve 4c Sticking choke 4d Choke setting rich	4a Trace and fix leak 4b Replace 4c Service choke 4d Adjust choke

NOTE: Due to the position of the air cleaner on some cars, a mirror may be necessary when observing the position of the air door.

4. Operate the throttle lever rapidly to ½–¾ of its opening and release it. The air door should open to allow outside air to enter and then close again.
5. Allow the engine to warm up to normal temperature. Watch the door. When it opens to the outside air, remove the cover from the air cleaner. The temperature should be over 90°F and no more than 130°F; 115°F is about normal. If the door does not work within these temperature ranges, or fails to work at all, check for linkage or door binding.

If binding is not present and the air door is not working, proceed with the vacuum tests, given below. If these indicate no faults in the vacuum motor and the door is not working, the temperature sensor is defective and must be replaced.

Vacuum Motor Tests

Ford

1. Detach the hose from the vacuum override motor. Connect a vacuum gauge to the hose.
2. With the engine at idle, the vacuum gauge should read 15 in. Hg or better. If it is less than this, check the vacuum lines and connections for leaks.
3. If the vacuum is at specification, install the hose back on the vacuum motor.
4. With the underhood temperature below 100°F, check the air door position. If the air door is less than halfway to the "heat on" position and no components are binding, remove the vacuum motor for bench-testing.
5. Connect the motor to an *alternate* vacuum source. If the rod on the motor moves at least ½ in., reinstall it and check for a defective thermostat bulb.
6. If the rod does not move at all or if it moves less than ½ in., the motor is defective and should be replaced.

GM and AMC

NOTE: Be sure that the vacuum hose that runs between the temperature switch and the vacuum motor is not pinched by the retaining clip under the air cleaner. This could prevent the air door from closing.

1. Check all of the vacuum lines and fittings for leaks. Correct any leaks. If none are found, proceed with the test.
2. Remove the hose which runs from the sensor to the vacuum motor. Run a hose directly from the manifold vacuum source to the vacuum motor.
3. If the motor closes the air door, it is functioning properly and the temperature sensor is defective.
4. If the motor does *not* close the door and no binding is present in its operation, the vacuum motor is defective and must be replaced.

NOTE: If an alternate vacuum source is applied to the motor, insert a vacuum gauge in the line by using a T-fitting. Apply at least 9 in. Hg of vacuum in order to operate the motor.

Chrysler Corp.

1. Remove the air cleaner from the carburetor and allow it to cool to 90°F. Connect a vacuum source to the sensor as well as a vacuum gauge.
2. Apply 20 in. Hg to the sensor, the door should be in the "heat on" (up) position. If it remains in the "off" position, test the vacuum motor.
3. Connect the motor to a vacuum source. In addition to the vacuum gauge, a hose clamp and a bleed valve are necessary. Connect them in the following order:
   a. Vacuum source
   b. Hose clamp (or shut-off valve)
   c. Bleed valve
   d. Vacuum gauge
   e. Vacuum motor
4. Apply 20 in. Hg vacuum to the motor. Use the hose clamp to block the line, so that the motor will retain the vacuum. The door operating motor should retain this amount of vacuum for five minutes. Release the hose clamp.

NOTE: If the vacuum cannot be built up to the specified amount, the diaphragm has a leak and the valve will require replacement.

5. By slowly closing the bleed valve, check the operation of the door. The door should start to raise at not less than 5 in. Hg and should be fully raised at no more than 9 in. Hg.
6. If the vacuum motor fails any of the tests in steps 3–5, it is defective. Replace it with a new unit.
7. If the door works properly but fails to pass step two, the sensor is a fault and should be replaced.

NOTE: If the engine has a dual snorkle air cleaner, check the right side as in steps 3–5, above. However, there is no temperature sensor on the right-side door.

Testing the vacuum motor — Chrysler heated air intake system
(© Chrysler Corp)

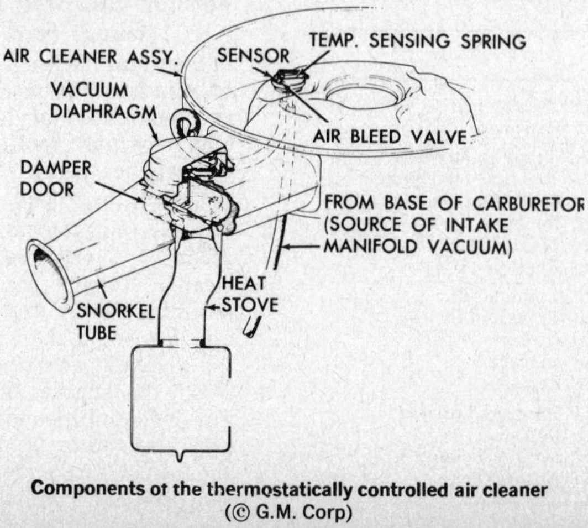
AIR CLEANER ASSY.
SENSOR
TEMP. SENSING SPRING
VACUUM DIAPHRAGM
AIR BLEED VALVE
DAMPER DOOR
FROM BASE OF CARBURETOR (SOURCE OF INTAKE MANIFOLD VACUUM)
HEAT STOVE
SNORKEL TUBE

Components of the thermostatically controlled air cleaner
(© G.M. Corp)

Distributor Controls

Dual Diaphragm Distributor Tests

1. Connect a timing light to the engine. Check the ignition timing.

NOTE: Before proceeding with the tests, disconnect any spark control devices, distributor vacuum valves,

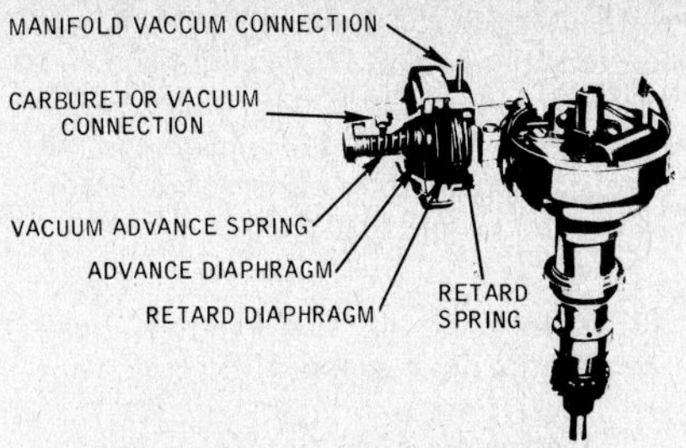
MANIFOLD VACCUM CONNECTION
CARBURETOR VACUUM CONNECTION
VACUUM ADVANCE SPRING
ADVANCE DIAPHRAGM
RETARD DIAPHRAGM
RETARD SPRING

Distributor with dual vacuum advance

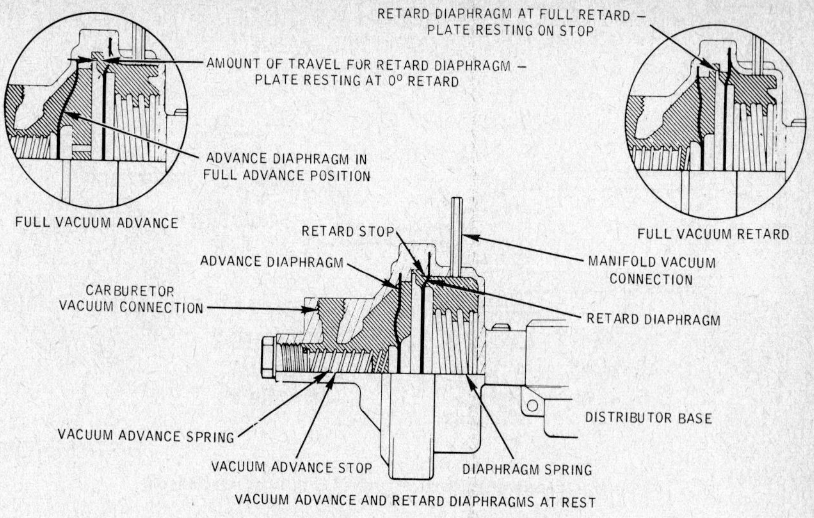
RETARD DIAPHRAGM AT FULL RETARD – PLATE RESTING ON STOP
AMOUNT OF TRAVEL FOR RETARD DIAPHRAGM – PLATE RESTING AT 0° RETARD
ADVANCE DIAPHRAGM IN FULL ADVANCE POSITION
FULL VACUUM ADVANCE
FULL VACUUM RETARD
RETARD STOP
ADVANCE DIAPHRAGM
MANIFOLD VACUUM CONNECTION
CARBURETOR VACUUM CONNECTION
RETARD DIAPHRAGM
DISTRIBUTOR BASE
VACUUM ADVANCE SPRING
VACUUM ADVANCE STOP
DIAPHRAGM SPRING
VACUUM ADVANCE AND RETARD DIAPHRAGMS AT REST

Dual diaphragm vacuum advance mechanism

etc. If these are left connected, inaccurate results may be obtained.

2. Remove the retard hose from the distributor and plug it. Increase the engine speed. The timing should advance. If it fails to do so, then the vacuum unit is faulty and must be replaced.
3. Check the timing with the engine at normal idle speed. Unplug the retard hose and connect it to the vacuum unit. The timing should instantly be retarded from 4–10°. If this does not occur, the retard diaphragm has a leak and the vacuum unit must be replaced.

Timing Retard Solenoid Test

A timing retard solenoid is used on some Chrysler Corp. products up to, and including the 1971 model year.

1. Connect a timing light to the engine and check the timing.
2. Detach the solenoid ground lead near its carburetor end. Timing should advance at least 5° and there should be an increase in engine speed.
3. Reconnect the ground lead. Timing should be retarded to the original position noted and the engine should slow down. Repeat the test several times.
4. If the timing does not behave in the manner indicated, the solenoid is defective and must be replaced; it cannot be adjusted or repaired.

DISCONNECT SOLENOID LEAD

Detach the timing retard solenoid leads at the carburetor end (© Chrysler Corp)

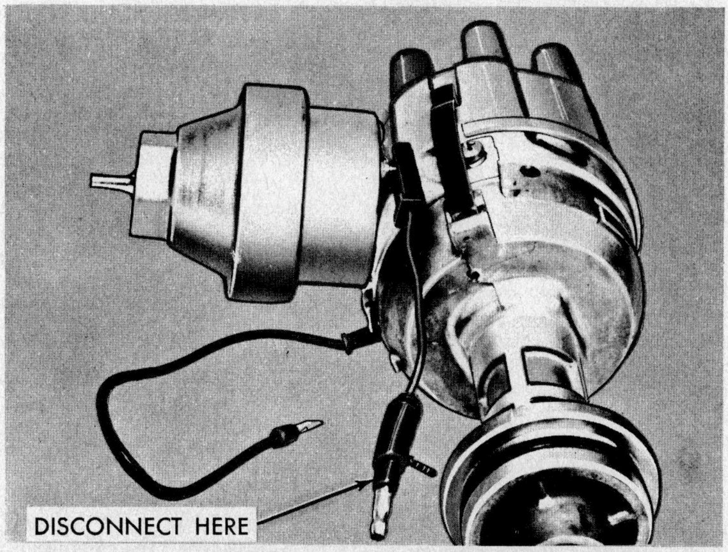
DISCONNECT HERE

Detach the timing advance solenoid where indicated (© Chrysler Corp)

Timing Advance Solenoid Test

NOTE: A timing advance solenoid is used on Chrysler products in 1972. It should not be confused with the retard solenoid, above. It is used only on the 400 cu. in. 4-bbl engine in 1973.

1. Attach a tachometer to the engine.
2. Detach the vacuum advance line from the distributor advance unit.
3. Run the engine at normal idle and check engine rpm with the tachometer.
4. Detach the solenoid lead wire at its connection, which is about 6 in. away from it. Run a jumper wire from the battery to the disconnected lead from the solenoid.
5. When the two leads are touched, the engine speed should increase by 50 rpm or, if a timing light is used, the timing should advance 7–8°.

NOTE: Do not touch the jumper wire to the solenoid lead for more than 30 seconds, or the solenoid will overheat.

6. If the engine speed does not increase or the timing advance, the solenoid is defective and must be replaced. Remember to reconnect it when through testing.

Deceleration Valve Tests

NOTE: Timing, idle speed and air/fuel mixture should be at proper specifications before starting this test.

1. Connect a vacuum gauge to the distributor vacuum advance line, by using a T-connection which has about the same inside diameter as the line. Do not clamp the line shut.

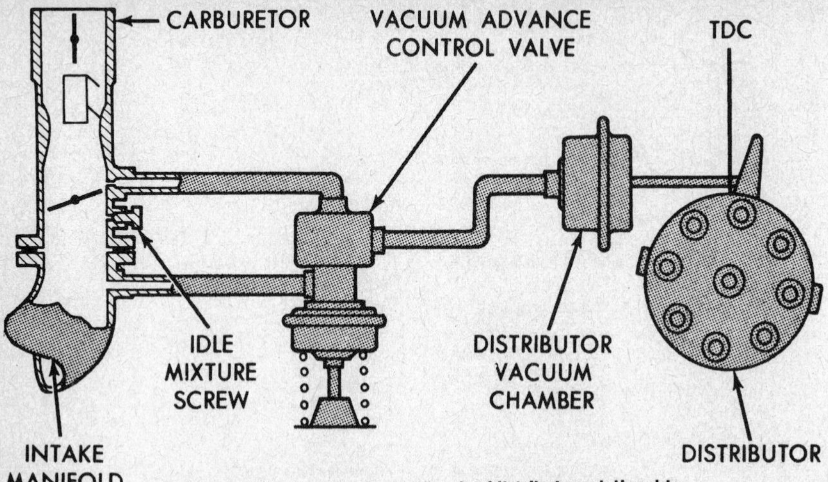
CARBURETOR
VACUUM ADVANCE
CONTROL VALVE
TDC
IDLE
MIXTURE
SCREW
DISTRIBUTOR
VACUUM
CHAMBER
INTAKE
MANIFOLD
DISTRIBUTOR

Carburetor/deceleration (control) valve/distributor relationship

2. If the carburetor is equipped with a dashpot, tape its plunger down so that it cannot touch the throttle lever at idle.
3. Speed the engine up to about 2,-000 rpm and retain this speed for about five seconds.
4. Release the throttle, allowing the engine to return to normal idle.
5. The vacuum reading should rise to about 15–16 in. Hg and stay there for one second. It should take about three seconds for the vacuum to return to its normal 6 in. Hg reading. These specifications do not apply to American Motors cars. See note under "Deceleration Valve Adjustment for American Motors Cars."
6. If the valve does not retain its high reading for about one second or if it takes over three seconds for the reading to return to normal, the valve should be adjusted, as outlined below.

To check for a leaking valve diaphragm, proceed as follows:

1. Remove the vacuum gauge and connect it to the manifold vacuum line with a T-connection.
2. Clamp the valve-to-distributor vacuum line and, with the engine at normal idle speed, check the vacuum reading.
3. Clamp the line shut between the deceleration valve and the T-connection. Check the vacuum gauge reading again.
4. If the second reading is higher than the first, the valve diaphragm is leaking and the valve should be replaced.

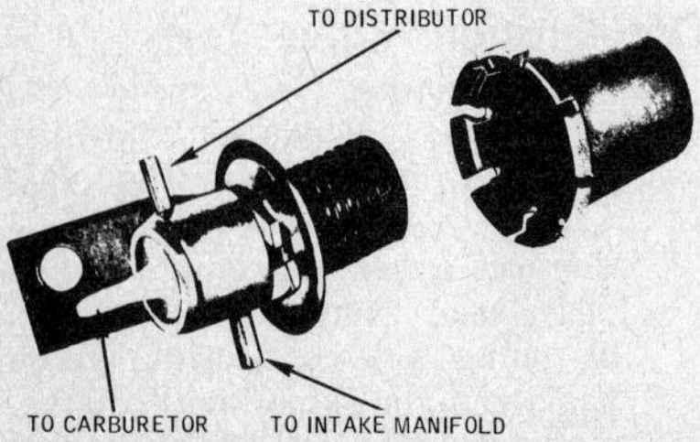
TO DISTRIBUTOR
TO CARBURETOR
TO INTAKE MANIFOLD

Distributor vacuum deceleration control valve

Deceleration Valve Adjustments

If the deceleration valve test indicated a need for adjustments, proceed as follows:

1. Remove the cover to gain access to the adjusting screw.
2. If an *increase* in valve opening time is desired, turn the adjusting screw counterclockwise.
3. If a *decrease* in time is desired, turn the adjusting screw clockwise.

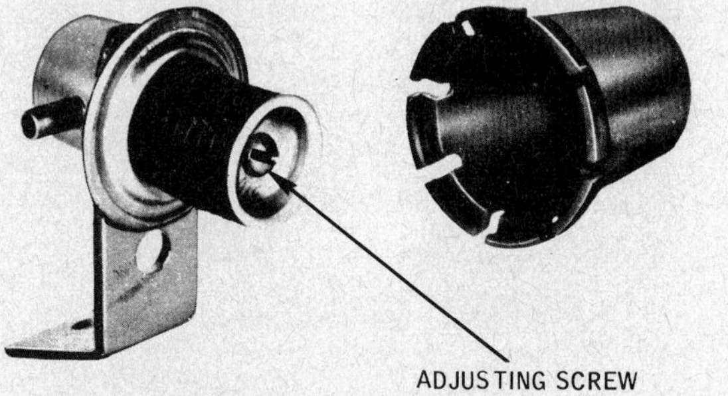
ADJUSTING SCREW

Adjustment of the deceleration valve
(© Ford Motor Co)

NOTE: Each complete turn of the adjusting screw equals ½ in. Hg. Thus, if the vacuum reading at the end of three seconds is 7½ in. Hg, it will take three turns of the screw to return it to the proper 6 in. Hg reading.

4. After finishing the adjustments, retest the valve, as outlined above. If the valve cannot be adjusted to proper specifications, it is defective and must be replaced.

NOTE: On 1970 American Motors cars equipped with a deceleration valve, the test and adjustment procedures are the same, but the specifications are different. Operate the engine at 2,000 rpm for ten seconds; the vacuum reading range should fall between 4 (low)–20 (high) in. Hg.

Coolant Temperature Operated Vacuum Valve Tests

NOTE: On some cars equipped with distributor control systems, this valve also is used to override the control system under overheating conditions. If a malfunction of the distributor control system occurs, remember to check the vacuum valve.

1. Check all of the vacuum hoses for proper installation and routing.
2. Connect a tachometer to the engine.
3. Run the engine until it reaches normal operating temperature but do not allow it to overheat. Be sure that the choke is open.
4. On Chrysler Corp., cars, detach the distributor solenoid ground lead at the carburetor (if so equipped).

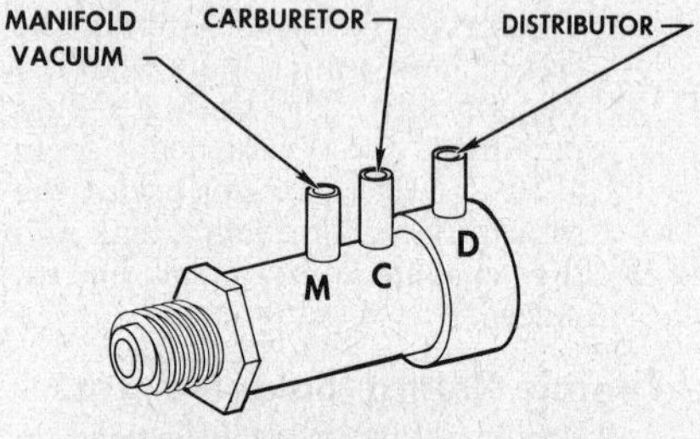
MANIFOLD
VACUUM
CARBURETOR
DISTRIBUTOR
M
C
D

Typical GM coolant temperature-operated vacuum valve
(© G.M. Corp)

5. Check engine rpm with the carburetor at curb idle.
6. Detach the vacuum line from the intake manifold at the valve end. Plug this hose.
7. Check the idle speed; there should be no change. If the idle speed drops 100 rpm or more, the valve is defective and must be replaced.
8. Check the coolant level and radiator cap. Reconnect the intake manifold hose to the temperature valve.
9. Cover the radiator to increase the coolant temperature. Then do one of the following:
   a. If the car is equipped with a temperature gauge, run the engine until the gauge registers near the top of the "Normal" range.
   b. On cars equipped with warning lights, run the engine until the red temperature light comes on.

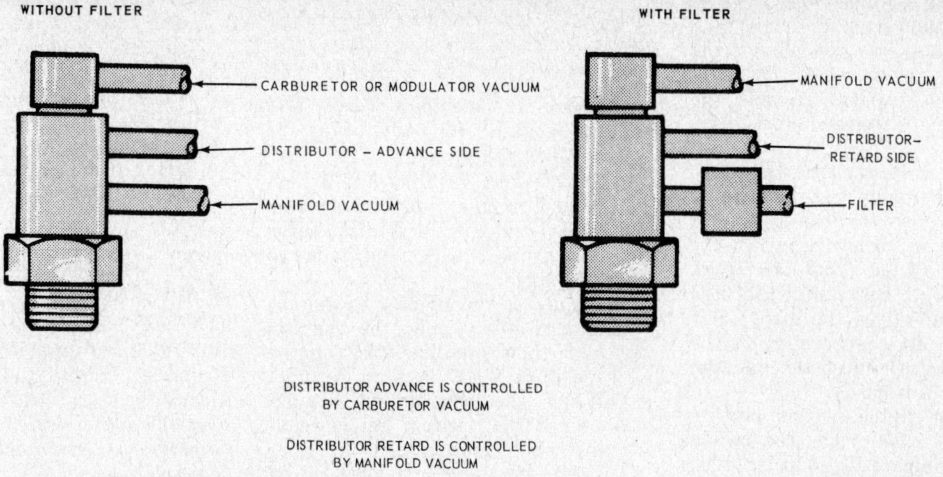
WITHOUT FILTER
CARBURETOR OR MODULATOR VACUUM
DISTRIBUTOR – ADVANCE SIDE
MANIFOLD VACUUM
WITH FILTER
MANIFOLD VACUUM
DISTRIBUTOR–
RETARD SIDE
FILTER
DISTRIBUTOR ADVANCE IS CONTROLLED
BY CARBURETOR VACUUM
DISTRIBUTOR RETARD IS CONTROLLED
BY MANIFOLD VACUUM

Typical Ford coolant temperature-operated vacuum valves (© Ford Motor Co)

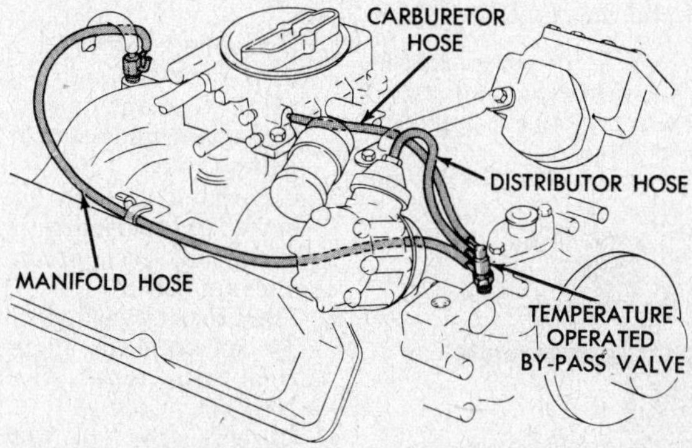
CARBURETOR
HOSE
DISTRIBUTOR HOSE
MANIFOLD HOSE
TEMPERATURE
OPERATED
BY-PASS VALVE

Basic hose routing for temperature-operated vacuum valve

Caution Do not run the engine at an abnormally high temperature for any longer than is required to test the valve. It is not necessary, nor desirable, to overheat an engine when the car uses a temperature gauge, i.e., the gauge should never be allowed to register "H" (Hot) when testing the valve.

10. If the engine speed has increased by at least 100 rpm, the valve is functioning properly. If there is little or no increase in engine speed, the valve is faulty and must be replaced.
11. Uncover the radiator and allow the car to cool by running the engine at idle.
12. On Chrysler products, remember to connect the distributor solenoid wire.

ENGINE VACUUM
FUEL PUMP TESTER

Testing the Ford spark delay valve—the black side should be connected to the vacuum source

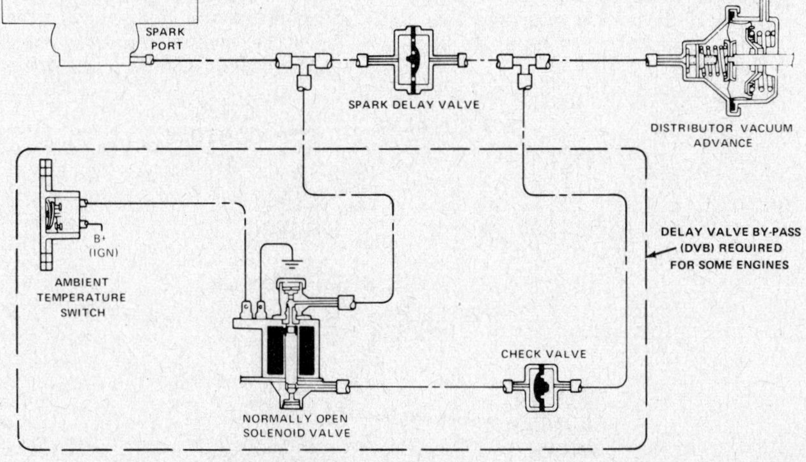
CARBURETOR
SPARK
PORT
SPARK DELAY VALVE
DISTRIBUTOR VACUUM
ADVANCE
B+
(IGN)
AMBIENT
TEMPERATURE
SWITCH
DELAY VALVE BY-PASS
(DVB) REQUIRED
FOR SOME ENGINES
CHECK VALVE
NORMALLY OPEN
SOLENOID VALVE

Ford spark delay valve circuit (© Ford Motor Co)

Ford Spark Delay Valve Tests

NOTE: If the distributor vacuum line contains a cut-off solenoid, it must be open during this test.

1. Detach the vacuum line from the distributor at the spark delay valve end. Connect a vacuum gauge to the valve, in its place.
2. Connect a tachometer to the engine. Start the engine and rapidly increase its speed to 2,000 rpm with the transmission in neutral.
3. As soon as the engine speed is increased, the vacuum gauge reading should drop to zero.

4. Hold the engine speed at a steady 2,000 rpm. It should take longer than two seconds for the gauge to register 6 in. Hg. If it takes less than two seconds, the valve is defective and must be replaced.
5. If it takes longer than the number of seconds specified in the chart below for the gauge to reach 6 in. Hg, disconnect the vacuum gauge from the spark delay valve. Disconnect the hose which runs from the spark delay valve to the carburetor at the valve end. Connect the vacuum gauge to this hose.
6. Start the engine and increase its speed to 2,000 rpm. The gauge should indicate 10–16 in Hg. If it does not, there is a blockage in the carburetor vacuum port or else the hose itself is plugged or broken. If the gauge reading is within specification, the valve is defective.
7. Reconnect all vacuum lines and remove the tachometer, once testing is completed.

Spark Delay Valve Color Code (Ford)

Color (With Black)	*1972 Time Delay Maximum (sec)*	*1973 Time Delay Maximum (sec)*
Green	20	20
Blue	15	16
Red	40	28
White	5	12
Yellow	10	14
Orange	—	24

Check Valve Test

If the spark delay valve is working properly, but vacuum still is not present when it should be, test the check valve for proper operation:

1. Remove the hoses from either side of the check valve, being careful to note the proper valve installation direction.
2. Connect the BLACK side of the valve to a vacuum source and the colored side to a vacuum gauge.
3. The gauge should show a vacuum reading, as soon as vacuum is applied to the valve.
4. Reverse the connections to the check valve; the vacuum gauge should read zero.
5. Replace the valve if it fails either of the above tests.

Chrysler Orifice Spark Advance Control (OSAC) Valve

NOTE: Air temperature around the car must be above 68° F for this test because the OSAC valve has a temperature sensor in it. Valves produced from around 1 March 1973 do not have an ambient temperature sensor built into them. They may be identified by their white gasket (old OSAC valves had a black one) and a pasted-on label with the part number (3755499) on it.

1. Check the vacuum hoses and connections for any signs of leaks or plugging.
2. Detach the vacuum line which runs from the distributor to the OSAC valve at the distributor end. Connect a vacuum gauge to this line.
3. Connect a tachometer to the engine. Rapidly open the throttle and then stabilize the engine speed at 2,000 rpm in neutral. When the throttle is rapidly opened the vacuum gauge reading should drop to zero.
4. With the engine speed at a steady 2,000 rpm, it should take about 15 seconds for the vacuum level to rise and then stabilize.

NOTE: The length of time may vary slightly with different engines; 15 seconds is an approximate figure.

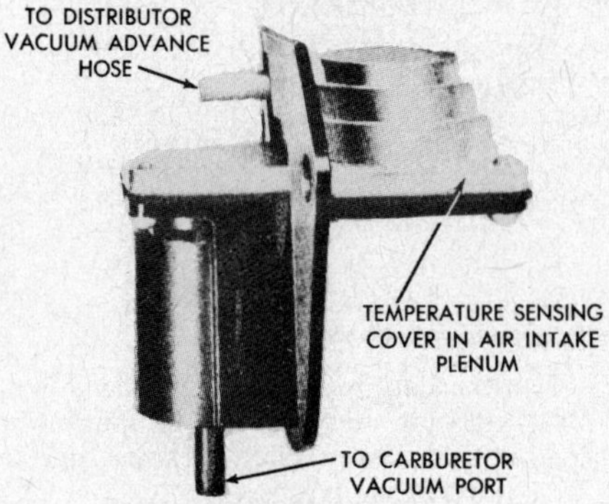
TO DISTRIBUTOR
VACUUM ADVANCE
HOSE
TEMPERATURE SENSING
COVER IN AIR INTAKE
PLENUM
TO CARBURETOR
VACUUM PORT

Chrysler orifice spark advance control (OSAC) valve (© Chrysler Corp)

5. If the vacuum level rises immediately, the valve is defective and must be replaced.
6. If there is no increase in vacuum at all, disconnect the hose which runs from the carburetor to the OSAC valve at the valve and connect a vacuum gauge to this hose. Speed the engine up to 2,000 rpm.
7. If there is no vacuum reading on the gauge, check for a clogged carburetor port, filters or hoses.
8. If there is a vacuum reading, the valve is defective and must be replaced.
9. Reconnect the vacuum hoses, after disconnecting the vacuum gauge. Disconnect the tachometer.

1973 Oldsmobile Spark Delay Valve Test

NOTE: The underhood temperature must be above 50°F for this test. Beginning with cars made on 15 March 1973, a plastic cover is used over the spark delay valve. It will be necessary to remove this cover in order to service the valve. Be sure to replace the cover after completing service, as it is required to meet Federal regulations.

1. Disconnect the vacuum hose that runs from the spark delay valve to the coolant temperature operated vacuum valve at the spark delay valve.
2. Connect a vacuum gauge to the end of the spark delay valve from which you just disconnected the vacuum hose.
3. Start the engine and rapidly raise the speed of the engine to 2,000 rpm with the transmission in Neutral.
4. Observe the reading on the vacuum gauge. As soon as the throttle is depressed, the vacuum gauge reading should drop to zero. The reading should remain at zero for about 35–40 seconds, after which time the vacuum should show a reading.
5. If the vacuum gauge does not react this way, and if the vacuum hose to the spark delay is not defective, the spark delay valve is defective and must be replaced.

1973 Oldsmobile Vacuum Reducing Valve Test

1. Allow the engine to warm up.
2. Disconnect the line which runs from the vacuum reducing valve to the coolant temperature oper-

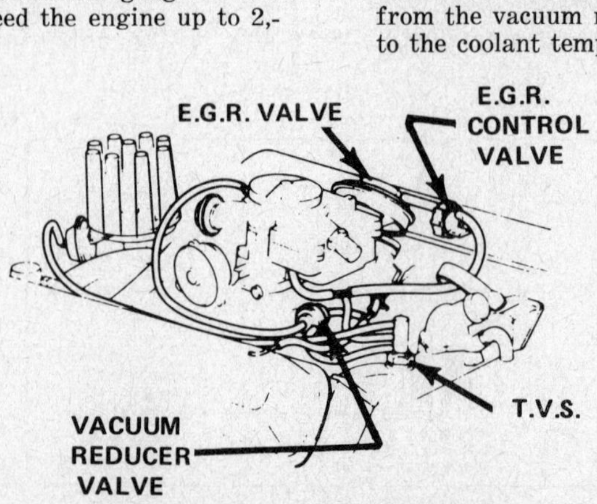
E.G.R. VALVE
E.G.R.
CONTROL
VALVE
T.V.S.
VACUUM
REDUCER
VALVE

Oldsmobile vacuum reducing valve location (© G.M. Corp)

ated vacuum valve at the temperature valve end. Plug the nipple on the temperature valve to prevent a vacuum leak.

3. Connect a vacuum gauge to the line, after being sure that the line is neither plugged nor pinched.
4. With the engine at idle, the vacuum gauge should register no more than 9 in. Hg. If the reading is higher than this, replace the vacuum reducing valve.

Transmission Controlled Spark System Tests

Ford

NOTE: When performing the following tests, be sure that the temperature switch is kept above 65°F, expect as noted. On models equipped with a spark delay valve, the spark delay valve must be removed for this test to be valid.

Manual Transmission System Test

1. Connect a vacuum gauge between the distributor and the distributor modulator valve, using a T-connector.
2. Start the engine. With the transmission in neutral, the vacuum gauge should read zero.
3. Increase engine speed to between 1,000–1,500 rpm with the clutch pedal depressed. The vacuum reading should remain at zero.
4. With the clutch still depressed, place the transmission in high gear. Increase engine speed, as before. The vacuum gauge should now read at least 6 in. Hg. If it does not, proceed further with testing. Remember to shift into netural or stop the engine before engaging the clutch.
5. Unfasten the transmission switch lead from the distributor modulator terminal. Connect the lead in series with a low amperage test lamp and the positive side of the battery.
6. Move the gear shift lever through all of the gears. The test lamp should remain on until high gear is entered.
7. If the lamp stays on when the transmission is in high, either the switch is defective or the circuit is grounded. If it fails to come on at all, the switch is defective or the circuit has a loose wire.
8. If the transmission switch is functioning properly but the system check indicates that something is still wrong, proceed with the temperature switch test below.

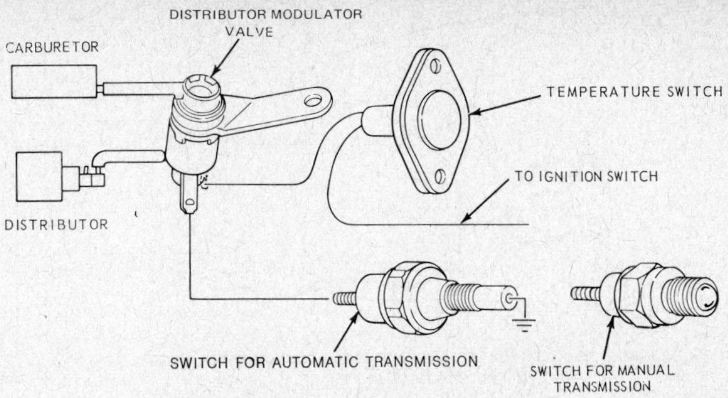
DISTRIBUTOR MODULATOR VALVE
CARBURETOR
TEMPERATURE SWITCH
TO IGNITION SWITCH
DISTRIBUTOR
SWITCH FOR AUTOMATIC TRANSMISSION
SWITCH FOR MANUAL TRANSMISSION

Ford transmission controlled spark system
(© Ford Motor Co)

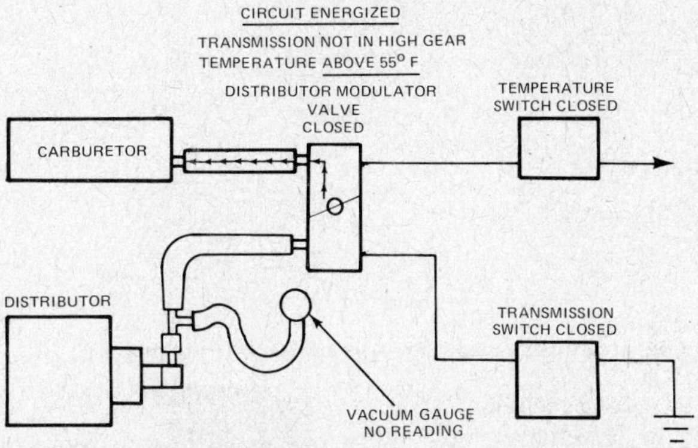
CIRCUIT ENERGIZED
TRANSMISSION NOT IN HIGH GEAR
TEMPERATURE ABOVE 55° F
DISTRIBUTOR MODULATOR VALVE CLOSED
TEMPERATURE SWITCH CLOSED
CARBURETOR
DISTRIBUTOR
TRANSMISSION SWITCH CLOSED
VACUUM GAUGE NO READING

Testing the transmission-controlled spark system with the circuit energized
(© Ford Motor Co)

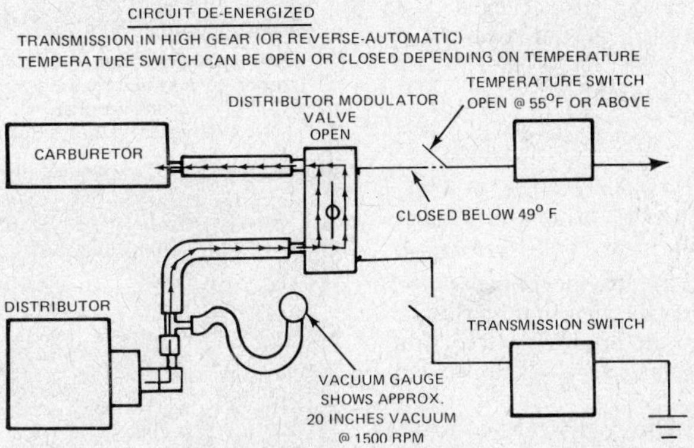
CIRCUIT DE-ENERGIZED
TRANSMISSION IN HIGH GEAR (OR REVERSE-AUTOMATIC)
TEMPERATURE SWITCH CAN BE OPEN OR CLOSED DEPENDING ON TEMPERATURE
TEMPERATURE SWITCH OPEN @ 55°F OR ABOVE
DISTRIBUTOR MODULATOR VALVE OPEN
CARBURETOR
CLOSED BELOW 49° F
DISTRIBUTOR
TRANSMISSION SWITCH
VACUUM GAUGE SHOWS APPROX. 20 INCHES VACUUM @ 1500 RPM

Testing the transmission-controlled spark system with the circuit de-energized
(© Ford Motor Co)

Automatic Transmission System Test

1. Connect a vacuum gauge between the distributor and the distributor modulator valve using a T-connection. Start the engine.
2. When the transmission is in Park or neutral, the vacuum gauge should read zero.
3. Apply the brakes and shift into Reverse. Increase the engine speed. The gauge may or may not register a vacuum.
4. If no vacuum is present, detach a wire from the distributor modulator valve and shift into neutral. Increase engine speed to between 1,000–1,500 rpm. This time the gauge should definitely show a vacuum reading.
5. If vacuum still is not present, disconnect the two vacuum lines from the distributor modulator valve and join them, using a nipple, to bypass the valve. Repeat step four.
6. If there is vacuum now, proceed with the rest of the tests. If no vacuum is present, check for loose, pinched, or plugged hoses. When finished, reconnect the wire to the valve.
7. Detach the transmission switch lead from the distributor modular valve. Connect the lead in series with a test lamp and the positive terminal of the battery.
8. Start the engine and apply the brakes. Move the transmission selector through all of the positions on the quadrant.
9. The lamp should go out only

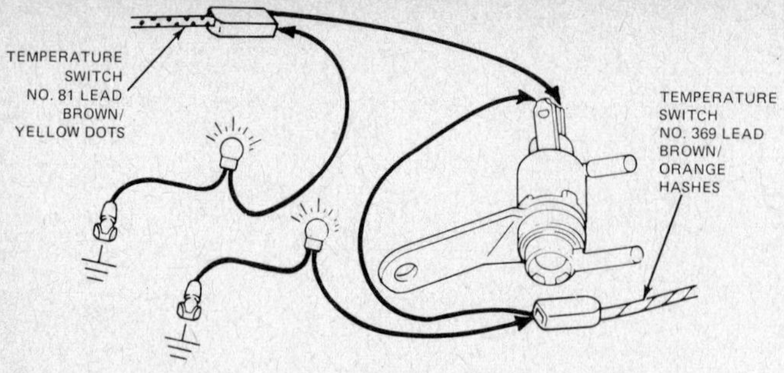
TEMPERATURE
SWITCH
NO. 81 LEAD
BROWN/
YELLOW DOTS
TEMPERATURE
SWITCH
NO. 369 LEAD
BROWN/
ORANGE
HASHES

Using a test lamp to check the temperature of the transmission switch
(© Ford Motor Co)

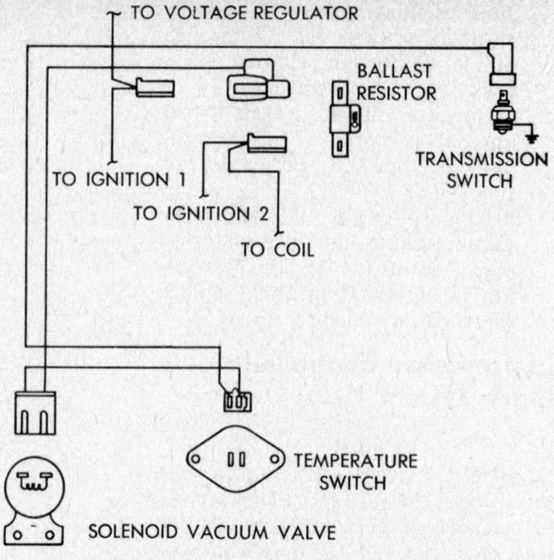
TO VOLTAGE REGULATOR
BALLAST
RESISTOR
TRANSMISSION
SWITCH
TO IGNITION 1
TO IGNITION 2
TO COIL
TEMPERATURE
SWITCH
SOLENOID VACUUM VALVE

NO_X (TCS) system schematic manual transmission
(© Chrysler Corp)

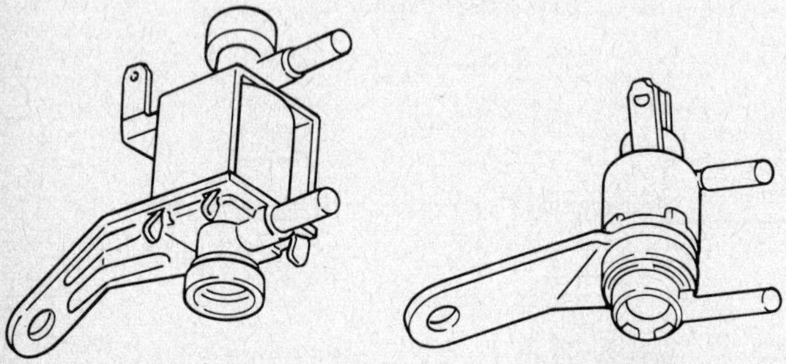

The two types of distributor modulator valve used on Ford products

when Reverse is selected. If it stays on in Reverse or fails to come on at all, either the switch is defective or the wiring is faulty.

10. If the transmission switch and wiring are in proper order, but vacuum still is not present, it will be necessary to test the temperature switch.

Temperature Switch Tests

NOTE: Cars made from 15 March 1973 do not use the ambient temperature switch with the TCS system.

1. Detach the temperature switch lead from its terminal or the distributor modulator valve. Connect the lead to a grounded test lamp.
2. Remove the temperature switch from either the right or left door pillar. Warm the switch by holding it in the palm of the hand. The lamp should come on once 65°F is reached.
3. Using ice, or an aerosol spray circuit cooler, cool the switch to below 49°F. The test lamp should go out.
4. If the lamp fails to go on or off when it should, the switch is defective and must be replaced.
5. If the temperature switch is functioning properly, and no vacuum was present in the system test, the distributor modulator valve is defective.

Distributor Modulator Valve Test

1. Perform the above system test.
2. If the other components, i.e., the transmission switch and the temperature switch, are functioning properly and vacuum is present when it should not be, or vice versa, the fault probably lies in the distributor modulator valve.
3. Before replacing the valve, however, remember to check for clogged, pinched, or loose vacuum hoses, as these could result in similar symptoms.

Location of American Motors ambient temperature switch on the front upper crossmember
(© American Motors Corp)

1973½ Solenoid vacuum valve (top) and transmission governor pressure switch (bottom)—AMC V8

American Motors

Manual Transmission Test

The transmission-controlled spark (TCS) system used on American Motors cars equipped with manual transmissions is similar to the one used by Ford for their cars with manual transmissions.

The major difference is in the temperature switch. The American Motors switch is located on the front upper crossmember and closes at 63°F. Also, American Motors refers to the "distributor modulator valve" (Ford) as the "solenoid vacuum valve."

NOTE: Cars made from 15 March 1973 do not use the ambient temperature switch with the TCS system.

Bearing these differences in mind, test the American Motors system in the same manner as outlined under "Ford—Manual Transmission," above.

1973½ Automatic Transmission

NOTE: The spark control system used on AMC cars, equipped with automatic transmissions and made after 15 March 1973, is controlled by a switch which operates on transmission governor oil pressure. Test procedures for cars made before this date may be found in the "Speed Controlled Spark Systems" section, below.

1. Disconnect the electrical lead from the terminal of the governor pressure switch.

NOTE: The switch may easily be reached with the hood opened. On sixes, the switch is located on the right rear of the cylinder block; on V8s, it is attached to a bracket at the rear of the right-hand rocker cover.

2. Connect a 12V test light in series, between the lead and the terminal on the switch.

Caution *Use a low amperage test light, so that the switch contacts will not be damaged.*

3. Raise the car, block the front wheels (if they are not off the ground), and securely support it so that the rear wheels are free to turn.
4. Apply the service brakes. Start

the engine. The test light should glow.

5. Place the gear selector in Drive (D), release the brake pedal and slowly depress the gas pedal.
6. Watch the speedometer and the test light; between 33-37 mph the switch should open and the test light should go out.
7. If the light does not go out within this speed range, adjust the switch by turning the 1/16 in. allen screw on the switch terminal. Turn the screw clockwise to increase or counterclockwise to decrease the switch cut-out speed. The switch should be adjusted to open at 35 mph.
8. If the switch cannot be adjusted to specification, replace it.
9. If the switch is working properly, but the TCS system is not working, the solenoid vacuum valve is probably defective.

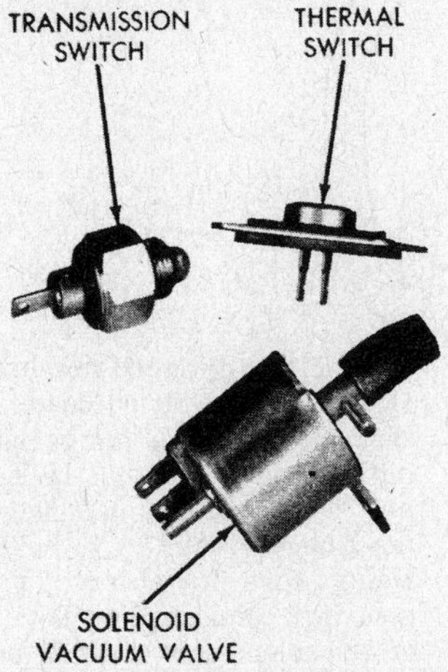
TRANSMISSION SWITCH
THERMAL SWITCH
SOLENOID VACUUM VALVE

NO_X (TCS) system components—manual transmission (© Chrysler Corp)

Chrysler

Manual Transmission

NOTE: For testing procedures to be used on Chrysler products that are equipped with an automatic transmission, see Speed Control Spark.

1. Turn the ignition switch to the "on" position. Place the transmission selector lever in the "neutral" position.
2. Disconnect the wire from the B+ terminal on the ignition system ballast resistor while holding the solenoid vacuum valve.
3. When the wire is disconnected, the valve should be felt to de-energize.
4. Reconnect the wire to the ballast resistor, the valve should be felt to energize. If the solenoid vacuum valve does not react this way, either the vacuum valve or the transmission switch is defective, or voltage is not present at the ballast resistor. Connect a test light to the B+ terminal of the resistor to check for voltage.
5. To test the solenoid vacuum valve, disconnect the wiring connector from the solenoid. Run a jumper wire from the piggyback connector on the ballast resistor to one of the terminals on the solenoid vacuum valve. Connect another jumper wire from the other terminal on the solenoid vacuum valve to a good ground. When the ignition switch is turned to the "on" position, the vacuum valve should be felt to energize. If the vacuum valve does not energize, it is defective. If the vacuum valve does energize, but did not energize in Steps 2–4, proceed to Step 6. Connect the lead wires to the vacuum valve.
6. Disconnect the lead wire from the transmission switch. Connect a jumper wire from the just disconnected switch lead to a good ground. When the ignition switch is turned to the "on" position the solenoid vacuum valve should be felt to energize. If the switch does energize when the lead wire to the switch was connected to ground, but failed to energize in Steps 2–4, the transmission switch is either defective or it has a bad ground. If the transmission switch is attached to the transmission with 180 in. lbs torque, it is correctly grounded.
7. If the vacuum valve energized in Step 5, but did not energize in Step 6, the lead wire from the ballast resistor to the vacuum valve is defective.

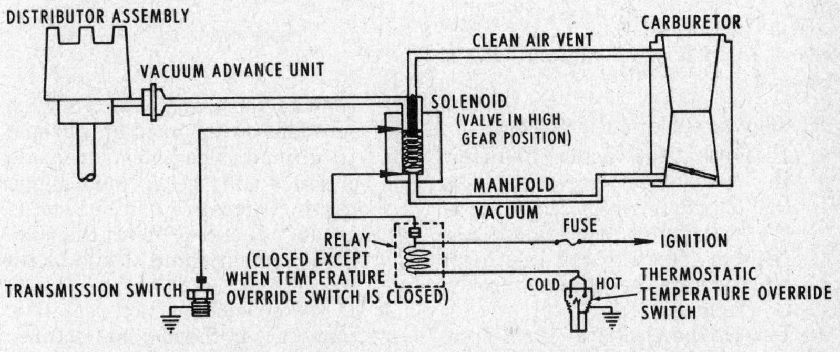
DISTRIBUTOR ASSEMBLY
VACUUM ADVANCE UNIT
CLEAN AIR VENT
CARBURETOR
SOLENOID
(VALVE IN HIGH GEAR POSITION)
MANIFOLD
VACUUM
FUSE
IGNITION
RELAY
(CLOSED EXCEPT WHEN TEMPERATURE OVERRIDE SWITCH IS CLOSED)
TRANSMISSION SWITCH
COLD
HOT
THERMOSTATIC TEMPERATURE OVERRIDE SWITCH

A typical transmission controlled spark system (© General Motors Corp)

GM Except All 1973 Pontiac Models

NOTE: The components used on the GM transmission-controlled spark (TCS) systems vary from model to model. For a description of the components used for each model, see the appropriate Car Section.

SYSTEM TEST

1. Connect a vacuum gauge to the vacuum source for the vacuum solenoid. With the transmission in neutral and the engine idling, vacuum should be present.
2. If there is no vacuum present, check for a clogged vacuum port, damaged vacuum lines or loose hose connections.
3. Disconnect the vacuum guage and reconnect the vacuum line.
4. Detach the vacuum line from the distributor vacuum unit and connect it to the vacuum gauge. This is the line which contains the vacuum advance solenoid or CEC solenoid.
5. With engine temperature above 95°F and the transmission in neutral, run the engine for at least 25 seconds. The vacuum gauge should read zero.

NOTE: All 1971 Cadillacs have a by-pass circuit to provide vacuum advance in both Park and neutral.

6. Do one of the following:
   a. Manual transmission — Depress the clutch pedal and move the shift lever through the gears. Increase engine speed in each gear, enough to cause vacuum advance. A vacuum should be present only in High gear.

NOTE: On 1970–71 models with four-speed transmissions, vacuum should also be present in third gear.

   b. Automatic transmission — Raise the rear wheels of the car off the ground. Support the car and block the front wheels, so that it cannot roll forward. Place the transmission in Drive and speed the engine up enough so that the transmission will shift into high gear; vacuum should only be present when the transmission enters high gear, and not while it is in lower gears.

NOTE: Some cars are equipped with a time-delay device, so it may take 20–25 seconds before vacuum is present once the proper gear has been reached. Do not run the engine any longer than necessary to complete the test.

7. If no vacuum is present when it should be or if it is present when it should not be, first check the TCS system fuse (if so equipped) and then proceed with the individual tests outlined below.

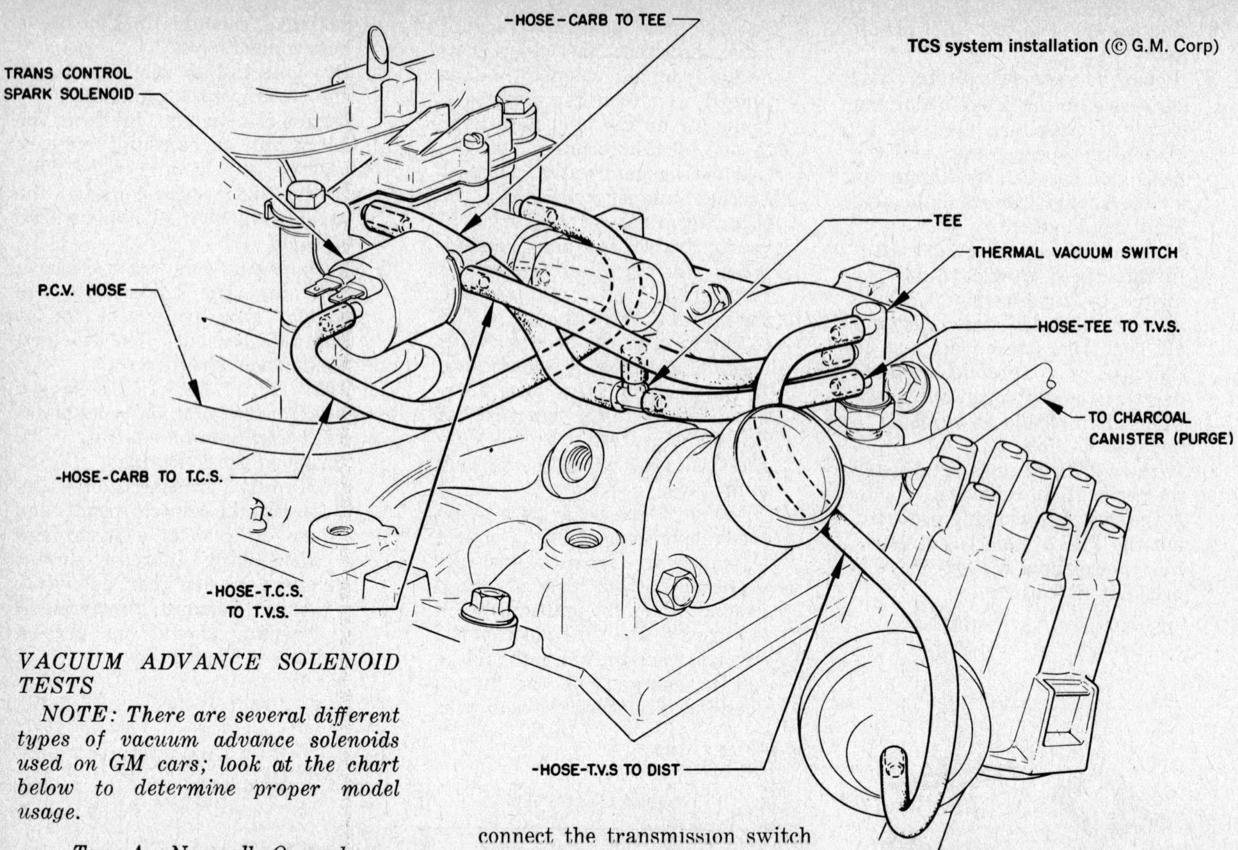

-HOSE-CARB TO TEE
TRANS CONTROL SPARK SOLENOID
P.C.V. HOSE
-HOSE-CARB TO T.C.S.
-HOSE-T.C.S. TO T.V.S.
TEE
THERMAL VACUUM SWITCH
HOSE-TEE TO T.V.S.
TO CHARCOAL CANISTER (PURGE)
-HOSE-T.V.S TO DIST

TCS system installation (© G.M. Corp)

VACUUM ADVANCE SOLENOID TESTS

NOTE: There are several different types of vacuum advance solenoids used on GM cars; look at the chart below to determine proper model usage.

Type A—Normally Opened

1. Disconnect the vacuum line from the vacuum advance solenoid to the distributor vacuum unit, at the distributor end. Connect a vacuum gauge to the line after making sure that it is not broken or clogged.
2. Detach the electrical leads from the solenoid. With the engine running, the vacuum gauge should register a vacuum. If it does not, the solenoid is faulty and must be replaced.
3. Using care to observe the proper polarity, connect one solenoid terminal to a 12 V power source. Using a jumper wire, connect the transmission switch terminal on the vacuum solenoid to ground. The solenoid should energize and the vacuum gauge reading should return to zero. If vacuum is still present, the solenoid is jammed and should be replaced.
4. If the solenoid is not defective, connect it in the original manner and go on to the next appropriate test.

Type B—Normally Closed

1. Disconnect the line which runs from the vacuum advance solenoid to the distributor vacuum unit. Connect a vacuum gauge to this line, after making sure that it is neither plugged nor broken.
2. Detach both electrical leads from the solenoid. The gauge should indicate zero vacuum. If it does not, the solenoid is defective and must be replaced.
3. Using care to observe proper polarity, connect the "hot" lead of the solenoid to a 12 V power source. Ground the other lead. Vacuum should now be present in the line. If it is not, the solenoid is defective and needs to be replaced.
4. If the solenoid is not defective, connect it in the original manner and go on with the next applicable test.

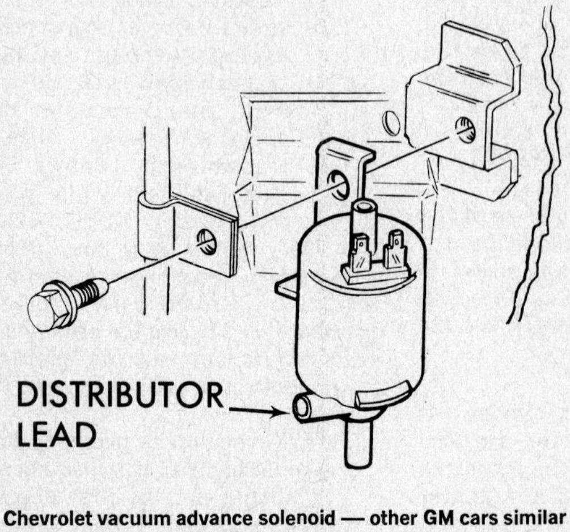

DISTRIBUTOR LEAD

Chevrolet vacuum advance solenoid — other GM cars similar
(© G.M. Corp)

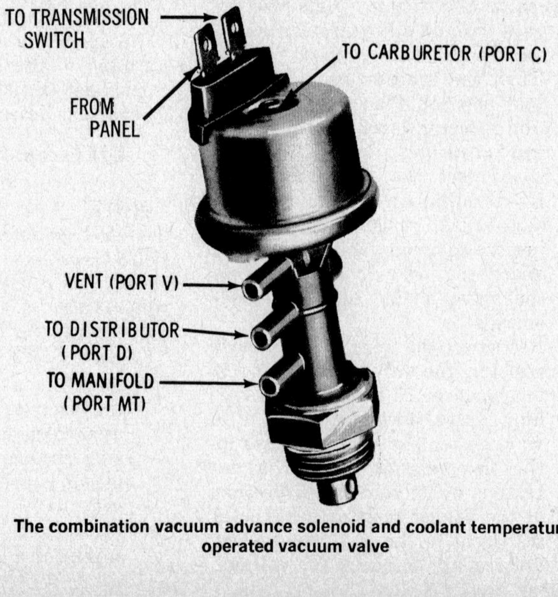

TO TRANSMISSION SWITCH
TO CARBURETOR (PORT C)
FROM PANEL
VENT (PORT V)
TO DISTRIBUTOR (PORT D)
TO MANIFOLD (PORT MT)

The combination vacuum advance solenoid and coolant temperature-operated vacuum valve

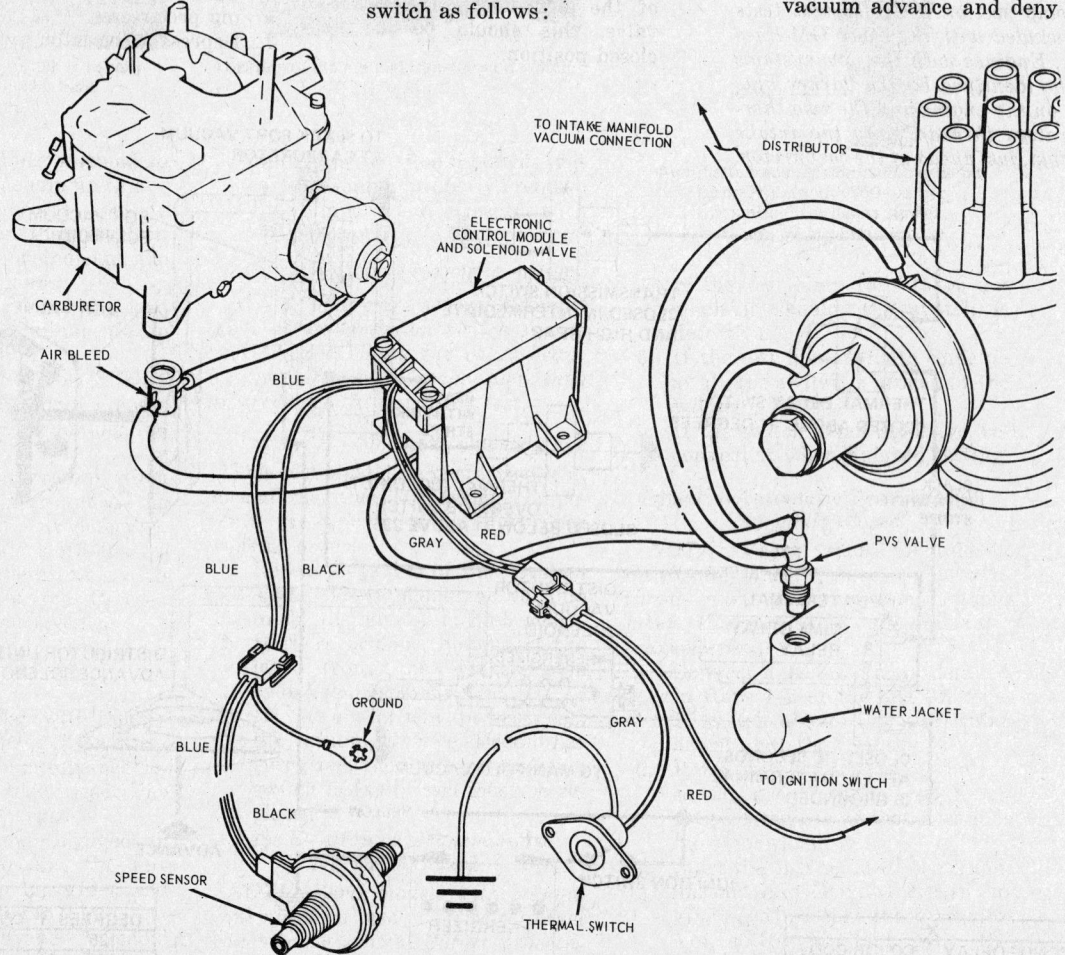

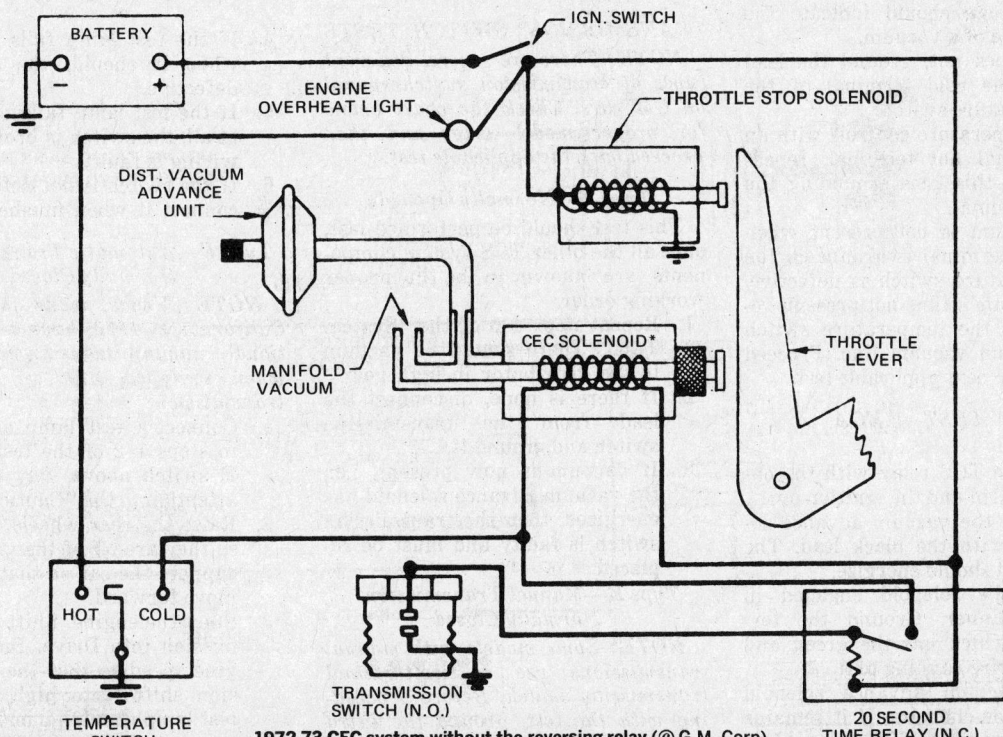

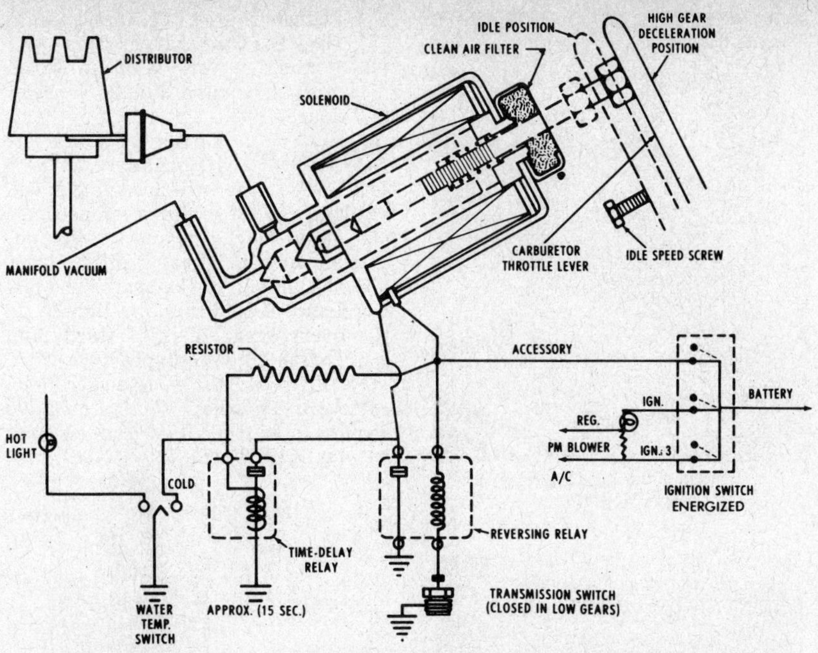
IDLE POSITION
CLEAN AIR FILTER
HIGH GEAR DECELERATION POSITION
DISTRIBUTOR
SOLENOID
MANIFOLD VACUUM
CARBURETOR THROTTLE LEVER
IDLE SPEED SCREW
RESISTOR
ACCESSORY
BATTERY
IGN.
REG.
PM BLOWER
IGN. 3
A/C
IGNITION SWITCH ENERGIZED
HOT LIGHT
COLD
TIME-DELAY RELAY
REVERSING RELAY
TRANSMISSION SWITCH (CLOSED IN LOW GEARS)
WATER TEMP. SWITCH
APPROX. (15 SEC.)

1970-71 CEC System
(© G.M. Corp)

Type C—CEC Solenoid and Relays

The test for the CEC solenoid is similar to that for the Type B vacuum advance solenoid, above, expect that a vacuum guage is not needed. With 12 V applied to the CEC solenoid, its plunger should extend. With no power applied to the solenoid, the plunger should retract. If it fails to do either properly, the solenoid is defective and must be replaced. If it is not defective, reconnect it.

NOTE: A defective CEC solenoid will also affect the operation of the throttle. For further details, see "Carburetor Modifications," below.

Models made prior to 1972 which are equipped with a CEC solenoid, use a reversing relay to provide proper switching action for the solenoid. To test relay operation:

1. Bypass the relay by grounding its single wire connector.
2. If the CEC solenoid plunger will now extend, and it did not extend in the above test, the reversing relay is defective.

A time-delay relay is used on some models equipped with a CEC solenoid to provide vacuum advance for 15–20 seconds after the ignition is switched on. To check its operation, proceed as follows:

1. Disconnect the electrical lead from the temperature switch.
2. Allow the relay to cool. Turn the ignition on. The CEC solenoid should energize (plunger extend) for about 15–20 seconds and then go off.
3. If it fails to go off, detach the blue lead from the time-delay relay. If the CEC solenoid now de-energizes, then the relay is faulty and must be replaced.

If none of the CEC system components which were tested are defective, go on to the next applicable test.

VACUUM DELAY RELAY TESTS

This relay is a solid-state unit which is used on some 1972 models. (It is not used with the CEC solenoid and should not be confused with the *time*-delay relay, above.) It is located underneath the dashboard, inside the passenger compartment. To test it proceed in the following manner:

1. Turn the ignition on. Then, using a lower amperage test lamp, check to see that the relay is getting power. If it is not, check its wiring.
2. Disconnect and ground the black lead.
3. Wait for 26 seconds. The vacuum advance solenoid should then energize. If it does not, the relay is faulty and must be replaced. If it does, reconnect the vacuum delay relay and proceed with the next applicable test.

TEMPERATURE SWITCH TEST

1. Connect a vacuum gauge to

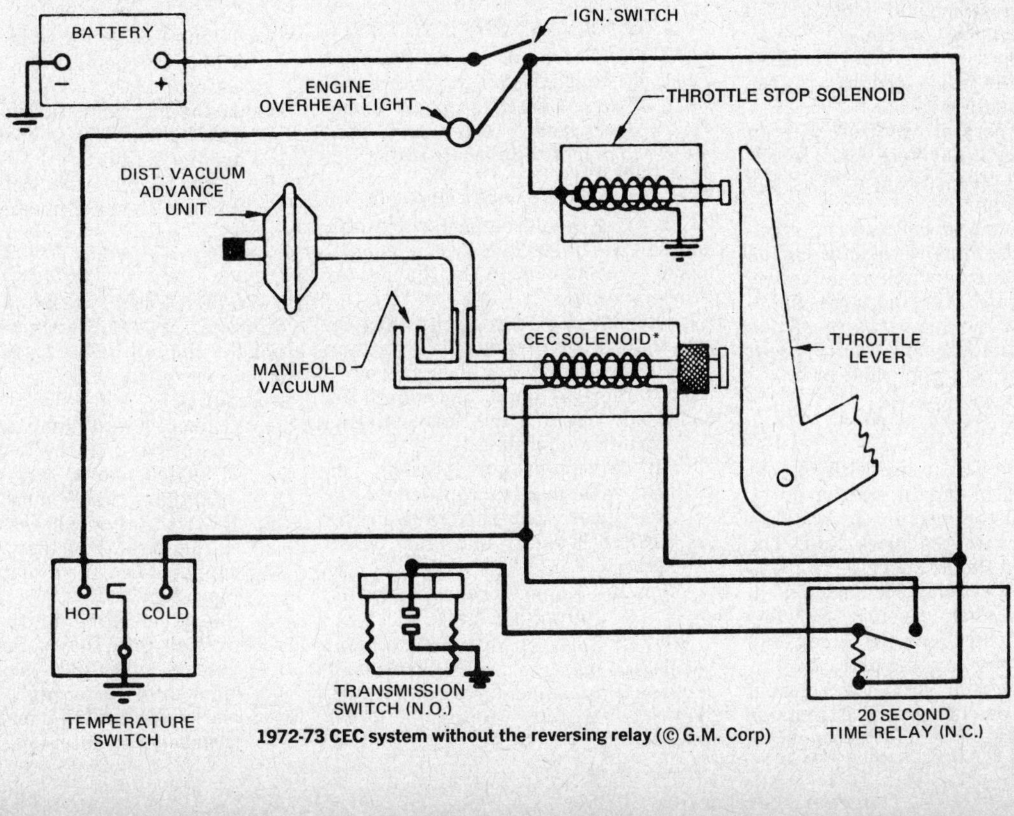
BATTERY
IGN. SWITCH
ENGINE OVERHEAT LIGHT
THROTTLE STOP SOLENOID
DIST. VACUUM ADVANCE UNIT
CEC SOLENOID*
THROTTLE LEVER
MANIFOLD VACUUM
HOT
COLD
TEMPERATURE SWITCH
TRANSMISSION SWITCH (N.O.)
20 SECOND TIME RELAY (N.C.)

1972-73 CEC system without the reversing relay (© G.M. Corp)

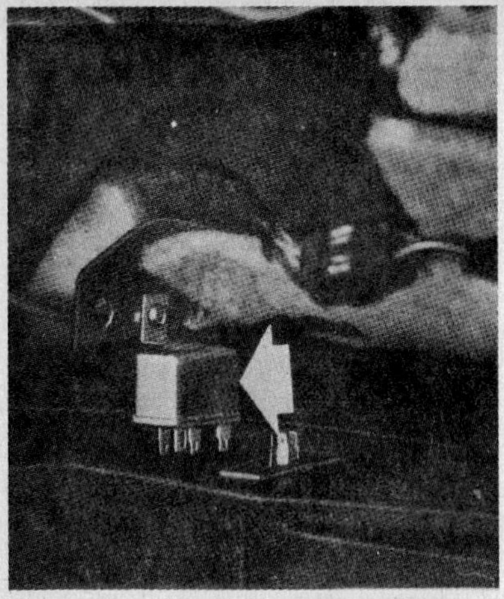
The vacuum delay relay is mounted underneath the dashboard
(© G.M. Corp)

Location of the Vega TCS relay
(© G.M. Corp)

The temperature sensing switch is usually threaded into the cylinder head
(© G.M. Corp)

Location of the manual transmission switch
(© G.M. Corp)

the vacuum advance solenoid to the distributor vacuum unit.

2. Allow the engine to cool to around 75°F and then start it. The gauge should indicate the presence of a vacuum.
3. If it does not, ground the lead from the cold terminal of the temperature switch.
4. On temperature controls with an additional hot terminal, repeat step 3—this time grounding the hot terminal.
5. If vacuum is not present when either terminal is grounded, the temperature switch is defective. If vacuum still is not present, reconnect the temperature switch leads and vacuum line. Proceed with the next applicable test.

TCS RELAY TEST—VEGA
1971–72

1. Test the TCS relay with the engine warm and the ignition on.
2. Ground the vacuum advance solenoid with the black lead. The solenoid should energize.
3. Keep the solenoid engaged in this manner. Ground the terminal which has the green and white wire running to it.
4. The vacuum advance solenoid should de-energize. If it remains energized, the TCS solenoid is faulty and must be replaced. If it is functioning properly, remove the jumpers and proceed with the next applicable test.

TRANSMISSION SWITCH TESTS

NOTE: There are several different types of transmission switches used on GM cars. Check the chart below for proper model usage and then proceed with the applicable test.

Type D—Normally Opened

This test should be performed last, once all the other TCS system components are known to be in proper working order.

1. Repeat steps 4–6 of the "System Test." There should be vacuum to the distributor in high gear.
2. If there is none, disconnect the lead from the transmission switch and ground it.
3. If vacuum is now present, i.e., the vacuum advance solenoid has energized, then the transmission switch is faulty and must be replaced.

Type E—Manual Transmission/ Normally Closed

NOTE: Some models with manual transmissions use a two-terminal transmission switch. Before proceeding with the test, ground the extra terminal.

1. Detach the switch connector at the side of the transmission.
2. Connect a test lamp in series with the switch and 12 V power source.

Caution Do not use a bulb any larger than 0.8 amp (no. 1893); the switch contacts will be damaged at a higher amperage.

3. With the engine and ignition off, move the gear shift lever through all of the gears. The test lamp should remain lighted in every gear except third and fourth (if so equipped).

NOTE: On 1972 models with four-speed transmissions, the lamp should remain lighted in third gear and not go out until fourth is selected.

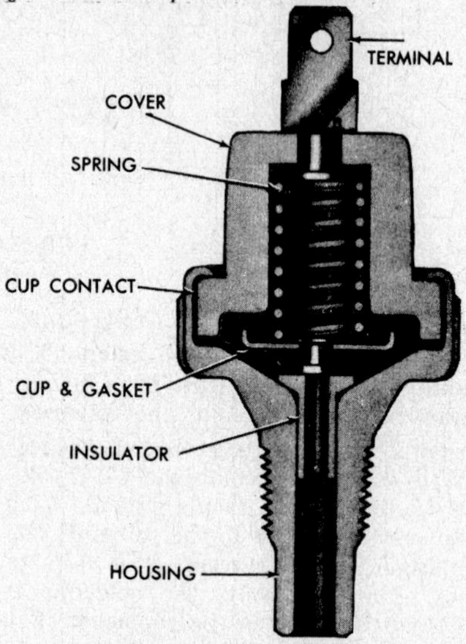
TERMINAL
COVER
SPRING
CUP CONTACT
CUP & GASKET
INSULATOR
HOUSING
Automatic transmission switch used on Turbo-Hydramatic 350—other transmission switches similar
(© G.M. Corp)

4. If the test lamp fails to go out when it should, the switch is defective.
5. If the test lamp fails to come on at all, the switch is broken or the wiring is faulty.
6. If the switch is not defective, reconnect it when finished testing.

Type F—Automatic Transmission Normally Closed

NOTE: Vegas, made for sale in California in 1972, have a non-functional, dummy transmission switch when equipped with an automatic transmission.

1. Connect a test lamp as detailed in steps 1–2 of the test for type E switch above. Pay particular attention to the "Caution."
2. Raise the rear wheels of the car so they are off of the ground and support the car so that it cannot move forward.
3. Start the engine. Shift the transmission into Drive. Increase engine speed so that the transmission shifts into high gear, the test lamp should go out when the transmission enters high gear.

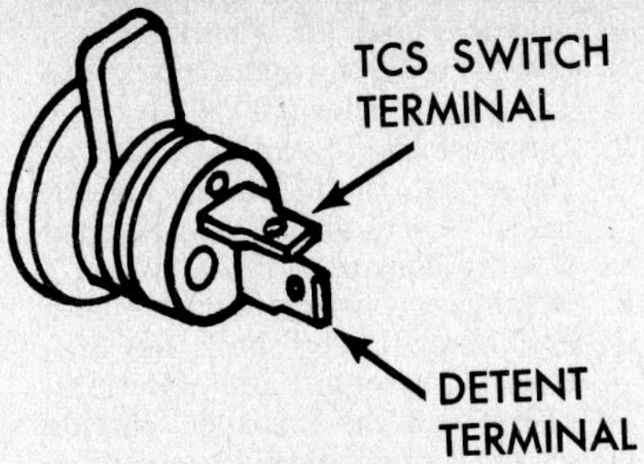
TCS SWITCH
TERMINAL
DETENT
TERMINAL

The terminals on the Turbo-Hydramatic 400 transmission switch
(© G.M. Corp)

4. Allow the engine to return to idle and apply the brakes. Shift into Reverse. The light should go out again, except on cars equipped with Powerglide or Torque Drive.
5. In all other gears the lamp should remain on. If it does not or if it fails to go out when it should, replace the switch.

VACUUM ADVANCE SOLENOID AND TRANSMISSION SWITCH USAGE

Make	*Year*	*Model*	*Test Section Used For:* *Vacuum Advance Solenoid*	*Transmission Switch*
Buick	1970–72	All	A	E, F
Cadillac	1970–71	All	A	F
Chevrolet	1970	All	A	E, F
	1971	L6, V8	C	E, F
		Vega	A	E, F
	1972–73	L6	C	D
		V8	C	D
	1972	Vega	A	E, F①
	1973	Vega	B	D
Pontiac	1970–71	All	A	E, F
	1972–73	L6	C	D
	1972	V8	A	E, F
Oldsmobile	1971–73	V8	A	E, F
	1973	L6	C	D

①—The transmission switch is not operative on Vegas sold in California when equipped with an automatic transmission.

1973 Pontiac Combination T.C.S.-E.G.R. System

NOTE: Cars produced on or after 15 March 1973 do not use the combined TCS-EGR system, instead two separate systems are used. For test procedures on the TCS system, see the following section. EGR system tests are included with the other GM lines below. Engines with the new systems may be identified by the darker blue paint on the engine and the two thermal valves threaded into the intake manifold, just ahead of the carburetor.

System Test

1. Apply parking brake, and securely block wheels. Connect a vacuum gauge to the distributor end of the vacuum line that runs from the T.C.S. solenoid to the distributor. Observe the position of the stem under the E.G.R. valve, this should be in the closed position.
2. The engine must be "overnight" cold with the ambient temperature below 71°. If this condition cannot be duplicated, follow the instructions below, skipping step four, and then use the "Simulated Temperature Switch Test" which follows the normal testing procedures.
3. Depress accelerator to set choke

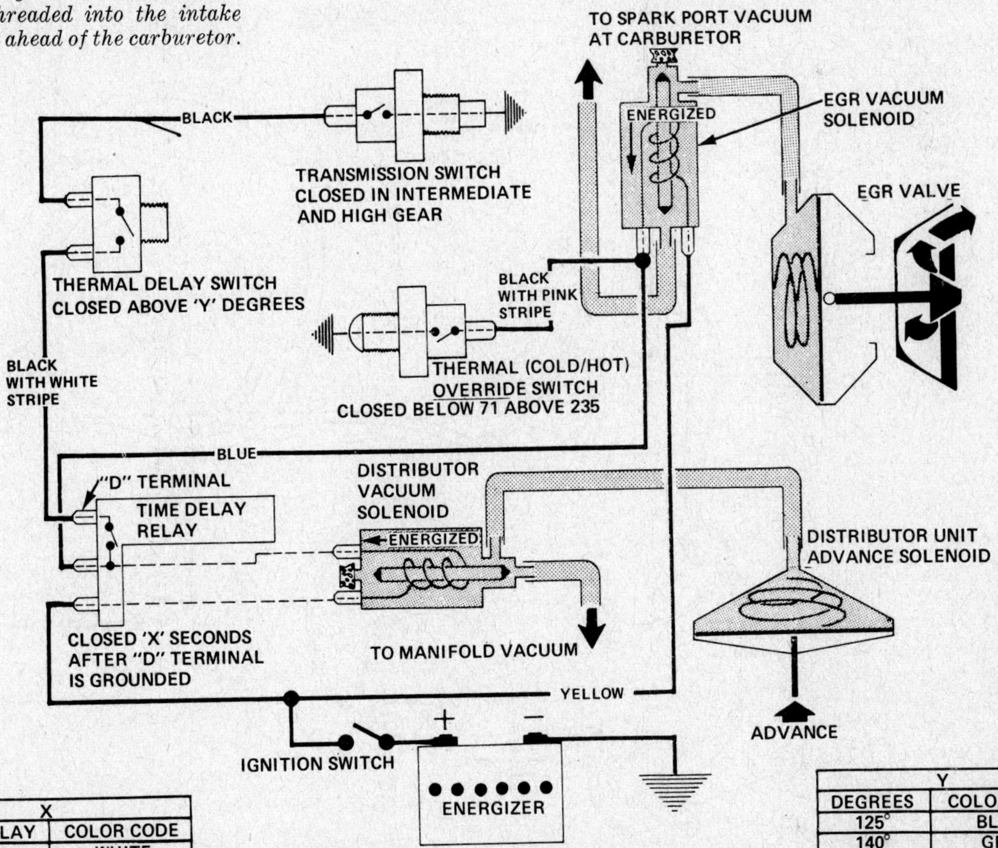
TO SPARK PORT VACUUM
AT CARBURETOR
ENERGIZED
EGR VACUUM
SOLENOID
BLACK
TRANSMISSION SWITCH
CLOSED IN INTERMEDIATE
AND HIGH GEAR
EGR VALVE
THERMAL DELAY SWITCH
CLOSED ABOVE 'Y' DEGREES
BLACK
WITH PINK
STRIPE
BLACK
WITH WHITE
STRIPE
THERMAL (COLD/HOT)
OVERRIDE SWITCH
CLOSED BELOW 71 ABOVE 235
BLUE
"D" TERMINAL
TIME DELAY
RELAY
DISTRIBUTOR
VACUUM
SOLENOID
ENERGIZED
DISTRIBUTOR UNIT
ADVANCE SOLENOID
CLOSED 'X' SECONDS
AFTER "D" TERMINAL
IS GROUNDED
TO MANIFOLD VACUUM
YELLOW
ADVANCE
IGNITION SWITCH
ENERGIZER

X	
SECONDS DELAY	COLOR CODE
30	WHITE
50	BLUE

Y	
DEGREES	COLOR CODE
125°	BLACK
140°	GREY
155°	GREEN

1973 Pontiac TCS-EGR system (© G.M. Corp)

and place throttle linkage on fast idle cam. Start the engine and allow throttle to remain on fast idle cam.

4. Vacuum gauge should indicate a high manifold vacuum and E.G.R. valve should remain fully closed.
5. When the engine reaches 71°, manifold vacuum should disappear and the E.G.R. valve should open.
6. Shut off the engine. Raise the rear of the car and place it on jackstands so wheels are off the floor. Release parking brake. Put automatic transmission in Drive, manual transmission in highest gear. Place throttle on fast idle cam. Make sure automatic transmission shifts out of first gear.
7. When engine temperature reaches 140° (well before coolant flows through radiator), the E.G.R. valve should close fully, and manifold vacuum should again show on the vacuum gauge. Shift transmission out of gear for several seconds, then put it back in gear. Vacuum should disappear and E.G.R. valve should open. 33–55 seconds. after the transmission shifts out of first gear, vacuum should come back and the E.G.R. valve should close.
8. Restrict the flow of air across the radiator core. Shift the transmission into neutral. Vacuum will disappear, and E.G.R. valve will open. At 235° (before temperature light comes on) vacuum should be restored and the E.G.R. valve should close.

NOTE: If the EGR valve is not operating properly, perform steps 5-7 of the GM EGR valve test, below.

Simulated Temperature Switch Test

If the other parts of the system function, but conditions would not permit testing the low temperature function, remove the temperature sensor from the rear of the left head as follows:

1. Allow engine to cool until radiator cap can be safely removed, then remove the cap.
2. Place a clean container under the drain cock and begin draining coolant.
3. Disconnect wiring and loosen switch at rear of left cylinder head to check for presence of coolant. As soon as switch can be removed without loss of coolant, close the radiator drain cock and remove the switch. Test the switch as follows:

1. Prepare a container of cold water or water and ice. Check with a thermometer to make sure temperature is below 60°.
2. Immerse the threaded portion of the switch in the water, and allow it to cool until it has reached the temperature of the water.
3. Remove the switch from the bath and immediately check for continuity between the electrical prong and the threaded portion of the switch. Replace a switch which shows no continuity under these conditions.

Symptoms and Appropriate Checks

1. System responds normally at operating temperatures but does not supply advance and deny EGR below 71° and/or above 235°. Operate engine at fast idle with transmission in neutral until normal operating temperature is reached. Jump the switch at the rear of the left cylinder head by grounding the wire which goes to the switch. If this produces vacuum and shuts off the EGR valve, replace the switch. Otherwise, check for defects in the wiring between this switch and the solenoids.
2. System responds to temperature changes, but does not provide vacuum advance and deny EGR

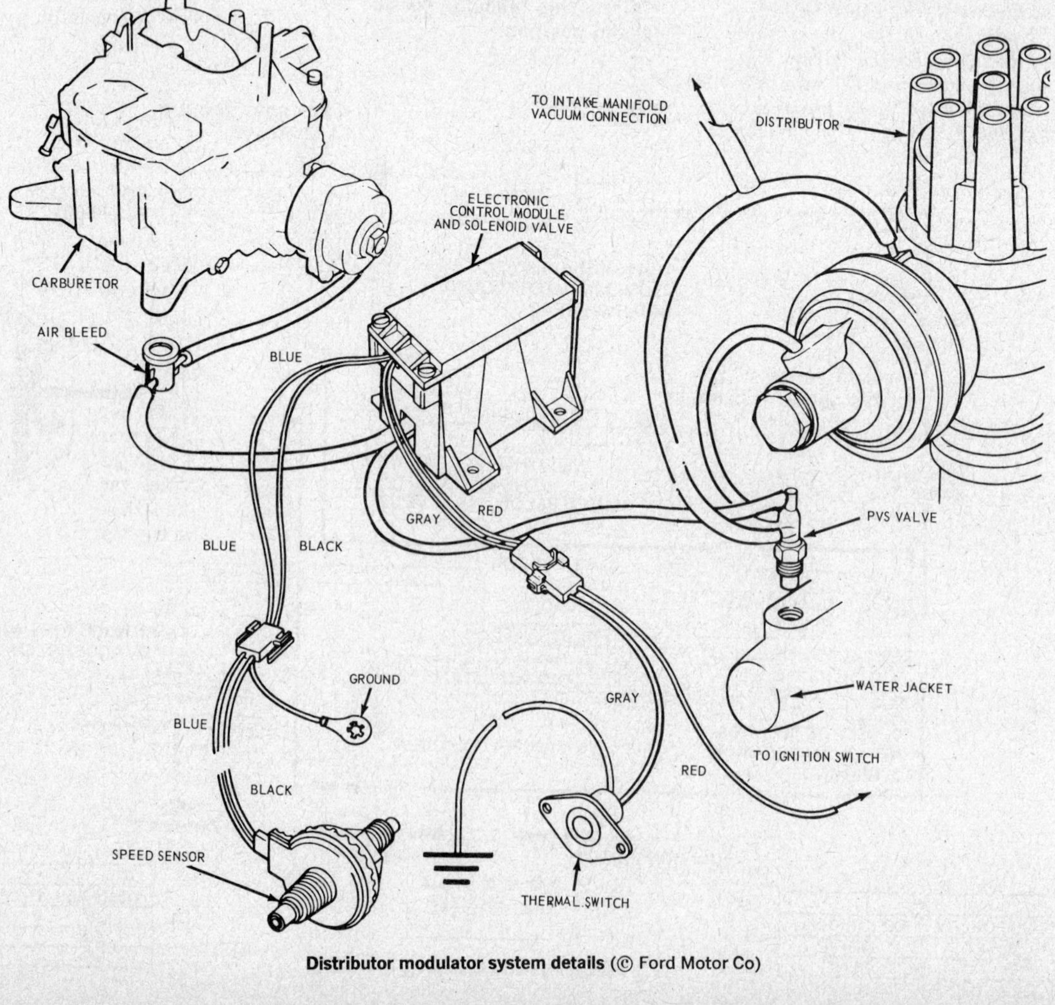
TO INTAKE MANIFOLD VACUUM CONNECTION
DISTRIBUTOR
ELECTRONIC CONTROL MODULE AND SOLENOID VALVE
CARBURETOR
AIR BLEED
BLUE
GRAY
RED
PVS VALVE
BLUE
BLACK
GROUND
WATER JACKET
GRAY
BLUE
TO IGNITION SWITCH
RED
BLACK
SPEED SENSOR
THERMAL SWITCH

Distributor modulator system details (© Ford Motor Co)

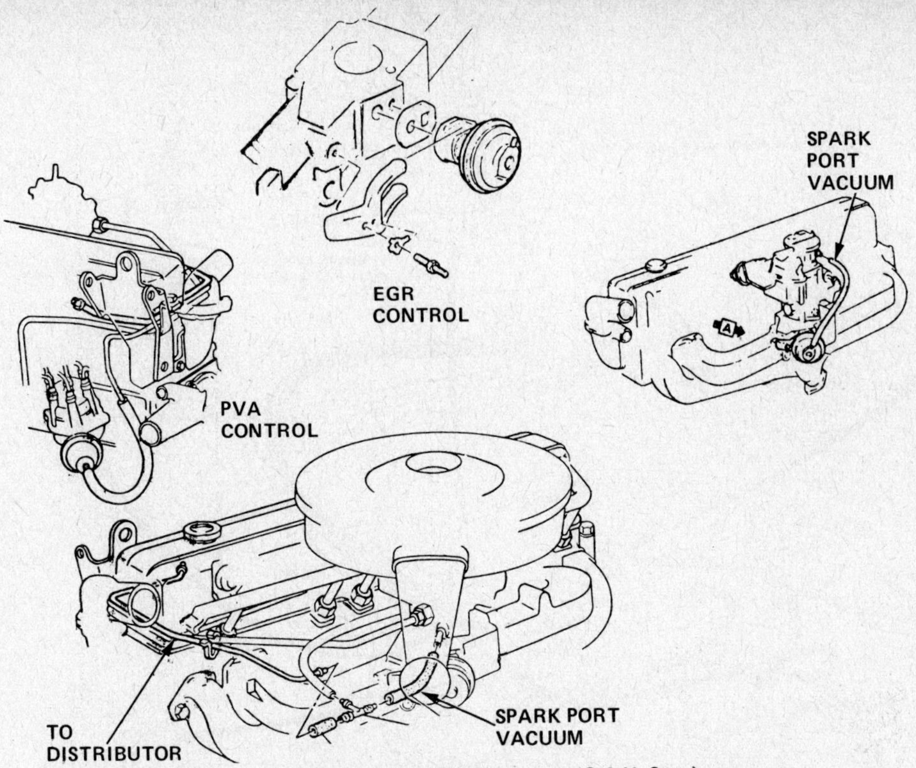
EGR
CONTROL
SPARK
PORT
VACUUM
PVA
CONTROL
TO
DISTRIBUTOR
SPARK PORT
VACUUM
Early 1973 Pontiac combined TCS/EGR system (© G.M. Corp.)

after transmission shifts to second gear. Operate engine at fast idle with transmission in Neutral until operating temperature is reached. Ground the switch on the right side of the transmission, by grounding the wire connected to it. Keep wire grounded one minute. If this produces vacuum advance and denies EGR, replace the transmission switch. Otherwise, bypass the switch on the right cylinder head and ground the wire to the transmission switch. If this produces vacuum advance and denies EGR after one minute, replace the sensor in the right head. Otherwise, the Time Delay Relay or associated wiring is defective. Bypass each to locate the defective component.

3. System responds normally except that EGR is denied and vacuum advance established as soon as transmission shifts to second gear. Replace Time Delay Relay.
4. Only one function responds as required, or system provides EGR and denies vacuum advance at all times; check wiring. Replace if defective. Otherwise, solenoid(s) are at fault.

1973½ Pontiac TCS System

A new TCS system is used on 1973 Pontiacs, beginning with cars produced on or after 15 March 1973. For testing the combined TCS-EGR system used before this date, see the preceding section.

System Test

NOTE: The following conditions must be met before beginning the TCS system test:

The car must be run for ten minutes, if it is at room temperature. If the car is cold, it must be run until it has reached normal operating temperature. This will allow the air/fuel mixture and the engine block to reach 62° and 155°F, respectively.

At no time during the test should the coolant temperature be allowed to go over 240°F (the temperature warning light will come on if it does).

1. Hook up a vacuum gauge to the vertical fitting at the back of the vacuum advance solenoid or, if the engine is equipped with a spark delay valve, hook up the gauge to the "DIST" port on the delay valve.
2. Place the vacuum gauge on the cowl, so that it can be seen from the driver's seat.
3. Run the engine until it is warmed-up. See the "Note" at the beginning of this section.
4. After the engine reaches normal operating temperature, turn it off.
5. Place the gearshift in Park or Neutral, and start the engine.
   a. The gauge should indicate vacuum for about 20 seconds, unless the car is equipped with a spark delay valve.
   b. The vacuum gauge reading will slowly rise to a peak in 10-15 seconds on spark delay valve equipped models.

The vacuum reading should disappear on all models after 20 seconds.

NOTE: In order to get a vacuum reading on cars having a manual transmission, open the throttle slightly, in order to uncover the carburetor vacuum port.

6. If no vacuum is registered on the gauge, check for a faulty time delay relay, as outlined under "Type C—CEC Solenoid and Relays", above. If the time delay relay is working properly, check the vacuum advance solenoid to see if it is defective. If both are working properly, go on to the next step.
7. On manual transmission-equipped cars, depress the clutch pedal, open the throttle slightly and shift into high gear, the gauge should show a vacuum. Remember to wait 10-15 seconds on spark delay valve equipped engines.
8. On cars having an automatic transmission, shift into Reverse. The gauge should register vacuum in at least 10-15 seconds.

Caution *Before shifting into Reverse, be sure that the parking brake is on and the service brake is fully applied to prevent the car from moving. Do not keep the car in Reverse any longer than necessary.*

9. If no vacuum is present, check for clogged, broken or misrouted vacuum lines. If the lines are in good condition, check the transmission switch or the vacuum advance solenoid, as outlined in the appropriate section, above.
10. If vacuum advance is always

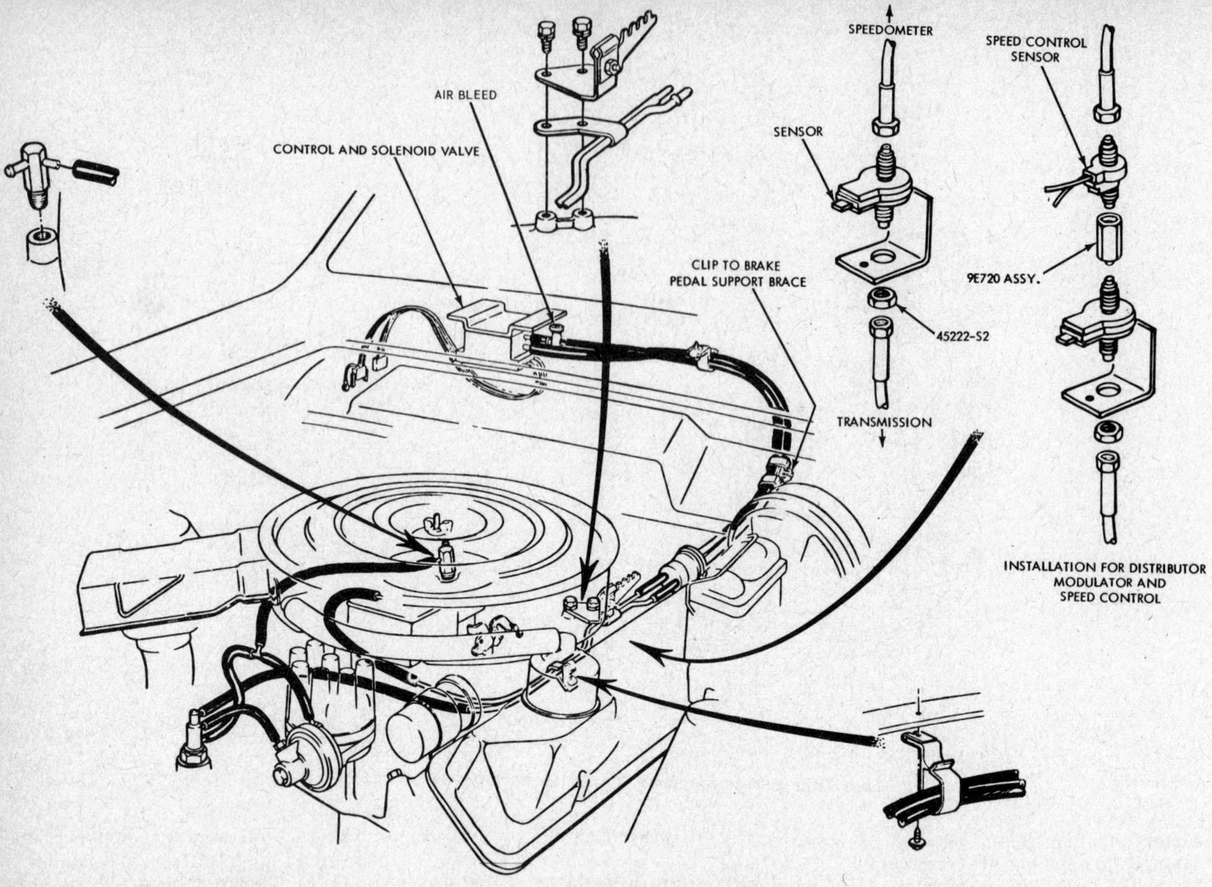
AIR BLEED
CONTROL AND SOLENOID VALVE
SPEEDOMETER
SPEED CONTROL SENSOR
SENSOR
CLIP TO BRAKE PEDAL SUPPORT BRACE
9E720 ASSY.
45222-S2
TRANSMISSION
INSTALLATION FOR DISTRIBUTOR MODULATOR AND SPEED CONTROL

Typical distributor modulator installation (© Ford Motor Co)

present, then check the following:

a. If the vacuum advance solenoid is always energized, check the red temperature warning light on the instrument panel. If it is on, either coolant temperature has reached 240°F or the temperature sensor is defective, which will cause the solenoid to remain energized. Allow the engine to cool to test the sensor's operation.

b. If the dash temperature light is not on, the engine block temperature is above 155°F, but the vacuum advance solenoid is still energized, the "cold feed" switch is probably defective and should be replaced.

c. If vacuum is always present, but the vacuum advance solenoid is NOT energized, then the air/fuel sensing valve is probably defective and should be replaced.

NOTE: This valve will provide vacuum advance all the time, unless the air/fuel mixture temperature is above 62°F.

Speed Controlled Spark Systems

Ford Distributor Modulator System—1970-71

System Tests

Check the distributor vacuum advance on an analyzer (distributor modulator system bypassed if distributor is left in engine for test). If it is functioning correctly, proceed with the tests outlined below.

1. Disconnect the distributor vacuum advance line from the carburetor and connect a vacuum gauge to vacuum line fitting on the carburetor. Run the engine at 1,500 rpm and take a vacuum reading. Make a note of the result. Disconnect the vacuum gauge and attach the vacuum line back on the carburetor.
2. Using a short length of rubber hose to bypass the distributor modulator control box, connect the distributor vacuum advance unit directly to the carburetor. Disconnect the vacuum line from the distributor vacuum advance unit and connect it to the vacuum gauge.
3. Run the engine at 1,500 rpm again. The vacuum gauge reading should be similar to that obtained above. If it is zero or much less than in step one, check for pinched or leaking vacuum lines.
4. Remove the hose used to bypass the distributor modulator and reconnect the vacuum lines as originally found. Leave the vacuum gauge connected to the distributor vacuum line, however.
5. Raise the rear wheels off the ground and support the car so that it cannot roll forward. Run the engine at idle until normal operating temperature is reached.
6. Remove the thermal switch from the door pillar. Hold the switch in the palm of the hand long enough to bring its temperature above 60° F.
7. Place the transmission selector in Drive. Accelerate to 35 mph. By the time this speed is reached, the vacuum gauge should show a reading.
8. If the vacuum gauge shows a reading below 20–35 mph, or if it does not show a reading above 35 mph, proceed with the individual component tests as required.

NOTE: Remember to check the coolant temperature operated vacuum valve, if so equipped, as possible cause of trouble. The test procedures may be found above.

Power Supply Test

1. Switch the ignition on. Take a voltage reading at the red lead which runs to the control module.
2. If the voltmeter reads zero, check for a blown system fuse or faulty wiring.
3. If the voltmeter registers normal battery voltage, the module is getting the proper power. Proceed with the next test.

DISTRIBUTOR MODULATOR SYSTEM TROUBLESHOOTING CHART

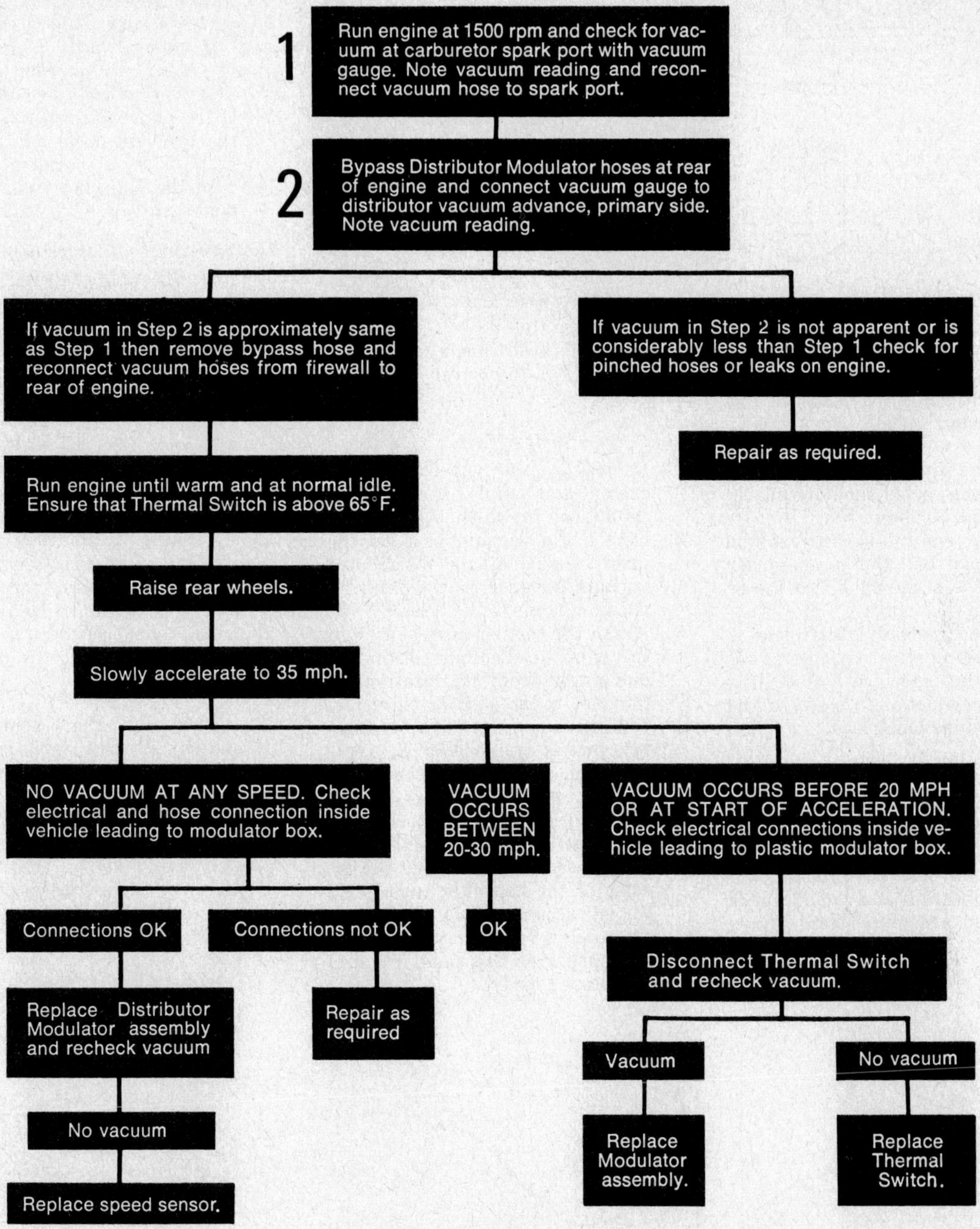
1
Run engine at 1500 rpm and check for vacuum at carburetor spark port with vacuum gauge. Note vacuum reading and reconnect vacuum hose to spark port.
2
Bypass Distributor Modulator hoses at rear of engine and connect vacuum gauge to distributor vacuum advance, primary side. Note vacuum reading.
If vacuum in Step 2 is approximately same as Step 1 then remove bypass hose and reconnect vacuum hoses from firewall to rear of engine.
If vacuum in Step 2 is not apparent or is considerably less than Step 1 check for pinched hoses or leaks on engine.
Repair as required.
Run engine until warm and at normal idle. Ensure that Thermal Switch is above 65°F.
Raise rear wheels.
Slowly accelerate to 35 mph.
NO VACUUM AT ANY SPEED. Check electrical and hose connection inside vehicle leading to modulator box.
VACUUM OCCURS BETWEEN 20-30 mph.
VACUUM OCCURS BEFORE 20 MPH OR AT START OF ACCELERATION. Check electrical connections inside vehicle leading to plastic modulator box.
Connections OK
Connections not OK
OK
Disconnect Thermal Switch and recheck vacuum.
Replace Distributor Modulator assembly and recheck vacuum
Repair as required
Vacuum
No vacuum
No vacuum
Replace Modulator assembly.
Replace Thermal Switch.
Replace speed sensor.

Thermal Switch Test

1. Disconnect the thermal switch at its multiconnector.
2. Connect an ohmmeter to the grey (or white) and black leads coming from the switch.
3. Warm the switch by holding it in the palm of the hand until it is above 68° F. There should be no reading (zero) on the ohmmeter. If there is a reading the switch is defective and needs to be replaced.
4. Chill the switch, using ice or cold water, to below 50° F. There should now be a reading (resistance indicated) on the meter. If there is no reading, the switch is defective and should be replaced.
5. If the temperature switch is functioning properly, proceed with the next test.

Control Module Test

1. Disconnect the thermal switch multiconnector from the module. Use a jumper lead to connect the two red wires leading from the two halves of multiconnector.
2. Attach a vacuum gauge to the distributor vacuum line fitting on the carburetor. Run the engine at fast idle and note the reading. Disconnect the gauge and reconnect the vacuum line to the port.
3. Connect the vacuum gauge to the vacuum hose that runs to the distributor vacuum advance unit.
4. Use another jumper lead to connect the grey (or white) wire, which runs from the control module to the thermal switch connector, to ground.
5. Run the engine at fast idle again and note the vacuum reading. It should be almost the same as that taken at the carburetor port.
6. If the reading is zero or lower than that at the carburetor port, the module is defective and must be replaced.
7. If the module is functioning properly, reconnect it and go on with the next test.

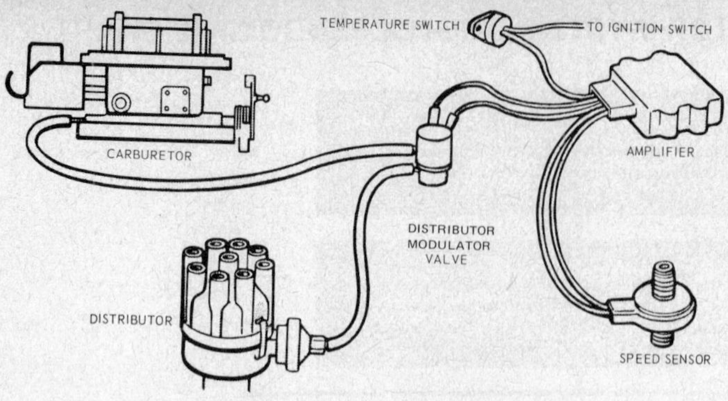
TEMPERATURE SWITCH
TO IGNITION SWITCH
CARBURETOR
AMPLIFIER
DISTRIBUTOR
MODULATOR
VALVE
DISTRIBUTOR
SPEED SENSOR

Components of the Ford ECS system
(© Ford Motor Co)

Speed Sensor Test

1. Detach the speed sensor leads at its multiconnector. Connect the test prods of an ohmmeter to them.
2. With the sensor at room temperature, the meter should read between 40–60 ohms.
3. Test for continuity between the black lead and the speed sensor case. There should be no meter reading.
4. The speed sensor is defective if the reading in step 2 does not fall within specifications or if a reading is obtained between the case and the black lead.

Ford Electronic Spark Control (ESC)—1972-73

This system replaces the distributor modulator system, above. The test procedures for the two systems are somewhat different and should not be interchanged, except as noted.

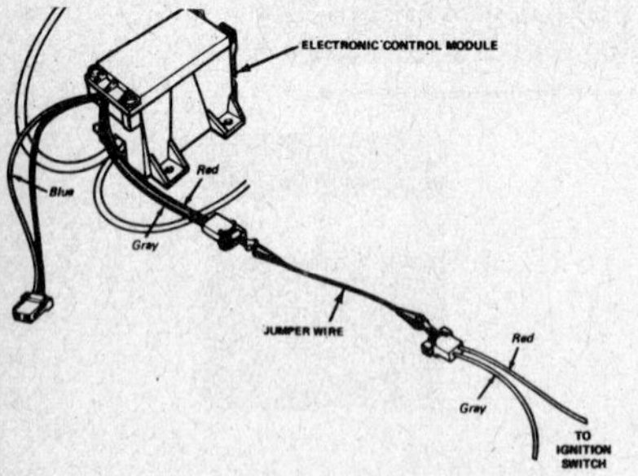
ELECTRONIC CONTROL MODULE
Blue
Red
Grey
JUMPER WIRE
Red
Grey
TO IGNITION SWITCH

Connect the two red wires of the multiconnector by using a jumper lead
(© Ford Motor Co)

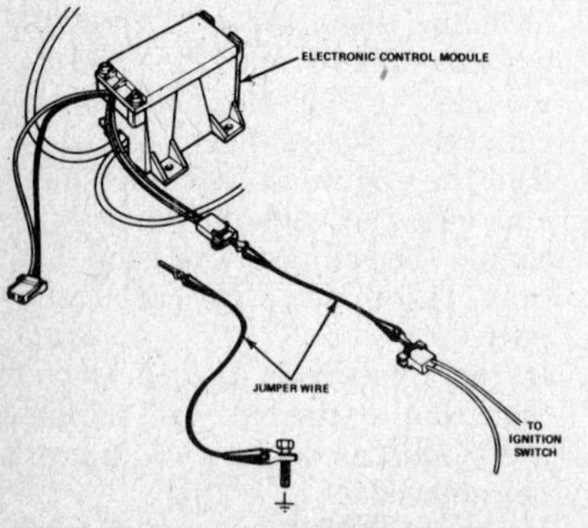
ELECTRONIC CONTROL MODULE
JUMPER WIRE
TO IGNITION SWITCH

Connect the grey (or white) wire to ground by using a jumper lead
(© Ford Motor Co)

NOTE: Vehicles made on or after 15 March 1973 do not use a temperature switch.

System Test

1. Raise the rear wheels off the ground and support the car so it cannot roll forward.
2. Detach the vacuum hose on the primary side of the distributor vacuum advance unit. Connect a vacuum gauge to the hose.
3. Warm the temperature sensor in the palm of the hand, after removing it from its location on the door pillar (left or right, depending upon model). Be sure it is heated to above 65°F.
4. Start the engine. Place the transmission selector in Drive. Accelerate until the speed specified in the chart is reached (see below). This speed is determined by the color of the amplifier case. Wait for 40 seconds; this allows the time delay valve to work (if so equipped). At this point vacuum should be present.

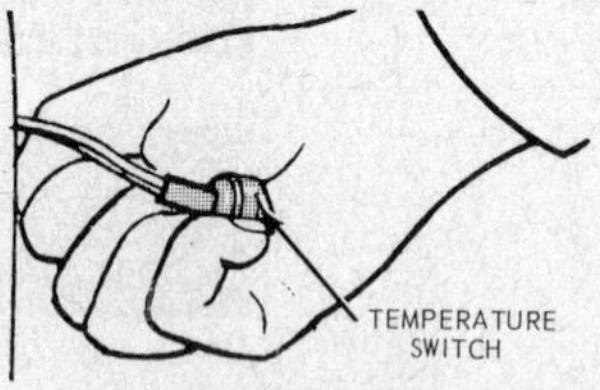
TEMPERATURE
SWITCH

Warm the temperature switch in the palm of your hand
(© Ford Motor Co)

Amplifier Case Color	*Vacuum Advance Cut-in Speed (mph)*
Black	23
White	28
Blue	33
Grey	35

5. If there is no vacuum, first check for a clogged carburetor vacuum port.
6. Then check the vacuum lines to see if they are pinched, clogged or misrouted.

NOTE: Remember to check the coolant temperature-operated vacuum valve, if so equipped, as a possible source of the malfunction. The test procedures for it are given above.

7. If the above checks indicate that the problem does not lie in the vacuum supply system, proceed with the ESC individual component tests.

Distributor Modulator Solenoid Test

1. Disconnect the electrical leads from the distributor modulator solenoid.
2. Increase engine speed. If there is no vacuum reading, with the gauge connected as in the System Test, the solenoid is defective and must be replaced. Reconnect the electrical leads to the distributor modulator solenoid and allow the engine to slow down.
3. If vacuum occurs below the specified cut-in speeds (see the chart in step 4, above), the solenoid is not being energized and the trouble lies elsewhere in the system. Proceed with the next test.

Temperature Switch Tests

1. Disconnect the temperature switch at the multiconnector. Connect an ohmmeter to the switch terminals.
2. Warm the switch by placing it in the palm of the hand. The ohmmeter should show a reading. If it does not, the switch is defective.
3. Chill the switch to 49°F or below, by using ice or cold water. There should be no reading (zero) on the ohmmeter. If a resistance is indicated, the temperature switch is defective.

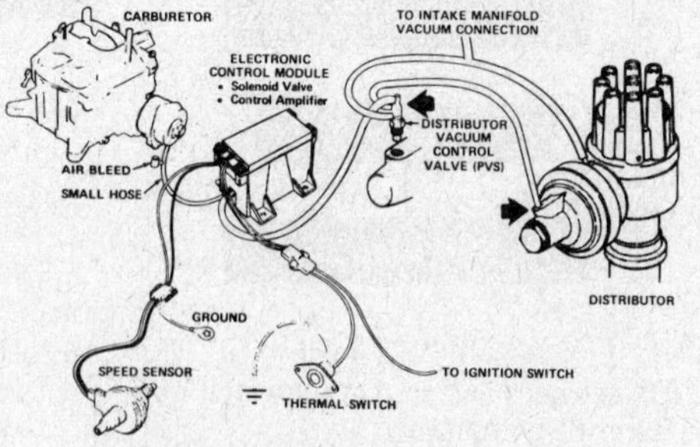
CARBURETOR
TO INTAKE MANIFOLD
VACUUM CONNECTION
ELECTRONIC
CONTROL MODULE
• Solenoid Valve
• Control Amplifier
DISTRIBUTOR
VACUUM
CONTROL
VALVE (PVS)
AIR BLEED
SMALL HOSE
GROUND
DISTRIBUTOR
SPEED SENSOR
TO IGNITION SWITCH
THERMAL SWITCH

Arrows show the vacuum gauge hook-up points used during control module tests
(© Ford Motor Co)

4. Replace the switch if defective. If it is not, proceed with the next test.

Power Supply Test

1. Ground one side of a low-amperage test lamp and connect the other side to the temperature switch connector of the instrument panel wiring (red/yellow hash lead).

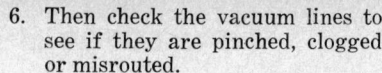

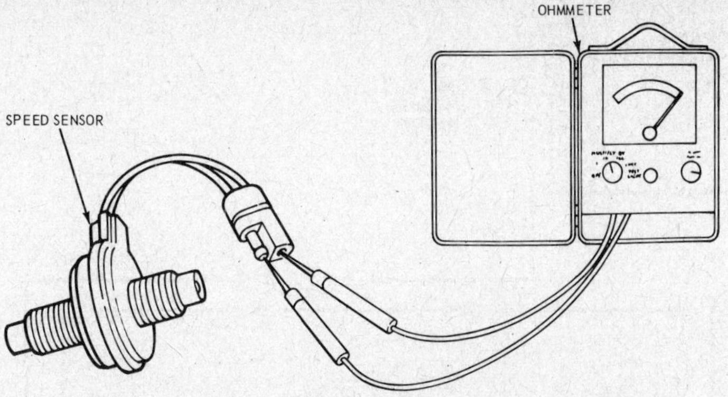
OHMMETER
SPEED SENSOR

Checking the impedance of the speed sensor with an ohmmeter
(© Ford Motor Co)

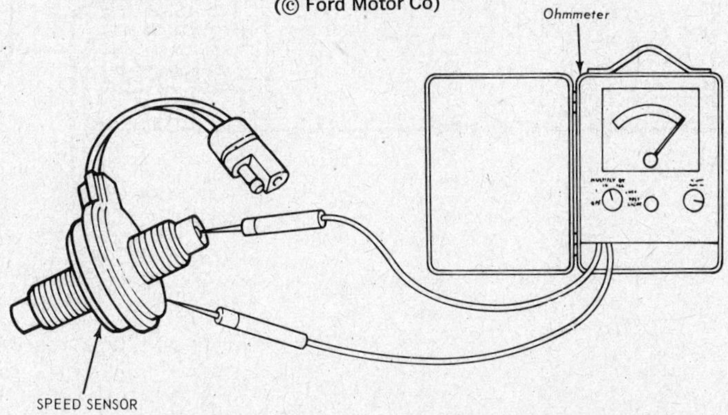
Ohmmeter
SPEED SENSOR

Using an ohmmeter to see if the speed sensor is grounded to the case
(© Ford Motor Co)

2. T-connect a vacuum gauge between the distributor and the solenoid vacuum valve.
3. Raise the car on a lift, with the wheels hanging free.
4. Disconnect the vacuum line at the vacuum switch on the control unit.
5. Start the engine and run at a speed above 850 rpm. Vacuum gauge should read zero.
6. Disconnect the wire from the control unit. The vacuum gauge should read normal advance unit operating vacuum. Reconnect the wire. The gauge should drop to zero.
7. Unplug and reconnect the vacuum line to the vacuum switch. Disconnect the wire from the control unit to the speed switch. The gauge should read normal advance unit operating vacuum.
8. Place transmission in Drive. Sharp acceleration should cause the gauge reading to drop sharply to zero. Do not exceed 40 mph.
9. Accelerate above 30 mph. The gauge should read normal vacuum advance unit operating vacuum.
10. If solenoid valve did not operate during the tests, replace control unit.

2. Turn on the ignition. The lamp should light. If it fails to do so, check the wiring to the ignition switch or check the ignition switch itself.
3. If the ESC system is getting power, proceed with the next test.

Speed Sensor Test

This test is exactly the same as that for the speed sensor used in the distributor modulator system.

Perform the speed sensor test as outlined in the "Distributor Modulator" section, above.

Amplifier

If everything else in the ESC system is functioning properly, the fault lies with the amplifier module. Replace the amplifier and repeat the "System Test".

Chrysler Corp.

Automatic Transmission System Test

1. Warm the engine to normal operating temperature. Be sure the ambient temperature is well above 70°F.

American Motors and Pontiac

NOTE: Although American Motors calls all of their spark control systems "Transmission - Controlled Spark" (TCS), the one used with automatic transmissions is really a speed-controlled spark system (SCS). American Motors cars made on or after 15 March 1973 do not use an SCS system, but have, instead, a transmission controlled spark (TCS) system. Consult the appropriate section above for system testing.

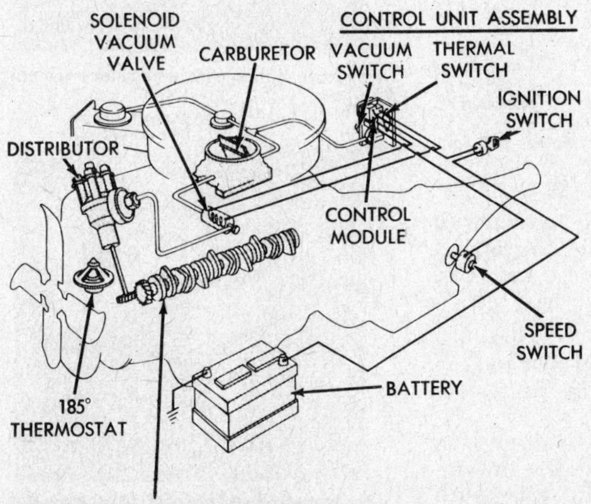
SOLENOID VACUUM VALVE
CARBURETOR
CONTROL UNIT ASSEMBLY
VACUUM SWITCH
THERMAL SWITCH
IGNITION SWITCH
DISTRIBUTOR
CONTROL MODULE
SPEED SWITCH
BATTERY
185° THERMOSTAT
INCREASED-OVERLAP CAMSHAFT

NO_X (SCS) system—automatic transmission
(© Chrysler Corp)

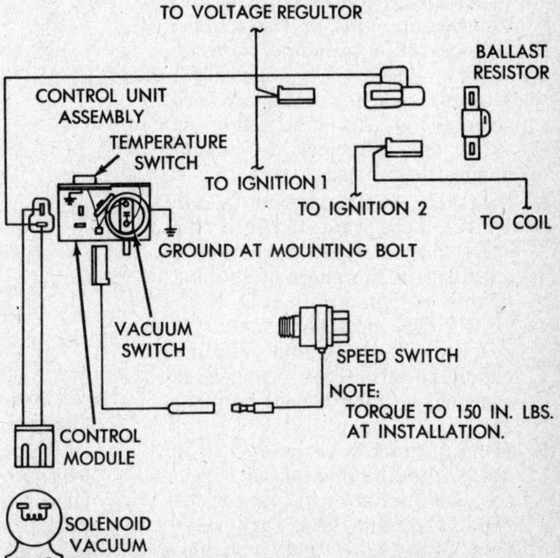
TO VOLTAGE REGULTOR
BALLAST RESISTOR
CONTROL UNIT ASSEMBLY
TEMPERATURE SWITCH
TO IGNITION 1
TO IGNITION 2
TO COIL
GROUND AT MOUNTING BOLT
VACUUM SWITCH
SPEED SWITCH
NOTE:
TORQUE TO 150 IN. LBS.
AT INSTALLATION.
CONTROL MODULE
SOLENOID VACUUM VALVE

NO_X (SCS) system schematic—automatic transmission
(© Chrysler Corp)

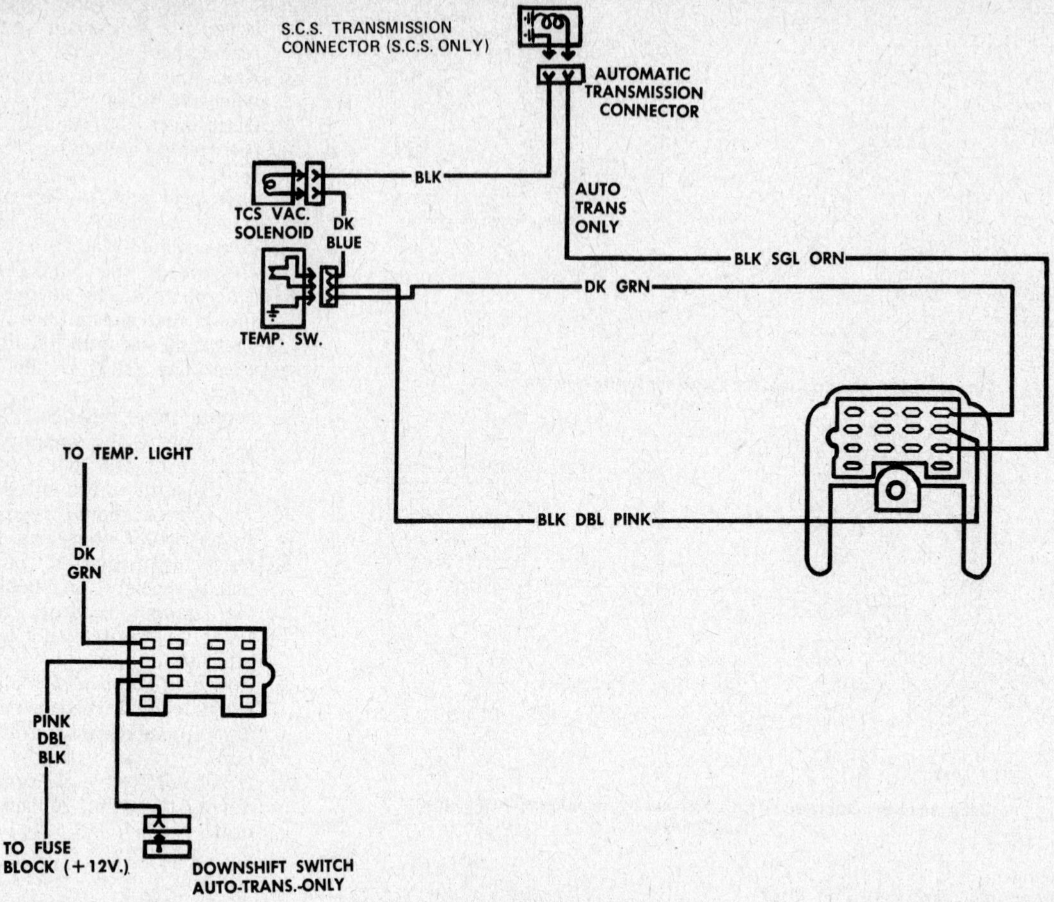
S.C.S. TRANSMISSION
CONNECTOR (S.C.S. ONLY)
AUTOMATIC
TRANSMISSION
CONNECTOR
BLK
TCS VAC.
SOLENOID
DK
BLUE
AUTO
TRANS
ONLY
BLK SGL ORN
DK GRN
TEMP. SW.
TO TEMP. LIGHT
BLK DBL PINK
DK
GRN
PINK
DBL
BLK
TO FUSE
BLOCK (+12V.)
DOWNSHIFT SWITCH
AUTO-TRANS.-ONLY

Schematic for Pontiac SCS system (© G.M. Corp)

System Test

This test should be performed with the air temperature above 65°F and the coolant temperature above 160°F (American Motors V8) or with the engine temperature between 95° and 230°F (Pontiac).

1. Raise the rear wheels off the ground and support the car so it cannot roll forward.
2. Disconnect the vacuum hose which runs between the distributor vacuum unit or the coolant temperature vacuum override valve (1972–73 American Motors) and the vacuum advance solenoid at the distributor or valve end. Connect a vacuum gauge to the hose.
3. Start the engine and shift into Drive. Accelerate to until the speedometer registers the speed specified in the chart at the end of this section.
4. Until the specified speed is reached, the vacuum reading should be zero. Once this speed is reached, vacuum should be present.
5. If no vacuum is registered at or above the specified speed, check the vacuum lines and connections first. Examine the carburetor port to be sure that it is not clogged.

NOTE: Remember to check the coolant temperature vacuum override valve, if so equipped, as its failure could cause a loss of vacuum. Test procedures for it are given earlier in this section.

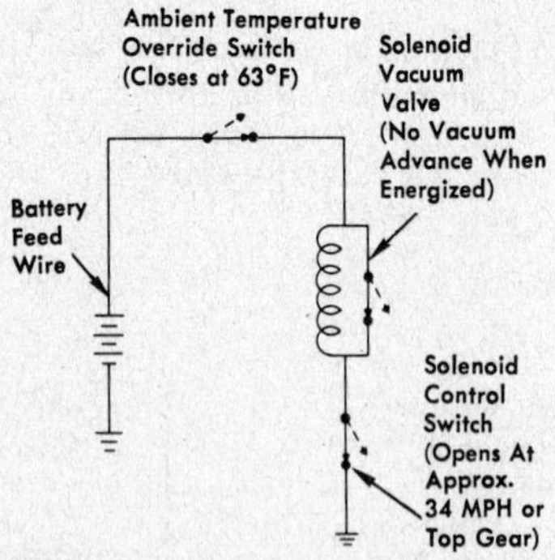
Ambient Temperature
Override Switch
(Closes at 63°F)
Solenoid
Vacuum
Valve
(No Vacuum
Advance When
Energized)
Battery
Feed
Wire
Solenoid
Control
Switch
(Opens At
Approx.
34 MPH or
Top Gear)

Schematic for the American Motors SCS (or TCS) system
(© American Motors Corp)

6. If there is nothing wrong with the vacuum supply, disconnect the gauge, reconnect the hose and proceed with the next test.

Transmission Switch Tests

1. Leave the rear wheels of the car off the ground as in the system test above.
2. Disconnect the transmission switch leads. Connect a low-amperage test lamp in series with the switch and the positive side of the battery.
3. Accelerate to the specified speed (see chart below) and watch the test lamp. It should remain on until the specified speed is reached. If the lamp fails to go out or if it does not light at all, the switch is defective and must be replaced.

American Motors vacuum advance solenoid location
(© American Motors Corp)

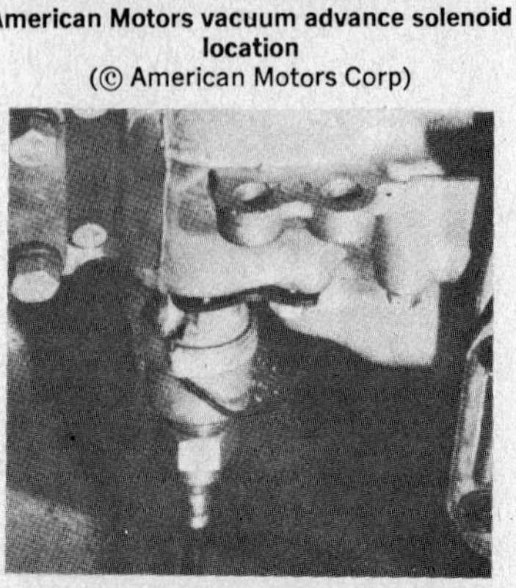

Transmission switch location on American Motors cars
(© American Motors Corp)

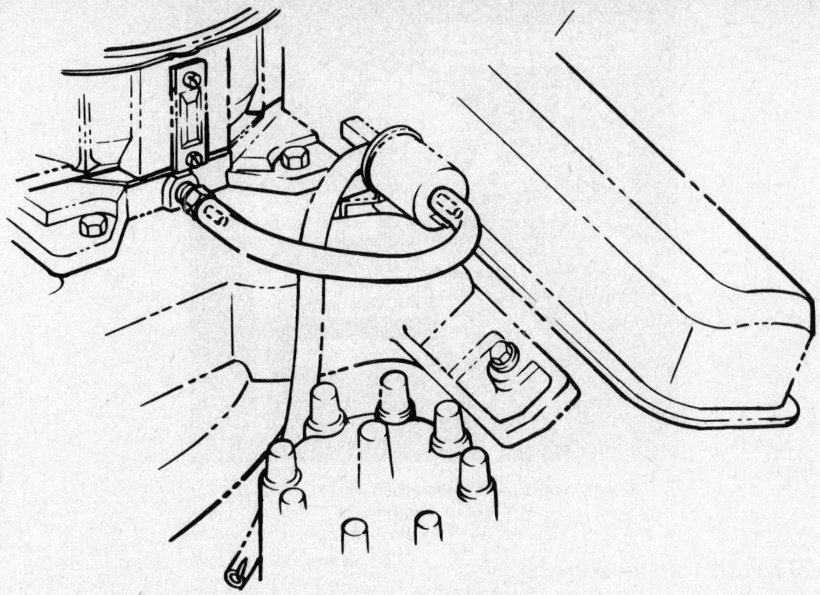

Pontiac vacuum solenoid location
(© G.M. Corp)

4. If the switch is working properly, reconnect it and go on with the next test.

Vacuum Advance Solenoid Test

1. Disconnect the vacuum advance solenoid leads. Connect a vacuum gauge to the solenoid hose as in the system test.
2. Place the transmission in neutral and start the engine. Increase engine speed. The gauge should indicate the presence of a vacuum.
3. Connect the hot lead to a 12 V power source. Ground the other lead. Increase the engine speed again. The solenoid should energize, resulting in a vacuum reading of zero.
4. Replace the vacuum advance solenoid if it is faulty. If it is not, reconnect the wiring and go on with the next appropriate test.

Ambient Temperature Override Switch—American Motors

1. Disconnect the ambient temperature switch leads.
2. Replace the switch in the circuit with a jumper wire.
3. Repeat the system test. If the vacuum gauge now reads zero or below the specified speed, i.e., the solenoid energizes, the temperature switch is defective.
4. If the switch proves not to be defective when tested in step 3, reconnect it after removing the jumper lead.

5. Cool the switch, using either ice, cold water, or an aerosol spray circuit tester, to below 63°F. Repeat the system test. If there is no vacuum below the specified speed, the switch is stuck closed and must be replaced.

Engine Temperature Switch—Pontiac

If vacuum advance is present when it should not be, i.e., below the speed specified in the chart, the temperature switch is defective if the other SCS System components are functioning properly and the engine temperature is 95–230°F. Replace it and repeat the system test.

If, on the other hand, vacuum is not being supplied when it should be, with the engine temperature below 95°F or above 230°F, and the other components are functioning properly, the fault again lies in the temperature switch. Replace it and repeat the system test with the engine below 95°F (cold). Vacuum advance should be present at all speeds.

Cadillac

The Cadillac speed-controlled spark system used on *rear*-wheel-drive models (all models except Eldorado) may be tested in a similar manner to the American Motors and Pontiac systems above.

NOTE: Since Cadillac does not use this component, the temperature switch tests are unnecessary.

Cadillac recommends a road test procedure because the front wheels of the Eldorado should not be raised off the ground for test purposes. The procedure outlined below may be used for rear-wheel-drive Cadillac models, as well.

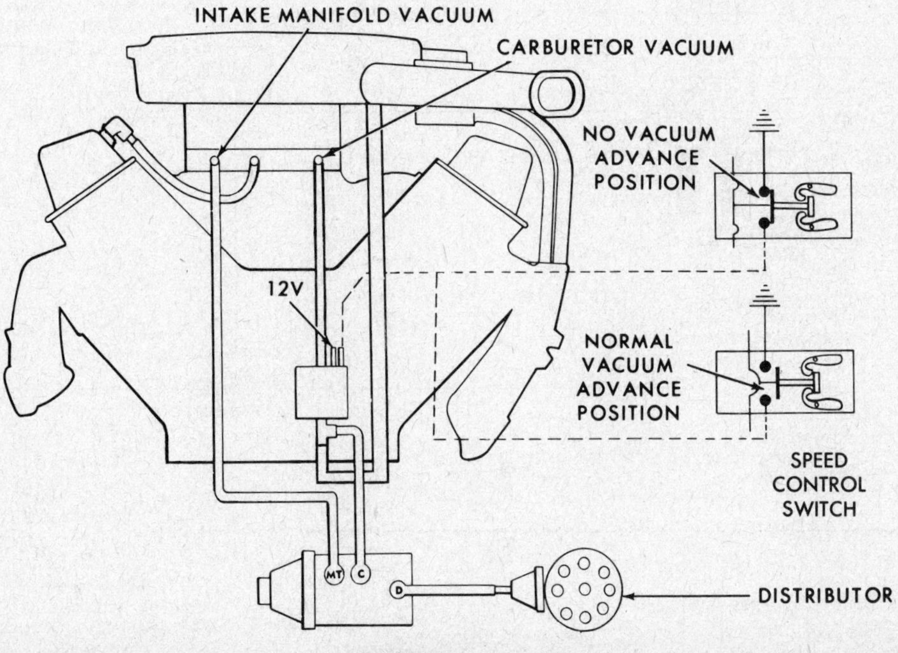
INTAKE MANIFOLD VACUUM
CARBURETOR VACUUM
NO VACUUM ADVANCE POSITION
12V
NORMAL VACUUM ADVANCE POSITION
SPEED CONTROL SWITCH
MT
C
D
DISTRIBUTOR

Cadillac SCS system
(© General Motors Corp)

Caution Never test the SCS system used on the Eldorado with its front (drive) wheels off the ground. Working near the front wheels while they are rotating could result in personal injury or vehicle damage.

1. Unfasten the double connector at the vacuum advance solenoid. Install a low-amperage test lamp, with long leads, between the wires on the connector.
2. Tape the test lamp to the car so that it is visible to the driver (hood, fender, cowl, etc.,) and close the hood.
3. Road-test the car while watching the test lamp (and traffic). Once 33 mph (± 2 mph) is reached, the test lamp should go out. Slow down; when 25 mph is reached, the lamp should come back on again.
4. If the test lamp fails to operate as indicated, jump the black wire to ground with the ignition turned on. If the lamp comes on now, replace the speed sensor switch and repeat step three. If the lamp does not come on, remove the jumper and proceed with the next step.
5. Install a jumper between one of the solenoid terminals and ground. Momentarily connect the other solenoid terminal to the positive (+) side of the battery.
6. The solenoid should energize when this is done, i.e., a "click" should be heard. If the solenoid fails to operate it is defective.
7. If both the solenoid and transmission switch are functioning properly, reconnect the leads to the solenoid and check for faulty wiring.

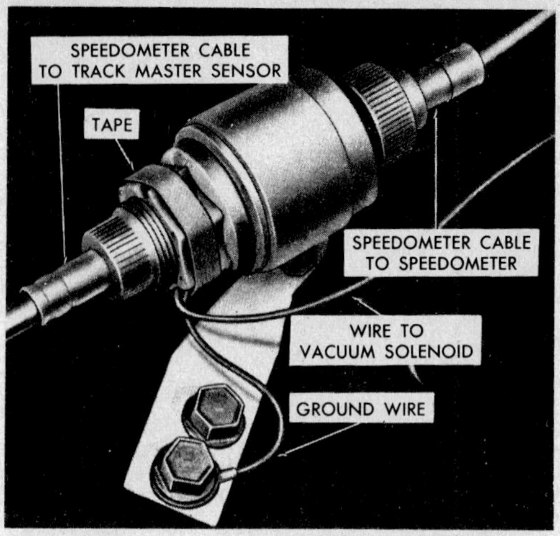

SPEEDOMETER CABLE TO TRACK MASTER SENSOR
TAPE
SPEEDOMETER CABLE TO SPEEDOMETER
WIRE TO VACUUM SOLENOID
GROUND WIRE

Speed control switch when used with Track-Master (except Eldorado)
(© G.M. Corp)

1973 Ford Temperature Activated Vacuum System (TAV)

System Test

1. Disconnect the vacuum line from the primary port of the distributor. Connect a vacuum gauge to the line by means of a T-fitting. Connect the other end of the T-fitting to the distributor.
2. Be sure that the air temperature is above 65°F. Hot water may be used to warm the temperature switch, which is located in the front door pillar.
3. Place the transmission in Park or Neutral. Start the engine.
4. Run the engine at idle; the vacuum gauge should read zero.
5. Increase the engine speed to 1,-500 rpm or slightly more. The gauge should read 5 in. Hg or better.
6. If there is no vacuum reading, check for leaking, plugged, or pinched lines and fittings.
7. Detach the EGR port hose and plug up the carburetor line. The vacuum gauge should read zero.
8. If it does not, check the lines and then proceed with the three-way vacuum valve test, below. If it does, go on to Step 9.
9. Next, detach one of the power leads from the three-way vacuum valve.
10. Speed the engine up to 1,500 rpm or more. The vacuum gauge should now read 6 in. Hg or better.

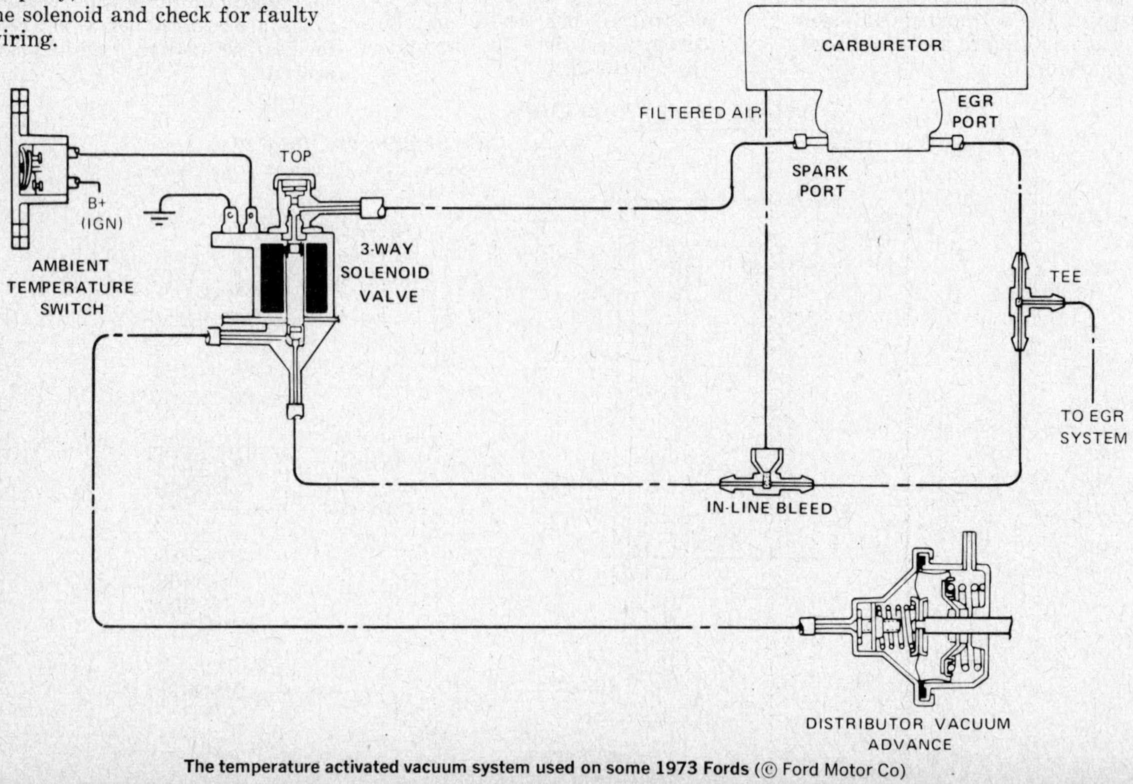

CARBURETOR
FILTERED AIR
EGR PORT
SPARK PORT
TOP
B+ (IGN)
AMBIENT TEMPERATURE SWITCH
3-WAY SOLENOID VALVE
TEE
TO EGR SYSTEM
IN-LINE BLEED
DISTRIBUTOR VACUUM ADVANCE

The temperature activated vacuum system used on some 1973 Fords (© Ford Motor Co)

11. If the system fails to function as outlined, check the ambient temperature switch, the EGR valve, or the three-way vacuum valve.
12. If everything is functioning properly, reconnect the leads and vacuum lines after disconnecting the vacuum gauge.

Temperature Switch Test

Test the ambient temperature switch, as outlined under "Ford Electronic Spark Control—1972–73," above. The switch is in either the left or right front door pillar.

Three-way Vacuum Valve Test

1. Remove the three-way vacuum valve from the car.
2. Connect a vacuum gauge to the horizontal port at the *bottom* of the valve.
3. Apply a vacuum source to the horizontal port at the *top* of the valve.
4. Ground one of the valve terminals while connecting the other terminal to a 12V power supply. The vacuum gauge should read zero.
5. With the valve energized, connect the vacuum source to the bottom *vertical* port. The vacuum gauge should now indicate an amount of vacuum equal to the output of the vacuum source.
6. Disconnect the leads from the valve. The vacuum gauge reading should return to zero.
7. If the valve fails to function as outlined, replace it. If it is functioning correctly, check the EGR valve operation as detailed in the appropriate section below.

SCS VACUUM ADVANCE

Make	*Year*	*No vacuum advance below*	*With engine temperature (deg F)*
American Motors	1971	30 mph	All temperatures①
	1972–73	34 mph	above 160①②
Cadillac	1972	33±2 mph	All temperatures
Pontiac	1972	38 mph	Between 95–230

①—Air temperature above 63°F
②—V8 only

Carburetor Controls

Antidieseling Solenoid Tests

NOTE: Antidieseling solenoids are also referred to as, "throttle stop" or "idle stop" solenoids.

1. Turn the ignition key on and open the throttle. The solenoid plunger should extend (solenoid energize).
2. Turn the ignition off. The plunger should retract, allowing the throttle to close.

NOTE: With the antidieseling solenoid de-energized, the carburetor idle speed adjusting screw must make contact with the throttle shaft to prevent the throttle plates from jamming in the throttle bore when the engine is turned off.

3. If the solenoid is functioning properly and the engine is still dieseling, check for one of the following:
   a. High idle or engine shut off speed;
   b. Engine timing not set to specification;
   c. Binding throttle linkage;
   d. Too low an octane fuel being used.

Correct any of these problems, as necessary.

4. If the solenoid fails to function as outlined in steps 1–2, disconnect the solenoid leads; the solenoid should de-enegerize. If it does not, it is jammed and must be replaced.
5. Connect the solenoid to a 12 V power source and to ground. Open the throttle so that the plunger can extend. If it does not, the solenoid is defective.
6. If the solenoid is functioning correctly and no other source of trouble can be found, the fault probably lies in the wiring between the solenoid and the ignition switch or in the ignition switch itself. Remember to reconnect the solenoid when finished testing.

NOTE: On some 1970–71 Ford models, dieseling may occur when the engine is turned off because of feedback through the alternator warning light circuit. A diode kit is available from Ford to cure this problem. A failure of this diode may also lead to a similar problem.

A/C Operated Antidieseling Device Tests

1. Run the engine and turn off all of the air conditioning controls.
2. Turn the engine off. The air conditioner compressor clutch should engage for several seconds to slow the engine down.
3. If the compressor clutch engagement does not occur, check the wiring for a loose connection, at either the compressor or the antidieseling relay.
4. Check to see that the relay is properly grounded to its mounting. Examine the air conditioner fuse(s) to see that they are not blown.
5. Start the engine and turn on the air conditioner. The clutch should engage. If it does not, the problem lies in the air conditioner circuit.
6. If the car is equipped with a blocking relay, remove it for bench-testing. Connect a 12 V test lamp between the two outboard connectors. Ground the mounting bracket. Connect a 12 V power source to the center terminal. The lamp should come on. If it does not, the blocking relay is defective and must be replaced.
7. If all of the other components are functioning properly, the an-

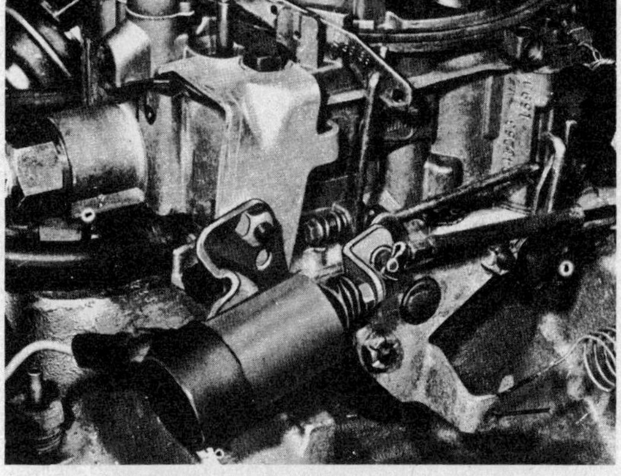

A typical anti-dieseling solenoid installation
(© G.M. Corp)

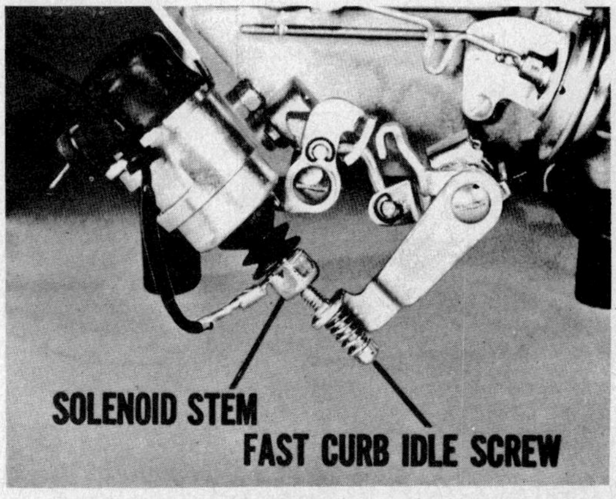
SOLENOID STEM
FAST CURB IDLE SCREW

When the anti-dieseling solenoid is energized, its plunger should make contact with the (fast) curb idle screw
(© Chrysler Corp)

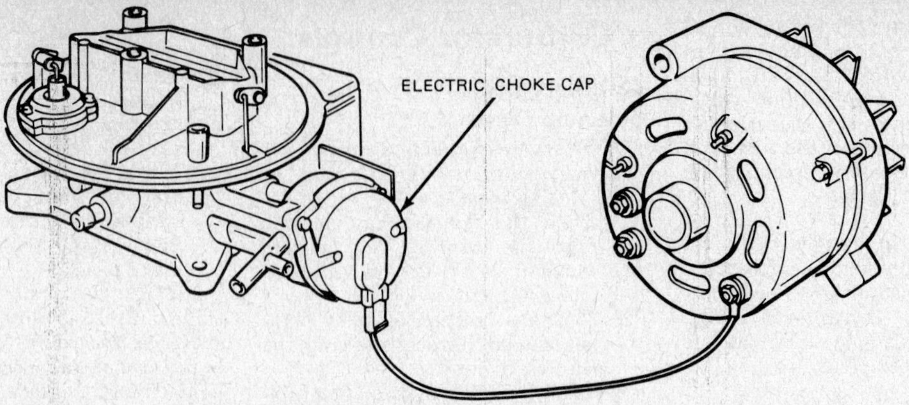
ELECTRIC CHOKE CAP

Ford and AMC electrically assisted choke hook-up (© Ford Motor Co)

tidieseling relay is defective and requires replacement.

CEC Solenoid Operation

The CEC solenoid is used on some GM models. It has two functions; one is to regulate distributor vacuum and the other is operate as a throttle positioner. When the solenoid is energized, the throttle blade is held off its seat by a plunger located at one end of the CEC solenoid. This provides higher engine rpm during deceleration, thus reducing exhaust emissions.

Because of its dual function, failure of this valve can lead to higher emission levels or an idle which is considerably faster than normal. If the CEC solenoid is suspected of not working properly, follow the complete set of test procedures for it in "Distributor Controls," above.

NOTE: On 1971 Buicks, the CEC solenoid is divided into two separate parts: a regular TCS solenoid and a solenoid to hold the throttle open during high gear deceleration. Testing and service should be carried out in the same manner as they would be for a regular CEC valve.

CEC SOLENOID
IDLE STOP SOLENOID

A typical CEC solenoid mounting (© G.M. Corp)

Electrically Assisted Choke

Ford and AMC

1. Detach the electrical lead from the choke cap.
2. Use a jumper lead to connect the terminal on the choke cap and the wire terminal, so that the electrical circuit is still completed.
3. Start the engine.
4. Hook up a test light between the connector on the choke lead and ground.
5. The test light should glow. If it does not, current is not being supplied to the electrically assisted choke.
6. Connect the test light between the terminal on the alternator and the terminal on the choke cap. If the light now glows, replace the lead, since it is not passing current to the choke assist.

Caution Do not ground the terminal on the alternator while performing Step 6.

7. If the light still does not glow, the fault lies somewhere in the electrical system. Check the system out.

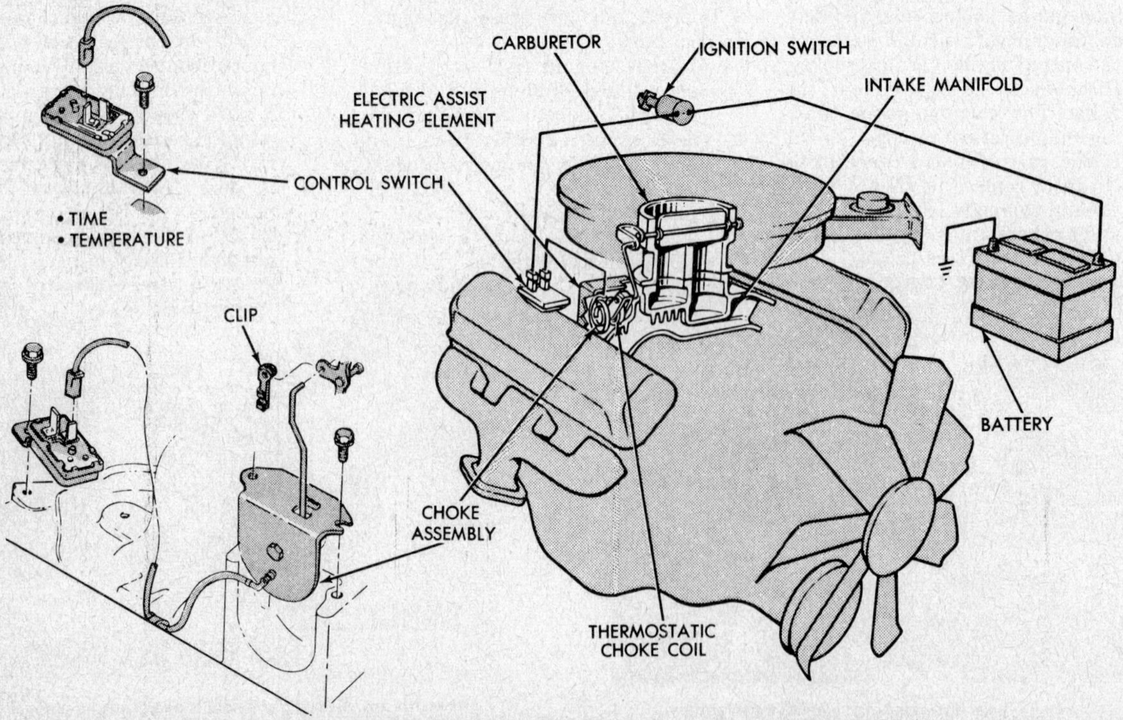
CARBURETOR
IGNITION SWITCH
INTAKE MANIFOLD
ELECTRIC ASSIST
HEATING ELEMENT
CONTROL SWITCH
• TIME
• TEMPERATURE
CLIP
BATTERY
CHOKE
ASSEMBLY
THERMOSTATIC
CHOKE COIL

Chrysler electrically assisted choke system components (© Chrysler Corp)

If the electrically assisted choke receives power but still does not appear to be functioning properly, reconnect the choke lead and proceed with the rest of the test.

8. Tape the bulb end of the thermometer to the metallic portion of the choke housing.
9. If the electrically assisted choke operates below 55°F, it is defective and must be replaced.
10. Allow the engine to warm up to between 80 and 110°F; at these temperatures the choke should operate for about 1½ minutes.
11. If it does not operate for this length of time, check the bi-metallic spring to see if it is connected to the tang on the choke lever.
12. If the spring is connected and the choke is not operating properly, replace the cap assembly.

Chrysler Corp.

Caution Do not immerse the choke heating element in any type of liquid, especially solvent, for any reason.

NOTE: A short circuit .in the choke wiring or in the heater will show up as a short in the ignition system.

1. Disconnect the electrical leads from the choke control switch before starting the engine.
2. Connect a test light between the smaller of the two terminals on the choke control switch and a ground.
3. Start the engine and run it until it reaches normal operating temperature.
4. Apply power from a 12V source to the terminal marked "BAT" on the choke control switch.
5. The test light should light for at least a few seconds or for as long as five minutes. If the light does not come on at all or if it stays on longer than five minutes, replace the switch.
6. Disconnect the test light and reconnect the electrical leads to the choke switch, if it is functioning properly.
7. Detach the lead from the choke switch which runs to the choke heating element.
8. Connect the lead from an ohmmeter to the crimped section at the choke end of the wire, which was removed in Step 7.

Caution Do not connect the ohmmeter to the metallic heater housing.

9. Ground the other ohmmeter test lead to the engine manifold.
10. The meter should indicate a resistance of 4–6 ohms.
11. If the reading is not within specifications, or if it indicates an opened (zero resistance) or a shorted (infinite resistance) heater coil, replace the heater assembly.

NOTE: The electrically assisted choke does not change any carburetor service procedures. If any parts of the electrically assisted choke are defective, they must be replaced. Adjustment is not possible.

Evaporative Emission Control System

There are several things to check for if a malfunction of the evaporative emission control system is suspected.

1. Leaks may be traced by using an infrared hydrocarbon tester. Run the test probe along the lines and connections. The meter will indicate the presence of a leak by a high hydrocarbon (HC) reading. This method is much more accurate than a visual inspection which would indicate only the presence of a leak large enough to pass liquid.
2. Leaks may be caused by any of the following, so always check these areas when looking for them:
   a. Defective or worn lines;
   b. Disconnected or pinched lines;
   c. Improperly routed lines;
   d. A defective filler cap.

   NOTE: If it becomes necessary to replace any of the lines used in the evaporative emission control system, use only those hoses which are fuel resistant or are marked "EVAP."
3. If the fuel tank has collapsed, it may be the fault of clogged or pinched vent lines, a defective vapor separator, or a plugged or incorrect fuel filler cap.
4. To test the filler cap, clean it and place it against the mouth. Blow into the relief valve housing. If the cap passes pressure with light blowing or if it fails to release with hard blowing, it is defective and must be replaced.

NOTE: Replace the cap with one marked "pressure/vacuum" only. An incorrect cap will render the system inoperative or damage its components.

Exhaust Gas Recirculation (EGR) Systems

1972 Buick and All 1973 GM EGR Valve Tests

NOTE: Skip steps 1–4 when checking 1973 Pontiacs with combined EGR/TCS systems. Start with step 5. See TCS section above for further tests.

1. Start the engine. Allow it to warm up and reach normal idle speed.

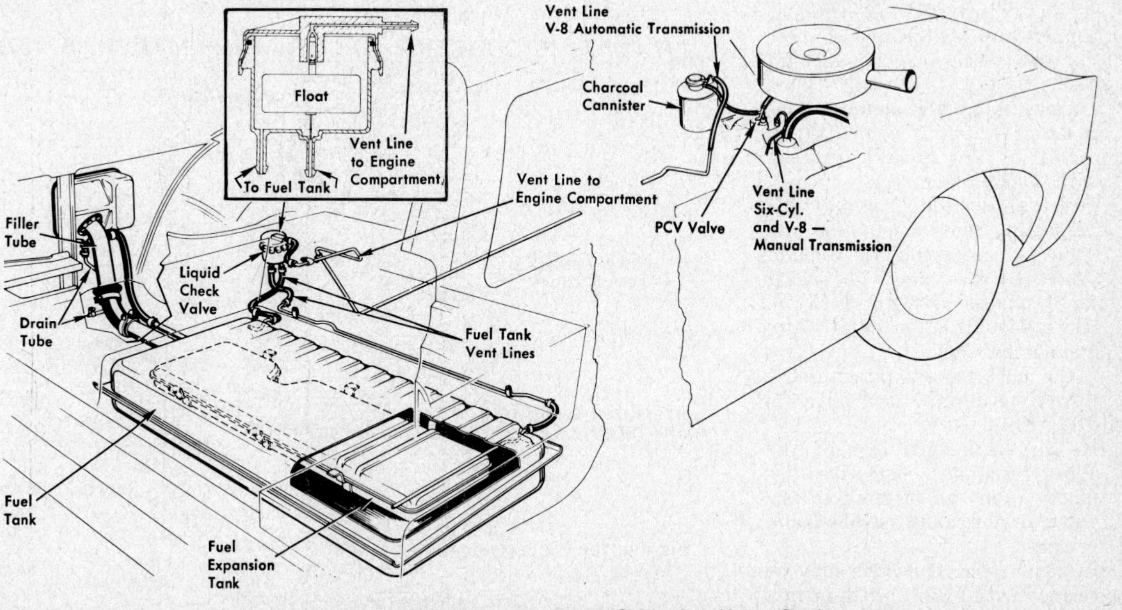
Vent Line
V-8 Automatic Transmission
Charcoal
Cannister
Float
Vent Line
to Engine
Compartment
To Fuel Tank
Vent Line to
Engine Compartment
PCV Valve
Vent Line
Six-Cyl.
and V-8 —
Manual Transmission
Filler
Tube
Liquid
Check
Valve
Drain
Tube
Fuel Tank
Vent Lines
Fuel
Tank
Fuel
Expansion
Tank

Vapor emission control system components (© American Motors Corp)

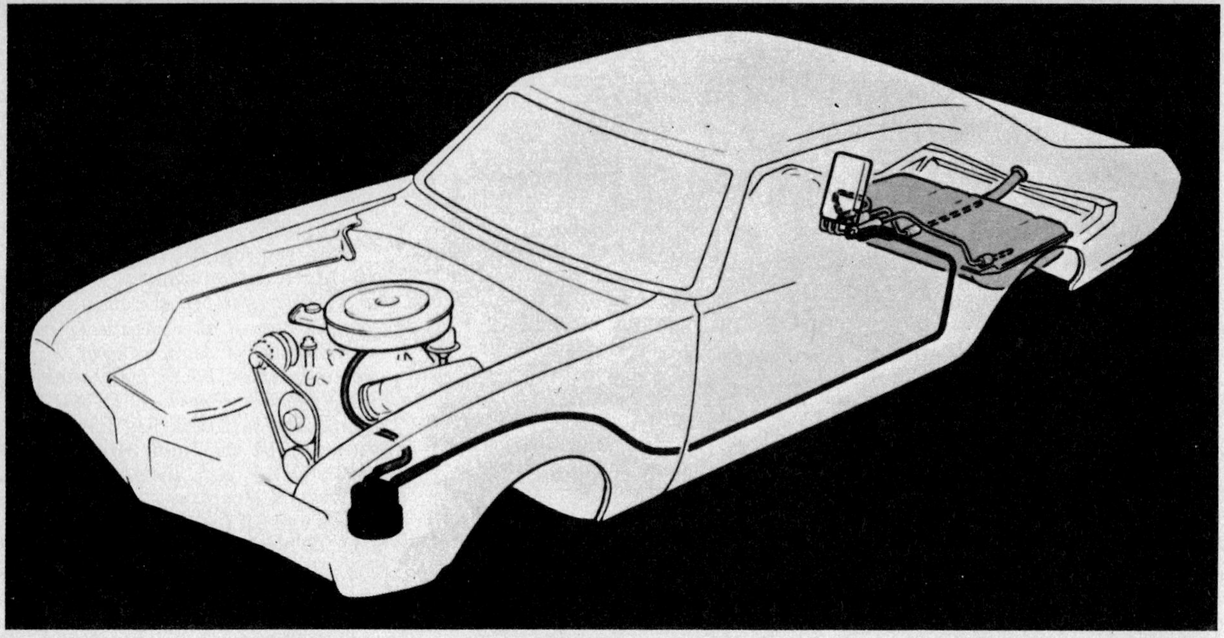

Typical hose routing and component layout for an evaporative emission control system
(© G.M. Corp)

NOTE: 1973 Oldsmobiles, Cadillacs, and Buicks are equipped with an ambient temperature switch. Be sure that under-hood temperature is above 50–60°F, before testing the EGR valve.

2. Increase the engine speed to 1,200–1,500 rpm and watch the EGR valve shaft. The shaft should move upward at this speed.
3. Allow the engine to return to normal idle; the valve shaft should go down.
4. If the shaft fails to raise in step two, check the vacuum line which runs from the carburetor port to the valve. Make sure that it is not loose, clogged, or pinched. On 1973 Cadillacs, Buicks, and Oldsmobiles with V8 engines, disconnect the ambient temperature switch and connect the two pieces of the vacuum hose. If the EGR valve now works, replace the ambient temperature switch. If none of these conditions are present, proceed with the next step.
5. Test the valve diaphragm by disconnecting the vacuum line and applying an outside vacuum source to the valve. The shaft should raise between 8–10 in. Hg. It should retain the pressure and not leak down.
6. If the valve shaft is frozen in the raised position, the valve is defective.
7. If the valve fails any of the above tests, it is defective. Replace it as an assembly; the valve cannot be disassembled and repaired.
8. In some cases the valve may be cleaned with a wire brush or in a spark plug cleaning machine, to loosen deposits which may cause the valve to stick.

NOTE: If the engine is to be tested by "shorting out" the cylinders when it is equipped with an EGR valve, first disconnect the vacuum hose at the valve and plug it. Failure to do this will cause uneven idling and indicate false test results.

1973½ Pontiac EGR System

NOTE: Pontiac models made on or after 15 March 1973 use separate systems for TCS and EGR. For TCS system checking procedures, see the appropriate section above.

The testing procedure for the Pontiac EGR valve is basically the same as that outlined for the other GM cars, in the preceding section. However, there are several points which should be noted:

1. The engine must be warmed up until the coolant temperature is above 95°F.
2. The air cleaner must be removed in order to see the EGR valve shaft.
3. If the EGR valve is not getting vacuum, check the vacuum hoses, then check the coolant temperature operated vacuum valve as outlined in the appropriate section above. The valve should work when the coolant temperature is above 95°F.

PONTIAC'S EMISSIONS CONTROL SYSTEM
— PARTS LOCATION —

1973 LATE PRODUCTION (ON OR AFTER MARCH 15, 1973)

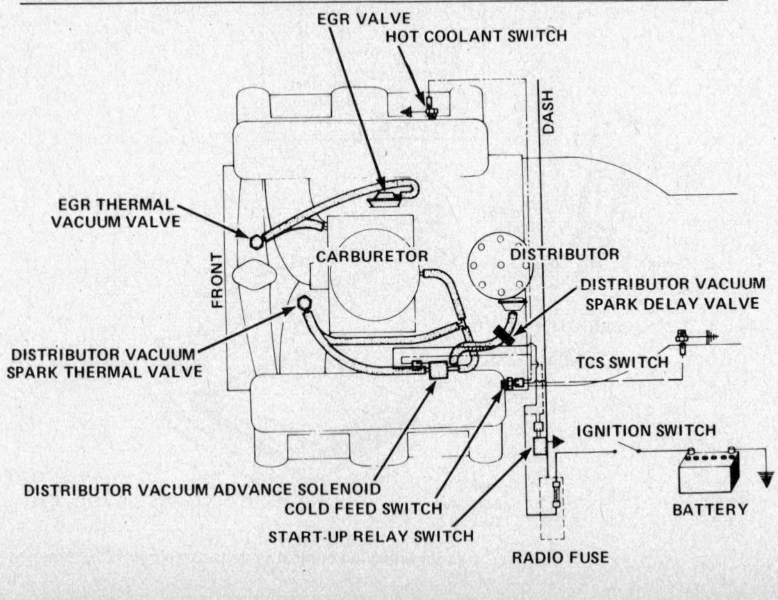
EGR VALVE
HOT COOLANT SWITCH
DASH
EGR THERMAL VACUUM VALVE
FRONT
CARBURETOR
DISTRIBUTOR
DISTRIBUTOR VACUUM SPARK DELAY VALVE
DISTRIBUTOR VACUUM SPARK THERMAL VALVE
TCS SWITCH
IGNITION SWITCH
DISTRIBUTOR VACUUM ADVANCE SOLENOID
COLD FEED SWITCH
START-UP RELAY SWITCH
BATTERY
RADIO FUSE

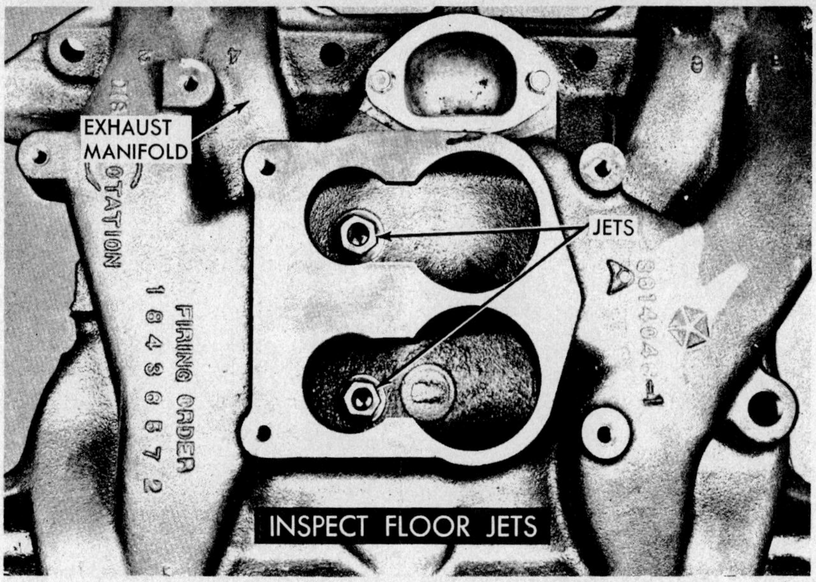
EXHAUST MANIFOLD
JETS
FIRING ORDER
1 8 4 3 6 5 7 2
INSPECT FLOOR JETS

Floor jet location in Chrysler Corp V8s — sixes use only one jet (© Chrysler Corp)

Chrysler Corp. Floor Jet Service

All six-cylinder engines have one floor jet, while all V8s have two.

1. Turn the engine off. Remove the air cleaner assembly from the carburetor.
2. Hold the choke and throttle valves open. Shine a flashlight through the carburetor to inspect the floor jet(s). The jet(s) is/are in satisfactory condition if the passage shows an open path to the orifice.
3. If the jet (s) is/are clogged, completely remove the carburetor. Withdraw the jet and clean it.

Caution Use care when handling the jets. They have very thin walls and are, therefore, easily damaged. Because they are made out of stainless steel, they are not magnetic and cannot be retrieved readily if dropped into the manifold.

4. Install the jet(s) and tighten to 25 ft lbs. Install the carburetor and attach the air cleaner.

NOTE: "Shorting out" cylinders on engines equipped with floor jets is not a reliable test proceedure. The unburned mixture is circulated to the other cylinders, causing the engine speed to fluctuate. Because of this, false test results may be obtained.

Chrysler Corp. 1973 Proportional EGR System Tests

NOTE: Air temperature should be above 68°F for this test.

1. Check all of the vacuum hoses which run between the carburetor, intake manifold, EGR valve, and the vacuum amplifier (if so equipped). Replace the hoses and tighten the connections, as required.
2. Allow the engine to warm up. Connect a tachometer to it. Start with the engine idling in neutral and rapidly increase the engine speed to 2,000 rpm.
3. If the EGR valve stem moves (watch the groove on the stem), the valve and the rest of the system are functioning properly. If the stem does not move, proceed with the rest of the EGR system tests.
4. Disconnect the vacuum supply hose from the EGR valve. Apply a vacuum of at least 10 in. Hg to

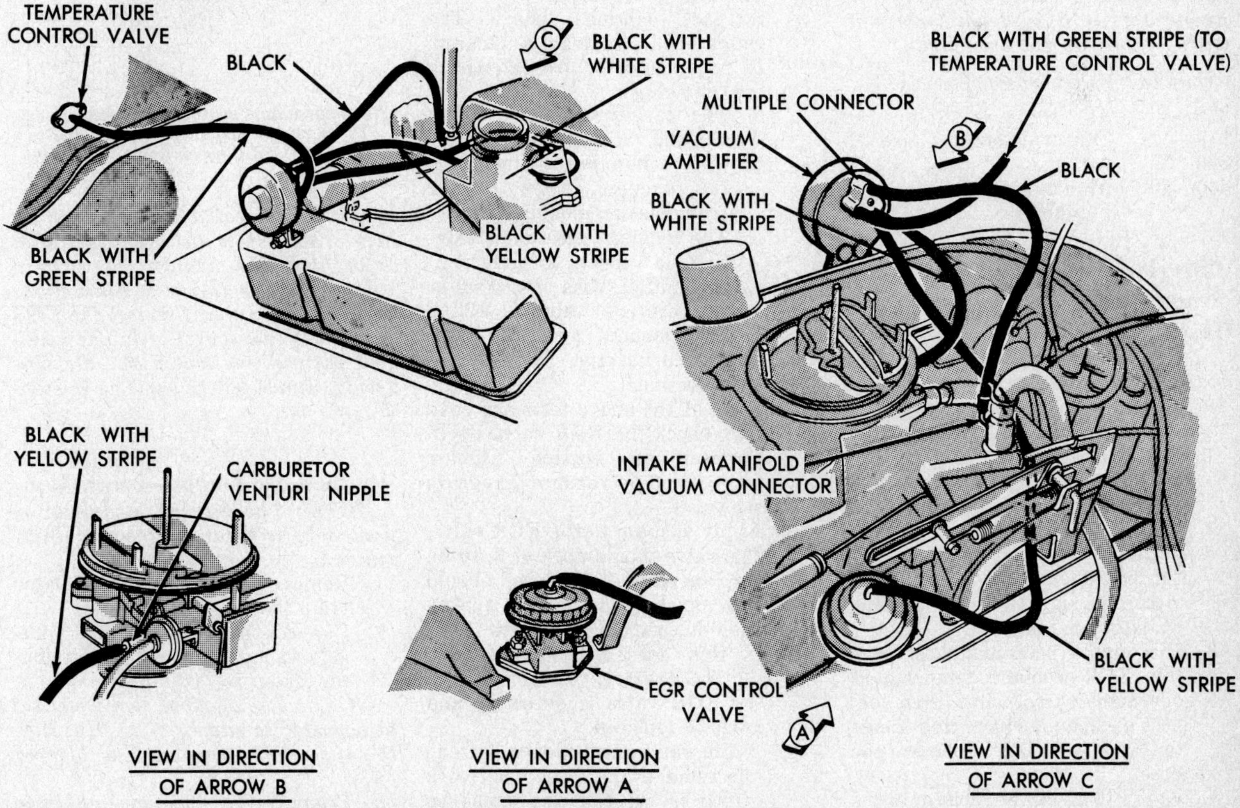
TEMPERATURE CONTROL VALVE
BLACK
C
BLACK WITH WHITE STRIPE
BLACK WITH GREEN STRIPE (TO TEMPERATURE CONTROL VALVE)
MULTIPLE CONNECTOR
VACUUM AMPLIFIER
B
BLACK
BLACK WITH WHITE STRIPE
BLACK WITH YELLOW STRIPE
BLACK WITH GREEN STRIPE
BLACK WITH YELLOW STRIPE
CARBURETOR VENTURI NIPPLE
INTAKE MANIFOLD VACUUM CONNECTOR
BLACK WITH YELLOW STRIPE
EGR CONTROL VALVE
A
VIEW IN DIRECTION OF ARROW B
VIEW IN DIRECTION OF ARROW A
VIEW IN DIRECTION OF ARROW C

Typical hose routing and component layout of a Chrysler Proportional EGR system

the valve with the engine warmed-up and idling and the transmission in neutral.

NOTE: A source of more than adequate vacuum is the intake manifold vacuum connection. Run a hose from the EGR valve directly to the connection.

5. When vacuum is applied to the EGR valve, the engine speed should drop at least 150 rpm. In some cases the engine may even stall. If the engine does not slow down and the EGR valve does not operate, the valve is defective or dirty. Replace it or remove the deposits from it.

NOTE: Always replace the EGR valve gasket with a new one when the valve is removed for service, even if the valve itself is not replaced.

6. If the EGR valve is functioning properly, reconnect its vacuum line and test the temperature control valve.
7. Disconnect the vacuum hose which runs to the temperature control valve and plug it. Repeat steps 2–3. If the EGR valve now functions, the temperature control valve is defective and must be replaced.
8. If everything else is functioning properly, the EGR system does not work and the engine is equipped with a vacuum amplifier (see the chart below), the amplifier is at fault. Replace it and repeat the system test.

NOTE: Before replacng the amplifier, check the vacuum port in the carburetor. If it is clogged, clean it with solvent; do not use a drill.

Engine	*Vacuum amplifier used on:*
225—6	All
318—V8	California only
360—V8	All
440—V8	All non-high-performance engines

Chrysler Corp. 1973 Proportional EGR System Tests

NOTE: This system is used starting with cars made on or after 15 March 1973. It replaces the system tested in the above section.

1. Perform steps 1-6 of the 1973 proportional EGR system tests, detailed in the above section.
2. Test the EGR system coolant temperature operated control valve for leaks. The valve is located on either the right or left side of the radiator top tank.
3. Disconnect the vacuum hose from the EGR coolant temperature operated control valve, then connect a vacuum source and gauge to the valve fitting, in place of the hose.
4. Apply 10 in. Hg of vacuum to the valve. If the valve loses more than 1 in. Hg in one minute, the valve is defective and must be replaced.
5. Proceed with step 8 in the above section.

The 1973½ EGR temperature control valve is located on the top tank of the radiator on Chrysler products

1973 Ford EGR System Tests

1. Allow the engine to warm up, so that the coolant temperature has reached at least 125°F.
2. Disconnect the vacuum hose which runs from the temperature cut-in valve to the EGR valve at the EGR valve end. Connect a vacuum gauge to this hose with a T-fitting.
3. Increase engine speed. The gauge should indicate a vacuum. If no vacuum is present, check the following:
   a. The carburetor—look for a clogged vacuum port.
   b. The vacuum hoses—including the vacuum hoses to the transmission modulator.
   c. The temperature cut-in valve —if no vacuum is present at its outlet with the engine temperature above 125°F and vacuum available from the carburetor, the valve is defective.
4. If all of the above tests are positive, check the EGR valve itself.
5. Connect an outside vacuum source and a vacuum gauge to the valve.
6. Apply vacuum to the EGR valve. The valve should open at 3–10 in. Hg, the engine idle speed should slow down, and the idle quality should become more rough.
7. If this does not happen, i.e., the EGR valve remains closed, the EGR valve is defective and must be replaced.
8. If the valve stem moves but the idle remains the same, the valve orifice is clogged and must be cleaned.

NOTE: If an outside vacuum source is not available, disconnect the hose which runs between the EGR valve and the temperature cut-in valve and plug the hose connections on the cut-in valve. Connect the EGR valve hose to a source of intake manifold vacuum and watch the idle. The results should be the same as in steps 6–7, above.

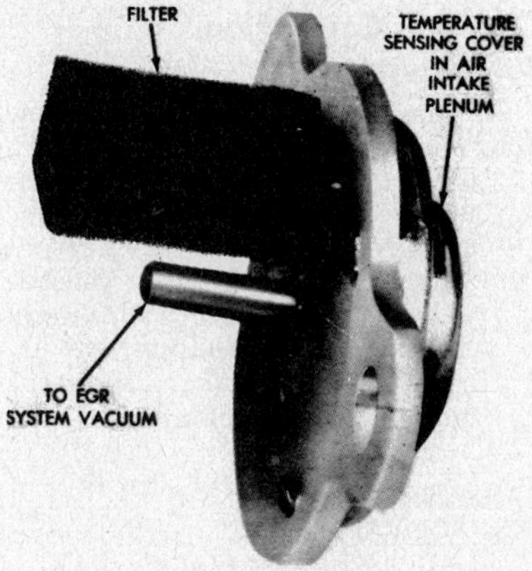
FILTER
TEMPERATURE SENSING COVER IN AIR INTAKE PLENUM
TO EGR SYSTEM VACUUM

The temperature sensing valve used prior to 15 March 1973 on Chrysler EGR systems (© Chrysler Corp)

Vacuum Modulator—Bench Test

NOTE: The vacuum modulator is used only with an automatic transmission.

1. Remove the vacuum modulator from the car.
2. Connect the modulator to an outside vacuum source: a distributor tester, for example.

NOTE: The vacuum source should be adjusted to supply 18 in. Hg, with the end of the vacuum line blocked off.

3. Connect the vacuum line from the vacuum source to the EGR port on the vacuum modulator.

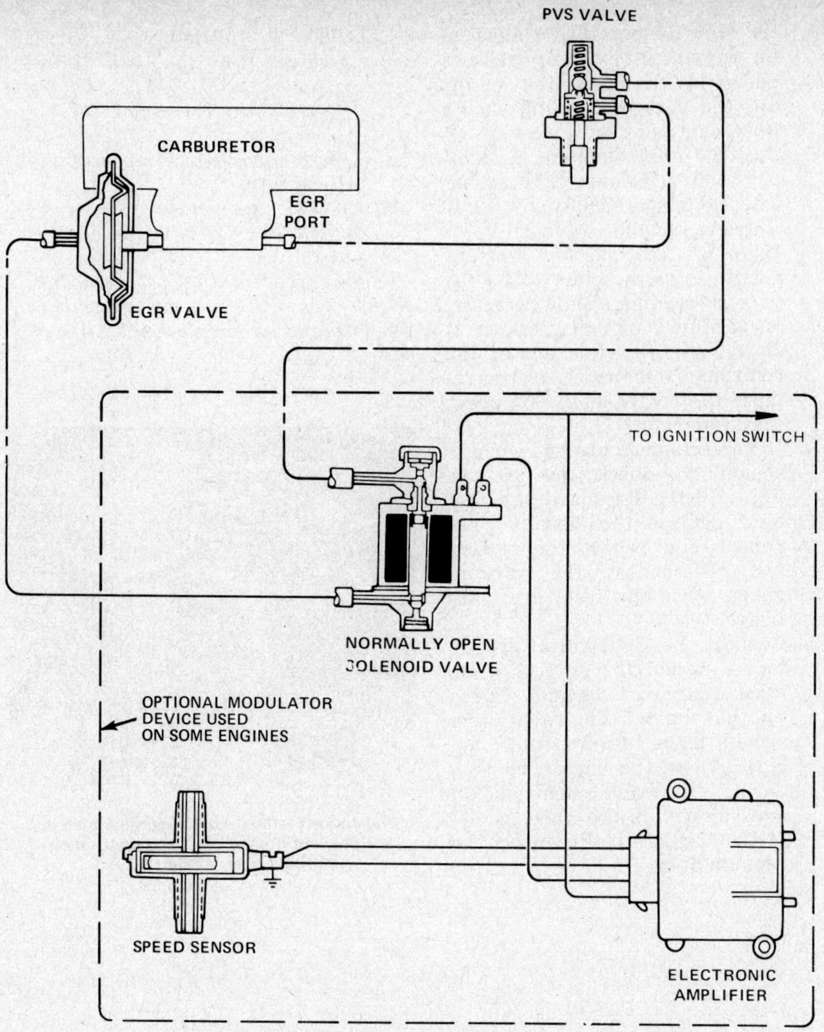
PVS VALVE
CARBURETOR
EGR
PORT
EGR VALVE
TO IGNITION SWITCH
NORMALLY OPEN
SOLENOID VALVE
OPTIONAL MODULATOR
DEVICE USED
ON SOME ENGINES
SPEED SENSOR
ELECTRONIC
AMPLIFIER

Ford exhaust gas recirculation (EGR) system (© Ford Motor Co)

4. The vacuum modulator should hold the 18 in. Hg reading. If it does not, then the diaphragm is leaking and must be replaced.

Temperature Cut-In Valve—Bench Test

1. Remove the valve from the engine.
2. Connect an outside source of vacuum to the top port on the valve. Leave the bottom port vented to the atmosphere.
3. Use ice or an aerosol spray to cool the valve below 60°F.
4. Apply 20 in. Hg vacuum to the valve. The valve should hold a minimum of 19 in. Hg vacuum for five minutes without leaking down.
5. Leave the vacuum source connected to the valve and place it, along with a high temperature thermometer, into a non-metallic, heat-resistant container full of water.
6. Heat the water. The vacuum in the valve should drop to zero once the temperature of the water reaches about 125°F.
7. Replace the valve if it fails either of the tests.

1973 Ford High Speed EGR Modulator—System Tests

NOTE: Before beginning this test, check the EGR valve and the other related components as outlined in the section above.

1. Detach the line from the EGR valve. Connect a vacuum gauge to the line, using a T-fitting, and reconnect the EGR valve.

NOTE: Position the vacuum gauge so that it can be seen from the driver's seat.

2. Raise the rear wheels of the car off the ground, supporting it so that it cannot roll forward.
3. Start the engine and allow it to warm up at *fast* idle for 3–4 minutes.
4. Return the engine to normal idle; the vacuum gauge reading should return to zero.
5. Place the transmission in Third gear (manual) or Drive (automatic). Increase the engine speed; vacuum should also increase.
6. At an indicated speed of approximately 67 mph, the vacuum gauge reading should drop to zero.

If the system is functioning properly, lower the car, disconnect the vacuum gauge, and reconnect the vacuum lines. If the system is malfunctioning, proceed with the tests below.

Power Supply Tests

Caution Do not use a self-powered test light; damage to the amplifier could result.

1. Check the electrical leads which run to and from the vacuum solenoid valve with a low-amperage test light. The car should be running so that power is being supplied to the system.
2. If there is no current at the valve, trace the wiring back to its power source to determine the reason for the failure.
3. If there is current at the valve, remove the power connector from the amplifier and check for current at the connector. If there is none, replace the wiring between the amplifier and the vacuum valve.

Speed Sensor Tests

1. Check the resistance of the speed sensor by touching its leads with the test prods of an ohmmeter. The ohmmeter should read 40–60 ohms.
2. Replace the speed sensor if its resistance is not within specifications.
3. Check the connector on the speed sensor to be sure that it is tight. If the ground interlock loop between the connectors is loose, the circuit will not be grounded and the speed sensor will appear not to be functioning.

Vacuum Solenoid Valve Tests

1. Disconnect the leads from the vacuum solenoid valve which run to the amplifier.

Caution Never connect a jumper lead or a self-powered test light to the valve while it is still connected to the amplifier; damage to the amplifier could result.

2. Connect a vacuum gauge to the EGR valve port on the vacuum valve.
3. With the valve disconnected from the amplifier, connect the valve directly to a 12V power source (the battery) with jumper leads.
4. With the transmission in Neutral and current flowing to the valve, increase the engine speed to 1,500 rpm. The vacuum gauge should read zero. If it does not, replace the valve.
5. Disconnect the 12V power source from the valve. The gauge should show a vacuum reading with the engine speed at 1,500 rpm.

If the valve is not functioning properly, replace it. If it is functioning properly and the system still is not, the only other possible source of trouble is the amplifier; replace it.

NOTE: There is no way to test amplifier operation other than by process of elimination or by substitution. Attempts to check it will probably lead to its failure, if it is not already defective.

1973 American Motors EGR System Test

NOTE: Start the test with the engine cold.

1. Disconnect the vacuum line at the EGR valve. Connect a vacuum gauge to the vacuum line.
2. Heat the low ambient compensator (located in front of the radiator) in the palm of the hand, until it is above 60°F.
3. Start the engine; increase engine speed. There should be no vacuum reading on the gauge. Allow the engine to warm up to at least 125°F (160°F—304 V8/manual). With the ambient temperature compensator above 60°F and the engine coolant temperature above 125°F (160°F), vacuum should be present when the engine speed is increased.
4. Using a trouble light or some other suitable heat source, heat the *high* temperature compensator (mounted on the firewall) to above 115°F. Speed the engine up; the vacuum reading should be zero or quite low.
5. Cool the *high* temperature compensator to below 115°F, using ice; the gauge should now show a strong vacuum reading.
6. Using ice, cool the *low* ambient compensator to below 60°F; the vacuum reading should decrease.
7. If vacuum is present when it should not be, while one of the components is being tested, replace the component and repeat the system test.
8. If *no* vacuum is present when it should be, check the vacuum lines. If the lines are satisfactory, replace the suspect component and repeat the system test. Disconnect the vacuum gauge when the tests are completed.
9. Connect the EGR valve directly to the carburetor port or some other source of vacuum. Speed up the engine; the valve stem should move upward (8-10 in. Hg). Allow the engine to slow down; the valve stem should move down. If the valve is defective, replace it. Reconnect the vacuum lines.

NOTE: The following components were dropped from the EGR system on, or after 15 March 1973:

1. *High temperature compensator—All engines.*
2. *Low temperature compensator—All engines.*
3. *Coolant temperature override switch — Six-cylinder engines only.*

Those steps of the test procedure which deal with these components are not required on models made after 15 March 1973.

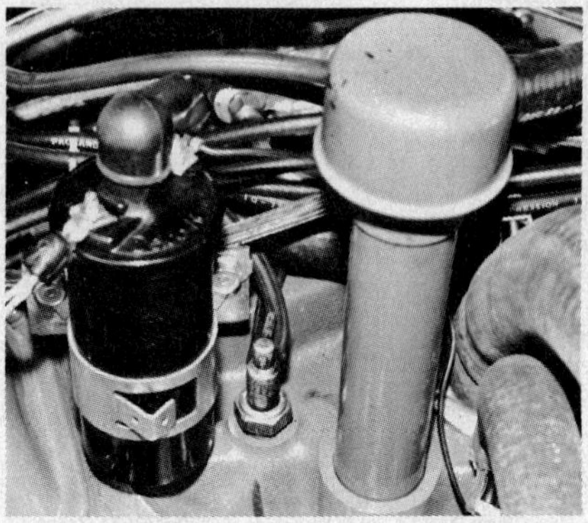

The coolant temperature override switch is the only control for EGR vacuum used on AMC V8s after 15 March 1973

INDEX

Windshield Wiper Systems

Wiper System Components

Wiper Motors

There are three types of windshield wiper motors presently in use on American automobiles: electric motors, hydraulic motors, and vacuum motors. The electric motor is by far the most common, and is the only type for which automobile manufacturers provide internal replacement parts. Both the hydraulic and the vacuum motor are non-repairable, and must be replaced, should they become defective.

Several different versions of the electric windshield wiper motor are produced, each manufacturer having a preference for a particular type.

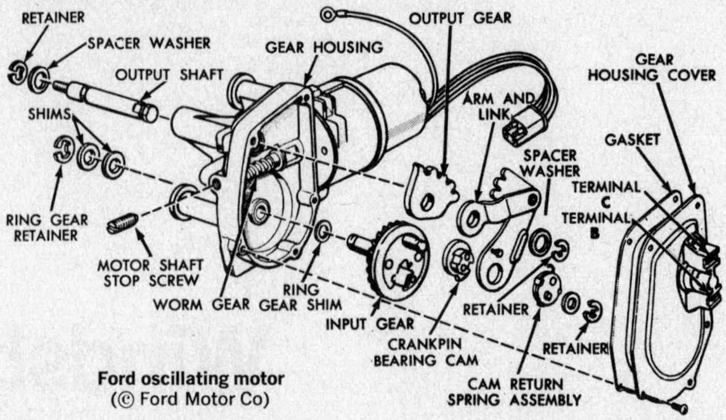
RETAINER
SPACER WASHER
OUTPUT SHAFT
SHIMS
RING GEAR RETAINER
MOTOR SHAFT STOP SCREW
WORM GEAR
RING GEAR SHIM
INPUT GEAR
CRANKPIN BEARING CAM
CAM RETURN SPRING ASSEMBLY
RETAINER
RETAINER
GEAR HOUSING
OUTPUT GEAR
GEAR HOUSING COVER
ARM AND LINK
GASKET
SPACER WASHER
TERMINAL C
TERMINAL B

Ford oscillating motor
(© Ford Motor Co)

Ford Motor Co. products use two types of electric wiper motors: permanent magnet and oscillating motors. The output shaft of the permanent magnet motor rotates 360°, and this circular motion is converted into reciprocating motion by the windshield wiper linkage. The permanent magnet motor derives its name from the fact that the magnetic field in which the armature of the motor rotates is created only by permanent magnets, without the use of electrical windings to increase the strength of the field. The oscillating motor however, does use electrical windings, making it a wound field motor. The oscillating motor derives its name from the fact that the circular motion of the motor armature is converted into oscillating motion in the gear box section of the motor.

General Motors products employ two types of electric wiper motors: a single pole-rectangularly shaped motor and a two pole-circular motor. All circular motors are compound wound, while some rectangular motors are compound wound and some are shunt wound. This difference in field winding is one method of altering windshield wiper speed to produce multi-speed windshield wiper systems.

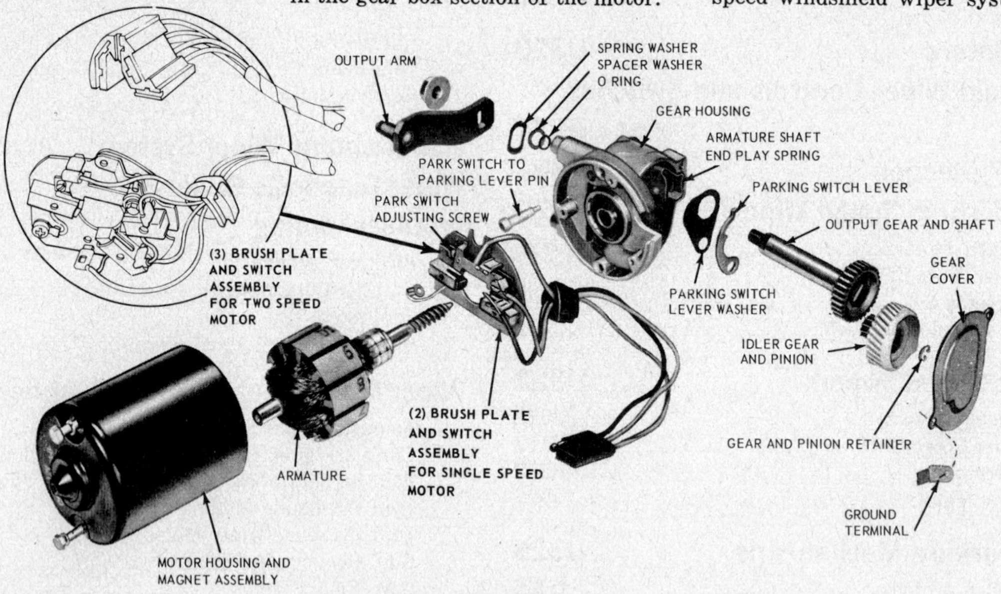
OUTPUT ARM
SPRING WASHER
SPACER WASHER
O RING
GEAR HOUSING
ARMATURE SHAFT
END PLAY SPRING
PARK SWITCH TO
PARKING LEVER PIN
PARKING SWITCH LEVER
PARK SWITCH
ADJUSTING SCREW
OUTPUT GEAR AND SHAFT
(3) BRUSH PLATE
AND SWITCH
ASSEMBLY
FOR TWO SPEED
MOTOR
GEAR
COVER
PARKING SWITCH
LEVER WASHER
IDLER GEAR
AND PINION
(2) BRUSH PLATE
AND SWITCH
ASSEMBLY
FOR SINGLE SPEED
MOTOR
ARMATURE
GEAR AND PINION RETAINER
GROUND
TERMINAL
MOTOR HOUSING AND
MAGNET ASSEMBLY

Ford permanent magnet motor (© Ford Motor Co)

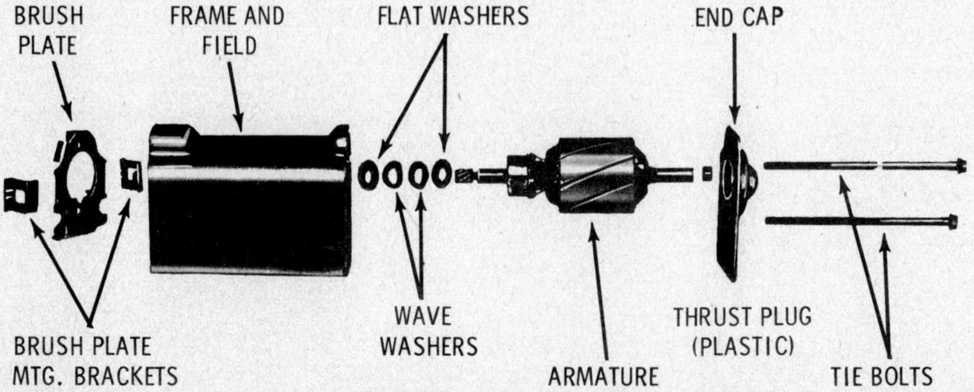
BRUSH
PLATE
FRAME AND
FIELD
FLAT WASHERS
END CAP
BRUSH PLATE
MTG. BRACKETS
WAVE
WASHERS
ARMATURE
THRUST PLUG
(PLASTIC)
TIE BOLTS

G.M. rectangular motor (© G.M. Corp)

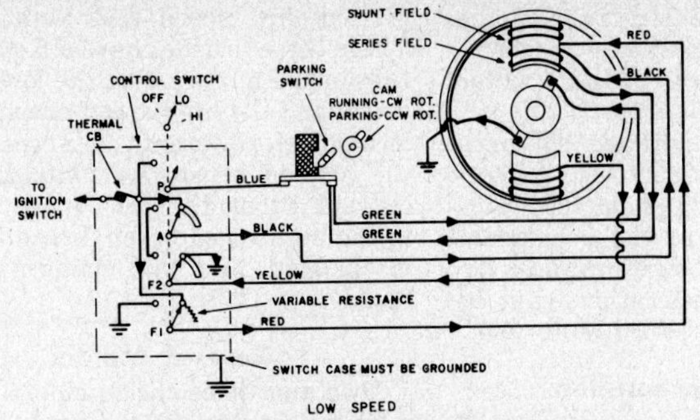
SHUNT FIELD
SERIES FIELD
RED
BLACK
CONTROL SWITCH
OFF LO
HI
PARKING SWITCH
CAM
RUNNING-CW ROT.
PARKING-CCW ROT.
THERMAL CB
TO IGNITION SWITCH
P
BLUE
YELLOW
GREEN
GREEN
A
BLACK
F2
YELLOW
VARIABLE RESISTANCE
F1
RED
SWITCH CASE MUST BE GROUNDED
LOW SPEED

American Motors low-speed circuit (1967-72)
(© American Motors Corp)

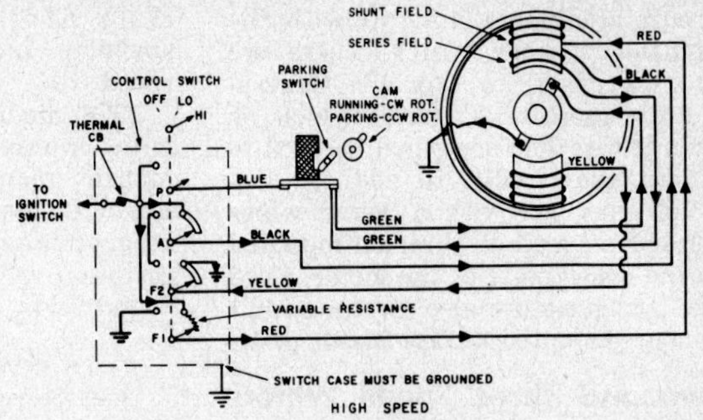
SHUNT FIELD
SERIES FIELD
RED
BLACK
CONTROL SWITCH
OFF LO
HI
PARKING SWITCH
CAM
RUNNING-CW ROT.
PARKING-CCW ROT.
THERMAL CB
TO IGNITION SWITCH
P
BLUE
YELLOW
GREEN
GREEN
A
BLACK
F2
YELLOW
VARIABLE RESISTANCE
F1
RED
SWITCH CASE MUST BE GROUNDED
HIGH SPEED

American Motors high-speed circuit
(© American Motors Corp)

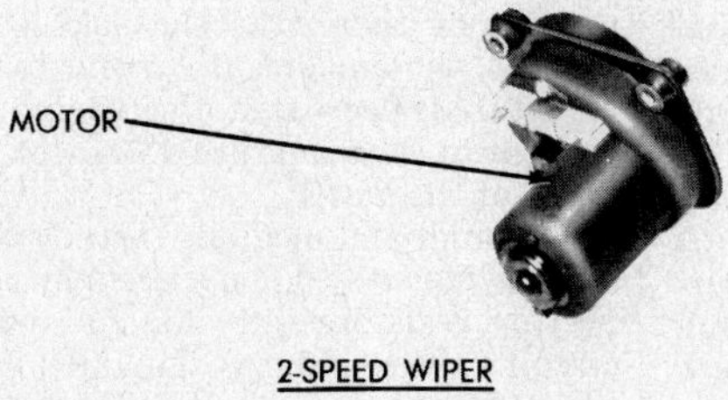
MOTOR
2-SPEED WIPER

3-SPEED WIPER

Chrysler wiper motors
(© Chrysler Corp)

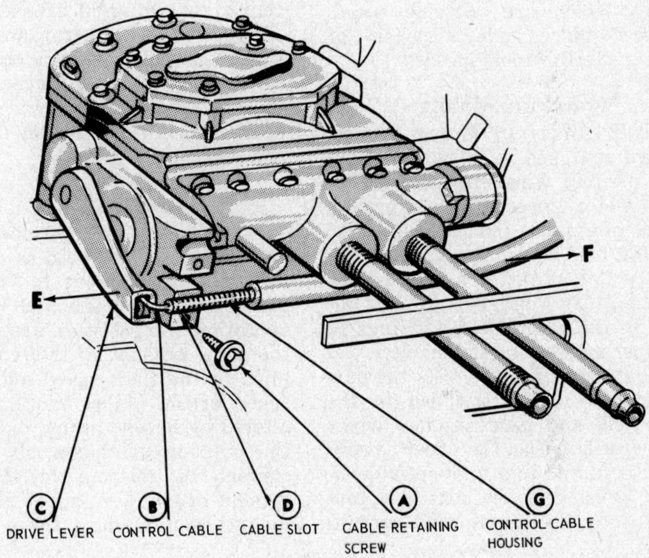
E
F
C DRIVE LEVER
B CONTROL CABLE
D CABLE SLOT
A CABLE RETAINING SCREW
G CONTROL CABLE HOUSING

Ford hydraulic wiper motor
(© Ford Motor Co)

Chrysler Corporation automobiles use permanent magnet and wound field windshield wiper motors. Variable speed wiper motors are wound field motors with an additional shunt winding to control motor speed. In permanent magnet motors, the magnetic field in which the motor armature turns is created by permanent magnets that are attached to the body of the wiper motor housing. In wound field motors, the magnetic field is created by electromagnetic windings, instead of by permanent magnets.

1967-72 American Motors models that are equipped with electric windshield wipers use only shunt wound motors. In this type of motor, shunt windings are used in addition to field windings to control wiper motor speed. In 1973, American Motors switched to permanent magnet wiper motors.

Thunderbird, Lincoln Continental, and Lincoln Mark III and IV models are the only vehicles that currently use hydraulic windshield wipers. In this system, hydraulic power to operate the windshield wiper motor is obtained from the power steering unit. Hydraulic fluid flows from the power steering pump to the steering gear, and then to the windshield wiper motor and back to the steering pump reservoir. During windshield wiper operation, part of the fluid is bypassed through the wiper motor by the pressure regulator valve on the motor. The speed of the wipers is controlled by adjusting the pressure regulator valve. A bowden wire connects the windshield wiper switch to the pressure regulator valve.

Some six cylinder American Motors cars are equipped with vacuum operated windshield wipers as standard equipment. The wiper motor is powered by vacuum which is obtained from the intake manifold and boosted by the fuel pump.

Windshield Wiper Controls and Switches

The windshield wiper motor constitutes only a small part of the windshield wiper system. With the advent of multi-speed and variable speed wipers, depressed park and hidden windshield wipers and the necessary controls for these systems, the possible sources of windshield wiper failure are greatly increased. To properly diagnose these systems, the mechanic must first have an understanding of their operation.

Circuit Protection

Most electric windshield wiper systems are equipped with a circuit breaker to protect the electrical components of the system from overheating, which may be caused by overloading, excessive resistance, or a short circuit. On most models, the circuit breaker is integral with the windshield wiper switch. There are two exceptions to this. On General Motors models, a fuse, which is mounted in the fuse panel, is used to protect the circuit. In addition, vehicles equipped with a round wiper motor have a circuit breaker mounted on the brush plate of the motor. Ford oscillating motors also have a circuit breaker mounted on the brush plate.

Two and Three Speed Wipers

There are many ways in which windshield wiper motor speed can be varied to produce multi-speed wipers. As is the case with types of electric wiper motors, each vehicle manufacturer has a preference for a particular way of controlling wiper motor speed. This section pertains only to wiper systems which offer a selection of two or three preset wiper speeds. It does not apply to wiper systems which are variable speed, i.e. those which have a variety of closely related wiper speeds.

American Motors

1970-72 American Motors models that are equipped with two or three speed electric wiper motors control wiper motor speed by varying the amount of current that is supplied to the shunt field in the motor. When the wiper switch is in the low speed position, battery voltage is applied directly to the shunt field windings in the wiper motor. The strong electrical field that this creates offsets the current that is being supplied to the series field and produces low wiper motor speeds. When the wiper control switch is moved to a high speed position, a resistor in the switch is connected into the shunt field circuit. This decreases the strength of the shunt field and produces a corresponding increase in wiper motor speed.

1973 models which are equipped with two speed wipers use a permanent magnet wiper motor. This motor is identical to the permanent magnet motor used by Ford and a description of its operation can be found below under "Ford Motor Co."

Chrysler Corporation

1967-68 two speed wipers and all three speed wipers are controlled by resistors in the field circuit. The high speed resistor is located on the windshield wiper switch, and the medium speed resistor (three speed wipers only) consists of resistance wire in the wiper motor wiring harness.

1969-73 two speed wipers have permanent magnet motors, which control wiper speed by feeding current to two different brushes for high and low speed operation. For low speed, the current flows through the torque limiting resistor and then to the low speed brush. For high speed operation, current is fed directly to the high speed brush.

Ford Motor Co.

On models with a permanent magnet motor, wiper speed is controlled by supplying current to two different brushes for high and low speed operation. No resistors are used, and the same amount of current is supplied to the high speed and the low speed brush. Wiper motor speed is altered by brush timing, or changing the position of the brush receiving current in relation to the motor ground brush. Two speed permanent magnet motors have three brushes: ground, low speed and high speed. These three brushes have a fixed position in the motor, with the low speed brush and the high speed brush being located at different distances from the ground brush. By switching the current from the low speed brush to the high speed brush, brush timing is changed, and this changes motor speed.

General Motors

Two and three speed wipers utilize a shunt in the field circuit of the wiper motor. Wound field motors divide the amount of current supplied to the motor between the field and the armature of the motor. If the amount of current to the field is increased, the amount of current to the armature is decreased. Decreasing the current to the armature decreases the speed of the motor.

The high and medium (three speed only) wiper speed is obtained by connecting resistors into the shunt field circuit, which reduces the amount of the current to the shunt field, and increases wiper speed. The greater the amount of resistance in the shunt field circuit, the higher the motor output. Therefore, the high speed shunt field circuit has more resistance than the medium speed (three speed wipers only).

Variable Speed Wipers

Variable speed wipers are of two types: those which vary the number of wiper blade strokes per minute, and those which vary the amount of time the wiper blades pause at the downward limit of their stroke before starting upward on a new stroke.

American Motors

Vacuum windshield wiper speed is

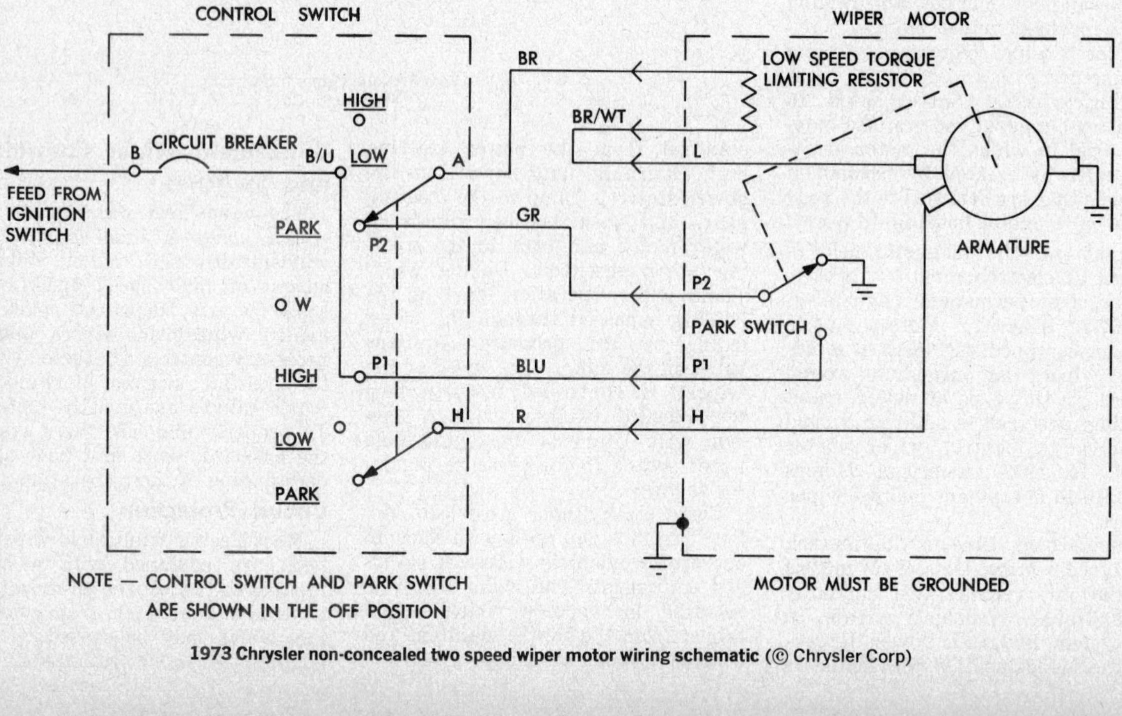

CONTROL SWITCH
WIPER MOTOR
BR
LOW SPEED TORQUE
LIMITING RESISTOR
HIGH
BR/WT
B
CIRCUIT BREAKER
B/U
LOW
A
L
FEED FROM
IGNITION
SWITCH
PARK
GR
P2
ARMATURE
O W
P2
PARK SWITCH
HIGH
P1
BLU
P1
H
R
H
LOW
PARK
NOTE — CONTROL SWITCH AND PARK SWITCH
ARE SHOWN IN THE OFF POSITION
MOTOR MUST BE GROUNDED

1973 Chrysler non-concealed two speed wiper motor wiring schematic (© Chrysler Corp)

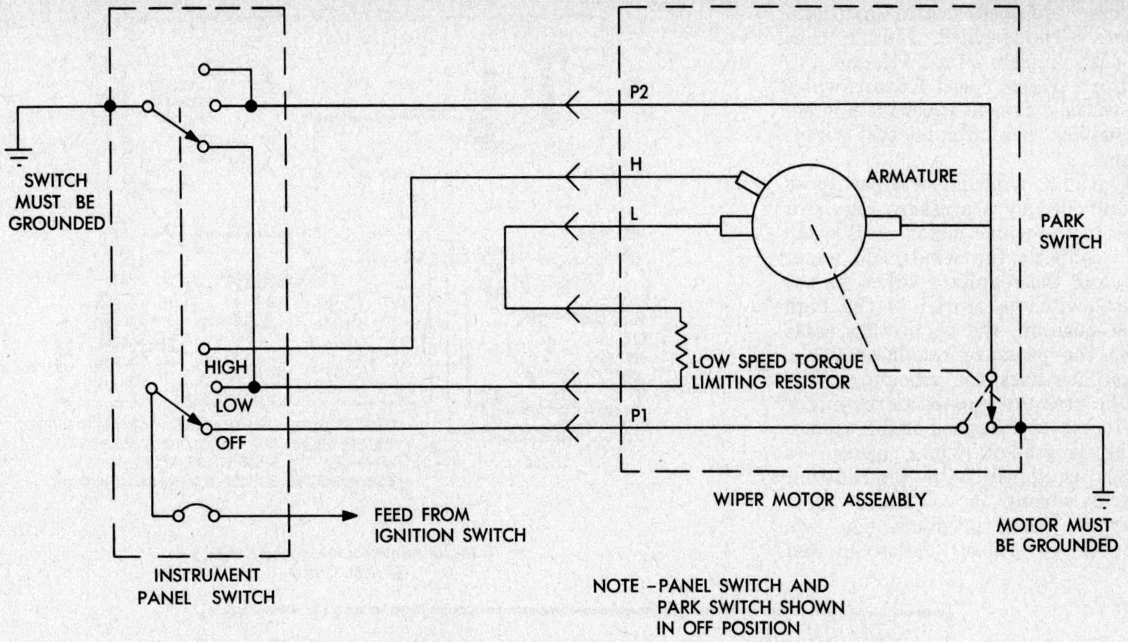
P2
H
L
ARMATURE
PARK
SWITCH
SWITCH
MUST BE
GROUNDED
HIGH
LOW
OFF
LOW SPEED TORQUE
LIMITING RESISTOR
P1
WIPER MOTOR ASSEMBLY
FEED FROM
IGNITION SWITCH
MOTOR MUST
BE GROUNDED
INSTRUMENT
PANEL SWITCH
NOTE – PANEL SWITCH AND
PARK SWITCH SHOWN
IN OFF POSITION

1973 Chrysler concealed park two-speed wiper motor schematic (© Chrysler Corp)

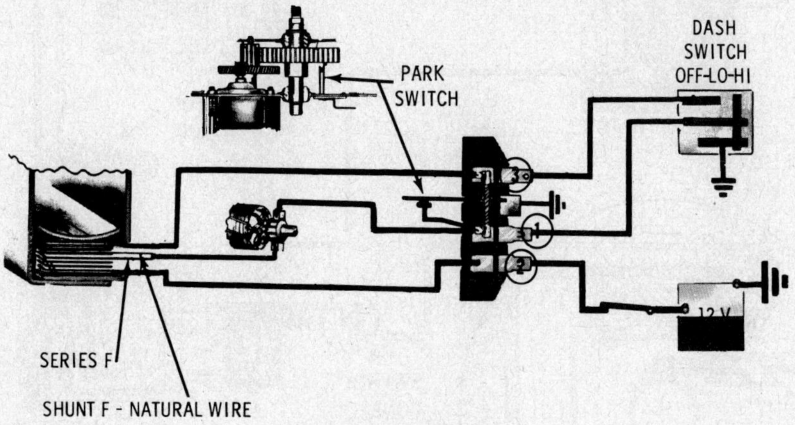
PARK
SWITCH
DASH
SWITCH
OFF-LO-HI
12 V
SERIES F
SHUNT F - NATURAL WIRE

G.M. rectangular motor
(© G.M. Corp)

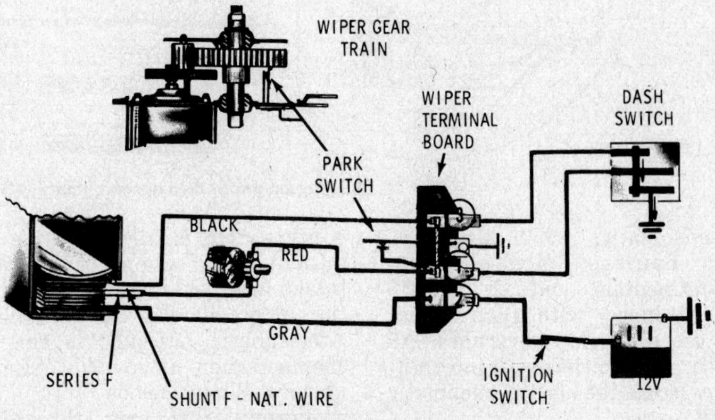
WIPER GEAR
TRAIN
WIPER
TERMINAL
BOARD
DASH
SWITCH
PARK
SWITCH
BLACK
RED
GRAY
12V
SERIES F
SHUNT F - NAT. WIRE
IGNITION
SWITCH

G.M. rectangular motor low-speed circuit
(© G.M. Corp)

controlled by a pressure regulator valve in the motor. A cable connects the windshield wiper switch to the pressure valve on the motor. As the windshield wiper switch is rotated toward the high speed position, the connecting cable opens the pressure regulator valve, which increases the amount of vacuum applied to the motor, and thus increases the speed of the wipers.

Electric windshield wiper speed on pre-1973 models is controlled by a resistor, which is contained in the windshield wiper switch. As the wiper switch is moved toward the high speed position, the amount of resistance in the shunt field circuit of the motor increases. This decreases the amount of current at the shunt field, which increases the current to the armature of the motor. Increasing the current at the armature raises motor speed.

On 1973 models with variable speed wipers, the wiper circuit contains a governor which controls the amount of time the wipers pause between strokes. A variable resistor in the wiper switch controls the current sent to the governor.

Chrysler Corporation

Electric wiper speed is governed by a rheostat which is built into the wiper control switch. The rheostat, when turned, regulates the amount of current which is delivered to the wiper motor. Raising the current at the motor increases motor speed.

Ford Motor Co.

All Ford products equipped with variable speed electric wipers are of the design that vary the length of the pause between wiper strokes. All models equipped with hydraulic wipers (Thunderbird, Lincoln Continental, Lincoln Mark III and IV) have a variable speed feature which allows the driver to select the number of strokes per minute the wipers make.

Hydraulic windshield wiper speed is controlled by a pressure regulator valve in the wiper motor. A Bowden cable connects the windshield wiper switch to the regulator valve. As the wiper switch is moved to the high speed position, the connecting cable opens the pressure regulator valve, which increases the amount of hydraulic pressure applied to the motor and increases the speed of the wipers.

The length of wiper pause, on models equipped with intermittent electric wipers, is controlled by a governor. Ford products use two types of governors: electronic and electro-pneumatic. 1970 Mustangs, Cougars, Fairlanes, Montegos, Lincoln Continentals, and all 1971-73 models equipped with intermittent wipers use electronic governors. All other years and models with intermittent wipers use the electro-pneumatic governor.

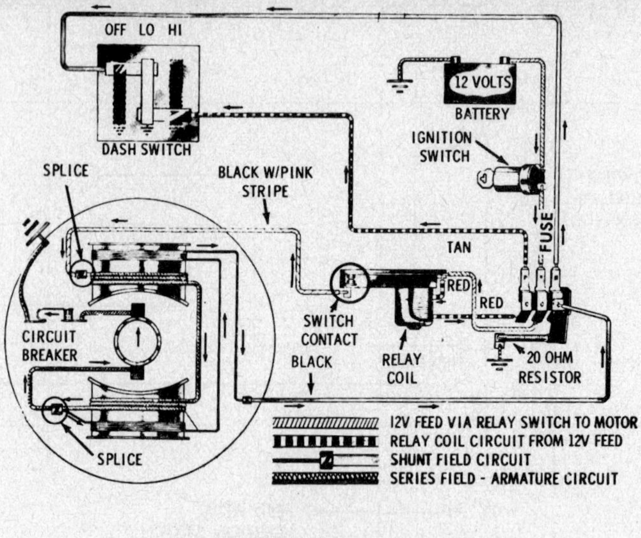
OFF LO HI
DASH SWITCH
12 VOLTS
BATTERY
IGNITION SWITCH
SPLICE
BLACK W/PINK STRIPE
FUSE
TAN
RED
RED
SWITCH CONTACT
CIRCUIT BREAKER
RELAY COIL
BLACK
20 OHM RESISTOR
SPLICE
12V FEED VIA RELAY SWITCH TO MOTOR
RELAY COIL CIRCUIT FROM 12V FEED
SHUNT FIELD CIRCUIT
SERIES FIELD - ARMATURE CIRCUIT

G.M. round motor low-speed circuit (© G.M. Corp)

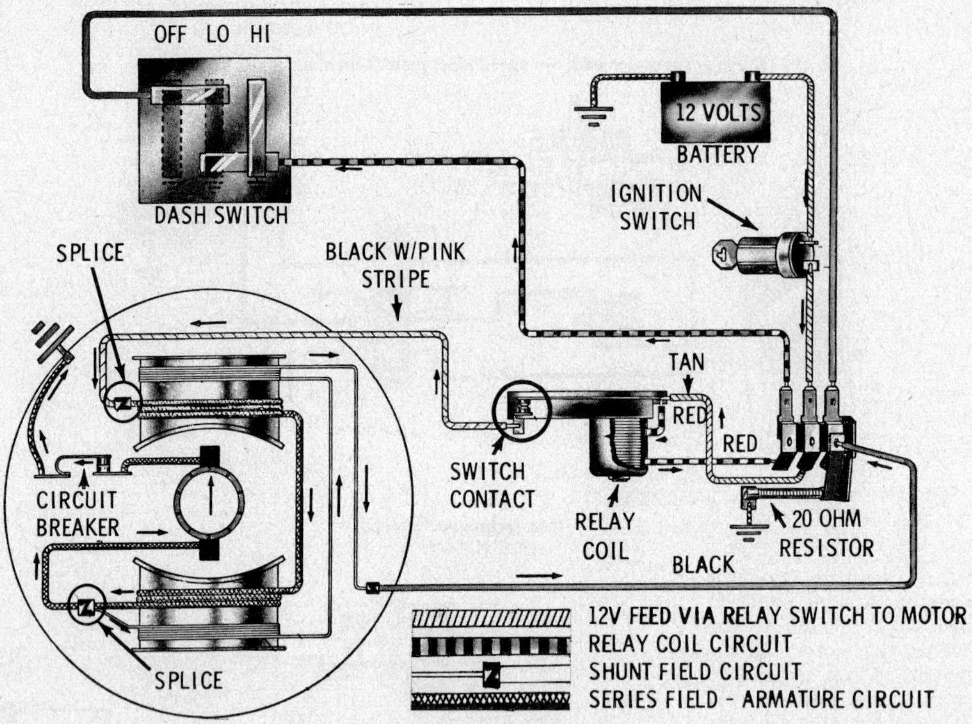
OFF LO HI
DASH SWITCH
12 VOLTS
BATTERY
IGNITION SWITCH
SPLICE
BLACK W/PINK STRIPE
TAN
RED
RED
SWITCH CONTACT
CIRCUIT BREAKER
RELAY COIL
BLACK
20 OHM RESISTOR
SPLICE
12V FEED VIA RELAY SWITCH TO MOTOR
RELAY COIL CIRCUIT
SHUNT FIELD CIRCUIT
SERIES FIELD - ARMATURE CIRCUIT

G.M. round motor high-speed circuit (© G.M. Corp)

The windshield wiper switch, on models equipped with an electronic governor, contains a resistor. As the wiper switch is turned the amount of resistance in the switch increases. This decreases the amount of current which is applied to the governor, which increases the time interval between wiper blade sweeps.

On models equipped with an electro-pneumatic governor, when the wiper switch is turned to the intermittent wiper action position, engine intake manifold vacuum is applied to the upper chamber of the governor. Atmospheric pressure in the lower chamber then moves the diaphragm upward. Simultaneous rotation of the governor valve cam through the spiral action of the follower applies manifold vacuum to the diaphragm of the normally closed electrical switch. The switch diaphragm is moved downward, compressing the diaphragm spring and moving the switch into the park position. The wiper blades move to the park position and remain there.

The rotation of the governor valve that applies vacuum to the governor switch also opens the upper governor chamber to the atmosphere. The compressed diaphragm spring applies downward pressure to the diaphragm, creating higher than atmospheric pressure in the lower chamber. This is allowed to bleed from the lower chamber through a variable orifice in the control selector. The size of the orifice is determined by the position of the wiper control switch. As the size of the orifice is increased, the length of the wiper dwell period between cycles will decrease.

As the diaphragm moves downward, the governor valve cam is rotated through the spiral action of the cam follower, opening the lower chamber of the electric switch dia-

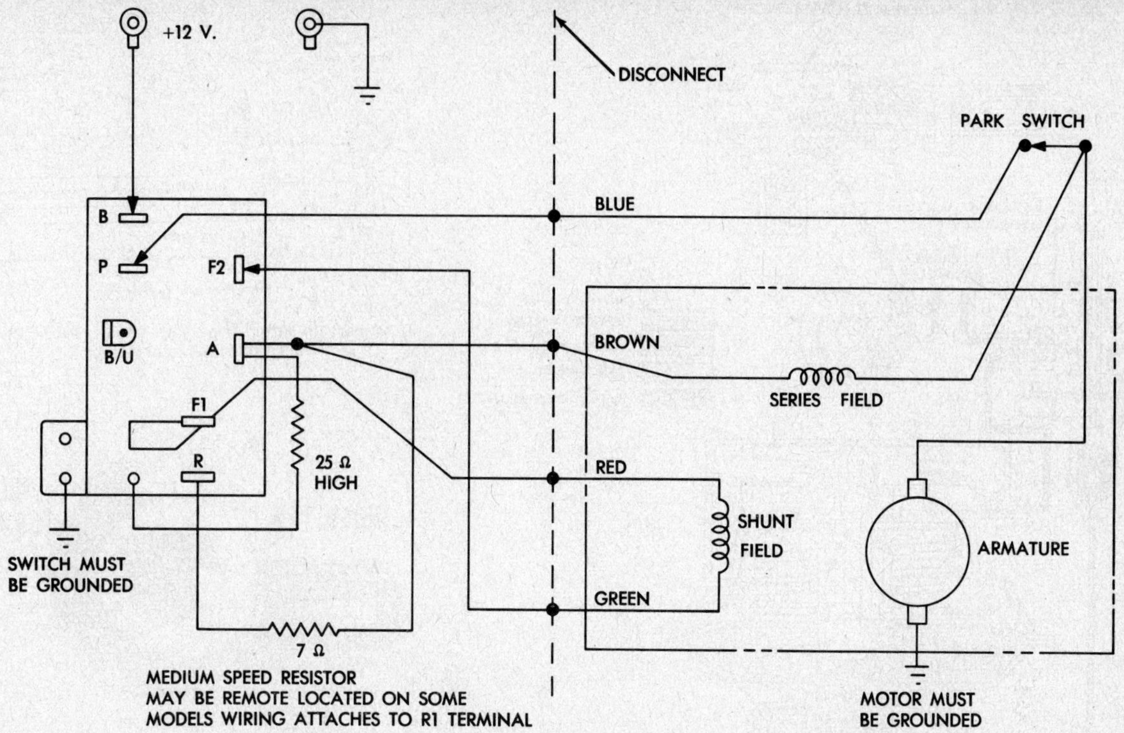
+12 V.
DISCONNECT
PARK SWITCH
B
P
F2
BLUE
B/U
A
BROWN
SERIES FIELD
F1
25 Ω
HIGH
R
RED
SHUNT
FIELD
ARMATURE
SWITCH MUST
BE GROUNDED
GREEN
7 Ω
MEDIUM SPEED RESISTOR
MAY BE REMOTE LOCATED ON SOME
MODELS WIRING ATTACHES TO R1 TERMINAL
MOTOR MUST
BE GROUNDED

1973 Chrysler three-speed wiper motor wiring schematic (© Chrysler Corp)

phragm to atmosphere. The compressed diaphragm spring moves the switch into the closed position, actuating the wiper motor. Simultaneously, the rotational movement of the valve cam applies manifold vacuum to the upper chamber of the governor, and a new wiper cycle begins.

General Motors

See Two and Three Speed Wipers.

Wiper Parking Mechanisms

There are two types of windshield wiper parking mechanisms: those which park the wiper blades at the downward limit of their normal stroke, and those which have a depressed parking feature which parks the wiper blades near the bottom of the windshield, or beneath the hood on models with concealed wipers.

American Motors

On pre-1973 models equipped with electric wipers, when the switch is turned to the Off position, the parking switch is engaged. The wipers continue the stroke they were on at the time the switch was turned Off, until they reach a fixed position on the wiper stroke. Here, the parking switch connects to the motor, and reverses the direction of the current flow to the motor, which reverses the direction of the wipers. When the wipers reach the rest position, the park switch opens the parking circuit, and the motor stops.

1973 models are equipped with a Ford wiper motor. For a description of the parking mechanism on this motor, see the "Ford Motor Co." paragraph below.

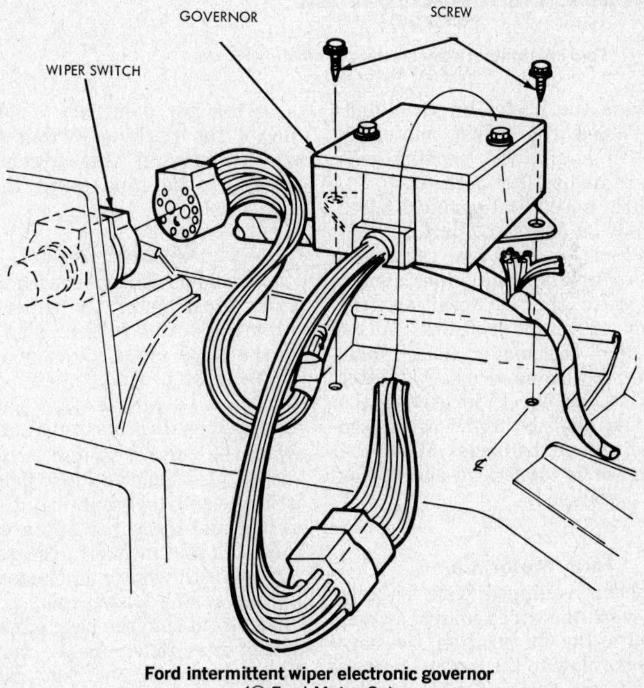
GOVERNOR
SCREW
WIPER SWITCH

Ford intermittent wiper electronic governor
(© Ford Motor Co)

On models equipped with vacuum wipers, when the switch is moved to the Off position, the pressure regulator valve closes, which halts the action of the wipers. Then the spring loaded diaphragm in the wiper motor returns the wipers to the rest position.

Chrysler Corporation

On models with a non-depressed parking position, when the wiper control switch is turned to the Off position, the wipers will complete the wipe cycle and return to the rest position.

The two speed wiper system, on models which feature depressed or concealed wipers, accomplishes its depressed parking action by means of a parking cam on the wiper motor crank pin. When the wiper control switch is turned Off, the motor reverses direction, and at the same time, the parking cam rotates 180°. This lengthens the drive link slightly

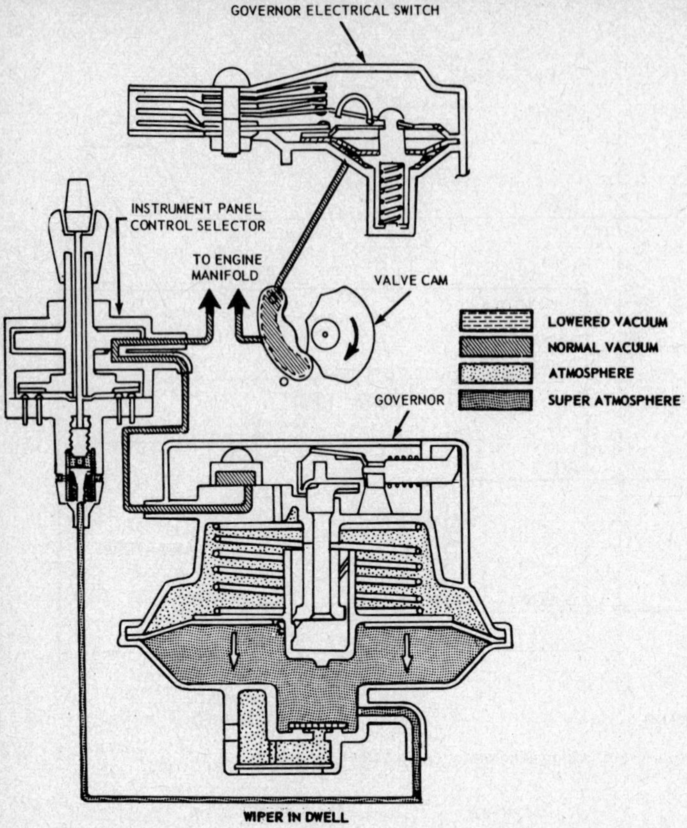
GOVERNOR ELECTRICAL SWITCH
INSTRUMENT PANEL CONTROL SELECTOR
TO ENGINE MANIFOLD
VALVE CAM
LOWERED VACUUM
NORMAL VACUUM
ATMOSPHERE
SUPER ATMOSPHERE
GOVERNOR
WIPER IN DWELL

Ford intermittent wiper electro-pneumatic governor
(© Ford Motor Co)

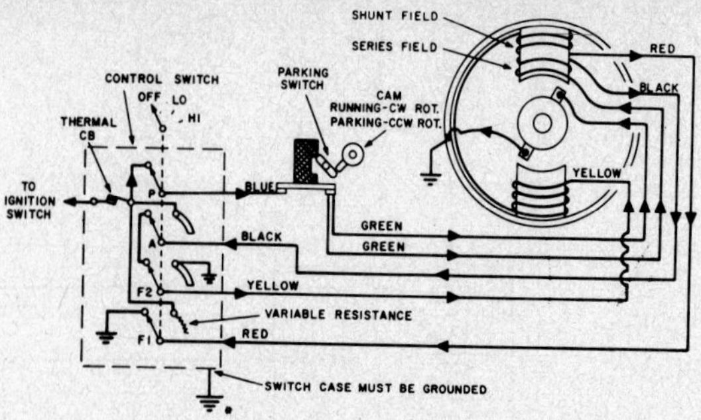
SHUNT FIELD
SERIES FIELD
RED
CONTROL SWITCH
OFF LO HI
PARKING SWITCH
CAM
RUNNING-CW ROT.
PARKING-CCW ROT.
BLACK
THERMAL CB
TO IGNITION SWITCH
P
BLUE
YELLOW
GREEN
GREEN
A
BLACK
F2
YELLOW
VARIABLE RESISTANCE
F1
RED
SWITCH CASE MUST BE GROUNDED

American Motors wiper park circuit (1967-72)
(© American Motors Corp)

INNER TAB
PIN TURNS

Chrysler two-speed wiper crank arm with the parking cam in the running position
(© Chrysler Corp)

and lowers the blades on the windshield. When the wiper motor is turned On again, the parking cam returns to its original position.

All three speed and variable speed wipers have a depressed parking feature, which utilizes an eccentric motor shaft. When the wiper switch is turned to the Off position, the direction of motor rotation is reversed, and the motor inner shaft stops, while the outer shaft rotates 180°. This, in effect, lengthens the drive link slightly and lowers the park position of the blades. When the wiper motor is turned On again, this action is reversed.

Ford Motor Co.

On models equipped with electric wipers, when the wiper control switch is turned to the Off position, the normal current flow to the motor brushes is shut off, and replaced with current which flows through the park switch. The park switch is mounted inside the wiper motor. This system features a cam and lever assembly which switches off the current to the motor when the wipers reach the park position. When the wipers are turned Off, and the wiper blades are in any position other than their normal park position, the parking cam and lever hold the park switch closed and current continues to be delivered to the brushes. As the wiper blades reach their park position, the parking cam is at the low point of its lobe. This allows the parking switch to open, which shuts off the current to the wiper brushes and stops the wiper motor.

General Motors

On models equipped with a rectangular wiper motor, the wiper parking circuit operates in the same manner as the Ford motor described above.

The round wiper motor does not contain a parking switch. On models equipped with this type of motor, when the control switch is turned to the Off position, the shunt field circuit is connected to ground at the wiper switch and the wiper operates in low speed. Simultaneously, the relay coil circuit in the motor is opened, allowing the spring loaded relay latch arm to move out into the path of the motor output gear pawl. As the motor continues to rotate, the relay latch arm engages the motor output gear pawl. This unlocks the gear from the drive pawl, lock pawl, and the drive plate of the output shaft assembly. Since the gear shaft is mounted on the output shaft at an offset location, the rotation of the gear causes a cam action between the output shaft and the gear shaft. This action causes the gear drive pawl to move into the relay switch slot and push the relay latch arm against the relay-switch flexible contact. This action opens the relay-switch contacts, cutting off current to the motor.

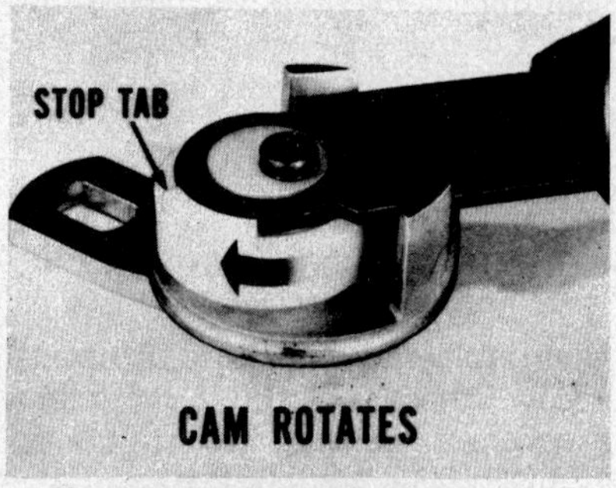
STOP TAB
CAM ROTATES

Chrysler two-speed wiper crank arm with the parking cam in the park position
(© Chrysler Corp)

G.M. Demand Wiper System

The wiper motor used with the demand wiper system is the G.M. round motor. This system requires the use of an extra relay (demand relay), a dual set of holding switches, and an extra switch located in the end of the shift lever.

Weather conditions such as light rain, mist, fog, etc. that do not require continuous wiper operation require the driver to repeatedly turn the wiper control switch on and off. With the demand wiper system the driver merely depresses the shift lever button to the first detent position and releases it. The wipers will then make one complete wiping stroke and automatically shut Off. If the button is held in the first detent position, the wiper will operate until the button is released.

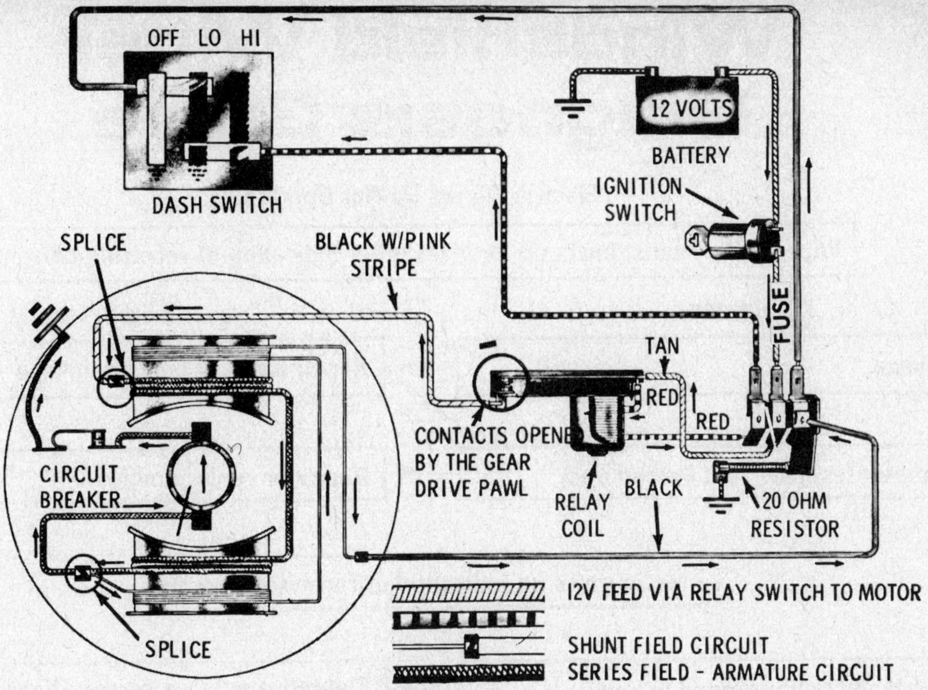
OFF LO HI
DASH SWITCH
12 VOLTS
BATTERY
IGNITION SWITCH
SPLICE
BLACK W/PINK STRIPE
FUSE
TAN
RED
RED
CONTACTS OPENED BY THE GEAR DRIVE PAWL
CIRCUIT BREAKER
RELAY COIL
BLACK
20 OHM RESISTOR
SPLICE
12V FEED VIA RELAY SWITCH TO MOTOR
SHUNT FIELD CIRCUIT
SERIES FIELD - ARMATURE CIRCUIT

G.M. round motor parking circuit (© G.M. Corp)

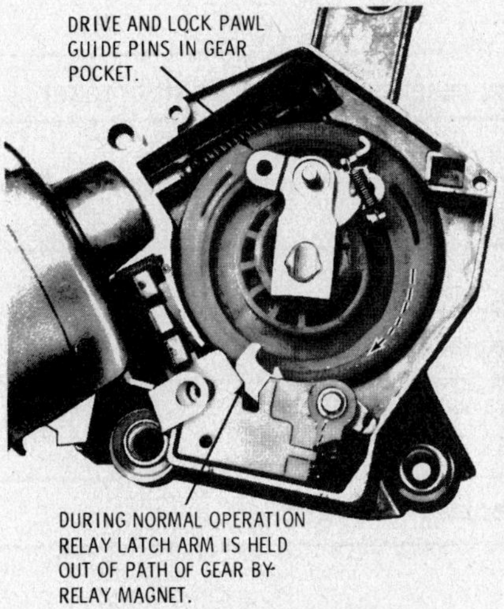
DRIVE AND LOCK PAWL GUIDE PINS IN GEAR POCKET.
DURING NORMAL OPERATION RELAY LATCH ARM IS HELD OUT OF PATH OF GEAR BY RELAY MAGNET.

G.M. round motor output gear in the run position
(© G.M. Corp)

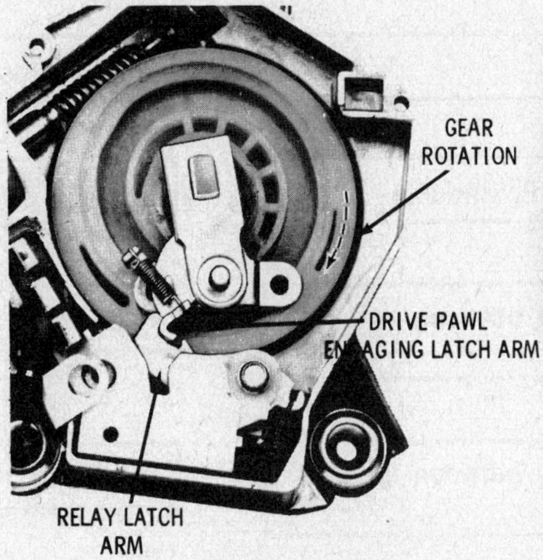
GEAR ROTATION
DRIVE PAWL ENGAGING LATCH ARM
RELAY LATCH ARM

G.M. round motor shutting off
(© G.M. Corp)

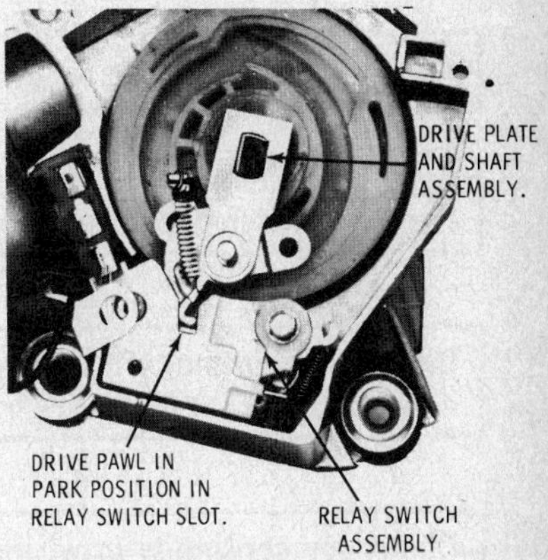
DRIVE PLATE AND SHAFT ASSEMBLY.
DRIVE PAWL IN PARK POSITION IN RELAY SWITCH SLOT.
RELAY SWITCH ASSEMBLY

G.M. round motor shut off in the park position
(© G.M. Corp)

Troubleshooting

American Motors Electric Wipers

Wiper Motor Does Not Operate—1967-72

Disconnect the brown current supply wire from the wiper switch and check it for battery voltage with the ignition switch on. If no voltage is present, repair brown wire or connection at the ignition switch.

If current is present at the brown wire, disconnect the three wire plug and the blue wire at the wiper switch. Connect a jumper wire from the brown supply wire to the black wire in the three wire plug. If the wiper motor operates, the wiper switch is defective.

If the wiper motor does not operate, check the black wire for continuity, and for a good connection at the wiper motor. If an instrument is not available to check the black wire for continuity, run a jumper wire from the supply wire to the terminal of the motor for the black wire. If the motor does not operate with the jumper wire in place, or if the black wire is found to have continuity, the wiper motor is defective.

Wipers Do Not Operate on "Low-Speed"—1967-72

Connect jumper wires from the positive battery terminal to the red and black wires at the wiper motor. Connect another wire from the negative battery terminal to the yellow wire at the wiper motor. If the motor runs at low speed, check the wires from the wiper switch to the wiper motor for continuity. If the wires

Windshield Wiper Diagnosis Guide

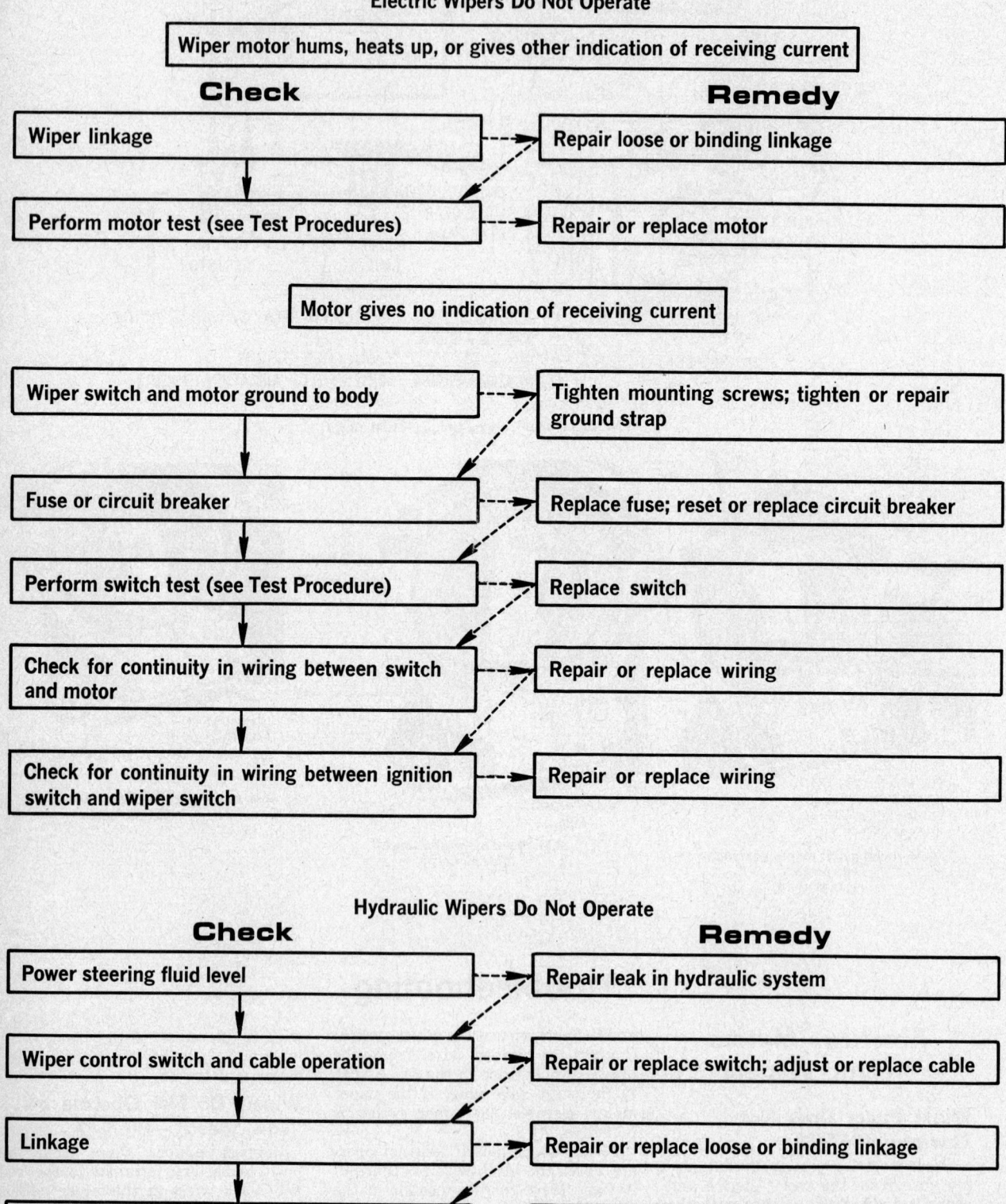

Electric Wipers Do Not Operate

Wiper motor hums, heats up, or gives other indication of receiving current

Check	Remedy
Wiper linkage	Repair loose or binding linkage
Perform motor test (see Test Procedures)	Repair or replace motor

Motor gives no indication of receiving current

Check	Remedy
Wiper switch and motor ground to body	Tighten mounting screws; tighten or repair ground strap
Fuse or circuit breaker	Replace fuse; reset or replace circuit breaker
Perform switch test (see Test Procedure)	Replace switch
Check for continuity in wiring between switch and motor	Repair or replace wiring
Check for continuity in wiring between ignition switch and wiper switch	Repair or replace wiring

Hydraulic Wipers Do Not Operate

Check	Remedy
Power steering fluid level	Repair leak in hydraulic system
Wiper control switch and cable operation	Repair or replace switch; adjust or replace cable
Linkage	Repair or replace loose or binding linkage
Motor	Replace motor

Vacuum Wipers Do Not Operate

Check		Remedy
15-17 in. of Mercury (vacuum) at the motor	--->	Replace defective hose or fitting; replace defective fuel pump
Wiper control switch and cable operation	--->	Repair or replace switch; adjust or replace cable
Linkage	--->	Repair or replace loose or binding linkage
Motor	--->	Replace motor

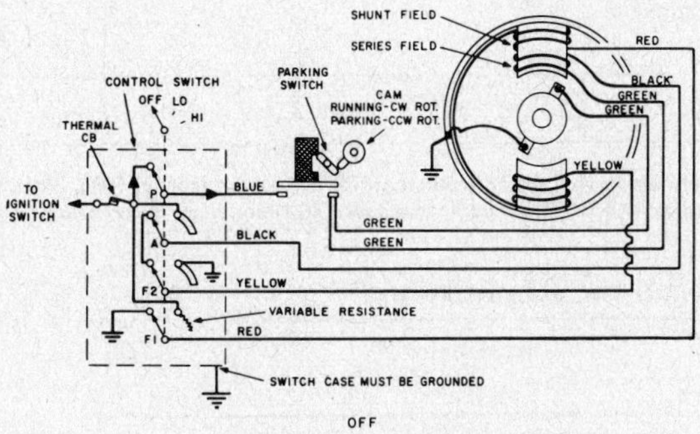
SHUNT FIELD
SERIES FIELD
RED
CONTROL SWITCH
OFF LO
HI
PARKING SWITCH
CAM
RUNNING-CW ROT.
PARKING-CCW ROT.
BLACK
GREEN
GREEN
THERMAL CB
YELLOW
TO IGNITION SWITCH
P
BLUE
GREEN
GREEN
A
BLACK
YELLOW
F2
VARIABLE RESISTANCE
F1
RED
SWITCH CASE MUST BE GROUNDED
OFF

American Motors electronic wiper circuit
(© American Motors Corp)

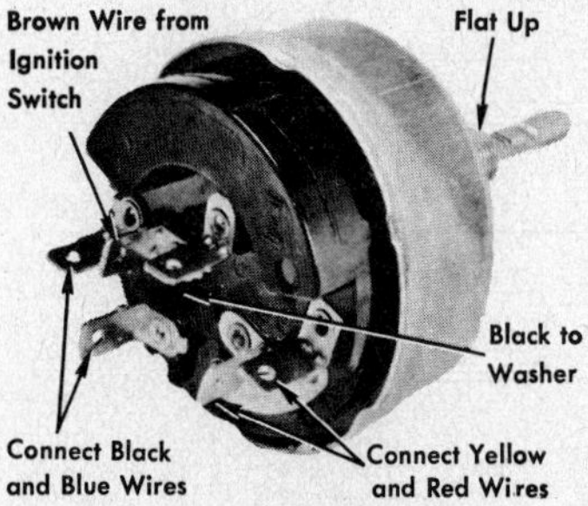
Brown Wire from Ignition Switch
Flat Up
Black to Washer
Connect Black and Blue Wires
Connect Yellow and Red Wires

Rambler wiper switch wire locations
(© American Motors Corp)

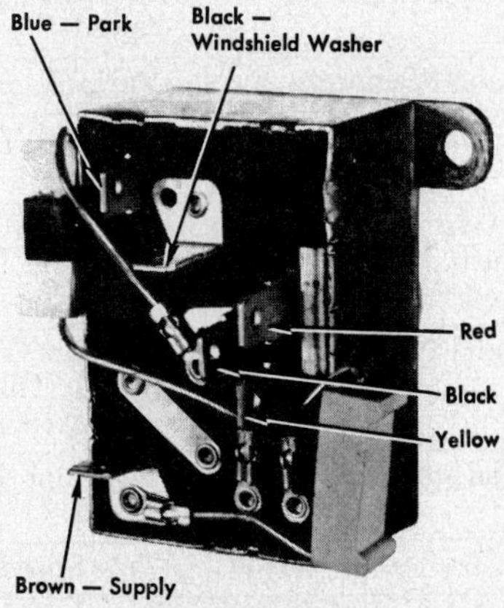
Blue — Park
Black — Windshield Washer
Red
Black
Yellow
Brown — Supply

Rebel and Ambassador wiper switch wire location
(© American Motors Corp)

have continuity, the wiper switch is defective. If the wiper motor did not run with the jumper wires attached, the motor is defective.

Wipers Will Not Park —1967-72

Disconnect the wires from the rear of the wiper switch. Connect the black and yellow wires together, and connect the brown current supply wire to the blue wire. Connect the red wire to ground. If the wipers park with these wires in place, the wiper switch is defective. If the wipers do not park, momentarily connect a jumper wire from the green wire to the blue wire at the wiper motor. If the wipers operate only with this jumper wire in place, the park switch is defective. If the wipers still do not operate, check the blue wire for battery current.

1973 Wiper Switch Test

Disconnect the wiring from the rear of the windshield wiper control switch and, using a self-powered test light or ohmmeter, check for continuity (no resistance) between the terminals of the switch listed in the accompanying illustration. If continuity does not exist between the proper terminals in any switch position, the switch is defective and must be replaced.

1973 Wiper Motor Current Draw Test

Disconnect the positive battery cable from the battery. Either remove the wiper arms and blades from the wiper pivot shafts or disconnect the wiper motor from the windshield wiper linkage. Disconnect the wiring connector from the wiper motor. Connect the positive lead of an ammeter to the positive battery post and connect the other lead to the white wire terminal on the wiper motor wiring harness. Note the reading on the ammeter, then move the ammeter lead from the white wire terminal to the blue wire terminal on the wiper motor wiring harness. Again, note the reading on the ammeter. If the wiper motor current draw in either of the two above tests exceeded 3 amps, the wiper motor is defective and must be replaced.

1973 Wiper Motor Parking Test

Run the wiper motor until the wiper blades are in the middle of the windshield. Turn the ignition key to the OFF position to stop the blades in this position. Disconnect the wiper motor wiring connector from the car wiring. Connect a jumper wire from the white wire terminal to the black wire terminal on the wiper motor connector. Connect another jumper wire from the red wire terminal on the wiper motor connector to the positive battery cable.

With the jumper wires installed, the wiper blades should make not more than one sweep and then return to the park position.

If the wipers do not respond this way, the wiper motor is defective. If the wipers parked correctly with the jumpers in place, but do not park when connected normally, the wiper switch or wiring is defective.

Chrysler Corporation

Wiper Switch Tests

Two Speed, Three Speed and Variable Speed Wipers

Remove the wiper switch from the dash. Using a continuity tester or ohmmeter, test for continuity (no resistance) between the terminals of the switch shown in the charts below. The heading of each column indicates the position the switch should be in for continuity to exist between the terminals of the switch listed in that column. For test purposes, the Park position is when the switch is turned to the Off detent. On models with variable speed wipers, the Low Speed position is immediately past the Off detent, and the High Speed position is the extreme position of switch travel. The word *ground* in the charts means to connect one lead of the tester to the case of the switch.

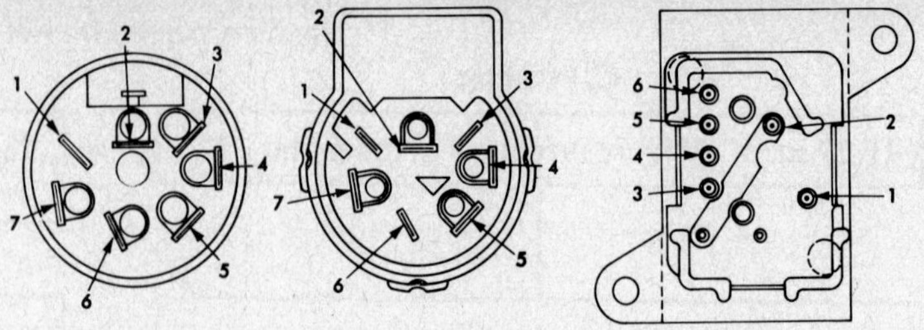
1
2
3
4
5
6
7

	STANDARD 01-10-40-80 Series	STANDARD 70 Series	INTERMITTENT 01-10-40-80 Series
Off or Park	1-2 3-4	1-2 3-4	1-2 4-5
Low Speed	1-2-3	1-2 4-5	1-2 5 to Case 4-5
High Speed	1-2-5	1-2 5-6	1-2-3 5 to Case 4-5
Intermittent			1-2 5 to Case Variable Resist. 4-5 1-9K to 7K
Wash	1-2 6-7		1-2 6-7

1973 American Motors wiper switch continuity test for Hornet (01), Matador (10), Gremlin (40), Javelin (70), and Ambassador (80) series (© American Motors Corp)

Test Procedure Applications

Year	*Models*	*Wipers*	*Test No.*
1967	Belvedere, Coronet, Charger, Dart, Satellite, and Valiant	Two Speed	2
	Chrysler, Fury, Imperial, and VIP	Two and Three Speed	1
	All Dodge and Plymouth	Variable Speed	1
1968	Barracuda, Dart, and Valiant	Chrysler Two Speed	4
	Belvedere, Coronet, Charger, Fury, Monaco, Polara, Satellite, and VIP	Chrysler Two Speed	3
	All Dodge and Plymouth	Non-Chrysler Two Speed; Three Speed and Variable Speed	1
	Chrysler and Imperial	Two and Three Speed	1
1969	Barracuda, Dart and Valiant	Two Speed	4
	Belvedere, Coronet, Charger, and Satellite	Two Speed	3
	Fury, Monaco, Polara, and VIP	Two Speed	5
	All Dodge and Plymouth	Three Speed and Variable Speed	1
	Chrysler and Imperial	Two Speed	5
	Chrysler and Imperial	Three Speed	1
1970	Dart, Valiant	Two Speed	4
	Belvedere, Charger, Coronet, and Satellite	Two Speed	3
	Baracuda, Fury, Monaco, and Polara	Two Speed	5
	Challenger	Two Speed	6

Test Procedure Applications

Year	*Models*	*Wipers*	*Test No.*
	All Dodge and Plymouth	Three Speed and Variable Speed	1
	Chrysler and Imperial	Two Speed	7
	Chrysler and Imperial	Three Speed	1
1971-73	All models with non-concealed wipers	Two Speed	4
	All models with concealed wipers	Two Speed	5
	All models	Three Speed and Variable Speed	1

Test No. 1

	Switch Position			
	Park	*Low*	*Medium**	*High*
Continuity Between	B to B/U	B to B/U	B to B/U	B to B/U
	B/U to P	B/U to A	B/U to A	B/U to A
	A to F-2	A to F-1	F-1 to R-1①	A through rheostat or resistor to F-1②
	F-1 to ground	F-2 to ground	F-2 to ground	F-2 to ground
		P-open④	P-open	P-open
				F-1 to R-2③

*—Three speed wipers only.
①—1967 Fury and VIP; 1968 All Dodge and Plymouth; 1969 Dart, Coronet, and Charger; 1970 Charger and Coronet: A to R-1.
②—On models with variable speed wipers only, as the switch is rotated, the resistance shown on the ohmmeter should vary from a high reading to a low reading in a smooth rate of change. If a continuity tester is used, the light should vary from bright to dim.
③—1969-70 models only.
④—Except 1967 models.

Test No. 2

	Switch Position		
	Park	*Low*	*High*
Continuity Between	B to B/U	B to B/U	B to B/U
	B/U to P	B/U to A	B/U to A
	A to F	A to F	A through resistor to F
			P-open

Test No. 3

	Switch Position		
	Park	*Low*	*High*
Continuity Between	B to B/U	B to B/U	B to B/U
	B to P	B to P	B to P
	A to F-2	B to A	B to F-1
	F-1-open	F-2-open	F-2-open
		F-1-open	A-open

Test No. 4

	Switch Position		
	Park	*Low*	*High*
Continuity Between	B to B/U	B to B/U	B to B/U
	B to P-1	B to P-1	B to P-1
	A to P-2	B to A	B to H
	H-open	P-2-open	P-2-open
		H-open	A-open

Test No. 5

	Switch Position		
	Park	*Low*	*High*
Continuity Between	B to B/U	B to B/U	B to B/U
	B to P	B to A	B to H
	A to ground	H-open	F-2 to ground
	F-2-open	P-open	A-open
	H-open	F-2 to ground	P-open

Test No. 6

Continuity Between	Switch Position: Park	Low	High
	B to B/U	B to B/U	B to B/U
	B to P	B to A	B to F-1
	A to ground	F-2 to ground	F-2 to ground
	F-2-open	F-1-open	P-open
	F-1-open	H-open	A-open

Test No. 7

Continuity Between	Switch Position: Park	Low	High
	B to B/U	B to B/U	B to B/U
	B to P	B to A	B to F-1
	A to ground	F-2 to ground	F-2 to ground
	F-2-open	F-1-open	A-open
	F-1-open	P-open	

Wiper Motor Tests

Caution Wiper motor can be damaged if test leads are connected to the wrong terminals on the wiper motor during testing.

Two Speed Wipers—Chrysler Motors

1967 Compacts and Intermediates

1. Disconnect the lead wires from the wiper motor.
2. Connect a jumper wire from the negative battery cable to the wiper motor ground strap.
3. Connect a jumper wire from the positive battery terminal to the black wire and the red wire on the wiper motor. The motor should run continuously.

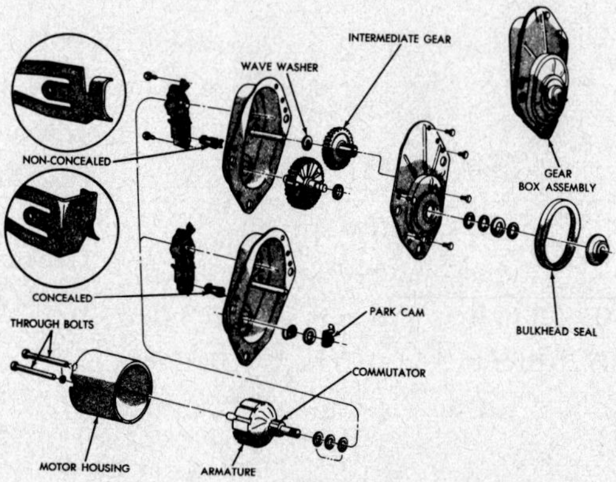
INTERMEDIATE GEAR
WAVE WASHER
NON-CONCEALED
GEAR BOX ASSEMBLY
CONCEALED
PARK CAM
THROUGH BOLTS
BULKHEAD SEAL
COMMUTATOR
MOTOR HOUSING
ARMATURE

Disassembled view of Chrysler two-speed wiper motor
(© Chrysler Corp)

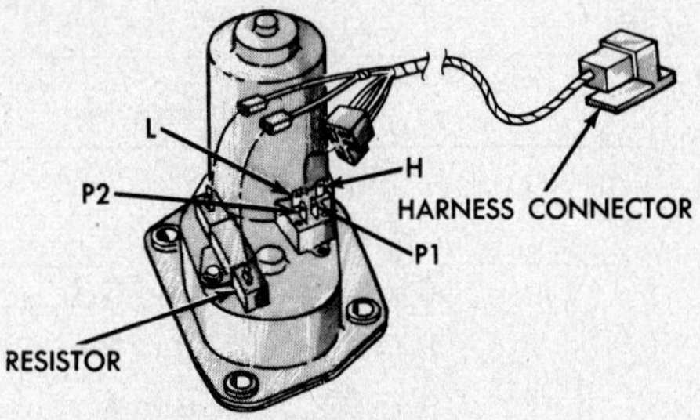
L
H
P2
HARNESS CONNECTOR
P1
RESISTOR

Chrysler design two speed wiper motor
(© Chrysler Corp)

1968 Fury, Monaco, and Polara
1968-69 All Intermediates and Compacts
1970 Belvedere, Charger, Coronet, Satellite, and Valiant
1971-73 All With Non-Concealed Wipers

1. Disconnect the lead wires from the wiper motor.
2. Connect a jumper wire from the positive battery terminal to the *H* terminal on the wiper motor. The motor should run on high speed. Remove the jumper.
3. Connect a jumper wire from the positive battery terminal to the resistor terminal on the wiper motor.
4. Connect a jumper wire from the *L* terminal of the wiper motor to the second resistor terminal. The motor should operate at low speed. Remove the jumpers.
5. Connect a jumper wire from the positive battery terminal to the *P-1* terminal on the wiper motor.
6. Connect a jumper wire from the *P-2* terminal on the wiper motor to the *L* terminal. The wipers should park.

1969-70 Chrysler, Fury, Imperial, Monaco, and Polara
1970 Barracuda, Challenger, and Dart
1971-73 All With Two Speed Concealed Wipers

1. Disconnect the lead wires from the wiper motor.
2. Connect a jumper wire from the positive battery terminal to the *H* terminal on the wiper motor.
3. Connect a jumper wire from the *P-2* terminal on the wiper motor to ground. The wipers should operate at high speed.
4. Remove the jumper wires that were used for the high speed test. Connect a jumper wire from the positive battery terminal to one of the resistor terminals on the wiper motor. Connect a second jumper wire from the (*L*) terminal on the wiper motor to the other resistor terminal. Connect a third jumper wire from the (*P-2*) terminal on the wiper motor to ground.
5. The wiper motor should operate at low speed. Remove all the jumper wires.
6. Connect a jumper wire from the positive battery terminal to the *P-1* terminal on the wiper motor.
7. Connect a jumper wire from the *L* terminal on the wiper motor to ground. On 1972 and 1973 models, connect a jumper wire from the wiper motor ground strap to ground. The wipers should park.

Two Speed Wipers—Non-Chrysler Motors
Three Speed Wipers
Variable Speed Wipers

1967-1973 All Models With: Two Speed Wipers With Non-Chrysler Motor, Three Speed Wipers, and Variable Speed Wipers

1. Disconnect the lead wires from the wiper motor.
2. Connect a jumper wire from the green wire on the wiper motor to ground. On 1967 models, connect a jumper wire from the negative battery terminal to the wiper motor ground strap.

3. Connect a jumper wire from the positive battery terminal to the brown wire and the red wire on the wiper motor. The motor should run continuously.
4. If the motor does not run, make sure the ground strap on the wiper motor has a good connection to the body of the vehicle. If the motor still does not run, and appears to be shorted, unsolder the two green wires from the wiper park switch. With the jumper wires connected as described above, fasten the two green wires together. If the motor runs, the park switch is defective. Resolder the green wires to the park switch. Disconnect the jumpers.
5. Connect a jumper wire from the green wire on the wiper motor to the brown wire.
6. Connect a jumper wire from the red wire on the wiper motor to ground.
7. Connect a jumper wire from the positive battery terminal to the blue wire on the wiper motor. The wipers should park.

Ford Motor Co.

Wiper Switch Test

Check the terminals of the switch listed in the illustrations for continuity (no resistance). If continuity does not exist between all of the terminals listed, the switch is defective and must be replaced.

Wiper Motor Current Draw Test

Disconnect the positive battery cable from the battery. Either remove

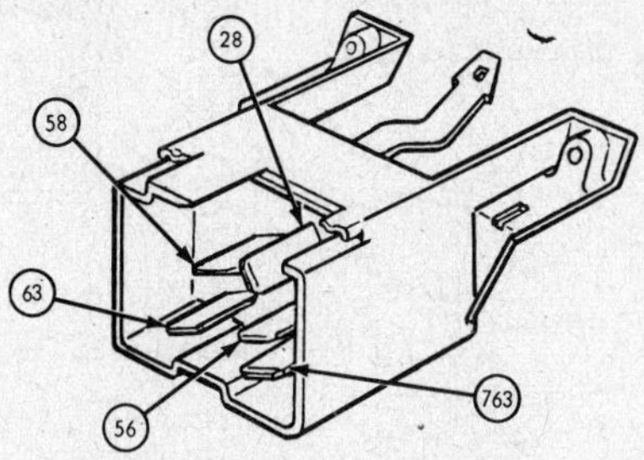
28
58
63
56
763

SWITCH POSITION	CONTINUITY BETWEEN TERMINALS
Off (Park)	63-763 28-58
Low	58-63-763
High	56-63-763
Washer On	950A-951

1967-68 Fairlane switch test
(© Ford Motor Co)

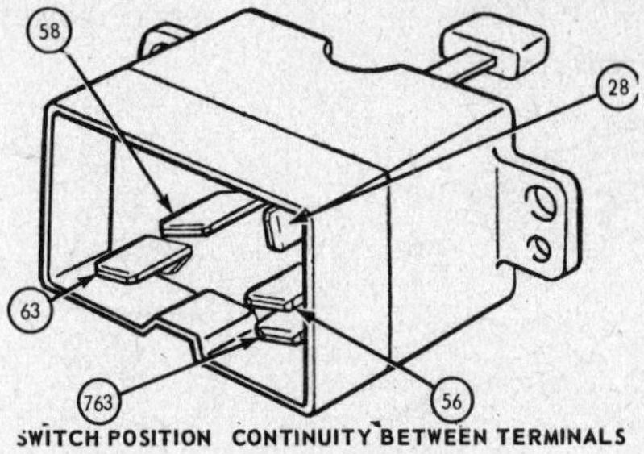
58
28
63
763
56

SWITCH POSITION	CONTINUITY BETWEEN TERMINALS
Off (Park)	63-763 28-58
Low	58-63-763
High	56-63-763
Washer On	58A-63A

1967-68 Cougar switch test
(© Ford Motor Co)

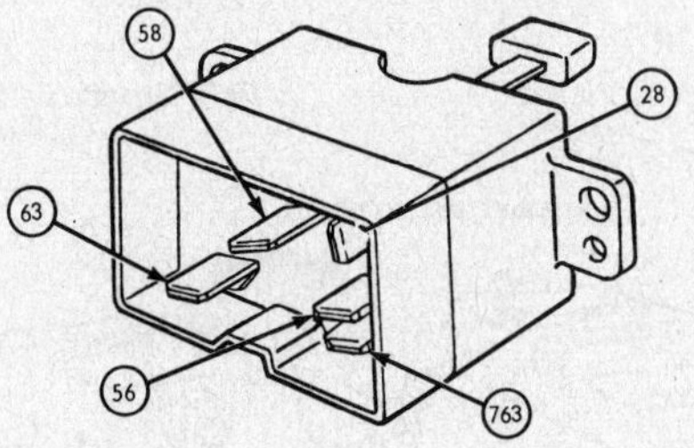
58
28
63
56
763

SWITCH POSITION	CONTINUITY BETWEEN TERMINALS
Off (Park)	63-763 28-58
Low	58-63-763
High	56-63-763
Washer On	58A-63A

1967-68 Mustang switch test
(© Ford Motor Co)

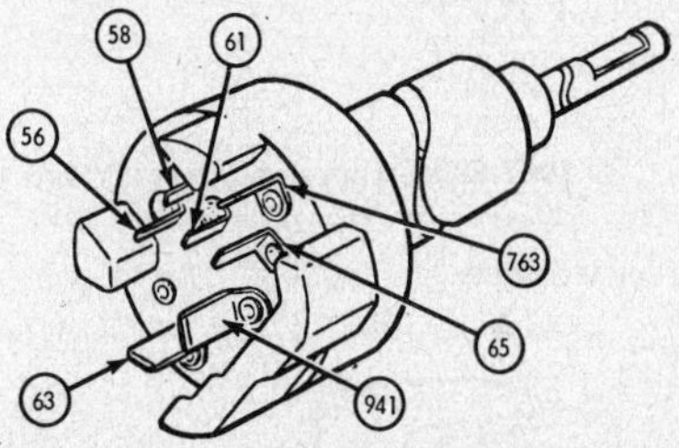
58
61
56
763
65
63
941

SWITCH POSITION	CONTINUITY BETWEEN TERMINALS
Off (Park)	65-763 56-63 58-61
Low	61-63-763 56-58
High	61-763 56-58
Washer On	763-941

1967-68 Falcon switch test
(© Ford Motor Co)

(INTERMITTENT SYSTEM)

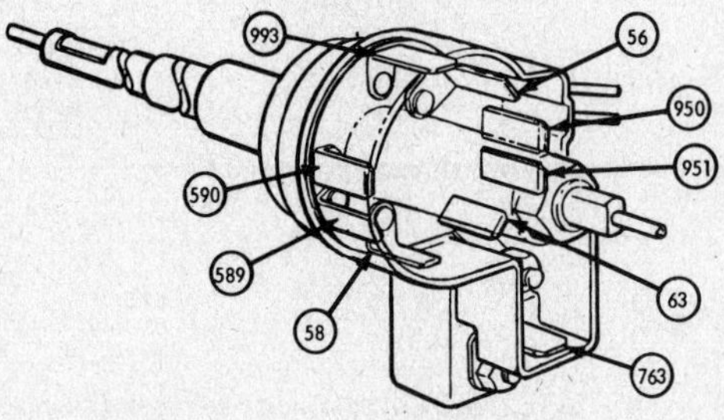
993
56
950
951
590
589
58
63
763

SWITCH POSITION	CONTINUITY BETWEEN TERMINALS
Off (Park)	63-763 58-589
Low	58-63-763
High	56-63-763
Intermittent	63-763 56-993 58-590
Washer On	950-951

(STANDARD SYSTEM)

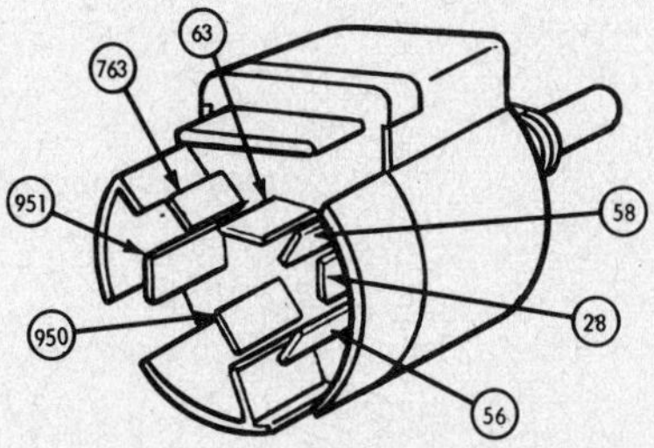
63
763
951
58
28
950
56

SWITCH POSITION	CONTINUITY BETWEEN TERMINALS
Off (Park)	763-63 28-58
Low	763-63-58
High	763-63-56
Washer On	951-950

1967-68 Mercury intermediate switch test (© Ford Motor Co)

the wiper arms and blades from the wiper pivot shafts or disconnect the windshield wiper linkage from the wiper motor. Connect an ammeter in series with the wiper motor and install jumper wires as shown in the accompanying illustrations. Operate the wiper motor on high and low speeds and note the current draw on the ammeter. On oscillating and non-depressed park permanent magnet wiper motors, the current draw should not exceed 3 amps. On depressed park permanent magnet wiper motors, the current draw should not exceed 3.5 amps.

Park Switch Test

Stop the wiper system by turning off the ignition switch when the wipers reach a position approximately 90° from the park position. Connect jumper wires to the motor as shown in the illustrations. If the wipers park correctly with the jumper wires in place, but would not park when controlled by the wiper switch, the wiper control switch is defective.

On 1969-1973 full size Ford products, the wiper motor output arm should reverse direction for approximately 10-15°. If the output arm reverses more than 15°, or if the motor stalls or jams while the arm is reversing, replace the output arm and wind-latch.

If the wipers still fail to park with the jumpers in place, repair or replace the park switch. On 1967-68 models equipped with a permanent magnet motor, the park switch is adjustable.

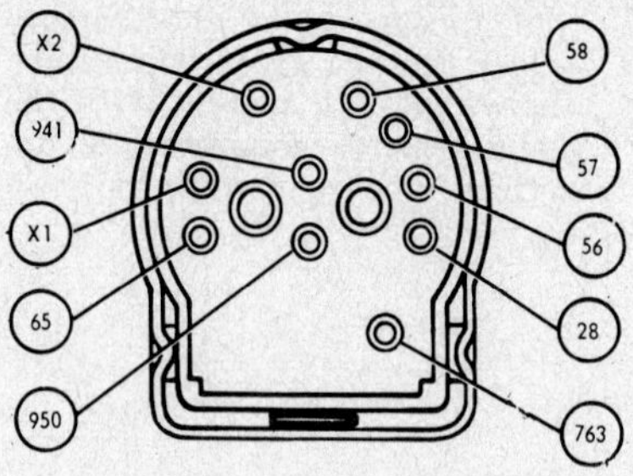
X2
58
941
57
X1
56
65
28
950
763

SWITCH POSITION	CONTINUITY BETWEEN TERMINALS
OFF (PARK)	65-763 28-56 X1-X2
INTERMITTENT	65-763 56-57 56-X2
LOW	X1-X2 – (100-900 ohms @ 1st detent and up to 7000 ohms through 10 detents.) 65-763 56-57 56-X1-X2
HIGH	65-763 57-58 58-X1-X2
WASHER ON	941-950

1970 Lincoln/Early Production switch test (© Ford Motor Co)

(INTERMTTTENT SYSTEM)

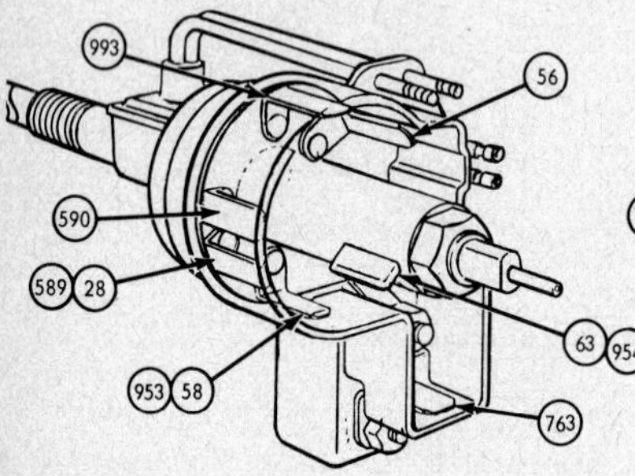
993
56
590
589
28
63
954
953
58
763

SWITCH POSITION	CONTINUITY BETWEEN TERMINALS
Off (Park)	63-763 28-58
Low	58-63-763
High	56-63-763
Intermittent	63-763 56-993 58-590
Washer On	953-954

(STANDARD SYSTEM)

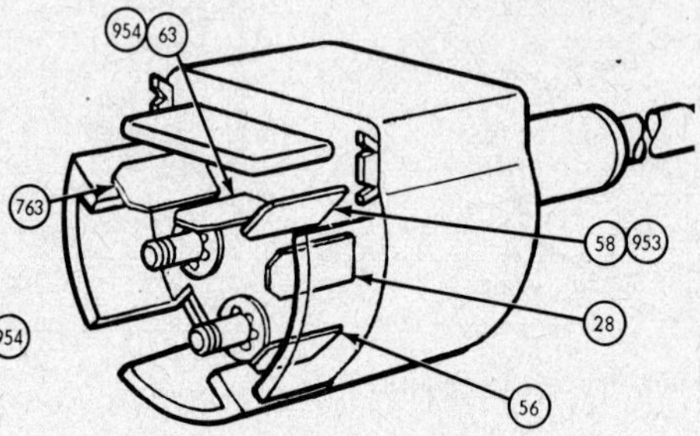
954
63
763
58
953
28
56

SWITCH POSITION	CONTINUITY BETWEEN TERMINALS
Off (Park)	63-763 28-58
Low	58-63-763
High	56-63-763
Washer On	953-954

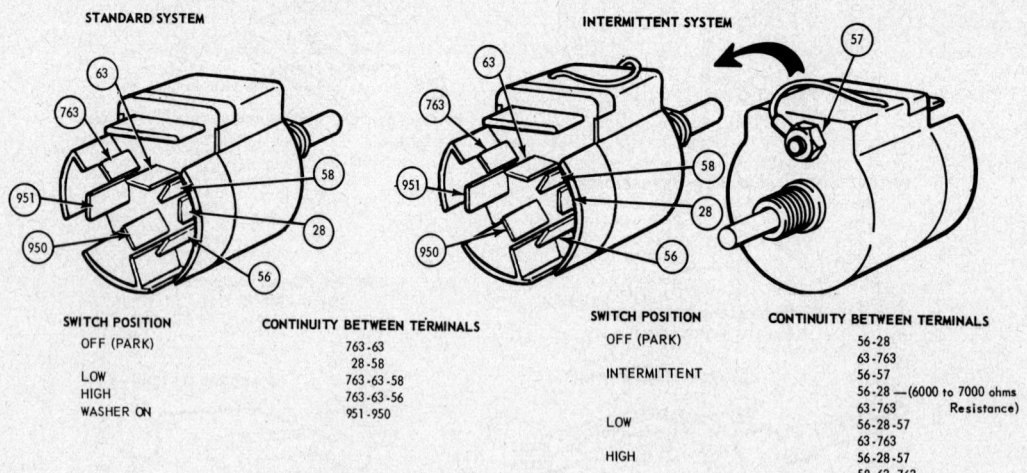

1967-68 Mercury switch test (© Ford Motor Co)

STANDARD SYSTEM

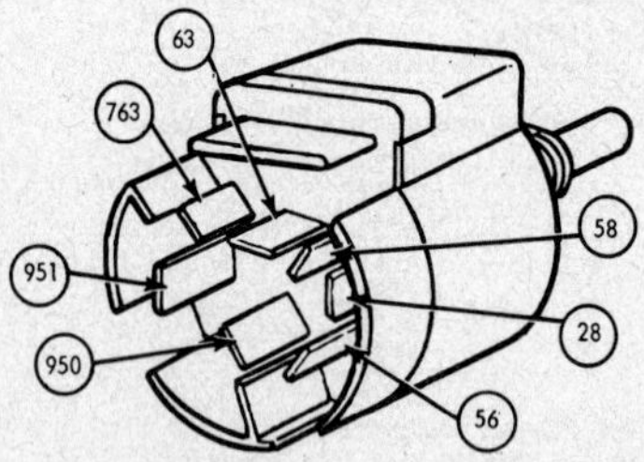
63
763
58
951
28
950
56

SWITCH POSITION	CONTINUITY BETWEEN TERMINALS
OFF (PARK)	763-63 28-58
LOW	763-63-58
HIGH	763-63-56
WASHER ON	951-950

INTERMITTENT SYSTEM

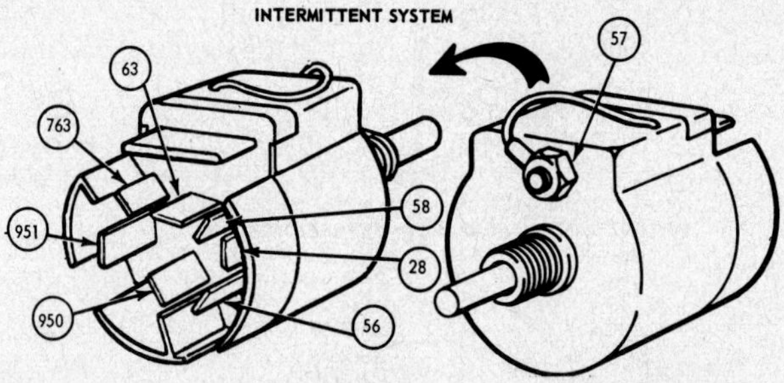
57
63
763
58
951
28
950
56

SWITCH POSITION	CONTINUITY BETWEEN TERMINALS
OFF (PARK)	56-28 63-763
INTERMITTENT	56-57 56-28 —(6000 to 7000 ohms Resistance) 63-763
LOW	56-28-57 63-763
HIGH	56-28-57 58-63-763

1969-70 Compact and Intermediate switch test (© Ford Motor Co)

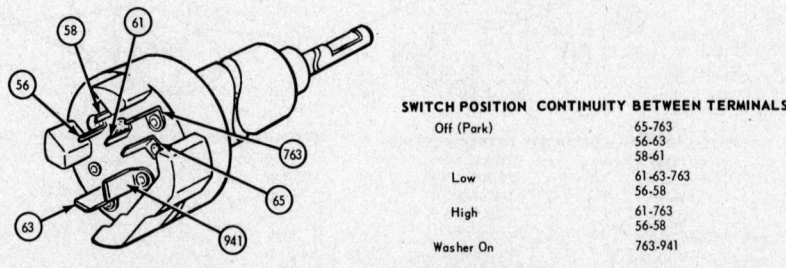

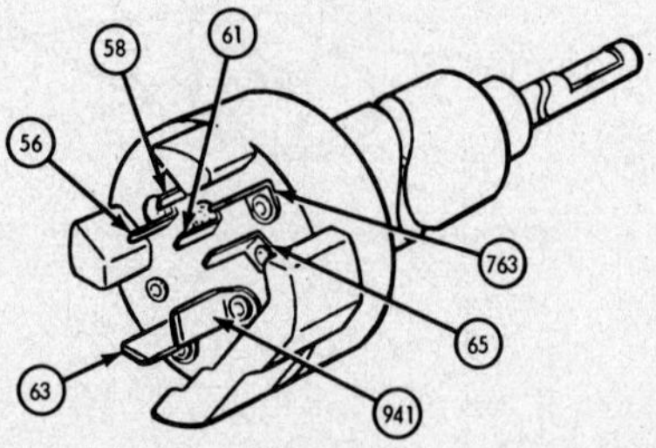
58
61
56
763
65
63
941

SWITCH POSITION	CONTINUITY BETWEEN TERMINALS
Off (Park)	65-763 56-63 58-61
Low	61-63-763 56-58
High	61-763 56-58
Washer On	763-941

1967-68 Ford switch test
(© Ford Motor Co)

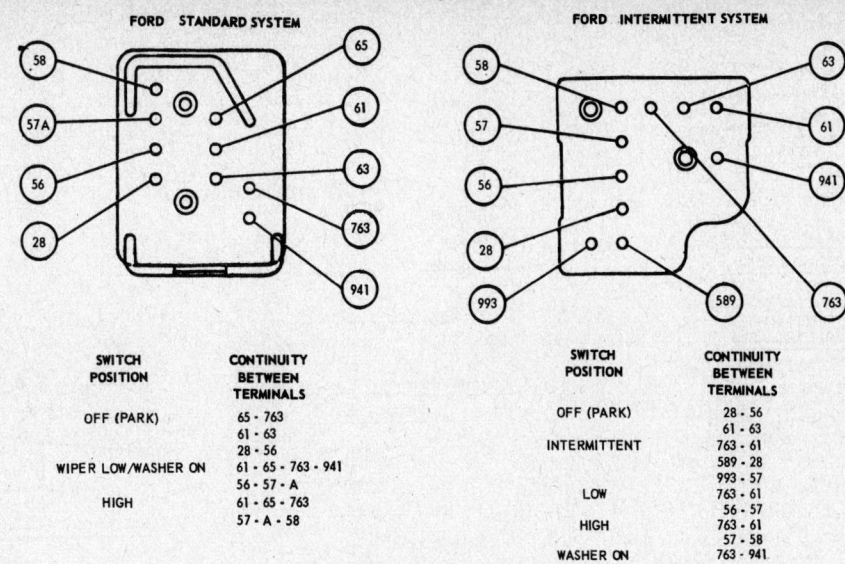

FORD STANDARD SYSTEM

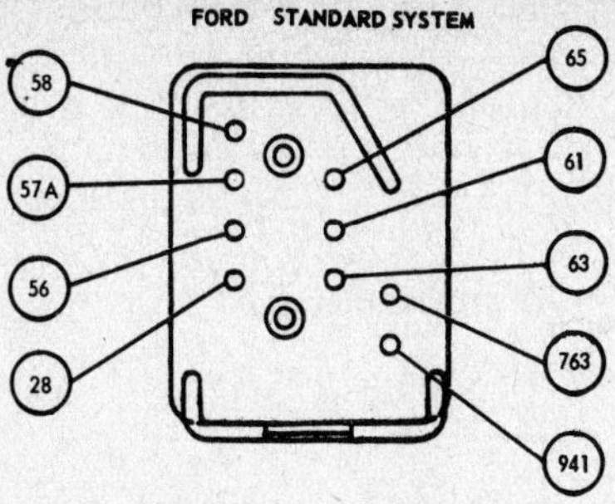
58
57A
56
28
65
61
63
763
941

SWITCH POSITION	CONTINUITY BETWEEN TERMINALS
OFF (PARK)	65 - 763
	61 - 63
	28 - 56
WIPER LOW/WASHER ON	61 - 65 - 763 - 941
	56 - 57 - A
HIGH	61 - 65 - 763
	57 - A - 58

FORD INTERMITTENT SYSTEM

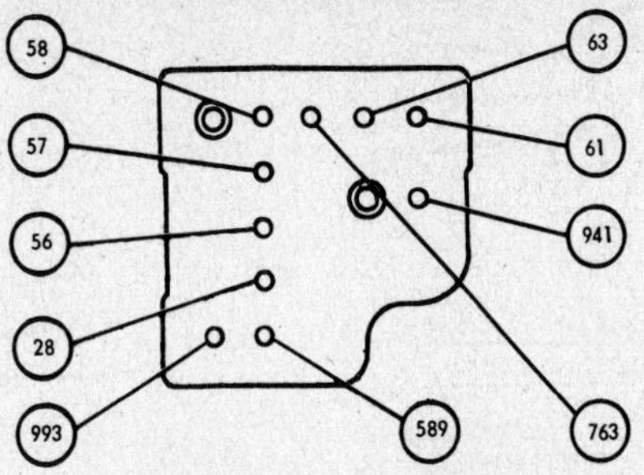
58
57
56
28
993
589
763
63
61
941

SWITCH POSITION	CONTINUITY BETWEEN TERMINALS
OFF (PARK)	28 - 56
	61 - 63
INTERMITTENT	763 - 61
	589 - 28
	993 - 57
LOW	763 - 61
	56 - 57
HIGH	763 - 61
	57 - 58
WASHER ON	763 - 941

1969-70 Ford switch test
(© Ford Motor Co)

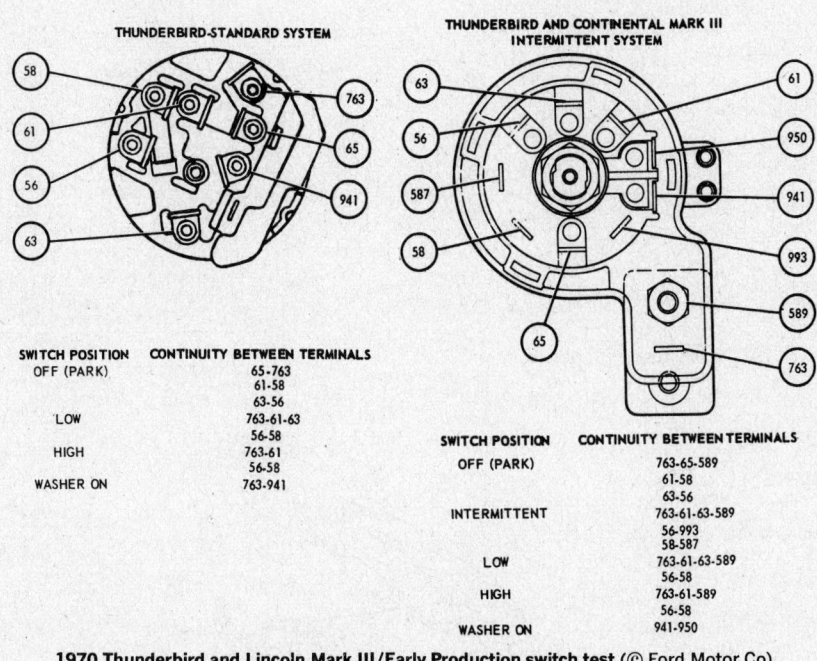

THUNDERBIRD-STANDARD SYSTEM

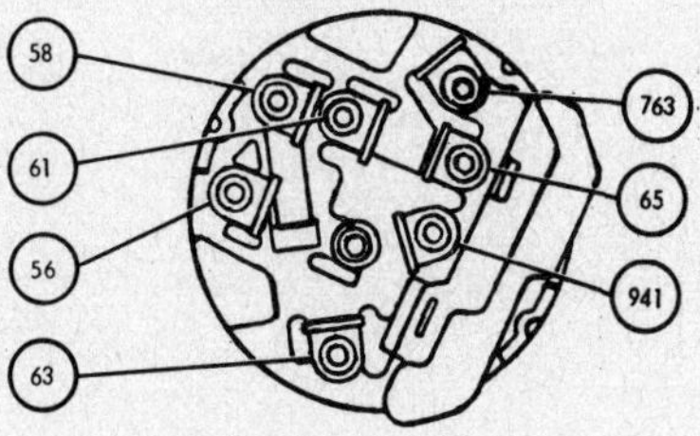
58
61
56
63
763
65
941

SWITCH POSITION	CONTINUITY BETWEEN TERMINALS
OFF (PARK)	65-763
	61-58
	63-56
LOW	763-61-63
	56-58
HIGH	763-61
	56-58
WASHER ON	763-941

THUNDERBIRD AND CONTINENTAL MARK III INTERMITTENT SYSTEM

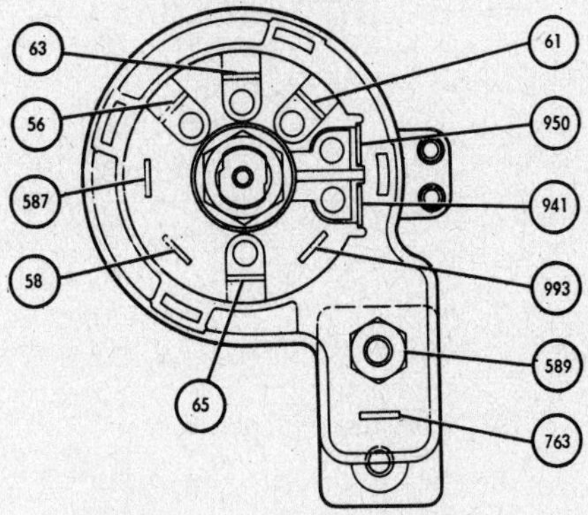
63
56
587
58
65
61
950
941
993
589
763

SWITCH POSITION	CONTINUITY BETWEEN TERMINALS
OFF (PARK)	763-65-589
	61-58
	63-56
INTERMITTENT	763-61-63-589
	56-993
	58-587
LOW	763-61-63-589
	56-58
HIGH	763-61-589
	56-58
WASHER ON	941-950

1970 Thunderbird and Lincoln Mark III/Early Production switch test (© Ford Motor Co)

MERCURY - STANDARD SYSTEM

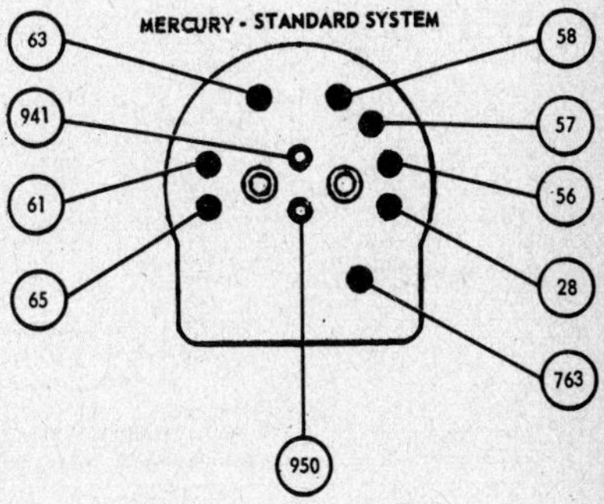
63
941
61
65
58
57
56
28
763
950

SWITCH POSITION	CONTINUITY BETWEEN TERMINALS
OFF (PARK)	763 - 65
	61 - 63
	28 - 56
LOW	763 - 61 - 65
	56 - 57
HIGH	763 - 61 - 65
	57 - 58
WASHER ON	763 - 65
	941 - 950

1969-70 Mercury switch test
(© Ford Motor Co)

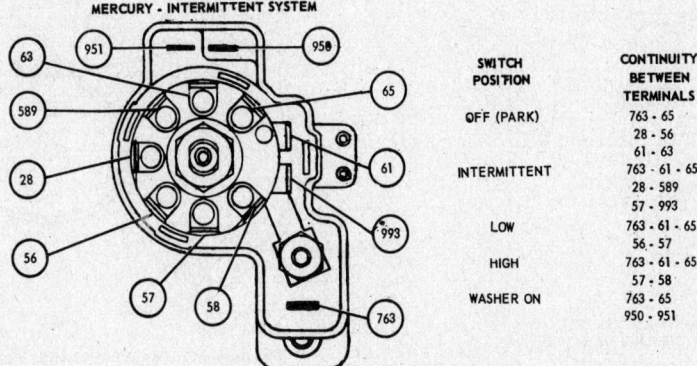

MERCURY - INTERMITTENT SYSTEM

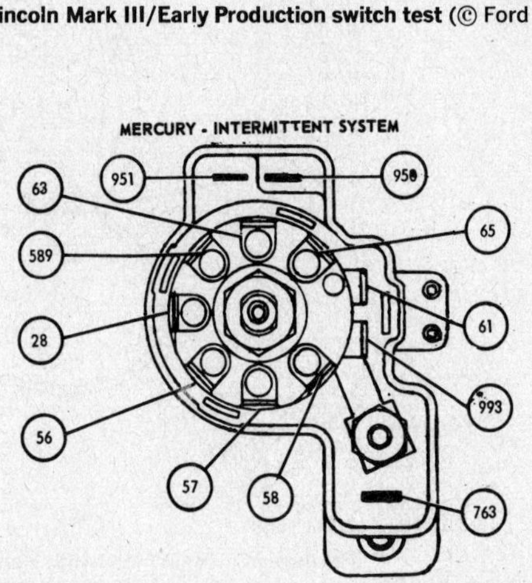
951
950
63
589
28
56
57
58
65
61
993
763

SWITCH POSITION	CONTINUITY BETWEEN TERMINALS
OFF (PARK)	763 - 65
	28 - 56
	61 - 63
INTERMITTENT	763 - 61 - 65
	28 - 589
	57 - 993
LOW	763 - 61 - 65
	56 - 57
HIGH	763 - 61 - 65
	57 - 58
WASHER ON	763 - 65
	950 - 951

1969-70 Mercury switch test
(© Ford Motor Co)

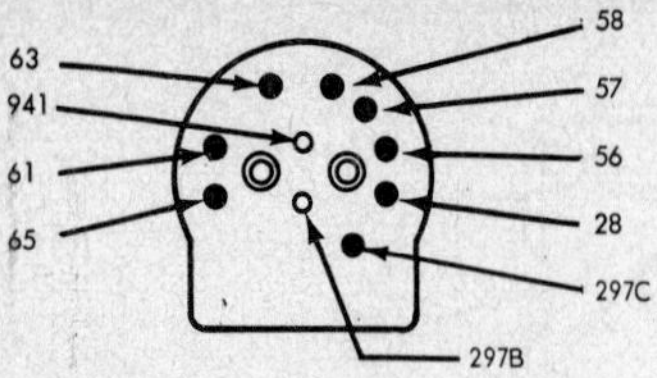
63
941
61
65
58
57
56
28
297C
297B

FORD, MERCURY, METEOR AND LINCOLN
STANDARD EQUIPMENT AND 2 SPEED

SWITCH POSITION	CONTINUITY BETWEEN TERMINALS
OFF (PARK)	61-63 28-56 65-297
LOW	61-65-297 56-57
HIGH	57-58 65-297-61
WASH	941-298-LINCOLN 941-296-FORD, MERCURY, METEOR

INTERMITTENT

SWITCH POSITION	CONTINUITY BETWEEN TERMINALS
OFF (PARK)	28-56 65-297 61-63
LOW	56-61-63-57 65-297
HIGH	65-297 57-58-61-63
INTERMITTENT	56-57-63 65-297 VARIABLE RESISTANCE BETWEEN 61 AND 63-MIN. 100-900 ohms MAX. 5600-8400 ohms
WASH	298-941 LINCOLN 941-296 FORD, MERCURY, METEOR

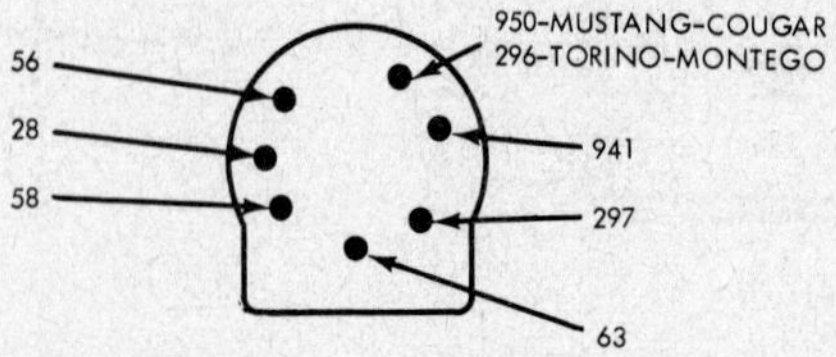
56
28
58
950-MUSTANG-COUGAR
296-TORINO-MONTEGO
941
297
63

MUSTANG-COUGAR-TORINO-MONTEGO
INTERMITTENT

SWITCH POSITION	CONTINUITY BETWEEN TERMINALS
OFF (PARK)	28-56 63-297
LOW	63-297 56-57-28
HIGH	56-57-28 58-63-297
INTERMITTENT	63-297 56-57 VARIABLE RESISTANCE BETWEEN 28-57-MIN. 100-900 ohms MAX. 5600-8400 ohms
WASH	296-941

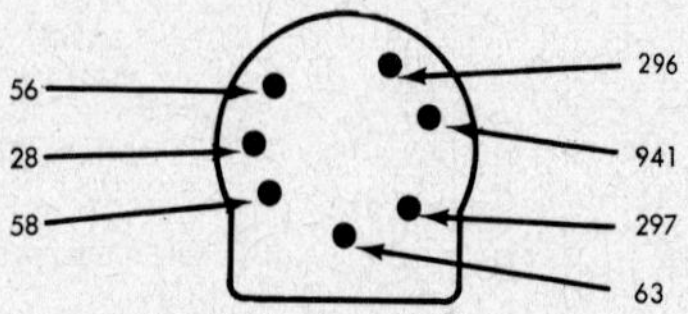
56
28
58
296
941
297
63

MUSTANG-COUGAR-MAVERICK TORINO-COMET
2-SPEED

SWITCH POSITION	CONTINUITY BETWEEN TERMINALS
OFF (PARK)	297-63 28-58
LOW	297-58-63
HIGH	297-63-56
WASH	296-941

1971 switch test (© Ford Motor Co)

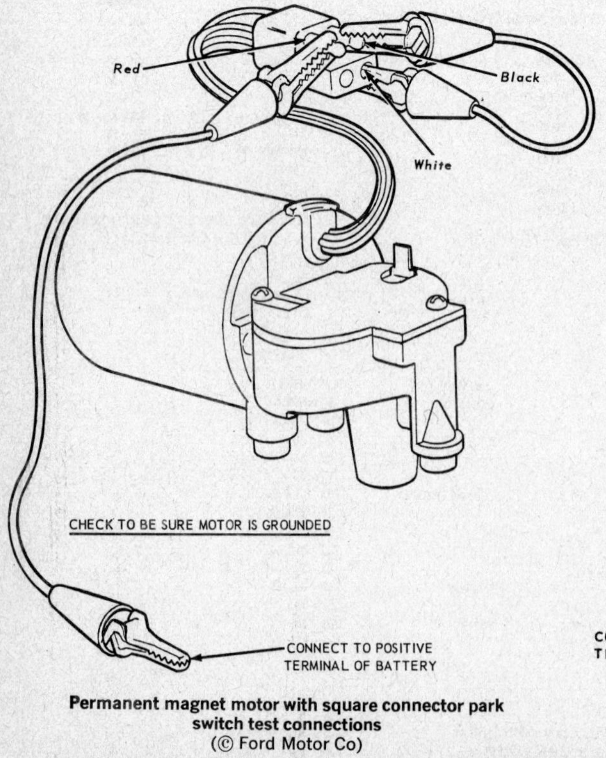
Red
Black
White
CHECK TO BE SURE MOTOR IS GROUNDED
CONNECT TO POSITIVE
TERMINAL OF BATTERY

Permanent magnet motor with square connector park switch test connections
(© Ford Motor Co)

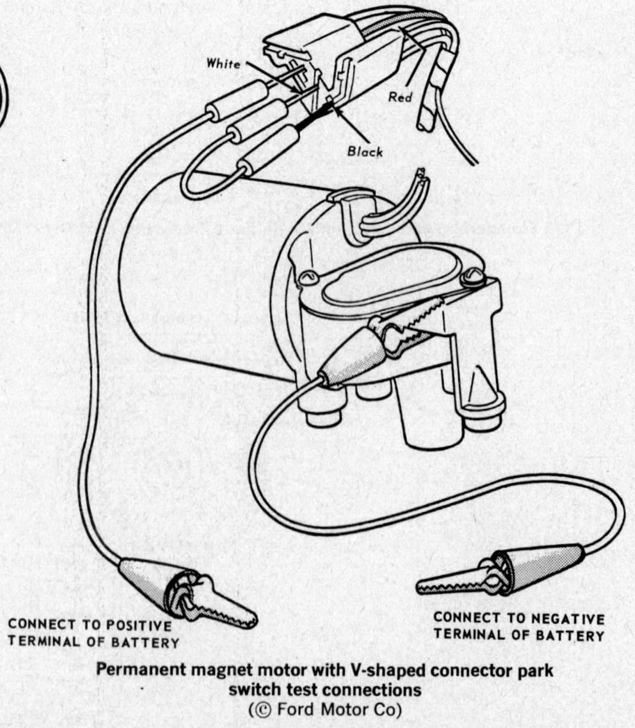
White
Red
Black
CONNECT TO POSITIVE
TERMINAL OF BATTERY
CONNECT TO NEGATIVE
TERMINAL OF BATTERY

Permanent magnet motor with V-shaped connector park switch test connections
(© Ford Motor Co)

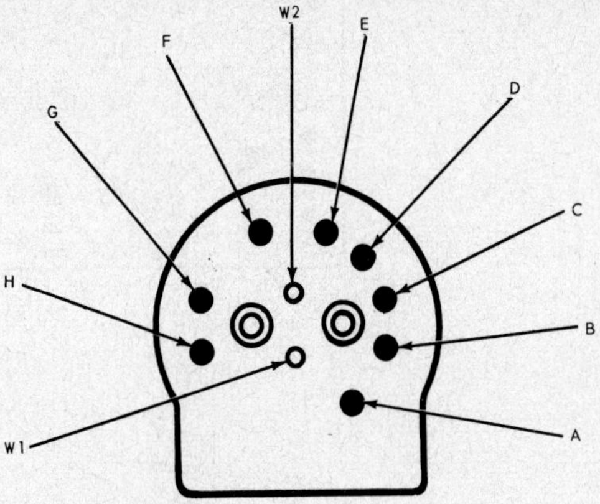
W2
F
E
G
D
C
H
B
W1
A

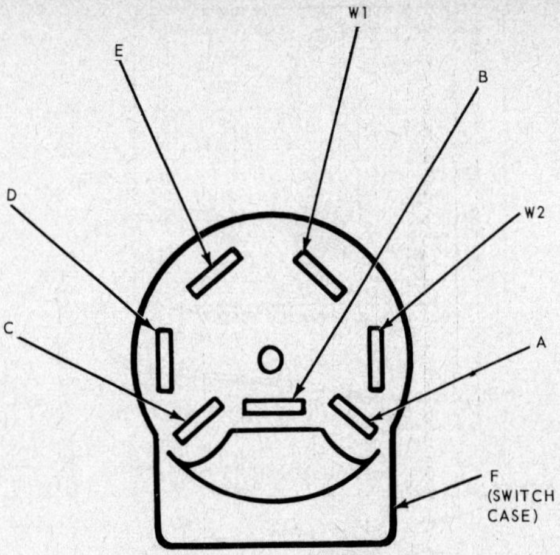
W1
E
B
D
W2
C
A
F
(SWITCH
CASE)

PIN-TYPE SWITCH
STANDARD EQUIPMENT (2 SPEED)

SWITCH POSITION	CONTINUITY BETWEEN TERMINALS
OFF (PARK)	B-C A-H F-G
LOW	C-D A-G-H
HIGH	D-E A-G-H
WASH	W,-W2

INTERMITTENT

SWITCH POSITION	CONTINUITY BETWEEN TERMINALS
OFF (PARK)	B-C A-H F-G
LOW	C-D-F-G A-H
HIGH	D-E-F-G A-H
INTERMITTENT	A-H C-D-F VARIABLE RESISTANCE BETWEEN F AND G-MIN. 100-900 ohms MAX. 5600-8400 ohms
WASH	W1-W2

BLADE-TYPE SWITCH (2 SPEED)

SWITCH POSITION	CONTINUITY BETWEEN TERMINALS
OFF (PARK)	C-D A-B
LOW	A-B-C
HIGH	A-B-E
WASH	W1-W2

INTERMITTENT

SWITCH POSITION	CONTINUITY BETWEEN TERMINALS
OFF (PARK)	A-B D-E
LOW	A-B D-E-F
HIGH	D-E-F A-B-C
INTERMITTENT	63-297 E-F 56-57 A-B VARIABLE RESISTANCE BETWEEN D-E-MIN. 100-900 ohms MAX. 5600-8400 ohms
WASH	296-941

1972-73 Ford wiper switch continuity test (© Ford Motor Co)

SLIDE WIPER SWITCH CONTINUITY TEST

STANDARD SWITCH

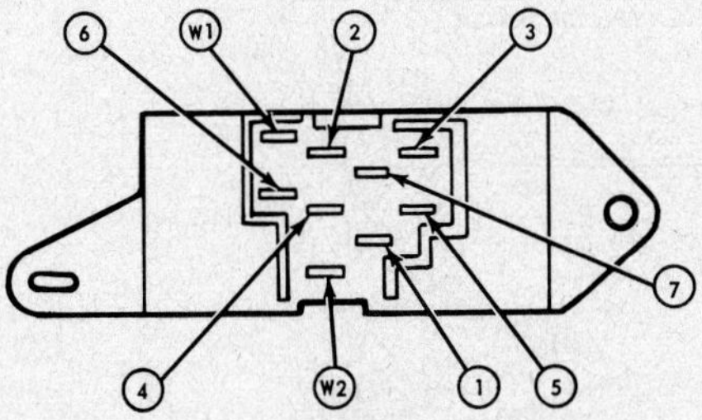
6
W1
2
3
7
4
W2
1
5

SWITCH POSITION	CONTINUITY BETWEEN TERMINALS
OFF	1-5, 3-7
LO	1-4, 2-7
HI	1-4, 2-6
WASH	W1-W2

* RESISTANCE BETWEEN TERMINALS F AND C VARIES FROM 500Ω ± 400 AT MIN. DWELL TO 10KΩ ± 20% AT MAX. DWELL

INTERMITTENT SWITCH

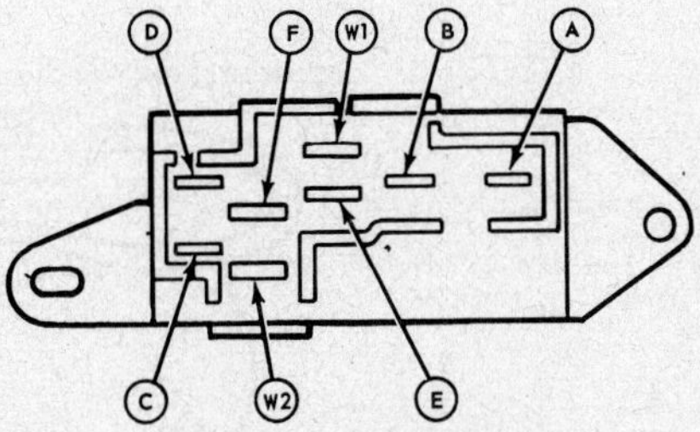
D
F
W1
B
A
C
W2
E

SWITCH POSITION	CONTINUITY BETWEEN TERMINALS
OFF	A-E
INT.	B-E-F, *
LO	B-E-F-C
HI	D-B-F-C
WASH	W1-W2

SLIDE WIPER/WASHER SWITCH

1973 Ford sliding wiper switch continuity test (© Ford Motor Co)

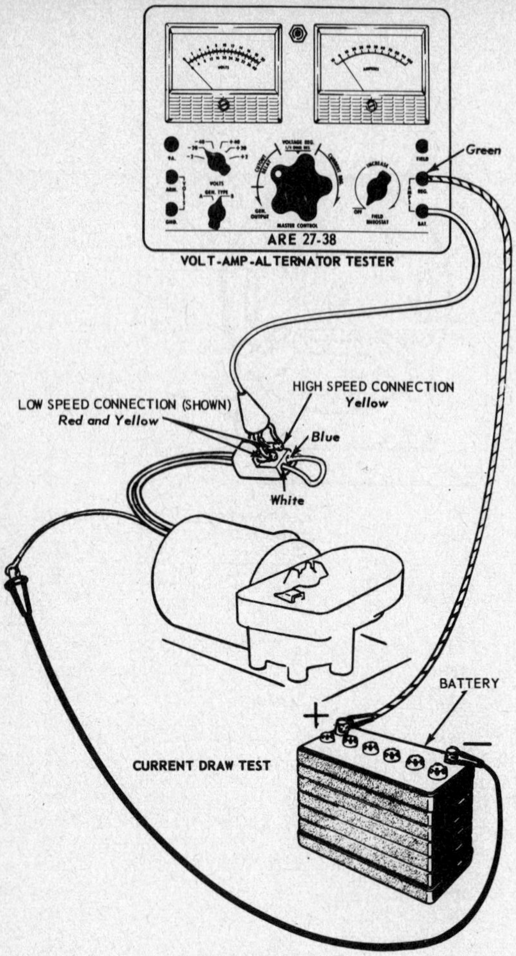
ARE 27-38
VOLT-AMP-ALTERNATOR TESTER
Green
HIGH SPEED CONNECTION
Yellow
LOW SPEED CONNECTION (SHOWN)
Red and Yellow
Blue
White
BATTERY
CURRENT DRAW TEST

Test connections for current draw test on Ford oscillating wiper motor
(© Ford Motor Co)

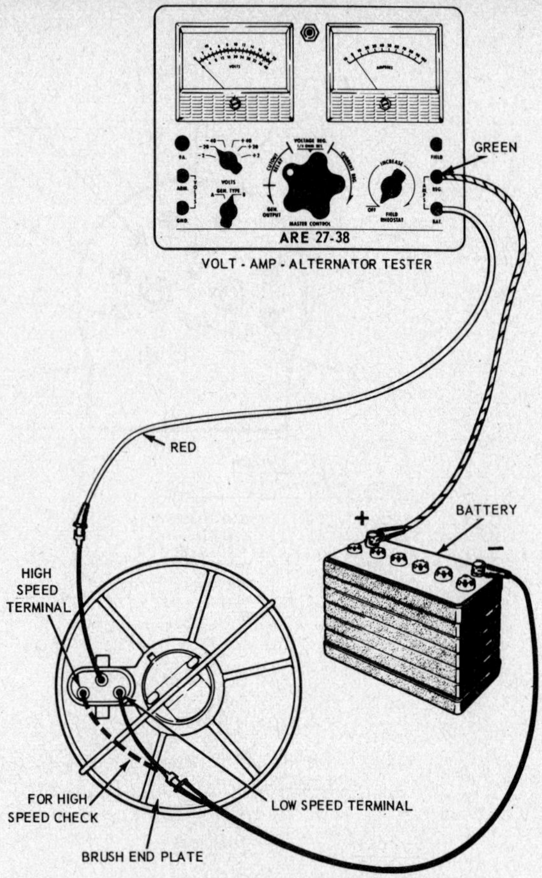
ARE 27-38
VOLT - AMP - ALTERNATOR TESTER
GREEN
RED
BATTERY
HIGH SPEED TERMINAL
FOR HIGH SPEED CHECK
LOW SPEED TERMINAL
BRUSH END PLATE

Test connections for current draw test on Ford depressed park permanent magnet wiper motor
(© Ford Motor Co)

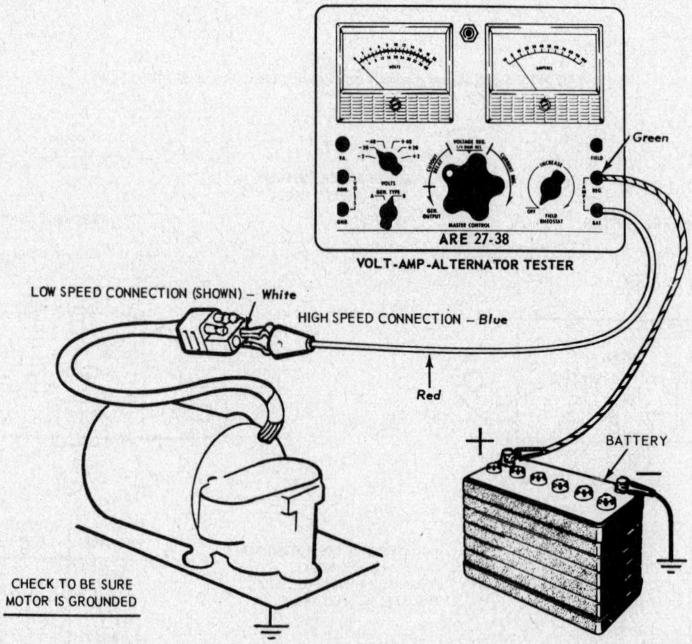
ARE 27-38
VOLT-AMP-ALTERNATOR TESTER
Green
LOW SPEED CONNECTION (SHOWN) – White
HIGH SPEED CONNECTION – Blue
Red
BATTERY
CHECK TO BE SURE MOTOR IS GROUNDED

Test connections for current draw test on Ford non-depressed park permanent magnet wiper motor
(© Ford Motor Co)

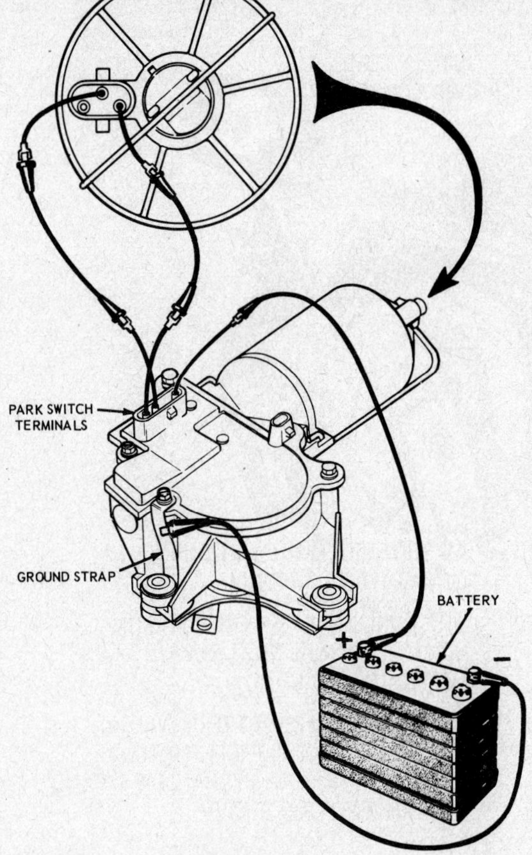
PARK SWITCH TERMINALS
GROUND STRAP
BATTERY
+
–
1969-71 depressed park wiper motor park switch test
(© Ford Motor Co)

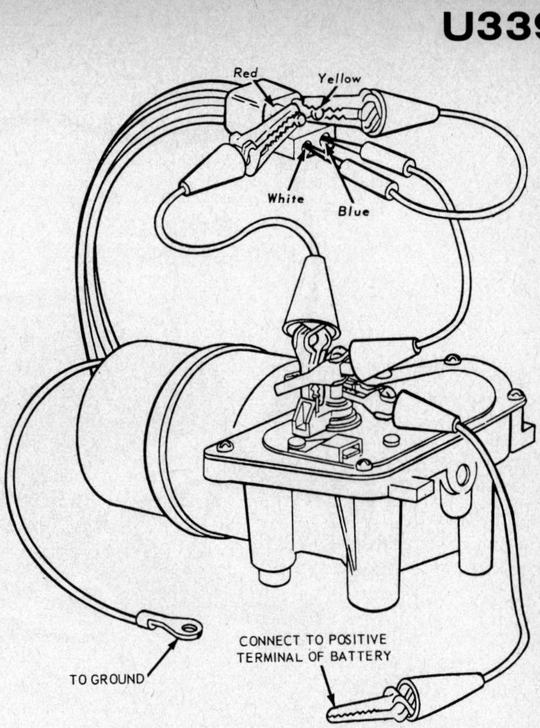
Red
Yellow
White
Blue
CONNECT TO POSITIVE TERMINAL OF BATTERY
TO GROUND
Oscillating motor park switch test connections
(© Ford Motor Co)

General Motors

Rectangular Wiper Motor Test

1. Disconnect the lead wires from the wiper motor.
2. Connect a jumper wire from the positive battery terminal to the No. 2 terminal on the wiper motor.
3. Connect a jumper wire from the No. 1 terminal on the motor to ground.
4. Connect a jumper wire from the No. 3 terminal to ground. The wipers should operate at low speed.
5. Remove the jumper wire installed in Step No. 4. The wiper motor should operate at high speed.
6. Remove the jumper wire installed in Step No. 3. Connect a jumper wire from the No. 1 terminal on the wiper motor to the No. 3 terminal. The wipers should park.

This procedure isolates the wiper motor and linkage from the rest of the windshield wiper system. If the wipers operated correctly with the jumper wires in place, but do not operate correctly when controlled by the wiper switch, the wiper switch or wiring is defective. If the wipers did not operate properly with the jumpers in place, the wiper motor

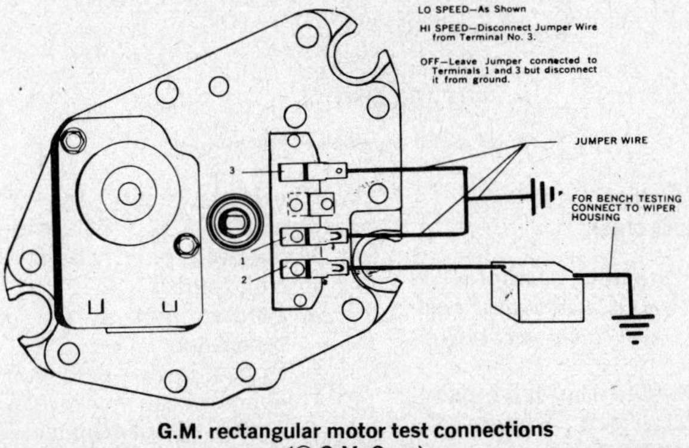
LO SPEED—As Shown
HI SPEED—Disconnect Jumper Wire from Terminal No. 3.
OFF—Leave Jumper connected to Terminals 1 and 3 but disconnect it from ground.
JUMPER WIRE
FOR BENCH TESTING CONNECT TO WIPER HOUSING
3
1
2
G.M. rectangular motor test connections
(© G.M. Corp)

is defective or the linkage is loose or binding.

Round Wiper Motor Test

Wiper Motor Does Not Operate

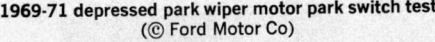

1. Remove washer pump (if so equipped) to gain access to relay switch assembly.
2. Connect 12-volt source to wiper, positive side to center terminal, ground side to gear housing. Do not connect jumper to terminal 1 and 3.
3. To determine if relay coil is open, connect test lamp to wiper terminal No. 1. Test lamp should light.
4. Test relay switch as follows:
   a. If gear mechanism is in full park position, insert a small screwdriver into the switch slot (between the drive pawl and the relay latch arm) and push relay latch arm down and toward the relay coil in the direction of the arrow. Next, remove a small amount of insulation from black lead with pink tracer and touch test lamp to exposed wire.
   b. If test lamp lights but motor doesn't run, proceed to Step 5.
   c. If test lamp doesn't light, relay switch is defective. NOTE: *cover exposed wire with tape after the test.*
5. Disassemble motor section and check for the following:
   a. Hung or sticking brush.
   b. Loose solder connections at brush holders.
   c. Loose splice joints at field coil connections to leads.
   d. Open armature.
   e. Poor circuit breaker ground

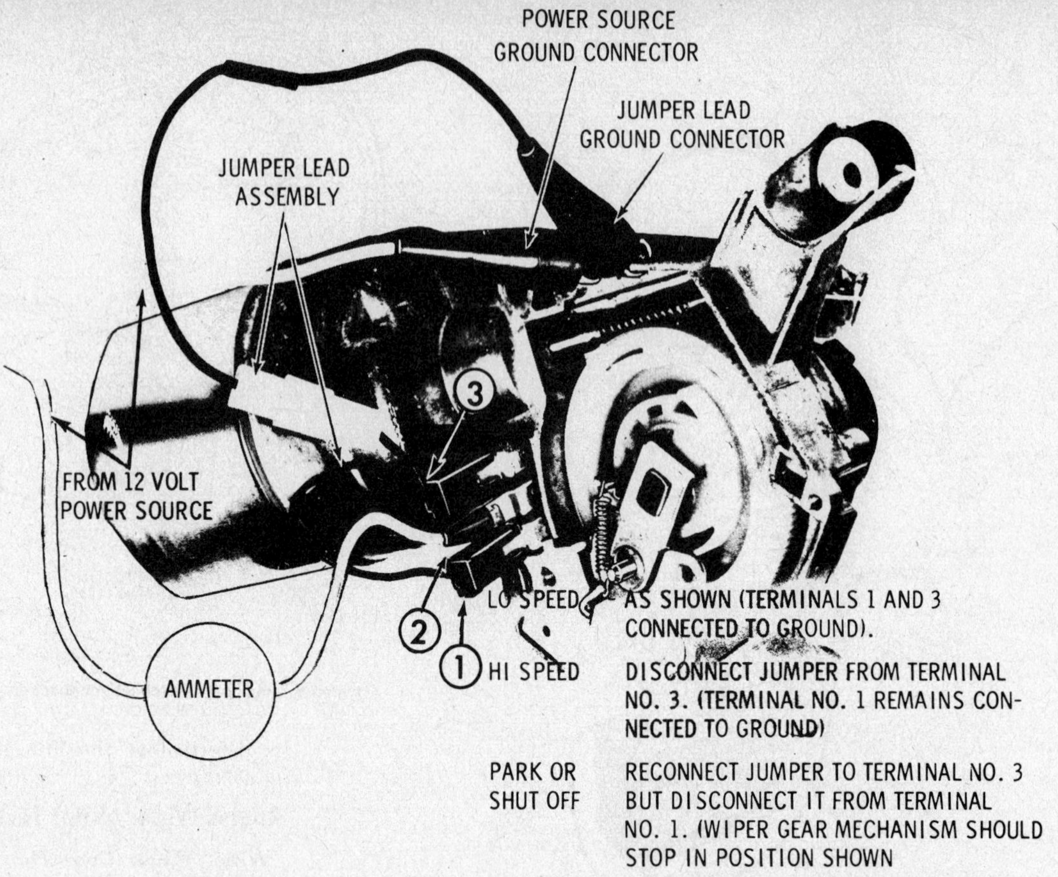
POWER SOURCE
GROUND CONNECTOR
JUMPER LEAD
GROUND CONNECTOR
JUMPER LEAD
ASSEMBLY
FROM 12 VOLT
POWER SOURCE
AMMETER
3
2
1
LO SPEED
AS SHOWN (TERMINALS 1 AND 3
CONNECTED TO GROUND).
HI SPEED
DISCONNECT JUMPER FROM TERMINAL
NO. 3. (TERMINAL NO. 1 REMAINS CON-
NECTED TO GROUND)
PARK OR
SHUT OFF
RECONNECT JUMPER TO TERMINAL NO. 3
BUT DISCONNECT IT FROM TERMINAL
NO. 1. (WIPER GEAR MECHANISM SHOULD
STOP IN POSITION SHOWN

G.M. round wiper motor test connections (© G.M. Corp)

connection on field lamination. To check the circuit breaker, disassemble motor section of wiper and visually inspect the circuit breaker for dirty or burned contacts, or loose connections to circuit breaker terminals.

Wipers Will Not Shut Off (Crankarm Rotates 360°)

1. Check to see if the relay latch arm spring is connected properly.
2. Manually operate the latch arm to check it for possible binding condition.
3. If the items in steps one and two check out, connect a power source to the wiper and connect the jumper wire from terminal no. 3 to the wiper housing. DO NOT make any connections from terminal no. 1. Manually actuate the latch arm in the direction of the arrow and see if it remains in the energized position (inside plastic switch housing out of path of gear drive pawl). If it remains in the energized position, check for a grounded red lead from the coil to terminal no. 1. If the red lead is not grounded, the coil is probably grounded internally and the relay switch should be replaced.

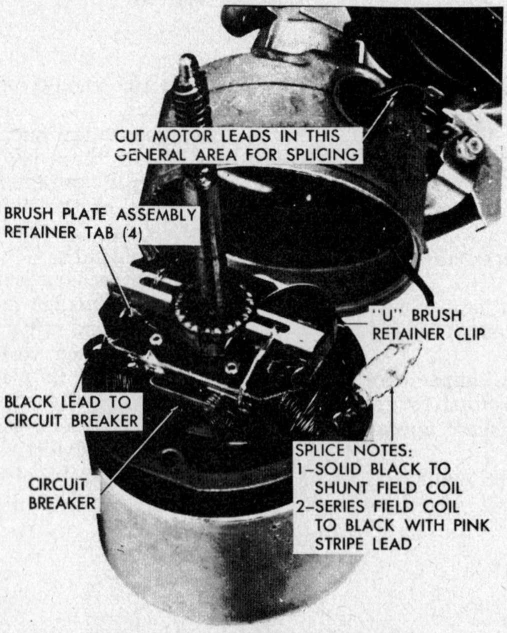
CUT MOTOR LEADS IN THIS
GENERAL AREA FOR SPLICING
BRUSH PLATE ASSEMBLY
RETAINER TAB (4)
"U" BRUSH
RETAINER CLIP
BLACK LEAD TO
CIRCUIT BREAKER
CIRCUIT
BREAKER
SPLICE NOTES:
1-SOLID BLACK TO
SHUNT FIELD COIL
2-SERIES FIELD COIL
TO BLACK WITH PINK
STRIPE LEAD

G.M. round motor brush plate assembly (© G.M. Corp)

Wipers Will Not Shut Off (Recycles)

NOTE: the crankarm oscillates in a horizontal plane and is accompanied by a loud knock with each revolution of the gear.

1. Check to see that the drive pawl and relay latch arm springs are properly connected.
2. Check the wiper for low-speed operation. If the wiper has high-speed only, check the following items:
   a. Solder joint at no. 3 wiper terminal.
   b. Splice joint—field coil cross-over splice.
   c. Splice joint—black lead to field coil.

3. Check relay switch as follows:
   a. Remove a small amount of insulation from the black lead with pink stripe and connect a test light between the exposed wire and the wiper housing.
   b. Connect the positive side of the power source to terminal no. 2 and the negative side to the motor case. Install a jumper wire from terminal no. 1 to the motor case. Observe whether the test light goes out once for each revolution of the gear, or if the light glows steadily. If the light glows steadily, the relay switch contacts are not opening and the switch is defective. If the light goes out each time the drive pawl moves into the relay switch slot, the relay switch is functioning correctly.

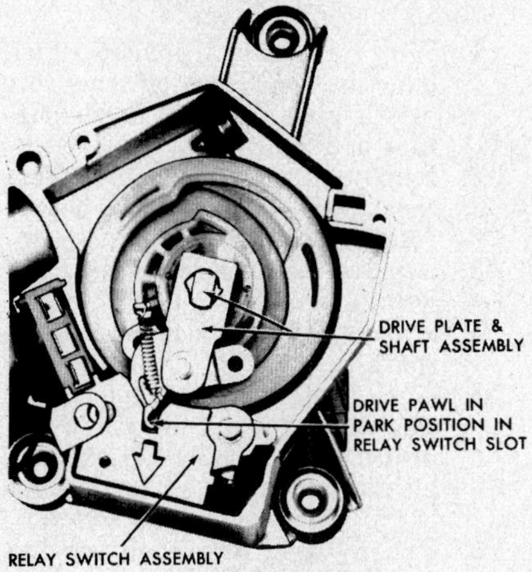
DRIVE PLATE &
SHAFT ASSEMBLY
DRIVE PAWL IN
PARK POSITION IN
RELAY SWITCH SLOT
RELAY SWITCH ASSEMBLY

Relay switch test
(© G.M. Corp)

Wipers Operate on Low-Speed Only

1. Check for a grounded condition in the wiper internal black lead that connects to wiper terminal no. 3.
2. Disassemble the motor section of the wiper and check for a grounded shunt field coil.

Wiper Operation Intermittent

1. Check the solder connections at the wiper terminal board.
2. Connect the wiper to operate in low-speed. Connect an ammeter (range 0-30 amps) in the feed wire circuit to the wiper and observe current draw. Allow the motor to run until it becomes hot.
   a. If current draw is normal and the wiper cycles on and off, a weak circuit breaker is indicated. Replace the brush plate assembly.
   b. If current draw exceeds specification, proceed to steps three, four, and five.
3. Adjust the armature endplay as required and recheck current draw.
4. Adjust the gear assembly endplay as required and recheck current draw.
5. If the adjustments in steps three and four fail to correct an excessive current draw condition, disassemble the motor section of the wiper and check the armature for a shorted or grounded condition.

Wiper Motor Repairs and Adjustments

This section contains repair and adjustment procedures for those motors on which these operations can be performed. On some wiper motors, no adjustments or repairs can be performed.

American Motors

1967-72 Electric Motor Park Switch Adjustment

To adjust the park switch, the wiper motor must be removed from the car.

When the motor is in the park position, the motor crank arm should be approximately 13° above a horizontal line from the crank drive. The horizontal line should be parallel to the base of the worm drive housing. The actuator cam must be installed with the letter R facing away from the motor.

The park switch can be adjusted by moving the adjustment tab. Do not move the tab beyond the range shown in the illustration.

Incorrect installation of the park switch plate will cause incorrect parking of the wiper blades. When the contact plate is installed, the stud on the plate must be positioned between the tabs on the wiper motor output gear.

1973 Electric Motor

See Ford Permanent Magnet Motor.

Chrysler Variable and Three Speed Motors

Gear and Park Switch Replacement

1. Run motor out of park to close hook and to prevent damage to park switch. If motor does not run check for open or excessive current. See Motor Testing.
2. Remove the five switch plate screws and ground strap.
3. Carefully remove park switch plate and gasket. Hook should be closed, as shown. If the latch is open, motor is unlatched, and the latch assembly must be replaced.
4. Remove the motor from the car if required to gain adequate clearance to replace park switch.
5. Remove gear and latch assembly from gear box.
6. Inspect all components for damage or wear paying special attention to the following:
   a. Bent parking switch blade.
   b. Melted switch cam.
   c. Chipped, scraped or broken islands.
   d. Chipped or scraped inner or outer cam.
   e. Bent hook where it latches to inner cam.
   f. Loose hook.

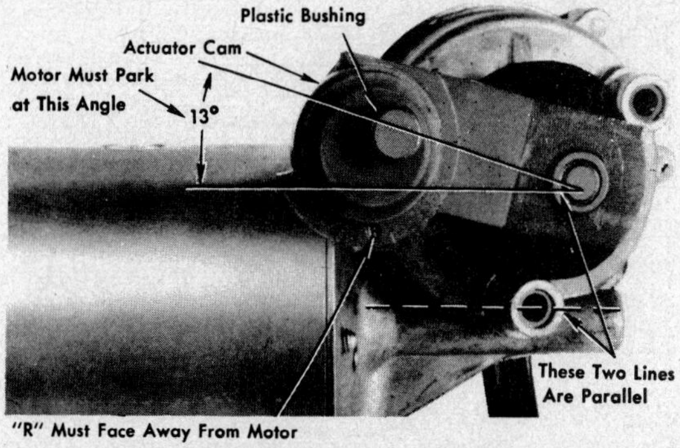
Plastic Bushing
Actuator Cam
Motor Must Park
at This Angle
13°
These Two Lines
Are Parallel
"R" Must Face Away From Motor

Crank arm in the park position
(© American Motors Corp)

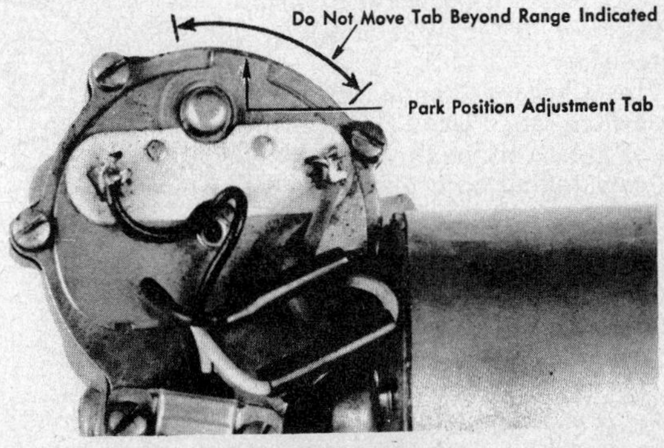
Do Not Move Tab Beyond Range Indicated
Park Position Adjustment Tab

Park switch tab adjustment
(© American Motors Corp)

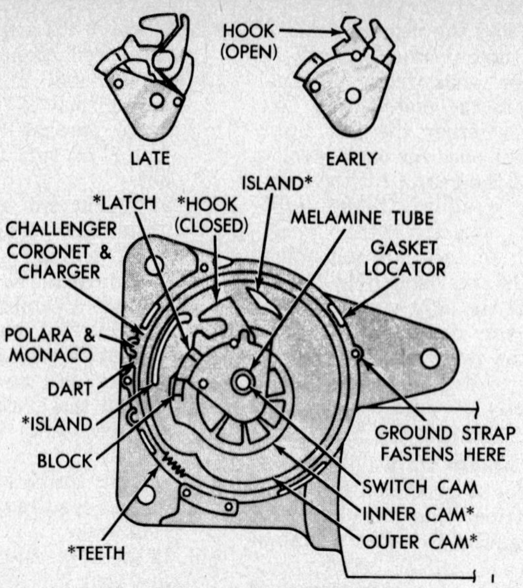
HOOK
(OPEN)
LATE
EARLY
ISLAND*
*LATCH
*HOOK
(CLOSED)
MELAMINE TUBE
CHALLENGER
CORONET &
CHARGER
GASKET
LOCATOR
POLARA &
MONACO
DART
*ISLAND
BLOCK
GROUND STRAP
FASTENS HERE
SWITCH CAM
INNER CAM*
OUTER CAM*
*TEETH

Gear and park switch replacement
(© Chrysler Corp)

g. High reinforcement pin in inner cam.

NOTE: when replacing components, lubricate all areas marked (*) *and metal surfaces with lubricant contained in package.*

7. Unsolder switch plate leads. Solder leads to new switch plate, making sure the two green leads are together in their original location.
8. Insert latch assembly into gear. The early latch assembly is to be inserted open. Rotate the early latch assembly counterclockwise until it stops against the block. Rotate the hook counterclockwise until it closes against the latch. Closing the latch should require some force. Re-examine latch and gear at this time if they do not fit snugly. The latch assembly is spring loaded and inserted closed with the latch against the block as shown. The late latch assembly may be used with either a steel inner cam (preferred) or the plastic inner cam. Insert gear and latch assembly, with washer between gear and gearbox, with the gear approximately in the position as shown.

NOTE: the gear and latch assembly must be in the position shown with the latch closed when the switch plate is installed to prevent damage to switch plate.

9. Install the melamine tube on the switch cam. Place a small amount of grease on the tip of the switch cam taking care to keep grease off the melamine tube.
10. Install the gasket with the slot over the gasket locator.
11. Rotate the rocker arm lever, which is riveted to the switch plate, counterclockwise to its stop. Install the switch plate so that the tab aligns with the correct notch as indicated. Replace the five screws, making sure the ground strap is under the screw next to the gasket locator.
12. Bench test motor. Motor must be grounded when bench testing.
13. Install motor.

Ford Permanent Magnet Motor

Cover and Switch Assembly —1969 and Later Models

Remove the four cover retaining screws to remove the assembly. Replace with the appropriate kit. Be sure to reassemble the ground strap under the cover screw. Use the new screws supplied with the kit and tighten to 15-25 in. lbs.

Brush End Plate—1969 and Later Models

Carefully observe the original position of the bale retainer and pry it off with a screw driver. Remove the end plate and plug. Replace it with the appropriate kit.

When installing the end plate, use a fine wire probe through the hub opening to position the brushes on the commutator. Rotate end plate to position the key in the notch and assemble the plug. Reinstall the bale retainer carefully with a screwdriver to avoid overbending.

Output Arm and Windlatch Assembly—1969 and Later Models

Removal

1. With a sharp pointed tool, puncture and pry off the soft plastic plug from the upper surface of the arm.
2. Remove the retaining bolt from the shaft being certain not to rotate the shaft.
3. Remove the arm from the shaft with a suitable puller. Do not attempt to drift the arm from the shaft.
4. Note the correct positioning of the windlatch in its guide for proper reassembly. Lift the plastic windlatch out of the integral cover plate and guide.
5. Unclip the windlatch spring from the guide and remove it.

Installation

1. Snap the windlatch spring in place.
2. Parts in the kits are supplied with a special water wash resistant lubricant. Do not remove

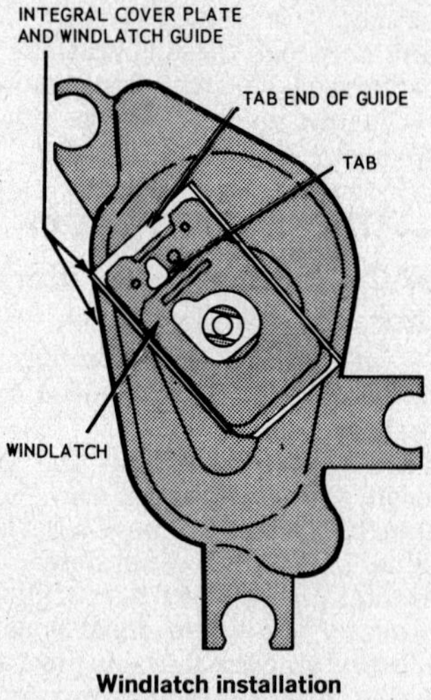
INTEGRAL COVER PLATE
AND WINDLATCH GUIDE
TAB END OF GUIDE
TAB
WINDLATCH

Windlatch installation
(© Ford Motor Co)

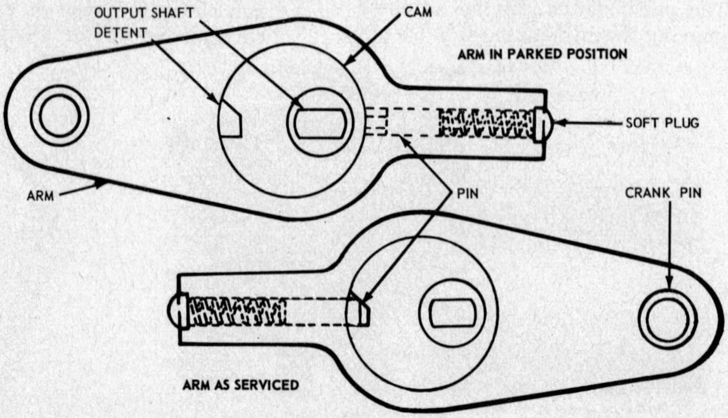
OUTPUT SHAFT
DETENT
CAM
ARM IN PARKED POSITION
SOFT PLUG
ARM
PIN
CRANK PIN
ARM AS SERVICED

Wiper output arm
(© Ford Motor Co)

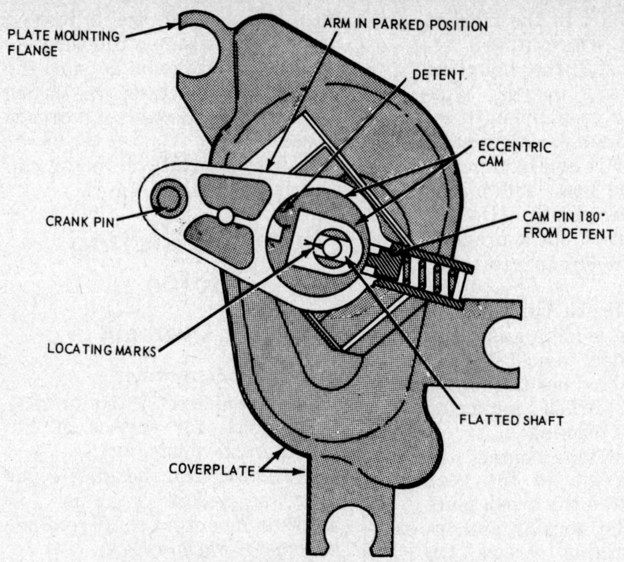
PLATE MOUNTING FLANGE
ARM IN PARKED POSITION
DETENT
ECCENTRIC CAM
CRANK PIN
CAM PIN 180° FROM DETENT
LOCATING MARKS
FLATTED SHAFT
COVERPLATE

Wiper motor output arm in the park position (© Ford Motor Co)

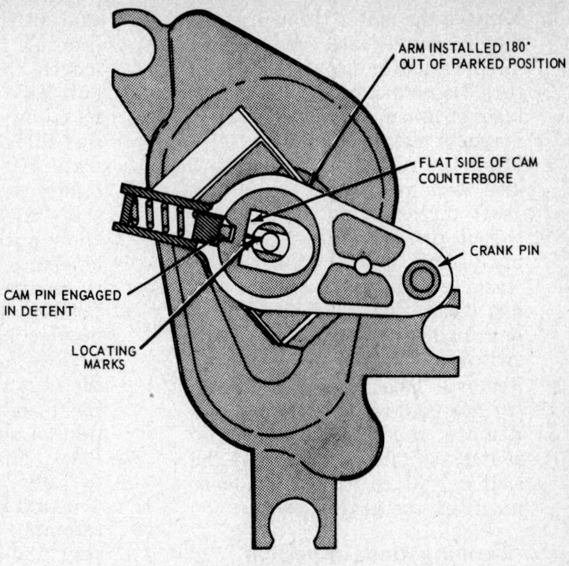
ARM INSTALLED 180° OUT OF PARKED POSITION
FLAT SIDE OF CAM COUNTERBORE
CRANK PIN
CAM PIN ENGAGED IN DETENT
LOCATING MARKS

Service replacement output arm installation (© Ford Motor Co)

the lubricant and do not add any lubricant. Position the windlatch in the integral cover plate and guide as shown.

3. Position the arm and cam assembly on the shaft so that the locating marks are aligned. Note that the service replacement arm comes with the cam pin engaged in the detent. Therefore, when installed with the correct cam-to-shaft relationship (marks aligned), the arm will be 180 degrees out of parked position. It will be returned to park position when you perform the final step of this procedure.
4. Draw the arm and cam assembly onto the output shaft with the retaining screw, applying 8-10 ft. lbs. of torque. Before tightening the screw, however, slide the windlatch in its guide to make sure that the upstanding tab clears the underside of the arm as it is being drawn onto the shaft.
5. Install a new soft plastic plug.
6. Make sure that the output arm is in park position as outlined in the following procedure.

Before attempting to install the motor in the vehicle, be sure that the output arm is in the park position as shown. If it is not in park position as in the case of the service replacement, proceed as follows:

7. Place the motor on the left fender near the feed wires at the dash panel.
8. Temporarily connect the motor to the feed wires (2 plugs).
9. Ground the motor by connecting a jumper wire from the ground strap to the body.
10. Move the control switch lever in the vehicle to operate the motor. The output arm and cam will move together in clockwise rotation.
11. Allow the arm and cam to move at least one full revolution, and then move the control switch to off position. This will cause the motor output arm to proceed through the following cycle: rotate in the normal direction; reverse direction of rotation for approximately 10 degrees to 15 degrees; stop rotating while the crank pin moves radially outward in 2 semi-circular motion; and stop in the final park position.

Wiper Motor

Disassembly

1. Remove the gear cover retaining screws, ground terminal and cover.
2. Remove the idler gear by pressing shaft with retainer out of the motorhousing. On 1965-68 models, remove the idler gear and pinion and thrust washer.

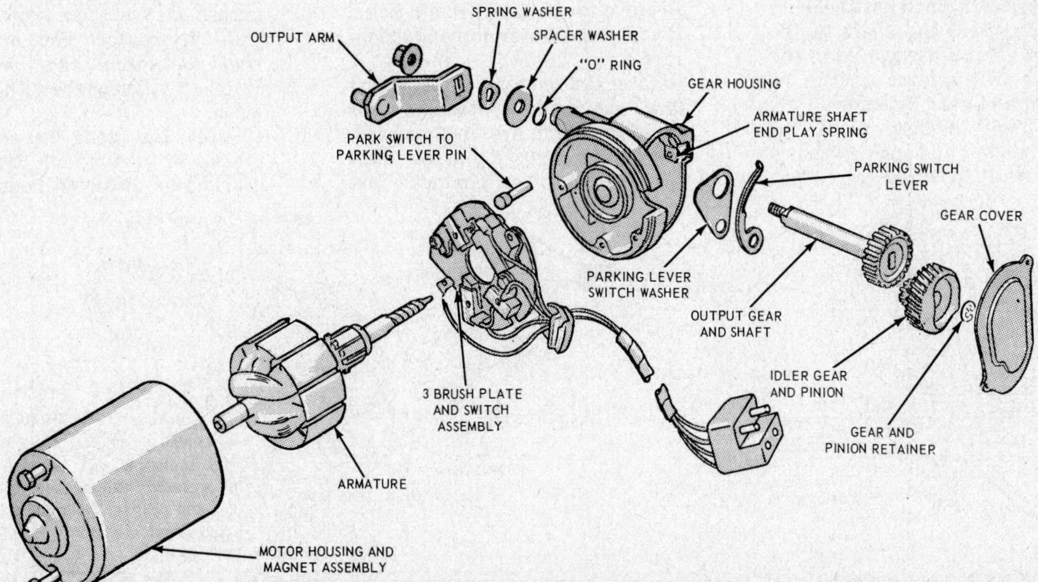
SPRING WASHER
OUTPUT ARM
SPACER WASHER
"O" RING
GEAR HOUSING
ARMATURE SHAFT END PLAY SPRING
PARK SWITCH TO PARKING LEVER PIN
PARKING SWITCH LEVER
GEAR COVER
PARKING LEVER SWITCH WASHER
OUTPUT GEAR AND SHAFT
IDLER GEAR AND PINION
3 BRUSH PLATE AND SWITCH ASSEMBLY
GEAR AND PINION RETAINER
ARMATURE
MOTOR HOUSING AND MAGNET ASSEMBLY

Permanent magnet motor disassembled (© Ford Motor Co)

3. Remove the motor through bolts, motor round case, switch terminal insulator sleeve, and armature. Do not pound the motor case magnet assembly as the ceramic magnets may be damaged.
4. Mark the position of the output arm with respect to the output shaft for assembly. Remove the output arm retaining nut, output arm, wave washer, flat washer, O-ring, leaf spring, output gear/shaft assembly, and parking switch lever and parking switch lever plate.
5. Remove the brushes, bush springs, and wire harness.
6. Remove the brush plate and switch assembly, and remove the switch contact to parking lever pin from the gear housing.

Cleaning and Inspection

1. Clean the gear housing of all old grease. *Do not allow any cleaning fluid to contact the armature shaft and output shaft bearings.*
2. Wipe all other parts with a clean cloth.
3. Inspect the gear housing for cracks or distortion. Replace a cracked or distorted housing.
4. Check all shafts, bushings, and gears for scored surfaces. Replace damaged parts, and add new grease to the housing and gears.

Assembly

It is essential that the idler gear shaft with the push-nut be reset to the original, proper depth in the gear housing.

1. Place the housing on a flat surface with the inside of the housing facing up.
2. Position the parking switch lever and lever plate with the cam rider pointing toward the gear housing output shaft hole.
3. Apply a film of grease to the output gear teeth and shaft bearing surface. Insert the shaft in the bearing. Make certain that the parking switch lever is clear of the cam and gear assembly.
4. On 1967-68 models, place the spacer washer and spring washer on the shaft, position the output arm on the shaft in the marked position from which it was removed, and install the mounting nut. On 1969-72 models, after installing idler gear on shaft, insert shaft through park lever and plate. Use a drift and hammer to lightly tap the gear and pinion shaft to proper depth. (Do not allow push-nut to put a pre-load on gear. A .001-007 in. clearance is required.)
5. Position the brush springs and brushes in the holders and wrap wire around them to hold them in the fully retracted position. Push the insulated brush connector into the switch terminal.
6. Place the switch contact to parking lever pin in the gear housing. Position the brush plate assembly to the housing and install the retaining screws. On 1967-68 models, adjust the park switch.
7. Apply grease to the ball bearing in the end of the armature shaft. Position the armature shaft in the gear housing and remove the brush retracting wires.
8. Holding the armature in position, install the motor case and magnet assembly, and through bolts. Align indicator marks on motor case and gear box housing before inserting through bolts. On 1967-68 models, seal the area where the terminal insulator sleeve seats against the motor and gear housings.
9. Apply grease to the worm gear and pinion and idle gear. Install end play spring in housing. On 1967-68 models, install the thrust washer and retainer.
10. Apply a generous amount of grease to the area around the end of the armature shaft. Install the gear housing cover.

1967-68 Park Switch Adjustment

1. Remove the motor through bolts.
2. Remove the motor cup and armature.
3. Rotate the motor output shaft until the lower contacts on the parking switch are firmly closed.
4. Rotate the adjusting screw until the switch lower contacts just open, then turn the adjusting screw clockwise one full turn.
5. Check the bridge to be sure the legs are contacting the brush plate when the lower contacts are closed.
6. Install the armature, motor cup and through bolts.

Ford Oscillating Motor

Wiper Motor Overhaul

Disassembly

The two-speed electric motor may be disassembled for service of the drive mechanism parts.

1. Remove the gear housing cover plate and gasket.
2. Remove the output shaft retainer and spacer washer.
3. Remove the crankpin bearing retainer and remove the spacer washer and cam return spring assembly.
4. Remove the arm and link assembly.
5. Remove the crankpin bearing cam.
6. Remove the input gear retainer and outer spacer shim, and remove the input gear and inner spacer shim.
7. Remove the wiper arm lever nut and lock washer.
8. Remove the wiper arm lever and spacer, and remove the output shaft and gear assembly from the housing.
9. The output gear may be removed from its shaft by tapping with a fiber hammer. Be careful not to damage the end of the shaft.

The worm drive gear and armature assembly is not serviced.

Cleaning and Inspection

1. Clean the gear housing of all old grease. *Do not allow any cleaning fluid to contact the armature shaft and output shaft bearings.*
2. Wipe all other parts with a clean cloth.
3. Inspect the gear housing for cracks or distortion. Replace a cracked or distorted housing.

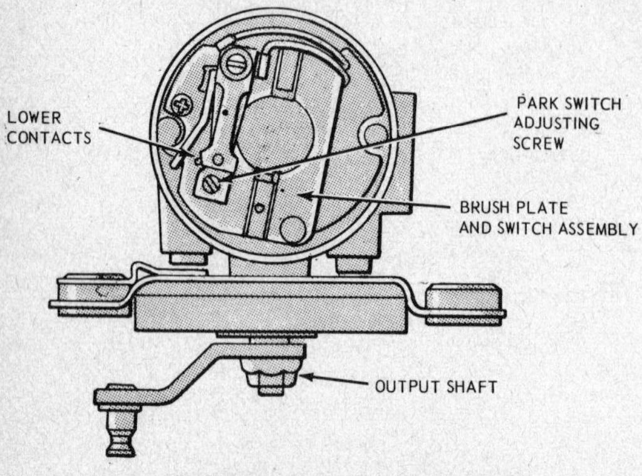

LOWER CONTACTS
PARK SWITCH ADJUSTING SCREW
BRUSH PLATE AND SWITCH ASSEMBLY
OUTPUT SHAFT

1967-68 park switch adjustment
(© Ford Motor Co)

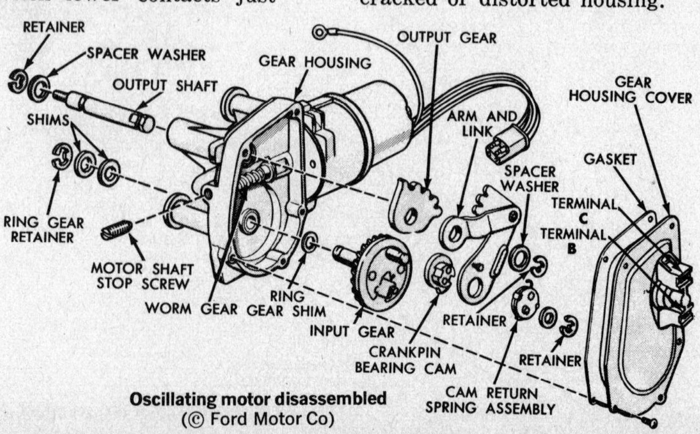

RETAINER
SPACER WASHER
OUTPUT SHAFT
SHIMS
OUTPUT GEAR
GEAR HOUSING
GEAR HOUSING COVER
ARM AND LINK
GASKET
SPACER WASHER
TERMINAL C
TERMINAL B
RING GEAR RETAINER
MOTOR SHAFT STOP SCREW
WORM GEAR
RING GEAR SHIM
INPUT GEAR
RETAINER
CRANKPIN BEARING CAM
RETAINER
CAM RETURN SPRING ASSEMBLY

Oscillating motor disassembled
(© Ford Motor Co)

4. Check all shafts, bushings, and gears for scored surfaces. Replace damaged parts.

Assembly

1. Tighten the motor cover. Adjust the motor shaft end play 0.000-0.005 in. by turning the shaft stop screw. Measure with a feeler gauge between the stop screw and the motor shaft.
2. Install the input gear shim on the input gear shaft and install the gear in the housing. Adjust the end play to 0.005 to 0.010 in. by adding or removing shims under the input gear retainer. Install the retainer.
3. Install the output gear on the output shaft. Make sure that the gear is bottomed on the shaft.
4. Install the output shaft and gear assembly into the housing with the gear teeth facing the motor. Install one spacer washer to the outside end of the output shaft and assemble the wiper arm lever to the output shaft, with the linkage studs facing away from and above the shaft. Secure the lever with a lock washer and nut.
5. Place the bearing cam on the crankpin with the small diameter portion of the cam facing outward.
6. Install the arm and link assembly to the bearing cam. As the arm is placed on the shaft, the gears must be meshed and the link which is riveted to the arm must be installed to the output shaft at the same time. Proper gear indexing is obtained when the bottom tooth of the arm and gear segment will be in mesh with the bottom valley of the output shaft gear.
7. Install the output shaft spacer washer and retainer. Check the end play of the output shaft (0.005-0.010 in.). Remove or install spacer washers under the shaft retainer to adjust the end play.
8. Install the cam return spring assembly.
9. Install the bearing spacer and retainer. If the retainer cannot be installed, one or more coils of the spring clutch are probably out of place. If the bearing has excessive end play on the crankpin, the projection of the bearing may ride out of the semi-circular slot in the end plate. Add spacer washers under the retainer if necessary.
10. Apply generous amounts of grease to all moving parts. Install the gear housing cover plate.

When operating the unit on the bench, do not place hands or fingers between the wiper lever and the case, or inside the gear housing, as considerable power is developed by the gear reduction.

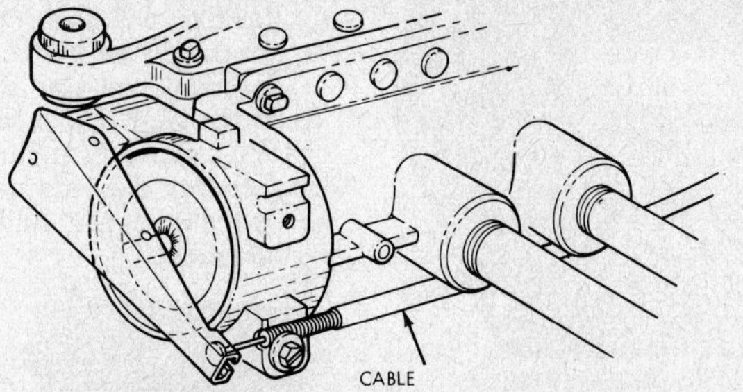
(OFF POSITION)
CABLE
Hydraulic motor control cable installation
(© Ford Motor Co)

Ford Hydraulic Wiper Motor

Control Cable Adjustment

1. Remove the carburetor air cleaner.
2. Remove the screw that retains the hydraulic line seal to the dash and pull the seal back over the lines.
3. Loosen the control cable retaining screw.
4. Insert the control cable into the mounting slot and position the wire end in the motor drive lever slot.
5. Position the motor drive lever at the extreme position of its travel, hold the lever in this position, and force the cable housing in the opposite direction until a positive stop is felt.
6. Release the control cable housing, hold the motor control lever in its extreme position, and tighten the cable mounting screws.
7. Position the hydraulic line seal on the dash and install the retaining screws.
8. Install the carburetor air cleaner.

G.M. Rectangular Motor

The disassembly-reassembly procedures for the wiper are broken down into two major areas: the motor section and gear box section.

Gear Box Disassembly

1. Remove washer pump (if so equipped) as follows:
   a. Remove the two washer pump mounting screws and carefully lift the washer pump off the wiper motor.
   b. Remove the washer pump four lobe drive cam. The cam is a press fit on the wiper gearshaft and it may be necessary to pry off with a screw driver or similar tool.
   c. Remove the felt washer from the wiper gearshaft.
2. Clamp crankarm in a vise and remove crankarm retaining nut.

NOTE: failure to clamp crankarm may result in stripping of wiper gears.

3. Remove crankarm, seal cap, Tru-Arc retaining ring and end play washers.

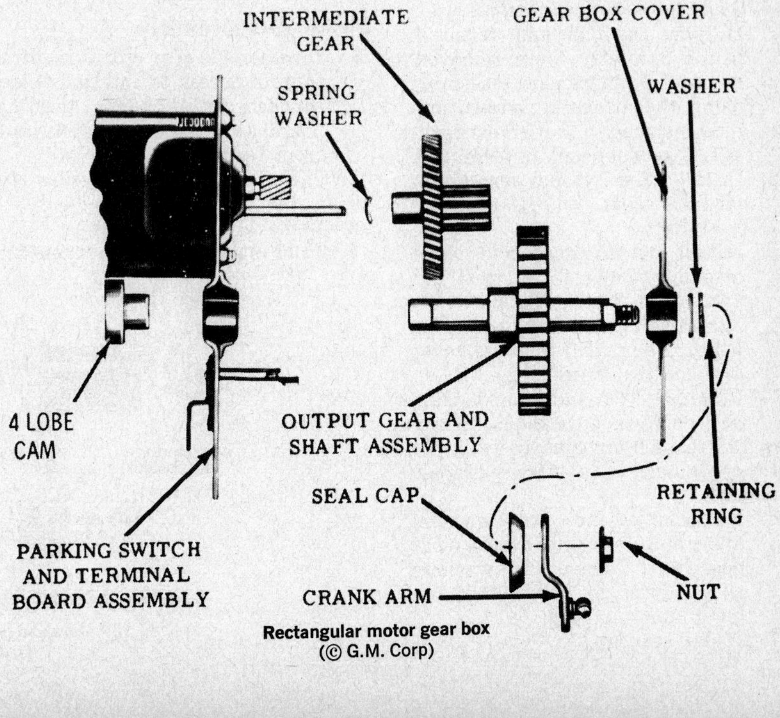
INTERMEDIATE GEAR
GEAR BOX COVER
SPRING WASHER
WASHER
4 LOBE CAM
OUTPUT GEAR AND SHAFT ASSEMBLY
SEAL CAP
RETAINING RING
PARKING SWITCH AND TERMINAL BOARD ASSEMBLY
CRANK ARM
NUT
Rectangular motor gear box
(© G.M. Corp)

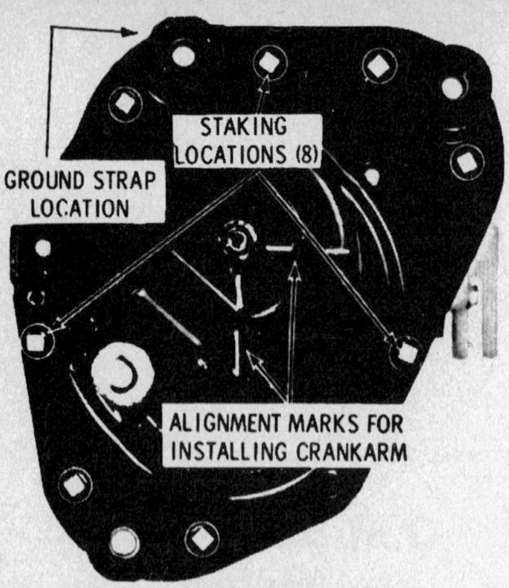
GROUND STRAP LOCATION
STAKING LOCATIONS (8)
ALIGNMENT MARKS FOR INSTALLING CRANKARM

Gear box cover staking locations
(© G.M. Corp)

NOTE: seal cap should be cleaned and repacked with a waterproof type grease before reassembly.

4. Drill out staking that secures gear box cover. Use a 9/32 in. drill.

NOTE: mark ground strap location and save ground strap for reassembly.

5. Remove output gear and shaft assembly, then slide intermediate gear and pinion assembly off shaft.
6. If required, remove terminal board and park switch assembly as follows:
   a. *Note position of motor leads on terminals,* then unsolder.
   b. Drill out rivets that secure terminal board and park switch ground strap to plate. Use a 7/64 in. drill.

NOTE: screws, nuts and washers for attaching a replacement terminal board and park switch are included with a replacement assembly.

Gear Box Reassembly

NOTE: lubricate gear teeth.

1. If park switch and terminal board assembly were removed, reinstall replacement assembly using the attaching screws and nuts included in the service package. Resolder leads to terminals.
2. Install wave washer and intermediate gear on intermediate gearshaft.
3. Install output gear and shaft assembly with cam at least 90° away from park switch.
4. Assemble gear box cover to wiper. Be careful to locate cover over locating dowels.
5. Be sure to reinstall ground strap.

NOTE: screws, nuts and lockwashers for reassembling cover to wiper are contained in a service repair package.

6. Reassemble end play washers and retaining ring over output gearshaft. Use end play washers as required to obtain .005 in. maximum end play.
7. Install seal cap.
8. To reassemble crankarm in proper position, operate wiper to Park or Off position, and install crankarm so that index marks on crankarm line up with those on the gear box cover.

NOTE: clamp crankarm in vise before securing the retaining nut.

9. Operate wiper and check performance.

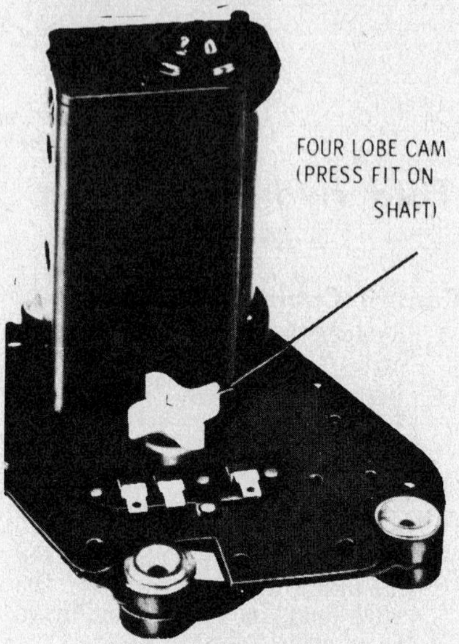
FOUR LOBE CAM (PRESS FIT ON SHAFT)

Washer cam installation
(© G.M. Corp)

10. Reinstall washer pump to wiper, reversing removal Steps 1 (a) through 1 (c). Observe precautions listed below.
11. Support crankarm end of wiper output shaft (threaded end) and using a suitable mallet, drive the four lobe cam on the wiper output shaft until it bottoms against the shoulders of the shaft flat.
12. Position four lobe cam as shown. It may be necessary to manually rotate crankarm.

Motor Disassembly

1. Disassemble gear box as required to gain access to internal solder connections at wiper terminal board and unsolder motor leads from terminals.

NOTE: step 1 is necessary for frame and field replacement only.

2. Remove motor tie bolts.
3. Hold end cap against frame and field and disengage complete motor section from gear box.
4. Turn motor section as required to gain access to brush plate assembly and release brush spring pressure against brushes.
5. Move brushes away from armature commutator and remove armature and end cap from frame and field assembly.
6. Remove end cap from end of armature shaft.

NOTE: be careful not to lose the plastic thrust plug in end of armature.

7. Remove end play washers from commutator end of armature shaft. When reassembling armature in wiper, install washers as shown.
8. To replace brushes, cut brush pigtail approximately ¼ in. from splicing clip. Splice the new brush pigtail to the ¼ in. of pigtail left from the original brush.

NOTE: splicing clips are provided in the replacement brush packages.

Motor Reassembly

Reverse disassembly Steps 1 through 7 and reassemble gear.

NOTE: make sure that brush plate mounting brackets are properly seated into housing.

G.M. Round Motor

Motor Disassembly and Assembly Procedure

Brush Plate and Circuit Breaker Removal

1. Scribe a reference line along the side of the casting and end cap for proper reassembly.
2. Remove the two motor tie bolts.
3. Feed exposed excess length of motor leads through the casting grommet and carefully back the case and field assembly plus the armature away from the casting.

NOTE: it may be necessary to remove the armature end play adjusting screw and insert a rod through the opening in order to apply pressure against the end of the armature.

4. Unsolder the black lead from circuit breaker.

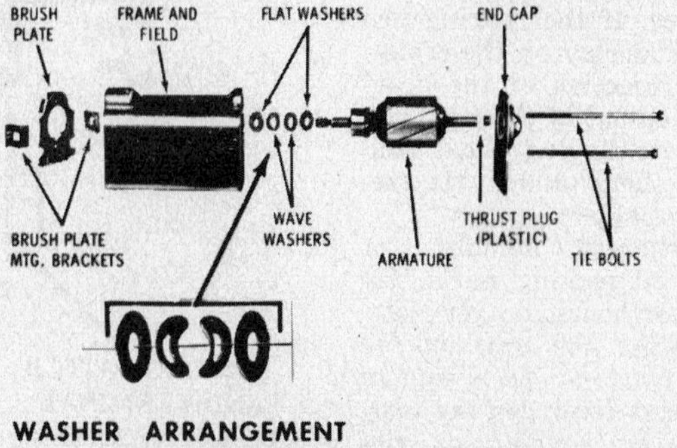
BRUSH PLATE
FRAME AND FIELD
FLAT WASHERS
END CAP
BRUSH PLATE MTG. BRACKETS
WAVE WASHERS
ARMATURE
THRUST PLUG (PLASTIC)
TIE BOLTS
WASHER ARRANGEMENT

Armature end play washer installation
(© G.M. Corp)

5. Straighten out the four tabs that secure the brush plate to the field coil retainers.

NOTE: be careful not to break any of the retainer tabs.

6. Install U shaped brush retainer clip over brush holder that has brush lead attached to circuit breaker.
7. Holding the opposite brush from that retained in Step 6, carefully lift the brush holder off the mounting tabs far enough to clear the armature commutator.
8. Allow the brush held in Step 7 to move out of its holder. Remove the brush spring and lift the brush holder off the armature shaft.

Armature Removal

1. Follow Steps 1 thru 8 under brush plate removal.
2. Lift armature out of case and field assembly.
3. Remove thrust ball from end of armature shaft and save for reassembly.

NOTE: thrust ball may be easily removed with a magnet.

Case and Field Assembly Removal

1. Remove brush plate and armature.
2. The end case and field assembly is serviced as a unit. To free the field and case assembly, cut the solid black and black with pink stripe leads in a location convenient for splicing preferably near the wiper terminal board.
3. Remove steel thrust plate and rubber disc from case bearing.

Motor Reassembly

1. If new field and case assembly is being installed, splice the black and black with pink stripe leads of the new field with the corresponding leads of the wiper.
2. Install the rubber thrust disc, steel thrust disc and felt lubricating washer in the case assembly bearing in the order indicated.
3. Lubricate end of armature shaft that fits in case bearing with recommended type grease. Next, install thrust ball in end of shaft.
4. Assemble armature in the case and field assembly.
5. Position the partially assembled brush plate over the armature shaft far enough to allow reassembly of the remaining brush in its brush holder; then position the brush plate assembly on the mounting tabs.

NOTE: circuit breaker ground lead will not reach circuit breaker terminal if brush plate is wrongly positioned.

6. Center the brush plate mounting holes over the mounting tabs and bend the tabs toward the brush holders as required to secure the brush plate in position.

NOTE: be sure tabs are centered in brush plate mounting holes.

7. Remove brush retainer clips and resolder circuit breaker ground lead to circuit breaker.
8. If new case and field assembly is used, scribe a line on it in the old case. This will insure proper alignment of the new case with the scribed line made on the housing.
9. Position armature worm shaft inside the housing and, using the scribed reference marks, line up as near as possible the case and field assembly with the housing.
10. Maintaining the armature in its assembled position in the case, start the armature worm shaft through the field and housing bearing until it starts to mesh with the drive gear. At the same time carefully pull the excess black and black with pink stripe leads through the housing grommet.

NOTE: it may be necessary at this point to rotate armature slightly before the armature worm will engage with drive gear teeth.

11. Rotate the case as required to align the bolt holes in the case with those in the housing.
12. Secure the case to the housing with the two tie bolts.

Gear Box—Disassembly and Assembly Procedures

Relay Switch Latch Assembly Terminal Board Removal

1. Remove washer pump, if so equipped.
2. If wiper gear drive pawl is in full park position, remove gear assembly. (See Drive Gear Disassembly).

If wiper gear mechanism is not in park position (drive pawl away from latch arm) proceed to Step 3.

3. Remove relay switch attaching screw and carefully lift the relay switch assembly out of the gear box. Unsolder leads from switch terminals as required.
4. To remove terminal board assembly, simply slide it out of housing and unsolder leads as required.

Reassembly of Relay Switch-Latch and Terminal Board

1. Resolder red coil lead to wiper terminal board as required.
2. Slide terminal board into wiper housing being careful to position the terminal board resistor lead out of the way of the output gear.

NOTE: with the relay switch assembly replaced in the housing and washer pump reinstalled, the relay switch plastic housing applies pressure against the resistor lead to form a positive ground connection to the wiper housing.

3. Resolder leads to relay switch assembly as required.
4. Position relay switch assembly in housing.

NOTE: be very careful to route leads in such a manner as to avoid having them pinched between relay and wiper housing.

5. Install relay switch attaching screw.
6. Reassemble washer pump to gear (reassemble drive gear assembly if removed).

Drive Gear Disassembly

1. Remove crankarm retaining nut, crankarm, rubber seal cap, retaining ring, shim washers, shield and spacer washer in the order indicated.
2. Slide gear assembly out of housing.
3. Slide drive plate and shaft out of gear and remove the drive pawl, lock pawl, and coil spring as required.

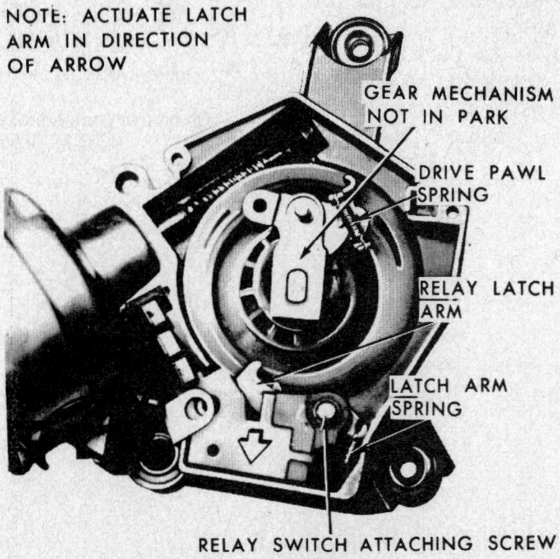
NOTE: ACTUATE LATCH ARM IN DIRECTION OF ARROW
GEAR MECHANISM NOT IN PARK
DRIVE PAWL SPRING
RELAY LATCH ARM
LATCH ARM SPRING
RELAY SWITCH ATTACHING SCREW

Relay latch mechanism
(© G.M. Corp)

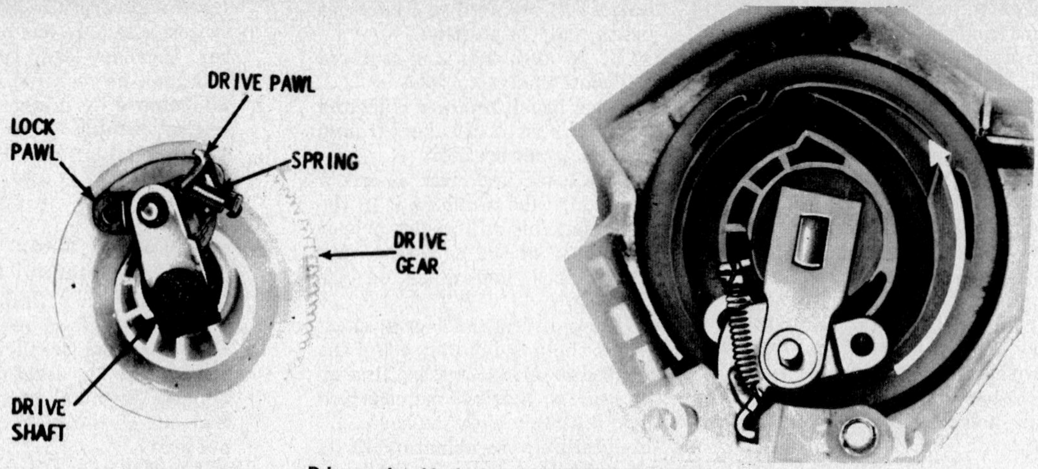
DRIVE PAWL
LOCK PAWL
SPRING
DRIVE GEAR
DRIVE SHAFT

Drive pawl and lock pin installation (© G.M. Corp)

Drive Gear Reassembly

1. Position drive pawl on drive plate.
2. Assemble lock pawl over drive pawl.
3. Slide gear and tube over the drive shaft. (More drive and lock pawls as required to allow their respective pins to fit in the gear guide channel.)
4. Holding the gear, manually rotate the drive plate in the direction of the arrow until the drive and lock pawl guide pins snap into their respective pockets in the gear.
5. Reinstall coil spring between lock and drive pawls.

NOTE: be very careful to maintain lock and drive pawl guide pins in their respective pockets during Step 6.

6. Assemble inner spacer washer over gearshaft and assemble gear mechanism in housing so that it is positioned with respect to the housing in the approximate location shown.
7. Reassemble the outer spacer washer, shield, shim washers, as

   or minus .002 in.) end play, snap ring and rubber seal cap in the order indicated.
8. Operate wiper to park position and install crankarm in the approximate position shown.
9. Reassemble washer pump to gear.

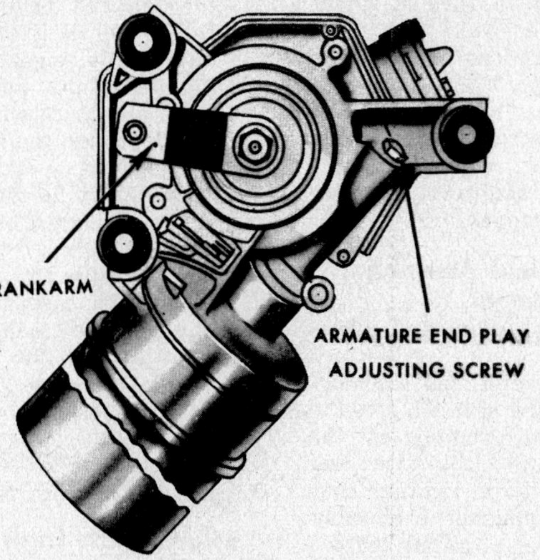
CRANKARM
ARMATURE END PLAY
ADJUSTING SCREW

Crankarm in the park position
(© G.M. Corp)

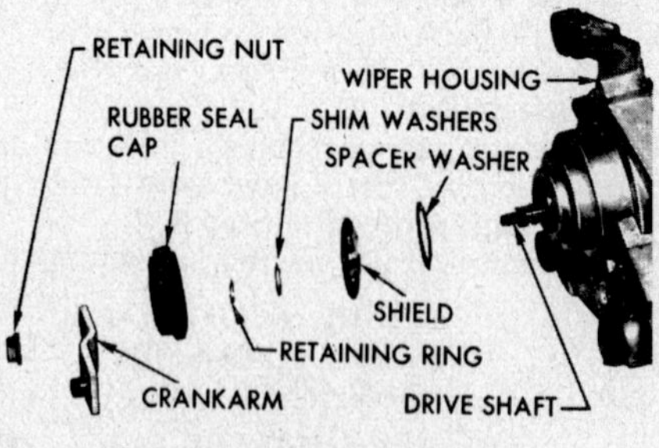
RETAINING NUT
WIPER HOUSING
RUBBER SEAL CAP
SHIM WASHERS
SPACER WASHER
SHIELD
RETAINING RING
CRANKARM
DRIVE SHAFT

Crankarm component installation
(© G.M. Corp)

Wiper Motor Adjustments

Armature End Play

1. Loosen adjusting screw locknut and tighten or loosen the adjusting screw as required until end of screw barely touches end of armature.
2. Back off adjusting screw 1/4 turn and tighten locknut.

Gear Assembly End Play

1. Add or remove shim washers as required to obtain .004 in. (plus or minus .002 in.) end play.

Wankel Engine

By JAN P. NORBYE

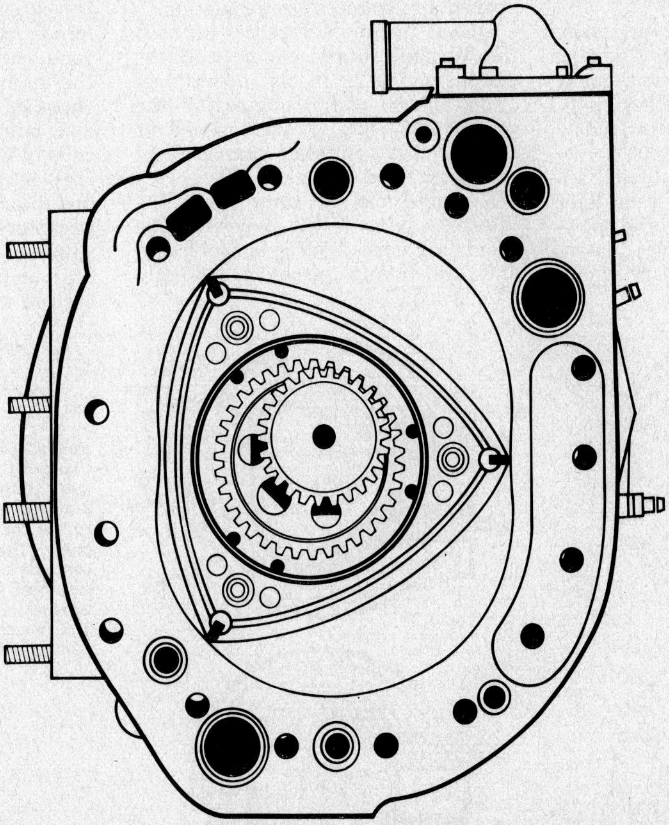

Mr. Norbye is the author of the definitive work entitled *The Wankel Engine*, 1971, Chilton Book Co., 519 pages, $15.00. (This book can be purchased from your bookstore or from Chilton Book Co., Chilton Way, Radnor, Pennsylvania 19089.

The Wankel Engine

The Wankel engine is a rotary internal-combustion engine working on the four-stroke cycle. It differs from the conventional piston engine in having purely rotary motion, without pistons that move up and down. It runs on the same kind of gasoline; the charge is fired by spark plugs; and the exhaust fumes have similar composition. The Wankel engine has many advantages over the conventional piston engines and 22 automobile manufacturers have signed license agreements for the rights to build it.

The leading producers of Wankel engines are Mazda in Japan, with an output of about 25,000 Wankel-powered cars a month, and NSU in Germany, with an output of 85,000 Wankel-powered cars a year. General Motors is reportedly planning the introduction of its first Wankel-powered car in the 1974 model year. Other licensees are Mercedes-Benz, Toyota, Datsun, Comotor (jointly owned by NSU and Citroën), Alfa Romeo, Fichtel & Sachs, Rolls-Royce, Ford of Germany, Outboard Marine Corp., and Curtiss-Wright.

Applications

The Wankel engine is primarily considered as an automotive engine for passenger car installation, but it is also suitable for many other applications. It can be made in widely different sizes, from 3 to 1,000 horsepower. A partial list of potential applications includes marine uses, light aircraft, motorcycles, scooters, snowmobiles, all-terrain vehicles, lawnmowers, golf carts, stationary pumping sets, generator sets, industrial utility vehicles, construction machinery, agricultural equipment, and military vehicles.

How the Wankel Engine Works

The cylinders are replaced by chambers, and the pistons are replaced by rotors. The chambers are not circular in section, but have a curved circumference that is identified as an *epitrochoid.* An epitrochoid is the curve described by a given point on a circle as the circle rolls around the periphery of another circle of twice the radius of the generating circle.

The rotor is three-cornered, with curved sides. All three corners are in permanent contact with the epitrochoidal surface as the rotor moves around the chamber. This motion is both orbital and rotational, as the rotor is mounted off center. The crankshaft of a piston engine is replaced by a rotor shaft, and crank throws are replaced by eccentrics. Each rotor is carried on an eccentric. Any number of rotors is possible, but most engines have one or two rotors. The valves of the piston engine are replaced by ports in the Wankel engine housing. They are opened and closed by rotor motion.

One of the key differences between the Wankel rotary engine and the piston engine is in the operational cycle. In the piston engine, all the events take place at the top end of the cylinder (intake, compression, expansion, and exhaust). The events are spaced out in time only. The Wankel engine is the opposite. The events are spaced out geographically, and are taking place concurrently and continuously around the epitrochoidal surface.

The intake phase takes place in the area following the intake port, and overlaps with the area used for compression. Expansion takes place in the area opposite the ports, and the exhaust phase takes place in the area preceding the exhaust port, overlapping with the latter part of the expansion phase. All three rotor faces are engaged in one of the four phases at all times.

In other words, one rotor gives three working spaces, all of which are permanently in action. As one rotor apex sweeps past the intake port, it ends the intake phase in the leading space, and starts it in the trailing space. The third space is then engaged in its expansion phase. As rotor motion continues, the leading space will approach the point of maximum compression and ignition, while the trailing space will enter the compression phase as the following apex closes it off from the intake port.

The trochoidal shape of the chamber, combined with the orbital motion of the rotor, produces large variations in displacement in the three spaces. Displacement is at its minimum on one rotor face when its opposite apex is centered on the minor axis. The minor axis is the line across the chamber where it is narrowest, and the major axis is the line across the chamber where it is widest. The major and minor axes intersect perpendicularly in the center of the chamber. Displacement is at its maximum on one rotor face when its opposite apex is centered on the major axis. These differences in displacement produce the pumping action required for operation as an engine.

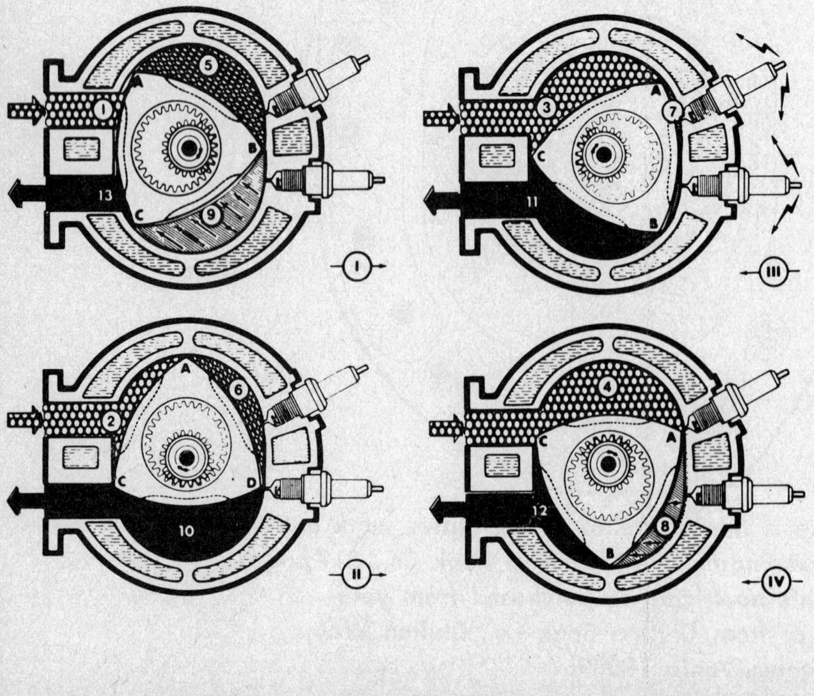

I
II
III
IV

How the Wankel engine works

Here's how the Wankel engine works: As the triangular rotor goes through its mixed sliding/turning motions, a fuel air mixture is drawn in (1, 2, 3, 4) and then compressed (5, 6) before being ignited by the spark plugs. The high-pressure gases created by combustion drive the rotor around (7, 8, 9) and after doing their work are swept out the exhaust port by the rotor (10, 11, 12, 13). The process is continuous on all the rotor's flanks, with power taken off at the gear hub.

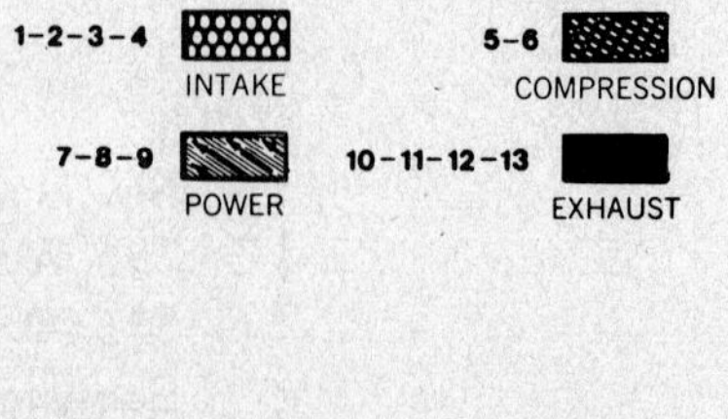

1-2-3-4
INTAKE
5-6
COMPRESSION
7-8-9
POWER
10-11-12-13
EXHAUST

How does rotor motion turn the rotor shaft? by exerting pressure on the eccentric. Here is what happens. Gas pressure on the rotor face during the expansion phase produces rotor motion. That means rotation. But the rotor is not free to spin—it is mounted on its eccentric, and has to follow an eccentric path. The rotor transfers the gas pressure to the eccentric. That moves the eccentric, which is part of the rotor shaft, and as the eccentric moves, it causes the shaft to rotate.

The relationship between the eccentric and the position of the rotor apices is quite intricate. Each apex is always in contact with the epitrochoidal surface, and to avoid jamming the rotor at some point, its position relative to the eccentric's position must be closely controlled.

This phasing is controlled by a stationary reaction gear that meshes with an internal ring gear in the rotor. It is important to note that this gearing has nothing to do with power flow or torque transmission. It is simply a phasing gear to assure smooth rotation of the eccentric and its rotor.

The stationary reaction gear is carried by a sleeve fixed to the end cover. The gear ratio is 3:2. If the reaction gear has 36 teeth, the rotor ring gear must have 54 teeth. A corresponding 3:1 ratio exists between the rotor and the rotor shaft (eccentric bearing). When the rotor makes one revolution, the shaft makes three revolutions.

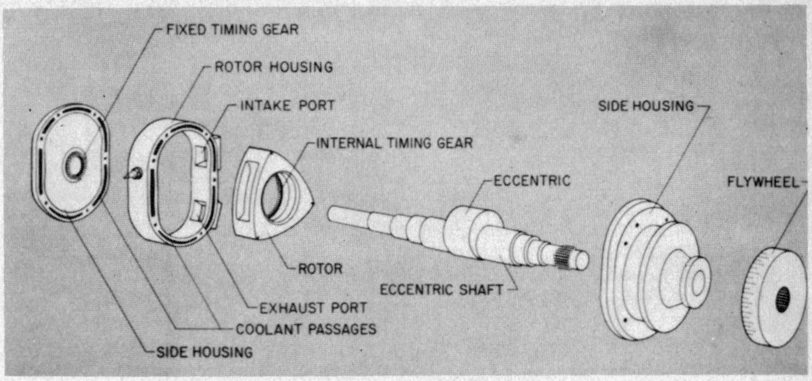
FIXED TIMING GEAR
ROTOR HOUSING
INTAKE PORT
INTERNAL TIMING GEAR
ECCENTRIC
SIDE HOUSING
FLYWHEEL
ROTOR
ECCENTRIC SHAFT
EXHAUST PORT
COOLANT PASSAGES
SIDE HOUSING

The main parts in the Wankel engine

When the rotor advances 30°, the eccentric advances 90°. For each time a rotor apex passes the intake port, the main shaft starts another complete revolution. There is a power impulse for each 1/3 turn of each rotor. That gives one expansion (or power) phase for each main shaft revolution.

In passenger car Wankel engines, the housing is water-cooled and the rotor is oil-cooled. The coolant passages in most engines run axially, and the passages are dimensioned to provide the most cooling in the area around the spark plugs(s).

The oil supply can be carried in the sump or in a separate reservoir. It is fed in through the rotor shaft, circulates inside the rotor, and returns to the reservoir (often via a heat exchanger cooled by water). The same oil that cools the rotor also lubricates the eccentric bearing.

It is not exactly true that the rotor touches the epitrochoidal surface. The rotor comes close, but is never in direct contact with the surface or the end covers. To seal the spaces for gas leaks, there is a complex seal system. Its duties are similar to those of piston rings in conventional engines.

A radial slot in each apex has a seal strip that rubs against the chamber surface. It is spring-loaded, and designed to make use of gas pressure to increase its sealing effectiveness. The rotor flanks have a seal grid intersecting with the trunnions that provide the mounting base for the apex seals. In order to fulfill their sealing duties, the seals must be lubricated. This oil is, of course,

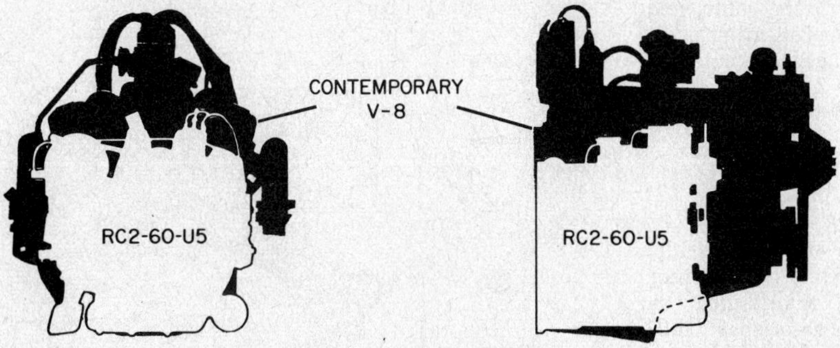
CONTEMPORARY
V-8
RC2-60-U5
RC2-60-U5

	RC2-60-U5	CONTEMPORARY V-8
HORSEPOWER / RPM	185/5000	195/4800
WEIGHT - LBS	237	607
L x W x H - IN	18.0 x 22.1 x 21.5	29.5 x 28 x 31.5
VOLUME - CU. FT.	5	15
NUMBER OF PARTS	633	1029
NUMBER OF MOVING PARTS IN POWER SECTION AND DRIVE LINE	154	388

Comparison between Wankel engine and contemporary V-8 engine

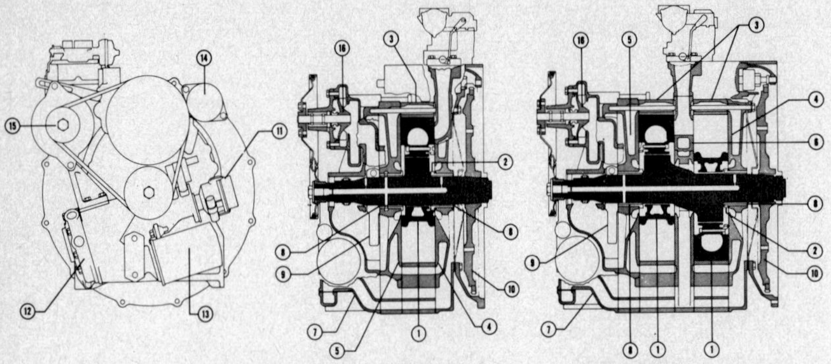

Elevation of Curtiss Wright single and twin rotor power units

1 Rotor	6 Intermediate housing	11 Ignition contact maker
2 Stationary gear	7 Accessory housing	12 Oil pumps
3 Rotor housing	8 Main bearing	13 Oil filter
4 Side housing—drive side	9 Balance weight	14 Starter
5 Side housing—anti-drive side	10 Flywheel cum balance weight	15 Generator
		16 Water pump

burned. The amounts needed are minute, and oil consumption is on a par with modern V-8 engines. The lube oil for the seals can be mixed with the gasoline (for instance in the carburetor float bowl) or injected separately by a metering pump.

There are two types of intake ports: peripheral ports, and side ports. Examples of both are illustrated. Side ports produce a gas flow that tends to give higher low-range torque, while peripheral ports produce a gas flow that tends to give higher peak power. All Wankel engines have peripheral exhaust ports.

In the air-cooled Fichtel & Sachs and Outboard Marine engines, the rotor is also air-cooled. The incoming charge is led through the rotor, and thereby undergoes a preheating process. This type of engine is not considered suitable for automotive purposes.

Advantages of the Wankel Engine

Since the Wankel engine has no reciprocating parts, it is practically free of vibration. In a single-rotor engine, balance is maintained by counterweight on the rotor shaft, 180° opposite the eccentric. In a twin-rotor engine, the eccentrics are spaced 180° and automatically cancel any imbalance.

The Wankel engine has far fewer parts than a piston engine of comparable power output, and especially fewer moving parts (see the comparison chart).

The Wankel engine is smaller and lighter than a piston engine of comparable power output. It has less than half the space requirement, and the weight saving is about 50 percent. That doubles the power-to-weight ratio of a piston engine.

The Wankel engine has higher volumetric efficiency. An engine's efficiency depends on how much air it can consume in a given time, and the Wankel engine breathes much better than the piston engine. That is because it fills the chamber with a fresh combustion charge during 270° of rotor shaft rotation, against only 180° of crankshaft rotation in a piston engine.

The Wankel engine has smoother torque output, which means smoother running, because it delivers power during two-thirds of the combustion phase, against only one-quarter of the expansion stroke in a piston engine.

Due to the absence of reciprocating motion, the Wankel engine has a higher limit on rotational speeds. That offers a further potential increase in power-to-weight ratio.

The Wankel engine is uncritical of gasoline antiknock properties. It can digest fuels of wide octane rating variations. Mazda has made tests with 68 octane gasoline under wide-open-throttle conditions, without causing abnormal combustion, and without any loss in power or economy. The Wankel engine does not require lead or other additives.

The Wankel engine is also uncritical of lube oil quality. There are no blow-by gases entering the oil system. Foaming or cavitation is not a problem. Sludge caused by dirt does not form. Raw fuel is not present in the oil system. As a result, oil contamination is not a serious problem.

The Wankel engine's compactness facilitates installation and makes for improved space utilization in the car. It offers greater design freedom and better opportunities to develop new vehicle concepts. The simplicity of the engine promises lower cost. Many parts are eliminated (the entire valve

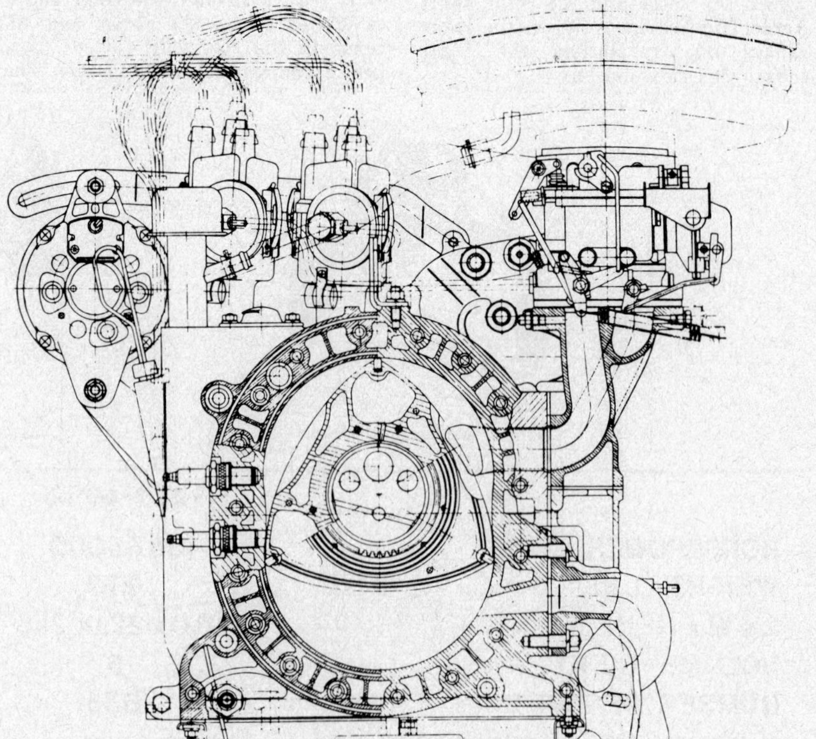

Cross section of Mazda 0813 engine

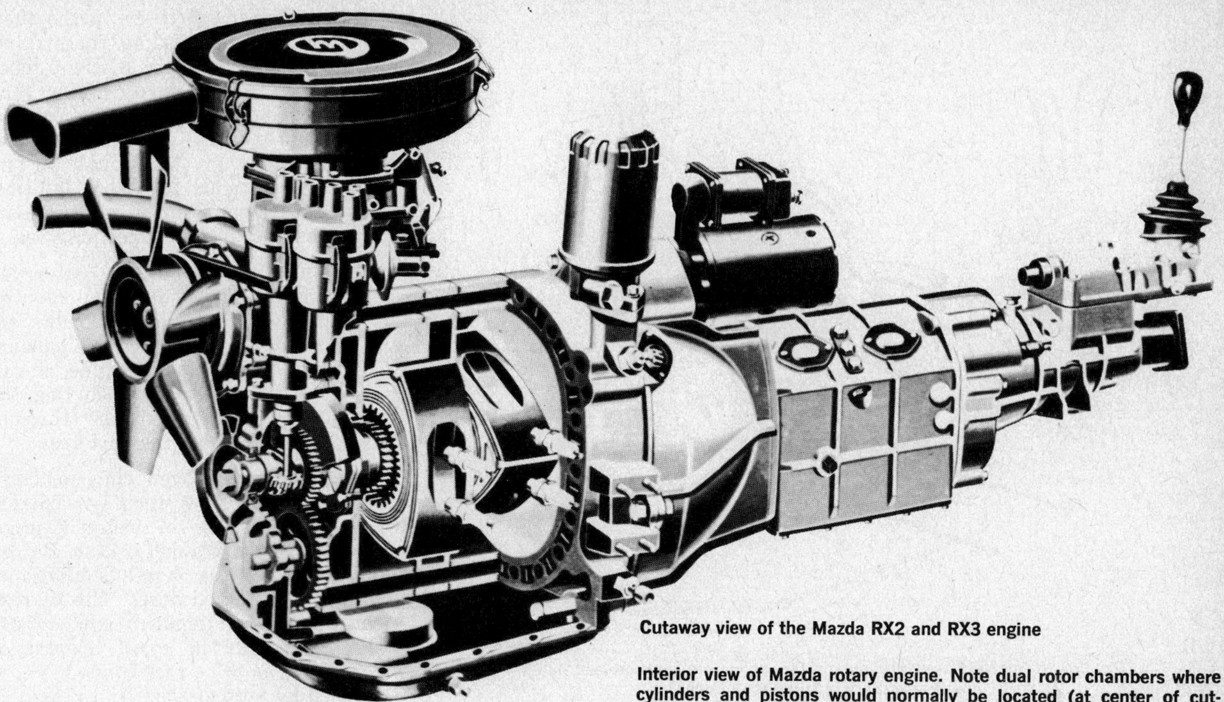

Cutaway view of the Mazda RX2 and RX3 engine

Interior view of Mazda rotary engine. Note dual rotor chambers where cylinders and pistons would normally be located (at center of cutaway). The unique Mazda rotary engine offers superior high-speed performance, better throttle response and about twice the horsepower per pound of a conventional piston engine. It also operates on unleaded, low octane gasoline and is virtually vibration free.

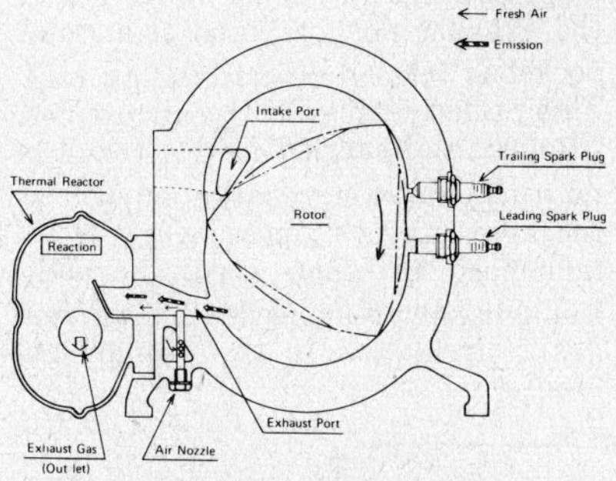
Fresh Air
Emission
Intake Port
Trailing Spark Plug
Thermal Reactor
Rotor
Leading Spark Plug
Reaction
Exhaust Port
Exhaust Gas
(Out let)
Air Nozzle

Mazda rotary engine with thermal reactor and additional air injection

train, for instance.) The design also lends itself well to automated manufacture and assembly.

Wankel Engine Emissions

Since it is an internal-combustion engine with spark ignition, it emits the same types of pollutants as the conventional piston engine. Three types of pollutants are now limited by federal standards: carbon monoxide, hydrocarbons, and oxides of nitrogen.

The same types of emission control devices that work on piston engines can be used on the Wankel. That includes such basic modifications as retarded ignition timing and leaner air-fuel mixtures. It also includes exhaust gas recirculation and thermal reactors (a type of afterburner). The Wankel engine does not require a catalytic converter (as now considered necessary for piston engines) to meet the 1975 standards.

Most of the reasons for the Wankel engine's advantages in the emission

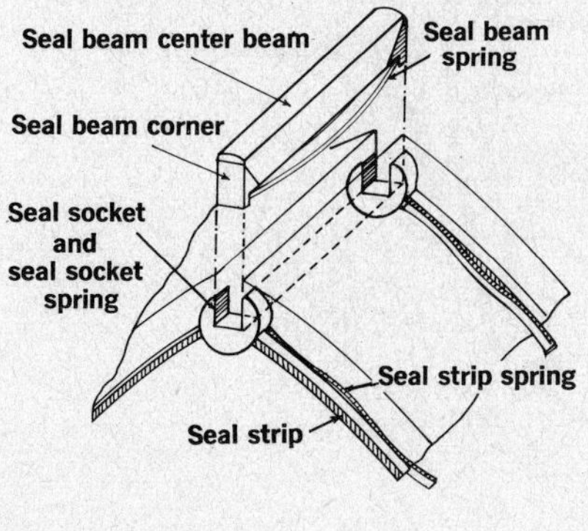
Seal beam center beam
Seal beam spring
Seal beam corner
Seal socket and seal socket spring
Seal strip spring
Seal strip

Apex seal configuration developed by Mercedes-Benz

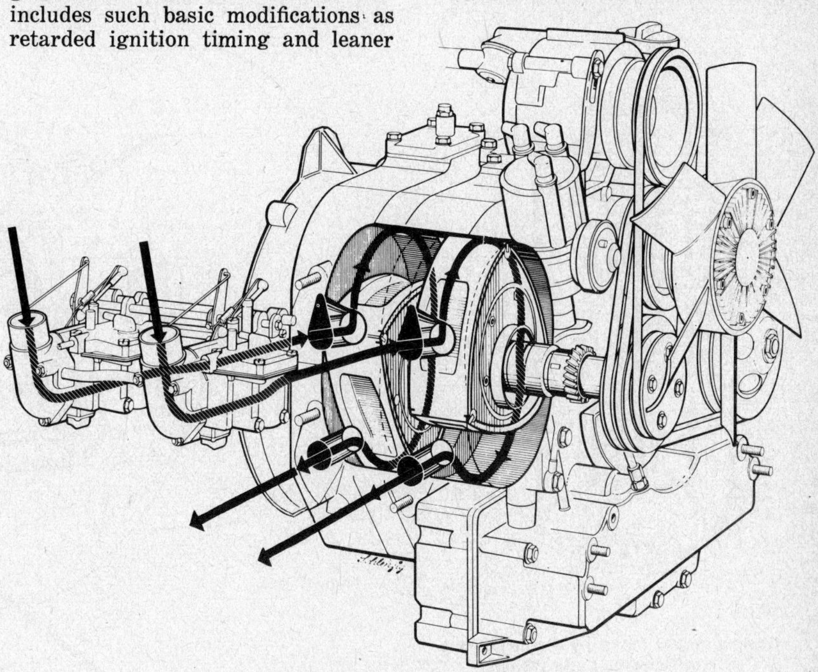

Gas flow in the NSU Ro 80 engine

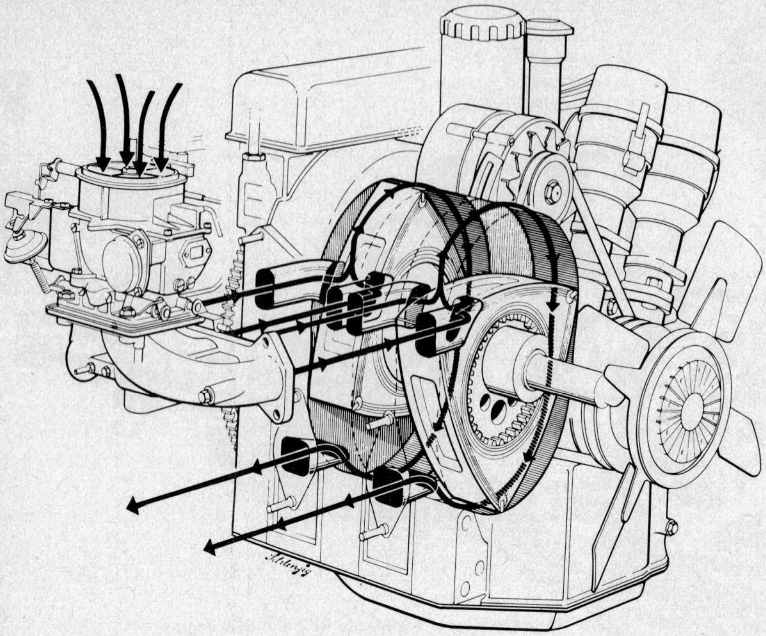

Gas flow in the NSU/Wankel-system rotary piston engine produced by the Japanese manufacturer Toyo Kogyo

control area are to be found in the combustion process. As one rotor face goes through the compression and expansion phases, the combustion chamber is transported along the epitrochoidal surface, and is constantly changing its shape. The combustion process takes up more time than in a piston engine with equal flame front velocity. As a result, the burning rate of the air-fuel mixture is slower in the Wankel engine, and peak combustion temperature is lower.

Average (as opposed to *peak*) combustion temperature is higher in the Wankel engine. That translates into higher exhaust gas temperature, which normally would be considered as an energy loss, but is turned into an advantage from the point of view of emission control.

Higher exhaust gas temperature means higher efficiency in the thermal reactor. The same thermal reactor would be more efficient when mounted on a Wankel engine than when installed on a piston engine, because exhaust gas heat assures better burning. Additional air injection is needed to assure ignition, but the system again is more efficient than is possible in piston engines.

Additional air does a better job the closer to the combustion chamber it can be injected. In the piston engine, that's right behind the exhaust valve. In the Wankel engine, it can be injected anywhere, including the combustion chamber itself (through the end cover) and the port area.

Oxides of nitrogen emissions are controlled by a system of exhaust gas recirculation in piston engines as well as the Wankel engine. But on the piston engine, it means additional valves, pipes, and hoses. The Wankel engine has automatic exhaust gas recirculation. The exact amount of exhaust gas to be recirculated is controlled by port location and design.

When the rotor apex slides across the exhaust port, a small triangular pocket is formed on its trailing face. This pocket is filled with exhaust gas, trapped, and carried forward to mix with the incoming charge as soon as the apex starts to pass over the intake port. In other words, no additional hardware is needed for exhaust gas recirculation in the Wankel engine.

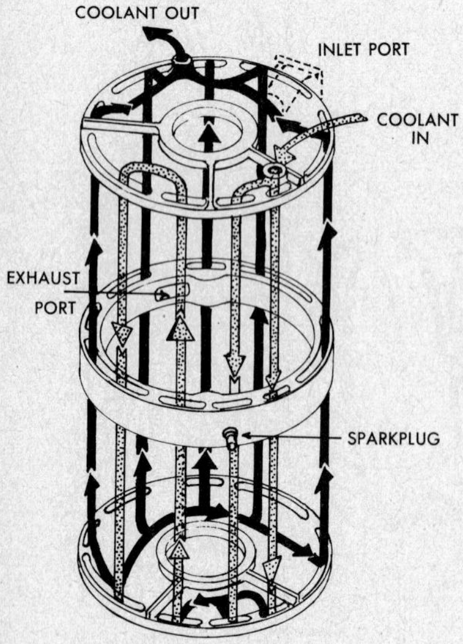
COOLANT OUT
INLET PORT
COOLANT IN
EXHAUST PORT
SPARKPLUG

Cooling system for rotary engine housing as developed by Curtiss Wright

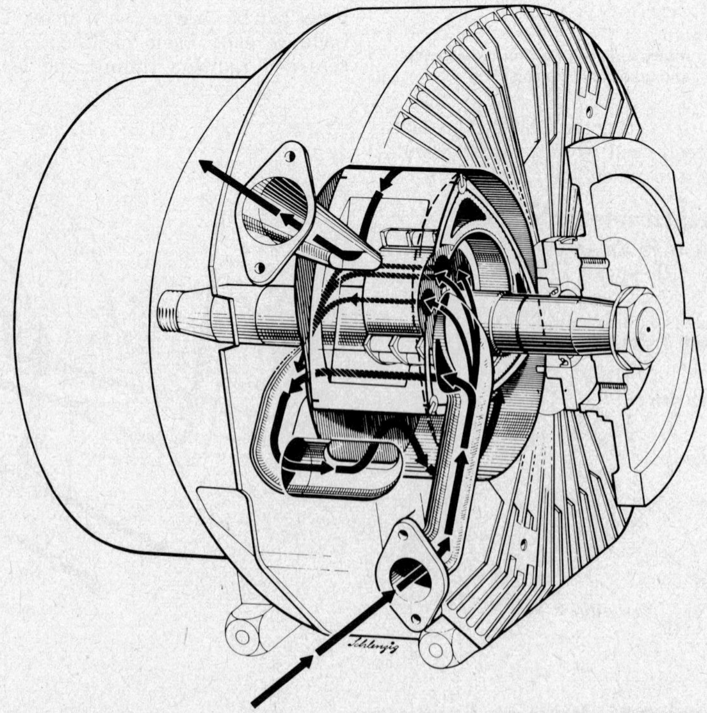

Gas flow in the air-cooled Fichtel & Sachs rotary piston engine (NSU/Wankel system)

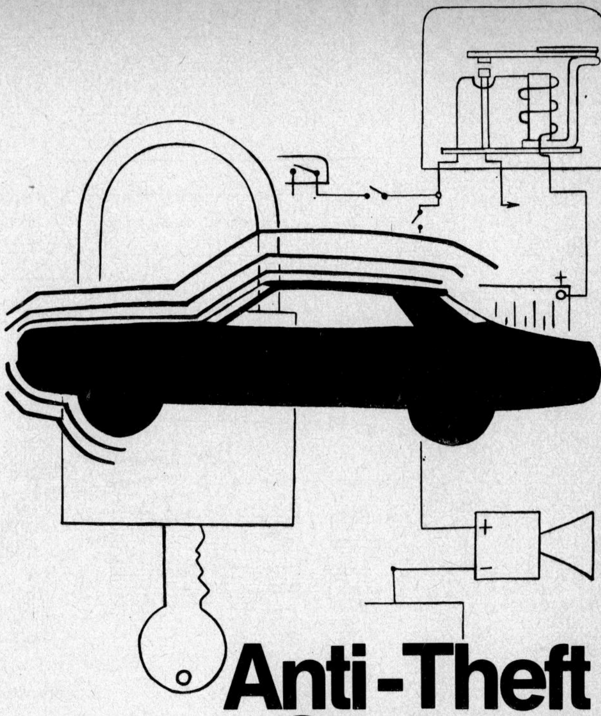

Anti-Theft Systems

Preface

Due to the increasing rate of auto theft, automotive anti-theft systems have recently come into general use. Installation of these devices by automobile manufacturers began in 1968, with the installation of key warning buzzers. This buzzer sounds whenever the key is in the ignition switch with the driver's door open. In 1969, the first steering column-transmission locks were installed. Prior to removing the ignition key from the lock, the driver must place the transmission in reverse (manual) or Park (automatic). Upon removal of the key, the steering column and the transmission linkage lock. This device is standard equipment on all 1970 and later model cars.

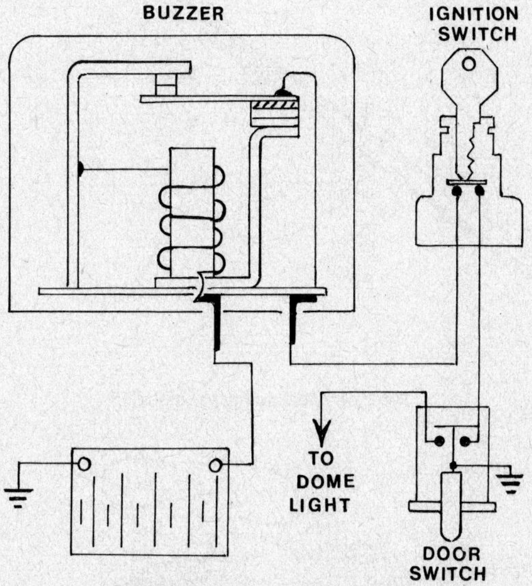
BUZZER
IGNITION SWITCH
TO DOME LIGHT
DOOR SWITCH

Typical key warning buzzer circuit

Aftermarket Systems

Aftermarket installations of anti-theft systems, on earlier model cars, or in addition to the above mentioned original equipment systems are becoming increasingly widespread. This section describes the various types of anti-theft devices that are presently commercially available, or readily fabricated.

Two basic types of systems will be considered. Type A are devices which mechanically or electrically inhibit movement of the car. Type B are warning systems (burglar alarms), which deter theft or tampering. In many cases, a system which performs both functions may be devised by combining or modifying the above.

Type A, Movement Inhibitors

The most common systems available inhibit the movement of the brake pedal and/or the steering wheel. Of these, the most prevalent (best known by its trade name—Krooklok®) is a locking, telescoping steel bar, with a hook at each end. In use, one hook is positioned around a steering wheel spoke, and the other around the brake pedal arm. The steel shaft is then telescoped down, and locked into position, preventing movement of the brake pedal and limiting steering wheel movement. A similar system utilizes a long steel bar, which hooks and locks onto the steering wheel, and prevents it from turning beyond a certain point by wedging against interior components.

Both of the above devices have the added advantage of being visible from outside the car, to act as a visual deterrent. The disadvantage of these devices is that they are somewhat awkward, and must be re-

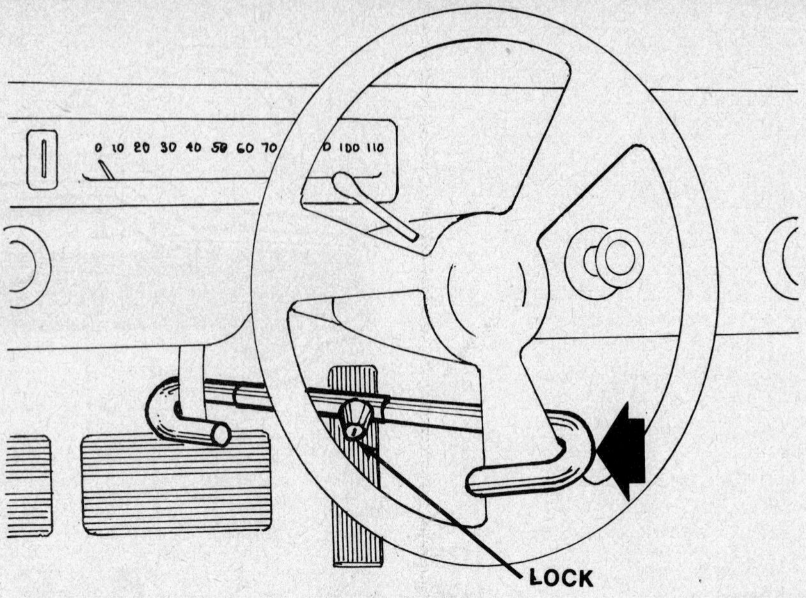
0 10 20 30 40 50 60 70
0 100 110
LOCK

Krooklok® installed

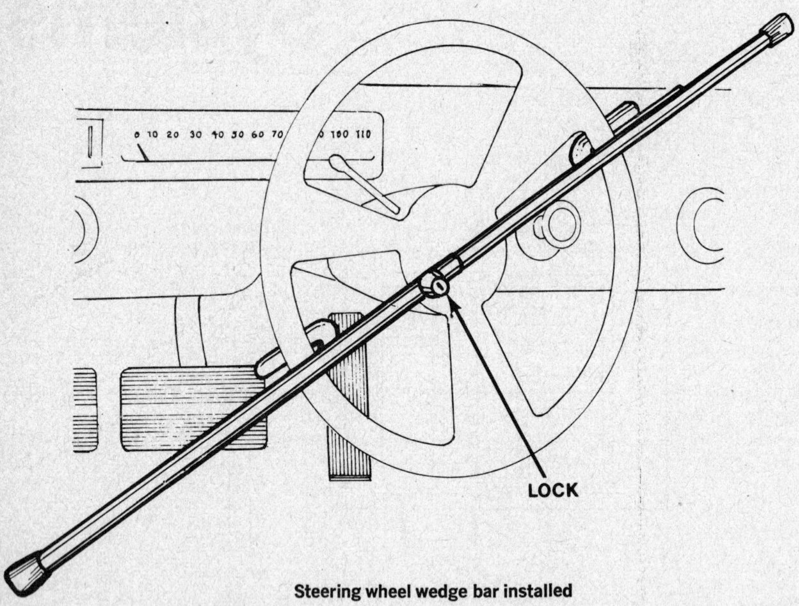
0 10 20 30 40 50 60 70
0 100 110
LOCK

Steering wheel wedge bar installed

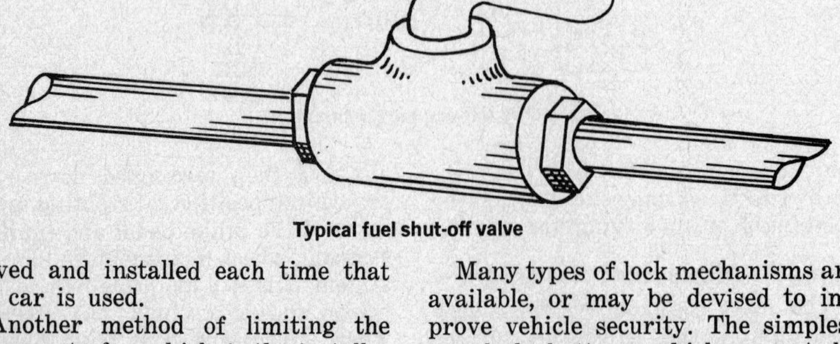

Typical fuel shut-off valve

moved and installed each time that the car is used.

Another method of limiting the movement of a vehicle is the installation of a fuel shut-off valve in the fuel line, in an inconspicuous place. However, this method is not recommended, as the engine will run until the fuel supply in the float bowl is exhausted, permitting the car to be moved.

Many types of lock mechanisms are available, or may be devised to improve vehicle security. The simplest are lock buttons which cannot be pulled up from outside the car. In many cases, these may be made from the original lock buttons, by removing the raised lip at the top of the button. In cases where the door locks are released by the inside door handles, the lock button may be positioned so that it is flush with the door when the door is locked. It is also advisable (where applicable) to position the door handles so that they cannot be moved from outside the car.

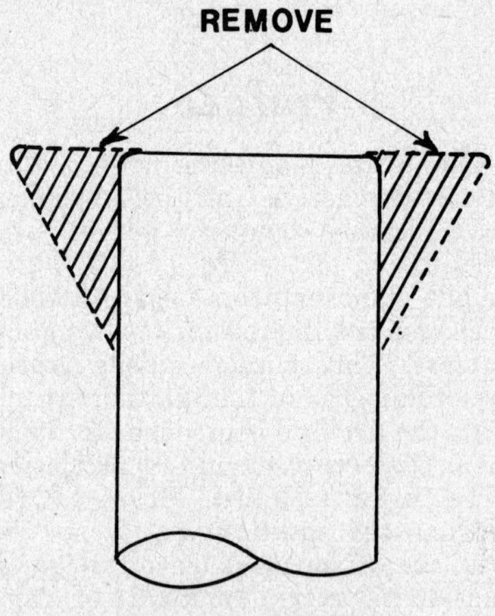
REMOVE

Altered door lock button

Hood lock mechanisms are available in two basic types—those which are visible when installed, and those that are not. Visible locks (e.g., locking hood pins, flush mount locks) not only deter opening the engine compartment, but act as a visual deterrent. Hidden mechanisms usually consist of a cable actuated release for the hood latch replacing the exterior latch release, or a secondary latch mechanism. Hood locks have the advantage of protecting the engine compartment from theft in addition to protecting the entire vehicle. Their disadvantage lies in the fact that the hood need not be open to start the engine in many cases; therefore, it is advisable to use hood locks in combination with other anti-theft devices.

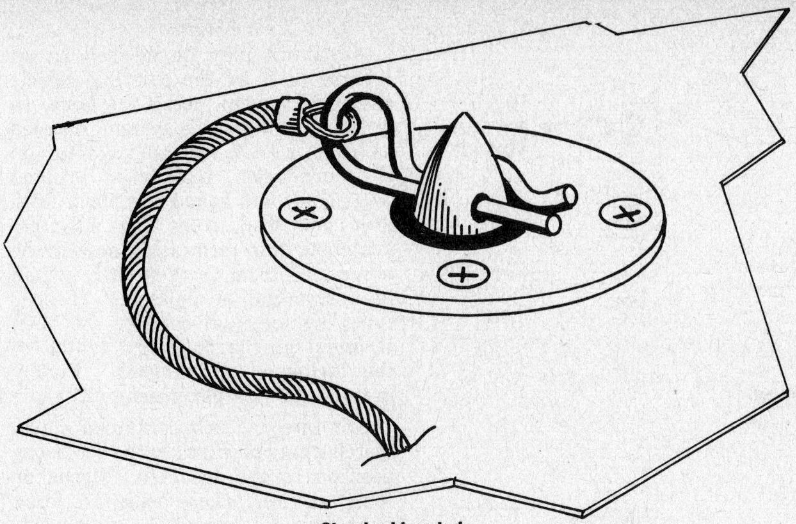

Standard hood pin

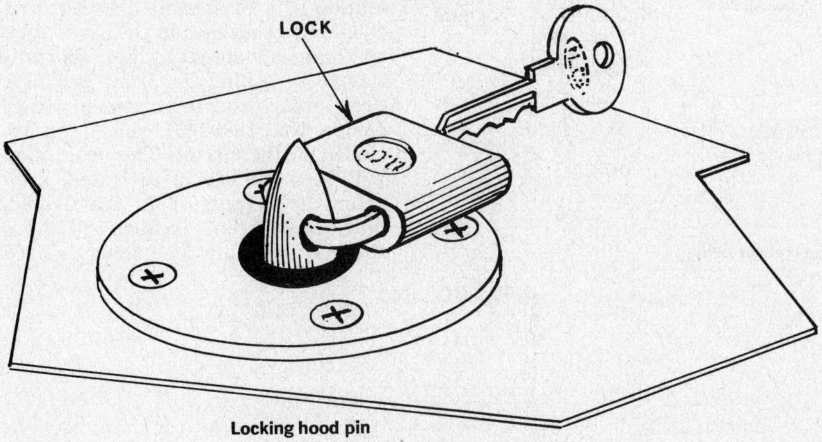
LOCK

Locking hood pin

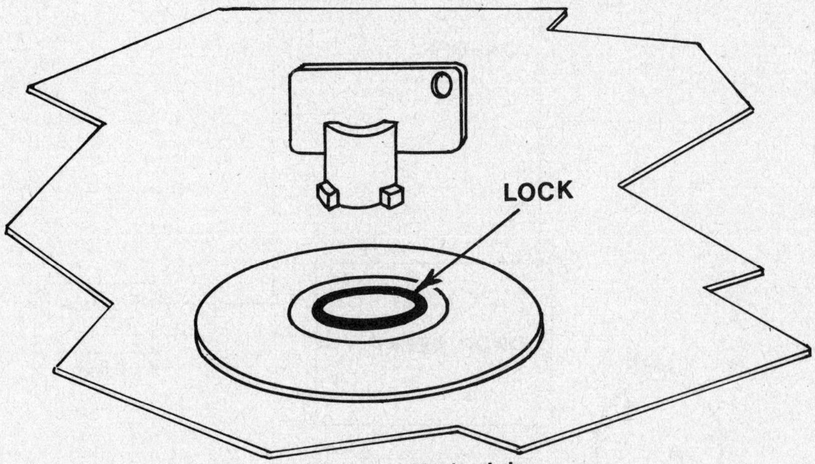
LOCK

Flush-mount locking hood pin

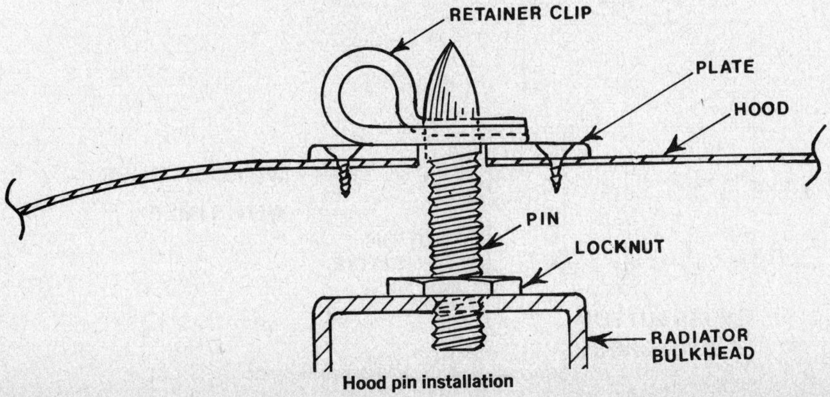
RETAINER CLIP
PLATE
HOOD
PIN
LOCKNUT
RADIATOR BULKHEAD

Hood pin installation

Electrical Systems

The most effective, and simplest electrical anti-theft device is an ignition ground switch, which will prevent the engine from being started. A single pole single throw switch is wired between the distributor primary lead and ground, and mounted inconspicuously in the interior (e.g., in the glove box, under the dashboard, etc.). When the switch is open, the ignition will function normally. When the switch is closed, the ignition is grounded, and the engine will not run.

An alternate method includes a switch in the distributor primary wire (see illustration). In this case, the system will function only when the switch is closed.

Solenoid actuated hood latches or fuel shut off valves, controlled by interior mounted switches are effective and easy to conceal; however, each has the disadvantages of the mechanical version of the same device.

Type B, Warning Systems

Warning systems can be broken down into three basic components: the trigger, trigger control, and alarm. Each will be considered separately.

Trigger Mechanisms

The trigger mechanism is the device used to actuate the alarm. In most cases, the trigger consists of a switch, or switches, and a drop relay. A drop relay is a relay that once activated will not recycle until reset manually; therefore, the alarm will not stop functioning even if the trigger switch is deactivated.

Motion sensitive switches (e.g., mercury switches, pendulum switches, reed vibrator switches) are excellent means of detecting tampering. The switch may be mounted anywhere in the car, and its sensitivity may be adjusted to the desired level. The disadvantage of a motion sensitive switch is the accuracy with which it must be adjusted. The switch must respond to the opening of a door, the hood or trunk, but not to parking on an incline, being bumped by a pedestrian, or traffic passing by. Once the proper sensitivity is determined, it is a good idea to include a timer in the trigger circuit, to shut the alarm off after a certain period of time if it is accidentally triggered when the car is disturbed.

Pushbutton switches (i.e., interior lighting door jamb switches), mounted on all doors and the hood and trunk, may also be used to trigger an alarm. These spring loaded, normally closed switches may be positioned adjacent to the existing switches on the door jambs, and on the hood and trunk latch plates. A combination system of motion sensitive and pushbutton switches will provide excellent

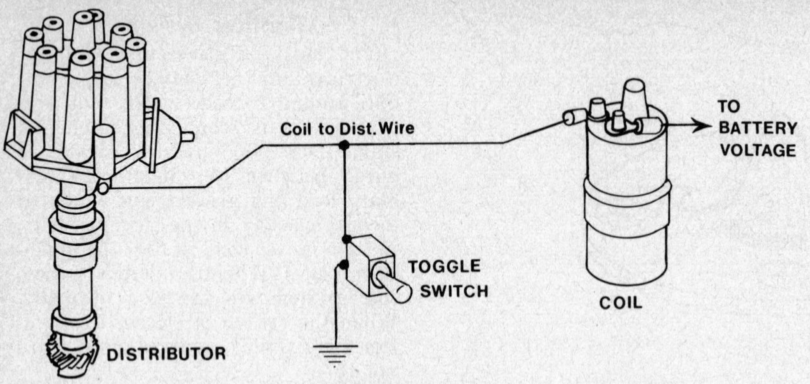
Coil to Dist. Wire
TO
BATTERY
VOLTAGE
TOGGLE
SWITCH
COIL
DISTRIBUTOR

Ignition ground switch

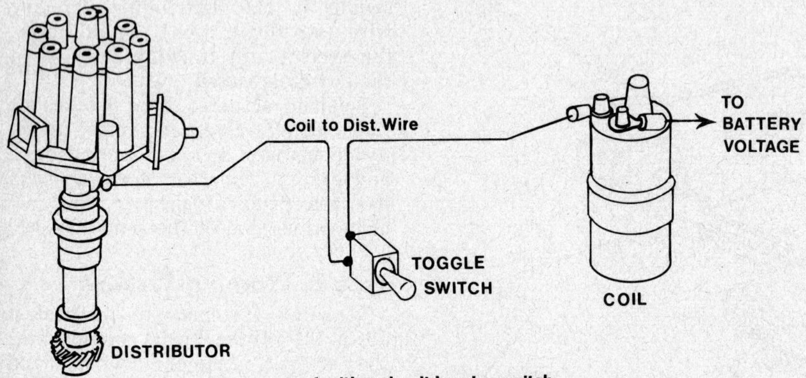
Coil to Dist. Wire
TO
BATTERY
VOLTAGE
TOGGLE
SWITCH
COIL
DISTRIBUTOR

Ignition circuit breaker switch

Alarms

An alarm may be devised as an integral part of the existing vehicle electrical system, using the horn. In order to connect this system, proceed as follows: Locate the terminal on the horn relay, that when bridged to ground, will sound the horn. Connect one lead from the ON-OFF switch to this terminal. Connect the other lead from the ON-OFF switch to a terminal of pulsating (flasher type) switch, and connect the open terminal of the pulsating switch to the trigger mechanisms. Firmly ground the trigger mechanisms.

Non-integral, self contained alarm systems may be wired to the accessory position in the fuse box. Sirens or other devices (i.e., bells, buzzers) must be loud enough to attract attention at a reasonable distance, and should be positioned in the car to take maximum advantage of their capabilities (e.g., behind the front grill). A drop relay and/or a timer (e.g., Dodge No. 2889565) should be included in the circuit. The drop relay will keep the alarm activated, even after the trigger(s) is deactivated, until all current is removed from the alarm circuit. The timer is used

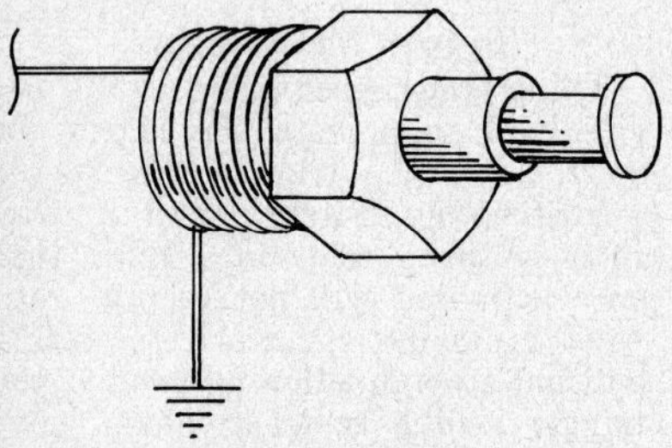

Pushbutton switch

protection. Mercury switches used to activate hood and trunk lights may be used as triggers, in lieu of pushbutton switches, on the hood and trunk.

Trigger Control Switches

The trigger control switch acts as an ON-OFF switch for the alarm system. It must be arranged in such a manner that the owner may enter the vehicle without triggering the alarm, but that a thief will be unable to detect or disarm.

The simplest control switch is a toggle switch mounted outside the car in an inconspicuous place. (e.g., under the rocker panel, inside a fender well). For this usage, the switch and the wiring must be weatherproofed.

The most popular type of control switch is the locking type which may be mounted anywhere on the outside of the car. These switches use cylindrical "pickproof" locks, and provide excellent protection, in addition to acting as a visual deterrent.

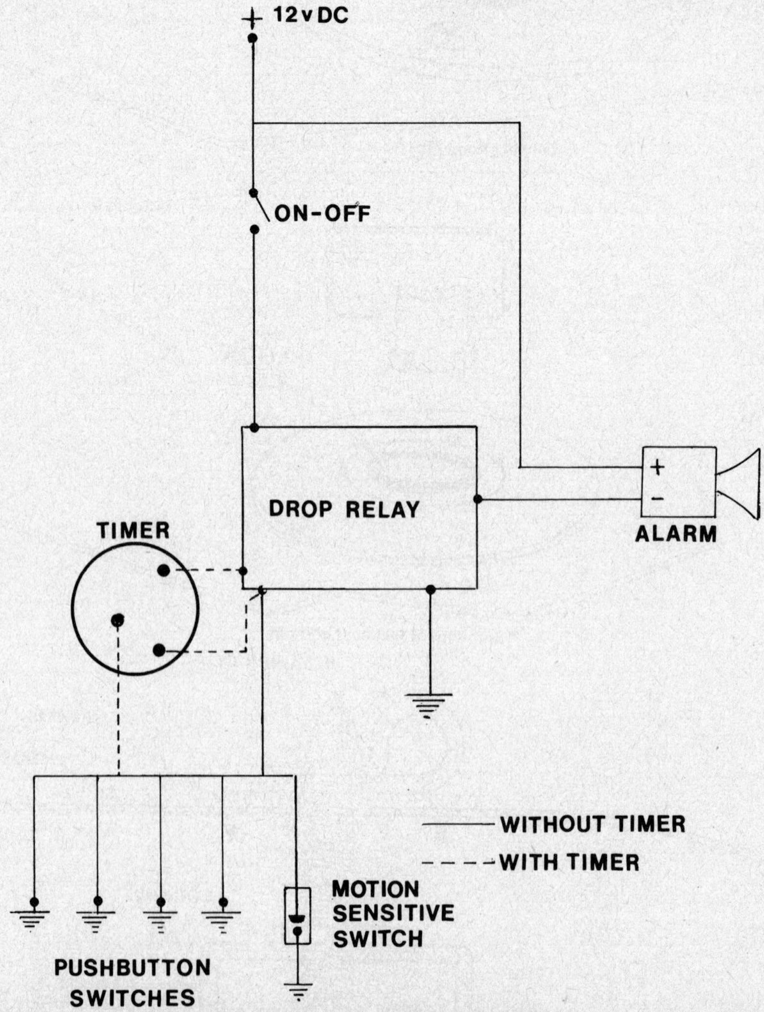
+ 12 v DC
ON-OFF
DROP RELAY
+
−
ALARM
TIMER
WITHOUT TIMER
WITH TIMER
MOTION
SENSITIVE
SWITCH
PUSHBUTTON
SWITCHES

Self-contained alarm system schematic

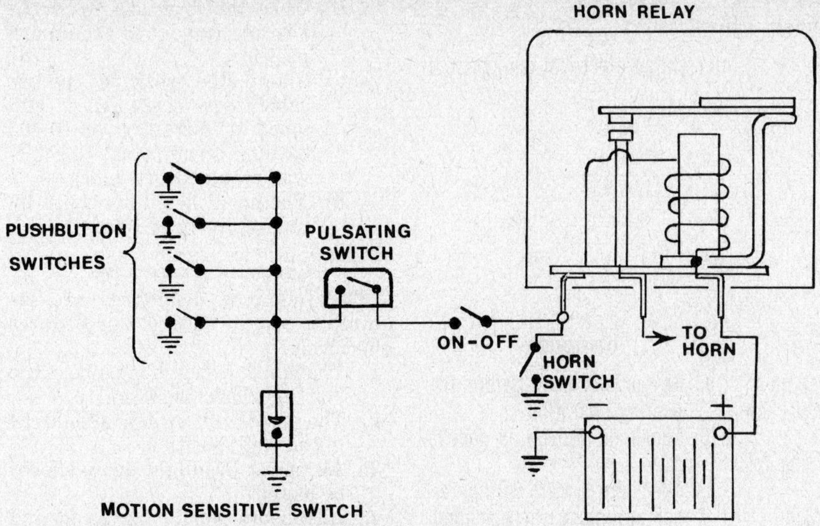
HORN RELAY
PUSHBUTTON SWITCHES
PULSATING SWITCH
ON-OFF
TO HORN
HORN SWITCH
MOTION SENSITIVE SWITCH
Integral alarm circuit schematic

to deactivate the alarm a certain period of time after the trigger is deactivated, to prevent the alarm running down the battery or disturbing the peace after accidental triggering.

In addition to, or in lieu of the above, it is suggested that a "Protected by Alarm" sticker be mounted on the window. This will act as an excellent visual deterrent to theft, and costs little or nothing. These stickers may be obtained from many burglar alarm manufacturers.

Factory-Installed Systems

Chrysler Corporation—All Models

Description

The theft warning system is armed when either front door is locked with the key. When the system is armed, forced entry of the doors, hood, trunk, tailgate, or application of voltage to the accessory circuit of the ignition switch will activate the alarm. When one of the mechanisms is triggered the control unit flashes the headlamps, tail and side marker lamps and simultaneously sounds the horns at a rate of ninety times per minute. The alarm will continue to operate for three to five minutes or until the system is turned off by using the key.

Testing Procedures

1. If the hood cannot be opened because of a run down battery, the following steps must be taken to open the hood.
   a) Using jumper cables, attach the negative cable to a ground. Use the courtesy light door switch.

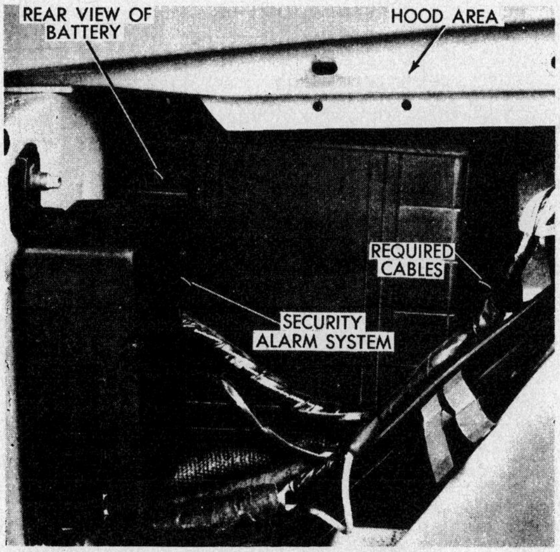
REAR VIEW OF BATTERY
HOOD AREA
REQUIRED CABLES
SECURITY ALARM SYSTEM
Control unit location
(© Chrysler Corp)

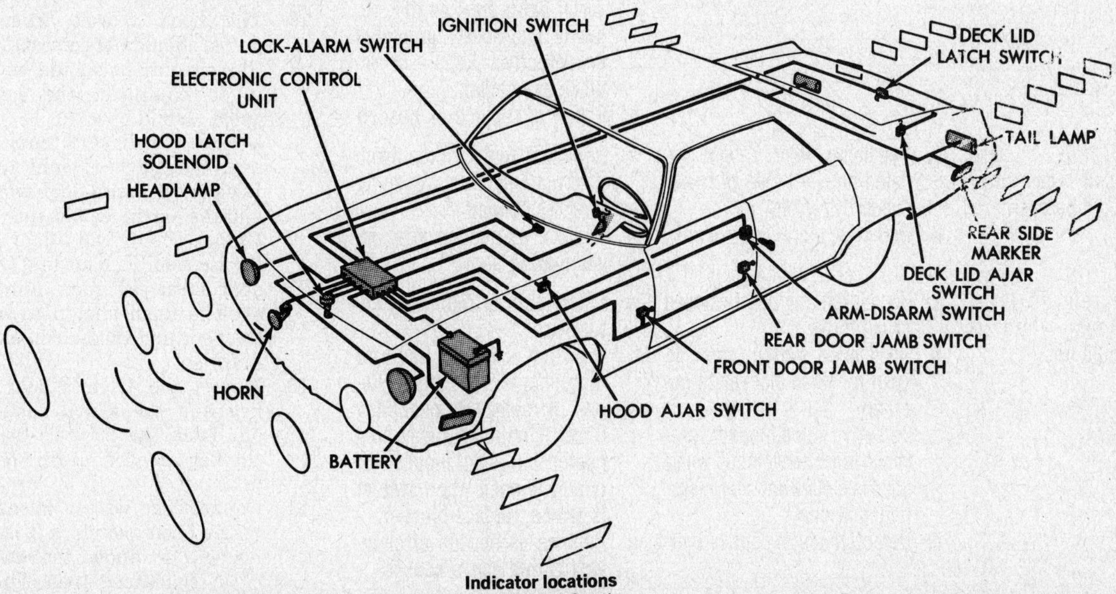
IGNITION SWITCH
LOCK-ALARM SWITCH
ELECTRONIC CONTROL UNIT
HOOD LATCH SOLENOID
HEADLAMP
DECK LID LATCH SWITCH
TAIL LAMP
REAR SIDE MARKER
DECK LID AJAR SWITCH
ARM-DISARM SWITCH
REAR DOOR JAMB SWITCH
FRONT DOOR JAMB SWITCH
HOOD AJAR SWITCH
HORN
BATTERY
Indicator locations
(© Chrysler Corp)

Chrysler Diagnosis Chart

Before using the Diagnosis Chart, check the following interrelated electrical components for proper operation:

1. Horns
2. Headlights
3. Taillights
4. Side marker lights
5. Courtesy lights

COMPLAINT	POSSIBLE CAUSE	CORRECTION
Alarm on when it should be off	a. Ignition switch turned on after doors have been key-locked b. Defective in one of the following switches: Trunk/tailgate latch switch Trunk/tailgate open switch Door lock alarm switch Hood latch switch Hood open switch c. Defective system wiring d. Defective alarm control unit	a. Key unlock door before repeating operation b. Repair or replace as necessary c. Check-out system wiring; repair or replace where needed d. Replace as needed after investigating above causes
Alarm system inoperative	a. Improperly grounded or defective hood or trunk open switch (closes when hood or trunk is opened) b. Defective trunk/tailgate latch switch (closes when trunk/tailgate is shut) c. Defective door lock switch d. Defective system wiring (especially battery, ground, or ignition feed) e. Defective alarm control unit	a. Repair or replace as needed b. Same as above c. Same as above d. Check-out system wiring; repair or replace as needed e. Replace as needed after investigating previous causes
Headlamps on when alarm is switched off	a. Headlamp time delay by-pass relay defective or improperly grounded b. Defective alarm control unit	a. Turn ignition ON. Then turn headlight switch ON, then OFF. Turn ignition OFF. If headlights remain ON, remove by-pass relay connector. If lights then go OFF, relay is improperly grounded or defective. Repair or replace as needed. b. Repair or replace as needed
Headlamp doors closed when they should be open	a. Headlamp door relays (located on right side of brake support bracket) b. Defective alarm control unit	a. Repair or replace (headlamp door holding or door opening relay) as needed b. Replace as needed after investigating above.
Hood release lever moves when it should not	a. Hood latch improperly closed or defective b. Hood open switch (must be open for hood blocker to operate) c. Defective hood blocker (prevents latch movement when hood is closed and alarm system is armed d. Defective alarm control unit	a. Close latch or replace if defective. b. If switch is closed, open or disconnect it to check. Repair or replace as needed c. Check circuit at 2-way connector on hood blocker. If circuit is open when system is armed, replace blocker. d. Replace as needed after investigating above causes

b) Turn the door lock with the key and leave it in the unlock position.
c) Clamp the positive jumper cable to a screwdriver and touch the screwdriver to the battery terminal of the firewall mounted fuse block.
d) The hood should now open by pulling the hood release.

Checkout Procedures

The following conditions are required to use the checkout procedures effectively.

1. The ignition switch must be in the "off" or "lock" position.
2. The headlight switch should be in the "off" position.
3. All power headlight doors should be closed.
4. All dooors should be closed and unlocked.
5. Put the driver's door and tailgate glass in the full down position.
6. The hood should be opened with the latch manually closed. The hood switch should either be disconnected or clamped open.
7. Keep the ignition and trunk key available.

Follow the checkout procedures step by step until the problem area is detected.

1. With the alarm control unit not armed and all the wiring properly connected the alarm should stay off.
2. Open and close the left rear door and when the dome light goes on the alarm should stay off.
3. Open the driver's door and while open, lock the door with the key. The alarm should stay off.
4. Turn the ignition to the "on" position and the alarm should go on.
5. Turn the ignition to the "off" position and the alarm should stay on.
6. The hood release lever when pulled should not release.
7. The headlamps should be off and if so equipped, the headlamp doors should be open.
8. Unlock the driver's door with a key, the alarm should turn off. Lock the driver's door with a key and the alarm should stay off.
9. Unlock the driver's door by lifting the door lock button. Open the door until the dome lamp turns on. The alarm should go on. Close the door and the alarm should remain on.
10. Unlock the driver's door with a key and the alarm should turn off. Lock the driver's door with the key and the alarm should remain off.
11. Connect the wiring harness lead to the hood switch if it is disconnected, or allow the switch to close if clamped open. The alarm should go on.

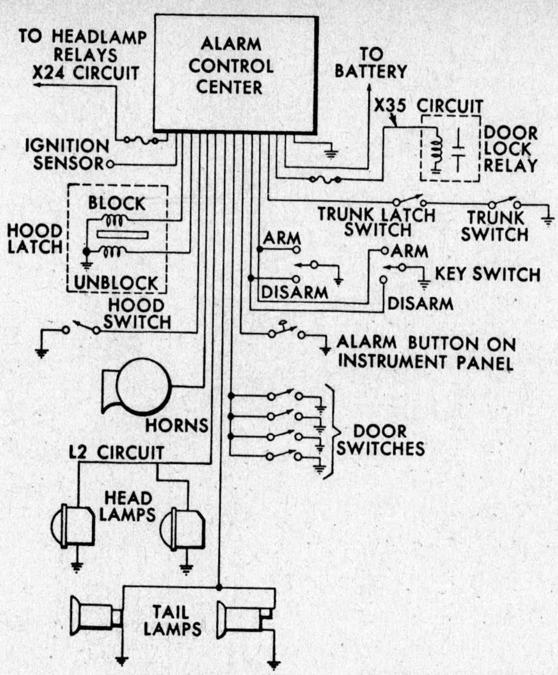
TO HEADLAMP RELAYS X24 CIRCUIT
ALARM CONTROL CENTER
TO BATTERY
X35 CIRCUIT
DOOR LOCK RELAY
IGNITION SENSOR
BLOCK
HOOD LATCH
UNBLOCK
HOOD SWITCH
TRUNK LATCH SWITCH
TRUNK SWITCH
ARM
DISARM
ARM
KEY SWITCH
DISARM
ALARM BUTTON ON INSTRUMENT PANEL
HORNS
DOOR SWITCHES
L2 CIRCUIT
HEAD LAMPS
TAIL LAMPS

Vehicle security alarm circuit system
(© Chrysler Corp)

12. On the right side of the car both doors should be locked. Unlock the front door with the key. The alarm should turn off. Lock the door using the key.
13. Push the hood switch down, then release the switch and the alarm should go off. Disconnect the wiring harness connector or clamp the hood switch open. Headlamps should be flashing.
14. Unlock the passenger's door with the key and the alarm should turn off. Open the door and the alarm should stay off and the dome light should operate.
15. Press the lock alarm switch by reaching in the car and the alarm should go on.
16. Unlock the passenger's door with the key and the alarm should turn off. Unlock the rear door, then close the passenger's door. Open the rear door and observe the dome lamp operation. Lock the passenger's door with the key.
17. Open the trunk and the alarm should stay off.
18. Manually close the trunk latch, and the alarm should go on. Unlock the latch and close the trunk. The alarm should stay on. (All models other than Stationwagons proceed to step #22.)
19. The tailgate should be locked. Unlock the tailgate by lifting the door lock button. The alarm should go on. Open the tailgate and push the door lock button down. The alarm should stay on.
20. Unlock the tailgate using the key and the alarm should stay on. Lock the tailgate using the key then close the tailgate. The alarm should stay on.
21. Unlock the tailgate by lifting the door lock button. The alarm should stay on.
22. Using a key, unlock the driver's door. The alarm should turn off. Pull the hood release and the handle should allow the hood latch to release. Turn the ignition key to "on" and the alarm should stay off. The headlamp doors should close.
23. Turn the ignition off and connect the wire to the hood switch. Close the hood.

Ford and Mercury

Description

The theft warning system is armed by locking either front door with a key and then removing the key from the cylinder. When the trunk lid or doors are opened, the alarm is activated and the horns sound intermittently, for approximately five minutes. The horns can only be turned off by inserting the key in the ignition switch and turning it to the Accessory or Run position.

The hood latch release used with this system can only be opened from inside the car by using the trunk key and pulling on the hood release handle.

The warning system is controlled by a transistorized sensor (actuator) which is mounted to a bracket and lo-

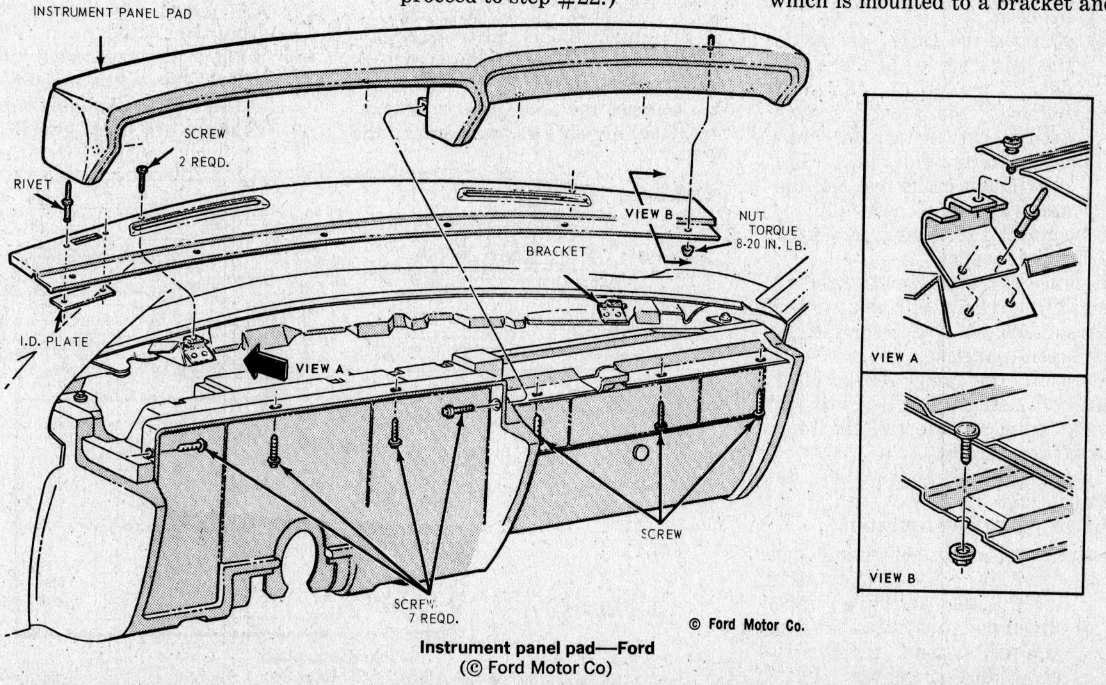
INSTRUMENT PANEL PAD
SCREW
2 REQD.
RIVET
VIEW B
NUT
TORQUE
8-20 IN. LB.
BRACKET
I.D. PLATE
VIEW A
SCREW
SCREW
7 REQD.
VIEW A
VIEW B
© Ford Motor Co.

Instrument panel pad—Ford
(© Ford Motor Co)

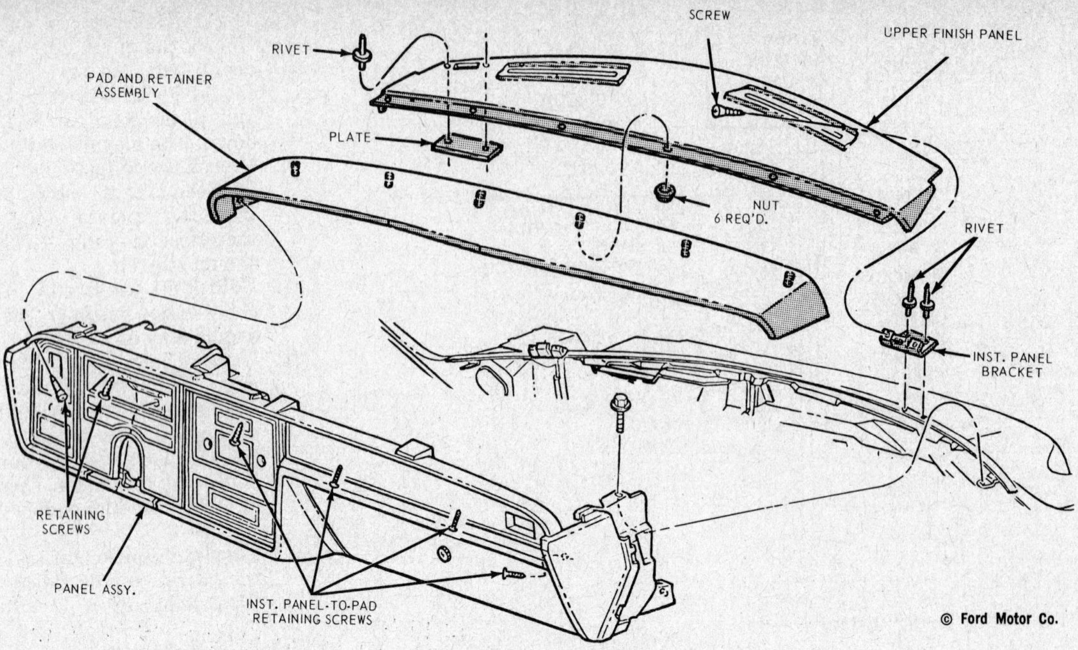
SCREW
UPPER FINISH PANEL
RIVET
PAD AND RETAINER ASSEMBLY
PLATE
NUT 6 REQ'D.
RIVET
INST. PANEL BRACKET
RETAINING SCREWS
PANEL ASSY.
INST. PANEL-TO-PAD RETAINING SCREWS
© Ford Motor Co.

Instrument panel pad—Mercury
(© Ford Motor Co)

cated under the instrument panel top pad and above the glove compartment door. The sensor receives its power from the battery and is electrically connected to the trunk warning switch and door lock cylinder switches. The sensor unit cannot be repaired and must be replaced if found defective.

Sensor (Actuator) Removal and Installation

Ford

1. Remove the instrument panel pad.
   a) Remove one screw on each side of the defroster nozzle opening.
   b) Remove the three screws on the ledge above the glove box door.
   c) Remove the four screws around the instrument cluster opening and remove the instrument panel pad and the upper finish pad assembly.
2. Disconnect the wiring connector from the sensor.
3. Remove the four sensor bracket attaching screws and remove the sensor and bracket from the instrument panel.
4. Position the new sensor and bracket assembly to the instrument panel and install the four attaching screws.
5. Connect the wiring harness to the sensor.
6. Check for proper operation.
7. Install the instrument panel pad.
   a) Position the instrument panel pad and the upper finish pad and install the four screws around the instrument cluster opening.
   b) Install the three screws above the glove box door.
   c) Install each screw on the sides of the defroster nozzle opening.

Mercury

1. Remove the instrument panel pad.
   a) Remove one screw on each side of the defroster nozzle opening.
   b) Remove the four screws going up into the entire length of the pad.
   c) Remove the one screw at each end of the inboard side of the pad and remove the upper instrument panel pad and the upper finish panel assembly.
2. Disconnect the wiring harness from the sensor.
3. Remove the four sensor bracket attaching screws and remove the sensor and bracket from the instrument panel.
4. Position the new sensor and bracket assembly to the instrument panel and install the four attaching screws.
5. Connect the wiring harness to the sensor.
6. Check for proper operation.
7. Install the instrument panel pad.
   a) Position the upper instrument panel pad and the upper finish panel assembly and install all the attaching screws.

Trunk Lid Switch Removal and Installation

1. Open the trunk lid.
2. Disconnect the wire connector from the switch.
3. Remove the one screw which attaches the switch and bracket to the left hinge support assembly.
4. Position the new switch to the

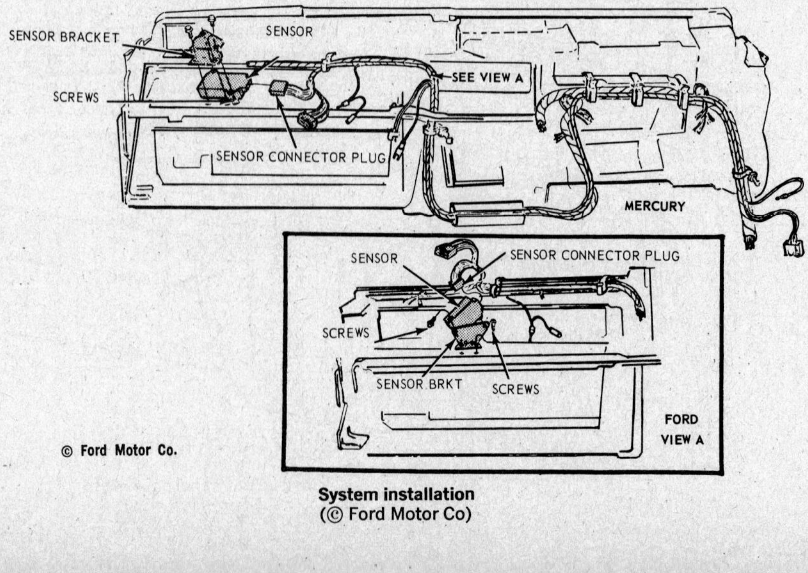
SENSOR BRACKET
SENSOR
SEE VIEW A
SCREWS
SENSOR CONNECTOR PLUG
MERCURY
SENSOR
SENSOR CONNECTOR PLUG
SCREWS
SENSOR BRKT
SCREWS
FORD
VIEW A
© Ford Motor Co.

System installation
(© Ford Motor Co)

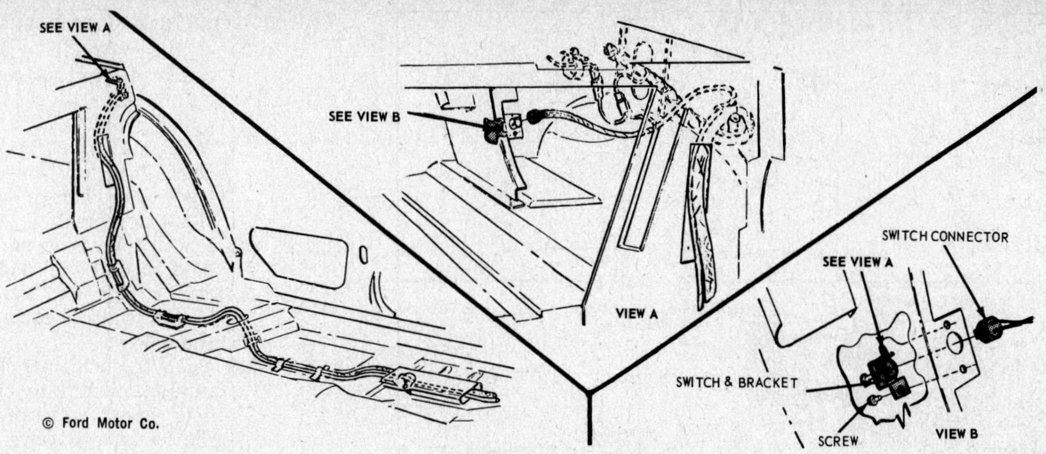
SEE VIEW A
SEE VIEW B
VIEW A
SWITCH CONNECTOR
SEE VIEW A
SWITCH & BRACKET
SCREW
VIEW B
© Ford Motor Co.

Trunk lid switch installation
(© Ford Motor Co)

left hinge support assembly and install the retaining screw.

5. Connect the wire connector to the switch.
6. Close the trunk lid and check the operation of the switch.

Door Lock Cylinder Switch Removal and Installation

1. Remove the door trim panel.

NOTE: If some of the following steps do not apply to the particular model being worked on, proceed to the next step.

a) Remove the door lock push button and garnish moulding.
b) Remove the window regulator handle screw access cover and remove the screw and handle.
c) Remove the door latch handle retaining screw access cover, if so equipped, and remove the door latch handle screws.
d) Remove the screws from the

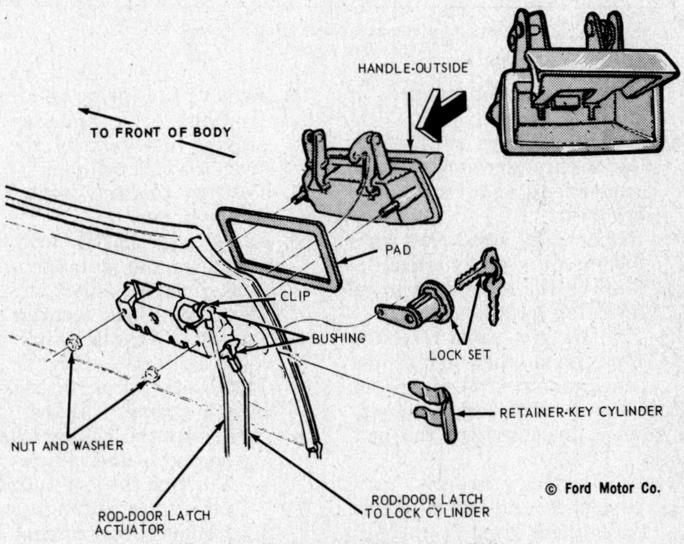
HANDLE-OUTSIDE
TO FRONT OF BODY
PAD
CLIP
BUSHING
LOCK SET
RETAINER-KEY CYLINDER
NUT AND WASHER
ROD-DOOR LATCH ACTUATOR
ROD-DOOR LATCH TO LOCK CYLINDER
© Ford Motor Co.

Door handle and lock cylinder installation
(© Ford Motor Co)

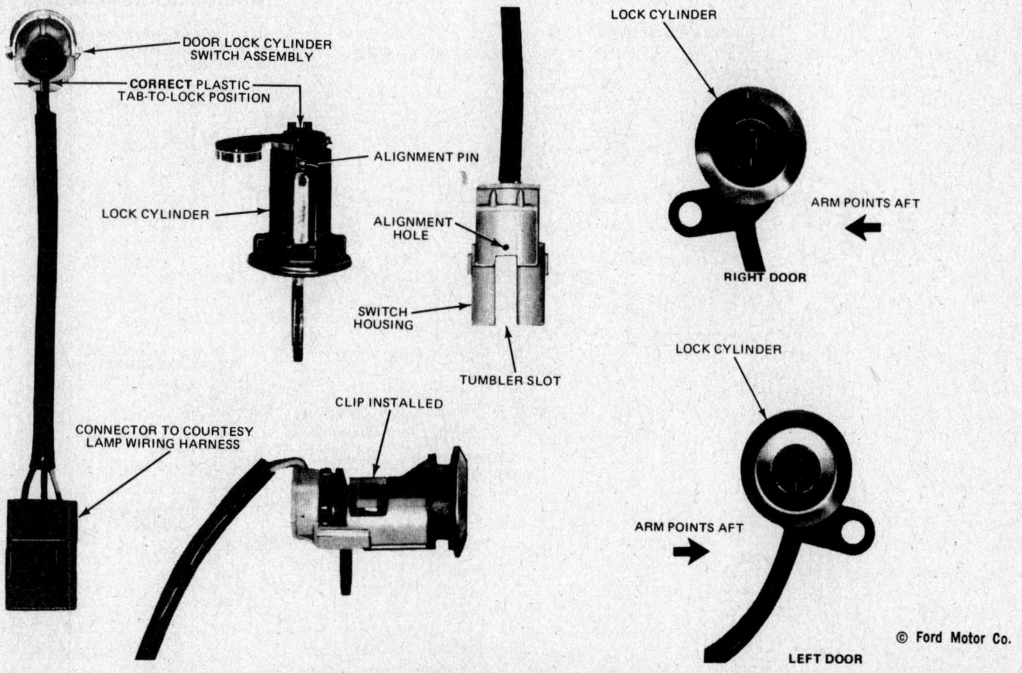
DOOR LOCK CYLINDER SWITCH ASSEMBLY
CORRECT PLASTIC TAB-TO-LOCK POSITION
ALIGNMENT PIN
LOCK CYLINDER
ALIGNMENT HOLE
SWITCH HOUSING
TUMBLER SLOT
CLIP INSTALLED
CONNECTOR TO COURTESY LAMP WIRING HARNESS
LOCK CYLINDER
ARM POINTS AFT
RIGHT DOOR
LOCK CYLINDER
ARM POINTS AFT
LEFT DOOR
© Ford Motor Co.

Door lock cylinder and switch assembly
(© Ford Motor Co)

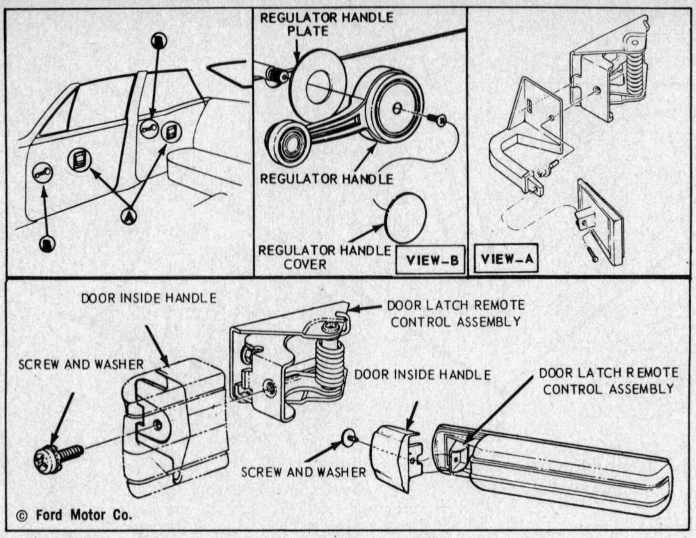
REGULATOR HANDLE PLATE
REGULATOR HANDLE
REGULATOR HANDLE COVER
VIEW—B
VIEW—A
DOOR INSIDE HANDLE
DOOR LATCH REMOTE CONTROL ASSEMBLY
SCREW AND WASHER
DOOR INSIDE HANDLE
DOOR LATCH REMOTE CONTROL ASSEMBLY
SCREW AND WASHER
© Ford Motor Co.

Door and window regulator handle installation
(© Ford Motor Co)

armrest door pull cup area, if so equipped.

e) Remove the arm rest retaining screws and any wiring connections and remove the arm rest.

f) Remove the bezel nut from the mirror remote control.

g) Remove the door trim panel retaining screws.

h) Pry the trim panel retaining clips from the door inner panel and separate the panel.

2. Disconnect the lock cylinder switch connector from the harness.
3. Remove the lock cylinder.
   a) Disconnect the control rod at the cylinder arm.
   b) Remove the door lock cylinder retainer and remove the lock cylinder.
4. Remove the spring retaining clip from the lock cylinder switch assembly and remove the switch from the lock cylinder.
5. Position the new switch to the lock cylinder.
6. Align the plastic arm of the switch to the metal tang on the back of the lock cylinder.
7. Install and lock securely the retaining clip to the switch housing tabs.
8. Install the lock cylinder and switch assembly to the door and make sure the locking arm points to the rear of the vehicle.
   a) Position the lock cylinder and install the retainer.
   b) Connect the control rod at the cylinder arm.
9. Test the alarm system for proper operation.
10. Install the door trim panel.
    a) If the watershield has been removed, position it correctly before installing the trim panel.
    b) Make sure that the arm rest retaining clips are properly positioned before installing the watershield.
    c) Position the trim panel to the door inner panel and connect any wiring and reroute the mirror control cable through the hole.
    d) Push the trim panel and retaining clips into the inner door panel holes and install the retaining screws.
    e) Install the bezel nut for the remote control mirror.
    f) Position the arm rest to the trim panel, connect any wiring and install the retaining screws.
    g) Install the arm rest finish panel, if so equipped.
    h) Position the door latch and window regulator handles and install the retaining screws.
    i) Tape the access cover back in place.
    j) Install the garnish moulding and the lock push button control knob.

NOTE: If for any reason the switch is separated from the lock cylinder a new switch must be installed.

Cadillac

Description

The theft warning system is operated by the ignition switch. When the ignition is turned off, the system is automatically armed within one and a

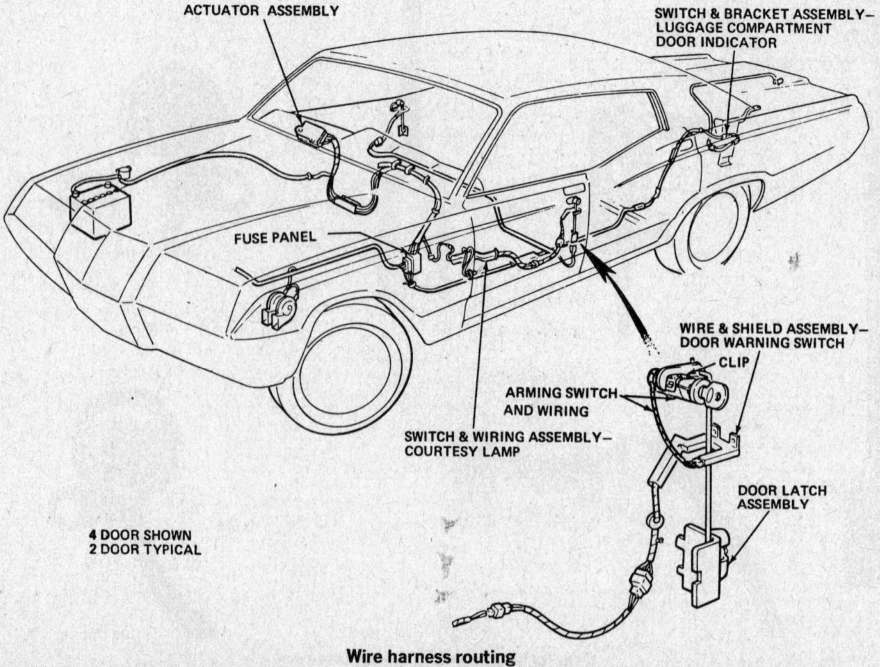
ACTUATOR ASSEMBLY
SWITCH & BRACKET ASSEMBLY—LUGGAGE COMPARTMENT DOOR INDICATOR
FUSE PANEL
WIRE & SHIELD ASSEMBLY—DOOR WARNING SWITCH
CLIP
ARMING SWITCH AND WIRING
SWITCH & WIRING ASSEMBLY—COURTESY LAMP
DOOR LATCH ASSEMBLY
4 DOOR SHOWN
2 DOOR TYPICAL

Wire harness routing
(© Ford Motor Co)

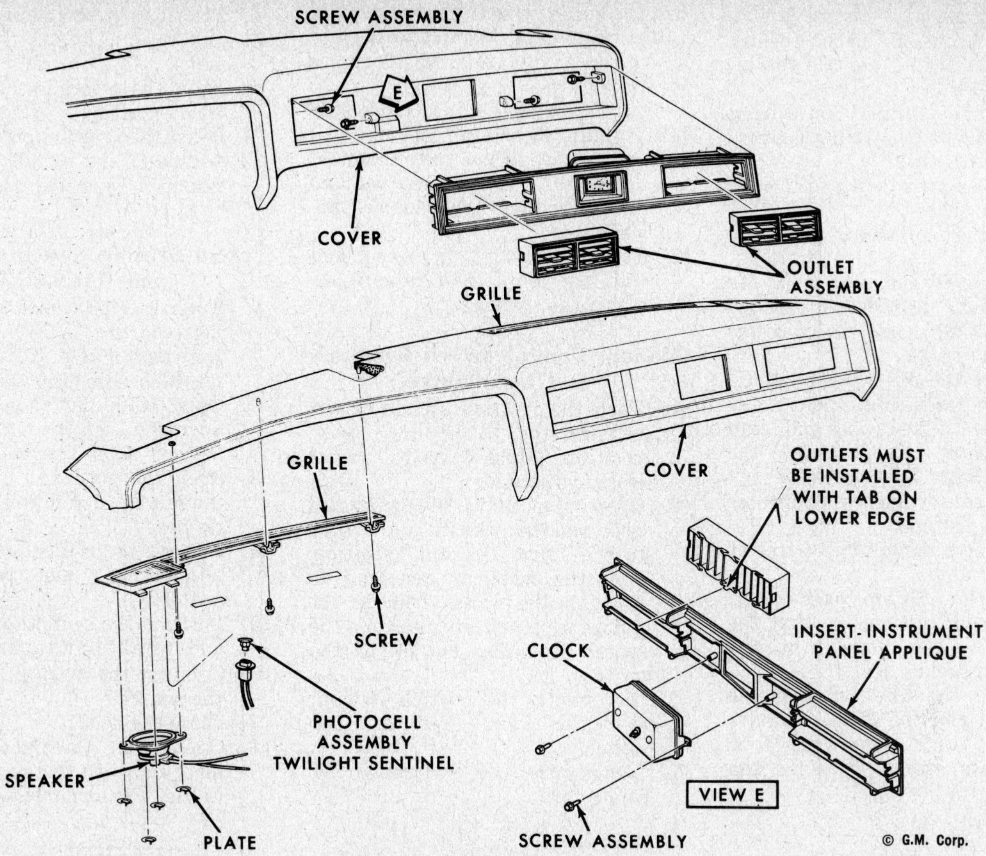
SCREW ASSEMBLY
E
COVER
OUTLET ASSEMBLY
GRILLE
GRILLE
COVER
OUTLETS MUST BE INSTALLED WITH TAB ON LOWER EDGE
SCREW
CLOCK
INSERT- INSTRUMENT PANEL APPLIQUE
PHOTOCELL ASSEMBLY TWILIGHT SENTINEL
SPEAKER
VIEW E
PLATE
SCREW ASSEMBLY
© G.M. Corp.

Instrument panel top cover—Cadillac
(© G.M. Corp)

half minutes. The system is disarmed when the ignition is turned to the run position within fifteen seconds after any door is opened. After fifteen seconds the alarm will go off.

The system may be prevented from being armed by actuating a two position switch located in the glove compartment. When the switch is turned to the "Arm Prevent" position with the ignition switch on or within thirty seconds after the ignition is switched off, the system will remain disarmed until the switch is turned to the "Arm Enable" position. A second arm prevent method is by turning the ignition switch to the accessory position for five seconds before withdrawing the key. This will allow the car to be moved or parked one time without the alarm going off.

After the system is armed the alarm will be actuated electrically by seven different trigger mechanisms: (1) A plunger type switch is located on the left side of the radiator tie bar in a position where it can sense any small movement of the hood, (2) Within fifteen seconds after any door is opened, the door pillar switches activate the alarm, (3) When the trunk lid is lifted and the inside bulb goes on, (4) A special cover is placed over the fuse block and held in place by the horn and window circuit breakers. When the horn circuit breaker is removed the alarm goes off, (5) If a resistance-type electrical load is turned on, (6) When the glove box is opened, (7) If the control switch in the glove compartment is turned to the disarm position.

The electronic sensor or control box is mounted on the instrument panel center brace. Access to the control can only be made by removing the top instrument panel cover. The controller contains an internal timing circuit and relay which flash the parking, side marker, tail and license lamps and simultaneously sound the horns at a rate of fifty cycles per minute.

In order to conserve the battery the alarm automatically shuts off after three to five minutes of operation then rearms itself.

Control Box Removal and Installation

1. Cycle the ignition switch slowly between "ACC" and the "lock" position.
2. Open the glove compartment door and move the manual switch to the "Arm Prevent" position.
3. Remove the instrument panel top cover.
   a) Disconnect the negative battery cable.
   b) Open the glove compartment and remove the two screws which secure the top cover to the instrument panel. On air conditioned cars, remove the aspirator hose from the sensor through the top of the glove compartment.
   c) Remove the four screws which secure the top cover to the instrument panel bezel assembly.
   d) Carefully lift up and pull the top cover rearward to separate it from the cowl.

   NOTE: On models equipped with a tilt wheel, removal can be accomplished by placing the wheel in the low position.

   e) Disconnect the speaker wires from the radio.
   f) Raise the top cover high enough to disconnect the Twilight Sentinel photocell at the left from speaker opening and sensor harness connector from the sensor, if so equipped.
   g) Disconnect the clock electrical feed wires and remove the top cover.
4. Remove the air conditioner center outlet duct hose.
5. Disconnect the control box wiring connectors from the wiring harness connectors.
6. Remove the two screws which secure the control box to the instrument panel center brace and remove the control box.

NOTE: The control box cannot be repaired and must be replaced if defective.

7. Position the new control box to the instrument panel center brace and install the two retaining screws.
8. Connect the control box wiring connectors to the wiring harness connectors.
9. Install the air conditioner center outlet duct hose.
10. Install the instrument panel top cover.

NOTE: Install the screws in the following order to prevent damage to the plastic bosses if stresses are present in the panel.

a) Place the top cover over the instrument panel and connect the clock feed wires and lamp assembly, also connect the Twilight Sentinel photocell and sensor harness connector if so equipped.
b) Connect the speaker wires at the radio.
c) Position the top cover on the instrument panel so that the three clips engage at the windshield.
d) Align the screw holes in the bezel and the glove compartment and install the four screws which attach the top cover to the bezel.
e) From within the glove compartment, install the two top cover to instrument panel screws.
f) On air conditioned models install the aspirator hose.

11. Open the glove compartment door and move the manual switch to the "Arm Enable" position.
12. Turn the ignition on and off and wait one and a half minutes to rearm the system.

Manual Control Switch Removal and Installation

1. Turn the ignition switch slowly between the "ACC" and "lock" position. (Hold at "ACC" for at least five seconds).
2. Open the glove compartment door and turn the manual switch to the "Arm Prevent" position.
3. Hold the switch by reaching up through the access hole in the top of the glove box and turn the switch mounting nut off of the switch.
4. Disconnect the switch wiring connector and remove the switch.
5. Connect the new switch wiring connector.
6. Position the switch in the mounting hole and install the retaining nut.
7. Turn the switch to the "Arm Enable" position.
8. Turn the ignition on and off and wait one and a half minutes to rearm the system.

Hood Sensing System Removal and Installation

1. Turn the ignition switch slowly between the "ACC" and "lock" positions. (Hold at "ACC" for at least five seconds.)
2. Open the glove compartment door and turn the manual switch to the "Arm Prevent" position.
3. Open the hood and reach under the left hand side of the radiator tie bar.
4. Remove the switch to tie bar retaining nut and remove the switch.
5. Position the switch to the tie bar and install the retaining nut.
6. Connect the wiring harness to the switch.
7. Close the hood.
8. Open the glove compartment door and turn the manual switch to the "Arm Enable" position.

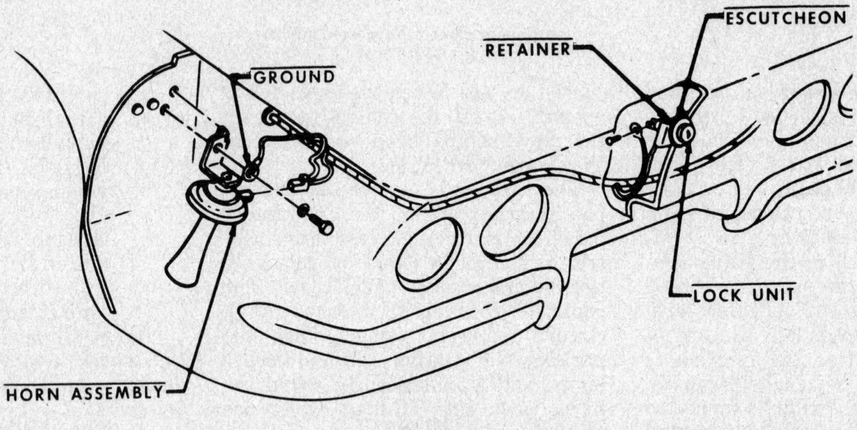
ESCUTCHEON
RETAINER
GROUND
LOCK UNIT
HORN ASSEMBLY

REAR END

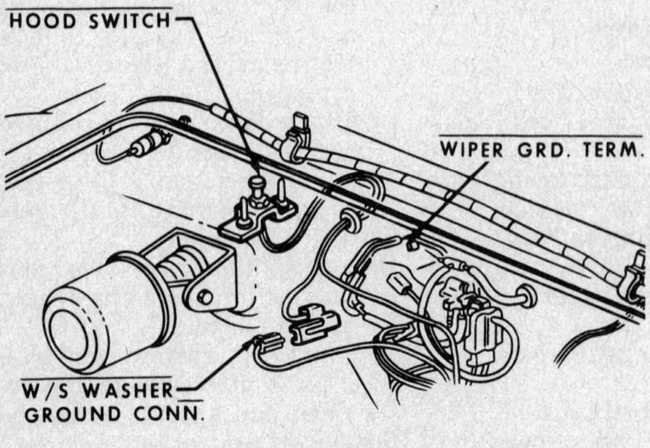
HOOD SWITCH
WIPER GRD. TERM.
W/S WASHER
GROUND CONN.

UNDER HOOD

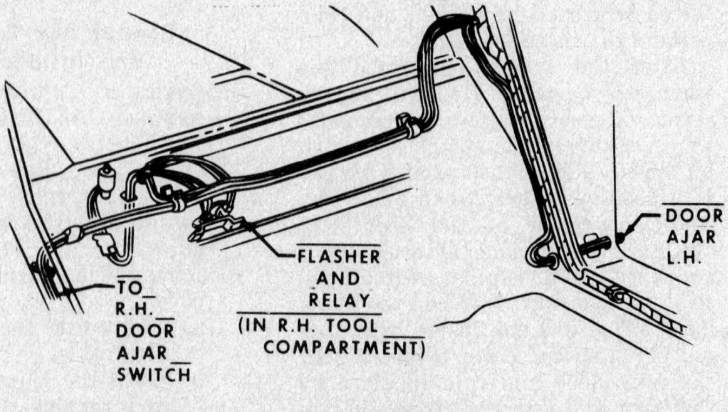
DOOR
AJAR
L.H.
FLASHER
AND
RELAY
(IN R.H. TOOL
COMPARTMENT)
TO
R.H.
DOOR
AJAR
SWITCH

INSIDE VEHICLE

Corvette installation
(© G.M. Corp)

9. Turn the ignition on and off and wait for one and a half minutes for the system to rearm itself.
10. Check the system by opening the hood.

Hood Sensing Switch Adjustment

1. Make sure that the hood panel and latches are properly aligned.
2. Turn the ignition switch on and off and wait ten seconds.
3. With the hood locked, lift upward at the left front corner.
4. If the alarm sounds remove the switch and shim with washers as required.
5. Pull the hood release cable and open the hood.
6. If the alarm does not sound, stretch the hood pop-up spring to raise the hood fully to the secondary latch position.

Fuse Box Cover Removal and Installation

1. Turn the ignition switch to "ACC" and hold there for at least five seconds. Then turn to the "lock" position.
2. Open the glove compartment and turn the manual switch to the "Arm Prevent" position.
3. Remove the two circuit breakers from the fuse block cover and remove the cover.
4. Position the fuse block cover on the fuse block and retain by installing the two circuit breakers through the cover.
5. From inside the glove compartment move the manual switch to the "Arm Enable" position.
6. Turn the ignition on and off and wait one and a half minutes for the system to rearm itself.

NOTE: When using jumper cables or reconnecting battery cables to a car equipped with the theft warning system, it is normal for the alarm to be activated and the horns and lights to operate. The alarm may be shut off by turning the ignition switch to the accessory or run position.

Corvette

Description

The theft warning system is armed when the glove compartment and spare tire key is inserted into the tail panel lock cylinder and turned clockwise ninety degrees. Plunger type switches are located in both the door jambs and under the right side of the hood. When the system is armed and the hood or doors are opened, the triggered switches complete the circuit and actuate the warning horn located above the left rear tire in the wheelhouse.

The only way to shut off the alarm is to insert the key into the tail panel lock cylinder and turn it ninety degrees counter-clockwise.

Lock Cylinder Switch Removal and Installation

1. Remove the ground cable from the battery.
2. Remove the license plate.
3. Remove the two license lamp housing retaining screws and remove the housing.
4. After the license lamp housing is removed, reach through the access hole created and pull the clip which retains the control switch.
5. Note the location of the switch wires and remove both from the switch.
6. Position the new switch and install the wires and retaining clip.
7. Position the license lamp housing and install the two retaining screws.
8. Replace the license plate.
9. Replace the ground cable on the battery.

Warning Horn Removal and Installation

1. Raise the car and lower the left tail pipe assembly.
2. Remove the wiring connector from the horn.
3. Remove the bolt which retains the warning horn to the wheelhouse panel above the left rear tire.
4. Position the new horn and install the retaining bolt.
5. Install the wire connector.
6. Check the operation of the system.
7. Raise the tailpipe and secure in place.

General Motors Diagnosis Chart

Before using the "THEFT DETERRENT DIAGNOSIS CHART", check the following interrelated electrical components for proper operation:

1. Horns
2. Courtesy lamps
3. Trunk lamp

COMPLAINT	PROBABLE CAUSE	CORRECTION
System inoperative	a. Manual switch in "ARM PREVENT" b. Open in one of the following wires: 1. Battery feed 2. Ground wire 3. Ignition feed c. Short in manual switch wire d. Defective or reversed manual switch e. Defective controller	a. Place manual switch in "ARM ENABLE" b. Repair or replace as needed. Refer to electrical check-out procedure c. Same as above d. Same as above e. Replace after investigating previously listed causes.
Alarm activates shortly after key is turned from "ON" to "OFF"	a. Misadjusted (closed) hood switch b. Open in one of the following wires: 1. Horn breaker 2. Accessory feed c. Short in hood switch wire d. Defective controller	a. Readjust b. Repair or replace as needed. Refer to electrical check-out procedure. c. Same as above d. Replace after investigating previously listed causes.
Alarm can be activated even though switch placed in "ARM PREVENT"	a. Open in manual switch wire b. Defective or reversed manual switch c. Defective controller	a. Repair or replace as needed. Refer to electrical check-out procedure. b. Same as above c. Replace after investigating previously listed causes
System operates normally except alarm will not activate when hood opened	a. Open in hood switch wire b. Defective hood switch c. Defective controller	a. Repair or replace as needed. Refer to electrical check-out procedure b. Same as above c. Replace after investigating previously listed causes.
System operates normally except alarm activates immediately upon door opening (no entrance delay)	a. Open in door jamb switch wiring to controller b. Defective controller	a. Repair or replace as needed. Refer to electrical check-out procedure b. Replace after investigating previously listed cause.

INDEX

Volkswagen

Introduction

In 1932, Ferdinand Porsche produced prototypes for the NSU company of Germany. These led to the design of the Volkswagen. The prototypes had a rear, air-cooled engine, torsion-bar suspension, and the spare tire mounted at an angle in the front luggage compartment. In 1936, Porsche produced three Volkswagen prototypes, one of which was a 995 cc, horizontally opposed, four-cylinder automobile. In 1945 Volkswagen production began and 1,785 beetles were built. The Volkswagen convertible was introduced in 1949, the year when only two Volkswagens were sold in the entire U.S.A. The year 1950 marked the beginning of the sunroof models and the transporter series. The Volkswagen Karmann Ghia was introduced in 1956, and is still of the same basic styling format. The "big" Volkswagen, the 1500 Squareback, was introduced in Europe in 1961, and sold in the U.S.A. in 1966 as a member of the new type 3 series (Fastback and Squareback). The Type 4 was introduced to the U.S.A. with the 1971 model line.

BASIC BODY TYPES

411 4-Door Sedan, Type 4

411 3-Door Sedan, Type 4

Micro Bus, Type 2

Sedan (Beetle), Type 1

Convertible, Type 1

Fastback sedan, Type 3

Karmann Ghia, Type 1

Squareback Sedan, Type 3

Vehicle and Engine Serial Number Identification

Volkswagen Types

Volkswagen models are differentiated by type. Type 1 is the beetle and Karmann Ghia. Type 2 is the transporter, or bus and truck, series. Type 3 is the Fastback and Squareback. Type 4 is the 411 sedan and wagon. The current model numbers are as follow:

Model No. (LHD)	*Description*
111	VW 1300A sedan, 1971 1600 sedan
115	VW 1300A sedan with folding sunroof
113	VW 1500 sedan, 1971 1600 Super Beetle
117	VW 1500 sedan with steel sunroof
141	VW 1500 Karmann Ghia Convertible
143	VW 1500 Karmann Ghia Coupe
151	VW 1500 Convertible (4 seater)
211–215	Delivery Van
221–225	Micro Bus
231–237	Kombi
241	Deluxe Micro Bus (9 seater)
251	Deluxe Micro Bus (7 seater)
261–267	Pickup
271–273	Ambulance
281–285	Micro Bus (7 seater)
311	Fastback sedan (1600TL)
313	Fastback sedan with steel sunroof
315	1600A sedan
317	1600A sedan with steel sunroof
343	1600L Karmann Ghia Coupe
345	1600L Karmann Ghia Coupe with steel sunroof
361	1600L Squareback sedan
363	1600L Squareback sedan with steel sunroof
365	1600A Squareback sedan
367	1600A Squareback sedan with steel sunroof
411	411 Four door sedan
411	411 Three door sedan (wagon)

Chassis Number

The chassis number is on the frame tunnel under the back seat in the Types 1 and 3. In the Type 2, the chassis number is on the right engine cover plate in the engine compartment.

Beginning with the 1965 model year, a nine-digit serial number system was instituted. In this system, the first two numbers are the first two digits of the car's model number and the third digit stands for the car's model year—"5" stands for 1965, "8" stands for 1968, etc. A tenth digit was added when production passed one million.

Identification Plate

The identification plate carries the vehicle serial number and paint, body, and assembly codes. It is behind the spare tire in the luggage compartment on Type 1 models, and on the right side of the overhead air duct in early Type 2 vehicles. The Type 3 identification plate is next to the hood latch, in front of the spare tire in the luggage compartment. Starting 1970, all models have an identification plate on top of the driver's side of the instrument panel. This plate may be seen through the windshield.

Engine Number

On type 1 and 2 vehicles, which have the upright engine fan housing, the engine number is on the crankcase flange for the generator support. The number can readily be seen by looking through the center of the fan belt. On type 3 and 4 engines, which have the fan on the end of the crankshaft, the number is along the crankcase joint between the oil cooler and the air cleaner. The engine can be identified by the letter preceding the serial number. Refer to the Engine Identification Chart.

VEHICLE IDENTIFICATION—TYPES 1, 2, AND 3

H5752261
Type 1 Engine number location

Type 1 chassis number location

Type 1 identification plate location

		SAE Output	from Chassis No.	from Date	to Chassis No.	to Date
VEHICLE, TYPE 1						
Standard Sedan		36 bhp	1-0575 415	Dec. 1953	6 502 399	July 1964
Standard Sedan, Sedan A		36 bhp	115 000 001	Aug. 1964	115 979 202	July 1965
Deluxe Sedan, Karmann Ghia Models, VW Convertible		36 bhp	1-0575 415	Dec. 1953	3192 506	July 1960
		42 bhp	3192 507	Aug. 1960	6 502 399	July 1964
			115 000 001	Aug. 1964	115 979 202	July 1965
1200A		42 bhp	116 000 001	Aug. 1965	1161 021 297	July 1966
VW 1200		42 bhp	117 483 306	Jan. 1967	117 844 900	July 1967
			118 000 001	Aug. 1967	1181 061 095	July 1968
			119 000 001	Aug. 1968	1191 093 701	July 1969
			110 2000 001	Aug. 1969		
VW 1300 Sedan, Karmann Ghia Models, VW Convertible		50 bhp	116 000 001	Aug. 1965	1161 021 298	July 1966
VW 1300 A		50 bhp	117 000 001	Aug. 1966	117 403 305	Jan. 1967
VW 1300 Sedan		50 bhp	117 000 001	Aug. 1966	117 844 901	July 1967
			118 000 001	Aug. 1967	1181 016 096	July 1968
			119 000 002	Aug. 1968	1191 093 702	July 1969
			110 2000 002	Aug. 1969		
VW 1500 Sedan, Karmann Ghia Models, VW Convertible		53 bhp	117 000 001	Aug. 1966	117 844 902	July 1967
			118 000 001	Aug. 1967	118 1016 097	July 1968
			119 000 003	Aug. 1968	119 1093 703	July 1969
			110 2000 003	Aug. 1969		
		57 bhp	110 2000 004	Aug. 1969		
VW 1600 Sedan, Karmann Ghia Models, VW Convertible		57 bhp		1970		
VW 1600 Sedan, Super Beetle, Karmann Ghia Models, VW Convertible		60 bhp		1971		
VEHICLE, TYPE 2						
Transporter	1200	36 bhp	20-069 409	Dec. 1953	614 455	May 1960
		42 bhp	614 456	June 1960	1 328 271	July 1964
			215 000 001	Aug. 1964	215 036 378	Sept. 1964
	1500	51 bhp	1041 014	Jan. 1963	1 328 271	July 1964
			215 000 001	Aug. 1964	215 176 339	July 1965
		53 bhp	216 000 001	Aug. 1965	216 179 668	July 1966
			217 000 001	Aug. 1966	217 148 459	July 1967
	1600	57 bhp	218 000 001	Aug. 1967	218 202 251	July 1968
			219 000 001	Aug. 1968	219 238 131	July 1969
			210 2000 001	Aug. 1969		
		60 bhp		1971		
VEHICLE, TYPE 3						
Volkswagen 1500		54 bhp	0 000 001	Apr. 1961	0 483 592	July 1964
			315 000 001	Aug. 1964	315 220 883	July 1965
			316 000 001	Aug. 1965	316 316 237	July 1966
			317 000 001	Aug. 1966	317 283 852	July 1967
			318 000 001	Aug. 1967	318 235 387	July 1968
			319 000 001	Aug. 1968	319 264 031	July 1969
			310 2000 002	Aug. 1969		

VEHICLE IDENTIFICATION—TYPES 1, 2, AND 3

	SAE Output	from Chassis No.	from Date	to Chassis No.	to Date
Volkswagen 1600	66 bhp	0 221975	Aug. 1963	0 483 592	July 1964
		315 000 001	Aug. 1964	315 220 883	July 1965
		316 000 001	Aug. 1965	316 316 238	July 1966
		317 000 001	Aug. 1966	317 233 853	July 1967
		318 000 002	Aug. 1967	318 235 387	July 1968
		319 000 002	Aug. 1968	319 264 032	July 1969
		310 2000 002	Aug. 1969		
VEHICLE, TYPE 4					
Volkswagen 411	85 bhp		Aug. 1970		

ENGINE IDENTIFICATION

Common Designation	Number Of Cylinders	CC Displacement (cu in.)	Type Engine	Type Vehicle	Engine Code Letter	Year
—	4	1,131 (69.02)	Upright fan	1	—	To December, 1953
1,200	4	1,192 (72.74)	Upright fan	1,2	A	To July, 1960
1,200	4	1,192 (72.74)	Upright fan	1,2	D	From August, 1960
1,300	4	1,285 (78.4)	Upright fan	1,2	F	From August, 1965
1,500	4	1,493 (91.1)	Upright fan	1,2	H	From August, 1967①
1,600	4	1,584 (96.6)	Upright fan	1,2	B	From August, 1969②
1,500	4	1,493 (91.1)	Upright fan	2	G	To July, 1965
1,500	4	1,493 (91.1)	Suitcase engine	3	K	To July, 1965③ From August, 1965④
1,500S	4	1,493 (91.1)	Suitcase engine	3 1500S	R	To July, 1965
1,600	4	1,584 (96.6)	Suitcase engine	3	T	From August, 1965
1,600	4	1,584 (96.6)	Suitcase engine	3 injected	U	From August, 1967
1,600	4	1,584 (96.6)	Upright fan	1,2	AD	From August, 1970
1,700	4	1,679	Suitcase engine	4 injected	W	From August, 1970
1,700	4	1,679	Suitcase engine	2	CB	From August, 1971
1,600	4	1,584	Upright fan	1,2	AE	From August, 1970
1,600	4	1,584	Upright fan	1	AH	From August, 1971
1,600	4	1,584	Suitcase engine	3	X	From August, 1971

① Type 2 from August, 1965
② Type 2 from August, 1967
③ High compression
④ Low compression

GENERAL ENGINE SPECIFICATIONS

Engine Code①	CC Displacement (cu in.)	Carburetor	Developed Horsepower (SAE) @ rpm	Developed Torque (ft lbs) @ rpm	Bore x Stroke (in.)	Compression Ratio	Normal Oil Pressure (psi) @ 2,500 rpm
—	1,131 (69.02)	Single-barrel downdraft	25 @ 3,300	51 @ 2,000	2.953 x 2.520	5.8:1	42⑤
A	1,192 (72.74)	Single-barrel downdraft	36 @ 3,700	60 @ 2,400	3.03 x 2.52	6.6:1	42⑤
D	1,192 (72.74)	Single-barrel downdraft	41.5 @ 3,900	65 @ 2,400	3.03 x 2.52	7.0:1	42⑤
F	1,285 (78.4)	Single-barrel downdraft	50 @ 4,600	69 @ 2,600	3.03 x 2.72	7.3:1	42⑤
H	1,493 (91.1)	Single-barrel downdraft	53 @ 4,200	78 @ 2,600	3.27 x 2.72	7.5:1	42⑤
B	1,584 (96.6)	Single-barrel downdraft	57 @ 4,400	113 @ 3,000②	3.36 x 2.72	7.5:1③	42⑤
G	1,493 (91.1)	Single-barrel downdraft	51 @ 4,000	74 @ 2,600	3.27 x 2.72	7.8:1	42⑤
K	1,493 (91.1)	Single-barrel downdraft	54 @ 4,200	84 @ 2,800	3.27 x 2.72	7.8:1④	42⑤
R	1,493 (91.1)	Two single-barrel downdraft	66 @ 4,800	84 @ 3,000	3.27 x 2.72	8.5:1	42⑤
T	1,584 (96.6)	Two single-barrel downdraft	65 @ 4,600	87 @ 2,800	3.36 x 2.72	7.5:1	42⑤
U	1,584 (96.6)	Electronic fuel injection	65 @ 4,600	87 @ 2,800	3.36 x 2.72	7.7:1	42⑤
AD	1,584 (96.6)	Single-barrel downdraft	60 @ 4,400	81.6 @ 3,000	3.36 x 2.72	7.5:1	42⑤
W	1,679	Electronic fuel injection	85 @ 5,000	99.5 @ 3,500	3.54 x 2.60	8.2:1	42
X	1,584	Electronic fuel injection	65 @ 4,600	86.8 @ 2,800	3.36 x 2.72	7.3:1	42⑤
CB	1,679	Two single-barrel downdraft	74 @ 5,000	88 @ 2,800	3.54 x 2.60	7.3:1	42⑤
AE	1,584	Single-barrel downdraft	60 @ 4,400	81.7 @ 3,000	3.36 x 2.72	7.5:1	42⑤
AH	1,584	Single-barrel downdraft	60 @ 4,400	78.8 @ 2,600	3.36 x 2.72	7.3:1	42⑤

① See Engine Identification Chart for explanation of codes
② Type 2—82 @ 3,000
③ Type 2—7.7:1
④ To July 1965; 7.5:1 from August 1965
⑤ Minimum—28 @ 2,500 rpm, 7 @ idle rpm

ENGINE REBUILDING SPECIFICATIONS FROM 1971 TO 1972

Engines	Bore (in.)	Number of Oversizes	1st O/S (in.)	2nd O/S (in.)	Piston to Cylinder Clearance (in.)	Wrist Pin Diameter (in.)	Ring Specifications: Side Clearance (in.) Top Ring	Side Clearance (in.) 2nd Ring	Side Clearance (in.) Oil Ring	End Gap (in.) Top Ring	End Gap (in.) 2nd Ring	End Gap (in.) Oil Ring
Type 1 Type 2, 1600 engine Type 3, 1600 engine	3.366①	2	.020	.040	.0016-.0023	.8658-.8661	.0027-.0039	.0016-.0027	.0011-.0019	.012-.018	.012-.018	.010-.016
Type 2, 1700 engine Type 4	3.543①	2	.020	.040	.0016-.0023	.9445-.9448	.0023-.0035	.0016-.0027	.0008-.0019	.014-.021	.012-.014	.010-.016

① All pistons, rings, and cylinders are matched and color-coded blue, pink and green. This figure is the nominal size for the standard bore, with a pink color code. To get the blue color code, subtract .01 in. To get the green color code, add .01 in.

ENGINE REBUILDING SPECIFICATIONS TO 1970—CRANKSHAFT

Engine	Main Bearing Journals (in.) Journal Diameter Journal 1, 2, 3		Journal 4		Oil Clearance Journal 1-4		Shaft End-Play	Thrust On No.	Connecting Rod Journals (in.) Journal Diameter		Oil Clearance	End-Play	Max Journal Out-of-Round (in.)
36 hp, A engine-type 1, Type 2 engine-before May, 1959③	Std	1.9681, 1.9675	Std	1.5748, 1.5742	.002-.004	.002-.004	.0027-.005	1 (at flywheel)	Std	1.9861, 1.9675	.0008-.0024	.0067-.016	.001
	1st U/S	1.9583, 1.9577	1st U/S	1.5650, 1.5643					1st U/S	1.9583, 1.9577			
	2nd U/S	1.9484, 1.9478	2nd U/S	1.5551, 1.5545					2nd U/S	1.9484, 1.9478			
	3rd U/S	1.9386, 1.9380	3rd U/S	1.5453, 1.5446					3rd U/S	1.9386, 1.9380			
All later engines to 1970①	Std	2.1648, 2.1642	Std	1.5748, 1.5742	②	.002-.004	.0027-.005	1 (at flywheel)	Std	2.1650, 2.1645	.0008-.003④	.004-.016	.001
	1st U/S	2.1551, 2.1544	1st U/S	1.5650, 1.5643					1st U/S	2.1553, 2.1544			
	2nd U/S	2.1453, 2.1445	2nd U/S	1.5551, 1.5545					2nd U/S	2.1455, 2.1448			
	3rd U/S	2.1353, 2.1347	3rd U/S	1.5452, 1.5446					3rd U/S	2.1355, 2.1350			

NOTE: The crankshaft of type 1/1,200 cc engines may be reground only twice

U/S undersize

① Including modified 36 hp type 2 engine from May, 1959 (chassis 469477, engine 3400000)

② Bearings No. 1 and 3 from August, 1965: .0016-.004 in. Bearings No. 1, 2, 3; to engine 3520332: .0016-.0035 in. ① to engine 3472699: .001-.0035 in. ① Steel-backed bearing No. 2 from August, 1965 and all other steel-backed bearings (used in cold countries): .001-.0035 in.

③ Also 25 hp

④ All 1,500 and 1,600 cc: .0008 in.

ENGINE REBUILDING SPECIFICATIONS FROM 1971 TO 1972—CRANKSHAFT

Engines	Undersizes① 1st U/S (in.)	2nd U/S (in.)	3rd U/S (in.)	Main Bearing Journal Dia Standard Journals 1, 2, 3 (in.)	Journal 4 (in.)	Crank-shaft End-play (in.)	Connecting Rod Journals Journal Dia Standard (in.)	End-play (in.)
Type 1 Type 2 Type 3, 1600 engine	.010	.020	.030	2.1640-2.1648	1.5739-1.5748	.0027-.005	2.1644-2.1653	.004-.016
Type 2, 1700 engine Type 4	.010	.020	.030	2.3609-2.3617	1.5739-1.5748	.0027-.005	2.1644-2.1653	.004-.016

① Undersizes applicable to main bearing and connecting rod journal

ENGINE REBUILDING SPECIFICATIONS TO 1970—PISTONS, CYLINDERS, AND RINGS

Engines to 1970	Color Coding ③	CYLINDERS Cylinder Diameter (mm) Std	1st O/S	2nd O/S	PISTONS Piston Diameter (mm) Std	1st O/S	2nd O/S	Wrist Pin ② Diameter (in.) No Mark	Green	RINGS Side Clearance (in.) Top	2nd	Oil Scraper	End Gap (in.) Top 2nd	Oil Scraper
1,131, 1,200, and 1,300 cc	B	76.99	77.49	77.99	76.95	77.45	77.95	19.996-20.00①	20.001-20.004①	.002-.0027	.002-.0027	.001-.002	.012-.018	.010-.016
	P	77.00	77.50	78.00	76.96	77.46	77.96							
	G	77.01	77.51	78.01	76.97	77.47	77.97							
1,500 cc	B	82.99	83.49	83.99	82.95	83.45	83.95	21.996-22.000	22.001-22.004	.0027-.0035	.002-.0027	.001-.002	.012-.018	.010-.016
	P	83.00	83.50	84.00	82.96	83.46	83.96							
	G	83.01	83.51	84.01	82.97	83.47	83.97							
1,600 cc	B	85.49	85.99	86.49	85.45	85.95	86.45	21.996-22.000	22.001-22.004	.0027-.0035	.002-.0027	.001-.002	.012-.018	.010-.016
	P	85.50	86.00	86.50	85.46	85.96	86.46							
	G	85.51	86.01	86.51	85.47	85.97	86.47							

O/S Oversize

① Pin diameter given applies to 1,131 and 1,200 cc engines only. Pins for the 1,300 cc engine are the same as for the 1,500 and 1,600

② Pin should be light push fit in piston. Piston pin to connecting rod clearance: .0004-.001 in.-maximum-.002 in.

③ Color coding of cylinders and matching pistons: B—blue; P—pink; G—Green

ENGINE REBUILDING SPECIFICATIONS—VALVES

Engine	Seat Angle (deg)	Valve Seat Width (in.)		Spring Pressure (lbs @ in.)	Stem (in.) Diameter		Stem-to-Guide Rock (in.)		Valve Guide Removeable
		Intake	Exhaust		Intake	Exhaust	Intake	Exhaust	
25 hp, 36 hp, A engine-Type 1, and Type 2 engine-before May, 1959	45	.05-.09		73.5 ± 3.7 @ 1.1	.2739-.2736	.2736-.2732	.011-.012		With Special Equipment
All Later Engines to 1970	45	.05-.09		①	.3130-.3126	.3118-.3114	.008-.009	.011-.012	With Special Equipment

① Engine Code	To Engine No.	Spring Pressure
G	0627578	96.4 ± 6.6 @ 1.32 in.
K, R, T	0663330	
D	6805938 (type 2) 6850939 (type 1) 0042987	102.0 ± 5.0 @ 1.35 in.
K Engines with progressively wound springs		126.0 ± 8.8 @ 1.22 in.

NOTE: Cylinder head combustion chamber volumes are as follows:

Engine	Volume (cc)
A	45.5-47.0
D	43.0-45.0
F	44.0-46.0
All 1,500 and 1,600 cc	48.0-50.0

ENGINE REBUILDING SPECIFICATIONS 1971-72—VALVES

Engine	Seat Angle (deg)	Valve Seat Width (in.)		Spring Pressure (lbs @ in.)	Stem (in.) Diameter		Stem-to-Guide Rock (in.)		Valve Guide Removeable
		Intake	Exhaust		Intake	Exhaust	Intake	Exhaust	
Type 1 Type 2 1,600 Type 3 1,600	45	.05-.10		117.2-134.8	.3125-.3129	.3125-.3117	.009-.010		With Special Equipment
Type 2 1,700 Type 4 1,700	Intake 30 Exhaust 45	.07-.08	.078-.098	168-186	.3125-.3129	.3507-.3511	.018 (new)		With Special Equipment

ELECTRICAL SPECIFICATIONS 1971-1972—GENERATOR AND REGULATOR

	GENERATOR		REGULATOR	
	Max Output	Average Regulating Voltage	Cut-In Voltage (volts)	Voltage Setting (no load)
Type 1, 2, and 3	30 amps	14V @ 2000 rpm	12.4-13.1	13.5-14.5

	ALTERNATOR		REGULATOR	
	Max Output	Average Regulating Voltage	Cut-In Speed	Output
Type 2/1700 Type 4	55 amps	14V @ 2000 rpm	1000 rpm	10 amps @ 1350 rpm 36 amps @ 2200 rpm 55 amps @ 6000 rpm

ELECTRICAL SPECIFICATIONS—GENERATOR AND REGULATOR

Generator				Regulator		
Part Number	Brush Spring Pressure (oz)	Field Resistance (ohms)	Max Output	Part Number	Cut-in Voltage	Voltage Setting (No Load)
25 hp Bosch RED 130/ 6-2600 AL 16	16-21	1.20-1.32	NA	Bosch RS/G130/ 6/11 (on generator)	NA	7.3-8.6
36 hp 1,200 cc Bosch LJ/ REF 160/ 2500 L4	16-21	1.20-1.32	NA	Bosch RS/TA 160/ 6/A1 (on generator)	5.5-6.3	7.3-8.6
36 hp 1,200 cc Bosch LJ/ REF 160/6/ 2500 L17	16-21	1.20-1.32	NA	Bosch RS/TAA 160/ 6/1 (on generator)	6.4-6.7	7.4-8.1
40 hp 1,200 cc Bosch 111 903 021 G	16-21	1.20-1.32	270 Watts	Bosch RS/TAA 180/ 6/A4	6.2-6.8	7.3-8.0
40 hp 1,200 cc VW 113 903 021 C	16-21	1.20-1.32	270 Watts	VW 113 903 801 C	6.4-6.7	7.4-8.1
Late 1,200 and 1,300 cc Bosch 113 903 021 H	16-21	1.20-1.32	NA	Bosch 113 903 801F	6.2-6.8	7.4-8.1
Late 1,200 and 1,300 cc VW 111 903 021 J	16-21	1.20-1.32	NA	VW 113 903 801G	6.4-6.7	7.4-8.1
Karmann Ghia 1,300 and Type 1 1,500 Bosch 131 903 021	16-21	NA	30 Amps	Bosch 131 903 801	6.2-6.8	7.3-8.0
Bosch 450 M 12/ 3700-14 38A 32 (12 Volt)	16-21	NA	38 Amps	Bosch UA 14 V 38A	12.5-13.2	13.5-14.5
Bosch E(L) 14V 38A 32, EG (R) 14V 38A 32 (12 Volt)	16-21	NA	38 Amps	Bosch RS/VA 14V 38A	12.4-13.1	13.6-14.4
Bosch G(L) 14V 30A 20	16-21	NA	30 Amps	Bosch RS/VA 14V 30A	12.4-13.1	13.6-14.4

NA Information not available

ELECTRICAL SPECIFICATIONS—BATTERY AND STARTER

Model	BATTERY			STARTER						
	Capacity (Amp Hours)	Volts	Grounded Terminal	Model	Lock Test			No Load Test		
					Amps	Volts	Torque (ft lbs)	Amps	Volts	rpm
Type 1 up to Chassis No. 929745	70	6	Neg	25, 36 hp Bosch EED 0.4/6L/4	500	3.5	NA	80	5.5	5,400
Type 1 from Chassis No. 929746	66	6	Neg	40 hp 1,200 cc Bosch EEF 0.5/ 6L/1	450-520	3.5	8.0	60-80	5.5	5,500-7,300
Type 1 from Chassis No. 118000001①	36	12	Neg	40 hp 1,200 and 1,300 cc-VW 113 911 021 A	450-520	3.5	8.0	60-80	5.5	5,500-7,300
Type 2 up to Chassis No. 117901	84	6	Neg	40 hp 1,200 and 1,300 cc-Bosch 113 911 021 B	450-520	3.5	8.0	60-80	5.5	5,500-7,300
Type 2 from Chassis No. 117902	77	6	Neg	Bosch AL/EEF 0.8/12L1 (12 Volt)	250-285	6.0	6.5 8.2	38-45	12	6,400-7,900
Type 2 from Chassis No. 217000001	45	12	Neg	1,500 cc-111 911 021 G (12 Volt)②	250-285	NA	NA	38-45	12	7,150
Type 3 from Chassis No. 0000001	77	6	Neg	—	—	—	—	—	—	—
Type 3 from Chassis No. 317000001	36	12	Neg	—	—	—	—	—	—	—
Type 1, 2, 3, 4 from 1971 to 1972	45	12	Neg	311 911 023B	220-260	6.0	—	35-45	12	7,400-9,100
				111 911 023A	270-290	6.0	—	25-40	12	6,200-7,800
				003 911 023A	250-300	6.0	—	35-50	12	6,400-7,600

① Excluding VW 1,200, Type 1
② Test figures for 6 Volt units on 1,500 cc engines should be the same as for previous 6 volt units
NA Not available

TUNE-UP SPECIFICATIONS

Year	Engine Code,⑨ SAE HP Rating Displacement	SPARK PLUGS Make, Type⑧	SPARK PLUGS Gap (in.)	DISTRIBUTOR Approx Point Dwell (deg)	DISTRIBUTOR Point Gap (in.)	Basic Ignition Timing (deg)	Cranking Comp. Pressure (psi)	VALVES Clearance (in.) Intake	VALVES Clearance (in.) Exhaust	VALVES Intake Opens (deg)①	Idle Speed (rpm)
To Dec., 1953	25 hp, 1,100	Bosch W175T1, Champion L-10	.026	50	.016	5 BTDC	85-107	.004	.004	2½ BTDC	550
To July, 1960	A, 36 hp, 1,200	Bosch W175T1, Champion L-10	.026	50	.016	7.5 BTDC	100-114	.004	.004	2½ BTDC	550
From Aug., 1960	D, 42 hp, 1,200	Bosch W175T1, Champion L-87Y	.026	50	.016	10 BTDC	100-128	.004 ②	.004 ②	6 BTDC	550
From Aug., 1965	F, 50 hp, 1,300	Bosch W175T1, Champion L-87Y	.028	50	.016	7.5 BTDC	107-135	.004	.004	7½ BTDC	550
From Aug., 1965-Type 2, From Aug., 1967-Type 1	H, 53 hp, 1,500	Bosch③ W175T1, Champion L-87Y	.028	42-58	.016	7.5 BTDC④	114-142	.004	.004	7½ BTDC	550⑤
From Aug., 1969-Type 1, From Aug., 1967-Type 2	B, 57 hp, 1,600	Bosch W145T1	.026	47-53	.016	TDC	114-142	.004	.004	7½ BTDC	850
To July 1963	G, 51 hp, 1,500	Bosch W145T1	.028	42-58	.016	10 BTDC	121-142	.004 ②	.004 ②	7½ BTDC	550
From Aug., 1970	W, 85 hp, 1,700	Bosch W175T2	.028	44-50	.016	27 BTDC⑩ At 3500 rpm	128-156	.006	.006	12 BTDC	900
From Aug., 1971	X, 65 hp, 1,600	Champion L-88A, Bosch W145T1	.028	44-50	.016	TDC⑩	128-156	.004	.004	7½ BTDC	850
From Aug., 1971	CB, 74 hp, 1,700	Champion L-88A, Bosch W145T1	.028	44-50	.016	5 ATDC⑪	128-156	.004	.004	7½ BTDC	850

① With valve clearance of .04 in. (This clearance is used for checking valve timing only)

② Before 1965, some 1,200 and 1,500 cc engines used long rocker arm mounting studs which pass through the full thickness of the cylinder head. Valve clearances on engines with long studs must be set at .008 in. (intake), and .012 in. (exhaust). These engines are:

Engine Code	Up to Engine No.
D	9205699
G	0710799
K	0672748
R	0672297

Some of these engines have had short studs installed in one or both heads. In this case, the valves are set at .004 in. (intake and exhaust); The only sure way to determine what clearance to use on these engines is by a sticker on the engine, or by feeling the stud ends between the pushrod tubes under the engine.

③ Type 1—Bosch W145T1

④ Type 1 with throttle positioner—TDC

⑤ Type 1—850 rpm

⑥ High compression

⑦ Low compression

⑧ The Bosch W175T1 plug can be used to replace the W145T1 for sustained high speeds

⑨ See Engine Identification Chart for explanation of codes

⑩ Vacuum hoses off

⑪ Vacuum hoses on

NOTE: If any of this tune-up information conflicts with the information on the engine sticker(s), use the sticker figures

TUNE-UP SPECIFICATIONS • Continued

Year	Engine Code,⑨ SAE HP Rating Displacement	SPARK PLUGS Make, Type⑧	SPARK PLUGS Gap (in.)	DISTRIBUTOR Approx Point Dwell (deg)	DISTRIBUTOR Point Gap (in.)	Basic Ignition Timing (deg)	Cranking Comp. Pressure (psi)	VALVES Clearance (in.) Intake	VALVES Clearance (in.) Exhaust	VALVES Intake Opens (deg)①	Idle Speed (rpm)
From Aug., 1970	AE, 60 hp, 1,600	Champion L-88A, Bosch W145T1	.028	44-55	.016	5-ATDC⑪	128-156	.004	.004	7½ BTDC	850
From Aug., 1971	AH, 60 hp, 1,600	Champion L-88A, Bosch W145T1	.028	44-55	.016	5 ATDC⑪	128-156	.004	.004	7½ BTDC	850
To July, 1965⑥ From Aug., 1965⑦	K, 54 hp, 1,500	Bosch W175T1	.026	50	.016	10 BTDC⑥ 7.5 BTDC⑦	121-142 ⑥ 114-142 ⑦	.004 ②	.004 ②	7½ BTDC	550
To July, 1965	R, 66 hp, 1,500S	Bosch W175T1	.026	50	.016	10 BTDC	135-164	.004 ②	.004 ②	7½ BTDC	750
From Aug., 1965	T, 65 hp, 1,600	Bosch W175T1	.028	50	.016	7.5 BTDC	114-142	.004	.004	7½ BTDC	750
From Aug., 1967, Injected	U, 65 hp, 1,600	Bosch W175T1	.028	47-53	.016	TDC	114-142	.004	.004	7½ BTDC	850
From Aug., 1970	AD, 60 hp, 1,600	Bosch W145T1	.028	44-50	.016	5 ATDC	114-142	.004	.004	7½ BTDC	850

TORQUE SPECIFICATIONS
TRANSMISSION AND REAR AXLE

Fastener	Size Thread	Torque (ft lbs)
Transmission and Rear Axle (Standard and Partly Synchronized Transmission) Type 1 and 2		
Transmission housing nuts and bolts①	M 8 x 1.25	14
Oil drain plug	M 18 x 1.5	22-29
Oil filler plug	M 24 x 1.5	14
Axle shaft nut	M 24 x 1.5	217
Transmission carrier-to-frame	M 18 x 1.5	166
Spring plate nuts/bolts	M 12 x 1.5	72
Transmission and Rear Axle (fully synchronized) all Types		
Axle tube retainer nuts	M 8 x 1.25	14
Rear wheel bearing retainer screws	M 10 x 1.5	43
Oil drain plug	M 24 x 1.5	14
Oil filler plug		
Rear axle shaft nut (Types 1 and 3)	M 24 x 1.5	217
Nut on driven shaft (Type 2 from August 1963)	M 30 x 1.5	108
Nut on rear axle driven shaft (Type 2) up to Chassis No. 1144302	M 24 x 1.5	217②
from Chassis No. 1144303	M 30 x 1.5	217②
Transmission carrier on frame	M 18 x1 .5	166
Spring plate/ reduction gear housing screw (Type 2)	M 12 x 1.5	72-87

Fastener	Size Thread	Torque (ft lbs)
Additional torques for transmission and rear axle (Stick-shift automatic)		
Temperature switch/Selector switch/Starter inhibtor switch	M 14 x 1.5	18
Converter to drive plate screws	M 8 x 1.25	18
Retaining nut for taper roller bearing	M 80 x 1	159
Nut for converter housing	M 8 x 1.25	14
Screw for one-way clutch support	M 6 x 1	11③
Screw for clutch	M 6 x 1	11
Lockscrew	M 8 x 1.25	7
Clamp screw for clutch lever	M 8 x 1.25	18
Screw for transmission oil pan and lockplate	M 7 x 1.25	7
Union for oil pressure line	M 12 x 1.5	25
Union for oil return line	M 14 x 1.5	25
Screw for drive shaft	M 8 x 1.25	25
Fitted screw in diagonal arm	M 14 x 1.5	87

① Note tightening sequence
② If cotter pin holes are not in line, tighten to a maximum of 250 ft lbs. If hole is still not in line, fit a different nut
③ Use new screws
④ Tighten to 32 ft lbs first, slacken off, and tighten to 22 ft lbs
⑤ With reinforced spacer sleeve: at least 253 ft lbs then turn on to cotter pin hole

TORQUE SPECIFICATIONS— TRANSMISSION AND REAR AXLE

Fastener	Thread Size	Torque (ft lbs)
Transmission and Rear Axle (fully synchronized) Type 2 from Chassis No. 218 000-001		
Double taper roller bearing retainer	M 9 x 1.25	22④
Final drive side covers	M 8 x 1.25	14
Brake backplate-to-housing	M 8	18
Brake backplate-to-housing	M 10	25
Slotted nut on rear wheel shaft	M 30 x 1.5	230-253⑤
Joint-to-flange (socket head screw)	M 8	25
Control arm-to-frame	M 12 x 1.5	58
Cover/spring plate mounting	M 10	32
Control arm-to-bearing housing	M 14 x 1.5	94
Shock absorber-to-frame and bearing housing	M 12 x 1.5	43

TORQUE SPECIFICATIONS— FRONT AXLE AND STEERING GEAR

Fastener	Thread Size	Torque (ft lbs)
TYPE 1 FRONT AXLE		
Front axle-to-frame	M 12 x 1.5	22-25
Shock absorber screw on side plate	M 12 x 1.5	36
Shock absorber nut on side plate	M 10	14
Shock absorber nut on lower tension arm	M 10	22-25
Hexagon nuts for steering ball joints⑤	M 12 x 1.5 or M 10 x 1	36-50 29-36
Inner wheel bearing nut	M 18 x 1.5	29①
Locknut for wheel bearing	M 18 x 1.5	50①
Socket head screw in clamp nut	M 7 M 12 x 1.5	 7—max 9②
Slotted nut on tie rod	M 10 x 1	22③
Steering damper nut on tie rod⑤	M 10 x 1 M 10 x 1	18③ 18
Steering damper screw on axle tube	M 10	29-32
Setscrew for torsion bars	M 14 x 1.5	29-36
Locknut for setscrew	M 14 x 1.5	29-36
Caliper to steering knuckle	M 10	36
Clamping screw link pin to torsion arm	M 10	32
Screw for front axle support/front axle	M 12 x 1.5	40-43
Screw for front axle/frame	M 10	40-43
TYPE 2 FRONT AXLE		
Front axle/frame bolts (side member)	M 12 x 1.5	65-90
Shock absorber nut and bolt	M 12 x 1.5	36
upper (from Chassis No. 971550)	M 10	29-32
Shock absorber securing bolt, upper (up to Chassis No. 971549)	M 12 x 1.5	25-32
Shock absorber securing nut, lower	M 10	18-22
Steering knuckle/torsion arm (link pin bolts)	M 10	29-32
Ball joints-to-steering knuckle⑤	M 18 x 1.5	72
Inner wheel bearing nut	M 18 x 1 or M 22 x 1.5	25④
Wheel bearing locknut	M 18 x 1 or M 22 x 1.5	50④
Tie rod and draglink nuts	M 12 x 1.5 M 10 x 1	22③ 18③
TYPES 1 and 3 STEERING GEAR		
Steering gear-to-axle Type 1	M 10	18-22
Steering gear-to-axle Type 3	M 10	18-22
Locknut for roller shaft adjusting screw	M 10 x 1	18
Steering gear cover screws	M 8 x 1.25	14-18
Screw securing drop arm to roller shaft	M 12 x 1.5	50
Steering wheel nut	M 18 x 1.5	36
Locknut for steering worm adjustment screw	M 35 x 1.5	36-43
Hex bolt for steering coupling-to-steering worm	M 8	14-18
Hex nut flange-to-coupling disc	M 8	11
Fillister head screw for self-cancelling ring on steering wheel	AM 3.5	3.6
Locknut for tapered ring-to-tie rod	M 14 x 1.5	18
Clamping screw for tie rod retaining clip	M 8 x 1	11
Hex bolt for steering column mounting plate-to-instrument panel	M 8	11
Screw for retainer eccentric bearing	M 8	11
TYPE 2 STEERING GEAR		
Bracket-to-frame screws	M 10 x 22	29-32
Steering boss to bracket	M 10 x 40	25-36
Drop arm nut	M 20 x 1.5	58-80
Swing lever pinch bolt (from Chassis No. 20-117 901)	M 12 x 1.5	43
Upper and lower steering arm bolts (up to Chassis No. 20-117 901)	M 12 x 1.5	47-54
Steering wheel nut	M 16 x 1.5	18-22
Hex nut for flange-to-steering worm	M 8	14
Castellated nut for coupling disc-to-flange	M 8	11
Cheese-head screw for steering column cap-to-floor plate	M 6	3.6
Steering gear case cover bolt	M 8	18
Steering gear and cover bolt	M 6	11

① Tighten inner nut to 29 ft lbs first, fit new lock plate, and slacken nut 72° (distance from one wheel bolt hole in drum to next). Tighten outer nut to 50 ft lbs

② Tighten nut while turning the wheel. Slacken the nut until the specified axial play of .03-.12mm (.001-.005 in.) is obtained. If front axle tends to be noisy, keep play to lower limit (.03-.06mm). When play is correct, tighten socket head screw to the correct torque

③ Turn on to cotter pin hole

④ Tighten inner nut to 25 ft lbs first, while turning the wheel. Then fit a new lockplate and slacken the nut until the specified axial play of .03-.12mm (.001-.005 in.) is obtained. If front axle tends to be noisy, keep play to lower limit (.03-.06mm). When play is correct, tighten outer locknut to 50 ft lbs

⑤ Always use new self-locking nuts after removal

⑥ Tighten clamp screw to 29 ft lbs first, then tighten adjusting screw to 7 ft lbs and lock it

TORQUE SPECIFICATIONS— FRONT AXLE AND STEERING GEAR

Fastener	Thread Size	Torque (ft lbs)
Steering damper/frame bolt and nut (up to Chassis No. 851 389)	M 10 x 45	32
Steering damper/axle tube screw (from Chassis No. 851 390)	M 10 x 40	29-32
Steering damper/swing lever screw	M 10 x 72	29-32
Setscrew for torsion bars	M 14 x 1.5	29
Locknut for setscrew	M 14 x 1.5	29
Stabilizer to torsion arm	M 10	25-36
	M 8	18
Screw for brake back-plate to steering knuckle	M 10	36-43
Clamping screw for link pins to torsion bar	M 10	29-36
TYPE 3 FRONT AXLE		
Front axle securing bolts		
a—upper and lower	M 10	22
b—center	M 10	29
Grub screw securing torsion bars	M 14 x 1.5	22
Grub screw securing stabilizer	M 14 x 1.5	32-40
Locknut for grub screw	M 14 x 1.5	29
Torsion bar to axle beam screws	M 10	29
Clamp screw stabilizer	M 10	29
Adjusting screw for stabilizer	M 8	7⑥
Shock absorber-to-axle beam screws	M 12 x 1.5	22-25
Shock absorber nut on torsion arm	M 10	22-25
Steering arm on steering knuckle	M 10 x 1	40
Nuts for upper and lower ball joints	M 20 x 1.5 or M 18 x 1.5	80
Clamp screws for upper and lower ball joints	M 10 x 40	40
up to Chassis No. 0273513 (October 1963)	M 8 x 40	25
Socket head screw in split nut	M 7	7—max 9
Inner wheel bearing nut up to Chassis No. 315 220 883	M 16 x 1.5	11②
Wheel bearing locknut	M 16 x 1.5	50②
Tie rod nuts	M 12 x 1.5	22④
	M 10 x 1	18④
Steering damper screw on axle	M 10	29-32
Steering damper nut on drop arm	M 10	18

TORQUE SPECIFICATIONS— BRAKES AND WHEELS

Fastener	Thread Size	Torque (ft lbs)
BRAKES, TYPE 1		
Master cylinder-to-frame	M 8	14-22
Screws for bearing cover/backplate/bearing flange	M 10	40-47
Backplate/steering knuckle screws	M 10	36
Brake hose unions	M 10 x 1	11-14
Brake pipe unions	M 10 x 1	11-14
Stoplight switch	M 10 x 1	11-14
Wheel cylinder-to-backplate	M 8	14-22
Caliper-to-steering knuckle	M 10	36
Residual pressure valve in tandem master cylinder	M 12 x 1	14
BRAKES TYPE 2		
Screws for bearing cover-to-rear brake backplate	M 10	40-43
Brake backplate/wheel cylinder front	M 10	40-43
Brake hose unions	M 10 x 1	11-14
Brake pipe unions	M 10 x 1	11-14
Stoplight switch	M 10 x 1	11-14
Tandem master cyinder-to-brake servo	M 8	9
Brake servo-to-retaining plate/front axle	M 8	9
BRAKES TYPE 3		
Master cylinder-to-frame	M 8	14-22
Screws for bearing cover/backplate rear	M 10 x 1.5	40-47
Wheel cylinders		
a—rear on backplate	M 8	18
b—front on backplate/steering knuckle	M 10 x 1	32
Disc brake caliper housing-to-steering knuckle	M 10	43
Brake hose at		
a—brake pipe	M 10 x 1	11-14
b—wheel cylinder	M 10 x 1	11-14
c—disc brake caliper housing	M 10 x 1	11
Stoplight switch	M 10 x 1	11-14
WHEELS		
Wheel bolts		
Type 1	M 12 x 1.5	72
from August 1965 (four-hole wheel)①	M 14 x 1.5	108
Type 2	M 14 x 1.5	94
Type 3	M 12 x 1.5	72
from August 1965 (four-hole wheel)	M 14 x 1.5	108

① Only on vehicles with disc brakes. For all from Chassis No. 118 000 001

TORQUE SPECIFICATIONS—ENGINE

Fastener	Thread Size	Torque (ft lbs)
ALL ENGINES		
1-Nuts for crankcase halves	M 12 x 1.5	25①
2-Screws and nuts for crankcase halves⑥	M 8	14
3-Cylinder head nuts②	M 10	23
4-Rocker shaft nuts⑦	M 8	14-18
5-Flywheel gland nut	M 28 x 1.5	217
6-Connecting rod bolts and nuts	M 9 x 1	22-25④
7-Special nut for fan	M 12 x 1.5	40-47
8-Generator pulley nut	M 12 x 1.5	40-47
9-Crankshaft pulley bolt	M 20 x 1.5	29-36
10-Spark plugs	M 14 x 1.25	22-29
11-Oil drain plug	M 14 x 1.5	25⑧
12-Clutch-to-flywheel	M 8 x 1.5	18
13-Self-locking nuts for engine carrier to the crankcase	M 8	18⑤
14-Nuts for oil pump	M 8	14
15-Cap nut for oil filter cover	M 6	5
16-Nuts for engine mounting	M 10	22
17-Screws for converter-to-drive plate	M 8	18

TORQUE SPECIFICATIONS—ENGINE

Fastener	Thread Size	Torque (ft lbs)
25 and 36 hp—EXCEPTIONS		
1-Nuts for crankcase halves	M 10	22
3-Cylinder head nuts②	M 10	26-27
11-Oil drain plug③	M 18 x 1.5	22-29
13-Insert for spark plug	M 18 x 1.5	50-54
TYPE 3—EXCEPTIONS		
8-Generator pulley nut	M 12 x 1.5	40-47
9-Special bolt for fan and crankshaft pulley	M 20 x 1.5	94-108
17-Screws for converter-to-drive plate	M 8	14
19-Self-locking nuts for engine carrier to body	M 8	18⑤

① For cap nuts: 18 ft lbs
② See tightening sequences
③ As above from August 1959
④ Contact surfaces oiled
1,300 cc and earlier—28-36 ft lbs
⑤ Renew
⑥ Type 1, 2, 3/1600 1971-72 Nonsealing nuts 14, sealing nuts 18, Type 2/1700 and Type 4 sealing nuts 23 ft lbs
⑦ Type 2/1700, Type 4 1971-72 11 ft lbs
⑧ Type 2/1700, Type 4 1971-72 16 ft lbs

BRAKE SPECIFICATIONS

Vehicle	Model	TYPE		BRAKE CYLINDER BORE (in.)			BRAKE DRUM OR DISC DIAMETER (in.)	
		Front	Rear	Master Cylinder	Wheel Cylinder			
					Front	Rear	Front	Rear
Type 1	25 hp, 36 hp 1,200 cc	Drum①	Drum	.750	.750	.690	9.05 ±.008	9.05 ±.008
	40 hp 1,200 and 1,300 cc	Drum	Drum	.687	.874	.750	9.059 ±.008	9.055 ±.008
	1,500 and 1,600 cc Single Master Cylinder	Drum	Drum	.687	.875	.687	9.059 ±.008	9.055 ±.008
	1,500 and 1,600 cc-Tandem Master Cylinder	Drum	Drum	.750	.875	.687	9.059 ±.008	9.055 ±.008
	1971 Models	Drum	Drum	.750	.94	.690	9.76	9.06
	Karmann Ghia	Disc	Drum	NA	1.574	.687	10.9	NA
	Karmann Ghia, 1971-72	Disc	Drum	.750	1.575②	.687	10.9	9.06
	1972 Models	Drum	Drum	.750	.938	.687	9.768 ±.008	9.06 ±.008
Type 2	Tandem Master Cylinder	Drum	Drum	.875	1.00	.875	9.843 ±.008	9.843 ±.008
	1971-72 Models	Disc	Drum	.938	2.126	.875	10.9	9.92
Type 3	Tandem Master Cylinder	Disc	Drum	.750	1.653	.875	10.9	9.768 ±.008
	1971 Models	Disc	Drum	.813	NA	.875	10.9	9.92
	1972 Models	Disc	Drum	.750	1.654	.874	—	9.768 ±.008
Type 4	1971-72 Models	Disc	Drum	.750	1.654	.874	—	9.768 ±.008

① Some early models have mechanical brakes
② After ch. no. 142 2000001 Dia is 1.654 in.

CHASSIS AND WHEEL ALIGNMENT SPECIFICATIONS

Vehicle	Model	CHASSIS (in.)			WHEEL ALIGNMENT						
		Wheel-base	Track		Caster (deg or in.)	Camber (deg)	Toe-in (in or deg) ④	King Pin Inclination (deg)	Rear Wheel Camber (deg)	Wheel Pivot Ratio (deg)	
			Front	Rear						Inner Wheel	Outer Wheel
Type 1	25 hp and 36 hp 1,200 cc	94.5	51	49.2	2°30′ ± 30′	0°40′ ± 30′	.04-.12	4°20′	NA	NA	NA
	42 hp 1,200 cc	94.5	51.4	50.7	2° ± 15′	0°40′ ± 30′	.08-.16	4°20′	3° ± 30′	34	28
	42 hp 1,200 and 1,300 cc-after August, 1965	94.5	51.4	51.2	2° ± 15′	0°30′ ± 15′	.08-.16	4°20′	3° ± 30′①	34	28
	1,500 cc-Swing Axles	94.5	51.4	53.5	2° ± 15′	0°30′ ± 15′	.08-.18	4°20′	1° ± 1°①	34	28
	1,500 cc and 1,600 cc-Double Jointed Rear Axles	94.5	51.57	NA	3°30′ ±1°	30′ ± 20′	30′ ± 15′	5°	− 1°20′ ± 40′	34 ± 2	28-1
	1971-72 Beetle Torsion Bar Front Suspension	94.5	51.6	53.1	3°20′ ±1°	0°30′ ± 20′	30′ ± 15′	NA	1° ± 1°	—	—
	1971-72 Super Beetle with Strut Suspension	95.3	54.1	53.1	2° ± 35′	1°20′ ± 40′	30′ ± 10′	NA	− 1°20′ ± 40′	—	—
Type 2	Pre-1968-Swing Axles	94.5	54.1	53.5	3° ± 40′	40′ ± 30′	± .04 (5′ ± 10′)	NA	3° ± 30′②	NA	NA
	1968-70 Double-Jointed Rear Axles	94.5	54.5	56.2	3° ± 40′	40′ ± 15′	10′ ± 10′	5°	− 50′ ± 30′	32	24
	1971-72	94.5	54.5	56.6	3° ± 40′	40′ ± 20′	15′± 15′	NA	− 50′ ± 30′	—	—
Type 3	With Swing Axles	94.5	51.58	52.99	4° ± 40′	1°20′ ± 20′	40′ ± 5′	NA	2°30′ ± 1°③	NA	NA
	With Double Jointed Rear Axles	94.5	51.58	53.14	4° ± 40′	1°20′ ± 20′	40′ ± 15′	5°10′	− 1°20′ ± 40′	30	27-1
	1971-72	94.5	51.6	53.1	4° ± 40′	1°20′ ± 20′	40′ ± 15′	NA	− 1°20′ ± 40′	—	—
Type 4	1971-72	98.4	54.7	52.8	1°10′ ± 35′	1°10′ + 25′ − 30′	20′ ± 15′	NA	− 1° ± 30′	—	—

NA Information not available

① 1967 sedan: 1° ± 1°
1967 Karmann Ghia and VW convertible: 15′ ± 1°

② After chassis No. 117 901:
Van: 4° ± 30′
Kombi: 3°30′ ± 30′
Bus: 3° ± 30′

③ 1967 and later Notchback and Type 3 Karmann Ghia: 1°45′ ± 1°

④

Size Wheel	**10′ toe-in equals:**
14 in.	.043 in.
15 in.	.047 in.
16 in.	.051 in.

CARBURETOR SPECIFICATIONS—TYPES 1 AND 2

Vehicle	Engine	Carburetor	Venturi (mm dia)	Main Jet	Air Correction Jet	Pilot Jet	Pilot Jet Air Bleed or Pilot Air Jet (mm dia)	Pump Fuel Jet	Pump Air Correction Jet	Power Fuel Jet (mm dia)	Emulsion Tube	Float Needle Valve (mm dia)	Float Needle Valve Washer (mm)	Float Weight (g)	Accel Pump Cap (cc Stroke)
Type 1	1,131 cc 25 hp	Solex 28 PCI	20	105	190	50	.8	50	2.0	—	10	1.5	—	12.5	—
Type 1	1,200 cc 36 hp from No. 695282	Solex 28 PCI	21.5	122.5	200	g50	.8	50	2.0	—	29⑧	1.5	—	5.7	.4-.6
Type 1	1,200 cc 36 hp from No. 849905	Solex 28 PCI	21.5	117.5	195	g50	.8	50	2.0	—	29⑧	1.5	—	5.7	.4-.6
Karmann Ghia-Type 1	1,200 cc 36 hp from No. 1118403	Solex 28 PCI	21.5	117.5	180	g50	.8	50	2.0	—	29⑧	1.5	—	5.7	.4-.6
Type 2	1,200 cc 36 hp from No. 991590	Solex 28 PCI	21.5	117.5	180	g50	.8	50	2.0	—	29⑧	1.5	—	5.7	.4-.6
Type 1 & 2	1,200 cc 42 hp from No. 5000 001	Solex 28 PICT(-1)	22.5	122.5	130Y/ 140Z/ 135Z/	g55	2.0	.5	—	1.0/75	①	1.5	—	5.7	1.1-1.4/ .8-1.0
Type 2	1,500 cc 51 hp from No. 0143543	Solex 28 PICT-2	22.5	115	145Y/ 150Z/	g45	1.55	.5	—	.7	①	1.5	—	5.7	1.1-1.4/ 1.2-1.3
Type 1	1,300 cc 50 hp from No. F0 000 001	Solex 30 PICT-1	24.0	125	125Z ②	g55	150	50	—	— ③	①	1.5	—	5.7	1.3-1.6
Type 2	1,500 cc 53 hp from No. H0000001	Solex 30 PICT-1	24.0	115	135Z	g60	150	50	—	75	①	1.5	—	5.7	1.3-1.6
Type 1 & 2	1,600 cc 57 hp from No. B0000001	Solex 30 PICT-1	24.0	120	135Z	55	140	50	—	50	①	1.5	—	5.7	1.3-1.6
Type 1	1,300 cc 50 hp Automatic from No. F1462682	Solex 30 PICT-2	24.0	x120	170Z	55	140	50	—	50	①	1.5	—	8.5	1.3-1.6
Type 1	1,500 cc 53 hp Automatic from No. H0879927	Solex 30 PICT-2	24.0	x120	125Z ④	55	140	50	—	50	①	1.5	—	8.5	1.3-1.6/ 1.05-1.35
Type 1	1,500 cc 53 hp from No. H0204001	Solex 30 PICT-2	24.0	x120	125Z ④	g55	150 ⑤	50	—	50	①	1.5	—	5.7 ⑥	1.3-1.6/ 1.05-1.35

① Fixed to air correction jet
② Karmann Ghia—170Z
③ Karmann Ghia—75
④ Karmann Ghia—135Z
⑤ From engine No. H087400—140
⑥ From No. H0874200—8.5
⑦ With emission control
⑧ Emulsion tube carrier dia (mm)—5.0

CARBURETOR SPECIFICATIONS—TYPES 1 AND 2

Vehicle	Engine	Carburetor	Venturi (mm dia)	Main Jet	Air Correction Jet	Pilot Jet	Pilot Jet Air Bleed or Pilot Air Jet (mm dia)	Pump Fuel Jet	Pump Air Correction Jet	Power Fuel Jet (mm dia)	Emulsion Tube	Float Needle Valve (mm dia)	Float Needle Valve Washer (mm)	Float Weight (g)	Accel Pump Cap (cc Stroke)
Type 1 & 2	1,500 cc 53 hp⑦ from No. H5000001	Solex 30 PICT-2	24.0	x116	125Z	55	140/ 135	50	—	60	①	1.5	—	8.5	1.3-1.6/ 1.05-1.35
Type 1 & 2	1,600 cc 57 hp from No. B5000001	Solex 30 PICT-2	24.0	x116	125Z	55	140	50	—	60	①	1.5	—	8.5	1.3-1.6
Type 1	1,600 cc 57 hp from No. B6000001	Solex 30 PICT-3	24.0	x122.5	125Z	65	135	—	—	100	①	1.5	1.5	8.5	1.2-1.35
Type 1	1,600 cc 57 hp Automatic from No. B6000002	Solex 30 PICT-3	24.0	x112.5	125Z	65	135	—	—	100	①	1.5	1.5	8.5	1.2-1.35
Type 1	1,600 cc 57 hp from No. B5116437	Solex 30 PICT-3													
Type 1	1,600 cc 60 hp AE 1971-72 Models	Solex 34 PICT-3	26.0	130	75Z	60	147.5	—	—	100	—	1.5	.5	8.5	—
Type 1	1971-72 AH	Solex 34 PICT-3	26.0	127.5x 130	75Z 80Z	55	147.5	—	—	100	—	1.5	.5	8.5	1.3-1.6
Type 2	1,600 cc 1971-72 AE	Solex 34 PICT-3	26.0 26.0	125	60Z	60	147.5	—	—	95	—	1.5	.5	8.5	1.45-1.75
Type 2	1,700 cc 1971-72 CE	Solex 34 PDSIT-2(-3)	26.0	137.5	155/ 050	55	120	—	—	—	—	1.2	.5	7.0	.7 ± 15

CARBURETOR SPECIFICATIONS—TYPE 3

Vehicle	Engine	Carburetor	Venturi (mm dia)	Main Jet	Air Correction Jet	Pilot Jet	Idling Air Drilling	Pump Injector Tube (mm dia)	Power Fuel Jet (mm dia)	Emulsion Tube (No.)	Float Needle Valve (mm dia)	Float Needle Valve Washer (mm)	Float Weight (g)	Accel Pump Cap (cc Stroke)	Throttle Valve Gap (mm)
Type 3 Single Carbu-retor	From No. 0 000 001	Solex 32 PHN	23.5	137.5	125	g45 g50	—	.8	1.05	48	1.5	—	12.5	.9-1.2/ 1.2-1.5	.8-.9
	From No. 0 084 752	Solex 32 PHN-1	23.5	132.5	115	g45	—	.8	.7	48	1.5	—	12.5	.9-1.2	.8-.9
	From No. 0220137	Solex 32 PHN-1	23.5	127.5	115	g45	—	.8	.7	48	1.5	—	12.5	.9-1.2	.8-.9
	From No. 0319841	Solex 32 PHN	23.5	130.0	115	g50	—	.7	.7	48	1.5	—	12.5	.8-1.0	.8-.9
	From No. K0150001	Solex 32 PHN	23.5	130.0	115	—	1.4	.7	.7	48	1.5	—	12.5	.8-1.0	.8-.9

① 2 - Left carburetor, with distributor vacuum connection
3 - Right carburetor
② Return valve for accelerator pump - .3

CARBURETOR SPECIFICATIONS—TYPE 3

Vehicle	Engine	Carburetor	Venturi (mm dia)	Main Jet	Air Correction Jet	Pilot Jet	Idling Air Drilling	Pump Injector Tube (mm dia)	Power Fuel Jet (mm dia)	Emulsion Tube (No.)	Float Needle Valve (mm dia)	Float Needle Valve Washer (mm)	Float Weight (g)	Accel Pump Cap (cc Stroke)	Throttle Valve Gap (mm)
Type 3 Dual Carbu- retors	1,500 cc From No. 0255001	Solex 32 PDSIT-2(-3)①	21.5	x125	180	g45	—	.5 (12 mm)	.9 (9.5 mm)	—	1.2	—	7.3	.35-.55	.60-.65
	1,500 cc From No. 0633331	Solex 32 PDSIT-2(-3)①	23	x135	180	g45	—	.5 (15 mm)	.8 (10.5 mm)	—	1.2	1.5	7.3	.35-.55	.60-.65
	1,600 cc From No. T0000001	Solex 32 PDSIT-2(-3)①	23	x130	240	g45	—	50 (12 mm)	80 (15 mm)	—	1.2	1.5	7.3	.35-.55	.60-.65
	1,600 cc From No. T0244544	Solex 32 PDSIT-2 (Left)	24	x132.5	150	g50	—	.5 (9 mm)	—	—	1.2	.5	7.3	.35-.55	.60-.65
		Solex 32 PDSIT-3 (Right)	24	x130	120	g50	—	.5 (9 mm)	—	—	1.2	.5	7.3	.35-.55	.60-.65
	1,600 cc From No. T0576724	Solex 32 PDSIT-2 (Left)	24	x132.5	150	50	—	.5	—	—	1.2	.5	7.0	.35-.55	.60-.65
		Solex 32 PDSIT-3 (Right)	24	x130	120	50	—	.5	—	—	1.2	.5	7.0	.35-.55	.60-.65
Type 3 Dual Carbu- retors— Auto- matic	1,600 cc From No. T0690001	Solex 32 PDSIT-2 (Left)	24	x130	155	—	135	—	—	—	1.2	.5	7.0	.3-.45	.7
		Solex 32 PDSIT-3 (Right)	24	x127.5	120	—	135	—	—	—	1.2	.5	7.0	.3-.45	.7
	1,600 cc From No. T0463930	Solex 32 PDSIT-2 (Left)	24	130	155	50	—	.5 (9 mm)	—	—	1.2	.5	7.0	.25-.4	.60-.65
		Solex 32 PDSIT-3 (Right)	24	127.5	120	50	—	.5 (9 mm)	—	—	1.2	.5	7.0	.25-.4	.60-.65
	1,600 cc From No. T069000	Solex 32 PDSIT-2 (Left)	24	130	155	—	135	—	—	—	1.2	.5	7.0	.23-.4②	.9
		Solex 32 PDSIT-3 (Right)	24	127.5	120	—	135	—	—	—	1.2	.5	7.0	.23-.4②	.9

FUSES

Model	Circuit	Amp
1,300 Type 1 (6 Volt)	Horn, flashers, stoplight, wipers	16
	High-beam warning light, left high-beam	8
	Right high-beam	8
	Left low-beam	8
	Right low-beam	8
	Left parking light, left taillight	8
	Right parking light, right taillight license plate light	8
	Headlight dimmer, radio, interior light	16
1,500 Type 1 (12 Volt)	Turn signals, horn, Stoplights brake warning light, Automatic Stickshift and rear window defroster switch current	8
	Wipers	8
	High-beam warning light, left high-beam	8
	Right high-beam	8
	Left low-beam	8
	Right low-beam	8
	Left parking light, left taillight	8
	License plate light, right parking light, right taillight	8
	Interior light, emergency blinkers	8
	Spare fuse	—
	Rear window defroster main current (under rear seat, left side)	8
	Back-up lights (right side of engine fan housing)	8
	Automatic Stickshift control valve (left side of engine fan housing)	8
1,500 Type 2 (6 Volt)	Left low-beam	8
	Right low-beam	8
	Left high-beam, high-beam warning light	8
	Right high-beam	8
	Left taillight	8
	Right taillight, license plate light, parking lights	8
	Stoplights, turn indicators	16
	Horn, interior lights, wipers, headlight dimmer	16
1,600 Type 3 (6 Volt)	Right parking light, left parking light left taillight, luggage compartment light	8
	Right taillight, license plate light	8
	Left low-beam	8
	Right low-beam	8
	Left high-beam, high-beam warning light	8
	Right high-beam	8
	Spare fuse	—
	Emergency blinkers, interior light, horn, clock, radio	16
	Stoplights, turn signals	8
	Wipers, fuel gauge, warning lights	16

LIGHT BULBS

Model	Usage	U.S. Replacement Bulbs	VW Part No.	Wattage
36 hp 1,200 Type 1 (6 Volt) January, 1954—August 1955	Headlights	—	—	35/35
	Parking lights	—	—	1.5
	Stoplights	—	—	15
	Taillights	—	—	5
	License plate light	—	—	5
	Interior light	—	—	10
	All warning lights	—	—	1.2
	Instrument lighting	—	—	1.2
	Turn signals	—	—	3
36 hp 1,200 Type 1 (6 Volt) from August, 1955	Headlights	—	—	35/35
	Parking lights	—	—	2
	Stoplights	—	—	20
	Taillights	—	—	5
	License plate light (tubular bulb)	—	—	5
	Interior light	—	—	10
	Semaphore type	—	—	3
	Turn signals (tubular bulbs)	—	—	1.2
	All warning lights	—	—	1.2
	Instrument lighting	—	—	1.2
36 hp 1,200 Type 1 (6 Volt) Karmann Ghia, from August, 1955	Headlights	—	—	35/35
	Parking lights	—	—	3
	Taillights	—	—	5
	Rear stop/turn signal	—	—	15
	License plate lights	—	—	5
	Interior light	—	—	5
	Front turn signals	—	—	15
42 hp 1,200 and 1,300 Type 1 6 (Volt) Sedan and Convertible	Headlights	—	N177051	45/40
	Parking lights	—	N177171	4
	Stoplight/taillight	—	N177371	18/5
	Turn signals	—	N177311	18
	License plate light	—	N177191	10 ①
	Interior light	—	N177231	10
	Warning and instrument lights	—	N177221	1.2
42 hp 1,200 and 1,300 Type 1 (6 Volt) Karmann Ghia	Headlights	—	—	45/40
	Parking lights	—	—	4
	Taillights	—	—	5
	Stoplights	—	—	18
	Turn signals	—	—	18
	License plate lights	—	—	5
	Interior light	—	—	10
	Warning, instrument lights, clock	—	—	1.2
1,300 Type 1 (12 Volt)	Headlights	6012	11194126A	45/40
	License plate light	—	—	10
	Interior light	—	—	10
	Instrument and warning lights	—	—	2
	Parking lights	—	—	4
	Turn signals	—	—	18
	Stoplight/taillight	—	—	18/5
1,500 and 1,600 Type 1 (12 Volt) Sedan and Convertible	Headlights	6012	111941261A	—
	Parking/turn signal, taillight/stoplight	1034	N177382	—
	Rear turn signal	1073	N177322	—
	License plate light	89	N177192	—
	Backup lights	1073	N177332	—
	Instrument and warning lights	—	N177222	—
	Sedan interior light	—	N177232	—
	Convertible interior light	—	N177252	—

LIGHT BULBS

Model	Usage	U.S. Replacement Bulbs	VW Part No.	Wattage
	Warning lights for emergency flasher, brake, rear window defroster	—	N177512	—
1,500 Type 2 (6 Volt)	Headlights	—	N177051	45/40
	Parking lights	—	N177171	4
	Turn signals	—	N177311	18
	Taillights/stoplights	—	N177371	5/18
	License plate light	—	N177191	10
	Warning lights, instrument lights	—	N177221	1.2
	Dome lights	—	N177251	5
	Clock	—	N177221	1.2
1,600 Type 3 (6 Volt)	Headlights	6006, Type 2	N177051	—
	Front parking/turn signal	1154	N177171	5/18
	Rear turn signal, stoplight	1129	N177311	18
	Taillight	81	N177181	5
	License plate light	81	N177191	10
	Warning, instrument lights	—	N177221	1.2
	Interior and luggage compartment lights	—	N177231	10

① 1,200 uses 5 watt bulb after August, 1965.

FUSES

Model	Circuit	Amps
1600 Type 1 (12 volt)	Left parking and side marker lights, left tail lights	8
	Parking and side marker lights (right side), right tail light	8
	Low beam (left side)	8
	Low beam (right side)	8
	High beam (left side)	8
	High beam (right side), high beam indicator light	8
	License plate light	8
	Emergency flasher system	8
	Interior light	16
	Windshield wipers, rear window defroster, fresh air fan	16
	Horn, stop lights, transmission control valve and Automatic Stick Shift warning light	8
	Fuel gauge, turn signals, warning lights for brake and oil pressure, turn signals and generator	8
1700 Type 2 (12 volt)	Chart is the same as above except that the license plate light fuse is an accessory outlet. It holds an 8 amp fuse.	
1600 Type 3 (12 volt)	Right tail light, license plate light, parking and side marker lights; luggage compartment light	8
	Left tail light	8
	Left low beam	8
	Right low beam	8
	Left high beam; high beam indicator light	8
	Right high beam	8
	Electric fuel pump	8
	Emergency flasher; interior light Buzzer	16
	Windshield wipers; fresh air fan; rear window defogger	16
	Stop lights; turn signals; horn; brake warning light; back-up lights	8
	Accessories	8
1600 Type 1 (Ghia)	Parking and side marker lights; right tail light license plate lights	8
	Left tail light	8
	Left low beam	8
	Right low beam	8
	Left high beam; high beam indicator light	8
	Right high beam	8
	Accessories	8
	Emergency flasher	8
	Buzzer alarm; interior light	16
	Windshield wipers; rear window defogger	16
	Horn; stop lights, control valve	8
	Warning lights for turn signals, oil pressure and generator, turn signals, fuel gauge and brake warning light	8
1700 Type 4 (12 volt)	Left/right parking lights, left tail light, left rear side marker light	8
	Right tail light, right rear side marker light, license plate light, selector lever console light (Automatic)	8
	Left low beam	8
	Right low beam	8
	Left high beam	8
	Right high beam, high beam indicator light	8
	Fuel pump	8
	Interior light, emergency flasher, buzzer	8
	Cigarette lighter, heater switch	16
	Windshield wipers, fresh air fan, heater, rear window defogger	16
	Turn signals, back-up lights, warning lamps, oil pressure and fuel gauge	8
	Horn, brake warning light, stop lights	8

CAPACITIES AND PRESSURES

Model	Crankcase Refill After Draining (pts)	TRANSMISSION REFILL AFTER DRAINING (pts) Standard	Auto Stick Shift	Fully Auto	Reduction Gears	Final Drive (pts)	Air Cleaner (pts)⑧	Fuel Tank (gals)	Normal Fuel Pressure (psi)
Type 1	5.3	6.3	6.3①	—	—	②	.5③	10.5⑨	⑩
Type 2	5.3	7.4	—	—	.5 each	②	.63④	15.8	⑩
Type 3	5.3	6.3	—	6.3-8.4⑥	—	2.1⑦	.85⑤	10.5	⑩
Type 4	7.4	—	—	6.3⑥	—	2.1	.9	13.2	3-5 max @ 4000 rpm

— Not applicable to this vehicle
① The total capacity of the Automatic Stickshift torque converter circuit is 7.6 pts ATF. The refill capacity is somewhat less.
② In unit with transmission
③ 1,300 cc Karmann Ghia—.63 pt, 1,500 cc Karmann Ghia—.96 pt, 1,500 cc sedan and convertible—.85 pt
④ 1,200 cc—.44 pt, Late 1,500 and 1,600 cc—.95 pt
⑤ Single-carburetor engine; 44 pts fuel injected engine .53 pt
⑥ Total capacity—12.6 pts ATF
⑦ Only with automatic transmission; otherwise, note ② applies.
⑧ Since so many different air cleaners have been used in production, it is best to rely on the full mark on the air cleaner body. If there is no such mark, these figures may be used.
⑨ Super Beetle—11.1 gals
⑩

Pump Marking	Pressure @ rpm
Unmarked (36 hp & earlier)	1.3-1.8 @ 1,000-3,000
Unmarked	2.5 @ 3,000-3,400
VW 2	5.0 @ 3,800
VW 3	3.5 @ 3,400-3,800
VW 4	3.5 @ 3,800
VW 6	5.0 @ 3,800
VW 7	3.5 @ 3,800
VW 8	3.5 @ 3,800

CYLINDER HEAD BOLT TIGHTENING SEQUENCE

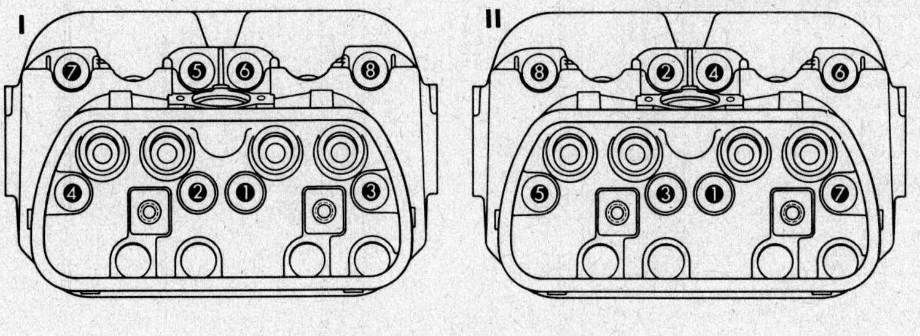
I
7 5 6 8
4 2 1 3
II
8 2 4 6
5 3 1 7

The cylinder head nuts should initially be tightened to 7 ft. lbs. in order I, then tightened to the recommended torque in order II.

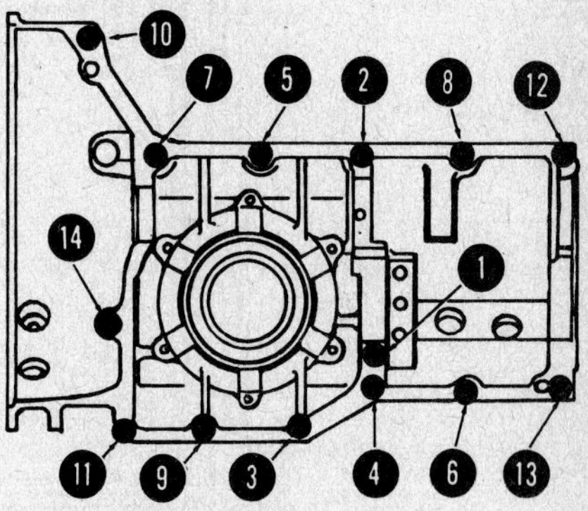
10
7 5 2 8 12
14
1
11 9 3 4 6 13

Split-type trans-axle.

U390

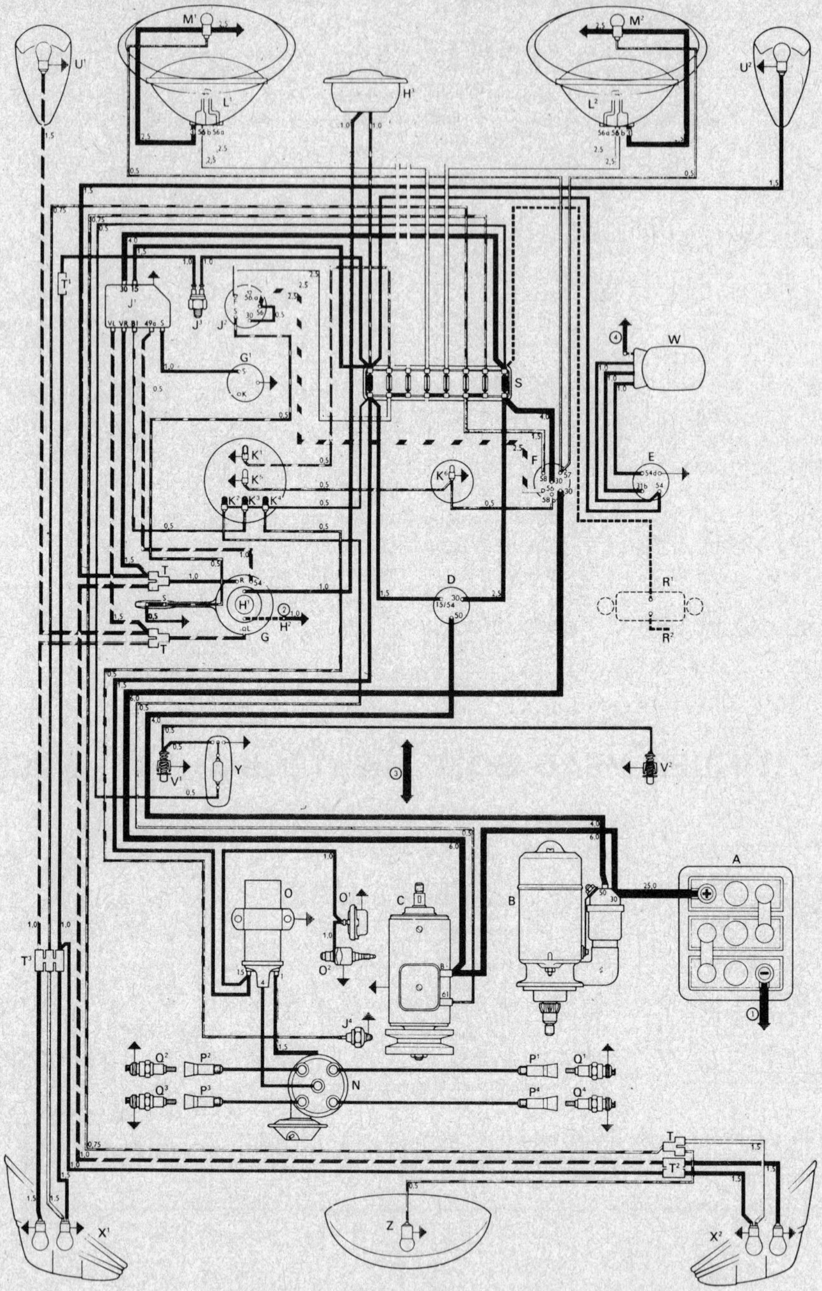

U^1
M^1
H^1
M^2
U^2
L^1
L^2
J^1
J^3
J^2
G^1
K^1
K^2
K^3
K^4
K^5
K^6
W
S
F
E
D
T
G
H^2
R^1
R^2
Y
V^1
V^2
T^1
T^3
A
B
C
O
O^1
O^2
J^4
N
P^1
P^2
P^3
P^4
Q^1
Q^2
Q^3
Q^4
T^2
Z
X^1
X^2

Wiring diagram, VW 1300 (from August, 1965). © Volkswagen

A Battery
B Starter
C Generator
D Ignition/starter switch
E Windshield wiper switch
F Lighting switch
G Turn signal switch with dimmer switch
G^1 Emergency light switch
H^1 Horn half ring
H^2 Steering column connection
H^3 Horn
J^1 Flasher and emergency light relay
J^2 Dimming relay
J^3 Brake light switch
J^4 Oil pressure switch
K^1 High beam warning light
K^2 Generator warning light
K^3 Turn signal warning light
K^4 Oil pressure warning light
K^5 Speedometer light
K^6 Fuel gauge light

L^1 Sealed-beam unit, left
L^2 Sealed-beam unit, right
M^1 Parking light, left
M^2 Parking light, right
N Distributor
O Ignition coil
O^1 Automatic choke
O^2 Electromagnetic pilot jet
P^1 Spark plug connector, No. 1 cylinder
P^2 Spark plug connector, No. 2 cylinder
P^3 Spark plug connector, No. 3 cylinder
P^4 Spark plug connector, No. 4 cylinder
Q^1 Spark plug for No. 1 cylinder
Q^2 Spark plug for No. 2 cylinder
Q^3 Spark plug for No. 3 cylinder
Q^4 Spark plug for No. 4 cylinder
R^1 Radio
R^2 Aerial connection
S Fuse box
white fuses: 8 Ampere
red fuses: 16 Ampere

T Cable adaptor
T^1 Cable connector, single
T^2 Cable connector, double
T^3 Cable connector, triple
U^1 Turn signal, left
U^2 Turn signal, right
V^1 Door switch, left
V^2 Door switch, right
W Windshield wiper motor
X^1 Brake, turn signal and tail lights, left
X^2 Brake, turn signal and tail lights, right
Y Interior light
Z License plate light
① Battery to frame ground strap
② Horn ring to steering coupling ground connection
③ Transmission to frame ground strap
④ Wiper motor to body ground strap

Black dotted line = Service installation

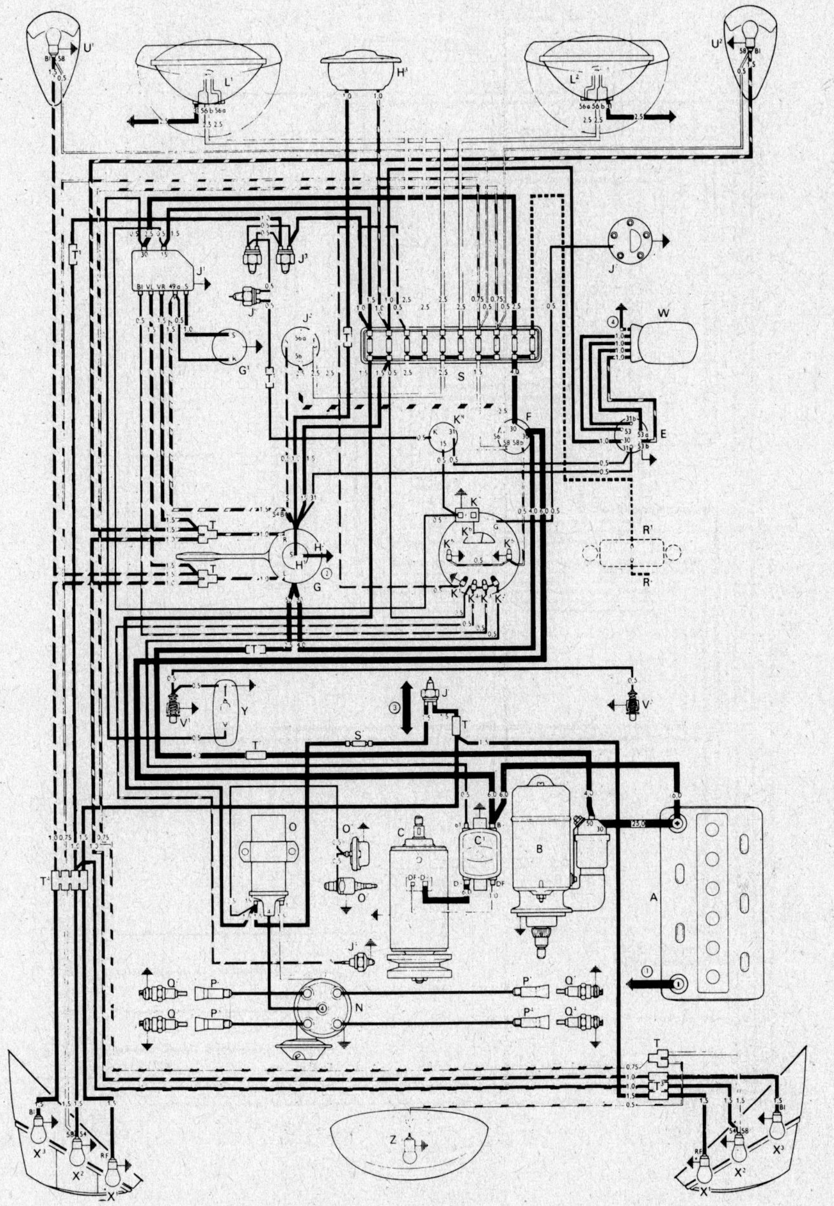

Wiring diagram, VW 1500 sedan and convertible (1968). © Volkswagen

A Battery
B Starter
C Generator
C^1 Regulator
E Windshield wiper switch
F Lighting switch
G Turn signal switch with automatic canceling, hand dimmer button and ignition/starter switch
G^1 Emergency light switch
H^1 Horn half ring
H^2 Steering column connection
H^3 Horn
J^1 Turning signal and emergency light relay
J^2 Dimmer relay
J^3 Brake light switch (2 X)
J^4 Oil pressure switch
J^5 Back-up light switch
J^6 Warning switch for brake system
J^7 Fuel gauge sender unit
K^1 High beam warning light
K^2 Generator warning light
K^3 Turn signal warning light
K^4 Oil pressure warning light
K^5 Speedometer light
K^6 Fuel gauge light
K^7 Resistance for fuel gauge
K^8 Brake warning lamp with test button
L^1 Sealed-beam insert, left
L^2 Sealed-beam insert, right
N Distributor
O Ignition coil
O^1 Automatic choke
O^2 Electromagnetic pilot jet
P^1 Spark plug connector, No. 1 cylinder
P^2 Spark plug connector, No. 2 cylinder
P^3 Spark plug connector, No. 3 cylinder
P^4 Spark plug connector, No. 4 cylinder
Q^1 Spark plug for No. 1 cylinder
Q^2 Spark plug for No. 2 cylinder
Q^3 Spark plug for No. 3 cylinder
Q^4 Spark plug for No. 4 cylinder
R^1 Radio
R^2 Aerial connection
S Fuse box
T Cable adapter
T^1 Cable connector, single
T^2 Cable connector for horn under front luggage compartment lining
T^3 Cable connector, triple
U^1 Front turn signal and parking light, left
U^2 Front turn signal and parking light, right
V^1 Door contact switch, left
V^2 Door contact switch, right
W Windshield wiper motor
X^1 Back-up lights
X^2 Brake and tail lights
X^3 Turn signal lights
Y Interior light
Z License plate light
① Battery to frame ground strap
② Horn ring to steering coupling ground connection
③ Transmission to frame ground strap
④ Wiper motor to body ground strap

Black dotted line = Optional extras or service installation.

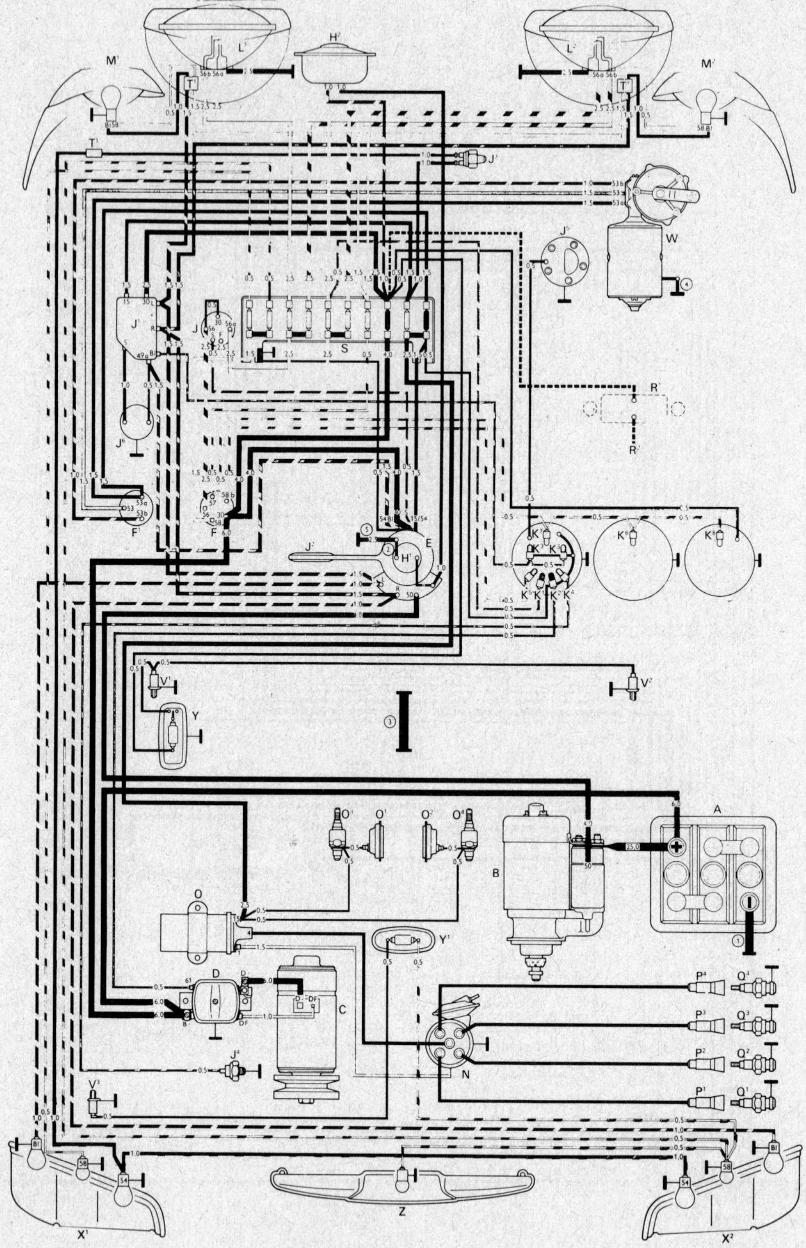

Wiring diagram, VW 1600 (from August, 1965). © Volkswagen

A Battery
B Starter
C Generator
D Regulator
E Turn signal switch with ignition starter lock
F Lighting switch
F^1 Windshield wiper switch
H^1 Horn half ring
H^2 Horn
J Hand dimmer relay
J^1 Flasher and emergency light relay
J^2 Headlamp flasher button
J^3 Brake light switch
J^4 Oil pressure switch
J^5 Fuel gauge sender unit
J^6 Emergency light switch
K^1 High beam warning light
K^2 Generator warning light
K^3 Turn signal warning light
K^4 Oil pressure warning light
K^5 Parking light warning light
K^6 Speedometer light
K^7 Fuel gauge light
K^8 Clock light
L^1 Headlamp, left
L^2 Headlamp, right
M^1 Parking light and turn signal light, left
M^2 Parking light and turn signal light, right
N Distributor
O Ignition coil
O^1 Automatic choke, left
O^2 Automatic choke, right
O^3 Electromagnetic pilot jet, left
O^4 Electromagnetic pilot jet, right
P^1 Spark plug connector, No. 1 cylinder
P^2 Spark plug connector, No. 2 cylinder
P^3 Spark plug connector, No. 3 cylinder
P^4 Spark plug connector, No. 4 cylinder
Q^1 Spark plug for No. 1 cylinder
Q^2 Spark plug for No. 2 cylinder
Q^3 Spark plug for No. 3 cylinder
Q^4 Spark plug for No. 4 cylinder
R^1 Radio
R^2 Aerial connection
S Fuse box—10 fuses
T^1 Cable connector, single
T^2 Cable connector, double
V^1 Door switch, left
V^2 Door switch, right
V^3 Luggage compartment light switch
W Windshield wiper motor
X^1 Tail light, left
X^2 Tail light, right
Y Interior light
Y^1 Luggage compartment light
Z License plate light
① Battery to frame ground strap
② Horn half ring steering coupling ground connection
③ Transmission to frame ground connection
④ Windshield wiper motor to body ground strap
⑤ Front axle to frame ground strap

Black dotted lines = Service installation
1.5; 0.5 etc.: Cable cross section

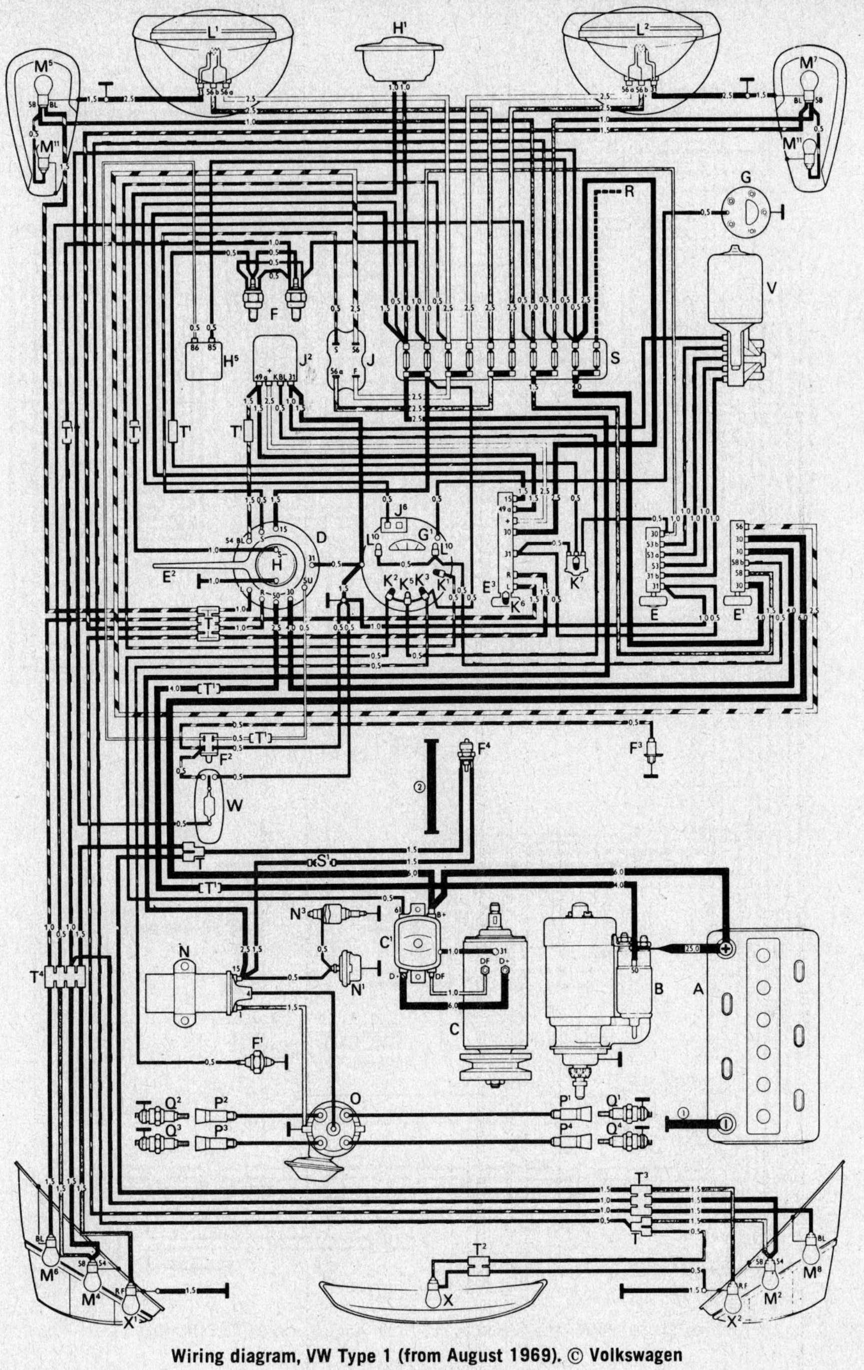
S
R
G
V
F
J
D
W
T
N
C
B
A
O
X
E

Wiring diagram, VW Type 1 (from August 1969). © Volkswagen

A Battery
B Starter
C Generator
C^1 Regulator
D Ignition/starter switch
E Windshield wiper switch
E^1 Light switch
E^2 Turn signal and headlight dimmer switch
E^3 Emergency flasher switch
F Brake light switch with warning switch
F^1 Oil pressure switch
F^2 Door contact switch, left, with contact for buzzer H 5
F^3 Door contact switch, right
F^4 Back-up light switch
G Fuel gauge sending unit
G^1 Fuel gauge
H Horn button
H^1 Horn
H^5 Ignition key warning buzzer
J Dimmer relay
J^2 Emergency flasher relay
J^6 Vibrator for fuel gauge
K^1 High beam warning light
K^2 Generator charging warning light
K^3 Oil pressure warning light
K^5 Turn signal warning light
K^6 Emergency flasher warning light
K^7 Dual circuit brake system warning light
L^1 Sealed beam unit, left headlight
L^2 Sealed beam unit, right headlight
L^{10} Instrument panel light
M^2 Tail and brake light, right
M^4 Tail and brake light, left
M^5 Turn signal and parking light, front, left
M^6 Turn signal, rear, left
M^7 Turn signal and parking light, front, right
M^8 Turn signal, rear, right
M^{11} Side marker light, front
N Ignition coil
N^1 Automatic choke
N^3 Electro-magnetic pilot jet
O Ignition distributor
P^1 Spark plug connector, No. 1 cylinder
P^2 Spark plug connector, No. 2 cylinder
P^3 Spark plug connector, No. 3 cylinder
P^4 Spark plug connector, No. 4 cylinder
Q^1 Spark plug, No. 1 cylinder
Q^2 Spark plug, No. 2 cylinder
Q^3 Spark plug, No. 3 cylinder
Q^4 Spark plug, No. 4 cylinder
R Radio connection
S Fuse box
S^1 Back-up light fuse
T Cable adapter
T^1 Cable connector, single
T^2 Cable connector, double
T^3 Cable connector, triple
T^4 Cable connector (four connections)
V Windshield wiper motor
W Interior light
X License plate light
X^1 Back-up light, left
X^2 Back-up light, right
① Battery to frame ground strap
② Transmission to frame ground strap

U394

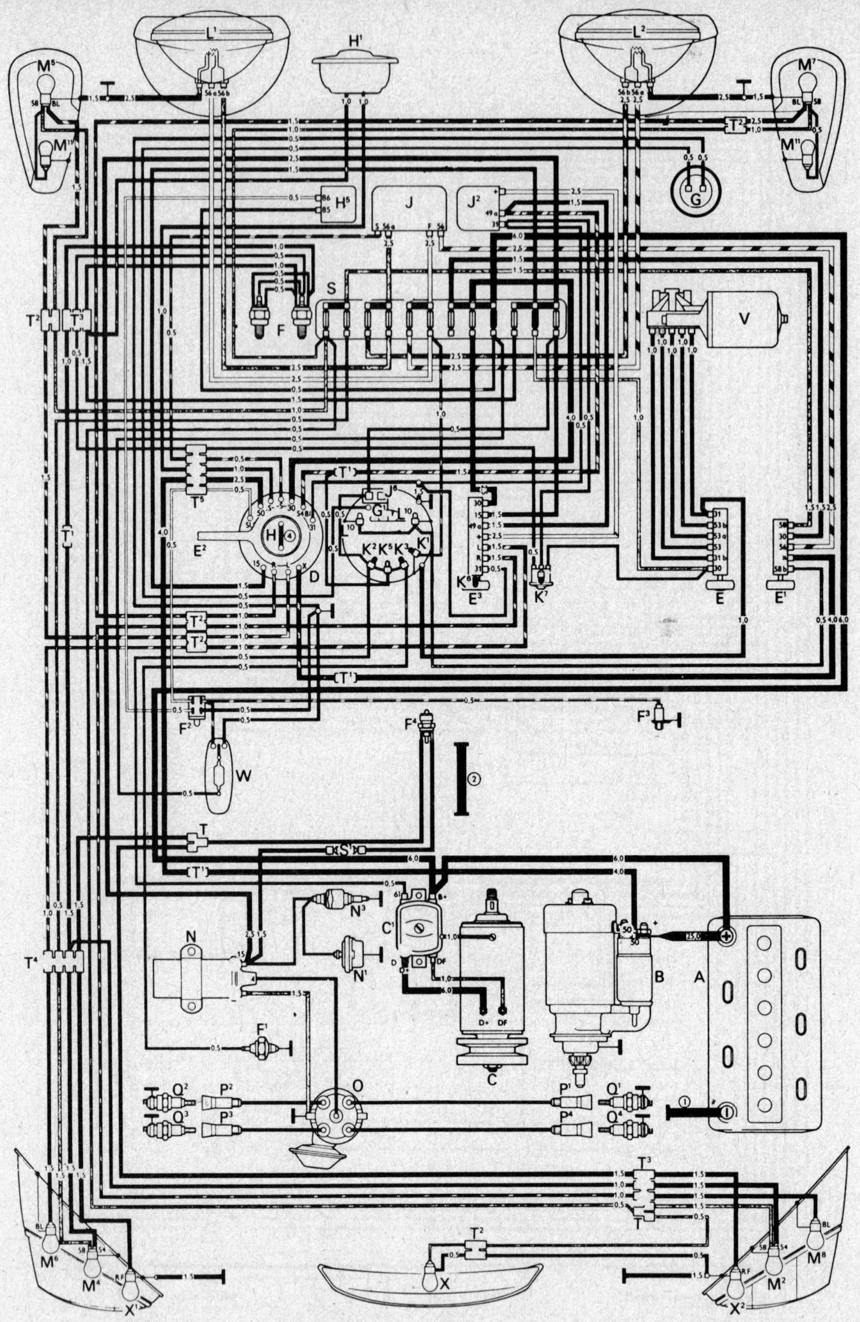

Wiring Diagram, VW Type 1/Sedan 113 (from August, 1970). © Volkswagen

A Battery
B Starter
C Generator
C^1 Regulator
D Ignition/starter switch
E Windshield wiper switch
E^1 Light switch
E^2 Turn signal and headlight dimmer switch
E^3 Emergency flasher switch
F Brake light switch
F^1 Oil pressure switch
F^2 Door contact and buzzer alarm switch, left
F^3 Door contact switch, right
F^4 Back-up light switch
G Fuel gauge sending unit
G^1 Fuel gauge
H Horn button
H^1 Horn
H^5 Ignition key warning buzzer
J Dimmer relay
J^2 Emergency flasher relay
J^6 Fuel gauge vibrator
K^1 High beam warning light
K^2 Generator charging warning light
K^3 Oil pressure warning light
K^5 Turn signal warning light
K^6 Emergency flasher warning light
K^7 Dual circuit brake warning light
L^1 Sealed-Beam unit, left headlight
L^2 Sealed-Beam unit, right headlight
L^{10} Instrument panel light
M^1 Parking light, left
M^2 Tail/brake light, right
M^4 Tail/brake light, left
M^5 Turn signal and parking light front left
M^6 Turn signal, rear, left
M^7 Turn signal and parking light front right
M^8 Turn signal, rear, right
M^{11} Side marker light, front
N Ignition coil
N^1 Automatic choke
N^3 Electromagnetic pilot jet
O Distributor
P^1 Spark plug connector, No. 1 cylinder
P^2 Spark plug connector, No. 2 cylinder
P^3 Spark plug connector, No. 3 cylinder
P^4 Spark plug connector, No. 4 cylinder
Q^1 Spark plug, No. 1 cylinder
Q^2 Spark plug, No. 2 cylinder
Q^3 Sparg plug, No. 3 cylinder
Q^4 Spark plug, No. 4 cylinder
S Fuse box
S^1 Back-up light in-line fuse
T Cable adapter
T^1 Cable connector, single
T^2 Cable connector, double
T^3 Cable connector, triple
T^4 Cable connector (four connections)
T^5 Cable connector (five connections)
V Windshield wiper motor
W Interior light
X License plate light
X^1 Back-up light, left
X^2 Back-up light, right
① Ground strap from battery to frame
② Ground strap from transmission to frame
④ Ground cable from front axle to frame

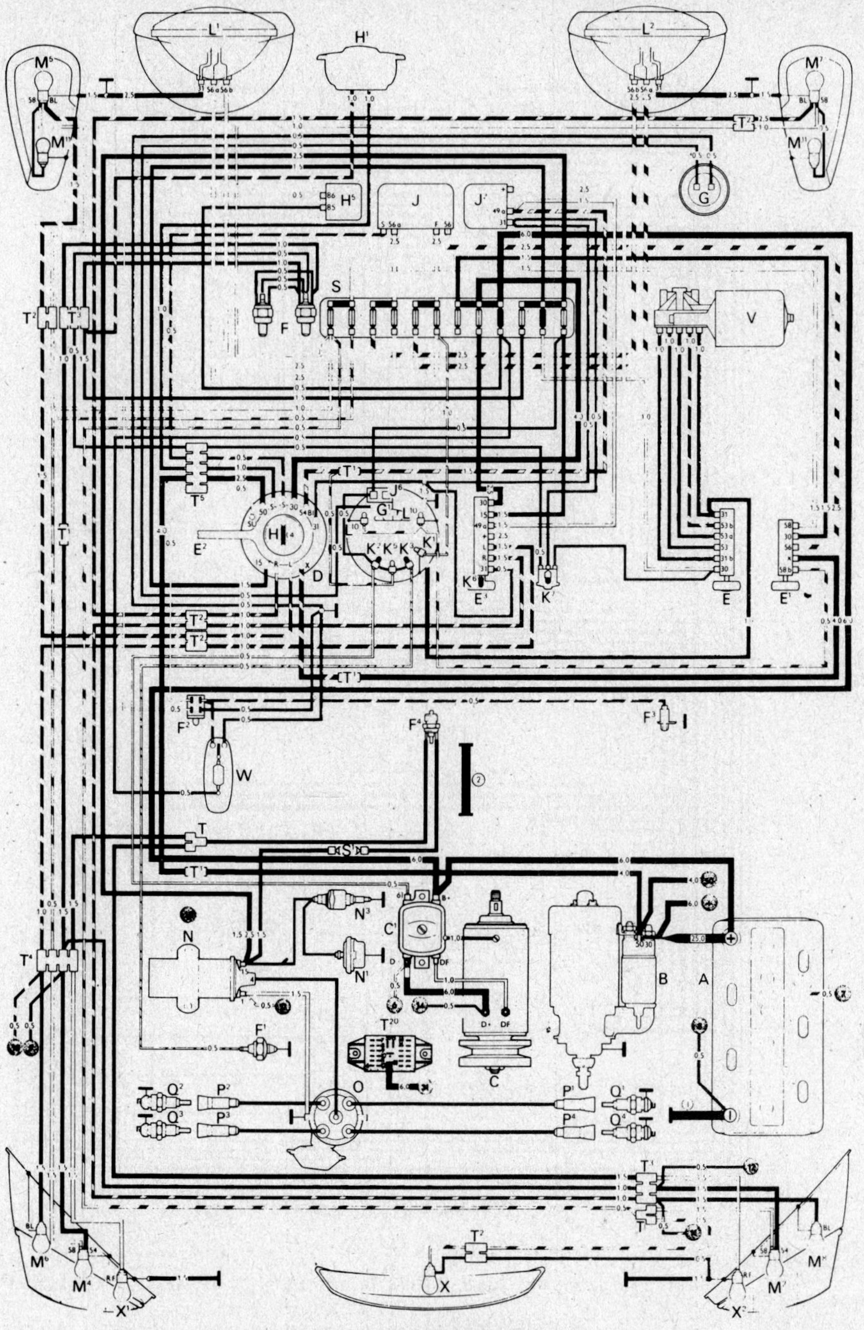

Wiring diagram, VW Type 1/Sedan 113 (from June, 1971). © Volkswagen

- A Battery
- B Starter
- C Generator
- C^1 Regulator
- D Ignition/starter switch
- E Windshield wiper switch
- E^1 Light switch
- E^2 Turn signal and headlight dimmer switch
- E^3 Emergency flasher switch
- F Brake light switch
- F^1 Oil pressure switch
- F^2 Door contact and buzzer alarm switch, left
- F^3 Door contact switch, right
- F^4 Back-up light switch
- G Fuel gauge sending unit
- G^1 Fuel gauge
- H Horn button
- H^1 Horn
- H^5 Ignition key warning buzzer
- J Dimmer relay
- J^2 Emergency flasher relay
- J^6 Fuel gauge vibrator
- K^1 High beam warning light
- K^2 Generator charging warning light
- K^3 Oil pressure warning light
- K^5 Turn signal warning light
- K^6 Emergency flasher warning light
- K^7 Dual circuit brake warning light
- L^1 Sealed-Beam unit, left headlight
- L^2 Sealed-Beam unit, right headlight
- L^{10} Instrument panel light
- M^1 Parking light, left
- M^2 Tail/brake light, right
- M^4 Tail/brake light, left
- M^5 Turn signal and parking light front left
- M^6 Turn signal, rear, left
- M^7 Turn signal and parking light front right
- M^8 Turn signal, rear, right
- M^{11} Side marker, light, front
- N Ignition coil
- N^1 Automatic choke
- N^3 Electromagnetic pilot jet
- O Distributor
- P^1 Spark plug connector, No. 1 cylinder
- P^2 Spark plug connector, No. 2 cylinder
- P^3 Spark plug connector, No. 3 cylinder
- P^4 Spark plug connector, No. 4 cylinder
- Q^1 Spark plug, No. 1 cylinder
- Q^2 Spark plug, No. 2 cylinder
- Q^3 Spark plug, No. 3 cylinder
- Q^4 Spark plug, No. 4 cylinder
- S Fuse box
- S^1 Back-up light in-line fuse
- T Cable adapter
- T^1 Cable connector, single
- T^2 Cable connector, double
- T^3 Cable connector, triple
- T^4 Cable connector (four connections)
- T^5 Cable connector (five connections)
- T^{20} Test network, central plug
- V Windshield wiper motor
- W Interior light
- X License plate light
- X^1 Back-up light, left
- X^2 Back-up light, right
- ① Ground strap from battery to frame
- ② Ground strap from transmission to frame
- ④ Ground cable from front axle to frame

U396

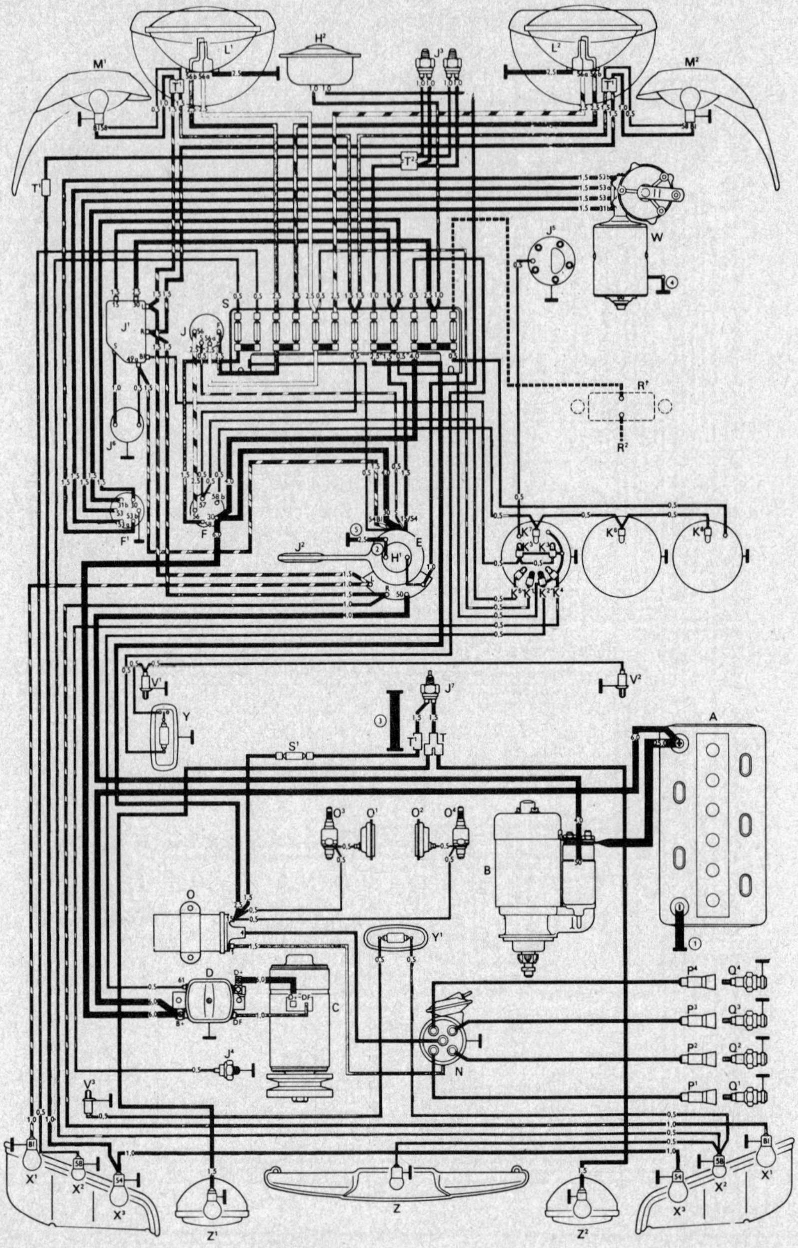

Wiring diagram, VW Type 3, 1600 (from August, 1966)—US version. © Volkswagen

A Battery
B Starter
C Generator
D Regulator
E Turn signal switch with ignition/starter lock
F Light switch
F^1 Windshield wiper switch
H^1 Horn half ring
H^2 Horn
J Hand dimmer relay
J^1 Turn signal/emergency flasher
J^2 Hand dimmer switch
J^3 Brake light switch
J^4 Oil pressure switch
J^5 Fuel gauge sender unit
J^6 Emergency flasher switch
J^7 Back-up light switch
K^1 High beam warning light
K^2 Generator charging warning light
K^3 Turn signal warning lights
K^4 Oil pressure warning light
K^5 Parking light warning light
K^6 Speedometer light
K^7 Fuel gauge light
K^8 Clock light
L^1 Sealed beam unit, left
L^2 Sealed beam unit, right
M^1 Parking light and turn signal light, left
M^2 Parking light and turn signal light, right
N Distributor
O Ignition coil
O^1 Automatic choke, left
O^2 Automatic choke, right
O^3 Electromagnetic pilot, jet, left
O^4 Electromagnetic pilot jet, right
P^1 Spark plug connector, No. 1 cylinder
P^2 Spark plug connector, No. 2 cylinder
P^3 Spark plug connector, No. 3 cylinder
P^4 Spark plug connector, No. 4 cylinder
Q^1 Spark plug, No. 1 cylinder
Q^2 Spark plug, No. 2 cylinder
Q^3 Spark plug, No. 3 cylinder
Q^4 Spark plug, No. 4 cylinder
R Radio
R^2 Aerial connection
S Fuse box
S^1 Back-up light fuse
T^1 Cable connector, single
T^2 Cable connector, double
V^1 Door contact switch, left
V^2 Door contact switch, right
V^3 Luggage compartment light switch
W Windshield wiper motor
X^1 Turn signal lights
X^2 Tail lights
X^3 Brake lights
Y Interior light
Y^1 Luggage compartment light
Z License plate light
Z^1 Back-up light, left
Z^2 Back-up light, right
① Battery to frame ground strap
② Horn half ring to steering coupling ground cable
③ Transmission to frame ground strap
④ Windshield wiper motor to body ground strap
⑤ Front axle to frame ground cable

Black dotted lines = optional extras
1.5; 0.5 etc.: cable cross section

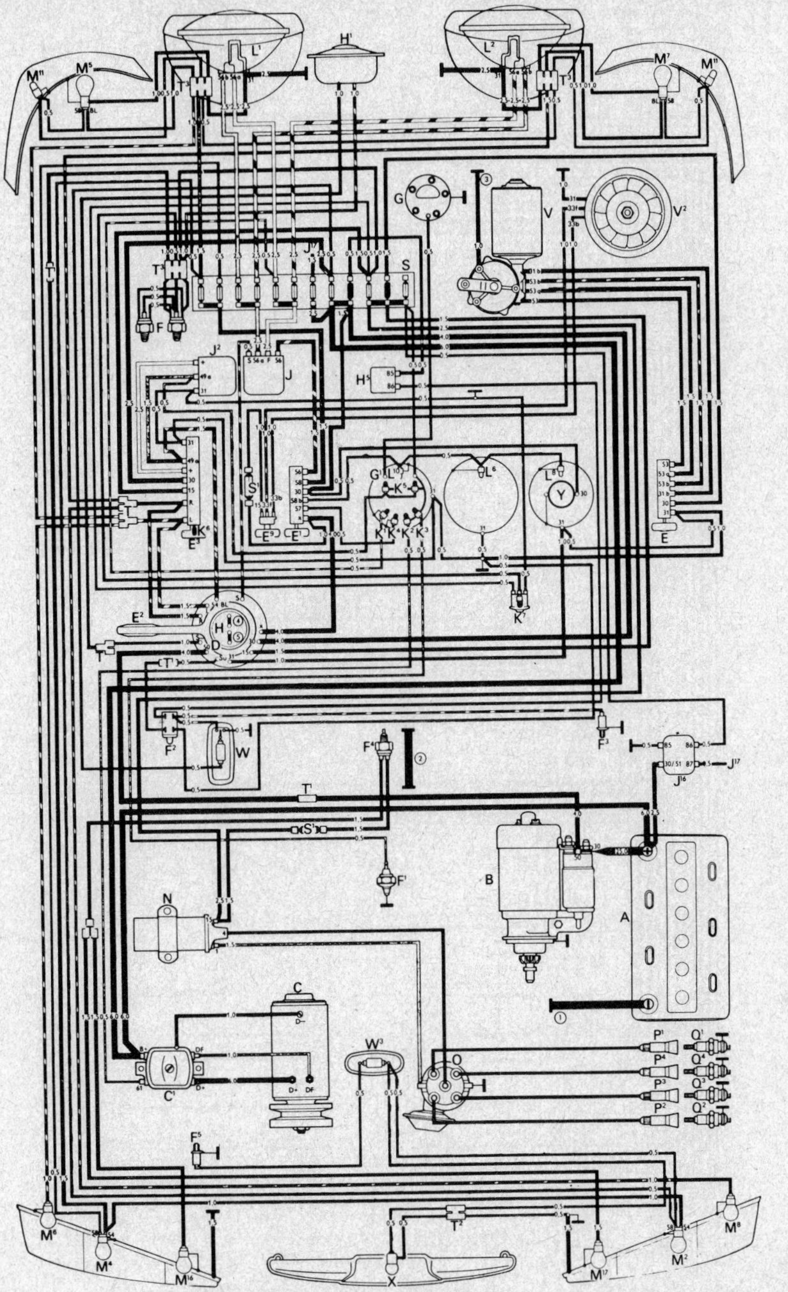

Wiring diagram, VW Type 3 (from August, 1970). © Volkswagen

A Battery
B Starter
C Generator
C^1 Regulator
D Ignition/starter switch
E Windshield wiper switch
E^1 Light switch
E^2 Turn signal and headlight dimmer switch
E^3 Emergency flasher switch
E^9 Fresh air fan motor switch
F Brake light switch
F^1 Oil pressure switch
F^2 Door contact and buzzer alarm switch, left
F^3 Door contact switch, right
F^4 Back-up light switch
F^5 Luggage compartment light switch
G Fuel tank sending unit
G^1 Fuel gauge
H Horn button
H^1 Horn
H^5 Ignition key warning buzzer
J Dimmer relay
J^2 Emergency flasher relay
J^{16} Power supply relay for fuel injection
J^{17} Connection to fuel pump relay
K^1 High beam warning light
K^2 Generator charging warning light
K^3 Oil pressure warning light
K^4 Parking light warning light
K^5 Turn signal warning light
K^6 Emergency flasher warning light
K^7 Dual brake circuit warning light
L^1 Sealed-Beam unit left headlight
L^2 Sealed-Beam unit right headlight
L^6 Speedometer light
L^8 Clock light
L^{10} Instrument panel light
M^2 Tail/brake light, right
M^4 Tail/brake light, left
M^5 Turn signal and parking light/front, left
M^6 Turn signal, rear, left
M^7 Turn signal and parking light, front, right
M^8 Turn signal, rear, right
M^{11} Side marker light, front
M^{16} Back-up light, left
M^{17} Back-up light, right
N Ignition coil
O Distributor
P^1 Spark plug connector, No. 1 cylinder
P^2 Spark plug connector, No. 2 cylinder
P^3 Spark plug connector, No. 3 cylinder
P^4 Spark plug connector, No. 4 cylinder
Q^1 Spark plug, No. 1 cylinder
Q^2 Spark plug, No. 2 cylinder
Q^3 Spark plug, No. 3 cylinder
Q^4 Spark plug, No. 4 cylinder
S Fuse box
S^1 In-line fuse for back-up lights and fresh air fan motor
T Cable adapter
T^1 Cable connector, single
T^2 Cable connector, double
T^3 Cable connector, triple
V Windshield wiper motor
V^2 Fresh air motor front
W Interior light
W^3 Luggage compartment light
X License plate light
Y Clock
① Ground strap from battery to frame
② Ground strap from transmission to frame
④ Ground cable from horn to steering coupling
⑤ Ground cable from front axle to frame

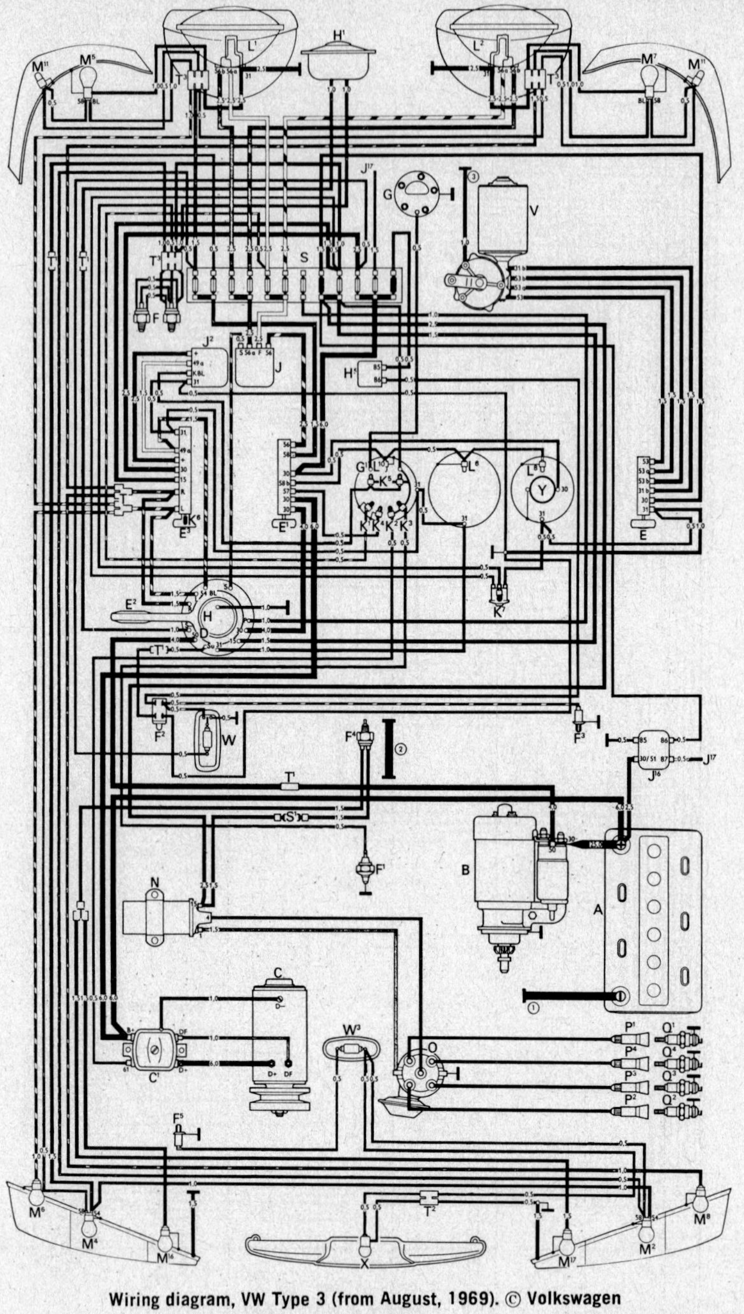

Wiring diagram, VW Type 3 (from August, 1969). © **Volkswagen**

A Battery
B Starter
C Generator
C^1 Regulator
D Ignition/starter switch
E Windshield wiper switch
E^1 Light switch
E^2 Turn signal and head light dimmer switch
E^3 Emergency flasher switch
F Brake light switch
F^1 Oil pressure switch
F^2 Door contact switch, left, with contact for buzzer
F^3 Door contact switch, right
F^4 Back-up light switch
F^5 Luggage compartment light switch
G Fuel gauge sending unit
G^1 Fuel gauge
H Horn button
H^1 Horn
H^5 Ignition key warning buzzer
J Dimmer relay
J^2 Emergency flasher relay
J^{16} Power supply relay for fuel injection system
J^{17} To fuel pump relay
K^1 High beam warning light
K^2 Generator charging warning light
K^3 Oil pressure warning light
K^4 Parking light warning light
K^5 Turn signal warning lights
K^6 Hazard warning light
K^7 Dual circuit brake system warning light
L^1 Sealed beam unit, left
L^2 Sealed beam unit, right
L^6 Speedometer light
L^8 Clock light
L^{10} Instrument panel light
M^2 Tail and brake light, right
M^4 Tail and brake light, left
M^5 Turn signal and parking light, front, left
M^6 Turn signal and parking light, front, right
M^7 Turn signal, rear, left
M^8 Turn signal, rear, right
M^{11} Side marker light, front
M^{16} Back-up light, left
M^{17} Back-up light, right
N Ignition coil
O Distributor
P^1 Spark plug connector, No. 1 cylinder
P^2 Spark plug connector, No. 2 cylinder
P^3 Spark plug connector, No. 3 cylinder
P^4 Spark plug connector, No. 4 cylinder
Q^1 Spark plug, No. 1 cylinder
Q^2 Spark plug, No. 2 cylinder
Q^3 Spark plug, No. 3 cylinder
Q^4 Spark plug, No. 4 cylinder
S Fuse box
S^1 Back-up light in-line fuse
T Cable adapter
T^1 Cable connector, single
T^2 Cable connector, double
T^3 Cable connector, triple
V Windshield wiper motor
W Interior light
W^3 Luggage compartment light
X License plate light
① Battery to frame ground strap
② Transmission to frame ground strap
③ Windshield wiper motor to body ground strap

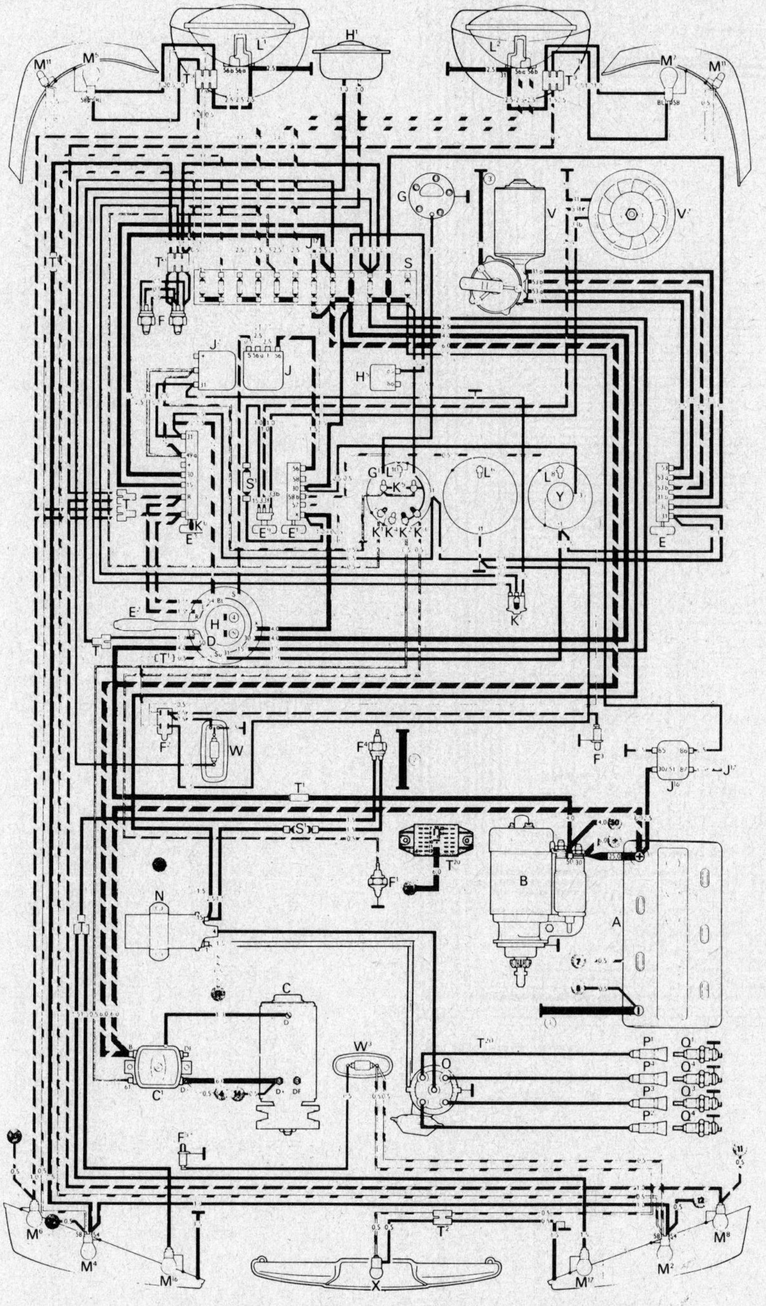

Wiring diagram, VW Type 3 (from May 1971). © Volkswagen

A	Battery
B	Starter
C	Generator
C^1	Regulator
D	Ignition/starter switch
E	Windshield wiper switch
E^1	Light switch
E^2	Turn signal and headlight dimmer switch
E^3	Emergency flasher switch
E^9	Fresh air fan motor switch
F	Brake light switch
F^1	Oil pressure switch
F^2	Door contact and buzzzer alarm switch, left
F^3	Door contact switch, right
F^4	Back-up light switch
F^5	Luggage compartment light switch
G	Fuel gauge sending unit
G^1	Fuel gauge
H	Horn button
H^1	Horn
H^5	Ignition key warning buzzer
J	Dimmer relay
J^2	Emergency flasher relay
J^{16}	Power supply relay for fuel injection
J^{17}	Connection to fuel pump relay
K^1	High beam warning light
K^2	Generator charging warning light
K^3	Oil pressure warning light
K^4	Parking light warning light
K^5	Turn signal warning light
K^6	Emergency flasher warning light
K^7	Dual brake circuit warning light
L^1	Sealed-Beam unit left headlight
L^2	Sealed-Beam unit right headlight
L^6	Speedometer light
L^8	Clock light
L^{10}	Instrument panel light
M^2	Tail/brake light, right
M^4	Tail/brake light, left
M^5	Turn signal and parking light, front, left
M^6	Turn signal, rear, left
M^7	Turn signal and parking light, front, right
M^8	Turn signal, rear, right
M^{11}	Side marker light, front
M^{16}	Back-up light, left
M^{17}	Back-up light, right
N	Ignition coil
O	Distributor
P^1	Spark plug connector, No. 1 cylinder
P^2	Spark plug connector, No. 2 cylinder
P^3	Spark plug connector, No. 3 cylinder
P^4	Spark plug connector, No. 4 cylinder
Q^1	Spark plug, No. 1 cylinder
Q^2	Spark plug, No. 2 cylinder
Q^3	Spark plug, No. 3 cylinder
Q^4	Spark plug, No. 4 cylinder
S	Fuse box
S^1	In-line fuse for back-up lights and fresh air fan motor
T	Cable adapter
T^1	Cable connector, single
T^2	Cable connector, double
T^3	Cable connector, triple
T^{20}	Test network, central plug
V	Windshield wiper motor
V^2	Fresh air motor front
W	Interior light
W^3	Luggage compartment light
X	License plate light
Y	Clock
①	Ground strap from battery to frame
②	Ground strap from transmission to frame
④	Ground cable from horn to steering coupling
⑤	Ground cable from front axle to frame

Test network

The orange colored spots are the connections in the test network which are wired to the central plug. The numbers in the spots correspond to the terminals in the central plug.

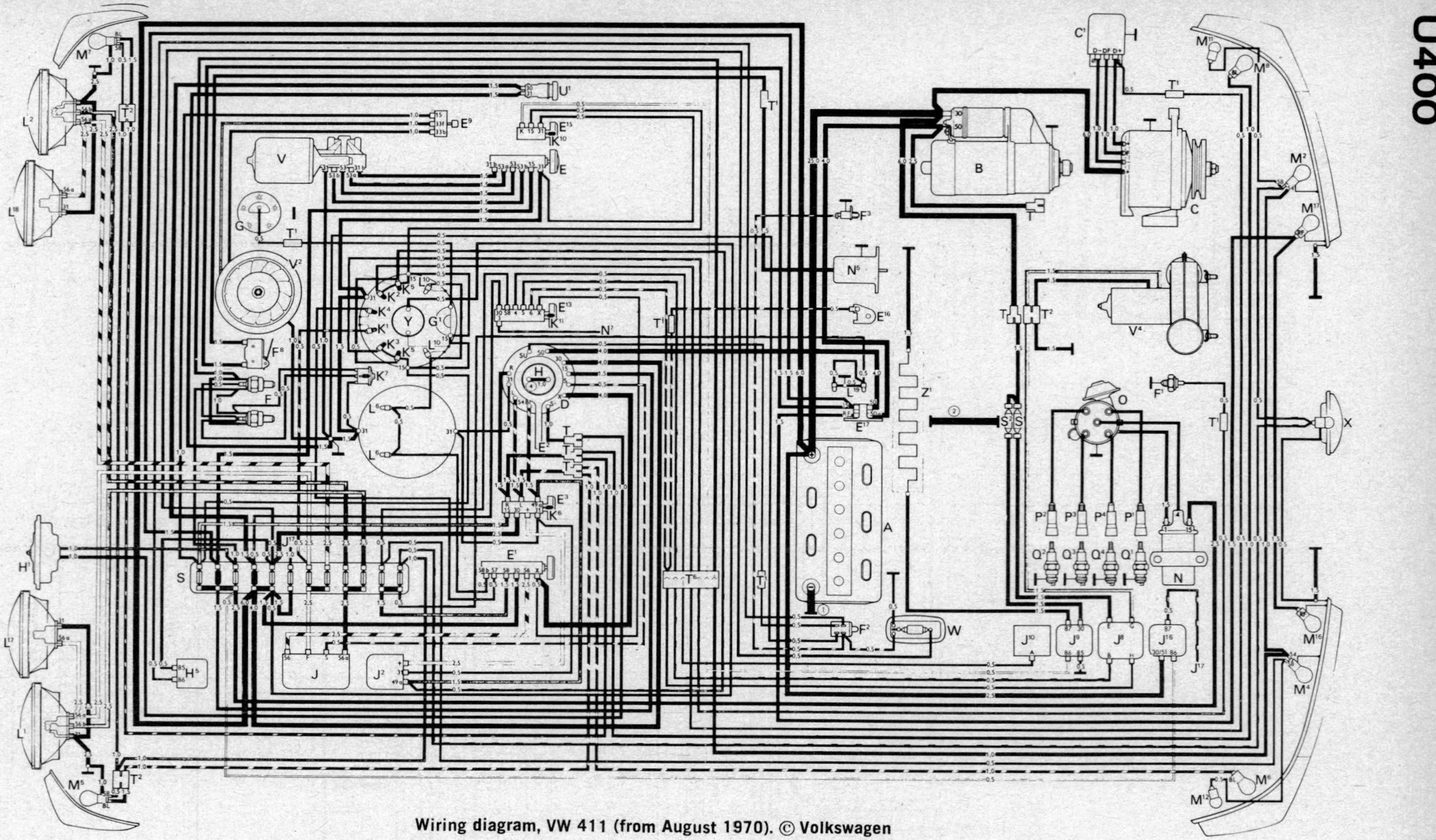

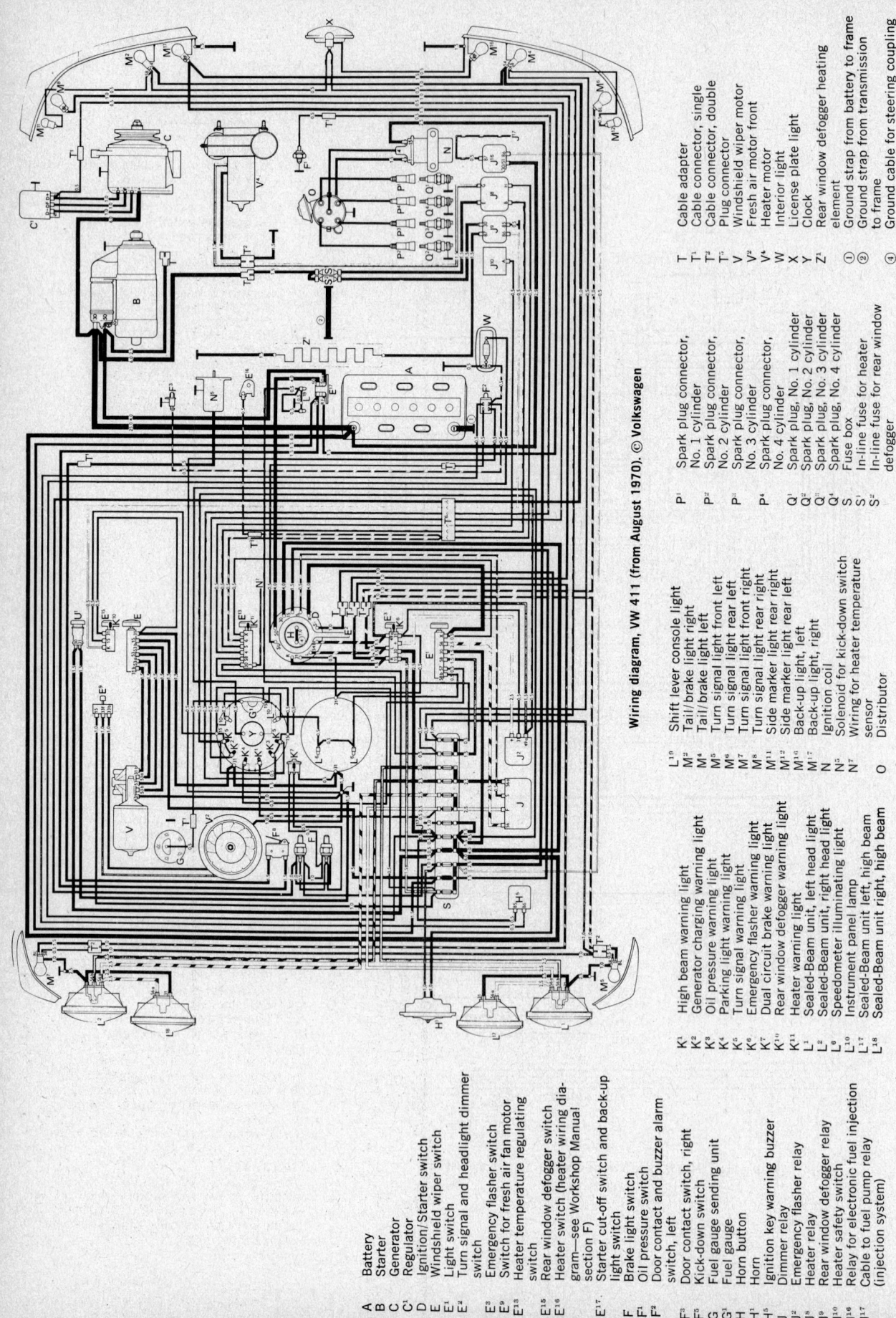

Wiring diagram, VW 411 (from August 1970). © Volkswagen

- A Battery
- B Starter
- C Generator
- C^1 Regulator
- D Ignition/Starter switch
- E Windshield wiper switch
- E^1 Light switch
- E^2 Turn signal and headlight dimmer switch
- E^3 Emergency flasher switch
- E^9 Switch for fresh air fan motor
- E^{13} Heater temperature regulating switch
- E^{15} Rear window defogger switch
- E^{16} Heater switch (heater wiring diagram—see Workshop Manual section F)
- E^{17} Starter cut-off switch and back-up light switch
- F Brake light switch
- F^1 Oil pressure switch
- F^2 Door contact and buzzer alarm switch, left
- F^3 Door contact switch, right
- F^5 Kick-down switch
- G Fuel gauge sending unit
- G^1 Fuel gauge
- H Horn button
- H^1 Horn
- H^5 Ignition key warning buzzer
- J Dimmer relay
- J^2 Emergency flasher relay
- J^8 Heater relay
- J^9 Rear window defogger relay
- J^{10} Heater safety switch
- J^{16} Relay for electronic fuel injection
- J^{17} Cable to fuel pump relay (injection system)
- K^1 High beam warning light
- K^2 Generator charging warning light
- K^3 Oil pressure warning light
- K^4 Parking light warning light
- K^5 Turn signal warning light
- K^6 Emergency flasher warning light
- K^7 Dual circuit brake warning light
- K^{10} Rear window defogger warning light
- K^{11} Heater warning light
- L^1 Sealed-Beam unit, left head light
- L^2 Sealed-Beam unit, right head light
- L^6 Speedometer illuminating light
- L^{10} Instrument panel lamp
- L^{17} Sealed-Beam unit left, high beam
- L^{18} Sealed-Beam unit right, high beam
- L^{19} Shift lever console light
- M^2 Tail/brake light right
- M^4 Tail/brake light left
- M^5 Turn signal light front left
- M^6 Turn signal light rear left
- M^7 Turn signal light front right
- M^8 Turn signal light rear right
- M^{11} Side marker light rear right
- M^{12} Side marker light rear left
- M^{16} Back-up light, left
- M^{17} Back-up light, right
- N Ignition coil
- N^5 Solenoid for kick-down switch
- N^7 Wiring for heater temperature sensor
- O Distributor
- P^1 Spark plug connector, No. 1 cylinder
- P^2 Spark plug connector, No. 2 cylinder
- P^3 Spark plug connector, No. 3 cylinder
- P^4 Spark plug connector, No. 4 cylinder
- Q^1 Spark plug, No. 1 cylinder
- Q^2 Spark plug, No. 2 cylinder
- Q^3 Spark plug, No. 3 cylinder
- Q^4 Spark plug, No. 4 cylinder
- S Fuse box
- S^1 In-line fuse for heater
- S^2 In-line fuse for rear window defogger
- T Cable adapter
- T^1 Cable connector, single
- T^2 Cable connector, double
- T^5 Plug connector
- V Windshield wiper motor
- V^2 Fresh air motor front
- V^4 Heater motor
- W Interior light
- X License plate light
- Y Clock
- Z^1 Rear window defogger heating element
- ① Ground strap from battery to frame
- ② Ground strap from transmission to frame
- ④ Ground cable for steering coupling

IGNITION SYSTEM

Distributor

Distributor R & R

Take off the vacuum hose at the distributor. Disconnect cable one at the ignition coil and remove the distributor cap. Mark the relationship between the distributor body and the engine case. Unscrew the distributor retaining screw on the crankcase and lift out the distributor.

1 Breaker plate with ground cable
2 Condenser
3 Vacuum advance unit
4 Sealing ring
5 Distributor cap
6 Rotor
7 Distributor shaft
8 Fiber washer
9 Contact breaker arm with spring
10 Return spring
11 Contact breaker point
12 Distributor housing
13 Steel washers
14 Driving dog
15 Pin
16 Locking ring

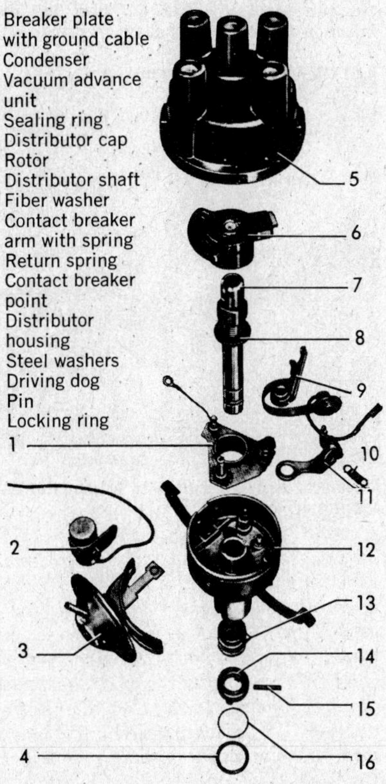
1
2
3
4
5
6
7
8
9
10
11
12
13
14
15
16

Exploded view, typical VW distributor.

NOTE: Before removing the distributor, it is best to turn the engine until the rotor points to number one cylinder lead; i.e., toward the notch in the distributor housing. In this way one can be sure of having the rotor pointing in the proper direction when the distributor is reinstalled.

Installation is in the reverse sequence. Align the marks made before removal. When the distributor is reinstalled in the engine, the timing must then be adjusted.

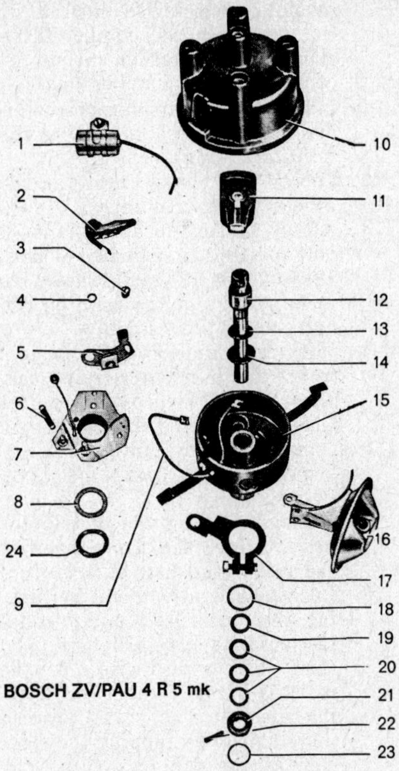
BOSCH ZV/PAU 4 R 5 mk

1 Condenser
2 Contact breaker arm
3 Securing screw with flat and spring washers
4 Insulating washer
5 Contact breaker point
6 Return spring
7 Breaker plate with ground cable
8 Plastic washer
9 Low-tension cable
10 Distributor cap
11 Rotor
12 Distributor shaft
13 Steel washer
14 Fiber washer
15 Distributor housing
16 Vacuum advance
17 Clip
18 Sealing ring
19 Fiber washer
20 Shim
21 Driving dog
22 Pin
23 Locking spring
24 Shim

Exploded view, typical Bosch distributor.

Contact Point Adjustment

The breaker points are the heart of the Volkswagen ignition system and must be given their share of attention. All Volkswagens ever made require a breaker point gap of .016 in. (COLD) and a dwell angle of 50 degrees (50°). In adjusting the contact points, the following steps are taken:

1. Remove the distributor cap and rotor.
2. Turn the engine by hand until the fiber block on the movable breaker point rests on a high point of the cam lobe.
3. With a screwdriver, loosen the locking screw of the stationary breaker point.
4. Manipulate the stationary point plate so that the clearance between the points is .016 in.
5. Tighten the locking screw of the stationary point.
6. Recheck gap and correct if it has changed from step (4) due to the tightening of the locking screw.

When replacing points, the same steps as above are followed, except that in between steps three and four, the old points are taken out and the new points inserted. Points should be replaced when they have been badly burned or have been in use so long that correct adjustment is no longer possible.

If necessary, multipurpose grease should be applied to the breaker arm fiber block whenever the points are inspected. Use enough to do the job but avoid excess grease that could come into contact with the breaker points and cause misfiring of the ignition system.

1 2 3 4 5 6 7
8 9 10 11 12 13 14

1 Spring for breaker arm
2 Breaker arm
3 Distributor with cam
4 Connection for contact
5 Breaker plate
6 Vacuum unit
7 Condenser
8 Insulator
9 Securing screw
10 Pins on breaker plate
11 Breaker point
12 Eccentrics for return springs
13 Return springs
14 Pull rod

Details of typical distributor.

Ignition Timing

It is only after adjusting the breaker points properly that the ignition timing should be adjusted. It is most important that the ignition timing adjustment be carried out only when the engine is dead cold, because rising engine temperature causes the setting to become different.

If, in exceptional cases, it is necessary **to adjust the timing** with a warm engine, not exceeding 122°F, the timing should be advanced about 2.5° beyond the normal setting. The timing must then be rechecked at the first opportunity with the engine cold.

VW engines have had several different arrangements of crankshaft pulley timing marks. On early Type 1 engines, the pulley bore two timing marks, 7.5° before top dead center and 10° before top dead center, reading clockwise. Later, with the introduction of emission controls, a 0° top dead center mark was added. The

Right mark is 10° BTDC, one on left is 7.5° BTDC on early Type 1 and 2 engines. See text for details of markings on other engines.

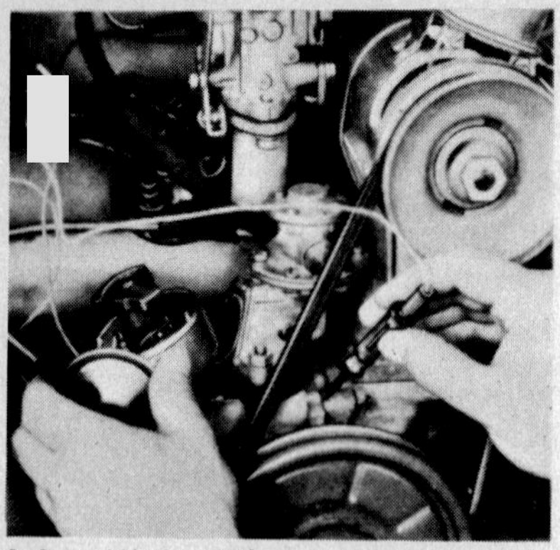

A 6 or 12 volt static test lamp is used in setting the ignition timing of all pre-1968 VW engines. One lead of the test lamp is connected to terminal 1 of the coil, the other to ground.

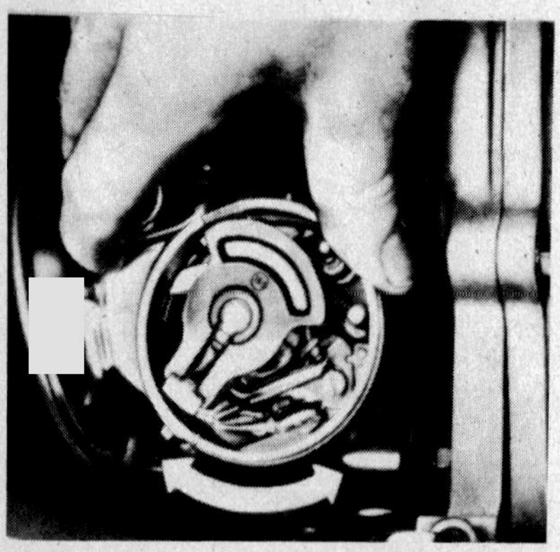

Turning the distributor body clockwise retards the ignition timing; turning counterclockwise advances the timing.

7.5° and 10° marks were subsequently removed, leaving only the 0° mark. Current engines have only a 5° after top dead center mark. Type 2 engines are generally the same as Type 1 models. Early Type 3 engines have marks at 7.5° and 10° before top dead center; later engines have marks at 7.5°, 10°, and 12.5° before top dead center. Fuel-injected Type 3 engines have marks corresponding to 0°, 7.5°, 10°, and 12.5° before top dead center.

Timing Procedure

1. Turn the engine by hand until the appropriate mark on the crankshaft pulley is lined up with the crankcase dividing line. (On Type 3 models, the mark is to be lined up with the timing setting surface, or pointer, on the fan housing. At the same time the appropriate mark is opposite the dividing line, the rotor must be pointing to the lead wire of cylinder number one (the cylinder toward the front of the car on the passenger [right] side). Number one position is indicated by a mark on the rim of the distributor. See the illustration showing cylinder numbering. If the rotor is not pointed toward number one cylinder, the crankshaft must be turned one more revolution clockwise until it is. On recent models, number three cylinder is retarded about 4° compared with number one cylinder and only number one cylinder is to be used in setting the ignition timing.
2. Loosen the clamp screw at the base of the distributor.
3. Attach the lead of a test lamp (6 volt for 1966 and earlier models, 12 volt for 1967 and later) to terminal one of the ignition coil and ground the test lamp.
4. With the ignition switched on, rotate the distributor body clockwise until the contact points close, and then rotate it slowly counterclockwise until the points begin to open and the lamp lights.
5. Without moving the distributor body, tighten the clamp screw at the base of the distributor.
6. Recheck the adjustment by turning the crankshaft pulley counterclockwise one-half turn, and then turning clockwise until the mark is within 1 in. of the dividing line. At this point, proceed more slowly by tapping the right side of the fan belt with your hand. Such tapping will cause the fan belt to move in either moderate or very small jumps, depending on the strength of the tap. Slight taps toward the end of the check will ensure the finest pssible check on the accuracy of the adjustment. If, upon rechecking, the lamp lights before the mark gets to the dividing line, the timing will have to be retarded slightly by loosening the clamp screw and rotating the distributor body in the clockwise direction. Rotating the distributor clockwise retards the timing, while rotation in the counterclockwise direction advances the timing.

NOTE: Adjustment of ignition timing on 1967 and earlier engines must always be done with a test lamp. A stroboscopic timing light should not be used, as it will alter the engine setting range. It is, however, recommended that exhaust emission controlled engines 1968 and later and Type 3 and 4 fuel-injected engines be timed with a stroboscopic light. These engines should be timed at idle speed, with the distributor vacuum line disconnected and the engine at normal operating temperature.

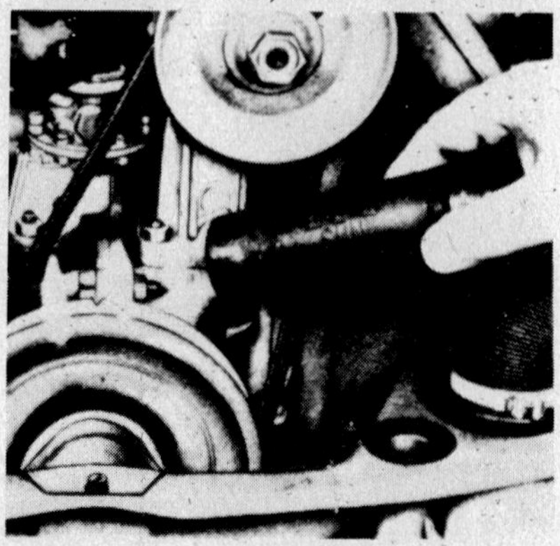

A stroboscopic timing light must be used to set the ignition timing of all 1968 and later exhaust emission controlled VW engines.

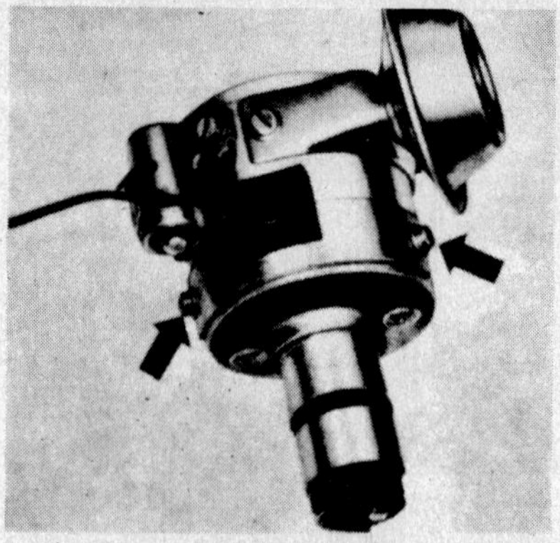

Distributor used with fuel-injected engines. The two screws pointed out hold the fuel injection trigger contact plate in place.

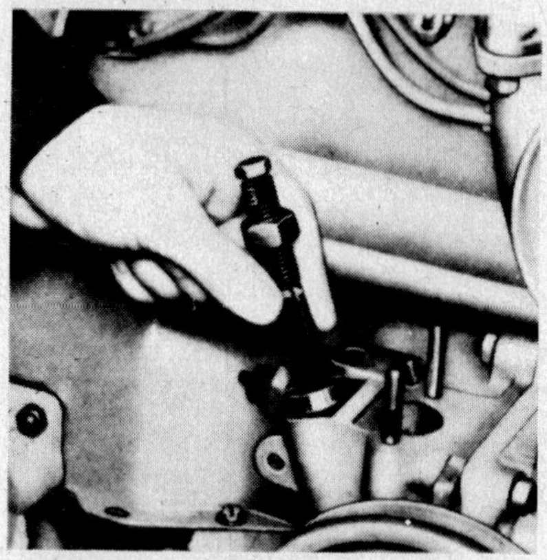

A removal tool is required to extract the distributor driveshaft.

Distributor Trigger Contact R & R

The distributor on fuel-injected engines has two breaker plates. The first is the normal breaker point plate for the ignition system. The second plate, mounted in the base of the distributor head, carries two similar breaker assemblies which regulate fuel injection. There is no adjustment provided for the injection trigger contact breakers. To replace the trigger contacts:

1. Remove the distributor cap. Pull out the triple plug and disconnect the flat plug at terminal one of the coil. Loosen the clamp and remove the distributor after noting the rotor position and marking the relationship between the engine block and the distributor body.
2. Remove the two contact plate holding screws.
3. Pull out the plate holder.

4. Reverse the procedure to install the new plate holder. If ignition timing is correct, the injection timing will also be correct.

Distributor Driveshaft R & R

To remove the distributor driveshaft, loosen the distributor clamp bolt, turn the engine so that the rotor is pointing to number one cylinder (the notch on the distributor housing), and lift out the distributor. Re-

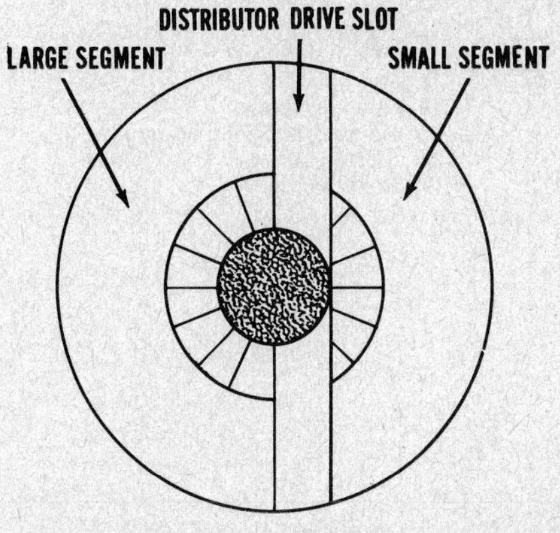
DISTRIBUTOR DRIVE SLOT
LARGE SEGMENT
SMALL SEGMENT

Detail of top of distributor driveshaft, showing offset slot referred to in text.

move fuel pump and intermediate flange, gaskets, and fuel pump push rod. Remove the distance spring on the distributor driveshaft. Be sure that number one cylinder is at its firing point, and withdraw the driveshaft via a removal tool by pulling with the extractor and turning the driveshaft to the left at the same time.

Remove the washer(s) under the driveshaft, being careful not to drop a washer into the crankcase. When the engine is installed, a magnet is handy for removing these washers.

When installing, the reverse of the previous procedure applies. The fuel-pump push rod drive eccentric and the pinion teeth should be checked for wear. If the teeth are badly worn, the teeth on the crankshaft should also be examined. Check the washer under the driveshaft for wear and replace it if necessary. Position number one

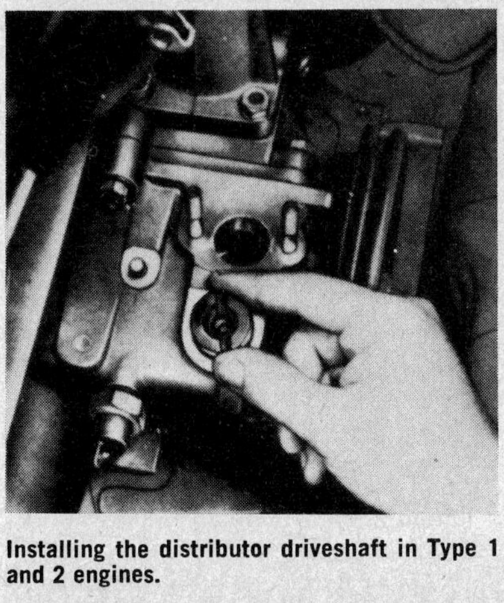

Installing the distributor driveshaft in Type 1 and 2 engines.

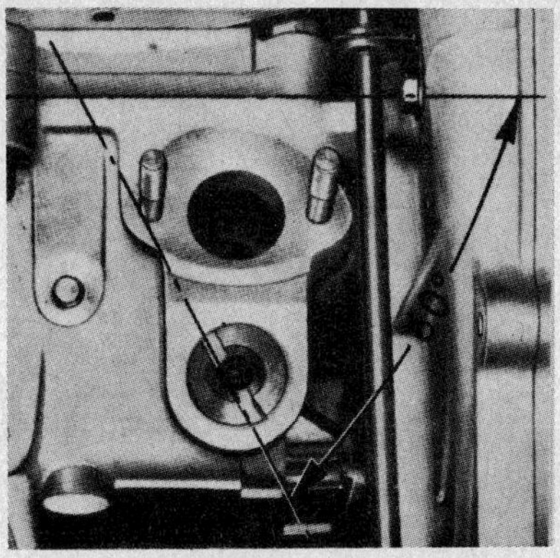

Installing the distributor driveshaft in Type 3 engines. With No. 1 cylinder at its firing point, the slot of the driveshaft must form an angle of approximately 60°, with the smaller segment toward the oil cooler. See the text for details on other engines.

cylinder at its firing point and insert the distributor driveshaft.

The slot in the top of the distributor driveshaft is offset, dividing the top of the driveshaft into two unequal segments. The driveshaft is installed as follows:

Insert the distance spring, install the distributor, set the ignition timing, and install the fuel pump. *NOTE: When the engine has been completely disassembled, it is necessary that the oil pump, the fan housing, the fan, and the crankshaft pulley be installed before the distributor driveshaft is inserted.*)

CHARGING SYSTEM

Different types of generators have been used throughout the years and models. Refer to the "Generator and Regulator Electrical Equipment Specifications" chart for details.

The generator warning light in the speedometer housing connects to the voltage regulator by means of terminals in the ignition switch. The warning lamp lights as soon as the ignition is turned on, and goes out when the voltage of the generator approaches that of the battery. The warning lamp simply gives a "yes-no" answer to the question of whether the generator is charging or not. As such, it is potentially useful in detecting broken fan belts, because when a fan belt is broken, the generator is no longer being turned and will not charge. In a Type 1 or 2, a broken belt means that the entire car is out of commission, but with the Type 3, the fan is mounted directly on the crankshaft and the car can be driven until the battery runs out of electricity.

The generator is equipped with ball bearings that are packed with special high melting-point grease. Lubrication of the generator is not necessary under normal conditions. However, if the unit has been disassembled and/or overhauled, it is then necessary to provide new lubricant for the bearings. Under no circumstances should ordinary grease be used, for it will not hold up under operating conditions.

Testing Generator No-Load Voltage

In testing the no-load voltage of the generator, the cable from terminal B+(51) at the regulator must first be disconnected. The positive lead of the voltmeter to be used should be attached to terminal B+(51) of the regulator and the negative lead of the meter grounded. With the engine running, the speed should be increased gradually until the reading of the voltmeter peaks out. If the regulator is functioning properly, the peaking point of the no-load voltage should be approximately 7.4–8.1 volts (V) for the 6 volt system and 13.6–14.4 for the 12 volt system. When the engine is turned off, the needle of the voltmeter should drop from 6 V (12 V) to zero just before the engine stops.

Testing Generator Without Regulator

The generator can be given a very quick check without the regulator. It is most important that the duration of the test be very brief (only a few seconds) in order that the generator field windings will not be overloaded during the test.

Disconnect the D+ and DF leads from the generator. Connect terminal DF of the generator to the D—terminal. Connect the positive terminal of the voltmeter to terminal D+ and the negative terminal to the generator ground. For 6 V systems, approximately 6 V should be generated at 1500 rpm and about 15 at 3000 rpm. For 12 V systems, 12 V should be generated at 1500 rpm and 36 V at 3000 rpm. A circuit diagram for this test is included in this section.

Regulator R & R

On pre-1967 models, the regulator is located on top of the generator. Take off the connections from terminals B+ (51) and 61 at the regulator. Remove the screws that hold the reg-

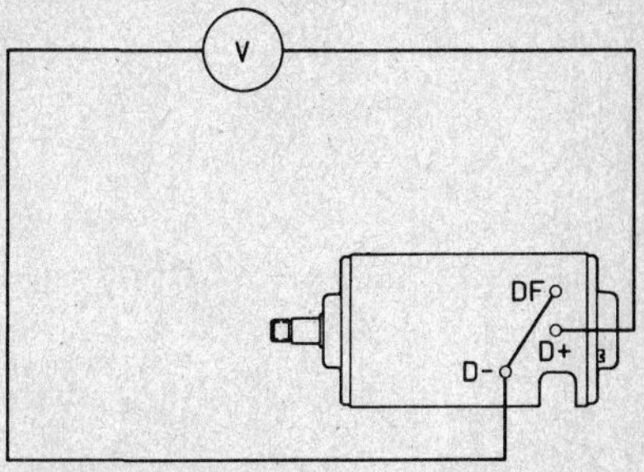
V
DF
D+
D-

Circuit diagram for making quick check of generator without regulator. Test must not take longer than a few seconds or generator will be damaged.

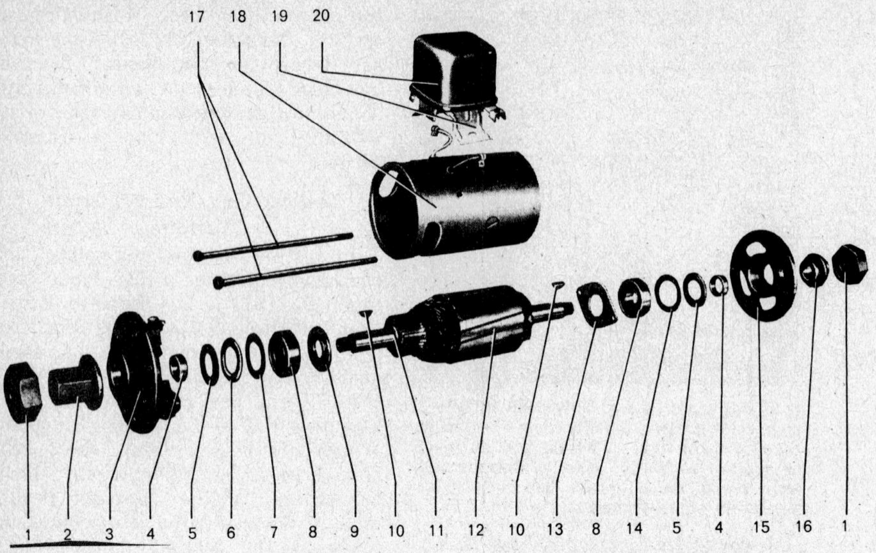
17 18 19 20
1 2 3 4 5 6 7 8 9 10 11 12 10 13 8 14 5 4 15 16 1

1 Nut
2 Pulley hub
3 Brush holder end plate
4 Spacer ring
5 Felt washer
6 Retainer
7 Thrust ring
8 Ball bearing
9 Washer
10 Key
11 Spacer
12 Armature
13 Bearing retainer
14 Thrust ring
15 End plate
16 Fan hub
17 Housing screws
18 Housing and field assembly
19 Slotted screw
20 Regulator

Exploded view, VW generator.

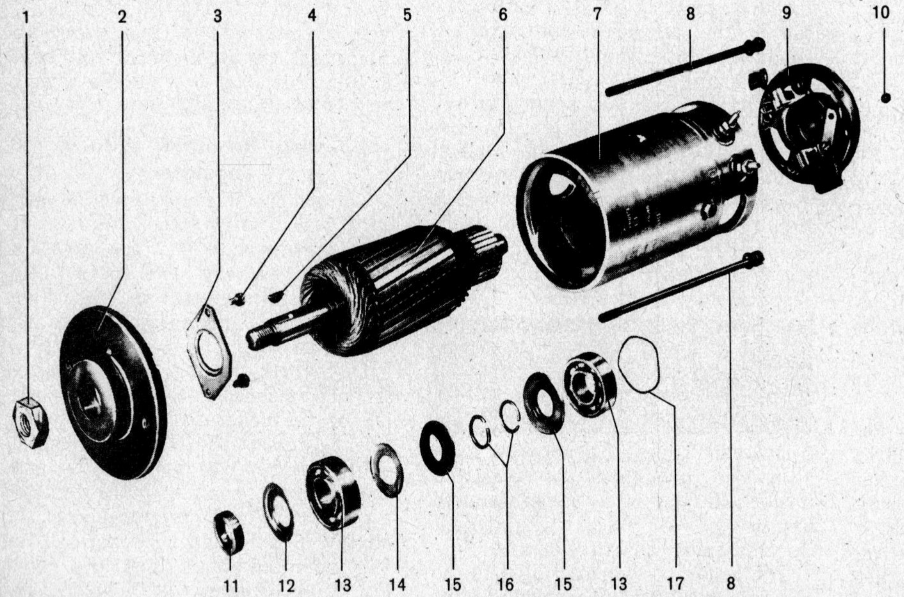
1 2 3 4 5 6 7 8 9 10
11 12 13 14 15 16 15 13 17 8

1 Nut
2 End plate
3 Retaining plate
4 Screw
5 Woodruff key
6 Armature
7 Pole housing
8 Housing screw
9 End plate with brush holders
10 Screw
11 Spacer
12 Washer
13 Bearing
14 Washer
15 Washer
16 Circlip
17 Spring ring

Exploded view, Bosch generator.

ulator onto the generator and remove the regulator from its position on the generator. Disconnect the electrical cables from the bottom of the regulator. These are marked + (D+) and F (DF).

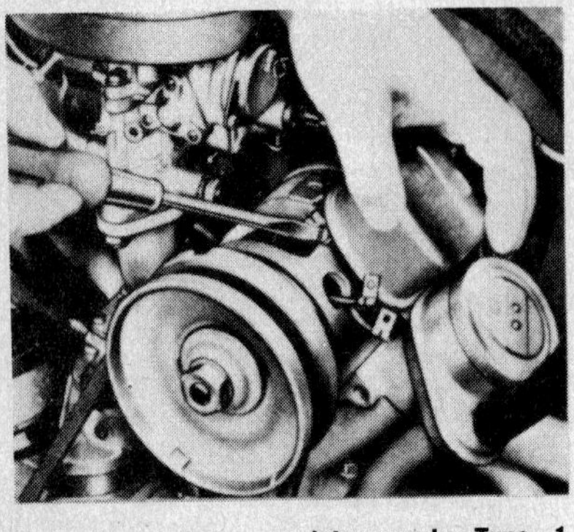

Removing voltage regulator, early Type 1 vehicles.

Installation of the regulator is the reverse of the preceding, but it should be noted that the thicker cable (coming from the positive brush of the generator) must be attached at the regulator bottom to terminal + (D+). The thin cable coming from the generator field windings should be attached to the F (DF) terminal at the bottom of the regulator. If the replacement of the regulator does not correct a deficiency in the charging system, chances are that the generator itself is defective.

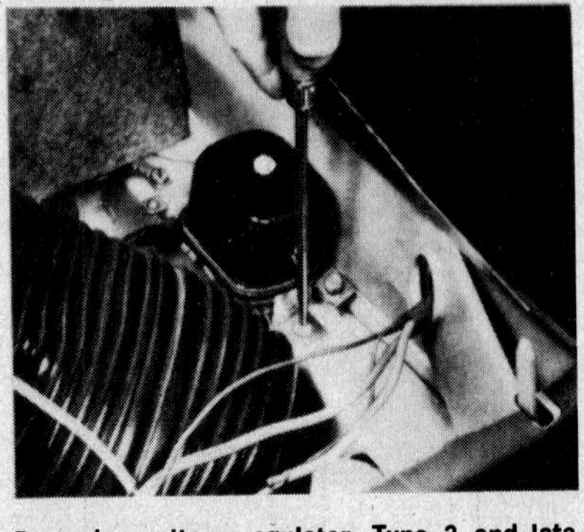

Removing voltage regulator, Type 3 and late Type 1 vehicles.

Checking Generator Brushes

The generator brushes should be examined periodically for wear. If they are worn to the point where they no longer extend from their holders, they should be replaced.

Alternator R & R Type 4

NOTE: The factory procedure recommends removing the engine to remove the alternator, however, it is possible to reach the alternator by first removing the right heater box which will provide access to the alternator.

1. Remove the engine. Disconnect the battery.
2. Remove the dipstick and the rear engine cover plate.
3. Remove the fan belt.
4. Remove the lower alternator bolt and the alternator cover plate.
5. Disconnect the wiring harness.
6. Remove the allen-head screws holding the fan, then remove the fan.
7. Remove the rubber elbow from the fan housing that provides alternator cooling.
8. Remove the alternator adjusting bracket.
9. Remove the alternator.
10. Reverse the above steps to install.

Regulator Type 4

The regulator is located near the air cleaner, mounted either on the air cleaner or on the firewall. Make careful note of the wiring.

Generator R & R

Disconnect the ground strap of the battery and disconnect the leads from the regulator. Remove the air cleaner and the carburetor and take off the fan belt. Remove the retaining strap from the generator. Remove the cooling air thermostat. Remove hot air hoses from the fan housing, take out the fan housing screws, and lift off the housing. After removing the fan housing screws, the generator can be lifted off along with the fan.

Installation is the reverse of the preceding. Except on Type 3, where the generator must be installed so that the mark on the housing is in line with the notch on the clamping strap.

STARTING SYSTEM

Battery

The electrical system of the Volkswagen is of the negative-ground type, the negative terminal of the battery being grounded. In most VW models, the battery is located under the right-hand side of the rear seat. In the Karmann Ghia and Transporter models, it is in the engine compartment.

The 6V electrical system was standard on all Volkswagens through the 1966 models. Beginning with the 1967 models (August 1966), the change was made to the 12 V system.

Starter

The starter is flange-mounted on the right-hand side of the transmission housing. Attached to the starter motor housing is a solenoid which engages the pinion and connects the starting motor to the battery when the ignition key is turned on. When the engine starts and the key is released from the start position, the solenoid circuit is opened and the pinion is returned to its original position by the return spring. If for any reason the starter is not switched off immediately after the engine starts, a pinion free-wheeling device stops the armature from being driven so that the starter will not be damaged.

Starter R & R

Disconnect the ground strap of the battery and remove the cable from terminal 30 and the lead from terminal 50 of the solenoid. After removal of the two retaining screws, the starter can be taken out. One of the starter attaching bolts is located in the engine compartment.

Prior to installation, the outboard bushing should be lubricated with special lithium grease, and sealing compound should be applied to the mating surfaces between the starter and the transmission. After putting the long screw into the hole in the flange, locate the starter on the transmission housing. Be sure that the cables are tightly connected to the terminals and that the contact points between the cables and terminals are clean.

Solenoid R & R

Unscrew the hexagon nut and remove the connector strip. Take out the two retaining screws on the mounting bracket and withdraw the solenoid after it has been unhooked from its actuating lever. When replacing a defective solenoid with a new one, care should be taken to see that the distance "a" in the accompanying diagram is 19+ or —.1 mm when the magnet is drawn in. The actuating rod can be adjusted after loosening the locknut.

Installation of the solenoid is the reverse of the preceding. Be certain that the rubber seal on the starter mounting bracket is properly seated. A small strip of VW Sealing Compound D 14 should be placed on the

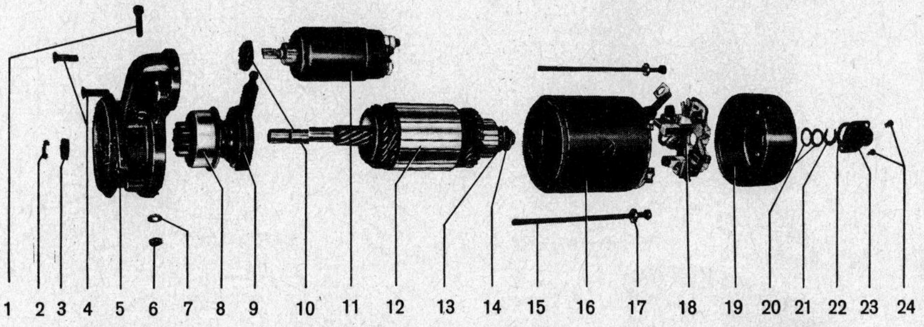
1 2 3 4 5 6 7 8 9 10 11 12 13 14 15 16 17 18 19 20 21 22 23 24

1 Lever bearing pin
2 Circlip
3 Stop-ring
4 Securing screws
5 Mounting bracket
6 Nut
7 Spring washer
8 Pinion
9 Operating lever
10 Rubber seal
11 Solenoid
12 Armature
13 Steel washer
14 Synthetic washer
15 Housing screw
16 Pole housing
17 Washer
18 Brush holder
19 End plate
20 Shims
21 Lockwasher
22 Sealing ring
23 End cap
24 Screws

Exploded view of typical Bosch starter.

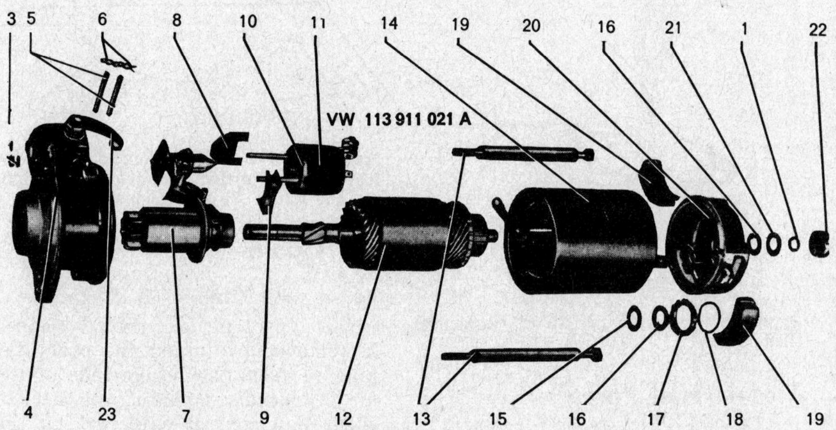
3 5 6 8 10 11 14 19 20 16 21 1 22
VW 113 911 021 A
4 23 7 9 12 13 15 16 17 18 19

1 Circlip
2 Cup washer
3 Nuts and lockwashers
4 Intermediate bracket
5 Pivot pins
6 Spring clips
7 Drive pinion with linkage and solenoid core
8 Insulating plate
9 Molded rubber seal
10 Insulating disc
11 Solenoid housing
12 Armature
13 Housing screws
14 Housing and field assembly
15 Steel washer
16 Bronze washer
17 Friction washer
18 Thrust ring
19 Brush inspection cover
20 Commutator end plate
21 Steel washer
22 Cap
23 Connecting strip

Exploded view of typical VW starter.

outside of the switch. In order to facilitate engagement of the actuating rod, the pinion should be pulled out as far as possible when the solenoid is inserted.

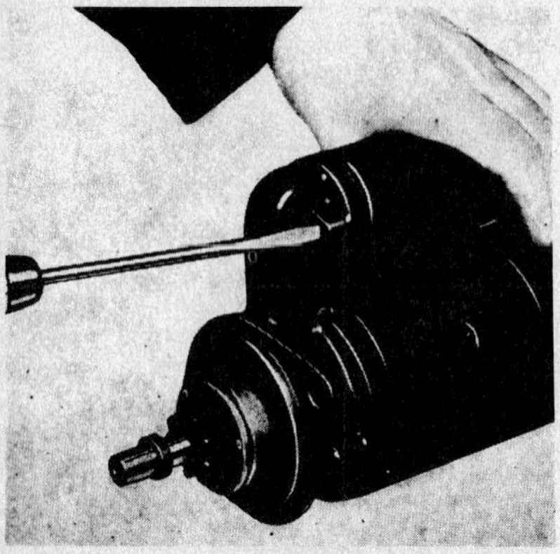

The solenoid may be withdrawn after removal of the two screws securing it to the starter motor intermediate bracket.

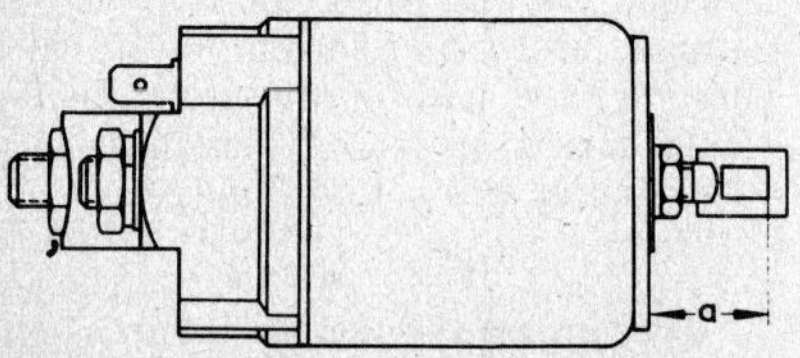
a

When installing a new solenoid, distance "a" should be 19 ± .1 mm with the magnet drawn in.

FUEL SYSTEM

The Fuel Pump

The Volkswagen fuel pump, except on fuel-injected engines, is mechanical, and of the diaphragm type, being push-rod operated from a cam on the distributor drive gear.

Other than cleaning the filter of the pump at regular intervals, no other maintenance is necessary. The push rod and pump rocker arm are lubricated by the lubricant in the lower part of the pump. The fuel pump filter on recent Volkswagen models is removed by unscrewing the hexagonal head plug from the side of the fuel pump assembly.

Mechanical Fuel Pump R & R

The fuel pump is removed by taking off the fuel line, disconnecting the hose from the pump, and removing the retaining nuts from the mounting studs. After the pump has been removed, the intermediate flange, push rod, and gaskets can be removed. Be careful in handling the push rod, as it could be inconvenient to have to fish it out of the crankcase.

Once removed, the stroke of the fuel pump is adjusted by insertion or removal of the proper number of flange gaskets. Adjustment is checked after installing the intermediate flange with two gaskets and push rod, and nuts are tightened to the same tightness as if the entire pump were being installed. Normal full-stroke is approximately 4 mm. The length of the push-rod stroke is measured from the pump contact surface on the intermediate flange, including gaskets.

When installing the fuel pump, care must be taken to install the intermediate flange before the push rod, otherwise the rod may fall through into the crankcase. Before installing the fuel pump, the lower chamber should be filled with universal grease. Tighten nuts to mounting studs, taking care not to overtighten. (Nuts should be retightened when the engine has reached operating temperature.) Connect the fuel line and hose, and check for correct seating of the fuel line rubber grommet in the panel of the engine compartment.

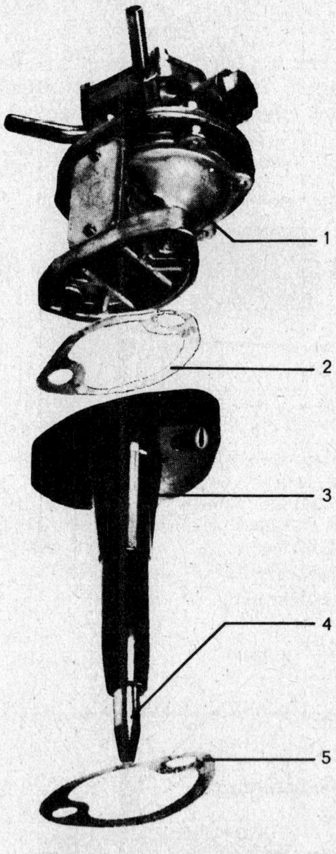
1
2
3
4
5

1 Fuel pump
2 Gasket
3 Plastic intermediate flange
4 Push rod
5 Gasket

Exploded view, lower portion of mechanical fuel pump.

Electric Fuel Pump

Electric Fuel Pump R & R

The electric fuel pump is mounted at the front of the chassis. There are three fuel lines: suction, pressure, and return.

To remove the pump:

1. Pinch-clamp the fuel lines shut to prevent leakage.
2. Unplug the electrical cable plug.
3. Cut off the original hose clamps Pull off the hoses and catch the fuel which drains out.
4. Raise the pressure hose to prevent draining the fuel loop line.
5. Unbolt and remove the pump.

To replace the pump:

1. Connect the three fuel hoses. Install screw type hose clamps at all three connections.
2. Bolt the pump to the mounting supports.
3. Remove the pinch clamps from the hoses.
4. Install the cable plug. The brown, negative ground wire must be to the bottom and the half circular cavity toward the right. Install the protective plug cap.

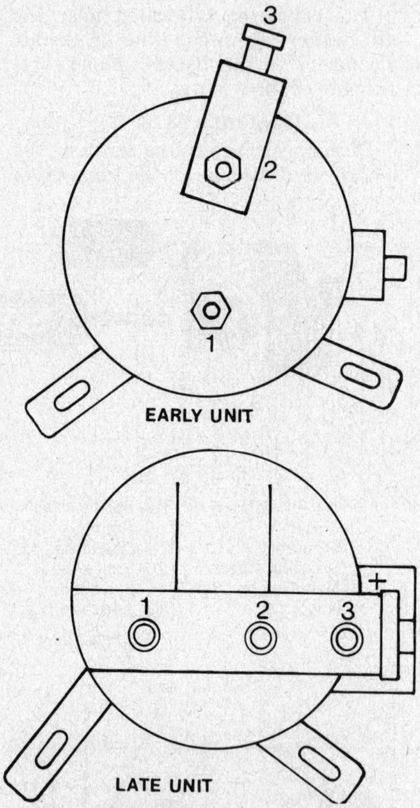
3
2
1
EARLY UNIT
+
1
2
3
LATE UNIT

Front view of electric fuel pumps used with fuel injection system. Suction (1), pressure (2), and return (3) connections are shown.

Air Cleaner

Air Cleaner R & R

On Type 1 models, the air cleaner is removed by taking the preheater pipe(s) from the intake tube of the air cleaner, disconnecting the thermostatic flap control wire, pulling the crankcase breather hose from the cleaner, and loosening the clamp screw that holds the cleaner onto the carburetor throat. After the air cleaner has been removed, the top part can be separated from the lower part by removing the clips that hold the halves together.

When the cleaner has been taken

The dual-carburetor, Type 3 engine's air cleaner is fastened down at three points. The center wingnut should always be loosened first and tightened last to avoid disturbing the linkage adjustment.

apart, the dirty oil should be poured out and the lower part cleaned. The upper part does not generally require cleaning. The bottom part of the air cleaner should then be filled to the mark with new engine oil of the same viscosity as that used in the engine. If there is no mark, refill with the quantity of oil specified in the "Capacities and Pressures" chart.

Removal of the air cleaner in the Type 3, dual-carburetor engine is slightly more complex, but accomplished in much the same manner. The right-hand connecting rod must be removed from between the rotating lever and the carburetor, the cables removed from the automatic choke and electromagnetic pilot jet, the crankcase ventilation hose taken off the air cleaner, and the three wing nuts unscrewed. The center wing nut is removed before removing the air cleaner; those at each of the carburetors remain in place. After the center wing nut is removed, the air cleaner can be lifted from its position and the upper and lower parts separated.

When installing the air cleaner of the Type 3 engine, care should be taken to see that the oil is up to the mark, that the rubber sealing ring on each carburetor is secure, that the water drain hole is free in the lower part of the air cleaner, and that the marks' are lined up when the upper and lower halves are put back together. If the marks do not line up exactly, the intake pipe will point in the wrong direction and be either difficult or impossible to connect to the intake extension. When tightning the wing nuts of the air cleaner, it is very important that the outer wing nuts are tightened down first. There is an expansion-contraction joint between the left outer wing nut and the center wing nut which makes these not quite so critical. However, there is no such joint between the center and right-hand wing nuts. Subsequently, if the center nut is tightened first, and then the right-hand nut, the result could be a slight movement on the part of the right-hand carburetor, thus causing an alteration in a very sensitive adjustment. Tighten down the center wing nut only after the two outer wing nuts have been fully tightened.

To remove the air cleaner from fuel injected engines:

1. Detach crankcase and auxiliary air regulator hoses.
2. Loosen the hose clamps at either end of the air cleaner. Pull off the rubber hoses.
3. Remove the wingnut and air cleaner.

To clean, refill, and replace the air cleaner on fuel-injected engines:

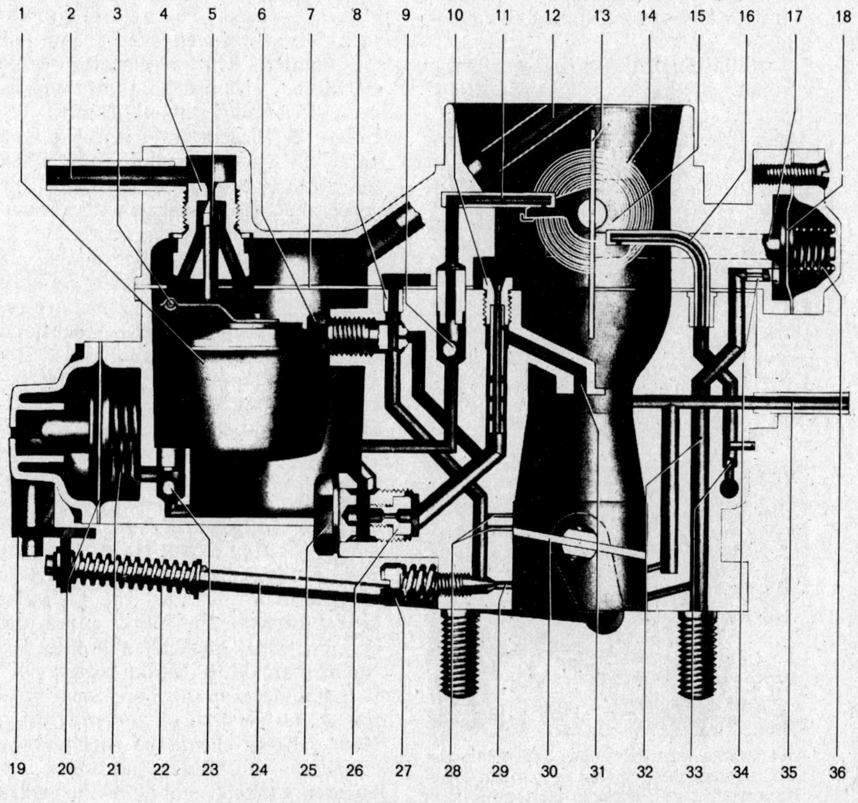

1 Float
2 Fuel line
3 Float lever
4 Float needle valve
5 Float needle
6 Pilot jet
7 Gasket
8 Pilot air drilling
9 Ball check valve in power fuel system
10 Air correction jet with emulsion tube
11 Power fuel tube
12 Float bowl vent tube
13 Choke valve
14 Bimetal spring
15 Operating lever
16 Accelerator pump discharge tube
17 Diaphragm rod
18 Vacuum diaphragm
19 Pump lever
20 Pump diaphragm
21 Spring
22 Push rod spring
23 Ball check valve for accelerator pump
24 Pump connector rod
25 Main jet carrier
26 Main jet
27 Volume control screw
28 Bypass port
29 Idle port
30 Throttle valve
31 Discharge arm
32 Vacuum drilling
33 Ball check valve in accelerator pump drilling
34 Jet in vacuum drilling
35 Vacuum connection
36 Diaphragm spring

Solex 28 PICT-1 carburetor used on 1,200 cc engines.

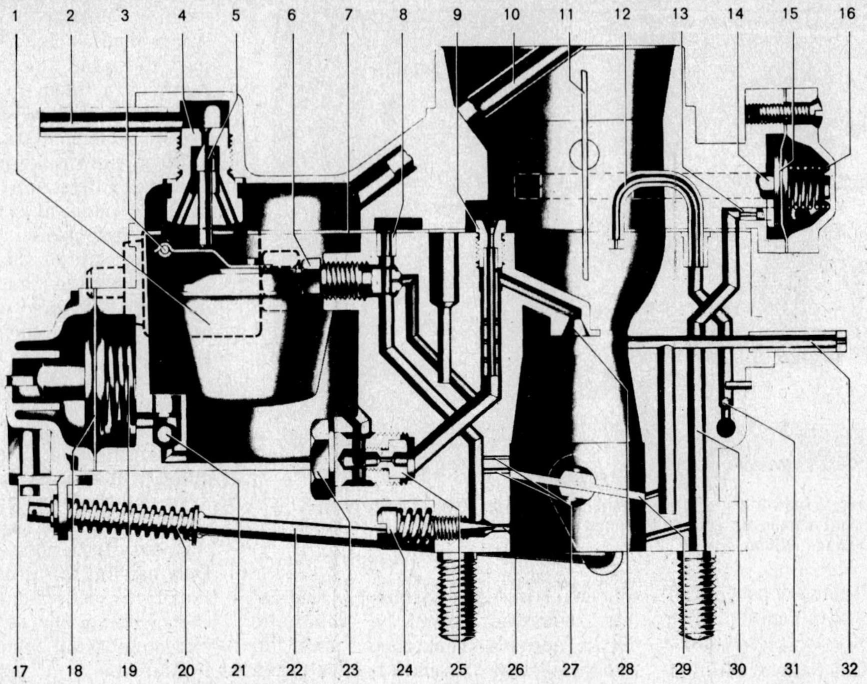
1 2 3 4 5 6 7 8 9 10 11 12 13 14 15 16
17 18 19 20 21 22 23 24 25 26 27 28 29 30 31 32

1 Float
2 Fuel line
3 Float lever
4 Float needle valve
5 Float needle
6 Electromagnetic pilot jet
7 Gasket
8 Pilot air drilling
9 Air correction jet with emulsion tube
10 Float bowl vent tube
11 Choke valve
12 Accelerator pump discharge tube
13 Jet in vacuum drilling
14 Diaphragm rod
15 Vacuum diaphragm
16 Spring for vacuum diaphragm
17 Pump lever
18 Pump diaphragm
19 Pump spring
20 Spring
21 Ball check valve for accelerator pump
22 Pull rod for accelerator pump
23 Main jet carrier
24 Volume control screw
25 Main jet
26 Idle port
27 Bypass port
28 Discharge arm
29 Throttle valve
30 Vacuum drilling
31 Ball check valve in accelerator pump drilling
32 Vacuum connection

The carburetors on the Karmann Ghia models are fitted with a power fuel system.

Solex 30 PICT-1 carburetor used on 1,300 and 1,500 cc engines.

1. Release the three clips. Remove the top section.
2. Clean the filter assembly out and refill it with SAE 30 oil to the red mark. SAE 10 may be used in arctic climates.
3. Be sure that the red arrows on the top and bottom sections are aligned when reassembling.
4. Reconnect the hoses, and tighten the clamps and wingnut.

Carburetor

Carburetor R & R

On the Type 1, remove the preheat hose from the air cleaner intake pipe. Disconnect the thermostatic flap control wire. Disconnect the crankcase breather hose from the air cleaner intake. Loosen the air cleaner holding clamp and remove the air cleaner. Disconnect the fuel and vacuum hoses from the carburetor. Disconnect the wires from the automatic choke and the electromagnetic pilot jet. Disconnect the throttle cable at the carburetor and take off the spring, pin, and spring retaining plate. Take off the two carburetor retaining nuts and remove the carburetor from the intake manifold. The throttle positioner may be removed in unit with the carburetor. It would, at this point, be a good idea to stuff part of a clean rag into the intake manifold hole in order to ensure that dirt and other foreign matter will not find its way into the manifold and cause damage to the engine.

Installation of the carburetor is the reverse of the previous operation.

SOLEX
1
2

Main jet can be removed after unscrewing plug 1. 2 is idle mixture control screw.

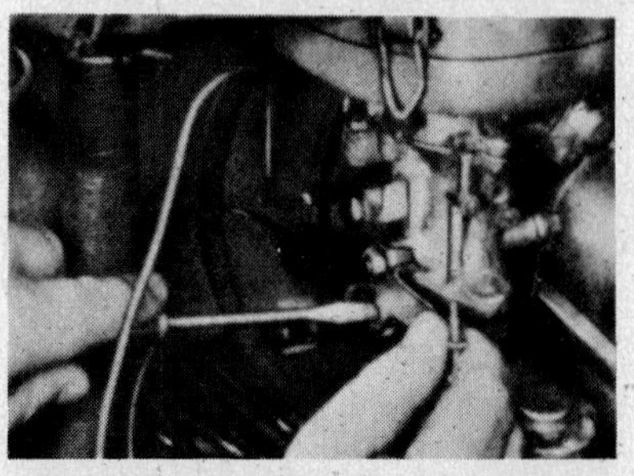

With throttle valve fully open and accelerator pedal floored, there should be a slight clearance (about 1 mm) between the throttle lever and the stop on the carburetor body.

When installing the carburetor, it is advisable that a new intake manifold gasket be used. The retaining nuts should be tightened evenly, but not too tightly. The accelerator cable should be adjusted so that there is very little play (about 1 mm) between the throttle lever and the stop point on the carburetor body when the pedal is fully depressed. The idle speed should be checked with the engine at operating temperature.

On the Type 3, remove the air cleaner as described earlier. Be sure that the electrical connections are removed from the automatic chokes and the electromagnetic pilot jets. Remove the connecting rods from between the center lever and the left- and right-hand carburetors. Disconnect the carburetor return springs and pull off the spark plug connecting caps. Remove the balance tube from between the carburetors by pulling it out of the connecting hoses on either side. Remove the nuts that hold the intake manifolds to the cylinder heads. Remove the intake pipes and cylinder head gaskets, and take the carburetors off the intake pipes.

Installation of the Type 3 carburetor is the reverse of the preceding. New gaskets should be used on the cylinder head intake, and the carburetor gaskets should be inspected for damage and replaced if necessary.

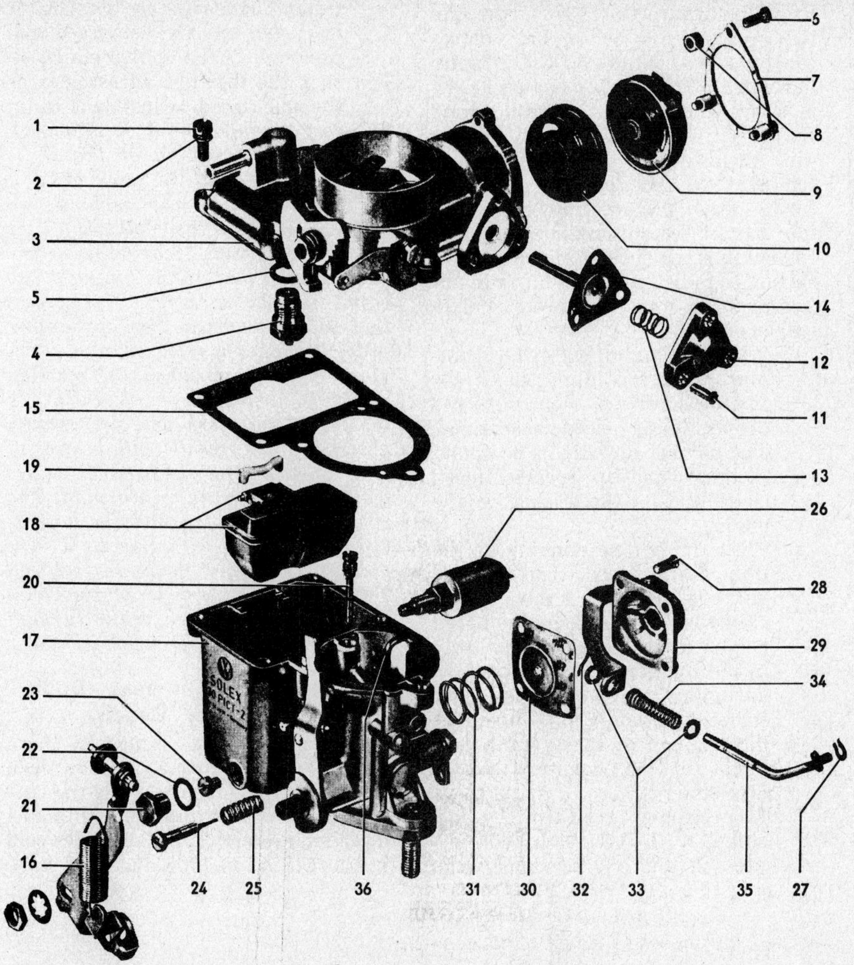
1
2
3
5
4
15
19
18
20
17
23
22
21
16
24
25
36
31
30
32
33
35
27
6
7
8
9
10
14
12
11
13
26
28
29
34
SOLEX
30 PICT-2

1 Screw for carburetor upper part
2 Spring washer
3 Carburetor upper part
4 Float needle valve 1.5mm diameter
5 Washer 15 x 12 x 1 mm for float needle valve
6 Screw for retaining ring
7 Retaining ring for cap
8 Spacer for retaining ring
9 Choke unit with spring and heater element
10 Plastic cap
11 Fillister head screw
12 Cover for vacuum diaphragm
13 Diaphragm spring
14 Vacuum diaphragm
15 Gasket
16 Return spring for accelerator cable
17 Carburetor lower part
17 Float and pin
19 Bracket for float pin
20 Air correction jet
21 Plug for main jet
22 Plug seal
23 Main jet
24 Volume control screw (designation 1, 2, and 3)
25 Spring
26 Pilot jet cut-off valve "A"
27 Circlip
28 Fillister head screw
29 Cover for pump
30 Pump diaphragm
31 Spring for diaphragm
32 Cotter pin 1.5 x 15 mm
33 Washer 4.2 mm
34 Spring for connecting rod
35 Connecting rod
36 Injector tube for accelerator pump

Solex 30 PICT-2 carburetor used on 1968-69, 1,500 cc engines with throttle positioner.

Checking Electromagnetic Pilot Jet

If the engine is equipped with an electromagnetic pilot jet in the carburetor, and still shows a tendency to "run-on" after being shut off, chances are that the electromagnetic jet is defective. Operation can be checked by turning on the ignition and touching the slip-on connector against the terminal of the jet. If the jet is operating properly, a clicking sound will be heard each time the connector touches the terminal. When the current is off, the needle of this jet moves so as to block off the fuel supply, so when the connector is removed while the engine is running, it should stop the engine.

On 1971 Type 1 and 2 engines, with the Solex 34 PICT-3 carburetor, the pilot jet cut-off valve has been replaced by an idle bypass mixture cut-off valve. The new unit performs the same function.

Choke housing cover alignment, Type 1 single carburetor shown.

1 Air by-pass drilling
2 Throttle valve
3 Air by-pass screw
4 Volume control screw
5 Fuel drilling

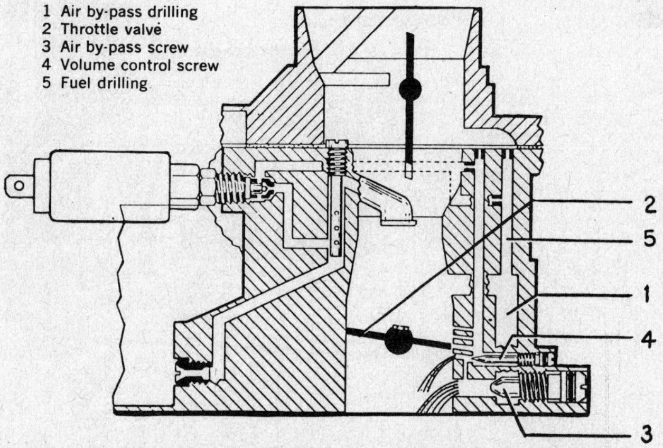
2
5
1
4
3

Solex 30 PICT-3 carburetor used on 1970 1,600 cc Type 1 and 2 engines. Idling speed adjustments are made with the air bypass screw.

Carburetor Adjustment

As a part of a routine tune-up it is necessary only to adjust the idling speed and mixture screws on the carburetors of most single carburetor Volkswagens. On 1970 and later Type 1 and 2 engines, the volume control screw is factory set and the throttle valve remains closed during idling. Idling speed adjustments are made with the air bypass screw. On the 30

Idle speed adjustment, pre-1970 Type 1 and 2.

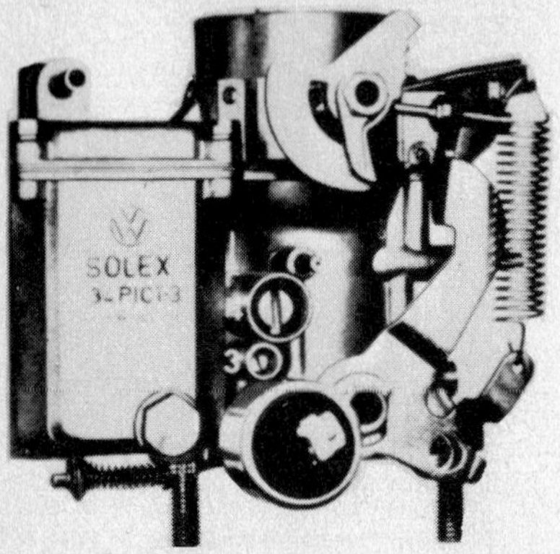
SOLEX

Adjustment screws on Solex 34 PICT-3 carburetor, 1971 Type 1 and 2. 3 is the volume screw. 4 is the air bypass screw.

PICT-3 carburetor (1970), the air bypass screw is below the volume control screw. On the 34 PICT-3 carburetor (1971), the air bypass screw is above the volume control screw. Before adjustment is begun, the engine should be at normal operating temperature and the idle adjusting screw must not be resting on the fast idle cam of the automatic choke. The following steps should be followed in setting the idle speed and mixture adjustments on single-carburetor Volkswagen engines:

1. With the engine warm and running, turn the idling speed adjusting screw in or out until the proper idling speed is attained. The correct speed can be found in the "Tune-Up Specifications" chart and on the sticker on the engine.
2. With the engine running at the proper idle speed, turn the idle mixture control screw slowly clockwise until the engine speed begins to drop, then turn slowly in the counterclockwise direction until the engine is running smoothly again. Now turn the mixture control screw another ¼ turn in the counterclockwise direction.
3. If necessary, readjust the idle speed. With the clutch pedal depressed, the engine should continue to run after the accelerator has been quickly depressed and released. If the engine stalls, either the mixture adjustment or the idle speed adjustment is incorrect and should be remedied.

NOTE: The setting of the slow-speed (idle) mixture will have a great influence on the performance and economy of the Volkswagen at speeds as great as 50 or 60 miles per hour. If the mixture is too rich, the result will be excess fuel consumption, stalling when the accelerator pedal is suddenly released, and possible "running on" when the ignition switch is turned off. If the mixture is too lean (too much air, not enough gasoline), the result will be better fuel consumption, but exhaust valves may suffer burning or warping. The previously given method for adjusting the slow-speed adjustment will give the proper mixture setting. Turning the mixture screw clockwise will lean the mixture, while turning counterclockwise will enrich it.

Carburetor Adjustment—Dual Carburetor Models

On certain Type 3 models, there are two carburetors—one for each bank of two cylinders. While the current models are equipped with a fuel injection system, Type 3 vehicles sold in the U.S.A. in 1966 and 1967 have

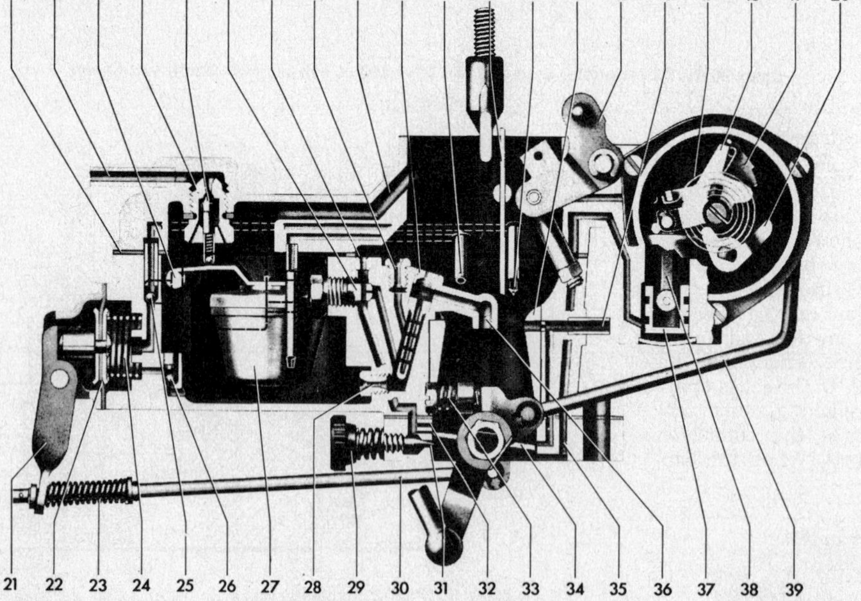
1 2 3 4 5 6 7 8 9 10 11 12 13 14 15 16 17 18 19 20
21 22 23 24 25 26 27 28 29 30 31 32 33 34 35 36 37 38 39

1 Gasket
2 Fuel pipe
3 Float pin
4 Float needle valve
5 Float needle
6 Pilot jet
7 Pilot air bleed drilling
8 Air correction jet
9 Vent passage for float chamber
10 Emulsion tube with ventilation jet
11 Power fuel pipe
12 Choke valve
13 Injector tube accelerator pump
14 Venturi
15 Relay lever
16 Vacuum connection
17 Bimetal coil
18 Intermediate lever
19 Fast idle cam
20 Stop lever
21 Pump lever
22 Pump diaphragm
23 Connecting rod spring
24 Diaphragm spring
25 Ball pressure valve
26 Ball suction valve
27 Float
28 Main jet
29 Volume control screw
30 Connecting rod
31 Idling mixture port
32 Bypass port
33 Idle adjustment screw
34 Throttle valve
35 Vacuum drilling
36 Discharge arm
37 Vacuum piston
38 Piston rod
39 Operating rod

Solex 32 PDSIT-2 carburetor used on dual-carburetor Type 3 engine. The 32 PDSIT-2 is the left carburetor, and has a double vacuum drilling for the distributor advance mechanism.

4
3
1
2
4

1 Accelerator cable
2 Connecting rod, right
3 Connecting rod, left
4 Carburetor pull rod with return spring

Dual carburetor linkage.

dual carburetors and require slightly more sophistication in the tune-up operation. Adjusting the carburetors on the dual-carb models requires the use of a special instrument to measure air flow. A commonly used product is that known as the Uni-Syn, available for under $10 from most mail-order auto accessory sources. This device measures the vacuum created by carburetor suction by means of a red piston which rides up and down inside a graded glass tube. The higher the vacuum, the higher the piston is raised.

Besides the synchronizing device mentioned above, a small frozen-juice can will also be required in order that the device will fit on the air horns of the carburetors. Because of the screws that stick straight up from the air horn for the purpose of holding the air cleaner, the small can (open on both ends) is needed. By mounting it on top of the can, the test device will clear the screws without losing vacuum. Before attempting adjustment, the engine must be at operating temperature.

Adjustment Steps

1. Remove the right-hand connecting rod of the carburetor linkage system. This is the rod which connects the center bellcrank with the right-hand carburetor throttle.
2. Remove the air cleaner. It is held on by two wing nuts on each carburetor and one wing nut in the center. The connections to the air intake and to the crankcase ventilation system must also be removed.
3. With the engine running, adjust the idle speed adjusting screw of each carburetor until the correct idling speed is attained. Each carburetor should then be drawing the same amount of air. When the test device is moved from one carburetor to the other, the height of the red piston should not change more than 1 in., preferably less.
4. In adjusting the volume control screw of each carburetor, slowly turn the screw clockwise until the engine speed begins to drop, then turn counterclockwise until the engine runs smoothly once again, then a further 1/4 of a turn in the counterclockwise direction.
5. Recheck the idle speed adjustment, and if necessary increase or decrease the idle speed of each carburetor so that the correct speed is maintained and the test device shows the same reading when it is moved from one carburetor to the other without moving the disc on the device.
6. Recheck the adjustment on the mixture control screws. On the 1600 models, there is a raised portion on the outside perimeter of each screw. This will enable one to feel the position of the screw when he cannot see it. The correct position for the mixture control screw will be approximately 1 1/2 turns from the screwed-in position. When turning the screw fully in the closed position, care should be taken not to apply too much torque, for the seat or needle of the screw could be damaged in this way.
7. After the mixture adjustment has been rechecked, the idle speed and balance should also be checked again and corrected if necessary.
8. In checking the balance of the carburetors at an increased speed, it is necessary to install once again the right-hand connecting rod which was removed in step (1). By means of a suitable object (e.g., a tool box) wedged against the accelerator pedal, the engine speed should be maintained at approximately 1,200–1,500 rpm in order to check the higher speed balance of the two carburetors.
9. Apply the test device to the left-hand carburetor and adjust the disc until the red piston rides in the center of the range. Now move the device over to the right-hand carburetor and, without moving the disc, compare the height of the piston here with the height achieved at the left carburetor. If the height of the piston is higher on the right side, the length of the right-hand connecting rod must be increased slightly. If the height of the piston is lower on the right side, the length of the right-hand connecting rod will have to be decreased. Changing the length of the right-hand connecting rod is accomplished by loosening the nuts on both ends and twisting the rod while leaving the ends stationary. The opposite ends have threads which tighten in opposite directions. The length of the right control rod must be adjusted until there is little or no difference between the readings of the test device when it is moved from one carburetor to the other.
10. After low-speed and high-speed balance has been checked, the connecting rods should be lubricated at their ends with lithium grease and the carburetor's moving parts lubricated with a light oil.
11. Reinstall the oil bath air cleaner, being careful to tighten the two outer wing nuts first, and then the center wing nut. If the center wing nut is tightened first, it is possible that the adjustment of the right-hand carburetor will be altered when the air cleaner is fastened tightly to the screw protruding from its air horn. Replace the crankcase ventilation hose and air intake connections. In order to install the air cleaner it will be necessary to remove the right-hand carburetor connecting rod temporarily. Take care not to bend this rod.

Accelerator Cable R & R, Type 1

The Volkswagen accelerator cable runs from the accelerator pedal to the carburetor by means of the central tunnel, the fan housing and the throttle valve lever. Guide tubes are used in both the central frame tunnel and the fan housing, while a plastic hose is present between the tunnel and the front engine cover plate.

To remove the accelerator cable, disconnect the cable from the throttle lever pin, raise the rear of the car,

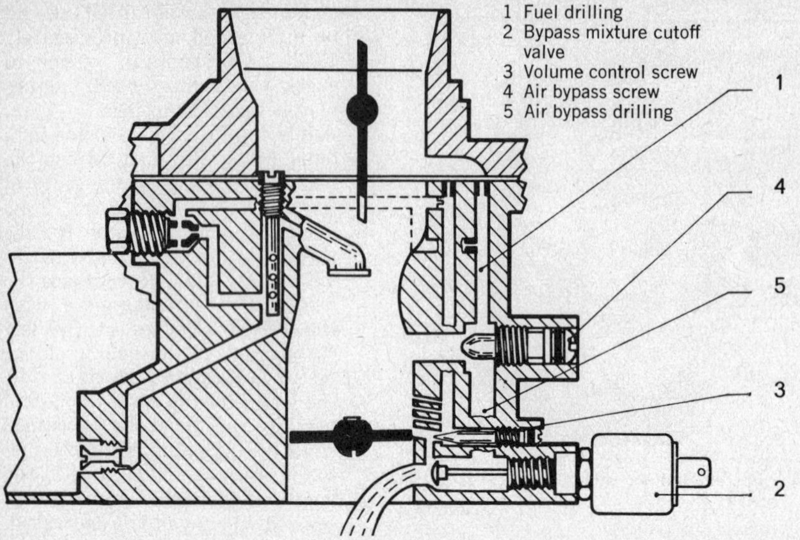
1 Fuel drilling
2 Bypass mixture cutoff valve
3 Volume control screw
4 Air bypass screw
5 Air bypass drilling
1
4
5
3
2

Solex 34 PICT-3 carburetor used on 1971 1,600 cc Type 1 and 2 engines. The volume control screw is factory set. Idling speed adjustments are made with the air bypass screw.

and pull the cable through from the front of the car after disconnecting the rod from the accelerator pedal.

Installation is the reverse of the removal. Grease the cable well before inserting from the front of the car. Be sure that the rear rubber boot and hose are properly seated, so that water will not enter the guide tubes. In order to avoid excessive strain of the throttle cable and assembly, there should be about 1 mm (.04 in.) clearance between the throttle stop and the carburetor body when the throttle is in the wide-open position. For this reason, it is advisable that the cable be tightened down at the carburetor end only when the accelerator pedal is at the fully floored position.

Fuel Injection System

The Bosch electronic fuel injection system is used on all Type 3 and 4 vehicles, beginning with 1968 models. Fuel pressure in the system is maintained at a constant 28 psi by an electric pump and a pressure regulator. Excess fuel bled off by the pressure regulator is routed back to the tank. Opening of the injector valves is timed by a pair of breaker trigger contacts in the base of the ignition distributor. The injector valves open in pairs; cylinders No. 1 and 4, and 2 and 3. The duration of the injector opening, and thus the volume of fuel injected, is regulated by the famous black box, or electronic computer. This unit takes into account inputs from sensors which measure engine temperature, air temperature, engine vacuum, air density, and throttle opening.

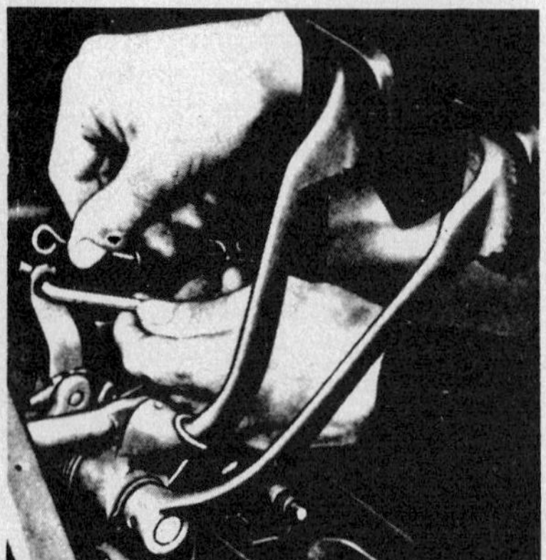

Accelerator cable is removed from the front of the car and is attached as shown.

Testing and troubleshooting of the fuel injection system requires special Bosch electronic testing apparatus. For this reason, these operations are best left to qualified personnel at an authorized dealer's shop. Removal and replacement of components, and adjustments that can be made without special equipment are covered in this section.

Idle Speed Adjustment

The only tune-up adjustment possible on the Bosch electronic fuel injection system is that for idle speed. The adjusting screw is located on the left side of the intake air distributor. Early models have a knurled screw with a lockspring; current models have a locknut on the adjusting screw. After adjusting the idle speed to specifications, make sure that the throttle valve is completely closed at idle.

Throttle Valve Switch Adjustment

The throttle valve switch is mounted to a base plate with graduated markings secured to the intake air distributor inlet. An alignment mark is located on the air distributor housing. The switch is affixed by two mounting screws and an electrical plug. To adjust the switch:

1. Remove the air cleaner for access.
2. Close the throttle valve completely.
3. Loosen the base plate mounting screws. Slowly rotate the switch and plate assembly counterclockwise until a click is heard.
4. Continue rotating the switch and plate assembly counterclockwise one more graduation. (Each graduation indicates 2°.)
5. Tighten the base plate mounting screws.
6. The throttle valve switch should come into operation when throttle has moved 4° from the closed position. Unhook the throttle return spring and check to see that the throttle is not binding.
7. Replace the throttle spring and air cleaner.

Pressure Regulator Adjustment

The pressure regulator is located on the front engine cover plate beneath the right side of the intake manifold. It is fitted with an adjusting nut and a locknut. There is a T-fitting for a pressure gauge in the fuel loop line between the takeoff points for the right side injector units. This fitting is normally plugged with a stopscrew.

NOTE: Before making any adjustment, be absolutely certain that the pressure gauge being used is accurate.

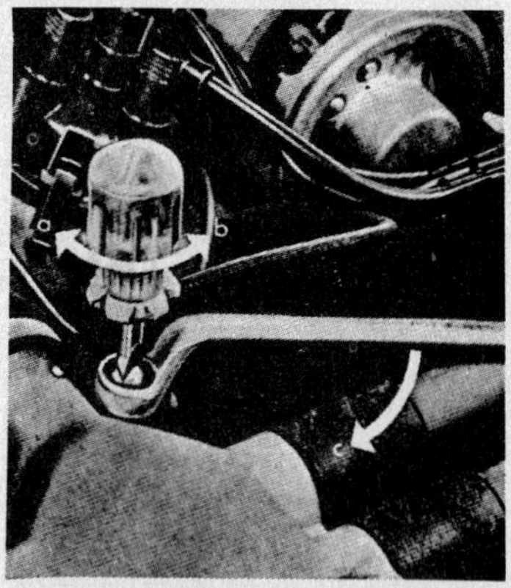

Adjusting idle speed on fuel-injected engine. Turn screw toward a to increase speed. Turn the locknut toward c to tighten.

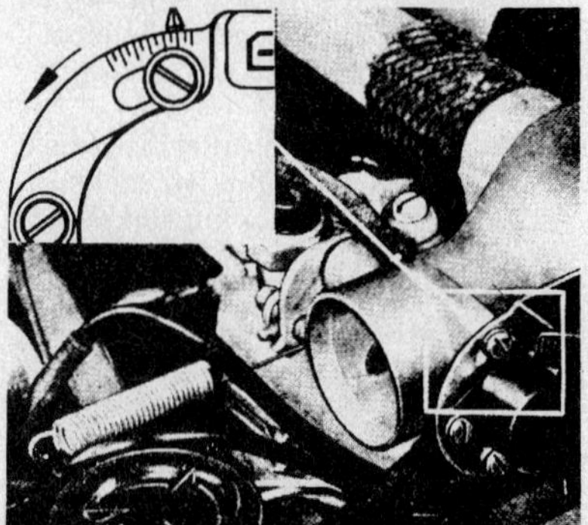

Throttle valve switch details. Each graduation indicates 2°.

To adjust the pressure regulator:

1. Remove the air cleaner for access.
2. Attach the pressure gauge securely to the T-fitting.
3. Start the engine and allow it to idle. Make sure that the idle speed is correct. Adjustment of idling speed is explained in chapter two.
4. If the pressure reading is not 28 psi (2 atmospheres), loosen the locknut and regulate the pressure with the adjusting nut.
5. Tighten the locknut. Check to see that the pressure is still correct.
6. Stop the engine. Disconnect the pressure gauge and plug the T-fitting with a stopscrew. Replace the air cleaner.

Injector R & R

To remove the injectors on either side of the engine.

1. Remove both cable plugs.
2. Unscrew both retainer plate nuts.
3. Pull out both injectors with the retainer plate, centering bushings, base plate, and stud sleeves. Be sure to remove the inner bushings from the intake manifold base.
4. Loosen the hose clamps and pull out the injectors. Be careful not to damage the needles.
5. Reverse the procedure to replace the injectors. Use lockwashers under the retaining nuts. Torque them to 4.3 ft lbs. Install the cable plug with the gray protective cap toward the rear of the car, and the plug with the black cap at the front.

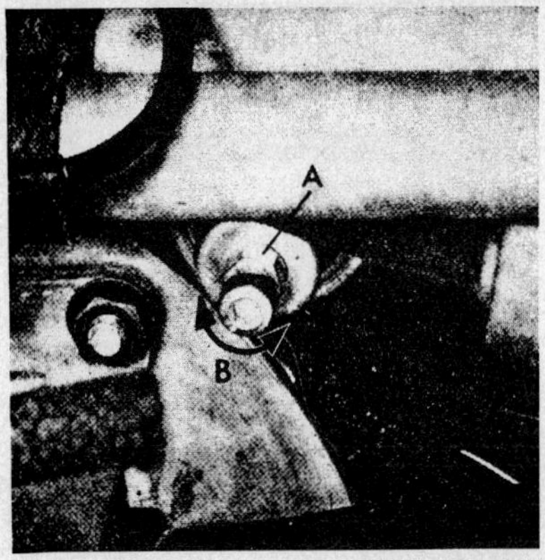
A
B

Pressure regulator, located under the right side of the intake manifold. A is the locknut; B is the adjusting nut.

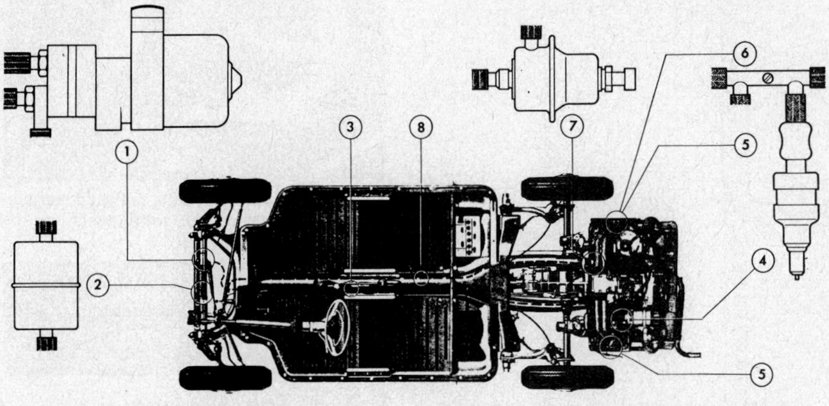

Fuel system of the fuel-injected engine: (1) electric fuel pump, (2) filter, (3) pressure line, (4) ring main, (5) electromagnetic fuel injectors, (6) distributor pipes, (7) pressure regulator, and (8) return line.

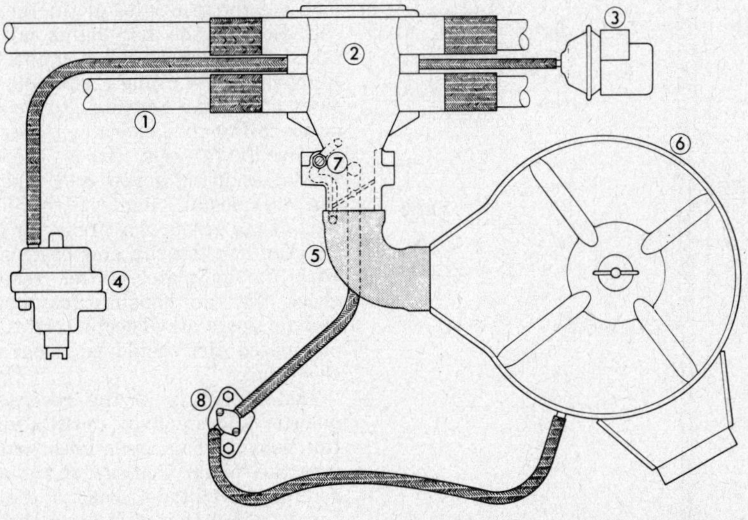

Air system of the fuel-injected engine: (1) intake pipes, (2) intake air distributor, (3) pressure switch, (4) pressure sensor, (5) idle air circuit, (6) air cleaner, (7) idling air screw, (8) auxiliary air regulator.

Fuel Filter R & R

The fuel filter is in the pump suction line, either near to, or mounted on, the fuel pump. It should be replaced every 6,000 miles. To replace the filter:

1. Pinch-clamp the fuel lines shut on either side of the filter.
2. Remove the pin holding the filter bracket to the pump. Remove the filter.
3. Install the new filter, making sure that the arrow points to the pump. Replace the bracket and pin.
4. Install screw type hose clamps on the fuel lines.

Exhaust System

Exhaust Pipe, Muffler, and Tail Pipe

R & R, Muffler

To remove the muffler from all Volkswagen models, first remove the clamps from the muffler and heat exchangers. (Early 1963 and earlier models do not have exchangers.) Remove the clips connecting the warm air channels. Loosen the clamps on the tail pipe(s) and remove the tail pipe(s). Remove the nuts from the muffler flange and the preheater adaptor pipe. Remove the four screws from the manifold preheater pipe and take off the muffler, including the gaskets. Check the muffler to be installed and the exhaust pipes for leaks or damage. If necessary, exhaust pipes can be reused. However, in practice, it is often difficult to remove tailpipes from an old muffler without damaging them extensively. This generally occurs with old mufflers that have become rusty, and in such cases it is advisable to install new tailpipes. Type 1 tailpipes should protrude about 7.5 in. on pre-1968 models; 8.3 in. on later models. New gaskets should be used in installing the muffler.

R & R, Heat Exchangers

To remove the heat exchangers, remove the exhaust pipe clamps, the clamps between the heat exchanger and the exhaust pipe, and the rear engine cover plate (Type 1 and 2). Remove the nuts on the cylinder head and the warm air pipe connecting clips. The heat exchanger can now be removed. Check the outer shell and exhaust pipes for damage and leakage. If the heat exchangers leak, there could be a possibility of poisonous gases entering the heating system. Sealing surfaces must be clean and smooth, and flanges that are distorted or bent through excessive tightening should be straightened or machined. Use new gaskets and ensure that all connections are gastight. Heat exchangers must be attached at the cylinder heads with self-locking, 8 mm hexagon nuts. It is not permissible for any other types of nuts to be used, even with lockwashers.

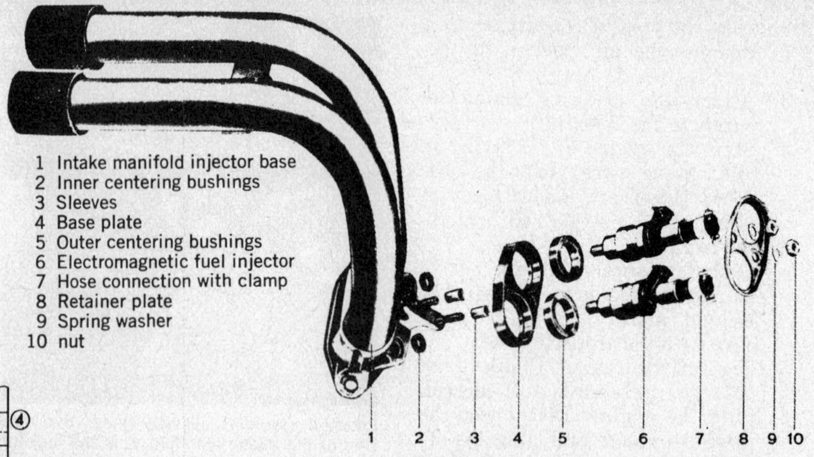
1 Intake manifold injector base
2 Inner centering bushings
3 Sleeves
4 Base plate
5 Outer centering bushings
6 Electromagnetic fuel injector
7 Hose connection with clamp
8 Retainer plate
9 Spring washer
10 nut

Details of injectors and the right side of the intake manifold.

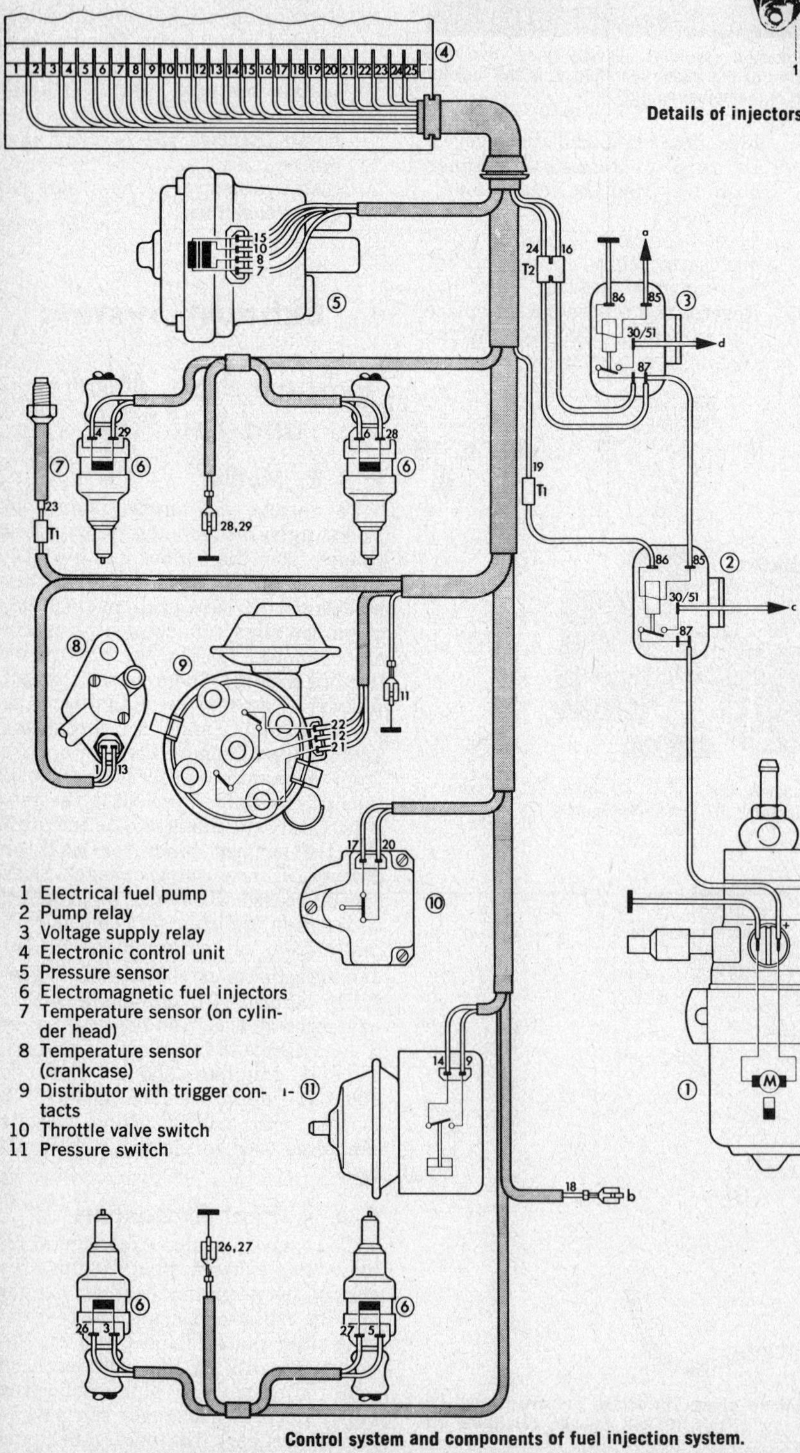
1 Electrical fuel pump
2 Pump relay
3 Voltage supply relay
4 Electronic control unit
5 Pressure sensor
6 Electromagnetic fuel injectors
7 Temperature sensor (on cylinder head)
8 Temperature sensor (crankcase)
9 Distributor with trigger contacts
10 Throttle valve switch
11 Pressure switch

Control system and components of fuel injection system.

Fuel filter, which must be replaced periodically. The arrow shown must point to the pump.

COOLING SYSTEM

R & R, Fan Housing

Removal of the Type 1 and 2 fan housing is as follows: Remove the two heater hoses and generator strap. Pull out the lead wire of the ignition coil. Remove the distributor cap and take off the spark plug connectors. Remove the retaining screws on both sides of the fan housing. Remove the outer half of the generator pulley and remove the fan belt. Remove the thermostat securing screw and take out the thermostat. Remove the lower part of the carburetor preheater duct. The fan housing can now be removed with the generator. After removal, check the fan housing for damage and for loose air-deflector plates. Accumulated dirt should be removed at this time.

Installation is in the reverse sequence, and involves installation of fan housing flap assemblies and the insertion of the thermostat actuating rod in the cylinder head and lower fan housing. It is necessary that the fan housing fit properly on the cylinder cover plates so that loss of cool-

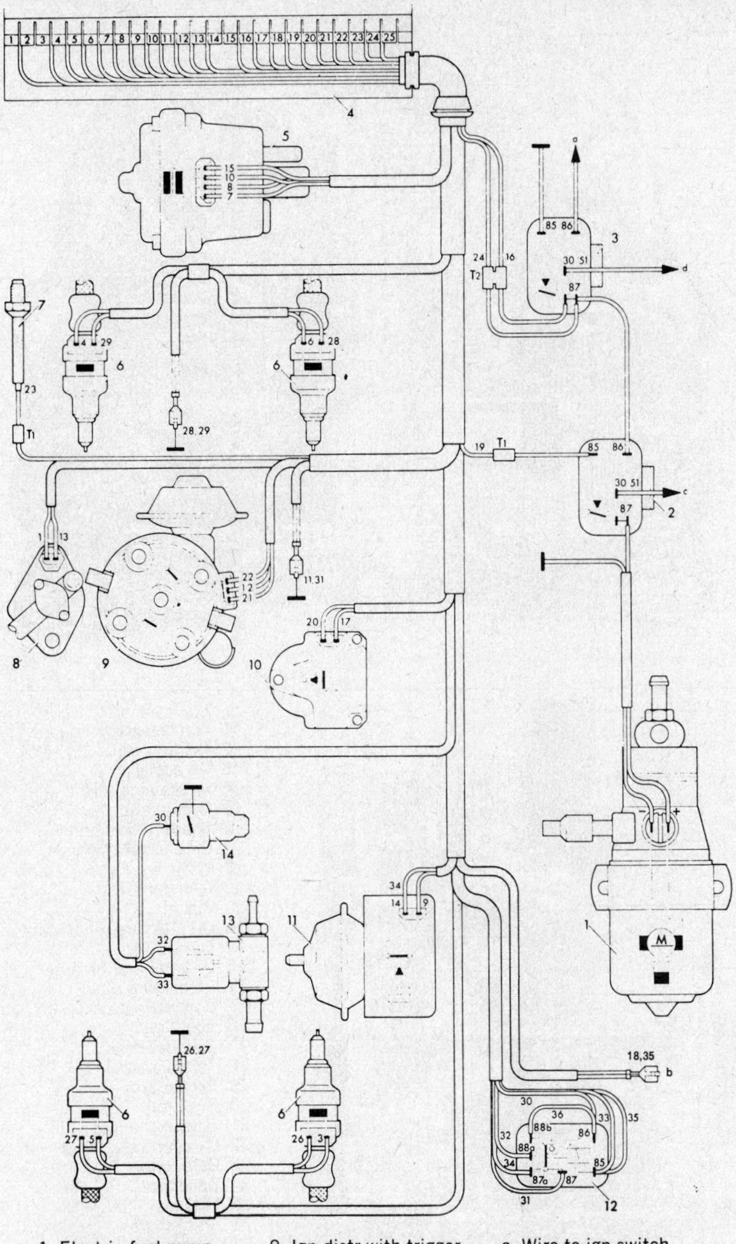

1 Electric fuel pump
2 Pump relay (relay 1)
3 Voltage supply relay (relay 2)
4 Electronic control unit
5 Pressure sensor
6 Elec magnetic fuel injectors
7 Temp sensor (cyl head)
8 Temp sensor (crank-case)
9 Ign distr with trigger contacts
10 Throttle valve switch
11 Pressure switch (no longer used)
12 Relay (cold starting jet)
13 Elec magnetic cut-off (cold starting jet)
14 Thermo switch (cold starting)

a Wire to ign switch (terminal 15)
b Wire to starter solenoid (term. 50)
c Wire to terminal 30
d Wire to pos battery terminal

Control system and components of fuel injection system with cold starting device.

ing air will be avoided. In order to achieve proper fit, the cover plates may have to be bent slightly.

The removal of the fan housing of the Type 3 is accomplished in a slightly different manner due to the different layout of the cooling system of this engine. Remove the crankshaft pulley, the rear fan housing half, and the fan. Unhook the linkage and spring at the right-hand air control flap. Remove the attaching screws of the front half of the fan housing. Prior to installation, the front half of the fan housing should be checked for damage.

In installing the fan housing, first install the front half of the fan housing, ensuring correct sealing with the cylinder cover plates. Replace and tighten the two lower mounting screws slightly. Turn the two halves of the fan housing to the left until the left crankcase half is contacted by the front lug. Tighten the two lower mounting screws fully. Loosen the nuts at the breather support until it can be moved. Insert and tighten the mounting screws of the upper fan housing half. Tighten the breather support nuts fully. Connect the linkage and spring to the right-hand air control flap. Install the fan and the rear half of the fan housing.

R & R, Fan

The cooling fan of the Type 1 and 2 models is removed as follows: using a T-wrench, remove the four retaining screws on the fan cover. Remove the generator and fan. While holding the fan to keep it from rotating, unscrew the fan retaining nut and take off the fan, spacer washers, and hub.

Installation of the fan is as follows: place the hub on the generator shaft, making sure that the woodruff key is securely positioned. Insert the spacer washers. (Note: the distance between the fan and the fan cover should be 1.5–1.8 mm (.06–.07 in.). Place the fan into position and tighten its retaining nut with a torque wrench and socket to 40–47 ft lbs. Check the distance from the fan to the cover. Correct spacing is achieved by inserting the proper number of spacer washers between the hub and the thrust washer. When only one washer is used, the other two should be positioned between the lockwasher and the fan. Insert the generator in the fan housing and tighten the retaining screws on the fan housing cover. (With 1967 and more recent models, be sure that the cooling air intake slot is at the bottom when the retaining plate is screwed onto the fan housing.)

On the Type 3, fan removal begins with the removal of the crankshaft pulley, coil, and the rear half of the fan housing. The fan can then be removed.

On installation of the fan, check the condition of the oil return thread on the fan hub, and install rear half of fan housing, coil and crankshaft pulley.

R & R Fan and Fan Housing Type 4

1. Remove the engine. Remove the fan belt.
2. Remove the allen head screws (3) and remove the belt pulley and fan as an assembly.

NOTE: It is not necessary to remove the alternator to remove the fan housing.

3. Remove the spacer, alternator cover plate, and alternator if necessary.
4. Disconnect the cooling air regulating cable at the shaft.
5. Remove the nuts (4) and remove both halves of the fan housing at the same time.
6. Installation is the reverse of the removal procedure.

ENGINE

The Volkswagen engine's flat four (i.e., pancake) design has proven itself in automotive, industrial, and aerial applications as one of the most rugged and reliable made in the world today. The four-cycle, overhead valve engine has two pairs of cylinders horizontally opposed; it is attached to the transmission case by four bolts, and is easily removed for service.

The engine in the Type 3 (Fastback and Squareback) series is similar to the "Beetle" engine, the main exception being the location of the cooling fan on the crankshaft rather than on the generator shaft. With the Type 3 engine, there is no chance of cooling fan failure due to fan belt breakage, because there is no fan belt. If the generator belt should fail, the driver could drive some distance in daylight before running out of electricity for the ignition. In addition, the Type 3 engine is slightly different in the location of the oil cooler and, of course, in the layout of the cooling ductwork.

1
2
3
4
5
6
7
8
9
10
11
12
13
14
15
16
17
18
19
20
21
22

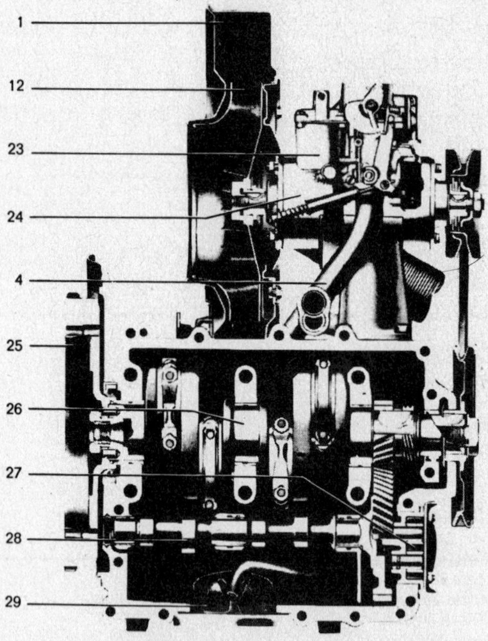
1
12
23
24
4
25
26
27
28
29

1 Fan housing
2 Ignition coil
3 Oil cooler
4 Intake manifold
5 Fuel pump
6 Ignition distributor
7 Oil pressure switch
8 Valve
9 Cylinder
10 Piston
11 Oil pressure relief valve
12 Fan
13 Oil filter and breather
14 Preheating pipe
15 Connecting rod
16 Spark plug
17 Cylinder head
18 Thermostat
19 Rocker arm
20 Push rod
21 Heat exchanger
22 Cam follower
23 Carburetor
24 Generator
25 Flywheel
26 Crankshaft
27 Oil pump
28 Camshaft
29 Oil strainer

Type 1 and 2 engine.

Fan Belt

Adjusting Fan Belt Tension

If belt tension is too great, the result will be a shortening of the life of the generator bearings due to unnecessary stress. If the belt is too loose, the result will be a loss of cooling efficiency in Beetles and a loss of generating power in both the small and large Volkswagens. The following steps should be followed in adjusting the fan belt tension on all Volkswagens, regardless of year:

1. Remove the holding nut from the generator pulley shaft. In Type 3 models, the pulley must be held from turning by using a suitable wrench. In the smaller Volkswagens the pulley is held by a screwdriver wedged between the notch in the generator pulley and the upper generator housing bolt.
2. Remove the outer half of the generator pulley and adjust the fan belt tension by fitting the proper number of spacer washers between the halves of the pulley. Each washer added or removed changes the play in the belt about 1/4 in.
3. If the fan belt is too loose, one or more spacer washers will have to be removed from between the pulley halves. Any spacers not used are installed on the outside of the outer pulley half. If the belt is too tight, one or more washers will have to be added between the pulley halves.
4. When correct adjustment has been achieved, the belt will deflect approximately .6 in. (15 mm) when pressed by thumb pressure at its midpoint.
5. Tighten the pulley nut.

If the belt has stretched to the extent that correct adjustment can no longer be achieved by removing spacers from between the pulley halves, the belt should be replaced. Also, if a belt has frayed edges or cracks, it should be replaced. Fan belts should be kept free from grease and oil.

It is recommended that a new belt be inspected regularly during the first several hundred miles of use, since new belts have a tendency to stretch slightly.

Exhaust Emission Control

Throttle Regulator Adjustment

The exhaust emission control device used on type 1 and 2 vehicles, 1968–72, is the throttle valve regulator. This device holds the throttle open slightly on deceleration to prevent an excessively rich mixture.

On 1970–72 models, the throttle regulator consists of two parts, connected by a hose. The operating part is mounted at the carburetor, and the control part is located on the left sidewall of the engine compartment. The The 1968–69 unit is one piece, mounted at the carburetor.

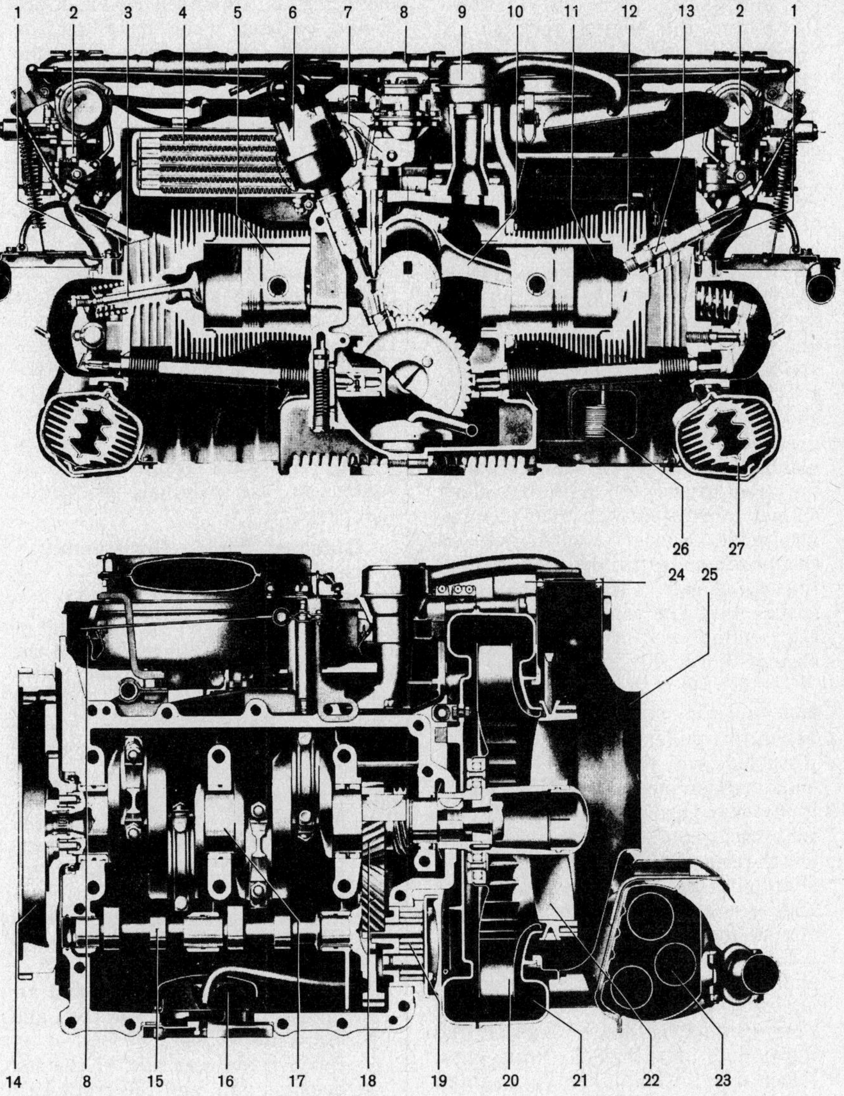
1 2 3 4 5 6 7 8 9 10 11 12 13 2 1
26 27
24 25
14 8 15 16 17 18 19 20 21 22 23

1 Intake pipe
2 Carburetor
3 Valve
4 Oil cooler
5 Piston
6 Distributor
7 Fuel pump
8 Air cleaner
9 Crankcase breather
10 Connecting rod
11 Cylinder
12 Cylinder head
13 Spark plug
14 Flywheel
15 Camshaft
16 Oil strainer
17 Crankshaft
18 Camshaft drive gears
19 Oil pump
20 Fan
21 Fan housing
22 Crankshaft pulley
23 Muffler
24 Coil
25 Cooling air intake housing
26 Thermostat
27 Heat exchanger

Dual carburetor Type 3 engine.

1. The engine must be at operating temperature, with the automatic choke fully open.
2. Start the engine. Turn the regulator adjusting screw clockwise until the control rod just starts to move the throttle valve lever. The stop collar on the control rod will be against the regulator body. Engine speed should be 1,700–1,800 rpm.
3. If speed is too high, shorten the control rod.
4. After adjustment, tighten the locknuts on the control rod.
5. Turn the regulator adjusting screw counterclockwise until an idle speed of 850 rpm is obtained.
6. Increase the engine speed to 3,000 rpm, then release the throttle valve lever. The engine should take 3–4 seconds to return to idle.

Incorrect throttle regulator adjustment may cause erratic idle, excessively high idle speed, and backfiring on deceleration.

Engine Assembly

Engine Removal

NOTE: On Type 4 cars the engine and transmission must be removed as an assembly. The procedure for removing the engine and transmission assembly is found in the transmission removal procedures.

The Volkswagen engine is mounted on the transmission, which in turn is attached to the frame. In the Beetle models, there are four attaching points—two bolts and two studs while on the Type 3 there is an extra mounting point at the rear of the engine. Type 3 vehicles with automatic transmission have front and rear engine and transmission mounts. At the front, the gearbox is supported by the rear tubular crossmember; at the rear, a crossmember is bolted to the crankcase and mounted to the body at either end. When removing the engine from the car, it is recommended that the rear of the car be about three feet off the ground. The engine is removed by bringing it out from underneath the car. However, before raising the car, the following steps should be followed:

1. Disconnect the ground strap from the battery, and cables from the generator (and, in Beetle models, regulator).
2. Remove the air cleaner from the engine, and the rear engine cover plate on Beetle models. Remove the throttle positioner. In Type 2 Volkswagens, with 1600cc engines, remove the rear crossmember.
3. Rotate the distributor of Beetle models so that this part will be able to clear the rear cover plate. *(NOTE: on 1967 and later models, the rear cover plate need not be removed, since the redesigned rear deck and compartment allow sufficient room for engine withdrawal from the car.)*
4. Disconnect the throttle cable from the carburetor(s), and remove the electrical connections to the automatic choke, coil, electromagnetic cut-off jet, and the oil pressure sending unit.
5. Disconnect the fuel hose at the front engine cover plate and seal it to prevent leakage.
6. On Type 3 models, remove the oil dipstick and the rubber boot between the oil filler and body.
7. Remove the cooling air intake bellows on Type 3 models after loosening the clip that secures the unit.
8. Remove the warm air hose on the Type 3 models.
9. After disconnecting the appropriate electrical and control cables, remove the rear engine support (Type 3) and raise the car off the ground.
10. After removing the flexible air hoses between the engine and heat exchangers, disconnect the heater flap cables, unscrew the two lower engine mounting nuts, and slide a jack under the engine. Be sure that it is suitable for supporting the weight of the engine without placing undue

strain on the components. (On Type 2 with 1600cc engine, remove the two bolts from the rubber engine mounts by the muffler.

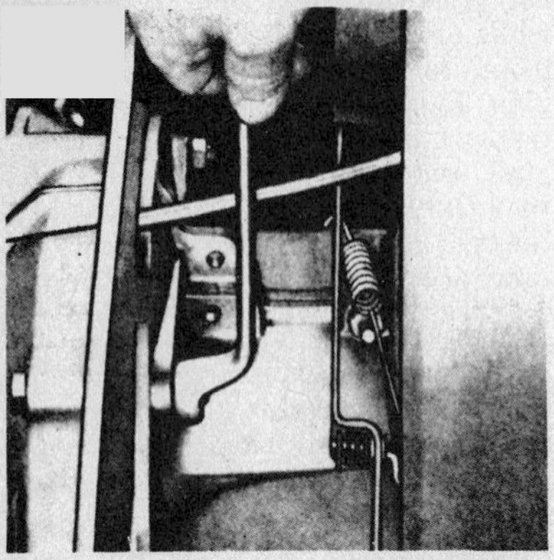

Removing upper engine mounting bolts, Type 1.

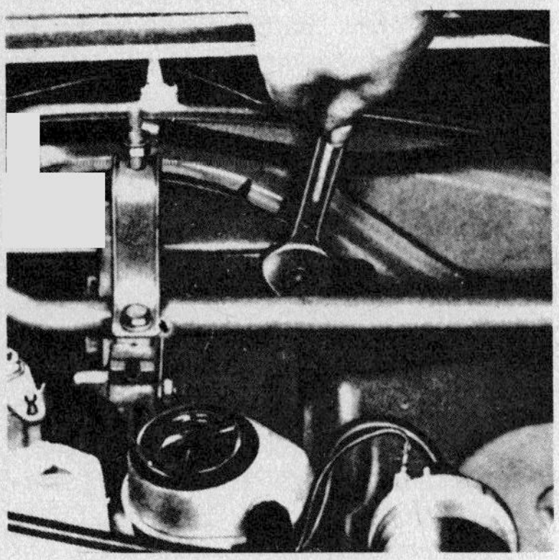

Removing upper engine mounting bolts, Type 3.

On Type 1 Automatic Stickshift models, disconnect the control valve cable and manifold vacuum hoses. Disconnect the ATF suction line and plug it with a 16 X 1.5 mm cap. On Type 3 fully automatic models, disconnect the vacuum hose and kick-down cable. On either model, remove the four 8 mm bolts from the converter drive plate through the holes in the transmission case. After removing the engine, hold the torque converter in place on the transmission with a strap. On fuel-injected Type 3 models, the fuel pressure and return lines must be clamped off and disconnected, and the injection unit wiring disconnected.

11. Raise the jack until it just contacts the engine, and have an assistant hold the bolts of the two upper engine mounts so that you will be able to unscrew the nuts.
12. When the engine mounts are disconnected and there are no remaining cables or controls linking the engine with the car, move the engine backward slightly so that the release plate will be able to clear the main driveshaft.
13. Lower the engine very slowly and be sure that the clutch release plate does not contact the main driveshaft of the transmission.

Engine Installation

Engine installation is the reverse of the preceding operation, although it is important that some special precautions be taken. Before replacing the engine, the clutch plate must be centered, the clutch release bearing and release plate checked for wear, and a number of components greased or cleaned. The starter shaft bush should be lubricated with lithium grease, the needle bearing in the gland nut supplied with one gram of universal grease, the main driveshaft splines lubricated with molybdenum-disulphide powder applied with a clean cloth or brush. Before installing the engine, care must also be taken to ensure that the mating surfaces of the engine and transmission are cleaned thoroughly.

The engine is then lifted into position and the engine rotated via the generator pulley so that the clutch plate hub will engage the transmission shaft splines. In pushing the engine home, care must be taken to see that the gland nut needle bearing, clutch release bearing and main driveshaft are not damaged. After the engine is in position, put the lower engine mounting bolts through the holes in the flange of the transmission case and press the engine against the flange so that proper and even contact is made. Tighten the upper nuts first, then the lower ones. After this initial tightening, tighten all nuts evenly in this same sequence.

On the Type 3 reinstallation, synthetic washers are used to raise the engine about 2–3 mm when the rear engine mounting is attached and tightened. Use only enough washers in the rear mount so that the engine is lifted no more than 3 mm when the mounting is tightened down. Care should be used when installing the rear intake housing bellows of the Type 3 engine, for this unit can be easily damaged through careless handling. Reconnect the cables and controls. Attach the thick lead to terminal D+ of the generator. Adjust the accelerator cable with the engine at full throttle and set the ignition timing.

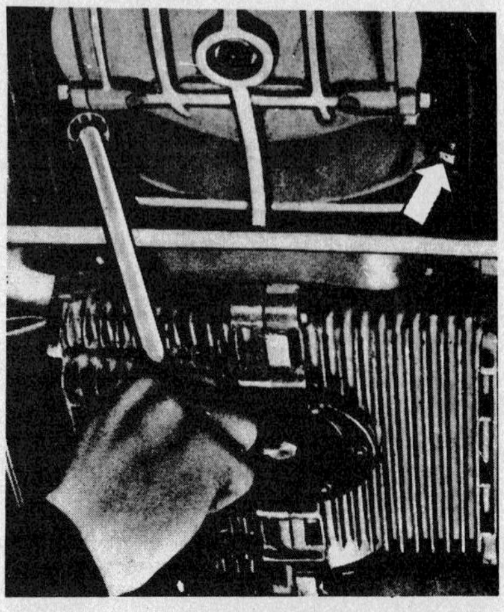

Removing lower engine mounting nuts, Type 1.

To avoid interference with the function of the automatic stickshift clutch, take care to route the connecting hoses so that they are not kinked or jammed when installing the engine. This applies particularly to the small-diameter pipe from the control valve to the carburetor venturi, which will work properly only if routed in the original production manner.

Order of Engine Disassembly Operations

The disassembly of the Type 3 and type 4 engine is different from that of the other VW engines mainly in the removal of the engine cover plates and cooling ductwork. In tearing down a Volkswagen engine, the following is the recommended sequence of operations:

1. Drain the engine oil.
2. Remove the hoses between the engine and the heat exchangers.
3. Remove the front engine cover plate.
4. Remove the muffler and intake manifold, including the carburetor(s).
5. Remove the fan belt, cooling air intake housing, generator, and crankshaft pulley.
6. Remove the rear half of the fan housing, fan, and the front half of the fan housing.
7. Remove the distributor and fuel pump, and take out the distributor drive pinion.
8. Remove the cooling air ductwork from the cylinder area.
9. Remove the oil cooler.
10. Remove the rocker arm shaft and cylinder heads.
11. Remove the cylinders and pistons.
12. Remove the clutch assembly and flywheel.
13. Remove the oil pump and oil strainer.
14. Disassemble the crankcase and remove the camshaft, crankshaft, and connecting rods.

Assembly, generally speaking, is the reverse of the foregoing procedure.

NOTE: The torque, capacity, tune-up, and clearance figures given in the text apply, generally, to the most common engines. However, since there are so many variations in production, it is always best to consult the applicable chart for the figure in question.

Cylinder Heads

R & R

In order to remove the cylinder head of either pair of cylinders, it is first necessary that the rocker arm assembly be removed. The cylinder head is held in place by eight studs. Since the cylinder head also holds the cylinders in place in the VW engine, if it is not desired that the cylinders be removed, they should be held in place with an appropriate holding clamp. After the rocker arm cover, the rocker arm retaining nuts and rocker arm assembly have been removed, the cylinder head nuts can be removed and the cylinder head lifted off.

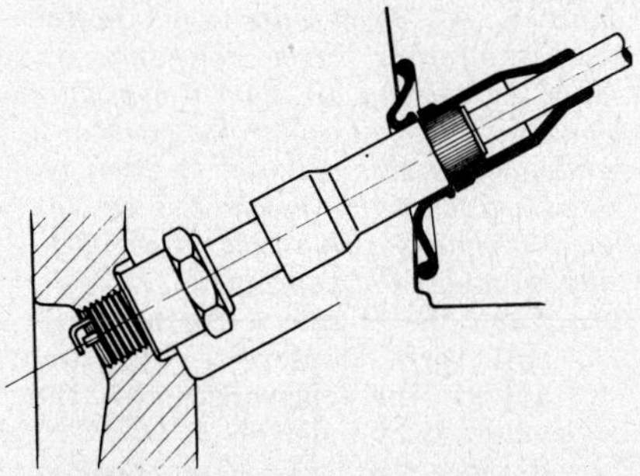

The rubber spark plug seals should fit snugly against the cooling ducts so that cooling air does not escape.

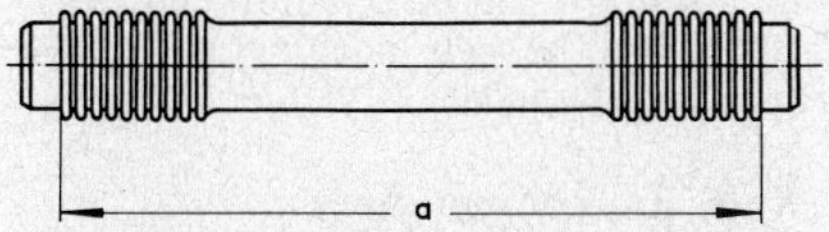
a

Push rod tube length (distance a) is 190-191 mm for 1,300, 1,500, and 1,600 cc engines, and 180.5-181.5mm for the 40 hp 1,200 cc engines. No measurement is given for earlier engines.

When reinstalling the cylinder head, several points must be remembered. The cylinder head should be checked for cracks both in the combustion chamber and in the intake and exhaust ports. Cracked cylinder heads should be replaced. Spark plug threads should be checked at this time for tightness. If the threads are stripped, they can be corrected by means of Heli-coil threaded inserts. On 1963 and later engines, no gasket is necessary between the cylinder head and the cylinders. However, on earlier models, which do not have a fresh air heating system, a gasket should be fitted. New seals should be used on the push rod tube ends, and should be checked for proper seating.

The push rod tubes should be turned so that the seam faces upward. In order to ensure perfect sealing, used tubes should be stretched to the correct length of 190–191mm before they are installed. (Note: in the 40 hp engine, the correct length is 180.5–181.5 mm On the 40 hp engine, the sealing ring between the outer shoulder of the cylinder and the cylinder head should be renewed, placing the slotted side of the ring toward the cylinder head. On the 50 hp engine of 1966 and subsequent engines, no sealing ring is needed.)

After inserting the cylinder head nut washers, the cylinder head nuts should be tightened slightly, and then to a torque of 7 ft lbs before fully tightening them to a torque of 23 ft lbs (27 ft lbs in 1959 and earlier models). The sequence of tightening shown in the tightening sequence diagram should be followed. (Note the different sequences for the initial and final tightening procedures.)

Cylinders

R & R

Before removing the cylinders, the cylinder head, valve push rods, push rod tubes, and deflector plate below the cylinders must be taken out. The cylinders may then be pulled off. Match-mark the cylinders for reassembly.

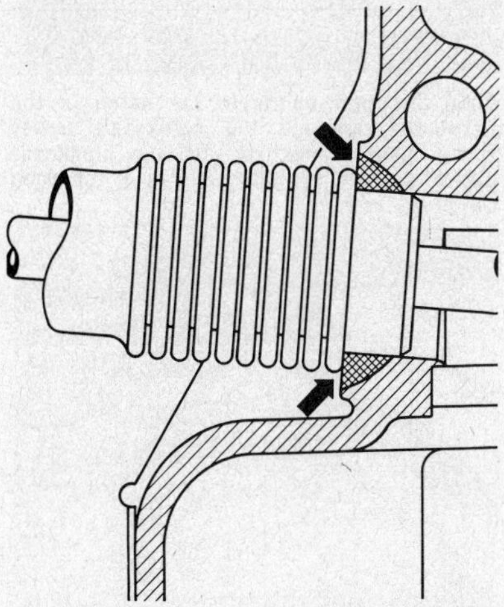

The oil seals at the ends of the push rod tubes must be properly seated to prevent leakage.

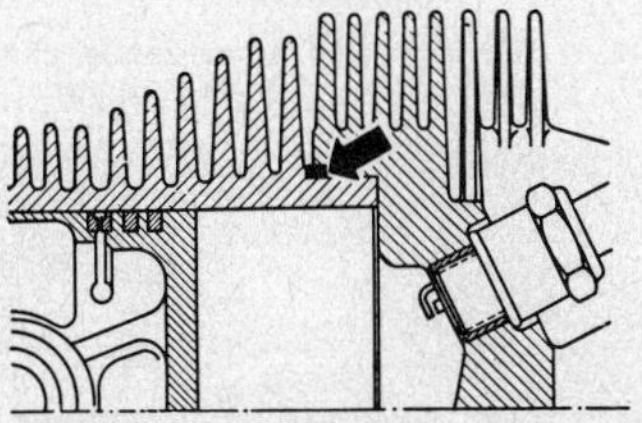

On pre-1963 engines a cylinder head gasket is used. The slotted side of the gasket must be toward the cylinder head.

Reinstall the cylinders as follows:

Cylinders should be checked for wear, and if necessary replaced with another matched cylinder and piston assembly of the same size. Also check the cylinder seating surface on the crankcase, cylinder shoulder, and gasket, for cleanliness. Foreign matter here could cause leaks due to distortion of the mating parts. When reinstalling the cylinders, a new gasket should be used between each cylinder and the crankcase.

The piston rings and piston pin should be liberally oiled (a MoS_2 based lubricant is suitable). Compress the rings with a compression tool. Be sure that ring gaps are adequate and staggered on the piston with the oil ring inserted into the cylinder so that its gap is positioned UP when the pistons are in their horizontal position in the engine.

Lubricate the cylinder wall and slide the cylinder over the piston. Crankcase studs should not contact the cylinder cooling fins. Install the deflector plates under the cylinders, bending slightly if necessary to make them seat tightly on the cylinder head studs.

Install the push rod tubes and push rods, ensuring that the tubes are inserted with the seam facing upward and are of the proper length.

Valve Train

Adjusting Valve Clearance

If valve clearances in the Volkswagen engine are too small, the valves can be seriously damaged by warping or burning, and compression will eventually suffer from the lack of proper valve sealing. On the other hand, if the valve clearance is too great, the result will be rough run-

The deflector plates under the cylinders must be tight against the cylinder studs to prevent rattles.

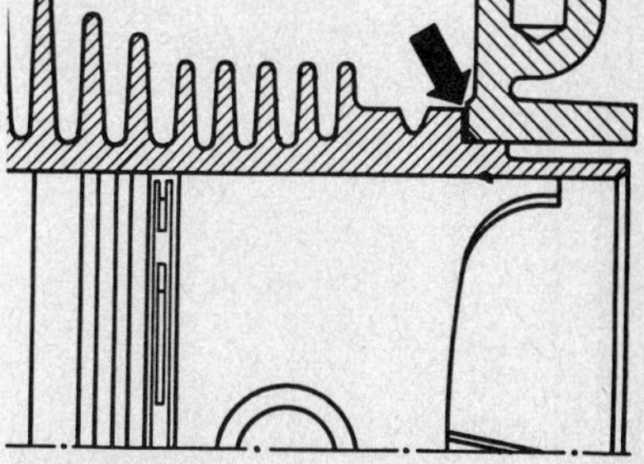

Foreign matter between the cylinder and the crankcase could cause distortion of the cylinder. The gasket indicated should not be reused.

ning, loss of power, and excessive wear of the valve train components.

Before the valves can be adjusted in any Volkswagen, the engine must be cold, preferably after sitting overnight. Volkswagen valve clearances vary somewhat between models of different years. To determine the correct setting, refer to both the "Tune-Up Specifications" chart and the engine sticker.

Preference is to be given to the valve clearance specified on the engine fan housing sticker, if one is present. On models built after late 1964, such a sticker will be on the fan housing. Such stickers will also be present on all factory rebuilt engines, regardless of horsepower output, and the clearances specified should be followed closely.

Steps in Adjustment

1. Remove the distributor cap and turn the engine until the rotor points to the notch in the distributor rim and the crankshaft pulley timing mark is aligned with the crankcase split or pointer. No. 1 cylinder is now at top dead center of its compression stroke. See the illustration showing cylinder numbering.
2. Remove the rocker arm cover of cylinders no. 1 and 2.
3. With the proper feeler gauge, check the clearance between the adjusting screw and the valve stem of both valves for no. 1 cylinder. If the feeler gauge slides in snugly without being forced, the clearance is correct.
4. If the clearance is incorrect, the lock-nut must be loosened and the adjusting screw turned until the proper clearance is attained. After tightening the locknut, it is advisable to recheck the clearance, because it is possible to alter the adjustment when tightening the locknut.
5. Turn the engine one-half revolution in the counterclockwise direction. This will turn the distributor rotor 90° in the counterclockwise direction so that it will now point to the lead wire for cylinder no. 2. No. 2 cylinder is now at top dead center.
6. Repeat the adjustment process for cylinder no. 2.
7. Replace valve rocker arm cover on cylinders no. 1 and 2, using a new gasket and cleaning off the seating surfaces to guard against leakage.
8. Remove the valve rocker arm cover on cylinders no. 3 and 4.
9. Turn the engine another one-half turn in the counterclockwise direction so that the distributor rotor now points to the lead wire of cylinder no. 3. No. 3 cylinder is now at top dead center.
10. Adjust the clearances on cylinder no. 3.

NOTE: On pre-1971 Type 1 and 2 engines, no. 3 cylinder runs hotter than the other three cylinders because its cooling air flow is partially blocked by the oil cooler. To counter a tendency for this cylinder to burn exhaust valves, some mechanics set the no. 3 exhaust valve clearance .001–.002 in. wider than specified.

11. Turn the engine a further one-half turn counterclockwise and adjust the clearances of the valves in cylinder no. 4.
12. Replace the rocker arm cover of cylinders no. 3 and 4, cleaning the sealing surfaces and using a new gasket.
13. Replace the distributor cap. Replace the belt housing cover in Type 3 models.

When sliding the cylinder over the piston, the crankcase studs must not be allowed to contact the cylinder cooling fins.

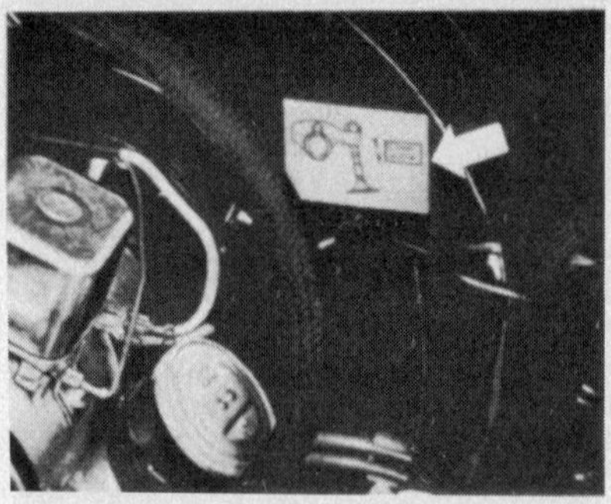

Most late model engines have the correct valve clearance indicated on a sticker on the fan housing.

When the rotor points to the notch in the distributor rim and the crankshaft pulley timing mark is aligned with the crankcase split or pointer, cylinder no. 1 is at top dead center.

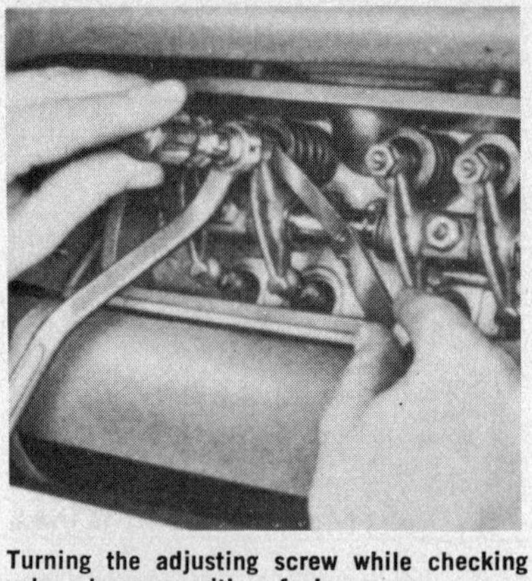

Turning the adjusting screw while checking valve clearance with a feeler gauge.

90°

If the engine is turned backward one-half revolution from the firing point for no. 1 cylinder, the distributor rotor will turn backward one quarter turn to the firing point for no. 2 cylinder. Proceeding backward in this manner, the valves can be adjusted in 1-2-3-4 order.

R & R, Rocker Arm Mechanism

Before the valve rocker assembly can be reached, it is necessary to undo the clip that retains the cover plate. Remove the rocker arm retaining nuts, the rocker arm shaft and the rocker arms. Remove the stud seals.

Before installing the rocker arm mechanism, be sure that the parts are as clean as possible, including the inside of the cover plate. Install the stud seals and the rocker shaft, making sure that the chamfered edges of the supports are pointing outward and the slots, upward. Tighten the retaining nuts to a torque of 14–18 ft lbs. The only type of retaining nuts which should be used are 8 mm nuts of the 8 G grade. These nuts are distinguishable by their copper color. Ball ends of the push rods must be centered in the sockets of the rocker arms. In addition, to help valves rotate during operation, the rocker arm adjusting screws should contact the tip of the valve slightly off center. It should be neither in the center nor all the way to one side, but exactly in the middle of the two extremes. After adjusting valves to their proper clearance, reinstall the cover plate with a new gasket. Be sure that the proper cover plate gasket is used. There are two types of gaskets, early and late. the late type is straight across the top edge, while the early type has a tab in the center of the top edge. After the engine has been run for a brief period, check the cover plates for oil leakage.

Disassembly and Assembly of Rocker Arm Mechanism

Remove the spring clips from the rocker arm shaft. Remove the washers, rocker arms, and bearing supports. Before installation, check the rocker arm shaft for wear, and the seats and ball sockets of the rocker arm adjusting screws. Loosen the adjusting screws before installing the rocker arms. Otherwise, installation is the reverse of the disassembly procedure.

R & R, Valves

In order to remove the valves, the cylinder head must first be taken off. With the cylinder head removed, compress the valve springs with a special tool and remove valve keys, valve spring caps, valve springs, and oil deflector rings. Remove the valves from cylinder head after removing any burrs that may be present near the seating surface of the keys on the valve stem. While the valve springs are out, they should be tested. Proper valve spring pressures are given in the "Engine Rebuilding Specifications" chart for "valves." Valve keys should be checked prior to installation, and new and worn keys ground at the joining faces until it is still possible to turn the valve when the key halves are pressed together. Valve stems should be checked for run-out and valve guides for wear. Valves should be checked for leaks and for wear. Because exhaust valves generally do heavy-duty work in the air-cooled engine of the Volkswagen, it is good practice to replace them since their cost is not great and the engine is already apart. If the stems of the valves are hammered in, the valves can still be used again after valve caps have been installed. Polish rough valve stems carefully with emery cloth. After coating the valve stems with a moly paste, insert them into their guides and fit oil deflector rings. Install valve springs with the close-wound coils facing the cylinder head. Used valves must be refaced before being reinstalled. Damaged seats must also be reconditioned.

Crankcase

Disassembly and Assembly of the Crankcase

With the cylinders, pistons, and cylinder heads removed, the crankcase is split as follows:

1. Remove the oil strainer, oil pressure switch, and crankcase nuts. Remove the flywheel and oil pump.
2. Keep the cam followers of the right crankcase half in position by using the retaining springs.
3. Use a rubber hammer to break the seal between the crankcase halves. Never insert sharp tools, wedges, etc., between the crankcase halves; this will surely lead to serious leakage of lubricant.

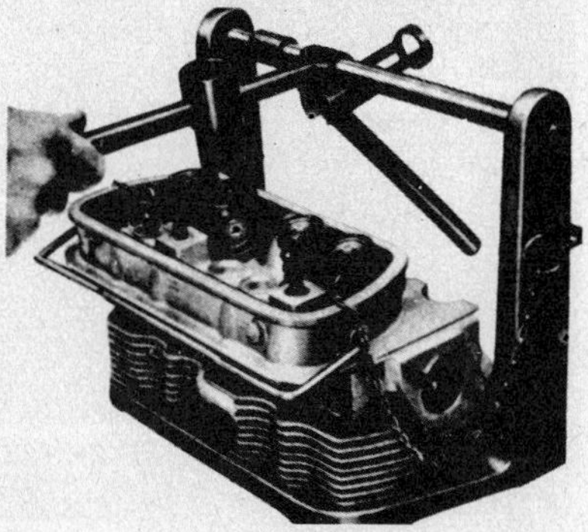

Use of a valve spring compressor to remove valves.

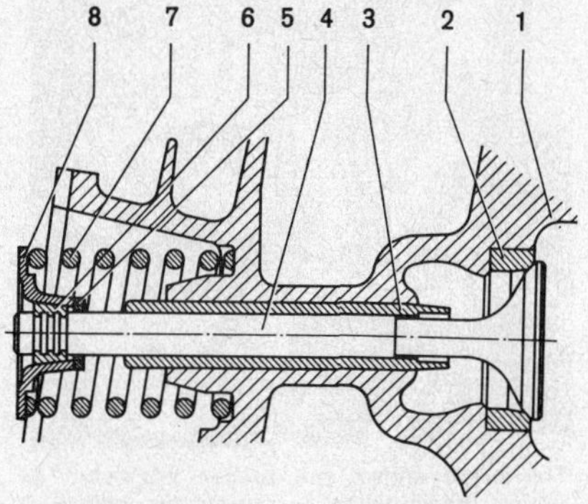
8
7
6
5
4
3
2
1

1 Cylinder head
2 Valve seat insert
3 Valve guide
4 Valve
5 Oil deflector ring
6 Valve cotter
7 Valve spring
8 Valve spring cap

Details of a typical valve.

4. After the seal between the mating surfaces has been broken, remove the right-hand crankcase half, the crankshaft oil seal and camshaft end plug, and lift out the camshaft and the crankshaft.
5. Remove the cam followers, bearing shells, and oil-pressure relief valve.

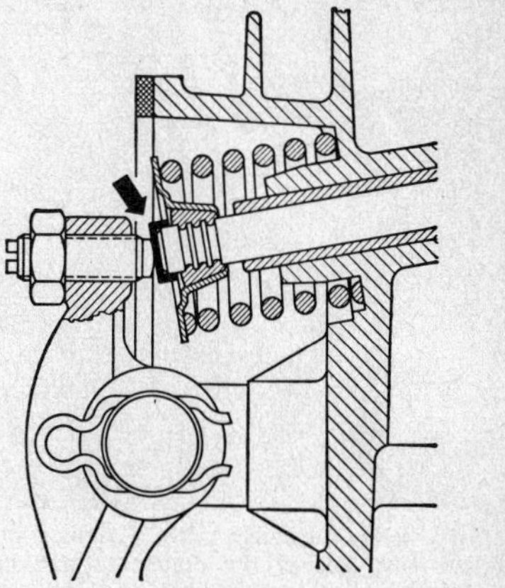

Valves with a damaged stem can be reused after fitting a cap.

Assembly is generally the reverse of the foregoing procedure, but includes the following:

1. Before reassembling the crankcase, check it for damage and cracks after cleaning thoroughly. Mating and sealing surfaces should be cleaned especially well. A solvent should be used to remove traces of the old sealant from the mating surfaces.
2. Flush and blow out all ducts and oil passages.
3. Check the oil suction pipe for leaks.
4. Check the studs for tightness. If tapped holes are worn, correction involves the installation of Helicoil inserts.
5. Insert the cam followers after checking both the followers and their bores in the crankcase.
6. Install the crankshaft bearing dowel pins and bearing shells for crankshaft and camshaft.
7. Install the crankshaft and camshaft after bearings have been well lubricated. (When installing the crankshaft, note the position of the timing marks on the timing gears.)
8. Install the camshaft end plug, using sealing compound.
9. Install the thrust washers and crankshaft oil seal. The oil seal must rest squarely on the bottom of its recess in the crankcase.
10. Check and install the oil pressure switch.
11. Spread a thin film of sealing compound on the crankcase joining faces. Use care so that no sealing compound enters the oil passages of the crankshaft or the camshaft bearings.
12. Keep the cam followers of the right crankcase half in place by using retaining springs.
13. Join the crankcase halves and evenly torque the fasteners to the torque specified in the "Engine Torque Specifications" chart.

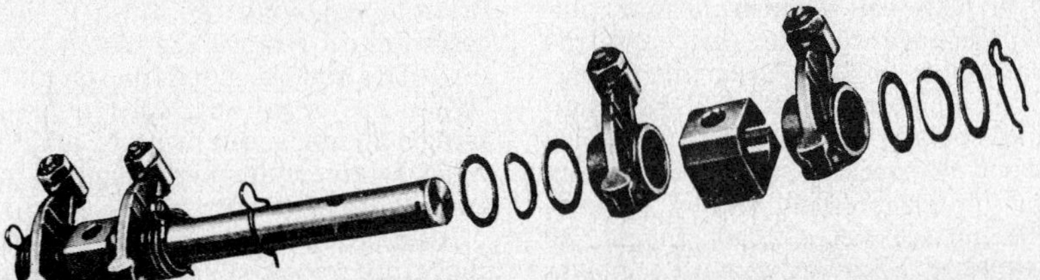

Exploded view, rocker arm mechanism.

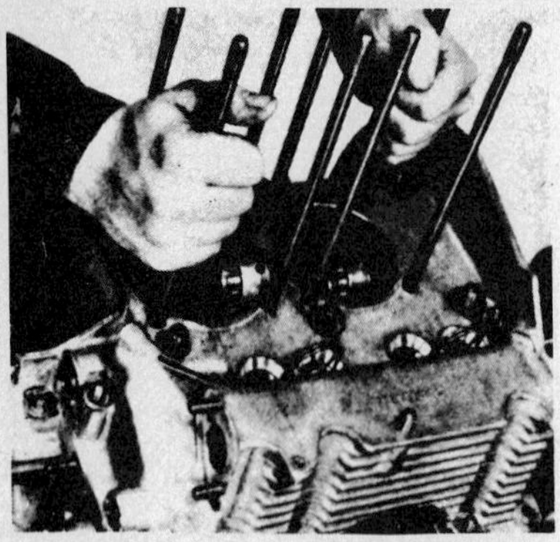

After being loosened with a rubber mallet, the right half of the crankcase can be removed. Prying tools should never be used to separate the crankcase halves.

The 8 mm nut pointed out must be tightened fully before the 12 mm nuts are tightened.

NOTE: First tighten the 8 mm nut which is beside the 12 mm stud of the no. 1 crankshaft bearing. Only then should the 12 mm nuts be tightened fully.)

14. Turn the crankshaft to check for ease of movement, and check the endplay of the crankshaft. The crankshaft end-play is measured with the engine assembled and the flywheel installed.

Camshaft and Timing Gears

R & R. Camshaft

Removal of the camshaft requires splitting of the crankcase. The camshaft and camshaft bearing shells are then easily removed. Before reinstalling the camshaft, it should be checked for wear of the bearing faces and bearing points. In addition, the riveted joint between the camshaft timing gear and the camshaft should be examined for security. If there is slight damage to the camshaft, it may be smoothed with a silicon carbide oilstone. A 100–120 grit stone is first used to smooth the damaged area, and then a 280–320 stone may be used for final polishing. The camshaft should be checked for run-out, which should not exceed .0008 in. The timing gear should be checked for correct tooth contact and for wear, and the edges of the camshaft bearing bores lightly chamfered to avoid seizure. If the camshaft shells removed are either worn or damaged, new shells should be fitted. The camshaft bearing shells should be installed with the tabs engaging the notches in the crankcase. Before installing the camshaft, the bearing journals and cams should be generously coated with oil. When the camshaft is installed, care should be taken to ensure that the timing gear tooth marked "O" is located between the two teeth of the crankshaft timing gear marked by a center punch. The end-play at the thrust bearing (bearing no. 3) is .06–.11 mm (.002–.004 in.) and the wear limit is .14 mm (.006 in.).

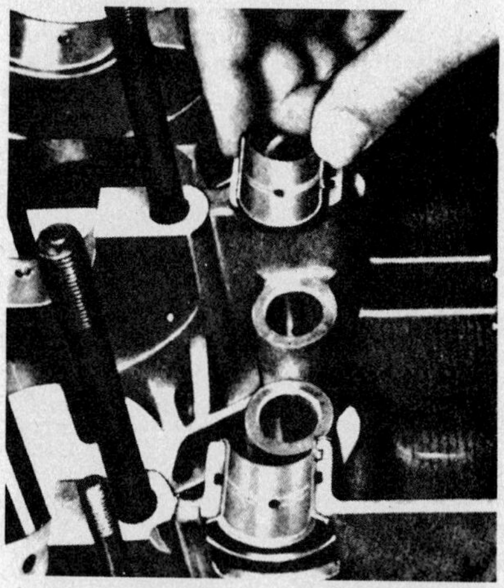

Camshaft bearings. Note the thrust flange on bearing no. 3, in the foreground.

The arrow shows the proper alignment of timing marks when installing the camshaft and crankshaft.

Crankshaft

R & R, Crankshaft Pulley

On the Type 1 and 2, the crankshaft pulley can be removed while the engine is still in the car. However, in this instance it is necessary for the rear cover plate of the engine to be removed. Remove the cover plate after taking out the screws in the cover plate below the crankshaft pulley. Remove the fan belt and the crankshaft pulley securing screw. Using a puller tool, remove the crankshaft pulley. The crankshaft pulley should be checked for proper seating and for proper belt contact surface. The oil return thread should be cleaned and lubricated with a molybdenum-disulphide based oil. The crankshaft pulley should be installed in the reverse sequence, and should have no run-out.

On the Type 3, the crankshaft pulley can be removed only when the engine is out of the car and the muffler, generator, and cooling air intake housing are removed. After these parts have been removed, take out the plastic cap on the pulley. This can be done easily with a screwdriver. Remove the crankshaft pulley retaining bolt and remove the pulley.

Installation is the reverse of the preceding but the following should be noted: when installing, use a new paper gasket between the fan and the crankshaft pulley. If shims are used, do not forget them. No more than two shims may be used. When inserting the pulley, make sure that the pin engages the hole in the fan. The crankshaft pulley retaining bolt should be tightened to a torque of 94–108 ft lbs. Ensure that the clearance between the generator belt and the intake housing is at least 4 mm and that the belt is parallel to the housing. Check the seal on the cooling air intake housing and if damaged, cement a new seal into place. On the Type 4, the pulley is removed with the fan.

Crankshaft End-Play

With the engine installed, the crankshaft end-play can be read with a dial indicator mounted at the pulley side of the engine. End-play should be as specified with an upper wear limit of .15 mm (.006 in.). When the engine is not installed, crankshaft end-play can be measured at the flywheel end with an indicator mounted on the flywheel. Desirable end-play is obtained by adding or subtracting shims at the outer end of the main bearing. Shims for this purpose are available in various thicknesses. Never use more than one gasket.

R & R, Flywheel

The flywheel is attached to the crankshaft with a gland nut, and is located by four dowels. Some models have a paper gasket between the flywheel and the crankshaft; others have a metal gasket. Beginning with the 1967 model year, a metal sealing gasket is no longer present between the flywheel and crankshaft. An oil seal is recessed in the crankcase casting at no. 1 main bearing. A needle bearing, which supports the main driveshaft, is located in the gland nut. Prior to removing the flywheel, it is necessary to remove the clutch pressure plate and the clutch driven plate. Loosen the gland nut and remove it, using a 36 mm special wrench and flywheel retainer. Remove the gland nut and withdraw the flywheel.

Installation is the reverse of the above procedure, plus the following: check the flywheel teeth for wear and

With the engine assembled and the flywheel installed, crankshaft end-play should be .06-.12 mm (.003-.005 in.) with a wear limit of .15 mm (.006 in.).

damage. Check the dowel holes in the flywheel and crankshaft, and renew the dowels if necessary. Adjust the crankshaft end-play and check the needle bearing in the gland for wear.

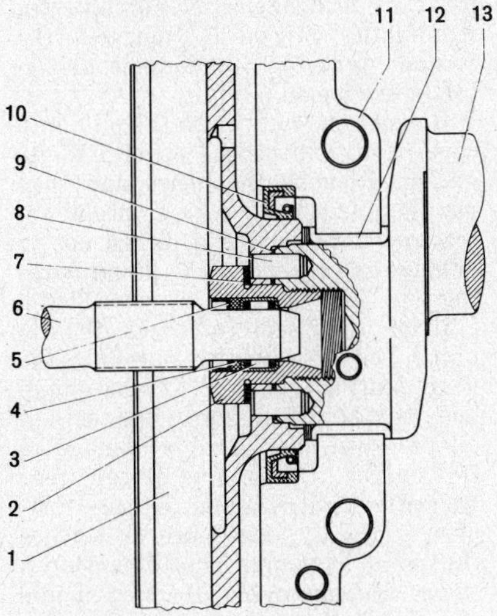

11
12
13
10
9
8
7
6
5
4
3
2
1

1 Flywheel
2 Gland nut
3 Needle bearing
4 Felt ring
5 Retaining ring
6 Main driveshaft
7 Lockwasher
8 Dowel pin
9 Paper or metal gasket
10 Oil seal
11 Crankcase
12 Crankshaft bearing
13 Crankshaft

Cross-sectional view of flywheel and crankshaft end.

Lubricate the needle bearing with about 10 grams of universal grease. Insert the flywheel gasket, if one is used in the engine. (Note: to minimize engine imbalance, the crankshaft, flywheel, and clutch are marked at their heaviest points. Upon assembly, be sure that the marks on these units are offset by 120°. If but two of these parts are marked, the marks should be offset by 180°. Tighten flywheel gland nut to 217 ft lbs and check flywheel run-out, which should be a maximum of .3 mm (.012 in.).

R & R, Crankshaft Oil Seal (engine assembled)

Oil losses at the flywheel could well be the result of a leaky crankshaft oil

The flywheel gland nut is torqued to 30 mkg (217 ft lbs).

seal. This seal is removed after removing the flywheel. After the flywheel is removed, inspect the surface on the flywheel joining flange where the oil seal makes contact. Remove the old oil seal by prying it out of its counterbore. Before installing a new crankshaft oil seal, clean the crankcase oil seal recess and coat it thinly with sealing compound. The sharp edges should be slightly chamfered so that the outer edge of the seal is not damaged. Using VW tool 204b, press in the new seal, being sure that it rests squarely on the bottom of its recess. Remove the tool and reinstall the flywheel after coating the oil seal contact surface with oil.

R & R, Crankshaft and Connecting Rods

Removal of the crankshaft requires splitting of the crankcase halves and the withdrawal of the camshaft. When installing the crankshaft, check to see that the crankcase does not have sharp edges at the points of junction. If foreign matter has become lodged in the main bearings, it will be necessary to remove it with a scraper, taking care not to remove material from the bearing shell itself. Check the dowel pins for tightness. Place one half of no. 2 crankshaft bearing in the crankcase. Slide on crankshaft bearing no. 1 so that the dowel pin hole is toward the flywheel. Install the crankshaft, making sure that the dowel pins are correctly seated in the crankshaft bearings.

A special tool is needed to install the crankshaft oil seal.

When installing the camshaft, note the marks on the timing gears.

After the crankshaft has been removed and clamped into position, remove the connecting rod clamping bolts and the connecting rods and caps. Inspect the piston pin bushing. With a new bushing, the correct clearance is indicated by a light finger push-fit of the pin at room temperature. Check and, if necessary, correct connecting rod alignment. Reinsert the connecting rod bearing shells after all parts have been thoroughly cleaned and assemble the connecting rods on the crankshaft. The identification numbers stamped on the connecting rods and bearing caps must both be on one side.

NOTE: New connecting rod screws should always be used and the wax removed from the screws before they are installed.

Tighten the connecting rod bolts to the specified torque. A slight pretension between the bearing halves, which is likely to occur when tightening connecting rod bolts, can be eliminated by light hammer taps. The connecting rods, lubricated with engine oil prior to assembly, must slide on the crankpin by their own weight. The connecting rod bushings must not be scraped, reamed or filed during assembly. Using a peening chisel, secure the connecting rod bolts in place.

Engine Lubrication

R & R, Oil Strainer

All Volkswagen models are equipped with the same type of oil strainer, a view of which is shown in the accompanying diagram. The oil strainer can be easily removed simply by removing the restraining nuts, washers, oil strainer plate, strainer and gaskets. Once taken out, the strainer must be thoroughly cleaned and all traces of old gaskets removed prior to fitting new ones. The suction pipe should be checked for tightness

cylinder 1
cylinder 2
cylinder 3
cylinder 4

Note that the marks on the connecting rods are pointing upward, while the rods are pointing toward their respective cylinders.

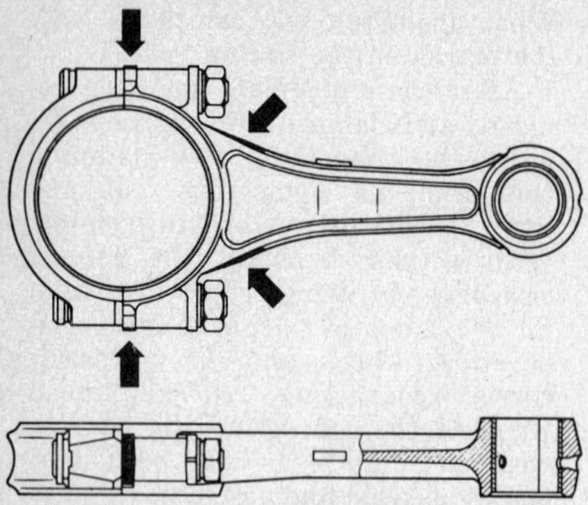

Maximum allowable weight difference between connecting rods in one engine is 10 grams. Metal may be removed from the portions of the connecting rod indicated.

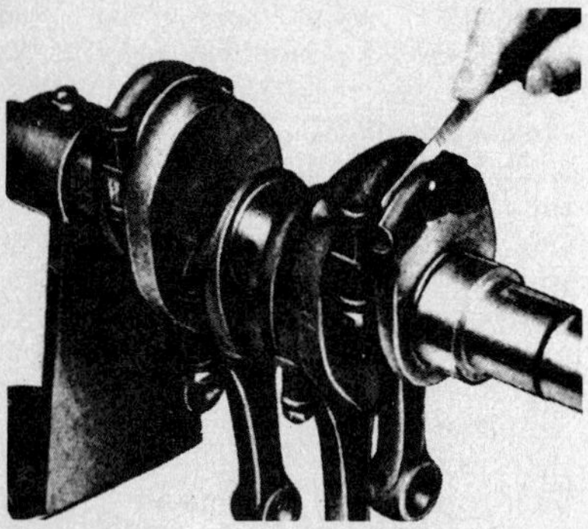

Measuring the axial (side) play of the connecting rods with a feeler gauge.

and proper position. When the strainer is installed, be sure that the suction pipe is correctly seated in the strainer. If necessary, the strainer may be bent slightly. The measurement from the strainer flange to the tip of the suction pipe should be 10 mm, plus or minus 1 mm. The measurement from the flange to the bottom of the strainer should be 6 mm plus or minus 1 mm. The cap nuts at the bottom of the strainer should not be overtightened, for the bottom plate may become distorted and lead to leakage of engine lubricant. If it is desired, the strainer can be equipped with a permanent magnet designed to retain metal particles that are circulating in the oil. This magnet is held in place by means of a spring clip, and should be removed and cleaned whenever the strainer is removed for the same purpose. Magnetic drain plugs are also available. Type 4 engines have an oil filter that is a replaceable cartridge.

R & R, Oil Cooler

The Volkswagen oil cooler is mounted on the crankcase and is positioned in the path of the cooling air. The oil cooler in the Type 1 can be removed with the engine in the car, but it is first necessary that the fan housing be removed. The oil cooler can be removed after the three oil cooler retaining nuts have been taken off. The gaskets should be removed along with the oil cooler and replaced with new ones when the cooler is installed. Before installation, the oil cooler should be checked for leaks at a pressure of 85 psi. If the cooler is found to leak, the oil pressure relief valve should also be checked. The studs and bracket on the cooler should be checked for tightness. See that the hollow ribs of the oil cooler do not touch one another. Clean the contact surfaces on the crankcase, install new gaskets, and attach the oil cooler. Tighten the retaining nuts. On the

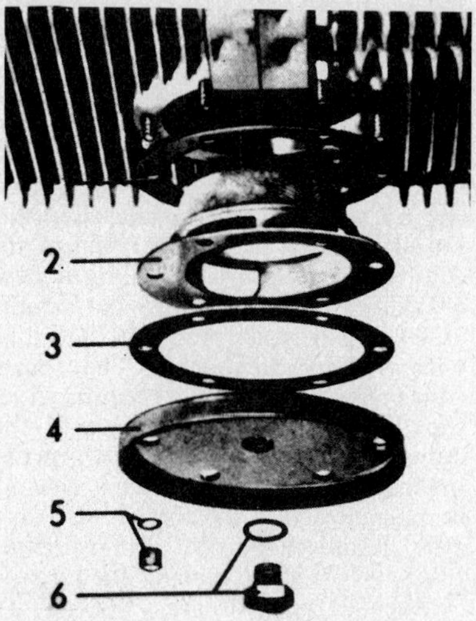
2
3
4
5
6

1 Gasket
2 Oil strainer
3 Gasket
4 Cover plate
5 Cap nut with washer
6 Plug with washer

Crankcase oil strainer components. The strainer must be cleaned at each oil change, and new gaskets must be used.

1
2
3
4
5
6

1 Gasket
2 Oil pump body
3 Gears
4 Gasket
5 Oil pump cover
6 Nut and spring washer

Oil pump components, Type 1.

Types 3 and 4, be sure that a spacer ring is present between the crankcase and the cooler at each securing screw. If these rings are omitted, the seals may be squeezed too tightly, resulting in a stoppage of oil flow and consequent damage to the engine. The Type 3 oil cooler is similar in design to that of the Type 1 and 2, except that it lies horizontally cross-wise in the path of the air, while that of the other models is in a vertical position.

Beginning 1971, the Type 1 and 2 oil cooler is mounted farther forward on an intermediate flange and has its own cooling air supply through the fan housing. This prevents the oil cooler from blocking off the cooling air to no. 3 cylinder and causing that cylinder to run hot.

R & R, Oil Pump

An exploded view of the Volkswagen oil pump is given in the accompanying illustration. In the Type 3, the oil pump can be taken out only after the engine is removed from the car and the air intake housing, the belt pulley fan housing, and the fan are dismantled. On the Types 1 and 2, the pump can be removed with the engine in the car, but it is first necessary to remove the cover plate, the crankshaft pulley, and the cover plate under the pulley. Removal from all model Volkswagens is similar. On Automatic Stickshift models, the torque converter oil pump is driven by the engine oil pump.

Remove the nuts from the oil pump cover and remove the cover and its gasket. Remove the gears and take out the pump body with a special extractor. Care should be taken not to damage the inside of the pump housing.

Prior to assembly, check the oil pump body for wear, especially the gear seating surface. If the pump body is worn, the result will be loss of oil pressure and possible damage to the engine. Check the driven gear shaft for tightness and, if necessary, peen it tightly into place or replace the pump housing. The dimension *a* in the accompanying diagram should be .5–1.0 mm (.02–.04 in.) The

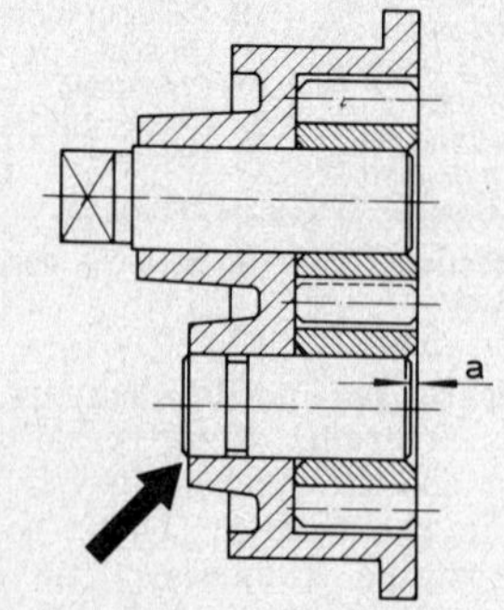
a

Arrow shows driven shaft of gear type oil pump. Dimension a should be .02-.04 in.

gears should be checked for wear, backlash, and end-play. Backlash may be from .03–.08 mm (.0012–.0031 in.) and the maximum end-play, without gasket, .1 mm (.004 in.). The end-play can be checked using a T-square and a feeler gauge. Check the mating surfaces of the pump body and crankcase for damage and clean them. Install the pump body with gasket, but without sealing com-

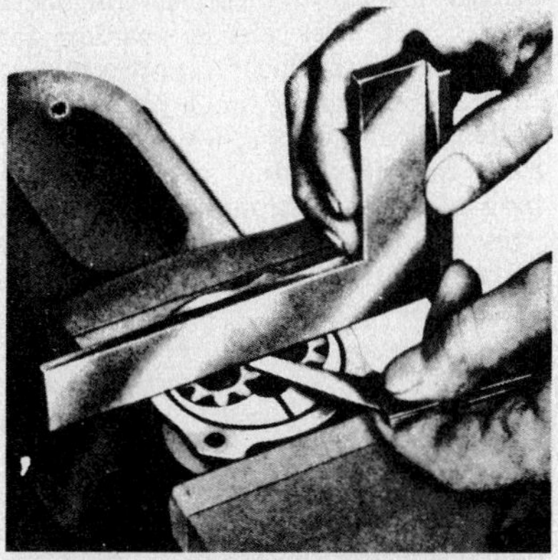

Maximum end-play of the oil pump gears, measured without a gasket, should be .1 mm.

pound. Insert the oil pump pilot instead of the oil pump driveshaft into the pump body. Turn the camshaft by 360°. (One complete turn of the camshaft requires two complete turns of the crankshaft.) This will ensure the centering of the pump body opposite the slot in the camshaft. Mark the pump body so that the correct fit of the oil pump can be checked after the cover has been installed. Remove the oil pump pilot and install the gears. Check the cover for wear—worn covers should be either machined or replaced. Before installing the cover, new gaskets should be fitted and secured with sealing compound. Install the cover and tighten the nuts without disturbing the position of the pump housing.

R & R Oil Pressure Relief Valve

When the oil is cold and thick, and oil pressure is very high, the pressure relief valve plunger is in its lowest position and oil flows directly to the lubrication points; some of it back to the crankcase. When the oil warms and thins, the oil pressure drops, the plunger covers the bypass port and oil flows to the lubrication points both directly and via the oil cooler. After the oil has warmed to normal operating temperature and is thin, oil pressure is low, the plunger of the relief

1
2
3
4

1 Plunger 3 Gasket
2 Spring 4 Plug

Components of oil pressure relief valve.

valve is in its highest position, and the oil goes to the lubrication points only after it has passed through the oil cooler.

The oil pressure relief valve should be checked whenever there is any disturbance in oil circulation, and especially when the oil cooler is found to be leaky. If the plunger should stick at its highest point when the oil is thick, there is danger of the oil cooler leaking from excess pressure. If, on the other hand, the plunger sticks in the bottom of its travel, the oil will tend to flow directly back to the sump and lubrication will be lacking when the engine is warm.

The oil pressure relief valve is removed by unscrewing the end plug and removing the gasket ring, spring, and plunger. If the plunger is stuck, it can be removed by screwing a 10 mm tap into it. Prior to installation, check the plunger and the bore in the crankcase for signs of seizure. If necessary, the plunger should be renewed. The spring should be checked to make sure that it conforms to the following specifications:

Condition	*Length*	*Load in lbs*
Unloaded	2.44–2.52 in.	0
Loaded	.93 in.	17.1 lbs

When installing the relief valve, care should be taken to ensure that the upper end of the spring does not scratch the wall of the bore. The gasket should be removed and the end plug tightened securely.

There are two types of oil pressure relief valve plungers available. The first is the plain type normally found in Type 1 and 2 engines. The second type is longer and has an annular groove. This is used in some Type 3 engines. It has been found that if the grooved plunger is substituted for the plain plunger, the result will be more oil flow through the cooler and a drop in oil temperature of about 15°F. This, as all other engine modifications, is discouraged by the VW factory.

1970 and later Type 1 and 2 engines have two oil pressure relief valves. The second valve is located at the flywheel side of the oil sump and is identical to the first.

Pistons and Connecting Rods

Pistons R & R

Following the removal of the cylinder head and the cylinder, the pistons should be marked with a number (cylinder number) and an arrow (pointing to clutch side of engine) if they are to be reinstalled in the engine. The pistons are removed as follows:

Using piston circlip pliers, remove the circlips used to retain the piston wrist pin. Heat the piston to 80°C (176°F), remove the piston pin and take the piston off the end of the connecting rod. Heating the pistons to

Oil pressure relief valve plungers; the grooved type gives increased oil cooling.

remove the piston pin is accomplished by boiling a rag in water and wrapping the hot rag around the piston. If it is necessary to remove the piston rings, use piston ring pliers in order to avoid damage.

Install the piston as follows: First, clean the piston and the ring grooves, taking care to see that the ring grooves are not scratched or otherwise damaged. The piston should then be checked for wear and, if necessary, replaced by one of corresponding size and weight. Weight between pistons must not be greater than 10 grams. If the running clearance between the piston and cylinder is .2 mm (.008 in.) or more, the piston and cylinder should be replaced by a set of the same size grading. If, however, the cylinder of a worn or damaged piston shows no signs of wear, it is permissible to install a new piston of appropriate size. See the accompanying diagram for piston markings.

After making a decision concerning the piston to be used, select piston rings of the correct size. After the ring has been inserted in the cylinder and pushed down about .2 in. by the piston, check the gap with a feeler gauge. After using a piston ring tool to install the rings, check the side clearance of the rings in their grooves with a feeler gauge.

Ring side clearance and end-gap should be as specified in the "Engine Rebuilding Specifications" chart for pistons, cylinders, and rings.

Because the compression rings are slightly tapered, they should be installed with the marking "Top" or "Oben" toward the top of the piston.

II
I

The pistons should be marked in this manner before removal.

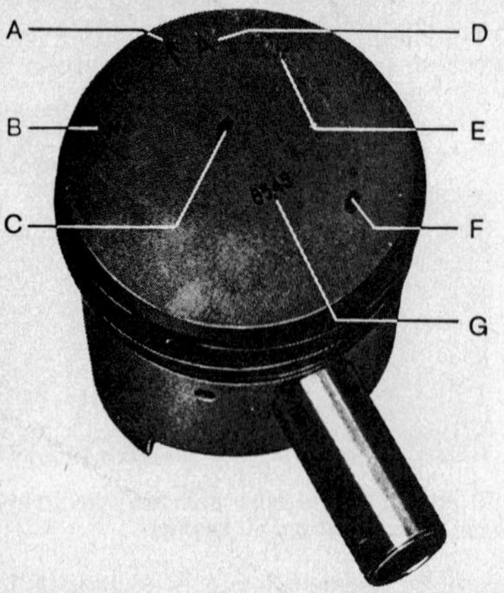
A
B
C
D
E
F
G

A. Arrow (indented or stamped on) which must point toward the flywheel when piston is installed.
B. Details of piston pin bore size indented or stamped on (s = black, w = white).
C. Paint spot indicating matching size (blue, pink, green).
D. The letter near the arrow corresponds to the index of the part number of the piston concerned. It serves as an identification mark.
E. Details of weight grading (+ or —) indented or stamped on.
F. Paint spot indicating weight grading (brown = — weight, grey = + weight).
G. Details of piston size in mm.

An explanation of the markings on new pistons.

Measuring ring end-gap.

Measuring ring side clearance.

Insert the piston pin circlip which faces toward the flywheel. Because piston pin holes are offset, make sure that the arrow (or word "vorn") points toward the flywheel. This offset is to help accommodate thrust loads which amplify and lead to objectionable piston slap.

Check and fit the piston pin. The pin may be found to be a light finger-push fit in the piston, even when the piston is cold. This condition is normal, even to the extent of the pin sliding out of the piston under its own weight. Clearance between the piston pin and the connecting rod bushing should be as specified in the "Engine Rebuilding Specifications" chart. If the clearance is near the wear limit, renew the piston pin and the rod bushing. It is not advisable to install an oversize pin in this case. In all cases where the pin is not a light finger-push fit in the cold piston, heat the piston in oil to about 176°F. Insert the second circlip and make sure that the circlips fit perfectly in their grooves. A good barometer in deciding whether or not a new cylinder and piston should be installed is oil consumption. If the engine uses more than one quart of oil each 600 miles, it is quite likely that the engine is in need of reconditioning.

CLUTCH

Clutch R & R

Manual Transmission

To remove the clutch, first remove the engine; then remove the clutch-to-flywheel attaching bolts by gradually and alternately backing the bolts out of the flywheel; finally take off the clutch cover and lift out the clutch driven plate.

Installation of the clutch is the reverse of the preceding. Before installing, inspect and resurface the pressure plate if it is worn in excess of .008 in. The friction surface should be polished. Inspect the driven plate and renew it if there is any doubt as to its reliability. Examine the release plate, release levers, and springs for damage. Check the release bearing for damage and replace if necessary. If the release bearing has a plastic ring, it must be roughed up with emery cloth and lubricated sparingly with molybdenum disulphide paste. This prevents an annoying whistling sound which sometimes comes from the release bearing. Inspect the bearing points of the clutch operating shaft for wear. Lubricate the needle bearing in the flywheel gland nut with approximately 10 grams of universal grease. Reinstall the driven (lined) plate, using a pilot mandrel to ensure correct centering alignment. Evenly and alternately tighten the clutch-to-flywheel bolts. Check for proper distance and parallelism between the clutch cover contact face at flywheel and the clutch release plate with a clutch adjustment gauge. Adjust free-play at the clutch pedal to .4–.8 in.

Clearance between cylinder and piston should not exceed .20 mm (.008 in.). Clearance is determined by measuring both piston and cylinder. The cylinder diameter is measured 10-15 mm below the upper edge.

Automatic Stickshift

To remove the clutch, the engine and then the transmission must first be removed. Proceed as follows:

1. Pull off the torque converter. Seal off the hub opening.
2. Mount the transmission in a repair stand or on a suitable bench.
3. Loosen the clamp screw and pull off the clutch operating lever. Remove the transmission cover. Remove the hex nuts between the clutch housing and the transmission case (two inside the differential housing).
4. The oil need not be drained if the clutch is removed with the cover opening up and the gearshift housing breather blocked.
5. Pull the transmission off the clutch housing studs.
6. Turn the clutch lever shaft to disengage the release bearing.
7. Remove both lower engine mounting bolts.
8. Loosen the clutch retaining bolts gradually and alternately to prevent distortion. Remove the bolts, diaphragm clutch, clutch plate, and release bearing.
9. Do not wash the release bearing. Wipe dry only.

To replace the clutch:

10. Check the clutch plate, pressure plate, and release bearing for wear and damage. Check the clutch carrier plate, needle bearing, and seat for wear. Replace all parts as necessary.
11. If the clutch is wet with ATF, replace the clutch carrier plate seal and clutch. If the clutch is wet with transmission oil, replace the transmission case seal and clutch.
12. Coat the release bearing guide on the transmission case neck and both lugs on the release bearing with lithium grease containing a

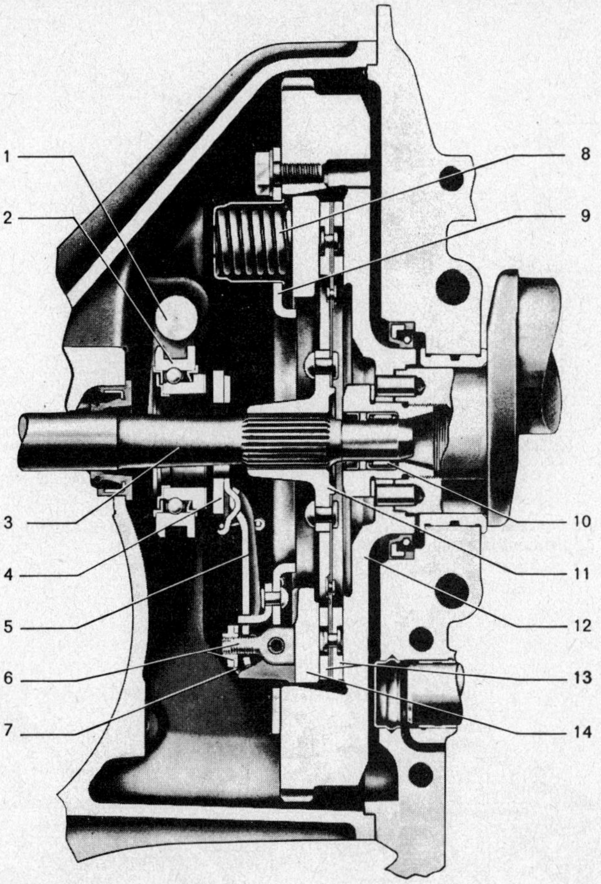
1
2
3
4
5
6
7
8
9
10
11
12
13
14

1 Operating shaft
2 Release bearing
3 Main driveshaft
4 Release plate
5 Release lever
6 Bolt and special nut
7 Release lever spring
8 Thrust spring
9 Cover
10 Needle bearing for gland nut
11 Driven plate
12 Flywheel
13 Lining
14 Pressure plate

Cross-sectional view of clutch assembly.

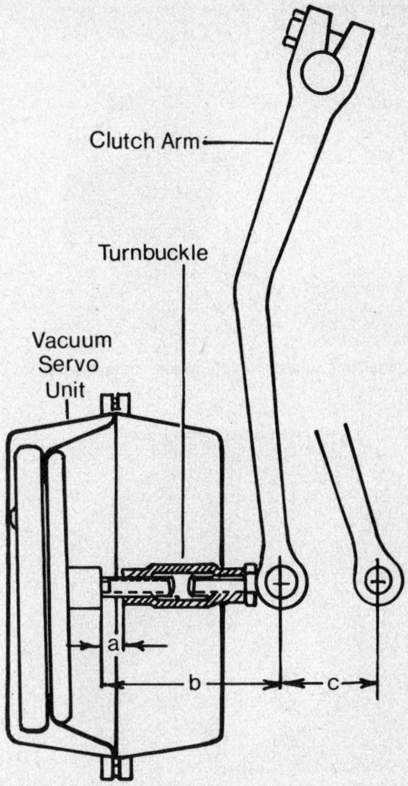
Clutch Arm
Turnbuckle
Vacuum
Servo
Unit
a
b
c

Adjustment dimensions required after installing new clutch in Automatic Stickshift unit. a should be .335 in., b should be 3.03 in., and c should be 1.6 in.

molybdenum disulphide additive. Insert the bearing into the clutch.

13. Apply lithium grease to the carrier plate needle bearing. Install the clutch plate and clutch, centering the plate with an old main driveshaft or a suitable dummy shaft.
14. Tighten the clutch retaining bolts evenly and alternately. Make sure that the release bearing is correctly located in the diaphragm spring.
15. Insert the lower engine mounting bolts from the front. Replace the sealing rings if necessary. Some units have aluminum sealing rings and cap nuts.
16. Push the transmission onto the converter housing studs. Insert the clutch lever shaft behind the release bearing lugs. Push the release bearing onto the transmission case neck. Tighten the hex bolts holding the clutch housing to the transmission case.
17. Install the clutch operating lever.

To adjust a new clutch:

18. The clutch operating lever should contact the clutch housing. Tighten the lever clamp screw slightly.
19. Refer to the adjustment illustration. Adjust dimension a to .335 in., b to 3.03 in., and c to 1.6 in. Tighten the clutch lever clamp screw fully.
20. Push the torque converter onto the support tube. Insert it into the turbine shaft by turning.
21. Check clutch play after installing the transmission and engine.

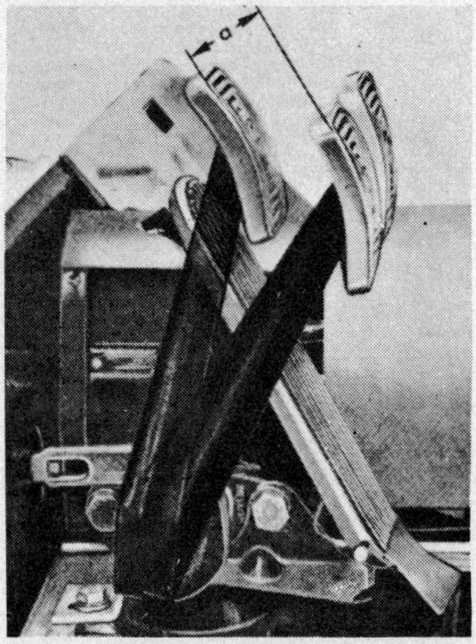
a

Clutch pedal free-play should be 10-20 mm (.4-.8 mm.).

R & R, Clutch Cable

Manual Transmission

The clutch cable runs from the pedal to the release bearing, which in turn presses against the release plate and moves it axially. To remove the cable, first remove the left rear wheel. Disconnect the cable from its operating lever on the transmission. Pull the rubber boot from the guide tube and cable. Disconnect the brake master cylinder push rod and unbolt the pedal assembly. Unhook the cable from the pedal cluster and pull it forward through the hole from which the pedal cluster was removed. To gain access to the cable end, on Type 1 cars remove the pedal cluster, on Type 2 cars, remove the cover under the pedal cluster, on Type 3, a frame head cover is located under the pedal cluster under the car.

Installation is the reverse of the above. The cable should be lubricated thoroughly with universal grease. While the pedal assembly is out of the frame tunnel, it is a good idea to lubricate this part well also. The cable

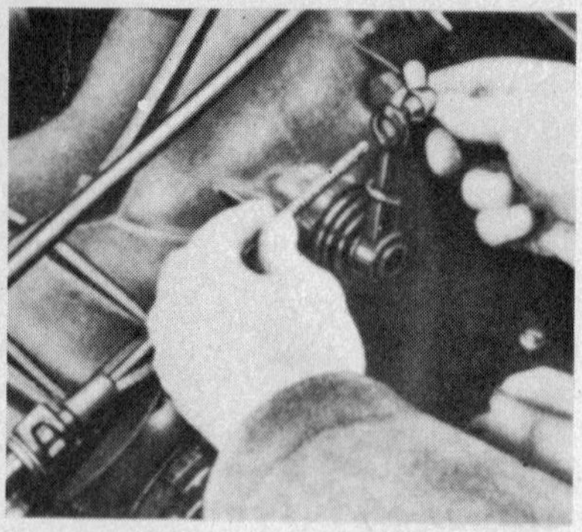

Disconnecting clutch cable from operating lever.

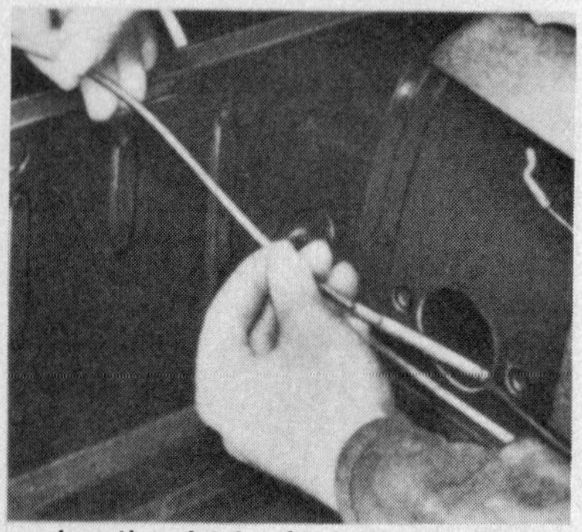

Inserting clutch cable into guide tube.

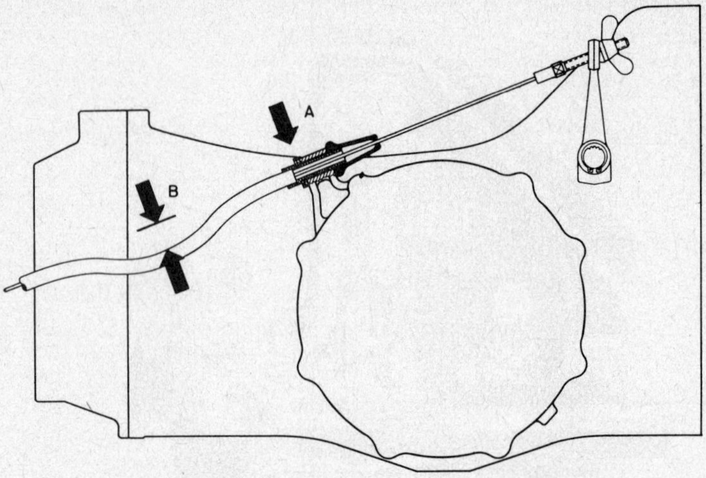
A
B

Smooth clutch action requires a slight sag in the cable. Dimension B should be 1.0-1.7 in. Adjustment is made by washers at point A.

guide should be bent slightly by inserting a suitable number of washers between the transmission case bracket and the end of the cable guide (A). (See illustration.) Adjust pedal free-play.

Clutch Adjustment—Manual Transmission

The Volkswagen clutch is a dry, singleplate unit fitted to the flywheel. Earlier models had a carbon throwout bearing, while the later models are equipped with the ball bearing type. With the carbon type bearing, wear on the bearing was significant when the clutch pedal was depressed for any length of time, although in normal and proper use the carbon bearings generally lasted for the life of the clutch lining. Neither the carbon bearing nor the ball type bearing requires periodic maintenance.

Routine clutch maintenance is limited to adjusting the free-play present at the clutch pedal. As the clutch lining wears, clearance between the release bearing and release plate is reduced until these parts touch. Such a condition can lead to damage or excessive wear, as well as clutch slipping and burning of the lining. The proper clutch pedal free-play is 10–20 mm (.4–.8 in.) measured at the pedal.

Adjustment is carried out at the rear of the car, at the cable end of the clutch. First loosen the locking nut and then the adjusting nut. On 1966 and subsequent models, a single wing

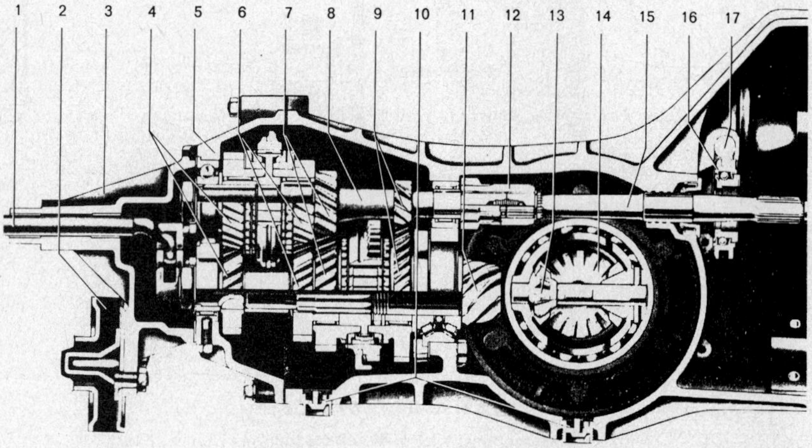
1
2
3
4
5
6
7
8
9
10
11
12
13
14
15
16
17

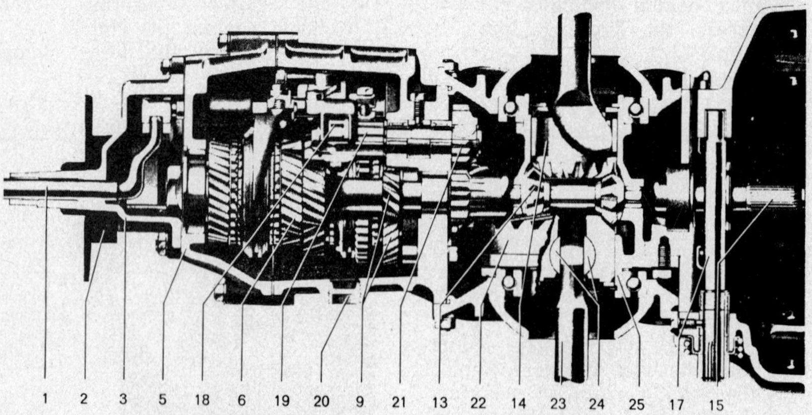
1
2
3
5
18
6
19
20
9
21
13
22
14
23
24
25
17
15

1 Transmission shift lever
2 Bonded rubber mounting
3 Gearshift housing
4 4th speed
5 Gear carrier
6 3rd speed
7 2nd speed
8 Main driveshaft, front
9 1st speed
10 Oil drain plugs
11 Drive pinion
12 Reverse gear
13 Differential pinion
14 Differential side gear
15 Main driveshaft, rear
16 Clutch release bearing
17 Clutch operating shaft
18 Reverse sliding gear
19 Reverse shaft
20 Oil filler plug
21 Reverse drive gear
22 Ring gear
23 Rear axle shaft
24 Fulcrum plate
25 Differential housing

Cross-sectional view of one-piece transaxle with four-speed transmission.

nut serves both purposes. The adjusting nut is turned until the proper amount of free-play is evident at the pedal. The locknut, if present, is tightened, after which the pedal should be depressed several times and the free-play rechecked. After the clutch is adjusted, the thread on the cable end should be greased.

Clutch Adjustment— Automatic Stickshift

Checking Clutch Play

A minimum clutch play is required to prevent slippage and excessive wear. The adjustment is made on the linkage between the clutch arm and the vacuum servo unit. To check the clutch play:

1. Pull off the servo vacuum hose.
2. Measure the clearance between the upper edge of the servo unit mounting bracket and the lower edge of the adjusting turnbuckle. If the clearance is .16 in. or more, the clutch needs adjustment.
3. Replace the vacuum hose.

Adjusting Clutch Play

To adjust the clutch:

1. Pull off the servo vacuum hose. Loosen the turnbuckle locknut slightly. Turn the turnbuckle 5–5½ turns away from the locknut. There should now be .25 in. clearance between the locknut and the turnbuckle.
2. Tighten the locknut against the turnbuckle.
3. Replace the vacuum hose.
4. The clutch adjustment is correct when there is no slippage and reverse can be engaged silently. If the clutch arm contacts the clutch housing, there is no more adjustment possible and the clutch plate must be replaced.

Adjusting Speed of Engagement

The clutch should normally take a full second to engage after shifting down from 2 to 1, at 44 mph without accelerating. Engagement speed may be adjusted to suit personal preference, within certain limits. Excessively fast clutch action may, however, cause transmission damage, while excessively slow action may cause overheating and rapid lining wear. Speed of clutch engagement is adjusted at the reducing valve, to the left of the ignition coil. The adjusting screw is on top of the unit, under a cap. In the normal position, the adjusting screw has two threads protruding from the unit.

To adjust the speed of clutch engagement:

1. Remove the reducing valve cap.
2. To slow engagement, turn the adjusting screw ¼–½ turn clockwise. To speed engagement, turn screw ¼–½ turn counterclockwise.
3. Replace the cap.
4. Test operation by shifting from 2 to 1 at 44 mph without depressing the accelerator.

Trans-Axle

Recent transmission cases are of one-piece, die-cast construction. Transmissions of 1960 and earlier models (36 hp with a non-synchromesh first gear) are of a split type construction. With the 40 hp engine introduced on the 1961 models, all transmissions have been of the one-piece type. In the case of the split type cases, both halves must be replaced at the same time, since they are cast and machined in pairs.

The transmission has four speeds forward and one reverse, with various ratios.

Transmission work of any kind requires removal of the engine.

Transaxle R & R

Manual Transmission With Swing Axles

1. With the engine removed from the car, remove the rear wheels and disconnect the brake lines at the rear wheels and plug the lines.
2. Disconnect the parking brake cables from the push bar at the frame and withdraw the cables from their conduit tubes.
3. Remove the bolts at the rear axle shaft bearing.
4. Disconnect the clutch release cable from the operating shaft lever and pull it from its guide plate.
5. From the access hole under the rear seat, disconnect the shift rod in back of the coupling.
6. Remove the nuts from the mounting studs at the front of the transmission.
7. Remove the lower shock absorber mounting bolts and mark the position of the rear torsion bar radius arm in relation to the rear axle bearing housing by using a chisel.
8. Disconnect the wires from the starter motor.
9. Disconnect the ground strap from the frame and remove the nuts from the auxiliary spring rods (1966 Squareback and 1967–68 Beetles).
10. Place a suitable jack under the unit, and remove the two bolts at the transmission attachments with a 27 mm wrench.
11. Withdraw the transaxle toward the rear of the car. Be sure that the main driveshaft is not damaged or bent when the unit is placed on the ground.

Installation of the transaxle unit is accomplished by reversing the above procedure. The two bolts at the transmission carrier should be greased before being tightened. When a new rear axle is being installed, it is advisable that the retaining nuts of the transmission cradle be tightened fully only after the front mounting has been securely tightened. This tightening sequence is necessary to prevent distortion and premature wear of the rubber mountings.

When the shift rod coupling is reinstalled, the point of the coupling screw should be correctly engaged in the recess. The screw should be secured with a piece of wire. After replacing the ground strap, install the rear axle tubes in their correct positions. The mounting bolts on the spring plate should be tightened to a torque of about 80 ft lbs. Tighten the lower mounting bolts of the shock absorbers securely. Install the engine and adjust the clutch pedal free-play to .4–.8 in. and tighten the rear axle shaft nuts to 217 ft lbs. If the cotter pin cannot be aligned, turn further until it can be inserted. Bleed the brakes and adjust the hand brakes. Note: when a new axle, frame, spring plate, or front transmission mounting is installed, the rear wheels must be realigned. A special optical alignment gauge is necessary for this purpose. An accurate setting is not possible otherwise.

Manual Transmission with Double-Jointed Axles

This procedure is similar to that for vehicles with swing axles; however, the rear wheels and brakes need not be removed or disconnected. The driveshafts should be unbolted at both ends and removed. If the vehicle is not to be moved, the driveshafts may be unbolted at the inner ends only and wired to the body. It is a good idea to cover the axle joints with plastic bags to keep out dirt.

Automatic Stickshift

All Automatic Stickshift models have double-jointed axles. After removing the engine:

1. Detach the gearshift rod coupling.
2. Remove or disconnect and support the driveshafts.
3. Disconnect the ATF hoses from the transmission. Seal the openings. Disconnect the temperature switch, neutral safety switch, and back-up light switch.
4. Pull off the vacuum servo hose.
5. Disconnect the starter cables. (Battery ground strap was disconnected during engine removal.)
6. Remove the front transaxle mounting nuts.
7. Loosen the rear transaxle mounting bolts. Support the unit and remove the bolts.
8. Remove the transaxle.

To replace the transaxle:

9. Raise the transaxle into place. Tighten the nuts for the front mounting. Insert the rear mounting bolts loosely.
10. Replace the vacuum servo hose.
11. Connect the ATF hoses, using new washers.
12. Connect the temperature switch and starter cables.
13. Install the driveshafts, using new lockwashers. Turn the convex sides of the washers toward the screw heads.
14. Align the transaxle and tighten the mounting bolts, being careful that the axle joints cannot rub on the frame fork.
15. Insert the shift rod coupling, tighten the screw, and secure it with wire.
16. After installing engine, bleed the ATF lines if return flow has not started after 2–3 minutes.

R & R, Gearshift Lever—Standard Transmission

The gearshift lever can be removed after the front floor mat has been lifted and the screws removed that attach the gearshift lever ball housing to the central frame tunnel. After the two retaining screws have been removed, the gearshift lever, ball housing, rubber boot, and spring are removed as a unit. The spring will have to be turned in order to clear the pin. Remove the stop plate and clean all components and check them for wear.

Installation of the gearshift lever is the reverse of the preceding. Replace any worn parts. Be sure that the locating pin is a firm fit, but not overly tight. The spring in the steel ball should be checked for tension and replaced if necessary. When installing the stop plate, be sure that the turned-up ramp is on the right-hand side. Lubricate all parts generously with universal grease. After installation is completed, operate the various gears in order to check ease of movement.

VW Automatic Stickshift

Since 1968, Volkswagen has offered an automatic clutch control three-speed transmission. This unit is called the Automatic Stickshift.

It consists of a three-speed gearbox connected to the engine through a hydrodynamic torque converter. Between the converter and gearbox is a vacuum-operated clutch, which automatically separates the power flow from the torque converter while in the process of changing gear ratios.

The converter functions as a conventional clutch for starting and stopping. The shift clutch serves only for engaging and changing the speed ranges. It is very lightly loaded in terms of friction.

There is an independent oil supply for the converter provided by an engine-driven pump and a reservoir. The converter oil pump, driven off

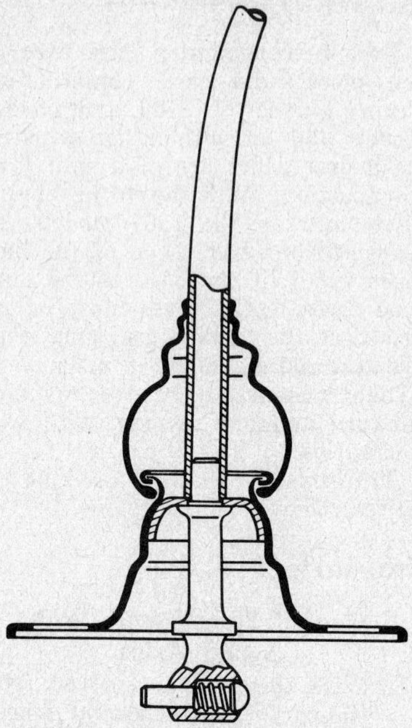

Details of gearshift lever.

the engine oil pump, draws fluid from the reservoir and drives it around a circuit leading through the converter and back to the reservoir.

This circuit also furnishes cooling for the converter fluid.

Operation

The control valve is activated by a very light touch to the top of the shift selector knob which, in turn, is connected to an electromagnet. It has two functions.

At the beginning of the selection process, it has to conduct the vacuum promptly from the intake manifold to the clutch servo, so that the shift clutch disengages at once, and thus interrupts the power flow between converter and transmission. At the end of the selection process, it must, according to driving conditions, automatically ensure shift clutch engagement at the proper speed. It may neither slip nor engage too harshly. The control valve can be adjusted for this purpose.

Clutch engagement takes place, quickly or slowly, according to engine loading. The clutch will engage suddenly, for example, at full throttle, and can transform the full drive movement into acceleration of the car. This can also be effected slowly and gently if the braking force of the engine is to be used on overrun. In the part-load range, too, the duration of clutch reengagement depends on the throttle opening, and thus the depression in the carburetor venturi. This results in smooth, pleasant driving under all conditions.

Vanes on the outside of the converter housing aid in cooling. In the case of abnormal prolonged loading, however (lugging a trailer over mountain roads in second or third speed), converter heat may exceed maximum permissible temperature. This condition will cause a red warning light to function in the speedometer.

There is also a starter locking switch. This, combined with a bridging switch, is operated by the inner transmission shift lever. It performs two functions:

1. With a speed range engaged, the electrical connection to the starter is interrupted. The en-

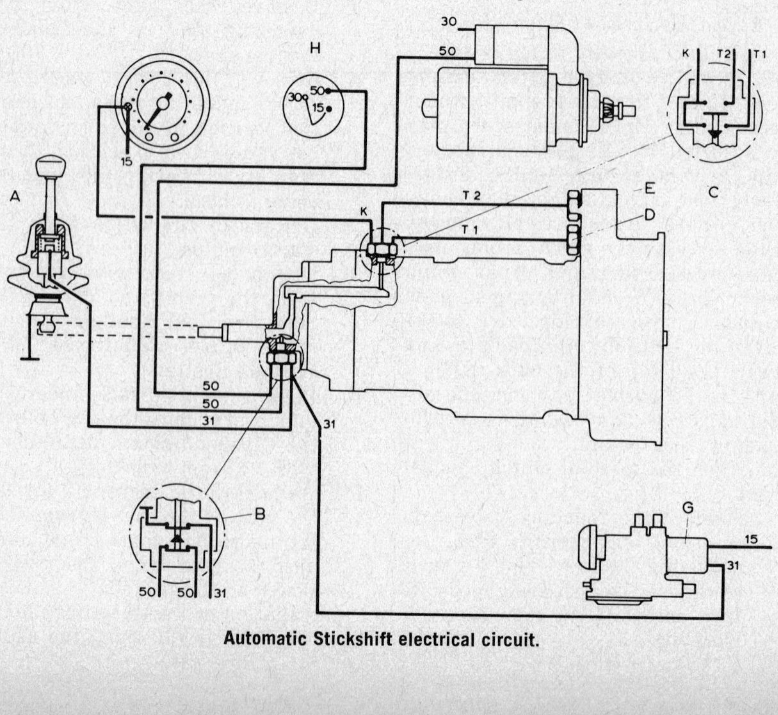

J
30
50
H
K
T2
T1
A
E
C
D
T 2
T 1
15
50
50
31
31
B
G
15
31
50
50
31

Automatic Stickshift electrical circuit.

gine, therefore, can only be started in neutral.

2. The contacts in the selector lever are not closed in the neutral position. Instead, the bridging switch transmits a voltage to the electromagnets of the control valve. This ensures that the separator clutch is also disengaged in the neutral shifter position.

Fully Automatic Transmission

The fully automatic transmission, consisting of an automatically shifted, three-speed planetary transmission and a torque converter, was introduced in 1969.

The torque converter is a conventional three-element design. The three elements are an impeller (driving member), a stator (reaction member), and the turbine (driven member). Maximum torque multiplication, with the vehicle starting from rest, is two and one-half to one. Maximum converter efficiency is about 96 percent.

The automatic transmission is a planetary unit with three forward speeds which engage automatically depending on engine loading and road speed. The converter, planetary unit, and control system are incorporated together with the final drive in a single housing. The final drive is located between the converter and the planetary gearbox.

1
2
3
4
5
6

1 Small sungear
2 Planet carrier
3 Large sungear
4 Large sungear
5 Small planet gear
6 Ring gear

Automatic transmission planetary gear unit.

The transmission control system includes a gear type oil pump, a centrifugal governor which regulates shift points, a throttle modulator valve which evaluates engine loading according to intake manifold pressure, and numerous other regulating components assembled in the transmission valve body.

Transmission ranges are Park, Reverse, Neutral, Drive (3), Second (2), and First (1).

Transmission R & R

NOTE: The engine and transmission must be removed as an assembly.

Removal

1. Remove the battery ground cable.
2. On the sedan, remove the cooling air intake duct with the heating fan and hoses. Remove the cooling air intake connection and bellows, then detach the hoses to the air cleaner.
3. On the station wagons, remove the warm air hoses and air cleaner. Remove the boot between the dipstick tube and the body and the boot between the oil filler neck and the body. Disconnect the cooling air bellows at the body.
4. Disconnect the wires at the regulator and the alternator wires at the snap-connector located by the regulator. Disconnect the auxiliary air regulator and the oil pressure switch at the snap-connectors located by the distributor.
5. Disconnect the fuel injection wiring. There are 12 connections and are listed as follows;
   a. Fuel injector cyl 2, 2 pole—protective gray cap
   b. Fuel injector cyl 1, 2 pole—protective black cap
   c. Starter, 1 pole—white
   d. Throttle valve switch, 4 pole
   e. Distributor, 3 pole
   f. Thermo switch, 1 pole—white
   g. Cold start valve, 3 pole
   h. Temperature sensor crankcase, 2 pole
   i. Ground connection, 3 pole—white wires
   j. Temperature sensor for the cyl head, 1 pole
   k. Fuel injector cyl 3, 2 pole—protective black cap
   l. Fuel injector cyl 4, 2 pole—protective gray cap
6. Disconnect the accelerator cable.
7. Disconnect the right fuel return line.
8. Raise the car.
9. Disconnect the warm air hoses from the heat exchangers.
10. Disconnect the starter wires and push the engine wiring harness through the engine cover plate.
11. Disconnect the fuel supply line and plug it.
12. Remove the heater booster exhaust pipe.
13. Remove the rear axles and cover the ends to protect them from dirt.
14. Remove the selector cable by unscrewing the cable sleeve.
15. Remove the wire from the kickdown switch.
16. Remove the bolts from the rubber transmission mountings, taking careful note of the position, number, and thickness of the spacers that are present. These spacers must be reinstalled exactly as they were removed. Do not detach the transmission carrier from the body.
17. Support the engine and transmission assembly in such a way that it may be lowered and moved rearward at the same time.
18. Remove the engine carrier bolts and the engine/transmission assembly from the car.
19. Match-mark the flywheel and the torque converter and remove the three attaching bolts.
20. Remove the engine-to-transmission bolts and separate the engine and transmission. Care must be taken when separating the engine and transmission as the torque converter will easily slip off the input shaft if the transmission is tilted downward.

Installation

1. Install and tighten the engine-to-transmission bolts.
2. Align the converter-to-flywheel match marks and install the bolts.
3. Make sure the rubber buffer is in place and the two securing studs do not project more than 0.7 in. from the transmission case.
4. Tie a cord to the slot in the engine compartment seal. This will make positioning the seal easier.
5. Lift the assembly far enough to allow the accelerator cable to be pushed through the front engine cover.
6. Continue lifting the assembly into place. Slide the rubber

1 Impeller with housing
2 Stator
3 Turbine
4 Housing cover
5 Drive plate

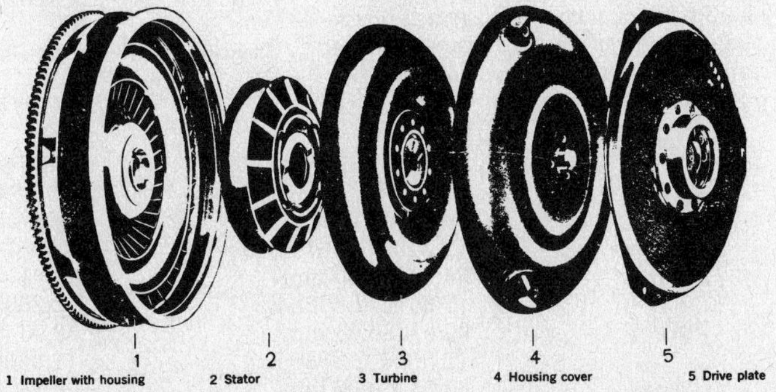
1
2
3
4
5
1 Impeller with housing
2 Stator
3 Turbine
4 Housing cover
5 Drive plate

Automatic transmission torque converter.

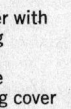

buffer into the locating tube in the rear axle carrier.

7. Insert the engine carrier bolts and raise the engine until the bolts are at the top of their elongated slots. Tighten the bolts.

NOTE: A set of three gauges must be obtained to check the alignment of the rubber buffer in its locating tube. The dimensions are given in the illustration as is the measuring technique. The rubber buffer is centered horizontally when the 11 mm gauge can be inserted on both sides. The buffer is located vertically when the 10 mm gauge can be inserted on the bottom side and the 12 mm gauge can be inserted on the top side.

8. Install the rubber transmission mount bolts with spacers of the correct thickness. The purpose of the spacers is to center the rubber buffer vertically in its support tube. The buffer is not supposed to carry any weight, it absorbs torsional forces only.
9. To locate the buffer horizontally in its locating tube, the engine carrier must be vertical and parallel to the fan housing. It is adjusted by moving the engine carrier bolts in elongated slots. Further travel may be obtained by moving the brackets attached to the body. It may be necessary to adjust the two rear suspension wishbones with the center of the transmission after the rubber buffer is horizontally centered.
10. Adjust the selector lever cable.
11. Connect the wire to the kickdown switch.
12. Install the rear axles. Make sure the lockwashers are placed with the convex side out.
13. Reconnect the fuel hoses and heat exchanger hoses. Install the pipe for the heater booster.
14. Lower the car and pull the engine compartment seal into place with the cord.
15. Reconnect the fuel injection and engine wiring. Push the starter wires through the engine cover plate and connect the wires to the starter.
16. Install the intake duct with the fan and hoses, also the cooling air intake.

Selector Cable Adjustment

1. Place the gearshift lever in Park.

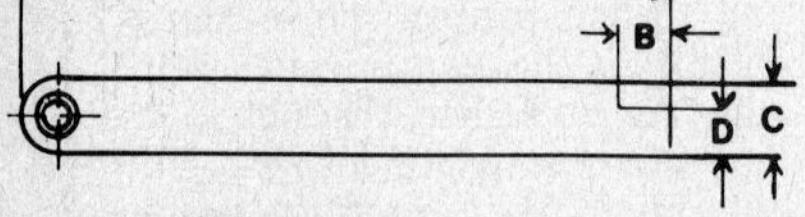
A
B
C
D

A = 150 mm (5.905 in.)
B = 12 mm (.472 in.)
C = 15 mm (.590 in.)
D = 10, 11, 12 mm (.393, .433, .472 in.)
4 mm (.157 in.) thick strip

Alignment gauges.

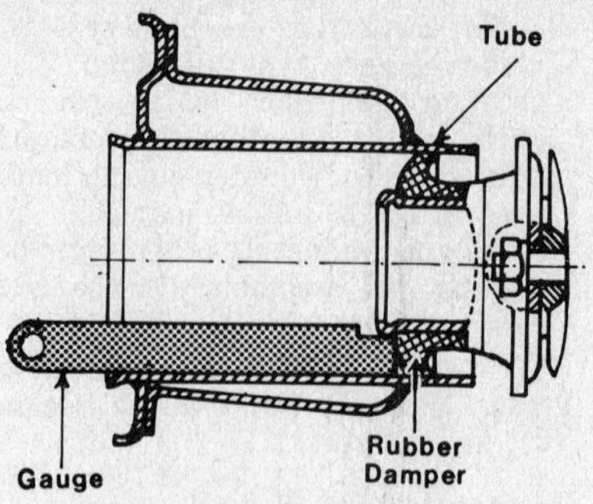
Tube
Gauge
Rubber
Damper

Rubber buffer in locating tube

2. Press the lever on the transmission as far rearward as possible so that the manual valve is against its stop in the valve body.
3. With the transmission lever in this position, tighten the clamp.
4. Check the shift pattern. The brakes must be firmly applied when the pattern is checked.

DRIVE AXLES

Swing Axles

Rear Axle Tube and Shaft R & R

The rear axle tube and shaft can be removed while the transmission is still in the car.

1. Remove the brake drums, bearing cover, back plate, and rear wheel bearing.
2. Remove the nuts of the axle tube retainer and remove the axle tube and retainer.
3. Take off the gasket and plastic packing.
4. Remove the differential side gear lockring, the differential side gear thrust washer, and the axle shaft.
5. After removing the differential side gear and fulcrum plates from the differential housing, knock the dowel pin from the bearing ange.
6. Remove the rear axle dust sleeve.
7. Press the axle tube out of its bearing flange.

Installation is mainly the reverse of the preceding. The rear axle boot should be checked for wear and replaced if necessary. The tube retainer and its seat should be cleaned thoroughly. The clearance between the flat end of the rear axle shaft and the inner diameter of the side gear should be .03–.1 mm (.0012–.004 in.). The axles and gears are coded according to color, and fall into four tolerance groups: yellow, blue, pink, and green. Only parts in the same size group should be mated.

The maximum allowable run-out for the rear axle is .05 mm (.002 in.) This measurement is taken at the seat of the ball bearing. Axles that are slightly bent can be straightened cold. A feeler gauge is used to measure the side clearance between the flat ends of the axle and the fulcrum plates. This clearance should be .035–.244 mm (.0014–.0096 in.). Excessive clearance can be taken care of by installing oversize fulcrum plates which have a groove on the face.

Install the differential side gear, axle, and thrust washer in the differential housing and insert a lockring. Install the retainer gasket and the axle tube with retainer. There should be no end-play between the axle tube and the axle tube retainer. This is accomplished by choosing a gasket of suitable thickness. The axle tube retainer nuts should be tightened to a torque of 14 ft lbs. Over- or undertightening should be avoided, for this will lead either to rapid wear or to leaks. Axle boots should not be tightened before the car is on the ground, axle intact. Otherwise, the boots may become twisted and damaged.

Rear Axle Boot R & R

The original rear axle boots (dust sleeves) are of a one-piece design and must be cut open in order to be removed for replacement. A split type axle boot is available for replacement

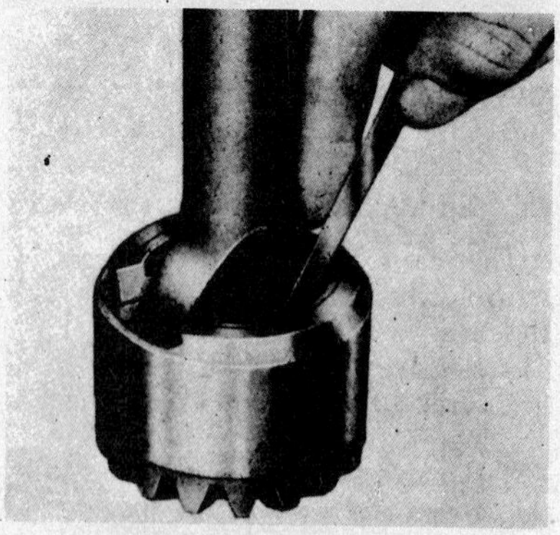

Checking clearance between rear axle shaft and fulcrum plates and between fulcrum plates and differential side gear.

Paint Mark	*Inner Diameter Side Gear*	*Outer Diameter Axle Shaft*
Yellow	59.93–59.97 mm (2.3200–2.3610 in.)	59.87–59.90 mm (2.357–2.3582 in.)
Blue	59.98–60.00 mm (2.3610–2.3622 in.)	59.91–59.94 mm (2.3583–2.3598 in.)
Pink	60.01–60.04 mm (2.3626–2.3638 in.)	59.95–59.97 mm (2.3602–2.3610 in.)
Green	60.05–60.07 mm (2.3642–2.3650 in.)	59.98–60.00 mm (2.3614–2.3622 in.)

which can be installed and then tightened down. To remove the axle boot, take off the retaining clip at each end, and cut off the damaged boot. Clean both the axle tube and the axle tube retainer thoroughly so that the new boot will fit securely.

Upon installation, put a light coating of sealing compound on the join-

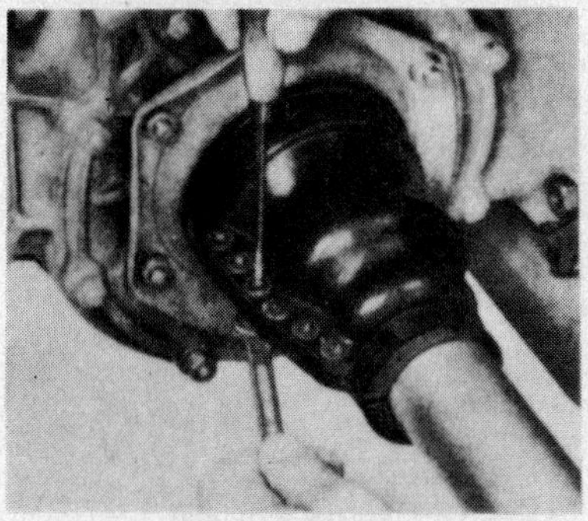

Installation of boot for rear swing axle. The seam must be horizontal, as shown.

ing faces of the boot and ensure that the smaller diameter of the boot is equal to 89 mm. When positioning the new boot, keep the joining faces in a horizontal plane and on the rear of the axle. Tighten the joining screws and the retaining clips (do not overtighten) only after the rear axle is in a loaded condition, and be sure that the boot is not twisted.

Constant Velocity U-Joints and Axle R & R

1. Remove the bolts securing the joints at each end of the shaft, tilt the shaft down, and remove the shaft.
2. Loosen the clamps securing the rubber boot to the axle and slide the boot back on the axle.
3. Drive the stamped steel cover off the joint with a drift.

NOTE: After the cover is removed, do not tilt the ball hub as the balls will fall out of the hub.

4. Remove the circlip from the end of the axle and press the axle out of the joint.
5. Reverse the above steps to install. The position of the dished washer is dependent on the type of transmission. On automatic transmissions it is placed between the ball hub and the circlip. On manual transmission it is placed between the ball hub and the shoulder on the shaft. Be sure to pack the joint with grease.

Disassembly of Constant Velocity U-Joint

1. Remove the ball hub and ball bearing cage from the outer hub.
2. Remove the balls from the cage.
3. Align two grooves in the ball hub and remove the bearing cage from the ball hub.
4. Assembly is the reverse of the disassembly procedure. The chamfer on the splined inside diameter of the ball hub faces the shoulder on the driveshaft.

Suspension

Trailing Arm Front Suspension

The trailing arm type front suspension of the Volkswagen has taken two basically different forms over the years. Models prior to 1966 used link (king) pins to connect the front wheel spindles to the suspension trailing arms. All Volkswagens since the 1966 model year employ ball joints in the front end along with the transverse torsion bars which had always been used.

Strut Front Suspension

The Type 4 and the Type 1 Super Beetle use a strut front suspension. Each wheel is suspended independently on a shock absorber strut surrounded by a coil spring. The strut is located at the bottom by a track control arm and a ball joint, and at the top by a ball bearing which is rubber-mounted to the body.

Greasing Front Wheel Bearings

Beginning with the 1966 models, tapered roller bearings were used in the front wheels of all model Volkswagens. Previously, all models were equipped with ball bearings in the front wheels. The front wheel bearings should be cleaned and repacked with grease at intervals of 30,000 miles. In servicing the front wheel bearings, the following procedures should be followed:

Ball Bearing Equipped Models

NOTE: It is always a good idea to use new plastic seals and locking plates. When working on the left front wheel, take note that this wheel drives the speedometer cable. After

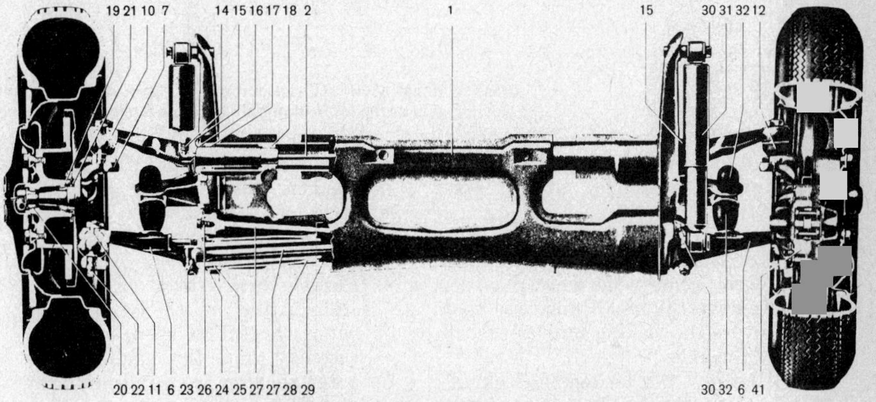
19 21 10 7
14 15 16 17 18 2
1
15
30 31 32 12
20 22 11 6 23 26 24 25 27 27 28 29
30 32 6 41

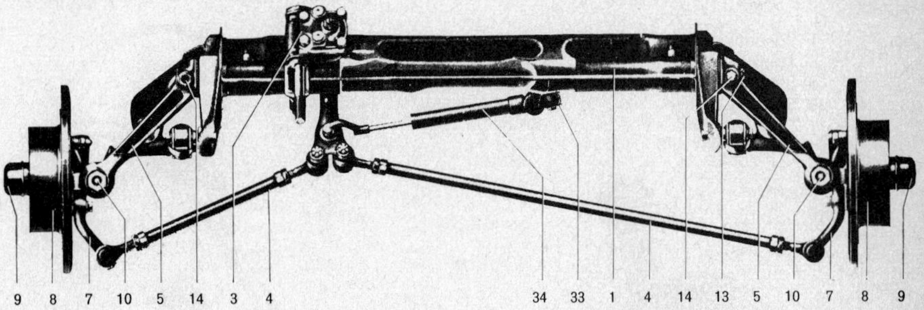
9 8 7 10 5 14 3 4
34 33 1 4 14 13 5 10 7 8 9

1 Front axle beam
2 Stabilizer
3 Steering gear
4 Tie rods
5 Torsion arm, upper
6 Torsion arm, lower
7 Steering arm
8 Brake disc
9 Grease cap
10 Upper ball joint
11 Lower ball joint
12 Dust seal
13 Adjust screw for upper torsion arm axial play
14 Grub screw
15 Seal, upper
16 Thrust ring
17 Needle bearing, upper
18 Plastic sleeve with metal bush
19 Front wheel bearing, inner
20 Front wheel bearing, outer
21 Seal

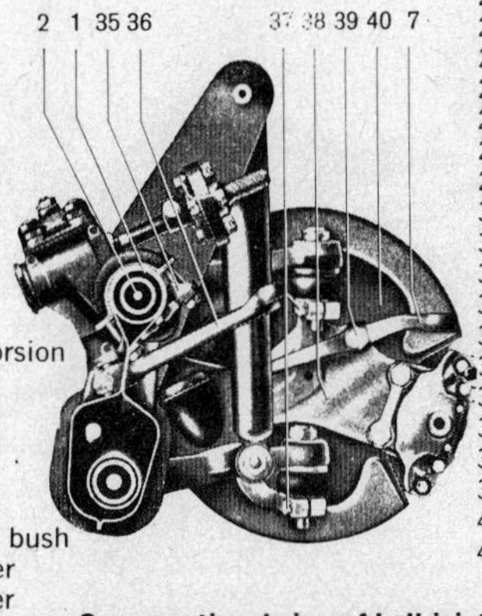
2 1 35 36
37 38 39 40 7

22 Eccentric for camber adjustment
23 Grub screw
24 Seal, lower
25 Needle bearing, lower
26 Retaining bolt
27 Torsion bars
28 Plastic sleeve with metal bush, lower
29 Reinforcement plate
30 Shock absorber mounting bolt
31 Shock absorber
32 Rubber stop
33 Steering damper mounting bolt
34 Steering damper
35 Steering gear mounting clamp
36 Steering drop arm
37 Clamping screw
38 Steering knuckle
39 Steering arm mounting bolt
40 Brake back plate
41 Caliper

Cross-sectional view of ball joint front suspension currently in use.

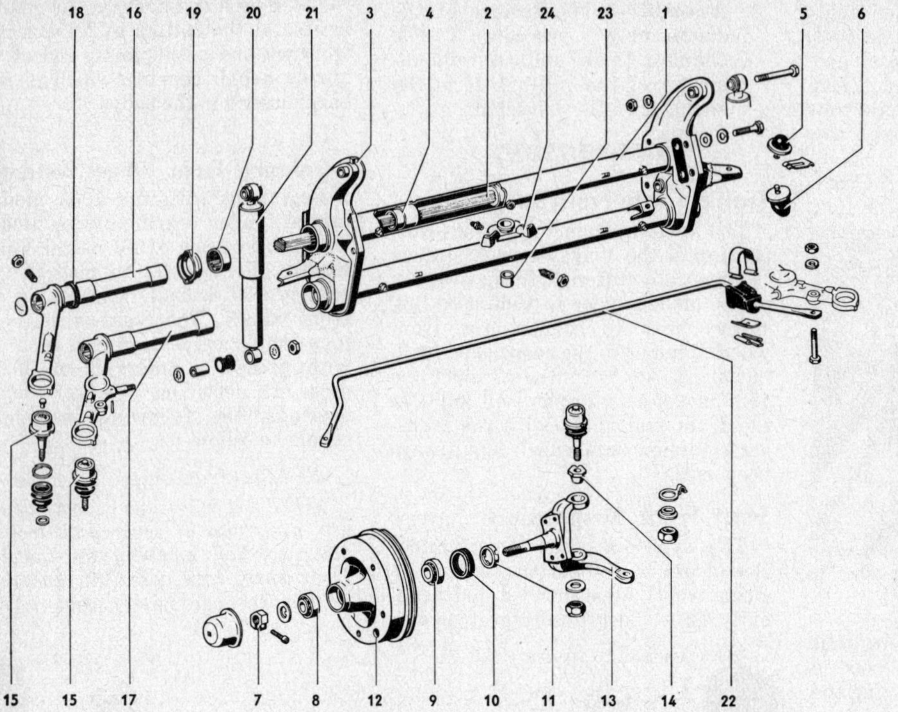
18
16
19
20
21
3
4
2
24
23
1
5
6
15
15
17
7
8
12
9
10
11
13
14
22

1 Front axle beam
2 Torsion bar
3 Side plate
4 Torsion arm bush
5 Upper rubber buffer
6 Lower rubber buffer
7 Clamp nut for wheel bearing adjustment
8 Outer front wheel bearing
9 Inner front wheel bearing
10 Front wheel bearing seal
11 Spacer ring
12 Brake drum
13 Steering knuckle
14 Eccentric bush for camber adjustment
15 Ball joint
16 Upper torsion arm
17 Lower torsion arm
18 Seal for torsion arm
19 Seal retainer
20 Torsion arm needle bearing
21 Shock absorber
22 Stabilizer
23 Swing lever shaft bush
24 Swing lever stop

Cross-sectional view of transporter ball joint front suspension. Note steering gear swing lever in middle of lower torsion bar housing.

removing the cotter pin and the driving end of the cable, proceed normally.

1. Jack up the side of the car; remove the hub cap from the wheel; remove the wheel.
2. Remove the small dust cap that covers the locking nuts at the tip of the axle.
3. Unscrew the hexagonal locknut, remove the locking plate, inner hexagonal nut, and the thrust washer. Nuts on the left axle have left-hand threads; those on the right have right-hand threads.
4. Pull the brake drum off the axle stub, while at the same time being careful to keep the inner raceway and the cage of the outer bearing from falling in the dirt. If brake drum resists being removed, it may be necessary to back off the brake adjustment slightly and also bolt the wheel back onto the brake drum so as to have more leverage in pulling on the drum.
5. Remove the plastic grease seal from the hub and take out the cage of the inner bearing.
6. Leaving the inner raceway in place on the axle, and the outer raceway in place in the hub, clean all components in solvent and clean the inside of the brake drum, being careful to keep any grease or oil from touching the interior surface of the drum. Caution should also be exercised in order that the brake shoes themselves will remain free of grease.
7. Repack the inner bearing cage with grease and place it within the hub. Now the plastic seal can be reinstalled by tapping it in lightly until it achieves a flush position. A flat piece of wood placed atop the seal may prove helpful in this operation.
8. The inner raceway on the axle should now be greased and the wheel replaced. After repacking the outer bearing cage, this part can now be inserted in the hub. Bearing installation is completed with the installation of the inner race, thrust washer, and hexagonal nut.
9. Tighten the hexagonal nut until the thrust washer can just be moved sideways with a screwdriver. Replace the locking plate

1 Suspension strut
2 Track control arm
3 Stabilizer
4 Steering gear
5 Tie rods
6 Idler arm and bracket
7 Safety steering column
8 Frame head

1
7
6
4
5
5
3
2

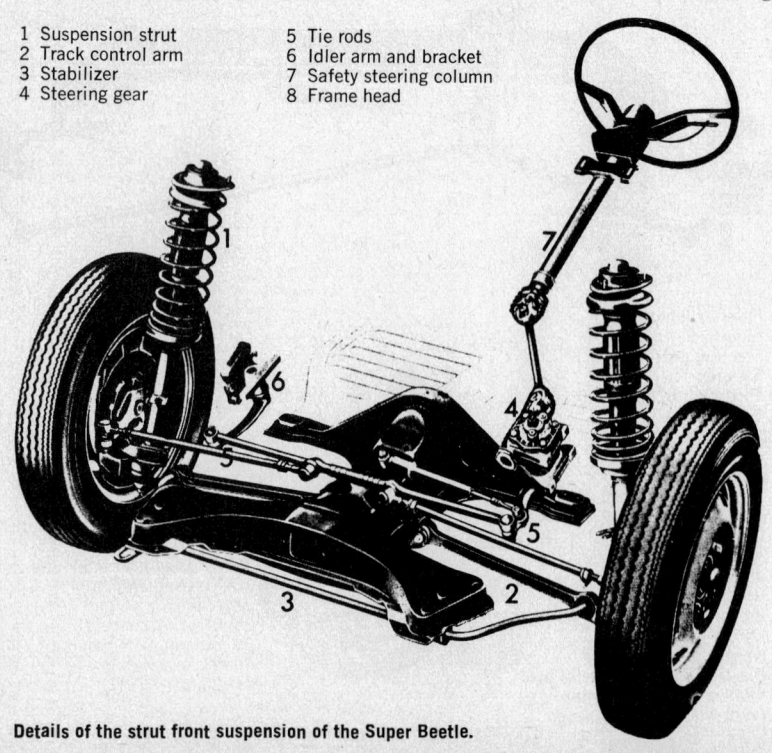

Details of the strut front suspension of the Super Beetle.

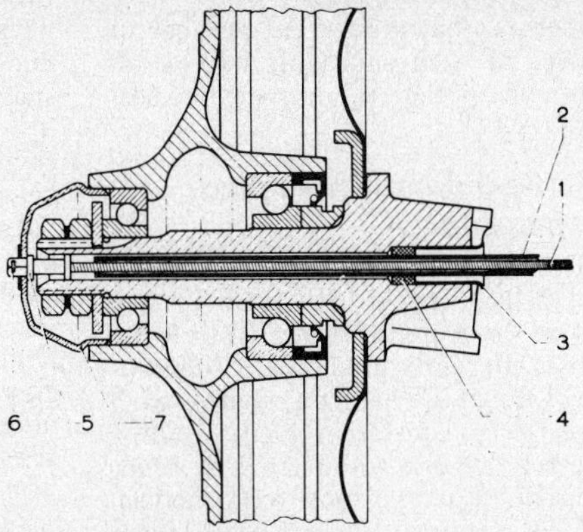
1
2
3
4
5
6
7

1 Cable
2 Plastic sheath
3 Metal sleeve
4 Rubber sleeve
5 Square drive end
6 Cotter pin
7 Hub cap with square hole

Cross-sectional view of left front wheel bearing. The right side is the same, but does not have the speedometer drive assembly.

(renew if unusable) and the locknut. The locking plate tabs should be bent over, and the hexagonal nut tightened down.

Roller Bearing Equipped Models

Roller bearing equipped models include the Type 3 and the Type 1 Karmann Ghia and Beetle models of 1966 and later.

On Beetle models, equipped with drum brakes, the procedure is much the same as that listed for ball bearing equipped models except that the final adjustment will be more exacting. Adjustment requires that the following procedure be followed:

1. Loosen the clamp nut screw.
2. Tighten the clamp nut to a torque of 11 ft lbs, while at the same time turning the wheel.
3. Loosen the clamp nut until the axial play of the wheel is .03–.12 mm (.001–.005 in.).
4. Tighten the clamp nut screw to 7 ft lbs and recheck axial play.
5. Install the hub cap.

The following directions apply to Type 3 and 1971 and later Type 2 models, and the 1500 and 1600 Karmann Ghia, supplied with disc brakes:

1. After removing the front wheel and disc cap, bend up the lockplates on the caliper securing screws and remove both the screws and the caliper assembly.
2. Secure the caliper to the brake hose bracket by means of a piece of wire or rope. The caliper should not be allowed to hang by the brake hose.
3. Loosen the socket head screw of the clamp nut. Unscrew the clamp nut.
4. Remove the wheel bearing thrust washer.
5. Remove the disc.
6. The parts removed should be cleaned thoroughly in a cleaning solvent solution.
7. Lubricate the bearings with a lithium grease of the proper type, pressing grease into the cages and fill the grease cavity of the disc. Grease should not be put into the disc cap.

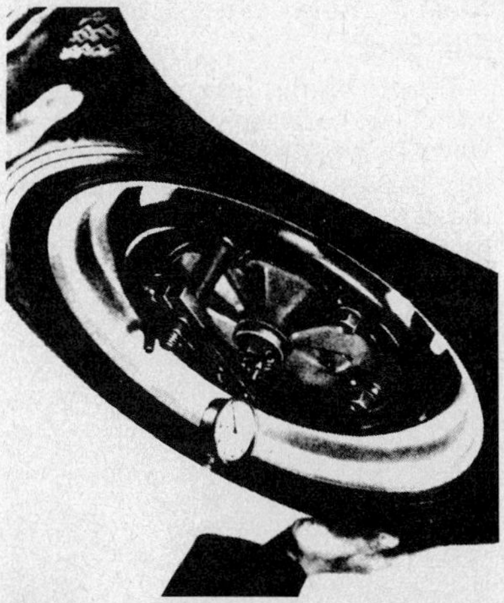

Checking axial (side) play of front wheel bearings with a dial indicator.

Loosening wheel nut pinch bolt at left front wheel. The pinch bolt should be torqued to 7 ft lbs on reinstallation.

8. Press in the outer race of the inner bearing.
9. Fit the inner race and cage, and insert the grease seal. When fitting the grease seal, drive it in by tapping lightly with a rubber hammer; avoid tilting the seal.
10. Press in the outer race of the outer bearing.
11. Install the thrust washer and make sure that it is not tilted.
12. Adjust the bearings so that axial play is .03–.12 mm (.001–.005 in.). The adjustment process is as described in the preceding section on adjusting front wheel bearings on Beetle models equipped with roller bearings.

Torsion Bar R & R

1. Remove wheels and both steering knuckles, complete with brake drums and backing plates. Attach the assemblies to the axle with wire.
2. Remove the shock absorber. Remove the torsion arms on one side.
3. On Type 2 disconnect the front gearshift rod at coupling.
4. Loosen the setscrew locknuts and remove the screws.
5. Remove the torsion bars.

To install:

1. Coat the torsion bars with lithium grease.
2. Tape the end of the torsion bar leaves. Insert the torsion bars, noting the positions of the countersinks for the set screws.
3. Install the remaining parts and lubricate the torsion arm bearings with general purpose grease.

Link Pin R & R

1. Raise the front end.
2. Remove the front wheels, drums, and backing plates. Disconnect the speedometer cable and the outer tie rod.
3. Remove the torsion arm pinch bolts.
4. Remove the torsion arm link and stub axle by driving out both link pins.
5. Examine all parts carefully and replace them as necessary.

To install:

1. Measure the offset of the torsion arm eye faces. By using .5 mm shims, set the offset to 7 mm.

NOTE: There must always be eight shims and one retainer with a dust excluder fitted to one torsion arm link pin.

2. Install the link pins and shims with universal grease.
3. Replace the remaining parts.
4. Adjust the torsion arm pins, front wheel bearings, and front end alignment, then bleed and adjust the brakes.

Ball Joint R & R

1. Remove the wheel and brake drum. Disconnect the stabilizer bar and speedometer cables.
2. Remove the torsion arms.
3. Press out the ball joints. Check ball joint free-play (.3–2 mm is allowable) and dust seals.

To install:

1. Ball joints and torsion arms are available in standard and oversizes. Press a new joint into the torsion arm, making sure that the notches on the ball joint

align with the projection on the torsion arm.
2. Check the camber and toe-in after reassembly.

Stabilizer Bar R & R

1. Remove the clamp retaining clip.
2. Bend up the clamps and remove the plates.
3. Remove the nut from the securing bolt on lower torsion arm.
4. Remove the stabilizer bar, check for damaged parts, and replace as necessary.
5. Reverse the procedure to install. Torque the securing nut on the lower torsion arm to the figure specified in the "Torque Specifications" chart.

Swing Axle Rear Suspension

The rear wheels of the Volkswagen are independently sprung by means of torsion bars. The inside ends of the torsion bars are anchored to a body crossmember via a splined tube which is welded to the frame. The torsion bar at each side of the rear suspension has a different number of splines at each end. This makes adjustment of the rear suspension possible.

Double-Jointed Axle Rear Suspension

This rear suspension system was first introduced on the 1968 Type 2 and on the Automatic Stickshift Type 1. It is currently used on all Volkswagen vehicles. The axle shafts each have two, constant-velocity joints. The rear wheels are located by trailing arms as on swing axle models, and by diagonal control arms from the rear crossmember.

R & R, Rear Wheel Bearing, Oil Seal

Details of the rear wheel bearing and oil seal are shown in an exploded view. To remove the oil seal and bearing, remove the rear axle nut, raise the car and take off the brake drum. Remove the retaining screws from the cover and take off the cover along with the oil seal. Remove the brake line, and take off the back plate, outer spacer, the gasket between the bearing and the spacer, the washer, and cover gasket. Remove the rear wheel bearing and inner spacer.

Installation is the reverse of the preceding but, in addition, certain other steps should be taken. The bearing should be examined and replaced if necessary. Replace the two sealing rings. If the oil seal is damaged or uneven, it should also be replaced. When installing a new oil seal, coat it with oil and press it into the bearing cover. The outer spacer should be examined for wear, replaced if scored or cracked, and lightly coated with oil when installed. Clean the oil hole in the cover and replace the cover. The splines in the brake drum hub should be inspected and the brake drum replaced if the splines show signs of excessive wear. Tighten the rear axle shaft nut to 217 ft lbs, using a new cotter pin and turning the nut slightly tighter if necessary to line up the holes for the cotter pin.

Check the level of lubricant in the transmission and top up if necessary. The oil should be at a level even with the lower edge of the filler hole. Bleed and adjust the brakes.

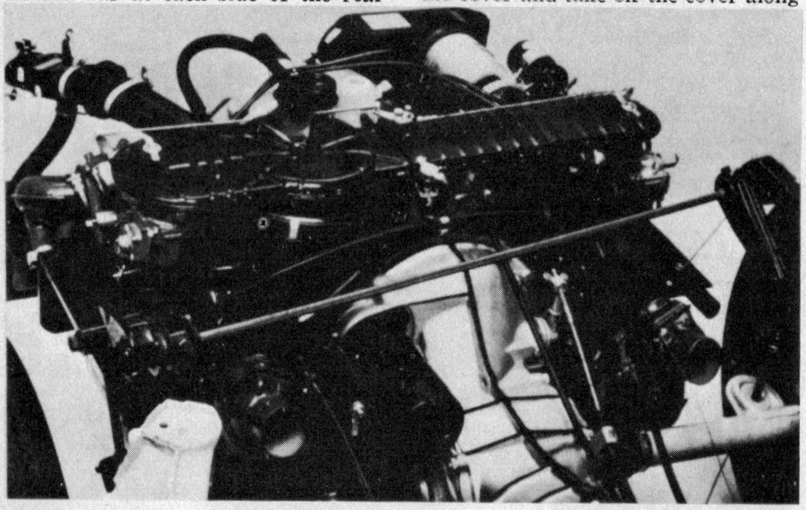

Swing axle rear suspension. This is a type 3 vehicle with a transverse reinforcing torsion bar.

Double-jointed axle rear suspension. The model shown is a Type 2.

STEERING

General

Type 1 and 3 steering is of the roller type. The Type 2 uses worm and peg steering. All models since

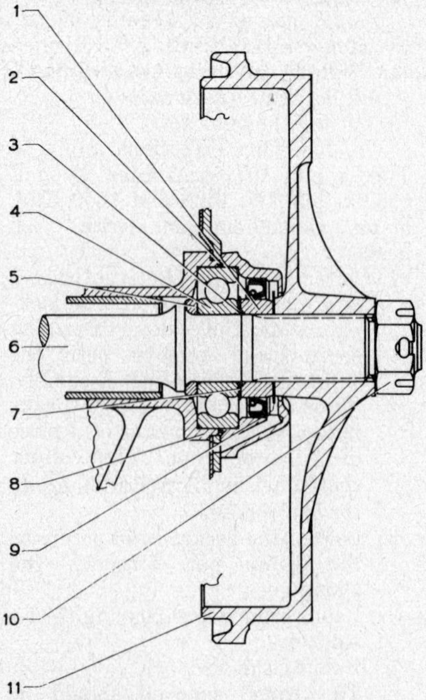
1
2
3
4
5
6
7
8
9
10
11

1 Outer spacer
2 Sealing ring
3 Sealing ring
4 Ball bearing
5 Inner spacer
6 Axle shaft
7 Washer
8 Bearing housing
9 Oil seal
10 Nut
11 Brake drum

Cross-sectional view of rear wheel bearing.

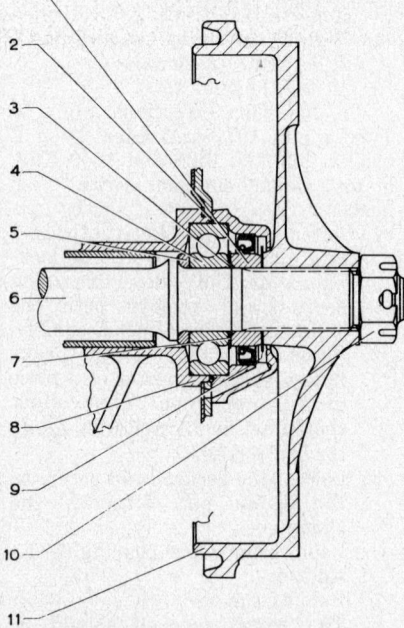

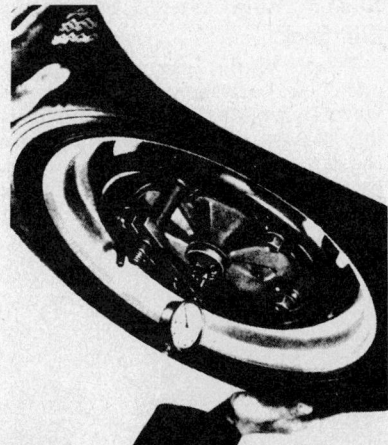

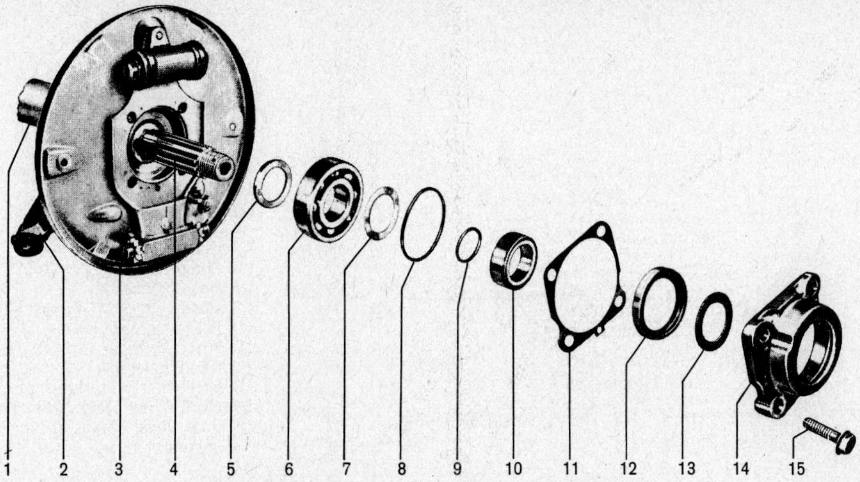
1 2 3 4 5 6 7 8 9 10 11 12 13 14 15
1 Rear axle tube
2 Shock absorber bracket
3 Brake back plate
4 Axle shaft
5 Inner spacer
6 Ball bearing
7 Washer
8 Sealing ring
9 Sealing ring
10 Outer spacer
11 Paper gasket
12 Oil seal
13 Oil deflector
14 Cover
15 Cover retaining screw

Exploded view of rear wheel bearing assembly.

The correct torque for the rear wheel nut is 217 ft. lbs.

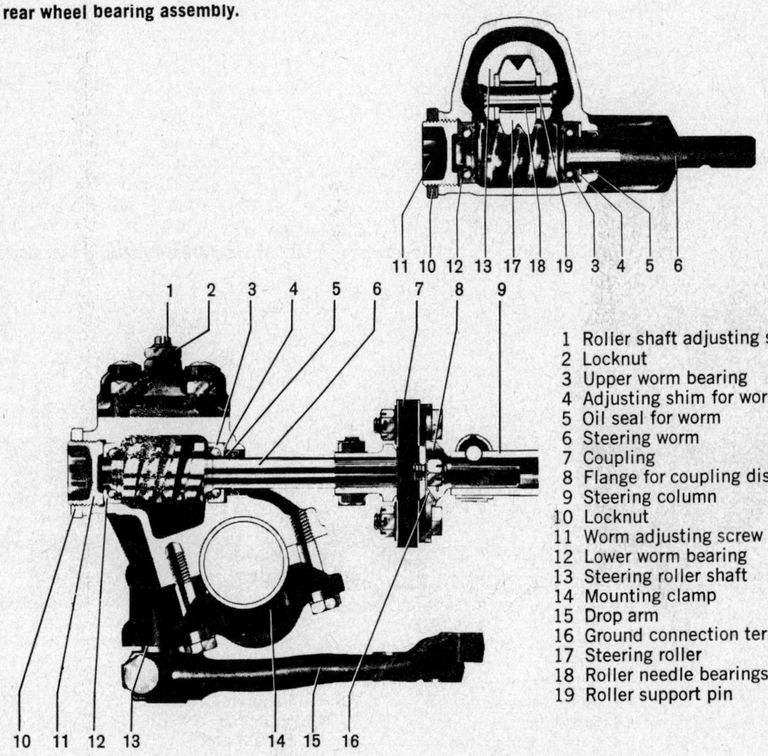
11 10 12 13 17 18 19 3 4 5 6
1 2 3 4 5 6 7 8 9
10 11 12 13 14 15 16
1 Roller shaft adjusting screw
2 Locknut
3 Upper worm bearing
4 Adjusting shim for worm
5 Oil seal for worm
6 Steering worm
7 Coupling
8 Flange for coupling disc
9 Steering column
10 Locknut
11 Worm adjusting screw
12 Lower worm bearing
13 Steering roller shaft
14 Mounting clamp
15 Drop arm
16 Ground connection terminal
17 Steering roller
18 Roller needle bearings
19 Roller support pin

Cross-sectional view of roller type steering gear.

1968 have collapsible or break-away steering column arrangements for crash protection.

The worm in the steering case is adjustable, and is engaged by a roller shaft with a needle-bearing-mounted roller. The roller shaft is held by bronze bushings in the housing and housing cover, while the worm spindle is mounted in ball bearings. The spindle and the roller shaft are both adjustable, the former by a washer fitted under the upper bearing, and the latter by a screw in the housing cover.

Steering and Front-End Geometry

The critical geometrical angles in the front end of the Volkswagen vary significantly from model to model and even change somewhat from early models to later models. Refer to the "Chassis and Wheel Alignment Chart" for the correct figures for each model.

BRAKES

The Hydraulic Brake System

Since 1950, all Volkswagens imported to the U.S. have been equipped with hydraulic brakes. The brakes of the Squareback and Fastback sedans are of the disc/drum type, with discs on the front and conventional drums at the rear. The 1500 Karmann Ghia is also provided with discs at the front, while the Beetle models are, at this writing, still equipped with drums front and rear. The Type 2 models were equipped with front discs starting in 1971.

The VW handbrake is mechanically actuated and operates on the rear wheels via a cable running to the rear.

Master Cylinder

Steps applying to the early single-cylinder type are not covered here; only steps that apply to the dual type are used.

Fluid Reservoir

A dual-section reservoir is used so that loss of fluid in one portion will not cause failure of the entire system.

Push Rod

To obtain proper master cylinder action, the push rod must be set to obtain pedal free movement of 0.02–0.28 in.

If a new rod is to be used, it must be an exact predetermined length. That is, from end of ball to center of pin hole—5.433 ± .019 in. Push rod length is set at the factory.

Master Cylinder Repair

1. Remove the boot.
2. Remove the stop screw.
3. Remove the spring stop-ring.
4. Remove the internal parts.
5. Remove the residual pressure valves and light switches.

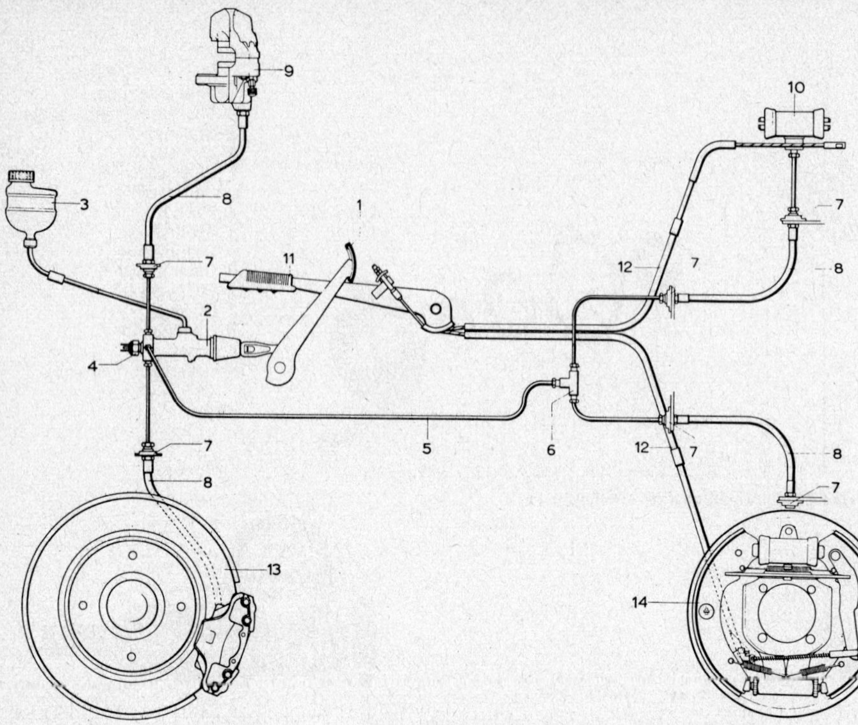
1
2
3
4
5
6
7
8
9
10
11
12
13
14

1 Brake pedal
2 Master cylinder
3 Fluid reservoir
4 Stop light switch
5 Brake line
6 Connector
7 Hose bracket
8 Hose
9 Brake caliper
10 Wheel cylinder
11 Hand brake lever
12 Cable and guide tube
13 Front wheel brakes (disc brakes)
14 Rear wheel brakes (drum brakes)

Typical single circuit disc/drum hydraulic brake system.

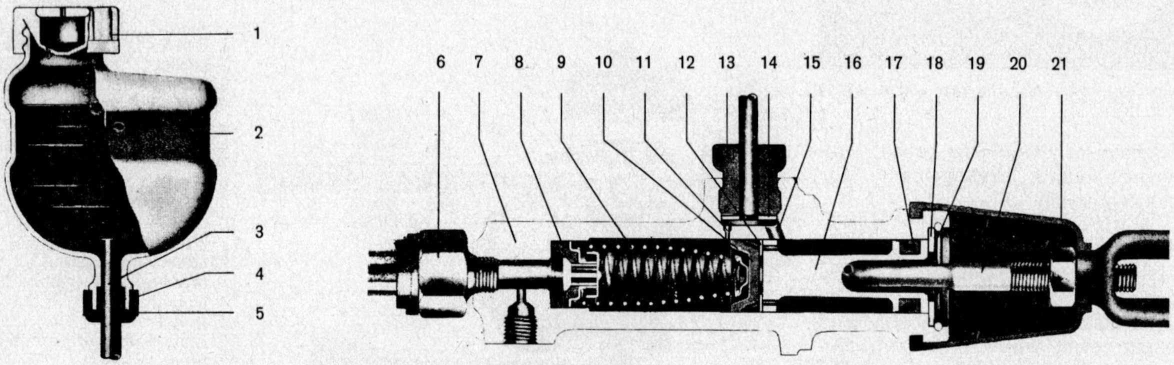
1
2
3
4
5
6 7 8 9 10 11 12 13 14 15 16 17 18 19 20 21

1 Screw cap
2 Fluid reservoir
3 Brake line
4 Line attaching nut
5 Seal for brake line
6 Stop light switch
7 Master cylinder body
8 Special check valve
9 Piston return spring
10 Main cup
11 Bypass port
12 Piston washer
13 Rubber plug
14 Washer for rubber plug
15 Intake port
16 Piston
17 Secondary cup
18 Piston stop-plate
19 Lockring
20 Piston push rod
21 Rubber boot

Cross-sectional view, single-circuit master cylinder and reservoir.

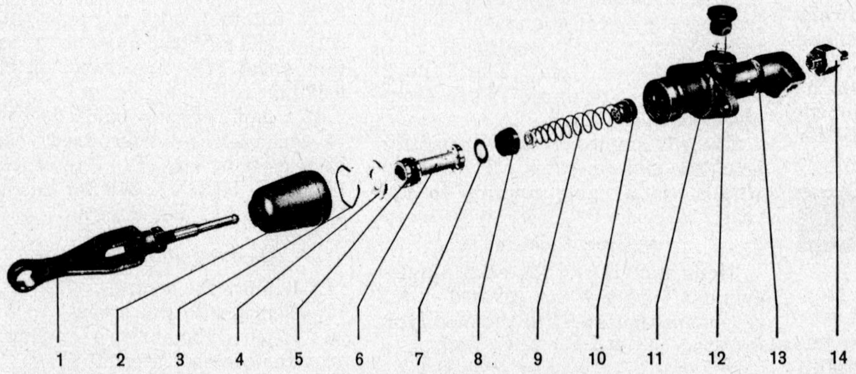
1 2 3 4 5 6 7 8 9 10 11 12 13 14

1 Push rod
2 Rubber boot
3 Lockring
4 Stop washer
5 Secondary cup
6 Piston
7 Piston washer
8 Main cup
9 Return spring
10 Special check valve
11 Washer for sealing plug
12 Sealing plug
13 Cylinder housing
14 Stop light switch

Exploded view, single-circuit master cylinder.

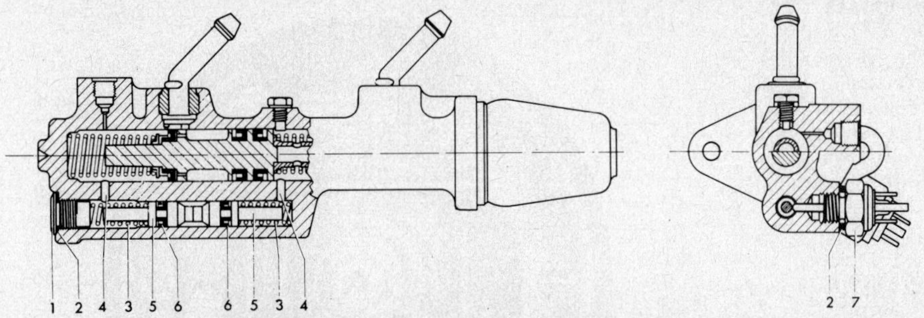
1 Plug
2 Washer
3 Spring
4 Drilling
5 Pistons for warning device
6 Cups for pistons
7 Switch
1 2 4 3 5 6 6 5 3 4
2 7

Cross-sectional view of dual-circuit brake master cylinder. Each half of the system serves two brakes. A warning light tells when either half has failed.

6. Replace in the reverse sequence of removal. All parts must be cleaned in methylated spirits or brake fluid. No burrs or corrosive conditions should be overlooked.
7. The residual pressure valves and the brake light switches should be installed and tightened to 11–14 ft lbs.
8. Install the protective cap with the breather hole downward.

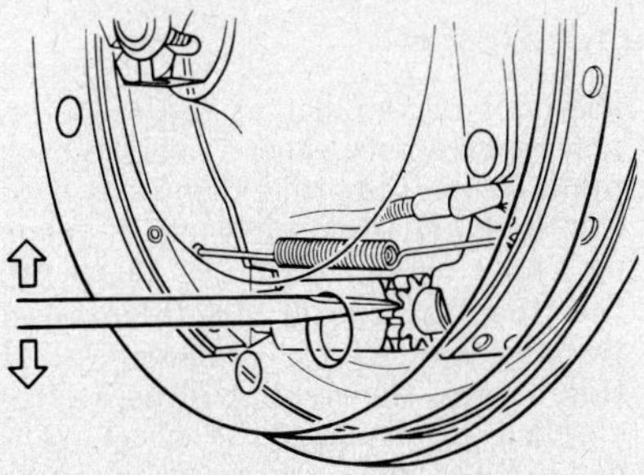

Drum brake adjustment. Later models have two adjusting holes in the backing plate.

Drum Brakes—Adjustment

The only equipment needed to adjust the drum brakes of the Volkswagen is a screwdriver. Pre-1966 Volkswagens have an adjuster hole in the outside of the brake drum for the purpose of adjustment. Models of 1966 and later have adjustment holes in the back plate.

Before adjusting the brakes, press the pedal down several times to centralize the shoes in the drums. Turn the wheel so that an adjusting nut is visible through the adjustment hole. Using the screwdriver, turn the adjustment nut until a slight drag is felt when the wheel is rotated by hand. At this point, back off the adjusting nut until the wheel turns freely. (About three or four teeth of the adjusting nut will pass the adjustment hole.) Move on to the other adjusting nut of the wheel. The adjustment nuts on each wheel turn in opposite directions, so whichever direction of rotation was needed to tighten one shoe will loosen the adjustment of the other shoe. The handbrake is adjusted by means of adjusting nuts at the rear of the control lever inside the car. However, when the rear brakes are adjusted, the handbrake is automatically adjusted also. If this is not enough to hold the rear wheels at four notches, the handbrake should be adjusted by means of the adjusting nuts. When the brake lever is applied by two notches, both rear wheels should resist turning by an equal amount of force. If for some reason, it was necessary to use the handbrake to stop in an emergency, it could be dangerous if both rear wheels did not lock equally.

Parking Brake Adjustment

Unless adjustments are of major proportions, or parts replacement needed, the parking brake may be adjusted inside the vehicle.

1. Raise both rear wheels.
2. Slide off the rubber ring, then fold back the parking brake lever rubber boot until the cable adjusting nuts are accessible.
3. Back off the locknuts, then tighten the adjusting nuts to a point where the rear wheels will still turn freely when the handbrake is off.
4. Pull the handlever up two notches, then check to make sure that both rear wheels have the same value of brake hold. Application to the fourth notch should lock the wheels to hand-turning.
5. Secure the locknuts and reposition the handlever rubber boot.

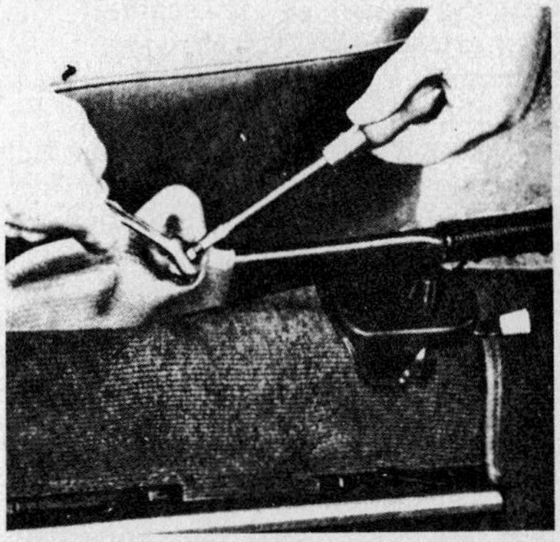

Parking brake adjustment. Each side should be adjusted equally.

Parking Brake Repair

On parking brake levers of this type, the ratchet sometimes disengages itself, making the brake inoperative. The reason for this is that the rear wheel brakes gradually wear down, thus requiring more travel in the parking brake mechanism to tighten them. Eventually, a point is reached where the ratchet can no longer cope with the increasing travel and the unit comes apart. To repair,

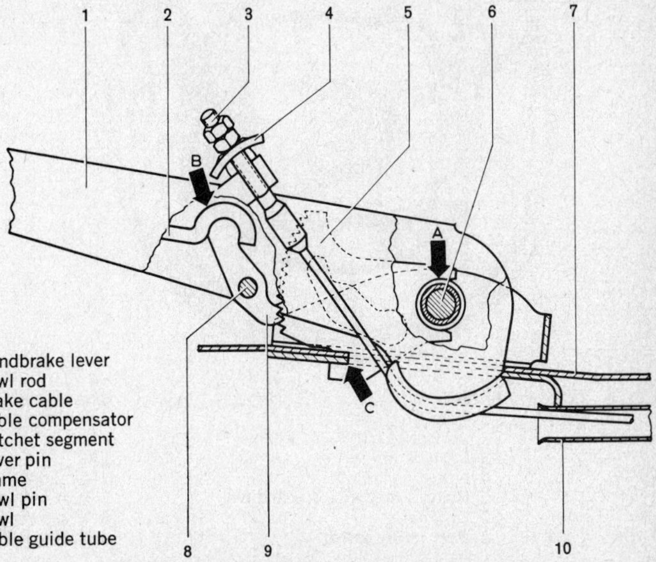
1 2 3 4 5 6 7
B
A
C
8 9 10
1 Handbrake lever
2 Pawl rod
3 Brake cable
4 Cable compensator
5 Ratchet segment
6 Lever pin
7 Frame
8 Pawl pin
9 Pawl
10 Cable guide tube

Details of parking brake assembly.

follow the numbered steps, but remember, a lasting repair can only be accomplished by adjusting the system back to normal operating tolerance.

1. Completely remove the four nuts which secure and lock the cables to the mechanism.
2. Lift the lever to its uppermost position and examine the pawl rod, checking to see that it is not physically broken. Slowly drop the rod to about the halfway position.
3. Pull the pawl rod off the pawl (see illustration) and reposition the pawl so it contacts the ratchet (B). At the same time, push down on the pawl rod so that it hooks over the pawl.
4. Slowly lower the lever to the full down position, then carefully check for proper operation by pushing the button and slowly pulling up on the lever a short distance. The ratchet mechanism should make a clicking sound, indicating that the pawl rod is successfully hooked over the pawl.
5. If the lever comes free, the operation must be repeated. A study of the illustration will help greatly, as it indicates the correct positioning of the components.
6. When the operation of the parking brake lever is satisfactory, place two of the nuts on the cable ends and adjust them.

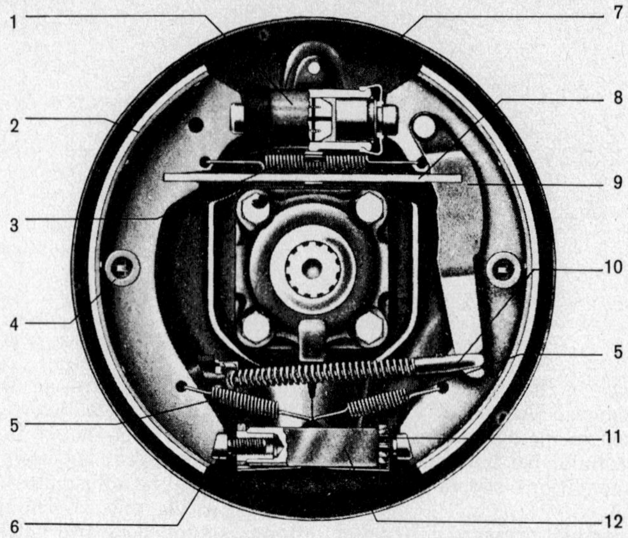
1
2
3
4
5
6
7
8
9
10
5
11
12

1 Cylinder
2 Brake shoe with lining
3 Upper return spring
4 Spring with cup and pin
5 Lower return spring
6 Adjusting screw
7 Back plate
8 Connecting link
9 Lever
10 Brake cable
11 Adjusting nut
12 Anchor block

Rear drum brake of Type 3 vehicle.

Drum Brakes

The amount of brake lining remaining can be checked by looking through the holes provided in the drums.

Shoe Replacement—Drum Brakes (Front)

Remove the front wheel and grease cap. Remove the cotter pin from the speedometer drive cable (left wheel) before removing the grease cap. Remove the brake drum, the shoe retainer spring assemblies, and the front shoe return springs. Take one brake shoe out of the slot of the adjuster, and remove both shoes from the back plate. When the brake drum has been removed and the brake shoes taken out, care should be taken to ensure that the brake pedal is not depressed through accident or carelessness. If this occurs, the result will be an unchecked expansion of the wheel cylinder and its parts, and a loss of brake fluid.

Before installing new brake shoes,

Front wheel brake

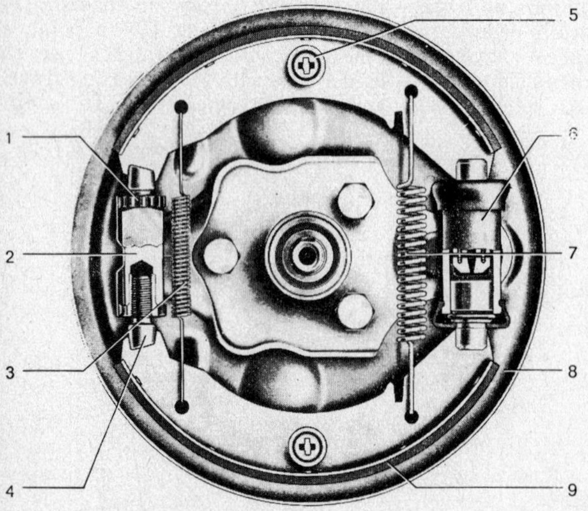
1
2
3
4
5
6
7
8
9

Rear wheel brake

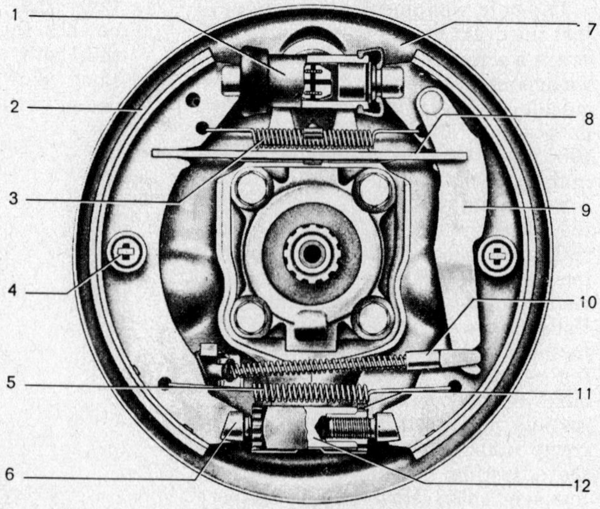
1
2
3
4
5
6
7
8
9
10
11
12

FRONT
1 Adjusting screw
2 Anchor block
3 Front return spring
4 Adjusting nut
5 Guide spring with cup and pin
6 Cylinder
7 Rear return spring
8 Back plate
9 Brake shoe with lining

REAR
1 Cylinder
2 Brake shoe with lining
3 Upper return spring
4 Spring with cup and pin
5 Lower return spring
6 Adjusting screw
7 Back plate
8 Connecting link
9 Lever
10 Brake cable
11 Adjusting nut
12 Anchor block

Front and rear drum brakes, Type 1.

be sure that both front wheels are using the same type of lining. Any difference in lining type, or the use of a lining of the wrong width, can lead only to uneven braking at best, and to a dangerous accident at worst. Care should also be taken to install the shoes correctly. The stronger return spring and the slots in the brake shoes should be at the wheel cylinder side of the assembly. The adjuster slots should be positioned as shown in the accompanying illustration. The brake shoe return springs should be hooked in from the front so that there is no chance of interference with shoe operation. The two brake shoe retainers should also be replaced at this time. The slotted retainer cup should be inspected for wear and replaced if necessary. If the slot has become too large or shows evidence of possible weakness, it should be replaced. Once the brake shoes are installed and retained, they should be centered. Before replacing the brake drum, inspect the oil seal. Adjust the front wheel bearings and adjust and bleed the brakes. Road-test the car and check braking action.

Shoe Replacement—Drum Brakes (Rear)

Remove the wheel and brake drum. (On the Type 3, the drum can be removed after the two drum retaining bolts have been taken out. This eliminates the need to remove the axle shaft nuts in order to remove the drum.) Remove the brake shoe retainers and unhook the lower return spring. (There are two lower return springs on the rear brakes of the Type 3.) Remove the upper return spring, handbrake cable, and the brake shoe with the lever. The lever is held onto the rear brake shoe by a circlip.

Installation of the rear brake shoes is in the opposite sequence. Be sure to install the proper linings on each of the rear wheels. Install the front brake shoe and attach its retaining assembly. The front brake shoe of the Type 3 should be positioned as shown in the accompanying picture. Install the rear brake shoe with the handbrake lever, connecting link, and the upper return spring and clip. Fasten the retainer assembly to the rear brake shoe and attach the handbrake cable end to the lever on the rear shoe. Be sure to position the adjuster slots properly. Install the lower return spring(s), adjust the brakes, and bleed the brake system. If the axle nut was removed to allow removal of the brake drum, tighten it to 217 ft lbs.

Disc Brakes

The principal components of the disc brakes are the disc, friction pad, caliper, and splash shield.

R & R Friction Pads

Replacement of the friction pads is easily done. After raising the front of the car, remove the wheel. Use a punch to drive out the upper retaining pin. Remove the friction pad expander spring and drive out the lower retaining pin.

Push the pistons away from the disc. Before carrying out this part of the operation, however, it is a good idea to remove some fluid from the brake fluid reservoir so that it does not overflow. Clean the calipers with alcohol. Sharp-edged tools and mineral-based solvents should not be used. The retaining plates are removed for the purpose of cleaning, and should

Disconnecting parking brake cable from operating lever.

be replaced if damaged or corroded. When replacing the retaining plate, be sure that it is installed so that the center part is firmly pressed into the center of the piston, and is below the piston cutaway. The piston should be

1
2
3

1 Splash shield 2 Brake disc
3 Brake caliper

Basic components of disc brake.

at an angle of 20°.

The brake pads may now be inserted. Care should be taken to ensure free movement in the caliper housing. Insert the lower retaining pin, using a punch of a larger diameter than the pin itself. Install a new friction pad expanding spring. Insert the upper retaining pin, while at the same time pressing down on the expander spring. While the vehicle is stationary, depress the brake pedal several times to enable the brake pads to settle into their correct positions. The level of brake fluid in the reservoir should be checked and

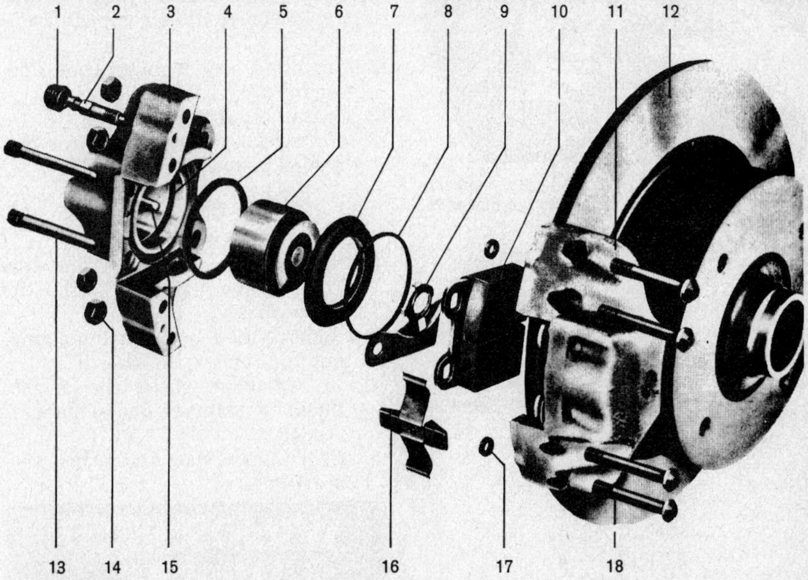
1 2 3 4 5 6 7 8 9 10 11 12
13 14 15 16 17 18

1 Bleeder valve dust cap
2 Bleeder valve
3 Brake caliper inner housing
4 Groove for rubber seal
5 Rubber seal
6 Brake caliper piston
7 Rubber boot
8 Spring ring
9 Piston retaining plate
10 Friction pad
11 Brake caliper outer housing
12 Brake disc
13 Friction pad retaining pin
14 Nut
15 Cylindrical pin (pressed in)
16 Spreader spring
17 Fluid channel O-ring
18 Caliper housing securing bolts

Exploded view of Type 3 disc brake.

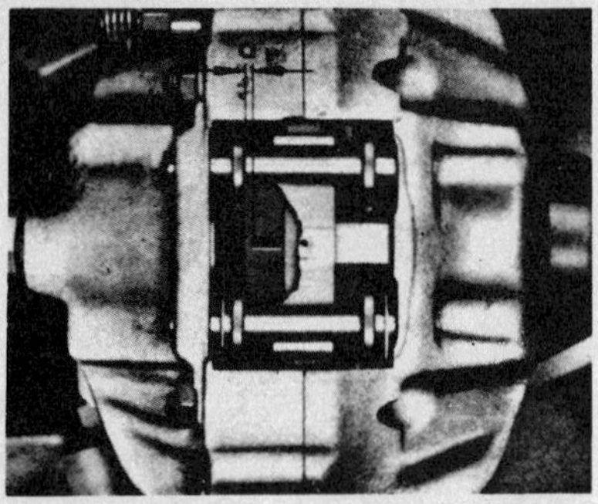

Disc brake friction pads should be checked for wear every 6,000 miles. When the pad thickness, a, is 2 mm or less, the pads must be replaced.

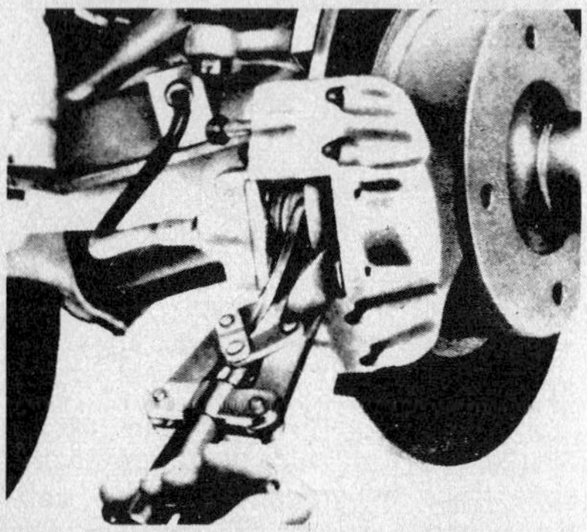

These special pliers are useful in pushing the pistons back into the cylinders.

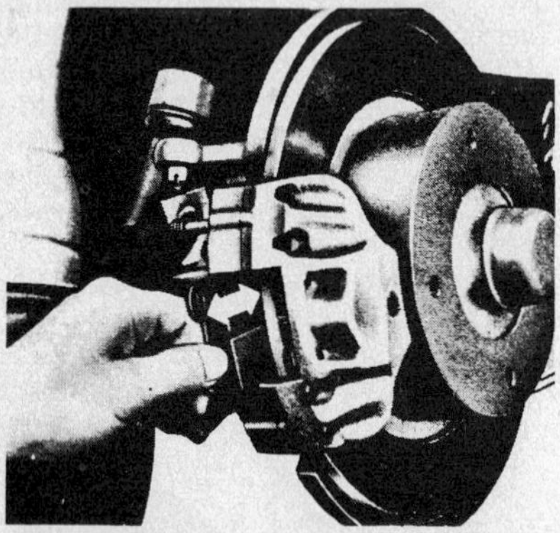

Insertion or removal of friction pads. A special hook is often needed to remove the old pads.

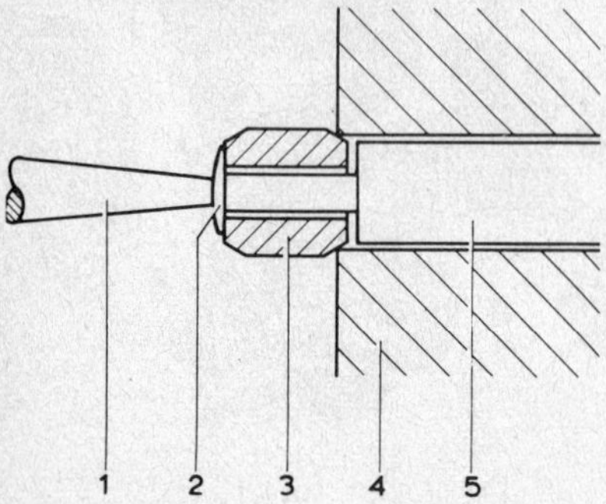
1 2 3 4 5

1 Punch (too small)
2 Endangered retaining pin shoulder
3 Split clamping bush
4 Housing
5 Retaining pin

The punch shown is too small to safely drive in the friction pad retaining pin. If the pin is driven in with this size punch, the pin head may shear off and allow the pin to fall out.

the car taken on a test run.

Brake Caliper R & R

1. Remove the front wheel.
2. Remove the brake hose, cap, and bleeder valve dust cap.
3. Bend back the mounting bolt lockplate.
4. Remove the caliper attaching bolts.
5. Remove the caliper.
6. In reinstalling, clean all mating surfaces and steering knuckle.
7. Install the mounting bolts and torque to 43 ft lbs. The bolts and locking plates should be renewed.
8. Bleed the brake system. Be sure to replace the dust caps on the bleeder valves.
9. Road-test.

Brake Caliper Repair

1. Remove the friction pads.
2. Remove the caliper.
3. Mount the caliper in a vise using vise clamps.
4. Remove the piston retaining plates.
5. With a screwdriver, pry out the rubber boot spring ring. Do not damage the boot.
6. With a plastic rod, remove the boot.
7. Remove one piston with air pressure, holding the second piston with retaining pliers.
8. Remove the rubber seal with a plastic rod.
9. To reassemble, first clean with methylated spirits or brake fluid.
10. Replace any parts showing wear, corrosion, or physical damage. A damaged cylinder requires the replacement of a complete caliper.
11. Install a new rubber boot and spring ring.
12. Install the retaining plate.
13. Follow above procedures for the second piston.

Brake Disc R & R

1. Remove the wheel.
2. Remove the caliper from the knuckle and hang it on the tie rod with a wire hook.
3. Remove the wheel bearing clamp nut and remove the disc.
4. In replacing, check the splash shield for damage and replace if needed.
5. Reinstall the disc and adjust the bearing.

WINDSHIELD WIPERS

Windshield Wiper Motor R & R, Type 1

1. Disconnect the battery ground cable.
2. Loosen the clamp screws and remove the wiper arms.
3. Remove both wiper bearing hex nuts and washers. Take off the outer bearing seals.
4. Remove the back of the instrument panel from the luggage compartment.
5. Disconnect the cable from the wiper motor.
6. Remove the glove compartment box.
7. Remove the screw securing the wiper frame to the body.
8. Remove the frame and motor, with the linkage.

When replacing the motor and linkage:

1. The pressed lug on the wiper frame must engage the groove in the wiper bearing. Make sure that the wiper spindles are vertical to the windshield.
2. Check the linkage bushings for wear.
3. The hollow side of the links must face toward the frame, with the angled end of the driving link toward the right bearing.
4. The inner bearing seal should be placed so that the shoulder of the rubber molding faces the wiper arm.

Windshield Wiper Motor R & R, Type 2

1. Disconnect the ground wire from the battery.
2. Remove both wiper arms.
3. Remove the bearing cover and nut.
4. Remove the heater branch connections under the instrument panel.
5. Disconnect the wiper motor wiring harness.
6. Remove the wiper motor securing screws and remove the motor.
7. Reverse the above steps to install.

Windshield Wiper Motor R & R, Type 3

1. Disconnect the battery.
2. Remove the ashtray and glove compartment.
3. Remove the fresh air controls.
4. Remove the cover for the heater and water drainage hoses.
5. Disconnect the motor wiring.
6. Remove the wiper arms.
7. Remove the bearing covers and nuts, washers, and outer bearing seals.
8. Remove the wiper motor securing screw and remove the motor.
9. Reverse the above steps to install.

Engine Tune-Up

Engine tune-up is a procedure performed to restore engine performance, deteriorated due to normal wear and loss of adjustment. The three major areas considered in a routine tune-up are compression, ignition, and carburetion, although valve adjustment may be included.

A tune-up is performed in three steps: *analysis*, in which it is determined whether normal wear is responsible for performance loss, and which parts require replacement or service; *parts replacement or service*; and *adjustment*, in which engine adjustments are returned to original specifications. Since the advent of emission control equipment, precision adjustment has become increasingly critical, in order to maintain pollutant emission levels.

Analysis

The procedures below are used to indicate where adjustments, parts service or replacement are necessary within the realm of a normal tune-up. If, following these tests, all systems appear to be functioning properly, proceed to the Troubleshooting Section for further diagnosis.

—Remove all spark plugs, noting the cylinder in which they were installed. Remove the air cleaner, and position the throttle and choke in the full open position. Disconnect the coil high tension lead from the coil and the distributor cap. Insert a compression gauge into the spark plug port of each cylinder, in succession, and crank the engine with the starter to obtain the highest possible reading. Record the readings, and compare the highest to the lowest on the compression pressure limit chart. If the difference exceeds the limits on the chart, or if all readings are excessively low, proceed to a wet compression check (see Troubleshooting Section).

Maxi. Press. Lbs. Sq. In.	*Min. Press. Lbs. Sq. In.*	*Max. Press. Lbs. Sq. In.*	*Min. Press. Lbs. Sq. In.*
134	101	188	141
136	102	190	142
138	104	192	144
140	105	194	145
142	107	196	147
146	110	198	148
148	111	200	150
150	113	202	151
152	114	204	153
154	115	206	154
156	117	208	156
158	118	210	157
160	120	212	158
162	121	214	160
164	123	216	162
166	124	218	163
168	126	220	165
170	127	222	166
172	129	224	168
174	131	226	169
176	132	228	171
178	133	230	172
180	135	232	174
182	136	234	175
184	138	236	177
186	140	238	178

Compression pressure limits
(© Buick Div. G.M. Corp.)

—Evaluate the spark plugs according to the spark plug chart in the Troubleshooting Section, and proceed as indicated in the chart.

—Remove the distributor cap, and inspect it inside and out for cracks and/or carbon tracks, and inside for excessive wear or burning of the rotor contacts. If any of these faults are evident, the cap must be replaced.

—Check the breaker points for burning, pitting or wear, and the contact heel resting on the distributor cam for excessive wear. If defects are noted, replace the entire breaker point set.

—Remove and inspect the rotor. If the contacts are burned or worn, or if the rotor is excessively loose on the distributor shaft (where applicable), the rotor must be replaced.

—Inspect the spark plug leads and the coil high tension lead for cracks or brittleness. If any of the wires appear defective, the entire set should be replaced.

—Check the air filter to ensure that it is functioning properly.

Parts Replacement and Service

The determination of whether to replace or service parts is at the mechanic's discretion; however, it is suggested that any parts in questionable condition be replaced rather than reused.

—Clean and regap, or replace, the spark plugs as needed. Lightly coat the threads with engine oil and install the plugs. CAUTION: *Do not over-torque taper-seat spark plugs, or plugs being installed in aluminum cylinder heads.*

SPARK PLUG TORQUE

Thread size	*Cast-Iron Heads*	*Aluminum Heads*
10 mm.	14	11
14 mm.	30	27
18 mm.	34*	32
7/8 in.—18	37	35

* 17 ft. lbs. for tapered plugs using no gaskets.

—If the distributor cap is to be reused, clean the inside with a dry rag, and remove corrosion from the rotor contact points with fine emery cloth. Remove the spark plug wires one by one, and clean the wire ends and the inside of the towers. If the boots are loose, they should be replaced.

If the cap is to be replaced, transfer the wires one by one, cleaning the wire ends and replacing the boots if necessary.

—If the original points are to remain in service, clean them lightly with emery cloth, lubricate the contact heel with grease specifically designed for this purpose. Rotate the crankshaft until the heel rests on a high point of the distributor cam, and adjust the point gap to specifications.

When replacing the points, remove the original points and condenser, and wipe out the inside of the distributor housing with a clean, dry rag. Lightly lubricate the contact heel and pivot point, and install the points and condenser. Rotate the crankshaft until the heel rests on a high point of the distributor cam, and adjust the point gap to specifications. NOTE: *Always replace the condenser when changing the points.*

—If the rotor is to be reused, clean the contacts with solvent. Do not alter the spring tension of the rotor center contact. Install the rotor and the distributor cap.

—Replace the coil high tension lead and/or the spark plug leads as necessary.

—Clean the carburetor using a spray solvent (e.g., Gumout Spray). Remove the varnish from the throttle bores, and clean the linkage. Disconnect and plug the fuel line, and run the engine until it runs out of fuel. Partially fill the float chamber with solvent, and reconnect the fuel line. In extreme cases, the jets can be pressure flushed by inserting a rubber plug into the float vent, running the spray nozzle through it, and spraying the solvent until it squirts out of the venturi fuel dump.

—Clean and tighten all wiring connections in the primary electrical circuit.

Additional Services

The following services *should* be performed in conjunction with a routine tune-up to ensure efficient performance.

—Inspect the battery and fill to the proper level with distilled water. Remove the cable clamps, clean clamps and posts thoroughly, coat the posts lightly with petroleum jelly, reinstall and tighten.

—Inspect all belts, replace and/or adjust as necessary.

—Test the PCV valve (if so equipped), and clean or replace as indicated. Clean all crankcase ventilation hoses, or replace if cracked or hardened.

—Adjust the valves (if necessary) to manufacturer's specifications.

Adjustments

—Connect a dwell-tachometer between the distributor primary lead and ground. Remove the distributor cap and rotor (unless equipped with Delco externally adjustable distributor). With the ignition off, crank the engine with a remote starter switch and measure the point dwell angle. Adjust the dwell angle to specifications. NOTE: *Increasing the gap decreases the dwell angle and vice-versa.* Install the rotor and distributor cap.

—Connect a timing light according to the manufacturer's specifications. Identify the proper timing marks with chalk or paint. NOTE: *Luminescent (day-glo) paint is excellent for this purpose.* Start the engine, and run it until it reaches operating temperature. Disconnect and plug any distributor vacuum lines, and adjust idle to the speed required to adjust timing, according to specifications. Loosen the distributor clamp and adjust timing to specifications by rotating the distributor in the engine. NOTE: *To advance timing, rotate distributor opposite normal direction of rotor rotation, and vice-versa.*

—Synchronize the throttles and mixture of multiple carburetors (if so equipped) according to procedures given in the individual car sections.

—Adjust the idle speed, mixture, and idle quality, as specified in the car sections. Final idle adjustments should be made with the air cleaner installed. CAUTION: *Due to strict emission control requirements on 1969 and later models, special test equipment (CO meter, SUN Tester) may be necessary to properly adjust idle mixture to specifications.*

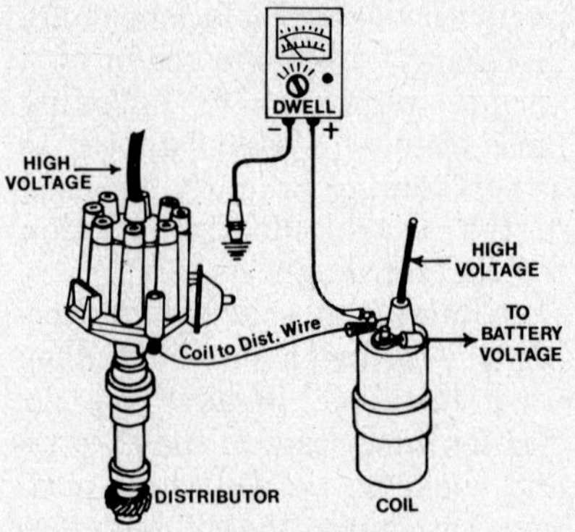
DWELL
HIGH VOLTAGE
HIGH VOLTAGE
TO BATTERY VOLTAGE
Coil to Dist. Wire
DISTRIBUTOR
COIL

Dwell meter hook-up

Engine Troubleshooting

The following section is designed to aid in the rapid diagnosis of engine problems. The systematic format is used to diagnose problems ranging from engine starting difficulties to the need for engine overhaul. It is assumed that the user is equipped with basic hand tools and test equipment (tach-dwell meter, timing light, voltmeter, and ohmmeter).

Troubleshooting is divided into two sections. The first, *General Diagnosis*, is used to locate the problem area. In the second, *Specific Diagnosis*, the problem is systematically evaluated.

General Diagnosis

PROBLEM: *Symptom*	*Begin diagnosis at Section Two, Number* ———
Engine won't start:	
Starter doesn't turn	1.1, 2.1
Starter turns, engine doesn't	2.1
Starter turns engine very slowly	1.1, 2.4
Starter turns engine normally	3.1, 4.1
Starter turns engine very quickly	6.1
Engine fires intermittently	4.1
Engine fires consistently	5.1, 6.1
Engine runs poorly:	
Hard starting	3.1, 4.1, 5.1, 8.1
Rough idle	4.1, 5.1, 8.1
Stalling	3.1, 4.1, 5.1, 8.1
Engine dies at high speeds	4.1, 5.1
Hesitation (on acceleration from standing stop)	5.1, 8.1
Poor pickup	4.1, 5.1, 8.1
Lack of power	3.1, 4.1, 5.1, 8.1
Backfire through the carburetor	4.1, 8.1, 9.1
Backfire through the exhaust	4.1, 8.1, 9.1
Blue exhaust gases	6.1, 7.1
Black exhaust gases	5.1
Running on (after the ignition is shut off)	3.1, 8.1
Susceptible to moisture	4.1
Engine misfires under load	4.1, 7.1, 8.4, 9.1
Engine misfires at speed	4.1, 8.4
Engine misfires at idle	3.1, 4.1, 5.1, 7.1, 8.4

PROBLEM: *Symptom*	*Probable Cause*
Engine noises: ①	
Metallic grind while starting	Starter drive not engaging completely
Constant grind or rumble	*Starter drive not releasing, worn main bearings
Constant knock	Worn connecting rod bearings
Knock under load	Fuel octane too low, worn connecting rod bearings
Double knock	Loose piston pin
Metallic tap	*Collapsed or sticky valve lifter, excessive valve clearance, excessive end play in a rotating shaft
Scrape	*Fan belt contacting a stationary surface
Tick while starting	S.U. electric fuel pump (normal), starter brushes
Constant tick	*Generator brushes, shreaded fan belt
Squeal	* Improperly tensioned fan belt
Hiss or roar	*Steam escaping through a leak in the cooling system or the radiator overflow vent
Whistle	* Vacuum leak
Wheeze	Loose or cracked spark plug

①—It is extremely difficult to evaluate vehicle noises. While the above are general definitions of engine noises, those starred (*) should be considered as possibly originating elsewhere in the car. To aid diagnosis, the following list considers other potential sources of these sounds.

Metallic grind:
Throwout bearing; transmission gears, bearings, or synchronizers; differential bearings, gears; something metallic in contact with brake drum or disc.

Metallic tap:
U-joints; fan-to-radiator (or shroud) contact.

Scrape:
Brake shoe or pad dragging; tire to body contact; suspension contacting undercarriage or exhaust; something non-metallic contacting brake shoe or drum.

Tick:
Transmission gears; differential gears; lack of radio suppression; resonant vibration of body panels; windshield wiper motor or transmission; heater motor and blower.

Squeal:
Brake shoe or pad not fully releasing; tires (excessive wear, uneven wear, improper inflation); front or rear wheel alignment (most commonly due to improper toe-in).

Hiss or whistle:
Wind leaks (body or window); heater motor and blower fan.

Roar:
Wheel bearings; wind leaks (body and window).

Specific Diagnosis

This section is arranged so that following each test, instructions are given to proceed to another, until a problem is diagnosed.

INDEX

Group		Topic
1	*	Battery
2	*	Cranking system
3	*	Primary electrical system
4	*	Secondary electrical system
5	*	Fuel system
6	*	Engine compression
7	**	Engine vacuum
8	**	Secondary electrical system
9	**	Valve train
10	**	Exhaust system
11	**	Cooling system
12	**	Engine lubrication

*—The engine need not be running.
**—The engine must be running.

SAMPLE SECTION

Test and Procedure	*Results and Indications*	*Proceed to*
4.1—Check for spark: Hold each spark plug wire approximately ¼″ from ground with gloves or a heavy, dry rag. Crank the engine and observe the spark.	→ If no spark is evident: →	4.2
	→ If spark is good in some cases: →	4.3
	→ If spark is good in all cases: →	4.6

DIAGNOSIS

1.1—Inspect the battery visually for case condition (corrosion, cracks) and water level.

If case is cracked, replace battery: 1.4

If the case is intact, remove corrosion with a solution of baking soda and water (CAUTION: *do not get the solution into the battery*), and fill with water: 1.2

1.2—Check the battery cable connections: Insert a screwdriver between the battery post and the cable clamp. Turn the headlights on high beam, and observe them as the screwdriver is gently twisted to ensure good metal to metal contact.

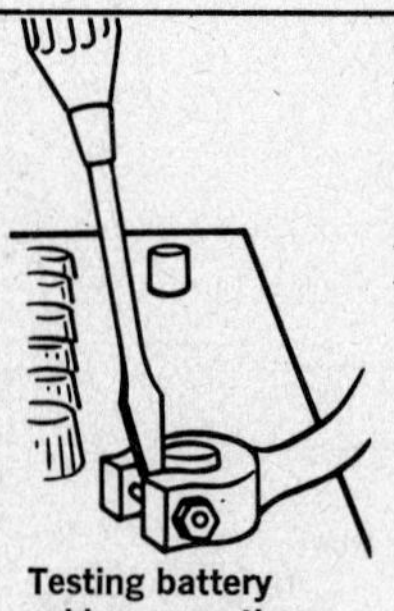

Testing battery cable connections using a screwdriver

If the lights brighten, remove and clean the clamp and post; coat the post with petroleum jelly, install and tighten the clamp: 1.4

If no improvement is noted: 1.3

1.3—Test the state of charge of the battery using an individual cell tester or hydrometer.

Spec. Grav. Reading	*Charged Condition*
1.260-1.280	Fully Charged
1.230-1.250	Three Quarter Charged
1.200-1.220	One Half Charged
1.170-1.190	One Quarter Charged
1.140-1.160	Just About Flat
1.110-1.130	All The Way Down

State of battery charge

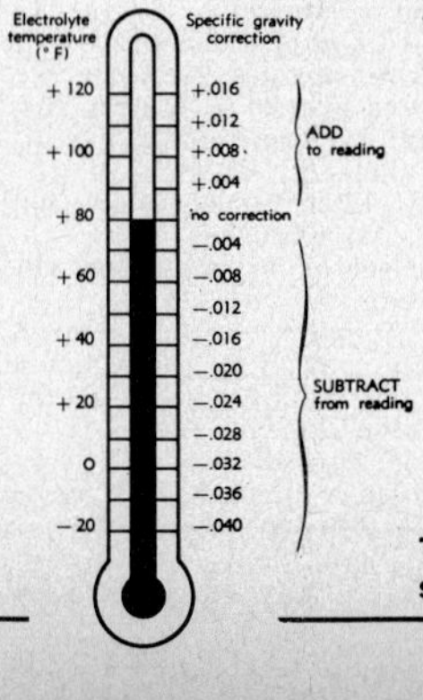

Electrolyte temperature (°F)
Specific gravity correction
+ 120
+ 100
+ 80
+ 60
+ 40
+ 20
0
− 20
+.016
+.012
+.008
+.004
no correction
−.004
−.008
−.012
−.016
−.020
−.024
−.028
−.032
−.036
−.040
ADD to reading
SUBTRACT from reading

The effect of temperature on the specific gravity of battery electrolyte

If indicated, charge the battery. NOTE: *If no obvious reason exists for the low state of charge (i.e., battery age, prolonged storage), the charging system should be tested:* 1.4

Test and Procedure	*Results and Indications*	*Proceed to*
1.4—Visually inspect battery cables for cracking, bad connection to ground, or bad connection to starter.	If necessary, tighten connections or replace the cables:	2.1

Tests in Group 2 are performed with coil high tension lead disconnected to prevent accidental starting.

Test and Procedure	*Results and Indications*	*Proceed to*
2.1—Test the starter motor and solenoid: Connect a jumper from the battery post of the solenoid (or relay) to the ignition switch post of the solenoid (or relay).	If starter turns the engine normally:	2.2
	If the starter buzzes, or turns the engine very slowly:	2.4
	If no response, replace the solenoid (or relay).	3.1
	If the starter turns, but the engine doesn't, ensure that the flywheel ring gear is intact. If the gear is undamaged, replace the starter drive.	3.1
2.2—Determine whether ignition override switches are functioning properly (clutch start switch, neutral safety switch), by connecting a jumper across the switch(es), and turning the ignition switch to "start".	If starter operates, adjust or replace switch:	3.1
	If the starter doesn't operate:	2.3
2.3—Check the ignition switch "start" position: Connect a 12V test lamp between the starter post of the solenoid (or relay) and ground. Turn the ignition switch to the "start" position, and jiggle the key.	If the lamp doesn't light when the switch is turned, check the ignition switch for loose connections, cracked insulation, or broken wires. Repair or replace as necessary:	3.1
	If the lamp flickers when the key is jiggled, replace the ignition switch.	3.3

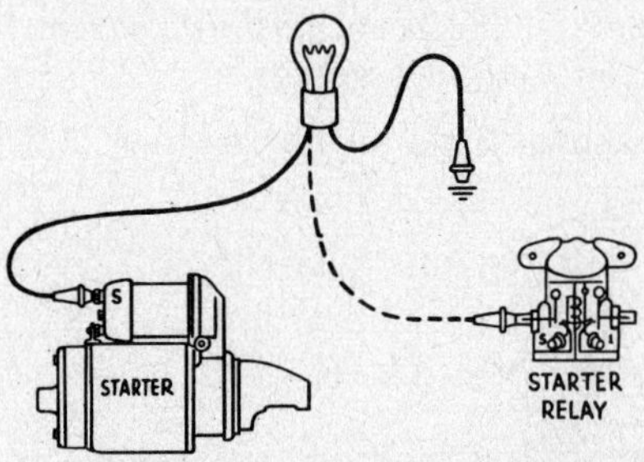
STARTER
STARTER RELAY
Checking the ignition switch "start" position

Test and Procedure	*Results and Indications*	*Proceed to*
2.4—Remove and bench test the starter, according to specifications in the car section.	If the starter does not meet specifications, repair or replace as needed:	3.1
	If the starter is operating properly:	2.5
2.5—Determine whether the engine can turn freely: Remove the spark plugs, and check for water in the cylinders. Check for water on the dipstick, or oil in the radiator. Attempt to turn the engine using an 18″ flex drive and socket on the crankshaft pulley nut or bolt.	If the engine will turn freely only with the spark plugs out, and hydrostatic lock (water in the cylinders) is ruled out, check valve timing:	9.2
	If engine will not turn freely, and it is known that the clutch and transmission are free, the engine must be disassembled for further evaluation:	Next Chapter

<table>
<tr><th>Tests and Procedures</th><th>Results and Indications</th><th>Proceed to</th></tr>
<tr><td>3.1—Check the ignition switch "on" position: Connect a jumper wire between the distributor side of the coil and ground, and a 12V test lamp between the switch side of the coil and ground. Remove the high tension lead from the coil. Turn the ignition switch on and jiggle the key.
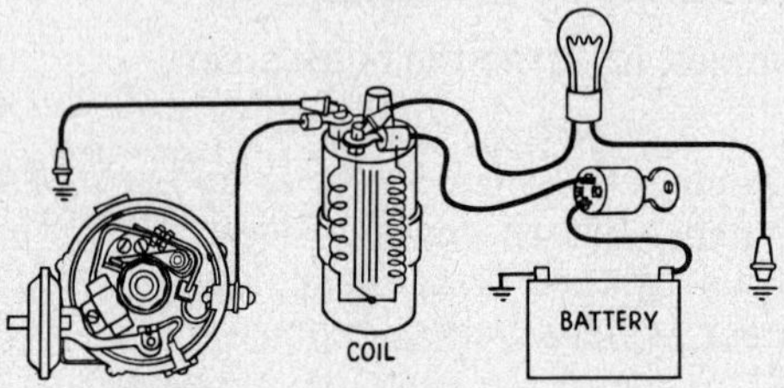
COIL
BATTERY
Checking the ignition switch "on" position</td><td>If the lamp lights:
If the lamp flickers when the key is jiggled, replace the ignition switch:
If the lamp doesn't light, check for loose or open connections. If none are found, remove the ignition switch and check for continuity. If the switch is faulty, replace it:</td><td>3.2
3.3
3.3</td></tr>
<tr><td>3.2—Check the ballast resistor or resistance wire for an open circuit, using an ohmmeter.</td><td>Replace the resistor or the resistance wire if the resistance is zero.</td><td>3.3</td></tr>
<tr><td>3.3—Visually inspect the breaker points for burning, pitting, or excessive wear. Gray coloring of the point contact surfaces is normal. Rotate the crankshaft until the contact heel rests on a high point of the distributor cam, and adjust the point gap to specifications.</td><td>If the breaker points are intact, clean the contact surfaces with fine emery cloth, and adjust the point gap to specifications. If pitted or worn, replace the points and condenser, and adjust the gap to specifications:
NOTE: Always lubricate the distributor cam according to manufacturer's recommendations when servicing the breaker points.</td><td>3.4</td></tr>
<tr><td>3.4—Connect a dwell meter between the distributor primary lead and ground. Crank the engine and observe the point dwell angle.
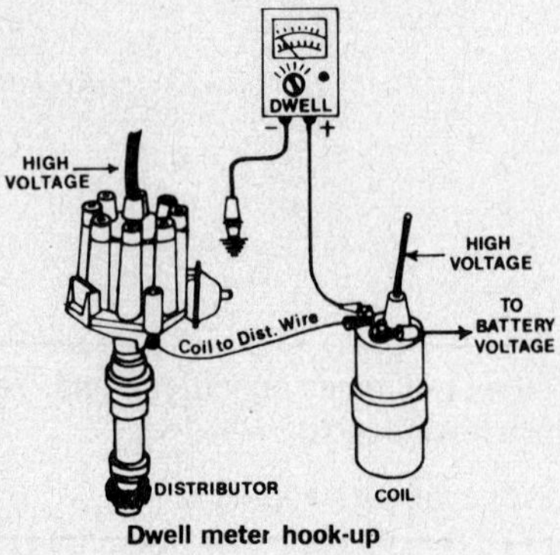
DWELL
HIGH VOLTAGE
HIGH VOLTAGE
TO BATTERY VOLTAGE
Coil to Dist. Wire
DISTRIBUTOR
COIL
Dwell meter hook-up</td><td>If necessary, adjust the point dwell angle: NOTE: Increasing the point gap decreases the dwell angle, and vice-versa.
If dwell meter shows little or no reading:
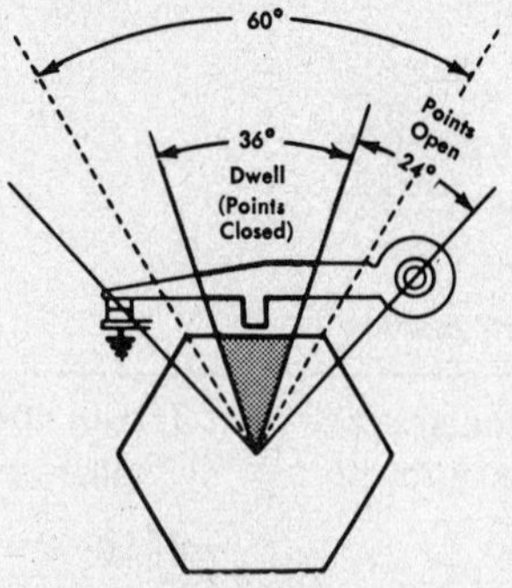
60°
36°
Dwell (Points Closed)
Points Open
24°
Dwell angle</td><td>3.6
3.5</td></tr>
<tr><td>3.5—Check the condenser for short: Connect an ohmmeter across the condenser body and the pigtail lead.
Checking the condenser for short
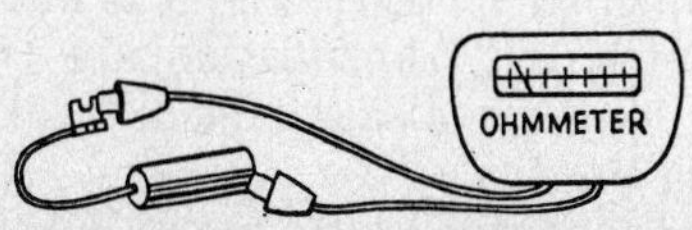
OHMMETER</td><td>If any reading other than infinite resistance is noted, replace the condenser:</td><td>3.6</td></tr>
</table>

Test and Procedure	*Results and Indications*	*Proceed to*
3.6—Test the coil primary resistance: Connect an ohmmeter across the coil primary terminals, and read the resistance on the low scale. Note whether an external ballast resistor or resistance wire is utilized. 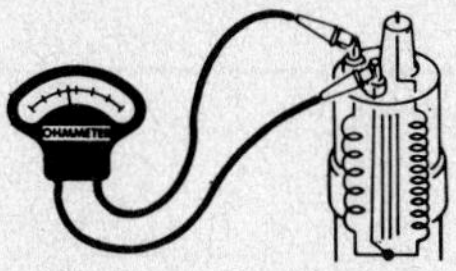 Testing the coil primary resistance	Coils utilizing ballast resistors or resistance wires should have approximately 1.0Ω resistance; coils with internal resistors should have approximately 4.0Ω resistance. If values far from the above are noted, replace the coil:	4.1
4.1—Check for spark: Hold each spark plug wire approximately 1/4″ from ground with gloves or a heavy, dry rag. Crank the engine, and observe the spark.	If no spark is evident:	4.2
	If spark is good in some cylinders:	4.3
	If spark is good in all cylinders:	4.6
4.2—Check for spark at the coil high tension lead: Remove the coil high tension lead from the distributor and position it approximately 1/4″ from ground. Crank the engine and observe spark. CAUTION: *This test should not be performed on cars equipped with transistorized ignition.*	If the spark is good and consistent:	4.3
	If the spark is good but intermittent, test the primary electrical system starting at 3.3:	3.3
	If the spark is weak or non-existent, replace the coil high tension lead, clean and tighten all connections and retest. If no improvement is noted:	4.4
4.3—Visually inspect the distributor cap and rotor for burned or corroded contacts, cracks, carbon tracks, or moisture. Also check the fit of the rotor on the distributor shaft (where applicable).	If moisture is present, dry thoroughly, and retest per 4.1:	4.1
	If burned or excessively corroded contacts, cracks, or carbon tracks are noted, replace the defective part(s) and retest per 4.1:	4.1
	If the rotor and cap appear intact, or are only slightly corroded, clean the contacts thoroughly (including the cap towers and spark plug wire ends) and retest per 4.1:	
	If the spark is good in all cases:	4.6
	If the spark is poor in all cases:	4.5
4.4—Check the coil secondary resistance: Connect an ohmmeter across the distributor side of the coil and the coil tower. Read the resistance on the high scale of the ohmmeter. 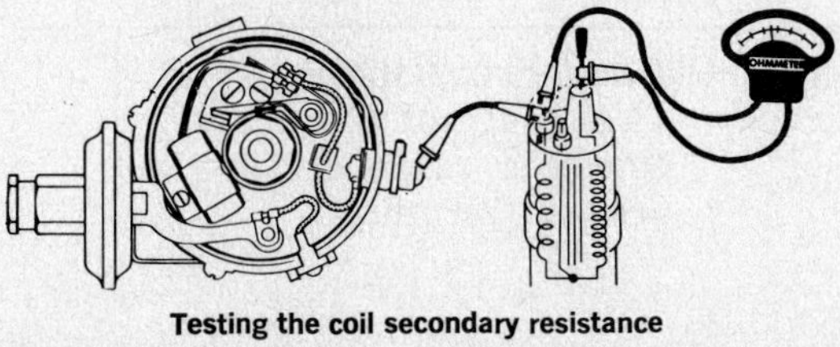 Testing the coil secondary resistance	The resistance of a satisfactory coil should be between 4KΩ and 10KΩ. If the resistance is considerably higher (i.e., 40KΩ) replace the coil, and retest per 4.1: NOTE: *This does not apply to high performance coils.*	4.1

Test and Procedure	*Results and Indications*	*Proceed to*
4.5—Visually inspect the spark plug wires for cracking or brittleness. Ensure that no two wires are positioned so as to cause induction firing (adjacent and parallel). Remove each wire, one by one, and check resistance with an ohmmeter.	Replace any cracked or brittle wires. If any of the wires are defective, replace the entire set. Replace any wires with excessive resistance (over 8000Ω per foot for suppression wire), and separate any wires that might cause induction firing.	4.6
4.6—Remove the spark plugs, noting the cylinders from which they were removed, and evaluate according to the chart below.	See below.	See below.

	Condition	*Cause*	*Remedy*	*Proceed to*
	Electrodes eroded, light brown deposits.	Normal wear. Normal wear is indicated by approximately .001″ wear per 1000 miles.	Clean and regap the spark plug if wear is not excessive: Replace the spark plug if excessively worn:	4.7
	Carbon fouling (black, dry, fluffy deposits).	If present on one or two plugs:		
		Faulty high tension lead(s).	Test the high tension leads:	4.5
		Burnt or sticking valve(s).	Check the valve train: (Clean and regap the plugs in either case.)	9.1
		If present on most or all plugs: Overly rich fuel mixture, due to restricted air filter, improper carburetor adjustment, improper choke or heat riser adjustment or operation.	Check the fuel system:	5.1
	Oil fouling (wet black deposits)	Worn engine components. NOTE: *Oil fouling may occur in new or recently rebuilt engines until broken in.*	Check engine vacuum and compression:	6.1
			Replace with new spark plug	
	Lead fouling (gray, black, tan, or yellow deposits, which appear glazed or cinder-like).	Combustion by-products.	Clean and regap the plugs: (Use plugs of a different heat range if the problem recurs.)	4.7

	Condition	Cause	Remedy	Proceed to
	Gap bridging (deposits lodged between the electrodes).	Incomplete combustion, or transfer of deposits from the combustion chamber.	Replace the spark plugs:	4.7
	Overheating (burnt electrodes, and extremely white insulator with small black spots).	Ignition timing advanced too far.	Adjust timing to specifications:	8.2
		Overly lean fuel mixture.	Check the fuel system:	5.1
		Spark plugs not seated properly.	Clean spark plug seat and install a new gasket washer: (Replace the spark plugs in all cases.)	4.7
	Fused spot deposits on the insulator.	Combustion chamber blow-by.	Clean and regap the spark plugs:	4.7
	Pre-ignition (melted or severely burned electrodes, blistered or cracked insulators, or metallic deposits on the insulator).	Incorrect spark plug heat range.	Replace with plugs of the proper heat range:	4.7
		Ignition timing advanced too far.	Adjust timing to specifications:	8.2
		Spark plugs not being cooled efficiently.	Clean the spark plug seat, and check the cooling system:	11.1
		Fuel mixture too lean.	Check the fuel system:	5.1
		Poor compression.	Check compression:	6.1
		Fuel grade too low.	Use higher octane fuel:	4.7

Test and Procedure	Results and Indications	Proceed to
4.7—Determine the static ignition timing: Using the flywheel or crankshaft pulley timing marks as a guide, locate top dead center on the *compression* stroke of the No. 1 cylinder. Remove the distributor cap.	Adjust the distributor so that the rotor points toward the No. 1 tower in the distributor cap, and the points are just opening:	4.8
4.8—Check coil polarity: Connect a voltmeter negative lead to the coil high tension lead, and the positive lead to ground (NOTE: *reverse the hook-up for positive ground cars*). Crank the engine momentarily.  VOLTS Checking coil polarity	If the voltmeter reads up-scale, the polarity is correct:	5.1
	If the voltmeter reads down-scale, reverse the coil polarity (switch the primary leads):	5.1

Test and Procedure	Results and Indications	Proceed to
5.1—Determine that the air filter is functioning efficiently: Hold paper elements up to a strong light, and attempt to see light through the filter.	Clean permanent air filters in gasoline (or manufacturer's recommendation), and allow to dry. Replace paper elements through which light cannot be seen:	5.2
5.2—Determine whether a flooding condition exists: Flooding is identified by a strong gasoline odor, and excessive gasoline present in the throttle bore(s) of the carburetor.	If flooding is not evident:	5.3
	If flooding is evident, permit the gasoline to dry for a few moments and restart.	
	If flooding doesn't recur:	5.6
	If flooding is persistant:	5.5
5.3—Check that fuel is reaching the carburetor: Detach the fuel line at the carburetor inlet. Hold the end of the line in a cup (not styrofoam), and crank the engine.	If fuel flows smoothly:	5.6
	If fuel doesn't flow (NOTE: *Make sure that there is fuel in the tank*), or flows erratically:	5.4
5.4—Test the fuel pump: Disconnect all fuel lines from the fuel pump. Hold a finger over the input fitting, crank the engine (with electric pump, turn the ignition or pump on), and feel for suction.	If suction is evident, blow out the fuel line to the tank with low pressure compressed air until bubbling is heard from the fuel filler neck. Also blow out the carburetor fuel line (both ends disconnected):	5.6
	If no suction is evident, replace or repair the fuel pump:	5.6
	NOTE: *Repeated oil fouling of the spark plugs, or a no-start condition, could be the result of a ruptured vacuum booster pump diaphragm, through which oil or gasoline is being drawn into the intake manifold (where applicable).*	
5.5—Check the needle and seat: Tap the carburetor in the area of the needle and seat.	If flooding stops, a gasoline additive (e.g., Gumout) will often cure the problem:	5.6
	If flooding continues, check the fuel pump for excessive pressure at the carburetor (according to specifications). If the pressure is normal, the needle and seat must be removed and checked, and/or the float level adjusted:	5.6
5.6—Test the accelerator pump by looking into the throttle bores while operating the throttle.	If the accelerator pump appears to be operating normally:	5.7
	If the accelerator pump is not operating, the pump must be reconditioned. Where possible, service the pump with the carburetor(s) installed on the engine. If necessary, remove the carburetor. Prior to removal:	5.7
5.7—Determine whether the carburetor main fuel system is functioning: Spray a commercial starting fluid into the carburetor while attempting to start the engine.	If the engine starts, runs for a few seconds, and dies:	5.8
	If the engine doesn't start:	6.1

Test and Procedures	*Results and Indications*	*Proceed to*
5.8—Uncommon fuel system malfunctions: See below:	If the problem is solved:	6.1
	If the problem remains, remove and recondition the carburetor.	

Condition	*Indication*	*Test*	*Usual Weather Conditions*	*Remedy*
Vapor lock	Car will not restart shortly after running.	Cool the components of the fuel system until the engine starts.	Hot to very hot	Ensure that the exhaust manifold heat control valve is operating. Check with the vehicle manufacturer for the recommended solution to vapor lock on the model in question.
Carburetor icing	Car will not idle, stalls at low speeds.	Visually inspect the throttle plate area of the throttle bores for frost.	High humidity, 32-40° F.	Ensure that the exhaust manifold heat control valve is operating, and that the intake manifold heat riser is not blocked.
Water in the fuel	Engine sputters and stalls; may not start.	Pump a small amount of fuel into a glass jar. Allow to stand, and inspect for droplets or a layer of water.	High humidity, extreme temperature changes.	For droplets, use one or two cans of commercial gas dryer (Dry Gas) For a layer of water, the tank must be drained, and the fuel lines blown out with compressed air.

Test and Procedure	*Results and Indications*	*Proceed to*
6.1—Test engine compression: Remove all spark plugs. Insert a compression gauge into a spark plug port, crank the engine to obtain the maximum reading, and record.	If compression is within limits on all cylinders:	7.1
	If gauge reading is extremely low on all cylinders:	6.2
	If gauge reading is low on one or two cylinders:	6.2
	(If gauge readings are identical and low on two or more adjacent cylinders, the head gasket must be replaced.)	

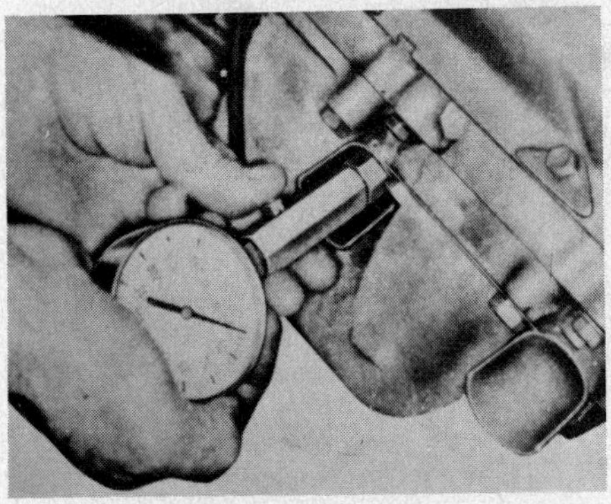

Testing compression
(© Chevrolet Div. G.M. Corp.)

Maxi. Press. Lbs. Sq. In.	*Min. Press. Lbs. Sq. In.*	*Maxi. Press. Lbs. Sq. In.*	*Min. Press. Lbs. Sq. In.*	*Max. Press. Lbs. Sq. In.*	*Min. Press. Lbs. Sq. In.*	*Max. Press. Lbs. Sq. In.*	*Min. Press. Lbs. Sq. In.*
134	101	162	121	188	141	214	160
136	102	164	123	190	142	216	162
138	104	166	124	192	144	218	163
140	105	168	126	194	145	220	165
142	107	170	127	196	147	222	166
146	110	172	129	198	148	224	168
148	111	174	131	200	150	226	169
150	113	176	132	202	151	228	171
152	114	178	133	204	153	230	172
154	115	180	135	206	154	232	174
156	117	182	136	208	156	234	175
158	118	184	138	210	157	236	177
160	120	186	140	212	158	238	178

Compression pressure limits
(© Buick Div. G.M. Corp.)

Test and Procedure	Results and Indications	Proceed to
6.2—Test engine compression (wet): Squirt approximately 30 cc. of engine oil into each cylinder, and retest per 6.1.	If the readings improve, worn or cracked rings or broken pistons are indicated:	Next Chapter
	If the readings do not improve, burned or excessively carboned valves or a jumped timing chain are indicated: NOTE: *A jumped timing chain is often indicated by difficult cranking.*	7.1
7.1—Perform a vacuum check of the engine: Attach a vacuum gauge to the intake manifold beyond the throttle plate. Start the engine, and observe the action of the needle over the range of engine speeds.	See below.	See below

	Reading	Indications	Proceed to
 10 15 5 20 0 25	Steady, from 17-22 in. Hg.	Normal.	8.1
 10 15 5 20 0 25	Low and steady.	Late ignition or valve timing, or low compression:	6.1
 10 15 5 20 0 25	Very low	Vacuum leak:	
 10 15 5 20 0 25	Needle fluctuates as engine speed increases.	Ignition miss, blown cylinder head gasket, leaking valve or weak valve spring:	6.1, 8.3
 10 15 5 20 0 25	Gradual drop in reading at idle.	Excessive back pressure in the exhaust system:	10.1
 10 15 5 20 0 25	Intermittent fluctuation at idle.	Ignition miss, sticking valve:	8.3, 9.1
 10 15 5 20 0 25	Drifting needle.	Improper idle mixture adjustment, carburetors not synchronized (where applicable), or minor intake leak. Synchronize the carburetors, adjust the idle, and retest. If the condition persists:	7.2
 10 15 5 20 0 25	High and steady.	Early ignition timing:	8.2

Test and Procedure	*Results and Indications*	*Proceed to*
7.2—Attach a vacuum gauge per 7.1, and test for an intake manifold leak. Squirt a small amount of oil around the intake manifold gaskets, carburetor gaskets, plugs and fittings. Observe the action of the vacuum gauge.	If the reading improves, replace the indicated gasket, or seal the indicated fitting or plug: If the reading remains low:	8.1 7.3
7.3—Test all vacuum hoses and accessories for leaks as described in 7.2. Also check the carburetor body (dashpots, automatic choke mechanism, throttle shafts) for leaks in the same manner.	If the reading improves, service or replace the offending part(s): If the reading remains low:	8.1 6.1
8.1—Check the point dwell angle: Connect a dwell meter between the distributor primary wire and ground. Start the engine, and observe the dwell angle from idle to 3000 rpm.	If necessary, adjust the dwell angle. NOTE: *Increasing the point gap reduces the dwell angle and vice-versa.* If the dwell angle moves outside specifications as engine speed increases, the distributor should be removed and checked for cam accuracy, shaft endplay and concentricity, bushing wear, and adequate point arm tension (NOTE: *Most of these items may be checked with the distributor installed in the engine, using an oscilloscope*):	8.2
8.2—Connect a timing light (per manufacturer's recommendation) and check the dynamic ignition timing. Disconnect and plug the vacuum hose(s) to the distributor if specified, start the engine, and observe the timing marks at the specified engine speed.	If the timing is not correct, adjust to specifications by rotating the distributor in the engine: (Advance timing by rotating distributor opposite normal direction of rotor rotation, retard timing by rotating distributor in same direction as rotor rotation.)	8.3
8.3—Check the operation of the distributor advance mechanism(s): To test the mechanical advance, disconnect all but the mechanical advance, and observe the timing marks with a timing light as the engine speed is increased from idle. If the mark moves smoothly, without hesitation, it may be assumed that the mechanical advance is functioning properly. To test vacuum advance and/or retard systems, alternately crimp and release the vacuum line, and observe the timing mark for movement. If movement is noted, the system is operating.	If the systems are functioning: If the systems are not functioning, remove the distributor, and test on a distributor tester:	8.4 8.4
8.4—Locate an ignition miss: With the engine running, remove each spark plug wire, one by one, until one is found that doesn't cause the engine to roughen and slow down.	When the missing cylinder is identified:	4.1

Test and Procedure	Results and Indications	Proceed to
9.1—Evaluate the valve train: Remove the valve cover, and ensure that the valves are adjusted to specifications. A mechanic's stethoscope may be used to aid in the diagnosis of the valve train. By pushing the probe on or near push rods or rockers, valve noise often can be isolated. A timing light also may be used to diagnose valve problems. Connect the light according to manufacturer's recommendations, and start the engine. Vary the firing moment of the light by increasing the engine speed (and therefore the ignition advance), and moving the trigger from cylinder to cylinder. Observe the movement of each valve.	See below	See below

Observation	Probable Cause	Remedy	Proceed to
Metallic tap heard through the stethoscope.	Sticking hydraulic lifter or excessive valve clearance.	Adjust valve. If tap persists, remove and replace the lifter:	10.1
Metallic tap through the stethoscope, able to push the rocker arm (lifter side) down by hand.	Collapsed valve lifter.	Remove and replace the lifter:	10.1
Erratic, irregular motion of the valve stem.*	Sticking valve, burned valve.	Recondition the valve and/or valve guide:	Next Chapter
Eccentric motion of the pushrod at the rocker arm.*	Bent pushrod.	Replace the pushrod:	10.1
Valve retainer bounces as the valve closes.*	Weak valve spring or damper.	Remove and test the spring and damper. Replace if necessary:	10.1

*—When observed with a timing light.

Test and Procedure	Results and Indications	Proceed to
9.2—Check the valve timing: Locate top dead center of the No. 1 piston, and install a degree wheel or tape on the crankshaft pulley or damper with zero corresponding to an index mark on the engine. Rotate the crankshaft in its direction of rotation, and observe the opening of the No. 1 cylinder intake valve. The opening should correspond with the correct mark on the degree wheel according to specifications.	If the timing is not correct, the timing cover must be removed for further investigation:	

Test and Procedure	*Results and Indications*	*Proceed to*
10.1—Determine whether the exhaust manifold heat control valve is operating: Operate the valve by hand to determine whether it is free to move. If the valve is free, run the engine to operating temperature and observe the action of the valve, to ensure that it is opening.	If the valve sticks, spray it with a suitable solvent, open and close the valve to free it, and retest.	
	If the valve functions properly:	10.2
	If the valve does not free, or does not operate, replace the valve:	10.2
10.2—Ensure that there are no exhaust restrictions: Visually inspect the exhaust system for kinks, dents, or crushing. Also note that gasses are flowing freely from the tailpipe at all engine speeds, indicating no restriction in the muffler or resonator.	Replace any damaged portion of the system:	11.1
11.1—Visually inspect the fan belt for glazing, cracks, and fraying, and replace if necessary. Tighten the belt so that the longest span has approximately ½″ play at its midpoint under thumb pressure.	Replace or tighten the fan belt as necessary:	11.2

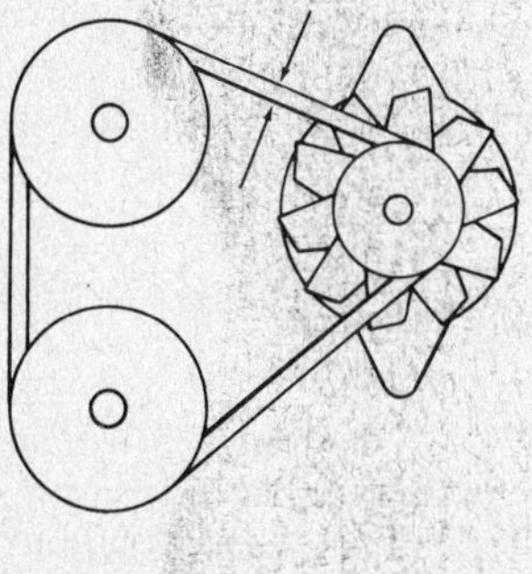

Checking the fan belt tension
(© Outboard Marine Corp.)

Test and Procedure	*Results and Indications*	*Proceed to*
11.2—Check the fluid level of the cooling system.	If full or slightly low, fill as necessary:	11.5
	If extremely low:	11.3
11.3—Visually inspect the external portions of the cooling system (radiator, radiator hoses, thermostat elbow, water pump seals, heater hoses, etc.) for leaks. If none are found, pressurize the cooling system to 14-15 psi.	If cooling system holds the pressure:	11.5
	If cooling system loses pressure rapidly, reinspect external parts of the system for leaks under pressure. If none are found, check dipstick for coolant in crankcase. If no coolant is present, but pressure loss continues:	11.4
	If coolant is evident in crankcase, remove cylinder head(s), and check gasket(s). If gaskets are intact, block and cylinder head(s) should be checked for cracks or holes.	
	If the gasket(s) is blown, replace, and purge the crankcase of coolant:	12.6
	NOTE: *Occasionally, due to atmospheric and driving conditions, condensation of water can occur in the crankcase. This causes the oil to appear milky white. To remedy, run the engine until hot, and change the oil and oil filter.*	

Test and Procedure	Results and Indication	Proceed to
11.4—Check for combustion leaks into the cooling system: Pressurize the cooling system as above. Start the engine, and observe the pressure gauge. If the needle fluctuates, remove each spark plug wire, one by one, noting which cylinder(s) reduce or eliminate the fluctuation.  **Radiator pressure tester** (© American Motors Corp.)	Cylinders which reduce or eliminate the fluctuation, when the spark plug wire is removed, are leaking into the cooling system. Replace the head gasket on the affected cylinder bank(s).	
11.5—Check the radiator pressure cap: Attach a radiator pressure tester to the radiator cap (wet the seal prior to installation). Quickly pump up the pressure, noting the point at which the cap releases.  **Testing the radiator pressure cap** (© American Motors Corp.)	If the cap releases within ± 1 psi of the specified rating, it is operating properly:	11.6
	If the cap releases at more than ± 1 psi of the specified rating, it should be replaced:	11.6
11.6—Test the thermostat: Start the engine cold, remove the radiator cap, and insert a thermometer into the radiator. Allow the engine to idle. After a short while, there will be a sudden, rapid increase in coolant temperature. The temperature at which this sharp rise stops is the thermostat opening temperature.	If the thermostat opens at or about the specified temperature:	11.7
	If the temperature doesn't increase: (If the temperature increases slowly and gradually, replace the thermostat.)	11.7
11.7—Check the water pump: Remove the thermostat elbow and the thermostat, disconnect the coil high tension lead (to prevent starting), and crank the engine momentarily.	If coolant flows, replace the thermostat and retest per 11.6:	11.6
	If coolant doesn't flow, reverse flush the cooling system to alleviate any blockage that might exist. If system is not blocked, and coolant will not flow, recondition the water pump.	—
12.1—Check the oil pressure gauge or warning light: If the gauge shows low pressure, or the light is on, for no obvious reason, remove the oil pressure sender. Install an accurate oil pressure gauge and run the engine momentarily.	If oil pressure builds normally, run engine for a few moments to determine that it is functioning normally, and replace the sender.	—
	If the pressure remains low:	12.2
	If the pressure surges:	12.3
	If the oil pressure is zero:	12.3

Test and Procedure	*Results and Indications*	*Proceed to*
12.2—Visually inspect the oil: If the oil is watery or very thin, milky, or foamy, replace the oil and oil filter.	If the oil is normal:	12.3
	If after replacing oil the pressure remains low:	12.3
	If after replacing oil the pressure becomes normal:	—
12.3—Inspect the oil pressure relief valve and spring, to ensure that it is not sticking or stuck. Remove and thoroughly clean the valve, spring, and the valve body.	If the oil pressure improves:	—
	If no improvement is noted:	12.4

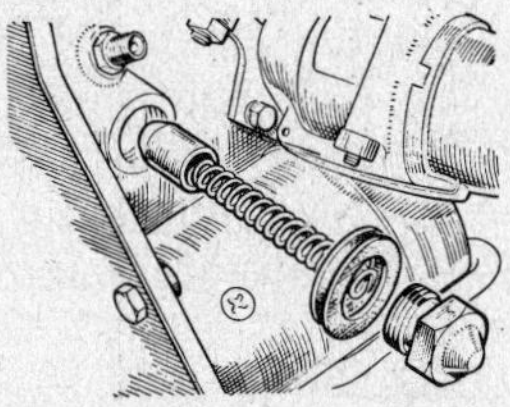

Oil pressure relief valve
(© British Leyland Motors)

Test and Procedure	*Results and Indications*	*Proceed to*
12.4—Check to ensure that the oil pump is not cavitating (sucking air instead of oil): See that the crankcase is neither over nor underfull, and that the pickup in the sump is in the proper position and free from sludge.	Fill or drain the crankcase to the proper capacity, and clean the pickup screen in solvent if necessary. If no improvement is noted:	12.5
12.5—Inspect the oil pump drive and the oil pump:	If the pump drive or the oil pump appear to be defective, service as necessary and retest per 12.1:	12.1
	If the pump drive and pump appear to be operating normally, the engine should be disassembled to determine where blockage exists:	Next Chapter
12.6—Purge the engine of ethylene glycol coolant: Completely drain the crankcase and the oil filter. Obtain a commercial butyl cellosolve base solvent, designated for this purpose, and follow the instructions precisely. Following this, install a new oil filter and refill the crankcase with the proper weight oil. The next oil and filter change should follow shortly thereafter (1000 miles).		

Engine Rebuilding

This section describes, in detail, the procedures involved in rebuilding a typical engine. The procedures specifically refer to an inline engine, however, they are basically identical to those used in rebuilding engines of nearly all design and configurations. Procedures for servicing atypical engines (i.e., horizontally opposed) are described in the appropriate section, although in most cases, cylinder head reconditioning procedures described in this chapter will apply.

The section is divided into two sections. The first, Cylinder Head Reconditioning, assumes that the cylinder head is removed from the engine, all manifolds are removed, and the cylinder head is on a workbench. The camshaft should be removed from overhead cam cylinder heads. The second section, Cylinder Block Reconditioning, covers the block, pistons, connecting rods and crankshaft. It is assumed that the engine is mounted on a work stand, and the cylinder head and all accessories are removed.

Procedures are identified as follows:

Unmarked—Basic procedures that must be performed in order to successfully complete the rebuilding process.

Starred (*)—Procedures that should be performed to ensure maximum performance and engine life.

Double starred (**)—Procedures that may be performed to increase engine performance and reliability. These procedures are usually reserved for extremely heavy-duty or competition usage.

In many cases, a choice of methods is also provided. Methods are identified in the same manner as procedures. The choice of method for a procedure is at the discretion of the user.

The tools required for the basic rebuilding procedure should, with minor exceptions, be those

TORQUE (ft. lbs.)*

U.S.

Bolt Diameter (inches)	*Bolt Grade (SAE)* 1 and 2	5	6	8	*Wrench Size (inches)* Bolt	Nut
1/4	5	7	10	10.5	3/8	7/16
5/16	9	14	19	22	1/2	9/16
3/8	15	25	34	37	9/16	5/8
7/16	24	40	55	60	5/8	3/4
1/2	37	60	85	92	3/4	13/16
9/16	53	88	120	132	7/8	7/8
5/8	74	120	167	180	15/16	1
3/4	120	200	280	296	1-1/8	1-1/8
7/8	190	302	440	473	1-5/16	1-5/16
1	282	466	660	714	1-1/2	1-1/2

Metric

Bolt Diameter (mm)	*Bolt Grade* 5D	8G	10K	12K	*Wrench Size (mm) Bolt and Nut*
6	5	6	8	10	10
8	10	16	22	27	14
10	19	31	40	49	17
12	34	54	70	86	19
14	55	89	117	137	22
16	83	132	175	208	24
18	111	182	236	283	27
22	182	284	394	464	32
24	261	419	570	689	36

*—Torque values are for lightly oiled bolts. CAUTION: Bolts threaded into aluminum require much less torque.

General Torque Specifications

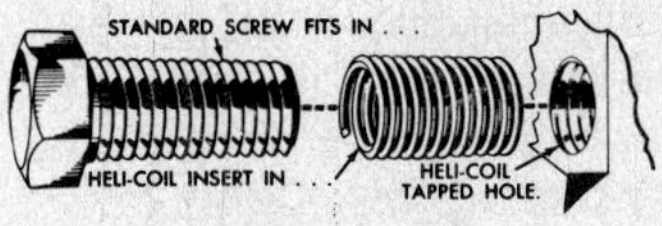
STANDARD SCREW FITS IN . . .
HELI-COIL INSERT IN . . .
HELI-COIL
TAPPED HOLE.

Heli-Coil installation
(© Chrysler Corp.)

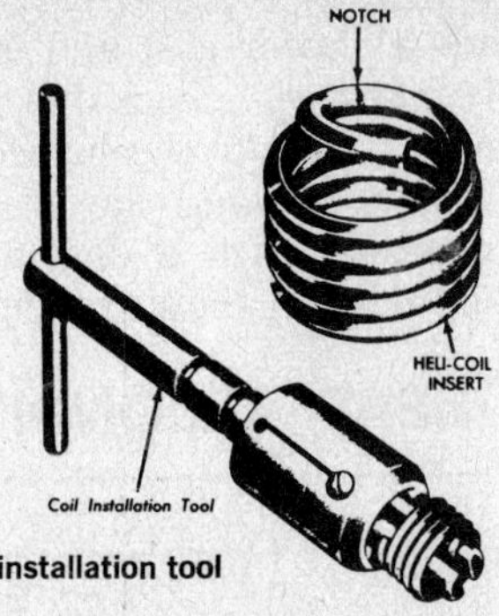
NOTCH
HELI-COIL
INSERT
Coil Installation Tool

Heli-Coil and installation tool

Heli-Coil Insert			*Drill*	*Tap*	*Insert. Tool*	*Extracting Tool*
Thread Size	*Part No.*	*Insert Length (In.)*	*Size*	*Part No.*	*Part No.*	*Part No.*
1/2 -20	1185-4	3/8	17/64(.266)	4 CPB	528-4N	1227-6
5/16-18	1185-5	15/32	Q(.332)	5 CPB	528-5N	1227-6
3/8 -16	1185-6	9/16	X(.397)	6 CPB	528-6N	1227-6
7/16-14	1185-7	21/32	29/64(.453)	7 CPB	528-7N	1227-16
1/2 -13	1185-8	3/4	33/64(.516)	8 CPB	528-8N	1227-16

Heli-Coil Specifications

included in a mechanic's tool kit. An accurate torque wrench, and a dial indicator (reading in thousandths) mounted on a universal base should be available. Bolts and nuts with no torque specification should be tightened according to size (see chart). Special tools, where required, all are readily available from the major tool suppliers (i.e., Craftsman, Snap-On, K-D). The services of a competent automotive machine shop must also be readily available.

When assembling the engine, any parts that will be in frictional contact must be pre-lubricated, to provide protection on initial start-up. Vortex Pre-Lube, STP, or any product specifically formulated for this purpose may be used. NOTE: *Do not use engine oil.* Where semi-permanent (locked but removable) installation of bolts or nuts is desired, threads should be cleaned and coated with Loctite. Studs may be permanently installed using Loctite Stud and Bearing Mount.

Aluminum has become increasingly popular for use in engines, due to its low weight and excellent heat transfer characteristics. The following precautions must be observed when handling aluminum engine parts:

—Never hot-tank aluminum parts.

—Remove all aluminum parts (identification tags, etc.) from engine parts before hot-tanking (otherwise they will be removed during the process).

—Always coat threads lightly with engine oil or anti-seize compounds before installation, to prevent seizure.

—Never over-torque bolts or spark plugs in aluminum threads. Should stripping occur, threads can be restored according to the following procedure, using Heli-Coil thread inserts:

Tap drill the hole with the stripped threads to the specified size (see chart). Using the specified tap (NOTE: *Heli-Coil tap sizes refer to the size thread being replaced, rather than the actual tap size*), tap the hole for the Heli-Coil. Place the insert on the proper installation tool (see chart). Apply pressure on the insert while winding it clockwise into the hole, until the top of the insert is one turn below the surface. Remove the installation tool, and break the installation tang from the bottom of the insert by moving it up and down. If the Heli-Coil must be removed, tap the removal tool firmly into the hole, so that it engages the top thread, and turn the tool counter-clockwise to extract the insert.

Snapped bolts or studs may be removed, using a stud extractor (unthreaded) or Vise-Grip pliers (threaded). Penetrating oil (e.g., Liquid Wrench) will often aid in breaking frozen threads. In cases where the stud or bolt is flush with, or below the surface, proceed as follows:

Drill a hole in the broken stud or bolt, approximately ½ its diameter. Select a screw extractor (e.g., Easy-Out) of the proper size, and tap it into the stud or bolt. Turn the extractor counterclockwise to remove the stud or bolt.

Magnaflux and Zyglo are inspection techniques used to locate material flaws, such as stress cracks. Magnafluxing coats the part with fine magnetic particles, and subjects the part to a magnetic field. Cracks cause breaks

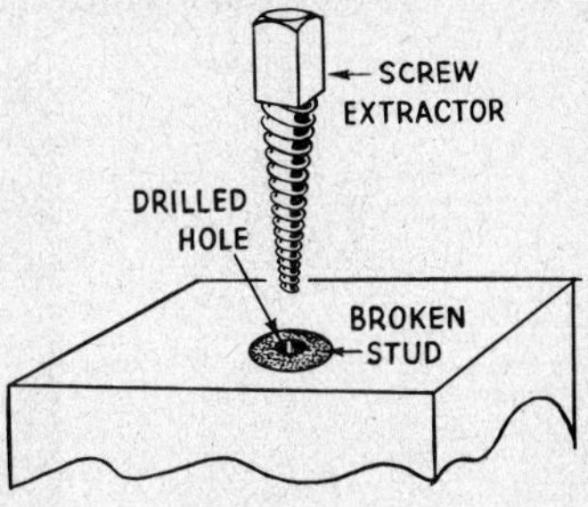
SCREW
EXTRACTOR
DRILLED
HOLE
BROKEN
STUD

Screw extractor

in the magnetic field, which are outlined by the particles. Since Magnaflux is a magnetic process, it is applicable only to ferrous materials. The Zyglo process coats the material with a fluorescent dye penetrant, and then subjects it to blacklight inspection, under which cracks glow bright-

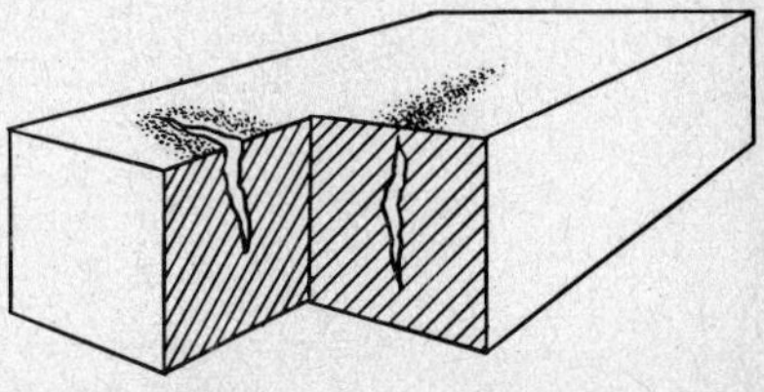

Magnaflux indication of cracks

ly. Parts made of any material may be tested using Zyglo. While Magnaflux and Zyglo are excellent for general inspection, and locating hidden defects, specific checks of suspected cracks may be made at lower cost and more readily using spot check dye. The dye is sprayed onto the suspected area, wiped off, and the area is then sprayed with a developer. Cracks then will show up brightly. Spot check dyes will only indicate surface cracks; therefore, structural cracks below the surface may escape detection. When questionable, the part should be tested using Magnaflux or Zyglo.

CYLINDER HEAD RECONDITIONING

Procedure	*Method*
Identify the valves:	Invert the cylinder head, and number the valve faces front to rear, using a permanent felt-tip marker.

Valve identification
(© SAAB)

Remove the rocker arms:	Remove the rocker arms with shaft(s) or balls and nuts. Wire the sets of rockers, balls and nuts together, and identify according to the corresponding valve.
Remove the valves and springs:	Using an appropriate valve spring compressor (depending on the configuration of the cylinder head), compress the valve springs. Lift out the keepers with needlenose pliers, release the compressor, and remove the valve, spring, and spring retainer.
Check the valve stem-to-guide clearance:	Clean the valve stem with lacquer thinner or a similar solvent to remove all gum and varnish. Clean the valve guides using solvent and an expanding wire-type valve guide cleaner. Mount a dial indicator so that the stem is at 90° to the valve stem, as close to the valve guide as possible. Move the valve off its seat, and measure the valve guide-to-stem clearance by moving the stem back and forth to actuate the dial indicator. Measure the valve stems using a micrometer, and compare to specifications, to determine whether stem or guide wear is responsible for excessive clearance.

Checking the valve stem-to-guide clearance
(© American Motors Corp.)

De-carbon the cylinder head and valves:	Chip carbon away from the valve heads, combustion chambers, and ports, using a chisel made of hardwood. Remove the remaining deposits with a stiff wire brush. NOTE: *Ensure that the deposits are actually removed, rather than burnished.*

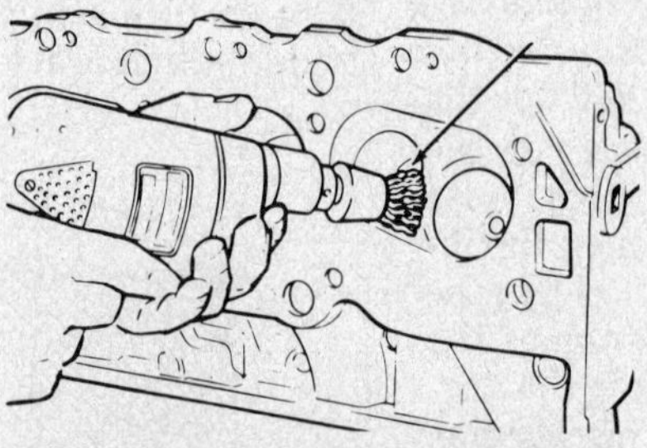

Removing carbon from the cylinder head
(© Outboard Marine Corp.)

Procedure	*Method*
Hot-tank the cylinder head:	Have the cylinder head hot-tanked to remove grease, corrosion, and scale from the water passages. NOTE: *In the case of overhead cam cylinder heads, consult the operator to determine whether the camshaft bearings will be damaged by the caustic solution.*
Degrease the remaining cylinder head parts:	Using solvent (i.e., Gunk), clean the rockers, rocker shaft(s) (where applicable), rocker balls and nuts, springs, spring retainers, and keepers. Do not remove the protective coating from the springs.

Check the cylinder head for warpage:

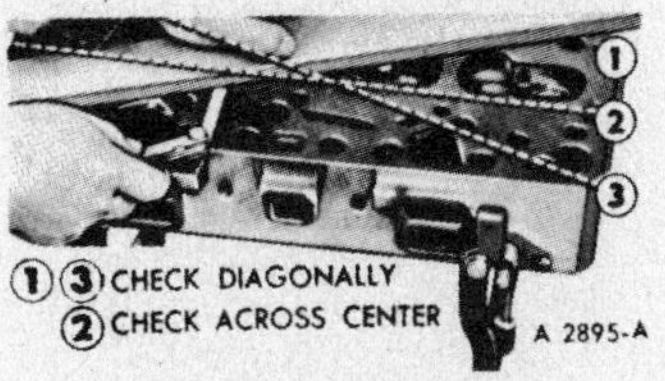
1
2
3
1 3 CHECK DIAGONALLY
2 CHECK ACROSS CENTER
A 2895-A

Checking the cylinder head for warpage
(© Ford Motor Co.)

Place a straight-edge across the gasket surface of the cylinder head. Using feeler gauges, determine the clearance at the center of the straight-edge. Measure across both diagonals, along the longitudinal centerline, and across the cylinder head at several points. If warpage exceeds .003″ in a 6″ span, or .006″ over the total length, the cylinder head must be resurfaced. NOTE: *If warpage exceeds the manufacturers maximum tolerance for material removal, the cylinder head must be replaced.* When milling the cylinder heads of V-type engines, the intake manifold mounting position is altered, and must be corrected by milling the manifold flange a proportionate amount.

** Porting and gasket matching:

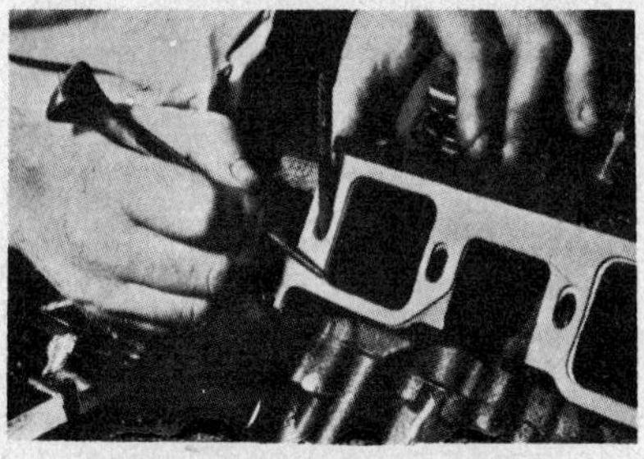

Marking the cylinder head for gasket matching
(© Petersen Publishing Co.)

Port configuration before and after gasket matching
(© Petersen Publishing Co.)

** Coat the manifold flanges of the cylinder head with Prussian blue dye. Glue intake and exhaust gaskets to the cylinder head in their installed position using rubber cement and scribe the outline of the ports on the manifold flanges. Remove the gaskets. Using a small cutter in a hand-held power tool (i.e., Dremel Moto-Tool), gradually taper the walls of the port out to the scribed outline of the gasket. Further enlargement of the ports should include the removal of sharp edges and radiusing of sharp corners. Do not alter the valve guides. NOTE: *The most efficient port configuration is determined only by extensive testing. Therefore, it is best to consult someone experienced with the head in question to determine the optimum alterations.*

Procedure	*Method*

** Polish the ports:

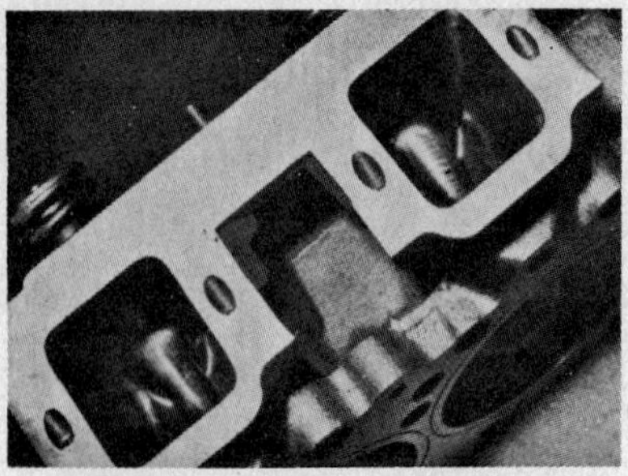

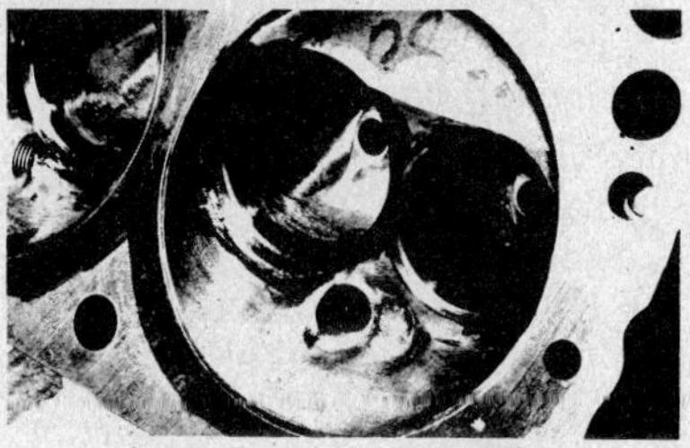

Polished combustion chamber
(© Petersen Publishing Co.)

** Using a grinding stone with the above mentioned tool, polish the walls of the intake and exhaust ports, and combustion chamber. Use progressively finer stones until all surface imperfections are removed. NOTE: *Through testing, it has been determined that a smooth surface is more effective than a mirror polished surface in intake ports, and vice-versa in exhaust ports.*

* Knurling the valve guides:

Cut-away view of a knurled valve guide
(© Petersen Publishing Co.)

* Valve guides which are not excessively worn or distorted may, in some cases, be knurled rather than replaced. Knurling is a process in which metal is displaced and raised, thereby reducing clearance. Knurling also provides excellent oil control. The possibility of knurling rather than replacing valve guides should be discussed with a machinist.

Replacing the valve guides: NOTE: *Valve guides should only be replaced if damaged or if an oversize valve stem is not available.*

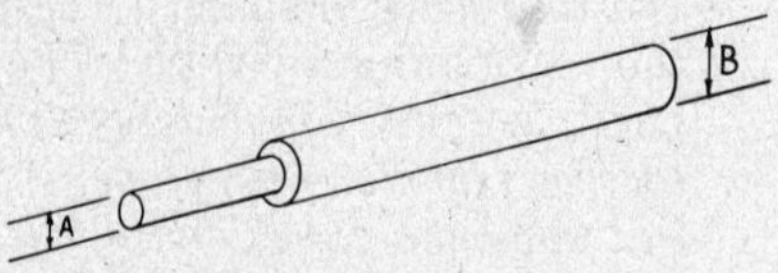
A
B

A-VALVE GUIDE I.D.
B-SLIGHTLY SMALLER THAN VALVE GUIDE O.D.

Valve guide removal tool

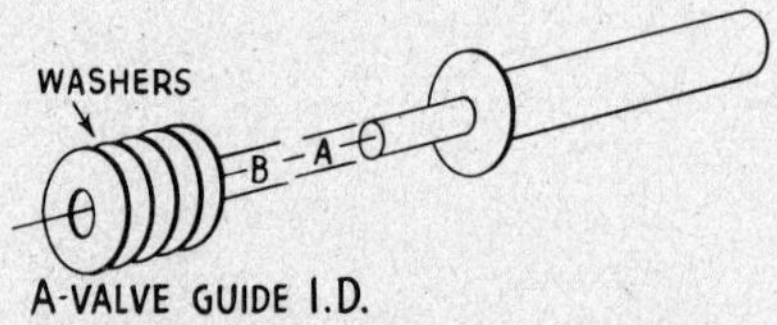
WASHERS
B
A

A-VALVE GUIDE I.D.
B-LARGER THAN THE VALVE GUIDE O.D.

Valve guide installation tool (with washers used during installation)

Depending on the type of cylinder head, valve guides may be pressed, hammered, or shrunk in. In cases where the guides are shrunk into the head, replacement should be left to an equipped machine shop. In other cases, the guides are replaced as follows: Press or tap the valve guides out of the head using a stepped drift (see illustration). Determine the height above the boss that the guide must extend, and obtain a stack of washers, their I.D. similar to the guide's O.D., of that height. Place the stack of washers on the guide, and insert the guide into the boss. NOTE: *Valve guides are often tapered or beveled for installation.* Using the stepped installation tool (see illustration), press or tap the guides into position. Ream the guides according to the size of the valve stem.

Procedure | *Method*

Replacing valve seat inserts:

Replacement of valve seat inserts which are worn beyond resurfacing or broken, if feasible, must be done by a machine shop.

Resurfacing (grinding) the valve face:

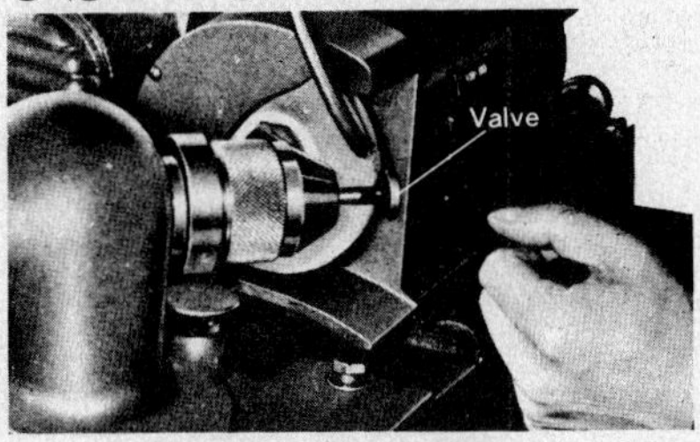
Valve

Grinding a valve
(© Subaru)

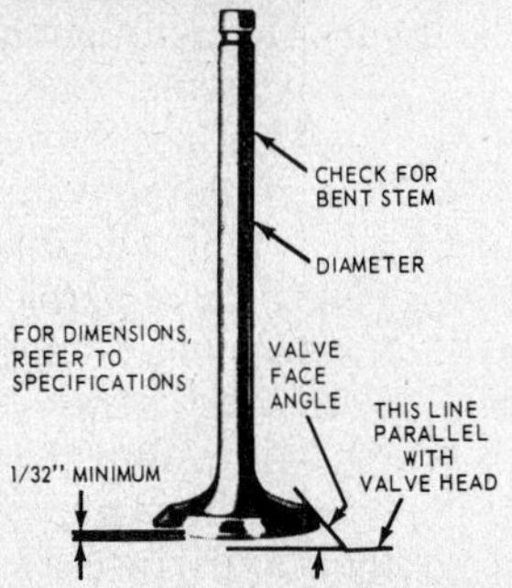
CHECK FOR
BENT STEM
DIAMETER
FOR DIMENSIONS,
REFER TO
SPECIFICATIONS
VALVE
FACE
ANGLE
THIS LINE
PARALLEL
WITH
VALVE HEAD
1/32" MINIMUM

Critical valve dimensions
(© Ford Motor Co.)

Using a valve grinder, resurface the valves according to specifications. CAUTION: *Valve face angle is not always identical to valve seat angle.* A minimum margin of 1/32" should remain after grinding the valve. The valve stem tip should also be squared and resurfaced, by placing the stem in the V-block of the grinder, and turning it while pressing lightly against the grinding wheel.

Resurfacing the valve seats using reamers:

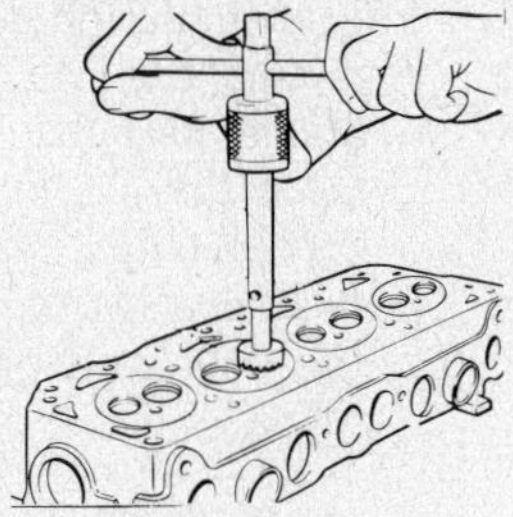

Reaming the valve seat
(© Outboard Marine Corp)

45°
VALVE SEAT
WIDTH
A 2897-A

Valve seat width and centering
(© Ford Motor Co.)

Select a reamer of the correct seat angle, slightly larger than the diameter of the valve seat, and assemble it with a pilot of the correct size. Install the pilot into the valve guide, and using steady pressure, turn the reamer clockwise. CAUTION: *Do not turn the reamer counter-clockwise.* Remove only as much material as necessary to clean the seat. Check the concentricity of the seat (see below). If the dye method is not used, coat the valve face with Prussian blue dye, install and rotate it on the valve seat. Using the dye marked area as a centering guide, center and narrow the valve seat to specifications with correction cutters. NOTE: *When no specifications are available, minimum seat width for exhaust valves should be 5/64", intake valves 1/16"*. After making correction cuts, check the position of the valve seat on the valve face using Prussian blue dye.

* Resurfacing the valve seats using a grinder:

Valve grinder

Grinding a valve seat
(© Subaru)

Select a pilot of the correct size, and a coarse stone of the correct seat angle. Lubricate the pilot if necessary, and install the tool in the valve guide. Move the stone on and off the seat at approximately two cycles per second, until all flaws are removed from the seat. Install a fine stone, and finish the seat. Center and narrow the seat using correction stones, as described above.

Procedure	*Method*
Checking the valve seat concentricity:	Coat the valve face with Prussian blue dye, install the valve, and rotate it on the valve seat. If the entire seat becomes coated, and the valve is known to be concentric, the seat is concentric.
	* Install the dial gauge pilot into the guide, and rest the arm on the valve seat. Zero the gauge, and rotate the arm around the seat. Run-out should not exceed .002″.

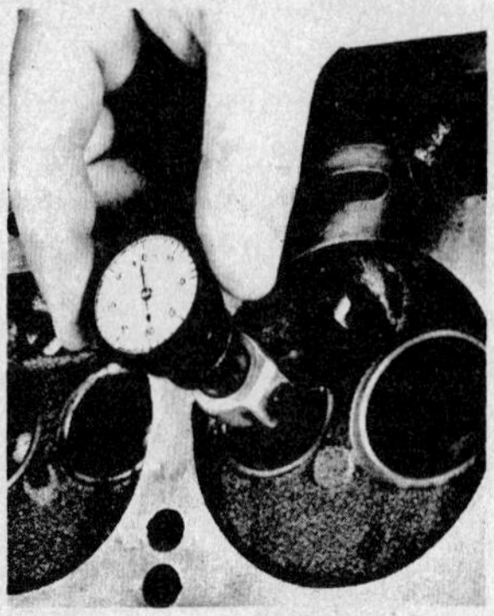

Checking the valve seat concentricity using a dial gauge (© American Motors Corp.)

Procedure	*Method*
* Lapping the valves: NOTE: *Valve lapping is done to ensure efficient sealing of resurfaced valves and seats. Valve lapping alone is not recommended for use as a resurfacing procedure.*	* Invert the cylinder head, lightly lubricate the valve stems, and install the valves in the head as numbered. Coat valve seats with fine grinding compound, and attach the lapping tool suction cup to a valve head (NOTE: *Moisten the suction cup*). Rotate the tool between the palms, changing position and lifting the tool often to prevent grooving. Lap the valve until a smooth, polished seat is evident. Remove the valve and tool, and rinse away all traces of grinding compound.
	** Fasten a suction cup to a piece of drill rod, and mount the rod in a hand drill. Proceed as above, using the hand drill as a lapping tool. CAUTION: *Due to the higher speeds involved when using the hand drill, care must be exercised to avoid grooving the seat.* Lift the tool and change direction of rotation often.

Hand lapping the valves

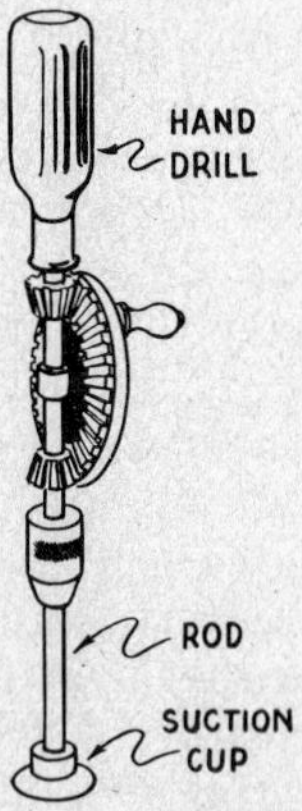
HAND
DRILL
ROD
SUCTION
CUP

Home made mechanical valve lapping tool

Procedure	*Method*
Check the valve springs:	Place the spring on a flat surface next to a square. Measure the height of the spring, and rotate it against the edge of the square to measure distortion. If spring height varies (by comparison) by more than 1/16″ or if distortion exceeds 1/16″, replace the spring.
	** In addition to evaluating the spring as above, test the spring pressure at the installed and compressed (installed height minus valve lift) height using a valve spring tester. Springs used on small displacement engines (up to 3 liters) should be ± 1 lb. of all other springs in either position. A tolerance of ± 5 lbs. is permissible on larger engines.

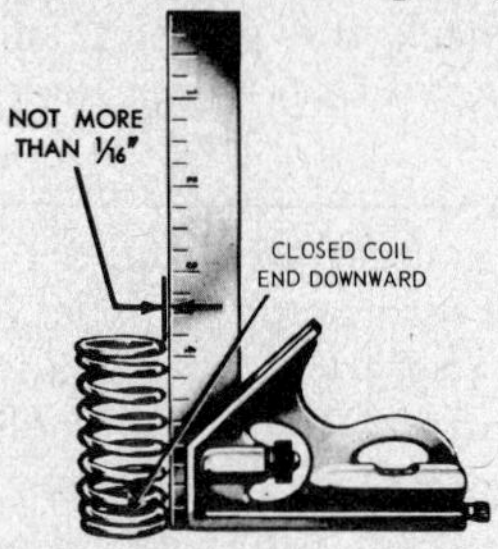
NOT MORE
THAN 1/16″
CLOSED COIL
END DOWNWARD

Checking the valve spring free length and squareness (© Ford Motor Co.)

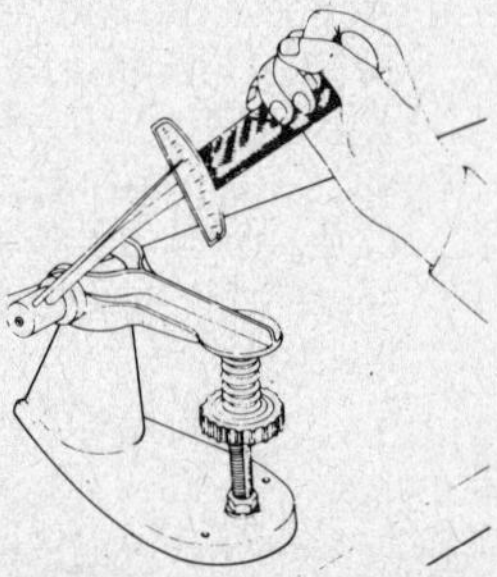

(© Outboard Marine Corp.)

Procedure	*Method*

* Install valve stem seals:

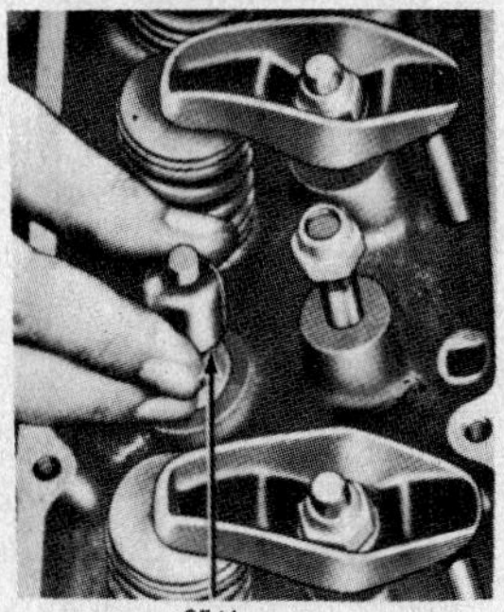
SEAL

Valve stem seal installation
(© Ford Motor Co.)

* Due to the pressure differential that exists at the ends of the intake valve guides (atmospheric pressure above, manifold vacuum below), oil is drawn through the valve guides into the intake port. This has been alleviated somewhat since the addition of positive crankcase ventilation, which lowers the pressure above the guides. Several types of valve stem seals are available to reduce blow-by. Certain seals simply slip over the stem and guide boss, while others require that the boss be machined. Recently, Teflon guide seals have become popular. Consult a parts supplier or machinist concerning availability and suggested usages. NOTE: *When installing seals, ensure that a small amount of oil is able to pass the seal to lubricate the valve guides; otherwise, excessive wear may result.*

Install the valves:

Lubricate the valve stems, and install the valves in the cylinder head as numbered. Lubricate and position the seals (if used, see above) and the valve springs. Install the spring retainers, compress the springs, and insert the keys using needlenose pliers or a tool designed for this purpose. NOTE: *Retain the keys with wheel bearing grease during installation.*

Checking valve spring installed height:

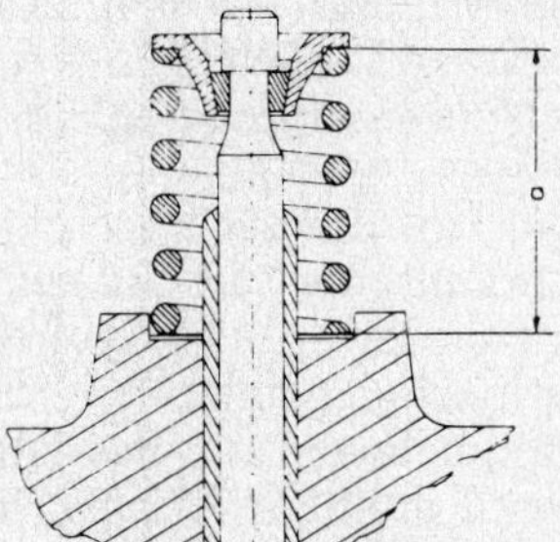

Valve spring installed height dimension
(© Porsche)

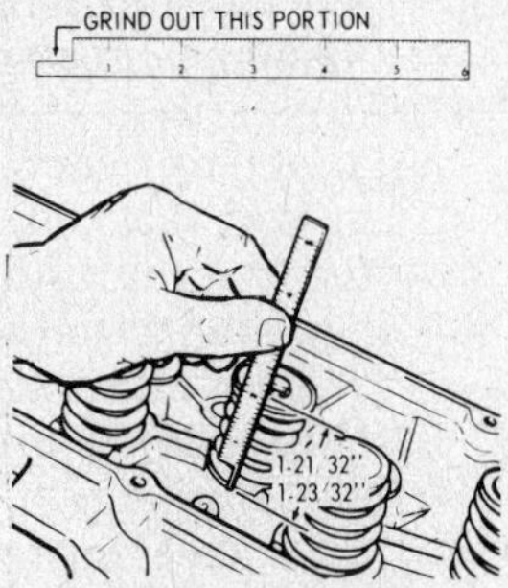
GRIND OUT THIS PORTION
1-21/32"
1-23/32"

Measuring valve spring installed height
(© Outboard Marine Corp.)

Measure the distance between the spring pad and the lower edge of the spring retainer, and compare to specifications. If the installed height is incorrect, add shim washers between the spring pad and the spring. CAUTION: *Use only washers designed for this purpose.*

** CC'ing the combustion chambers:

** Invert the cylinder head and place a bead of sealer around a combustion chamber. Install an apparatus designed for this purpose (burette mounted on a clear plate; see illustration) over the combustion chamber, and fill with the specified fluid to an even mark on the burette. Record the burette reading, and fill the combustion chamber with fluid. (NOTE: *A hole drilled in the plate will permit air to escape*). Subtract the burette reading, with the combustion chamber filled, from the previous reading, to determine combustion chamber volume in cc's. Duplicate this procedure in all combustion

Procedure | *Method*

CC'ing the combustion chamber (© Petersen Publishing Co.)

chambers on the cylinder head, and compare the readings. The volume of all combustion chambers should be made equal to that of the largest. Combustion chamber volume may be increased in two ways. When only a small change is required (usually), a small cutter or coarse stone may be used to remove material from the combustion chamber. NOTE: *Check volume frequently.* Remove material over a wide area, so as not to change the configuration of the combustion chamber. When a larger change is required, the valve seat may be sunk (lowered into the head). NOTE: *When altering valve seat, remember to compensate for the change in spring installed height.*

Inspect the rocker arms, balls, studs, and nuts (where applicable):

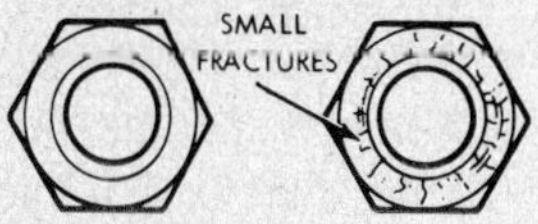
SMALL
FRACTURES

Stress cracks in rocker nuts (© Ford Motor Co.)

Visually inspect the rocker arms, balls, studs, and nuts for cracks, galling, burning, scoring, or wear. If all parts are intact, liberally lubricate the rocker arms and balls, and install them on the cylinder head. If wear is noted on a rocker arm at the point of valve contact, grind it smooth and square, removing as little material as possible. Replace the rocker arm if excessively worn. If a rocker stud shows signs of wear, it must be replaced (see below). If a rocker nut shows stress cracks, replace it. If an exhaust ball is galled or burned, substitute the intake ball from the same cylinder (if it is intact), and install a new intake ball. NOTE: *Avoid using new rocker balls on exhaust valves.*

Replacing rocker studs:

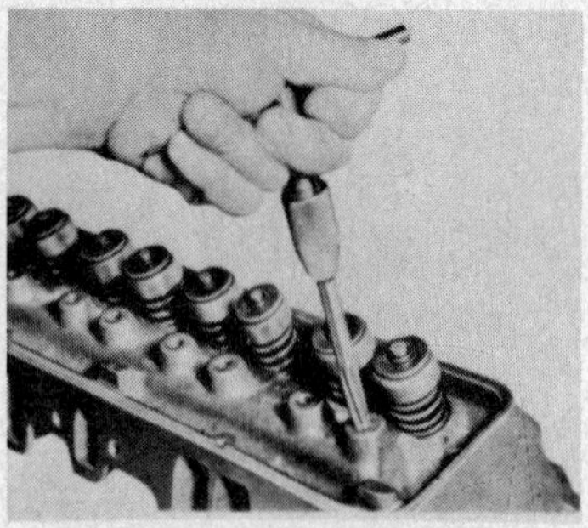

Reaming the stud bore for oversize rocker studs (© Buick Div. G.M. Corp.)

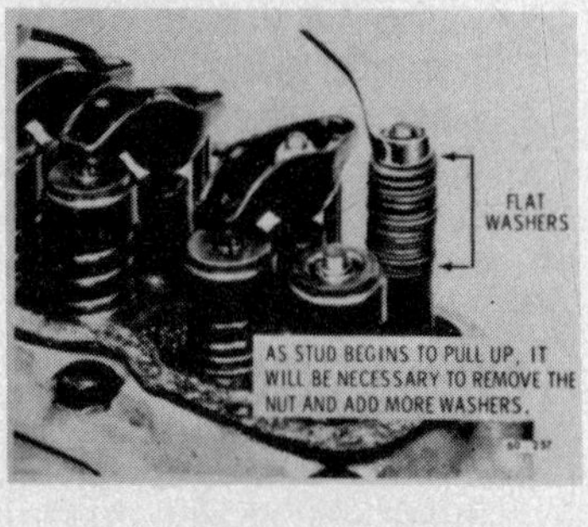
FLAT
WASHERS
AS STUD BEGINS TO PULL UP, IT
WILL BE NECESSARY TO REMOVE THE
NUT AND ADD MORE WASHERS.

Extracting a pressed in rocker stud (© Buick Div. G.M. Corp.)

In order to remove a threaded stud, lock two nuts on the stud, and unscrew the stud using the lower nut. Coat the lower threads of the new stud with Loctite, and install.

Two alternative methods are available for replacing pressed in studs. Remove the damaged stud using a stack of washers and a nut (see illustration). In the first, the boss is reamed .005-.006″ oversize, and an oversize stud pressed in. Control the stud extension over the boss using washers, in the same manner as valve guides. Before installing the stud, coat it with white lead and grease. To retain the stud more positively, drill a hole through the stud and boss, and install a roll pin. In the second method, the boss is tapped, and a threaded stud installed. Retain the stud using Loctite Stud and Bearing Mount.

Procedure	*Method*
Inspect the rocker shaft(s) and rocker arms (where applicable):	Remove rocker arms, springs and washers from rocker shaft. NOTE: *Lay out parts in the order they are removed.* Inspect rocker arms for pitting or wear on the valve contact point, or excessive bushing wear. Bushings need only be replaced if wear is excessive, because the rocker arm normally contacts the shaft at one point only. Grind the valve contact point of rocker arm smooth if necessary, removing as little material as possible. If excessive material must be removed to smooth and square the arm, it should be replaced. Clean out all oil holes and passages in rocker shaft. If shaft is grooved or worn, replace it. Lubricate and assemble the rocker shaft.

Disassembled rocker shaft parts arranged for inspection
(© American Motors Corp.)

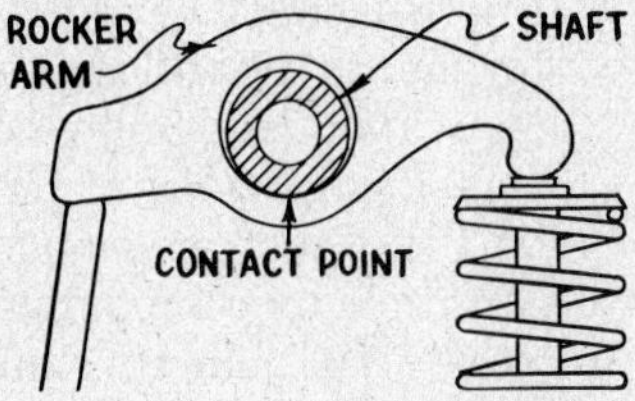
ROCKER ARM
SHAFT
CONTACT POINT

Rocker arm to rocker shaft contact

Procedure	*Method*
Inspect the camshaft bushings and the camshaft (overhead cam engines):	See next section.
Inspect the pushrods:	Remove the pushrods, and, if hollow, clean out the oil passages using fine wire. Roll each pushrod over a piece of clean glass. If a distinct clicking sound is heard as the pushrod rolls, the rod is bent, and must be replaced.
	* The length of all pushrods must be equal. Measure the length of the pushrods, compare to specifications, and replace as necessary.
Inspect the valve lifters:	Remove lifters from their bores, and remove gum and varnish, using solvent. Clean walls of lifter bores. Check lifters for concave wear as illustrated. If face is worn concave, replace lifter, and carefully inspect the camshaft. Lightly lubricate lifter and insert it into its bore. If play is excessive, an oversize lifter must be installed (where possible). Consult a machinist concerning feasibility. If play is satisfactory, remove, lubricate, and reinstall the lifter.

Check for Concave Wear on Face of Tappet Using Tappet for Straight Edge

Checking the lifter face
(© American Motors Corp.)

Procedure	*Method*
* Testing hydraulic lifter leak down:	Submerge lifter in a container of kerosene. Chuck a used pushrod or its equivalent into a drill press. Position container of kerosene so pushrod acts on the lifter plunger. Pump lifter with the drill press, until resistance increases. Pump several more times to bleed any air out of lifter. Apply very firm, constant pressure to the lifter, and observe rate at which fluid bleeds out of lifter. If the fluid bleeds very quickly (less than 15 seconds), lifter is defective. If the time exceeds 60 seconds, lifter is sticking. In either case, recondition or replace lifter. If lifter is operating properly (leak down time 15-60 seconds), lubricate and install it.

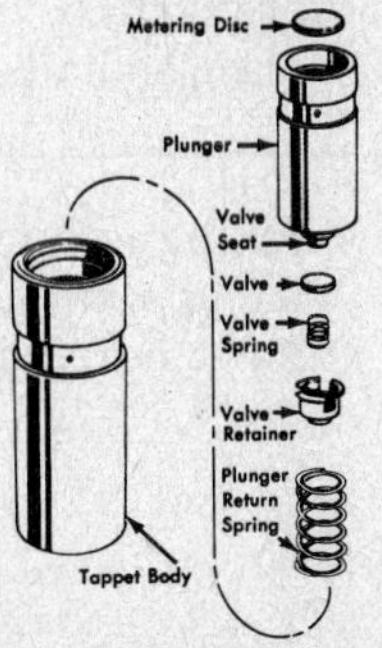
Lock Ring
Plunger Cap
Push Rod Socket
Metering Disc
Plunger
Valve Seat
Valve
Valve Spring
Valve Retainer
Plunger Return Spring
Tappet Body

Exploded view of a typical hydraulic lifter
(© American Motors Corp.)

CYLINDER BLOCK RECONDITIONING

Procedure	*Method*

Checking the main bearing clearance:

Plastigage installed on main bearing journal
(© Chevrolet Div. G.M. Corp.)

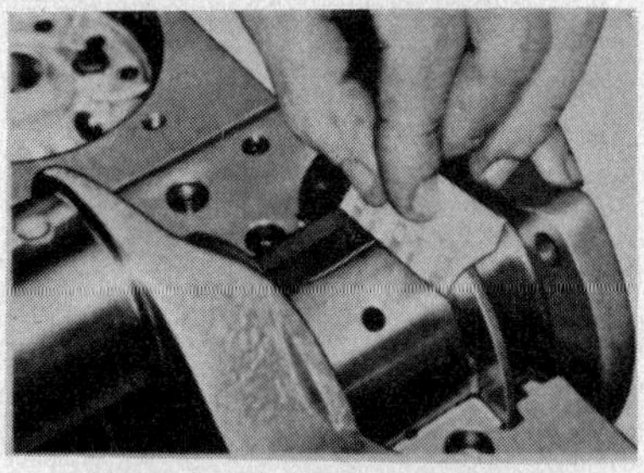

Measuring Plastigage to determine main bearing clearance
(© Chevrolet Div. G.M. Corp.)

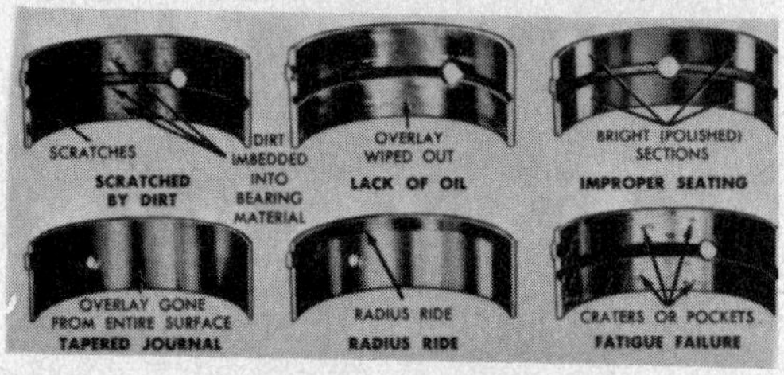
SCRATCHES
DIRT IMBEDDED INTO BEARING MATERIAL
SCRATCHED BY DIRT
OVERLAY WIPED OUT
LACK OF OIL
BRIGHT (POLISHED) SECTIONS
IMPROPER SEATING
OVERLAY GONE FROM ENTIRE SURFACE
TAPERED JOURNAL
RADIUS RIDE
RADIUS RIDE
CRATERS OR POCKETS
FATIGUE FAILURE

Causes of bearing failure
(© Ford Motor Co.)

Invert engine, and remove cap from the bearing to be checked. Using a clean, dry rag, thoroughly clean all oil from crankshaft journal and bearing insert. NOTE: *Plastigage is soluble in oil; therefore, oil on the journal or bearing could result in erroneous readings.* Place a piece of Plastigage along the full length of journal, reinstall cap, and torque to specifications. Remove bearing cap, and determine bearing clearance by comparing width of Plastigage to the scale on Plastigage envelope. Journal taper is determined by comparing width of the Plastigage strip near its ends. Rotate crankshaft 90° and retest, to determine journal eccentricity. NOTE: *Do not rotate crankshaft with Plastigage installed.* If bearing insert and journal appear intact, and are within tolerances, no further main bearing service is required. If bearing or journal appear defective, cause of failure should be determined before replacement.

* Remove crankshaft from block (see below). Measure the main bearing journals at each end twice (90° apart) using a micrometer, to determine diameter, journal taper and eccentricity. If journals are within tolerances, reinstall bearing caps at their specified torque. Using a telescope gauge and micrometer, measure bearing I.D. parallel to piston axis and at 30° on each side of piston axis. Subtract journal O.D. from bearing I.D. to determine oil clearance. If crankshaft journals appear defective, or do not meet tolerances, there is no need to measure bearings; for the crankshaft will require grinding and/or undersize bearings will be required. If bearing appears defective, cause for failure should be determined prior to replacement.

Checking the connecting rod bearing clearance:

Plastigage installed on connecting rod bearing journal
(© Chevrolet Div. G.M. Corp.)

Connecting rod bearing clearance is checked in the same manner as main bearing clearance, using Plastigage. Before removing the crankshaft, connecting rod side clearance also should be measured and recorded.

* Checking connecting rod bearing clearance, using a micrometer, is identical to checking main bearing clearance. If no other service

Procedure	*Method*

is required, the piston and rod assemblies need not be removed.

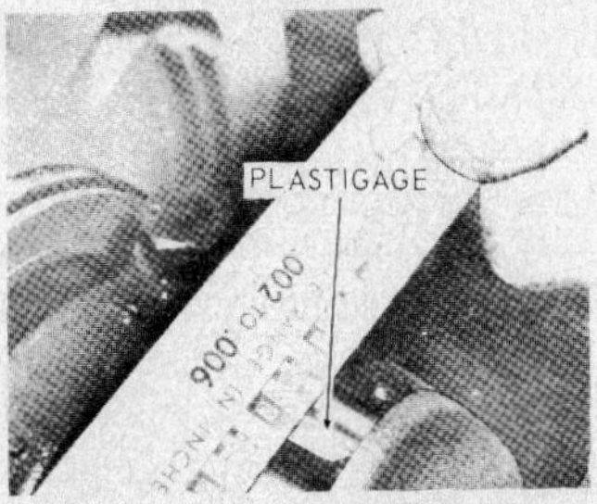
PLASTIGAGE

Measuring Plastigage to determine connecting rod bearing clearance
(© Outboard Marine Corp.)

Removing the crankshaft:

Connecting rod matching marks
(© Ford Motor Co.)

Using a punch, mark the corresponding main bearing caps and saddles according to position (i.e., one punch on the front main cap and saddle, two on the second, three on the third, etc.). Using number stamps, identify the corresponding connecting rods and caps, according to cylinder (if no numbers are present). Remove the main and connecting rod caps, and place sleeves of plastic tubing over the connecting rod bolts, to protect the journals as the crankshaft is removed. Lift the crankshaft out of the block.

Remove the ridge from the top of the cylinder:

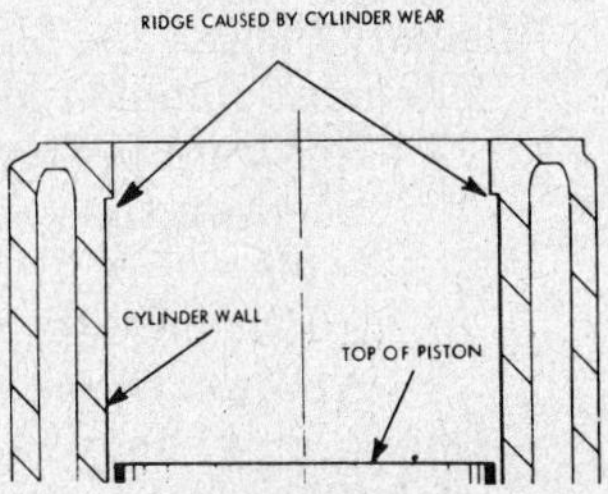
RIDGE CAUSED BY CYLINDER WEAR
CYLINDER WALL
TOP OF PISTON

Cylinder bore ridge
(© Pontiac Div. G.M. Corp.)

In order to facilitate removal of the piston and connecting rod, the ridge at the top of the cylinder (unworn area; see illustration) must be removed. Place the piston at the bottom of the bore, and cover it with a rag. Cut the ridge away using a ridge reamer, exercising extreme care to avoid cutting too deeply. Remove the rag, and remove cuttings that remain on the piston. CAUTION: *If the ridge is not removed, and new rings are installed, damage to rings will result.*

Removing the piston and connecting rod:

Removing the piston
(© SAAB)

Invert the engine, and push the pistons and connecting rods out of the cylinders. If necessary, tap the connecting rod boss with a wooden hammer handle, to force the piston out. CAUTION: *Do not attempt to force the piston past the cylinder ridge* (see above).

Procedure	Method
Service the crankshaft:	Ensure that all oil holes and passages in the crankshaft are open and free of sludge. If necessary, have the crankshaft ground to the largest possible undersize.
	** Have the crankshaft Magnafluxed, to locate stress cracks. Consult a machinist concerning additional service procedures, such as surface hardening (e.g., nitriding, Tuftriding) to improve wear characteristics, cross drilling and chamfering the oil holes to improve lubrication, and balancing.
Removing freeze plugs:	Drill a hole in the center of the freeze plugs, and pry them out using a screwdriver or drift.
Remove the oil gallery plugs:	Threaded plugs should be removed using an appropriate (usually square) wrench. To remove soft, pressed in plugs, drill a hole in the plug, and thread in a sheet metal screw. Pull the plug out by the screw using pliers.
Hot-tank the block:	Have the block hot-tanked to remove grease, corrosion, and scale from the water jackets. NOTE: *Consult the operator to determine whether the camshaft bearings will be damaged during the hot-tank process.*
Check the block for cracks:	Visually inspect the block for cracks or chips. The most common locations are as follows: Adjacent to freeze plugs. Between the cylinders and water jackets. Adjacent to the main bearing saddles. At the extreme bottom of the cylinders. Check only suspected cracks using spot check dye (see introduction). If a crack is located, consult a machinist concerning possible repairs.
	** Magnaflux the block to locate hidden cracks. If cracks are located, consult a machinist about feasibility of repair.
Install the oil gallery plugs and freeze plugs:	Coat freeze plugs with sealer and tap into position using a piece of pipe, slightly smaller than the plug, as a driver. To ensure retention, stake the edges of the plugs. Coat threaded oil gallery plugs with sealer and install. Drive replacement soft plugs into block using a large drift as a driver.
	* Rather than reinstalling lead plugs, drill and tap the holes, and install threaded plugs.

Procedure	Method
Check the bore diameter and surface:	Visually inspect the cylinder bores for roughness, scoring, or scuffing. If evident, the cylinder bore must be bored or honed oversize to eliminate imperfections, and the smallest possible oversize piston used. The new pistons should be given to the machinist with the block, so that the cylinders can be bored or honed exactly to the piston size (plus clearance). If no flaws are evident, measure the bore diameter using a telescope gauge and micrometer, or dial gauge, parallel and perpendicular to the engine centerline, at the top (below the ridge) and bottom of the bore. Subtract the bottom measurements from the top to determine taper, and the parallel to the centerline measurements from the perpendicular measurements to determine eccentricity. If the measurements are not within specifications, the cylinder must be bored or honed, and an oversize piston installed. If the measurements are within specifications the cylinder may be used as is, with only finish honing (see below). NOTE: *Prior to submitting the block for boring, perform the following operation(s).*

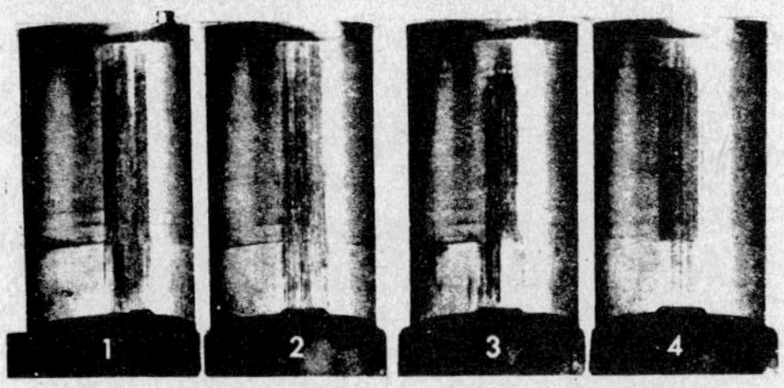

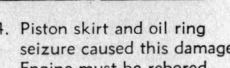

1, 2, 3 Piston skirt seizure resulted in this pattern. Engine must be rebored

4. Piston skirt and oil ring seizure caused this damage. Engine must be rebored

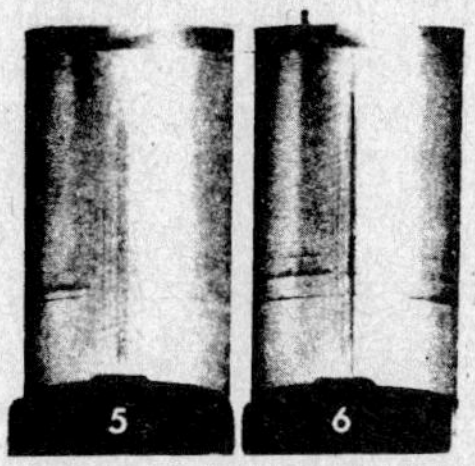

5, 6 Score marks caused by a split piston skirt. Damage is not serious enough to warrant reboring

7. Ring seized longitudinally, causing a score mark 1 3/16" wide, on the land side of the piston groove. The honing pattern is destroyed and the cylinder must be rebored

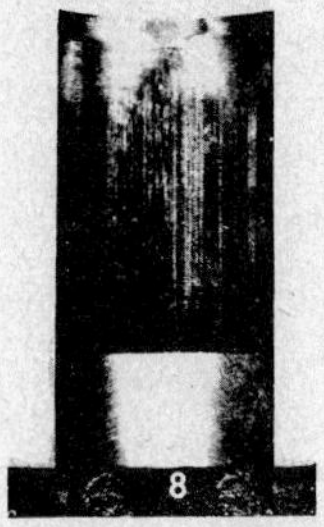

8. Result of oil ring seizure. Engine must be rebored

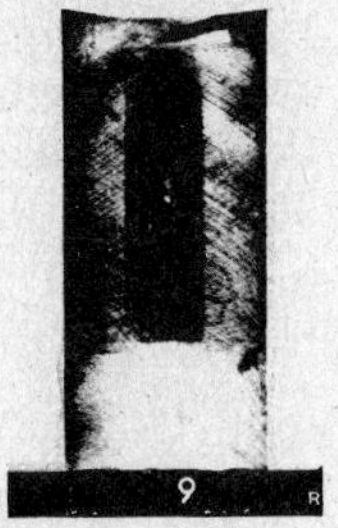

9. Oil ring seizure here was not serious enough to warrant reboring. The honing marks are still visible

Cylinder wall damage
(© Daimler-Benz A.G.)

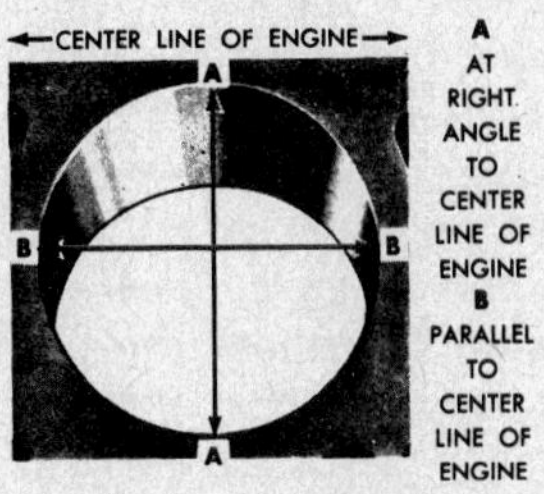
CENTER LINE OF ENGINE
A
B
B
A
A AT RIGHT ANGLE TO CENTER LINE OF ENGINE
B PARALLEL TO CENTER LINE OF ENGINE

Cylinder bore measuring positions
(© Ford Motor Co.)

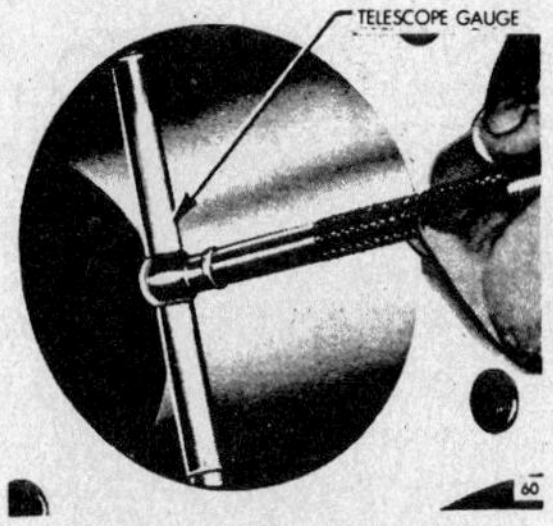
TELESCOPE GAUGE

Measuring the cylinder bore with a telescope gauge
(© Buick Div. G.M. Corp.)

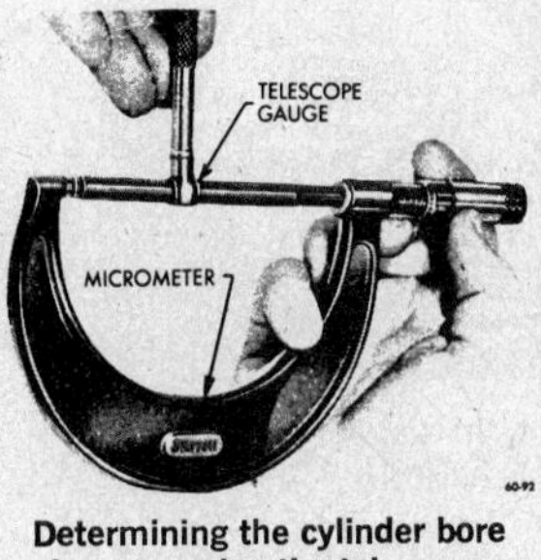
TELESCOPE GAUGE
MICROMETER

Determining the cylinder bore by measuring the telescope gauge with a micrometer
(© Buick Div. G.M. Corp.)

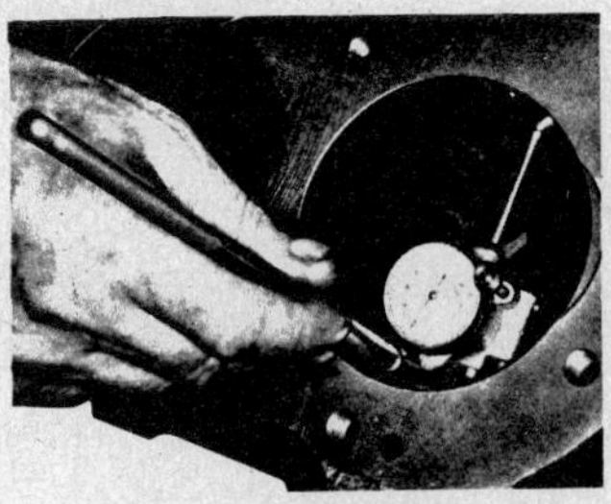

Measuring the cylinder bore with a dial gauge
(© Chevrolet Div. G.M. Corp.)

Procedure	*Method*
Check the block deck for warpage:	Using a straightedge and feeler gauges, check the block deck for warpage in the same manner that the cylinder head is checked (see Cylinder Head Reconditioning). If warpage exceeds specifications, have the deck resurfaced. NOTE: *In certain cases a specification for total material removal (Cylinder head and block deck) is provided. This specification must not be exceeded.*
* Check the deck height:	The deck height is the distance from the crankshaft centerline to the block deck. To measure, invert the engine, and install the crankshaft, retaining it with the center main cap. Measure the distance from the crankshaft journal to the block deck, parallel to the cylinder centerline. Measure the diameter of the end (front and rear) main journals, parallel to the centerline of the cylinders, divide the diameter in half, and subtract it from the previous measurement. The results of the front and rear measurements should be identical. If the difference exceeds .005″, the deck height should be corrected. NOTE: *Block deck height and warpage should be corrected concurrently.*
Check the cylinder block bearing alignment: 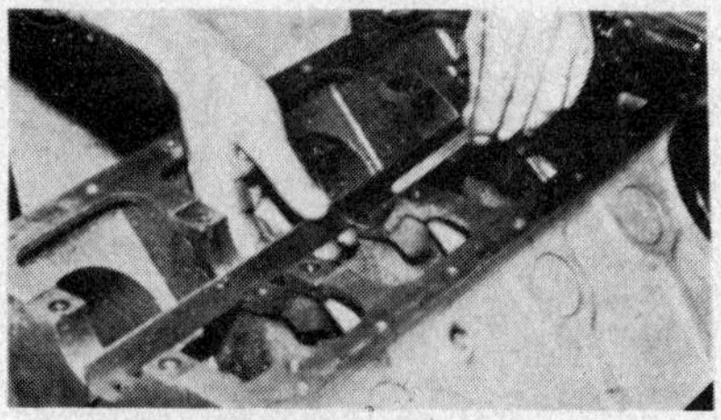 **Checking main bearing saddle alignment** (© Petersen Publishing Co.)	Remove the upper bearing inserts. Place a straightedge in the bearing saddles along the centerline of the crankshaft. If clearance exists between the straightedge and the center saddle, the block must be alignbored.
Clean and inspect the pistons and connecting rods: 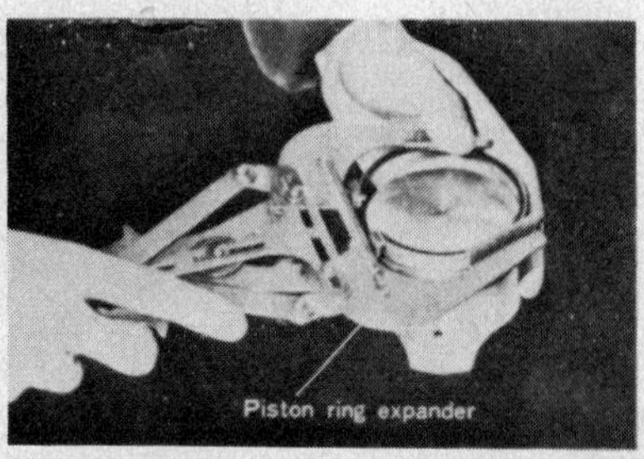 Piston ring expander **Removing the piston rings** (© Subaru)	Using a ring expander, remove the rings from the piston. Remove the retaining rings (if so equipped) and remove piston pin. NOTE: *If the piston pin must be pressed out, determine the proper method and use the proper tools; otherwise the piston will distort.* Clean the ring grooves using an appropriate tool, exercising care to avoid cutting too deeply. Thoroughly clean all carbon and varnish from the piston with solvent. CAUTION: *Do not use a wire brush or caustic solvent on pistons.* Inspect the pistons for scuffing, scoring, cracks, pitting, or excessive ring groove wear. If wear is evident, the piston must be replaced. Check the connecting rod length by measuring the rod from the inside of the large end to the inside of the small end using calipers (see

Procedure	*Method*

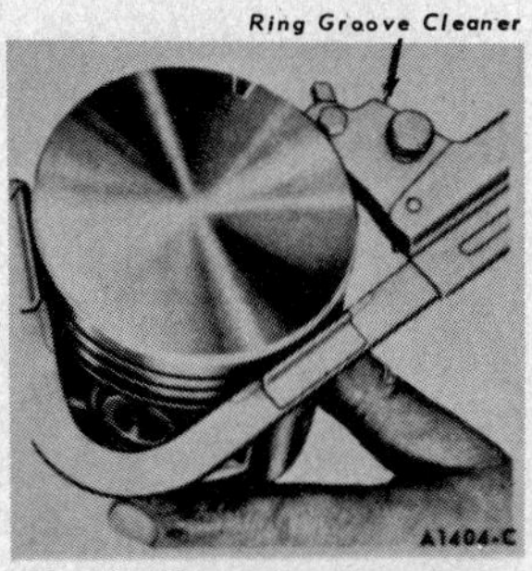
Ring Groove Cleaner
A1404-C

Cleaning the piston ring grooves
(© Ford Motor Co.)

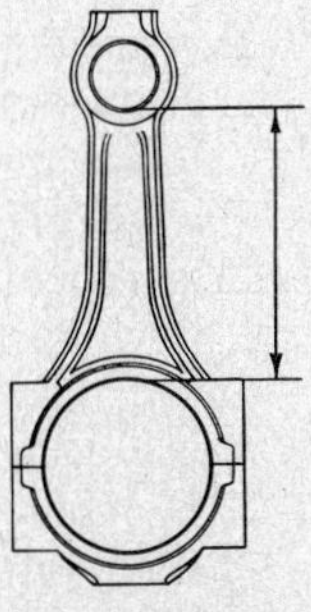

Connecting rod length checking dimension

illustration). All connecting rods should be equal length. Replace any rod that differs from the others in the engine.

* Have the connecting rod alignment checked in an alignment fixture by a machinist. Replace any twisted or bent rods.

* Magnaflux the connecting rods to locate stress cracks. If cracks are found, replace the connecting rod.

Fit the pistons to the cylinders:

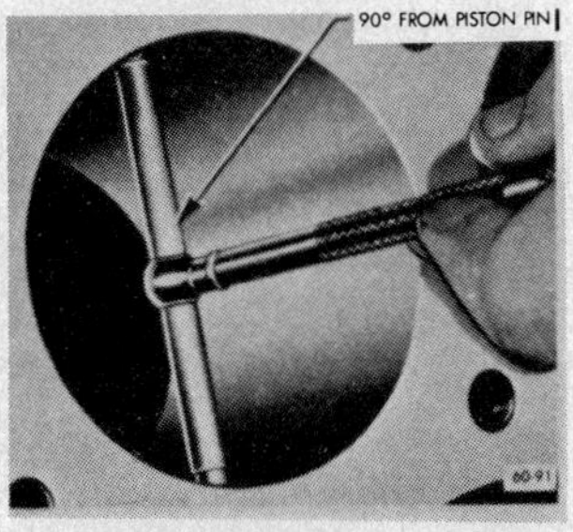
90° FROM PISTON PIN

Measuring the cylinder with a telescope gauge for piston fitting
(© Buick Div. G.M. Corp.)

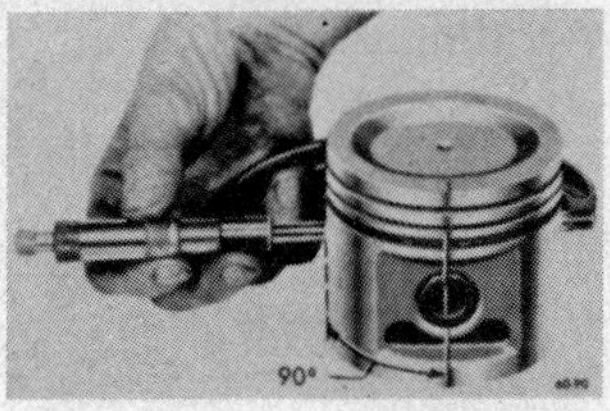
90°

Measuring the piston for fitting
(© Buick Div. G.M. Corp.)

Using a telescope gauge and micrometer, or a dial gauge, measure the cylinder bore diameter perpendicular to the piston pin, $2\frac{1}{2}''$ below the deck. Measure the piston perpendicular to its pin on the skirt. The difference between the two measurements is the piston clearance. If the clearance is within specifications or slightly below (after boring or honing), finish honing is all that is required. If the clearance is excessive, try to obtain a slightly larger piston to bring clearance within specifications. Where this is not possible, obtain the first oversize piston, and hone (or if necessary, bore) the cylinder to size.

Assemble the pistons and connecting rods:

Installing piston pin lock rings
(© Nissan Motor Co., Ltd.)

Inspect piston pin, connecting rod small end bushing, and piston bore for galling, scoring, or excessive wear. If evident, replace defective part(s). Measure the I.D. of the piston boss and connecting rod small end, and the O.D. of the piston pin. If within specifications, assemble piston pin and rod. CAUTION: *If piston pin must be pressed in, determine the proper method and use the proper tools; otherwise the piston will distort.* Install the lock rings; ensure that they seat properly. If the parts are not within specifications, determine the service method for the type of engine. In some cases, piston and pin are serviced as an assembly when either is defective. Others specify reaming the piston and connecting rods for an oversize pin. If the connecting rod bushing is worn, it may in many cases be replaced. Reaming the piston and replacing the rod bushing are machine shop operations.

Procedure	Method

Clean and inspect the camshaft:

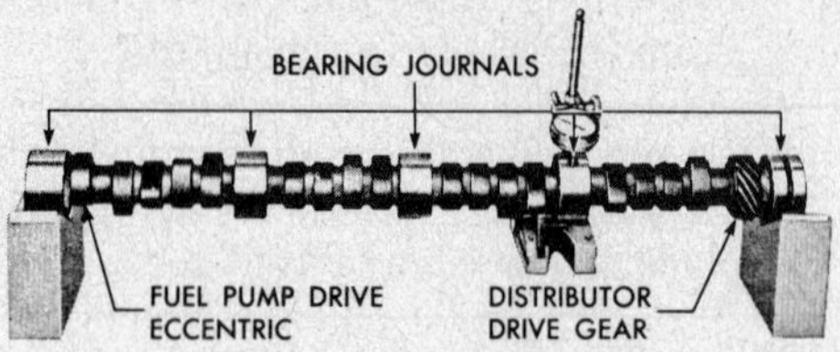
BEARING JOURNALS
FUEL PUMP DRIVE ECCENTRIC
DISTRIBUTOR DRIVE GEAR

Checking the camshaft for straightness
(© Chevrolet Motor Div. G.M. Corp.)

Degrease the camshaft, using solvent, and clean out all oil holes. Visually inspect cam lobes and bearing journals for excessive wear. If a lobe is questionable, check all lobes as indicated below. If a journal or lobe is worn, the camshaft must be reground or replaced. NOTE: *If a journal is worn, there is a good chance that the bushings are worn.* If lobes and journals appear intact, place the front and rear journals in V-blocks, and rest a dial indicator on the center journal. Rotate the camshaft to check straightness. If deviation exceeds .001″, replace the camshaft.

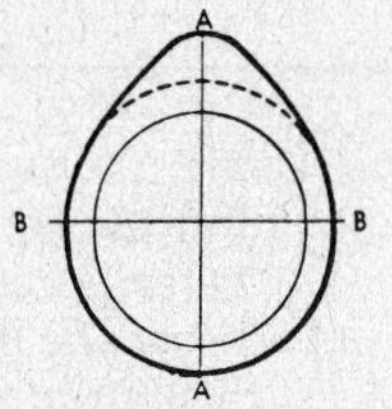
A
B
B
A

Camshaft lobe measurement
(© Ford Motor Co.)

* Check the camshaft lobes with a micrometer, by measuring the lobes from the nose to base and again at 90° (see illustration). The lift is determined by subtracting the second measurement from the first. If all exhaust lobes and all intake lobes are not identical, the camshaft must be reground or replaced.

Replace the camshaft bearings:

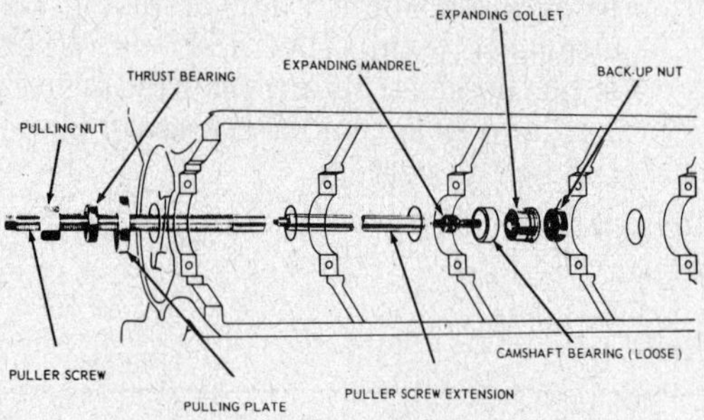
EXPANDING COLLET
EXPANDING MANDREL
THRUST BEARING
BACK-UP NUT
PULLING NUT
CAMSHAFT BEARING (LOOSE)
PULLER SCREW
PULLER SCREW EXTENSION
PULLING PLATE

Camshaft removal and installation tool (typical)
(© Ford Motor Co.)

If excessive wear is indicated, or if the engine is being completely rebuilt, camshaft bearings should be replaced as follows: Drive the camshaft rear plug from the block. Assemble the removal puller with its shoulder on the bearing to be removed. Gradually tighten the puller nut until bearing is removed. Remove remaining bearings, leaving the front and rear for last. To remove front and rear bearings, reverse position of the tool, so as to pull the bearings in toward the center of the block. Leave the tool in this position, pilot the new front and rear bearings on the installer, and pull them into position. Return the tool to its original position and pull remaining bearings into position. NOTE: *Ensure that oil holes align when installing bearings.* Replace camshaft rear plug, and stake it into position to aid retention.

Finish hone the cylinders:

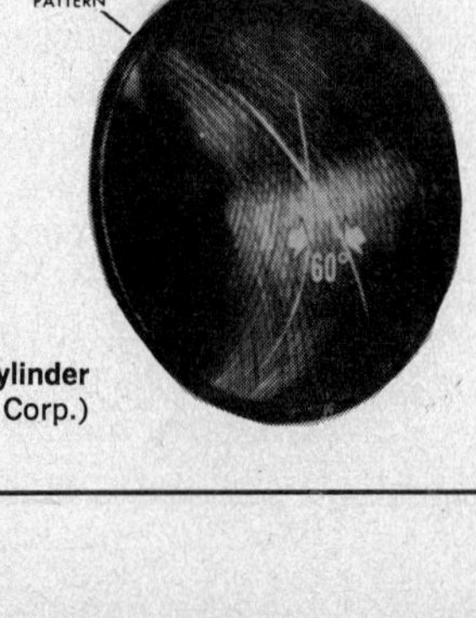
CROSS-HATCH PATTERN
60°

Finish honed cylinder
(© Chrysler Corp.)

Chuck a flexible drive hone into a power drill, and insert it into the cylinder. Start the hone, and move it up and down in the cylinder at a rate which will produce approximately a 60° cross-hatch pattern (see illustration). NOTE: *Do not extend the hone below the cylinder bore.* After developing the pattern, remove the hone and recheck piston fit. Wash the cylinders with a detergent and water solution to remove abrasive dust, dry, and wipe several times with a rag soaked in engine oil.

Procedure	*Method*
Check piston ring end-gap:	Compress the piston rings to be used in a cylinder, one at a time, into that cylinder, and press them approximately 1″ below the deck with an inverted piston. Using feeler gauges, measure the ring end-gap, and compare to specifications. Pull the ring out of the cylinder and file the ends with a fine file to obtain proper clearance. CAUTION: *If inadequate ring end-gap is utilized, ring breakage will result.*

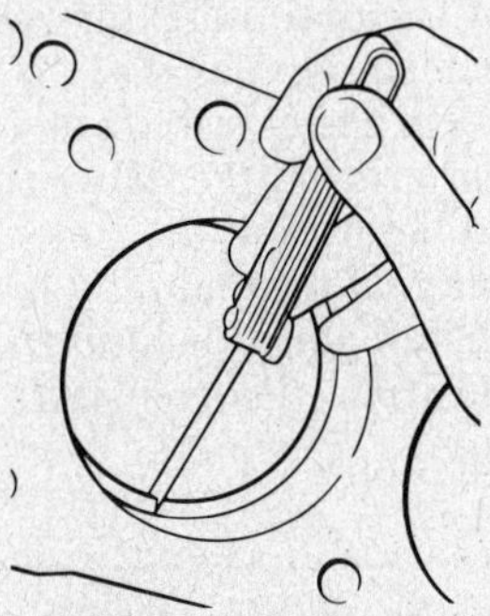

Checking ring end-gap
(© Outboard Marine Corp.)

Install the piston rings:	Inspect the ring grooves in the piston for excessive wear or taper. If necessary, recut the groove(s) for use with an overwidth ring or a standard ring and spacer. If the groove is worn uniformly, overwidth rings, or standard rings and spacers may be installed without recutting. Roll the outside of the ring around the groove to check for burrs or deposits. If any are found, remove with a fine file. Hold the ring in the groove, and measure side clearance. If necessary, correct as indicated above. NOTE: *Always install any additional spacers above the piston ring.* The ring groove must be deep enough to allow the ring to seat below the lands (see illustration). In many cases, a "go-no-go" depth gauge will be provided with the piston rings. Shallow grooves may be corrected by recutting, while deep grooves require some type of filler or expander behind the piston. Consult the piston ring supplier concerning the suggested method. Install the rings on the piston, lowest ring first, using a ring expander. NOTE: *Position the ring markings as specified by the manufacturer (see car section).*

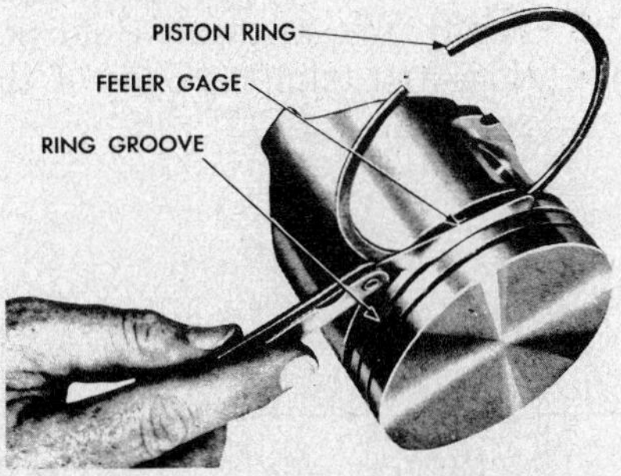
PISTON RING
FEELER GAGE
RING GROOVE

Checking ring side clearance
(© Chrysler Corp.)

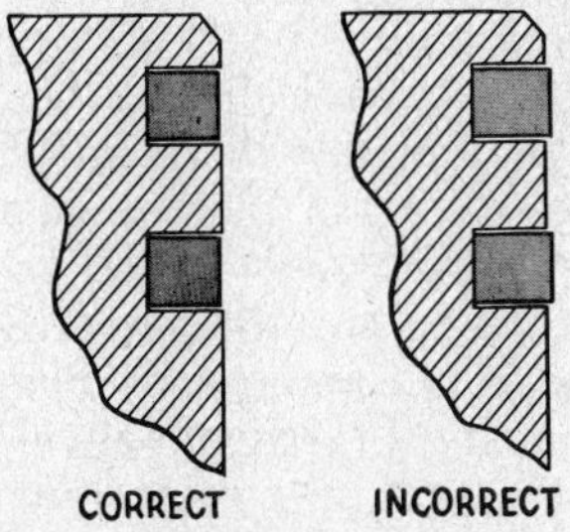
CORRECT
INCORRECT

Piston groove depth

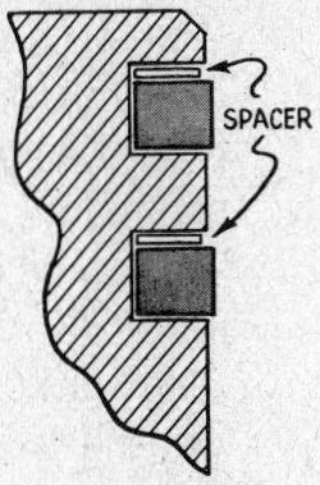
SPACER

Correct ring spacer installation

Install the camshaft:	Liberally lubricate the camshaft lobes and journals, and slide the camshaft into the block. CAUTION: *Exercise extreme care to avoid damaging the bearings when inserting the camshaft.* Install and tighten the camshaft thrust plate retaining bolts.
Check camshaft end-play:	Using feeler gauges, determine whether the clearance between the camshaft boss (or gear) and backing plate is within specifications. Install shims behind the thrust plate, or reposition the camshaft gear and retest end-play.

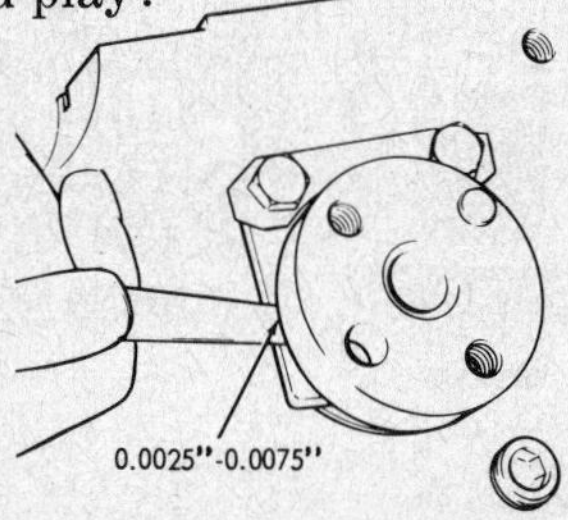
0.0025"-0.0075"

Checking camshaft end-play with a feeler gauge
(© Outboard Marine Corp.)

Procedure	Method
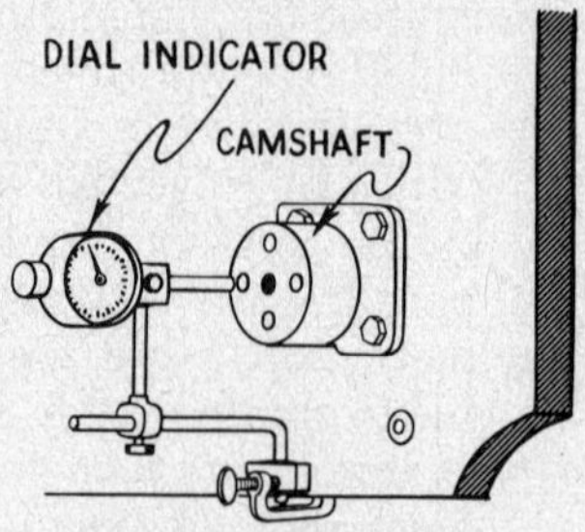 DIAL INDICATOR CAMSHAFT Checking camshaft end-play with a dial indicator	* Mount a dial indicator stand so that the stem of the dial indicator rests on the nose of the camshaft, parallel to the camshaft axis. Push the camshaft as far in as possible and zero the gauge. Move the camshaft outward to determine the amount of camshaft end-play. If the end-play is not within tolerance, install shims behind the thrust plate, or re-position the camshaft gear and retest.
Install the rear main seal (where applicable): 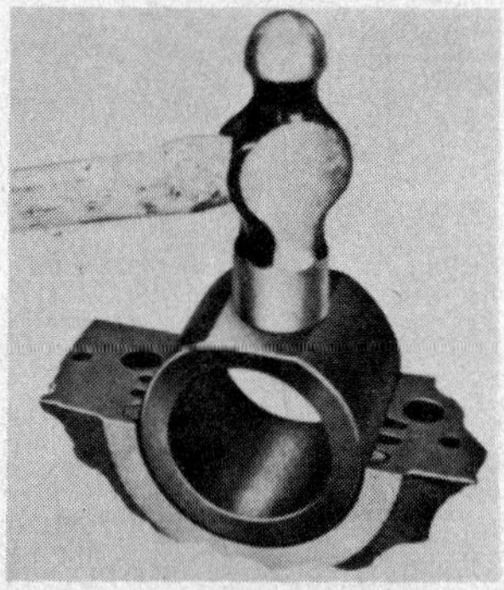 Seating the rear main seal (© Buick Div. G.M. Corp.)	Position the block with the bearing saddles facing upward. Lay the rear main seal in its groove and press it lightly into its seat. Place a piece of pipe the same diameter as the crankshaft journal into the saddle, and firmly seat the seal. Hold the pipe in position, and trim the ends of the seal flush if required.
Install the crankshaft: 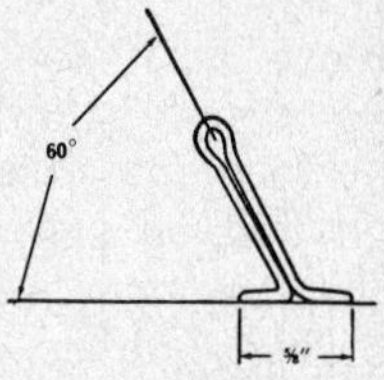 60° ⅝" Home made bearing roll-out pin (© Pontiac Div. G.M. Corp.) 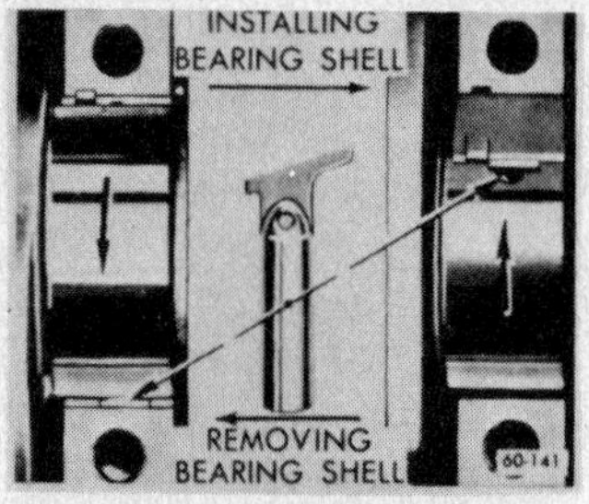 INSTALLING BEARING SHELL REMOVING BEARING SHELL 60-141 Removal and installation of upper bearing insert using a roll-out pin (© Buick Div. G.M. Corp.)	Thoroughly clean the main bearing saddles and caps. Place the upper halves of the bearing inserts on the saddles and press into position. NOTE: *Ensure that the oil holes align.* Press the corresponding bearing inserts into the main bearing caps. Lubricate the upper main bearings, and lay the crankshaft in position. Place a strip of Plastigage on each of the crankshaft journals, install the main caps, and torque to specifications. Remove the main caps, and compare the Plastigage to the scale on the Plastigage envelope. If clearances are within tolerances, remove the Plastigage, turn the crankshaft 90°, wipe off all oil and retest. If all clearances are correct, remove all Plastigage, thoroughly

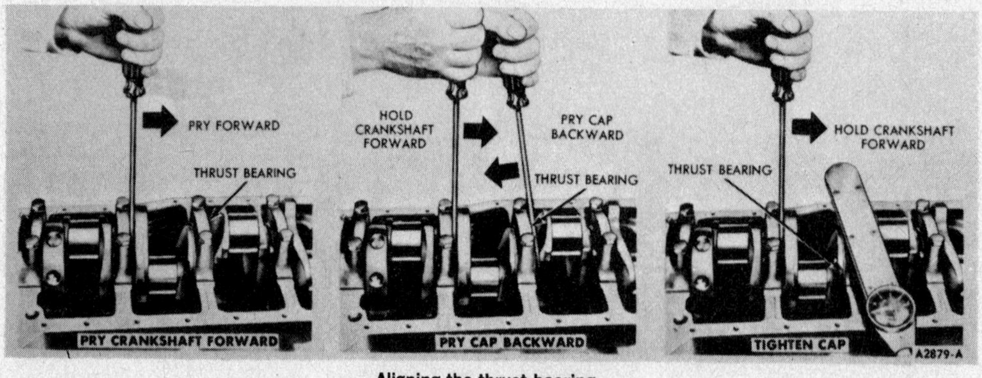
PRY FORWARD
THRUST BEARING
PRY CRANKSHAFT FORWARD
HOLD CRANKSHAFT FORWARD
PRY CAP BACKWARD
THRUST BEARING
PRY CAP BACKWARD
THRUST BEARING
HOLD CRANKSHAFT FORWARD
TIGHTEN CAP
A2879-A
Aligning the thrust bearing
(© Ford Motor Co.)

Procedure	*Method*
	lubricate the main caps and bearing journals, and install the main caps. If clearances are not within tolerance, the upper bearing inserts may be removed, without removing the crankshaft, using a bearing roll out pin (see illustration). Roll in a bearing that will provide proper clearance, and retest. Torque all main caps, excluding the thrust bearing cap, to specifications. Tighten the thrust bearing cap finger tight. To properly align the thrust bearing, pry the crankshaft the extent of its axial travel several times, the last movement held toward the front of the engine, and torque the thrust bearing cap to specifications. Determine the crankshaft end-play (see below), and bring within tolerance with thrust washers.
Measure crankshaft end-play:	Mount a dial indicator stand on the front of the block, with the dial indicator stem resting on the nose of the crankshaft, parallel to the crankshaft axis. Pry the crankshaft the extent of its travel rearward, and zero the indicator. Pry the crankshaft forward and record crankshaft end-play. NOTE: *Crankshaft end-play also may be measured at the thrust bearing, using feeler gauges* (see illustration).

A 2908-A

Checking crankshaft end-play with a dial indicator
(© Ford Motor Co.)

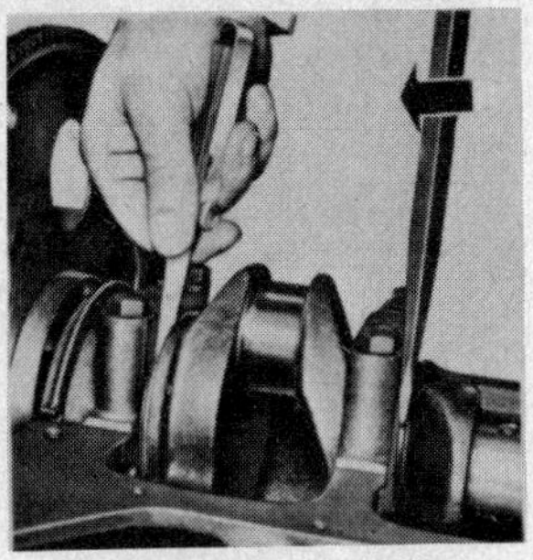

Checking crankshaft end-play with a feeler gauge
(© Outboard Marine Corp.)

Procedure	*Method*
Install the pistons:	Press the upper connecting rod bearing halves into the connecting rods, and the lower halves into the connecting rod caps. Position the piston ring gaps according to specifications (see car section), and lubricate the pistons. Install a ring compresser on a piston, and press two long (8″) pieces of plastic tubing over the rod bolts. Using the plastic tubes as a guide, press the pistons into the bores and onto the crankshaft with a wooden hammer handle. After seating the rod on the crankshaft journal, remove the tubes and install the cap finger tight. Install the remaining pistons in the same man-

Procedure	*Method*

USE A SHORT
PIECE OF 3/8"
HOSE AS A
GUIDE

Tubing used as guide when installing a piston
(© Oldsmobile Div. G.M. Corp.)

ner. Invert the engine and check the bearing clearance at two points (90° apart) on each journal with Plastigage. NOTE: *Do not turn the crankshaft with Plastigage installed.* If clearance is within tolerances, remove *all* Plastigage, thoroughly lubricate the journals, and torque the rod caps to specifications. If clearance is not within specifications, install different thickness bearing inserts and recheck. CAUTION: *Never shim or file the connecting rods or caps.* Always install plastic tube sleeves over the rod bolts when the caps are not installed, to protect the crankshaft journals.

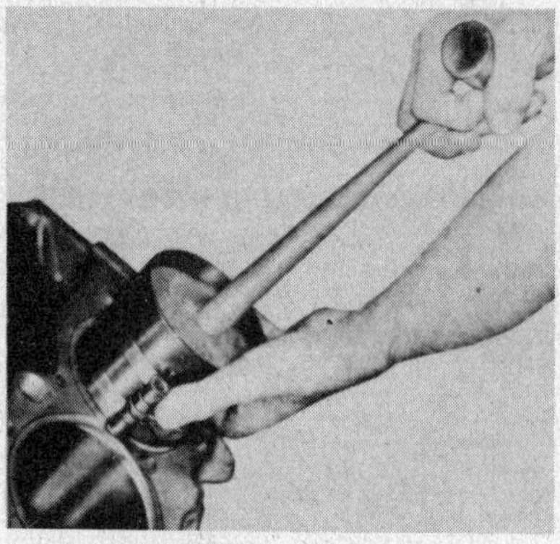

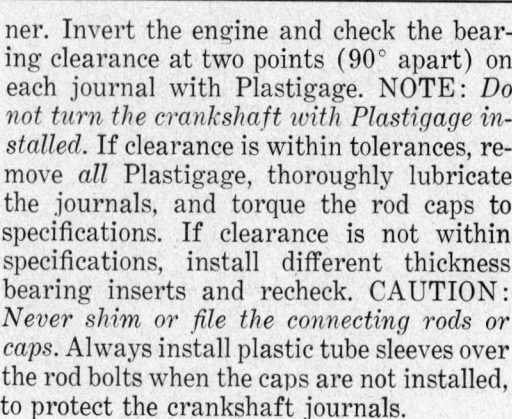

Installing a piston
(© Chevrolet Div. G.M. Corp.)

Check connecting rod side clearance:

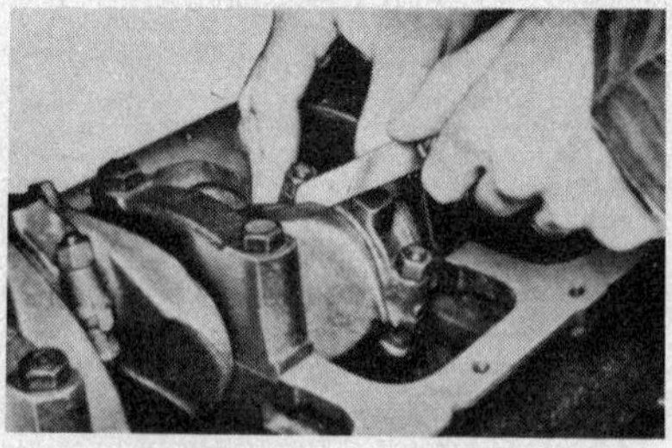

Checking connecting rod side clearance
(© Chevrolet Div. G.M. Corp.)

Determine the clearance between the sides of the connecting rods and the crankshaft, using feeler gauges. If clearance is below the minimum tolerance, the rod may be machined to provide adequate clearance. If clearance is excessive, substitute an unworn rod, and recheck. If clearance is still outside specifications, the crankshaft must be welded and reground, or replaced.

Inspect the timing chain:

Visually inspect the timing chain for broken or loose links, and replace the chain if any are found. If the chain will flex sideways, it must be replaced. Install the timing chain as specified. NOTE: *If the original timing chain is to be reused, install it in its original position.*

Procedure	Method
Check timing gear backlash and runout:	Mount a dial indicator with its stem resting on a tooth of the camshaft gear (as illustrated). Rotate the gear until all slack is removed, and zero the indicator. Rotate the gear in the opposite direction until slack is removed, and record gear backlash. Mount the indicator with its stem resting on the edge of the camshaft gear, parallel to the axis of the camshaft. Zero the indicator, and turn the camshaft gear one full turn, recording the runout. If either backlash or runout exceed specifications, replace the worn gear(s).

Checking camshaft gear backlash
(© Chevrolet Div. G.M. Corp.)

Checking camshaft gear runout
(© Chevrolet Div. G.M. Corp.)

Completing the Rebuilding Process

Following the above procedures, complete the rebuilding process as follows:

Fill the oil pump with oil, to prevent cavitating (sucking air) on initial engine start up. Install the oil pump and the pickup tube on the engine. Coat the oil pan gasket as necessary, and install the gasket and the oil pan. Mount the flywheel and the crankshaft vibrational damper or pulley on the crankshaft. NOTE: *Always use new bolts when installing the flywheel.* Inspect the clutch shaft pilot bushing in the crankshaft. If the bushing is excessively worn, remove it with an expanding puller and a slide hammer, and tap a new bushing into place.

Position the engine, cylinder head side up. Lubricate the lifters, and install them into their bores. Install the cylinder head, and torque it as specified in the car section. Insert the pushrods (where applicable), and install the rocker shaft(s) (if so equipped) or position the rocker arms on the pushrods. If solid lifters are utilized, adjust the valves to the "cold" specifications.

Mount the intake and exhaust manifolds, the carburetor(s), the distributor and spark plugs. Adjust the point gap and the static ignition timing. Mount all accessories and install the engine in the car. Fill the radiator with coolant, and the crankcase with high quality engine oil.

Break-in Procedure

Start the engine, and allow it to run at low speed for a few minutes, while checking for leaks. Stop the engine, check the oil level, and fill as necessary. Restart the engine, and fill the cooling system to capacity. Check the point dwell angle and adjust the ignition timing and the valves. Run the engine at low to medium speed (800-2500 rpm) for approximately ½ hour, and retorque the cylinder head bolts. Road test the car, and check again for leaks.

Follow the manufacturer's recommended engine break-in procedure and maintenance schedule for new engines.

Diagnostic Charts

STARTING SYSTEM DIAGNOSIS

Problems

● Most probable causes
✓ Possible causes

Causes	Repeated clicking from starter	Cranks very slowly	Starter Spins, but does not turn engine	Starter clunks, but does not turn engine	No sound from starter	Excessive Starter Current draw
Battery Not Fully Charged	●	●		●	●	
Loose Battery Cables	●	●		●	✓	✓
Defective Battery	✓	✓		✓	✓	✓
Shorted or Loose Starter Wire	✓	✓		✓	✓	✓
Defective Solenoid	✓				✓	✓
Engine Overheated		✓		✓		
Low Temperature		●		✓		
Thick Oil		✓		✓		
Internal Engine Malfunction		✓		✓		
Defective Starter		✓		✓		
Defective Starter Drive		✓	●			
Open Circuit in Solenoid Armature, or Field Coils				●		●
Short in Field or Armature Coils				●		●
Neutral Safety Switch Misadjusted					✓	
Fusible Link Melted					✓	
Defective Ignition Switch					✓	
Clutch Switch Misadjusted					✓	

CLUTCH AND MANUAL TRANSMISSION DIAGNOSIS

Problems

● Most probable causes
✓ Possible causes

Causes	Noisy in Forward Speeds	Noisy in Reverse	Noisy in Neutral	Hard Shifting	Jumping Out of Gear	Sticking in Gear	Gears Clash	Locks in Two Gears	Leaks
Low or Wrong Lubricant	✓	✓	✓	✓		✓	✓		✓
Transmission Misaligned or Loose	✓	✓	✓		✓				
Maindrive Gear or Bearing Damaged	●	✓	✓			✓	✓		
Speedometer Drive Noise	✓	✓							
Mainshaft Gears or Bearing Damaged	●	✓	✓		●				
Incorrect End Play on Shafts	✓	✓	✓		✓				
Reverse Idler Gear or Shaft Damaged		●	✓						
Incorrect Clutch Adjustment			●	✓		●	●		
Shift Linkage Misadjusted				●	✓	✓		●	
Bent Shifter Forks or Shafts				✓	✓	✓		✓	
Damaged Synchronizers				✓	✓	✓	●		
Speed Too High on Downshift				●			✓		
Front Main Bearing Damaged	✓	✓	✓		✓				
Bent Output Shaft					✓				
High Idle Speed							✓		
Wait 3-4 Sec. Before Shifting Into a Non-synchronized Gear							●		
Bent Shift Rods								✓	
Overfilled									●
Seals at Covers or Extension Housing Bad									✓
Loose Main Drive Gear Bearing Retainer									✓
Operating Shaft Seals Bad									✓
Worn Extension Housing Bushing									✓

CHRYSLER TORQUEFLITE AUTOMATIC TRANSMISSION DIAGNOSIS

Problems

✓ Possible causes

Causes	Oil level	Control linkage	Oil pressure check	Kickdown band	Low-reverse band	Improper engine idle	Servo linkage	Accumulator	Valve body assembly	Manual valve lever	Air pressure check	Servo link	Governor	Gear shift cable	Regulator valve	Strainer	Converter control valve	Breather clogged	Cooler or lines
Harsh N to D or N to R shift			✓	✓	✓	✓	✓		✓	✓									
Delayed Shift—N to D	✓		✓						✓										
Runaway on upshift—2-3 kickdown	✓	✓	✓	✓				✓	✓			✓							
Harsh upshift and 3-2 kickdown		✓	✓	✓				✓	✓			✓							
No upshift	✓	✓	✓	✓				✓	✓	✓	✓	✓	✓						
No kickdown on normal downshift	✓	✓	✓	✓				✓	✓		✓		✓	✓					
Erratic shifts	✓	✓	✓			✓								✓	✓	✓			
Slips in forward drive positions	✓		✓					✓	✓		✓								
Slips in Reverse only			✓		✓		✓		✓		✓								
Slips in all positions	✓		✓						✓		✓				✓				
No drive in any positions	✓		✓						✓	✓	✓					✓			
No drive in forward positions			✓	✓				✓	✓		✓	✓			✓				
No drive in Reverse			✓		✓		✓		✓		✓		✓						
Drives in Neutral									✓	✓				✓					
Drags or locks				✓	✓		✓					✓							
Noises	✓								✓	✓			✓		✓		✓		
Hard to fill or blows out	✓								✓							✓	✓	✓	✓
Transmission overheats	✓			✓	✓				✓				✓		✓		✓		✓

This transmission is used on all Chrysler Corporation cars since 1967 and on American Motors products since 1973.

FORD C-6 AUTOMATIC TRANSMISSION DIAGNOSIS

Causes

● Most probable causes
✓ Possible causes

Problems	Fluid level	Vacuum diaphragm	Manual linkage	Governor	Valve body	Pressure regulator	Intermediate band	Low-reverse clutch	Intermediate servo	Engine idle speed	Downshift linkage	Perform air pressure check	Extension rear oil seal	Perform pressure check	Engine performance
No drive in D, 2, and 1			✓		✓							✓		✓	
1-2 or 2-3 shift points erratic	✓	✓	✓	✓	✓						✓	✓		✓	
Rough 1-2 upshifts		✓			✓	✓	✓		✓			✓		✓	
Rough 2-3 upshifts		✓			✓	✓	✓		✓			✓		✓	
Dragged out 1-2 shift	✓	✓			✓	✓	✓		✓			✓		✓	
No 1-2 or 2-3 shift		✓	✓	✓	✓		✓		✓		✓	✓		✓	
No 3-1 shift in D				✓	✓										
No forced downshifts		✓			✓						✓				
Runaway engine on 3-2 downshift		✓			✓	✓	✓		✓			✓		✓	
Rough 3-2 or 3-1 shift at closed throttle		✓			✓	✓			✓	✓					
Shifts 1-3 in D		✓		✓	✓		✓		✓						
Creeps excessively										●					
Slips in first gear, D	✓	✓			✓	✓						✓		✓	
Slips in second gear	✓	✓			✓	✓	✓		✓			✓		✓	
Slips or chatters in R	✓	✓			✓	✓		✓				✓		✓	
No drive in D only			✓		✓							✓		✓	
No drive in 2 only	✓		✓		✓				✓			✓		✓	
No drive in 1 only	✓		✓		✓							✓		✓	
No drive in R only	✓		✓		✓			✓				✓		✓	
No drive in any lever position	✓		✓		✓	✓						✓		✓	
Lockup in 2 only								●							
Parking lock broken			✓												
Transmission overheats		✓				✓						✓		✓	
Maximum speed too low															✓
Transmission noisy in N and P	✓					✓									
Transmission noisy in all gears	✓					✓									
Fluid leak	✓	✓							✓				✓		
Car moves forward in N			✓												

This transmission is available on many Ford Motor Company cars from 1967.

GENERAL MOTORS TURBO HYDRA-MATIC 350 AUTOMATIC TRANSMISSION DIAGNOSIS

Causes

● Most probable causes
✓ Possible causes

Problems	Low oil level/water in oil	Vacuum leak	Modulator and/or valve	Strainer and/or gasket	Governor valve/screen	Valve body gasket/plate	Pressure regulator valve	1-2 shift valve	2-3 shift valve	Manual low-control valve	Detent valve and linkage	2-3 accumulator	Manual valve linkage	Pump gears	Gasket screen-pressure
Slips in all ranges	✓		✓	✓		✓	✓						✓		✓
Drive slips—no First gear	✓		✓	✓		✓	✓						✓		✓
No 1-2 upshift		✓			✓	✓	✓	✓							
Slips, 1-2 upshift	✓		✓			✓	✓	✓				✓			
Harsh 1-2 upshift		✓	✓				✓								
No 2-3 upshift						✓			✓						
2-3 upshift early or late		✓			✓	✓	✓		✓		✓				
Slips, 2-3 upshift	✓		✓			✓	✓		✓						
No full throttle downshift		✓	✓				✓		✓			✓			
2-3 upshift, full throttle only		✓									✓				
Car drives in Neutral											●				
Slips in Reverse	✓		✓	✓		✓	✓	✓					✓	✓	✓
1-2 or 2-3 shifts noisy	●														
Noisy in all ranges	✓			✓		✓									✓
Spews oil out of the breather	✓			✓											

This transmission is available on many General Motors cars since 1969.

FRONT SUSPENSION DIAGNOSIS

● Most probable causes
✓ Possible causes

Causes \ Problems	Front Wheel Shimmy	Pull to One Side	Excessive Play in Steering	Wheel Tramp	Excessive Tire Wear	Hard Steering	Wandering	Front End Noise
Out of Balance Tires	●			●	✓			
Worn or Out of Adjustment Wheel Bearings	✓					✓		
Worn Tie Rod Ends	✓							
Worn Ball Joints	✓							
Incorrect Wheel Alignment	●	✓			✓	✓	●	
Incorrect Ride Height	✓							
Low or Uneven Tire Pressures		●			●	●	✓	
Front or Rear Brake Dragging		✓						
Grease or Brake Fluid on Brake Linings		✓						
Broken or Sagging Front Spring		✓				✓	✓	
Incorrect Steering Gear Adjustment			✓					
Worn Front End Parts			●					●
Shock Absorber Inoperative or Loose				✓		✓	✓	✓
Ball Joint Needs Lubrication						✓		✓
Loose Stabilizer Bar								✓
Loose Lugnuts								✓
Loose Brake Parts								✓
Improper Tire Size					✓			
Bent or Worn Steering Linkage						✓	✓	

HYDRAULIC BRAKES DIAGNOSIS

● Most probable causes
✓ Possible causes

Problems / **Causes**

Causes	Brake Tell-Tale Glows During Stop	Brakes Chatter (Roughness)	Brakes Squeak During Application	Scraping Noise from Brakes	Uneven Braking Action (Front to Rear)	Uneven Braking Action (Pulls to Side)	Brakes Drag	Brakes Slow to Release	Brakes Slow to Respond	Excessive Braking Action	Excessive Brake Pedal Effort	Pedal Travel Gradually Increases	Excessive Brake Pedal Travel
Leaking Brake Line or Connection	●				✓							●	✓
Leaking Wheel Cylinder or Piston Seal	✓					✓				✓		●	✓
Leaking Master Cylinder	✓											●	✓
Restricted Brake Fluid Passage					✓	✓	✓	✓	✓		✓	✓	
Air In Brake System	●				✓								●
Contaminated or Improper Brake Fluid	✓						✓	✓	✓				
Faulty Metering Valve (Disc Only)	✓				✓		✓	✓	✓	✓	✓		✓
Sticking Wheel Cylinder or Caliper Pistons					✓	✓	✓	✓			✓		
Improperly Adjusted Master Cylinder Push Rod	✓						●	✓					✓
Leaking Vacuum System									✓		●		
Restricted Air Passage In Power Unit								✓	●		✓		
Improperly Assembled Power Unit							●	✓	✓	✓	✓		
Damaged Power Unit							✓	✓	✓	✓	✓		
Brake Assembly Attachments—Missing or Loose		✓		✓	✓	✓	✓						✓
Brake Pedal Linkage Interference or Binding							●	●	✓		✓		
Worn Out Brake Lining—Replace			✓	✓	✓	✓					✓		
Uneven Brake Lining Wear—Replace	✓		✓	✓	✓	✓							✓
Glazed Brake Lining—Sand Lightly			✓		✓	✓			✓		●		
Incorrect Lining Material—Replace		✓	●		✓	✓			✓	✓	✓		
Contaminated Brake Lining—Replace		✓	✓	✓	●	●			✓	●			
Linings Damaged By Abusive Use—Replace			✓	✓	✓	✓				●	✓		
Excessive Brake Lining Dust—Remove with Air			✓		●	●				●	✓		
Brake Drums or Rotors Heat Spotted or Scored		●	✓		✓	✓				✓			
Out-of-Round or Vibrating Brake Drums		●											
Out-of-Parallel Brake Rotors		●											
Excessive Rotor Run-Out		✓											
Faulty Automatic Adjusters	✓				✓	✓	✓					●	✓
Weak or Incorrect Brake Shoe Return Springs			✓	●	✓	✓	●	✓		✓			
Drums Tapered or Threaded				●									
Incorrect Wheel Cylinder Sizes					✓	✓				✓	✓		
Improperly Adjusted Parking Brake							✓						
Incorrect Front End Alignment						●							
Incorrect Tire Pressure					✓	✓							
Incorrect Wheel Bearing Adjustment		✓		✓									✓
Loose Front Suspension Attachments		✓		●		✓							
Out-of-Balance Wheel Assemblies		●											
Driver Riding Brake Pedal					✓		✓				✓	✓	✓
Faulty Proportioning Valve							✓	✓	✓		✓		
Insufficient Brake Shoe Pad Lubricant			●	●	✓		✓	✓					

DISC BRAKE DIAGNOSIS

● Most probable causes
✓ Possible causes

Causes \ Problems	Excessive Pedal Travel	Hard Pedal	Grabbing or Pulling	Fading Pedal	Noise and Chatter	Dragging Brakes
Master Cylinder Fluid Low	●		✓	✓		
Air in Hydraulic System	●		✓			
Hoses Soft or Weak	●			✓		
Caliper Seals Soft or Broken	●		●		✓	●
Power Brake Malfunctioning		●				
Lining Soiled With Brake Fluid		●	●			
Lines or Hoses Kinked or Collapsed		●	●			●
Caliper Pistons Frozen or Seized		●	●		✓	●
Master Cylinder Cups Swollen		●				●
Master Cylinder Bore Rough		●	●	●		
Caliper Cylinder Bore Rough or Worn		●	●	●	✓	●
Pedal Push Rod and Linkage Binding		●	✓			
Metering Valve Not Working		●	●			
Hydraulic Connections Loose or Ruptured	✓		✓	●		
Caliper Cylinder Seals Worn or Damaged	✓			●	✓	●
Bleed Screw Open	✓			●		
Lines or Hoses Ruptured	✓			●		
Disc Has Excessive Internal Runout					●	✓
Disc Out of Parallel			✓		●	✓
Disc Has Casting Imperfections					●	✓
Restricted Port in Master Cylinder		✓				●
Residual Pressure Check Valve		✓				●
Push Rod on Master Cylinder Out of Adjustment		✓				●
Caliper Loose			●		✓	
Poor Quality Brake Fluid				●		
Poor Quality Brake Lining				●	●	

TIRE WEAR DIAGNOSIS

● Most probable causes
✓ Possible causes

Causes \ Problems	Rapid wear at shoulders	Rapid wear at center	Cracked Treads	Wear on one side	Feathered Edge	Bald spots
Underinflation	●		✓			
Overinflation		●				
Excessive speed			●			
Excessive camber				●		
Incorrect toe-in					●	
Wheel unbalanced						●
Corrections	Adjust pressure to specifications with tire cool	Adjust pressure to specifications with tire cool	Adjust pressure to specifications with tire cool or replace tire	Adjust camber to specifications	Adjust toe-in	Dynamic cr static balance the wheels

COOLING SYSTEM DIAGNOSIS

Problems

● Most probable causes
✓ Possible causes

Causes	External Leakage	Internal Leakage	Poor Circulation	Overheating	Overflow Loss	Corrosion	Temp Too Low (Slow Engine Warm Up)	Water Pump Noisy
Hose Leaking	●			●				
Water Pump Leaking	●			●				
Damaged Gasket	●	●		●				
Leaking Heater Core	●			✓				
Cracked Cylinder Block	●	●		✓				
Faulty Pressure Cap	●	●		●	●			
Oil Cooler Fittings Loose	●	●		✓				
Faulty Head Gasket	●	●		✓				
Loose Cylinder Head Bolts	●	●		✓				
Cracked Valve Port		●		✓				
Cracked Cylinder Wall		●		✓				
Leaking Oil Cooler		●						
Low Coolant Level			●	●				
Collapsed Radiator Hose			●	●				
Fan Belt Loose			●	✓				✓
Air Leak Through Bottom Hose	✓		●					
Faulty Thermostat			●	●			●	
Water Pump Impeller Broken			●					●
Restricted Radiator Core			●	●				
Restricted Engine Water Jacket			●					
Incorrect Ignition Timing				●				
Inaccurate Temperature Gauge				●			●	
Excessive Engine Idling				●				
Frozen Coolant				●				
Faulty Vacuum By Pass Valve			✓	●				
Overfilling					●			
Blown Head Gasket	✓				●			
Coolant Foaming					●			
Insufficient Corrosion Inhibitor			✓	✓		●		
Extended Use of Anti-Freeze			✓	✓		●		
High Mineral and Lime Content of Coolant			✓	✓		●		
Faulty Temperature Sending Unit							●	
Faulty Heater Controls			✓				●	
Defective Seal								●
Bearing Corroded								●

AIR CONDITIONING DIAGNOSIS

● Most probable causes
✓ Possible causes

Problems

Causes	Compressor Discharge Pressure Too High	Compressor Discharge Pressure Too Low	P.O.A. Valve Inlet Pressure Too High	P.O.A. Valve Inlet Pressure Too Low	Nozzle Outlet Temperature Too Warm	Nozzle Outlet Temperature Too Cold	Blown Thermal Limiter	Compressor Clutch Slips	Evaporator Pressure Too High	Water Blowing Out Discharge Nozzle	Compressor Not Operating	Water Drains Onto Floor
Engine Overheated	●				✓			✓	✓			
Overcharge of Refrigerant or Air in System	●				✓			✓	✓			
Restriction in Condenser	●				✓		✓	✓				
Restriction in Receiver-Dehydrator		●		✓	✓		✓					
Restriction in Any High Pressure Line	●	✓		✓	✓		✓	✓	✓			
Condenser Air Flow Blocked	●				✓		✓	✓	✓			
P.O.A. Valve Inlet Pressure Too High	●											
Insufficient Refrigerant		●		✓	●		●				✓	
Defective Compressor		●	✓		✓			✓	✓		●	
Plug in Refrigerant System	✓	●	✓	✓	✓		✓	✓	✓		✓	
P.O.A. Valve Inlet Pressure Too Low		●				✓	✓				✓	
P.O.A. Valve Stuck Open					✓	✓	✓				✓	
Capillary Tube to Evaporator Tube Contact	✓		●		✓	✓		●	✓			
Expansion Valve Inoperative	✓	✓	●	✓	●		●	✓	●		✓	
Inlet Screen Plugged or Valve Fails		✓		●	✓		✓				✓	
Restriction in System Hoses or Tubes	✓	✓		●	✓	✓	✓	✓	✓		✓	
Poor Seal Evaporator to Evaporator Inlet Case		✓		✓	●							
Poor Seal Evaporator to Heater Case		✓		✓	●							
Defective or Missing Evaporator Drain Hose										●		●
Air Ducts Not Properly Connected		✓		✓	●	✓						
Vacuum Hoses Not Connected Properly					●	✓						
P.O.A. Valve Faulty			●		●	●						
Low Charge or Discharged System		✓	✓	✓	✓		●		✓		✓	
Thermal Limiter Improperly Installed							●				✓	
Thermal Limiter Blown											●	
Faulty Superheat Shut Off Switch							●				✓	
Head Pressure Too High								●				
Pulley Wobbles								●				
Loose Compressor Drive Belt		✓	✓		✓				●		●	
Defective Clutch or Coil		✓	✓		✓				●		●	
Restriction in Suction Line		✓	✓		✓				●		✓	
Defective Suction Throttling Valve		✓	✓	●					✓			
Defective Expansion Valve	✓		●	✓	✓		✓		✓			
Plugged or Kinked Evaporator Drain Hose										●		
Broken Compressor Drive Belt											●	
No Power to Clutch							✓				●	
Faulty Switch or Wiring								✓			●	

INDEX

Lifting and Towing

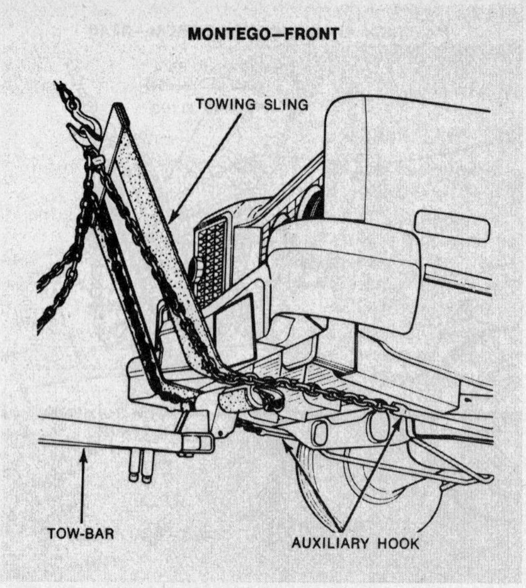
MONTEGO—FRONT
TOWING SLING
TOW-BAR
AUXILIARY HOOK

Attachments to Montego
(© Ford Motor Co)

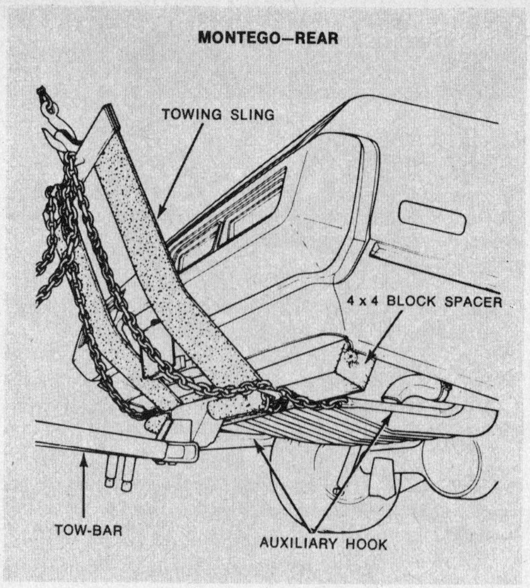
MONTEGO—REAR
TOWING SLING
4 x 4 BLOCK SPACER
TOW-BAR
AUXILIARY HOOK

Attachments to Montego
(© Ford Motor Co)

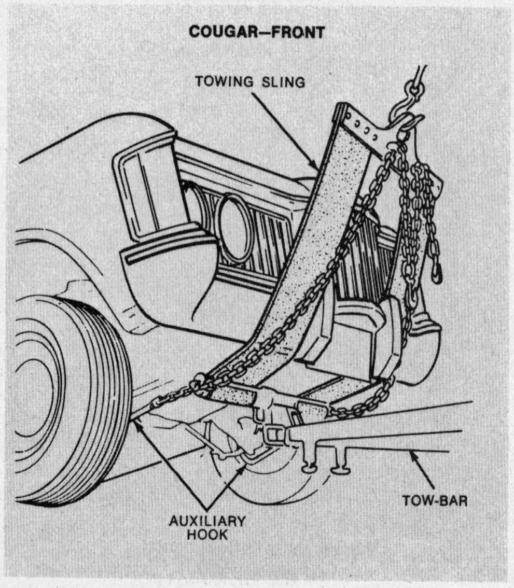
COUGAR—FRONT
TOWING SLING
AUXILIARY HOOK
TOW-BAR

Attachments to Cougar
(© Ford Motor Co)

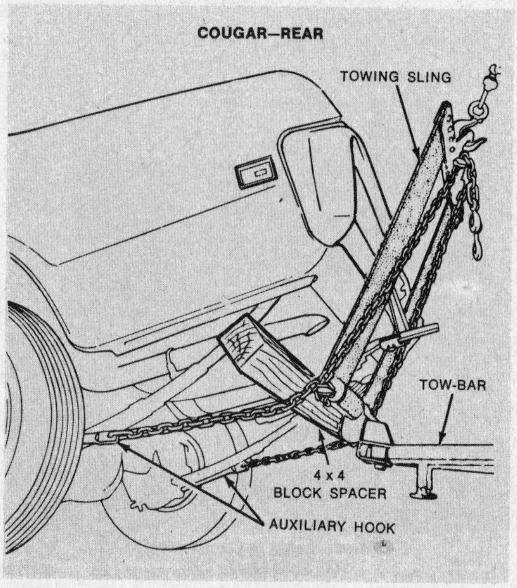
COUGAR—REAR
TOWING SLING
TOW-BAR
4 x 4
BLOCK SPACER
AUXILIARY HOOK

Attachments to Cougar
(© Ford Motor Co)

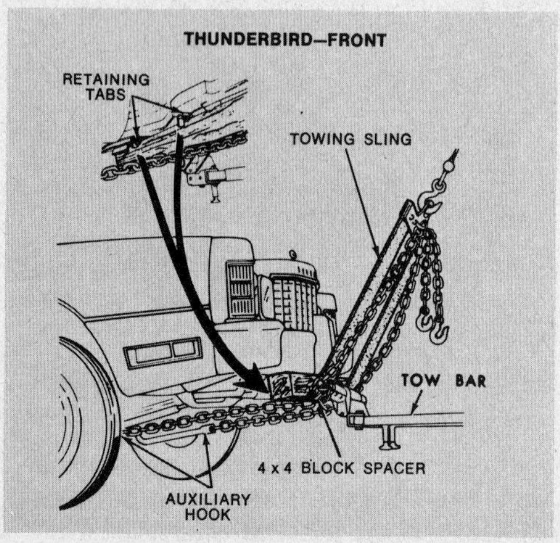
THUNDERBIRD—FRONT
RETAINING
TABS
TOWING SLING
TOW BAR
4 x 4 BLOCK SPACER
AUXILIARY
HOOK

Attachments to Thunderbird
(© Ford Motor Co)

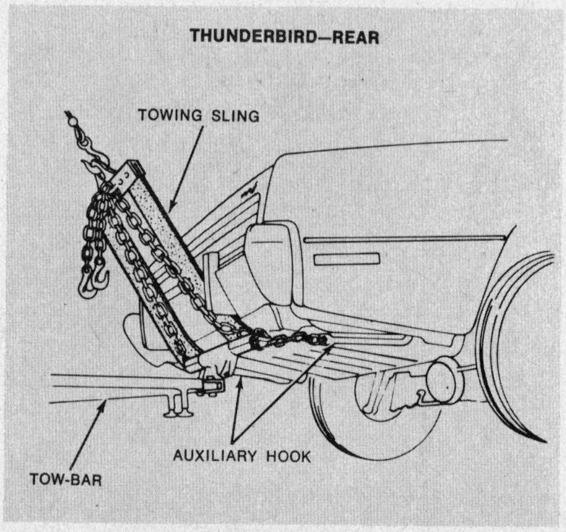
THUNDERBIRD—REAR
TOWING SLING
AUXILIARY HOOK
TOW-BAR

Attachments to Thunderbird
(© Ford Motor Co)

Lifting and Towing

Introduction

With the advent of the 1973 impact absorbing bumper syster , towing a disabled vehicle is not a, easy as it used to be. If the vehicle is not attached correctly permanent damage could be done to the bumper mechanisms. Therefore, it is of great importance that attachment to the tow vehicle be done in the correct manner.

This section contains the factory recommended procedure for attaching 1973 cars to wreckers. By following the recommendations, damage to the towed vehicle will be avoided.

General Information

If the vehicle to be towed is equipped with a locking steering column and the wheels are positioned in other than the straight ahead driving position with no ignition key available, it must be towed from the front or a dolly must be placed under the front wheels if it is to be towed from the rear.

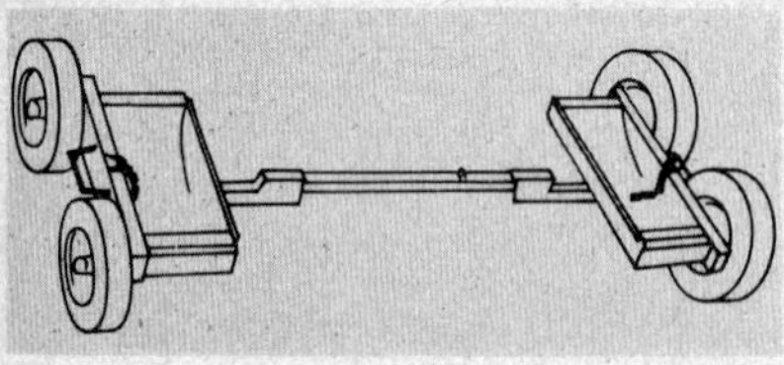

Dolly
(© Ford Motor Co)

If the vehicle is not equipped with a steering column lock or the lock is damaged, the wheel must be secured in some manner. One means is the steering column clamp. This is a hook type device which is fastened to the bottom of the steering wheel and the seat. It applies tension to the bottom of the wheel and keeps it in the straight ahead driving position. There are many devices like this on the market and all do a good job.

As a general rule, if a vehicle is towed on its rear wheels, the speed should NEVER exceed 30 mph. Towing distance should not exceed 15 miles. If this is not possible, the vehicle should be raised from the rear or the driveshaft must be disconnected.

Front wheel drive vehicles may be towed on their rear wheels for any period of time at speed not in excess of 50 mph. The parking brake must be released and the transmission placed in Neutral.

Caution Vehicles should never be towed at speeds over 50 mph.

Front wheel drive vehicles may be towed on their front wheels at speeds under 35 mph for distances of less than 50 miles. The steering wheel must be positioned straight ahead and clamped. This is done with a steering wheel clamping device. It is not sufficient to use the steering column lock to hold the wheel in this position. If the speed or the distance traveled with the disabled vehicle will be exceeded and the car cannot be towed from the front, the front wheels must be supported while towing from the rear.

Towing Safety

It is important, during any towing operation, to guard against injury to any person and damage to the tow vehicle or the vehicle being towed.

Examine the attaching points on the disabled vehicle for strength and security. If there is excessive damage, other secure attachments should be made. Also, all wreckers should be equipped with safety chains which are separate from the normal lifting mechanism.

All loose or damaged portions of the sheet metal which protrude must be modified. Also, if damage has been done to the locking mechanism of the doors, hood, or trunk, they must be tied shut.

Caution Never crawl under a vehicle which is supported by only the wrecker lifting mechanism.

It is imperative that no person ride in any vehicle which is being towed by a wrecker.

Common sense plays an important part in safety when towing a disabled vehicle. Towing speed is dependent on weather, traffic, and other conditions; so remember, "Safety First".

Equipment

Slings

For 1973 car models, it is recommended that a special wide belt sling be used. Its use will avoid any contact or damage to the bumper mechanism or the underside sheet metal. It should be noted that it is necessary to remove license plate holders and front fiberglass spoilers from vehicles before attempting to hook up the tow assembly. This will prevent damage to these components.

Spacer Blocks

A spacer block is usually a 4 in. x 4 in. piece of solid wood which is used as added leverage or support to the hitch. By means of the spacer, the weight is taken off the front of the hitch (the portion which contacts the sheet metal) and placed on the spacer

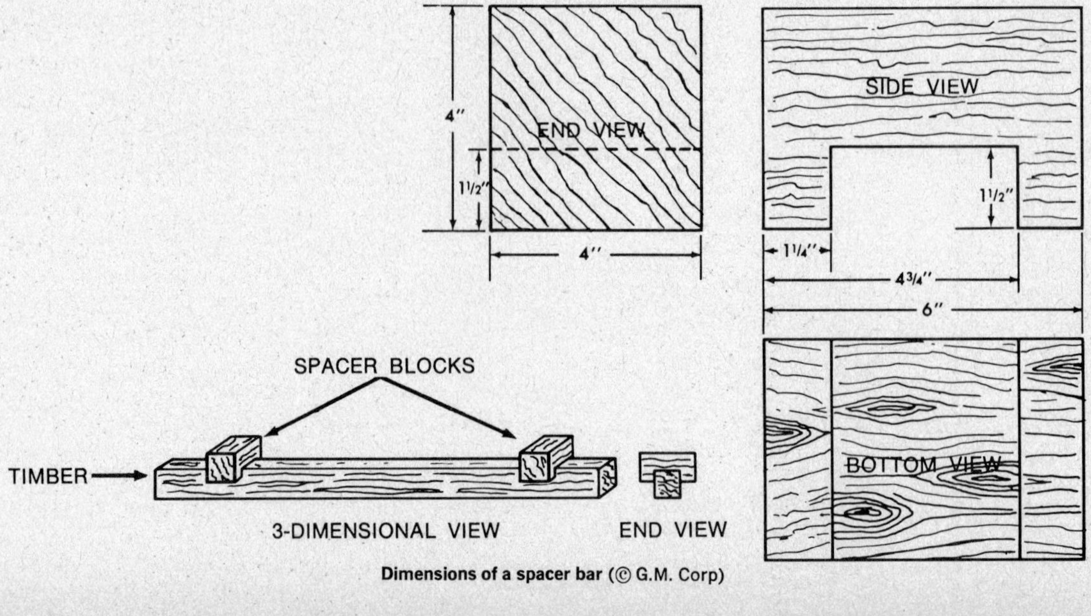
4"
END VIEW
1½"
4"
SIDE VIEW
1½"
1¼"
4¾"
6"
BOTTOM VIEW
SPACER BLOCKS
TIMBER
3-DIMENSIONAL VIEW
END VIEW

Dimensions of a spacer bar (© G.M. Corp)

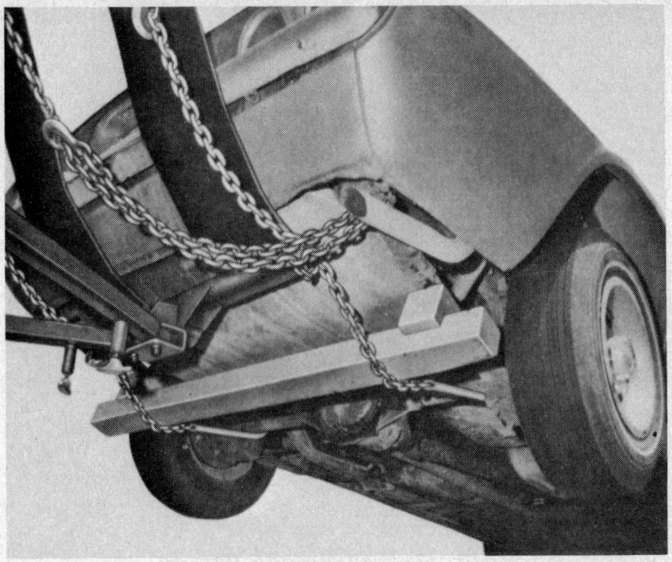

Positioning the spacer bar
(© G.M. Corp)

bar which ideally should contact the frame. The bar should be used when the pressure on the straps is too great and the possibility of sheet metal damage is present. Insert the bar between the chain hooks and the tow bar extension.

Do's and Don'ts

1. Never place a tow hook over the top of an axle or an upper A-arm. There is always the danger of the hook releasing in this position. Always position the hook so that the pressure is applied to the bend of the hook, never to the tip. Also never position the hook over the tie-rods or steering linkage, as damage to these components will occur.

NOTE: When the vehicle is lifted from the front, place the hook on the lower suspension arms with the tip of the hook pointing upward. When the vehicle is towed from the front, attach the hooks to the rear axle also with the hooks in the upward position.

2. Make certain that the hook chains are attached securely to the grab hooks.
3. It is important to unlatch the hood of the disabled vehicle. Leave the safety catch attached. This is done to prevent damage to the hood due to stress on the front end during lifting.
4. Position the lower bar of the sling so that it will contact the vehicle frame or other secure lifting point. Also guard against pressure to the gas tank and exhaust components.
5. If the vehicle has extensive damage to the end where it must be lifted, guard against damage to your straps. Attach chains so that the weight of the vehicle is on the chains as the straps hang loose. If possible, place wood blocks or an old tire in front of the sling to avoid damage from the jagged metal.
6. Keep a watchful eye on your equipment for defects and wear. Replace the hooks, chains or straps if they are defective and use only approved replacements.

Towing Procedures

Ford Products

When towing 1973 standard size Fords, Mustangs, Pintos, Torinos, Mavericks, Continentals, Mercurys, Montegos and Cougars from the front, no wood spacers are necessary; just attach the auxiliary hooks to the lower "A" frame of the vehicle.

When raising the front of Thunderbirds and the Lincoln Mark IVs, position the wooden spacer bar forward of the retaining tabs which are located directly under the bumper guards. The auxiliary hook may be attached to the stabilizer bar outside of the rubber insulator blocks.

When towing standard Ford and Mercury vehicles from the rear, no wood spacers are necessary. The auxiliary hooks may be attached to the axle housing inside of the springs.

On Thunderbirds, Torinos, Mark IVs, Lincolns, and Montegos, place the 4 in. x 4 in. spacer bar across the rear crossmember. There are shipping tie-down holes in the frame. These may be used to locate the auxiliary hooks. The holes are located 2 ft to the rear of the axle.

NOTE: On Lincolns, do not connect the hooks to the axle housing as this might damage the fuel tank.

On Pintos, Mustangs, Mavericks, and Cougars, place the spacer bar under the rear bumper beneath the bumper guards. The auxiliary hooks are attached to the axle housing between the springs and the wheel. If the vehicle is not equipped with bumper guards, position the spacer against the lower bumper panel.

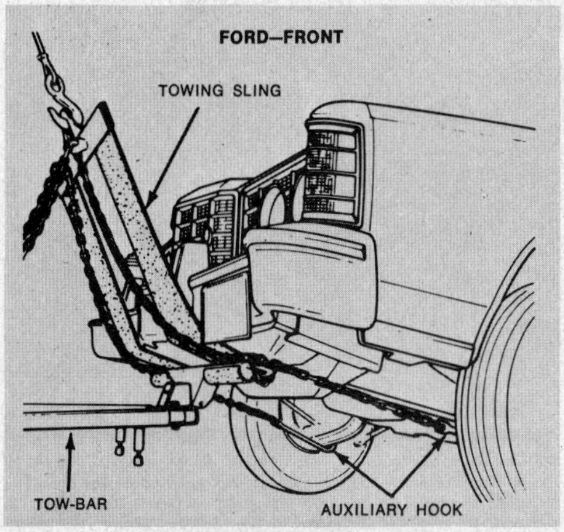
FORD—FRONT
TOWING SLING
TOW-BAR
AUXILIARY HOOK

Attachments to full size Ford
(© Ford Motor Co)

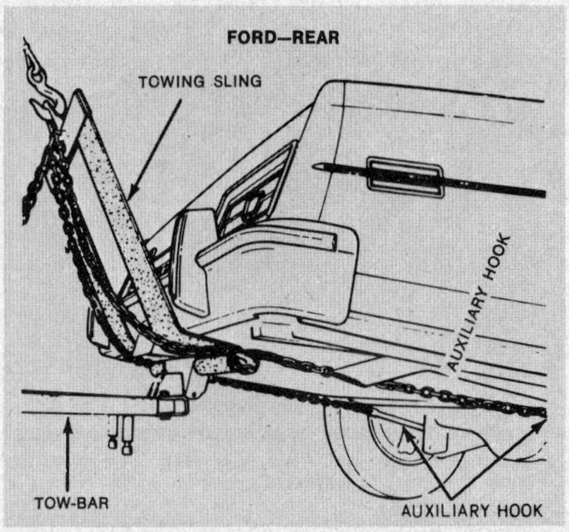
FORD—REAR
TOWING SLING
AUXILIARY HOOK
TOW-BAR
AUXILIARY HOOK

Attachments to Ford
(© Ford Motor Co)

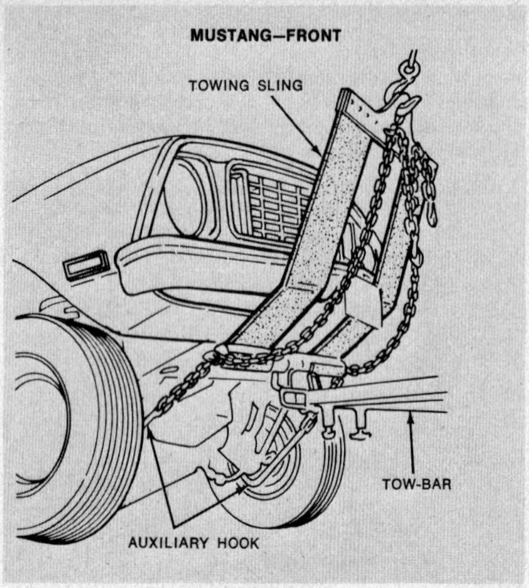
MUSTANG—FRONT
TOWING SLING
TOW-BAR
AUXILIARY HOOK

Attachments to Mustang
(© Ford Motor Co)

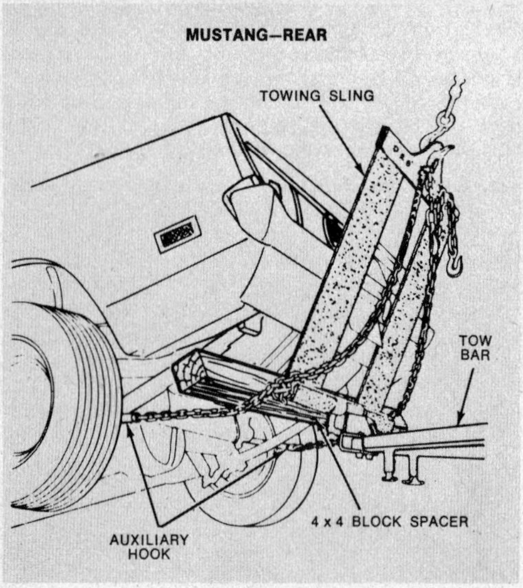
MUSTANG—REAR
TOWING SLING
TOW BAR
AUXILIARY HOOK
4 x 4 BLOCK SPACER

Attachments to Mustang
(© Ford Motor Co)

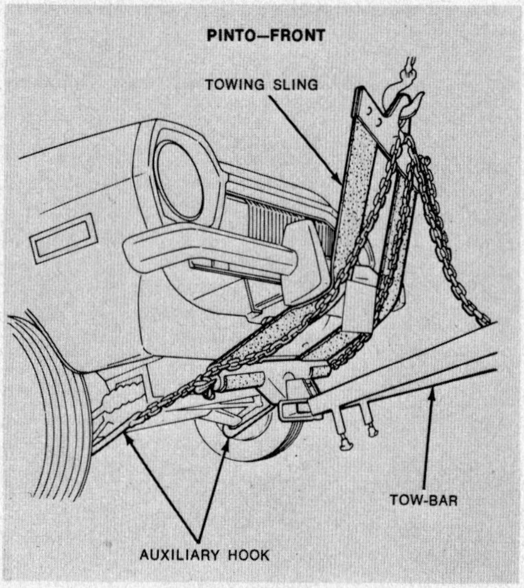
PINTO—FRONT
TOWING SLING
TOW-BAR
AUXILIARY HOOK

Attachments to Pinto
(© Ford Motor Co)

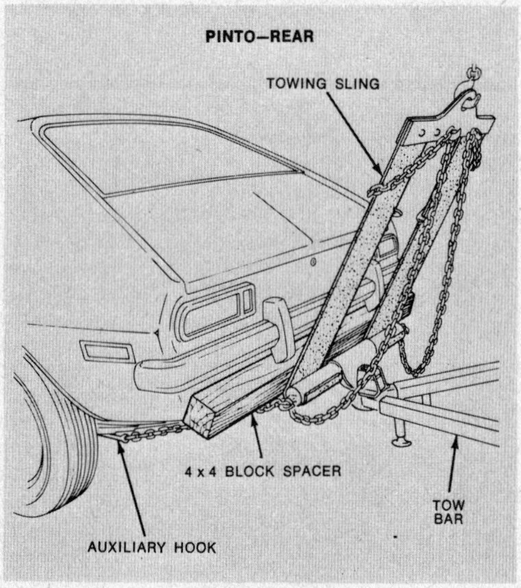
PINTO—REAR
TOWING SLING
4 x 4 BLOCK SPACER
TOW BAR
AUXILIARY HOOK

Attachments to Pinto
(© Ford Motor Co)

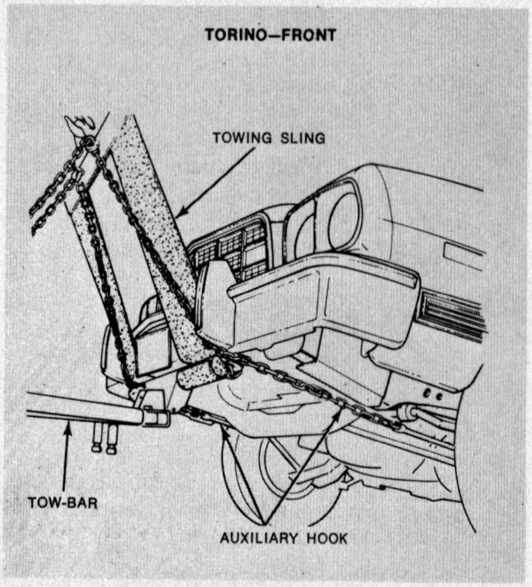
TORINO—FRONT
TOWING SLING
TOW-BAR
AUXILIARY HOOK

Attachments to Torino
(© Ford Motor Co)

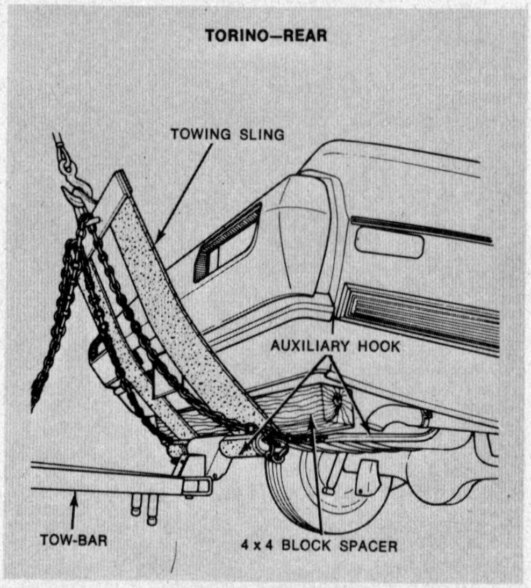
TORINO—REAR
TOWING SLING
AUXILIARY HOOK
TOW-BAR
4 x 4 BLOCK SPACER

Attachments to Torino
(© Ford Motor Co)

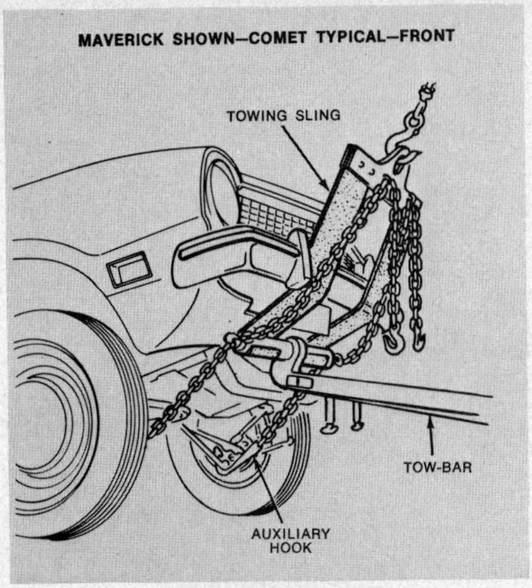
MAVERICK SHOWN—COMET TYPICAL—FRONT
TOWING SLING
TOW-BAR
AUXILIARY
HOOK

Attachments to Maverick
(© Ford Motor Co)

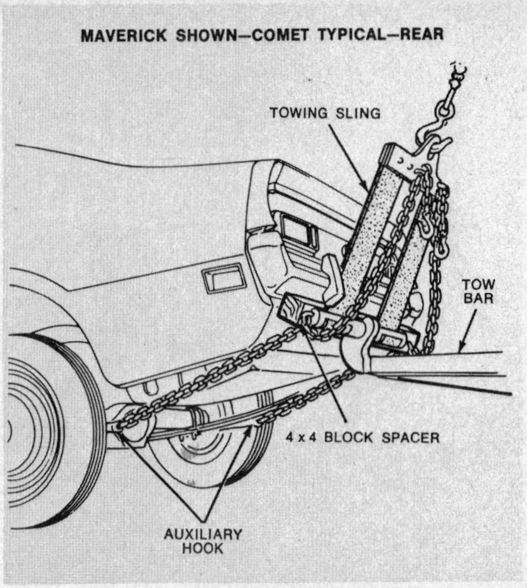
MAVERICK SHOWN—COMET TYPICAL—REAR
TOWING SLING
TOW
BAR
4 x 4 BLOCK SPACER
AUXILIARY
HOOK

Attachments to Maverick
(© Ford Motor Co)

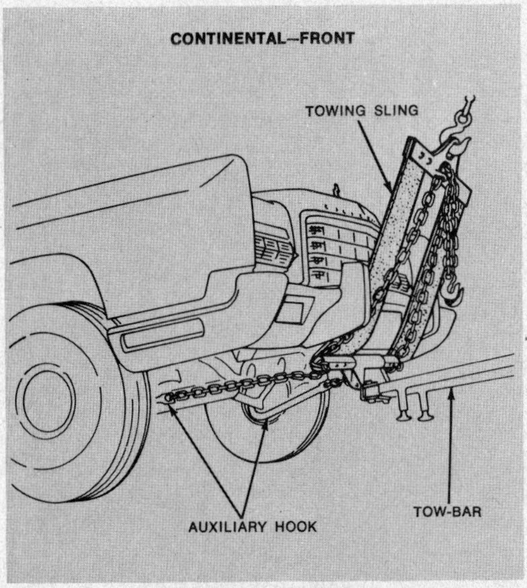
CONTINENTAL—FRONT
TOWING SLING
AUXILIARY HOOK
TOW-BAR

Attachments to Continental
(© Ford Motor Co)

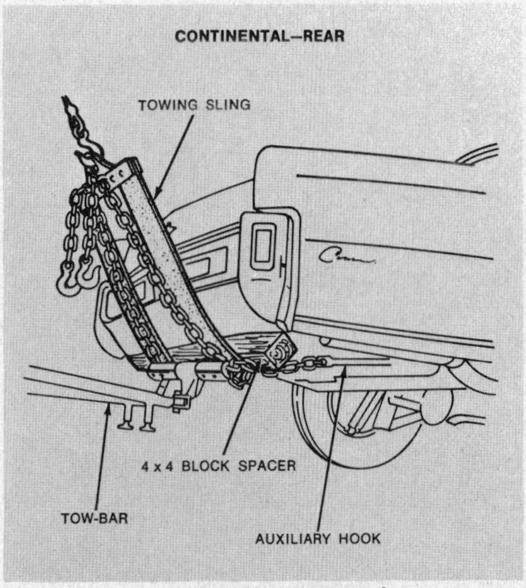
CONTINENTAL—REAR
TOWING SLING
4 x 4 BLOCK SPACER
TOW-BAR
AUXILIARY HOOK

Attachments to Continental
(© Ford Motor Co)

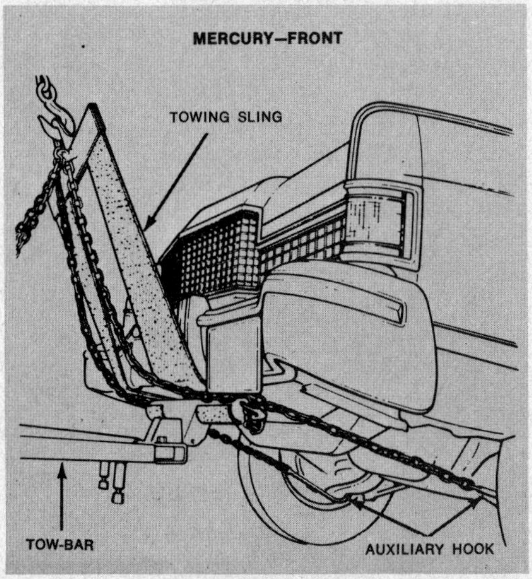
MERCURY—FRONT
TOWING SLING
TOW-BAR
AUXILIARY HOOK

Attachments to Mercury
(© Ford Motor Co)

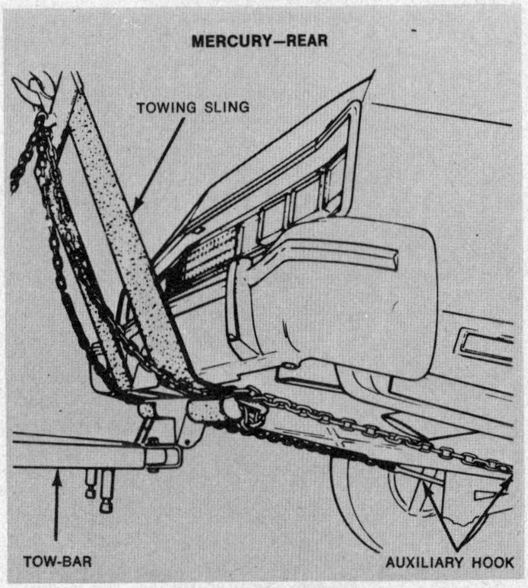
MERCURY—REAR
TOWING SLING
TOW-BAR
AUXILIARY HOOK

Attachments to Mercury
(© Ford Motor Co)

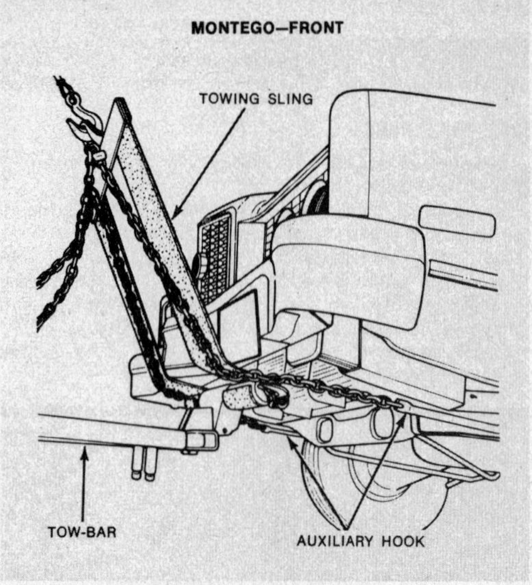
MONTEGO—FRONT
TOWING SLING
TOW-BAR
AUXILIARY HOOK

Attachments to Montego
(© Ford Motor Co)

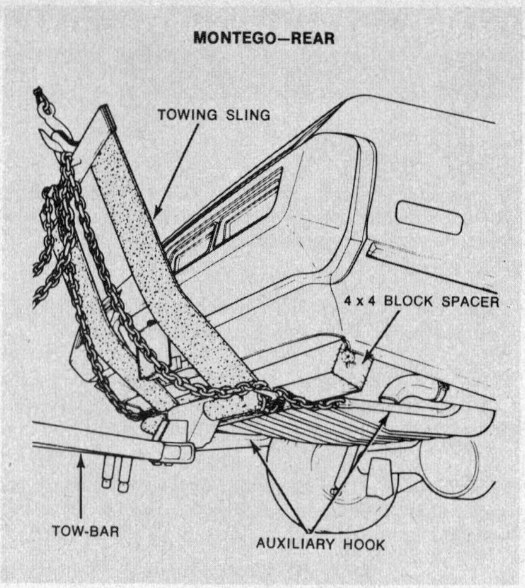
MONTEGO—REAR
TOWING SLING
4 x 4 BLOCK SPACER
TOW-BAR
AUXILIARY HOOK

Attachments to Montego
(© Ford Motor Co)

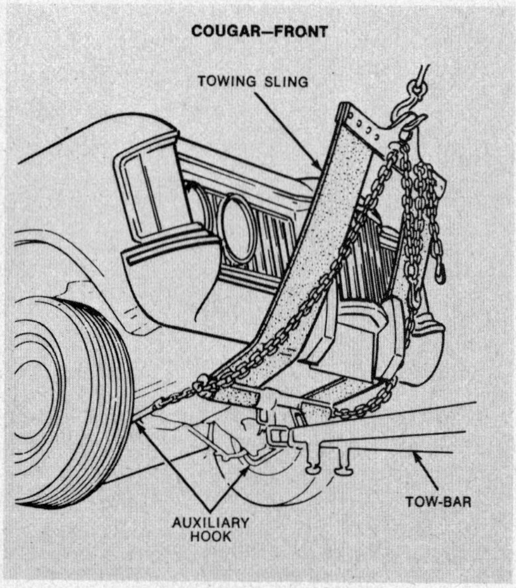
COUGAR—FRONT
TOWING SLING
AUXILIARY HOOK
TOW-BAR

Attachments to Cougar
(© Ford Motor Co)

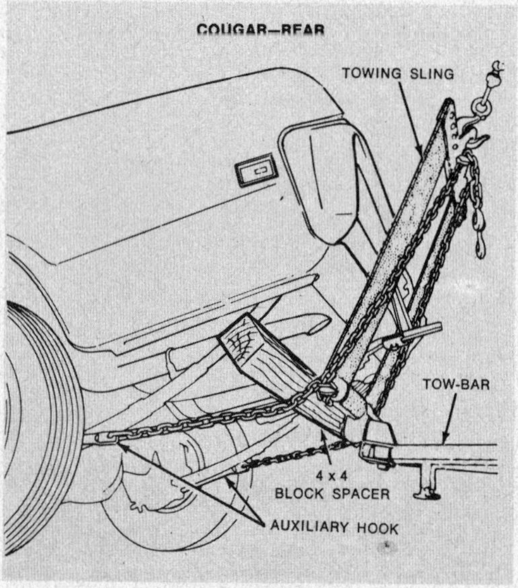
COUGAR—REAR
TOWING SLING
TOW-BAR
4 x 4
BLOCK SPACER
AUXILIARY HOOK

Attachments to Cougar
(© Ford Motor Co)

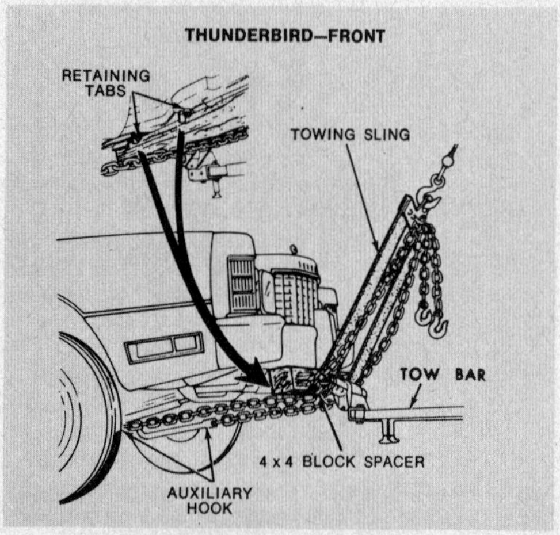
THUNDERBIRD—FRONT
RETAINING TABS
TOWING SLING
TOW BAR
4 x 4 BLOCK SPACER
AUXILIARY HOOK

Attachments to Thunderbird
(© Ford Motor Co)

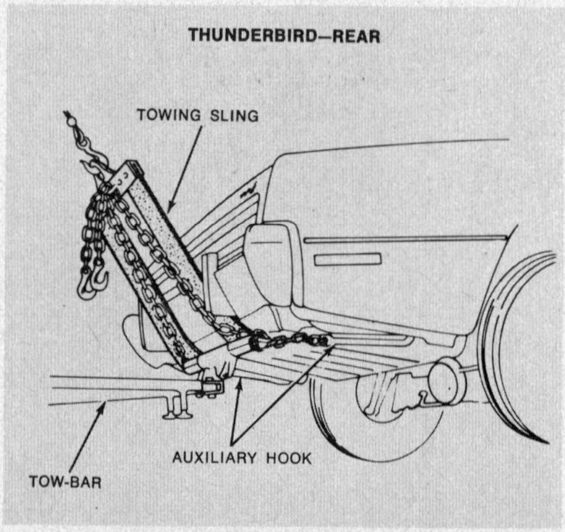
THUNDERBIRD—REAR
TOWING SLING
AUXILIARY HOOK
TOW-BAR

Attachments to Thunderbird
(© Ford Motor Co)

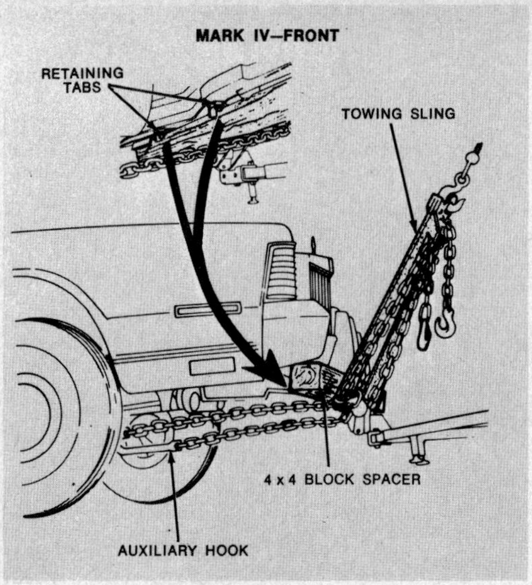
MARK IV—FRONT
RETAINING TABS
TOWING SLING
4 x 4 BLOCK SPACER
AUXILIARY HOOK

Attachments to Lincoln Mark IV
(© Ford Motor Co)

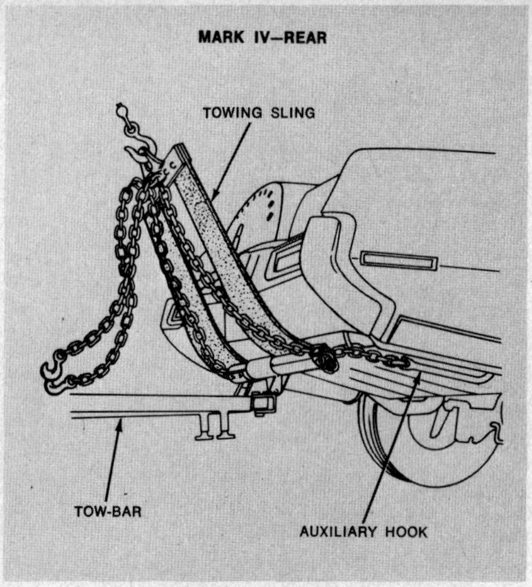
MARK IV—REAR
TOWING SLING
TOW-BAR
AUXILIARY HOOK

Attachments to Mark IV
(© Ford Motor Co)

GM Products

Chevrolet

All 1973 Chevrolet cars which are to be towed from the front are lifted in the same manner. Attach the "J" hooks to the inside ends of the lower control arms and place the sling cross bar behind the edge of the front bumper. On Camaro, Vega, and Corvette, place the spacer bar between the sling chains and the frame. On the Camaro, the spacer must contact the frame at the bumper brackets while the Vega bar must be positioned under the reinforcement struts. Place the spacer bar on Corvettes behind the front spoiler, making sure that it contacts the front crossmember.

Caution Because of the fiberglass construction of the Corvette, make certain that the sling crossbar is 2 to 4 in. ahead of the front spoiler. The position is important in order to prevent fiberglass damage.

To tow 1973 Chevrolet vehicles from the rear, place the "J" hooks into the access holes in the side rails. On Vega and Nova, attach the hooks to the outboard end of the axle tube. On Vegas, place the hooks on the outside ends of the suspension, while on Nova position the hooks just inside of the springs. Attach the "J" hooks on Corvettes to the lower end of the shock absorber mounts at the suspension link. Make certain that the sling bar is 2 to 4 in. behind the lower panel. For security, attach the safety chains around the ends of the springs.

To relieve pressure on the fuel tank on both Vega and Nova, place the wooden spacer block across the tank with its outer edges contacting the leaf springs at a point 5 in. in front of the spring shackle.

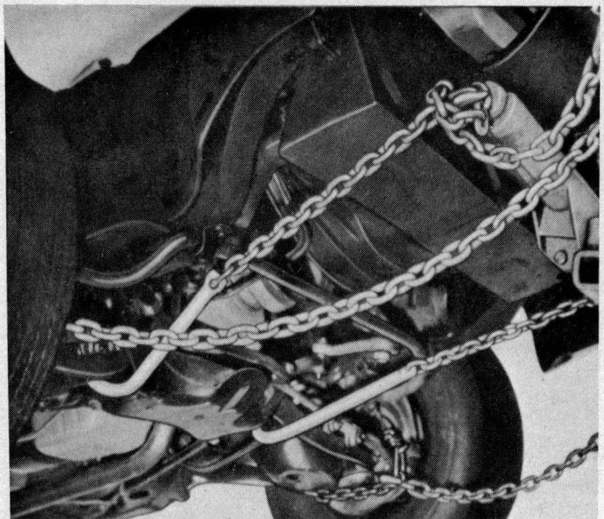

Front attachments to Chevrolet cars
(© G.M. Corp)

Placement of spacer bar
(© G.M. Corp)

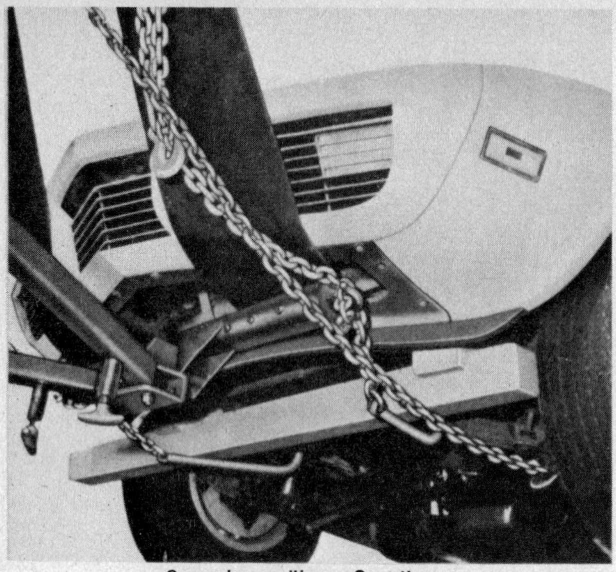
Spacer bar position on Corvette
(© G.M. Corp)

Spacer bar position on Vega
(© G.M. Corp)

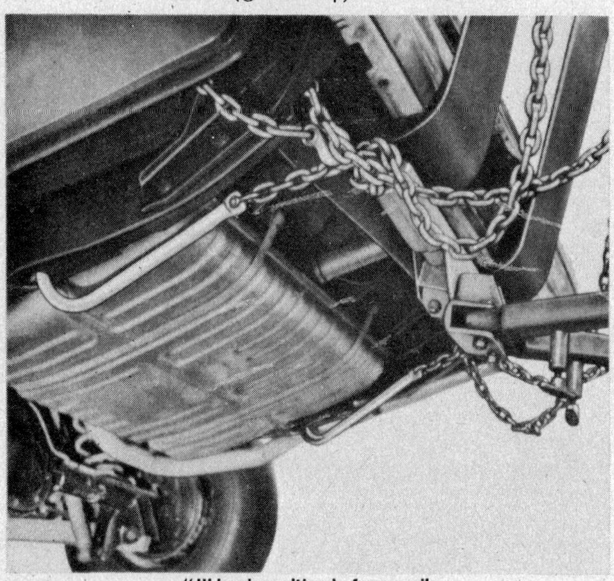
"J" hook position in frame rails
(© G.M. Corp)

"J" hook position on Nova
(© G.M. Corp)

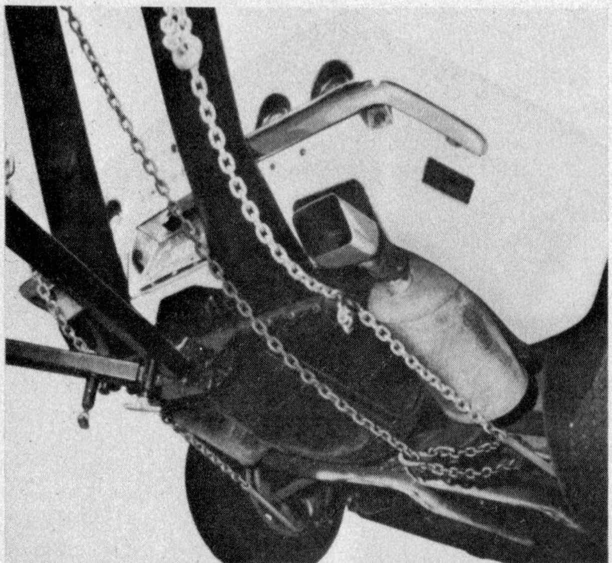
"J" hook position on Corvette
(© G.M. Corp)

Spacer block location on Vega
(© G.M. Corp)

Pontiac

On 1973 Pontiac cars which are to be towed from the front, attach the "J" hooks to the front inside ends of the lower control arms at the point where the arms attach to the frame.

In order to lift Pontiac vehicles from the front, all models except the LeMans and the LeMans Safari Wagon must use the wooden spacer block. On the LeMans and the LeMans Wagon it is necessary to place the sling crossbar under the lower edge of the radiator support while on all other models the wooden spacer is necessary to prevent lower sheet metal damage. On most models, position the spacer bar across the end of the "J" hooks with the ends of the spacer contacting the frame.

For added security, attach the safety chains around the lower control arms at their outside edge.

When lifting most 1973 Pontiac vehicles from the rear, attach the "J" hooks at the holes in the frame side rails. The only exceptions are the Trans Am, Safari, and Safari Wagon. On these models, attach the hooks to the ends of the axle tubes just outside of the springs.

On all models, with the exception of Grandville, Bonneville, Catalina, and LeMans Safari Wagon, use the wooden spacer bar. It is placed across the sling chain and it must contact the frame. Make certain that the spacer is clear of sheet metal.

Attach the safety chains to the vehicle bumper brackets.

"J" hook position on 1973 Pontiacs
(© G.M. Corp)

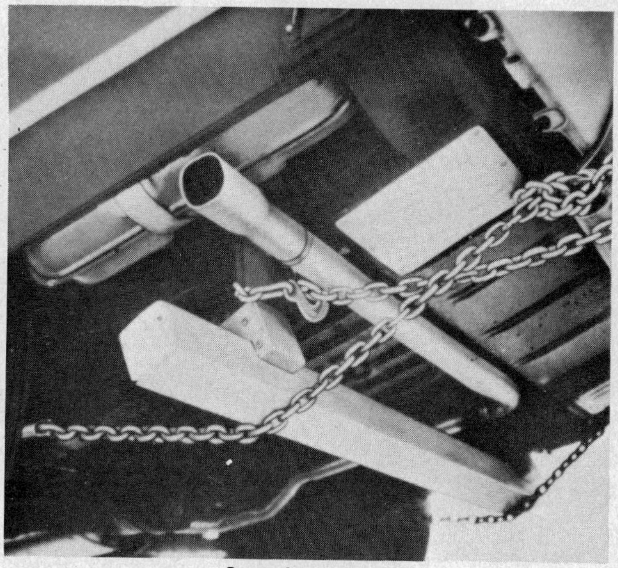

Spacer bar position
(© G.M. Corp)

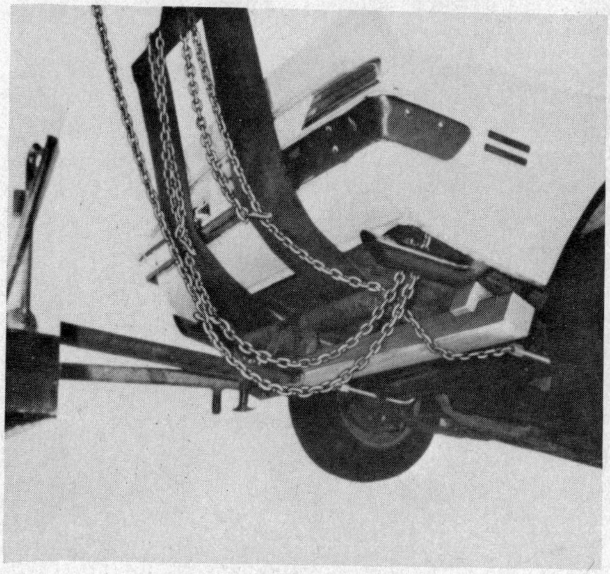

Spacer and "J" hook position on Trans Am
(© G.M. Corp)

"J" hook position in side rail holes
(© G.M. Corp)

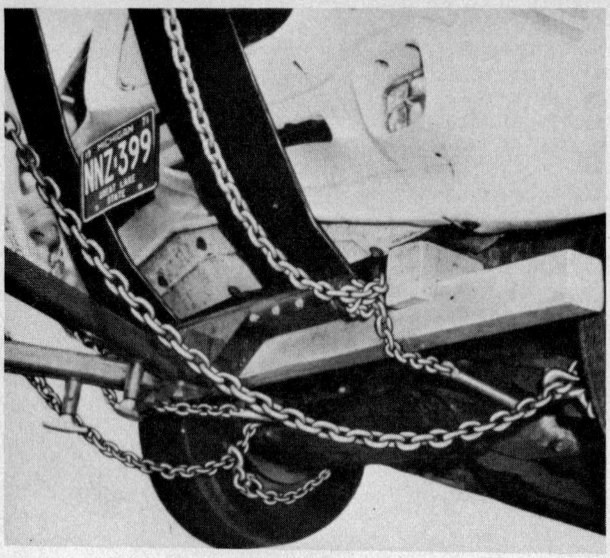
NNZ-399

Safety chain position
(© G.M. Corp)

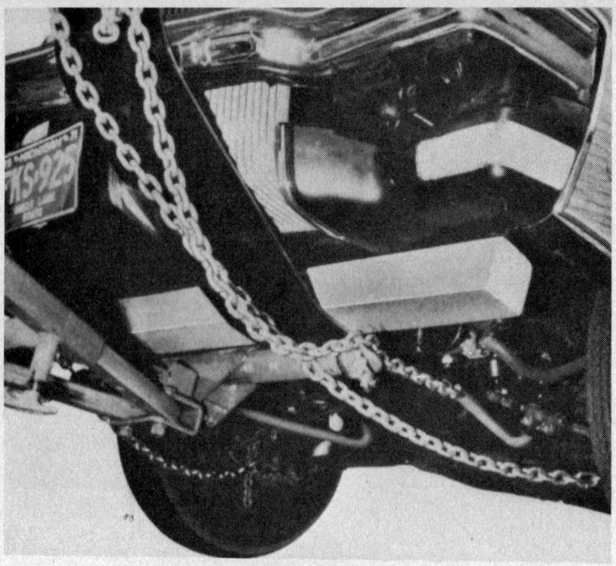

"J" hook position
(© G.M. Corp)

Oldsmobile

Position the "J" hooks on all 1973 models at the inside ends of the lower control arms at the frame.

It is necessary to use the wooden spacer on all Oldsmobile cars. The spacer should be placed across the sling chains with its ends contacting the vehicle frame.

Caution

Because of minimal ground clearance on the 98 Model, it is necessary to place the rear wheels on a dolly if the vehicle is to be towed over rough road. This will avoid damage to the rear of the car.

The sling crossbar should be positioned at a secure point ahead of the spacer. Avoid putting pressure on any sheet metal surfaces with the crossbar.

Attach the safety chains to the lower control arms just inside the wheel.

When towing the vehicle from the rear, attach the "J" hooks to the rear frame rails. There are holes in the lower side of the rails. On the Omega and the 88 Station Wagon, the "J" hooks should be secured around the axle tubes just inside the springs.

The wooden spacer bar is needed to lift the 88 Wagon and the Omega but all other models can be lifted safely with the "J" hooks and the crossbar in the proper positions. On the 88 Wagon and the Omega, the spacer bar should be placed across the left rear spring shackles.

The crossbar should be positioned some distance behind the edge of the bumper so that it is secure. For added safety, attach the safety chains either around the bumper brackets or the rear spring shackles.

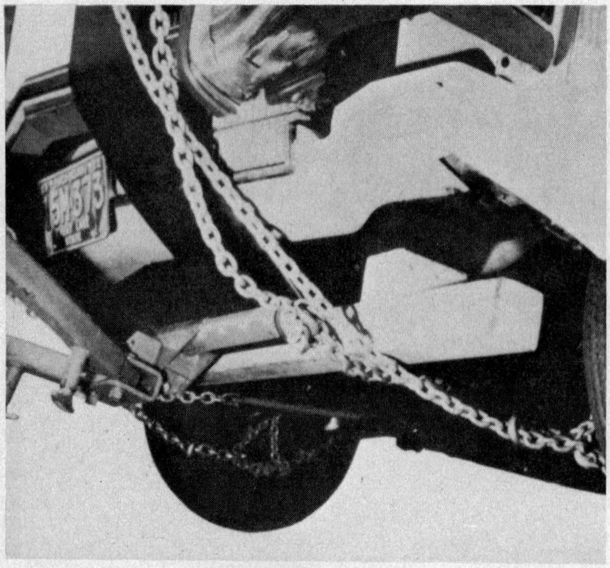

Sling crossbar position
(© G.M. Corp)

Spacer bar position
(© G.M. Corp)

Buick

Place the "J" hooks, on all 1973 models, around the lower end of the control arms where they meet the frame.

NOTE: Wooden spacer blocks are not needed to raise any 1973 model from the front.

Place the sling crossbar to the front of any lower front sheet metal. Attach safety chains around the outside ends of the lower control arms.

Caution Because of low ground clearance on the Electra 225 and the Riviera, it may be necessary to remove the front wheels and lower the vehicle so that it is closer to level with the rear wheels. If this cannot be done, the rear wheels must be placed on a dolly.

When towing Buicks from the rear, attach the "J" hooks to the holes in the lower side of the frame rails.

The wooden spacer bar is not needed on any models except the Estate Wagon and Riviera. On these models the spacer should be positioned across the sling chains with the ends of the spacer contacting the rear leaf spring shackles.

Position the sling crossbar on the rear frame. On the Estate Wagon, place the bar 6 to 8 in. ahead of the lower edge of the bumper.

Attach the safety chains either to the bumper brackets or the lower spring shackles, whichever is most convenient.

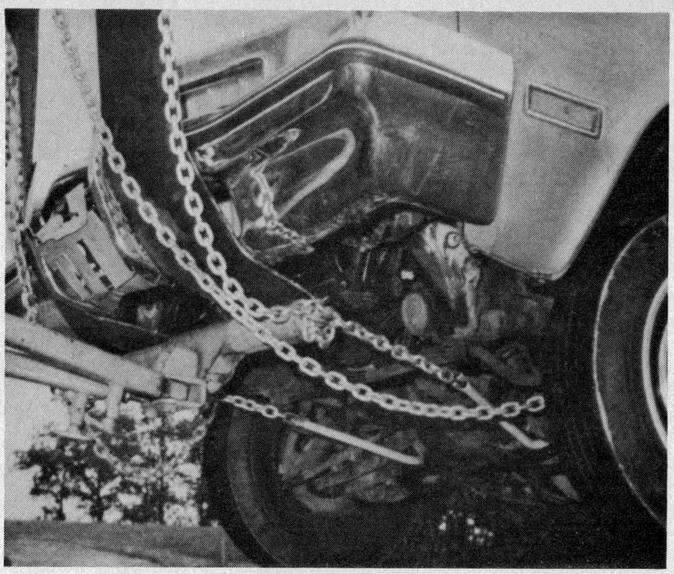

"J" hook position
(© G.M. Corp)

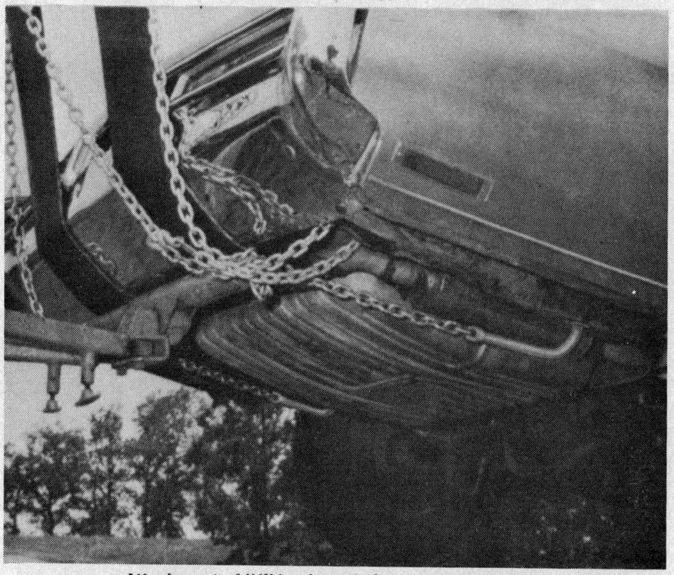

Attachment of "J" hooks to holes in the rear frame
(© G.M. Corp)

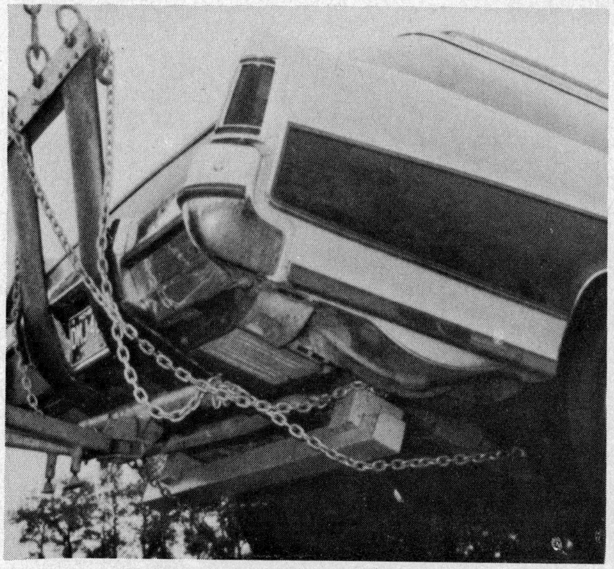

Position of spacer bar on the Estate Wagon
(© G.M. Corp)

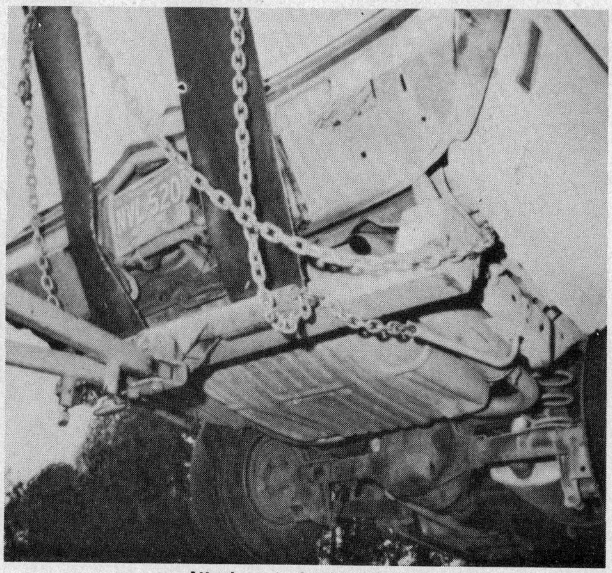

Attachment of safety chains
(© G.M. Corp)

Cadillac

To lift 1973 Cadillacs from the front, attach the "J" hooks to the inside ends of the lower control arms where they meet the frame. On the Eldorado, secure the hooks to the rear edge of the front lower control arms. Place the hooks just inside the shock absorber lower mounting bracket.

Caution When towing the Eldorado from the front, always release the hood latch.

Place the sling crossbar 2 to 4 in. behind the lower edge of the bumper on both Cadillac and Eldorado.

The safety chains should be attached to the front frame crossmember.

When towing the vehicle from the rear, attach the "J" hooks to the holes in the lower frame rails.

Place the sling crossbar behind the edge of the bumper and secure the safety chains to the rear bumper brackets.

KLY-911

Front attachments to Cadillac
(© G.M. Corp)

Front attachments to Eldorado
(© G.M. Corp)

Rear attachments to Cadillac
(© G.M. Corp)

INDEX

Buick

YEAR IDENTIFICATION

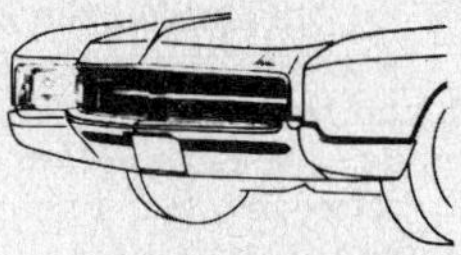
1967 Riviera

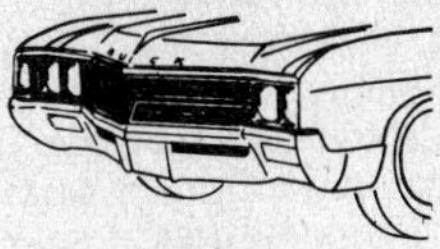
1967 Wildcat

1967 Electra-Le Sabre

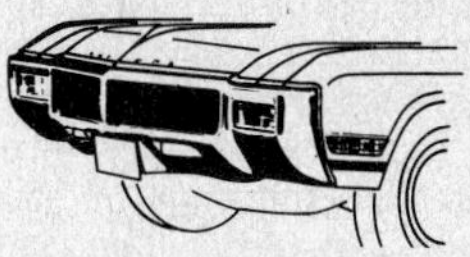
1968-69 Riviera

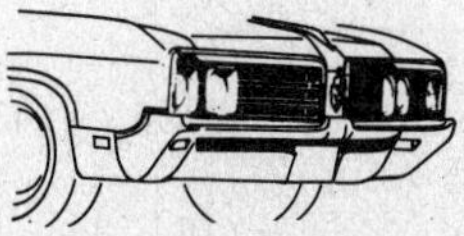
1968 Wildcat

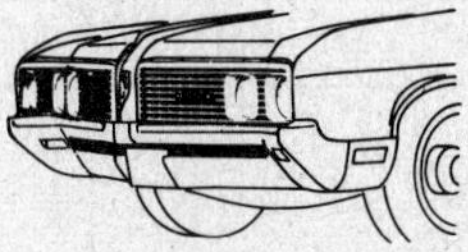
1968 Electra

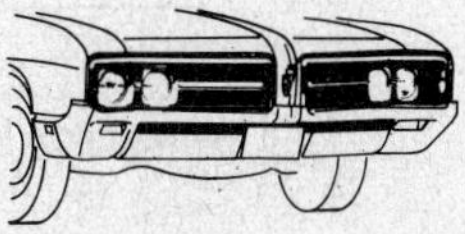
1968 Le Sabre

1969 Wildcat

1969 Le Sabre

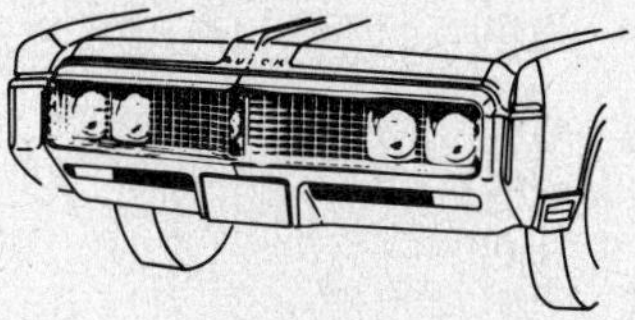
1969 Electra

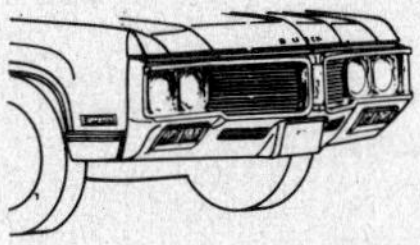
1970 Le Sabre

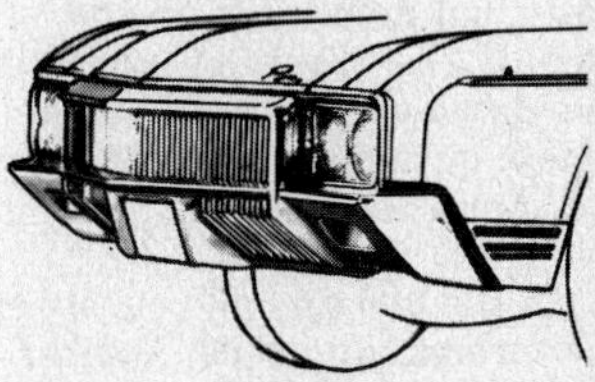
1970 Riviera

1971 Electra

1971 Riviera

1971 Le Sabre

1971 Centurion

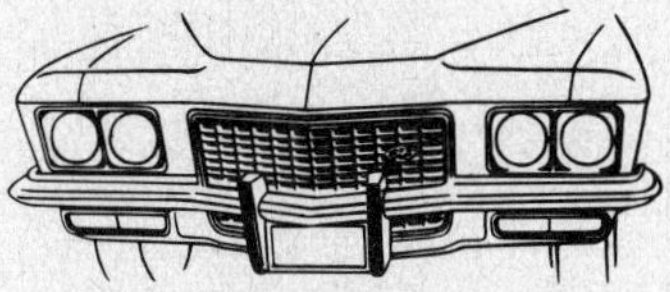
1972 Riviera

1972 Electra

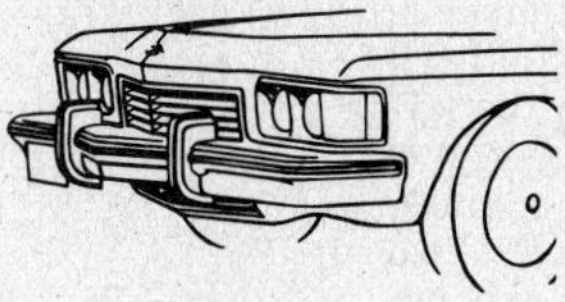
1973 Riviera

1973 Buick

1974 Electra

1974 Riviera

1974 Le Sabre

FIRING ORDER

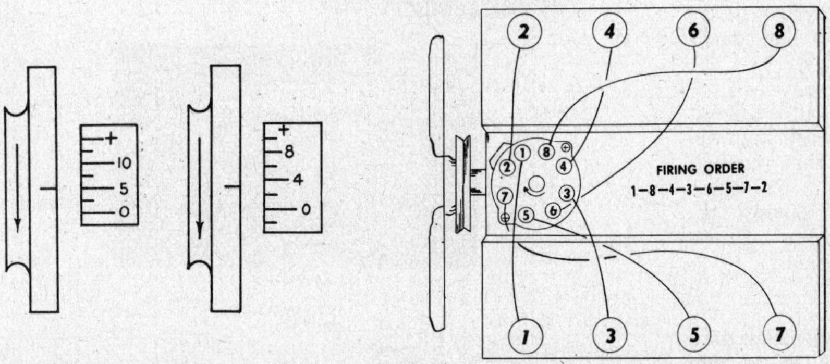
+
10
5
0
+
8
4
0
2 4 6 8
FIRING ORDER
1—8—4—3—6—5—7—2
1 3 5 7

1967-'74 350, 400, 430, 455 cu. in. (Left timing mark 1967-69)

CAR SERIAL NUMBER LOCATION AND ENGINE IDENTIFICATION

The car serial number is used for registration and other legal records. This number is unique to the individual car. The production code number identifies the type of engine and its production date. The Engine Identification Code chart can be used to determine the type of engine in the particular vehicle. The engine number also appears on the vehicle identification plate following model and series identification.

1967

The car serial number identification plate is attached to the left front body hinge pillar.

On the 300 and 340 cu. in. engines, the serial number is on the left front face of the crankcase to the side of the distributor cap. The production code number is between the two middle branches of the right exhaust manifold.

On the 400 and 430 cu. in. engines, the production code number is between the two front branches of the right exhaust manifold, while the engine serial number is between the two rear branches.

1968

The serial number identification plate is attached to the left front body hinge pillar.

On the 350 cu. in. engine, the serial number is on the front of the left cylinder bank just below the cylinder head. The production code number is between the left exhaust manifold and the two front spark plugs on the left bank.

On the 400 and 430 cu. in. engines, the serial number is between the two front spark plugs and the exhaust manifold on the left side. The production code number is between the two rear spark plugs and the exhaust manifold, also on the left side.

1969

The serial number identification plate is attached to the top of the instrument panel on the left side.

On the 350 cu. in. engine, the serial number is on the front of the left cylinder bank just below the cylinder head. The production code number is between the left exhaust manifold and the two front spark plugs on the left bank.

On the 400 and 430 cu. in. engines, the serial number is between the two front spark plugs and the exhaust manifold on the left side. The production code number is between the two rear spark plugs and the exhaust manifold, also on the left side.

1970-74

The serial number identification plate is attached to the top of the instrument panel on the left side.

On the 350 cu. in. engine, the serial number is on the front of the left cylinder bank just below the cylinder head. The production code number is between the left exhaust manifold and the two front spark plugs on the left bank.

On the 455 cu. in. engine, the serial number is between the two front spark plugs and the exhaust manifold on the left side. The production code number is between the two rear spark plugs and the exhaust manifold, also on the left side.

ENGINE PRODUCTION CODE

Disp	Bbl	Hp	'67	'68	'69	'70	'71	'72	'73	'74
8-Cylinder Models										
340	2	220	NA							
340	4	260	NB							
350	2	150, 165# (net)							XC	YC
350	2	155 (net)						WC		
350	4	175, 195# (net)							XB	YB
350	4	180 (net)						WB		
350	2	230		PO	RO		TC TO			
350	2	260				SO				
350	4	260					TB TD			
350	4	280		PP	RP					
350	4	285				SB				
350	4	315				SP				
430	4	360								
455	2	175, 190# (net)								—
455	4	225, 250# (net)		ND MD	PD	RD		WF	XF	
455	4	210, 230# (net)								YF
455	4	260 (net)						WA	XA	
Stage 1										
455	4	245 (net)								YA
455	4	315					TR			
455	4	330					TA			
455	4	350				SR				
455	4	370				SF				

\# Dual exhaust

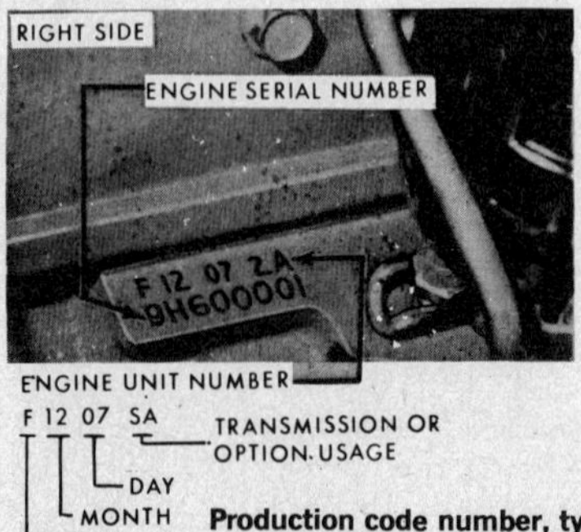
RIGHT SIDE
ENGINE SERIAL NUMBER
F 12 07 ZA
9H600001
ENGINE UNIT NUMBER
F 12 07 SA
TRANSMISSION OR OPTION USAGE
DAY
MONTH
PLANT

Production code number, typical
(© Buick Div., G.M. Corp.)

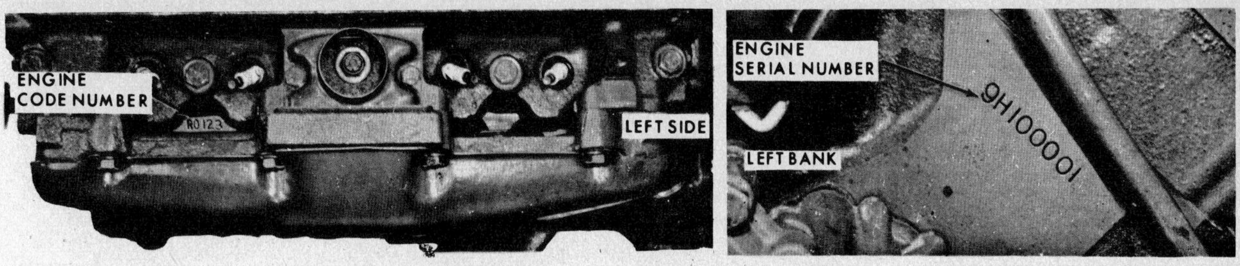
ENGINE
CODE NUMBER
R0123
LEFT SIDE
ENGINE
SERIAL NUMBER
LEFT BANK

Engine numbers, 1968–'74 350 cu. in. (© Buick Div., G.M. Corp.)

TUNE-UP SPECIFICATIONS

When analyzing compression test results, look for uniformity among cylinders rather than specific pressures.

	ENGINE		SPARK PLUGS		DISTRIBUTOR		IGNITION TIMING (deg) ▲		VALVES	Fuel	IDLE SPEED (rpm) ▲	
Year	No. Cyl Displacement (cu in.)	hp	Type §	Gap (in.)	Point Dwell (deg)	Point Gap (in.)	Man Trans	Auto Trans	Intake Opens ■ (deg)	Pump Pressure (psi)	Man Trans	Auto Trans
'67	8-340	220	44S	.035	30	.016	2½B	2½B	32	4¼-5¾	550①(600)	550①(600)
	8-340	260	44S	.035	30	.016	2½B	2½B	N.A.	4¼-5¾	550①(600)	550①(600)
	8-430	360	44TS	.035	30	.016	2½B	2½B	14	5½-7	550①(600)	550①(600)
'68	8-350	230	45TS	.030	30	.016	TDC	TDC	24	4¼-5¾	700	550
	8-350	280	45TS	.030	30	.016	TDC	TDC	24	4¼-5¾	700	550
	8-430	360	44TS	.030	30	.016	TDC	TDC	14	5½-7	550	550
'69	8-350	230	R-45TS	.030	30	.016	TDC	TDC	24	4¼-5¾	700	600
	8-350	280	R-45TS	.030	30	.016	TDC	TDC	24	4¼-5¾	700	600
	8-430	360	R-44TS	.030	30	.016	—	TDC	14	5½-7	—	550
'70	8-350	260	R-45TS	.030	30	.016	6B	6B	24	4¼-5¾	700	600
	8-350	285	R-45TS	.030	30	.016	6B	6B	24	4¼-5¾	700	600
	8-350	315	R-45TS	.030	30	.016	6B	6B	24	4¼-5¾	700	600
	8-455	350	R-44TS	.030	30	.016	6B	6B	18	4¼-5¾	700	600
	8-455	370	R-44TS	.030	30	.016	6B	6B	18	4¼-5¾	700	600
'71	8-350	230	R-45TS	.030	30	.016	6B	10B②	24	4¼-5¾	1100/800③	600
	8-350	260	R-45TS	.030	30	.016	6B	4B	28	4¼-5¾	1100/800③	600
	8-455	315	R-45TS	.030	30	.016	6B	4B	12	4¼-5¾	1100/700③	600
	8-455	330	R-44TS	.030	30	.016	10B	10B	12	4¼-5¾	1100/700③	600
'72	8-350	155	R-45TS	.040	30	.016	4B	4B	24	4¼-5¾	800③/600	650③/500
	8-350	180	R-45TS	.040	30	.016	4B	4B	24	4¼-5¾	800③/600	650③/500
	8-455	225	R-45TS	.040	30	.016	4B	4B	12(14)④	4¼-5¾	900③/600	650③/500
	8-455	250	R-45TS	.040	30	.016	4B	4B	12(14)④	4¼-5¾	900③/600	650③/500
	8-455	260	R-45TS	.040	30	.016	4B	4B	12(14)④	4¼-5¾	900③/600	650③/500
'73	8-350	150	R-45TS	.040	30	.016	—	4B	24	4¼-5¾	—	600/500③
	8-350	175	R-45TS	.040	30	.016	—	4B	24	4¼-5¾	—	600/500③
	8-455	225	R-45TS	.040	30	.016	—	4B	14	4¼-5¾	—	650/500③
	8-455	250	R-45TS	.040	30	.016	—	4B	14	4¼-5¾	—	650/500③
	8-455	260	R-45TS	.040	30	.016	—	4B	14	4¼-5¾	—	650/500③
'74	All 350	—	R-45TS	.040	30	.016	—	4B	19⑤	4¼-5¾	—	650/500③
	All 455	—	R-45TS	.040	30	.016	—	4B	10⑤	4¼-5¾	—	650/500③

▲ See text for procedure
■ All figures Before Top Dead Center
§ All spark plug listings are A.C. original equipment numbers
① Adjust idle on air conditioned vehicles 50 rpm higher with A/C off, except on California vehicles.
② 4B for LeSabre
③ Lower figure indicates idle speed with solenoid disconnected
④ Lower figure indicates California vehicle.
⑤ These figures do not represent a change from 1973; however, the reference point is changed from .004 in. valve lift to .004 in. cam lift to be consistent with information required for government certification.
B Before Top Dead Center
N.A. Not available
TDC Top Dead Center
— Not applicable

GENERAL ENGINE SPECIFICATIONS

Year	Engine Cu. In. Displacement	Carburetor Type	Advertised Horsepower @ rpm ■	Advertised Torque @ rpm (ft lbs) ■	Bore and Stroke (in.)	Advertised Compression Ratio	Oil Pressure @ 2400 rpm (psi)
'67	8-340	2 bbl	220 @4200	340 @ 2400	3.750 x 3.850	9.0:1	40
	8-340	4 bbl	260 @ 4200	365 @ 2800	3.750 x 3.850	10.25:1	40
	8-430	4 bbl	360 @ 5000	475 @ 3200	4.1875 x 3.900	10.25:1	40
'68	8-350	2 bbl	230 @ 4400	350 @ 2400	3.800 x 3.500	9.0:1	37
	8-350	4 bbl	280 @ 4800	375 @3200	3.800 x 3.850	10.25:1	37
	8-430	4 bbl	360 @ 5000	475 @ 3200	4.1875 x 3.900	10.25:1	40
'69	8-350	2 bbl	230 @ 4400	350 @ 2400	3.800 x 3.500	9.0:1	37
	8-350	4 bbl	280 @ 4600	375 @ 3200	3.800 x 3.850	10.25:1	37
	8-430	4 bbl	360 @ 5000	475 @ 3200	4.1875 x 3.900	10.25:1	40
'70	8-350	2 bbl	260 @ 4600	360 @ 2600	3.800 x 3.850	9.0:1	37
	8-350	4 bbl	285 @ 4600	375 @ 3200	3.800 x 3.850	10.25:1	37
	8-350	4 bbl	315 @ 4800	410 @ 3200	3.800 x 3.850	10.25:1	37
	8-455	4 bbl	370 @ 4600	510 @ 2800	4.3125 x 3.900	10.0:1	40
'71	8-350	2 bbl	230 @ 4400	350 @ 2400	3.800 x 3.850	8.5:1	37
	8-350	4 bbl	260 @ 4600	360 @ 3000	3.800 x 3.850	8.5:1	37
	8-455	4 bbl	315 @ 4400	450 @ 2800	4.3125 x 3.900	8.5:1	40
	8-455	4 bbl	330 @ 4600	455 @ 2800	4.3125 x 3.900	8.5:1	40
'72	8-350	2 bbl	155 @ 3800①	270 @ 2400②	3.800 x 3.850	8.5:1	37③
	8-350	4 bbl	180 @ 3800④	275 @ 2400⑤	3.800 x 3.850	8.5:1	37③
	8-455	4 bbl	225 @ 4000	360 @ 2600	4.3125 x 3.900	8.5:1	40
	8-455 DE	4 bbl	250 @ 4000	375 @ 2800	4.3125 x 3.900	8.5:1	40
	8-455	4 bbl	260 @ 4400	380 @ 2800	4.3125 x 3.900	8.5:1	40
'73	8-350	2 bbl	150 @ 3800	265 @ 2400	3.800 x 3.850	8.5:1	37
	8-350	4 bbl	175 @ 3800	270 @ 2400	3.800 x 3.850	8.5:1	37
	8-455	4 bbl	225 @ 4000	360 @ 2600	4.3125 x 3.900	8.5:1	37
	8-455 DE	4 bbl	250 @ 4000	375 @ 2800	4.3125 x 3.900	8.5:1	37
	8-455	4 bbl	260 @ 4400	380 @ 2800	4.3125 x 3.900	8.5:1	37
'74	8-350 SE	2 bbl	150 @ 3600	270 @ 2000	3.800 x 3.850	8.5:1	37
	8-350 DE	2 bbl	165 @ 3800	285 @ 2000	3.800 x 3.850	8.5:1	37
	8-350 SE	4 bbl	175 @ 3800	260 @ 2000	3.800 x 3.850	8.5:1	37
	8-350 DE	4 bbl	195 @ 4000	280 @ 2000	3.800 x 3.850	8.5:1	37
	8-455 SE	2 bbl	175 @ 3400	355 @ 2000	4.3125 x 3.900	8.5:1	37
	8-455 DE	2 bbl	190 @ 3600	370 @ 2000	4.3125 x 3.900	8.5:1	37
	8-455 SE	4 bbl	210 @ 3600	335 @ 2200	4.3125 x 3.900	8.5:1	37
	8-455 DE	4 bbl	230 @ 3800	355 @ 2200	4.3125 x 3.900	8.5:1	37
	8-455 DE⑥	4 bbl	245 @ 4000	360 @ 2400	4.3125 x 3.900	8.5:1	37
	8-455 DE⑦	4 bbl	255 @ 4400	370 @ 2800	4.3125 x 3.900	8.5:1	37

■ Beginning 1972 horsepower and torque are SAE net figures. They are measured at the rear of the transmission with all accessories installed and operating. Since the figures vary when a given engine is installed in different models, some are representative rather than exact.

SE Single Exhaust

DE Dual Exhaust

① For California vehicles, advertised horsepower is 150 @ 3800 rpm

② For California vehicles, advertised torque is 265 @ 2400 rpm

③ Adjust oil pressure at 2600 rpm

④ For California vehicles, advertised horsepower is 175 @ 3800 rpm

⑤ For California vehicles, advertised torque is 270 @ 2400 rpm

⑥ Stage I Riviera

⑦ Stage I Gran Sport

PISTON CLEARANCE

Year	Engine	Piston to Bore Clearance (in.)
'67	8-340	.0011-.0017
	8-430	.0007-.0013
'68	8-350	.0008-.0014
	8-430	.0007-.0013
'69	8-350	.0008-.0014
	8-430	.0007-.0013
'70-'74	8-350	.0008-.0020
	8-455	.0010-.0016

CRANKSHAFT AND CONNECTING ROD SPECIFICATIONS

All measurements are given in in.

Year	Engine Displace. (cu in.)	CRANKSHAFT Main Brg. Journal Dia	CRANKSHAFT Main Brg. Oil Clearance	CRANKSHAFT Shaft End-Play	CRANKSHAFT Thrust on No.	CONNECTING ROD Journal Diameter	CONNECTING ROD Oil Clearance	CONNECTING ROD Side Clearance
'67	340	2.9995	.0004-.0015	.004-.008	3	2.0000	.0020-.0023	.006-.014
	430	3.2500	.0007-.0018	.003-.009	3	2.2495	.0002-.0023	.005-.012
'68-'69	350	2.9995	.0004-.0015	.003-.009	3	2.0000	.0002-.0023	.006-.014
	430	3.2500	.0007-.0018	.003-.009	3	2.2495	.0002-.0023	.005-.012
'70-'74	350	2.9995	.0004-.0015	.003-.009	3	2.0000	.0002-.0023	.006-.014
	455	3.2500	.0007-.0018	.003-.009	3	2.2495	.0002-.0023	.005-.012

CAPACITIES

Year	ENGINE No. Cyl. Displacement (Cu. In.)	Engine Crankcase Add 1 Qt For New Filter	TRANSMISSION Pts To Refill After Draining Manual 3-Speed	Manual 4-Speed	Automatic ●	Drive Axle (pts)	Gasoline Tank (gals)	COOLING SYSTEM (qts) With Heater	With A/C
'67	8-340	4	3.4	—	5	2.75	25	12.7	14.7
	8-430	4	3.5	—	5	4.25	25	16.7	17
	Riviera	4	—	—	5	4.25	21	16.7	17
'68	8-350	4	3.4	—	5	3	25	13.2	13.6
	8-430	4	3.5	—	5	4.25	25	16.7	17
	Riviera	4	—	—	5	4.25	21	16.7	17
'69	8-350	4	3.5	—	5	3	25	13.2	13.6
	8-430	4	3.5	—	7	4.25	25	16.7	17
	Riviera	4	—	—	7	4.25	21	16.7	17
'70	8-350	4	3.5	—	6	3	25	16.2	16.6
	8-455	4	3.5	—	7	4.25	25①	19.7	20
	Riviera	4	—	—	7	4.25	21	19.7	20
'71	8-350	4	3.5	—	6	4.25	25	16.2	16.6
	8-455	4	3.5	—	7	5.5	25②	18.7	19
	Riviera	4	—	—	7	5.5	24	19.7	20
'72	8-350	4	—	—	6	4.25	25	19	19.3
	8-455	4	—	—	7	5.5	25②	18.7	19
	Riviera	4	—	—	7	5.5	24	18.7	19
'73	8-350	4	—	—	6	4.25	26	18.9	19.3
	8-455	4	—	—	7	5.4	26③	18.7	19④
	Riviera	4	—	—	7	5.4	26	18.7	19④
'74	8-350	4	—	—	6	4.25	26	18.9	19.3
	8-455	4	—	—	7	5.4	26	18.7	19④
	Riviera	4	—	—	7	5.4	26	18.7	19④

● Specifications do not include torque convertor
① Estate wagon—24 gals
② Estate wagon—23 gals
③ Estate wagon—22 gals
④ 20.2 with H.D. cooling
— Not applicable

ALTERNATOR AND REGULATOR SPECIFICATIONS

	ALTERNATOR			REGULATOR	Field Relay			Regulator		
Year	Part No. or Manufacturer	Field Current @ 12 V	Output (amps)	Part No. or Manufacturer	Air Gap (in.)	Point Gap (in.)	Volts to Close	Air Gap (in.)	Point Gap (in.)	Volts @ 75°
'67-'70	1100691	2.2-2.6	42	1119515	.015	.030	1.5-3.2	.067	.014	13.6-14.4
	1100774	2.2-2.6	55	1119507	.015	.030	3.8-7.2	.067	.014	13.6-14.4
	1100774	2.2-2.6	55	1119515	.015	.030	1.5-3.2	.067	.014	13.6-14.4
	1100860	2.2-2.6	61	1119515	.015	.030	1.5-3.2	.067	.014	13.6-14.4
'71	1100943	2.2-2.6	42	1119515	.015	.030	1.5-3.2	.067	.014	13.5-14.5
	1100926	4.0-4.5	42	1116384	Transistor type—no adjustment					13.6-14.3
	1100931	2.2-2.6	55	1119515	.015	.030	1.5-3.2	.067	.014	13.5-14.5
	1100932	2.2-2.6	61	1119515	.015	.030	1.5-3.2	.067	.014	13.5-14.5
	1100933	2.8-3.2	63	1119519	.015	.030	1.5-3.2	.067	.014	13.5-14.5
	1100924	4.0-4.5	55	1116384	Transistor type—no adjustment					13.6-14.3
'72	1102449	2.2-2.6	37	1119515	.015	.030	1.5-3.2	.067	.014	13.5-14.4
	1102448	2.2-2.6	55	1119515	.015	.030	1.5-3.2	.067	.014	13.5-14.4
	1102442	2.2-2.6	55	1119515	.015	.030	1.5-3.2	.067	.014	13.5-14.4
	1102450	2.2-2.6	61	1119515	.015	.030	1.5-3.2	.067	.014	13.5-14.4
	1102447	2.8-3.2	63	1119519	.015	.030	1.5-3.2	.067	.014	13.5-14.4
	1100926	4.0-4.5	42	1116384	Transistor type—no adjustment					13.6-14.3
	1100924	4.0-4.5	55	1116384	Transistor type—no adjustment					13.6-14.3
	1100948	4.0-4.5	61	1116384	Transistor type—no adjustment					13.6-14.2
	1100925	4.0-4.5	63	1116384	Transistor type—no adjustment					13.6-14.2
'73-'74	1100947	4.0-4.5	32	1116384	Transistor type—no adjustment					13.5-14.5
	1100926	4.0-4.5	37	1116384	Transistor type—no adjustment					13.5-14.5
	1101018	4.0-4.5	74	1116384	Transistor type—no adjustment					13.5-14.5
	1100946	4.0-4.5	50	1116384	Transistor type—no adjustment					13.5-14.5
	1100948	4.0-4.5	55	1116384	Transistor type—no adjustment					13.5-14.5
	1100925	4.0-4.5	58	1116384	Transistor type—no adjustment					13.5-14.5

WHEEL ALIGNMENT SPECIFICATIONS

		CASTER		CAMBER				WHEEL PIVOT RATIO (deg)	
Year	Model	Range (deg)	Pref Setting (deg)	Range (deg)	Pref Setting (deg)	Toe-in (in.)	Steering Axis Inclin.	Inner Wheel	Wheel Outer
'67-'68	All	$\frac{1}{2}$P to 1$\frac{1}{2}$P	1P	0 to 1P	$\frac{1}{4}$P	$\frac{7}{32}$ to $\frac{5}{16}$	10.75	20	17①
'69	All exc. Riviera	$\frac{1}{4}$P to 1$\frac{1}{4}$P	$\frac{3}{4}$P	$\frac{1}{2}$N to $\frac{1}{2}$P	0	$\frac{3}{16}$ to $\frac{5}{16}$	10.75	20	19$\frac{1}{2}$
	Riviera	$\frac{1}{2}$P to 1$\frac{1}{2}$P	1P	$\frac{1}{4}$N to $\frac{3}{4}$P	$\frac{1}{4}$P	$\frac{5}{32}$ to $\frac{9}{32}$	10.75	20	16$\frac{3}{4}$
'70	All exc. Riviera	$\frac{1}{4}$P to 1$\frac{1}{4}$P	$\frac{3}{4}$P	$\frac{1}{2}$N to $\frac{1}{2}$P	0	$\frac{3}{16}$ to $\frac{5}{16}$	10.5	20	19$\frac{1}{2}$
	Riviera	$\frac{1}{2}$P to 1$\frac{1}{2}$P	1P	$\frac{1}{4}$N to $\frac{3}{4}$P	$\frac{1}{4}$P	$\frac{1}{8}$ to $\frac{1}{4}$	10.5	20	16$\frac{3}{4}$
'71	All	$\frac{1}{2}$P to 1$\frac{1}{2}$P	1P	$\frac{1}{4}$N to $\frac{3}{4}$P	$\frac{1}{4}$P	$\frac{1}{8}$ to $\frac{1}{4}$	10.5	20	18$\frac{1}{2}$
'72	All	$\frac{1}{2}$P to 1$\frac{1}{2}$P	1P	0 to 1P	$\frac{1}{2}$P	$\frac{1}{8}$ to $\frac{1}{4}$	9.0	20	18$\frac{1}{2}$
'73	All	$\frac{1}{2}$P to 1$\frac{1}{2}$P	1P	$\frac{1}{4}$N to $\frac{3}{4}$P	$\frac{1}{4}$P	$\frac{1}{8}$ to $\frac{1}{4}$	9.6②	20	18$\frac{1}{2}$
'74	All	$\frac{1}{2}$P to 1$\frac{1}{2}$P	1P	$\frac{1}{2}$P LH 1P RH	—	$\frac{1}{8}$ to $\frac{1}{4}$	9.6②	20	18$\frac{1}{2}$

① 18° for 1967 Le Sabre
② Estate Wagon 10.8
N Negative P Positive

TORQUE SPECIFICATIONS

All readings in ft lbs

Year	Engine Displacement (cu in.)	Cylinder Head Bolts	Rod Bearing Bolts	Main Bearing Bolts	Crankshaft Pulley Bolt	Flywheel to Crankshaft Bolts	MANIFOLD Intake	MANIFOLD Exhaust
'67	340	65-80	30-40	95-120	140	50-65	45-55	15-20
	430	100-120	45-50	80-115	200	50-65	45-55	15-20
'68	350	75	35	110	140	60	50	18
	430	100	45	110	200	60	50	18
'69-'72	350	75	35	95	120	60	55	18
	430, 455	100	35①	110	200	60	55②	18
'73-'74	350	80	35	115	140	60	55	18
	455	100	45	115	200	60	65	18

① 1970 455 cu in.—45 ft. lbs.
② 1970-72 455 cu in.—65 ft. lbs.

BATTERY AND STARTER SPECIFICATIONS

Year	Engine Displacement (cu in.)	BATTERY Ampere Hour Capacity	BATTERY Volts	BATTERY Terminal Grounded	STARTERS Lock Test Amps	STARTERS Lock Test Volts	STARTERS Lock Test Torque (ft lbs)	STARTERS No-Load Test Amps	STARTERS No-Load Test Volts	STARTERS No-Load Test RPM	Brush Spring Tension (oz)
'67-'68	300, 340, 350	61	12	Neg.	330	3.5	—	65-100	10.6	3,600-5,100	35
	400, 430	70	12	Neg.	510	3.0	—	70-105	10.6	3,800-6,200	35
'69-'70	350	61	12	Neg.	Not Recommended			55-85	9	3,100-4,900	35
	430, 455	70	12	Neg.	Not Recommended			48-74	9	4,100-6,300	35
'71-'72	350	61	12	Neg.	Not Recommended			80	9	3,500-6,000	35
	455	70	12	Neg.	Not Recommended			45-80	9	4,000-6,500	35
'73-'74	350	①	12	Neg.	Not Recommended			80	9	3,500-6,000	35
	455	②	12	Neg.	Not Recommended			45-80	9	4,000-6,500	35

① Side Terminal—Cranking power 2,900 watts @ 0°F
② Side Terminal—Cranking power 3,000 watts @ 0°F

BRAKE SPECIFICATIONS

(All measurements are given in in.)

Year	Model	MASTER CYLINDER Disc	MASTER CYLINDER Drum	WHEEL CYLINDER Front Disc	WHEEL CYLINDER Front Drum	WHEEL CYLINDER Rear	BRAKE DISC OR DRUM DIAMETER Front Disc	BRAKE DISC OR DRUM DIAMETER Front Drum	BRAKE DISC OR DRUM DIAMETER Rear
'67	All	1.125	1.00	2.125	1.188	1.00①	11.920	12.002	12.002
'68	All	1.125	1.00	2.125	1.188	1.00①	11.920	12.002	12.002
'69	All	1.125	1.00	2.125	1.188	1.00①	11.920	12.002	12.002
'70	All	1.125	1.00	2.937	1.188	1.00①	11.00	12.002	12.002
'71-'74	All	1.125	—	2.937	—	.9375②	11.86	—	11.002③

① Riviera—.9375
② Station Wagon—1.00
③ Station Wagon—12.002
— Not applicable

RING GAP

Year	Engine	Top Compression	Bottom Compression	Oil Control
'67-'70	8-340, 350	.010-.020	.010-.020	.015-.035
'67-'70	8-430, 455	.013-.023	.013-.023	.015-.055
'71-'74	8-350, 455	.013-.023	.013-.023	.015-.035

RING SIDE CLEARANCE

Year	Engine	Top Compression	Bottom Compression	Oil Control
'67-'74	All engines	.003-.005	.003-.005	.0035-.0095

VALVE SPECIFICATIONS

Year	Engine No. Cyl. Displacement (cu in.)	Seat Angle (deg)	Face Angle (deg)	Spring Test Pressure (lbs @ in.)	Spring Installed Height (in.)	STEM TO GUIDE Clearance (in.)		STEM Diameter (in.)	
						Intake	Exhaust	Intake	Exhaust
'67	8-340	45	45	164 @ 1.34	1 23/32	.0012-.0032	.0015-.0035	.3410	.3405
	8-430	45	45	177 @ 1.45	1 29/32	.0015-.0035	.0015-.0035	.3725	.3725
'68	8-350	45	45	180 @ 1.34	1 23/32	.0015-.0035	.0015-.0035	.3725	.3725
	8-430	45	45	177 @ 1.45	1 29/32	.0015-.0035	.0015-.0035	.3725	.3725
'69	8-350	45	45	180 @ 1.34	1 23/32	.0015-.0025	.0015-.0032	.3725	.3727
	8-430	45	45	177 @ 1.45	1 29/32	.0015-.0035	.0015-.0032	.3725	.3727
'70	8-350	45	45	180 @ 1.34	1 23/32	.0015-.0025	.0015-.0032	.3725	.3725
	8-455	45	45	177 @ 1.45	1 29/32	.0015-.0035	.0015-.0032	.3725	.3725
'71	8-350	45	45	180 @ 1.34	1 23/32	.0015-.0035	.0015-.0032	.3725	.3725
	8-455	45	45	177 @ 1.45	1 29/32	.0015-.0035	.0015-.0032	.3725	.3727
'72	8-350	45	45	180 @ 1.34	1 23/32	.0015-.0035	.0015-.0032	.3725	.3727
	8-455	45	45	177 @ 1.45	1 29/32	.0015-.0035	.0015-.0032	.3725	.3727
'73	8-350	45	45	180 @ 1.34	1 23/32	.0015-.0035	.0015-.0032	.3725	.3730
	8-455	45	45	177 @ 1.45	1 29/32	.0015-.0035	.0015-.0032	.3725	.3730
'74	8-350	45	45	180 @ 1.34	1 23/32	.0015-.0035	.0015-.0032	.3725	.3730
	8-455	45	45	177 @ 1.45	1 29/32	.0015-.0035	.0015-.0032	.3725	.3730

ENGINE
SERIAL
NUMBER
275100001

ENGINE
CODE
NUMBER
LL 123

Engine numbers, 1967 300 and 340 cu in. (© Buick Div., G.M. Corp)

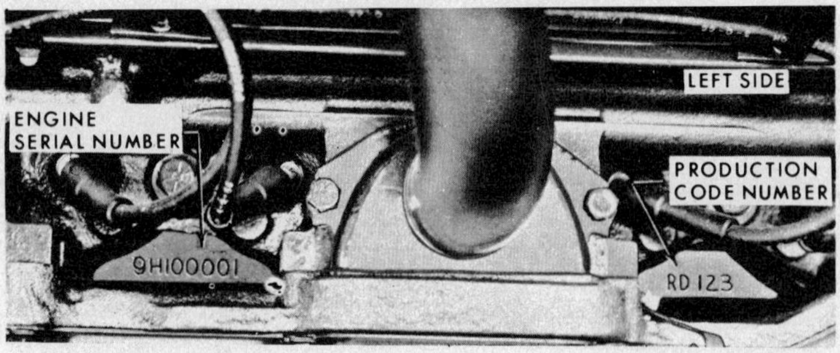
LEFT SIDE
ENGINE
SERIAL NUMBER
PRODUCTION
CODE NUMBER
9H100001
RD 123

Engine numbers, 1967–'74 400, 430, and 455 cu. in. (© Buick Div., G.M. Corp.)

CHARGING SYSTEM

See the "Unit Repair Section" for rebuilding procedures and trouble-shooting.

Caution Since the Delcotron and regulator are designed for use on only one polarity system, the following precautions must be observed:

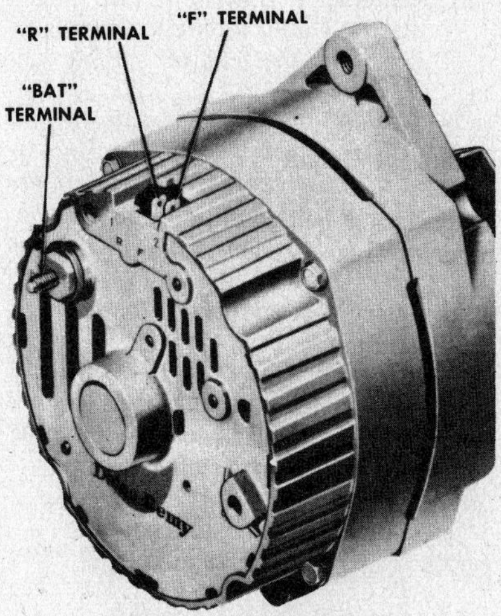
"R" TERMINAL
"F" TERMINAL
"BAT" TERMINAL

Delcotron wire connections
(© Buick Div., G.M. Corp)

1. The polarity of the battery, generator and regulator must be matched and considered before making any electrical connections in the system.
2. When connecting a booster battery, be sure to connect the negative battery terminals together and the positive battery terminals together.
3. When connecting a charger to the battery, connect the charger positive lead to the battery positive terminal. Connect the charger negative lead to the battery negative terminal.
4. Never operate the Delcotron on open circuit. Be sure that all connections in the circuit are clean and tight.
5. Do not short across or ground any of the terminals on the Delcotron regulator.
6. Do not attempt to polarize the Delcotron.
7. Do not use test lamps of more than 12 volts for checking diode continuity.
8. Avoid long soldering times when replacing diodes or transistors. Prolonged heat is damaging to these units.
9. Disconnect the battery ground terminal when servicing any component of the charging system.

Voltage Regulator R & R 1967-70

Removal and Installation

1. Disconnect the battery cables.
2. Disconnect the wiring from the voltage regulator.
3. Remove the screws holding the regulator to the firewall or front bulkhead depending on the car.
4. Reverse the removal procedures to install.

Voltage Regulator R & R 1971-74

The voltage regulator is inside the alternator. For R&R procedures see the Starting and Charging Systems in the Unit Repair Section.

Alternator Removal and Installation

Unfasten bolt holding tension bar to generator. On some models, it may be necessary to loosen and rotate fan shroud to get at pivot bolt. Push generator in toward engine to release drive belt. Unfasten generator mounting bolt to release generator from engine.

When reinstalling, adjust generator drive belt to allow ½ in. play on the longest run between pulleys.

NOTE: on A/C models, remove brace.

STARTING SYSTEM

See the "Unit Repair Section" for rebuilding procedures and trouble-shooting.

Starter R & R

1967-74

1. Disconnect battery.
2. Jack up car and remove the four flywheel inspection cover screws (⅜ in.).
3. Disconnect wires from solenoid.
4. Remove bolt from starter bracket (½ in.), then remove two 9/16 in. starter bolts.
5. Remove starter.

NOTE: On some models, it may be necessary to move exhaust pipe to gain clearance.

6. Reverse the above steps to install.

Starter Drive Removal and Replacement

1. Remove the bolt which holds the field leads to the solenoid motor terminal and disconnect the leads. Remove the two solenoid attaching bolts, rotate and remove the solenoid.
2. Remove the two through bolts, end frame, and field frame assembly.
3. Pull both brush holder pivot pins and lift out each pair of brush holder assemblies. Disconnect the leads and brushes.
4. Remove the shift lever pivot bolt, plunger, shift lever, and armature from the drive housing.
5. Remove the drive assembly from the armature by first using a suitable tool (such as a ½ in. pipe coupling) to disengage the snap-ring retainer from the snap-ring. After removing the snap ring and retainer, slide the drive assembly off of the armature shaft.
6. Inspect all parts for wear or damage and replace where necessary. When cleaning all parts, be sure not to use any degreasing or high temperature method on the armature, field coils, and drive assembly.
7. To reassemble, reverse the above steps. Be sure to lubricate the armature shaft, drive frame bushing, shift lever linkage, and the bushing in the commutator end frame when reassembling.

NOTE: When assembling the field frame over the armature to the drive end frame, spread the brush holders apart enough for the brushes to clear the commutator without damage to either.

IGNITION SYSTEM

Distributor Removal

Disconnect the distributor primary wire from the coil and the hose from the vacuum unit. Remove distributor cap by inserting a screwdriver into upper slotted end of cap latches, pressing down and turning 90° counterclockwise.

Make a mark on the distributor body in line with the rotor. Matchmark position of vacuum unit to the engine.

Remove clamp to release distributor and remove from crankcase.

NOTE: 1970-74 distributors have a radio interference shield over the contact points. Only snap-lock point sets can be used because screw-type connectors will hit this shield and short ignition.

Distributor Installation

If engine was inadvertently turned over while distributor was out, proceed as follows:

Remove right rocker arm cover. Using a wrench on the crankshaft pulley bolt, turn the engine over until both valves for No. 1 cylinder are closed. The timing mark on the harmonic balancer behind the crankshaft pulley should be aligned with the zero degree mark. No. 1 cylinder is now at firing point.

Install distributor in engine with rotor in position to fire No. 1 cylinder. The vacuum unit should align with the match-mark made when distributor was removed. Press down lightly on distributor if it does not seat correctly. Use starter to turn engine until the tang on the distributor shaft slips into the slot in the oil pump shaft. This will not disturb the relationship between the distributor and the camshaft because the drive gear engages before the tang. However, it will be necessary to return the engine to the No. 1 firing point and check that rotor is also at No. 1 firing point. Reconnect vacuum tube and primary wire. Rotate the distributor body

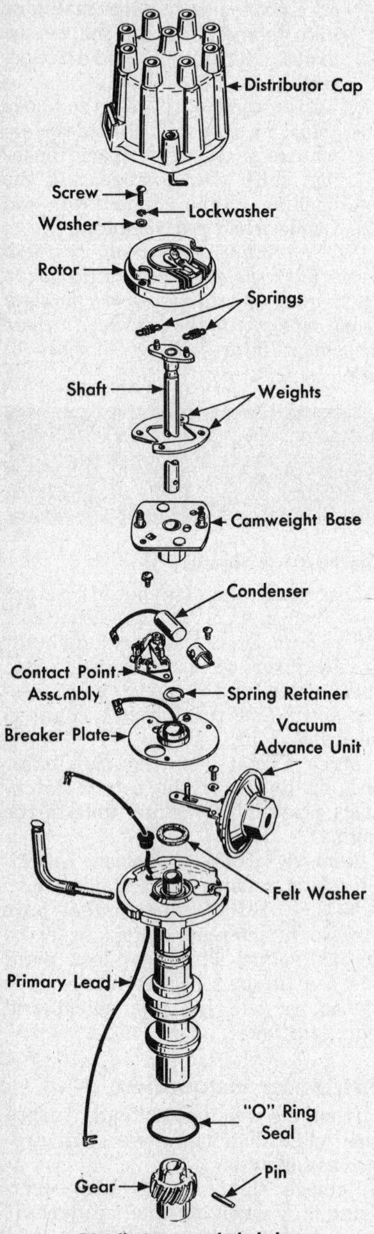
Distributor Cap
Screw
Lockwasher
Washer
Rotor
Springs
Shaft
Weights
Camweight Base
Condenser
Contact Point Assembly
Spring Retainer
Breaker Plate
Vacuum Advance Unit
Felt Washer
Primary Lead
"O" Ring Seal
Pin
Gear

Distributor—exploded view
(© Buick Div., G.M. Corp)

slightly until contacts just start to open. Install and tighten distributor clamp. Install distributor cap. Start engine and adjust point dwell.

Install RFI shield 1971-74
(© Buick Div., G.M. Corp)

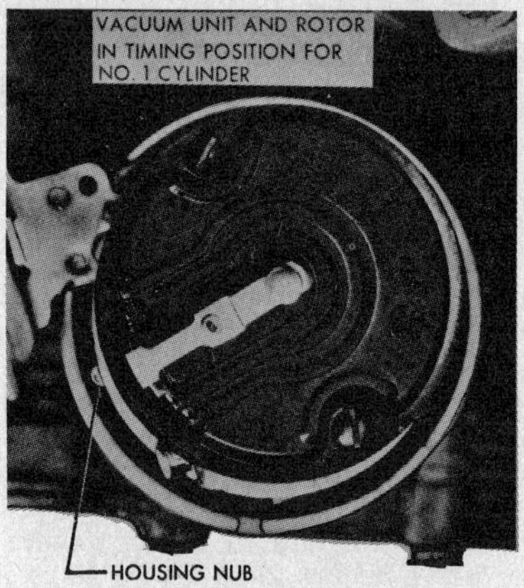
VACUUM UNIT AND ROTOR IN TIMING POSITION FOR NO. 1 CYLINDER
HOUSING NUB

Distributor installation 350, 455 V8
(© Buick Div., G.M. Corp)

If the engine has not been disturbed since the distributor was removed proceed as follows:

Insert distributor into the block so that the rotor is pointing to the mark made on distributor housing and the vacuum advance unit is aligned with the match-mark made on the engine. Connect the vacuum tube, primary wire, and install the distributor cap. Install distributor clamp. Check that spark plug wires are correctly routed. Start engine and adjust point dwell and then adjust ignition timing. Rotate distributor body counterclockwise to advance the timing.

Contact Point Replacement and Adjustment

NOTE: the condenser should be replaced when the points are replaced.

1. Remove the distributor cap and rotor. If equipped with an interference shield, remove the shield.
2. Loosen the two screws holding the contact point set in place and remove the point set.
3. Disconnect the condenser and primary leads from their terminals on the points.
4. Connect the wires to a new set of points and install them into the distributor.
5. Put a small amount of grease on the breaker cam.
6. Turn the engine over slowly to open the points to the maximum gap.
7. Using an allen wrench (1/8 in.), adjust the gap to specification and reinstall the shield, rotor, and cap. Install the shield half that covers the points first.
8. If a dwell meter is available, adjust the dwell to specification.
9. Check the timing.

Ignition Timing

Timing marks are located on the front engine cover and on the harmonic balancer.

1. Disconnect the distributor vacuum advance hose from the distributor and plug the hose.
2. Make sure the point gap is adjusted. Using a dwell meter is an alternate method of setting the gap.

NOTE: it may be necessary to put a small amount of white paint or chalk on the timing marks to make them more visible.

3. Connect a timing light to no. one cylinder.
4. Loosen the distributor clamp.
5. Start the engine and rotate the distributor until the correct marks line up. Tighten the distributor clamp and recheck the timing.
6. Reconnect the vacuum hose.

1974 Solid State Ignition

In 1974, a solid state, high energy ignition system is offered as an option on all Buick engines. There are no points or capacitor to replace, nor any cam or rubbing block to wear out. Precision timing and proper tuning are maintained over a greater interval than conventional point-and-capacitor systems, and the high energy coil delivers 50 to 75% more voltage than a conventional electronic system. In addition, the high energy system is completely unitized.

FUEL SYSTEM

Fuel Pump

1967-74

These models use a single action fuel pump mounted on the lower side of the engine front cover. Flexible type gas lines are used.

Beginning 1966, the repairable fuel pump was discontinued. If the fuel pump is unsatisfactory, renew the unit.

1969-70 Riviera Only

These models have a turbine type electric fuel pump mounted at the bottom of the fuel tank. This pump maintains a steady pressure whenever the engine is running. The electrical circuit to the pump is completed by an oil pressure switch which is bypassed for starting. If oil pressure fails, the fuel pump will not operate.

1967-70 All Engines with Air Conditioners, All 400, 430, 455 Cu. In.

All air-conditioner equipped cars have a special fuel pump with a metering outlet for a vapor return system. Hot fuel and fuel vapor is returned to the fuel tank. The fuel pump is continuously cooled by circulating fuel from the tank, thus greatly reducing the possibility of vapor lock.

Fuel Pump R & R

Removal

1. Disconnect the fuel inlet, outlet, and vapor return hoses.
2. Remove the two bolts holding the pump to the engine.
3. Remove the old fuel pump.

Installation

1. Install a new pump and gasket.
2. Install the two bolts.
3. Reconnect the hoses to the pump. Do not force the threaded fittings, use very light pressure until it is obvious that the threads are started properly.
4. Start the engine and check for leaks.

Fuel Filter Replacement

The filter is located in the carburetor inlet behind the large hex nut. This is a small pleated paper or sintered bronze filter.

1. Remove the fuel inlet line from the carburetor.
2. Remove the large nut from the carburetor body.
3. Remove the old filter.
4. Reinstall a new filter with the spring inserted before the filter.
5. Install the large hex nut and fuel line.
6. Start the engine and check for leaks.

Idle Speed and Mixture Adjustments

1967

Adjust with air cleaner removed.

1. If equipped with Automatic Level Control, disconnect vacuum line from compressor at the storage tank and plug it with a pencil.
2. Make sure that the PCV system is operative (not plugged).
3. Remove the air cleaner; connect the tachometer.
4. Start the engine and allow it to come to normal operating temperature.
5. Place manual transmission in Neutral, automatic in Drive (wheels blocked) and brakes locked.
6. Adjust the throttle stop screw to obtain the specified idle speed.
7. Adjust the mixture needles alternately to obtain a 20 rpm drop

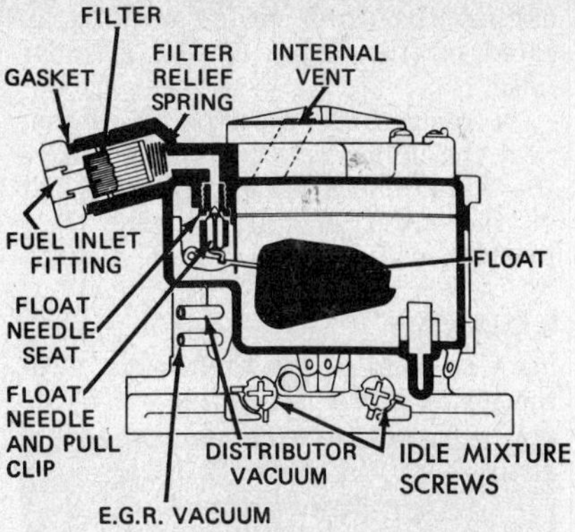
FILTER
GASKET
FILTER RELIEF SPRING
INTERNAL VENT
FUEL INLET FITTING
FLOAT
FLOAT NEEDLE SEAT
FLOAT NEEDLE AND PULL CLIP
DISTRIBUTOR VACUUM
IDLE MIXTURE SCREWS
E.G.R. VACUUM
2 bbl carburetor
(© Buick Div., G.M. Corp)

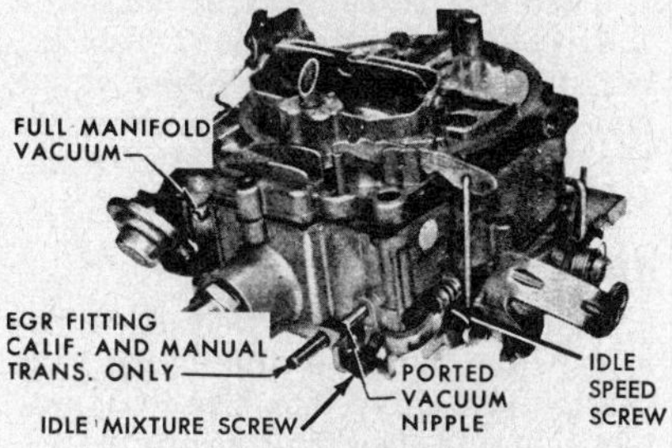
FULL MANIFOLD VACUUM
EGR FITTING CALIF. AND MANUAL TRANS. ONLY
PORTED VACUUM NIPPLE
IDLE SPEED SCREW
IDLE MIXTURE SCREW
4 bbl carburetor
(© Buick Div., G.M. Corp)

from specified idle, then open them 1/4 turn each. If this does not restore idle speed to specifications, turn them out 1/8 turn at a time until the best lean idle is obtained.
8. Make sure the transmission idle stator switch on the linkage is closed by disconnecting its wire. If idle speed doesn't decrease, the switch is not closed and should be adjusted.
9. Press down on the hot idle compensator valve, if so equipped. If the idle drops, the valve is open and should be unstuck and the idle reset.

1968-70

In 1968, the stator switch for the transmission was eliminated. The changing stator blade angle featured previously was discontinued that year. *Air cleaner must be in place to get proper idle, starting in 1968.*

1. Check PCV system for proper operation.
2. Connect tachometer; warm engine to normal operating temperature.
3. Place manual transmission in N, automatic in D (wheels blocked).
4. To make sure the Thermo Vacuum switch does not switch distributor vacuum over to full manifold vacuum due to overheated coolant, remove the hose from the distributor and plug.

NOTE: check that the compressor for the Automatic Level Control. if so equipped, is not running. The compressor now has a regulating valve to shut off vacuum at idle speed. If the compressor is running, this valve is faulty and must be replaced before a good idle can be obtained.

5. Adjust throttle stop screw to obtain an idle speed 20 rpm faster than specified.
6. Turn in each mixture needle, alternately, to obtain an idle speed 10 rpm less *per needle* than the basic idle setting of Step 5 (for a total of 20 rpm less).
7. Press down on the hot idle compensator, if so equipped. If idle drops, valve is open and should be unstuck and idle reset.

1971

Air cleaner must be in place to get proper, emission-free, idle speed.

1. Check PCV system for proper operation.
2. Connect tachometer; warm engine to normal operating temperature.
3. Place manual transmission in N, automatic in D (wheels blocked).
4. Remove distributor hose and plug.

NOTE: check that the compressor for the Automatic Level Control, if so equipped, is not running. The compressor has a regulating valve to shut off vacuum at idle speed. If the compressor is running, this valve is faulty and must be replaced before a good idle can be obtained.

5. Adjust throttle stop screw to obtain specified idle speed.
6. Adjust idle mixture needles, alternately, to obtain highest tachometer reading.
7. Readjust throttle stop and mixture screws as required to obtain an idle speed 50 rpm faster than specified, then turn in each screw (leaner) to reduce idle speed 25 rpm *per needle* (for a total reduction of 50 rpm).
8. Adjust fast idle speed.

1972-73 (2 & 4 bbl.)

1. Connect a tachometer to the engine.
2. Start the engine and run it until it is warmed up.
3. Remove and plug the vacuum hose to the distributor.
4. Place manual transmissions in neutral and automatic transmissions in D.
5. Open the throttle sufficiently to allow the solenoid to extend and contact the throttle lever pad in the idle position.
6. Adjust the solenoid set screw to obtain the specified rpm. This is the higher figure in the specification chart.
7. Disconnect the solenoid wire to disengage solenoid.
8. Adjust the carburetor idle screw to obtain specified idle speed, which is the lower figure in the specification chart.
9. Reconnect the solenoid wire.

10. Adjust the idle mixture needles, one at a time, to obtain the highest tachometer reading. After the highest reading is reached, readjust the solenoid plunger to obtain 50 rpm over the specified idle speed. Turn each mixture needle in to reduce the idle speed 25 rpm for each needle. This reduces the idle speed to the recommended rpm.
11. Adjust the fast idle speed on all four-barrel carburetors. Fast idle must be adjusted after slow idle speed and mixture have been adjusted. Automatic transmission cars are adjusted on the low step of the fast idle cam in Drive to 700 RPM. Manual transmission cars are adjusted on the low cam step to 820 RPM for 350 engines, and 920 RPM for 455 engines.
12. Connect the distributor vacuum hose.
13. Install the "red" service idle needle limiter caps on the mixture screws.

Throttle Adjustment

Buick uses a throttle cable which is not adjustable. Make sure that the cable is not kinked or rubbing against anything, and that it is properly lubricated.

COOLING SYSTEM

Radiator Core R & R

1967-74

On models equipped with a fan shroud, remove the shroud from the radiator and position it rearward over the fan.

Remove the capscrews that hold the fan blades to the fan hub and take off the blades, spacer and pump pulley. Remove the top and bottom radiator hoses and the two hoses which connect the oil cooler to the radiator. Remove the bolts that hold the radiator core to the cradle and lift the core straight up. Reverse the above steps to install.

Water Pump Removal

It is possible to remove and replace the water pump on all Buicks without disturbing the radiator core. This is accomplished by removing the fan belt, fan blades, and pulley, disconnecting the hoses and removing the water pump attaching bolts. Reverse the removal procedure to install. Use a new gasket and make sure all gasket surfaces are clean.

Thermostat Removal

1967-74 All Engines

The thermostat is contained in the water outlet elbow mounted on the front of the intake manifold. On L-6 engines the water outlet elbow is located on the front of the cylinder head.

To replace the thermostat, disconnect the upper radiator hose, remove the water outlet attaching bolts, lift off the outlet and take out the thermostat.

Caution When installing a thermostat always place the end of the thermostat with the spring inside the engine.

EMISSION CONTROLS

There are three types of emissions to be controlled: crankcase emissions, carburetor and gas tank fuel vapor emissions, and exhaust emissions. See the "Unit Repair Section" for troubleshooting and repair information.

1967

Buick controlled crankcase emissions with the positive crankcase ventilation (PCV) system. The PCV system connects the crankcase to the intake manifold. Crankcase gases are returned to the intake manifold to be reburned.

The Air Injection Reactor, (AIR), system was used to treat exhaust emissions. It consists of an air pump, a special air cleaner, a by-pass valve, and tubes and hoses used to inject the air into the exhaust manifolds. The pump, driven by the engine, compresses, distributes, and injects clean air at the exhaust port for each cylinder. In the exhaust manifolds, the air combines with the unburned hydrocarbons and carbon monoxide to produce a low-emission exhaust.

1968-69

Buick elected to adopt a special system of terminal exhaust treatment. This plan supercedes the method used to conform to 1966–67 California laws. The new system cancels out, except in special purpose applications, the use of the AIR method previously used.

The new concept, Combustion Control System, (CCS), uses engine modifications. Essentially, the CCS increases combustion efficiency through carburetor and distributor calibrations and by increasing engine operating temperature.

Carburetors are calibrated leaner and initial ignition timing is retarded. Another carburetor feature is the idle fuel mixture limiting orifice. It is located at the base of the idle mixture screw and makes sure that even if the idle mixture screw is turned out too far, the fuel enrichment will not greatly affect exhaust emissions.

The CCS incorporates a higher engine operation temperature with a 195°F thermostat. Engines that run hotter provide more complete vaporazation of the fuel and reduce quench area in the combustion chamber. Quench area is the relatively cool area near the cylinder wall and combustion chamber surfaces. Fuel in these areas does not burn properly because of the lower temperatures. This incomplete burning increases emissions.

The CCS uses a thermostatically controlled air cleaner called the Auto-Therm air cleaner. It is designed to keep the temperature of the air entering the carburetor at approximately 100°F. This allows the lean carburetor to work properly, minimizes carburetor icing, and improves engine warm-up characteristics. A sensor unit, located on the clean air side of the air filter, senses the temperature of the air passing over it and regulates the vacuum supplied to a vacuum diaphragm in the inlet tube of the air cleaner. The colder the air, the greater the amount of vacuum supplied to the vacuum diaphragm. The vacuum diaphragm, depending on the vacuum supplied to it, opens or closes a damper door in the inlet tube of the air cleaner. If the door is open, it allows air from the engine compartment to go to the carburetor. If the door is closed, air flows from the heat stove that is located on the exhaust manifold into the carburetor. It is in this way that heated air is supplied to the carburetor during cold days and when first starting the engine and warming it up.

1970-71

The more stringent 1970 laws require tighter control of emissions. Crankcase emissions are controlled by the Closed Positive Crankcase Ventilation System, and exhaust emissions by the engine Controlled Combustion System (CCS), in conjunction with the new Transmission Controlled Spark System (TCS).

In addition, cars sold in California are equipped with an Evaporation Control System that limits the amount of gasoline vapor discharged into the atmosphere (usually from the carburetor and fuel tank).

The TCS system consists of a transmission switch, a solenoid valve, and a temperature switch. Under normal conditions, the system permits the vacuum distributor (spark) advance to operate only in high gear (both manual and automatic transmissions) and reverse.

The transmission switch is located on the transmission and senses when the transmission is in one of the lower gears. When in a lower gear, the switch activates the vacuum solenoid valve. This valve is located in the vacuum line that runs from the carburetor to the distributor and shuts off vacuum to the distributor advance when it is activated. There is also an engine-temperature sensing

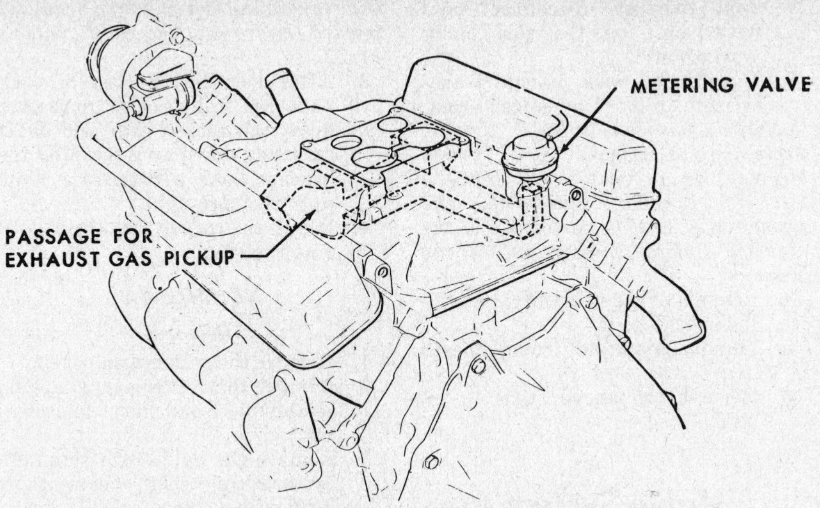
METERING VALVE
PASSAGE FOR
EXHAUST GAS PICKUP

1973 Buick Exhaust Gas Recirculation system
(© Buick Div., G.M. Corp)

switch which overrides the transmission switch. It will allow vacuum advance in the lower gears when engine temperature is below 85°F or above 220°F. There is always vacuum advance in high gear and reverse.

The Evaporative Emission Control System was introduced in 1970. Vapors generated in the gas tank while the car is at rest are transferred to an activated charcoal canister located in the engine compartment. When the car is running the vapors are removed from the canister and burned by the engine.

1972

In 1972, all engines are equipped with positive crankcase ventilation, transmission controlled vacuum spark advance (TCS) and the controlled combustion system (CCS). The air injection reactor system is standard on all engines except the non-California 350 cu in. with automatic transmissions. All California cars and all cars with manual transmissions have Exhaust Gas Recirculation (EGR).

CCS is explained in the above 1968–69 section, and TCS in the 1970–71 section.

The EGR system is used to reduce oxides of nitrogen emissions. To lower the formation of nitrogen oxides, it is necessary to reduce combustion temperatures. This is done by introducing exhaust gases into the intake manifold to be burned.

An EGR valve is mounted on the right rear of the intake manifold and is used to regulate the amount of exhaust gases and the time the exhaust gases enter the intake manifold. As the engine speeds up, carburetor vacuum is applied to the valve which opens a port connecting the intake manifold to the exhaust gas passage that is cast in the intake manifold. This allows exhaust gases to pass into the intake manifold. The EGR system is not in operation during engine idle.

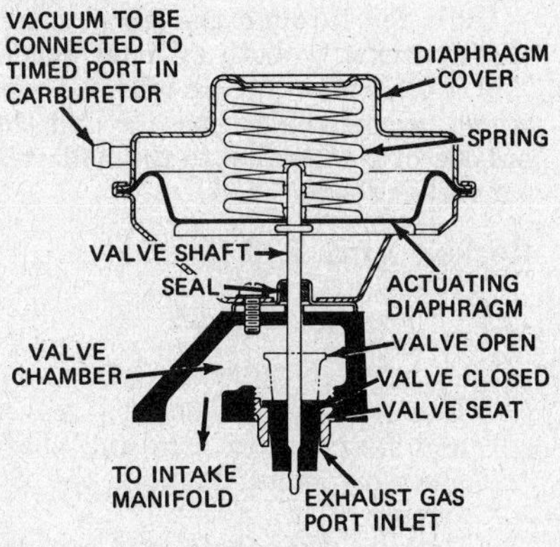
VACUUM TO BE
CONNECTED TO
TIMED PORT IN
CARBURETOR
DIAPHRAGM
COVER
SPRING
VALVE SHAFT
SEAL
ACTUATING
DIAPHRAGM
VALVE
CHAMBER
VALVE OPEN
VALVE CLOSED
VALVE SEAT
TO INTAKE
MANIFOLD
EXHAUST GAS
PORT INLET

EGR valve
(© Buick Div., G.M. Corp)

1973

All engines are equipped with Positive Crankcase Ventilation, Controlled Combustion, Air Injection Reactor System, Exhaust Gas Recirculation, Transmission Controlled Vacuum Spark Advance System and Evaporative Emission Control. With the exception of a low temperature cut-out valve that was added to the EGR system, the emission control systems remain unchanged from previous years.

The EGR system is the same one that was used on 1972 California cars with a new temperature valve. This black and white plastic valve is located in the vacuum line to the EGR valve and it senses ambient temperature above the engine intake manifold. At temperatures below 55°F, the temperature valve closes to prevent carburetor vacuum from opening the EGR valve. When the temperature above the manifold rises above 60°F, the valve opens and allows carburetor vacuum to control the operation of the EGR valve. Whenever installing a new valve, always make sure the side of the valve marked EGR faces toward the EGR valve.

1974

The 1974 Buick emission control system is unchanged from 1973, except for the required change in the EGR temperature sensor. The Environmental Protection Agency order necessitated that the EGR ambient temperature sensor either be removed or changed to record coolant temperature. Although the system design remains unchanged, there has been an extensive refinement and recalibration of components to insure greater efficiency.

1974 Federal Emission standards are unchanged from 1973½, however, California engines are required to reduce oxides of nitrogen by 1/3.

ENGINE

Engine R & R

All Models—1967-74

1. Drain cooling system.
2. Scribe hinge outline on underside of hood. Remove hood attaching bolts and remove hood.
3. Disconnect battery cables.
4. Remove radiator and heater hoses.
5. Disconnect transmission oil cooler lines. Remove fan shroud.
6. Remove attaching bolts and lift out radiator.
7. Disconnect exhaust pipe or pipes at the exhaust manifold/s.
8. Disconnect vacuum line to power brake unit.
9. Disconnect accelerator to carburetor linkage.
10. Disconnect all engine component wiring that would interfere with engine removal, such as generator wires, gauge sending unit wires, primary ignition wires, etc.
11. Disconnect gas line at fuel pump.
12. Detach power steering pump and position to the left. Do not disconnect the hoses.
13. Detach air conditioner compressor at bracket and position to the right. Do not disconnect hoses.

Caution If the compressor refrigerant lines do not have enough slack to position the compressor out of the way without disconnecting the refrigerant lines, the air conditioning system will have to be removed by a trained air conditioning specialist. Under no conditions should an untrained person attempt to disconnect the air conditioning refrigerant lines. These lines contain pressurized freon which can be extremely dangerous to the untrained.

14. Disconnect transmission control linkage.
15. Disconnect vapor emission lines on 1970-74 models.

16. Attach lifting device to the engine and raise enough to support the engine weight.
17. Remove flywheel cover pan. On cars equipped with an automatic transmission, remove the flywheel to-torque converter bolts. Match-mark the flywheel and torque converter for reassembly.
18. Separate engine from transmission at bell housing on cars equipped with automatic transmission. On cars equipped with a manual transmission, separate the transmission from the bell-housing.
19. Remove engine attachment thru-bolts at the engine mounts.
20. Lift engine forward and upward to clear engine compartment.
21. Install by reversing above procedure. When installing an engine, the front mounting pad to frame bolts should be the last mounting bolts to be tightened. Note that there are dowel pins in the block that have matching holes in the bellhousing. These pins must be in almost perfect alignment before the engine will go together with the transmission.

Manifolds

Intake Manifold R & R

1. Drain the cooling system.
2. Remove carburetor air cleaner. Disconnect all tubes and hoses from the carburetor. Disconnect and remove the coil.
3. Disconnect temperature indicator wire from sending unit.
4. Disconnect accelerator and transmission linkage at carburetor. Disconnect throttle return spring.
5. Slide front thermostat by-pass hose clamp back on the hose. Disconnect upper radiator hose at outlet.
6. Disconnect heater hose at the temperature control valve inlet. Force the end of the hose down to permit coolant to drain from intake manifold.
7. Remove manifold-to-head attaching bolts.
8. Remove intake manifold and carburetor as an assembly by sliding rearward to disengage the thermostat by-pass hose from the water pump. Remove intake manifold gasket.
9. Reverse the above steps to install.

NOTE: New intake manifold gasket and seals must be used whenever a manifold is removed.

Exhaust Manifolds R & R

1. Jack up car and support on axle stands.
2. Disconnect exhaust pipe from manifolds on both sides of engine and lower. If equipped with dual exhaust, disconnect and lower only on the side being worked on.
3. If equipped with manual transmission, remove equalizer shaft.

NOTE: on right side, it may be necessary to remove A/C, power steering, or alternator. On 1971–74 left-side exhaust manifolds, the pitman arm must be removed and the steering linkage pushed out of the way.

4. Remove exhaust manifold-to-cylinder head bolts.
5. Remove manifold from beneath car.
6. Reverse the above steps to install.

Valve System

Rocker Shaft Lubrication

Oil is fed through the front rocker shaft bracket on both cylinder heads. The front bracket has an oversize bore which permits oil to pass around the outside of the bolt up to the hollowed out rocker shaft.

Rocker Arm R & R

V8 1967-69

Removal

1. Remove the rocker arm cover and four rocker arm and shaft assembly bolts. Remove the assembly.
2. Remove the shaft end-cap by splitting the side of the cap with a chisel.
3. Remove the rocker arms and springs. Keep the parts in order.

Installation

1. Install the rocker arms and springs on the shaft and lubricate the shaft with oil as the rocker arms are installed.
2. Install a new end-cap on the rocker arm shaft.

NOTE: when installing the rocker arm shaft assembly, be sure that the drill mark is facing up and toward the rear on the left cylinder head and toward the front of the right cylinder head.

3. After locating the top of each push rod in its rocker arm seat, draw the rocker arm and shaft assembly down by tightening the bracket bolts a little at a time until they are tight.
4. Install the rocker arm cover with a new gasket.

11
7
3
1
5
9
12
8
4
2
6
10

Intake manifold tightening sequence—1971-74 350 and 455 V8
(© Buick Div., G.M. Corp)

V8 1970-74

Removal

1. Remove the rocker arm cover.
2. Remove the rocker arm shaft assembly bolts and then the assembly.
3. Remove the nylon arm retainers by breaking them below their head with a chisel.
4. Remove the rocker arms.

Installation

1. Install the rocker arms on the shaft and lubricate them with oil.

NOTCH
FRONT
FRONT OF RIGHT ROCKER ARM SHAFT
NOTCH
FRONT
REAR OF LEFT ROCKER ARM SHAFT

Rocker arm and shaft—300, 340 1967
(© Buick Div., G.M. Corp)

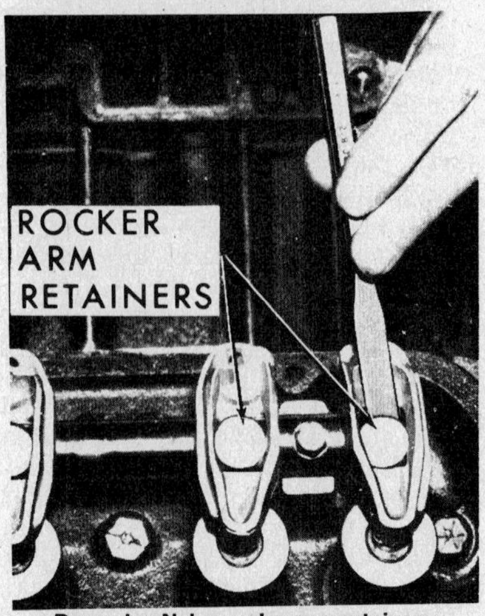

ROCKER
ARM
RETAINERS

Removing Nylon rocker arm retainers —1971-74 350 and 455 V8
(© Buick Div., G.M. Corp)

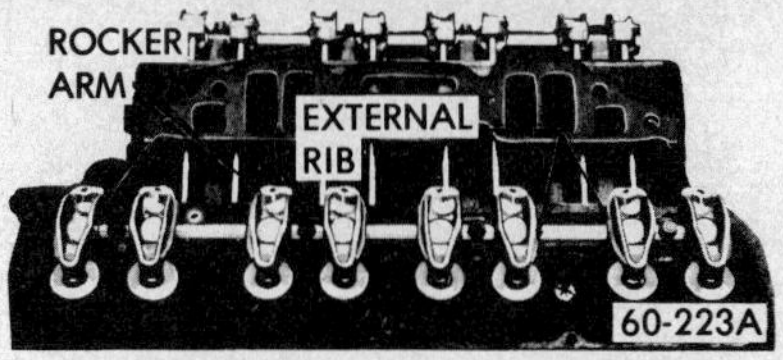
ROCKER ARM
EXTERNAL RIB
60-223A
Position of external ribs on rocker arms
(© Buick Div., G.M. Corp)

2. Center each arm on the ¼ in. hole in the shaft. Install new nylon rocker arm retainers in the holes using a drift ½ in. in diameter.

NOTE: each pair of rocker arms must be installed so that the external rib on each arm points away from the rocker arm shaft bolt that is located between each pair of rocker arms.

3. Locate the push rods in the rocker arms and insert the shaft-to-cylinder head bolts. Tighten the bolts a little at a time until they are tight.
4. Install the rocker cover and use a new gasket.

Valve Adjustment

These engines use rocker arm shafts; after the shaft assembly-to-cylinder head bolts are torqued to specification, the valves are adjusted.

Valve Guide Replacement

Valve guides are cast into the cylinder heads of all engines. The valve guides must be reamed and fitted with valves with oversize stems to be repaired.

Valve Springs

To check the condition of the valve springs, line up the intake valve springs on a flat surface and, using a straightedge, compare the height of the springs. If all of the springs are the same height, as determined by the straightedge, it may be assumed that the springs are in good condition, since it is very unlikely that all of the springs would collapse the same amount.

If one or more of the springs are lower than the rest it is advisable to procure at least one new spring and then compare the other springs with the new one for free length.

Replace all springs that do not come up to the standard established by the new one.

Repeat the operation on the exhaust valve springs.

Valve Removal

Remove the air cleaner, the rocker cover, the rockers and the intake manifold. Disconnect the exhaust manifolds at their flanges, leaving the manifold attached to the heads.

From the right bank, remove the generator mounting bracket, and from the left, the power steering pump. Disconnect the heat indicator, remove fuel and vacuum lines. Remove the bolts that hold the water manifolds, if applicable, to the cylinder heads, unbolt and remove the cylinder heads. Take the heads to a bench and, using a C-type or lever type valve spring compressor, compress the valve springs, remove the keepers, release the valve springs, and push the valves to the combustion chamber side of the head.

Hydraulic Lifters, Removal

To remove the lifters, remove the rocker cover and take off the rocker shaft assemblies and lift out the pushrods. Then remove the intake manifold.

The valve chamber cover plate can then be removed giving access to the lifters.

The lifters are barrel type which come right up out of their bores requiring no other tools than the fingers.

If more effort is required than can be given by the fingers, it indicates gum or sticky substances present in the oil which probably caused the failure.

NOTE: V8 lifters have a spherical shaped base to ensure lifter rotation. Do not grind these lifters to remove score marks.

Cylinder Head

R & R All V8

1. Disconnect the battery.
2. Drain the coolant.
3. Remove the air cleaner.
4. Remove the air conditioning, but do not disconnect any lines.
5. Remove the intake manifold.
6. When removing the right cylinder head, loosen the alternator belt and remove the alternator; if equipped with an air conditioning compressor, remove the compressor from the mounting bracket and position it out of the way WITH THE HOSES CONNECTED, then remove the alternator with the mounting bracket; finally, disconnect the metal temperature indicator wire (1973-4 models only).
7. When removing the left cylinder head, remove the dipstick and the power steering pump.
8. Disconnect the plug wires.
9. Disconnect the exhaust manifold from the head being removed.
10. Remove the rocker arm cover and rocker shaft assembly. Lift out the push rods. Disconnect the AIR hoses from the cylinder head.

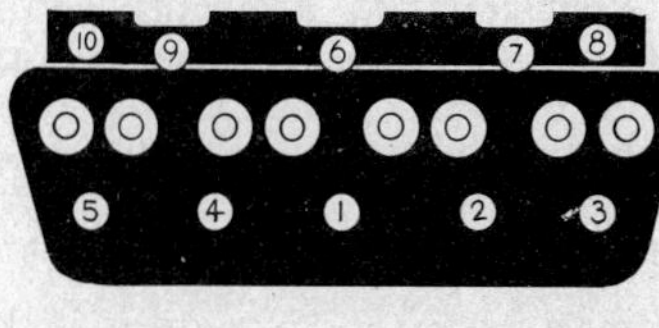
10 9 6 7 8
5 4 1 2 3
1967 300, 340 cu in. 1967-69 400, 430 cu in. 1968-69 350 cu in.

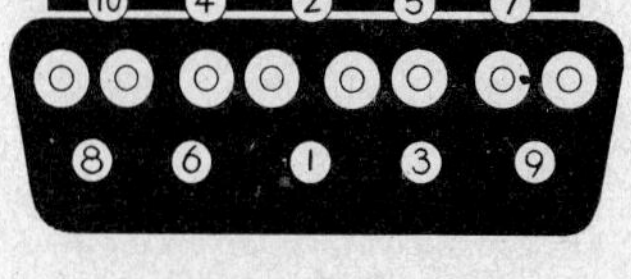
10 4 2 5 7
8 6 1 3 9
1970-74 350, 455 cu in.

11. Remove the cylinder head bolts.
12. Remove the cylinder head and gasket.
13. Reverse the above steps to install. Torque the head bolts to specifications in three steps.

Chilton's

TIME SAVER

The following is a method for replacing valve springs, oil seals or spring retainers without removing the cylinder head.

1. **Obtain a spark plug hole air chuck adaptor from an auto parts store.**
2. **Add an air chuck to this adaptor so the hose from an air compressor can be attached. This assembly will be used later to pressurize the cylinder.**
3. **Remove the valve rocker cover. Remove the rocker arm from the valve to be worked on.**
4. **Remove the spark plug from the cylinder to be worked on.**
5. **Turn the crankshaft to bring the piston of this cylinder down, away from possible contact with the valve head. Sharply tap the valve retainer to loosen the valve lock.**
6. **Then turn the crankshaft to bring the piston in this cylinder to the Exact Top of its Compression Stroke.**
7. **Screw in the chuck-equipped tool.**
8. **Hook up an air hose to the chuck and turn on the pressure (about 200 lbs.).**
9. **With a strong and constant supply of air holding the valve closed, compress the valve spring and remove the lock and retainer.**
10. **Make the necessary replacements and reassemble.**

NOTE: it is important that the operation be performed exactly as stated, in this order. The piston in the cylinder must be on exact top-center to prevent air pressure from turning the crankshaft.

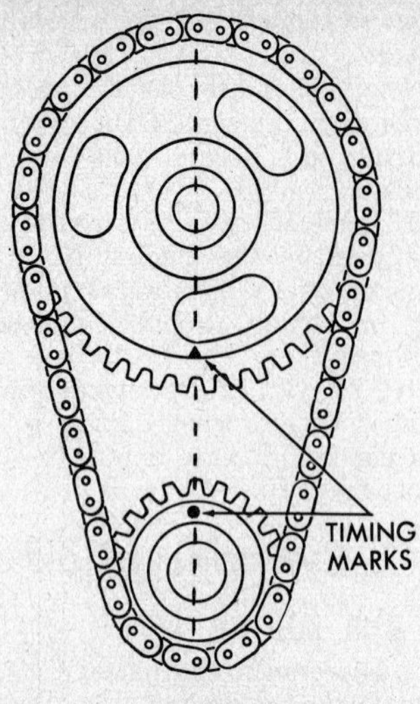
TIMING
MARKS

Timing chain and sprocket marks

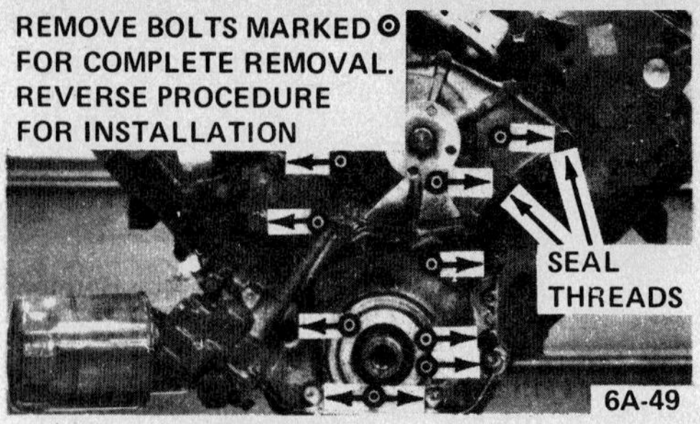
REMOVE BOLTS MARKED ⊙
FOR COMPLETE REMOVAL.
REVERSE PROCEDURE
FOR INSTALLATION
SEAL
THREADS
6A-49

350 timing cover bolts
(© Buick Div., G.M. Corp)

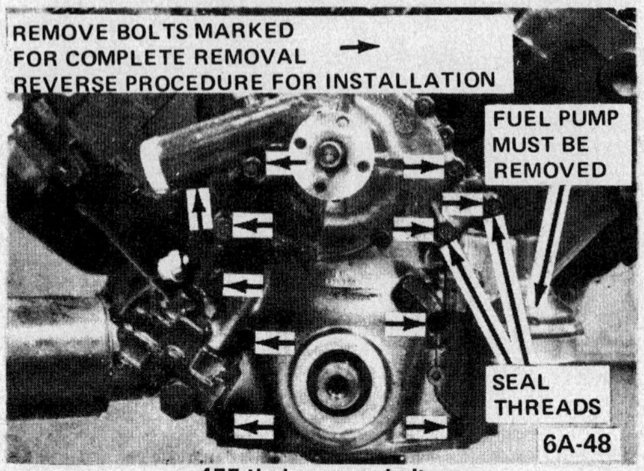
REMOVE BOLTS MARKED
FOR COMPLETE REMOVAL →
REVERSE PROCEDURE FOR INSTALLATION
FUEL PUMP
MUST BE
REMOVED
SEAL
THREADS
6A-48

455 timing cover bolts
(© Buick Div., G.M. Corp)

TIMING CASE COVER, Timing Chain and Camshaft

Vibration Damper Removal

Remove the radiator core and take out the cap screws that hold the fan pulley to the vibration damper. Remove the large bolt from the center of the crankshaft and insert a bolt type puller into the holes which held the fan pulley. Pull off the vibration damper.

Timing Chain and Front Oil Seal Replacement

1967-74 300, 340, 350 Cu. In.

1. Drain cooling system and remove radiator, shroud, fan, pulleys, and belts.
2. Remove crankshaft pulley, fuel pump and distributor.
3. Remove Delcotron and power steering pump, if necessary.
4. Loosen and slide rearward front clamp on thermostat by-pass hose. Remove harmonic balancer.
5. Remove bolts attaching timing chain cover to cylinder block and oil pan to timing chain cover bolts. Remove timing chain cover assembly and gasket. Clean cover thoroughly, being careful not to damage the gasket surface.
6. Turn the crankshaft so that the timing marks on the sprockets are adjacent to each other on a line with the shaft centers.
7. Remove crankshaft oil slinger.
8. Remove bolt, special washer, distributor drive gear, and fuel pump eccentric from camshaft.
9. Pry camshaft and crankshaft sprockets forward until camshaft sprocket is free. Then remove both sprockets and chain.

   If oil seal appears worn or has been leaking, replace as follows:
10. Use a punch to drive out the old seal and retainer. Drive from front to rear of the timing chain cover.
11. Coil new packing around opening so that ends are at top. Drive in retainer. Stake the retainer in at least three places. Size the packing by rotating a hammer handle, etc. around the packing until the balancer hub fits through the packing.

    If engine has been disturbed since chain and sprockets were removed:
12. Turn crankshaft until No. 1 piston is at top dead center.
13. Mount sprocket temporarily and turn camshaft so that timing mark is straight down.
14. Assemble chain and sprockets and mount on shafts with their timing marks closest to each other.
15. Mount slinger on sprocket with the concave side to the front.
16. Reinstall fuel pump eccentric, distributor drive gear, special washer, and bolt on camshaft. Reinstall Woodruff key with oil groove forward.
17. Remove oil pump cover and pack the space around the oil pump gears full of petroleum jelly, leaving no air spaces. Reinstall oil pump cover with new gasket. This step is very important. If it is not done the oil pump will not begin to pump oil as soon as the engine is started.
18. Reinstall timing chain cover with new gasket.

Keep engine speed low for a short time after installation of a new oil seal.

1967-74 400, 430, 455 Cu. In.

This procedure is identical to that outlined above for 300, 340, and 350 cu. in. engines with the substitution of the following steps:

8. Remove oil pan. Remove camshaft sprocket bolts.
16. Reinstall oil pan. Reinstall camshaft sprocket bolts.

Camshaft R & R

1. Remove the intake manifold, distributor, and grille.
2. Remove the rocker arm covers.
3. Remove the rocker arm and shaft assemblies, push rods, and valve lifters.
4. Remove the timing chain cover, timing chain, and sprocket.
5. Slide the camshaft forward, through the grille opening, and out from the bearing bores. Carefully avoid marring the bearing surfaces.
6. Reverse the above steps to install.

Connecting Rods, Rings And Pistons

When new rings are installed without reboring the cylinders, cylinder wall glaze should be broken. This can be done by using the finest grade stones in a cylinder home. Check the piston - to - cylinder wall clearance after honing.

New piston rings must be checked for clearance in cylinder bores and for gap and for side-clearance while installed on the piston.

If piston pin bosses are worn out of round or oversize, the piston and pin should be replaced. Oversize pins are not practical because the pin is a press fit in the connecting rod. Piston pins must fit the piston with an easy finger push at 70°F.

When the rod assemblies are replaced in the engine, the connecting rod bearing oil spurt hole must point up toward the camshaft.

Piston Assembly Removal

1. Remove cylinder heads.
2. Remove oil pan.
3. Examine cylinder bores for a ring ridge. If ridge exists, remove it before taking pistons out.
4. Number all the pistons, connecting rods and caps.

All V8 engines are numbered 1-3-5-7, left; and 2-4-6-8, right.

5. With No. 1 crankpin straight down, remove cap and bearing shell from No. 1 connecting rod.
6. Push piston and rod assembly up out of the cylinder. Then remove bolt guides and reinstall cap and bearing shell on the rod.
7. Remove the remaining rod and piston assemblies in the same manner.
8. Carefully remove old rings with piston ring expander.
9. Carefully press out the old pin.

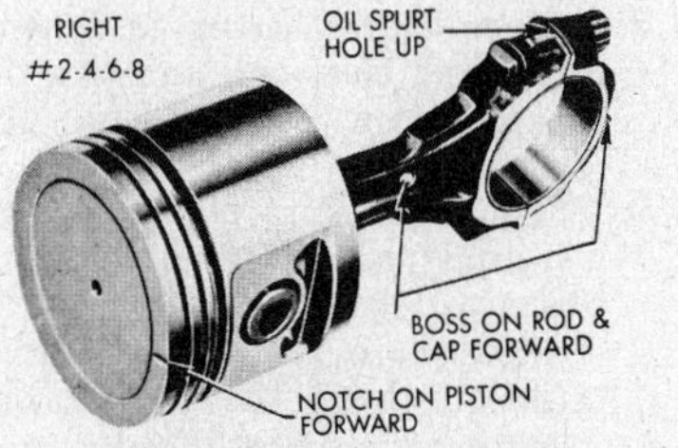
RIGHT
#2-4-6-8
OIL SPURT HOLE UP
BOSS ON ROD & CAP FORWARD
NOTCH ON PISTON FORWARD

300, 340, 400, 430 piston and connecting rod assemblies—right bank
(© Buick Div., G.M. Corp)

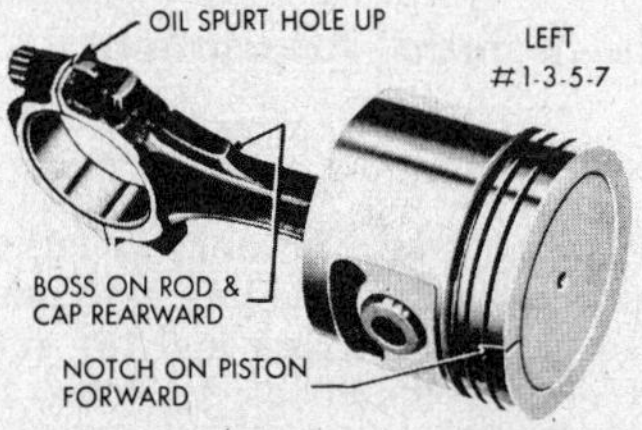
OIL SPURT HOLE UP
LEFT
#1-3-5-7
BOSS ON ROD & CAP REARWARD
NOTCH ON PISTON FORWARD

300, 340, 400, 430 piston and connecting rod assemblies—left bank
(© Buick Div., G.M. Corp)

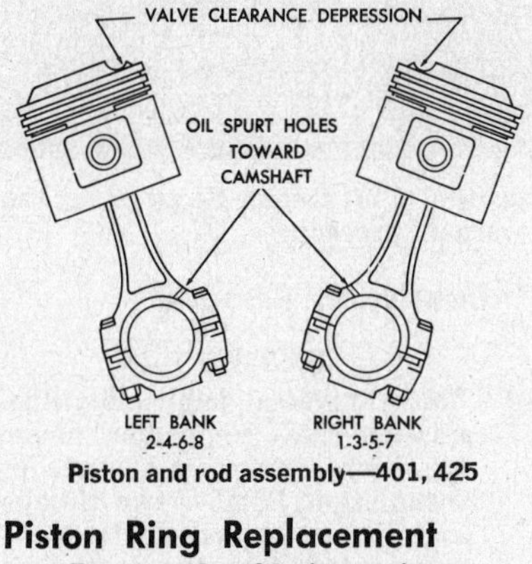
VALVE CLEARANCE DEPRESSION
OIL SPURT HOLES TOWARD CAMSHAFT
LEFT BANK
2-4-6-8
RIGHT BANK
1-3-5-7

Piston and rod assembly—401, 425

Piston Ring Replacement

1. Remove the old piston rings.
2. Clean any carbon, varnish, or other deposits from the surfaces of the piston. A piece of broken ring may be used to clean the ring grooves by scraping the grooves with the sharp edge of the broken ring.
3. Place the ring at the bottom of the bore in that portion that is traveled by the rings. Measure the gap between the ends of the ring. If the gap is too wide, the ring is worn out. If the gap is too narrow file the end of the ring until it is gapped to specification.

NOTE: square the ring in the bore with a piston.

Piston and Connecting Rod Replacement

1. Lubricate all the cylinder bores and bearings with oil.
2. Make sure the piston and connecting rod are aligned correctly and then insert the assembly into its bore.

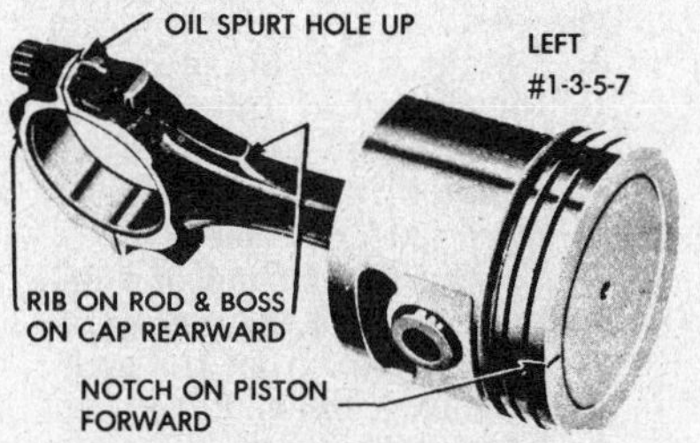
OIL SPURT HOLE UP
LEFT
#1-3-5-7
RIB ON ROD & BOSS ON CAP REARWARD
NOTCH ON PISTON FORWARD

350 piston and connecting rod assembly—left bank
(© Buick Div., G.M. Corp)

OIL SPURT HOLE UP
RIGHT #2-4-6-8
RIB ON ROD & BOSS ON CAP FORWARD
NOTCH ON PISTON FORWARD

350 piston and connecting rod assembly—right bank
(© Buick Div., G.M. Corp)

3. Pull the assembly onto its crankpin and install the bearing cap.
4. Install the oil pan and cylinder heads.

Engine Lubrication

Oil Pan R & R—1967-74

1. Disconnect the battery.
2. Remove the fan shroud-to-radiator tie bar screws.
3. Remove the air cleaner and disconnect the throttle linkage.
4. Raise the car and support it on jackstands.
5. Drain the oil.
6. On cars equipped with manual transmission, loosen the clutch equalizer bracket - to - frame attaching bolts and remove the exhaust crossover pipe.
7. On cars equipped with automatic transmissions, remove the lower flywheel housing, remove the shift linkage attaching bolt and swing it out of the way, and disconnect the exhaust crossover pipe at the engine.
8. Disconnect the idler arm at the frame and push the steering linkage forward to the crossmember.
9. Remove the front engine mounting bolts.
10. Raise the engine by placing a jack under the crankshaft pulley mounting.
11. Remove the oil pan bolts and remove the pan. It may be necessary to rotate the crankshaft to get enough clearance to remove the pan.
12. Reverse the above steps to install. Use gasket sealer and new gaskets.

Oil Pump Removal

The oil pump is located in the timing chain cover on the right-hand side. It is connected by a drilled passage in the crankcase to an oil screen housing and pipe assembly. The screen is submerged in the oil supply in the oil pan.

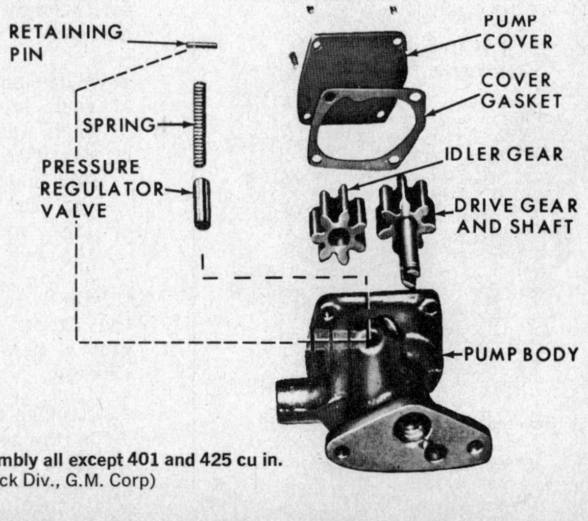
RETAINING PIN
SPRING
PRESSURE REGULATOR VALVE
PUMP COVER
COVER GASKET
IDLER GEAR
DRIVE GEAR AND SHAFT
PUMP BODY

Typical oil pump assembly all except 401 and 425 cu in.
(© Buick Div., G.M. Corp)

Rear Main Bearing Oil Seal Replacement

Buick uses an oil slinger and groove, a braided fabric seal and two neoprene strips to seal the rear main bearing. The braided fabric seal can be installed in the crankcase half (upper) only when crankshaft is removed. However, the seal can be replaced in the lower half whenever the lower half (cap) has been removed. To renew the seals in the cap proceed as follows:

Remove the oil pan. Remove the old seals and clean the cap. Place new braided seal in groove with both ends projecting above parting surface of cap. Force seal into groove by rubbing down with a hammer handle or other smooth tool until seal is seated in groove and ends project above the parting face of the cap not more than 1/16 in. Using a razor blade, cut off ends flush with parting surface.

Just before installing the bearing cap, lightly lubricate the neoprene seals and install in bearing cap with the upper ends protruding about 1/16 in. The seals must not be cut to length. After installing the cap, force the seals up into the cap with a blunt instrument to insure a seal at the line between the cap and the case.

NOTE: the 1968-70 430 and 455 cu. in. engines use a rear bearing cap which does not have the neoprene seals. These engines are sealed at this point by a rear oil pan seal.

Caution The engine must be operated at slow speed when first started after installation of new braided seals.

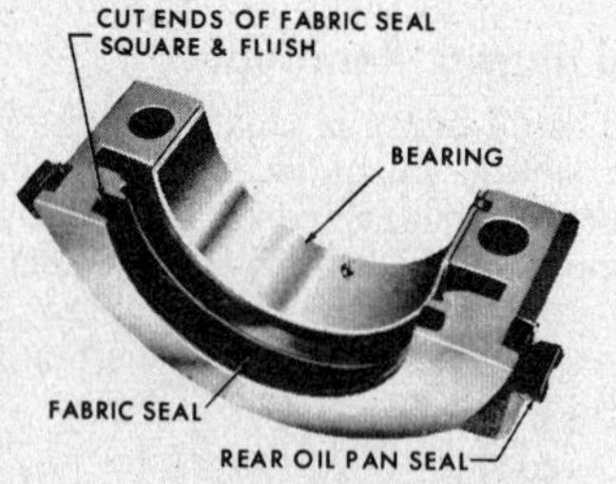
CUT ENDS OF FABRIC SEAL SQUARE & FLUSH
BEARING
FABRIC SEAL
REAR OIL PAN SEAL

Rear main bearing cap—430 and 455 cu in.
(© Buick Div., G.M. Corp)

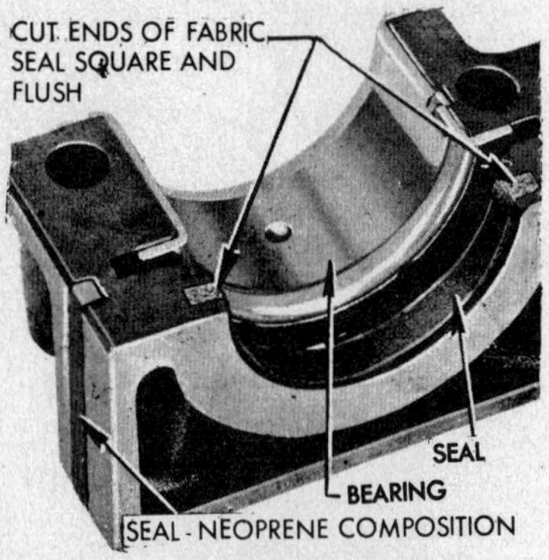
CUT ENDS OF FABRIC SEAL SQUARE AND FLUSH
SEAL
BEARING
SEAL - NEOPRENE COMPOSITION

Rear main bearing cap—except 430 and 455 cu in.
(© Buick Div., G.M. Corp)

Chilton's TIME SAVER

Top Half, Rear Main Bearing Oil Seal Replacement

1. Drain engine oil and remove oil pan.
2. Remove rear main bearing cap.
3. With a 6 in. length of 3/16 in. brazing rod, drive up on either exposed end of the top half oil seal. When the opposite end of the seal starts to protrude, have a helper grasp it with pliers and pull gently while the driven end is being tapped. It is surprising how easily most of these seals can be removed by this method.

To replace the woven fabric-type seal:

1. Obtain a 12 in. piece of copper wire (about the same gauge as that used in the strands of an insulated battery cable).
2. Thread one strand of this wire through the new seal, about ½ in. from the end, bend back and make secure.
3. Thoroughly saturate the new seal with engine oil.
4. Push the copper wire up through the oil seal groove until it comes down on the opposite side of the bearing.
5. Pull (with pliers) on the protruding copper wire while the crankshaft is being turned and the new seal is slowly fed into place.

CAUTION: this snaking operation slightly reduces the diameter of the new seal and care will have to be used to keep the seal from slipping too far through the top half of the bearing.

6. When an equal amount of seal is extending from each side, cut off the copper wire close to the seal and tamp both ends of the seal up into the groove (this will tend to expand the seal again).

NOTE: don't worry about the copper wire left in the groove, it is too soft to cause damage.

7. Replace the seal in the cap in the usual way and replace the oil pan.

CLUTCH

1967-74

The only service adjustment that can be made on a Buick clutch is that of pedal clearance. If difficulty is experienced with the clutch and adjusting the clearance does not correct it, it will be necessary to remove the clutch from the car, since no practical in-car service is possible.

Clutch Removal and Installation

1967-74

1. Remove transmission.
2. Release equalizer assembly.
3. Remove pedal return spring from clutch fork. Disconnect rod assembly from clutch fork.
4. Remove flywheel housing.
5. Remove throwout bearing from clutch fork.
6. Disconnect clutch fork from ball stud by moving toward center of flywheel housing.
7. Mark clutch cover and flywheel so that cover can be reinstalled in the same position. This is important to proper balance.
8. Loosen clutch cover to flywheel attaching bolts one turn at a time to maintain even spring pressure.
9. Support pressure plate and cover assembly while removing bolts. Remove pressure plate and driven plate. Caution should be used to keep the driven plate clean.
10. Reinstall by reversing procedure Tighten pressure plate to 30-40 ft lbs.

Clutch Pedal Adjustment

1967-74
All Models

Clutch pedal clearance is adjusted under the car at the link between the clutch throwout fork and the equalizer. There should be ⅝-⅞ in. freeplay of the clutch pedal before the throwout bearing strikes the fingers (or diaphragm).

MANUAL TRANSMISSION

See the "Unit Repair Section" for the overhaul procedures.

Transmission Removal

1967-74

1. Mark universal joint and transmission shaft companion flange for proper indexing at time of installation. Remove two U-bolts and disconnect driveshaft at the front joint. Slide the driveshaft rearward as far as possible and remove.

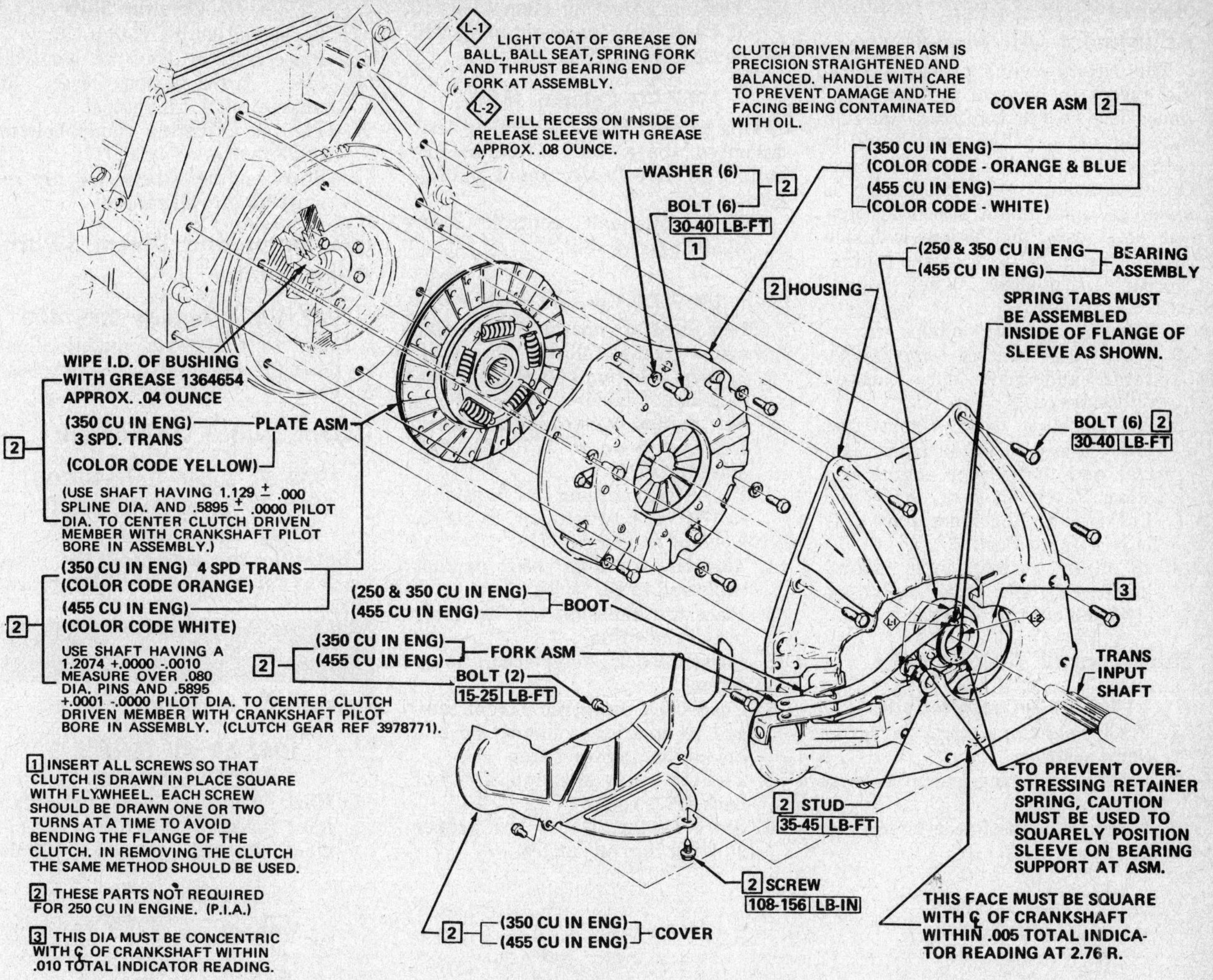

L-1 LIGHT COAT OF GREASE ON BALL, BALL SEAT, SPRING FORK AND THRUST BEARING END OF FORK AT ASSEMBLY.
L-2 FILL RECESS ON INSIDE OF RELEASE SLEEVE WITH GREASE APPROX. .08 OUNCE.
CLUTCH DRIVEN MEMBER ASM IS PRECISION STRAIGHTENED AND BALANCED. HANDLE WITH CARE TO PREVENT DAMAGE AND THE FACING BEING CONTAMINATED WITH OIL.
COVER ASM 2
(350 CU IN ENG) (COLOR CODE - ORANGE & BLUE
(455 CU IN ENG) (COLOR CODE - WHITE)
WASHER (6) 2
BOLT (6) 30-40 LB-FT 1
(250 & 350 CU IN ENG) (455 CU IN ENG) BEARING ASSEMBLY
2 HOUSING
SPRING TABS MUST BE ASSEMBLED INSIDE OF FLANGE OF SLEEVE AS SHOWN.
WIPE I.D. OF BUSHING WITH GREASE 1364654 APPROX. .04 OUNCE
2 (350 CU IN ENG) 3 SPD. TRANS (COLOR CODE YELLOW) PLATE ASM
(USE SHAFT HAVING 1.129 ± .000 SPLINE DIA. AND .5895 ± .0000 PILOT DIA. TO CENTER CLUTCH DRIVEN MEMBER WITH CRANKSHAFT PILOT BORE IN ASSEMBLY.)
BOLT (6) 2 30-40 LB-FT
2 (350 CU IN ENG) 4 SPD TRANS (COLOR CODE ORANGE) (455 CU IN ENG) (COLOR CODE WHITE)
USE SHAFT HAVING A 1.2074 +.0000 -.0010 MEASURE OVER .080 DIA. PINS AND .5895 +.0001 -.0000 PILOT DIA. TO CENTER CLUTCH DRIVEN MEMBER WITH CRANKSHAFT PILOT BORE IN ASSEMBLY. (CLUTCH GEAR REF 3978771).
(250 & 350 CU IN ENG) (455 CU IN ENG) BOOT
3
2 (350 CU IN ENG) (455 CU IN ENG) FORK ASM
BOLT (2) 15-25 LB-FT
TRANS INPUT SHAFT
1 INSERT ALL SCREWS SO THAT CLUTCH IS DRAWN IN PLACE SQUARE WITH FLYWHEEL. EACH SCREW SHOULD BE DRAWN ONE OR TWO TURNS AT A TIME TO AVOID BENDING THE FLANGE OF THE CLUTCH. IN REMOVING THE CLUTCH THE SAME METHOD SHOULD BE USED.
2 THESE PARTS NOT REQUIRED FOR 250 CU IN ENGINE. (P.I.A.)
3 THIS DIA MUST BE CONCENTRIC WITH ℄ OF CRANKSHAFT WITHIN .010 TOTAL INDICATOR READING.
2 STUD 35-45 LB-FT
TO PREVENT OVER-STRESSING RETAINER SPRING, CAUTION MUST BE USED TO SQUARELY POSITION SLEEVE ON BEARING SUPPORT AT ASM.
2 SCREW 108-156 LB-IN
THIS FACE MUST BE SQUARE WITH ℄ OF CRANKSHAFT WITHIN .005 TOTAL INDICATOR READING AT 2.76 R.
2 (350 CU IN ENG) (455 CU IN ENG) COVER

Typical clutch assembly sequence—1971-74 illustrated (© Buick Div., G.M. Corp)

2. Disconnect shift linkage from transmission.
3. Disconnect speedometer cable at transmission. Remove driven gear and sleeve.
4. Loosen all three exhaust pipe ball joints to permit transmission and rear of engine to be lowered.
5. Remove two bolts holding transmission mounting pad to transmission support. Leave mounting pad bolted to transmission.
6. With a padded jack under the engine, raise the unit until the transmission mounting pad clears the transmission support.
7. Remove four bolts holding transmission support to body members. Remove support, then lower the jack to allow transmission to clear the underbody.
8. Remove the two top transmission-to-flywheel housing bolts and insert guide pins.

NOTE: If guide pins are not used, damage to the clutch driven plate can result.

9. Remove the two lower transmission attaching bolts. Slide the transmission back until the drive gear shaft disengages the clutch disc and clears the flywheel housing. Lower the transmission.
10. Install transmission by reversing the above procedure.

Shift Control Adjustment—Three-Speed Column Shift

1967-68

1. Place the transmission levers in Neutral.
2. Loosen the shift rod adjusting clamp bolts.
3. Install a 3/16 in. rod through the holes in the first/reverse lever, the selector plate, the second/third lever and the alignment plate at the bottom of the steering column.
4. Lift the column selector lever straight up toward the steering wheel several times to assure that the neutral positions in both the first/reverse and the second/third planes are aligned. If they are not aligned, shorten the first/reverse rod by pulling it through the swivel no more than 3/16 in.

1969-74

1. Place column selector lever in reverse position. Loosen first-reverse adjusting clamp bolts.
2. Shift first-reverse transmission lever into reverse. Tighten first-reverse adjusting clamp bolt to 17-23 ft. lbs.
3. Shift transmission levers into neutral positions. Loosen second-third adjusting clamp.
4. Install 3/16 in. rod into alignment holes. Tighten second-third adjusting clamp bolt to 17-23 ft. lbs.

AUTOMATIC TRANSMISSION

The Super Turbine 300 transmission is standard equipment on Le Sabre models with the smallest engine, 1967-69. The Super Turbine 400 is optional on the small engine Le Sabres and standard on all other models, 1967-68. In 1969, the Super Turbine 400 is replaced by the virtually identical Turbo Hydra-Matic 400; it is optional on small engine Le Sabres and standard on all other models. In 1970, the Super Turbine 300 is eliminated; the Turbo Hydra-Matic 350 and 400 are the only automatic transmissions used 1970 to present.

Neutral Start Switch Adjustment—All Models

This safety switch prevents starting except in Neutral or Park positions. The switch combines function with the back-up light switch and is actuated by the transmission linkage. On column shift cars, the switch is under the instrument panel. On console shift cars, the switch is inside the console up to 1970, on the column thereafter. To check switch adjustment:

1. Turn on ignition switch.
2. Place shift control lever in Reverse, and make sure back-up lights are on.
3. Set parking brake. Hold foot brake. Place shift control in Neutral and make sure engine will start. Repeat in Park, Drive, and Reverse. Engine must start only in Neutral or Park.
4. To adjust switch, loosen mounting screws and move switch on slotted mounting holes.

Shift Control Adjustment

1967-68—Console Shift

1. Place manual control lever in Park position.
2. Loosen adjusting clamp bolt at transmission.
3. Place transmission lever in Park position.
4. Tighten adjusting clamp bolt to 17-23 ft. lbs. Overtightening will cause hard shifting.

1967-70 Column Shift

This procedure is identical to that described above for 1967-68 console shift with the substitution of the following step:

1. Place manual control lever against Drive stop.

1969-74 Console Shift

These units are operated by a cable linkage. Adjust as follows:

1. Loosen trunnion bolt at transmission end of cable.
2. Set manual control lever against Drive stop up to 1970, Neutral starting 1971.
3. Place transmission bar assembly in Drive position up to 1970, Neutral starting 1971.
4. Tighten trunnion bolt against cable end to 6-9 ft. lbs.
5. Place transmission bar assembly in Park position.
6. Loosen back drive rod clamp screw.
7. Push back drive rod (from linkage to steering column) up and hold lightly against stop.
8. Tighten screw in clamp at end of back drive rod to 17-23 ft. lbs.
9. Start engine. Check for proper shifting into all ranges.

1971-74 Column Shift

1. Loosen adjusting clamp bolt.
2. Place selector lever in Neutral.
3. Place transmission lever, at transmission, in Neutral.
4. Tighten adjusting clamp bolt to 17-23 ft. lbs.
5. Start engine. Check for proper shifting into all ranges.

Idle Stator and Detent Switch Adjustments

1967 Super Turbine 300, 400

Refer to the accompanying illustrations for these adjustment procedures.

Detent Switch Adjustment

1968-69 Super Turbine 300
1968-74 Super Turbine 400, Turbo Hydra-Matic 400

Refer to the accompanying illustrations for these adjustment procedures.

U-JOINTS

Driveshaft Removal

1967-68 All Models
1969-70 Riviera

1. Mark pinion flange and rear joint for reassembly. At rear pinion flange, remove U-bolt

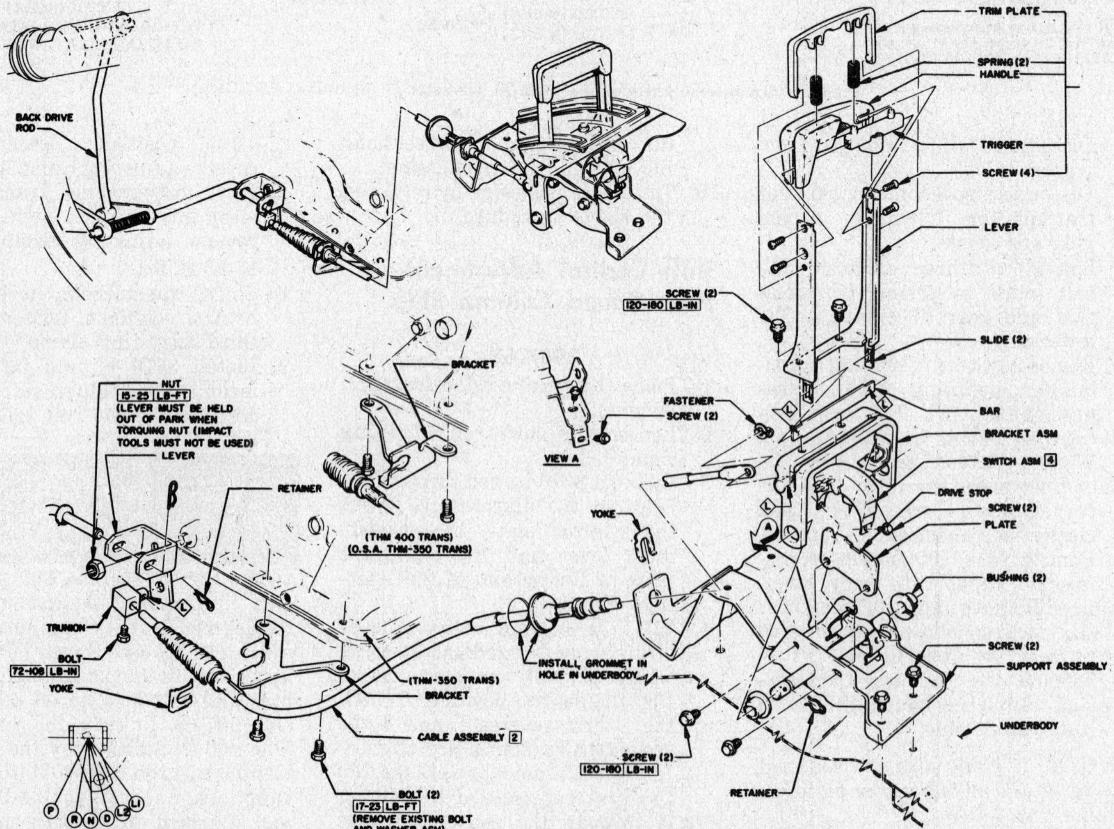

BACK DRIVE ROD
TRIM PLATE
SPRING (2)
HANDLE
TRIGGER
SCREW (4)
LEVER
SCREW (2)
120-180 LB-IN
SLIDE (2)
BRACKET
NUT
15-25 LB-FT
(LEVER MUST BE HELD OUT OF PARK WHEN TORQUING NUT (IMPACT TOOLS MUST NOT BE USED)
LEVER
RETAINER
(THM 400 TRANS)
(O.S.A. THM-350 TRANS)
VIEW A
FASTENER
SCREW (2)
BAR
BRACKET ASM
SWITCH ASM 4
DRIVE STOP
SCREW (2)
PLATE
YOKE
BUSHING (2)
TRUNION
BOLT
72-108 LB-IN
YOKE
(THM-350 TRANS)
BRACKET
INSTALL GROMMET IN HOLE IN UNDERBODY
SCREW (2)
SUPPORT ASSEMBLY
UNDERBODY
CABLE ASSEMBLY 2
SCREW (2)
120-180 LB-IN
RETAINER
BOLT (2)
17-23 LB-FT
(REMOVE EXISTING BOLT AND WASHER ASM)
P R N D L2 L1
VIEW OF TRANS SHIFT LEVER

Cable type console shift linkage—starting 1969 Turbo-Hydramatic 400
(© Buick Div., G.M. Corp)

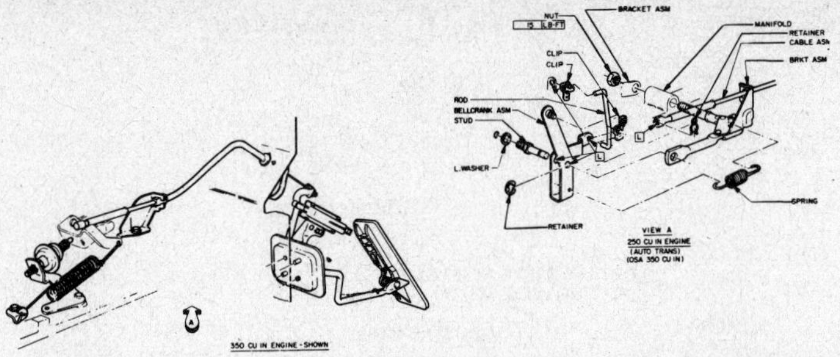
NUT
15 LB-FT
BRACKET ASM
MANIFOLD
RETAINER
CABLE ASM
BRKT ASM
CLIP
CLIP
ROD
BELLCRANK ASM
STUD
L.WASHER
RETAINER
SPRING
VIEW A
250 CU IN ENGINE
(AUTO TRANS)
(OSA 350 CU IN)
350 CU IN ENGINE - SHOWN

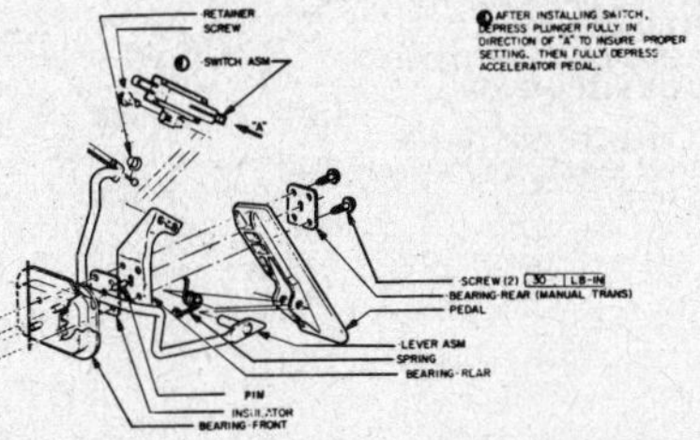
RETAINER
SCREW
SWITCH ASM
"A"
AFTER INSTALLING SWITCH, DEPRESS PLUNGER FULLY IN DIRECTION OF "A" TO INSURE PROPER SETTING. THEN FULLY DEPRESS ACCELERATOR PEDAL.
SCREW (2) 30 LB-IN
BEARING-REAR (MANUAL TRANS)
PEDAL
LEVER ASM
SPRING
BEARING-REAR
PIN
INSULATOR
BEARING-FRONT

1968-69 Super Turbine 300 detent switch adjustment (© Buick Div., G.M. Corp)

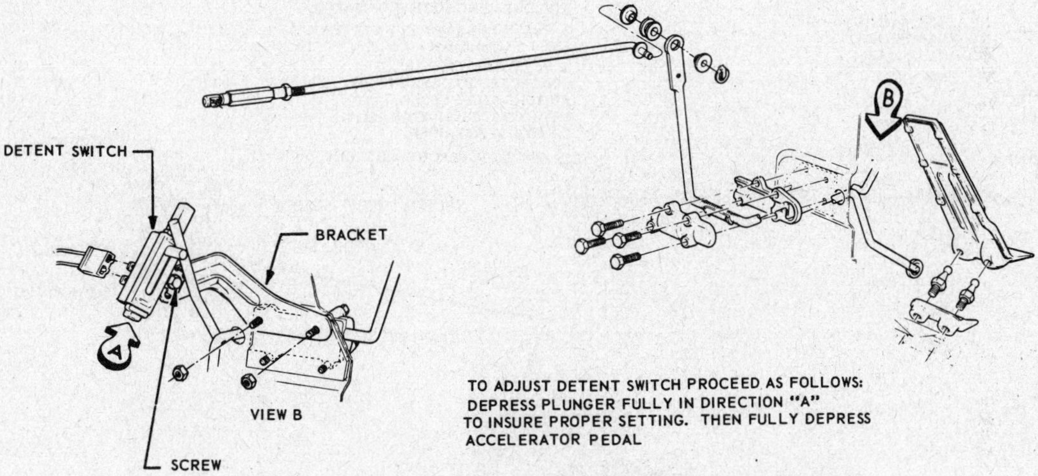
DETENT SWITCH
BRACKET
B
A
VIEW B
SCREW
TO ADJUST DETENT SWITCH PROCEED AS FOLLOWS:
DEPRESS PLUNGER FULLY IN DIRECTION "A"
TO INSURE PROPER SETTING. THEN FULLY DEPRESS
ACCELERATOR PEDAL

1968-70 Super Turbine 400 and Turbo-Hydramatic 400 detent switch adjustment
(© Buick Div., G.M. Corp)

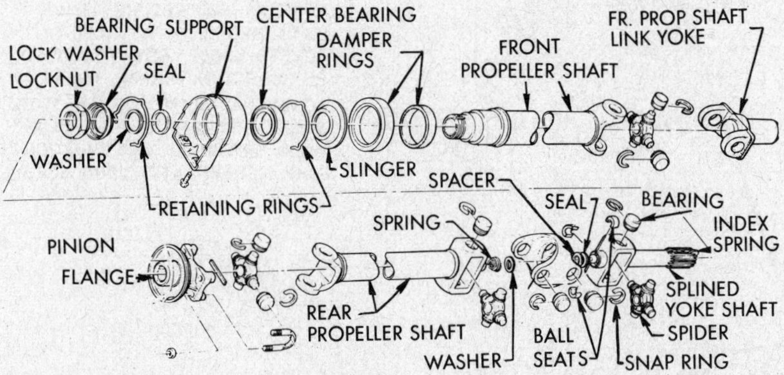
BEARING SUPPORT
CENTER BEARING
DAMPER RINGS
FRONT PROPELLER SHAFT
FR. PROP SHAFT LINK YOKE
LOCK WASHER
LOCKNUT
SEAL
WASHER
SLINGER
RETAINING RINGS
SPACER
SEAL
BEARING
INDEX SPRING
SPRING
PINION FLANGE
REAR PROPELLER SHAFT
WASHER
BALL SEATS
SNAP RING
SPLINED YOKE SHAFT
SPIDER

Typical constant velocity universal joint 1967-68
(© Buick Div., G.M. Corp)

clamps from rear universal; on Riviera, remove four rear CV joint to pinion flange bolts. Use tape to secure bearings on the spider.

2. Remove four center bearing attaching bolts; two bolts on Riviera.
3. Support rear end of shaft. Slide assembly rearward until front yoke is free of transmission shaft splines. On Riviera, slide complete shaft assembly rearward through frame tunnel.
4. Protect the oil seal surface on the front yoke from dirt or marring.

NOTE: do not bend CV joint to its extreme angle at any time.

1969-70, Except Riviera, All 1971-74

1. Mark shaft and pinion flange for reassembly.
2. Remove U-bolts from rear pinion flange. Use tape to secure bearings on the spider.
3. Remove shaft assembly by sliding rearward to disengage splines on transmission shaft.

Driveshaft Disassembly

Single Universal Joint 1967-74

Nylon-injected composite universal joints are used.

1. Remove the driveshaft.
2. By using a piece of pipe or similar tool, slightly larger than 1⅛ in. to encircle the bearing shell, apply force on the yoke until downward movement of the yoke and stationary position of journal force the bearing assembly almost out of the top of the yoke (the force applied on the yoke will shear nylon retainers which lock bearings in place).
3. Rotate propeller shaft 180° and repeat preceding step to partially remove the opposite bearing.
4. Complete removal of these bearings by tapping around the circumference of exposed portion of bearing.
5. Remove journal from driveshaft rear yoke.
6. Remove bearings and journal from splined yoke in the same way.

NOTE: new bearings and journal assembly kits must be used upon reassembly. The kit includes snaprings and Delrin washers.

7. Install by inserting one bearing one-quarter way in one side of

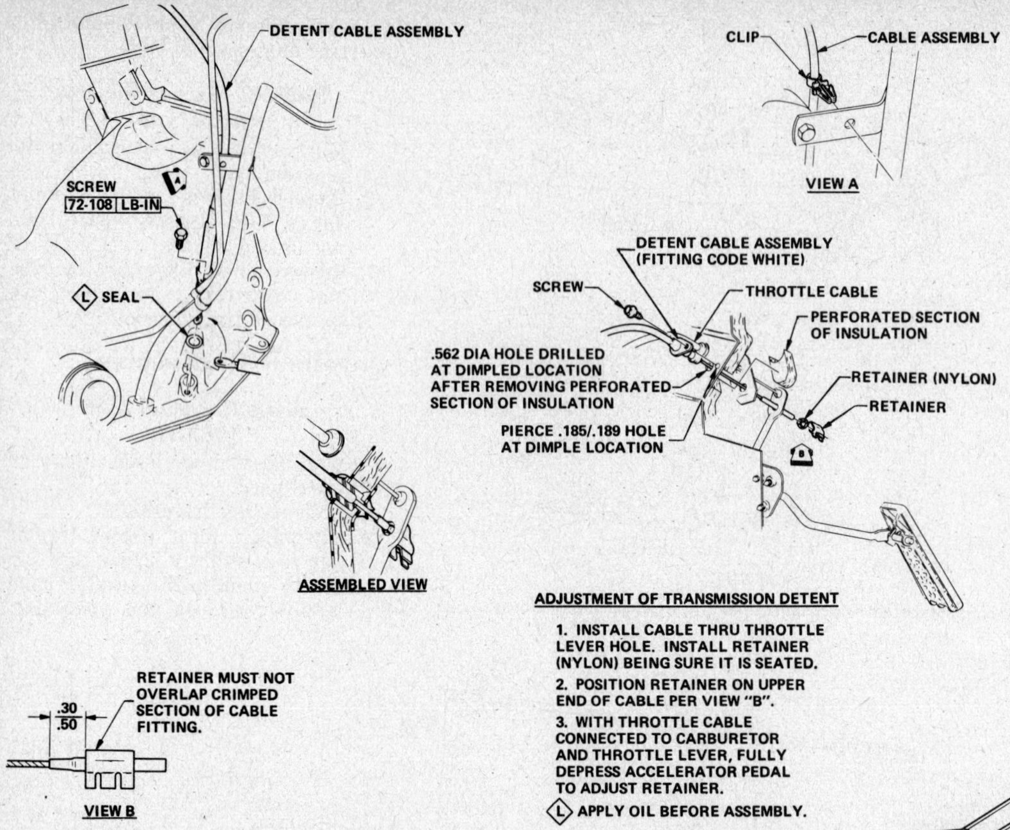
DETENT CABLE ASSEMBLY
SCREW
72-108 LB-IN
SEAL
ASSEMBLED VIEW
CLIP
CABLE ASSEMBLY
VIEW A
DETENT CABLE ASSEMBLY (FITTING CODE WHITE)
SCREW
THROTTLE CABLE
PERFORATED SECTION OF INSULATION
.562 DIA HOLE DRILLED AT DIMPLED LOCATION AFTER REMOVING PERFORATED SECTION OF INSULATION
RETAINER (NYLON)
RETAINER
PIERCE .185/.189 HOLE AT DIMPLE LOCATION
ADJUSTMENT OF TRANSMISSION DETENT
1. INSTALL CABLE THRU THROTTLE LEVER HOLE. INSTALL RETAINER (NYLON) BEING SURE IT IS SEATED.
2. POSITION RETAINER ON UPPER END OF CABLE PER VIEW "B".
3. WITH THROTTLE CABLE CONNECTED TO CARBURETOR AND THROTTLE LEVER, FULLY DEPRESS ACCELERATOR PEDAL TO ADJUST RETAINER.
L APPLY OIL BEFORE ASSEMBLY.
RETAINER MUST NOT OVERLAP CRIMPED SECTION OF CABLE FITTING.
.30
.50
VIEW B

Detent switch adjustment—starting 1971 (© Buick Div., G.M. Corp)

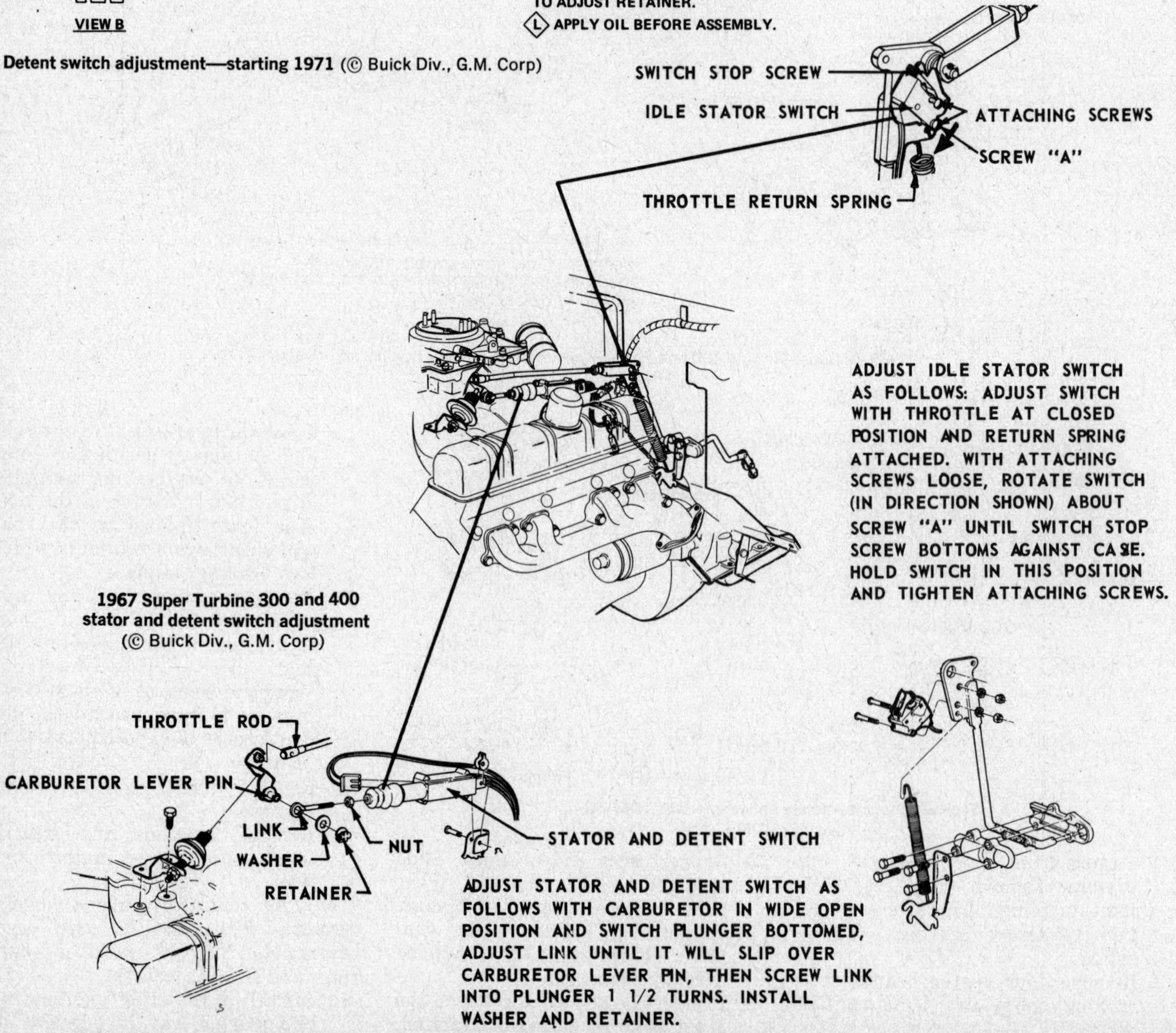
SWITCH STOP SCREW
IDLE STATOR SWITCH
ATTACHING SCREWS
SCREW "A"
THROTTLE RETURN SPRING
ADJUST IDLE STATOR SWITCH AS FOLLOWS: ADJUST SWITCH WITH THROTTLE AT CLOSED POSITION AND RETURN SPRING ATTACHED. WITH ATTACHING SCREWS LOOSE, ROTATE SWITCH (IN DIRECTION SHOWN) ABOUT SCREW "A" UNTIL SWITCH STOP SCREW BOTTOMS AGAINST CASE. HOLD SWITCH IN THIS POSITION AND TIGHTEN ATTACHING SCREWS.
THROTTLE ROD
CARBURETOR LEVER PIN
LINK
WASHER
RETAINER
NUT
STATOR AND DETENT SWITCH
ADJUST STATOR AND DETENT SWITCH AS FOLLOWS WITH CARBURETOR IN WIDE OPEN POSITION AND SWITCH PLUNGER BOTTOMED, ADJUST LINK UNTIL IT WILL SLIP OVER CARBURETOR LEVER PIN, THEN SCREW LINK INTO PLUNGER 1 1/2 TURNS. INSTALL WASHER AND RETAINER.

1967 Super Turbine 300 and 400 stator and detent switch adjustment (© Buick Div., G.M. Corp)

splined yoke, using brass hammer.

8. Insert journal into splined yoke (with dust shields installed).
9. Install opposite bearing, ensuring that the bearing rollers do not jam on journal. Check free rotary movement of journal in bearing.
10. Now, press both bearings into place (just far enough to install snap rings).
11. Assemble opposite end universal in the same way.

Double Cardon Constant-Velocity Rear U-Joint R&R

Removal

1. Mark the link yoke and the adjoining yokes, with a punch, before disassembly to ensure proper reassembly and driveshaft balance.

NOTE: it is easier to remove the flange yoke first. The first pair of flange yoke universal joint bearings to be removed is the pair in the link yoke.

2. With the driveshaft in a horizontal position, solidly support the link yoke. (A 1⅞ in. pipe will do.)
3. Apply force to the bearing cup on the opposite side with a 1⅛ in. pipe or a socket the size of the bearing cup. Use a hammer, vise, or press to apply force. Force the cup inward as far as possible.

NOTE: in the absence of a press, a heavy vise may be used, but make sure that the universal to be removed is at a right angle to the jaws of the vise. Do not cock the bearing cups in their bores.

4. Remove the pieces of pipe and complete the removal of the protruding bearing cup by tapping around the circumference of the exposed portion of the bearing with a small hammer.
5. Reverse the positions of the pieces of pipe and apply force to the exposed journal end. This will force the other bearing cup out of its bore and allow removal of the flange.

NOTE: there is a ball joint located between the two universals. The ball portion of this joint is on the inner end of the flange yoke. Care must be taken not to damage the ball. On 1973-74 models the centering ball is a press-fit and is replaceable. On previous models the ball can not be removed. The ball seat is in the end of the driveshaft. To remove the seat, pry the seal out with a screwdriver.

6. To remove the journal from the flange, use steps two through five.
7. Remove the universal joint bearings from the driveshaft using the steps from two through five. The first pair of bearing caps that should be removed is the pair in the link yoke.

Installation

1. Examine the ball stud seat and ball stud for scores or wear. Worn seats can be replaced with a kit. A worn ball, however, requires the replacement of the entire propeller shaft yoke and flange assembly on all except 1973 models. Clean the ball seat cavity and fill it with grease. Install the spring, washer, ball seats, and spacer, if removed.
2. Install the universal joints in the opposite order from which they were disassembled.
3. Install a bearing ¼ of the way into one side of the yoke.
4. Insert the journal into the yoke so that an arm of the journal seats into the bearing.
5. Press the bearing in the remaining distance and install its snapring.
6. Install the opposite bearing. Do not allow the bearing rollers to jam. Continually check for free movement of the journal in the bearings as they are pressed into the yoke.
7. Install the rest of the bearings in the same manner.

Jacking and Hoisting

1967-74

Jack car at front spring seat of lower control arm or center of crossmember.

Jack car at rear, at axle housing.

To lift at frame, use side rails in front of body floor pan and at rear side rail at lower control arm front pivot.

1973 constant velocity U-joint with replaceable centering ball
(© Buick Div., G.M. Corp)

FRONT SUSPENSION

Figures covering the caster, camber, toe-in, king pin inclination, and turning radius can be found in the Wheel Alignment table.

Shock Absorber R & R

1. Remove the upper shock absorber attaching nut, grommet retainer, and grommet.
2. Remove the lower retaining screws. Lower the shock through the hole in the lower control arm.
3. Reverse the above steps to install.

Ball Joint Inspection

1967-72

NOTE: before performing this inspection, make sure that the wheel bearings are adjusted correctly and that the A-arm bushings are in good condition.

1. Jack the car up under the front lower control arm at the spring seat.
2. Raise the car until there is 1–2 in. of clearance under the wheel.
3. Insert a bar under the wheel and pry upward. If the wheel raises more than 1/8 in., the ball joints are worn. Determine whether the upper or lower ball joint is worn by visual inspection while prying on the wheel.

NOTE: due to the distribution of forces in the suspension, the lower ball joint is usually the defective joint.

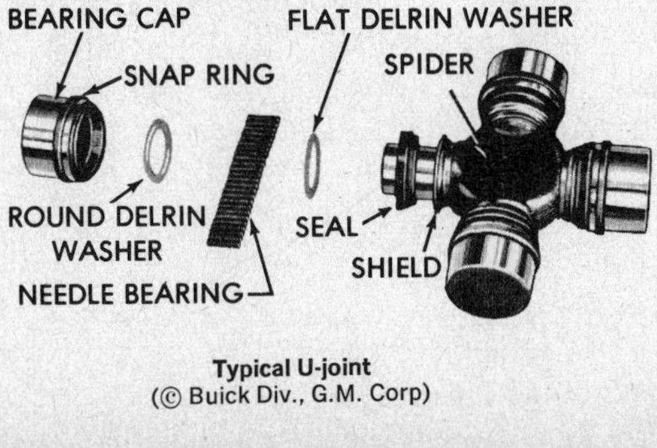
BEARING CAP
SNAP RING
FLAT DELRIN WASHER
SPIDER
ROUND DELRIN WASHER
NEEDLE BEARING
SEAL
SHIELD

Typical U-joint
(© Buick Div., G.M. Corp)

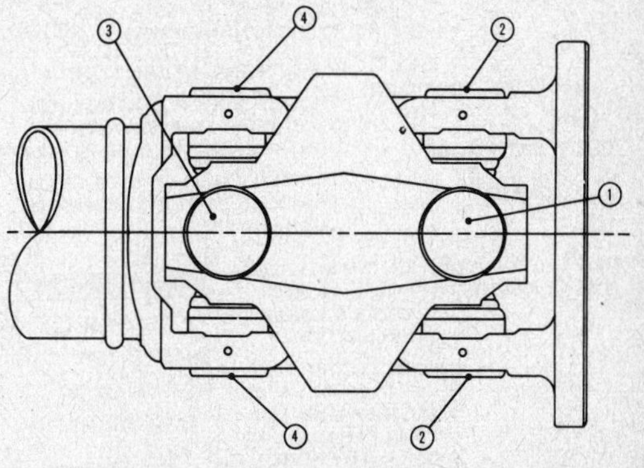
3
4
2
1
4
2

Bearing cap removal sequence—double Cardon joint starting 1971
(© Buick Div., G.M. Corp)

1973-74

1973-74 lower ball joints contain a visual wear indicator. The lower ball joint grease plug screws into the wear indicator which protrudes from the bottom of the ball joint housing. As long as the wear indicator extends out of the ball joint housing, the ball joint is not worn. If the tip of the wear indicator is parallel with, or recessed into the ball joint housing, the ball joint is defective.

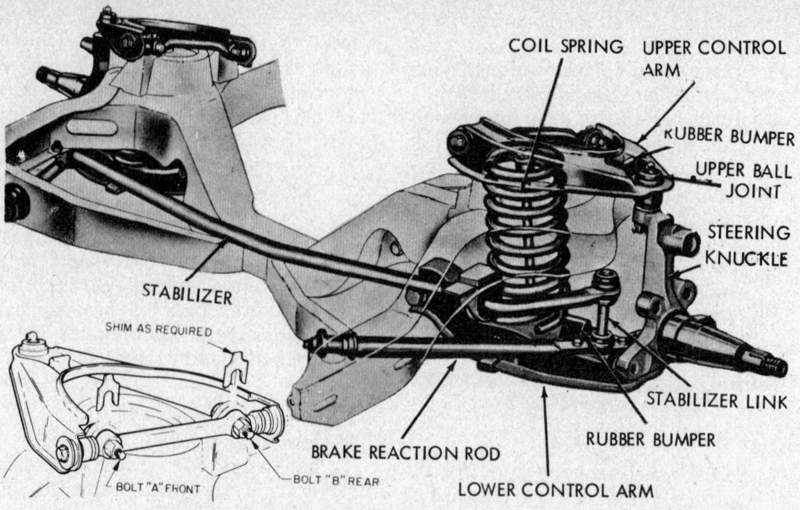
COIL SPRING
UPPER CONTROL ARM
RUBBER BUMPER
UPPER BALL JOINT
STEERING KNUCKLE
STABILIZER
SHIM AS REQUIRED
STABILIZER LINK
RUBBER BUMPER
BRAKE REACTION ROD
BOLT "A" FRONT
BOLT "B" REAR
LOWER CONTROL ARM

Typical front suspension—1967-70 (© Buick Div., G.M. Corp)

Control Arms, and/or Ball Joint, Spring—R & R

Upper Control Arm

1. Raise car with jack under the frame. Remove wheel and tire.
2. Remove cotter pin from upper ball joint stud.
3. Loosen, but do not remove nut. Rap the knuckle sharply in the area of the tapered stud to free the stud from the knuckle.
4. With another jack, support the car weight under the outer edge of the lower control arm. Raise jack enough to free upper control arm from upper ball stud.
5. Wire brake and knuckle in place to prevent brake hose damage, then, lift upper arm from knuckle.

NOTE: if only ball joints are to be replaced, stop at this point. Center punch and drill out the four rivets, then chisel off their heads. Remove old ball joint—the new joint comes with four specially hardened bolts, which must be torqued to 8 ft. lbs. The nut goes on top.

6. Remove the upper control arm shaft-to-bracket nuts and lock washers. Carefully note the number, thickness, and location of the adjusting shims. Remove control arm assembly.
7. Reverse the above to install.

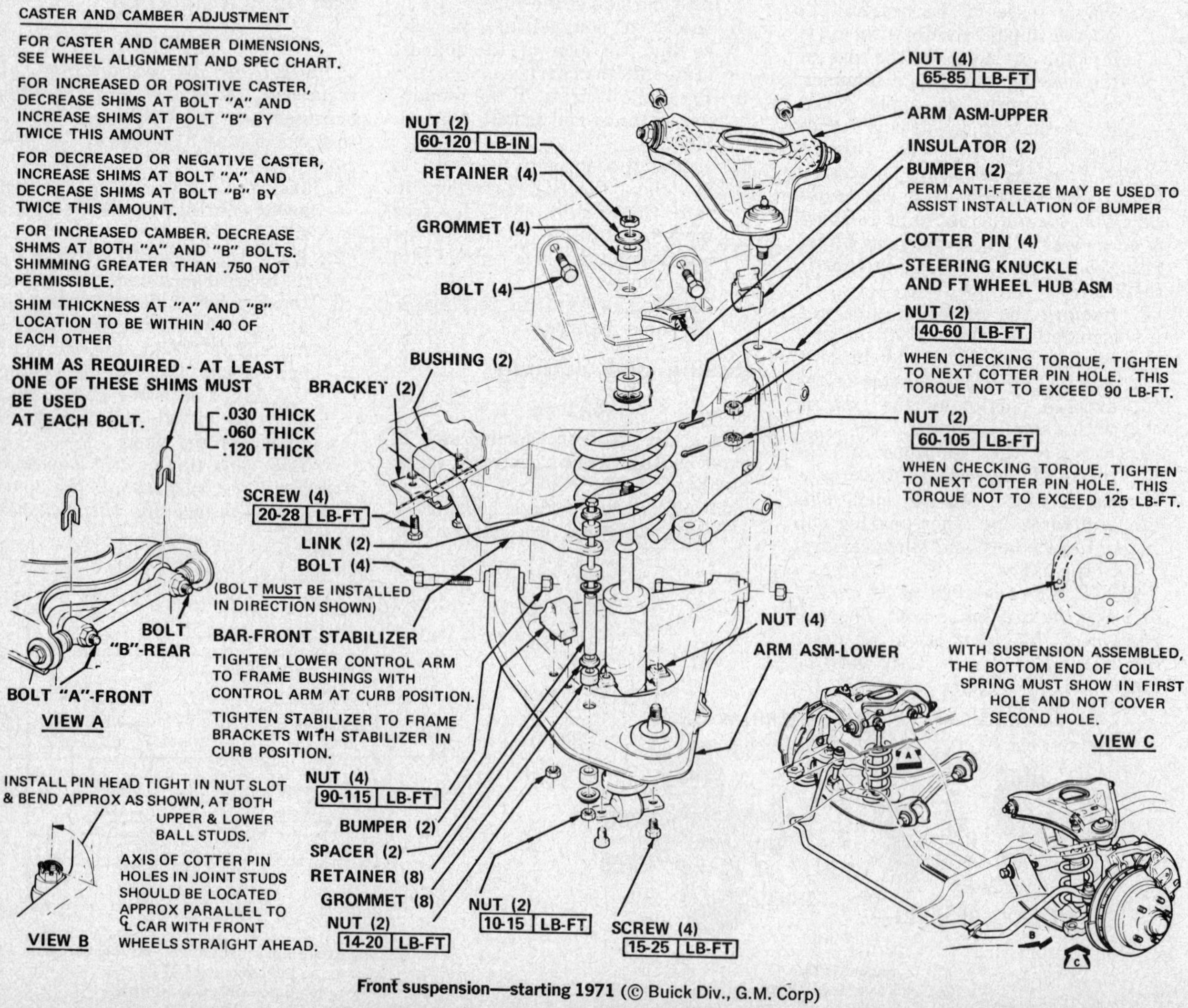
CASTER AND CAMBER ADJUSTMENT
FOR CASTER AND CAMBER DIMENSIONS, SEE WHEEL ALIGNMENT AND SPEC CHART.
FOR INCREASED OR POSITIVE CASTER, DECREASE SHIMS AT BOLT "A" AND INCREASE SHIMS AT BOLT "B" BY TWICE THIS AMOUNT
FOR DECREASED OR NEGATIVE CASTER, INCREASE SHIMS AT BOLT "A" AND DECREASE SHIMS AT BOLT "B" BY TWICE THIS AMOUNT.
FOR INCREASED CAMBER, DECREASE SHIMS AT BOTH "A" AND "B" BOLTS. SHIMMING GREATER THAN .750 NOT PERMISSIBLE.
SHIM THICKNESS AT "A" AND "B" LOCATION TO BE WITHIN .40 OF EACH OTHER
SHIM AS REQUIRED - AT LEAST ONE OF THESE SHIMS MUST BE USED AT EACH BOLT.
.030 THICK
.060 THICK
.120 THICK
BOLT "B"-REAR
BOLT "A"-FRONT
VIEW A
INSTALL PIN HEAD TIGHT IN NUT SLOT & BEND APPROX AS SHOWN, AT BOTH UPPER & LOWER BALL STUDS.
AXIS OF COTTER PIN HOLES IN JOINT STUDS SHOULD BE LOCATED APPROX PARALLEL TO ℄ CAR WITH FRONT WHEELS STRAIGHT AHEAD.
VIEW B
NUT (2) 60-120 LB-IN
RETAINER (4)
GROMMET (4)
BOLT (4)
BUSHING (2)
BRACKET (2)
SCREW (4) 20-28 LB-FT
LINK (2)
BOLT (4)
(BOLT MUST BE INSTALLED IN DIRECTION SHOWN)
BAR-FRONT STABILIZER
TIGHTEN LOWER CONTROL ARM TO FRAME BUSHINGS WITH CONTROL ARM AT CURB POSITION.
TIGHTEN STABILIZER TO FRAME BRACKETS WITH STABILIZER IN CURB POSITION.
NUT (4) 90-115 LB-FT
BUMPER (2)
SPACER (2)
RETAINER (8)
GROMMET (8)
NUT (2) 14-20 LB-FT
NUT (2) 10-15 LB-FT
SCREW (4) 15-25 LB-FT
NUT (4) 65-85 LB-FT
ARM ASM-UPPER
INSULATOR (2)
BUMPER (2)
PERM ANTI-FREEZE MAY BE USED TO ASSIST INSTALLATION OF BUMPER
COTTER PIN (4)
STEERING KNUCKLE AND FT WHEEL HUB ASM
NUT (2) 40-60 LB-FT
WHEN CHECKING TORQUE, TIGHTEN TO NEXT COTTER PIN HOLE. THIS TORQUE NOT TO EXCEED 90 LB-FT.
NUT (2) 60-105 LB-FT
WHEN CHECKING TORQUE, TIGHTEN TO NEXT COTTER PIN HOLE. THIS TORQUE NOT TO EXCEED 125 LB-FT.
NUT (4)
ARM ASM-LOWER
WITH SUSPENSION ASSEMBLED, THE BOTTOM END OF COIL SPRING MUST SHOW IN FIRST HOLE AND NOT COVER SECOND HOLE.
VIEW C

Front suspension—starting 1971 (© Buick Div., G.M. Corp)

Caution

When installing the cotter pin, never loosen the nut to align the cotter pin holes. Always tighten the nut to the next slot that lines up with the hole.

Lower Control Arm, or Spring

1. Raise the front of the car and remove the tires, wheels, hub and drum or rotor.
2. Disconnect . and remove shock absorber.
3. Remove front stabilizer rod link from lower control arm.
4. Disconnect brake reaction rod from lower control arm but leave it attached to the front frame crossmember up to 1970 models.
5. Remove control arm bumper up to 1970 models.
6. As a safety precaution and to gain maximum leverage, place a jack about ½ in. below the lower ball joint stud. Now, remove the ball stud cotter pin and loosen the nut about ⅛ in. Do not remove the nut.
7. Rap the steering knuckle in the area of the stud to separate the stud from the knuckle.
8. After the stud has broken loose from the knuckle, raise the jack against the control arm. Remove nut and separate the steering knuckle from the tapered stud.
9. Carefully lower jack under the control arm and release the spring. With the jack entirely lowered, it may be necessary to pry the spring off its seat on the lower control arm with a pry bar.
10. After the spring is removed, the lower control arm may be removed by removing the lock nut attaching the control arm to the frame.
11. Install by reversing removal procedure. Tighten castellated nut to 85 ft. lbs.

Lower Ball Joint R & R

1. Perform steps two through eight, inclusive, in the "Lower Control Arm R&R" procedure.
2. Remove the ball joint by pressing the joint from the lower control arm. It may be necessary to remove the ball joint and lower control arm as an assembly and have the ball joint removed in a press if suitable tools are not available.
3. Install a new ball joint and reverse the removal procedure.

Front Wheel Bearing Adjustment

1967-70

Adjustment of freshly cleaned and repacked roller bearings is as follows:

1. Torque spindle nut to 19 ft. lbs. while rotating the wheel.
2. Back off the nut until bearings are loose.
3. Retorque spindle nut to 11 ft. lbs. while rotating the wheel.
4. If either cotter pin hole in spindle lines up with nut castellations, back off the nut one-twelfth turn and install cotter pin. Otherwise, back off the nut to the first position that will accept a horizontal or vertical cotter pin.
5. Install cotter pin and lock spindle nut into position.

NOTE: .002-.006 in. end-play is normal.

1971-74

1. Lift the wheel off the ground by jacking under the lower control arm.
2. Remove the dust cap from the hub.

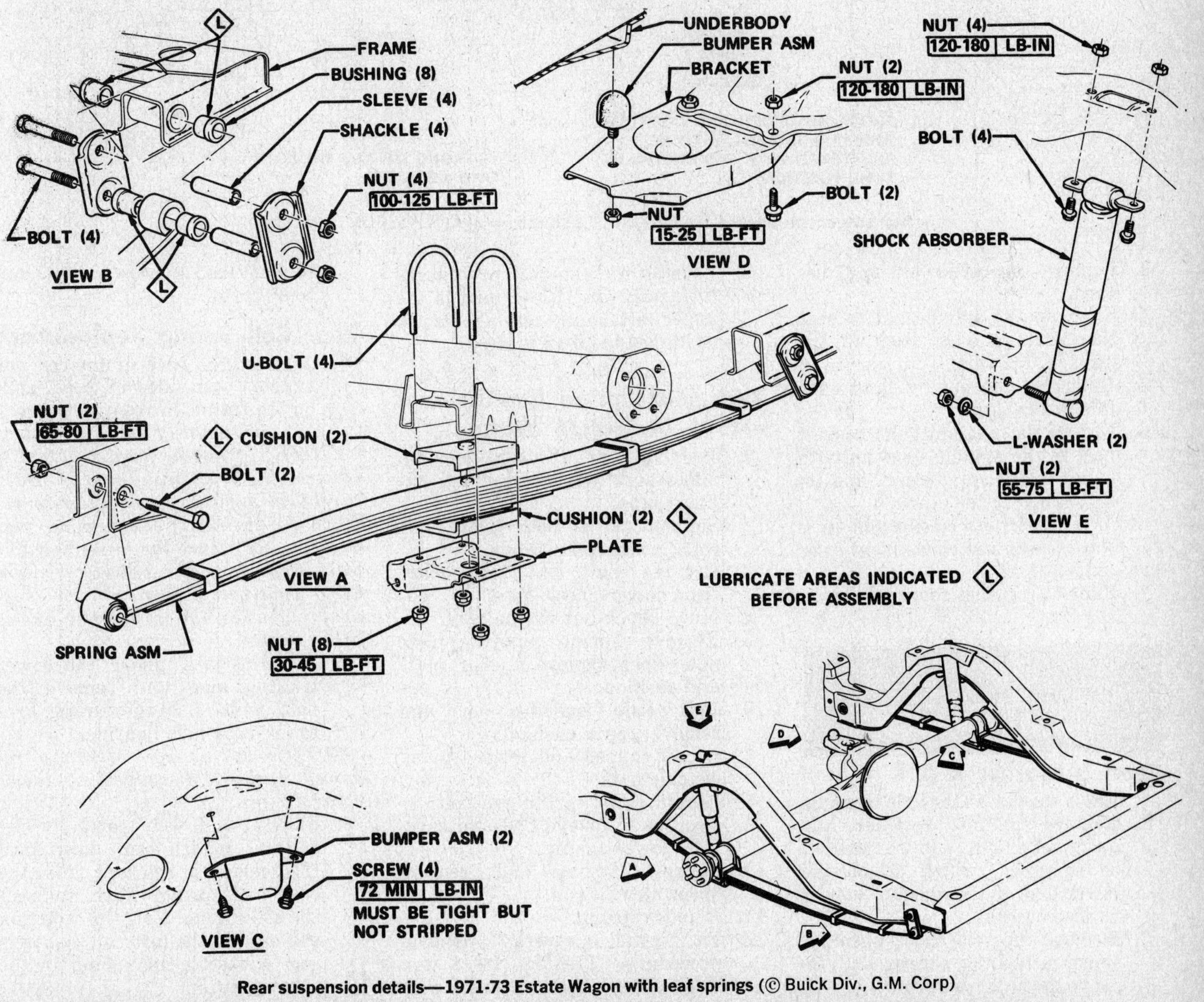
FRAME
BUSHING (8)
SLEEVE (4)
SHACKLE (4)
NUT (4)
100-125 LB-FT
BOLT (4)
VIEW B
UNDERBODY
BUMPER ASM
BRACKET
NUT (2)
120-180 LB-IN
NUT
15-25 LB-FT
BOLT (2)
VIEW D
NUT (4)
120-180 LB-IN
BOLT (4)
SHOCK ABSORBER
U-BOLT (4)
NUT (2)
65-80 LB-FT
CUSHION (2)
BOLT (2)
CUSHION (2)
PLATE
VIEW A
SPRING ASM
NUT (8)
30-45 LB-FT
L-WASHER (2)
NUT (2)
55-75 LB-FT
VIEW E
LUBRICATE AREAS INDICATED
BEFORE ASSEMBLY
BUMPER ASM (2)
SCREW (4)
72 MIN LB-IN
MUST BE TIGHT BUT
NOT STRIPPED
VIEW C

Rear suspension details—1971-73 Estate Wagon with leaf springs (© Buick Div., G.M. Corp)

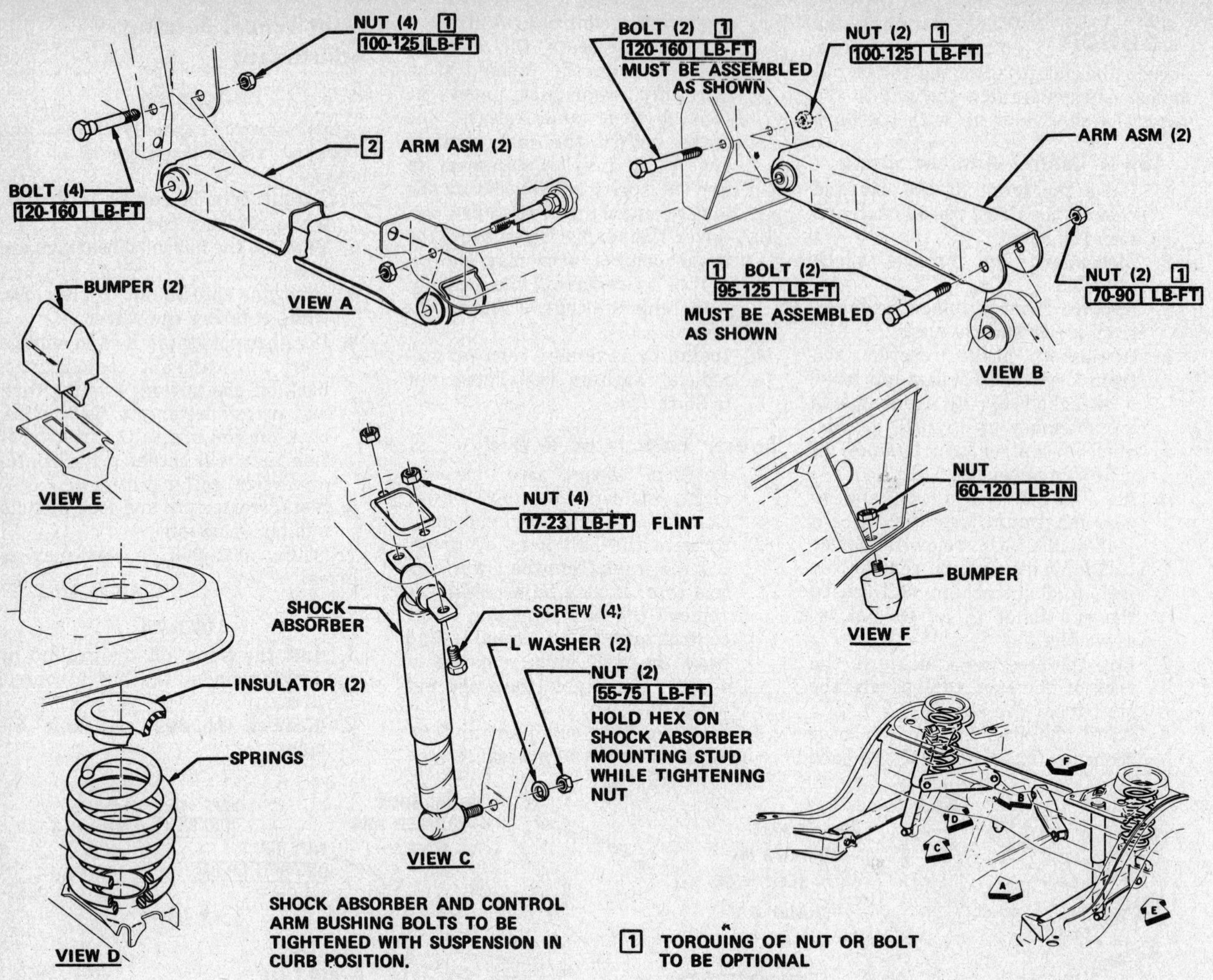
NUT (4) 1
100-125 LB-FT
BOLT (4)
120-160 LB-FT
2 ARM ASM (2)
VIEW A
BOLT (2) 1
120-160 LB-FT
MUST BE ASSEMBLED AS SHOWN
NUT (2) 1
100-125 LB-FT
ARM ASM (2)
1 BOLT (2)
95-125 LB-FT
MUST BE ASSEMBLED AS SHOWN
NUT (2) 1
70-90 LB-FT
VIEW B
BUMPER (2)
VIEW E
NUT (4)
17-23 LB-FT FLINT
NUT
60-120 LB-IN
BUMPER
VIEW F
SHOCK ABSORBER
SCREW (4)
L WASHER (2)
NUT (2)
55-75 LB-FT
HOLD HEX ON SHOCK ABSORBER MOUNTING STUD WHILE TIGHTENING NUT
INSULATOR (2)
SPRINGS
VIEW C
VIEW D
SHOCK ABSORBER AND CONTROL ARM BUSHING BOLTS TO BE TIGHTENED WITH SUSPENSION IN CURB POSITION.
1 TORQUING OF NUT OR BOLT TO BE OPTIONAL

Rear suspension details—typical 1967-72 with coil springs (© Buick Div., G.M. Corp)

3. Remove the cotter pin and discard.
4. Snug up the spindle nut to seat the bearings. Then back off the nut 1/4–1/2 turn.
5. Retighten the nut by hand until it is finger-tight.
6. Loosen the nut until the nearest hole in the spindle lines up with a slot in the spindle nut, and insert a new cotter pin.

NOTE: under no circumstances is the final bearing nut adjustment to be even finger-tight.

7. Replace the dust cover and lower the car.

REAR SUSPENSION

Shock Absorber R & R

1. Raise the car at the axle housing.
2. Remove the nut, retainer, and grommet or nut, and lockwasher, as equipped, which attach the lower end of the shock absorber to its mounting.
3. Remove the two shock absorber upper attaching screws and remove the shock absorber.
4. Reverse the removal procedures to install. On 1973-4 models the upper attaching nut should be tightened to 10-15 ft lbs.

Rear Leaf Spring Replacement —1971-74 Station Wagon

1. Jack up car at axle housing. Make sure you don't crush exhaust pipe.
2. Support car at both frame side rails, using axle stands.
3. Remove nut and lockwasher from lower shock stud.
4. Move shock out of the way.
5. Remove spring anchor plate nuts, then remove anchor plate and cushion.
6. Jack axle housing up and remove upper cushion.
7. Loosen upper and lower spring shackle nuts.
8. Loosen front spring eye bolt.
9. Remove front eye bolt and carefully lower spring.
10. Support spring and remove lower shackle pin.
11. Remove spring.
12. To install, reverse removal procedure. Tighten front eye bolt to 70-90 ft lbs., shackle nuts to 95 ft lbs., and lower shock nut to 65 ft lbs.

Rear Coil Spring Replacement

1. Jack up the back of the car and support both sides on stand jacks on the frame, in front of the rear axle. Disconnect shock absorber.

NOTE: It may be necessary to disconnect the rear brake line in order to obtain sufficient axle drop to remove the spring. If this is done, first depress and secure the brake pedal at least 1 in. from the relaxed position to prevent the master cylinder from draining when the rear brake line is disconnected.

2. Place a jack under the lower trailing arm and remove the bolts which hold the trailing arm to the rear axle housing.

NOTE: spring can often be removed without disconnecting lower control arm.

3. Slowly, and very carefully, let the trailing arm come down until the tension is released from the rear coil spring. Then, take off the coil spring. Note the direction the end of the last coil is pointing. Reinstall the spring in the same position.

4. When starting a new coil spring, make certain that the bottom of the coil is properly inserted into the socket in the frame and into the form plate on the trailing arm.
5. Jack the trailing arm into place and reinstall the trailing arm rear bolt.

BRAKES

Since 1967 a dual master cylinder is used on all models. Information on the dual type system and brake adjustments, lining replacement bleeding procedure, master and wheel cylinder overhaul can be found in the Unit Repair Section.

Information on the grease seals which may need replacement can be found in the Unit Repair Section.

Since 1967, some models are equipped with front wheel disc brakes. Beginning 1969 these disc brakes operate with single cylinder per wheel design. However, some 1969 models have the earlier four piston disc brakes. For details, consult the Unit Repair Section.

Master Cylinder R & R

1967-74

1. Disconnect brake pipe or pipes from master cylinder and tape end of pipe or pipes to prevent entrance of dirt.
2. Disconnect brake pedal from master cylinder at the pushrod.
3. Remove master cylinder-to-dash retaining bolts. Remove the master cylinder.
4. Reverse the above steps to install. Bleed the brakes and check for leaks after installation.

Power Brake Unit R & R

1967-74

1. Disconnect brake pipe or pipes from hydraulic master cylinder and tape pipe ends to exclude dirt.
2. Disconnect vacuum hose from power brake unit.
3. Remove four nuts holding power brake unit to dash.
4. Remove retainer and washer from brake pedal pin and disengage pushrod clevis.
5. Remove power brake unit from car.
6. Reverse the above steps to install. Bleed the brakes and check for leaks after installation.

Parking Brake Lever

The parking brake lever on all models is a foot-operated treadle.

To remove the treadle first disconnect the cable and then unbolt the treadle frame from its mounting under the dash.

Parking Brake Cable Replacement—1967-74

Front Cable

1. Raise car.
2. Remove jam nut and adjusting nut from equalizer. Remove retainer clip from rear portion of front cable at frame. The retainer clip is not used on the Riviera.
3. At front of cable, bend snap-in retainer fingers in, so that retainer can be removed.
4. Disconnect cable from pedal assembly and remove cable.

NOTE: installation of a new cable can be eased by tying a cord to either end of the cable being removed and then pulling the new cable through the proper routing by use of the same cord. This is necessary since the cable is not long enough to follow a new path.

5. Install cable by reversing removal procedure.

Center Cable

1. Raise car.
2. Remove jam nut and adjusting nut from equalizer.
3. Unhook connector at each end and disengage hooks and guides.
4. Install new cable by reversing removal procedure.

Rear Cable

1. Raise car.
2. Remove rear wheel and brake drum.
3. Loosen jam nut and adjusting nut at equalizer.
4. Disengage rear cable at connector.
5. Remove two bolts attaching cable assembly to backing plate. Disengage cable at brake shoe operating lever.
6. Install new cable by reversing removal procedure.

Parking Brake Adjustment—1967-74

Adjustment of the parking brake is necessary whenever the rear brake cables have been disconnected or the parking brake pedal can be depressed more than sixteen rachet clicks under have foot pressure. The car should first be raised on a lift.

1. Make sure that service brakes are properly adjusted.
2. Depress parking brake pedal three rachet clicks.
3. Loosen jam nut on equalizer adjusting nut. Tighten adjusting nut until rear wheels can just be turned rearward by hand but not forward.
4. Release rachet one click; the rear wheels should rotate rearward freely and forward with a slight drag.
5. Release rachet one more click; rear wheels should turn freely in either direction.

NOTE: be sure that the parking brake does not drag. An overtightened, dragging parking brake on a car with automatic brake adjusters will result in an extremely short life for rear brake linings.

STEERING

Instructions covering the overhaul of the steering gear will be found in the Unit Repair Section. No manual steering is available on full-size Buicks starting in 1971. Troubleshooting and overhaul procedures are given in the "Unit Repair Section."

Power Steering Pump Removal and Installation

Disconnect the drive belt and remove the pump pulley with a suitable puller. On some models, the pulley has bolt access holes which make pulley removal unnecessary. Disconnect the hoses from the pump and unbolt the pump from the bracket. Use caps or tape to cover the hose connectors, unions, and hose ends to keep out dirt.

Reinstall by reversing procedure. The drive belt should be adjusted to have about ½ in. play on the longest run between pulleys. After replacing pump, fill reservoir and bleed pump by idling engine for three minutes before moving the steering wheel. Then rotate steering wheel slowly throughout its entire range. Recheck oil level.

Tie Rod End Inspection

1. Raise the car under the lower control arm.
2. Make sure control arm ball joints are good and that the wheel bearings are adjusted. Grasp the tire on either side and move the tire from side to side. If excessive play is present (more than 1/16 in.), visually inspect the linkage as the tire is moved.

Tie Rod End R & R

1. Loosen the tie-rod adjuster sleeve clamp nuts.
2. Remove the tie-rod stud nut cotter pin and nut.
3. Remove the tie-rod stud from the steering arm or intermediate rod. This is a taper fit. Removal is accomplished using a ball joint removal tool or by hitting the tie rod stud sharply with a hammer. If the ball joint is to be reused, the removal tool must be used.
4. Unthread the tie rod from the adjuster sleeve. Outer tie rods have right-hand threads and inner tie rods have left-hand threads. Count the number of turns the tie rod must be rotated

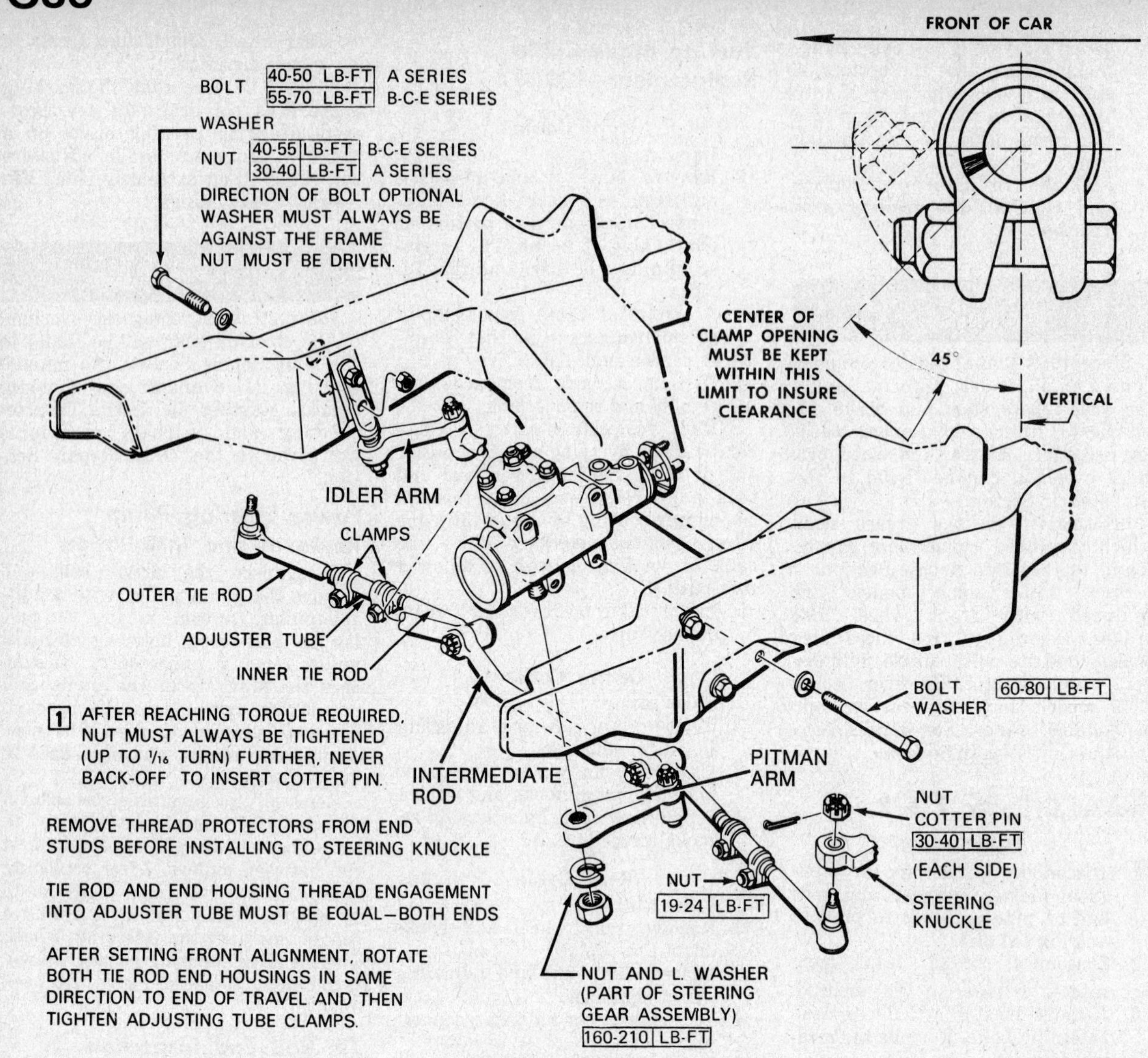
FRONT OF CAR
BOLT
40-50 LB-FT A SERIES
55-70 LB-FT B-C-E SERIES
WASHER
NUT
40-55 LB-FT B-C-E SERIES
30-40 LB-FT A SERIES
DIRECTION OF BOLT OPTIONAL
WASHER MUST ALWAYS BE
AGAINST THE FRAME
NUT MUST BE DRIVEN.
CENTER OF
CLAMP OPENING
MUST BE KEPT
WITHIN THIS
LIMIT TO INSURE
CLEARANCE
45°
VERTICAL
IDLER ARM
CLAMPS
OUTER TIE ROD
ADJUSTER TUBE
INNER TIE ROD
BOLT 60-80 LB-FT
WASHER
1 AFTER REACHING TORQUE REQUIRED, NUT MUST ALWAYS BE TIGHTENED (UP TO 1/16 TURN) FURTHER, NEVER BACK-OFF TO INSERT COTTER PIN.
INTERMEDIATE ROD
PITMAN ARM
NUT
COTTER PIN
30-40 LB-FT
(EACH SIDE)
REMOVE THREAD PROTECTORS FROM END STUDS BEFORE INSTALLING TO STEERING KNUCKLE
TIE ROD AND END HOUSING THREAD ENGAGEMENT INTO ADJUSTER TUBE MUST BE EQUAL—BOTH ENDS
NUT
19-24 LB-FT
STEERING
KNUCKLE
AFTER SETTING FRONT ALIGNMENT, ROTATE BOTH TIE ROD END HOUSINGS IN SAME DIRECTION TO END OF TRAVEL AND THEN TIGHTEN ADJUSTING TUBE CLAMPS.
NUT AND L. WASHER
(PART OF STEERING
GEAR ASSEMBLY)
160-210 LB-FT

Steering linkage (© Buick Div., G.M. Corp)

to remove it from the adjusting sleeve. This will allow a reasonably accurate realignment upon reassembly.

5. Reverse the removal procedures to install. Clean rust and dirt from the threads. Check the alignment and adjust if necessary.

Intermediate Rod R & R

1. Remove the left and right-side inner tie-rod ends from the intermediate rod. These are taper fits; remove them as described in the tie rod section.
2. Remove the intermediate rod studs from the idler and pitman arms. These are taper fits.
3. Remove the intermediate rod.
4. Reverse the above steps to install.

Pitman Arm R & R

1. Remove the intermediate rod stud from the pitman arm. This is a taper fit, remove it as described in the tie rod section.
2. Remove the pitman arm nut and lockwasher from the pitman shaft.
3. Remove the pitman arm from the pitman shaft using a puller. Do not hammer on the end of the puller or serious internal damage will be done to the steering gear box.
4. Reverse the above steps to install.

Idler Arm R & R

1. Remove the intermediate arm stud. This is a taper fit; see the tie rod section for removal.
2. Remove the two bolts attaching the idler arm to the frame.
3. Remove the idler arm from the intermediate rod by tapping the intermediate rod with a hammer, using a heavy hammer as a backing.
4. Reverse the above steps to install.

Steering Wheel R & R

Removal

1. Unplug the horn wire connector from the steering column.
2. On cars with standard wheel or optional wood-rim wheel, pull off cap, remove three screws and bushing spacer, receiver cup, and Belleville spring. On cars with bar-type horn actuator remove screws securing actuator from underside of steering wheel, pull out lead connector plug, and remove actuator assembly.
3. Loosen steering wheel nut.
4. Apply steering wheel puller and pull wheel up to the nut. Now remove puller, nut and steering wheel.

Installation

NOTE: location marks are provided on the steering wheel and shaft to simplify proper indexing at the time of installation.

1. Install wheel with the location mark aligned with that of the shaft.
2. Install the wheel nut and torque to 30 ft. lbs.
3. Reinstall horn button or actuator assembly.

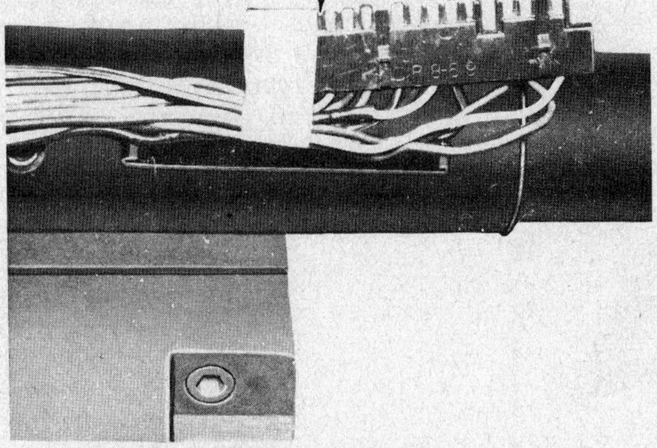
TAPE CONNECTOR
TO WIRES

Tape connector wires to connector before removing turn signal switch
(© Buick Div., G.M. Corp)

Turn Signal Switch R & R

1967-68 Tilt Column

NOTE: it is necessary to loosen the steering column brackets and drop the steering column slightly to remove the turn signal wires. When the column is loose, use extreme care to prevent bending the column. The column must be securely supported at all times.

1. Remove the steering wheel, turn signal cancelling cam, and spring.
2. Lower the column slightly.
3. Remove the turn signal lever and push the hazard warning switch in and remove the knob.
4. Remove the screws holding the turn signal switch to the column.
5. Disconnect the turn signal wiring harness at the base of the steering column.
6. To withdraw the switch wiring harness, it is necessary to remove the wire terminals from the curved connector. This is done by inserting a small screwdriver between the curved connector and each wire terminal and bending the metal tab, which secures the terminal to the connector, toward the terminal. After the wires have been removed from the connector, tape the wires together.
7. Withdraw the switch and harness assembly from the steering column.
8. Installation is the reverse of the removal procedure.

1967-68 Non-Tilt Column

NOTE: the steering column must always be supported. Use extreme care not to bend the steering column.

1. Remove the steering wheel, spring, and turn signal cancelling cam.
2. Lower the column slightly. Disconnect the switch wiring harness at the base of the steering column.

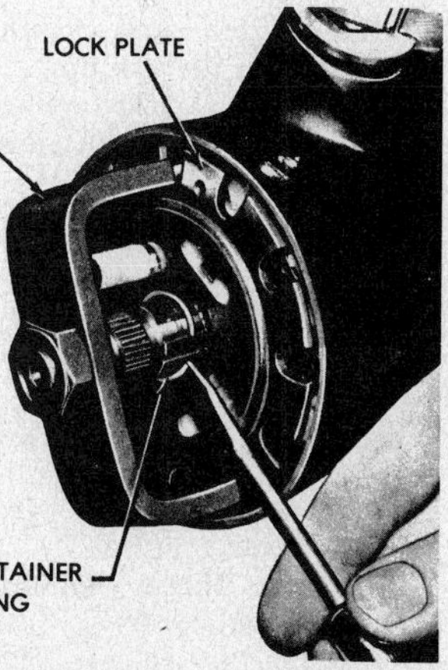
LOCK PLATE
J-23653
RETAINER
RING

Depressing lockplate and removing the snap-ring
(© Buick Div., G.M. Corp)

3. Remove the turn signal lever and hazard warning knob.
4. Depress the lockplate and remove the retaining ring from the upper portion of the steering shaft.
5. Remove the switch assembly, housing assembly, cover, springs, and lockplate as a unit by loosening, but not removing, the three screws in the cover. Push in on the cover and then rotate the cover in a counterclockwise direction. Lift off the assembly.
5. Disassemble the above unit by removing the three screws. This will free all parts in this unit. Carefully note the position of all parts before disassembly.
6. Install a new switch and reverse the above steps to install.

1969-74 Tilt and Non-Tilt Column

NOTE: the steering wheel must always be supported. Use extreme care not to bend steering column.

1. Remove the steering wheel.
2. Remove the three cover screws and remove the cover.
3. Depress the lockplate and remove the snap-ring. Remove the lockplate.
4. Remove the spring and horn contact signal cancelling cam.
5. Remove the turn signal lever, depress and remove the hazard warning knob, and tilt column lever, if equipped.
6. Remove the three turn signal switch mounting screws. Pull the connector out from the bracket on the column.
7. Pull the switch straight up with the wire protector and wire harness.
8. Reverse the above steps to install.

INSTRUMENT PANEL

Ignition Switch

Lock Cylinder Replacement —to 1968

1. Insert key and turn to Acc position.
2. With stiff wire (paper clip) in hole in face of switch depress lock pin and rotate cylinder counterclockwise and pull out.

Switch Replacement—to 1968

1. Disconnect battery.
2. Remove cylinder (as above).
3. Disconnect the wire connector from the rear of the switch and remove ignition switch nut.
4. Install in reverse of above.

Lock Cylinder and/or Switch Replacement—1969-74

The ignition switch has been relocated. It is no longer in its familiar place on the instrument panel, but it occupies a position on the steering column, just above the gear selector lever. This lock also prevents shifting the transmission and locks the steering. The ignition lock cylinder cannot be removed until the steering column is partially disassembled to gain access to the internal lock cylinder retainer. The steering wheel, lock plate, and turn signal switch assembly must be removed first.

Standard Column

1. Remove steering wheel using proper puller.
2. Remove three cover screws and cover; remove retainers.
3. Depress lock plate, then remove wire snap-ring and lock plate.
4. Slide upper bearing preload spring and cancelling cam off shaft.
5. Slide thrust washer off shaft, then remove turn signal lever screw and lever.
6. Push in four-way flasher switch; remove knob.
7. Remove three turn signal switch mounting screws, pull connector

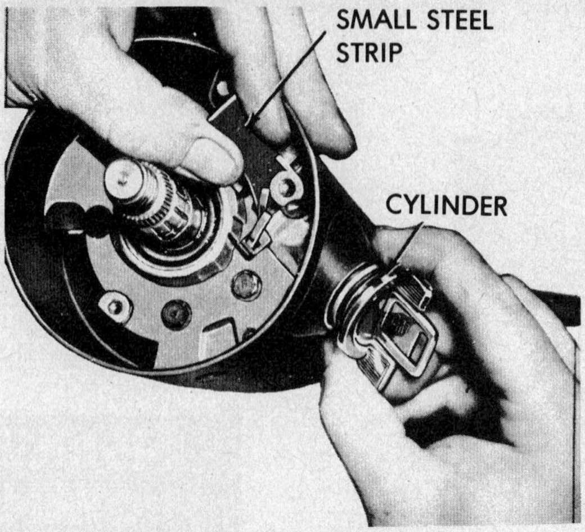
SMALL STEEL
STRIP
CYLINDER

Removing ignition lock cylinder
(© Buick Div., G.M. Corp)

out of its bracket on the column and tape the upper part of connector and wires together.

8. Pull turn signal switch out of column jacket.
9. Insert a small screwdriver into the slot next to the turn signal switch mounting screw boss (right-hand slot), depress spring latch and remove key lock.
10. Pull buzzer switch straight out. depressing switch clip with pliers. If the ignition switch is to be removed, disconnect the steering column mounting bracket from the lower edge of the instrument panel and lower the steering column. Support the column so that it does not flex.
11. Place ignition switch in accessory position by pulling up on connecting rod until there is a definite stop or detent felt.
12. Remove two attaching screws and ignition switch.
13. Assembly is the reverse of the above. However, note the following steps before proceeding with the reassembly.
14. To install the steering lock, hold the lock cylinder sleeve and rotate the knob clockwise against the stop. Insert the cylinder into the cover bore with the key on the cylinder sleeve aligned with the keyway in the housing. Then push the cylinder in until it bottoms. Maintaining a light inward pressure, rotate the knob counterclockwise until the drive section of the cylinder mates with the drive shaft. Push in until the snap ring pops into the groove and the lock cylinder is secured in the cover. Check for free rotation.
15. When installing the ignition switch, be sure the lock cylinder is in the lock position. Put the shift bowl or shroud in the park position. Make sure the ignition switch is in the lock position. Then insert the actuator rod into the switch and assemble the switch to the column.
16. The neutral start switch is adjusted with the shift lever in the drive position.

Tilt Column

1. Remove column mounting bracket from column.

NOTE: be careful not to damage the "breakaway" capsules.

2. Remove steering wheel using proper puller.
3. Remove turn signal wire protector (lower column).
4. Remove three column cover screws and cover.
5. Remove tilt release lever, turn signal switch lever, push four-way flasher knob in and remove knob, and remove upper shift lever.
6. Depress lock plate and remove the snap-ring; remove lock plate.
7. Remove cancelling cam and spring.
8. Remove three turn signal switch screws, tape wires to wire connector at upper end and place shift bowl in Low. Pull switch straight up and out.
9. Insert a small screwdriver into the slot next to the turn signal switch mounting screw boss (right-hand slot), depress spring latch and remove key lock.
10. If ignition switch is to be replaced, remove buzzer switch straight out, depressing switch clip with pliers.
11. Remove three housing cover screws and cover.
12. Install tilt release lever and place column in full UP position.
13. Place screwdriver in slot of tilt spring retainer, press in about 3/16 in. and turn counterclockwise. Remove spring and guide.

NOTE: spring is very strong—be careful.

14. Place column in neutral position, push in on upper steering shaft, remove inner race seat and race.
15. Remove upper flange pinch bolt, place ignition switch in accessory position, remove two switch mounting screws and switch.

NOTE: neutral start switch can be removed at this time, if necessary.

16. Assembly is the reverse of the above. However, note the following steps before proceeding with the reassembly.
17. To install the steering lock, hold the lock cylinder sleeve and rotate the knob clockwise against the stop. Insert the cylinder into the cover bore with the key on the cylinder sleeve aligned with the keyway in the housing. Then push the cylinder in until it bottoms. Maintaining a light inward pressure, rotate the knob counterclockwise until the drive section of the cylinder mates with the drive shaft. Push in until the snap ring pops into the groove and the lock cylinder is secured in the cover. Check for free rotation.
18. When installing the ignition switch, be sure the lock cylinder is in the lock position. Put the shift bowl or shroud in the park position. Make sure the ignition switch is in the lock position. Then insert the actuator rod into the switch and assemble the switch to the column.
19. The neutral start switch is adjusted with the shift lever in the drive position.

Lighting Switch

Replacement

1. Disconnect battery.
2. Remove screws that retain vent control plate or access door to instrument panel. (N.A.—1971-74).
3. Pull switch knob to last notch and depress spring loaded latch button on top of switch, while pulling knob and rod out of switch.
4. Remove escutcheon. Remove switch from cluster.

NOTE: remove left trim panel on 1971-74 models.

5. Disconnect multiple connector.
6. Install in reverse of above.

WINDSHIELD WIPERS

Motor R & R

1967-74

1. Disconnect wire connectors from motor and pump.
2. Remove washer hoses from the pump.
3. Remove left side air intake grille.
4. Remove spring retainer clip from wiper motor shaft lever.

NOTE: on 1971-73 models, loosen two 3/8 in. adjusting nuts and slip drive link off crank arm.

5. Lift transmission drive links off motor shaft lever.
6. Remove motor attaching bolts, then lift out motor.
7. Install by reversing the above procedure.

Wiper Transmission

1967-74

1. Remove the wiper blade and arm, shaft and escutcheon retaining nuts and the escutcheon from the transmission shaft.
2. Remove air intake grille.
3. Remove spring retainer clip from wiper motor shaft. Lift drive links off motor shaft.

NOTE: on 1971-74 models, loosen adjusting nuts and slip drive link off crank arm.

4. Remove the transmission retaining screws.
5. Slide transmission and drive link toward opposite side of car. Lift transmission up at opening and remove.
6. Install by reversing the above procedure.

RADIO

Always disconnect the battery ground cable before working on any part of the instrument panel.

Removal and Installation

1967 Riviera

1. Remove ash tray assembly.
2. Pry out chrome strip at center of instrument panel.
3. Remove two screws securing center outlet, lift off center outlet, and pull out plastic duct.
4. Remove knobs, two nuts, and escutcheon.
5. Disconnect antenna and wiring leads.
6. Remove radio support.
7. Lower radio through ash tray opening.
8. Install by reversing procedure.

1967 Except Riviera

1. Remove knobs and hex nuts.
2. Remove six screws and remove instrument panel cover.
3. Remove left and right mounting bracket screws.
4. Disconnect antenna and wiring leads.
5. Lift out radio.
6. Install by reversing procedure.

1968 All Models, 1969-70 Riviera

1. Remove ash tray assembly.
2. Remove knobs, escutcheons, and hex nuts.
3. Unplug antenna and wiring leads.
4. Remove radio downward.
5. Install by reversing procedure.

1969-70 Except Riviera

1. Remove center air-conditioning duct.
2. Remove right instrument trim panel and screw in bottom of radio.
3. Remove radio knobs, escutcheons, and two hex nuts.
4. Unplug antenna and wiring leads.
5. Remove radio downward.
6. Install by reversing procedure.

1971-74 All Models

1. Remove knobs and escutcheons from radio. If equipped with Trip-Set and/or Speed-Alert, remove cone-shaped knobs.
2. Remove face plate by pulling outward. *Disconnect Seelight before completely removing face plate, if equipped with Trip-Set/Speed-Alert.*
3. Remove the two hex nuts from the control shafts.
4. Remove ash tray and frame.
5. Disconnect the two connectors behind dash and unplug antenna.
6. Unscrew the support bracket nuts and remove radio to the rear and downwards.
7. Install by reversing removal procedure.

HEATER

NOTE: On procedures which call for removal of fender in order to gain access to the blower motor, it is possible to cut a trap door in the inner fender panel to gain access to the blower motor. Using a torch or sheet metal cutter, cut the door on three sides and bend it out of the way. Remove and install the motor. Bend the trap door back and weld it in place. Then, spray the welds and door with undercoating.

Blower and Heater Core Assembly R & R w/o A/C

1967 Riviera

1. Support the hood and remove the right hood hinge and hinge support.
2. Disconnect the vacuum hoses.
3. Disconnect the wire that is attached to the motor and remove the connector from the blower resistor. If just the blower motor is to be replaced, remove the blower motor attaching screws and the blower.
4. Disconnect the control wire attached to the temperature door lever.
5. Drain the coolant and remove the heater hoses at the firewall.
6. Remove the 12 screws securing the blower and heater assembly to the firewall and remove the assembly.
7. Reverse the above steps to install.

1968-70 Riviera

1. Remove the right front fender.
2. Continue with steps two through seven in the 1967 procedure to finish the removal.

Blower Only R & R w/o A/C

1967-70 All Models Except Riviera

1. Remove the right front fender.
2. Disconnect the blower motor wire.
3. Remove the blower motor attaching screws and remove the motor.
4. Reverse the above steps to install.

1971-74 All Models

1. Support the hood and loosen the hood hinge from the extension and plate assembly.
2. Remove the extension and plate assembly.
3. Disconnect the blower motor wire.
4. Remove the blower motor attaching screws and the motor.

Heater Core R & R w/o A/C

1967-74 All Models Except 1967-70 Riviera

1. Drain the radiator and disconnect the heater inlet and outlet hoses at the dash.
2. Disconnect the control wires from the defroster door and vacuum hose diverter door actuator diaphragm and control cable from the temperature door lever.
3. Remove the five nuts (four in 1971–72) securing the heater assembly to the dash.
4. Remove the screw securing the defroster outlet tab to the heater assembly.
5. Remove the heater from the car.
6. Reverse the above steps to install.

Blower Motor R & R with A/C

1967 Riviera

1. Open and support the hood.
2. Remove the right hood hinge and hood hinge support.
3. Remove the blower cooling tube and disconnect the blower wires.
4. Remove the five sheet metal screws securing the blower motor in place, and remove the blower.
5. Reverse the above steps to install.

1968 Riviera

1. Remove the right front fender.
2. Remove the blower motor wires.

3. Remove the five blower motor screws and remove the motor.
4. Reverse the above steps to install.

1969-70 Riviera

1. Remove the right front fender inner panel.
2. Remove the motor wires.
3. Remove the five blower motor securing screws and remove the motor.
4. Reverse the above steps to install.

1966-70 All Models Except Riviera

1. Remove the blower motor wires.
2. Remove the five blower motor securing screws and remove the motor.
3. Reverse the above steps to install.

1971-74 All Models Including Riviera

1. Support the hood and loosen the hood hinge from the extension and plate assembly.
2. Remove the extension and plate assembly.
3. Disconnect the blower motor wires.
4. Remove the blower motor securing screws and remove the motor.

Heater Core R & R with A/C

1967 Riviera

1. Drain the coolant from the radiator.
2. Disconnect the inlet and outlet hoses from the heater core.
3. Disconnect the temperature control wire from the lever on the heater assembly.
4. Disconnect the vacuum hose from the diverter door.
5. Reconnect the rear end of the diverter door return spring to the operating lever pin to hold the door in the air condition position.
6. Remove the six sheet metal bolts holding the assembly to the firewall and remove the assembly.
7. Reverse the above steps to install.

1968-70 Riviera

1. Drain the radiator and disconnect the heater hoses from the heater core.
2. Disconnect the temperature door control cable and blower wires.
3. Remove the six screws securing the air conditioner assembly to the firewall and remove the assembly.
4. Reverse the above steps to install.

1967 All Models except Riviera

1. Drain the radiator and disconnect the heater hoses from the heater core.
2. Remove the distributor duct that is to the left of the core assembly.
3. Remove the four screws securing the heater center outlet to the core assembly, and remove the outlet.
4. Disconnect the temperature and defroster control cables.
5. Disconnect the vacuum hose from the assembly.
6. Remove the two screws from the defroster manifold, and move out of the way.
7. Remove the nine screws, seven of which are located under the instrument panel, securing the core assembly to the firewall.
8. Remove the assembly.
9. Reverse the above steps to install.

1968-70 All Models except Riviera

1. Drain the radiator and disconnect the hoses from the heater core.
2. Remove the instrument panel cover with the center A/C outlet and right A/C outlet with hose attached.
3. Remove the center A/C duct, A/C distributor duct and defroster outlet manifold assembly.
4. Disconnect the defroster and temperature control wires and the pink hose from the mode door diaphragm.
5. Remove the seven screws from the inside and the two screws from the engine compartment and remove the core assembly.

1971-74 All Models Including Riviera

1. Drain the radiator and disconnect the hoses from the core.
2. Disconnect the wires from the defroster door, diverter door and temperature door.
3. Remove the four nuts securing the core assembly to the dash.

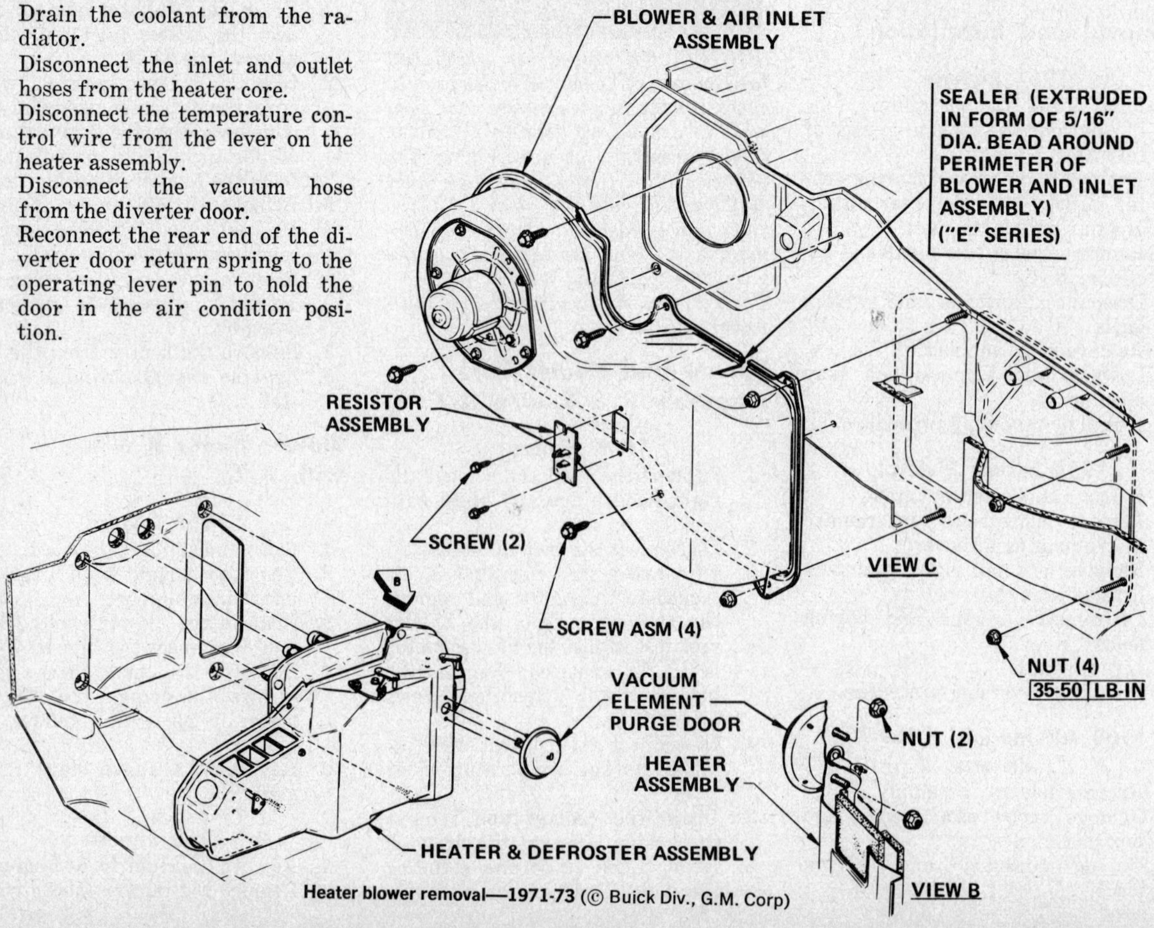
BLOWER & AIR INLET ASSEMBLY
SEALER (EXTRUDED IN FORM OF 5/16" DIA. BEAD AROUND PERIMETER OF BLOWER AND INLET ASSEMBLY) ("E" SERIES)
RESISTOR ASSEMBLY
SCREW (2)
SCREW ASM (4)
VIEW C
NUT (4)
35-50 LB-IN
B
VACUUM ELEMENT PURGE DOOR
NUT (2)
HEATER ASSEMBLY
HEATER & DEFROSTER ASSEMBLY
VIEW B

Heater blower removal—1971-73 (© Buick Div., G.M. Corp)

4. Remove the screw securing the defroster outlet tab to the heater assembly.
5. Remove the core assembly.
6. Reverse the above steps to install.

SEAT BELTS

Buzzer System—1973

The front seat belt warning system consists of a switch in each belt retractor, a sensor switch in the seat cushion on the passenger side, a reminder light, and a warning buzzer. The circuit wiring is routed through the ignition switch and the parking brake warning switch on manual transmission models, or through the ignition switch and the transmission switch on models equipped with automatic transmissions.

With the ignition switch on and the parking brake released (manual transmission), or with the selector in a forward position on automatic transmission models, the warning circuit (light and buzzer) is closed (activated) until the driver's seat belt is extended to open (deactivate) the circuit. The seat sensor on the passenger side will react to weights in excess of 0-47 lbs on the seat cushion and close the warning circuit. Extending the passenger belt will open the circuit.

Seat Belt/Starter Interlock System—1974

The seat belt/starter interlock system makes it necessary for outboard front seat occupants to fasten their seat belts before the engine can be started. Employing seat weight sensors similar to 1973 models, the new system does not require a passenger occupying the middle portion of the front seat to buckle up, but failure to do so will cause the seat belt alarm buzzer to sound.

When an outboard front seat is occupied, a sensor under the seat signals an electronic relay module which then requires vertification from a switch in the buckle, indicating the belt has been fastened, before completing the starting circuit. An override by-pass switch under the hood, which is activated with the ignition key in the ON position, permits starting in the event of system malfunction.

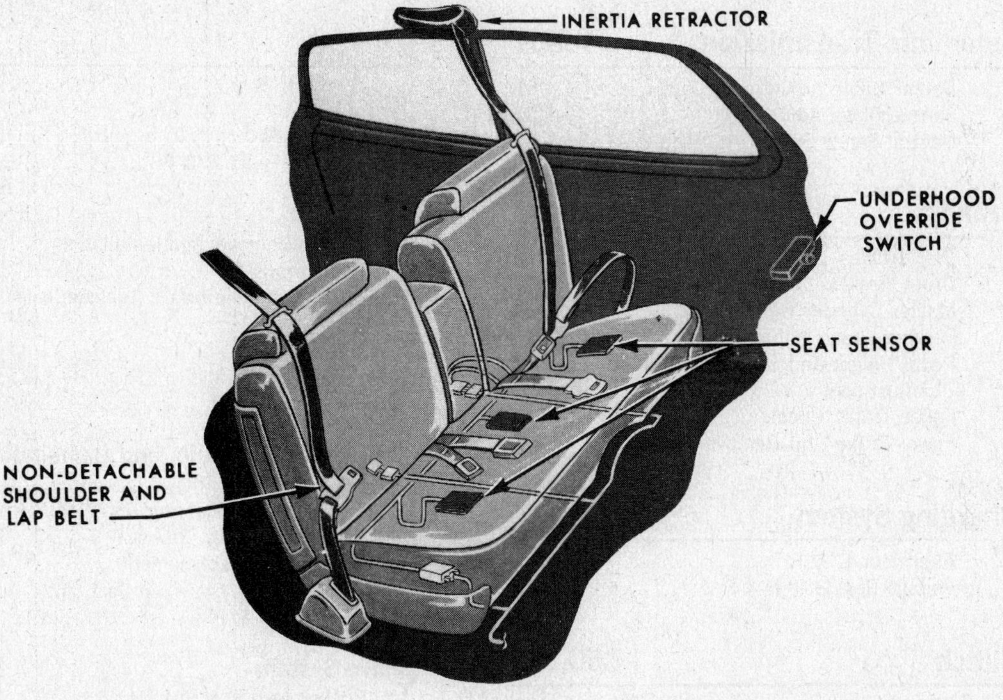
INERTIA RETRACTOR
UNDERHOOD OVERRIDE SWITCH
SEAT SENSOR
NON-DETACHABLE SHOULDER AND LAP BELT

1974 seat belt/ignition interlock system (© Buick Div., G.M. Corp)

INDEX

Buick Special • Gran Sport Century • Regal • Apollo

YEAR IDENTIFICATION

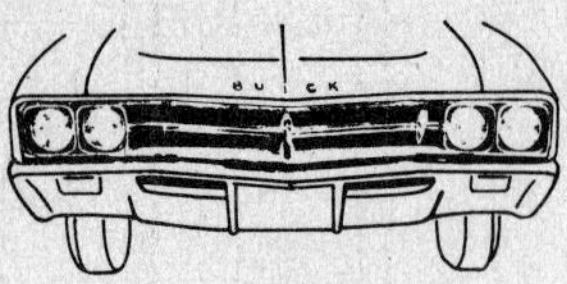
1967

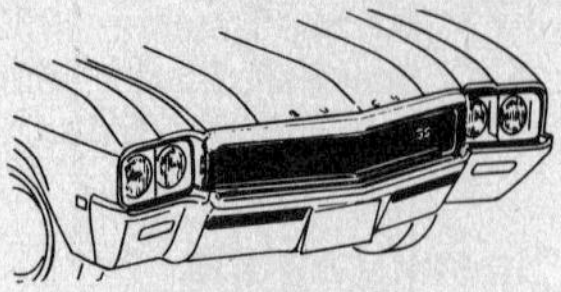
1968 G.S. 400

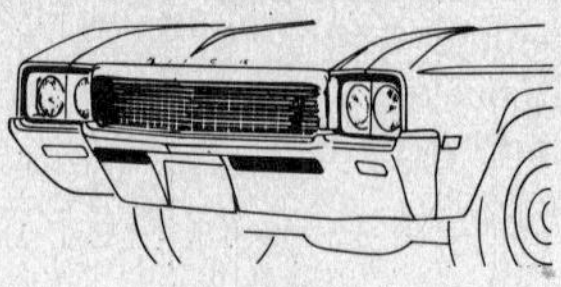
1968 Special

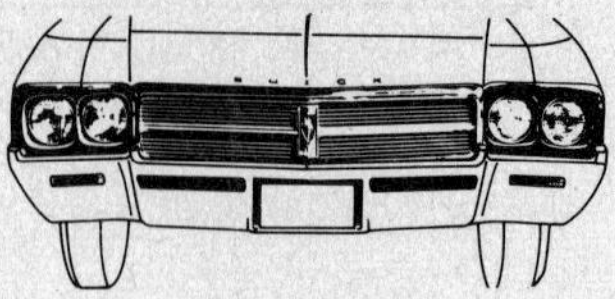
1969 Special

1969 G.S. 400

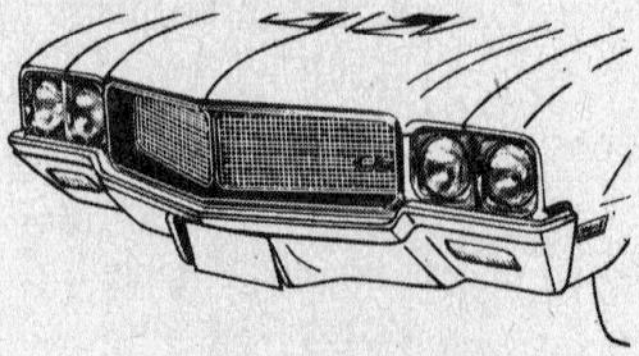
1970 Buick Special

1971 Skylark

1971 G.S.

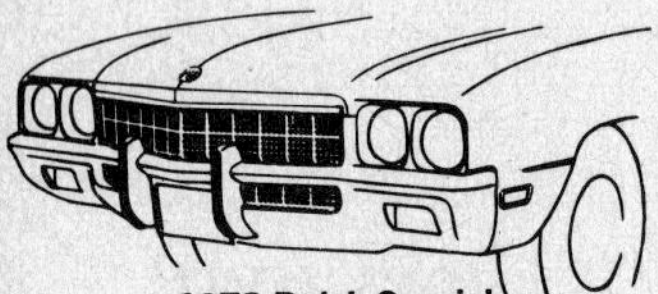
1972 Buick Special

1972 Buick Gran Sport

1973 Buick Century

1973 Buick Regal

1974 Apollo

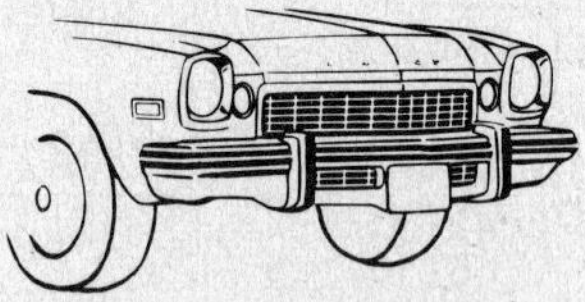
1974 Buick Century

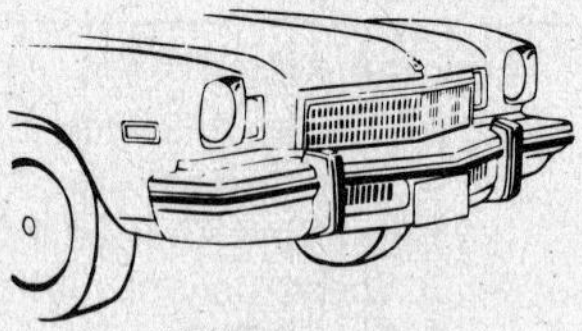
1974 Buick Regal

FIRING ORDER

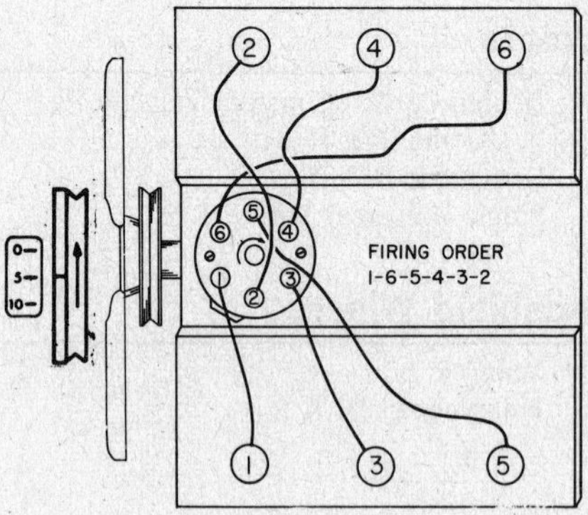
FIRING ORDER
1-6-5-4-3-2

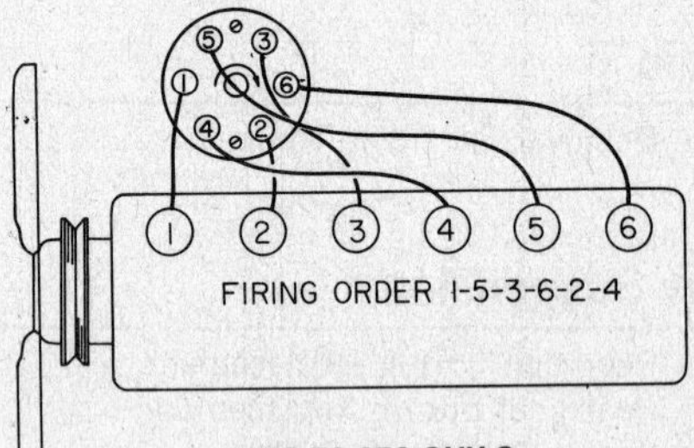
FIRING ORDER 1-5-3-6-2-4
1968-72 250 OHV-6

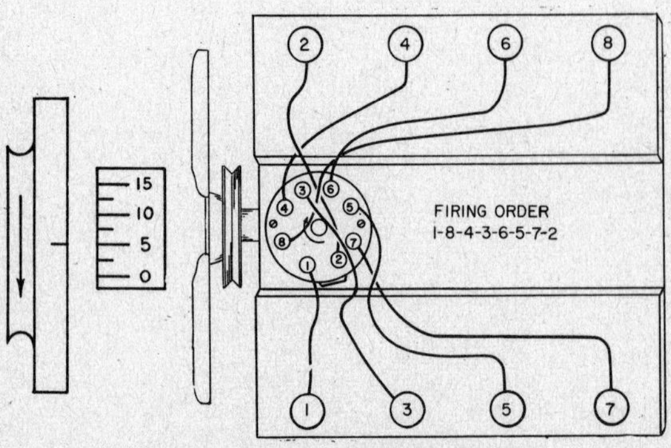
FIRING ORDER
1-8-4-3-6-5-7-2
1966–67 300, 340 cu. in.
(© Buick Div., G.M. Corp.)

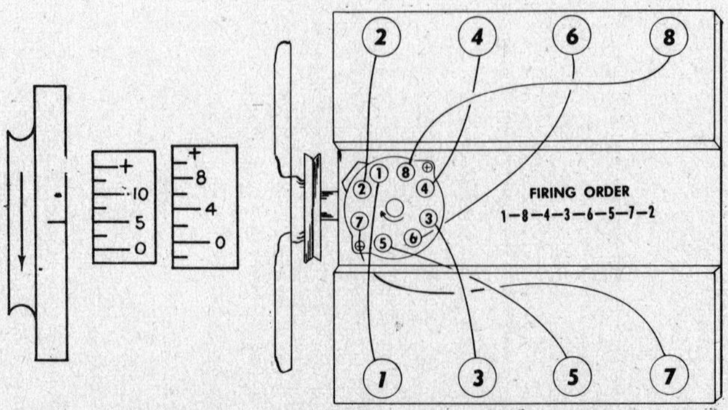
FIRING ORDER
1–8–4–3–6–5–7–2
1967–73 350, 400, 455 cu. in. (Left timing mark 1967–69)
(© Buick Div., G.M. Corp.)

CAR SERIAL NUMBER LOCATION AND ENGINE IDENTIFICATION

The car serial number is used for registrations and other legal records. This number is unique to the individual car. The production code number identifies the type of engine and its production date. The Engine Identification Code chart can be used to determine the type of engine installed in the vehicle. The engine serial number also appears on the vehicle identification plate following model and series identification. The engine serial and car serial numbers are the same.

1967

The serial number identification plate is attached to the left front body hinge pillar.

On the 225 cu. in. V6 engine, the production code number is between the front and middle branches of the right exhaust manifold. The engine number is just below the front of the left cylinder head.

On the 300 and 340 cu. in. engines, the production code number is between the middle branches of the right exhaust manifold. The engine number is just below the front of the left cylinder head.

On the 400 cu. in. engine, the production code number is between the two forward branches of the right exhaust manifold and the engine number is between the rear branches.

1968

The serial number identification plate is attached to the left front body hinge pillar.

On the 250 cu. in. OHV6 engine, the engine number and the production code number are on the right side of the engine, to the rear of the distributor.

On the 350 cu. in. V8 engine, the engine number is stamped on the front of the left cylinder bank. The production code number is between the left exhaust manifold and the two front spark plugs.

On the 400 cu. in. engine, the engine number is between the two front spark plugs and the left exhaust manifold, and the production code number is between the two rear plugs and the exhaust manifold, also on the left.

1969

The serial number identification plate is attached to the top of the instrument panel on the left side and can be seen through the windshield.

On the 250 cu. in. OHV6 engine, the engine number and the production code number are on the right side, rearward of the distributor.

On the 350 cu. in. V8 engine, the engine number is on the front of the left bank of cylinders. The production code number is between the left exhaust manifold and the two front spark plugs.

On the 400 cu. in. engine, the production code number is between the two rear spark plugs and the left exhaust manifold. The engine number is between the two front plugs and the left exhaust manifold.

1970-74

The serial number identification plate is attached to the top left of the instrument panel. It can be seen through the windshield.

On the 250 cu. in. OHV6 engine, the engine number and production code number are on the right side, to the rear of the distributor.

On the 350 cu. in. V8 engine, the engine number is on the front of the left bank of cylinders. The production code number is between the left exhaust manifold and the two front spark plugs.

On the 455 cu. in. engine, the production code number is between the two rear spark plugs and the left exhaust manifold. The engine number is between the two front spark plugs and the exhaust manifold.

ENGINE CODE

Buick Special, Gran Sport, Century, Regal, Apollo

Disp	Bbl	Hp	'67	'68	'69	'70	'71	'72	'73	'74
6-Cylinder Models										
225	2	160	NH							
250	1	145					ZB ZG			
250	1	155		CA CM CQ CR	LA LE MA ME	SA SB				
250	1	100 (net)								—
8-Cylinder Models										
300	2	210	NL							
340	2	220	NA							
340	4	260	NB							
350	2	150, 165# (net)							XC	YC
350	2	155 (net)						WC		
350	4	175, 190# (net)							XB	YB
350	4	180, 195# (net)						WB		
350	2	230		PO	RO		TC TO			
350	2	260				SO				
350	4	260					TB TD			
350	4	280		PP	RP					
350	4	285				SB				
350	4	315				SP				
400	4	340		PR	RR					—
455	2	190 (net)								—
455	4	225 (net)						WF WA	XF	YF
Stage 1 455	4	255 (net)								YS
455	4	270 (net)						WS	XS	

Disp	Bbl	Hp	'67	'68	'69	'70	'71	'72	'73	'74
Stage 1										
455	4	315					TR			
455	4	345					TS			
Stage 1										
455	4	450				SR				
455	4	360				SS				
Stage 1										

Dual exhaust

ENGINE SERIAL NUMBER
PRODUCTION CODE NUMBER
8H100001
ND163
400 & 430 ENGINES
RIGHT SIDE
00—2A

Serial number and production code location (400 cu in.)
(© Buick Div., G.M. Corp)

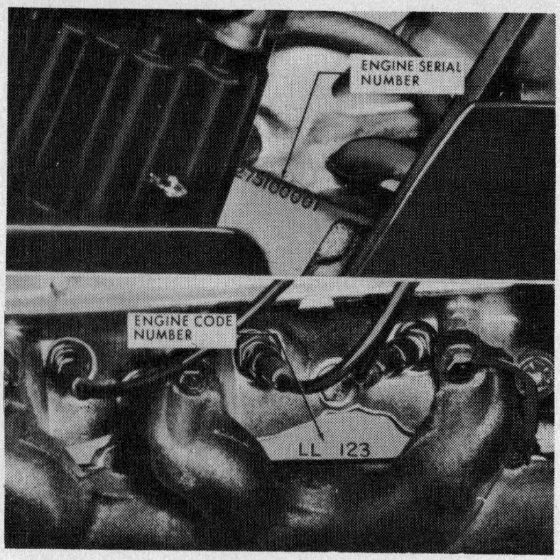
ENGINE SERIAL NUMBER
ENGINE CODE NUMBER
LL 123

Serial number and production code location—1967 300 and 340 cu in. (© Buick Div., G.M. Corp)

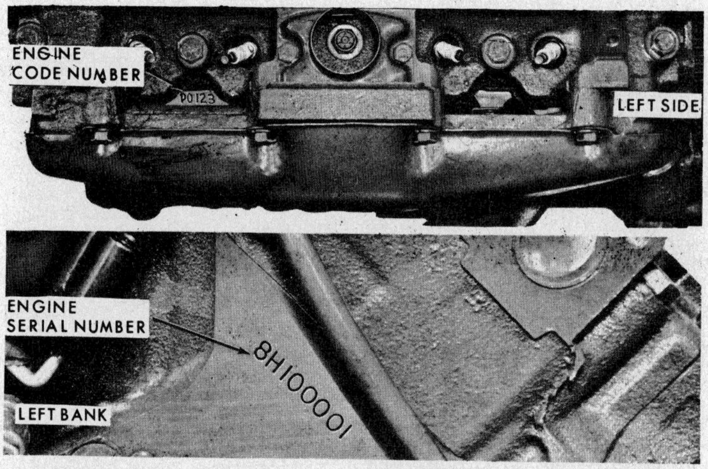
ENGINE CODE NUMBER
PD123
LEFT SIDE
ENGINE SERIAL NUMBER
8H100001
LEFT BANK

Serial number and production code number location (350 cu in.), 1968-74 Buick Special, Skylark, and Century
(© Buick Div., G.M. Corp)

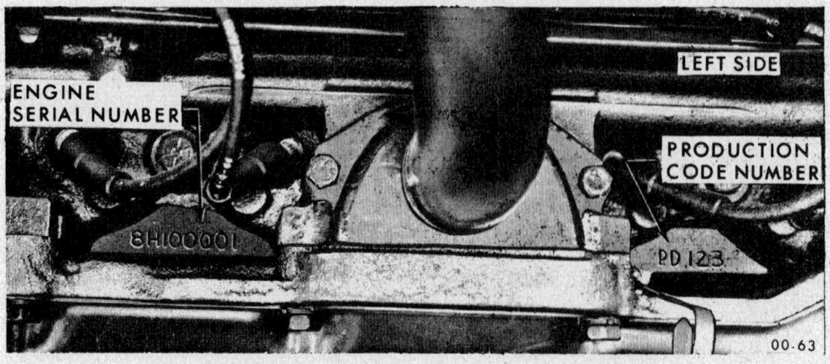
LEFT SIDE
ENGINE SERIAL NUMBER
PRODUCTION CODE NUMBER
8H100001
PD123
00-63

Serial number and production code location (400 and 455 cu in.)—1968-74 Buick Special, Skylark, Century

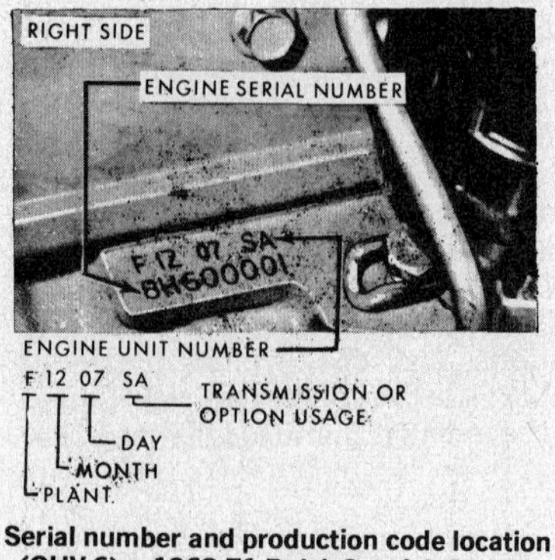
RIGHT SIDE
ENGINE SERIAL NUMBER
F 12 07 SA
8H600001
ENGINE UNIT NUMBER
F 12 07 SA
TRANSMISSION OR OPTION USAGE
DAY
MONTH
PLANT

Serial number and production code location (OHV 6)—1968-71 Buick Special, Skylark
(© Buick Div., G.M. Corp)

Buick Special, Grand Sport

GENERAL ENGINE SPECIFICATIONS

Year	Engine Cu. In. Displacement	Carburetor Type	Advertised Horsepower @ rpm ■	Advertised Torque @ rpm (ft lbs) ■	Bore and Stroke (in.)	Advertised Compression Ratio	Oil Pressure @ 2400 rpm
'67	6-225	2 bbl	160 @ 4200	235 @ 2400	3.750 x 3.400	9.0:1	40
	8-300	2 bbl	210 @ 4400	310 @ 2400	3.750 x 3.400	9.0:1	40
	8-340	2 bbl	220 @ 4200	340 @ 2400	3.750 x 3.850	9.0:1	40
	8-340	4 bbl	260 @ 4200	365 @ 2800	3.750 x 3.850	10.25:1	40
	8-400	4 bbl	340 @ 5000	440 @ 3200	4.040 x 3.900	10.25:1	40
'68	6-250	1 bbl	155 @ 4200	235 @ 1600	3.875 x 3.530	8.5:1	37①
	8-350	2 bbl	230 @ 4400	350 @ 2400	3.800 x 3.500	9.0:1	37
	8-350	4 bbl	280 @ 4800	375 @ 3200	3.800 x 3.850	10.25:1	37
	8-400	4 bbl	340 @ 5000	440 @ 3200	4.040 x 3.900	10.25:1	40
'69	6-250	1 bbl	155 @ 4200	235 @ 1600	3.875 x 3.530	8.5:1	37①
	8-350	2 bbl	230 @ 4400	350 @ 2400	3.800 x 3.500	9.0:1	37
	8-350	4 bbl	280 @ 4600	375 @ 3200	3.800 x 3.850	10.25:1	37
	8-400	4 bbl	340 @ 5000	440 @ 3200	4.040 x 3.900	10.25:1	40
'70	6-250	1 bbl	155 @ 4200	235 @ 1600	3.875 x 3.530	8.5:1	37①
	8-350	2 bbl	260 @ 4600	360 @ 2600	3.800 x 3.850	9.0:1	37
	8-350	4 bbl	285 @ 4600	375 @ 3000	3.800 x 3.850	9.0:1	37
	8-350	4 bbl	315 @ 4800	410 @ 3200	3.800 x 3.850	10.25:1	37
	8-455	4 bbl	350 @ 4600	510 @ 2600	4.3125 x 3.900	10.0:1	40
	8-455 Stage 1	4 bbl	360 @ 4600	510 @ 2600	4.3125 x 3.900	10.5:1	40
'71	6-250	1 bbl	145 @ 4000	235 @ 2400	3.875 x 3.530	8.5:1	37①
	8-350	2 bbl	230 @ 4400	350 @ 2400	3.800 x 3.850	8.5:1	37
	8-350	4 bbl	260 @ 4600	360 @ 3000	3.800 x 3.850	8.5:1	37
	8-455	4 bbl	315 @ 4400	450 @ 2800	4.3125 x 3.900	8.5:1	40
	8-455 Stage 1	4 bbl	345 @ 5000	460 @ 3000	4.3125 x 3.900	8.5:1	40
'72	8-350	2 bbl	155 @ 3800②	270 @ 2400③	3.800 x 3.850	8.5:1	37④
	8-350	4 bbl	180 @ 3800⑤	275 @ 2400	3.800 x 3.850	8.5:1	37④
	8-350⑥	4 bbl	195 @ 4000⑦	290 @ 2800⑧	3.800 x 3.850	8.5:1	37④
	8-455	4 bbl	225 @ 4000	360 @ 2600	4.3125 x 3.900	8.5:1	40
	8-455 Stage 1	4 bbl	270 @ 4400	390 @ 3000	4.3125 x 3.900	8.5:1	40
'73	8-350	2 bbl	150 @ 3800	265 @ 2400	3.800 x 3.850	8.5:1	37
	8-350	4 bbl	175 @ 3800	270 @ 2400	3.800 x 3.850	8.5:1	37
	8-350	4 bbl	190 @ 4000	285 @ 2800	3.800 x 3.850	8.5:1	37
	8-455	4 bbl	225 @ 4000	360 @ 2600	4.3125 x 3.900	8.5:1	37
	8-455	4 bbl	270 @ 4400	390 @ 3000	4.3125 x 3.900	8.5:1	37
'74	6-250 SE	1 bbl	100 @ 3600	175 @ 1600	3.875 x 3.530	8.25:1	37
	8-350 SE	2 bbl	150 @ 3600	270 @ 2000	3.800 x 3.850	8.5:1	37
	8-350 DE	2 bbl	165 @ 3800	285 @ 2000	3.800 x 3.850	8.5:1	37
	8-350 SE	4 bbl	175 @ 3800	260 @ 2000	3.800 x 3.850	8.5:1	37
	8-350 DE	4 bbl	195 @ 4000	280 @ 2000	3.800 x 3.850	8.5:1	37
	8-455 SE	2 bbl	175 @ 3400	355 @ 2000	4.3125 x 3.900	8.5:1	37
	8-455 DE	2 bbl	190 @ 3600	370 @ 2000	4.3125 x 3.900	8.5:1	37
	8-455 SE	4 bbl	210 @ 3600	335 @ 2200	4.3125 x 3.900	8.5:1	37
	8-455 DE	4 bbl	230 @ 3300	355 @ 2200	4.3125 x 3.900	8.5:1	37
	8-455 DE⑧	4 bbl	255 @ 4400	370 @ 2800	4.3125 x 3.900	8.5:1	37

■ Beginning 1972 horsepower and torque are SAE net figures. They are measured at the rear of the transmission with all accessories installed and operating. Since the figures vary when a given engine is installed in different models, some are representative rather than exact.

① Oil pressure at 1500 rpm

② For California vehicles, advertised horsepower is 150 @ 3800 rpm

③ For California vehicles, advertised torque is 265 @ 2400 rpm

④ Oil pressure at 2600 rpm

⑤ For California vehicles, advertised torque is 285 @ 2800 rpm

⑥ Dual exhaust

⑦ For California vehicles, advertised horsepower is 190 @ 4000 rpm

⑧ Stage I Gran Sport

TUNE-UP SPECIFICATIONS

When analyzing compression test results, look for uniformity among cylinders rather than specific pressures.

	ENGINE		SPARK PLUGS		DISTRIBUTOR		IGNITION TIMING (deg) ▲		VALVES	Fuel	IDLE SPEED (rpm) ▲	
Year	No. Cyl Displacement (cu in.)	hp	Type §	Gap (in.)	Point Dwell (deg)	Point Gap (in.)	Man Trans	Auto Trans	Intake Opens ■ (deg) ●	Pump Pressure (psi)	Man Trans	Auto Trans
'67	V6-225	160	44S	.035	30	.016	5B	5B	24	4¼-5¾	550①(600)	550①(600)
	8-300	210	44S	.035	30	.016	2½B	2½B	30	4¼-5¾	550①(600)	550①(600)
	8-340	220	44S	.035	30	.016	2½B	2½B	32	4¼-5¾	550①(600)	550①(600)
	8-340	260	44S	.035	30	.016	2½B	2½B	N.A.	4¼-5¾	550①(600)	550①(600)
'68	6-250	155	46N	.030	32½	.019	TDC	4B	62	4-5	700	500②
	8-350	230	45TS	.030	30	.016	TDC	TDC	24	4¼-5¾	700	550
	8-350	280	45TS	.030	30	.016	TDC	TDC	24	4¼-5¾	700	550
	8-400	340	44TS	.030	30	.016	TDC	TDC	14	4¼-5¾	700	550
'69	6-250	155	R-46N	.035	32½	.019	TDC	4B	62	4-5	700/400	500/400
	8-350	230	R-45TS	.030	30	.016	TDC	TDC	24	4¼-5¾	700	600
	8-350	280	R-45TS	.030	30	.016	TDC	TDC	24	4¼-5¾	700	600
	8-400	340	R-44TS	.030	30	.016	TDC	2½B	14	4¼-5¾	700	600
'70	6-250	155	R-46T	.035	32½	.019	TDC	4B	16	4-5	750/400	600/400
	8-350	260	R-45TS	.030	30	.016	6B	6B	24	4¼-5¾	700	600
	8-350	285	R-45TS	.030	30	.016	6B	6B	24	4¼-5¾	700	600
	8-350	315	R-45TS	.030	30	.016	6B	6B	24	4¼-5¾	700	600
	8-455	350	R-44TS	.030	30	.016	6B	6B	18	4¼-5¾	700	600
	8-455 Stage 1	360	R-44TS	.030	30	.016	10B	10B	18	4¼-5¾	700	600
'71	6-250	145	R-46T	.035	32½	.019	4B	4B	16	4-5	550	600
	8-350	230	R-45TS	.030	30	.016	6B	10B	24	4¼-5¾	800	600
	8-350	260	R-45TS	.030	30	.016	6B	6B	28	4¼-5¾	800	600
	8-455	315	R-45TS	.030	30	.016	6B	6B	12	4¼-5¾	700	600
	8-455 Stage 1	270	R-45TS	.030	30	.016	10B	10B	28	4¼-5¾	700	600
'72	8-350	155	R-45TS	.040	30	.016	4B	4B	24	4¼-5¾	800③/600	650③/500
	8-350	180	R-45TS	.040	30	.016	4B	4B	24	4¼-5¾	800③/600	650③/500
	8-350	195	R-45TS	.040	30	.016	4B	4B	24	4¼-5¾	800③/600	650③/500
	8-455	225	R-45TS	.040	30	.016	4B	4B	24(14)	4¼-5¾	900③/600	650③/500
	8-455 Stage 1	360	R-45TS	.040	30	.016	8B	10B	24(14)	4¼-5¾	900③/600	650③/500
'73	8-350	150	R-45TS	.040	30	.016	4B	4B	24	4¼-5¾	800/600③	650/500
	8-350	175	R-45TS	.040	30	.016	4B	4B	24	4¼-5¾	800/600③	650/500
	8-350	190	R-45TS	.040	30	.016	4B	4B	24	4¼-5¾	800/600③	650/500
	8-455	225	R-45TS	.040	30	.016	4B	4B	24	4¼-5¾	900/600③	650/500
	8-455 Stage 1	270	R-45TS	.040	30	.016	8B	10B	24	4¼-5¾	900/600③	650/500
'74	6-250	All	ACR-46T	.035	32½	.019	6B	6B	16④	4-5	1100/700③	600/500
	8-350	All	R-45TS	.040	30	.016	—	4B	19④	4¼-5¾	—	650/500
	8-455	All	R-45TS	.040	30	.016	—	4B	19④	4¼-5¾	—	650/500

▲ See text for procedure
● Figure in parentheses indicates California engine
■ All figures Before Top Dead Center
§ All spark plug listings are A.C. original equipment numbers
① Adjust idle on air conditioned 50 rpm higher with A/C off, except on California vehicles.
② A/C on
③ Lower figure indicates idle speed with solenoid disconnected
④ These figures do not represent a change from 1973; however, the reference point is changed (from .004 inch valve lift to .004 inch cam lift) to be consistent with information required for Government certification.
B Before Top Dead Center
TDC Top Dead Center

Buick Special & Gran Sport CAPACITIES

Year	ENGINE No. Cyl. (Cu. In.) Displacement	Engine Crankcase Add 1 Qt For New Filter	TRANSMISSION Pts To Refill After Draining Manual 3-Speed	4-Speed	Automatic	Drive Axle (pts)	Gasoline Tank (gals)	COOLING SYSTEM (qts) With Heater	With A/C
'67	6-225	4	3.4	—	5	2.75	20	11.2	11.2
	8-300	4	3.4	—	5	2.75	20	12.7	14
	8-340	4	3.4	—	5	2.75	20	12.7	14.7
	8-400	4	3.5	3	5	2.75	20	16.7	17
'68	6-250	4	3.4	—	5	3	20	11.3	13
	8-350	4	3.4	—	5	3	20	13.5	13.5
	8-350GS	4	3.5	3	5	3	20	13.5	13.5
	8-400GS	4	3.5	3	5	3	20	16.2	16.7
'69	6-250	4	3.4	—	5	3	20	11.3	13
	8-350	4	3.4	—	5	3	20	13.5	13.5
	8-350GS	4	3.4	3	6	3	20	13.5	13.5
	8-400GS	4	3.5	3	7	3	20	16.2	16.7
'70	6-250	4	3.4	—	6	3	20	16	16
	8-350	4	3.4	—	6	3	20②	16.5	16.5
	8-350GS	4	3.5	3	7	3	20	16.5	16.5
	8-455	4	3.5	3	7	4.25	20	19.2	19.7
'71	6-250	4	3.4	—	6	4.25	20	16	16
	8-350	4	3.4	—	6	4.25	20②	16.5	16.5
	8-350GS	4	3.4	3	6	4.25	20	16.5	16.5
	8-455	4	—	3	7	5.5	20	19.2	19.7
'72	8-350	4	3.4	—	6	4.25	20②	16.5	16.9
	8-350GS	4	3.4	3	6	4.25	20	16.2	16.6
	8-455	4	—	3	7	5.5	20	19.2	19.7
'73	8-350	4	3.4	—	6	4.25	22	16.5	16.9
	8-350GS	4	3.4	3.4	6	4.25	22	16.5	16.9
	8-455	4	—	3.4	6	4.25	22	16.2	16.6
'74	6-250	4	3.5	—	6	4.25	21	16.5③	16.9④
	8-350	4	—	—	6	4.25	22	16.5⑤	16.9⑥
	8-455	4	—	—	6	4.25	22	16.2	16.6

- • Specifications do not include torque converter
- ① Station wagon—14 qts
- ② Sportwagon—23 gals
- ③ Apollo—14 qts
- ④ Apollo—16 qts
- ⑤ Apollo—18.9 qts
- ⑥ Apollo—19.3 qts
- GS Gran Sport
- —— Not applicable

TORQUE SPECIFICATIONS

All readings in ft lbs

Year	Engine Displacement (cu in.)	Cylinder Head Bolts	Rod Bearing Bolts	Main Bearing Bolts	Crankshaft Pulley Bolt	Flywheel to Crankshaft Bolts	MANIFOLD Intake	Exhaust
'67	V6	65-70	30-35	100-125	140-160	50-60	25-30	10-15
	8	65-70①	30-35	50-55②	140-160	50-60	25-30	10-15
'68-'69	L6	90-95	35-45	60-70	Press fit	55-65	25-35	③
	8-350	65-70	30-35	50-55②	140-160	50-60	25-30	10-15
	8-400	100	45	110	200	50-60	55	18
'70-'74	L6	95	35	60-70	Press fit	55-65	25-35	③
	8-350	75	35	95	120④	60	55	18
	8-455	100	45	110	200④	58	65	18

- ① 8-400—100-120 ft. lbs.
- ② Rear Main Bearing—65-75
- ③ Center Bolts 25-30; End Bolts 15-20
- ④ Minimum

VALVE SPECIFICATIONS

Year	Engine No. Cyl. Displacement (cu in.)	Seat Angle (deg)	Face Angle (deg)	Spring Test Pressure (lbs @ in.)	Spring Installed Height (in.)	STEM TO GUIDE Clearance (in.)		STEM Diameter (in.)	
						Intake	Exhaust	Intake	Exhaust
'67	6-225	45	45	168 @ 1.25	1 23/32	.0012-.0032	.0015-.0035	.3410	.3405
	8-300	45	45	164 @ 1.34	1 23/32	.0012-.0032	.0015-.0035	.3410	.3405
	8-340	45	45	164 @ 1.34	1 23/32	.0012-.0032	.0015-.0035	.3410	.3405
	8-400	45	45	177 @ 1.45	1 29/32	.0015-.0035	.0015-.0035	.3725	.3725
'68	6-250	46	45	186 @ 1.27	1 21/32	.0010-.0027	.0010-.0027	.3414	.3414
	8-350	45	45	180 @ 1.34	1 23/32	.0015-.0035	.0015-.0035	.3725	.3725
	8-400	45	45	177 @ 1.45	1 29/32	.0015-.0035	.0015-.0035	.3725	.3725
'69	6-250	46	45	186 @ 1.27	1 21/32	.0010-.0027	.0010-.0027	.3414	.3414
	8-350	45	45	180 @ 1.34	1 23/32	.0015-.0025	.0015-.0032	.3725	.372
	8-400	45	45	177 @ 1.45	1 29/32	.0015-.0035	.0015-.0032	.3725	.3727
'70	6-250	46	45	186 @ 1.27	1 21/32	.0010-.0027	.0010-.0027	.3414	.3414
	8-350	45	45	180 @ 1.34	1 23/32	.0015-.0025	.0015-.0032	.3725	.3727
	8-455	45	45	177 @ 1.45	1 29/32	.0015-.0035	.0015-.0032	.3725	.3727
'71	6-250	46	45	186 @ 1.27	1 21/32	.0010-.0027	.0010-.0027	.3414	.3414
	8-350	45	45	180 @ 1.34	1 23/32	.0015-.0035	.0015-.0032	.3725	.3727
	8-455	45	45	177 @ 1.45	1 29/32	.0015-.0035	.0015-.0032	.3725	.3727
'72	8-350	45	45	180 @ 1.34	1 23/32	.0015-.0035	.0015-.0032	.3725	.3727
	8-455	45	45	198 @ 1.45	1 29/32	.0015-.0035	.0015-.0032	.3725	.3727
'73	8-350	45	45	180 @ 1.34	1 23/32	.0015-.0035	.0015-.0032	.3720	.3730
	8-455	45	45	198 @ 1.45	1 29/32	.0015-.0035	.0015-.0032	.3725	.3727
'74	6-250	46	45	186 @ 1.27	1 21/32	.0010-.0027	.0010-.0027	.3413	.3413
	8-350	45	45	180 @ 1.34	1 29/32	.0015-.0035	.0015-.0032	.3725	.3727
	8-455	45	45	198 @ 1.45	1 29/32	.0015-.0035	.0015-.0032	.3725	.3727

① Inner spring test pressure—76 @ 1.25

RING GAP

Year	Engine	Top Compression	Bottom Compression
'67-'70	6,225, 250 300, 340, 350	.010-.020	.010-.020
'67-'69	8-400	.013-.023	.013-.023
'70-'74	8-455	.013-.023	.013-.023
'71-'74	6-250	.010-.020	.010-.020
'71-'74	8-350	.013-.023	.013-.023

Year	Engine	Oil Control
'67-'74	6-255, 8-300, 340, 350	.015-.035
'67-'74	8-400, 425, 455	.015-.055
'68-'71	6-250	.015-.025
'74	6-250	.015-.055

RING SIDE CLEARANCE

Year	Engine	Top Compression	Bottom Compression	Oil Control
'67-'74	All Exc. 6-250	.003-.005	.003-.005	.0035-.0095
'67-'71, '74	6-250	.0012-.0027	.0012-.0032	.0000-.0050

PISTON CLEARANCE

Year	Engine	Piston to Bore Clearance (in.)
'67	6-225	.0011-.0017
	8-300	.0011-.0017
	8-340	.0011-.0017
	8-400	.0007-.0013
'68-'69	6-250	.0005-.0011
	8-350	.0008-.0014
	8-400	.0007-.0013
'70-'71	6-250	.0005-.0011
	8-350	.0008-.0020
	8-455	.0010-.0016
'72-'73	8-350	.0008-.0020
	8-455	.0010-.0016
'74	6-250	.0005-.0015
	8-350	.0008-.0014
	8-455	.0010-.0016

CRANKSHAFT AND CONNECTING ROD SPECIFICATIONS

All measurements are given in in.

Year	Engine Displace. (cu in.)	Crankshaft: Main Brg. Journal Dia	Crankshaft: Main Brg. Oil Clearance	Crankshaft: Shaft End-Play	Crankshaft: Thrust on No.	Connecting Rod: Journal Diameter	Connecting Rod: Oil Clearance	Connecting Rod: Side Clearance
'67	6-225	2.4995	.0004-.0015	.006	2	2.0000	.0020-.0023	.006-.014
	8-300	2.4995	.0004-.0015	.006	3	2.0000	.0020-.0023	.006-.014
	8-340	2.9995	.0004-.0015	.006	3	2.0000	.0020-.0023	.006-.014
'68-'69	L6-250	2.3004	.0003-.0029	.004	7	2.0000	.0007-.0027	.009-.013
	8-350	2.9995	.0004-.0015	.006	3	2.0000	.0002-.0023	.006-.014
	8-400	3.2500	.0007-.0018	.006	3	2.2500	.0002-.0023	.005-.012
'70-'74	L6-250①	2.3004	.0003-.0029	.002-.006	7	2.0000	.0007-.0027	.009-.013③
	8-350	2.9995	.0004-.0015	.002-.006②	3	2.0000	.0002-.0023	.006-.014
	8-455	3.2500	.0007-.0018	.003-.009	3	2.2500	.0002-.0023	.005-.012

① 1970-71, '74
② 1972, V8—350; .003-.009 in.
③ 1974—.007-.016

BATTERY AND STARTER SPECIFICATIONS

Year	Engine Displacement (cu in.)	Battery: Ampere Hour Capacity	Battery: Volts	Battery: Terminal Grounded	Starters Lock Test: Amps	Starters Lock Test: Volts	Starters Lock Test: Torque (ft lbs)	Starters No-Load Test: Amps	Starters No-Load Test: Volts	Starters No-Load Test: RPM	Brush Spring Tension (oz)
'67	6-225	44	12	Neg.	Not Recommended			58	10.6	6,200	35
	8-300, 340	66	12	Neg.	Not Recommended			85	10.6	3,600	35
	8-400	70	12	Neg.	Not Recommended			85	10.6	6,200	35
'68	L6-250	45	12	Neg.	Not Recommended			58	10.6	6,200	35
	8-350	61	12	Neg.	Not Recommended			85	10.6	3,600	35
	8-400	70	12	Neg.	Not Recommended			85	10.6	3,600	35
'69	L6-250	44	12	Neg.	Not Recommended			68	10.6	6,700	35
	8-350	61	12	Neg.	Not Recommended			70	9	4,000	35
	8-350 G.S.	61	12	Neg.	Not Recommended			70	9	4,000	35
	8-400 G.S.	70	12	Neg.	Not Recommended			61	9	5,200	35
'70-'72	L6-250	44	12	Neg.	Not Recommended			49-87	9	6,200-10,700	35
	8-350	61	12	Neg.	Not Recommended			55-85	9	3,100-6,000①	35
	8-455	70	12	Neg.	Not Recommended			48-80	9	4,100-6,500②	35
'73	8-350	③	12	Neg.	Not Recommended			55-85	9	3,500-6,000	35
	8-455	④	12	Neg.	Not Recommended			48-80	9	4,000-6,500	35
'74	6-250	⑤	12	Neg.	Not Recommended			49-87	9	6,200-10,700	35
	8-350	③	12	Neg.	Not Recommended			55-85	9	3,500-6,000	35
	8-455	④	12	Neg.	Not Recommended			48-80	9	4,000-6,500	35

① 1972—3,500-6,000 rpm
② 1972—4,000-6,500 rpm

③ Side Terminal—Cranking power 2,900 watts @ 0°F
④ Side Terminal—Cranking power 3,250 watts @ 0°F
⑤ Side Terminal—Cranking power 2,300 watts @ 0°F

ALTERNATOR AND REGULATOR SPECIFICATIONS

Year	Alternator: Part No. or Manufacturer	Alternator: Field Current @ 12 V	Alternator: Output (amps)	Regulator: Part No. or Manufacturer	Regulator: Field Relay Air Gap (in.)	Regulator: Field Relay Point Gap (in.)	Regulator: Field Relay Volts to Close	Regulator: Regulator Air Gap (in.)	Regulator: Regulator Point Gap (in.)	Regulator: Volts @ 75°
'67-'69	1100761	2.2-2.6	37	1119515	.015	.030	2.3-3.7	.060	.014	13.6-14.4
	1100691	2.2-2.6	42	1119515	.015	.030	2.3-3.7	.060	.014	13.6-14.4
'70	1100761	2.2-2.6	37	1119515	.015	.030	2.3-3.7	.060	.014	13.6-14.4
	1100691	2.2-2.6	42	1119515	.015	.030	2.3-3.7	.060	.014	13.6-14.4
'71	1100905	2.2-2.6	37	1119515	.015	.030	1.5-3.2	.067	.014	13.5-14.4
	1100931	2.2-2.6	55	1119515	.015	.030	1.5-3.2	.067	.014	13.5-14.4
'72	1102449	2.2-2.6	37	1119515	.015	.030	1.5-3.2	.067	.014	13.5-14.4
	1102448	2.2-2.6	55	1119515	.015	.030	1.5-3.2	.067	.014	13.5-14.4
'73	1100947	2.2-2.6	37	Transistor type, integral with alternator, no adjustment						13.6-14.2
	1100946	2.2-2.6	55	Transistor type, integral with alternator, no adjustment						13.6-14.2
'74	1100947	2.2-2.6	37	Transistor type, integral with alternator, no adjustment						13.6-14.2
	1100926	2.2-2.6	①	Transistor type, integral with alternator, no adjustment						13.6-14.2

① 350 V8—37 amps; with A/C 55 amps
455 V8—42 amps; with A/C 61 amps

BRAKE SPECIFICATIONS

Year	Model	Master Cylinder: Disc	Master Cylinder: Drum	Wheel Cylinder: Front Disc	Wheel Cylinder: Front Drum	Wheel Cylinder: Rear	Brake Disc or Drum Diameter: Front Disc	Brake Disc or Drum Diameter: Front Drum	Brake Disc or Drum Diameter: Rear
'67	Special, Skylark, GS	1.125	1.0	2.937	1.125	.938	11.0	9.5	9.5
	Sportwagon	1.125	1.0	2.937	1.125	1.0	11.0	9.5	9.5
'68-'69	Special, Skylark, GS	1.125	1.0	2.937	1.125	.875	11.0	9.5	9.5
	Sportwagon	1.125	1.0	2.937	1.125	1.0	11.0	9.5	9.5
'70-'72	All	1.125	1.0	2.937	1.125	.875	11.0	9.495-9.505	9.495-9.505
'73	All	1.000①	—	2.937	—	.875	11.0	—	9.495-9.505
'74		1.125	1.0	2.937	1.125	.875	11.0	9.5	9.5

GS Gran Sport
① Power disc—1.125
— Not applicable

WHEEL ALIGNMENT SPECIFICATIONS

Year	Model	Caster: Range (deg)	Caster: Pref Setting (deg)	Camber: Range (deg)	Camber: Pref Setting (deg)	Toe-in (in.)	Steering Axis Inclin.	Wheel Pivot Ratio (deg): Inner Wheel	Wheel Pivot Ratio (deg): Wheel Outer
'67-'69	All	1N to 0	½N	0 to 1P	½P	⅛ to ¼	8	20	18½
'70-'72	All	1N to 0	½N	0 to 1P	½P	⅛ to ¼	8	20	18½
'73	All	0 to 1P	½P	0 to 1P①	½P	1/16 to ⅛	8	N.A.	N.A.
'74	Apollo	½N to 1½P	½P	½N to 1P	¾P	1/16 to 5/16	9	N.A.	N.A.
	Century, Regal	½P	—	½P RH 1P LH	—	± 1/16	8	N.A.	N.A.

① Right wheel given, left wheel is 0 to 2P, preferred 1P
N Negative P Positive

RH Right hand side
LH Left hand side

CHARGING SYSTEM

Complete information on charging system troubleshooting and repairs can be found in the "Unit Repair Section."

Caution Since the Delcotron and regulator are designed for use on only one polarity system, the following precautions must be observed:

1. The polarity of the battery, generator and regulator must be matched and considered before making any electrical connections in the system.
2. When connecting a booster battery, be sure to connect the negative battery terminals together and the positive battery terminals together.
3. When connecting a charger to the battery, connect the charger positive lead to the battery positive terminal. Connect the charger negative lead to the battery negative terminal.
4. Never operate the Delcotron on open circuit. Be sure that all connections in the circuit are clean and tight.
5. Do not short across or ground any of the terminals on the Delcotron regulator.
6. Do not attempt to polarize the Delcotron.
7. Do not use test lamps of more than 12 volts for checking diode continuity.
8. Avoid long soldering times when replacing diodes or transistors. Prolonged heat is damaging to these units.
9. Disconnect the battery ground terminal when servicing any AC system. This will prevent the possibility of accidental reversing of polarity.

Alternator R & R

Remove bolt holding tension bar to unit. Release drive belt. Unfasten mounting bolt to release Delcotron from engine. When reinstalling, adjust drive belt to allow ½ in. play on the longest run between pulleys.

NOTE: on some models, it may be necessary to loosen and rotate fan shroud. On all A/C models, remove compressor bracket.

Voltage Regulator R & R 1967-70

Removal

1. Disconnect the battery cables.
2. Disconnect the wiring from the voltage regulator.
3. Remove the screws holding the regulator to the firewall or front bulkhead, depending on the car.

Installation

1. Reverse the removal procedures to install.

Voltage Regulator R & R 1971-74

The voltage regulator is inside the alternator. For R&R procedures see "Starting and Charging Systems" in the "Unit Repair Section."

STARTING SYSTEM

The starter circuit consists of the battery, battery cables, starting motor, starter motor solenoid switch, ignition-starter switch and the neutral safety switch (used on cars with automatic transmission).

The starting motor and solenoid assembly is mounted on the right side of the engine. The solenoid switch closes the circuit between the battery and the starting motor. It also operates the shift lever that moves the drive pinion into mesh with the flywheel ring gear.

Starter R & R

L-6

1. Disconnect battery and solenoid wires.
2. Remove attaching bolts and lift out starter.

V8

1. Disconnect battery.
2. Jack up car.
3. Remove four screws (3/8 in.) that hold flywheel inspection cover.
4. Disconnect wires from solenoid.
5. Remove one bolt from starter bracket to engine block, then remove two rear starter bolts using a 9/16 in. socket.

NOTE: the bracket bolt is hidden and must be removed using a short ½ in. open-end wrench. This bolt must be started by hand when installing.

6. Remove starter motor.

Starter Drive Removal and Installation

1. Remove the bolt which holds the field leads to the solenoid motor terminal and disconnect the leads. Remove the two solenoid attaching bolts, rotate, and remove the solenoid.
2. Remove the two through-bolts, end frame, and field frame assembly.
3. Pull both brush holder pivot pins and lift out each pair of brush holder assemblies. Disconnect the leads and brushes.
4. Remove the shift lever pivot bolt, plunger, shift lever, and armature from the drive housing.
5. Remove the drive assembly from the armature by first using a suitable tool (such as a ½ in. pipe coupling) to disengage the snap-ring retainer from the snap-ring. After removing the snap-ring and retainer, slide the drive assembly off of the armature shaft.
6. Inspect all parts for wear or damage and replace where necessary. When cleaning all parts, be sure not to use any degreasing or high temperature method on the armature, field coils, and drive assembly.
7. To reassemble, reverse the above steps. Be sure to lubricate the armature shaft, drive frame bushing, shift lever linkage, and the bushing in the commutator end frame when reassembling.

NOTE: When assembling the field frame over the armature to the drive end frame, spread the brush holders apart enough for the brushes to clear the commutator without damage to either.

IGNITION SYSTEM

The distributor on the OHV 6 is located on the right side of the engine. On the V6, and most V8's, the distributor is located between the two cylinder banks, up front. On the early 400 cu. in. V8, the distributor is at the rear of the engine. The rotor turns clockwise, viewed from the top.

Engine timing requirements are satisfied by centrifugal and vacuum advance mechanisms. Vacuum advance is controlled by the effort of a vacuum diaphragm working against spring tension. The diaphragm moves the breaker plate counterclockwise to advance the timing, and the springs move the plate clockwise to retard the timing. The degree of vacuum advance is determined by the amount of vacuum applied to the spring loaded diaphragm and breaker plate. Centrifugal advance is governed by engine speed. As speed increases, advance weights push against an advance cam which is integral with the distributor shaft. This causes the spark to be mechanically advanced. As speed decreases, the weights are returned by springs, returning the timing to the initial setting.

Caution Design of the V6-90° engine requires a special form of distributor cam. The engine will not run in balance if No. 1 spark plug wire is inserted into No. 6 distributor cap tower, even though each wire in firing sequence is advanced to the next distributor tower. There is a difference between the firing intervals of each succeeding cylinder through the 720° engine cycle.

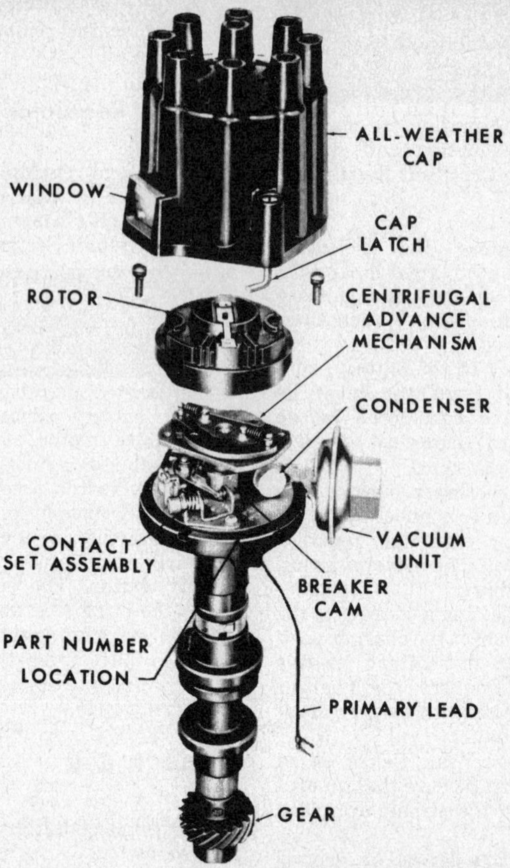
ALL-WEATHER CAP
WINDOW
CAP LATCH
ROTOR
CENTRIFUGAL ADVANCE MECHANISM
CONDENSER
CONTACT SET ASSEMBLY
VACUUM UNIT
BREAKER CAM
PART NUMBER LOCATION
PRIMARY LEAD
GEAR

Distributor assembly, R.F.I. shield was installed after 1970
(© Buick Div., G.M. Corp)

Distributor Removal

1. Remove distributor cap, primary wire and vacuum line at the distributor.
2. Scribe a mark on the distributor body, locating the position of the rotor and scribe another mark on the engine block, showing the position of the body in the block.
3. Remove the hold-down clamp and lift the distributor out of the block.

NOTE: 1970-74 distributors have a radio interference shield over the contact points. Only snap-lock point sets can be used because screw-type connectors will hit this shield and short the ignition.

Distributor Installation

For firing order and cylinder numbering, see specifications.

1. If engine has been disturbed, rotate the crankshaft to bring the piston of No. 1 cylinder to the top of its compression stroke. If the engine has not been disturbed, insert the distributor into the engine, making sure the tip of the rotor is aligned with the marks that were scribed on the distributor housing and the engine block.
2. Position the distributor in the block with the rotor at No. 1 firing position. Make sure the oil pump intermediate drive shaft is properly seated in the oil pump.
3. Install the distributor lock but do not tighten.
4. Rotate the distributor body clockwise until the breaker points are just starting to open. Tighten the retaining screw.
5. Connect the primary wire and the vacuum line to the distributor, then install distributor cap.
6. Start the engine and check the timing with a timing light.

NOTCH
DISTRIBUTOR POSITION FOR FIRING #1

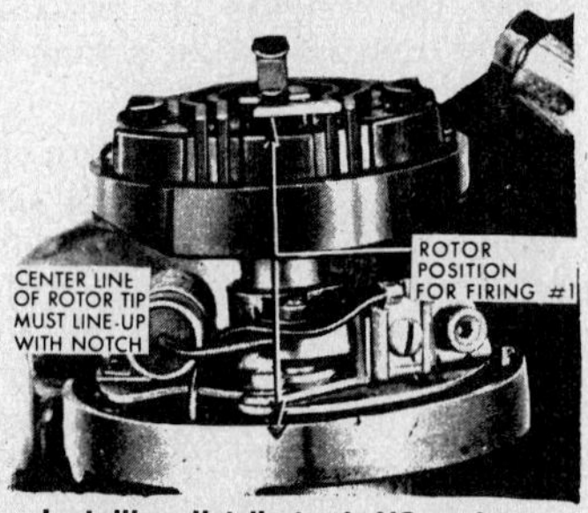
CENTER LINE OF ROTOR TIP MUST LINE-UP WITH NOTCH
ROTOR POSITION FOR FIRING #1

Installing distributor in V6 engine
(© Buick Div., G.M. Corp)

Contact Point Replacement and Adjustment

NOTE: the condenser should be replaced when the points are replaced.

1. Remove the distributor cap and rotor. If equipped with an interference shield, remove the shield.
2. Loosen the two screws holding the contact point set in place and remove point set.
3. Disconnect the condenser and primary leads from their terminal on the points.
4. Connect the wires to a new set of points and install them into the distributor.
5. Put a small amount of grease on the breaker cam.
6. Turn the engine over slowly to open the points on the maximum gap.
7. Using an Allen wrench (1/8 in.), adjust the gap to specification and reinstall the shield, rotor, and cap. Install the shield half that covers the points first.
8. If a dwell meter is available adjust the dwell to specifications.
9. Check the timing.

Installing R.F.I. shield
(© Buick Div., G.M. Corp)

Ignition Timing

Timing marks are located on the front engine cover and on the harmonic balancer.

1. Disconnect the distributor vacuum advance hose from the distributor and plug the hose.
2. Make sure the point gap is adjusted. Using a dwell meter is an alternate method of setting the gap.

NOTE: it may be necessary to put a small amount of white paint or chalk on the timing marks to make them more visible.

3. Connect a timing light to no. 1 cylinder.
4. Loosen the distributor clamp.

5. Start the engine and rotate the distributor until the correct marks line up. Tighten the distributor clamp and recheck the timing.
6. Reconnect the vacuum hose.

1974 Solid State Ignition

In 1974, a solid state, high energy ignition system is offered as an option on all Buick engines. There are no points or capacitor to replace, nor any cam or rubbing block to wear out. Precision timing and proper tuning are maintained over a greater interval than conventional point-and-capacitor systems, and the high energy coil delivers 50 to 75% more voltage than a conventional electronic system. In addition, the high energy system is completely unitized.

FUEL SYSTEM

Throttle Linkage and Dashpot Adjustments

1967

The procedure for adjusting throttle linkage is identical on standard or automatic transmission cars. On automatic transmission cars, however, the linkage actuates other linkage connected to a valve in the transmission.

1. To adjust throttle linkage, make sure the accelerator pedal is free.
2. On automatic transmission equipped cars, see Throttle Linkage Adjustment of Automatic Transmission.
3. Disconnect rear end of throttle rod from throttle operating lever.
4. While a helper presses the accelerator firmly against the floor, hold throttle in wide open position. Hold rear end of throttle rod at hole in throttle operating lever. The rod end must be 1/16 in. short of entering the hole in the lever. Adjust throttle rod length to obtain this condition.
5. Connect throttle rod to operating lever and attach cotter pin.
6. Now, press accelerator to the floor and recheck throttle for wide open position.
7. Hold choke valve closed and move throttle lever to wide open position to check adjustment of choke unloader.
8. Finally check that there is a full opening of the throttle valve as the accelerator pedal just strikes the floor.
9. Now adjust the dashpot by turning the plunger until it just touches the throttle lever.
10. With the gear selector in drive and the brakes firmly set, jab the accelerator and release it quickly. Note engine operation as the throttle closes.
11. If engine stalls due to too quick deceleration, move the dashpot plunger toward the throttle lever until the stalling is corrected. If too much time is required for throttle to close, move the plunger away from the throttle lever.
12. If correct control cannot be obtained, renew the dashpot.

1968-74

These models have a flexible cable type throttle linkage, which is not adjustable. Dashpot adjustment is the same as that shown above for 1967 models, Steps 9-12.

Idle Speed and Mixture Adjustment

1967 All

1. If equipped with Automatic Level Control (Sportwagon), disconnect vacuum line from compressor at storage tank and plug it with a pencil.
2. Make sure that the PCV system is operative (not plugged).
3. Remove the air cleaner and connect the tachometer.
4. Start the engine and allow it to come to normal operating temperature.
5. Place manual transmissions in Neutral, automatics in Drive (wheels blocked).
6. Adjust the throttle stop screw to obtain the specified idle speed.
7. Adjust the mixture needles alternately to obtain a 20 rpm drop from the specified idle, then open them 1/4 turn each. If this does not restore idle speed to specifications, turn them out 1/8 turn at a time until the lean best idle is obtained.
8. Make sure the transmission idle stator switch on the linkage is closed by disconnecting its wire. If the idle speed doesn't decrease, the switch is not closed and should be adjusted.
9. Press down on the hot idle compensator valve, if so equipped. If the idle drops, the valve is open and should be unstuck and the idle reset.

1968-71 V8
1968 L-6

1. Connect a tachometer to the engine.
2. Start the engine until it is warmed up.
3. Remove and plug the vacuum hose to the distributor.
4. Place a manual transmission in neutral, and an automatic transmission in Drive.

NOTE: check to see that the compressor for the Automatic Level Control, if equipped, is not running. The compressor now has a regulating valve to turn off vacuum at idle speed. If the compressor is running, this valve is faulty and must be adjusted or replaced before a good idle can be obtained.

5. Adjust the throttle stopscrew to set the idle speed according to specifications.
6. Adjust the idle mixture needles, one at a time, to obtain the highest tachometer reading. Readjust the throttle stopscrew to obtain 20 revolutions per minute (rpm) faster than specified idle speed. Turn each mixture needle to reduce engine speed 10 rpm. This reduces idle speed to specifications.

1969 6 Cyl

See Note in previous procedure about Automatic Level Control.

1. Connect a tachometer to the engine.
2. Start the engine and warm it up.
3. Remove and plug the vacuum hose to the distributor.
4. Place manual transmissions in neutral and automatics in Drive. Make sure the wheels are blocked and the brakes are securely set.
5. Adjust the solenoid plunger screw to set the specified idle speed. This is the higher figure in the specification table.
6. Adjust the idle mixture needles, one at a time, to obtain the highest tachometer reading. Readjust the solenoid plunger to obtain 20 rpm higher than the specified idle.

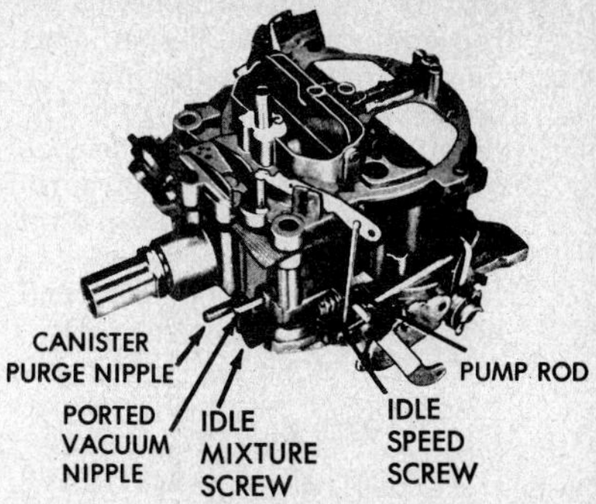
CANISTER
PURGE NIPPLE
PUMP ROD
PORTED
VACUUM
NIPPLE
IDLE
MIXTURE
SCREW
IDLE
SPEED
SCREW
4 bbl carburetor
(© Buick Div., G.M. Corp)

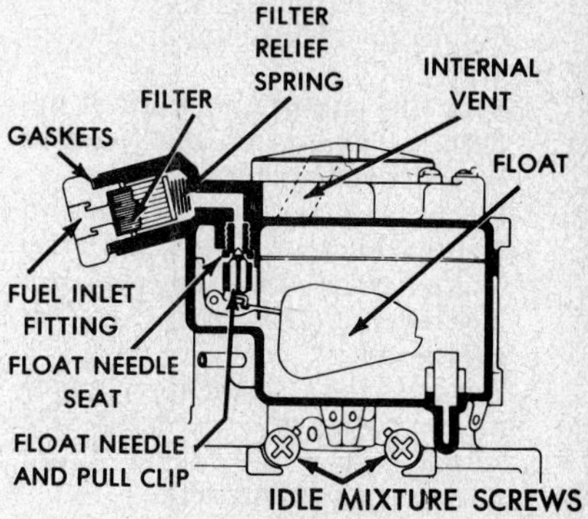
FILTER
RELIEF
SPRING
INTERNAL
VENT
FILTER
GASKETS
FLOAT
FUEL INLET
FITTING
FLOAT NEEDLE
SEAT
FLOAT NEEDLE
AND PULL CLIP
IDLE MIXTURE SCREWS
2 bbl carburetor
(© Buick Div., G.M. Corp)

7. Turn in the mixture needle to drop engine speed 20 rpm. This will achieve the specified idle.
8. Disconnect the wire from the idle stop solenoid to de-energize the solenoid. Adjust the carburetor throttle stopscrew to obtain the specified slow-idle speed.
9. Reconnect the solenoid wire and check the fast-idle speed.

1970 6 Cyl.

See the note in the 1968–70 V8, 1968 L-6 section on Automatic Level Control.

1. Connect a tachometer to the engine.
2. Start the engine and warm it up.
3. Remove and plug the vacuum hose to the distributor.
4. Place manual transmissions in Neutral and automatics in Drive. Make sure the wheels are blocked and the brakes are securely set.
5. Adjust the solenoid plunger screw to set the specified idle speed. This is the higher figure in the specification table.
6. Stop the engine and turn the mixture screw in until it contacts the seat lightly, then turn it out four turns. Restart the engine.
7. Readjust the solenoid screw to get 830 rpm for manual transmissions and 630 rpm for automatics.
8. Adjust the mixture screw in to achieve the specified idle speed.
9. Disconnect the wire from the idle stop solenoid to de-energize the solenoid.
10. Adjust the carburetor throttle stopscrew to obtain specified slow-idle speed. This is the lower figure in the specification table. Reconnect the solenoid wire and check the fast-idle speed.

1971 All

Note: on models with a V8 engine and manual transmission, the relay and solenoid located near the carburetor are emission control devices and should not be adjusted. See the note in the 1968–70 V8 procedure on automatic level control.

1. Connect a tachometer to the engine.
2. Start the engine and warm it up.
3. Remove the hose to the distributor and plug it up.
4. Adjust the throttle stopscrew to set the specified idle speed.
5. Adjust the idle mixture screws (one screw on 6 cyl) to obtain the highest idle within the limited travel of the screws.
6. Readjust the throttle stopscrew to obtain the specified idle speed.

1972-73 All

See the note in the 1968–70 V8 procedure on automatic level control.

1. Connect a tachometer to the engine.
2. Start the engine and run it until it is warmed up.
3. Remove and plug the vacuum hose to the distributor.
4. Place manual transmissions in Neutral and automatic transmissions in Drive.
5. Open the throttle sufficiently to allow the solenoid to extend and contact the throttle lever pad in the idle position.
6. Adjust the solenoid plunger to obtain the specified rpm. This is the higher figure in the specification chart.
7. Disconnect the solenoid wire to disengage solenoid.
8. Adjust the carburetor idle screw to obtain specified idle speed, this is the lower figure in the specification chart.
9. Reconnect the solenoid wire.
10. Adjust the idle mixture needles, one at a time, to obtain the highest tachometer reading. After the highest reading is reached, readjust the solenoid plunger to obtain 50 rpm over the specified idle speed. Turn each mixture needle in to reduce the idle speed 25 rpm for each needle. This reduces the idle speed to the recommended rpm.
11. Adjust the fast idle speed on all four-barrel carburetors. Fast idle must be adjusted after the slow idle speed and mixture have been adjusted. Automatic transmission cars are adjusted on the low step of the fast idle cam, in Drive, to 700 rpm. Manual transmission cars are adjusted on the low cam step to 820 rpm for 350 engines, and 920 rpm for 455 engines.
12. Connect the distributor vacuum hose.
13. Install the red service idle needle limiter caps on the mixture screws.

Fuel Pump

An AC fuel pump is used. The pump lever works from the underside of a camshaft eccentric. It is of the single-action diaphragm type and is equipped with a pulsation dampening chamber for stabilizing fuel flow. Beginning 1966, fuel pumps are sealed units. They are not to be repaired.

Beginning 1966, all air conditioned cars with V8 engines and all cars with 400 and 455 cu. in. engines have a special fuel pump. This pump has a vapor return line which returns hot fuel and fuel vapor to the fuel tank. The possibility of vapor lock is thus greatly reduced by keeping cool fuel circulating through the pump.

Fuel Pump R & R

Removal

1. Disconnect the fuel inlet hose from the pump. Disconnect the vapor return hose, if equipped. Disconnect the outlet hose.
2. Remove the two $\frac{1}{2}$ inch (in.) bolts.
3. Remove the fuel pump.

Installation

1. Install a new gasket.
2. Install a new pump and bolts.
3. Tighten the bolts alternately and evenly.
4. Reconnect the hoses, start the engine, and check for leaks.

Fuel Filter

V6 Engine

The V6 engine gas filter is located in the carburetor fuel inlet. The element is sintered bronze and placed with the cupped end outward. The element is spring loaded as to permit fuel by-pass in the event of element clogging.

The element should be removed and cleaned in a good solvent at 12,000 mile or 12 month periods.

1967-74 OHV 6 & V8 Engines

These engines have a pleated paper fuel filter located in the carburetor inlet. The filter should be replaced every 12,000 miles.

Fuel Filter Replacement 1967-74

1. Disconnect the fuel line connection at the inlet of the carburetor.
2. Remove the inlet fuel filter nut from the carburetor with a box wrench.
3. Remove the filter element and spring.
4. If a bronze element, blow through the cone end—the element should allow air to pass freely.
5. Install the element spring and a new element into the carburetor. Bronze elements are installed with the small section of the cone facing outward.
6. Install a new gasket on the fitting nut and install the nut.
7. Install the fuel line and tighten it securely. Start the engine and check for leaks.

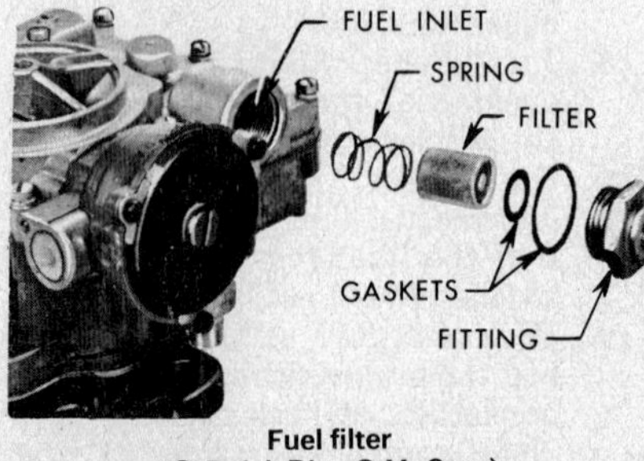
FUEL INLET
SPRING
FILTER
GASKETS
FITTING

Fuel filter
(© Buick Div., G.M. Corp)

COOLING SYSTEM

The cooling system is pressurized to 15 psi. Coolant temperature is controlled by a thermostat housed in the forward (outlet) end of the intake manifold.

In the OHV 6 engine, the thermostat is in the top front of the cylinder head. This thermostat controls circulation and temperature in the intake manifold as well as in the engine.

Thermostat R & R

To replace the thermostat, remove the two bolts holding the water neck in place. Remove the water neck and the thermostat will lift out. Use a new gasket when reinstalling a new thermostat.

Caution Be sure the thermostat is not reversed in its installed position. The temperature-sensitive side should extend toward the rear or down.

Water Pump

Removal—1967-74

1. Drain cooling system.
2. Loosen belt or belts, then remove fan blades and pulley or pulleys from hub on water pump shaft. Remove belt or belts.
3. Disconnect hose from water pump inlet and heater hose from nipple. Remove bolts, then remove pump and gasket from the timing case cover.

Installation—1967-74

1. Install pump assembly with new gasket. Bolts and lock washers must be torqued evenly.
2. Connect radiator hose to pump inlet and heater hose to nipple. Fill cooling system and check all points of possible coolant leaks.
3. Install fan pulley or pulleys and fan blade. Install belt or belts and adjust for correct tension.

Radiator R & R

The radiator mounting is a four-point system using rubber inserts on U-shaped brackets for the lower mounting. The radiator upper mounting points are part of the upper radiator panel. The radiator is removed by removing the upper radiator panel, disconnecting the hoses and automatic transmission lines if equipped, and lifting the radiator out of the car. On models equipped with a fan shroud, remove the shroud from the radiator and position it rearward over the fan. Installation is the reverse of removal.

Engine Temperature and Oil Pressure Sending Unit

Temperature Gauge—1967-74

A temperature switch controls the operation of the temperature indicator light located in the instrument cluster. The temperature switch is located in the thermostat housing on the OHV 6 and in the right front of the intake manifold on the V6 and all other V8 engines.

If the engine cooling system is not working properly and the coolant temperature reaches approximately 250°F, the temperature indicator light will light in the instrument cluster.

Oil Pressure—1967-74

The oil pressure sending unit is located in the oil pump cover and operates an indicator light in the instrument cluster.

If engine oil pressure drops below a safe level during operation, the circuit is completed through the sending unit to ground. This will cause the oil indicator light in the cluster to burn.

EMISSION CONTROLS

There are three types of emissions to be controlled: crankcase emissions, carburetor and gas tank gas vapor emissions, and exhaust emissions. See the "Unit Repair Section" for troubleshooting and repair information.

1967

Buick controlled crankcase emissions with the positive crankcase ventilation system. The PCV system connects the crankcase to the intake manifold. Crankcase gases are returned to the intake manifold to be reburned.

The Air Injection Reactor (AIR) system was used to treat exhaust emissions. It consists of an air pump, a special air cleaner, a by-pass valve, and tubes and hoses used to inject the air into the exhaust manifolds. The pump, driven by the engine, compresses, distributes, and injects clean air at the exhaust port for each cylinder. In the exhaust manifolds, the air combines with the unburned hydrocarbons and carbon monoxide to produce an exhaust low in emissions.

1968-69

Buick elected to adopt a special system of terminal exhaust treatment. This plan supersedes the method used to conform to 1967 California laws. The new system cancels out—except in special purpose applications—the use of the AIR method previously used.

The new concept, Combustion Control System (CCS) utilizes engine modifications. Essentially the CCS increases combustion efficiency through carburetor and distributor calibrations and by increasing engine operating temperature.

Carburetors are calibrated leaner and initial ignition timing is retarded. Another carburetor feature is the idle fuel mixture limiting orifice. It is located at the base of the idle mixture screw and makes sure that fuel enrichment will not greatly affect exhaust emissions even if the idle mixture screw is turned out too far.

The CCS also incorporates a higher engine operation temperature. A 195° thermostat is used. Engines running hotter provide more complete vaporation of the fuel and reduce quench area in the combustion chamber. Quench area is the relatively cool area near the cylinder wall and combustion chamber surfaces. Fuel in these areas does not burn properly because of the lower temperatures. This incomplete burning increases emissions.

The CCS uses a thermostatically controlled air cleaner called the Auto-Therm air cleaner. It is designed to keep the temperature of the air entering the carburetor at approximately 100°. This allows the lean carburetor to work properly, minimizes carburetor icing, and improves engine warm-up characteristics. A sensor unit located on the clean air side of the air filter senses the temperature of the air passing over it and regulates the vacuum supplied to a vacuum diaphragm in the inlet tube of the air cleaner. The colder the air the greater the amount of vacuum supplied to the vacuum diaphragm. The vacuum diaphragm, depending on the vacuum supplied to it, opens or closes a damper door in the inlet tube of the air cleaner. If the door is open, it allows air from the engine compartment to go to the carburetor. If the door is closed, air flows from the heat stove located on the exhaust manifold into the carburetor. In this way heated air is supplied to the carburetor during cold days and when first starting the engine and warming it up.

1970-71

The more stringent 1970 laws require tighter control of emissions. Crankcase emissions are controlled by the Closed Positive Crankcase Ventilation System; exhaust emissions are controlled by the engine Controlled Combustion System (CCS), in conjunction with the new Transmission Controlled Spark System (TCS).

In addition, cars sold in California in 1970 and all 1971 models are equipped with an Evaporation Control System that limits the amount of gasoline vapor discharged into the atmosphere (usually from the carburetor and fuel tank).

The TCS system consists of a transmission switch, a solenoid valve, and a temperature switch. Under normal conditions, the system permits the vacuum distributor (spark) advance to operate only in high gear (both manual and automatic transmissions) and reverse.

The transmission switch is located on the transmission and senses when the transmission is in one of the lower gears. When in a lower gear, the switch activates the vacuum solenoid valve. This valve is located in the vacuum line that runs from the carburetor to the distributor and shuts off vacuum to the distributor advance when it is activated. There is also an engine-temperature sensing switch which overrides the transmission switch. It will allow vacuum advance in the lower gears when the engine temperature is below 85° or above 220°. There is always vacuum advance in high gear and reverse.

The Evaporative Emission Control System was introduced in 1970. Vapors generated in the gas tank while the car is at rest are transferred to an activated charcoal canister located in the engine compartment. When the car is running the vapors are removed from the canister and burned by the engine.

1972

In 1972, all engines are equipped with Positive Crankcase Ventilation, Transmission Controlled Vacuum Spark Advance, and the Controlled Combustion System. See the 1970-71 section for an explanation of TCS. The Air Injection Reactor System is standard on all engines except non-California 350 cu in. engines with automatic transmissions. All California cars and all cars with manual transmissions have Exhaust Gas Recirculation (EGR).

The EGR System is used to reduce oxides of nitrogen emissions. To lower the formation of nitrogen oxides, it is necessary to reduce combustion temperatures. This is done by introducing exhaust gases into the intake manifold to be burned.

An EGR valve is mounted on the right rear of the intake manifold and is used to regulate the amount of exhaust gases and the time the exhaust gases enter the intake manifold. As the engine speeds up, carburetor vacuum is applied to the valve which opens a port connecting the intake manifold to the exhaust gas passage that is cast in the intake manifold. This allows exhaust gases to pass into the intake manifold. The EGR system is not in operation during engine idle.

1973

All engines are equipped with Positive Crankcase Ventilation, Controlled Combustion, Air Injection Reactor System, Exhaust Gas Recirculation, Transmission Controlled Vacuum Spark Advance System, and Evaporative Emission Control. With the exception of a low temperature cut-out valve that added to the EGR system, the emission control systems remain unchanged from previous years.

The EGR system is the same one that was used on 1972 California cars with a new temperature valve. This black and white plastic valve is located in the vacuum line to the EGR valve and it senses ambient temperature above the engine intake manifold. At temperatures below 55°F, the temperature valve closes to prevent carburetor vacuum from opening the EGR valve. When the temperature above the manifold rises above 60°F, the valve opens and allows carburetor vacuum to control the operation of the EGR valve. Whenever installing a new valve, always make sure the side of the valve marked EGR faces toward the EGR valve.

1974

The 1974 Buick emission control system is unchanged from 1973, except for the required change in the EGR temperature sensor. The Environmental Protection Agency order necessitated that the EGR ambient temperature sensor either be removed or changed to record coolant temperature. Although the system design remains unchanged, there has been an extensive refinement and recalibration of components to insure greater efficiency.

1974 Federal Emission standards are unchanged from 1973½, however, California engines are required to reduce oxides of nitrogen by 1/3.

1974 EXHAUST EMISSION STANDARDS

	FEDERAL (grams/mi)	CALIFORNIA (grams/mi)
HYDRO-CARBONS	3.4	3.2
CARBON MONOXIDE	39	39
OXIDES OF NITROGEN	3.0	2.0

ENGINE

Engine Removal

1. Scribe marks at the hood hinges and the hinge brackets. Remove the hood.
2. Disconnect the battery and drain the coolant.
3. Remove the air cleaner.
4. On cars with air conditioning (A/C), disconnect the compressor ground wire from the bracket. Remove the electrical connector from the compressor. Remove the compressor and position the compressor out of the way. Do not disconnect any hoses.

Caution If the compressor refrigerant lines do not have enough slack to position the compressor out of the way without disconnecting the refrigerant lines, the air conditioning system will have to be removed by a trained air conditioning specialist. Under no conditions should an untrained person attempt to disconnect the air conditioning refrigerant lines. These lines contain pressurized freon, which can be extremely dangerous to the untrained.

5. Remove the fan blade, pulley, and belts.
6. Disconnect the radiator and heater hoses. Remove the radiator and shroud assembly.
7. Remove the power steering pump and move it out of the way. Do not disconnect any hoses.
8. Remove the fuel pump hoses and plug them.
9. Disconnect the vapor emission lines, on 1970-74 models, from the carburetor, the vacuum supply hose from the carburetor to the vacuum manifold, and the power brake vacuum hoses, if equipped.
10. Disconnect the throttle control cable at the carburetor.
11. Disconnect the oil and coolant switch.
12. Disconnect the engine-to-body ground strap.
13. Raise the car and disconnect the starter wires.
14. Disconnect the crossover pipe from the exhaust manifolds and support the exhaust system.
15. Remove the flywheel and converter cover.
16. On cars equipped with automatic transmissions, remove the flywheel-to-converter attaching

10
6
9
2
5
4
8
1
3
7
V6 intake manifold bolt tightening sequence
(© Buick Div., G.M. Corp)

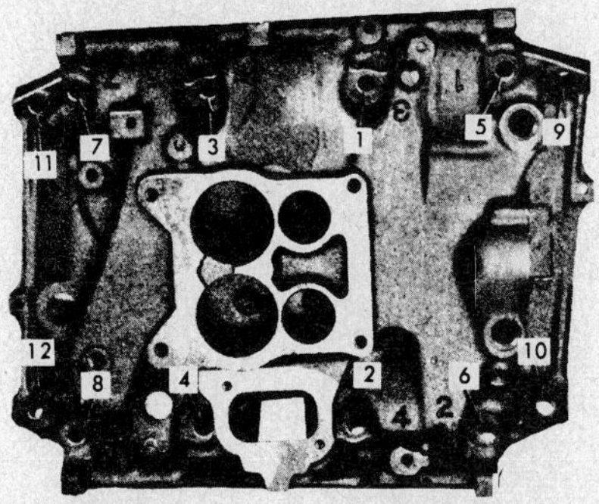
11
7
3
1
5
9
12
8
4
2
6
10
V8 intake manifold bolt tightening sequence
(© Buick Div., G.M. Corp)

bolts. Match-mark the converter to the flywheel. On standard transmission models, disconnect the clutch linkage.

17. Remove the transmission-to-engine attaching bolts.
18. Support the transmission.
19. Remove the thru-bolts from the motor mounts.
20. Lower the car, making sure the transmission is adequately supported.
21. Disengage the engine from the transmission and remove the engine from the car.

Engine Installation

Install the engine in the reverse order of removal.

Note that there are dowel pins in the block that have matching holes in the bellhousing. These dowel pins must be in almost perfect alignment before the engine will go together with the transmission.

Manifolds

L6 Models R & R

This engine uses a combined intake and exhaust manifold, equipped with thermostatic heat-riser valve.

To remove the manifold assembly, disconnect the exhaust pipe flange and remove all connections to the carburetor. Take off the vacuum lines at the manifold and also at the carburetor. Remove power steering pump and bracket.

Remove the carburetor. Unbolt the manifold from the side of the cylinder head. The intake manifold can be separated from the exhaust manifold by removing one bolt and two nuts. These fasteners should be tightened to 15-30 ft lbs after the manifolds are bolted to the engine.

Before reinstalling the manifold, thoroughly clean out the ports to prevent turbulence, particularly on the intake manifold.

Intake Manifold

V6 & V8 Engines

These engines have a low restriction, dual intake manifold. The manifold incorporates an exhaust heat passage to warm the carburetor throttle body. Engine coolant flows out of the engine through the water passages in the manifold and through the thermostat and water outlet elbow located at the front of the manifold.

Intake Manifold R & R

1. Drain cooling system and disconnect the battery.
2. Remove carburetor air cleaner. Disconnect all tubes and hoses from the carburetor. Disconnect and remove the coil.
3. Disconnect temperature indicator wire from sending unit.
4. Disconnect accelerator and transmission linkage at carburetor. Disconnect throttle return spring.
5. Slide front thermostat by-pass hose clamp back on the hose. Disconnect upper radiator hose at outlet.
6. Disconnect heater hose at the temperature control valve inlet. Force the end of the hose down to permit coolant to drain from intake manifold.
7. Remove manifold-to-head attaching bolts.
8. Remove intake manifold and carburetor as an assembly by sliding rearward to disengage the thermostat by-pass hose from the water pump. Remove intake manifold gasket. Reverse the above steps to install.

Exhaust Manifold R & R

1967-74 V6 and V8

1. Jack up car and support on axle stands.
2. Disconnect exhaust pipe from manifolds on both sides of engine and lower. If equipped with dual exhaust, disconnect and lower only on the side being worked on.
3. If equipped with manual transmission, remove equalizer shaft.

NOTE: on right side, it may be necessary to remove A/C, power steering, or alternator.

4. Remove exhaust manifold-to-cylinder head bolts.
5. Remove manifold from beneath car.

NOTE: on GS 400 models, it may be necessary to pull pitman arm from pitman shaft and to swing steering linkage forward to gain clearance.

6. Reverse the above to install. Always use the bolt locks.

Valve System

All V8 and V6 engines use rocker arm shafts while the L6 engine uses rocker arm studs. All lifters are the hydraulic type.

Rocker Arm R & R

L6 1968-71, 1974

NOTE: these rocker arms are of the individual pedestal design and need not be removed to remove head.

1. Remove rocker arm cover.
2. Remove rocker arm nuts, rocker arm balls, rocker arms, and push rods. These should be reinstalled in their original locations.

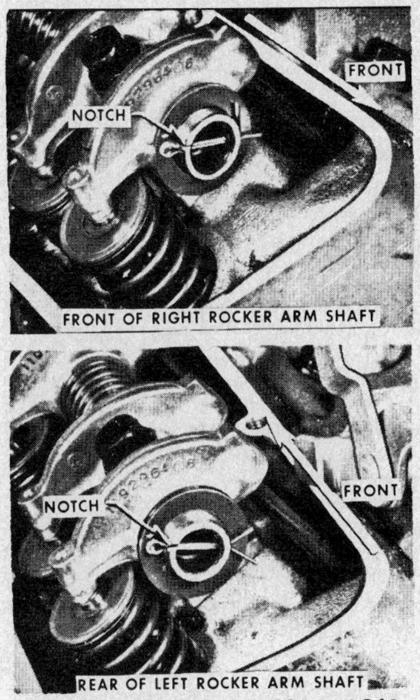
FRONT
NOTCH
FRONT OF RIGHT ROCKER ARM SHAFT
NOTCH
FRONT
REAR OF LEFT ROCKER ARM SHAFT
Rocker arm and shaft—300 and 340 cu in. 1967
(© Buick Div., G.M. Corp)

V8 1967-69, V6 1967

Removal

1. Remove the rocker arm cover and four rocker arm and shaft assembly bolts. Remove the assembly.
2. Remove the shaft end cap by splitting the side of the cap with a chisel.
3. Remove the rocker arms and springs. Keep the parts in order.

Installation

1. Install the rocker arms and springs on the shaft and lubricate the shaft with oil as the rocker arms are installed.
2. Install a new end cap on the rocker arm shaft.

NOTE: When installing the rocker arm shaft assembly, be sure that the drill mark is facing up and toward the rear on the left cylinder head and toward the front on the right cylinder head.

3. After locating the top of each push rod in its rocker arm seat, draw the rocker arm and shaft assembly down by tightening the bracket bolts a little at a time until tight.
4. Install the rocker arm cover with a new gasket.

V8 1970-74

Removal

1. Remove the rocker arm cover.
2. Remove the rocker arm shaft assembly bolts and the assembly.
3. Remove the nylon arm retainers by breaking them below their head with a chisel.
4. Remove the rocker arms.

Installation

NOTE: Each pair of rocker arms must be installed so that the external rib on each arm points away from the rocker arm shaft bolt that is located between each pair of rocker arms.

1. Install the rocker arms on the shaft and lubricate them with oil.
2. Center each arm on the 1/4 in. hole in the shaft. Install new nylon rocker arm retainers in the holes using a 1/2 in. drift.
3. Locate the push rods in the rocker arms and insert the shaft-to-cylinder head bolts. Tighten the bolts a little at a time until they are tight.
4. Install the rocker cover and use a new gasket.

Rocker Arm Stud Removal and Installation

1968-71, 1974 L6

1. Remove the rocker cover and rocker arms.
2. File two slots 3/32-1/8 in. deep on opposite sides of the stud. The bottom of the slots should be 1/2 in. from the top of the stud hole.
3. Place a spacer washer (or tool J-6392-3) over the stud, then position a stud remover (or tool J-6392-1) on the stud and tighten it securely.
4. Place a spacer (socket or J-6392-2) over the stud remover, then thread a 7/8 in. nut on the stud remover and turn in until the stud pulls from the head.
5. If an oversize stud is to be used (0.003 and 0.013 in. oversize studs are available), ream the stud hole to the proper size.
6. To install, coat the press-fit area of the stud with axle lube, then press or hammer it into place.

NOTE: The factory recommends that tool J-6880 be used for this job. This tool is simply a sleeve that is held in place with an allen screw and it protects the threads from damage. Any homemade tool similar to the one illustrated will work if care is exercised. Do not hammer directly on the stud because it is hardened to the point where it will fracture if subjected to shock.

ROCKER ARM
EXTERNAL RIB
Rocker arms and shaft, 455 cu in.
(© Buick Div., G.M. Corp)

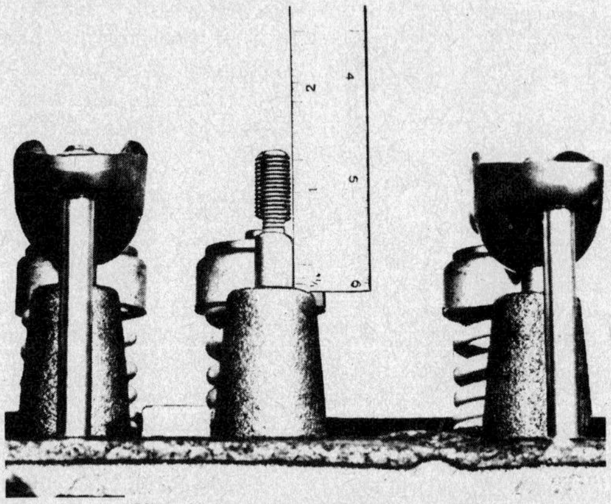
Slots for removing rocker arm stud
(© Buick Div., G.M. Corp)

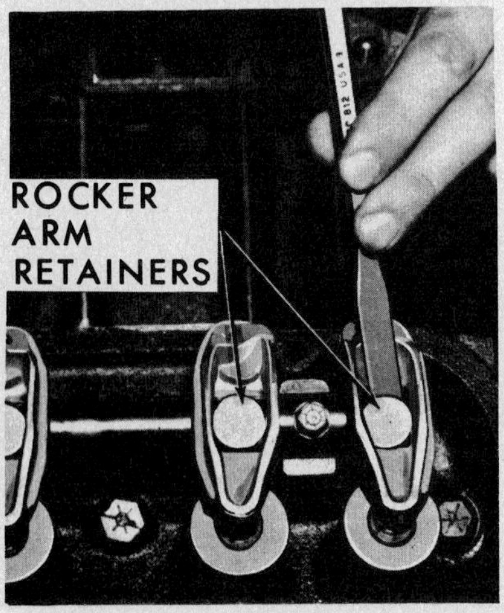
ROCKER ARM RETAINERS
Removing nylon rocker arm retainer
(© Buick Div., G.M. Corp)

Valve Adjustment—L6

1. Mark the distributor housing with chalk at each plug wire position. Then remove the distributor cap and plug wire assembly.
2. Crank the engine until the distributor rotor points to no. 1 cylinder position and the breaker points are fully open. This step places the lifter on the base circle of the cam for each cylinder.
3. Adjust the lifters for this cylinder by backing out the adjusting nut until free-play is felt at the push rod, then turn in the nut until the push rods cannot be turned with the fingers. When play has been removed, turn the adjusting nut in one full additional turn to center the lifter plunger.
4. Repeat step three on each cylinder, following the firing order of the engine.

Valve Adjustment V6 and V8

These engines use rocker arm shafts. After the shaft assembly to cylinder head bolts are torqued to specification, the valves are adjusted.

Valve Guide Replacement

Valve guides are cast into the cylinder heads of all engines. The valve guides must be reamed and fitted with valves with oversize stems to be repaired.

Cylinder Head R & R

Installation L6

1. Clean all gasket surfaces, install a new gasket, and place the head on the block.
2. Install the head bolts. Torque the head bolts to specifications in three stages.

Installing new rocker arm stud
(© Buick Div., G.M. Corp)

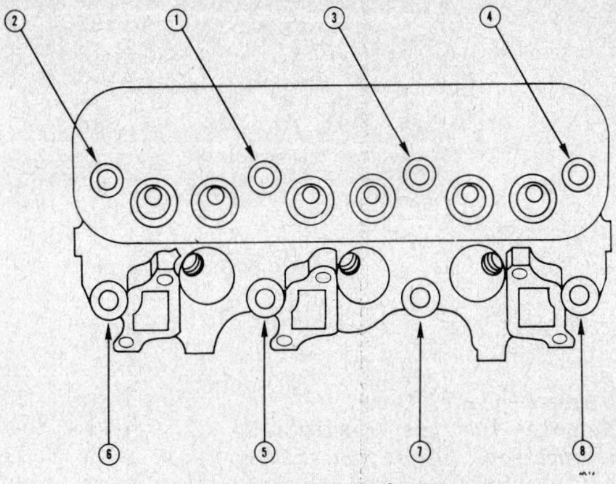

V6 cylinder head bolt tightening sequence
(© Buick Div., G.M. Corp)

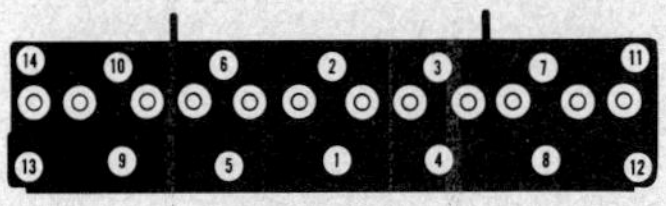

1968-71, 1974 L6

3. Reverse steps one through eight to finish installation.

Removal L6

1. Drain coolant.
2. Disconnect the exhaust pipe at the manifold flange, then remove the manifold bolts and clamps and remove the manifolds and carburetor as an assembly.
3. Remove the air conditioning compressor, if equipped, *but do not disconnect any lines.*
4. Disconnect the spark plug wires from the plugs.
5. Disconnect the fuel and vacuum lines from the retaining clip at the water outlet. Disconnect the wires from the temperature sending unit, and accelerator pedal at bellcrank.
6. Remove the upper radiator hose.
7. Remove the coil and rocker arm cover.
8. Loosen the rocker arm nuts and rotate the rocker arms so the pushrods can be removed, then remove the pushrods and store them so they can be installed in their original locations.

Chilton's TIME SAVER

The following is a method for replacing valve springs, oil seals, or spring retainers without removing the cylinder head.

1. **Obtain a spark plug hole air chuck adaptor from an auto parts store.**
2. **Add an air chuck to this adaptor so the hose from an air compressor can be attached. This assembly will be used later to pressurize the cylinder.**
3. **Remove the valve rocker cover. Remove the rocker arm from the valve to be worked on.**
4. **Remove the spark plug from the cylinder to be worked on.**
5. **Turn the crankshaft to bring the piston of this cylinder down, away from possible contact with the valve head. Sharply tap the valve retainer to loosen the valve lock.**
6. **Turn the crankshaft to bring the piston in this cylinder to the exact top of its compression stroke.**
7. **Screw in the chuck-equipped tool.**
8. **Hook up an air hose to the chuck and turn on the pressure (about 200 lbs).**
9. **With a strong and constant supply of air holding the valve closed, compress the valve spring and remove the lock and retainer.**
10. **Make the necessary replacements and reassemble.**

NOTE: it is important that the operation be performed exactly as stated, in this order. The piston in the cylinder must be on exact top-center to prevent air pressure from turning the crankshaft.

9. Remove the cylinder head bolts, cylinder head, and gasket.

V6

1. Drain coolant and disconnect battery ground strap.
2. Remove intake manifold.
3. For right head only: Remove Delcotron and air conditioning compressor. Do not disconnect compressor hoses.
4. For left head only: Remove dipstick, power steering pump, and A.I.R. equipment. Do not disconnect steering unit hoses.
5. Disconnect exhaust pipe from manifold, remove manifold.
6. Remove rocker cover, rocker shaft assembly, and pushrods. The pushrods should be reinstalled in their original locations. It is important to protect the hydraulic lifters from dirt.
7. Loosen all head bolts, then remove all bolts and remove head and gasket. Reverse the above steps to install. Torque head bolts to specifications in three stages.

1967-74 V8

1. Disconnect the battery.
2. Drain the coolant.

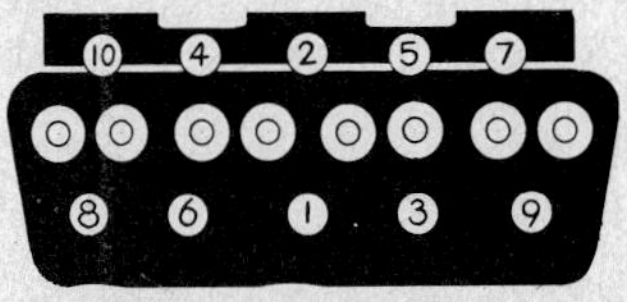

1970-74 350, 455 cu in.

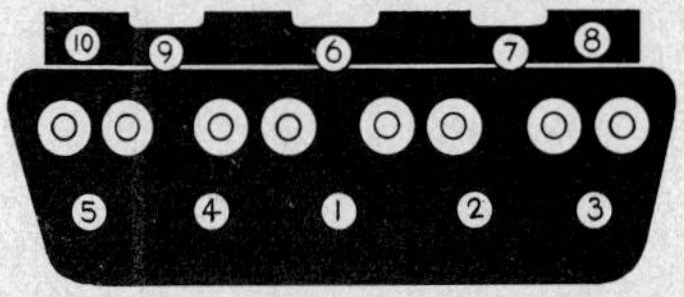

1967 300, 340 cu in., 1967-69 400 cu in., 1968-69 350 cu in.

9
3
1
6
8
7
5
2
4
10

1970-74 350, 455 cu in.

3. Remove the air cleaner.
4. Remove the air conditioning compressor, *but do not disconnect any lines.*
5. Remove the intake manifold.
6. When removing the right cylinder head, loosen the alternator belt and remove the alternator.
7. When removing the left cylinder head, remove the dipstick, power steering pump and AIR pump if so equipped.
8. Disconnect the plug wires.
9. Disconnect exhaust manifold from the head being removed.
10. Remove the rocker arm cover and rocker shaft assembly. Lift out the push rods.
11. Remove the cylinder head bolts.
12. Remove the cylinder head and gasket.
13. Reverse the above steps to install. Torque the head bolts to specifications in three steps.

Timing Cover, Chain, and Camshaft

Timing Chain, Cover Oil Seal, & Cover R & R

L6 Removal and Installation

1. Drain the cooling system and disconnect the radiator hoses at the radiator.
2. Remove the fan and water pump pulley.
3. Remove the radiator and fan belt.
4. Remove the harmonic balancer, using a puller.
5. Loosen the oil pan bolts and allow the pan to rest against the front crossmember.
6. Remove the timing gear cover bolts, then remove the cover and gasket.
7. Pry out the oil seal using a screwdriver.

NOTE: The seal can be replaced with the cover installed.

8. Install a new seal with the lip toward the inside of the cover. Drive it into place, using the proper seal installer or an old wheel bearing outer race.
9. Inspect the oil nozzle for damage and replace it if necessary, then clean all gasket surfaces.
10. Install the cover and gasket (stick the gasket to the block with Petroleum jelly or wheel bearing grease), making sure the cover is centered properly on the crankshaft end.
11. Tighten the cover bolts to 7 ft lbs, then install the oil pan and harmonic balancer.

Removal V6

1. Drain cooling system.
2. Disconnect radiator and heater hoses at water pump and disconnect lower radiator hose at radiator. Remove attaching bolts and brackets and remove radiator.
3. Remove fan, fan pulleys and belt, or belts.
4. Remove crankshaft pulley.
5. Remove harmonic balancer from crankshaft.
6. If car has power steering remove the pump bracket bolts and move the steering pump out of the way.
7. Disconnect lines and remove the fuel pump.
8. Remove generator.
9. Remove distributor cap and spark plug wire retainers from brackets on rocker arm cover. Swing distributor cap, with wires, out of the way. Disconnect distributor primary wire.
10. Remove distributor.
11. Loosen and slide front clamp on thermostat by-pass hose rearward.
12. Remove bolts attaching timing cover to cylinder block. Remove two oil pan to timing cover bolts.
13. Lift off the timing case cover. Pry the seal out with a screwdriver. Do not distort the cover.
14. Temporarily install harmonic balancer bolt and washer to the end of crankshaft. Rotate crankshaft so sprockets are positioned as for timing, (shafts and sprocket O-marks on a centerline). Now remove harmonic balancer bolt with a sharp rap on the wrench handle to prevent changing the position of the sprockets.
15. Remove front crankshaft oil slinger.
16. Remove bolt and special washer holding the camshaft distributor drive gear and fuel pump eccentric to the camshaft. Slide gear and eccentric off the shaft.
17. Use two large screwdrivers to alternately pry the camshaft sprocket then the crankshaft sprocket forward and off their respective shafts.
18. Thoroughly clean the sprockets, distributor drive gear, fuel pump eccentric and crankshaft oil slinger.

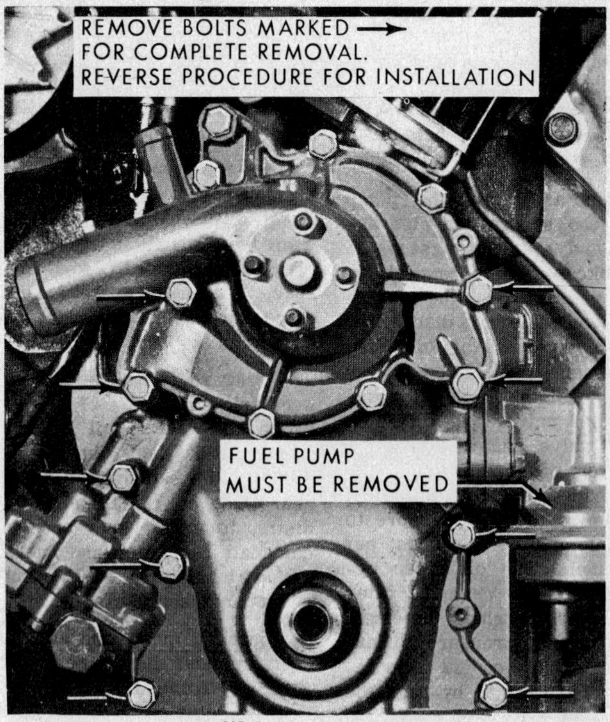
REMOVE BOLTS MARKED →
FOR COMPLETE REMOVAL.
REVERSE PROCEDURE FOR INSTALLATION
FUEL PUMP
MUST BE REMOVED

V6 timing chain cover
(© Buick Div., G.M. Corp)

REMOVE BOLTS MARKED →
FOR COMPLETE REMOVAL.
REVERSE PROCEDURE FOR INSTALLATION
FUEL PUMP
MUST BE
REMOVED

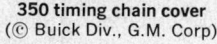

350 timing chain cover
(© Buick Div., G.M. Corp)

REMOVE BOLTS MARKED *
FOR COMPLETE REMOVAL.
REVERSE PROCEDURE
FOR INSTALLATION

455 timing chain cover
(© Buick Div., G.M. Corp)

Removal 400 Cu. In. 1967-69, 300, 340, 350 Cu. In. 1967-74

This procedure is the same as that detailed above for the 455 cu. in. engine with the substitution of the following steps:

9. Delete Step 9.
10. Remove bolt, special washer, camshaft distributor drive gear, and fuel pump eccentric from camshaft. Remove crankshaft oil slinger.

Installation V6 and V8, Except 1970-74 455 Cu. In.

1. Make sure, with sprockets temporarily installed, that No. 1 piston is at top dead center and the camshaft sprocket O-mark is straight down and on the centerline of both shafts.
2. Remove the camshaft sprocket and assemble the timing chain on both sprockets. Then slide the sprockets-and-chain assembly on the shafts with the O-marks in their closest together position and on a centerline with the sprocket hubs.
3. Assemble slinger on crankshaft with I.D. against the sprocket, (concave side toward front of engine).
4. Slide fuel pump eccentric on camshaft and Woodruff key with oil groove forward.
5. Install distributor drive gear.
6. Install drive gear and eccentric bolt and retaining washer. Torque to 40-55 ft. lbs.
7. Reinstall timing case cover. Install a new seal by lightly tapping it in place. The lip of the seal faces inward. By reversing removal procedure, paying particular attention to the following points.
   A. Remove oil pump cover and pack space around the oil pump gears completely full of petroleum jelly. There must be no air space left inside the pump. Reinstall the pump cover using new gasket.
   B. The gasket surface of the block and timing chain cover must be clean and smooth. Use a new gasket correctly positioned.
   C. Install chain cover being certain the dowel pins engage the dowel pin holes before starting the attaching bolts.
   D. Lube the bolt threads before installation and install them.
   E. If the car has power steering, the front pump bracket should be installed at this time.
   F. Lube the O.D. of the harmonic balancer hub before installation to prevent damage to the seal when starting the engine.

Installation 455 Cu. In.

This procedure is similar to that above for V6 and V8, except 1970-73 455 cu. in., with the substitution of the following steps:

4. Delete Step 4.
5. Reinstall oil pan.
6. Install camshaft sprocket bolts. Torque to 22 ft. lbs.

Camshaft R & R

L6—1968-71, 1974

1. Drain cooling system.
2. Remove radiator, fan, and water pump pulley.
3. Remove grille.
4. Remove valve cover and gasket, then loosen rocker arm nuts and pivot rockers out of the way.
5. Remove pushrods.
6. Remove distributor, fuel pump, and spark plugs.
7. Remove coil, pushrod (tappet gallery) covers and gasket; reach in and remove tappets, keeping them in order.
8. Remove harmonic balancer, then loosen oil pan bolts and allow pan to drop.
9. Remove timing gear cover.
10. Remove two camshaft thrust plate bolts by rotating cam gear holes to gain clearance.
11. Remove the camshaft by pulling it straight forward.

NOTE: do not wiggle the camshaft; cam bearings could be dislodged.

12. If cam gear is to be replaced, press it from the shaft using an arbor press.

NOTE: thrust plate must be positioned so that Woodruff key does not damage it during removal.

13. New cam gear must be pressed onto the shaft, with the shaft supported in back of the front bearing journal.

NOTE: the thrust plate end-play should be 0.001-0.005 in. If less than 0.001 in., replace spacer ring; if greater than 0.005 in., replace thrust plate.

14. Carefully install the camshaft into the engine, then turn crankshaft and camshaft so that timing marks coincide; tighten thrust plate bolts to 5–8 ft. lbs. Lubricate the camshaft lobes and bearings with heavy oil.
15. Check camshaft and crankshaft gear runout using a dial indicator. Cam gear runout should not exceed 0.004 in., crank gear runout should not exceed 0.003 in.

NOTE: if runout is excessive, remove gear and clean burrs from shaft.

16. Check gear backlash using a dial indicator; it should not exceed 0.006 in. and should not be less than 0.004 in.
17. To complete installation, reverse Steps 1-9.

NOTE: install distributor with No. 1 piston at TDC on compression stroke so that vacuum diaphragm faces forward and rotor points to No. 1 spark plug wire cap tower.

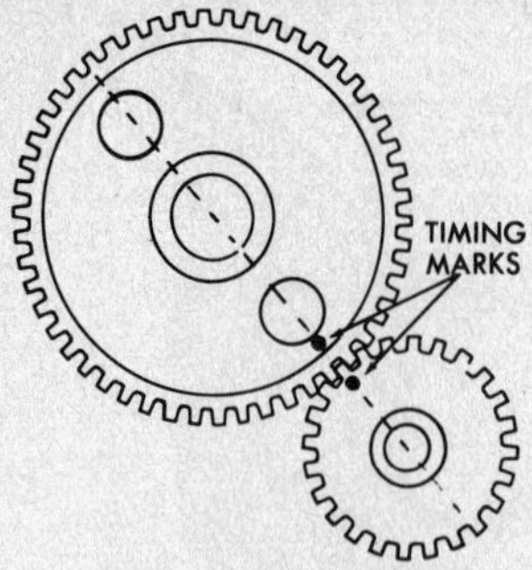
TIMING
MARKS

Timing marks—inline 6

Make sure oil pump drive shaft is properly indexed with distributor drive shaft.

V6 and V8

1. Drain the cooling system.
2. Remove the radiator, fan, and water pump pulley.
3. Remove the grille.
4. Remove the valve cover, rocker shaft assemblies, and push rods. Keep these parts in order. They must be reassembled in the same order.
5. Remove the distributor and fuel pump.
6. Remove the harmonic balancer, water pump timing chain cover assembly, timing chain, and sprocket.
7. Remove the intake manifold and the valley cover.
8. Remove the hydraulic lifters and keep them in order.
9. Slide the camshaft forward out of the bearing bores. Do this very carefully to avoid marring the bearing surfaces.
10. Reverse the above steps to install. Clean all gasket surfaces and use new gaskets. Make sure the camshaft timing marks are aligned. Lubricate the camshaft lobes and bearings with heavy oil.

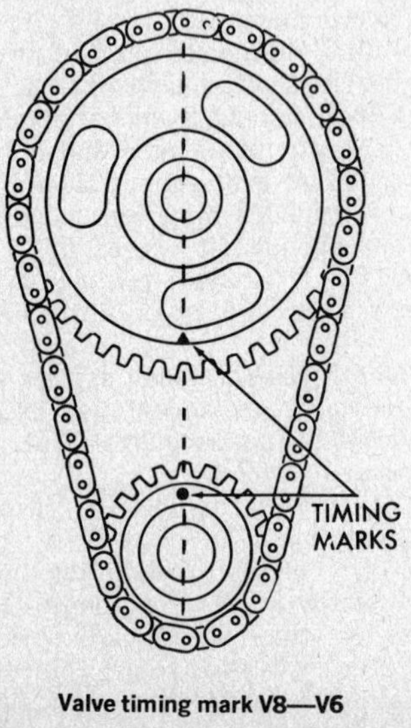
TIMING
MARKS

Valve timing mark V8—V6

Piston Assembly Removal

1. Remove cylinder heads.
2. Remove oil pan.
3. Examine cylinder bores for a ring ridge. If ridge exists, remove it before taking pistons out.

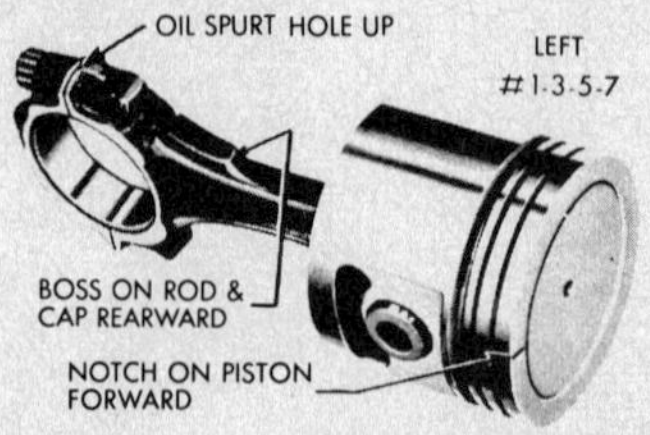
OIL SPURT HOLE UP
LEFT
#1-3-5-7
BOSS ON ROD &
CAP REARWARD
NOTCH ON PISTON
FORWARD

Piston and rod assembly, left bank—300, 340, 350, 455, starting 1967 400
(© Buick Div., G.M. Corp)

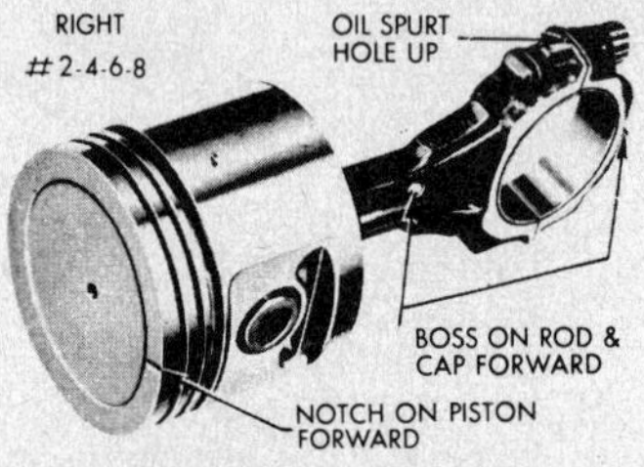
RIGHT
#2-4-6-8
OIL SPURT
HOLE UP
BOSS ON ROD &
CAP FORWARD
NOTCH ON PISTON
FORWARD

Piston and rod assembly, right bank—300, 340, 350, 455, starting 1967 400
(© Buick Div., G.M. Corp)

4. Number all the pistons, connecting rods and caps.

With the V6 engine the right bank is numbered 2-4-6. The left bank, 1-3-5, from the front. All V8 engines are numbered 1-3-5-7, left; and 2-4-6-8, right. The OHV 6 engine is numbered 1-2-3-4-5-6, front to rear.

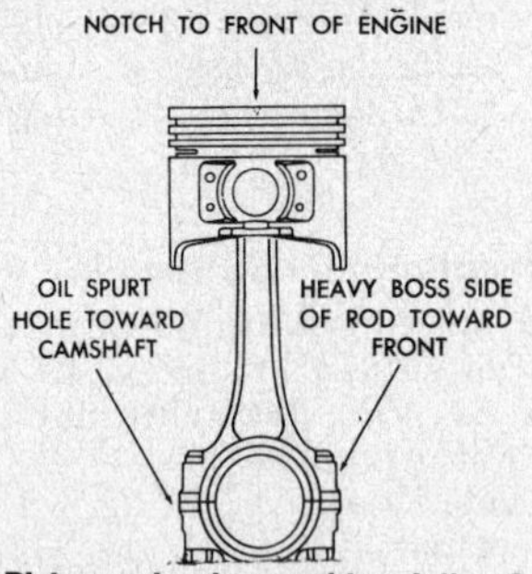
NOTCH TO FRONT OF ENGINE
OIL SPURT
HOLE TOWARD
CAMSHAFT
HEAVY BOSS SIDE
OF ROD TOWARD
FRONT

Piston and rod assembly—inline 6

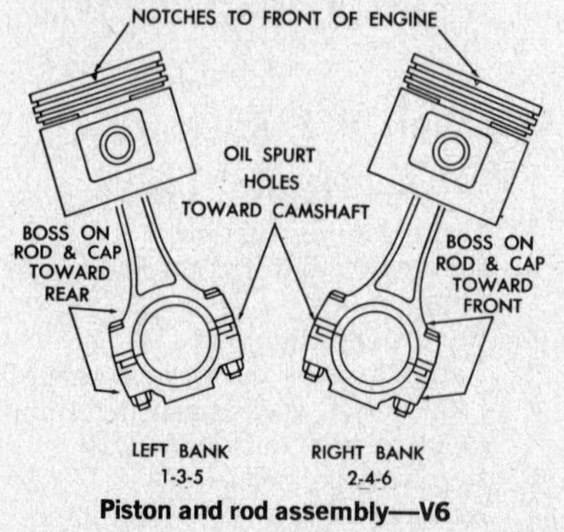
NOTCHES TO FRONT OF ENGINE
OIL SPURT
HOLES
TOWARD CAMSHAFT
BOSS ON
ROD & CAP
TOWARD
REAR
BOSS ON
ROD & CAP
TOWARD
FRONT
LEFT BANK
1-3-5
RIGHT BANK
2-4-6

Piston and rod assembly—V6

5. With No. 1 crankpin straight down, remove cap and bearing shell from No. 1 connecting rod.
6. Push piston and rod assembly up out of the cylinder. Then remove bolt guides and reinstall cap and bearing shell on the rod.
7. Remove the remaining rod and piston assemblies in the same manner.
8. Carefully remove old rings with piston ring expander.
9. Carefully press out the old pin.

NOTE: check the cylinder bores for distortion, taper or other damage. Any cylinders requiring attention may be bored or honed as required.

Piston Ring Replacement

1. Remove the old piston rings.
2. Clean any carbon, varnish, and any other deposits from the piston surfaces. The ring grooves may be cleaned with a suitable tool. A piece of broken ring may be used by scraping the ring groove with the sharp edge of the broken ring.
3. Place the ring at the bottom of the bore in that portion that is traveled by the rings. Measure the gap between the ends of the ring. If the gap is too wide, the ring is worn out. If the gap is too narrow, file the end of the ring until it is gapped to specification.

NOTE: square the ring in the bore with a piston.

Piston and Connecting Rod Replacement

1. Lubricate all the cylinder bores and bearings with oil.
2. Make sure the piston and connecting rod are aligned correctly and insert the assembly into its bore using a piston ring compressor tool.
3. Pull the assembly onto its crankpin, install the bearing cap, and tighten the bolts to specifications.
4. Install the oil pan and cylinder heads.

Lubrication

The engine lubrication system is the force feed type, in which oil is supplied under pressure to the crankshaft, connecting rods, camshaft bearings and valve lifters. Oil is supplied under controlled volume to the rocker arm bearings and pushrods. All other moving engine parts are lubricated by gravity flow or splash.

Oil Pump Removal and Installation

On the OHV 6, the oil pump is located in the oil pan and mounted to the front section of the cylinder block where it is connected to an oil screen housing and pipe assembly. On the V6 and V8s, the oil pump is located in the left side of the timing chain cover, where it is connected by a

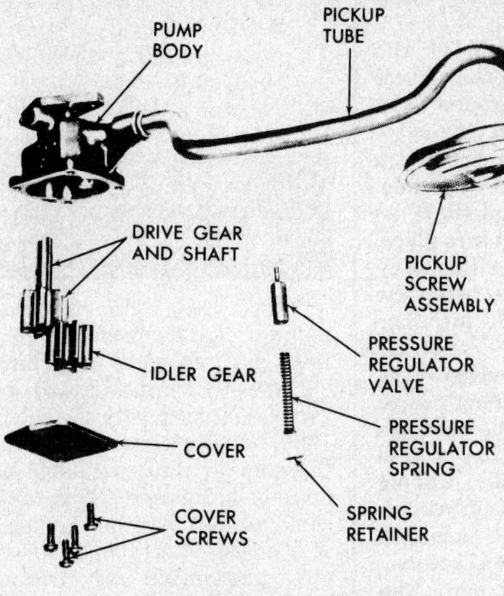
PUMP
BODY
PICKUP
TUBE
DRIVE GEAR
AND SHAFT
PICKUP
SCREW
ASSEMBLY
PRESSURE
REGULATOR
VALVE
IDLER GEAR
PRESSURE
REGULATOR
SPRING
COVER
COVER
SCREWS
SPRING
RETAINER

OHV 6 oil pump—exploded view
(© Buick Div., G.M. Corp)

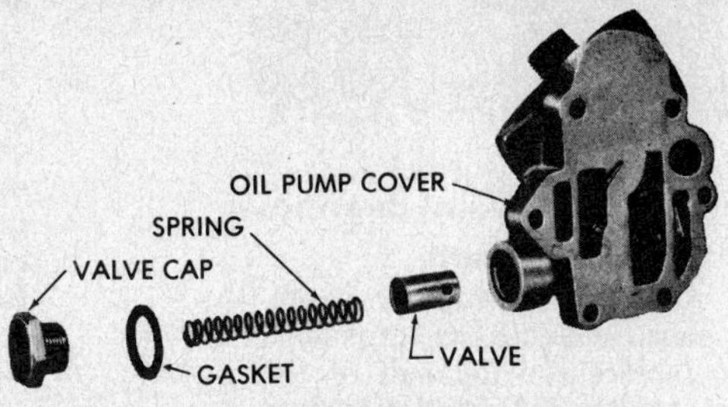
OIL PUMP COVER
SPRING
VALVE CAP
GASKET
VALVE

Oil pump cover and pressure relief valve—V8
(© Buick Div., G.M. Corp)

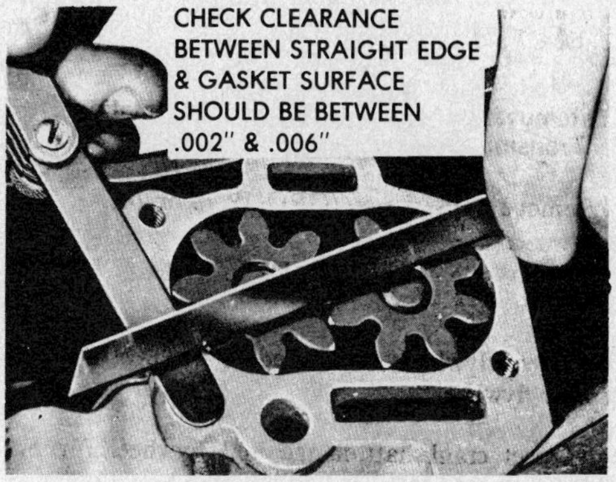
CHECK CLEARANCE
BETWEEN STRAIGHT EDGE
& GASKET SURFACE
SHOULD BE BETWEEN
.002" & .006"

Checking oil pump end clearance—V6 & V8
(© Buick Div., G.M. Corp)

drilled passage in the cylinder crankcase to an oil screen housing and standpipe assembly.

L6

1. Drain the oil and remove the oil pan.
2. Remove the two flange mounting bolts and nuts from the elongated No. 6 main bearing cap bolt and remove the pump and screen as an assembly.
3. To install, reverse the above procedure, being sure to tighten the mounting bolts to 9 ft lbs.

NOTE: The oil pump should slide easily into place. If not, remove it and relocate the slot.

V6 & V8

1. Remove the oil filter.
2. Remove the screws which attach the oil pump cover assembly to the timing chain cover. Remove the cover assembly and slide out the oil pump gears.
3. To install, reverse the removal procedure, being sure to check the clearance between the gear faces and the pump gasket surface. Clearance should be between 0.002 and 0.006 in.

NOTE: Pack the pump gears with petroleum jelly only. Unless the pump is packed with petroleum jelly, it may not prime itself when the engine is started.

Oil Pan Removal and Installation

V6 and V8 Engines

1. Raise car and support on stands.
2. Drain engine oil.
3. Disconnect exhaust pipe at crossover.
4. If standard transmission equipped, loosen clutch equalizer-to-frame attaching bolts.
5. Remove steering idler arm bracket-to-suspension crossmember attaching bolts.
6. Support engine with a padded jack under the crankshaft pulley mounting.
7. Remove engine mounting bolts.
8. Raise engine.
9. Remove flywheel housing inspection cover bolts. Then remove the inspection cover.
10. Remove oil pan bolts and lower the oil pan enough to remove oil pump pipe and screen-to-cylinder block attaching bolts.
11. Rotate crankshaft to provide maximum clearance at the front end of oil pan. Move the front of the pan to the right and lower the pan through opening between crossmember and steering linkage intermediate shaft.
12. Install by reversing removal procedure.

L6—1968-69

To remove the oil pan, it is necessary to remove the engine from the car. See Engine Removal.

L6—1970-71, 1974

1. Disconnect battery, remove air cleaner and disconnect throttle linkage.
2. Remove fan shroud-to-radiator tie bar screws.
3. Jack up car and support on axle stands under lower A-frames.
4. Drain engine oil.
5. If equipped with automatic transmission:
   a. Remove flywheel housing inspection cover.
   b. Remove shift linkage bolt and swing linkage out of way.
   c. Disconnect exhaust pipe at manifold.
6. Remove front motor mount bolts.
7. Jack up engine as far as it will go, with padded jack under crank pully mounting.
8. Remove front motor mounts completely to gain clearance.
9. Remove oil pan bolts and oil pan.
10. To install, reverse removal procedure, tightening pan bolts to 10 ft. lbs.

NOTE: Bolts into the timing gear cover should be installed last. They are installed at an angle and the holes line up after the rest of the oil pan bolts are tightened finger-tight.

Rear Main Bearing Oil Seal Replacement

L6

1. The rear main bearing oil seal can be replaced without removing the crankshaft. Remove the oil pan and rear main bearing cap.
2. Remove the seal from the bearing cap and clean the groove.
3. Remove the upper seal half by tapping the seal out with a brass punch until it can be grasped with pliers.
4. To replace the bearing cap seal, lubricate the groove in the cap

Chilton's TIME SAVER

Top Half, Rear Main Bearing Oil Seal Replacement

Although the factory recommends removing the crankshaft to replace the top half of the oil seal, the following procedure can be used without removing the crankshaft.

1. **Remove the oil pan and rear main bearing cap.**
2. **Loosen the rest of the crankshaft main bearings and allow the crankshaft to drop about 1/16 in.**
3. **Remove the old upper half of the oil seal.**
4. **Wrap some soft copper wire around the end of the new seal and leave about 12 in. on the end. Generously lubricate the new seal with oil.**
5. **Slip the free end of the copper wire into the oil seal groove and around the crankshaft. Pull the wire until the seal protrudes an equal amount on each side. Rotate the crankshaft as the seal is pulled into place.**
6. **Remove the wire. Push any excess seal that may be protruding back into the groove.**
7. **Before tightening the crankshaft bearing caps, visually check the bearings to make sure they are in place. Torque the bearing cap bolts to specifications. Make sure there is no oil on the parting surfaces.**
8. **Replace the oil pan. Run the engine slowly for the first few minutes of operation.**

and lightly press the seal in place. Do not cut the end of the seal. Do not get any oil on the parting line surface.

5. To replace the upper seal, lubricate the new seal with oil. Gradually push the seal in the groove in the block, while turning the crankshaft, until the seal is rolled into place.
6. Install the rear main bearing cap and torque it to specifications. Be sure the cross seal tabs are in place and properly seated. Make sure there is no oil on the parting line between the bearing cap and the block. Run the engine slowly for the first few minutes.

V6 and V8

1. Braided fabric seals are used. The upper seal half cannot be replaced without removing the crankshaft.
2. Remove the oil pan and rear main bearing cap.
3. Remove the old seal from the bearing cap and place a new seal in the groove with both ends projecting above the parting surface of the cap.
4. Force the seal into the groove by rubbing down with a hammer handle or smooth tool, until the seal projects above the groove not more than 1/16 in. Cut the ends off flush with the surface of the cap. Use a razor blade.
5. Use the same procedure to install a new upper seal half after removing the engine from the car and the crankshaft from the engine.

CLUTCH

A single plate, dry disc clutch is used in cars with manual transmissions. The unit is conventional in design with a diaphragm spring assembly. The clutch is not adjustable except for pedal clearance.

Clutch Removal

1967-74

1. Remove pedal return spring from clutch fork. Remove the transmission. On the 1966 Grand Sport, disconnect the lower clutch release rod assembly from the equalizer. Remove the equalizer.
2. Remove flywheel housing.
3. Remove throw-out bearing from clutch fork.
4. Disconnect clutch fork from ball stud.
5. Mark clutch cover and flywheel to assure proper balance on reassembly.
6. Loosen clutch cover to flywheel bolts one turn at a time until spring pressure is released.
7. Support pressure plate and cover assembly while removing last bolts, then remove cover assembly and driven plate.

Clutch Installation

Install clutch by reversing removal procedure. Use a clutch aligning pilot or a spare main drive gear through the hub of driven plate and into the pilot bushing. Be sure to align the clutch cover-to-flywheel index marks.

Clutch Linkage Adjustment

Check pedal lash (free-play) by pushing down on the pedal by hand. Lash should be approximately ¾ in. measured at the pedal pad.

1. Make sure the pedal is at full release position, contacting the rubber bumper stop. Remove return spring.
2. Adjust clutch release rod underneath car to give zero lash at the clutch pedal.
3. Back off release rod adjustment 2-3 turns to give ¾ in. lash at pedal pad. (Equals 1/16-1/8 in. at pushrod.)
4. Tighten locknut on clutch release rod.

MANUAL TRANSMISSION

There are three basic types of manual transmissions used. The first, a three-speed unit having synchromesh on all forward gears, became the basic three-speed unit in 1966. The second is a heavy duty three-speed unit, available only with floorshift linkage. This unit is the same as that used on the larger series of Buicks. The third is a four-speed, all synchromesh unit, equipped only with floorshift linkage.

For repair procedures see Unit Repair Section.

Removal and Installation

1. Mark the universal joint and transmission shaft companion flange for proper indexing at the time of installation. Remove the two U-bolts and disconnect the driveshaft at the rear joint. Slide the driveshaft rearward as far as possible and remove it.
2. Disconnect the shift linkage from the transmission.
3. Disconnect the speedometer cable at the transmission.
4. Loosen all three exhaust pipe ball joints to permit the transmission and the rear of the engine to be lowered if necessary.
5. Remove the two bolts holding the transmission mounting pad to the transmission support. Leave the mounting pad bolted to the transmission.
6. With a padded jack under the engine, raise the unit until the transmission mounting pad just clears the transmission support.
7. Remove the four bolts holding the transmission support to the body members. Remove the support, then lower the jack to allow the transmission to clear the underbody.
8. Remove the two top transmission-to-flywheel housing bolts and install a guide pin.

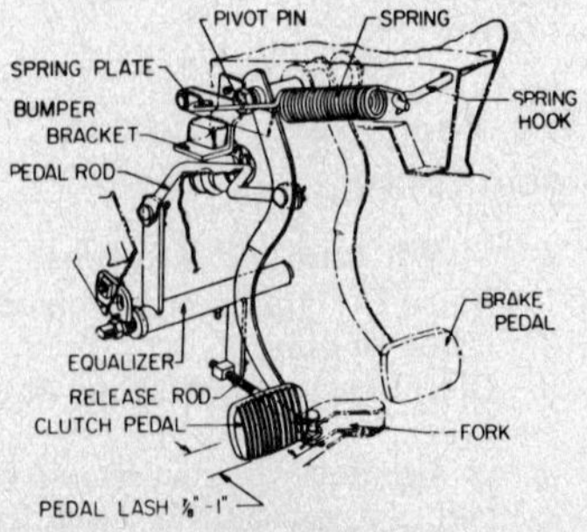
PIVOT PIN
SPRING
SPRING PLATE
BUMPER
BRACKET
SPRING HOOK
PEDAL ROD
BRAKE PEDAL
EQUALIZER
RELEASE ROD
CLUTCH PEDAL
FORK
PEDAL LASH ¾"-1"

Clutch linkage

NOTE: If guide pins are not used, damage to the clutch driven plate can result.

9. Remove the other transmission attaching bolts. Slide the transmission back until the drive gear shaft disengages the clutch disc and clears the flywheel housing. Lower the transmission.

Linkage Adjustment

Three-Speed Column Shift

1967

1. Place column shift lever in Neutral.
2. Place transmission levers into neutral positions.
3. Loosen shift rod adjusting clamp bolts.
4. Install a 3/16 in. dia. rod through first-reverse lever, selector plate, and second-third lever at bottom of steering column.
5. Push second-third shift rod through clamp until it sticks out from clamp ¼-½ in.
6. Tighten shift rod adjusting clamps to 17-23 ft. lbs.
7. Lift column shift lever straight up toward steering wheel several times to assure a free neutral crossover. If neutral detents do not line up, loosen first-reverse rod clamp, pull first-reverse rod through clamp no more than 3/16 in., and tighten clamp.

1968

This procedure is similar to that for 1967 models, with the substitution of the following step:

4. Install a 3/16 in. dia. rod through second-third lever, selector plate, first-reverse lever, and alignment plate.

1969-74

1. Place column shift lever in Reverse.
2. Loosen first-reverse clamp bolt.
3. Place transmission first-reverse lever into reverse position. Tighten clamp bolt to 17-23 ft. lbs.
4. Shift transmission levers into neutral positions.
5. Loosen second-third clamp bolt.
6. Install a 3/16 in. dia. rod through second-third lever, selector plate, first-reverse lever, and alignment plate.
7. Tighten second-third clamp bolt to 17-23 ft. lbs.

Three-Speed Floorshift

1. Place transmission levers into neutral.
2. Loosen shift rod adjusting clamp bolts.
3. Place a 5/16 in. dia. rod in notch in rear portion of shift bracket assembly.
4. Move both shift levers back against rod.
5. Tighten shift rod adjusting bolts to 17-23 ft. lbs.

Four-Speed Floorshift

1. Place transmission levers in neutral positions.
2. Place a 5/16 in. dia. rod in rear lower portion of shift bracket assembly.
3. Adjust all three shift levers back against rod.
4. Tighten adjusting clamp bolts to 17-23 ft. lbs.

Hurst Shift Linkage Adjustment

1. Shift transmission into Reverse.
2. Push "back drive" (steering lock) rod up into reverse detent in steering column (if applicable).
3. Tighten clamp screw to 17-23 ft. lbs.
4. Place all transmission and control levers in Neutral.
5. Insert a ¼ in. drill rod through adjustment hole in shifter and make sure all shift rods fit into their respective levers without tension. Adjust length of rods as necessary, then tighten swivel nuts.

Clutch Start Switch—1969-74

On all cars with manual transmission, a clutch start switch on the clutch pedal bracket prevents starting unless the clutch pedal is fully depressed. This switch is connected in series with the circuit from the ignition switch to the starter solenoid; therefore a no-start condition could be caused by its failure.

AUTOMATIC TRANSMISSION

Detent Cable Adjustment

Refer to the accompanying illustration for this procedure.

Shift Linkage Adjustment

Column Shift All Models

1. Place selector lever in Drive (Neutral for 1971 up).
2. Loosen adjusting clamp bolt.
3. Place lever at transmission in drive (Neutral for 1971 up) position.
4. Tighten clamp bolt to 17-23 ft. lbs.

Console Shift 1967

1. Place selector lever in Drive.
2. Loosen adjusting clamp bolt.
3. Place transmission in drive position.
4. Tighten clamp bolt to 17-23 ft. lbs.

Console Shift 1968-74

This linkage uses a cable rather than a shifting rod.

1. Loosen trunnion bolt.
2. Set selector lever in Drive.
3. Place transmission in drive position.
4. Tighten trunnion bolt to 6-9 ft. lbs.
5. For 1969-74 models only: Place selector lever in Park. Place transmission in park position. Push back drive rod (to steering column) up to stop and hold lightly. Tighten back drive rod clamp screw.

Neutral Safety Switch

This switch prevents the engine from being started in any transmis-

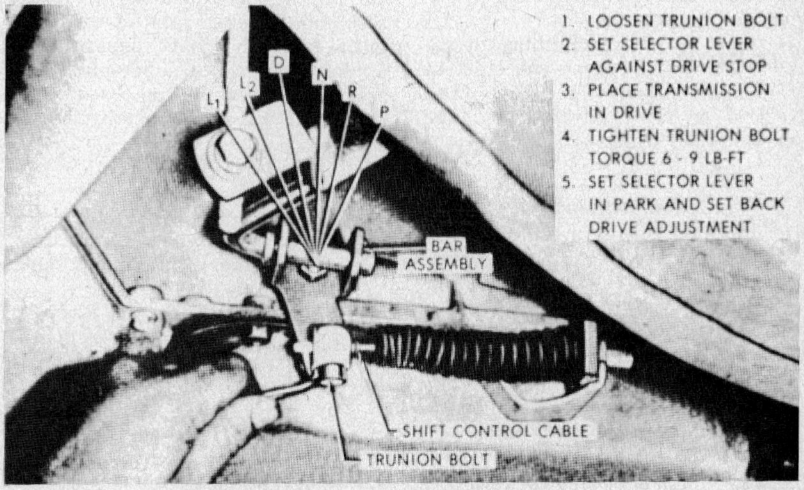

L1
L2
D
N
R
P
1. LOOSEN TRUNION BOLT
2. SET SELECTOR LEVER AGAINST DRIVE STOP
3. PLACE TRANSMISSION IN DRIVE
4. TIGHTEN TRUNION BOLT TORQUE 6 - 9 LB-FT
5. SET SELECTOR LEVER IN PARK AND SET BACK DRIVE ADJUSTMENT
BAR ASSEMBLY
SHIFT CONTROL CABLE
TRUNION BOLT

Turbo-Hydramatic 350 and 400 linkage adjustment console shifter
(© Buick Div., G.M. Corp)

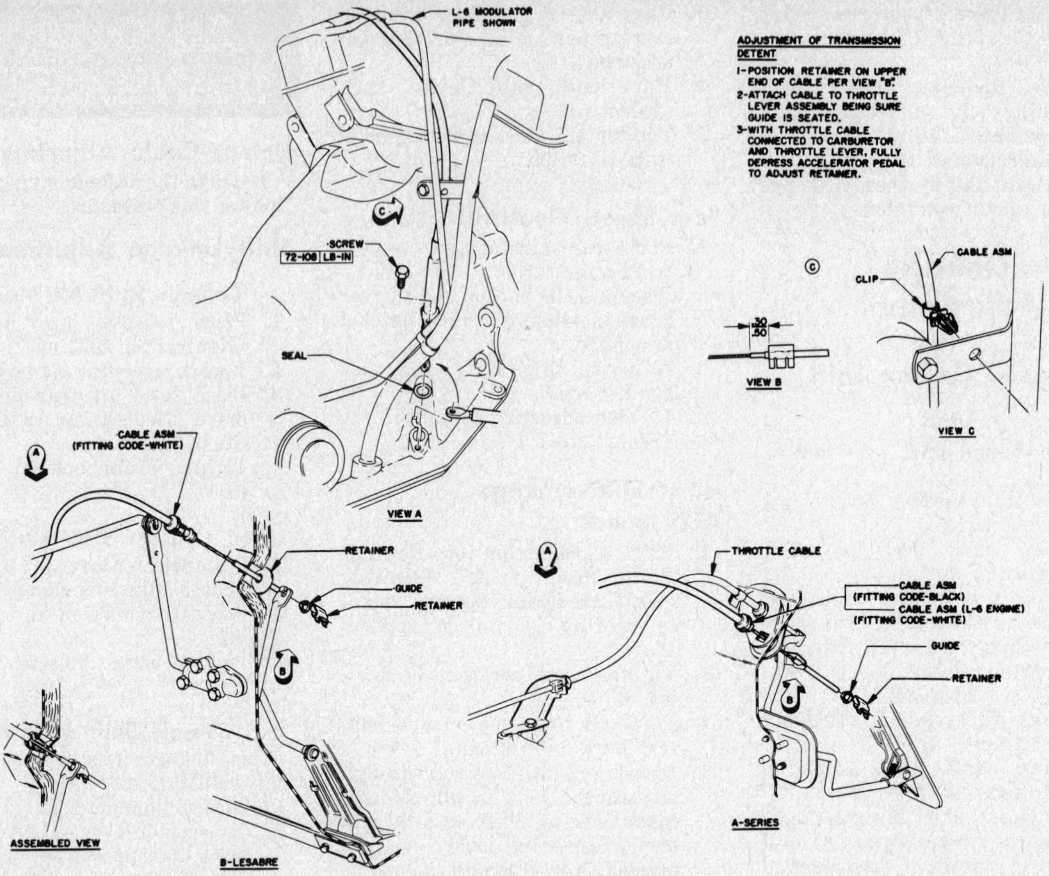
L-6 MODULATOR PIPE SHOWN
ADJUSTMENT OF TRANSMISSION DETENT
1-POSITION RETAINER ON UPPER END OF CABLE PER VIEW "B".
2-ATTACH CABLE TO THROTTLE LEVER ASSEMBLY BEING SURE GUIDE IS SEATED.
3-WITH THROTTLE CABLE CONNECTED TO CARBURETOR AND THROTTLE LEVER, FULLY DEPRESS ACCELERATOR PEDAL TO ADJUST RETAINER.
SCREW
72-108 LB-IN
SEAL
CABLE ASM
CLIP
.30
.50
VIEW B
VIEW C
CABLE ASM (FITTING CODE-WHITE)
VIEW A
RETAINER
GUIDE
RETAINER
THROTTLE CABLE
CABLE ASM (FITTING CODE-BLACK)
CABLE ASM (L-6 ENGINE) (FITTING CODE-WHITE)
GUIDE
RETAINER
ASSEMBLED VIEW
B-LESABRE
A-SERIES

Transmission detent cable adjustment—Turbo-Hydramatic 350
(© Buick Div., G.M. Corp)

sion position except Neutral or Park. The back-up light switch is combined with the neutral safety switch. On column shift cars and 1971-74 models with console shift, the switch is located on the steering column under the instrument panel. On console shift cars, the switch is located inside the console. When the neutral start portion of the switch is correctly adjusted, the back-up portion is adjusted automatically. Slotted mounting screw holes permit switch movement for adjustment.

Caution when checking to see if engine will start in transmission positions other than Neutral or Park, always hold the service brake firmly.

Adjustment

1. Place the shifter lever in Park.
2. Loosen the switch retaining screws. Make sure the switch drive tang is engaged in the shifter tube slot and that it stays engaged during adjustment.
3. Rotate the switch in its slot until it is in the Park position and tighten the screws.
4. After observing the above caution, check the shifter pattern by placing the shifter lever in neutral. If the transmission does not shift into neutral, place the lever back in Park and rotate the switch slightly until the shift pattern is correct.
5. If it is possible to move the shift lever a large distance without having the transmission respond, check for a worn switch drive tang or bad electrical contacts inside the switch. In either case replace the switch.

U-JOINTS

The driveshaft is a one piece unit with a splined slip yoke and a universal joint at the transmission end, and a second universal joint at the differential end. The shaft, depending on application, can be a one-piece solid steel unit, or can be composed of two concentric tubes damped with rubber.

Driveshaft R & R

1. Mark the driveshaft rear yoke and the differential flange to assure correct alignment upon reassembly.
2. Remove the bolts and straps or four bolts on double cardon U-joint from the differential flange.
3. Remove the driveshaft assembly by first sliding the driveshaft sufficiently forward to disengage the differential flange and then slide the shaft downward and rearward to disengage the front splined yoke from the transmission output shaft.
4. Installation is the reverse of removal. Be sure to align the match marks made before disassembly.

Single Universal Joint R & R —1967-74

Nylon-injected composite universal joints are used. To replace universal joints:

1. Remove the driveshaft.
2. By using a piece of pipe or similar tool, slightly larger than $1\frac{1}{8}$ in. to encircle the bearing shell, apply force on the yoke until downward movement of the yoke and stationary position of journal force the bearing assembly almost out of the top of the yoke (the force applied on the yoke will shear nylon retainers which lock bearings in place).
3. Rotate propeller shaft 180° and repeat preceding step to partially remove the opposite bearing.
4. Complete removal of these bearings by tapping around the circumference of exposed portion of bearing.
5. Remove journal from driveshaft rear yoke.
6. Remove bearings and journal from splined yoke in the same way.

NOTE: new bearings and journal assembly kits must be used upon reassembly. The kit includes snaprings and Delrin washers.

7. Install by inserting one bearing

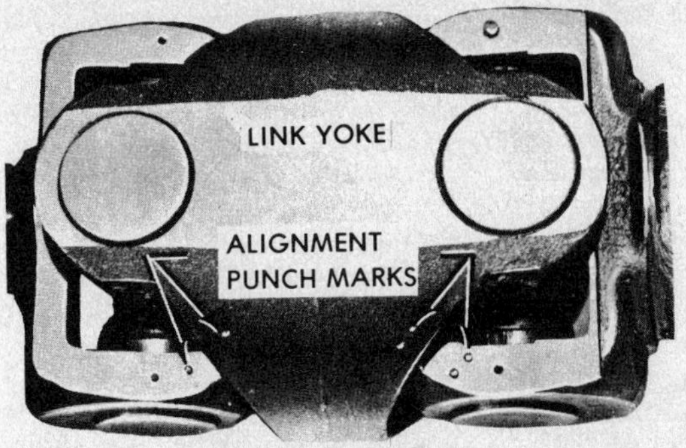
LINK YOKE
ALIGNMENT
PUNCH MARKS
Alignment punch marks
(© Buick Div., G.M. Corp)

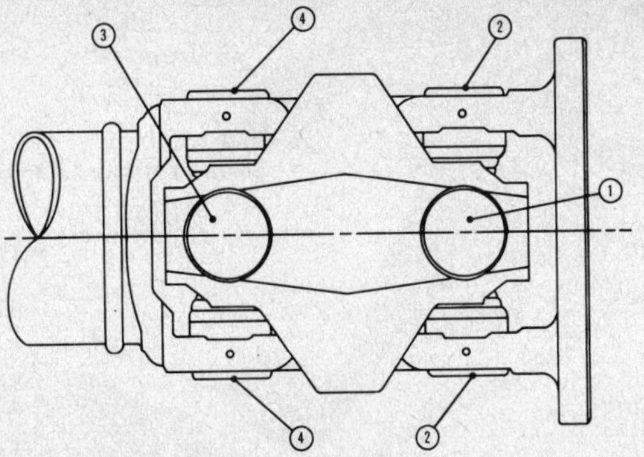
3
4
2
1
4
2
Bearing cup removal sequence
(© Buick Div., G.M. Corp)

one-quarter way in one side of splined yoke, using brass hammer.
8. Insert journal into splined yoke (with dust shields installed).
9. Install opposite bearing, ensuring that the bearing rollers do not jam on journal. Check free rotary movement of journal in bearing.
10. Now, press both bearings into place (just far enough to install snap rings).
11. Assemble opposite end universal in the same way.

Double Cardon Constant Velocity Rear U-Joint R & R

Removal

1. Using a punch, mark the link yoke and the adjoining yokes before disassembly to ensure proper reassembly and driveshaft balance.

NOTE: it is easier to remove the universal joint bearings from the flange yoke first. The first pair of flange yoke universal joint bearings to be removed is the pair in the link yoke.

2. With the driveshaft in a horizontal position, solidly support the link yoke (a 1⅞ in. pipe will do).
3. Apply force to the bearing cup on the opposite side with a 1⅛ in. pipe or a socket the size of the bearing cup. Use a hammer, vise, or press to apply force. Force the cup inward as far as possible.

NOTE: in the absence of a press, a heavy vise may be used, but make sure that the universal to be removed is at a right angle to the jaws of the vise. Do not cock the bearing cups in their bores.

4. Remove the pieces of pipe and complete the removal of the protruding bearing cup by tapping around the circumference of the exposed portion of the bearing with a small hammer.
5. Reverse the positions of the pieces of pipe and apply force to the exposed journal end. This

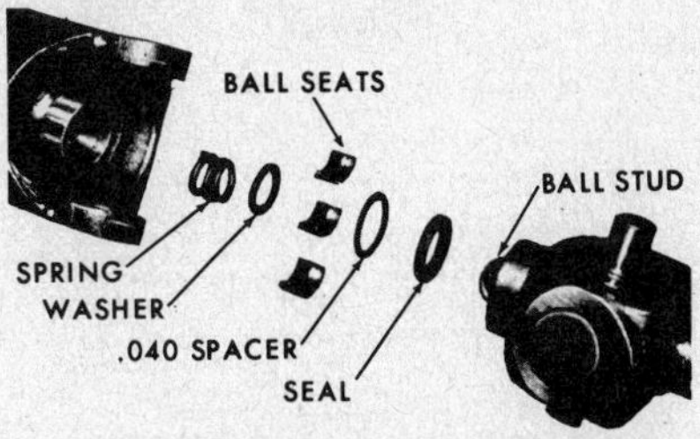
BALL SEATS
BALL STUD
SPRING
WASHER
.040 SPACER
SEAL
Exploded view ball joint double cardon rear universal
(© Buick Div., G.M. Corp)

will force the other bearing cup out of its bore and allow removal of the flange.

NOTE: there is a ball joint located between the two universals. The ball portion of this joint is on the inner end of the flange yoke. Care must be taken not to damage the ball. The ball seat is in the end of the driveshaft. To remove the seat, pry the seal out with a screwdriver.

6. To remove the journal from the flange, use steps two through five.
7. Remove the universal joint bearings from the driveshaft using the steps from two through five. The first pair of bearing cups that should be removed is the pair in the link yoke.

Installation

1. Examine ball stud seat and ball stud for scores or wear. Worn seats can be replaced with a kit, a worn ball however requires the replacement of the entire propeller shaft yoke and flange assembly. Clean the ball seat cavity and fill it with grease. Install the spring, washer, ball seats and spacer, if removed.
2. Install the universal joints opposite the order in which they were disassembled.
3. Install a bearing ¼ of the way into one side of the yoke.
4. Insert the journal into the yoke so that an arm of the journal seats into the bearing.
5. Press the bearing in the remaining distance and install its snap-ring.
6. Install the opposite bearing. Do not allow the bearing rollers to jam. Continually check for free movement of the journal in the bearings as they are pressed into the yoke.
7. Install the rest of the bearings in the same manner.

JACKING, HOISTING

Jack car at front spring seat of lower control arm or center of cross member.

Jack car at rear at axle housing.

To lift at frame, use side rails in front of body floor pan and at rear side rail at lower control arm front pivot.

FRONT SUSPENSION

Ball joints, located at the outer ends of the upper and lower control arms, act as pivot points for both the vertical movement of the wheel and rotation of the steering knuckle. The spherical joints have a fixed boot grease seal to protect against dirt and water. Steering knuckles and spindles are one-piece forgings.

Rubber bushings at the upper inner control arm ends pivot on shafts attached to the frame. By varying shim thickness at this point, caster and camber are adjusted. The inner ends of the lower control arms are also rubber mounted and are attached to the front crossmember by brackets.

The upper ends of the coil springs are seated in the frame, while the lower ends rest on the lower control arms. Double-action shock absorbers are located inside the coil springs, the rubber insulated upper end of each unit being fastened to the frame, the similarly insulated lower end to the lower control arm.

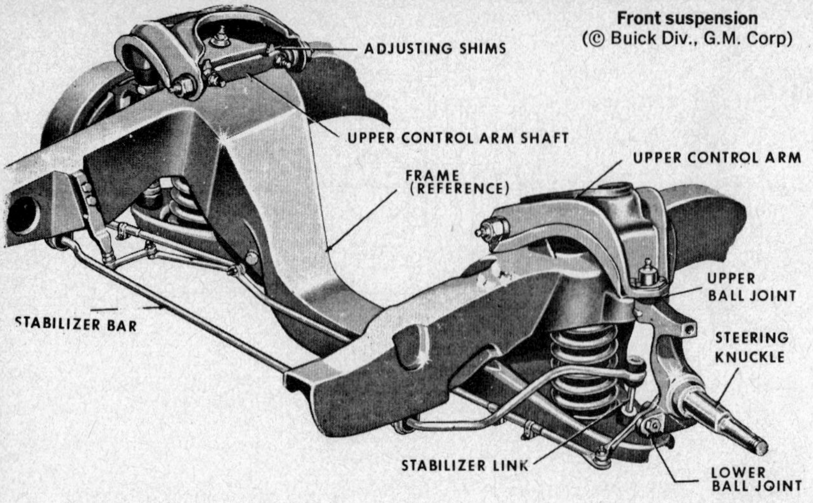
ADJUSTING SHIMS
UPPER CONTROL ARM SHAFT
UPPER CONTROL ARM
FRAME (REFERENCE)
UPPER BALL JOINT
STABILIZER BAR
STEERING KNUCKLE
STABILIZER LINK
LOWER BALL JOINT

Front suspension
(© Buick Div., G.M. Corp)

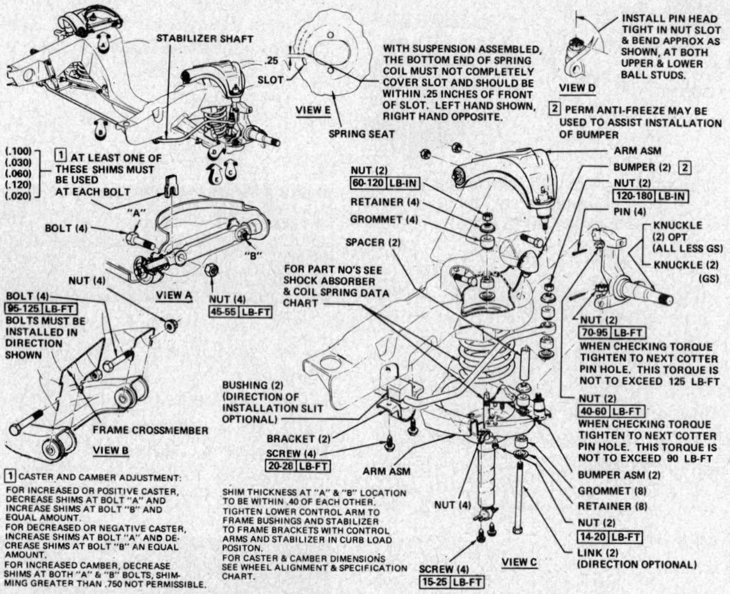
STABILIZER SHAFT
.25
SLOT
VIEW E
SPRING SEAT
WITH SUSPENSION ASSEMBLED, THE BOTTOM END OF SPRING COIL MUST NOT COMPLETELY COVER SLOT AND SHOULD BE WITHIN .25 INCHES OF FRONT OF SLOT. LEFT HAND SHOWN, RIGHT HAND OPPOSITE.
INSTALL PIN HEAD TIGHT IN NUT SLOT & BEND APPROX AS SHOWN, AT BOTH UPPER & LOWER BALL STUDS.
VIEW D
2 PERM ANTI-FREEZE MAY BE USED TO ASSIST INSTALLATION OF BUMPER
(.100) (.030) (.060) (.120) (.020)
1 AT LEAST ONE OF THESE SHIMS MUST BE USED AT EACH BOLT
"A"
"B"
BOLT (4)
NUT (4)
VIEW A
NUT (4) 45-55 LB-FT
BOLT (4) 95-125 LB-FT
BOLTS MUST BE INSTALLED IN DIRECTION SHOWN
FRAME CROSSMEMBER
VIEW B
NUT (2) 60-120 LB-IN
RETAINER (4)
GROMMET (4)
SPACER (2)
FOR PART NO'S SEE SHOCK ABSORBER & COIL SPRING DATA CHART
ARM ASM
BUMPER (2) 2
NUT (2) 120-180 LB-IN
PIN (4)
KNUCKLE (2) OPT (ALL LESS GS)
KNUCKLE (2) (GS)
NUT (2) 70-95 LB-FT
WHEN CHECKING TORQUE TIGHTEN TO NEXT COTTER PIN HOLE. THIS TORQUE IS NOT TO EXCEED 125 LB-FT
BUSHING (2) (DIRECTION OF INSTALLATION SLIT OPTIONAL)
BRACKET (2)
SCREW (4) 20-28 LB-FT
ARM ASM
NUT (2) 40-60 LB-FT
WHEN CHECKING TORQUE TIGHTEN TO NEXT COTTER PIN HOLE. THIS TORQUE IS NOT TO EXCEED 90 LB-FT
BUMPER ASM (2)
GROMMET (8)
RETAINER (8)
NUT (4)
NUT (2) 14-20 LB-FT
LINK (2) (DIRECTION OPTIONAL)
VIEW C
SCREW (4) 15-25 LB-FT
1 CASTER AND CAMBER ADJUSTMENT:
FOR INCREASED OR POSITIVE CASTER, DECREASE SHIMS AT BOLT "A" AND INCREASE SHIMS AT BOLT "B" AND EQUAL AMOUNT.
FOR DECREASED OR NEGATIVE CASTER, INCREASE SHIMS AT BOLT "A" AND DECREASE SHIMS AT BOLT "B" AN EQUAL AMOUNT.
FOR INCREASED CAMBER, DECREASE SHIMS AT BOTH "A" & "B" BOLTS, SHIMMING GREATER THAN .750 NOT PERMISSIBLE.
SHIM THICKNESS AT "A" & "B" LOCATION TO BE WITHIN .40 OF EACH OTHER.
TIGHTEN LOWER CONTROL ARM TO FRAME BUSHINGS AND STABILIZER TO FRAME BRACKETS WITH CONTROL ARMS AND STABILIZER IN CURB LOAD POSITON.
FOR CASTER & CAMBER DIMENSIONS SEE WHEEL ALIGNMENT & SPECIFICATION CHART.

Typical front suspension and wheel alignment details—1967-72
(© Buick Div., G.M. Corp)

For increased roll stability, a stabilizer bar is rubber mounted to the frame and is connected to the lower control arms via links at each end.

Ball Joint Inspection

NOTE: before performing this inspection, make sure the wheel bearings are adjusted correctly and that the A arm bushings are in good condition.

1. Jack up the car under the front lower control arm at the spring seat.
2. Raise the car until there is 1–2 in. of clearance under the wheel.
3. Insert a bar under the wheel and pry upward. If the wheel raises more than 1/8 in. the ball joints are worn. Determine if the upper or lower ball joint is worn by visual inspection while prying on the wheel.

NOTE: due to the distribution of forces in the suspension, the lower ball joint is usually the defective joint.

Control Arm, and/or Ball Joint, Spring—Removal and Installation

Upper Control Arm

1. Raise the car and place a jack under the frame. Remove the wheel and tire.
2. Remove the cotter pin from the upper ball joint stud.
3. Loosen, but do not remove, the nut. Rap the knuckle sharply in the area of the tapered stud to free the stud from the knuckle.
4. With another jack, support the car weight under the outer edge of the lower control arm. Raise the jack enough to free the upper control arm from the upper ball stud.
5. Wire the brake and knuckle in place to prevent brake hose damage, then lift the upper arm from the knuckle.

NOTE: If only the ball joints are to be replaced, stop at this point. Center punch and drill out the four rivets, then chisel off their heads. Remove the old ball joint. The new joint comes with four specially hardened bolts which must be torqued to 8 ft lbs. The nut goes on top.

6. Remove the upper control arm shaft-to-bracket nuts and lock washers. Carefully note the number, thickness, and location of the adjusting shims. Remove the control arm assembly.
7. Reverse the above steps to install.

Caution When installing the cotter pin, never loosen the nut to align the cotter pin holes. Always tighten the nut to the next slot that lines up with the hole.

Lower Control Arm or Spring

1. Raise the front of the car and remove the tires, wheels, hub, and drum or rotor.
2. Disconnect and remove the shock absorber.
3. Remove the front stabilizer rod link from the lower control arm.
4. Disconnect the brake reaction rod from the lower control arm but leave it attached to the front frame crossmember up to 1970 models.
5. Remove the control arm bumper up to 1970 models.
6. As a safety precaution and to gain maximum leverage, place a jack about 1/2 in. below the lower ball joint stud. Now, remove the ball stud cotter pin and loosen the nut about 1/8 in. Do not remove the nut.
7. Rap the steering knuckle in the area of the stud to separate the stud from the knuckle.
8. After the stud has broken loose from the knuckle, raise the jack against the control arm. Remove the nut and separate the steering knuckle from the tapered stud.
9. Carefully lower the jack under the control arm and release the spring. With the jack entirely lowered, it may be necessary to pry the spring off its seat on the lower control arm with a pry bar.
10. After the spring is removed, the lower control arm may be removed by removing the lock nut which attaches the control arm to the frame.
11. Install by reversing the removal procedure. Tighten the castellated nut to 85 ft lbs.

Lower Ball Joint Removal and Installation

1. Perform Steps 2-8, inclusive, in the "Lower Control Arm" procedure.
2. Remove the ball joint by pressing the joint from the lower control arm. It may be necessary to remove the ball joint and lower

control arm as an assembly and have the ball joint removed in a press if suitable tools are not available.

3. Install a new ball joint and reverse the removal procedure.

Front Wheel Bearing Adjustment

1967-70

Adjustment of freshly cleaned and repacked roller bearings is as follows:

1. Torque the spindle nut to 19 ft lbs while rotating the wheel.
2. Back off the nut until the bearings are loose.
3. Retorque the spindle nut to 11 ft lbs while rotating the wheel.
4. If either cotter pin hole in the spindle lines up with the nut castellations, back off the nut ½ turn and install the cotter pin. Otherwise, back off the nut to the first position that will accept a horizontal or vertical cotter pin.
5. Install the cotter pin and lock spindle nut into position.

NOTE: 0.002-0.006 in. end-play is normal.

1971-74

1. Lift the wheel off the ground by jacking under the lower control arm.
2. Remove the dust cap from the hub.
3. Remove the cotter pin and discard it.
4. Snug up the spindle nut to seat the bearings. Then back off the nut ¼-½ turn.
5. Retighten the nut by hand until it is finger-tight.
6. Loosen the nut until the nearest hole in the spindle lines up with a slot in the spindle nut, and insert a new cotter pin.

NOTE: Under no circumstance is the final bearing nut adjustment to be even finger-tight.

7. Feel the looseness in the hub assembly. There will be 0.002-0.006 in. end-play.
8. Replace the dust cover and lower the car.

Shock Absorber R & R

1. Remove the upper shock absorber attaching nut, grommet retainer, and grommet.
2. Remove the lower retaining screws. Lower the shock through the hole in the lower control arm.
3. Reverse the above steps to install.

REAR SUSPENSION

Shock Absorber R & R

1. Raise car at the axle housing.
2. Remove the nut, retainer, and grommet or nut and lockwasher, as equipped, which attach the lower end of the shock absorber to its mounting.
3. Remove the two shock absorber upper attaching screws and remove the shock absorber.
4. Reverse the removal procedures to install.

Rear Leaf Spring Replacement—1971-72 Station Wagon

1. Jack up car at axle housing. Make sure you don't crush the exhaust pipe.
2. Support the car at both frame side rails, using axle stands.
3. Remove the nut and lockwasher from the lower shock stud.
4. Move the shock out of the way.
5. Remove the spring anchor plate nuts, then remove the anchor plate and cushion.
6. Jack the axle housing up and remove the upper cushion.
7. Loosen the upper and lower spring shackle nuts.
8. Loosen the front spring eyebolt.
9. Remove the front eyebolt and carefully lower the spring.
10. Support the spring and remove the lower shackle pin.
11. Remove the spring.
12. To install, reverse the removal procedure. Tighten the front eyebolt to 75 ft lbs, shackle nuts to 95 ft lbs, and the lower shock nut to 65 ft lbs.

Rear Coil Spring Replacement

1. Jack up the back of the car and support both sides on stand jacks on the frame, in front of the rear axle. Disconnect the shock absorber.

NOTE: It may be necessary to disconnect the rear brake line in order to obtain sufficient axle drop to remove the spring. If this is done, first depress and secure the brake pedal at least 1 in. from the relaxed position to prevent the master cylinder from draining when the rear brake line is disconnected.

2. Place a jack under the lower trailing arm and remove the bolts which hold the trailing arm to the rear axle housing.

NOTE: the spring can often be removed without disconnecting the lower control arm.

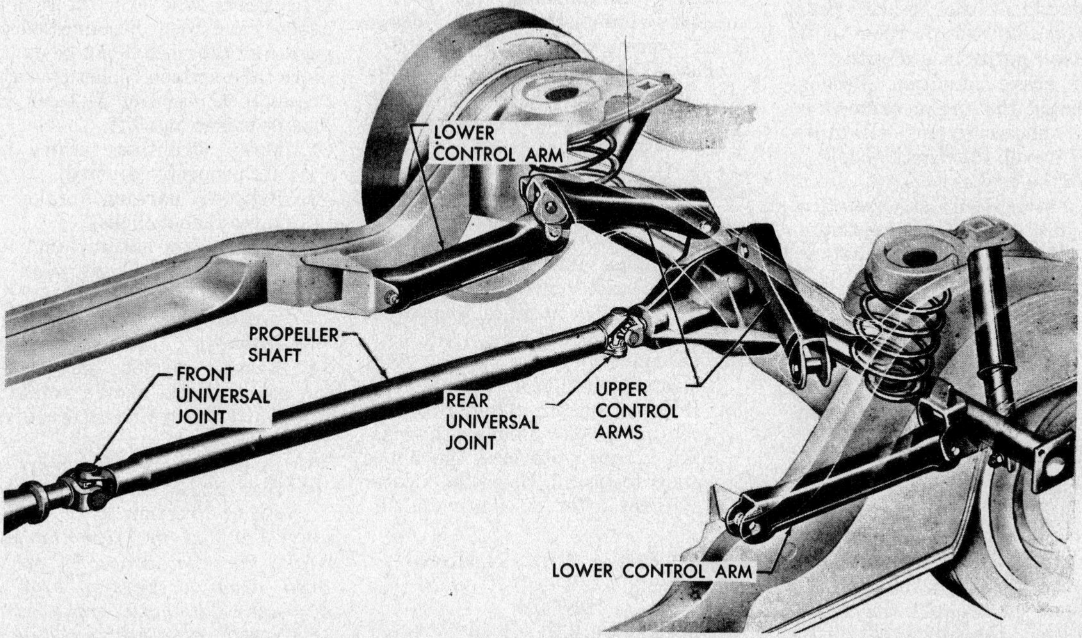
LOWER CONTROL ARM
PROPELLER SHAFT
FRONT UNIVERSAL JOINT
REAR UNIVERSAL JOINT
UPPER CONTROL ARMS
LOWER CONTROL ARM

Rear suspension except 1971-72 station wagon—1967-72 (© Buick Div., G.M. Corp)

3. Slowly, and very carefully, let the trailing arm come down until the tension is released from the rear coil spring. Then, take off the coil spring. Note the direction in which the end of the last coil is pointing. Reinstall the spring in the same position.
4. When starting a new coil spring, make certain that the bottom of the coil is properly inserted into the socket in the frame and into the form plate on the trailing arm.
5. Jack the trailing arm into place and reinstall the trailing arm rear bolt.

BRAKES

Drum Brakes

The service brakes are of the conventional type, hydraulically operated. The primary shoe lining is shorter than the secondary lining and is of different composition. The primary shoe goes toward the front of the car.

Brake drum lining-contact-surfaces are cast iron, however, the drum proper is pressed steel or cast aluminum with integral cooling fins.

The parking brake on all models is operated by a foot pedal and actuates the rear brakes only.

The brakes are self-adjusting. The system is designed to react and progressively tighten the star wheel adjuster, a notch at a time, as required. The self-adjusters only operate when the brakes are applied while the car is moving rearward.

For detailed service brake information, see Unit Repair Section.

Pedal Travel Check

The distance the brake pedal moves from its rest position to its fully applied position is a good indication of brake condition. Because heat expands the brake drums and increases shoe-to-drum clearance, and pedal travel, this check should be made with the brakes *cold*.

NOTE: dimensions are the *maximum* pedal travel—not optimum. Starred (*) dimensions are distance from floor.

Year	*Manual Drum*	*Power Drum(†)*
1967-70	*2¼″	*1½″
1971-74	4¾″	2⅜″

†Pump power brakes before checking.

Pedal Height and Stop Light Switch Adjustment

1967-74

Brake pedal height is not adjustable because of solid design pushrod. In addition, no brake pedal return spring is used; the spring within the master cylinder returns the brake to rest position. Stop light switch is adjusted by turning switch in or out so that plunger is fully depressed against plate with pedal in released position.

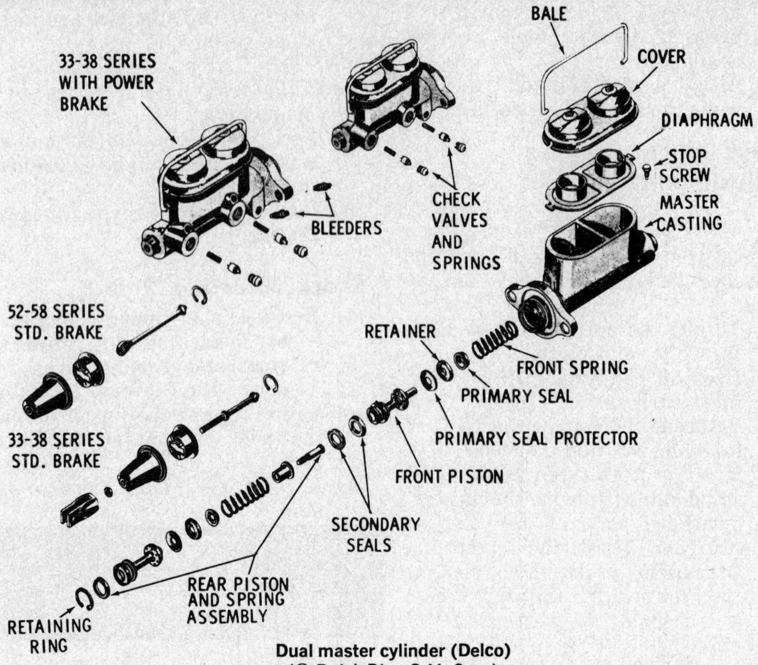
BALE
COVER
33-38 SERIES WITH POWER BRAKE
DIAPHRAGM
STOP SCREW
MASTER CASTING
BLEEDERS
CHECK VALVES AND SPRINGS
52-58 SERIES STD. BRAKE
RETAINER
FRONT SPRING
PRIMARY SEAL
PRIMARY SEAL PROTECTOR
33-38 SERIES STD. BRAKE
FRONT PISTON
SECONDARY SEALS
REAR PISTON AND SPRING ASSEMBLY
RETAINING RING

Dual master cylinder (Delco)
(© Buick Div., G.M. Corp)

Master Cylinder

A tandem master cylinder is standard equipment on all models. This type system is covered in the Unit Repair Section.

Disc Brakes

Disc brakes were optional on the front wheels of some models until the 1973 model year when they became standard equipment. For 1967-68 models, four-piston Delco-Moraine discs were optional. For 1969-73 models, a single-piston Delco-Moraine disc brake begin is utilized. Information on disc brakes is in the Unit Repair Section.

Master Cylinder Removal

1967-74

1. Disconnect brake pipe or pipes from master cylinder and tape end of pipe or pipes to prevent entrance of dirt.
2. Disconnect brake pedal from master cylinder at the pushrod.
3. Remove master cylinder-to-dash retaining bolts. Remove the master cylinder. Reverse the above steps to install. Bleed the master cylinder after it is reinstalled.

Power Brake Unit Removal

1967-74

1. Disconnect brake pipe or pipes from hydraulic master cylinder and tape pipe ends to exclude dirt.
2. Disconnect vacuum hose from power brake unit.
3. Remove four nuts holding power brake unit to dash.
4. Remove retainer and washer from brake pedal pin and disengage pushrod clevis.
5. Remove power brake unit from car. Reverse the above steps to install.

Parking Brake Adjustment—1967-74

Adjustment of the parking brake is necessary whenever the rear brake cables have been disconnected or the parking brake pedal can be depressed more than sixteen rachet clicks under heavy foot presure. The car should first be raised on a lift.

1. Make sure that service brakes are properly adjusted.
2. Depress parking brake pedal three rachet clicks.
3. Loosen jam nut on equalizer adjusting nut. Tighten adjusting nut until rear wheels can just be turned rearward by hand but not forward.
4. Release rachet one click; the rear wheels should rotate rearward freely and forward with a slight drag.
5. Release rachet one more click; rear wheels should turn freely in either direction.

NOTE: be sure that the parking brake does not drag. An overtightened, dragging parking brake on a car with automatic brake adjusters will result in an extremely short life for rear brake linings.

STEERING

The steering system consists of a steering wheel, steering column, universal joint, intermediate steering shaft, flexible coupling, manual or power steering gear, and steering linkage.

The manual steering gear is the recirculating ball nut type. The steering shaft, worm shaft, and worm nut are all in line. The steering shaft and worm shaft are separated by a flexible coupling. This coupling permits the gear to be removed independently of the steering shaft and steering column.

All Buicks use a variable-ratio power steering gear. The gear is the recirculating ball type incorporating a wormshaft and a rack-piston.

Hydraulic pressure for the power steering is provided by a constant displacement vane type pump. It is located on the left front of the engine and is belt driven off the engine crankshaft pulley.

See the "Unit Repair Section" for rebuilding procedures.

Refer to the Unit Repair Section for adjustments and repairs to steering gear, both manual and power-assisted.

Steering Wheel

Removal—1967-74

1. Unplug the horn wire connector from the steering column.
2. On cars with standard wheel or optional wood-rim wheel, pull off cap, remove three screws and bushing spacer, receiver cup, and Belleville spring. On cars with bar-type horn actuator, remove screws securing actuator from underside of steering wheel, pull out lead connector plug, and remove actuator assembly.
3. Loosen steering wheel nut.
4. Apply steering wheel puller and pull wheel up to the nut. Now remove puller, nut and steering wheel.

Installation—1967-74

NOTE: location marks are provided on the steering wheel and shaft to simplify proper indexing at the time of installation.

1. Install wheel with the location mark aligned with that of the shaft.
2. Install the wheel nut and torque to 30 ft. lbs.
3. Reinstall horn button or actuator assembly.

Tie-Rod End Inspection

1. Raise the car under the lower control arm.
2. Make sure the control arm ball joints are good and that the wheel bearings are adjusted. Grasp the tire on either side and move the tire from side to side. If excessive play is present (more than 1/16 in.) inspect the linkage as the tire is moved.

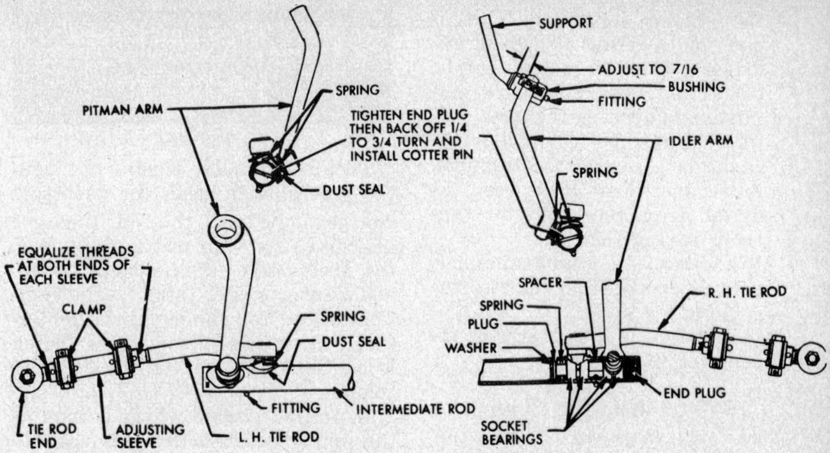
PITMAN ARM
SPRING
TIGHTEN END PLUG THEN BACK OFF 1/4 TO 3/4 TURN AND INSTALL COTTER PIN
DUST SEAL
EQUALIZE THREADS AT BOTH ENDS OF EACH SLEEVE
CLAMP
SPRING
DUST SEAL
FITTING
INTERMEDIATE ROD
TIE ROD END
ADJUSTING SLEEVE
L. H. TIE ROD
SUPPORT
ADJUST TO 7/16
BUSHING
FITTING
IDLER ARM
SPRING
SPACER
SPRING
PLUG
WASHER
R. H. TIE ROD
END PLUG
SOCKET BEARINGS
Manual and power steering linkage
(© Buick Div., G.M. Corp)

Tie-Rod End R & R

1. Loosen the tie-rod adjuster sleeve clamp nuts.
2. Remove the tie-rod stud nut cotter pin and nut.
3. Remove the tie-rod stud from the steering arm or intermediate rod. This is a taper fit. Removal is accomplished using a ball joint removal tool or by hitting the tie rod stud sharply with a hammer. If the ball joint is to be reused the removal tool must be used.
4. Unthread the tie rod from the adjuster sleeve. Outer tie rods have right-hand threads and inner tie rods have left-hand threads. Count the number of turns the tie rod must be rotated to remove it from the adjusting sleeve. This will allow a reasonably accurate realignment upon reassembly.
5. Reverse the removal procedures to install. Clean rust and dirt from the threads. Check the alignment and adjust if necessary.

Intermediate Rod R & R

1. Remove the left and right side inner tie-rod ends from the intermediate rod. These are taper fits, remove them as described in the tie rod section.
2. Remove the intermediate rod studs from the idler and pitman arms. These are taper fits.
3. Remove the idler arm from the intermediate rod by tapping the intermediate rod with a hammer, using another heavy hammer as a backing.
4. Reverse the above steps to install.

Pitman Arm R & R

1. Remove the intermediate rod stud from the pitman arm. This is a taper fit, remove it as described in the tie rod section.
2. Remove the pitman arm nut and lockwasher from the pitman shaft.
3. Remove the pitman arm from the pitman shaft using a puller. Do not hammer on the end of the puller or serious internal damage will be done to the steering gear box.
4. Reverse the above steps to install.

Idler Arm R & R

1. Remove the intermediate arm stud. This is a taper fit, see the tie rod section for removal.
2. Remove the two bolts attaching the idler arm to the frame.
3. Remove the idler arm.
4. Reverse the above steps to install.

Turn Signal Switch R & R

1967-68 Tilt Column

NOTE: it is necessary to loosen the steering column brackets and drop the steering column slightly to remove the turn signal wires. When the column is loose, use extreme care to prevent bending the column. The column must be securely supported at all times.

1. Remove the steering wheel, turn signal cancelling cam, and spring.
2. Lower the column slightly.
3. Remove the turn signal lever and push the hazard warning switch in and remove the knob.
4. Remove the screws holding the turn signal switch to the column.
5. Disconnect the turn signal wiring harness at the base of the steering column.
6. To withdraw the switch wiring harness, it is necessary to remove the wire terminals from

the curved connector. This is done by inserting a small screwdriver between the curved connector and each wire terminal and bending the metal tab, that secures the terminal to the connector, toward the terminal. After the wires have been removed from the connector tape the wires together.

7. Withdraw the switch and harness assembly from the steering column.
8. Installation is the reverse of the removal procedure.

1967-68 Non-Tilt Column

NOTE: the steering column must always be supported. Use extreme care not to bend the steering column.

1. Remove the steering wheel, spring, and turn signal cancelling cam.
2. Lower the column slightly. Disconnect the switch wiring harness at the base of the steering column.
3. Remove the turn signal lever and hazard warning knob.
4. Depress the lock plate and remove the retaining ring from the upper portion of the steering shaft.
5. Remove the switch assembly, housing assembly, cover, springs, and lockplate, as a unit, by loosening, but not removing, the three screws in the cover. Push in on the cover then rotate the cover in a counterclockwise direction. Lift off the assembly.
6. Disassemble the above unit by removing the three screws. This will free all parts in this unit. Carefully note the position of all parts before disassembly.
7. Install a new switch and reverse the above steps to install.

1969-74 Tilt and Non-Tilt Column

NOTE: the steering wheel must always be supported. Use extreme care not to bend the steering column.

1. Remove the steering wheel.
2. Remove the three cover screws and the cover.
3. Depress the lockplate and remove the snap-ring. Remove the lockplate.
4. Remove the spring and horn contact signal cancelling cam.
5. Remove the turn signal lever, depress the hazard warning knob, and remove the knob and tilt column lever—if equipped.
6. Remove the three turn signal switch mounting screws. Pull the connector out of the bracket on the column.
7. Pull the switch straight up with the wire protector and wire harness.
8. Reverse the above steps to install.

INSTRUMENT PANEL

1967-69

The instrument cluster includes the speedometer head, the generator charge indicator, the oil pressure indicator, the temperature indicator, the fuel gauge, light switch, wiper and washer switch, starter and ignition switch and the cigarette lighter. On 1969 models, the ignition switch is on the right side of the steering column.

A printed circuit which is part of the speedometer housing is used to complete the circuit for the fuel gauge and the lights in the cluster.

1970-72

The instrument cluster assembly is comprised of three individual units. The left unit houses the fuel gauge, indicator lights and/or oil pressure gauge and ammeter. The center unit contains the speedometer. The right unit contains the optional clock or tachometer. Each unit contains its own printed circuit, fastened by three screws on the rear of the housing.

1973-74

The new instrument cluster was designed with ease of service in mind. All switches, knobs, and instruments can be removed from the front of the panel.

Ignition Switch and Lock Cylinder R & R

1967-68

1. Disconnect battery ground strap.
2. Turn key to Accessory position.
3. Insert stiff wire into hole in face of lock cylinder to depress lock pin. Rotate cylinder counterclockwise and pull out.
4. To remove ignition switch, remove retaining nut and lower switch.

To reinstall:

5. Install switch, tighten nut.
6. Insert key in cylinder, place cylinder in switch slightly counterclockwise from Accessory position, press inward and turn cylinder clockwise.

1969-74

The ignition switch and lock is located, not in the instrument panel, but in the steering column. The ignition lock also locks the steering and the transmission.

Standard Column—1969-74

1. Remove steering wheel using proper puller.
2. Remove three cover screws and cover; remove retainers.
3. Depress lock plate, then remove wire snap-ring and lock plate.

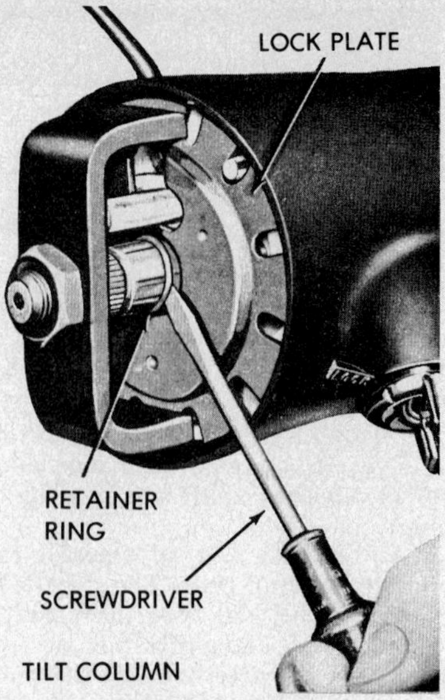
LOCK PLATE
RETAINER RING
SCREWDRIVER
TILT COLUMN
Removing lock plate
(© Buick Div., G.M. Corp)

4. Slide upper bearing preload spring and cancelling cam off shaft. Remove the steering column-to-instrument panel attaching bolts (2), and carefully lower the column.

NOTE: steering shaft is now unsupported and could slide out the bottom of the column.

5. Slide thrust washer off shaft, then remove turn signal lever screw and lever.
6. Push in four-way flasher switch; remove knob.
7. Remove three turn signal switch mounting screws, pull connector out of its bracket on the column and tape the upper part of connector and wires together.
8. Pull turn signal switch out of column jacket.
9. Insert a small screwdriver into the slot next to the turn signal switch mounting screw boss (right-hand slot), depress spring latch and remove key lock.
10. Pull buzzer switch straight out, depressing switch clip with pliers.
11. Place ignition switch in accessory position by pulling up on connecting rod until there is a definite stop or detent felt.
12. Remove two attaching screws and ignition switch.
13. Assembly is the reverse of the above. However, note the following steps before proceeding with the reassembly.
14. To install the steering lock, hold the lock cylinder sleeve and rotate the knob clockwise against the stop. Insert the cylinder into the cover bore with the key on the cylinder sleeve aligned with the keyway in the housing. Then push the cylinder in until it bottoms. Maintaining a light inward pressure, rotate the knob coun-

terclockwise until the drive section of the cylinder mates with the drive shaft. Push in until the snap-ring pops into the groove and the lock cylinder is secured in the cover. Check for free rotation.

15. When installing the ignition switch, be sure the lock cylinder is in the LOCK position. Put the shift bowl or shroud in the PARK position. Make sure the ignition switch is in the LOCK position. Then insert the actuator rod into the switch and assemble the switch to the column.
16. The neutral start switch is adjusted with the shift lever in the Drive position.

Tilt Column—1969-74

1. Remove column mounting bracket from column.

NOTE: be careful not to damage the "breakaway" capsules.

2. Remove steering wheel using proper puller.
3. Remove turn signal wire protector (lower column).
4. Remove three column cover screws and cover.
5. Remove tilt release lever, turn signal switch lever, push four-way flasher knob in and remove knob, and remove upper shift lever.
6. Depress lock plate and remove the snap-ring; remove lock plate.
7. Remove cancelling cam and spring.
8. Remove three turn signal switch screws, tape wires to wire connector at upper end and place shift bowl in Low. Pull switch straight up and out.
9. Insert a small screwdriver into the slot next to the turn signal switch mounting screw boss (right-hand slot), depress spring latch and remove key lock.
10. Remove buzzer switch straight out, depressing switch clip with pliers.
11. Remove three housing cover screws and cover.
12. Install tilt release lever and place column in full UP position.
13. Place screwdriver in slot of tilt spring retainer, press in about 3/16 in. and turn counterclockwise. Remove spring and guide.

NOTE: spring is very strong—be careful.

14. Place column in neutral position, push in on upper steering shaft, remove inner race seat and race.
15. Remove upper flange pinch bolt, place ignition switch in accessory position, remove two switch mounting screws and switch.

NOTE: neutral start switch can be removed at this time, if necessary.

16. Assembly is the reverse of the above. However, note the following steps before proceeding with

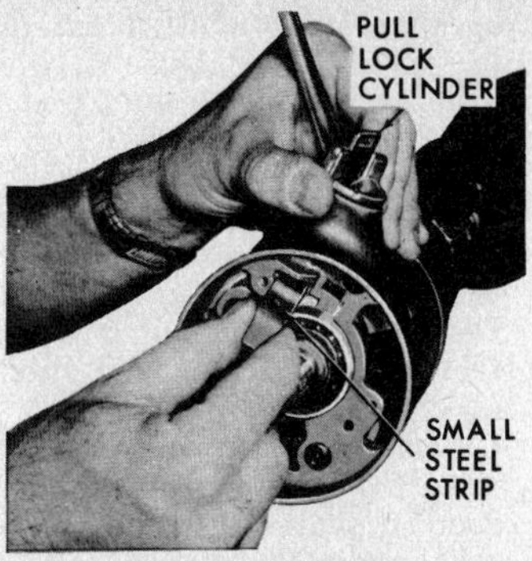
PULL
LOCK
CYLINDER
SMALL
STEEL
STRIP

Removing ignition lock cylinder—1969-74
(© Buick Div., G.M. Corp)

the reassembly.

17. To install the steering lock, hold the lock cylinder sleeve and rotate the knob clockwise against the stop. Insert the cylinder into the cover bore with the key on the cylinder sleeve aligned with the keyway in the housing. Then push the cylinder in until it bottoms. Maintaining a light inward pressure, rotate the knob counterclockwise until the drive section of the cylinder mates with the drive shaft. Push in until the snap-ring pops into the groove and the lock cylinder is secured in the cover. Check for free rotation.
18. When installing the ignition switch, be sure the lock cylinder is in the LOCK position. Put the shift bowl or shroud in the PARK position. Make sure the ignition switch is in the LOCK position. Then insert the actuator rod into the switch and assemble the switch to the column.
19. The neutral start switch is adjusted with the shift lever in the Drive position.

Lighting Switch Replacement

1. Disconnect battery.
2. Disconnect multiple connector from switch.
3. Pull switch knob to last notch and depress spring loaded latch button on top of switch while pulling knob and rod out of switch.

NOTE: on A/C cars, remove left duct if so equipped.

4. Remove escutcheon.
5. Install in reverse of above.

WINDSHIELD WIPERS

All wiper motors are located on the engine side of the firewall. The transmission and linkage are located on the passenger compartment side of the firewall directly forward of the instrument panel. The cowl screen must be removed to allow the drive link to be disconnected from the crank arm.

The wiper-washer switch is included in the instrument cluster.

Windshield Wiper Motor R & R

Non-Depressed Park

1. Disconnect the battery.
2. Remove the cowl screen.
3. Loosen the two nuts on the adjustable motor drive link at the crank arm and slip the drive link off.
4. Remove the electrical connectors from the washer motor and pump.
5. Disconnect the washer pump hoses.
6. Remove the three bolts securing the motor to the cowl and carefully lift the motor away from the cowl.
7. Reverse the above steps for installation.

Depressed Park

1. Disconnect the battery.
2. Remove the hoses from the washer nozzles.
3. Remove the rubber weatherstrip and cowl screen.
4. Loosen the two nuts on the adjustable motor drive link at the crank arm and slip the drive link off.
5. Disconnect the washer hoses and electrical connectors.
6. Remove the three wiper motor-to-cowl retaining screws and the motor.
7. Reverse the above steps to install.

Windshield Wiper Transmission R & R

1. Disconnect the washer hose from the washer nozzles.
2. Remove the rubber weatherstrip from the front of the cowl screen and the five snap-clips from the rear of the screen then remove the screen.
3. Loosen the two nuts on the drive link at the crank arm and slip the link off the crank arm.
4. Remove both wiper arm and blade assemblies.
5. Remove the three screws from the right and left transmission pilot shafts. The larger screw on the left side should be removed last.
6. With the transmission assembly loose, rotate it toward the front of the car and remove it through the access hole in the right side of the cowl.
7. Reverse the above steps to install.

RADIO

Radio Removal and Installation

1967

1. Disconnect battery ground lead.
2. Remove ashtray assembly.

3. Remove radio bracket to radio screw. Remove radio knobs, escutcheons, and hex nuts. Disconnect wiring connectors.
4. Remove radio downward.
5. Install in reverse order of removal.

1968-72

NOTE: if equipped with stereo tape, remove tape player before starting Step 2.

1. Disconnect battery ground lead.
2. Remove radio knobs, escutcheons, and hex nuts.
3. Remove two screws from radio filler plate and remove plate.
4. Remove ashtray assembly.
5. Remove center air conditioning duct, if so equipped.
6. Remove radio bracket.
7. Remove two instrument panel attaching nuts at radio face.
8. Disconnect wiring and remove radio downward.
9. Install in reverse order of removal.

1973-74

1. Disconnect the negative battery cable.
2. Remove the radio control knobs and the two radio attaching nuts from the front of the radio.
3. Disconnect the electrical leads from the radio and lower the radio from under the instrument panel.

HEATER

Heater Core R & R without A/C

1967

1. Remove right front wheel.
2. Draw an arc on inside of skirt, 11 in. from upper bolt of wheel opening. Draw another arc 16¾ in. from lower bolt of wheel opening and punch dimple at intersection of two arcs.
3. Drill a ¾ in. hole through skirt at this dimple. Remove lower right attaching nut from heater assembly stud through this hole.
4. Disconnect air control cables from defroster door and outside air door levers.
5. Disconnect temperature control cable from lever of temperature door on heater assembly.
6. Drain radiator.
7. Disconnect inlet and outlet hoses.
8. Remove connector from blower resistor assembly.
9. Remove nuts and washers securing assembly to cowl, then lift out assembly
10. Install in reverse of above.
11. Use ¾ in. body plug to close hole in skirt.

1968-72

1. Remove right front inner fender panel.
2. Drain radiator.
3. Disconnect control cables from defroster door and outside air inlet door. Disconnect temperature control cable from temperature door.
4. Remove nuts from heater assembly studs.
5. Disconnect inlet and outlet hoses.
6. Remove connector from blower motor resistor.
7. Remove screws securing defroster outlet assembly to top of heater assembly.
8. Work heater assembly rearward until studs clear dash. Remove heater assembly.
9. Install in reverse of above.

1973-74

1. Drain the radiator and disconnect the heater inlet and outlet hoses at the dash.
2. Disconnect the control wires from the defroster door and vacuum hose diverter door actuator diaphragm and control cable from the temperature door lever.
3. Remove the four nuts securing the heater assembly to the dash.
4. Remove the screw securing the defroster outlet tab to the heater assembly.
5. Remove the heater from the car.
6. Reverse the above steps to install.

Heater Blower R & R without A/C

1967

1. Remove right front fender.
2. Remove nuts and screws securing blower and air inlet assembly to cowl.
3. Disconnect blower motor wire and remove assembly.
4. Install in reverse of above.

1968-72

Follow procedure above for 1966-67 models, substituting this step:

1. Remove right front inner fender panel.

1973-74

1. Support the hood and loosen the hood hinge from the extension and plate assembly.
2. Remove the extension and plate assembly.
3. Disconnect the blower motor wire.
4. Remove the blower motor attaching screws and the motor.

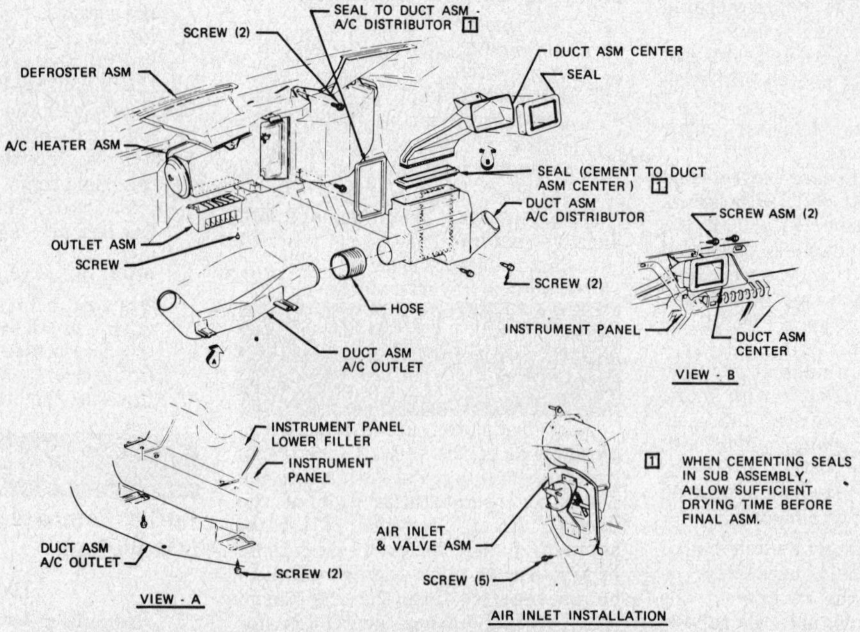

SEAL TO DUCT ASM - A/C DISTRIBUTOR 1
SCREW (2)
DUCT ASM CENTER
SEAL
DEFROSTER ASM
A/C HEATER ASM
SEAL (CEMENT TO DUCT ASM CENTER) 1
DUCT ASM A/C DISTRIBUTOR
SCREW ASM (2)
OUTLET ASM
SCREW
SCREW (2)
HOSE
INSTRUMENT PANEL
DUCT ASM CENTER
DUCT ASM A/C OUTLET
VIEW - B
INSTRUMENT PANEL LOWER FILLER
INSTRUMENT PANEL
1 WHEN CEMENTING SEALS IN SUB ASSEMBLY, ALLOW SUFFICIENT DRYING TIME BEFORE FINAL ASM.
AIR INLET & VALVE ASM
DUCT ASM A/C OUTLET
SCREW (2)
SCREW (5)
VIEW - A
AIR INLET INSTALLATION

1972 air conditioning ducts (© Buick Div., G.M. Corp)

Blower Motor R & R with A/C

1967

1. Open the hood and support it securely. Remove the right hood hinge and hood hinge support.
2. Remove the blower motor cooling tube and disconnect the blower motor wiring.
3. Remove the five sheet metal screws and the motor.
4. Reverse the above steps to install.

1968-70

1. On 1968 and 1970 cars, remove the right front inner fender panel. On 1969 models, remove the fender.
2. Disconnect the motor wiring.
3. Remove the five securing screws and remove the motor.
4. Reverse the above steps to install.

1971-72

1. Support the hood and remove the extension and plate assembly from the hood hinge.
2. Disconnect the motor wiring.
3. Remove the screws securing the motor to the firewall and remove the motor.
4. Reverse the above steps to install.

1973-74

1. Follow the same procedures as described in the Blower R&R without A/C.

Heater Core R & R with A/C

1967

1. Drain the coolant and disconnect the inlet and outlet hoses from the heater core.
2. Disconnect the temperature control wire from the lever on the assembly.
3. Disconnect the vacuum hose from the diverter door diaphragm.
4. Connect the rear end of the diverter door return spring to the operating lever pin to hold the door in the air condition position.
5. Remove the six sheet metal bolts holding the heater-air conditioner assembly and then remove the assembly.

1968-70

1. Drain the radiator and disconnect the heater hoses from the heater core.
2. Remove the instrument panel cover with the right-side A/C outlet and hose still attached.
3. Remove the center A/C duct, left A/C outlet duct, A/C distributor duct, and the defroster assembly.
4. Disconnect the defroster and temperature control wires.
5. Remove the four nuts and two screws securing the air conditioner heater assembly to the dash and remove the assembly.
6. Reverse the above steps to install.

1971-72

1. Drain the radiator and disconnect the heater inlet and outlet hoses from the dash.
2. Disconnect the control wires from the defroster door and vacuum hose diverter door actuator diaphragm and control cable from the temperature door lever.
3. Remove the four nuts securing the heater assembly to the dash.
4. Remove the screw securing the defroster outlet tab to the heater assembly.
5. Move the heater assembly rearward until the studs clear the dash and then remove the heater assembly.
6. Reverse the above steps to install.

1973-74

1. Follow the procedures as described in the Heater Core R&R without A/C.

1974 SEAT BELT INTERLOCK SYSTEM

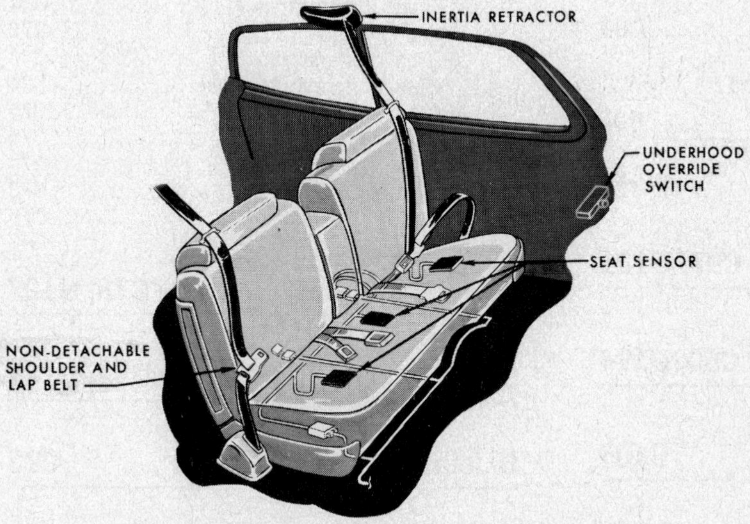
INERTIA RETRACTOR
UNDERHOOD OVERRIDE SWITCH
SEAT SENSOR
NON-DETACHABLE SHOULDER AND LAP BELT

1974 seat belt/ignition interlock system (© Buick Div., G.M. Corp)

SEAT BELTS

Buzzer System—1973

The front seat belt warning system consists of a switch in each belt retractor, a sensor switch in the seat cushion on the passenger side, a reminder light and a warning buzzer. The circuit wiring is routed through the ignition switch and parking brake warning switch on manual transmission models, or through the ignition switch and transmission switch on models equipped with automatic transmissions.

With the ignition switch on and the parking brake released with manual transmission, or with the selector in a forward position on automatic transmission models, the warning circuit (light and buzzer) is closed (activated) until the driver's seat belt is extended to open (deactivate) the circuit. The seat sensor on the passenger side will react to weights in excess of 0-47 lbs on the seat cushion and close the warning circuit. Extending the passenger belt will open the circuit.

Seat Belt/Starter Interlock System—1974

The seat belt/starter interlock system makes it necessary for outboard front seat occupants to fasten their seat belts before the engine can be started. Employing seat weight sensors similar to 1973 models, the new system does not require a passenger occupying the middle portion of the front seat to buckle up, but failure to do so will cause the seat belt alarm buzzer to sound.

When an outboard front seat is occupied, a sensor under the seat signals an electronic relay module which then requires verification from a switch in the buckle, indicating the belt has been fastened, before completing the starting circuit. An override by-pass switch under the hood, which is activated with the ignition key in the ON position, permits starting in the event of system malfunction.

Cadillac

YEAR IDENTIFICATION

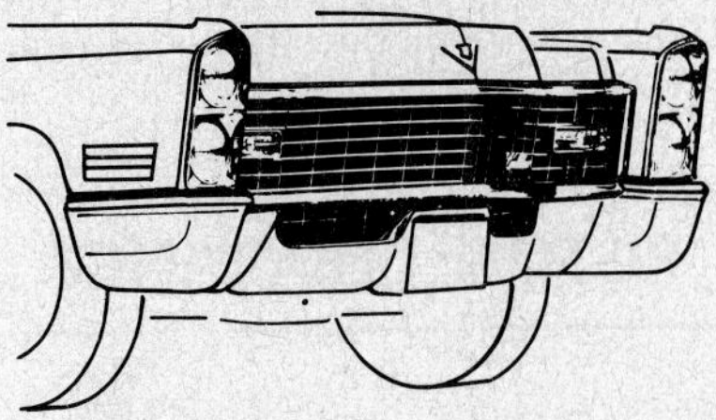

1967

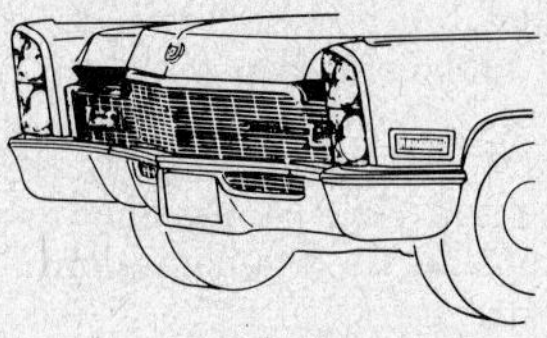

1968

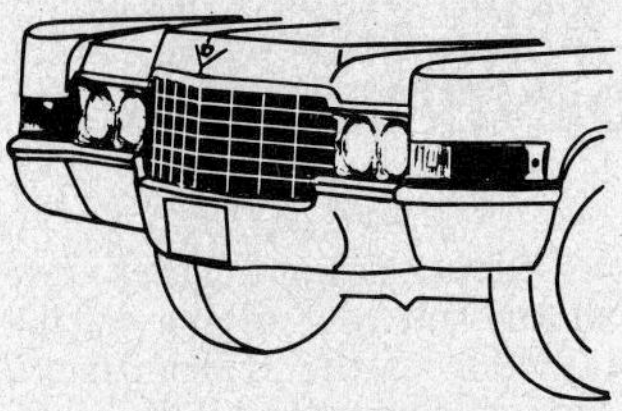

1969-70

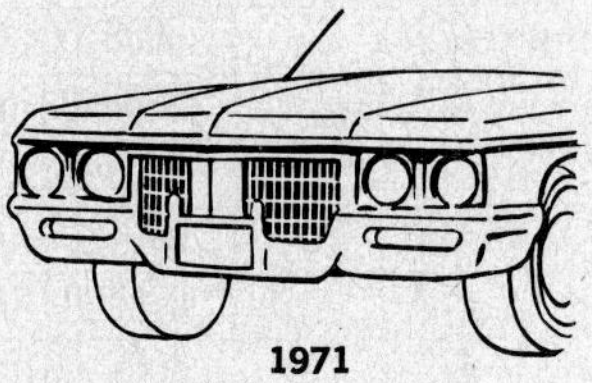

1971

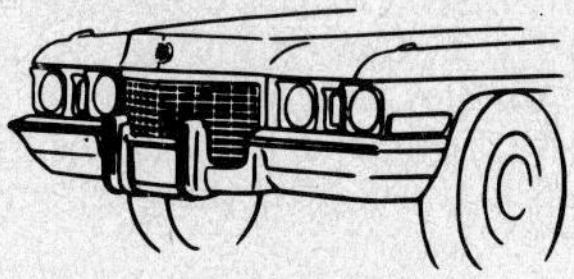

1972

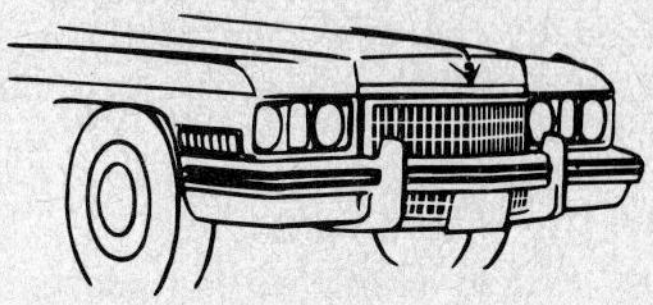

1973

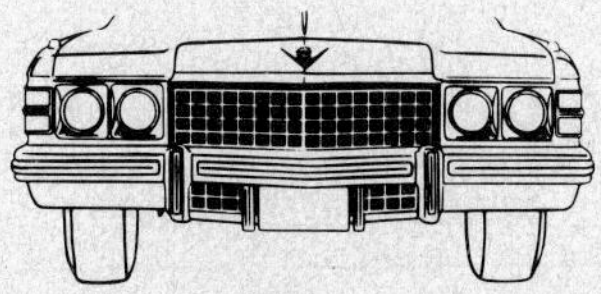

1974

FIRING ORDER

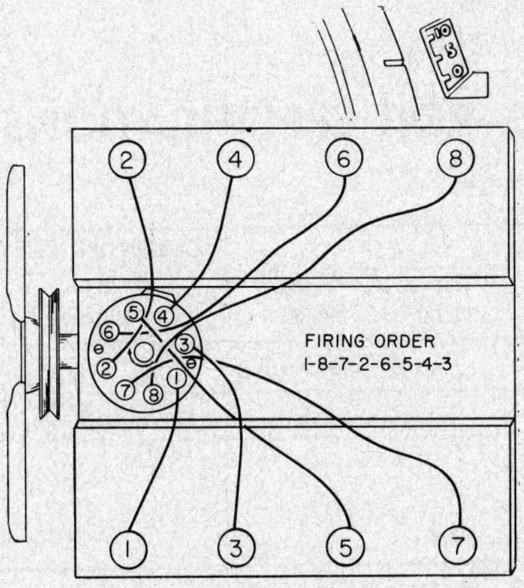
2
4
6
8
FIRING ORDER
1-8-7-2-6-5-4-3
1
3
5
7

1967
(© Cadillac Div., G.M. Corp.)

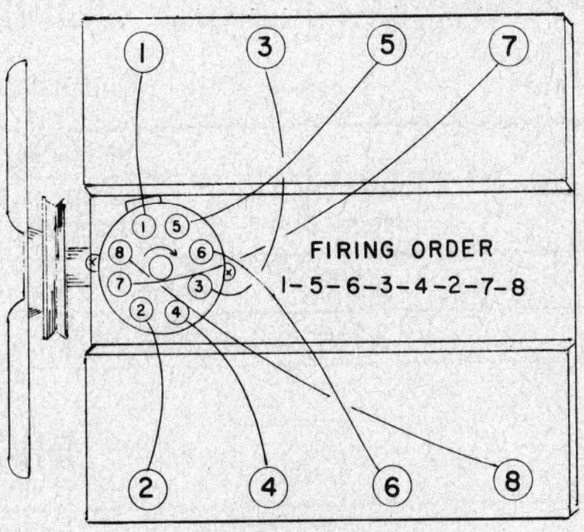
1
3
5
7
FIRING ORDER
1-5-6-3-4-2-7-8
2
4
6
8

1968-74
(© Cadillac Div., G.M. Corp.)

5° NOTCH ON TAB
NOTCH ON PULLEY

Timing marks—1968-70

8° ON TAB
NOTCH ON BALANCER

Timing marks—1971-74

CAR SERIAL NUMBER LOCATION AND ENGINE IDENTIFICATION

1967

Vehicle identification plates are located at the top rear of the engine block, adjacent to the transmission, and on the left front door lock pillar. The eight digit serial number consists of a sales code letter, the last digit of the model year (7), and a six digit sequential serial number.

All models utilize a 429 cu. in. V8 engine. The engine serial number is stamped at the left rear of the cylinder block, just below the cylinder head.

1968-70

The vehicle identification plate is located on the top left side of the dashboard, and is visible through the windshield. The eight digit serial number consists of a sales code letter, the last digit of the model year (8, 9, or 0), and a six digit sequential serial number.

All models utilize a 472 cu. in. V8 engine. The vehicle identification number, less sales code, is stamped on the top rear of the engine block, adjacent to the transmission.

1971-74

The vehicle identification plate is located on the top left side of the dashboard, and is visible through the windshield. The thirteen digit serial number consists of the G.M. Division Code (6), a four digit series and model number, the last digit of the model year (1 or 2), plant designation, and a six digit sequential serial number.

All models utilize a 472 cu. in. V8 engine. A derivative of the vehicle identification number is stamped on the top rear of the engine block, adjacent to the transmission.

1972-74 models have the engine code located on the left rear of the crankcase behind the intake manifold.

PISTON CLEARANCE

Year	Engine	Piston to Bore Clearance
'67	429	.0006-.0010
'68	472	.0006-.0010
'69	472	.0006-.0010
'70	472	.0006-.0010
'71	472	.0006-.0010
'72	472	.0006-.0010
'73	472	.0006-.0010
'74	472	.0006-.0010

TORQUE SPECIFICATIONS

All readings in ft lbs

Year	Engine Displacement (cu in.)	Cylinder Head Bolts	Rod Bearing Bolts	Main Bearing Bolts	Crankshaft Pulley Bolt	Flywheel to Crankshaft Bolts	MANIFOLD Intake	MANIFOLD Exhaust
'67	429	60	40	90-95	65-70	75	25	60
'68-'74	472	115	40	90	Press fit	75	30	35

NOTE—Some bolts and nuts are marked on the heads to indicate the grade of steel used. Do not use bolts of a lower grade than those originally installed. The marks consist of lines: SAE5—3 lines; SAE7—5 lines; SAE8—6 lines

CRANKSHAFT AND CONNECTING ROD SPECIFICATIONS

All measurements are given in in.

Year	Engine Displace. (cu in.)	CRANKSHAFT				CONNECTING ROD		
		Main Brg. Journal Dia	Main Brg. Oil Clearance	Shaft End-Play	Thrust on No.	Journal Diameter	Oil Clearance	Side Clearance
'67	429	3.000	.0008-.0029	.001-.007	3	2.2488-2.2493	.0005-.0035	.008-.014
'68-'74	472	3.250	.0003-.0026	.002-.012	3	2.5000	.0005-.0035	.008-.016

RING GAP

Year	Engine	Top Compression	Bottom Compression
'67	8-429	.013-.030	.013-.030
'68-'74	8-472	.013-.025	.013-.025

Year	Engine	Oil Control
'67-'74	All engines	.015-.055

RING SIDE CLEARANCE

Year	Engine	Top Compression	Bottom Compression
'67-'68	8-429, 472	.0022-.0035	.0022-.0035
'69-'74	8-472	.0017-.0040	.0017-.0040

Year	Engine	Oil Control
'67-'74	All engines	None (side sealing)

ALTERNATOR AND REGULATOR SPECIFICATIONS

	ALTERNATOR			REGULATOR						
					Field Relay			Regulator		
Year	Part No. or Manufacturer	Field Current @ 12 V	Output (amps)	Part No. or Manufacturer	Air Gap (in.)	Point Gap (in.)	Volts to Close	Air Gap (in.)	Point Gap (in.)	Volts @ 75°
'67	1100691	2.2-2.6	42	1119515	.015	.030	2.3-3.7	.060	.014	13.5-14.4
	1100692	2.2-2.6	55	1119515	.015	.030	2.3-3.7	.060	.014	13.5-14.4
	1100760	2.2-2.6	55	1119515	.015	.030	2.3-3.7	.060	.014	13.5-14.4
'68-'69	1100696	2.2-2.6	42	1119515	—	—	—	—	—	13.5-14.4
	1100694	2.2-2.6	55	1119515	—	—	—	—	—	13.5-14.4
	1100742	2.2-2.6	63	1119519	—	—	—	—	—	13.5-14.4
'70	1100908	2.2-2.6	42	1119515	—	—	—	—	—	13.5-14.4
	1100694	2.2-2.6	55	1119515	—	—	—	—	—	13.5-14.4
	1100910	2.8-3.2	63	1119519	—	—	—	—	—	13.5-14.4
'71-'74	1100558	2.2-2.6	42	1119515	—	—	—	—	—	13.5-14.4
	1100557	2.8-3.2	63	1119519	—	—	—	—	—	13.5-14.4
	1101015	4.0-4.5	80	—	Transistor type—no adjustment					

BATTERY AND STARTER SPECIFICATIONS

		BATTERY			STARTER						
					Lock Test			No-Load Test			
Year	Engine Displacement (cu in.)	Ampere Hour Capacity	Volts	Terminal Grounded	Amps	Volts	Torque (ft lbs)	Amps	Volts	RPM	Brush Spring Tension (oz)
'67	429	73	12	Neg.	510	30	Locked	88	10.6	4,000	35
'68-'70	472	74	12	Neg.	510	Not Recommended		70-99	10.6	7,800	35
'71-'74	472	74	12	Neg.	510	Not Recommended		65-90	9	7,000	35

BRAKE SPECIFICATIONS

All measurements are given in in.

		MASTER CYLINDER		WHEEL CYLINDER			BRAKE DISC OR DRUM DIAMETER		
				Front			Front		
Year	Model	Disc	Drum	Disc	Drum	Rear	Disc	Drum	Rear
'67	All Series		1.00		1 3/16	15/16 ①		12.0	12.0
'68	All Series	1.00	1.00	2 3/4	1 3/16	15/16 ①	12.0	12.0	12.0
'69	All Series	1.00		2 3/4		13/16 ②	12.0		12.0
'70	All Series	1.00		2 3/4		13/16 ②	11.9		12.0
'71-'74	All Series	1.12		2 15/16		15/16	11.9		12.0

① 1.00 for the Fleetwood 75 Sedan and Limousine
② 7/8 for the Fleetwood 75 Sedan and Limousine

WHEEL ALIGNMENT SPECIFICATIONS

		CASTER		CAMBER				WHEEL PIVOT RATIO (deg)	
Year	Model	Range (deg)	Pref Setting (deg)	Range (deg)	Pref Setting (deg)	Toe-in (in.)	Steering Axis Inclin.	Inner Wheel	Wheel Outer
'67	All Series	1 1/2N to 1/2N	1N	①	①	3/16 to 1/4	6	22 1/6	20
'68	All Series	1 1/2N to 1/2N	1N	①	①	3/16 to 1/4	6	20	18 1/6
'69-'70	All Series	1 1/2N to 1/2N	1N	3/8N to 3/8P	0	1/8 to 1/4	6	20	18
'71-'74	All Series	1 1/2N to 1/2N	1N	②	②	1/8 to 1/4	6	20	18

① Left 3/8P to 1/8N; zero preferred
Right 1/8P to 3/8N; 1/4N preferred
② Left 3/8P to 3/8N; zero preferred
Right 1/8P to 5/8N; 1/4N preferred

N Negative P Positive

GENERAL ENGINE SPECIFICATIONS

Year	Engine Cu. In. Displacement	Carburetor Type	Advertised Horsepower @ rpm ■	Advertised Torque @ rpm (ft lbs) ■	Bore and Stroke (in.)	Advertised Compression Ratio	Oil Pressure @ 2050 rpm
'67	8-429	4 bbl	340 @ 4600	480 @ 3000	4.130 x 4.000	10.5:1	33
'68	8-472	4 bbl	375 @ 4400	525 @ 3000	4.300 x 4.060	10.5:1	38
'69	8-472	4 bbl	375 @ 4400	525 @ 3000	4.300 x 4.060	10.5:1	38
'70	8-472	4 bbl	375 @ 4400	525 @ 3000	4.300 x 4.060	10.0:1	38
'71	8-472	4 bbl	345 @ 4400	500 @ 2800	4.300 x 4.060	8.5:1	38
'72	8-472	4 bbl	220 @ 4000	565 @ 2400	4.300 x 4.060	8.5:1	35
'73	8-472	4 bbl	220 @ 4000	565 @ 2400	4.300 x 4.060	8.5:1	35
'74	8-472	4 bbl	220 @ 4000	365 @ 2400	4.300 x 4.060	8.5:1	35

■ Beginning 1972 horsepower and torque are SAE net figures. They are measured at the rear of the transmission with all accessories installed and operating. Since the figures vary when a given engine is installed in different models, some are representative rather than exact.

TUNE-UP SPECIFICATIONS

When analyzing compression test results, look for uniformity among cylinders rather than specific pressures.

Year *	ENGINE No. Cyl Displacement (cu in.)	ENGINE hp	SPARK PLUGS Type §	SPARK PLUGS Gap (in.)	DISTRIBUTOR Point Dwell (deg)	DISTRIBUTOR Point Gap (in.)	IGNITION TIMING (deg) ▲ Man Trans	IGNITION TIMING (deg) ▲ Auto Trans	VALVES Intake Opens ■ (deg) ●	Fuel Pump Pressure (psi)	IDLE SPEED (rpm) ▲ Man Trans	IDLE SPEED (rpm) ▲ Auto Trans
'67	8-429	340	44	.035	30	.016	—	5B	39	5¼-6½	—	480① (550)②
'68	8-472	375	44-N	.035	30	.016	—	5B	18	5¼-6½	—	550①
'69	8-472	375	R-44-N	.035	30	.016	—	5B	18	5¼-6½	—	550③
'70	8-472	375	R-46-N	.035	30	.016	—	7½B	18	5¼-6½	—	600③
'71	8-472	345	R-46-N	.035	30	.016	—	8B	38	5¼-6½	—	600④/400
'72	8-472	220	R-46-N	.035	30	.016	—	8B	34	5¼-6½	—	600④/400
'73	8-472	220	R-46-N	.035	30	.016	—	8B	34	5¼-5¾	—	600④/400
'74	8-472	220	R-46-N	.035	30	.016	—	8B	34	5¼-5¾	—	600④/400

▲ See text for procedure
■ All figures Before Top Dead Center
§ All spark plug listings are A.C. original equipment listings
● Figures in parentheses are for California only
① For A/C equipped vehicles, adjust idle to 900-950 rpm in neutral with A/C and idle speed-up on
② A/C on
③ Adjust idle to 900-950 rpm with idle speed-up on. See text for special procedure.
④ Lower figure indicates idle speed with solenoid disconnected
B Before Top Dead Center
— Not applicable

*For '74 models with optional electronic ignition, see engine compartment decal for tune-up specifications.

VALVE SPECIFICATIONS

Year	Engine No. Cyl. Displacement (cu in.)	Seat Angle (deg)	Face Angle (deg)	Spring Test Pressure (lbs @ in.)	Spring Installed Height (in.)	STEM TO GUIDE Clearance (in.) Intake	STEM TO GUIDE Clearance (in.) Exhaust	STEM Diameter (in.) Intake	STEM Diameter (in.) Exhaust
'67	8-429	45	44	160 @ 1.50	1 15/16	.0005-.0025	.0010-.0025	.3420	.3418
'68	8-472	45	44	160 @ 1.50	1 15/16	.0005-.0025	.0010-.0025	.3420	.3418
'69	8-472	45	44	160 @ 1.50	1 15/16	.0005-.0025	.0010-.0025	.3420	.3418
'70	8-472	45	44	160 @ 1.50	1 15/16	.0005-.0025	.0010-.0025	.3420	.3418
'71	8-472	45	44	160 @ 1.50	1 15/16	.0010-.0027	.0010-.0025	.3420	.3418
'72	8-472	45	44	168 @ 1.50	1 15/16	.0010-.0027	.0012-.0027	.3420	.3418
'73	8-472	45	44	168 @ 1.50	1 15/16	.0010-.0027	.0012-.0027	.3420	.3418
'74	8-472	45	44	168 @ 1.50	1 15/16	.0010-.0027	.0012-.0027	.3420	.3418

CAPACITIES

Year	ENGINE No. Cyl. (Cu. In.) Displacement	Engine Crankcase Add 1 Qt For New Filter	TRANSMISSION Pts To Refill After Draining Manual 3-Speed	Manual 4-Speed	Automatic ●	Drive Axle (pts)	Gasoline Tank (gals)	COOLING SYSTEM (qts) With Heater	With A/C
'67	All	4	—	—	7	5	26①	18	19②
'68	All	4	—	—	8	5	26①	20.3	20.8③
'69	All	4	—	—	8	5	26①	21.3	21.8④
'70	All	4	—	—	8	5	26①	21.3	21.8④
'71	All	4	—	—	8	5	27.5	21.3	21.8④
'72	All	4	—	—	8	5	27.5	21.3	21.8④⑤
'73	All	4	—	—	8	5	27.5	21.3	21.8④⑤
'74	All	4	—	—	8	5	27.5	21.3	21.8④⑤

● Specifications do not include torque convertor
① Fleetwood—20 gals
② Fleetwood—20.7 qts
③ Fleetwood—23.8 qts
④ Fleetwood—24.8 qts
⑤ Trailer package—2 qts additional

CHARGING SYSTEM

Two types of alternators are used on the various Cadillac models, both of which consist of an integrated circuit regulator which is mounted inside the alternator. For charging system trouble shooting and repair information, consult the "Unit Repair Section."

Alternator Removal

All Models

Disconnect the battery. Disconnect the wire leads at the alternator. Remove alternator adjusting strap drive belt. Remove alternator.

NOTE: heavy duty alternator used on commercial chassis is slid backwards off its lower mounting bolts, after first loosening belt tensioner and removing fan belt and upper bolt.

Caution Since the Delcotron and regulator are designed for use on only one polarity system, the following precautions must be observed:

1. The polarity of the battery, generator, and regulator must be matched and considered before making any electrical connections in the system.
2. When connecting a booster battery, be sure to connect the negative battery terminals together and the positive battery terminals together.
3. When connecting a charger to the battery, connect the charger positive lead to the battery positive terminal. Connect the charger negative lead to the battery negative terminal.
4. Never operate the Delcotron on open circuit. Be sure that all connections in the circuit are clean and tight.
5. Do not short across or ground any of the terminals on the Delcotron regulator.
6. Do not attempt to polarize the Delcotron.
7. Do not use test lamps of more than 12 volts for checking diode continuity.
8. Avoid long soldering times when replacing diodes or transistors. Prolonged heat is damaging to these units.
9. Disconnect the battery ground terminal when servicing any A.C. system. This will prevent the possibility of accidental reversing of polarity.

STARTING SYSTEM

Cadillac starter motors are located on the right hand side of the engine and consist of four pole shoes and two series fields. When the ignition switch is closed, the solenoid is energized and this positions the drive pinion into mesh with the flywheel. The main contacts of the solenoid are closed and the battery current is transferred to the starter motor.

Information on starter overhaul & starter drive can be found in the Unit Repair Section.

Starter R & R

All Models

1. Disconnect battery cable and jack up car.
2. Disconnect battery lead and two wires from solenoid.
3. Remove bolt that holds support bracket to starter.
4. Remove two starter-to-engine bolts.
5. Remove motor by pulling it forward and down, or toward right front wheel and over linkage.
6. To install, reverse removal procedure, tightening starter-to-engine bolts to 46 ft. lbs. and bracket bolt to 12 ft. lbs.

Starter Drive Removal and Installation

Caution When the starter is disassembled, do not clean the starter drive, armature, or the field in solvent as this will dissolve the lubricant in the drive mechanism and damage the insulation on the armature.

1. Remove the field coil connector from the solenoid motor terminal.
2. Remove the two screws and lockwashers which secure the solenoid switch assembly to the starter drive housing. Pull off the solenoid and its return spring by turning the solenoid assembly counterclockwise to disengage the flange from the center frame.
3. Remove the housing throughbolts and the commutator end frame with the leather brake washer.
4. Remove the center frame assembly and the snap-ring which holds the shift lever pivot pin. Remove the pin.
5. Pull the plunger, shift lever, armature, and the starter drive from the drive housing.
6. Use the following procedure to remove the starter drive from the armature shaft.
   a. Remove the thrust collar from the armature shaft.
   b. Using a $5/8$ in. deep socket, slide it over the end of the shaft so that the end of the socket butts against the edge of the retainer. With a hammer, tap the end of the socket to drive the retainer toward the armature and off of the snap-ring.
   c. Remove the snap-ring. Examine its condition and replace if necessary.
   d. The drive can now be removed from the armature shaft.
7. To install the unit, reverse the removal proceure.

IGNITION SYSTEM

The distributor used in Cadillacs is a single-point type using clockwise rotation. It is constructed of allumium alloy and is located at the top left front of the engine. The distributor houses the contact points that make and break the primary circuit and it also directs the high voltage in the proper sequence to the spark plugs.

Detailed information on direction of distributor rotation, cylinder numbering, firing order, point gap, cam dwell, timing mark location, spark plugs, spark advance, and idle speed will be found in the front portion of this section.

Distributor Point Replacement

1967-74

1. Remove distributor cap by depressing and turning the retaining screws.
2. Remove two screws securing rotor cap and remove cap.
3. Remove condenser and primary leads from nylon insulated connection.
4. Loosen two screws holding base

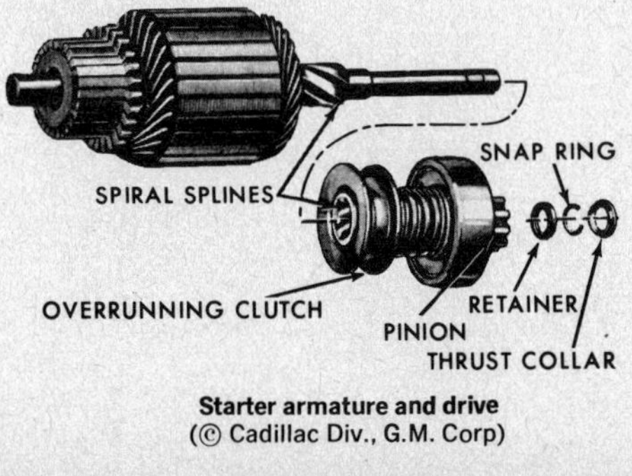
SNAP RING
SPIRAL SPLINES
OVERRUNNING CLUTCH
RETAINER
PINION
THRUST COLLAR

Starter armature and drive
(© Cadillac Div., G.M. Corp)

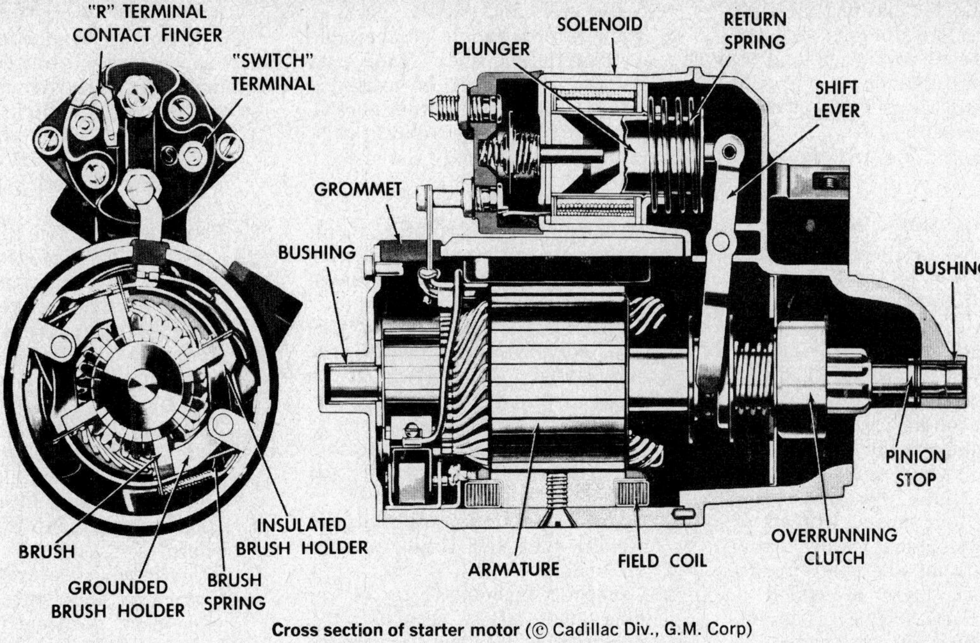
"R" TERMINAL
CONTACT FINGER
"SWITCH"
TERMINAL
SOLENOID
PLUNGER
RETURN
SPRING
SHIFT
LEVER
GROMMET
BUSHING
BUSHING
PINION
STOP
INSULATED
BRUSH HOLDER
OVERRUNNING
CLUTCH
BRUSH
ARMATURE
FIELD COIL
GROUNDED
BRUSH HOLDER
BRUSH
SPRING
Cross section of starter motor (© Cadillac Div., G.M. Corp)

of contact assembly in place and remove points.

5. Inspect weight assembly, replace or lubricate as required.
6. Place new points under the two screws and tighten screws.
7. Connect the condenser and primary leads at the nylon insulated connection.

NOTE: be sure leads do not interfere with cap, weight base, or breaker advance.

8. Install rotor cap. Square and round lugs must be properly aligned.
9. With 1/8 in. Allen wrench inserted, turn until points close while rubbing block is on high point of lobe. Then turn screw counterclockwise one-half turn.
10. Replace distributor cap.
11. With engine warmed up and off fast idle, set points to get proper dwell angle.

Distributor Removal

All Models

Remove distributor cap. Disconnect vacuum line. Disconnect primary lead at distributor.

Turn the engine to top dead center for No. 1 cylinder so that the rotor points to the No. 1 cylinder tower in the distributor cap and the pointer on the timing case cover points to the O-mark on the crankshaft pulley.

Using a scribe mark, index the vacuum advance unit to the cylinder block, and the tip of the rotor to the distributor housing so that the distributor body will be correctly replaced at reassembly. Remove clamp bolt and distributor.

Distributor Installation

All Models

Install the distributor so that the vacuum advance unit aligns with the match-mark made at removal. Turn the rotor slightly left of center so that as the gear engages the camshaft it will revolve into the proper position, pointing to the No. 1 contact in the cap.

NOTE: if the engine has been cranked, remove the No. 1 spark plug. Crank the engine until the No. 1 piston is in firing position with the pointer and the O-mark on the crank-shaft pulley aligned. Then proceed as above.

Install the hold-down clamp. Connect the primary lead and install the cap.

Fill the distributor oiler tube with 10W oil or rotate lubricator.

Plug the distributor vacuum line to the carburetor.

Insert an adapter pin alongside the No. 1 wire in the distributor cap and connect a timing light.

Clean the crankshaft pulley markings and the pointer.

Set the timing to specifications.

Tighten clamp bolt to 18 ft. lbs.

Remove plug and adapter pin and reconnect the vacuum line to the advance unit.

Distributor Installation (If Engine Has Been Disturbed)

If the engine has been disturbed (cranked) after removing the distributor, perform the following procedure for installation:

1. Crank the engine until no. 1 piston is at the top of its compression stroke. The compression stroke can be determined by removing the spark plug from no. 1 cylinder and placing your thumb over the hole while an assistant slowly cranks the engine. Crank until compression is felt at the hole and then continue cranking slowly until the timing mark on the crankshaft pulley lines up with the zero degrees (0°) timing mark located on the timing chain cover.
2. Position the distributor in the block but do not, at this time, allow it to engage with its drive gear at the base of the mounting hole. Observe the position of the vacuum control unit on the distributor. If the distributor is located correctly, the vacuum unit will be positioned normally so that the vacuum hose can easily connect to it.
3. Rotate the distributor shaft so that the rotor points to the front of the engine, turn the rotor counterclockwise about 1/8 turn toward the left (driver's side), and push the distributor down to engage the camshaft. It may be necessary to turn the rotor a small amount in either direction in order to achieve this engagement. If installed correctly, the rotor should point toward the no. 1 spark plug terminal in the distributor cap.
4. Press firmly downward on the distributor housing. This will ensure that the distributor shaft engages the oil pump shaft, thereby allowing the distributor to fully contact the engine block.
5. Install the hold-down clamp and tighten the bolt until it is snug.
6. Turn the distributor slightly until the points just open and then tighten down on the bolt.
7. Install the distributor cap, making sure that the rotor points to no. 1 terminal in the cap.
8. Attach all wires and the vacuum advance hose.
9. Start the engine. If it fails to start, or runs roughly, the dis-

tributor is 180° out of time. Lift up on the distributor, turn the rotor one-half revolution, and install the distributor. Repeat steps 1–9 if the engine continues to run poorly.
10. Check the timing and change it as necessary.

Thermal Vacuum Switch

Starting 1968, a thermal vacuum switch was added to the distributor vacuum circuit to prevent engine overheating in heavy traffic. This switch is so designed to provide full vacuum advance in prolonged idling, or high temperature, situations. Under these conditions, the switch sends full manifold vacuum, instead of the normal carburetor vacuum, to the advance unit. Vacuum switch units having four ports, instead of the normal three, allow manifold vacuum to operate an idle speed-up device (the adjustment of which is found under *Fuel System*). The cutoff temperature of the switch is 220°F. An overheating condition may be due to a faulty switch.

To check the switch, proceed as follows:

1. Idle engine at 600 rpm and at normal operating temperature.
2. With an assistant in the car with his foot on the brake, and transmission in Reverse, disconnect the line from the distributor advance unit and check that vacuum is available (from port D). If vacuum is not available, the separate vacuum solenoid may be at fault.
3. Remove the line between the switch and the vacuum break T at carb. Vacuum still should be available at distributor line (from port D) and should not be available at the line just removed from port MT.
4. Block radiator with a piece of cardboard until "Engine Temp" light comes on.
5. Reconnect line removed in Step 3 and disconnect line between carburetor and switch port C. Vacuum now should be available at distributor line (from port D) and should not be available at line disconnected from port C.
6. If the previous checks indicate a faulty switch, replace the unit.

FUEL FILTER
METAL GASKET
FUEL OUTLET NUT
Fuel filter—1969-74
(© Cadillac Div., G.M. Corp)

Ignition Timing

1. Loosen the distributor hold-down bolt so that the distributor can be turned without it being too loose.
2. Remove the hose from the vacuum advance and tape the free end closed. The end must be taped as a manifold leak will affect the timing.
3. Remove the vacuum hose from the parking brake and tape the end.
4. Connect the timing light. Make certain that the timing marks are visible.
5. Connect a tachometer to the engine and, after securing the parking brake, start the engine and place the selector lever in Drive.
6. Adjust the idle speed to 600 rpm.
7. Point the timing light at the pulley and observe the notch in the pulley in relation to the notches on the front cover. Check the specification chart for the correct timing setting.
8. If the setting is not correct, rotate the distributor until the correct timing is obtained then tighten the distributor clamp nut to 18 ft lbs and recheck the timing.
9. Untape and reconnect the vacuum hoses on the parking brake and the vacuum advance.

FUEL SYSTEM

Cadillac fuel system includes the fuel pump, fuel filter line, carburetor, and intake manifold.

Information covering operation and trouble shooting of the fuel gauge will be found in the Unit Repair Section.

Fuel Pump and Filter

The fuel pump is mounted on the engine front cover up to 1967, on the left-hand side of the engine from 1968 to 1974. The pump is driven by an eccentric machined as an integral part of the camshaft. There is a fuel filter between the fuel pump and the carburetor. Up to 1967, the filter is mounted on the oil filler bracket. In 1968, the filter is an inline unit mounted near the fuel pump, and from 1969 onward the filter is an integral part of the fuel pump. The filter should be replaced every 12,000 miles. On air conditioned cars, the fuel filter has a passage and a connecting line to the fuel tank to return fuel vapors to the tank under high temperature conditions.

R & R Pump—1967-74

NOTE: on air conditioned cars, be sure to disconnect the flexible line connecting the fuel filter to the vapor return line from the tank.

1. If equipped with A.I.R. system, it may be necessary to remove air pump and bracket for clearance.
2. Remove center coil wire.

2A. For 1968-74 models, jack up front of car and support on axle stands so that pump can be removed from underneath.

3. Loosen two mounting bolts (or one bolt and one stud nut from 1968).
4. Turn over engine so that tension on mounting bolts is relieved.
5. Disconnect pump inlet line and pump outlet line. Plug inlet line.
6. Remove two mounting bolts and pump.
7. To install, reverse removal procedure. Make sure pump arm is properly positioned on cam eccentric; tighten bolts to 15 ft. lbs.

R & R Filter—1969-74

1. Jack up car and support on stands.
2. Clamp or plug rubber section of inlet hose.
3. Disconnect fuel pump outlet line at fuel pump.
4. Remove fuel outlet nut and remove filter.

NOTE: use two wrenches to prevent loosening of nut welded to pump cover.

5. Install in reverse of above.

Air Valve (Dashpot)

A vacuum-operated throttle check is used on some models. It operates by a combination of spring pressure and engine vacuum. Adjust length of plunger for correct operation.

Adjustment is made by seating the vacuum diaphragm. With the diaphragm in this position there must be 0.030 in. clearance between the dashpot rod and the end of the slot in the air valve lever. When making this measurement, make certain that the diaphragm plunger is totally compressed inward. Bend the rod at the air valve end to make adjustments.

Speed-Up Control Adjustment

Cars equipped with air conditioning have a vacuum-powered, solenoid-operated speed-up control attached to the carburetor.

This device increases the engine idle speed to 900 rpm when the transmission is in neutral and the air conditioner switch is on.

1967-68

1. In Park, warm up engine.
2. Remove air cleaner.
3. Remove and plug vacuum hose from Automatic Climate Control power servo vacuum actuator.

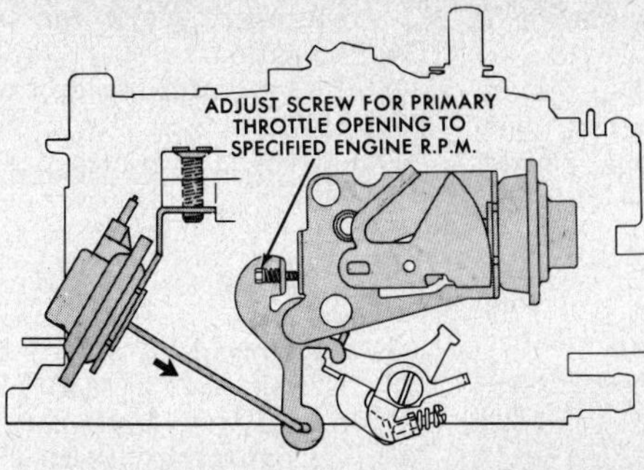
ADJUST SCREW FOR PRIMARY
THROTTLE OPENING TO
SPECIFIED ENGINE R.P.M.

Speed-up control adjustment. The adjustment is on the rod on earlier models
(© Cadillac Div., G.M. Corp)

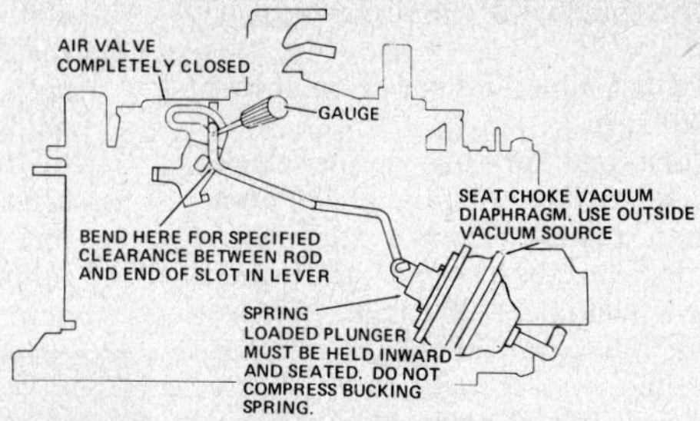
AIR VALVE
COMPLETELY CLOSED
GAUGE
SEAT CHOKE VACUUM
DIAPHRAGM. USE OUTSIDE
VACUUM SOURCE
BEND HERE FOR SPECIFIED
CLEARANCE BETWEEN ROD
AND END OF SLOT IN LEVER
SPRING
LOADED PLUNGER
MUST BE HELD INWARD
AND SEATED. DO NOT
COMPRESS BUCKING
SPRING.

Air valve adjustment
(© Cadillac Div., G.M. Corp)

4. Set Automatic Climate Control selector on AUTO.
5. On 1967 model, adjust nuts on speed-up control rod to idle speed of 900. On 1968 model, the adjustment is made by turning the screw located on speed-up control arm.
6. Shut off engine, reconnect vacuum hose and install air cleaner.

1969

On these models, the speed-up control is actuated by water temperature, working only when radiator reaches 220°F. Air conditioner does not have to be on to have idle speed up. Curb and fast idle adjustments should be made before attempting the speed-up idle adjustment.

1. Warm up engine.
2. With engine off, remove air cleaner.
3. Disconnect vacuum hose leading from thermo vacuum switch to reducing nipple near dash, at reducing nipple.
4. Disconnect vacuum hose at diverter valve and connect to reducing nipple.
5. Disconnect and plug distributor vacuum hose at vacuum unit.
6. Disconnect manifold vacuum hose from thermo vacuum switch nipple at "MT" and connect to distributor vacuum unit. This is the nipple closest to the block.
7. Turn air conditioner to HIGH and turn temperature dial to 65.
8. With transmission in Neutral or Park, start engine and make adjustment at screw on idle speed-up control arm (900-950 rpm).
9. Turn engine off, reconnect hoses and install air cleaner.

1970 Fleetwood 75 and Commercial

Operation is similar to 1969. Different vacuum routing requires a slightly different procedure.

1. Set curb and fast idle.
2. Stop engine and remove air cleaner and heat duct.
3. Disconnect and plug distributor advance hose.
4. Disconnect vacuum hose at vacuum break tank and connect it to distributor advance unit.
5. Disconnect vacuum hose that goes from Thermo Vacuum switch to reducing nipple, at the reducing nipple.
6. Disconnect vacuum hose connector at carburetor vacuum break T.
7. Connect a 25 in. section of 3/16 in. vacuum hose between T and reducing nipple.
8. Turn A/C to HIGH and set dial to 65°F.
9. Start and warm up engine, then adjust idle speed-up in Neutral. Turn adjusting screw, as illustrated, to maintain 900-950 rpm.

NOTE: pull rod on idle speed-up unit should move when selector lever is moved to Park or Neutral. If it does not, check neutral switch or for vacuum leaks.

10. Turn off engine, reconnect hoses and install air cleaner.

Idle Speed and Mixture Adjustments

1967-69

Make all adjustments with the air cleaner removed.

1. Make sure the PCV valve is clean and working properly.
2. Disconnect the parking brake vacuum hose at the vacuum cylinder and connect a vacuum gauge to the hose.
3. Connect a tachometer to the engine and set the parking brake. Allow the engine to reach normal operating temperature.
4. Remove the air cleaner and make certain that the dashpot is disengaged.
5. With the parking brake on, place the transmission in Drive. Make sure that the parking brake holds securely.
6. On 1968-69 cars, disconnect and plug distributor vacuum advance hose.

NOTE: plug parking brake vacuum hose instead of using a gauge.

7. Adjust air adjusting screw to obtain an idle speed of 480-500 rpm for cars without Air Injection Reactor system, 550 rpm for A.I.R. equipped cars. (A/C should be *off* for A.I.R. cars, *on* for all others.)

NOTE: press down on brass hot idle compensator pin while making adjustments. Be careful of the bimetallic strip, as it is easily damaged.

8. On 1967 cars with A/C, no A.I.R. , disconnect and plug vacuum line from power servo on firewall.
9. Set idle speed screw $1\frac{1}{2}$ turns in after contacting primary lever, both mixture screws out 4 turns from seated position.
10. Turn one idle mixture screw clockwise to obtain highest tach reading. Continue to turn screw until speed falls off 20 rpm—this is the lean idle fall-off point. Back off screw $\frac{1}{4}$ turn for non-A.I.R. cars, $1\frac{1}{8}$ turns for 1967 A.I.R. cars, $1\frac{1}{2}$ turns for 1968 A.I.R. cars, and 1 turn for 1969 A.I.R. cars.
11. Repeat Step 10, turning other mixture screw.
12. Reset idle speed as in Step 7, then repeat Steps 10 and 11 if speed exceeds 500 rpm for non-A.I.R. cars or 550 rpm for A.I.R. cars.
13. Install air cleaner and recheck idle speed.
14. Shut off engine, disconnect tach, connect parking brake vacuum line and, on 1968-69 models, reconnect distributor vacuum advance.

1970

Adjust with air cleaner removed.

1. Disconnect and plug distributor vacuum advance line.
2. Disconnect and plug parking brake vacuum line at vacuum release cylinder.
3. Connect a tachometer, set parking brake and remove air cleaner.
4. Make sure dashpot is not touching linkage, then turn slow idle speed screw in approximately $1\frac{1}{2}$ turns after it contacts primary throttle lever. Turn in both mixture screws until they seat gently, then unscrew them approximately 6 turns.
5. Place car in Drive after warming up engine. Turn off Air Conditioning.

NOTE: press down on hot idle compensator pin while making adjustments.

6. Adjust slow idle screw to obtain 620 rpm.
7. Turn one mixture screw clockwise until speed falls off 10 rpm, then repeat Steps 6 and 7 for other mixture screw. Idle speed now should be 600 rpm, indicating a 10 rpm drop per mixture needle.
8. Install air cleaner, shut off engine and disconnect tach.
9. Connect parking brake vacuum line and distributor vacuum line.

1971-74

Adjust with air cleaner removed.

Idle speed is adjusted at a new anti-dieseling solenoid located where the dashpot was located in previous years. The throttle must be opened slightly to allow the plunger to move out all the way, then it must be closed against the now-extended solenoid plunger before making the idle speed adjustment. The solenoid plunger will retract when the ignition is shut off.

1. Disconnect and plug distributor vacuum advance hose and parking brake vacuum hose (at the release cylinder).
2. Connect a tachometer and set the parking brake with transmission in Neutral.
3. Remove the air cleaner and turn in mixture screws until they seat gently, then turn the screws out approximately 6 turns.
4. Start engine and allow it to warm up.
5. Place car in Drive with A/C off.

NOTE: press down on hot idle compensator pin while making adjustments. This applies to Fleetwood 75 and Commercial models only.

6. Set idle speed to 620 rpm by adjusting anti-dieseling solenoid. Tighten jam nut.
7. Turn one mixture screw clockwise until idle speed falls off 10 rpm, then repeat for other screw. Idle speed now should be 600 rpm.
8. Install limiter caps, then disconnect wire that energizes solenoid. The plunger should retract to allow a slower idle speed of 350-400 rpm.
9. Shut off engine, disconnect tach, connect vacuum lines and solenoid wire and install air cleaner.

COOLING SYSTEM

All Cadillac models from 1967 to 1968 used a non-sealed, low capacity system while the 1969-74 models use a sealed cooling system. The sealed system is designed to remain sealed at all times. A coolant reservoir allows the pressurized system to be kept sealed even when fresh coolant is added. There is no need to open the radiator cap.

Information on the water temperature gauge can be found in the Unit Repair Section.

Radiator Core Removal

1967-74

1. Disconnect battery cable.
2. Drain cooling system.
3. Disconnect air conditioning compressor, if so equipped, and position out of the way without disconnecting hoses.
4. Remove clamp that holds A/C high pressure vapor line to cradle.
5. Loosen hose clamps and disconnect upper and lower radiator hoses.
6. Disconnect two transmission oil cooler lines and plug them.

NOTE: disconnect heater return hose, if so equipped.

7. Remove two top radiator cradle clamps or straps and fan shroud. Disconnect reservoir hose from 1969.
8. Remove vacuum hoses, if so equipped. Mark for proper installation.
9. Pull radiator straight up and out of car.

Water Pump Removal

1967

1. Disconnect negative battery cable.
2. Drain coolant.
3. Unbolt compressor and swing out of way (A/C cars) without disconnecting hoses.
4. Remove four capscrews and fan shroud.
5. Remove two radiator cradle clamp screws and clamps. Push radiator forward far enough to gain access to fan.
6. Remove power steering pump bracket and position pump and hoses to one side.
7. Remove power steering belt and fan, pulley and fan belt.

NOTE: place A/C fans aside in installed position to prevent silicone fluid loss.

8. Remove alternator - to - support bracket capscrew.
9. Disconnect water inlet and upper radiator hoses.
10. On A.I.R.-equipped cars, remove the three capscrews that hold the air pump bracket to the front engine cover. Loosen air pump adjusting bolt and bracket bolt, then remove belt.
11. Remove four capscrews that hold water outlet pipe to cylinder heads. Remove outlet pipe and discard gaskets.
12. Remove the nine remaining capscrews that hold water pump; remove pump.

1968-74

1. Disconnect negative battery cable.
2. Drain radiator and, on 1968 models, remove fan shroud.
3. Remove fan assembly. The screws cannot be removed entirely due to lack of clearance between fan and radiator. Slide

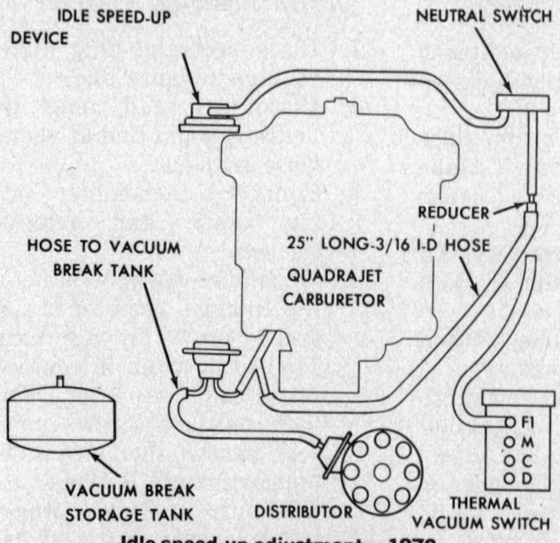
IDLE SPEED-UP DEVICE
NEUTRAL SWITCH
REDUCER
HOSE TO VACUUM BREAK TANK
25" LONG-3/16 I-D HOSE
QUADRAJET CARBURETOR
VACUUM BREAK STORAGE TANK
DISTRIBUTOR
THERMAL VACUUM SWITCH
FI
M
C
D

Idle speed-up adjustment—1970
(© Cadillac Div., G.M. Corp)

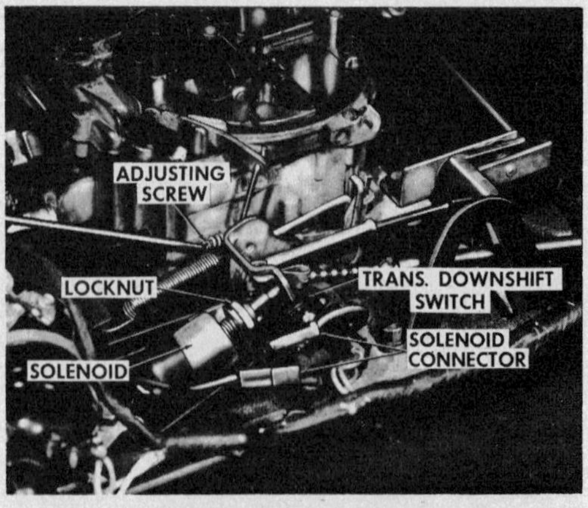
ADJUSTING SCREW
LOCKNUT
TRANS. DOWNSHIFT SWITCH
SOLENOID CONNECTOR
SOLENOID

Adjusting anti-dieseling solenoid—1971-74
(© Cadillac Div., G.M. Corp)

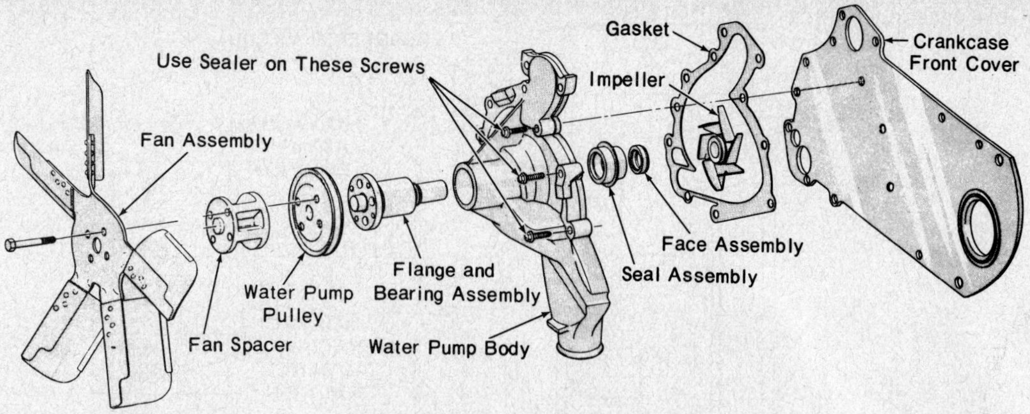
Gasket
Use Sealer on These Screws
Impeller
Crankcase Front Cover
Fan Assembly
Face Assembly
Flange and Bearing Assembly
Seal Assembly
Water Pump Pulley
Fan Spacer
Water Pump Body

Water pump—1968-72 (© Cadillac Div., G.M. Corp)

loosened assembly near power steering pump to remove bolts and spacer.

4. Loosen alternator mounting screws and remove generator belt.
5. Loosen power steering pump mounting screws and remove belts.
6. On applicable models, remove A.I.R. pump and belt.
7. Remove water pump pulley, disconnect water inlet and remove 11 screws and pump.

Thermostat R & R —1967-74

Removal

1. Drain the cooling system until the coolant level is below the level of the thermostat.
2. Remove the upper radiator hose at the thermostat housing.
3. Remove the thermostat housing.
4. Pull the thermostat from the engine block.

Installation

1. Position the thermostat in the block with the valve up.
2. Install a new gasket coated with sealer onto the engine block.
3. Position and secure the thermostat housing.
4. Connect the radiator hose and refill the system to the proper level.

EMISSION CONTROLS

The emission controls for the Cadillac have changed greatly through the years. The 1967 models were equipped with the Positive Crankcase Ventilation System (PCV) which by way of carburetor vacuum extracts and reburns crankcase vapors. With the increasingly strict pollution laws coming into effect, the 1968 and 1969 cars were equipped with an Air Injection Reactor (AIR) in addition to the PCV system. This AIR system consists of an engine-driven pump which forces air into the exhaust port of each cylinder to reduce the concentration of hydrocarbons. This compressed air causes further oxidation of the exhaust gases before they enter the exhaust pipe. The A.I.R. system passages are built into the engine castings after 1967, eliminating the need for some of the exterior air manifolding of previous years. It does, however, use the same principle as before.

Beginning 1968, all manufacturers Post complete tune-up specifications and instructions for making these settings in the engine compartment.

The 1970 models did not use the AIR system but substituted the Controlled Combustion System (CCS). The PCV system was retained on all 1970 models. The CCS system is composed of a thermac air cleaner and a transmission-controlled spark advance.

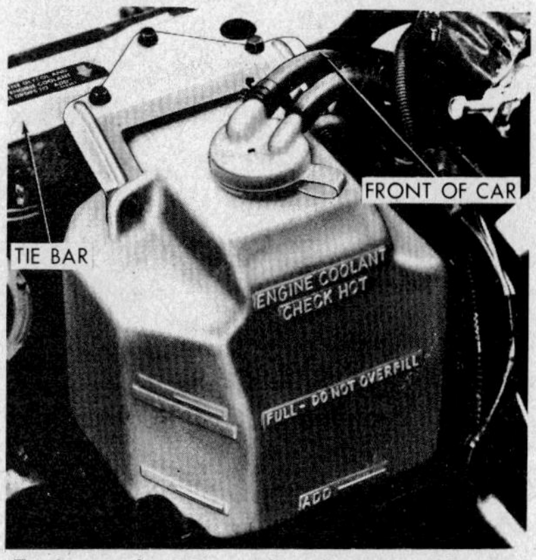
FRONT OF CAR
TIE BAR
ENGINE COOLANT CHECK HOT
FULL - DO NOT OVERFILL
ADD

Engine coolant reservoir—the FULL and ADD marks are two quarts apart (© Cadillac Div., G.M. Corp)

The thermatic air cleaner regulates the air temperature at the air cleaner inlet so that it maintains a constant temperature of 100° F. A damper in the air cleaner, when the engine is cold, allows the intake air to be heated by the exhaust manifold before it enters the carburetor. As the engine reaches operating temperature, the damper opens and allows a mixture of outside cool air and heated air to mix to obtain the 100° F intake air.

The transmission-controlled spark system is composed of a transmission switch, a thermal vacuum switch, and a vacuum solenoid. The switch is positioned in the block with vacuum lines from the intake manifold, the

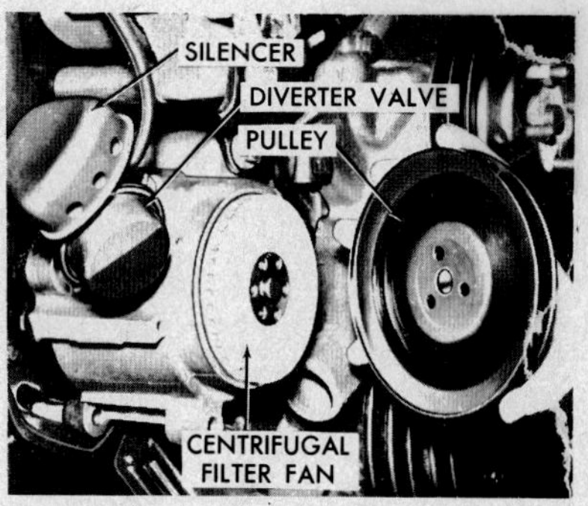
SILENCER
DIVERTER VALVE
PULLEY
CENTRIFUGAL FILTER FAN

Air pump (© Cadillac Div., G.M. Corp)

distributor and the carburetor running to it. The line between the carburetor and the thermal vacuum switch has the solenoid attached to it. The solenoid has a wire which connects it with the transmission. Inside the thermal vacuum switch there is a ball check valve system which opens and closes the ports in the switch.

The vacuum switch has two vacuum sources attached to it: intake manifold vacuum and carburetor vacuum. In the normal running position, the ball check blocks the passage of vacuum from the intake manifold to the distributor and allows vacuum to pass from the carburetor to the distributor. This vacuum is regulated by the transmission solenoid. If the engine should overheat at idle speed, the ball check valve blocks the carburetor-to-distributor vacuum and allows the intake manifold-to-distributor vacuum port to be uncovered allowing the stronger intake manifold vacuum to advance the ignition timing and cool the engine.

The vacuum solenoid is a type of regulator between the carburetor vacuum line, the thermal vacuum switch, the distributor, and the transmission. When the transmission is in neutral,

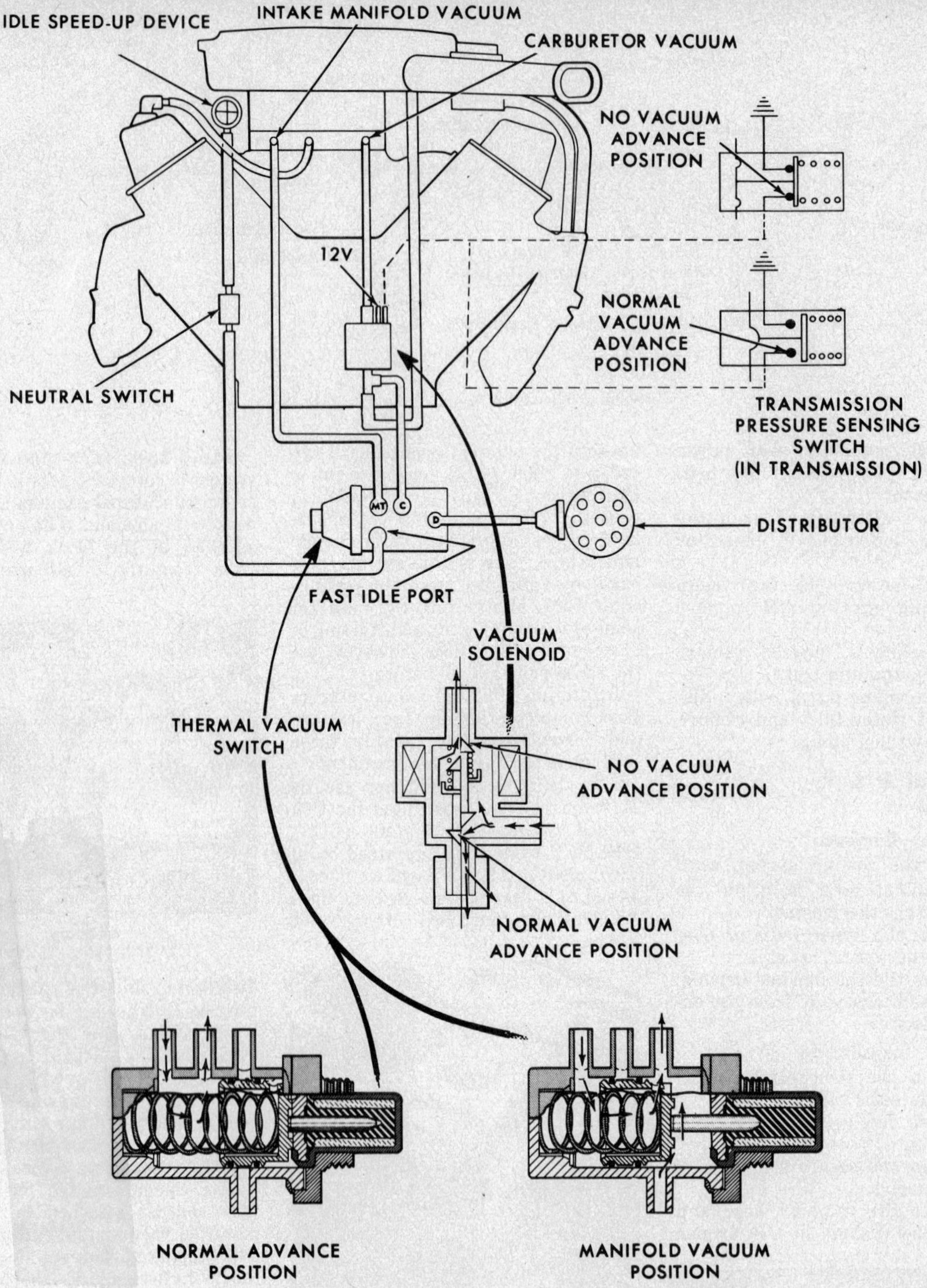
IDLE SPEED-UP DEVICE
INTAKE MANIFOLD VACUUM
CARBURETOR VACUUM
NO VACUUM
ADVANCE
POSITION
12V
NORMAL
VACUUM
ADVANCE
POSITION
NEUTRAL SWITCH
TRANSMISSION
PRESSURE SENSING
SWITCH
(IN TRANSMISSION)
MT
C
D
DISTRIBUTOR
FAST IDLE PORT
VACUUM
SOLENOID
THERMAL VACUUM
SWITCH
NO VACUUM
ADVANCE POSITION
NORMAL VACUUM
ADVANCE POSITION
NORMAL ADVANCE
POSITION
MANIFOLD VACUUM
POSITION

Vacuum advance controls—1970 (© Cadillac Div., G.M. Corp)

first, or second gear, the solenoid is energized which eliminates vacuum advance to the distributor. When the transmission shifts into third gear the solenoid is de-energized allowing the vacuum advance to pass to the distributor.

Evaporative Loss Control (ELC) was available in California cars in 1970 as it was considered an experimental emission control. The concept of this system is the venting of the fuel tank through a canister containing charcoal. Both liquid fuel and fuel vapors from the tank are fed into the liquid vapor separator which is located ahead of the fuel tank. The vapors are collected in the charcoal canister which is mounted on the front of the radiator. The vapors are drawn from the canister by a vacuum line which is connected to the air cleaner. The liquid fuel which is ducted to the separator is returned to the fuel tank.

The Exhaust Gas Recirculation System (EGR) is a control system used to reduce nitrous oxides released into the air. The basic function of the system is to reduce the temperature in the combustion chambers. This will lessen nitrogen oxidation and reduce pollution. It is accomplished by recirculating the engine exhaust through ports in the intake manifold and into the carburetor for reburning.

This channeling of exhaust is governed by the EGR valve which is mounted at the rear of the intake manifold. As the engine speed increases, vacuum is applied to the vacuum diaphragm in the valve and this opens the exhaust port allowing exhaust gases to enter. As vacuum decreases at idle speed and wide open

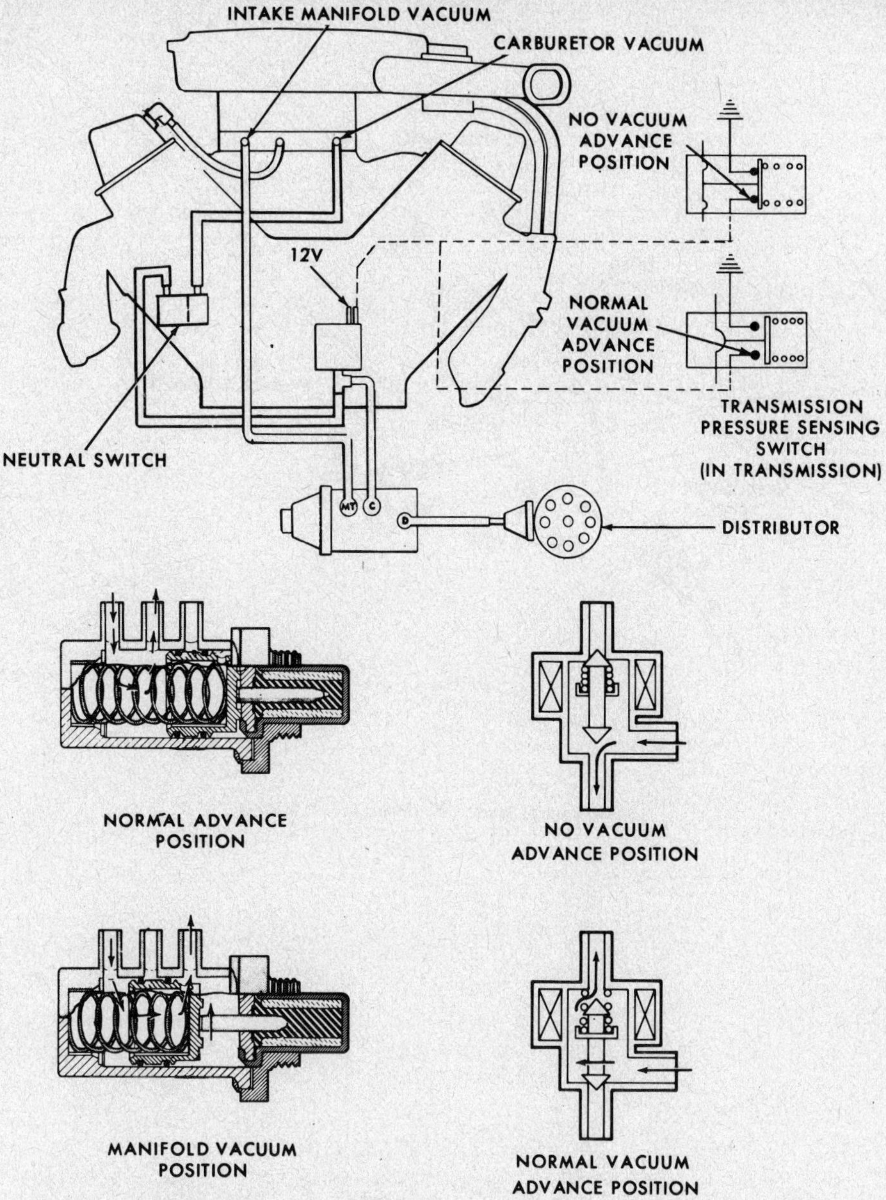
INTAKE MANIFOLD VACUUM
CARBURETOR VACUUM
NO VACUUM ADVANCE POSITION
12V
NORMAL VACUUM ADVANCE POSITION
TRANSMISSION PRESSURE SENSING SWITCH (IN TRANSMISSION)
NEUTRAL SWITCH
MT
C
DISTRIBUTOR
NORMAL ADVANCE POSITION
NO VACUUM ADVANCE POSITION
MANIFOLD VACUUM POSITION
NORMAL VACUUM ADVANCE POSITION

Vacuum advance controls—1971-74 (© Cadillac Div., G.M. Corp)

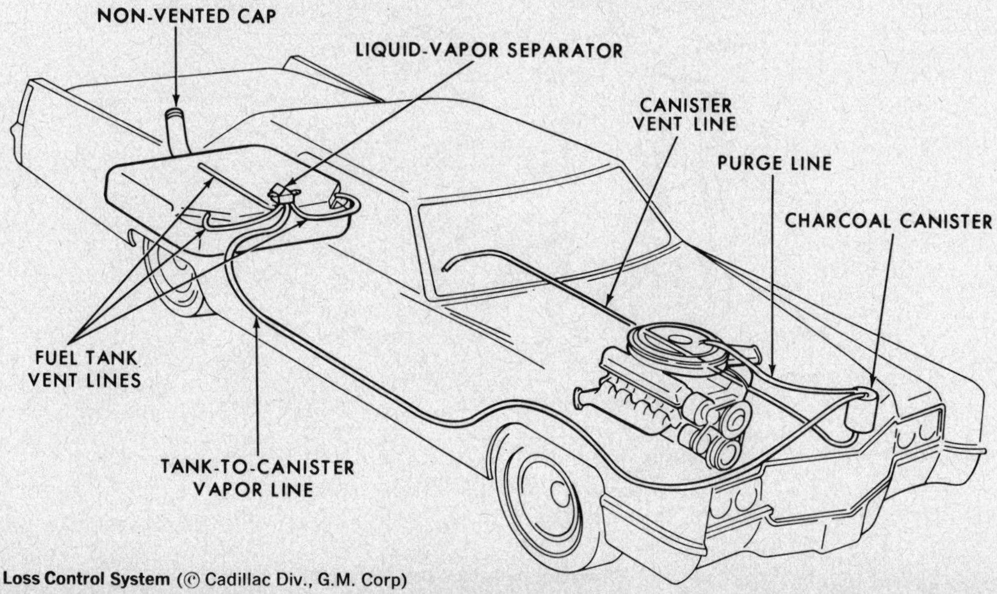
NON-VENTED CAP
LIQUID-VAPOR SEPARATOR
CANISTER VENT LINE
PURGE LINE
CHARCOAL CANISTER
FUEL TANK VENT LINES
TANK-TO-CANISTER VAPOR LINE

Evaporative Loss Control System (© Cadillac Div., G.M. Corp)

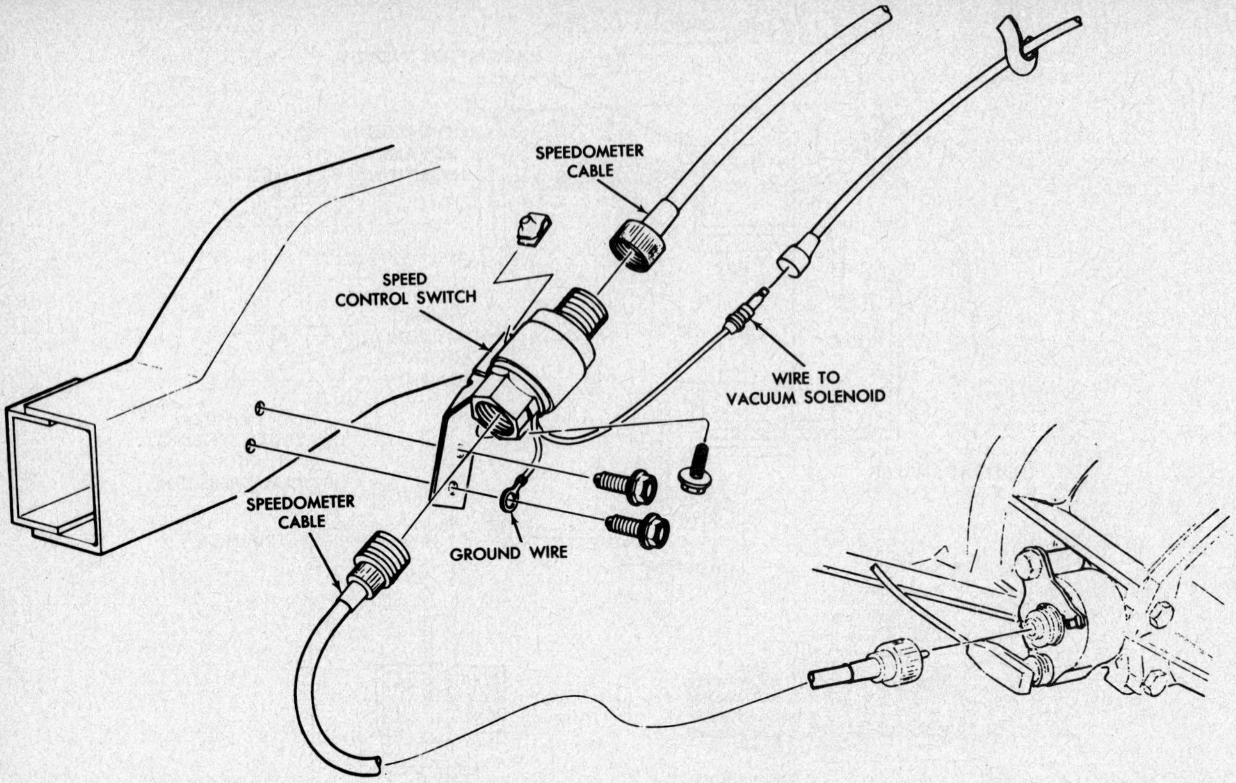
SPEEDOMETER
CABLE
SPEED
CONTROL SWITCH
WIRE TO
VACUUM SOLENOID
SPEEDOMETER
CABLE
GROUND WIRE

Speed Control Switch (© Cadillac Div., G.M. Corp)

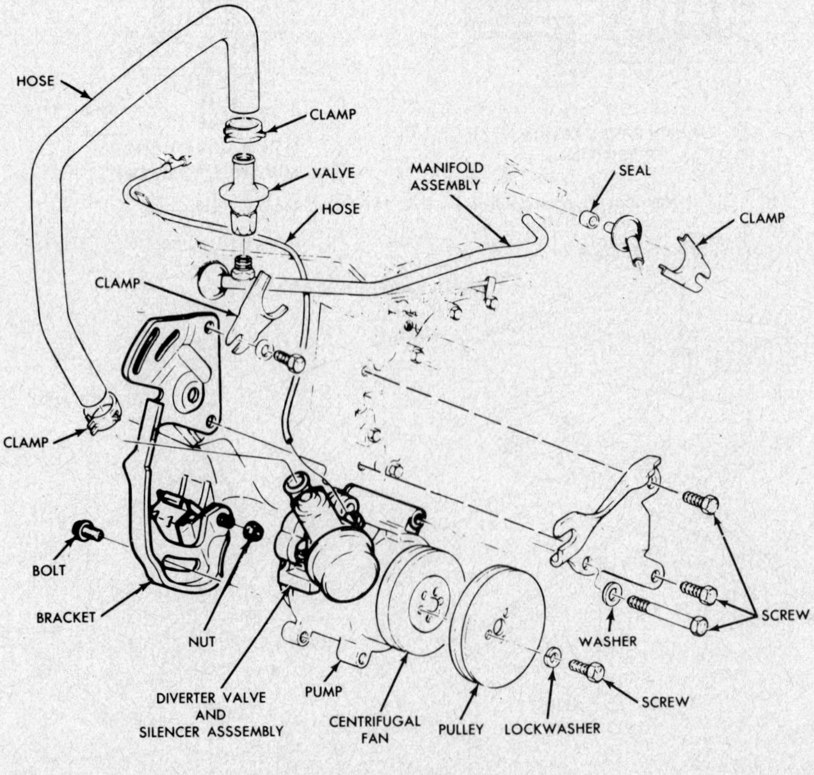
HOSE
CLAMP
VALVE
MANIFOLD
ASSEMBLY
SEAL
HOSE
CLAMP
CLAMP
CLAMP
BOLT
BRACKET
NUT
SCREW
WASHER
SCREW
DIVERTER VALVE
AND
SILENCER ASSSEMBLY
PUMP
CENTRIFUGAL
FAN
PULLEY
LOCKWASHER

AIR system (© Cadillac Div., G.M. Corp)

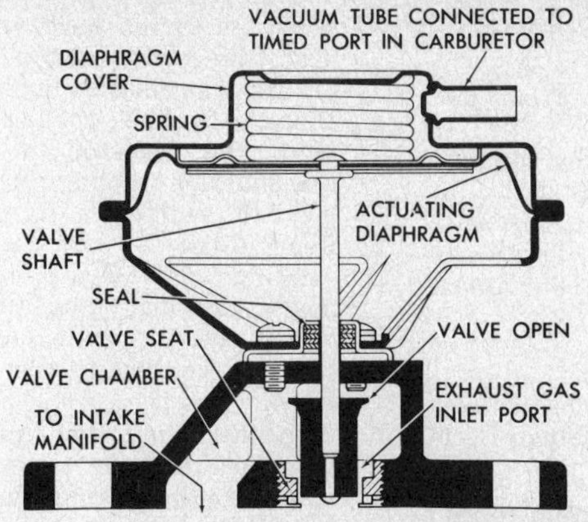
VACUUM TUBE CONNECTED TO TIMED PORT IN CARBURETOR
DIAPHRAGM COVER
SPRING
VALVE SHAFT
ACTUATING DIAPHRAGM
SEAL
VALVE SEAT
VALVE OPEN
VALVE CHAMBER
EXHAUST GAS INLET PORT
TO INTAKE MANIFOLD

E.G.R. valve in the open position
(© Cadillac Div., G.M. Corp)

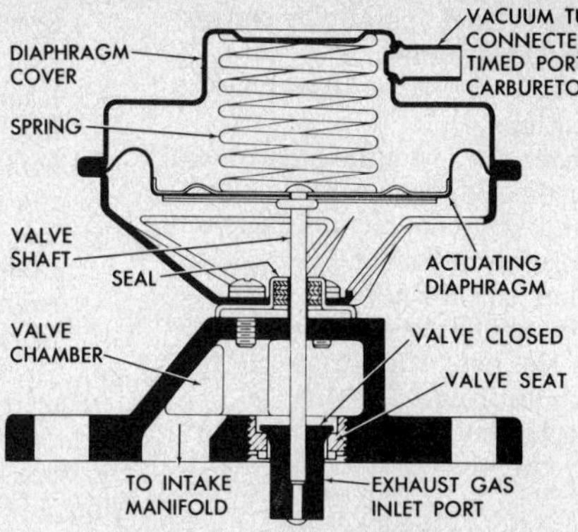
DIAPHRAGM COVER
VACUUM TUBE CONNECTED TO TIMED PORT IN CARBURETOR
SPRING
VALVE SHAFT
SEAL
ACTUATING DIAPHRAGM
VALVE CHAMBER
VALVE CLOSED
VALVE SEAT
TO INTAKE MANIFOLD
EXHAUST GAS INLET PORT

E.G.R. valve in the closed position
(© Cadillac Div., G.M. Corp)

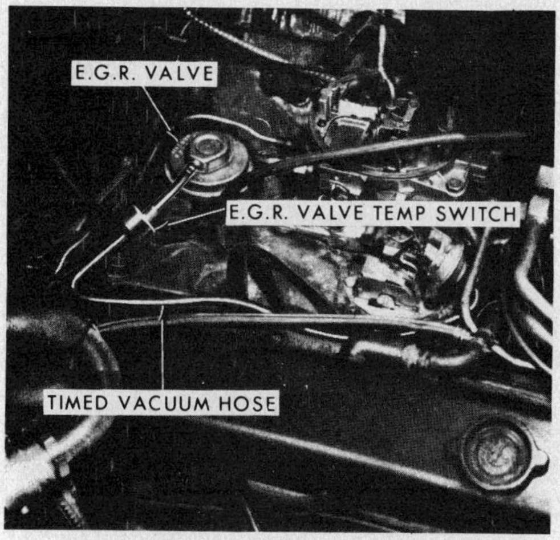
E.G.R. VALVE
E.G.R. VALVE TEMP SWITCH
TIMED VACUUM HOSE

Exhaust Gas Recirculation valve
(© Cadillac Div., G.M. Corp)

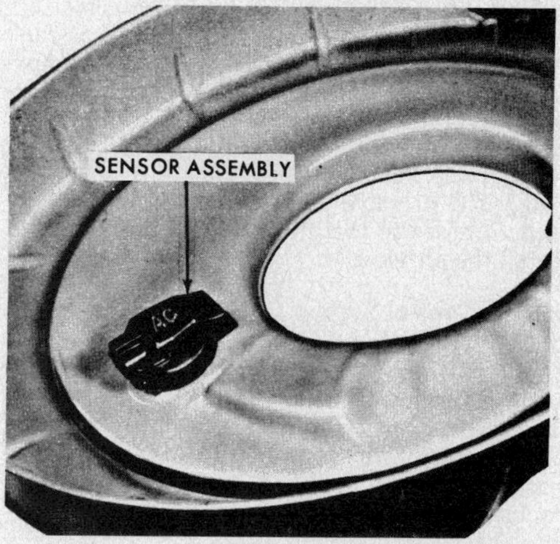
SENSOR ASSEMBLY

Location of the Thermac Air Cleaner Sensor
(© Cadillac Div., G.M. Corp)

throttle, the valve closes and the gases are cut off.

In the 1971 model year all cars were equipped with the PCV, AIR, and ELC systems.

The 1972 cars use the PCV, AIR, ELC, and a Speed Control Switch (SCS) which controls the spark advance to the distributor at low speeds. The switch is mounted within the transmission and connected to the speedometer gear. The switch is closed prior to 33 mph, allowing no vacuum advance to the distributor during speeds from 0 to 33 mph. When the vehicle reaches 33 mph, the contacts in the switch separate, allowing the vacuum port to be uncovered. Once the port is uncovered the vacuum causes the distributor to advance. 1973-74 models use EGR PCV, AIR, and ELC.

Component Removal and Installation

PCV Valve

1. Disconnect the valve from its connection in the valve cover.
2. Remove the hose clamp and the hose from the ventilator valve grommet.
3. To install, place a small amount of silicone sealer on both ends of the new valve and install the small end of the valve into the hose. Secure with the clamp.
4. Place the large end of the valve into the grommet in the valve cover.

AIR Pump

NOTE: Pump service should be limited to replacement of the entire unit. At no time should the pump be opened.

1. Raise and support the vehicle.
2. Remove the air hose from the diverter valve and disconnect the vacuum line from the other side of the valve.
3. Remove the three screws which hold the pulley to the pump and remove the pulley and belt.
4. Remove the mounting bolt from the top of the air pump and the adjusting bolt from the bottom rear.
5. Remove the pump and the diverter valve as an assembly.
6. To install, lift the pump through the space between the lower radiator hose and the oil filter. Turn the pump so that the diverter valve passes over the oil filter.
7. Place the pump against the mounting bracket and loosely install the upper screw and adjusting bolt.
8. Install the pulley and drive belt and adjust the belt.
9. The adjusting and mounting bolts should be torqued to 25 ft lbs.
10. Connect the air hose to the larger fitting of the diverter valve and tighten the clamp. The vacuum hose is installed on the small fitting of the valve.

Thermac Temperature Sensor

1. Remove the hose from between the sensor and the manifold fitting.
2. Remove the air cleaner.
3. Remove the hose between the sensor and the vacuum motor.
4. Pull the retainer from the sensor vacuum fittings and remove the retainer.
5. Pull the sensor from the air cleaner.
6. To install, place the gasket on

the sensor and install the sensor into the air cleaner.

7. Press the retainer on the vacuum connections.
8. Connect the vacuum hose between the sensor and the vacuum motor. Place the vacuum hose on the remaining fitting.
9. Position the air cleaner making certain that the heat tube engages the heat shroud on the exhaust manifold.
10. Connect the vacuum hose between the sensor and the manifold.

Exhaust Gas Recirculation Valve

1. Remove the air cleaner and the vacuum hoses from the air cleaner and the front of the carburetor.
2. Remove the valve attaching nuts and the vacuum signal line and remove the valve.
3. To install, place the valve on the manifold studs and install the attaching nuts.
4. Connect the vacuum signal line to the E.G.R. valve and the two vacuum hoses to the air cleaner.
5. Install the air cleaner.

Evaporative Control System Canister

1. Remove the hoses from the top of the canister.
2. Remove the canister strap bracket from the radiator cradle.
3. Remove both the strap and the canister from the cradle.
4. To install, position the canister onto the radiator cradle bracket with the fittings on the top facing toward the engine.
5. Tighten the hold-down strap and connect the two hoses to the top of the canister. The smaller diameter hose is connected to the carburetor while the larger diameter hose goes to the tank.

Evaporative Control System Canister Filter

1. Remove the canister from its cradle.
2. Pull out the element by squeezing it under the retainer bar.
3. To install, push the element under the bar and locate it evenly around the entire bottom of the canister.
4. Install the canister.

For troubleshooting and adjustment of the Cadillac emission control systems consult the "Unit Repair Section."

ENGINE

Engine Removal—1967

Cars of these years necessitate the removal of the engine and transmission as one onit.

1. Remove the hood after scribing aligning marks to aid in reassembly.
2. Remove the battery cables and the carburetor air cleaner.
3. Place the car on jackstands and drain the cooling system, engine oil, and transmission fluid.
4. Disconnect the cooling hoses from the radiator, with the transmission cooling lines. Remove the radiator.
5. Remove the fan and the power steering pump belts. Remove the power steering pump and position it away from the engine. It is not necessary to remove the hoses.
6. Disconnect the power brake vacuum hose and the transmission modulator hose from the intake manifold.
7. Remove the throttle control linkage and the return spring.
8. Disconnect the leads to the starter solenoid.
9. Disconnect the exhaust pipe at the manifold and at the resonator to remove the pipe.
10. From the transmission, disconnect the downshift switch, the clevis pin, and the shift rod. Remove the speedometer cable.

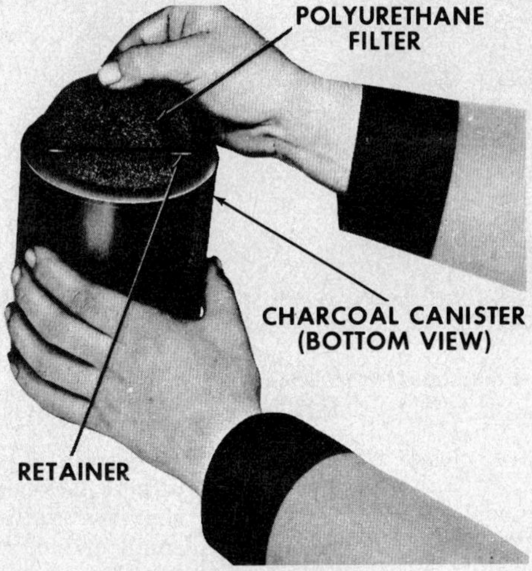
POLYURETHANE FILTER
CHARCOAL CANISTER (BOTTOM VIEW)
RETAINER

Removing the canister filter (© Cadillac Div., G.M. Corp)

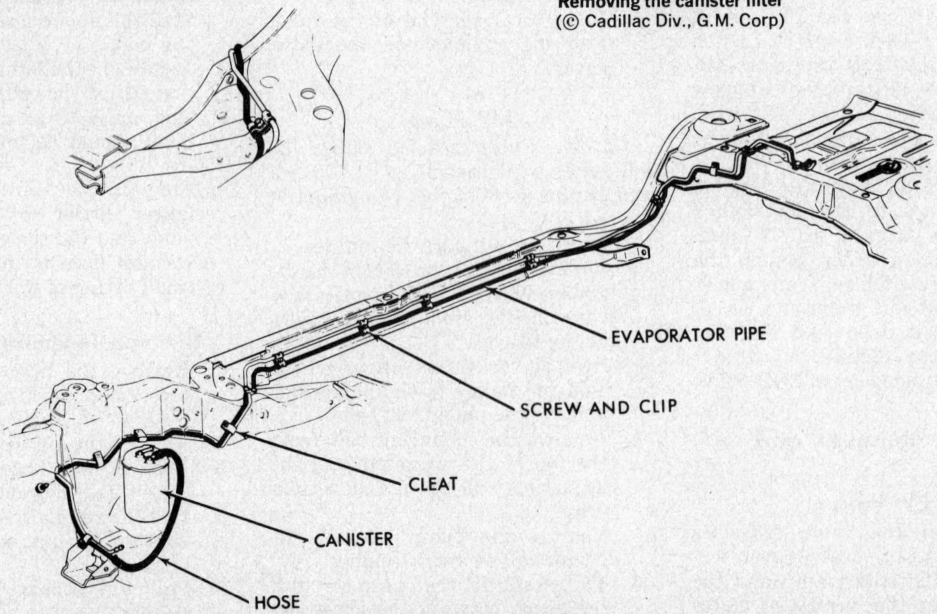
EVAPORATOR PIPE
SCREW AND CLIP
CLEAT
CANISTER
HOSE

Evaporative Control System (© Cadillac Div., G.M. Corp)

11. Remove the center bolts from the engine motor mounts.
12. With a jack positioned under the transmission, remove the transmission bolts and, raising the transmission slightly, remove the crossmember.
13. Hook the engine securely to a hoist and remove all the remaining wires and straps. Disconnect the fuel lines at the fuel pump.
14. Tilt the rear of the engine down at a 45° angle and lift the engine and transmission straight out.

1968-74

1. Disconnect negative battery cable.
2. Remove hood, after scribing hood hinge outline for proper alignment.
3. Remove air cleaner and heat shroud.
4. Drain cooling system.
5. Remove radiator hose bracket, radiator cover and fan.
6. Remove upper radiator hose.
7. Disconnect throttle and Cruise Control linkage at carburetor.
8. Remove Cruise Control power unit on cars so equipped.
9. Disconnect power steering pump bracket and swing pump out of way with hoses still connected. Position power steering fluid cooler out of the way.
10. Remove A/C compressor bracket bolts and swing compressor out of way with hoses still connected.
11. Disconnect temperature sender wire, idle speed-up wire (if so equipped), ignition primary wire, downshift switch wire, S.C.S. or T.C.S. solenoid (if so equipped) and anti-dieseling solenoid wires, and all ground straps.
12. Bend back clips and position wiring harness out of the way.
13. Disconnect all vacuum hoses, and purge hose from E.L.C. canister.
14. Disconnect alternator, heater switch and oil pressure sender wires.
15. Remove wiring harness from clips.
16. Remove water hose from fitting at rear of right-hand cylinder head.

NOTE: on A/C cars up to 1969, remove blower relay, power servo, and master switch from heater air selector.

17. Loosen and remove alternator and A.I.R. pumps and remove belts.
18. Disconnect tie struts and swing out of the way.
19. Remove upper two transmission-to-engine bolts. Remove two screws that secure right air deflector to lower radiator cradle.
20. Jack up car and support on axle stands.
21. Remove starter motor, then disconnect exhaust pipes from manifolds.
22. Remove front engine mount bolts, then disconnect and plug vapor return line at fuel pump (A/C cars only) and fuel inlet line. Remove oil filter, after draining engine oil.
23. Disconnect lower radiator hose and remove flywheel housing cover.
24. Remove the three screws that secure flex plate to converter. Engine must be rotated for access.
25. Remove four transmission-to-engine bolts.
26. Lower the car to the ground.
27. Connect a lifting bracket to the engine.
28. Support transmission with a wood-padded floor jack.
29. Raise engine slightly and pull forward to disengage from transmission, then pull engine up and out.
30. Reverse the above procedure to install the engine.

Manifolds

Exhaust Manifold Removal

To remove either of the exhaust manifolds, detach the manifold at the exhaust pipe flange and, in the case of the right manifold, remove the alternator and then remove the bolts that hold the manifold to the cylinder head.

On some models, particularly those with heater ducts, access is easier when the ducts are removed.

Intake Manifold Removal

1. Remove the negative battery cable, air cleaner, heat tube, and crankcase vent.
2. Disconnect the throttle linkage and the Cruise Control.
3. Remove the coil leads and the connector from the SCS solenoid.
4. Disconnect the downshift switch and the temperature sender. On some models it is necessary to remove the anti-dieseling solenoid and the SCS solenoid.
5. Disconnect all vacuum lines. Remove the carburetor fuel line.
6. On cars with air conditioning, it is necessary to partially remove the compressor.
7. Remove the manifold hold-down bolts and lift the manifold from the engine.
8. To install the intake manifold, reverse the above procedure. The intake manifold bolts are torqued to 30 ft lbs, using a diagonal torque pattern beginning from the center of the manifold and working toward the ends.

Valve System

All Cadillacs from 1967 to 1974 use hydraulic lifters. Valve systems with hydraulic lifters operate with zero clearance in the valve train. It should be noted that the rocker arms are non-adjustable. The lifter itself will compensate if there is slack in the system but if there is excessive play. the entire system should be examined.

Rocker Arm Removal and Installation

1967-74

The rocker arms are mounted in pairs (four pairs to each cylinder head). They are of the modified pedestal-mounted type.

Rocker arms may be removed in pairs and do not require cylinder-head removal.

Torque rocker arm mounting screws to 60 ft. lbs.

NOTE: do not install pre-1967 lifters in 1971 and later models.

Checking the Valve Guides

Check the valve stem to guide clearance using a 1/16 in. (wide) strip of 0.005 in shim stock. With the valve removed, bend the shim and hang it in the valve guide on the push-rod side. The shim should not extend more than ¼ in. into the guide. With the shim in the guide, place the valve stem into the guide. If it does not slide into the guide, it is within the allowable limits.

Valve Lifter Removal

Lifters may be removed without taking off the cylinder head.

Remove throttle and gas lines from the carburetor, disconnect hoses, vacuum lines and wires that pass over the rocker covers. Remove the distributor cap and disconnect the wires at the spark plugs. Remove the bolts that hold the rocker covers to the cylinder head and lift off the rocker covers leaving the spark plug wires attached to them. Remove the bolts that hold the intake manifold to the cylinder block and lift off the intake manifold. If desired, the carburetor can be detached from the manifold first, but this is not necessary. Remove the valve chamber cover plate. Remove the bolts that hold the rocker shafts to the cylinder head and lift off the rocker shafts. Pull the pushrods up through the holes in the cylinder heads, and the lifters can be pulled up out of their bores.

Sometimes gum residue forms on the bottom of the lifter, making it very difficult to pull the lifter up out of its bore.

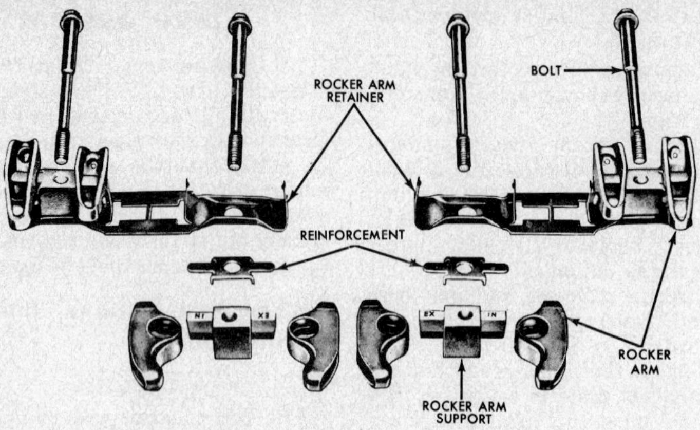
ROCKER ARM
RETAINER
BOLT
REINFORCEMENT
ROCKER
ARM
ROCKER ARM
SUPPORT

1967-74 rocker arm (© Cadillac Div., G.M. Corp)

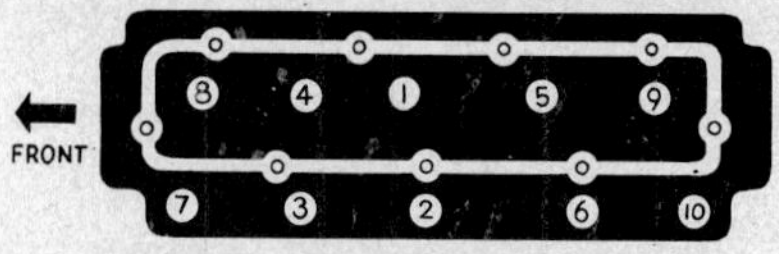
FRONT
8 4 1 5 9
7 3 2 6 10

Cylinder head bolt tightening torque —1968-74

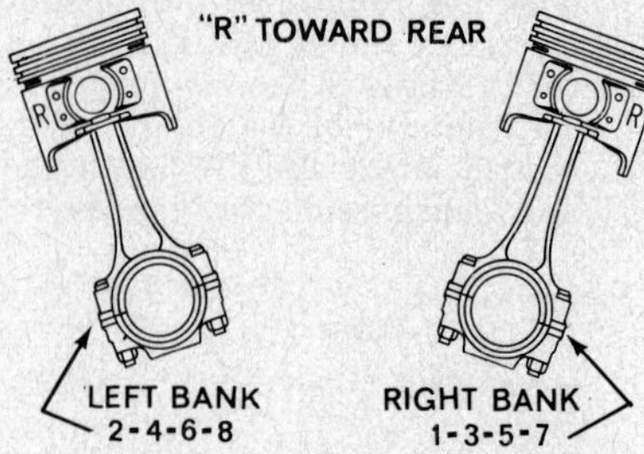
"R" TOWARD REAR
LEFT BANK
2-4-6-8
RIGHT BANK
1-3-5-7

Piston to connecting rod relationship —1968-74

VALVE LIFTER
REMOVER
J-3049

Valve lifter removal
(© Cadillac Div., G.M. Corp)

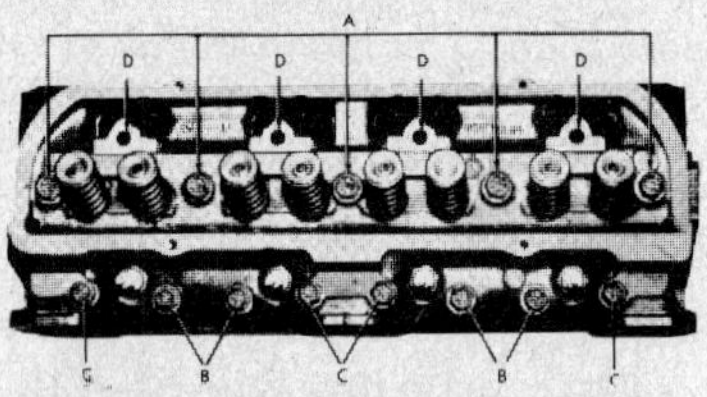
A
D
D
D
D

Cylinder head bolt location and length
1967 (© Cadillac Div., G.M. Corp)

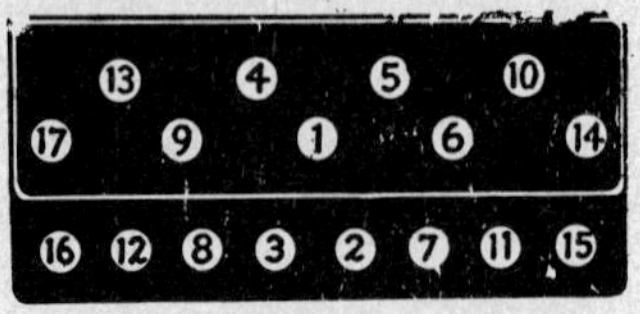
13 4 5 10
17 9 1 6 14
16 12 8 3 2 7 11 15

Cylinder head bolt tightening sequence—1967
(© Cadillac Div., G.M. Corp)

However, even when gum is present on the bottom of the lifter body, the lifter can be pulled up out of its bore using special pliers. These pliers are designed to grip the lifter firmly, without scoring or scratching it.

If a special tool isn't available, a good substitute can be made by grinding the teeth out of an ordinary pair of pliers and grinding a circle almost the size of the valve lifter body. When the pliers are squeezed down on the lifter body, it will contact a large surface, thus preventing scoring.

Cylinder Heads

Cylinder Head Removal and Installation

Service Note

Care must be used when replacing cylinder-head bolts. They are of different lengths.

1967

1. Disconnect the water manifold at the front of the cylinder head or heads. It is a good idea to remove the water pump and water manifold from the car. It is difficult to reinstall a cylinder head with the water pump in place on one head without damaging the water pump gasket.
2. Remove all vacuum lines and carburetor connections; disconnect all ignition, throttle and battery connections.
3. Take off the intake manifold with the carburetor in place or if desired remove the carburetor.
4. Remove the rocker covers.

NOTE: it is customary to remove the rocker covers together with the ignition wires and distributor cap as a unit unless service is to be done on the distributor.

5. Remove the alternator if the right cylinder head is to be removed. The exhaust manifolds may be disconnected either from the head or from the flange connection to the exhaust pipe. It is better to leave them connected to the head.
6. Remove the head bolts that hold the rocker assemblies to the cylinder head and lift off the rocker assemblies.
7. Remove the pushrods.
8. Remove the balance of the cylinder attaching bolts and lift the head off. It is very important that the head be handled carefully so as not to damage or mark the head gasket surface.
9. Installation is the reverse of the above.

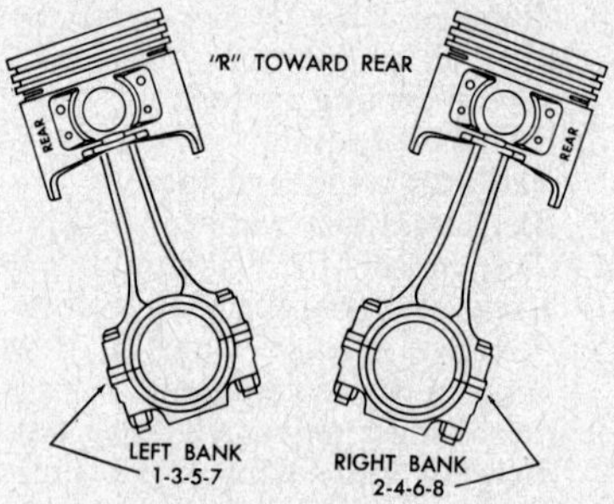
"R" TOWARD REAR
REAR
REAR
LEFT BANK
1-3-5-7
RIGHT BANK
2-4-6-8

Piston to connecting rod relationship—1967

1968-74

1. Remove intake manifold.
2. Drain engine coolant.
3. Disconnect ground strap at rear of cylinder heads from cowl. Disconnect wiring connector for high engine temperature warning system from sending unit at rear of left cylinder head.
4. Remove alternator, if working on the right cylinder head, or partially remove the steering pump if working on the left head.
5. Disconnect A.I.R. injection pump tubes from cylinder heads.
6. Remove clamps holding the wire harness to the cylinder heads and tie harness back out of the way.
7. Remove screws holding exhaust manifolds to cylinder heads.
8. Remove screws holding the rocker arm cover to the heads.
9. Remove cover.
10. Remove screws holding each rocker arm support to cylinder head, then remove rocker arm assemblies. Store these assemblies so that they may be reinstalled in their correct locations.
11. Remove pushrods and store them with their respective rocker arm assemblies.
12. Install two 7/16 x 6 in. screws to be used as lifting handles in two of the rocker arm support screw holes.

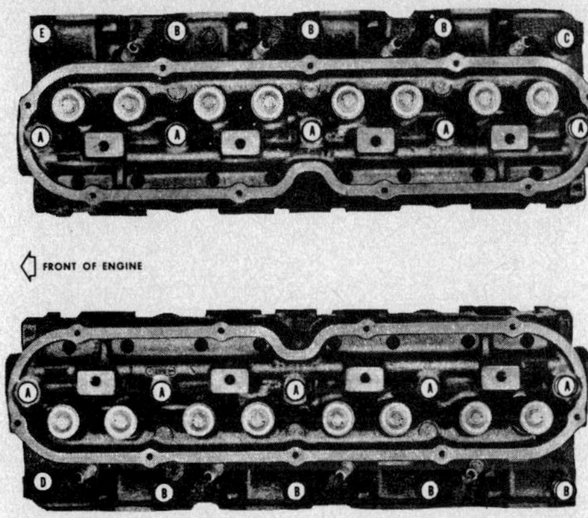
FRONT OF ENGINE

Bolt Location	Length
A (Bolt)	4.36"
B (Bolt)	4.77"
C (Bolt)	3.02"
D (Bolt/Stud)	3.02"
E (Bolt/Stud)	4.77"

Cylinder head bolt location and length—1968

FRONT OF ENGINE

Bolt Location	Length
A (Bolt)	4.36"
B (Bolt)	4.77"
C (Bolt)	3.02"

Cylinder head bolt location and length—1969

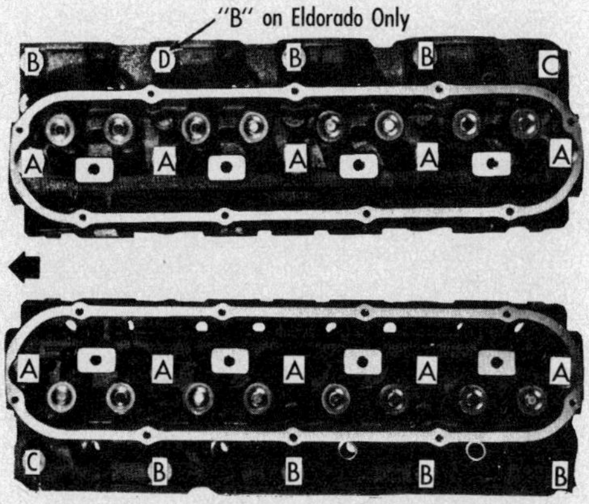
"B" on Eldorado Only

Cylinder head bolt location and length—1970-74

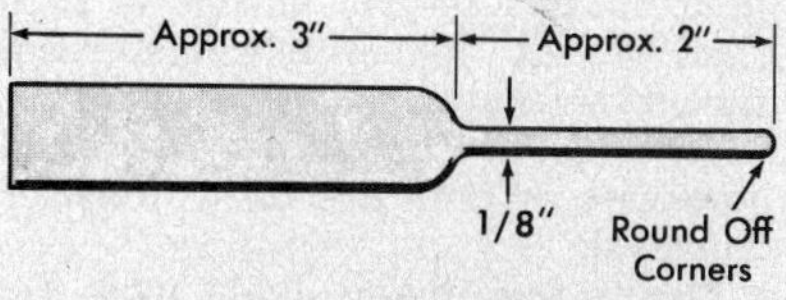
Approx. 3"
Approx. 2"
1/8"
Round Off Corners

Rear main bearing oil seal installation tool
(© Cadillac Div., G.M. Corp)

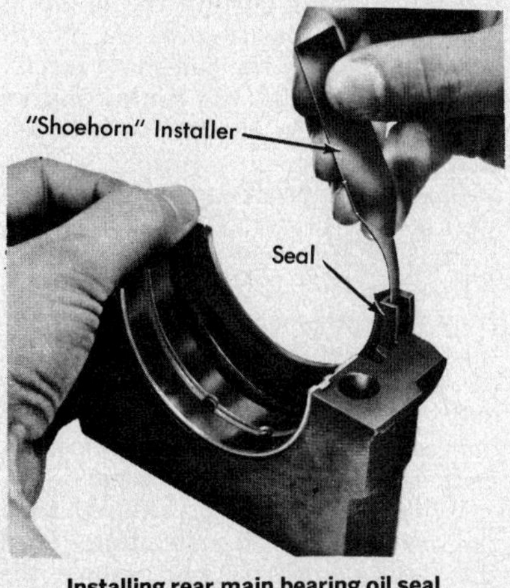
"Shoehorn" Installer
Seal

Installing rear main bearing oil seal
(© Cadillac Div., G.M. Corp)

13. Remove ten cylinder-head bolts.
14. Lift cylinder head off the block.
15. Remove all gasket material from the cylinder head and block mating surfaces.
16. Install by reversing removal procedures.

Cylinder Head Tightening

The cylinder head torque for 1967–69 cars is 60 ft lbs, with 1968 being the only exception. The 1968 head torque is 100 ft lbs. Cars from 1970 to 1974 use a head bolt torque of 115 ft lbs.

When torquing the head bolts, use the three-step method. Starting from the middle of the center row of bolts and working outward (toward each end), torque the bolts to 1/3 of the total torque listed. Once this is done, repeat the same procedure, this time torquing all the bolts to 2/3 of the total listed torque. Finally torque the bolts to the recommended torque.

By using this procedure, head warping is eliminated and it ensures equal pressure on the head gasket over its entire surface.

Piston and Rod Removal

Rod and piston assemblies on all models are removed through the top of the block.

It is possible to replace any and all of the rod or main bearings from underneath the car without removing the crankshaft.

Clean out carbon from top of cylinder bore and ream off the ridge at the top of the bore. This will prevent breakage of the piston ring lands. Push the piston and rod assemblies up and out of the tops of the cylinders. Be careful not to nick the lower edge of the bores and the crankshaft journals.

Piston Ring Replacement

All Cadillac pistons are equipped with two compression rings and one oil ring. When replacing the rings, use only molybdenum-filled upper compression rings and multi- piece oil rings.

There are "dimples" located on the rings near the end. These should be facing the top of the piston.

The end-gap of the compression rings should be 0.013–0.025 in. while the oil ring end-gap should be 0.015–0.055 in. Ring side-play should be no greater than 0.005 in. The ring gaps should be staggered 120° before installation.

Piston and Rod Installation

The numbers on the connecting rods face away from the camshaft; that is, the numbers on the left bank (odd numbers up to 1967, even from 1968) face to the left; the numbers on the right bank (even numbers up to 1967, odd from 1968) face to the right. As a double check, the word *rear,* (or "R"), stamped on the piston, faces the rear of the engine on both banks and an arrow on the piston top points to the front of the engine. The rod nuts are torqued to 40 ft lbs.

Rear Main Seal R & R

1. Remove the oil pan, after removing spark plug. wires and plugs.
2. Remove the rear main bearing cap and loosen the bolts holding the other four bearings about three turns each. Remove the old rear main bearing seals.
3. Clean the groove in the cap and in the block. Lubricate seals with engine oil.
4. Make an installation tool, as illustrated.
5. Start the upper half into the groove in the block with the lip facing forward and rotate it into position, using the tool as a guide. Press firmly on both ends to be sure it is protruding uniformly on each side.
6. Install the lower half of the seal into the bearing cap with the lip facing forward and one end of the seal over the ridge and flush with the split line. Hold one finger over this end to prevent it from slipping, and push the seal into seated position by applying pressure to the other end. Be sure the seal is firmly seated and protrudes evenly on each side. Do not apply pressure to the lip. This may damage the effectiveness of the seal.
7. Apply rubber cement to the mating surfaces of the block and cap being careful not to get any cement on the bearing, the crankshaft or the seal. The cement coating should be about .010 in. thick.
8. Install the bearing cap, tightening the bolts with the fingers only.
9. Move the crankshaft forward and rearward by pounding on the counterweight with a plastic hammer to assure alignment of the rear main bearing thrust surfaces.
10. Tighten the bearing bolts to 90-100 ft. lbs. Be sure to tighten the bolts of the other four bearings also.
11. Reinstall the oil pan.

Timing Case Cover—Chains and Camshaft

Timing Chain Cover, Chain, and Sprocket Removal

1967

1. Disconnect battery and remove carburetor air cleaner.
2. Drain coolant from engine cooling system.
3. Drain oil and remove engine oil pan.
4. Remove upper radiator hose.
5. Remove fan blade assembly, spacer and pulley.

NOTE: where air conditioning is involved, partially remove the compressor. Remove the compressor belt, then, remove the radiator fan shroud.

6. Remove power steering pump belt, generator belt and pulley.
7. Remove lower radiator hose.
8. Without disconnecting the hoses, remove the power steering pump bracket from the cylinder block. Position bracket out of the way.
9. Detach the generator support bracket from the cylinder-head water-outlet pipe and position the bracket out of the way.
10. Remove distributor assembly.
11. Remove fuel pump.
12. Remove four of the six cap screws that attach the crankshaft pulley to the harmonic balancer.
13. Remove cork plug from end of crankshaft, and install balancer puller pilot, J-21052-4 or equivalent in one bore in the end of the crankshaft.
14. Install puller base, J-21052-1 or equivalent on front of pulley, lining up index mark on puller base with key slot in harmonic balancer, and install attaching screws. Do not tighten screws.
15. Tighten puller screw to remove balancer. Remove pilot from end of crankshaft.

NOTE: on engines equipped with an Air Injector Reactor System. Remove the air pump and bracket assembly and swing it out of the way.

16. Remove oil filter from oil pump cover assembly.
17. Remove the four cap screws that hold the cylinder-head water-outlet pipe to cylinder heads and remove the outlet pipe.
18. Remove remaining cap screws that attach the front cover to the cylinder block and remove the cover with water pump attached.
19. Align the two sprocket timing marks, then, remove the two camshaft sprocket attaching screws.
20. Remove camshaft sprocket, with chain, from camshaft.
21. Remove crankshaft sprocket.
22. To assemble, reverse the above procedure.

1968-74

1. Disconnect negative battery cable and drain cooling system.
2. Detach upper radiator hose retainer from cradle and position hose out of the way.
3. Remove fan, generator belt and power steering belts.
4. Remove four capscrews that secure crank pulley to harmonic balancer, then remove both pulley and balancer.
5. Remove plug from end of crankshaft, then install a puller as in Step 13 of earlier procedure and remove balancer hub from end of crank.
6. Drain engine oil and remove oil pan.
7. Disconnect lower radiator hose from water pump, then remove the ten screws that hold front cover to engine. Remove cover with water pump attached.
8. Remove distributor and fuel pump.
9. Remove oil slinger and fuel pump eccentric.
10. Remove two capscrews that secure camshaft sprocket.
11. Remove camshaft sprocket along with timing chain.
12. To install, reverse removal procedure.

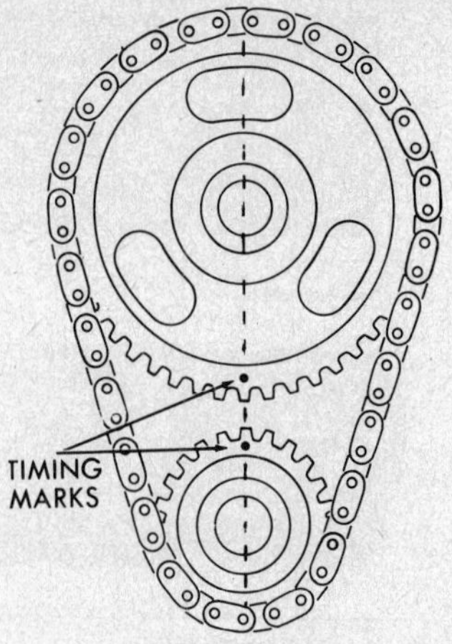
TIMING
MARKS
Timing mark alignment
(© Cadillac Div., G.M. Corp)

Valve Timing Procedure

The chain and sprocket assembly used on all Cadillac models is such that, unless deliberately disturbed, the valve timing will remain as set by the factory, unless the chain and sprockets or both are badly worn or damaged.

Mount the timing chain over the camshaft and the crankshaft sprocket and start the camshaft sprocket over the shaft, being certain the aligning dowel is in a position where it will enter the hole in the camshaft freely. Make certain that the timing marks on the sprockets are in line between shaft centers.

Camshaft sprockets sometimes install a little stiffly. However, a comparatively easy way to install a tight-fitting sprocket is to draw it on carefully with two bolts somewhat longer than the regular mounting bolts. By drawing alternately against each bolt, and tapping gently with a plastic hammer, even a very tight camshaft gear sprocket can be installed.

When the camshaft is secured, turn the engine two full revolutions until the timing marks again assume the original position. Check to make cer-

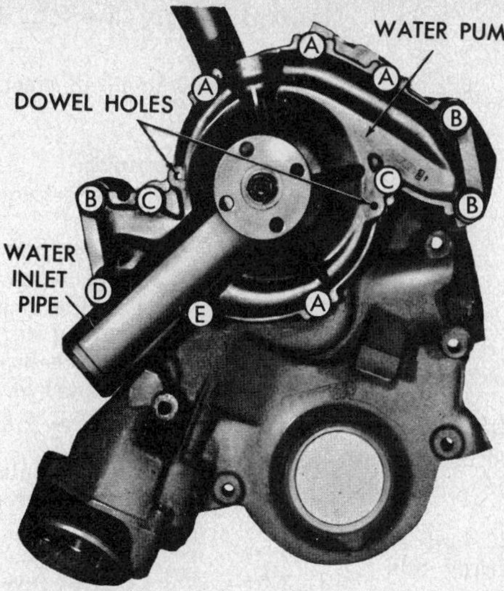
WATER PUMP
DOWEL HOLES
WATER
INLET
PIPE
A
B
C
D
E

A
C
D
E

Front cover and water pump—1968-74
(© Cadillac Div., G.M. Corp)

Key	No.	Size	Torque
A	(4)	1/4 -20 x 1-1/4	5 Foot-Pounds
B	(3)	3/8 -16 x 3-4/8	20 Foot-Pounds
C	(2)	5/16-18 x 3-1/4	10 Foot-Pounds
D	(1)	3/8 -16 x 5	20 Foot-Pounds
E	(1)	1/4 -20 x 2-1/4	5 Foot-Pounds

Front cover installation—1967
(© Cadillac Div., G.M. Corp)

Key	No.	Size	Torque
A	(4)	3/8 - 16 x 1-3/8	22 foot-pounds
B	(4)	1/4 - 20 x 1-1/8	70 inch-pounds
C	(3)	5/16 - 18 x 1-1/4	15 foot-pounds

tain that the punch marks, which are little round circles stamped into the front face of the sprockets, are in line between the shaft centers.

Timing Cover Oil Seal R & R

1967-74

These cars are equipped with a molded-type front cover crankshaft oil seal. The seal may be replaced without removing the engine front cover.

1. Disconnect the battery and remove carburetor air cleaner.
2. Remove power steering pump drive belt.
3. Remove generator drive belt.
4. On air conditioned cars, and cars equipped with the A.I.R. system. remove the pump drive belts.
5. Raise and support the front of the car stands. On 1968 to present cars, it will be necessary to remove the fan.
6. Remove pulley and harmonic balancer, as outlined in Timing Chain and Sprocket Removal.
7. With a thin blade screwdriver, pry out front cover oil seal.
8. Lubricate new dual-lip oil seal with wheel bearing grease. Position seal on end of crankshaft with garter spring side toward engine.
9. Using seal installer and adapter cover until it bottoms.
10. Assemble and install the remaining parts in reverse order of disassembly.

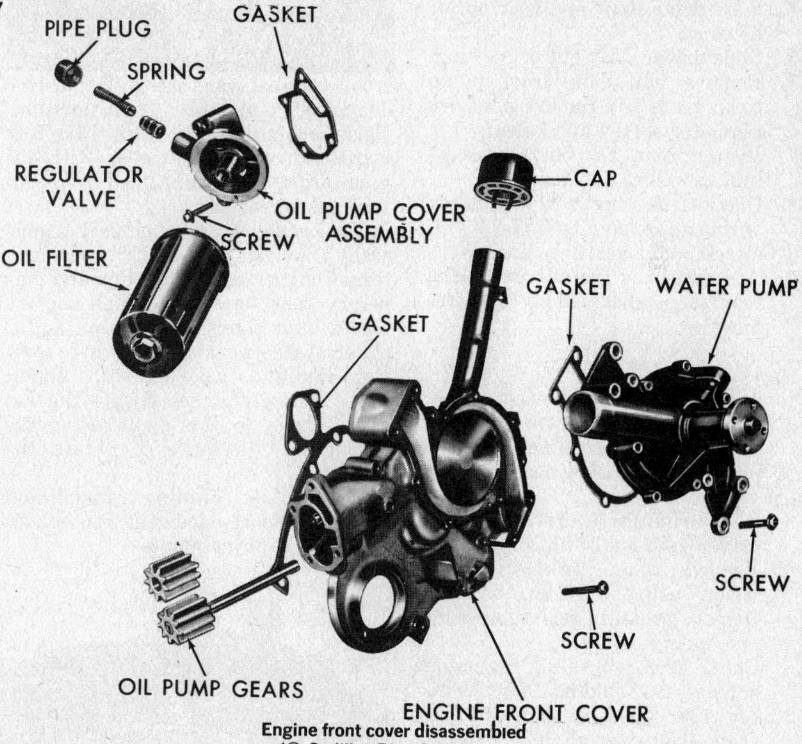
PIPE PLUG
GASKET
SPRING
REGULATOR
VALVE
CAP
OIL PUMP COVER
ASSEMBLY
SCREW
OIL FILTER
GASKET
WATER PUMP
GASKET
SCREW
SCREW
OIL PUMP GEARS
ENGINE FRONT COVER

Engine front cover disassembled
(© Cadillac Div., G.M. Corp)

Camshaft Removal and Replacement

1. Remove the radiator.
2. Remove the engine front cover and the distributor.
3. Remove the oil pump and the oil slinger from the crankshaft.
4. Remove the fuel pump and the fuel pump eccentric from the camshaft.
5. Remove the camshaft sprocket and the timing chain.

NOTE: make certain that the aligning marks on the two sprockets are correctly aligned before removing the timing chain.

6. Remove the lifters and slide the camshaft carefully out of the engine block without letting the camshaft lobes damage the cam bearings.
7. To install the camshaft, reverse the above procedure. Before installation, the camshaft should be lubricated with a thin coat of rear axle lubricant and then carefully inserted to avoid bearing damage.
8. The camshaft sprocket screws should be torqued to 18 ft lbs while the fuel pump eccentric screw is tightened to 35 ft lbs.

Lubrication

Oil Pump Removal and Installation

1967

1. Remove engine front cover. (See Timing Case Cover.)
2. Remove four capscrews that secure pump cover plate to housing.
3. Remove cover plate, making sure pump gears do not fall out.
4. Slide drive shaft and gear out of housing.
5. Slide driven gear out of housing.
6. Remove hex plug from pump cover plate and remove pressure regulator spring and valve.
7. Inspect gears for burrs or scoring, as well as housing.
8. Check free length of regulator spring—it should be 2.77-2.89 in.
9. Check pump clearance limits.
10. Assembly and installation is the reverse of disassembly and removal.

1968-74

1. Jack up car and remove oil filter.
2. Remove five capscrews that secure oil pump to engine.

NOTE: remove screw nearest pressure regulator last.

3. Slide drive shaft, drive gear and driven gear out of housing.
4. Remove plug from housing cover, using 5/16 in. wrench. Remove pressure regulator valve and spring.
5. Check free length of regulator spring—it should be 2.77-2.89 in. for 1968 models, 2.57-2.69 in. from 1969 through 1973 models.
6. Inspect gears and housing for burrs or scoring.
7. Check pump clearance limits.
8. Assembly, and installation is the reverse of disassembly and removal.

Oil Pump Specifications

Backlash between drive gears, 0.008-0.012 in.

Clearance between body and shaft not to exceed 0.005 in.

Clearance between body and gears not to exceed 0.005 in.

Gear end-play not to exceed 0.006 in.

Oil Pan Removal and Installation

1967-74

1. Drain engine oil and disconnect positive battery cable.
2. Disconnect exhaust crossover pipe at exhaust manifold.
3. Disconnect exhaust support bracket at transmission extension housing, and position exhaust system to one side.
4. Remove starter motor.
5. Remove two idler arm support mounting screws from frame side member, and lower support.
6. Disconnect pitman arm at drag link, and lower steering linkage.
7. Remove transmission lower cover.
8. Remove engine oil pan.
9. When reinstalling, reverse above procedure and torque oil pan screws and nuts to 10 ft lbs. The transmission cover screws should be torqued to 20 ft lbs.

AUTOMATIC TRANSMISSION

All Cadillac cars use a Turbo Hydra-matic automatic transmission. This transmission provides three forward and one reverse gear with engine torque being multipled by a centrifugal converter.

The inside of the transmission generally consists of a three-element torque converter and a compound planetary gear set. The system also includes dual bands for friction and a clutch system consisting of three multiple-disc and two roller-type clutch units. These clutches couple the engine torque to the planetary gears through oil pressure to obtain the gearing.

This section contains transmission removal and replacement procedures and linkage adjustments.

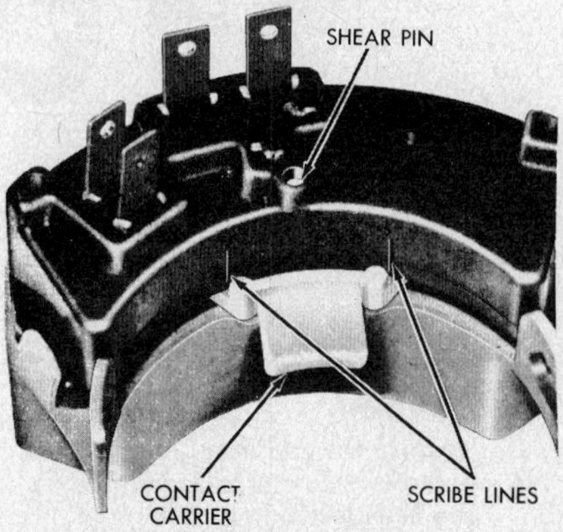
SHEAR PIN
CONTACT CARRIER
SCRIBE LINES

Neutral safety switch
(© Cadillac Div., G.M. Corp)

Neutral Safety Switch, All Models

NOTE: switch is on steering column under dash.

Removal

1. Position the gear selector in the Neutral position.
2. Release the clamp and remove the switch without moving the contact carrier. The position of the carrier should be marked.
3. Remove the vacuum hoses after they have been marked and disconnect the two wires from the switch.
4. Installation is accomplished by reversing the above procedure.

Adjustment

1. Check that the gear lever is correctly adjusted and that the neutral safety switch is properly positioned by this check.
2. Set the handbrake. Put the hand lever on the steering column in drive. Hold the ignition key on and slowly move the hand lever toward Neutral or Park until the starter cranks and the engine runs.
3. Without moving the lever farther, press the accelerator to determine whether the transmission is really in Neutral or Park.
4. If all is correct, the engine will have started when the hand lever got to the neutral position and the transmission will not be in gear. Also, back-up lights will go on with transmission in Reverse.

NOTE: a vacuum leak that can be corrected by moving shift lever is an indication that the switch only needs adjustment and is not defective.

5. Adjust the neutral safety switch by turning it and its mounting bracket until the above conditions are met.

Manual Linkage Adjustment

1. Loosen nut on steering column manual lever.
2. Pull relay rod up, positioning transmission shift valve in Park, then push rod down to the third or Neutral step.
3. Position selector lever in Neutral.

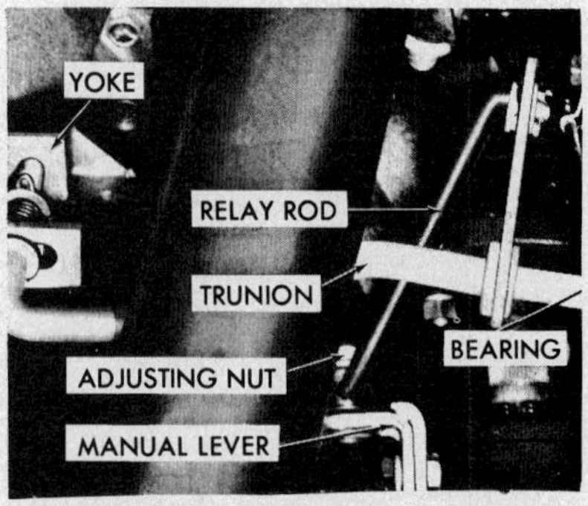
YOKE
RELAY ROD
TRUNION
BEARING
ADJUSTING NUT
MANUAL LEVER

Manual linkage adjustment—1970-74
(© Cadillac Div., G.M. Corp)

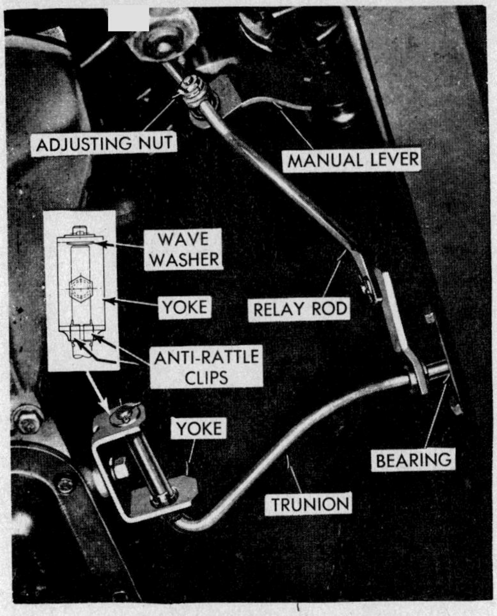
ADJUSTING NUT
MANUAL LEVER
WAVE WASHER
YOKE
RELAY ROD
ANTI-RATTLE CLIPS
YOKE
BEARING
TRUNION

Manual linkage adjustment—1967-68
(© Cadillac Div., G.M. Corp)

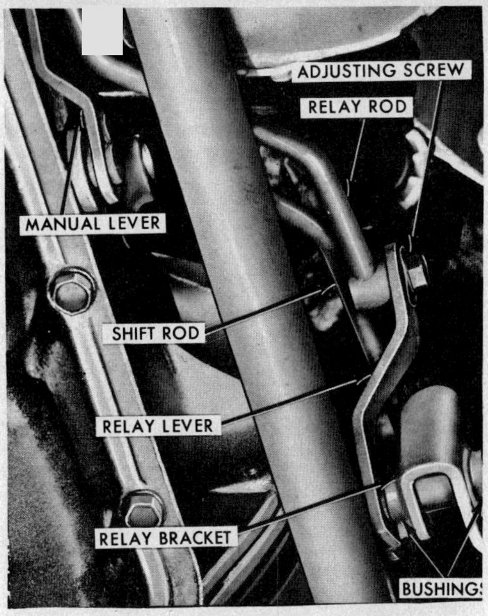
ADJUSTING SCREW
RELAY ROD
MANUAL LEVER
SHIFT ROD
RELAY LEVER
RELAY BRACKET
BUSHINGS

Manual linkage adjustment—1969
(© Cadillac Div., G.M. Corp)

4. Tighten nut on steering column manual lever.
5. Check that positions selected on selector lever correspond with appropriate detents on transmission.

Kickdown Adjustment

1. Remove the air cleaner.
2. Make certain that the idle speed is set correctly and that the carburetor is operating on the low-speed circuit.
3. Loosen the switch mounting screws and insert 0.094 in wire gauge into the hole in the lower wire terminal.
4. With the gauge in place, adjust the position of the switch so that the lever just touches the carburetor adaptor plate arm. The switch should make contact above 60° of throttle opening.
5. After adjusting, tighten the mounting screws and remove the gauge.
6. Reinstall the air cleaner.

U-JOINTS

Universal joints and drive lines can be divided into three groups: single-shaft models, two-piece shaft models (except Commercial after 1969), and two-piece shaft models (Commercial up to 1969).

Single-Piece Type

Two constant velocity universal joints are used on the single-shaft type: one at the front, and one at the rear. This type propeller shaft is serviced as a complete assembly.

Two-Piece-Shaft Type—Except 1967-69 Commercial Models

The two-piece propeller shaft uses three constant velocity universal joints, located at each end and at the approximate center of the shaft assembly. This shaft is used on 1970 up commercial models.

At the front end of the rear section of the propeller shaft is a splined male slip yoke that fits into a splined coupling in the rear end of the front section of the front shaft. This slip spline satisfies the normal lengthening

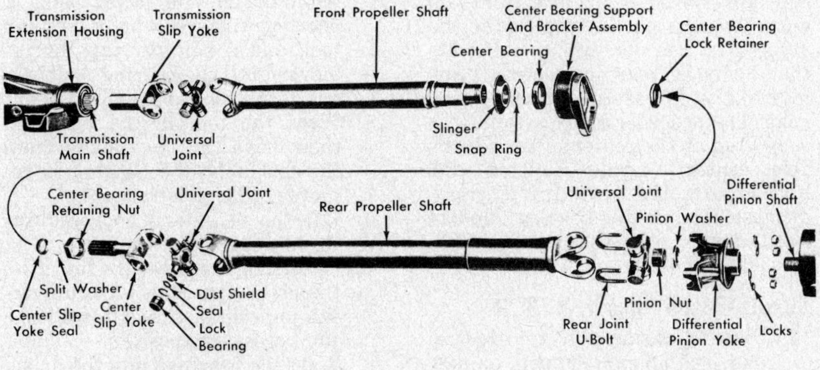
Transmission Extension Housing
Transmission Slip Yoke
Front Propeller Shaft
Center Bearing Support And Bracket Assembly
Center Bearing Lock Retainer
Center Bearing
Slinger
Snap Ring
Transmission Main Shaft
Universal Joint
Center Bearing Retaining Nut
Universal Joint
Rear Propeller Shaft
Universal Joint
Differential Pinion Shaft
Pinion Washer
Split Washer
Center Slip Yoke Seal
Center Slip Yoke
Dust Shield
Seal
Lock
Bearing
Pinion Nut
Rear Joint U-Bolt
Differential Pinion Yoke
Locks

Driveshaft 1967-69 Commercial (© Cadillac Div., G.M. Corp)

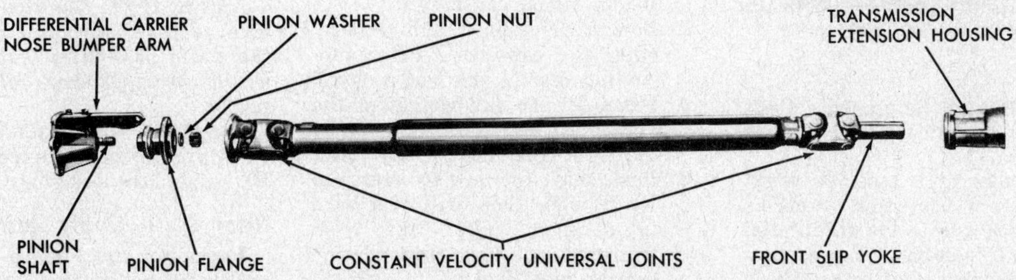
DIFFERENTIAL CARRIER NOSE BUMPER ARM
PINION WASHER
PINION NUT
TRANSMISSION EXTENSION HOUSING
PINION SHAFT
PINION FLANGE
CONSTANT VELOCITY UNIVERSAL JOINTS
FRONT SLIP YOKE

Single-piece driveshaft (© Cadillac Div., G.M. Corp)

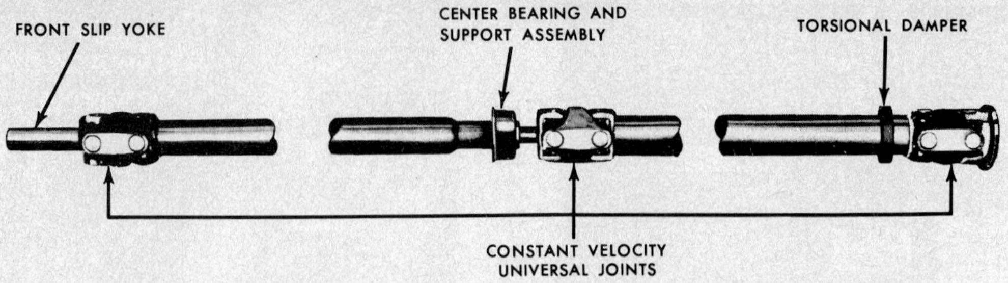
FRONT SLIP YOKE
CENTER BEARING AND SUPPORT ASSEMBLY
TORSIONAL DAMPER
CONSTANT VELOCITY UNIVERSAL JOINTS

Two-piece driveshaft with C.V. joints (© Cadillac Div., G.M. Corp)

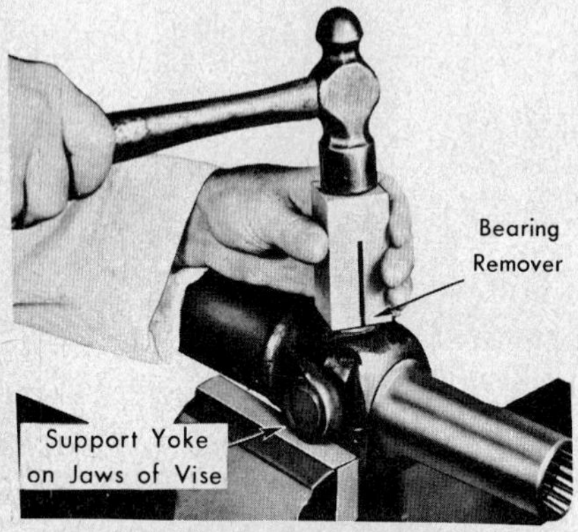
Bearing Remover
Support Yoke on Jaws of Vise

Using the bearing removal tool
(© Cadillac Div., G.M. Corp)

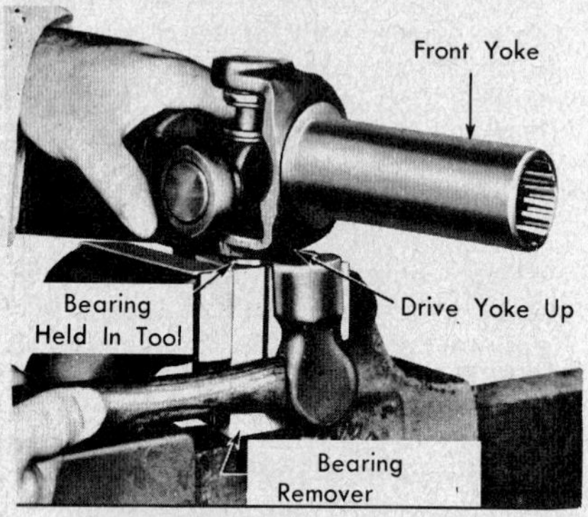
Front Yoke
Bearing Held In Tool
Drive Yoke Up
Bearing Remover

Removing the universal joint bearing
(© Cadillac Div., G.M. Corp)

Press Bearings In with Vise
Guide Cross Into Bearings

Installing the universal joint bearing

and shortening of the propeller shaft due to road conditions and rear axle movement.

The propeller shaft assembly is attached to the transmission by means of a slip yoke, and to the differential drive pinion by a double flange connection. The propeller shaft assembly is supported midway by a bracket and bearing combination attached to a frame crossmember.

With the exception of the center bearing and support combination, the propeller shaft is serviced as an assembly.

Two-Piece-Shaft Type—1967-69 Commercial Models

A two-piece propeller shaft assembly, using three standard universal joints, is used on commercial vehicles.

Standard joints are used at each end of the shaft assembly and at the center support.

The universal joints are replaceable, but cannot be repacked. On original universal joints, the injected nylon ring that locks the bearing cup in the slip yoke will shear off when the bearing is removed. There are no provisions for replacing this nylon ring. When the joint becomes noisy or otherwise needs attention, renew the joint.

Front and rear sections of this shaft are splined together the same as in two-piece passenger car models.

The commercial vehicle two-piece-shaft type unit is attached to the transmission by means of a front slip yoke. The assembly is attached to the differential carrier by two U-bolts that hold the rear joint cross bearings to the differential carrier pinion yoke. The propeller shaft assembly is supported at the center by an adjustable center bearing support and bracket attached to a frame crossmember. The center bearing support is adjustable to compensate for various load influences.

Single-Piece Shaft R & R

1. Place transmission in Neutral and jack up car; support on axle stands.
2. Remove the two accessible rear U-joint flange capscrews.
3. Rotate driveshaft and remove other two capscrews, after supporting rear of shaft on a chain. Never let the full weight of the driveshaft be supported only by the front constant velocity joint.
4. Push shaft forward to clear pinion flange, then pull rearward to disengage slip yoke from transmission. Plug transmission to prevent oil leak.
5. Lubricate slip yoke inside diameter with gear lube, outside of splines with A.T.F.
6. To install, reverse removal procedure, tightening rear U-joint fasteners to 70 ft. lbs. Place transmission in Park to hold shaft while tightening capscrews.

Two-Piece Shaft R & R

1. Follow Steps 1-6 of *Single-Piece Shaft R & R*, with the addition of the following step:

1A. Remove center bearing support after matchmarking it and crossmember. When installing, tighten the bolts to 16 ft. lbs.

U-Joint Removal and Installation

1. Remove the drive shaft.
2. Remove the lockrings from the bearings. If the original universal joints are being replaced, the nylon ring will sear off when the bearing is removed.
3. Match-mark the yoke and the shaft so that the shaft parts can be reassembled easily.
4. Position the yoke or bearing trunnion on vise jaws. Using a bearing remover, or a similar tool, and a hammer tap the remover until the bearing is driven out of the yoke about ½ in.
5. Place the tool in the vise and then drive the yoke away from the tool until the bearing is removed. (See illustration.)
6. Use the no. 4 and 5 procedures for all other bearings.
7. To install the bearings lubricate the cross arm ends with universal joint grease and install the joint cross into position.
8. Start the bearings into the driveshaft yoke and press them into position using a vise.

NOTE: if the bearings are not positioned with normal vise pressure, there is a possibility that one of the needle bearings has fallen out of place.

9. Use the same installation procedure for the other bearings.
10. Install the lock rings.

Rear Axle Shaft Removal

Raise car and remove wheels and brake drums. Remove retainer and backing plate to rear axle housing.

Attach slide hammer to axle shaft puller and install on studs of rear axle shaft flange. Drive outward and remove axle shaft.

JACKING, HOISTING

1967-74

When jacking under front suspension arms, make sure lift is made from the flattened portion on the flange of the lower arms.

When lifting on frame area, make sure of solid contact at the corners of the perimeter of the frame with the lift points close to the bend at front and rear of the frame.

FRONT SUSPENSION

All Cadillacs use the same front suspension system (except Eldorado). The system is a coiled-spring suspension which consists of two upper and two lower control arm assemblies, shock absorbers, front struts, a stabilizer bar and two steering knuckles, and a pair of steel coiled springs.

For further information on the front suspension consult the "Unit Repair Section."

Lower Control Arm and Coil Spring R & R

1. Disconnect front shock at its upper mount.
2. Raise car and support under front frame side rails.
3. Remove wheel and tire assembly.
4. Disconnect stabilizer link from lower arm or spring to be removed.
5. Disconnect tie-strut at lower arm.
6. Remove bolt holding shock to lower arm, and remove shock from car.
7. Remove nut from pivot bolt in lower arm at frame mount.
8. Position jack under outboard end of lower suspension arm so that jack is supporting the arm.
9. Remove locknut from lower ball joint stud. Install standard nut on joint stud and run nut to within two threads of knuckle.
10. Strike knuckle with a hammer in area of ball joint stud to loosen the joint. Raising the opposite rear corner of the car will help compress the spring and assist in removing the joint stud from the knuckle.
11. Use jack to lift spring load from nut and remove nut from joint stud.
12. Slowly lower jack and remove spring.

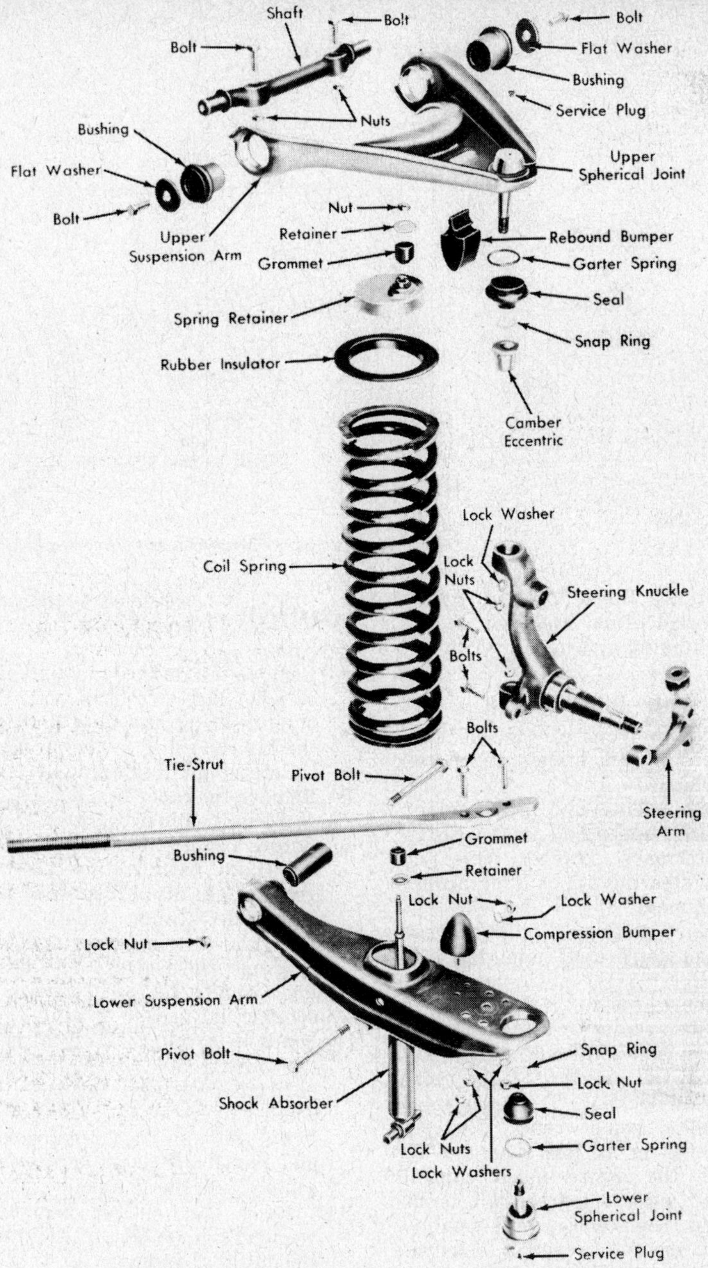
Shaft
Bolt
Bolt
Bolt
Flat Washer
Bushing
Service Plug
Nuts
Bushing
Flat Washer
Upper Spherical Joint
Bolt
Nut
Upper Suspension Arm
Retainer
Rebound Bumper
Grommet
Garter Spring
Seal
Spring Retainer
Snap Ring
Rubber Insulator
Camber Eccentric
Lock Washer
Coil Spring
Lock Nuts
Steering Knuckle
Bolts
Bolts
Tie-Strut
Pivot Bolt
Steering Arm
Grommet
Bushing
Retainer
Lock Nut
Lock Washer
Lock Nut
Compression Bumper
Lower Suspension Arm
Snap Ring
Pivot Bolt
Lock Nut
Seal
Shock Absorber
Garter Spring
Lock Nuts
Lock Washers
Lower Spherical Joint
Service Plug

Typical front suspension—1967-70 (© Cadillac Div., G.M. Corp)

13. Remove pivot bolt from lower arm at frame mount and remove the arm.
14. Install by reversing the removal procedure.

Ball Joint Inspection

NOTE: before performing this inspection, make sure the wheel bearings are adjusted correctly and that the A arm bushings are in good condition.

1. Jack the car up under the front lower control arm at the spring seat.
2. Raise the car until there is 1–2 in. of clearance under the wheel.
3. Insert a bar under the wheel and pry upward. If the wheel raises more than 1/8 in. the ball joints are worn. Determine if the upper or lower ball joint is worn by visual inspection while prying on the wheel.

NOTE: due to the distribution of forces in the suspension, the lower ball joint is usually the defective joint.

Lower Ball Joint R & R

1. Follow Steps 1-12 of *Lower Control Arm and Coil Spring R&R.*
2. Remove band and seal from ball joint.
3. If ball joint vertical movement exceeds 1/16 in. (.062 in.), press old ball joint out of lower control arm, using press tool.
4. Press new joint into arm until it bottoms on flange, using standard nut and flat washer to pull joint into position.

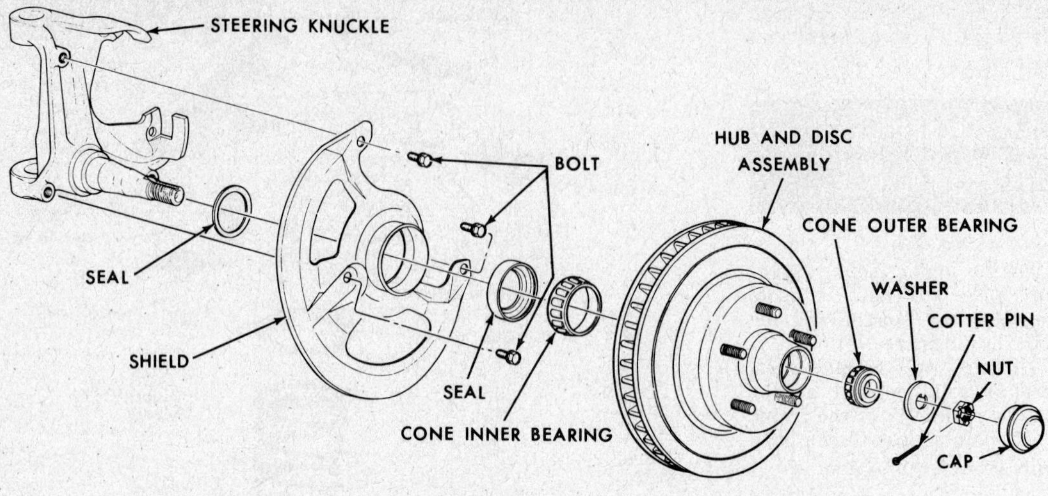
STEERING KNUCKLE
HUB AND DISC
ASSEMBLY
BOLT
CONE OUTER BEARING
SEAL
WASHER
COTTER PIN
SHIELD
NUT
SEAL
CONE INNER BEARING
CAP

Front wheel assembly with disc brake (© Cadillac Div., G.M. Corp)

5. Reverse Steps 1-12 of *Lower Control Arm and Coil Spring* tightening stud nut to 85 ft. lbs.

Upper Ball Joint R & R

1. Jack up front of car and support on jack stands under coil springs.
2. Remove wheel and tire assembly.
3. Loosen upper ball joint locknut.
4. Matchmark camber eccentric and steering knuckle for proper alignment.
5. Strike steering knuckle near upper joint until joint taper is free.
6. Remove locknut, then remove camber eccentric using a puller.
7. Clean ball joint and install another nut on top of the reinstalled locknut. Turn the joint using a torque wrench. If torque exceeds or is less than 2-4 ft. lbs., the entire upper control arm with integral ball joint must replace as an assembly.
8. To install, reverse removal procedure. Tighten locknut on stud of ball joint to 60 ft. lbs.

NOTE: use a standard ½-20 nut and washer to pull camber eccentric into position.

Wheel Bearing

Removal and Installation

1. Raise the vehicle and position it securely.
2. Remove the wheel and tire.
3. On drum brake models, remove the dust cap, cotter pin, spindle nut, washer, and the outer bearing assembly. Remove the brake drum from the steering knuckle spindle.
4. On disc brake models, remove the two bolts which hold the caliper to the knuckle and slide the caliper off the disc and secure it to the upper control arm.

Caution Never allow the caliper to hang from the brake hose.

Remove the dust cap, cotter pin, spindle nut, washer, and the outer bearing assembly. Pull off the hub and disc assembly from the steering knuckle spindle.

5. Remove the inner bearing grease seal and the inner bearing.
6. Before installation, lubricate the hub bore with a thin film of grease. (On disc brake units use #2 grade lithium type.) Also, pack the bearing cone and the bearings themselves. The bearings should be packed with a commercial packer or with your hands by forcing grease through the larger end of the bearing until it protrudes through the smaller end.
7. Install the inner bearing and seal and install the drum or disc assembly onto the spindle.
8. Install the outer bearings, washer, and spindle nut. Tighten the nut hand tight.
9. On disc brake models, install the caliper.
10. Replace the wheel and tire.
11. Adjust the wheel bearings. (See "Wheel Bearing Adjustment.")
12. Tighten the wheel lugs and lower the vehicle.

Inspection

1. Clean the bearing assemblies with clean solvent and, if there is damage, replace the complete assembly.
2. Check the bearing races and the hub surface for nicks or other defects. Replace if necessary.
3. Make certain that the inner race is not turning inside the hub. Replace the hub and race if necessary.
4. Examine the spindle bearing seats for wear. Replace if necessary.

Adjustment

Drum Brakes

1. Tighten the adjusting nut to 30 ft lbs while rotating the wheel.
2. Back off ¼ turn (90°) and insert the cotter pin. If the pin cannot be inserted, loosen the adjusting nut until it can be installed.
3. Peen the cotter pin over so that it cannot be moved within its hole.

Disc Brakes

1. Rotate the wheel and tighten the adjusting nut to 15 ft lbs.
2. Back off the nut until it is free and then tighten it finger tight.
3. Insert the cotter pin. If the pin cannot be installed in this position, back off the nut until the holes align. Make certain that the pin does not vibrate. If it can be moved with your fingers, it should be replaced.

REAR SUSPENSION

All Except Commercial

A four-link rear suspension system, consisting of upper and lower control arms, coil springs and shock absorbers is used. The coil springs are placed on brackets on the rear axle housing at their lower ends, the upper ends being seated in the frame crossmember. The upper and lower control arms are so placed to give the car good lateral stability. Cars can be equipped with Automatic Level Control, described later.

Commercial Chassis

The Commercial chassis uses semi-elliptic nine-leaf springs in 1967, seven-leaf springs from 1968 to 1974, they are approximately 2½ in.

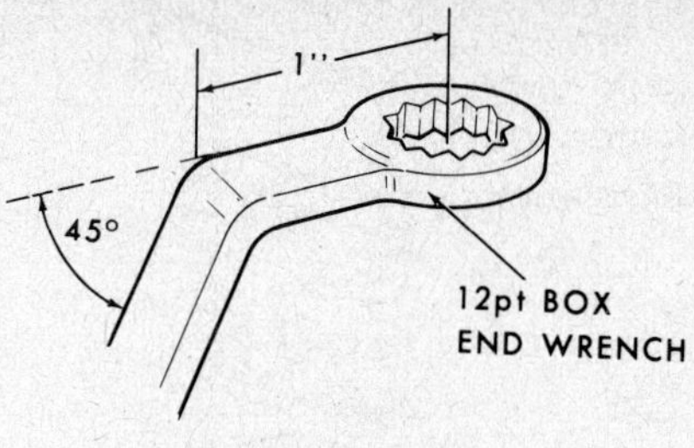
1"
45°
12pt BOX
END WRENCH

Rear shock absorber wrench
(© Cadillac Div., G.M. Corp)

wide in a conventional Hotchkiss drive layout. The springs have zinc or full length polyethylene inner liners between first four leaves to provide correct interleaf friction and to prevent corrosion. Direct acting shock absorbers are provided, connected between the U-bolt spring plates and brackets welded to the frame crossmember. Automatic Level Control, with individual valving, is optional.

Shock Absorber Removal and Installation

1. Raise the rear of the vehicle and support both the frame and the axle with separate jacks.
2. If the vehicle is equipped with Automatic Level Control, remove the air lines at the shocks.

Caution The shocks act as rebound stops for the rear suspension and under no circumstances should the rear end be raised excessively high while disconnecting the shocks, unless both the rear axle and the frame are supported.

3. Remove the upper retaining bolts and nuts. To perform this, bend a ½ in. box end wrench to form a 45° angle at a point one inch from the center of the box diameter. This is used to hold the upper mounting nut.
4. Remove the lower retaining nut while holding the stem by the grommet to keep the stem from turning. Pull the shock off.

Coil Spring R & R

1967-70

1. Jack up rear of car and place axle stands under frame side rails.
2. Place a jack under the differential housing.
3. Remove tire and wheel assemblies.
4. If car has A.L.C., disconnect link at overtravel lever and position it in center position.

Caution The shock absorbers act as stops for the suspension. Make certain that both the axle and frame are supported before proceeding further.

5. Remove shock absorber lower retaining nuts and washers.
6. Remove rear bolts from upper control arms, then free links from mountings.

NOTE: it may be necessary to place another jack under differential pinion housing to facilitate bolt removal.

7. If removing right spring, disconnect brake hose at crossmember bracket and disconnect parking brake cable strap. Lower jacks under differential.

Caution Do not allow the differential to wind up as it is lowered as the spring may fly out.

8. Place floor jack under control arm opposite of spring being removed. (If removing right spring, place jack under left control arm and vice-versa.)
9. Jack up on lower control arm until spring can be removed.
10. To install, reverse removal procedure. Tighten upper and lower control arm bolts to 75 ft. lbs.

1971-74

1. Follow Steps 1-5 of previous procedure.
2. Position container to catch brake fluid, then disconnect brake hose from steel line at frame.
3. Remove brake hose and clip from frame.
4. Disconnect rear U-joint and support driveshaft on a chain.
5. Remove nuts and bolts that secure both upper control arms to axle brackets.
6. Lower rear axle assembly slowly until springs are free.

Caution Do not allow the differential to wind up as it is lowered as the spring may fly out.

7. To install, reverse removal procedure. Tighten upper and lower control arm bolts to 75 ft. lbs.

Leaf Spring R & R

1. Jack up car and support on axle stands at frame side rails.
2. Place axle stands under axle housing, after jacking up housing.
3. Remove front eye bolt nut and drive out bolt.
4. Disconnect shock absorber from U-bolt plate.
5. Remove rear shackle nuts.
6. Remove U-bolt plate nuts, plate and insulators.
7. Disconnect rear shackle links and lower spring.
8. To install, reverse removal procedure. Tighten shackle nuts to 70 ft. lbs., U-bolt nuts to 45 ft. lbs., and lower shock nuts to 50 ft. lbs.

Automatic Level Control

The system consists of a vacuum-operated air compressor and a control valve mounted at rear suspension crossmember. The valve is then connected to Superlift rear shock absorbers.

The Superlift shock absorber is essentially a conventional shock absorber enclosed in an air chamber. A pliable nylon-reinforced neoprene boot seals the air dome to air piston. It will extend or retract under the pressure controlled by the valve.

As load is added to the vehicle, the control valve admits air under pressure to these shock absorbers, lifting vehicle to normal position. As load is reduced, the valve releases air and lowers vehicle to the previous normal level.

The valve is connected by a link to the right rear upper control link. A deflection of at least ½ in. is required to make it operative.

A delay mechanism is built into the valve housing. This requires that an attitude be assumed for four to 15 seconds in order for the valve to operate. It prevents operation during normal road motions.

Pressure at the shock absorber units is kept equal by means of the line connecting the two units, with only one unit connected directly to the control valve. This keeps approximately 8-15 psi. on shock absorber units at all times. The pressure is released at the control valve and the equalizing pressure is maintained through a check valve at the release fitting.

The compressor is located in the engine compartment. It is operated by vacuum surge through a line connected just forward of the carburetor insulator connection. Air, at atmospheric pressure, is taken into the compressor through a line connected to the air cleaner. The compressed air from the compressor is supplied to a reservoir and then to the control valve.

Any service work on this system, or other parts of the vehicle, that may cause deflation will require system reinflation to approximately 140 psi.

All lines are ⅛ in. diameter flexible black tubing. In working on this system, use care not to kink this tubing. Keep tubing away from the exhaust system.

BRAKES

All Cadillacs have power-assisted, hydraulic front and rear brakes. They also use a vacuum-release operated parking brake. Prior to 1968 all models were equipped with four wheel drum brakes as original equipment. From 1969 to 1974, all cars were equipped with single-piston, sliding-caliper front disc brakes and retained the rear drum system.

For information relating to brake shoe replacement and adjustment, wheel cylinder and caliper overhaul, and brake bleeding refer to the brake "Unit Repair Section."

A dual master cylinder was first used in 1966, with the front reservoir of the unit supplying the rear brakes and the rear reservoir supplying the front brakes. This system enables one pair of brakes to function even if the other pair fails. Use caution when installing the brake lines. They are connected front brakes to rear cylinder and rear brakes to front.

On the 1967 models, two different brake units were used, the Delco Moraine and the Bendix. The Bendix unit is painted all black.

Beginning in 1967, and continuing to 1974, Cadillac revised the design for the master cylinder. The master cylinder and the reservoir responsible for the front wheel brake application is now the front half of the cylinder instead of the rear, as in the earlier models. The front portion of the master cylinder serves the front wheels and the rear portion of the cylinder serves the rear wheels.

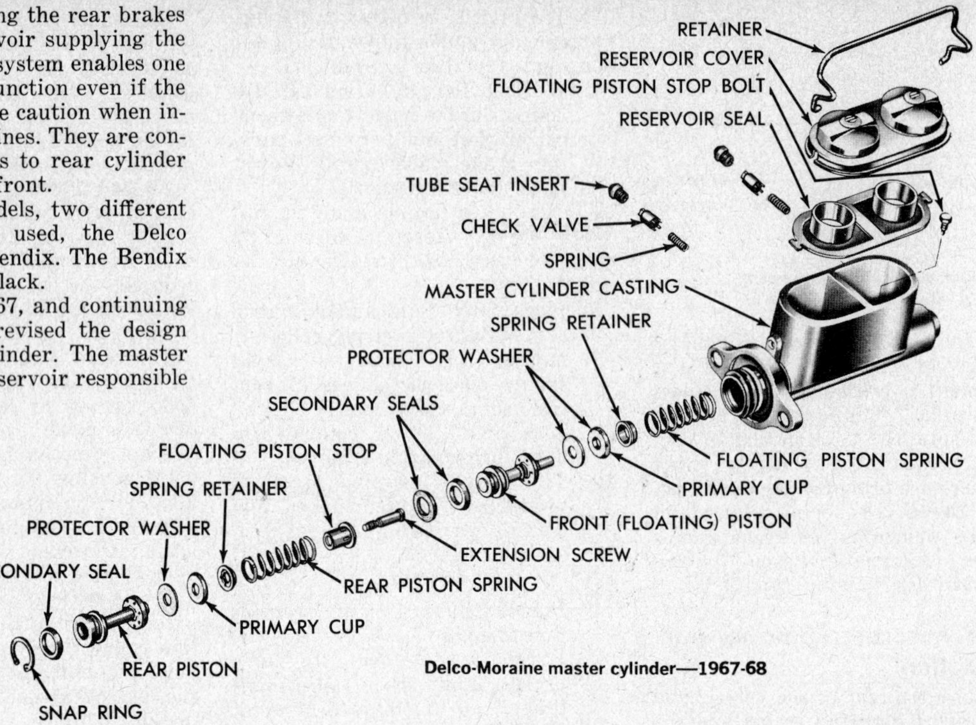
RETAINER
RESERVOIR COVER
FLOATING PISTON STOP BOLT
RESERVOIR SEAL
TUBE SEAT INSERT
CHECK VALVE
SPRING
MASTER CYLINDER CASTING
SPRING RETAINER
PROTECTOR WASHER
SECONDARY SEALS
FLOATING PISTON STOP
SPRING RETAINER
PROTECTOR WASHER
SECONDARY SEAL
FLOATING PISTON SPRING
PRIMARY CUP
FRONT (FLOATING) PISTON
EXTENSION SCREW
REAR PISTON SPRING
PRIMARY CUP
REAR PISTON
SNAP RING

Delco-Moraine master cylinder—1967-68

Power Brake Unit R & R

1967-74

1. Disconnect hydraulic lines from master cylinder.
2. Disconnect vacuum line from vacuum check valve on unit.
3. Remove steering column lower cover, as described under *Panel and Cluster R & R.*
4. Remove cotter pin, washer and spring spacer that secure power unit pushrod to brake pedal arm.
5. Remove the four nuts that secure power unit to firewall, then remove power unit.
6. To install, reverse removal procedure. The torque on the brake lines should be no greater than 20 ft lbs.

The rear braking system of all models consists of power-assisted, hydraulic service brakes.

The service brake has a self-adjusting brake shoe mechanism consisting of a link, actuator, pawl, and pawl return spring. The actuator is held against the secondary shoe by means of a hold-down cup and spring. The pawl is connected to the actuator and held in position by the pawl return spring.

The automatic adjustment takes place only when the brakes are applied when the car is moving rearward.

Over-adjustment is prevented by the shoe-to-drum clearance limiting secondary shoe travel to less than that required for the pawl to engage the next tooth of the star wheel.

Care must be used that the correct star wheel assembly is installed at the proper wheel, to insure that the self-adjusters work correctly.

Vacuum Release Parking Brake

A vacuum release assists the foot-operated parking brake. With the engine running, the brake automatically releases when the car is put into gear. This device eliminates the possibility of driving the car with the parking brake engaged.

Parking Brake Adjustment

NOTE: make certain that the rear brakes are properly adjusted before adjusting the parking brake.

1. Make a check of the parking brake linkage for the free movement of all the cables.
2. Making a correct measurement with a ruler, depress the parking brake pedal exactly 1 ¾ in.
3. Raise the rear wheels off the ground.
4. While holding the cable stud to keep it from turning, tighten the equalizer nut until a light drag is felt on either wheel when they are spun in the forward direction.

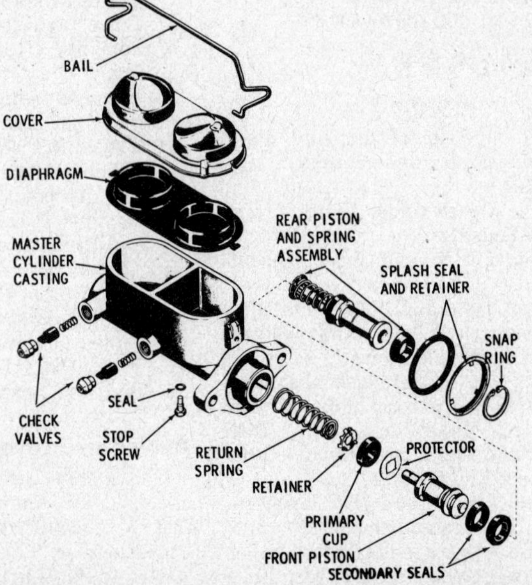
BAIL
COVER
DIAPHRAGM
MASTER CYLINDER CASTING
REAR PISTON AND SPRING ASSEMBLY
SPLASH SEAL AND RETAINER
SNAP RING
CHECK VALVES
SEAL
STOP SCREW
RETURN SPRING
RETAINER
PROTECTOR
PRIMARY CUP
FRONT PISTON
SECONDARY SEALS

Master cylinder (Bendix) used with drum brakes (© Cadillac Div., G.M. Corp)

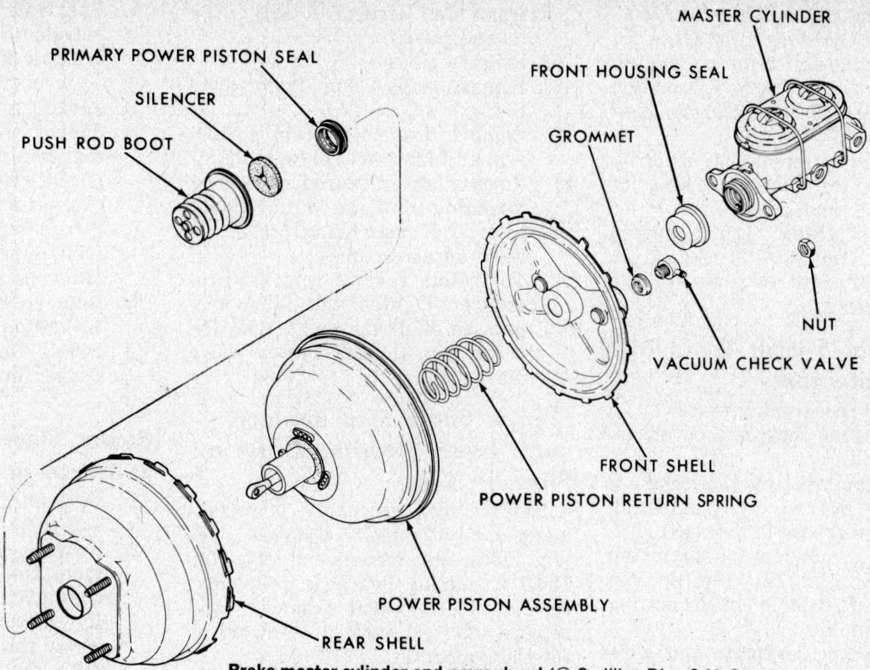
MASTER CYLINDER
PRIMARY POWER PISTON SEAL
FRONT HOUSING SEAL
SILENCER
GROMMET
PUSH ROD BOOT
NUT
VACUUM CHECK VALVE
FRONT SHELL
POWER PISTON RETURN SPRING
POWER PISTON ASSEMBLY
REAR SHELL
Brake master cylinder and power head (© Cadillac Div., G.M. Corp)

5. When the parking brake is released there should be no brake shoe drag.
6. When the brake is adjusted properly there should be 1⅛–2⅛ in. of pedal travel when a 50 lbs force is applied to the pedal.

Master Cylinder Removal and Installation

NOTE: It is possible to remove the master cylinder unit without removing the power head from the vehicle.

1. Disconnect and cover the front and rear brake lines.
2. Remove the two securing nuts which hold the master cylinder to the power head.
3. Remove the master cylinder.
4. To install, reverse the removal procedure.

Power Booster Removal and Installation

NOTE: To help in reassembly, scribe a mark on the top center of the front and rear power booster housings in line with the master cylinder reservoir cover.

1. Remove the master cylinder reservoir cover and diaphragm and drain the reservoir.
2. Remove the master cylinder attaching nuts and pull the master cylinder from its studs.
3. Disconnect the power piston rod and the rear shell attaching bolts and remove the assembly.
4. To install, reverse the removal procedure.

STEERING

Power Steering Gear and Linkage

Troubleshooting and repair instructions covering power steering gears are given in the Unit Repair Section. All 1967-74 Fleetwood 75 and Commercial models use a constant ratio power steering unit (17.5:1). All other models from 1966 use a variable ratio steering unit (16:1 on center, 11.5:1 at full lock for 1966–67 models; 16:1 on center, 12.2:1 at full lock for 1968 and 1969. The 1971 and 1973-74 models are 16:1 on center, 13.0:1 at full turn.)

NOTE: for power steering pump belt adjustment, loosen pump to mounting bracket screws, move pump upward until belt is tight. Tighten mounting bracket screws. Run the engine faster than idle speed, turn steering wheel full right or left. If belt squeals, it is too loose and should be tightened more.

The components of the steering linkage are the pitman arm, idler arm and bracket, two tie rod assemblies, and a drag link. The pitman arm is the middle section between the steering gear and the idler arm. The bracket assembly connects the drag link to the frame.

Adjustment to the tie rod linkage is made by adjusting the tubes at the tie rods. In this manner, the individual toe-in adjustment can be made for each wheel. It should be noted that these tubes should be kept lubricated to make the adjustment easier.

For steering gear overhaul see "The Unit Repair Section."

Horn Ring and Steering Wheel Removal

Remove the screws on the underside of the steering wheel spokes near the center and remove the pad assembly.

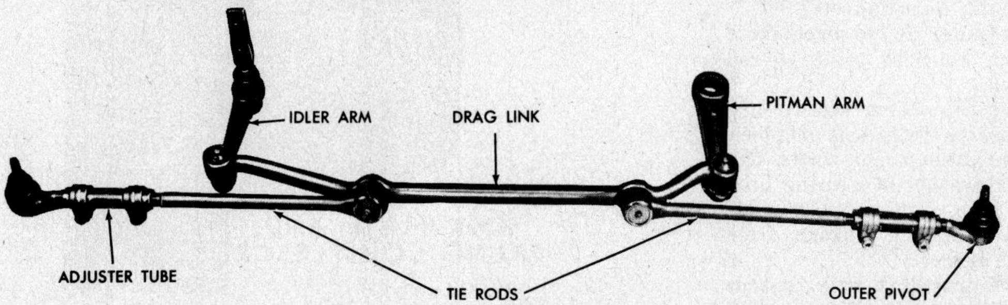
IDLER ARM
DRAG LINK
PITMAN ARM
ADJUSTER TUBE
TIE RODS
OUTER PIVOT
Steering linkage (© Cadillac Div., G.M. Corp)

Remove the nut holding the steering wheel to the steering shaft.

On tilt wheels, remove locking lever and flange and screw assembly. On all models, disconnect horn contact wire.

Use a puller to remove the steering wheel. Note the match-marking of the shaft and wheel.

When reinstalling, tighten nut to 30-35 ft. lbs. for 1967-70 models, 20 ft lbs for 1971 and 30 ft lbs for the 1972-74 models.

Turn Signal Switch Removal and Replacement

1. Remove the steering wheel.
2. Remove the lockplate cover assembly.
3. After compressing the lockplate spring, remove the snap-ring from the groove in the shaft.

Caution When the snap-ring is removed do not allow the shaft to slide out the bottom of the column.

4. Remove the lockplate and slide the turn signal cam and the upper bearing preload spring off the upper steering shaft.
5. Remove the thrust washer from the shaft.
6. Remove the hazard warning switch from the column along with the turn signal lever.
7. Use the following procedure if the car is equipped with Cruise Control.
   a. Attach a piece of piano wire to the connector on the Cruise Control switch harness.
   b. Gently pull the harness up and out of the column.
8. Remove the turn signal switch mounting screws.
9. Slide the switch connector out of the bracket on the steering column.
10. After freeing the switch wiring protector from its mounting, pull the turn signal switch straight up and remove the switch, switch harness, and the connector from the column.
11. To reassemble reverse the removal procedure.

Steering Linkage Removal and Disassembly

1. Remove cotter pins and nuts from outer tie-rod pivots.
2. Remove outer tie rod pivots from steering knuckles using tie-rod end puller.
3. Remove idler arm screws and lockwashers from side member.
4. Remove pitman arm cotter pin. nut and washer at steering linkage.
5. Remove steering linkage from pitman arm.
6. Remove drag link with tie-rods and idler arm attached.
7. Remove cotter pins and nuts from idler arm pivot and inner tie-rod pivots.
8. Remove tie-rod.
9. Remove idler arm from drag link.
10. Remove dust seals from pitman arm and idler arm pivot studs.
11. Remove outer tie-rod pivots by loosening nuts on outer clamp bolts and unscrewing the pivot- from adjuster tubes.
12. To install, reverse removal procedure. Tighten the idler arm nuts to 40 ft lbs and install the cotter pin. Do not tighten above 50 ft lbs.

Pitman Shaft Seal Replacement (with Steering Gear in Place in Car)

NOTE: this procedure is recommended only for 1971-74 models. Cadillac does not recommend this for 1967-70 due to clearance problems; remove steering gear from car and remove old seal with a screwdriver for these models.

1. Disconnect pitman arm from pitman shaft. Clean end of pitman shaft and housing. Tape the splines of the pitman shaft to keep them from cutting the seal. Use only one layer of tape. Too much tape will prevent passage of the seal. Using lock ring pliers remove the seal retaining ring.
2. Start the engine and turn the steering wheel to the left so that the oil pressure in the housing will force the seals out. Catch the seal and the oil in a container. Turn off the engine when the two seals are out. This method of seal removal eliminates the possible scoring of the seal seats while attempting to pry them out.
3. Inspect the two old seals for damage to the rubber covering on the outside diameter. If they are scored or scratched, inspect the housing for burrs, etc. and remove them before installing the new seals.
4. Lubricate the two new seals with petroleum jelly. Put the one with a single lip in first, then put in a washer. Drive seal in far enough to permit installation of double lip seal, washer and the seal retaining ring. The first seal is not supposed to bottom in its counterbore.
5. Fill reservoir to proper level, start engine, turn wheel to right and check for leaks.
6. Remove the tape and reinstall the pitman arm. Tighten nut to 140 ft. lbs for 1967-69, and 185 ft. lbs. for 1970-74.

Power Steering Pump Removal and Installation

1. Disconnect the pump lines and seal them to prevent fluid loss.
2. Remove the pump mounting from the engine block. Remove the drive belt.
3. By releasing the bottom pivot screw the pump can be removed with the mounting bracket attached.
4. The installation procedure is the reverse of the removal. Remember to adjust the pump belt tension and bleed the hydraulic line system.

INSTRUMENT PANEL

The instrument panels on 1967-1974 Cadillacs have varied in design but there has been little component change during the years. The warning light system is used for the engine water temperature, oil pressure, and alternator functioning while switches operate the windshield wipers, climate control, cruise control, headlights, and the power top.

This section will include procedures for the removal and reassembly of the ignition lock cylinder, ignition switch, and the headlight switch.

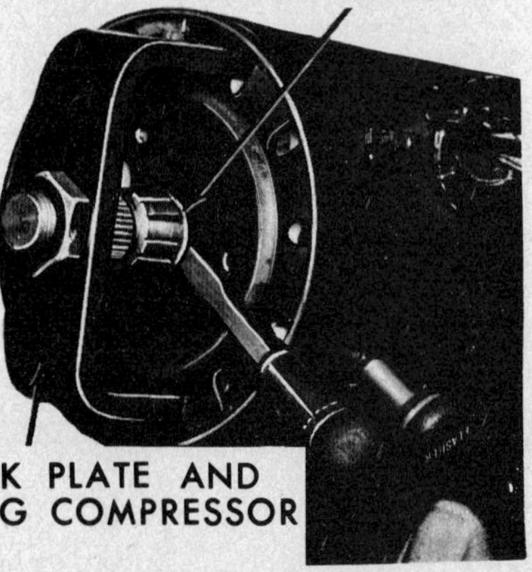
"C" RING
LOCK PLATE AND
SPRING COMPRESSOR

Removing the C-ring
(© Cadillac Div., G.M. Corp)

Ignition Switch Replacement

1967-68

1. Disconnect battery.
2. Remove lock cylinder.
3. Remove steering column lower cover.
4. Remove switch nut that holds the switch assembly to the panel.
5. Disconnect dial bulb socket and wiring harness from back of switch assembly.
6. Pull switch rearward out of instrument panel.
7. Install by reversing removal procedure.

1969-74

1. Disconnect battery.
2. Position lock cylinder in "lock" position.
3. Remove steering column lower cover.
4. Loosen two nuts on upper steering column, allowing column to drop.

CAUTION: Do not remove nuts, as column may bend under its own weight.

5. Disconnect ignition switch connector at switch.
6. Remove two screws securing ignition switch to steering column. Remove switch.
7. To install, first assemble ignition switch on actuator rod and adjust to "lock" position, as follows:
   a. *Standard Column*—Hold switch actuating rod stationary with one hand while moving switch toward bottom of column until switch reaches end of travel (Acc. position). Back off one detent, then, with key also in "lock" position, tighten two switch mounting screws to 35 in. lbs.
   b. *Tilt column*—Hold switch actuating rod stationary with one hand while moving switch toward upper end of column until switch reaches end of travel (Acc. position). Back off one detent, then, with key also in "lock" position, tighten two switch mounting screws to 35 in. lbs.
8. Connect wires, tighten two steering column nuts, install lower cover and reconnect battery.

Lock Cylinder Replacement

Up to 1968

1. Insert key and turn to left of Acc. position.
2. With stiff wire in hole depress lock pin and rotate cylinder counterclockwise and pull out.

1969-74 Standard Steering Column

1. Remove the steering wheel.
2. Remove the lockplate cover assembly.
3. After compressing the lockplate spring, remove the snap-ring from the groove in the shaft.

Caution When the snap-ring is removed do not allow the shaft to slide out the bottom of the column.

4. Remove the lockplate and slide the turn signal cam and the upper bearing preload spring off the upper steering shaft.
5. Remove the thrust washer from the shaft.
6. Remove the hazard warning switch from the column along with the turn signal lever.
7. Use the following procedure if the car is equipped with Cruise Control.
   a. Attach a piece of stiff wire to the connector on the Cruise Control switch harness.
   b. Gently pull the harness up and out of the column.
8. Remove the turn signal switch mounting screws.
9. Slide the switch connector out of the bracket on the steering column.
10. After freeing the switch wiring protector from its mounting, pull the turn signal switch straight up and remove the switch, switch harness and the connector from the column.
11. Turn the ignition switch to "on" or "run" and then insert a small screwdriver into the slot next to the switch mounting screw boss. Push the lock cylinder tab and remove the lock cylinder.

1969-74 Tilt Column

1. Remove the steering wheel.
2. Remove the rubber sleeve bumper from the steering shaft.
3. Using a small screwdriver remove the plastic retainer.
4. Using a spring compressor, compress the upper steering shaft spring and remove the C-ring. Release the steering shaft lockplate, the horn contact carrier, and the upper steering shaft preload spring.
5. Remove the four screws which hold the upper mounting bracket and then remove the bracket.
6. Slide the harness connector out of the bracket on the steering column. Tape the upper part of the harness and connector.
7. Disconnect the hazard button and position the shift bowl in Park. Remove the turn signal lever from the column.
8. Use the following procedure for cars with Cruise Control.
   a. Remove the harness protector from the harness.
   b. Attach a piece of piano wire to the switch harness connector.
   c. Before removing the turn signal lever, loop a piece of piano wire and insert it into the turn signal lever opening. Using the wire, pull the Cruise Control harness out through the opening.
   d. Pull the rest of the harness up through and out of the column.
   e. Remove the guide wire from the connector and secure the wire to the column.
   f. Remove the turn signal lever.
9. Pull the turn signal switch up until the end connector is within the shift bowl. Remove the hazard flasher level. Allow the switch to hang.
10. Place the ignition key in the "run" position.
11. Depress the center of the lock cylinder retaining tab with a screwdriver and then remove the lock cylinder.
12. To install reverse the above procedure.

Headlight Switch R & R

1. Remove the lower cover of the steering column.
2. Release the wiring harness retainer which runs below the headlight switch.

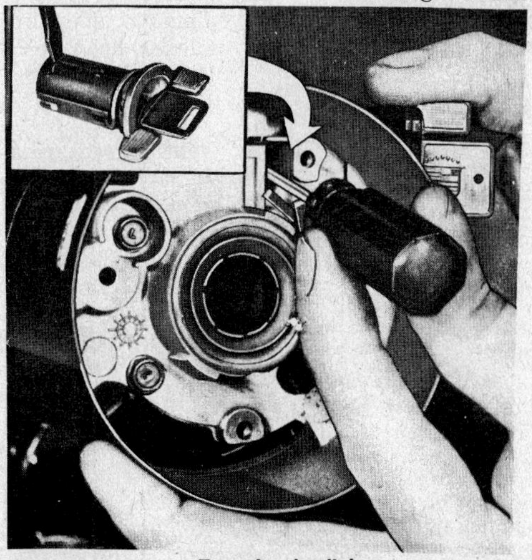

Turn signal switch
(© Cadillac Div., G.M. Corp)

3. Depress the knob release button which is located on the top of the headlight switch. While the button is depressed, remove the rod and knob.
4. Remove the two mounting screws and the ground wire which is located at the bottom of the switch housing.
5. Pull the headlight switch assembly down and rearward, disconnect the wiring harness connectors, and the two bulbs, and then remove the assembly.
6. Unfasten the hex-head sleeve which holds the headlight switch to the housing case, then remove the switch from the case.
7. On units with Guide-Matic or Twilight Sentinel, use the following additional procedure.
   a. Remove the two screws securing the backplate and the lens to the bezel. Then remove the backplate and the lens.
   b. Remove the control ring and the washer on units equipped with one of the systems only. On cars with both systems, a dual control with an inner and outer shaft is used.
   c. Remove the hex nut securing the control switch and then remove the switch from the backplate.
8. To reassemble reverse the removal procedure.

WINDSHIELD WIPERS

Wiper and Washer Motor R & R

1967-70

1. Disconnect negative battery cable.
2. Disconnect three washer hoses from control valve. Matchmark hoses and valve nipples for proper assembly sequence.
3. Disconnect two-way connector at washer unit and three-way connector at wiper unit.
4. Remove rubber grommet or cover plate above wiper motor on firewall.
5. Loosen two locknuts that secure crank arm to ball socket. Disengage arm from socket, without removing the locknuts.
6. Remove three screws that secure wiper/washer to firewall and remove assembly.
7. To install, reverse removal procedure, making sure wiper crank is in Park position.

1971-74

1. Disconnect negative battery cable, after raising hood.
2. Remove cowl screen.
3. Reach through opening and disengage transmission drive link from wiper crank arm by loosening two nuts.
4. Disconnect wiring and washer hoses.
5. Remove three screws that secure wiper/washer unit to firewall.
6. Remove entire assembly.
7. To install, reverse removal procedure, making sure wiper crank arm is in Park position.

Wiper Transmission R & R

1967

1. Remove both wiper arms.
2. Remove escutcheons, spanner nuts and washers.
3. Raise hood and remove eight capscrews that secure front and side edges of ventilator frame to firewall, noting location of any shims.

NOTE: end screws are hidden and are reached by opening doors and removing door hinge pillar inspection plates.

4. Raise front edge of ventilator frame and disengage washer hoses.
5. Raise rear edge of ventilator frame and slide it forward to disengage from molding; remove molding.
6. Remove rubber grommet or cover plate above wiper motor on firewall.
7. Disengage motor crank arm from linkage by loosening two retaining nuts.
8. Remove three transmission hold-down screws at right- and left-hand sides.
9. Remove four hold-down screws at bellcranks, then remove transmission linkage as an assembly.
10. To install, reverse removal procedure, after lubricating ball sockets.

NOTE: rivets can be drilled out to replace only one side of transmission.

1968

1. Remove both wiper arms.
2. Remove six clips that secure rubber hood seal to cowl. Position seal out of the way.
3. Remove screws that secure cowl vent screen; remove screen.
4. Remove the three screws on each side that hold transmissions to cowl.
5. Remove the three screws that secure bellcrank assembly.
6. Remove cover plate on firewall above wiper motor.
7. Loosen the two retaining locknuts and disengage motor crank arm.

Caution Do not remove lock nuts from the ball socket studs.

8. Remove transmission through right-hand cowl opening.
9. To install, reverse removal procedure, after lubricating ball sockets.

1969-74

Same as 1968 procedure, except delete Step 5.

RADIO

Removal

1967

1. Remove upper instrument panel cover.
2. Remove ash tray housing assembly.
3. Remove screws that secure ash tray frame to retaining plate, disconnect ash tray frame connector, and remove frame.
4. Remove knobs, springs and rings.
5. Using spanner nut wrench, remove spanner nuts that hold control shafts to instrument panel.
6. Remove screw on right side that secures radio bracket to frame.
7. Pull radio rearward and lower to gain access to wire connectors.
8. On AM-FM stereo radio, disconnect audio-amplifier connector.
9. Disconnect wire connector and antenna lead-in cable.
10. Disconnect dial bulb socket from radio.
11. Disconnect foot control plug, if so equipped.
12. On stereo, remove tape securing speaker leads; two on instrument panel cluster and two at panel frame above glove compartment door.
13. Remove radio through ash tray housing hole.

1968

1. Remove upper instrument panel cover.
2. Remove radio knobs, springs and rings.
3. Disconnect dial bulb socket from radio.
4. Disconnect wire connector and antenna lead-in cable.
5. Disconnect foot control plug, if so equipped, from radio.
6. Using spanner nut wrench, remove spanner nuts that secure control shafts to upper panel, then remove escutcheons.
7. Remove locknut that holds radio front bracket to stud.
8. Loosen screw that holds rear bracket to radio and remove screw to upper panel.
9. Pull radio rearward, then remove through opening at top of panel.

NOTE: on AM-FM stereo radios, disconnect audio-amplifier unit connector after Step 1. Remove center A/C duct at same time.

1969-70

1. Remove steering column lower cover.

2. Remove defroster hose behind radio.
3. Remove radio knobs, washers and rings by pulling straight out.
4. Using spanner nut wrench, remove spanner nuts securing control shafts to instrument panel.
5. Disconnect wire connectors and antenna lead-in cable. On cars with stereos, disconnect the single lead to the rear speaker and the four-way connector to the front speaker. Disconnect the two-way speaker connector on AM/FM units.
6. Remove screws securing support bracket to radio and panel center support and remove bracket.
7. Pull radio rearward and down.
8. Disconnect dial bulb socket and remove radio.

1971-74

This procedure is the same as 1969-70 procedure, except that Step 2 can be eliminated.

HEATER

Heater Blower— Non-Air-Conditioned Cars

1967-68

1. Drain cooling system.
2. Disconnect electrical connection to blower motor.
3. Remove blower motor mounting screws and remove blower.
4. Remove heater hoses from fittings on assembly, leaving clamps on fittings.
5. Disconnect cable to temperature valve at pivot point on assembly.

NOTE: disconnect vacuum manifold assembly and position out of the way, starting 1968.

6. Remove screws holding bottom of assembly to cowl.
7. Remove screws holding top of assembly to cowl, then remove assembly.
8. Install in reverse of above.

1969-70

1. Disconnect negative battery cable.
2. Drain cooling system.
3. Remove one screw that secures antenna bracket to wheelhousing.
4. Disconnect blower electrical connector.
5. Remove five screws that secure blower to case and remove blower motor by rotating it 180° while pulling out.
6. Remove heater hoses.
7. Disconnect green vacuum hose at vacuum power unit.
8. Disconnect temperature valve cable and remove cable clamp.
9. Remove screw that secures check valve and position valve out of the way.
10. Position power brake vacuum line out of the way.
11. Disconnect three-way connector at blower resistor.
12. Remove seat warmer relay, if so equipped.
13. Remove wiring harness from clip.
14. Remove seven screws that secure the bottom of the blower assembly to cowl.
15. Remove five screws and one nut that secure top of blower assembly to cowl.
16. Remove blower case assembly.
17. To install, reverse removal procedure.

1971-74

1. Disconnect negative battery cable.
2. Disconnect electrical connector.
3. Remove five blower-to-case screws and blower motor.

Heater Blower— Air-Conditioned Cars

1967-68

1. Disconnect battery.
2. Disconnect motor feed wire.
3. Disconnect air hose at motor.
4. Disconnect ground wire and capacitor from 1968.
5. Remove screws holding motor to evaporator and remove motor.
6. Install in the reverse of above.

1969-74

1. Disconnect negative battery cable.
2. On 1969-70 models only, remove screw that secures antenna bracket to wheelhousing.
3. Remove rubber cooling hose from nipple and blower motor.
4. Disconnect electrical connector.
5. Remove five screws that secure motor to case, then twist motor 180° and pull out.

Heater Core— Non-Air-Conditioned Cars

1967-70

1. Disconnect the negative battery cable.
2. Drain the cooling system.
3. Disconnect the electrical connector lead to the heater blower motor.
4. Remove the attaching screws of the blower motor and remove the motor.
5. Remove screws from each side of heater core, securing wire retaining clamps to blower case, then remove clamps.
6. Pull core out of case and remove grommets from inlet and outlet fittings.
7. Install in reverse of above.

1971-74

1. Drain cooling system.
2. Remove heater hoses from core nipples.
3. Remove instrument panel top cover.
4. Remove screws and position center ventilator duct and sleeve out of the way.
5. Remove vacuum hoses from diverter door and defroster door vacuum actuators.
6. Unfasten the bowden cable from temperature door and case and move out of way.
7. Take out the screws, securing heater case to cowl.
8. Work heater case from position under instrument panel.
9. Remove the screws and clips securing the core to heater case, and lift out core.
10. To install, reverse removal procedure.

Heater Core— Air-Conditioned Cars

1967-68

1. Drain cooling system.
2. Remove carburetor air cleaner.
3. Disconnect vacuum hose assembly connectors from servo vacuum valve and control vacuum valve on power servo unit.
4. Disconnect vacuum hose from power servo power unit.
5. Disconnect electrical connector from power servo unit.
6. Disconnect vacuum hoses and electrical connections from master switch.
7. Disconnect small diameter vacuum hose from center port of vacuum check valve.
8. Remove screw securing vacuum check valve mounting bracket to heater air-selector assembly, then position check valve and bracket out of way.
9. Disconnect vacuum hose from mode door vacuum power unit.
10. Disconnect cable from control valve on power servo unit.
11. Remove hoses from heater inlet and outlet fittings and disengage vacuum manifold from assembly, starting 1968.
12. Remove screws securing heater-air selector to cowl and remove assembly from engine compartment.
13. Remove screws securing heater core frame to heater-air selector case, then remove gasket from case.
14. Pull core frame, with core attached, away from heater-air selector case.
15. Remove grommets from inlet and outlet fittings.
16. Remove corner screws securing wire retaining clamps to core frame.
17. Remove clamps and core.
18. Install in reverse of above.

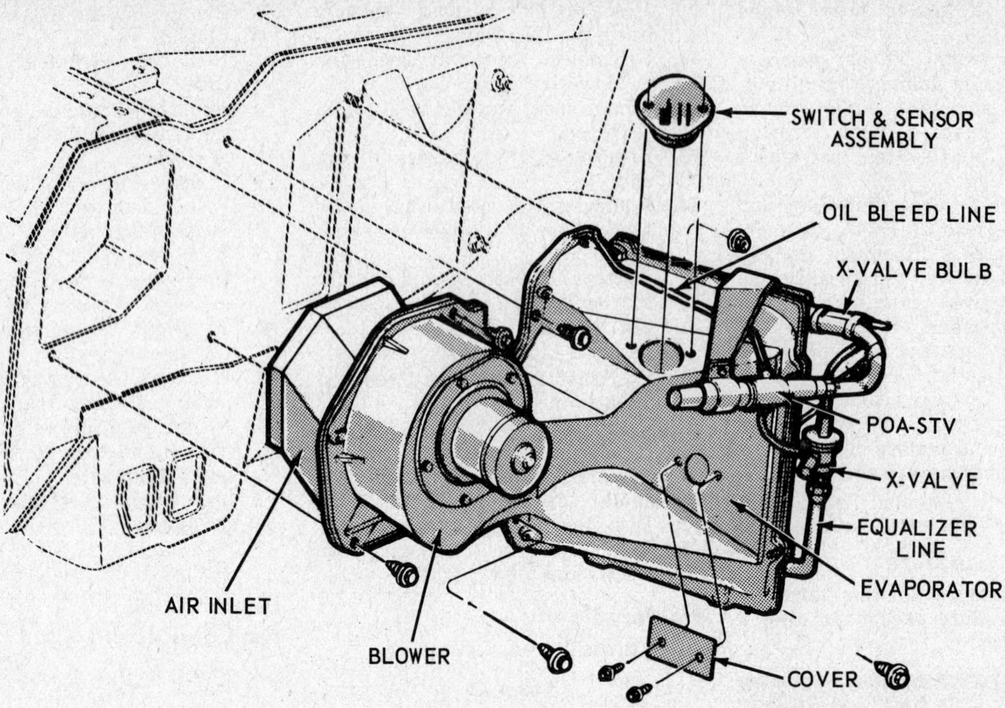
SWITCH & SENSOR ASSEMBLY
OIL BLEED LINE
X-VALVE BULB
POA-STV
X-VALVE
EQUALIZER LINE
EVAPORATOR
AIR INLET
BLOWER
COVER

1971-74 Blower, air inlet, and evaporator (© Cadillac Div., G.M. Corp)

1969-70

1. Disconnect negative battery cable.
2. Remove air cleaner.
3. Drain coolant.
4. Disconnect two heater hoses at heater air selector.
5. Remove blower relay connector.
6. Remove connector from power servo.
7. Remove neutral switch, vacuum storage tank, and Automatic Level Control hoses from vacuum check valve.
8. Remove right and left tie struts.

NOTE: if equipped with Automatic Level Control, position left tie strut out of the way in the engine compartment.

9. Disconnect Thermal Vacuum Switch hose.
10. Disengage wiring harness from clips, then remove white vacuum hose at water valve.
11. Remove vacuum harness connector from cowl, then remove six air selector to cowl screws.
12. Remove one nut and blower relay ground wire from air selector stud.
13. Remove fuse block and position it out of the way.
14. Remove four mode selector screws.
15. Pull vacuum harness connector into passenger compartment and disconnect.
16. Guide heater and air modulator assembly from engine compartment.
17. Remove four screws that secure heater core frame to case.
18. Remove gasket, then pull heater core and frame away from case.
19. Remove rubber grommets from air inlet and outlet fittings.
20. Remove four screws, retaining clamps and heater core.
21. To install, reverse removal procedure.

1971-74

1. Drain cooling system.
2. Remove hoses from heater core nipples.
3. Remove instrument panel top cover.
4. Remove right and left A/C outlet hoses and center outlet connector.
5. Remove screws securing A/C distributor to heater case and lift off distributor.
6. Remove defroster nozzle.
7. Remove glove box.
8. Disconnect vacuum hoses at recirculator door, water valve, control head and supply hose.
9. Disconnect aspirator hose from in-car sensor.
10. Take off instrument panel braces.
11. On engine side of cowl remove the nuts securing heater case to cowl.
12. Work the heater case out from under dash.
13. Remove rubber seals from around core nipples.
14. Remove the screw and clip from beneath the seal.
15. Take out screws and clip from opposite end of core and remove core.
16. Reverse the above procedure for installation.

INDEX

Cadillac Eldorado

YEAR IDENTIFICATION

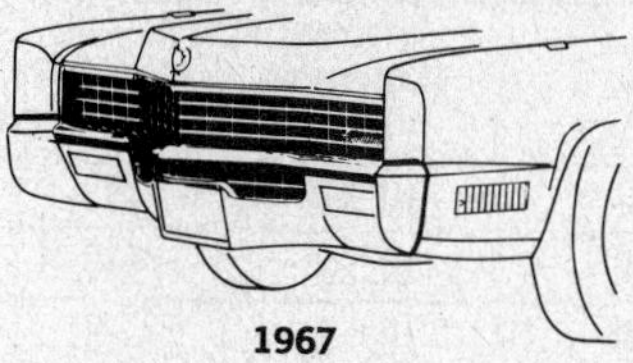
1967

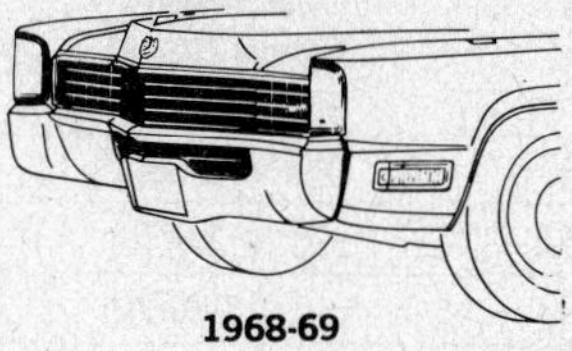
1968-69

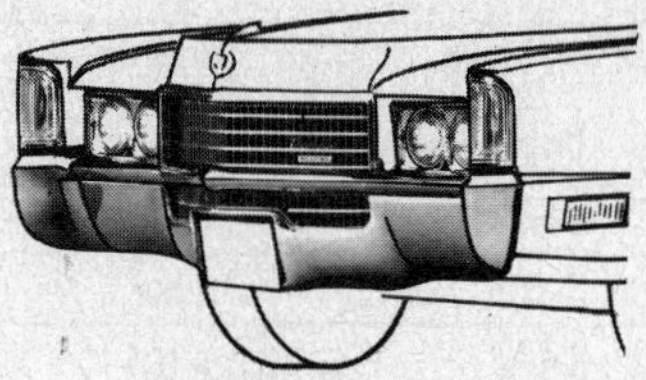
1970

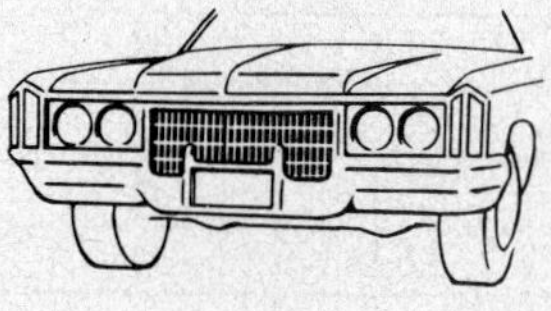
1971

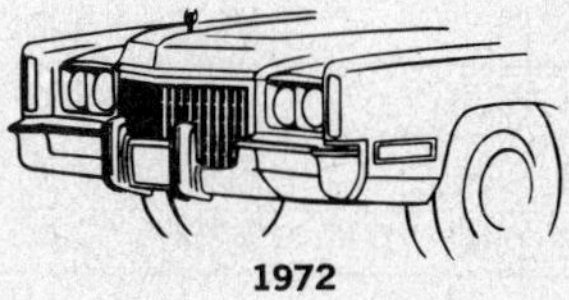
1972

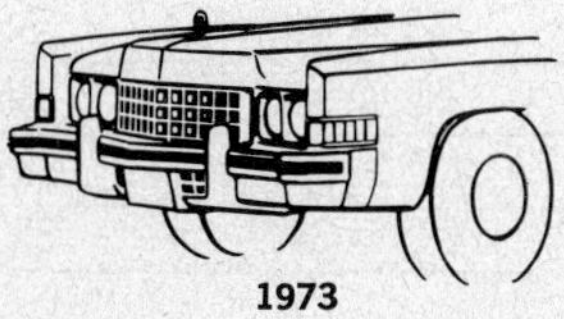
1973

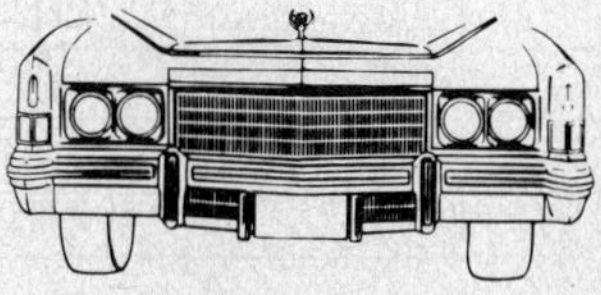
1974

FIRING ORDER

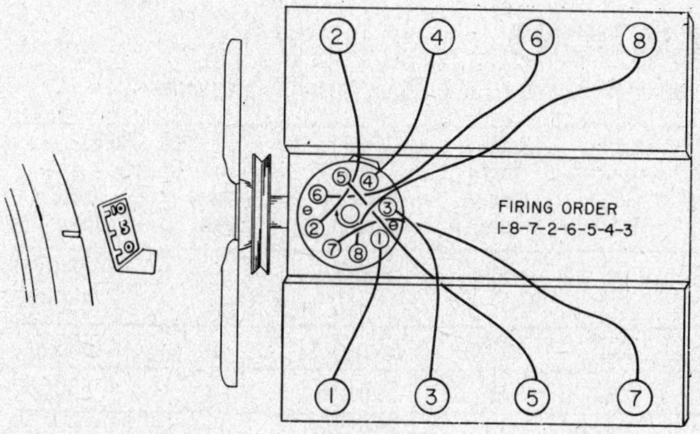
FIRING ORDER
1-8-7-2-6-5-4-3
1967

DIRECTION
OF ROTATION
Distributor numbering—1968 only

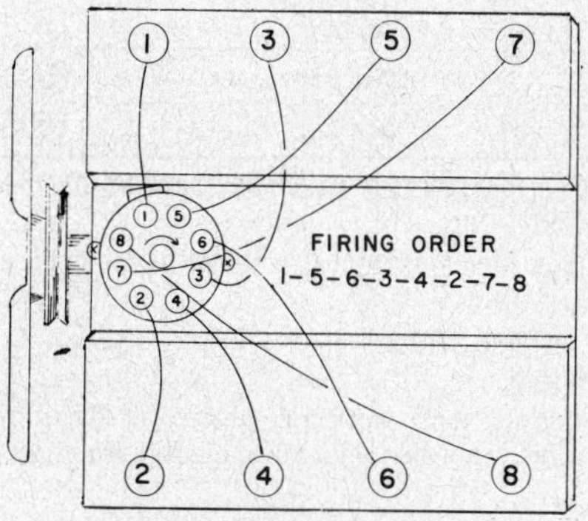
FIRING ORDER
1-5-6-3-4-2-7-8
1968-74
(© Cadillac Div., G.M. Corp.)

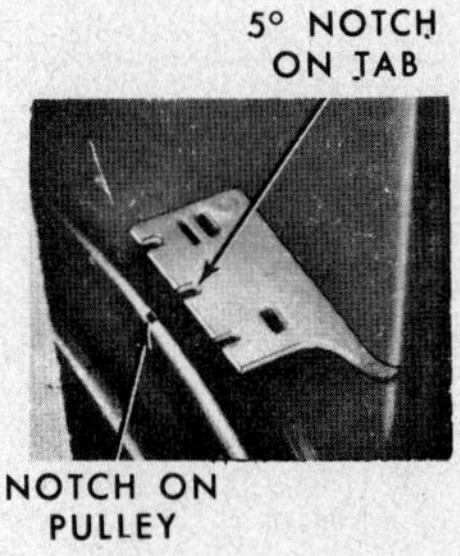
5° NOTCH
ON TAB
NOTCH ON
PULLEY
Timing marks—1968-70

8° ON TAB
NOTCH ON
BALANCER
Timing marks—1971-74
(© Cadillac Div., G.M. Corp.)

CAR SERIAL NUMBER LOCATION AND ENGINE IDENTIFICATION

1967

Vehicle identification plates are located at the top rear of the engine block, adjacent to the transmission, and on the left front door lock pillar. The eight digit serial number consists of a sales code letter, the last digit of the model year (7), and a six digit sequential serial number.

All models utilize a 429 cu. in. V8 engine. The engine serial number is stamped at the left rear of the cylinder block, just below the cylinder head.

1968-70

The vehicle identification plate is located on the top left side of the dashboard, and is visible through the windshield. The eight digit serial number consists of a sales code letter. The last digit of the model year (8, 9, or 0), and a six digit sequential number.

1968-69 models use a 472 cu. in. engine. A 500 cu. in. engine is used in 1970. The vehicle identification number, less sales code, is stamped on the top rear of the engine block, adjacent to the transmission.

1971-74

The vehicle identification plate is located on the top left side of the dashboard, and is visible through the windshield. The thirteen digit serial number consists of the G.M. Division Code (6), a four digit series and model number, the last digit of the model year, plant designation, and a six digit sequential serial number.

All models utilize a 500 cu. in. V8 engine. A derivative of the vehicle identification number is stamped on the top rear of the engine block, adjacent to the transmission.

1972-74 models have the engine code located on the left rear of the engine block, behind intake mani-fold.

GENERAL ENGINE SPECIFICATIONS

Year	Engine Cu. In. Displacement	Carburetor Type	Advertised Horsepower @ rpm ■	Advertised Torque @ rpm (ft lbs) ■	Bore and Stroke (in.)	Advertised Compression Ratio	Oil Pressure @ 2050 rpm
'67	8-429	4 bbl	340 @ 4600	480 @ 3000	4.130 x 4.000	10.5:1	33
'68	8-472	4 bbl	375 @ 4400	525 @ 3000	4.300 x 4.060	10.5:1	33
'69	8-472	4 bbl	375 @ 4400	525 @ 3000	4.300 x 4.060	10.5:1	38
'70	8-500	4 bbl	400 @ 4400	550 @ 3000	4.300 x 4.304	10.0:1	38
'71	8-500	4 bbl	365 @ 4400	535 @ 2800	4.300 x 4.304	8.5:1	38
'72	8-500	4 bbl	235 @ 3800	385 @ 2400	4.300 x 4.304	8.5:1	35
'73	8-500	4 bbl	235 @ 3800	385 @ 2400	4.300 x 4.304	8.5:1	35
'74	8-500	4 bbl	235 @ 3800	385 @ 2400	4.300 x 4.304	8.5:1	35

■ Beginning 1972 horsepower and torque are SAE net figures. They are measured at the rear of the transmission with all accessories installed and operating. Since the figures may vary when a given engine is installed in different models, some are representative rather than exact.

TUNE-UP SPECIFICATIONS

When analyzing compression test results, look for uniformity among cylinders rather than specific pressures.

Year *	ENGINE No. Cyl Displacement (cu in.)	ENGINE hp	SPARK PLUGS Type §	SPARK PLUGS Gap (in.)	DISTRIBUTOR Point Dwell (deg)	DISTRIBUTOR Point Gap (in.)	IGNITION TIMING (deg) ▲ Man Trans	IGNITION TIMING (deg) ▲ Auto Trans	VALVES Intake Opens ■ (deg) ●	Fuel Pump Pressure (psi)	IDLE SPEED (rpm) ▲ Man Trans	IDLE SPEED (rpm) ▲ Auto Trans
'67	8-429	340	44	.035	30	.016	—	5B	39	5¼-6½	—	480① (550)②
'68	8-472	375	44-N	.035	30	.016	—	5B	18	5¼-6½	—	550①
'69	8-472	375	R-44-N	.035	30	.016	—	5B	18	5¼-6½	—	550③
'70	8-500	400	R-46-N	.035	30	.016	—	7½B	18	5¼-6½	—	600④/400
'71	8-500	365	R-46-N	.035	30	.016	—	8B	38	5¼-6½	—	600④/400
'72	8-500	235	R-46-N	.035	30	.016	—	8B	34	5¼-6½	—	600④/400
'73	8-500	235	R-46-N	.035	30	.016	—	8B	34	5¼-6½	—	600④/400
'74	8-500	235	R-46-N	.035	30	.016	—	8B	34	5¼-6½	—	600④/400

▲ See text for procedure
■ All figures Before Top Dead Center
§ All spark plug listings are A.C. original equipment listings
● Figures in parentheses are for California only
① For A/C equipped vehicles, adjust idle to 900-950 rpm in neutral with A/C and idle speed-up on
② A/C on
③ Adjust idle to 900-950 rpm with idle speed-up on. See text for special procedure.
④ Lower figure indicates idle speed with solenoid disconnected
B Before Top Dead Center
— Not applicable
*For '74 models with optional electronic ignition, see engine compartment decal for tune-up specifications.

CAPACITIES

Year	ENGINE No. Cyl. (Cu. In.) Displacement	Engine Crankcase Add 1 Qt For New Filter	TRANSMISSION Pts To Refill After Draining Manual 3-Speed	Manual 4-Speed	Automatic ●	Drive Axle (pts)	Gasoline Tank (gals)	COOLING SYSTEM (qts) With Heater	With A/C
'67	All	4	—	—	11	4.5	24	17	17.5
'68	All	5	—	—	11.9	4.5	24	20.3	20.8
'69	All	5	—	—	11.9	4.5	24	21.3	21.8
'70	All	5	—	—	11.9	4.5	24①	21.3	21.8
'71	All	5	—	—	11.9	4	27.5	21.3	21.8
'72	All	5	—	—	11.9	4	27.5	21.3	21.8②
'73	All	5	—	—	11.9	4	27.5	21.3	21.8②
'74	All	5	—	—	11.9	4	27.5	21.3	21.8②

● Specifications do not include torque convertor
① California cars—22 gals
② Trailer package—2 qts additional
— Not applicable

VALVE SPECIFICATIONS

Year	Engine No. Cyl. Displacement (cu in.)	Seat Angle (deg)	Face Angle (deg)	Spring Test Pressure (lbs @ in.)	Spring Installed Height (in.)	STEM TO GUIDE Clearance (in.) Intake	STEM TO GUIDE Clearance (in.) Exhaust	STEM Diameter (in.) Intake	STEM Diameter (in.) Exhaust
'67	8-429	45	44	160 @ 1.50	1 15/16	.0005-.0025	.0010-.0025	.3420	.3418
'68	8-472	45	44	160 @ 1.50	1 15/16	.0005-.0025	.0010-.0025	.3420	.3418
'69	8-472	45	44	160 @ 1.50	1 15/16	.0005-.0025	.0010-.0025	.3420	.3418
'70	8-500	45	44	160 @ 1.50	1 15/16	.0005-.0025	.0010-.0025	.3420	.3418
'71	8-500	45	44	160 @ 1.50	1 15/16	.0010-.0027	.0010-.0025	.3420	.3418
'72	8-500	45	44	168 @ 1.50	1 15/16	.0010-.0027	.0012-.0027	.3418	.3416
'73	8-500	45	44	168 @ 1.50	1 15/16	.0010-.0027	.0012-.0027	.3418	.3416
'74	8-500	45	44	168 @ 1.50	1 15/16	.0010-.0027	.0012-.0027	.3418	.3416

TORQUE SPECIFICATIONS

All readings in ft lbs

Year	Engine Displacement (cu in.)	Cylinder Head Bolts	Rod Bearing Bolts	Main Bearing Bolts	Crankshaft Pulley Bolt	Flywheel to Crankshaft Bolts	MANIFOLD Intake	MANIFOLD Exhaust
'67	429	60	40	95	65-70	75	25	60
'68-'74	472, 500	115	40	90	Press fit	75	30	35

NOTE—Some bolts and nuts are marked on the heads to indicate the grade of steel used. Do not use bolts of a lower grade than those originally installed. The marks consist of lines: SAE5—3 lines; SAE7—5 lines; SAE8—6 lines

PISTON CLEARANCE

Year	Engine	Piston to Bore Clearance
'67	429	.0006-.0010
'68	472	.0006-.0010
'69	472	.0006-.0010
'70	500	.0006-.0010
'71	500	.0006-.0010
'72	500	.0006-.0010
'73	500	.0006-.0010
'74	500	.0006-.0010

RING GAP

Year	Engine	Top Compression	Bottom Compression
'67	8-429	.013-.030	.013-.030
'68-'74	8-472, 500	.013-.025	.013-.025

Year	Engine	Oil Control
'67-'74	All engines	.015-.055

RING SIDE CLEARANCE

Year	Engine	Top Compression	Bottom Compression
'67-'68	8-429, 472	.0022-.0035	.0022-.0035
'69-'74	8-500	.0017-.0040	.0017-.0040

Year	Engine	Oil Control
'67-'74	All engines	None (side sealing)

CRANKSHAFT AND CONNECTING ROD SPECIFICATIONS

All measurements are given in in.

Year	Engine Displace. (cu in.)	CRANKSHAFT Main Brg. Journal Dia	Main Brg. Oil Clearance	Shaft End-Play	Thrust on No.	CONNECTING ROD Journal Diameter	Oil Clearance	Side Clearance
'67	429	3.000	.0008-.0029	.001-.007	3	2.2488-2.2493	.0005-.0035	.008-.014
'68-74	472, 500	3.250	.0003-.0026	.002-.012	3	2.5000	.0005-.0035	.008-.016

WHEEL ALIGNMENT SPECIFICATIONS

Year	Model	CASTER Range (deg)	Pref Setting (deg)	CAMBER Range (deg)	Pref Setting (deg)	Toe-in (in.)	Steering Axis Inclin.	WHEEL PIVOT RATIO (deg) Inner Wheel	Wheel Outer
'67	Eldorado	$1\frac{1}{2}$N to $2\frac{1}{2}$	2N	$\frac{3}{8}$N to $\frac{3}{8}$P	0	0 to $\frac{1}{8}$	6	20	$18\frac{1}{6}$
'68-'70	Eldorado	$1\frac{1}{2}$N to $2\frac{1}{2}$N	2N	$\frac{3}{8}$N to $\frac{3}{8}$P	0	0 to $\frac{1}{8}$	11	20	$18\frac{1}{6}$
'71-'74	Eldorado	$\frac{1}{2}$N to $1\frac{1}{2}$N	1N	$\frac{3}{8}$N to $\frac{3}{8}$P	0	$\frac{1}{16}$N to $\frac{1}{16}$P	11	20	$18\frac{1}{6}$

N Negative P Positive

ALTERNATOR AND REGULATOR SPECIFICATIONS

Year	ALTERNATOR Part No. or Manufacturer	Field Current @ 12 V	Output (amps)	REGULATOR Part No. or Manufacturer	Field Relay Air Gap (in.)	Point Gap (in.)	Volts to Close	Regulator Air Gap (in.)	Point Gap (in.)	Volts @ 75°
'67	1100641	2.2-2.6	42	1119515	.015	.030	2.3-3.7	.060	.014	13.5-14.4
	1100760	2.2-2.6	55	1119515	.015	.030	2.3-3.7	.060	.014	13.5-14.4
'68-'69	1100734	2.2-2.6	42	1119515	.015	.030	2.3-3.7	.060	.014	13.5-14.4
	1100803	2.2-2.6	55	1119515	.015	.030	2.3-3.7	.060	.014	13.5-14.4
'70	1100908	2.2-2.6	42	1119515	—	—	—	—	—	13.5-14.4
	1100910	2.8-3.2	63	1119515	—	—	—	—	—	13.5-14.4
'71-'74	1100940	4.0-4.5	42	—	Transistor type—no adjustment					
	1100937	4.0-4.5	63	—	Transistor type—no adjustment					

BATTERY AND STARTER SPECIFICATIONS

Year	Engine Displacement (cu in.)	BATTERY Ampere Hour Capacity	Volts	Terminal Grounded	STARTERS Lock Test Amps	Volts	Torque (ft lbs)	No-Load Test Amps	Volts	RPM	Brush Spring Tension (oz)
'67	429	73	12	Neg.	510	30	Locked	70-99	10.6	7,800	35
'68-'70	472, 500	74	12	Neg.	Not Recommended			70-99	10.6	7,800	35
'71-'74	500	74	12	Neg.	Not Recommended			65-95	9	700	35

BRAKE SPECIFICATIONS

All measurements are given in in.

Year	Model	MASTER CYLINDER Disç	Drum	WHEEL CYLINDER Front Disc	Front Drum	Rear	BRAKE DISC OR DRUM DIAMETER Front Disc	Front Drum	Rear
'67-'68	Eldorado	1.00	1.00	$1\frac{15}{16}$	$1\frac{1}{8}$	$\frac{7}{8}$①	11.3	11.0	11.0
'69-'70	Eldorado	1.125	—	$2\frac{15}{16}$	—	$\frac{7}{8}$	11.0	—	11.0
'71-'74	Eldorado	1.125	—	$2\frac{15}{16}$	—	$\frac{15}{16}$	11.0	—	11.0

① Disc Brakes (1968)—$\frac{13}{16}$

CHARGING SYSTEM

The charging system on the Eldorado consists of a three-pole alternator. The large pole is connected from the battery side of the alternator through a relay box to the positive side of the battery. The two smaller poles are connected from the alternator's internal regulator to the battery through the ignition switch. The no. 1 wire from the regulator runs to a connection on the indicator lamp where it is split into two wires, one of which is transferred through the lamp switch to the key switch. The other half of no. 1 wire is ducted through a resistor to the battery side of the ignition switch. The ignition switch is connected to the relay by means of a single wire from the battery side of the ignition switch.

The no. 2 wire from the internal regulator is connected directly to the relay box.

The Delco-Remy Delcotron alternator is used on all Eldorado models. From 1967 to 1970, a 42 ampere unit was standard on cars without air conditioning and a 55 ampere unit standard on air conditioned models. In 1968, an optional 63 ampere alternator was made available for use in cars having radio equipment or other heavy electrical demands. The dual point (with field relay) regulators used with these alternators are mounted on the right-hand inner fender panel under the hood. The regulator used with the 63 ampere Delcotron is similar to the standard unit, with the addition of a field discharge diode in parallel with the voltage regulator contacts and the regulator "F" terminal to allow for the higher current.

In 1971 and 1974, the standard alternator for non-air conditioned Eldorado models became a 42 ampere, integrated circuit Delcotron, and the standard alternator on air conditioned models a 63 ampere unit of similar design. These alternators are unlike their predecessors in that the regulator is now an integral part of of the alternator itself and is nonadjustable.

Troubleshooting and repair of both the conventional Delcotron and the new integrated circuit type are covered in the Unit Repair Section.

Caution

The following are a few precautions to observe in servicing the Delcotron (AC) generator and the regulator.

1. When installing a battery, be certain that the ground polarity of the battery and the ground polarity of the generator and regulator are the same.
2. When connecting a booster battery, be sure to connect the correct battery terminals together.
3. When hooking up a charger, connect the correct charged leads to the battery terminals.
4. Never operate the generator on an open circuit. Be sure all connections in the charging circuit are tight.
5. Do not short across or ground any of the terminals on the generator or regulator.
6. Never polarize an AC system.

Alternator Removal and Installation

1967

1. Disconnect negative battery cable.
2. Disconnect wires and multiple connector from alternator.
3. Remove alternator bracket adjusting screw.
4. Remove front nut and washer from stud on exhaust manifold.
5. Remove V-belts.
6. Remove two screws that hold alternator support bracket to manifold.
7. Position alternator away from support brace and slide both alternator and bracket off locating stud.
8. To install, reverse removal procedure, tightening bracket-to-manifold screws to 18 ft. lbs.

NOTE: even if only one V-belt must be replaced, it is best to replace both so that tension is equally distributed between them.

1968-74

1. Disconnect negative battery cable.
2. Disconnect A.I.R. hose at check valve and remove heater hose clip from adjusting link.
3. For 1968-69 models, remove strut rod between adjusting link and cylinder head.
4. Remove cap, if installed, from "+" terminal.
5. Disconnect three wires from "+" terminal.
6. Unplug multiple connector.
7. Disconnect black wire from ground terminal.
8. Remove link adjusting screw and raise link, then loosen lower alternator mounting screw and remove V-belt.
9. Remove lower mounting screw, spacer and washer.

NOTE: it may be necessary to twist alternator towards fender to do this.

10. Remove alternator.
11. To install, reverse removal screws to 17 ft. lbs.

STARTING SYSTEM

The basic operation of the starting system is that the energy from the battery is transferred through the ignition switch to energize the starter

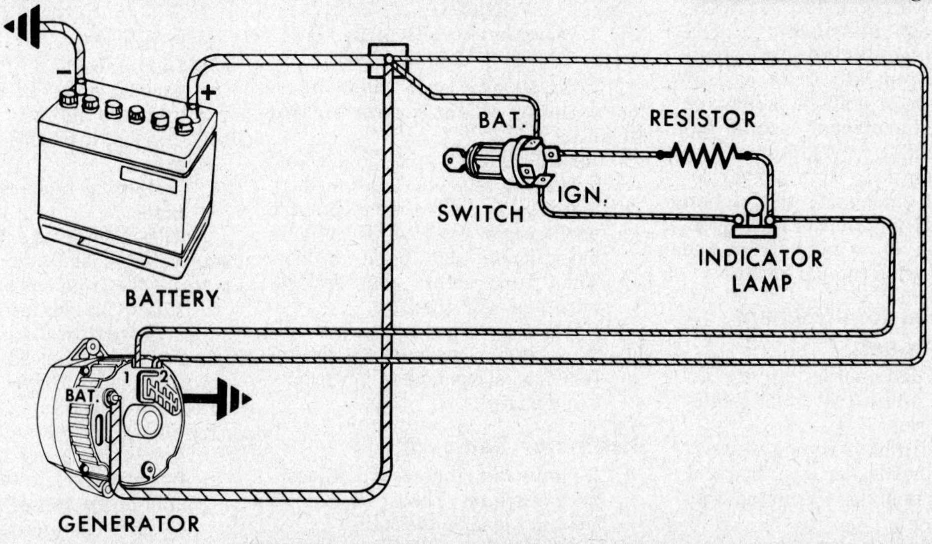
BAT.
RESISTOR
IGN.
SWITCH
INDICATOR LAMP
BATTERY
BAT.
1
2
GENERATOR

Charging system diagram (© Cadillac Div., G.M. Corp)

solenoid. The solenoid engages the starter pinion with the flywheel gear and then closes the main switch so that the battery current is delivered to the starter motor. With the starter rotating, the cranking motor pinion is meshed with the flywheel. When the key switch is released the pinion is drawn into the housing and the starter disengages.

For detailed testing and repair procedures consult the "Unit Repair Section."

Starter R & R

1967-74

1. Disconnect the negative battery cable.
2. Disconnect the starter harness which is located at the right rear of the engine.
3. Raise the front of the car.
4. Remove the spring clip securing wire which is attached to the solenoid housing.
5. Remove the support bracket which holds the starter to the crankcase.
6. Remove the two screws which attach the starter to the crankcase.
7. Remove the starter from the car by first pulling it forward and then toward the right front wheel and then up over the steering linkage.
8. To install the unit, position it properly onto the engine crankcase and then tighten the attaching screws to 46 ft lbs.
9. Install the support bracket. Tighten the screws to 12 ft lbs and the nut to 6 ft lbs.
10. Install the spring clip and lower the car. Connect the starter harness and the negative battery cable.

IGNITION SYSTEM

The Eldorado distributor is constructed of aluminum alloy and positioned at the top left, front part of the engine. It is of a single point type variety with an internal vacuum advance. The unit is driven by meshing the distributor gear with a gear located on the camshaft; this action drives the distributor cam in a clockwise direction as viewed from the front of the engine compartment.

Contact Point Replacement and Adjustment

1. Remove distributor cap by depressing and turning the retaining screws.
2. Remove the two rotor screws.
3. Remove condenser and primary leads from nylon insulated connection.
4. Loosen two screws holding base of contact assembly in place and remove points.
5. Inspect weight assembly, replace or lubricate as required.
6. Place new points under the two screws and tighten screws.
7. Connect the condenser and primary leads at the nylon insulated connection.

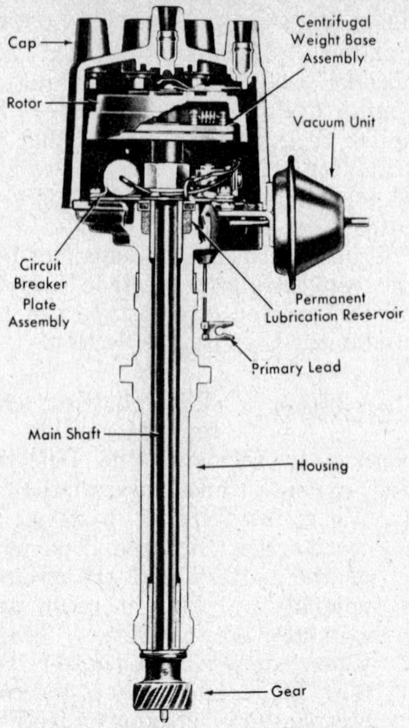
Cap
Rotor
Centrifugal Weight Base Assembly
Vacuum Unit
Circuit Breaker Plate Assembly
Permanent Lubrication Reservoir
Primary Lead
Main Shaft
Housing
Gear

Distributor showing major components
(© Cadillac Div., G.M. Corp)

Window
"Hex" Type Wrench
Adjusting Screw

Adjusting distributor points
(© Cadillac Div., G.M. Corp)

NOTE: be sure leads do not interfere with cap, weight base, or breaker advance.

8. Install rotor. Square and round lugs must be properly aligned.
9. With ⅛ in. Allen wrench, turn until points close while rubbing block is on high point of lobe. Then turn screw counterclockwise one-half turn.
10. Replace distributor cap.
11. With engine warmed up and off fast idle, set points to get proper dwell angle.

Distributor Removal

1. Remove distributor cap. Disconnect vacuum hose. Disconnect primary lead at the coil.
2. Turn the engine to top dead center for No. 1 cylinder, see firing order illustrations. The pointer on the timing case cover will point to the O-mark on the crankshaft pulley and the rotor will face No. 1 plug wire on the cap.
3. Match-mark the vacuum advance unit to the cylinder block so that the distributor body will be correctly replaced at reassembly.
4. Remove hold-down clamp and lift the distributor straight up.

Distributor Installation

1. Install rubber seal-ring below distributor housing mounting flange.
2. Install the distributor so that the vacuum advance unit aligns with the match-mark made at removal. Turn the rotor slightly left of center so that as the gear engages the camshaft it will revolve into the proper position, pointing to No. 1 contact in the cap.
3. Install the distributor hold-down and connect the distributor lead to the coil.
4. Check the condition of the contact points and the breaker gap.
5. Install the cap and set the timing. (See "Ignition Timing.")
6. Reconnect the vacuum hose to the vacuum advance unit.

NOTE: if the engine has been cranked, remove No. 1 spark plug. Crank the engine until No. 1 piston is in firing position with the pointer and the O-mark on the crankshaft pulley aligned. Lower the distributor into position with the rotor pointing to No. 1 contact on the distributor cap.

Ignition Timing

1. Loosen the distributor clamp enough to allow the distributor to be turned by hand without excessive looseness.
2. Disconnect the vacuum advance at the distributor and tape the end of the hose to prevent any air leaks.
3. Disconnect the parking brake vacuum hose at the diaphragm and tape the end.
4. Connect a timing light to the engine.
5. Connect a tachometer to the engine.

NOTE: Make sure that the timing mark on the pulley and the aligning plate on the front cover are clean.

6. Allow the engine to reach operating temperature.
7. Set the idle speed with the selector lever in Drive.
8. With the timing light set the timing correcting a wrong setting by rotating the distributor.
9. At the correct setting tighten the hold-down bolt of the distributor to 18 ft lbs. and recheck the timing.

10. Connect the two vacuum hoses and remove both the timing light and the tachometer from the engine.

FUEL SYSTEM

The fuel pump is mounted on the left-front of the engine and is driven by an eccentric on the camshaft. The fuel filter is located on the engine oil filler tube on 1967 models, is an inline type on 1968 models, and is an integral part of the fuel pump on 1969-74 models. The pump is serviced only as an assembly.

All air conditoned cars have a provision to return excess fuel vapor to the gasoline tank to prevent vapor lock under high temperature conditions. On 1967-68 models, the bypass line runs from the fuel filter, and on 1969 and later cars, the line runs directly from the fuel pump.

The filters should be changed at least every 12,000 miles. On 1967-68 models, the replacement procedure is obvious; on 1969 and later models, see the Cadillac section for replacement procedure. Remove filter from underneath car starting 1968.

Fuel Pump R & R

1. If equipped with A.I.R. system, it may be necessary to remove air pump and bracket for clearance.
2. Remove center coil wire.
3. For 1968-74 models, jack up front of car and support on axle stands so that pump can be removed from underneath.
4. Loosen two mounting bolts, or one bolt and one nut.
5. Turn over engine to relieve tension on pump arm.
6. Disconnect pump inlet and outlet lines. Plug inlet line.
7. Disconnect vapor return line on 1969 and later models.
8. Remove mounting bolts and fuel pump.
9. To install, reverse removal procedure.

Fuel Filter

See Cadillac section.

Thermal Vacuum Switch and Idle Speed-up Device

See Cadillac section.

Idle Speed and Mixture Adjustments

1967-69

Adjust with air cleaner removed.

1. Make sure PCV valve is free and working properly.
2. Disconnect parking brake vacuum hose at vacuum release cylinder and plug.
3. Connect a tachometer, set parking brake and allow engine to come up to normal operating temperature in Neutral.
4. Remove air cleaner and make sure dashpot is disengaged.
5. With wheels chocked, place transmission in Drive.
6. On 1968-69 cars, disconnect and plug distributor vacuum line.
7. Adjust air adjusting screw to obtain an idle speed of 550 rpm with A/C *off* for A.I.R. cars, 480-500 rpm with A/C *on* for non-A.I.R. cars.

NOTE: press down on brass hot idle compensator pin while making adjustments.

8. On 1967 cars having no A.I.R. but having A/C, disconnect and plug vacuum line from power servo on firewall.
9. Set idle speed screw 1½ turns in after contacting primary lever, both mixture screws out 4 turns from seated position.
10. Turn one mixture screw clockwise to obtain highest tach reading. Continue to turn screw until speed falls off 20 rpm—this is the lean idle fall off point. Back off screw ¼ turn for non-A.I.R. cars, 1⅛ turns for 1967 A.I.R. cars, 1½ turns for 1968 A.I.R. cars, and 1 turn for 1969 cars.
11. Repeat Step 10, turning other mixture screw.
12. Reset idle speed as in Step 7, then repeat Steps 10 and 11 if speed exceeds 500 rpm for non-A.I.R. cars or 550 rpm for A.I.R. cars.
13. Install air cleaner and recheck idle speed.
14. Shut off engine, disconnect tach, reconnect parking brake vacuum line and distributor vacuum line on 1968-69 models.

1970

Adjust with air cleaner removed.

1. Disconnect and plug distributor vacuum advance line.
2. Disconnect and plug parking brake vacuum line at vacuum release cylinder.
3. Connect a tachometer, set parking brake and remove air cleaner.
4. Make sure dashpot is not touching linkage, then turn slow idle speed screw in approximately 1½ turns after it contacts primary throttle lever. Turn in both mixture screws until they seat gently, then unscrew them approximately 6 turns.
5. Place car in Drive after warming up engine. Turn off A/C.

NOTE: press down on hot idle compensator pin while making adjustments.

6. Adjust slow idle screw to obtain 620 rpm.
7. Turn one mixture screw clockwise until speed falls off 10 rpm, then repeat Steps 6 and 7 for other mixture screw. Idle speed now should be 600 rpm, indicating a 10 rpm drop per mixture needle.
8. Install air cleaner, shut off engine and disconnect tach.
9. Connect parking brake vacuum line and distributor vacuum line.

1971-1974

Adjust with air cleaner removed.

Idle speed is adjusted at a new anti-dieseling solenoid located where the dashpot was located in previous years. The throttle must be opened slightly to allow the plunger to move out all the way, then it must be closed against the now-extended solenoid plunger before making the idle speed adjustment. The solenoid plunger will retract when the ignition is shut off.

1. Disconnect and plug distributor vacuum advance hose and parking brake vacuum hose (at the release cylinder).
2. Connect a tachometer and set the parking brake with transmission in Neutral.
3. Remove the air cleaner and turn in mixture screws until they seat gently, then turn the screws out approximately 6 turns.
4. Start engine and allow it to warm up.
5. Place car in Drive with A/C off.
6. Set idle speed to 620 rpm by adjusting anti-dieseling solenoid. Tighten jam nut.
7. Turn one mixture screw clockwise until idle speed falls off 10 rpm, then repeat for other screw. Idle speed now should be 600 rpm.
8. Disconnect wire that energizes solenoid. The plunger should retract to allow a slower idle speed of 350-400 rpm.
9. Shut off engine, disconnect tach, connect vacuum lines and solenoid wire and install air cleaner.

COOLING SYSTEM

1967-1974 Eldorados use a low-capacity sealed cooling system which maintains 15 lbs maximum pressure. The radiator is constructed with two vertical tanks that connect to the enclosed cross-flow tubing. The coolant enters the upper left-hand inlet tank and circulates through the cross-flow tubes and enters the right return tank.

Further information on the cooling system may be found in the Cadillac section under the same year model. Also, system capacities can be found in the "Capacities Table."

Radiator R & R

1. Remove the negative battery cable.

2. Open the drain plug on the radiator and drain the coolant. Remove the radiator cap so that the liquid flows more quickly.
3. On the 1967 models with air conditioning, position the compressor out of the way. Do not disconnect the hoses.
4. Remove the hose clamps and remove the upper hose.
5. Remove the heater return hose which is located at the right radiator tank.
6. Disconnect the two transmission cooler lines from the bottom of the radiator. Plug the ends of the lines to prevent loss of fluid.
7. On the 1967–1970 cars, remove the two top cradle clamps and then the three screws which fasten the finger guard to the cradle.
8. On 1971 through 1974 cars it is necessary to remove the screw which holds the upper radiator hose to the cover panel and then remove the cover panel by removing the six panel screws.
9. On 1967 models remove the hoses from the vacuum distributor switch if it is so equipped. Mark each hose before removal.
10. On 1971 through 1974 cars, remove the reservoir hose from the filler neck and the two straps from the top of the radiator.
11. Remove the radiator, being careful not to damage the radiator or the fan. Pull the unit straight up.

Water Pump and Thermostat R & R

See the Cadillac section under the specific year.

EMISSION CONTROLS

In compliance with anti-pollution laws involving all of the continental United States, the Cadillac Division of General Motors has adopted as standard equipment, an integrated Air Injector Reactor (A.I.R.) control system. This method is designed and built into the engine castings after 1967, and eliminates the need for some of the tubes and exterior air manifolding of previous plans. It does, however, use the same afterburner principle as that described in the Unit Repair Section. This method of control was not used on 1970 models, although it was revived for 1971 production. In 1970, a Controlled Combustion System (C.C.S.) was used, a major part of which is the T.C.S. Transmission Controlled Spark system. 1973-74 models use P.C.V., AIR, EGR, and ECS. (See "Cadillac" section for system explanation.)

Any of the present methods of terminal exhaust control require close and frequent attention to tune-up factors of engine maintenance.

Since 1968, all car manufacturers post idle speeds and other pertinent data relative to the specific engine-car application, in a conspicuous place in the engine compartment.

Transmission Controlled Spark

On 1970 models, the T.C.S. system plays a major part in the operation of the Controlled Combustion System, which consists of a thermostatic air cleaner to regulate the temperature of incoming carburetor intake air, and the T.C.S. system. The T.C.S. system itself consists of a pressure-sensitive switch in the transmission and a solenoid in the ported vacuum line between the carburetor and the thermal vacuum switch of the air cleaner. With the transmission in first or second gear, the solenoid is energized. This eliminates vacuum advance to the distributor to help reduce emissions. In third gear, the solenoid de-energizes and allows the vacuum advance to operate normally.

On the 1971 models, the system was modified slightly to bypass the T.C.S. solenoid in the Park and Neutral positions. The neutral switch senses when the transmission is shifted into Park or Neutral and allows distributor advance to be controlled through the Thermal Vacuum Switch, thus preventing overheating in traffic. The result is that there is spark advance at fast idle speed on 1971 models, whereas there was no spark advance at fast idle on 1970 models.

The 1972 cars are equipped with PCV and the AIR system which were introduced in the previous years. To these are added the Evaporative Loss Control (ELC) and a Speed Control Switch (SCS). An explanation of these two systems is outlined in the "Emissions Control Section" of Cadillac.

Troubleshooting and adjustment of the emission control system for Eldorado are found in the "Unit Repair Section."

ENGINE

The engine in all Eldorado models is an overhead valve 90° V8 design. The 1967 model engine has a displacement of 429 cu. in. developing 340 horsepower at 4,600 rpm. The 1968-69 models have an engine of 472 cu. in. displacement developing 375 horsepower at 4,400 rpm. The stroke on the 1970 engine has been increased, giving it 500 cu. in. displacement and developing 400 horsepower at 4,400 rpm. This engine is used on all 1970-72 Eldorado models.

Specifications tables are found at the beginning of this section. Other information may be found by referring to procedures given for the same year model in the Cadillac section.

Engine R & R

Caution If it is necessary to reposition the air conditioner compressor or the lines, do not disconnect the lines.

1967

1. Disconnect negative battery terminal.
2. Remove engine hood.
3. Remove two nuts holding the cowl rods at the wheel wells and pivot rods up from the cowl.
4. Remove the air cleaner.
5. Drain the cooling system.
6. Disconnect wires from generator.
7. On cars equipped with Automatic Climate Control, partially remove compressor.
8. Disconnect transmission cooler line at left front of final drive by removing the screw that holds attaching clip.
9. Remove heater hoses at engine and at water control valve.
10. Remove left and right shrouds by removing four screws that attach each shroud.
11. Remove four screws holding fan assembly to water pump pulley and remove as an assembly.

NOTE: fan clutches used on air-conditioned cars are always to be in an in-car position. When removed from car, support the assembly to keep clutch disc in a vertical plane to keep silicone fluid from leaking from clutch mechanism.

12. On cars equipped with Automatic Climate Control, disconnect vapor return line near fuel pump and remove clamp holding vacuum hoses to steel vapor return.
13. On cars equipped with exhaust emission control systems, remove the air pump.
14. Disconnect fuel line at the fuel pump and plug the end of the line.
15. Remove power steering pump bracket-to-cylinder block screws and position pump and bracket to one side. Remove pump belt. Do not disconnect power steering hoses.
16. Disconnect accelerator linkage at the carburetor.
17. Disconnect wiring connectors at transmission downshift switch.
18. Disconnect positive terminal wiring at coil and remove harness from two retaining clips on the left valve cover.
19. If car is equipped with Cruise Control, disconnect wiring connector at the power unit. Remove cotter pin securing accelerator linkage to exterior arm, remove washer and separate linkage from exterior arm. Also disconnect two cables at power unit.

20. Disconnect oil pressure switch connector at rear of engine.
21. Disconnect all vacuum hoses leading from intake manifold and carburetor.
22. Remove two nuts that hold left exhaust clamp to exhaust manifold and disconnect pipe.
23. Remove four upper transmission to adapter screws.
24. Remove right output shaft as described in later paragraph.
25. Disconnect starter motor retainer clamps by removing one screw at the bearing support and one screw at the engine mounting bracket.
26. Disconnect wiring at starter solenoid and remove two screws holding the starter motor to the engine and remove the starter.
27. Remove one screw at the brace at the final drive.
28. Remove two nuts holding the right exhaust pipe clamp at the exhaust manifold.
29. Remove four screws holding transmission front cover to transmission.

NOTE: the upper left screw is accessible with an extension and universal socket.

30. Remove three converter-to-flexplate attaching screws.

NOTE: this is done by removing the cork in the harmonic balancer and inserting a screw in the balancer. Rotate the screw to gain access to flexplate-to-converter screws. Do not pry on the flexplate ring gear to rotate the converter.

31. Remove vacuum modulator line at transmission and at engine.
32. Working through center crossmember, loosen, but do not remove, two transmission mounting nuts.
33. Remove two nuts and washers holding the engine mounting studs to front frame crossmember.

NOTE: there is one bolt left holding the final drive housing to the engine support bracket and two screws holding the transmission to the spacer to the engine. Do not proceed further until chain hoist is connected to the engine, because the engine may shift.

34. Attach chain hoist and take up slack.
35. Remove lower right and left transmission - to - adapter - to - cylinder-block screws.
36. Place small jack under final drive housing to support final drive and transmission.
37. Remove bolt and lockwasher holding final drive housing to engine support bracket.
38. Remove engine by pulling it slightly forward to disengage it from transmission and up from engine compartment. Turn engine slightly clockwise while removing to assist in clearing engine compartment.
39. Secure converter holding strap J-21366 to transmission case using a 5/16—18 nut, because the converter is now free.
40. Install by reversing removal procedure.

1968-74

1. Follow Steps 1-16 of 1968-72 procedure in Cadillac Section.
2. Disconnect left exhaust pipe at manifold flange.
3. Remove screw that holds transmission cooler lines to motor mount.
4. Remove nut that secures dipstick tube to manifold.
5. Jack up car.
6. Remove starter motor.
7. Disconnect right exhaust pipe at manifold flange.
8. Remove transmission inspection cover.
9. Disconnect and plug vapor return line and fuel inlet at fuel pump.
10. Remove lower radiator hose at water pump.
11. Remove three screws that secure flex plate to converter.
12. Remove four screws that secure engine to transmission.
13. Remove front motor mount bolts and bolt that secures final drive to mount.
14. Remove right drive axle spindle nut and cotter pin.
15. Remove drive axle-to-output shaft screws and lockwashers.

NOTE: discard screws and washers. Have an assistant hold brake pedal to prevent shaft from turning.

16. Remove shaft support-to-engine bolts, and one support-to-brace screw.
17. Rotate inboard end of drive axle rearward toward starter motor.
18. Pull output shaft straight out, then lower and remove from underside of car. Proceed with engine removal procedure.
19. Lower car, install lifting bracket and chain hoist and place a wood-padded jack under the transmission pan.
20. Raise engine and pull forward to disengage transmission. Lift engine out of car.
21. To install, reverse removal procedure. See Cadillac Section for flex plate alignment.

Manifolds

Intake Manifold R & R

1. Remove the negative battery cable.
2. Remove the air cleaner, heat tube, crankcase breather, carburetor linkage, and the Cruise Control linkage.
3. Remove the coil wires and disconnect the SCS solenoid.
4. Remove the primary coil wire and then remove the distributor cap.
5. Disconnect the single connector near the ignition coil and the green wire to the temperature sender.
6. Remove the two orange wires from the downshift switch and disconnect the antidieseling solenoid.
7. Remove the ignition coil, antidieseling solenoid, and the SCS solenoid.
8. Remove the power brake vacuum hose and the vacuum modulator hose which is located at the rear of the carburetor.
9. On air-conditioned cars, disconnect the compressor clutch electrical connection. Remove the vacuum hose for the air conditioner from the rear of the carburetor.
10. Remove the fuel line from the carburetor and remove the distributor vacuum advance at the carburetor.
11. Disconnect the PCV valve and remove the 12 manifold retaining bolts.
12. Remove the manifold. Also remove the inner manifold shield and gasket and the front and rear gaskets.
13. To reassemble reverse the above procedure.

Exhaust Manifold R & R

1. If the work is to be done on the left-side manifold, remove the carburetor air cleaner and the heat duct. Remove the nuts from no. 2 and no. 6 cylinders and the heat shroud from around the manifold.
2. Remove the dipstick tube.
3. Release the eight securing screws, disconnect the manifold from the exhaust pipe, and remove the manifold.
4. Use the same procedure for removing the other side.
5. Reassembly is accomplished by reversing the above procedure.

Valve System

Checking Valve Guides

An inspection of the valve guides are made with the valves removed from the cylinder head. With the head in this condition insert a piece of 0.005 in. shim stock which is approximately 1/16 in. wide. Bend the shim and insert it into the rocker arm side of the valve guide making sure that it does not extend more than 1/4 in. into the guide. With the shim in position, attempt to insert the valve into the guide. If the valve will enter the guide, the wear is excessive. Since the guides are not replaceable, it must be oversized.

Valve Lifter Removal

Lifters may be removed without taking off the cylinder head.

Remove throttle and gas lines from the carburetor, disconnect hoses, vacuum lines and wires that pass over the rocker covers. Remove the distributor cap and disconnect the wires at the spark plugs. Remove the bolts that hold the rocker covers to the cylinder head and lift off the rocker covers leaving the spark plug wires attached to them. Remove the bolts that hold the intake manifold to the cylinder block and lift off the intake manifold. If desired, the carburetor can be detached from the manifold first, but this is not necessary. Remove the valve chamber cover plate if applicable. Remove the bolts that hold the rockers or shafts to the cylinder head and lift off the rockers. Pull up the pushrods through the holes in the cylinder heads and the lifters can be pulled up out of their bores.

Sometimes gum residue forms on the bottom of the lifter, making it very difficult to pull the lifter up out of its bore. If this condition is suspected before the job is started, put a good solvent in the engine oil and run the engine for the time specified by the manufacturer of the solvent in order to dissolve this gum.

However, even when gum is present on the bottom of the lifter body, the lifter can be pulled up out of its bore using special pliers. These pliers are designed to grip the lifter body firmly without scoring or scratching it.

If a special tool isn't available, a good substitute can be made by grinding the teeth out of an ordinary pair of pliers and grinding a circle almost the size of the valve lifter body so that when the pliers are squeezed down on the lifter body it will contact a large surface of the lifter body, thus preventing scoring.

Rocker Arm R & R and Valve Adjustment

1967-74

Valve rocker arms are no longer fitted to one common shaft per head; they are mounted in pairs (four pairs to each cylinder head). They are of the modified pedestal-mounted type.

Rocker arms may be removed in pairs and do not require cylinder-head removal.

Torque rocker arm mounting screws to 60 ft lbs.

NOTE: Do not install pre-1967 lifters in the 1967 to 1974 models.

Cylinder Head Removal

Service Note

Care must be used when replacing cylinder-head bolts. They are of different lengths.

1967

1. Disconnect the water manifold at the front of the cylinder head or heads. It is a good idea to remove the water pump and water manifold from the car. It is difficult to reinstall a cylinder head with the water pump in place on one head without damaging the water pump gasket.
2. Remove all vacuum lines and carburetor connections; disconnect all ignition, throttle and battery connections.
3. Take off the intake manifold with the carburetor in place or if desired remove the carburetor.
4. Remove the rocker covers.

NOTE: it is customary to remove the rocker covers together with the ignition wires and distributor cap as a unit unless service is to be done on the distributor.

5. Remove the alternator if the right cylinder head is to be removed. The exhaust manifolds may be disconnected either from the head or from the flange connection to the exhaust pipe. It is better to leave them connected to the head.
6. Remove the head bolts that hold the rocker assemblies to the cylinder head and lift off the rocker assemblies.
7. Remove the pushrods.
8. Remove the balance of the cylinder attaching bolts and lift the head off. It is very important that the head be handled carefully so as not to damage or mark the head gasket surface.

1968-74

1. Remove intake manifold.
2. Drain engine coolant.
3. Disconnect ground strap at rear of cylinder heads from cowl. Disconnect wiring connector for high engine temperature warning system from sending unit at rear of left cylinder head.
4. Remove alternator, if working on the right cylinder head, or partially remove the steering pump if working on the left head.
5. Disconnect AIR injection pump tubes from cylinder heads.
6. Remove clamps holding the wire harness to the cylinder heads and tie harness back out of the way.
7. Remove screws holding exhaust manifolds to cylinder heads.
8. Remove screws holding the rocker arm cover to the heads.
9. Remove the cover.
10. Remove the screws holding each rocker arm support to cylinder head, then remove rocker arm assemblies. Store these assemblies so that they may be reinstalled in their correct locations.
11. Remove pushrods and store them with their respective rocker arm assemblies.
12. Install two 7/16 x 6 in. screws to be used as lifting handles in two of the rocker arm support screw holes.
13. Remove ten cylinder-head bolts.
14. Lift cylinder head off the block.
15. Remove all gasket material from the cylinder head and block mating surfaces.

Cylinder Head Installation

The cylinder head torque for 1967–69 cars is 60 ft lbs., with 1968 being the only exception. The 1968 head torque is 100 ft lbs. Cars from 1970 to 1974 use a head bolt torque of 115 ft lbs.

When torquing the head bolts, use the three-step method. Starting from the middle of the center row of bolts and working outward (toward each end), torque the bolts to 1/3 of the total torque listed. Once this is done, repeat the same procedure, this time torquing all the bolts to 2/3 of the total listed torque. Finally torque the bolts to the recommended torque.

By using this procedure, head warping is eliminated and it ensures equal pressure on the head gasket over its entire surface.

CYLINDER HEAD BOLT TIGHTENING SEQUENCE

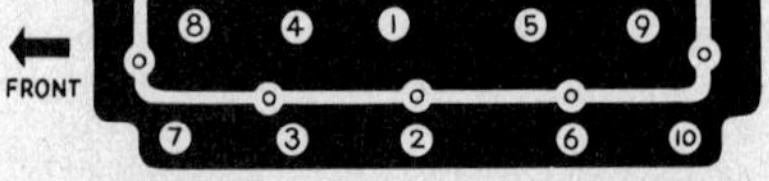
FRONT
8 4 1 5 9
7 3 2 6 10
1968-74 cylinder head bolt tightening sequence

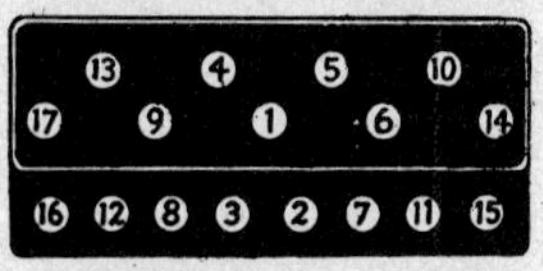
13 4 5 10
17 9 1 6 14
16 12 8 3 2 7 11 15
1967 cylinder head bolt tightening sequence

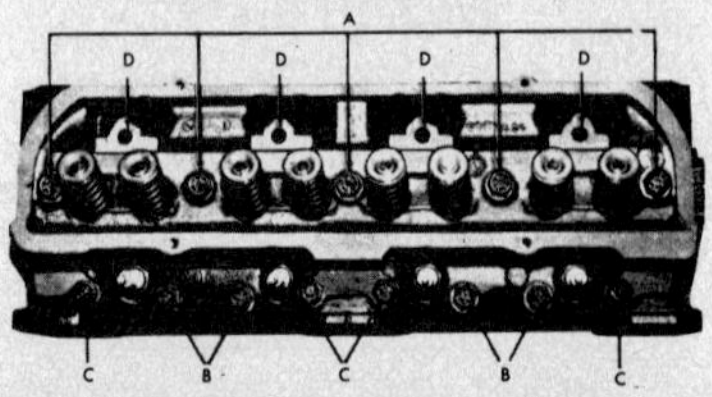
A
D D D D
C B C B C
1967 cylinder head cap screw location and length

Bolt Location	Length
A	4.06"
B	2.75"
C	3.69"
D	5.94"

See text in "Cadillac" section for 1968-74 bolt location and length

Piston and Rod Removal

Rod and piston assemblies on all models are removed through the top of the block.

It is possible to replace any and all of the rod or main bearings from underneath the car without removing the crankshaft.

Clean out carbon from top of cylinder bore and ream off the ridge at the top of the bore. This will prevent breakage of the piston ring lands. Push the piston and rod assemblies up and out of the tops of the cylinders. Be careful not to nick the lower edge of the bores and the crankshaft journals.

Piston Ring Replacement

All Cadillac pistons are equipped with two compression rings and one oil ring. When replacing the rings, use only molybdenum-filled upper compression rings and multi-piece oil rings.

There are "dimples" located on the rings near the end. These should be facing the top of the piston.

The ring gaps should be staggered 120° before installation.

Assembling Rod and Piston Assemblies to the Block

The numbers on the connecting rods face away from the camshaft; that is, the numbers on the left bank (odd numbers in 1967, even from 1968) face to the left; the numbers on the right bank (even numbers in 1967, odd from 1968) face to the right. As a double check, the word

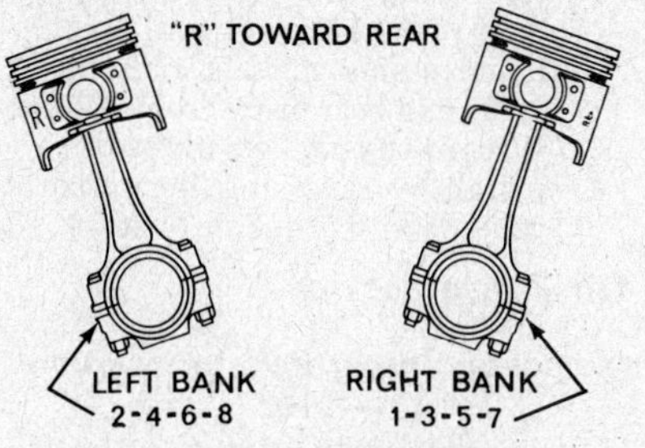
"R" TOWARD REAR
LEFT BANK
2-4-6-8
RIGHT BANK
1-3-5-7

Piston-to-connecting rod relationship —1968-74
(© Cadillac Div., G.M. Corp)

rear, (or "R"), stamped on the piston, faces the rear of the engine on both banks and an arrow on the piston top points to the front of the engine. The rod nuts are torqued to 40 ft lbs.

Rear Main Bearing Oil Seal Replacement

1. Remove the oil pan, after removing spark plug, wires and plugs.
2. Remove the rear main bearing cap and loosen the bolts holding the other four bearings about three turns each. Remove the old rear main bearing seals.
3. Clean the groove in the cap and in the block. Lubricate seals with engine oil.
4. Make an installation tool, as illustrated.
5. Start the upper half into the groove in the block with the lip facing forward and rotate it into position, using the tool as a guide. Press firmly on both ends to be sure it is protruding uniformly on each side.
6. Install the lower half of the seal into the bearing cap with the lip facing forward and one end of the seal over the ridge and flush with the split line. Hold one finger over this end to prevent it from slipping, and push the seal into seated position by applying pressure to the other end. Be sure the seal is firmly seated and protrudes evenly on each side. Do not apply pressure to the lip. This may damage the effectiveness of the seal.
7. Apply rubber cement to the mating surfaces of the block and cap being careful not to get any cement on the bearing, the crankshaft or the seal. The cement coating should be about .010 in. thick.
8. Install the bearing cap, tightening the bolts with the fingers only.
9. Move the crankshaft forward and rearward by pounding on the counterweight with a plastic hammer to assure alignment of the rear main bearing thrust surfaces.
10. Tighten the bearing bolts to 90–100 ft lbs. Be sure to tighten the bolts of the other four bearings also.
11. Reinstall the oil pan.

Timing Cover, Chain and Camshaft

Timing Cover, Chain and Sprockets R & R

1967

1. Disconnect battery.
2. Remove carburetor air cleaner.
3. Drain coolant.
4. Remove oil-pan-to-front cover nuts and studs.
5. Remove upper radiator hose.
6. Remove the cap screws that hold the fan blade assembly to the water pump and remove fan blade assembly, or hub spacer and fan on non-air conditioned cars.

NOTE: fan clutches on air-conditioned cars are to be kept in an in-car position. When removed from car for any service procedure, support assembly to keep clutch disc in a vertical plane to prevent silicone fluid from leaking.

7. Remove power steering pump belt, generator belt and pulley.
8. Remove lower radiator hose.
9. Without disconnecting hoses, remove the power steering pump and bracket. Tie back out of way.
10. Disconnect generator support bracket at the cylinder head. Tie back out of way.
11. On air-conditioned cars, partially remove compressor. Also remove compressor lower mounting bracket attached to engine front cover.
12. Remove distributor assembly.
13. Remove fuel pump as previously described.
14. Remove four of the six cap screws that hold the crankshaft pulley to the harmonic balancer.
15. Remove cork plug from end of crankshaft.
16. Install harmonic balancer puller pilot, J-21052-4 or equivalent in bore end of crankshaft.
17. Install holding base, J-21052-1 or equivalent, on front of pulley, lining up the scribe mark on base with key slot in harmonic balancer, and install four holding screws with washers finger tight. Do not use a wrench to tighten screws.
18. Thread puller screw, J-21052-2, into base until screw contacts pilot.
19. With a wrench, remove balancer from crankshaft.

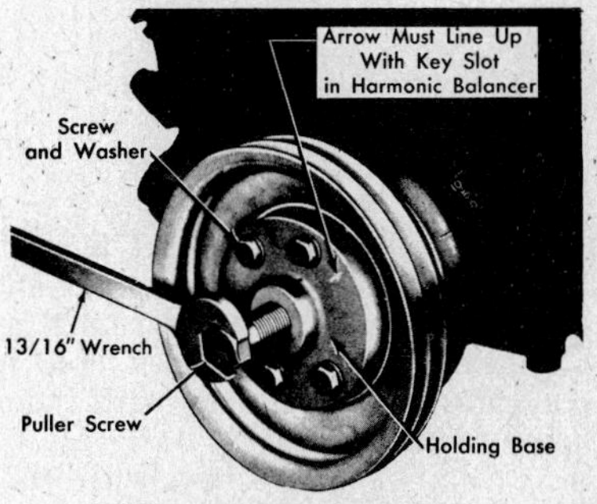
Arrow Must Line Up With Key Slot in Harmonic Balancer
Screw and Washer
13/16" Wrench
Puller Screw
Holding Base

Balancer assembly removal
(© Cadillac Div., G.M. Corp)

20. Remove pilot from end of crankshaft and remove the puller.
21. On cars with exhaust emission control systems, remove three cap screws that hold air pump front mounting bracket to engine front cover. Loosen air pump drive belt adjusting bolt and remove the belt. Swing air pump and bracket to one side.
22. Remove oil filter from oil pump cover assembly.
23. Remove four cap screws that hold the cylinder-head coolant-outlet pipe to the cylinder heads and remove outlet pipe.
24. Remove cap screw that holds fuel filter to bracket on oil filler tube.
25. Remove remaining nine cap screws that hold engine front cover to cylinder block and remove the cover with water pump attached.

26. Remove the cap screws that hold the camshaft sprocket to the camshaft.
27. Remove camshaft sprocket with chain, from camshaft.
28. Remove crankshaft sprocket from crankshaft.
29. Remove Woodruff key from crankshaft key slot.
30. Install chain and sprockets by, first seating Woodruff key in the crankshaft key slot.
31. Install crankshaft sprocket on the crankshaft in line with the keyway.
32. Install camshaft sprocket in timing chain with timing mark toward the front.
33. Place chain over crankshaft sprocket.
34. Line up timing marks on both sprockets.

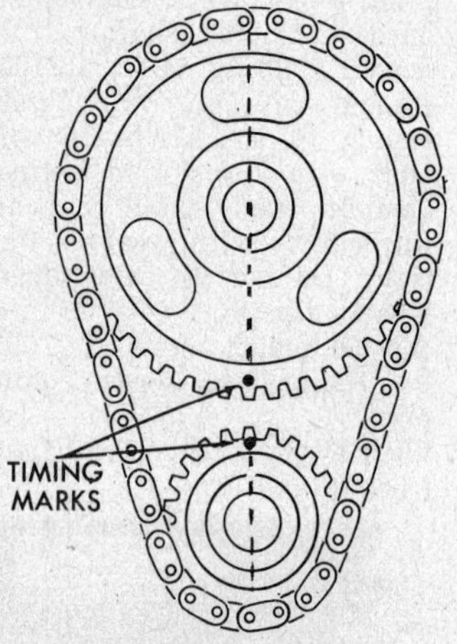
TIMING
MARKS

Timing gear location marks

35. Hold camshaft sprocket in position against end of camshaft and press sprocket on camshaft by hand, being sure index hole in camshaft is lined up with index hole in sprocket.
36. Install two cap screws with lockwashers in camshaft sprocket and torque to 18 ft. lbs.
37. Install oil seal in front cover by prying out the old seal with a thin blade and, pressing a well greased new one into place.

NOTE: it is not necessary to remove the engine front cover to replace an oil seal.

38. To install the cover, apply a small amount of gasket cement to the new front cover gasket and locate the gasket over locating dowels on cylinder block.
39. Install front cover with water pump attached, over end of crankshaft. Secure with 12 attaching screws. Refer to chart for screw locations and torque specifications.
40. Lubricate the new coolant outlet pipe to water pump O-ring seal with silicone, and install O-ring against shoulder in bore in pump body.
41. With cement on coolant outlet pipe flange surfaces, place new gaskets in position on coolant outlet pipe.
42. Install neck of coolant outlet pipe in bore in pump body, position flange surfaces against cylinder heads and install four attaching screws. Torque screws to 20 ft. lbs.
43. Install oil filter on oil pump cover assembly.
44. On cars with air-conditioning, install compressor lower mounting bracket to engine front cover. Also install compressor.
45. Install generator support bracket on coolant outlet pipe and secure with two attaching screws. Torque to 20 ft. lbs.
46. Secure fuel filter to bracket on oil filler tube with attaching screw and washer.
47. On cars with exhaust emission control system, position air pump and mounting bracket on engine front cover and secure with three attaching screws. See illustration for torque.
48. Install four pulley to harmonic balancer cap screws that were previously removed. Torque all six screws to 18 ft. lbs.
49. Lubricate bore of balancer with E.P. lubricant to prevent seizure.
50. Position balancer on the crankshaft, with key and keyway lined up.
51. Place holding base, J-21052-1, against front face of pulley and thread installer screw, J-21052-5, into end of crankshaft. Position thrust bearing with inner race forward, washer next, and installer nut, J-21052-6, last.
52. With a wrench, press harmonic balancer onto the crankshaft.
53. When balancer is in place on the crankshaft, remove the installer tool. Finish positioning the balancer all the way on the crankshaft by, threading an appropriate bolt, (a 1962 Cadillac balancer-to-crankshaft screw will do) and washer in the end of the crankshaft. Tighten screw to 125 ft. lbs.
54. Remove this screw from the crankshaft, and install cork plug.
55. Install fuel pump.
56. Install power steering pump with bracket on the cylinder block and secure with two attaching screws.
57. Connect lower radiator hose at radiator outlet and water pump inlet pipe.
58. Install pulley and fan blade assembly on water pump and secure with four attaching screws. Torque screws to 18 ft. lbs.
59. On cars equipped with exhaust emission control system, install air pump drive belt and adjust.
60. Install generator belt and adjust.
61. Install upper radiator hose.
62. Install power steering pump belt and adjust.
63. On air-conditioned cars, install compressor, and adjust belt. Install fan shroud on radiator cradle and secure with eight cap screws. Torque screws to 12 ft. lbs.
64. Install two oil pan to engine front cover studs and nuts.
65. Refill cooling system.
66. Reconnect battery.
67. Install distributor assembly and adjust timing to specifications.
68. Install carburetor air cleaner.
69. Run engine to check for coolant and oil leaks at all connections.

1968-74

The engine must be removed from the car before the front cover can be removed. The procedure is otherwise identical to that for the same year Cadillac as found in the Cadillac Section.

Camshaft R & R

See Cadillac section.

Lubrication

Oil Pan Removal

1967-74

1. Remove engine as previously described in Engine R & R.
2. Drain engine oil.
3. Remove two brackets-to-block bolts on each side of engine front mounting support.
4. Remove nuts and cap screws that hold oil pan to cylinder block and engine front cover, then remove the oil pan.
5. Remove side gaskets and rubber front and rear seals from oil pan. Discard the gaskets and seals.
6. Install by reversing the removal procedure. Torque to 10 ft lbs.

Oil Pump Service

Removal, Inspection, Installation —1967

1. Remove engine front cover, as described later, *or* pull engine from car.
2. Remove four capscrews that secure pump cover plate to housing.
3. Remove cover plate, making sure pump gears do not fall out.
4. Slide drive shaft and gear out of housing.
5. Slide driven gear out of housing.
6. Remove hex plug from pump cover plate and remove pressure regulator spring and valve.
7. Inspect gears for burrs or scoring, as well as housing.
8. Check free length of regulator spring—it should be 2.77-2.89 in.
9. Check pump clearance limits.
10. Assembly and installation is the reverse of disassembly and removal.

Removal, Inspection, Installation —1968-74

1. Jack up car and remove oil filter.
2. Remove five capscrews that secure oil pump to engine.

NOTE: remove screw nearest pressure regulator last.

3. Slide drive shaft, drive gear and driven gear out of housing.
4. Remove plug from housing cover, using 5/16 in. wrench. Remove pressure regulator valve and spring.
5. Check free length of regulator spring—it should be 2.77-2.89 in. for 1968 models, 2.57-2.69 in. from 1969 models.
6. Inspect gears and housing for burrs or scoring.
7. Check pump clearance limits.
8. Assembly, and installation is the reverse of disassembly and removal.

Oil Pump Specifications

Backlash between drive gears, 0.008-0.012 in.

Clearance between body and shaft not to exceed 0.005 in.

Clearance between body and gears not to exceed 0.005 in.

Gear end-play not to exceed 0.006 in.

AUTOMATIC TRANSMISSION

The Turbo Hydramatic transmission used on the Eldorado is a fully automatic transmission used for front wheel drive applications. It consists primarily of a three-element hydraulic torque converter, dual sprocket and link assembly, compound planetary gear set, three multiple-disc clutches, a sprag clutch, a roller clutch, two band assemblies, and an hydraulic control system.

Automatic Transmission R & R—1967-74

Removal

1. Disconnect the battery.
2. Remove the hood.
3. Remove the transmission dipstick, then remove the bolt holding the filler tube bracket to exhaust manifold and remove the filler tube. Discard the O-ring seal.
4. Remove bolts at locations A, B and C, holding the final drive case to the transmission. (See illustration).
5. Disconnect speedometer cable from the governor assembly, and unplug T.C.S. wiring if so equipped.
6. Disconnect oil cooler pipes at the transmission and at the radiator. Cap the pipes and plug connector holes in transmission and radiator.
7. Remove bolt holding the cooler pipe bracket to final drive bracket and position pipes outboard of governor assembly.
8. Remove nut at location H, holding final drive to the transmission.

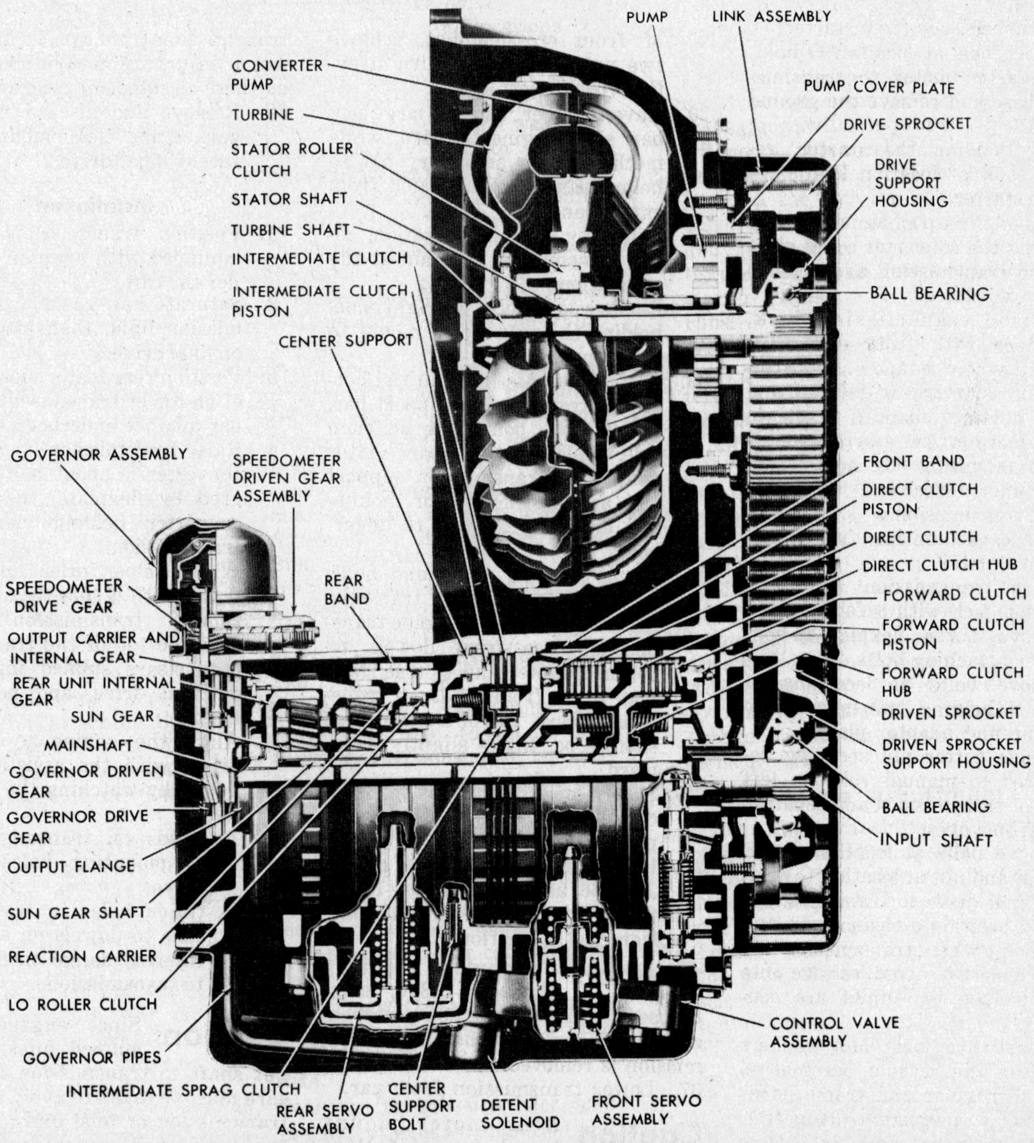
PUMP
LINK ASSEMBLY
CONVERTER PUMP
TURBINE
STATOR ROLLER CLUTCH
STATOR SHAFT
TURBINE SHAFT
INTERMEDIATE CLUTCH
INTERMEDIATE CLUTCH PISTON
CENTER SUPPORT
PUMP COVER PLATE
DRIVE SPROCKET
DRIVE SUPPORT HOUSING
BALL BEARING
GOVERNOR ASSEMBLY
SPEEDOMETER DRIVEN GEAR ASSEMBLY
SPEEDOMETER DRIVE GEAR
REAR BAND
OUTPUT CARRIER AND INTERNAL GEAR
REAR UNIT INTERNAL GEAR
SUN GEAR
MAINSHAFT
GOVERNOR DRIVEN GEAR
GOVERNOR DRIVE GEAR
OUTPUT FLANGE
SUN GEAR SHAFT
REACTION CARRIER
LO ROLLER CLUTCH
GOVERNOR PIPES
INTERMEDIATE SPRAG CLUTCH
REAR SERVO ASSEMBLY
CENTER SUPPORT BOLT
DETENT SOLENOID
FRONT SERVO ASSEMBLY
CONTROL VALVE ASSEMBLY
FRONT BAND
DIRECT CLUTCH PISTON
DIRECT CLUTCH
DIRECT CLUTCH HUB
FORWARD CLUTCH
FORWARD CLUTCH PISTON
FORWARD CLUTCH HUB
DRIVEN SPROCKET
DRIVEN SPROCKET SUPPORT HOUSING
BALL BEARING
INPUT SHAFT

Turbo-Hydramatic transmission components (© Cadillac Div., G.M. Corp)

stall washers and three spider leg balls, one at a time as a unit on the spider.

NOTE: when installing leg balls, use the leg ball washers as retainers for the spider rollers.

13. Pack inside of seal with special drive axle joint lubricant until the folds of the seal are full.
14. Pack housing with special drive axle joint lubricant and install by sliding housing over spider leg balls.
15. Position seal adapter over lip on joint housing and stake with blunt chisel.
16. Seat seal in groove on axle shaft, and secure keystone clamps.

JACKING, HOISTING

When jacking the front of the vehicle, make certain that the jack is placed so that it contacts the lower suspension arm just inside the stabilizer bar. If the vehicle is lifted from the rear, place the jack as far in to the middle of the frame as possible so that the Automatic Level Control and the fuel and brake lines are not damaged.

Ideally, the best lift is one which contacts both the front and rear suspension at the same time.

Caution The rear lower control arm should never be used as a lift point for the vehicle.

When working on the vehicle in the raised position, it is recommended that two jackstands be placed under the front frame cross member. Also, the vehicle should never be supported at the very ends of the frame with anything other than the jack provided with the car.

DIFFERENTIAL

Planetary-Type

1967

This type differential replaces the conventional spider and beveled axle drive pinions with a planetary gear set to distribute torque to the respective drive axles.

Engine torque is transmitted from the power train, to the main drive pinion and ring gear, to the differential housing. Torque is then applied through the planetary and sun gear mechanism to both drive axles at variable speed requirements.

While the car is moving straight ahead, the planetary gears are fixed and rotate with the differential case and ring gear as a unit. However, when turning, the planetary gears revolve upon their individual axles with differential action, allowing the drive axles to rotate at different speeds.

This unit is not a controlled or limited slip differential. The unit normally is serviced as an assembly with the exception of the various seals.

Bevel Gear-Type

Beginning 1968

Since 1968, a bevel gear-type differential is used on all front wheel drive models. This design supersedes the original planetary-type final

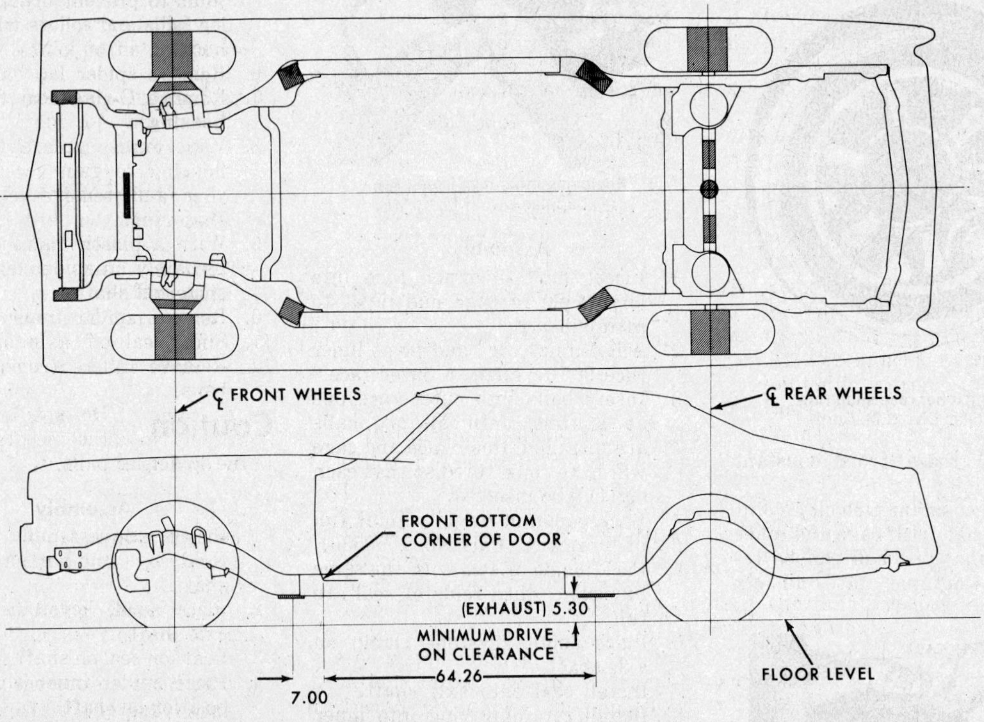
℄ FRONT WHEELS
℄ REAR WHEELS
FRONT BOTTOM
CORNER OF DOOR
(EXHAUST) 5.30
MINIMUM DRIVE
ON CLEARANCE
64.26
7.00
FLOOR LEVEL

Lift points

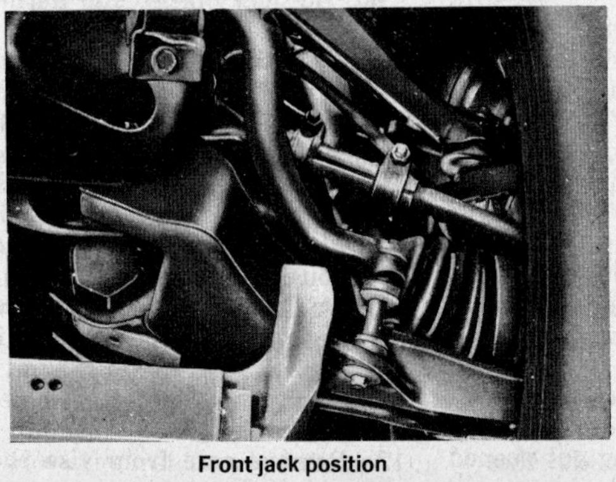

Front jack position

Rear jack position

Removal, Inspection, Installation —1968-74

1. Jack up car and remove oil filter.
2. Remove five capscrews that secure oil pump to engine.

NOTE: remove screw nearest pressure regulator last.

3. Slide drive shaft, drive gear and driven gear out of housing.
4. Remove plug from housing cover, using 5/16 in. wrench. Remove pressure regulator valve and spring.
5. Check free length of regulator spring—it should be 2.77-2.89 in. for 1968 models, 2.57-2.69 in. from 1969 models.
6. Inspect gears and housing for burrs or scoring.
7. Check pump clearance limits.
8. Assembly, and installation is the reverse of disassembly and removal.

Oil Pump Specifications

Backlash between drive gears, 0.008-0.012 in.

Clearance between body and shaft not to exceed 0.005 in.

Clearance between body and gears not to exceed 0.005 in.

Gear end-play not to exceed 0.006 in.

AUTOMATIC TRANSMISSION

The Turbo Hydramatic transmission used on the Eldorado is a fully automatic transmission used for front wheel drive applications. It consists primarily of a three-element hydraulic torque converter, dual sprocket and link assembly, compound planetary gear set, three multiple-disc clutches, a sprag clutch, a roller clutch, two band assemblies, and an hydraulic control system.

Automatic Transmission R & R—1967-74

Removal

1. Disconnect the battery.
2. Remove the hood.
3. Remove the transmission dipstick, then remove the bolt holding the filler tube bracket to exhaust manifold and remove the filler tube. Discard the O-ring seal.
4. Remove bolts at locations A, B and C, holding the final drive case to the transmission. (See illustration).
5. Disconnect speedometer cable from the governor assembly, and unplug T.C.S. wiring if so equipped.
6. Disconnect oil cooler pipes at the transmission and at the radiator. Cap the pipes and plug connector holes in transmission and radiator.
7. Remove bolt holding the cooler pipe bracket to final drive bracket and position pipes outboard of governor assembly.
8. Remove nut at location H, holding final drive to the transmission.

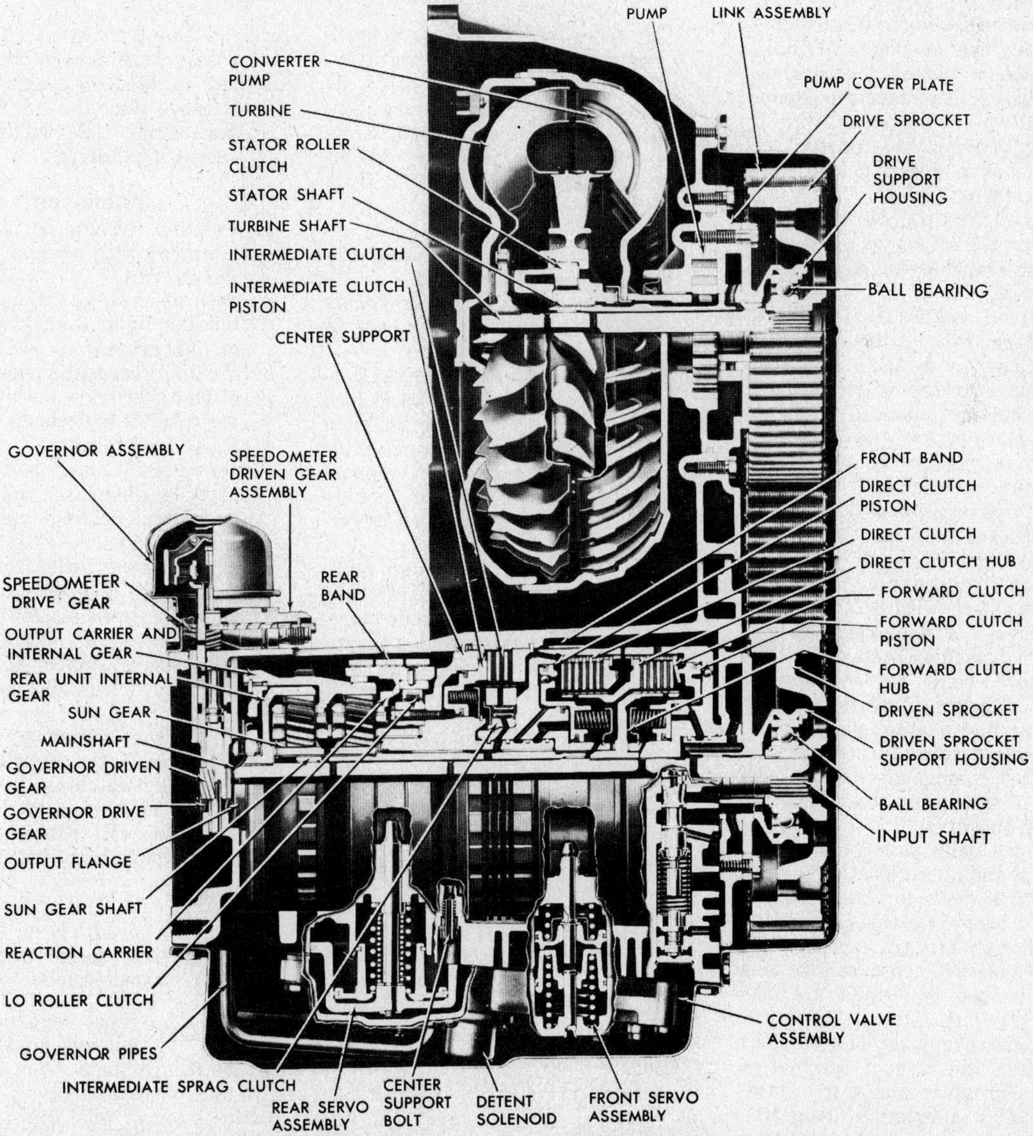
PUMP
LINK ASSEMBLY
CONVERTER PUMP
PUMP COVER PLATE
TURBINE
DRIVE SPROCKET
STATOR ROLLER CLUTCH
DRIVE SUPPORT HOUSING
STATOR SHAFT
TURBINE SHAFT
INTERMEDIATE CLUTCH
BALL BEARING
INTERMEDIATE CLUTCH PISTON
CENTER SUPPORT
GOVERNOR ASSEMBLY
SPEEDOMETER DRIVEN GEAR ASSEMBLY
FRONT BAND
DIRECT CLUTCH PISTON
DIRECT CLUTCH
DIRECT CLUTCH HUB
SPEEDOMETER DRIVE GEAR
REAR BAND
FORWARD CLUTCH
OUTPUT CARRIER AND INTERNAL GEAR
FORWARD CLUTCH PISTON
REAR UNIT INTERNAL GEAR
FORWARD CLUTCH HUB
SUN GEAR
DRIVEN SPROCKET
MAINSHAFT
DRIVEN SPROCKET SUPPORT HOUSING
GOVERNOR DRIVEN GEAR
BALL BEARING
GOVERNOR DRIVE GEAR
INPUT SHAFT
OUTPUT FLANGE
SUN GEAR SHAFT
REACTION CARRIER
LO ROLLER CLUTCH
CONTROL VALVE ASSEMBLY
GOVERNOR PIPES
INTERMEDIATE SPRAG CLUTCH
CENTER SUPPORT BOLT
REAR SERVO ASSEMBLY
DETENT SOLENOID
FRONT SERVO ASSEMBLY

Turbo-Hydramatic transmission components (© Cadillac Div., G.M. Corp)

9. Remove bolts at locations I, J, K and L, holding transmission to engine and adapter plate.
10. Remove upper left bolt holding rear motor mount bracket to the transmission.
11. Remove bolt holding the ground strap to left side of cowl. Remove ground strap.
12. Remove upper left bolt holding converter cover plate to transmission, (use 7/16 in. socket with universal and extension to reach underneath the left exhaust manifold).

NOTE: loosen two screws holding A.L.C. compressor and position compressor out of the way.

13. Position cable with looped ends under engine intake manifold and hook looped ends to chain fall and cable, putting engine mounts under tension.
14. Position safety chain over top of transmission.
15. Raise car and place on jack stands, adjusting chain fall as necessary.
16. Disconnect leads from starter.
17. Remove bolt at location O holding starter motor to transmission case and remove the ground strap.
18. While holding the starter, remove bolt at location P and remove starter.
19. Remove three remaining screws holding the converter cover plate to the transmission and remove the cover plate.
20. Position transmission jack, equipped with front end drive transmission adapter plate to transmission and install nut and bolt holding adapter brace to transmission at starter motor lower mounting bolt hole.
21. Disconnect electrical connector from transmission.
22. Remove vacuum line from vacuum modulator.
23. Secure transmission to transmission jack with safety chain.
24. Remove three flexplate-to-converter attaching bolts.
25. Remove bolts at locations M and N holding transmission to engine and adapter plate.
26. Remove cotter pin securing relay rod to manual yoke on left side of transmission and separate rod from yoke.
27. Remove bolts at locations D, E and F and nut at location G holding final drive to transmission.

NOTE: position a clean drain pan under a point where transmission and final drive meet to avoid leakage onto floor when the two units are separated.

28. Remove five bolts and washers holding the rear of acromat to front crossbar and frame horns and allow acromat to hang free.
29. Through access holes in bottom of front crossmember, remove two nuts and studs. Turn steering wheel to left lock.

L
K
M
J
N
I
A
H
B
O
G
C
P
D
F
E

Transmission attaching bolt location 1967-74
(© Cadillac Div., G.M. Corp)

30. Have a helper, using a large pry bar, shift engine forward, while mechanic uses small pry bar to help separate transmission from engine and final drive.
31. Following initial separation, allow transmission to drain at the separation.
32. Remove two bolts on right side, holding the rear motor mount to the transmission.
33. Through access holes in the bottom of transmission support bar, remove two bolts, one on each side, holding the rear motor mounts to transmission support bar, and position motor mounts and bracket rearward to underbody.
34. While a helper pries and holds engine forward, move transmission rearward to disengage transmission case from dowels on engine adapter and to disengage final drive from studs on transmission case. Top of transmission should be tilted slightly rearward.
35. Slowly lower transmission, until converter is about half-way exposed from flexplate.
36. Install converter holding clamp, J-21366, using a 5/16 in.—18 nut to hold clamp screw to transmission case at location N.

Caution Converter holding clamp, J-21366, must be used to prevent the converter becoming disengaged when the transmission is removed.

37. Lower transmission from car.

Caution Rear motor mount bracket will follow transmission from car. To avoid damage or injury, remove bracket as soon as there is sufficient clearance.

38. Remove and discard final drive gasket and clean mounting surface of final drive.

Installation

1. Position transmission on jack, equipped with adapter plate, under the car.
2. Saturate new gasket with transmission fluid, then place gasket on final drive.
3. Position rear motor mount bracket on top of transmission support bar against underbody.
4. Raise transmission in place until converter is about half-way covered by flexplate, then remove converter holding clamp from transmission.
5. While helper pries engine forward with a pry bar, continue raising transmission, making sure the top of the transmission case clears splined input shaft of final drive, and position to engine.
6. Align the engine to the final drive, with the assistance of a helper by watching the following items:
   A. Studs on transmission case to mounting holes in final drive.
   B. Guide holes in transmission case to dowels on adapter.
   C. Internal flange on final drive to transmission.

Caution Since engagement of splined final drive input shaft to transmission is hidden, care must be taken to avoid damaging transmission or final drive assembly.

   D. To help engagement of final

drive splines, rotate one front wheel while helper holds the other.

NOTE: when alignment is complete and correct, the gap between the final drive and transmission should not exceed 1/4 in.

7. Loosely install bolts at locations D and F attaching transmission to final drive and bolt at location N attaching transmission to engine through adapter, alternately tightening bolts to avoid cocking the transmission. Do not torque bolts.
8. Working in the engine compartment, loosely install bolt at location J attaching transmission to adapter. Do not torque at this time.
9. Install bolt at location M holding transmission to adapter plate. Do not torque.
10. Position rear motor mount bracket to transmission and loosely install three bolts holding bracket to transmission.

NOTE: upper left bolt is installed from engine compartment.

11. Position rear engine mounts and bracket to transmission support bar, and loosely install bolts through access holes in bottom of bar, attaching mounts to bar.
12. Reposition engine assembly, as necessary, and install left bolt securing front motor mount to front cross bar. Torque front motor mount bolts to 30 ft. lbs.
13. Separate safety chain, remove nut and bolt securing jack adapter plate to transmission case and remove jack.
14. Torque the following bolts as specified:
    A. Rear engine mounts to transmission support bar, 55 ft. lbs.
    B. Rear engine mounts to transmission (two on right side), 55 ft. lbs.
    C. Transmission to adapter to engine, 30 ft. lbs.
    D. Transmission to adapter (location M), 30 ft. lbs.

Caution The following procedure for attaching the converter to the flexplate must be strictly followed to prevent improper installation and damage to flexplate and transmission.

15. Rotate converter until two of the three weld nuts on the converter line up with two of the three bolt holes in the flexplate. Position converter so that weld nuts are flush with flexplate. Be sure converter is not cocked and that pilot in center of converter is properly seated in crankshaft.
16. Install two flexplate to converter attaching bolts through access holes in flexplate and torque to 28 ft. lbs.

NOTE: bolts must be tightened at this time to assure proper alignment of converter.

17. Rotate flexplate and converter until third bolt hole is accessible. Install third bolt and torque to 28 ft. lbs.
18. Install vacuum hose on vacuum modulator assembly.
19. Install electrical connector to transmission connector.
20. Position converter cover plate to transmission case and install two lower and one upper right bolts holding the cover plate to the transmission. Torque to 5 ft. lbs.
21. Position the starter to the transmission case and install bolt at P position.
22. Position ground strap to transmission and install bolt holding the ground strap and starter to the transmission at location O. Torque bolts at locations O and P to 25 ft. lbs.
23. Install leads to starter motor.
24. Install bolts at locations C and E and a nut at G holding transmission to final drive.
25. Torque bolts at locations C through F to 25 ft. lbs.
26. Position acromat to front cross bar and frame horns and install five retaining bolts and washers.
27. Position relay rod to manual yoke and secure with a cotter pin.
28. Check operation of manual linkage and adjust, if necessary.
29. Disconnect chain fall and lower the car.
30. Remove cable from intake manifold and safety chain from transmission.
31. Install bolts at locations A and B and nut at location H holding transmission to final drive. Torque bolts to 25 ft. lbs.
32. Install upper left bolt holding converter cover plate to transmission in the manner described for removing it, the reversal of Step 12.
33. Install bolts at locations I, K and L, holding transmission to engine and adapter.
34. Torque bolts at locations I, J, K and L to 25 ft. lbs.
35. Tighten brass cooler pipe connectors at case to 28 ft. lbs. Clean connections and connect cooler pipes at transmission, using cooler pipe wrench J-21477. Torque to 28 ft. lbs.
36. Connect oil cooler pipes to radiator with the same wrench. Torque to 40 ft. lbs.
37. Install cooler pipe clamp.
38. Install speedometer cable to governor.
39. Install new O-ring on transmission filler tube and install filler tube through hole in final drive case.
40. Position transmission filler tube bracket to exhaust manifold and install retaining bolt.
41. Install body ground strap to firewall and secure it with a nut.
42. Connect battery.
43. Bring transmission to fluid level. Bring engine to operating temperature, then recheck fluid level.
44. Thoroughly check entire power train for oil and coolant leaks.
45. Install and align hood assembly.

Neutral Safety Switch, All Models

NOTE: switch is on steering column under dash.

Removal

1. Position the gear selector in the Neutral positon.
2. Release the clamp and remove the switch without moving the contact carrier. The position of the carrier should be marked.
3. Remove the vacuum hoses after they have been marked and disconnect the two wires from the switch.
4. Installation is accomplished by reversing the above procedure.

Adjustment

1. Check that the gear lever is correctly adjusted and that the neutral safety switch is properly positioned by this check.
2. Set the handbrake. Put the hand lever on the steering column in drive. Hold the ignition key on and slowly move the hand lever toward Neutral or Park until the starter cranks and the engine runs.
3. Without moving the lever farther, press the accelerator to determine whether the transmission is really in Neutral or Park.
4. If all is correct, the engine will have started when the hand lever got to the neutral position and the transmission will not be in gear. Also, back-up lights will go on with transmission in Reverse.

NOTE: a vacuum leak that can be corrected by moving shift lever is an indication that the switch only needs adjustment and is not defective.

5. Adjust the neutral safety switch by turning it and its mounting bracket until the above conditions are met.

Manual Linkage Adjustment

1. Place the transmission shift valve into the Park position and then move the relay rod to the Neutral step which is the third one in the downward position.
2. Loosen the adjusting screw on the relay lever and place the selector lever in the Neutral detent position.
3. Tighten the relay rod adjusting screw with the shift lever held against the neutral stop.
4. Check the adjustment by:
    a. Moving the selector lever to

the Neutral detent making sure that the lever fits securely into the notch on the steering column.

b. Move the lever to Drive. Make sure that the lever is secure in this gear. Move the lever to Reverse and check for gear security.

Caution When the linkage is adjusted check the operation of the Neutral Safety Switch, parking brake release and the back-up lights.

Kickdown Adjustment

1. Remove the air cleaner.
2. Make certain that the idle speed is set correctly and that the carburetor is operating on the low-speed circuit.
3. Loosen the switch mounting screws and insert a 0.094 in. wire gauge into the hole in the lower wire terminal.
4. With the gauge in place, adjust the position of the switch so that the lever just touches the carburetor adaptor plate arm. The switch should make contact above 60° of throttle opening.
5. After adjusting, tighten the mounting screws and remove the gauge.
6. Reinstall the air cleaner.

Drive Sprocket

If it should be necessary to replace either the drive sprocket, chain, or driven sprocket, the three unit combination must be replaced as a set. They are matched and are not to be serviced separately.

Removal

1. Remove 18 cover housing attaching bolts.
2. Remove cover housing and gasket. Discard the gasket.

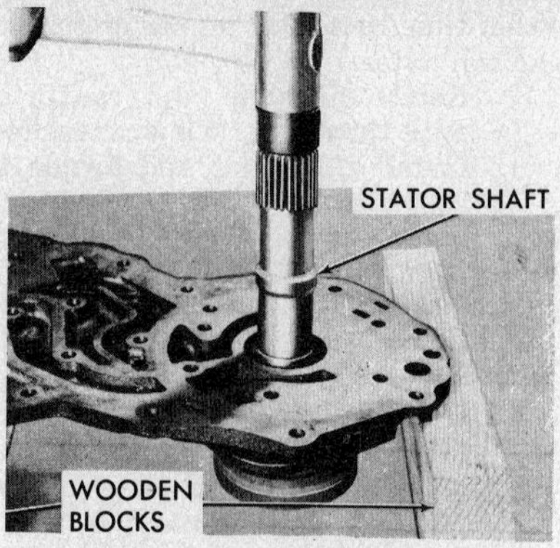
STATOR SHAFT
WOODEN BLOCKS

Removing drive sprocket support

NOTE: do not remove snap-rings from beneath the sprockets. Leave them in a loose position between the sprockets and the bearing assemblies.

4. Remove drive and driven sprockets, link assemblies, bearings and shaft simultaneously by alternately pulling upward on the drive and driven sprockets until the bearings are out of the drive and driven support housings.

NOTE: it may be necessary to pry up on the sprockets. Use care.

1/8 INCH MASONITE

Removing tight sprockets

7. Inspect drive and driven sprocket bearing assemblies for rough or defective bearings.

NOTE: do not remove bearing assemblies from drive or driven sprockets unless they need replacement.

8. If removal of bearing assembly from drive and/or driven sprockets is necessary, proceed as follows:
   A. Remove sprocket to bearing assembly retaining snap-ring using tool J-5589, snap-ring pliers.
   B. Mount sprocket with turbine or input shaft placed in hole in work bench on two 2 x 4 x 10 in. pieces of wood.
   C. With a hammer and brass rod, drive the inner race alternately through each of the access openings until the bearing assembly is removed from the sprocket hub. Drive the sprocket, and turbine shaft and link assembly.

Inspection

1. Inspect drive sprocket teeth for nicks, burrs, scoring, gauling and excessive wear.
2. Inspect drive sprocket to ball bearing retaining snap-ring for damage.
3. Inspect drive sprocket ball bearing inner race mounting surface for damage.
4. Inspect turbine shaft for open lubrication passages. Run a tag wire through the passages to be sure they are open.
5. Inspect spline for damage.
6. Inspect the ground bushing journals for damage.
7. Inspect the two hook-type oil seal grooves for damage or excessive wear.
8. Inspect the turbine shaft for cracks or distortion.

J-4646

Removing sprocket snap-ring

DRIVE SPROCKET
DRIVEN SPROCKET
LINK BELT

Removing sprockets and link assembly

3. Install J-4646 snap-ring pliers into sprocket bearing retaining snap-rings located under the drive and driven sprockets and remove snap-rings from retaining grooves in support housings.

Caution Do not pry on the guide links or the aluminum case. Pry only on the sprockets.

5. Remove link assembly from drive and driven sprockets.
6. Remove two hook type oil seal rings from turbine shaft.

9. Inspect the link assembly for damage or loose links.

NOTE: take particular notice of the guide links. They are the wide outside links on each side of the link assembly.

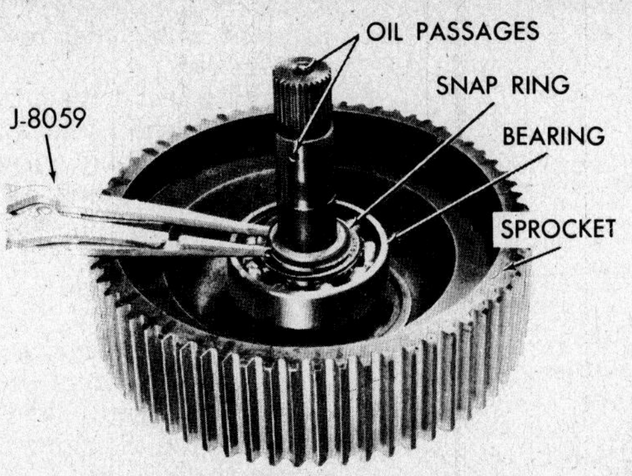
OIL PASSAGES
SNAP RING
J-8059
BEARING
SPROCKET

Removing sprocket bearing snap-ring

THICKNESS	COLOR
.060-.064	Yellow
.071-.075	Blue
.082-.086	Red
.093-.097	Brown
.104-.108	Green
.115-.119	Black
.126-.130	Purple

NOTE: An oil soaked washer may tend to discolor so that it will be necessary to measure the washer with a set of one inch micrometers to determine its actual thickness.

Selective thrust washer chart—Eldorado
(© Cadillac Div., G.M. Corp)

Driven Sprocket at Input Shaft

Inspection

1. Inspect driven sprocket teeth for nicks, burrs, scoring, gauling and excessive wear.
2. Inspect sprocket to ball bearing retaining snap-ring for damage.
3. Inspect ball bearing inner race mounting surface for damage.
4. Inspect input shaft for open lubrication holes. Run a tag wire through the holes to be sure they are open.
5. Inspect spline for damage.
6. Inspect ground bushing journals for damage.

Sprocket Bearings

Installation

1. Turn sprocket so that turbine or input shaft is pointing upward.
2. Install new sprocket bearing as follows:
   A. Install snap-ring, letter side down on shaft.
   B. Assemble bearing assembly on turbine or input shaft.
   C. Using tool, J-6133-A, drive the bearing assembly onto the hub of the sprocket until it is resting on the bearing seat of the sprocket.
   D. Install sprocket to bearing assembly retaining snap-ring into groove sprocket hub.
3. Install two hook-type oil seal rings on turbine shaft.

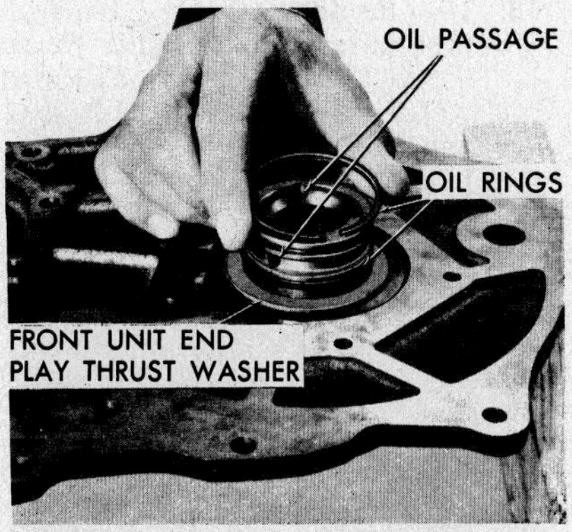
OIL PASSAGE
OIL RINGS
FRONT UNIT END
PLAY THRUST WASHER

Installing oil rings on driven sprocket support

USE BOLTS FOR
GUIDE PINS
WOODEN BLOCKS

Installing driven sprocket support

Front Unit End-Play Check

Make front unit end-play check as follows:

A. Install front unit end-play checking tool J-22241 into driven sprocket housing so that the urethane on the tool can engage the splines and the forward clutch housing. Let the tool bottom on the main shaft and then withdraw it approximately 1/16-1/8 in.

B. Remove two of the 5/16—18 bolts from the driven support housing.

C. Install 5/16—18 threaded hammer bolt with jam nut into one bolt hole in driven support housing.

NOTE: do not thread slide hammer bolt deep enough to interfere with forward clutch travel.

D. Mount dial indicator on rod and index indicator to register with the forward clutch drum that can be reached through second bolt removed from driven support housing.

E. Push end-play tool down to remove slack.

F. Push and hold output flange outward. Place a screwdriver in case opening at parking area and push upward on output carrier.

G. Place another screwdriver between the metal lip of the end-play tool and the drive sprocket housing. Now push upward on the metal lip of the end-play tool and read the resulting end-play. This should be between .003-.024 in. The selective washer controlling this end play is the phenolic thrust washer located between the driven support housing and the forward clutch housing. If more or less washer thickness is required to bring the end-play within specifications, select the proper washer from the chart.

U-JOINTS

See Drive Axle.

DRIVE AXLES

Drive axles are a complete flexible assembly and consist of an axle shaft and an inner tri-pot joint and outer constant velocity joint. The inner tri-pot joint has complete flexibility, plus inward and outward movement. The outer constant velocity joint has complete flexibility at the angle of operation.

Drive Axle—Right Side

Removal—1967-68

1. Hoist car under lower control arms.

NOTE: battery should be disconnected.

2. Remove drive axle, cotter pin, nut and washer.
3. Using a wood-padded hammer, tap on end of drive axle to unseat axle at hub assembly.

NOTE: install a piece of rubber hose over torsion bar connector at lower control arm to prevent *seal* damage.

4. Remove inner constant velocity joint attaching bolts.

NOTE: on 1967-68 models, disconnect tie-rod end at steering knuckle and disconnect upper ball joint before proceeding to Step 5.

5. Slide drive axle inward and disengage outer joint from steering knuckle.
6. Rotate axle toward rear of car and guide it down and out.

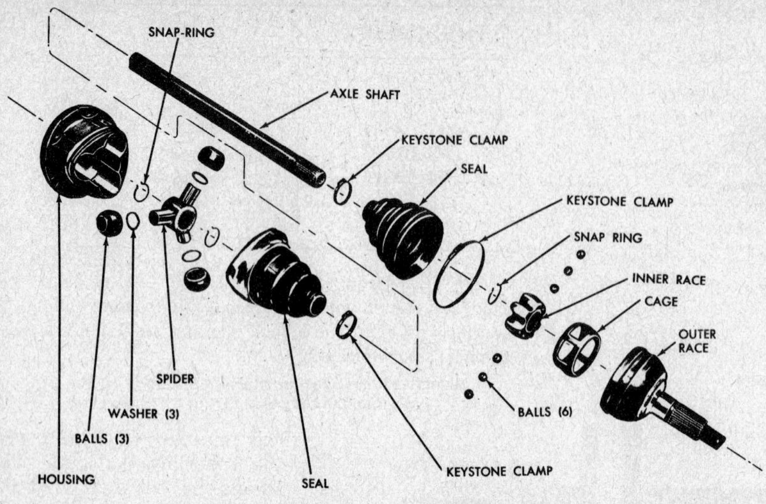
SNAP-RING
AXLE SHAFT
KEYSTONE CLAMP
SEAL
KEYSTONE CLAMP
SNAP RING
INNER RACE
CAGE
OUTER RACE
SPIDER
WASHER (3)
BALLS (3)
HOUSING
SEAL
BALLS (6)
KEYSTONE CLAMP
Drive axle exploded view
(© Cadillac Div., G.M. Corp)

Removal—1969-1971

1. Follow Steps 1-4 of 1967-68 procedure.
2. Remove two output shaft support-to-engine bolts and one support-to-brace screw.
3. Rotate inboard end of axle rearward toward starter motor.
4. Slide output shaft straight out and remove.
5. Rotate drive axle inboard and toward front of car, guiding over front crossmember.

Removal 1972-1974

1. Remove the negative battery cable and the wheel disc.
2. If the drive axle is to be removed, release the cotter pin and loosen but do not remove the spindle nut.
3. Raise the car at the lower control arms.
4. Loosen but do not remove the right front shock absorber lower mounting nut. Then pry the shock absorber along the lower mounting stud until it reaches the nut. Do not remove the shock absorber from the lower mount.
5. To keep the torsion bar connectors from being damaged, cover them with a short length of rubber hose.
6. Remove the screws securing the drive axle to the output shaft.
7. Position the inside end of the drive axle toward the starter motor to gain access to the output shaft. Then remove the screw which supports the output shaft to the final drive housing.
8. Remove the two screws which support the right output shaft support to the engine.
9. Remove the output shaft, support, and strut as an assembly in the following manner.
   a. Slide the output shaft outward to disengage the splines.
   b. Move the inside end of the assembly forward and downward until it is clear of the car.
10. If the drive axle is to be removed, use the following procedure.
    a. Using a hammer and a wooden block tap the end of the drive axle to unseat the axle at the hub.

NOTE: The spindle nut should be loosened but not removed.

    b. Rotate the axle inward and toward the front of the car positioning the axle over the front crossmember and out from under the car.

Caution Care must be exercised so that constant velocity joints do not turn to full extremes, and that seals are not damaged against shock absorber or stabilizer bar.

Installation—1967-68

1. Guide drive axle into position from underneath car. Lift it and slide it over lower control arm.
2. Insert splines into steering knuckle.
3. Reattach upper ball joint, not forgetting brake line clip. Tighten stud nut to 40 ft. lbs. and install cotter pin.
4. Attach brake line clip to frame.
5. Install six drive axle-to-output shaft screws and tighten to 65 ft. lbs.
6. Install washer and drive axle nut.
7. Remove protective piece of rubber hose from torsion bar connector.
8. Install wheel and tire.
9. Lower car to ground and tighten lug nuts to 105 ft. lbs. and drive axle nut to 105-110 ft. lbs.
10. Connect battery.

Installation—1969-74

1. Carefully place right-hand drive axle assembly into lower control arm and enter outer race splines into knuckle.
2. Lubricate final drive output shaft seal, with wheel bearing grease.
3. Install right-hand output shaft into final drive and attach the support bolts to engine and brakes. Torque the bolts to 50 ft. lbs. (1969 and later).
4. Install brace.
5. Move right-hand drive axle assembly toward front of car and align with right-hand output shaft. Install attaching bolts and torque to 65 ft. lbs.
6. Install washer and nut on drive axle.
7. Remove floor stands and lower hoist.
8. Tighten wheel lugs to 105 ft. lbs. and drive axle nut to 105–110 ft, lbs., 1972 to 150 ft lbs. Install cotter pin.

Drive Axle—Left Side

Removal and Installation —1967-74

1. Hoist car under lower control arms.
2. Remove wheel and tire.
3. Remove drive axle cotter pin, nut and washer.
4. Install a piece of rubber hose over lower control arm torsion bar connector.
5. Remove six drive axle-to-output shaft screws and washers.
6. Loosen upper shock mounting bolt. Disconnect stabilizer bar link up to 1970.
7. Remove upper control arm ball joint cotter pin and nut.
8. Using hammer and brass drift, drive on knuckle until upper ball joint stud is free.
9. Remove brake hose bracket from frame.
10. Tip upper part of knuckle and support outward so that brake hose is not damaged.
11. Carefully guide drive axle assembly outboard.

NOTE: care must be exercised so that constant velocity joints do not turn to full extremes and that seals are not damaged against shock absorber or stabilizer bar.

12. To install, reverse removal procedure. Tighten upper shock bolt to 75 ft. lbs., drive axle and wheel lug nuts to 105-110 ft. lbs., and output shaft-to-axle screws to 65 ft. lbs.

Constant Velocity Joint (Out of Car)

The constant velocity joints are to be replaced as a unit and are only disassembled for repacking and replacement of seals.

Outer C.V. Joint Disassembly

1. Insert axle assembly in vise. Hold by the mid-portion of the axle shaft.

2. Remove inner and outer seal clamps.
3. Slide seal down axle shaft to gain access to C. V. joint.
4. Using snap-ring pliers, spread retaining ring until C. V. joint can be removed from axle spline.
5. Remove retaining ring.

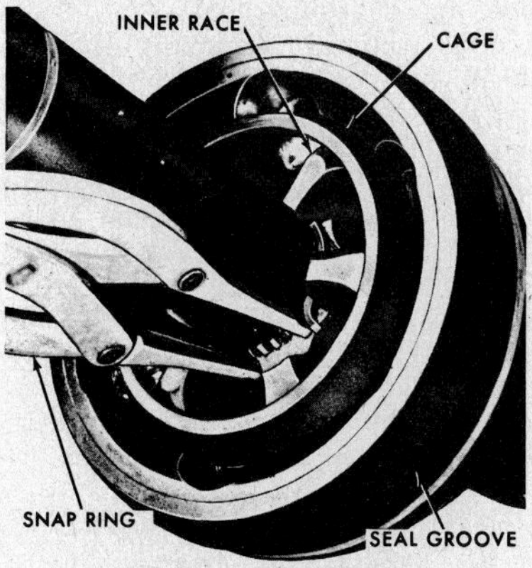
INNER RACE
CAGE
SNAP RING
SEAL GROOVE

Removing outer axle joint
(© Cadillac Div., G.M. Corp)

6. Slide seal from axle shaft.

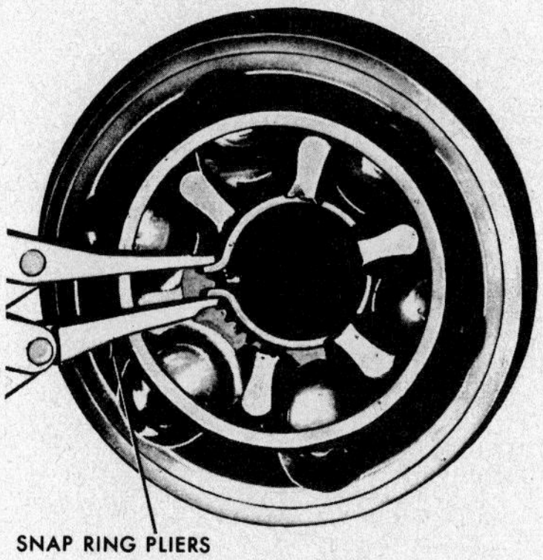
SNAP RING PLIERS

Removing inner race snap-ring
(© Cadillac Div., G.M. Corp)

7. Remove grease from constant velocity joint.
8. Holding constant velocity joint with one hand, tilt cage and inner race so that one ball can be removed. Continue until all six balls are removed.

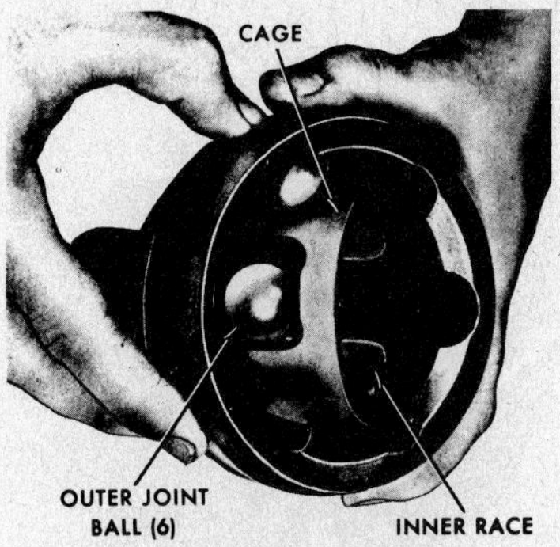
CAGE
OUTER JOINT BALL (6)
INNER RACE

Removing balls from outer joint
(© Cadillac Div., G.M. Corp)

9. Turn cage 90° and with large slot in cage aligned with land in outer race, lift out.

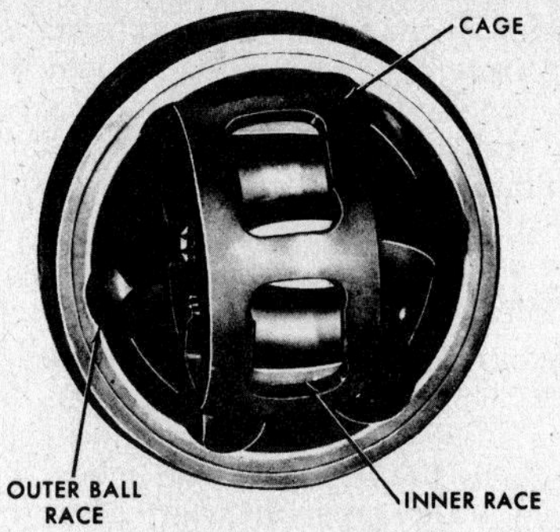
CAGE
OUTER BALL RACE
INNER RACE

Removing cage and inner race
(© Cadillac Div., G.M. Corp)

10. With cage and inner race assembly, turn inner race 90° to align with large hole in cage. Lift land on inner race up through large hole in cage and turn up and out to separate parts.

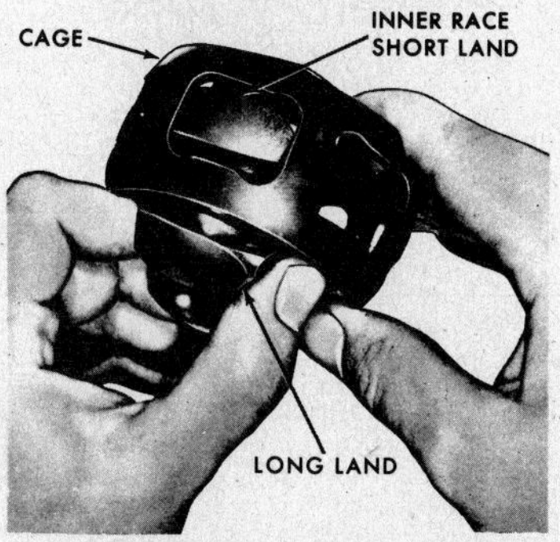
CAGE
INNER RACE SHORT LAND
LONG LAND

Removing inner race from cage
(© Cadillac Div., G.M. Corp)

Assembly

1. Insert land of inner race into large hole in cage and pivot to install in cage.
2. Align inner race and pivot inner race 90° to align in outer race.
3. Insert balls into outer race one at a time until all six balls are installed. Inner race and cage will have to be tilted so that each ball can be inserted.
4. Pack constant velocity joint full of lubricant (Part No. 1050530).
5. Pack inside of seal with the same lubricant, until folds of seal are full.
6. Place small keystone clamp on axle shaft.
7. Install seal onto axle shaft.
8. Install retaining ring into inner race.
9. Insert axle shaft into splines of outer constant velocity joint until retaining ring secures shaft.
10. Position seal in slot of outer race.
11. Install large keystone clamp over seal and secure.

Inner Tri-pot Joint Disassembly

1. Insert axle assembly in vise. Clamp on mid-portion of axle shaft.
2. Remove small seal clamp.
3. Remove large end of seal from C. V. joint by prying out peened

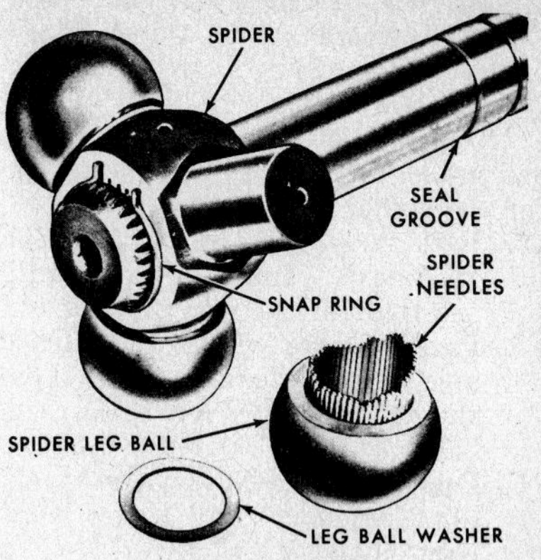
SPIDER
SEAL GROOVE
SPIDER NEEDLES
SNAP RING
SPIDER LEG BALL
LEG BALL WASHER

Spider assembly
(© Cadillac Div., G.M. Corp)

spots and driving off C. V. joint with hammer and chisel.
4. Slide the seal and adapter down the axle shaft until the tri-pot joint is exposed.

NOTE: the tri-pot housing is now free to slide off the joint. Use care to prevent the spider leg balls from sliding off the spider legs. Each leg ball contains multiple bearing rollers.

5. Cup one hand under the tri-pot joint to prevent dropping spider leg balls and rollers while sliding housing off of joint.
6. Remove spider leg ball.
7. Remove O-ring seal from outer housing.
8. Wipe excess grease from outer housing to gain access to snap ring and remove spider outer snap-ring.
9. With a plastic hammer, tap alternately on spider legs to drive spider off shaft.
10. Remove spider inner snap-ring.
11. Slide seal off axle shaft.
12. Remove rollers from spider leg balls.

Caution Do not lose any of the needle bearings in the spider leg balls.

Assembly

1. Insert axle assembly in a vise. Hold by mid-portion of axle shaft.
2. Place small keystone clamp on axle shaft.
3. Position seal on shaft.
4. Place spider inner snap-ring in position on shaft.
5. Apply lubricant to axle and the spider splines.
6. Align spider on axle shaft.
7. With a plastic hammer, tap alternately on spider legs to drive spider into position on axle shaft.
8. Install spider outer snap-ring on axle shaft.
9. Place O-ring on tri-pot joint housing.
10. Apply a thin coat of lubricant to inner race of leg balls, and install leg ball rollers.
11. Apply lubricant to spider leg balls and legs.
12. Remove axle from vise then in-

stall washers and three spider leg balls, one at a time as a unit on the spider.

NOTE: when installing leg balls, use the leg ball washers as retainers for the spider rollers.

13. Pack inside of seal with special drive axle joint lubricant until the folds of the seal are full.
14. Pack housing with special drive axle joint lubricant and install by sliding housing over spider leg balls.
15. Position seal adapter over lip on joint housing and stake with blunt chisel.
16. Seat seal in groove on axle shaft, and secure keystone clamps.

JACKING, HOISTING

When jacking the front of the vehicle, make certain that the jack is placed so that it contacts the lower suspension arm just inside the stabilizer bar. If the vehicle is lifted from the rear, place the jack as far in to the middle of the frame as possible so that the Automatic Level Control and the fuel and brake lines are not damaged.

Ideally, the best lift is one which contacts both the front and rear suspension at the same time.

Caution The rear lower control arm should never be used as a lift point for the vehicle.

When working on the vehicle in the raised position, it is recommended that two jackstands be placed under the front frame cross member. Also, the vehicle should never be supported at the very ends of the frame with anything other than the jack provided with the car.

DIFFERENTIAL

Planetary-Type

1967

This type differential replaces the conventional spider and beveled axle drive pinions with a planetary gear set to distribute torque to the respective drive axles.

Engine torque is transmitted from the power train, to the main drive pinion and ring gear, to the differential housing. Torque is then applied through the planetary and sun gear mechanism to both drive axles at variable speed requirements.

While the car is moving straight ahead, the planetary gears are fixed and rotate with the differential case and ring gear as a unit. However, when turning, the planetary gears revolve upon their individual axles with differential action, allowing the drive axles to rotate at different speeds.

This unit is not a controlled or limited slip differential. The unit normally is serviced as an assembly with the exception of the various seals.

Bevel Gear-Type

Beginning 1968

Since 1968, a bevel gear-type differential is used on all front wheel drive models. This design supersedes the original planetary-type final

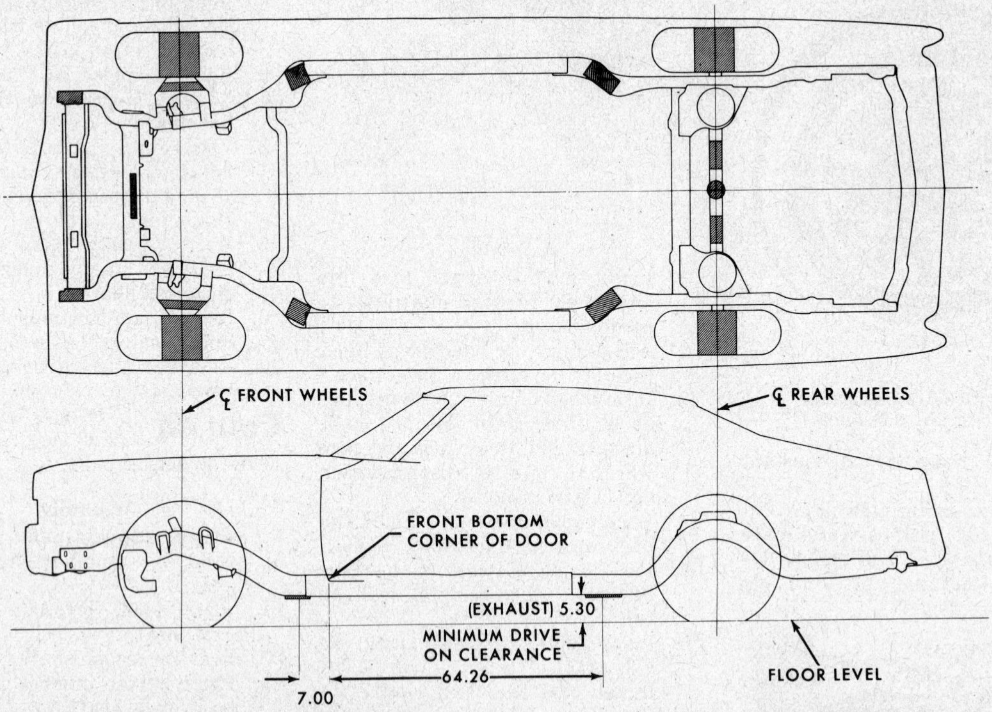
℄ FRONT WHEELS
℄ REAR WHEELS
FRONT BOTTOM CORNER OF DOOR
(EXHAUST) 5.30
MINIMUM DRIVE ON CLEARANCE
FLOOR LEVEL
7.00
64.26

Lift points

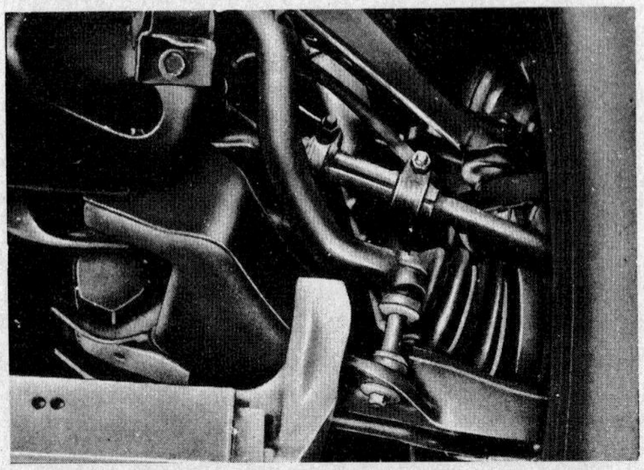

Front jack position

Rear jack position

drive. While unit removal and installation procedures are typical, the assembly, or its components are not interchangeable with the earlier design.

Overhauling the differential assembly is not encouraged. However, reconditioning procedures are found in later paragraphs of this final drive coverage. Differences in procedure are clearly indicated.

Output Shafts, Bearings and Seals

Right Side Shaft Removal

1. Disconnect battery.
2. Hoist car and remove the wheel.
3. Place a short length of rubber hose over control arm torsion bar connector.

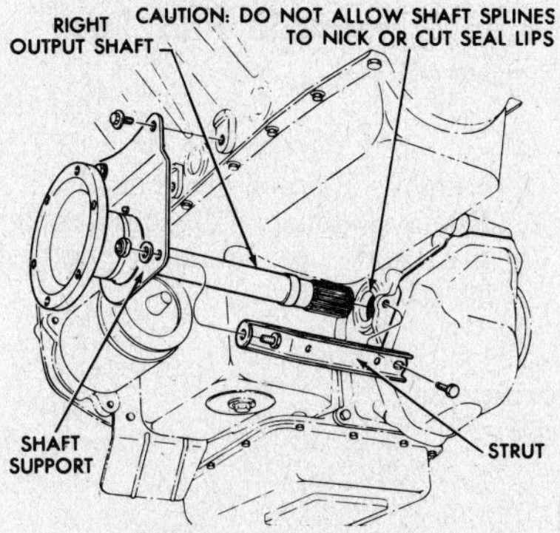
RIGHT OUTPUT SHAFT
CAUTION: DO NOT ALLOW SHAFT SPLINES TO NICK OR CUT SEAL LIPS
SHAFT SUPPORT
STRUT

Output shaft, right side
(© Cadillac Div., G.M. Corp)

4. Disconnect right-hand drive axle from the output shaft.
5. Disconnect support from engine and brace. Loosen lower shock bolt.
6. Rotate the inside end of the drive axle toward the starter motor and slide the output shaft straight out toward the side of the car.
7. When the splined end has cleared the drive unit, tilt and remove it from the underside of the car. Be careful not to damage the drive oil seal.
8. If seal is to be removed, pry it out with a large screwdriver.
9. If output shaft bearing is to be removed, it can be removed as follows:
   a. Remove three self-tapping screws that secure bearing retainer.
   b. Clamp output shaft in a vise.
   c. Make two steel plates ¼x3x8 in. and install as illustrated.
   d. Install four ⅜—24 bolts about 5 in. long through output shaft flange.
   e. Tighten bolts alternately and bearing will be forced from its seat.

Installation

1. If output bearing was removed, assemble parts as illustrated.
2. Position assembly in a press and install bearing until seated.
3. Pack area between bearing and retainer with wheel bearing grease, then install slinger.
4. If seal was removed, it can now be installed.
5. Apply special seal lubricant to output shaft seal, then install output shaft into final drive, indexing the splines of both units.
6. Install support to engine and brace bolts.

NOTE: seat washers in old grooves in output shaft support to ensure output shaft alignment. If new support is installed, carefully center output shaft in support with bolts loosely installed, then tighten bolts to 50 ft. lbs. Do not allow shaft to hang unsupported in final drive.

7. Connect drive axle to output shaft. Tighten screws to 65 ft. lbs.
8. Remove protective rubber hose.
9. Connect battery, check engine oil level and check for oil leaks.

Left Side Shaft Removal

1. Remove the cotter pin from the drive spindle and loosen the spindle nut.
2. Raise the car. Remove the wheel and the drive spindle nut.
3. Remove the left drive axle. (See "Left Drive Axle Removal.")
4. Remove the bolt which holds the left-hand output shaft.
5. Remove the output shaft by pulling it out in the same manner as was used in the right side removal procedure.

Installation

1. If seal was removed, install new seal.
2. Apply special seal lubricant to seal, then insert output shaft into final drive assembly, indexing splines of output shaft with splines of final drive.
3. Install left-hand output shaft retaining bolt and torque to 45 ft. lbs.
4. Install left drive axle.

Final Drive

Cadillac recommends that the final drive unit not be serviced. It is replaced, if defective, by installing a new unit. The removal and installation procedure is listed below.

Removal

1. Disconnect battery.
2. Pump about one gallon of transmission fluid out of filler tube. Remove bolt on the bracket that secures filler tube and remove filler tube, plugging the filler tube hole.
3. Remove bolts A and B and nut H. (See illustration.)
4. Remove support bracket bolts.
5. Raise car and remove wheels and tires.
6. Install lengths of rubber hose on both lower torsion bar connectors.
7. Loosen twelve screws and washers that secure drive axles to output shafts.
8. Loosen, but do not remove, lower shock nut on right side.
9. Remove right drive axle and output shaft.
10. Remove six screws and lockwashers that secure left output shaft to axle.
11. Loosen screws that secure final drive cover to final drive. Allow lubricant to drain then remove screws and cover.
12. Compress left drive axle inner constant velocity joint and secure drive axle to frame.
13. Remove final drive support bracket.
14. Remove bolts C, D, E, and F and nut G.
15. Disengage final drive splines from transmission.
16. Remove final drive unit, permitting ring gear to rotate up over steering gear.
17. Remove transmission to final drive gasket and discard.

Installation

1. Positioning new gasket on transmission, install final drive unit, permitting ring gear to rotate up over steering linkage.
2. Align final drive splines with splines in transmission.
3. Align bolt studs G and H on transmission with holes in final drive.
4. Install bolts C, D, E and F and nut G finger tight.
5. Install support bracket on final drive unit.
6. Install other support brackets.
7. Install bolt in oil cooler lines clamp and tighten to 8 ft. lbs.
8. Tighten bolts C, D, E and F and nut G to 25 ft. lbs.
9. Reposition left drive axle and install screws to 65 ft. lbs.
10. Install right output shaft and axle.
11. Position final drive cover to final drive and install screws to 30 ft. lbs.
12. Fill final drive unit. Tighten lower shock nut to 75 lbs.
13. Install wheels and tires, tightening nuts finger tight.
14. Lower car and tighten wheel nuts to 105 ft. lbs.
15. Install bolts A and B and nut H, tightening to 25 ft. lbs.
16. Install new O-ring on transmission filler tube, remove plug in filler tube hole and install filler tube.
17. Position the transmission cooler line clips and secure the support bracket with the screw torqued to 8 ft lbs.
18. Connect battery.
19. Check engine oil and transmis-

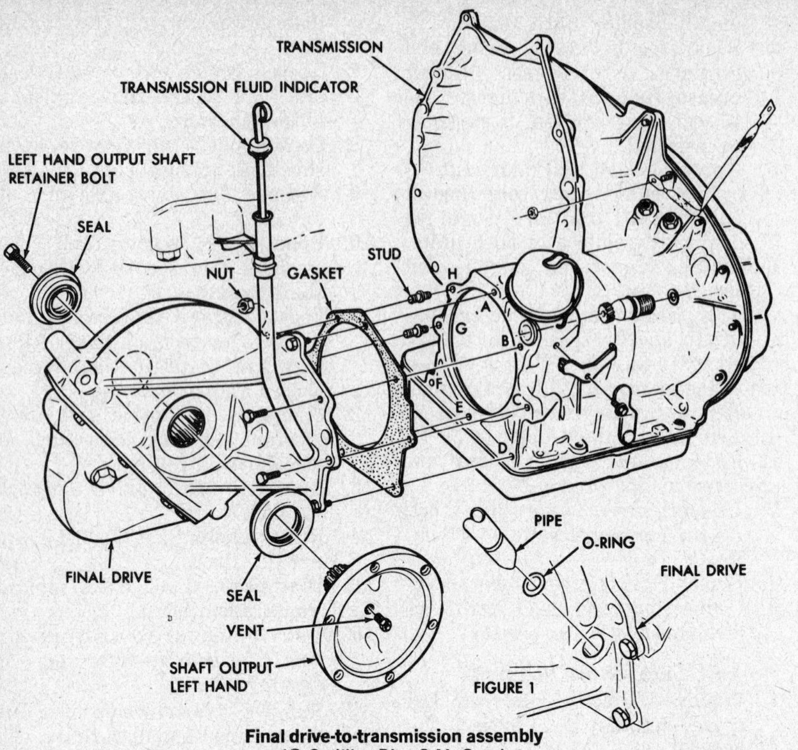
TRANSMISSION
TRANSMISSION FLUID INDICATOR
LEFT HAND OUTPUT SHAFT RETAINER BOLT
SEAL
NUT
GASKET
STUD
H
A
G
B
F
E
C
D
FINAL DRIVE
SEAL
VENT
SHAFT OUTPUT LEFT HAND
PIPE
O-RING
FINAL DRIVE
FIGURE 1

Final drive-to-transmission assembly
(© Cadillac Div., G.M. Corp)

sion fluid. Start engine and add fluid as needed.

20. After running check the seals for leaks.

FRONT SUSPENSION

The front suspension consists of control arms, stabilizer bar, shock absorbers and a right and left torsion bar. Torsion bars are used in place of conventional coil springs. The front end of the torsion bar is attached to the lower control arm. The rear of torsion bar is mounted into an adjustable arm at the torsion bar crossmember. The carrying height of the car is controlled by this adjustment.

Wheel Hub (Front) R & R

1967-74

1. Remove hub cap, loosen wheel nuts, remove drive axle cotter pin and loosen drive axle nut.
2. Jack up car and place axle stands under lower control arms.
3. Remove axle nut and wheel and tire assembly.
4. Remove brake drum, or with disc brakes remove brake hose and caliper.

NOTE: starting 1969, match-mark disc and hub, then remove disc.

5. Disconnect brake hose from steel line if equipped with drum brakes.
6. Remove upper ball joint cotter pin and loosen stud nut.
7. Strike steering knuckle near upper joint to separate it from taper.
8. Remove tie-rod end cotter pin and nut.
9. Separate tie-rod end from steering knuckle using a tie-rod splitter.
10. Remove lower ball joint cotter pin and stud nut.
11. Disconnect lower ball joint.
12. Remove hub, backing plate and steering knuckle as an assembly.
13. To install, reverse removal procedure. Tighten both ball joint stud nuts to 40 ft. lbs. up to 1969, 85 ft. lbs. starting 1970 and tie-rod nut to 30 ft. lbs. Drive axle nut must be tightened to 105–110 ft lbs. except 1972 which has a torque of 150 ft lbs. to prevent loosening in service.

Steering Knuckle and Seal Replacement

Removal

1. Remove hub and drum or disc.
2. Remove upper ball joint cotter pin and nut. Remove caliper starting 1969.

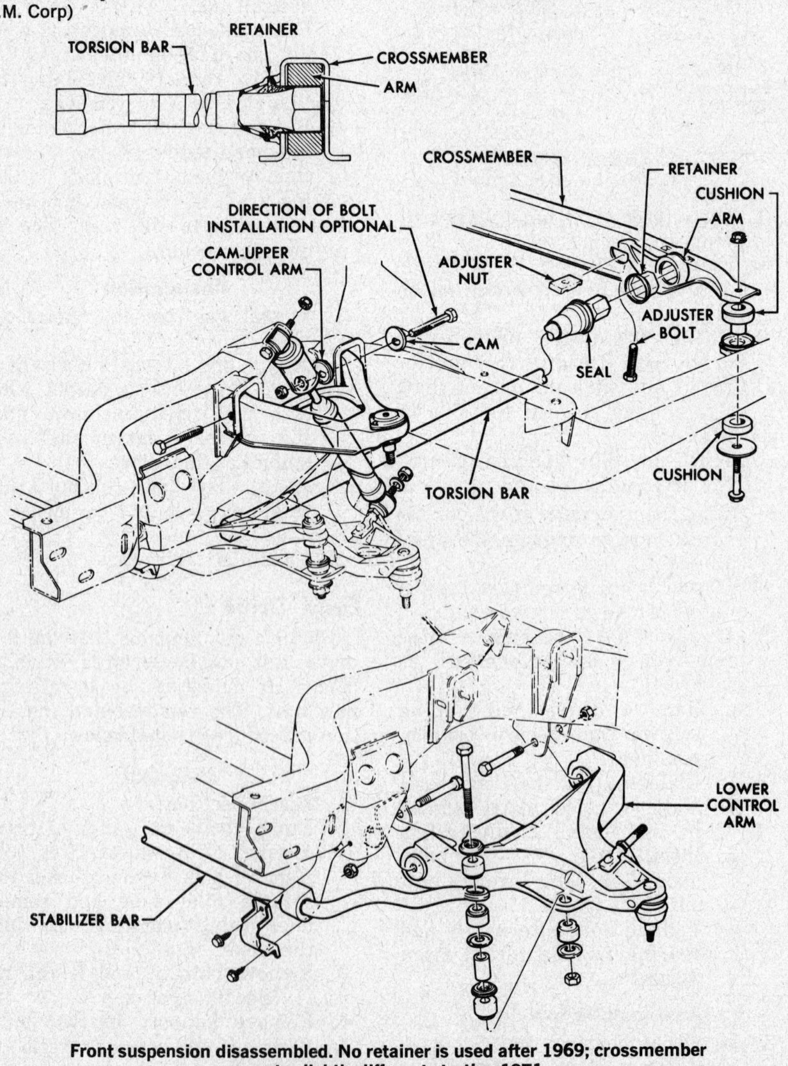
TORSION BAR
RETAINER
CROSSMEMBER
ARM
CROSSMEMBER
RETAINER
CUSHION
ARM
DIRECTION OF BOLT INSTALLATION OPTIONAL
CAM-UPPER CONTROL ARM
ADJUSTER NUT
CAM
SEAL
ADJUSTER BOLT
TORSION BAR
CUSHION
LOWER CONTROL ARM
STABILIZER BAR

Front suspension disassembled. No retainer is used after 1969; crossmember mounts slightly different starting 1971.
(© Cadillac Div., G.M. Corp)

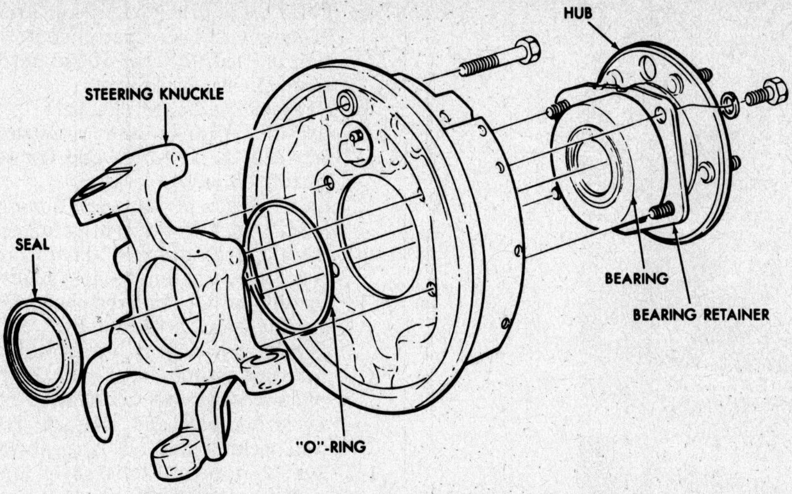
HUB
STEERING KNUCKLE
SEAL
BEARING
BEARING RETAINER
"O"-RING

Front hub, bearing, and retainer—1967-68 with drum brakes
(© Cadillac Div., G.M. Corp)

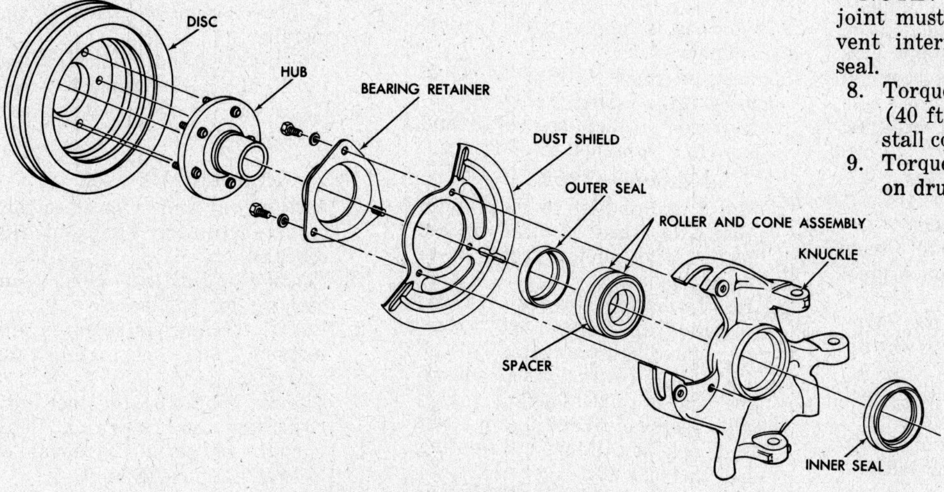
DISC
HUB
BEARING RETAINER
DUST SHIELD
OUTER SEAL
ROLLER AND CONE ASSEMBLY
KNUCKLE
SPACER
INNER SEAL

Front hub, bearing, and retainer—1969-74
(© Cadillac Div., G.M. Corp)

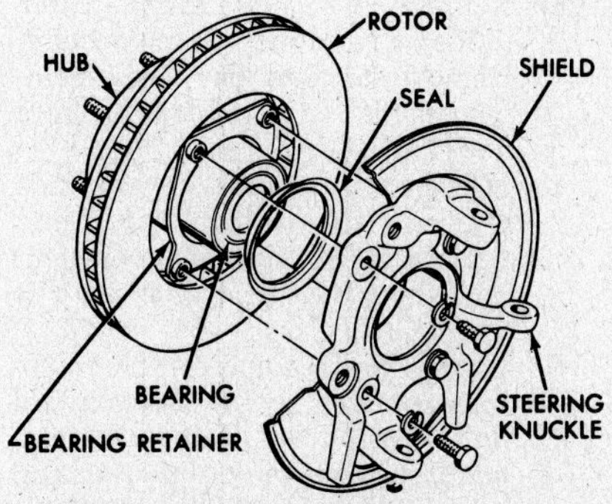
ROTOR
HUB
SHIELD
SEAL
BEARING
STEERING KNUCKLE
BEARING RETAINER

Front hub, bearing, and retainer—1967-68 with disc brakes
(© Cadillac Div., G.M. Corp)

3. Remove brake line hose clip from ball joint stud.

NOTE: do not loosen ball joint stud.

4. Bend lock plate on anchor bolt up and remove anchor bolt of cars with drum brakes.
5. Carefully lift brake backing plate outboard over end of axle shaft and support the brake assembly so that it is not hanging from the brake line.

NOTE: it is not necessary to remove dust shield on cars with disc brakes. If only the O-ring seal is to be replaced, it can be done at this time without further disassembly.

6. Place rubber pad over lower control arm torsion bar connector to protect C.V. joint seal.
7. Using a brass drift and hammer loosen upper ball joint stud.
8. Remove cotter pin and nut from tie-rod end.
9. Using brass drift and hammer, remove tie-rod end from knuckle.
10. Remove cotter pin and nut from lower ball joint.
11. Carefully place ball joint puller adapter between ball joint seal and knuckle.
12. Remove lower ball joint from knuckle.
13. Remove knuckle.
14. Knuckle seal can be pried from the knuckle at this time.

Installation

1. Using seal installer, install seal into knuckle. Seal should be packed with chassis grease.
2. Install lower ball joint stud into knuckle and attach nut. Do not tighten nut at this time.
3. Install tie-rod and stud into knuckle and attach nut. Do not tighten nut at this time.
4. Install upper ball joint stud into knuckle and attach nut. Do not tighten nut at this time.
5. Install backing plate onto knuckle with anchor bolt and lock plate. Do not tighten nut at this time.
6. Remove upper ball joint attaching nut and install brake line hose clip.
7. Torque ball joint nuts to a minimum of 40 ft. lbs. up to 1969, 85 ft. lbs. starting 1970 to 1971 and 60 ft. lbs. in 1972-74 models. Never back off to install cotter pins.

NOTE: cotter pin on upper ball joint must be bent up, only, to prevent interference with C. V. joint seal.

8. Torque tie-rod end to 30 ft. lbs. (40 ft. lbs. for 1972-74) and install cotter pin.
9. Torque anchor bolt to 135 ft. lbs. on drum brake models, and bend lock plate onto flat of bolt head.
10. Install hub assembly.
11. Install drum or disc and wheel; install drive axle nut.
12. Remove floor stand and lower car.
13. Be sure to check camber, caster and toe-in, and adjust if necessary. Tighten drive axle and lug nuts to 105-110 ft. lbs, 130 ft lbs for 1973-74 models.

Torsion Bar

Removal—1967

1. Loosen wheel lug nuts, jack up car and place on axle stands.
2. Remove wheel and tire assemblies.
3. Replace one nut per side on drum brake cars to prevent drum's falling off.
4. Remove hub cotter pin, nut and washer.
5. Remove brake line clip attached to frame.
6. Place a floor jack under the lower control arm of the side being worked on.
7. Using a hammer and brass drift,

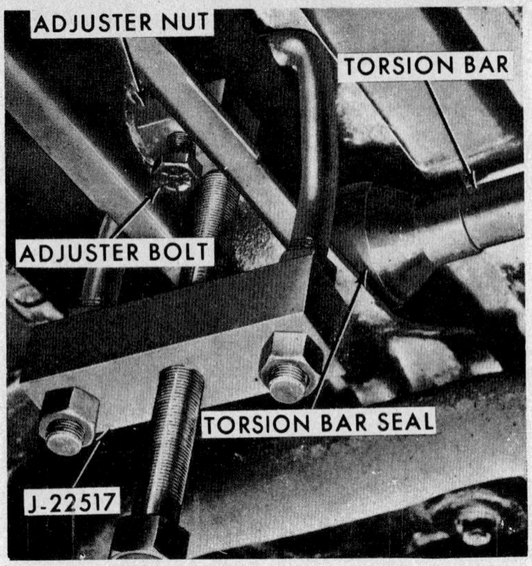
ADJUSTER NUT
TORSION BAR
ADJUSTER BOLT
TORSION BAR SEAL
J-22517

Torsion bar remover and installer
(© Cadillac Div., G.M. Corp)

disconnect upper ball joint, remove nut and brake line clip.

8. Disconnect shock absorber at lower mount.
9. Disconnect tie-rod at steering knuckle.
10. Disconnect stabilizer bar; discard nut and bolt.
11. Disconnect lower ball joint.
12. Disengage backing plate (drum brakes) and hang it on a piece of wire.
13. Remove lower control arm-to-frame attaching *nuts. Do not remove bolts yet.*
14. Slowly lower the floor jack under the lower control arm. The torsion bar is now unloaded.
15. Remove the torsion bar adjusting bolt at crossmember.
16. Pull down on lower control arm, while at the same time reaching back to remove torsion bar adjusting nut from crossmember.
17. Now, remove lower control arm-to-frame attaching *bolts.*
18. Disengage lower control arm from frame mounts.
19. Using extreme care, slide lower control arm off torsion bar. Slide torsion bar out of frame retainer and remove from car. *Any nicks on torsion bar can cause failure of the part.*

Installation—1967

1. Check rubber seal for damage and replace if necessary.
2. Lubricate about 3 in. of each end of bar with Lubriplate or Molykote.

NOTE: if retainers are used, they must be renewed each time bar is replaced.

3. Install torsion bar into lubricated retainer at crossmember.

NOTE: torsion bars are marked for proper installation.

4. Lubricate lower control arm bar connector and position lower arm on torsion bar. Make sure lower arm is level and that torsion bar is fully seated in crossmember.
5. Reverse Steps 1-18 of *Removal* procedure. Lower control arm-to-frame attaching bolts and nuts are tightened to 65 ft. lbs.

Removal—1968-70

1. Raise car and place jack under rear axle. Raise front of car and place jacks under front lower control arms.
2. Install torsion bar remover and installer on torsion bar crossmember. Tighten center bolt on this tool until torsion bar adjusting arm is raised enough to permit removal of adjusting bolt and lock nut. Remove adjusting bolt and lock nut.
3. Remove torsion bar installer and remover and install on other end of torsion bar crossmember and repeat Step 2. Remove tool.
4 Remove torsion bar crossmember mounting bolts, bushings, retainers and parking brake cable clip.
5. Drive crossmember down, then rearward until both torsion bars are free. Adjusting arms will fall out.
6. Lift up on crossmember. Remove torsion bars by sliding them out of lower control arm connectors.

Installation—1968-70

1. Lubricate both ends of torsion bar for approximately 3 in. with extreme pressure chassis lubricant.
2. Place torsion bar in retainer at chassis crossmember.
3. Lubricate lower control arm torsion bar connector and slide torsion bar into connector.

NOTE: The torsion bars are stamped "L" and "R" for left and right. The end which is stamped is inserted in the lower control arm torsion bar connector.

4. Repeat procedure for other torsion bar.
5. Place torsion bar adjusting arm in crossmember, then slide torsion bar toward rear of car until seated in adjusting arm.
6. Repeat for other torsion bar.
7. Install bushings and retainers between crossmember and frame on both sides.
8. Raise front of car, positioning jacks under lower control arms.
9. Install crossmember mounting bolts and tighten to 40 ft. lbs.
10. Install torsion bar remover and installer on crossmember and tighten center bolt until torsion bar adjusting arm is high enough to permit installation of adjusting bolt and locknut. Install locknut and adjusting bolt.
11. Remove torsion bar remover and installer and install on other end of crossmember and repeat Step 10 for other torsion bar.
12. Remove torsion bar remover and installer.
13. Check the standing height and the front wheel alignment.
14. Raise car, removing jacks, and lower car.

Removal—1971-74

1. Jack up car and support so that front suspension hangs at full rebound.
2. Remove adjusting bolt from both torsion bar locknuts.
3. Install torsion bar remover and installer tool on torsion bar crossmember.
4. Tighten center bolt of tool until adjusting arm is raised high enough to permit removal of locknut. Remove locknut.
5. Repeat Steps 3 and 4 on other side of crossmember.
6. Remove parking brake cable guide at right side of underbody.
7. Remove torsion bar crossmember bolts and retainers from both sides.
8. Move crossmember toward side opposite the torsion bar being removed. One side of crossmember should clear frame at this point.
9. Lower the free end on the crossmember and drive it rearward until torsion bar is free. It may be necessary to loosen parking brake adjuster nut to gain slack in cable.

NOTE: although both torsion bars can be removed at this point, it has been found much easier to do only one side at a time.

10. Remove torsion bar from lower control arm.

NOTE: nicks or scratches in torsion bar can cause its failure.

Installation—1971-74

1. Lubricate 3 in. of each end of torsion bar. Bars are marked L or R for left and right sides—do not interchange.

2. Slide torsion bar into lower control arm as far as it will go after installing the torsion bar seal.
3. Position adjusting arm in crossmember. Holding arm in place, slide torsion bar rearward until it is seated in adjusting arm. The torsion bars are stamped "L" for left and "R" for right. The stamped end is installed in the lower control arm.
4. Position crossmember to frame and reverse Steps 1-7 of *Removal* procedure.

Upper Control Arm

Removal

NOTE: the upper control arm can be serviced as an assembly, although bushings and upper ball joint kits are available.

1. Hoist car and remove wheel.
2. Remove upper shock absorber attaching bolt.
3. Remove cotter pin and nut on upper ball joint.
4. Disconnect brake hose clamp from ball joint stud. Remove caliper.
5. Using hammer and a drift, drive on spindle until upper ball joint stud is disengaged.
6. Remove upper control arm cam assemblies and remove control arm from car.

Installation

1. Guide upper control arm over shock absorber and install bushing ends into frame horns.
2. Install cam assemblies.

NOTE: front cam is mounted up, rear cam is mounted down.

3. Install ball joint stud into knuckle. Install caliper.
4. Install brake hose clip on ball joint stud.
5. Install ball joint nut. Torque to 40 ft. lbs. up to 1969, 85 ft. lbs. from 1970–1971 and 60 ft. lbs. in 1972-74, and insert cotter pin, crimp.

NOTE: cotter pin must be crimped toward upper control arm to prevent interference with outer C. V. joint seal.

6. Install upper shock attaching bolt and nut. Torque to 75 ft. lbs.
7. Install wheel.
8. Lower hoist.
9. Check camber, caster and toe-in, and adjust if necessary.

Upper Control Arm Bushing on the Car

The upper control arm bushings can be removed and installed without removing the control arm.

Removal

1. Hoist car and remove wheel.
2. Disconnect upper shock absorber attaching bolt.
3. Remove cam assemblies from control arms.
4. Move control arms out of frame horns and attach bushing removal tools.

Installation

1. Install tools and press bushings into control arm.
2. Move control arm into frame horns and install cam assemblies. Front cam is mounted up, rear cam is mounted down.
3. Connect upper shock absorber attaching bolt. Torque to 75 ft. lbs.
4. Replace wheel and lower car.
5. Align front wheels.

Lower Control Arm

Removal

1. Remove wheel disc and loosen wheel mounting nuts.
2. Remove hub cotter pin. Loosen nut.
3. Raise car and remove wheel and tire.
4. Remove torsion bar, as described previously.
5. Remove hub nut and washer, and brake line clips attached to frame.
6. Remove cotter pin, nut and brake line clip from upper ball joint and remove joint from steering knuckle with a hammer and drift.
7. Disconnect shock absorber and remove.
8. Disconnect tie-rod end at steering knuckle with tie-rod end puller.
9. Disconnect stablizer bar and nut and link bolt.
10. Disconnect lower ball joint with ball joint puller and adapter.
11. Disengage hub, knuckle and disc as an assembly and secure to upper control arm with wire.
12. Remove lower control arm to frame nuts and bolts and disengage arm from frame mounts.

Installation

1. Install hub, disc and knuckle assembly on drive axle.
2. Install lower control arms into mounts at chassis.

NOTE: do not tighten nuts now.

3. Install lower control arm ball joint into steering knuckle. Tighten nut to 40 ft. lbs. to 1969, 85 ft. lbs. from 1970 to 1971 and 80 ft. lbs. in 1972. Install the cotter pin.
4. Tighten lower control arm bolts to 75 ft. lbs.
5. Install shock absorber and tighten nut to 75 ft. lbs.
6. Install upper control arm ball joint into steering knuckle and install brake line clip. Tighten nut to 40 ft. lbs. to 1969, 85 ft. lbs. from 1970 to 1971 and 60 ft. lbs from 1972-74. Install cotter pin.
7. Install brake line clip to chassis.
8. Install tie-rod end in steering knuckle, tightening nut to 30 ft. lbs.
9. Install stabilizer bar.
10. Install hub to drive axle washer and nut.
11. Install torsion bar.
12. Install wheel and tire.
13. Lower car.
14. Tighten hub to drive axle nut to 110 ft. lbs. and install cotter pin. Tighten wheel nuts to 105 ft. lbs.
15. Install wheel disc.

Lower Control Arm Bushings

Removal

Remove lower control arm and press bushings out of arm. To install, press bushings into arm and install arm. Check standing height and front wheel alignment if necessary.

Ball Joint Checks

Vertical Check

1. Raise the car and position floor stands under the left and right lower control arm, as near as possible to each lower ball joint. Car must be stable and should not rock on floor stands.
2. Position dial indicator to register vertical movement at wheel hub.
3. Place a pry bar between the lower control arm and the outer race, and pry down on the bar. Care must be used so that the drive axle seal is not damaged. The vertical reading must not exceed .125 in.

Horizontal Check

1. Place car on floor stands as outlined in Step 1 in the Vertical Check.
2. Position dial indicator at the rim of the wheel, to indicate side play.
3. Grasp wheel, top and bottom, and push in on the bottom of the tire while pulling out at the top. Read gauge, then reverse the push-pull procedure. Horizontal deflection on the gauge should not exceed .125 in. at the wheel rim.

Lower Control Arm Ball Joint

Removal

1. Remove knuckle.
2. Using chisel, cut the three rivet heads off.
3. By using a 7/32 in. drill bit, drill side rivets 3/16 in. deep.
4. Using hammer and punch, drive center rivet of joint, until joint is out of the control arm.

Installation

1. Install service ball joint into control arm and torque bolts and nut.
2. Reverse knuckle removal.

Lower Control Arm Ball Joint Seal

The lower ball joint seal can be installed with lower control arm either in or out of the car.

Removal

1. Remove steering knuckle.
2. Using hammer and chisel, drive seal from ball joint.
3. Wipe grease from ball joint and stud.

Installation

1. Position new seal over ball joint stud.
2. Lubricate jaws of camber adjusting wrench and carefully slide jaw between seal and retainer.
3. Tap lightly with hammer on center bolt of the wrench until retainer is fully seated.
4. Install knuckle.
5. Lubricate the ball joint fitting until grease is apparent in seal.

Stabilizer Bar

Removal

1. Raise the car and support it on jack stands.
2. Remove link bolts, nuts, grommets, spacers and retainers from lower control arm. Discard bolts.
3. Remove two bolts attaching dust shield to frame, both sides.
4. Remove bracket to frame attaching bolts and remove stabilizer bar from front of car.

Installation

Reverse removal procedure.

NOTE: new link bolts are torqued to 14 ft. lbs., then cut off to leave ¼ in. of bolt remaining.

Front Shock Absorber

Replacement

1. Remove wheel disc and loosen wheel mounting nuts.
2. Raise car, place on jacks, and remove wheel and tire.
3. Place a hydraulic jack under lower control arm and raise so that load is taken off shock absorber.
4. Disconnect shock absorber at upper and lower mount.
5. Compress shock absorber, working lower mount free from mount bolt.
6. Remove shock absorber.
7. Install by reversing procedure above, tightening shock absorber nuts to 75 ft. lbs. and wheel mounting nuts to 105 ft. lbs.

Standing Height—1967-70

The standing height is controlled by the adjustment setting of the torsion bar adjusting bolts. Clockwise rotation of the bolts increases the front height. It is very important that this height be considered and made correct before steering geometry is established.

For quick checks only, the locations at frame-to-ground points A and B, as illustrated, can be used up to

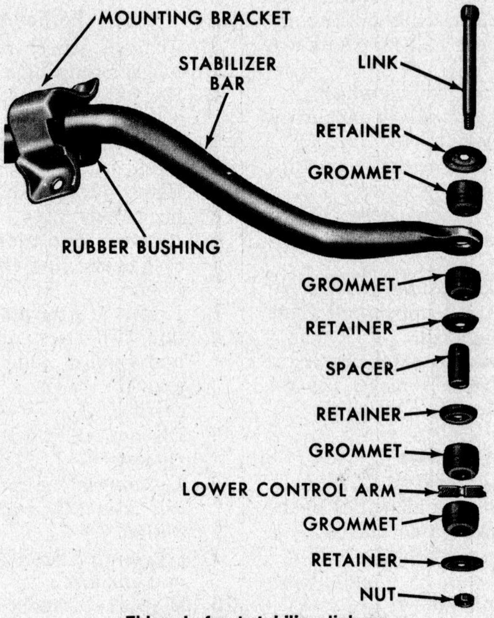
MOUNTING BRACKET
STABILIZER BAR
LINK
RETAINER
GROMMET
RUBBER BUSHING
GROMMET
RETAINER
SPACER
RETAINER
GROMMET
LOWER CONTROL ARM
GROMMET
RETAINER
NUT

Eldorado front stabilizer linkage
(© Cadillac Div., G.M. Corp)

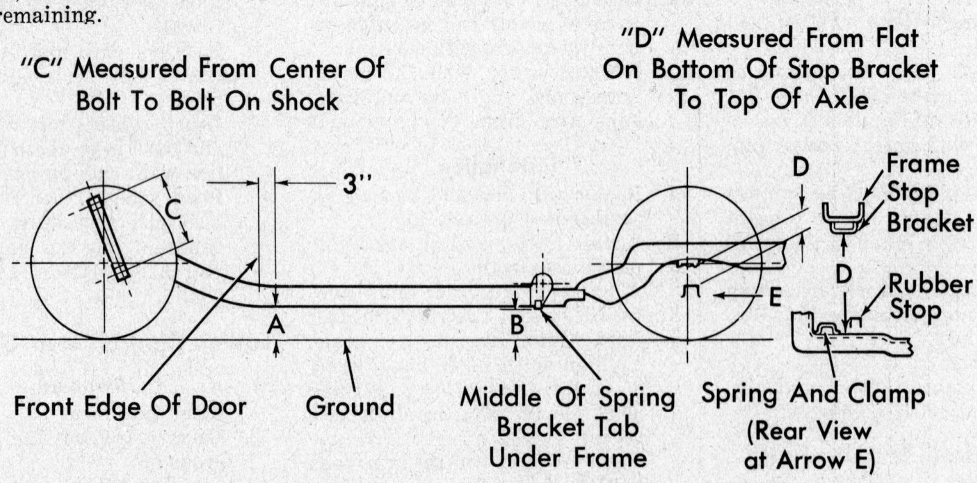
"C" Measured From Center Of Bolt To Bolt On Shock
"D" Measured From Flat On Bottom Of Stop Bracket To Top Of Axle
C
3"
A
B
D
D
E
Frame Stop Bracket
Rubber Stop
Front Edge Of Door
Ground
Middle Of Spring Bracket Tab Under Frame
Spring And Clamp (Rear View at Arrow E)

Reference Locations Frame To Ground		Preferred Locations	
"A" Front	"B" Rear	"C" Front True Shock Length	"D" Rear Standing Height
6¼" TO 6 7/16"	5 15/16" TO 6½"	14⅝" TO 14⅞"	4-23/32" To 5-15/32"

1969-70 Eldorado standing height chart (© Cadillac Div., G.M. Corp)

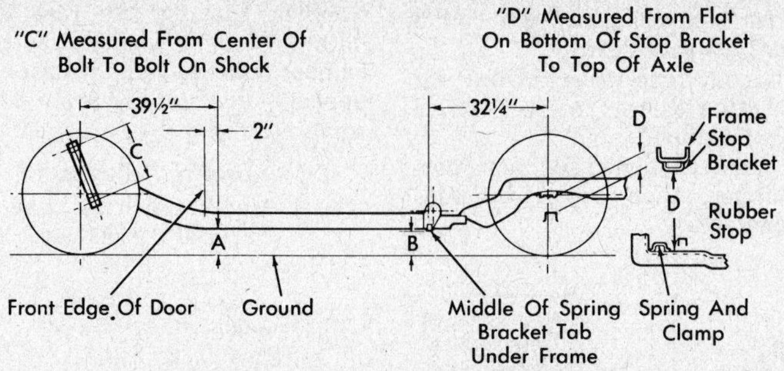
"C" Measured From Center Of
Bolt To Bolt On Shock
"D" Measured From Flat
On Bottom Of Stop Bracket
To Top Of Axle
39½"
2"
32¼"
C
D
Frame
Stop
Bracket
D
Rubber
Stop
A
B
Front Edge Of Door
Ground
Middle Of Spring
Bracket Tab
Under Frame
Spring And
Clamp

Reference Locations Frame To Ground		Preferred Locations	
"A" Front	"B" Rear	"C" Front True Shock Length	"D" Rear Standing Height
5-31/32" To 6-17/32"		14-15/32" To 14-23/32"	4-23/32" To 5-15/32"

1967-68 Eldorado standing height chart
(© Cadillac Div., G.M. Corp)

1970. However, locations C and D, are preferred and should always be used for proper measurements of standing heights up to 1970.

Measuring Height—All Years

Before measuring standing height, check and correct the following items:

1. Car must be on a level surface.
2. Gas tank should be full or a compensating weight added. Estimate the amount of gasoline in the tank and add weights in the trunk in the space immediately above the float access hole area.
3. Front seat should be adjusted all the way to its rearmost position.
4. Front and rear tires should be inflated to 24 and 22 lbs. respectively.
5. Both doors closed.
6. No passengers or additional weight should be in the car or trunk (except as indicated above).

Checking Rear Height with Automatic Level Control Disconnected

Though rear height readings can be taken without disconnecting the ALC, it is preferred that measurements be taken with the leveling system disconnected—to eliminate the possibility of the ALC system affecting the reading.

The ALC can be disconnected at the black line connection at the leveling valve.

After the measurement is taken and the black line is reconnected, the ALC system should be refilled by use of an air pressure hose to insure pressure reserve in the tank.

If rear of car raises when the automatic leveling system is reconnected, the leveling system should be checked and adjusted.

Quick Reference Locations —to 1970

Location A is at a point 2 in. behind the front edge of the door. This is 39½ in. from the centerline of the front wheel.

Location B is at the middle of the spring bracket tab under the frame. This is 32¼ in. forward of the rear axle centerline.

Preferred Locations—to 1970

Location C is from center to center of the shock absorber upper and lower mounting bolts.

Location D is from the flat on the bottom of the stop bracket to the top of the axle. The rear view of D, as illustrated, shows this location more clearly.

Standing Height—1971-74

The procedure for checking standing height has been modified slightly starting with 1971 production. A quick check of height on these models can be made by measuring the distance between the lower edge of the front shock absorber dust cover and the lower shock bolt centerline (front) and the distance between the lower edge of the frame "kickover" and the top of the axle tube (rear). If equipped with Automatic Level Control, loosen the air lines at the rear shocks to bleed all air from the system.

Standing Height—1971-74

Model	*Front*	*Rear*
Coupe	8.0-8.25"	3.88-4.64"
Convertible	8.0-8.25"	3.88-4.64"

Caution Do not accidentally slip the measuring rule or device into the slot for the rubber bumper in the rear axle, because doing so would give a false reading. Also remove all air from Automatic Level Control before the measurement.

Acceptable specifications are also given in illustration. Frame to ground dimensions must be within 1 in. from front to rear and within ⅝ in. from side to side.

If dimensions are not within tolerance, torsion bars wheel alignment must be adjusted.

Alignment Procedures Setting Camber & Caster

1. Check camber. The preferred setting for camber is in the specifications. To adjust proceed as follows:
   A. Loosen nut on upper control arm front cam bolt.
   B. Note camber reading and rotate front bolt to correct for one-half of the incorrect reading or as near to that amount as possible. Tighten front nut.
   C. Loosen nut on upper control arm rear cam bolt and rotate rear cam bolt to bring camber reading to 0°. Tighten rear nut.
   D. Check caster. Preferred reading is in the specifications.

NOTE: if caster requires adjustment, proceed with Step E; if not, move to Step I.

   E. Loosen front cam bolt nut.
   F. Using camber scale on alignment equipment, rotate front bolt so that the camber changes an amount equal to one-quarter of the desired caster change.

NOTE: if adjusting to correct for excessive negative caster, rotate front bolt to increase positive camber. If adjusting to correct for excessive positive caster, rotate front bolt to increase negative camber.

   G. Tighten front nut.
   H. Loosen nut on rear cam bolt and rotate the rear bolt until camber setting returns to 0°. This results in the correct caster setting.
   I. Tighten upper control arm cam nuts to 75 ft. lbs. up to 1969, 95 ft. lbs. starting 1970. Hold head of bolt securely; any movement of the cam will affect final setting and will require a recheck of the camber and caster adjustments.

CASTER - CAMBER CAMS

Caster, camber cam locations
(© Cadillac Div., G.M. Corp)

Relationship of Front and Rear Cams

When setting camber and caster, remember this relationship:

Front cams. If turned for more positive camber, then caster also becomes more positive.

In other words, when turning the front cams to obtain a more positive setting for camber, caster will follow to a more positive setting.

The same is true when turning for more positive caster: more positive camber will follow.

Rear cams. If turned for more positive camber, then caster becomes more negative.

When turning the rear cams to obtain a more positive setting for camber, caster will advance in the opposite direction toward a more negative setting.

Toe-in Adjustment

A. Center steering wheel, raise car and check wheel runout.

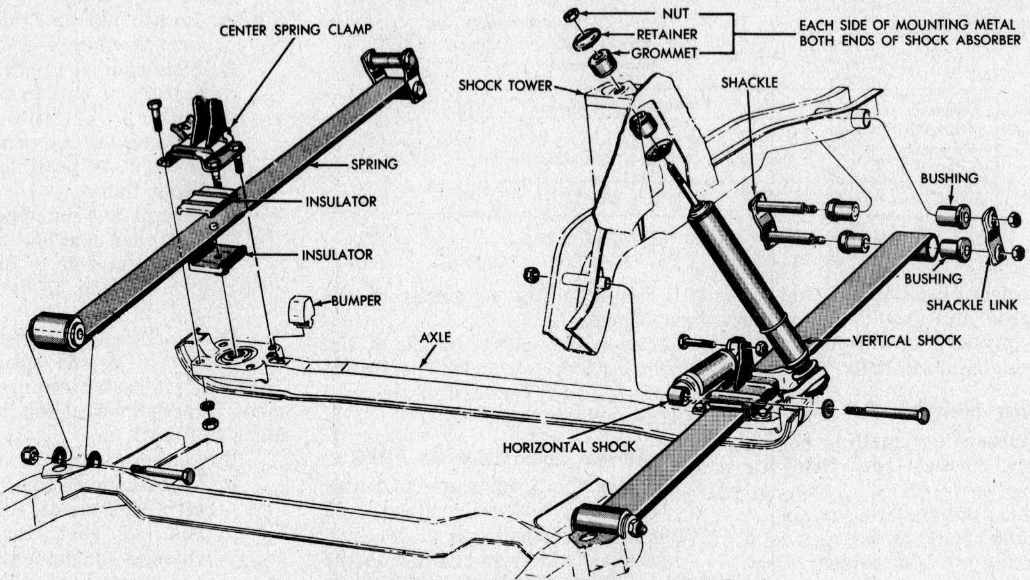
CENTER SPRING CLAMP
SPRING
INSULATOR
INSULATOR
BUMPER
AXLE
NUT
RETAINER
GROMMET
EACH SIDE OF MOUNTING METAL
BOTH ENDS OF SHOCK ABSORBER
SHOCK TOWER
SHACKLE
BUSHING
BUSHING
SHACKLE LINK
VERTICAL SHOCK
HORIZONTAL SHOCK

Rear suspension—1967-70 (© Cadillac Div., G.M. Corp)

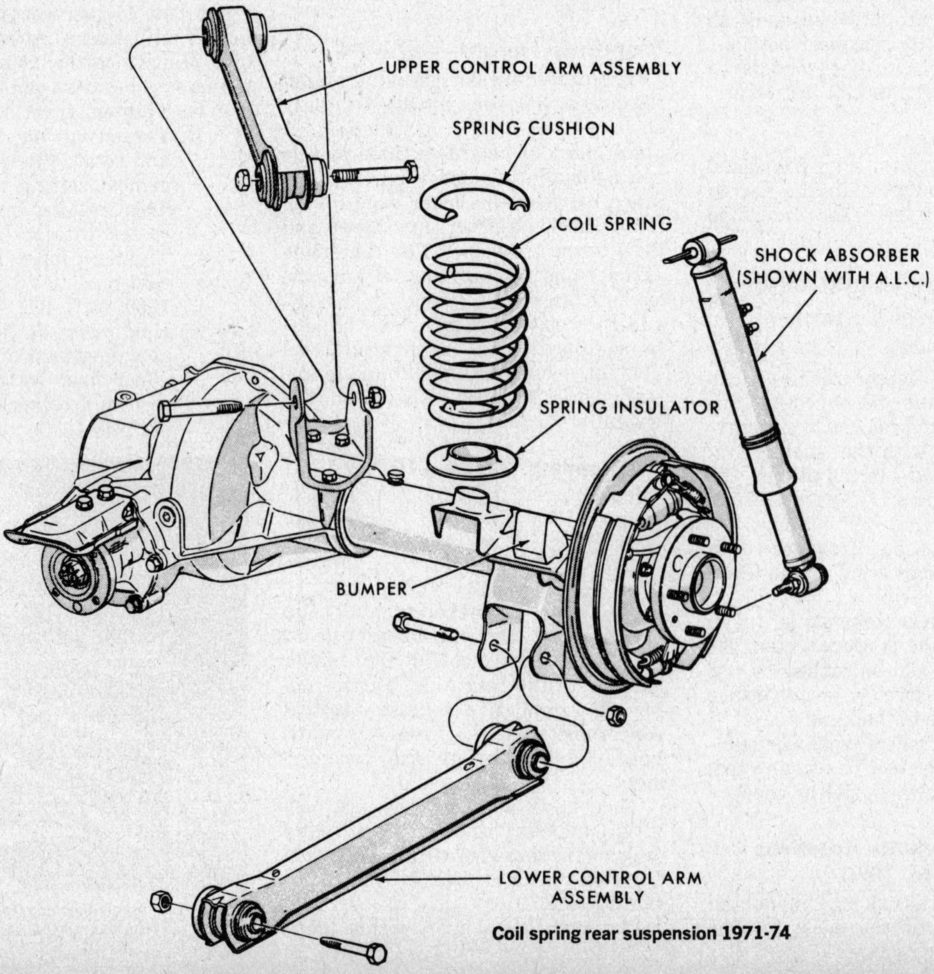
UPPER CONTROL ARM ASSEMBLY
SPRING CUSHION
COIL SPRING
SHOCK ABSORBER
(SHOWN WITH A.L.C.)
SPRING INSULATOR
BUMPER
LOWER CONTROL ARM
ASSEMBLY

Coil spring rear suspension 1971-74

B. Loosen tie-rod adjuster nuts, and adjust to proper setting.
C. Tighten tie-rod adjuster nuts. Torque nuts 22 ft. lbs. Position tie-rod clamps so operning of clamps are facing UP. This is a very necessary setting. Interference and a possible tie up of front end linkage could occur, if clamps hit anything while turning.

Front Wheel Bearing Adjustment

1. Raise the front of the car and remove the wheel covers from the wheels and the dust covers, nut locks and cotter pins from the spindles.
2. On 1967 to 1971 models tighten the adjusting nut to 30 ft lbs. while on 1972 to 1974 models torque the nut to 15 ft lbs.
3. Once the correct torque is obtained, on 1967 and 1968 models back the nut off one quarter turn (90°). On 1969 to 1971 models back the nut off to 0 pounds of torque. 1972 to 1974 models require that the nut be backed off until it is just loose.
4. Tighten the nut on 1967 to 1971 models to 6 ft lbs of torque. 1972-74 models are tightened finger tight only.
5. Install cotter pin.

NOTE: If the cotter pin cannot be installed, back the adjusting nut off to the next hole. DO NOT tighten the nut over 6 lbs on 1967 to 1971 models.

REAR SUSPENSION

1967-70

The rear suspension on the Cadillac Eldorado consists of two single leaf, semi-elliptical springs, two vertical and two horizontal shock absorbers.

1971-74

A new rear suspension system, introduced in 1971, has replaced the old leaf spring type used previously. This new system is a four-link, coil spring suspension having no components interchangeable with other Cadillac models. Instead of two vertical and two horizontal shock absorbers, as used on earlier models, Automatic Level Control Superlift shock absorbers are used exclusively.

Automatic Level Control

This system is basically the same as that used on other Cadillac models and functions identically. However, the on-car location of major components is different. Procedures will be found in the Cadillac section.

Rear Leaf Spring Removal —1967-70

1. Raise car.
2. Support rear axle at center with hydraulic jack.
3. Remove rear wheel from side being worked on.
4. Remove nut that secures Automatic Level Control link to axle bracket and remove link.
5. Remove nut that secures front of spring to frame bracket.

NOTE: do not remove bolt now.

6. Remove two nuts at rear shackle outer link and remove link.
7. Remove four nuts and lockwashers that secure center spring clamp to rear axle and position out of the way.
8. Lower hydraulic jack until axle is free from spring.
9. Remove rear shackle assembly from spring and body.
10. Remove bolt from front of spring and remove spring.

Upper Control Arm R & R—1971-74

1. Jack up car and support rear on axle stands under frame side members.
2. Disconnect Automatic Level Control system over-travel link at right upper control arm axle bracket, then position lever in "center" position.
3. Disconnect lower shock bolt and position shock out of the way.
4. Jack up under rear axle to unload upper control arm.
5. Remove bolt and nut that secures upper arm to axle bracket.
6. Remove bolt and nut that se-

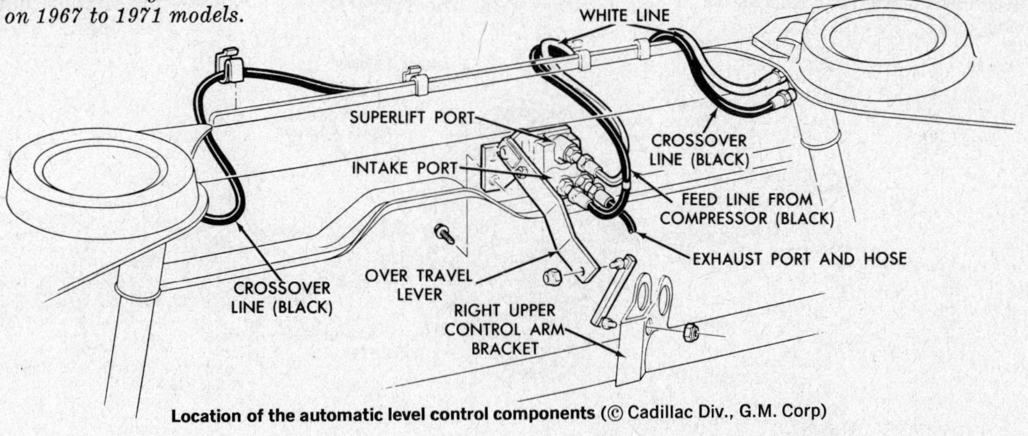
WHITE LINE
SUPERLIFT PORT
CROSSOVER LINE (BLACK)
INTAKE PORT
FEED LINE FROM COMPRESSOR (BLACK)
EXHAUST PORT AND HOSE
OVER TRAVEL LEVER
CROSSOVER LINE (BLACK)
RIGHT UPPER CONTROL ARM BRACKET

Location of the automatic level control components (© Cadillac Div., G.M. Corp)

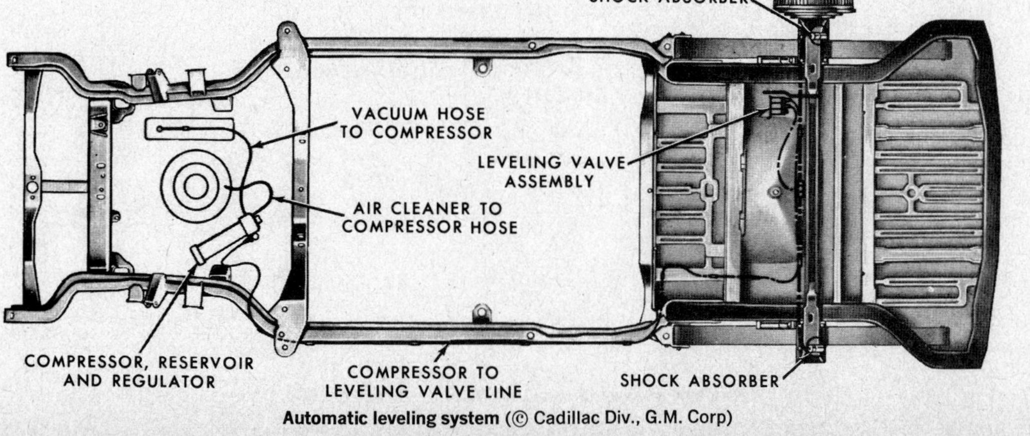
SHOCK ABSORBER
VACUUM HOSE TO COMPRESSOR
LEVELING VALVE ASSEMBLY
AIR CLEANER TO COMPRESSOR HOSE
COMPRESSOR, RESERVOIR AND REGULATOR
COMPRESSOR TO LEVELING VALVE LINE
SHOCK ABSORBER

Automatic leveling system (© Cadillac Div., G.M. Corp)

cures upper arm to crossmember; remove arm.

NOTE: bushings can be replaced at this point.

7. Install upper arm to brackets and install bolts and nuts. Do not tighten nuts at this time.
8. Install lower shock bolt and shock.
9. Jack up on rear axle and remove axle stands under frame side members.
10. With weight of car on axle only, tighten upper arm-to-crossmember nuts to 100 ft. lbs. and lower axle bracket nuts to 75 ft. lbs.
11. Install A.L.C. overtravel lever, lower car and inflate system to 140 psi.

NOTE: control arm pivot bolts must be tightened at standing height or ride rate will be affected.

12. Inspect brake lines for damage.

Lower Control Arm R & R—1971-74

1. Jack up car.
2. Remove bolts and nuts that secure lower arm to axle and frame.
3. Remove lower control arm.
4. Install lower arm and tighten bolts to 100 ft. lbs.

Rear Coil Spring R & R—1971-74

1. Remove both upper control arms from their axle mountings.
2. Disconnect both rear shocks at lower ends.
3. Disconnect brake hose and cap brake line.
4. Lower axle carefully, using a floor jack, until springs can be removed.

Caution If axle is lowered beyond full rebound, springs can jump from their seats with considerable force. For this reason, lower axle only far enough to allow springs to be lightly compressed by hand and removed.

5. Inspect rubber insulators for damage.
6. Insert springs and jack up axle until springs are compressed.
7. Reconnect shocks and upper control arms.
8. Connect brake hose and bleed rear brake circuit.

Rear Axle Assembly

1967-70

The rear axle consists of a welded beam-type, drop center axle having spindles pressed into and bolted to the axle flanges. The rear wheels run on tapered roller bearings very similar to those used on the front wheels of Cadillac models other than the Eldorado.

1971-74

The rear axle was changed in 1971 to a straight, hollow tube design. The spindles still are pressed and bolted to the axle flanges and tapered roller bearings are used. The Track Master system, optional on 1971 and later Eldorado models, uses a hollow spindle through which the drive cables for the speed sensors run.

Removal—1967-70

1. Raise car, and remove rear wheels.
2. Remove rear brake drum, then hub assembly.
3. Disconnect brake lines and hose and parking brake cable.
4. Disconnect overtravel lever link from bracket on rear axle.
5. Remove spring guides that hold parking brake cable to center spring clamp.
6. Remove brake backing plates.
7. Supporting rear axle at center with hydraulic jack, remove four nuts on each side of spring clamp assemblies.
8. Lower jack and remove rear axle.

Removal—1971-74

1. Jack up rear of car and support on stands under frame rails.
2. Remove both tire and wheel assemblies.
3. Remove hubs as follows:
   a. Remove brake drums.
   b. If equipped with Track Master, remove three screws that secure drive cap, remove cap, retainer rings, spindle nut, washer and bearings.
   c. If equipped with standard axle, remove dust cap, cotter pin, spindle nut, washer and bearings.

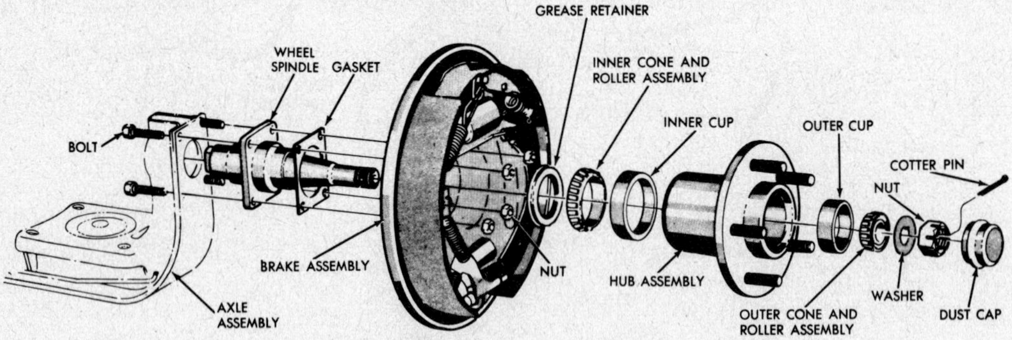
GREASE RETAINER
WHEEL SPINDLE
GASKET
INNER CONE AND ROLLER ASSEMBLY
INNER CUP
OUTER CUP
COTTER PIN
NUT
BOLT
BRAKE ASSEMBLY
NUT
HUB ASSEMBLY
WASHER
DUST CAP
AXLE ASSEMBLY
OUTER CONE AND ROLLER ASSEMBLY

Rear axle disassembled—1967-70 (© Cadillac Div., G.M. Corp)

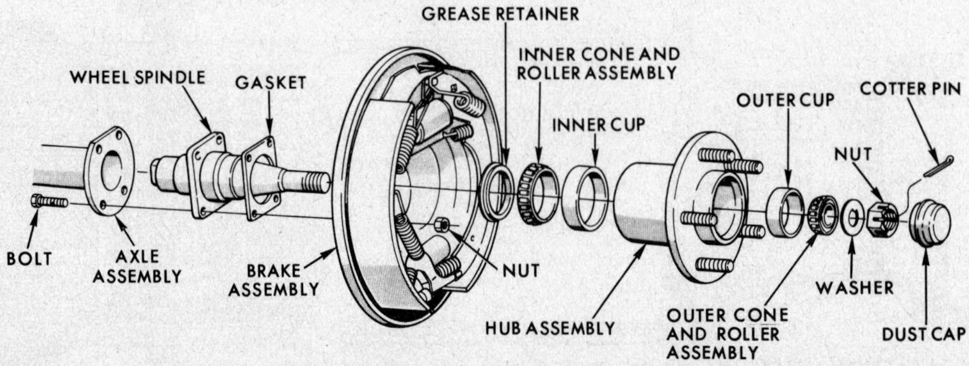
GREASE RETAINER
INNER CONE AND ROLLER ASSEMBLY
WHEEL SPINDLE
GASKET
INNER CUP
OUTER CUP
COTTER PIN
NUT
BOLT
AXLE ASSEMBLY
BRAKE ASSEMBLY
NUT
WASHER
HUB ASSEMBLY
OUTER CONE AND ROLLER ASSEMBLY
DUST CAP

Rear axle disassembled—1971-74 (© Cadillac Div., G.M. Corp)

d. Pull hub off spindle.
4. Disconect brake lines at wheel cylinders.
5. Disconnect rubber hose and cap to prevent brake fluid loss.
6. Disconnect overtravel link at axle bracket, then deflate shocks.
7. Remove brake backing plates and pull spindle using a slide hammer.

NOTE: make sure the sensor wiring is not damaged if equipped with T.M.

8. Disconnect brake lines from clips on axle.
9. If car is equipped with T.M., remove screw and clip that secures sensor cable to axle. Pull cable through 5/8 in. hole in axle and disconnect.
10. Disconnect lower shock bolts and position shocks out of the way.
11. Jack up on axle to relieve tension on upper control arm.
12. Remove bolts and nuts that secure upper control arms to axle.
13. Lower axle and remove coil springs.

Caution Stand clear of the axle assembly as the springs may snap from their seats.

14. Remove bolts and nuts that secure lower control arms to axle.
15. Remove brake junction from axle and rubber stop bumpers.
16. Remove axle from car.
17. To install, reverse removal procedure.

BRAKES

Description

The brake system used in 1967 and 1968 consists of standard power drum brakes front and rear, with four-piston disc brakes by Delco-Moraine optional on the front. Two master cylinder types are used, depending on the type brake system. A Delco-Moraine master cylinder is used on drum brake models, and a Bendix master cylinder on models having disc front brakes. The Bendix master cylinder has no check valve in the front outlet because no residual brake pressure is required with disc brakes.

Starting in 1969, single-piston, sliding caliper Delco-Moraine disc brakes became standard equipment on the front wheels of all Eldorado models. The master cylinders used with these brakes are the same as for the same year Cadillac, even though the Eldorado uses tandem power booster units.

On all models from 1967, a foot-operated, vacuum parking brake working on the rear drums via mechanical linkage is used. This is virtually identical to the parking brake used on other Cadillac models with the exception of cable length and configuration.

For brake service, see the Unit Repair Section of this manual.

Master Cylinder R & R

See Cadillac section.

Power Brake Booster R & R

1967-74

1. Disconnect hydraulic lines from master cylinder.
2. Disconnect vacuum line from vacuum check valve on unit.
3. Remove steering column lower cover.
4. Remove cotter pin, washer and spring spacer that secure power unit pushrod to brake pedal arm.
5. Remove the four nuts that secure power unit to firewall, then remove power unit.
6. To install, reverse removal procedure.

Brake System Check

1. Start engine and allow it to idle in Neutral. Depress brake pedal and hold—if pedal gradually falls away, a hydraulic system leak is indicated.
2. Check pedal travel from rest to full on position. Pedal travel should not exceed 1½ in. for 1967, 1¾ in. for 1968, 2 in. for 1967-70 with disc brakes, and 2 1/16 in. for 1971-74.
3. If pedal travel exceeds specifications, the system is probably contaminated by air bubbles and should be bled.

NOTE: disc brakes—tap calipers around piston area with plastic hammer to dislodge all air bubbles. Less common causes of excessive pedal travel include malfunctioning rear brake self-adjusters, tapered rear linings, worn out rear linings or complete loss of fluid from one brake circuit.

Parking Brake

Preliminary Check

1. Check vacuum cylinder piston travel (on brake pedal support) by running engine at idle and shifting from Drive to Neutral. The manual release lever should move up and down as vacuum is applied and released.
2. If no movement is observed, check for kinked or loose vacuum line connections all the way out to the intake manifold. Check neutral switch adjustment and vacuum release valve.
3. If movement is slow (greater than 2 seconds), vacuum diaphragm may be leaking or lines kinked partially closed.
4. If vacuum piston completes full stroke, but does not release brake, parking brake assembly is faulty and must be replaced as a unit.
5. If parking brake does not remain fully engaged in all gears with engine off, the assembly must be replaced.

Parking Brake Cable Adjustment

See Cadillac section.

STEERING

The steering linkage on the Eldorado is composed of a pitman arm, idler arm, a pair of tie rod assemblies, a drag link, and a shock absorber. The pitman arm connects the left side of the drag link to the steering gear while the idler arm connects the right side of the drag link to the frame. The small shock absorber connects the drag link to the frame and serves to

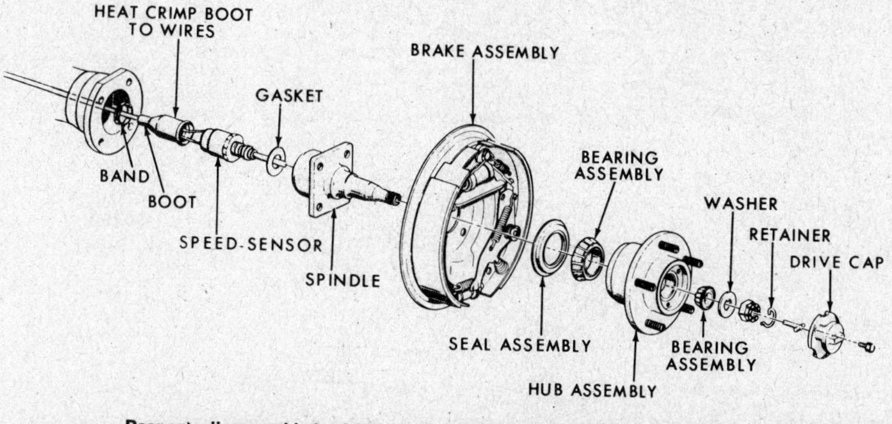
HEAT CRIMP BOOT TO WIRES
BRAKE ASSEMBLY
GASKET
BEARING ASSEMBLY
BAND
BOOT
WASHER
RETAINER
DRIVE CAP
SPEED-SENSOR
SPINDLE
SEAL ASSEMBLY
BEARING ASSEMBLY
HUB ASSEMBLY

Rear axle disassembled—1971-72 with Track Master (© Cadillac Div., G.M. Corp)

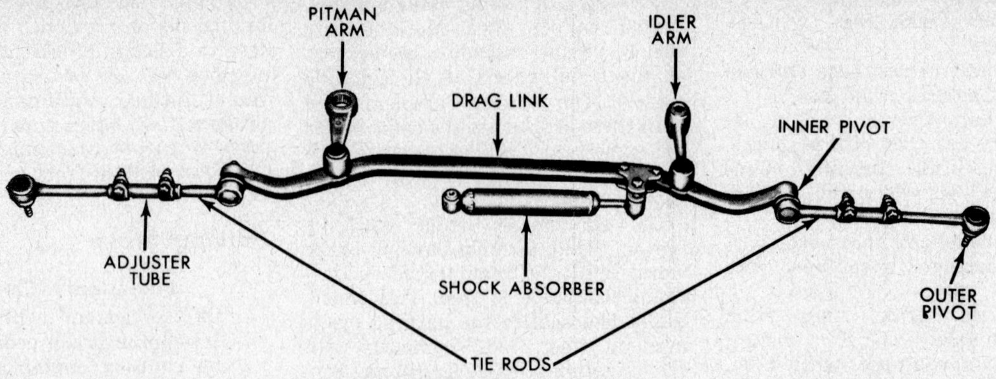
PITMAN ARM
IDLER ARM
DRAG LINK
INNER PIVOT
ADJUSTER TUBE
SHOCK ABSORBER
OUTER PIVOT
TIE RODS

Steering linkage (© Cadillac Div., G.M. Corp)

dampen the vibrations in the linkage. The tie rods connect the drag link with the steering knuckles.

For steering gear overhaul see the "Unit Repair Section."

Steering Gear R & R

1. Remove the pressure lines from the gear and tape or plug the lines.
2. Raise the car.
3. Remove the cotter pin and nut from the pitman arm and then, using a puller, disconnect the pitman arm from the drag link.
4. Separate the flexible coupling.
5. Release the three screws which hold the gear to the side frame rail. The gear is removed by pulling it forward and downward and out of the car.
6. Installation is the reverse of removal. If the pitman arm is removed from the shaft the nut should be torqued to 185 ft lbs upon assembly. The side rail mounting screws should be torqued to 70 ft lbs while the flexible coupling torque should be 20 ft lbs and the pitman arm nut which secures it to the drag link should be tightened to 60 ft lbs. The return line hoses should be tightened to 30 ft lbs.

Steering Linkage R & R

1. Remove the wheels.
2. Remove the steering damper from the frame.
3. Remove all the cotter pins and nuts from the pitman arm and the idler arm pivots on the drag link.
4. Using a puller, remove both the idler and pitman arm pivots from the drag link.

NOTE: It may be necessary to loosen the steering gear from the frame to remove the drag link from the pitman arm.

5. The cotter pins and nuts from the outer tie rod pivots should be

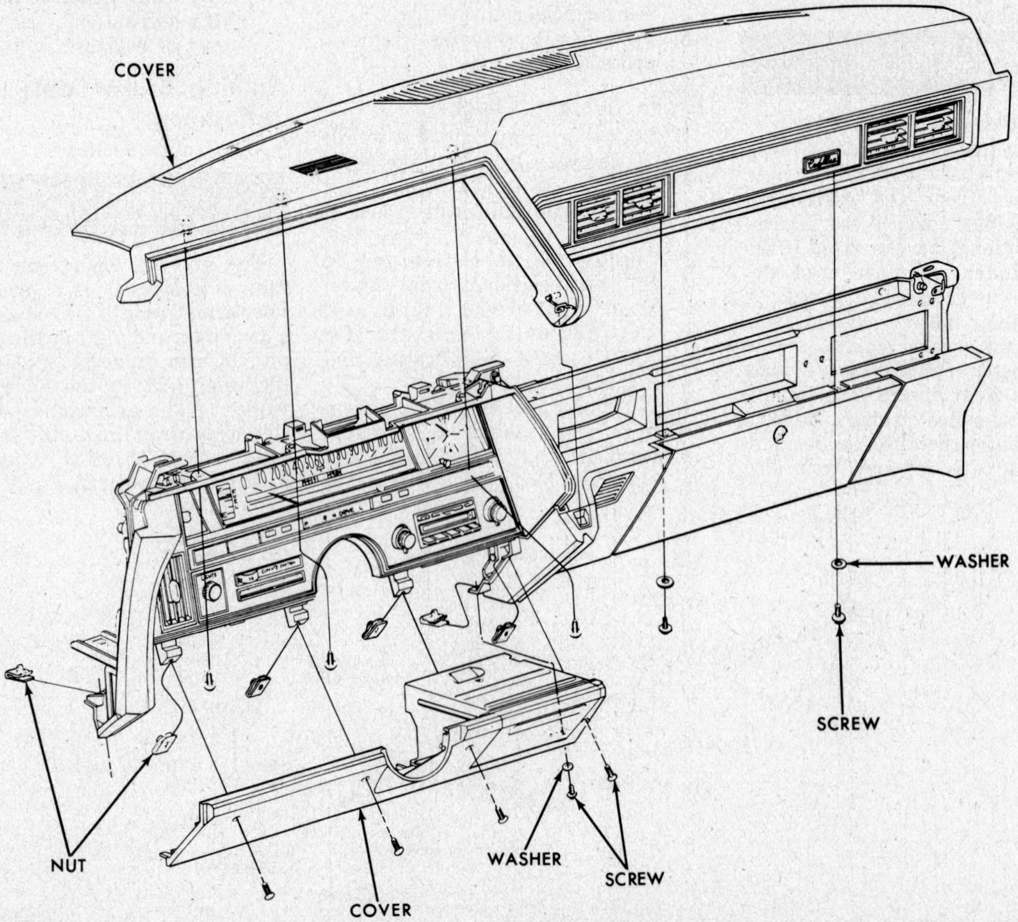
COVER
WASHER
SCREW
NUT
WASHER
SCREW
COVER

Typical instrument panel (© Cadillac Div., G.M. Corp)

removed at the steering knuckles. Then separate the tie rod pivots from the steering knuckles.

6. The linkage can be removed from the frame.
7. If the idler arm is to be removed, loosen the locknut and bolt which fastens it to the frame.
8. Installation is accomplished by reversing the removal procedure. The torque on the damper should be 40 ft lbs while the tie rod torque is 60 ft lbs. When installing the idler arm on the frame tighten the bolt to 95 ft lbs.

Power Steering Pump R & R, Steering Wheel R & R, and Turn Signal Switch R & R

See the Cadillac section.

INSTRUMENT PANEL

Basically the instrument panel of the Eldorado is the same as that of the Cadillac. For a general description of the instrument panel see the Cadillac section.

Upper Instrument Panel Cover Panel R & R

1967-68

1. Disconnect battery.
2. Remove three Phillips head screws holding the instrument panel cluster bezel to the upper cover.
3. From inside the glove compartment door, remove two upper screws holding the upper cover to the right panel.
4. Raise upper panel high enough for clearance, then disconnect the following wire connectors: radio speaker/or speakers, Twilight Sentinel photocell and Automatic Climate Control sensor.
5. Pull upper cover rearward to disengage three hooks at the front of cover from retainers on cowl, and remove cover.
6. Install by reversing removal procedure.

1969-70

1. Disconnect battery.
2. Disconnect radio speaker connection near radio.
3. Remove three Phillips head screws that secure right and left garnish moldings and remove moldings.
4. Inside glove compartment, remove two screws that secure cover to instrument panel.
5. Remove screws that secure cover to bezel assembly.
6. Lift cover up and rearward to disengage from cowl.
7. Disconnect Twilight Sentinel photocell and clock wires. Remove cover.
8. Install in reverse of above.

1971-74

Procedure is the same as for 1969–70, except eliminate Step 3. On 1972 cars with Air Conditioning, remove the aspirator hose from the sensor through the top of the glove box.

Steering Column Lower Cover R & R

1969-70

1. Disconnect battery.
2. Remove screws that secure lower cover to bezel assembly and loosen two screws that secure lower cover to lower instrument panel.
3. Pull lower cover up and out to disengage.
4. Disconnect ash tray wiring and Twilight Sentinel, if so equipped. Remove courtesy light bulb and socket.
5. Remove flasher units from clips on rear sides of cover.
6. Remove cover.
7. Install in reverse of above.

1971-74 (Tilt & Telescope)

1. Disconnect battery.
2. On cars equipped with tilt and telescope steering wheel, put wheel in up position.
3. Remove two Phillips head screws holding the lower end of the steering column lower cover to the lower instrument panel.
4. Remove one long special screw holding upper end of steering column lower cover to clamp.
5. Disengage steering column lower cover by pulling straight out to disengage two upper pins from cover and gain access to flasher unit on rear side of lower cover.
6. Remove flasher unit from mounting clip.
7. Install by reversing removal procedure.

1971-74

1. Disconnect negative battery cable.
2. Disconnect ash tray wires.
3. Pull out ash tray, remove two Phillips screws and ash tray door.
4. Remove ash tray.
5. Remove four screws that secure lower cover to upper cover. One is removed through ash tray opening.
6. Loosen two screws that secure lower cover to lower instrument panel.
7. Disengage lower cover by pulling straight out. Disconnect Twilight Sentinel wiring, remove courtesy lamp and turn signal flasher, then disconnect and remove ash tray light.
8. Remove lower cover.
9. To install, reverse removal procedure.

Speedometer Head R & R

1967-68

1. Remove cluster assembly as previously described.
2. Remove odometer reset knob retainer using a 1/16 in. Allen wrench.
3. Remove clock reset knob retainer using a 1/16 in. Allen wrench.
4. Remove lower clips that hold cluster lens to cluster case.
5. Remove self tapping screws that hold retainer to case.
6. With back of cluster case on the work bench, separate lens and retainer from cluster case.
7. Remove three screws and attached grommets that hold speedometer head to cluster case and place assembly with back of cluster case on the bench.
8. Remove speedometer head from cluster case.
9. Remove map light housing because it will have to be repositioned for assembly.
10. Install by reversing removal procedure.

1969-70

1. Remove cluster assembly.
2. Remove clips that secure cluster lens to case and remove lens.
3. Open staking along lower edges and remove sheet metal retainer and shift indicator dial.
4. Remove screws that secure speedometer head assembly to cluster case and remove assembly with back of cluster case.
5. Lift speedometer head assembly out of cluster case.
6. Install in reverse of above.

1971-74

1. Remove cluster assembly.
2. Remove seven screws that secure back case to dial assembly.
3. Remove three screws that secure printed circuit to fuel gauge; remove gauge.
4. Remove two nuts that secure speedometer head to dial assembly.
5. Slide speedometer head out of lens, making sure pointer is not damaged.
6. To install, reverse removal procedure.

Printed Circuit R & R

1967-68

1. Remove instrument panel cluster as previously described.
2. Remove one nut and wave washer holding printed circuit to clock.
3. Remove 12 wedge-base sockets and bulbs from cluster case.
4. Remove two screws from fuel gauge.
5. Remove two screws from temperature gauge.
6. Remove four screws that hold the printed circuit to cluster case and remove printed circuit.

NOTE: do not attempt to repair this printed circuit.

7. Install by reversing removal procedure.

1969-74

1. Remove instrument panel cluster.
2. Remove 14 sockets and bulbs from cluster case.
3. Snap off fuel gauge cover and remove screws that secure printed circuit flap to fuel gauge.
4. Remove screws that secure circuit to back of cluster case and remove circuit.
5. Install by reversing removal procedure.

Headlight Switch R & R

1967-68

1. Remove steering column lower cover as previously described.
2. Remove hoses at vacuum valve, which is integral with headlight switch.
3. Remove lower right screw holding headlight control switch housing to lower instrument panel.
4. On cars equipped with Automatic Climate Control, remove left outlet hose at inboard side to gain access to upper left screw.
5. Remove upper left screw that holds headlight control switch housing to lower instrument panel.
6. Pull headlight control switch assembly rearward, disconnect wiring harness connectors and two bulbs, then remove assembly.
7. Install by reversing removal procedure.

1969

1. Remove instrument panel upper cover.
2. Remove steering column lower cover.
3. Remove two screws that secure air conditioning duct to bezel assembly and remove duct.
4. Disconnect wiring harness that is below headlight switch assembly.
5. Depress spring loaded release button on top of headlight switch and remove switch, knob and rod assembly.
6. Remove screws that secure switch assembly to bezel.
7. Pull assembly rearward, disconnect wiring connectors, two bulbs and remove assembly.
8. Install in reverse of above.

1970-74

1. Remove steering column lower cover.
2. Disconnect wiring harness retainer below headlight switch assembly.
3. Depress spring loaded release button on top of headlight switch and remove switch, knob and rod assembly.
4. Remove screw with ground wire at bottom of switch housing.
5. Pull assembly down and rearward, disconnect wiring harness connectors, two bulbs and remove assembly.
6. Install in reverse of above.

Ignition Switch R & R

See *Cadillac Section* for same year Eldorado.

Ignition Lock Cylinder R & R

See *Cadillac Section.*

WINDSHIELD WIPERS

The windshield wiper system consists of the wiper motor and transmission assembly. It is similar to that used on other Cadillac models.

Transmission R & R

1967

1. Remove both wiper arm and blade assemblies.
2. Raise hood and remove nine screws that retain front and side edges of ventilator frame to cowl, noting locations of any shims.

NOTE: to reach end screws, open doors and remove cover plates.

3. Carefully raise front edge of ventilator frame and disengage washer hoses.
4. Raise rear edge of frame and slide it forward. Remove vent frame and grill.
5. Remove two screws and cover plate on firewall.
6. Remove locknut that secures wiper crank to ball socket.
7. Remove three transmission mounting screws (each side) and both transmissions, after disengaging ball socket.
8. To install, reverse removal procedure, making sure ball socket is fully seated.

1968-70

1. Remove wiper arm and blade assemblies.
2. Remove screws that secure air inlet screen to cowl; remove screen.
3. Follow Steps 5-8 of 1967 procedure.

NOTE: driver side transmission arm must point *down*, passenger side *up*.

1971-74

1. Raise hood and remove cowl vent screen.
2. Remove wiper arm and blade assembly from side being serviced.
3. Loosen, but do not remove, attaching nuts securing transmission drive linkage to motor crank arm. If only left transmission is being removed, it is not necessary to loosen right attaching nuts.
4. Disconnect transmission drive linkage from motor crank arm.
5. Remove the attaching screws of the transmission being serviced, then remove transmission through plenum chamber opening.
6. To install, reverse removal procedure. Motor must be in "Park" position.

Motor R & R

See Cadillac section.

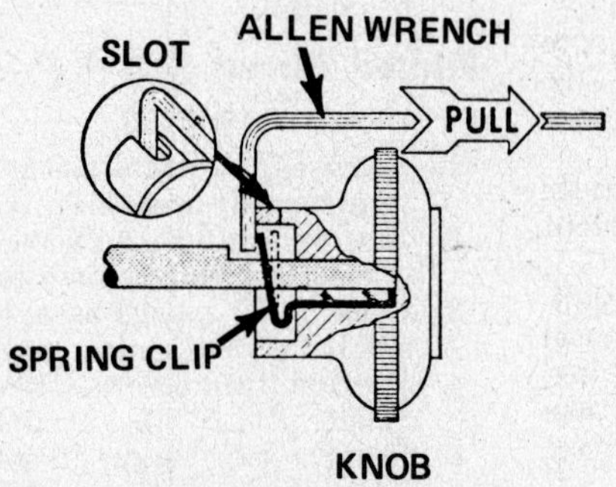
ALLEN WRENCH
SLOT
PULL
SPRING CLIP
KNOB

1971-74 Radio knob removal
(© Cadillac Div., G.M. Corp)

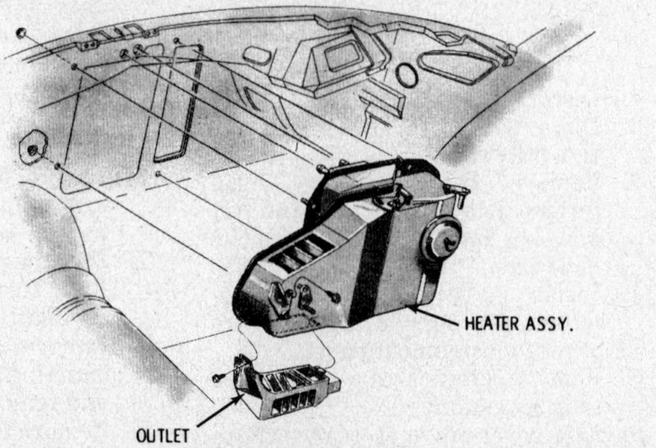
HEATER ASSY.
OUTLET

1969-74 Heater assembly
(© Cadillac Div., G.M. Corp)

RADIO

Procedures for removal and installation of radio may be found under instructions for same year model listed in the Cadillac section. On Eldorado models, it is not necessary to remove the defroster hose, otherwise the procedures for Cadillac apply.

HEATER

Blower Assembly and Motor R & R

1967-70

1. Drain cooling system.
2. Remove rubber cooling hose from nipple and blower motor.
3. Disconnect blower motor electrical connector.
4. Remove five attaching screws and blower motor.
5. Remove left cowl-to-fender strut rod.
6. Remove heater hoses from blower case.
7. Disconnect Bowden cable from temperature door.
8. Disconnect connector from motor resistor.
9. Disconnect vacuum hoses, then remove twelve screws from blower case.
10. Pull blower assembly away from cowl and remove from car.
11. To install, reverse removal procedure, using a new gasket.

1971-74

See Cadillac section.

Heater Core R & R

1967-70

1. Remove heater blower motor and assembly.
2. Remove four screws, two on each side, that secure retaining clamps.
3. Remove retaining clamps and heater core.

1971-74

See Cadillac section.

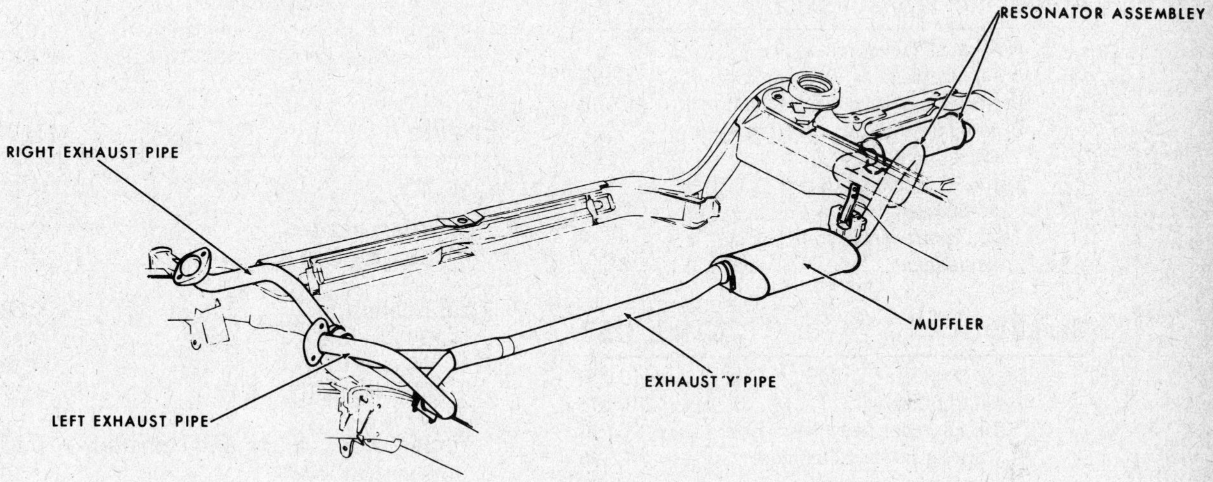
RESONATOR ASSEMBLEY
RIGHT EXHAUST PIPE
MUFFLER
EXHAUST 'Y' PIPE
LEFT EXHAUST PIPE

Exhaust system (1972)—Eldorado (© G.M. Corp)

INDEX

Camaro • Chevelle Chevy II • Monte Carlo

YEAR IDENTIFICATION

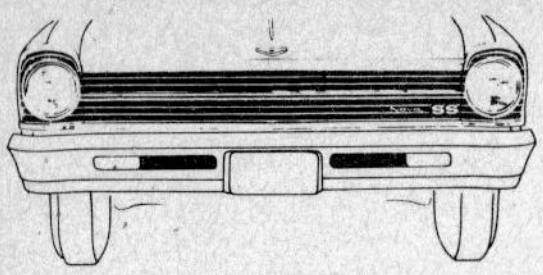
1967 Chevy II

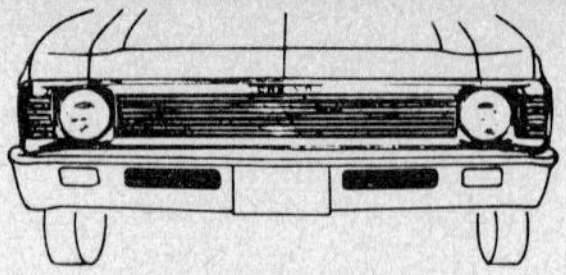
1968 Chevy II

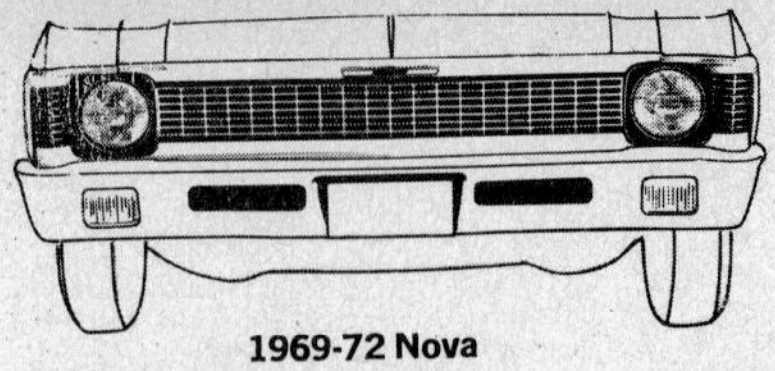
1969-72 Nova

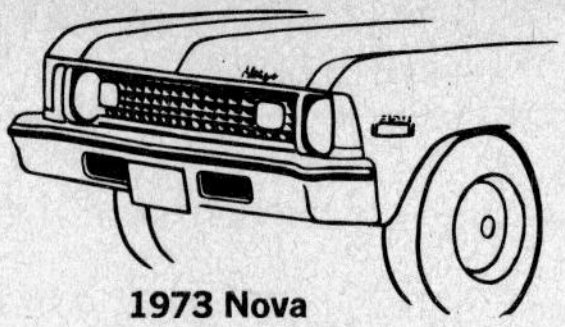
1973 Nova

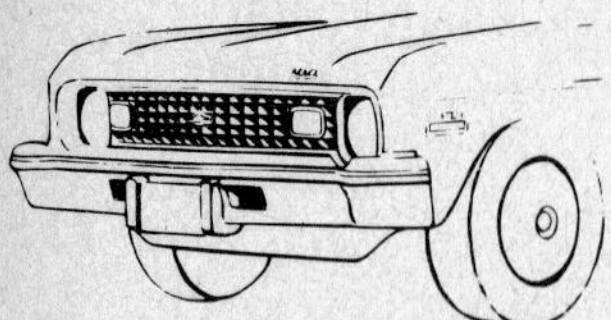
1974 Nova

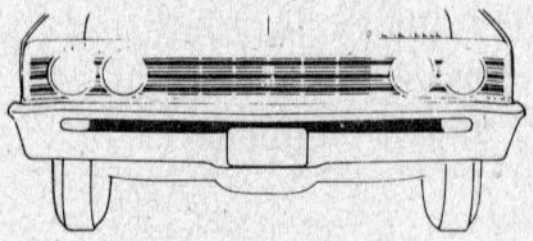
1967 Chevelle

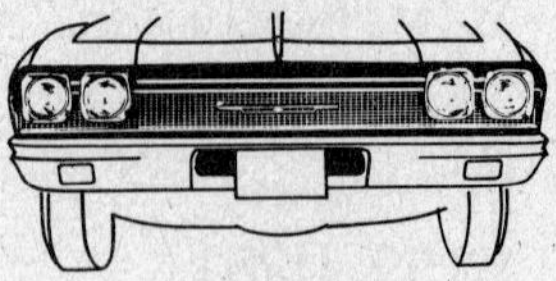
1968 Chevelle

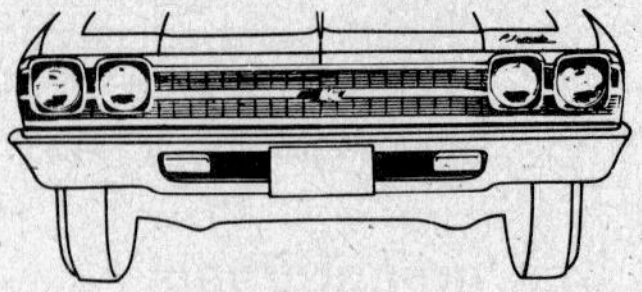
1969 Chevelle

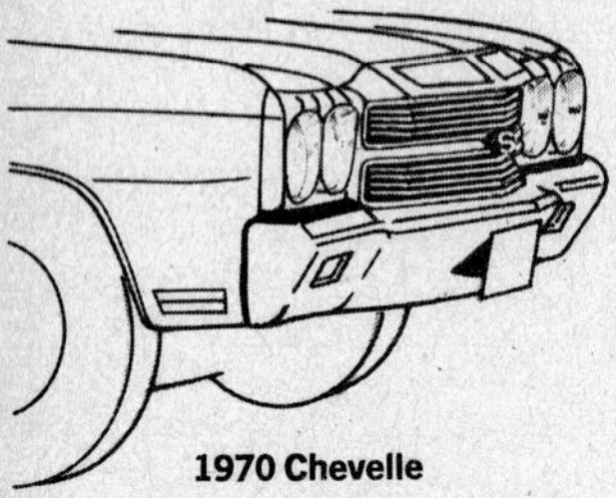
1970 Chevelle

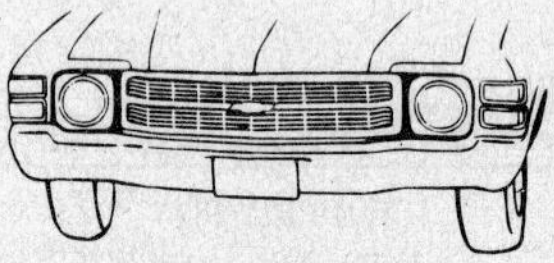
1971 Chevelle

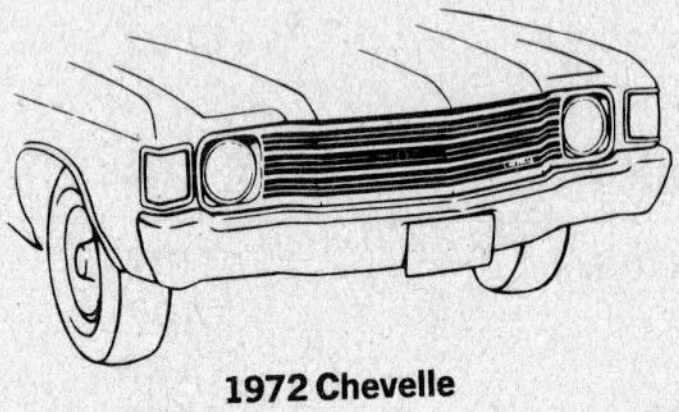
1972 Chevelle

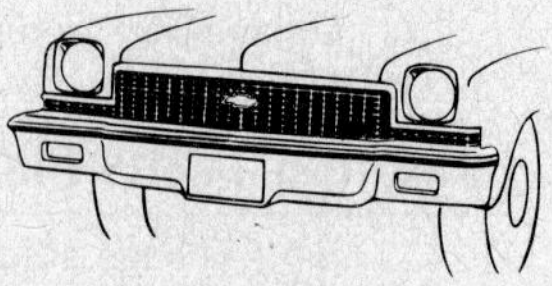
1973 Chevelle

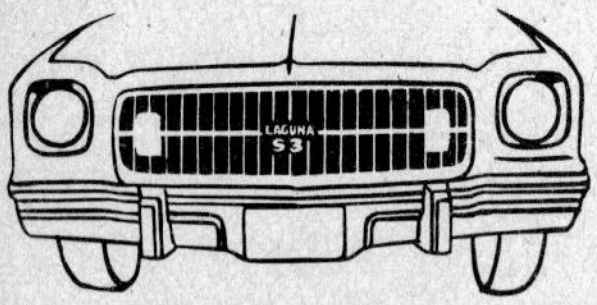
LAGUNA
S3
1974 Chevelle Laguna

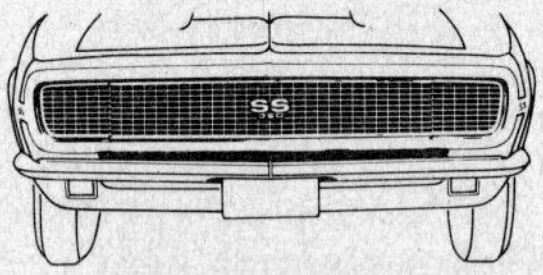
SS
1967 Camaro SS

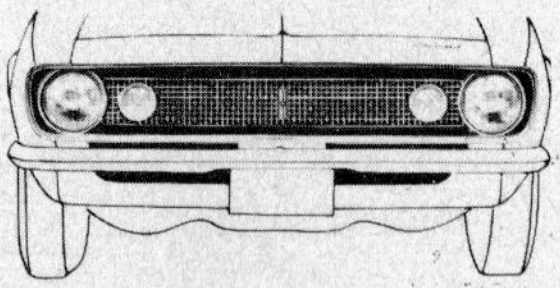
1967 Camaro

350
1968 Camaro SS

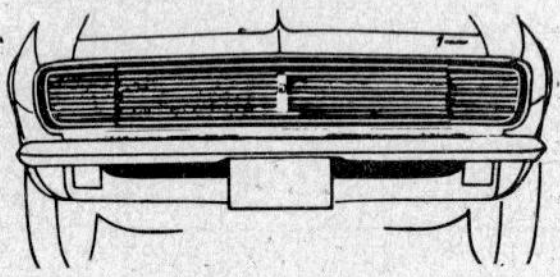
1968 Camaro

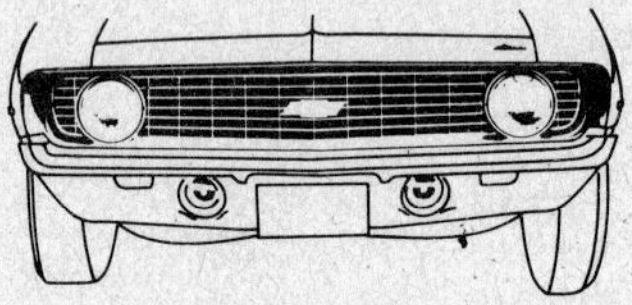
1969 Camaro

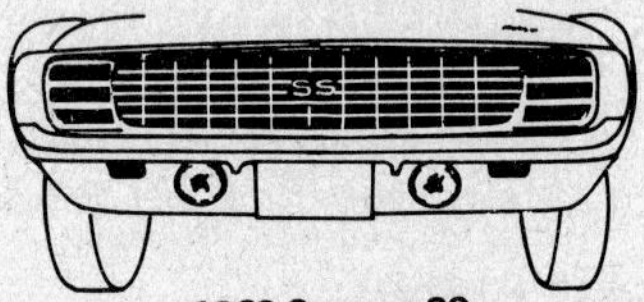
SS
1969 Camaro SS

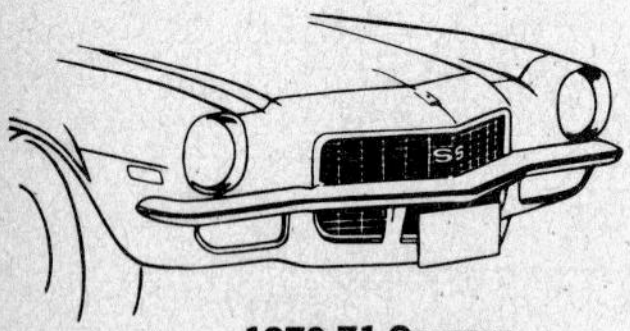
SS
1970-71 Camaro

1972 Camaro

1973 Camaro

1974 Camaro

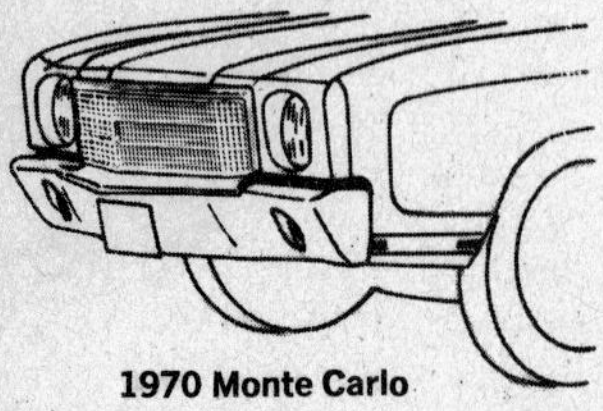
1970 Monte Carlo

1971 Monte Carlo

1972 Monte Carlo

1973 Monte Carlo

1974 Monte Carlo

FIRING ORDER

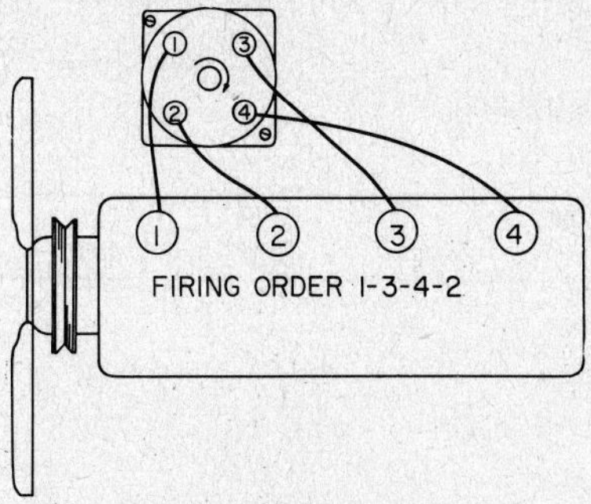

1
2
3
4
FIRING ORDER I-3-4-2

153 4-cyl

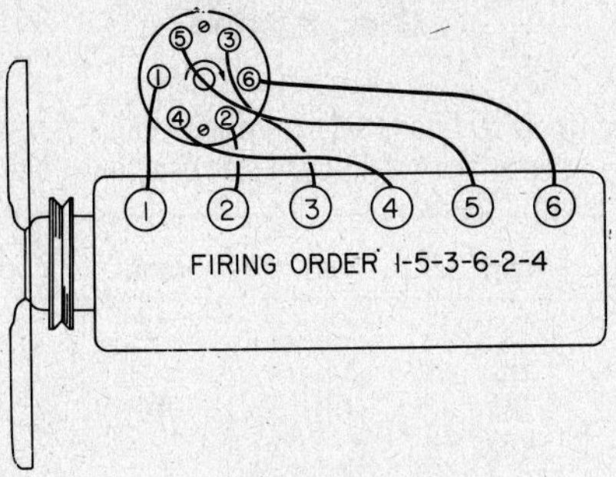

1
2
3
4
5
6
FIRING ORDER I-5-3-6-2-4

194, 230, 250 6-cyl

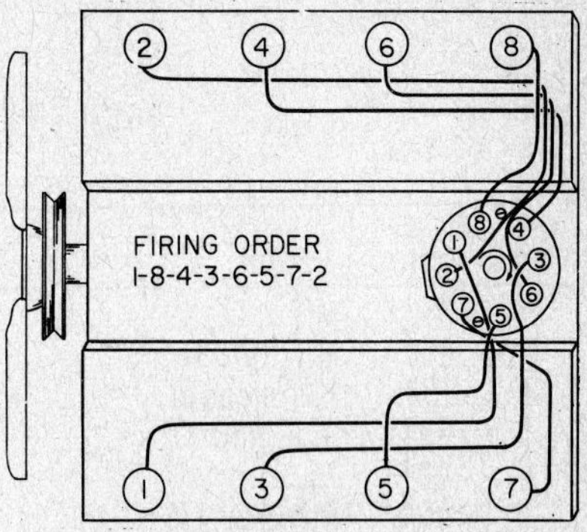

2
4
6
8
FIRING ORDER
I-8-4-3-6-5-7-2
1
3
5
7

283, 307, 327, 350, 396, 400, 454 V8

CAR SERIAL NUMBER LOCATION

1967

Car serial number is found on a plate attached to the left front door hinge pillar.

1968-74

Car serial number is located on the top left-hand side of the instrument panel, visible through the windshield.

Car Serial Number Interpretation

A typical vehicle serial number tag yields manufacturer's identity, vehicle type, model year, assembly plant and production unit number when broken down as shown in the following chart.

Mfr. Identity[1]	*Body Style*[2]	*Model Year*[3]	*Assy. Plant*[4]	*Unit No.*[5]
1	5645	8	F	100025

1. Manufacturer's identity number assigned to all Chevrolet built vehicles.
2. Model Identification
3. Last number of model year (1968).
4. F-Flint
5. Unit numbering will start at 100,001 at all plants.

Engine Identification

Six Cylinder Engines

The production code letters immediately follow the engine serial number. The number is found on a pad at the front right-hand side of the cylinder block, just to the rear of the distributor.

V8 Engines

The production code letters immediately follow the engine serial number. The number is found on a pad at the front right-hand side of the cylinder block.

ALTERNATOR AND REGULATOR SPECIFICATIONS

	ALTERNATOR			REGULATOR						
					Field Relay			Regulator		
Year	Part No. or Manufacturer	Field Current @ 12 V	Output (amps)	Part No. or Manufacturer	Air Gap (in.)	Point Gap (in.)	Volts to Close	Air Gap (in.)	Point Gap (in.)	Volts @ 75°
'67	1100693	2.2-2.6	37	1119515	.015	.030	2.3-3.7	.067	.014	13.5-14.4
	1100695	2.2-2.6	32	1119515	.015	.030	2.3-3.7	.067	.014	13.5-14.4
	1100794	2.2-2.6	37	1119515	.015	.030	2.3-3.7	.067	.014	13.5-14.4
'68	1100813	2.2-2.6	37	1119515	.015	.030	2.3-3.7	.067	.014	13.5-14.4
	1100693	2.2-2.6	37	1119515	.015	.030	2.3-3.7	.067	.014	13.5-14.4
'69	1100834	2.2-2.6	37	1119515	.015	.030	2.3-3.7	.067	.014	13.5-14.4
	1100836	2.2-2.6	37	1119515	.015	.030	2.3-3.7	.067	.014	13.5-14.4
'70	1100834	2.2-2.6	37	1119515	.015	.030	2.3-3.7	.067	.014	13.5-14.4
	1100837	2.2-2.6	37	1119515	.015	.030	2.3-3.7	.067	.014	13.5-14.4
'71	1100838	2.2-2.6	37	1119515	.015	.030	2.3-3.7	.067	.014	13.5-14.4
	1100839	2.2-2.6	37	1119515	.015	.030	2.3-3.7	.067	.014	13.5-14.4
'72	1100566	2.2-2.6	35	1119515	.015	.030	1.5-3.2	.067	.014	13.8-14.8
	1100917	2.8-3.2	59	1119519	.030	.030	1.5-3.2	.067	.014	13.8-14.8
	1100843	2.8-3.2	58	Integrated with alternator						13.8-14.8
'73-'74	1100497	2.8-3.2	36	Integrated with alternator						13.8-14.8
	1100934	2.8-3.2	37	Integrated with alternator						13.8-14.8

ENGINE IDENTIFICATION CODE, LOCATION

Chevy II/Nova

4-6 Cyl.—Pad at front right-hand side of cylinder block at rear of distributor.
V8—Pad at front right-hand side of cylinder block.

No. Cyls.	Cu. In. Displ.	Type	YEAR AND CODE 1967	1968	1969	1970	1971	1972	1973
4	153	M.T.		OA	AA				
4	153	M.T., HDC	OC	OC					
4	153	PG, Torque Dr.	OH	OH	AB				
6	194	M.T., HDC	OM						
6	194	PG	OR						
6	194	PG, w/ex. EM	ZX						
6	194	w/ex. EM	ZY						
6	230	PG		BF					
6	230	PG, w/ex. EM			AN				
6	230	HDC, AC		BB					
6	230	HDC		BC					
6	230	PG, AC		BH	AQ				
6	230	T.H. 350			AO				
6	230	AC			AP				
6	230	T.H. 350, AC			AR				
6	230	M.T.	PV		AM				
6	230	Torque Dr.			AN	CCD			
6	250	M.T., or OD	PC, PV	CB	BE	CCG, CRF	CCI, CCL	CBG, CDM	CCC
6	250	PG, w/ex. EM	PI, PX	CQ	BB	CCM		CSD	CCA
6	250	PG, AC			BC				
6	250	T.H. 350			BD	CCK			
6	250	AC			BF				
6	250	T.H. 350, AC			BH				
6	250	Torque Dr.			BB, BC				
6	250	M.T.				CAA			
6	250	PG, TD				CAB			
6	250	M.T., w/NB2							CCD
6	250	PG, w/NB2							CCB
8	283	M.T., 4-spd.	PL						
8	283	4-spd., AC	PM						
8	283	M.T., 3-spd.	PD						
8	283	PG	PN						
8	283	PG, AC	PP						
8	283	w/ex. EM	PE						
8	283	AC	PF						
8	283	4-spd., w/ex. EM	PQ						
8	283	PG, w/ex. EM	PU						
8	307	M.T.						CKG	CHB
8	307	PG						CKH	
8	307	T.H.						CTK	CHH
8	307	M.T., w/ex. EM						CAR	
8	307	PG, w/ex. EM						CAZ	
8	307	T.H., w/ex. EM						CMA	
8	307	M.T., w/NB2							CHD
8	307	T.H., w/NB2							CHC

AC—air conditioned
HDC—heavy duty clutch
HP—high performance engine
SHP—special high performance engine
PCV—positive crankcase ventilation
w/ex. EM, or EM—with exhaust emission
M.T.—manual transmission
PG—Powerglide transmission
3-spd.—three speed transmission
4-spd.—four speed transmission
T.H.—Turbo Hydra-Matic
#—Aluminum heads
TD—Torque Drive
NB2—Calif. only

Chevy II/Nova

4-6 Cyl.—Pad at front right-hand side of cylinder block at rear of distributor.
V8—Pad at front right-hand side of cylinder block.

No. Cyls.	Cu. In. Displ.	Type	1967	1968	1969	1970	1971	1972	1973
			YEAR AND CODE						
8	307	M.T.		MB	DA	CNC			
8	307	SHP		ML					
8	307	PG		MM	DC	CNE			
8	307	T.H. 350			DD	CNF			
8	307	4-spd.			DE	CND			
8	307	M.T.				CCA	CCA		
8	307	PG				CCC	CCC		
8	327	M.T.	ZA	MK					
8	327	w/ex. EM	ZB						
8	327	w/ex. EM, PG	ZD						
8	327	M.T., AC	ZE						
8	327	SHP		ML					
8	327	PG	ZK	MM					
8	327	PG, AC	ZM						
8	350	M.T.			HA, HQ	CNI(250), CNJ(300)		CKA CKK	CKA, CKB
8	350	T.H.			HB, HD	CNN(250), CRE(300)		CTL CKD	CKW CKW
8	350	2-BBL.			HC				
8	350	PG			HE, HR	CNK, CNM			
8	350	PG, 2-BBL.			HF				
8	350	T.H.			HS				
8	350	PG				CGB(250)	CGB		
8	350	M.T.				CGK(300)	CGK		
8	350	T.H. 350				CGL(300) CJD(300)	CGL	CDD CMD	
8	350	M.T.				CJG(300)		CDG	
8	350	M.T., w/NB2							CKC, CKH
8	350	A.T., w/NB2							CKK, CKD
8	396	HP			JF				
8	396	SHP			JH, KA, KC				
8	396	HP, T.H. 400			JI				
8	396	SHP, T.H. 400			JL				
8	396	T.H. 400			JM	CTW(350), CTY(375), CKN(325)			
8	396	PG			JU				
8	396	M.T.			KE	CTX(350), CKO(375)			
8	396	T.H. 400#				CKP(375)			
8	396	M.T., HDC				CTZ(350), CKQ(375)			
8	396	B.T., HDC#				CKU(375)			
8	396	M.T.#				CKT(375)			
8	402	M.T.				CKR(330)			
8	402	M.T., HDC				CKS(300)			

AC—air conditioned
HDC—heavy duty clutch
HP—high performance engine
SHP—special high performance engine
PCV—positive crankcase ventilation
OD—overdrive
w/ex. EM, or EM—with exhaust emission
M.T.—manual transmission
PG—Powerglide transmission.
3-spd.—three speed transmission
4-spd.—four speed transmission
T.H.—Turbo Hydra-Matic
#—Aluminum heads
TD—Torque Drive
NB2—Calif. only

Chevelle and Monte Carlo Engine Identification Code Location

Engine identification code letter follows immediately after engine serial number.
6 Cyl.—Pad at front right-hand side of cylinder block at rear of distributor.
V8—Pad at front right-hand side of cylinder block.

No. Cyls.	Cu. In. Displ.	Type	YEAR AND CODE 1967	1968	1969	1970	1971	1972	1973
6	230	HDC	BC	BC	BC				
6	230	HDC, AC	BB	BB	BB				
6	230	PG		BF	BF				
6	230	PG, w/ex. EM			AN				
6	230	T.H., AC			AR				
6	230	T.H.			AD				
6	230	M.T.	CA	BA	AM				
6	230	3-spd. AC	CB		AP				
6	230	PG	CC						
6	230	PG, AC	CD	BH	AQ				
6	250	3-spd. or OD	CM	CM	BE	CCL			
6	250	3-spd. AC	CN	CN	BF				
6	250	3-spd. or OD w/ex. EM	CO						
6	250	3-spd. AC w/ex. EM	CP						
6	250	PG	CQ	CQ	BB	CCM		CBJ	
6	250	PG, AC	CR	CR	BC				
6	250	T.H.			BD	CCK			CCA
6	250	PG, w/ex. EM	CS						
6	250	T.H., AC			BH				
6	250	PG, AC w/ex. EM	CT						
6	250	M.T.					CAA	CBG	CCC
6	250	M.T., w/NB2							CCD
6	250	T.H., w/NB2							CCB
8	283	3-spd.	DA						
8	283	4-spd.	DB						
8	283	PG	DE						
8	283	w/ex. EM	DI						
8	283	PG, w/ex. EM	DJ						
8	283	4-spd., w/ex. EM	DK						
8	283	HDC	DN						
8	307	T.H.			DD	CNF		CTK	CMA
8	307	M.T.		DA	DA	CNC			CHB
8	307	4-spd.		DE	DE	CND			
8	307	PG		DB	DC	CNE		CKH	
8	307	HDC		DN					
8	307	M.T.					CCA	CKG	
8	300	T.H., w/NB2							CHC
8	327	M.T.	EA	EA					
8	327	w/ex. EM	EB						
8	327	PG, w/ex. EM	EC						
8	327	3- or 4-spd. (325 hp)	EP						
8	327	HDC, 3- or 4-spd. w/ex. EM (325 hp)	ER						
8	327	HDC (325 hp)	ES	ES					
8	327	HDC (275 hp)	ED	ED					
8	327	PG	EE	EE					

AC—air conditioned
HDC—heavy duty clutch
HP—high performance
M.T.—manual transmission
OD—overdrive
PG—powerglide transmission
PCV—positive crankcase ventilation
w/ex. EM—with exhaust emission
w/T. Ign.—with transistor ignition
4-BBL.—four-barrel carburetor
T.H.—Turbo Hydra-Matic
#—Aluminum heads
NB2—Calif. only

Chevelle and Monte Carlo Engine Identification Code Location

Engine identification code letter follows immediately after engine serial number.
6 Cyl.—Pad at front right-hand side of cylinder block at rear of distributor.
V8—Pad at front right-hand side of cylinder block.

No. Cyls.	Cu. In. Displ.	Type	YEAR AND CODE 1967	1968	1969	1970	1971	1972	1973
8	350	M.T.			HA			CKK, CKA	CKA, CKB
8	350	T.H.			HB				
8	350	2-BBL.			HC				
8	350	2-BBL., T.H.			HD				
8	350	PG			HE	CNM(250)			
8	350	PG, 2-BBL.			HF				
8	350	M.T.			HP	CNI(250)			
8	350	M.T.			HR	CNJ(300)			
8	350	PG			HR	CNK(300)		CKB, CDB	
8	350	T.H.			HS	CRE(300)		CT, CKD	CKL, CKJ
8	350	M.T.					CGA(245)		
8	350	PG					CGB(245)		
8	350	M.T.					CGK(270)		
8	350	T.H. 350					CGL(270) CJD(270)		
8	350	M.T.					CJJ(270)		
8	350	M.T., w/NB2							CKC, CKH
8	350	T.H., w/NB2							CKD, CKK
8	396	HDC	ED	ED	ED				
8	396	HP	EF	EF	JC				
8	396	SHP		EG	JD				
8	396	w/ex. EM	EH						
8	396	HP, w/ex. EM	EJ						
8	396	PG	EK	EK	EK				
8	396	PG, HP	EL	EL	EL				
8	396	PG, w/ex. EM	EM						
8	396	PG, HP, w/ex. EM	EN						
8	396	T.H. (325 hp)	ET	ET	ET				
8	396	T.H. (350 hp)	EU	EU	EU				
8	396	w/ex. EM (325 hp)	EV						
8	396	w/ex. EM (350 hp)	EW						
8	396	M.T.			JA	CTX(350) CKT(375) CKO(375)			
8	396	HP, 3-spd. T.H. 400			JE				
8	396	T.H. 400			JK	CTW(350)			
8	396	SHP, T.H. 400 (#—CKP only)			KF	CTY(375), CKP(375) CKU(375)			
8	396	M.T.			KG				
8	396	T.H. 400			KH	CKN(325)			
8	396	M.T., HP			KB				
8	396	M.T.			JV				
8	396	SHP, M.T.			KD				
8	396	M.T.			KI				
8	396	M.T., HDC				CTZ(350), CKQ(375)			
8	402	M.T.				CKR			
8	402	M.T., HDC (330 hp)				CKS		CLA, CLS	
8	402	T.H. 350 (Mk. IV)							
8	402	T.H. 400 (Mk. IV)					CLB	CLB	
8	402	M.T. (Mk. IV)							
8	402	4-spd. (Mk. IV)					CLL		
8	402	M.T. Police (Mk. IV)					CLR		
8	402	M.T. (Mk. IV)					CLS		

AC—air conditioned
HDC—heavy duty clutch
HP—high performance
M.T.—manual transmission
OD—overdrive
PG—powerglide transmission
PCV—positive crankcase ventilation
w/ex. EM—with exhaust emission
w/T. Ign.—with transistor ignition
4-BBL.—four-barrel carburetor
T.H.—Turbo Hydra-Matic
#—Aluminum heads
NB2—Calif. only

Chevelle and Monte Carlo Engine Identification Code location (cont'd.)

Engine identification code letter follows immediately after engine serial number.
6 Cyl.—Pad at front right-hand side of cylinder block at rear of distributor.
V8—Pad at front right-hand side of cylinder block.

No. Cyls.	Cu. In. Displ.	Type	YEAR AND CODE 1967	1968	1969	1970	1971	1972	1973
8	402	M.T. (Mk. IV)					CPR		
8	400	M.T. (Mk. IV)					CPA	CPA	
							CPG		
							CPD		
							CPP		
8	454	M.T. (390 hp)				CRN, CRT			
8	454	T.H. 400				CRQ			
8	454	T.H. 400 (450 hp)				CRR		CPD	
8	454	T.H. 400# (450 hp)				CRS			
8	454	M.T.				CRV			CWA
8	454	T.H.							CWB
8	454	M.T., w/NB2							CWC
8	454	T.H. w/NB2							CWD

AC—air conditioned
HDC—heavy duty clutch
HP—high performance
M.T.—manual transmission
OD—overdrive
PG—powerglide transmission
PCV—positive crankcase ventilation
w/ex. EM—with exhaust emission
w/T. Ign.—with transistor ignition
4-BBL.—four-barrel carburetor
T.H.—Turbo Hydra-Matic
#—Aluminum heads
NB2—Calif. only

Camaro
Engine Identification Code Location

Engine identification code letter follows immediately after engine serial number.
6 Cyl.—Pad at front right-hand side of cylinder block at rear of distributor.
V8—Pad at front right-hand side of cylinder block.

No. Cyls.	Cu. In. Displ.	Type	YEAR AND CODE 1967	1968	1969	1970	1971	1972	1973
6	230	3 or 4-spd.	LA	BA	AM	CCC			
6	230	3 or 4-spd. AC	LB	BB					
6	230	3 or 4-spd. w/ex. EM	LC						
6	230	3 or 4-spd. AC, w/ex. EM	LD						
6	230	PG, Torque Dr.	LE	BF	AN	CCD			
6	230	PG, AC	LH, LF	BH	AQ				
6	230	T.H. 350			AO				
6	230	AC			AP				
6	230	T.H. 350, AC			AR				
6	230	PG, w/ex. EM	LG						
6	250	3 or 4-spd.	LN	CM	BE				
6	250	3 or 4-spd. AC	LO	CN					
6	250	PG, w/ex. EM	LP						
6	250	3 or 4-spd. w/ex. EM	LQ						
6	250	AC			BF				
6	250	PG, Torque Dr.	FM	CQ	BB				
6	250	PG, AC	FR	CR	BC				
6	250	PG, w/ex. EM	GP					CDL	
6	250	PG, AC, w/ex. EM	GQ		BC				
6	250	T.H. 350			BD				
6	250	T.H. 350, AC			BH				
6	250	M.T.					CAA	CBG	CCC
6	250	PG					CCA	CBJ	
6	250	T.H.							CCA
6	250	M.T., w/NB2							CCP
6	250	T.H., w/NB2							CCB
8	302	Z28		DZ	DZ*				
8	307	M.T.			DA	CNC			
8	307	P.G.			DC	CNE			
8	307	T.H. 350			DD	CNF		CTK	CHH
8	307	4-spd.			DE	CND			

Camaro
Engine Identification Code Location

Engine identification code letter follows immediately after engine serial number.
6 Cyl.—Pad at front right-hand side of cylinder block at rear of distributor.
V8—Pad at front right-hand side of cylinder block.

No. Cyls.	Cu. In. Displ.	Type	YEAR AND CODE 1967	1968	1969	1970	1971	1972	1973
8	307	M.T.					CCA	CKG	CHB
8	307	PG					CCA	CKH	
8	307	M.T., w/NB2							CHJ
8	307	T.H., w/NB2							CHK
8	327	3 or 4-spd. (210)	MA	MA					
8	327	3 or 4-spd. w/ex. EM	MB						
8	327	PG (210 hp)	ME	ME					
8	327	PG, w/ex. EM	MF						
8	327	3 or 4-spd. (275 hp)	MK						
8	327	3 or 4-spd. w/ex. EM	ML						
8	327	PG (275 hp)	MM						
8	327	PG, w/ex. EM	MN						
8	350	3 or 4-spd.	MS	MS	HA, HQ	CNJ(300)			
8	350	3 or 4-spd. w/ex. EM	MT						
8	350	PG	MU	MU	HE, HR	CNK(300)			
8	350	PG, w/ex. EM	MV						
8	350	T.H.			HB, HS	CRE(300)		CKD	
8	350	2-BBL.			HC	CNJ(250)			
8	350	T.H., 2-BBL.			HD	CNM(250)			
8	350	PG, 2-BBL.			HF	CNN(250)			
8	350	PG					CGB(245)		
8	350	T.H. 400					CGR(330)		CLK
8	350	M.T.					CGK(270)	CKA	CKB
							CJG(270)	CRG	
8	350	T.H. 350					CGL(270)	CTL	CKU
							CJD(270)	CRD	CKW
8	350	M.T.					CJG(330)	CKK	
8	350	M.T., 4-spd.							CLJ
									CKA
8	350	M.T., w/NB2							CLM
									CKY
8	350	T.H., w/NB2							CKH
									CLL
									CKX
									CKD
8	396	M.T. & PG	MW	MW					
8	396	M.T. & PG w/ex. EM	MX						
8	396	T.H. 400	MY	MY	JG	CJI(350)			
8	396	T.H. w/ex. EM	MZ						
8	396	SHP		MQ	JH				
8	396	HP, T.H.		MR	JI				
8	396	SHP#		MT					
8	396	HP		MX	JF				
8	396	PG			JB				
8	396	M.T.#			JJ, KE				
8	396	SHP, T.H. 400			JL	CJL(375)			
8	396	T.H. 400#			JM				
8	396	M.T.			JU	CJF(350)			
8	396	M.T., SHP			KA, KC	CJH(375)			
8	402	T.H.				CTW(350),		CTB	
						CKN(325),			
						CTY(375)			
8	402	M.T.				CTX(350),		CLA	
						CKO(375)		CTA	
8	402	T.H.					CLD(300)	CLB	
8	402	M.T.					CLC(300)		

AC—air conditioned
HDC—heavy duty clutch
HP—high performance
SHP—special high performance
M.T.—manual transmission
PG—Powerglide transmission
w/ex. EM—with exhaust emission
4-BBL.—four-barrel carburetor
2-BBL.—two-barrel carburetor
T.H.—Turbo Hydra-Matic
*—CNA = late production
#—Aluminum heads
NB2—Calif. only

GENERAL ENGINE SPECIFICATIONS

Year	Engine Cu. In. Displacement	Carburetor Type	Advertised Horsepower @ rpm ■	Advertised Torque @ rpm (ft lbs) ■	Bore and Stroke (in.)	Advertised Compression Ratio	Oil Pressure @ 2000 rpm
'67	4-153	1 bbl	90 @ 4000	152 @ 2400	3.875 x 3.250	8.5:1	38
	6-194	1 bbl	120 @ 4000	177 @ 2400	3.563 x 3.250	8.5:1	38
	6 230	1 bbl	140 @ 4400	220 @ 1600	3.875 x 3.250	8.5:1	38
	6-250	1 bbl	155 @ 4200	235 @ 1600	3.875 x 3.530	8.5:1	38①
	8-283	2 bbl	195 @ 4600	285 @ 2400	3.875 x 3.000	9.25:1	38①
	8-327	2 bbl	210 @ 4600	320 @ 2400	4.001 x 3.250	8.75:1	38①
	8-327	4 bbl	275 @ 4800	355 @ 3200	4.001 x 3.250	10.0:1	38①
	8-350	4 bbl	295 @ 4800	380 @ 3200	4.000 x 3.480	10.25:1	38①
	8-396	4 bbl	325 @ 4800	410 @ 3200	4.094 x 3.760	10.25:1	57
	8-396	4 bbl	350 @ 5200	415 @ 3400	4.094 x 3.760	10.25:1	57
'68	4-153	1 bbl	90 @ 4000	152 @ 2400	3.875 x 3.250	8.5:1	58
	6-230	1 bbl	145 @ 4400	220 @ 1600	3.875 x 3.250	8.5:1	58
	6-250	1 bbl	155 @ 4200	235 @ 1600	3.875 x 3.530	8.5:1	58
	8-302	4 bbl	290 @ 5800	290 @ 4200	4.000 x 3.000	11.0:1	45
	8-307	2 bbl	200 @ 4600	300 @ 2400	3.875 x 3.250	9.0:1	58
	8-327	2 bbl	210 @ 4600	320 @ 2400	4.001 x 3.250	8.75:1	58
	8-327	4 bbl	275 @ 4800	355 @ 3200	4.001 x 3.250	10.0:1	58
	8-350	4 bbl	295 @ 4800	380 @ 3200	4.000 x 3.480	10.25:1	58
	8-396	4 bbl	325 @ 4800	410 @ 3200	4.094 x 3.760	10.25:1	62
	8-396	4 bbl	350 @ 5200	415 @ 3400	4.094 x 3.760	10.25:1	62
	8-396	4 bbl	375 @ 5600	415 @ 3600	4.094 x 3.760	11.0:1	62
'69	4-153	1 bbl	90 @ 4000	152 @ 2400	3.875 x 3.250	8.5:1	58
	6-230	1 bbl	140 @ 4400	220 @ 1600	3.875 x 3.250	8.5:1	58
	6-250	1 bbl	155 @ 4200	235 @ 1600	3.875 x 3.530	8.5:1	58
	8-302	4 bbl	290 @ 5800	290 @ 4200	4.000 x 3.000	11.0:1	45
	8-307	2 bbl	200 @ 4600	300 @ 2400	3.875 x 3.250	9.0:1	58
	8-350	2 bbl	250 @ 4800	345 @ 2800	4.000 x 3.480	9.0:1	62
	8-350	4 bbl	300 @ 4800	380 @ 3200	4.000 x 3.480	10.25:1	62
	8-396	4 bbl	325 @ 4800	410 @ 3200	4.094 x 3.760	10.25:1	62
	8-396	4 bbl	350 @ 5200	415 @ 3400	4.094 x 3.760	10.25:1	62
	8-396	4 bbl	375 @ 5600	415 @ 3600	4.094 x 3.760	11.0:1	62
'70	4-153	1 bbl	90 @ 4000	152 @ 2400	3.875 x 3.250	8.5:1	40
	6-230	1 bbl	140 @ 4400	220 @ 1600	3.875 x 3.250	8.5:1	40
	6-250	1 bbl	155 @ 4200	235 @ 1600	3.875 x 3.530	8.5:1	40
	8-307	2 bbl	200 @ 4600	300 @ 2400	3.875 x 3.250	9.0:1	40
	8-350	2 bbl	250 @ 4800	345 @ 2800	4.000 x 3.480	9.0:1	40
	8-350	4 bbl	300 @ 4800	380 @ 3200	4.000 x 3.480	10.25:1	40
	8-400	2 bbl	265 @ 4400	400 @ 2400	4.125 x 3.760	9.0:1	40
	8-402	4 bbl	330 @ 4800	410 @ 3200	4.126 x 3.760	10.25:1	40
	8-402	4 bbl	350 @ 5200	415 @ 3400	4.126 x 3.760	10.25:1	40
	8-454	4 bbl	360 @ 4400	500 @ 3200	4.251 x 4.000	10.25:1	40
'71	6-250	1 bbl	145 @ 4200	230 @ 1600	3.875 x 3.530	8.5:1	40
	8-307	2 bbl	200 @ 4600	300 @ 2400	3.875 x 3.250	8.5:1	40
	8-350	2 bbl	245 @ 4800	350 @ 2800	4.000 x 3.480	8.5:1	40
	8-350	4 bbl	270 @ 4800	360 @ 3200	4.000 x 3.480	8.5:1	40
	8-350	4 bbl	330 @ 5000	275 @ 5600	4.000 x 3.480	9.0:1	40
	8-402	4 bbl	300 @ 4800	400 @ 3200	4.126 x 3.760	8.5:1	40
	8-454	4 bbl	365 @ 4800	465 @ 3200	4.251 x 4.000	8.5:1	40
	8-454	4 bbl	425 @ 5600	475 @ 4000	4.251 x 4.000	9.0:1	40

GENERAL ENGINE SPECIFICATIONS

Year	Engine Cu. In. Displacement	Carburetor Type	Advertised Horsepower @ rpm ■	Advertised Torque @ rpm (ft lbs) ■	Bore and Stroke (in.)	Advertised Compression Ratio	Oil Pressure @ 2000 rpm
'72	6-250	1 bbl	110 @ 3800	185 @ 1600	3.875 x 3.530	8.5:1	40
	8-307	2 bbl	130 @ 4000	230 @ 2400	3.875 x 3.250	8.5:1	40
	8-350	2 bbl	165 @ 4000	280 @ 2400	4.000 x 3.480	8.5:1	40
	8-350	4 bbl	200 @ 4400	300 @ 2800	4.000 x 3.480	8.5:1	40
	8-350	4 bbl	255 @ 5600	280 @ 4000	4.000 x 3.480	9.0:1	40
	8-402	4 bbl	240 @ 4400	345 @ 3200	4.126 x 3.760	8.5:1	40
	8-454	4 bbl	220 @ 4000	390 @ 3200	4.251 x 4.000	8.5:1	40
'73	6-250	1 bbl	100 @ 3800	175 @ 1600	3.875 x 3.530	8.25:1	40
	8-307	2 bbl	115 @ 4000	205 @ 2000	3.875 x 3.250	8.5:1	40
	8-350	2 bbl	145 @ 4000	255 @ 2400	4.000 x 3.480	8.5:1	40
	8-350	4 bbl	175 @ 4400	270 @ 2400	4.000 x 3.480	8.5:1	40
	8-350	4 bbl	245 @ 5200	280 @ 4000	4.000 x 3.480	9.0:1	40
	8-454	4 bbl	245 @ 4000	375 @ 2800	4.251 x 4.000	8.5:1	40
'74	6-250	1 bbl	100 @ 3600	175 @ 1800	3.875 x 3.530	8.25:1	40
	8-350②	2 bbl	145 @ 3600	250 @ 2200	4.000 x 3.480	8.5:1	40
	8-350③	4 bbl	160 @ 3800	245 @ 2400	4.000 x 3.480	8.5:1	40
	8-350	4 bbl	185 @ 4000	270 @ 2600	4.000 x 3.480	8.5:1	40
	8-350/Z28	4 bbl	245 @ 5400	280 @ 4000	4.000 x 3.480	9.0:1	40
	8-400②	2 bbl	150 @ 3200	295 @ 2600	4.126 x 3.750	8.5:1	40
	8-400③	4 bbl	180 @ 3800	290 @ 2400	4.126 x 3.750	8.5:1	40
	8-454	4 bbl	235 @ 4000	360 @ 2800	4.251 x 4.000	8.25:1	44

■ Starting 1972, horsepower and torque are SAE net figures. They are measured at the rear of the transmission with all accessories installed and operating. Since the figures vary when a given engine is installed in different models, some are representative rather than exact.

① Oil pressure at 1500 rpm
② Not available—Calif.
③ Calif. only

Camaro

TUNE-UP SPECIFICATIONS

When analyzing compression test results, look for uniformity among cylinders rather than specific pressures.

Year	ENGINE: No. Cyl Displacement (cu in.)	ENGINE: hp	SPARK PLUGS: Type §	SPARK PLUGS: Gap (in.)	DISTRIBUTOR: Point Dwell (deg)	DISTRIBUTOR: Point Gap (in.)	IGNITION TIMING (deg) ▲: Man Trans	IGNITION TIMING (deg) ▲: Auto Trans	VALVES Intake Opens ■ (deg) ●	Fuel Pump Pressure (psi)	IDLE SPEED (rpm) ▲: Man Trans	IDLE SPEED (rpm) ▲: Auto Trans
'67	6-230	140	46N	.035	31-34	.019	4B	4B	62	3½-4½	500②	500②
	6-230①	140	46N	.035	31-34	.019	4B	4B	62	3½-4½	700	500
	6-250	155	46N	.035	31-34	.019	4B	4B	62	3½-4½	500②	500②
	6-250①	155	46N	.035	31-34	.019	4B	4B	62	3½-4½	700	500
	8-327	210	44	.035	28-32	.019	2B	2B	36	5¼-6½	500②	600②
	8-327①	210	44	.035	28-32	.019	2B	2B	36	5¼-6½	700	600
	8-327	275	44	.035	28-32	.019	8B	8B	38	5¼-6½	500②	500②
	8-327①	275	44	.035	28-32	.019	6B	6B	38	5¼-6½	700	600
	8-350	295	44	.035	28-32	.019	4B	4B	38	5¼-6½	500②	500②
	8-350①	295	44	.035	28-32	.019	4B	4B	38	5¼-6½	700②	500②
	8-396	325	43N	.035	28-32	.019	4B	4B	40	5-8½	700	600
	8-396	350	43N	.035	28-32	.019	TDC	4B	40	5-8½	750	600
	8-396	375	43N	.035	28-32	.019	4B	—	N.A.	5-8½	700	—
'68	6-230	140	46N	.035	31-34	.019	TDC	4B	16	3½-4½	700	600②/400
	6-250	155	46N	.035	31-34	.019	TDC	4B	16	3½-4½	700	600②/400
	8-302	290	43	.035	28-32	.019	4B	—	N.A.	5¼-6½	900	—
	8-327	210	44	.035	28-32	.019	2A	2B	28	5-6½	700	600
	8-327	275	44	.035	28-32	.019	TDC	4B	28	5-6½	700②	600

TUNE-UP SPECIFICATIONS

When analyzing compression test results, look for uniformity among cylinders rather than specific pressures.

	ENGINE		SPARK PLUGS		DISTRIBUTOR		IGNITION TIMING (deg) ▲		VALVES	Fuel	IDLE SPEED (rpm) ▲	
Year	No. Cyl Displacement (cu in.)	hp	Type §	Gap (in.)	Point Dwell (deg)	Point Gap (in.)	Man Trans	Auto Trans	Intake Opens ■ (deg) ●	Pump Pressure (psi)	Man Trans	Auto Trans
'68	8-350	295	44	.035	28-32	.019	TDC	4B	28	5-6½	700	600
	8-396	325	43N	.035	28-32	.019	4B	4B	40	7-8½	700	600
	8-396	350	43N	.035	28-32	.019	TDC	4B	40	7-8½	700	600
	8-396	375	43N	.035	28-32	.019	4B	—	N.A.	7-8½	750	—
'69	6-230	140	R-46N	.035	31-34	.019	TDC	4B	16	4-5	700	500/400③
	6-250	155	R-46N	.035	31-34	.019	TDC	4B	16	4-5	700	500/400③
	8-302	290	R-43	.035	28-32	.019	4B	—	N.A.	5-6½	900	—
	8-307	200	R-45S	.035	28-32	.019	2B	2B	28	5-7½	700	600
	8-327	210	R-45S	.035	28-32	.019	2A	2B	28	5-6½	700	600
	8-350	255	R-44	.035	28-32	.019	TDC	4B	28	5-6½	700	600
	8-350	300	R-44	.035	28-32	.019	TDC	4B	28	5-6½	700	600
	8-396	325	R-44N	.035	28-32	.019	4B	4B	28	5-8½	800	600
	8-396	350	R-43N	.035	28-32	.019	TDC	4B	56	5-8½	800	600
	8-396	375	R-43N	.035	28-32	.019	4B	4B	N.A.	5-8½	750	750/400
'70	6-250	155	R-43	.035	29-31	.019	TDC	4B	16	3½-4½	750	650/400③
	8-307	200	R-46T	.035	31-34	.019	2B	8B	28	5-6½	700	600/450③
	8-350	250	R-44	.035	29-31	.019	TDC	4B	28	7-8½	750	600/450③
	8-350	300	R-44	.035	29-31	.019	TDC	4B	28	7-8½	700	600
	8-350	360	R-43	.035	29-31	.019	8B	8B	42½	7-8½	800	750/500③
	8-396	350	R-44T	.035	29-31	.019	TDC	4B	56	5-8½	700	600
	8-396	375	R-43T	.035	29-31	.019	4B	4B	N.A.	5-8½	750	700
'71	6-250	145	R-46TS	.035	31-34	.019	4B	4B	16	3½-4½	550	550②
	8-307	200	R-45TS	.035	29-31	.019	4B	8B	28	5-6½	600	550②
	8-350	245	R-45TS	.035	29-31	.019	2B	6B	28	7-8½	600	550②
	8-350	270	R-44TS	.035	29-31	.019	4B	8B	28	7-8½	600	550②
	8-350	300	R-43TS	.035	29-31	.019	8B	12B	42⅔	7-8½	700	700
	8-402	300	R-44TS	.035	28-30	.019	8B	8B	28	7-8½	600	600
'72	6-250	110	R-46T	.035	31-34	.019	4B	4B	16	3½-4½	700	600
	8-307	130	R-44T	.035	29-31	.019	4B	8B	28	5-6½	900	600
	8-350	165	R-44T	.035	29-31	.019	6B	6B	28(44)	7-8½	900	600
	8-350	200	R-44T	.035	29-31	.019	4B	8B	28(44)	7-8½	800	600
	8-350	255	R-44T	.035	29-31	.019	8B	12B	42⅔	7-8½	900	700
	8-402	240	R-44TS	.035	28-30	.019	8B	8B	28	7-8½	800	600
'73	6-250	100	R-46T	.035	31-34	.019	6B	6B	16	3½-4½	700/450③	600/450
	8-307	115	R-44T	.035	29-31	.019	4B	4B	28	5-6½	900/450③	600/450
	8-350	145	R-44T	.035	29-31	.019	8B	8B	28	7½-8½	900/450③	600/450
	8-350	175	R-44T	.035	29-31	.019	8B	12B	28	7½-8½	900/450③	600/450
	8-350	245	R-44T	.035	29-31	.019	8B	12B	52	7½-8½	900/450③	700/450

Camaro

TUNE-UP SPECIFICATIONS

When analyzing compression test results, look for uniformity among cylinders rather than specific pressures.

	ENGINE		SPARK PLUGS		DISTRIBUTOR		IGNITION TIMING (deg) ▲		VALVES	Fuel	IDLE SPEED (rpm) ▲	
Year	No. Cyl Displacement (cu in.)	hp	Type §	Gap (in.)	Point Dwell (deg)	Point Gap (in.)	Man Trans	Auto Trans	Intake Opens ■ (deg) ●	Pump Pressure (psi)	Man Trans	Auto Trans
'74	6-250	100	R-46T	.035	31-34	.019	6B	6B	16	4-5	800/450③	600/450
	8-350	145	R-44T	.035	29-31	.019	4B	8B	28	7½-9	900/450③	600/450
	8-350	160	R-44T	.035	29-31	.019	4B	8B	44	7½-9	900/450③	600/450
	8-350	185	R-44T	.035	29-31	.019	4B	8B	28	7½-9	900/450③	600/450
	8-350	245	R-44T	.035	29-31	.019	8B	8B	52	7½-9	900/450③	700/450

▲ See text for procedure. For those cars equipped with an idle solenoid, disconnect solenoid and adjust idle to 450 rpm
● Figure in parentheses indicates California engine
■ All figures Before Top Dead Center
§ All spark plug listings are A.C. original equipment numbers
① Equipped with Air Injection Reactor System
② A/C on
③ Lower figure with Idle Solenoid disconnected
A After Top Dead Center
B Before Top Dead Center
N.A. Not available
TDC Top Dead Center
— Not applicable

MECHANICAL VALVE LIFTER CLEARANCE

Year	Engine		Intake (Hot) In.	Exhaust (Hot) In.
1967-1969	V8-302	290 hp	.030	.030
1970	V8-350	360 hp	.024	.030
1971	V8-350	300 hp	.024	.030
1972	V8-350	255 hp	.024	.030

Chevy II-Nova

TUNE-UP SPECIFICATIONS

When analyzing compression test results, look for uniformity among cylinders rather than specific pressures.

	ENGINE		SPARK PLUGS		DISTRIBUTOR		IGNITION TIMING (deg) ▲		VALVES	Fuel	IDLE SPEED (rpm) ▲	
Year	No. Cyl Displacement (cu in.)	hp	Type §	Gap (in.)	Point Dwell (deg)	Point Gap (in.)	Man Trans	Auto Trans	Intake Opens ■ (deg) ●	Pump Pressure (psi)	Man Trans	Auto Trans
'67	4-153	90	46N	.035	31-34	.019	4B	4B	33½	3½-4½	500②	500②
	6-194	120	46N	.035	31-34	.019	4B	4B	62	3½-4½	500②	500②
	6-194①	120	46N	.035	31-34	.019	2B	4B	62	3½-4½	700	600
	6-250	155	46N	.035	31-34	.019	4B	4B	62	3½-4½	500②	500②
	6-250①	155	46N	.035	31-34	.019	4B	4B	62	3½-4½	700	500
	8-283	195	45	.035	28-32	.019	4B	4B	36	5¼-6½	500②	500②
	8-283①	195	45	.035	28-32	.019	TDC	4B	36	5¼-6½	700	600
	8-327	275	44	.035	28-32	.019	8B	8B	38	5¼-6½	500②	500②
	8-327①	275	44	.035	28-32	.019	6B	6B	38	5¼-6½	700	600
'68	4-153	90	46N	.035	31-34	.019	TDC	4B	17½	3½-4½	750	600
	6-230	140	46N	.035	31-34	.019	TDC	4B	48	3½-4½	700 ②	600②/400③
	6-250	155	46N	.035	31-34	.019	TDC	4B	16	3½-4½	700②	500②/400③
	8-307	200	45S	.035	28-32	.019	2B	2B	28	5-6½	700	600
	8-327	275	44	.035	28-32	.019	TDC	4B	28	5-6½	700②	600②
	8-350	295	44	.035	28-32	.019	TDC	4B	28	5-6½	700	500
	8-396	300	43N	.035	28-32	.019	TDC	4B	40	5-7½	700	600
	8-396④	375	43N	.035	28-32	.019	4B	—	44	5-8½	750	—
'69	4-153	90	D-46N	.035	31-34	.019	TDC	4B	28	4-5	750	600
	6-230	140	R-46N	.035	31-34	.019	TDC	4B	16	4-5	700	550/400③
	6-250	155	R-46N	.035	31-34	.019	TDC	4B	16	4-5	700	550/400③
	8-307	200	R-45S	.035	31-34	.019	2B	2B	28	5½-7½	700	600
	8-350	250	R-45S	.035	29-31	.019	TDC	4B	28	5½-7½	700	600
	8-350	300	R-44S	.035	29-31	.019	TDC	4B	28	7½-9	700	600
	8-396	350	R-43N	.035	28-32	.019	TDC	4B	56	5-8½	800	600
	8-396④	375	R-43N	.035	28-32	.019	4B	4B	44	5-8½	750	750/400

Chevy II, Nova — TUNE-UP SPECIFICATIONS

When analyzing compression test results, look for uniformity among cylinders rather than specific pressures.

	ENGINE		SPARK PLUGS		DISTRIBUTOR		IGNITION TIMING (deg) ▲		VALVES	Fuel	IDLE SPEED (rpm) ▲	
Year	No. Cyl Displacement (cu in.)	hp	Type §	Gap (in.)	Point Dwell (deg)	Point Gap (in.)	Man Trans	Auto Trans	Intake Opens ■ (deg) ●	Pump Pressure (psi)	Man Trans	Auto Trans
'70	4-153	90	R-46N	.035	31-34	.019	TDC	4B	17½	4-5	750	650
	6-230	140	R-46N	.035	31-34	.019	TDC	4B	16	4-5	700	550/400③
	6-250	155	R-46N	.035	31-34	.019	TDC	4B	16	4-5	700	550/400③
	8-307	200	R-45	.035	29-31	.019	2B	8B	28	5½-7½	700	600/450③
	8-350	250	R-44	.035	29-31	.019	TDC	4B	28	5½-7½	750	600/450③
	8-350	300	R-44	.035	29-31	.019	TDC	4B	28	7½-9	700	600
'71	6-250	145	R-46TS	.035	31-34	.019	4B	4B	16	4-5	550	500
	8-307	200	R-45TS	.035	29-31	.019	4B	8B	28	5½-7½	600	550②
	8-350	245	R-45TS	.035	29-31	.019	2B	6B	28	7½-9	600	550②
	8-350	270	R-44TS	.035	29-31	.019	4B	8B	28	7½-9	600	550②
'72	6-250	110	R-46T	.035	31-34	.019	4B	4B	16	4-5	700	600
	8-307	130	R-44T	.035	29-31	.019	4B	8B	28	5½-7½	900	600
	8-350	165	R-44T	.035	29-31	.019	6B	6B	28(44)	7½-9	900	600
	8-350	200	R-44T	.035	29-31	.019	4B	8B	28(44)	7½-9	800	600
'73	6-250	100	R-46T	.035	31-34	.019	6B	6B	16	3½-4½	700/450③	600/450
	8-307	115	R-44T	.035	29-31	.019	4B	8B	28	5-6½	900/450③	600/450
	8-350	145	R-44T	.035	29-31	.019	8B	8B	28	7-8½	900/450③	600/450
	8-350	175	R-44T	.035	29-31	.019	8B	12B	28	7-8½	900/450③	600/450
'74	6-250	100	R-46T	.035	31-34	.019	6B	6B	16	4-5	800/450③	600/450
	8-350	145	R-44T	.035	29-31	.019	4B	8B	28	7½-9	900/450③	600/450
	8-350	160	R-44T	.035	29-31	.019	4B	8B	44	7½-9	900/450③	600/450
	8-350	185	R-44T	.035	29-31	.019	4B	8B	28	7½-9	900/450③	600/450

▲ See text for procedure
● Figure in parentheses indicates California engine
■ All figures Before Top Dead Center
§ All spark plug listings are A.C. original equipment numbers
① Equipped with Air Injection Reactor System
② A/C on
③ Lower figure with Idle Solenoid disconnected
④ Adjust mechanical valve lifter clearance to .024 inches for intake with engine hot, and to .028 inches for exhaust with engine hot
A After Top Dead Center
B Before Top Dead Center
TDC Top Dead Center
— Not applicable

Chevelle — TUNE-UP SPECIFICATIONS

When analyzing compression test results, look for uniformity among cylinders rather than specific pressures.

	ENGINE		SPARK PLUGS		DISTRIBUTOR		IGNITION TIMING (deg) ▲		VALVES	Fuel	IDLE SPEED (rpm) ▲	
Year	No. Cyl Displacement (cu in.)	hp	Type §	Gap (in.)	Point Dwell (deg)	Point Gap (in.)	Man Trans	Auto Trans	Intake Opens ■ (deg) ●	Pump Pressure (psi)	Man Trans	Auto Trans
'67	6-230	140	46N	.035	31-34	.019	4B	4B	62	3½-4½	500②	500②
	6-230①	140	46N	.035	31-34	.019	4B	4B	62	3½-4½	700	500
	6-250	155	46N	.035	31-34	.019	4B	4B	62	3½-4½	500②	500②
	6-250①	155	46N	.035	31-34	.019	4B	4B	62	3½-4½	700	500
	8-283	195	45	.035	28-32	.019	4B	4B	38	5-6½	500②	500②
	8-283①	195	45	.035	28-32	.019	TDC	4B	38	5-6½	700	600
	8-327	275	44	.035	28-32	.019	8B	8B	38	5¼-6½	500②	500②
	8-327①	275	44	.035	28-32	.019	6B	6B	38	5¼-6½	700	600
	8-327	325	44	.035	28-32	.019	10B	—	54	5-6½	700②	—
	8-327①	325	44	.035	28-32	.019	10B	—	54	5-6½	750②	—
	8-396	325	43N	.035	28-32	.019	4B	4B	40	5-6½	500②	500②
	8-396①	325	43N	.035	28-32	.019	4B	4B	40	5-6½	700②	500②
	396	350	43N	.035	28-32	.019	4B	4B	56	7¼-8½	550②	550②
	396①	350	43N	.035	28-32	.019	4B	4B	56	7¼-8½	700②	500②
	8-396	375	R-43N	.035	28-32	.019	4B	—	44	5-8½	750	—

TUNE-UP SPECIFICATIONS

When analyzing compression test results, look for uniformity among cylinders rather than specific pressures.

	ENGINE		SPARK PLUGS		DISTRIBUTOR		IGNITION TIMING (deg) ▲		VALVES	Fuel	IDLE SPEED (rpm) ▲	
Year	No. Cyl Displacement (cu in.)	hp	Type §	Gap (in.)	Point Dwell (deg)	Point Gap (in.)	Man Trans	Auto Trans	Intake Opens ■ (deg) ●	Pump Pressure (psi)	Man Trans	Auto Trans
'68	6-230	140	46N	.035	31-34	.019	TDC	4B	16	3½-4½	700	500②/400
	6-250	155	46N	.035	31-34	.019	TDC	4B	16	3½-4½	700	500②/400
	8-307	200	45S	.035	28-32	.019	2B	2B	28	5-6½	700	600
	8-327	275	44	.035	28-32	.019	TDC	4B	28	5-6½	700	600
	8-327	325	44	.035	28-32	.019	4B	—	40	5-6½	750②	—
	8-396	325	43N	.035	28-32	.019	4B	4B	28	5-6½	700②	600②
	8-396	350	43N	.035	28-32	.019	TDC	4B	40	7¼-8½	700	600
	8-396	375	R-43N	.035	28-32	.019	4B	—	44	5-8½	750	—
'69	6-230	140	R-46N	.035	31-34	.019	TDC	4B	16	3-4½	700	550/400③
	6-250	155	R-46N	.035	31-34	.019	TDC	4B	16	3-4½	700	550/400③
	8-307	200	R-45S	.035	28-32	.019	2B	2B	28	5-6½	700	600
	8-350	250	R-44	.035	28-32	.019	TDC	4B	28	5-6½	700	600
	8-350	300	R-44	.035	28-32	.019	TDC	4B	28	5-6½	700	600
	8-396	325	R-44N	.035	28-32	.019	4B	4B	28	5-8½	800	600
	8-396	350	R-43N	.035	28-32	.019	TDC	4B	56	5-8½	800	600
	8-396	375	R-43N	.035	28-32	.019	4B	4B	44	5-8½	750	750/400
'70	6-250	155	R-46T	.035	31-34	.019	TDC	4B	16	3-4½	750	600/400③
	8-307	200	R-43	.035	28-32	.019	2B	8B	28	5-6½	700	600/450③
	8-350	250	R-44	.035	28-32	.019	TDC	4B	28	5-6½	750	600/450③
	8-350	300	R-44	.035	28-32	.019	TDC	4B	28	5-6½	700	600
	8-396	350	R-44T	.035	28-32	.019	TDC	4B	56	5-8½	700	600
	8-396	375	R-43T	.035	28-32	.019	4B	4B	N.A.	5-8½	750	700
	8-400	265	R-44	.035	28-32	.019	4B	8B	28	5-8½	700	600/450③
	8-400	330	R-44T	.035	28-32	.019	4B	4B	28	5-8½	700	600
	8-454	360	R-43T	.035	28-32	.019	6B	6B	56	5-8½	700	600
'71	6-250	145	R-46TS	.035	31-34	.019	4B	4B	16	3½-4½	550	500
	8-307	200	R-45TS	.035	29-31	.019	4B	8B	28	5-6½	600	550
	8-350	245	R-45TS	.035	29-31	.019	2B	6B	28	7-8½	600	550
	8-350	270	R-44TS	.035	29-31	.019	4B	8B	28	7-8½	600	550
	8-400	255	R-44TS	.035	29-31	.019	4B	8B	28	7-8½	600	550
	8-402	300	R-44TS	.035	29-31	.019	8B	8B	28	7-8½	600	600
	8-454	365	R-42TS	.035	29-31	.019	8B	8B	56	7-8½	600	600
	8-454	425	R-42TS	.035	29-31	.019	8B	12B	44	7-8½	700	700
'72	6-250	110	R-46TS	.035	31-34	.019	4B	4B	16	3½-4½	700	600
	8-307	130	R-44T	.035	29-31	.019	4B	8B	28	5-6½	900	600
	8-350	165	R-44T	.035	29-31	.019	6B	6B	28	7-8½	900	600
	8-350	175	R-44T	.035	29-31	.019	4B	8B	28	7-8½	800	600
	8-402	240	R-44T	.035	29-31	.019	8B	8B	30	7-8½	750	600
	8-454	270	R-44T	.035	29-31	.019	8B	8B	56	7-8½	750	600

Chevelle — TUNE-UP SPECIFICATIONS, Continued

When analyzing compression test results, look for uniformity among cylinders rather than specific pressures.

Year	ENGINE No. Cyl Displacement (cu in.)	ENGINE hp	SPARK PLUGS Type §	SPARK PLUGS Gap (in.)	DISTRIBUTOR Point Dwell (deg)	DISTRIBUTOR Point Gap (in.)	IGNITION TIMING (deg) ▲ Man Trans	IGNITION TIMING (deg) ▲ Auto Trans	VALVES Intake Opens ■ (deg) ●	Fuel Pump Pressure (psi)	IDLE SPEED (rpm) ▲ Man Trans	IDLE SPEED (rpm) ▲ Auto Trans
'73	6-250	100	R-46T	.035	31-34	.019	6B	6B	16	3½-4½	700/450③	600/450
	8-307	115	R-44T	.035	29-31	.019	4B	8B	28	5-6½	900/450③	600/450
	8-350	145	R-44T	.035	29-31	.019	8B	8B	28	7-8½	900/450③	600/450
	8-350	175	R-44T	.035	29-31	.019	8B	12B	28	7-8½	900/450③	600/450
	8-454	245	R-44T	.035	29-31	.019	10B	10B	55	7-8½	900/450③	600/450
'74	6-250	100	R-46T	.035	31-34	.019	6B	6B	16	4-5	800/450③	600/450
	8-350	145	R-44T	.035	29-31	.019	4B	8B	28	7½-9	900/450③	600/450
	8-350	160	R-44T	.035	29-31	.019	4B	8B	44	7½-9	900/450③	600/450
	8-400	150	R-44T	.035	29-31	.019	—	8B	28	7½-9	—③	600/450
	8-400	180	R-44T	.035	29-31	.019	—	8B	44	7½-9	—③	600/450
	8-454	235	R-44T	.035	29-31	.019	10B	10B	55	7½-9	800/450③	600/450

▲ See text for procedure
● Figure in parentheses indicates California engine
■ All figures Before Top Dead Center
① Equipped with Air Injection Reactor System
② A/C on
③ Lower figure with idle solenoid disconnected
§ All spark plug listings are A.C. original equipment numbers
A After Top Dead Center
B Before Top Dead Center
TDC Top Dead Center
— Not applicable

MECHANICAL VALVE LIFTER CLEARANCE

Year	Engine		Intake (Hot) in.	Exhaust (Hot) in.
1967-1971	V8-396	375 hp	.024	.028
1971	V8-454	425 hp	.024	.028

Chevy II, Nova, Camaro, Chevelle, Monte Carlo — CAPACITIES

Year	ENGINE No. Cyl. Displacement (Cu. In.)	Engine Crankcase Add 1 Qt For New Filter*	TRANSMISSION Pts To Refill After Draining Manual 3-Speed	TRANSMISSION Manual 4-Speed	TRANSMISSION Automatic ●	Drive Axle (pts)	Gasoline Tank (gals) See chart below	COOLING SYSTEM (qts) With Heater	COOLING SYSTEM (qts) With A/C
'67	4-153	3.5	3	—	6	3.5		9	9
	6-194	4	3③	3③	6	3.5		12	12
	6-230	4	3③	3③	6	3.5		14	14
	6-250	4	3③	3③	6	3.5		13⑥	14
	8-283	4	3③	3③	6	3.5		16	17
	8-327	4	3③	3③	6	3.5		15	18
	8-350	4	3③	3③	6	3.5		17	17
	8-396	4	3③	3③	6	3.5		23	23
'68	4-153	3.5	3	—	6	3.5		9	9
	6-230	4	3	3	6	3.5		12	12
	6-250	4	3	3	6	3.5		12	12
	8-302	4	3	3	6	3.5		16	—
	8-307	4	3	3	6	3.5		17	17
	8-327	4	3②	3	6	3.5		16	16
	8-350	4	3②	3	6	3.5		16	16
	8-396	4	3②	3	6⑫	3.5		23	23
'69	4-153	3.5	3	—	6	3.5		9	9
	6-230	4	3③	—	6⑬	3.5④		13	13
	6-250	4	3③	—	6⑬	3.5④		13	13
	8-302	4	3③	3	6⑬	3.5④		17	—

CAPACITIES

Year	ENGINE No. Cyl. Displacement (Cu. In.)	Engine Crankcase Add 1 Qt For New Filter*	TRANSMISSION Pts To Refill After Draining — Manual 3-Speed	Manual 4-Speed	Automatic ●	Drive Axle (pts)	Gasoline Tank (gals) See chart below	COOLING SYSTEM (qts) With Heater	With A/C
'69	8-307	4	3③	3	6⑬	3.5④		17	18⑦
	8-350	4	3③	3	6⑬	3.5④		16	17⑦
	8-396	4	3③	3	8	3.5④		23	24
'70	4-153	3.5	3	—	6	3.75⑧		9	9
	6-230	4	3	—	6⑬	3.75⑧		12	13
	6-250	4	3	—	6⑬	3.75⑧		12	13
	8-307	4	3	—	6⑬	3.75⑧		15	16
	8-350	4	3	3	6.5⑨⑬	3.75⑧		16	16
	8-400	4	3	3	8	3.75⑧		16	16
	8-396	4	3	3	8	3.75⑧		23	24
	8-400	4	3	3	8	3.75⑧		23	24
	8-454	4	3	3	8	3.75⑧		22	23
'71	6-250	4	3	—	6	3.75		12	—
	8-307	4	3	—	6⑬	3.75		15	16
	8-350	4	3	3	6.5⑬	3.75		16	16
	8-400	4	3	3	8	3.75		23	23
	8-454	4	—	3	8	3.75		22	23
'72	6-250	4	3	—	6⑬	4.25		12	—
	8-307	4	3	—	6⑬	4.25		15	16
	8-350	4	3	3	6.5⑩⑬	4.25		16	16
	8-402	4	—	3	8	4.25⑪		24	24
	8-454	4	—	3	8	4.25⑪		23	24
'73	6-250	4	3	—	6⑬	4.25		12.5	—
	8-307	4	3	—	5	4.25		16⑭	17⑮
	8-350	4	3	3	5⑩	4.25		16⑭	17⑮
	8-454	4	—	3	8	4.25⑪		23	24
'74	6-250	4	3	—	8	4.25		12.5	—
	8-350	4	3	3	8	4.25		16⑭	17⑮
	8-400	4	—	—	8	4.25⑪		16	17
	8-454	4	—	3	9	4.9		23	24

* Add ½ qt with filter change on 4 cyl engine
● Specifications do not include torque convertor
① Not used
② 2.5 pts on Chevelle
③ 3.5 pts with heavy duty transmission
④ 4 pts with 8.875 in. ring gear
⑤ Not used
⑥ 14 qts on Camaro
⑦ Less one qt on Nova
⑧ 4:25 pts with 8.875 in. ring gear
⑨ 8 pts with 360 hp engine
⑩ 8 pts with Z-28 350
⑪ 4.9 pts in Monte Carlo or Chevelle with 8.875 in. ring gear
⑫ 8 pts with Turbo Hydramatic 400
⑬ 5 pts with Turbo Hydramatic 350
⑭ 15.5 Nova
⑮ 16.5 Nova
— Not applicable

GAS TANK CAPACITIES (Gals)

Year	Chevy II, Nova	Chevelle, Monte Carlo	Camaro
'67	16	20	18
'68	18	20	18
'69	18	20①	18
'70	18	20②	19
'71	16	19②	17
'72	16	19②	18
'73	21	22③	18
'74	21	22③	21

① 22 gals in station wagon
② 18 gals in station wagon
③ 26 gals in El Camino

VALVE SPECIFICATIONS

Year	Engine No. Cyl. Displacement (cu in.)	Seat Angle (deg)	Face Angle (deg)	Spring Test Pressure (lbs @ in.)	Spring Installed Height (in.)	STEM TO GUIDE Clearance (in.) Intake	STEM TO GUIDE Clearance (in.) Exhaust	STEM Diameter (in.) Intake	STEM Diameter (in.) Exhaust
'67	4-153	46③	45	82 @ 1.66	1 21/32	.0010-.0037	.0010-.0047	.3414	.3414
	6-194	46③	45	60 @ 1.66	1 21/32	.0010-.0037	.0015-.0052	.3414	.3414
	6-230	46③	45	60 @ 1.66	1 21/32	.0010-.0037	.0015-.0052	.3414	.3414
	6-250	46③	45	60 @ 1.66	1 21/32	.0010-.0047	.0015-.0052	.3414	.3414
	8-283	46③	45	80 @ 1.70	1 5/32	.0010-.0037	.0010-.0047	.3414	.3414
	8-327	46③	45	80 @ 1.70	1 5/32	.0010-.0037	.0010-.0047	.3414	.3414
	8-350	46③	45	80 @ 1.70	1 5/32	.0010-.0037	.0010-.0047	.3414	.3414
	8-396①	46③	45	90 @ 1.88	1 7/8	.0010-.0035	.0012-.0047	.3717	.3717
	8-396②	46③	45	100 @ 1.88	1 7/8	.0010-.0035	.0012-.0047	.3717	.3717
'68	4-153	46③	45	81 @ 1.66	1 21/32	.0010-.0037	.0015-.0052	.3414	.3414
	6-230	46③	45	59 @ 1.66	1 21/32	.0010-.0037	.0015-.0052	.3414	.3414
	6-250	46③	45	59 @ 1.66	1 21/32	.0010-.0037	.0015-.0052	.3414	.3414
	8-302	46③	45	80 @ 1.70	1 5/32	.0010-.0037	.0010-.0047	.3414	.3414
	8-307	46③	45	80 @ 1.70	1 5/32	.0010-.0037	.0010-.0047	.3414	.3414
	8-327	46③	45	80 @ 1.70	1 5/32	.0010-.0037	.0010-.0047	.3414	.3414
	8-350	46③	45	80 @ 1.70	1 5/32	.0010-.0037	.0010-.0047	.3414	.3414
	8-396	46③	45	90 @ 1.88	1 7/8	.0010-.0035	.0012-.0047	.3719	.3717
'69	4-153	46③	45	81 @ 1.66	1 21/32	.0010-.0037	.0015-.0052	.3414	.3414
	6-230	46③	45	59 @ 1.66	1 21/32	.0010-.0037	.0015-.0052	.3414	.3414
	6-250	46③	45	59 @ 1.66	1 21/37	.0010-.0037	.0015-.0052	.3414	.3414
	8-302	46③	45	80 @ 1.70	1 5/32	.0010-.0037	.0010-.0047	.3414	.3414
	8-307	46③	45	80 @ 1.70	1 5/32	.0010-.0037	.0010-.0047	.3414	.3414
	8-350	46③	45	80 @ 1.70	1 5/32	.0010-.0037	.0010-.0047	.3414	.3414
	8-396①	46③	45	90 @ 1.88	1 7/8	.0010-.0035	.0012-.0047	.3719	.3719
	8-396④	46③	45	100 @ 1.88	1 7/8	.0010-.0035	.0012-.0047	.3719	.3719
'70	4-153	46③	45	81 @ 1.66	1 21/32	.0010-.0037	.0015-.0052	.3414	.3414
	6-230	46③	45	59 @ 1.66	1 21/32	.0010-.0037	.0015-.0052	.3414	.3414
	6-250	46③	45	59 @ 1.66	1 21/32	.0010-.0037	.0015-.0052	.3414	.3414
	8-307	46③	45	80 @ 1.70	1 23/32	.0010-.0037	.0012-.0049	.3414	.3414
	8-350	46③	45	80 @ 1.70	1 23/32	.0010-.0037	.0012-.0049	.3414	.3414
	8-400	46③	45	80 @ 1.70	1 7/8	.0010-.0037	.0012-.0047	.3414	.3414
	8-402	46③	45	75 @ 1.88⑤	1 7/8	.0010-.0037	.0012-.0047	.3719	.3717
	8-454	46④	45	75 @ 1.88⑤	1 7/8	.0010-.0037	.0012-.0047	.3717	.3719
'71	6-250	46	45	60 @ 1.66	1 21/32	.0010-.0037	.0015-.0052	.3414	.3414
	8-307	46	45	80 @ 1.70	1 23/32	.0010-.0037	.0012-.0049	.3414	.3414
	8-350	46	45	80 @ 1.70	1 23/32	.0010-.0037	.0012-.0049	.3414	.3414
	8-402	46	45	75 @ 1.88⑤	1 7/8	.0010-.0037	.0012-.0047	.3719	.3717
	8-454	46	45	75 @ 1.88⑤	1 7/8	.0010-.0037	.0012-.0047	.3719	.3717
'72	6-250	46	45	60 @ 1.66	1 21/32	.0010-.0037	.0015-.0052	.3414	.3414
	8-307	46	45	80 @ 1.70	1 23/32	.0010-.0037	.0012-.0049	.3414	.3414
	8-350	46	45	80 @ 1.70	1 23/32	.0010-.0037	.0012-.0049	.3414	.3414
	8-402	46	45	75 @ 1.88⑤	1 7/8	.0010-.0037	.0012-.0047	.3719	.3717
	8-454	46	45	75 @ 1.88⑤	1 7/8	.0010-.0037	.0012-.0047	.3719	.3717

VALVE SPECIFICATIONS

Year	Engine No. Cyl. Displacement (cu in.)	Seat Angle (deg)	Face Angle (deg)	Spring Test Pressure (lbs @ in.)	Spring Installed Height (in.)	STEM TO GUIDE Clearance (in.) Intake	STEM TO GUIDE Clearance (in.) Exhaust	STEM Diameter (in.) Intake	STEM Diameter (in.) Exhaust
'73	6-250	46	45	60 @ 1.66	1 21/32	.0010-.0027	.0015-.0032	.3414	.3414
	8-307	46	45	80 @ 1.61	1 5/8	.0010-.0027	.0012-.0029	.3414	.3414
	8-350	46	45	80 @ 1.70	1 23/32	.0010-.0027	.0012-.0027	.3414	.3414
	8-454	46	45	80 @ 1.88	1 7/8	.0010-.0027	.0012-.0027	.3719	.3417
'74	6-250	46	45	60 @ 1.66	1 21/32	.0010-.0027	.0010-.0027	.3414	.3414
	8-350	46	45	80 @ 1.70	1 23/32	.0010-.0027	.0010-.0027	.3414	.3414
	8-400	46	45	80 @ 1.70	1 23/32	.0010-.0027	.0010-.0027	.3414	.3414
	8-454	46	45	80 @ 1.88	1 7/8	.0010-.0027	.0010-.0027	.3719	.3719

① 325 hp
② 360 hp and 375 hp
③ 45° on aluminum heads
④ 350 hp
⑤ Inner spring—30 @ 1.78

RING SIDE CLEARANCE

Year	Engine	Top Compression	Bottom Compression
'67-'74	4-153, 6-194, 230, 8-283, 302, 307, 327, 400	.0012-.0027	.0012-.0032
'67	8-396	.0012-.0032	.0012-.0032
'68-'69	8-396	.0017-.0032	.0017-.0032
'67	6-250	.0020-.0035	.0020-.0040
'67-'74	6-250	.0012-.0027	.0012-.0032
'67-'74	8-350	.0012-.0032	.0012-.0027②
'70-'74	8-402, 454	.0017-.0032	.0017-.0032

Year	Engine	Oil Control
'67-'74	4-153, 6-194, 230, 250, 8-283, 302, 307, 327, 350, 400	.0000-.0050
'67	8-396	.0012-.0060
'68-'74	8-396, 402, 454	.0005-.0065

① 300, 325, 350 hp 327 cu in. engines
Top .0012-.0032
2nd .0012-.0027
② 165, 245, 250 hp 350 cu in. engine
.0012-.0032
③ 330 hp 400 cu in. engine
Top .0017-.0032
2nd .0017-.0032

RING GAP

Year	Engine	Top Compression	Bottom Compression
'67-'74	4-153, 6-194, 230, 250, 8-283, 307, 396, 400, 402, 454	.010-.020	.010-.020
'67-'69	8-302, 327	.013-.023①	.013-.025①
'68	8-350	.010-.020	.013-.023
'69	8-350	.013-.023②	.013-.025②
'70-'72	8-350	.010-.020②	.013-.025②
'73-'74	8-350	.010-.020	.013-.025

Year	Engine	Oil Control
'67-'74	All engines	.015-.055
'67-'69	8-396	.010-.030

① 325, 350 hp Top .010-.020
2nd .013-.023
② 255, 330, 350, 370 hp Top .010-.020
2nd .013-.023

CRANKSHAFT AND CONNECTING ROD SPECIFICATIONS

All measurements are given in in.

Year	Engine Displace. (cu in.)	CRANKSHAFT				CONNECTING ROD		
		Main Brg. Journal Dia	Main Brg. Oil Clearance	Shaft End-Play	Thrust on No.	Journal Diameter	Oil Clearance	Side Clearance
'67	4-153	2.2983-2.2993	.0003-.0029	.002-.006	5	1.999-2.000	.0007-.0027	.009-.013
	6-194	2.2983-2.2993	.0003-.0029	.002-.006	7	1.999-2.000	.0007-.0027	.009-.013
	6-230	2.2983-2.2993	.0003-.0029	.002-.006	7	1.999-2.000	.0007-.0027	.009-.013
	6-250	2.2983-2.2993	.0003-.0029	.002-.006	7	1.999-2.000	.0007-.0027	.009-.013
	8-283	⑤	⑦	.003-.011	5	1.999-2.000	.0007-.0027	.009-.013
	8-327	⑤	⑦	.003-.011	5	1.999-2.000	.0007-.0028	.009-.013
	8-350	2.24493-2.4493⑥	.0008-.002⑧	.003-.011	5	2.099-2.100	.0007-.0028	.009-.013
	8-396	③	④	.006-.010	5	2.199-2.200	.0007-.0028	.015-.021
'68	4-153	2.2983-2.2993	.0003-.0029	.002-.006	5	1.999-2.000	.0007-.0027	.009-.013
	6-230	2.2983-2.2993	.0003-.0029	.002-.006	7	1.999-2.000	.0007-.0027	.009-.013
	6-250	2.2983-2.2993	.0003-.0029	.002-.006	7	1.999-2.000	.0007-.0027	.009-.013
	8-302 (Z28)	2.4479-2.4488	.0008-.003	.003-.011	5	2.099-2.100	.0007-.0028	.009-.013
	8-307	2.4484-2.4493⑥	.0008-.002⑧	.003-.011	5	2.099-2.100	.0007-.0027	.009-.013
	8-327	2.4484-2.4493⑥	.0008-.002⑧	.003-.011	5	2.099-2.100	.0007-.0028	.009-.013
	8-350	2.4484-2.4493⑥	.0008-.002⑧	.003-.011	5	2.099-2.100	.0007-.0028	.009-.013
	8-396	⑨	⑪	.006-.010	5	2.199-2.200	.0009-.0025	.015-.021
	8-396 (375 H.P.)	⑩	.0013-.0025⑫	.006-.010	5	2.1985-2.1995	.0014-.0030	.019-.025
'69	4-153	2.2983-2.2993	.0003-.0029	.002-.006	5	1.999-2.000	.0007-.0027	.009-.013
	6-230	2.2983-2.2993	.0003-.0029	.002-.006	7	1.999-2.000	.0007-.0027	.009-.013
	6-250	2.2983-2.2993	.0003-.0029	.002-.006	7	1.999-2.000	.0007-.0027	.009-.013
	8-302 (Z28)	2.4479-2.4488	.0008-.003	.003-.011	5	2.099-2.100	.0007-.0028	.009-.013
	8-307	2.4479-2.4488	.0008-.002⑧	.003-.011	5	2.099-2.100	.0007-.0027	.009-.013
	8-327	2.4479-2.4488	.0008-.002⑧	.003-.011	5	2.099-2.100	.0007-.0028	.009-.013
	8-350	2.4479-2.4488	.0008-.002⑧	.003-.011	5	2.099-2.100	.0007-.0028	.009-.013
	8-396	⑨	⑪	.006-.010	5	2.199-2.200	.0009-.0025	.015-.021
	8-396 (375 H.P.)	⑩	.0013-.0025⑫	.006-.010	5	2.1985-2.1995	.0014-.0030	.019-.025
'70	4-153	2.2983-2.2993	.0003-.0029	.002-.006	5	1.999-2.000	.0007-.0027	.009-.013
	6-230	2.2983-2.2993	.0003-.0029	.002-.006	7	1.999-2.000	.0007-.0027	.009-.013
	6-250	2.2983-2.2993	.0003-.0029	.002-.006	7	1.999-2.000	.0007-.0027	.009-.013
	8-307, 350	2.4484-2.4493⑥	.0003-.0015⑬	.002-.006	5	2.099-2.100	.0007-.0028	.008-.014
	8-350 (Z28)	2.4484-2.4493⑥	.0013-.0025⑭	.002-.006	5	2.099-2.100	.0013-.0035	.008-.014
	8-400 (Monte Carlo)	2.6584-2.6493⑱	.0008-.0020㉑	.002-.006	5	2.099-2.100	.0009-.0025	.008-.014
	8-402	2.7487-2.7496⑮	.0007-.0019⑯	.006-.010	5	2.199-2.200	.0009-.0025	.013-.023
	8-454	2.7485-2.7494⑩	.0013-.0025⑰	.006-.010	5	2.199-2.200	.0009-.0025	.015-.021
'71	6-250	2.2983-2.2993	.0003-.0029	.002-.006	7	1.999-2.000	.0007-.0027	.009-.014
	8-307, 350	2.4484-2.4493⑳	.0008-.0020㉑	.002-.006	5	2.099-2.100	.0013-.0035	.008-.014
	8-350 (Z28)	2.4484-2.4493⑳	.0013-.0025⑭	.002-.006	5	2.099-2.100	.0013-.0035	.008-.014
	8-402	2.7487-2.7496⑮	.0007-.0019⑯	.006-.010	5	2.199-2.200	.0009-.0025	.013-.023
	8-454 (365 H.P.)	2.7485-2.7494⑩	.0013-.0025⑰	.006-.010	5	2.199-2.200	.0009-.0025	.015-.021
	8-454 (425 H.P.)	2.7481-2.7490⑥	.0013-.0025⑲	.006-.010	5	2.1985-2.1995	.0009-.0025	.019-.025
'72	6-250	2.2983-2.2993	.0003-.0029	.002-.006	7	1.999-2.000	.0007-.0027	.009-.014
	8-307, 350	2.4484-2.4493⑳	.0008-.0020㉑	.002-.006	5	2.099-2.100	.0013-.0035	.008-.014
	8-350 (Z28)	2.4484-2.4493⑳	.0013-.0025⑭	.002-.006	5	2.099-2.100	.0013-.0035	.008-.014
	8-402	2.7487-2.7496⑮	.0007-.0019⑯	.006-.010	5	2.199-2.200	.0009-.0025	.013-.023
	8-454	2.7485-2.7494⑩	.0013-.0025⑰	.006-.010	5	2.199-2.200	.0009-.0025	.015-.021
'73	6-250	2.3004	.0003-.0029	.002-.006	7	1.999-2.000	.0007-.0027	.009-.014
	8-307, 350	2.4502㉒	.0008-.0020㉑	.002-.007	5	2.099-2.100	.0013-.0035	.008-.014
	8-454	2.7492㉓	.0007-.0019㉔	.006-.010	5	2.199-2.200	.0009-.0025	.015-.023

CRANKSHAFT AND CONNECTING ROD SPECIFICATIONS (Continued)

All measurements are given in in.

Year	Engine Displace. (cu in.)	CRANKSHAFT Main Brg. Journal Dia	CRANKSHAFT Main Brg. Oil Clearance	CRANKSHAFT Shaft End-Play	CRANKSHAFT Thrust on No.	CONNECTING ROD Journal Diameter	CONNECTING ROD Oil Clearance	CONNECTING ROD Side Clearance
'74	6-250	2.3004	.0003-.0029	.002-.006	7	1.999-2.000	.0007-.0027	.007-.016
	8-350	2.4502㉒	.0008-.0020㉑	.002-.007	5	2.099-2.100	.0013-.0025	.008-.014
	8-400	2.6503㉕	.0008-.0020㉑	.002-.007	5	2.099-2.100	.0013-.0025	.008-.014
	8-454	2.7499 §	.0007-.0019㉔	.006-.010	5	2.199-2.200	.0013-.0035	.015-.023

① Not used
② Not used
③ Nos. 1-2—2.7487-2.7497
Nos. 3-4—2.7482-2.7492
No. 5—2.7478-2.7488
④ Nos. 1-2—.0004-.002
Nos. 3-4—.0009-.0025
No. 5—.0013-.0029
⑤ No. 1—2.2984-2.2993
Nos. 2-4—2.2983-2.2993
No. 5—2.2978-2.2988
⑥ No. 5—2.4478-2.4488
⑦ No. 1—.0008-.002
Nos. 2-4—.0018-.002
No. 5—.0010-.0036
⑧ No. 5—.0018-.0034
⑨ Nos. 1-2—2.7484-2.7493
Nos. 3-4—2.7481-2.7490
No. 5—2.7478-2.7488
⑩ No. 1—2.7484-2.7493
Nos. 2-4—2.7481-2.7490
No. 5—2.7478-2.7488
⑪ Nos. 1-2—.0010-.0022
Nos. 3-4—.0013-.0025
No. 5—.0015-.0031
⑫ No. 5—.0015-.0031
⑬ Nos. 2-4—.0006-.0018
No. 5—.0008-.0023
⑭ w/Man. trans.—No. 5—.0023-.0033
w/Auto. trans.—No. 1—.0019-.0031
Nos. 2-4—.0013-.0025
No. 5—.0023-.0033
⑮ Nos. 3-4—2.7481-2.7490
No. 5—2.7473-2.7483
⑯ Nos. 2-4—.0013-.0025
No. 5—.0019-.0035
⑰ No. 5—.0024-.0040
⑱ No. 5—2.6479-2.6488
⑲ No. 5—.0029-.0045
⑳ Nos. 2-4—2.4481-2.4490
No. 5—2.4479-2.4488
㉑ Nos. 2-4—.0011-.0023
No. 5—.0017-.0033
㉒ No. 5—2.4508
㉓ Nos. 2-4—2.7504
No. 5—2.7499
㉔ Nos. 2-4—.0013-.0028
No. 5—.0019-.0035
㉕ No. 5—2.6509
§ Nos. 2-4—2.7504
No. 5—2.7505

BATTERY AND STARTER SPECIFICATIONS

Year	Engine Displacement (cu in.)	BATTERY Ampere Hour Capacity	BATTERY Volts	BATTERY Terminal Grounded	STARTER Lock Test Amps	STARTER Lock Test Volts	STARTER Lock Test Torque (ft lbs)	STARTER No-Load Test Amps	STARTER No-Load Test Volts	STARTER No-Load Test RPM	Brush Spring Tension (oz)
'67	4 & 6, 8-283	44	12	Neg.	Not Recommended			49-76	10.6	7,800	35
	8-327, 396	61	12	Neg.	Not Recommended			65-100	10.6	4,200①	35
'68-'69	4 & 6, 8-307	45	12	Neg.	Not Recommended			—	10.6	—	35
	8-302, 327, 350, 396	61	12	Neg.	Not Recommended			—	9	—	35
'70-'71	4 & 6, 8-307	45	12	Neg.	Not Recommended			50-80	9	5,500-10,500	35
	8-350	61	12	Neg.	Not Recommended			55-80	9	3,500-6,000	35
	8-402 (396)	61	12	Neg.	Not Recommended			65-95	9	7,500-10,500	35
	8-454	62	12	Neg.	Not Recommended			65-95	9	7,500-10,500	35
'72	6	45	12	Neg.	Not Recommended			50-80	9	5,500-10,500	35
	8-307, 350, 402	61	12	Neg.	Not Recommended			50-80②	9	5,500-10,500	35
	8-454	76	12	Neg.	Not Recommended			65-95	9	7,500-10,500	35
'73-'74	6	45	12	Neg.	Not Recommended			50-80	9	5,500-10,500	35
	8-307	61	12	Neg.	Not Recommended			50-80	9	5,500-10,500	35
	8-350, 454	76	12	Neg.	Not Recommended			65-95	9	7,500-10,500	35

① Camaro—230 & 327 cu in. = 9,750
② 350 & 402 use 454 starter below

PISTON CLEARANCE

Year	Engine	Horsepower	Piston to Bore Maximum Clearance (in.)
'67	L4, L6, 8-283,	All	.0025
	8-350, 8-396	All	.0025
'68-'69	L4, L6, 8-307, 8-350	All	.0025
	8-302	All	.0050
	8-396	325, 350	.0025
	8-396	370	.0065
'70	L4, L6, 8-307	All	.0025
	8-302	All	.0061
	8-350	250, 300	.0027
	8-400	265	.0034
	8-402	All	.0038
	8-454	360	.0049
'71-'72	L6, 8-307	All	.0025
	8-350	245, 270	.0027
	8-350	330	.0061
	8-402	All	.0035
	8-454	365	.0049
	8-454①	425	.0065
'73	L6, 8-307	All	.0025
	8-350	145, 175	.0027
	8-350	245	.0061
	8-454	All	.0035
'74	L6	100	.0010
	8-350	145, 160, 185	.0012
	8-350	245	.0051
	8-400	150, 180	.0019
	8-454	All	.0023

① 1971 Only

TORQUE SPECIFICATIONS

All readings in ft lbs

Year	Engine Displacement (cu in.)	Cylinder Head Bolts	Rod Bearing Bolts	Main Bearing Bolts	Crankshaft Pulley Bolt	Flywheel to Crankshaft Bolts	MANIFOLD Intake	MANIFOLD Exhaust
'67-'74	6	95	35	65	—	60	30⑧	25⑦
'67	8-283, 327	60-70	35	80	60⑥	60	30	20
'67-'74	8-302, 307, 350, 400	60-70	45	75②	60⑥	60	30	⑤
'67-'74	8-396, 402 (Big Block)	80①	50	105③	85⑥	65	30	30
	8-427, 454	80①	50④	105③	85	65	30	30

① Aluminum Heads—Short bolts 65, Long bolts 75
② Engines with 4-bolt mains—Outer bolts 65
③ 1967-68 2-bolt mains 95
1967 4-bolt mains 115
④ 7/16 Rod bolts—70
⑤ Center bolts—25-30, end bolts 15-20
⑥ Where applicable
⑦ Exhaust-to-intake
⑧ Manifold-to-head

BRAKE SPECIFICATIONS

Year	Model	MASTER CYLINDER Disc	MASTER CYLINDER Drum	WHEEL CYLINDER Front Disc	WHEEL CYLINDER Front Drum	WHEEL CYLINDER Rear	BRAKE DISC OR DRUM DIAMETER Front Disc	BRAKE DISC OR DRUM DIAMETER Front Drum	BRAKE DISC OR DRUM DIAMETER Rear
'67-'68	Chevelle	1.125	1.0①	2.063	1.125	.938	11.0	9.5	9.5
'67	Chevy II	1.00	1.0①	1.875	1.06	.875	11.0	9.5	9.5
	Camaro	1.00	1.0①	1.875	1.125	.875	11.0	9.5	9.5
'68	Chevy II, Camaro	1.125	1.0	2.063	1.125	.875	11.0	9.5	9.5
'69	Chevelle	1.00	1.0	2.063	1.125	.938②	11.0	9.5	9.5
	Nova, Camaro	1.125	1.0	2.938	1.125	.875	11.0	9.5	9.5
'70-'74	Chevelle, Nova⑥	1.125③	1.0	2.938	1.125	.875⑤	11.0	9.5	9.5④
	Camaro, Monte Carlo	1.125③	—	2.938	—	.875	11.0	—	9.5

① .875 with metallic linings
② .875 with disc brakes
③ 1.000 with power disc brakes
④ 11.0 for 1973 station wagon models
⑤ .938 for 1973-'74 station wagon models
⑥ Disc brakes (front)—standard on 1973-'74 Chevelle
— Not applicable

WHEEL ALIGNMENT SPECIFICATIONS

Year	Model	CASTER Range (deg)	CASTER Pref Setting (deg)	CAMBER Range (deg)	CAMBER Pref Setting (deg)	Toe-in	Steering Axis Inclin.	WHEEL PIVOT RATIO (deg) Inner Wheel	WHEEL PIVOT RATIO (deg) Wheel Outer
'67	Chevy II	1/2P to 1 1/2P	1P	0 to 1P	1/2P	1/8 to 1/4	7	20	18 3/4
	Chevelle	1 1/2N to 1/2N①	1N	0 to 1P	1/2P	1/8 to 1/4	8 1/4	20	18 3/4
	Camaro	0 to 1P	1/2P	1/4N to 3/4P	1/4P	1/8 to 1/4	8 3/4	20	18 3/4
'68-'69	Chevy II (Nova)	0 to 1P	1/2P	1/4N to 3/4P	1/2P	1/8 to 1/4	8 3/4	20	N.A.
	Chevelle	1 1/2N to 1/2N①	1N	0 to 1P	1/2P	1/8 to 1/4	8 1/4	20	18 1/2
	Camaro	0 to 1P	1/2P	1/4N to 3/4P	1/2P	1/8 to 1/4	8 3/4	20	N.A.
'70-'71	Nova	0 to 1P	1/2P	1/4N to 3/4P	1/2P	1/8 to 1/4	8 1/4 to 9 1/4	20	N.A.
	Chevelle, Monte Carlo	1 1/2N to 1/2N①	1N	0 to 1P	1/2P	1/8 to 1/4	7 3/4 to 8 3/4	20	N.A.
	Camaro	0 to 2P	1P	1/4N to 1 3/4P	3/4P	1/8 to 1/4	10 to 11	20	N.A.
'72	Nova	0 to 1P	1/2P	1/4N to 3/4P	1/4P	1/8 to 1/4	8 3/4 to 9 1/4	N.A.	N.A.
	Chevelle	1 1/2N to 1/2N	1N	1/4P to 1 1/4P	3/4P	1/8 to 1/4	7 3/4 to 8 3/4	N.A.	N.A.
	Monte Carlo	1/2N to 1/2P	0	1/4P to 1 1/4P	3/4P	1/8 to 1/4	7 3/4 to 8 3/4	N.A.	N.A.
	Camaro	1/2N to 1/2P	0	1/2P to 1 1/2P	1P	1/8 to 1/4	9 to 10	N.A.	N.A.
	Camaro (Z28)	1 1/2N to 1/2N	1N	1/4P to 1 1/4P	3/4P	1/8 to 1/4	9 1/4 to 10 1/4	N.A.	N.A.
'73-'74	Nova	1/2N to 1 1/2P	1/2P	1/2N to 1P	3/4P	1/16 to 5/16	9	N.A.	N.A.
	Chevelle	1 3/4N to 3/4N	1 1/4N	1/2P to 1 1/2P	1P②	1/8 to 1/4	9 1/2	N.A.	N.A.
	Monte Carlo	4 1/4P to 5 1/4P	4 3/4P	1/2P to 1 1/2P	1P②	0 to 1/8	9 1/2	N.A.	N.A.
	Camaro	1N to 1P	0	1/4P to 1 3/4P	1P	1/16 to 5/16	10 1/2	N.A.	N.A.
	Camaro (Z28)	2N to 0	1N	1 1/2N to 0	3/4N	1/16 to 5/16	10 1/2	N.A.	N.A.

N Negative P Positive

① SS 396 + El Camino—0 to 1P

② Left wheel given, right wheel is 1/2P ± 1/2

CHARGING SYSTEM

AC generator and regulator troubleshooting and repair are covered in the Unit Repair Section.

AC Generator

The following are a few precautions to observe in servicing the Delcotron (AC) generator and the regulator.

1. When installing a battery, be certain that the ground polarity of the battery and the ground polarity of the generator and regulator are the same.
2. When connecting a booster battery, be sure to connect the correct battery terminals together.
3. When hooking up a charger, connect the correct leads to the battery terminals.
4. Never operate the generator on an open circuit. Be sure all connections in the charging circuit are tight.
5. Do not short across or ground any of the terminals on the generator or regulator.
6. Never polarize an AC system.
7. Do not use test lamps of more than 12 volts for checking diode continuity.
8. Avoid long soldering times when replacing diodes or transistors, as prolonged heat will damage them. Always use a heat sink.
9. Always disconnect the battery ground terminal when servicing any AC system. This will prevent accidentally reversing polarity.
10. Always disconnect the battery and AC generator if electric arc welding equipment is being used on the car.

Delcotron Removal and Installation

1. Disconnect battery ground cable to prevent diode damage.
2. Disconnect Delcotron wiring.
3. Remove generator brace bolt. If power steering equipped, loosen pump brace and mount nuts. Detach drive belt(s).
4. Support generator and remove mount bolt(s). Remove unit from vehicle.
5. Reverse procedure to install. Adjust drive belt to have ¼-½ in. play on longest run of belt.

Regulator R & R

1. Disconnect the ground cable at the battery.
2. Disconnect the wiring harness from the regulator.
3. Remove the mounting screws and remove the regulator.
4. Make sure that the regulator base gasket is in place before installation.
5. Clean the attaching area for proper grounding.
6. Install the regulator. Do not overtighten the mounting screws, as this will cancel the cushioning effect of the rubber grommets.

NOTE: an integral alternator-/regulator has been optionally available since 1969. Separate removal or adjustment of the regulator is not possible with this unit. Complete disassembly of this unit is described in the "Unit Repair Section."

STARTING SYSTEM

Starter motor troubleshooting and repairs are covered in the Unit Repair Section.

Starter Removal and Installation

1. Disconnect battery ground cable.
2. Raise and support vehicle.
3. Disconnect all wires at solenoid terminals. Note color coding of wires for reinstallation.
4. Remove starter front bracket and two mount bolts. On engines with solenoid heat shield, remove front bracket upper bolt and detach bracket from starter motor.
5. Remove front bracket bolt or nut. Rotate bracket clear. Lower starter front end first. Remove starter.

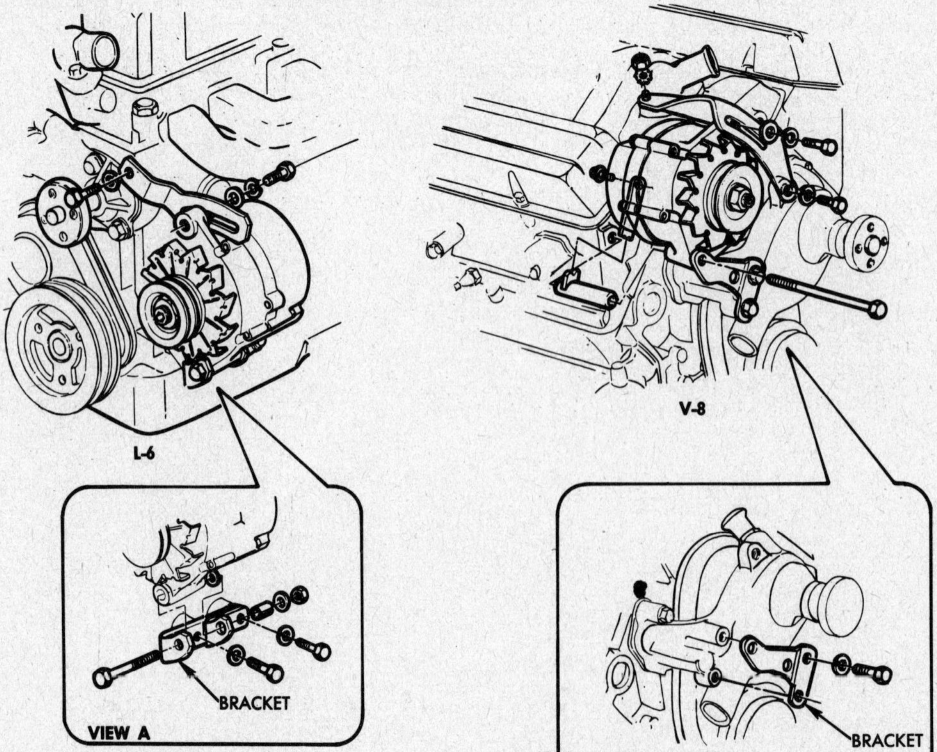
L-6
V-8
BRACKET
VIEW A
BRACKET
VIEW B

Delcotron installation (© Chevrolet Div., G.M. Corp)

6. Reverse procedure to install. Torque mount bolts to 25-35 ft. lbs.

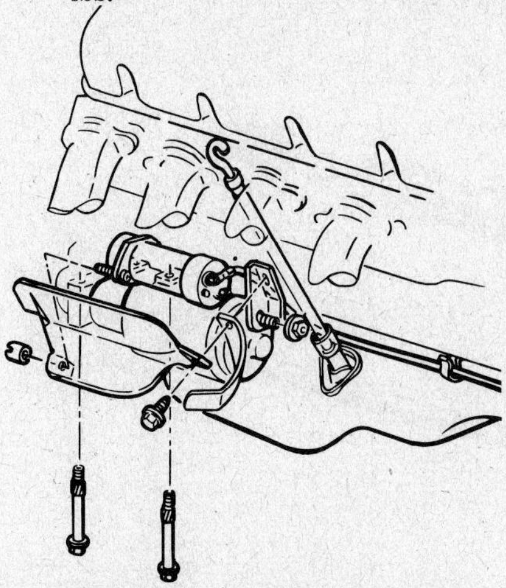

V-8 WITH SOLENOID HEAT SHIELD

Starter motor installation
(© Chevrolet Div., G.M. Corp)

IGNITION SYSTEM

Caution When using an auxiliary starter switch for bumping the engine into position for timing or compression test, the primary distributor lead must be disconnected from the negative post of the ignition coil and the ignition switch must be on. Failure to do this may cause damage to the grounding circuit in the ignition switch.

4 and 6 Cylinder Models

The four and six cylinder distributors, except for number of cam lobes and distributor caps, are similar. Mounting is on the forward right side of the engine. Both units use centrifugal and vacuum controlled advance mechanism. Direction of rotation (as viewed from the top) is clockwise for both models. Other pertinent distributor specifications can be found in the Tune-Up Specifications charts.

V8 Models

The distributor is located between the two banks of cylinders at the back of the block.

Distributor Removal

4 and 6 Cylinder Models

1. Remove distributor cap, primary wire and vacuum line at distributor.
2. Scribe a mark on the distributor body, locating the position of the rotor. Scribe another mark on the engine block, showing the position of the body in the block.
3. Remove the distributor hold-down screw and lift the distributor up and out of the engine.

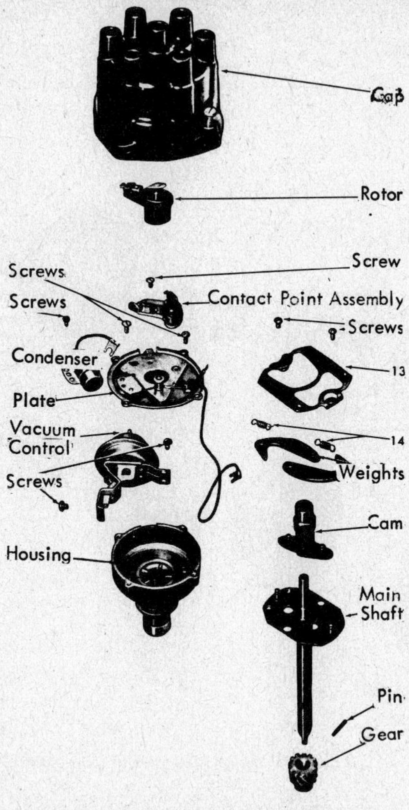
Cap
Rotor
Screws
Screw
Screws
Contact Point Assembly
Screws
Condenser
13
Plate
Vacuum Control
14
Screws
Weights
Cam
Housing
Main Shaft
Pin
Gear

6 cylinder distributor exploded view—typical
(© Chevrolet Div., G.M. Corp)

V8 Models

The drive gear is attached to the distributor shaft. If it becomes necessary to remove the distributor, carefully mark the position of the rotor in relation to the engine block and the distributor housing so that, if the engine is not turned after the distributor is taken out, the rotor can be returned to the position from which it was removed without difficulty.

To remove the distributor, take off the carburetor air cleaner, disconnect the coil primary wire and the vacuum line, remove the distributor cap, take out the single hold-down bolt located under the distributor body. With a pencil, mark the position of the body relative to the block, and then work the distributor up out of the block.

When installing the distributor, make sure the rotor aligns with the marks that were scribed on the distributor housing and the engine block during removal.

Distributor Installation (Engine Disturbed)

1. Turn the crankshaft until the No. 1 cylinder is at the top of its compression stroke. Remove the No. 1 spark plug to feel the compression.
2. Align the timing mark on the flywheel or vibration damper with the TDC indicator or 0 mark on the timing scale.
3. With distributor body oriented in its normal position, hold the rotor pointing toward the front of the engine, then turn the rotor approximately 1/8 turn counterclockwise and push the distributor down until it engages the camshaft, rotating the shaft slightly if necessary.

NOTE: on Mark IV engines there is a punch mark on the distributor drive gear which indicates the rotor position. Thus, the distributor may be installed with the cap in place. Align the punch mark 2° clockwise from the No. 1 cap terminal, then rotate the distributor body clockwise 1/8 turn counterclockwise and push the distributor down into the block.

4. Press down on the distributor and crank the engine to make sure the oil pump shaft is engaged.
5. Return the crankshaft to No. 1 cylinder compression stroke with the timing marks aligned.
6. Turn the distributor body counterclockwise until the points are just beginning to open, then tighten the distributor clamp bolt.
7. Install the distributor cap, checking that the rotor points to the No. 1 terminal. Make sure that the spark plug wires are in their supports and are securely connected.
8. Connect distributor vacuum line and primary wire.
9. Start engine and set the timing.

Breaker Point Adjustment

NOTE: 1970 and later distributors are equipped with a radio static-shield which must be removed for access to the points.

Breaker point gap (dwell) adjustment is accomplished for four and six cylinder engines by loosening the point assembly attaching screw and adjusting it with a screwdriver until the correct gap clearance is obtained (use a feeler gauge). Tighten the point assembly attaching screw and install the distributor cap. Use a dwell meter, if available, to check the dwell angle, readjusting if necessary.

On V8 models there is a window in the distributor cap so that the dwell angle may be set while the engine is running. Use an Allen (hex) wrench to make the adjustment.

See Tune-Up Specifications at the beginning of this section for correct breaker point gap and dwell angle.

The distributor cam lubricator should be rotated 180° (L4 and 6 engines) or switched end-for-end (V8 engines) every 12,000 miles, and replaced every 24,000 miles. Do not oil these lubricator wicks.

Caution On V8 models the distributor body is involved in the engine lubricating system. The lubricating circuit to the

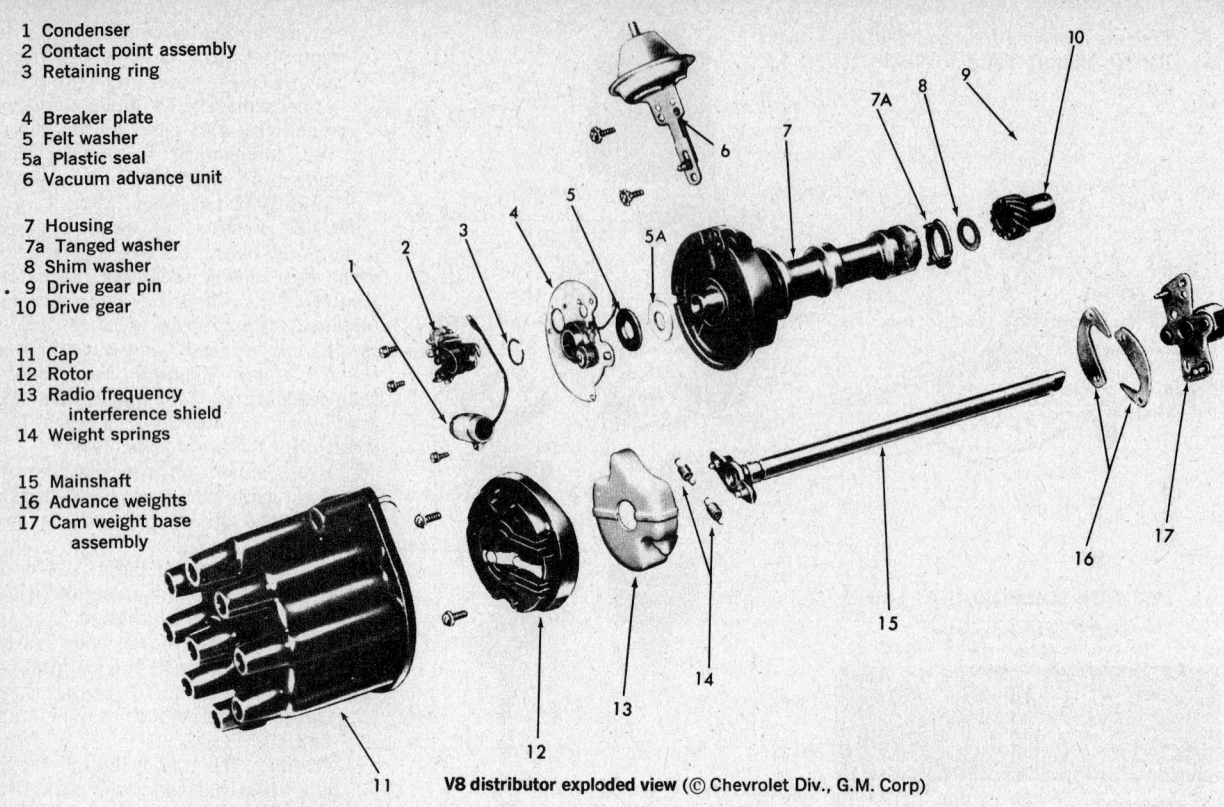

1 Condenser
2 Contact point assembly
3 Retaining ring

4 Breaker plate
5 Felt washer
5a Plastic seal
6 Vacuum advance unit

7 Housing
7a Tanged washer
8 Shim washer
9 Drive gear pin
10 Drive gear

11 Cap
12 Rotor
13 Radio frequency interference shield
14 Weight springs

15 Mainshaft
16 Advance weights
17 Cam weight base assembly

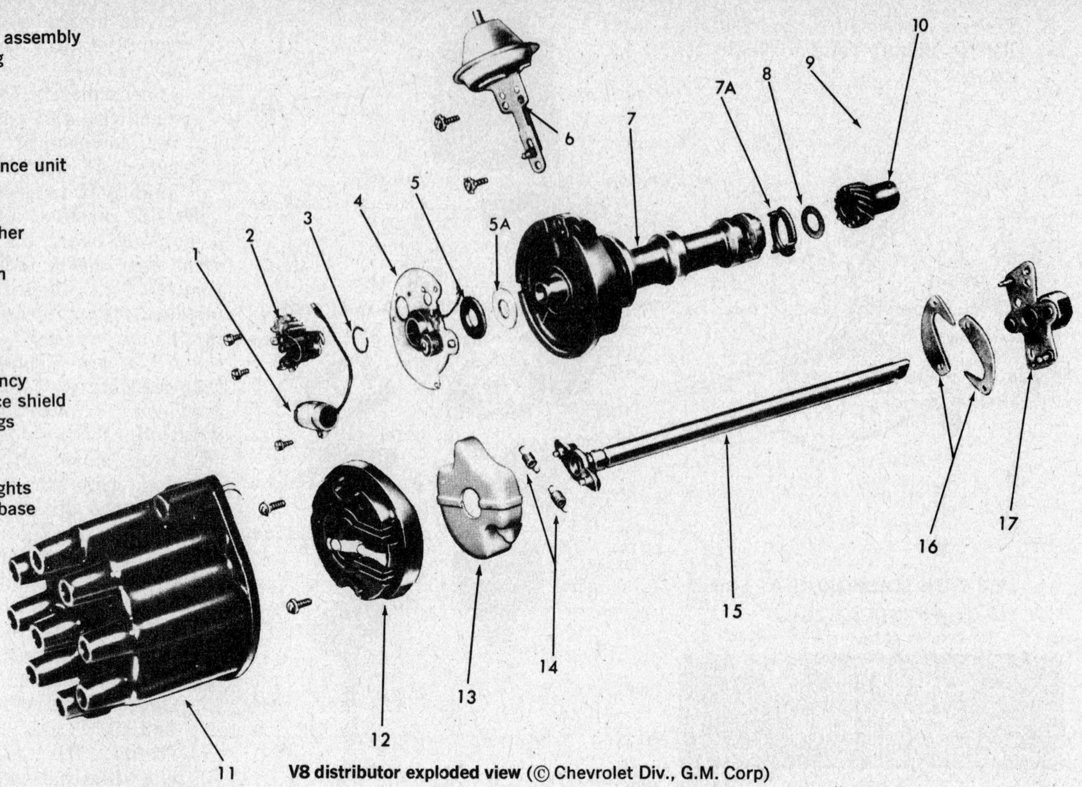

1
2
3
4
5
5A
6
7
7A
8
9
10
11
12
13
14
15
16
17

V8 distributor exploded view (© Chevrolet Div., G.M. Corp)

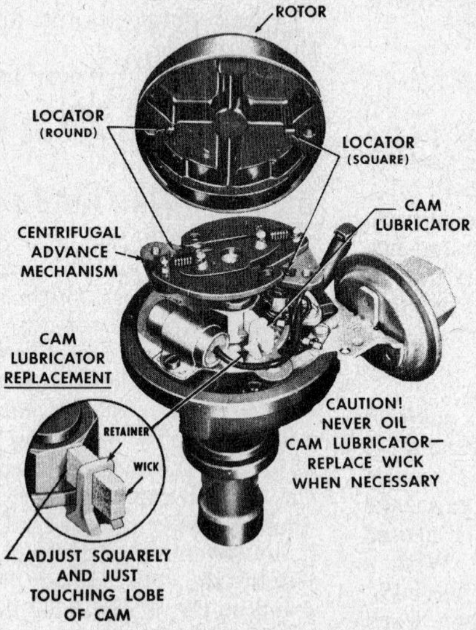

ROTOR
LOCATOR (ROUND)
LOCATOR (SQUARE)
CAM LUBRICATOR
CENTRIFUGAL ADVANCE MECHANISM
CAM LUBRICATOR REPLACEMENT
RETAINER
WICK
CAUTION! NEVER OIL CAM LUBRICATOR— REPLACE WICK WHEN NECESSARY
ADJUST SQUARELY AND JUST TOUCHING LOBE OF CAM

V8 distributor cam lubricator
(© Chevrolet Div., G.M. Corp)

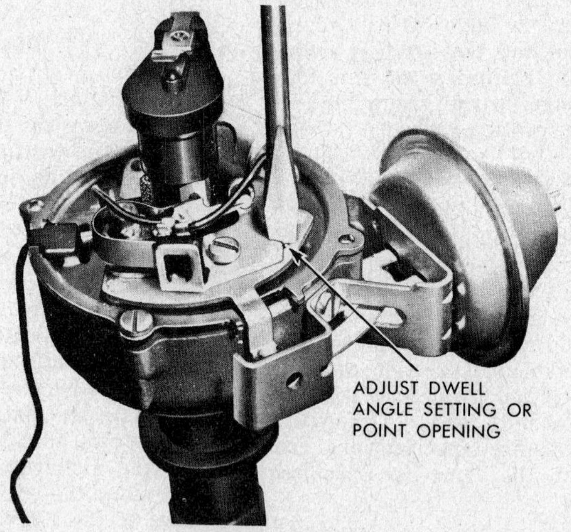

ADJUST DWELL ANGLE SETTING OR POINT OPENING

L6 point adjustment
(© Chevrolet Div., G.M. Corp)

right-bank valve train can be interrupted by mis-alignment of the distributor body. This can cause serious trouble and may be hard to diagnose. See Firing Order and Timing illustrations for correct distributor positioning.

Ignition Timing

Remove the spark plug wire from No. 1 plug and attach a timing light between the wire and the plug. Disconnect the distributor spark advance hose and plug the vacuum opening. Start the engine and run it at idle speed. Aim the timing light at the degree scale just over the harmonic balancer. The markings on the scale are in 2° increments with the greatest number of markings on the before side of the "0." Adjust the timing by loosening the securing clamp and rotating the distributor until the desired ignition advance is achieved, then tighten the clamp. To advance the timing, rotate the distributor opposite to the normal direction of rotor rotation. Retard the timing by rotating the distributor in the normal direction of rotor rotation.

FUEL SYSTEM

Fuel Pump

The fuel pump is the single action AC diaphragm type.

The pump is actuated by an eccentric located on the engine camshaft. On inline engines, the eccentric actuates the pump rocker arm. On V8 engines, a pushrod between the camshaft eccentric and the fuel pump actuates the pump rocker arm.

Fuel Pump R & R—1967-74

1. Disconnect fuel inlet and outlet lines at pump and plug pump inlet line.
2. Remove two pump mounting bolts and lockwashers; remove pump and gasket.
3. On all small-block engines, including Z28, if rocker arm pushrod is to be removed: take out the two adapter bolts and lockwashers and remove adapter and gasket.
4. On big-block V8 engines, 396, 402, 427, 454 cu. in., if rocker arm pushrod is to be removed: take out pipe plug.
5. Install pump with new gasket coated with sealer. Coat mounting bolt threads with sealer and tighten bolts.

NOTE: on V8 engines, mechanical fingers or heavy grease can be used to hold pump pushrod in place during installation. Coat pipe plug threads or adapter gasket with sealer if pushrod was removed.

6. Connect inlet and outlet lines, start engine and check for leaks.

Chilton's TIME SAVER

When replacing a fuel pump on a 283, 307, 327, 350, and 400 cu. in. engine, considerable time can be saved as follows:

1. **Before removing the old pump, remove the upper bolt from the engine's right front mounting boss. This bolt hole is in direct alignment with the fuel pump pushrod. The threaded bolt hole continues into the pump pushrod bore. The bolt acts as an oil plug.**
2. **Temporarily insert a longer bolt, (about 3/8—16 x 2 in.) into the hole. Screw the bolt into the bore until it bottoms against the pump pushrod. (Don't tighten the bolt with a wrench or the rod can be damaged.)**
3. **The mechanic is now free to remove and install the fuel pump without worrying about fuel pump pushrod misalignment.**

CAUTION: don't forget to reinstall original motor bolt.

Fuel Filter R & R

Paper and Bronze Types —1967-74

1. Disconnect fuel line connection at inlet of carburetor.
2. Remove inlet fuel filter nut from carburetor using a box wrench.

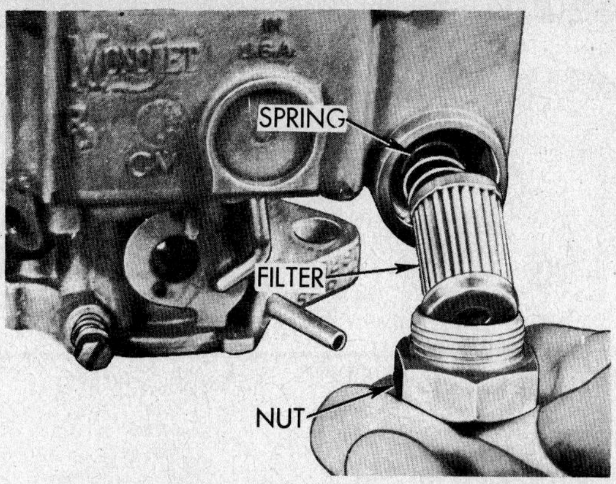
SPRING
FILTER
NUT
Paper fuel filter
(© Chevrolet Div., G.M. Corp)

Carburetor Usage Chart

Year	*Engine*	*Carburetor Make & Model*	*Application*
1967	L-4 153	Carter YF	Chevy II
	L-6 194	Rochester BV (man.) Carter YF (auto.)	Chevy II
	L-6 230	Rochester BV	Chevelle
	L-6 230	Carter YF	Chevy II, Camaro (auto.)
	L-6 250	Rochester BV (man.) Carter YF (auto.)	Chevelle, Chevy II, Camaro
	V8 283 (195)	Rochester 2GV	Chevelle, Chevy II, Camaro
	V8 283 (210)	Rochester 2GV	Camaro
	V8 327 (275)	Rochester 4MV	Chevelle, Chevy II, Camaro
	V8 327 (325)	Holley 4150 (side)	Chevelle
	V8 350 (295)	Rochester 4MV	Camaro
	V8 396 (325)	Rochester 4MV	Chevelle
	V8 396 (350)	Holley 4160	Chevelle
1968	L-4 153	Rochester M	Chevy II
	L-6 230, 250	Rochester MV	Chevelle, Chevy II, Camaro
	V8 302 (290 Z28)	Holley 4150	Camaro
	V8 307 (200)	Rochester 2GV	Chevelle, Chevy II
	V8 327 (210)	Rochester 2GV	Camaro
	V8 327 (250)	Rochester 4MV	Chevelle
	V8 327 (275)	Rochester 4MV	Chevelle, Chevy II, Camaro
	V8 327 (325)	Rochester 4MV	Chevelle, Chevy II
	V8 350 (295)	Rochester 4MV	Chevy II, Camaro
	V8 396 (325)	Rochester 4MV	Chevelle, Chevy II
	V8 396 (350)	Rochester 4MV	Chevelle, Chevy II
	V8 396 (375)	Holley 4150	Chevelle, Chevy II

3. Remove filter element and spring.
4. If a bronze element, blow through cone end—element should allow air to pass freely.
5. Install element spring and new element into carburetor. Bronze elements are installed with small section of cone facing outward.
6. Install new gasket on fitting nut and install nut.
7. Install fuel line and tighten securely. Start engine and check for leaks.

Idle Speed and Mixture Adjustments

NOTE: the *Carburetor Usage Chart* will help in identifying the type of carburetor installed on a particular car. The carburetor illustrations show the locations of idle speed and mixture adjustment screws for each type carburetor.

NOTE: idle speed figures listed in this section are approximate. Consult the tune-up chart in the front of this section for exact figures.

ROCHESTER MV

IDLE SPEED
IDLE MIXTURE
Rochester MV
(© Chevrolet Div., G.M. Corp)

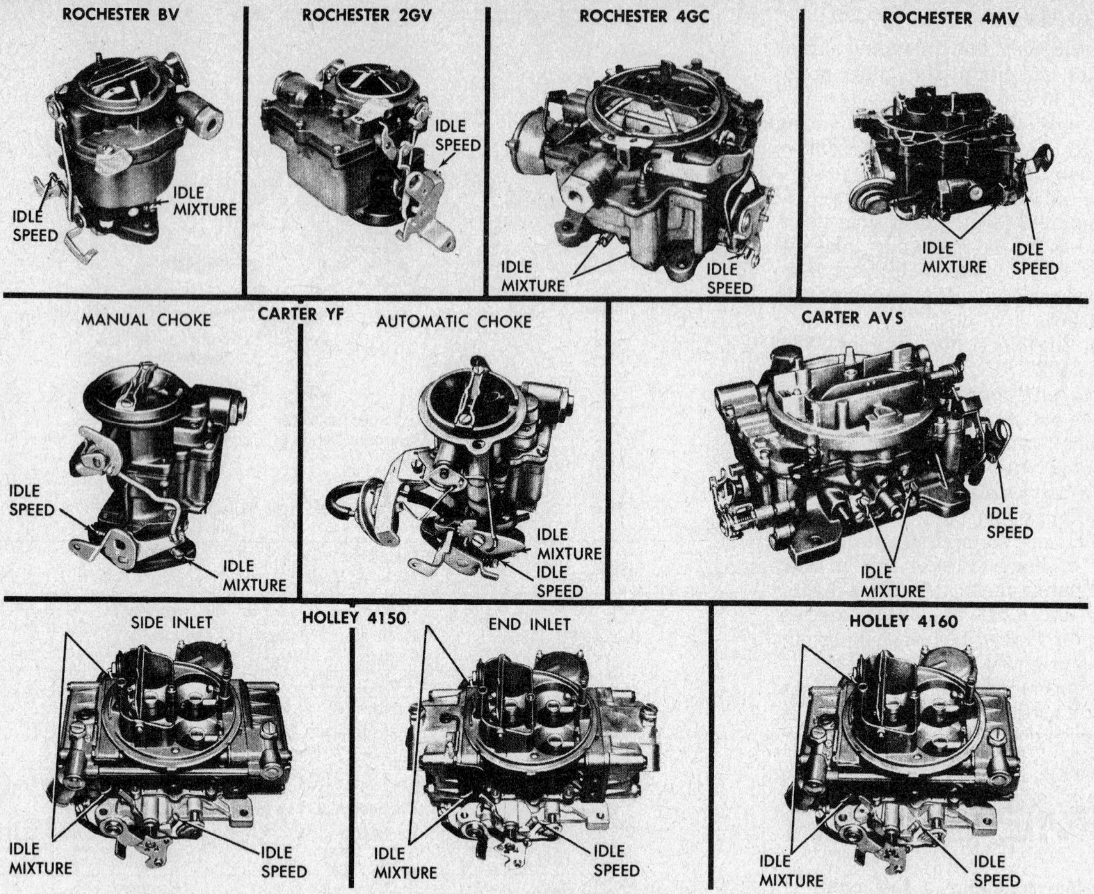

ROCHESTER BV
IDLE MIXTURE
IDLE SPEED
ROCHESTER 2GV
IDLE SPEED
ROCHESTER 4GC
IDLE MIXTURE
IDLE SPEED
ROCHESTER 4MV
IDLE MIXTURE
IDLE SPEED
MANUAL CHOKE
CARTER YF
AUTOMATIC CHOKE
IDLE SPEED
IDLE MIXTURE
IDLE MIXTURE
IDLE SPEED
CARTER AVS
IDLE SPEED
IDLE MIXTURE
SIDE INLET
HOLLEY 4150
END INLET
IDLE MIXTURE
IDLE SPEED
IDLE MIXTURE
IDLE SPEED
HOLLEY 4160
IDLE MIXTURE
IDLE SPEED

Carburetor identification (© Chevrolet Div., G.M. Corp)

IDLE MIXTURE
IDLE SPEED
CARTER AFB
ROCHESTER 2GV (1-½)
IDLE SPEED
IDLE MIXTURE
ROCHESTER M
IDLE SPEED
IDLE MIXTURE

CEC SOLENOID
IDLE SPEED (SOLENOID) SCREW
IDLE SPEED (SOLENOID) SCREW
IDLE SPEED (SOLENOID) SCREW

Rochester carburetor idle speed adjustment locations (© Chevrolet Div., G.M. Corp)

Year	Engine	Carburetor Make & Model	Application
1969	L-4 153	Rochester M	Nova
	L-6 230, 250	Rochester MV	Chevelle, Nova, Camaro
	V8 302 (290 Z28)	Holley 4150	Camaro
	V8 307 (200)	Rochester 2GV (1¼)	Chevelle, Nova
	V8 327 (210)	Rochester 2GV (1¼)	Camaro
	V8 350 (300)	Rochester 4MV	Chevelle, Nova, Camaro
	V8 396 (325)	Rochester 4MV	Chevelle, Camaro
	V8 396 (350) (375)	Holley 4150	Chevelle, Nova, Camaro
1970 exc. below	L-4 153	Rochester M	Nova
	L-6 230	Rochester MV	Nova
	L-6 250	Rochester MV	Nova, Chevelle
	V8 307 (200)	Rochester 2GV (1¼)	Nova, Chevelle
	V8 350 (250)	Rochester 2GV (1½)	Chevelle, Monte Carlo, Chevelle
	V8 350 (300)	Rochester 4MV	Nova, Monte Carlo, Chevelle
	V8 400 (265)	Rochester 2GV (1½)	Monte Carlo
	V8 402 (330)	Rochester 4MV	Monte Carlo, Chevelle (396)
	V8 454 (360)	Rochester 4MV	Monte Carlo, Chevelle
	V8 400 (350)	Rochester 4MV	Chevelle
1970½ and 1971	L-6 250	Rochester MV	Chevelle, Nova, Camaro
	V8 307 (200)	Rochester 2GV (1¼)	Chevelle, Nova, Camaro
	V8 350 (245)	Rochester 2GV	Nova, Monte Carlo, Chevelle, Camaro
	V8 350 (270)	Rochester 4MV	Nova, Monte Carlo, Chevelle, Camaro
	V8 350 (330 Z28)	Holley 4150	Camaro
	V8 402 (300)	Rochester 4MV	Chevelle, Monte Carlo, Camaro
	V8 454 (365)	Rochester 4MV	Monte Carlo, Chevelle
	V8 454 (425)	Holley 4150	Monte Carlo, Chevelle
1972	L6-250	Rochester MV	Chevelle, Camaro, Nova
	V8-307	Rochester 2GV (1¼)	Chevelle, Camaro, Nova
	V8-350	Rochester 2GV (1½)	Chevelle, Monte Carlo, Camaro, Nova
	V8-350 Z28	Holley 4150	Camaro
	V8-350	Rochester 4MV	Chevelle, Monte Carlo, Camaro, Nova
	V8-402	Rochester 4MV	Chevelle, Camaro
	V8-454	Rochester 4MV	Chevelle, Monte Carlo
1973	L6-250	Rochester MV	Chevelle, Camaro, Nova
	V8-307	Rochester 2GV (1¼)	Chevelle, Camaro, Nova
	V8-350	Rochester 2GV (1½)	Nova, Chevelle, Monte Carlo, Camaro
	V8-350	Rochester 4MV	Chevelle, Monte Carlo, Nova, Camaro (incl. Z28)
	V8-454	Rochester 4MV	Chevelle, Monte Carlo

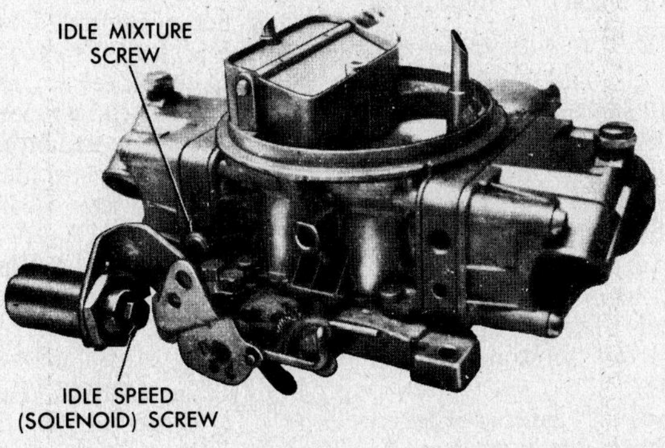
IDLE MIXTURE SCREW
IDLE SPEED (SOLENOID) SCREW

Holley 4150 idle speed adjustment location
(© Chevrolet Div., G.M. Corp)

1967 Without A.I.R.

Adjust with air cleaner removed.

1. Remove air cleaner.
2. Connect a tachometer and vacuum gauge to engine, set parking brake and place transmission in Neutral.
3. Turn in idle mixture screws until they gently seat, then back out 1½ turns.
4. Start engine and allow it to come to normal operating temperature. Make sure choke is fully open, then adjust idle speed screw to obtain specified idle speed (automatic in Drive, manual in Neutral).
5. Adjust idle mixture screw/s to obtain highest steady vacuum at specified idle speed, except for Rochester BV. For this carburetor, adjust idle mixture screw out ¼ turn from lean "drop off", the point where a 20-30 rpm drop is achieved by leaning the mixture.

NOTE: on carburetors having a hot idle compensator valve (A/C models), hold brass valve down with a pencil while making mixture adjustment.

6. Repeat Steps 4 and 5 if necessary.
7. Shut off engine, remove gauges and install air cleaner.

1967 With A.I.R.

Adjust with air cleaner removed.

1. Remove air cleaner.
2. Connect a tachometer and a vacuum gauge to engine, set parking brake and place transmission in Neutral.
3. Turn in idle mixture screw/s until they gently seat, then back out three turns.
4. Start engine and allow it to come up to normal operating temperature. Make sure choke is fully open, then adjust idle speed screw/s to obtain specified idle speed (automatic in Drive, manual in Neutral).
5. Turn the idle mixture screw/s clockwise (in) to the point where a 20-30 rpm drop in speed is achieved—this is the lean "drop off" point. Back out the screws ¼ turn from this point.

NOTE: during this adjustment, A/C should be off on L-4, L-6, 283, 327 and 350 engines. On 396 engines, A/C should be on and hot idle compensator pin depressed.

6. Repeat Steps 4 and 5 if necessary.
7. Shut off engine, remove gauges and install air cleaner.

1968-69

Adjust with air cleaner installed.

1. Turn in idle mixture screw/s until they seat gently, then back out three turns.

2. Start engine and allow it to come up to operating temperature. Make sure choke is fully open and preheater valve is open, then adjust idle speed screw to obtain specified idle speed (automatic in Drive, manual in Neutral).

NOTE: on A/C cars, turn off A/C *except* on L-4 and L-6 with auto transmission and 327 (325/350 H.P.) with manual transmission. On these engines, idle is set with A/C on.

3. Adjust idle mixture screw/s to obtain highest steady idle speed, then readjust idle speed screw to obtain specified speed. On cars having idle stop solenoid, adjust as follows:
   a. Adjust idle speed to 500 rpm L-6 or 600 rpm V8 by turning hex on solenoid plunger.
   b. Disconnect wire at solenoid. This allows throttle lever to seat against idle screw.
   c. Adjust idle screw to obtain 400 rpm, then reconnect wire.
4. Adjust one mixture screw to obtain a 20 rpm drop in idle speed, then back out screw 1/4 turn from this point.
5. Repeat Steps 3 and 4 for second mixture screw, if so equipped.
6. Readjust idle speed to obtain specified idle speed.

1970

Adjust with air cleaner installed.

1. Disconnect "FUEL TANK" line from vapor canister (E.E.C.).
2. Connect a tachometer to engine, start engine and allow it to come up to operating temperature. Make sure choke and preheater valves are fully open.
3. Turn off A/C and set parking brake. Disconnect and plug distributor vacuum line.
4. Make the following adjustments:

L-4 153

a. Set mixture screw to obtain maximum idle rpm.

b. Adjust idle speed screw to obtain 750 rpm for manual transmission (in Neutral), 650 rpm for automatic (in Drive).

c. Adjust mixture screw to obtain a 20 rpm drop in idle speed, then back out 1/4 turn from this point.

d. Readjust idle speed to obtain specified rpm, then reconnect vacuum line.

L-6 230/250

a. Turn in mixture screw until it gently seats, then back out screw four turns.

b. Adjust solenoid screw to obtain 830 rpm for manual transmission (in Neutral) or 630 rpm for automatic (in Drive).

c. Adjust mixture screw to obtain 750 rpm for manual transmission (in Neutral) or 600 rpm for automatic (in Drive).

d. Disconnect solenoid wire and set idle speed to 400 rpm, then reconnect.

e. Reconnect distributor vacuum line.

V8 307 and 400 (265 H.P.)

a. Turn in mixture screws until they seat gently, then back out four turns.

b. Adjust carburetor idle speed screw to obtain 800 rpm for manual transmission (in Neutral), or adjust solenoid screw to obtain 630 rpm for automatic transmission (in Drive).

c. Adjust both mixture screws equally inward to obtain 700 rpm for manual transmission, 600 rpm for automatic (in Drive).

d. On cars with automatic, disconnect solenoid wire, set carburetor idle screw to obtain 450 rpm and reconnect solenoid.

e. Reconnect distributor vacuum line.

V8 350 (250 H.P.)

a. Turn in mixture screws until they gently seat, then back out four turns.

b. Adjust solenoid screw to obtain 830 rpm for manual transmission (in Neutral), 630 rpm for automatic (in Drive).

c. Adjust both mixture screws equally inward to obtain 750 rpm for manual transmission or 600 rpm for automatic (in Drive).

d. Disconnect solenoid wire, set carburetor idle screw to obtain 450 rpm and reconnect solenoid.

e. Reconnect distributor vacuum line.

V8 350 (300 H.P.) and 400 (330 H.P.)

a. Turn in both mixture screws until they gently seat, then back out four turns.

b. Adjust carburetor idle screw to obtain 775 rpm for manual transmission, 630 rpm for automatic (in Drive).

c. Adjust mixture screws equally to obtain 700 rpm for manual transmission, 600 rpm for automatic (in Drive).

d. Reconnect distributor vacuum line.

V8 396 (350 H.P.) and 454 (360 H.P.)

a. Turn in both mixture screws until they gently seat, then back out four turns.

b. Adjust carburetor idle screw to obtain 700 rpm for manual transmission or 630 rpm for automatic (in Drive).

c. For cars with automatic transmission: adjust mixture screws equally to obtain 600 rpm with transmission in Drive.

d. For cars with manual transmission: turn in *one* mixture screw until speed drops to 400 rpm, then adjust carburetor idle screw to obtain 700 rpm. Turn in the *other* mixture screw until speed drops 40 rpm, then regain 700 rpm by adjusting carburetor idle screw.

e. Reconnect distributor vacuum line.

5. Disconnect tachometer and reconnect fuel vapor line.

1971

Adjust with air cleaner installed.

The idle stop solenoid is no longer used, having been replaced by the combination emission control valve. This valve is energized through the transmission to increase idle speed under conditions of high gear deceleration and to provide full vacuum spark advance during high gear operation. The valve is de-energized at curb idle and in the lower gears to provide a retarded spark under these conditions, the result of which is lower hydrocarbon emission. *The valve need not be adjusted unless the solenoid or throttle body is removed, or the carburetor overhauled.*

On all 1971 vehicles except those with solid lifter cams, i.e., 350/330 (Z28) and 454/425 (LS-6), idle limiter caps are installed on the mixture screws of the carburetors. Chevrolet does not recommend removing these caps, and does not recommend adjusting the mixture. Adjusting the mixture without the proper test gear will result in hydrocarbon emission levels in excess of the specified minimum.

1. Follow Steps 1-3 of 1970 procedure.
2. Make the following adjustments:

L-6 250

a. Adjust carburetor idle speed screw to obtain 550 rpm for manual transmission (in Neutral) or 500 rpm for automatic (in Drive). *Do not adjust solenoid screw.*

b. Reconnect vapor line and distributor vacuum advance line.

V8 307 (200 H.P.) and 350 (245 H.P.)

a. Adjust carburetor idle speed screw to obtain 600 rpm for manual transmission (in Neutral) with A/C off, or 550 rpm for automatic (in Drive) with A/C on. *Do not adjust solenoid screw.*

b. Reconnect vapor line and distributor vacuum advance line.

V8 350 (270 H.P.)

a. Adjust carburetor idle speed screw to obtain 600 rpm for manual transmission (in Neutral) with A/C off, or 550 rpm for automatic (in Drive) with A/C on. *Do not adjust solenoid screw.*

b. Place fast idle cam follower on second step of fast idle cam, turn A/C off and adjust fast idle to 1,350 rpm for manual transmission (in Neutral) or 1,500 rpm for automatic (in Park).

c. Reconnect vapor line and distributor vacuum advance line.

V8 350 (330 H.P. Z28) and 454 (425 H.P.)

a. Adjust mixture screws to obtain maximum speed (rpm at idle), then adjust carburetor idle speed screw to obtain 700 rpm (manual in Neutral and automatic in Drive).

b. Turn in one mixture screw to obtain a 20 rpm drop in speed, then back out 1/4 turn.

c. Repeat Step "b" for other mixture screw, then reset idle to 700 rpm. *Do not adjust solenoid screw.*

d. Reconnect vapor line and distributor vacuum line.

V8 396 (300 H.P.) and 454 (365 H.P.)

a. Turn off A/C and adjust carburetor idle speed screw to obtain 600 rpm with manual transmission in Neutral and automatic in Drive. *Do not adjust solenoid screw.*

b. Place fast idle cam follower on second step of fast idle cam, turn off A/C and adjust fast idle to 1,350 rpm for manual transmission (in Neutral) or 1,500 rpm for automatic (in Park).

c. Reconnect vapor line and distributor vacuum line.

1972

Disconnect the fuel tank line from the vapor canister on Chevrolet models. Remove the fuel tank cap on Corvettes, but do not remove the vapor line. Disconnect the distributor vacuum hose and plug the opening. All carburetors are equipped with idle mixture limiter caps. Do not try to adjust the mixture or remove the caps. Adjust the idle speed with the engine running at its normal temperature, choke open, and parking brake set. Turn the air conditioner off, if so equipped. Chock the wheels on automatic transmission cars. Manual transmissions should be in Neutral, and automatic transmissions in Drive.

250 cu in. L6

Adjust the idle stop solenoid (not the C.E.C. solenoid, which is the larger of the two carburetor-mounted solenoids) for a speed of 700 rpm (M.T.) or 600 rpm (A.T.).

350 and 400 cu in. V8s (two-barrel carburetor)

Adjust the idle stop solenoid screw for 900 rpm (M.T.) or 600 rpm (A.T.). Set the carburetor fast idle cam screw for 1850 rpm on 307 engines and 2200 rpm on 350 engines.

350 cu in. V8 (Quadrajet four-barrel carburetor)

Adjust the idle stop solenoid screw to obtain 800 rpm (M.T.) or 600 rpm (A.T.). Position the fast idle follower on the second step of the fast idle cam and set the fast idle to 1350 rpm (M.T.) or 1500 rpm (A.T.).

350 cu in. V8 (Holley four-barrel carburetor)

Adjust the idle stop solenoid screw for 900 rpm.

402 and 454 cu in. V8s (Quadrajet four-barrel carburetor)

Adjust the idle stop solenoid screw for 800 rpm (M.T.) or 600 rpm (A.T.). Position the fast idle follower on the second step of the fast idle cam and set the fast idle at 1350 rpm (M.T.) or 1500 rpm (A.T.).

NOTE: only use this procedure when the idle solenoid has been removed from the carburetor.

1972-74 Idle Solenoid Adjustment

All 1972–74 models are equipped with an idle solenoid on the carburetor. The solenoid should allow the throttle plate to close further when the ignition is turned off. If it does not, the solenoid must be replaced. The same preconditions necessary for the idle adjustment procedure also apply here.

Caution Do not turn the solenoid more than one complete turn unless the electrical wire is disconnected.

One-barrel Carburetors

The solenoid is turned clockwise for an rpm increase and counterclockwise for a decrease.

1. Disconnect the fuel tank line from the charcoal canister.
2. Disconnect and plug the distributor vacuum line.
3. Set the final idle speed by turning the idle solenoid plunger, with the idle solenoid energized, to the specification in the chart.
4. Adjust the low idle speed, with the solenoid de-energized, to 450 rpm. Use an allen wrench in the end of the solenoid for this adjustment.

Two and Four-barrel Carburetors

1. Disconnect the fuel tank line from the charcoal canister.
2. Disconnect and plug the distributor vacuum line.
3. Turn the solenoid plunger to obtain the higher of the two idle speeds listed in the tune-up specifications. Disconnect the idle solenoid wire.
4. Turn the curb idle adjusting screw to set the low idle to 450 rpm with the adjustment screw on the low step of the cam.
5. Adjust the dwell angle and timing, and again check the low idle speed.
6. Reconnect the solenoid wire.
7. Open the throttle for a moment and adjust the solenoid plunger screw to the idle specified in the "Tune-Up Specifications" table.

Heat Riser R & R

The V8 heat riser is located between the exhaust manifold and the exhaust pipe. To replace the valve, lower the exhaust pipe from the manifold on the side where the valve is located. Remove the valve assembly from the exhaust manifold studs. Install the replacement valve, raise the exhaust pipe, and tighten the exhaust manifold stud nuts to 20 ft lbs.

COOLING SYSTEM

A standard pressure cooling system is used on all models. The radiator cap is designed to maintain a cooling system pressure of about 13 or 15 psi above atmospheric. The water pump requires no attention except to make certain the air vent at the top of the hosing and the drain holes in the bottom do not become clogged.

Radiator Removal—1967-74

1. Drain radiator.
2. Disconnect hoses and oil cooler lines.
3. Remove radiator upper panel and shroud (if so equipped).
4. Remove radiator attaching bolts and lift radiator out of car.

Radiator Installation—1967-74

1. Slide radiator into position.
2. Install attaching bolts, shroud, and upper panel.
3. Install hoses and close drain.
4. Fill cooling system, run engine until operating temperature has been reached. Again fill cooling system and check for leaks.

Water Pump R & R

1. Drain the radiator and loosen the fan pulley bolts.
2. Disconnect the heater hose, lower radiator hose and, if applicable, the bypass hose at the water pump.
3. On V8 engines, remove the Delcotron upper brace. Loosen the swivel bolt and remove the fan belt.
4. On Mark IV engines, disconnect the power steering and air conditioning belts and swivel the power steering pump to one side.
5. Remove the fan blade and pulley. Replace a bent or damaged fan.

NOTE: thermostatic fan clutches must be kept in an "in-car" position. When removed from the car the assembly should be supported so that the clutch disc remains in a vertical plane to prevent silicone fluid leakage.

6. Remove the water pump attaching bolts and, if applicable, the power steering-to-pump bolts and remove the pump and gasket.

NOTE: on four and six-cylinder engines, pull the pump straight out of the block first to avoid damage to the impeller.

7. Install the pump assembly using a new gasket. Coat the gasket on both sides with sealer. Tighten the 5/16 in. bolts to 15 ft lbs. (four and six-cylinder) and the 3/8 in. bolts (V8) to 30 ft lbs.
8. Install the pulley and fan.
9. On Mark IV engines, install the power steering and air conditioning bolts.
10. Connect the hoses and fill the cooling system.
11. On V8 engines, install the Delcotron upper brace and fan belt. Install the power steering pump bolt.
12. Adjust the belts, then start the engine and check for leaks.

Thermostat R & R

The thermostat is located inside a housing on the front of the cylinder head on four and six-cylinder engines and inside the front of the intake manifold casting on V8 engines. It is not necessary to remove the radiator hose from the thermostat housing when removing the thermostat.

1. Remove the two retaining bolts from the thermostat housing and lift up the housing with the hose attached. Remove the thermostat.
2. Insert the new thermostat, spring end down, and install the housing with a new gasket. Tighten the housing retaining bolts to 30 ft lbs on four and six-cylinder engines.

EMISSION CONTROLS

NOTE: see the Unit Repair Section for emission control systems troubleshooting.

Positive Crankcase Ventilation

In this system, crankcase vapors are drawn into the intake manifold and burned as part of engine combustion. Positive ventilation uses a vented-mesh oil filler cap for clean air intake to the crankcase and the closed positive system draws clean air from the carburetor air cleaner. After 1968, only the closed system is used. The ventilation flow is regulated by PCV valve.

Air Injection Reactor

This system was first introduced on California cars in 1966. The AIR system injects compressed air into the exhaust system, near enough to the exhaust valves to continue the burning of the normally unburned segment of the exhaust gases. To do this it employs an air injection pump and a system of hoses, valves, tubes, etc., necessary to carry the compressed air from the pump to the exhaust manifolds. Carburetors and distributors for AIR engines have specific modifications to adapt them to the air injection system; those components should not be interchanged with those intended for use on engines that do not have the system. All 1973 engines are equipped with AIR.

A diverter valve is used to prevent backfiring. The valve senses sudden increases in manifold vacuum and ceases the injection of air during fuel-rich periods. During coasting, this valve diverts the entire air flow through the pump muffler and during high engine speeds, expels it through a relief valve. Check valves in the system prevent exhaust gases from entering the pump.

Air Pump R & R

Caution Do not pry on the pump housing or clamp the pump in a vise: the housing is soft and may become distorted.

1. Disconnect the air hoses at the pump.
2. Hold the pump pulley from turning and loosen the pulley bolts.
3. Loosen the pump mounting bolt and adjustment bracket bolt. Remove the drive belt.
4. Remove the mounting bolts, and then remove the pump.
5. Install the pump using a reverse of the removal procedure.

Diverter (Anti-afterburn) Valve R & R

1. Detach the vacuum sensing line from the valve.
2. Remove the other hose(s) from the valve.
3. Unfasten the diverter valve from the elbow or the pump body.

Installation is performed in the reverse order of removal. Always use a new gasket. Tighten the valve securing bolts to 85 in. lbs.

Controlled Combustion System

C.C.S. increases combustion efficiency through leaner carburetor adjustments and revised distributor calibration. Thermostatically controlled air intakes are also used on most models. A higher temperature thermostat is used on C.C.S. cars.

Evaporative Emission Control

Introduced on California cars in 1970, and nationwide in 1971, this system reduces the amount of escaping gasoline vapors. Float bowl emissions are controlled by internal carburetor modifications. Redesigned bowl vents, reduced bowl capacity, heat shields, and improved intake manifold-to-carburetor insulation serve to reduce vapor loss into the atmosphere. The venting of fuel tank vapors into the air has been stopped. Fuel vapors are now directed through lines to a canister containing an activated charcoal filter. Unburned vapors are trapped here until the engine is started. When the engine is running, the canister is purged by air drawn in by manifold vacuum. The air and fuel vapors are then directed into the engine to be burned. All 1973 models, except Camaro, have integral vapor separators within the fuel tank.

Charcoal Canister R & R

1. Raise the vehicle and securely support it on jackstands.
2. Note the proper installation positions of the hose connections on the canister and then remove the hoses.
3. Loosen the screws which secure the canister mounting clamps and remove the canister assembly.
4. If the filter requires replacement, withdraw it from the bottom of the canister with your fingers.

Check the condition of the hoses and hose fittings. Replace as required.

NOTE: If new hoses are being used, use only those which are fuel resistant and are marked "EVAP".

Check the purge valve which is located on the top of the canister, by applying vacuum to it. A good valve should retain the vacuum. If the valve is defective, slowly unsnap its top (the diaphragm is held in place by spring tension). Withdraw the diaphragm, spring, and spring retainer. Assemble the valve in the reverse order of disassembly.

Replace the filter in the bottom of the canister if necessary. Install the canister assembly in the vehicle in the reverse order of removal.

Transmission Controlled Spark

Introduced in 1970, this system controls exhaust emissions by eliminating vacuum advance in the lower forward gears.

The 1970 system consists of a transmission switch, solenoid vacuum switch, time delay relay, and a thermostatic water temperature switch. The solenoid vacuum switch is energized in the lower gears via the transmission switch and closes off distributor vacuum. The two-way transmission switch is activated by the shifter shaft on manual transmissions, and by oil pressure on automatic transmissions. The switch de-energizes the solenoid in high gear, the plunger extends and uncovers the vacuum port, and the distributor receives full vacuum. The temperature switch overrides the system when engine temperature is below 63° or above 232°. This allows vacuum advance in all gears. A time delay relay opens 15 seconds after the ignition is switched on. Full vacuum advance during this delay eliminates the possibility of stalling.

The 1971 system is similar, except that the vacuum solenoid (now called a Combination Emissions Control or CEC solenoid) serves two functions. One function is to control distributor vacuum; the added function is to act as a deceleration throttle stop in high gear. This cuts down on emissions when the vehicle is coming to a stop in high gear. The CEC solenoid is controlled by a temperature switch, a transmission switch, and a 20 second time delay relay. This system also contains a reversing relay, which energizes the solenoid when the transmission switch, temperature switch or time delay completes the CEC circuit to ground. This system is directly opposite the 1970 system in operation. The 1970 vacuum solenoid was normally open to allow vacuum advance and when energized, closed to block vacuum. The 1971 system is normally closed blocking vacuum advance and when energized, opens to allow vacuum advance. The temperature switch completes the CEC circuit to ground when engine temperature is below 82°. Some Camaros and Corvettes also have a high temperature terminal on the switch to complete the CEC circuit when coolant temperature reaches 232°. The time delay relay allows vacuum advance (and raised idle speed) for 20 seconds after the ignition key is turned to the "on" position. Models with an automatic transmission and air conditioning also have a solid state timing device which engages the air conditioning compressor for three seconds after the ignition key is turned to the "off" position to prevent the engine from running-on.

The 1972 L6 system is similar to that used in 1971, except that an idle stop solenoid has been added to the system. In the energized position, the solenoid maintains engine speed at a predetermined fast idle. When the solenoid is de-energized by turning off the ignition, the solenoid allows the throttle plates to close beyond the normal idle position; thus cutting off the air supply and preventing engine run-on. The L6 is the only 1972 engine with a C.E.C. valve, which serves the same deceleration function as in 1971. The 1972 time delay relay delays full vacuum 20 seconds after the transmission is shifted into high gear. V8 engines use a vacuum advance solenoid similar to that used in 1970. This relay is normally closed to block vacuum and opens when energized to allow vacuum advance. The solenoid controls distributor vacuum advance and performs no throttle positioning function. The idle stop solenoid used operates in the same manner as the one on L6 engines. All air-conditioned cars have an additional anti-diesel (run-on) solenoid which engages the compressor clutch for three seconds after the ignition is switched off. The 1973 TCS system differs from the 1972 system in three ways. The 23 second upshift delay has been replaced by a 20 second starting relay. This relay closes to complete the TCS circuit and open the TCS solenoid, allowing vacuum advance, for 20 seconds after the key is turned to the "on" position. The operating temperature of the temperature overide switch has been raised to 93°, and the switch that was used to engage the A/C compressor when the key was turned "off" has been eliminated. All models are equipped with an electric throttle control solenoid to prevent run-on. The 1973 TCS system is used on all models equipped with a 307 engine. all V8 models equipped with a manual transmission, and all full-size station wagons equipped with a 165 hp 350 or a 170 hp 400.

For diagnosis procedures, see the Unit Repair Section. Any of the methods of exhaust emission control requires close and frequent attention to tune-up factors of engine maintenance.

Exhaust Gas Recirculation

1973-'74 engines are equipped with exhaust gas recirculation (EGR). This system consists of a metering valve, a vacuum line to the carburetor, and cast-in exhaust gas passages in the intake manifold. The EGR valve is controlled by carburetor vacuum, and accordingly opens and closes to admit exhaust gases into the fuel/air mixture. The exhaust gases lower the combustion temperature, and reduce the amount of oxides of nitrogen (NO_x) produced. The valve is closed at idle and wide open throttle, but is open between the two extreme throttle positions.

EGR Valve R & R

1. Pull the vacuum sensing line from the fitting on top of the EGR valve.
2. Unfasten the bolt which secures the valve clamp to the manifold.

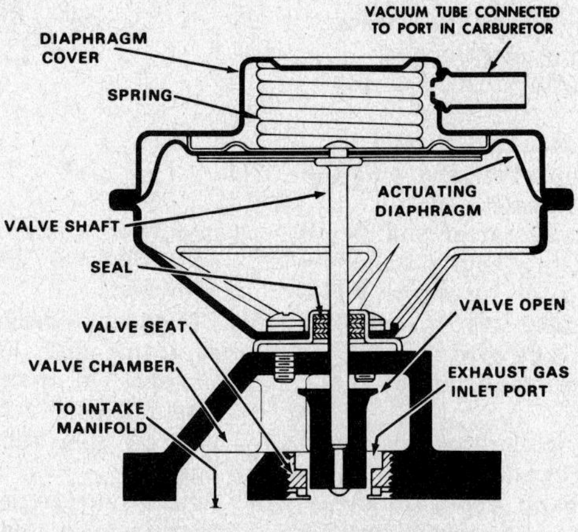
VACUUM TUBE CONNECTED TO PORT IN CARBURETOR
DIAPHRAGM COVER
SPRING
ACTUATING DIAPHRAGM
VALVE SHAFT
SEAL
VALVE OPEN
VALVE SEAT
VALVE CHAMBER
EXHAUST GAS INLET PORT
TO INTAKE MANIFOLD

Cutaway view of an EGR valve
(© Chevrolet Div., G.M. Corp)

3. Withdraw the clamp and the EGR valve from the manifold.

Install the EGR valve in the reverse order of removal. Use a new valve gasket. Tighten the clamp bolt to 25 ft lbs and lock it with its tab.

ENGINE

Four, six, and eight cylinder engines are used. The four cylinder engine is a 153 cu. in. inline design with five main bearings. The six cylinder engines are also of the inline type, with seven main bearings. They have been built in 230 and 250 cu. in. displacements. V8 engines are of two basic types. All engines of each type are generally similar in design and have some interchangeability of parts. The first type is the small V8 series. This includes the 283, 302, 307, 327, 350, and 400 cu. in. engines. The second type is the large, or Mark IV, V8 series. This includes engines of 396, 402, and 454 cu. in. displacement. A small-block 400 cu. in. engine is available only in 2-BBL form. This engine must not be confused with the Mark IV 402, which is also called a "396" in some cars.

Pertinent engine data can be found in the General Engine Specifications chart.

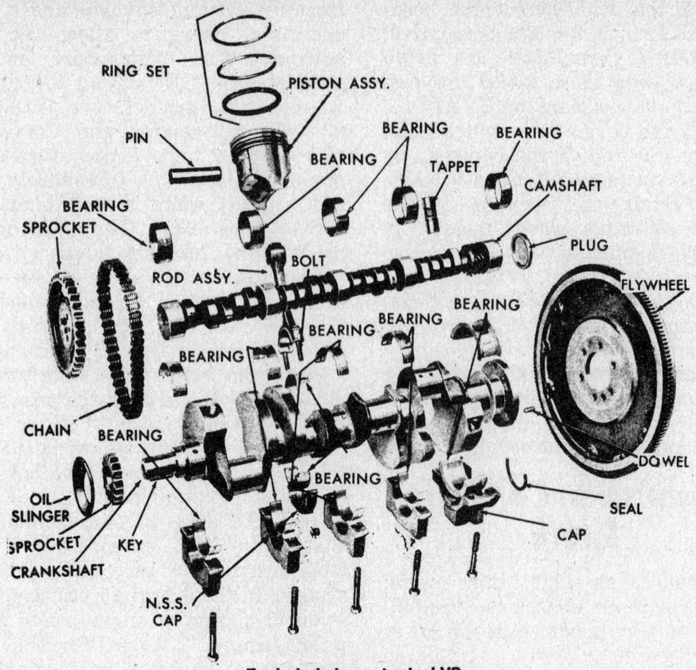
RING SET
PISTON ASSY.
PIN
BEARING
BEARING
BEARING
TAPPET
CAMSHAFT
BEARING
SPROCKET
PLUG
ROD ASSY.
BOLT
FLYWHEEL
BEARING
BEARING
BEARING
BEARING
CHAIN
BEARING
DOWEL
OIL SLINGER
BEARING
SEAL
SPROCKET
KEY
CAP
CRANKSHAFT
N.S.S. CAP

Exploded view—typical V8
(© Chevrolet Div., G.M. Corp)

Exploded view 6 cylinder engine—typical
(© Chevrolet Div., G.M. Corp)

Engine R & R

NOTE: unless otherwise stated, the following operations cover the 4 cylinder, 6 cylinder and V8 engines.

Caution Do not discharge the compressor or disconnect the A/C lines. Damage to the A/C system or personal injury could result.

Removal—1967-74

1. Raise car and place on jackstands.
2. Drain cooling system, transmission, and crankcase.
3. Scribe alignment marks on underside of hood and around hood hinges, and remove hood from hinges.
4. Disconnect coolant and heater hoses at engine attachment.
5. Disconnect battery cables at battery.
6. Remove radiator and shroud assembly. Remove fan and pulley.
7. Remove air cleaner.
8. Disconnect coil, starter and Delcotron wires, engine-to-body ground strap, oil pressure and engine temperature sender wires, and C.E.C. wire.
9. Disconnect gas tank line at fuel pump.
10. Disconnect accelerator control linkage at firewall.
11. Disconnect hand choke linkage (4 cylinder), and power brake vacuum line.
12. Disconnect exhaust pipe from manifold. Disconnect the crossover pipe on V8 models, if so equipped.
13. Disconnect clutch shaft bracket at frame and disconnect clutch linkage. On automatic transmission models, remove transmission oil filler tube and plug the opening.
14. Attach engine lifting tool. Attach to hoist and secure the engine.
15. Remove driveshaft.
16. Remove and set aside power steering pump and air conditioning compressor. Do not disconnect hoses.
17. Remove engine rear mounting bolts.
18. Disconnect speedometer cable, transmission control rod linkage lower ends, T.C.S. switch, and transmission oil cooler lines.
19. Loosen front engine mounting bolts.
20. Raise engine slightly and remove

bolts.

21. Remove transmission crossmember and free the transmission rear mounting.
22. Remove engine and transmission as a unit from the car.

Installation—1967-74

1. Bolt engine lifting tool to engine and lower engine and transmission into chassis as a unit. Guide engine to align front engine mounts with mounts on frame.
2. Install one rear transmission crossmember side bolt, swing crossmember up under transmission mount and install bolt in opposite side rail.
3. Align and install rear mount bolts.
4. Install engine front mount bolts and remove lifting tool from engine.
5. Install and connect all items in reverse order of engine removal procedure.

Separating Transmission and Clutch from Engine

Manual Transmission

1. Remove clutch housing cover plate screws.
2. Remove bolts holding clutch housing to engine block. Remove clutch housing and transmission assembly.
3. Remove starter and clutch housing cover plate.
4. Loosen clutch-to-flywheel bolts, alternately, until spring pressure is released. Remove all bolts, clutch disc and pressure plate assembly.
5. Re-attach transmission by reversing above process.

Automatic Transmission

1. Lower the engine and support it on suitable blocks.
2. Remove starter and converter housing underpan.
3. Remove flywheel-to-converter assembly attaching bolts.
4. Support transmission on blocks.
5. Remove transmission-to-engine mounting bolts.
6. With engine hoist attached, remove blocks from engine only and slowly guide the engine from the transmission.
7. Re-attach automatic transmission by reversing above process.

Valve System

Chevrolet uses a hydraulically operated tappet system with adjustable rocker nuts to obtain zero lash.

Valve specifications may be obtained from the Valve Specifications chart and the Tune-up Specifications chart.

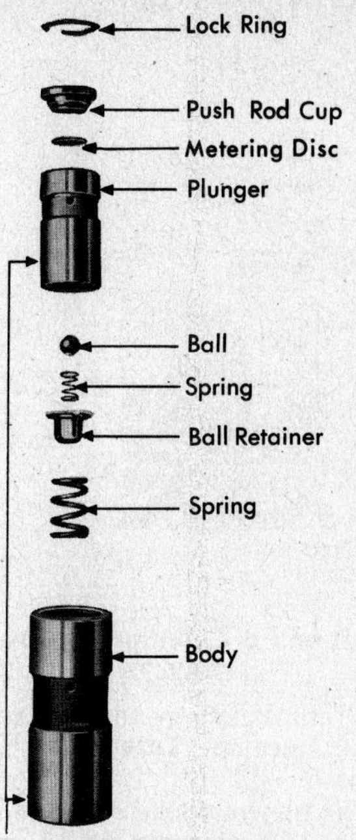
Lock Ring
Push Rod Cup
Metering Disc
Plunger
Ball
Spring
Ball Retainer
Spring
Body

Plunger and body are fitted pairs and must not be mismated
(© Chevrolet Div., G.M. Corp)

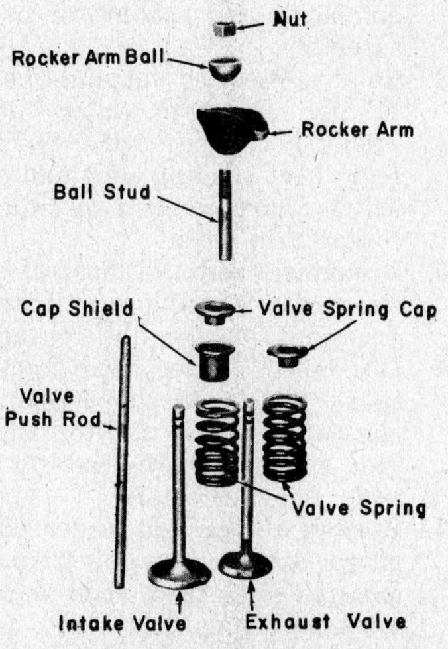
Nut
Rocker Arm Ball
Rocker Arm
Ball Stud
Cap Shield
Valve Spring Cap
Valve
Push Rod
Valve Spring
Intake Valve
Exhaust Valve

V8 valve assembly
(© Chevrolet Div., G.M. Corp)

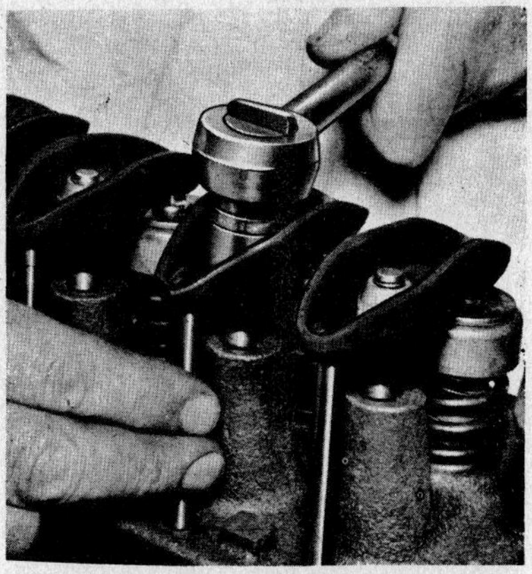

Adjusting valve clearance—6 cyl w/hydraulic lifters
(© Chevrolet Div., G.M. Corp)

Hydraulic Valve Lifter Adjustment

Preliminary Adjustment

In the case of disassembly, or any other cause for valve tappet adjustment, proceed as follows:

1. Adjust rocker arm nuts to eliminate lash. This must be done when lifter is on base of circle of cam.
2. Remove distributor cap and crank engine until distributor rotor points to No. 1 cylinder terminal, with points open.

The following valves can be adjusted with the engine in No. 1 firing position:

OHV 4—Intake No. 1, 2, Exhaust No. 1, 3
OHV 6—Intake No. 1, 2, 4, Exhaust No. 1, 3, 5
V8—Intake No. 1, 2, 5, 7, Exhaust No. 1, 3, 4, 8

3. Turn adjusting nut until all lash is removed from this particular valve train. This can be determined by checking pushrod side play while turning the adjustment. When all play has been removed, turn adjusting nut one more turn. This will place the lifter plunger in the center of its travel.
4. Follow steps 2 and 3 to adjust remaining valves.

The following valves can be adjusted with the engine in the No. 6 firing position (No. 4 on OHV 4):

OHV 4—Intake No. 3, 4, Exhaust No. 2, 4
OHV 6—Intake No. 3, 5, 6, Exhaust No. 2, 4, 6
V8—Intake No. 3, 4, 6, 8, Exhaust No. 2, 5, 6, 7

Readjust the lifters as follows with the engine hot and running.

1. Remove rocker arm covers and gaskets.
2. Place oil deflector clips on rocker arms.
3. With engine running at idle, back off rocker arm nut until it starts to clatter.
4. Turn nut down until clatter stops. This is the zero lash position.
5. Tighten nut down one-quarter turn. Pause ten seconds. Repeat additional quarter turns and ten second pauses until nut has been tightened down one full turn from the zero lash position.
6. Repeat steps 3, 4, and 5 for all rocker arms.
7. Remove oil deflector clips and replace rocker arm covers.

Mechanical Valve Lifter Adjustment

1. Set engine in No. 1 firing position.
2. Adjust the clearance between the valve stems and the rocker

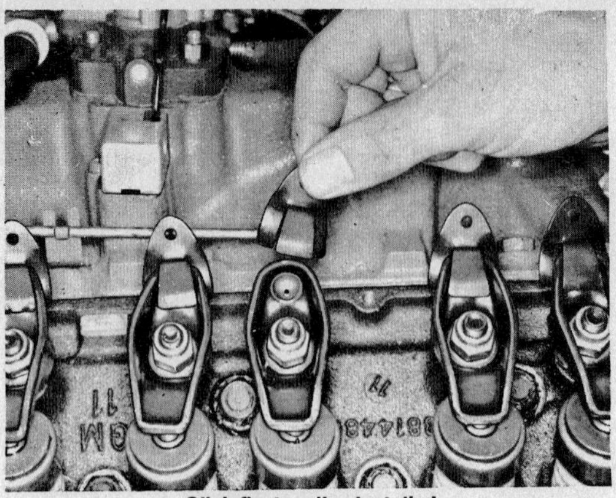

Oil deflector clips installed
(© Chevrolet Div., G.M. Corp)

Adjusting valve clearance—V8 w/mechanical lifters
(© Chevrolet Div., G.M. Corp)

arms using a feeler gauge. Check the Tune-Up Specifications table for the proper clearance. Adjust the following Valves in No. 1 firing position: Intake No. 2, 7, Exhaust No. 4, 8.

3. Turn crankshaft one-half revolution clockwise. Adjust the following valves: Intake No. 1, 8, Exhaust No. 3, 6.
4. Turn crankshaft one-half revolution clockwise to No. 6 firing position. Adjust the following valves in No. 6 firing position: Intake No. 3, 4, Exhaust No. 5, 7.
5. Turn crankshaft one-half revolution clockwise. Adjust the following valves: Intake No. 5, 6, Exhaust No. 1, 2.
6. Run engine until normal operating temperature is reached. Reset all clearances, using oil deflectors.

Cylinder Head

R & R

Caution Do not discharge the compressor or disconnect the A/C lines. Damage to the A/C system or personal injury could result.

4 and 6 Cylinder Engines 1967-74

1. Drain cooling system and remove air cleaner. Disconnect P.C.V. hose.
2. Disconnect choke cable (4 cylinder), accelerator pedal rod at bell crank on manifold, and fuel and vacuum lines at carburetor.
3. Disconnect exhaust pipe at manifold flange, then remove manifold bolts and clamps and remove manifolds and carburetor as an assembly.
4. Remove fuel and vacuum line retaining clip from water outlet. Then disconnect wire harness from heat sending unit and coil, leaving harness clear of clips on rocker arm cover.
5. Disconnect radiator hose at water outlet housing and battery ground strap at cylinder head.
6. Disconnect wires and remove spark plugs. On the 6 cylinder engine disconnect coil to distributor primary wire lead at coil and remove the coil.
7. Remove rocker arm cover. Back off rocker arm nuts, pivot rocker arms to clear push rods and remove push rods.
8. Remove cylinder-head bolts, cylinder head and gasket.
9. Place a new cylinder-head gasket over dowel pins in cylinder block.
10. Guide and lower cylinder head into place over dowels and gasket.
11. Oil cylinder-head bolts, install and run them down snug.
12. Tighten the cylinder-head bolts a little at a time with a torque wrench in the correct sequence, Final torque should be 90 to 95 ft. lbs.
13. Install valve pushrods down through the cylinder-head openings and seat them in their lifter sockets.
14. Install rocker arms, balls and nuts and tighten rocker arm nuts until all pushrod play is taken up.
15. Install thermostat, thermostat housing and water outlet using new gaskets. Then connect radiator hose.
16. Install heat sending switch and torque to 15–20 ft. lbs.
17. Clean spark plugs or install new ones. Set gaps to .035 in.
18. Torque 13/16 in. hex plugs to 20 ft lbs and 5/8 in. hex plugs to 15 ft lbs. Tapered seat plugs are used on some engines starting in 1970 and all engines beginning in 1971.
19. Install coil (on six cylinder engine) then connect heat sending unit and coil primary wires, and connect battery ground cable at the cylinder head.

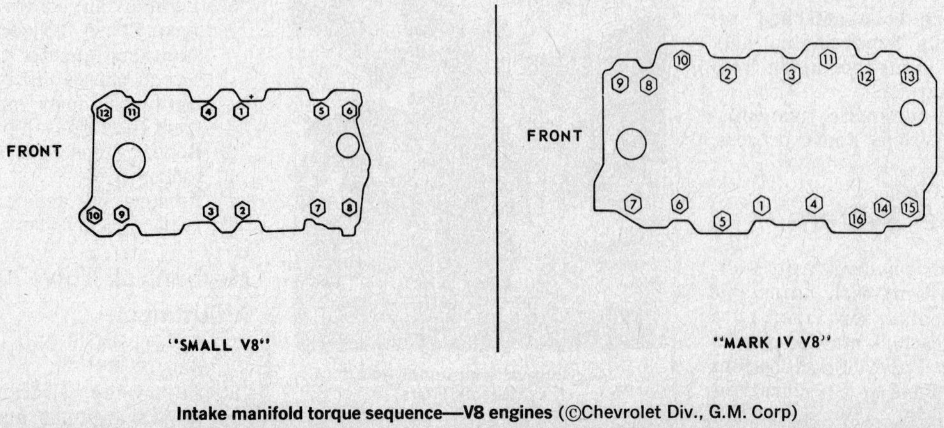
FRONT
"SMALL V8"
FRONT
"MARK IV V8"

Intake manifold torque sequence—V8 engines (©Chevrolet Div., G.M. Corp)

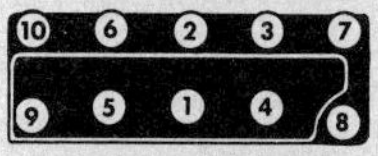

4 cylinder
(© Chevrolet Div., G.M. Corp)

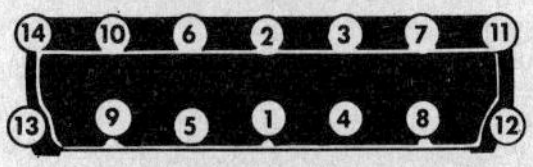

6 cylinder
(© Chevrolet Div., G.M. Corp)

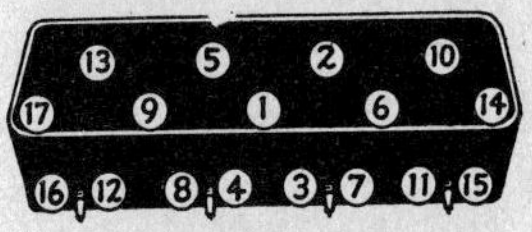

283, 302, Z28, 307, 327, 350, 400 (small block) V8s
(© Chevrolet Div., G.M. Corp)

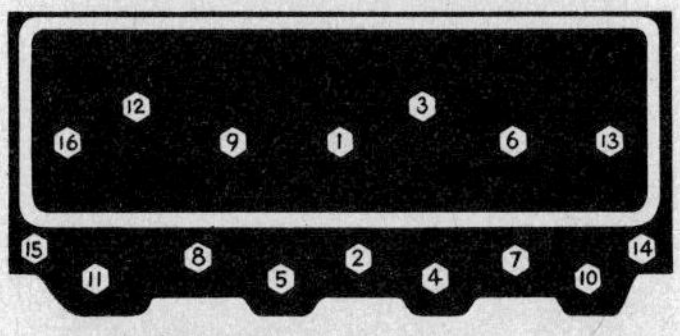

396, 400, (big block 402) 427, 454, V8s
(© Chevrolet Div., G.M. Corp)

20. Clean surfaces and install new gasket over manifold studs. Install manifold. Install bolts and clamps and torque as specified.
21. Connect throttle linkage, and choke wire (on four cylinder engine).
22. Connect P.C.V., fuel and vacuum lines and secure lines in clip at water outlet.
23. Fill cooling system and check for leaks.
24. Adjust valve lash.
25. Install rocker arm cover and position wiring harness in clips.
26. Clean and install air cleaner.

V8 Engines

Removal and Installation

1. Drain coolant. Remove air cleaner.
2. Disconnect:
   a. battery
   b. radiator and heater hose from manifold
   c. throttle linkage
   d. fuel line
   e. coil wires
   f. temperature sending unit
   g. power brake hose, distributor vacuum hose, and crankcase vent hoses.
3. Remove:
   a. distributor, marking position
   b. Delcotron upper bracket
   c. coil and bracket
   d. manifold attaching bolts
   e. intake manifold and carburetor.
4. Remove:
   a. rocker arm covers
   b. rocker arm nuts, balls, rocker arms, and push rods. These items must be replaced in their original locations.
5. Remove cylinder head bolts, cylinder head, and gasket.
6. Reverse procedure to install. Tighten head bolts evenly to the specified torque. On engines having steel gasket, use sealer on both sides. No sealer should be used on steel-asbestos gaskets.

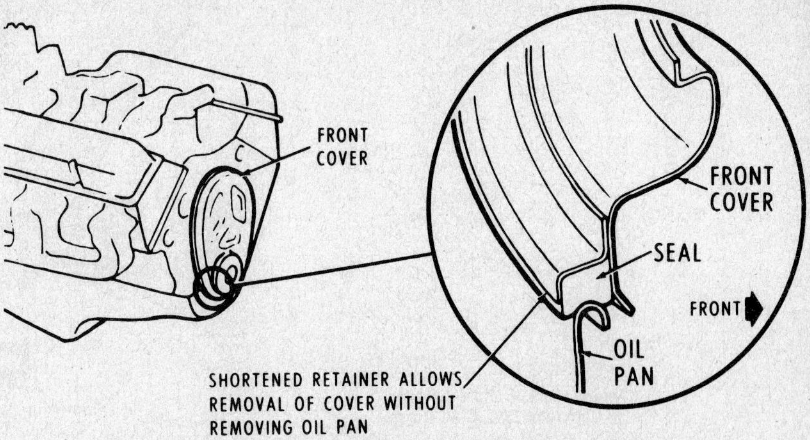
FRONT COVER
FRONT COVER
SEAL
FRONT
OIL PAN
SHORTENED RETAINER ALLOWS REMOVAL OF COVER WITHOUT REMOVING OIL PAN

It is unnecessary to first remove the oil pan in order to remove the timing cover
(© Chevrolet Div., G.M. Corp)

Timing Cover, Chain, and Camshaft

All 4 and 6 cylinder engines have gear driven camshafts, while all V8 camshafts are driven by a timing chain. 4 or 6 cylinder timing gear replacement requires camshaft removal.

NOTE: the 6 cylinder engine uses a harmonic balancer that closely resembles the Chevrolet V8-type. The removal procedure for this damper will be the same as that used for the Chevrolet V8. Driving the damper back onto the crankshaft without supporting the pulley can cause damage. A replacement tool must be used during the reassembly operation.

Caution The 6 and 8 cylinder engines use a harmonic balancer. Breakage may occur where the balancer has been hammered back onto the crankshaft.

This balancer must be drawn back into place.

Chilton's TIME SAVER

When replacing the crankshaft damper, it has been found that lightly polishing the inside diameter with crocus cloth will greatly ease replacement. This procedure will also assist in any future removals, as it is sometimes difficult to pull a damper even with a puller. Be sure that the polishing is not overdone, or the damper will wobble on the crankshaft.

Cover Removal and Installation

1. Drain and remove radiator.
2. Remove harmonic balancer, (6 and 8 cylinder) or a crankshaft pulley, (4 cylinder) using a puller.
3. Drain engine oil and remove oil pan. Remove V8 water pump.
4. Remove timing gear cover attaching screws, and cover and gasket.
5. Reverse procedure to install.

Oil Seal R & R

1. After removing gear cover, pry oil seal out of front of cover with large screwdriver.
2. Install new lip seal with lip (open side of seal) inside and drive or press seal carefully into place.

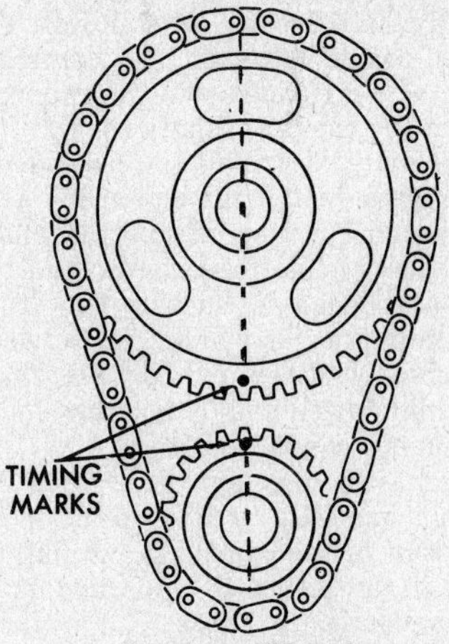
TIMING MARKS

Timing mark V8 engine
(© Chevrolet Div., G.M. Corp)

Timing Chain Replacement

V8 Models

V8 models are equipped with a timing chain. To replace the chain, remove the radiator, water pump harmonic balancer, and the crankcase front cover. This will allow access to the timing chain. Crank the engine until the zero marks punched on both sprockets are closest to one another and in line between the shaft centers. Take out the three bolts that hold the camshaft gear to the cam-

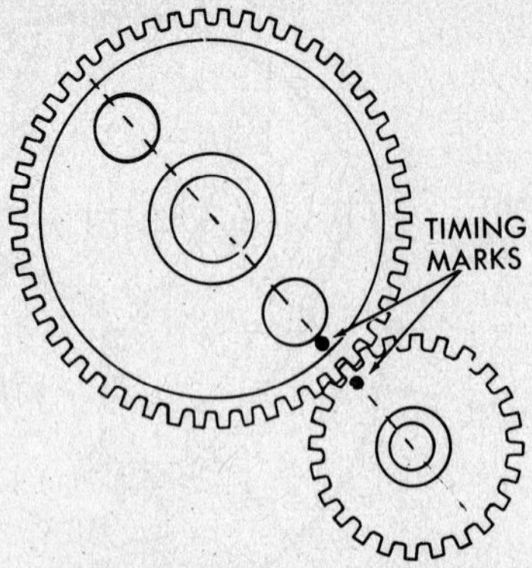
TIMING
MARKS

Timing mark, 4 and 6 cylinder
(© Chevrolet Div., G.M. Corp)

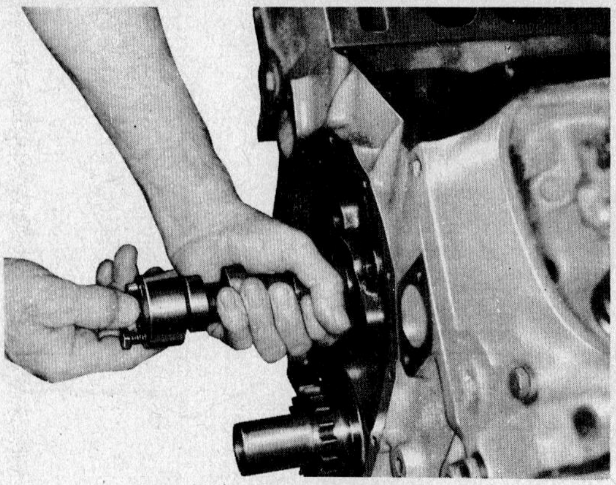

Removing camshaft—V8 engine
(© Chevrolet Div., G.M. Corp)

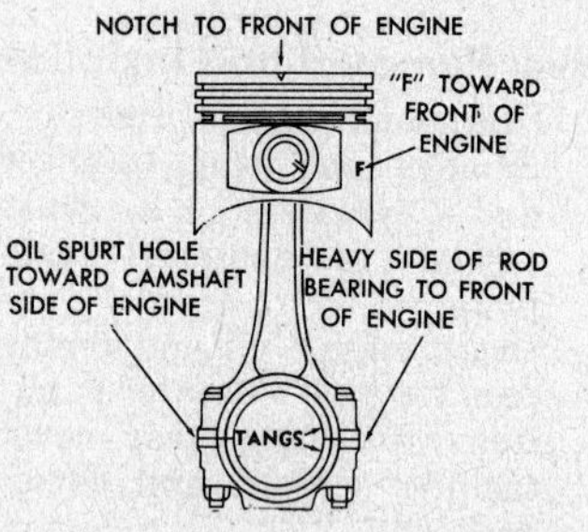
NOTCH TO FRONT OF ENGINE
"F" TOWARD
FRONT OF
ENGINE
OIL SPURT HOLE
TOWARD CAMSHAFT
SIDE OF ENGINE
HEAVY SIDE OF ROD
BEARING TO FRONT
OF ENGINE
TANGS

Piston and rod assembly—4 and 6 cylinder
(© Chevrolet Div., G.M. Corp)

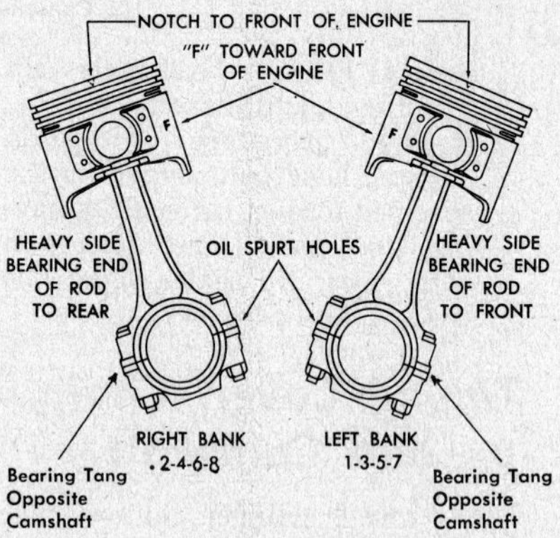
NOTCH TO FRONT OF ENGINE
"F" TOWARD FRONT
OF ENGINE
HEAVY SIDE
BEARING END
OF ROD
TO REAR
OIL SPURT HOLES
HEAVY SIDE
BEARING END
OF ROD
TO FRONT
RIGHT BANK
2-4-6-8
LEFT BANK
1-3-5-7
Bearing Tang
Opposite
Camshaft
Bearing Tang
Opposite
Camshaft

Piston-to-rod relationship—small block V8
(© Chevrolet Div., G.M. Corp)

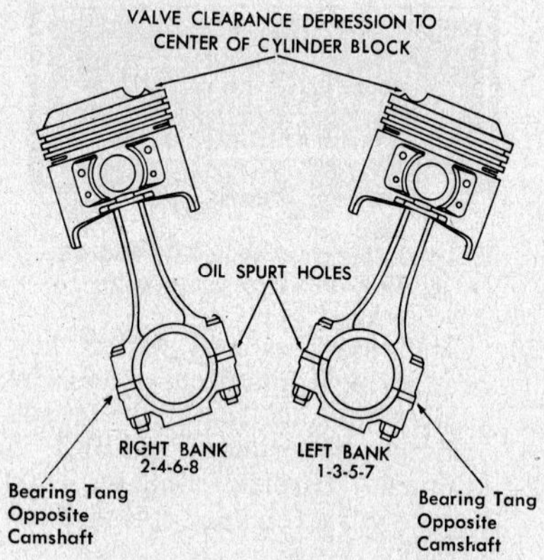
VALVE CLEARANCE DEPRESSION TO
CENTER OF CYLINDER BLOCK
OIL SPURT HOLES
RIGHT BANK
2-4-6-8
LEFT BANK
1-3-5-7
Bearing Tang
Opposite
Camshaft
Bearing Tang
Opposite
Camshaft

Piston-to-rod relationship—Mk IV V8
(© Chevrolet Div., G.M. Corp)

shaft. This gear is a light press fit on the camshaft and will come off readily. It is located by a dowel. The chain comes off with the camshaft gear. A gear puller will be required to remove the crankshaft gear.

Without disturbing the position of the engine, mount the new crank gear on the shaft, then mount the chain over the camshaft gear. Arrange the camshaft gear in such a way that the timing marks will line up between the shaft centers and the camshaft locating dowel will enter the dowel hole in the cam sprocket.

Place the cam sprocket, with its chain mounted over it, in position on the front of the camshaft and pull up with the three bolts that hold it to the camshaft.

After the gears are in place, turn the engine two full revolutions to make certain that the timing marks are in correct alignment between the shaft centers.

Camshaft R & R

1967-74 4 and 6 Cylinder Except Camaro

1. In addition to removing the timing gear cover, remove the grille assembly.
2. Remove valve cover and gasket, loosen all the valve rocker arm nuts and pivot the arms clear of the pushrods.
3. Remove distributor and fuel pump.
4. Remove coil, side cover and gasket. Remove pushrods and valve lifters.
5. Remove the two camshaft thrust plate retaining screws by working through holes in the camshaft gear.
6. Remove camshaft and gear assembly by pulling it out through the front of the block.

NOTE: if renewing either camshaft or camshaft gear, the gear must be pressed off the camshaft. The replacement parts must be assembled in the same manner (under pressure). In placing the gear on the camshaft, press the gear onto the shaft until it bottoms against the gear spacer ring. The end clearance of the thrust plate should be .001 to .005 in.

7. Install camshaft assembly in the engine.
8. Turn crankshaft and camshaft to align and bring the timing marks together. Push the camshaft into this aligned position. Install camshaft thrust plate-to-block screws and torque them to 6-7½ ft. lbs.
9. Runout on either crankshaft or camshaft gear should not exceed .003 in.
10. Backlash between the two gears should be between .004 and .006 in.
11. Install timing gear cover and gasket.
12. Install oil pan and gaskets.
13. Install harmonic balancer.
14. Line up keyway in balancer with key on crankshaft and drive balancer onto shaft until it bottoms against crankshaft gear.
15. Install valve lifters and pushrods. Install side cover with new gasket. Attach coil wires; install fuel pump.
16. Install distributor and set timing as described under distributor at the beginning of the section.
17. Pivot rocker arms over pushrods and lash the valves as described in a previous paragraph, Valve Tappets Adjustment.
18. Add oil to the engine. Install and adjust fan belt.
19. Install radiator or shroud.
20. Install grille assembly.
21. Fill cooling system, start engine and check for leaks.
22. Check and adjust timing.

1967-74 Camaro—6 Cylinder

Remove engine from car, then proceed as in *1967-74 Except Camaro.*

V8 Engines

1. Remove intake manifold, valve

lifters and timing chain cover (requires oil pan removal), as described in this section.
2. Remove grille, except on 1969-72 Nova and 1969 Camaro. On these models, remove both front motor mount bolts and right motor mount, then lower engine until it rests on frame.
3. On 1969-73 Nova and 1969 Camaro, remove the two center bolts and the one lower bolt that secure the hood latch support. This will give adequate clearance for the cam.
4. Remove fuel pump and pump pushrod.
5. Remove camshaft sprocket bolts, sprocket and timing chain. A light blow to the lower edge of a tight sprocket should free it (use a plastic mallet).
6. Install two 5/16—18 x 4 in. bolts in cam bolt holes and pull cam from block.
7. To install, reverse removal procedure, aligning timing marks as illustrated.

NOTE: cam lobes must be lubricated with Molykote or SAE 90 gear oil before installation. All cam journals are the same diameter, so be careful that the cam bearings are not dislodged during installation.

Piston Removal

1. Drain crankcase and remove oil pan.
2. Drain cooling system and remove cylinder heads.
3. Remove any ridge or deposits from the upper end of cylinder bores with a ridge reamer.
4. Check rods and pistons for identification numbers and, if necessary, number them.
5. Remove connecting rod cap nuts and caps. Push the rods away from the crankshaft and install rubber hose over both cap bolts.
6. Push piston and rod assemblies up and out of the cylinders.

Piston Ring Installation

1. Before replacing rings, inspect cylinder bores. If cylinder bore is in satisfactory condition, place each ring in its bore in turn and square it in bore with head of piston. Measure ring end gap. If gap is greater than limit, get new ring. If gap is less than limit, file end of ring to obtain correct gap.
2. Check ring side clearance by installing rings on piston, and inserting feeler gauge of correct dimension between ring and lower land. Gauge should slide freely around ring circumference without binding. Any wear will form a step on lower land. Replace any pistons having high steps. Before checking ring side clearance be sure ring grooves are clean and free of carbon, sludge, or grit.
3. Space ring gaps at equal intervals around piston circumference. Be sure to install piston in its original bore. Install piston and rod assembly with connecting rod bearing tang slots on the side opposite the camshaft on V8 engines. Inline engine pistons must have the piston notch facing the front of the engine. Install short lengths of rubber tubing over connecting rod bolts to prevent damage to the rod journals. Install ring compressor over rings on piston. Lower piston and rod assembly into bore until ring compressor contacts block. Using wooden handle of hammer push piston into bore while guiding rod onto journal.

Lubrication

Oil Pan R & R

1967 Chevy II—4 and 6 Cylinder

1. Disconnect battery ground strap at battery.
2. Drain oil from engine.
3. Disconnect all wires from starter. Remove starter.
4. Disconnect steering idler arm bracket at right hand frame rail. Swing linkage down for pan clearance.
5. On 6 cylinder only, remove front crossmember.

NOTE: on station wagon, let stabilizer bar hang while removing crossmember.

6. Remove oil pan bolts, drop the pan and clean off gaskets and end seals.

1968-74 Chevy II and Nova, 1967-74 Camaro—4 and 6 Cylinder

1. Disconnect battery ground cable.
2. Remove front engine mount bolts.

NOTE: 1970 up, remove upper radiator panel or side mount bolts.

3. Drain coolant. Remove radiator hoses.
4. Remove fan.
5. Drain engine oil.
6. Disconnect and remove starter.
7. Disconnect oil cooler lines and remove converter housing underpan.
8. Disconnect steering rod at idler lever. Swing linkage to one side for pan clearance.
9. Rotate crankshaft until timing mark on torsional damper is at 6:00 o'clock position.
10. Raise engine enough to insert 2 X 4 in. blocks under engine mounts.
11. Unbolt oil pan. On some models it may be necessary to remove the oil pump and intake pipe or remove the left engine mount for clearance. Lower pan.

1967-68 Chevelle, 1969 Chevelle with Standard Transmission 6 Cylinder

1. Remove engine from car.
2. Place engine on stands, supported at each front mount and at transmission extension.

Caution As a safety precaution, leave engine lift attached and most of the weight supported from above.

3. On cars equipped with automatic transmission, remove converter housing underpan.
4. Remove starter, then the oil pan.

1969 Chevelle with Automatic Transmission, 1970-74 Chevelle 6 Cylinder

1. Disconnect battery ground cable.
2. Remove radiator upper mounting panel. Place a piece of heavy cardboard between fan and radiator.
3. Remove starter. Disconnect fuel line.
4. Drain engine oil; disconnect brake line from front crossmember.
5. Remove converter housing underpan and splash shield.
6. Rotate crankshaft until timing mark on torsional damper is at 6:00 o'clock position.

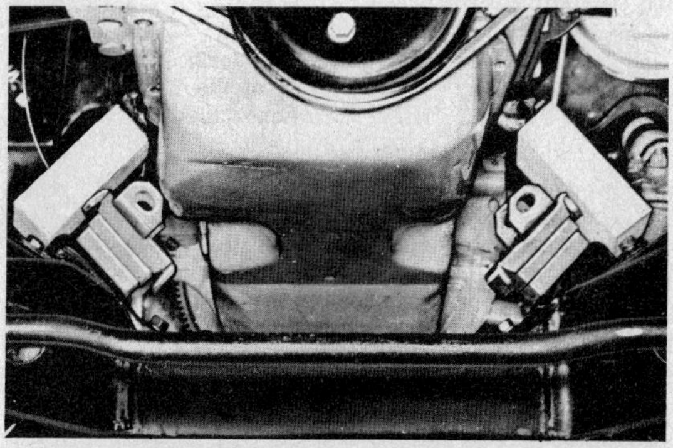

Installing blocks for oil pan removal—V8
(© Chevrolet Div., G.M. Corp)

7. Remove front engine mount through bolts.
8. Raise engine approximately three inches, remove engine mounts, and lower oil pan.

1967 Chevy II—V8

1. Disconnect battery ground cable.
2. Drain engine oil.
3. Disconnect and remove starter.
4. Disconnect steering idler arm bracket at right frame rail. Swing linkage down for clearance.
5. Disconnect exhaust pipes at manifolds.
6. Remove oil pan.

1967-68 Chevelle—V8

This procedure is the same as that for 1967-68 Chevelle models with inline engines.

1967-69 Camaro, 1968-74 Chevy II and Nova, 1969-74 Chevelle, 1970-74 Monte Carlo—V8

1. Disconnect battery ground cable.
2. Remove distributor cap.
3. Remove radiator upper mounting panel.
4. Remove fan. On Mark IV engine models, place a piece of heavy cardboard between the radiator and fan.
5. Drain engine oil.
6. Disconnect exhaust or crossover pipes.
7. Remove converter housing underpan and splash shield.
8. On all except 1970-72 Chevelle, disconnect steering idler lever at the frame. Swing linkage down.
9. Rotate crankshaft until timing mark on torsional damper is at 6:00 o'clock position.
10. Remove starter.
11. On small V8, remove fuel pump.
12. Remove front engine mount through bolts.
13. Raise engine and insert blocks under engine mounts. Block thickness should be 2 in. for Nova and Camaro, and 3 in. for Chevelle.
14. Remove oil pan.

1969 Chevelle with 396 Engine or Manual Transmission, 1970-74 Chevelle 396, 454

1. Disconnect battery ground cable.
2. Remove:
   a. air cleaner
   b. dipstick
   c. distributor cap
   d. radiator shroud and upper mounting panel.
3. On 396 models, place a piece of heavy cardboard between radiator and fan.
4. Disconnect engine ground straps. Remove fuel pump on 307 and 350 engines.
5. Disconnect accelerator control cable.
6. Drain oil. Remove filter on 307 and 350 engines.
7. Remove driveshaft and plug rear of transmission.
8. Remove starter.
9. Disconnect transmission linkage at transmission or remove floorshift lever.
10. Disconnect speedometer cable and back-up switch connector.
11. On manual transmission vehicles disconnect clutch cordon shaft at frame. On automatic transmission vehicles, disconnect cooler lines, detent cable, rod or switch wire, and modulator pipe.
12. Remove crossmember bolts. Jack up engine. Move crossmember rearward.
13. Remove crossover or disconnect dual exhaust pipes.
14. Remove:
    a. flywheel housing cover
    b. transmission
    c. flywheel housing and throwout bearing (manual transmission)
    d. front engine mount through bolts.
15. Raise rear of engine approximately 4 inches. Support engine by hoist.
16. Raise front of engine approximately 4 inches and insert 2 in. blocks under front engine mounts.
17. Rotate crankshaft until timing mark on torsional damper is at 6:00 o'clock position.
18. Unbolt and remove oil pan.

Oil Pump R & R

1. Remove oil pan.
2. Remove pump and pickup tube and screen assembly.
3. To install, reverse removal procedure.

Rear Main Seal R & R

The rear main bearing seal may be replaced without removing the crankshaft. Seals should only be replaced as a pair. Fabrication of a seal installation tool as shown in the figure will prevent damaging the bead on the cylinder block. The seal lips should face the front of the engine when properly installed.

1. Remove the oil pan and pump as previously outlined, and remove the rear main bearing cap.
2. Pry the lower seal out of the bearing cap with a screwdriver, being careful not to gouge the cap surface.
3. Remove the upper seal by lightly tapping on one end with a brass pin punch until the other end can be grasped and pulled out with pliers.

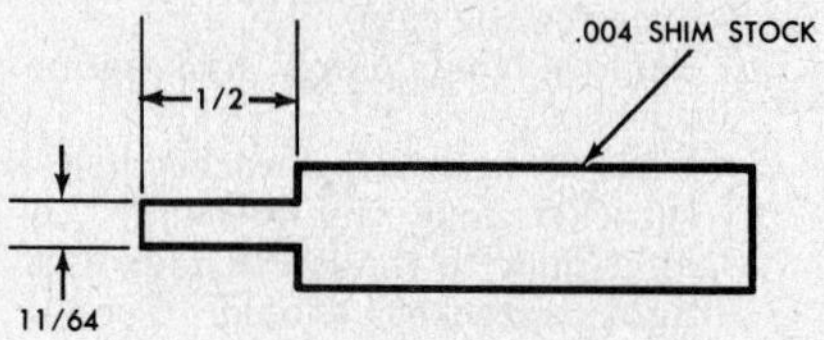
.004 SHIM STOCK
1/2
11/64

Rear main bearing seal installation tool
(© Chevrolet Div., G.M. Corp)

4. Clean the bearing cap, cylinder block, and crankshaft mating surfaces with solvent. Inspect all these surfaces for gouges, nicks, and burrs.
5. Apply light engine oil on the seal lips and bead, but keep the seal ends clean.
6. Insert the tip of the installation tool between the crankshaft and the seal seat of the cylinder block. Place the seal between the tip of the tool and the crankshaft, so that the bead contacts the tip of the tool.
7. Be sure that the seal lip is facing the front of the engine, and work the seal around the crankshaft, using the installation tool to protect the seal from the corner of the cylinder block.

NOTE: do not remove the tool until the opposite end of the seal is flush with the cylinder block surface.

8. Remove the installation tool, being careful not to pull the seal out at the same time.

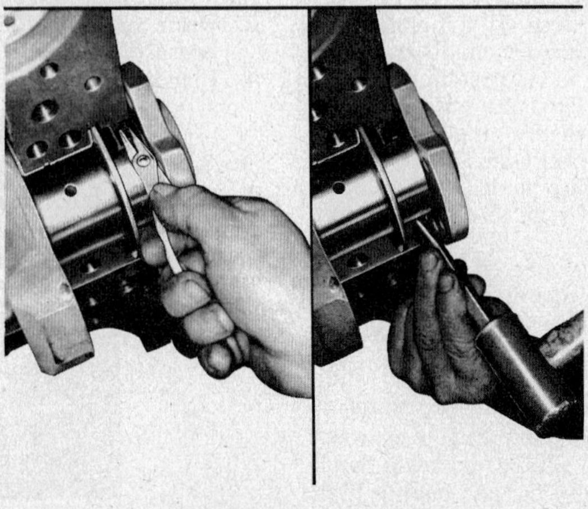

Rear main seal installation
(© Chevrolet Div., G.M. Corp)

9. Using the same procedure, install the lower seal into the bearing cap. Use your finger and thumb to lever the seal into the cap.
10. Apply sealer to the cylinder block only where the cap mates to the surface. Do not apply sealer to the seal ends.
11. Install the rear cap and torque the bolts to specifications. Install the oil pan and pump as previously described.

CLUTCH

A diaphragm type clutch assembly is used with all manual transmissions. A flat finger diaphragm clutch is used for normal service. V8 engines with four speed transmissions have a bent finger, centrifugal diaphragm clutch assembly. In this design the release fingers are bent back to gain a centrifugal boost and to insure quick re-engagement at high engine speeds. The centrifugal type clutch has the advantage of low pedal effort with high plate load.

The clutch release bearings used with the flat and bent finger diaphragms are not interchangeable. Using the flat finger release bearing with the bent finger clutch assembly will result in slippage and rapid wear.

The only service adjustment necessary on the clutch is to maintain the correct pedal free play. Clutch pedal free play, or throwout bearing lash, decreases with driven disc wear.

Further information on clutches may be found in the Unit Repair Section.

Removal—1967-74

1. Support engine and remove transmission.
2. Disconnect clutch fork push rod and spring.
3. Remove flywheel housing.
4. Slide clutch fork from ball stud and remove fork from dust boot. Ball stud is threaded into clutch housing and may be replaced, if necessary.
5. Install an alignment tool to support the clutch assembly during removal. Mark flywheel and clutch cover for reinstallation, if they do not already have X marks.

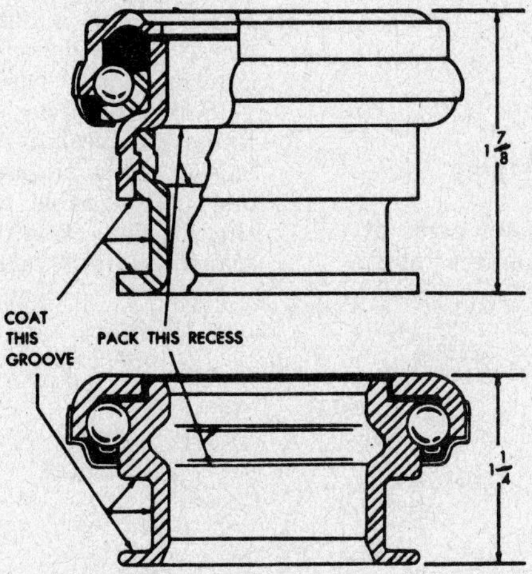
1 7/8
COAT
THIS
GROOVE
PACK THIS RECESS
1 1/4

Clutch release bearing lubrication, flat finger type at top, bent finger type at bottom
(© Chevrolet Div., G.M. Corp)

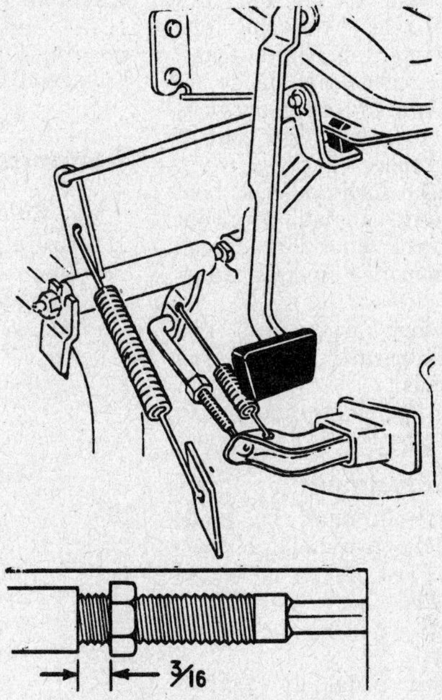
3/16

Clutch linkage—1967 Chevelle
(© Chevrolet Div., G.M. Corp)

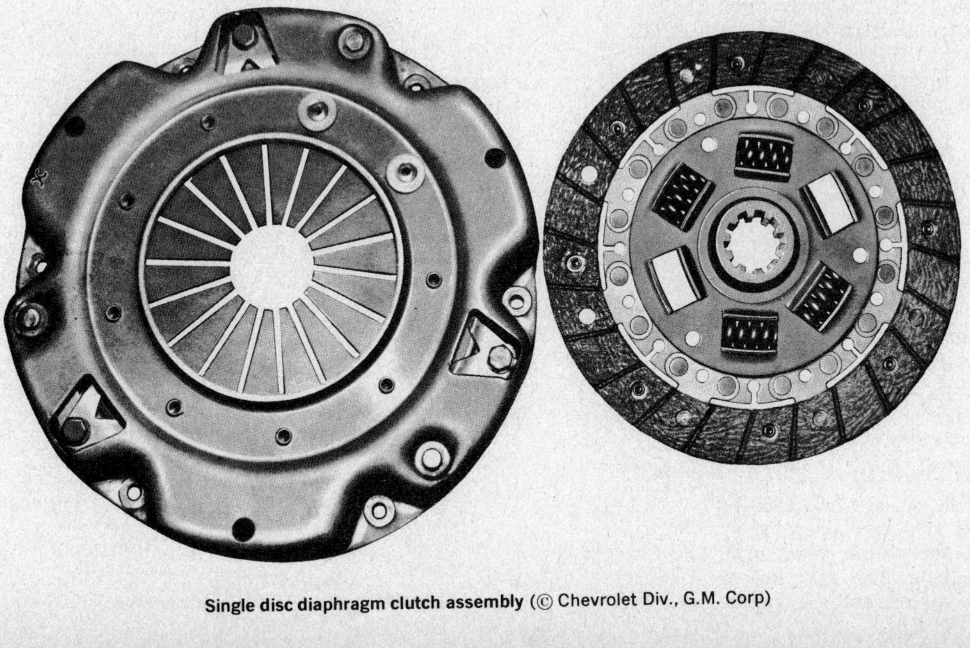

Single disc diaphragm clutch assembly (© Chevrolet Div., G.M. Corp)

6. Loosen clutch to flywheel attaching bolts evenly, one turn at a time, until spring pressure is released. Remove bolts and clutch assembly.

Installation—1967-74

1. Clean pressure plate and flywheel face.
2. Support clutch disc and pressure plate with alignment tool. The driven disc is installed with the damper springs on the transmission side. The grease slinger is always on the transmission side.
3. Turn clutch assembly until mark on cover lines up with mark on flywheel, then install bolts. Tighten down evenly and gradually to avoid distortion.
4. Remove alignment tool.
5. Lubricate ball socket and fork fingers at release bearing end with high melting point grease. Lubricate recess on inside of throwout bearing and throwout fork groove with a light coat of graphite grease.
6. Install clutch fork and dust boot into housing. Install throwout bearing to throwout fork. Install flywheel housing. Install transmission.
7. Connect fork push rod and spring. Lubricate spring and pushrod ends.
8. Adjust shift linkage and clutch pedal free play.

Free Play Adjustment

This adjustment must be made under the vehicle on the clutch operating linkage. Free play is measured at the clutch pedal.

1. Disconnect return spring at clutch fork.
2. Hold clutch pedal up against stop. Loosen locknut.
3. Adjust pushrod to allow correct free play. Tighten locknut.

NOTE: see 1971-72 Camaro and Chevelle linkage illustration for alternate method.

4. Reinstall return spring and recheck free play.

Clutch Pedal Free Play

Vehicle	Free Play at Pedal Pad (in.)
1967 Chevy II, 1971-74 Nova, 1967 Chevelle	1-1½
1967-69 Camaro, 1968-70 Chevy II and Nova	1-1⅛
1968-74 Chevelle, 1970-74 Camaro	1⅛-1¾

Clutch Start Switch

This switch, used on 1969-74 standard shift models, is operated by linkage from the clutch pedal arm, inside the vehicle. The function of the clutch is to prevent the engine from being started unless the clutch pedal is fully depressed. There is no adjustment necessary for this switch.

MANUAL TRANSMISSION

Three and four speed transmissions are available on all models. Three speed transmissions have all three forward gears synchronized. A heavy duty three speed transmission is optionally available.

All four speed transmissions have synchromesh in all forward gears. For 1967-74 models, a heavy duty four speed transmission is available.

A planetary overdrive, in combination with a three speed transmission, is available from 1967-69.

See the Unit Repair Section for transmission repairs,and Hurst shift linkage adjustments.

Transmission R & R

Column Shift Models

1. Drain transmission.
2. Disconnect speedometer cable at transmission. Disconnect shift control rods from shift levers at the transmission. Disconnect the TCS switch wiring.
3. Remove driveshaft.
4. Support rear of engine. Remove crossmember.
5. Remove two top transmission to clutch housing capscrews and install two long transmission guide pins in these holes.
6. Remove the two lower transmission mounting capscrews.
7. Slide the transmission straight back on the guide pins until the clutch gear is free of splines in the clutch disc.
8. Remove transmission from under car.
9. Install transmission in reverse order of removal.

Floorshift Models

1. Remove shift lever trim plate and dust boot.
2. Remove shift lever assembly.
3. Raise car on a hoist, then disconnect speedometer cable at transmission. Disconnect the TCS switch wiring.
4. Remove driveshaft, then support engine at the oil pan with a padded jack capable of supporting the engine weight when the transmission is removed.

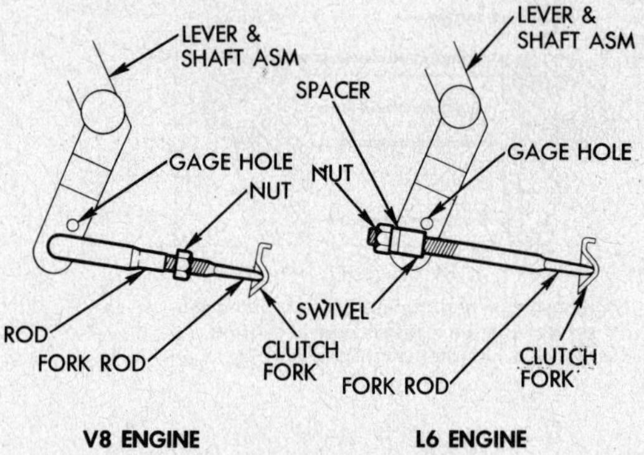
LEVER & SHAFT ASM
GAGE HOLE
NUT
ROD
FORK ROD
CLUTCH FORK
SWIVEL
V8 ENGINE
LEVER & SHAFT ASM
SPACER
NUT
GAGE HOLE
FORK ROD
CLUTCH FORK
L6 ENGINE

Clutch pedal free-play adjustment
(© Chevrolet Div., G.M. Corp)

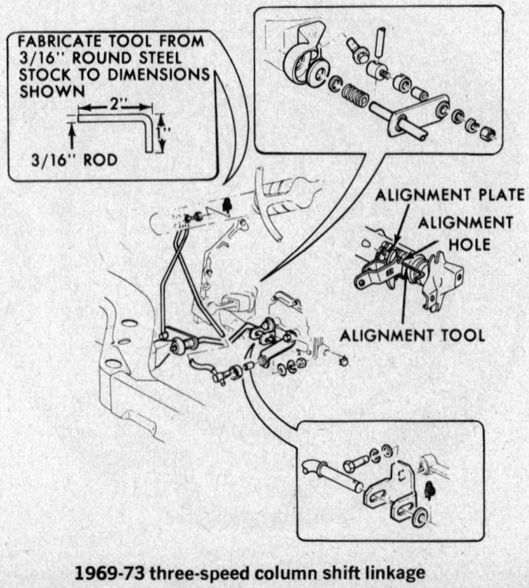
FABRICATE TOOL FROM 3/16" ROUND STEEL STOCK TO DIMENSIONS SHOWN
2"
1"
3/16" ROD
ALIGNMENT PLATE
ALIGNMENT HOLE
ALIGNMENT TOOL

1969-73 three-speed column shift linkage

5. Disconnect shift lever bracket. Remove all transmission shift levers and linkage. Disconnect the backdrive rod at the bellcrank, if so equipped.
6. Remove crossmember attaching bolts.
7. Loosen transmission crossmember and move rearward or remove.
8. Remove transmission-to-clutch housing retaining bolts and install two guide pins in top holes.
9. Slide transmission straight back to free the input shaft from the clutch hub.
10. When transmission has moved rearward enough, tilt front of transmission down and lower unit from car.
11. Install by reversing removal procedure.

Shift Linkage Adjustment

For adjustment on Hurst shift linkages, see the Unit Repair Section.

1967-68 Three Speed Column Shift

1. With transmission shifter rods disconnected at transmission levers, move both levers into neutral detents.
2. Move manual selector lever into neutral position.
3. Align first and reverse shifter tube lever with second and high shifter tube lever on the mast jacket. In some cases, a pin may be used to hold the levers in alignment.

NOTE: the key is engaged with the slot on the second and third shifter tube lever when selector lever is in the neutral position.

4. Loosen control rod clamp bolts. Install control rods on mast jacket shifter levers and secure with retaining clips.
5. Adjust length of first-reverse rod. Tighten clamp bolt.
6. Adjust length of second-third control rod. Tighten clamp bolt.
7. Shift through all positions to check adjustment, and to insure positive and full gear engagement.

1969-74 Three Speed Column Shift

1. With transmission in Reverse, place ignition switch in Off position up to 1970, Lock for 1971-74.
2. Loosen shift rod lock nuts.
3. Set transmission first-reverse lever in reverse position. Push up on first-reverse control rod to 1970, pull down for 1971-74 until column lever is in reverse detent position. Tighten first-reverse lock nut.
4. Shift column and transmission levers to neutral position. Insert a 3/16 in. dia. rod into alignment holes in levers and alignment plate.
5. Tighten second-third locknut.
6. Remove alignment rod. Shift column lever to reverse. Turn key to Lock. Ignition switch must move freely to Lock position and it must not be possible to turn key to Lock when in any transmission position other than reverse. If this interlock binds, leave switch in Lock position and readjust first-reverse rod.
7. Check shifting.

1967-68 Three Speed Floorshift

1. Loosen shift rod locknuts.
2. Set shift lever in neutral and install locating pin into control lever bracket assembly. On some linkages, a flat locating gauge is used. This gauge is 1/8 thick X 41/64 wide X 3 in. long.
3. Place transmission shift levers in neutral positions.
4. Adjust length of control rods. Tighten locknuts.
5. Remove gauge or pin. Check shifting operation.

1969-74 Three Speed Floorshift

1. Turn ignition switch to Lock position up to 1970, Off starting 1971.
2. Loosen locknuts on shift rods and back drive rod.
3. Set transmission levers in neutral positions.

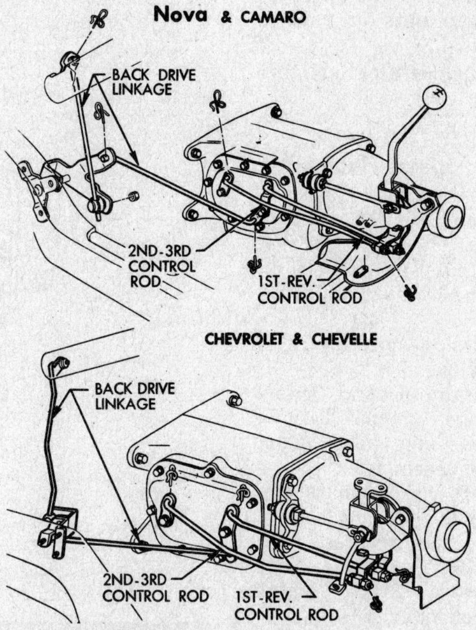
Nova & CAMARO
BACK DRIVE LINKAGE
2ND-3RD CONTROL ROD
1ST-REV. CONTROL ROD
CHEVROLET & CHEVELLE
BACK DRIVE LINKAGE
2ND-3RD CONTROL ROD
1ST-REV. CONTROL ROD

Typical three speed floorshift linkage
(© Chevrolet Div., G.M. Corp)

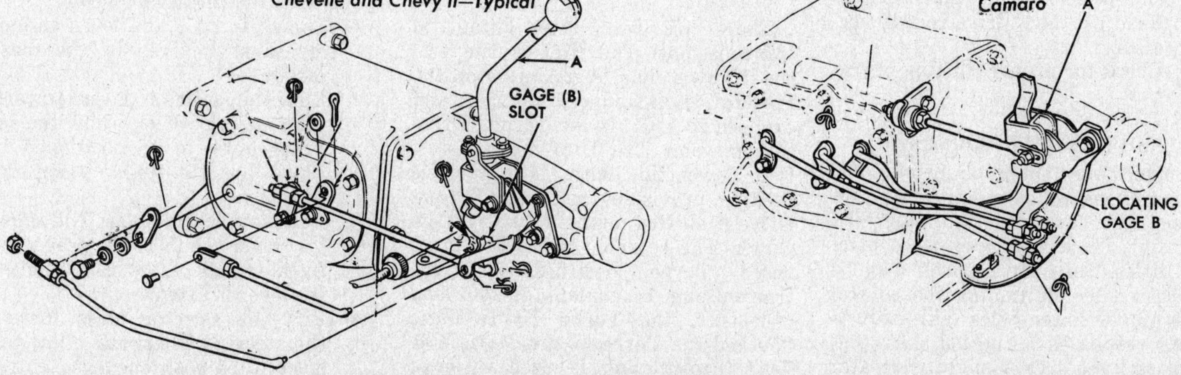
Chevelle and Chevy II—Typical
A
GAGE (B) SLOT
Camaro
A
LOCATING GAGE B

Typical four speed floorshift linkage (© Chevrolet Div., G.M. Corp)

4. Set floorshift lever in neutral. Install locating gauge, 1/8 thick X 41/64 wide X 3 in. long, into control lever bracket assembly.
5. Adjust length of shift rods. Tighten locknuts.
6. Remove locating gauge. Shift into reverse.
7. Pull down slightly on back drive rod to remove any slack and tighten locknut. Ignition switch must move freely to Lock position and it must not be possible to turn key to Lock when in any transmission position other than reverse. If this interlock binds, leave the switch in Lock position and readjust back drive rod.
8. Check shifting operation.

1967-68 Four Speed Floorshift

1. Loosen shift rod clamp nuts or remove clevis pins.
2. Set transmission shift levers in neutral positions.
3. Insert locating gauge, 1/8 thick X 41/64 wide X 3 in. long, into control lever bracket assembly.
4. Adjust length of shifting rods. Tighten clamp nuts or replace clevis pins.
5. Remove gauge. Check shifting operation.

1969-74 Four Speed Floorshift

1. Place ignition switch in Lock position up to 1970, Off starting 1971.
2. Loosen locknuts at swivels on shift rods and back drive control rod.
3. Set transmission shift levers in neutral positions.
4. Shift lever into neutral. Insert locating gauge, 1/8 thick X 41/64 wide X 3 in. long, into control lever bracket assembly.
5. Tighten shift rod locknuts and remove gauge.
6. Shift lever into reverse, then pull down slightly on back drive rod to remove slack. Tighten back drive rod locknut.
7. Ignition switch must move freely to Lock position and it must not be possible to turn key to Lock when in any transmission position other than reverse. Readjust back drive rod, if necessary.
8. Check for proper shifting operation.

Short Throw Shift Adjustment

Some four speed transmissions, primarily heavy duty units, have an adjustment for quicker shifting. The transmission levers have two control rod holes. Shift lever travel may be decreased by positioning the control rods in the lower holes. This adjustment results in a tighter shift pattern and requires a slightly greater shifting effort.

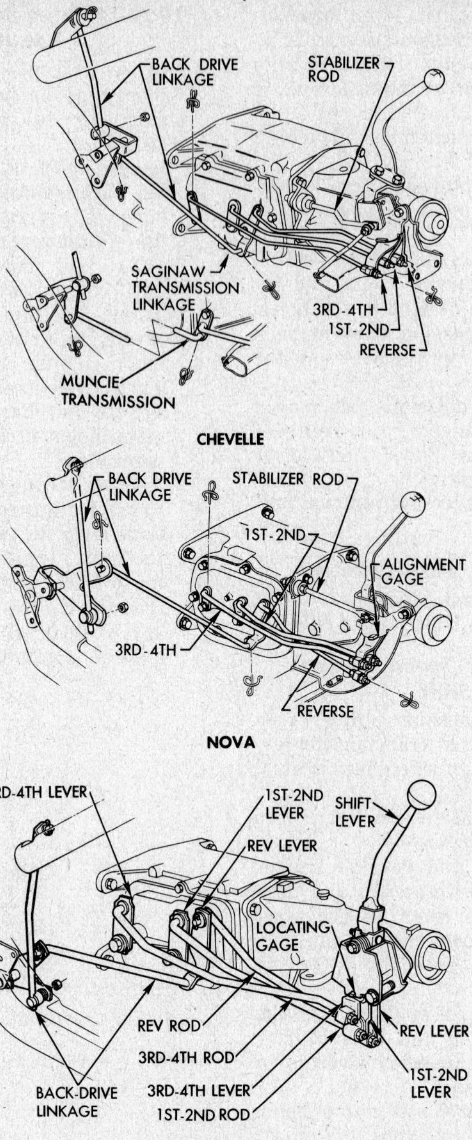
BACK DRIVE LINKAGE
STABILIZER ROD
SAGINAW TRANSMISSION LINKAGE
3RD-4TH
1ST-2ND
REVERSE
MUNCIE TRANSMISSION
CHEVELLE
BACK DRIVE LINKAGE
STABILIZER ROD
1ST-2ND
ALIGNMENT GAGE
3RD-4TH
REVERSE
NOVA
3RD-4TH LEVER
1ST-2ND LEVER
SHIFT LEVER
REV LEVER
LOCATING GAGE
REV ROD
REV LEVER
3RD-4TH ROD
1ST-2ND LEVER
BACK-DRIVE LINKAGE
3RD-4TH LEVER
1ST-2ND ROD
CAMARO

Saginaw four speed linkages
(© Chevrolet Div., G.M. Corp)

AUTOMATIC TRANSMISSION

There are two basic automatic transmissions. The first is the two speed Powerglide. A variation on the Powerglide, introduced in 1969 and dropped in 1972, is the Torque Drive transmission. The Torque Drive unit is a Powerglide with the automatic shifting provisions removed. Torque Drive is shifted manually, but has no clutch. The second type is the three speed Turbo Hydra-Matic. This transmission is available in two load capacities, the Turbo Hydra-Matic 350 and the Turbo Hydra-Matic 400. This transmission is used in most General Motors vehicles.

Powerglide Shift Linkage Adjustment

1967-73 Column Shift

Check adjustment as follows:

1. The shift tube and lever assembly must be free in the mast jacket.
2. Lift the selector lever toward the steering wheel. Allow the selector lever to be positioned in Drive by the transmission detent.
3. Release selector lever. The selector lever should be prevented from engaging Low range unless the lever is lifted.
4. Lift the selector lever toward the steering wheel and allow the lever to be positioned in Neutral by the transmission detent.

5. Release the selector lever. The selector lever should now be prevented from engaging Reverse unless the lever is lifted. If the linkage is adjusted correctly, the selector lever should be prevented from moving beyond both the Neutral detent and the Drive detent unless the lever is lifted to pass over the mechanical stop in the steering column.

Adjust as follows:

6. Loosen adjustment clamp at cross-shaft. Set transmission lever in drive by rotating lever counterclockwise to low detent, then clockwise one detent to drive.
7. Set selector lever in Drive. Remove any free play by holding cross-shaft upward and pulling shift rod downward.
8. Tighten clamp and recheck adjustment.

For 1969-73 models:

9. Place shift lever in Park and ignition switch in Lock. Loosen back drive rod clamp nut. Remove column lash and tighten clamp nut.
10. With selector lever in Park, the ignition key should move freely to Lock position. Lock position should be obtainable only when transmission is in Park.

1969-72 Torque Drive

1. Loosen swivel at idler lever.
2. Place transmission lever in Hi position.
3. Set shift lever at lower end of column up against first position stop.
4. Adjust rod in swivel and tighten retaining nut.
5. Place shift lever in Park and ignition switch in Lock. Loosen back drive rod clamp nut. Remove column lash and tighten clamp nut.
6. With selector lever in Park, the ignition key should move freely to Lock position. Lock position should be obtainable only when transmission is in Park.

1967 Chevelle Floorshift

1. Loosen adjustment nuts at swivel. Set transmission lever in drive position by moving counterclockwise to low detent, then clockwise one detent position to drive.
2. Set floorshift lever in Drive. Hold floorshift unit lower operating lever forward against shift lever detent.
3. Place a 7/64 (.11 in.) spacer between rear nut and swivel. Tighten rear nut against spacer.
4. Remove spacer and tighten front nut against swivel, locking swivel between nuts.

1967-68 Chevy II, 1969-73 Nova, 1967 Camaro Floorshift

This procedure is identical to that for 1967 Chevelle floorshift models, with the exception of the following steps:

3. Place a 3/32 (.09 in.) spacer between rear nut and swivel. Tighten rear nut against spacer.
5. Place shift lever in Park position. Adjust column (back drive) rod. With shift lever in Park, the ignition key must move freely to Lock, and Lock position must not be obtainable in any transmission position other than Park.

1968-73 Chevelle, 1968-73 Camaro, 1970-73 Monte Carlo Floorshift

These models use a cable operated linkage.

1. Place shift lever in Drive position.
2. Disconnect cable from transmission lever. Place transmission lever in drive by rotating lever counterclockwise to low detent, then clockwise one detent to drive.
3. Measure distance from rearward face of attachment bracket to center of cable attachment pin. Adjust this dimension to 5.5 in. by loosening and moving cable end stud nut.

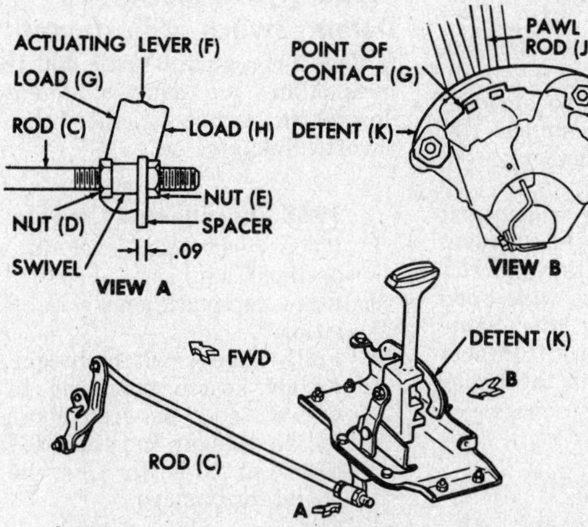
ACTUATING LEVER (F)
LOAD (G)
ROD (C)
LOAD (H)
NUT (E)
NUT (D)
SPACER
SWIVEL
.09
VIEW A
POINT OF CONTACT (G)
PAWL ROD (J)
DETENT (K)
VIEW B
FWD
DETENT (K)
B
ROD (C)
A

Automatic transmission rod operated floorshift linkage, Chevy II and Nova
(© Chevrolet Div., G.M. Corp)

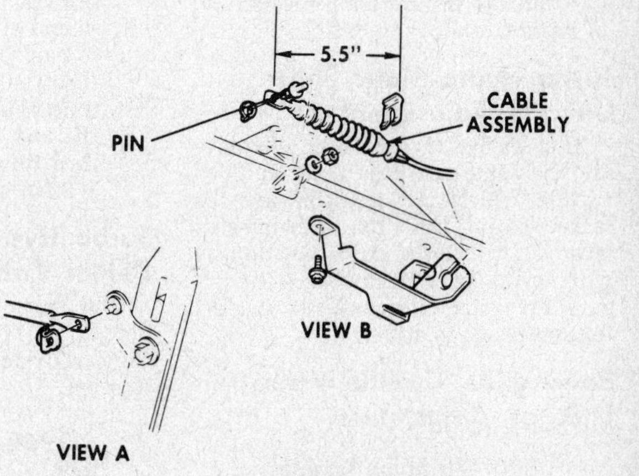
5.5"
CABLE ASSEMBLY
PIN
VIEW B
VIEW A

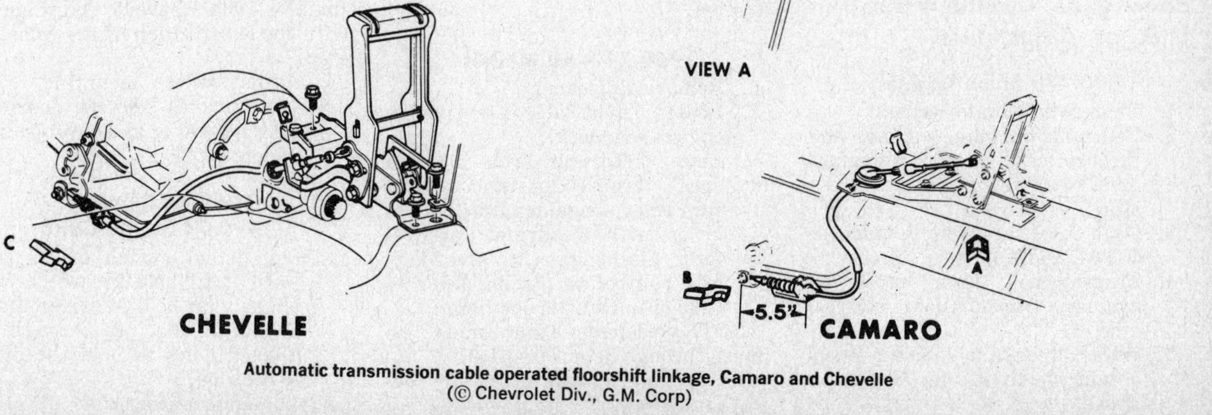
C
CHEVELLE
B
5.5"
A
CAMARO

Automatic transmission cable operated floorshift linkage, Camaro and Chevelle
(© Chevrolet Div., G.M. Corp)

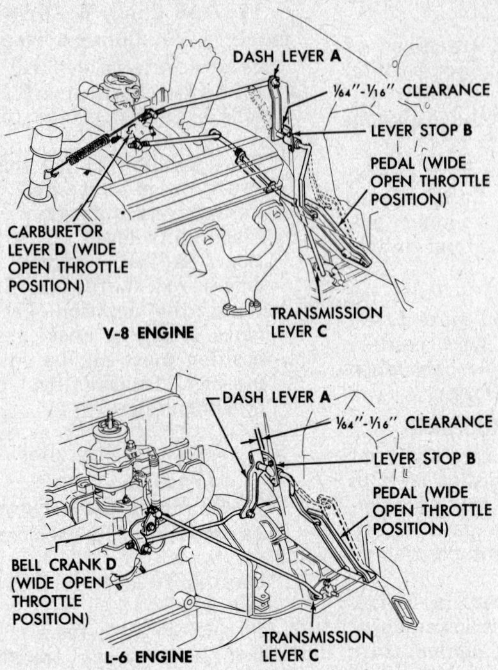
DASH LEVER A
1/64"-1/16" CLEARANCE
LEVER STOP B
PEDAL (WIDE OPEN THROTTLE POSITION)
CARBURETOR LEVER D (WIDE OPEN THROTTLE POSITION)
TRANSMISSION LEVER C
V-8 ENGINE
DASH LEVER A
1/64"-1/16" CLEARANCE
LEVER STOP B
PEDAL (WIDE OPEN THROTTLE POSITION)
BELL CRANK D (WIDE OPEN THROTTLE POSITION)
TRANSMISSION LEVER C
L-6 ENGINE

Powerglide throttle valve linkage adjustment V8, 1967-73 inline engines
(© Chevrolet Div., G.M. Corp)

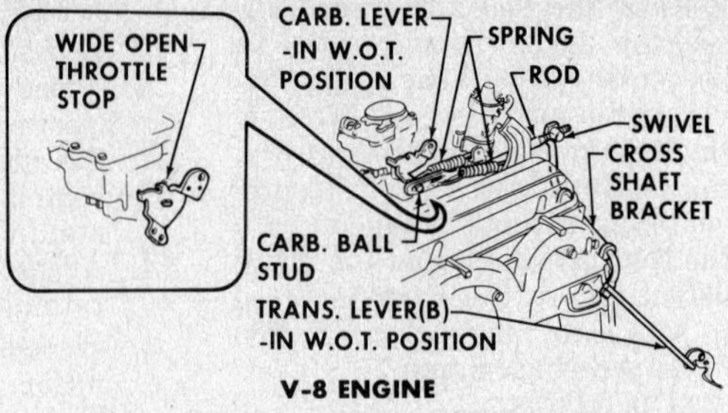
WIDE OPEN THROTTLE STOP
CARB. LEVER -IN W.O.T. POSITION
SPRING
ROD
SWIVEL
CROSS SHAFT BRACKET
CARB. BALL STUD
TRANS. LEVER(B) -IN W.O.T. POSITION
V-8 ENGINE

Powerglide throttle valve linkage—1967-72 V8
(© Chevrolet Div., G.M. Corp)

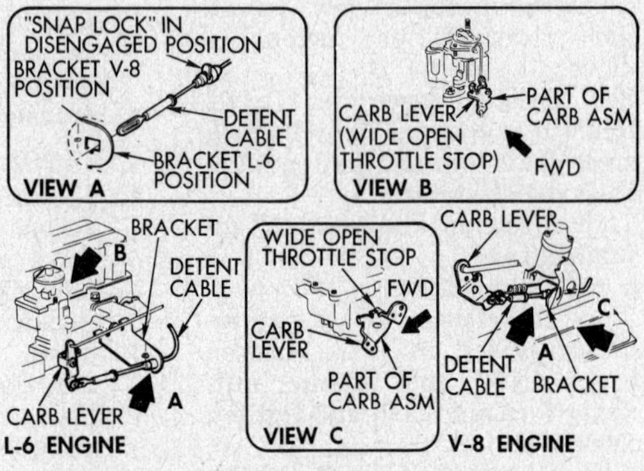
"SNAP LOCK" IN DISENGAGED POSITION
BRACKET V-8 POSITION
DETENT CABLE
BRACKET L-6 POSITION
VIEW A
CARB LEVER (WIDE OPEN THROTTLE STOP)
PART OF CARB ASM
FWD
VIEW B
BRACKET
B
DETENT CABLE
A
CARB LEVER
L-6 ENGINE
WIDE OPEN THROTTLE STOP
FWD
CARB LEVER
PART OF CARB ASM
VIEW C
CARB LEVER
C
A
DETENT CABLE
BRACKET
V-8 ENGINE

1969-'74 Turbo Hydra-Matic 350 detent cable adjustment
(© Chevrolet Div., G.M. Corp)

For 1969-72 models:

4. Place shift lever in Park and ignition switch in Lock position.
5. Loosen and adjust column (back drive) rod.
6. With selector lever in Park position, the ignition key should move freely to Lock position. Lock position should not be obtainable in any transmission position other than Park.

Turbo Hydra-Matic Shift Linkage Adjustment

The Turbo Hydra-Matic linkages are the same as those used on Powerglide models. Adjustments are the same, except that the transmission lever is adjusted to drive position by moving the lever clockwise to the low detent, then counterclockwise two detent positions to drive.

Powerglide Throttle Valve Linkage Adjustment

1967-73 Inline Engines

1. Depress accelerator pedal.
2. Bellcrank on inline engines and carburetor lever on V8 engines must be at wide open throttle position.
3. Dash lever at firewall must be 1/64-1/16 in. off lever stop.
4. Transmission lever must be against transmission internal stop.
5. Adjust linkage to simultaneously obtain conditions in Steps 1-4, above.

1967-72 V8 Engines

1. Remove air cleaner.
2. Disconnect accelerator linkage at carburetor.
3. Disconnect both return springs.
4. Pull throttle valve upper rod forward until transmission is through detent.
5. Open carburetor to wide open throttle position. Adjust swivel on end of upper throttle valve rod so carburetor reaches wide open throttle position at the same time that the ball stud contacts the end of the slot in the upper throttle valve rod. A tolerance of 1/32 in. is allowable.

Turbo Hydra-Matic 350 Detent Cable Adjustment

The Turbo Hydra-Matic 350 has a detent, or downshift, cable between the carburetor linkage and the transmission.

1969-74—All Models

1. Remove air cleaner.
2. Loosen detent cable screw or disengage snap lock.
3. Place carburetor lever in wide open throttle position. Make sure lever is against stop. On vehicles with Quadrajet carburetors, disengage the secondary lock out before placing lever in wide open throttle position.

NOTE: detent cable must be pulled through detent position.

4. Engage snap lock or tighten detent screw.

Turbo Hydra-Matic 400 Detent Switch Adjustment

The Turbo Hydra-Matic 400 transmission has an electrical detent, or downshift, switch operated by the throttle linkage.

1968 Chevelle and Camaro

1. Place carburetor lever in wide open position.
2. Place automatic choke in off position.
3. Fully depress switch plunger.
4. Adjust switch mounting to obtain distance between depressed switch plunger and throttle lever paddle of .05 in. for Chevelle and .20 in. for Camaro.

1969-74 Nova, 1969-74 Camaro

This procedure is the same as that for the 1968 Chevelle and Camaro, with the substitution of the following step:

4. Adjust switch mounting to obtain distance between depressed switch plunger and throttle lever paddle of .22-.24 in.

1969-74 Chevelle, 1970-74 Monte Carlo

1. Pull detent switch driver rearward until hole in switch body aligns with hold in driver. Insert a .092 in. dia. pin through the aligned holes to hold the driver in position.
2. Loosen mounting bolt.

3. Depress accelerator to wide open throttle position. Move switch forward until driver contacts accelerator lever.
4. Tighten mounting bolt. Remove pin.

Neutral Safety Switch

The neutral safety switch prevents the engine from being started in any transmission position except Neutral or Park. On column shift models, the switch is located on the upper side of the steering column under the instrument panel. On floorshift models, the switch is located inside the shift console.

Switch Replacement

1. Remove console for access on floorshift models.
2. Disconnect wiring connectors.
3. Remove switch.
4. Position shift lever in Neutral. On column shift models, locate lever tang against transmission selector plate.
5. Align slot in contact support with hole in switch. Insert 3/32 in. dia. pin to hold support in place. Switch is now aligned in drive position.

NOTE: 1973-74 neutral safety switches have a shear-pin installed to aid in proper switch alignment so that insertion of a pin is unnecessary. Moving the shift lever from Neutral shears the pin.

6. Place contact support drive slot over drive tang. Install screws.
7. Remove pin. Connect wiring. Replace console.
8. Set parking brake and footbrake. Check to see that engine will start only in Drive or Neutral.

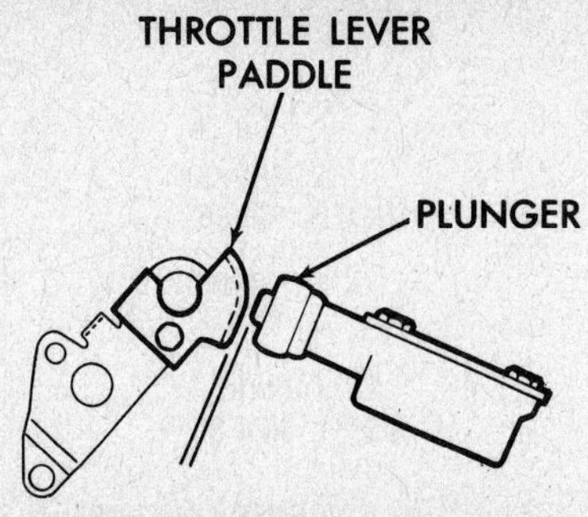
THROTTLE LEVER
PADDLE
PLUNGER

Turbo Hydra-Matic 400 detent switch adjustment 1968 Chevelle, 1969-74 Nova, 1968-74 Camaro
(© Chevrolet Div., G.M. Corp)

U-JOINTS

Driveshafts are of a one-piece design, using Cardan type universal joints. The universal joints are lubricated and sealed at the factory and require no periodic maintenance. The front yoke is splined, providing a slip joint for length variations in the drive line. There is a damper on some models: this damper is not serviced separately.

Two basic universal joints are used. The Dana or Cleveland type uses snap-ring bearing cap retainers. The Saginaw uses injection molded plastic to retain the bearing caps. On the Saginaw type there is a snap-ring groove in the bearing housing inboard of the yoke to hold the bearings in place.

Driveshaft R & R

Disconnect the rear universal joint flange. On some models, the bearing caps are bolted directly to the differential flange with clamps or U-bolts. Pull the front yoke from the transmission. Watch for oil leaks from the transmission output housing. Install in the reverse order of removal.

Universal Joint R & R

Dana and Cleveland Type

1. Remove the driveshaft.
2. Remove the snap-rings from the trunnion yoke.
3. Using a vise and suitably sized sockets, press on the trunnion until the bearing cap is almost out. Grasp the cap in the vise and work it out of the yoke. Repeat the above procedure for the rest of the bearing caps.
4. Pack the rollers in grease and fill the grease reservoir.
5. To install, position the trunnion in the yoke and partially install one bearing cap. Start the trunnion in the bearing cap and partially install the other cap. Align the trunnion with the caps and press into place.
6. If necessary, repeat Step 5 above for the other yoke.
7. Install the snap-rings.
8. Install the driveshaft in the vehicle.

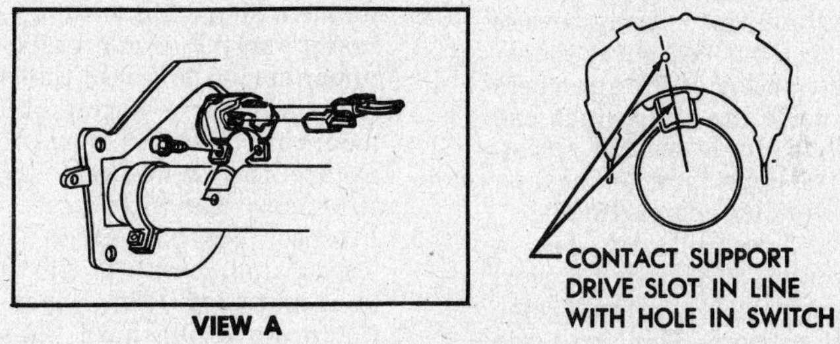
VIEW A
CONTACT SUPPORT
DRIVE SLOT IN LINE
WITH HOLE IN SWITCH

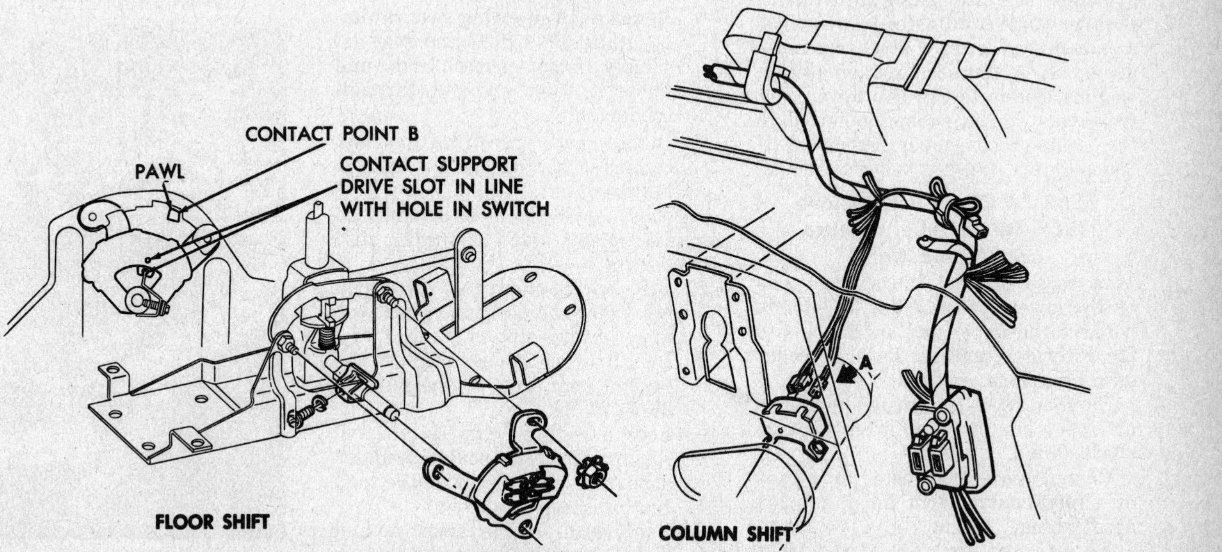
CONTACT POINT B
PAWL
CONTACT SUPPORT
DRIVE SLOT IN LINE
WITH HOLE IN SWITCH
FLOOR SHIFT
A
COLUMN SHIFT

Typical neutral safety switch installation (© Chevrolet Div., G.M. Corp)

Saginaw Type

Remove and install the bearing caps and trunnion as described for the Dana and Cleveland type universal joints. On an original universal joint, however, the bearing caps will be secured in the yokes with injected plastic. The plastic will shear when the bearing caps are pressed. Service snap-rings are installed in the groove on the inside (of yoke) of the installed caps.

JACKING, HOISTING

1. Jack car at front spring seat of lower control arm. Jack car at rear axle housing except when equipped with rear stabilizer bar. On these models, jack at frame rails.
2. To lift at frame, use side rails in front of body floor pan and at rear corner at squared off corner of box ahead of rear wheel.

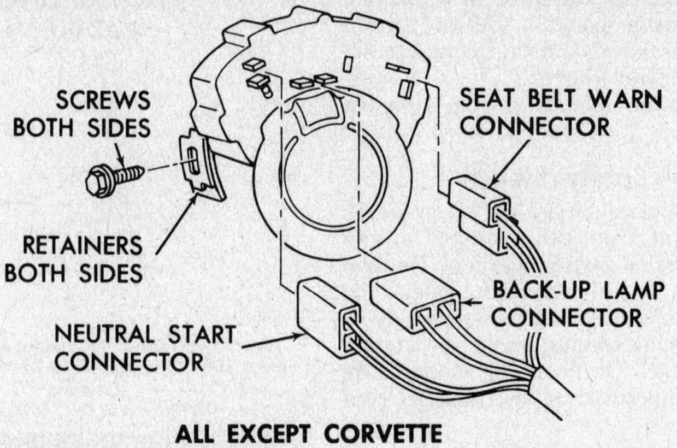

SCREWS BOTH SIDES
SEAT BELT WARN CONNECTOR
RETAINERS BOTH SIDES
BACK-UP LAMP CONNECTOR
NEUTRAL START CONNECTOR
ALL EXCEPT CORVETTE

1973 combination neutral start switch connections
(© Chevrolet Div., G.M. Corp)

FRONT SUSPENSION

1967 Chevy II

Front suspension is an independent coil-spring, ball-joint-type with rubber bushed, pivoting upper and lower control arms. The coil springs are positioned at their lower ends on a pivoting spring seat bolted to the upper control arm. The upper end of the spring extends into spring towers formed in the front end sheet metal. Direct, double-acting shock absorbers are located inside the coil springs and are attached to the lower coil spring seat and to the upper bracket, accessible from the engine compartment.

Each lower control arm has a strut rod running diagonally forward to a brace attached between frame and radiator support. This strut rod provides for caster angle adjustment. Camber angle is adjusted by means of a cam-shaped lower control arm inner pivot bolt. A stabilizer rod, on station wagons, connects the two lower control arms and is rubber mounted to the front crossmember. Front wheel bearings are tapered roller bearings.

1968-74 Chevy II and Nova 1967-74 Chevelle, Camaro and Monte Carlo

In these models, the springs ride on the lower control arms. Ball joints connect the upper and lower arms to the steering knuckle. Tapered roller wheel bearings are used.

Camber angle is adjusted by means of upper control arm inner support shaft shims.

Caster angle is adjusted by means of upper control arm inner support shaft shims.

Periodic maintenance of the front suspension includes lubrication of the four ball joints, spring seat lower pivot shafts and adjustment and lubrication of the front wheel bearings.

Further data on front end alignment can be obtained from the Front Wheel Alignment chart and from the Unit Repair Section.

Coil Spring R & R

1967 Chevy II

1. Raise car and remove wheel.
2. Support lower control arm with adjustable jackstand and raise slightly from full rebound position.
3. Remove shock absorber.
4. Insert spring compressor into upper spring tower so that lower U-bolt fits into shock absorber mounting holes in spring seat. Secure the two lower studs to the spring seat with nuts.
5. Fit tool upper pilot to top of spring and compress the spring by tightening the upper nut. Compress spring until the screw is bottomed out.
6. Remove lower spring seat retaining nuts, lift spring and seat assembly from control arm and guide it down and out through fender skirt.
7. Install new spring into tool and compress spring until screw is bottomed out.

NOTE: spring coil ends must be against spring stops in upper and lower seats.

8. Lift spring and tool assembly into place and position so that the upper spring stop is inboard.
9. Install lower spring seat to the control arm. Torque the nuts to 25-35 ft. lbs.
10. Loosen spring compressor until spring is properly seated in upper spring tower and remove the tool.
11. Install shock absorber.
12. Remove adjustable jackstand and install wheel and tire. Lower car to the floor.

1967-74 Chevelle, 1968-74 Chevy II and Nova, 1967-74 Camaro, 1970-74 Monte Carlo

1. Hold the shock absorber upper stem from turning, then disconnect the shock absorber at the top.
2. Support the car by the frame, so the control arms hang free, remove wheel assembly (replace one wheel nut to hold the brake drum), shock absorber, and stabilizer bar to lower control arm link.
3. Place a steel bar through the shock absorber mounting hole in the lower control arm so that the notch seats over the bottom spring coil and the bar extends outboard beyond the end of the control arm and slightly toward the front of the car.
4. With a suitable jack, raise the end of the bar.
5. Remove lower ball stud cotter pin and nut, then remove the ball stud from the knuckle.

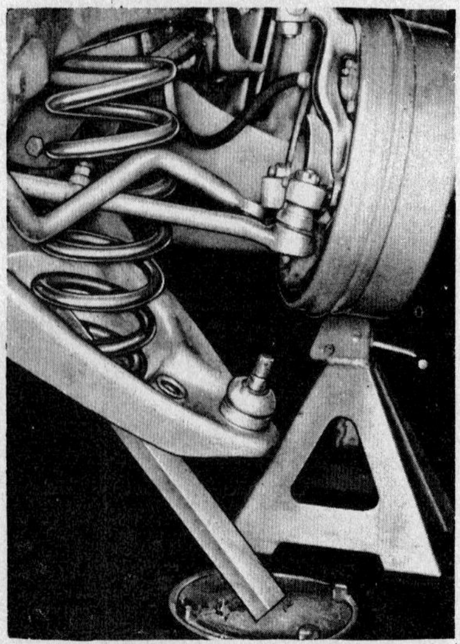

Front spring removal
(© Chevrolet Div., G.M. Corp)

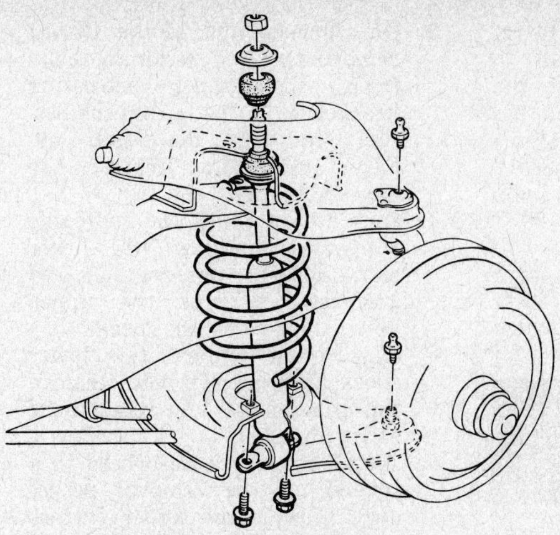

Chevelle, Camaro, 1968-69 Chevy II and Nova shock absorber installation
(© Chevrolet Div., G.M. Corp)

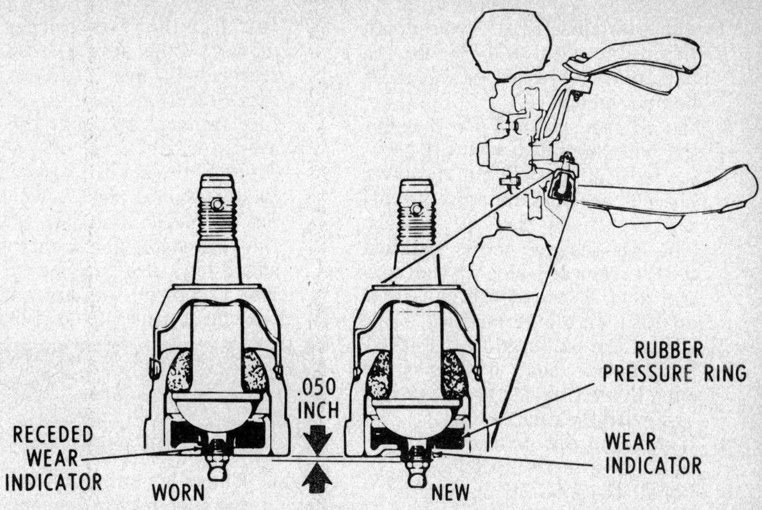
RUBBER
PRESSURE RING
.050
INCH
RECEDED
WEAR
INDICATOR
WEAR
INDICATOR
WORN
NEW

1974 Chevelle and Monte Carlo models use the same ball joint wear indicator first used on the 1973 full-size Chevrolets
(© Chevrolet Div., G.M. Corp)

NOTE: place a chain around spring and through lower arm for safety.

6. Lower the jack supporting the steel bar and control arm until the spring can be removed.
7. Install by reversing removal procedure.

Shock Absorber R & R

1967 Chevy II

1. Insert a 4½ in. support between the upper control arm and the frame before jacking the car off the ground.
2. Raise the car and remove the wheel(s).
3. Remove the lower nuts, lockwashers, and rubber washers.
4. Remove the upper mounting bolts and pull the shock absorber and bracket out as a unit.
5. Separate the shock absorber and bracket and remove the bushings and washers.
6. Install the shock absorber using a reverse of the removal procedure. Torque the upper shaft nut to 8 ft lbs, the bracket-to-spring tower nuts and the lower mounting nuts to 9 ft lbs.

1968-74 Chevy II and Nova 1967-74 Chevelle, Camaro, and Nova

1. Remove the upper stem nut while holding the stem to keep it from turning.
2. Remove the two bolts holding the shock absorber to the lower control arm, and pull the shock through the arm.
3. Extend the shock absorber and insert it up through the lower control arm. Make sure that the upper stem goes through the hole in the upper control arm frame bracket.
4. Install the grommet, retainer cup, and nut to the shock absorber upper stem.
5. Hold the shock absorber stem and tighten the upper nut to 8 ft lbs.
6. Install the lower control arm retaining bolts and tighten to 20 ft lbs.

Front Wheel Bearing Adjustment

1. Jack the car up and support it at the lower arm.
2. Remove the hub dust cover, spindle cotter pin, and spindle nut.
3. While spinning the wheel, snug the nut down to seat the bearings. Do not exert over 12 ft lbs of force on the nut.
4. Back the nut off ¼–½ a turn. Line up the cotter pin hole in the spindle with the hole in the nut.
5. Insert the cotter pin. End-play should be between 0.001 and 0.008 in. If play exceeds this tolerance, the wheel bearings should be replaced.

Ball Joints

Ball Joint Inspection

NOTE: before performing this inspection, make sure the wheel bearings are adjusted correctly and that the A-arm bushings are in good condition.

1. Jack the car up under the front lower control arm at the spring seat.
2. Raise the car until there is 1–2 in. of clearance under the wheel.
3. Insert a bar under the wheel and pry upward. If the wheel raises more than ⅛ in., the ball joints are worn. Determine if the upper or lower ball joint is worn by visual inspection while prying on the wheel.

NOTE: due to the distribution of forces in the suspension, the lower ball joint is usually the defective joint. Because of this, 1974 Chevelle and Monte Carlo models are equipped with wear indicators on the lower ball joint. As long as the indicator extends below the ball stud seat, replacement is unnecessary.

Upper Ball Joint R & R

1. Raise the car on a hoist.
2. Remove the tire and wheel assembly.
3. Support the lower control arm with a jack.
4. Remove the upper ball stud nut.
5. Remove the ball stud from the knuckle.
6. Chisel or grind off the ball joint mounting rivets.
7. Drill out the ball stud attaching holes to accept the service ball joint attaching bolts.
8. Install the ball joint with the nuts and bolts supplied with the new joint.
9. Install the lube fitting in the new joint.
10. Mate the upper control arm to the steering knuckle and install the ball stud through the knuckle boss.
11. Tighten the ball stud nut to 50 ft lbs. plus whatever is necessary to align the cotter pin holes. Install the cotter pin.

NOTE: Do not back off on the nut to align the cotter pin.

12. Install the wheel and lower the vehicle.

Lower Ball Joint R & R

1. Raise the vehicle on a hoist and remove the wheel. On vehicles equipped with disc brakes, remove the caliper assembly.
2. Support the lower control arm with a jack.
3. Loosen the lower ball stud nut. Break the ball stud loose. Remove the ball stud nut.
4. Remove the ball stud from the steering knuckle.
5. The ball joint in 1967-70 models is attached with rivets which

must be chiseled or ground off. Beginning with 1971 models, the ball joint is pressed in and must be pressed out.

6. Install the new ball joint, using the bolts supplied with the service ball joint (drill out the rivet hoses to accommodate the mounting bolts) on 1967-70 models. The thick-headed bolt is installed on the forward side of the control arm. Press in the ball joint on 1971 and later models.
7. Install the ball stud in the steering knuckle boss. This may be done by raising the lower control arm with the jack.
8. Install the nut on the ball stud, tightening to 89-90 ft lbs.
9. Install the lube fitting.

Lower Control Arm R & R

1. Remove the spring as described above.
2. Remove the ball stud from the steering knuckle as described above.
3. Remove the control arm pivot bolts and remove the control arm.
4. To install, reverse the above procedure. Tighten the shaft nuts-/bolts to 85 ft lbs.

Upper Control Arm R & R

1. Raise the vehicle on a hoist.
2. Support the outer end of the lower control arm, with a jack.
3. Remove the wheel.
4. Separate the upper ball joint from the steering knuckle as described above under "Upper Ball Joint R&R"
5. Remove the control arm shaft to frame nuts.

NOTE: tape the shims together and identify them so that they can be installed in the positions from which they were removed.

6. Remove the bolts which attach the control arm shaft to the frame and remove the control arm. Note the positions of the bolts.
7. Install in the reverse order of removal. Make sure the shaft to frame bolts are installed in the same position they were in before removal and that the shims are in their original positions. Tighten the shaft to frame bolts to 55 ft lbs. on the Chevelle, 50 ft lbs. on theNova, and 80 ft lbs. on the Camaro. The control arm shaft nuts are torqued to 40 ft lbs., except on Camaro on which they are torqued to 60 ft lbs.

REAR SUSPENSION

The Chevelle and Monte Carlo have a coil spring rear suspension located by two lower control arms and two diagonally mounted upper control arms. Fore and aft axle movement is prevented by the lower control arms. Lateral movement is prevented by the upper control arms and the axle-to-frame tie-rod.

The Camaro, Chevy II, and Nova all have a leaf spring rear suspension. Some light duty models and all Chevy II models, up to 1967, have single leaf rear springs. Other models use the more conventional multiple leaf springs.

All models, starting 1968, use staggered shock absorbers to prevent axle hop on hard acceleration. The right shock absorber is mounted forward of the axle and the left shock absorber is mounted behind the axle.

Rear Shock Absorber R & R

1. Jack the car to a convenient working height.
2. If the car is equipped with superlift shock absorbers, disconnect the air line.
3. On Chevelle and Monte Carlo: remove the two retaining bolts from the upper mounting bracket. Hold the hex on the bottom stud and disconnect the lower mounting. Remove the shock absorber.
4. On Camaro: with the rear axle supported, remove the lower shock absorber nut, retainer, and grommet. Remove the upper bolts, and remove the shock.
5. On Nova: remove the lower shock absorber eye bolt. Remove the upper bolts, and remove the shock absorber.
6. Install the shock absorbers in a reverse of the removal procedure. Torque the upper fasteners: 12 ft lbs on Chevelle and Monte Carlo and 18 ft lbs on Nova and Camaro. Torque the bottom fasteners: 65 ft lbs on Chevelle and Monte Carlo, 45 ft lbs on Nova, and 8 ft lbs on Camaro.

Rear Spring R & R

Chevelle and Monte Carlo

1. Raise rear of vehicle and place jack stands under frame. Support weight of vehicle at rear axle housing separately from above frame position.
2. Remove both rear wheels.
3. With car supported as in Step 1, and springs compressed by weight of vehicle:
   a. Disconnect both rear shocks from anchor pin lower connection.
   b. Loosen the upper control arm(s) rear pivot bolt (do not remove the nut).
   c. Loosen both left and right lower control arm rear attachment (do not disconnect from axle brackets).

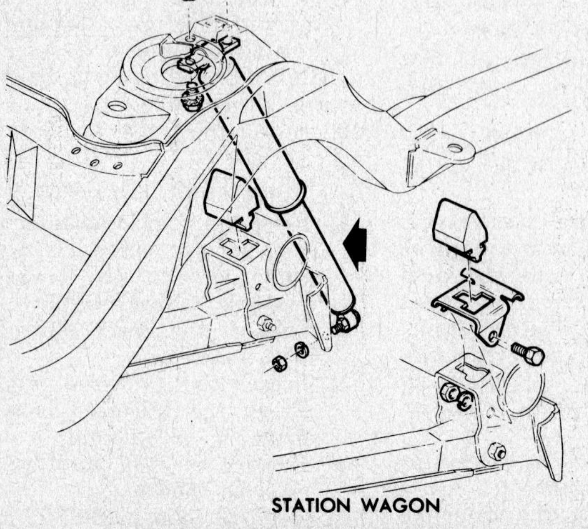
STATION WAGON

Chevelle rear shock absorber mounting
(© Chevrolet Div., G.M. Corp)

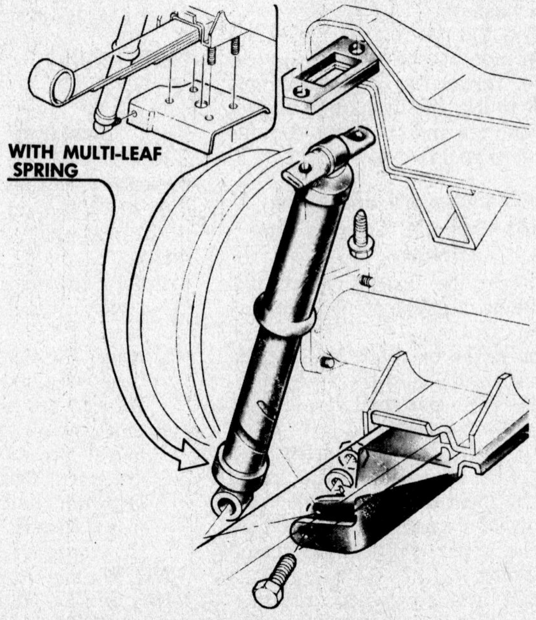
WITH MULTI-LEAF SPRING

Nova rear shock absorber mounting
(© Chevrolet Div., G.M. Corp)

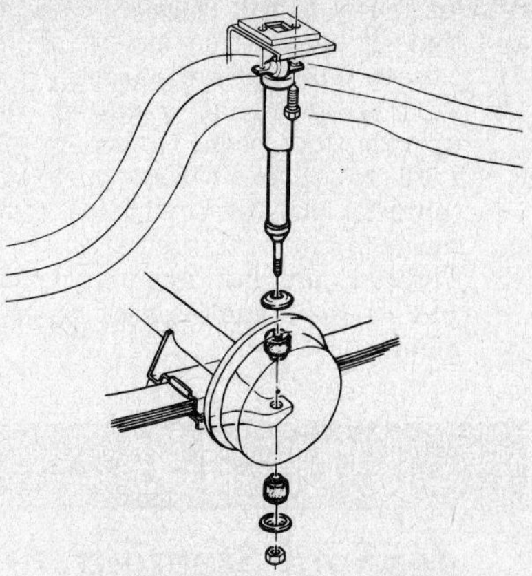

Camaro rear shock absorber mounting
(© Chevrolet Div., G.M. Corp)

d. Remove rear suspension tie rod from stud on axle tube.

4. Slightly loosen the nut on the bolt that retains the spring and seat to control arm at lower seat of both rear springs. When bolt has been backed off the maximum distance, all threads of the nut should still be engaged on the bolt.

Caution Under no condition should the nut, at this time, be removed from the bolt in the seat of either spring.

5. Slowly lower the rear axle assembly, allowing the axle to swing down, carrying the springs out of the upper seat. This provides access for spring removal.
6. Remove the lower seat attaching parts from each spring, then remove springs from vehicle.
7. Position springs in upper seat and install lower seat parts on control arm. Install nut of spring retaining bolt finger-tight.

NOTE: omit lockwasher under the special high carbon bolt, so that sufficient threads will be available to start the nut. Lockwashers will be installed later.

8. Alternately raise the axle slightly and retighten the nut on each spring lower seat bolt. Continue in until the weight is fully supported on the jack or lift. With spring now completely compressed to approximate curb position, completely position the springs in the lower seats by torquing the nut on the lower seat bolt.
9. Reconnect shock absorbers, torque rear attachment of upper and lower control arms, and reconnect the axle tie-rod.
10. While still jacked under axle, remove the nut from the lower seat bolt of one rear spring and install lockwasher and replace nut and tighten. Similarly install lockwasher at other spring.
11. Install rear wheels and lower car to floor.

Chevy II, Nova, and Camaro

1. Raise the vehicle on a hoist and place an adjustable jack under the axle.
2. Raise the axle until all tension is relieved from the spring.
3. Disconnect the shock absorber from the spring retainer plate.
4. Remove the upper shackle retaining bolt, then the front spring eye bolt.
5. Remove the spring/axle U-bolts, lower plate, spring pads, and spring.
6. Remove the shackle from the spring.
7. Before installing the spring, install the shackle on the rearward end.
8. Place the upper cushion on the spring, then insert the front of the spring into the frame and attach the rear shackle, leaving the bolt loose.
9. Install the lower spring pad and retainer plate, tightening the U-bolt nuts to 40 ft lbs.
10. Tighten the rear shackle bolts to 50 ft lbs.
11. Tighten the front eye bolt to 75 ft lbs.
12. Attach the shock absorber to spring retainer plate.
13. Remove the jack and lower the vehicle.

BRAKES

Description

General Motors cars have as standard equipment the duo-servo single anchor type service brake. Brake shoe linings are bonded and the shoes are self-adjusting. Drums are of cast iron.

Wheel cylinders are conventional double piston type.

Since 1967, a dual type master cylinder is used. The front portion of the master cylinder supplies hydraulic pressure for the front wheels. Pressure for rear wheel brake application is supplied from the rear portion of the master cylinder.

Brake lining replacement and ad-

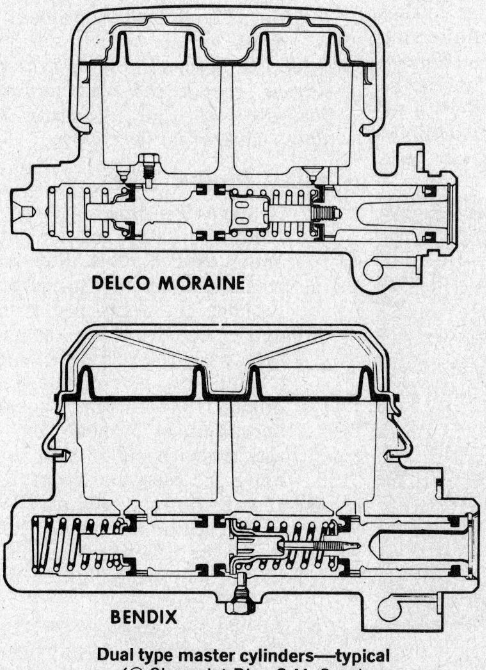
DELCO MORAINE
BENDIX

Dual type master cylinders—typical
(© Chevrolet Div., G.M. Corp)

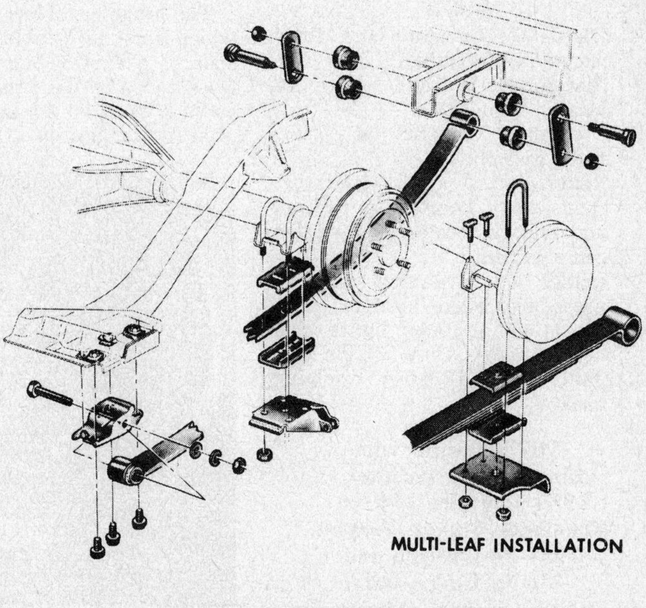
MULTI-LEAF INSTALLATION

Rear spring mounting—Nova and Camaro
(© Chevrolet Div., G.M. Corp)

justment, wheel and master cylinder overhaul and brake bleeding procedures can be found in the Unit Repair Section.

As an option, both Bendix and Moraine power brakes are available. Data on these two power brakes can be found in the Unit Repair Section.

Front wheel disc brakes are standard on the 1970-74 Camaro, SS396 and 454 Chevelles, 1970-74 Monte Carlo and Chevelle. Repair procedures for disc brakes are given in the Unit Repair Section.

Master Cylinder R & R

1967-74

1. Disconnect hydraulic line/s at master cylinder.
2. Remove the two retaining nuts and lockwashers that hold cylinder to firewall. Disconnect pushrod at brake pedal.
3. Remove the master cylinder, gasket and rubber boot.
4. Position master cylinder on firewall, making sure pushrod goes through the rubber boot into the piston. Reconnect pushrod clevis to brake pedal.
5. Install nuts and lockwashers.
6. Install hydraulic line/s, then check brake pedal free play.
7. Bleed brakes, as described in Unit Repair Section.

NOTE: cars having disc brakes do not have a check valve in the front outlet port of the master cylinder. If one is installed, front discs will immediately wear out due to residual hydraulic pressure holding pads against rotor.

Power Brake Booster R & R

1967-74 Except the Following Chevelle and Monte Carlo Models

1. Disconnect vacuum hose from vacuum check valve.
2. Disconnect hydraulic lines at master cylinder.
3. Disconnect pushrod at brake pedal assembly.
4. Remove nuts and lockwashers that secure booster to firewall and remove booster from engine compartment.
5. Install by reversing removal procedure. Make sure to check operation of stop lights and bleed brakes. Allow engine vacuum to build before applying brakes.

1969 Chevelle with Manual Transmission, 1970 Chevelle 116 in. Wheelbase Station Wagon, 1971-74 Chevelle and Monte Carlo—All

1. Remove master cylinder from vacuum booster.
2. Remove vacuum line from vacuum check valve.
3. On 1971-74 models, remove brake line clip from booster.
4. From inside vehicle, remove nuts and lockwashers that secure booster to firewall.
5. Push brake pedal to the floor. This will disengage booster from firewall and adequate clearance for removal of the pushrod pivot pin will be gained.
6. Remove clip from pivot pin, then remove power unit from car.
7. Install by reversing removal procedure. Make sure to check operation of stop lights and bleed brakes. Allow engine vacuum to build before applying brakes.

Parking Brake

The parking brake is hand operated by a lever attached to the dash panel, just to the right of the steering column on the 1967 Chevy II and pedal operated on all other models. It functions through an equalizer and cables to the rear brake shoes.

Parking Brake Adjustment

1. Jack up rear of car and support with both rear wheels off floor.
2. Apply parking brake two notches from fully released position.
3. Loosen the equalizer front jam nut, then tighten rear nut until a light to moderate drag is felt when rear wheels are rotated.
4. Tighten jam nuts.
5. Fully release parking brake and rotate rear wheels—no drag should be felt.

Brake Pedal Free Play Check

Caution Do not use this procedure for disc brakes.

The brake pedal has a definite stop, which is not adjustable. This stop consists of a rubber bumper at the release end of pedal travel. Before adjusting pushrod to master cylinder clearance, make sure the brake pedal returns freely to full release position and that spring has not lost tension.

1. Loosen jam nut on pushrod.
2. Turn pushrod as required to provide for a pedal movement of 1/16 to ¼ in. before pushrod contacts master cylinder piston/s.
3. Tighten jam nut against clevis (14 ft. lbs.) and recheck movement.

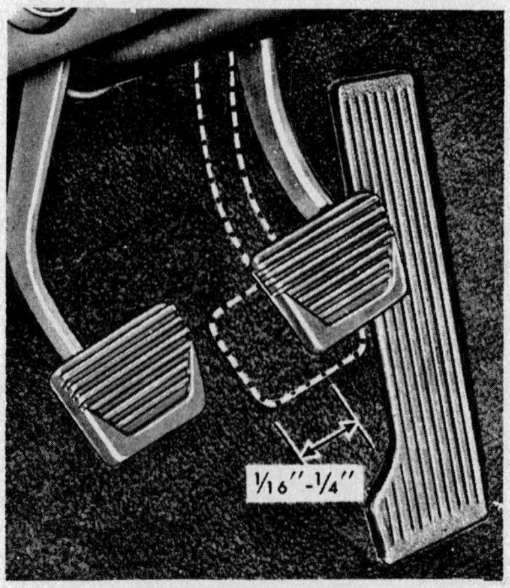
1/16"-1/4"
Brake pedal free-play check
(© Chevrolet Div., G.M. Corp)

STEERING

Manual Steering Gear

Tie-Rod R & R

1. Remove the cotter pins and nuts from the tie-rod end studs.
2. Tap on the steering arm near the tie-rod end (use another hammer as backing) and pull down on the tie-rod, if necessary, to free it.
3. Remove the inner stud in the same manner as the outer.
4. Loosen the clamp bolts and unscrew the ends if they are being replaced.
5. Lubricate the tie-rod end threads with chassis grease if they were removed. Install each end assembly an equal distance from the sleeve.
6. Ensure that the tie-rod end stud threads and nut are clean. Install new seals and install the studs into the steering arms and relay rod.
7. Install the stud nuts. Tighten the outer end nut to 35 ft lbs and the inner nut to 60 ft lbs.
8. Adjust the toe-in as described in the "Front End Alignment" section.

NOTE: before tightening the sleeve clamps, ensure that the clamps are positioned so that adjusting sleeve slot is covered by the clamp.

Relay Rod R & R

1. Remove the inner tie-rod ends from the relay rod as outlined under tie-rod R&R. Remove the steering damper, if so equipped.
2. Remove the relay rod stud nut and cotter pin from the pitman arm. Free the relay rod from the pitman arm, moving the steering linkage if necessary. Repeat this operation to remove the relay rod from the idler arm and remove the relay rod from the car.
3. Install the relay rod on the idler arm. Tighten the nut to 40 ft lbs.
4. Raise the relay and install it on the pitman arm. Tighten the nut to 45 ft lbs.
5. Adjust the toe-in as described in the "Front End Alignment" section.

Pitman Arm R & R

1. Remove the pitman arm stud nut and cotter pin.
2. Tap the relay rod off the pitman arm, using another hammer as backing. Pull the relay rod off the pitman arm stud.
3. Remove the pitman arm nut and mark the arm-to-shaft relationship.
4. Remove the pitman arm using a puller.
5. Install the pitman arm on the shaft, aligning the previously made marks. Install the pitman shaft nut and tighten it to 180 ft lbs.
6. Install the relay rod on the pitman arm. Tighten the nut to 45 ft lbs. and install a cotter pin.

Idler Arm R & R

Chevy II 1967

1. Remove the idler arm-to-relay rod cotter pin, nut, and washer.
2. Remove the relay rod from the idler arm.
3. On power steering, disconnect the power cylinder shaft from the idler arm bracket.
4. Remove the idler arm-to-frame bracket fasteners and remove the bracket and idler arm assembly.
5. Remove the idler arm-to-bracket nut and bolt. Press the idler arm bushing out, if replacement is necessary.
6. Reverse the removal procedure to install the idler arm. Make sure that the wheels are straight ahead during installation.

All Other Cars

1. Remove the idler arm-to-frame nut, washer, and bolt.
2. Remove the cotter pin and nut from the idler arm-to-relay rod ball end stud.
3. Tap the relay rod with a hammer, using another hammer as backing, to remove the relay rod from the idler arm.
4. Remove the idler arm.
5. Place the idler arm on the frame and install the bolts, washers, and nuts. Tighten to 35 ft lbs.
6. Install the relay rod to the idler arm, making sure that the stud seal is in place. Tighten the nut to 50 ft lbs and insert a cotter pin.

Recirculating ball type gear is used on General Motors cars. Adjustment and overhaul procedures are found in the Unit Repair Section.

Power Steering

Two types of power steering are used. The 1967 Chevy II uses the linkage assist type of gear with a

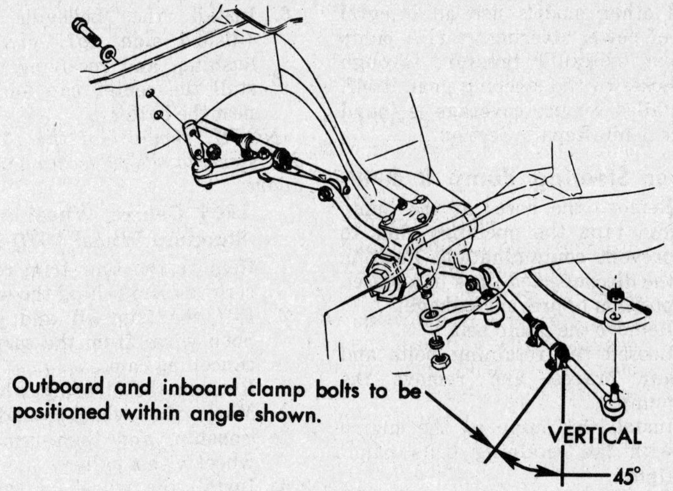
Outboard and inboard clamp bolts to be positioned within angle shown.
VERTICAL
45°
Chevelle and Monte Carlo steering linkage
(© Chevrolet Div., G.M. Corp)

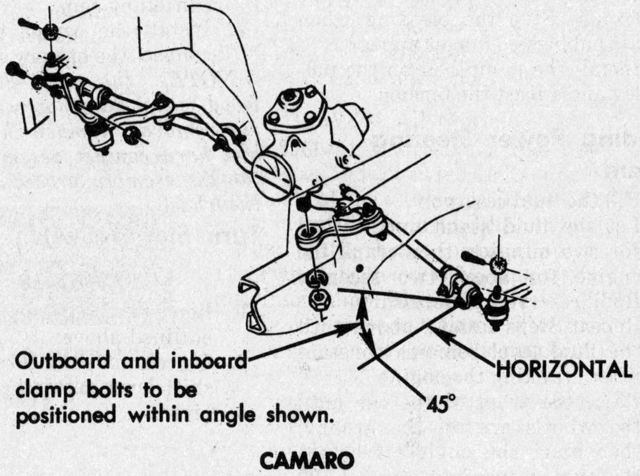
Outboard and inboard clamp bolts to be positioned within angle shown.
HORIZONTAL
45°
CAMARO
Camaro steering linkage
(© Chevrolet Div., G.M. Corp)

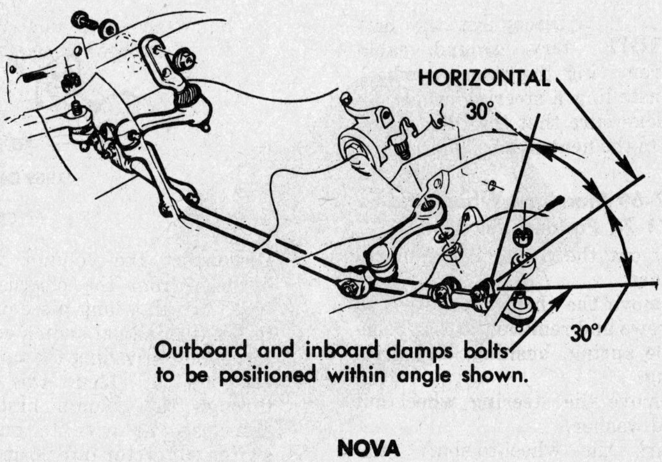
HORIZONTAL
30°
30°
Outboard and inboard clamps bolts to be positioned within angle shown.
NOVA
Nova steering linkage
(© Chevrolet Div., G.M. Corp)

2. Drain radiator.
3. Disconnect heater hoses. Plug core inlet and outlet.
4. Remove nuts from air distributor duct studs on firewall.
5. On Chevy II, remove glove compartment and door assembly.
6. From under dash, drill out lower right hand distributor duct stud with a ¼ in. drill.
7. On 1970 and later Camaro: remove glove box and radio, then defroster duct to distributor duct screw.
8. Pull distributor duct from firewall mounting. Remove resistor wires. Lay duct on floor.
9. Remove core assembly from distributor duct.
10. Reverse procedure to install.

NOTE: the two procedures above are not applicable to air-conditioned cars, except pre-1970 models with the dealer installed, under-dash unit.

1967 Chevelle with Air Conditioning

1. Remove the battery ground cable and drain the cooling system. It is not necessary to evacuate the A.C. refrigerant.
2. Remove the right front fender and inside panel.
3. Remove the heater hoses at the firewall.
4. Remove the glove compartment door and compartment interior.
5. Remove the right, left, and center air conditioning outlet hoses from the distributor.
6. Remove the distributor duct from the heater housing.
7. Disconnect the hose and cable clamps from the housing.
8. From the engine compartment, remove the three retaining nuts on the housing studs. Remove the single screw from under the dash.
9. Pull the housing off the firewall and out of the car.
10. Remove the heater housing cover and withdraw the core, which is retained by four screws and two U-clamps.
11. Use a non-hardening sealer to install the core into the heater housing and install using a reverse of the removal procedure.

1968-74 Chevelle and Monte Carlo with Air Conditioning

1. Drain the cooling system and disconnect the battery ground cable. It is not necessary to purge the A.C. refrigerant.
2. Remove the heater hoses at the firewall and plug the openings.
3. Remove the case stud nuts from the firewall.
4. Remove the glove compartment on 1967-69 models.
5. Remove the right kick pad cover and the recirculating air valve.
6. Remove the center duct from the distributor, and remove the floor distributor duct.
7. From inside the passenger compartment, drill the lower right distributor duct stud out.
8. Remove the remaining air distributor-to-firewall screws, electrical connectors, and control cables.
9. Scribe the temperature door camming plate - to - distributor duct relationship and remove the plate.
10. Remove the heater core housing and core.
11. Reverse the removal procedure to install the core. Replace the drilled-out stud with a screw and speed nut.

1968-74 Chevy II and Nova with Air Conditioning

1. Disconnect the battery ground cable and drain the cooling system. It is not necessary to purge the refrigerant from the A.C. system.
2. Disconnect the heater hose from the upper pipe at the firewall.
3. Remove the nuts from the heater studs in the firewall.
4. Remove the right front inner fender panel screws and lower the panel onto the tire.
5. Remove the remaining stud nut and the lower heater hose.
6. Remove the glove compartment.
7. Remove the right kick pad recirculating air valve.
8. Detach the center duct from the selector duct.
9. Remove the floor duct and separate the two selector halves.
10. Remove the selector duct from the firewall.
11. Disconnect the control cables and electrical wires.
12. Scribe the temperature door camming plate-to-selector duct relationship and remove the plate.
13. Place the selector duct on the floor and remove the heater core housing and core.
14. Reverse the removal steps to install the core.

1967-69 Camaro with Air Conditioning

1. Drain the cooling system and disconnect the battery ground cable. It is not necessary to purge the refrigerant from the A.C. system.
2. Disconnect the upper heater hose at the firewall.
3. Remove all accessible heater stud nuts from the firewall.
4. Remove the lower right side rocker molding.
5. Remove the bottom fender retaining bolts, inner panel-to-fender, and inner panel-to-reinforcement screws.
6. Pull the lower part of the fender out and pry the skirt away from the fender flange and firewall. Insert a 2 x 4 in. block of wood to hold the skirt out.
7. Disconnect the bottom heater hose and remove the lower right hand stud nut.
8. Remove the glove compartment and right kick pad recirculating valve.
9. Disconnect both side and center dash outlet hoses from the center duct. Remove the center duct from the distributor assembly.
10. Remove the floor outlet duct and separate the two distributor halves.
11. Detach the distributor from the firewall and carefully lower it. Remove the control cables and electrical connections.
12. Remove the distributor. Scribe the temperature door camming plate-to-distributor relationship and remove the plate.
13. Remove the heater core housing and core from the distributor.
14. Reverse the removal procedure to install the heater core.

1970-74 Camaro with Air Conditioning

1. Disconnect the battery ground cable and drain the cooling system. It is not necessary to purge the refrigerant from the cooling system.
2. Disconnect the heater hoses at the firewall and plug the openings.
3. Remove the nuts from the heater studs protruding through the firewall.
4. Remove the glove compartment and radio.
5. Remove the defroster duct-to-distributor duct screw and pull the defroster duct rearward.
6. Pull the distributor duct from its dash mounting. Disconnect the control cables and electrical wires when there is sufficient clearance.
7. Remove the distributor duct and core from the car.
8. Remove the retainers and remove the heater core.
9. Reverse the removal procedure to install the heater core.

SEAT BELTS

Seat Belt/Ignition Interlock System

1974

As required by law, all 1974 Chevrolet passenger cars cannot be started until the front seat occupants are seated and have fastened their seat belts. If the proper sequence is not followed, e.g., the occupants fasten the seat belts and then sit on them, the engine cannot be started.

Pitman Arm R & R

1. Remove the pitman arm stud nut and cotter pin.
2. Tap the relay rod off the pitman arm, using another hammer as backing. Pull the relay rod off the pitman arm stud.
3. Remove the pitman arm nut and mark the arm-to-shaft relationship.
4. Remove the pitman arm using a puller.
5. Install the pitman arm on the shaft, aligning the previously made marks. Install the pitman shaft nut and tighten it to 180 ft lbs.
6. Install the relay rod on the pitman arm. Tighten the nut to 45 ft lbs. and install a cotter pin.

Idler Arm R & R

Chevy II 1967

1. Remove the idler arm-to-relay rod cotter pin, nut, and washer.
2. Remove the relay rod from the idler arm.
3. On power steering, disconnect the power cylinder shaft from the idler arm bracket.
4. Remove the idler arm-to-frame bracket fasteners and remove the bracket and idler arm assembly.
5. Remove the idler arm-to-bracket nut and bolt. Press the idler arm bushing out, if replacement is necessary.
6. Reverse the removal procedure to install the idler arm. Make sure that the wheels are straight ahead during installation.

All Other Cars

1. Remove the idler arm-to-frame nut, washer, and bolt.
2. Remove the cotter pin and nut from the idler arm-to-relay rod ball end stud.
3. Tap the relay rod with a hammer, using another hammer as backing, to remove the relay rod from the idler arm.
4. Remove the idler arm.
5. Place the idler arm on the frame and install the bolts, washers, and nuts. Tighten to 35 ft lbs.
6. Install the relay rod to the idler arm, making sure that the stud seal is in place. Tighten the nut to 50 ft lbs and insert a cotter pin.

Recirculating ball type gear is used on General Motors cars. Adjustment and overhaul procedures are found in the Unit Repair Section.

Power Steering

Two types of power steering are used. The 1967 Chevy II uses the linkage assist type of gear with a

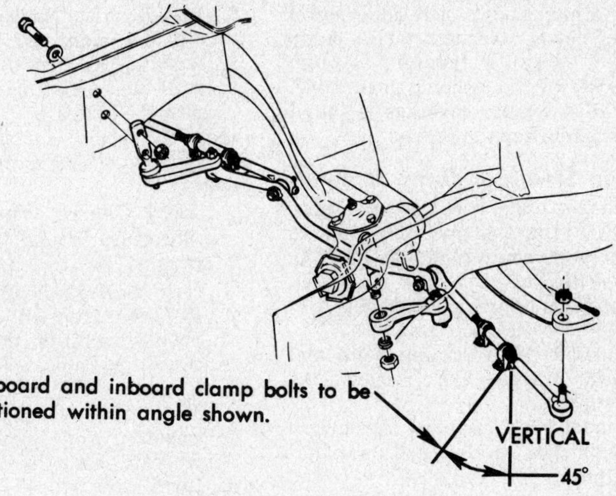
Outboard and inboard clamp bolts to be positioned within angle shown.
VERTICAL
45°

Chevelle and Monte Carlo steering linkage
(© Chevrolet Div., G.M. Corp)

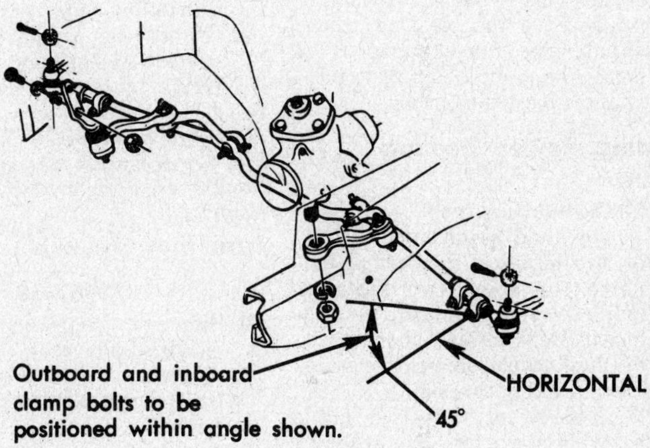
Outboard and inboard clamp bolts to be positioned within angle shown.
HORIZONTAL
45°

CAMARO

Camaro steering linkage
(© Chevrolet Div., G.M. Corp)

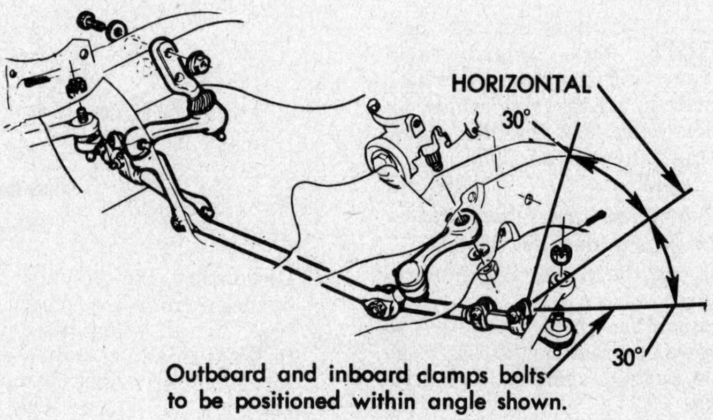
HORIZONTAL
30°
30°
Outboard and inboard clamps bolts to be positioned within angle shown.

NOVA

Nova steering linkage
(© Chevrolet Div., G.M. Corp)

pump delivering an assist to a power cylinder attached to the steering linkage..

All other models use an integral type of power steering gear. A pump delivers hydraulic pressure through two hoses to the steering gear itself.

Detailed service coverage is found in the Unit Repair Section.

Power Steering Pump R & R

1. Remove the hoses at the pump and tape the openings shut to prevent contamination. Position the disconnected lines in a raised position to prevent leakage.
2. Remove the pump belt.
3. Loosen the retaining bolts and any braces, and remove the pump.
4. Install the pump on the engine with the retaining bolts hand-tight.
5. Connect and tighten the hose fittings.
6. Refill the pump with fluid and bleed by turning the pulley counterclockwise (viewed from the front). Stop the bleeding when air bubbles no longer appear.
7. Install the pump belt on the pulley and adjust the tension.

Bleeding Power Steering System

1. Fill the fluid reservoir.
2. Let the fluid stand undisturbed for two minutes, then crank the engine for about two seconds. Refill reservoir if necessary.
3. Repeat Steps 1 and 2 above until the fluid level remains constant after cranking the engine.
4. Raise the front of the car until the wheels are off the ground, then start the engine. Increase the engine speed to about 1,500 rpm.
5. Turn the wheels to the left and right, checking the fluid level and refilling if necessary.

Steering Wheel R & R

Caution Disconnect the battery ground cable before removing the steering wheel. When installing a steering wheel, always make sure that the turn signal lever is in the neutral position.

1967-69 Standard Wheel and 1971-74 Padded Rim Wheel

1. Pry out the center cap and retainer.
2. Remove the three receiving cup screws and remove the cup, belleville spring, bushing, and pivot ring.
3. Remove the steering wheel nut and washer.
4. Mark the wheel-to-shaft relationship, and then remove the wheel with a puller.
5. Install the wheel on the shaft, aligning the previously made marks. Tighten the nut to 35 ft lbs.
6. Install the belleville spring (dished side up), pivot ring, bushing, and receiving cup. Install the center cap and reconnect the battery.

NOTE: removal of the 1970 padded steering wheel is similar to the above.

1969 Deluxe Wheel and Standard Wheel 1970-74

1. Remove the four trim retaining screws from behind the wheel.
2. Lift the trim off and pull the horn wires from the turn signal cancelling cam.
3. Remove the steering wheel nut.
4. Mark the wheel-to-shaft relationship, and then remove the wheel with a puller.
5. Install the wheel on the shaft, aligning the previously made marks. Tighten the nut to 30 ft lbs.
6. Insert the horn wires into the cancelling cam.
7. Install the center trim and reconnect the battery cable.

NOTE: the 1967–69 simulated wood wheel does not require pulling for removal. Remove the center cap and horn contact assembly. Reverse the disassembly procedure to install the wheel.

Turn Signal Switch R & R

1967-68

1. Remove the steering wheel as outlined above.
2. On column shift cars, remove the shift lever retaining pin and the lever.

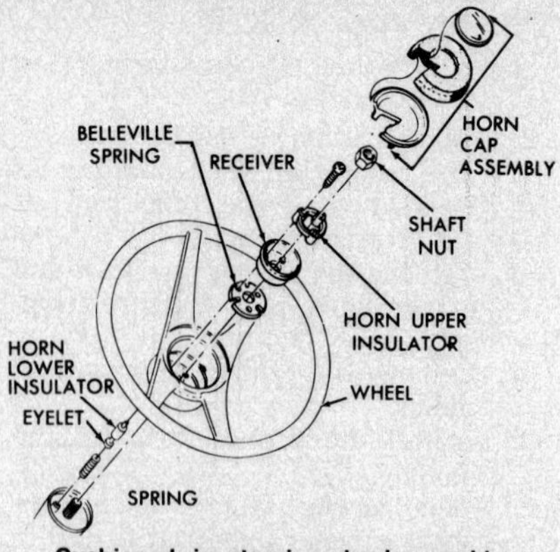
BELLEVILLE SPRING
RECEIVER
HORN CAP ASSEMBLY
SHAFT NUT
HORN UPPER INSULATOR
HORN LOWER INSULATOR
EYELET
WHEEL
SPRING
Cushioned rim steering wheel assembly
(© Chevrolet Div., G.M. Corp)

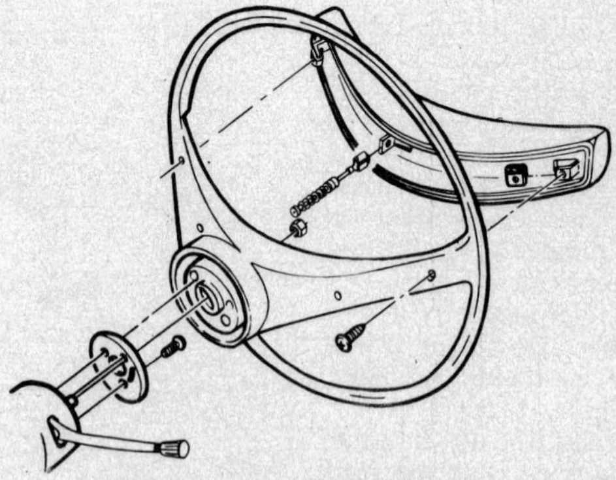
1969 Deluxe and 1970-74 standard steering wheel
(© Chevrolet Div., G.M. Corp)

3. Disconnect the column wiring harness from the chassis harness. Attach a long piece of wire to the turn signal switch connector. When installing the turn signal switch, feed this wire through the column first, and then use the wire to pull the switch connector into position.
4. Remove the lower trim plate and the upper mast jacket clamp. On automatic cars, remove the indicator retaining screw and the pointer.
5. Remove the three turn signal-to-housing screws.
6. Using snap-ring pliers, remove the C-ring from the upper steering shaft. Slide the thrust and wave washers off the steering shaft.
7. Loosen, but do not remove, the three turn signal mounting screws.
8. Turn the switch counterclockwise. Pull the switch out of the mast jacket and let it hang by its wiring.
9. Support the columm, and then remove the upper mounting bracket. Remove the wiring harness cover and clip, and then reinstall the upper bracket hand-tight.
10. Remove the shift lever bowl from the mast jacket and disconnect it from the wiring harness.
11. Remove the switch retaining screws, being careful not to lose the springs.
12. Remove the switch and upper bearing housing from the switch cover.
13. Install the upper bearing housing assembly and the switch into the cover, working the switch wires through the cover.
14. Install the remaining components in a reverse order of removal.

NOTE: the procedure for the tilt wheel is similar, with the exceptions that turn signal cover removal requires a slide hammer and special attachment and that the switch wiring connector must be cut.

1969-74

1. Remove the steering wheel as previously outlined.
2. Loosen the three cover screws and lift the cover off the shaft.
3. Position the special lockplate compressing tool (J-23131 1969-70 or J-23653 1971-74) on the end of the steering shaft and compress the lock plate by turning the shaft nut clockwise. Pry the wire snap-ring out of the shaft groove.

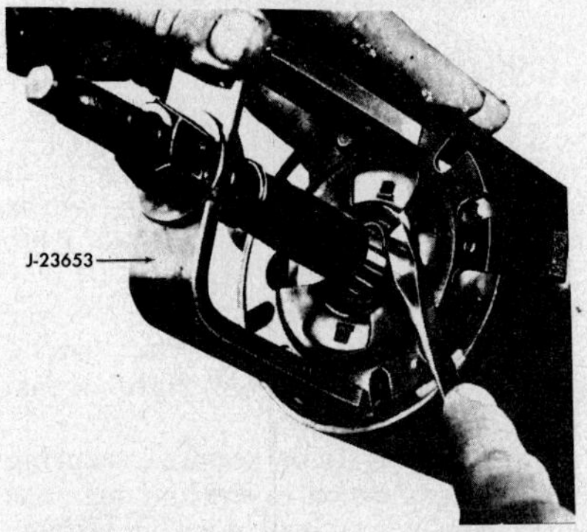
J-23653

Depressing the lock plate and removing the snap-ring
(© Chevrolet Div., G.M. Corp)

4. Remove the tool and lift the lockplate off the shaft.
5. Slip the cancelling cam, upper bearing preload spring, and thrust washer off the shaft.
6. Remove the turn signal lever. Push the flasher knob in and unscrew it.
7. Pull the switch connector out of the mast jacket and tape the upper part to facilitate switch removal. Attach a long piece of wire to the turn signal switch connector. When installing the turn signal switch, feed this wire through the column first, and then use this wire to pull the switch connector into position. On tilt wheels, place the turn signal and shifter housing in Low position and remove the harness cover.
8. Remove the three switch mounting screws. Remove the switch by pulling it straight up while guiding the wiring harness cover through the column.
9. Install the replacement switch by working the connector and cover down through the housing and under the bracket. On tilt models, the connector is worked down through the housing, under the bracket, and then the cover is installed on the harness.
10. Install the switch mounting screws and the connector on the mast jacket bracket. Install the column-to-dash trim plate.
11. Install the flasher knob and the turn signal lever.
12. With the turn signal lever in neutral and the flasher knob out, slide the thrust washer, upper bearing preload spring, and cancelling cam onto the shaft.
13. Position the lock plate on the shaft and press it down until a new snap-ring can be inserted in the shaft groove.
14. Install the cover and the steering wheel.

INSTRUMENT PANEL

Ignition Switch Replacement

1967-68 Chevy II

1. Disconnect battery.
2. Remove lock cylinder by placing in off position and inserting a wire in the small hole in cylinder face. While pushing on the wire, continue to turn cylinder counterclockwise. Pull cylinder from case.
3. Remove nut from passenger side of dash.
4. Pull switch from under dash and remove wiring connector.
5. To remove the theft resistant connector, the switch must be removed from under the dash. With screwdriver, depress tangs and separate the connector.
6. Install in reverse of above.

1967-68 Chevelle

1. Disconnect battery ground cable.
2. Remove:
   a. ash tray
   b. ash tray retainer
   c. Radio knobs, nuts, connectors, bracket, and radio.
3. Remove lock cylinder by positioning switch in Accessory position and inserting wire in hole in cylinder face. Push in wire and turn key counterclockwise to remove cylinder.
4. Remove bezel nut and pull out ignition switch.
5. Unsnap locking tangs on connector with a screwdriver. Unplug connector.
6. Reverse procedure to install.

1967-68 Camaro

This procedure is the same as that given above for the 1967-68 Chevelle, with the deletion of Step 2.

1969-74 All Models

All 1969-74 models have the ignition lock cylinder located on the upper right side of the steering column. The ignition switch is inside the channel section of the brake pedal support. The switch is inaccessible unless the steering column is lowered.

1. Lower steering column. The column must be carefully supported to prevent damage.
2. Remove lock cylinder as above.

NOTE: pull actuating rod for switch up until a definite stop is felt, then push it down one detent to Lock position.

3. Remove two switch screws and switch assembly.
4. When replacing switch, make sure switch and lock are in Lock position. Do not use switch screws longer than the originals, or the compressibility feature of the column may be lost.

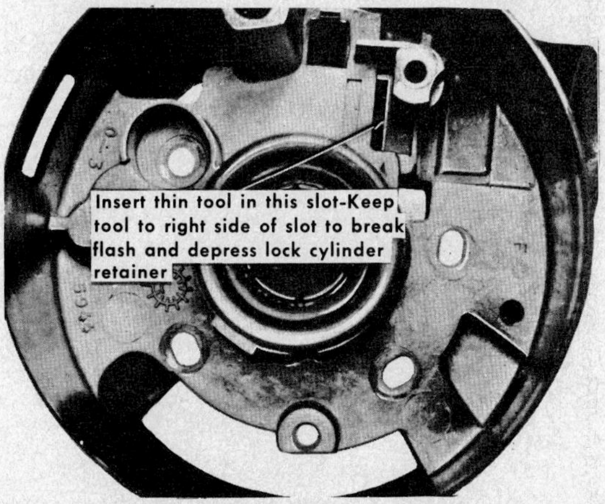
Insert thin tool in this slot-Keep tool to right side of slot to break flash and depress lock cylinder retainer

Removing 1969-74 lock cylinder
(© Chevrolet Div., G.M. Corp)

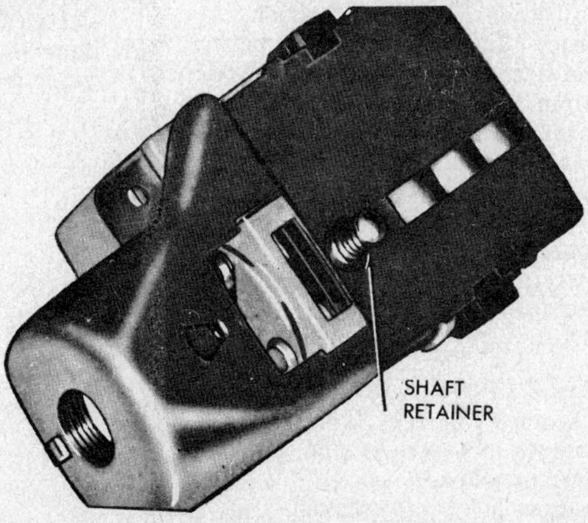
SHAFT RETAINER

Light switch—1967-74
(© Chevrolet Div., G.M. Corp)

Lock Cylinder R & R—1969-74

1. Remove steering wheel and directional signal switch as previously outlined in "Steering."
2. Place lock cylinder in Lock position up to 1970, Run position starting 1971.

NOTE: considerable force may be necessary to break this casting flash, but be careful not to damage any other parts. When ordering a new lock cylinder, specify a cylinder assembly. This will save assembling the cylinder, washer, sleeve, and adaptor.

Caution Do not remove the ignition key buzzer.

3. Insert a small screwdriver into the turn signal housing slot. Keeping the screwdriver to the right side of the slot, break the housing flash loose and depress the spring latch at the lower end of the lock cylinder. Remove the lock cylinder.
4. To install, hold the lock cylinder sleeve and rotate the knob clockwise against the stop. Insert the cylinder into the housing, aligning the key and keyway. Hold a .070 in. drill between the lock bezel and housing. Rotate the cylinder counterclockwise, maintaining a light pressure until the drive section of the cylinder mates with the sector. Push in until the snap ring pops into the grooves. Remove drill. Check cylinder operation.

Caution The drill prevents forcing the lock cylinder inward beyond its normal position. The buzzer switch and spring latch can hold the lock cylinder in too far. Complete disassembly of the upper bearing housing is necessary to release an improperly installed lock cylinder.

Lighting Switch Replacement

1967-68 Chevy II, 1969-74 Nova, 1967-69 Camaro and Chevelle

1. Disconnect battery.
2. Pull knob out to on position.
3. Reach under instrument panel and depress the switch shaft retainer, and remove knob and shaft assembly.
4. Remove the retaining ferrule nut.
5. Remove switch from instrument panel.
6. Disconnect the multi-plug connector from the switch.
7. Install in reverse of above.

1970-74 Chevelle, Monte Carlo

1. Disconnect battery ground cable.
2. Remove six screws and instrument panel pad.
3. Remove left radio speaker.
4. Pull knob to on position.
5. Reach behind instrument panel and depress switch shaft retainer. Remove knob and shaft assembly.
6. Remove ferrule nut and switch assembly from instrument panel.
7. Reverse procedure to install.

1970-74 Camaro

1. Disconnect battery negative cable.
2. Remove steering column lower cover (six screws).
3. Reach up under cluster on the left side and depress light switch shaft retainer, while pulling gently on shaft.
4. Remove nut that secures switch to cluster carrier.
5. Remove four cluster carrier screws in front and two from rear, then tilt right side of cluster out. Cigarette lighter grounding ring may have to be freed.
6. Unplug harness connector from switch.
7. Remove switch.
8. To install, reverse removal procedure. Make sure all ground connections are refastened.

WINDSHIELD WIPERS

Motor R & R

1967 Chevelle and Chevy II

1. Make certain wiper motor is in park position.
2. Working under instrument panel, remove transmission linkage from motor crank arm.
3. Disconnect electrical connectors and washer hoses.
4. Remove motor retaining bolts and remove motor.
5. Reverse procedure to install, checking sealing gaskets at motor.

1967 Camaro

1. Make certain wiper motor is in park position.
2. Disconnect washer hoses and electrical connectors.
3. Remove three motor bolts. Pull wiper motor assembly from cowl opening and loosen nuts retaining drive rod ball stud to crank arm.
4. Reverse procedure to install, checking sealing gaskets at motor.

1968-74 All Models

1. Make sure wiper motor is in park position.
2. Disconnect washer hoses and electrical connectors.
3. Remove the plenum chamber grille or access cover. Remove the nut retaining the crank arm to the motor assembly.
4. Remove the retaining screws or nuts and remove motor.
5. Reverse procedure to install, checking sealing gaskets at motor.

Transmission R & R

1967 Chevy II

1. Make certain wiper motor is in park position. Remove wiper arm and blade assemblies from transmission shaft.
2. Remove linkage from wiper crank arm. Remove left transmission link from right transmission.
3. Remove two screws securing transmission to cowl on one side. Remove transmission from under dash.
4. Reverse procedure to install, checking gasket.

1967 Chevelle

1. Make certain wiper motor is in park position. Remove wiper arm and blade assemblies from transmission shaft.
2. Remove plenum chamber grille.
3. Detach linkage from wiper crank arm.
4. Remove transmission retaining screws, lower assembly into plenum chamber, and remove unit.
5. Reverse procedure to install.

1967 Camaro, 1968-74 All Models

1. Make sure wiper motor is in park position.
2. Disconnect battery ground cable.
3. Remove wiper arm and blade as-

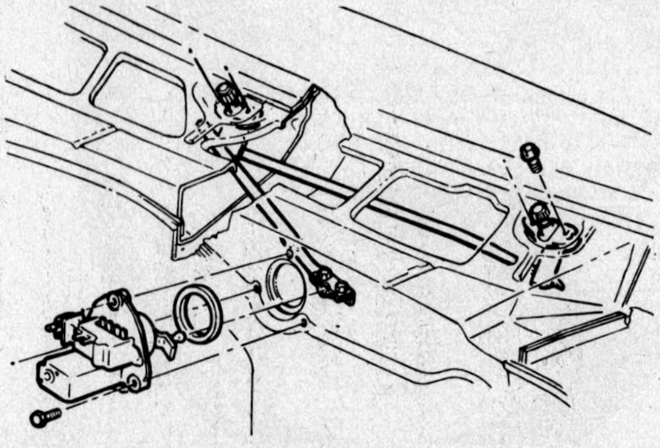

Wiper motor and linkage—Camaro
(© Chevrolet Div., G.M. Corp)

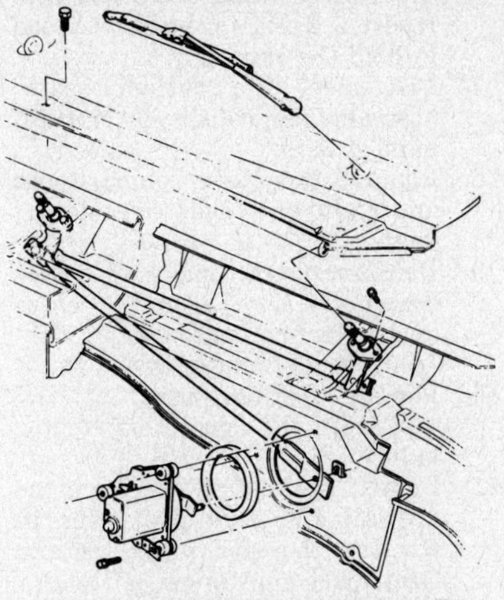

Wiper motor and linkage—1967 Chevelle
(© Chevrolet Div., G.M. Corp)

semblies from transmission. On articulated left arm assemblies, remove carburetor type clip retaining pinned arm to blade arm.

4. Remove plenum chamber air intake grille or screen.
5. Loosen nuts retaining drive rod ball stud to crank arm and detach drive rod from crank arm.
6. Remove transmission retaining screws. Lower transmission and drive rod assemblies into plenum chamber.
7. Remove transmission and linkage from plenum chamber through cowl opening.
8. Reverse procedure to install, making sure wiper blade assemblies are installed in park position.

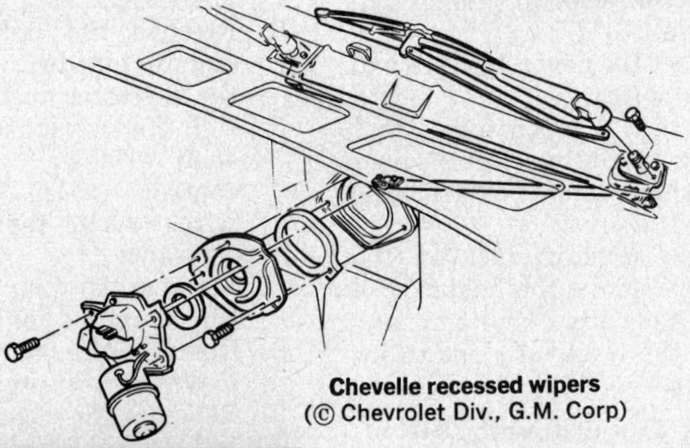

Chevelle recessed wipers
(© Chevrolet Div., G.M. Corp)

HEATER

Heater Blower R & R

1967 Chevy II

1. Remove screws attaching the motor and blower to heater assembly. Remove the motor air-cooling hose on air-conditioned cars.
2. Remove retainer attaching blower to motor shaft.
3. Install in reverse of above.

1967 Chevelle

1. Disconnect battery.
2. Unclip hoses from fender skirt.
3. Disconnect electrical feed from motor. Remove the air-cooling hose on air-conditioned cars.
4. Turn vehicle front wheels to extreme right.
5. Remove right front fender skirt bolts and allow skirt to drop, resting it on top of tire. It may be wedged away from fender lower flange with block of wood to provide better access to bolts.
6. Remove screws attaching motor mounting plate to air inlet housing.
7. Remove screws attaching motor to mounting plate.
8. Remove clip attaching cage to shaft and remove blower motor.
9. Install in reverse of above.

1967-69 Camaro

1. Disconnect battery ground cable.
2. Disconnect hoses and wiring from fender skirt.
3. Remove wheel opening trim.
4. Remove rocker panel molding.
5. Loosen rear lower fender to body bolt.
6. Remove nine rearmost fender skirt attaching screws.
7. Pull lower rear edge of fender out. Pull skirt down. Place a block of wood between fender and skirt.
8. Remove blower to case attaching screws. Remove the air-cooling hose from the motor on air-conditioned cars. Remove blower assembly.
9. Remove blower wheel retaining nut. Separate blower and motor.
10. Reverse procedure to install. Open end of blower should be away from motor.

1968 Chevy II, 1969 Nova, 1968-69 Chevelle, 1970-74 All Models

1. Disconnect battery ground cable.
2. Disconnect hoses and wiring from right side inner fender panel.
3. Remove all right side inner fender panel attaching bolts except those attaching panel to radiator support.
4. Pull out, then down, on panel. Place a block between panel and fender.
5. Remove blower to case attaching screws. Remove the air-cooling hose from the motor on air-conditioned cars. Remove blower assembly.
6. Remove blower wheel retaining nut and separate the motor and wheel.
7. Reverse procedure to install. Open end of blower should be away from motor.

Heater Core R & R

1967 Chevy II

1. Drain radiator.
2. From engine compartment, remove hoses from inlet and outlet connections.
3. Remove nuts around blower motor holding heater to dash panel.
4. From inside vehicle, remove glove compartment and glove compartment door.
5. Remove screws attaching heater distributor bracket to dash.
6. Remove screw holding case bracket to adaptor bracket.
7. Detach heater assembly from dash panel and adaptor assembly, then lower toward floor.
8. Disconnect all cable connections, wire connector and defroster hoses.
9. Remove assembly from vehicle.
10. Remove screws attaching core cover to heater.
11. Remove core mounting screws and remove core from heater.
12. Install in reverse of above.

1967 Chevelle (Except Air-Conditioned Cars)

1. Drain radiator.
2. Remove heater hoses at connections beside air inlet assembly.
3. Remove cable and electrical connectors from heater and defroster assembly.
4. On engine side of dash, remove screws and nuts holding air inlet to dash panel.
5. Inside vehicle, pull entire assembly from the firewall and remove assembly from vehicle.
6. Remove core assembly retaining springs and remove core.
7. Install in reverse of above.

1968-74 All Models (Except Air-Conditioned Cars)

1. Disconnect battery ground cable.

RADIO

1967-74

1. Disconnect battery ground cable.
2. Remove ash tray and ash tray housing as necessary.
3. Remove knobs, controls, washers, trim plate, and nuts from radio.
4. Remove hoses from center air conditioning duct as necessary.
5. Disconnect all wiring leads.
6. Remove screw from radio rear mounting bracket and lower radio.
7. To install, reverse above procedure.

2. Drain radiator.
3. Disconnect heater hoses. Plug core inlet and outlet.
4. Remove nuts from air distributor duct studs on firewall.
5. On Chevy II, remove glove compartment and door assembly.
6. From under dash, drill out lower right hand distributor duct stud with a 1/4 in. drill.
7. On 1970 and later Camaro: remove glove box and radio, then defroster duct to distributor duct screw.
8. Pull distributor duct from firewall mounting. Remove resistor wires. Lay duct on floor.
9. Remove core assembly from distributor duct.
10. Reverse procedure to install.

NOTE: the two procedures above are not applicable to air-conditioned cars, except pre-1970 models with the dealer installed, under-dash unit.

1967 Chevelle with Air Conditioning

1. Remove the battery ground cable and drain the cooling system. It is not necessary to evacuate the A.C. refrigerant.
2. Remove the right front fender and inside panel.
3. Remove the heater hoses at the firewall.
4. Remove the glove compartment door and compartment interior.
5. Remove the right, left, and center air conditioning outlet hoses from the distributor.
6. Remove the distributor duct from the heater housing.
7. Disconnect the hose and cable clamps from the housing.
8. From the engine compartment, remove the three retaining nuts on the housing studs. Remove the single screw from under the dash.
9. Pull the housing off the firewall and out of the car.
10. Remove the heater housing cover and withdraw the core, which is retained by four screws and two U-clamps.
11. Use a non-hardening sealer to install the core into the heater housing and install using a reverse of the removal procedure.

1968-74 Chevelle and Monte Carlo with Air Conditioning

1. Drain the cooling system and disconnect the battery ground cable. It is not necessary to purge the A.C. refrigerant.
2. Remove the heater hoses at the firewall and plug the openings.
3. Remove the case stud nuts from the firewall.
4. Remove the glove compartment on 1967-69 models.
5. Remove the right kick pad cover and the recirculating air valve.
6. Remove the center duct from the distributor, and remove the floor distributor duct.
7. From inside the passenger compartment, drill the lower right distributor duct stud out.
8. Remove the remaining air distributor-to-firewall screws, electrical connectors, and control cables.
9. Scribe the temperature door camming plate - to - distributor duct relationship and remove the plate.
10. Remove the heater core housing and core.
11. Reverse the removal procedure to install the core. Replace the drilled-out stud with a screw and speed nut.

1968-74 Chevy II and Nova with Air Conditioning

1. Disconnect the battery ground cable and drain the cooling system. It is not necessary to purge the refrigerant from the A.C. system.
2. Disconnect the heater hose from the upper pipe at the firewall.
3. Remove the nuts from the heater studs in the firewall.
4. Remove the right front inner fender panel screws and lower the panel onto the tire.
5. Remove the remaining stud nut and the lower heater hose.
6. Remove the glove compartment.
7. Remove the right kick pad recirculating air valve.
8. Detach the center duct from the selector duct.
9. Remove the floor duct and separate the two selector halves.
10. Remove the selector duct from the firewall.
11. Disconnect the control cables and electrical wires.
12. Scribe the temperature door camming plate-to-selector duct relationship and remove the plate.
13. Place the selector duct on the floor and remove the heater core housing and core.
14. Reverse the removal steps to install the core.

1967-69 Camaro with Air Conditioning

1. Drain the cooling system and disconnect the battery ground cable. It is not necessary to purge the refrigerant from the A.C. system.
2. Disconnect the upper heater hose at the firewall.
3. Remove all accessible heater stud nuts from the firewall.
4. Remove the lower right side rocker molding.
5. Remove the bottom fender retaining bolts, inner panel-to-fender, and inner panel-to-reinforcement screws.
6. Pull the lower part of the fender out and pry the skirt away from the fender flange and firewall. Insert a 2 x 4 in. block of wood to hold the skirt out.
7. Disconnect the bottom heater hose and remove the lower right hand stud nut.
8. Remove the glove compartment and right kick pad recirculating valve.
9. Disconnect both side and center dash outlet hoses from the center duct. Remove the center duct from the distributor assembly.
10. Remove the floor outlet duct and separate the two distributor halves.
11. Detach the distributor from the firewall and carefully lower it. Remove the control cables and electrical connections.
12. Remove the distributor. Scribe the temperature door camming plate-to-distributor relationship and remove the plate.
13. Remove the heater core housing and core from the distributor.
14. Reverse the removal procedure to install the heater core.

1970-74 Camaro with Air Conditioning

1. Disconnect the battery ground cable and drain the cooling system. It is not necessary to purge the refrigerant from the cooling system.
2. Disconnect the heater hoses at the firewall and plug the openings.
3. Remove the nuts from the heater studs protruding through the firewall.
4. Remove the glove compartment and radio.
5. Remove the defroster duct-to-distributor duct screw and pull the defroster duct rearward.
6. Pull the distributor duct from its dash mounting. Disconnect the control cables and electrical wires when there is sufficient clearance.
7. Remove the distributor duct and core from the car.
8. Remove the retainers and remove the heater core.
9. Reverse the removal procedure to install the heater core.

SEAT BELTS

Seat Belt/Ignition Interlock System

1974

As required by law, all 1974 Chevrolet passenger cars cannot be started until the front seat occupants are seated and have fastened their seat belts. If the proper sequence is not followed, e.g., the occupants fasten the seat belts and then sit on them, the engine cannot be started.

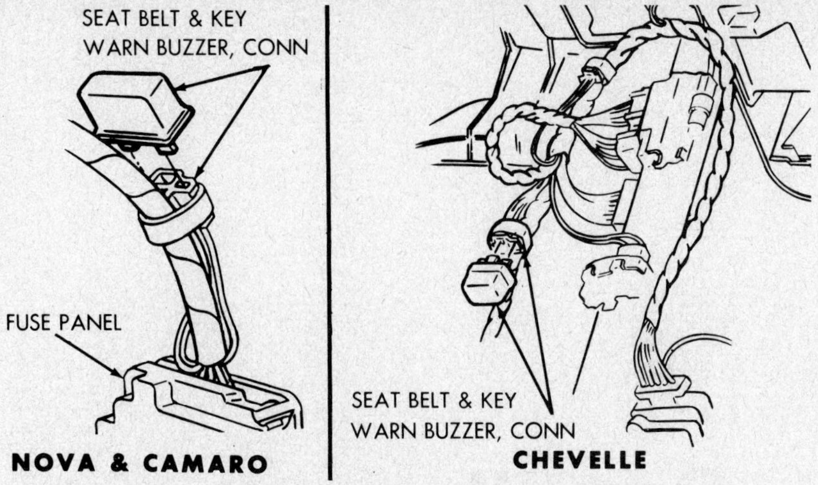
SEAT BELT & KEY
WARN BUZZER, CONN
FUSE PANEL
NOVA & CAMARO
SEAT BELT & KEY
WARN BUZZER, CONN
CHEVELLE

Seat belt/ignition switch warning buzzer location (© Chevrolet Div., G.M. Corp)

If, after the car is started, the seat belts are unfastened, a warning buzzer and light will be activated in a similar manner to that described above for 1972-73 models.

The shoulder harness and lap belt are permanently fastened together, so that they both must be worn. The shoulder harness uses an inertia-lock reel to allow freedom of movement under normal driving conditions.

NOTE: This type of reel locks up when the car decelerates rapidly, as during a crash.

The lap belts use the same ratchet-type retractors that the 1972-73 models use.

The switches for the interlock system have been removed from the lap belt retractors and placed in the belt buckles. The seat sensors remain the same as those used in 1972-73.

For ease of service, the car may be started from outside, by reaching in and turning the key, but without depressing the seat sensors.

In case of system failure, an override switch is located under the hood. This is a "one start" switch and it must be reset each time it is used.

On Chevrolet products, this system consists of seat belt retractor switches, pressure sensitive front seat switches, a parking brake switch, (M.T.), or a transmission switch (A.T.), a warning light, and a buzzer.

The seat belt warning system is wired through the 20 amp "Gauges" fuse.

The warning light is located in the instrument cluster; and the buzzer, which is shared with the ignition key warning system, is taped to the instrument cluster wiring harness.

The warning system is activated when the ignition switch is ON, the front seats are occupied, and the seat belts are left in their retractors. Only when the front seat belts are extended and properly fastened, will the warning light and buzzer stop.

Two different types of switches are used to control the operation of the system, depending upon the type of transmission used:

On manual transmission-equipped cars, the parking brake warning light switch is used to activate the seat belt warning circuit through a relay as soon as the parking brake is released. A diode is used in the circuit to prevent feedback to the brake warning system.

On automatic transmission equipped models, the seat belt warning system is activated by the neutral safety/back-up lamp switch, when the car is placed into any forward gear and the seat belts are not used.

NEW THREE POINT SEAT-SHOULDER BELT IGNITION INTERLOCK SYSTEM

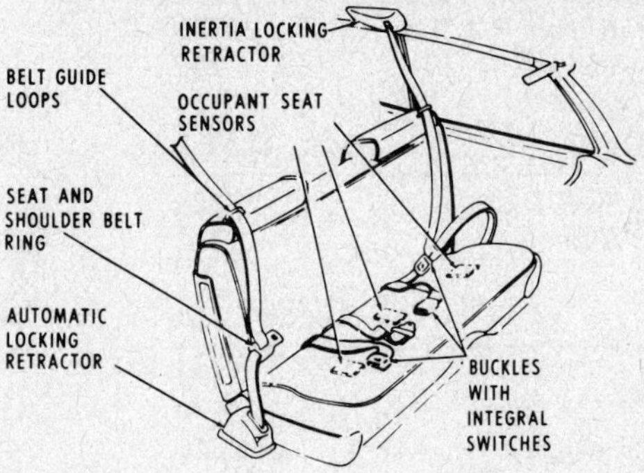
INERTIA LOCKING
RETRACTOR
BELT GUIDE
LOOPS
OCCUPANT SEAT
SENSORS
SEAT AND
SHOULDER BELT
RING
AUTOMATIC
LOCKING
RETRACTOR
BUCKLES
WITH
INTEGRAL
SWITCHES

INDEX

Chevrolet · Corvette

YEAR IDENTIFICATION

CHEVROLET:

1967

1968

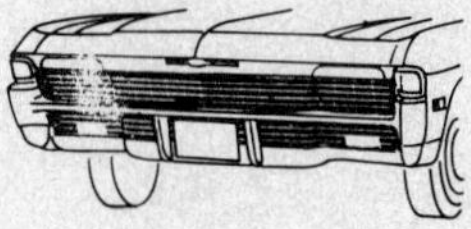

1968 Caprice

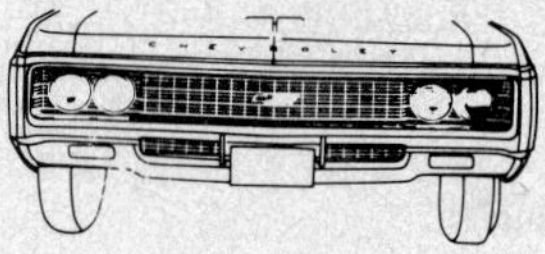

1969

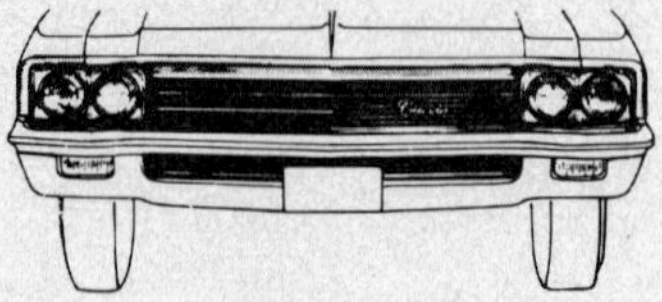

1970

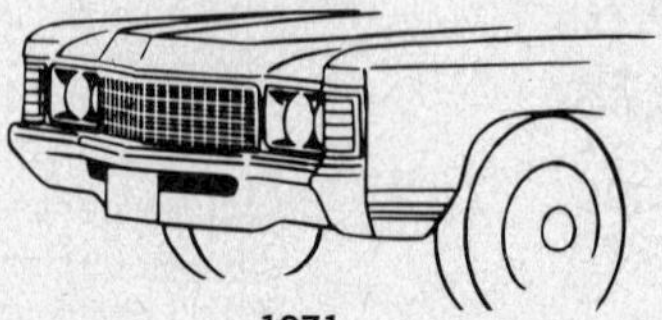

1971

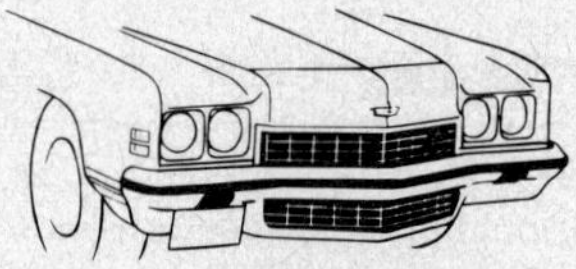

1972 Caprice

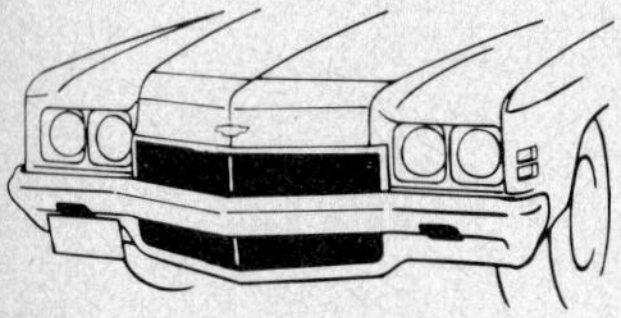

1972 Impala

1973 Impala

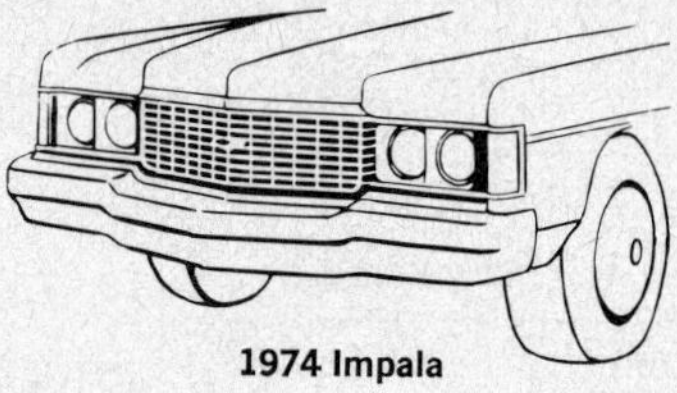

1974 Impala

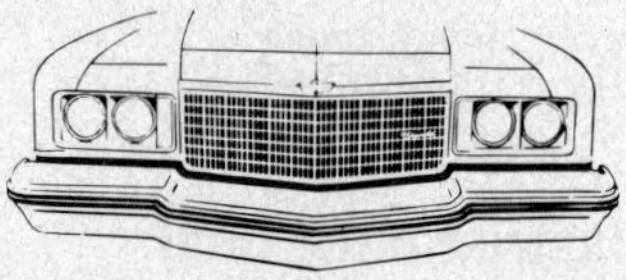

1974 Caprice

CORVETTE:

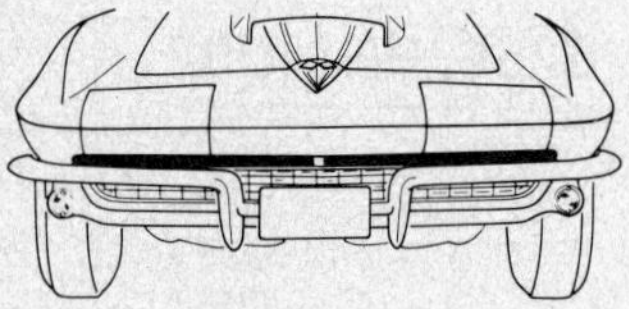

1967

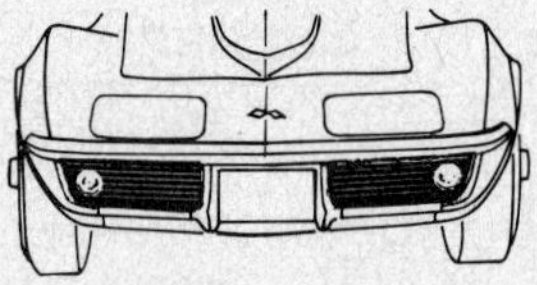

1968-69

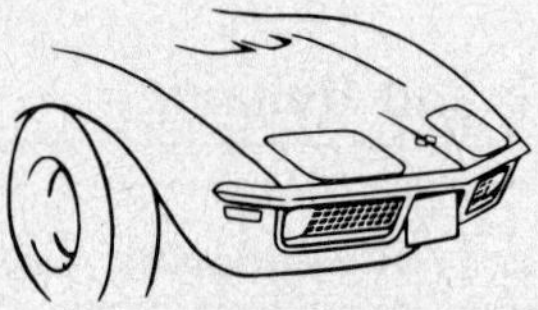

1972

1973

1974 Corvette

FIRING ORDER

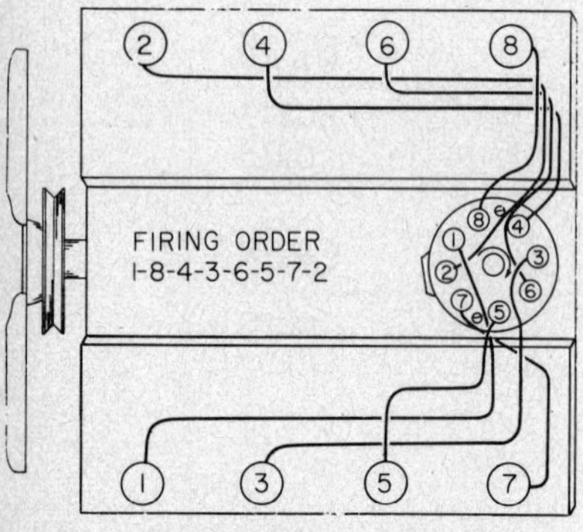
2
4
6
8
FIRING ORDER
1-8-4-3-6-5-7-2
1
3
5
7

1967-74 283, 327, 350, 307, 396, 400, 427, 454 cu. in. V8
(© Chevrolet Div., G.M. Corp)

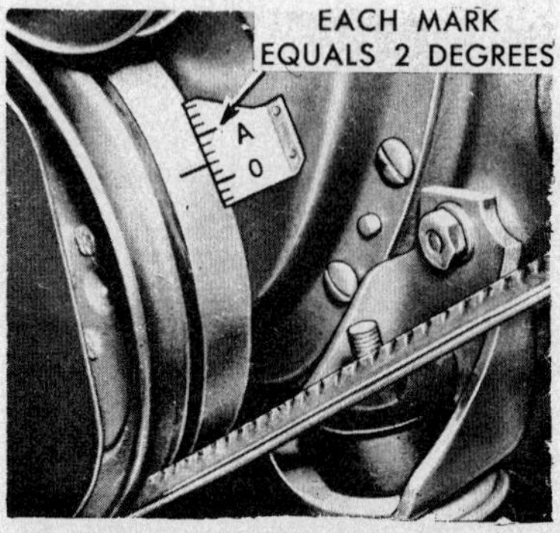
EACH MARK
EQUALS 2 DEGREES
A
0

Ignition timing marks V8 engine
(© Chevrolet Div., G.M. Corp)

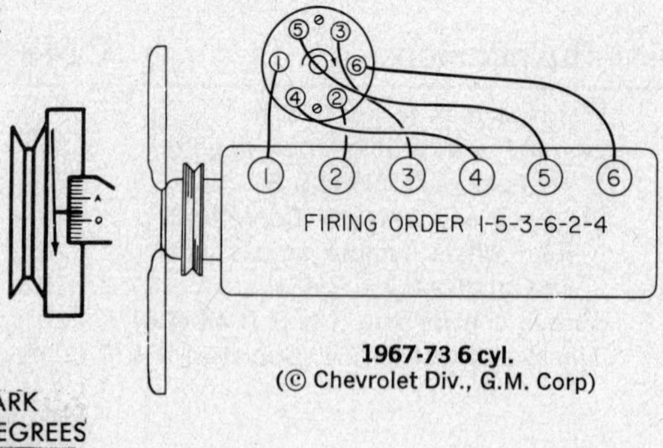
1
2
3
4
5
6
FIRING ORDER 1-5-3-6-2-4

1967-73 6 cyl.
(© Chevrolet Div., G.M. Corp)

CAR SERIAL NUMBER LOCATION

1967

Vehicle serial number is found on a plate attached to left front door hinge pillar.

1968-74

Vehicle serial number is found on a plate on the top left side of the instrument panel, visible through the windshield.

Car Serial Number Interpretation

A typical vehicle serial number tag yields manufacturer's identity, vehicle type, model year, assembly plant and production unit number when broken down as shown in the following chart.

Mfr. Identity[1]	*Body Style*[2]	*Model Year*[3]	*Assy. Plant*[4]	*Unit No.*[5]
1	5645	8	F	100025

1. Manufacturer's identity number assigned to all Chevrolet built vehicles.
2. Model identification.
3. Last number of model year (1968).
4. F-Flint.
5. Unit numbering will start at 100,001 at all plants.

Engine Identification

Six Cylinder Engines

The production code letters immediately follow the engine serial number. The number is found on a pad at the front right-hand side of the cylinder block, just to the rear of the distributor.

V8 Engines

The production code letters immediately follow the engine serial number. The number is found on a pad at the front right-hand side of the cylinder block.

Chevrolet

ENGINE IDENTIFICATION

No. Cyls.	Cu. in. Displ.	Type	YEAR AND CODE 1967	1968	1969	1970	1971	1972	1973
6	250	PG, AC, w/ex. EM	GQ	CR	BO				
6	250	M.T.	FA	CA	BA	CCG, CCH,	CAA	CNJ	
						CCZ, CRF, CRG		CDL	CCL
6	250	M.T. California							CCM
6	250	PG, w/AIR							
6	250	HDC, M.T.	CJ						
6	250	HDC, M.T., AC	FF	CK					
6	250	M.T., AC	FL	CN	BG			CBH	
6	250	Taxi, Police, M.T.			BP	CCL	CAC	CBJ	
6	250	PG	FM	CQ			CAB	CBK	
6	250	PG, Taxi, Police			BJ, BL	CCM	CAD		
6	250	PG, AC	FR	CR	BO				
6	250	AC			BQ				
6	250	PG, w/ex. EM	GP	CQ					
6	250	T.H. 350, Police				CCK			
8	283	M.T.	GA						
8	283	PG	GF						
8	283	4 spd., w/ex. EM	GS						
8	283	PG, w/ex. EM	GT						
8	283	HDC	GU						
8	283	4 spd.	GC						
8	283	w/ex. EM	GK						
8	307	M.T.		DO					
8	307	4 spd. SS		DP					
8	307	HDC		DQ					
8	307	PG		DR					
8	327	M.T.	HA	HA	FA, FJ				
8	327	M.T., HP							
8	327	w/ex. EM	HB						
8	327	PG	HC	HC	FB, FK				
8	327	PG, HP							
8	327	PG, w/ex. EM	HF	HF					
8	327	T.H. 350	KL	HF	FC, FL				
8	327	HDC	KE						
8	327	T.H. 400			FH				
8	327	Police			FG				
8	327	M.T., Taxi			FY				
8	327	PG, Taxi			FZ				

Chevrolet

No. Cyls.	Cu. in. Displ.	Type	YEAR AND CODE 1967	1968	1969	1970	1971	1972	1973
8	327	T.H. 350, Taxi			GA				
8	327	T.H. 400, Taxi			GB				
8	350	PG			GE, HK				
8	350	T.H. 350, 2-BBL.			HD, HM				
8	350	PG, 2-BBL.			HF, HL				
8	350	M.T.			HG, HD	CND (250), CNQ (300)	CGA (245)		
8	350	T.H. 400			HH, IA			CKB	
8	350	2-BBL.			HI				
8	350	T.H. 400, 2-BBL.			HJ				
8	350	T.H. 350			HN, HY	CNR (300) CNV (250)			
8	350	M.T.			HP, HT			CSJ	
8	350	PG			HU	CNS (300), CNU (250)	CGB		
8	350	M.T., Taxi, 2-BBL.			IL				
8	350	PG, Taxi, 2-BBL.			IM				
8	350	T.H. 350, Taxi, 2-BBL.			IN		CGJ		
8	350	T.H., 2-BBL.							CKL
8	350	T.H., 2-BBL., California							CKK
8	350	T.H., 2-BBL., Wagon							CLU
8	350	T.H., 2-BBL., Wagon, Calif.							CLT
8	350	T.H. 400, Taxi, 2-BBL.			IP				
8	350	M.T., Taxi, Police			IQ, IR	CNP (250)	CJB, CJH		
8	350	PG, Taxi, Police			IS, IX	CNW (250)		CAR, CSH	
8	350	T.H. 350, Taxi			IT, IY	CNT (300), CNX (250)	CGJ		
8	350	T.H. 400, Taxi			IV, IZ				
8	350	M.T., Taxi			IW				
8	350	T.H., 4-BBL.							CKJ
8	350	T.H., 4-BBL., California							CKD
8	396	M.T.	IA	IA	JT				
8	396	w/ex. EM	IB						
8	396	M.T., w/ex. EM							
8	396	PG, w/ex. EM	IC						
8	396	M.T., SHP							
8	396	PG	IG	IG					
8	396	PG, Trans. Ign.							
8	396	T.H., w/ex. EM	IN						
8	396	T.H.	IV	IV					
8	396	T.H., Trans. Ign.							
8	396	M.T., 2-BBL.			JN				
8	396	T.H. 400, Police, 2-BBL.			JO				
8	396	2-BBL., Police			JP				
8	396	T.H. 400, 2-BBL.			JQ				
8	396	M.T., Police			JR				
8	400	M.T. (265 hp)				CGR			
8	400	T.H. 350				CLK (265)		CDL, CDM	
8	400	T.H.							CSA
8	400	T.H., California							CSD
8	400	T.H., Wagon							CSK
8	400	T.H., Wagon, California							CSM

Chevrolet

No. Cyls.	Cu. in. Displ.	Type	YEAR AND CODE 1967	1968	1969	1970	1971	1972	1973
8	402	T.H. 350 (Mk. IV)			CKR	CLP (300)			
8	402	M.T., Police (Mk. IV)			CKN	CLR (330)		CLR, CTB	
8	402	M.T.						CLB	
8	402	M.T., w/AIR, Police						CTJ	
8	427	M.T., HDC							
8	427	SHP							
8	427	T.H., w/ex. EM							
8	427	w/ex. EM	II						
8	427	M.T.	IH	IH	MA				
8	427	T.H.	IJ	IJ					
8	427	T.H., HP, w/ex. EM	IO						
8	427	SS Hyd.	IF						
8	427	HP			LA				
8	427	4-BBL.			LB				
8	427	T.H. 400, HP			LC				
8	427	M.T., SHP			LD				
8	427	T.H. 400, 4-BBL.			LE				
8	427	T.H., Police, HP			LF				
8	427	M.T., Police, HP			LG, LZ, MB				
8	427	M.T., HP			LH, MC				
8	427	T.H. 400			LI				
8	427	T.H. 400, Police, 4-BBL.			LJ				
8	427	M.T., Police, 4-BBL.			LK				
8	427	T.H. 400, SHP			LS				
8	427	M.T., Police			LY				
8	427	M.T., SHP			MD				
8	454	M.T.				CGV (345), CGU (390)	CPD (365)		
8	454	M.T., Police				CGS (345), CGT (390)	CPG (365)		
8	454	T.H.						CPD	
8	454	T.H., Police						CPG	
8	454	T.H., w/AIR						CRW	
8	454	T.H., Police, w/AIR						CRY	
8	454	T.H.							CWL
8	454	T.H., California							CWD

AC—Air conditioned
HDC—Heavy duty clutch
HP—High performance
SHP—Special high performance
M.T.—Manual transmission
PG—Powerglide transmission
T.H.—Turbo-Hydramatic transmission
w/ex. EM—With exhaust emission controls
Trans. Ign.—Transistorized ignition
TD—Torque Drive
MT—Manual Transmission

Corvette

ENGINE IDENTIFICATION

No. Cyls.	Cu. in. Displ.	Type	YEAR AND CODE 1967	1968	1969	1970	1971	1972	1973
8	327	SHP, w/ex. EM	HD						
8	327		HE						
8	327	T.H.	HO						
8	327	SHP, T.H.	HT						
8	327	PS, AC							
8	327	SHP							

C210

Corvette

No. Cyls.	Cu. in. Displ.	Type	YEAR AND CODE 1967	1968	1969	1970	1971	1972	1973
8	327	4 Speed	HT						
8	350	HP			HW	CTN			
8	350	HP, AC			HX	CTO			
8	350	M.T.			HY	CTL			
8	350	T.H. 400			HZ	CTM			
8	350	HP, T. Ign.				CTP			
8	350	HP, T. Ign., AC				CTQ			
8	350	SHP				CTR			
8	350	SHP, T. Ign.				CTU			
8	350	SHP, T. Ign., M.T.				CTV			
8	350	M.T. (270 hp)					CGS		
8	350	M.T. (330 hp)					CGZ		
8	350	M.T. (200 hp)						CKW	
8	350	M.T., w/ex. EM (200 hp)						CDH	
8	350	T.H. (200 hp)						CKX	
8	350	T.H., w/ex. EM (200 hp)						CDJ	
8	350	M.T. (255 hp)						CKY	
8	350	HDMT (255 hp)						CKZ	
8	350	M.T., w/AIR (255 hp)						CRT	
8	350	T.H., w/AIR (255 hp)						CRS	
8	350	Hyd. 400 (270 hp)					CGT		
8	350	4-Spd. (330 hp)					CGY		
8	350	M.T. (190 hp)							CKZ
8	350	M.T., California (190 hp)							CLB
8	350	T.H. (190 hp)							CLA
8	350	T.H., California (190 hp)							CLC
8	350	M.T. (250 hp)							CLR
8	350	M.T., California (250 hp)							CLS
8	350	T.H. (250 hp)							CLD
8	350	T.H., California (250 hp)							CLH
8	427	SHP							
8	427	HP (390 hp), T.H.	IL	IL	LL, LM				
8	427	w/ex. EM (390 hp)	IM						
8	427	SHP		IT	LO				
8	427	(390 hp), T.H.	IQ	IQ					
8	427	PG, w/ex. EM (390 hp)	IR						
8	427	SHP (435 hp)	IT	IR	LR				
8	427	Aluminum Heads (435 hp)	IU	IU	LP				
8	427	4 Speed w/ex. EM (435 hp)	JA						
8	427	4 Speed (400 hp)	JC						
8	427	PG or T.H. (400 hp)	JD	IO					
8	427	4 Speed (435 hp)	JE						
8	427	4 Speed, w/ex. EM (400 hp)	JF	IM					
8	427	PG w/ex. EM (400 hp)	JG						
8	427	Aluminum Heads w/ex. EM (435 hp)	JH						
8	427	HP, T.H. 400, 3-2-BBL.			LN				
8	427	HP, 3-2-BBL.			LQ				
8	427	SHP, HDC, 3-2-BBL.			LT				
8	427	Aluminum Heads, HDC			LU				
8	427	Aluminum Heads, T.H. 400			LW				
8	427	T.H. 400 (heavy duty)			LV				

Corvette

No. Cyls.	Cu. in. Displ.	Type	1967	1968	1969	1970	1971	1972	1973
			YEAR AND CODE						
8	427	SHP, T.H .400			LX				
8	454	HP, 4-BBL., T.H. 400				CGW			
8	454	HP, 4-BBL.				CZU			
8	454	Heavy duty, 4-BBL.				CZL			
8	454	T.H. 400, 4-BBL.				CZN			
8	454	HP, 4-BBL., T. Ign.				CRI			
8	454	T.H. 400 (365 hp)					CPJ		
8	454	M.T. (365 hp)					CPH		
8	454	M.T. (425 hp)					CPW		
8	454	T.H. 400 (425 hp)					CPX		
8	454	M.T. (270 hp)						CPH	
8	454	T.H. (270 hp)						CPJ	
8	454	w/AIR (270 hp)						CSR	
8	454	w/AIR (270 hp)						CSS	
8	454	M.T.							CWM
8	454	M.T., California							CWT
8	454	T.H.							CWR
8	454	T.H., California							CWS

AC—Air conditioned
HP—High performance
SHP—Special high performance
M.T.—Manual transmission
PG—Powerglide Transmission
HDC—Heavy duty clutch
PS—Power steering
w/ex. EM—With exhaust emission
w/F.I.—With fuel injection
T. Ign.—With transistor ignition
4-BBL.—Four barrel carburetor
T.H.—With Turbo-Hydramatic
HDMT—Heavy duty 4-speed
w/AIR—With Air Injection Reactor

Chevrolet, Corvette

GENERAL ENGINE SPECIFICATIONS

Year	Engine Cu. In. Displacement	Carburetor Type	Advertised Horsepower @ rpm ■	Advertised Torque @ rpm (ft lbs) ■	Bore and Stroke (in.)	Advertised Compression Ratio	Oil Pressure @ 2050 rpm
'67	6-250	1 bbl	155 @4200	235 @ 1600	3.875 x 3.530	8.5:1	38 @ 1500
	8-283	2 bbl	195 @ 4800	285 @ 2800	3.875 x 3.000	9.25:1	38 @ 1500
	8-327	4 bbl	275 @ 4800	355 @ 3200	4.000 x 3.250	10.25:1	38 @ 1500
	8-327	4 bbl	300 @ 5000	360 @ 4000	4.000 x 3.250	10.25:1	38 @ 1500
	8-327	4 bbl	350 @ 5800	360 @ 3600	4.000 x 3.250	11.0:1	38 @ 1500
	8-396	4 bbl	325 @ 4800	410 @3200	4.094 x 3.760	10.25:1	62 @ 2000
	8-427	4 bbl	385 @ 5200	460 @ 3600	4.251 x 3.760	10.25:1	62 @ 2000
	8-427	4 bbl	390 @ 5400	460 @ 3600	4.251 x 3.760	10.25:1	62 @ 2000
	8-427	3 x 2 bbl	400 @ 5400	460 @ 3600	4.251 x 3.760	10.25:1	62 @ 2000
	8-427	4 bbl	430 @ 5200	450 @ 4400	4.251 x 3.760	12.5:1	62 @ 2000
	8-427	3 x 2 bbl	435 @ 5800	460 @ 4000	4.251 x 3.760	11.0:1	62 @ 2000
'68	6-250	1 bbl	155 @ 4200	235 @ 1600	3.875 x 3.530	8.5:1	58 @ 2000
	8-307	2 bbl	200 @ 4600	300 @ 2400	3.875 x 3.250	9.0:1	58 @ 2000
	8-327	4 bbl	250 @ 4800	335 @ 3200	4.001 x 3.250	8.75:1	58 @ 2000
	8-327	4 bbl	275 @ 4800	355 @ 3200	4.001 x 3.250	10.00:1	58 @ 2000
	8-327	4 bbl	300 @ 5000	360 @ 3400	4.000 x 3.250	10.00:1	38 @ 1500
	8-327	4 bbl	350 @ 5800	360 @ 3600	4.000 x 3.250	11.0:1	38 @ 1500
	8-396	4 bbl	325 @ 4800	410 @ 3200	4.094 x 3.760	10.25:1	62 @ 2000
	8-427	4 bbl	385 @ 5200	460 @ 3400	4.251 x 3.760	10.25:1	62 @ 2000
	8-427	4 bbl	390 @ 5400	460 @ 3600	4.250 x 3.760	10.25:1	62 @ 2000
	8-427	3 x 2 bbl	400 @ 5400	460 @ 3600	4.250 x 3.760	10.25:1	62 @ 2000
	8-427	3 x 2 bbl	435 @ 5800	460 @ 4000	4.250 x 3.760	11.0:1	62 @ 2000
'69	6-250	1 bbl	155 @ 4200	235 @ 1600	3.875 x 3.530	8.5:1	58 @ 2000
	8-327	2 bbl	235 @ 4800	325 @ 2800	3.875 x 3.530	9.0:1	58 @ 2000

Year	Engine Cu. In. Displacement	Carburetor Type	Advertised Horsepower @ rpm ■	Advertised Torque @ rpm (ft lbs) ■	Bore and Stroke (in.)	Advertised Compression Ratio	Oil Pressure @ 2050 rpm
'69	8-350	4 bbl	255 @ 4800	365 @ 3200	4.000 x 3.480	9.0:1	58 @ 2000
	8-350	4 bbl	300 @ 4800	380 @ 3200	4.000 x 3.480	10.25:1	58 @ 2000
	8-350	4 bbl	350 @ 5600	380 @ 3600	4.000 x 3.480	11.0:1	58 @ 2000
	8-396	2 bbl	265 @ 4800	400 @ 2800	4.094 x 3.760	9.0:1	62 @ 2000
	8-427	4 bbl	335 @ 4800	460 @ 3200	4.251 x 3.760	10.25:1	62 @ 2000
	8-427	4 bbl	390 @ 4800	460 @ 3600	4.251 x 3.760	10.25:1	62 @ 2000
	8-427	3 x 2 bbl	400 @ 5400	460 @ 3600	4.251 x 3.760	10.25:1	62 @ 2000
	8-427	3 x 2 bbl	435 @ 5800	460 @ 4000	4.251 x 3.760	11.0:1	62 @ 2000
'70	6-250	1 bbl	155 @ 4200	235 @ 1600	3.875 x 3.530	8.5:1	58 @ 2000
	8-350	2 bbl	250 @ 4800	345 @ 2800	4.000 x 3.480	9.0:1	58 @ 2000
	8-350	4 bbl	300 @ 4800	380 @ 3200	4.000 x 3.480	10.25:1	58 @ 2000①
	8-350	4 bbl	350 @ 5600	380 @ 3600	4.000 x 3.480	11.0:1	40 @ 2000
	8-350	4 bbl	370 @ 6000	380 @ 4000	4.000 x 3.480	11.0:1	40 @ 2000
	8-400	2 bbl	265 @ 4400	400 @ 2400	4.125 x 3.750	9.0:1	58 @ 2000
	8-454	4 bbl	345 @ 4400	500 @ 3000	4.251 x 4.000	10.25:1	62 @ 2000
	8-454	4 bbl	390 @ 4800	500 @ 3400	4.251 x 4.000	10.25:1	62 @ 2000①
	8-454	4 bbl	460 @ 5600	490 @ 3600	4.251 x 4.000	11.25:1	62 @ 2000①
'71	6-250	1 bbl	145 @ 4200	230 @ 1600	3.875 x 3.530	8.5:1	40 @ 2000
	8-350	2 bbl	245 @ 4800	350 @ 2800	4.000 x 3.480	8.5:1	40 @ 2000
	8-350	4 bbl	270 @ 4800	360 @ 3200	4.000 x 3.480	8.5:1	40 @ 2000
	8-350	4 bbl	330 @ 5600	360 @ 4000	4.000 x 3.480	9.0:1	40 @ 2000
	8-400	2 bbl	255 @ 4400	390 @ 2400	4.125 x 3.750	8.5:1	40 @ 2000
	8-400 (402 Cu. In.)	4 bbl	300 @ 4800	400 @ 3200	4.126 x 3.760	8.5:1	40 @ 2000
	8-454	4 bbl	365 @ 4800	465 @ 4000	4.251 x 4.000	8.5:1	40 @ 2000
	8-454	4 bbl	425 @ 5600	475 @ 4000	4.251 x 4.000	9.0:1	40 @ 2000
'72	6-250	1 bbl	110 @ 3800	185 @ 1600	3.875 x 3.530	8.5:1	40 @ 2000
	8-350	2 bbl	165 @ 4000	280 @ 2400	4.000 x 3.480	8.5:1	40 @ 2000
	8-350	4 bbl	200 @ 4400	300 @ 2800	4.000 x 3.480	8.5:1	40 @ 2000
	8-350	4 bbl	255 @ 5600	280 @ 4000	4.000 x 3.480	9.0:1	40 @ 2000
	8-400	2 bbl	170 @ 3400	325 @ 2000	4.126 x 3.750	8.5:1	40 @2000
	8-402	4 bbl	210 @ 4400	320 @ 2400	4.126 x 3.760	8.5:1	40 @ 2000
	8-454	4 bbl	270 @ 4000	390 @ 3200	4.251 x 4.000	8.5:1	40 @ 2000
'73	6-250	1 bbl	100 @ 3600	175 @ 1600	3.875 x 3.530	8.25:1	40 @ 2000
	8-350	2 bbl	145 @ 4000	255 @ 2400	4.000 x 3.480	8.5:1	40 @ 2000
	8-350	4 bbl	175 @ 4000	260 @ 2800	4.000 x 3.480	8.5:1	40 @ 2000
	8-350	4 bbl	190 @ 4400	270 @ 2800	4.000 x 3.480	8.5:1	40 @ 2000
	8-350	4 bbl	250 @ 5200	285 @ 4000	4.000 x 3.480	9.0:1	40 @ 2000
	8-400	2 bbl	150 @ 3200	295 @ 2000	4.126 x 3.750	8.5:1	40 @ 2000
	8-454	4 bbl	245 @ 4000②	375 @ 2800③	4.251 x 4.000	8.25:1	40 @ 2000
	8-454	4 bbl	275 @ 4400	395 @ 2800	4.251 x 4.000	8.25:1	40 @ 2000
'74	8-350	2 bbl	145 @ 3600	250 @ 2200	4.000 x 3.480	8.5:1	40 @ 2000
	8-350	4 bbl	160 @ 3800	245 @ 2400	4.000 x 3.480	8.5:1	40 @ 2000
	8-350	4 bbl	195 @ 4400	275 @ 2800	4.000 x 3.480	8.5:1	40 @ 2000
	8-350	4 bbl	250 @ 5200	285 @ 4000	4.000 x 3.480	9.0:1	40 @ 2000
	8-400	2 bbl	150 @ 3200	295 @ 2000	4.126 x 3.750	8.5:1	40 @ 2000
	8-400	4 bbl	180 @ 3800	290 @ 2400	4.126 x 3.750	8.5:1	40 @ 2000
	8-454	4 bbl	235 @ 4000	360 @ 2800	4.251 x 4.000	8.25:1	44 @ 2000
	8-454	4 bbi	270 @ 4400	380 @ 2800	4.251 x 4.000	8.25:1	40 @ 2000

■ Beginning 1972, horsepower and torque are SAE net figures. They are measured at the rear of the transmission with all accessories installed and operating. Since the figures vary when a given engine is installed in different models, some are representative rather than exact.

① For Corvettes, oil pressure is 40 psi at 2000 rpm
② 215 in wagon
③ 345 in wagon

Chevrolet

TUNE-UP SPECIFICATIONS

When analyzing compression test results, look for uniformity among cylinders rather than specific pressures.

	ENGINE		SPARK PLUGS		DISTRIBUTOR		IGNITION TIMING (deg) ▲		VALVES	Fuel	IDLE SPEED (rpm) ▲	
Year	No. Cyl Displacement (cu in.)	hp	Type §	Gap (in.)	Point Dwell (deg)	Point Gap (in.)	Man Trans	Auto Trans ●	Intake Opens ■ (deg) ●	Pump Pressure (psi)	Man Trans	Auto Trans
'67	6-250	155	46N	.035	31-34	.019	4B	4B	62	3½-4½	500②	500②
	6-250①	155	46N	.035	31-34	.019	4B	4B	62	3½-4½	700	500
	8-283	195	45	.035	28-32	.019	4B	4B	38	5-6½	500②	500②
	8-283①	195	45	.035	28-32	.019	TDC	4B	38	5-6½	700	600
	8-327	275	44	.035	28-32	.019	8B	8B	36	5¼-6½	500②	500②
	8-327①	275	44	.035	28-32	.019	6B	6B	36	5½-6½	700	600
	8-396	325	43N	.035	28-32	.019	10B	—	40	5-6½	700②	—
	8-396①	325	43N	.035	28-32	.019	10B	—	40	5-6½	750②	—
	8-427	385	43N	.035	28-32	.019	4B	4B	56	5-6½	550②	550②
	8-427①	385	43N	.035	28-32	.019	4B	4B	56	5-6½	700②	550②
'68	6-250	155	46N	.035	31-34	.019	TDC	4B	16	3½-4½	700②	600②/ 400③
	8-307	200	45S	.035	28-32	.019	2B	2B	28	5-6½	700	600
	8-327	250	44S	.035	28-32	.019	4B	4B	28	5-6½	700②	600
	8-327	275	44	.035	28-32	.019	TDC	4B	28	5-6½	700②	600②
	8-396	325	43N	.035	28-32	.019	4B	4B	28	5-6½	700	600
	8-427	385	43N	.035	28-32	.019	4B	4B	40	7-8½	700	600
'69	6-250	155	R46N	.035	31-34	.019	TDC	4B	16	4-5	700	550/400③
	8-327	235	R45S	.035	29-31	.019	2A	2B	28	7½-9	700	600
	8-350	255	R44S	.035	29-31	.019	TDC	4B	28	7½-9	700	600
	8-350	300	R44S	.035	29-31	.019	TDC	4B	28	7½-9	700	600
	8-396	265	R44N	.035	29-31	.019	TDC	4B	28	7½-9	700	600
	8-427	335	R44N	.035	29-31	.019	4B	4B	28	7½-9	700	600
	8-427	390	R43N	.035	29-31	.019	4B	4B	56	7½-9	800②	600②
'70	6-250	155	R46T	.035	31-34	.019	TDC	4B	16	4-5	750/400③	600/400②
	8-350	250	R44	.035	29-31	.019	TDC	4B	28	7½-9	700/450③	600/450③
	8-350	300	R44	.035	29-31	.019	TDC	4B	28	7½-9	700	600
	8-400	265	R44	.035	29-31	.019	4B	8B	28	7½-9	700	600/450②
	8-454	345	R44T	.035	28-30	.019	6B	6B	30	7½-9	700	600
	8-454	390	R43T	.035	28-30	.019	6B	6B	56	7½-9	700	600

TUNE-UP SPECIFICATIONS

When analyzing compression test results, look for uniformity among cylinders rather than specific pressures.

Year	ENGINE No. Cyl Displacement (cu in.)	ENGINE hp	SPARK PLUGS Type §	SPARK PLUGS Gap (in.)	DISTRIBUTOR Point Dwell (deg)	DISTRIBUTOR Point Gap (in.)	IGNITION TIMING (deg) ▲ Man Trans	IGNITION TIMING (deg) ▲ Auto Trans ●	VALVES Intake Opens ■ (deg) ●	Fuel Pump Pressure (psi)	IDLE SPEED (rpm) ▲ Man Trans	IDLE SPEED (rpm) ▲ Auto Trans
'71	6-250	145	R46TS	.035	31-34	.019	4B	4B	16	4-5	550	500②
	8-350	245	R44TS	.035	29-31	.019	2B	6B	28	7½-9	600	550②
	8-350	270	R44TS	.035	29-31	.019	4B	8B	28	7½-9	600	550②
	8-400	255	R44TS	.035	29-31	.019	4B	8B	28	7½-9	600	550②
	8-402	300	R44TS	.035	29-31	.019	8B	8B	28	7½-9	600	600②
	8-454	365	R43TS	.035	28-30	.019	8B	8B	56	7½-9	600	600
'72	6-250	110	R46T	.035	31-34	.019	4B	4B	16	4-5	700	600
	8-350	165	R44T	.035	29-31	.019	6B	6B	28(44)	7½-9	900	600
	8-400	170	R44T	.035	29-31	.019	2B	6B	28(44)	7½-9	900	600
	8-402	210	R44T	.035	29-31	.019	8B	8B	30(44)	7½-9	750	600
	8-454	270	R44T	.035	29-31	.019	8B	8B	56	7½-9	750	600
'73	6-250	100	R46T	.035	31-34	.019	6B	—	16	3½-4½	700/450③	—
	8-350	145	R44T	.035	29-31	.019	—	8B	28	7½-9	—	600/450③
	8-350	175	R44T	.035	29-31	.019	—	12B	28	7½-9	—	600/450③
	8-400	140	R44T	.035	29-31	.019	—	8B	28	7½-9	—	600/450③
	8-454	245⑤	R44T	.035	29-31	.019	—	10B	55	7½-9	—	600/450③
'74	8-350	145	R44T	.035	29-31	.019	—	8B	28(44)	7½-9	—	600
	8-350	160	R44T	.035	29-31	.019	—	12B(8B)	28(44)	7½-9	—	600
	8-400	150	R44T	.035	29-31	.019	—	8B	28(44)	7½-9	—	600
	8-400	180	R44T	.035	29-31	.019	—	8B	28(44)	7½-9	—	600
	8-454	235	R44T	.035	29-31	.019	—	10B	55	7½-9	—	600

▲ See text for procedure
● Figure in parentheses indicates California engine
■ All figures Before Top Dead Center
§ All spark plug listings are A.C. original equipment numbers
① Equipped with Air Injection Reactor System
② A/C on
③ Lower figure with Idle Solenoid disconnected
④ Adjust mechanical valve lifter clearance to .020 inches for intake with engine hot and to .024 inches for exhaust with engine hot.
⑤ 215 in wagons
A After Top Dead Center
B Before Top Dead Center
TDC Top Dead Center
— Not applicable

Corvette

TUNE-UP SPECIFICATIONS

When analyzing compression test results, look for uniformity among cylinders rather than specific pressures.

Year	ENGINE No. Cyl Displacement (cu in.)	ENGINE hp	SPARK PLUGS Type §	SPARK PLUGS Gap (in.)	DISTRIBUTOR Point Dwell (deg)	DISTRIBUTOR Point Gap (in.)	IGNITION TIMING (deg) ▲ Man Trans ●	IGNITION TIMING (deg) ▲ Auto Trans	VALVES Intake Opens ■ (deg) ●	Fuel Pump Pressure (psi)	IDLE SPEED (rpm) ▲ Man Trans	IDLE SPEED (rpm) ▲ Auto Trans
'67	8-327	300	44	.035	28-32	.019	6B	6B	32½	5¼-6½	500②	500②
	8-327①	300	44	.035	28-32	.019	6B	4A	32½	5¼-6½	700	600
	8-327	350	44	.035	28-32	.019	10B	—	54	5-6½	700②	—
	8-327①	350	44	.035	28-32	.019	10B	—	54	5-6½	750②	—
	8-427	390	43N	.035	28-32	.019	4B	4B	56	5½-7	550②	550②
	8-427①	390	43N	.035	28-32	.019	4B	4B	56	5½-7	700②	550②
	8-427	435	43N	.035	—	—	10B	—	54	5½-7	1000②	—
'68	8-327	300	44N	.035	28-32	.019	4B	4B	28	5-6½	700②	600
	8-327	350	44	.035	28-32	.019	4B	—	40	5-6½	750②	—
	8-427	390	43N	.035	28-32	.019	4B	4B	40	5-8½	700	600
	8-427	400	43N	.035	28-32	.019	4B	4B	40	5-8½	750	600
	8-427	430	C43XL	.035	28-32	.019	12R	—	54	5-8½	1000	—
	8-427	435	43N	.035	28-32	.019	4B	—	44	5-8½	750	—
'69	8-350	300	R44S	.035	28-32	.019	TDC	4B	28	7½-9	700	600
	8-350	350	R44	.035	28-32	.019	4B	—	52	7½-9	750	—
	8-427	390	43N	.035	28-32	.019	4B	4B	56	7½-9	800②	600②
	8-427	400	43N	.035	28-32	.019	4B	4B	56	7½-9	800②	600②
	8-427	435	43N	.035	28-32	.019	4B	4B	44	7½-9	750	750/400
'70	8-350	300	R44	.035	29-31	.019	4B	4B	28	7½-9	700	600
	8-350	350	R44	.035	29-31	.019	4B	—	52	7½-9	750	—
	8-350	370	R43T	.035	—	—	8B	12B	42½	7½-9	700	—
	8-454	390	R43T	.035	28-30	.019	6B	6B	56	7½-9	800	600
	8-454	460	R43XL	.035	—	—	4B	4B	62	7½-9	750	600
'71	8-350	270	R44TS	.035	29-31	.019	8B	8B	28	7½-9	600	550
	8-350	330	R43TS	.035	—	—	8B	12B	42½	7½-9	700	700
	8-454	365	R43TS	.035	28-30	.019	8B	8B	56	7½-9	600	600
	8-454	425	R44TS	.035	—	—	8B	12B	44	7½-9	700	700
'72	8-350	200	R44T	.035	29-31	.019	8B	8B	28(44)	7½-9	800	600
	8-350	255	R44T	.035	29-31	.019	4B	8B	42½	7½-9	900	700
	8-454	270	R44T	.035	29-31	.019	8B	8B	56	7½-9	800	600
'73	8-350	190	R44T	.035	29-31	.019	12B	12B	28	7½-9	900/450③	600/450
	8-350	250	R44T	.035	29-31	.019	8B	8B	52	7½-9	900/450③	700/450
	8-454	275	R44T	.035	29-31	.019	10B	10B	55	7½-9	900/450③	600/450
'74	8-350	195	R44T	.035	29-31	.019	8B(4B)	8B	28(44)	7½-9	900	600
	8-350	250	R44T	.035	29-31	.019	8B	8B	52	7½-9	900	700
	8-454	270	R44T	.035	29-31	.019	10B	10B	55	7½-9	800	600

▲ See text for procedure
● Figure in parentheses indicates California engine
■ All figures Before Top Dead Center
§ All spark plug listings are A.C original equipment numbers
① Equipped with Air Injection Reactor System
② A/C on
③ Lower figure with Idle Solenoid disconnected
④ With A/C
⑤ Adjust solenoid screw with A/C on. Adjust idle screw with A/C off
A After Top Dead Center
B Before Top Dead Center
TDC Top Dead Center
— Not applicable

MECHANICAL VALVE LIFTER CLEARANCE

Year	Engine		Intake (Hot) In.	Exhaust (Hot) In.
1967-1968	V8-427	430 hp	.022	.024
1967-1969	V8-427	435 hp	.024	.028
1970	V8-350	370 hp	.024	.030
1970	V8-454	460 hp	.024	.028
1971	V8-350	330 hp	.024	.030
1971	V8-454	425 hp	.024	.028
1972	V8-350	255 hp	.024	.030

CAPACITIES

Year	ENGINE No. Cyl. (Cu. In.) Displacement	Engine Crankcase Add 1 Qt For New Filter	TRANSMISSION Pts To Refill After Draining Manual 3-Speed	Manual 4-Speed	Automatic ●	Drive Axle (pts)	Gasoline Tank (gals) ■	COOLING SYSTEM (qts) With Heater	With A/C
'67	6-250	4	3	—	6	3.5①	24	12	13
	8-283	4	3	3	6	3.5①	24	17	18
	8-327	4	3	3	6.5	4.0	24	15	16
	8-396	4	3③	3	6.5⑥	4.0	24	23	23
	8-427	4	3③	3	8	4.0	24	22	22
'68	6-250	4	3	3	6⑦	3.5	24	12	13
	8-307	4	3	3	6	3.5	24	17	18
	8-327	4	3	3	6.5⑥	3.5	24	15	16
	8-396	4	3③	3	6.5⑥	3.5	24	22	22
	8-427	4	3③	3	8	3.5	24	22	22
'69	6-250	4	3	3	6⑦	3.5①	24	12	12
	8-327	4	3	3	6.5⑥	3.5①	24	17	17
	8-350	4	3.5	3	6.5⑥	3.5①	24	15	16
	8-396	4	3.5	3	6.5⑥	3.5①	24	23	24
	8-427	4	3.5	3	8	3.5①	24	22	23
'70	6-250	4	3	—	6	3.5①	25	12	12
	8-350	4	3	—	6.5⑦	3.5①	25	16	16④
	8-400	4	—	—	5⑥	3.5①	25	16	17
	8-454	4	—	—	8	3.5①	25	22	22
'71	6-250	4	3	—	6	3.5①	24	12	—
	8-350	4	3	—	6.5⑦	3.5①	24	16	17
	8-400	4	3	—	5⑥	3.5①	24	16	17
	8-402	4	—	—	8	3.5①	24	23	24
	8-454	4	—	—	8	3.5①	24	22	23
'72	6-250	4	3	—	6	4.25⑤	23	12	—
	8-350	4	—	—	5	4.25⑤	23	16	17
	8-400	4	—	—	5	4.25⑤	23	16	17
	8-402	4	—	—	8	4.25⑤	23	23	24
	8-454	4	—	—	8	4.25⑤	23	22	23
'73	6-250	4	3	—	5	4.25⑤	26	12	12
	8-350	4	—	—	5	4.25⑤	26	16	17
	8-400	4	—	—	5	4.25⑤	26	16.5	17.5
	8-454	4	—	—	8	4.25⑤	26	23	24
'74	8-350	4	—	—	8	4.25⑤	26	16	16
	8-400	4	—	—	8⑧	4.25⑤	26	16	16
	8-454	4	—	—	9	4.25⑤	26	22	23

● Specifications do not include torque convertor
■ Station wagons: '67-69—24 gals, '70—22 gals, '71—23 gals, '72-'74—22 gals
① 4 pts with 8.875 diameter ring gear
② 425 hp 427—23 qts
③ 3.5 pts with heavy duty 3-speed
④ 17 qts with 300 hp engine
⑤ 4.9 pts with 8.875 ring gear
⑥ 8 pts with 3-speed Turbo Hydramatic 400
⑦ 5 pts with 3-speed Turbo Hydramatic 350
⑧ 9 with 400 4 bbl
— Not applicable

Corvette

CAPACITIES

Year	ENGINE No. Cyl. (Cu. In.) Displacement	Engine Crankcase Add 1 Qt For New Filter	TRANSMISSION Pts To Refill After Draining Manual 3-Speed	Manual 4-Speed	Automatic ●	Drive Axle (pts)	Gasoline Tank (gals)	COOLING SYSTEM (qts) With Heater	With A/C
'67	8-327	5	3	3	4.6	3.7	20	19	19
	8-427	5	—	3	4.6	3.7	20	22	22
'68	8-327	4	3	3	—	3.7	20	15	15
	8-427	5	3	3	8	3.7	20	22	22
'69	8-350	4	3	3	8	4	20	15	15
	8-427	5	—	3	8	4	20	22	22
'70	8-350	4	—	3	8	4	20	15①	18
	8-454	5	—	3	8	4	20	22	22
'71	8-350	4	—	3	8	4	18	15②	18
	8-454	5	—	3	8	4	18	22	22
'72	8-350	4	—	3	8	4	18	15②	18
	8-454	5	—	3	8	4	18	22	24
'73	8-350	4	—	3	8	4	18	18	18
	8-454	5	—	3	8	4	18	24	24
'74	8-350	4	—	3	8	4	18	17	17
	8-454	5	—	3	8	4	18	22	23

● Specifications do not include torque converter
① 18 qts with 370 hp
② 18 qts with 330 hp
— Not applicable

VALVE SPECIFICATIONS

Year	Engine No. Cyl. Displacement (cu in.)	Seat Angle (deg)	Face Angle (deg)	Spring Test Pressure (lbs @ in.)	Spring Installed Height (in.)	STEM TO GUIDE Clearance (in.) Intake	Exhaust	STEM Diameter (in.) Intake	Exhaust
'67	6-250	46②	45	60 @ 1.66	1 21/32	.0010-.0037	.0010-.0047	.3414	.3414
	8-283	46②	45	80 @ 1.70	1 5/32	.0010-.0037	.0010-.0047	.3414	.3414
	8-327	46②	45	80 @ 1.70	1 5/32	.0010-.0037	.0010-.0047	.3414	.3414
	8-396	46②	45	100 @ 1.88	1 7/8	.0010-.0037	.0010-.0047	.3718	.3718
	8-427	46②	45	100 @ 1.88	1 7/8	.0010-.0037	.0010-.0047	.3718	.3718
	8-427③	46②	45	75 @ 1.88④	1 7/8	.0010-.0037	.0010-.0047	.3718	.3718
'68	6-250	46②	45	60 @ 1.66	1 21/32	.0010-.0037	.0010-.0047	.3414	.3414
	8-307	46②	45	80 @ 1.70	1 5/32	.0010-.0037	.0010-.0047	.3414	.3414
	8-327	46②	45	80 @ 1.70	1 5/32	.0010-.0037	.0010-.0047	.3414	.3414
	8-396	46②	45	90 @ 1.88	1 7/8	.0010-.0037	.0015-.0052	.3719	.3717
	8-396⑤	46②	45	100 @ 1.88	1 7/8	.0010-.0037	.0015-.0052	.3719	.3717
	8-427	46②	45	100 @ 1.88	1 7/8	.0010-.0037	.0015-.0052	.3719	.3717
	8-427③	46②	45	75 @ 1.88	1 7/8	.0010-.0037	.0015-.0052	.3719	.3717
'69	6-250	46②	45	60 @ 1.66	1 21/32	.0010-.0037	.0010-.0047	.3414	.3414
	8-327	46②	45	80 @ 1.70	1 5/32	.0010-.0037	.0010-.0047	.3414	.3414
	8-350	46②	45	80 @ 1.70	1 5/32	.0010-.0037	.0010-.0047	.3414	.3414
	8-396	46②	45	90 @ 1.88	1 7/8	.0010-.0037	.0010-.0037	.3719	.3719
	8-427	46②	45	90 @ 1.88	1 7/8	.0010-.0037	.0010-.0037	.3719	.3719
	8-427③	46②	45	75 @ 1.88④	1 7/8	.0010-.0037	.0010-.0037	.3719	.3719
'70	6-250	46	45	60 @ 1.66	1 21/32	.0010-.0037	.0010-.0047	.3414	.3414
	8-350	46	45	80 @ 1.70	1 23/32	.0010-.0037	.0010-.0047	.3414	.3414
	8-400	46	45	80 @ 1.70	1 7/8	.0010-.0037	.0010-.0047	.3414	.3414
	8-454	46	45	75 @ 1.88⑥	1 7/8	.0010-.0037	.0010-.0047	.3718	.3718
	8-454⑦	46	45	75 @ 1.88⑧	1 7/8	.0010-.0037	.0010-.0047	.3718	.3718

Year	Engine No. Cyl. Displacement (cu in.)	Seat Angle (deg)	Face Angle (deg)	Spring Test Pressure (lbs @ in.)	Spring Installed Height (in.)	STEM TO GUIDE Clearance (in.)		STEM Diameter (in.)	
						Intake	Exhaust	Intake	Exhaust
'71	6-250	46	45	60 @ 1.66	1 21/32	.0010-.0037	.0010-.0047	.3414	.3714
	8-350	46	45	80 @ 1.70	1 23/32	.0010-.0037	.0010-.0047	.3414	.3714
	8-400	46	45	80 @ 1.70	1 23/32	.0010-.0037	.0010-.0047	.3414	.3714
	8-400⑨	46	45	75 @ 1.88⑥	1 7/8	.0010-.0037	.0010-.0047	.3719	.3717
	8-454	46	45	75 @ 1.88⑥	1 7/8	.0010-.0037	.0010-.0047	.3719	.3717
'72	6-250	46	45	60 @ 1.66	1 21/32	.0010-.0037	.0010-.0047	.3414	.3414
	8-350	46	45	80 @ 1.70	1 23/32	.0010-.0037	.0010-.0047	.3414	.3414
	8-400	46	45	80 @ 1.70	1 23/32	.0010-.0037	.0010-.0047	.3414	.3414
	8-402	46	45	90 @ 1.88	1 7/8	.0010-.0037	.0010-.0047	.3719	.3717
	8-454	46	45	75 @ 1.88⑥	1 7/8	.0010-.0037	.0010-.0047	.3719	.3717
'73	6-250	46	45	60 @ 1.66	1 21/32	.0010-.0027	.0010-.0027	.3414	.3414
	8-350	46	45	80 @ 1.70	1 23/32	.0010-.0027	.0010-.0027	.3414	.3414
	8-400	46	45	80 @ 1.70	1 23/32	.0010-.0027	.0010-.0027	.3414	.3414
	8-454	46	45	80 @ 1.88	1 7/8	.0010-.0027	.0010-.0027	.3719	.3717
'74	8-350	46	45	80 @ 1.70	1 23/32	.0010-.0027	.0010-.0027	.3414	.3414
	8-400	46	45	80 @ 1.70	1 23/32	.0010-.0027	.0010-.0027	.3414	.3414
	8-454	46	45	80 @ 1.88	1 7/8	.0010-.0027	.0010-.0027	.3719	.3717

① 360 hp
② 45° on engines with aluminum heads
③ 430 hp
④ Inner spring 41 @ 1.78
⑤ 350 hp
⑥ Inner spring 30 @ 1.78
⑦ 460 hp
⑧ Inner spring 41 @ 1.78
⑨ 300 hp

CRANKSHAFT AND CONNECTING ROD SPECIFICATIONS

All measurements are given in in.

Year	Engine Displace. (cu in.)	CRANKSHAFT				CONNECTING ROD		
		Main Brg. Journal Dia	Main Brg. Oil Clearance	Shaft End-Play	Thrust on No.	Journal Diameter	Oil Clearance	Side Clearance
'67	6-250	2.2983-2.2993	.0003-.0029	.002-.006	7	1.9990-2.0000	.0007-.0027	.0085-.0135
	8-283	2.2987-2.2997④	.0003-.0029⑤	.003-.011	5	1.9990-2.0000	.0007-.0027	.009-.013
	8-327	2.2987-2.2997④	.0003-.0034⑤	.003-.011	5	1.9990-2.0000	.0007-.0028	.009-.013
	8-396	2.7487-2.7497①	.0004-.0020②	.006-.010	5	2.1990-2.2000	.0007-.0028	.015-.021
	8-427	2.7487-2.7497①	.0004-.0020②	.006-.010	5	2.1990-2.2000	.0007-.0028	.015-.021⑥
	8-427 (435 H.P.)	2.7487-2.7497①	.0004-.0020②	.006-.010	5	2.1990-2.2000	.0007-.0028	.019-.025
'68-'69	6-250	2.2983-2.2993	.0003-.0029	.002-.006	7	1.9990-2.0000	.0007-.0027	.009-.013
	8-307, 327	2.4484-2.4493⑦	.0008-.0020⑧	.003-.011	5	2.0990-2.1000	.0007-.0028	.009-.013
	8-350**	2.4484-2.4493⑦	.0008-.0020⑧	.003-.011	5	2.0990-2.1000	.0007-.0028	.009-.013
	8-396	2.7484-2.7493⑨	.0010-.0022⑩	.006-.010	5	2.1990-2.2000	.0009-.0025	.015-.021
	8-427	2.7481-2.7490⑪	.0013-.0025⑫	.006-.010	5	2.1990-2.2000	.0009-.0025	.015-.021
	8-427 (435 H.P.)	2.7481-2.7490⑪	.0013-.0025⑫	.006-.010	5	2.1985-2.1995	.0014-.0030	.019-.025
'70	6-250	2.2983-2.2993	.0003-.0029	.002-.006	7	1.9990-2.0000	.0007-.0027	.009-.014
	8-350	2.4484-2.4493⑬	.0003-.0015⑭	.002-.006	5	2.0990-2.1000	.0007-.0028	.008-.014
	8-400 (265 H.P.)	2.6509	.0008-.0020⑮	.002-.006	5	2.0990-2.1000	.0009-.0030	.008-.014
	8-454	2.7485-2.7494⑨	.0013-.0025⑯	.006-.010	5	2.1990-2.2000	.0009-.0025	.015-.021
	8-454 (460 H.P.)	2.7481-2.7490⑪	.0013-.0025⑰	.006-.010	5	2.1985-2.1995	.0014-.0030	.019-.025

Year	Engine Displace. (cu in.)	CRANKSHAFT				CONNECTING ROD		
		Main Brg. Journal Dia	Main Brg. Oil Clearance	Shaft End-Play	Thrust on No.	Journal Diameter	Oil Clearance	Side Clearance
'71	6-250	2.2983-2.2993	.0003-.0029	.002-.006	7	1.9990-2.0000	.0007-.0027	.009-.014
	8-350	2.4484-2.4493⑬	.0008-.0020⑮	.002-.006	5	2.0990-2.1000	.0013-.0035	.008-.014
	8-350 (330 H.P.)	2.4484-2.4493⑬	.0013-.0025⑲	.002-.006	5	2.0990-2.1000	.0013-.0035	.008-.014
	8-400 (255 H.P.)	2.6484-2.6493⑳	.0008-.0020⑮	.002-.006	5	2.0990-2.1000	.0013-.0035	.008-.014
	8-402 (300 H.P.) (Mk. IV)	2.7487-2.7496㉑	.0007-.0019㉒	.006-.010	5	2.1990-2.2000	.0009-.0025	.013-.023
	8-454 (365 H.P.)	2.7485-2.7494㉓	.0013-.0025⑯	.006-.010	5	2.1990-2.2000	.0009-.0025	.015-.021
	8-454 (425 H.P.)	2.7481-2.7490⑪	.0013-.0025⑰	.006-.010	5	2.1985-2.1995	.0009-.0025	.019-.025
'72	6-250	2.2983-2.2993	.0003-.0029	.002-.006	7	1.9990-2.0000	.0007-.0027	.009-.014
	8-350	2.4484-2.4493⑱	.0008-.0020⑮	.002-.006	5	2.0990-2.1000	.0013-.0035	.008-.014
	8-350 (255 H.P.)	2.4484-2.4493⑱	.0013-.0025⑲	.002-.006	5	2.0990-2.1000	.0013-.0035	.008-.014
	8-400 (170 H.P.)	2.6484-2.6493⑳	.0008-.0020⑮	.002-.006	5	2.0990-2.1000	.0013-.0035	.008-.014
	8-402 (210 H.P.)	2.7487-2.7496㉑	.0007-.0019㉒	.006-.010	5	2.1990-2.2000	.0009-.0025	.013-.023
	8-454 (270 H.P.)	2.7485-2.7494㉓	.0013-.0025⑯	.006-.010	5	2.1990-2.2000	.0009-.0025	.015-.021
'73-'74	6-250	2.3004	.0003-.0029	.002-.006	7	1.9990-2.0000	.0007-.0027	.007-.016
	8-350	2.4502㉔	.0008-.0020⑮	.002-.006	5	2.0990-2.1000	.0013-.0035	.008-.014
	8-350	2.4502㉔	.0013-.0025⑲	.002-.006	5	2.0990-2.1000	.0013-.0035	.008-.014
	8-400	2.6503㉕	.0008-.0020⑮	.002-.007	5	2.0990-2.1000	.0013-.0035	.008-.014
	8-454	2.7504 [26]	.0007-.0019㉒	.006-.010	5	2.1990-2.2000	.0009-.0025	.015-.021

① No.'s 3, 4—2.7482-2.7492; No. 5—2.7478-2.7488
② No.'s 3, 4—.0009-.0025; No. 5—.0013-.0029
③ No. 5—2.4977-2.4987
④ No. 1 (1967)—2.2984-2.2993; No.'s 2, 3, 4—2.2983-2.993; No. 5—2.2978-2.2988
⑤ No. 5—.0010-.0036
⑥ 427 cu in. (425 H.P.)—.019-.025
⑦ No. 5—2.4470-2.4488
⑧ No. 5—.0018-.0034
⑨ No.'s 3, 4—2.4781-2.7490; No. 5—2.7478-2.7488
⑩ No.'s 3, 4—.0013-.0025; No. 5—.0015-.0031
⑪ No. 5—2.7478-2.7488
⑫ No. 5—.0015-.0031
** Not available in 1968
⑬ No. 5—2.4479-2.4488
⑭ No.'s 2, 3, 4—.0006-.0018; No. 5—.0008-.0023
⑮ No.'s 2, 3, 4—.011-.0023; No. 5—.0017-.0033
⑯ No. 5—.0024-.0040
⑰ No. 5—.0029-.0045
⑱ No.'s 2, 3, 4—2.4481-2.4490; No. 5—2.4479-2.4488
⑲ No. 5—.0023-.0033; with auto. trans. No. 1—.0019-.0031
⑳ No. 5—2.6479-2.6488
㉑ No.'s 3, 4—2.7481-2.7490; No. 5—2.7473-2.7483
㉒ No.'s 2, 3, 4—.0013-.0025; No. 5—.0019-.0035
㉓ No.'s 2, 3, 4—2.7481-2.7490; No. 5—2.7478-2.7488
㉔ No. 5—2.4508
㉕ No. 5—2.6509
[26] No.'s 1, 5—2.7499

TORQUE SPECIFICATIONS

All readings in ft lbs

Year	Engine Displacement (cu in.)	Cylinder Head Bolts	Rod Bearing Bolts	Main Bearing Bolts	Crankshaft Pulley Bolt	Flywheel to Crankshaft Bolts	MANIFOLD	
							Intake	Exhaust
'67-'73	6	95	35	65	—	60	30⑧	25⑦
'67	8-283, 327	60-70	35	80	60⑥	60	30	20
'68-'73	8-302, 307, 350, 400	60-70	45	75②	60⑥	60	30	⑤
'67-'74	8-396, 402 (Big Block)	80①	50	105③	85⑥	65	30	30
	8-427, 454	80①	50④	105③	85	65	30	30

① Aluminum Heads—Short bolts 65, Long bolts 75
② Engines with 4-bolt mains—Outer bolts 65
③ 1967-68 2-bolt mains 95
1967 4-bolt mains 115
④ 7/16 Rod bolts—70
⑤ Center bolts—25-30, end bolts 15-20
⑥ Where applicable
⑦ Exhaust-to-intake
⑧ Manifold-to-head

RING GAP

All measurements given in in.

Year	Engine	Top Compression	Bottom Compression
'67-'74	6-250, 8-283	.010-.020	.010-.020
'67-'69	8-327	.013-.023①	.013-.025①
'69-'71	8-350 .	.010-.020②	.013-.025②
'67-'72	8-396, 400, 402 427, 454	.010-.020	.010-.020
	All except 8-350	.010-.020	.010-.020
'73-'74	8-350	.010-.020	.013-.025③

① 325, 350 hp 327 cu in. Top .010.-020
2nd .013-.023
② 250, 300 hp 350 cu in. Top .013-.023
2nd .013-.025
③ 250, 255 hp 350 cu in. .013-.023

Year	Engine	Oil Control
'67-'74	All engines except 8-396, 427	.015-.055
'67-'69	8-396, 427	.010-.030

RING SIDE CLEARANCE

Year	Engine	Top Compression	Bottom Compression
'67	6-250	.0020-.0035	.0020-.0040
'68-'73	6-250	.0012-.0027	.0012-.0032
'67	8-283	.0012-.0027	.0012-.0032
'67-'69	8-327	.0012-.0032①	.0012-.0027①
'69	8-350	.0012-.0032	.0012-.0027
'70-'74	8-350 2 bbl	.0012-.0032	.0012-.0032
'70-'74	8-350 4 bbl	.0012-.0032	.0012-.0027
'67	8-396	.0012-.0032	.0012-.0032
'68-'69	8-396	.0017-.0032	.0017-.0032
'70-'74	8-400	.0012-.0027②	.0012-.0032②
'67	8-427	.0012-.0032	.0012-.0032
'68-'69	8-427	.0017-.0032	.0017-.0032
'71-'72	8-402	.0017-.0032	.0017-.0032
'71-'74	8-454	.0017-.0032	.0017-.0032

① 250, 275 hp 327 cu in.
Top .0012-.0027
2nd .0012-.0032
② 330 hp 400 cu in.
Top .0017-.0032
2nd .0012-.0032
③ 330 hp 400 cu in.
.0005-.0065

Year	Engine	Oil Control
'67-'74	6-250, 8-283	
	327, 400	.000-.005③
'69-'74	8-350 2 bbl	.002-.007
'69-'74	8-350 4 bbl	.000-.005
'67	8-396	.0012-.0060
'68-'69	8-396	.0005-.0065
'71-'72	8-402	.0005-.0065
'67	8-427	.0012-.0060
'68-'69	8-427	.0005-.0065
'70-'74	8-454	.0005-.0065

PISTON CLEARANCE

Year	Engine Displacement cu in.	Engine Advertised H.P.	Piston to Bore Clearance (in.)
'67-'73	250		.0005-.0025
	283, 307, 327	All	.0005-.0025
	350	145, 190, 250	.0007-.0027
		300	.0007-.0027
		350	.0020-.0036
		370	.0036-.0061
	396	350	.0018-.0038
		375	.0036-.0065
	400	150, 265	.0014-.0034
		330	.0018-.0038

Year	Engine Displacement cu in.	Engine Advertised H.P.	Piston to Bore Clearance (in.)
	427	390	.0024-.0045
		400	.0024-.0045
		430	.0058-.0080
		435	.0040-.0065
	454	215, 245, 275	.0018-.0035
		345	.0024-.0049
		360	.0024-.0049
		390	.0024-.0049
		450	.0040-.0065

ALTERNATOR AND REGULATOR SPECIFICATIONS

	ALTERNATOR			REGULATOR						
					Field Relay			Regulator		
Year	Part No. or Manufacturer	Field Current @ 12 V	Output (amps)	Part No. or Manufacturer	Air Gap (in.)	Point Gap (in.)	Volts to Close	Air Gap (in.)	Point Gap (in.)	Volts @ 75°
'67	1100693	2.2-2.6	37	1119515	.015	.030	2.3-3.7	.067	.014	13.5-14.4
	1100696	2.2-2.6	42	1119515	.015	.030	2.3-3.7	.067	.014	13.5-14.4
'68	1100693	2.2-2.6	37	1119515	.015	.030	2.3-3.7	.067	.014	13.5-14.4
	1100794	2.2-2.6	37	1119515	.015	.030	2.3-3.7	.067	.014	13.5-14.4
	1100696	2.2-2.6	42	1119515	.015	.030	2.3-3.7	.067	.014	13.5-14.4
'69	1100834	2.2-2.6	37	1119515	.015	.030	2.3-3.7	.067	.014	13.5-14.4
	1100836	2.2-2.6	37	1119515	.015	.030	2.3-3.7	.067	.014	13.5-14.4
	1100696	2.2-2.6	37	1119515	.015	.030	2.3-3.7	.067	.014	13.5-14.4
'70	1100834	2.2-2.6	37	1119515	.015	.030	2.3-3.7	.067	.014	13.5-14.4
	1100900	2.2-2.6	37	1119515	.015	.030	2.3-3.7	.067	.014	13.5-14.4
	1100901	2.2-2.6	37	1119515	.015	.030	2.3-3.7	.067	.014	13.5-14.4
'71-'72	1100544	4.0-4.5	55	1119515	.015	.030	1.5-3.2	.067	.014	13.8-14.8
	1100543, 1100950	4.0-4.5	37	1119515	.015	.030	1.5-3.2	.067	.014	13.8-14.8
	1100566, 1100836, 1100837	2.2-2.6	35	1119515	.015	.030	1.5-3.2	.067	.014	13.8-14.8
	1100843	2.2-2.6	58	1119515	.015	.030	1.5-3.2	.067	.014	13.8-14.8
	1100917	2.8-3.2	59	1119519	.030	.030	1.5-3.2	.067	.014	13.8-14.8
	1100567	2.2-2.6	40	1119515	.015	.030	1.5-3.2	.067	.014	13.8-14.8
	1100497	2.8-3.2	37		Integrated with alternator					13.8-14.8
	1100934	2.8-3.2	37		Integrated with alternator					13.8-14.8
'73-'74	1100544	4.0-4.5	61		Integrated with alternator					13.8-14.8
	1102353, 1100573, 1102346, 1100950	4.0-4.5	42		Integrated with alternator					13.8-14.8
	1100934, 1100497	4.0-4.5	37		Integrated with alternator					13.8-14.8
	1102354, 1100542	4.0-4.5	63		Integrated with alternator					13.8-14.8

BATTERY AND STARTER SPECIFICATIONS

Year	Engine Displacement (cu in.)	BATTERY Ampere Hour Capacity	BATTERY Volts	BATTERY Terminal Grounded	STARTERS Lock Test Amps	STARTERS Lock Test Volts	STARTERS Lock Test Torque (ft lbs)	STARTERS No-Load Test Amps	STARTERS No-Load Test Volts	STARTERS No-Load Test RPM	Brush Spring Tension (oz)
'67	6 & 8-283	45	12	Neg.	Not Recommended			73	10.6	9,575	35
	8-327	61	12	Neg.	Not Recommended			83	10.6	4,250	35
	8-396, 427	61	12	Neg.	Not Recommended			85	10.6	9,900	35
'68	6 & 8-307, 327 (250 H.P.)	45	12	Neg.	Not Recommended			73	10.6	4,500	35
	8-327 (275 H.P.), 396, 427	61	12	Neg.	Not Recommended			85	10.6	10,000	35
	All Corvette Engines	62	12	Neg.	Not Recommended			85	10.6	10,000	35
'69	6 & 8-327, 396	45	12	Neg.	Not Recommended			73	9	4,500	35
	8-350, 427	61	12	Neg.	Not Recommended			85	9	10,000	35
	All Corvette Engines	62	12	Neg.	Not Recommended			85	9	10,000	35
'70	6	45	12	Neg.	Not Recommended			50-80	9	5,500-10,500	35
	8-350	61	12	Neg.	Not Recommended			55-80	9	3,500-6,000	35
	All Corvette Engines	62	12	Neg.	Not Recommended			55-80	9	3,500-6,000	35
	8-400	62	12	Neg.	Not Recommended			55-80	9	3,500-6,000	35
	8-454	62	12	Neg.	Not Recommended			65-95	9	7,500-10,500	35
'71-'72	6	45	12	Neg.	Not Recommended			50-80	9	5,500-10,500	35
	8-350	61	12	Neg.	Not Recommended			65-95	9	7,500-10,500	35
	8-400	61	12	Neg.	Not Recommended			65-95	9	7,500-10,500	35
	8-402	61	12	Neg.	Not Recommended			65-95	9	7,500-10,500	35
	8-454	76	12	Neg.	Not Recommended			65-95	9	7,500-10,500	35
	Corvette 350	62	12	Neg.	Not Recommended			65-95	9	7,500-10,500	35
	Corvette 454	76	12	Neg.	Not Recommended			65-95	9	7,500-10,500	35
'73-'74	6	①	12	Neg.	Not Recommended			50-80	9	5,500-10,500	35
	8-350, 400	②	12	Neg.	Not Recommended			65-95	9	7,500-10,500	35
	8-454	④	12	Neg.	Not Recommended			65-95	9	7,500-10,500	35
	Corvette 350	③	12	Neg.	Not Recommended			65-95	9	7,500-10,500	35
	Corvette 454	④	12	Neg.	Not Recommended			65-95	9	7,500-10,500	35

① Side Terminal—Cranking power 2,300 watts @ 0°F
② Side Terminal—Cranking power 2,900 watts @ 0°F
③ Side Terminal—Cranking power 3,250 watts @ 0°F
④ Side Terminal—Cranking power 3,750 watts @ 0°F

BRAKE SPECIFICATIONS

Year	Model	Master Cylinder Disc	Master Cylinder Drum	Wheel Cylinder Front Disc	Wheel Cylinder Front Drum	Wheel Cylinder Rear	Brake Disc or Drum Diameter Front Disc	Brake Disc or Drum Diameter Front Drum	Brake Disc or Drum Diameter Rear
CHEVROLET									
'67-'68	All	1.0	1.0①	2 15/16	1 3/16	1.00	11.75	11.0	11.0
'69-'70	All	1 1/8	1.0	2 15/16	1 3/16	1.00	11.75	11.0	11.0
'71-'74	Exc. Sta. Wag.	1 1/8	—	2 15/16	—	15/16	11.86	—	11.0
	Sta. Wag.	1 1/8	—	2 15/16	—	1.00	11.86	—	12.0
CORVETTE									
'67-'71	All	1.0	—	1 7/8	—	1 3/8	11.75	—	11.75③
'72-'74	All	1.0②	—	1 7/8	—	1 3/8	11.75	—	11.75③

① Metallic linings—7/8 in.
② Power brakes—1 1/8
② Power brakes—1 1/8 except 1974
③ Disc
— Not applicable

WHEEL ALIGNMENT SPECIFICATIONS

Year	Model	Caster Range (deg)	Caster Pref Setting (deg)	Camber Range (deg)	Camber Pref Setting (deg)	Toe-in (in.)	Steering Axis Inclin.	Wheel Pivot Ratio (deg) Inner Wheel	Wheel Pivot Ratio (deg) Wheel Outer
'67	Chevrolet	1/4P to 1 1/4P	1/4P	1/4P to 3/4P	1/4P	1/8 to 1/4	7 to 8	20	20 1/4
	Corvette	1/2P to 1 1/2P	1P	1/4P to 1 1/4P③	3/4P	3/16 to 5/16①	6 1/2 to 7 1/2	20	18 1/2
'68-'69	Chevrolet	1/4P to 1 1/4P	1/4P	1/4N to 3/4P	1/4P	1/8 to 1/4	7 to 8	20	18
	Corvette	1/2P to 1 1/2P④	1P	1/2P to 1 1/4P⑤	3/4P	3/16 to 5/16⑤	6 1/2 to 7 1/2	20	18 1/2
'70	Chevrolet	1/4P to 1 1/4P	1/4P	1/4N to 3/4P	1/4P	1/8 to 1/4	7 to 8	20	18
	Corvette	1/2P to 1 1/2P④	1P	1/2P to 1 1/4P⑤	3/4P	3/16 to 5/16⑤	6 1/2 to 7 1/2	20	18 1/2
'71	Chevrolet	1 1/2N to 1/2N	1N	0 to 1P	1/2P	1/8 to 1/4	9 1/2 to 10 1/2	N.A.	N.A.
'71-'72	Corvette	1/2P to 1 1/2P④	1P	1/4P to 1 1/4P	3/4P	3/16 to 5/16	6 1/2 to 7 1/2	N.A.	N.A.
'72	Chevrolet	1/2P to 1 1/2P	1P	0 to 1P	1/2P	3/16 to 5/16	9 1/2 to 10 1/2	N.A.	N.A.
'73	Chevrolet	0 to 2P	1P	1/4P to 1 3/4P⑨	1P	1/16N to 3/16P	10 1/2	N.A.	N.A.
	Corvette	0 to 2P⑦	1P	0 to 1 1/2P⑧	3/4P	1/8 to 3/8⑧	6 7/8	N.A.	N.A.
'74	Chevrolet	0-2P	1P	0-2P⑨	1P⑪	1/16 to 3/16	9 1/2	N.A.	N.A.
	Corvette	1/2P-1 1/2P④	1P	1/4P-1 1/4P⑩	3/4P	3/32 to 5/32	7 3/4	N.A.	N.A.

① Rear wheels—1/16 to 3/16
③ Rear wheels—1/2° ± 1/2°
④ W/power steering—1 3/4P to 2 3/4P
⑤ Rear wheel alignment: camber 1 1/8N to 5/8N toe-in 1/32 to 3/32
⑥ Power steering—1 1/4P to 3 1/4P
⑦ W/power steering—1 1/4P to 3 1/4P, 2 1/4 preferred
⑧ Rear wheel alignment: camber 7/8N ± 1/4, toe-in 2/32 ± 1/32
⑨ Left wheel given, right wheel is 1/4N to 1 1/4P, preferred 1/2P
⑩ Rear wheel alignment: Camber 1/2N ± 1/4. Toe-in 3/32 ± 1/32
⑪ Left wheel given, right wheel is 1/2P
N Negative P Positive

CHARGING SYSTEM

Repair and test details on the Delcotron and its regulators can be found in the Unit Repair Section.

A resistance wire is used between the "ACC" connector of the ignition switch and the regulator.

Caution Since the Delcotron and regulator are designed for use on a single polarity system, the following precautions must be observed:

1. The polarity of the battery, generator, and regulator must be matched and considered before making any electrical connections in the system.
2. When connecting a booster battery, be sure to connect the negative battery terminals with one another, and the positive battery terminals with one another.
3. When connecting a charger to the battery, connect the charger positive lead to the battery positive terminal. Connect the charger negative lead to the battery negative terminal.
4. Never operate the Delcotron on open circuit. Be sure that all connections in the circuit are clean and tight.
5. Do not short across or ground any of the terminals on the Delcotron regulator.
6. Do not attempt to polarize the Delcotron.
7. Do not use test lamps of more than 12 volts or high amperage for checking diode continuity.
8. Avoid long soldering times when replacing diodes or transistors. Prolonged heat is damaging to these units. Always use a heat-sink when soldering these solid state devices.
9. Disconnect the battery ground terminal when servicing any AC system. This will prevent the possibility of accidentally reversing polarity.

Alternator R & R

1. Disconnect the battery cables from the battery terminals.
2. Disconnect and identify the wire leads from the alternator.
3. Remove the alternator brace bolt, then remove belt(s).
4. Remove the alternator pivot attaching bolt and remove alternator from vehicle.
5. To install, reverse the above procedure and adjust belt tension.

Regulator R & R

1. Disconnect the ground cable at the battery.
2. Disconnect the wiring harness from the regulator.
3. Remove the mounting screws and remove the regulator.
4. Make sure that the regulator base gasket is in place before installation.
5. Clean the attaching area for proper grounding.
6. Install the regulator. Do not overtighten the mounting screws, as this will cancel the cushioning effect of the rubber grommets.

NOTE: An integral alternator/regulator has been optionally available since 1969. Separate removal or adjustment of the regulator is not possible with this unit. Complete disassembly of this unit is described in the "Unit Repair Section."

STARTING SYSTEM

Detailed information on the starter can be found in the Starter Specifications table of this section. More information on starters can be found in the Unit Repair Section under Charging and Starting Systems.

Starter R & R

1. Disconnect the battery and the wires from the solenoid.
2. Remove the starter mounting bolt and lock washers. On V8s, a stud nut and lock washer are at the front of the starter.
3. Pull starter forward and out of car.
4. To install, reverse the above procedure.

IGNITION SYSTEM

Two types of ignition systems have been available: a conventional breaker type and an optional (on Corvette) magnetic pulse, breakerless system. The magnetic pulse distributor, which was discontinued in 1972, requires no maintenance. A resistance wire connects the ignition switch and the coil on the breaker type system, while the breakerless system utilizes two; one between the negative coil terminal and ground, the other resistance wire provides a voltage drop for the engine run circuit. Troubleshooting of the breakerless distributor is contained in the "Unit Repair Section."

Distributor Removal

6 Cylinder Models

The distributor assembly is mounted on the right side of the block and is driven directly from the camshaft.

To remove the distributor, first detach the vacuum lines from the vacuum advance unit and lift off the distributor cap.

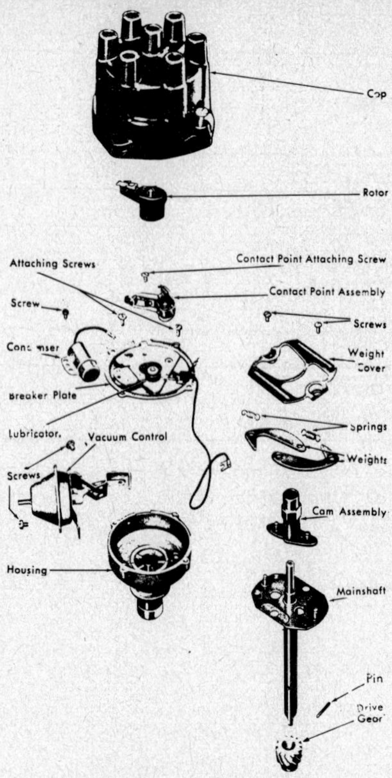
Cap
Rotor
Attaching Screws
Contact Point Attaching Screw
Contact Point Assembly
Screw
Screws
Weight Cover
Breaker Plate
Lubricator
Vacuum Control
Screws
Cam Assembly
Housing
Mainshaft
Pin
Drive Gear

6-cylinder distributor, typical
(© Chevrolet Div., G.M. Corp)

The distributor body is fastened to the block by a single cap screw which holds the octane selector plate down against the block. Scribe marks so that the distributor body and rotor can be installed in their original locations. Do not turn engine while the distributor is removed. Remove the retaining screw and lift the distributor out of the block.

V8 Models—Standard Distributor

The distributor is located between the two banks of cylinders at the back of the block.

The drive gear is attached to the distributor shaft; therefore, if it becomes necessary to remove the distributor, carefully mark the position of the rotor. Then, if the engine is not turned after the distributor is taken out, it can be installed in the same position from which is was removed.

To remove the distributor, disconnect the carburetor air cleaner, disconnect the coil primary wire and the vacuum line, remove the distributor cap, take out the single hold-down bolt located under the distributor body, mark the position of the body relative to the block and then work the distributor up out of the block.

Breakerless Distributor

1. Disconnect pick-up coil connector.
2. Remove distributor cap.

1 Condenser
2 Contact points
2A Cam lubricator
3 Retaining ring
4 Breaker plate
5 Felt washer
5A Plastic seal
6 Vacuum advance unit
7 Housing
8 Shim washer
9 Drive gear pin
10 Drive gear
11 Cap
12 Rotor
13 Radio frequency interference shield
14 Weight springs
15 Mainshaft
16 Advance weights
17 Weight base assembly

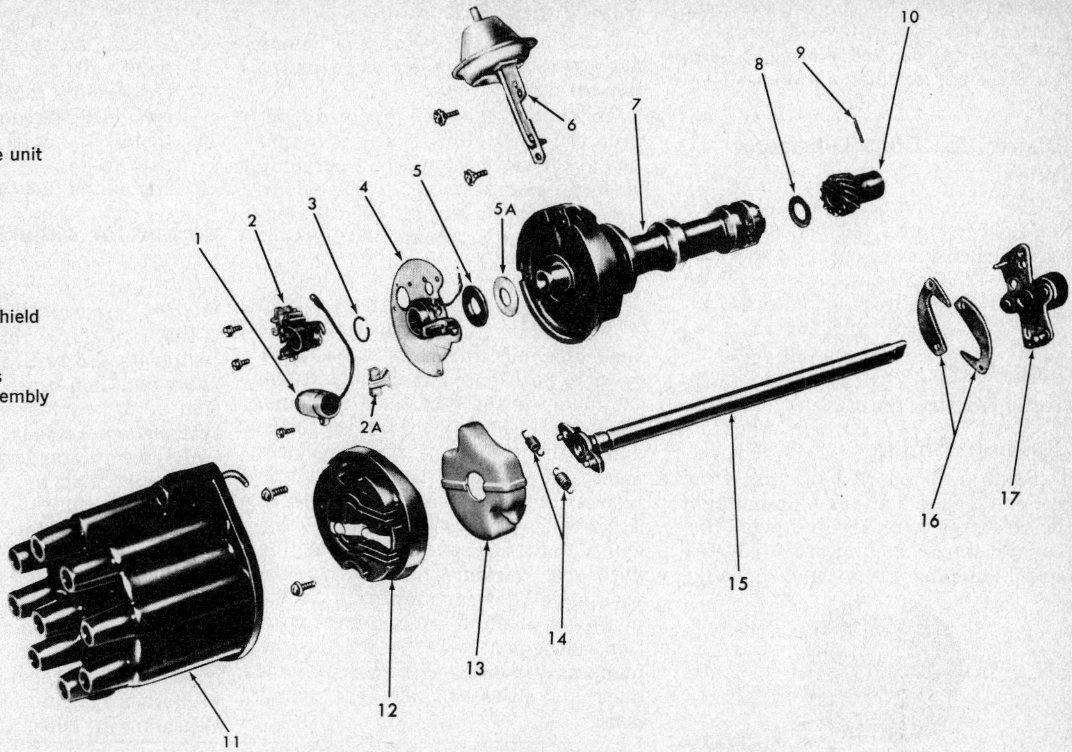
1
2
2A
3
4
5
5A
6
7
8
9
10
11
12
13
14
15
16
17

Typical V8 distributor (© Chevrolet Div., G.M. Corp)

3. Crank engine so that rotor points to No. 1 cylinder plug tower and timing mark on crankshaft pulley is indexed with pointer. Mark the position of the tip of the rotor on the engine block.
4. Remove distributor vacuum line.
5. Remove distributor hold-down bolt and clamp, then remove distributor.
6. When installing the distributor, align the tip of the rotor with the mark that was made on the block.

Distributor Installation (Engine Disturbed)

1. Turn crank until the No. 1 cylinder is at the top of its compression stroke. Remove the No. 1 spark plug to feel the compression.
2. Align the timing mark on the flywheel or vibration damper with the indicator.
3. With distributor body oriented in its normal position, hold the rotor pointing toward the front of the engine, then turn the rotor approximately 1/8 turn counterclockwise and push the distributor down until it engages the camshaft, rotating the shaft slightly if necessary.

NOTE: on Mark IV engines there is a punch mark on the distributor drive gear which indicates the rotor position. Thus, the distributor may be installed with the cap in place. Align the punch mark 2° clockwise from the No. 1 cap terminal, then rotate the distributor body clockwise 1/8 turn counterclockwise and push the distributor down into the block.

4. Press down on the distributor and crank the engine to make sure the oil pump shaft is engaged.
5. Return the crankshaft to No. 1 cylinder compression stroke with the timing marks aligned.
6. Turn the distributor body counterclockwise until the points are just beginning to open, then tighten the distributor clamp bolt.
7. Install the distributor cap, checking that the rotor points to the No. 1 terminal. Make sure that the spark plug wires are in their supports and are securely connected.
8. Connect distributor vacuum line and primary wire.
9. Start engine and set the timing.

Caution When using an auxiliary starter switch for bumping the engine into position for timing, the primary distributor lead must be disconnected from the negative post of the ignition coil and the switch must be in the on position. Failure to do this may cause damage to the grounding circuit in the ignition switch.

Breaker Point Adjustment

NOTE: 1970 and later distributors are equipped with a radio static shield, which must be removed for access to the points.

Breaker point gap (dwell) adjustment is accomplished for 6-cylinder engines by loosening the point assembly attaching screw and adjusting it with a screwdriver until correct gap clearance is obtained (use a feeler gauge). Tighten the point assembly attaching screws and install the distributor cap. Use a dwell meter, if available, to check the dwell angle, readjusting if necessary.

ADJUST DWELL
ANGLE SETTING OR
POINT OPENING

6-cylinder point adjustment
(© Chevrolet Div., G.M. Corp)

On V8 models there is a window in the distributor cap so that the dwell angle may be set while the engine is running. Use an Allen (hex) wrench to make the adjustment.

See Tune-Up Specifications at the beginning of this section for correct breaker point gap and dwell angle.

Caution On V8 models the distributor body is involved in the engine lubricating system. The lubricating circuit to the right-bank valve train can be interrupted by mis-alignment of the distributor body. This can cause serious trouble and may be hard to diagnose. See Firing Order and Timing illustrations for correct distributor positioning.

Distributor Cam Lubricator Wick

The distributor cam lubricator should be rotated 180° (L6 engines) or switched end for end (V8 engines) every 12,000 miles, and replaced every 24,000 miles.

Caution Do not oil these lubricator wicks or directly lubricate the cam.

Ignition Timing

Remove the spark plug wire from no. one plug and attach a timing light between the wire and the plug. Disconnect the distributor spark advance hose and plug the vacuum opening.

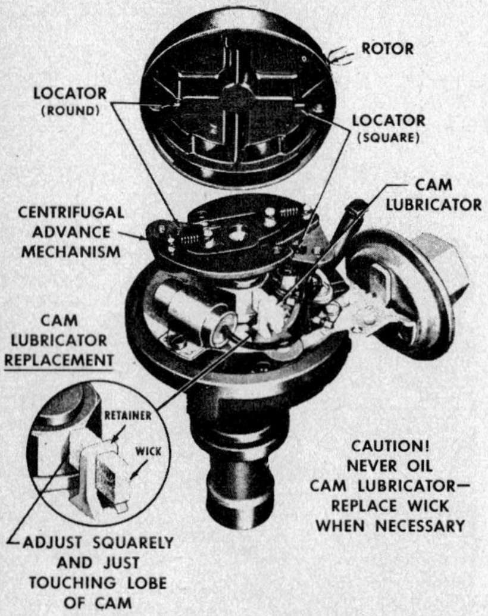
ROTOR
LOCATOR (ROUND)
LOCATOR (SQUARE)
CAM LUBRICATOR
CENTRIFUGAL ADVANCE MECHANISM
CAM LUBRICATOR REPLACEMENT
RETAINER
WICK
CAUTION! NEVER OIL CAM LUBRICATOR—REPLACE WICK WHEN NECESSARY
ADJUST SQUARELY AND JUST TOUCHING LOBE OF CAM

V8 distributor showing details of cam lubricator
(© Chevrolet Div., G.M. Corp)

Start the engine and run it at idle speed. Aim the timing light at the degree scale just over the harmonic balancer. The markings on the scale are in 2° increments with the greatest number of markings on the *before* side of the 0. Adjust the timing by loosening the securing clamp and rotating the distributor until the desired ignition advance is achieved, then tighten the clamp. To advance the timing, rotate the distributor opposite to the normal direction of rotor rotation. Retard the timing by rotating the distributor in the normal direction of rotor rotation.

FUEL SYSTEM

Data on capacity of the gas tank can be found in the Capacities table. Data on correct engine idle speed and fuel pump pressure can be found in the Tune-up Specifications table.

Information covering operation and troubles of the fuel gauge is in the Unit Repair Section.

Fuel Pump R & R

NOTE: two types of fuel pump are used; a serviceable type and a non-serviceable type.

To remove the fuel pump, disconnect the input line and the output line to the carburetor. The fuel pump then can be unbolted from the side of the block and lifted off. On V8 models, the pump is actuated by a pushrod in the block.

Caution A fuel pump may fail to function at the time of replacement as a result of error in positioning or damage to the fuel pump pushrod of the V8 engine. This pushrod can slip out of place during the process of pump replacement and result in no pump action from the newly replaced unit. Before tightening the fuel pump to the engine, have someone spin the engine with the starter while feeling the fuel pump body for movement. If the pump and pushrod are in correct position, movement will be felt in the pump as the pushrod pressure is applied and released from the pump arm.

Chilton's TIME SAVER

283, 307, 327, 350, 400 cu. in.

When replacing a fuel pump on a 283, 307, 327, 350, and 400 cu. in. engine, considerable time can be saved as follows:

1. **Before removing the old pump, remove the upper bolt from the engine's right front mounting boss. This bolt hole is in direct alignment with the fuel pump pushrod. The threaded bolt hole continues into the pump pushrod bore. The bolt acts as an oil plug.**
2. **Temporarily insert a longer bolt, (about ⅜—16 x 2 in.) into the hole. Screw the bolt into the bore until it bottoms against the pump pushrod. (Don't tighten the bolt with a wrench or the rod can be damaged.)**
3. **The mechanic is now free to remove and install the fuel pump without worrying about fuel pump pushrod misalignment.**

CAUTION: don't forget to reinstall original motor bolt.

396, 427 and 454 cu. in.

The design of these engines prevents the use of the method of simplifying fuel pump pushrod positioning while installing a fuel pump. However, to hold the pump pushrod in position while installing the fuel pump, the following works satisfactorily;

1. **Clean oil from pushrod.**
2. **Pack a small quantity of non-fibrous grease in the area around the fuel pump pushrod to hold it in suspension long enough to position the fuel pump.**
3. **Install and check pump action, then torque attaching bolts.**

Fuel Filter R&R

Fuel filters are integral with the carburetor body. The filter element can be replaced as follows:

1. Disconnect the fuel line.
2. Remove the fuel filter nut from the carburetor.
3. Remove the filter element and spring. Blow through the filter end. If the air does not flow freely, replace the element. Do not attempt to clean the filter element.
4. Install the spring, then the element. Bronze filters in Holley carburetors must have the small section of the cone facing out.
5. Install the inlet fitting using a new gasket.
6. Install the fuel line.

Carburetor Adjustments

NOTE: refer to the illustrations in the Camaro Section for idle speed and mixture screw locations.

Idle mixture and speed adjustments are critical aspects of exhaust emission control. For a discussion of the various emission control systems see Exhaust Emission Control Systems later in this section. It is important that all tune-up instructions be carefully followed to ensure satisfactory engine performance and minimum exhaust pollution. The different combinations of emission systems application on the different engine models have resulted in a great variety of tune-up specifications. See the Tune-Up Specifications at the beginning of this section. Beginning in 1968, all models have a decal conspicuously placed somewhere in the engine compartment giving tune-up specifications.

When adjusting a carburetor with two idle mixture screws, adjust them alternately and evenly, unless otherwise stated.

See the Unit Repair Section for illustrations and adjustment specifications of Carter, Holley and Rochester carburetors. In the following adjustment procedures the term "lean roll" means turning the mixture adjusting screws in (clockwise) from optimum setting to obtain an obvious drop in engine speed (usually 20 rpm).

All 1967 Without A.I.R.

Adjust with air cleaner removed.

1. Connect a tachometer and vacuum gauge to the engine, then set the parking brake and shift the manual transmission into Neutral, automatic into Drive.
2. Turn the idle mixture screw/s in until lightly seated, then back out 1½ turns.
3. With engine running, adjust the idle speed screw to obtain the specified rpm.
4. Adjust the idle mixture screw/s to obtain the highest steady manifold vacuum at the specified speed. If necessary, reset the idle speed screw while adjusting mixture.

NOTE: on air conditioned models, the air conditioner is turned on and the hot idle compensator valve is held closed while adjusting idle speed and mixture.

NOTE: on Rochester BV carburetors, turn the idle mixture screw to "lean roll" position, then back it out ¼ turn.

5. Final adjustment should be made with the air cleaner installed.
6. Remove tachometer and vacuum gauge.

1967 With A.I.R.

Adjust with air cleaner removed.

1. Connect a tachometer to the engine, place manual transmission in Neutral, automatic in Drive.
2. Turn idle mixture screw/s in until lightly seated, then back out 3 turns.
3. With engine running, adjust the idle speed screw to obtain the specified idle speed.
4. Adjust the idle mixture screw/s in to "lean roll" position, then back them out (rich) ¼ turn. Readjust the idle speed screw to keep the engine at the specified idle speed while adjusting the mixture.

NOTE: on air conditioned cars, turn the air conditioner off with L6, 283, 327 and 350 cu. in. engines. Air conditioner must be on and hot idle compensator held closed with 396 and 427 cu. in. engines.

5. Final adjustment should be made with the air cleaner installed.
6. Remove the tachometer.

All 1968-69

Adjust with air cleaner installed.

1. Turn the idle mixture screw/s in until lightly seated, then back out 3 turns.
2. With engine at operating temperature, adjust idle speed screw to obtain specified rpm, manual transmission in Neutral and automatic in Drive.

NOTE: on all 1968 models *except* L6 with automatic transmission and the 325 H.P. and 350 H.P. 327 cu. in. with manual transmission, the air conditioner is turned *off*. On the above-mentioned vehicles the air conditioner is left *on*. On 1969 models, turn the air conditioner either on or off according to the instructions on the tune-up decal.

3. Adjust one idle mixture screw to obtain the highest steady idle speed.
4. Adjust the idle speed screw to the speed specified on the tune-up decal.

NOTE: on models equipped with an idle solenoid, adjust the solenoid plunger hex to obtain 500 rpm on the L6 engine and 600 rpm on V8 engines. Disconnect the wire at the solenoid to de-energize it, allowing the throttle lever to contact the carburetor idle speed screw. Adjust the carburetor idle screw to obtain 400 rpm.

5. Adjust the mixture screw in to "lean roll" position, then back out (rich) ¼ turn.
6. Repeat Steps 3, 4 and 5 for the other idle mixture screw for 2-BBL. and 4-BBL. engines.
7. Readjust the idle speed screw to obtain final specified rpm, if necessary.

1970 Chevrolet

Adjust with air cleaner installed.

If the vehicle is equipped with Evaporative Emission, disconnect the fuel tank line from the vapor canister while making the idle speed and mixture adjustments. Warm up the engine and leave it running with the choke and, if applicable, air cleaner damper door fully open and the air conditioning off.

250 Engine

1. Disconnect and plug the distributor vacuum hose at the distributor end.
2. Turn the idle mixture screw in until it lightly contacts the seat, back it out 4 turns.
3. Adjust the solenoid plunger to obtain 830 rpm (manual transmission in Neutral) or 630 rpm (automatic transmission in Drive).
4. Adjust mixture screw in to obtain 750 rpm (manual transmission in Neutral) or 600 rpm (automatic transmission in Drive).
5. Disconnect the solenoid wire and, with the solenoid plunger depressed, adjust the carburetor idle speed screw to obtain 400 rpm.
6. Reconnect the solenoid wire and distributor vacuum hose.

350 (250 H.P.) Engine

1. Disconnect and plug the distributor vacuum hose at the distributor end.
2. Turn the idle mixture screws in until they lightly contact the seats, then back them out 4 turns.
3. With manual transmission in Neutral, adjust the solenoid plunger to obtain 830 rpm. With automatic transmission in Drive, adjust the solenoid plunger to obtain 630 rpm.
4. Adjust the idle mixture screws in equally to obtain 750 rpm (manual transmission in Neutral) or 600 rpm (automatic transmission in Drive).
5. Disconnect the solenoid wire and, with the solenoid plunger fully depressed, set the carburetor idle speed screw to obtain 450 rpm.
6. Reconnect the solenoid wire and distributor vacuum hose.

350 (300 H.P.) Engine

1. Disconnect the vacuum hose at the distributor and plug the hose.
2. Turn the idle mixture screws in until they lightly contact the seats, then back them out 4 turns.
3. With manual transmission in Neutral, adjust the carburetor idle speed screw to obtain 775 rpm. With automatic transmission in Drive, adjust the carburetor idle speed screw to obtain 630 rpm.
4. Adjust the mixture screws in equally to obtain 700 rpm (manual transmission in Neutral) or 600 rpm (automatic transmission in Drive).
5. Reconnect the distributor vacuum hose.

400 (265 H.P.) Engine

1. Disconnect and plug the distributor vacuum hose at the distributor end.
2. Turn the idle mixture screws in until they lightly contact the seats, then back them out 4 turns.
3. With manual transmission in Neutral, adjust the carburetor idle speed screw to obtain 800 rpm. With automatic transmission in Drive, adjust the solenoid plunger to obtain 630 rpm.
4. Adjust the idle mixture screws in equally to obtain 700 rpm (manual transmission in Neutral) or 600 rpm (automatic transmission in Drive).
5. If equipped with automatic transmission, disconnect the solenoid wire and, with solenoid plunger depressed, set the carburetor idle speed screw to obtain 450 rpm.
6. Reconnect the solenoid wire and the distributor vacuum hose.

454 (450 H.P.) Engine

1. *Remove the air cleaner.*
2. Disconnect the distributor vacuum hose at the distributor and plug the hose.
3. Adjust the mixture screws for maximum idle speed.
4. With manual transmission in Neutral, adjust the carburetor idle speed screw to obtain 750 rpm. With automatic transmission in Drive, adjust the carburetor idle speed screw to obtain 700 rpm.
5. Turn one idle mixture screw to obtain a 20 rpm drop in idle speed, then back the screw out 1/4 turn. Repeat for the second idle mixture screw.
6. Repeat Step 4 above.
7. Reconnect the distributor vacuum hose and install the air cleaner.

454 (345 H.P.) and 454 (390 H.P.) Engines

1. Disconnect the distributor vacuum hose at the distributor and plug the hose.
2. Turn the idle mixture screws in they are lightly seated, then back them out 4 turns.
3. With automatic transmission in Drive, adjust the carburetor idle speed screw to obtain 630 rpm. Adjust the idle mixture screws in equally to obtain 600 rpm.
4. With manual transmission in Neutral, adjust the carburetor idle speed screw to obtain 700 rpm. Turn one of the mixture screws in until the engine speed drops to 400 rpm. Readjust the idle speed screw to obtain 700 rpm. Turn in the other mixture screw until the engine speed drops 40 rpm. Readjust the idle speed screw to obtain 700 rpm.
5. Reconnect the distributor vacuum hose.

1970 Corvette

Adjust with air cleaner installed.

If the vehicle is equipped with Evaporative Emission, disconnect the fuel tank line from the vapor canister while making the idle speed and mixture adjustments. Warm up the engine and leave it running while adjusting. The choke valve and, if applicable, air cleaner damper door should remain open. Leave the air conditioning off.

350 (300, 350 and 370 H.P.) Engines

1. Adjust the idle mixture screws equally to obtain maximum idle speed.
2. On the 300 H.P. engine with manual transmission in Neutral adjust the idle speed screw to obtain 700 rpm. On the 300 H.P. engine with automatic transmission in Drive, adjust the idle speed screw to obtain 600 rpm.
3. On the 350 and 370 H.P. engines, adjust the idle speed screw to obtain 750 rpm with the manual transmission in Neutral.

427 (390 H.P. and 400 H.P.) Without Air Conditioning

1. Adjust the idle mixture screws to obtain the maximum idle rpm.
2. On the 390 H.P. engine with manual transmission in Neutral, adjust the idle speed screw to obtain 800 rpm. On the 390 engine with automatic transmission in Drive, adjust the idle speed screw to obtain 600 rpm.
3. On the 400 H.P. engine with manual transmission in Neutral, adjust the idle speed screw to obtain 750 rpm. On the 400 H.P. engine with automatic transmission in Drive, adjust the idle speed screw to obtain 600 rpm.

427 (390 and 400 H.P.) With Manual Transmission and Air Conditioning

1. Turn the air conditioning off and disconnect the wire from the idle-stop solenoid.
2. Adjust the idle mixture screws to obtain the maximum idle speed.
3. With transmission in Neutral, adjust the idle speed screw to obtain 550 rpm.
4. Turn each idle mixture screw in to obtain a 20 rpm drop, then back out each screw 1/4 turn.
5. Turn on the air conditioning and reconnect the wire to the idle-stop solenoid.
6. Adjust the solenoid plunger to obtain 1,000 rpm.

427 (390 and 400 H.P.) with Automatic Transmission and Air Conditioning

1. Turn the air conditioning on.
2. Adjust the mixture screws to obtain the maximum idle speed.
3. Adjust the solenoid plunger to obtain 650 rpm with the transmission in Drive.
4. Adjust each mixture screw to obtain a 20 rpm drop in engine speed, then back out each screw 1/4 turn.
5. Readjust the solenoid plunger to obtain 650 rpm.
6. Disconnect the solenoid wire and, with the plunger depressed, adjust the carburetor idle speed screw to obtain 500 rpm.
7. Reconnect the solenoid wire.

427 (430 and 435 H.P.) Engines

1. Adjust the idle mixture screws alternately and evenly to obtain the maximum smooth idle speed.
2. With the automatic transmission in Drive, adjust the solenoid plunger to obtain 750 rpm.
3. With the manual transmission in Neutral, adjust the carburetor idle speed screw to obtain 750 rpm (435 H.P.) or 1,000 rpm (430 H.P.).
4. Disconnect the solenoid wire (automatic transmission models only) and, with the solenoid plunger fully depressed, adjust the carburetor idle speed screw to obtain 500 rpm.
5. If necessary, readjust the carburetor idle screw (manual transmission) or the solenoid plunger (automatic transmission) to obtain the speeds specified in Steps 2 and 3.

All 1971—Initial Adjustments

Adjust with air cleaner installed.

The following initial idle adjustments are part of the normal engine tune-up. There is a tune-up decal placed conspicuously in the engine compartment outlining the specific procedure and settings for each engine application. Follow all of the instructions when adjusting the idle. These tuning procedures are necessary to obtain the delicate balance of variables for the maintenance of both reliable engine performance and efficient exhaust emission control.

NOTE: all engines except the 350 (330 H.P.) and 454 (425 H.P.) have limiter caps on the mixture adjusting screws. The idle mixture is preset and the limiter caps installed at the factory in order to meet emission control standards. Do not remove these limiter caps unless all other possible causes of poor idle condition have been thoroughly checked out. Procedures for setting the idle mixture with the limiter caps removed are described under the heading "Complete Adjustment" later on.

The solenoid used on 1971 carburetors is different from the one used on earlier models. Combination Emission Control System (C.E.C. solenoid) valve regulates distributor vacuum as a function of transmission gear position.

Caution The C.E.C. solenoid is adjusted only after: 1) replacement of the solenoid, 2) major carburetor overhaul, or 3) after the throttle body is removed or replaced.

Instructions for C.E.C. solenoid plunger adjustment are contained in the Unit Repair Section.

All initial adjustments described below are made:

1. With the engine warmed up and running.
2. With the choke fully open.
3. With the fuel tank line disconnected from the Evaporative Emission canister on all models except the Corvette.
4. With the fuel tank gas cap removed on the Corvette.
5. With the vacuum hose disconnected at the distributor and plugged.

Be sure to reconnect the distributor vacuum hose and to connect the fuel tank to evaporative emission canister line or install the gas cap when idle adjustments are complete.

250 6-Cylinder Engine

Adjust the carburetor idle speed screw (NOT the solenoid plunger) to obtain 550 rpm (manual transmission in Neutral) or 500 rpm (automatic transmission in Drive).

350 and 400 (2-BBL) and 350 (4-BBL Quadrajet) Engines

Adjust the carburetor idle speed screw (NOT the solenoid plunger) to obtain 600 rpm (manual transmission in Neutral with the air conditioner off) or 550 rpm (automatic transmission in Drive with the air conditioner on).

350 and 454 (4-BBL Holley) Engines —Corvette

1. Adjust the carburetor idle speed screw (NOT the solenoid plunger) to obtain 700 rpm (manual transmission in Neutral or automatic transmission in Drive).
2. Adjust the idle mixture screws alternately to obtain the maximum smooth idle speed.
3. Adjust one of the idle mixture screws to obtain a 20 rpm drop ("lean roll"), then back it out ¼ turn.
4. Repeat Step 4 above for the other idle mixture screw.
5. Readjust the carburetor idle speed screw to obtain 700 rpm if necessary.

402 and 454 (4-BBL Quadrajet) Engines

Turn the air conditioner off. Adjust the carburetor idle speed screw (NOT the solenoid plunger) to obtain 600 rpm (manual transmission in Neutral or automatic transmission in Drive).

All 1971—Complete Adjustment

The adjustment of the idle mixture requiring the removal of the limiter caps is only made after carburetor overhaul, throttle body part replacement, mixture needle part replacement or limiter cap and needle removal. Before proceeding, follow the tuning instructions on the tune-up decal (refer to "All 1971—Initial Adjustment").

1. Turn the idle mixture screw/s in until lightly contact the seat, then back out 4 turns.
2. Referring to the chart ("Idle Mixture Adjustment"), adjust the idle speed screw (NOT the solenoid plunger) to obtain the "initial idle speed" listed in Column #1.
3. Hook-up a CO (carbon monoxide) gas analyzer to the vehicle.
4. Adjust the idle mixture screw (both screws equally on 2- and 4-BBL carburetors) to obtain the specified %CO reading (Column #3).
5. Readjust the idle speed screw (NOT the solenoid plunger) to obtain the specified "final idle speed" (Column #2).
6. Install service idle mixture screw limiter cap/s on the idle mixture screws (except on Holley carburetors).
7. Reconnect the distributor vacuum hose.
8. Reconnect the fuel tank vapor hose or, on Corvettes, install the fuel tank cap.

NOTE: if a CO analyzer is unavailable, the following alternate procedure may be used to adjust the idle mixture.

1. Turn the idle mixture screw/s in until lightly seated, then back out 4 full turns.
2. Adjust the carburetor idle speed screw (NOT the solenoid plunger) to obtain the "initial idle speed" (see Column #1 of "Idle Mixture Adjustment" chart).
3. Adjust the idle mixture screw/s to obtain the "final idle speed" (see Column #2 in the "Idle Mixture Adjustment" chart).
4. Install service idle limiter cap/s on mixture screws.
5. Reconnect the distributor vacuum hose and fuel vapor line.

1972-74

NOTE: all carburetors are equipped with idle limiter caps and idle mixture is preset at the factory and should not require adjustment.

1. On Chevrolet models, disconnect the fuel tank line from the vapor storage canister. On Corvettes, remove the fuel filler cap but do not remove the vapor line.
2. Detach the distributor vacuum hose and plug the hose.
3. Set the parking brake and turn the air conditioner (if so equipped) off. On cars equipped with an automatic transmission, chock the wheels.
4. Allow the engine to reach normal operating temperature. Be sure that the choke is open.
5. If the car has an automatic transmission, set the selector in Drive. If the car has a manual transmission keep the transmission in Neutral.
6. Adjust the anti-dieseling solenoid to the *higher* of the two rpm figures given in the specifications.

Caution Do not turn the solenoid more than one complete turn unless the electrical lead is disconnected (solenoid de-energized).

7. Disconnect the solenoid lead and set the idle speed to the *lower* of the two figures given in the specifications. Use an allen wrench in the end of the solenoid for this adjustment, on six cylinder engines. On V8's use the normal idle speed adjusting screw.

NOTE: if no lower figure is given, adjust the idle to 450 rpm.

8. Reconnect all of the wires and hoses which were disconnected in order to perform these adjustments.

COOLING SYSTEM

Chevrolet engine cooling systems function at high pressure for increased cooling efficiency. The radiator cap has both pressure and vacuum relief valves.

Cooling system capacities for the various models can be found in the Capacities table at the beginning of this section. Information on the water temperature gauge can be found in the Unit Repair Section.

Radiator R & R

Chevrolet

1. Drain the cooling system.
2. Disconnect the radiator upper and lower hoses and, if applicable, transmission coolant lines. Remove the coolant recovery system line, if so equipped.
3. Remove the radiator upper panel if so equipped.
4. If there is a radiator shroud in front of the radiator, the radiator and shrould are removed as an assembly.
5. If there is a fan shroud, remove the shroud attaching screws let the shroud hang on the fan.
6. Remove the radiator attaching bolts and remove the radiator.
7. Installation is the reverse of the removal procedure.

Fan Shroud—1967 Corvette

1. Drain the radiator.
2. Raise the hood and install a bolt in the hole of the hood support bracket.
3. Disconnect the upper radiator hose and the supply tank hose at the radiator connection.
4. Remove the six shroud bolts.
5. Carefully remove the shroud.
6. Install in reverse order of removal.

Aluminum Radiator—1967 Corvette

1. Remove the fan shroud as described above.
2. Disconnect the lower radiator hose.
3. Remove the radiator upper mount bracket, then lift out radiator.

4. To install, reverse the removal procedure.

Copper Radiator—1967 Corvette

1. Scribe the location of the hood panel bracket, then remove the hood panel assembly.
2. Drain the radiator and disconnect the hoses.
3. Remove the fan.
4. Remove the four bolts along the top of the radiator support, the right and left radiator hold-down clamps and the shroud center bracket.
5. Remove the horns and bolts retaining the fan shroud to the radiator support.
6. Remove the radiator and fan shroud from the vehicle.
7. Installation is the reverse of the removal procedure.

1968-74 Corvette

1. Drain the radiator.
2. Raise the hood and insert a bolt in the hole of the hood support.
3. Remove the radiator inlet and outlet hoses and, if applicable, the transmission coolant hoses.
4. If applicable, remove the supply tank hose at the radiator connection.
5. Remove the shroud to radiator support bracket screws (the L88 engine does not have a fan shroud).
6. Remove the shroud to radiator baffle bracket screws and let the shroud rest on the fan.
7. Remove the radiator upper support bracket screws and carefully lift the radiator from the car.
8. Install in the reverse order of removal.

Water Pump R & R

1. Drain the radiator and loosen the fan pulley bolts.
2. Disconnect the heater hose, lower radiator hose and, if applicable, the bypass hose at the water pump.
3. On V8 engines, remove the Delcotron upper brace. Loosen the swivel bolt and remove the fan belt.
4. On Mark IV engines, disconnect the power steering and air conditioning belts and swivel the power steering pump to one side.
5. Remove the fan blade and pulley. Replace a bent or damaged fan.

NOTE: thermostatic fan clutches must be kept in an "in-car" position. When removed from the car the assembly should be supported so that the clutch disc remains in a vertical plane to prevent silicone fluid leakage.

6. Remove the water pump attaching bolts and, if applicable, the power steering-to-pump bolts and remove the pump and gasket.

NOTE: on six-cylinder engines, pull the pump straight out of the block first to avoid damage to the impeller.

7. Install the pump assembly using a new gasket. Coat the gasket on both sides with sealer. Tighten the 5/16 in. bolts to 15 ft. lbs. (six-cylinder) and the 3/8 in. bolts (V8) to 30 ft. lbs.
8. Install the pulley and fan.
9. On Mark IV engines, install the power steering and air conditioning bolts.
10. Connect the hoses and fill the cooling system.
11. On V8 engines, install the Delcotron upper brace and fan belt. Install the power steering pump bolt.
12. Adjust the belts, then start the engine and check for leaks.

Thermostat R & R

The thermostat is located inside a housing on the front of the cylinder head on six-cylinder engines and between the intake manifold and the cylinder head (forward) on V8 engines. It is not necessary to remove the radiator hose from the thermostat housing.

1. Remove the two retaining bolts from the thermostat housing and lift up the housing with the hose attached. Remove the thermostat.
2. Insert the new thermostat, spring end down, and install the housing with a new gasket.

EMISSION CONTROLS

Positive Crankcase Ventilation

In this system, crankcase vapors are drawn into the intake manifold and burned as part of the engine combustion. The "positive" ventilation uses a vented-mesh oil filler cap for clean air intake to the crankcase and the "closed positive" system draws clean air from the carburetor air cleaner. Only the closed system is used after 1968. The ventilation flow is regulated by a PCV valve.

Air Injection Reactor

The A.I.R. system injects compressed air into the exhaust system, close enough to the exhaust valves to continue the burning of the normally unburned segment of the exhaust gases. To do this it employs an air injection pump and a system of hoses, valves, tubes, etc., necessary to carry the compressed air from the pump to the exhaust manifolds. Carburetors and distributors for A.I.R. engines have specific modifications to adapt them to the air injection system; these components should not be interchanged with those intended for use on engines that do not have the system.

A diverter valve is used to prevent backfiring. The valve senses sudden increases in manifold vacuum and ceases the injection of air during fuel-rich periods. During coasting, this valve diverts the entire air flow through the muffler and during high engines speeds, expels it through a relief valve. Check valves in the system prevent exhaust gases from entering the pump.

Air Pump R & R

1. Disconnect the air hoses at the pump.
2. Hold the pump pulley from turning and loosen the pulley bolts.
3. Loosen the pump mounting bolt and adjustment bracket bolt. Remove the drive belt.
4. Remove the mounting bolts and then remove the pump.
5. Install the pump using a reverse of the removal procedure.

Controlled Combustion System

This system increases combustion efficiency by means of leaner carburetor mixtures and revised distributor calibration. On most installations, thermostatically controlled air cleaner intakes draw warm air from an exhaust manifold shroud. This allows leaner carburetor settings and improves engine warm-up. A higher temperature thermostat is employed on C.C.S. cars.

Particular attention must be paid to the tuning of C.C.S. equipped engines to maintain performance and efficient exhaust emission control.

Evaporative Emission Control

Introduced on California cars in 1970, and nationwide in 1971, this system reduces the amount of escaping gasoline vapors. Float bowl emissions are controlled by internal carburetor modifications. Redesigned bowl vents, reduced bowl capacity, heat shields, and improved intake manifold - to - carburetor insulation serve to reduce vapor loss into the atmosphere. The venting of fuel tank vapors into the air has been stopped. Fuel vapors are now directed through lines to a canister containing an activated charcoal filter. Unburned vapors are trapped here until the engine is started. When the engine is running, the canister is purged by air drawn in by manifold vacuum. The air and fuel vapors are then directed into the engine to be burned. This system is designed to reduce fuel vapor emission. The canister filter should be replaced every 12 months or 12,000 miles. To remove the canister and replace the filter, proceed as follows:

1. Note the positions of the hoses, then disconnect them from the canister.
2. Loosen the clamps and remove the canister.
3. Remove the bottom of the canister and pull out the filter.
4. Install a new filter and assemble the bottom to the canister.
5. Install the canister and tighten the clamp bolts.
6. Install the hoses in their original positions.

Anti-Dieseling Solenoid

Beginning in 1968 some models may have an idle speed solenoid on the carburetor. All 1972-74 models have idle solenoids. Due to the leaner carburetor settings required for emission control, the engine may have a tendency to "diesel" or "run-on" after the ignition is turned off. The carburetor solenoid, energized when the ignition is on, maintains the normal idle speed. When the ignition is turned off, the solenoid is de-energized and permits the throttle valves to fully close, thus preventing run-on. For adjustment of carburetors with idle solenoids see Carburetor Adjustments.

Transmission Controlled Spark

Introduced in 1970, this system controls exhaust emissions by eliminating vacuum advance in the lower forward gears.

1970

The 1970 system consists of a transmission switch, solenoid vacuum switch, time delay relay, and a thermostatic water temperature switch. The solenoid vacuum switch is energized in the lower gears via the transmission switch and closes off distributor vacuum. The two-way transmission switch is activated by the shifter shaft on manual transmissions, and by oil pressure on automatic transmissions. The switch de-energizes the solenoid in high gear, the plunger extends and uncovers the vacuum port, and the distributor receives full vacuum. The temperature switch overrides the system when engine temperature is below 63° or above 232°. This allows vacuum advance in all gears. A time delay relay opens 15 seconds after the ignition is switched on. Full vacuum advance during this delay eliminates the possibility of stalling.

1971

The 1971 system is similar, except that the vacuum solenoid (now called a Combination Emissions Control solenoid) serves two functions. One function is to control distributor vacuum; the added function is to act as a deceleration throttle stop in high gear. This cuts down on emissions when the vehicle is coming to a stop in high gear. The CEC solenoid is controlled by a temperature switch, a transmission switch, and a 20 second time delay relay. This system also contains a reversing relay, which energizes the solenoid when the transmission switch, temperature switch or time delay completes the CEC circuit to ground. This system is directly opposite the 1970 system in operation. The 1970 vacuum solenoid was normally open to allow vacuum advance and when energized, closed to block vacuum. The 1971 system is normally closed blocking vacuum advance and when energized, opens to allow vacuum advance. The temperature switch completes the CEC circuit to ground when engine temperature is below 82°. Some Camaros and Corvettes also have a high temperature terminal on the switch to complete the CEC circuit when coolant temperature reaches 232°. The time delay relay allows vacuum advance (and raised idle speed) for 20 seconds after the ignition key is turned to the "on" position. Models with an automatic transmission and air conditioning also have a solid state timing device which engages the air conditioning compressor for three seconds after the ignition key is turned to the "off" position to prevent the engine from running-on. Two throttle settings are necessary; one for curb idle and one for emission control on coast. Both settings are described in the tune-up section.

1972-74

The 1972-74 L6 system is similar to that used in 1971, except that an idle stop solenoid has been added to the system. In the energized position, the solenoid maintains engine speed at a predetermined fast idle. When de-energized the solenoid allows the throttle plates to close beyond the normal idle position; thus cutting off the air supply and preventing engine run-on. The L6 is the only 1972-74 engine with a CEC valve, which serves the same deceleration function as in 1971. The 1972 time delay relay delays full vacuum 20 seconds after the transmission is shifted into high gear. On 1973-74 models, the delay relay is replaced by a time relay which energizes the CEC valve for 20 seconds after the key is turned to the On position. This relay is not used on 1973 V8 engines with small blocks. V8 engines use a vacuum advance solenoid similar to that used in 1970. This relay is normally closed to block vacuum and opens when energized to allow vacuum advance. The solenoid controls distributor vacuum advance and performs no throttle positioning function. The idle stop solenoid used operates in the same manner as the one on L6 engines. All air-conditioned cars have an additional anti-diesel (run-on) solenoid which engages the compressor clutch for three seconds after the ignition is switched off. The

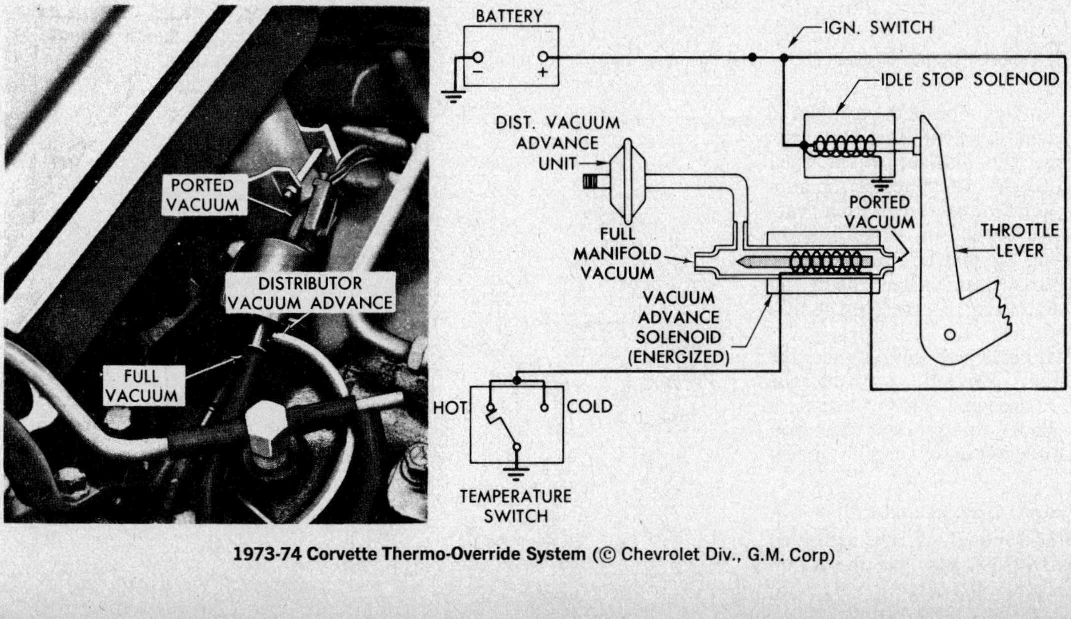
PORTED VACUUM
DISTRIBUTOR VACUUM ADVANCE
FULL VACUUM
BATTERY
IGN. SWITCH
IDLE STOP SOLENOID
DIST. VACUUM ADVANCE UNIT
PORTED VACUUM
FULL MANIFOLD VACUUM
THROTTLE LEVER
VACUUM ADVANCE SOLENOID (ENERGIZED)
HOT
COLD
TEMPERATURE SWITCH

1973-74 Corvette Thermo-Override System (© Chevrolet Div., G.M. Corp)

1973-74 Chevrolet TCS system differs from the 1972 system in three ways. The 23 second upshift delay has been replaced by a 20 second starting relay. This relay closes to complete the TCS circuit and open the TCS solenoid, allowing vacuum advance, for 20 seconds after the key is turned to the "on" position. The operating temperature of the temperature override switch has been raised to 93°, and the switch that was used to engage the A/C compressor when the key was turned "off" has been eliminated. All models are equipped with an electric throttle control solenoid to prevent run-on. The 1973 TCS system is used on all full-size station wagons equipped with a 165 hp 350 or a 170 hp 400.

1973-74 Corvette models are equipped with a Thermo-Override system instead of the normal TCS system. This system consists of a three-position temperature switch, which is mounted in the right cylinder head and a two-position vacuum advance solenoid. Three vacuum lines are connected to the solenoid, a ported vacuum line from the carburetor, a vacuum line from the intake manifold, and a vacuum line that runs to the distributor vacuum advance unit. When the engine temperature is between 93°F and 232°F, the temperature switch contacts are open and the vacuum solenoid is de-energized. This causes carburetor-ported vacuum to control the operation of the distributor vacuum advance unit. When the engine temperature is below 93°F or above 232°F, the temperature switch contacts are closed and the vacuum solenoid is energized. This moves the plunger in the solenoid to block the ported vacuum opening and connect manifold vacuum to the distributor. When the engine reaches normal temperature, the temperature switch contacts open and ported vacuum is restored to the distributor.

For diagnosis procedures, see the Unit Repair Section. Any of the methods of exhaust emission control requires close and frequent attention to tune-up factors of engine maintenance.

Exhaust Gas Recirculation

All 1973-74 engines are equipped with exhaust gas recirculation (EGR). This system consists of a metering valve, a vacuum line to the carburetor, and cast-in exhaust gas passages in the intake manifold. The EGR valve is controlled by carburetor vacuum, and accordingly opens and closes to admit exhaust gases into the fuel/air mixture. The exhaust gases lower the combustion temperature, and reduce the amount of oxides of nitrogen (NO_X) produced. The valve is closed at idle and wide open throttle, but is open between the two extreme throttle positions.

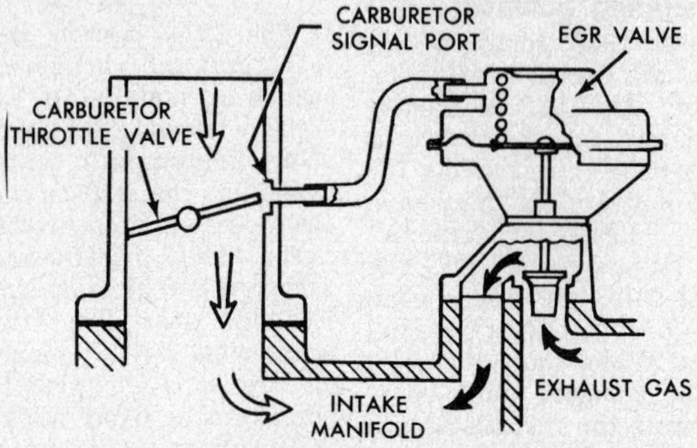
CARBURETOR
SIGNAL PORT
EGR VALVE
CARBURETOR
THROTTLE VALVE
INTAKE
MANIFOLD
EXHAUST GAS

EGR system schematic
(© Chevrolet Div., G.M. Corp)

As the car accelerates, the carburetor throttle plate uncovers the vacuum port for the EGR valve. At 3–5 in. Hg, the EGR valve opens and then some of the exhaust gases are allowed to flow into the air/fuel mixture to lower the combustion temperature. At full-throttle the valve closes again.

EGR Valve R & R

1. Detach the vacuum line from the EGR valve.
2. Unfasten the two bolts which attach the valve to the manifold. Withdraw the valve.
3. Installation is the reverse of removal. Always use a new gasket between the valve and the manifold.

ENGINE

Engine application and specification tables may be found at the beginning of this section.

The following service procedures apply to all engines, except where differences are specified. The 396, 402, 427 and 454 V8 (Mark IV large blocks) are essentially the same engine. Similarly, the 283, 307, 327, 350, and 400 small block series engines all utilize the same design.

Engine R & R

Chevrolet

1. Remove the hood. Scribe lines

1 Cap nipple
2 Rotor
3 Spring clip
4 Distributor
5 Distributor gear
6 Gasket
7 Intake manifold
8 Gasket
12 Oil pump shaft
13 Oil pump
14 Sleeve
15 Drain plug
16 Cylinder block
17 Gasket
18 Gasket
19 Timing cover
20 Damper
21 Pulley
22 Fan
23 Spacer
24 Pulley
25 Water pump
26 Thermostat
27 Water neck
28 Carburetor stud
29 Gasket
30 Shaft
31 Vacuum unit
32 Distributor cap

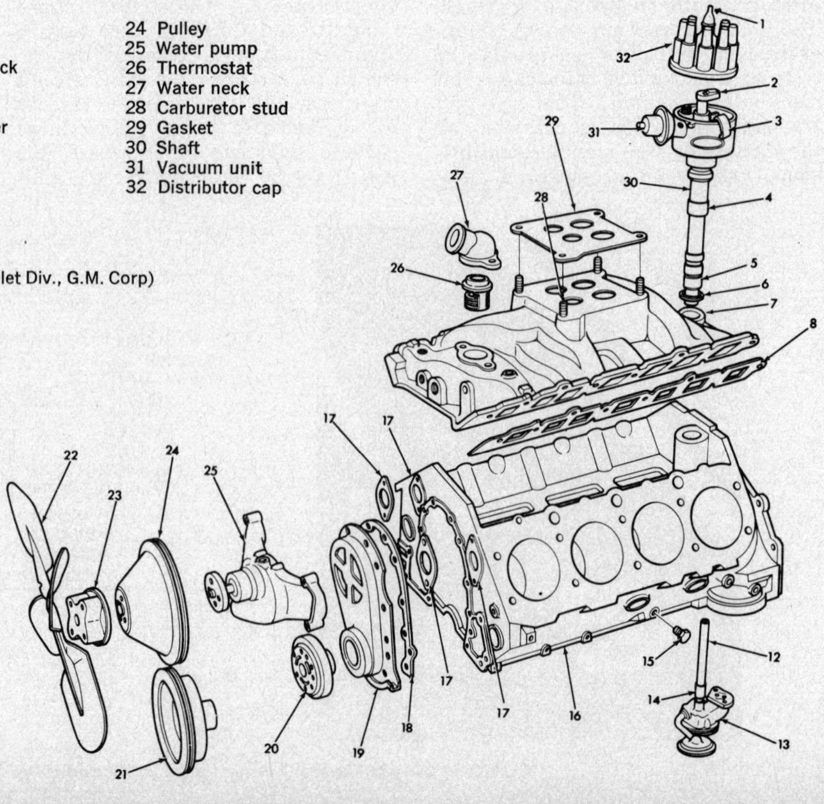

Mark IV V8 exploded view (© Chevrolet Div., G.M. Corp)

around the hinges so that the hood can be installed in its original location.

2. Remove the air cleaner.
3. Disconnect the battery cables at the battery.
4. Remove the radiator and shroud.
5. Remove the fan blade and pulley.
6. Disconnect wires at:
   a. C.E.C. solenoid.
   b. Coil.
   c. Temperature switch.
   d. Delcotron.
   e. Starter solenoid.
   f. Oil pressure sending unit.
7. Disconnect:
   a. Accelerator linkage at the pedal.
   b. Oil pressure gauge line, if so equipped.
   c. Exhaust pipes at the manifold flanges.
   d. Engine cooler lines, if so equipped.
   e. Vacuum line to the power brake unit, if so equipped.
   f. Fuel line (front tank) at the fuel pump.
8. Remove the power steering pump, leaving the hoses attached to the pump.
9. Raise the car on a hoist.
10. Drain the cooling system and the crankcase.
11. Remove the driveshaft.

NOTE: if a plug for the driveshaft opening in the transmission is not available, drain the transmission.

12. Disconnect:
    a. Shift linkage at the transmission.
    b. Speedometer cable at the transmission.
    c. Transmission cooler lines, if so equipped.
    d. TCS switch at the transmission.
13. On vehicles with synchromesh transmissions, disconnect the clutch linkage at the cross-shaft then remove the cross-shaft at the frame bracket.
14. Lower the vehicle and remove the rocker arm covers and install engine lifting adapter on the cylinder heads.
15. Raise the engine enough to take the weight off the front mounts, then remove the front mount through bolts.
16. Remove the rear mount to crossmember bolts.
17. Raise the engine enough to take the weight off the rear mount, then remove the crossmember.

NOTE: on Chevrolets it is necessary to remove the mount from the transmission before the crossmember can be removed.

18. Remove the engine/transmission assembly as a unit.
19. To remove the clutch and transmission from the engine:
    a. Remove the clutch housing cover plate screws.
    b. Remove the clutch housing to engine attaching bolts, then, remove the transmission and clutch housing as a unit.

Caution Do not let the weight of the transmission hang on the spline because the clutch disc may be easily damaged.

    c. Remove the starter and clutch housing rear cover plate.
    d. Loosen the clutch mounting bolts one turn at a time (to prevent distortion of the clutch cover) until the spring pressure is released. Remove all the bolts, clutch disc and pressure plate assembly.
20. To remove the automatic transmission:
    a. Remove the starter and the converter housing underpan.
    b. Remove the flywheel to converter attaching bolts.
    c. Supporting both the engine and transmission, remove the transmission to engine mounting bolts.
    d. Slowly guide the engine from the transmission.

Corvette

This procedure is basically the same for all engines regardless of size and model year. Certain pieces of optional equipment require minor specific changes but the overall operation remains the same.

1. The engine may be removed separately from the transmission, through the top of the engine compartment. Begin by draining the cooling system and the engine crankcase.
2. Disconnect the battery cables from the battery terminals and remove the air cleaner and ignition shields. Cover the carburetor.
3. Disconnect wiring at the alternator, temperature sending unit, oil pressure switch, primary coil lead, and CEC solenoid when applicable. Also disconnect the engine ground wires and the accelerator rod at the bellcrank.
4. Disconnect the power brake hose at the manifold end when applicable. Disconnect the tachometer drive cable at the distributor and the throttle valve if so equipped. Scribe the hood hinge locations on the support brackets and remove the hood.
5. Remove the radiator shroud and radiator, then the fan and fan assembly. If the car is equipped with power steering, remove the pump mounting bolts and push the pump into the vacant radiator opening. An alternate method is to disconnect the pump lines and plug both ends.
6. Remove the heater hose from the clip at the alternator bracket, then disconnect the hose from the engine connections and move back for extra clearance. Remove the rocker arm covers and place the vehicle on jack stands.
7. Remove the center head bolt on each head, and install the lift tool to the engine. Unhook the distributor cap and move it forward. Cover the distributor with a clean cloth.
8. Disconnect the exhaust pipes at the manifold flanges. On cars equipped with large block engines, the front stud on each manifold must be removed before the exhaust pipes can be removed.
9. Disconnect the wire leads at the starter solenoid. Remove the gas tank line at the fuel pump and plug the line to prevent fuel siphoning.
10. Block the clutch pedal in the return position and remove the clutch cross-shaft. Remove the oil filter and oil cooler lines if so equipped. Remove the starting motor. If the Corvette is equipped with a manual transmission, remove the flywheel cover plate. If equiped with an automatic transmission, remove the converter underpan.
11. Remove the front engine mount thru-bolts. Support the transmission with a floor jack and remove the transmission-to-engine bolts. If the car has an automatic transmission, remove the converter-to-flywheel bolts and install the converter holding bracket to the transmission.
12. Move the engine forward and upward as needed to clear the engine compartment.
13. Replacement is the reversal of this procedure.

Manifolds

Combination Manifold Used on 6 Cylinder Engines

All Chevrolet six cylinder engines are equipped with a combination intake and exhaust manifold. The exhaust manifold is equipped with a heat riser valve which, when the engine is cold, deflects the hot exhaust gases against the intake manifold to assist in rapid warm up.

If the engine doesn't seem to warm up properly or, when operated at a high speed, acts lean, it is a good idea to check this heat riser valve to be certain that it is functioning freely. Failure of the heat riser valve to open will increase the time required to warm the engine. Failure of the heat riser valve to close after the manifold is hot will cause the engine to run lean.

To remove the manifold assembly, disconnect the exhaust pipe flange and remove all connections to the carburetor. Take off the vacuum lines at the manifold and at the carburetor.

Remove the carburetor, and the manifold may be unbolted from the side of the cylinder head using socket wrenches and box wrenches. If necessary to remove either exhaust or intake manifolds they may be separated by removing one bolt and two nuts at center of assembly.

Before reinstalling the manifold, thoroughly clean all mating surfaces.

Intake Manifold R & R—V8

1. Remove the air cleaner.
2. Drain the radiator.
3. Disconnect:
   a. Battery cables at the battery.
   b. Upper radiator and heater hoses at the manifold.
   c. Crankcase ventilation hoses as required.
   d. Fuel line at the carburetor.
   e. Accelerator linkage at the pedal lever.
   f. Vacuum hose at the distributor.
   g. Power brake hose at the carburetor base or manifold, if applicable.
   h. Ignition coil and temperature sending switch wires.
4. Remove the distributor cap and scribe the rotor position relative to distributor body.
5. Remove the distributor.
6. If applicable, remove the Delcotron upper bracket.
7. Remove the manifold to head attaching bolts, then remove the manifold and carburetor as an assembly.
8. If the manifold is to be replaced, transfer the carburetor (and mounting studs), water outlet and thermostat (use a new gasket), heater hose adapter and, if applicable, the choke coil and EGR valve with its vacuum line.
9. Before installing the manifold, thoroughly clean the gasket and seal surfaces of the cylinder heads and manifold.
10. Install the manifold end seals, folding the tabs if applicable, and the manifold/head gaskets, using a sealing compound around the water passages. Make sure the gaskets are firmly cemented in place before installing the manifold.
11. When installing the manifold, care should be taken not to dislocate the end seals. It is helpful to use a pilot in the distributor opening. Tighten the manifold bolts to 30 ft. lbs. in the sequence illustrated.
12. Install the ignition coil.
13. Install the distributor with the rotor in its original location as indicated by the scribe line. If the engine has been disturbed, refer to "Distributor R&R" above.
14. If applicable, install the Delcotron upper bracket and adjust the belt tension.
15. Connect all components disconnected in Step 3 above.
16. Fill the cooling system, start the engine, check for leaks and adjust the ignition timing and carburetor idle speed and mixture.

Exhaust Manifold R & R—V8

1. If equipped with A.I.R., remove the air injector manifold assembly. The 1/4 in. pipe threads in the manifold are straight threads. Do not use a 1/4 in. tapered pipe tap.
2. Disconnect the battery.
3. If applicable, remove the air cleaner pre-heater shroud.
4. Remove the exhaust pipe flange nuts, then hang the pipe with wire.
5. Remove the manifold mounting bolts (end bolts first), then remove the manifold.
6. To install, clean the mating surfaces, then install the manifold with the center bolts first. Install the end bolts, then tighten all bolts to 20 ft. lbs.
7. To complete installation, reverse Steps 1 through 3.

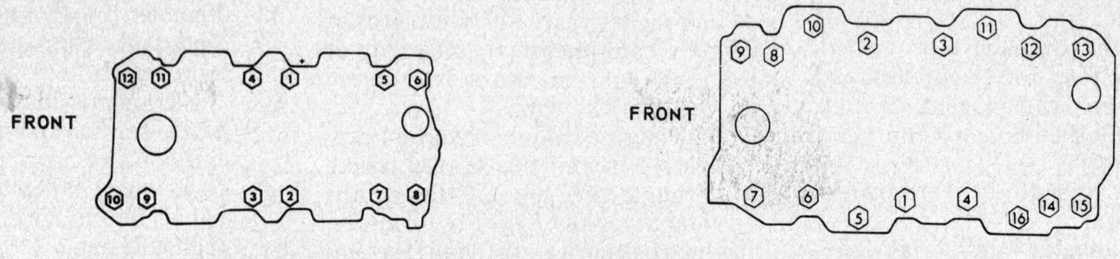
FRONT
FRONT

Intake manifold tightening sequence (left—small block V8; right—Mk. IV V8)
(© Chevrolet Div., G.M. Corp)

Valve System

Valve tappet clearances are listed in the Tune-Up Specifications table. Complete valve specifications are found in the Valve Specifications table.

Valve Guides

Valve guides are integral with the cylinder head. Valve guide bores may be reamed to accommodate oversize valve stems or the guides may be knurled (if wear permits) to allow the retention of standard size valves. Maximum allowable valve stem to guide bore clearance is .0027 in.

Valve Replacement

With cylinder head on bench and the rockers removed, compress the valve spring and remove the valve lock, seal, spring cap and spring.

Line the valve springs up on a flat surface. All should be the same height. Replace those that do not match with new.

Rocker Arm R & R

Rocker arms are removed by removing the adjusting nut. Be sure to adjust valve lash after replacing rocker arms.

NOTE: when replacing an exhaust rocker, move an old intake rocker to the exhaust rocker arm stud and install the new rocker arm on the intake stud.

Rocker arm studs that have damaged threads or are loose in the cylinder heads may be replaced with new studs available in 0.003 in. and 0.013 in. oversize or the bores may be tapped and screw-in replacement studs used. Do not attempt to install an oversize stud without reaming the stud bore. Studs are press-fit. Mark IV and late high-performance small-block engines use screw-in studs and pushrod guide plates.

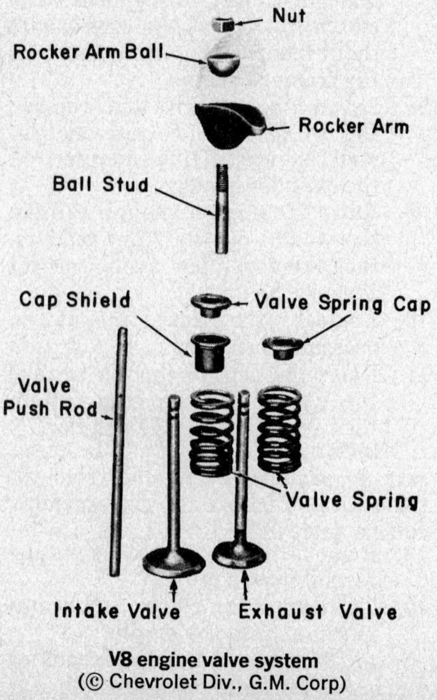
Nut
Rocker Arm Ball
Rocker Arm
Ball Stud
Cap Shield
Valve Spring Cap
Valve Push Rod
Valve Spring
Intake Valve
Exhaust Valve

V8 engine valve system
(© Chevrolet Div., G.M. Corp)

NOTE: if engine is equipped with the A.I.R. exhaust emission control system, the interfering components of the system must be removed. Disconnect the lines at the air injection nozzles in the exhaust manifolds.

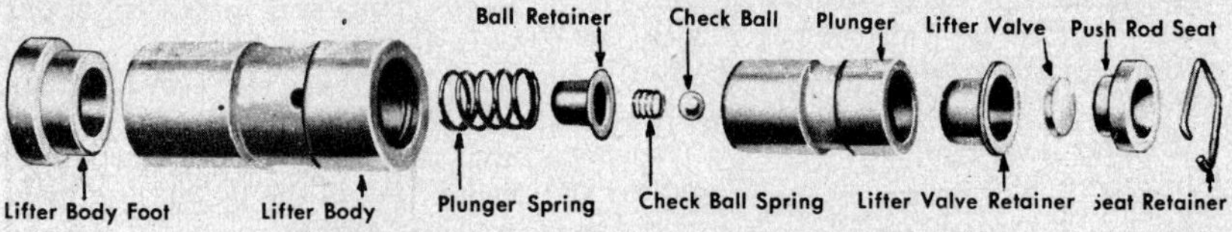

Ball Retainer
Check Ball
Plunger
Lifter Valve
Push Rod Seat
Lifter Body Foot
Lifter Body
Plunger Spring
Check Ball Spring
Lifter Valve Retainer
Seat Retainer

Typical hydraulic lifter exploded (© Chevrolet Div., G.M. Corp)

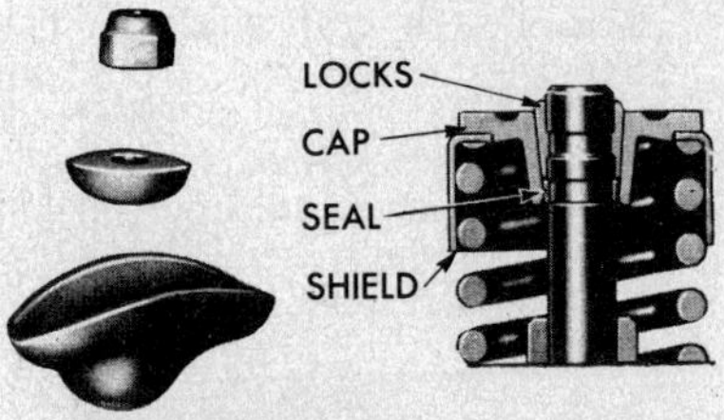

LOCKS
CAP
SEAL
SHIELD

6-cylinder head and rocker arm assembly, 230 cu. in. engine
(© Chevrolet Div., G.M. Corp)

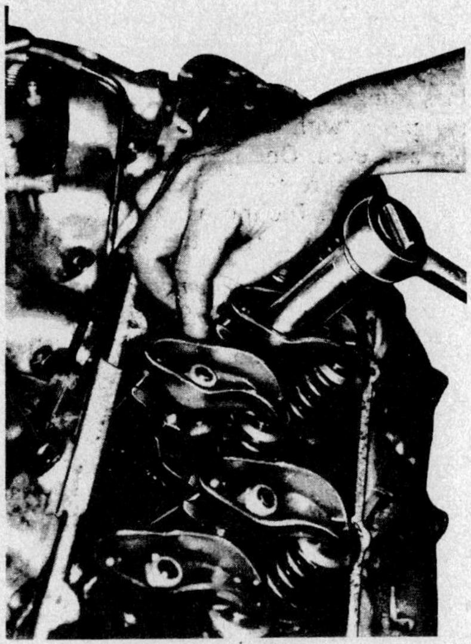

V8 valve adjustment
(© Chevrolet Div., G.M. Corp)

Valve Tappet Adjustment

Hydraulic Lifters

On six-cylinder engines, crank the engine until the distributor rotor points to the No. 1 firing position and the breaker points are just opening. The following valves may be adjusted:

No. 1	exhaust	intake
No. 2		intake
No. 3	exhaust	
No. 4		intake
No. 5	exhaust	

To adjust the rest of the valves, crank the engine until the distributor rotor points to the No. 6 firing position and the breaker points are just opening. The following valves may be adjusted:

No. 2	exhaust	
No. 3		intake
No. 4	exhaust	
No. 5		intake
No. 6	exhaust	intake

On V8 engines, crank the engine until the No. 1 piston is at TDC of its compression stroke (the compression can be felt by placing a finger over the spark plug hole or by feeling the valves as the timing mark passes "0"—if the valves don't move, the No. 1 piston is at the top of its compression stroke). With the crankshaft in this position the following valves may be adjusted:

Exhaust—1, 3, 4, 8
Intake—1, 2, 5, 7

Rotate the crankshaft one full revolution until the timing pointer is again aligned with the "0". With the crankshaft thus in No. 6 cylinder firing position, the following valves may be adjusted:

Exhaust—2, 5, 6, 7
Intake—3, 4, 6, 8

Adjustment is made by backing off the rocker arm adjusting nut until there is play in the pushrod. Tighten the nut to remove the pushrod clearance (this can be felt by rotating the pushrod with the fingers while tightening the adjusting nut). When the pushrod cannot be freely turned, tighten the nut one additional turn to place the hydraulic lifter in the center of its travel. No further adjustment is required.

Mechanical Lifters

Position the crankshaft for No. 1, then No. 6 cylinder firing positions as described for adjusting hydraulic lifters above. In the case of mechanical lifters, however, use a feeler gauge between the rocker arm and the valve stem to obtain the correct clearance. The final valve lash setting is made with the engine running at normal operating temperature. Specified valve lash (hot) can be found in the Tune-Up Specifications at the beginning of this section.

Cylinder Head

R & R

6 Cylinder Models

To remove the cylinder head, detach the air cleaner and all rods, lines and vacuum tubes at the carburetor and manifold.

NOTE: if the engine is equipped with an exhaust emission control system, the injector connections must be disconnected at the cylinder head.

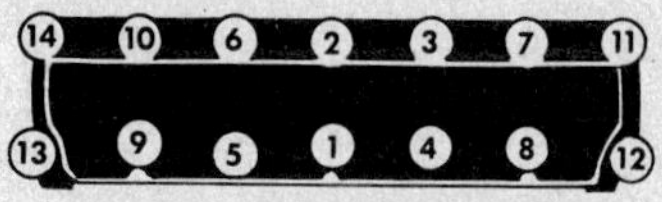

OHV 6 cylinder
(© Chevrolet Div., G.M. Corp)

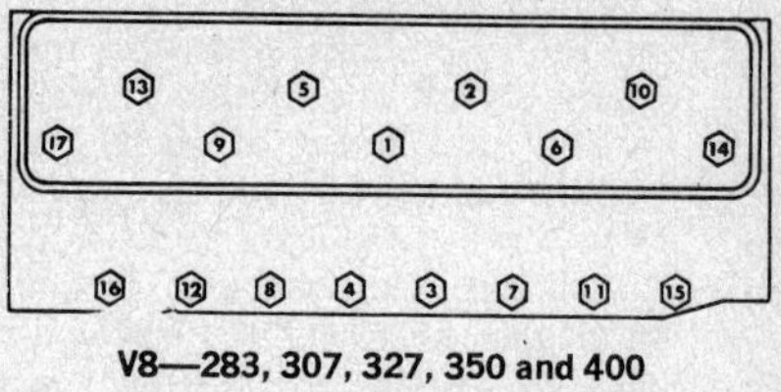

V8—283, 307, 327, 350 and 400

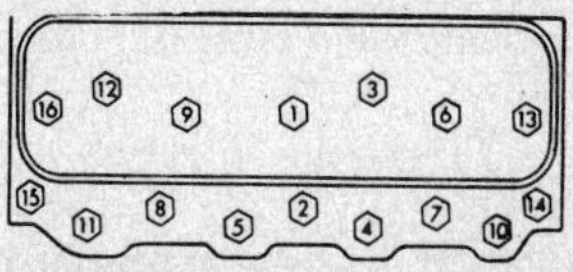

V8—396, 402, 427, 454

Disconnect any interfering components and tie back out of the way.

When installing, do not use sealer on the composition steel asbestos gasket. Coat the threads of the head bolts with sealing compound before installation. Tighten the head bolts in sequence (see the illustration at the beginning of this section) a little at a time until each is torqued to 95 ft. lbs. Install all components which were removed. Adjust the valve mechanism as described later.

Caution The 1/4 in. pipe threads at the cylinder head air injection nozzles are a straight pipe thread. Do not use a 1/4 in. tapered pipe tap. Hoses used in this air injection system are of special material. Do not substitute.

1. Unbolt the manifold from the cylinder head, but not from the exhaust pipe flange. The manifold is simply pulled away from the head.
2. Remove the engine side plate covers and the gas lines at the fuel pump. Unbolt and lift off the rocker cover, disconnect the oil line leads to the rockers.
3. The rocker levers are supported separately and may be left intact until the head is removed.
4. Unbolt and lift off the cylinder head.

V8 Models

1. Remove the intake manifold as described above.
2. Remove the exhaust manifolds as described above.

3. Back off the rocker arm nuts and pivot the rocker arms out of the way so that the pushrods can be removed. Identify the pushrods so that they can be reinstalled in their original locations.
4. Remove the cylinder head bolts and cylinder heads.
5. Install using new gaskets. The head gasket is installed with the bead up.

NOTE: coat a STEEL gasket on both sides with sealer. If a STEEL ASBESTOS gasket is used, do not apply sealer. Clean the bolt threads, apply sealing compound and install the bolts finger tight.

6. Tighten the head bolts a little at a time in the sequence illustrated in the Specifications at the beginning of this section. Tighten to a final torque of 65 ft. lbs. (small V8) or 85 ft. lbs. (Mark IV).
7. Install the exhaust and intake manifolds as described previously.
8. Adjust the valves as described later.

Timing Case

Crankshaft Pulley Replacement

NOTE: to prevent vibration damper damage, it is important that a puller be used to draw the pulley on the crankshaft.

6 Cylinder Models

1. Remove the radiator core and the fan belt. Remove accessory drive pulley and belt, if so equipped.
2. Use a screw-type puller to remove the balancer-pulley assembly.

V8 Models

1. Drain radiator and disconnect the hoses. Take off the fan belt, and the fan pulley assembly. Remove the battery.
2. Remove the fan shroud. Remove the radiator core. Unbolt the pulley portion of the balancer-pulley assembly.
3. Install screw-type puller and remove the balancer portion from the crankshaft.

Chilton's TIME SAVER

When replacing the crankshaft damper, it has been found that lightly polishing the crankshaft snout with crocus cloth will greatly ease replacement. This procedure will also assist in any future removals, as it is sometimes difficult to pull a damper even with a puller. Be sure that the polishing is not overdone, or the damper will wobble on the crankshaft.

Timing Case Cover and Front Oil Seal Replacement

NOTE: the timing case cover oil seal may be replaced without removing the case cover on all Corvettes and Chevrolets.

After gaining access to the oil seal, pry the old seal out of the cover with a screwdriver. Then lubricate the new seal and drive it into place with tool J-8340, or equivalent.

6 Cylinder and 396, 402, 427, 454 V8

1. Remove the radiator, fan belts and, using a puller, remove the crankshaft pulley. On V8 engines, remove the water pump.
2. Remove the timing case-to-engine attaching bolts and remove the two oil pan-to-timing case bolts. The front cover is changed, beginning 1974.

Cutting oil pan front seal
(© Chevrolet Div., G.M. Corp)

3. Slide the front cover forward until a knife can be positioned behind the cover, then cut the ends of the oil pan front seal off flush with the cylinder block on the two ends of the front cover.
4. Remove the front cover and clean all gasket mounting surfaces on the front cover, the block and the exposed portion of the oil pan.
5. Temporarily position a new oil pan front seal on the front of the oil pan and trim off the edges of the new seal so that it will fit flush with the engine block.
6. Remove the new front seal, coat it with sealer and install it on the front cover. Apply a bead of silicone rubber sealer to the place on the front of the oil pan where the cut off portion of the old seal will mate with the new oil pan front seal.
7. Install a centering tool in the crankshaft snout hole in the front cover and install the front cover on the engine.
8. Install the front cover bolts finger tight, remove the centering tool and tighten the cover bolts. Install the pulley, fan belts and radiator.

283, 327, 350 and 400 V8

1. Remove the crankshaft pulley. Remove the oil pan. The pan need not be removed on 1974 and later engines. Remove the water pump. Remove the screws holding the timing case cover to the block and remove the cover and gaskets.
2. Use a large screwdriver to pry the old seal out of the front face of the cover.
3. Install the new seal so that open end is toward the inside of the cover.
4. Check that the timing chain oil slinger is in place against the crankshaft sprocket.
5. Install the cover carefully onto the locating dowels.
6. Tighten the attaching screws to 6-8 ft. lbs.

Timing Chain Replacement

6 Cylinder Engines

Chevrolet timing gears are arranged so that (unless deliberately

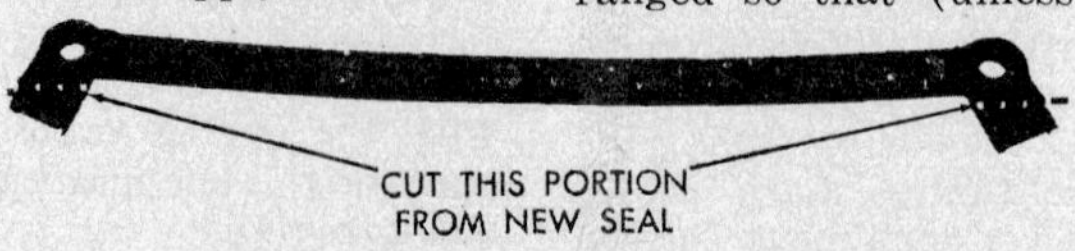
CUT THIS PORTION
FROM NEW SEAL

Fitting new oil pan front seal
(© Chevrolet Div., G.M. Corp)

disturbed) the valve timing will remain as set at the factory. Unless the gears are badly worn or seriously damaged, the valve timing will remain constant within reasonable limits.

If it becomes necessary to replace the timing gears due to wear or damage, remove the radiator core, disconnect the front motor mounts and jack up the front of the engine. Remove the fan belt, fan pulley, oil pan and timing case cover.

NOTE: the manufacturer recommends that the camshaft be removed from the car in order to remove and replace the gear in an arbor press.

Sometimes when the gear is being pressed on in place on the car, damage results to the thrust washer in back of the cam gear. Unfortunately, this damage is not noticed until the engine is started.

To replace the gear by removing the camshaft, remove the rocker arm assemblies and the distributor, take out all of the pushrods and all of the lifters. The camshaft may then be pulled out toward the front of the engine. It will be necessary to retime the ignition.

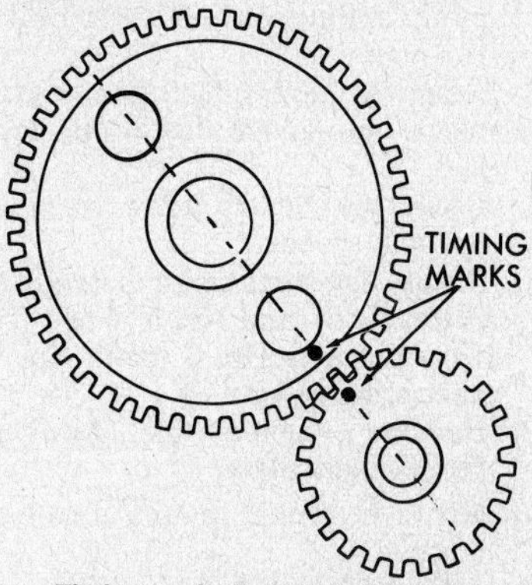
TIMING
MARKS
Timing mark alignment, 6 cylinder

Runout of the timing gear should not exceed .004 in. Backlash between the two gears should not be less than .004 in. nor more than .006 in. End clearance of the thrust plate should be .001 to .005 in.

Caution The use of a dial indicator will reduce the possibility of driving the gear too far onto the camshaft. This would alter the desired camshaft thrust clearance of .001 to .005 in. Use care when approaching the final position of the gear on the shaft, because it is impossible to increase the thrust clearance without pulling the new gear. In the absence of a dial indicator, this end thrust can be measured with a feeler gauge. In this case, the thrust clearance is to be measured between the camshaft gear hub and the thrust plate. A feeler gauge strip, inserted in either of the two large gear holes, will reach this point.

Timing Chain Replacement

V8 Models

To replace the chain, remove the radiator core, water pump, the harmonic balancer and the crankcase front cover. This will allow access to the timing chain. Crank the engine until the timing marks on both sprockets are nearest each other and in line between the shaft centers.

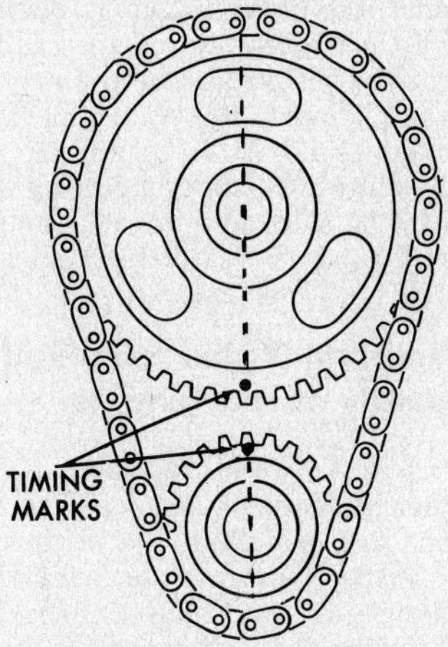
TIMING
MARKS
Timing mark alignment, V8

Then take out the three bolts that hold the camshaft gear to the camshaft. This gear is a light press fit on the camshaft and will come off easily. It is located by a dowel.

The chain comes off with the camshaft gear.

A gear puller will be required to remove the crankshaft gear.

Without disturbing the position of the engine, mount the new crankshaft gear on the shaft, and mount the chain over the camshaft gear. Arrange the camshaft gear in such a way that the timing marks will line up between the shaft centers and the camshaft locating dowel will enter the dowel hole in the cam sprocket.

Place the cam sprocket, with its chain mounted over it, in position on the front of the car and pull up with the three bolts that hold it to the camshaft.

After the gears are in place, turn the engine two full revolutions to make certain that the timing marks are in correct alignment between the shaft centers.

End-play of the V8 camshaft is zero.

Camshaft Replacement

6 Cylinder Engines

Due to the length of the six cylinder camshaft, a large amount of working room will be required in front of the engine to remove the camshaft. There are two ways to go about this task: either remove the engine assembly from the car, or remove the radiator, grille and supports that are mounted directly in front of the engine, disconnect the motor mounts and raise the front of the engine as required to gain enough clearance to remove the cam from the engine. In either case the following equipment will have to be removed from the engine:

1. Remove the valve cover. Loosen each rocker arm mounting stud enough to turn it sideways and remove the pushrods. Keep the pushrods in their proper order.
2. Remove the fuel pump.
3. Remove the inspection plates from the side of the engine and remove the valve lifters. Keep the lifters in order when they are removed.
5. Remove the timing case cover.
6. Turn the crankshaft until the timing marks on the camshaft and crankshaft gears are aligned.
7. Remove the distributor cap and mark the position of the distributor rotor relative to the distributor body and the position of the distributor body relative to the engine block. Remove the distributor.
8. Remove the camshaft from the engine.

V8

1. Drain the cooling system and remove the radiator. On Corvettes, remove the hood.
2. Remove the water pump and the timing case cover.
3. Turn the crankshaft until the timing marks on the camshaft and crankshaft gears are aligned.
4. Remove the valve covers and loosen each rocker arm nut enough to turn the rocker to the side and remove the pushrods. Keep the pushrods in order when they are removed from the engine.
5. Remove the distributor cap and mark the position of the rotor relative to the distributor body and the position of the distributor body relative to the engine. Remove the distributor.
6. Remove the intake manifold, then remove the valve lifters from the engine. Keep the lifters in order when they are removed from the engine.
7. Remove the fuel pump.
8. Remove the timing chain and sprockets from the engine.
9. Install two 5/16 in. 18x4 bolts in the holes in the front of the cam and carefully slide it out of the engine.

NOTE: On some engine and model combinations it will be necessary to disconnect the motor mounts and jack up the front of the engine or remove the grille from the car in order to gain adequate clearance in front of the engine to get the camshaft out of the engine.

Pistons and Connecting Rods

Assembling Piston to Connecting Rod

6 Cylinder Engines

Where split skirt-type pistons are being installed, the split in the skirt of the piston should be placed opposite the clamp screw of the wrist-pin. This is also opposite the number on the bottom of the connecting rod.

Where solid skirt slipper-type pistons are being replaced, it is unimportant which way the piston is mounted onto the connecting rod. However, if the old pistons are being reinstalled, the piston should be carefully marked before it is detached from the connecting rod in order that it may be replaced on the same side from which it was removed.

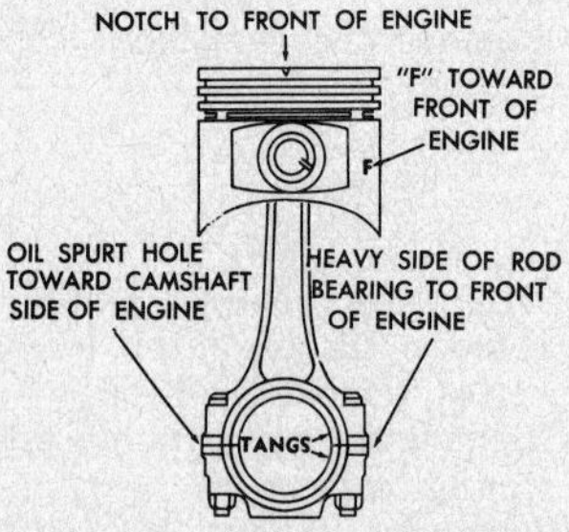

NOTCH TO FRONT OF ENGINE
"F" TOWARD FRONT OF ENGINE
OIL SPURT HOLE TOWARD CAMSHAFT SIDE OF ENGINE
HEAVY SIDE OF ROD BEARING TO FRONT OF ENGINE
TANGS

Correct relation of piston to rod, 6-cylinder 230 and 250 cu. in. engines

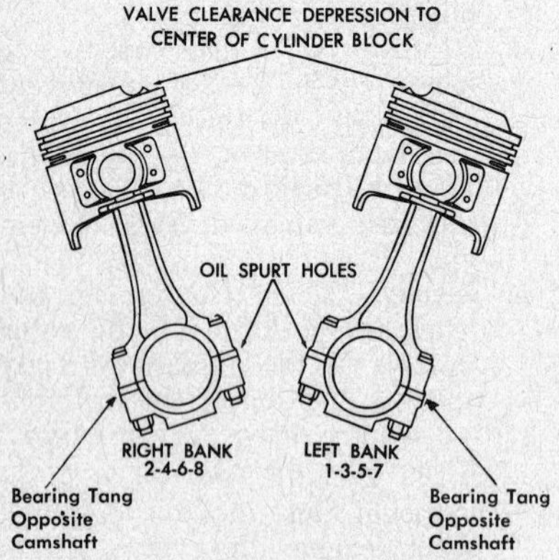

VALVE CLEARANCE DEPRESSION TO CENTER OF CYLINDER BLOCK
OIL SPURT HOLES
RIGHT BANK 2-4-6-8
LEFT BANK 1-3-5-7
Bearing Tang Opposite Camshaft
Bearing Tang Opposite Camshaft

Piston-to-rod relationship—Mk. IV V8

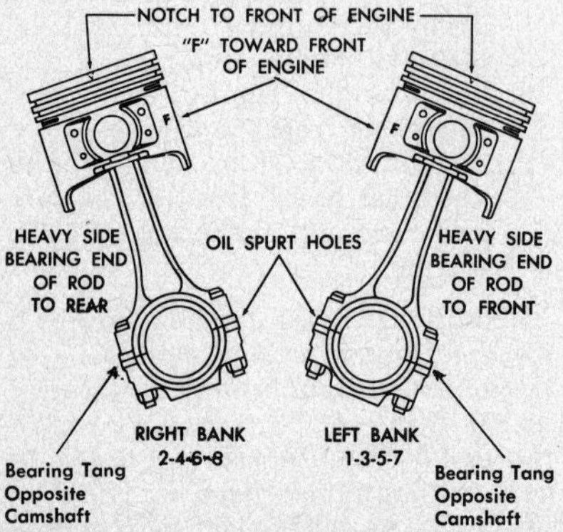

NOTCH TO FRONT OF ENGINE
"F" TOWARD FRONT OF ENGINE
HEAVY SIDE BEARING END OF ROD TO REAR
OIL SPURT HOLES
HEAVY SIDE BEARING END OF ROD TO FRONT
RIGHT BANK 2-4-6-8
LEFT BANK 1-3-5-7
Bearing Tang Opposite Camshaft
Bearing Tang Opposite Camshaft

Piston-to-rod relationship—small block V8

V8 Engines

Pistons are marked with a cast depression at the top of the piston and also the letter F on the piston strut. This depression and F always go toward the front.

For the left bank, pistons Nos. 1, 3, 5, and 7, the heavy flange at the bottom of the connecting rod goes on the side of the piston having the depression and F mark. For the right bank, cylinders Nos. 2, 4, 6, and 8, the heavy flange on the connecting rod goes to the side opposite the stamped letter F and the cast depression in the top of the piston.

Assembling Piston and Rod Assembly to the Engine

6 Cylinder Models

When assembling the rods to the pistons and installing the pistons in their respective bores, be sure that the flange, or heavy side of the rod at the bearing end, is toward the front of the piston (cast depression in top of piston head). The oil hole in the connecting rod goes toward the camshaft side of the engine.

V8 Models

Place the piston and rod assemblies into the cylinder so that the depression cast into the top of the piston (and the letter F stamped on the boss of the piston) face front. Double check that the pistons are in the correct bank by noting that on the left bank, pistons Nos. 1, 3, 5 and 7, the heavy flange on the connecting rod will also face forward, but on the right bank, cylinders Nos. 2, 4, 6 and 8, the heavy flange on the connecting rod will face toward the rear.

Piston Rings

Replacement

Before replacing rings, inspect cylinder bores.

1. Using an internal micrometer, check the cylinder bores for taper. The bore must not be out of round by more than 0.005 in. and it must not "taper" more than 0.010 in. "Taper" is the difference in wear between two bore measurements in any cylinder. Bore any cylinder beyond limits of out of roundness or taper to diameter of next available oversize piston that will clean up wear.
2. If bore is within limits dimensionally, examine bore visually. It should be dull silver in color and exhibit pattern of machining cross hatching intersecting at about 45 degrees.
3. If cylinder bore is in satisfactory condition, place each ring in bore in turn and square it in bore with head of piston. Measure ring gap.
4. Check ring side clearance by installing rings on piston, and inserting feeler gauge of correct dimension between ring and lower land.
5. Space ring gaps at equidistant intervals around piston circumference. Be sure to install piston in its original bore. Install short lengths of rubber tubing over connecting rod bolts to prevent damage to rod journal. Install ring compressor over rings on piston. Lower piston rod assembly into bore until ring compressor contacts block. Using wooden handle of hammer push piston into bore while guiding rod onto journal.

Engine Lubrication

Oil Pan Removal

Chevrolet 6 Cylinder Manual Transmission

The oil pan can be removed, either after removing engine, or as follows:

1. Drain radiator and oil pan.
2. Disconnect gas tank line at fuel pump and upper and lower radiator hoses.
3. Remove clutch housing-to-engine block bolt above dowel on right side.
4. Raise vehicle on hoist or place on jack stands.
5. Rotate engine to align distributor rotor No. 3. and No. 5 plug wire. (This locates No. 6 crank throw part way up.)
6. Remove starter and flywheel front cover plate.
7. Remove front mount through bolts.
8. Jack up front of engine. Raise as far as possible always using care by checking various dash and body tunnel clearances.
9. Remove front engine mount frame bracket on right side and remove oil filter where necessary.
10. Remove oil pan screws and lower pan to frame.
11. Remove oil pump to gain clearance, then remove oil pan by sliding and rotating front to right and then to rear, and down at an angle. (On certain earlier models, these procedures may be varied in some self-evident areas.)
12. Install in reverse of above.

NOTE: gasket can be replaced by completely removing pan from vehicle.

Chevrolet 6 Cylinder Automatic Transmission

1. Drain radiator and crankcase.
2. Disconnect gas tank line at fuel pump, and radiator hoses at radiator.

3. Remove clutch housing-to-engine block bolt above dowel pin on each side.
4. Rotate engine to align distributor between No. 3 and No. 5 plug wires. (This locates No. 6 crank throw part way up.)
5. Raise vehicle on hoist or on jack stands.
6. Remove converter cover pan, and starter assembly.
7. Follow Steps 7 through 12, listed above.

Chevrolet—V8

1. Disconnect battery negative cable.
2. Remove distributor cap from distributor to prevent breakage against firewall.
3. Drain cooling system. Remove radiator hoses, and remove oil dipstick and tube, where necessary.
4. Remove fan blade assembly.
5. Raise car, and drain engine oil.
6. Remove bolts from engine front mounts. Disconnect and remove starter.
7. On cars with automatic transmissions, remove converter housing underpan.
8. Disconnect the exhaust Y pipe from the manifolds.
9. Rotate crankshaft until timing mark on the damper is at six o'clock position.
10. Using a block of wood and a suitable jack, raise engine enough to insert 2 x 4 in. wood blocks under engine mounts then lower engine onto blocks.
11. Remove engine oil pan.
12. Install by reversing removal procedures.

NOTE: the 396, 402, 427, and 454 cu. in. engines use three 1/4 in. attaching bolts at crankcase front cover; one at each corner, and one at the lower center.

Corvette

1. Disconnect battery, and remove dipstick and tube.
2. Raise car and support on stands. Drain engine oil.
3. Remove starter and flywheel underpan.
4. Disconnect steering idler arm and lower steering linkage.
5. Remove oil pan and discard gaskets and seals.
6. On high performance engines, the oil baffle must be removed before additional operations can be performed.

NOTE: on the 427 and 454 cu. in. engine, the oil pan has three 1/4 in. attaching bolts at crankcase front cover; one at each front corner, and one at lower center.

7. Install by reversing removal procedure.

Oil Filter

The V8 oil filter is located under the engine at the left side just forward of the flywheel housing and is accessible from underneath the car. The L6 filter is on the lower, right, front side of the block.

Torque on the filter should be 25 ft. lbs. This is equivalent to one and one-third turns after the filter has been brought up snug to the case.

Oil Pump Replacement

On all Chevrolet engines, the oil pump is located in the oil pan, and it is driven by a tang from the distributor shaft.

On six-cylinder engines, the pump is flange-mounted to the under side of the crankcase with two cap screws.

On V8 models, the oil pump is bolted to the rear, main bearing cap. Oil is fed from the pump up through the rear, main bearing cap.

Rear Main Bearing Oil Seal Replacement

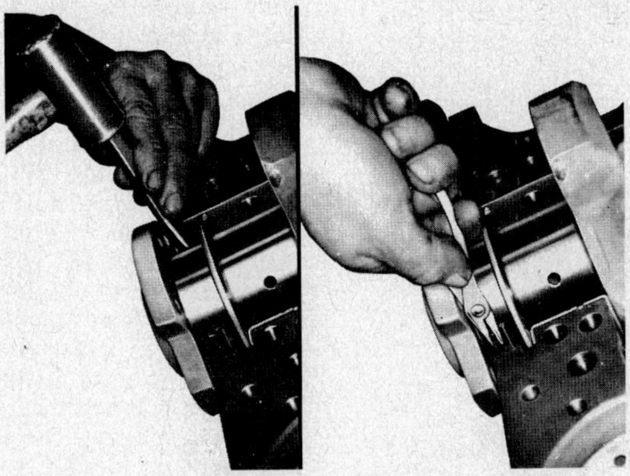

Rear main seal removal
(© Chevrolet Div., G.M. Corp)

Neoprene Seal

1. Remove rear main bearing cap and pry old seal from groove. Insert new seal with lubricant only on the lip. Do not get oil on the glue-treated parting line surfaces. Lip faces front of engine.
2. Using a hammer and small punch, revolve the upper half of the seal until it protrudes far enough to remove with pliers.
3. Oil the seal except at the glue-treated ends and, using a hammer handle, roll the seal into place in the block.
4. These seals are made to size and require no trimming. Install the lower half over the crankshaft and in place onto the block.

CLUTCH

Clutches are of the diaphragm spring type. The throwout bearing is a ball bearing with no provision for lubrication. The throwout fork pivots on a ball stud which is mounted in the rear face of the bellhousing.

Clutch R & R

All Models

1. Support the engine and remove the transmission as described in "Manual Transmission R&R."
2. Disconnect the clutch fork push-rod and spring.
3. Remove the flywheel housing.
4. Slide the clutch fork from the ball stud and remove the fork from the dust boot. The ball stud is threaded into the clutch housing and is easily replaced, if necessary.
5. Install a clutch pilot tool.

NOTE: look for the assembly markings "X" on the flywheel and the clutch cover (pressure plate assembly). If there are none, scribe marks to identify the position of the clutch cover relative to the flywheel.

6. Loosen the clutch cover bolts evenly until the spring pressure is relieved, then remove the bolts and clutch assembly.
7. Before installing, clean the pressure plate and the flywheel face.
8. Position the disc and pressure plate assembly on the flywheel and install a pilot tool.

NOTE: the disc on six-cylinder engines is installed with the springs facing the flywheel. On V8 engines, the grease slinger must face the transmission.

9. Install the pressure plate assembly bolts. Make sure the mark on the cover is aligned with the mark on the flywheel. Tighten the bolts alternately and evenly to 35 ft. lbs.
10. Remove the pilot tool.
11. Remove the release fork and lubricate the ball socket and the fork fingers at the throwout bearing with graphite or Moly Grease. Reinstall the release fork.
12. Lubricate the inside recess and the fork groove of the throwout bearing with a light coat of graphite or Moly Grease.

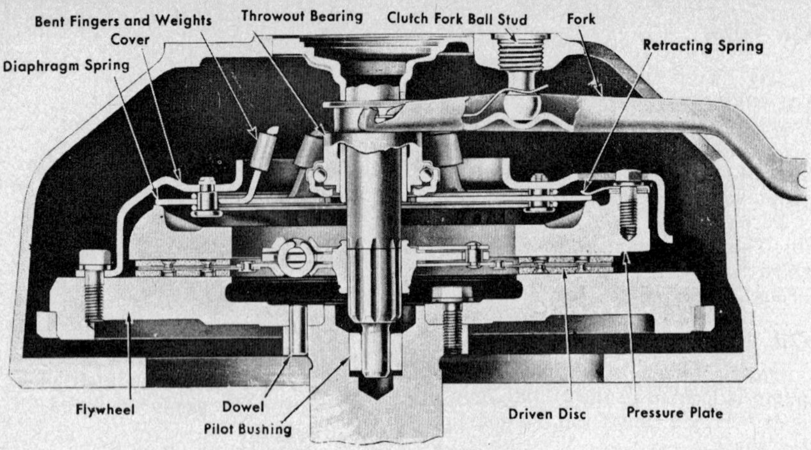
Bent Fingers and Weights
Cover
Diaphragm Spring
Throwout Bearing
Clutch Fork Ball Stud
Fork
Retracting Spring
Flywheel
Dowel
Pilot Bushing
Driven Disc
Pressure Plate

Typical V8 clutch cross-section
(© Chevrolet Div., G.M. Corp)

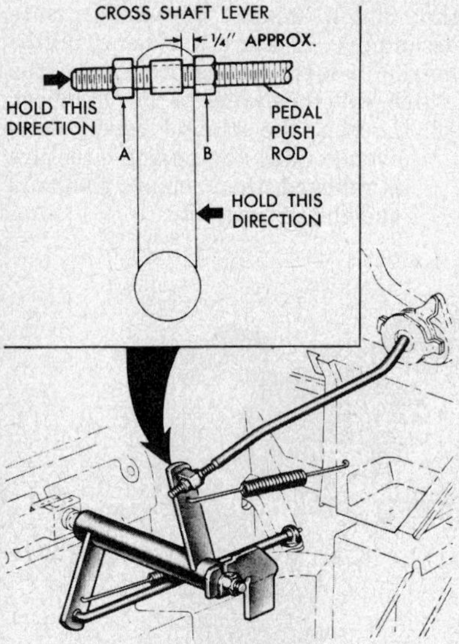
CROSS SHAFT LEVER
1/4" APPROX.
HOLD THIS DIRECTION
PEDAL PUSH ROD
A
B
HOLD THIS DIRECTION

Typical clutch linkage
(© Chevrolet Div., G.M. Corp)

13. Install the clutch release fork and dust boot in the clutch housing and the throwout bearing on the fork, then install the flywheel housing. Tighten flywheel housing bolts to 30 ft. lbs.
14. Connect the fork pushrod and spring.
15. Adjust the shift linkage as described later.
16. Adjust the clutch pedal free play as described previously.

Clutch Pedal Free-Travel

The pedal should travel 1 in. to $1\frac{1}{2}$ in. for Chevrolet, $1\frac{1}{4}$ in. to 2 in. for standard Corvette and 2 in. to $2\frac{1}{2}$ in. for heavy duty Corvette before the throw-out bearing engages the diaphragm spring.

This should be checked at the pedal by hand; $\frac{3}{4}$ in. true free-travel of the bearing will approximate 1 in. feel at the pedal.

The adjustment is made on the fork pushrod running from the lever and shaft assembly to the clutch fork. On some models, the adjustment is made at the fork end by changing the position of two jam nuts. On other models, the adjustment is made at the front end of the rod by turning an adjustable swivel. On this type, one turn of the swivel equals approximately 3/16 in. at the pedal. The adjustment can be made by holding the fork pushrod rearward to remove all lash, then adjusting the swivel to line up a conical point stamped on the swivel with a dimple stamped on the lever to which it attaches.

Clutch Pedal Height

The top of the clutch pedal pad should be at least 7 in. above the deadener felt glued to the metal floor pan. Do not measure to the floor mat.

If less than 7 in., cut off the rubber pedal stop to obtain proper pedal height. On some models, the rubber pedal stop is fastened to a metal piece held to the instrument panel brace by a bolt and nut. A slotted hole in the brace allows for adjustment of the bumper holding piece.

If more than 7 in. of pedal travel occurs, it may be that the diaphragm spring is being overstressed.

MANUAL TRANSMISSION

Transmission refill capacities are in the Capacities table of this section.

Troubleshooting and repair of manual transmissions is covered in the Unit Repair Section.

Shift Linkage Adjustment

1967-68 Three Speed Column Shift

1. With transmission shifter rods disconnected at transmission levers, move both levers into neutral detents.
2. Move manual selector lever into neutral position.
3. Align first and reverse shifter tube lever with second and high shifter tube lever on the mast jacket. In some cases, a pin may be used to hold the levers in alignment.

NOTE: the key is engaged with the slot on the second and third shifter tube lever when selector lever is in the neutral position.

4. Loosen control rod clamp bolts. Install control rods on mast jacket shifter levers and secure with retaining clips.
5. Adjust length of first-reverse rod. Tighten clamp bolt.
6. Adjust length of second-third control rod. Tighten clamp bolt.
7. Shift through all positions to check adjustment, and to insure positive and full gear engagement.

1969-74 Three Speed Column Shift

1. With transmission in Reverse, place ignition switch in Off position up to 1970, Lock for 1971-74.
2. Loosen shift rod lock nuts.
3. Set transmission first-reverse lever in reverse position. Push up on first-reverse control rod to 1970, pull down for 1971-74 until column lever is in reverse detent position. Tighten first-reverse lock nut.
4. Shift column and transmission levers to neutral position. Insert a 3/16 in. dia. rod into alignment holes in levers and alignment plate.
5. Tighten second-third locknut.
6. Remove alignment rod. Shift column lever to reverse. Turn key to Lock. Ignition switch must move freely to Lock position and it must not be possible to turn key to Lock when in any transmission position other than reverse. If this interlock binds, leave switch in Lock position and readjust first-reverse rod.
7. Check shifting.

1967-68 Three Speed Floorshift

1. Loosen shift rod locknuts.
2. Set shift lever in neutral and install locating pin into control lever bracket assembly. On some linkages, a flat locating gauge is used. This gauge is $\frac{1}{8}$ thick X 41/64 wide X 3 in. long.
3. Place transmission shift levers in neutral positions.
4. Adjust length of control rods. Tighten locknuts.
5. Remove gauge or pin. Check shifting operation.

1969 Chevrolet Three Speed Floorshift

1. Turn ignition switch to Lock position.
2. Loosen locknuts on shift rods and back drive rod.
3. Set transmission levers in neutral positions.
4. Set floorshift lever in neutral. Install locating gauge, $\frac{1}{8}$ thick X

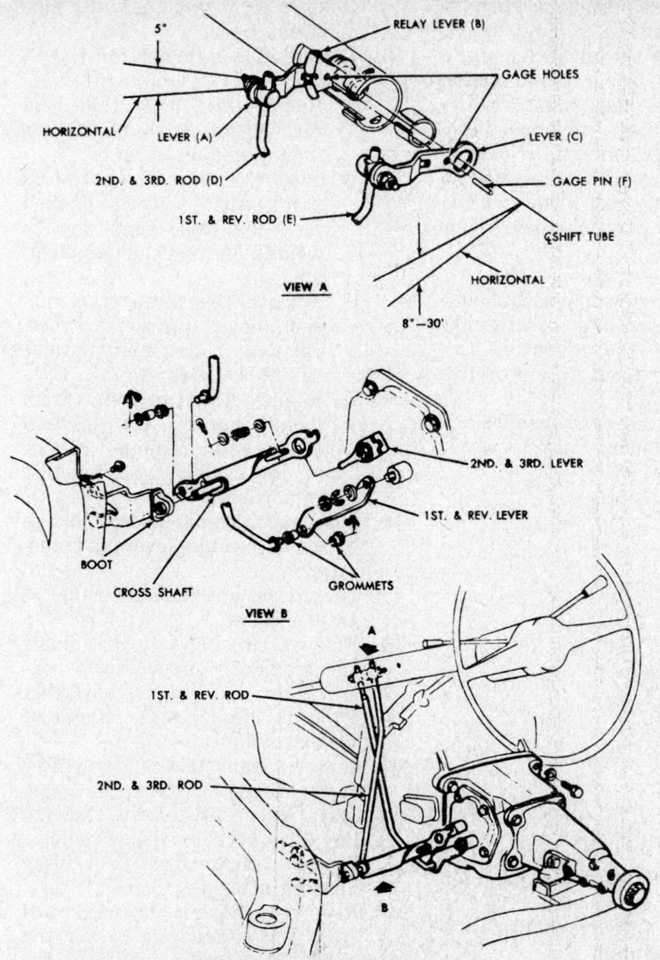
5°
RELAY LEVER (B)
GAGE HOLES
HORIZONTAL
LEVER (A)
LEVER (C)
2ND. & 3RD. ROD (D)
GAGE PIN (F)
1ST. & REV. ROD (E)
SHIFT TUBE
VIEW A
HORIZONTAL
8°—30'
2ND. & 3RD. LEVER
1ST. & REV. LEVER
BOOT
CROSS SHAFT
GROMMETS
VIEW B
A
1ST. & REV. ROD
2ND. & 3RD. ROD
B

1967-68 3-speed linkage adjustment
(© Chevrolet Div., G.M. Corp)

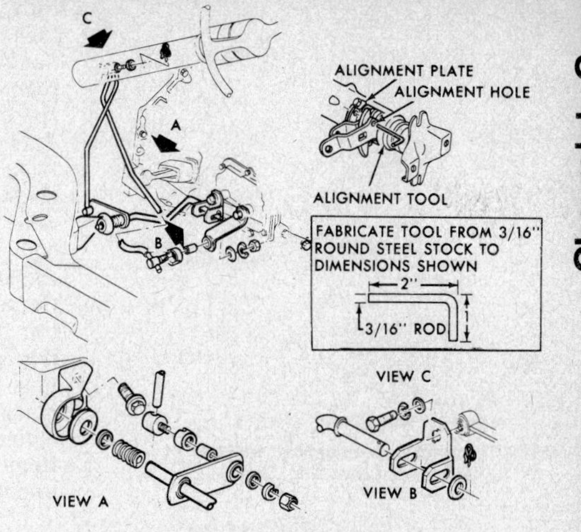
C
A
B
ALIGNMENT PLATE
ALIGNMENT HOLE
ALIGNMENT TOOL
FABRICATE TOOL FROM 3/16"
ROUND STEEL STOCK TO
DIMENSIONS SHOWN
2"
3/16" ROD
VIEW C
VIEW A
VIEW B

1969-73 3-speed column shift linkage adjustment
(© Chevrolet Div., G.M. Corp)

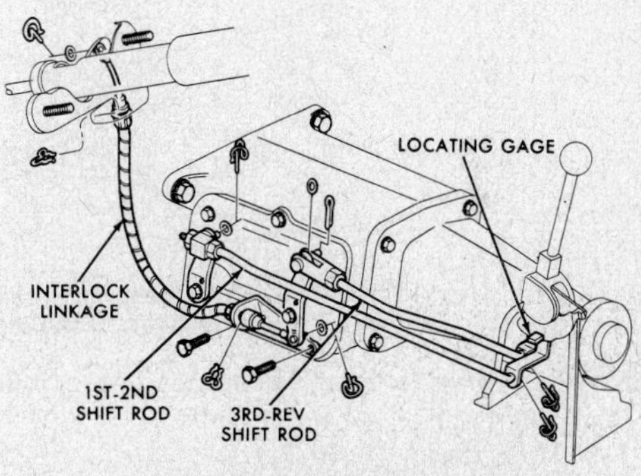
LOCATING GAGE
INTERLOCK
LINKAGE
1ST-2ND
SHIFT ROD
3RD-REV
SHIFT ROD

1969 Corvette 3-speed linkage adjustment
(© Chevrolet Div., G.M. Corp)

41/64 wide X 3 in. long, into control lever bracket assembly.

5. Adjust length of shift rods. Tighten locknuts.
6. Remove locating gauge. Shift into reverse.
7. Pull down slightly on back drive rod to remove any slack and tighten locknut. Ignition switch must move freely to Lock position and it must not be possible to turn key to Lock when in any transmission position other than reverse. If this interlock binds, leave the switch in Lock position and readjust back drive rod.
8. Check shifting operation.

1969 Corvette Three-Speed Floorshift

1. Put the ignition switch in "off" and loosen the shift rod swivel locknuts. Set the transmission levers in to the neutral detent position.
2. Install a 1/8 thick X 41/64 wide X 3 in. long gauge in the bracket assembly.
3. Adjust the length of the shift rods for easy entry into the levers.
4. Remove the gauge and check the shift operation.
5. Shift the transmission into reverse.
6. Loosen the interlock bracket assembly bolts at the bottom of the steering column. Make sure that the bracket is not stuck to the dash and then tighten the bracket again.
7. Move the ignition key through "off" and "lock." If there is any binding, readjust the interlock linkage.

Four-Speed—1967-74

Since 1967, two makes of four-speed transmission have been used, Muncie and Saginaw. Linkage adjustments, however, are typical. Four-speeds were not available in the Chevrolet after 1969. A gauge 1/8 in. thick by 41/64 in. wide and 3 in. long should be used to locate and maintain neutral detent position of the shift lever while making linkage adjustments.

1967-68 Four Speed Floorshift

1. Loosen shift rod clamp nuts or remove clevis pins.
2. Set transmissions shift levers in neutral positions.
3. Insert locating gauge, 1/8 thick X 41/64 wide X 3 in. long, into control lever bracket assembly.
4. Adjust length of shifting rods. Tighten clamp nuts or replace clevis pins.
5. Remove gauge. Check shifting operation.

1969 Chevrolet Four Speed Floorshift

1. Place ignition switch in Lock position.
2. Loosen locknuts at swivels on shift rods and back drive control rod.
3. Set transmission shift levers in neutral positions.
4. Shift lever into neutral. Insert locating gauge, 1/8 thick X 41/64 wide X 3 in. long, into control lever bracket assembly.
5. Tighten shift rod locknuts and remove gauge.
6. Shift lever into reverse, then pull down slightly on back drive rod to remove slack. Tighten back drive rod locknut.
7. Ignition switch must move freely to Lock position and it must not be possible to turn key to Lock when in any transmission position other than reverse. Readjust back drive rod, if necessary.
8. Check for proper shifting operation.

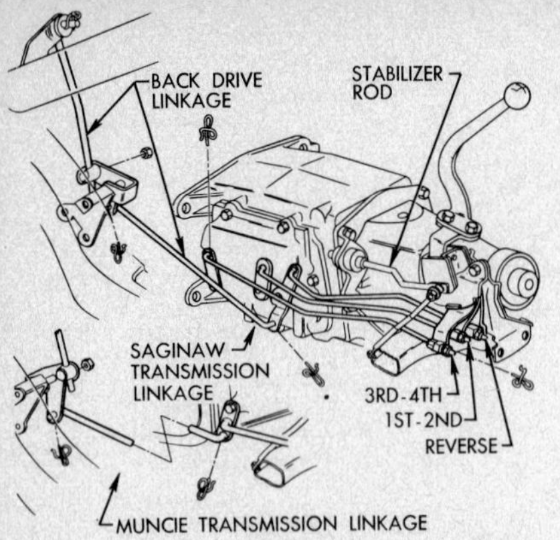
BACK DRIVE LINKAGE
STABILIZER ROD
SAGINAW TRANSMISSION LINKAGE
3RD-4TH
1ST-2ND
REVERSE
MUNCIE TRANSMISSION LINKAGE

1969 Chevrolet 4-speed linkage adjustment
(© Chevrolet Div., G.M. Corp)

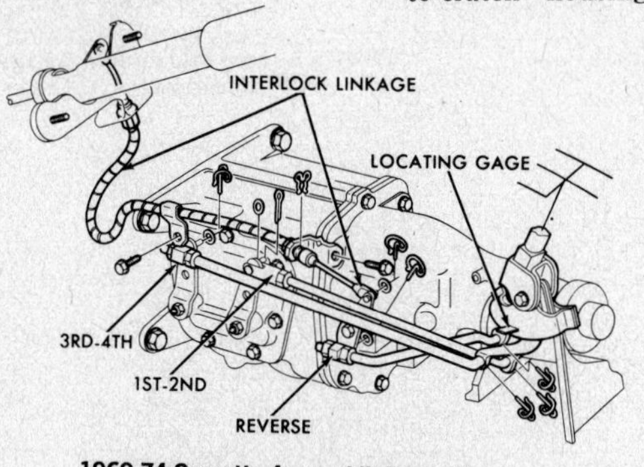
INTERLOCK LINKAGE
LOCATING GAGE
3RD-4TH
1ST-2ND
REVERSE

1969-74 Corvette 4-speed linkage adjustment
(© Chevrolet Div., G.M. Corp)

1969-74 Corvette Four-Speed

1. Place the ignition switch in "off" (1969) or "lock" (1970-74).
2. Perform steps two through five above, and then check the shifting operation.
3. Loosen the interlock bracket assembly bolts at the bottom of the steering column. Make sure that the bracket is not stuck to the dash and then tighten the bracket again.
4. Move the ignition key through "off" and "lock" positions. If there is any binding, readjust the interlock linkage.

Short Throw Shift Adjustment

Some four speed transmissions, primarily heavy duty units, have an adjustment for quicker shifting. The transmission levers have two control rod holes. Shift lever travel may be decreased by positioning the controls rods in the lower holes. This adjustment results in a tighter shift pattern and requires a slightly greater shifting effort.

Transmission Removal (Except Corvette)

1. Raise the car on a hoist and drain the transmission. Disconnect the speedometer cable and the control levers. Disconnect the propeller shaft. Remove two bolts attaching the center bearing to the frame. Remove nuts and U-bolts retaining the rear universal joint bearing to the differential pinion drive flange. Move the propeller shaft rearward to the left and under the rear axle housing to withdraw the front universal joint from the transmission output shaft. Remove the transmission rear mounting pad bolts and unbolt the support member from the frame.
2. On all models, remove the two top transmission-to-clutch housing cap screws, and insert guide pins to keep the weight of the transmission from falling on the clutch assembly.
3. Remove the lower transmission-to-clutch housing cap screws. Slide the transmission straight back on the guide pins until the input shaft of the transmission is free of the clutch.
4. Remove the transmission from under the car.
5. Install in reverse order of removal.

Transmission Removal (Corvette)

1967

1. Disconnect battery.
2. Disassemble shift control lever assembly.
3. Raise car on a hoist.
4. Place a block of wood between the top of the differential housing and the underbody.
5. Disconnect differential carrier front support from the frame bracket at the biscuit mount.
6. Pry the carrier support down, while removing the two center mounting bolts from the carrier front support.
7. Pivot carrier support downward for access to propeller shaft U-joint.
8. Disconnect propeller shaft U-joints, front and rear.
9. Disconnect parking brake cable from ball socket at idler lever near center of underbody.
10. Remove propeller shaft.
11. Remove heat deflectors from right and left exhaust pipes.
12. Remove left bank exhaust pipe. Remove right bank exhaust pipe and heat riser.
13. Disassemble transmission mount as follows:
    A. Remove two bolts that hold rear mount cushion to rear mount bracket.
    B. Support engine under the oil pan (with a well padded jack) and raise engine to take weight off rear mount cushion.
    C. Remove the three transmission mount bracket-to-crossmember bolts, and remove mount bracket.
    D. Remove the two bolts from mount pad to transmission case, and remove rubber mount cushion and exhaust pipe yoke.
14. Disconnect transmission linkage by removing shift levers at transmission.
15. Disconnect speedometer cable at transmission.
16. Remove two bolts to disconnect the transmission gearshift control lever and bracket assembly from its adapter plate on side of transmission.
17. Lower transmission assembly from the car, letting the gearshift lever slide down through the dust boot in the console.
18. Remove transmission - to - clutch housing attaching bolts.
19. Remove transmission rearward from the clutch and rotate the assembly to gain access to the three flathead machine screws in the control lever bracket adapter plate. Rotate transmission back to upright position.
20. Slowly lower rear of engine until tachometer drive cable at distributor clears the ledge across front of dash.
21. Slide transmission rearward out of clutch, then tip front of transmission down and lower the assembly out of the car.
22. Install by reversing removal procedure.

1968-74

1. Disconnect the battery ground cable.
2. Remove the shifter ball and "T" handle.
3. Remove the console trim plate.
4. Raise the vehicle on a hoist.
5. Remove the right and left exhaust pipes.
6. Disconnect the driveshaft at the transmission, lower the driveshaft and remove the slip yoke from the transmission.
7. Remove the rear mount to bracket bolts, then jack the engine enough to raise the transmission from the mount.
8. Remove the transmission linkage mounting bracket to frame bolts.

9. Disconnect the shift levers at the transmission.
10. Remove the bolts attaching gearshift assembly to mounting bracket and remove the mounting bracket. Remove the shifter mechanism with the rods attached.
11. Disconnect the speedometer cable and the TCS switch wiring.
12. Remove the transmission mount bracket.
13. Remove the transmission to clutch housing retaining bolts and the lower left extension bolt.
14. Pull the transmission rearward until it is clear of the clutch housing, then rotate it clockwise while pulling to the rear. Carefully lower the rear of the engine until the tachometer drive cable at the distributor just clears the firewall.

Caution The tachometer cable is easily damaged if it hits the firewall. Slide the transmission rearward until it clears the clutch, then tilt the front of it down and lower it from the car.

15. Installation is the reverse of removal. Adjust the shift linkage.

AUTOMATIC TRANSMISSION

Automatic transmissions used are the Powerglide, Turbo Hydra-Matic 350, and Turbo Hydra-Matic 400. Powerglide is a two-speed planetary transmission and the two Turbos are three-speed transmissions. Transmission linkage adjustments are covered in the following paragraphs.

Neutral Safety Switch Adjustment

In all models the adjustment is made with the shift lever in Drive position. Loosen the switch mounting screws. Align the slot in the contact support with the hole in the switch and insert a 3/32 in. pin to hold the support in place.

On column shift models, place the contact support drive slot over the shifter tube drive tang and tighten the screws.

On Corvettes, the shift control lever must be disconnected from the control rod and the shift control knob removed. Then remove the trim plate to get at the switch. Proceed as described in the first paragraph above, then place the contact support drive slot over the drive tang. Tighten the switch mounting screws, then remove the pin. Reinstall the shift control lever and trim plate.

On Chevrolet models with floor shift, the ash tray, trim plate assembly and indicator lens and housing must be removed from the console before proceding as described in the first paragraph above. Clamp the control lever pawl against the contact point of the detent. Tighten the switch mounting screws, then remove the pin and reinstall all the console components which were removed.

Linkage Adjustments

Column Shift—All Models

1. Make sure that the shift lever works freely in the mast jacket.
2. Check for proper linkage adjustment:
   a. Pull the selector lever back and allow the lever to be positioned in Drive by the transmission detent.

NOTE: do not use the indicator pointer as a reference. The indicator pointer will be adjusted after the linkage.

   b. Release the lever. The lever should not go into Low range unless it is lifted.
   c. Lift the shift lever and allow the lever to be positioned in Neutral by the transmission detent.
   d. Release the lever. The lever should not go into Reverse unless it is lifted.
   e. If the selector lever can move beyond the Neutral and Drive detents without being lifted, then the mechanical stops in the steering column are not coordinated with the transmission detents and adjustment is required.
3. To adjust, place the selector lever in Drive as determined by the transmission detent.
4. Loosen the adjustment clamp or swivel at the cross-shaft and position the selector lever in Drive.
5. With the selector lever in Drive and the transmission lever in Drive detent position, tighten the clamp or swivel bolt.
6. Repeat Step 2 above to check for proper adjustment.
7. If necessary, readjust the selector pointer to agree with the transmission detents.
8. Readjust the neutral safety switch if necessary.
9. When properly adjusted:
   a. From Reverse to Drive position travel, the transmission detent must be noted and related to the indicated position on the dial.
   b. In Drive and Reverse positions, the selector lever must drop back into position freely when lifted.

1967 Chevrolet Floorshift

See illustration.

1968-69 Chevrolet Floorshift

NOTE: this procedure covers both Powerglide and Turbo Hydra-Matic transmissions.

1. Shift the lever into Drive.
2. Remove the cable clip and disconnect the cable from the lever. Position the transmission lever in Drive.
3. Measure the distance from the rear face of the attaching bracket to the stud on the transmission bracket. If this distance is not 5.5 in., loosen the stud and adjust it.
4. Adjust the end of the cable and reinstall it on the stud.
5. Remove the console quadrant cover and disconnect the cable from the shift lever.

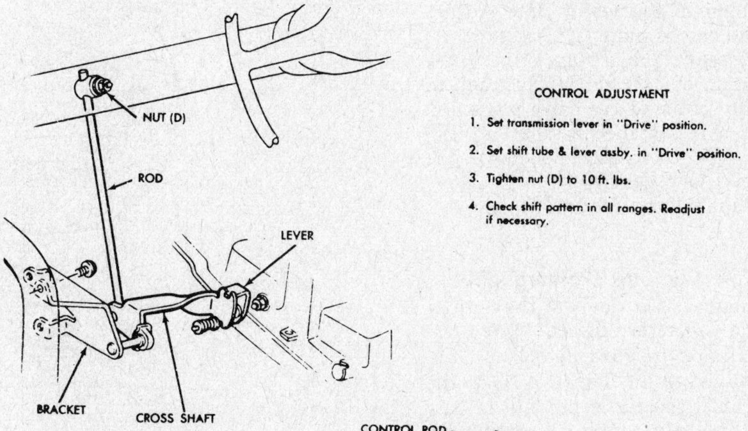
NUT (D)
ROD
LEVER
BRACKET
CROSS SHAFT
CONTROL ADJUSTMENT
1. Set transmission lever in "Drive" position.
2. Set shift tube & lever assby. in "Drive" position.
3. Tighten nut (D) to 10 ft. lbs.
4. Check shift pattern in all ranges. Readjust if necessary.

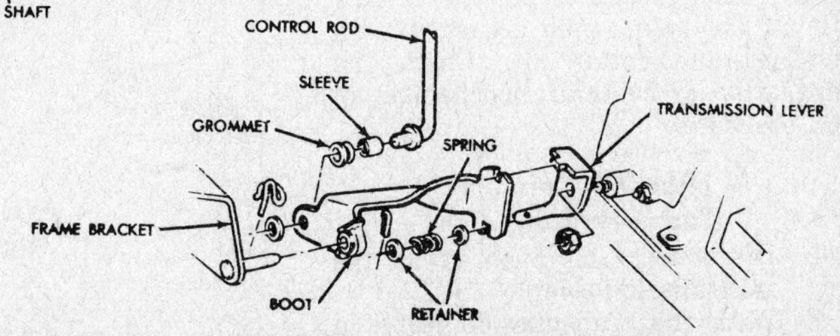
CONTROL ROD
SLEEVE
GROMMET
SPRING
TRANSMISSION LEVER
FRAME BRACKET
BOOT
RETAINER

Turbo Hydra-Matic column linkage adjustment (© Chevrolet Div., G.M. Corp)

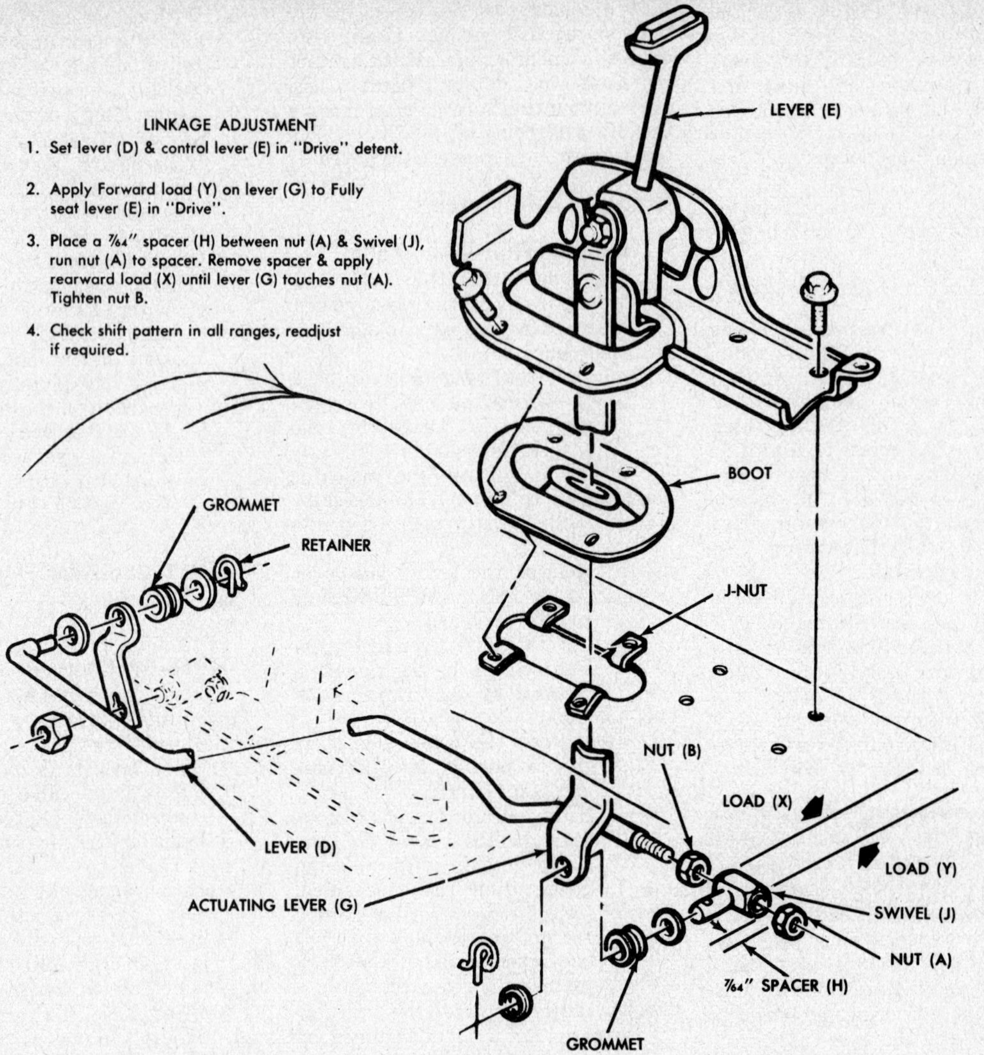
LINKAGE ADJUSTMENT
1. Set lever (D) & control lever (E) in "Drive" detent.
2. Apply Forward load (Y) on lever (G) to Fully seat lever (E) in "Drive".
3. Place a 7/64" spacer (H) between nut (A) & Swivel (J), run nut (A) to spacer. Remove spacer & apply rearward load (X) until lever (G) touches nut (A). Tighten nut B.
4. Check shift pattern in all ranges, readjust if required.
LEVER (E)
BOOT
GROMMET
RETAINER
J-NUT
NUT (B)
LOAD (X)
LEVER (D)
LOAD (Y)
ACTUATING LEVER (G)
SWIVEL (J)
NUT (A)
7/64" SPACER (H)
GROMMET

1967 Chevrolet Turbo Hydra-Matic console linkage adjustment (©Chevrolet Div., G.M. Corp)

6. A 0.07 in. feeler gauge should fit between the pawl and the Drive detent of the detent plate. Adjust the detent plate, if necessary.
7. Measure the distance from the front of the shifter bracket to the center of the cable pivot pin. If this distance is not 6.25 in., loosen the bolt and move the lever as necessary.
8. Reinstall the quadrant cover.

1967 Corvette (Powerglide)

Disconnect the clevis at the bottom of the selector lever. Put the transmission in Park detent and the selector lever in Park. Adjust the clevis until the clevis pin will fit easily in the holes, then secure it with washer and cotter pin. Check the operation of the shift mechanism in all positions.

1968-74 Corvette (Turbo-Hydramatic)

1. Disconnect the pushrod at the transmission lever.
2. With the transmission lever in Drive detent and the selector

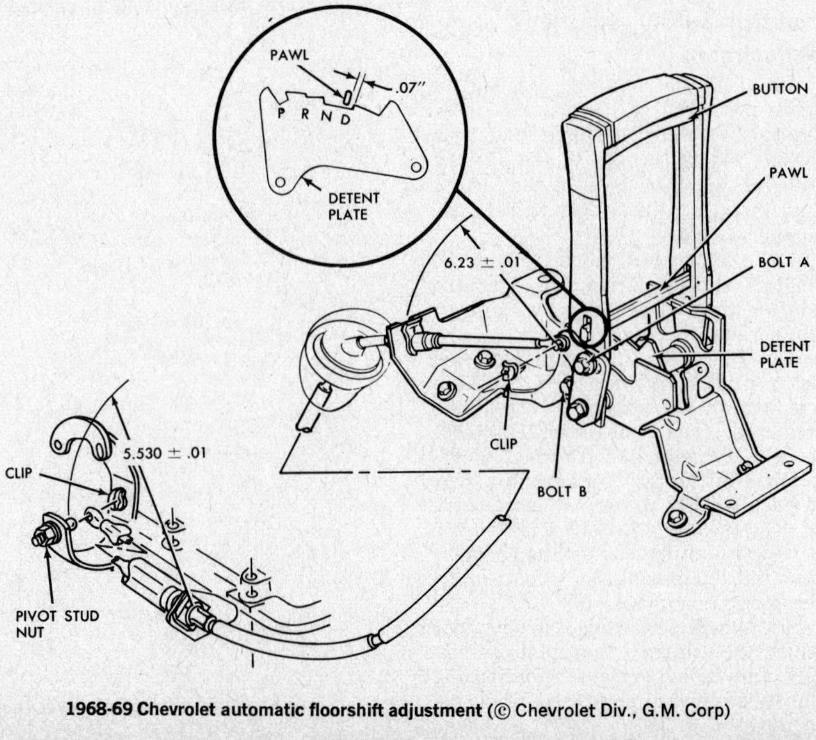
PAWL
.07"
P R N D
DETENT PLATE
BUTTON
PAWL
BOLT A
6.23 ± .01
DETENT PLATE
CLIP
BOLT B
5.530 ± .01
CLIP
PIVOT STUD NUT

1968-69 Chevrolet automatic floorshift adjustment (© Chevrolet Div., G.M. Corp)

lever in Drive, rotate the pushrod until the hole lines up with the lever pin.

3. Install the pushrod on the pin and install the retainer clip.

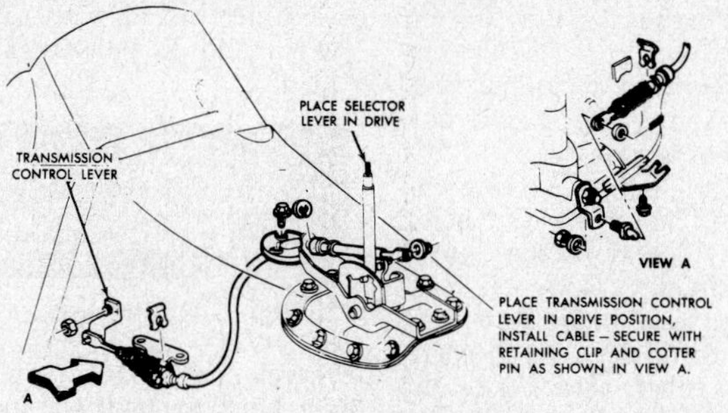
PLACE SELECTOR LEVER IN DRIVE
TRANSMISSION CONTROL LEVER
VIEW A
PLACE TRANSMISSION CONTROL LEVER IN DRIVE POSITION, INSTALL CABLE – SECURE WITH RETAINING CLIP AND COTTER PIN AS SHOWN IN VIEW A.
A

1968-74 Corvette Turbo Hydra-Matic linkage adjustment
(© Chevrolet Div., G.M. Corp)

4. Check operation of the linkage in all positions.

Throttle Valve Adjustment

1967-73 6-Cylinder

Adjustment is made with the throttle pedal completely depressed and the bellcrank (six-cylinder) or carburetor lever (V8) in wide open position.

Adjust the length of the linkage to obtain a 1/64 in. to 1/16 in. clearance between the lever on the firewall and its stop when the transmission lever is against its stop.

1967-72 V8 Powerglide

1. Remove the air cleaner and disconnect:
   a. Accelerator linkage at the carburetor.
   b. Accelerator return spring.
   c. Throttle valve rod return spring.
2. Pull the throttle valve upper rod forward until the transmission is through detent and place the carburetor in wide open position. The carburetor must reach wide open position at the same time that the ball stud contacts the end of the slot in the upper throttle valve rod.
3. Adjust the swivel on the end of the upper throttle valve rod to obtain the setting described in Step 2 above. Allowable tolerance is approximately 1/32 in.
4. Connect and adjust the carburetor linkage.

Detent Switch Adjustment

1969-74 Turbo Hydra-Matic 350 (Chevrolet)

1. Disengage the snap lock on the detent cable.
2. Place the carburetor in wide open position (lever against the stop). On Quadrajet carburetors, disengage the secondary locknut before placing the lever in wide open position.

NOTE: detent cable must be through detent.

3. Holding the carburetor in wide open position, push the snap lock on the detent cable downward until the top is flush with the cable.

1968-74 Turbo Hydra-Matic 400 (Corvette)

The detent switch is located on the carburetor.

1. Pull the detent switch driver rearward until the hole in the switch body aligns with the hole in the driver.
2. Insert a 0.092 in. pin through the aligned holes to a depth of 0.10 in. to hold the driver in position.
3. Loosen the switch mounting bolt.
4. With the throttle held in wide open position, move the switch forward until the driver contacts the accelerator lever.
5. Tighten the mounting bolt and remove the pin.

1968-74 Turbo Hydra-Matic 400 (Chevrolet)

The detent switch is located on the carburetor.

1. Loosen the switch mounting bolt.
2. Holding the throttle in wide open position (choke fully open), depress the detent switch plunger until it bottoms in the switch. Move the switch toward the throttle lever paddle until there is a clearance of 0.23 ± 0.01 in. (1969-74 models), 0.20 in. (1968 models with 396 or 427 engine) or 0.05 in. (1968 models with 307 or 327 engine) between the face of the lever paddle and the depressed detent switch plunger.
3. Tighten the switch mounting bolts.

U-JOINTS

Driveshafts are of a one-piece design, using Cardan type universal joints. The universal joints are lube-sealed at the factory and require no periodic maintenance. The front yoke is splined, providing a slip joint for slight length variations in the drive line. There is a damper on some models: this damper is not serviced separately.

Two basic universal joints are used. The Dana or Cleveland type uses snap-ring bearing cap retainers. The Saginaw uses injection molded plastic to retain the bearing caps. On the Saginaw type there is a snap-ring groove in the bearing housing inboard of the yoke to hold the bearings in place.

Driveshaft R & R

Disconnect the rear universal joint flange. On some models, the bearing caps are bolted directly to the differential flange with clamps or U-bolts. Pull the front yoke from the transmission. Watch for oil leaks from the transmission output housing. Install in the reverse order of removal.

Universal Joint R & R

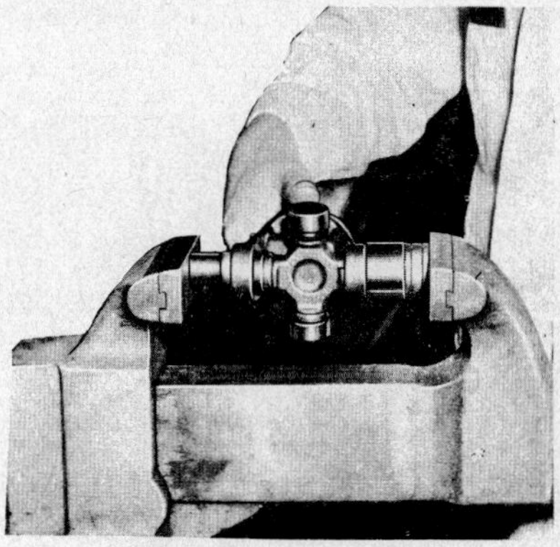

Assembling universal joint
(© Chevrolet Div., G.M. Corp)

Dana and Cleveland Type

1. Remove the driveshaft.
2. Remove the snap-rings from the trunnion yoke.
3. Using a vise and suitably sized sockets, press on the trunnion until the bearing cap is almost out. Grasp the cap in the vise and work it out of the yoke. Repeat the above procedure for the rest of the bearing caps.
4. Pack the rollers in grease and fill the grease reservoir.
5. To install, position the trunnion in the yoke and partially install one bearing cap. Start the trunnion in the bearing cap and partially install the other cap. Align the trunnion with the caps and press into place.
6. If necessary, repeat Step 5 above for the other yoke.
7. Install the snap-rings.
8. Install the driveshaft in the vehicle.

Saginaw Type

Remove and install the bearing caps and trunnion as described for the Dana and Cleveland type universal joints. On an original universal joint, however, the bearing caps will be secured in the yokes with injected plastic. The plastic will shear when the bearing caps are pressed. Service snap-rings are installed in the groove on the inside (of yoke) of the installed caps.

Constant Velocity Type

Some models are equipped with driveshafts which incorporate constant velocity U-joints. The driveshaft yokes on each end of the driveshaft contain two U-joints which are connected within the yoke by a centering ball. Factory installed U-joints do not have grooves for snap-rings and are retained in the yokes by injected plastic. This makes the joints non-repairable by conventional methods. Some aftermarket kits are available with screw-in bearing caps to repair this type of joint.

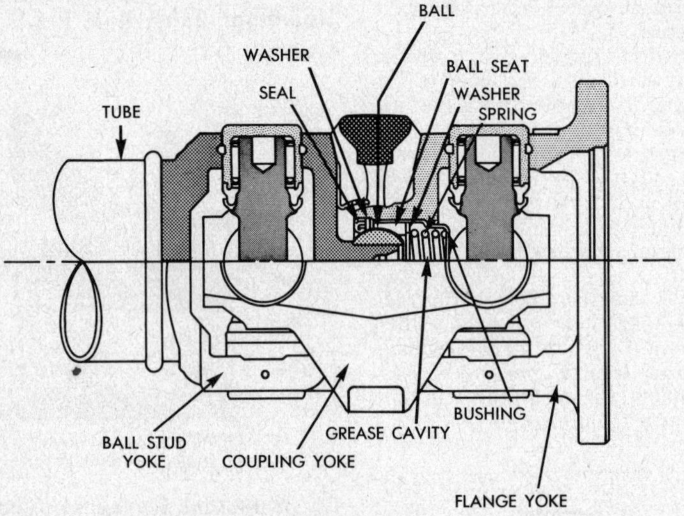
BALL
WASHER
BALL SEAT
SEAL
WASHER
SPRING
TUBE
BUSHING
GREASE CAVITY
BALL STUD
YOKE
COUPLING YOKE
FLANGE YOKE

Constant velocity U-joint
(© Chevrolet Div., G.M. Corp)

DRIVE AXLES

Corvette, 1967-74

Corvette is equipped with an independent rear suspension. The differential is solidly attached to the car frame, the rear wheels being driven through tubular rear axles, each fitted with two universal joints. A transverse, multiple leaf rear spring provides rear suspension. Brake torque and driving forces are transmitted through radius arms to the frame. The spring supports vertical loads, while lateral forces, on turns etc., are taken by the axles and control rods to the fixed differential and to the frame.

1. Raise the vehicle on a hoist.
2. Disconnect the spring and link bolts.
3. Disconnect the axle shafts at the carrier by removing the U-bolts on the universal joint trunnions.
4. Disconnect the carrier front support bracket at the frame crossmember.
5. Disconnect the driveshaft at the companion flange.
6. Scribe marks indicating the cam and bolt relative location on the strut rod bracket and loosen the cam bolts.
7. Remove the four bolts which secure the bracket to the carrier lower surface and drop the bracket. Remove the camber cam bolts and swing the strut rods up and out of the way.
8. Remove the eight carrier to cover bolts, loosening the bolts gradually to permit the lubricant to drain out.
9. Pull the carrier partially out of the cover, drop the nose to clear the crossmember, then gradually work the carrier down and out.
10. To install, clean the carrier cover and grease the gasket surface.
11. Using a new gasket and two ½-13 x 1-¼ in. studs as aligning studs, raise the carrier into position.
12. Install the carrier to cover bolts, tightening securely.
13. Install the driveshaft to the companion flange, tightening the clamp bolts securely.
14. Install the rubber cushion on the bracket and position to the frame crossmember. Install the nut, tightening to 50 ft. lbs.
15. Install the axle trunnions to the yokes with the U-bolts.
16. Assemble the strut rods to the bracket and raise the bracket into position under the carrier. Install the four bolts, tightening to 35 ft. lbs.
17. Move the camber cams to the marked locations and tighten the cam nuts.
18. Connect the spring end link bolts.
19. Fill the housing with lubricant to the level of the filler hole.

Positraction Differential

No special attention is required in this area, except with the lubricant used.

Under no circumstances use anything but special Positraction lubricant.

Failure to follow these instructions may result in permanent damage to the unit.

JACKING, HOISTING

When jacking the car, place the jack at the spring seat of the lower control arm in the front and at the axle housing in the rear. A bumper jack may be used on Chevrolet models, but not Corvettes.

To hoist the car, position the hoist arms at the frame side rails immediately in front of the rear wheels and immediately behind the front wheels.

FRONT SUSPENSION

Both Chevrolet and Corvette utilize conventional short-long arm suspension, with coil springs and tube shocks. A stabilizer bar is used between the lower arms to reduce roll.

Figures covering the caster, camber, toe-in, kingpin inclination, and turning radius can be found in the Wheel Alignment table of this section.

Shock Absorber R & R

1. Remove the upper stem nut while holding the stem to keep it from turning.
2. Remove the two bolts holding the shock absorber to the lower control arm and pull the shock through the arm.
3. Extend the shock absorber and insert it up through the lower control arm. Make sure that the upper stem goes through the hole in the upper control arm frame bracket.
4. Install the grommet, retainer cup, and nut to the shock absorber upper stem.
5. Hold the shock absorber stem and tighten the upper nut to 8 ft lbs.
6. Install the lower control arm retaining bolts and tighten to 20 ft lbs. (Chevrolet) or 13 ft lbs. (Corvette).

Front Wheel Bearing Adjustment

1. Jack the car up and support it at the lower arm.
2. Remove the hub dust cover and spindle cotter pin.
3. While spinning the wheel, snug the nut down to seat the bearings. Do not exert over 12 ft lbs of force on the nut.

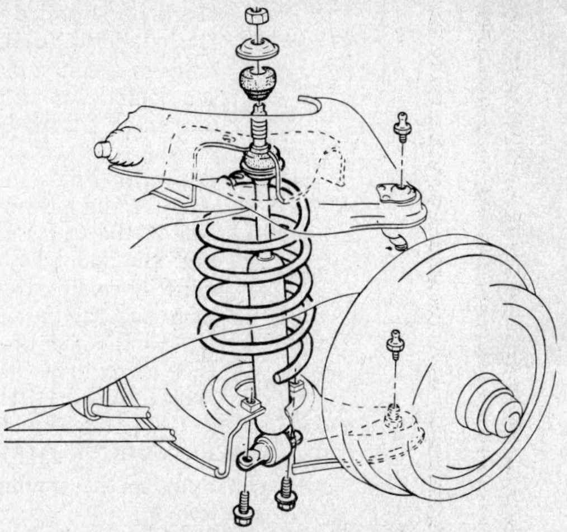

Installing shock absorbers—typical
(© Chevrolet Div., G.M. Corp)

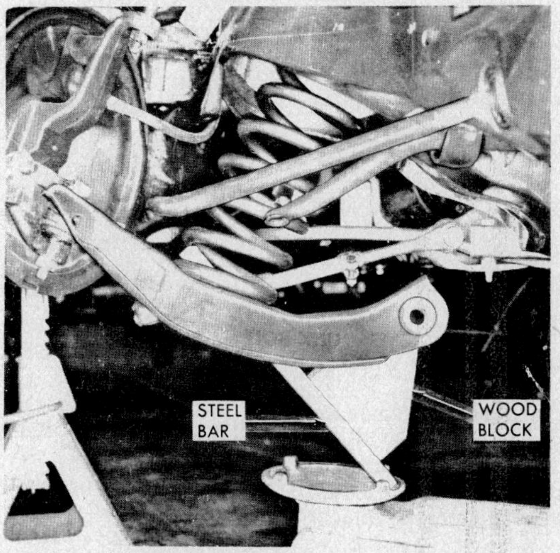
STEEL
BAR
WOOD
BLOCK

Chevrolet front spring removal
(© Chevrolet Div., G.M. Corp)

4. Back the nut off ¼–½ a turn. Tighten the nut *finger-tight* (if the roller bearings are preloaded with the wheel off the ground, the inner edges of the bearings will be forced against the bearing cage), then *loosen* the nut as required to line up the cotter pin hole in the spindle with the hole in the nut.
5. Insert the cotter pin. End-play should be between 0.001 and 0.008 in. If play exceeds this tolerance, the wheel bearings should be replaced.

Front Springs R & R

Chevrolet 1967-70

1. Remove shock absorber upper stem retaining nut and grommet.
2. Support the car by the frame so that the control arms hang free. Remove the wheel assembly, shock absorber, stabilizer to lower control arm link, strut rod to lower control arm attaching nuts, bolts and lockwashers, and the tie-rod end.
3. Scribe the position of the inner pivot camber adjusting cam bolt and then remove the nut, lock washer and outer cam.
4. Install a steel bar through the shock absorber mounting hole in the lower control arm so that the notch in the bar seats over the bottom spring coil and the bar extends inboard and under the inner bushing. Fit a 5 in. wood block between the bar and the lower arm inner support bushing.
5. With a floor jack, raise the end of the steel bar enough to remove tension from the inner pivot cam bolt. The bolt can then be removed.
6. Carefully lower the inner end of the control arm. Tension on the spring must be removed before the spring can be taken out of the car.
7. Remove the spring.
8. Install by reversing removal procedure.

Corvette—1967

1. Support car by the frame to allow control arms to swing free. Remove wheel assembly, stabilizer bar and shock absorber. Loosen lower ball joint to steering knuckle nut, and the two lower control arm cross-shaft bushing bolts.
2. Place tool J-6874-1 across top of sixth coil of the spring. Then, loosely secure tool J-6874-2 to the upper shoe, with attaching capscrews and lockwashers. The upper shoe V notch and lower shoe raised land should contact the spring.

NOTE: These special tools allow compression of the spring within the control arms. This permits the spring to be removed while compressed, and then slowly released once out of the car. Commercial tools are available that perform this same function.

3. Insert tool J-6874 up through center of spring and attach to upper and lower shoe assembly.
4. Position spacers under shock absorber mounting hole and against bottom of lower control arm. Install special bearing washer and tool J-6874-5. Locate bearing against spacer and large washer against bearing. Feed screw up through large washer bearing and spacer and thread into tool J-6874 and tighten.
5. Center shoe assembly on spring and tighten screw until a very slight compression is exerted on the spring. Then, firmly tighten the two capscrews holding the upper and lower shoes to lock these shoes to the spring.
6. Tighten the spring compressor enough to permit the spring to clear the spring tower, then remove the lower ball joint to steering knuckle nut.
7. Disconnect lower ball joint from the steering knuckle and lower control arm while the spring is compressed. Immediately release compression on spring by backing off the tool screw. Release spring and tool and remove the spring.
8. Install by reversing the removal procedure.

Chevrolet 1971-74
Corvette—1968-74

1. Raise car on hoist and remove nut, retainer and grommet from top of shock absorber. Support car so that control arms swing free.
2. Disconnect stabilizer bar from lower control arm and remove shock absorber.
3. Bolt spring remover tool (J-22944) to a suitable jack and place it under the lower control arm bushings so that the bushings seat in the grooves of the tool.

NOTE: This tool is a cradle which, when fastened to a hydraulic jack, allows the lowering of the control arm

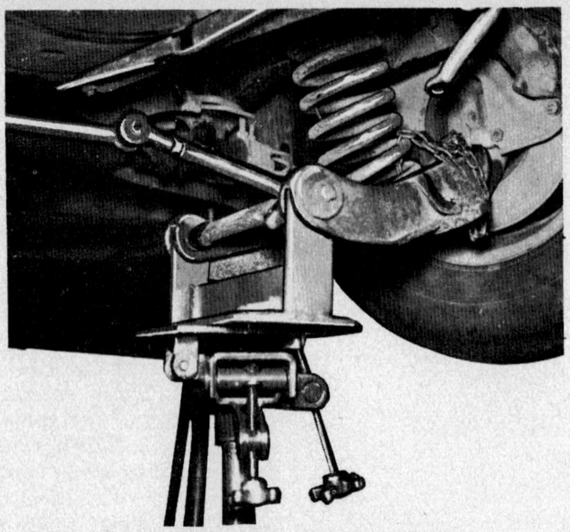

1968-74 Corvette front spring removal
(© Chevrolet Div., G.M. Corp)

and slow decompression of the spring. A similar tool can be fabricated in the shop. Always safety-chain the spring and control arm when using this method.

4. Remove cross shaft rear retaining nut and the two front retaining bolts.
5. Slowly release jack, swing control arm forward, then remove spring.
6. Install by reversing procedure above.

NOTE: Chevrolet recommends this cradle spring removal tool for all models, beginning in 1971. Either of the other two methods may be used, depending on the availability of tools.

Ball Joint Inspection

NOTE: before performing this inspection, make sure the wheel bearings are adjusted correctly and that the A arm bushings are in good condition.

1. Jack the car up under the front lower control arm at the spring seat.
2. Raise the car until there is 1-2 in. of clearance under the wheel.
3. Insert a bar under the wheel and pry upward. If the wheel raises more than 1/8 in. the ball joints are worn. Determine if the upper or lower ball joint is worn by visual inspection while prying on the wheel.

NOTE: due to the distribution of forces is the suspension, the lower ball joint is usually the defective joint. Also, 1973 and later Chevrolets are equipped with wear indicators on the lower ball joint. As long as the wear indicator neck extends below the ball stud seat, replacement is unnecessary.

Upper Ball Joint R & R

1. Raise the car on a hoist.
2. Remove the tire and wheel assembly.
3. Support the lower control arm with a jack.
4. Loosen the upper ball stud nut.
5. Install a ball joint remover tool and unseat the upper joint from the steering knuckle. Remove the upper stud nut and install a block of wood under the upper A-arm.
6. Chisel or grind off the ball joint mounting rivets.
7. Drill out the ball stud attaching holes to accept the service ball joint attaching bolts.
8. Install the ball joint with the nuts and bolts supplied with the new joint.
9. Install the lube fitting in the new joint.
10. Mate the upper control arm to the steering knuckle and install the ball stud through the knuckle boss.
11. Tighten the ball stud nut to 50 ft. lbs. plus whatever is necessary to align the cotter pin holes. Install the cotter pin.
12. Install the wheel and lower the vehicle.

Lower Ball Joint R & R

NOTE: On the 1971-74 Corvette, the lower ball joint removal and installation is the same as that described for the upper ball joint above. For all others:

1. On pre-1971 models, raise the vehicle on a hoist and remove the wheel. On vehicles equipped with disc brakes, remove the caliper assembly.
2. Support the lower control arm with a jack.
3. Loosen the lower ball stud nut. Break the ball stud loose. Remove the ball stud nut.
4. Remove the ball stud from the steering knuckle.
5. The ball joint in 1967-70 models is attached with rivets which must be chiseled or ground off. Beginning with 1971 models, the ball joint is pressed in and must be pressed out.
6. Install the new ball joint, using the bolts supplied with the service ball joint (drill out the rivet holes to accommodate the mounting bolts) on 1967-70 models. The thick-headed bolt is installed on the forward side of the control arm. Press in the ball joint on 1971 and later models.
7. Install the ball stud in the steering knuckle boss. This may be done by raising the lower control arm with the jack.
8. Install the nut on the ball stud, tightening to 80-90 ft. lbs.
9. Install the lube fitting.

Lower Control Arm R & R

1. Remove the spring as described above.
2. Remove the ball stud from the steering knuckle as described above.
3. Remove the control arm pivot bolts and remove the control arm. On some Corvettes, the pivot bolt is secured to the frame with two bolts.
4. To install, reverse the above procedure.

Upper Control Arm R & R

1. Raise the vehicle on a hoist.
2. Support the outer end of the lower control arm, with a jack.
3. Remove the wheel.
4. Separate the upper ball joint from the steering knuckle as described above under "Upper Ball Joint R&R"
5. Remove the control arm shaft to frame nuts.

NOTE: tape the shims together and identify them so that they can be installed in the positions from which they were removed.

6. Remove the bolts which attach the control arm shaft to the frame and remove the control arm. Note the positions of the bolts.
7. Install in the reverse order of removal. Make sure the shaft to frame bolts are installed in the same position they were in before removal and that the shims are in their original positions. Tighten the shaft to frame bolts to 85 ft. lbs. on the Chevrolet and to 55 ft. lbs. on the Corvette. The control arm shaft nuts are torqued to 60 ft. lbs.

REAR SUSPENSION

The Chevrolet uses a coil sprung Salisbury axle located by two trailing arms on each side, except the 1971–74 station wagon which has semi-elliptical leaf springs. The Corvette uses a three-link, independent suspension with a nine-leaf, transverse spring.

Rear Shock Absorber R & R

Chevrolet

1. Jack the car to a convenient working height.
2. If the car is equipped with superlift shock absorbers, disconnect the air line.
3. Remove the two retaining bolts from the upper mounting bracket.
4. Hold the hex on the bottom stud and disconnect the lower mounting. Remove the shock absorber.
5. Install the top two bolts hand-tight.

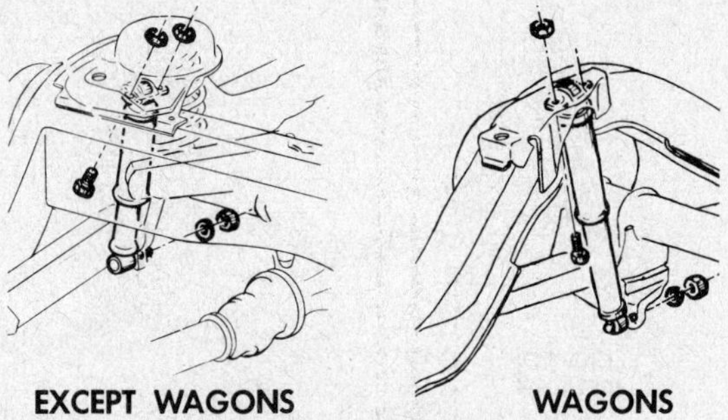
EXCEPT WAGONS
WAGONS

Chevrolet rear shock absorber mounting
(© Chevrolet Div., G.M. Corp)

6. Install the lower stud into the axle bracket and install the lockwasher and nut hand-tight.
7. Torque the upper bolts to 12 ft lbs.
8. While holding the hex stud, torque the nut to 65 ft lbs.
9. Attach the air line, if so equipped, and lower the car.

Corvette

1. Jack the car to a convenient working height.
2. Remove the upper bolt and nut.
3. Remove the lower mounting nut and washers.
4. Pivot the top of the shock absorber out the frame bracket and pull the bottom off the strut shaft.
5. Slide the upper shock absorber eye into the frame bracket and install the bolt, lockwasher, and nut.
6. Install the rubber grommets on the lower shock eye and place the shock over the strut shaft. Install the washers and nut.
7. Torque the upper bolt to 50 ft lbs and the lower nut to 35 ft lbs. Lower the car.

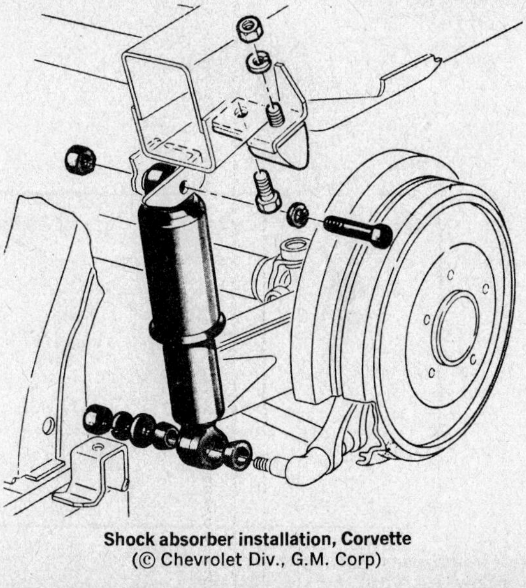

Shock absorber installation, Corvette
(© Chevrolet Div., G.M. Corp)

Coil Type Rear Springs (Chevrolet)

1967-74 R & R

1. Raise rear of vehicle and place jack stands under frame. Support weight of vehicle at rear axle housing separately from above frame position.
2. Remove both rear wheels.
3. With car supported as in Step 1, and springs compressed by weight of vehicle:
   a. Disconnect both rear shocks from anchor pin lower connection.
   b. Loosen the upper control arm(s) rear pivot bolt (do not remove the nut).
   c. Loosen both left and right lower control arm rear attachment (do not disconnect from axle brackets).
   d. Remove rear suspension tie rod from stud on axle tube.
4. Slightly loosen the nut on the bolt that retains the spring and seat to control arm at lower seat of both rear springs. When bolt has been backed off the maximum distance, all threads of the nut should still be engaged on the bolt.

Caution Under no condition should the nut, at this time, be removed from the bolt in the seat of either spring.

5. Slowly lower the rear axle assembly, allowing the axle to swing down, carrying the springs out of the upper seat. This provides access for spring removal.

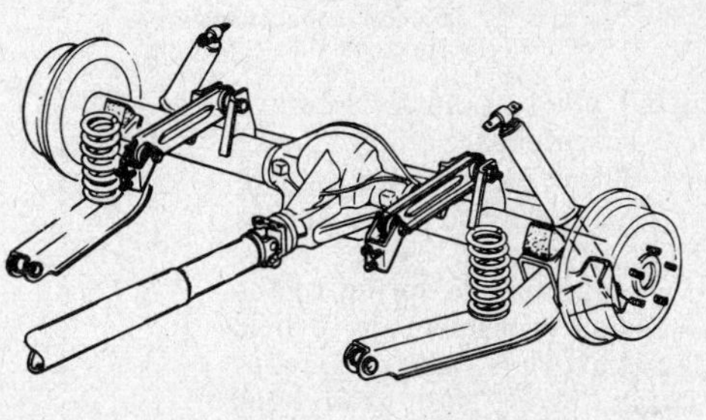

Chevrolet rear suspension except 1971-74 station wagon
(© Chevrolet Div., G.M. Corp)

6. Remove the lower seat attaching parts from each spring, then remove springs from vehicle.
7. Position springs in upper seat and install lower seat parts on control arm. Install nut of spring retaining bolt finger-tight.

NOTE: Omit lockwasher under the special high carbon bolt, so that sufficient threads will be available to start the nut. Lockwashers will be installed later.

8. Alternately raise the axle slightly and retighten the nut on each spring lower seat bolt. Continue in until the weight is fully supported on the jack or lift. With spring now completely compressed to approximate curb position, completely position the springs in the lower seats by torquing the nut on the lower seat bolt.
9. Reconnect shock absorbers, torque rear attachment of upper and lower control arms, and reconnect the axle tie-rod.
10. While still jacked under axle, remove the nut from the lower seat bolt of one rear spring and install lockwasher and replace nut and tighten. Similarly install lockwasher at other spring.
11. Install rear wheels and lower car to floor.

Transverse Leaf Spring (Corvette)

1967-74 R & R

1. Raise car and support it by the frame, slightly forward of torque

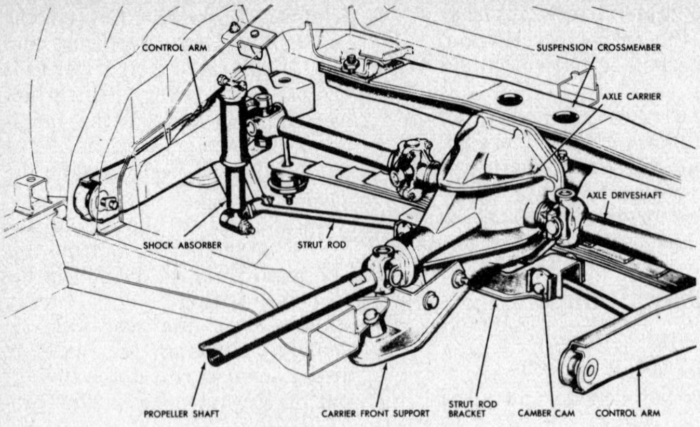
CONTROL ARM
SUSPENSION CROSSMEMBER
AXLE CARRIER
AXLE DRIVESHAFT
SHOCK ABSORBER
STRUT ROD
PROPELLER SHAFT
CARRIER FRONT SUPPORT
STRUT ROD BRACKET
CAMBER CAM
CONTROL ARM

Corvette rear suspension
(© Chevrolet Div., G.M. Corp)

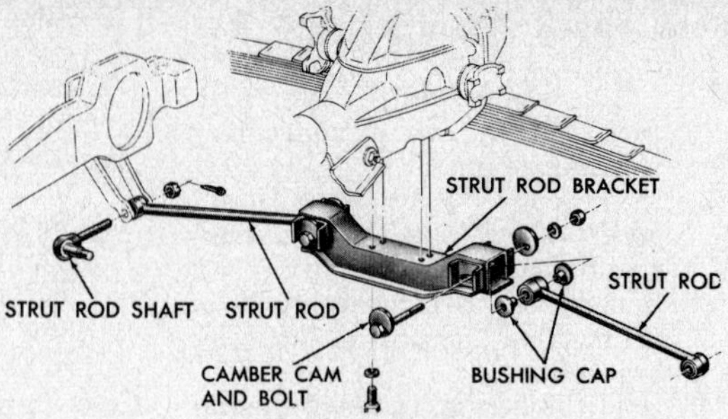
STRUT ROD BRACKET
STRUT ROD
STRUT ROD SHAFT
STRUT ROD
CAMBER CAM
AND BOLT
BUSHING CAP

Strut rods, Corvette
(© Chevrolet Div., G.M. Corp)

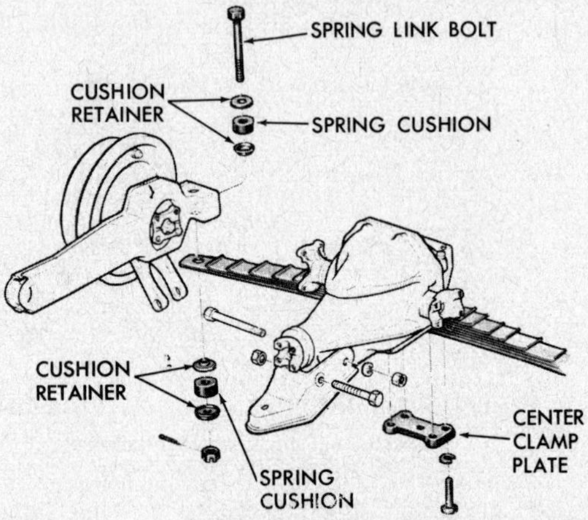
SPRING LINK BOLT
CUSHION
RETAINER
SPRING CUSHION
CUSHION
RETAINER
SPRING
CUSHION
CENTER
CLAMP
PLATE

Spring mounting, Corvette
(© Chevrolet Div., G.M. Corp)

control pivot points. Remove wheel assemblies.

2. Place floor jack under spring near link bolt, and raise spring until nearly flat.
3. Tie the end of the spring to the suspension crossmember to hold this flat attitude, with a 1/4 in. or 5/16 in. chain and grab hook wrapped around the spring and crossmember. To prevent chain slipping, use a C-clamp on the spring adjacent to the chain.
4. Remove link bolt and rubber bushings.
5. Support and raise spring end, as before, and remove chain.
6. Carefully lower jack to completely relax spring.
7. Repeat foregoing procedure on the other side of car.
8. Remove four bolts and washers attaching the spring at the center.
9. Remove the spring by sliding it over the exhaust pipes and out one side of the car.
10. Install by reversing removal procedure.

Leaf Spring R & R Chevrolet 126 In. W.B. Station Wagon

1971-74

1. Raise the vehicle on a hoist and place an adjustable jack under the axle.
2. Raise the axle until all tension is relieved from the spring.
3. Disconnect the shock absorber from the spring retainer plate.
4. Remove the upper shackle retaining bolt, then the front spring eye bolt.
5. Remove the spring/axle U-bolts, lower plate, spring pads, and spring.
6. Remove the shackle from the spring.
7. Before installing the spring, install the shackle on the rearward end.
8. Place the upper cushion on the

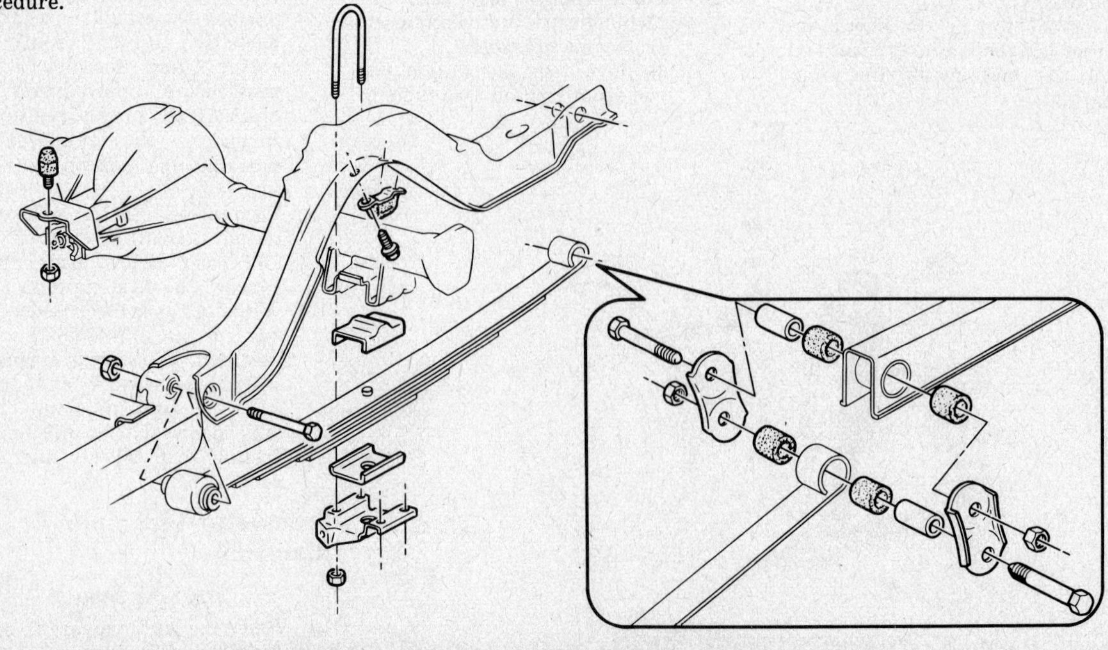

1971-74 126 in. W.B. station wagon rear suspension (© Chevrolet Div., G.M. Corp)

spring, then insert the front of the spring into the frame and attach the rear shackle, leaving the bolt loose.

9. Install the lower spring pad and retainer plate, tightening the U-bolt nuts to 40 ft. lbs.
10. Tighten the rear shackle bolts to 80 ft. lbs.
11. Tighten the front eye bolt to 115 ft. lbs.
12. Attach the shock absorber to spring retainer plate, tightening to 65 ft. lbs.
13. Remove the jack and lower the vehicle.

Strut Rod and Bracket (Corvette)

Rear Wheel Camber Adjustment

Due to the design of this rear suspension, it is important that the strut rod and rear wheel camber adjusting specifications and procedures be included.

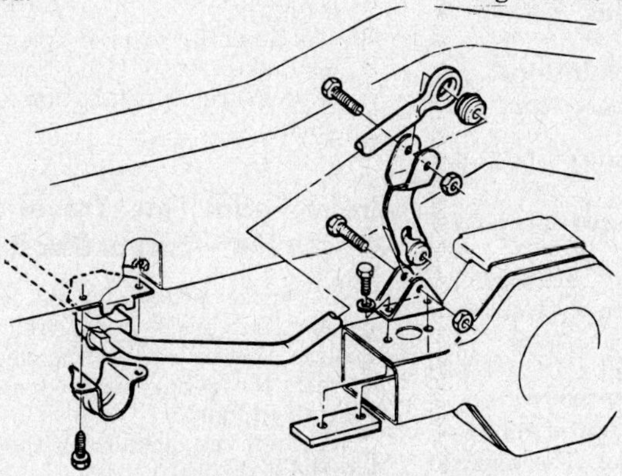

Stabilizer shaft installation, Corvette
(© Chevrolet Div., G.M. Corp)

Rod and Bracket—Removal

1. Raise car on a hoist.
2. Disconnect shock absorber lower eye from strut rod shaft.
3. Remove strut rod shaft cotter pin and nut. Withdraw shaft by pulling toward the front of the car.
4. Mark related position of camber adjustment, so that adjustment is maintained upon reassembly.
5. Loosen camber bolt and nut. Remove four bolts holding strut rod bracket to carrier and lower the bracket.
6. Remove cam bolt and cam bolt assembly. Pull strut down out of bracket and remove bushing caps.
7. Inspect strut rod bushings for wear and replace where necessary. Replace strut rod if it is bent or damaged in any way.
8. Install by reversing removal procedure.
9. Check rear wheel camber and adjust to specifications.

Torque Control Arm R & R (Corvette)

1. Disconnect spring on the side from which the torque arm is to be removed. Follow procedure for Springs R & R.

NOTE: if so equipped, disconnect stabilizer rod from torque arm.

2. Remove shock absorber lower eye from strut rod shaft.
3. Disconnect and remove strut rod shaft and swing strut rod down.
4. Remove four bolts holding the axle driveshaft to spindle flange and disconnect drive shaft.
5. Disconnect brake line at wheel cylinder inlet or caliper and from torque arm. Disconnect parking brake cable.
6. Remove torque arm pivot bolt and toe-in shims, then pull torque arm out of frame. Tape shims together to assure relationship for reassembly.
7. To install, place torque arm in frame opening.
8. Position toe-in shims in original location on both sides of torque arm. Install pivot bolt and lightly tighten at this time.
9. Raise axle driveshaft into position and install to drive flange. Torque bolts to 75 ft. lbs.
10. Raise strut into position and insert strut rod shaft so that flat lines up with flat in spindle support fork. Install nut and torque to 80 ft. lbs.
11. Install shock absorber lower eye and tighten nut to 35 ft. lbs.
12. Connect spring end as outlined under Leaf Type Rear Springs R & R.

NOTE: if car is so equipped, connect stabilizer shaft.

13. Install brake drum or disc and caliper, and wheel. Then lower the car. Tighten torque pivot bolt to 50 ft. lbs.
14. Bleed brakes and check camber and toe-in.

BRAKES

Specific information on brake cylinder sizes can be found in the Brake Specifications table.

Brake adjustments, lining replacement, bleeding procedure, master and wheel cylinder overhaul can be found in the Unit Repair Section.

1967-74

Beginning with 1967 models, a dual hydraulic brake system is employed. The front and rear brakes are each separate systems with a common tandem master cylinder. In the event of a failure in either of the systems, the other will remain operable.

Corvette Parking Brake Adjustment

1. Jack the rear wheels off the ground and remove the wheels.
2. Rotate the disc until the adjusting screw can be seen through the hole in the disc.
3. Insert a screwdriver and adjust with an up-and-down motion.
4. Tighten the adjuster until the disc cannot move, then back off 6 to 8 notches.
5. Apply the parking brake to the fourth notch. Tighten the cables at the equalizer to give a light drag with the wheel mounted.
6. Release the parking brake and check for a no drag condition.

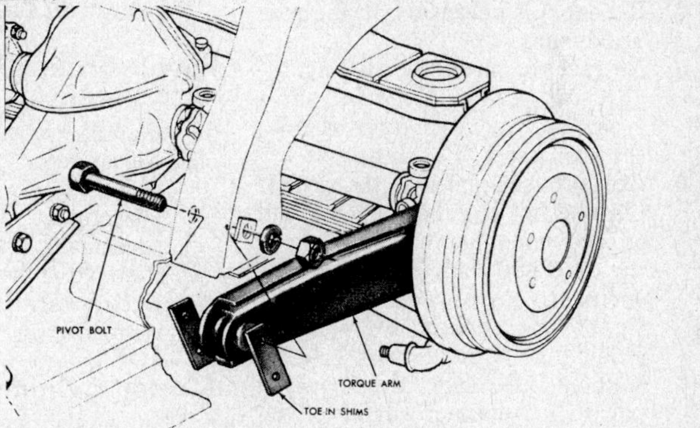
PIVOT BOLT
TORQUE ARM
TOE IN SHIMS

Torque control arm, Corvette
(© Chevrolet Div., G.M. Corp)

Corvette Parking Brake Shoe Removal and Replacement

1. Jack the car up and remove the rear wheels and tires.
2. Remove the brake caliper from the disc. Do not disconnect the brake line, but remove the line clip from the control arm and hang the caliper above the disc with wire.
3. Drill the disc retaining rivets out and remove the disc from the axle hub. It is not necessary to replace the rivets when the disc is reinstalled.
4. Insert a screwdriver into the adjusting hole and turn the screw several times to expand the shoes.
5. Push the brake shoes forward until the front shoe hold-down spring can be seen through the adjusting hole.

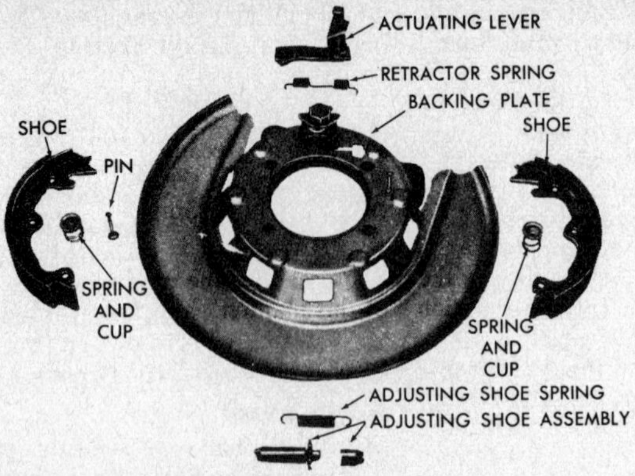
ACTUATING LEVER
RETRACTOR SPRING
BACKING PLATE
SHOE
SHOE
PIN
SPRING
AND
CUP
SPRING
AND
CUP
ADJUSTING SHOE SPRING
ADJUSTING SHOE ASSEMBLY

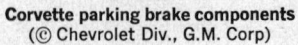

Corvette parking brake components
(© Chevrolet Div., G.M. Corp)

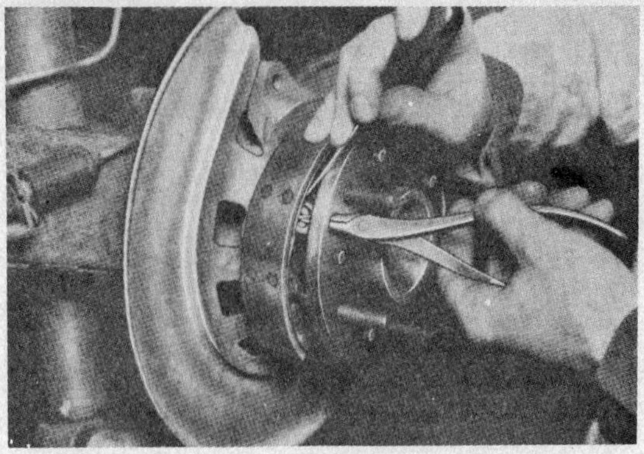

Removing Corvette parking brake shoe spring retainer
(© Chevrolet Div., G.M. Corp)

6. Insert a pair of needle-nosed pliers through the hole and grasp the hold-down pin. Depress the spring with a screwdriver inserted from the side and turn the pin 90° to free the spring and retainer. Remove the spring and retainer.
7. Repeat this operation on the rear brake shoe.
8. Retract the shoes by turning the adjuster screw. Pull the shoes from the adjuster and remove the adjuster and spring.
9. Separate the shoes at the anchor pin and lift the shoes up and out of the housing, while allowing the straight part of the return spring to go between the outer tip of the anchor pin and the axle flange plate.
10. Lightly lubricate the backing plate shoe contact surfaces, anchor pin, and adjusting screw threads.
11. Install the return spring on the replacement shoes and position the shoes on the anchor pin.
12. Install the adjuster spring and adjuster. Turn the adjuster screw to expand the shoes.
13. Turn the axle shaft flange so that the adjustment hole aligns with the front hold-down spring pin.
14. Push the shoe forward and over the hold-down pin.
15. Install the spring and retainer over the hold-down pin and using needle-nosed pliers and a screwdriver as in step 6, depress the spring and twist the pin 90°.
16. Repeat the above step on the rear shoe. Another pair of needle-nosed pliers will have to be utilized to hold the pin in position, as head of this pin is not accessible.
17. Turn the adjuster screw to retract the shoes.
18. Install the brake disc onto the studs, making sure that the adjustment holes in the disc and flange align.
19. Install the caliper.
20. Adjust the parking brake as described above.
21. Install the tire and wheel and lower the car.
22. After installation of new parking brake linings. the shoes should be burnished. At a speed of 50 mph, apply the parking brakes until a slight drag is felt. Keep the brakes on for approximately 50-60 seconds.

Power Brake Unit Removal

1. Remove vacuum hose from vacuum check valve.
2. Disconnect hydraulic lines at unit.
3. Disconnect push rod at brake pedal assembly.
4. Remove nuts and lockwashers that secure unit to firewall and remove unit.

Master Cylinder Removal

The pedals are pivoted from underneath the dash panel. The master cylinder is located on the engine side of the firewall.

1. To remove the master cylinder, disconnect the hydraulic lines, remove the clevis that connects the brake pushrod to the brake pedal from under the dash.
2. Remove the mounting bolts that hold the master cylinder to the firewall and lift off the master cylinder.
3. To install, reverse the above procedure, and bleed the brake system when installation is complete.

Brake Pedal Free Travel Adjustment—Except Disc Brakes

The brake pedal stop is not adjustable, but brake pedal free travel is adjustable by setting the clearance between the pedal pushrod and the master cylinder.

1. Loosen the locknut on the pushrod.
2. Turn the pushrod until there is

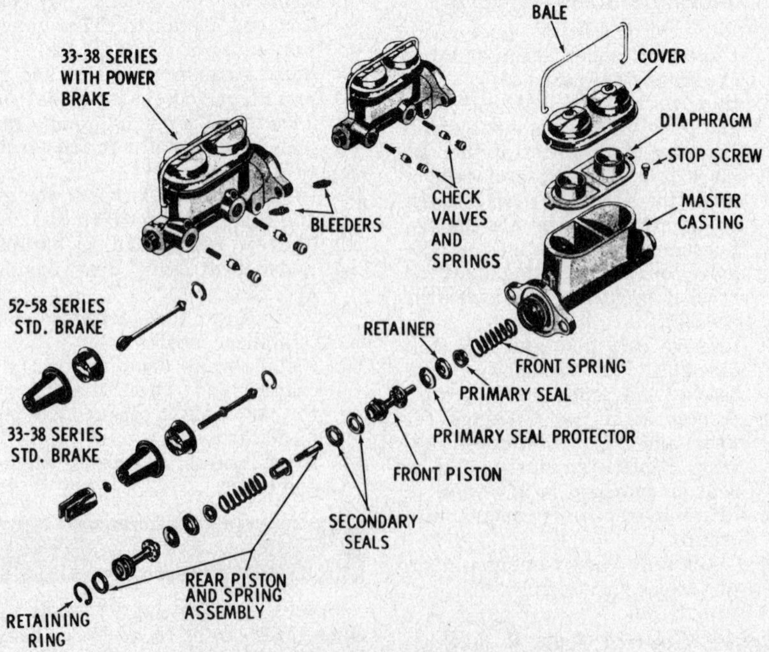
BALE
33-38 SERIES
WITH POWER
BRAKE
COVER
DIAPHRAGM
STOP SCREW
MASTER
CASTING
BLEEDERS
CHECK
VALVES
AND
SPRINGS
52-58 SERIES
STD. BRAKE
RETAINER
FRONT SPRING
PRIMARY SEAL
PRIMARY SEAL PROTECTOR
33-38 SERIES
STD. BRAKE
FRONT PISTON
SECONDARY
SEALS
REAR PISTON
AND SPRING
ASSEMBLY
RETAINING
RING

Master cylinder (Bendix) No front check valve with front disc brake
(© Chevrolet Div., G.M. Corp)

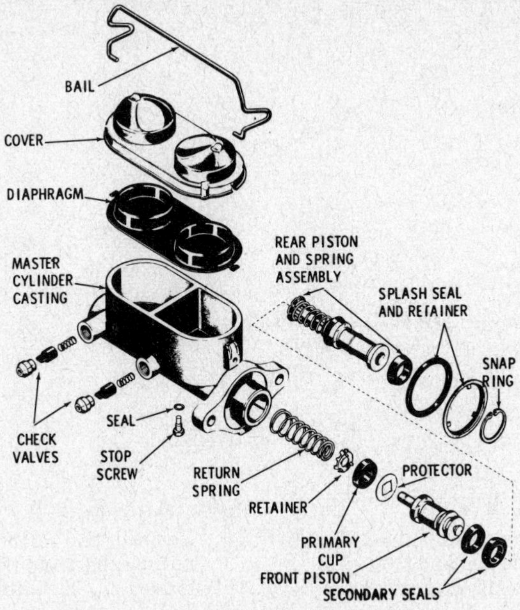
BAIL
COVER
DIAPHRAGM
MASTER CYLINDER CASTING
REAR PISTON AND SPRING ASSEMBLY
SPLASH SEAL AND RETAINER
SNAP RING
SEAL
CHECK VALVES
STOP SCREW
RETURN SPRING
RETAINER
PROTECTOR
PRIMARY CUP
FRONT PISTON
SECONDARY SEALS

Master cylinder (Moraine) No front check valve with front disc brake
(© Chevrolet Div., G.M. Corp)

1/16 to 1/4 in. pedal free travel (movement before the pushrod contacts the master cylinder pistons).

3. Tighten the locknut against the clevis and recheck the free travel.

Parking Brake Cable R & R

Before working under the dash to remove the front parking brake cable, disconnect the battery to avoid the possibility of shorting out any of the circuits.

1967-70 Chevrolet

There are three parking brake cables: the front cable runs between the pedal assembly and the looped center cable; the center cable is a large loop, each end connected to the short rear cables and the center (forward) attached to the front cable with the equalizer; the rear cables are attached to brake shoe actuating levers.

To remove any of the cables, first release the brake pedal and loosen the equalizer adjusting nuts. The front cable slips into a clevis at the pedal lever and is connected to the equalizer by means of a threaded rod. The outer cable has locking fingers which secure it in a hole in the firewall.

The center cable is removed by disconnecting the equalizer, disconnecting each end from the rear cables and by removing it from the frame guides and hook. The rear cables are removed by disconnecting the forward end from the center cable, removing the retainers at the frame and by removing the rear end from the brake actuating levers. The brake drum and shoes must be removed to disconnect the rear cable from the actuating lever.

Adjust the parking brake after replacing any of the cables. Adjustment is made at the equalizer while the parking brake pedal is applied two notches from the full release position. Loosen the forward equalizer adjusting nut, tighten the rear nut until slight brake drag is obtained, then tighten the forward adjusting nut. Check operation after adjustment.

1971-74 Chevrolet

The parking brake cable design is essentially the same as that used in 1967-70 models with a forward, center and two rear cables. The front outer cable, however, is clipped to the pedal bracket. When replacing the front cable, tie a rope onto the top of the old cable and pull it through the cable route so that it may be used to pull the new cable into place. Remove the rear screws holding the inner

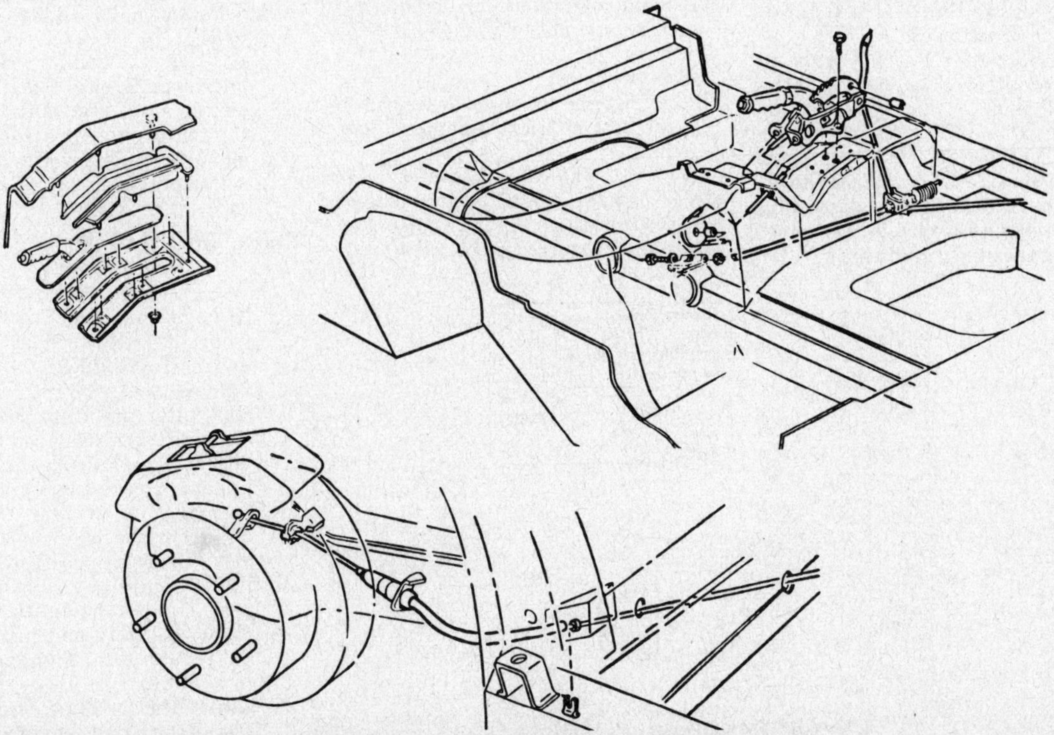

Corvette parking brake cables (© Chevrolet Div., G.M. Corp)

fender panel to the fender to get at the cable grommet in the firewall. Adjustment is the same as that described for the 1967-1970 models above.

1967-74 Corvette

To remove the front cable, remove the parking brake lever and the pulley. Remove the cable ball end from the hand lever. Remove the seal grommet from the underbody cable hole and pull the cable out of the vehicle. Installation is the reverse of the removal procedure.

To remove the rear cables, remove the retainer clips at the frame and disconnect the cables at the rear flange plate. Remove the ball from the recess of the brake lever clevis and disconnect the cables from the equalizer. Install in the reverse order of removal.

Adjustment of the parking brake is made with the lever set at two notches from the fully released position. Tighten the equalizer adjusting nuts until slight drag is felt at the rear wheels.

STEERING

Manual steering gear on both the Chevrolet and Corvette is of the recirculating ball type. Relay-type steering linkage is used on all models, with a pitman arm connected to one end of a relay rod and a frame-mounted idler arm at the other end. Two tie-rods assemblies connect the relay rod to the steering arms. The tie-rod ends are threaded into sleeves to provide adjustment.

Chevrolet power steering is the integral-gear type. The only external hydraulic lines on this system are the pressure and return hoses to the pump. The Corvette uses a linkage assist system. A valve attached to the linkage modulates pressure according to power requirements. A power cylinder supplies the actual assist.

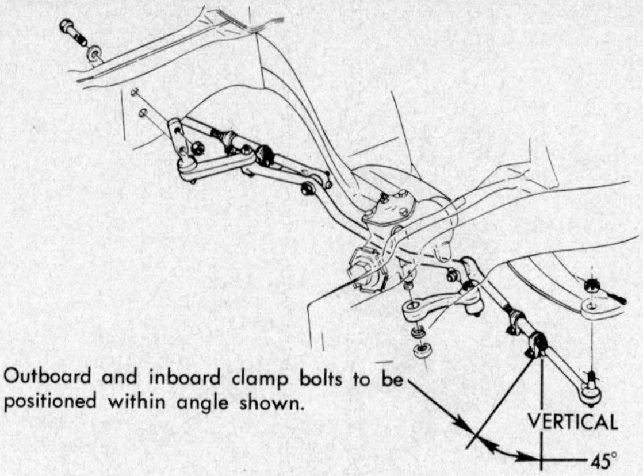
Outboard and inboard clamp bolts to be positioned within angle shown.
VERTICAL
45°

Chevrolet steering linkage
(© Chevrolet Div., G.M. Corp)

Tie-Rod R & R

1. Remove the cotter pins and nuts from the tie-rod end studs.
2. Tap on the steering arm near the tie-rod end (use another hammer as backing) and pull down on the tie rod, if necessary, to free it.
3. Remove the inner stud in the same manner as the outer.
4. Loosen the clamp bolts and unscrew the ends if they are being replaced.
5. Lubricate the tie-rod end threads with chassis grease if they were removed. Install each end assembly an equal distance from the sleeve.
6. Ensure that the tie-rod end stud threads and nut are clean. Install new seals and install the studs into the steering arms and relay rod.
7. Install the stud nuts. Tighten the outer end nut to 35 ft lbs and the inner nut to 60 ft lbs (35 ft lbs on Corvette)
8. Adjust the toe-in as described in the "Front End Alignment" section.

NOTE: before tightening the sleeve clamps, ensure that the clamps are positioned so that the adjusting sleeve slot is covered by the clamp.

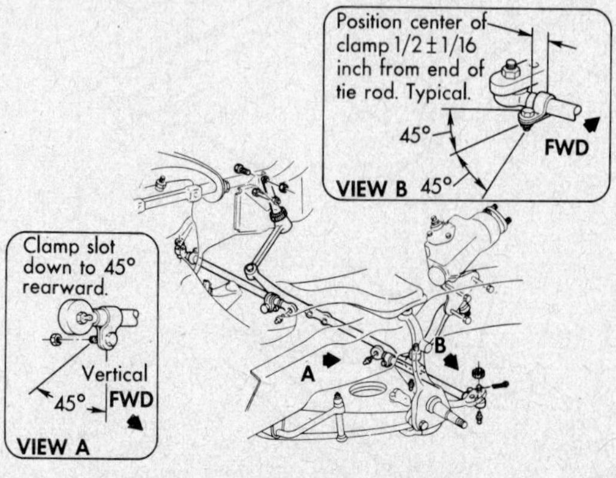
Position center of clamp 1/2 ± 1/16 inch from end of tie rod. Typical.
45°
FWD
VIEW B 45°
Clamp slot down to 45° rearward.
Vertical
45°
FWD
VIEW A
A
B

Corvette steering linkage
(© Chevrolet Div., G.M. Corp)

Idler Arm R & R

1. Remove the idler arm-to-frame nut, washer, and bolt (no washer is used on Corvette).
2. Remove the cotter pin and nut from the idler arm-to-relay rod ball end stud.
3. Tap the relay rod firmly with a hammer, using another heavy hammer as backing on the opposite side of the relay rod to remove the relay rod from the idler arm.
4. Remove the idler arm.
5. To install the idler arm on a Chevrolet, install the seal on the idler arm stud; position the stud up through the frame, and install the lockwasher and nut. Tighten the nut to 45 ft lbs.
6. To install the idler arm on a Corvette, place the idler arm on the frame and install the retaining bolts and nuts. Tighten the nuts to 35 ft lbs.
7. Position the relay rod on the idler arm. Ensure that the seal is on the stud. Install the nut and tighten to 40 ft lbs (Chevrolet) or 35 ft lbs (Corvette). Install a cotter pin.

Relay Rod R & R

Chevrolet

1. Remove the inner tie-rod ends from the relay rod as outlined under "Tie-Rod R&R."
2. Remove the relay rod stud nut and cotter pin from the pitman arm. Free the relay rod from the pitman arm, moving the steering linkage if necessary. Repeat this operation to remove the relay rod from the idler arm and remove the relay rod from the car.
3. Install the relay rod on the idler arm. Tighten the nut to 40 ft lbs.
4. Raise the relay and install it on the pitman arm. Tighten the nut to 45 ft lbs.
5. Adjust the toe-in as described in the "Front End Alignment" section.

Corvette

1. Remove the inner tie-rod ends from the relay rod as outlined in "Tie-Rod R&R."
2. Disconnect the relay rod at the pitman arm. Tap the stud out of the pitman arm and lower the relay rod.
3. Disconnect the relay rod from the idler arm and remove the rod. Remove the idler arm washer and seal.
4. Position the relay rod on the idler arm stud, ensuring that the seal and washer are in place, and then install the nut. Tighten the nut to 35 ft lbs and install a cotter pin.
5. Install a new pitman arm seal and clamp.
6. Install the inner spring seat and spring on the relay rod.
7. Raise the relay rod and install it on the pitman arm. Install the spring seat, spring, and end-plug.
8. Tighten the end-plug until the springs are compressed and the plug abuts, and then back it off ¾ of a turn. Insert a cotter pin to hold the adjustment.
9. Install the tie-rod ends as outlined under "Tie-Rod R&R."
10. Apply grease to the tie-rod ends and pitman arm-to-relay rod ball joint.
11. Adjust the toe-in as outlined in "Front End Alignment."

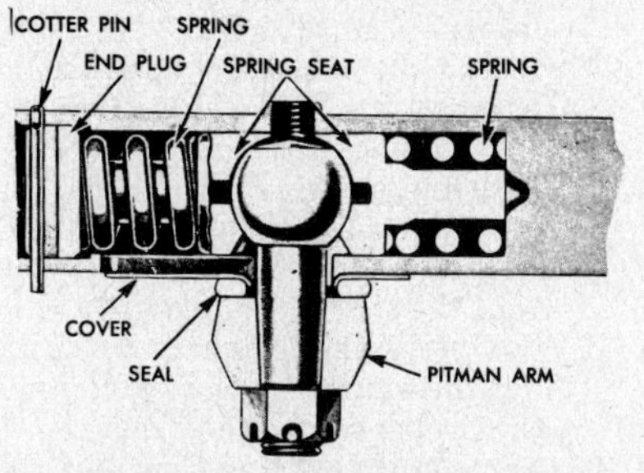
COTTER PIN
SPRING
END PLUG
SPRING SEAT
SPRING
COVER
SEAL
PITMAN ARM

Corvette pitman arm attachment to relay rod
(© Chevrolet Div., G.M. Corp)

Pitman Arm R & R

1. Remove the pitman arm stud nut and cotter pin.
2. Tap the relay rod off the pitman arm, using another hammer as backing. Pull the relay rod off the pitman arm stud.
3. Remove the pitman arm nut and mark the arm-to-shaft relationship.
4. Remove the pitman arm using a puller.
5. Install the pitman arm on the shaft, aligning the previously made marks. Install the pitman shaft nut and tighten it to 180 ft lbs (Chevrolet) or 140 ft lbs (Corvette).
6. Install the relay rod on the pitman arm. Tighten the nut to 45 ft lbs and install a cotter pin.

Power Steering Pump R & R

1. Remove the hoses at the pump and tape the openings shut to prevent contamination. Position the disconnected lines in a raised position to prevent leakage.
2. Remove the pump belt. On 427 and 454 Corvettes, loosen the alternator and remove the pump-to-alternator belt.
3. Loosen the retaining bolts and any braces, and remove the pump.
4. Install the pump on the engine with the retaining bolts hand-tight.
5. Connect and tighten the hose fittings.
6. Refill the pump and bleed by turning the pulley counterclockwise (viewed from the front). Stop the bleeding when air bubbles no longer appear.
7. Install the pump belt on the pulley and adjust the tension.

Steering Wheel R & R

Caution Disconnect the battery ground cable before removing the steering wheel. When installing a steering wheel, always make sure that the turn signal lever is in the neutral position.

Chevrolet and Corvette 1967-68

1. Pry out the center cap and retainer.
2. Remove the three receiving cup screws and the cup, belleville spring, bushing, and pivot ring.
3. Remove the steering wheel nut and washer.
4. Mark the wheel-to-shaft relationship, and then remove the wheel with a puller.
5. Install the wheel on the shaft, aligning the previously made marks. Tighten the nut to 35 ft lbs.
6. Install the belleville spring (dished side up), pivot ring, bushing, and receiving cup. Install the center cap and reconnect the battery.

NOTE: removal of the 1970 padded steering wheel is similar to the above.

Chevrolet 1969 Deluxe Wheel and Standard Wheel 1970-74

1. Remove the four trim retaining screws from behind the wheel.
2. Lift the trim off and pull the horn wires from the turn signal cancelling cam.
3. Remove the steering wheel nut.
4. Mark the wheel-to-shaft relationship, and then remove the wheel with a puller.
5. Install the wheel on the shaft, aligning the previously made marks. Tighten the nut to 30 ft lbs.
6. Insert the horn wires into the cancelling cam.
7. Install the center trim and reconnect the battery cable.

NOTE: The 1967–69 Chevrolet simulated wood wheel, the 1973 Chevrolet cushioned rim wheel, and the 1969-74 Corvette wheel do not require pulling for removal. Pry off the center cap and horn contact assembly. On the tilt/telescope Corvette wheel, remove the shim, center lockscrew, lock lever or knob, and the spacer. The wheel is held to the hub by phillips screws. Reverse the disassembly procedure to install the wheel.

Turn Signal Switch R & R

Chevrolet 1967-68

1 Remove the steering wheel as outlined above.
2. On column-shift cars, remove the shift lever retaining pin and the lever.
3. Disconnect the column wiring harness from the chassis harness.
4. Remove the lower trim plate and the upper mast jacket clamp. On automatic cars, remove the indicator retaining screw and the pointer.
5. Remove the wiring harness clamps, sliding the components up on the column to expose the upper clamp.
6. Using snap-ring pliers, remove the C-ring from the upper steering shaft. Slide the thrust and wave washers off the steering shaft.

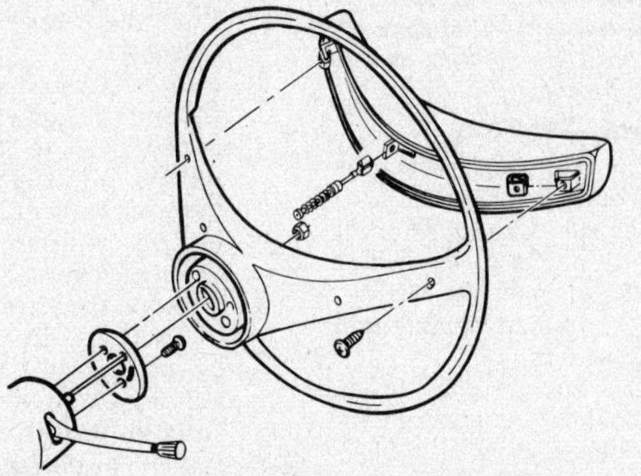

1969 Chevrolet Deluxe and 1970-74 standard steering wheel
(© Chevrolet Div., G.M. Corp)

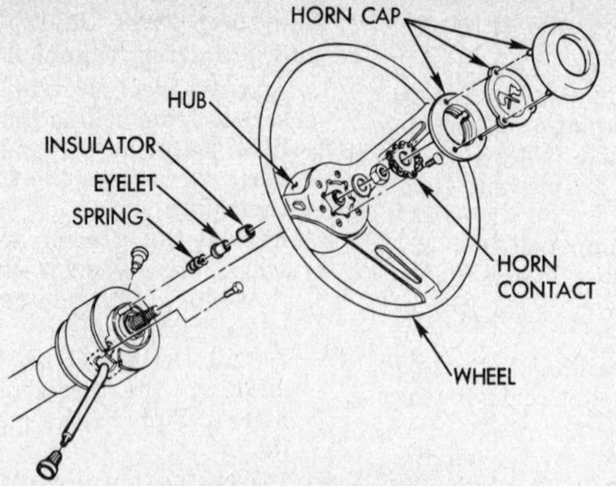
HORN CAP
HUB
INSULATOR
EYELET
SPRING
HORN CONTACT
WHEEL

1969-74 Corvette steering wheel
(© Chevrolet Div., G.M. Corp)

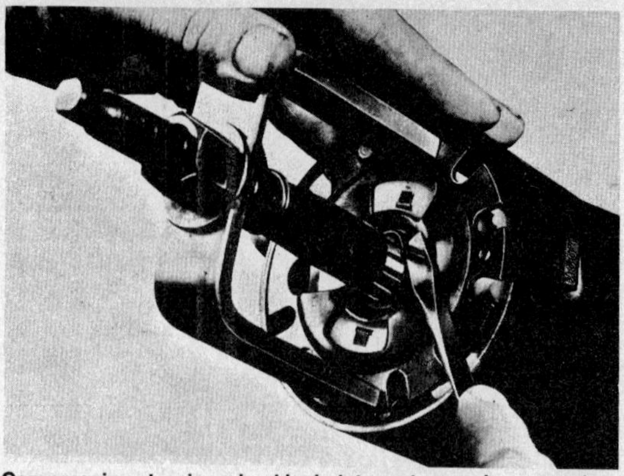

Compressing steering wheel lockplate and removing snap-ring
(© Chevrolet Div., G.M. Corp)

7. Loosen, but do not remove, the three turn signal mounting screws.
8. Turn the switch counterclockwise. Pull the switch out of the mast jacket and let it hang by its wiring.
9. Support the column, and then remove the upper mounting bracket. Remove the wiring harness cover and clip, and then reinstall the upper bracket hand-tight.
10. Remove the shift lever bowl from the mast jacket and disconnect it from the wiring harness.
11. Remove the switch retaining screws, being careful not to lose the springs.
12. Remove the switch and upper bearing housing from the switch cover.
13. Install the upper bearing housing assembly and the switch into the cover, working the switch wires through the cover.
14. Install the remaining components in a reverse order of removal.

NOTE: the procedure for the tilt wheel is similar, with the exceptions that turn signal cover removal requires a slide hammer and special attachment and that the switch wiring connector must be cut.

Corvette 1967-68

1. Remove the steering wheel as previously outlined.
2. From under the dash, disconnect the switch harness connector from the chassis harness.
3. Remove the preload spring and the cancelling cam.
4. Remove the turn signal lever. Push the flasher knob in and remove it by unscrewing.
5. Remove the lower trim cover.
6. Remove the retaining ring and the thrust and wave washers from the top of the steering shaft. Cut the wiring above the connector.
7. Unscrew the switch, and slide it, the cover, and the upper bearing housing out of the column. Pull the wire through the column protector and escutcheon.
8. Install the new switch by assembling it and the upper bearing housing into the switch cover, and then working the wire down through the escutcheon and column protector until the switch can be positioned on the mast jacket.
9. Install the switch and remaining components in a reverse order of removal.

Chevrolet and Corvette 1969-74

1. Remove the steering wheel as previously outlined.
2. Loosen the three cover screws and lift the cover off the shaft.
3. Position the special lockplate compressing tool (J-23131 1969–70 or J-23653 1971–73) on the end of the steering shaft and compress the lockplate by turning the shaft nut clockwise. Pry the wire snap-ring out of the shaft groove.
4. Remove the tool and lift the lockplate off the shaft.
5. Slip the cancelling cam, upper bearing pre-load spring, and thrust washer off the shaft.
6. Remove the turn signal lever. Push the flasher knob in and unscrew it.
7. Pull the switch connector out of the mast jacket and tape the upper part to facilitate switch removal. On tilt wheels, place the turn signal and shifter housing in Low position and remove the harness cover.
8. Remove the three switch mounting screws. Remove the switch by pulling it straight up while guiding the wiring harness cover through the column.
9. Install the replacement switch by working the connector and cover down through the housing and under the bracket. On tilt models, the connector is worked down through the housing, under the bracket, and then the cover is installed on the harness.
10. Install the switch mounting screws and the connector on the mast jacket bracket. Install the column-to-dash trim plate.
11. Install the flasher knob and the turn signal lever.
12. With the turn signal lever in neutral and the flasher knob out, slide the thrust washer, upper bearing pre-load spring, and cancelling cam onto the shaft.
13. Position the lockplate on the shaft and press it down until a new snap-ring can be inserted in the shaft groove.
14. Install the cover and the steering wheel.

Corvette Tilt-Telescope 1969-74

1. Remove the steering wheel as previously outlined and press off the hub with a puller.
2. Remove the steering column/dash trim cover.
3. Remove the C-ring plastic retainer, if so equipped.
4. Install the special lockplate compressing tool (J-23131 1969–70 or J-23653 1971–72) over the steering shaft. Position a 5/16 in. nut under each tool leg and reinstall the star screw to prevent the shaft from moving.
5. Compress the lockplate by turning the shaft nut clockwise until the C-ring can be removed.
6. Remove the tool and lift out the lock plate, horn contact carrier, and the upper bearing preload spring.

NOTE: 1969 Corvette assembly order is: horn control carrier, lockplate, and upper bearing preload spring.

7. Pull the switch connector out of the mast jacket and tape the upper part to facilitate switch removal.
8. Remove the turn signal lever. Push the flasher in and unscrew it.
9. Position the turn signal and shifter housing in Low position. Remove the switch by pulling it straight up while guiding the wiring harness out of the housing.
10. Install the replacement switch by working the harness connector down through the housing and under the mounting bracket.

11. Install the harness cover and clip the connector to the mast jacket.
12. Install the switch mounting screws, signal lever, and the flasher knob.
13. With the turn signal lever in neutral and the flasher knob out, install the upper bearing pre-load spring, horn contact carrier, and lockplate onto the shaft. Horn contact carrier is last on 1969 models.
14. Position the tool as in step four and compress the plate far enough to allow the C-ring to be installed.
15. Remove the tool. Install the plastic C-ring retainer.
16. Install the column/dash trim cover. Install the steering wheel.

Pitman Shaft Seal R & R

The pitman shaft seal can be replaced without removing the steering gear from the vehicle as follows:

1. Place the steering wheel in center position.
2. Remove the bolts which secure the gear side housing, then remove the pitman shaft and side cover as a unit.
3. Remove the pitman shaft seal from the steering gear body.
4. Grease the new seal and drive it into place with a suitable socket.
5. Install the side cover and pitman shaft assembly, being careful not to damage the new seal and using a new cover gasket.
6. Install the side cover retaining bolts.

Steering Knuckle R & R

1. Raise the vehicle on a hoist.
2. Support the lower control arm with a jack.
3. Remove the wheel.
4. Remove the brake drum and backing plate or the caliper, disc and splash shield. Do not disconnect the brake hydraulic line and do not let the backing plate or caliper hang by the hydraulic line.
5. Remove the upper and lower ball studs from the steering knuckle as described in "Ball Joint R&R."
6. Install in the reverse order of removal, referring to "Ball Joint R&R" if necessary.

Power Steering Control Valve R & R

Corvette

The rubber seal for the control valve ball stud (to which the pitman arm connects) may be replaced without removing the control valve. Remove the pitman arm, then remove the bolt and clamp which retain the ball stud. When installing the new seal, make sure the lips of the seal mate with the clamp.

To remove the control valve:

1. Raise the front of the car and place it on stands.
2. Remove the relay rod to control valve clamp bolt.
3. Disconnect and drain the hydraulic hoses.
4. Remove the ball stud nut and disconnect the control valve from the pitman arm.
5. Unscrew the control valve from the relay rod.
6. To install, reverse the above procedure. Bleed the hydraulic system as described below. Grease the ball joint.

Power Cylinder R & R

Corvette

1. Place the car on a hoist.
2. Disconnect the two hydraulic lines, letting them drain.
3. Remove the cotter pin, nut, retainer and grommet from the power cylinder rod end. Inspect the grommet in the bracket, replacing if necessary.
4. Remove the cotter pin, nut and ball stud at the relay rod and remove the power cylinder.
5. To install, reverse the removal procedure. Bleed the hydraulic system as described below. Grease the ball joint.

Bleeding Power Steering System

1. Fill the fluid reservoir.
2. Let the fluid stand undisturbed for two minutes, then crank the engine for about two seconds. Refill reservoir if necessary.
3. Repeat Steps 1 and 2 above until the fluid level remains constant after cranking the engine.
4. Raise the front of the car until the wheels are off the ground, then start the engine. Increase the engine speed to about 1,500 rpm.
5. Turn the wheels to the left and right, checking the fluid level and refilling if necessary.

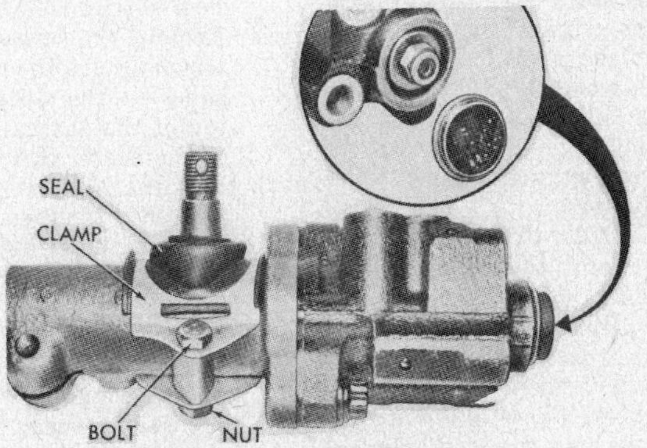

SEAL
CLAMP
BOLT
NUT

Control valve ball stud seal—Corvette
(© Chevrolet Div., G.M. Corp)

INSTRUMENT PANEL

Caution Disconnect battery while working on the speedometer or gauges.

Ignition Switch Replacement

1967-68 All Models

1. Disconnect battery.
2. Remove cylinder by placing in lock position and insert stiff wire in small hole to depress plunger. Turn cylinder counterclockwise until cylinder can be removed.
3. Remove holding nut. (Tool J-7607 will assist.)
4. Pull switch from under dash and remove connectors.
5. Using a screwdriver, unsnap the locking tangs of the "theft resistant" connector.
6. Install in reverse of above.

1968 Corvette

The ignition switch replacement procedure is the same as that described above, except that the "CORVETTE" cover plate in the top center of the cluster assembly must be removed first.

1969-74 Chevrolet & Corvette

The switch is located inside the channel section of the brake pedal support and is completely inaccessible without first lowering the steering column. The switch is actuated by a rod and rack assembly. A gear on the end of the lock cylinder engages the toothed upper end of the rod.

1. Remove or lower the steering column as described under *Steering*. If steering column is lowered, be sure to properly support it.
2. Put the switch in "Lock" position. With the cylinder removed, the rod is in "Lock" position when it is in the next to the uppermost detent.

3. Remove the two switch screws and remove the switch assembly.
4. Before installing, place the new switch in "Lock" position and make sure the lock cylinder and actuating rod are in "Lock" position (second detent from the top).
5. Install the activating rod into the switch and assemble the switch on the column. Tighten the mounting screws. Use only the specified screws since overlength screws could impair the collapsibility of the column.
6. Reinstall the steering column.

Lock Cylinder R & R—1969-74

1. Remove steering wheel and directional signal switch.

NOTE: see *Steering.*

2. Place lock cylinder in Lock position up to 1970, Run position starting 1971.

Caution Do not remove the ignition key buzzer.

3. Insert a small screwdriver into the turn signal housing slot. Keeping the screwdriver to the right side of the slot, break the housing flash loose and depress the spring latch at the lower end of the lock cylinder. Remove the lock cylinder.

NOTE: Considerable force may be necessary to break this casting flash, but be careful not to damage any other parts. When ordering a new lock cylinder, specify a cylinder assembly. This will save assembling the cylinder, washer, sleeve and adaptor.

4. To install, hold the lock cylinder sleeve and rotate the knob clockwise against the stop. Insert the cylinder into the housing, aligning the key and keyway. Hold a .070 in. drill between the lock bezel and housing. Rotate the cylinder counterclockwise, maintaining a light pressure until the drive section of the cylinder mates with the sector. Push in until the snap ring pops into the grooves. Remove drill. Check cylinder operation.

Caution The drill prevents forcing the lock cylinder inward beyond its normal position. The buzzer switch and spring latch can hold the lock cylinder in too far. Complete disassembly of the upper bearing housing is necessary to release an improperly installed lock cylinder.

Headlight Switch Replacement

1967-74 Except as Noted

1. Disconnect battery.
2. Pull knob out to on position.
3. Reach under instrument panel and depress the switch shaft retainer. Remove knob and shaft assembly.
4. Remove the retaining ferrule nut. (Tool J-4880 will assist.)
5. Remove switch from instrument panel.
6. Disconnect the multi-plug connector from the switch.
7. Replace in reverse of above. (In checking lights before installation, switch must be grounded to test dome light.)

1968 Corvette

The headlight switch replacement procedure is the same as that described immediately above, except that the instrument panel must be unscrewed and pulled forward to provide access to the switch. Also, when disconnecting the switch, identify the vacuum lines so that they can be correctly reconnected.

1969-74 Corvette

1. Disconnect the battery.
2. Remove mast jacket trim covers.
3. Unclip and remove the left forward console side trim panel.
4. Lower the steering column as described under *Steering.*
5. Remove the screws and washers which secure the left instrument panel to the door opening, the top of the dash and the left side of the center instrument cluster.
6. Pull the cluster assembly down and tilt it forward.
7. Depress the switch shaft retainer and remove the knob and shaft assembly.
8. Remove the switch retaining bezel.
9. Disconnect the vacuum lines, identifying them for correct reconnection.
10. Pry the connector from the switch.
11. Install in the reverse order of removal.

WINDSHIELD WIPERS

Motor R & R

1967 Chevrolet

1. Make sure the battery is disconnected and the wiper motor is in parked position.
2. Remove washer hoses, if present, and all electrical connectors.
3. Remove plenum chamber ventilator grille.
4. Disconnect transmission drive linkage from wiper motor crank arm.
5. Remove motor retaining bolts, then remove the motor.
6. Install motor by reversing the removal procedure.

NOTE: make sure the wiper motor is properly grounded.

1967 Corvette

1. Disconnect battery.
2. Remove ignition distributor shielding and left bank plug wire vertical shield.
3. Disconnect left bank plug wire bracket-to-manifold, position assembly to one side.
4. Disconnect ignition resistor at firewall, then remove washer pump inlet and outlet hose at pump valve assembly.
5. Remove ignition distributor cap and position to one side, then disconnect washer pump and motor assembly wires.
6. Remove glove compartment door and compartment.
7. Make sure wiper arms and motor are both in parked position. Remove transmission retaining clip and disconnect both transmission and spacer from crank arm.
8. Remove four wiper motor-to-dash wall mounting bolts and remove wiper motor from the car.
9. Install motor by reversing removal procedure.

1968-74 Corvette and Chevrolet

1. With wiper motor in park position and hood open, disconnect the washer hoses and all wiring from the motor assembly.
2. Remove the plenum chamber grill on Corvettes or the access cover on Chevrolet models.
3. Loosen the nuts which retain the drive link to the crank arm ball stud on Chevrolet models. Remove the nut which retains the crank arm to the motor assembly on Corvette models.
4. On Corvettes, remove the ignition shield and distributor cap. Remove and identify the left bank spark plug leads.
5. Remove the motor mounting screws or nuts and remove the motor.
6. To install, reverse the above procedure.

Transmission R & R

1967 Chevrolet

1. With the wiper motor in parked position, remove shroud top ventilator grille.
2. Detach transmission drive linkage from wiper motor assembly.
3. Remove screws holding transmission to body, then lower transmission into plenum chamber.
4. Remove the assembly from the plenum chamber.
5. To install, reverse the removal procedure.

1967 Corvette

1. Remove wiper block and arm assembly from transmission.
2. Remove glove compartment door and compartment.
3. Remove three transmission-to-cowl retaining screws.
4. Remove wiper transmission retaining clip and remove transmission from crank arm. Then, remove transmission through the glove compartment opening.

5. To install, reverse removal procedure.

1968-74 Chevrolet and Corvette

1. Open the hood and disconnect the battery.
2. Make sure that the wiper motor is in park position.
3. On 1968–72 Corvette models, remove the rubber plug from the front of the wiper door actuator, then insert a screwdriver, pushing the internal piston rearward to open the door.
4. Remove the wiper arm and blade. On the articulated left hand arm assembly, remove the retaining clip from the pin on the drive arm.
5. Remove the plenum chamber air intake grill or screen.
6. Loosen the nuts which retain the drive rod ball stud to the crank arm and detach the drive rod from the crank arm.
7. Remove the transmission retaining screws or nuts, then lower the drive rod assemblies into the plenum chamber.
8. Remove the transmission and linkage from the plenum chamber through the cowl opening.
9. To install, reverse the above procedure.

RADIO

R & R

1967-72 Chevrolet

1. Disconnect battery.
2. Remove ash tray, retainer attaching screws and retainer.
3. Remove heater control panel retaining screws and push panel assembly from console.

NOTE: if interference between control panel and radio is met, loosen radio retaining nuts.

4. Remove radio control knobs, bezels and retaining nuts.
5. Disconnect radio wiring harness, and antenna lead-in.
6. Remove radio rear brace attaching screw, and remove radio from the car.
7. Remove speaker retaining bolt and remove speaker.
8. To install, reverse removal procedure.

1973-74 Chevrolet

1. Disconnect the negative battery cable.
2. On cars with A/C, remove the lap cooler duct.
3. Turn the radio control knobs until the slots in the bottom of the knobs are visible. Depress the metal retainers with a screwdriver and remove the knobs and bezels.
4. Remove the control shaft nuts and washers.
5. Remove the right side bracket-to-instrument panel bolt and the stud nut on the left side of the radio.
6. Pull the radio forward and disconnect the wiring from the radio and remove the radio from the car.

1967-71 Corvette Coupe

1. Disconnect battery.
2. Remove right and left door sill plates and kick pads.
3. Disconnect right and left side radio-to-speaker connectors.
4. Remove right side dash pad.
5. Remove right and left console forward trim pads.
6. Remove bolt and remove the heater floor outlet duct by pulling it through left hand opening.
7. From front of console, tape radio push buttons in depressed position. From rear of console, disconnect electrical connector, brace and antenna lead-in.
8. Remove radio knobs and bezel retaining nuts. Push radio assembly forward and remove from rear through right side opening.
9. Install by reversing procedure above.

1967-71 Corvette Convertible

1. Disconnect battery.
2. Remove right instrument panel pad.
3. Disconnect speaker connectors.
4. Remove wiper switch trim plate screws to gain access to switch connector and remove connector and trim plate from cluster assembly.
5. Unclip and remove right and left console forward trim pads and remove forwardmost screw on right and left side of console.
6. Inserting a flexible drive socket between the console and metal horseshoe brace, remove the nuts from the two studs on the lower edge of the console cluster. Remove the remaining screws that retain the cluster assembly to the instrument panel.
7. From rear of console, disconnect electric connector, brace and antenna lead-in.
8. Remove radio knobs and bezel retaining nuts.
9. Pull radio assembly forward and remove through right side opening.
10. Install by reversing procedure above.

1972-74 Corvette

1. Disconnect the negative battery cable and remove the right instrument panel pad.
2. Disconnect the radio speaker connectors.
3. Remove the wiper switch trim plate screws and tip the plate forward to gain access to the switch connector. Remove the switch connector and trim plate from the dash.
4. Unclip and remove the right and left forward console trim pads. Remove the forwardmost screw on the left and right sides of the console.
5. Working with a flexible drive socket between the console and the metal horseshoe brace, remove the nuts from the studs on the lower edge of the console cluster.
6. Remove the remaining console attaching screws and disconnect the radio electrical connectors, antenna wire and radio brace from the rear of the console. Remove the radio knobs and nuts.
7. Pull the top of the console rearward and separate the radio from the console and remove it from the right side opening.

NOTE: The center instrument cluster trim panel is designed to collapse under impact. Do not deflect the panel to gain access to the radio. Also, the remotely located radio heat sink should be removed with the radio when servicing is required.

HEATER

Heater Blower R & R

1967-74 Chevrolet

1. Disconnect battery.
2. Unclip hoses from fender skirt.
3. Disconnect electrical feed from motor. Disconnect the motor air-cooling hose on air-conditioned cars.
4. Turn vehicle front wheels to extreme right.
5. Remove right front fender skirt bolts and allow skirt to drop, resting it on top of tire. It may be wedged away from fender lower flange with block of wood to provide better access to bolts.
6. Remove screws attaching motor mounting plate to air inlet housing.
7. Remove screws attaching motor to mounting plate.
8. Remove clip attaching cage to shaft and remove blower motor.
9. Install in reverse of above.

1967-74 Corvette (Non-Air Conditioned)

1. Remove the radiator supply tank from its retaining straps. Move it out of the way. Disconnect the battery.
2. Remove blower motor electrical connectors.
3. Scribe a reference mark on the blower motor mounting plate and the blower motor.
4. Remove the five screws that mount the blower mounting plate to the blower inlet assembly.
5. Withdraw the blower assembly from the inlet assembly.

6. Install in reverse of removal procedure.

NOTE: 1967 air-conditioned cars have the same R&R procedure with the addition of removing and installing the motor air cooling hose.

1968-74 Corvette with Air Conditioning

1. Remove the battery ground cable.
2. Disconnect the air cooling tube and electrical wire from the blower motor.
3. Remove the first three sill molding screws and pry the molding out to allow access to the right splash shield bolts.
4. Remove the splash shield.
5. Remove the motor retaining screws and drop the motor out through the splash shield opening. Pry on the mounting flange gently, if necessary to break the motor loose.
6. Reverse the removal steps to install the motor.

Heater Core R & R

All Except Air Conditioned Cars

1. Drain radiator.
2. Remove heater hoses at connections beside air inlet assembly.
3. Remove cable and electrical connectors from heater and defroster assembly.
4. On engine side of dash, remove screws and nuts holding air inlet to dash panel.
5. Inside vehicle, pull entire assembly from firewall and remove assembly from vehicle.
6. Remove core assembly retaining springs and remove core.
7. Install in reverse of above.

NOTE: This procedure is not applicable to air-conditioned cars, except pre-1970 models with the dealer-installed, under dash unit.

1967 Chevrolet with Air Conditioning

1. Remove the battery ground cable and drain the cooling system. It is not necessary to evacuate the A.C. refrigerant.
2. Remove the right front fender and inside panel.
3. Remove the heater hoses at the firewall.
4. Remove the glove compartment door and compartment interior.
5. Remove the right, left, and center air conditioning outlet hoses from the distributor.
6. Remove the distributor duct from the heater housing.
7. Disconnect the hose and cable clamps from the housing.
8. From the engine compartment, remove the three retaining nuts on the housing studs. Remove the single screw from under the dash.
9. Pull the housing off the firewall and out of the car.
10. Remove the heater housing cover and withdraw the core, which is retained by four screws and two U-clamps.
11. Use a non-hardening sealer to install the core into the heater housing and install using a reverse of the removal procedure.

1967 Corvette with Air Conditioning

1. Drain the cooling system. It is not necessary to evacuate the A.C. refrigerant.
2. Remove the heater hoses at the firewall.
3. Remove the cover retaining nuts and the cover around the heater core pipes.
4. Remove the glove compartment assembly.
5. Remove the right kick panel and left and right center console trim panels.
6. Remove the radio.
7. Remove the defroster duct.
8. Remove the radio speaker and its grille.
9. Remove the right air conditioner outlet duct.
10. Disconnect the cables on the distributor assembly.
11. Disconnect the flex tubes from the center and left side outlet ducts on the distributor.
12. Remove the heater air ducts from the distributor.
13. Remove the last distributor-to-dash nut from the right side of the distributor.
14. Pull the distributor assembly out of the car. Remove the heater core from the distributor.
15. Install using a reverse of the removal procedure.

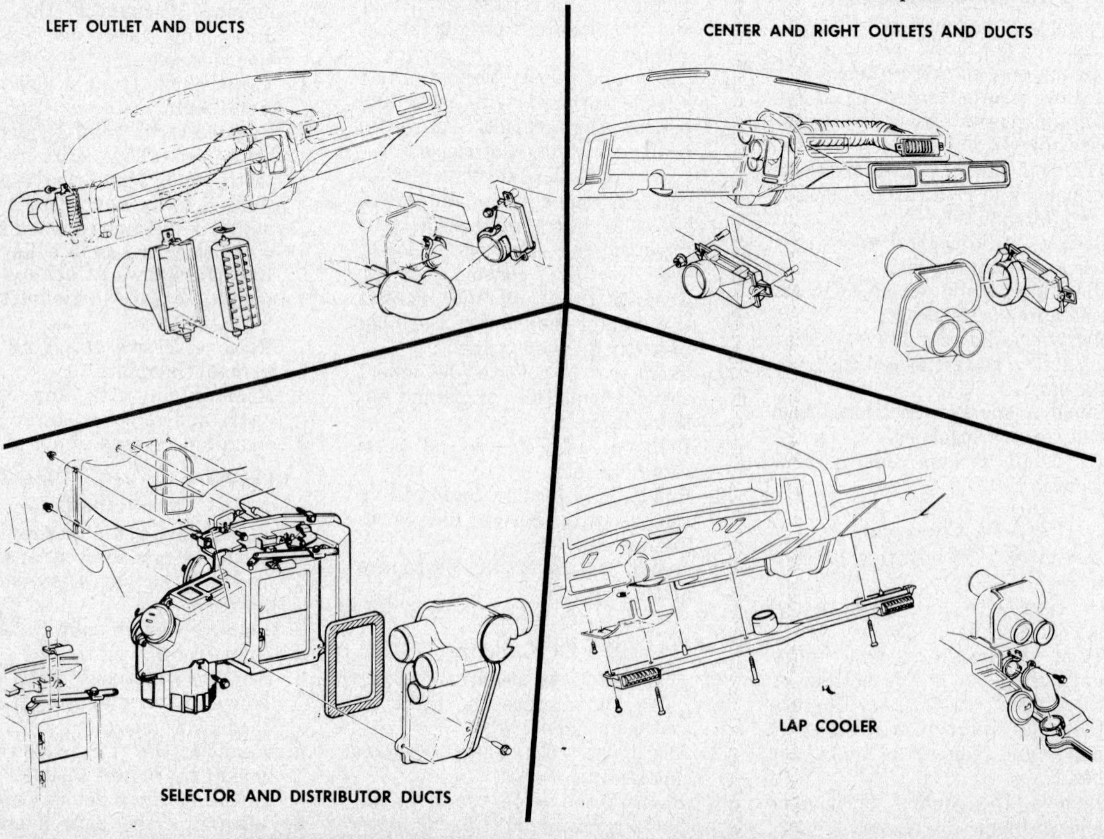
LEFT OUTLET AND DUCTS
CENTER AND RIGHT OUTLETS AND DUCTS
SELECTOR AND DISTRIBUTOR DUCTS
LAP COOLER

1972 Chevrolet air conditioning selector and ducts (© Chevrolet Div., G.M. Corp)

1968-71 Chevrolet with Air Conditioning

1. Remove the battery ground cable.
2. Drain the cooling system. It is not necessary to evacuate the A.C. refrigerant.
3. Remove the heater hoses at the firewall.
4. Remove the nuts from the heater distributor studs protruding through the firewall.
5. Remove the glove compartment.
6. Remove the five center distributor duct hoses, duct cables, center duct-to-selector duct screws, and the center duct.
7. From inside the car, drill out the lower case stud using a 1/4 in. drill.
8. Remove the floor distributor duct.
9. Remove the firewall screws and pull the selector from the firewall.
10. Remove all wires, vacuum lines, and cables attached to the assembly, and remove it from the car.
11. Scribe the temperature door camming plate-to-selector duct relationship and remove the plate.
12. Remove the heater core and core housing from the selector duct.
13. Reverse the removal steps to install.

1972-74 Chevrolet with Air Conditioning

1. Drain the cooling system. It is not necessary to evacuate the A.C. refrigerant.
2. Disconnect the battery ground cable and compressor clutch connector.
3. Disconnect the vacuum line from the vacuum check valve and push the grommet through the firewall into the passenger compartment.
4. Disconnect the heater hoses at the firewall.
5. Remove the three screws and nuts retaining the heater and selector duct. The inner fender must be pried out from the firewall to gain access to one screw.
6. Remove the lap cooler assembly.
7. Remove the glove compartment.
8. Remove the floor outlet duct and dash panel pad.
9. Disconnect the distributor duct hoses and connector.
10. Remove the duct from the selector.
11. Loosen the defroster duct and move it to provide access to the selector and core assembly.
12. Disconnect the temperature door cable.
13. Separate the inline vacuum connector and the outside air diaphragm line.
14. Lift the heater and air selector duct out as an assembly.
15. Remove the retaining screws and remove the heater core from the selector.

1968-74 Corvette with Air Conditioning

1. Disconnect the battery ground cable.
2. Drain the cooling system. It is not necessary to evacuate the A.C. refrigerant.
3. Disconnect the heater hoses at the firewall and plug the pipes.
4. Remove the nuts from the distributor studs protruding through the firewall.
5. Remove the right side dash pad and center dash cluster (described under "Instruments").
6. Disconnect the right dash outlet from the center duct.
7. Remove the center duct from the selector duct.
8. Remove the selector duct to the dash panel and pull it to the right and to the rear.
9. Remove the cables and wiring connectors from the selector and remove it from the car.
10. Remove the temperature door cam plate from the selector duct.
11. Remove the heater core and housing from the selector.
12. Reverse the removal procedure to install.

SEAT BELTS

Warning System

1972-73

The seat belt warning system consists of lap belt retractor switches, a pressure-sensitive switch underneath the right-hand front passenger's seat, a warning lamp and a buzzer.

On manual transmission-equipped cars, the circuit is wired through the ignition switch, the parking brake warning light switch, and a relay, which is located between the instrument cluster wiring and the switch on the parking brake. A diode is used to prevent feedback into the parking brake warning circuit.

On cars having automatic transmissions, the seat belt warning circuit is wired through the ignition switch and the combination back-up lamp/neutral safety switch.

With the ignition key in the "RUN" position, a weight of 40-50 lbs on the driver's or passenger's seat (pressure-sensitive switch) energizes the circuit when the parking brake is released (M/T) or the gear selector placed in a forward drive range (A/T).

A warning light will glow and a buzzer will sound with the circuit energized, unless the seat belts are withdrawn from the retractors and fastened over the laps of the two outboard front seat occupants.

Seat Belt/Starter Interlock System

1974

As required by law, all 1974 Chevrolet passenger cars cannot be started until the front seat occupants are seated and have fastened their seat belts. If the proper sequence is not followed, e.g., the occupants fasten their seat belts and then sit on them, the engine cannot be started.

If, after the car is started, the seat belts are unfastened, a warning buzzer and light will be activated in a similar manner to that described for 1972-73 models.

The shoulder harness and lap belt are permanently fastened together, so that they both must be worn. The shoulder harness uses an inertia-lock reel to allow freedom of movement under normal driving conditions.

NOTE: This type of reel locks up when the car decelerates rapidly, as during a crash.

The lap belts use the same ratchet-type retractors that the 1972-73 models use.

The switches for the interlock system have been removed from the lap belt retractors and placed in the belt buckles. The seat sensors remain the same as those used in 1972-73.

For ease of service, the car may be started from outside, by reaching in and turning the key, but without depressing the seat sensors.

In case of system failure or for service, an override switch is located under the hood. This is a "one start" switch and it must be reset each time it is used.

INDEX

Chrysler • Imperial

YEAR IDENTIFICATION

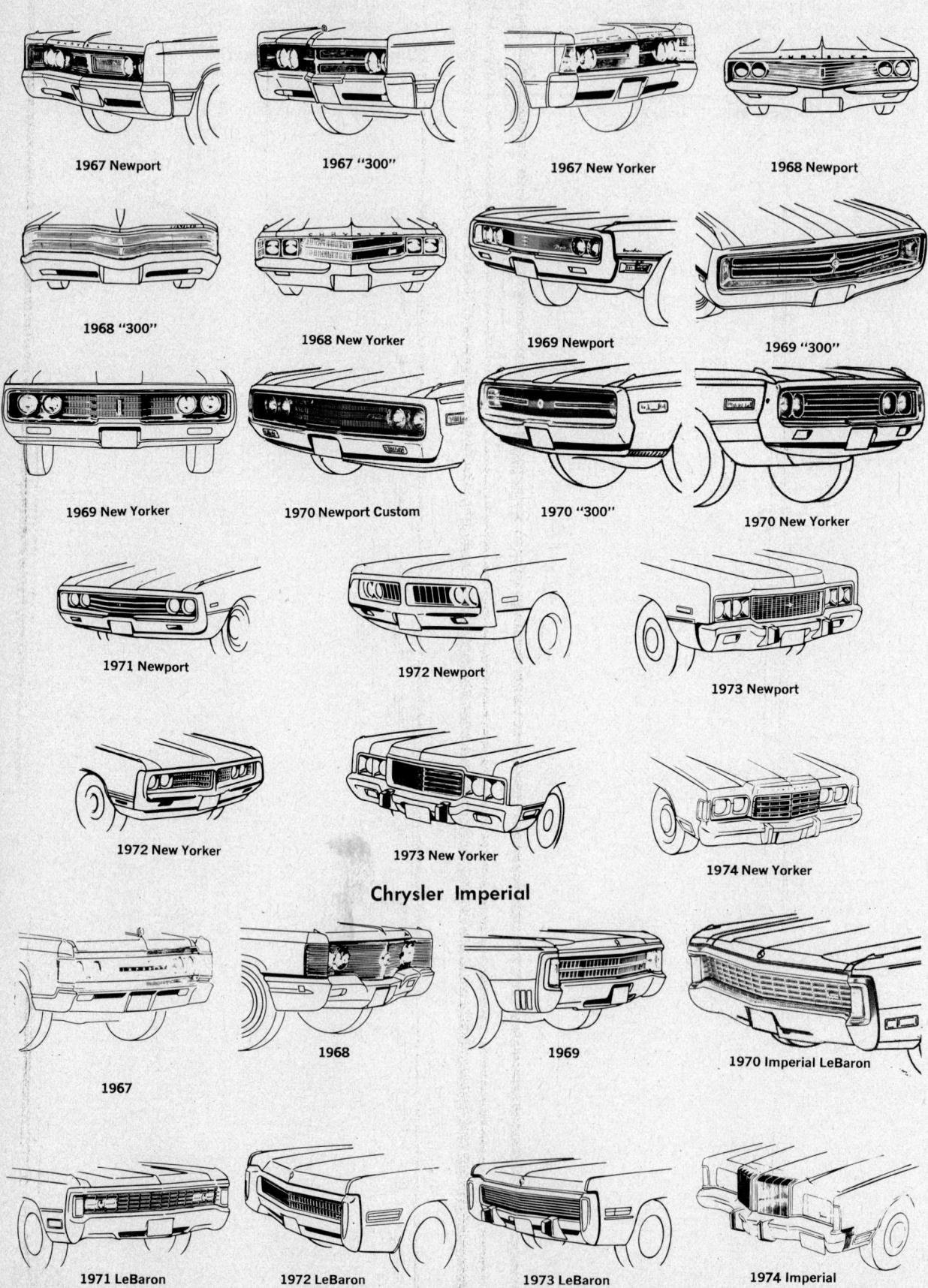

Chrysler

1967 Newport

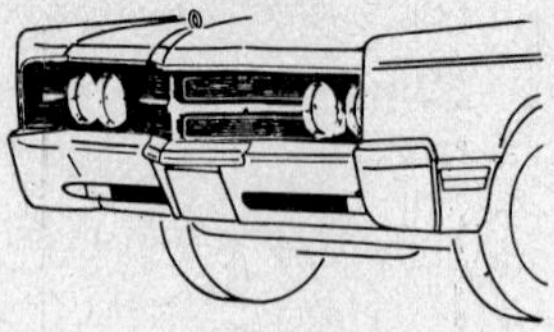
1967 "300"

1967 New Yorker

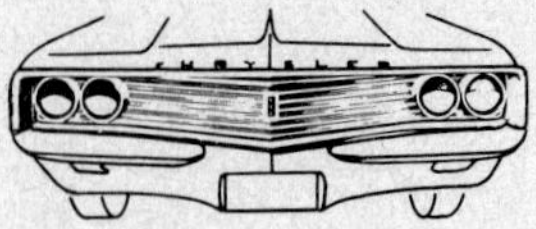
1968 Newport

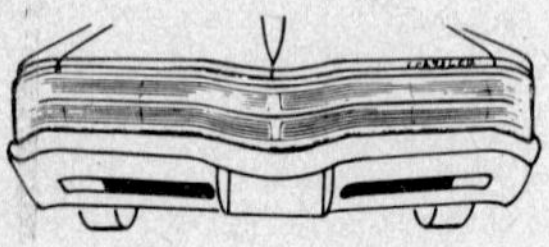
1968 "300"

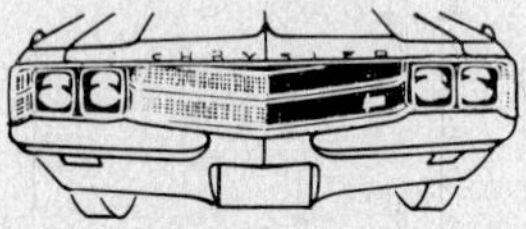
1968 New Yorker

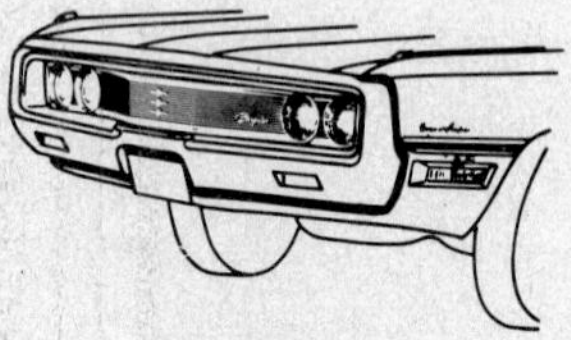
1969 Newport

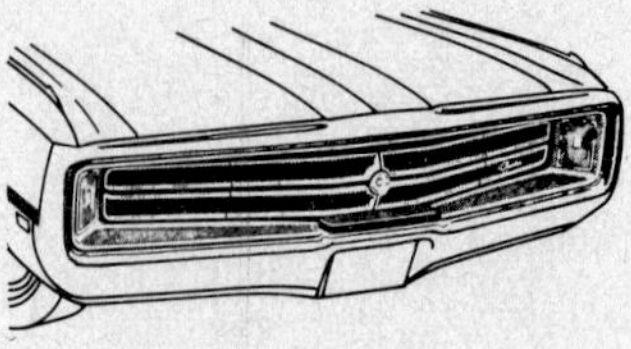
1969 "300"

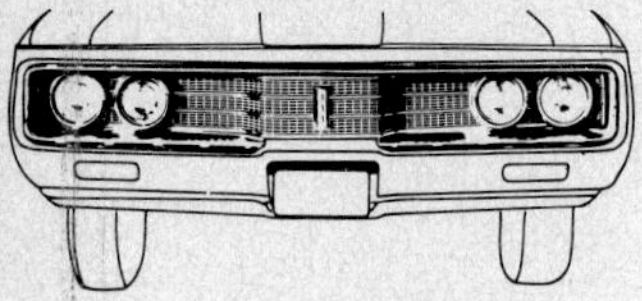
1969 New Yorker

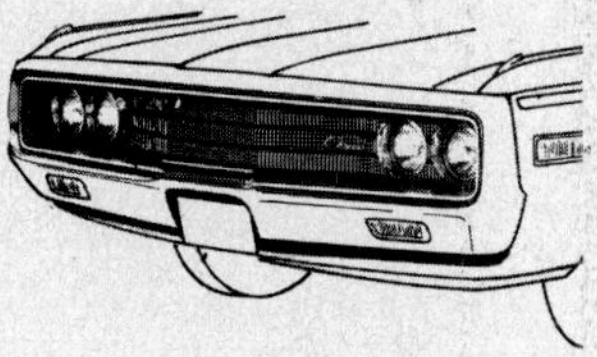
1970 Newport Custom

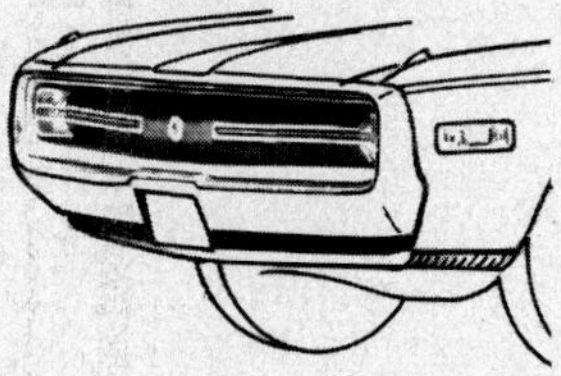
1970 "300"

1970 New Yorker

1971 Newport

1972 Newport

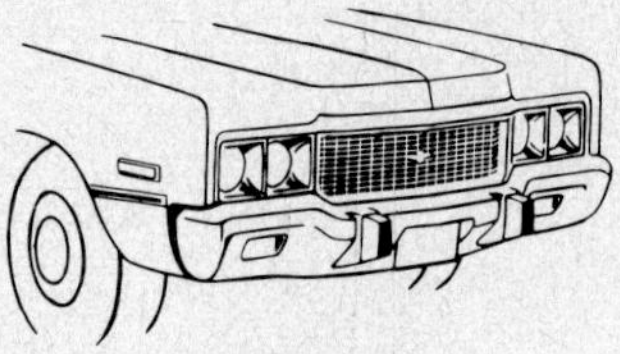
1973 Newport

1972 New Yorker

1973 New Yorker

1974 New Yorker

Chrysler Imperial

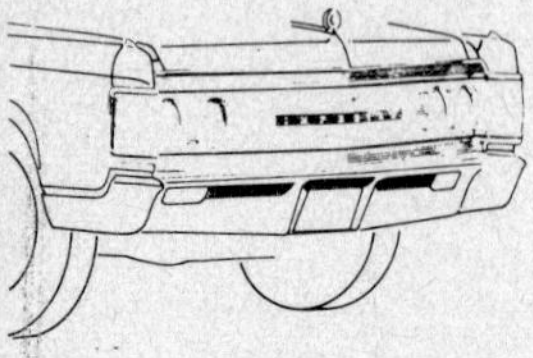
1967

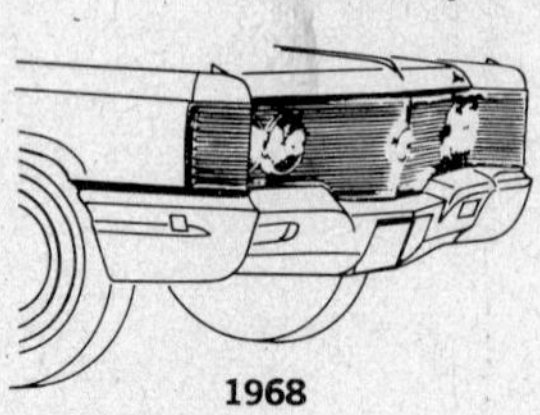
1968

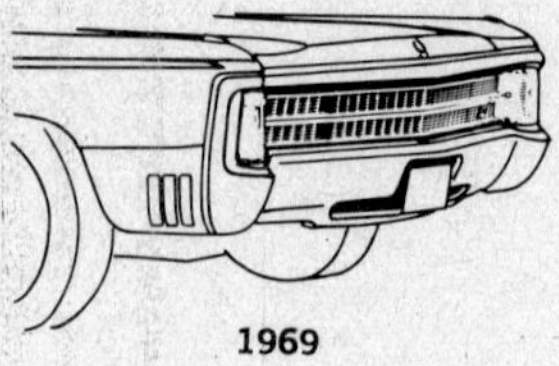
1969

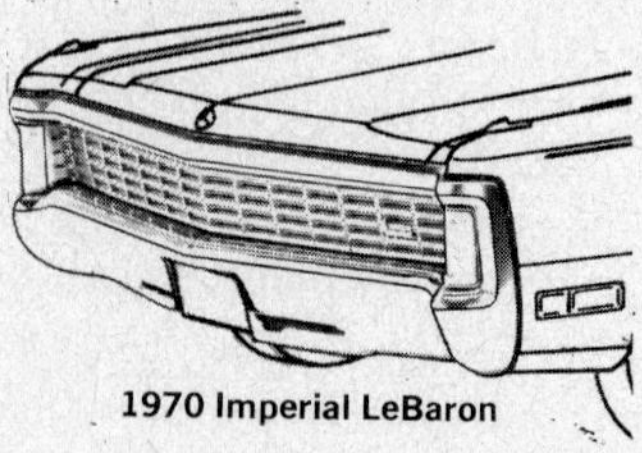
1970 Imperial LeBaron

1971 LeBaron

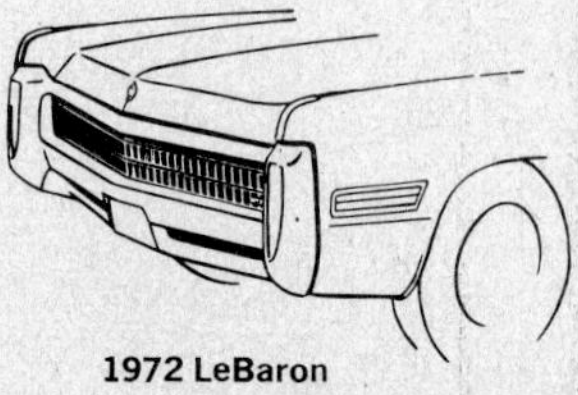
1972 LeBaron

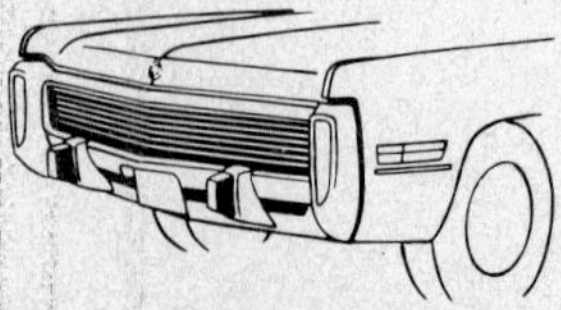
1973 LeBaron

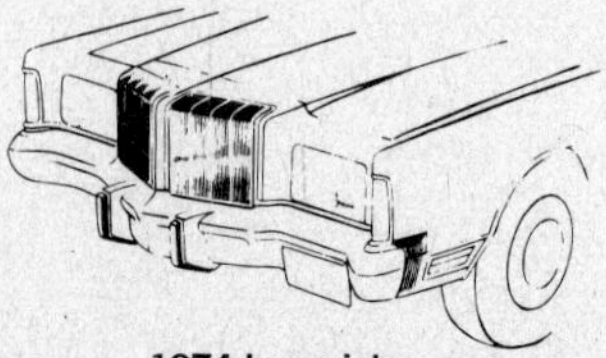
1974 Imperial

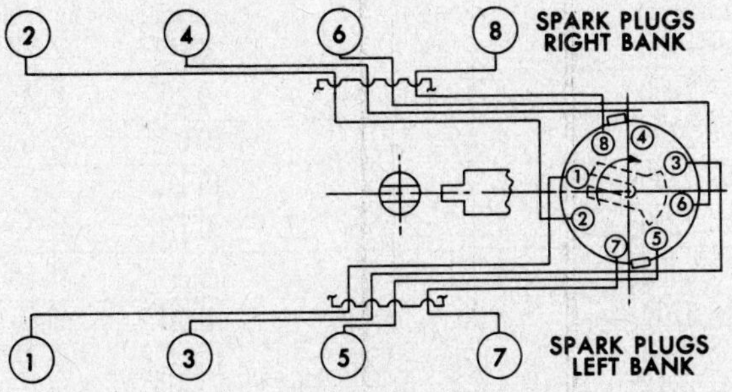
SPARK PLUGS
RIGHT BANK
SPARK PLUGS
LEFT BANK

360 cu in engines—distributor rotates clockwise

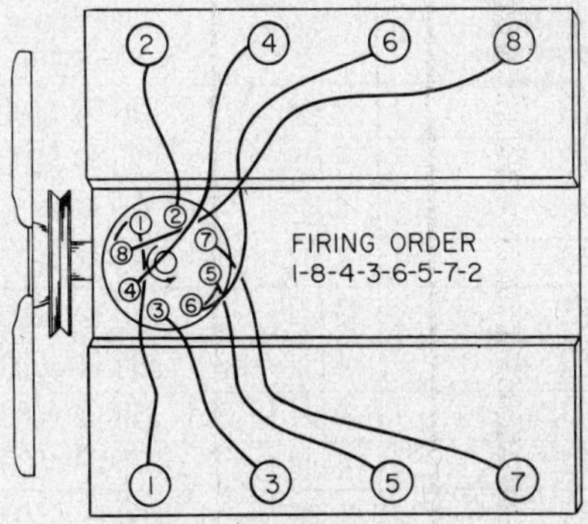
FIRING ORDER
1-8-4-3-6-5-7-2

383, 400 and 440 cu in engines—distributor rotates counterclockwise

ENGINE CODE

Chrysler, Chrysler Imperial

The engine code designation is the 5th digit of the vehicle identification number (V.I.N.). The V.I.N. is stamped on a plate located at the left front door hinge pillar on 1967 models, located at the left side of the instrument panel visible through the windshield on 1968-74 models, and located to the rear of the right engine mount on 1969-74 models.

Disp	Bbl	Hp	'67	'68	'69	'70	'71	'72	'73	'74
8-Cylinder Models										
360	2	175 (net)						K		
360	2	255					K			
383	2	270	G							
383	2	275					L			
383	2	290		G	G	L				
383	4	300					N			
383	4	325	H							
383	2	330		H	H	N				
400	4	185 (net)							M	M
400	4	255 (net)						P		
440	4	215 (net)							T	T
440	4	280 (net)						U		
440	4	335					T			
440	4	350	K	K	K	T				
440	4	370					U			
440	4	375	L	L	L	U				

Chrysler-Imperial GENERAL ENGINE SPECIFICATIONS

Year	Engine Cu. In. Displacement	Carburetor Type	Advertised Horsepower @ rpm ■	Advertised Torque @ rpm (ft lbs) ■	Bore and Stroke (in.)	Advertised Compression Ratio	Oil Pressure @ 2050 rpm
'67	8-383	2 bbl	270 @ 4400	390 @ 2800	4.250 x 3.375	9.2:1	45-65
	8-383	4 bbl	325 @ 4800	425 @ 2800	4.250 x 3.375	10.0:1	45-65
	8-440	4 bbl	350 @ 4400	480 @ 2800	4.320 x 3.750	10.1:1	45-65
	8-440	4 bbl	375 @ 4600	480 @ 3200	4.320 x 3.750	10.1:1	45-65
'68	8-383	2 bbl	270 @ 4400	390 @ 2800	4.250 x 3.375	9.2:1	45-65
	8-383	4 bbl	330 @ 5000	425 @ 3200	4.250 x 3.375	10.0:1	45-65
	8-440	4 bbl	350 @ 4400	480 @2800	4.320 x 3.750	10.1:1	45-65
	8-440	4 bbl	375 @ 4600	480 @ 3200	4.320 x 3.750	10.1:1	45-65
'69	8-383	2 bbl	290 @ 4400	390 @ 2800	4.250 x 3.375	9.2:1	45-65
	8-383	4 bbl	330 @ 5000	425 @ 3200	4.250 x 3.375	10.0:1	45-65
	8-440	4 bbl	350 @ 4400	480 @ 2800	4.320 x 3.750	10.1:1	45-65
	8-440	4 bbl	375 @ 4600	480 @ 3200	4.320 x 3.750	10.1:1	45-65
'70	8-383	2 bbl	290 @ 4400	390 @ 2800	4.250 x 3.375	8.7:1	45-65
	8-383	4 bbl	330 @ 5000	425 @ 3200	4.250 x 3.375	9.5:1	45-65
	8-440	4 bbl	350 @ 4400	480 @ 2800	4.320 x 3.750	9.7:1	45-65
	8-440	4 bbl	375 @ 4600	480 @ 3200	4.320 x 3.750	9.7:1	45-65
'71	8-360	2 bbl	255 @ 4000	360 @ 2400	4.000 x 3.580	8.7:1	45-65
	8-383	2 bbl	275 @ 4400	375 @ 2800	4.250 x 3.375	8.5:1	45-65
	8-383	4 bbl	300 @ 4800	410 @ 3400	4.250 x 3.375	8.5:1	45-65
	8-440	4 bbl	335 @ 4400	460 @ 3200	4.320 x 3.750	8.5:1	45-65
	8-440	4 bbl	370 @ 4600	480 @ 3200	4.320 x 3.750	9.5:1	45-65
'72	8-360	2 bbl	175 @ 4000	285 @ 2400	4.000 x 3.580	8.8:1	45-65
	8-400	2 bbl	190 @ 4400	310 @ 2400	4.342 x 3.375	8.2:1	45-65
	8-440	4 bbl	225 @ 4400	345 @ 3200	4.320 x 3.750	8.2:1	45-65
'73	8-400	2 bbl	185 @ 3600	310 @ 2400	4.340 x 3.380	8.2:1	45-65
	8-440	4 bbl	215 @ 3600①	345 @ 2000①	4.320 x 3.750	8.2:1	45-65
'74	8-400	2 bbl	175 @ 3600	305 @ 2400	4.340 x 3.380	8.2:1	45-65
	8-400	4 bbl	185 @ 3600	310 @ 2400	4.340 x 3.380	8.2:1	45-65
	8-440	4 bbl	215 @ 3600	345 @ 2000	4.320 x 3.750	8.2:1	45-65

① California cars hp 208 @ 3600, torque 340 @ 2000

■ Starting 1972, horsepower and torque are SAE net figures. They are measured at the rear of the transmission with all accessories installed and operating. Since the figures vary when a given engine is installed in different models, some are representative rather than exact.

CRANKSHAFT AND CONNECTING ROD SPECIFICATIONS

All measurements are given in in.

Year	Engine Displace. (cu in.)	CRANKSHAFT				CONNECTING ROD		
		Main Brg. Journal Dia	Main Brg. Oil Clearance	Shaft End-Play	Thrust on No.	Journal Diameter	Oil Clearance	Side Clearance
'71-'72	8-360	2.8095-2.8105	.0005-.0025	.002-.007	3	2.124-2.125	.0005-.0020	.009-.017
'67-'74	8-383, 400	2.6245-2.6255	.0005-.0015	.002-.007	3	2.3740-2.3750	.0005-.0015	.009-.017
'67-'74	8-440	2.7495-2.7505	.0005-.0015	.002-.007	3	2.3750-2.3750	.0007-.0032	.009-.017

Chrysler, Imperial — TUNE-UP SPECIFICATIONS

When analyzing compression test results, look for uniformity among cylinders rather than specific pressures.

Year	ENGINE No. Cyl Displacement (cu in.)	ENGINE hp	SPARK PLUGS Type §	SPARK PLUGS Gap (in.)	DISTRIBUTOR Point Dwell (deg)	DISTRIBUTOR Point Gap (in.)	IGNITION TIMING (deg) ▲ Man Trans	IGNITION TIMING (deg) ▲ Auto Trans	VALVES Intake Opens ■ (deg) ●	Fuel Pump Pressure (psi)	IDLE SPEED (rpm) ▲ Man Trans	IDLE SPEED (rpm) ▲ Auto Trans
'67	8-383	270	J-14Y	.035	28-32	.017	12½B(TDC)	12½B(5B)	16	3½-5	550②(650)	550(600)②
	8-383	325	J-13Y	.035	28-32	.017	12½B(TDC)	12½B(5B)	16	3½-5	500(650)②	500(600)②
	8-440	350	J-13Y	.035	28-32	.017	12½B(TDC)	12½B(5B)	16	3½-5	650②	650②
	8-440	375	J-11Y	.035	28-32	.017	12½B(TDC)	12½B(5B)	19	3½-5	650②	650②
'68	8-383	290	J-14Y	.035	28-32	.017	TDC	7B	18	3½-5	650	600
	8-383	330	J-11Y	.035	28-32	.017	TDC	5B	18	3½-5	650	600
	8-440	350	J-13Y	.035	28-32	.017	TDC	7½B	18	3½-5	650	650
	8-440	375	J-11Y	.035	28-32	.017	TDC	5B	21	3½-5	750	750
'69	8-383	290	J-14Y	.035	30-35	.017	TDC	7½B	18	3½-5	700	600
	8-383	330	J-11Y	.035	30-35	.017	—	5B	18	3½-5	700	650
	8-440	350	J-13Y	.035	30-35	.017	—	7½B	18	3½-5	700	600N
	8-440	375	J-11Y	.035	30-35	.017	TDC	5B	21	3½-5	700	650N
'70	8-383	290	J-14Y	.035	28½-32½	.018	TDC	2½B	18	3½-5	750	650
	8-383	330	J-11Y	.035	28½-32½	.018	TDC	2½B	18	3½-5	—	700
	8-440	350	J-13Y	.035	28½-32½	.018	—	5B	18	3½-5	—	650
	8-440	375	J-11Y	.035	28½-32½	.018	TDC	2½B	21	3½-5	900	800
'71	8-360	255	J-13Y	.035	30-34	.017	2½B	2½B	16	3½-5	750	700
	8-383	275	J-14Y	.035	30-34	.017	TDC	2½B	18	3½-5	750	700
	8-383	300	J-14Y	.035	28½-32½	.017	TDC	2½B	21	3½-5	900	800
	8-440	335	J-13Y	.035	28½-32½	.017	—	5B	18	3½-5	—	750
	8-440	370	J-11Y	.035	28½-32½	.017	TDC	2½B	21	3½-5	900	900
'72	8-360	175	N-13Y	.035	28½-32½	.017	—	TDC	16	5-7	—	700
	8-400	255	J-13Y	.035	28½-32½	.018	—	③5B(2½B)	18	3½-5	—	700
	8-440	280	J-11Y	.035	28½-32½	.018	—	10B(5B)	18	3½-5	—	900
'73	8-400	185	J-13Y	.035	Electronic		—	10B	18	4-5½	—	700
	8-440	215	J-11Y	.035	Electronic		—	10B	18	4-5½	—	700
'74	8-400	175	J-13Y	.035	Electronic		—	10B(5B)	18	4-5½	—	750
	8-400	260	J-11Y	.035	Electronic		5B	10B(2½B)	21	4-5½	900	850
	8-440	275	J-11Y	.035	Electronic		—	10B	21	7-8.2	—	800

▲ See text for procedure
● Figure in parentheses indicates California engine
■ All figures Before Top Dead Center
§ All spark plug listings are Champion original equipment listings
① Equipped with Air Injection Reactor System

② A/C on
③ Non-California cars built after Feb. 2, 7½B
A After Top Dead Center
B Before Top Dead Center
TDC Top Dead Center
— Not applicable

Chrysler & Imperial

CAPACITIES

Year	ENGINE No. Cyl. (Cu. In.) Displacement	Engine Crankcase Add 1 Qt For New Filter	TRANSMISSION Pts To Refill After Draining Manual 3-Speed	Manual 4-Speed	Automatic	Drive Axle (pts)	Gasoline Tank (gals)	COOLING SYSTEM (qts) With Heater ▲	With A/C
'67	8-383	4	6.5	—	18.5	4	25	17	18
	8-440	4	—	—	18.5	4	25	18	19
	8-440 "300"	4	—	—	18.5	4	25	18	19
	Town & Country	4	—	—	18.5	4	22	18	19
	Imperial	4	—	—	18.5	4	25	18	19
'68	8-383	4	6	—	18.5	4	24	17	18
	8-440	4	—	—	18.5	4	24	18	19
	Town & Country	4	—	—	18.5	4	22	17	18
	Imperial	4	—	—	18.5	4	24	18	18
'69	8-383	4	6	—	18.5①	4	24	17	17
	8-440	4	—	—	18.5	4	24	17	18
	Town & Country	4	—	—	18.5①	4	23	16	17
	Imperial	4	—	—	18.5	4	24	19	19
'70	8-383	4	4.75	—	19.0①	4	24	14.5②	16②
	8-440	4	—	—	19.0	4	24	15.5	17
	Town & Country	4	—	—	19.0①	4	23	16	17
	Imperial	4	—	—	19.0	4.4	24	18	18
'71	8-360	4	4.75	—	16.3	4.5	23	15.5	16
	8-383	4	4.75③	—	19.0①	4.5	23	14.5	15
	8-440	4	—	—	19.0	4.5	23	15.5	17
	Town & Country	4	—	—	19.0①	4.5	23	16	17
	Imperial	4	—	—	19.0	4.5	23	17.5	17.5
'72	8-360	4	—	—	16.3	4.4	23	15.5	16.5
	8-400	4	—	—	19.0	4.4	23	14.5	15.5
	8-440	4	—	—	19.0	4.4	23	17.5	17.5
	Town & Country	4	—	—	19.0	4.4	23	16	17
	Imperial	4	—	—	19.0	4.4	23	17.5	17.5
'73	8-400	4	—	—	19.0	4.5	23	16	16
	8-440	4	—	—	19.0	4.5	23	15.5	15.5
	Imperial	4	—	—	19.0	4.5	23	18	18
'74	8-400	4	—	7.5	18.9④	4.5	19.5	16.5	—
	8-440	4	—	—	16.1	4.5	19.5	16	16

▲ Add 1.5 qts if equipped with rear seat heater
① 4 bbl carb—16 pts
② 4 bbl carb—15.5-17 pts
③ 2 bbl only
④ 16.1 with HP400 engine
— Not applicable

TORQUE SPECIFICATIONS

All readings in ft lbs

Year	Engine Displacement (cu in.)	Cylinder Head Bolts	Rod Bearing Bolts	Main Bearing Bolts	Crankshaft Pulley Bolt	Flywheel to Crankshaft Bolts	MANIFOLD Intake	Exhaust
'71-'72	8-360	95	45	85	①	65	40	30
'67-'74	8-383, 400, 440	70	45	85	①	55	40	30

① Vibration damper bolts—15 ft. lbs. for 1967-69, 9 ft. lbs. for 1970-72. End of crankshaft bolt (except 1971 360 engine) 135 ft. lbs. 1971 360 engine—100 ft. lbs.

VALVE SPECIFICATIONS

Year	Engine No. Cyl. Displacement (cu in.)	Seat Angle (deg)	Face Angle (deg)	Spring Test Pressure (lbs @ in.)	Spring Installed Height (in.)	STEM TO GUIDE Clearance (in.) Intake	STEM TO GUIDE Clearance (in.) Exhaust	STEM Diameter (in.) Intake	STEM Diameter (in.) Exhaust
'67	8-383①	45	45	195 @ 1.47	1 7/8	.0010-.0030	.0020-.0040	.3725	.3715
	8-383②	45	45	200 @ 1.44	1 7/8	.0010-.0030	.0020-.0040	.3725	.3715
	8-440②	45	45	200 @ 1.44	1 7/8	.0010-.0030	.0020-.0040	.3725	.3715
	8-440③	45	45	245 @ 1.36	1 7/8	.0010-.0030	.0020-.0040	.3275	.3715
'68	8-383①	45	45	200 @ 1.44	1 7/8	.0010-.0030	.0020-.0040	.3725	.3715
	8-383②	45	45	230 @ 1.41	1 7/8	.0010-.0030	.0020-.0040	.3725	.3715
	8-440	45	45	200 @ 1.44	1 7/8	.0010-.0030	.0020-.0040	.3725	.3715
	8-440③	45	45	230 @ 1.41	1 7/8	.0010-.0030	.0020-.0040	.3725	.3715
'69	8-383①	45	45	200 @ 1.44	1 7/8	.0010-.0030	.0020-.0040	.3725	.3715
	8-383②	45	45	246 @ 1.36	1 7/8	.0010-.0030	.0020-.0040	.3725	.3715
	8-440	45	45	200 @ 1.44	1 7/8	.0010-.0030	.0020-.0040	.3725	.3715
	8-440③	45	45	246 @ 1.36	1 7/8	.0010-.0030	.0020-.0040	.3725	.3715
'70	8-383	45	45	200 @ 1.44	1 7/8	.0010-.0030	.0020-.0040	.3725	.3715
	8-440	45	45	200 @ 1.44	1 7/8	.0010-.0030	.0020-.0040	.3725	.3715
	8-440③	45	45	246 @ 1.36	1 7/8	.0010-.0030	.0020-.0040	.3725	.3715
'71	8-360	45	④	177 @ 1.31	1 11/16	.0010-.0030	.0020-.0040	.3725	.3715
	8-383①	45	45	200 @ 1.44	1 7/8	.0010-.0030	.0020-.0040	.3727	.3715
	8-383②	45	45	246 @ 1.36	1 7/8	.0015-.0032	.0025-.0042	.3722	.3712
	8-440	45	45	200 @ 1.44	1 7/8	.0010-.0030	.0020-.0040	.3727	.3717
	8-440③	45	45	246 @ 1.36	1 7/8	.0015-.0032	.0025-.0042	.3722	.3712
'72	8-360	45	④	177 @ 1.31	1 11/16	.0010-.0030	.0020-.0040	.3725	.3715
	8-400	45	45	200 @ 1.44	1 7/8	.0010-.0030	.0020-.0040	.3725	.3715
	8-440	45	45	200 @ 1.44	1 7/8	.0010-.0030	.0020-.0040	.3725	.3715
'73	8-400	45	45	200 @ 1.42	1 55/64	.0015-.0032	⑤	.3722	⑥
	8-440	45	45	200 @ 1.42	1 55/64	.0015-.0032	⑤	.3722	⑥
'74	8-400	45	45	200 @ 1.43	1 55/64	.0010-.0027	⑤	.3727	⑥
	8-400⑤	45	45	234 @ 1.40	1 55/64	.0015-.0032	⑥	.3722	⑥
	8-440	45	45	234 @ 1.40	1 55/64	.0015-.0032	⑥	.3722	⑥

① 2 bbl
② 4 bbl
③ Hi-Performance
④ Intake valve face angle 45°
Exhaust valve face angle 43°
⑤ Hot end—.0020-.0037, cold end—.0010-.0027
⑥ Hot end—.3716, cold end—.3726

BATTERY AND STARTER SPECIFICATIONS

Year	Engine Displacement (cu in.)	BATTERY Ampere Hour Capacity	BATTERY Volts	BATTERY Terminal Grounded	STARTERS Lock Test Amps	STARTERS Lock Test Volts	STARTERS Lock Test Torque (ft lbs)	STARTERS No-Load Test Amps	STARTERS No-Load Test Volts	STARTERS No-Load Test RPM	STARTERS Brush Spring Tension (oz)
'67-'69	8-383, 440, wo/AC	59①	12	Neg.	400-450	4	—	90	11	1,925-2,600	32-36
	All others	70	12	Neg.	400-450	4	—	90	11	1,925-2,600	32-36
'70-'71	8-360, 383, 400	59①	12	Neg.	400-450	4	—	90	11	1,925-2,600	32-36
	8-440	70	12	Neg.	400-450	4	—	90	11	1,925-2,600	32-36
'72-'74	8-360	55①	12	Neg.	400-450	4	—	90	11	1,925-2,600	32-36
	8-400	59①	12	Neg.	400-450	4	—	90	11	1,925-2,600	32-36
	8-440	70	12	Neg.	400-450	4	—	90	11	1,925-2,600	32-36

① 70 amp model available as special equipment

ALTERNATOR AND REGULATOR SPECIFICATIONS

	ALTERNATOR			REGULATOR						
					Field Relay			Regulator		
Year	Part No. or Manufacturer	Field Current @ 12 V	Output (amps)	Part No. or Manufacturer	Air Gap (in.)	Point Gap (in.)	Volts to Close	Air Gap (in.)	Point Gap (in.)	Volts @ 75°
'67-'68	Standard	2.38-2.75	35	2098300②	.050②	.014	13.8	.015	.050	13.8-14.4
	Heavy Duty	2.38-2.75③	44	2098300②	.050②	.014	13.8	.015	.050	13.8-14.4
'69	Chrysler	2.38-2.75	35	2098300	.050②	.014	13.8	.015	.050	13.8-14.4
	Imperial	2.38-2.75	35	2875400	.050②	.014	13.8	.015	.050	13.8-14.4
'70-'71	Standard	2.38-2.75	34.5 ± 3	3438150	—	—	—	Not Adjustable		13.8-14.4
	Hvy. Duty and/or A/C	2.38-2.75	44.5 ± 3	3438150	—	—	—	Not Adjustable		13.8-14.4
'72-'74	Chrysler	2.5-3.1	41④	3438150	—	—	—	Not Adjustable		13.8-14.4
	Imperial	2.5-3.1	50	3438150	—	—	—	Not Adjustable		13.8-14.4
	Special Equip. and A/C	2.5-3.1	60 ± 3⑤	3438150	—	—	—	Not Adjustable		13.8-14.4

① 51 amp model available as special equipment
② Essex wire regulator, #2444980, used interchangeably. Air gap setting is .032-.042 in. All other dimensions are identical to #2098300
③ 41 amp model used with A/C, 51 amp model available as special equipment
④ Beginning 1974, 50 amp
⑤ Beginning 1974, 65 amp

RING SIDE CLEARANCE

Year	Engine	Top Compression	Bottom Compression
'67-'74	8-383, 400, 440	.013-.025	.013-.025
'71-'72	8-360	.010-.020	.010-.020

Year	Engine	Oil Control
'67-'74	All engines	.015-.055

RING GAP

Year	Engine	Top Compression	Bottom Compression
'67-'74	8-383, 400, 440	.013-.023	.013-.023

Year	Engine	Oil Control
'67-'74	8-383, 400, 440	.0000-.005
'71-'72	8-360	.0002-.005

BRAKE SPECIFICATIONS

		MASTER CYLINDER		WHEEL CYLINDER			BRAKE DISC OR DRUM DIAMETER		
				Front			Front		
Year	Model	Disc	Drum	Disc	Drum	Rear	Disc	Drum	Rear
'67-'68	All	1.125	1.0	2.375	1.125	.9375	11.87	11.0	11.0
'69-'72	All with 4 wheel drums	—	1.0①	—	1.187	.9375	—	11.0	11.0
	All with Budd disc brakes	1.125①	—	2.375	—	.9375	11.87	—	11.0
	All with Kelsey Hayes disc	1.125①	—	2.75	—	.9375	11.75	—	11.0
'73-'74	Chrysler	1.03	—	2.75②	—	.9375	11.56	—	11.0③
	Imperial	1.03	—	2.75②	—	.9375	11.56	—	11.0③

① 1971-72 models—1.03 in.
— Not applicable
② 3.100 beginning 1974
③ 11.6 beginning 1974

WHEEL ALIGNMENT SPECIFICATIONS

Year	Model	CASTER Range (deg)	CASTER Pref Setting (deg)	CAMBER Range (deg)	CAMBER Pref Setting (deg)	Toe-in (in.)	Steering Axis Inclin.	WHEEL PIVOT RATIO (deg) Inner Wheel	WHEEL PIVOT RATIO (deg) Wheel Outer
'67	Chrysler, Manual	1N to 0	1/2N	①	①	3/32 to 5/32	7 1/2	20	18.8
	Chrysler, Power	1/4P to 1 1/4P	3/4P	①	①	3/32 to 5/32	7 1/2	20	18.8
	Imperial, Power	1/4P to 1 1/4P	3/4P	①	①	3/32 to 5/32	9	20	17.9
'68	Manual Steering	1N to 0	1/2N	①	①	3/32 to 5/32	7 1/2②	20	18.8
	Power Steering	1/4P to 1 1/4P	3/4P	①	①	3/32 to 5/32	7 1/2②	20	18.8③
'69	Man, Pow. exc. Imp.	1N to 0	1/2N	①	①	3/32 to 5/32	7 1/2②	20	18.8
	Power Steering Imp.	1/4P to 1 1/4P	3/4P	①	①	3/32 to 5/32	9	20	17.9
'70-'72	Manual Steering	1/2N ± 9/16	1/2N	④	⑤	3/32 to 5/32	7 1/2	20	18.8
	Power Steering Chry.	1/2N ± 9/16⑥	1/2N	④	⑤	3/32 to 5/32	7 1/2	20	18.8
	Power Steering Imp.	3/4P ± 9/16⑥	3/4P	④	⑤	3/32 to 5/32	9	20	17.9
'73-'74	Chrysler	1/16N to 1 5/16P	5/8P	⑦	⑤	1/8 ± 3/32	7 1/2	20	18.8
	Imperial	1/16N to 1 5/16P	5/8P	⑦	⑤	1/8 ± 3/32	9	20	17.9

① Left side—P1/4 to P3/4. Preferred P1/2.
Right side—0 to P1/2. Preferred P1/4.
② Imperial 9 degrees.
③ Imperial 17.9
④ Left side—1/2P ± 1/4; Right side—1/4P ± 1/4
⑤ Left side—1/2P; Right side—1/4P
⑥ 1971-72—3/4P ± 1/2
⑦ Left side—1/8P to 7/8P
Right side—1/8N to 5/8P
N Negative P Positive

FRONT END HEIGHT▲

Year	Model	Front End Height
'67-'74	Chrysler	1 1/8 ± 1/8
	Imperial	1 3/4 ± 1/8

▲ See text for procedure

PISTON CLEARANCE

Year	Engine	Piston to bore clearance (in.)
1967	383, 440	.0005-.0015
1968	383, 440	.0005-.0015
1969	383, 440	.0003-.0015
1970	383, 440	.0003-.0013
1971	360	.0005-.0015
	383, 440	.0003-.0013
1972	360	.0005-.0015
	400, 440	.0003-.0013
1973	400, 440	.0003-.0013
1974	400, 440	.0003-.0013

NOTE: Service procedures for the Charging System, Starting System, Ignition System, Fuel System, Cooling System, Emission Control System, Engine and Clutch on Chrysler and Imperial cars can be found in the Dodge-Plymouth section.

MANUAL TRANSMISSION

Linkage Adjustment

1967

1. Disconnect the second and third control rod from the steering column lever. Disconnect the first and reverse control rod from the transmission lever.
2. Place both transmission levers in the neutral position. To do this, the neutral detent balls must be engaged. To determine that they are engaged, disengage the clutch and start the engine. Slowly release the clutch; the transmission should be in neutral.

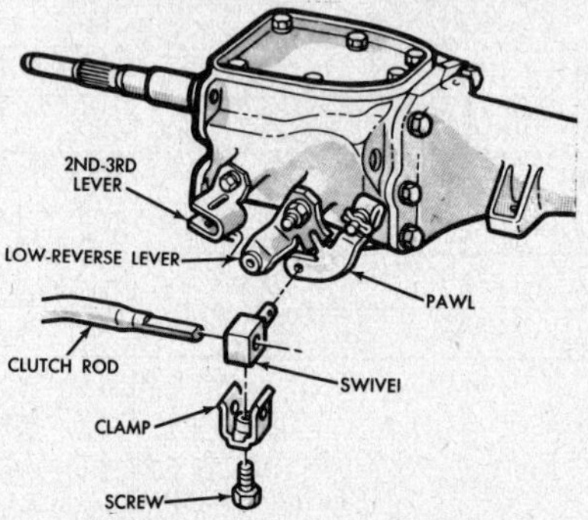

2ND-3RD LEVER
LOW-REVERSE LEVER
PAWL
CLUTCH ROD
SWIVEL
CLAMP
SCREW

Three-speed interlock—1967
(© Chrysler Corp)

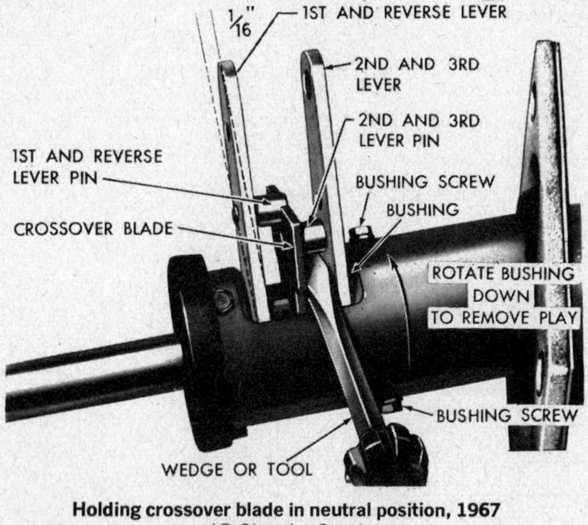

1/16"
1ST AND REVERSE LEVER
2ND AND 3RD LEVER
2ND AND 3RD LEVER PIN
1ST AND REVERSE LEVER PIN
BUSHING SCREW
BUSHING
CROSSOVER BLADE
ROTATE BUSHING DOWN TO REMOVE PLAY
BUSHING SCREW
WEDGE OR TOOL

Holding crossover blade in neutral position, 1967
(© Chrysler Corp)

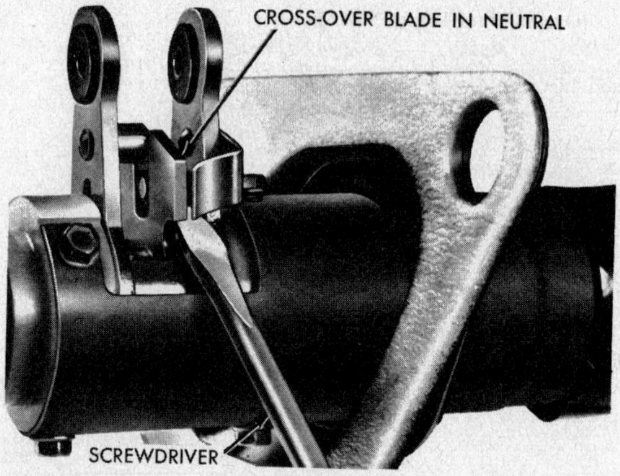

CROSS-OVER BLADE IN NEUTRAL
SCREWDRIVER

Holding the crossover blades in neutral—1968-71

3. Inspect the back-and-forth movement of the shift levers in the steering column. If the movement at the lever outer ends is more than 1/16 in., loosen the two upper bushing screws and turn the bushing downward. Rotate the bushing downward till all free-play in the levers has been removed; then tighten the bushing screws.
4. Using an appropriate wedge type tool, insert it between the crossover blade and the second and third levers. The crossover blade must be engaged with both lever crossover pins.
5. Adjust the length of the second and third control rods until the control rod stub shaft (or swivel) enters the column lever hole. Install the washer and clip and torque the swivel locknut to 70 in. lbs. While this step is being performed, the second and third control rods should be adjusted to position the column selector lever 5° above the horizontal.
6. Position the clamp and swivel on the end of the first and reverse control rod so the swivel stub shaft will enter the hole in the transmission lever. Secure it in position with its clip and washers. Determine the point of middle backlash in the linkage, hold the rod in that position, and tighten the control rod locknut.
7. Remove the wedge type positioning tool from the crossover blade and lever. Move the selector lever through all positions to check the adjustments and crossover smoothness.
8. Shift the transmission into neutral. Check to see whether the clutch pedal free-play is correctly adjusted. If the free-play requires adjustment, refer to the proper procedure and perform this operation now.
9. Loosen the clutch interlock rod clamp bolt. Place the clutch pedal in the fully returned position and secure it there. Slide the interlock rod swivel along the rod so as to fully engage the pawl with the lever; tighten the swivel clamp bolt. *NOTE: Do not pull the interlock rod rearward to engage the swivel in the pawl.*
10. Shift the transmission from neutral to first, then from neutral to reverse. Be sure to disengage the clutch while shifting and engage it while in gear. If the operation is not normal, perform the following steps. Disconnect the interlock rod from the pawl and check the free-play at the clutch. Connect the interlock rod and adjust as previously stated above. Now disengage the clutch. Place the transmission halfway between neutral and first. Slowly

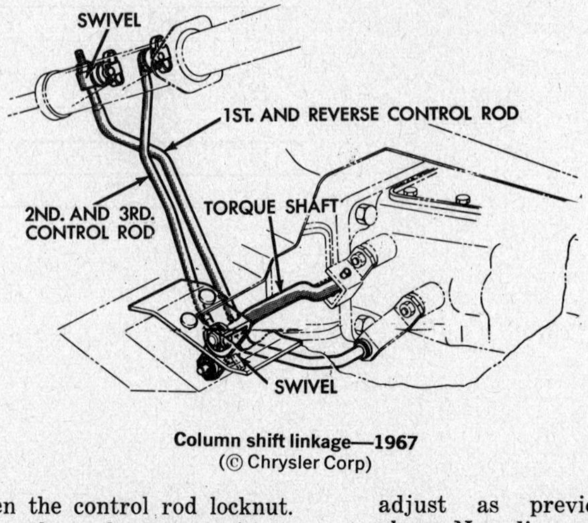

SWIVEL
1ST. AND REVERSE CONTROL ROD
2ND. AND 3RD. CONTROL ROD
TORQUE SHAFT
SWIVEL

Column shift linkage—1967
(© Chrysler Corp)

engage the clutch. When the interlock is properly adjusted, it should allow the clutch pedal to return to approximately 1 in. from the floor.

1968-69

1. Remove the first and reverse rod swivel from the steering column; remove the second and third rod swivel from the torque shaft lever.
2. Be sure the transmission levers are in the neutral (middle detent) position. Adjust the second and third rod swivel by loosening the clamp bolt and positioning the swivel on the rod so it will enter the torque shaft lever while the gear selector on the steering column is held approximately 12° above the horizontal. Secure it in position with its washers and clip, and torque the swivel clamp bolt to 100 in. lbs.
3. Insert a screwdriver between the crossover blade and the second and third lever at the steering column. Be sure that both lever pins are engaged by the crossover blade.
4. Adjust the first and reverse rod swivel by loosening its locknut and rotating the swivel so it will enter the first and reverse lever at the steering column. Install the washers and clip, and torque the swivel locknut to 70 in. lbs.
5. Remove the screwdriver from the crossover blade at the steering column. Shift through all the gears to check the adjustment and crossover smoothness.
6. Disconnect the clutch rod swivel from the interlock pawl. Check the clutch pedal free-play; if it requires adjustment, refer to the proper procedure and perform this operation now.
7. Adjust the first and reverse lever on the transmission so that when it is in the neutral (middle detent) position, the interlock pawl will enter the slot in the first and reverse lever.
8. Loosen the swivel clamp bolt and position the swivel on the rod so it will enter the pawl; install its clip and washers. With the interlock lever held forward, torque the swivel clamp bolt to 100 in. lbs. While this adjustment is being performed, the clutch pedal must be in the fully returned position. *NOTE: do not pull the interlock rod rearward to engage the swivel with the pawl.*
9. Disengage the clutch, and shift in the normal manner from neutral to first, and then from neutral to reverse. Be sure to perform the above as you normally would while driving.
10. The action of the clutch should be normal. Disengage the clutch and shift halfway to first or reverse. If everything is properly operating, the clutch should be held down to between 1 to 2 in. off the floor by the interlock.

1970-71

1. Remove the shift rod swivels from the transmission shift levers. Be sure the transmission shift levers are in the neutral (middle detent) position.
2. Position the shift levers to align the locating slots in the bottom of the steering column shift and bearing housing. Install a suitable holding tool in the slot and lock the ignition switch.
3. Insert a screwdriver between the crossover blade and the second and third lever at the steering column. Both lever pins must be engaged by the crossover blade.
4. Rotate (clockwise) the first and reverse lever on the transmission to obtain the reverse position.
5. Adjust the first and reverse rod swivel by loosening the clamp bolt and positioning the swivel on the rod so it will enter the first and reverse lever at the transmission. Install its washers and clip; torque the swivel bolt to 100 in. lbs.
6. Remove the gearshift housing locating tool, unlock the ignition switch, and shift the steering column lever to the neutral position.
7. Adjust the second and third rod swivel by loosening the clamp bolt and positioning the swivel on the rod so it will enter the second and third lever at the transmission. Install its washers and clip; torque the swivel bolt to 100 in. lbs.
8. Remove the tool from the crossover blade at the steering column. Shift through all the gears to check the adjustment.
9. Check the operation of the steering lock in the reverse (1970–

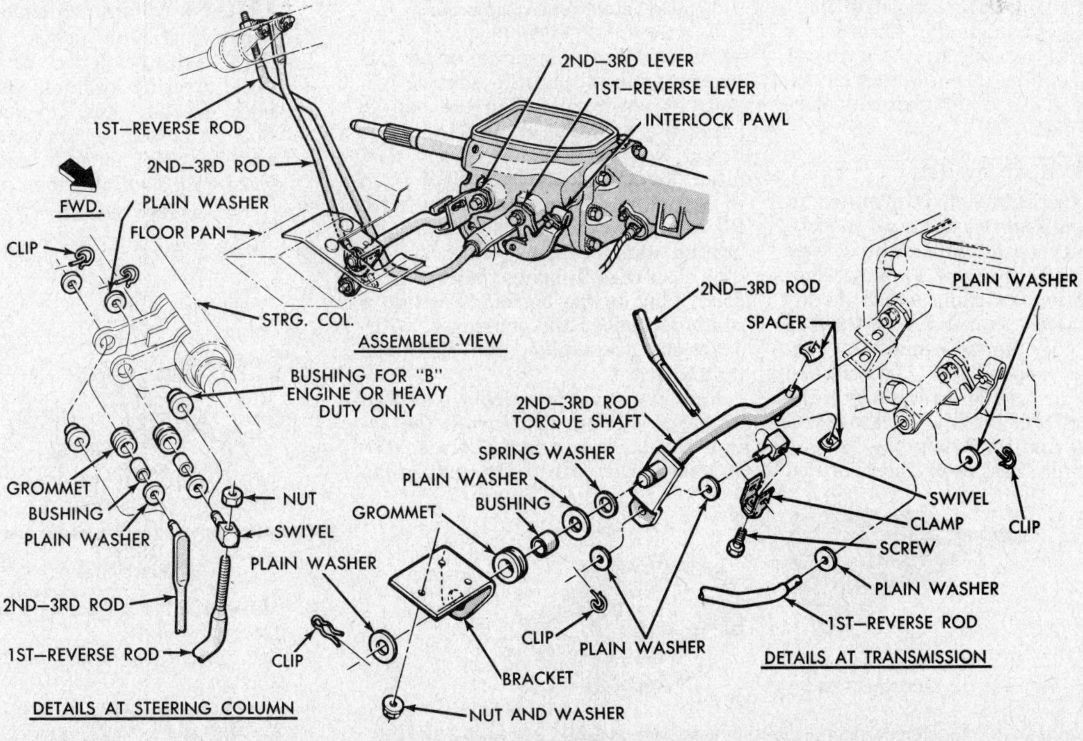
2ND–3RD LEVER
1ST–REVERSE LEVER
INTERLOCK PAWL
1ST–REVERSE ROD
2ND–3RD ROD
FWD.
PLAIN WASHER
FLOOR PAN
CLIP
STRG. COL.
ASSEMBLED VIEW
BUSHING FOR "B" ENGINE OR HEAVY DUTY ONLY
GROMMET
BUSHING
PLAIN WASHER
NUT
SWIVEL
2ND–3RD ROD
1ST–REVERSE ROD
DETAILS AT STEERING COLUMN
2ND–3RD ROD TORQUE SHAFT
SPRING WASHER
PLAIN WASHER
BUSHING
GROMMET
PLAIN WASHER
CLIP
CLIP
PLAIN WASHER
BRACKET
NUT AND WASHER
2ND–3RD ROD
SPACER
PLAIN WASHER
SWIVEL
CLAMP
CLIP
SCREW
PLAIN WASHER
1ST–REVERSE ROD
DETAILS AT TRANSMISSION

Typical linkage—1968-71 (© Chrysler Corp)

71) and second gear (1970 only) positions. With the linkage properly adjusted (for all years) the column should lock in the reverse position only.

Manual Transmission Service

For all manual transmission service procedures, please refer to the Dodge-Plymouth section.

AUTOMATIC TRANSMISSION

Model identification appears in large letters embossed on the lower side of the bell housing. While designs and servicing procedures are similar for all vehicles, internal parts are necessarily different. Therefore, when replacing parts refer to the 7-digit part number stamped on the left side of the transmission oil flange.

The transmission combines a torque converter and fully automatic 3-speed gear system. Converter housing and transmission case are an integral aluminum casting. The transmission consists of two multiple disc clutches, an overrunning clutch, two servos and bands, and two planetary gear sets to provide three forward ratios and a reverse ratio. The common sun gear of the planetary gear sets is connected to the front clutch by a driving shell splined to the sun gear and to the front clutch retainer. The hydraulic system consists of the oil pump and a single valve body that contains all valves except the governor valve.

Cooling the converter is accomplished by circulating the transmission fluid through an oil-to-water type cooler located in the radiator lower tank. The torque converter assembly is a sealed unit that cannot be disassembled.

Neutral Start Switch

The neutral switch is mounted in the transmission case on all models. When the transmission manual lever is placed in either the Park or Neutral position, a cam, which is attached to the transmission throttle lever inside the transmission, contacts the neutral start switch and provides a ground to complete the starter solenoid circuit. On late model Chryslers and Imperials, the back-up light switch has been incorporated into the neutral switch. The combination neutral and back-up light switch can be identified by the three electrical terminals on the rear of the switch. On this type of switch, the center terminal is for the neutral switch and the two outer terminals are for the back-up lights.

NOTE: in order for the neutral start switch to function properly, the transmission manual linkage must be properly adjusted and the actuator cam in the transmission must be centered in the neutral switch mounting hole in the transmission.

To remove the switch, remove all the electrical leads while taking note of their position. Remove the switch with a wrench. Have a container of adequate size at hand to catch the draining fluid. When replacing the switch, be sure to use a new seal. Torque the switch to 24 ft lbs and replace the fluid.

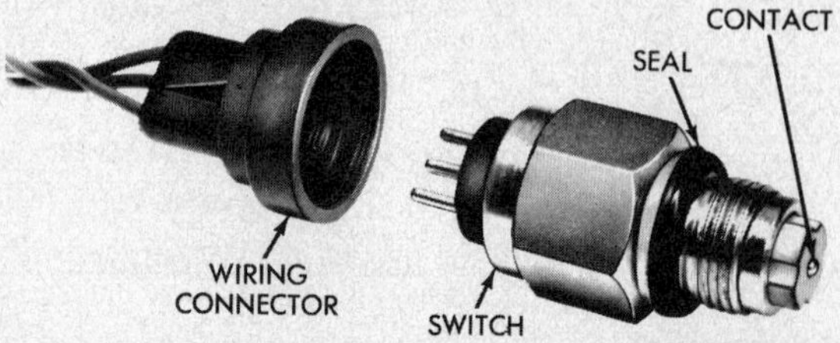
CONTACT
SEAL
WIRING CONNECTOR
SWITCH

Combination neutral start and back-up light
(© Chrysler Corp)

Draining, Refilling, and Filter Service

To drain the transmission fluid, raise the car on a hoist or jack up the front of the car and support it with suitable stands. Place a container,

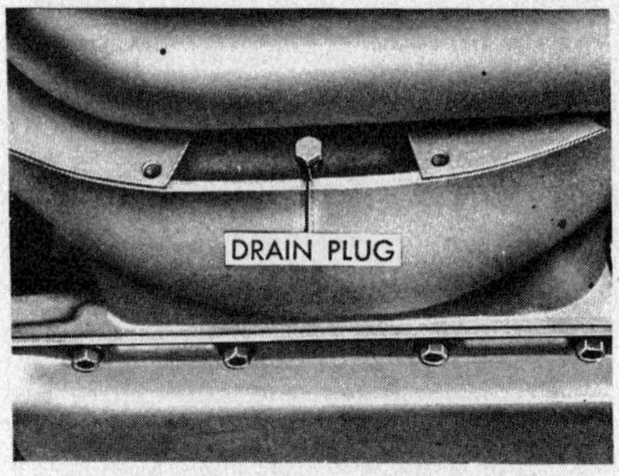
DRAIN PLUG

Torque converter drain plug location
(© Chrysler Corp)

which has a large opening, under the transmission oil pan. Loosen the pan bolts at one corner, tap the pan to break the seal, and allow the fluid to drain. Now remove the oil pan and filter. Remove the access plate from in front of the torque converter. With the aid of a socket wrench on the vibration damper bolt, rotate the engine clockwise to bring the converter drain plug to the bottom. Position a container under the converter, withdraw the drain plug, and allow the fluid to drain.

Refit the converter drain plug and torque to 110 in. lbs. Install the access plate. Place a new filter on the bottom of the valve body and torque its retaining screws to 35 in. lbs. Clean the oil pan, fit a new gasket, and install the assembly. Torque the pan bolts to 150 in. lbs. Remove the container and lower the car.

Fill the transmission with 6 qt of Dexron Type A automatic transmission fluid. Start the engine and allow it to idle. Thoroughly warm the transmission and recheck the fluid level.

Shift Linkage Adjustment

1967-69 Console Selector, 1967-69 Column Selector

1. Place selector lever in Park.

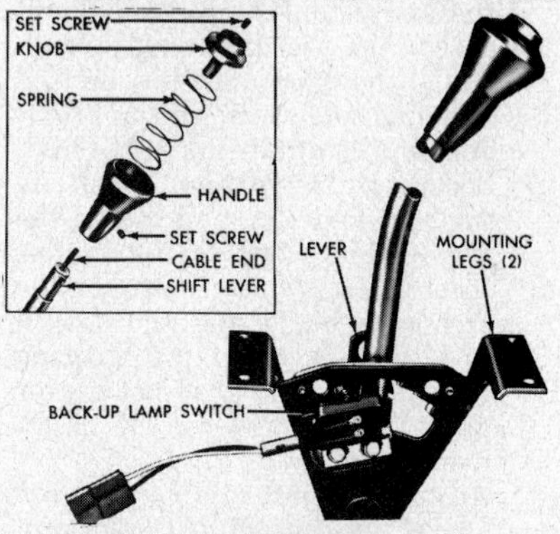
SET SCREW
KNOB
SPRING
HANDLE
SET SCREW
CABLE END
SHIFT LEVER
LEVER
MOUNTING LEGS (2)
BACK-UP LAMP SWITCH

Automatic transmission console shifter—1967-74
(© Chrysler Corp)

Loosen control rod swivel clamp.
2. Move selector to rear of Park detent.
3. Check that transmission lever is in park position. Tighten swivel clamp screw to 100 in. lbs.

1970-74 Console Selector 1970-74 Column Selector

1. Free adjustable rod ends.
2. Place selector lever in Park. Lock steering column. On console selector, line up locating slots in bottom of shift housing and bearing housing. Hold in place with a suitable tool.

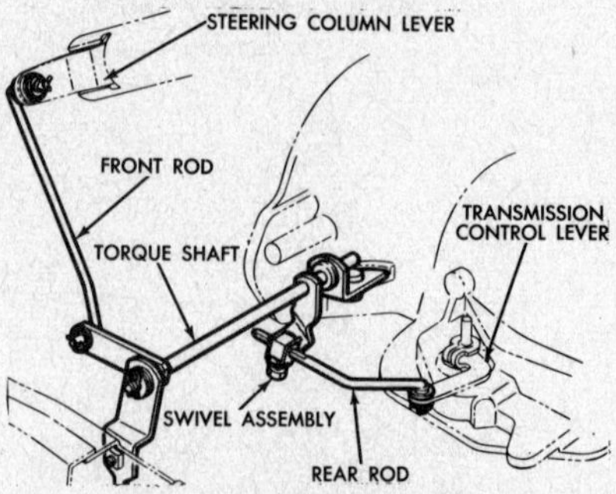
STEERING COLUMN LEVER
FRONT ROD
TORQUE SHAFT
TRANSMISSION CONTROL LEVER
SWIVEL ASSEMBLY
REAR ROD

Typical automatic transmission column shift linkage
(© Chrysler Corp)

3. Move selector to rear of Park detent.
4. Set adjustable rods to proper length.
5. Check adjustment:
   a. Detents and gate stops should be positive.

b. Selector lever must not remain out of detent position when placed against gate and then released.
c. Key start must occur with selector lever held against Park gate.

Band Adjustments

Kick-down Band

The kick-down band adjusting screw is located on the left-hand side of the transmission case near the throttle lever shaft.

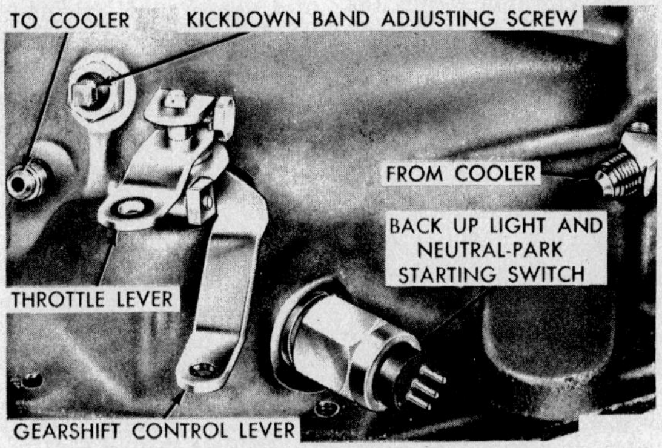

TO COOLER
KICKDOWN BAND ADJUSTING SCREW
FROM COOLER
BACK UP LIGHT AND NEUTRAL-PARK STARTING SWITCH
THROTTLE LEVER
GEARSHIFT CONTROL LEVER

TorqueFlite transmission external controls, showing the location of the kick-down band adjustment.
(© Chrysler Corp)

1. Loosen the locknut and back it off about five turns. Be sure that the adjusting screw is free in the case.
2. Using an inch pounds torque wrench torque the adjusting screw to 72 in. lbs.
3. Back off the adjusting screw the exact number of turns specified below. Keep the screw from turning and torque the locknut to the value specified below.

1967-70 ....2 turns
1971-74 ....$2\frac{1}{2}$ turns
Kick-down band adjusting screw locknut torque ....29 ft lbs

Low and Reverse Band

The oil pan must be removed from the transmission to gain access to the low and reverse band adjusting screw.

1. Drain the transmission and remove the oil pan.
2. Loosen the band adjusting screw locknut and back it off about five turns. Be sure that the adjusting screw turns freely in the lever.
3. Using an inch pounds torque wrench, tighten the adjusting screw to 72 in. lbs if an adaptor is not used.
4. Back off the adjusting screw the exact number of turns specified below. Keep the screw from turning and torque the locknut to the value specified below.

1967-74 ....2 turns
Low and reverse band adjusting screw locknut torque ....35 ft lbs

5. Using a new gasket, install the oil pan and tighten the attaching bolts to 150 in. lbs.
6. Fill the transmission.

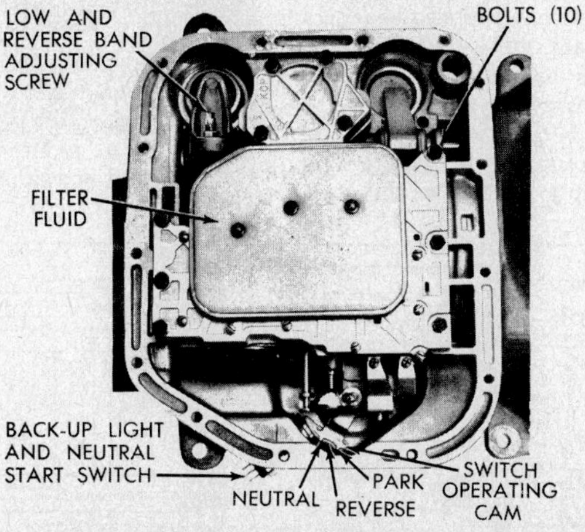

LOW AND REVERSE BAND ADJUSTING SCREW
BOLTS (10)
FILTER-FLUID
BACK-UP LIGHT AND NEUTRAL START SWITCH
NEUTRAL
PARK
REVERSE
SWITCH OPERATING CAM

TorqueFlite transmission with the oil pan removed. Note the low and reverse band adjusting screw location
(© Chrysler Corp)

U-JOINTS

All Chrysler models, and Imperial from 1967, use one-piece driveshafts with two U-joints. All Chrysler models have two cross-and-roller joints with a slip spline at the front U-joint. There are two constant-velocity U-joints with a sliding yoke at the front of 1967-74 Imperials.

Two basic types of driveshafts are utilized; a solid tube type, and one that incorporates an internal vibration damper inside the tube itself. On certain applications, the driveshaft may be found to incorporate an inertia type ring at the front U-joint. Servicing of all driveshafts is identical.

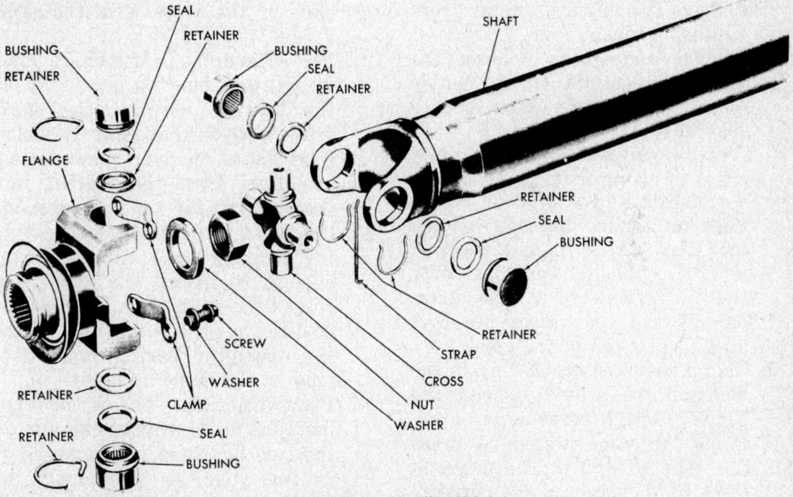

SEAL
RETAINER
BUSHING
RETAINER
BUSHING
SEAL
RETAINER
SHAFT
FLANGE
RETAINER
SEAL
BUSHING
SCREW
WASHER
CLAMP
RETAINER
STRAP
CROSS
NUT
WASHER
RETAINER
SEAL
RETAINER
BUSHING

Rear cross and roller U-joint
(© Chrysler Corp)

Driveshaft Removal

1967-74 All Models

1. Scribe alignment marks on the driveshaft, rear U-joint, and the drive pinion flange. This is necessary to ensure proper drive train balance upon installation of the various parts.
2. Remove both of the U-joint roller and bushing assembly clamps from the rear axle drive pinion flange. Be sure not to disturb the retaining strap (if so equipped) which holds the bushing assemblies on the U-joint cross. Do not allow the driveshaft to hang loose while removing either U-joint.

3. Slide the driveshaft with the front yoke from the transmission output shaft. Be careful not to damage the splines on the output shaft and the yoke. Do not disturb the yoke seal unless it is damaged or leaking. Remove the driveshaft and protect the sliding yoke from damage.
4. To install the driveshaft, clean the sliding yoke and inspect its machined surface. File off burrs if necessary. Carefully engage the yoke splines with the splines on the end of the transmission output shaft.
5. At the rear, align the scribe marks and install the U-joint cross and roller bushings into the drive pinion flange. Fit the bushing clamps and securing screws and torque to specifications.

Constant Velocity Universal Joint

Disassembly

Remove the driveshaft and, before disassembling any parts, mark the joints for proper indexing at the time of assembly.

1. Remove four screws and lockwashers. Remove spline yoke.
2. Remove two loose bearings from centering socket yoke.
3. Remove snap-rings holding the bearing assemblies in the center socket yoke shaft, and center yoke bores.
4. Press bearing assemblies from the yokes by using a ¾ in. socket as a remover and a pipe or socket with an inside diameter of not less than 1 1/16 in. as a receiver on the opposite bearing. With the aid of a press or vise, press one of the rear yoke bearings about ⅜ in. out of the yoke.
5. Clamp the exposed bearing in the vise and drive the yoke from the bearing with a brass drift.
6. Using the same procedure, press the exposed end of the cross to force the bearing on the opposite end about ⅜ in. out of the yoke. Remove the bearing from the yoke as previously described in Step 5.
7. Remove the remaining set of bearings from the propeller shaft yoke in the same way.
8. With the shaft held in the vise, press in on the yoke shaft and work the center joint off the cross.
9. Remove the cross from the propeller shaft yoke. Remove centering stud spring from the propeller shaft.
10. Remove the four roller bearing assemblies to separate the yoke shaft from the center yoke, as previously described.

If it is necessary to remove the centering ball and socket assembly, proceed as follows:

11. Carefully pry the centering ball seal assembly from the yoke shaft.
12. Remove seal from the centering stud seal retainer and the bearing rollers from the centering ball.
13. Fill the cavity behind the centering ball and inside the ball with lithium base grease.
14. Insert a rod, slightly smaller than the inside diameter of the centering ball, into the ball, then strike it sharply with a hammer. The force applied should force the ball and retainer from the yoke.

Assembly

1. Position the centering assembly in the yoke with the large diameter hole up, and press it firmly into its seat.
2. Apply grease on the inside surface of the centering ball. Install the 34 rollers. Install the centering stud seal in the ball.
3. Install centering ball seal assembly on the yoke and press firmly into place.
4. Coat the inside surfaces of the bearing races with the same grease, and install the 32 rollers. Also, pack the reservoirs in the ends of the cross with the same grease.
5. Place the cross in the shaft yoke. Insert one bearing assembly in the bearing bore of the shaft yoke. With the bar stock or socket used as a remover when disassembling, press the bearing into the bore. At the same time, guide the cross into the bearing. Press the bearing into the yoke far enough to install the snap-ring. Install the snap-ring. Reverse the position of the yoke and install the opposite bearing and snap-ring in the same manner.
6. Place the center yoke on the cross installed in the shaft yoke. Install the two bearings and snap-rings in the yoke, as previously described.
7. Install the cross and two bearings in the shaft yoke, in the same manner as previously described. Install snap-rings.
8. Install centering stud spring on the centering stud, (large end first). Apply grease to the stud.
9. Position the cross in the center universal joint of the propeller shaft while guiding the centering ball on the centering stud, applying pressure at the same time. Work the center yoke over the cross. Don't damage the cross seals.
10. Install the two bearing assemblies in the rear bores of the center yoke as previously described. Install snap-rings.
11. Coat the splines of the center socket yoke with grease.
12. Install slip spline yoke on the constant velocity joints with screws and lockwashers. Torque to specifications.

Cross and Roller Bearing U-Joints

Disassembly and Assembly

1. To disassemble the joint, remove the four bolts that hold the two bearing assemblies to the companion flange and knock the bearings off the flange.
2. To remove the bearings from the yoke, first remove the bearing retainer lock washers or C-washers, then pressing on one of the bearings, drive the bearing in toward the center of the joint. This will force the cross to push the opposite bearing out of the universal joint yoke. After it has been pushed all the way out of the yoke, pull up the cross slightly and pack some washers under it. Then press on the end of the cross from which the bearing was just removed to force the first bearing out of the yoke.
3. Perhaps the easiest way to reassemble is to start both bearing retainers into the yoke at the same time, hold the cross carefully in the fingers and squeeze both bearings in a vise or heavy C-clamp. Driving the bearings into place usually cocks the little rollers, greatly reducing the life of the bearings.
4. Install the locking devices.

JACKING, HOISTING

Jack car at front under lower control arm and at rear under axle housing.

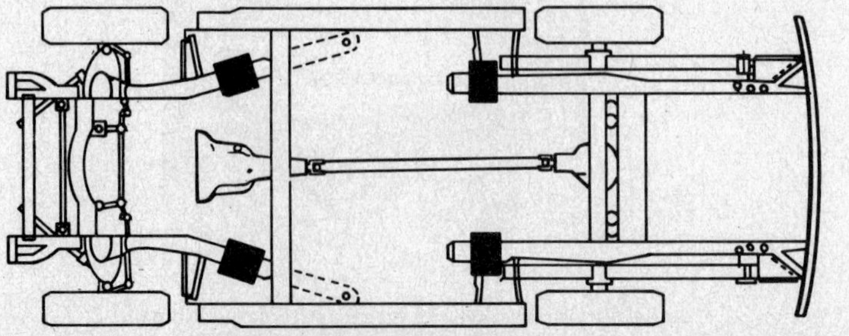

Positioning lift adapter
(© Chrysler Corp)

To lift at frame, use adapters so that contact will be made at points shown. Lifting pad must extend beyond sides of supporting structure.

FRONT SUSPENSION

All models utilize torsion bar front suspension. The rear anchors of the torsion bars are integral with the engine rear support crossmember; the front anchor points are part of the lower control arms, and are the means used to adjust the height of the vehicle. Compression type lower ball joints are used on all models. The lower ball joints are preloaded on Imperials only, beginning in 1967. The ball joints and torsion bars at the front of the rear anchors use balloon type flexible seals; this serves to protect the components from road splash and dirt. When it is necessary to lubricate these balloon seals, avoid pressure type lubrication guns; these seals burst easily, and should be filled slowly and manually only.

Imperials received a redesigned front suspension in 1967. In addition to the preloaded (zero axial endplay) ball joints mentioned above, the frame received a front "K" type crossmember. It is effectively isolated from the stub frame by four large rubber bushing insulators. The crossmember that supports the torsion bar rear anchor is further isolated from the stub frame's crossmember by sandwich type insulators. The upper control arm is mounted on a pivot bar and the front wheel alignment is adjusted by two vertically mounted cam bolts. A link type sway bar is fitted; it mounts to the lower control arm and front crossmember.

When servicing Chrysler and Imperial vehicles, it is important to remember that all front suspension parts containing rubber should be tightened only when the suspension is at the proper height, and that the full weight of the vehicle must be on the wheels. Moreover, do not lubricate the rubber bushings with oil at any time.

Front Shock Absorber Removal and Installation

1. Remove the nut and retainer from the shock absorber top.
2. Jack the front of the vehicle. It is sometimes necessary to remove the tire and wheel assembly, from Imperials, and perform the removal operation from beneath the fender.
3. Remove the shock absorber lower attaching bolt nut. Remove the bolt from the shock absorber eye and lower the control arm mounting bracket.
4. Push upward on the shock absorber and fully compress it; pull the shock downward and out of its upper mounting bushings and remove from the vehicle. On all Imperial models the dust shield is removed with the shock absorber. It may be necessary to remove the upper control arm bumper, on some models, to obtain enough clearance to remove the shock absorber assembly.
5. To begin the installation procedure fully compress the shock. Insert the rod through the upper bushing, install the retainer and nut, and tighten the nut. On Imperial models, place the retainer on the shock absorber upper rod; now install the dust shield. Install the rod to the upper bushing with its nut and retainer and tighten the nut. *NOTE: All retainers must be installed with the concave (sunken) side in contact with the rubber.* Align the shock lower eye with its lower control arm mountings. Install its retaining nut and bolt finger tight. Lower the vehicle and tighten the nut with the full weight of the vehicle on the wheels.

Front Height Adjustment

1. Jounce vehicle several times, releasing it on downward motion.
2. Measure distance A. For 1967-74 Chrysler models, the measurement is taken from the lowest point of the adjusting blade. For 1967-74 Imperial models, measure from the lowest point of the front torsion bar anchor at the rear of the lower control arm flange.
3. Measure distance B. This is the distance between the lowest point of the lower ball joint housing and the floor.
4. Subtract distance A from distance B to obtain front suspension height. Check this figure against the figure listed in the front end alignment table in the front of this section.
5. Measure the other side. There should be no more than 1/8 in. difference in height from one side to the other.
6. Adjust height, as necessary, by turning torsion bar adjusting bolt clockwise to increase height and counterclockwise to decrease height.

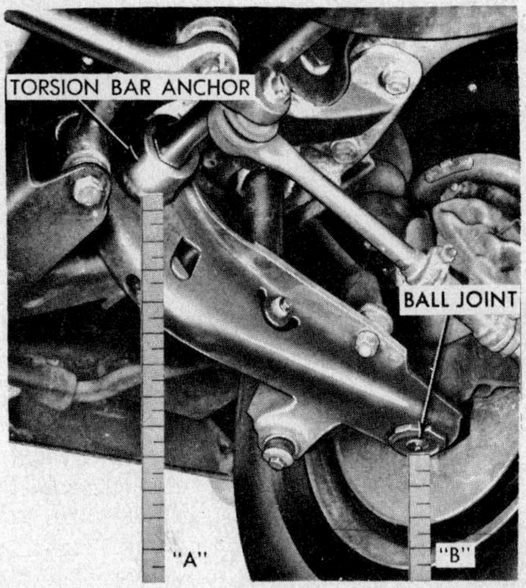
TORSION BAR ANCHOR
BALL JOINT
"A"
"B"

Measuring front suspension height—1967-74 Imperial
(© Chrysler Corp)

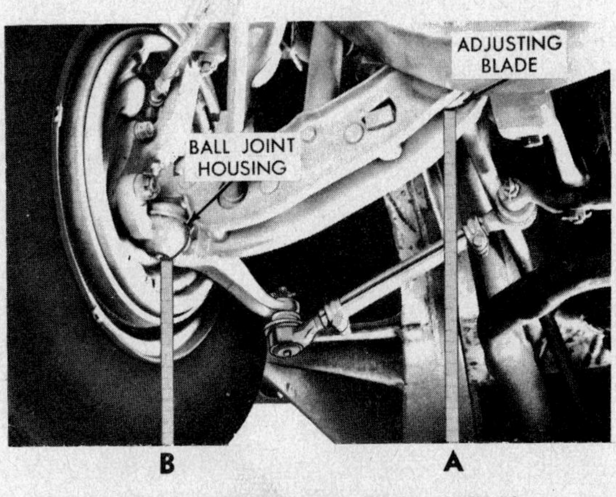
ADJUSTING BLADE
BALL JOINT HOUSING
B
A

Measuring front suspension height—1967-74
(© Chrysler Corp)

Wheel Bearing Adjustment

1967-69

1. Jack the vehicle and remove the hub cap and grease cup. Take out the cotter pin, remove the nut lock and loosen the adjusting nut.
2. While rotating the wheel, tighten the wheel bearing adjusting nut to 90 in. lbs.
3. Align the nut lock on the nut so that one pair of slots is in line with the cotter pin hole.
4. Back off the adjusting nut lock assembly one slot and install a new cotter pin. This should yield an adjustment between zero (no preload) and 0.003 in. end-play.
5. Clean the grease cup. Coat, but do not fill, the inside of the cup with wheel bearing lubricant and install it on the vehicle. Install the hub caps and lower the vehicle.

1970-74

1. Raise the front of the car to allow the wheels to spin freely.
2. Remove the wheel cover, grease cup, cotterpin, and lock nut.
3. Tighten the wheel bearing adjusting nut to 240-300 in. lbs while spinning the wheel.
4. Back the nut off and retighten to finger tight.
5. Reinstall the lock nut, cotter pin, grease cup, and wheel cover.
6. Lower the car.

Lower Ball Joint

Inspection

1. Raise the front of the vehicle by placing a floor jack under the lower control arm. Position the lifting point of the jack as close to the wheel as possible.
2. Have an assistant raise and lower the tire and wheel assembly and observe any movement at the lower ball joint.
3. On 1967 Chryslers, replace the ball joint if the axial (up and down) play of the ball joint housing arm in relation to the ball joint stud exceeds 0.050 in. On 1968-74 Chryslers, replace the ball joint if the axial play exceeds 0.070 in. On 1967-74 Imperials, the lower ball joints are preloaded and, if any free play exists, the lower ball joint-control arm assembly must be replaced.

Removal—1967-74 Chrysler

The lower ball joint is integral with the steering arm and is not serviced separately.

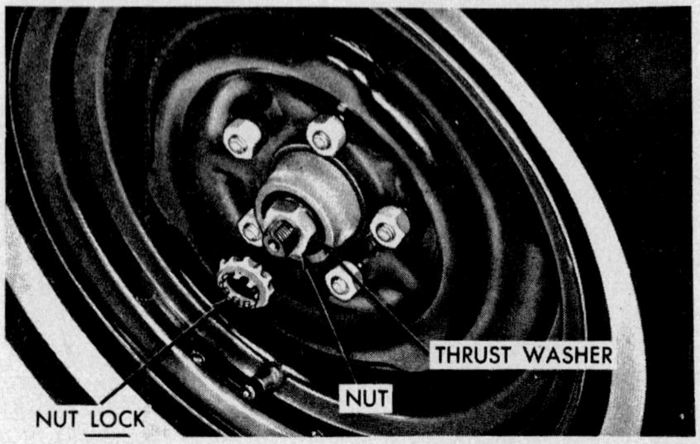
THRUST WASHER
NUT
NUT LOCK

Adjusting the wheel bearings
(© Chrysler Corp)

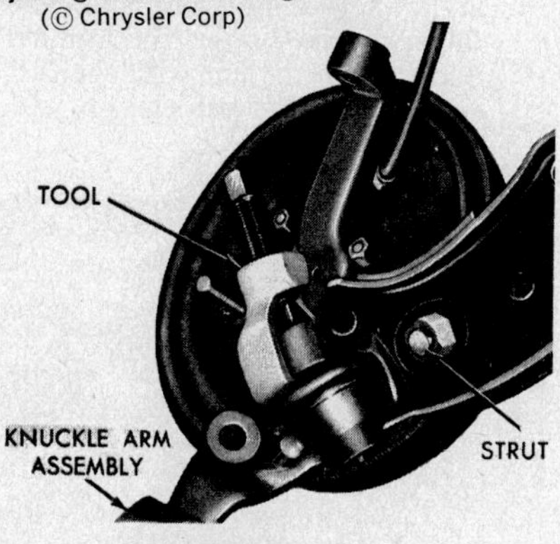
TOOL
KNUCKLE ARM ASSEMBLY
STRUT

Removing the lower ball joint stud
(© Chrysler Corp)

1. Raise the vehicle on a hoist so the front suspension will drop to the downward limit of its travel.
2. Place a jack stand under the lower control arm, near the ball joint.
3. Lower the vehicle onto the jack stand.
4. Remove the tire, wheel, and brake drum from the vehicle as an assembly. If equipped with disc brakes, remove the tire and wheel. Remove the brake pads, and remove the caliper from the steering knuckle and position it out of the way with the brake line attached. Remove the rotor from the spindle.
5. Remove the two lower bolts that attach the steering arm-ball joint assembly to the brake assembly mounting plate.
6. Using a suitable tool, disconnect the tie rod end from the steering arm.
7. Remove the ball joint stud retaining nut and cotter pin.
8. Using a suitable tool, separate and remove the ball joint from the lower contol arm.

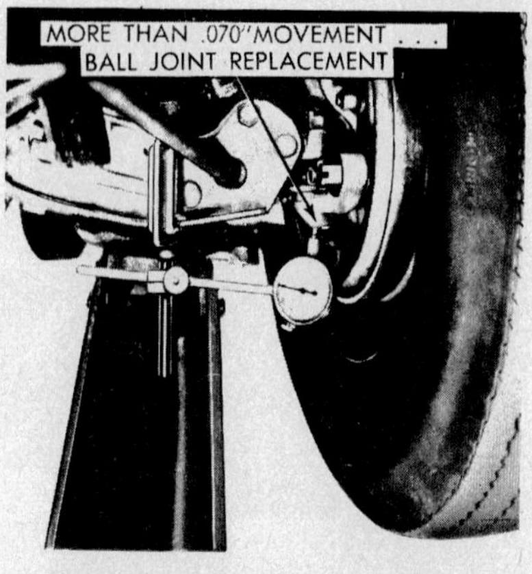
MORE THAN .070" MOVEMENT . . .
BALL JOINT REPLACEMENT

Measuring lower ball joint axial travel
(© Chrysler Corp)

Installation

1. Position ball joint-steering arm assembly on the steering knuckle and install the two retaining bolts.
2. Insert the ball joint stud in the lower control arm and install the retaining nut and cotter pin.
3. Position the tie rod end in the steering knuckle and install the retaining nut and cotter pin.
4. Place a load on the torsion bar by turning the adjusting bolt in a clockwise direction.
5. Install the tire, wheel and brake drum assembly. If equipped with disc brakes, install the rotor, caliper, brake pads and tire and wheel assembly.
6. Lower vehicle and install upper control arm rebound bumper if so equipped.
7. Check and adjust front suspension height as required.

Removal—1967-74 Imperial

Lower ball joints on these Imperial models are serviced only as ball joint-control arm assemblies.

1. Raise the vehicle on a hoist so the front suspension drops to the downward limit of its travel.
2. Remove the wheel and tire as an assembly.
3. Remove the load from *both* torsion bars by turning the adjusting bolts in a counterclockwise direction.
4. Disconnect the shock absorber from the lower control arm and position the shock out of the way. Disconnect the strut bar from the lower control arm.
5. Disconnect the brake hose from the caliper.
6. Remove the lower ball joint retaining nut and cotter pin.
7. Using a suitable tool, separate the ball joint stud from the steering knuckle.
8. Remove the nut and washer that attaches the lower control arm pivot shaft to the frame.
9. Using a brass drift and hammer, tap the end of the pivot shaft to

loosen it (the shaft is a tapered fit in the front crossmember).

10. Remove the lower control arm and shaft from the vehicle as an assembly.
11. Position the control arm assembly in a press with the hex opening for the torsion bar in the up position and place a support under the outer edge of the control arm.
12. Insert a brass drift in the hex opening and press the shaft out of the control arm. The bushing inner arm will remain on the shaft.
13. Remove the torsion bar adjusting bolt and swivel from the control arm.

Installation

1. Position a new bushing on the pivot shaft (flange end of the bushing first) and seat the bushing on the shoulder of the pivot shaft.
2. Press the shaft and bushing assembly into the new control arm.
3. Install the torsion bar adjusting bolt and swivel on the new control arm.
4. Position a new seal on the ball joint and install the seal. To ease installation of the seal, the ball joint stud should be perpendicular to the body of the ball joint.
5. Position the control arm assembly on the crossmember in approximate operating position and install the nut and washer. *Do not tighten the nut until the full weight of the vehicle is on the wheels.*
6. Insert the lower ball joint stud in the steering knuckle and install the retaining nut and cotter pin.
7. Install the strut bar rear bushing and retainer on the strut bar and insert the strut bar through the crossmember.
8. Install the front strut bar bushing and retainer on the strut bar and install the retaining nut finger tight only.
9. Position the rear of the strut bar over the lower control arm and install the bumper and plate.
10. Connect the shock absorber to the lower control arm and install the retaining nut finger tight. Place a load on each torsion bar by turning the adjusting bolt clockwise.
11. Connect the brake line to the disc brake caliper and bleed the brakes.
12. Install the tire and wheel assembly.
13. Lower the vehicle to the floor. Tighten the strut bar, shock absorber and lower control arm attaching nuts.
14. Check and adjust front end height as required.

Upper Ball Joint

Replacement

1. Raise the vehicle by placing a floor jack under the lower control arm. Place the lifting point of the jack as close as possible to the wheel.
2. Remove the wheel, tire and drum as an assembly. On models with disc brakes, remove the tire and wheel, remove the disc brake pads, remove the disc brake caliper from the steering knuckle and position the caliper out of the way with the brake line attached. Remove the brake rotor from the steering knuckle.
3. Remove the nut that attaches the upper ball joint to the steering knuckle and, using a suitable tool, loosen the ball joint stud from the steering knuckle.
4. Unscrew the upper ball joint from the upper control arm and remove it from the vehicle.
5. Position new ball joint on the upper control arm, screw the ball joint into the control arm until it bottoms and tighten the ball joint to a minimum of 125 ft. lbs. for Chrysler models, 150 ft. lbs for Imperial models.

NOTE: when installing a ball joint, make certain the ball joint threads engage those of the upper control arm squarely if the original control arm is being used.

6. Position a new seal on the ball joint stud and install the seal in the ball joint making sure the seal is fully seated on the ball joint housing.
7. Position ball joint stud in the steering knuckle and install the retaining nut.
8. Lubricate ball joint and, if replacement ball joint is equipped with knock-off type grease fitting, break off that portion of the fitting over which the lubrication gun was installed.
9. If equipped with disc brakes, install the rotor, caliper and brake pads. Install the tire and wheel.
10. Lower the vehicle and adjust front suspension height as required.

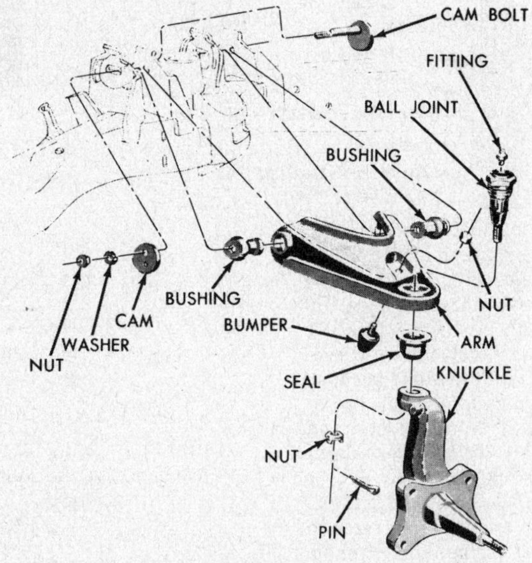
CAM BOLT
FITTING
BALL JOINT
BUSHING
BUSHING
NUT
CAM
WASHER
NUT
BUMPER
ARM
SEAL
KNUCKLE
NUT
PIN

Chrysler upper control arm
(© Chrysler Corp)

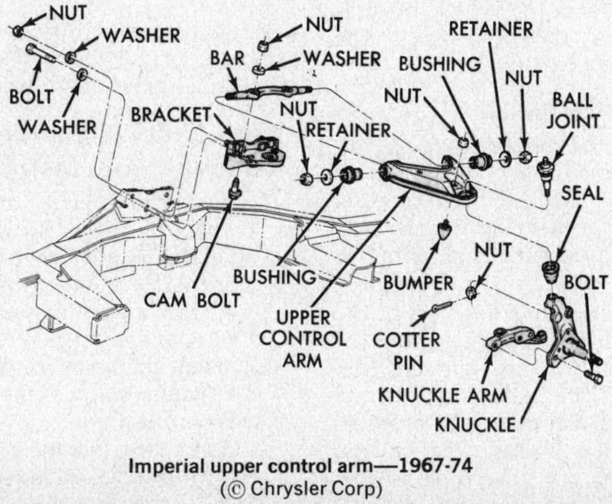
NUT
WASHER
BOLT
WASHER
NUT
BAR
WASHER
BRACKET
NUT
RETAINER
RETAINER
BUSHING
NUT
NUT
BALL JOINT
SEAL
NUT
BOLT
BUSHING
BUMPER
CAM BOLT
UPPER CONTROL ARM
COTTER PIN
KNUCKLE ARM
KNUCKLE

Imperial upper control arm—1967-74
(© Chrysler Corp)

Torsion Bar

Contrary to appearance, the torsion bars are not interchangeable from right to left. They are marked with an R or an L, according to their location.

Torsion Bar Removal and Replacement

Removal

1. Raise the vehicle so the front suspension drops to the limit of its downward travel.
2. Remove the upper control arm rebound bumper if so equipped.
3. On all models except 1967-72 Imperials, remove the tension from the torsion bar to be replaced by turning the anchor adjusting bolt in a counterclockwise direction and removing the adjusting bolt and swivel. On 1967-74 Imperials, release the load on both torsion bars by turning each anchor adjusting bolt in a counterclockwise direction. This is necessary because the rubber insulator rear crossmember would be under load and could possibly cause severe damage or personal injury.
4. Slide rear anchor balloon seal off of the rear anchor and remove the lockring from the anchor. On Imperial models remove the balloon seal clamp.
5. On all models, remove the torsion bar from the vehicle by sliding it rearward and out of the torsion bar rear anchor.

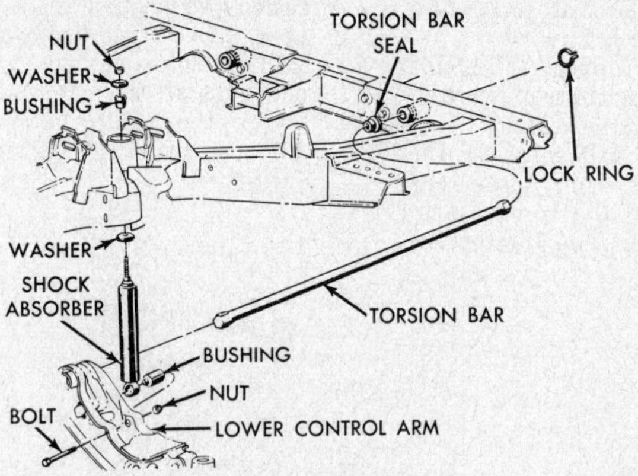
TORSION BAR
SEAL
NUT
WASHER
BUSHING
LOCK RING
WASHER
SHOCK
ABSORBER
TORSION BAR
BUSHING
NUT
BOLT
LOWER CONTROL ARM

Chrysler torsion bar 1967-74
(© Chrysler Corp)

Installation

1. Position the torsion bar in the chassis and apply a coating of chassis lubricant to both ends.
2. Install the lockring in the anchor, making sure it is seated in the groove.
3. Pack the annular opening in the rear anchor completely full of chassis lubricant and position the lip of the balloon seal in the groove of the anchor. On Imperial models, install the balloon seal clamp.
4. On all Chrysler models, turn the adjusting bolt in a clockwise direction to place a load on the torsion bar. On all other Imperial models, turn both adjusting bolts to load both torsion bars.
5. Lower the vehicle to the floor and adjust front end height as required.

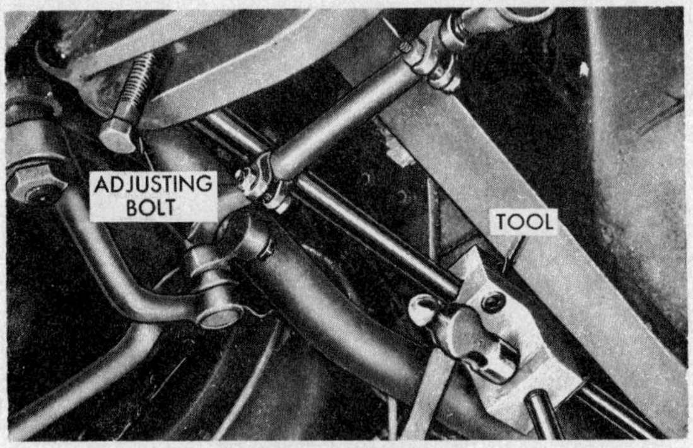
ADJUSTING
BOLT
TOOL

Removing the torsion bar
(© Chrysler Corp)

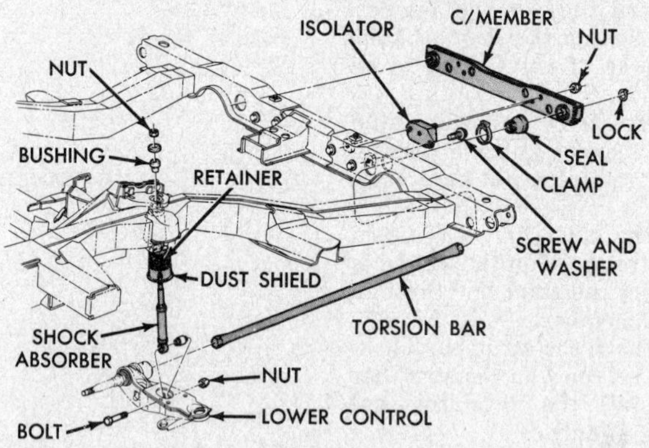
ISOLATOR
C/MEMBER
NUT
NUT
LOCK
BUSHING
SEAL
RETAINER
CLAMP
SCREW AND
WASHER
DUST SHIELD
TORSION BAR
SHOCK
ABSORBER
NUT
BOLT
LOWER CONTROL

1967-74 Imperial torsion bar
(© Chrysler Corp)

REAR SUSPENSION

All Chrysler and Imperial models use a leaf-spring rear suspension and double-acting shock absorbers. The springs are of the semi-elliptical type, with zinc interleaves between the normal leaves to increase spring life and reduce corrosion. On most models, rubber insulators are used where the springs attach to the body to reduce road noise and vibration.

Rear Shock Absorber Removal and Installation

1. Jack the vehicle under the rear axle. Position the jackstands in such a manner that the shock absorbers are under no load.
2. At the bottom mount, remove the nut and retainer securing the shock to the spring seat isolator retainer plate; remove the shock from the stud.
3. At the top mount, remove the retaining nut and washer and then remove the shock. To replace the shock absorber, reverse the removal procedure. Remember that the shock absorber mounting bolts must not be fully tightened until the full vehicle weight is resting on the wheels.

Rear Spring R & R

1. Raise the vehicle on a hoist.
2. Place jack stands under the differential and lower the vehicle until the weight is removed from the rear springs.
3. Disconnect the rear shock absorber. If so equipped, remove the sway bar.
4. Loosen and remove the U-bolt nuts and U-bolts. Remove the spring plate.
5. Loosen and remove the nuts holding the front spring hanger to the front body mounting bracket.
6. Remove the rear spring hanger bolts and let the spring drop far enough to pull the front spring hanger bolts out of the body mounting bracket.
7. Remove the front pivot bolt from the front spring hanger.
8. Loosen and remove rear shackle nuts and remove the rear shackle from the spring.
9. Remove rear spring from the vehicle.
10. Reverse above procedure to install. When installing the front

and rear pivot nuts and bolts, **do** not tighten the bolts until the vehicle has been lowered to the floor and weight is on the wheels.

BRAKES

In 1967, front wheel disc brakes were optional on some models. Disc brakes continued as optional equipment until 1973 when they became standard equipment. Information on this type of brake is in the Unit Repair Section. Starting in 1967, a compound brake system is used on all models. This system is, in effect, two independent hydraulic systems, one for the front brakes and another for the rear brakes. The master cylinder has two pistons in tandem and two fluid outlets. The front outlet tube is connected to the hydraulic system safety switch and to the rear brakes. The rear outlet tube is also connected to the safety switch and the front brakes. In the event of a pressure loss in either branch of the system, the safety switch causes a warning light to be illuminated on the instrument panel. Power brakes are available on all models. The power brake unit features a direct pedal connection to a vacuum unit mounted on the firewall with a master cylinder directly mounted to a vacuum booster.

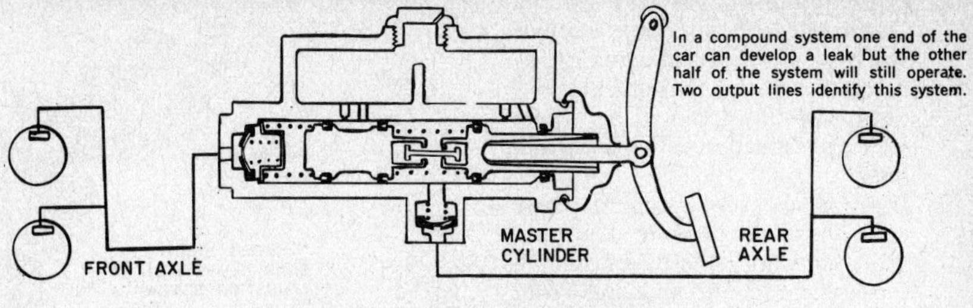
In a compound system one end of the car can develop a leak but the other half of the system will still operate. Two output lines identify this system.
FRONT AXLE
MASTER CYLINDER
REAR AXLE

Dual master cylinder, typical—1967-74
(© Chrysler Corp)

This vacuum-suspended system utilizes engine intake manifold vacuum and atmospheric pressure for its power boost to the master cylinder.

The 1974 Imperial uses rear disc brakes. The system is similar to that employed on domestic sportscars, with internal drum brake shoes for the parking brake.

NOTE: Procedures for brake shoe or pad replacement and adjustment, wheel and master cylinder overhaul, and brake bleeding can be found in the "Unit Repair Section."

Master Cylinder Removal

1. Disconnect fluid lines. On disc brake cylinders, plug brake outlets to prevent leakage.
2. Remove nuts attaching master cylinder to cowl panel or to power brake unit.

NOTE: it is not necessary to disconnect the pedal push rod as it is possible to separate the master cylinder from the rod by pulling them apart after the master cylinder attaching nuts have been removed.

3. Disconnect pedal push rod (non-power brakes) from brake pedal.
4. Remove master cylinder from vehicle.
5. Reverse procedure to install.
6. Bleed brake system.

Power Brake Booster R & R

1. Remove the nuts attaching the master cylinder to the brake booster and position the master

1. Housing assembly
2. Bleeder valve
3. Parking brake assembly with backing plate
4. Bracket assembly with cable and hose mounting
5. Caliper mounting bolts
6. Gasket
7. Hose
8. Rotor and brake disc
9. Retainer
10. Parking brake cable
11. Nut (8 required)
12. Axle
13. Axle housing
14. Lock
15. Nut

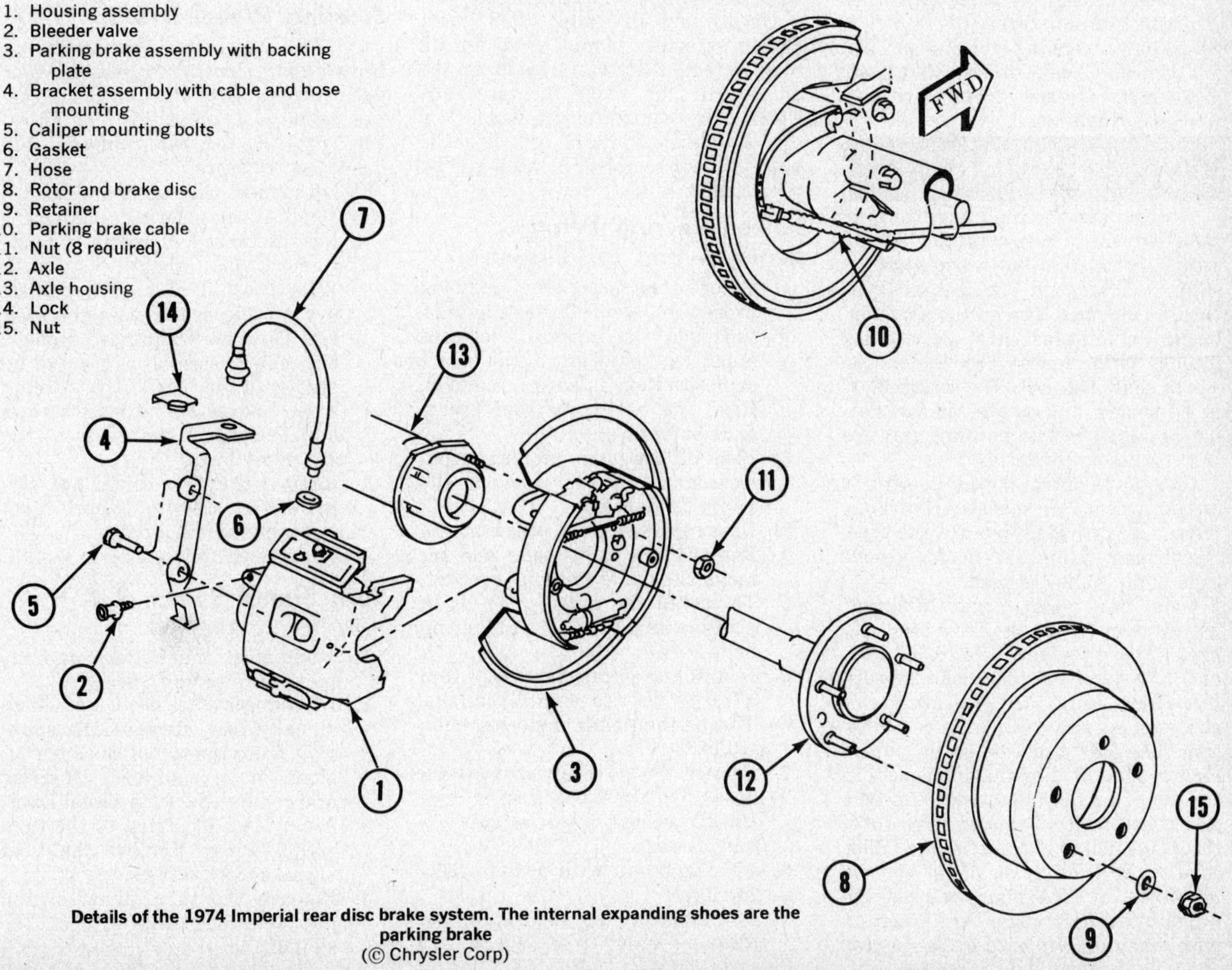
FWD
1
2
3
4
5
6
7
8
9
10
11
12
13
14
15

Details of the 1974 Imperial rear disc brake system. The internal expanding shoes are the parking brake
(© Chrysler Corp)

cylinder out of the way. If the brake lines do not have enough slack to allow the master cylinder to be moved without kinking the brake lines, it will be necessary to disconnect the brake lines.
2. Disconnect the vacuum hose from the brake booster.
3. Working under the dash, remove the attaching nut and bolt from the brake booster pushrod and disconnect the pushrod from the brake pedal. On linkage type power brake boosters, remove the lower pivot mounting bolt.
4. Remove the four nuts and washers that attach the brake booster to the interior side of the firewall.
5. Remove the booster from under the hood.
6. Reverse above procedure to install.
7. If the brake lines were disconnected, bleed the brake system.

Parking Brake Adjustment

1. Raise and support vehicle. Release parking brake lever. Loosen cable adjusting nut.
2. Tighten cable adjusting nut until a slight drag is felt while rotating wheel.
3. Loosen cable adjusting nut until both rear wheels can be rotated freely. Back off cable adjusting nut two full turns.
4. Apply parking brake several times. Check to see that rear wheels rotate freely without dragging.

STEERING

A worm and recirculating ball type steering gear is used with the manual steering system. The worm shaft is supported at each end by ball type thrust bearings. The sector shaft includes an integral sector gear which meshes with helical grooves on the worm shaft ball nut. The sector shaft is supported, and rotates, in two needle bearings in the housing and one in the housing cover.

Constant-Control power steering is an option on all models. Hydraulic power is provided by a vane-type, belt-driven pump. A double-groove type pump pulley is used.

Over the years four different power steering pumps have been utilized. These include 0.94, 0.96, 1.06, and 1.20 cu in. displacement models. Use varies with the particular vehicle, engine, and rear axle combination. The 0.94 and 1.06 cu in. pumps may be identified by the differences in the shape of the filler tube (the 0.94 pump has an oval-shaped filler tube, the 1.06 pump has a round filler tube). The 0.96 cu in. pump may be identified by the plain end of the pump driveshaft while the 1.20 cu in. pump may be identified by the hexagonal hole in the driveshaft pulley end. The 0.96 and 1.20 cu in. pumps were last installed on production models in 1968. After that date, only the 0.94 and 1.06 cu in. pumps have been used.

Some power steering pumps were equipped from the factory with oil coolers. These were used on vehicles with air conditioning, high-performance engines, and/or vehicles equipped with special axle ratios.

Up to and including 1968, most power steering pumps used an oil filter screen that was located in the oil return tube inside the reservoir. These only require service when they are completely clogged or when the pump is disassembled. Servicing is by replacement only.

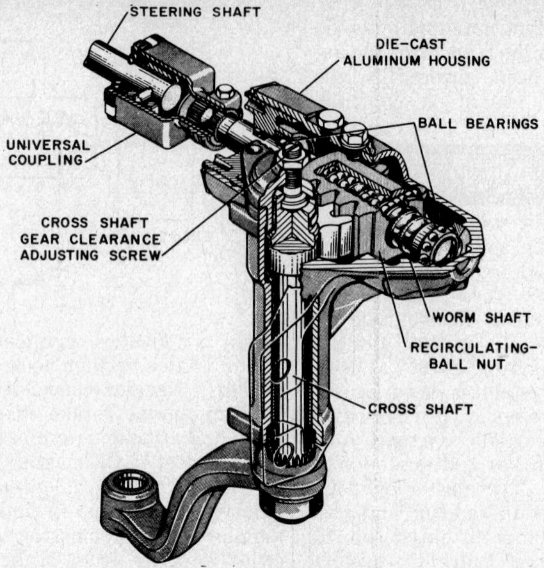
STEERING SHAFT
DIE-CAST
ALUMINUM HOUSING
BALL BEARINGS
UNIVERSAL
COUPLING
CROSS SHAFT
GEAR CLEARANCE
ADJUSTING SCREW
WORM SHAFT
RECIRCULATING-
BALL NUT
CROSS SHAFT
Manual steering gear
(© Chrysler Corp)

Power Steering Pump Removal and Installation

1. Before beginning the removal procedure, carefully take note of the exact hose routing. The hoses must be installed in the exact same position as before removal. Read the entire removal procedure before beginning.
2. Back off the pump mounting and locking bolts and remove the pump drive belt.
3. Disconnect all hoses at the pump.
4. Remove the pump bolts and remove the pump with its bracket.
5. To install the pump, place it in position and install the mounting bolts.
6. Install the pump drive belt and adjust it to specifications. Torque the pump mounting bolts to 25–30 ft lbs.
7. Connect the pressure and return hoses. On the 1.06 cu in. pump, install a new pressure-hose O-ring.
8. Fill the pump with power steering fluid.
9. Start the engine and rotate the steering wheel from stop to stop at least 10 times. This will help to bleed the system. Check the pump oil level and fill as required.
10. Torque the pump end hose fitting to 24 ft lbs, and the gear end fitting to 160 in. lbs. Be certain the hoses are at least 2 in. from the exhaust manifolds and are not kinked or twisted.

Steering Wheel R & R

NOTE: Be careful when removing the steering wheel from vehicles that are equipped with a collapsible steering column. A sharp blow or excessive pressure on the column could cause it to collapse.

1. Disconnect the battery.
2. Depress the steering wheel center assembly and rotate it counterclockwise about 1/4 turn. With the aid of a screwdriver, pry off the center assembly. On rim blow horn equipped models, the center assembly is secured by screws in the rear of the steering wheel spokes. Remove the screws and disconnect the wires to the rim blow horn.
3. Remove the large center nut. Remove the steering wheel from the column with a puller.
4. Reverse the procedure to install.

Turn Signal Switch R & R
1967-69

1. Disconnect the battery and remove the steering wheel.
2. Disconnect the horn and turn signal wires. Remove the snapring from the top of the steering shaft, if so equipped. Unscrew and remove the turn signal lever.
3. Tie a piece of string to the turn signal wires. Remove the turn signal switch screws.
4. Remove the turn signal switch retainer ring and extract the switch.

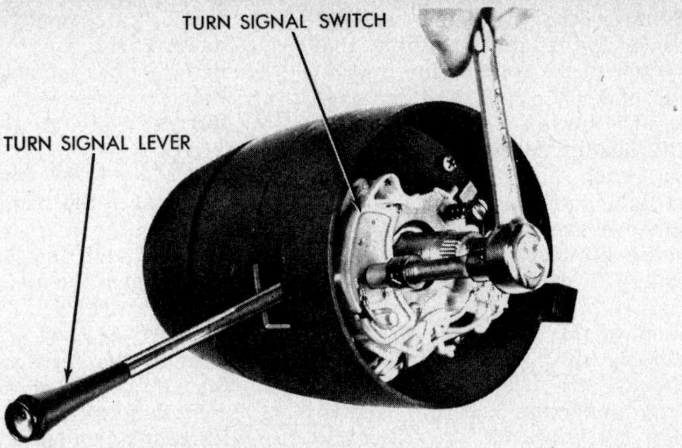
TURN SIGNAL SWITCH
TURN SIGNAL LEVER
Removing the turn signal switch
(© Chrysler Corp)

5. To install the switch, reverse the removal procedure. Transfer the string that was attached to the old switch to the new switch, and pull on the opposite end of the string to guide the wires through the column.

1970-74

1. Remove the steering wheel.
2. Remove the three screws which fasten the turn signal switch to the steering column.
3. Remove the turn signal lever.
4. Unfasten the moulded wiring connector from the turn signal switch and withdraw the switch.
5. Installation is the reverse of the removal procedure.

INSTRUMENT PANEL

Ignition Switch Replacement —1967-69

1967-69 All Models

1. Remove switch bezel nut.
2. Push switch through panel.
3. Disconnect wiring connector.
4. Remove switch.
5. To install, reverse procedure. Align key on switch with slot in panel.

Ignition Lock Cylinder Replacement—1967-69

1. Insert the ignition key into the lock cylinder.
2. Insert a piece of stiff wire into the small hole in the front face of the cylinder, and apply pressure to the wire.
3. Turn the ignition key counterclockwise toward the "acc" position.
4. Pull the lock cylinder and key from the instrument panel.
5. Insert a new lock cylinder into the instrument panel and it will lock itself in place.

Ignition Lock Cylinder and/or Ignition Switch Replacement —1970-74

1970-74 Standard Steering Column

1. Disconnect the negative battery cable. Remove the steering wheel.
2. Remove the screw that attaches the turn signal lever to the steering column.
3. Remove the three screws that attach the upper bearing retainer to the turn signal switch.
4. Pull the turn signal switch as far upward as possible.
5. Remove the upper bearing housing snap-ring from the steering shaft with snap-ring pliers.
6. Remove the screw that attaches the ignition key light assembly to the upper bearing housing.
7. Being careful not to damage any components, pry the upper bearing housing off the steering shaft by lifting upward on alternate sides of the bearing housing with screwdrivers.
8. Lift upward on the steering shaft lockplate and place a screwdriver, or a substitute under it to hold it in the raised position. If this operation does not provide adequate working room beneath the lockplate, it will be necessary to press out the pin that attaches the lockplate to the steering shaft and remove the lockplate from the steering shaft. If the ignition switch is being replaced the lockplate must be removed.
9. Using an offset screwdriver, remove the two screws that attach the lock lever guide plate to the steering column.
10. With the ignition lock cylinder in the "lock" position and the ignition key removed, insert a stiff wire into the lock cylinder release hole in the steering column. Push in on the wire to release the spring-loaded lock retainer and pull the lock cylinder out from the steering column.
11. If the ignition switch is being replaced, remove the two screws that attach the ignition key buzzer switch to the steering column and the three screws that attach the ignition switch to the steering column. Lift the ignition switch out of the housing.
12. Reverse the above procedure for installation.

1970-74 Tilt Steering Column

1. Disconnect the negative battery cable.
2. Remove the steering wheel.
3. Remove the three attaching screws and remove the shaft lock cover.
4. Remove the screws that attach the tilt control lever and the turn signal lever to the steering column and remove the levers.
5. Push the hazard warning knob in and unscrew the knob from the turn signal switch. Remove the ignition key lamp assembly.
6. Using a suitable tool, repress the lockplate to gain access to the lockplate retaining snap-ring. Remove the snap-ring from the steering shaft.
7. Remove the lockplate, cancelling cam, and spring.
8. Remove the three turn signal switch attaching screws, place the shift lever in the low (1) position, and pull the switch and wires as far upward as possible.
9. With the ignition lock cylinder in the "lock" position, insert a small screwdriver into the lock release slot in the housing cover.
10. Press down with the screwdriver to release the spring latch at the bottom of the slot and pull the lock cylinder from the housing. The following steps are for ignition switch replacement only.
11. Remove the three screws that attach the upper steering column housing to the steering column and remove the housing.
12. Install the column tilt control lever and move the column to the full "up" position.
13. Insert a screwdriver into the slot in the spring retainer and press the retainer in approximately 3/16 in. Turn the retainer approximately 1/8 turn to the left until the ears align with the grooves in the housing. Remove the spring retainer, spring, and guide.
14. Push the steering shaft inward to enable removal of the inner race and seat. Remove the race and seat.
15. Make sure the ignition switch is in the "lock" position, then remove the wire connector from the ignition switch and remove the screws that attach the ignition switch to the outside of the steering column.

16. Lift the ignition switch from the column and twist it to disengage the switch actuating rod from the rack. Remove the switch.
17. To install the ignition lock cylinder, insert the cylinder into the housing with the cylinder in the lock position and the key *removed.*
18. Move the cylinder into the housing until it contacts the switch actuator. Move the switch actuator rod up and down to align the parts. When the parts are aligned the cylinder will move inward, where it will snap and lock into position.
19. With the ignition switch in the "lock" position insert the actuating rod into the steering column.
20. Twist the switch and rod assembly as required to engage the actuating rod with the rack. Make sure the ignition lock cylinder is in the lock position.
21. Install the ignition switch mounting screws but do not tighten them.
22. Move the ignition switch downward, away from the steering wheel, and tighten the switch mounting screws. Make sure the ignition switch has not moved out of the "lock" detent.
23. Attach the switch wiring connector.

Headlight Switch Replacement

1967-68 All Models

1. Remove the instrument cluster bezel.
2. Remove headlamp switch from rear of bezel.
3. Install in reverse of above.

1969-70 All Models

1. Remove instrument cluster.
2. Remove headlamp switch from rear of cluster.
3. Install in reverse of above.

Chilton's TIME SAVER

Although the Chrysler service literature calls for the removal of the instrument cluster to remove the headlight switch, the switch may be removed with the cluster in place. Working from under the instrument panel, remove the wires from the switch. Remove the switch retaining screws using a stubby screwdriver. Remove the switch from the panel.

1971-74 All Models

1. Disconnect the battery. If equipped with air conditioning, remove the left air conditioning duct.
2. Remove the headlight switch shaft and knob by pulling the switch to the On position, reaching under the dash, and depressing the button on the bottom of the headlight switch case. Pull the knob and shaft from the switch.
3. Remove the sentinel and automatic dimmer control knobs if equipped with automatic headlight dimmer.
4. Remove the headlight switch attaching nut.
5. Remove the headlight switch from under the dash and disconnect the wires.
6. Reverse above procedure to install.

WINDSHIELD WIPERS

Wiper Motor Removal and Installation

1967-68 All Models

1. Disconnect battery ground cable.
2. Remove wiper arm and blade assemblies.
3. Remove windshield lower moulding.
4. Remove cowl grille panel.
5. Remove drive crank arm retaining nut and drive crank. Disconnect motor wiring.
6. Remove three nuts mounting motor to bulkhead and remove motor.
7. Reverse procedure to install.

1969-70 All Models

1. Disconnect battery ground cable.
2. Lift the wiper arm and insert a .090 pin or drill. Pull wiper arm from shaft with a rocking motion.
3. Remove windshield lower moulding.
4. Remove cowl screen.
5. Remove drive crank arm retaining nut and drive crank. To prevent damage to the gears, hold the crank arm nut with a wrench when removing the crank arm from the motor. Disconnect motor wiring.
6. Remove three mounting nuts. Remove motor.
7. Reverse procedure to install.

1971-74 All Models

1. Disconnect the negative battery cable.
2. Lift the latch on each wiper arm and remove the arms and blades as an assembly.
3. Remove the cowl screen.
4. Remove the drive crank retaining nut and drive crank. To prevent damage to the gears, hold the crank arm nut with a wrench when removing the crank arm from the motor. Disconnect motor wiring.
5. Disconnect the lead wires from the wiper motor.
6. Remove the three wiper motor mounting bolts and remove the motor from the vehicle.
7. Reverse above procedure to install. When installing the wiper arms and blades, make sure the wiper motor is in the Park position.

Wiper Transmission

1967-68 All Models

1. Remove the wiper arm and blade assemblies.
2. Remove the lower windshield moulding.
3. Remove the cowl grille.
4. Remove the nut or clip that attaches the crank arm to the wiper motor output pin.
5. Remove the clip, felt and brass washer from the right pivot and remove the connecting link from the right pivot.
6. Remove the bolts that attach the left pivot to the body of the vehicle.
7. Remove the links and left pivot from the vehicle through the cowl opening.
8. Reverse above procedure to install.

1969-74 All Models

1. Disconnect the battery. Insert a

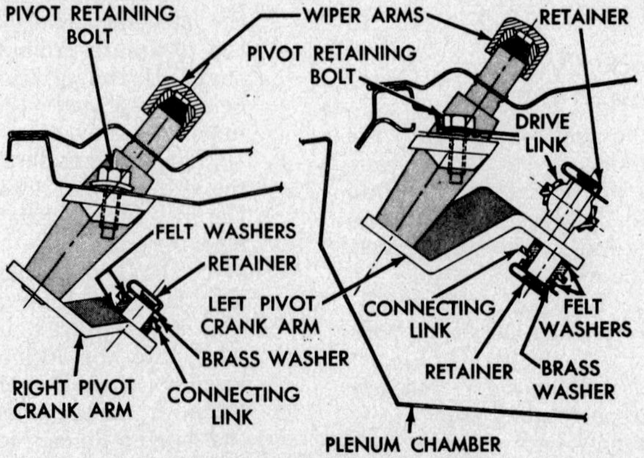
PIVOT RETAINING BOLT
WIPER ARMS
RETAINER
PIVOT RETAINING BOLT
DRIVE LINK
FELT WASHERS
RETAINER
LEFT PIVOT CRANK ARM
BRASS WASHER
CONNECTING LINK
FELT WASHERS
RETAINER
BRASS WASHER
RIGHT PIVOT CRANK ARM
CONNECTING LINK
PLENUM CHAMBER
1968 Chrysler windshield wiper pivots
(© Chrysler Corp)

0.090 in. pin in the base of each wiper arm and remove the arm and blade assemblies from the wiper pivots.
2. On 1969 models, remove the windshield lower moulding.
3. Remove the cowl screen.
4. Remove the crank arm retaining nut and crank arm from the wiper motor. To prevent stressing the gears, hold the motor crank with a wrench while removing the crank arm nut.
5. Remove the bolts that attach the right and left pivots to the body of the vehicle.
6. Remove the links and pivots as an assembly through the cowl opening.
7. Reverse above procedure to install.

RADIO

Removal and Installation

1967-68 Imperial

1. Disconnect battery ground cable.
2. Remove air conditioning duct and hoses.
3. Disconnect heater blower motor wire connectors from resistor.
4. Disconnect radio wiring.
5. Remove radio support bracket.
6. Remove radio knobs and mounting nuts. Slide radio down and to the right. Rotate front of radio up and remove.
7. Reverse procedure to install.

1967 Chrysler

1. Disconnect battery ground cable.
2. Remove ash tray and housing.
3. Remove air conditioning ducts and hoses.
4. Remove bezels next to map light.
5. Remove two upper radio bezel screws now exposed and remove screw in lower center edge of bezel.
6. Disconnect antenna cable. Remove radio mounting screws from instrument panel.
7. Remove support bracket screw at lower lip of instrument panel and loosen nut on mounting stud at back of radio.
8. Rotate rear edge of radio out and down enough to disconnect speaker and feed wires. Remove radio.
9. Reverse procedure to install.

1968 Chrysler Without Air Conditioning

1. Disconnect battery ground cable.
2. Remove ash tray. Lower ash tray housing. Disconnect two ash tray lights and remove housing.
3. Remove heater temperature control knob.
4. Remove blower switch connector.
5. Remove heater control plate attaching nuts and drop controls down to ash tray opening.
6. Disconnect electrical connector, tions, vacuum switch connector, and bowden cable.
7. Remove heater controls through ash tray opening.
8. Remove fader cover plate and reverberator cover plate.
9. Open glove compartment and remove center bezel (three screws).
10. Remove radio mounting nuts.
11. Remove radio mounting bracket.
12. Disconnect radio wiring.
13. Tilt radio toward instrument panel and slightly toward right to disconnect stereo plug, if so equipped. Remove radio through ash tray opening.
14. Reverse procedure to install.

1968 Chrysler Models with Air Conditioning

1. Disconnect the battery. Remove the ash tray by disconnecting the lighter wires and pushing up on two spring clips located on the ash tray bottom.
2. The Auto-Temp controls must be removed. To remove the ash tray receiver housing, remove its six mounting screws and lower the housing slightly. Disconnect the two ash tray lights and remove the housing from the panel.
3. Remove the knob from the temperature control arm and the two mounting nuts securing the control to the panel. Remove the panel through the ash tray opening.
4. Disconnect the vacuum and electrical connections from the controls; secure the controls and connections out of the way.
5. Remove the radio knobs and their mounting nuts.
6. Remove both the upper left and right stereo switch assemblies (if so equipped).
7. Remove the center bezel by removing the two mounting screws at the upper left and right corners and one screw from the lower center. Open the glove box door and move the center bezel far enough over so that the center air outlet duct can be disconnected; remove the bezel from the panel.
8. Take out the two radio panel screws.
9. At the back of the radio, disconnect the radio mounting bracket and swing it toward the glove box.
10. Working through the ash tray opening, disconnect all radio and antenna electrical leads.
11. Remove the radio by tilting it toward the dash panel and to the right. Remove the radio through the ash tray opening.
12. To install the radio and Auto-Temp controls, reverse the removal procedure.

1969-74 All Models

1. Disconnect battery ground cable.
2. Remove left ash tray.
3. On all except 1972 to 1974 models, remove the steering column cover.
4. Unscrew stereo tape reset knob, if so equipped.
5. Disconnect radio wiring.
6. Move defroster vacuum actuator to facilitate radio removal.
7. Remove two radio mounting screws through access openings in lower instrument panel. On search-tune and AM radios, remove knobs, bezels, and nuts.
8. Remove radio support bracket (if so equipped) mounting screw from lower reinforcement. Support radio.
9. Remove radio support bracket or mounting screws through the access openings in the lower instrument panel. Remove radio from under instrument panel.
10. Reverse procedure to install.

HEATER SYSTEM

Heater Blower R & R—Non-Air Conditioned Models

1967-68 All Models

1. Disconnect battery ground cable.
2. Disconnect water hoses at dash panel (engine side). Plug heater hose fittings to prevent spilling water in passenger area.
3. Under instrument panel, remove bracket from top of heater to dash.
4. Remove defroster hoses at heater, and disconnect vacuum lines at heater.
5. Disconnect wiring at heater blower motor resistor.
6. Remove glove compartment.
7. Disconnect control cable at heater end.
8. Unclamp flexible connector at right end of heater. Do not remove connector from cowl side.
9. Pull carpet or mat from under instrument panel.
10. From engine compartment, remove nuts mounting the assembly to the instrument panel.
11. Pull heater toward rear to clear mounting studs from dash. Rotate heater assembly until studs are down, then remove heater.
12. Disconnect wiring from heater assembly to blower motor.
13. Remove motor cooler tube.
14. Remove heater back plate.
15. Remove fan from motor shaft.
16. Remove blower motor from back plate.
17. Install in reverse of above.

1969-74 All Models

The blower motor is mounted to

the engine side housing under the right front fender between the inner fender shield and the fender. The inner fender shield must be removed to service the blower motor.

Heater Core R & R—Non-Air Conditioned Models

1967-68 All Models

1. Follow Steps 1 through 11 under Heater Blower R&R, 1967-68 All Models.
2. Remove heater cover plate.
3. Remove screws attaching heater core to heater, and remove core.
4. Install in reverse of above.

1969-74 All Models

1. Disconnect battery ground cable. Drain coolant.
2. Disconnect heater hoses and plug fittings.
3. Slide front seat back. Unplug antenna from radio.
4. Remove vacuum hoses from trunk lock, if so equipped.
5. Disconnect blower motor resistor block.
6. Remove vacuum hoses from defroster actuator and heater shut off door actuator.
7. Swing support bracket up out of the way.
8. Remove four retaining nuts from studs on engine side housing.
9. Remove locating bolt from bottom center of passenger side housing.
10. Roll or tip housing out from under instrument panel.
11. Remove temperature control cable retaining clip and cable from heat shut off door crank.
12. From inside housing, remove two retaining nuts from right side of heater core and four screws from outside of housing.
13. Remove core tube locating metal screw from top of housing.
14. Carefully pull heater core out of housing.
15. Reverse procedure to install.

Blower Motor Removal—Air Conditioned Models

1967-74 All Models

1. For all 1967-68 models, blower motor service is performed from the engine compartment. For all 1969-74 models, the blower motor is mounted on the engine side housing, under the right front fender, between the inner fender shield and the fender. To service the motor, it is necessary to remove the inner fender panel by extracting its securing bolts. If the vehicle is equipped with a power antenna, it is necessary to disconnect it before the inner fender panel is removed.
2. For all models, disconnect the battery and feed wires and remove the air tube (if so equipped). Remove its mounting bolts and remove the blower assembly.
3. Installation is the reverse of the above.

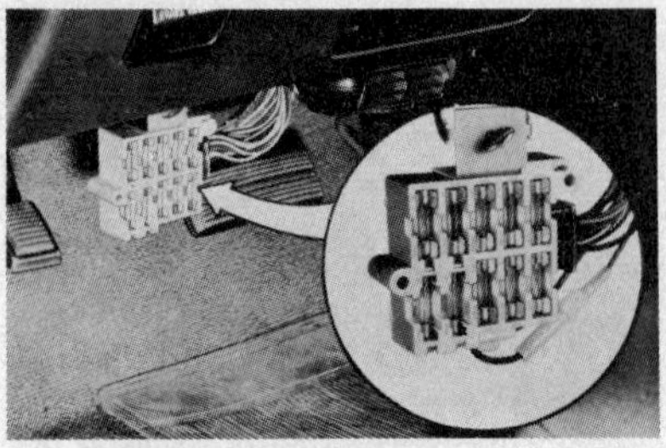

Fold-down fuse panel, used on all full-size models beginning 1974
(© Chrysler Corp)

Heater Core Removal—Air Conditioned Models

1967-68 Chrysler Models and 1967-68 Imperial

1. The heater core is positioned behind a separate cover forward of the instrument panel and attached to the evaporator case.
2. Disconnect the battery and drain the cooling system. Remove the air cleaner and disconnect the heater hoses.
3. Remove the glove box, the distribution housing, and the heater core intake and outlet tube assembly. Remove the fresh air recirculating air intake hose.
4. Disconnect the floor air actuator rod from its linkage. Disconnect the vacuum hoses from the actuator and remove the fresh air recirculating door housing assembly.
5. Disconnect the defroster hoses and remove the electrical connections from the bypass switch and the resistor block.
6. Take out the screws securing the water bypass valve to the heater cover. Remove the operating link attaching screw.
7. Remove the air conditioning door actuator from its mounting bracket with its support braces.
8. Remove the retainer spring clips and the screws attaching the cover to the case.
9. Remove the heater core and cover by pulling the lower edge rearward; lift the assembly 3/8 in. to release the cover lip from the case, and carefully lower the assembly to the right side.
10. To begin the installation procedure, install the water bypass valve with its linkage to the heater core. Use a new O-ring on the intake and outlet tubes.
11. Install the heater core in the evaporator case. Install the cover by hooking its lip on the evaporator case and rolling it down and into position. Secure the cover by replacing its spring clips and screws.
12. Install the water bypass valve to the heater cover; install the operating link to the air conditioning door.
13. Replace the air conditioning door actuator with its vacuum hoses. (The hose with the red stripe must be on the rod side.) Replace the support braces.
14. Connect all electrical leads to the resistor block and bypass switch.
15. This step applies to 1967 models only. The electrical bypass switch-operating arm must be adjusted to provide 0.020-0.060 in. operating clearance between the operating arm and the actuator rod. Do this by turning the threaded adjuster to obtain the desired clearance.
16. Replace the vacuum hoses to the floor air actuator and the fresh air recirculating actuator. The hose with the red stripe must be on the rod side. Install the floor air actuator rod to its linkage by replacing the retaining clip.
17. Connect the fresh air recirculating air intake hose.
18. Place a few drops of clean water on the heater core intake and outlet tube assembly O-rings and then install the assembly into position.
19. Replace the temperature control valve capillary tube in the heater core cover.
20. With the air conditioning door open about 1 in., replace the distribution housing.
21. From this point, reverse the removal procedure.

1969-74 Chrysler and Imperial

1. The heater core is located in the front cover of the passenger side housing. The air conditioning system need not be discharged to remove the heater core.
2. Disconnect the battery and drain the cooling system. Remove the air cleaner and disconnect the heater hoses. Plug the heater core tubes to prevent fluid loss.
3. Remove the left spot cooler duct and the steering column cover. On 1972 models, remove the linkage shield.
4. Disconnect the two actuator rods at the linkage on the left side of the housing. Remove the two cover retaining screws.
5. Remove the heat distribution duct securing screws, the duct, and the now-exposed screws in the bottom lip of the front cover.
6. Remove the glove box and the center spot cooler duct; also the right spot cooler duct and the air distribution housing.
7. Working in the glove box opening, remove the top and right side retaining screws from the housing. On vehicles with Auto-

Temp, remove the aspirator tube from its clip before performing the above.

8. Disconnect all electrical leads at the resistor block. Remove the vacuum hoses from the recirculating housing actuator. On cars with Auto-Temp, remove the wires from the plastic strips and metal clip; remove the amplifier, master, and compressor switches.
9. Remove the nut from the housing end of the support bracket. Swing the bracket upward and out of the way, and carefully roll the heater core and front cover out from beneath the instrument panel. On 1972 models, remove the core from the housing by cutting the adhesive away, grasping it at the top, and pulling it from the housing.
10. (This step applies to 1969–71 models only.) To begin the installation procedure, install the heater core in the front cover and place the core and cover on the evaporator housing. Hold the front cover in position and swing the support bracket down over the stud on the front cover face. Install its retaining nut.
11. This step applies to 1972-74 models only. To begin the installation procedure, remove the condensate seal from the heater core flange and cement a new seal in position. Install the heater core in the rear housing and secure with a screw at either end. Install the core and rear housing to the front housing. Hold the rear housing in position and swing the support bracket down and over the stud on the rear housing face; install its retaining nut.
12. Working through the glove box opening, install the housing top retaining screws and the screws at the right side of the front cover (1969–71) or the screws at the right side of the rear housing (1972-74).
13. Working beneath the instrument panel, replace all the screws securing the housings together. On 1972-74 models, install the two screws on the left side of the rear housing. (On these models, it is not necessary to reinstall the linkage shield.)
14. Install the heat distribution duct to the bottom of the housing.
15. Connect the actuator rods.
16. Connect all of the vacuum hoses to the actuators; install all electrical connections to the resistor block. On cars with Auto-Temp, secure the wires with the plastic straps and metal clip. Install the aspirator tube in the clip.
17. Working through the glove box opening, replace the air distribution housing, the center spot cooler duct, and the right spot cooler duct.
18. Install the steering column cover and the left spot cooler duct. Replace the glove box assembly. On Auto-Temp equipped vehicles, install the amplifier, master, and compressor switches.
19. From this point, reverse the removal procedure.

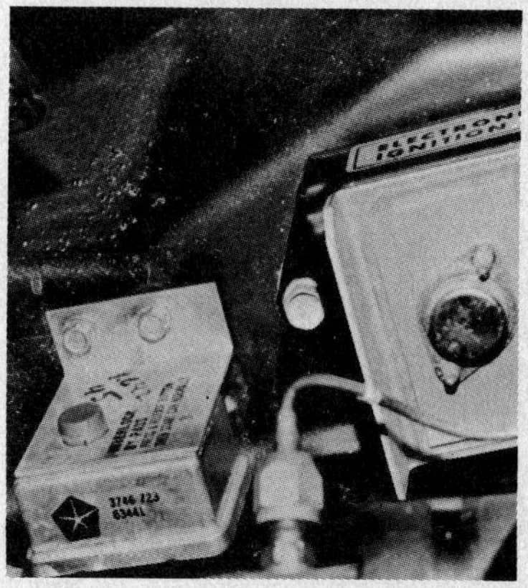

Seat belt interlock override switch; pushing the switch button will permit the car to be started once for servicing purposes, without an occupant using the seat restraint system
(© Chrysler Corp)

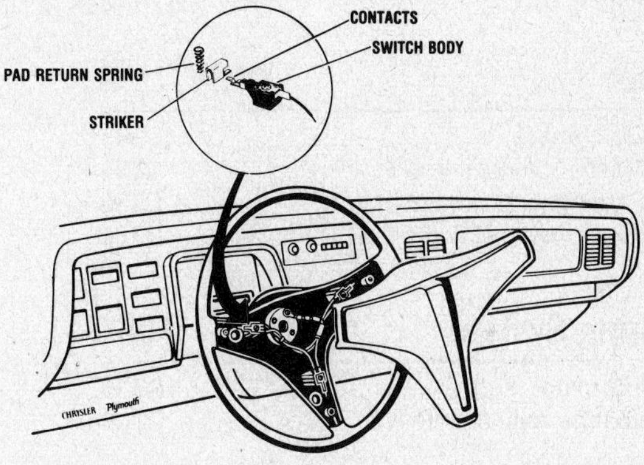
CONTACTS
SWITCH BODY
PAD RETURN SPRING
STRIKER

Horn switch, used on all full-size Chrysler products beginning 1974
(© Chrysler Corp)

INDEX

Dodge · Plymouth

MODEL IDENTIFICATION

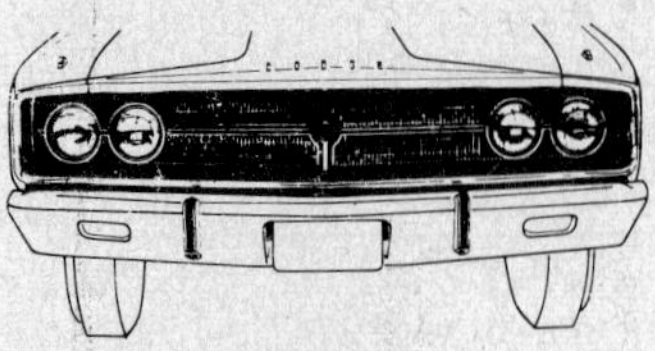
1967 Coronet

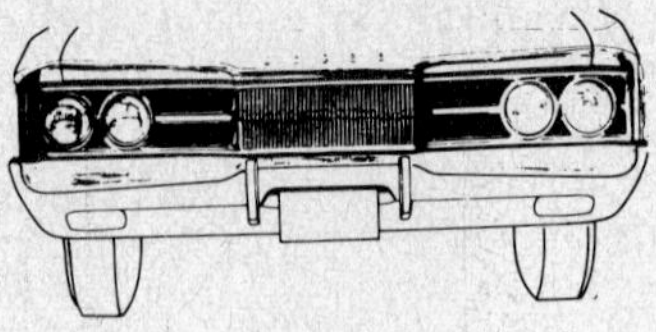
1967 Polara

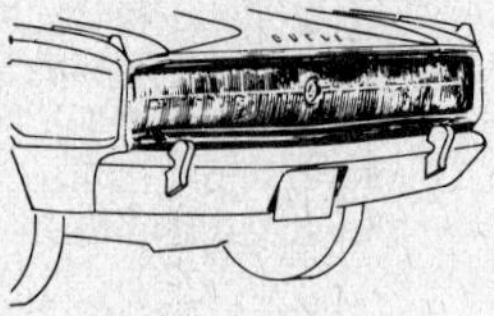
1967 Charger

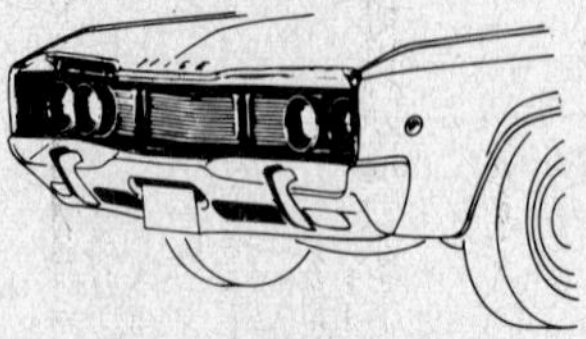
1968 Polara

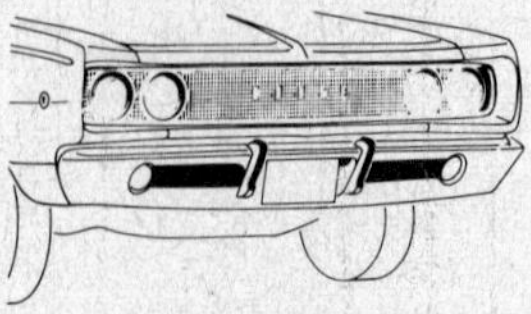
1968 Coronet

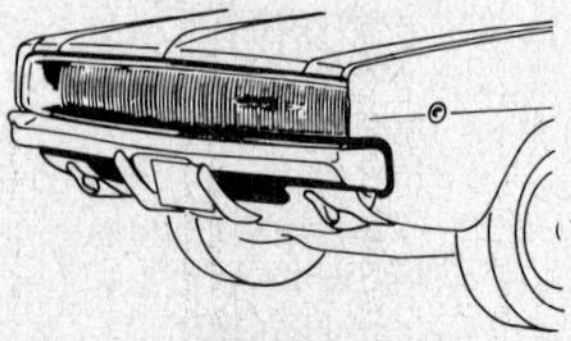
1968 Charger

1969 Polara

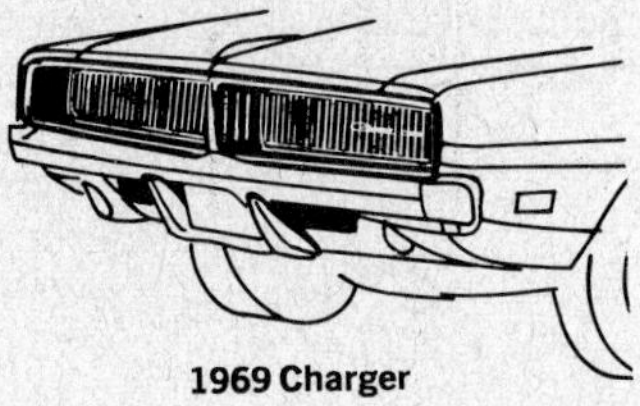
1969 Charger

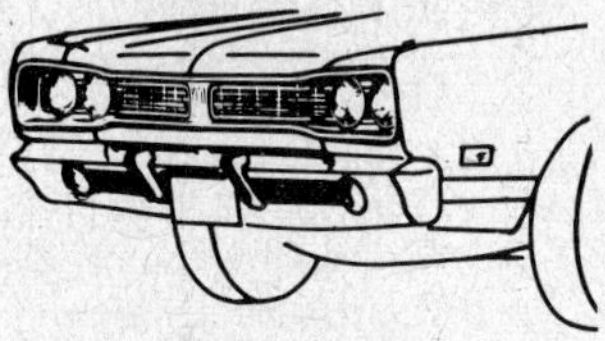
1969 Coronet

1970 Coronet 500

1970 Polara

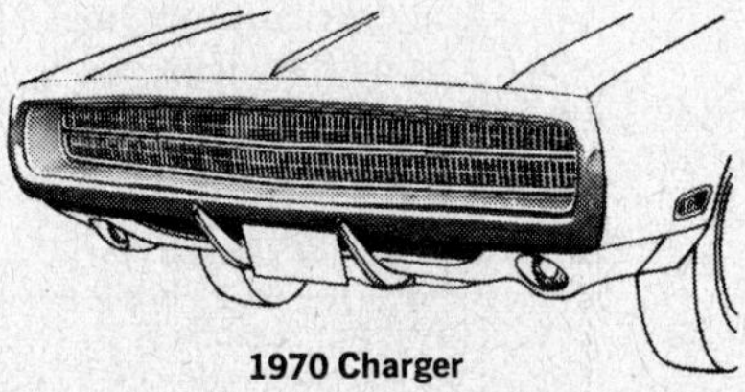
1970 Charger

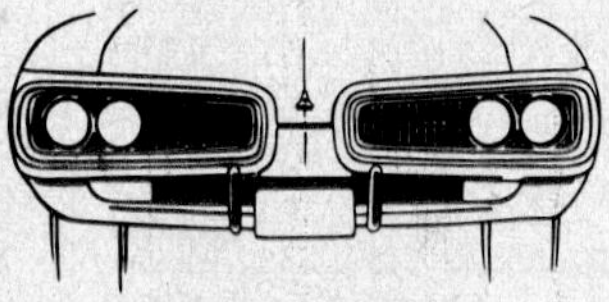
1970 Coronet 440

1971 Coronet

1971 Charger

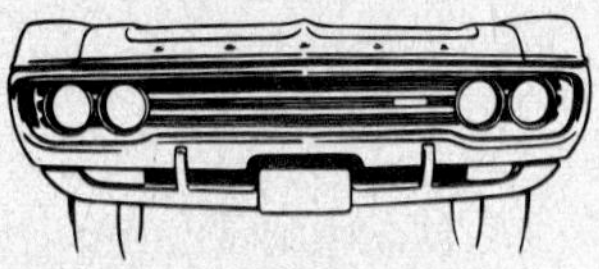
1971 Polara

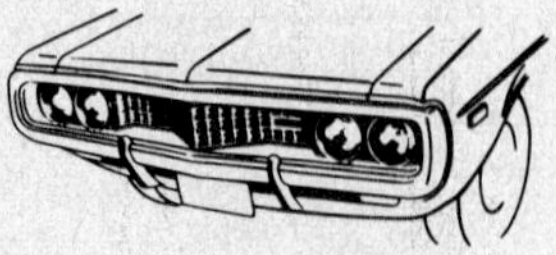
1972 Coronet

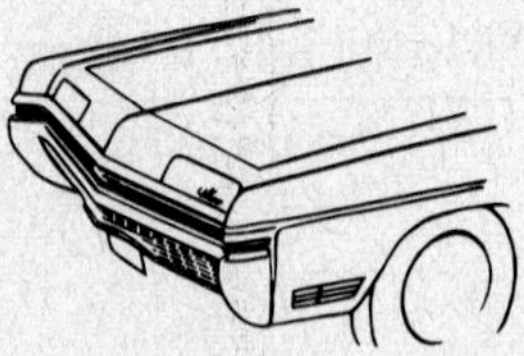
1972 Monaco

1972 Charger

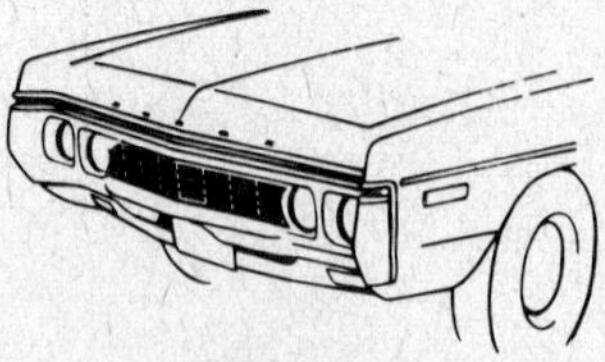
1972 Polara

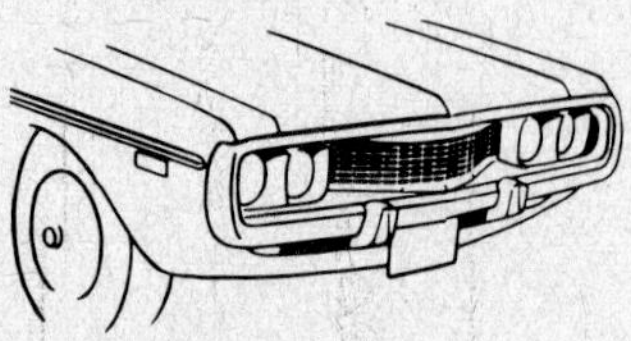
1973 Coronet

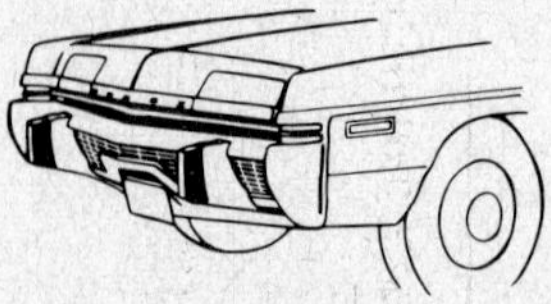
1973 Monaco

1973 Charger

1973 Polara

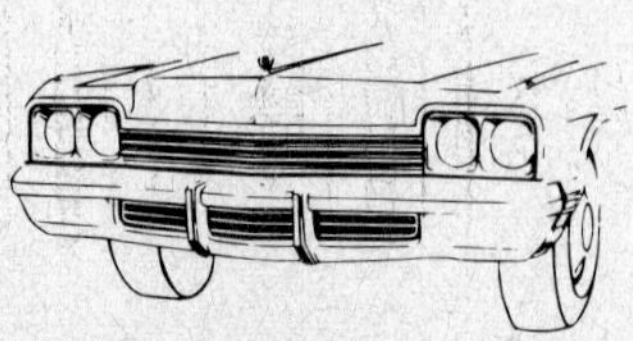
1974 Monaco

1974 Charger

MODEL IDENTIFICATION

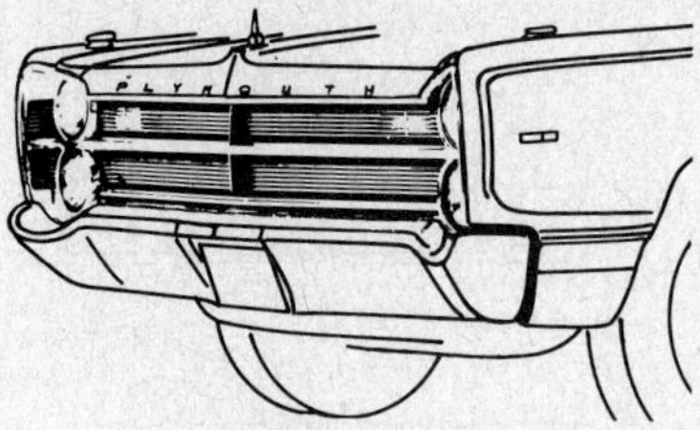

1967 Fury

1967

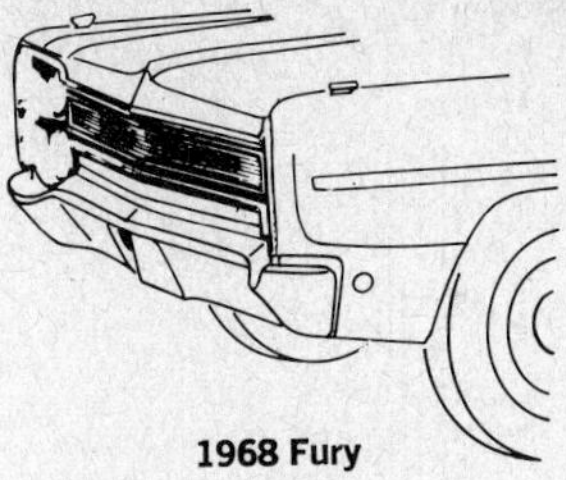

1968 Fury

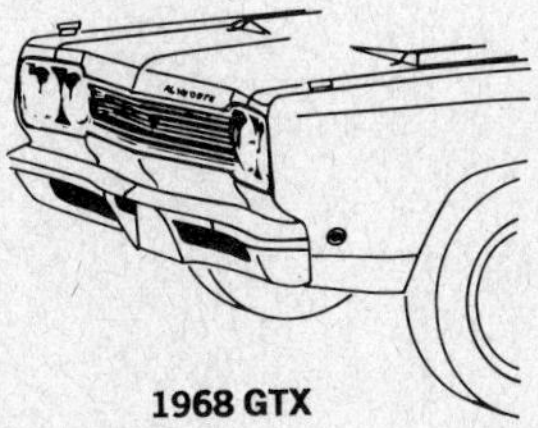

1968 GTX

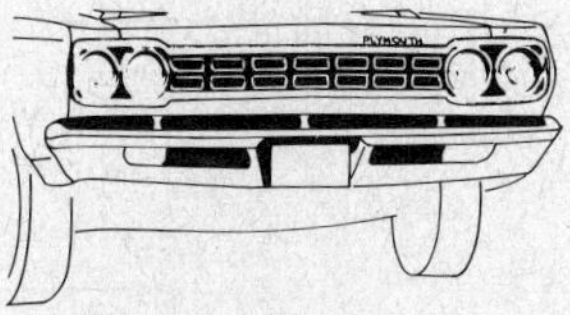

1968 Road Runner

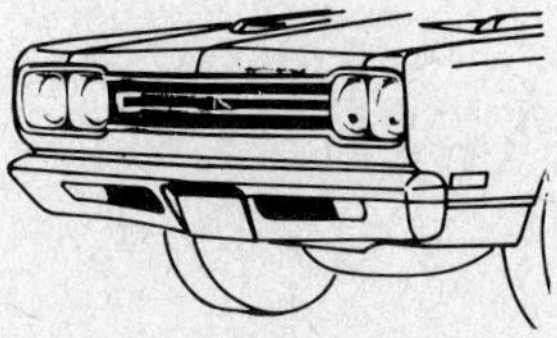

1969

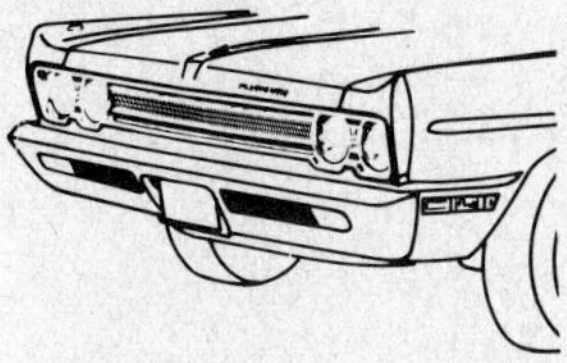

1969 Fury

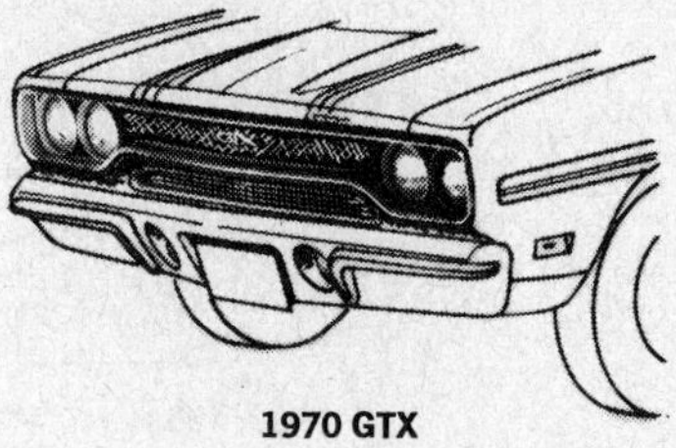

1970 GTX

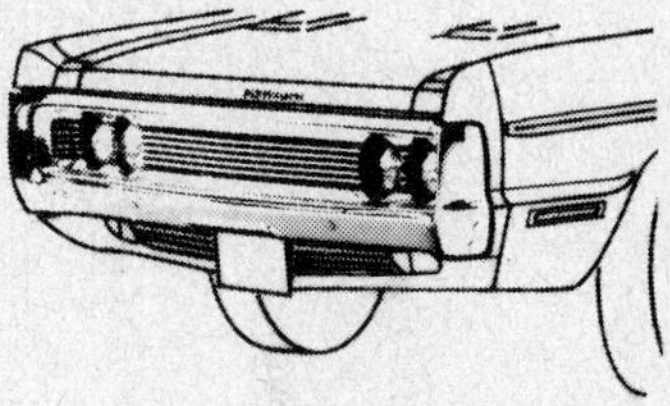

1970 Fury

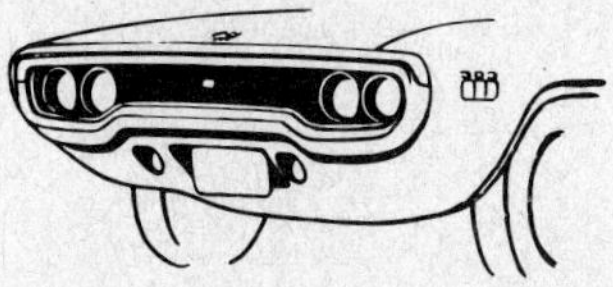

1971 Sebring

1971 Road Runner

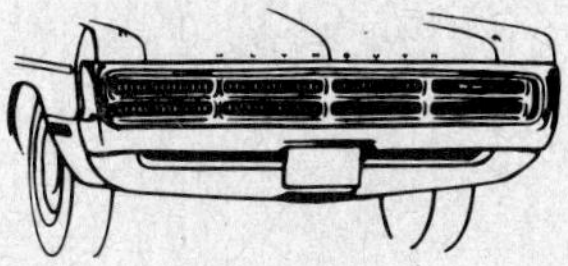

1971 Fury

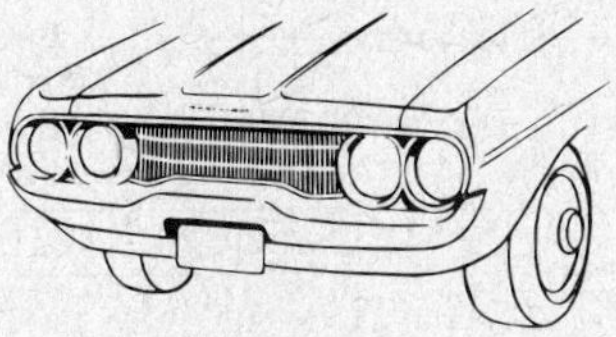

1972 Satellite

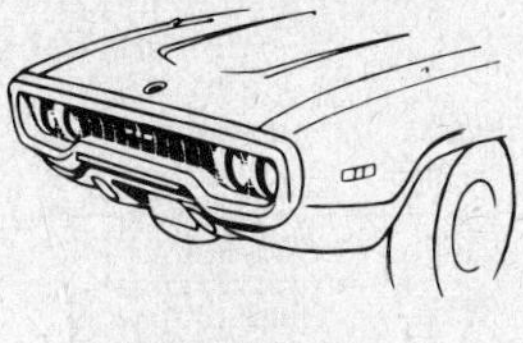

1972 Sebring

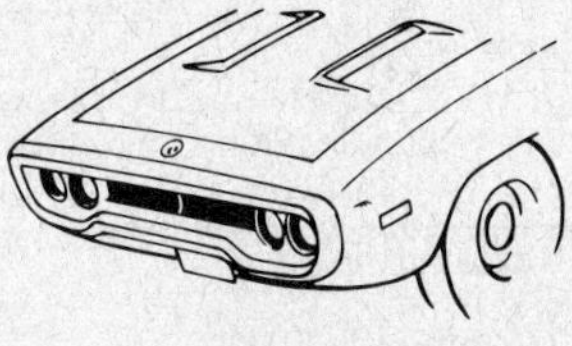

1972 Road Runner

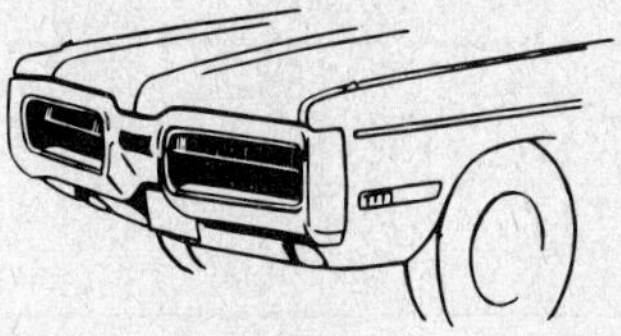

1972 Fury

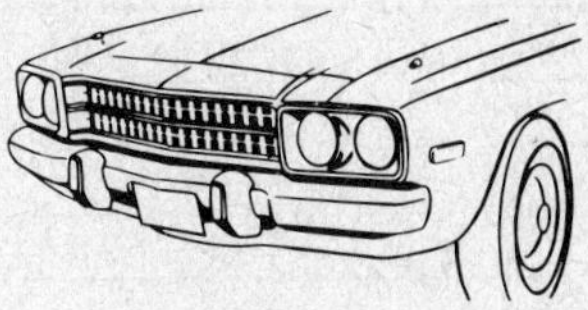

1973 Satellite

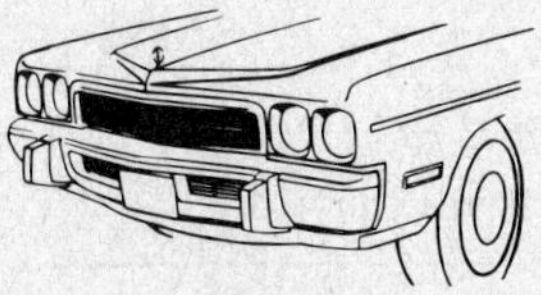

1973 Fury

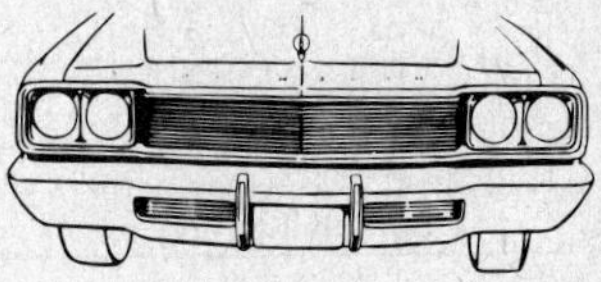

1974 Fury

CAR SERIAL NUMBER LOCATION

1967

Plate on left front door hinge post.

1968-74

Top of instrument panel, visible through windshield.

FIRING ORDER

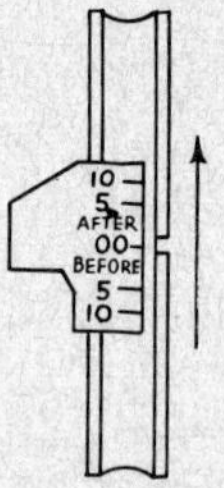
10
5
AFTER
00
BEFORE
5
10

Timing marks—6 cylinder
(© Chrysler Corp)

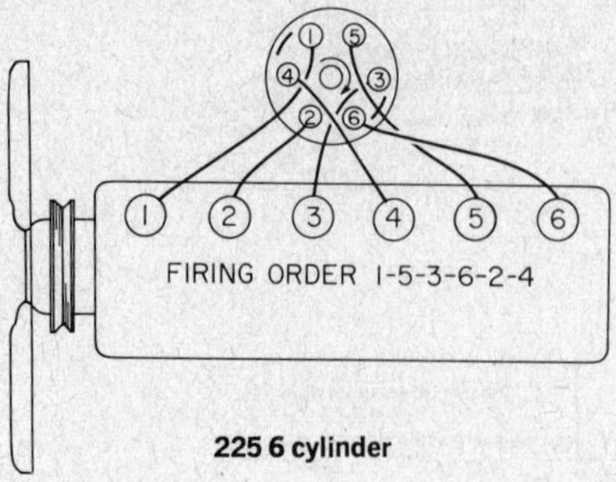
FIRING ORDER 1-5-3-6-2-4

225 6 cylinder

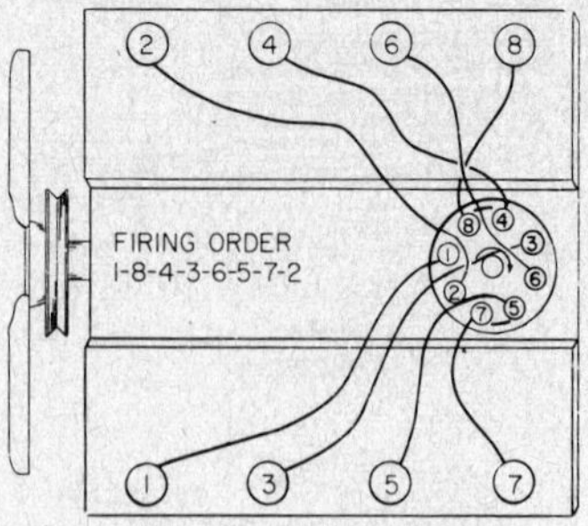
FIRING ORDER
1-8-4-3-6-5-7-2

273, 318, 340, 360 cu. in. V8

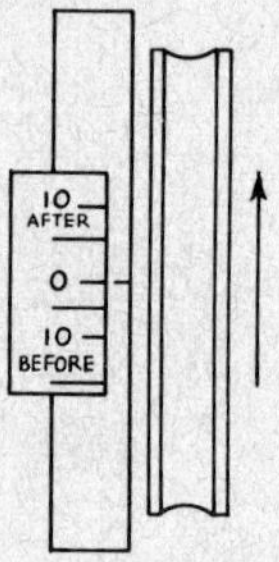
10
AFTER
0
10
BEFORE

Timing marks—1967-74 V8
(© Chrysler Corp)

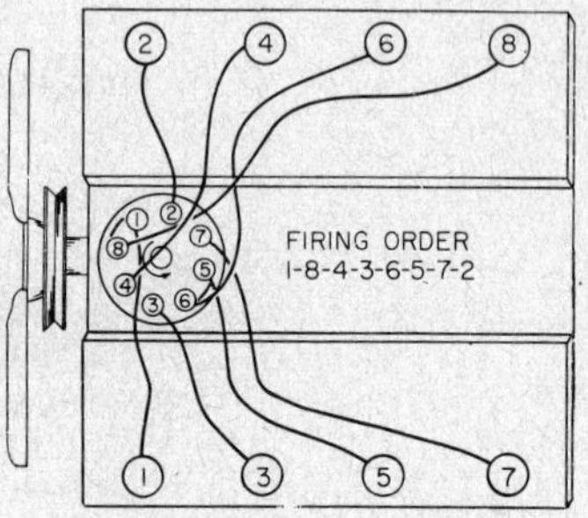
FIRING ORDER
1-8-4-3-6-5-7-2

383, 426 Hemi, 400, 440 cu. in. with Chrysler distributor (No. 1 one space CW for Autolite and Prestolite distributors)

BATTERY AND STARTER SPECIFICATIONS

		BATTERY			STARTER						
					Lock Test			No-Load Test			
Year	Engine Displacement (cu in.)	Ampere Hour Capacity	Volts	Terminal Grounded	Amps	Volts	Torque (ft lbs)	Amps	Volts	RPM	Brush Spring Tension (oz)
'67-'69	6-225, 8-318, 273	48	12	Neg.	400-450	4	—	90	11	1,925-2,600①	32-36
	8-361	59	12	Neg.	400-450	4	—	90	11	1,925-2,600①	32-36
	8-383, 426, 440	70	12	Neg.	400-450	4	—	90	11	1,925-2,600	32-36
	Opt. all others										
	8-426	70	12	Neg.	310-445	4	—	78	11	3,800	32-36
'70-'74	6-225, 8-318, 340	46	12	Neg.	400-450	4	—	90	11	1,925-2,600	32-36
	8-360, 383, 400	59②	12	Neg.	400-450	4	—	90	11	1,925-2,600	32-36
	8-426, 440	70	12	Neg.	400-450	4	—	90	11	1,925-2,600	32-36
	Opt. all others										

① 1,925-2,400 rpm, '66
② 55 amps for '72 8-360, 8-400

ENGINE CODE

Dodge, Plymouth

The engine code designation is the 5th digit of the vehicle identification number (V.I.N.). The V.I.N. is stamped on a plate located at the left front door hinge pillar on 1967 models, located at the left side of the instrument panel visible through the windshield on 1968-74 models, and located to the rear of the right engine mount on the oil pan rail on 1969-74 models.

Disp	Bbl	Hp	'67	'68	'69	'70	'71	'72	'73	'74
6-Cylinder Models										
225	1	105 (net)							C	
225	1	110 (net)						C		
225	1	145	B	B	B	C	C			
8-Cylinder Models										
273	2	180	D	D						
318	2	150, 170 (net)*						G	G	
318	2	230	F	F	F	G	G			
340	4	240 (net)						H	H	
340	4	275					H			
383	2	270	G							
383	2	275					L			
383	2	290		G	G	L				
383	4	300					N			
383	4	325	H							
383	4	330		H	H	L				
383	4	335		H	H	N				
400	2	190 (net)						M		
400	2	175 (net)							M	
400	4	255 (net)④						P		
400	4	260 (net)							P	
426	8	425	J	J	J	R	R			
440	4	275, 280 (net)*							U	
440	4	290 (net)						U		
440	4	370					U			
440	4	375	L	L	L	U				
440	6	385					V			
440	6	390				V				

* Net horsepower rating varies with model application
④ Non-California cars with Fresh Air Packs—265 (net)

Dodge, Plymouth GENERAL ENGINE SPECIFICATIONS

Year	Engine Cu. In. Displacement	Carburetor Type	Advertised Horsepower @ rpm ■	Advertised Torque @ rpm (ft lbs) ■	Bore and Stroke (in.)	Advertised Compression Ratio	Oil Pressure @ 2050 rpm
'67	6-225	1 bbl	145 @ 4000	215 @ 2400	3.400 x 4.125	8.40:1	55
	8-273	2 bbl	180 @ 4200	260 @ 1600	3.625 x 3.310	9.20:1	55
	8-318	2 bbl	230 @ 4400	340 @ 2400	3.910 x 3.310	9.20:1	55
	8-383	2 bbl	270 @ 4400	390 @ 2800	4.250 x 3.375	9.20:1	55
	8-383	4 bbl	325 @ 4800	425 @ 2800	4.250 x 3.375	10.00:1	55
	8-426 Hemi	2 x 4 bbl	425 @ 5000	490 @ 4000	4.250 x 3.750	10.25:1	55
	8-440	4 bbl	350 @ 4400	480 @ 2800	4.320 x 3.750	10.00:1	55
	8-440 HP	4 bbl	375 @ 4600	480 @ 3200	4.320 x 3.750	10.00:1	55
'68	6-225	1 bbl	145 @ 4000	215 @ 2400	3.400 x 4.125	8.40:1	55
	8-273	2 bbl	190 @ 4400	260 @ 2000	3.625 x 3.310	9.00:1	55
	8-318	2 bbl	230 @ 4400	340 @ 2400	3.910 x 3.310	9.20:1	55
	8-383	2 bbl	290 @ 4400	390 @ 2800	4.250 x 3.375	9.20:1	55
	8-383	4 bbl	330 @ 5000	425 @ 3200	4.250 x 3.375	10.00:1	55
	8-383	4 bbl	335 @ 5200	425 @ 3400	4.250 x 3.375	10.00:1	55
	8-426 Hemi	2 x 4 bbl	425 @ 5000	490 @ 4000	4.250 x 3.750	10.25:1	55
	8-440	4 bbl	350 @ 4400	480 @ 2800	4.320 x 3.750	10.01:1	55
	8-440 HP	4 bbl	375 @ 4600	480 @ 3200	4.320 x 3.750	10.01:1	55
'69	6-225	1 bbl	195 @ 4000	215 @ 2400	3.400 x 4.125	84.0:1	55
	8-318	2 bbl	230 @ 4400	340 @ 2400	3.910 x 3.310	9.20:1	55
	8-383	2 bbl	290 @ 4400	390 @ 2800	4.250 x 3.375	9.20:1	55
	8-383	4 bbl	330 @ 5000	425 @ 3200	4.250 x 3.375	10.00:1	55
	8-383	4 bbl	335 @ 5200	425 @ 3400	4.250 x 3.375	10.00:1	55
	8-426 Hemi	2 x 4 bbl	425 @ 5000	490 @ 4000	4.250 x 3.750	10.25:1	55
	8-440	4 bbl	350 @ 4400	480 @ 2800	4.320 x 3.750	10.01:1	55
	8-440 HP	4 bbl	375 @ 4600	480 @ 3200	4.320 x 3.750	10.01:1	55
'70	6-225	1 bbl	145 @ 4000	215 @ 2400	3.400 x 4.125	8.40:1	55
	8-318	2 bbl	230 @ 4400	320 @ 2000	3.910 x 3.310	8.80:1	55
	8-383	2 bbl	290 @ 4400	390 @ 2800	4.250 x 3.375	8.70:1	55
	8-383	4 bbl	330 @ 5000	425 @ 3200	4.250 x 3.375	9.50:1	55
	8-383 HP	4 bbl	335 @ 5200	425 @ 3400	4.250 x 3.375	9.50:1	55
	8-426 Hemi	2 x 4 bbl	425 @ 5000	490 @ 4000	4.250 x 3.750	10.20:1	55

Dodge, Plymouth GENERAL ENGINE SPECIFICATIONS, Continued

Year	Engine Cu. In. Displacement	Carburetor Type	Advertised Horsepower @ rpm ■	Advertised Torque @ rpm (ft lbs) ■	Bore and Stroke (in.)	Advertised Compression Ratio	Oil Pressure @ 2050 rpm
'70	8-440	4 bbl	350 @ 4400	480 @ 2800	4.320 x 3.750	9.70:1	55
	8-440 HP	4 bbl	375 @ 4600	480 @ 3200	4.320 x 3.750	9.70:1	55
	8-440	3 x 2 bbl	390 @ 4700	490 @ 3200	4.320 x 3.750	10.50:1	55
'71	6-225	1 bbl	145 @ 4000	215 @ 2400	3.400 x 4.125	8.40:1	55
	8-318	2 bbl	230 @ 4400	320 @ 2000	3.910 x 3.310	8.60:1	55
	8-340	4 bbl	275 @ 5000	340 @ 3200	4.040 x 3.310	10.30:1	55
	8-360	2 bbl	255 @ 4400	360 @ 2400	4.000 x 3.580	8.70:1	55
	8-383	2 bbl	275 @ 4400	375 @ 2800	4.250 x 3.375	8.50:1	55
	8-383 HP	4 bbl	300 @ 4800	410 @ 3400	4.250 x 3.375	8.50:1	55
	8-426 Hemi	2 x 4 bbl	425 @ 5000	490 @ 4000	4.250 x 3.750	10.20:1	55
	8-440	4 bbl	335 @ 4400	460 @ 3200	4.320 x 3.750	8.50:1	55
	8-440 HP	4 bbl	370 @ 4600	480 @ 3200	4.320 x 3.750	9.50:1	55
	8-440	3 x 2 bbl	385 @ 4700	490 @ 3200	4.320 x 3.750	10.30:1	55
'72	6-225	1 bbl	110 @ 4000①	185 @ 2000②	3.400 x 4.125	8.40:1	55
	8-318	2 bbl	150 @ 4000	260 @ 1600	3.910 x 3.310	8.60:1	55
	8-340	4 bbl	240 @ 4800	290 @ 3600	4.040 x 3.310	8.50:1	55
	8-360	2 bbl	175 @ 4000	285 @ 2400	4.000 x 3.580	8.80:1	55
	8-400	2 bbl	190 @ 4400③	310 @ 2400④	4.340 x 3.380	8.20:1	55
	8-400	4 bbl	255 @ 4800⑤	340 @ 3200⑥	4.340 x 3.380	8.20:1	55
	8-400⑪	4 bbl	265 @ 4800	345 @ 3200	4.340 x 3.380	8.20:1	55
	8-440	4 bbl	225 @ 4400⑦	345 @ 3200⑧	4.320 x 3.750	8.20:1	55
	8-440	4 bbl	280 @ 4800⑨	375 @ 3200⑩	4.320 x 3.750	8.20:1	55
	8-440⑪	4 bbl	290 @ 4800	380 @ 3200	4.320 x 3750	8.20:1	55
'73	6-225	1 bbl	105 @ 4000	185 @ 1600	3.400 x 4.125	8.4:1	55
	8-318	2 bbl	150 @ 3600	265 @ 2000	3.910 x 3.310	8.6:1	55
	8-340	2 bbl	240 @ 4800	295 @ 3600	4.040 x 3.310	8.5:1	55
	8-340	4 bbl	240 @ 4800	295 @ 3600	4.040 x 3.310	8.5:1	55
	8-360	2 bbl	170 @ 4000	285 @ 2400	4.000 x 3.580	8.4:1	55
	8-400	2 bbl	185 @ 3600	310 @ 2400	4.340 x 3.380	8.2:1	55
	8-400	4 bbl	260 @ 4800	335 @ 3600	4.340 x 3.380	8.2:1	55
	8-440	4 bbl	220 @ 3600	350 @ 2400	4.320 x 3.750	8.2:1	55
	8-440	4 bbl	275 @ 4800	380 @ 3200	4.320 x 3.750	8.2:1	55
'74	6-225	1 bbl	105 @ 4000	185 @ 1600	3.400 x 4.125	8.4:1	55
	8-318	2 bbl	150 @ 3600	265 @ 2000	3.910 x 3.310	8.6:1	55
	8-360	2 bbl	160 @ 3600	285 @ 2400	4.000 x 3.580	8.4:1	55
	8-360	4 bbl	170 @ 4000	285 @ 2400	4.000 x 3.580	8.4:1	55
	8-400	2 bbl	175 @ 3600	305 @ 2400	4.340 x 3.380	8.2:1	55
	8-400	4 bbl	185 @ 3600	310 @ 2400	4.340 x 3.380	8.2:1	55
	8-440	4 bbl	220 @ 3600	350 @ 2400	4.320 x 3.750	8.2:1	55
	8-440	4 bbl	280 @ 4800	380 @ 3200	4.320 x 3.750	8.2:1	55

■ Beginning 1972, horsepower and torque are SAE net figures. They are measured at the rear of the transmission with all accessories installed and operating. Since the figures vary when a given engine is installed in different models, some are representative rather than exact.

① For California vehicles, advertised horsepower is 97 @ 4000 rpm

② For California vehicles, advertised torque is 180 @ 2000 rpm

③ For California vehicles, advertised horsepower is 181 @ 4400 rpm

④ For California vehicles, advertised torque is 305 @ 2400 rpm

⑤ For California vehicles, advertised horsepower is 246 @ 4800 rpm

⑥ For California vehicles, advertised torque is 335 @ 3200 rpm

⑦ For California vehicles, advertised horsepower is 216 @ 4400 rpm

⑤ For California vehicles, advertised torque is 340 @ 3200 rpm

⑨ For California vehicles, advertised horsepower is 271 @ 4800 rpm

⑩ For California vehicles, advertised torque is 370 @ 3200 rpm

⑪ Not available in California

HP High Performance

Belvedere, Satellite, Coronet, Charger

TUNE-UP SPECIFICATIONS

When analyzing compression test results, look for uniformity among cylinders rather than specific pressures.

	ENGINE		SPARK PLUGS		DISTRIBUTOR		IGNITION TIMING (deg) ▲		VALVES	Fuel	IDLE SPEED (rpm) ▲	
Year	No. Cyl Displacement (cu in.)	hp	Type §	Gap (in.)	Point Dwell (deg)	Point Gap (in.)	Man Trans	Auto Trans	Intake Opens ■ (deg) ●	Pump Pressure (psi)	Man Trans	Auto Trans
'67	6-225	145	N-14Y	.035	43	.020	5B(TDC)	5B(TDC)	10	3½-5	550(650)	550(650)
	8-273	180	N-14Y	.035	30	.017	5B(5A)	10B(5A)	14	5-7	500(700)	500(650)
	8-318	230	N-14Y	.035	30	.017	5B(5A)	10B(5A)	14	5-7	500(650)	500(600)
	8-383	270	J-14Y	.035	30	.017	12½B(TDC)	12½B(5B)	16	3½-5	550(650)	550(600)
	8-383	325	J-13Y	.035	30	.017	12½B(TDC)	12½B(5B)	16	3½-5	500(650)	500(600)
	8-426	425	N-10Y	.035	30①	.017	12½B(TDC)	12½B(TDC)	30	7-8½	750	750
	8-440	375	J-11Y	.035	30	.017	12½B(TDC)	12½B(5B)	19	6-7½	650	650
'68	6-225	145	N-14Y	.035	43	.029	5B(TDC)	5B(TDC)	10	3½-5	550(650)	550(650)
	8-273	190	N-14Y	.035	31	.017	5A	2½A	10	5-7	700	650
	8-318	230	N-14Y	.035	31	.017	5B(5A)	10B(2½)A	10	5-7	500(650)	500(600)
	8-383	290	J-14Y	.035	31	.017	TDC	7½B	18	3½-5	650	600
	8-383	330	J-11Y	.035	31	.017	TDC	5B	18	3½-5	650	650
	8-383	335	J-11Y	.035	31	.017	TDC	5B	21	3½-5	650	650
	8-426	425	N-10Y	.035	30①	.017	TDC	TDC	36	7-8½	750	650
	8-440	375	J-11Y	.035	31①	.017	TDC	5B	21	6-7½	650	650
'69	6-225	145	N-14Y	.035	45	.020	TDC	TDC	10	3½-5	700	650
	8-318	230	N-14Y	.035	33	.017	TDC	TDC	10	5-7	700	650
	8-383	290	J-14Y	.035	33	.017	TDC	7½B	18	3½-5	700	600
	8-383	330	J-11Y	.035	33	.017	TDC	5B	18	3½-5	700	650
	8-383	335	J-11Y	.035	30①	.017	TDC	5B	21	3½-5	700	650
	8-426	425	N-10Y	.035	30①	.017	TDC	TDC	36	7-8½	800	800
	8-440	375	J-11Y	.035	33②	.017	TDC	5B	21	6-7½	700	650
'70	6-225	145	N-14Y	.035	44	.020	TDC	TDC	10	3½-5	700	650
	8-318	230	N-14Y	.035	32	.017	TDC	TDC	10	5-7	750	700
	8-383	290	J-14Y	.035	30	.018	TDC	2½B	18	3½-5	750	650
	8-383	330	J-11Y	.035	30	.018	TDC	2½B	18	3½-5	750	750
	8-383	335	J-11Y	.035	30	.018	TDC	2½B	21	3½-5	750	750
	8-426	425	N-10Y	.035	30①	.017	TDC	5B	36	7-8½	900	900
	8-440	375	J-11Y	.035	30	.018	TDC	2½B	18	3½-5	900	800
	8-440	390	J-11Y	.035	30①	.017	5B	5B	21	6-7½	900	900
'71	6-225	145	N-14Y	.035	44	.020	TDC(2½B)	TDC(2½B)	16	3½-5	750	750
	8-318	230	N-14Y	.035	32	.017	TDC	TDC	10	5-7	750	700
	8-340	275	N-9Y	.035	33②	.017	5B	5B	22	5-7	900	900
	8-383	275	J-14Y	.035	30	.018	TDC	2½B	18	3½-5	750	700
	8-383	300	N-11Y	.035	30	.018	TDC	2½B	21	3½-5	900	800
	8-426	425	N-10Y	.035	30①	.017	TDC	2½B	36	7-8½	950	950
	8-440	370	J-11Y	.035	30	.018	TDC	2½B	18	3½-5	900	800
	8-440	385	J-11Y	.035	30①	.017	12½B	12½B	21	6-7½	900	900
'72	6-225	110	N-14Y	.035	44	.020	TDC	TDC	16	3½-5	750(700)	750(700)
	8-318	150	N-13Y	.035	32	.017	TDC	TDC	10	5-7	750	750(700)
	8-340	240	N-9Y	.035	Electronic		2½B	2½B	22	5-7	900(850	750
	8-400	190	J-13Y	.035	30	.018	—	5B③	18	3½-5	—	700
	8-400	255④	J-11Y	.035	Electronic		TDC(2½B)	10B(5B)	21	3½-5	900(800)	750
	8-440	290	J-11Y	.035	Electronic		2½B	10B(5B)	21	3½-5	900(800)	900

Belvedere, Satellite, Coronet, Charger

TUNE-UP SPECIFICATIONS, Continued

When analyzing compression test results, look for uniformity among cylinders rather than specific pressures.

Year	ENGINE No. Cyl Displacement (cu in.)	ENGINE hp	SPARK PLUGS Type §	SPARK PLUGS Gap (in.)	DISTRIBUTOR Point Dwell (deg)	DISTRIBUTOR Point Gap (in.)	IGNITION TIMING (deg) ▲ Man Trans	IGNITION TIMING (deg) ▲ Auto Trans	VALVES Intake Opens ■ (deg) ●	Fuel Pump Pressure (psi)	IDLE SPEED (rpm) ▲ Man Trans	IDLE SPEED (rpm) ▲ Auto Trans
'73	6-225	105	N-14Y	.035	Electronic		TDC	TDC	16	4-5½	750	750
	8-318	150	N-13Y	.035	Electronic		2½B	TDC	10	6-7½	750	700
	8-340	240	N-9Y	.035	Electronic		5B	2½B	22	6-7½	850	850
	8-400	175	J-13Y	.035	Electronic		—	10B	18	4-5½	—	700
	8-400	260	J-11Y	.035	Electronic		2½B	10B	21	4-5½	900	850
	8-440	275	J-11Y	.035	Electronic		—	10B	21	4-5½	—	800
'74	6-225	105	N-14Y	.035	Electronic		TDC	TDC	16	3½-5	800	750
	8-318	150	N-13Y	.035	Electronic		TDC	TDC	10	5-7	750	750
	8-360	170	N-12Y	.035	Electronic		5B(2½B)	5B	22	5-7	850	850
	8-400	175	J-13Y	.035	Electronic		—	10B(5B)	18	4-5½	—	750
	8-400	260	J-11Y	.035	Electronic		5B	10B(2½B)	21	4-5½	900	850
	8-440	275	J-11Y	.035	Electronic		—	10B	21	7-8.2	—	800

▲ See text for procedure
● Figure in parentheses indicates California engine
■ All figures Before Top Dead Center
§ All spark plug listings are Champion original equipment numbers
① Adjust each set of points to this figure. With both sets connected, the total reading should be 40 degrees.
② For vehicles with manual transmission, adjust each set of points to 30 degrees. With both sets connected, the total reading should be 40 degrees.
③ For non-California vehicles built after February 2, 1972, adjust ignition timing to 7½ degrees Before Top Dead Center
④ For non-California vehicles equipped with Fresh Air Packs, figure is 265 hp

A After Top Dead Center
B Before Top Dead Center
TDC Top Dead Center
— Not applicable

MECHANICAL VALVE LIFTER CLEARANCE

Year	Engine	Intake (Hot) In.	Exhaust (Hot) In.
1967-1974	All 6 cylinders	.010	.020
1967	273 V8	.013	.021
1967-1969	426 Hemi	.028 (Cold)	.032 (Cold)

Fury, Polara, Monaco

TUNE-UP SPECIFICATIONS

When analyzing compression test results, look for uniformity among cylinders rather than specific pressures.

Year	ENGINE No. Cyl Displacement (cu in.)	ENGINE hp	SPARK PLUGS Type §	SPARK PLUGS Gap (in.)	DISTRIBUTOR Point Dwell (deg)	DISTRIBUTOR Point Gap (in.)	IGNITION TIMING (deg) ▲ Man Trans	IGNITION TIMING (deg) ▲ Auto Trans	VALVES Intake Opens ■ (deg) ●	Fuel Pump Pressure (psi)	IDLE SPEED (rpm) ▲ Man Trans	IDLE SPEED (rpm) ▲ Auto Trans
'67	6-225	145	N-14Y	.035	40-45	.020	5B(TDC)	5B(TDC)	10	3½-5	550(650)③	550(650)③
	8-318	230	N-14Y	.035	28-32	.017	5B(5A)	10B(5A)	14	5-7	500(650)③	500(600)③
	8-383	270	J-14Y	.035	28-32	.017	12½B(TDC)	12½B(5B)	16	3½-5	550(650)③	550(600)③
	8-383	325	J-13Y	.035	28-32	.017	12½B(TDC)	12½B(5B)	16	3½-5	500(650)③	500(600)③
	8-440	350	J-13Y	.035	28-32	.017	12½B(5B)	12½B(5B)	16	3½-5	650③	650③
	8-440	375	J-11Y	.035	28-32	.017	12½B(TDC)	12½B(5B)	19	6-7½	650(650)③	650(650)③
'68	6-225	145	N-14Y	.035	40-45	.020	5B(TDC)	5B(TDC)	10	3½-5	550(650)	550(650)
	8-318	230	N-14Y	.035	28-33	.017	5B(5A)	10B(2½A)	10	5-7	550(650)	500(600)
	8-383	290	J-14Y	.035	28-33	.017	TDC	7½B	18	3½-7	650	600
	8-383	330	J-11Y	.035	28-33	.017	TDC	5B	18	3½-5	650	650
	8-440	350	J-13Y	.035	28-33	.017	—	7½B	18	3½-5	—	600
	8-440	375	J-11Y	.035	28-33①	.017	TDC	5B	21	6-7½	650	650

Fury, Polara, Monaco

TUNE-UP SPECIFICATIONS, Continued

When analyzing compression test results, look for uniformity among cylinders rather than specific pressures.

	ENGINE		SPARK PLUGS		DISTRIBUTOR		IGNITION TIMING (deg) ▲		VALVES	Fuel	IDLE SPEED (rpm) ▲	
Year	No. Cyl Displacement (cu in.)	hp	Type §	Gap (in.)	Point Dwell (deg)	Point Gap (in.)	Man Trans	Auto Trans	Intake Opens ■ (deg) ●	Pump Pressure (psi)	Man Trans	Auto Trans
'69	6-225	145	N-11Y	.035	42-47	.020	TDC	TDC	10	3½-5	700	650
	8-318	230	N-14Y	.035	30-35	.017	TDC	TDC	10	5-7	700	650
	8-383	290	J-14Y	.035	30-35	.017	TDC	7½B	18	3½-5	700	600
	8-383	330	J-11Y	.035	30-35	.017	TDC	5B	18	3½-5	700	650
	8-440	350	J-13Y	.035	28-33	.017	—	7½B	18	3½-5	—	600
	8-440	375	J-11Y	.035	②	.017	TDC	5B	21	6-7½	700	650
'70	6-225	145	N-14Y	.035	41-46	.020	TDC	TDC	10	3½-5	700	650
	8-318	230	N-14Y	.035	30-34	.017	TDC	TDC	10	5-7	750	700
	8-383	290	J-14Y	.035	28-32	.018	TDC	2½B	18	3½-5	750	650
	8-383	330	J-11Y	.035	28-32	.018	TDC	2½B	18	3½-5	750	750
	8-440	350	J-13Y	.035	28-33	.018	—	12½B	18	3½-5	—	650
	8-440	390	J-11Y	.035	27-32①	.017	5B	5B	21	6-7½	900	900
'71	6-225	145	N-14Y	.035	41-46	.020	TDC(2½B)	TDC(2½B)	16	3½-5	750	750
	8-318	230	N-14Y	.035	30-34	.017	TDC	TDC	10	5-7	750	700
	8-360	255	N-13Y	.035	30-34	.017	2½B	2½B	16	3½-5	750	700
	8-383	275	J-14Y	.035	28-32	.018	TDC	2½B	18	3½-5	750	700
	8-383	300	J-11Y	.035	28-32	.018	TDC	2½B	21	3½-5	900	800
	8-440	335	J-13Y	.035	28-32	.018	—	5B	18	3½-5	—	750
	8-440	370	J-11Y	.035	28-32	.018	TDC	2½B	21	3½-5	900	800
'72	8-318	150	N-13Y	.035	30-34	.017	—	TDC	10	5-7	—	750(700)
	8-360	175	N-13Y	.035	30-34	.017	—	TDC	16	5-7	—	750
	8-400	190	J-13Y	.035	28-32	.018	—	5B④	18	3½-5	—	700
	8-440	225	J-11Y	.035	28-32	.018	—	10B	18	3½-5	—	750(700)
'73	8-318	150	N-13Y	.035	Electronic		—	TDC	10	6-7½	—	700
	8-360	170	N-13Y	.035	Electronic		—	TDC	16	6-7½	—	750
	8-400	185	J-13Y	.035	Electronic		—	10B	18	4-5½	—	700
	8-440	220	J-11Y	.035	Electronic		—	10B	18	4-5½	—	700
'74	8-360	160	N-12Y	.035	Electronic		—	5B	16	5-7	—	750
	8-360	170	N-12Y	.035	Electronic		5B(2½B)	5B	22	5-7	850	850
	8-400	175	J-13Y	.035	Electronic		—	10B(5B)	18	4-5½	—	750
	8-400	260	J-11Y	.035	Electronic		5B	10B(2½B)	21	4-5½	900	850
	8-440	275	J-11Y	.035	Electronic		—	10B	21	7-8.2	—	800

▲ See text for procedure
■ Before Top Dead Center
● Figure in parentheses indicates California engine
§ All spark plug listings are Champion original equipment numbers
① Both sets 37°-40°
② Automatic transmission 30°-50°
Manual 27°-32°, both sets 37°-40°
③ A/C on
④ Non-California cars built after Feb. 2, 7½B

A After Top Dead Center
B Before Top Dead Center
TDC Top Dead Center

MECHANICAL VALVE LIFTER CLEARANCE

Year	Engine	Intake (Hot) In.	Exhaust (Hot) In.
1967-1974	All six cylinders	.010	.020

Dodge & Plymouth CAPACITIES

Year	ENGINE No. Cyl. (Cu. In.) Displacement	Engine Crankcase Add 1 Qt For New Filter	TRANSMISSION Pts To Refill After Draining: Manual 3-Speed	Manual 4-Speed	Automatic	Drive Axle (pts)	Gasoline Tank (gals)	COOLING SYSTEM (qts): With Heater	With A/C
'67	6-225	4	6.5	—	16	2④	19⑧	13	14
	8-273	4	6.5	—	16	4	19	19	20
	8-318	4	6.5	—	18.5	4	19⑧	18	19
	8-383	4	6.5	8.5	18.5	4	19⑧	17	18
	8-426	5	—	8.5	18.5	4	19	18	—
	8-440	4	6.5	9	18.5	4	19	18⑫	19⑫
'68	6-225	4	6.5	—	15.5	2④	19⑩	13	14
	8-273	4	6	—	15.5	4	19	19	20
	8-318	4	6	—	19.5	4	19⑩	18	19
	8-383	4	6	9	15.5	4	19⑩	17	18
	8-426	6	—	9	15.5	4⑤	19	18	—
	8-440	4	—	9	15.5	4	19⑩	17⑬	18⑬
'69	6-225	4	6.5	—	15.5	2④	19⑩	13	15
	8-318	4	6	—	15.5	4	19⑩	16	19
	8-383⑭	4	6	7	18.5	4	19⑩	16	17
	8-383⑮	4	—	7.5	15.5	4	19⑩	16	17
	8-426	6	—	7.5	16	4⑤	19	18	—
	8-440	4	—	7.5	18.5	4⑤	19⑩	17	18
'70	6-225	4	4.75	—	17	2④	19⑩	13	15
	8-318	4	4.75	—	16	4	19⑩	16	19
	8-383⑭	4	4.75	—	19	4	19⑩	16	17
	8-383⑮	4	4.75	7.5	16	4	19⑩	16	17
	8-426	6	—	7.5	17	5.5	19	18	—
	8-440	4①	—	7.5	19	5.5⑥	19⑩	17	18
'71	6-225	4	6.5②	—	17	4⑦	21⑪	13	13
	8-318	4	4.75	—	17	4⑦	21⑪	16	16.5
	8-340	4	4.75	7.5	16.3	4	21	15	15
	8-360	4	4.75	—	16	4.5	23	15.5	15
	8-383	4	4.75	7.5	16③	4⑦	21⑪	14.5	15
	8-426	6	—	7.5	17	5.5	21	15.5	—
	8-440	4①	—	7.5	19	5.5⑦	21⑪	15.5	17
'72	6-225	4	6.5	—	17	4.5	21	13	14
	8-318	4	4.75	—	17	4.5	21⑪	16	17.5
	8-340	4	—	7.5	16.3	4.5	21	15	15.5
	8-360	4	—	—	16.3	4.5	23	16	16
	8-400⑭	4	—	—	19	4.5	21⑪	14.5	15
	8-440⑮	4	4.75	7.5	16.3	4.5	21⑪	14.5	14.5
'73	6-225	4	4.75	—	17	4.5	19.5	13	13
	8-318	4	4.75	7.5	17	4.5	19.5⑪⑱	16	17.5
	8-340	4	—	7.5	16.3	4.5	19.5	15	15.5
	8-360	4	—	—	16.3	4.5	19.5⑪	15.5	16
	8-400	4	—	7.5	19⑯	4.5	19.5⑪⑱	16	17⑲
	8-440	4	—	—	16.3⑰	4.5	19.5⑪	16.5⑳	16.5⑳

Dodge & Plymouth — CAPACITIES, Continued

Year	Engine No. Cyl. (Cu. In.) Displacement	Engine Crankcase Add 1 Qt For New Filter	Transmission Pts To Refill After Draining: Manual 3-Speed	Manual 4-Speed	Automatic	Drive Axle (pts)	Gasoline Tank (gals)	Cooling System (qts) With Heater	With A/C
'74	6-225	4	4.75	—	16.5	4.5	19.5⑱	13	—
	8-318	4	4.75	7.5	16.5	4.5	19.5⑱	16	18
	8-360	4	—	7.5	16.1	4.5	19.5⑱㉒	16.5	16.5
	8-400	4	—	7.5	18.9㉑	4.5	19.5⑱㉒	16.5	16.5
	8-440	4	—	—	16.1	4.5	19.5⑱㉒	16	16

① 3-2 bbl—6 qts
② Fury, Polara, Monaco—4.75 pts
③ 2 bbl—19 pts
④ Fury, station wagon—4 pts
⑤ Manual transmissions—5.5 pts
⑥ Fury, Polara, Monaco—4 pts
⑦ Fury, Polara, Monaco—4.5 pts
⑧ Fury, Polara, Monaco—25 gals, station wagon—22 gals
⑨ Station wagon—22 gals
⑩ Fury, Polara, Monaco—24 gals, station wagon—23 gals
⑪ Fury, Polara, Monaco—23 gals
⑫ Fury, Polara, Monaco without A/C 17 qts, with A/C 18 qts
⑬ With Hi-performance option 18 qts, with A/C 19 qts
⑭ With 2 bbl carburetor
⑮ With 4 bbl carburetor
⑯ Charger, Coronet, Satellite with 4 bbl—16.3 pts
⑰ Fury. Polara, Monaco—19 pts
⑱ Station wagons—21 gals
⑲ Fury, Polara, Monaco—16 qts
⑳ Fury, Polara, Monaco—15.5 qts
㉑ 16.1 with HP 400 engine
㉒ Fury, Polara, Monaco—25 gals, station wagon—24 gals
—— Not applicable

VALVE SPECIFICATIONS

Year	Engine No. Cyl. Displacement (cu in.)	Seat Angle (deg)	Face Angle (deg)	Spring Test Pressure (lbs @ in.)	Spring Installed Height (in.)	Stem to Guide Clearance (in.) Intake	Exhaust	Stem Diameter (in.) Intake	Exhaust
'67	6-225	45	45②	144 @ 1.31	1 11/16	.0010-.0030	.0020-.0040	.3725	.3715
	8-273③	45	45	144 @ 1.31	1 11/16	.0010-.0030	.0020-.0040	.3725	.3715
	8-273④	45	45	177 @ 1.31	1 11/16	.0010-.0030	.0020-.0040	.3725	.3715
	8-318	45	45	177 @ 1.31	1 11/16	.0010-.0030	.0020-.0040	.3725	.3715
	8-383③	45	45	195 @ 1.47	1 7/8	.0010-.0030	.0020-.0040	.3725	.3715
	8-383④	45	45	200 @ 1.44	1 7/8	.0010-.0030	.0020-.0040	.3725	.3715
	8-426	45	45	184 @ 1.41	1 7/8	.0020-.0040	.0030-.0050	.3090	.3080
	8-440⑥	45	45	246 @ 1.36	1 7/8	.0010-.0030	.0020-.0040	.3725	.3715
	8-440	45	45	200 @ 1.44	1 7/8	.0010-.0030	.0020-.0040	.3725	.3715
'68	6-225	45	45①	144 @ 1.31	1 11/16	.0010-.0030	.0020-.0040	.3725	.3715
	8-273	45	45①	177 @ 1.31	1 11/16	.0010-.0030	.0020-.0040	.3725	.3715
	8-318	45	45①	177 @ 1.31	1 11/16	.0010-.0030	.0020-.0040	.3725	.3715
	8-383③	45	45	200 @ 1.44	1 7/8	.0010-.0030	.0020-.0040	.3725	.3715
	8-383④	45	45	230 @ 1.41	1 7/8	.0010-.0030	.0020-.0040	.3725	.3715
	8-426	45	45	280 @ 1.38	1 7/8	.0020-.0040	.0030-.0050	.3090	.3080
	8-440	45	45	200 @ 1.44	1 7/8	.0010-.0030	.0020-.0040	.3725	.3715
	8-440	45	45	230 @ 1.41	1 7/8	.0010-.0030	.0020-.0040	.3725	.3715
'69	6-225	45	45①	144 @ 1.31	1 11/16	.0010-.0030	.0020-.0040	.3725	.3715
	8-318	45	45①	177 @ 1.31	1 11/16	.0010-.0030	.0020-.0040	.3725	.3715
	8-383③	45	45	200 @ 1.44	1 7/8	.0010-.0030	.0020-.0040	.3725	.3715
	8-383④	45	45	246 @ 1.36	1 7/8	.0010-.0030	.0020-.0040	.3725	.3715
	8-426	45	45	280 @ 1.38	1 7/8	.0020-.0040	.0030-.0050	.3090	.3080
	8-440	45	45	200 @ 1.44	1 7/8	.0010-.0030	.0020-.0040	.3725	.3715
	8-440⑥	45	45	246 @ 1.36	1 7/8	.0010-.0030	.0020-.0040	.3725	.3715

VALVE SPECIFICATIONS, Continued

Year	Engine No. Cyl. Displacement (cu in.)	Seat Angle (deg)	Face Angle (deg)	Spring Test Pressure (lbs @ in.)	Spring Installed Height (in.)	STEM TO GUIDE Clearance (in.) Intake	Exhaust	STEM Diameter (In.) Intake	Exhaust
'70	6-225	45	45①	144 @ 1.31	1 11/16	.0010-.0030	.0020-.0040	.3725	.3715
	8-318	45	45①	177 @ 1.31	1 11/16	.0010-.0030	.0020-.0040	.3725	.3715
	8-383③	45	45	200 @ 1.44	1 7/8	.0010-.0030	.0020-.0040	.3727	.3717
	8-383④	45	45	246 @ 1.72	1 7/8	.0015-.0032	.0025-.0042	.3722	.3712
	8-426	45	45	200 @ 1.44	1 7/8	.0020-.0040	.0030-.0050	.3090	.3080
	8-440	45	45	246 @ 1.72	1 7/8	.0010-.0030	.0020-.0040	.3727	.3717
	8-440⑥	45	45	310 @ 1.38	1 7/8	.0015-.0032	.0025-.0042	.3722	.3712
'71	6-225	45	45①	144 @ 1.31	1 11/16	.0010-.0030	.0020-.0040	.3725	.3715
	8-318	45	45①	177 @ 1.31	1 11/16	.0010-.0030	.0020-.0040	.3725	.3715
	8-340	45	45①	238 @ 1.31	1 11/16	.0015-.0035	.0025-.0045	.3720	.3710
	8-360	45	45①	177 @ 1.31	1 11/16	.0010-.0030	.0020-.0040	.3725	.3715
	8-383③	45	45	200 @ 1.44	1 7/8	.0010-.0030	.0020-.0040	.3727	.3717
	8-383④	45	45	246 @ 1.72	1 7/8	.0015-.0032	.0025-.0042	.3722	.3712
	8-426	45	45	310 @ 1.28	1 7/8	.0020-.0040	.0030-.0050	.3090	.3080
	8-440	45	45	200 @ 1.44	1 7/8	.0010-.0030	.0020-.0040	.3722	.3717
	8-440⑥	45	45	246 @ 1.72	1 7/8	.0015-.0032	.0025-.0042	.3722	.3712
'72	6-225	45	45①	144 @ 1.31	1 11/16	.0010-.0030	.0020-.0040	.3725	.3715
	8-318	45	45①	177 @ 1.31	1 11/16	.0010-.0030	.0020-.0040	.3725	.3715
	8-340	45	45①	208 @ 1.31	1 11/16	.0015-.0035	.0025-.0045	.3720	.3710
	8-360	45	45①	177 @ 1.31	1 11/16	.0010-.0030	.0020-.0040	.3725	.3715
	8-400③	45	45	200 @ 1.44	1 7/8	.0010-.0030	.0020-.0040	.3727	.3717
	8-400④	45	45	246 @ 1.72	1 7/8	.0015-.0032	.0025-.0042	.3722	.3712
	8-440	45	45	200 @ 1.44	1 7/8	.0010-.0030	.0020-.0040	.3727	.3717
	8-440⑥	45	45	246 @ 1.72	1 7/8	.0015-.0032	.0025-.0042	.3722	.3712
'73	6-225	45	45②	160 @ 1.24	1 21/32	.0010-.0030	.0020-.0040	.3725	.3715
	8-318	45	45②	189 @ 1.28	1 21/32	.0010-.0030	.0020-.0040	.3725	.3715
	8-340	45	45②	238 @ 1.22	1 21/32	.0015-.0035	.0025-.0045	.3720	.3710
	8-360	45	45②	195 @ 1.24	1 21/32	.0010-.0030	.0020-.0040	.3725	.3715
	8-400③	45	45	200 @ 1.42	1 55/64	.0010-.0027	⑦	.3727	⑨
	8-400④	45	45	234 @ 1.40	1 55/64	.0015-.0032	⑧	.3722	⑩
	8-440	45	45	200 @ 1.42	1 55/64	.0010-.0027	⑦	.3727	⑨
	8-440⑥	45	45	234 @ 1.40	1 55/64	.0015-.0032	⑧	.3722	⑩
'74	6-225	45	45	160 @ 1.24	1 21/32	.0010-.0030	.0020-.0040	.3725	.3715
	8-318	45	45	189 @ 1.28	1 21/32	.0010-.0030	.0020-.0040	.3725	.3715
	8-360	45	45	238 @ 1.22⑪	1 21/32	.0010-.0030	.0025-.0045	.3725	.3710
	8-400	45	45	200 @ 1.43	1 55/64	.0010-.0027	⑦	.3727	⑨
	8-400⑥	45	45	234 @ 1.40	1 55/64	.0015-.0032	⑩	.3722	⑩
	8-440	45	45	234 @ 1.40	1 55/64	.0015-.0032	⑩	.3722	⑩

① Exhaust 43°
② Exhaust 47°
③ 2 bbl carburetor
④ 4 bbl carburetor
⑤ Hemi
⑥ Hi-Performance
⑦ Hot end—.0020-.0037, cold end—.0010-.0027
⑧ Hot end—.0025-.0042, cold end—.0015-.0032
⑨ Hot end—.3716, cold end—.3726
⑩ Hot end—.3711, cold end—.3721
⑪ 195 @ 1.24 on 2 bbl engine

TORQUE SPECIFICATIONS

All readings in ft lbs

Year	Engine Displacement (cu in.)	Cylinder Head Bolts	Rod Bearing Bolts	Main Bearing Bolts	Crankshaft Pulley Bolt	Flywheel to Crankshaft Bolts	MANIFOLD Intake	MANIFOLD Exhaust
'67-'74	6-All	70	45	85	Press fit	55	10①	10
'67-'74	8-273, 318, 340, 360	95	45	85	135②	65	40	30
	8-361, 383, 400, 440	70	45	85	135②	55	40	30
'67-'72	8-426	75	75	100③	135	70	④	35

① Intake to exhaust bolts—20 ft. lbs.
② '71 318, 340, 360 cu in. engines—100 ft. lbs.
③ Cross bolt mains—45 ft. lbs.
④ 4 center bolts on either side—6 ft. lbs., others 4 ft. lbs.

CRANKSHAFT AND CONNECTING ROD SPECIFICATIONS

All measurements are given in in.

Year	Engine Displace. (cu in.)	CRANKSHAFT Main Brg. Journal Dia	CRANKSHAFT Main Brg. Oil Clearance	CRANKSHAFT Shaft End-Play	CRANKSHAFT Thrust on No.	CONNECTING ROD Journal Diameter	CONNECTING ROD Oil Clearance	CONNECTING ROD Side Clearance
'67-'74	6-225	2.7495-2.7505	.0005-.0015	.002-.007	3	2.1865-2.1875	.0005-.0015	.006-.012
'67-'68	8-273, 318	2.4495-2.5005	.0005-.0015	.002-.007	3	2.124-2.125	.0005-.0025	.006-.014
'69-'74	8-318, 340	2.4495-2.5005	.0005-.0015	.002-.007	3	2.124-2.125	.0005-.0025	.009-.017
'71-'74	8-360	2.8095-2.8105	.0005-.0025	.002-.007	3	2.124-2.125	.0005-.0015	.009-.017
'67-'74	8-361, 383, 400	2.6245-2.6255	.0005-.0015	.002-.007	3	2.3740-2.3750	.0005-.0015	.009-.017
'67-'74	426, 440	2.7495-2.7505	.0005-.0015	.002-.007	3	2.3740-2.3750	.001-.0020	.009-.017
'67-'68	426 Hemi	2.7495-2.7505	.0015-.0025	.002-.007	3	2.374-2.375	.0015-.0025	.009-.013
'69-'70	426 Hemi	2.7495-2.7505	.0015-.0025	.002-.007	3	2.374-2.375	.0015-.0025	.009-.017
'71	426 Hemi	2.7490-2.7500	.0015-.0030	.002-.007	3	2.3738-2.3745	.0015-.0025	.013-.017

RING GAP

Year	Engine	Top Compression	Bottom Compression
'67	8-273, 318	.010-.020	.010-.020
	6-225, 383, 426, 440	.013-.023	.013-.023
'68-'72	6-225, 8-273	.010-.020	.010-.020
	318, 340, 360 8-383, 400, 426, 440	.013-.023	.013-.023
'73-'74	6-225, 8-318, 360	.010-.020	.010-.020
'73-'74	8-340, 400, 440	.013-.023	.013-.023

Year	Engine	Oil Control
'67-'74	All engines	.015-.055

RING SIDE CLEARANCE

Year	Engine	Top Compression	Bottom Compression
'67-'74	All engines	.0015-.0030	.0015-.0030

Year	Engine	Oil Control
'67	8-273, 318, 426	.0002-.005
	6-225, 8-383, 440	.0000-.005
'68-'74	6-225, 8-273, 318 426, 340, 360	.0002-.005
	8-383, 440, 400	.0000-.005

ALTERNATOR AND REGULATOR SPECIFICATIONS

	ALTERNATOR			REGULATOR	Field Relay			Regulator		
Year	Part No. or Manufacturer	Field Current @ 12 V	Output (amps)	Part No. or Manufacturer	Air Gap (in.)	Point Gap (in.)	Volts to Close	Air Gap (in.)	Point Gap (in.)	Volts @ 75°
'67-'69	6 Cyl Models	2.38-2.75	26 ± 3	2098300①	.050①	.014	13.8	.015	.050	13.8-14.4
	V8 Std.—All	2.38-2.75	34.5 ± 3	2098300①	.050①	.014	13.8	.015	.050	13.8-14.4
	Heavy Duty, A/C	2.38-2.75	44 ± 3②	2098300①	.050①	.014	13.8	.015	.050	13.8-14.4
'70-'71	6 Cyl Models	2.38-2.75	26 ± 3	3438150			Not Adjustable			13.8-14.4
	V8 Std.—All	2.38-2.75	34.5 ± 3	3438150			Not Adjustable			13.8-14.4
	Heavy Duty, A/C	2.38-2.75	44.5 ± 3	3438150			Not Adjustable			13.8-14.4
	Special Equip.	2.38-2.75	51 ± 3	3438150			Not Adjustable			13.8-14.4
'72-'73	6 Cyl Models	2.5-3.1	26	3438150			Not Adjustable			13.8-14.4
	V8 Std.	2.5-3.1	39	3438150			Not Adjustable			13.8-14.4
	Heavy Duty, A/C	2.5-3.1	50	3438150			Not Adjustable			13.8-14.4
	Special Equip.	2.5-3.1	60	3438150			Not Adjustable			13.8-14.4
'74	6 Cyl Models	2.5-3.1	41	3438150			Not Adjustable			13.8-14.4
	V8 Std.	2.5-3.1	50	3438150			Not Adjustable			13.8-14.4
	Special Equip.	2.5-3.1	65	3438150			Not Adjustable			13.8-14.4

① Chrysler built-used interchangeably with #2444900, which is Essex wire built. Air gap setting is .032-.042 in., all other dimensions are identical with #2098300

② 51 amp special equipment model available

BRAKE SPECIFICATIONS

		MASTER CYLINDER		WHEEL CYLINDER			BRAKE DISC OR DRUM DIAMETER		
				Front			Front		
Year	Model	Disc	Drum	Disc	Drum	Rear	Disc	Drum	Rear
'67	Belvedere, Coronet	—	1.0	—	1.125	.9375	—	10.0	10.0
	Fury, VIP, Polara, Monaco	1.125	1.0①	②	1.125	.9375③	11.87	11.0	11.0
'68-'69	Coronet, Charger, Belvedere, Satellite	—	1.0	—	1.125	.9375	—	10.0④	10.0④
	Polara, Monaco, Fury, VIP	—	1.0	—	1.125	.9375	—	11.0	11.0
	Coronet, Charger, Belvedere, Satellite	1.125	—	2.00	—	.9375	11.75	—	10.0
	Fury, Polara, Monaco, VIP	1.125	—	2.375⑤	—	.9375	11.75	—	11.0
'70	Coronet, Charger, Belvedere, Satellite	—	1.0	—	1.125	.9375	—	10.0⑥	10.0⑥
	Polara, Monaco	—	1.0	—	1.125	.9375	—	11.0	11.0
	Coronet, Charger, Belvedere, Satellite models with disc brakes	1.125	—	2.750	—	.9375	10.72	—	11.0
	Fury, Polara, Monaco	1.125	—	2.750	—	.9375	11.75	—	11.0
'71-'72	Coronet, Charger, Satellite	—	1.0	—	1.187	.9375	—	10.0④	10.0④
	Polara, Monaco	—	1.0	—	1.187	.9375	—	11.0④	11.0④
	All with disc brakes	1.00⑦	—	2.750	—	.9375	11.75	—	11.0
'73-'74	Coronet, Charger, Satellite	1.00⑧	—	2.750	—	.9375	10.84	—	10.0⑨
	Polara, Monaco, Fury	1.03	—	2.750⑩	—	.9375	11.56	—	11.0⑪

① Budd type disc brakes—1.125 in.

② Budd type disc brakes—2.375 in., Kelsey Hayes, 1.638 in., Bendix, 2.00 in.

③ When car is equipped with front disc—.875 in.

④ 11 in. standard on some models, optional on all others

⑤ 1969—2.750 in.

⑥ 11 in. brakes optional

⑦ 1⅛ in. with Hemi engine

⑧ 1.03 with power brakes

⑨ 11 in. on station wagons

⑩ 3.100 beginning 1974

⑪ 11.6 beginning 1974

— Not applicable

PISTON CLEARANCE

Year	Engine	Piston to Bore Clearance (in.)
'67-'74	6-225	.0005-.0015
	8-318, 340, 360	.0005-.0015
	8-383, 400, 440	.0003-.0013
'67-'71	8-426 Hemi	.0025-.0035

WHEEL ALIGNMENT SPECIFICATIONS

Year	Model	Caster Range (deg)	Caster Pref Setting (deg)	Camber Range (deg)	Camber Pref Setting (deg)	Toe-in (in.)	Steering Axis Inclin.	Wheel Pivot Ratio (deg) Inner Wheel	Wheel Pivot Ratio (deg) Wheel Outer
'67-'69	M.S.—Coronet, Charger, Belvedere, Satellite	0 to 1N	½N	①	①	3/32 to 5/32	7½	20	17.8
	P.S.—Coronet, Charger, Belvedere, Satellite	¼P to 1¼P	¾P	①	①	3/32 to 5/32	7½	20	17.8
	M.S.—Fury, Monaco, Polara	0 to 1N	½N	①	①	3/32 to 5/32	7½	20	18.8
	P.S.—Fury, Monaco, Polara	¼P to 1¼P	¾P	①	①	3/32 to 5/32	7½	20	18.8
'70-'72	M.S.—Coronet, Charger, Belvedere, Satellite	½N ± ½	½N	①	①	3/32 to 5/32	7½	20	17.8
	P.S.—Coronet, Charger, Belvedere, Satellite	¾P ± ½	¾P	①	①	3/32 to 5/32	7½	20	17.8
	M.S.—Fury, Monaco, Polara	½N ± ½	½N	①	①	3/32 to 5/32	7½	20	18.8
	P.S.—Fury, Monaco, Polara	¼ to 1¼P⑤	¾P⑤	①	①	3/32 to 5/32	7½	20	18.8
'73-'74	M.S.—Coronet, Charger, Satellite	1 5/16N to 1/16P	5/8N	⑥	⑥	⅛ ± 3/32	7½	20	17.8
	P.S.—Coronet Charger, Satellite	1/16N to 1 5/16P	5/8P	⑥	⑥	⅛ ± 3/32	7½	20	17.8
	P.S.—Fury, Monaco, Polara	1/16N to 1 5/16P	5/8P	⑥	⑥	⅛ ± 3/32	7½	20	18.8

M.S. Manual steering
P.S. Power steering
N Negative
P Positive

① Left—¼P to ¾P; ½P preferred
Right 0 to ½P; ¼P preferred
② Heavy duty—2⅛ ± ⅛
③ Fury sta. wag., Monaco, Polara, Custom 880—1⅛ ± ⅛
④ Sta. wag.—1¾ ± ⅛
⑤ 1970—0 to 1N (½N preferred)
⑥ Left—⅛P to ⅞P; ½P preferred
Right—⅛N to ⅝P; ¼P preferred

FRONT END HEIGHT

Year	Model	Front End Height ▲
'67-'69	M.S.—Coronet, Charger, Belvedere, Satellite	1⅞ ± ⅛
	P.S.—Coronet, Charger, Belvedere, Satellite	1⅞ ± ⅛
	M.S.—Fury, Monaco, Polara	1⅜ ± ⅛①
	P.S.—Fury, Monaco, Polara	1⅜ ± ⅛①
'70-'74	M.S.—Coronet, Charger, Belvedere, Satellite	1⅞ ± ⅛②
	P.S.—Coronet, Charger, Belvedere, Satellite	1⅞ ± ⅛②
	M.S.—Fury, Monaco, Polara	1⅜ ± ⅛①
	P.S.—Fury, Monaco, Polara	1⅜ ± ⅛①

① Monaco, Polara—1⅛ ± ⅛
② '71-'74—1⅝ ± ⅛
▲ See text for procedure

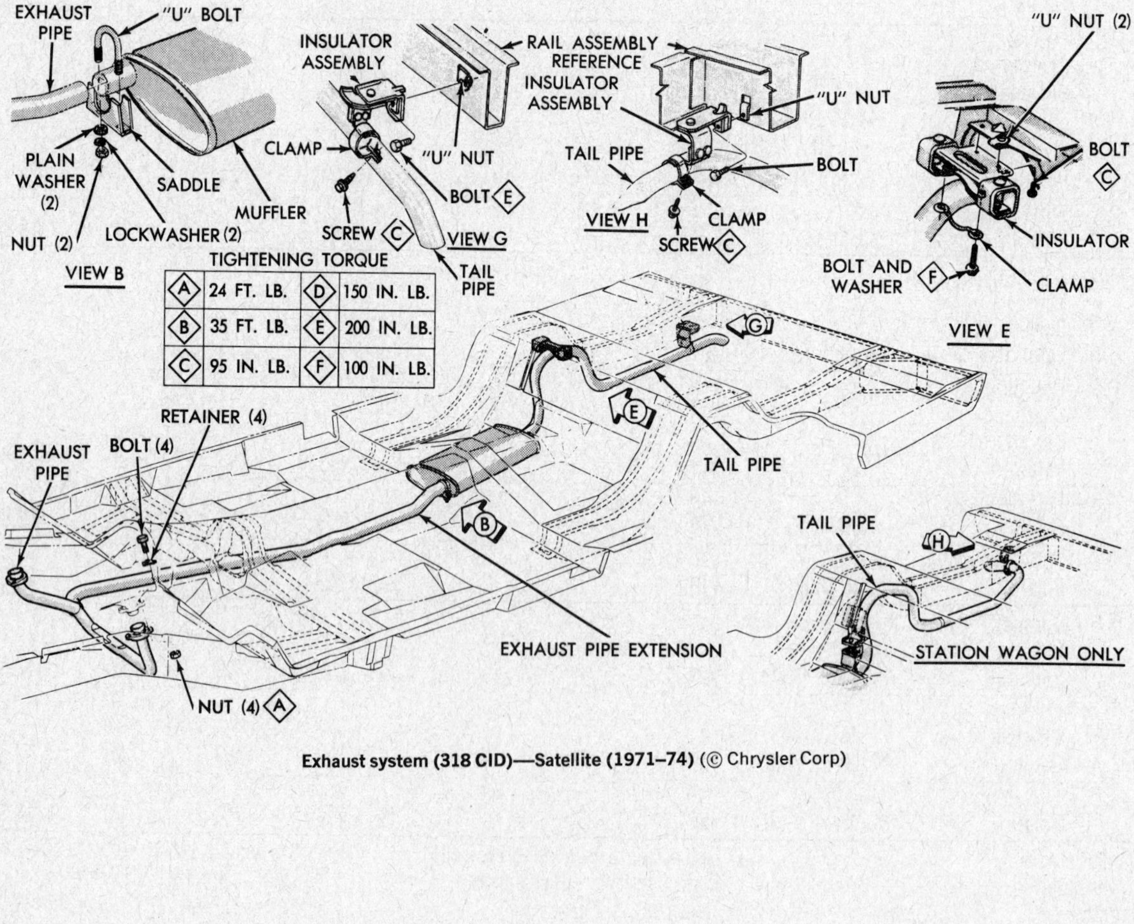
EXHAUST PIPE
"U" BOLT
PLAIN WASHER (2)
SADDLE
MUFFLER
NUT (2)
LOCKWASHER (2)
VIEW B
INSULATOR ASSEMBLY
CLAMP
"U" NUT
BOLT E
SCREW C
VIEW G
TAIL PIPE
RAIL ASSEMBLY REFERENCE
INSULATOR ASSEMBLY
"U" NUT
TAIL PIPE
BOLT
VIEW H
CLAMP
SCREW C
"U" NUT (2)
BOLT C
INSULATOR
BOLT AND WASHER F
CLAMP
VIEW E
TIGHTENING TORQUE
A 24 FT. LB.
B 35 FT. LB.
C 95 IN. LB.
D 150 IN. LB.
E 200 IN. LB.
F 100 IN. LB.
RETAINER (4)
EXHAUST PIPE
BOLT (4)
TAIL PIPE
EXHAUST PIPE EXTENSION
NUT (4) A
TAIL PIPE
STATION WAGON ONLY

Exhaust system (318 CID)—Satellite (1971–74) (© Chrysler Corp)

NOTE: Service procedures for the Charging System, Starting System, Ignition System, Cooling System, Fuel System, Emission Control Systems, Engine and Clutch apply to Chrysler and Imperial models, as well.

CHARGING SYSTEM

The alternator is basically an alternating current generator with solid-state rectifiers to convert AC current to DC current for charging the battery. The solid-state rectifiers are located between the battery alternator coils; since they are one-way current flow devices, they eliminate any need in the charging circuit for a cutout relay. A solid-state voltage regulator, used since 1970, maintains correct charging voltage by varying the duty cycle of a series of pulses to the alternator field. Pulse rate is controlled by the ignition frequency of the engine.

Before undertaking any electrical system service, the battery must be disconnected. Never attempt to polarize or short any component of the system.

Charging System troubleshooting and repairs can be found in the Unit Repair Section.

Alternator R&R

To remove alternator:

1. Disconnect battery.
2. Disconnect Bat. and Fld. leads from alternator.
3. Remove alternator by removing two mounting bolts and belt tensioner bracket bolt.
4. To reinstall: reverse the above.

Never attempt to polarize an alternator, and never short the regulator.

Regulator

Removal and Installation

1. Disconnect the battery.
2. Remove all electrical leads.
3. Remove all attaching bolts and lift off regulator.
4. To install, reverse the removal procedure.

Caution Never attempt to short the regulator.

STARTING SYSTEM

All Chrysler models are equipped with one of two types of starter: a direct-drive type, or a 3.5 : 1 reduction gear type. The reduction gear type of starter may be identified by the battery terminal on the starter being installed at an angle; the direct-drive type starter battery terminal is parallel to the starter case.

Both types of starters have solenoids which are mounted directly on the starter assembly. Therefore, the starter must be removed from the car to service the solenoid and motor brushes.

Starter

Removal and Installation

1. Disconnect the ground cable at the battery.
2. Remove the cable from the starter.
3. Disconnect the solenoid leads at their solenoid terminals.
4. Remove the starter securing bolts and withdraw the starter from the engine flywheel housing. On some models with automatic transmissions, the oil cooler tube bracket will interfere with starter removal. In this case, remove the starter securing bolts, slide the cooler tube bracket off the stud and then withdraw the starter.
5. Installation is the reverse of the above. Be sure that the starter and flywheel housing mating surfaces are free of dirt and oil.

IGNITION SYSTEM

Chrysler ignition systems may be divided into two circuits: a low-voltage primary section, consisting of the ammeter, battery, ignition switch, ballast resistor, ignition coil primary winding, vehicle frame, contact points, and condenser; and a secondary high-voltage section, consisting of the coil secondary winding, distributor cap and rotor, spark plugs, and vehicle frame.

Any ignition systems trouble should include a check of the ballast resistor. Its function is to reduce current flow during low-speed operation and allow high-current flow during high-speed operation. This tends to increase contact point life. While the starter is operating, the ballast resistor is bypassed, allowing full battery voltage to flow into the ignition primary system.

Ignition Retard Solenoid

1971 and Earlier Models

This unit's function is to retard ignition timing at closed throttle. *Located on the distributor side, this solenoid must be operating when ignition timing is checked.* To check whether the solenoid is operating, disconnect the ground lead after timing is set. If engine idle speed increases noticeably, the solenoid is functioning properly.

Ignition Advance Solenoid

1972-74 Models

This solenoid, located on the distributor side, is connected to the starter relay so that it operates only during engine cranking to improve starting.

When the engine fires, this solenoid ceases to operate. If the solenoid is not operating, it will affect starting, but not drivability. A possible sign of non-operation is popping through the carburetor during engine cranking.

To check operation, idle engine and connect a jumper wire from the battery to the solenoid lead. If the solenoid is operating properly, the engine speed will increase noticeably.

Caution Disconnect jumper wire as soon as possible after checking solenoid operation.

Electronic Ignition

An electronic ignition system is now standard on Dodge/Plymouth vehicles. This type of ignition system has no contact points; consequently, there is no dwell adjustment. The only regular ignition system maintenance required is inspection of the wiring and spark plug replacement (check timing on occasion only).

To determine whether a car is equipped with electronic ignition, check for a double primary lead from the distributor, a dual ballast resistor located on the firewall, and a control unit located either on the left wheel housing or the firewall.

If the electronic ignition is not functioning properly but the wiring is in good condition, refer to the Unit Repair section for proper service.

Detailed information on distributor drive, direction of distributor rotation, cylinder numbering, firing order, point gap, point dwell, timing mark location, spark plugs, and spark advance will be found in the Specification Tables.

Distributor Assembly Removal

1. Take off the cap and wire assembly.
2. Disconnect the primary coil wire and vacuum control tube.
3. Mark the relative positions of the distributor and rotor on the engine block.
4. Loosen the distributor mounting and lift out the distributor.

NOTE: to simplify reinstallation, do not disturb the engine while the distributor is out.

5. Reinstall by reversing the above procedure, aligning the distributor rotor and the mark on the block when installing the distributor.

Distributor Replacement (When Engine has been Disturbed)

Slant 6 Engine

1. Remove No. 1 spark plug and, with the thumb closing the hole,

rotate the engine until No. 1 piston is up on compression at top dead center. This is determined by the pressure on the thumb and the 0 mark on the crankshaft pully hub being aligned with the timing pointer.

2. Rotate the rotor to a position just ahead of the No. 1 distributor cap terminal.
3. Lower the distributor into the opening, engaging distributor gear with drive gear on camshaft. With distributor fully seated on engine, rotor should be under the cap No. 1 tower with distributor contact points just opening.
4. Install cap, tighten hold-down arm screw and check timing with a timing light.

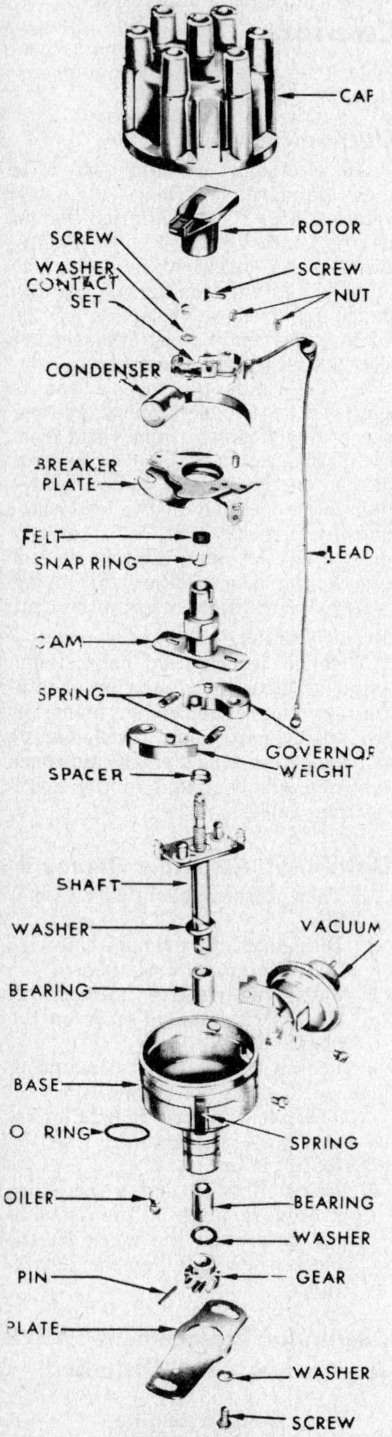

CAP
ROTOR
SCREW
WASHER
CONTACT SET
SCREW
NUT
CONDENSER
BREAKER PLATE
FELT
SNAP RING
LEAD
CAM
SPRING
GOVERNOR WEIGHT
SPACER
SHAFT
WASHER
VACUUM
BEARING
BASE
O RING
SPRING
OILER
BEARING
WASHER
PIN
GEAR
PLATE
WASHER
SCREW

6 cylinder distributor
(© Chrysler Corp)

V8 Engine

Rotate the crankshaft until No. 1 cylinder is at top dead center. The pointer on the chain case cover should be over the 0 mark on the crankshaft pulley. The slot in the intermediate shaft which carries the gear that drives the oil pump and the distributor, should be parallel with the crankshaft.

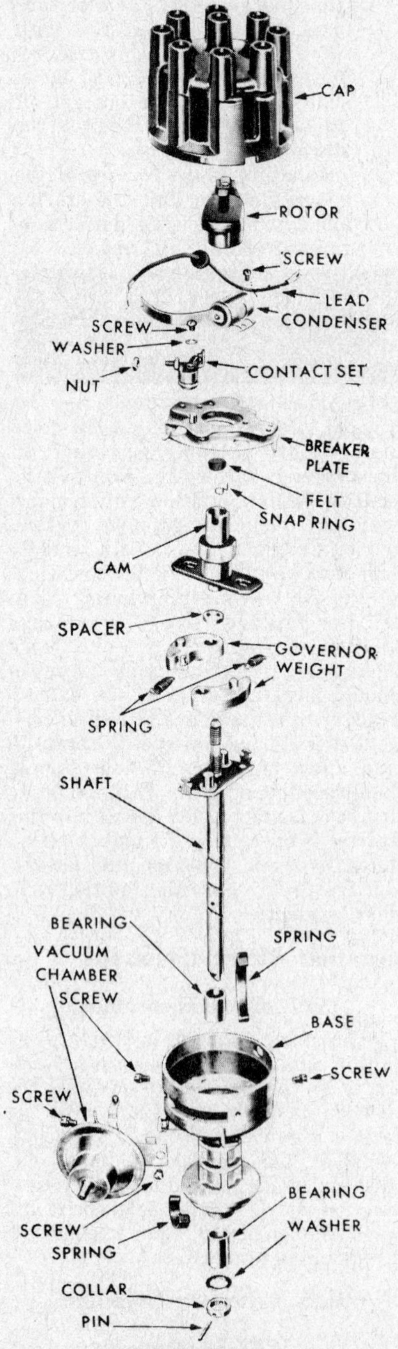

CAP
ROTOR
SCREW
LEAD
CONDENSER
SCREW
WASHER
NUT
CONTACT SET
BREAKER PLATE
FELT
SNAP RING
CAM
SPACER
GOVERNOR WEIGHT
SPRING
SHAFT
BEARING
VACUUM CHAMBER
SCREW
SPRING
BASE
SCREW
SCREW
BEARING
WASHER
SCREW
SPRING
COLLAR
PIN

V8 distributor
(© Chrysler Corp)

Hold the distributor over the mounting pad on the cylinder block so that the distributor body flange coincides with the mounting pad and the rotor points to the No. 1 cylinder firing position.

Install the distributor while holding the rotor in position, allowing it to move only enough to engage the slot in the drive gear.

Breaker Points and Condenser Replacement

Single Point Distributor

1. Remove the distributor cap. Do not pull the wires from the cap. Pull the rotor from the shaft.
2. Carefully note the position of all leads and remove the securing nut. Loosen the point plate lockscrew and remove the points and condenser from the vehicle.
3. With a clean, lint-free rag, wipe any of the old cam grease from the distributor cam. Apply fresh cam lubricant sparingly.
4. Insert a new point set with the contact heel resting on the highest point of the cam lobe. Set point gap to specifications with a feeler gauge. The setting is correct when the feeler gauge is removed with a light drag. Install the condenser and secure the leads. Lock the point securing screws.
5. Replace the distributor cap and rotor. Check the dwell with a dwell meter. Adjust the point gap as necessary.
6. Road-test vehicle.

Dual Point Distributor

The removal and installation of dual contact points is the same as for a single point set. The point adjustment is also the same, except that each set must be set while its rubbing block is on the high point of the cam lobe. The dwell adjustment of dual points is slightly different because one set of contacts must be blocked open with a clean insulator while the opposite point set is adjusted to specifications. When correctly adjusted, tighten the lockscrew. Block open this contact set and adjust this contact set in the same manner as the first. Check the point dwell. If the contacts have been installed and adjusted correctly, the dwell angle should be as specified for both contact sets.

Distributor (Point) Dwell Checking

Correct distributor dwell angle is essential to good ignition performance and contact life. To test:

1. Disconnect the vacuum line. If the vehicle is equipped with an ignition retard solenoid (some 1971 and earlier models only), disconnect it.
2. Connect the red lead of the dwell

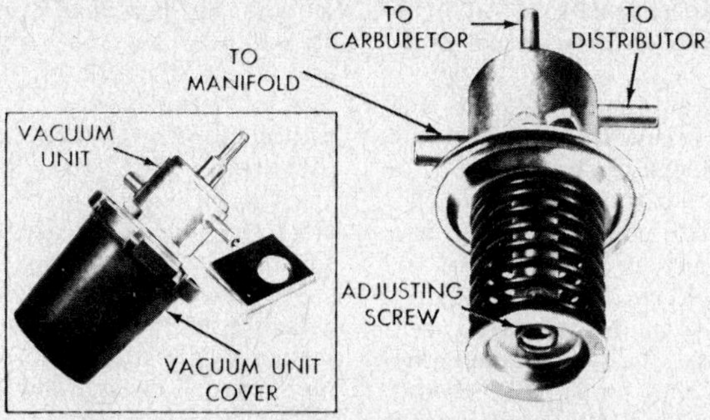
TO CARBURETOR
TO DISTRIBUTOR
TO MANIFOLD
VACUUM UNIT
ADJUSTING SCREW
VACUUM UNIT COVER

Distributor vacuum unit
(© Chrysler Corp)

meter to distributor terminal of the coil and the black lead to ground. Set the selector switch to proper number of engine cylinders.

3. Start the engine and allow it to operate at idle speed.
4. Observe the dwell meter reading. If it is not within specifications, the contact gap may be incorrect, the cam may be worn, or the movable contact arm may be distorted. Connect the ignition retard solenoid (if so equipped) and the vacuum line.

Ignition Timing

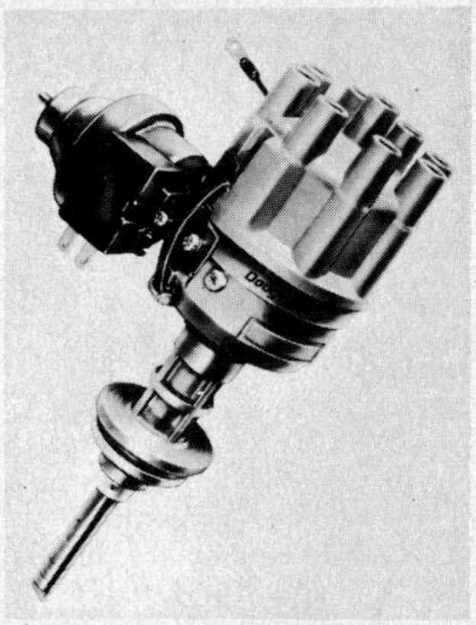

High performance distributor with solenoid retard
(©Chrysler Corp)

NOTE: Before timing engine, check information on ignition retard/advance solenoids.

The ignition timing test indicates correct timing of the engine only at idle and with the engine hot. Check timing as follows:

1. Disconnect the vacuum hose at the distributor and plug the line.
2. Connect a strobe light to No. 1 spark plug and to the battery terminals.
3. Start the engine and set it to the specified idle speed with the transmission in Neutral.
4. Loosen the distributor locking screw so that the housing can be rotated.
5. Check the timing by aiming the strobe light at the vibration damper. If timing is ahead of the mark, turn the distributor housing in the direction of rotor-rotation. This will retard timing. If it is past the mark, rotate the distributor against its direction of rotation to advance the timing. When timing is adjusted to specifications, tighten the distributor lockscrew and reconnect the vacuum hose to the distributor.

FUEL SYSTEM

The fuel system consists of three basic parts: the fuel pump; filter, and carburetor(s). The fuel pumps used on the six-cylinder and all big blocks (361–440 cu in.) are driven by a small cam eccentric cast into the main camshaft. On the 273, 318, 340, and 360 engines, the pump is driven by a pressed steel eccentric secured on the gear end of the camshaft. On the six-cylinder and 273, 318, 340, and 360 engines, the pump is driven directly by the pump rocker arm pressing on the cam eccentric. On the big block engines, there is a push rod located between the pump rocker arm and the driving eccentric.

All Dodge and Plymouth vehicles are equipped with a fuel filter located in the fuel line between the fuel pump and carburetor. Servicing is by replacement only.

Since 1967, Dodge and Plymouth vehicles have utilized many different types of carburetors. Some 1967 and all 1968 and later carburetors incorporate modifications to reduce engine exhaust emissions. Carburetor modifications for 1967–69 are part of Chrysler's Cleaner Air Package and 1970 and later models are part of the Cleaner Air System. The only carburetor changes used with the Cleaner Air Package are the installation of carburetor mixture limiter stops on the carburetor idle mixture adjustment screws, and leaner air-/fuel mixture. With the Cleaner Air System, in addition to the above mentioned changes, faster-acting chokes were added, and as of 1972 the choke is not adjustable. On some models, solenoid-operated throttle stops and distributor retard (until 1971) mechanisms were installed. In 1972. the distributor retard was exchanged for a distributor advance solenoid. The throttle stop raises the engine idle speed to reduce engine emissions, but de-energizes when the ignition is shut off to prevent the engine from dieseling. The distributor retard solenoid is activated when the idle speed adjustment screw returns to the curb idle position and contacts a sensor. This sensor, mounted on the carburetor, retards ignition timing when the engine idles. The distributor advance solenoid is connected to the starter relay so that it is activated only during engine cranking. It does not operate when the engine is running.

Some carburetors incorporate an internally mounted hot idle compensator. This compensator is designed to induct additional air to the carburetor during low-speed, high-temperature operation.

Until 1971, both the 426 Hemi and the 440 Six Pack engines were equipped with multiple carburetors. The Hemi used two Carter AFBs. Both carburetors were equipped with complete idle systems; they must be adjusted and synchronized to obtain a satisfactory engine idle. The 440 Six Pack was equipped with three Holley 2300 two-barrel carburetors. Only the center carburetor was equipped with an idle system; the inboard and outboard carburetors contained no idle adjustments.

Fuel Pump Removal

All Models

Remove all lines at the fuel pump, and the pump-to-block mounting screws. Remove the pump.

Fuel Filter

Removal and Installation

Locate the filter in the fuel line between the fuel pump and the carburetor. Using hose-clamp pliers, remove the attaching clamps and pull off the filter. Reverse the procedure to install. Be sure that the arrow on the filter is pointing toward the carburetor (direction of fuel flow).

Idle Speed and Mixture Adjustments

NOTE: 1967 CAP carburetors can be identified by a green tag attached to the air horn.

1967 Without CAP

Adjust with air cleaner installed.

1. Run engine at fast idle to stabilize engine temperature.
2. Make sure the choke plate is fully released.
3. Attach a tachometer of known accuracy to the engine.
4. If equipped with air conditioning, turn the air conditioner ON.
5. On models with six cylinder engine, turn the headlights on high beam.

6. Adjust the carburetor idle speed screw to obtain a curb idle speed of 500 rpm (550 if equipped with air conditioner).
7. Turn the idle mixture screws in or out to obtain the highest rpm possible. After obtaining the highest rpm, turn each idle mixture screw clockwise until the engine speed starts to drop, then turn the mixture screw counterclockwise just enough to regain the lost rpm.
8. If the mixture adjustment procedure has changed the curb idle speed, adjust the idle speed.

hot idle compensator valve is fully seated in the closed position.

8. Turn the engine idle speed adjustment screw in or out to adjust idle speed to specification. If equipped with an electric solenoid throttle positioner, turn the solenoid adjusting screw in or out to obtain specified rpm. Then, adjust the curb idle speed screw until it just touches the stop on the carburetor body. Now, back the curb idle speed adjusting screw out one full turn.

Holley 4V) have lead or cup plugs installed over the idle mixture screws and an additional off idle mixture control screw added to the body of the carburetor. When adjusting the carburetor idle speed and mixture, use the off idle adjustment screw to alter the idle speed air/fuel mixture so it conforms to the 14.2:1 ratio specified. If unable to obtain an acceptable engine idle by adjusting this screw, refer to the procedure to correct rough idle and low speed surge.

Rough Idle and Low Speed Surge—All 1967-74 Except Hemi

Rough idle and low speed surge

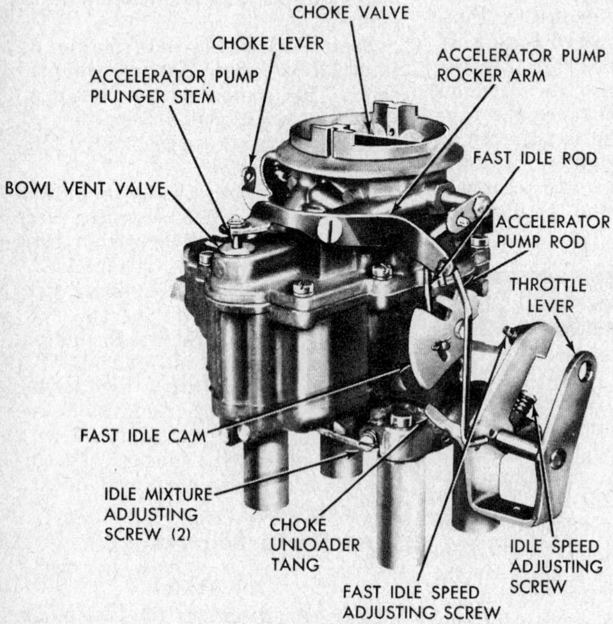
CHOKE VALVE
CHOKE LEVER
ACCELERATOR PUMP PLUNGER STEM
ACCELERATOR PUMP ROCKER ARM
BOWL VENT VALVE
FAST IDLE ROD
ACCELERATOR PUMP ROD
THROTTLE LEVER
FAST IDLE CAM
IDLE MIXTURE ADJUSTING SCREW (2)
CHOKE UNLOADER TANG
IDLE SPEED ADJUSTING SCREW
FAST IDLE SPEED ADJUSTING SCREW

Stromberg carburetor adjustments
(© Chrysler Corp)

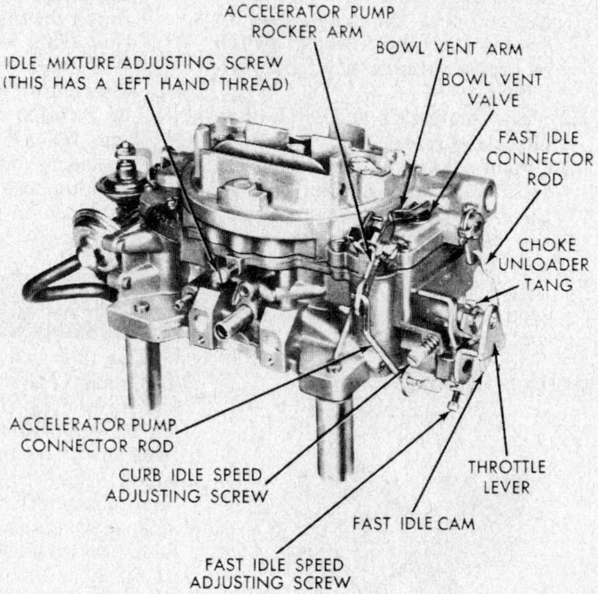
ACCELERATOR PUMP ROCKER ARM
BOWL VENT ARM
IDLE MIXTURE ADJUSTING SCREW (THIS HAS A LEFT HAND THREAD)
BOWL VENT VALVE
FAST IDLE CONNECTOR ROD
CHOKE UNLOADER TANG
ACCELERATOR PUMP CONNECTOR ROD
CURB IDLE SPEED ADJUSTING SCREW
THROTTLE LEVER
FAST IDLE CAM
FAST IDLE SPEED ADJUSTING SCREW

1968-69 Carter AVS carburetor adjustments
(© Chrysler Corp)

1967-74 with CAP or CAS Except 426 Hemi

Adjust with air cleaner installed.

NOTE: this is the basic carburetor adjustment procedure, any specific exceptions are listed below.

1. Run engine at fast idle to stabilize engine temperature.
2. Make sure choke plate is fully released.
3. Attach a tachometer of known accuracy to the engine.
4. Connect an exhaust analyzer to the engine and insert the probe as far into the tailpipe as possible. On vehicles with dual exhaust, insert the probe into the left tailpipe as this is the side without the heat riser valve.
5. Check ignition timing and adjust it as required to conform to specification.
6. If equipped with air conditioning, turn the air conditioner off. On models with six-cylinder engines, turn the headlights on high beam.
7. Place the transmission in the Neutral position. Make sure the
9. Turn each idle mixture adjustment screw 1/16 turn richer (counterclockwise). Wait 10 seconds and observe the reading on the exhaust gas analyzer. Continue this procedure until the meter indicates a definite increase in the richness of the mixture.

NOTE: this step is very important. A carburetor that is set too lean will cause the exhaust gas analyzer to give a false reading indicating a rich mixture. Because of this, the carburetor must first be known to have a rich mixture to verify the reading on the exhaust gas analyzer.

10. After verifying the reading obtained on the meter, adjust the mixture screws to get an air/fuel ratio of 14.2:1. Turn the mixture screws clockwise (leaner) to raise the meter reading or counterclockwise (richer) to lower the meter reading.

1968-69 383 and 440 V8

The carburetors used on these engines (Ball & Ball 2V, Carter 4V or

can be the result of improper balance of the idle mixture adjustment in the right and left carburetor bores. To correct this condition, perform the following operation.

1. On 1968-69 383 or 440 V8, remove the lead plugs from the two limiter screws in the base of the carburetor (Ball & Ball or Carter) or the cup plugs from the sides of the primary metering body (Holley). The best way to remove the lead plugs is with a small drill and easy-out. Use a sharp punch to remove cup plugs from a Holley carburetor.
2. On all other models, remove the plastic limiter caps from the idle mixture adjustment screws.
3. Perform Steps 1-8 of the idle speed and mixture adjustment procedure.
4. On 1968-69 383 or 440 V8, turn the single off idle mixture adjustment screw counterclockwise (richer) until it is seated, then turn it clockwise (lean) ¾ turn. Do not disturb this adjustment during the remainer of this procedure.

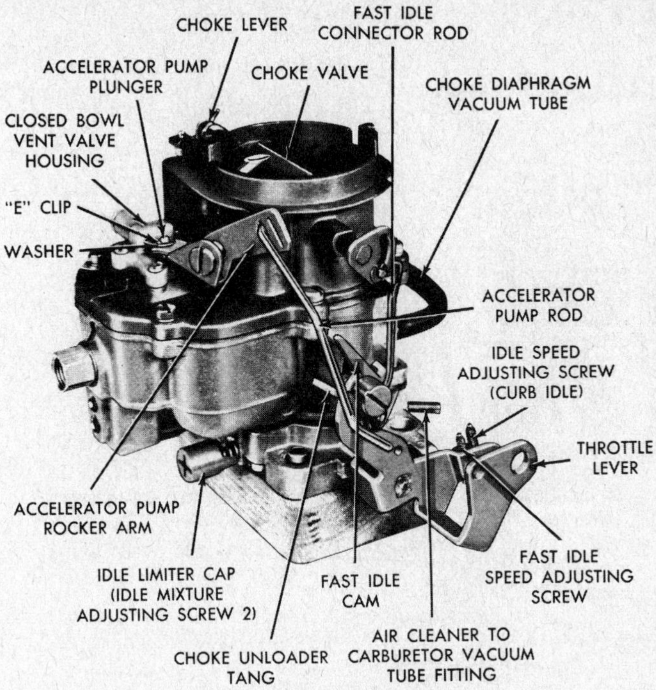
CHOKE LEVER
FAST IDLE CONNECTOR ROD
ACCELERATOR PUMP PLUNGER
CHOKE VALVE
CHOKE DIAPHRAGM VACUUM TUBE
CLOSED BOWL VENT VALVE HOUSING
"E" CLIP
WASHER
ACCELERATOR PUMP ROD
IDLE SPEED ADJUSTING SCREW (CURB IDLE)
THROTTLE LEVER
ACCELERATOR PUMP ROCKER ARM
FAST IDLE SPEED ADJUSTING SCREW
IDLE LIMITER CAP (IDLE MIXTURE ADJUSTING SCREW 2)
FAST IDLE CAM
AIR CLEANER TO CARBURETOR VACUUM TUBE FITTING
CHOKE UNLOADER TANG

Carter carburetor adjustments
(© Chrysler Corp)

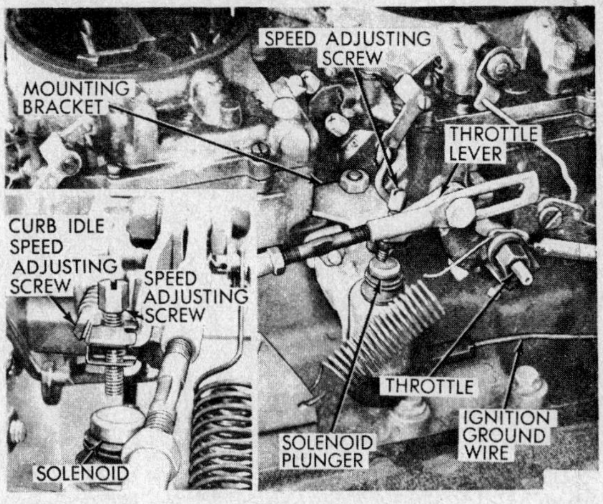
SPEED ADJUSTING SCREW
MOUNTING BRACKET
THROTTLE LEVER
CURB IDLE SPEED ADJUSTING SCREW
SPEED ADJUSTING SCREW
THROTTLE
IGNITION GROUND WIRE
SOLENOID PLUNGER
SOLENOID

Solenoid throttle positioner adjustment
(© Chrysler Corp)

5. Turn both idle mixture adjustment screws clockwise until they are lightly seated. On some models, the idle mixture screws have a prevailing torque feature which causes the screws to become more difficult to turn as they approach the seated position.
6. On Ball & Ball carburetors, turn both idle mixture screws 1½ turns counterclockwise. On Carter and Holley carburetors, turn both idle mixture screws 2-3 turns counterclockwise.
7. Start the engine and perform Steps 9-11 of the idle speed and mixture adjustment procedure.

NOTE: in order to obtain a smooth idle, it is important that both mixture adjustment screws are adjusted an equal number of turns from the fully seated position.

8. Install lead plugs, cup plugs, or plastic caps on the idle mixture screws.

426 Hemi

Because each carburetor is equipped with a complete idle system, accurate carburetor synchronization is very important. After adjusting the idle speed and mixture, it should be rechecked and rebalanced as required in the outside ambient temperature after a road test.

Adjust with air cleaner removed.

1. Run engine at fast idle to stabilize engine temperature.
2. Make sure the choke plate is fully released.
3. Attach a tachometer of known accuracy to the engine.
4. If equipped with a hot idle compensator valve, make sure it is fully seated in the closed position.

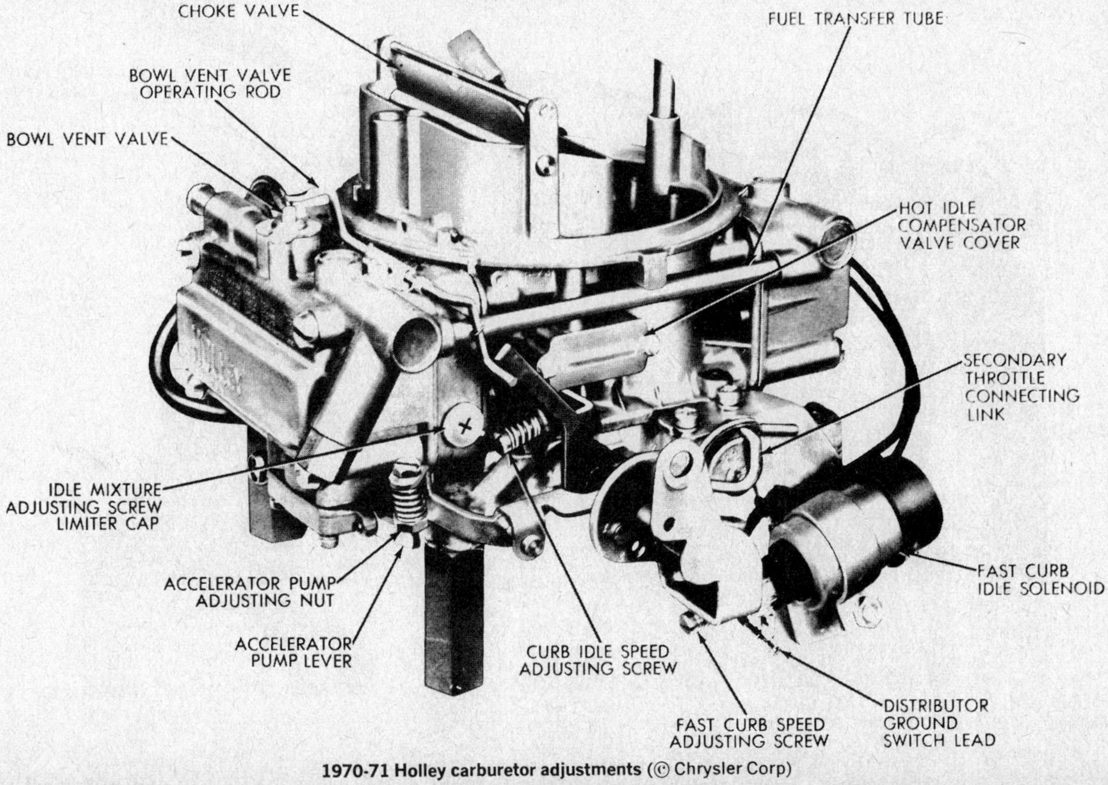
CHOKE VALVE
FUEL TRANSFER TUBE
BOWL VENT VALVE OPERATING ROD
BOWL VENT VALVE
HOT IDLE COMPENSATOR VALVE COVER
SECONDARY THROTTLE CONNECTING LINK
IDLE MIXTURE ADJUSTING SCREW LIMITER CAP
FAST CURB IDLE SOLENOID
ACCELERATOR PUMP ADJUSTING NUT
ACCELERATOR PUMP LEVER
CURB IDLE SPEED ADJUSTING SCREW
DISTRIBUTOR GROUND SWITCH LEAD
FAST CURB SPEED ADJUSTING SCREW

1970-71 Holley carburetor adjustments (© Chrysler Corp)

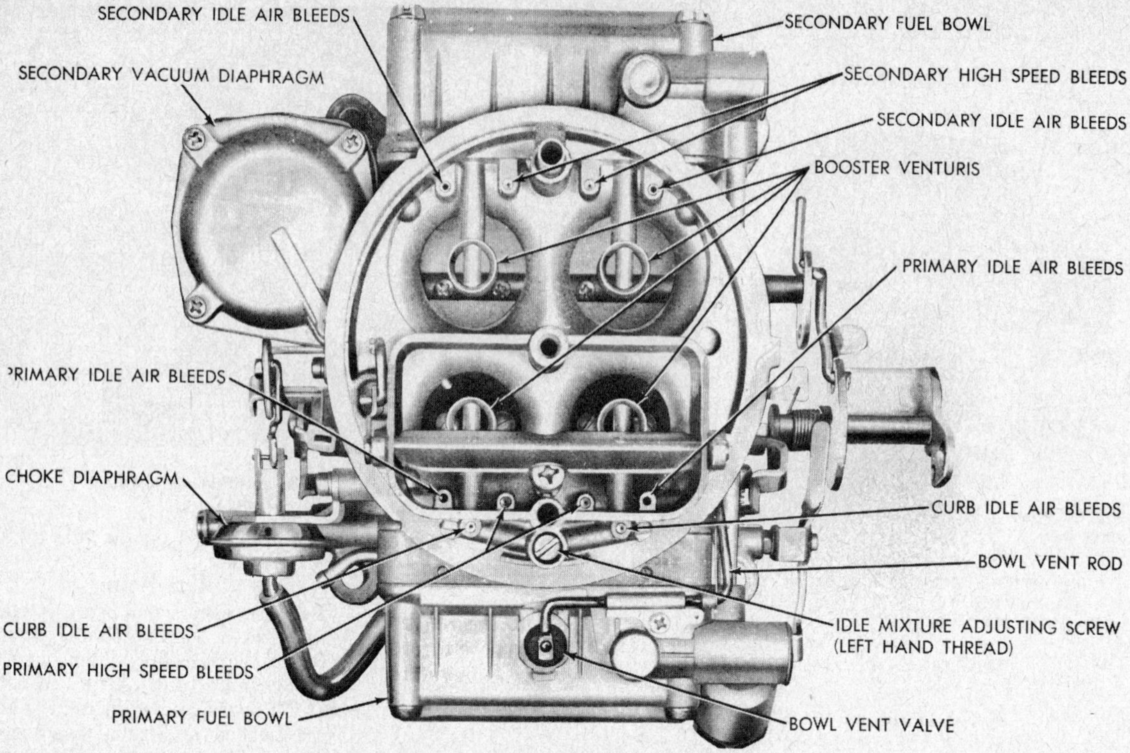
SECONDARY IDLE AIR BLEEDS
SECONDARY FUEL BOWL
SECONDARY VACUUM DIAPHRAGM
SECONDARY HIGH SPEED BLEEDS
SECONDARY IDLE AIR BLEEDS
BOOSTER VENTURIS
PRIMARY IDLE AIR BLEEDS
PRIMARY IDLE AIR BLEEDS
CHOKE DIAPHRAGM
CURB IDLE AIR BLEEDS
BOWL VENT ROD
IDLE MIXTURE ADJUSTING SCREW (LEFT HAND THREAD)
CURB IDLE AIR BLEEDS
PRIMARY HIGH SPEED BLEEDS
PRIMARY FUEL BOWL
BOWL VENT VALVE

1968-69 Holley carburetor adjustments (© Chrysler Corp)

5. Place the transmission in the Neutral position.
6. Turn the idle speed adjustment screws in or out to adjust the engine idle speed to specification. If equipped with an electric solenoid throttle positioner, turn the solenoid adjusting screw in or out to obtain specified engine idle speed. Then, turn the curb idle speed adjusting screw clockwise until it just touches the stop on the carburetor throttle body. Next, back the curb idle speed adjusting screw out one full turn.
7. Adjust each idle mixture screw to obtain the highest rpm possible. Repeat this operation until all four mixture adjustment screws have been properly adjusted and balanced.
8. If the idle mixture adjustment procedure has changed the engine idle speed, adjust the idle speed.

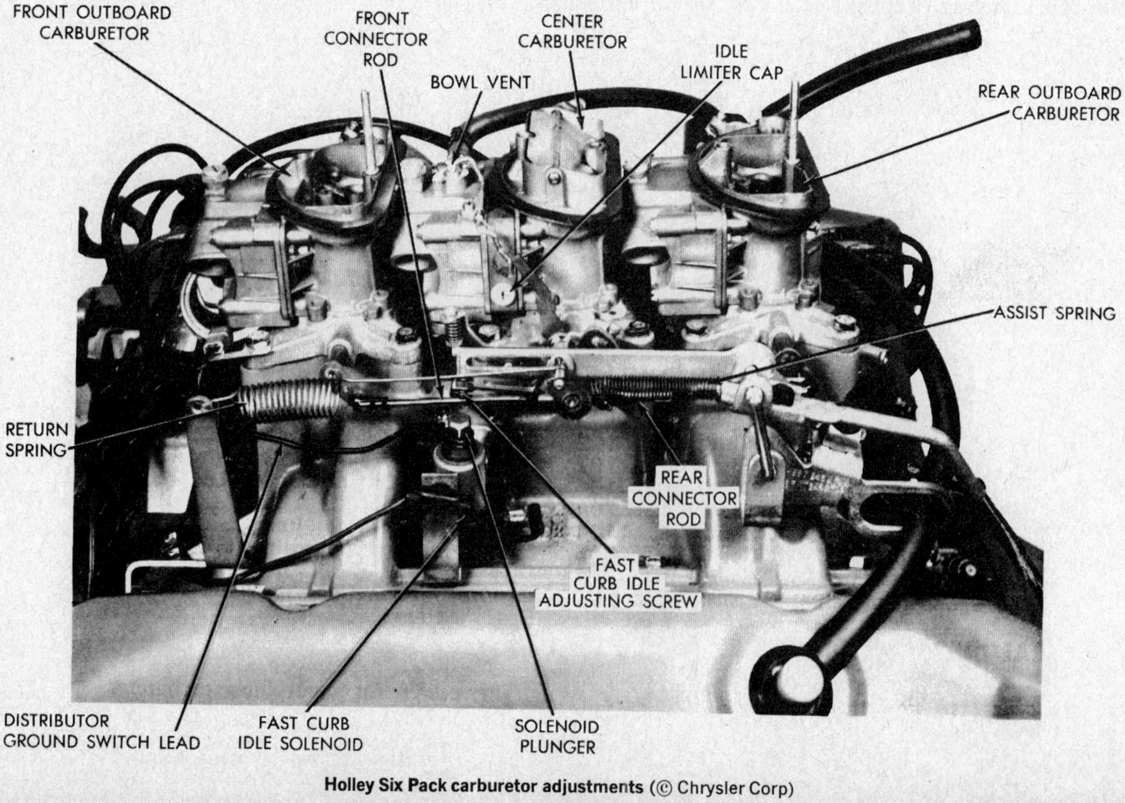
FRONT OUTBOARD CARBURETOR
FRONT CONNECTOR ROD
BOWL VENT
CENTER CARBURETOR
IDLE LIMITER CAP
REAR OUTBOARD CARBURETOR
ASSIST SPRING
RETURN SPRING
REAR CONNECTOR ROD
FAST CURB IDLE ADJUSTING SCREW
DISTRIBUTOR GROUND SWITCH LEAD
FAST CURB IDLE SOLENOID
SOLENOID PLUNGER

Holley Six Pack carburetor adjustments (© Chrysler Corp)

Balancing Multiple-Carburetor Installations

426 Hemi

There is no actual adjustment of the external carburetor linkage to synchronize the twin carburetors. Proper balancing of the carburetor idle speeds as described in the idle speed for the 426 Hemi will ensure correct and mixture adjustment procedure carburetor synchronization.

440 Six Pack

Because only the center carburetor has provisions for adjusting the engine idle speed and fuel mixture, these adjustments are performed using the procedure for single-carburetor installations. The throttle rods which connect each outboard carburetor to the center carburetor can be adjusted for correct throttle synchronization using the procedure below.

1. Remove the air cleaner.
2. Remove the outboard throttle rod securing clips and disengage the front and rear rods from the throttle levers.
3. Be sure that the ignition switch is turned off. (This de-energizes the fast curb idle solenoid so that clearance can be obtained between the plunger and the fast curb idle adjusting screw.)
4. Close the throttle valves of all three carburetors and hold them in the closed position.
5. Shorten or lengthen the front and rear connector rods by turning each rod into or out of the threaded sleeve until the rod end can be inserted into the hole in the throttle lever smoothly.
6. Fit each throttle connector rod into its corresponding throttle lever and secure each rod with a clip.

Fast Curb Idle Speed Solenoid Adjustment

1970-74 Models (If So Equipped)

1. Bring the engine to operating temperature and attach a tachometer.
2. With the engine running, adjust the fast curb idle screw to the proper rpm for the vehicle in question.
3. Adjust the slow curb idle screw until the screw end just contacts the stop. Back the screw off one full turn; this should return the vehicle to the slow curb idle setting.
4. Test the above procedure by disconnecting the solenoid wire at the connector. Be sure not to let the lead short to the engine. Now reconnect the wire. The fast curb idle speed solenoid should not advance the throttle.

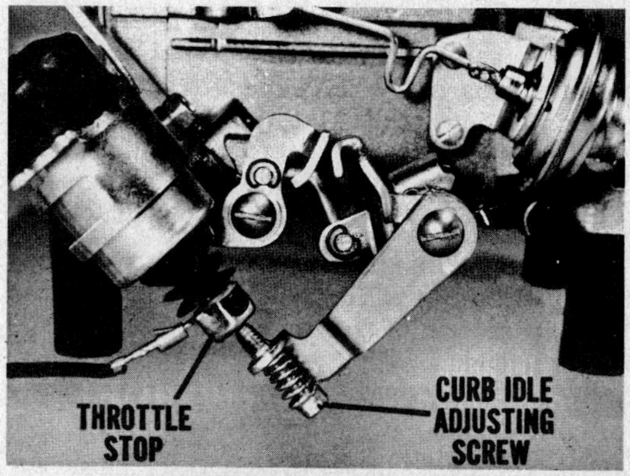
THROTTLE STOP
CURB IDLE ADJUSTING SCREW

Curb idle speed adjustment
(© Chrysler Corp)

COOLING SYSTEM

The main cooling system components are a tube and spacer-type radiator, a thermostat (temperature specifications vary with year and model), a fan which may have a varying number of blades (and may be a viscous-drive type), and a water pump. The type of fan and radiator size/equipment (such as a radiator shroud) vary with engine, accessories, and intended usage. Information on the water temperature gauge may be found in the Unit Repair Section.

Radiator Removal and Installation

1. Allow the cooling system to drain. On those vehicles with automatic transmissions, disconnect the oil cooler lines from the radiator bottom.
2. Remove both upper and lower radiator hoses. Remove the hose which runs to the coolant reserves system (if so equipped).
3. Remove the radiator shroud attaching bolts and tilt the shroud out of the way.
4. Remove the radiator attaching bolts. Remove radiator.

NOTE: When lifting the radiator, be sure not to damage the cooling fins.

5. To install the radiator, reverse the removal procedure. After finishing the installation, be sure to check the level of the coolant and the transmission oil.

Water Pump Removal

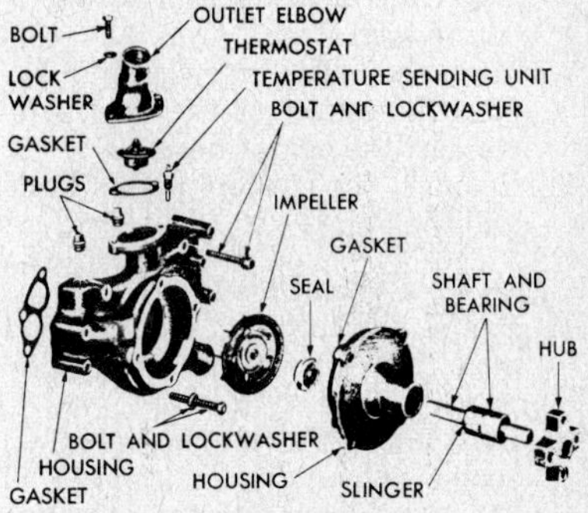
BOLT
OUTLET ELBOW
THERMOSTAT
LOCK WASHER
TEMPERATURE SENDING UNIT
BOLT AND LOCKWASHER
GASKET
PLUGS
IMPELLER
GASKET
SEAL
SHAFT AND BEARING
HUB
BOLT AND LOCKWASHER
HOUSING
GASKET
HOUSING
SLINGER

Typical water pump—B block engines
(© Chrysler Corp)

1967-71

1. Drain cooling system. Remove upper half of fan shroud if so equipped or set one piece shroud back on engine.
2. Loosen power steering pump, idler pulley and alternator. Remove all belts.
3. Remove fan, spacer or fluid drive, and pulley.

Caution Do not place a fluid drive unit with the shaft pointing downwards. Silicon fluid will drain into fan drive bearing and ruin grease.

4. Remove bolts attaching water pump to housing. Remove water pump and discard gasket.

1972-74

6 Cylinder Models without Air Conditioning and/or Air Pump

1. Drain the cooling system. If the engine is equipped with a fan shroud, remove and swing it back over the engine.
2. Remove the power steering and alternator belts.
3. Take off the fan, spacer, pulley, and bolts as a unit.
4. Move the lower hose clamp to bypass the center of the hose. Disconnect the heater hose and the lower hose of the water pump.
5. Remove the water pump bolts and the pump.

6 Cylinder Models with Air Conditioning and/or Air Pump

1. Remove the battery and drain the cooling system. Remove the fan shroud and swing it back over the engine.
2. Disconnect the transmission oil cooler lines (if automatic transmission) and remove the lower radiator hoses. Cap the openings to prevent the entry of dirt and excessive fluid loss.
3. Remove the radiator.

4. Loosen the alternator, power steering pump, idler pulley, and air pump.
5. Take off the fan, spacer, pulley, and bolts as an assembly. Remove all belts.
6. Remove the compressor and/or air pump bracket and secure it out of way.
7. Move the lower hose clamp to by-pass the center of the hose. Disconnect the heater hose.
8. Remove the water pump bolts and the pump.

V8 Removal

1. Drain the cooling system and move the fan shroud out of the way.
2. Disconnect the transmission oil cooler lines (automatic) and all radiator hoses. Cap the openings to prevent the entry of dirt or excessive fluid loss.
3. Remove the radiator, if necessary.
4. Loosen the alternator adjusting strap bolts. Remove the belts.
5. On 318-360 engines with no air conditioning, remove the alternator bracket bolts from the water pump. Swing the alternator out of the way and tighten the pivot bolt. On 318–360 engines with air conditioning, remove the idler pulley assembly and alternator with adjusting bracket.
6. Remove the fan, spacer/fluid drive, pulley, and bolts as an assembly.

Caution Do not let fluid drain into the fan-drive bearing.

7. Disconnect the heater and all by-pass hoses.
8. Remove the compressor-to-front mounting bracket bolts.
9. Remove the water pump attaching bolts and the water pump.
10. Carefully lift the compressor out of the way.

V8 Installation

1. Install the by-pass hose and position the clamp in the center of the hose.
2. Install the pump with a new gasket and torque it to 30 ft. lbs. Be sure that the pump turns freely.
3. Install the heater hose and route it near the by-pass hose clamps.
4. On V8s with air conditioning, install the front bracket on the compressor. Torque to 50 ft lbs. Torque the pump bolts to 30 ft lbs.
5. Replace the alternator, bracket, and idler pulley assembly. Torque to 30 ft lbs.
6. Install the compressor clutch assembly (if applicable).
7. Install the fan assembly. Check and adjust all belts.
8. Install the radiator, hoses, and transmission cooling lines.
9. Install fan shroud and fill the cooling system. Check the oil level in the transmission.

Thermostat

Removal and Installation

1. Drain the cooling system to below the level of the thermostat.
2. Remove the upper radiator hose from the thermostat housing flange. Remove the housing bolts, thermostat, and housing.
3. To install a thermostat, use a new gasket. On V8s, be sure that the pellet end is facing toward engine. Six-cylinder models must have the vent hole facing up. From this point, reverse the removal procedure.

EMISSION CONTROLS

NOTE: Additional information on the Emission Control System may be found in the emission systems unit repair section.

Positive Crankcase Ventilation

All models are equipped with a positive crankcase ventilation system which draws air into the engine through the oil filler cap or the air cleaner and circulates it through the engine. The air combines with vapors in the crankcase and exits the engine through a metering valve mounted in the rocker arm cover. The air-vapor mixture then re-enters the engine through the carburetor or intake manifold and passes into the combustion chamber where it is burned.

Cleaner Air Package (CAP)

Some 1967 and all 1968-69 models use this package to reduce engine exhaust emissions. Changes include the addition of limiters to the carburetor idle mixture screws, leaner carburetor mixtures and vacuum controlled ignition timing retard mechanisms.

Cleaner Air System (CAS)

All 1970 and later models are equipped with this type of exhaust emission control. This system consists of: heated carburetor air cleaner intake ducts, carburetor modifications, ignition timing controls, and reduced engine compression ratios.

In addition to the aforementioned controls, many new ones were added or modified since.

Intake Manifold/Cylinder Head Design Change

A change has been incorporated in intake manifold design to place all manifold branch runners on one level. This is in contrast to the previous, two-level design. This change was made to improve fuel vaporization during warm-up, and hence, to allow the use of leaner fuel/air mixtures.

Cylinder head design has also been modified. By redesigning the intake ports to give more fuel turbulence and increasing the volume of the combustion chambers to increase quench area, the fuel/air mixture burns more uniformly and this results in a lower production of HC and CO.

Ignition Retard Solenoid 1971 and Earlier Models

The function of this unit is to retard the ignition timing at closed throttle. Located on the distributor side, this solenoid must be operating when the ignition timing is adjusted. To be sure that the solenoid is operating, disconnect the ground lead after the timing is set. If the engine idle speed increases noticeably, the solenoid is functioning properly.

In contrast to the above, disconnect the solenoid when checking the dwell. If this is not done, the dwell meter will not read accurately.

Ignition Advance Solenoid

This solenoid, located on the distributor side, is connected to the starter relay so that it operates only during engine cranking, to improve starting.

When the engine fires, this solenoid ceases to operate. It is designed to advance the timing only during cranking. If the solenoid is not operating, it will affect starting, but not drivability. A possible sign of failure is popping through the carburetor during engine cranking.

To check operation, idle the engine and connect a jumper wire from the battery to the solenoid lead. If the solenoid is operating properly, engine speed will increase noticeably.

Caution Disconnect the jumper wire as soon as possible when checking the operation of the solenoid.

Vapor Saver System

This system is used to prevent the loss of fuel vapor from the fuel tank and carburetor. By venting carburetor and fuel tank vapors to a charcoal canister for temporary storage fuel vapors are prevented from entering the atmosphere. The system is purged of vapors when the engine is running by means of air drawn through the canister by intake manifold vacuum.

In addition, a limiting valve is used to prevent fuel tank overfilling. Located in the fuel vapor vent line in the engine compartment, this valve prevents overfilling by closing when the filler tube is closed by incoming fuel.

Air Injection System (Air Pump)

In 1972 the air injection system

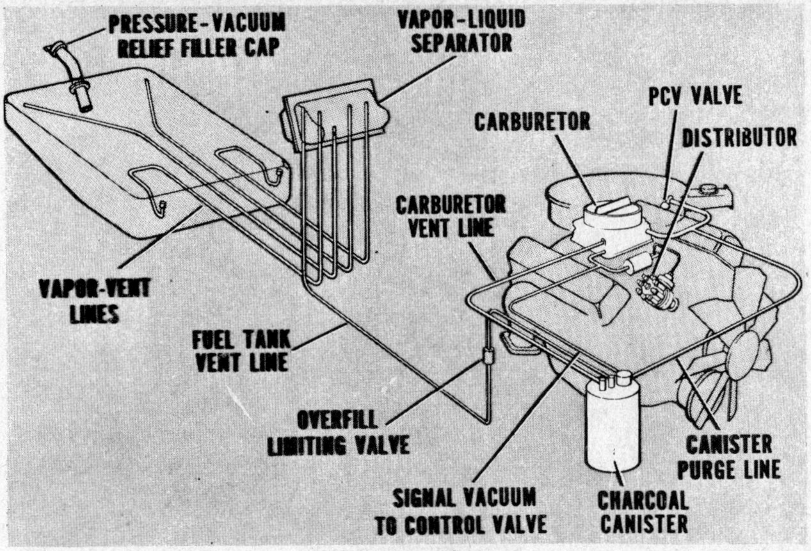
PRESSURE-VACUUM RELIEF FILLER CAP
VAPOR-LIQUID SEPARATOR
PCV VALVE
CARBURETOR
DISTRIBUTOR
CARBURETOR VENT LINE
VAPOR-VENT LINES
FUEL TANK VENT LINE
OVERFILL LIMITING VALVE
CANISTER PURGE LINE
SIGNAL VACUUM TO CONTROL VALVE
CHARCOAL CANISTER

Vapor saver system
(© Chrysler Corp)

was used on the 198, 225, 400 and 440 cu in. engines sold in California only. In 1973, the 225, 360 and 440 cu in. engines sold in California used air injection. In 1974, some of the 400 and 440 cu in. engines sold in California use air pumps, depending upon model usage.

A belt-driven air pump, mounted on the front of the engine, is used to inject air into the exhaust ports. This causes oxidation of these gases and a considerable reduction in carbon monoxide and hydrocarbons. The system consists of the pump, a check valve to protect the hoses and pump from hot gases, and a diverter-/pressure relief valve assembly.

Service to the air injection system is limited to belt tension adjustment every 12,000 miles. In addition, if any part fails in service, repair is effected by removal and replacement only.

Exhaust Gas Recirculation

In order to reduce the emission of oxides and nitrogen (NO_X), exhaust gases are ducted from the intake manifold crossover passage to contaminate the fuel/air mixture. (Do not confuse this system with other changes in the intake manifold.) These gases are introduced to the intake manifold floor by small jets. Every 12,000 miles, inspect these jets by looking through the carburetor. If the jet is plugged, remove, clean, and reinstall it.

1973—All

Starting with 1973, all Chrysler Corp. cars use exhaust gas recirculation (EGR). All engines have floor jets like those used on the 1972 models sold in California. The 340 and 400 cu in. engines equipped with 4-bbl carburetor use only floor jets for 1973.

In addition to the floor jets, all other 1973 engines use an EGR control valve. This valve directs exhaust gas from the crossover passage into the intake manifold. By using either ported-vacuum or venturi-vacuum signals, the EGR valve is able to proportion the exhaust gas flow to the amount of vacuum present in the carburetor. Ported-vacuum is used on the 318 cu in. (except California) and the 400 cu in. 2-bbl engines, as well as, the 440 cu in. 4-bbl high-performance engine. Venturi-vacuum is used on the six-cylinder engines, the 440 standard engines, and on the 318 2-bbl sold in California.

A thermal switch is used to de-energize the EGR valve when the outside temperature is below 58°F, to provide better driveability.

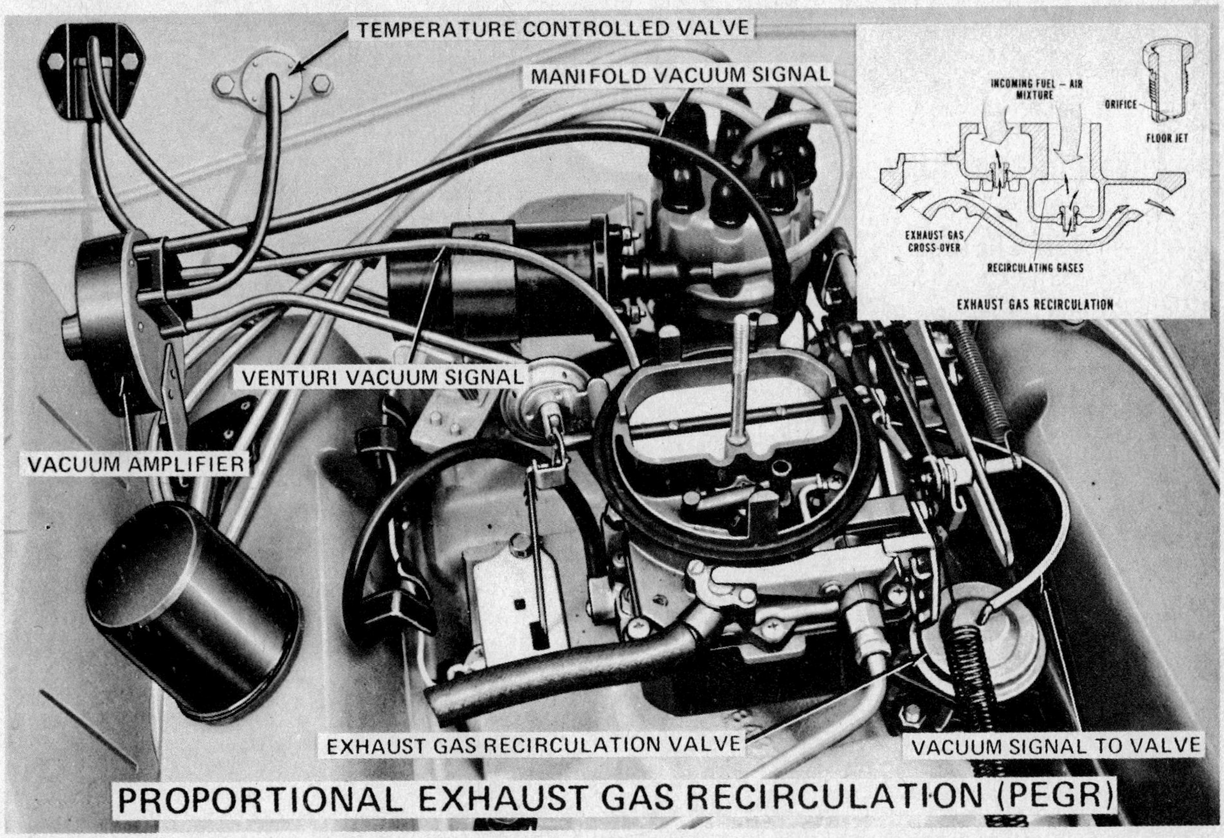
TEMPERATURE CONTROLLED VALVE
MANIFOLD VACUUM SIGNAL
INCOMING FUEL – AIR MIXTURE
ORIFICE
FLOOR JET
EXHAUST GAS CROSS-OVER
RECIRCULATING GASES
EXHAUST GAS RECIRCULATION
VENTURI VACUUM SIGNAL
VACUUM AMPLIFIER
EXHAUST GAS RECIRCULATION VALVE
VACUUM SIGNAL TO VALVE
PROPORTIONAL EXHAUST GAS RECIRCULATION (PEGR)

1973 exhaust gas recirculation system (© Chrysler Corp)

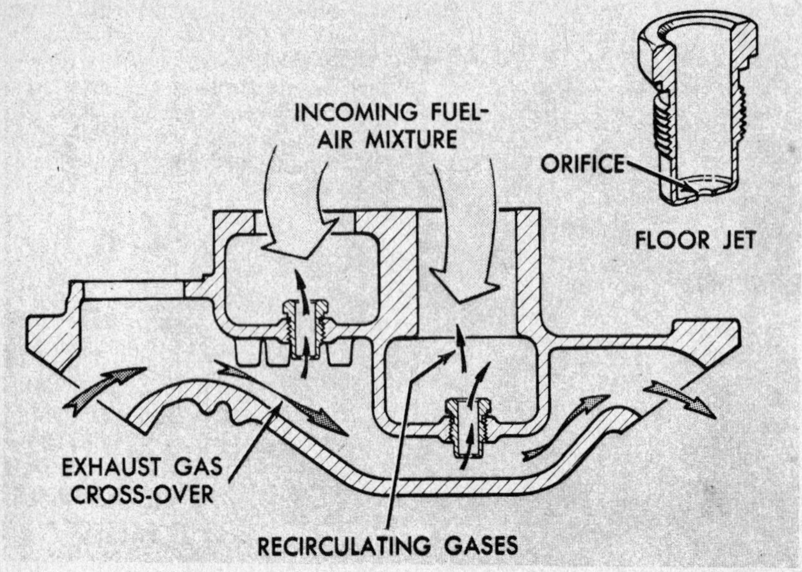
INCOMING FUEL-
AIR MIXTURE
ORIFICE
FLOOR JET
EXHAUST GAS
CROSS-OVER
RECIRCULATING GASES

Exhaust gas recirculation (© Chrysler Corp)

Starting around 15 March 1973, the ambient temperature sensor was dropped. It has been replaced by a thermostatic valve which is threaded into the top tank of the radiator. A hose runs from one valve nipple to the EGR vacuum amplifier. The other nipple has a filter fitted over it. When the coolant temperature is below 62°F, the valve is opened to the atmosphere, thus preventing the EGR valve diaphragm from getting vacuum. Above 62°F, the valve closes and the EGR valve is allowed to function.

Starting around 15 March 1973, the EGR temperature sensor was moved to the top tank of the radiator

1974—All

Floor jets have been dropped from all 1974 engines. The EGR temperature switch (mounted in the upper radiator tank), which was introduced in March 1973, has been retained.

NOTE: The thermostatic switch for the EGR system is mounted on the thermostat housing on the 360-4V engine.

All engines, except for the following, have a vacuum amplifier:

V8-318—All
V8-360—4-bbl High Performance
V8-400—4-bbl High Performance
V8-440—4-bbl High Performance

1973-74—Electric Assist Choke

During warm weather a heating element, located in the automatic choke well, comes on to shorten the period of choke operation and thus reduce hydro-carbon emissions. The heating element is operated by a time-delay control switch located next to the choke well. The assist choke draws about three amps of current during operation.

1974—Electric Assist Choke

A two-stage electric assist choke is used for 1974. The two-stage choke may be identified by its external resistor:

Blue resistor 5 ohm—all sixes/V8-318

White resistor 10 ohm—All other V8s

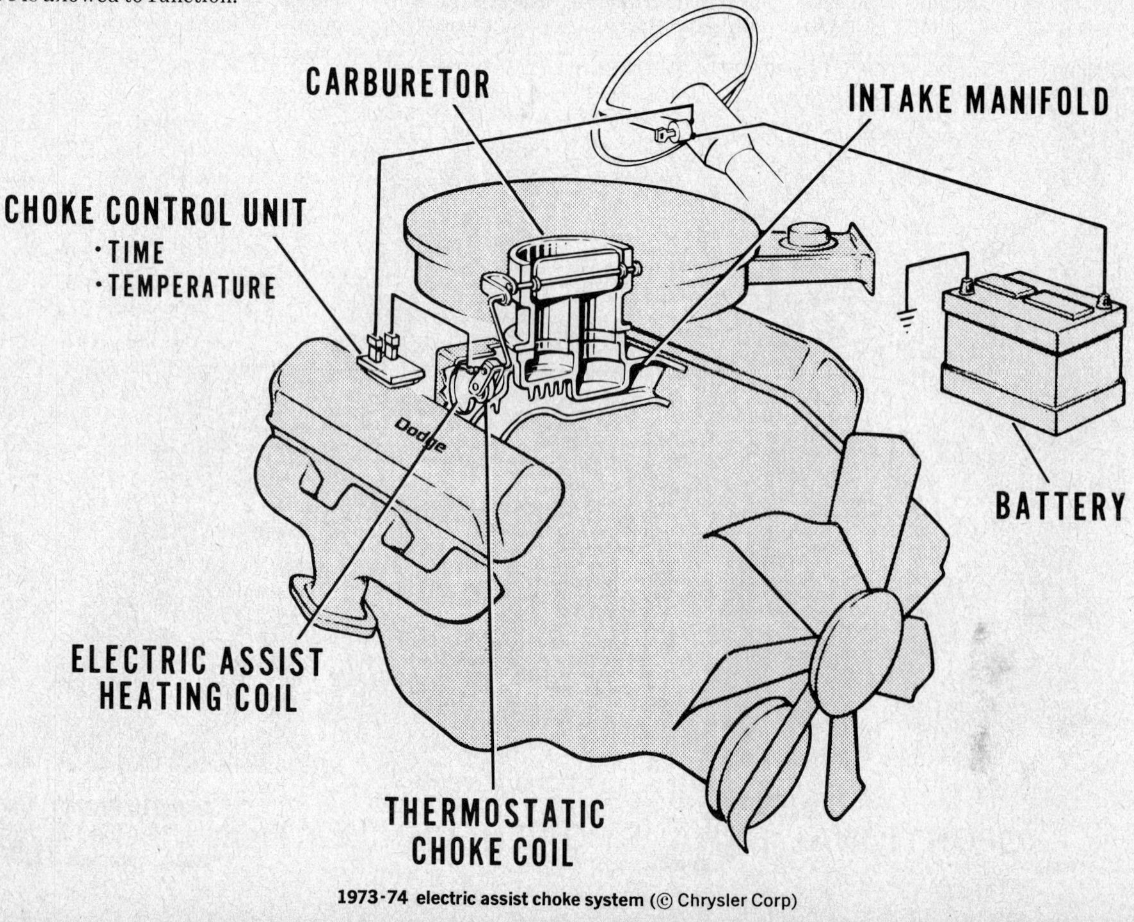
CARBURETOR
INTAKE MANIFOLD
CHOKE CONTROL UNIT
·TIME
·TEMPERATURE
Dodge
BATTERY
ELECTRIC ASSIST
HEATING COIL
THERMOSTATIC
CHOKE COIL

1973-74 electric assist choke system (© Chrysler Corp)

Below 58°F, the heating element gets full, low amperage current from the choke control. Above 58°F, the resistor cuts the current in half. After several minutes of operation above 58°F, the control opens the circuit so that the heating element gets no current at all.

Most engines use a 20-watt heating element, except for the following which have 4-bbl carburetors and use a 40-watt choke:

V8-440 (Thermo-Quad)—All states
V8-400 H.P. (Thermo-Quad)—All (except Calif.)
V8-440 H.P. (Thermo-Quad)—Calif. only
V8-360—All states
V8-360 H.P.—All states

The 40-watt choke has a white paint spot on the choke cover.

NOx System

Many 1971 and later vehicles have a NO_X system to control the emission of oxides of nitrogen. Engines with this system all have a special camshaft and a 185°F thermostat.

Manual Transmission

The manual transmission NO_X system uses a transmission switch, a thermal switch, and a solenoid vacuum valve. The transmission switch is screwed into the transmission housing and is closed, except in high gear. The thermal switch, mounted on the firewall, is open whenever the ambient temperature is above 70°F. With the transmission in any gear except high and the temperature above 70°, the solenoid vacuum valve is energized. This shuts off the distributor vacuum advance line preventing vacuum advance. Below 70°, the vacuum advance functions normally.

Automatic Transmission

The NO_X system for automatic transmissions is more complex than the manual transmission system. It prevents vacuum advance when the ambient temperature is above 70°F, speed is below 30 mph, or the car is accelerating. The solenoid vacuum valve is interchangeable with that used in the manual transmission system. The speed switch senses vehicle speed and is driven by the speedometer cable. The control unit is mounted on the firewall. It contains a control module, thermal switch, and a vacuum switch. The control unit senses ambient temperature and manifold vacuum.

1973—OSAC Valve

Starting with the 1973 models, an orifice spark advance control (OSAC) valve is used to delay distributor vacuum advance for about 15 seconds during acceleration.

NOTE: The amount of time-delay varies slightly from one engine size to another.

To aid in cold weather engine operation, a temperature sensing switch is built in to the OSAC valve so that it will not function when the air temperature is below 68°F.

Some time after 1 March and before 15 March 1973, the temperature sensor was removed from the OSAC valve, but the general appearance and location of the valve were not changed. The valve can be recognized by a white gasket and a stick-on label with the new part number (3755499).

At the same time, the ignition timing was changed to TDC.

NOTE: See the engine tune-up Specifications decal for further timing information.

1974—OSAC Valve

The OSAC valve has been moved from the firewall to the air cleaner for 1974 and the temperature control restored. There are six different time

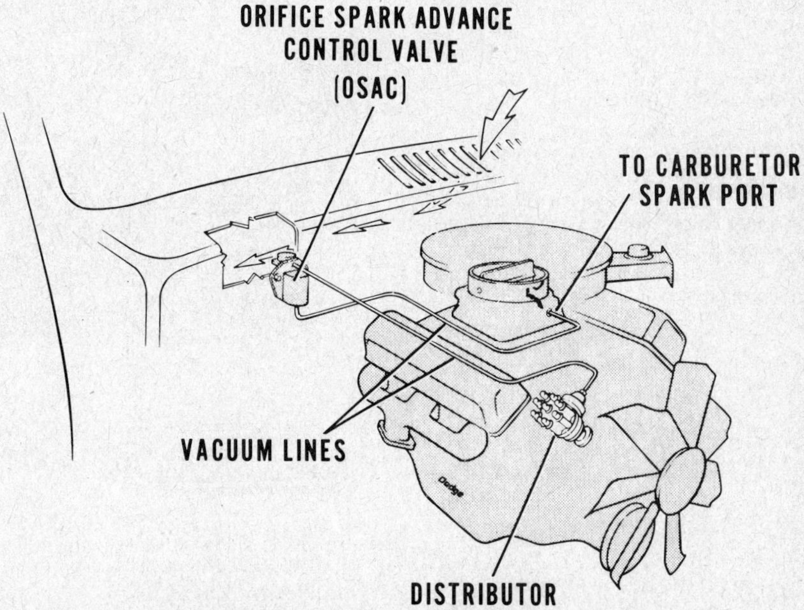
ORIFICE SPARK ADVANCE
CONTROL VALVE
(OSAC)
TO CARBURETOR
SPARK PORT
VACUUM LINES
DISTRIBUTOR

Orifice spark advance control (OSAC) valve (© Chrysler Corp)

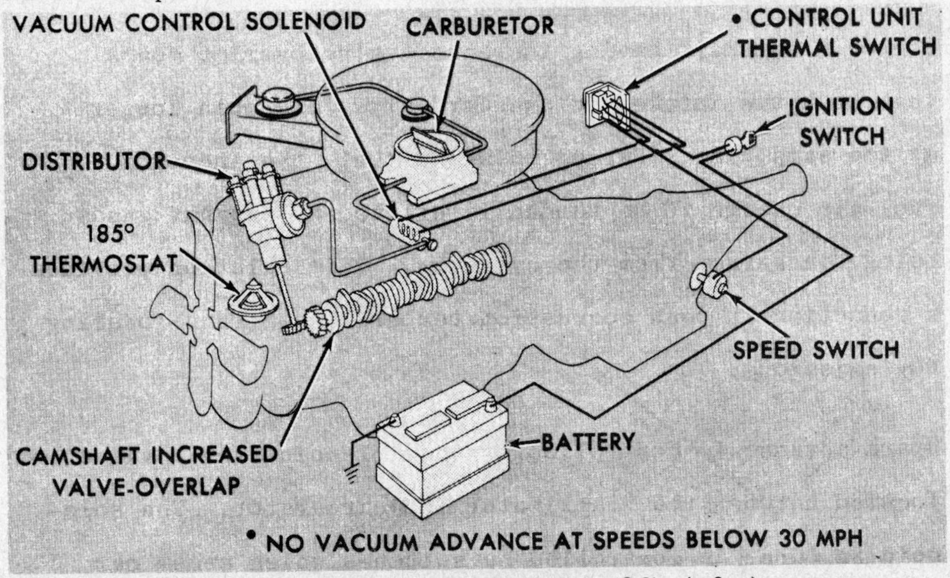
VACUUM CONTROL SOLENOID
CARBURETOR
• CONTROL UNIT
THERMAL SWITCH
IGNITION
SWITCH
DISTRIBUTOR
185°
THERMOSTAT
SPEED SWITCH
BATTERY
CAMSHAFT INCREASED
VALVE-OVERLAP
• NO VACUUM ADVANCE AT SPEEDS BELOW 30 MPH

NO_X control system—automatic transmission (© Chrysler Corp)

DIST

The 1974 OSAC valve is located in the air cleaner

delay and operating temperature combinations for the valve. These combinations are identified by a color code tape on the top of the valve. These codes are as follows:

Color	*Time (sec)*	*Temperature (°F)*
Green	17	58
Red	17	50
Blue	17	①
White	27	58
Orange	27	①
Yellow	27	58

①—No temperature control used

Caution Always replace the valve with one having the same color code. Failure to do so could result in poor vehicle performance or lack of compliance with the emission laws.

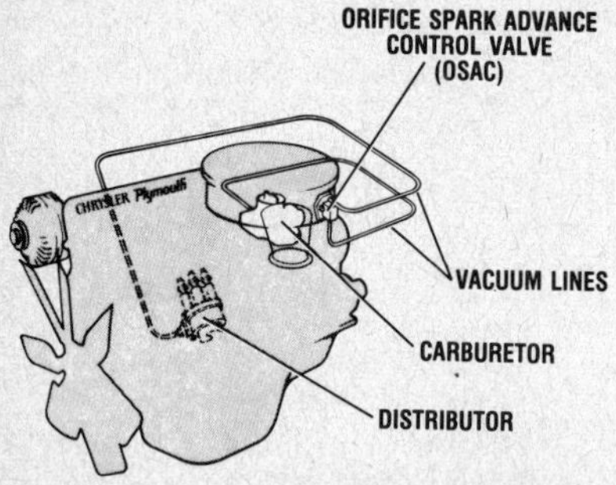
ORIFICE SPARK ADVANCE CONTROL VALVE (OSAC)
VACUUM LINES
CARBURETOR
DISTRIBUTOR

Typical OSAC valve vacuum hose routing and component layout
(© Chrysler Corp)

ENGINE

Dodge and Plymouth Engines 1967-74

The standard equipment engine in most Dodge and Plymouth car models is the 225 cu. in. slant six. Although this engine has a very long stroke by modern standards, it presents a low profile because the entire block is canted 30 degrees on the right.

The 273 cu. in. and 318 cu. in. engines are Chrysler Corporation's "A" block series of V8s. The oldest of the current "A" blocks, the 318, originally used polyspherical combustion chambers. When the 273 was introduced in 1964, it had the simpler wedged shaped combustion chambers, and in 1967 the 318 adopted them also. In 1971, a low compression 360 cu. in. V8 was added to the list of "A" block engines available.

Chrysler Corporation's "B" block series is really two series of engines, the low-block series and the raised-block series. These series differ in block deck height, main journal diameter, connecting rod length, and pushrod length. Otherwise these engines are similar and many parts interchange. The 383 and 400 cu. in. engines are low-block engines, and the 426 wedge head and 440 cu. in. V8s are raised-block engines. All these engines are conventional V8s with wedge shaped combustion chambers and deep blocks that extend well below crankshaft centerline.

The 426 Hemi is Dodge and Plymouth's largest, heaviest, most complicated, and most powerful engine. It is basically a "B" series, raised-block engine, but with so many differences that it must be treated as a completely separate engine. It has hemispherical combustion chambers with 2.25 in. intake and 1.95 in. exhaust valves actuated by rocker arms mounted on separate intake and exhaust rocker shafts. The spark plugs are centrally located in the combustion chambers, and aluminum tubes protect the plugs and wires from oil where they pass through the rocker covers. Because of the huge intake ports, there is no room for head bolts on the intake side. Instead studs are mounted in the head which extend down into the valley between the cylinder heads. To reduce piston side thrust, Hemis use longer connecting rods than other raised-block "B" engines, and to strengthen the lower end, the main caps are crossbolted. The Hemi engine was discontinued in 1971 and is no longer available.

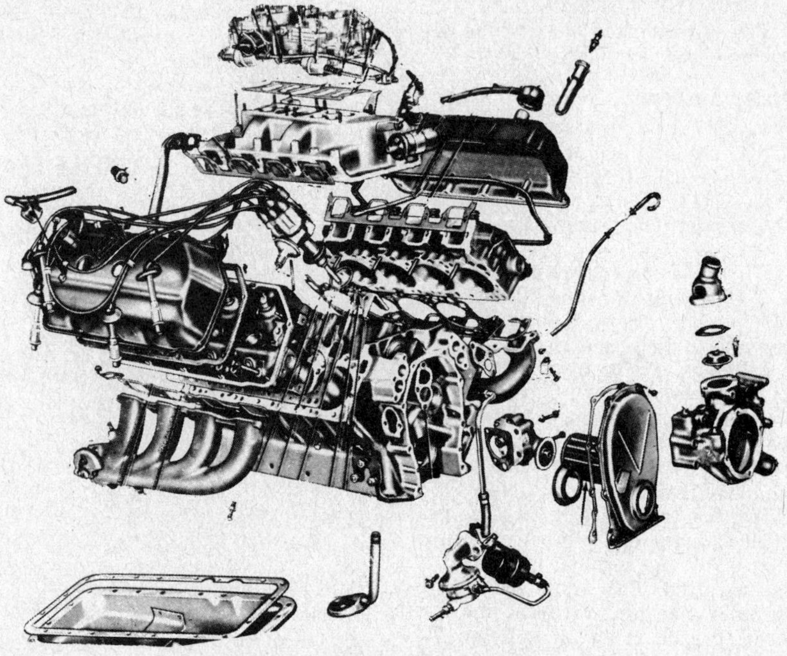

426 Hemi engine (© Chrysler Corp)

Special Engine Markings

Over and undersize engine components are identified by various marks. These marks may be located on top, right-front engine pads or on the crankshaft counterweights. In addition, some big-block engines may have oversize valve stem markings stamped on the ends of the cylinder head on the untapped boss.

Engine R & R

1. Scribe the outline of the hood hinge brackets on the bottom of the hood and remove the hood.
2. Drain the cooling system and remove the radiator.
3. Remove the battery.
4. Remove the fuel line from the fuel pump and plug the line.
5. Remove all wires and hoses that attach to the engine. Remove all emission control equipment that may be damaged by the engine removal procedure.
6. If equipped with air conditioning and/or power steering, remove the unit from the engine

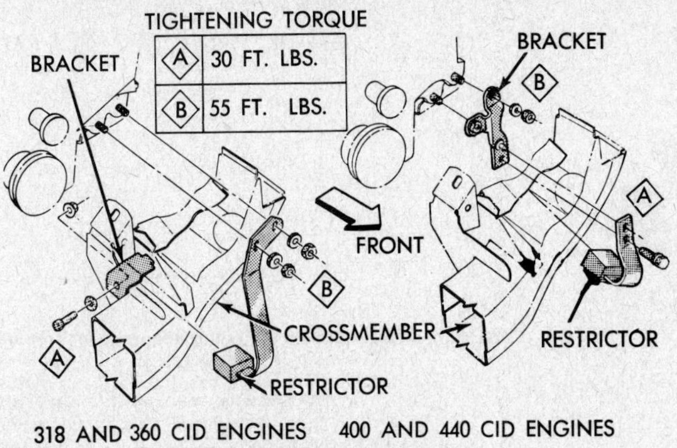
TIGHTENING TORQUE
A 30 FT. LBS.
B 55 FT. LBS.
BRACKET
BRACKET
FRONT
CROSSMEMBER
RESTRICTOR
RESTRICTOR
318 AND 360 CID ENGINES
400 AND 440 CID ENGINES

Spool-type engine mount tightening for 1973 Chrysler Corp. cars
(© Chrysler Corp)

and position it out of the way *without disconnecting the lines.*

7. Attach lifting sling to the engine. On V8 models (except the Hemi) remove the çarburetor and attach the engine lifting fixture to the carburetor flange studs on the intake manifold. On models equipped with a 426 Hemi engine, never attempt to remove the engine with the lifting sling attached to the intake manifold. Attach lifting straps to the front of the left cylinder head, and the rear strap to the rear of the right cylinder head.
8. Raise the vehicle on a hoist and install an engine support fixture to support the rear of the engine.
9. On automatic transmission models, drain the transmission and torque converter. On standard transmission models, disconnect the clutch torque shaft from the engine.
10. Disconnect the exhaust pipe/s from the exhaust manifold/s.
11. Remove the driveshaft.
12. Disconnect the transmission linkage and any wiring or cables that attach to the transmission.
13. Remove the engine rear support crossmember and remove the transmission.
14. Remove the bolts that attach the motor mounts to the chassis.
15. Lower the vehicle and attach a chain hoist or other lifting device to the engine.
16. Raise the engine and carefully remove it from the vehicle.
17. Reverse above procedure to install.

Manifolds

6 Cylinder Combination Manifold R&R

1. Remove the air cleaner and the fuel line from the carburetor.
2. Disconnect the accelerator linkage.
3. Disconnect the vacuum advance line at the carburetor.
4. Disconnect the exhaust pipe at the exhaust manifold flange.
5. Withdraw the manifold assemby-to-cylinder head bolts and remove the intake and exhaust manifolds, and the carburetor, as a single unit. The manifolds may be separated by removing the three bolts which hold them together.
6. Installation of the combination manifold and carburetor assembly is the reverse of the above. When installing the manifold assembly, use new gaskets and loosen the three bolts which secure the intake manifold to the exhaust manifold to maintain proper alignment. Torque these three bolts to 15 ft lbs in the sequence: inner bolt first, then the outer two bolts. Torque the manifold assembly-to-cylinder head bolts to 10 ft lbs.

Intake Manifold Removal

All V8 Engines Except 426 Hemi

1. Drain cooling system and disconnect battery.
2. Remove the air cleaner and fuel line from the carburetor.
3. Disconnect accelerator linkage.
4. Remove vacuum control between carburetor and distributor.
5. Remove distributor cap and wires.
6. Disconnect coil wires, temperature sending unit wire, heater hoses, and bypass hose.
7. Remove intake manifold, ignition coil, and carburetor as an assembly.

426 Hemi

1. Drain cooling system and disconnect battery.
2. Remove the air cleaner and fuel lines from the carburetors.
3. Disconnect accelerator linkage.
4. Remove vacuum control between carburetor and distributor.

TIME SAVER

It is possible to remove the engine without removing the transmission. If the engine is to be removed from the vehicle without removing the transmission, care must be exercised not to allow the weight of the engine to rest on the torque converter hub (automatic transmission) or transmission input shaft (standard transmission).

To remove the engine without removing the transmission, use the following operation. Perform Steps 1-7 and 10 of the above operation. If the vehicle is equipped with an automatic transmission, attach a remote starter switch to the engine, remove the inspection plate from the bellhousing, crank the engine to gain access to the torque converter-to-driveplate attaching nuts and remove the nuts. If the vehicle is equipped with a manual transmission, disconnect the clutch torque shaft from the engine block and the clutch linkage from the adjustment rod. Remove the bolt that attaches the transmission filler tube to the engine (automatic transmission). Support the transmission and remove the bolts that attach the transmission to the engine or clutch bellhousing. When removing the engine, place a block of wood on the lifting point of a floor jack and position the jack under the transmission. As the engine is removed from the vehicle, raise and lower the jack as required so the angle of the transmission duplicates as nearly as possible the angle of the engine.

When installing the engine into a vehicle with an automatic transmission, keep in mind that the crankshaft flange bolt circle, the inner and outer circle of holes in the driveplate, and the four tapped holes in the front face of the converter all have one hole offset. To ensure proper engine-torque converter balance, the torque converter must be mounted to the driveplate in the same location it was originally installed.

When installing the engine into a vehicle with a manual transmission, it may be necessary to disconnect the driveshaft and turn the transmission output shaft, with the transmission in gear, to get the transmission input shaft splines to mesh with the inner hub on the clutch disc.

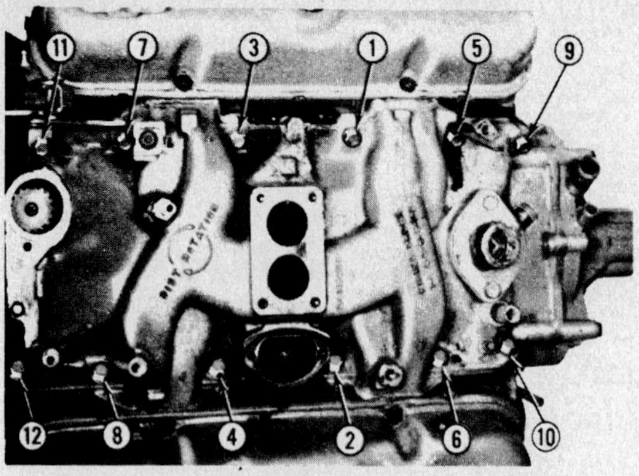
11
7
3
1
5
9
12
8
4
2
6
10

Typical intake manifold tightening sequence. Torque to specifications in two steps
(© Chrysler Corp)

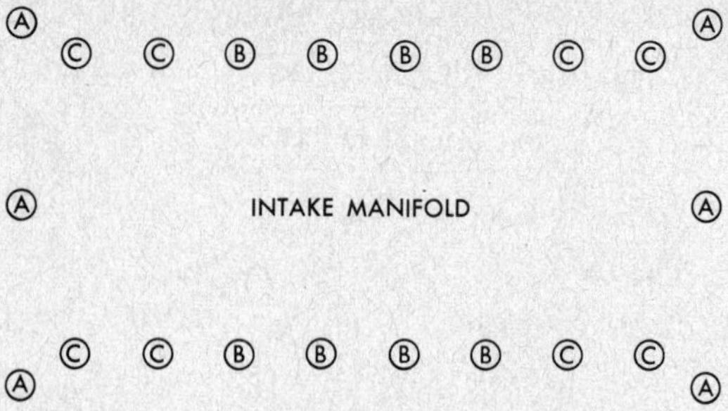
A C C B B B B C C A
A INTAKE MANIFOLD A
C C B B B B C C
A A

426 Hemi intake manifold tightening sequence in three steps
(© Chrysler Corp)

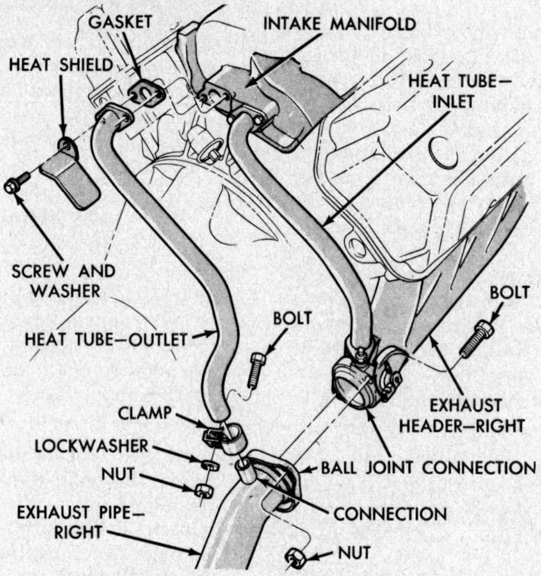
GASKET
INTAKE MANIFOLD
HEAT SHIELD
HEAT TUBE—INLET
SCREW AND WASHER
BOLT
BOLT
HEAT TUBE—OUTLET
EXHAUST HEADER—RIGHT
CLAMP
LOCKWASHER
NUT
BALL JOINT CONNECTION
EXHAUST PIPE—RIGHT
CONNECTION
NUT

Manifold heat tubes—426 Hemi
(© Chrysler Corp)

Remove distributor cap and wires.

5. Disconnect coil wires, heater hoses and bypass hose.
6. Remove two stud nuts and washers which retain intake manifold inlet heat tube to right hand exhaust header.
7. Remove screws attaching upper end of inlet tube to rear face of intake manifold.
8. Remove inlet tube and discard gaskets. Install new gaskets at assembly.
9. Remove nut, washer, and bolt from tube clamp at exhaust pipe. Remove clamp from outlet tube.
10. Remove screws attaching heat shield and outlet tube to rear face of intake manifold and remove tube and shield.
11. Remove intake manifold, coil and carburetors as an assembly.

Exhaust Manifold

Removal—All V8 Models

Disconnect the exhaust manifold at the pipe flange. Access to these bolts is underneath the vehicle. Disconnect the air injection nozzles and carburetor heated air stove (if so equipped). Remove the exhaust manifold by removing the securing bolts and washers. To reach these bolts, it may be necessary to jack the engine slightly off its front mounts. When the exhaust manifold is removed, sometimes the securing studs will come out with the nuts. If this occurs, the studs must be replaced with the aid of sealing compound on the coarse thread ends. If this is not done, water leaks may develop at the studs. To install the exhaust manifold, reverse the removal procedure.

Valve System

All valves used in Chrysler engines (except the 426 Hemi) are arranged in line in the cylinder head and ride in guides that are cast integrally. Service valves with overside stems are available; therefore, the valve guides may be reamed if that is required. Do not attempt to ream the guides in one step to their maximum .030 in. oversize; work in .005, .015, and .030 in. steps. This allows the guides to be reamed true in relation to valve seats.

All six-cylinder engines used in Chrysler vehicles are equipped with solid (mechanical) lifters. The 1967 273 V8s were also equipped with mechanical lifters. After the above dates, both engines switched to hydraulic lifters. The 426 Hemi engine used solid lifters until 1969; beginning in 1970, adjustable-type hydraulic lifters were used. All other V8 engines used in Dodge and Plymouth vehicles have used non-adjustable hydraulic lifters throughout their production.

Rocker Shaft Removal

All Engines except 426 Hemi

1. Remove the closed ventilation system (PCV). On V8s, remove the spark plug wires.
2. Remove the valve cover with its gasket.

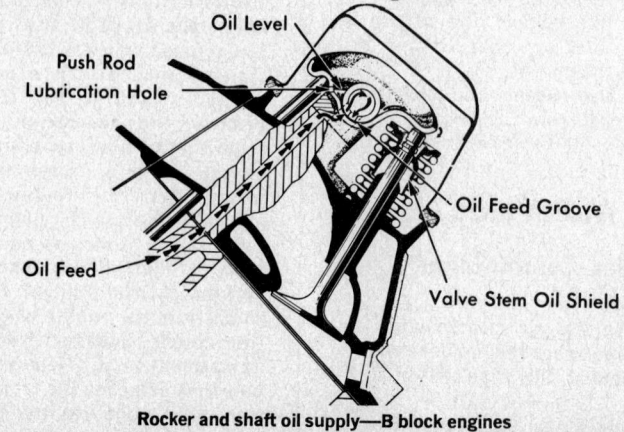

Oil Level
Push Rod
Lubrication Hole
Oil Feed Groove
Oil Feed
Valve Stem Oil Shield

Rocker and shaft oil supply—B block engines
(© Chrysler Corp)

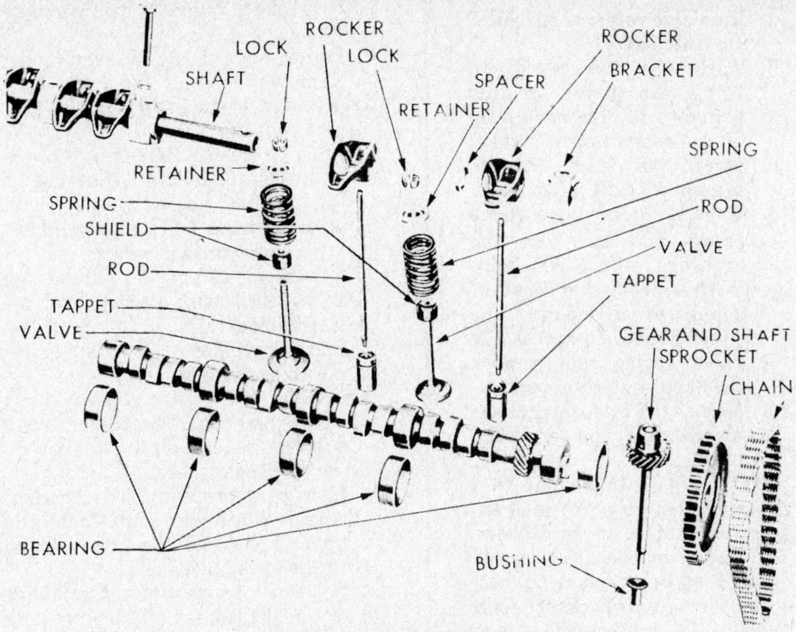

ROCKER
LOCK
LOCK
ROCKER
SHAFT
SPACER
BRACKET
RETAINER
SPRING
RETAINER
SPRING
ROD
SHIELD
VALVE
ROD
TAPPET
TAPPET
VALVE
GEAR AND SHAFT
SPROCKET
CHAIN
BEARING
BUSHING

Valve train components—B block engines
(© Chrysler Corp)

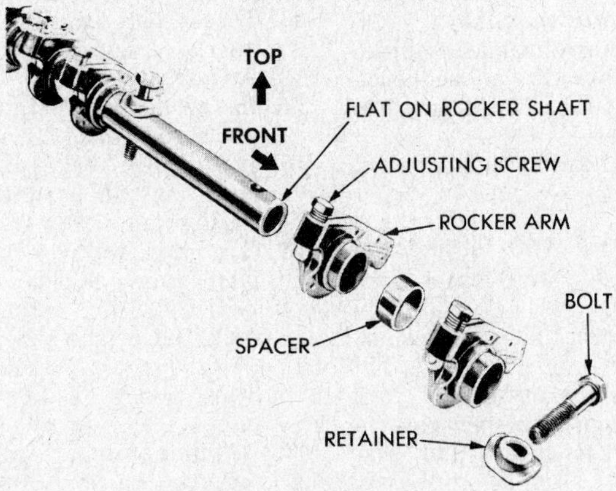

TOP
FLAT ON ROCKER SHAFT
FRONT
ADJUSTING SCREW
ROCKER ARM
BOLT
SPACER
RETAINER

Slant six shaft and rockers
(© Chrysler Corp)

3. Remove the rocker shaft bolts with their retainers.
4. To replace the rocker arms, reverse the removal procedure. Be sure to torque the rocker arm bolts to 25 ft lbs. On those engines with mechanical lifters, adjust the valves. When replacing the valve cover, use a new gasket.

NOTE: When replacing rocker arms, be sure to align the oil holes.

426 Hemi

1. Remove air cleaner, and distributor cap with spark plug cables and secondry coil cable as an assembly.
2. Grasp secondary cables at plastic spark covers and pull covers straight out.
3. Remove spark plugs.
4. On left bank, disconnect brake lines at master cylinder, and remove cotter pin and clevis pin from linkage in back of power brake.
5. Remove four nuts attaching booster to mounting bracket and remove power brake and master cylinder assembly.
6. Remove rocker covers and gaskets.
7. Remove five bolts that attach rocker shafts assembly on each head.

NOTE: these rocker shaft assembly bolts pass through the head and into the block. Anytime rocker shaft assembly is removed, remove that head, fit a new gasket, reassemble and torque.

8. Lift off rocker shafts assembly.

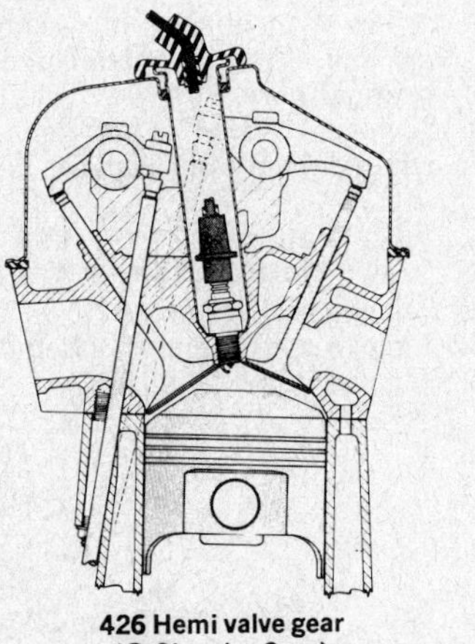

426 Hemi valve gear
(© Chrysler Corp)

Tappet Adjustment

6 Cylinder Engine

1. Start the engine and allow it to idle for 5 minutes.
2. Remove the rocker arm cover.
3. Start the engine and adjust the intake valves to have a clearance of 0.010 in. and the exhaust 0.020 in. with the engine HOT.

Tappet Adjustment—426 Hemi

1. Adjust ignition timing to TDC.
2. Mark crankshaft damper with chalk at TDC and 180° opposite TDC.
3. Rotate crankshaft until No. 1 cylinder is at TDC and points are just opening.
4. Adjust intake tappets on No. 2 and No. 7 cylinders and exhaust tappets on No. 4 and No. 8 cylinders. On 1967-69 engines, adjust the intake valves to have a clearance of .028 in. and the exhaust valves .032 in. with the engine COLD. On 1970-71 engines, adjust the valves to have zero lash, then tighten the adjustment screw an additional 1½ turns. Tighten the locknuts to 25 ft. lbs.
5. Rotate crankshaft 180° in normal direction of rotation until points open to fire No. 4 cylinder.
6. Adjust intake tappets on No. 1 and No. 8 cylinders and exhaust tappets on No. 3 and No. 6 cylinders as in Step 4.
7. Rotate crankshaft 180° in normal direction of rotation until points open to fire No. 6 cylinder.
8. Adjust intake tappets on No. 3 and No. 4 cylinders and exhaust tappets on No. 5 and No. 7 cylinders as in Step 4.
9. Rotate crankshaft 180° in normal direction of rotation until points open to fire No. 7 cylinder.
10. Adjust intake tappets on No. 5 and No. 6 cylinders and exhaust tappets on No. 1 and No. 2 cylinders as in Step 4.
11. Set ignition timing to operating specifications and install rocker covers.

Valve Guides

Dodge and Plymouth engines do not have separate valve guides. They do have, however, 0.005, 0.015, and 0.030 in. oversize valves (stem diameter). To use these, ream the worn guides to the smallest oversize that will clean up wear. Always start with the smallest reamer and proceed in steps to the largest, as this maintains the concentricity of the guide with the valve seat.

Chilton's TIME SAVER

The following is a method for replacing valve springs, oil seals or spring retainers without removing the cylinder head.

1. **Entirely dismantle a spark plug and save the threaded shell.**
2. **To this shell, braze or weld an air chuck.**
3. **Remove the valve rocker cover. Remove the rocker arm from the affected valve.**
4. **Remove the spark plug from the affected cylinder.**
5. **Turn the crankshaft to bring the piston of this cylinder down, away from possible contact with the valve head. Sharply tap the valve retainer to loosen the valve lock.**
6. **Turn the crankshaft to bring the piston in this cylinder to the exact top of its compression stroke.**
7. **Screw in the chuck-equipped spark plug shell.**
8. **Hook up an air hose to the chuck and turn on the pressure (about 200 lbs.).**
9. **With a strong and constant supply of air holding the valve closed, compress the valve spring and remove the lock and retainer.**
10. **Make the necessary replacements and reassemble.**

NOTE: it is important that the operation be performed exactly as stated, in this order. The piston in the affected cylinder must be on exact top center to prevent air pressure from turning the crankshaft.

As an alternate procedure, some local automotive machine shops bore out the stock guides and replace them with bronze or cast iron guides which are of stock internal dimensions.

Cylinder Head

Removal

Six Cylinder

1. Drain cooling system.
2. Remove air cleaner and fuel line.
3. Remove vacuum line at carburetor and distributor.
4. Disconnect accelerator linkage.
5. Disconnect spark plug wires by pulling straight out in line with plugs.
6. Disconnect heater hose and bypass hose clamp.
7. Disconnect temperature sending wire.
8. Disconnect exhaust pipe at exhaust manifold flange.
9. Remove intake and exhaust manifold as an assembly.
10. Remove closed vent system (PCV) and rocker cover.
11. Remove rocker shaft assembly.
12. Remove pushrods in sequence and save them to re-install in original bores.
13. Remove 14 head bolts.
14. Remove head.
15. Remove spark plugs and tubes.

273, 318, 340, 360 Engines

1. Drain cooling system and disconnect battery.
2. Remove intake manifold.

NOTE: Removing the intake manifold is only necessary if both heads are to be removed. Otherwise remove the bolts from the head and loosen the bolts on the other side. Slip the head from under the manifold.

3. Remove exhaust manifolds.
4. Remove rocker shaft assemblies.
5. Remove pushrods in sequence and save them to install in their original bores.
6. Remove ten head bolts from each cylinder head.

383, 400, and 440 Engines

1. Drain cooling system and disconnect battery.
2. Remove alternator, air cleaner, and fuel line.
3. Remove intake manifold.
4. Remove tappet chamber cover.
5. Remove rocker covers and gaskets.
6. Remove exhaust manifolds.
7. Remove rocker shaft assemblies.
8. Remove pushrods in sequence and save them to install in their original bore.
9. Remove 17 head bolts from each cylinder head and remove heads.

426 Hemi—Removal and Installation

1. Remove rocker covers.
2. Remove rocker shaft assemblies.
3. Remove intake manifold.
4. Disconnect exhaust headers, and tie out of way.
5. Remove eight lower head bolts. Remove the nuts from the four cylinder studs inside of the tappet chamber.
6. Remove heads. Do not set heads on studs at any time. Because of the unusual use of rocker shaft bolts as head bolts follow installation procedure carefully.
7. Coat new head gasket with sealer and install with raised bead towards block.
8. Install cylinder heads taking care not to damage studs.
9. Install nuts on cylinder head studs and short cylinder head bolts in outer bolt holes, but do not tighten either.
10. Install pushrods in their original bores. The short rods go in the upper holes and the long rods go in the lower holes.
11. Position rocker shafts assemblies on heads and install five long head bolts in each after lining up pushrods with rockers.
12. Torque bolts and stud nuts in sequence given at front of section.
13. Adjust valve lash.
14. Install headers with new gaskets and torque to 35 ft. lbs.
15. Install new rocker cover gaskets and install rocker covers. Tighten nuts to 10 ft. lbs.
16. Gap plugs to 0.035 in. Slide spark plug tube shields over tubes. With six in. extension install spark plugs and tubes. Torque to 30 ft. lbs. Do not drop or bang spark plugs for this may change gap.
17. Install manifold.

Cylinder Head Bolt Tightening Sequence

NOTE: Torque to specifications in three stages.

Timing Cover, Chain, and Camshaft

Removal and Installation

NOTE: On both 6 and V8 models, it is normal to find particles of rubber

STUD NUTS (4) EACH HEAD

Torquing Hemi head stud nuts
(© Chrysler Corp)

collected between the seal retainer and the crankshaft oil slinger after the seal has been in service. Check the slack in the chain after completion of chain installation (procedure will be found below):

the freeze plug in the rear of the engine block. Remove the distributor and the oil pump/distributor drive gear. Position the screwdriver against the rear side of the cam gear and be careful not to damage the cam lobes.

centric, cup washer, and camshaft sprocket lockbolt. Torque the lockbolt to 35 ft lbs. On 383 and 440 cu in. engines, install the washer and camshaft sprocket lockbolt. Torque the lockbolt to 35 ft lbs. Check that the rear

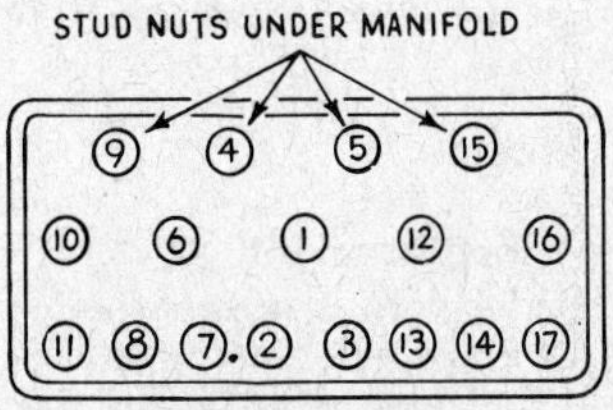
STUD NUTS UNDER MANIFOLD
9 4 5 15
10 6 1 12 16
11 8 7.2 3 13 14 17
426 Hemi V8

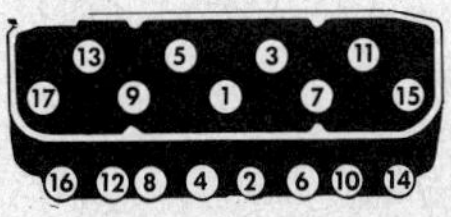
13 5 3 11
17 9 1 7 15
16 12 8 4 2 6 10 14
383, 400, 426 wedge, 440 V8

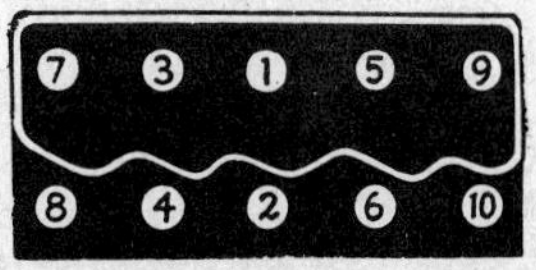
7 3 1 5 9
8 4 2 6 10
273, 318, 340, 360 cu. in. V8

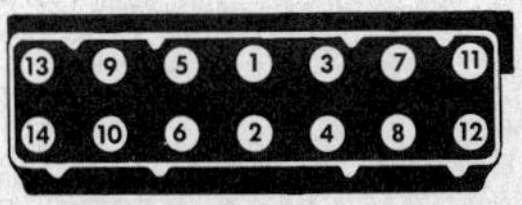
13 9 5 1 3 7 11
14 10 6 2 4 8 12
225 6 cylinder

Six Cylinder Models

1. Drain the cooling system and disconnect the battery.
2. Remove radiator and fan.
3. With puller, remove vibration damper.

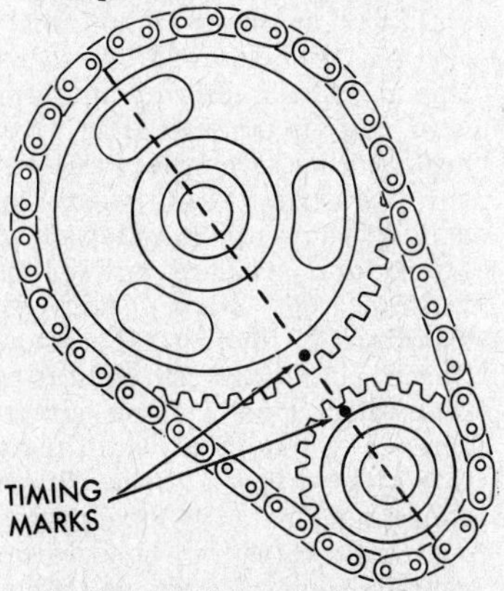
TIMING
MARKS
6 cylinder timing mark alignment

4. Loosen engine oil pan bolts to allow clearance, and remove timing case cover and gasket.
5. Slide crankshaft oil slinger off the front of crankshaft.
6. Remove the camshaft sprocket bolt.
7. Remove the timing chain with camshaft sprocket.

Installation

1. Turn crankshaft to line up the timing mark on the crankshaft sprocket with the centerline of canshaft (without the chain.)
2. Remove the camshaft sprocket and reinstall with chain.
3. Torque camshaft sprocket to 35 ft. lbs.
4. Replace oil slinger.
5. Reinstall timing case cover with new gasket and torque to 15 ft. lbs. Retighten engine oil pan to 17 ft. lbs.
6. Replace vibration damper.
7. Replace radiator and hoses.
8. Refill and bleed cooling system.

V8 Models

Caution When installing a timing chain on a V-8 engine, have an assistant support the camshaft with a screwdriver to prevent the camshaft from contacting

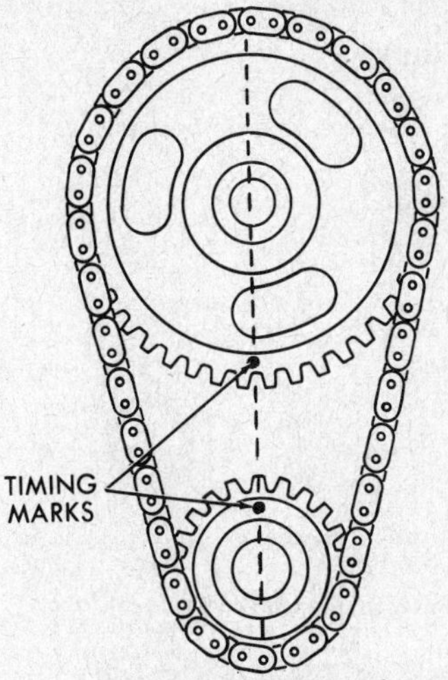
TIMING
MARKS
V8 timing mark alignment

1. Remove the timing gear cover and the crankshaft oil slinger.
2. On 273, 318, 340 and 360 cu in. engines, remove the camshaft sprocket lockbolt, securing cup washer, and fuel pump eccentric. Remove the timing chain with the camshaft and crankshaft sprockets. On 383, 400, 440, and 426 cu in. engines, remove the camshaft sprocket lockbolt and remove the timing chain with the camshaft and crankshaft sprockets.
3. Place the camshaft and crankshaft sprockets on a flat surface with their timing marker on an imaginary centerline through both sprocket borers.
4. Position the timing chain around both sprockets.
5. Turn the crankshaft and camshafts to line up with the keyway location in the crankshaft sprocket and the dowel hole in the camshaft sprocket.
6. Lift the sprockets and timing chains while keeping the sprockets tight against the chain in the correct position, and slide both sprockets evenly onto their respective shafts.
7. Use a straightedge to measure the alignment of the sprocket timing marks.
8. On 273, 318, 340, and 360 cu in. engines, install the fuel pump ec-

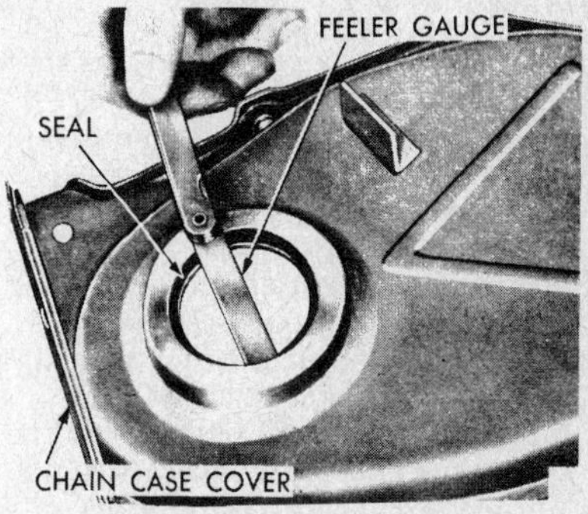
FEELER GAUGE
SEAL
CHAIN CASE COVER
Checking seal for proper clearance
(© Chrysler Corp)

face of the camshaft sprocket is flush with the camshaft end. On the 426 Hemi, install the washers and camshaft lockbolt. Torque the lockbolt to 40 ft lbs.

Checking Timing Chain Slack

To check timing chain slack, place a scale next to the timing chain to detect any movement in the chain. Place a torque wrench and socket on the camshaft sprocket attaching bolt. Apply either 30 ft lbs (if cylinder heads are installed on the engine) or 15 ft lbs (cylinder heads removed) of force to the bolt and rotate the bolt in the direction of crankshaft rotation to remove all slack from the chain. While applying torque to the camshaft sprocket bolt, the crankshaft should not be allowed to rotate. It may be necessary to block the crankshaft to prevent rotation. Position the scale over the edge of a timing chain link and apply an equal amount of torque in the opposite direction. If the movement of the chain exceeds 3/16 in., replace the chain.

Timing Gear Cover Seal Replacement

All Engines

1. Using a puller, separate the seal from the retainer.
2. Using fingers and a screwdriver, pull the seal from the case.
3. To install the seal place it in the case with the rubber side downward.
4. Seat the seal tightly against the cover face. There should be a

maximum clearance of .0014 in. between the seal and the cover. Be careful not to over-compress the seal.

Camshaft R&R

1. Remove the timing chain and cover.
2. Remove the intake manifold.

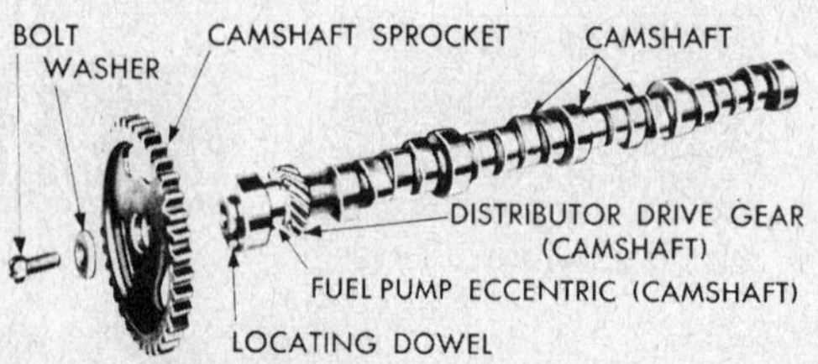
BOLT
WASHER
CAMSHAFT SPROCKET
CAMSHAFT
DISTRIBUTOR DRIVE GEAR (CAMSHAFT)
FUEL PUMP ECCENTRIC (CAMSHAFT)
LOCATING DOWEL

Camshaft and sprocket—318 V8
(© Chrysler Corp)

3. Remove the rocker arm covers and rocker arm assemblies.
4. Remove the pushrods and valve lifters and keep them in order so they can be returned to their original location in the engine.
5. Remove the distributor and distributor-oil pump driveshaft.
6. Remove the fuel pump from the engine and position it out of the way without disconnecting the fuel lines.
7. Remove the camshaft from the engine. Use care not to damage the lobes during removal.
8. Reverse above procedure to install, lubricating the cam before installation.

NOTE: when installing the camshaft and timing chain, do not allow the camshaft to contact the welch plug in the rear of the engine block as this could loosen the plug.

Pistons, Connecting Rods and Main Bearings

Rod and Piston Assembly Removal

All Models

1. Remove the cylinder head and oil pan.
2. Insert a good cylinder ridge reamer into the top of the bores accessible without turning the crankshaft, and remove the ridge. Detach the tool, turn the crankshaft, reattach the tool and remove the ridge on the next cylinder. Continue this process until all cylinder ridges have been removed.

Caution This is not a boring bar, so merely remove the ridge.

3. From underneath the car, select the connecting rods in the down position, and remove the locking device (pawl nut or cotter pin). Take off the two nuts that hold the cap to the lower end of the connecting rod. Tap the cap gently and slide it off the end of the bolts. Be careful not to lose the lower half of the rod bearing.
4. Start the connecting rod and piston assembly up toward the top of the bore, but, before pushing it out, replace the cap so that

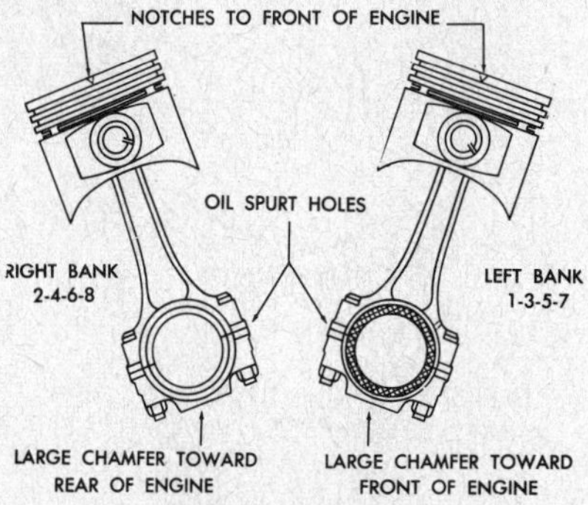
NOTCHES TO FRONT OF ENGINE
OIL SPURT HOLES
RIGHT BANK 2-4-6-8
LEFT BANK 1-3-5-7
LARGE CHAMFER TOWARD REAR OF ENGINE
LARGE CHAMFER TOWARD FRONT OF ENGINE

Relation of piston and rod—all V8s
(© Chrysler Corp)

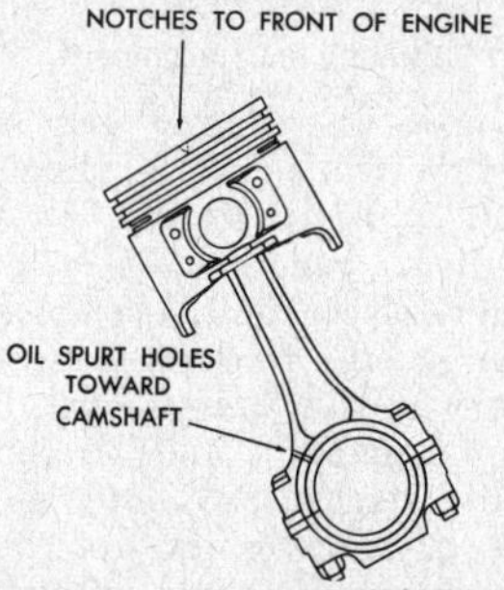
NOTCHES TO FRONT OF ENGINE
OIL SPURT HOLES TOWARD CAMSHAFT

Relation of piston and rod—slant six
(© Chrysler Corp)

there isn't the slightest chance of it getting mixed up or put on in the wrong way.

5. At this point, note whether the number of the cylinder is stamped on the connecting rod, and, if it is not, some provision will have to be made to mark the rod, such as a file mark or a punch mark. Push the rod and piston assembly up until the rings snap out of the cylinder.
6. When assembling pistons to connecting rods, and the assemblies to the engine, on the slant 6, be sure to locate the squirt hole to the proper side. The 1967-74 engine has the piston head notch at the front, with the oil squirt hole to the right side of the engine.

NOTE: Late in 1971, a new piston and crankshaft assembly was incorporated into the assembly of some 440 cu. in. non-high-performance engines. Because these pistons are lighter than the old style, they cannot be used as alternative replacements for the older engines. Engines equipped with this new style piston and crank assembly may be identified by the letter "C" on the information pad on the top, next to the left bank and tappet rail.

Piston Rings

Replacement

1. If cylinder bore is in satisfactory condition, place each ring in bore (in turn) and align using the head of a piston. Measure the ring end gap with feeler gauges; if gap is greater than limit, use new ring; if gap is less than limit, file end of ring to obtain correct gap. The correct ring gaps are found in the chart.
2. Check ring side clearance by installing rings onto piston and inserting feeler gauge of correct thickness between ring and lower land. Gauge should slide freely around ring circumference without binding. Any wear will usually show up as a step on the lower land; replace any pistons having high steps. Ring side clearance is found in the chart.
3. Space ring gaps at equidistant intervals around piston circumference. Be sure to install piston into its original bore. Install short lengths of rubber tubing over connecting rod bolts to prevent rod journal damage, then install ring compressor over rings on piston and lower piston-rod assembly into bore until ring compressor contacts block. Using a woden hammer handle, push piston into bore while guiding rod onto journal.

Engine Lubrication

All Chrysler engines utilize a full-flow, replaceable-type oil filter. Six-cylinder engines utilize an externally mounted rotor-type oil pump located on the lower right side of the cylinder block. The 273, 318, 340, and 360 V8s utilize an internally mounted oil pump. On the big-block engines, the pump is mounted externally, and is also of the rotor type.

Oil Pan Removal

Slant 6

1. Disconnect the battery and remove the oil dipstick. Jack up the vehicle and drain the oil.
2. Remove the steering arm center link. Remove the idler arm ball joints.
3. Disconnect the exhaust pipe from its manifold and secure it out of the way.
4. Take out the oil pan attaching bolts. Rotate the engine crank-

OVER LAP
REAR SEAL
NOTCH
NOTCH

On 360 engines, be sure that the pan gasket is positioned as shown
(© Chrysler Corp)

shaft in order to clear the counterweights. Remove the oil pan.
5. To install the pan, reverse the removal procedure. Torque the pan bolts to 200 in. lbs.

273, 318, 340, and 360 V8s

1. Disconnect the battery and remove the dipstick.
2. Jack up the vehicle and drain the oil. Remove the torque converter-to-engine left housing strut.
3. Remove the idler arm and steering linkage ball joints from the center link.
4. Disconnect the exhaust pipe(s) from the manifold and move it out of the way.
5. Remove the oil pan bolts and the oil pan.
6. To install the pan, be sure that the oil strainer will touch the bottom of the pan.
7. Using a new gasket, install the oil pan. Torque the bolts to 200 in. lbs. On 360 cu in. engines, be certain that the notches on the side gaskets overlap the rear seal.
8. Install the engine-to-converter housing strut.
9. From this point, reverse the removal procedure.

383, 400, 426, and 440 V8s

1. Disconnect the battery and remove the dipstick.
2. Jack up the vehicle and remove the steering linkage from the steering and idler arms.
3. Disconnect the exhaust pipes from the manifolds and move them out of the way.
4. Remove the clamp attaching the exhaust pipe to the extension and remove the exhaust pipe.
5. Drain the oil.
6. Remove the dust shield from the torque converter.
7. Extract the oil pan bolts. Rotate the flywheel until the counterweight and connecting rods at the front of the crank are at their highest position. This will provide sufficient clearance for the pan to be lowered. Rotate the pan counterclockwise to clear the oil screen and suction pipe; lower the pan.
8. To install the pan, reverse the removal procedure.

Oil Pump Removal

Six Cylinder

1. Drain radiator, disconnect upper and lower hoses, and remove fan shroud.
2. Raise vehicle on hoist, support front of engine with jackstand placed under right front corner of oil pan, and remove engine mount bolts. Do not support engine at crankshaft pulley or vibration damper.
3. Raise engine approximately 1½ to 2 in.
4. Remove oil filter, oil pump attaching bolts, and pump assembly.

273, 318, 340 and 360 Engines

1. Remove oil pan.
2. Remove oil pump from rear main bearing cap.

383, 400, 440, and 426 Hemi Engines

1. Because the oil pump is externally mounted, it is unnecessary to remove the oil pan.
2. Remove oil pump from bottom side of engine.

Rear Main Bearing Oil Seal

Service replacement seals are of split rubber type composition. This type of seal makes it possible to replace the upper half of the rear main oil seal without removing the engine from the car. When installing rubber seals, they must be replaced as a set and cannot be combined with the rope type rear main seal. The following procedure is for removing the rope type seal and replacing it with the rubber type seal.

Replacement

NOTE: on vehicles with a 426 Hemi engine, remove the transmission and vibration damper in addition to the procedure listed below.

1. Remove the oil pan.
2. Remove the rear seal retainer and the rear main bearing cap.
3. Remove the lower rope seal by prying from the side with a small screwdriver.
4. To remove the upper rope seal, drive up on either exposed end of the seal with a 6 in. piece of 3/16 in. brazing rod. When the opposite end of the seal starts to protrude from the block, have an assistant grasp it with pliers

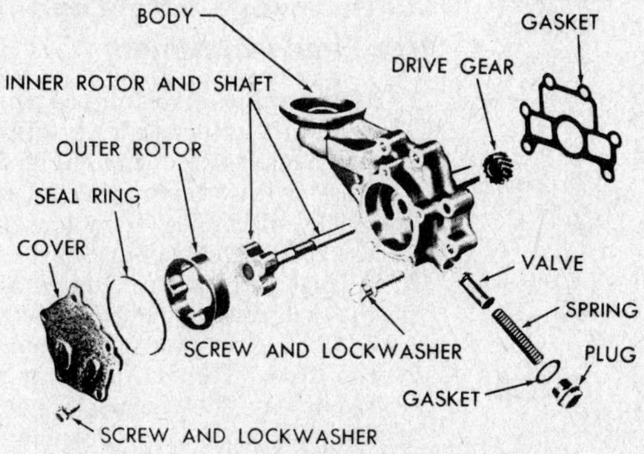
BODY
GASKET
INNER ROTOR AND SHAFT
DRIVE GEAR
OUTER ROTOR
SEAL RING
COVER
VALVE
SPRING
SCREW AND LOCKWASHER
PLUG
GASKET
SCREW AND LOCKWASHER

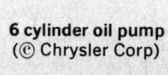

6 cylinder oil pump
(© Chrysler Corp)

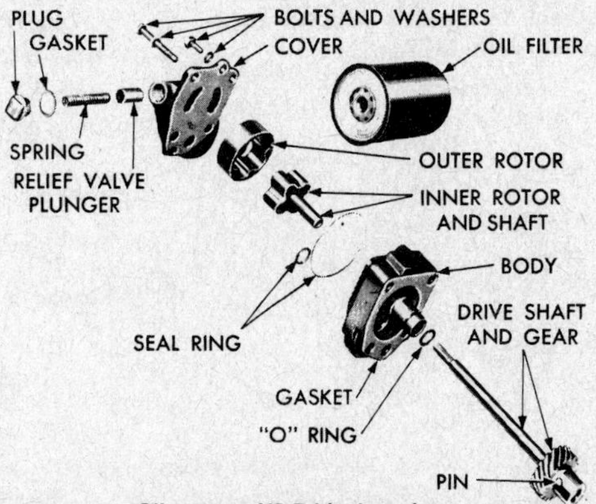
PLUG
GASKET
BOLTS AND WASHERS
COVER
OIL FILTER
SPRING
RELIEF VALVE
PLUNGER
OUTER ROTOR
INNER ROTOR
AND SHAFT
BODY
DRIVE SHAFT
AND GEAR
SEAL RING
GASKET
"O" RING
PIN

Oil pump—V8 B block engines
(© Chrysler Corp)

and gently pull it from the block while the opposite end is being driven.

5. Wipe crankshaft clean and lightly oil crankshaft and new seal before installing seal.
6. Loosen all main bearing caps slightly to lower the crankshaft which will ease installation.

Caution Do not allow the crankshaft to drop enough to permit the main bearings to become displaced on the crankshaft.

7. Hold the seal tightly against the crankshaft with the thumb (with paint stripe to the rear) and install the seal in the block groove. Rotate the crankshaft if necessary while installing the seal in the groove. *Make sure the sharp edges on the block groove do not cut or nick the rear of the seal.*
8. Install lower half of seal (with paint stripe to the rear) into the lower seal retainer.
9. Install rear main bearing cap.
10. Tighten all main bearing caps to specification.

Note: make sure all main bearings are located in their proper position before tightening the main bearing caps.

CLUTCH

All models utilize a single, dry-plate type of clutch which is operated by a pedal suspended under the dash. All models are equipped with a return spring; some models have centrifugal rollers assembled between the pressure plate and cover. Six-cylinder and light-duty V8 models utilize a non-centrifugal type of clutch; six-cylinder heavy-duty usage and most V8s use a semi-centrifugal type.

Clutch Removal

1967

1. Remove the transmission.
2. Remove the clutch housing pan.
3. Disconnect the clutch linkage and retracting spring at the release fork.
4. Remove the fork from the throw-out bearing assembly.
5. Punch-mark the clutch cover and flywheel to assure correct location when installing.
6. Loosen the clutch cover attaching bolts in two stages; this will prevent bending the cover flange.
7. Remove the clutch assembly. Be careful not to contaminate the clutch with grease or oil.

1968-74

1. Remove the transmission.
2. Remove the clutch housing pan.
3. Disconnect the fork return spring from the clutch housing and release the fork.
4. Take off the spring washer fastening fork rod-to-torque shaft lever pin. Remove the pin from the rod and release the fork.
5. On those models with three-speed transmissions (if this procedure is applicable to the vehicle in question) remove the clip and the plain washer which secures the interlock rod-to-torque shaft lever and remove the washers and rod from the torque shaft.
6. Remove the sleeve assembly and the clutch release bearing from the clutch release fork.
7. Punch-mark the clutch cover and flywheel so they may be installed in their same relative positions.
8. Loosen the clutch cover attaching screws in two stages to avoid bending the cover flange.
9. Remove the clutch assembly. Be careful not to contaminate the clutch with grease or oil.

Clutch Installation

1. Lightly lubricate the drive pinion bushing in the end of the crankshaft with ½ teaspoon of long-life chassis grease. The lubricant should be inserted in the radius in back of the bushing.
2. Thoroughly clean the surfaces of the flywheel and pressure plate with fine sandpaper. All oil or grease must be removed at this time.
3. Position the clutch disc, pressure plate, and cover in the mounting position. The springs on the disc damper must be facing away from the flywheel. Do not touch the disc facing at any time. Insert a clutch disc aligning arbor or suitable substitute (such as a spare transmission drive pinion) through the disc hub and into the bushing.
4. Align the punch marks that were made at removal. Install the clutch cover bolt but do not tighten it.
5. Tighten all bolts a few turns at a time in an alternate sequence. Torque 5/16 in. bolts to 200 in. lbs and 3/8 in. bolts to 30 ft lbs. Remove the alignment tool.
6. Pack the bearing sleeve cavity with an appropriate NLGI Grade 2 EP grease. Apply the same lubricant to the release fork pads of the sleeve.
7. Insert the release bearing and sleeve assembly into the clutch housing as far forward as possible. Lightly lubricate the fork fingers and retaining spring.
8. Insert the fork fingers under the clutch sleeve retaining springs. The retaining springs on the sleeve must have lateral freedom.
9. Make sure that the groove in the seal is properly seated in the seal-opening flange in the clutch housing. Replace the pedal rod on the torque shaft lever pin and secure it with spring washer.
10. Insert the threaded end of the fork rod assembly into the opening provided in the end of the release fork rod. Replace the eye end of the fork rod on the torque shaft lever pin and lock it in place with a spring washer.
11. If applicable, install the fork return spring between the release fork and the clutch housing.
12. If applicable, install the spring and plain washer with the interlock rod in the torque shaft lever and lock it in position with a washer and clip.
13. When installing the transmission, be careful that no grease settles on the splines or pilot end of the transmission drive pinion.
14. Install the transmission and adjust clutch pedal free-play.

Clutch Linkage (Height and Free-Play) Adjustment

1. If the vehicle is equipped with a gearshift interlock rod (six-cylinder models and some light-duty V8s with three-speeds after 1967), disconnect it by loosening the rod swivel clamp screw.
2. Adjust the fork rod by rotating the self-locking nut to provide 5/32 in. free-play at the end of the fork. This adjustment will result in the proper one-inch free-play at the clutch pedal.
3. If the gearshift interlock was disconnected, refer to its adjustment procedure below.

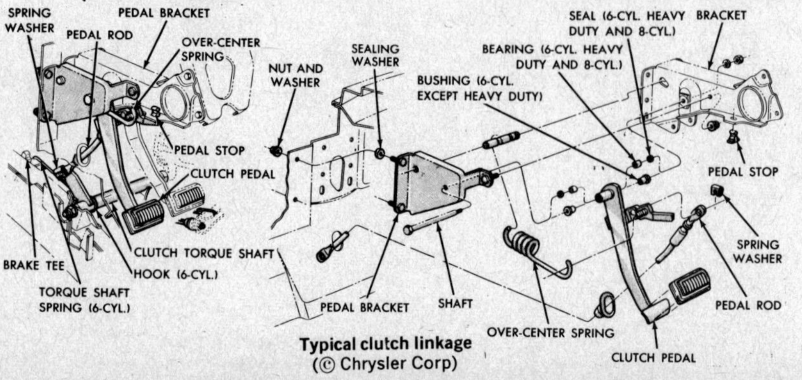
SPRING WASHER
PEDAL BRACKET
PEDAL ROD
OVER-CENTER SPRING
NUT AND WASHER
SEALING WASHER
BEARING (6-CYL. HEAVY DUTY AND 8-CYL.)
SEAL (6-CYL. HEAVY DUTY AND 8-CYL.)
BRACKET
BUSHING (6-CYL. EXCEPT HEAVY DUTY)
PEDAL STOP
CLUTCH PEDAL
PEDAL STOP
SPRING WASHER
BRAKE TEE
CLUTCH TORQUE SHAFT
HOOK (6-CYL.)
TORQUE SHAFT SPRING (6-CYL.)
PEDAL BRACKET
SHAFT
PEDAL ROD
OVER-CENTER SPRING
CLUTCH PEDAL

Typical clutch linkage
(© Chrysler Corp)

Gearshift Interlock Adjustment

1. Disconnect the interlock pawl from the clutch rod swivel.
2. Adjust clutch pedal free-play.
3. With the first-reverse lever of the transmission in the neutral (middle detent) position, the interlock pawl should enter the slot in the first-reverse lever.
4. Loosen the swivel clamp bolt and move the swivel on the rod to enter the pawl. Install the washers with a clip. Hold the interlock pawl forward and torque the swivel clamp bolt to 100–125 in. lbs. The clutch pedal must be in the fully returned position during this adjustment. Under no circumstance should the clutch rod be pulled rearward to engage the pawl swivel.
5. Shift the clutch through all of the gear positions at least three times, clutch action should be normal.
6. Disengage the clutch and shift halfway to first or reverse gear. The clutch should be held down by the interlock within 1–2 in. of floor.

MANUAL TRANSMISSION

Transmission Removal

Dodge and Plymouth have used four synchromesh manual transmissions in recent years. Six cylinders use a three speed, top cover transmission with synchromesh on second and third. V8s up to 1970 use a similar three speed, top cover transmission with synchromesh on second and third. 1970 and later V8s use a new fully synchromesh, side cover three speed. All Dodge and Plymouth four speed cars use a fully synchromesh, side cover four speed.

Transmission Removal

All Top Cover 3 Speed Transmissions

1. Drain the transmission.
2. Disconnect the driveshaft at the rear universal joint. Carefully pull the shaft yoke out of the transmission.
3. Disconnect the speedometer cable and the back-up light switch.
4. Install the engine support fixture or jack up the engine about 1 in. and block it in place.
5. Disconnect the transmission extension housing from the center crossmember.
6. Support the transmission with a jack and remove the crossmember. Remove the bolts that attach the transmission to the clutch housing.
7. Slide the transmission rearward until the pinion shaft clears the clutch disc before lowering the transmission.
8. Lower the transmission and remove it.

Fully Synchromesh, Side Cover Three Speed

1. Remove shift rods from transmission levers.
2. Drain transmission fluid.
3. Disconnect drive shaft at rear universal joint. Mark both parts for reassembly.
4. Carefully pull yoke out of transmission extension.
5. Disconnect speedometer and backup lights.
6. Remove part of exhaust if it blocks transmission.
7. Raise engine slightly and block in place.
8. Support transmission with jack, and remove crossmember.
9. Remove transmission to clutch housing bolts.
10. Slide transmission to rear until drive pinion shaft clears. Clear clutch disc, lower transmission, and remove from vehicle.

Four Speed

1. Raise vehicle on a hoist and drain transmission.
2. Disconnect all shift controls from transmission levers. Remove three bolts securing shift unit to extension housing.
3. Disconnect driveshaft at rear universal joint. Carefully pull yoke out of transmission extension.
4. Disconnect speedometer cable and backup light switch leads.
5. Disconnect left exhaust pipe or dual exhausts. Disconnect parking brake cable.
6. Raise engine slightly and block in place.
7. Disconnect transmission extension from crossmember.
8. Remove crossmember.
9. Support transmission with jack. Remove clutch housing to transmission bolts.
10. Slide transmission to rear until drive pinion shaft clears clutch disc.
11. Lower transmission and remove from vehicle.

Manual Transmission Installation

Lightly grease the inner end of the pilot shaft bushing in the flywheel. In addition, grease the pinion bearing retainer pilot at the clutch release shaft.

Position the transmission so that the drive pinion is centered in the clutch housing bore. Push the transmission forward until the pinion shaft enters the clutch disc. Place the transmission in gear. Twist the output shaft until the splines align. Push the transmission forward until it is seated against the clutch housing.

Caution The transmission must not hang after the pinion is inside the clutch.

Replace the transmission coupling bolts. Torque them to 50 ft lbs. With the aid of a drift, align the crossmember bolt holes and install and torque the bolts to 40–50 ft lbs. Remove the engine support fixture and hooks. Install the extension housing and bolt in position. If so equipped, tighten the engine mount-to-crossmember bolt. Install and perform the gearshift linkage adjustment. Connect the driveshaft and universal joints. Connect the exhaust system and fill the transmission with the appropriate lubricant. Road-test vehicle.

Manual Shift Adjustments

Column Mounted Shifter

Three Speed 1967 Dodge and Plymouth

1. With the second and third control rod disconnected from the lever on the column, and first and reverse control rod disconnected at the transmission lever, position both transmission levers in neutral.

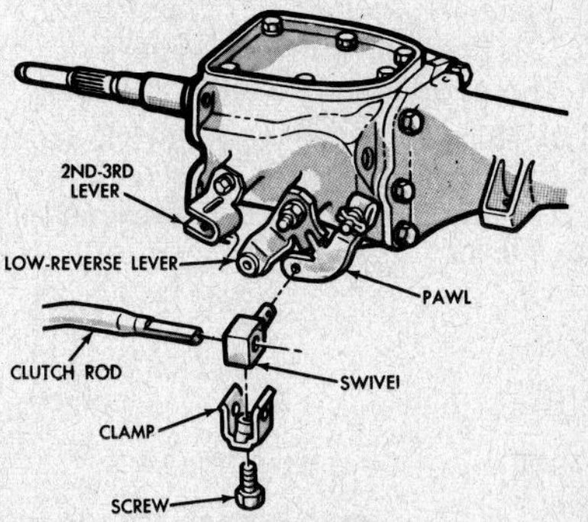
2ND-3RD LEVER
LOW-REVERSE LEVER
PAWL
CLUTCH ROD
SWIVEL
CLAMP
SCREW

3-speed shift linkage
(© Chrysler Corp)

2. Check for axial freedom of the shift levers in the column. If the outer ends of the levers move up or down along the column axis over 1/16 in., loosen the two upper bushing screws and rotate the plastic bushing, downward, until all of the axial play is eliminated. Retighten bushing screws.
3. Wedge a screwdriver between the crossover blade and the second and third lever, so that the crossover blade is engaged with both lever crossover pins.
4. Adjust the swivel on the end of second and third rod until the stub shaft of the swivel enters the hole in the column lever. Install washers and clip. Tighten swivel lock nut to 70 in. lbs.
5. Slide the clamp and swivel on the

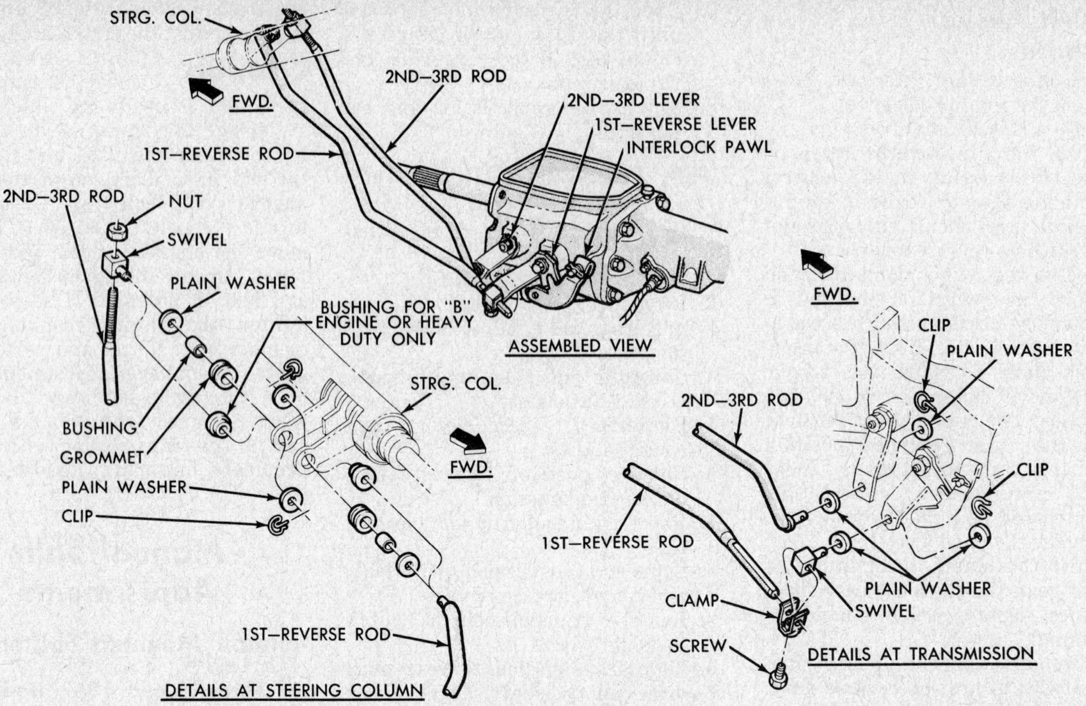

STRG. COL.
FWD.
2ND–3RD ROD
2ND–3RD LEVER
1ST–REVERSE LEVER
INTERLOCK PAWL
1ST–REVERSE ROD
2ND–3RD ROD
NUT
SWIVEL
PLAIN WASHER
BUSHING FOR "B" ENGINE OR HEAVY DUTY ONLY
ASSEMBLED VIEW
FWD.
CLIP
PLAIN WASHER
STRG. COL.
2ND–3RD ROD
BUSHING
GROMMET
FWD.
CLIP
PLAIN WASHER
CLIP
1ST–REVERSE ROD
PLAIN WASHER
CLAMP
SWIVEL
SCREW
DETAILS AT TRANSMISSION
1ST–REVERSE ROD
DETAILS AT STEERING COLUMN

1968-69 Coronet, Charger, and Belvedere gearshift linkage (© Chrysler Corp)

end of the first and reverse control rod until the swivel stub shaft enters the hole in the transmission lever. Install washers and clip. Tighten the swivel clamp bolt to 100 in. lbs.

Charger and Belvedere Three Speed 1968-69 Coronet,

1. Remove second-third swivel from steering column lever and first-reverse swivel from transmission lever.
2. Make sure transmission shift levers are in neutral (middle detent) position.
3. Loosen lock nut and adjust second-third swivel so it will enter second-third lever at steering column while hand lever on steering column is held 12 degrees above horizontal position. Install washers and clip. Tighten swivel nut to 70 in. lbs.
4. Place screwdriver or suitable tool between cross-over blade and second-third lever at steering column so that both lever pins are engaged by cross-over blade.
5. Adjust first reverse rod swivel by loosening clamp bolt and sliding swivel along rod so it will enter first-reverse lever at transmission. Install washers and slip. Tighten swivel bolt to 100 in. lbs.
6. Remove tool from cross-over blade at steering column and shift through all gears to check adjustment and cross over smoothness.

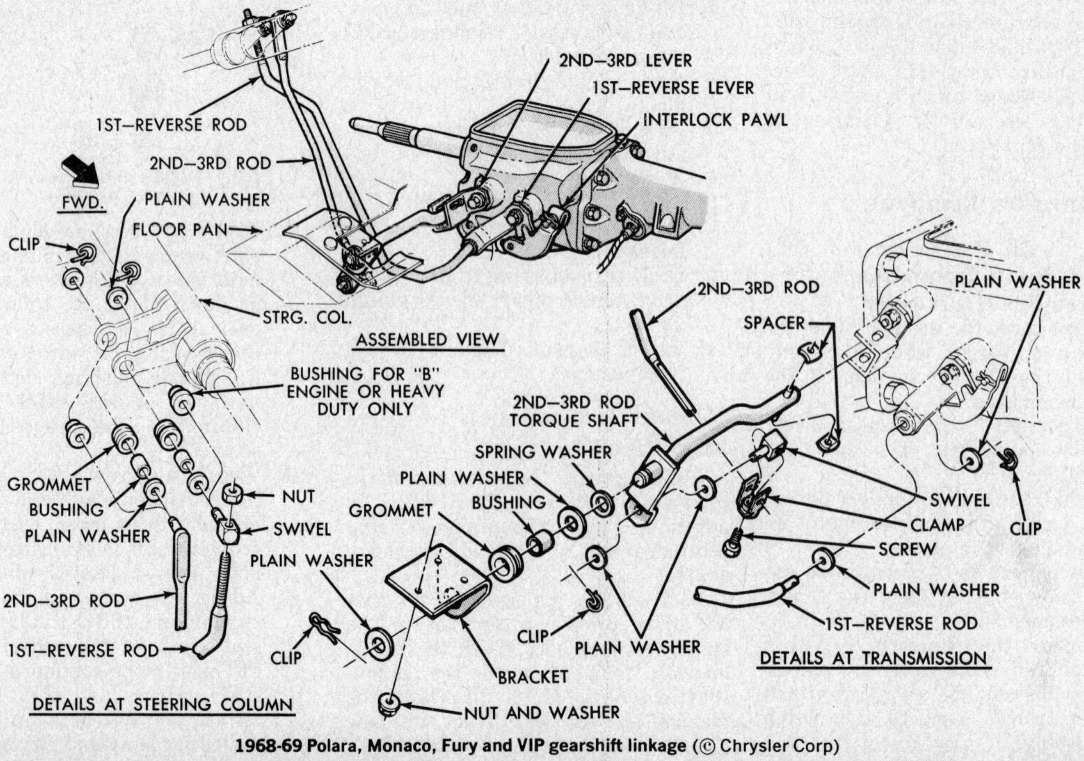

2ND–3RD LEVER
1ST–REVERSE LEVER
INTERLOCK PAWL
1ST–REVERSE ROD
2ND–3RD ROD
FWD.
PLAIN WASHER
FLOOR PAN
CLIP
STRG. COL.
ASSEMBLED VIEW
2ND–3RD ROD
PLAIN WASHER
SPACER
BUSHING FOR "B" ENGINE OR HEAVY DUTY ONLY
2ND–3RD ROD TORQUE SHAFT
SPRING WASHER
PLAIN WASHER
BUSHING
GROMMET
GROMMET
BUSHING
PLAIN WASHER
NUT
SWIVEL
PLAIN WASHER
SWIVEL
CLAMP
SCREW
CLIP
PLAIN WASHER
2ND–3RD ROD
1ST–REVERSE ROD
1ST–REVERSE ROD
CLIP
CLIP
PLAIN WASHER
BRACKET
DETAILS AT TRANSMISSION
DETAILS AT STEERING COLUMN
NUT AND WASHER

1968-69 Polara, Monaco, Fury and VIP gearshift linkage (© Chrysler Corp)

Three Speed 1968-69 Polara, Monaco, and Fury

1. Remove first-reverse rod swivel from steering column and second-third rod swivel from torque shaft lever.
2. Make sure transmission shift levers are in neutral (middle detent) position.
3. Adjust second-third rod swivel by loosening clamp bolt and sliding swivel along rod so it will enter torque shaft lever while hand lever on steering column is held 12 degrees above horizontal position. Install washers and clip. Tighten swivel clamp bolt to 100 in. lbs.
4. Place screwdriver or suitable tool between cross-over blade and second-third lever at steering column so that both lever pins are engaged by cross-over blade.
5. Adjust first-reverse rod swivel by loosening lock nut and turning swivel so it will enter first-reverse lever at steering column. Install washers and clip. Tighten swivel lock nut to 70 in. lbs.
6. Remove tool from cross-over blade at steering column and shift through all gears to check adjustment and cross-over smoothness.

Three Speed 1970-74

1. Remove both shift rod swivels from the transmission shift levers. Be sure that the transmission shift levers are in neutral (middle) position.
2. Move shift lever to line up locating slots in bottom of steering column shift housing and bearing housing. Place a suitable tool in the slot and lock the ignition switch.
3. Place a screwdriver or suitable tool between crossover blade and second-third lever at steering column so that both lever pins are engaged by cross-over blade.
4. Set first-reverse lever on transmission to reverse position (rotate clockwise).
5. Adjust first-reverse rod swivel by loosening clamp bolt and sliding swivel along rod. It should enter first-reverse lever at transmission. Install washers and clip. Tighten swivel bolt to 100 in. lbs.
6. Remove gearshift housing locating tool, unlock ignition switch, and shift column lever into neutral position.
7. Adjust second-third rod swivel by loosening clamp bolt and sliding swivel along rod so it will enter second-third lever at transmission. Install washers and clip. Tighten swivel bolt to 100 in. lbs.
8. Remove tool from crossover blade at steering column, and shift through all gears to check adjustment and cross-over smoothness.

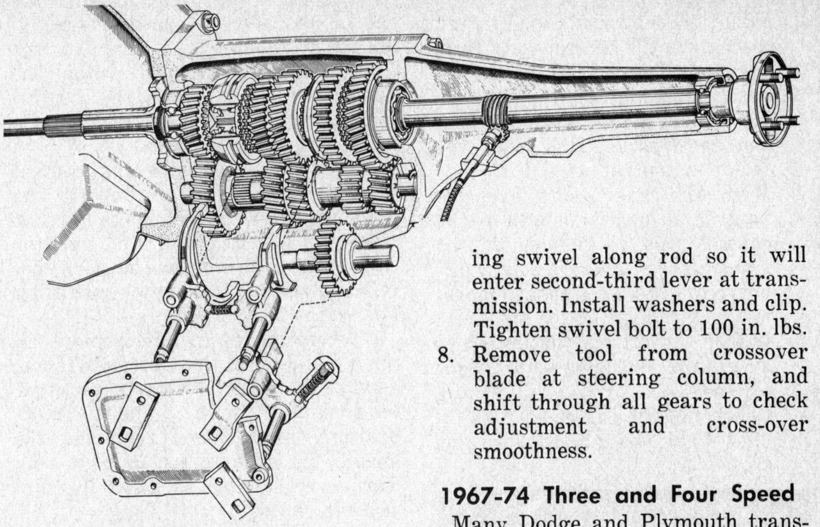
4-speed transmission
(© Chrysler Corp)

1967-74 Three and Four Speed

Many Dodge and Plymouth transmissions use Hurst shift linkages. To adjust these linkages, see Hurst Shift Linkage section. Adjust Chrysler Corporation linkages as follows:

1. Make up a lever aligning tool from 1/16 in. thick metal as in illustration.

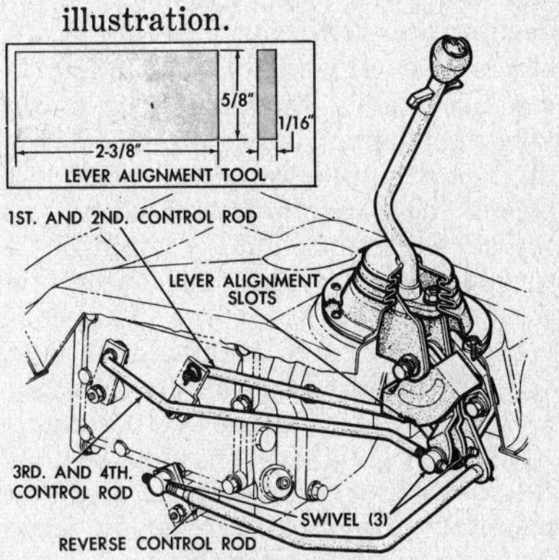
5/8"
1/16"
2-3/8"
LEVER ALIGNMENT TOOL
1ST. AND 2ND. CONTROL ROD
LEVER ALIGNMENT SLOTS
3RD. AND 4TH. CONTROL ROD
SWIVEL (3)
REVERSE CONTROL ROD
4-speed shift linkage
(© Chrysler Corp)

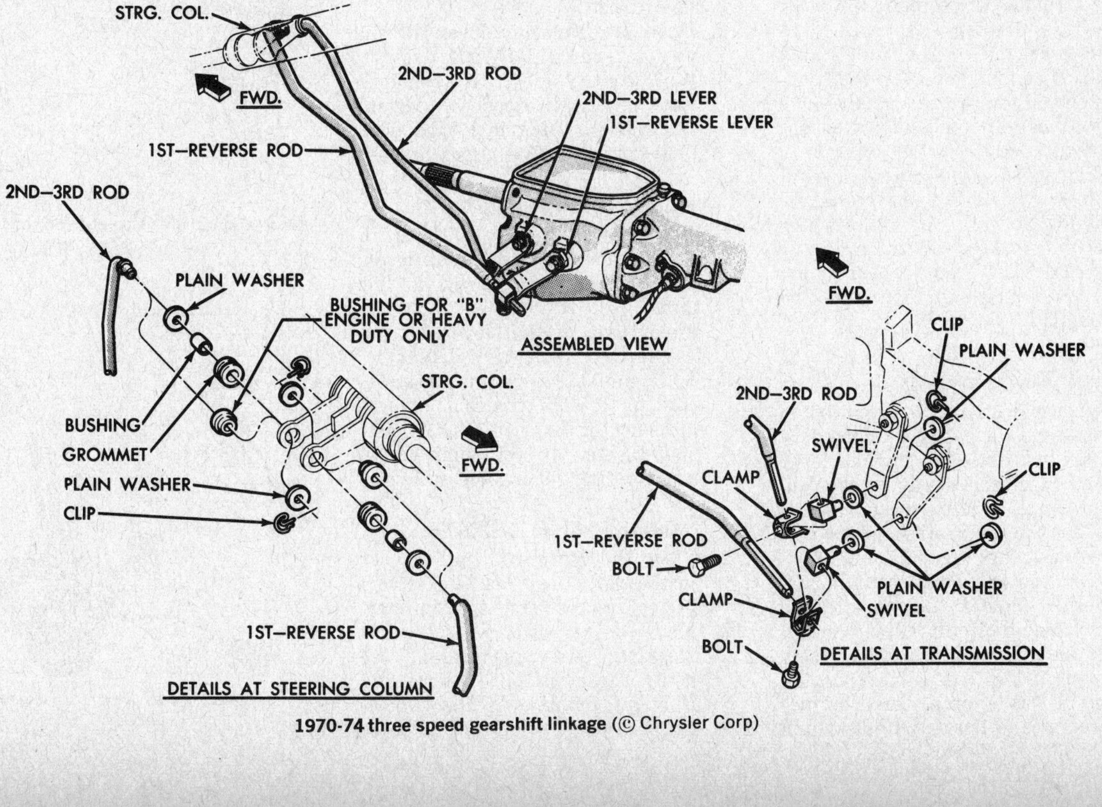
STRG. COL.
FWD.
2ND—3RD ROD
2ND—3RD LEVER
1ST—REVERSE LEVER
1ST—REVERSE ROD
2ND—3RD ROD
PLAIN WASHER
BUSHING FOR "B" ENGINE OR HEAVY DUTY ONLY
ASSEMBLED VIEW
FWD.
STRG. COL.
BUSHING
GROMMET
PLAIN WASHER
CLIP
FWD.
1ST—REVERSE ROD
DETAILS AT STEERING COLUMN
CLIP
PLAIN WASHER
2ND—3RD ROD
SWIVEL
CLAMP
CLIP
1ST—REVERSE ROD
BOLT
CLAMP
PLAIN WASHER
SWIVEL
BOLT
DETAILS AT TRANSMISSION
1970-74 three speed gearshift linkage (© Chrysler Corp)

2. With transmission in neutral, disconnect all control rods from the transmission levers.
3. Insert lever aligning tool through the slots in the levers and against the back plate. This locks the levers in neutral.
4. With all transmission levers in neutral, adjust the length of the control rods so they enter the transmission levers freely without rearward or forward movement.
5. Install control rod flat washers and retainers. Remove the aligning tool.
6. Check linkage for ease of shifting into all gears and for ease of crossover.

AUTOMATIC TRANSMISSION

Model identification appears in large letters embossed on the lower side of the bell housing. While designs and servicing procedures are similar for all vehicles, internal parts are necessarily different. Therefore, when replacing parts refer to the 7-digit part number stamped on the left side of the transmission oil flange.

The transmission combines a torque converter and fully automatic three-speed gear system. The converter housing and transmission case are an integral aluminum casting. The transmission consists of two multiple disc clutches, an overrunning clutch, two servos and bands, and two planetary gear sets to provide three forward ratios and a reverse ratio. The common sun gear of the planetary gear sets is connected to the front clutch by a driving shell splined to the sun gear and to the front clutch retainer. The hydraulic system consists of the oil pump and a single valve body that contains all valves except the governor valve.

Cooling of the converter is accomplished by circulating the transmission fluid through an oil-to-water type cooler located in the radiator lower tank. The torque converter assembly is a sealed unit that cannot be disassembled.

Neutral Start Switch

The neutral switch is mounted in the transmission case on all models. When the transmission manual lever is placed in either the Park or Neutral position, a cam, which is attached to the transmission throttle lever inside the transmission, contacts the neutral start switch and provides a ground to complete the starter solenoid circuit. On late model Dodges and Plymouths, the back-up light switch has been incorporated into the neutral switch. The combination neutral and back-up light switch can be identified by the three electrical terminals on the rear of the switch. On this type of switch, the center terminal is for the neutral switch and the two outer terminals are for the back-up lights.

NOTE: in order for the neutral start switch to function properly, the transmission manual linkage must be properly adjusted and the actuator cam in the transmission must be centered in the neutral switch mounting hole in the transmission.

To remove the switch, remove all wiring and, with the aid of a wrench, remove the switch. Have a container of adequate size at hand to catch draining fluid. When replacing the switch, be sure to use a new seal. Torque the switch to 24 ft lbs. Replace the fluid.

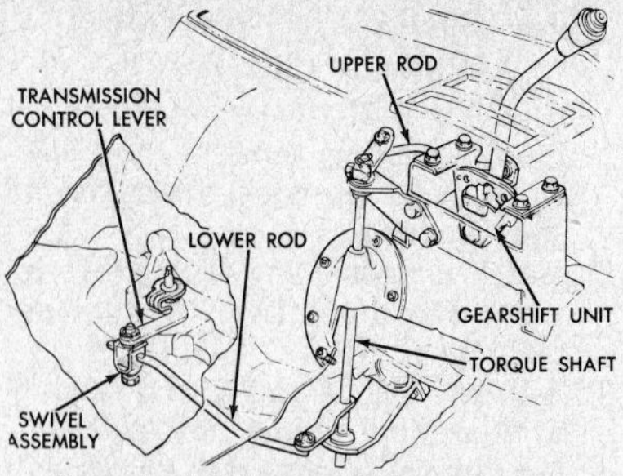
UPPER ROD
TRANSMISSION CONTROL LEVER
LOWER ROD
GEARSHIFT UNIT
TORQUE SHAFT
SWIVEL ASSEMBLY

Console shift linkage, 1969 and prior
(© Chrysler Corp)

3. Position the adjustable rod to the proper length and install it with no load in any direction on the linkage. Tighten the locknut.
4. Check the adjustment by determining that the shift effort is free and that the detents engage

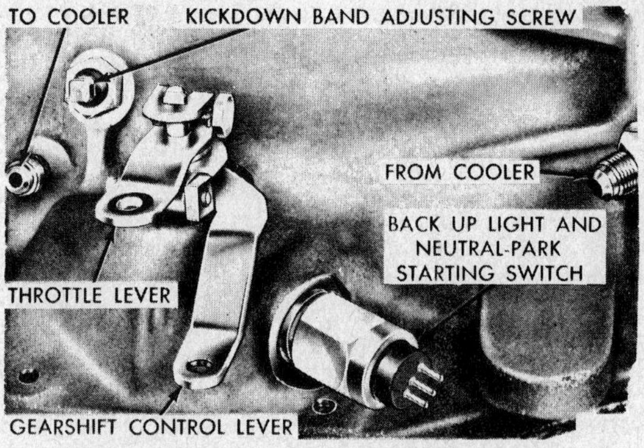
TO COOLER
KICKDOWN BAND ADJUSTING SCREW
FROM COOLER
BACK UP LIGHT AND NEUTRAL-PARK STARTING SWITCH
THROTTLE LEVER
GEARSHIFT CONTROL LEVER

Combination neutral start and back up light switch
(© Chrysler Corp)

Gearshift Linkage Adjustment

Column Shift 1967-69

1. Place gearshift selector lever in PARK position and loosen control rod swivel clamp screw a few turns.
2. Move transmission lever all the way to rear (in PARK detent).
3. With control lever on transmission in PARK position detent and selector lever in PARK position, tighten swivel clamp screw.

Console Shift 1967-69

1. Place gearshift selector lever in PARK position and loosen lower rod swivel clamp screw a few turns.
2. Move transmission lever all the way to rear (in PARK detent).
3. With control lever on transmission in PARK position detent, and selector lever in PARK position, tighten swivel clamp screw or adjusting lever bolt securely.

Column Shift 1970-74

1. Place the gearshift control lever in the park position. Lock steering column with the ignition key.
2. Move the gearshift control leaver (located on transmission, see neutral start switch illustration) fully rearward (in Park position).

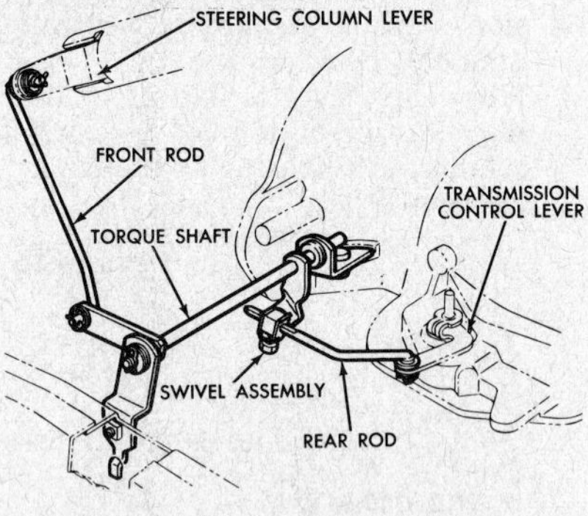
STEERING COLUMN LEVER
FRONT ROD
TRANSMISSION CONTROL LEVER
TORQUE SHAFT
SWIVEL ASSEMBLY
REAR ROD

Automatic transmission column shift linkage
(© Chrysler Corp)

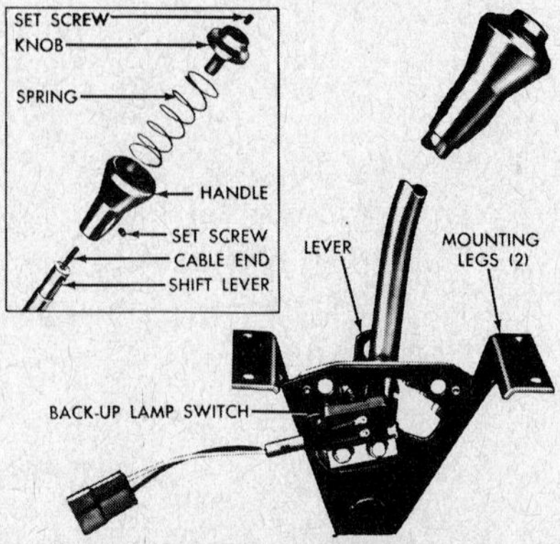
SET SCREW
KNOB
SPRING
HANDLE
SET SCREW
CABLE END
SHIFT LEVER
LEVER
MOUNTING LEGS (2)
BACK-UP LAMP SWITCH

Automatic transmission console shifter
(© Chrysler Corp)

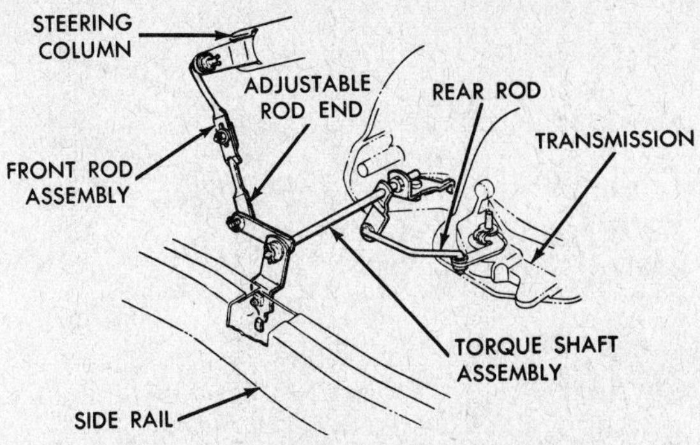
STEERING COLUMN
ADJUSTABLE ROD END
REAR ROD
TRANSMISSION
FRONT ROD ASSEMBLY
TORQUE SHAFT ASSEMBLY
SIDE RAIL
1970-74 column gearshift linkage (typical)
(© Chrysler Corp)

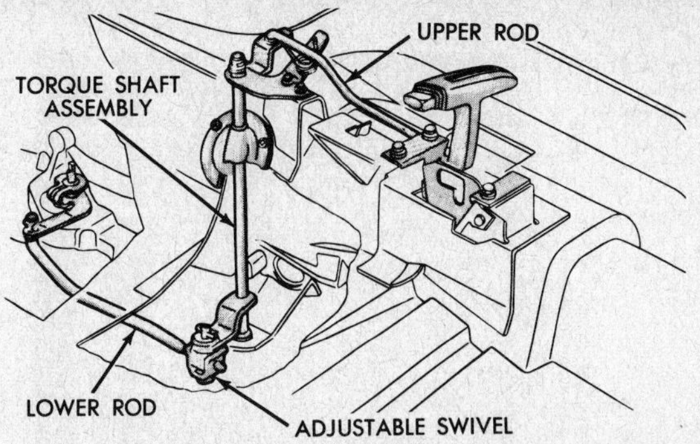
UPPER ROD
TORQUE SHAFT ASSEMBLY
LOWER ROD
ADJUSTABLE SWIVEL
1970-74 console gearshift linkage (typical)
(© Chrysler Corp)

crisply. The gate stops must be positive. The position of the detends should be close enough to the gate stops in Neutral and Drive that the handlever will slide into position when placed against the gate and then released. Key starts must occur only when the transmission shift lever is in the Neutral or Park positions.

Console Shift 1970-74

1. Align the locating slots in the bottom of the shift housing and the bearing housing at the upper end of the steering column. Install the appropriate tool to hold this alignment; lock the steering column with the ignition key.
2. Move the console lever to the Park position; move the gearshift control lever (located on the transmission, see neutral start switch illustration) fully rearward to the Park detent.
3. Position the adjustable rods to the correct length with no load, in any direction, on the rods or linkage. Tighten the locknut.
4. Check the adjustment by determining that the shift effort is free and that the detents engage crisply. The gate stops must be positive. The position of the detents should be close enough to the gate stops in Neutral and drive so that the handlever will slide into position when it is placed against the gate and then released. In addition, key starts must occur only when the transmission shift lever is in the Neutral or Park positions.

Draining, Refilling, Filter Service

The automatic transmission fluid need not be changed for most models in normal service. For vehicles used in abnormal service, and for an extra measure of protection, fluid should be changed at 36,000 mile intervals. If the vehicle is used in competition, or for trailer towing, it is recommended that the fluid be changed at 12,000 mile intervals.

To drain the transmission fluid, raise the car on a hoist or jack up the front of the car and support it with stands. Place a container, which has a large opening, under the transmission oil pan. Loosen the pan bolts at one corner, tap the pan to break the seal, and allow the fluid to drain. Remove the oil pan and filter. Remove the access plate from in front of the torque converter; with the aid of a socket wrench on the vibration damper bolt, rotate the engine clockwise to bring converter drain to bottom. Position the container under the converter, withdraw the drain plug, and allow the fluid to drain.

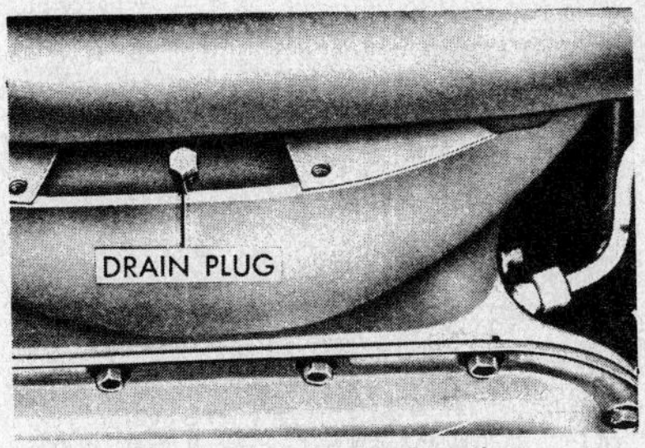
DRAIN PLUG
Converter drain plug location
(© Chrysler Corp)

Refit the converter drain plug and torque it to 100 in. lbs. Install the access plate. Place a new filter on the bottom of the valve body and tighten the retaining screws to 35 in. lbs. Clean the oil pan, fit a new gasket, and install the assembly. Torque the pan bolts to 150 in. lbs. Remove the container and lower the car.

Fill the transmission with six quarts of Dexron automatic transmission fluid. Start the engine and allow it to idle for at least two minutes. With the parking brake engaged, move the selector lever momentarily to each position, ending in the Neutral position. Add enough fluid to bring the level to the "add one pint" mark on the dipstick. Road-test the vehicle to thoroughly warm up the transmission and recheck the fluid level, with the engine idling and the parking brake engaged, after the transmission is at its normal operating temperature. The fluid level should then be between the "full" and "add one pint" marks.

Caution To prevent dirt from entering the transmission, be sure that the dipstick cap is fully seated onto the filler tube.

Band Adjustments

Kick-down Band

The kick-down band adjusting screw is located on the left-hand side of the transmission case near the throttle lever shaft.

1. Loosen the locknut and back it off about five turns. Be sure that the adjusting screw is free in the case.
2. Using a torque wrench and, if necessary, suitable adaptors, torque the adjusting screw to 50 in. lbs, if an adaptor is used, or to 72 in. lbs if an adaptor is not used.
3. Back off the adjusting screw the exact number of turns specified below. Keep the screw from turning and torque the locknut to the value specified below.

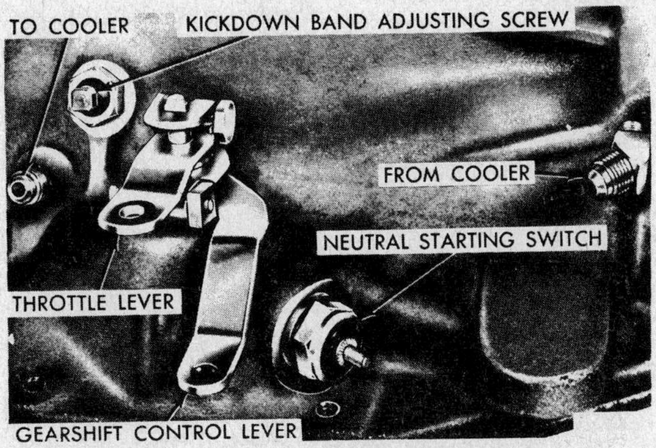
TO COOLER
KICKDOWN BAND ADJUSTING SCREW
FROM COOLER
NEUTRAL STARTING SWITCH
THROTTLE LEVER
GEARSHIFT CONTROL LEVER
Kick-down band adjusting screw
(© Chrysler Corp)

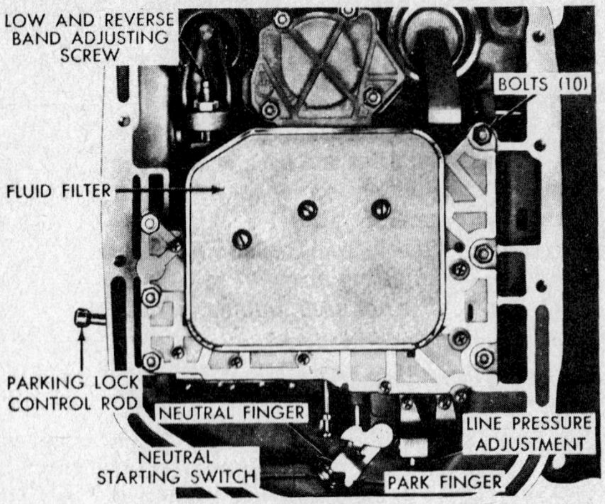
LOW AND REVERSE
BAND ADJUSTING
SCREW
BOLTS (10)
FLUID FILTER
PARKING LOCK
CONTROL ROD
NEUTRAL FINGER
LINE PRESSURE
ADJUSTMENT
NEUTRAL
STARTING SWITCH
PARK FINGER
Low and reverse band adjusting screw
(© Chrysler Corp)

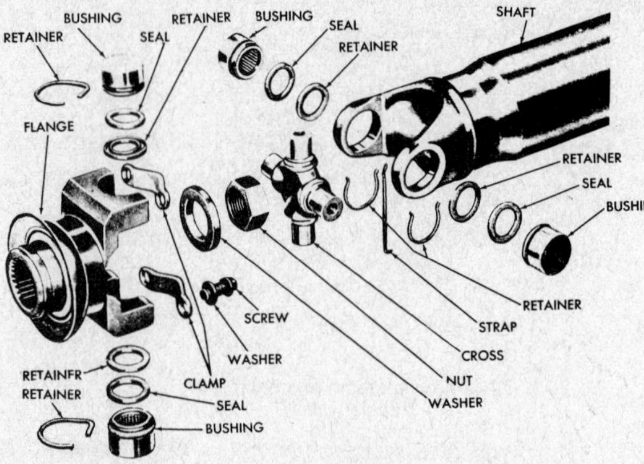
BUSHING
RETAINER
RETAINER
BUSHING
SEAL
SEAL
RETAINER
SHAFT
FLANGE
RETAINER
SEAL
BUSHING
RETAINER
STRAP
SCREW
CROSS
WASHER
NUT
RETAINFR
RETAINER
CLAMP
WASHER
SEAL
BUSHING
Exploded view—cross and bearing type universal joint
(© Chrysler Corp)

Kick-down Band Adjustment Specifications

A—904

1967-70 225 cu. in.	2 turns
1967-68 273 cu. in.	2 turns
1967-72 318 cu. in.	2 turns

A—727

1967-70 six and eight-cylinder engines except Hemi	2 turns
1968-71 Hemi and 440 Six Pack	1½ turns
1971-72 225, 318, 340, 360, 383, 400, and 440 cu in.	2½ turns
A-904 (1967-70) kick-down adjusting screw locknut torque	25 ft. lbs.
A-904 (1971-74) kick-down adjusting screw locknut torque	29 ft. lbs.
A—727 (1967-72) kick-down adjusting screw locknut torque	29 ft. lbs.

Low and Reverse Band

The oil pan must be removed from the transmission to gain access to the First and Reverse band adjusting screw.

1. Drain the transmission and remove the oil pan.
2. Loosen the band adjusting screw locknut and back it off about five turns. Be sure that the adjusting screw turns freely in the lever.
3. Using a torque wrench and, if necessary, suitable adaptors, torque the adjusting screw to 47–50 in. lbs, if an adaptor is used, or to 72 in. lbs if an adaptor is not used.
4. Back off the adjusting screw the exact number of turns specified below. Keep the screw from turning and torque the locknut to the value specified below.
5. Using a new gasket, refit the oil pan and torque the pan bolts to 150 in. lbs. Refill the transmission to the proper fluid level.

First and Reverse Band Adjustment Specifications

A—904

1967-74 All except 318 cu. in.	3¼ turns
1968-74 318 cu. in.	4 turns

A-727

1967-72 All	2 turns
A—904 (1967-70) First and Reverse band adjusting screw locknut torque	20 ft lbs
A—904 (1971-74) First and Reverse band adjusting screw locknut torque	35 ft lbs
A—727 (1967-74) First and Reverse band adjusting screw locknut torque	35 ft lbs

U-JOINTS

All Dodge and Plymouth vehicles use a cross and roller type universal joint at both the front and rear. Two basic types of driveshafts are used; a solid, tube type and a type that incorporates an internal vibration damper inside the tube itself. On certain applications, the driveshaft may be found to incorporate an inertia-type ring at the front universal joint. Servicing of all driveshafts is identical.

Cross and Roller Bearing-Type Joint Disassembly

1. To disassemble the joint, remove the four bolts that hold the two bearing assemblies to the companion flange and knock the bearings off the flange.
2. To remove the bearings from the yoke, first remove the bearing retainer lock washers or C-washers, then pressing on one of the bearings, drive the bearing in toward the center of the joint. This will force the cross to push the opposite bearing out of the universal joint yoke. After it has been pushed all the way out of the yoke, pull up the cross slightly and pack some washers under it. Then press on the end of the cross from which the bearing was just removed to force the first bearing out of the yoke.
3. Perhaps the easiest way to reassemble is to start both bearing retainers into the yoke at the same time, hold the cross carefully in the fingers and squeeze both bearings in a vise or heavy C-clamp. Driving the bearings into place usually cocks the little rollers, greatly reducing the life of the bearings.
4. Reinstall the locking devices.

JACKING, HOISTING

Jack car at front lower control arm and at rear under axle housing.

To lift at frame, use adapters so that contact will be made at points shown. Lifting pads must extend beyond sides of supporting structure.

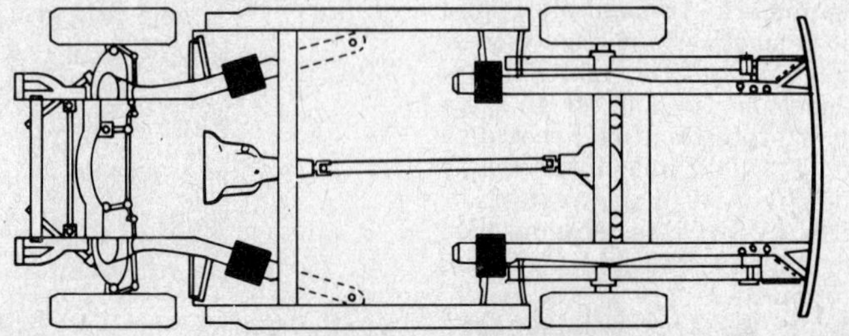
Positioning lift adapter

FRONT SUSPENSION

All Chrysler vehicles utilize a torsion-bar front suspension. The front torsion bar attachments are a part of the lower control arms; the rear fastenings are incorporated into the engine rear support crossmember. Compression-type lower ball joints are located in the steering arms. When servicing the front suspension, it should be kept in mind that rubber bushings must not be lubricated at any time. Any front suspension adjustments or servicing that is required on any part that contains rubber should be tightened with the suspension at the proper height and with the full vehicle weight on the point in question (if possible).

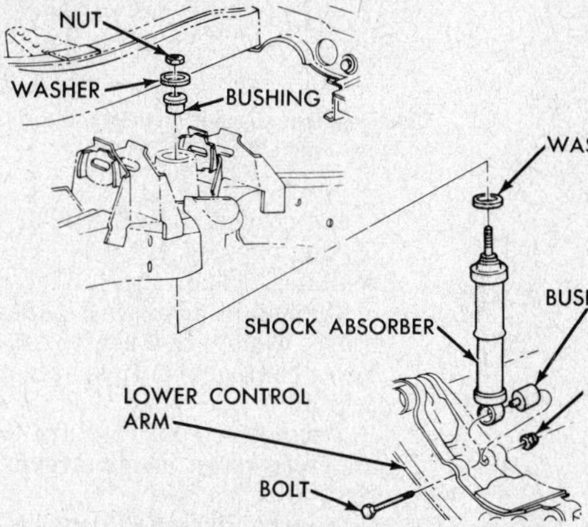
NUT
WASHER
BUSHING
WASHER
BUSHING
SHOCK ABSORBER
NUT
LOWER CONTROL ARM
BOLT
Front shock absorber replacement (typical)
(© Chrysler Corp)

Front Shock Absorbers

Removal and Installation

1. Remove the washer and nut from the upper end of the shock absorber. Be sure to note the positions of all small parts.
2. Jack the vehicle until the wheels are off the floor. Remove the shock absorber lower attaching bolt.
3. Fully compress the shock absorber by pulling upward. Pull the shock firmly and remove it from the vehicle.
4. Check the shock absorber bushings, if they are worn or scored, replace them. Remove and install the bushings with a press or a drift and hammer. To ease installation, lubricate with water.

Caution Do not use oil to ease installation.

5. To install the shock, compress it fully. Insert the mount through the upper bushing, replace the retainer and nut, and torque it to 25 ft lbs. Be sure that all of the retainers are installed with the concave side in contact with the rubber.
6. Position and align the lower mount of the shock absorber. Install the bolt (on some models it must be installed from the rear) with a nut and finger-tighten it. Lower the vehicle and torque the bolt to 50 ft lbs with the full weight of the vehicle on the wheels.

Lower Ball Joint

Inspection

1. Raise the front of the vehicle by placing a floor jack under the lower control arm. Position the lifting point of the jack as close to the wheel as possible.
2. Have an assistant raise and lower the tire and wheel assembly and observe any movement at the lower ball joint.
3. On 1967 models, replace the ball joint if the axial (up and down) play of the ball joint housing arm in relation to the ball joint stud exceeds 0.050 in. On 1968-74 models, replace the ball joint if the axial play exceeds 0.070 in.

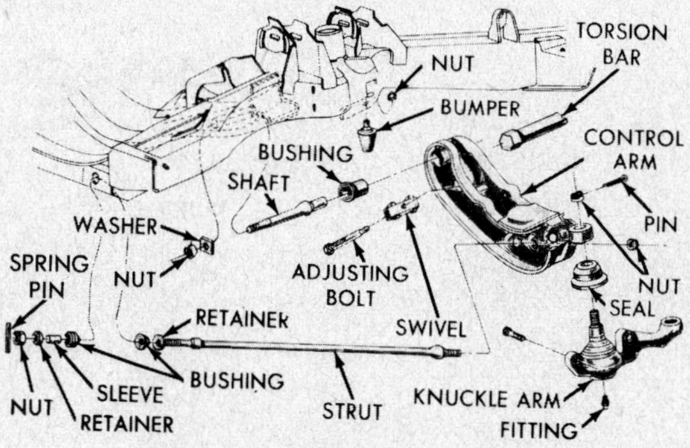
TORSION BAR
NUT
BUMPER
CONTROL ARM
BUSHING
SHAFT
PIN
WASHER
SPRING PIN
NUT
ADJUSTING BOLT
NUT
SEAL
RETAINER
SWIVEL
BUSHING
NUT
SLEEVE
RETAINER
STRUT
KNUCKLE ARM
FITTING
Lower control arm—Fury, Polara and Monaco
(© Chrysler Corp)

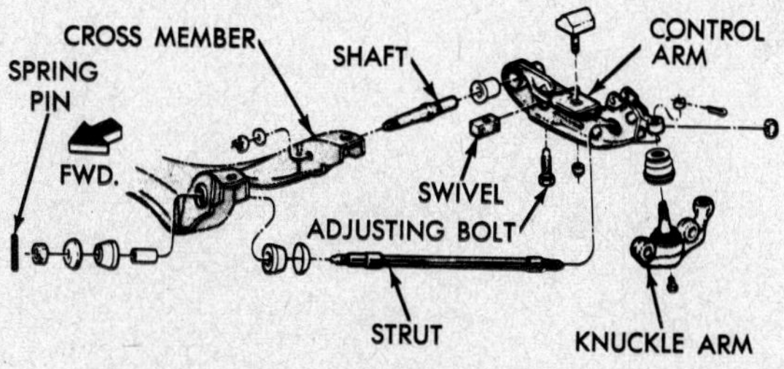
CROSS MEMBER
SHAFT
CONTROL ARM
SPRING PIN
FWD.
SWIVEL
ADJUSTING BOLT
STRUT
KNUCKLE ARM
Lower control arm—Belvedere, Satellite, Coronet and Charger
(© Chrysler Corp)

Removal

The lower ball joint is integral with the steering arm and is not serviced separately.

1. Raise the vehicle on a hoist so the front suspension will drop to the downward limit of its travel.
2. Place a jack stand under the lower control arm.
3. Lower the vehicle onto the jack stand.
4. Remove the tire, wheel, and brake drum from the vehicle as an assembly. If equipped with disc brakes, remove the tire and wheel, remove the brake pads, and remove the caliper from the steering knuckle and position it out of the way with the brake line attached. Remove the rotor from the spindle.
5. Remove the two lower and upper bolts that attach the steering arm-ball joint assembly to the brake assembly mounting plate and move the backing plate out of the way.
6. Using a suitable tool, disconnect the tie-rod end from the steering arm.
7. Remove the ball joint stud retaining nut and cotter pin.
8. Using a suitable tool, separate and remove the ball joint from the lower control arm.

Installation

1. Position ball joint-steering arm assembly on the steering knuckle and install the two retaining bolts.
2. Insert the ball joint stud in the lower control arm and install the retaining nut and cotter pin.
3. Position the tie-rod end in the steering knuckle and install the retaining nut and cotter pin.
4. Place a load on the torsion bar by turning the adjusting bolt in a clockwise direction. *Note: Loading the torsion bar is only necessary if it was removed.*
5. Install the tire, wheel and brake drum assembly. If equipped with

disc brakes, install the rotor, caliper, brake pads and tire and wheel assembly.
6. Lower vehicle and install upper control arm rebound bumper if so equipped and if it was removed.
7. Check and adjust front suspension height as required.

Upper Ball Joint

Replacement

1. Raise the vehicle by placing a floor jack under the lower control arm. Place the lifting point of the jack as close as possible to the wheel.

the upper ball joint to the steering knuckle and, using a suitable tool, loosen the ball joint stud from the steering knuckle.
4. Unscrew the upper ball joint from the upper control arm and remove it from the vehicle.
5. Position new ball joint on the upper control arm, screw the ball joint into the control arm until it bottoms on the control arm and tighten the ball joint to a minimum of 125 ft lbs.

NOTE: when installing a ball joint, make certain the ball joint threads engage those of the upper control arm squarely if the original control arm is being used.

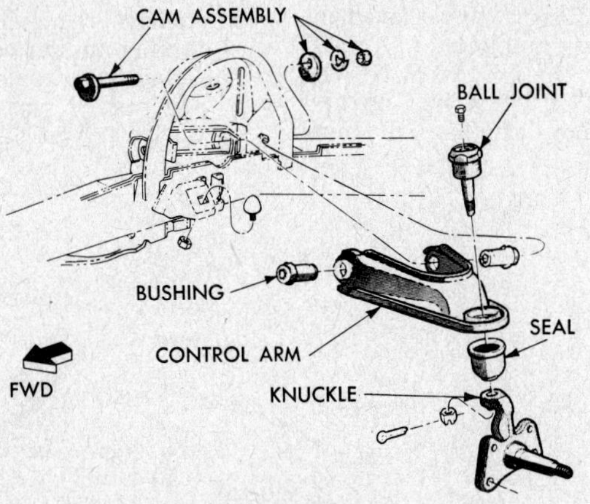
CAM ASSEMBLY
BALL JOINT
BUSHING
SEAL
CONTROL ARM
FWD
KNUCKLE

Upper control arm—Belvedere, Satellite, Coronet and Charger
(© Chrysler Corp)

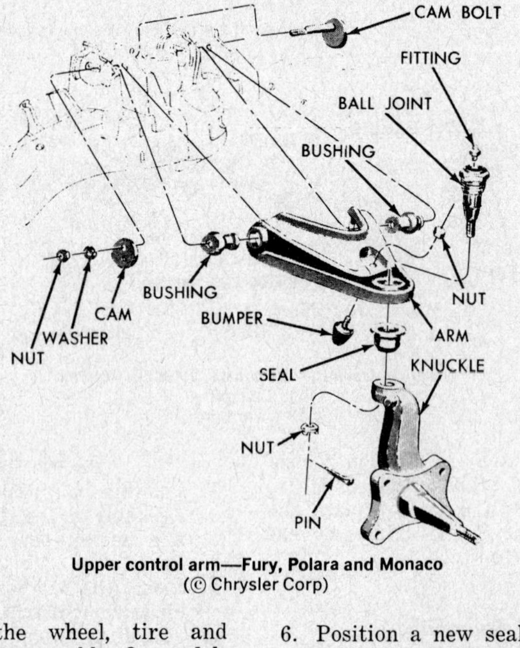
CAM BOLT
FITTING
BALL JOINT
BUSHING
BUSHING
NUT
CAM
WASHER
NUT
BUMPER
ARM
SEAL
KNUCKLE
NUT
PIN

Upper control arm—Fury, Polara and Monaco
(© Chrysler Corp)

2. Remove the wheel, tire and drum as an assembly. On models with disc brakes, remove the tire and wheel, remove the disc brake pads, remove the disc brake caliper from the steering knuckle and position the caliper out of the way with the brake line attached. Remove the brake rotor from the steering knuckle.
3. Remove the nut that attaches

6. Position a new seal on the ball joint stud and install the seal in the ball joint making sure the seal is fully seated on the ball joint housing.
7. Position ball joint stud in the steering knuckle and install the retaining nut.
8. Lubricate ball joint and, if replacement ball joint is equipped with knock-off type grease fitting, break off that portion of the fitting over which the lubrication gun was installed.
9. If equipped with disc brakes, install the rotor, caliper and brake pads. Install the tire and wheel.
10. Lower the vehicle and adjust front suspension height as required.

Front Suspension Height

1. Check to make sure that the vehicle is fully loaded with fuel, that the tire pressures are correct, and that the vehicle is positioned on a level floor.

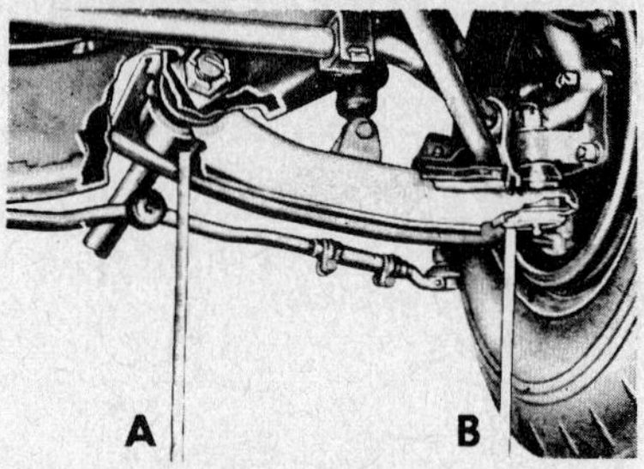
A
B

Checking front suspension height at ball joint and lower control arm
(© Chrysler Corp)

2. Clean road dirt from the bottom of the steering knuckle arm assemblies. Clean the lowest area of the height-adjusting blades directly below the center of the lower control arm inner pivot assembly.
3. Bounce vehicle at least five times and release on a downward motion.
4. Check the distance from the bottom of one adjusting blade to the floor (refer to illustration measurement A) and from the lowest point of the steering knuckle arm at the centerline on the same side of the vehicle (measurement B). Be sure to measure only one side at a time.
5. The difference in measurement between A and B is the front suspension height.
6. Refer to the specifications and make adjustments as necessary. Do this by rotating the torsion bar adjusting bolt clockwise to increase the height and counterclockwise to decrease the height. After each adjustment, bounce the vehicle as was done previously before checking the height. Both sides must be measured even though only one side may have been adjusted. Be sure that height does not vary more than $\frac{1}{8}$ in. from side to side.

Torsion Bars

Removal and Installation

NOTE: Torsion bars are not interchangable side-for-side. Do not mix them.

1. Remove the upper control arm rebound bumper (if so equipped).

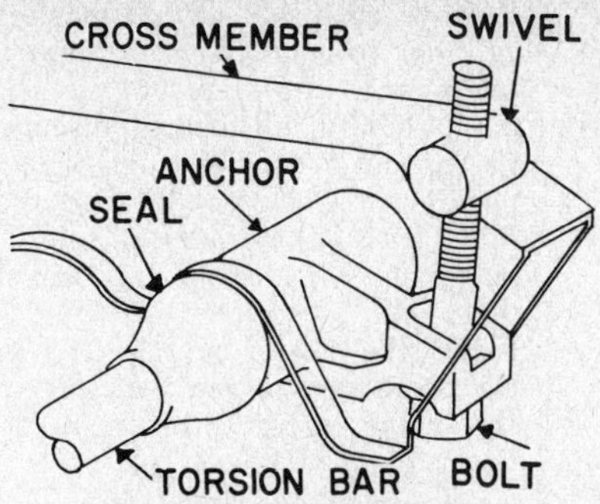
CROSS MEMBER
SWIVEL
ANCHOR
SEAL
TORSION BAR
BOLT
Torsion bar adjustment bolt
(© Chrysler Corp)

2. If the vehicle is jacked on a hoist, be sure that it is lifted on the body in such a manner that the front suspension is under no load. If the vehicle is to be lifted with a floor jack, at the center crossmember, first place a support between the jack and the crossmember. The front suspension must be under no load.
3. Remove all load from the torsion bars by rotating the anchor adjusting bolts counterclockwise.
4. At the torsion bar rear anchor, remove the lockring.
5. Using an appropriate tool, remove the torsion bar from its attachments.

Caution The torsion bar may be under some load so be careful when removing it. Heat must never be used to ease bar removal.

6. It may be necessary to move the rear balloon seal out of the way to ease removal of the torsion bar. Slide the torsion out through the rear of the anchor. Be careful not to damage the balloon seal at removal.
7. Inspect the torsion bar and lightly dress all sharp edges. Coat the area of repair with a rust preventive. Thoroughly clean the entire bar and lubricate it lightly to ease installation.
8. To begin replacement, slide the torsion bar into the rear anchor. Slide the balloon (if so equipped) seal over the bar with the cupped end toward the rear of the bar.
9. Lightly grease the hex ends of the bar. Insert the torsion bar through the hex opening of the lower control arm. Replace the lockring in the rear anchor.
10. Fully pack the ring opening in the rear anchor with grease.
11. Install the balloon seal on the rear anchor so the seal lip engages with the anchor groove.
12. Rotate the adjusting bolt clockwise to load the torsion bar. Lower the vehicle and adjust the front suspension height. Replace the upper control arm rebound bumper and torque it to 16 ft lbs.

Lower Control Arm and Steering Knuckle

Removal and Installation

1. Remove the wheel/tire and drum (or disc) as an assembly.
2. Remove the shock absorber at the bottom attachment and swing it up out of the way. Remove the torsion from its attachment at the lower control arm.
3. Using a puller, remove the tie rod end from the steering knuckle arm. Be careful not to damage the seal during this operation. At this point, it is a good idea to match-mark the wheel alignment cam to act as an aid in assembly.
4. Remove the sway bar link from the lower control arm (or strut attaching straps). Remove the knuckle arm-to-brake support bolts and remove the knuckle arm. Position the brake support assembly to one side.
5. With a puller, remove the ball joint stud from the lower control arm. Be sure not to damage the seal during this operation.
6. At the forward end of the crossmember, remove the strut spring, pin, nut, and retainer, taking note of their relative positions. Remove the nut and washer from the lower control arm shaft.
7. Using a non-metallic object, tap the end of the lower control arm shaft to aid in shaft removal from the crossmember. Take off the lower control arm, strut, and shaft as an assembly.
8. To begin installation (on some models), insert a new strut bushing into the crossmember with a twisting motion. Use water as a lubricant to aid installation—grease or oil must not be used. Position the strut bushing inner retainer on the strut and install the control arm, strut, and shaft assembly. Replace the shaft bushing retainer and finger-tighten the nut.
9. Replace the lower control arm shaft washer and finger-tighten the nut.
10. Replace the lower ball joint stud into the lower control arm and torque it to specifications. Install the cotter pin.
11. Install the brake support to the steering knuckle and replace the two upper bolts with nuts. Finger-tighten them only.
12. Install the steering knuckle on the steering knuckle arm and insert the two lower bolts with nuts. Torque the upper bolts to 55 ft lbs and the lower bolts to 120 ft lbs. Inspect the tie rod end seal and replace it if necessary. Install the tie rod end to the steering knuckle arm and torque it to 40 ft lbs. At this point, install the cotter pin.
13. Connect the shock absorber and finger-tighten it.
14. Replace the torsion bar assembly.
15. Install the wheel/tire/brake assembly.
16. Lower the vehicle. Adjust the front suspension height. Torque the strut nut at the crossmember of 52 ft lbs and insert the strut pin. Torque the lower control arm shaft nut to specifications and complete the installation of the shock absorber.
17. Align the front end as necessary.

Wheel Bearing Adjustment

1. The wheel must be rotated while the bearing adjusting nut is tightened. All models should be adjusted to 90 in. lbs.
2. Place the lock over the nut so that one pair of slots align with the cotter pin hole.
3. Back the nut and lock assembly off one slot. Install the cotter pin. This adjustment should yield zero to .003 in. end-play.
4. Clean the grease cap. Coat, but do not fill, the cap with grease. Install it on the hub.
5. Lower car and road test.

REAR SUSPENSION

All Dodge and Plymouth models utilize rear springs of the semi-elliptical leaf type. They are engineered to operate with little or no camber under conditions of small loads (including no load). Heavy-duty springs are offered as an option on all models. They increase the stability of the vehicle under conditions of heavy load. All vehicles equipped with leaf springs are constructed with zinc in-

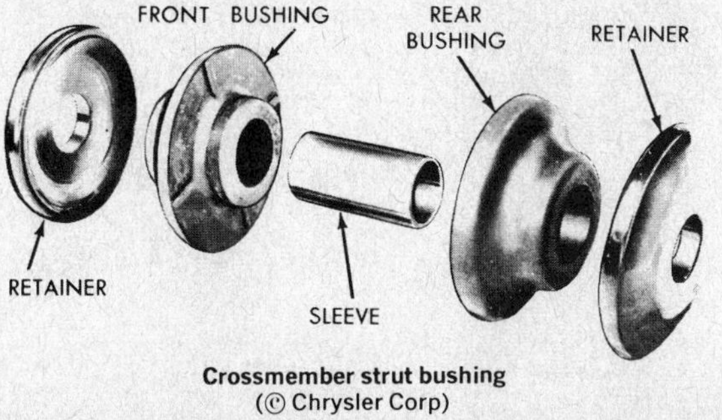
FRONT BUSHING
REAR BUSHING
RETAINER
RETAINER
SLEEVE
Crossmember strut bushing
(© Chrysler Corp)

terleaves between the normal leaves. They have the purpose of reducing spring corrosion and lengthening spring life.

Shock absorbers used on Chrysler vehicles are not used to support vehicle load. Their sole purpose is to control ride motion.

Chrysler shock absorbers have a built-in fluid weep. This is usually evident only during cold weather. Consequently, a slight fluid weep is not reason to replace a shock absorber.

Rear Shock Absorbers

Removal and Installation

1. Jack up the vehicle under the axle assembly in such a manner as to relieve the load from the shock absorbers.
2. Remove the nut attaching the shock to the spring mounting plate stud and withdraw bolt.
3. At the upper mount, remove shock attaching bolt and the shock.
4. To install the shock, position it so that the upper bolt may be inserted. Hand-tighten (only) the shock absorber bolt.
5. Align the shock with the spring mounting plate stud and install the bolt and nut. Hand-tighten only.
6. Lower the vehicle to the ground. Torque the lower nut to 50 ft lbs and the upper nut to 70 ft lbs.

Rear Springs

Removal and Installation

1. Jack up the vehicle and remove the wheels. Position the jack stands under the axle in such a manner so as to relieve the weight on the rear springs.
2. Disconnect the rear shock absorbers at the bottom attaching bolts. Lower the axle assembly to allow the rear springs to hang free.
3. Remove the U-bolt nuts and withdraw the bolts and spring plates. Remove the nuts securing the front spring hanger to the body mounting bracket.
4. Remove the rear spring hanger bolts and allow the spring to drop enough to allow the front spring hanger bolts to be removed.
5. Remove the front pivot bolt from the front spring hanger.
6. Remove the shackle nuts and remove the shackle from the rear spring.
7. To begin installation, assemble the shackle and bushings in the rear of the spring and hanger. Start the shackle bolt nuts. Do not lubricate the rubber bushings to ease installation. Do not tighten the bolt nut.
8. Install the front spring hanger to the front spring eye and insert the pivot bolt and nut. Do not tighten them.
9. Install the rear spring hanger to the body bracket and torque the bolts to 30 ft lbs.
10. With the aid of a helper, raise the spring and insert the bolts in the spring hanger mounting bracket holes. Install the nuts and torque them to 30 ft lbs.
11. Position the axle assembly so it is correctly aligned with the spring center bolt.
12. Position the center bolt over the lower spring plate. Insert the U-bolt and nut. Torque the bolt to 45 ft lbs and connect the shock absorbers.
13. Lower the vehicle. Torque the pivot bolts to 85 ft lbs. Torque the shackle nuts to 30 ft lbs.
14. After this operation, drive the vehicle. Return to the shop, check the front suspension height, and make adjustments as necessary.

BRAKES

Brake Information

Information on brake adjustments, lining replacement, disc brakes, bleeding procedure, master and wheel cylinder overhaul can be found in the Unit Repair Section.

Since 1967, a tandem-type master cylinder has been used on all models. This design divides the brake hydraulic system into two independent and hydraulically separated halves.

Details and repair procedures on this tandem system may be found in the Unit Repair Section.

Master Cylinder R & R

1967-74

1. Disconnect front and rear brake tubes from master cylinder.

NOTE: on drum brake master cylinders, residual pressure valves will keep cylinder from draining, but front brake outlet (rearmost) must be plugged on disc brake master cylinders.

2. Remove nuts that attach master cylinder to cowl panel or power brake unit.
3. On manual drum brakes, disconnect pedal pushrod from brake pedal.
4. Slide master cylinder straight out from cowl or power brake unit.
5. Install the master cylinder in the reverse order of removal. Bleed the brake system after installation is finished.

Power Brake

1967-74

Various types of power brakes are used. One is the vacuum-type, using a master cylinder and pedal linkage of the reaction type. A vacuum cylinder is combined with a conventional master cylinder.

Another is a tandem-diaphragm-type, consisting of a self-contained vacuum hydraulic power unit.

The basic elements are vacuum power chamber with a front and rear shell, a center plate, front and rear diaphragm, pushrod and diaphragm return spring.

A control valve integral with the diaphragms regulates the amount of application.

Removal and Installation

1. Remove the nuts that attach the master cylinder to the brake booster and position the master cylinder out of the way without disconnecting the lines. Use care not to kink the brake lines.
2. Disconnect the vacuum hose from the brake booster.
3. Working under the dash, remove the nut and bolt that attach the brake booster pushrod to the brake pedal. On linkage-type brake boosters, remove the lower pivot retaining bolt.
4. Remove the four brake booster attaching nuts and washers.
5. Remove the booster assembly from the vehicle.
6. Reverse the above procedure to install. The power brake unit is

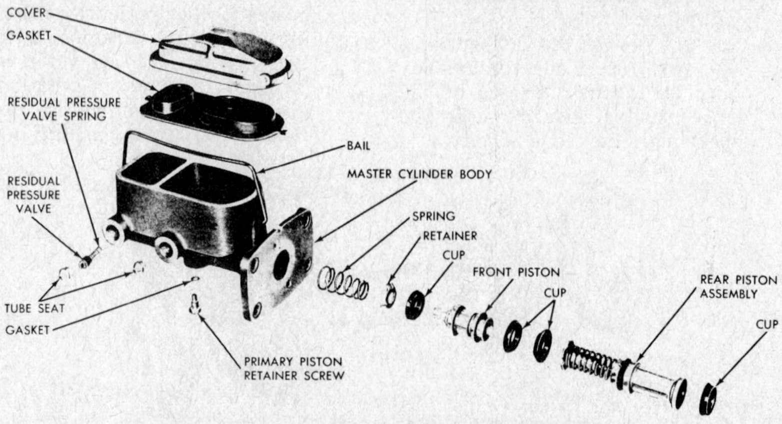
COVER
GASKET
RESIDUAL PRESSURE VALVE SPRING
BAIL
MASTER CYLINDER BODY
RESIDUAL PRESSURE VALVE
SPRING
RETAINER
CUP
FRONT PISTON
CUP
REAR PISTON ASSEMBLY
CUP
TUBE SEAT
GASKET
PRIMARY PISTON RETAINER SCREW

Dual type master cylinder used with disc brakes
(© Chrysler Corp)

serviced as an assembly only. Do not discard the old unit; it is needed as a trade-in on a rebuilt booster assembly.

Parking Brake Adjustment

NOTE: Adjust the service brakes properly before adjusting the parking brake.

1. Release parking brake lever and loosen cable adjusting nut to ensure cable is slack. Before loosening cable adjusting nut, clean threads with wire brush and lubricate.
2. Tighten cable adjusting nut until a slight drag is felt while rotating wheel. Loosen cable enough to allow both wheels to rotate freely. Back off cable adjusting nut two full turns.
3. Apply and release parking brake several times. Test to see that rear wheels rotate freely without grabbing.

Disc Brakes

Since 1967, disc brakes have been available on front wheels of some models. Sliding caliper disc brakes were introduced on full-size models for 1974. Complete service procedures are covered in the Unit Repair Section.

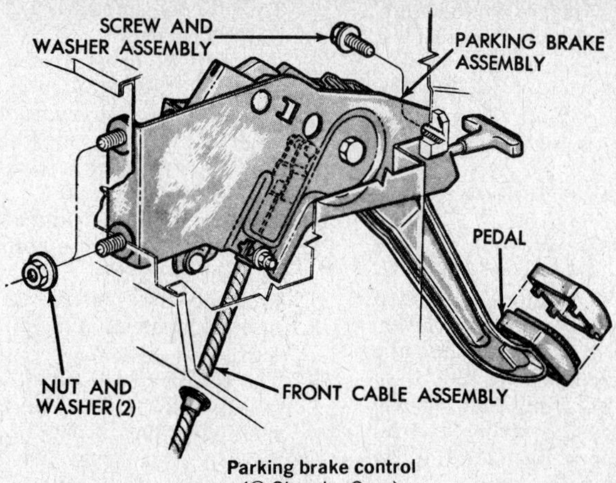
SCREW AND
WASHER ASSEMBLY
PARKING BRAKE
ASSEMBLY
PEDAL
NUT AND
WASHER (2)
FRONT CABLE ASSEMBLY
Parking brake control
(© Chrysler Corp)

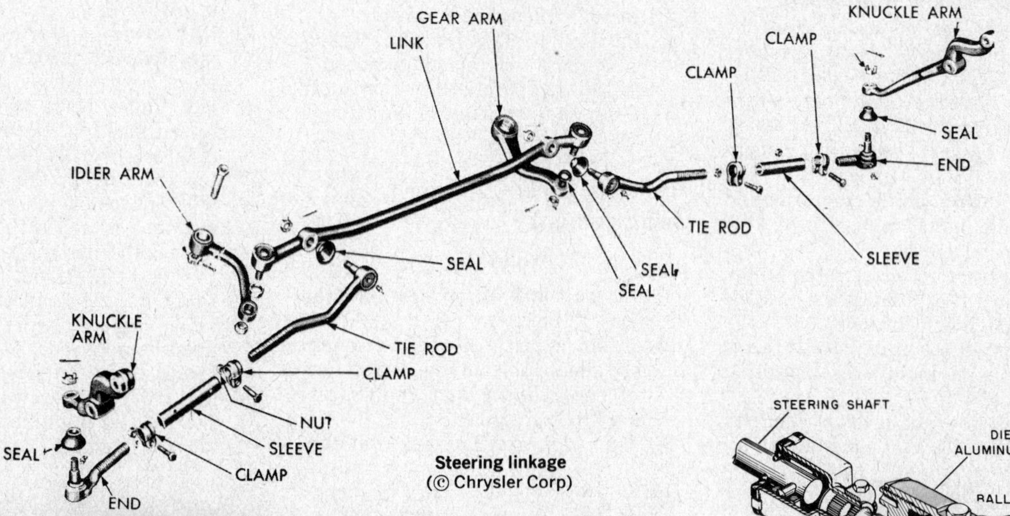
GEAR ARM
LINK
KNUCKLE ARM
CLAMP
CLAMP
SEAL
END
IDLER ARM
TIE ROD
SEAL
SEAL
SEAL
SLEEVE
KNUCKLE
ARM
TIE ROD
CLAMP
NUT
SEAL
SLEEVE
CLAMP
END
Steering linkage
(© Chrysler Corp)

STEERING

A worm and recirculating ball-type steering gear is used with the manual steering system.

The worm shaft is supported at each end by ball-type thrust bearings.

The sector shaft includes an integral sector gear which meshes with helical grooves on the worm shaft ball nut.

The sector shaft is supported, and rotates, in two needle bearings in the housing and one in the housing cover.

Constant-Control power steering is an option on all models. Hydraulic power is provided by a vane-type, belt-driven pump. A double-groove pump pulley is used.

Chrysler Corporation has utilized four different power steering pumps including 0.94, 0.96, 1.02, and 1.06 cu in. displacement models. Usage varies with the vehicle, engine, and rear axle combination. The 0.96 cu in. pump may be identified by the plain end of the pump driveshaft while the 1.02 cu in. pump may be identified by the hexagonal hole in the driveshaft pulley end. The 0.94 and 1.06 cu in. pumps may be identified by the differences in the filler tube shape (the 0.94 pump has an oval-shaped filler tube and the 1.06 pump has a round filler tube). The 0.96 and 1.02 cu in. pumps were last installed on production vehicles in 1968. After that date, only the 0.94 and 1.06 cu in. pumps were utilized.

Some power steering pumps were equipped by the factory with oil coolers. These were used on vehicles with high-performance engines and/or special axle ratios.

Up to, and including 1968, most power steering pumps utilized an oil filter screen located in the oil return tube inside the reservoir. These only require service when they are completely clogged or when the pump is disassembled. Servicing is by replacement only.

Steering Wheel

Removal and Installation

NOTE: Be careful when removing the steering wheel from those vehicles equipped with collapsible columns. A sharp blow or excessive pressure on the column could cause it to collapse; this renders it unfit for further use.

1. Disconnect the battery.
2. Remove the center, padded assembly with a screwdriver.

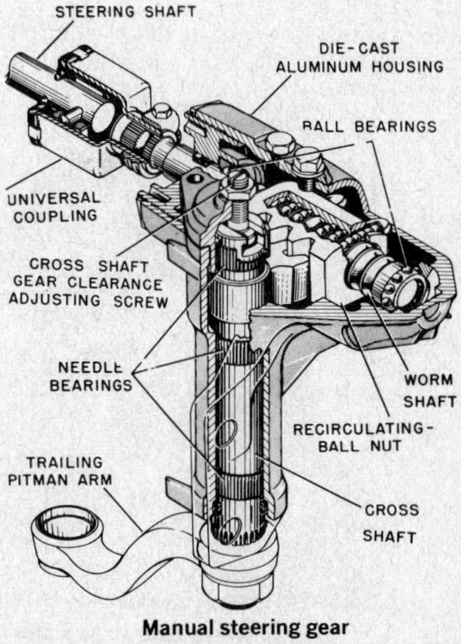
STEERING SHAFT
DIE-CAST
ALUMINUM HOUSING
BALL BEARINGS
UNIVERSAL
COUPLING
CROSS SHAFT
GEAR CLEARANCE
ADJUSTING SCREW
NEEDLE
BEARINGS
WORM
SHAFT
RECIRCULATING-
BALL NUT
TRAILING
PITMAN ARM
CROSS
SHAFT
Manual steering gear
(© Chrysler Corp)

3. Remove the large center nut. Using a puller, pull the steering wheel from the column.
4. To install the wheel, reverse the removal procedure. Torque the steering wheel nut to 28 ft lbs.

Turn Signal Switch R & R

1967-69

1. Remove the steering wheel.
2. If applicable, remove the horn wires and/or turn a signal lever.
3. Tie a piece of string to the turn signal wires. Remove the turn signal switch while holding the other end of the string to prevent the wires from falling inside the steering column.
4. To install the switch, reverse the removal procedure.

1970-74

1. Remove the steering wheel.
2. Remove the three screws which fasten the turn signal switch to the steering column.
3. Remove the turn signal lever.
4. Unfasten the moulded wiring connector from the turn signal switch and withdraw the switch.
5. Installation is the reverse of removal.

Power Steering Pump

Removal and Installation

NOTE: Before beginning removal, take careful note of the exact hose routing. Hoses must be routed and installed in the exact same manner as they were removed. Read the entire procdure before beginning pump service.

1. Back off the pump mounting and locking bolts and remove the pump drive belt.
2. Disconnect all hoses at the pump.
3. Remove the pump bolts and the pump with the bracket.
4. To install a pump, place it in position and install the mounting bolts.
5. Install the pump drive belt and adjust it to specifications. Torque the mounting bolts to 25–30 ft lbs.
6. Connect the pressure and return hoses. On the 1.06 cu in. pump, install a new pressure hose O-ring.
7. Fill the pump with power steering fluid.
8. Turn on the motor and rotate the steering wheel from stop to stop at least ten times. This will tend to bleed the system. Check the pump oil level and fill as required.
9. The torque of the pump-end hose fitting is 24 ft. lbs. The gear end fitting torque is 160 in. lbs. Be certain that hoses are at least two inches from exhaust manifolds and are not kinked or twisted.

INSTRUMENT PANEL

Ignition Switch Replacement

1967-69

1. Disconnect the push-on connector from the rear of the ignition switch, directly behind the ignition lock cylinder.
2. Remove the bezel nut that attaches the ignition switch to the rear of the instrument panel.
3. Remove the ignition switch.
4. Position a new ignition switch under the instrument panel and install and tighten the bezel nut.
5. Connect the wiring to the rear of the switch.

Ignition Lock Cylinder Replacement

1967-69

1. Insert the ignition key into the lock cylinder.
2. Insert a piece of stiff wire into the small hole in the front face of the cylinder and apply pressure to the wire.
3. Turn the ignition key counterclockwise toward the ACC position.
4. Pull the lock cylinder and key from the instrument panel.
5. Insert a new lock cylinder into the instrument panel and it will lock itself in place.

Ignition Switch and/or Ignition Lock Cylinder Replacement

1970-74 Standard Steering Column

1. Disconnect the negative battery cable. Remove the steering wheel.
2. Remove the screw that attaches the turn signal lever to the steering column.
3. Remove the three screws that attach the upper bearing retainer to the turn signal switch.
4. Pull the turn signal switch as far upward as possible.
5. Using snap-ring pliers, remove the upper bearing housing snapring from the steering shaft.
6. Remove the screw that attaches the ignition key light assembly to the upper bearing housing.
7. Using care not to damage any components, pry the upper bearing housing off the steering shaft by lifting upward on alternate sides of the bearing housing with screwdrivers.
8. Lift upward as far as possible on the steering shaft lock plate and place a screwdriver or other object under it to hold it in the raised position. If this operation does not provide adequate working room under the lock plate, it will be necessary to press out the pin that attaches the lock plate to the steering shaft and remove the lock plate from the steering shaft. If the ignition switch is being replaced, the lock plate must be removed.
9. Using an offset screwdriver, remove the two screws that attach the lock lever guide plate to the steering column.

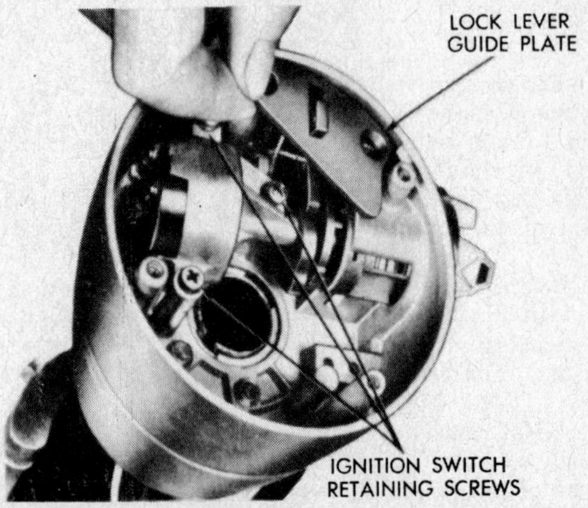
LOCK LEVER
GUIDE PLATE
IGNITION SWITCH
RETAINING SCREWS

Removing lock lever guide plate—standard column
(© Chrysler Corp)

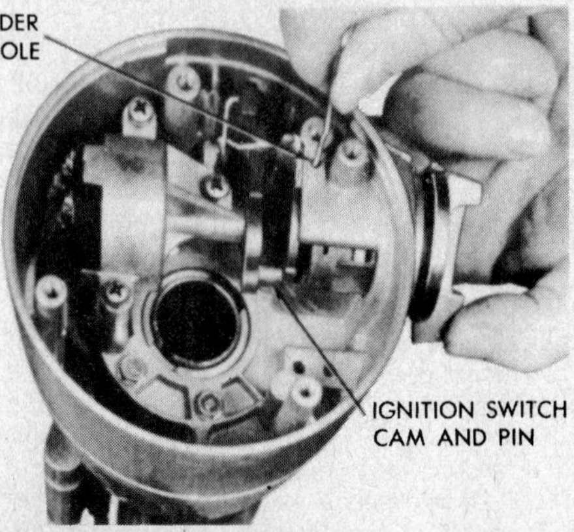
LOCK CYLINDER
RELEASE HOLE
IGNITION SWITCH
CAM AND PIN

Removing ignition lock cylinder—standard column
(© Chrysler Corp)

10. With the ignition lock cylinder in the "Lock" position and the ignition key removed, insert a stiff wire into the lock cylinder release hole in the steering column. Push in on the wire to release the spring-loaded lock retainer and pull the lock cylinder out of the steering column.
11. If the ignition switch is being replaced, remove the two screws that attach the ignition key buzzer switch to the steering column and the three screws that attach the ignition switch to the steering column. Lift off the ignition switch out of the housing.
12. Reverse the above procedure for installation.

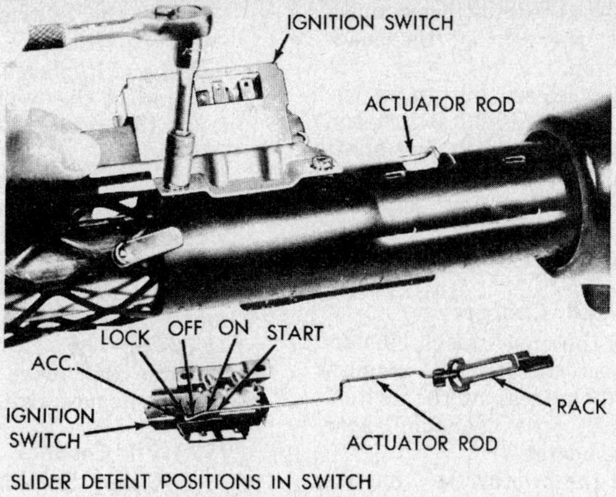
IGNITION SWITCH
ACTUATOR ROD
LOCK
OFF
ON
START
ACC.
IGNITION SWITCH
ACTUATOR ROD
RACK
SLIDER DETENT POSITIONS IN SWITCH

Removing ignition switch—tilt column
(© Chrysler Corp)

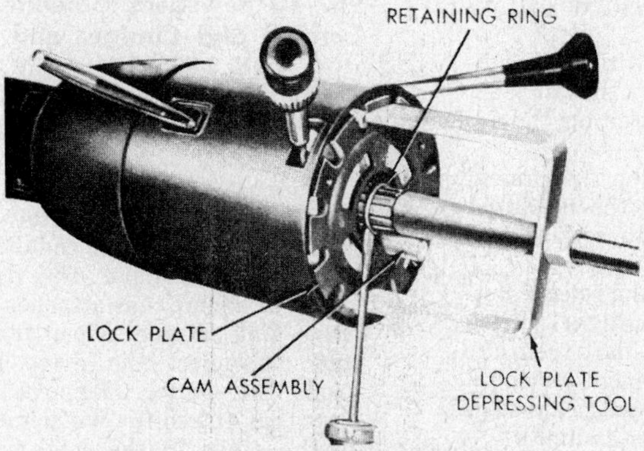
RETAINING RING
LOCK PLATE
CAM ASSEMBLY
LOCK PLATE DEPRESSING TOOL

Removing lock plate retaining ring—tilt column
(© Chrysler Corp)

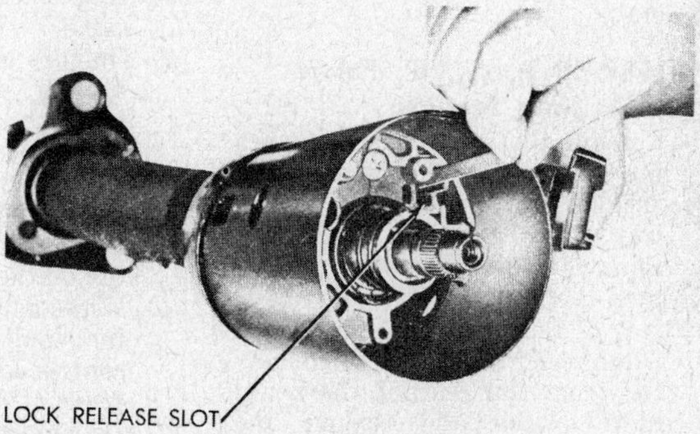
LOCK RELEASE SLOT

Removing ignition lock cylinder—tilt column
(© Chrysler Corp)

1970-74 Tilt Steering Column

1. Disconnect the negative battery cable.
2. Remove the steering wheel.
3. Remove the three attaching screws and remove the shaft lock cover.
4. Remove the screws that attach the tilt control lever and the turn signal lever to the steering column and then remove the levers.
5. Push in the hazard warning knob and unscrew the knob from the turn signal switch. Remove the ignition key lamp assembly.
6. Using a suitable tool, depress the lock plate to gain access to the lock plate retaining snap-ring. Remove the snap-ring from the steering shaft.
7. Remove the lock plate, cancelling cam, and spring.
8. Remove the three turn signal switch attaching screws, place the shift lever in the Low (L) position, and pull the switch and wires as far upward as possible.
9. With the ignition lock cylinder in the "Lock" position, insert a small screwdriver into the lock release slot in the housing cover.
10. Press down with the screwdriver to release the spring latch at the bottom of the slot and pull the lock cylinder from the housing. The following steps are for ignition switch replacement only.
11. Remove the three screws that attach the upper steering column housing to the steering column and remove the housing.
12. Install the column tilt control lever and move the column to the full "Up" position.
13. Insert a screwdriver into the slot in the spring retainer and press the retainer in approximately 3/16 in. Turn the retainer approximately 1/8 turn to the left until the ears align with the grooves in the housing. Remove the spring retainer, spring, and guide.
14. Push the steering shaft inward to enable removal of the inner race and seat. Remove the race and seat.
15. Make sure the ignition switch is in the "Lock" position, then remove the wire connector from the ignition switch and remove the screws that attach the ignition switch to the outside of the steering column.
16. Lift the ignition switch from the column and twist it to disengage the switch actuating rod from the rack. Remove the switch.
17. To install the ignition lock cylinder, insert the cylinder into the housing with the cylinder in the "Lock" position and the key *removed.*
18. Move the cylinder into the housing until it contacts the switch actuator. Move the switch actuator rod up and down to align the parts. When the parts are aligned, the cylinder will move inward and lock into place. The following steps are for ignition switch installation only.
19. With the ignition switch in the "Lock" position, insert the actuating rod into the steering column.
20. Twist the switch and rod assembly as required to engage the actuating rod with the rack. Make sure the ignition lock cylinder is in the "Lock" position.
21. Install the ignition switch mounting screws but do not tighten them.
22. Move the ignition switch downward, away from the steering wheel, and tighten the switch mounting screws. Make sure that the ignition switch has not moved out of the lock detent.
23. Attach the switch wiring connector.

Headlight Switch R & R

1967-68 Belvedere, Satellite, Coronet and 1967 Charger

1. Remove the screw that attaches the fuse box to the dash and position the fuse box out of the way.

2. Disconnect the multiple connector from the rear of the headlight switch.
3. Press the release button on the body of the headlight switch and pull the control knob and shaft from the switch.
4. Remove the bezel nut that attaches the headlight switch to the dash and remove the switch.

1968 Charger

1. Remove the instrument cluster.
2. Disconnect the multiple connector from the rear of the switch.
3. Disconnect the vacuum hose from the heater.
4. Remove the two screws that attach the headlight switch to the dash and remove the switch.
5. Reverse above procedure to install.

1967-68 Fury, VIP, Polara and Monaco

1. Remove the screw that attaches the fuse box to the dash and position the fuse box out of the way.
2. Remove the two screws that attach the headlight switch to the rear of the dash.
3. Disconnect the multiple connector from the rear of the headlight switch and remove the switch.

1969-70 Belvedere, Satellite and Coronet; 1969-71 Fury, Polara and Monaco

1. Disconnect the multiple connector from the rear of the headlight switch. On models with air conditioning, it may be necessary to disconnect the ducts to gain access to the wiring.
2. Remove the two screws that attach the headlight switch to the dash and remove the headlight switch from the vehicle.
3. Reverse above procedure to install.

1969-70 Charger

1. Disconnect the negative battery cable.
2. Remove the instrument cluster. See "Instrument Cluster Removal and Replacement."
3. Disconnect the wiring connector from the rear of the headlight switch.
4. Disconnect the two vacuum hoses from the heater switch to gain access to the headlight switch mounting screws.
5. Remove the headlight switch mounting screws and remove the switch.
6. Reverse the above procedure to install the new switch.

1971-74 Coronet, Charger and Satellite 1972-74 Fury, Polara, and Monaco

1. Disconnect the negative battery cable.
2. On cars equipped with air conditioning, disconnect the air duct from the spot cooler on the instrument panel.
3. Reach up under the instrument panel and depress the headlight switch control knob release button on the headlight switch.
4. While depressing the release button, pull the headlight switch control knob and shaft from the front of the instrument panel.
5. Disconnect the electrical leads from the rear of the switch.
6. Using a spanner wrench, remove the spanner nut that attaches the front of the headlight switch to the front of the instrument panel.
7. Remove the headlight switch from the rear of the instrument panel.
8. Reverse the above procedure to install the new switch.

WINDSHIELD WIPERS

Motor R & R

1967-70 Fury, Polara and Monaco

1. Remove the windshield wiper arm and blade assemblies. On 1969-70 models insert a 0.090 in. pin in the hole in the base of the wiper arm to release the assemblies from the pivots.
2. Remove the windshield lower moulding.
3. Remove the cowl grille.
4. Remove the nut that attaches the wiper link to the wiper motor drive pin or crank and disconnect the link from the motor.
5. Disconnect the wiper motor wiring at the multiple connector.
6. Remove the nuts that attach the wiper motor to the cowl panel and remove the motor through the cowl grille opening.

1967-70 Belvedere, Satellite, Coronet and Charger and All 1971-74 with Non-Concealed Wipers

1. Disconnect the negative battery cable.
2. Disconnect the wiper motor wiring at the multiple connector.
3. On models without air conditioning, working under the dash, remove the nut that attaches the drive link to the wiper motor and disconnect the drive link from the motor. Remove the nuts that attach the wiper motor to the studs in the cowl panel and remove the motor from the vehicle.

NOTE: Step 4 applies to 1967 and 68 models only, on all other models proceed to Step 5.

4. On models equipped with air conditioning, remove the instrument cluster to gain access to the left wiper pivot. Remove the drive link retaining clip from the left pivot. Remove the drive link and felt washer from the left pivot.
5. Remove the wiper motor mounting nuts. Work the motor off the mounting studs far enough to gain access to the nut that attaches the drive link to the wiper motor. *Do not force or pry the*

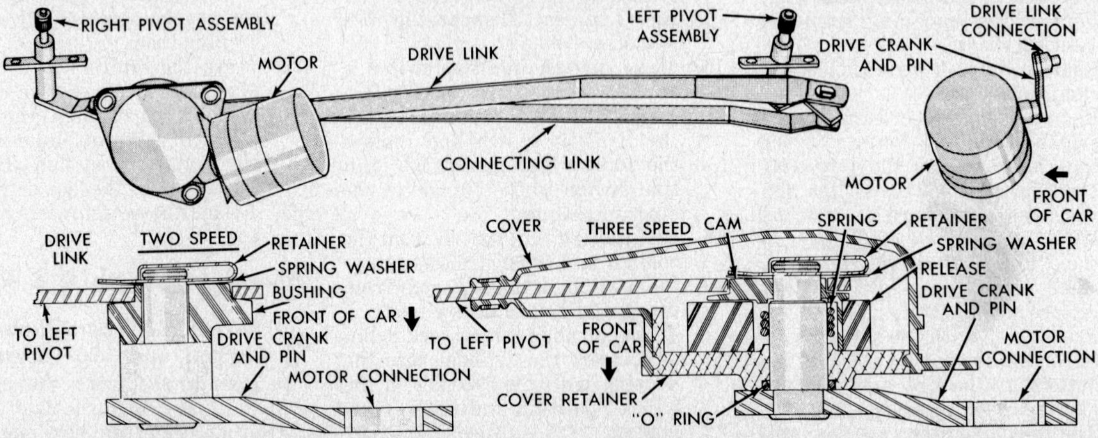
RIGHT PIVOT ASSEMBLY
MOTOR
DRIVE LINK
LEFT PIVOT ASSEMBLY
DRIVE CRANK AND PIN
DRIVE LINK CONNECTION
CONNECTING LINK
MOTOR
FRONT OF CAR
DRIVE LINK
TWO SPEED
RETAINER
SPRING WASHER
BUSHING
FRONT OF CAR
TO LEFT PIVOT
DRIVE CRANK AND PIN
MOTOR CONNECTION
COVER
THREE SPEED
CAM
SPRING
RETAINER
SPRING WASHER
RELEASE
DRIVE CRANK AND PIN
TO LEFT PIVOT
FRONT OF CAR
MOTOR CONNECTION
COVER RETAINER
"O" RING

Windshield wiper system—Fury, Polara and Monaco (© Chrysler Corp)

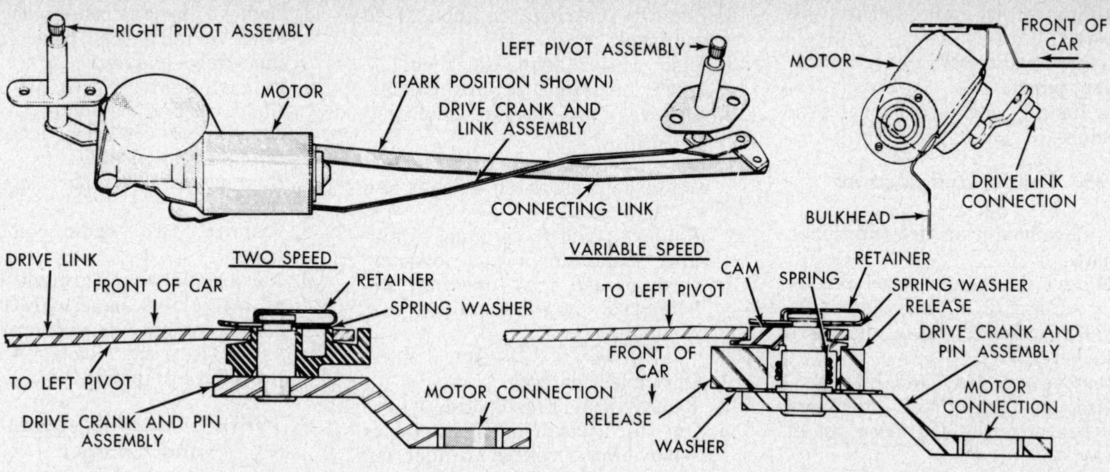
RIGHT PIVOT ASSEMBLY
MOTOR
LEFT PIVOT ASSEMBLY
(PARK POSITION SHOWN)
DRIVE CRANK AND LINK ASSEMBLY
CONNECTING LINK
FRONT OF CAR
MOTOR
DRIVE LINK CONNECTION
BULKHEAD
DRIVE LINK
TWO SPEED
FRONT OF CAR
RETAINER
SPRING WASHER
TO LEFT PIVOT
DRIVE CRANK AND PIN ASSEMBLY
MOTOR CONNECTION
VARIABLE SPEED
CAM
TO LEFT PIVOT
SPRING
RETAINER
SPRING WASHER
RELEASE
DRIVE CRANK AND PIN ASSEMBLY
FRONT OF CAR
RELEASE
WASHER
MOTOR CONNECTION

Windshield wiper system—Satellite, Belvedere, Coronet and Charger (© Chrysler Corp)

wiper motor off the mounting studs as this could damage the wiper drive link. Using a ½ in. open end wrench, remove the motor crank arm nut. Remove the arm from the wiper motor and remove the motor from the vehicle.

1971-74 All Models with Concealed Wipers

1. Disconnect the negative battery cable.
2. Lift the latch on each wiper arm and remove the arms and blades as an assembly.
3. Remove the cowl screen.
4. Remove the drive crank retaining nut and drive crank.
5. Disconnect the lead wires from the wiper motor.
6. Remove the three wiper motor mounting bolts and remove the motor from the vehicle.
7. Reverse the above procedure to install. When installing the wiper arms and blades, make sure the wiper motor is in the Park position.

Linkage and Pivots

1967-70 Belvedere, Satellite, Coronet and Charger

If car is air-conditioned, remove glove compartment to gain access to right pivot retainer.

1. Disconnect the negative battery cable. Remove the wiper arm and blade assemblies.
2. Remove the link retaining clip from the right pivot. On 1967 models, remove the fuse box and position it out of the way.
3. Remove wiper motor mounting nuts and pull motor out far enough to remove drive link from drive crank arm.
4. From under the panel, remove left pivot mounting nuts and right pivot retainer.
5. Remove the two links and left pivot as an assembly from under the panel or through the glove compartment.

1967-69 Fury, Polara and Monaco

1. Remove the wiper arm and blade assemblies.
2. Remove the windshield lower moulding.
3. Remove the cowl grille.
4. To remove the right pivot, disconnect the connecting link from the pivot, remove the bolts that attach the pivot to the cowl and remove the pivot.
5. To remove the left pivot, disconnect the connecting link from the right pivot. Disconnect the drive crank from the wiper motor. Remove the bolts that attach the left pivot to the cowl and remove the pivot and links through the cowl opening.

1970 Fury, Polara and Monaco

1. Remove the wiper arm and blade assemblies.
2. Remove the cowl screen.
3. Remove the crank arm nut and crank arm from the wiper motor.
4. Remove the bolts that attach the right and left pivots to the body.
5. Remove the pivots and linkage from the vehicle as an assembly through the cowl opening.

1971-74 All Models with Non-Concealed Wipers

1. Remove the wiper arm and blade assemblies.
2. If equipped with air conditioning, remove the left spot cooler duct to gain access to the left wiper pivot. Remove the glove box to gain access to the right wiper pivot.
3. Insert a wide blade screwdriver between the wiper link and the pivot crank arm and gently pry the link and plastic bushing from the pivot.
4. Remove the three wiper motor mounting nuts and move the motor outward on the mounting studs to gain access to the motor crank arm nut. Remove the crank arm nut and disconnect the crank arm from the wiper motor.
5. Remove the nut that attaches the pivot to the body of the vehicle and remove the pivot.

1971-74 All Models with Concealed Wipers

1. Insert a 0.090 in. pin in the base of each wiper arm and remove the arm and blade assemblies from the wiper pivots.
2. Remove the cowl screen.
3. Remove the crank arm retaining nut and crank arm from the wiper motor.
4. Remove the bolts that attach the right and left pivots to the body of the vehicle.
5. Remove the links and pivots as an assembly through the cowl opening.
6. Reverse the above procedure to install.

RADIO

R & R

1967 Belvedere and Satellite

1. Disconnect battery.
2. Remove control knobs and two mounting nuts.
3. On air-conditioned cars, remove spot cooler hoses and distribution duct, then disconnect speaker, power supply and antenna leads.
4. Remove radio support bracket.
5. Rotate front end of radio down and remove radio from under the dash panel.

1967 Coronet and Charger

1. Disconnect battery.
2. Remove upper half of glove compartment and disconnect wires from speaker.
3. Remove radio knobs and two mounting nuts.
4. Disconnect both defroster hoses at the heater.
5. Disconnect antenna cable and radio feed wires at connector.
6. Loosen radio support bracket re-

taining nut at radio and remove panel.
7. Remove radio from under instrument panel.
8. To install, reverse removal procedure.

1967 Polara and Monaco

1. Disconnect battery.
2. Remove heater or air-conditioner knobs.
3. Remove five center bezel retaining screws (3 in underside of lip and 2 in face of bezel.) Remove the bezel.
4. Remove ash tray and housing.
5. Disconnect right defroster hose at heater outlet. Tie hose out of way.
6. From ash tray opening, remove two heater or air-conditioner control mounting nuts and move the control assembly out of the way. It is not necessary to disconnect control cables.
7. Disconnect radio feed wires and antenna cable.
8. Remove two radio mounting screws from front of panel. Remove radio.

NOTE: on air-conditioned cars, the distribution duct must be removed.

9. To install, reverse removal procedure.

1967-68 Fury and VIP

1. Remove instrument cluster bezel. See Instrument Cluster Removal in this section.
2. From under panel, loosen radio support bracket nut at upper end.
3. Disconnect feed wires, speaker wires, and antenna cable at radio.
4. From front of instrument panel, remove three radio mounting screws and lift radio out of panel.
5. Reverse procedure to install.

1968 Polara and Monaco

1. Disconnect battery.
2. Disconnect cigar lighter lead and remove ash tray and housing.
3. Remove automatic temperature control, if so equipped.
4. Remove center air outlets, if so equipped.
5. Remove radio mounting bracket. (Loosen one nut at radio, remove one screw in lower reinforcement, and swing bracket toward glove box to clear area for radio removal.)
6. Remove eight bezel mounting screws (three in upper center trim bezel, three in upper right trim bezel, and two in lower center trim bezel).
7. Pull bezel out slightly and disconnect fader control harness and remove two fader control mounting screws from rear of fader and reverberator, if so equipped.
8. Remove reverberator knob, if so equipped.
9. Slide center trim bezel out of upper moulding toward cluster.
10. Remove two radio mounting screws.
11. Reach through ash tray opening and disconnect antenna leads and electrical leads.
12. Remove radio from panel by tipping radio down and lowering through ash tray opening. Reverse procedure to install.

1968-70 Charger

1. Disconnect battery.
2. Remove radio finish plate.
3. On air conditioned vehicles, remove lower center air duct, left air duct, and upper center duct.
4. Remove radio mounting bracket.
5. Remove two screws mounting radio to front of instrument panel.
6. Disconnect antenna and speaker leads.
7. Remove radio from under panel. Reverse procedure to install.

1968-70 Coronet and 1969-70 Belvedere and Satellite

1. Disconnect battery.
2. Remove radio upper trim panel.
3. Remove radio finish plate.
4. Remove radio rear mounting nut from mounting bracket.
5. Disconnect electrical wiring and antenna lead.
6. Remove two mounting screws from front of instrument panel.
7. Remove radio from instrument panel.

1968 Belvedere and Satellite and 1969-70 Polara and Monaco

1. Disconnect battery.
2. Remove automatic temperature control, if so equipped.
3. Remove radio bezel.
4. Remove two radio mounting bolts at front of instrument panel.
5. Remove air conditioner duct, if so equipped.
6. Disconnect electrical leads and antenna lead.
7. Loosen radio mounting bracket stud nut and slide radio and stud towards front of car from mounting bracket.
8. Carefully remove radio from under panel to avoid damaging electrical leads from main harness or automatic temperature control aspirator tube. Reverse procedure to install.

1969-74 Fury, VIP, and 1971-74 Polara and Monaco

1. Disconnect battery.
2. Remove nine lamp panel mounting screws, lower lamp panel assembly slightly, disconnect lamp harness from main harness, and remove lamp panel from instrument panel.
3. Remove steering column cover.
4. Remove radio trim bezel mounting screws and bezel.
5. Remove center lower air conditioner duct, if so equipped.
6. Disconnect electrical leads and antenna lead at radio.
7. Remove radio support mounting bracket.
8. Remove two radio mounting bolts.
9. Move radio down through bottom of instrument panel carefully to avoid damage to vacuum hoses and electrical leads. Reverse procedure to install.

1971-74 Satellite, Coronet and Charger

1. Disconnect the negative battery cable.
2. Remove the ash tray (1971 models only).
3. Remove the radio control knobs and retaining nuts. On 1972 models remove the rear radio support brackets.
4. Disconnect the lead wires from the radio and remove the radio from the vehicle.

HEATER

Heater Assembly R & R—Except Air-Conditioned Cars

1967-70 Belvedere, Satellite, Coronet and Charger

1. Drain radiator and disconnect battery. Remove the glove box.
2. On models equipped with a console, the console must be moved rearward before the heater assembly can be removed. From inside the console storage area, remove the two console mounting bolts and the two screws from the front sides of the console. Remove the two shift indicator bezel screws, move the transmission selector lever to the Drive position, and turn the bezel sideways and allow it to rest on the console. Remove the two screws from the rear of the gear selector mounting bracket and disconnect the back up light switch wiring. Remove the gear indicator light bulb, then move the console rearward.
3. Disconnect heater hoses at bulkhead. Plug hose fittings on heater to prevent spilling coolant on trim when removing heater.
4. From under instrument panel remove heater to cowl support bracket.
5. Remove defroster hoses and disconnect wiring from heater motor resistor.
6. Disconnect fresh air vent control and shut off door cables at heater from under instrument panel. Reaching through glove

box, disconnect temperature control door cable.
7. From inside engine compartment, remove three nuts that mount heater to bulkhead.
8. Rotate heater assembly until mounting studs are up and carefully remove heater from under instrument panel.
9. Reverse procedure to install.

1967-68 Fury, Polara and Monaco

1. Disconnect battery.
2. Disconnect hoses from heater and plug fittings to prevent coolant from leaking and spilling on inside of body when removed.
3. Remove bracket from top of heater to dash panel.
4. Remove defroster hoses at heater and vacuum actuator hose.
5. Disconnect wire at blower motor resistor.
6. Remove glove compartment.
7. Disconnect control cable at heater end.
8. Unclamp connector at right end of heater. Do not remove connector.
9. Pull carpet or mat from under instrument panel.
10. From inside engine compartment, remove nuts that attach heater assembly to dash panel.
11. Pull heater toward rear to clear mounting studs from dash panel and rotate heater until studs are down, then remove heater from panel.

1969-74 Fury, Polara and Monaco

NOTE: This is the removal procedure for the heater housing that attaches to the passenger compartment side of the firewall. Do not remove the part of the housing that attaches to the engine side of the firewall.

1. Disconnect battery and drain radiator.
2. Disconnect heater hoses at dash panel. Plug hose fittings on heater to prevent spilling coolant on trim.
3. Slide front seat back to allow room.
4. Disconnect radio antenna.
5. Disconnect electrical conductors from blower motor resistor block on face of housing.
6. Remove vacuum hoses from trunk lock if so equipped.
7. Remove control cables from defroster door crank and heat shut off door crank.
8. Remove bottom retaining nut from support bracket and swing bracket up and out of way.
9. In engine compartment remove four retaining nuts from studs on engine side housing.
10. Remove locating bolt from bottom center of passenger side housing.
11. Roll or tip housing out from under instrument panel.
12. Remove temperature control cable retaining clip and cable from heat shut off door crank.

1971-74 Satellite, Coronet and Charger

1. Disconnect the negative battery cable.
2. Drain the cooling system.
3. Disconnect the heater hoses from the heater core tubes at the dash panel. Plug the core tubes to prevent spilling coolant on the interior of the car.
4. Remove the three mounting nuts from the studs around the blower motor, the one nut from the heater housing near the center of the instrument panel, and remove the flange and air seal.
5. Disconnect the antenna lead wire from the radio and position it out of the way.
6. Remove the screw that attaches the housing to the support rod for the plenum. It is located on the right-side of the housing above the outside air opening.
7. Disconnect the three air door cables.
8. Disconnect the wires from the blower motor resistor.
9. Tip the heater assembly down and out from under the dash.

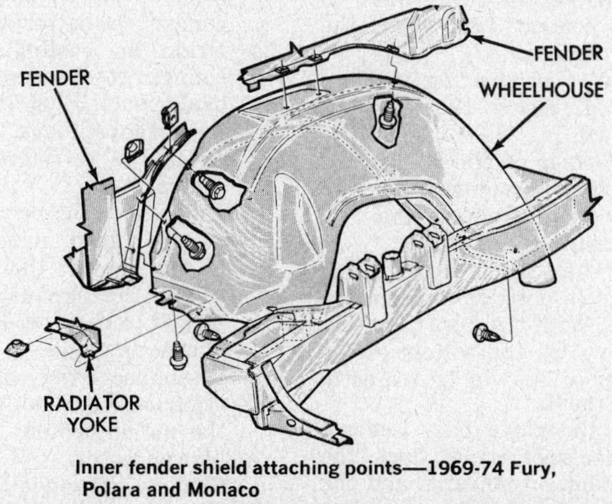
FENDER
WHEELHOUSE
FENDER
RADIATOR YOKE
Inner fender shield attaching points—1969-74 Fury, Polara and Monaco
(© Chrysler Corp)

Blower Motor

1967-68 All Models 1969-74 Belvedere, Satellite, Coronet and Charger

1. Remove heater assembly as outlined in Heater Assembly Removal.
2. Disconnect wiring from blower motor to heater assembly.
3. Remove motor cooler tube.
4. Remove heater back plate assembly from heater.
5. Remove fan from motor shaft.
6. Remove blower motor from back plate.

1969-74 Fury, Polara and Monaco

The blower motor is mounted to the engine side housing under the right front fender, between the inner fender shield and the fender. The inner fender shield must be removed to service the blower motor.

1. Raise the hood and remove all brackets and clips that attach to the inner fender shield under the hood.
2. Raise the car on a hoist and remove the right front tire and wheel assembly.
3. From under the fender, remove the bolts that attach the inner fender shield to the fender.
4. Remove the fender shield from the vehicle.
5. Disconnect the blower motor wiring at the multiple connector.
6. Remove the nuts that attach the blower motor to the heater housing and remove the blower motor.

Heater Core

1967-68 All Models 1969-70 Belvedere, Satellite, Coronet and Charger

1. Remove the heater assembly.
2. Remove the heater cover plate.
3. Remove the screws that attach the heater core to the heater assembly and remove the core.

1969-74 Fury, Polara and Monaco

1. Remove the heater assembly.
2. From inside the heater assembly, remove the two retaining nuts from the right-side of the heater core.
3. Remove the four heater core attaching screws from the outside of the heater housing.
4. Remove the heater core locating metal screw from the top of the heater housing.
5. Carefully pull the heater core from the heater housing.

1971-74 Belvedere, Satellite, Coronet and Charger

1. Remove the heater assembly.
2. Remove the screws that attach

the front cover to the heater housing.
3. Cut sponge rubber plenum-to-housing air seal in two places, where the front cover separates the cover from the housing.
4. Remove the one core tube retaining screw from behind the heater housing, between the heater core tubes.
5. Remove the sponge rubber gaskets from the heater core tubes. Remove the heater core from the heater housing.

Air Conditioner Heater Core Removal

1967-69 (except 1969 Fury, VIP, Polara, and Monaco) 1970 Charger, Coronet, and Satellite

The heater core is positioned behind a separate cover attached to the evaporator case. It is located just forward of the instrument panel.

1. Disconnect the battery and drain the cooling system. Remove the air cleaner and disconnect the heater hoses.
2. Remove the distribution housing, glove box, and the heater core intake-outlet tube assembly.
3. Remove the fresh air intake hose. Disconnect the floor air actuator rod.
4. Disconnect the actuator vacuum hoses. Remove the fresh air door housing assembly.
5. Remove the defroster hoses. Disconnect the resistor block and bypass switch electrical connections.
6. Extract the screws holding the water bypass valve to the heater cover. Remove the operating link attaching screw.
7. At its mounting bracket, disconnect the air conditioning door actuator and remove the supporting braces.
8. Remove the retainer spring clips and screws securing the cover to the case.
9. Pull the lower edge of the cover rearward; lift the assembly 3/8 in. This will release the cover lip from the case. Lower the assembly and remove it from the right side.
10. To begin the installation procedure, install the water bypass valve to the heater core (if it was removed). Be sure to use new O-rings on the intake and outlet tubes.
11. Place the heater core into the evaporator case. Install the cover by hooking the cover lip on the evaporator case and rolling it down into position. Replace the retainer spring clips and screws.
12. Install the water bypass valve to the heater cover. Connect the linkage to the air conditioning door.
13. Replace the air conditioning door actuator with its vacuum hoses. Be sure to replace the hose with the red stripe to the rod side. Install the two support braces.
14. Replace all electrical connections to the resistor block.
15. This step applies to 1967 models only. The electrical by-pass switch operating arm must be adjusted to .020-060 in. operating clearance between the actuator rod and the operating arm.
16. Connect the vacuum hoses to the floor air actuator and the fresh air recirculating actuator. Be sure the hose with the red stripe is facing the rod side. Replace the fresh air recirculating door housing. Connect the floor air actuator rod to its linkage.
17. Connect the fresh air recirculating air intake hose.
18. Replace the heater core intake-outlet tube assembly. Use a drop of water on the O-rings to ease installation. Replace the temperature control valve capillary tube in the heater core cover.
19. Open the air conditioning door about 1 in. Install the distribution housing.
20. Replace the flexible hoses to the instrument panel outlets.
21. Replace the glove box.
22. Connect the heater hoses and fill the cooling system with the proper amount and type of antifreeze.
23. Install the air cleaner and connect the battery. Test the operation of the heater.

1969-71 Fury, VIP, Polara, and Monaco

The air conditioning heater core is located in the front cover of the passenger side housing. To remove only the heater core, the air conditioning system need not be discharged.

1. Disconnect the battery and drain the cooling system. Disconnect the heater hoses and remove the air cleaner.
2. Plug the heater core tubes to prevent coolant loss when the core is removed.
3. Take off the steering column cover and remove the left spot cooler duct.
4. At the linkage on the left side of the housing, disconnect the two actuator rods. Remove the two cover retaining screws.
5. Remove the screws securing the heat duct in position and remove the duct. With the duct removed, the screws in the bottom of the front cover lip will be exposed. Remove them.
6. Remove the glove box. Remove the center spot cooler duct, the air distribution housing, and the right spot cooler duct.
7. Working in the glove box opening, remove the top retaining screws and the screws from the right side of the housing.
8. At the resistor block, disconnect all electrical connections. Disconnect the vacuum hoses from the recirculating housing actuator.
9. Take off the nut at the housing end of the cover support bracket. Swing the bracket upward and carefully roll the front cover and heater core outward. Remove it from under the instrument panel.
10. To begin installation, replace the heater core in the front cover. Position the core and cover on the evaporator housing. While holding the front cover in position, swing the support bracket downward over the stud on the front cover face. Install its retaining nut.
11. Working in the glove box opening, replace the top housing and right-side screws.
12. Working under the instrument panel, install the screws that retain the housing in position.
13. Replace the heat distribution duct to the housing bottom and connect the actuator rods.
14. Connect all the vacuum hoses to their actuators; install all electrical connections to the resistor block.
15. Through the glove box opening, install the air distribution housing, the center spot cooler duct, and the right spot cooler duct.
16. Replace the steering column cover and the left spot cooler duct. Replace the glove box assembly.
17. From this point, reverse the removal procedure. Be sure to fill cooling system with proper type and amount of antifreeze.

1971-74 Satellite, Coronet, and Charger

NOTE: this procedure requires evacuation of the refrigerant system which requires special tools and training.

1. Remove the air cleaner and disconnect the battery.
2. Drain the cooling system. Disconnect the heater hoses at the dash panel. Plug the core tubes to prevent spillage.
3. Discharge refrigerant from the system.
4. Disconnect the refrigerant lines at the dash panel (use two wrenches for this procedure). Leave the expansion valve attached to the line. Plug all refrigerant openings.
5. Disconnect the blower motor electrical connections. Remove the motor cooling tube and the blower motor.
6. Remove the glove box assembly.
7. Take the appearance shield from

the lower edge of the instrument panel.

8. Remove the left spot cooler duct and the air distribution housing.
9. Disconnect all wires from the blower motor resistor, and the antenna wire from the radio bottom.
10. Remove the radio.
11. Disconnect the vacuum harness from the control switch rear.
12. Remove the water valve cable from the bracket on the housing left end.
13. In the engine compartment, remove the nuts from the housing mounting studs.
14. Remove the rubber drain tube.
15. Remove the support bracket from the plenum-to-housing panel.
16. Remove the unit from beneath the instrument panel.
17. With the unit removed from the vehicle, remove the plenum air seal.
18. Remove the vacuum hose from the fresh air door actuator and bypass door actuator. Remove the air seal from the evaporator core tubes and heater.
19. Remove the 18 screws securing the front and rear covers; extract one screw from between the evaporator core tubes. Pull the housings apart.
20. Extract the three screws from the evaporator core access plate; remove the plate. With access now clear to the two evaporator core mounting screws, remove them. In addition, remove the four screws securing the evaporator core to the front cover; remove the core.
21. Carefully lift the left housing half seal from the rear cover. Do not remove the entire seal; the lower portion acts as a water seal.
22. Remove the two core retaining screws from the mounting plate. From the back of the rear cover, remove one screw from between the core tubes. Lift the heater core from the housing.
23. To begin assembly and installation, place the heat door in the up position. Place the heater core into the rear cover. Install its retaining screws.
24. Apply rubber cement to the bottom of the raised portion of the housing seal; carefully replace it in its original position over the heater core.
25. Insert the evaporator core into the front cover and replace its four securing screws.
26. Place the front and rear covers together. Make sure the cover seal is seated properly. Replace the 18 securing screws (and the screw between the evaporator core tubes at the back of the rear cover).
27. Replace the air seal over the heater and evaporator core tubes.
28. Connect all vacuum hoses to their respective actuators. Connect the hose with the red tracer to the actuator rod side.
29. Install the evaporator core access cover plate to the housing front and replace its three sheet metal screws.
30. Apply rubber cement to the plenum air seal and install it in position.
31. Position the housing up under the instrument panel. Connect the housing-to-plenum support bracket.
32. In the engine compartment, install four retaining nuts on the housing mounting studs: torque to 24 in. lbs.
33. Install the vacuum harness to the control switch rear. Install the water valve control cable in its retaining bracket.
34. Install the radio.
35. Install all blower motor resistor wiring. Plug the antenna lead into the radio bottom.
36. Replace the center outlet air distribution housing. Replace the left spot coller duct.
37. Replace the appearance shield at the instrument panel bottom.
38. Replace the glove box.
39. Replace the blower motor and connect its wiring. Install the blower motor cooling tube and replace the evaporator drain tube.
40. Connect the refrigerant lines to the evaporator core tubes. Freely lubricate fittings and O-rings with refrigerant oil. Use two wrenches to avoid twisting the tubes.
41. Connect the heater hoses to the core tubes. Fill the cooling system.
42. Sweep the system. Evacuate the system. Charge the system and check for leaks.

1972-74 Polara, Monaco, and Fury

To remove only the heater core, it is not necessary to discharge the air conditioning system. The heater core is positioned in the rear housing of the passenger-side unit.

1. Disconnect the battery and drain the cooling system. Remove the air cleaner and disconnect the heater hoses. Plug the heater core tubes to prevent coolant loss when the core is removed.
2. Remove the steering column cover and remove the left spot cooler duct.
3. On the left side of the housing, remove the linkage shield and disconnect the actuator rods. Remove the screws from the housing left side.
4. Remove the screws holding the heat distribution duct and remove it. With duct removed, the screws in the bottom lip of the rear housing will become visible. Remove them.
5. Remove the glove box. In addition, remove the right spot cooler duct, the air distribution housing, and the center outlet duct.
6. Working in the glove box opening, remove the top retaining screws and the right-side housing screws. If the vehicle is Auto-Temp equipped, remove the aspirator tube from the clip first and then remove the amplifier and master compressor switches. Now remove the right-side housing screws.
7. Disconnect all electrical connections at the resistor block. On Auto-Temp equipped vehicles, remove the wires from the two plastic straps and the metal clip.
8. Remove the nut from the hous-

MOUNTING STUDS
Blower motor removal—1969-74 Coronet, Belvedere, Charger and Satellite (© Chrysler Corp)

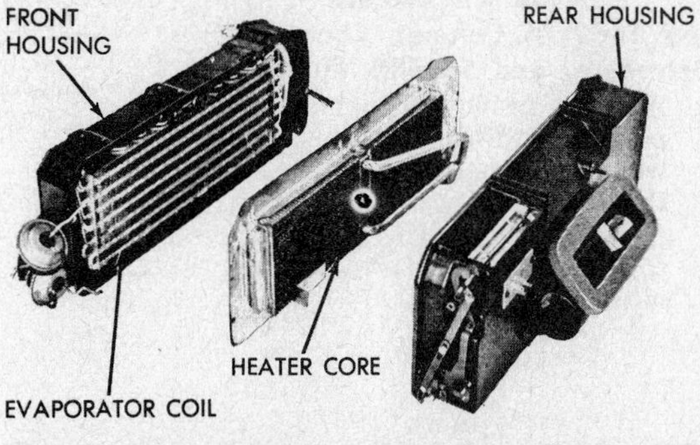
FRONT HOUSING
REAR HOUSING
HEATER CORE
EVAPORATOR COIL
Heater and evaporator core—1972-74 Polara, Monaco and Fury (© Chrysler Corp)

ing end of the support bracket. Swing the bracket upward and out of the way. Carefully roll the housing out from under the instrument panel. The heater core may be removed by pulling it out from the top. Cut the adhesive along the bottom and sides with a knife to ease removal.

9. To begin installation, scrape all remaining sealer from the heater core flange and fit a new seal. Position the heater core in the rear housing and secure with a screw at either end. Place the front housing in position; hold the rear housing in place and swing the support bracket down. Secure it in position with its retaining nut.
10. Working in the glove box opening, install the top two housing screws and the screws at the right side of the rear housing.
11. From beneath the instrument panel, install the screws along the housing bottom and the screws at the left side of the rear housing. It is not necessary to reinstall the linkage shield.
12. Replace the heat distribution duct to the housing bottom.
13. Connect the actuator rods.
14. Working in the glove box opening, connect the resistor block wires. Tighten the support bracket nuts. On Auto-Temp equipped vehicles, fasten the wires with the plastic straps and metal clip. Install the aspirator tube in the clip.
15. Replace the center outlet duct. the air distribution housing, and the right spot cooler duct.
16. Install the steering column cover, the left spot cooler duct. and the glove box assembly. On Auto-Temp equipped vehicles, install the amplifier and the master and compressor switches.
17. From this point, reverse the removal procedure. Be sure to fill the cooling system with the proper amount and type of antifreeze.

Air Conditioning Blower Motor Removal

1967-68 All Models and 1969-74 Coronet, Charger, Belvedere, and Satellite Models

1. Working inside the engine compartment, disconnect the feed wire and ground wire. Remove the air tube (if so equipped).
2. Remove the mounting screws located on the outer surface of the mounting plate.
3. Remove the mounting plate, blower motor, and fan as an assembly.
4. To install motor, if the motor was removed from its mounting plate, be sure mounting grommets are installed at the attaching bolts. In addition, be sure the blower wheel is free and does not rub.
5. Install the blower motor assembly to the evaporator casing with the air tube opening toward the bottom. Install its retaining screws.
6. Install the air tube, ground, and feed wires.
7. Check blower motor operation.

1969-74 Fury, Polara, Monaco, and VIP

The blower motor is located under the right front fender between the inner fender shield and the fender. Remove the inner fender shield to provide access to the blower motor. Service consists of removing its electrical leads and attaching screws. The blower motor is not repaired; remove and replace only.

SEAT BELTS

Buzzer System—1972-73

All Chrysler Corporation cars built after January 1, 1972 have front seat belts with a reminder light and buzzer system. The warning system consists of a buzzer and light, two lap belt retractor switches, a front passenger weight-sensing switch and a relay.

With only the driver in the front seat, the system will give warning when the ignition swich is on, the automatic transmission is in any gear or the parking brake is released on manual transmission models and the driver's seat belt has not been pulled out of the retractor at least ten inches.

With a passenger in the right front seat, the system will operate as for the driver alone unless the passenger's seat belt has also been extended.

Seat Belt/Starter Interlock—1974

The interlock system prevents the starter from being operated until all outboard front seat occupants have fastened their seat belts. An interlock control requires that the seat belts be fastened in all outboard front seats each time the engine is started.

For the convenience of the serviceman, there is an underhood bypass switch for the system. This enables him to start the engine once, without having to sit on the seat and fasten the seat belt.

The earlier light and buzzer reminder system is retained, with coverage for the center front seat position added.

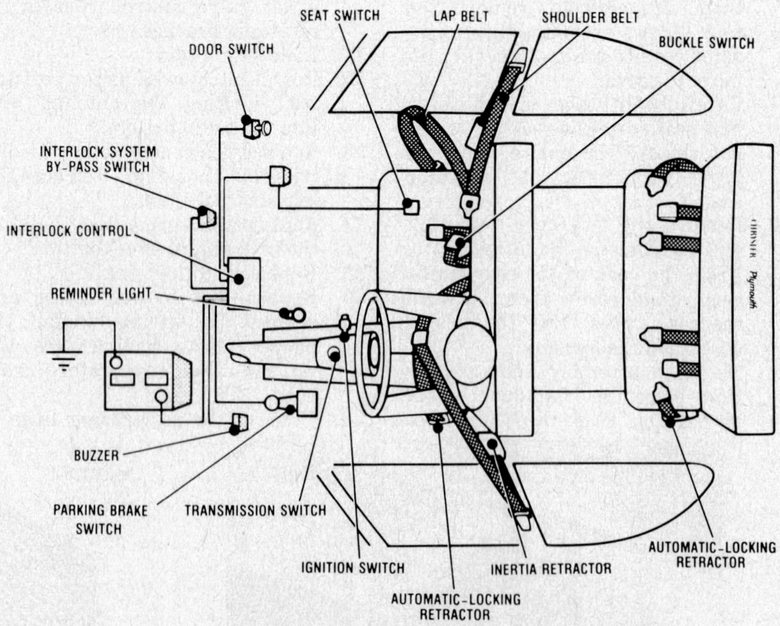
SEAT SWITCH
LAP BELT
SHOULDER BELT
BUCKLE SWITCH
DOOR SWITCH
INTERLOCK SYSTEM BY-PASS SWITCH
INTERLOCK CONTROL
REMINDER LIGHT
BUZZER
PARKING BRAKE SWITCH
TRANSMISSION SWITCH
IGNITION SWITCH
AUTOMATIC-LOCKING RETRACTOR
INERTIA RETRACTOR
AUTOMATIC-LOCKING RETRACTOR

The 1974 seat belt/starter interlock system (© Chrysler Corp)

Fairlane • Falcon • Mustang Comet • Cougar • Montego Maverick • Torino

YEAR IDENTIFICATION

FAIRLANE AND TORINO

1967

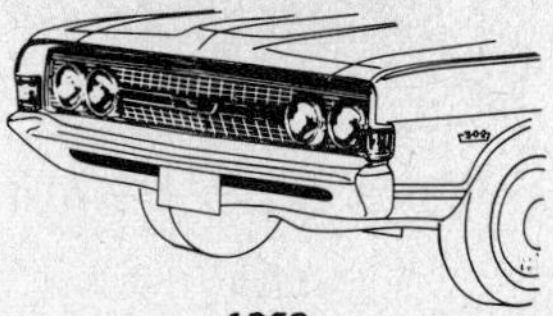
1968

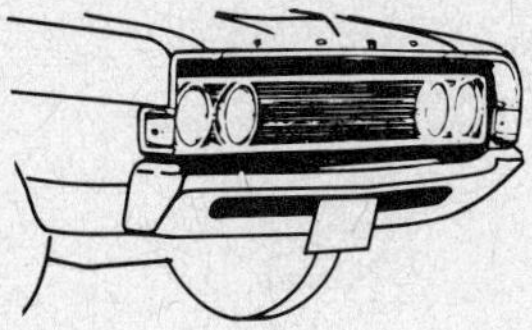
1969

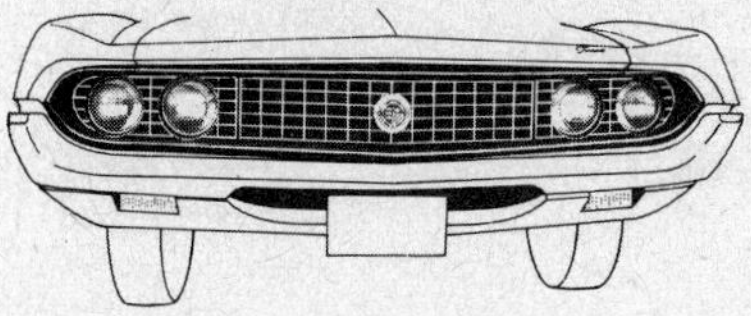
1970

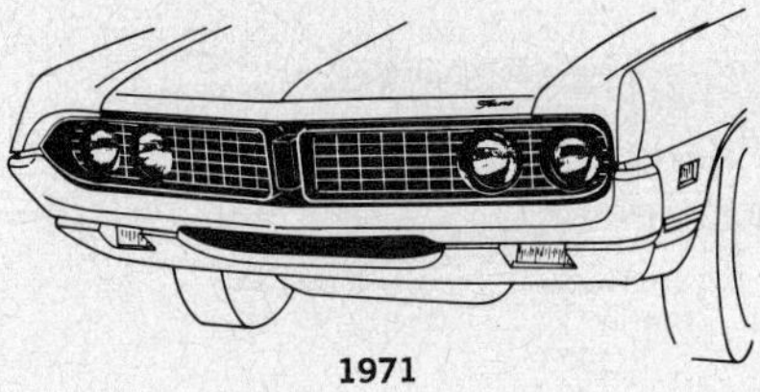
1971

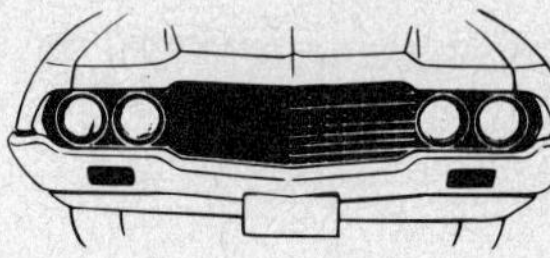
1972 Torino

1972 Gran Torino

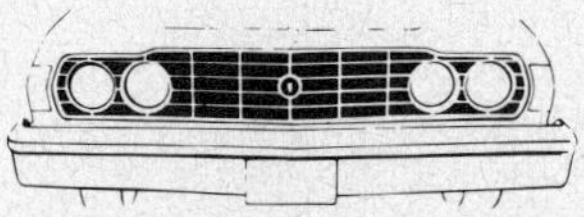
1973 Torino

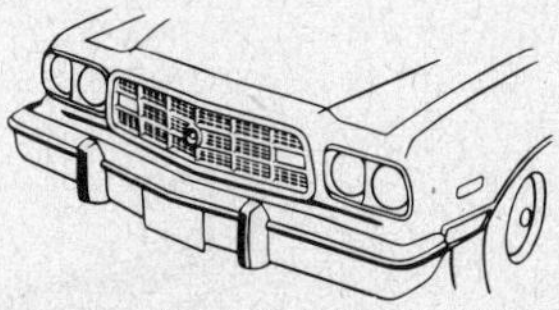
1973 Gran Torino

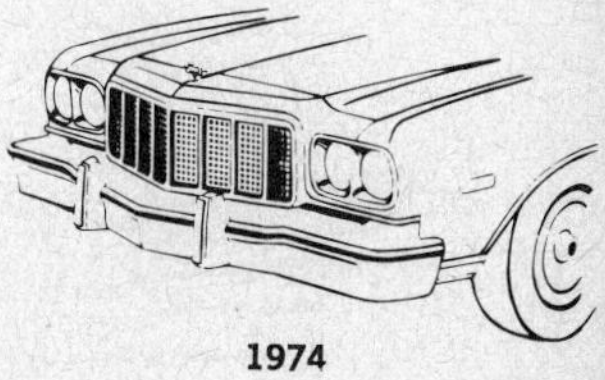
1974

FALCON

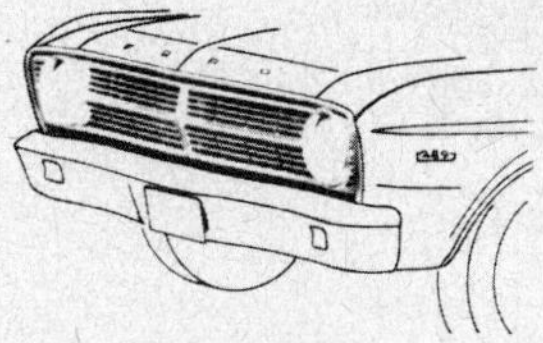
1967

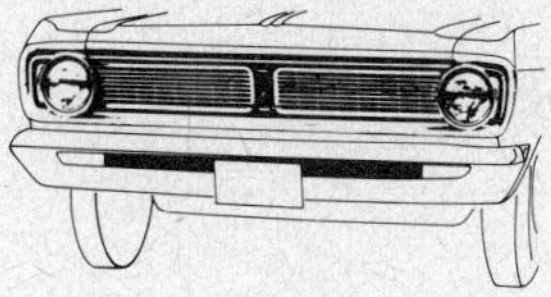
1968

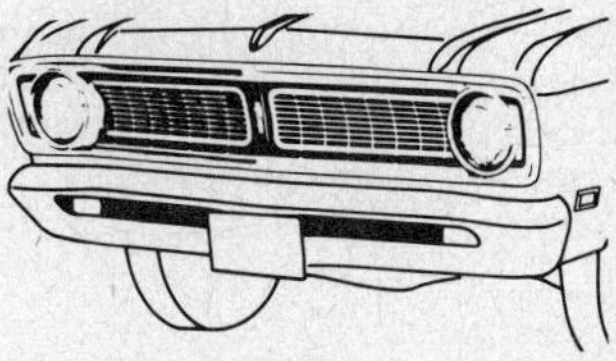
1969

COUGAR

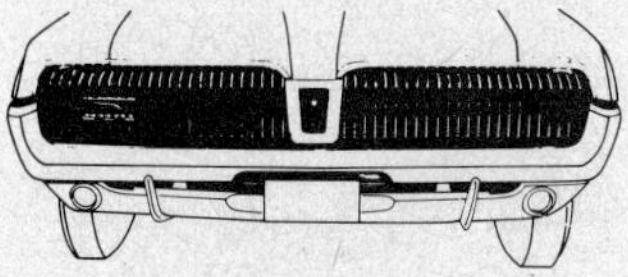
1967

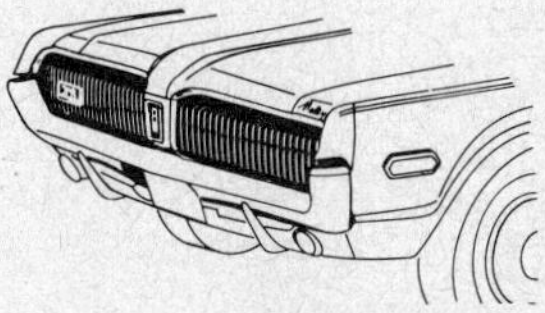
1968

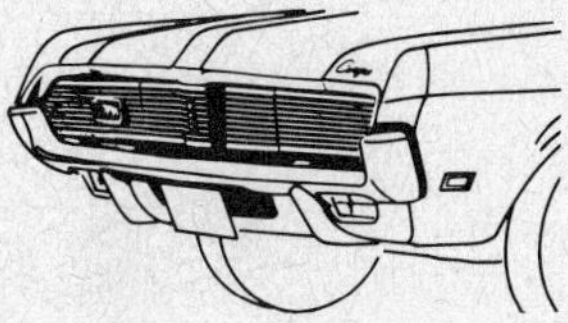
1969

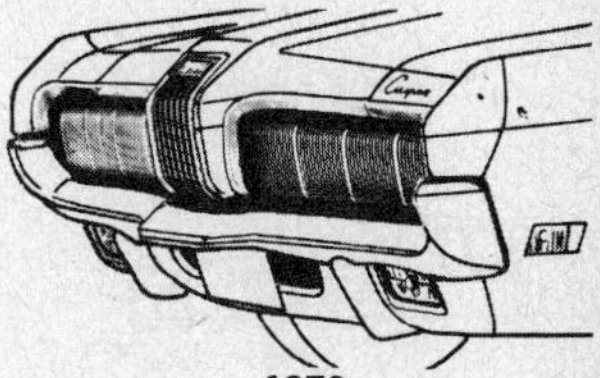
1970

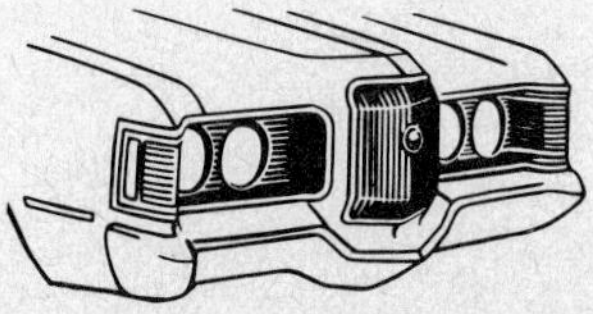
1971

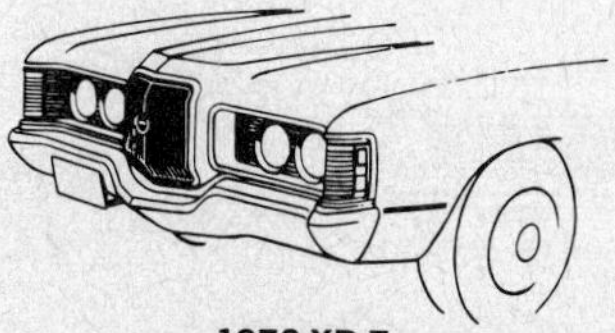
1972 XR-7

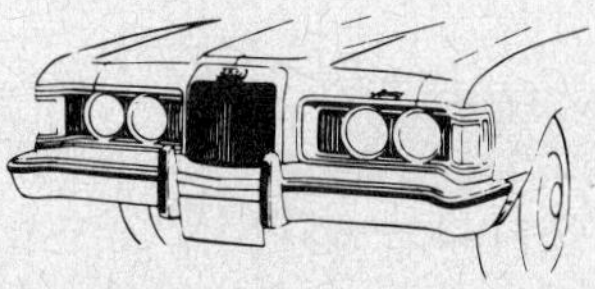
1973

MUSTANG

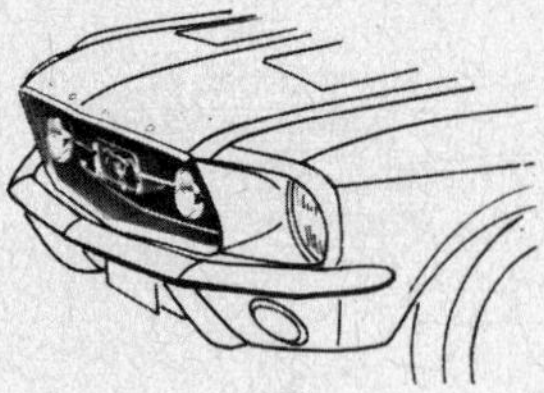
1967

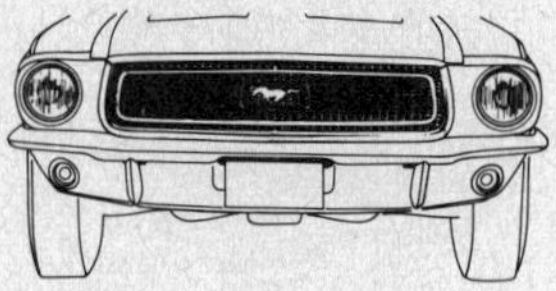
1968

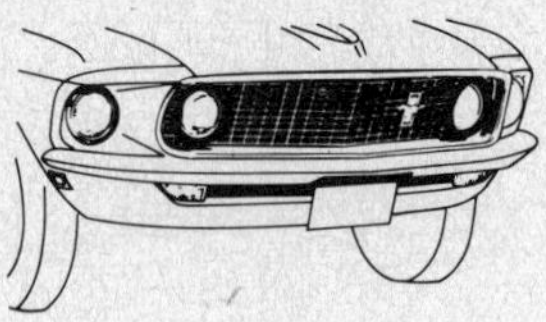
1969

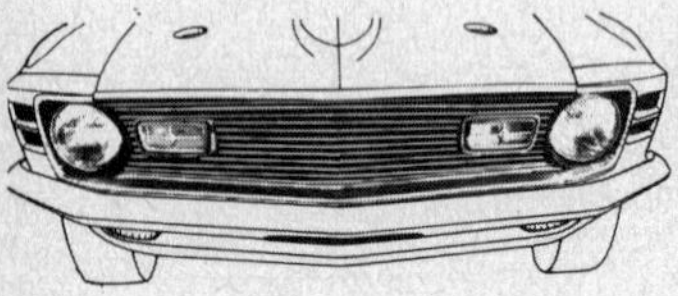
1970

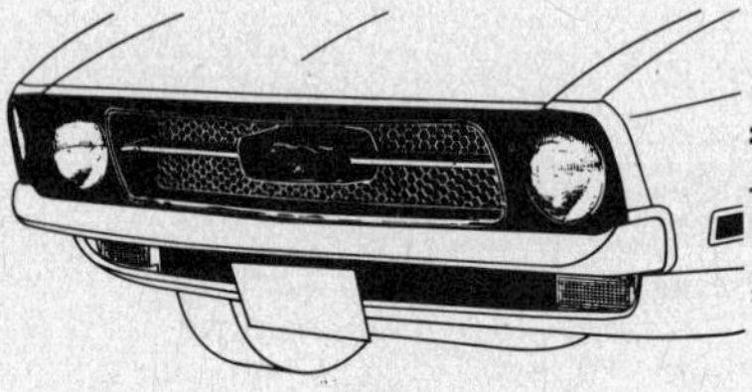
1971

1972

1973

COMET

1967

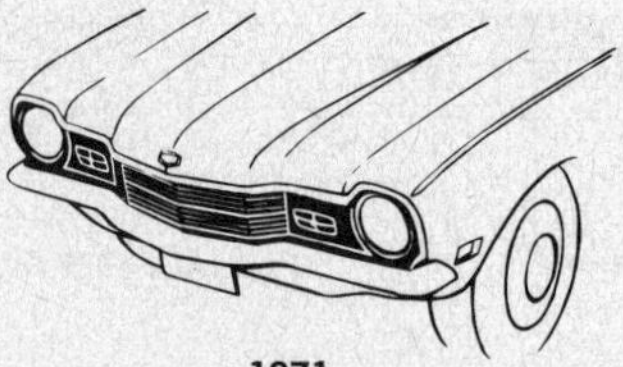
1971

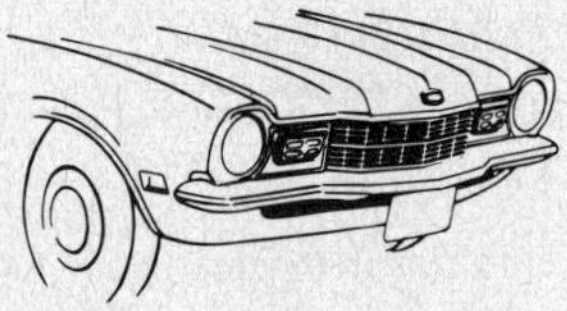
1972

1973

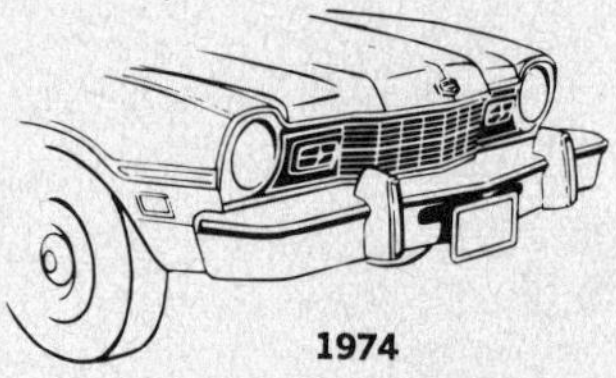
1974

MONTEGO

1968

1969

1970

1971

1972

1973

MAVERICK

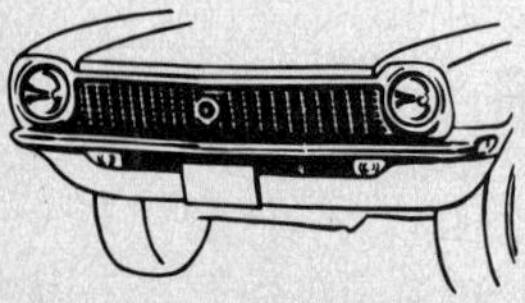
1970-72

1971-72 Grabber

1973

1974

FIRING ORDER

1968-74 289, 302 V8 timing marks

1967 390, 427 V8 timing marks

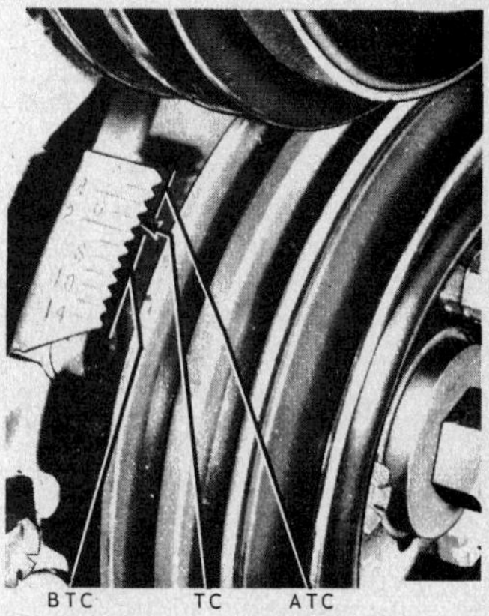
BTC
TC
ATC

1968-74 6 cyl timing marks

1967 260, 289 V8 timing marks

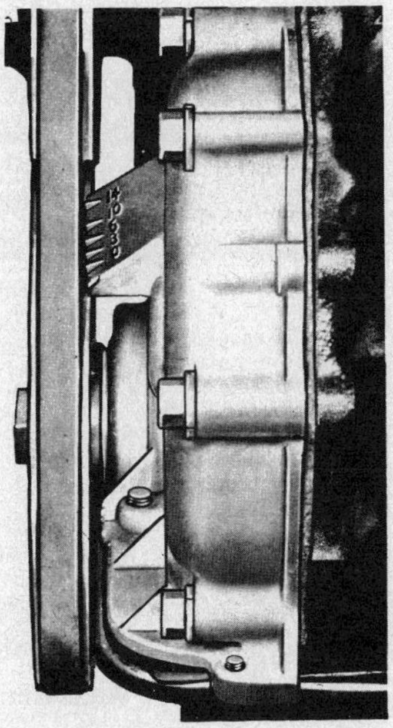

1967 6 cyl timing marks

1968-74 390, 427, 428, 429 V8 timing marks

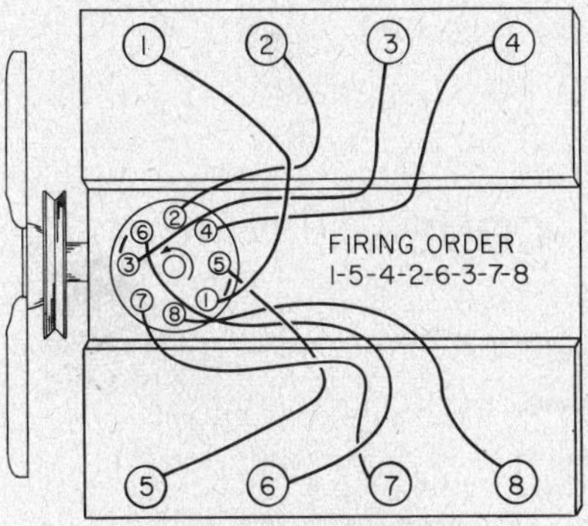
FIRING ORDER
1-5-4-2-6-3-7-8

All V8 except 351, 400 V8

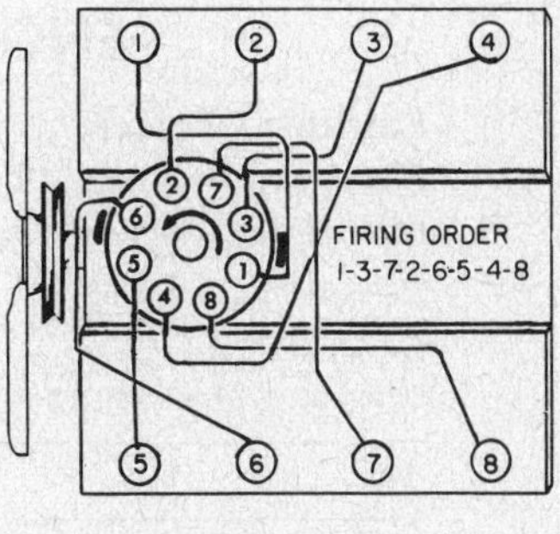
FIRING ORDER
1-3-7-2-6-5-4-8

351 and 400 V8

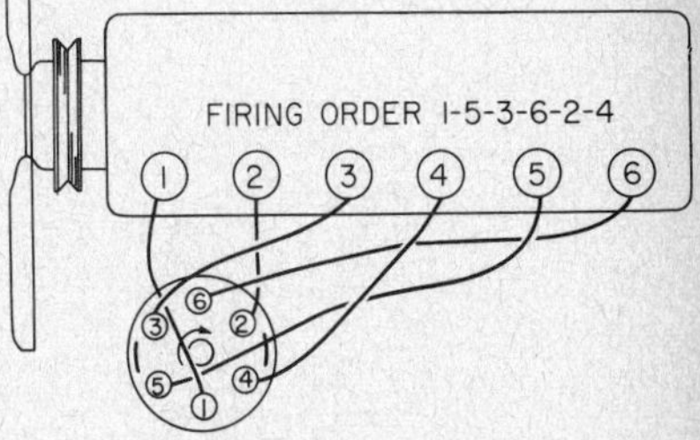
FIRING ORDER 1-5-3-6-2-4

All 6 cyl

CAR SERIAL NUMBER LOCATION AND ENGINE IDENTIFICATION

1967

Engine is identified through car serial number. Serial numbers, and other pertinent information, are to be found on a plate riveted to the rear edge of the left front door.

The engine number is stamped on the top surface of the engine block near the crankcase breather pipe, front left side.

The car serial number is composed of eleven digits, the first five giving the year, assembly plant, body serial code (2 digits), model and engine type. The second six digits are a sequential serial number.

1968-74

The serial number is on a plate attached to the top of the instrument panel, visible through the windshield. The plate is interpreted as per the illustrations.

Vehicle Certification Label 1970-74

The vehicle certification label is located on the rear of the driver's door. The upper half of the label contains the name of the manufacturer, the month and year of manufacture, and the certification statement. For interpretation of the lower half of the label, see the illustration.

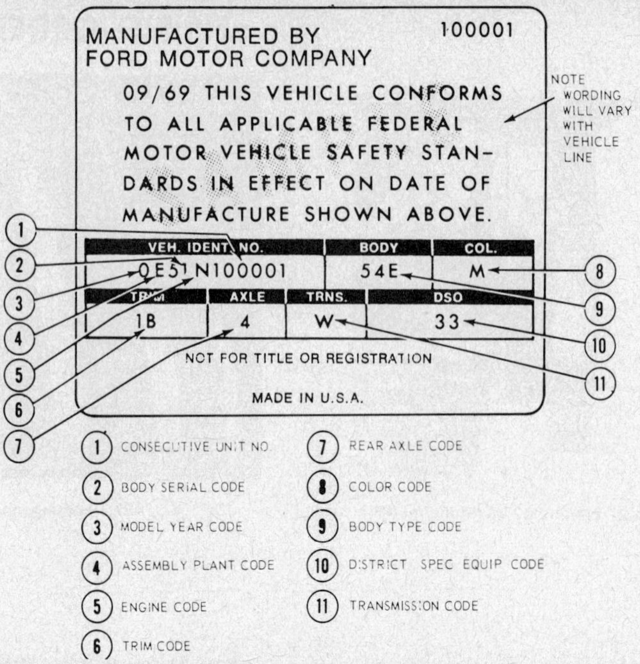
MANUFACTURED BY
FORD MOTOR COMPANY
100001
09/69 THIS VEHICLE CONFORMS TO ALL APPLICABLE FEDERAL MOTOR VEHICLE SAFETY STANDARDS IN EFFECT ON DATE OF MANUFACTURE SHOWN ABOVE.
NOTE WORDING WILL VARY WITH VEHICLE LINE
VEH. IDENT. NO.
BODY
COL.
0E51N100001
54E
M
TRIM
AXLE
TRNS.
DSO
1B
4
W
33
NOT FOR TITLE OR REGISTRATION
MADE IN U.S.A.
1 CONSECUTIVE UNIT NO
2 BODY SERIAL CODE
3 MODEL YEAR CODE
4 ASSEMBLY PLANT CODE
5 ENGINE CODE
6 TRIM CODE
7 REAR AXLE CODE
8 COLOR CODE
9 BODY TYPE CODE
10 DISTRICT SPEC EQUIP CODE
11 TRANSMISSION CODE

Vehicle certification label—1970-74

9Y83N100001

Typical vehicle identification number (VIN) tab

1 Model year code
2 Assembly plant code
3 Body serial code
4 Engine code
5 Consecutive unit number
6 Body type code
7 Color code
8 Trim code
9 Date code
10 District—special equipment code
11 Rear axle code
12 Transmission code

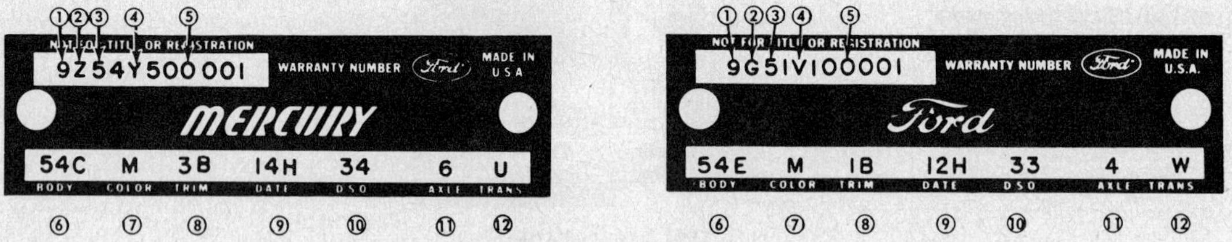
NOT FOR TITLE OR REGISTRATION
9Z54Y500001
WARRANTY NUMBER
MADE IN U.S.A.
MERCURY
54C M 3B 14H 34 6 U
BODY COLOR TRIM DATE DSO AXLE TRANS
NOT FOR TITLE OR REGISTRATION
9G51V100001
WARRANTY NUMBER
MADE IN U.S.A.
Ford
54E M 1B 12H 33 4 W
BODY COLOR TRIM DATE DSO AXLE TRANS

Engine number and code location V8 engines

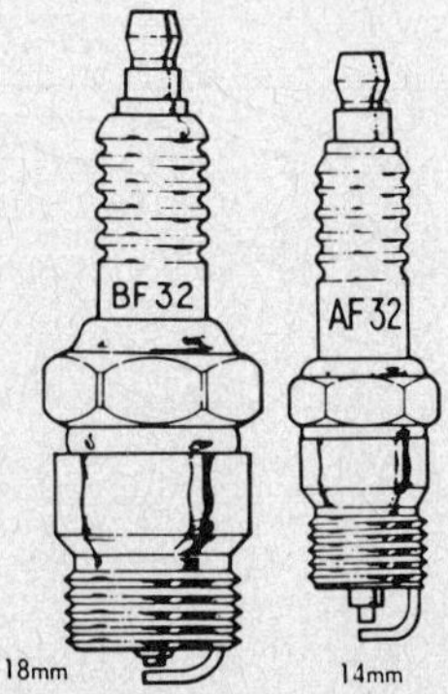
BF32
AF32
18mm
14mm

Left—Windsor spark plug; Right—Cleveland spark plug

ENGINE CODE

Fairlane, Falcon, Mustang, Comet, Cougar, Montego, Maverick, Torino

The engine code designation is the 5th digit of the vehicle identification number (V.I.N.). The V.I.N. is stamped on a plate located at the rear edge of the left front door on 1967 models and located at the left side of the instrument panel, visible through the windshield, on 1968-74 models.

Disp	Bbl	Hp	'67	'68	'69	'70	'71	'72	'73	'74
6-Cylinder Models										
170	1	82 (net)						U		
170	1	100					U			
170	1	105	U	U	U	U				
200	1	84 (net)							T	T

Disp	Bbl	Hp	'67	'68	'69	'70	'71	'72	'73	'74
6-Cylinder Models										
200	1	91 (net)						T		
200	1	115		T	T		T			
200	1	120	T			T				
250	1	88, 92, 99 (net)*							L	L
250	1	95, 98 (net)*						L		
250	1	145					L			
250	1	155			L	L				
8-Cylinder Models										
289	2	195		C						
289	2	200	C							
289	4	225	A							
289	4	271	K							
302	2	135, 137, 138, 141 (net)*							F	F
302	2	138, 140, 143 (net)*						F		
302	2	210		F		F	F			
302	2	220			F	F				
302	4	230		J						
302 (Boss)	4	290			G	G				
351W	2	156 (net)							H	H
351C	2	154, 159, 177 (net)*							H	H
351①	2	161, 164, 177 (net)*						H		
351CJ	4	246, 266 (net)*						Q	Q	Q
351HO	4	266 (net)						R		
351①	2	240					Q			
351①	2	250			H	H				
351①	4	280					M			
351①	4	285					R			
351①	4	290			M					
351①	4	300				M				
351 (Boss)	4	330					H			
390	2	265		Y						
390	2	270	H,Y							
390	2	280		X						
390	4	320	S							
390	4	325		S						
390	4	335	S							
400	2	163, 168 (net)*							S	S
400	2	168, 172 (net)*						S		
427	4	390		W						
427	8	425	R							
428	4	335		Q	Q	Q				
429	4	197, 201 (net)*							N	
429	4	205, 208, 212 (net)*						N		
429	4	360				N	N			
429CJ	4	370				C	C			
429SCJ	4	375				J	J			
429 (Boss)	4	375				Z				
460	4	202, 208 (net)*								A

① All 351 4V engines are Cleveland engines. Both Windsor and Cleveland versions of the 351 2V engine have been available. The quickest method of identification is to disconnect a spark plug wire and examine the size of the plug. Windsor engines are equipped with standard 18mm spark plugs. Cleveland engines are equipped with smaller 14mm spark plugs.

* Net horsepower rating varies with vehicle installation

CJ Cobra Jet
HO High output
W Windsor
C Cleveland
SCJ Super Cobra Jet

TRANSMISSION CODES

1967

1 .... Three speed manual
2 .... Overdrive
3 .... Three speed manual
5 .... Four speed manual
W .... Automatic C4
U .... Automatic C6

1968

1 .... Three speed manual
5 .... Four speed manual
W .... Automatic C4
U .... Automatic C6

1969

1 .... Three speed manual
5 .. Four speed manual-wide ratio
6 .. Four speed manual-close ratio
W .... Automatic C4
U .... Automatic C6
Y .... Automatic MX
X .... Automatic FMX
Z .... Automatic C6 Special for Police and trailer towing

1970-71

1 .... Three speed manual
5 .. Four speed manual-wide ratio
6 .. Four speed manual-close ratio
V .... Semi-Automatic stick shift
W .... Automatic C4
U .... Automatic C6
X .... Automatic FMX
Z .... Automatic C6 Special for Police and trailer towing

1972-74

1 .... Three speed manual
5 .... Four speed manual
U .... Automatic C6
W .... Automatic C4
X .... Automatic FMX
Z .... Automatic (C6 Special)

NOTE: All 351 4V engines are Cleveland engines. Both Windsor and Cleveland versions of the 351 2V engine are available. The quickest method of engine identification is to disconnect a spark plug wire at the spark plug and examine the size of the spark plug. Windsor engines are equipped with standard 18mm spark plugs. Cleveland engines are equipped with smaller 14mm spark plugs.

Fairlane, Falcon, Mustang, Comet, Cougar, Montego, Maverick, Torino

GENERAL ENGINE SPECIFICATIONS

Year	Engine Cu. In. Displacement	Carburetor Type	Advertised Horsepower @ rpm ■	Advertised Torque @ rpm (ft lbs) ■	Bore and Stroke (in.)	Advertised Compression Ratio	Oil Pressure @ 2050 rpm
'67	6-170	1 bbl	105 @ 4400	158 @ 2400	3.500 x 2.940	9.1:1	35-55
	6-200	1 bbl	120 @ 4400	190 @ 2400	3.680 x 3.130	9.2:1	35-55
	6-289	2 bbl	200 @ 4400	282 @ 2400	4.000 x 2.870	9.3:1	35-55
	8-289	4 bbl	225 @ 4800	305 @ 3200	4.000 x 2.870	9.8:1	35-55
	8-289 H.P.	4 bbl	271 @ 6000	312 @ 3400	4.000 x 2.870	10.0:1	35-55
	8-390	2 bbl	270 @ 4400	403 @ 2600	4.050 x 3.784	9.5:1	35-65
	8-390	4 bbl	320 @ 3600	427 @ 3200	4.050 x 3.784	10.5:1	35-65
	8-390 GT	4 bbl	335 @ 4800	427 @ 3200	4.050 x 3.784	10.5:1	35-65
	8-427	4 bbl	410 @ 5600	476 @ 3400	4.233 x 3.781	11.1:1	40-55
	8-427	2 x 4 bbl	425 @ 6000	480 @ 3700	4.233 x 3.781	11.1:1	40-55
'68	6-170	1 bbl	100 @ 4000	156 @ 2000	3.500 x 2.940	8.7:1	35-60
	6-200	1 bbl	115 @ 3800	190 @ 2200	3.680 x 3.130	8.8:1	35-60
	8-289	2 bbl	195 @ 4600	288 @ 2600	4.000 x 2.870	8.7:1	35-60
	8-302	2 bbl	210 @ 4600	300 @ 2600	4.000 x 3.000	9.0:1	35-60
	8-302	4 bbl	230 @ 4800	310 @ 2800	4.000 x 3.000	10.0:1	35-60
	8-390	2 bbl	265 @ 4400	390 @ 2600	4.050 x 3.784	9.5:1	35-60
	8-390	2 bbl	280 @ 4400	403 @ 2600	4.050 x 3.784	10.5:1	35-60
	8-390 GT	4 bbl	325 @ 4800	427 @ 3200	4.050 x 3.784	10.5:1	35-60
	8-427	4 bbl	390 @ 5600	460 @ 3200	4.236 x 3.781	10.9:1	35-60
	8-428 CJ	4 bbl	335 @ 5400	440 @ 3400	4.130 x 3.984	10.6:1	35-60
'69	6-170	1 bbl	105 @ 4400	158 @ 2400	3.500 x 2.940	9.1:1	35-60
	6-200	1 bbl	120 @ 4400	190 @ 2400	3.680 x 3.130	8.1:1	35-60
	6-250	1 bbl	155 @ 4000	240 @ 1600	3.682 x 3.910	9.0:1	35-60
	8-302	2 bbl	210 @ 4400	295 @ 2400	4.000 x 3.000	9.5:1	35-60
	8-302 BOSS	4 bbl	290 @ 5800	290 @ 4300	4.000 x 3.000	10.5:1	35-60
	8-351	2 bbl	250 @ 4600	355 @ 2600	4.000 x 3.000	9.5:1	35-60
	8-351 C	4 bbl	290 @ 4800	385 @ 3200	4.000 x 3.000	10.7:1	35-60
	8-390	4 bbl	320 @ 4600	427 @ 3200	4.050 x 3.784	10.5:1	35-60
	8-428 CJ	4 bbl	335 @ 5200	440 @ 3400	4.130 x 3.984	10.6:1	35-60
	8-429 BOSS	4 bbl	375 @ 5200	450 @ 3400	4.360 x 3.590	10.5:1	45-60
'70	6-170	1 bbl	105 @ 4400	158 @ 2400	3.500 x 2.940	8.7:1	35-60
	6-200	1 bbl	120 @ 4400	190 @ 2400	3.680 x 3.130	8.7:1	35-60
	6-250	1 bbl	155 @ 4400	240 @ 1600	3.682 x 3.910	9.0:1	35-60
	8-302	2 bbl	210 @ 4400	295 @ 2400	4.000 x 3.000	9.5:1	35-60
	8-302 BOSS	4 bbl	290 @ 5800	290 @ 4300	4.000 x 3.000	10.5:1	35-60
	8-351	2 bbl	250 @ 4600	355 @ 2600	4.000 x 3.500	9.5:1	35-60
	8-351 C	4 bbl	300 @ 5400	380 @ 3400	4.000 x 3.500	11.4:1	35-60
	8-428 CJ	4 bbl	335 @ 5200	440 @ 3400	4.130 x 3.984	10.6:1	35-60
	8-429	4 bbl	360 @ 4600	480 @ 2800	4.362 x 3.590	10.5:1	35-60
	8-429 CJ	4 bbl	370 @ 5400	450 @ 3400	4.362 x 3.590	11.3:1	35-60
	8-429 SCJ	4 bbl	375 @ 5600	450 @ 3400	4.362 x 3.590	10.5:1	35-60
	8-429 BOSS	4 bbl	375 @ 5200	450 @ 3400	4.362 x 3.590	10.5:1	45-60

GENERAL ENGINE SPECIFICATIONS

Year	Engine Cu. In. Displacement	Carburetor Type	Advertised Horsepower @ rpm ■	Advertised Torque @ rpm (ft lbs) ■	Bore and Stroke (in.)	Advertised Compression Ratio	Oil Pressure @ 2050 rpm
'71	6-170	1 bbl	100 @ 4200	148 @ 2600	3.500 x 2.940	8.7:1	35-60
	6-200	1 bbl	115 @ 4000	180 @ 2200	3.680 x 3.130	8.7:1	35-60
	6-250	1 bbl	145 @ 4000	232 @ 1600	3.682 x 3.910	9.0:1	35-60
	8-302	2 bbl	210 @ 4600	296 @ 2600	4.000 x 3.000	9.0:1	35-60
	8-351	2 bbl	240 @ 4600	355 @ 2600	4.000 x 3.500	9.5:1	35-60
	8-351 BOSS	4 bbl	330 @ 5800	380 @ 3400	4.000 x 3.500	11.0:1	35-60
	8-351 CJ	4 bbl	280 @ 5800	345 @ 3800	4.000 x 3.500	9.0:1	35-60
	8-351 C	4 bbl	285 @ 5400	370 @ 3400	4.000 x 3.500	10.7:1	35-60
	8-429	4 bbl	360 @ 4600	480 @ 2800	4.362 x 3.590	10.5:1	35-75
	8-429 CJ	4 bbl	370 @ 5400	450 @ 3400	4.362 x 3.590	11.3:1	35-75
	8-429 SCJ	4 bbl	375 @ 5600	450 @ 3400	4.362 x 3.590	11.3:1	35-75
'72	6-170	1 bbl	82 @ 4400	129 @ 1800	3.500 x 2.940	8.3:1	35-60
	6-200	1 bbl	91 @ 4000	154 @ 2200	3.680 x 3.130	8.3:1	35-60
	6-250	1 bbl	99 @ 3600	184 @ 1600	3.680 x 3.910	8.0:1	35-60
	8-302	2 bbl	141 @ 4000	242 @ 2000	4.000 x 3.000	8.5:1	35-60
	8-351	2 bbl	164 @ 4000	276 @ 2000	4.000 x 3.500	8.6:1	35-85
	8-351 CJ	4 bbl	248 @ 5400	290 @ 3800	4.000 x 3.500	8.6:1	35-85
	8-351 HO	4 bbl	266 @ 5400	301 @ 3600	4.000 x 3.500	8.6:1	35-85
	8-400	2 bbl	168 @ 4200	297 @ 2200	4.000 x 4.000	8.4:1	35-85
	8-429	4 bbl	205 @ 4400	322 @ 2600	4.362 x 3.590	8.5:1	35-75
'73	6-200	1 bbl	91 @ 4000	154 @ 2200	3.680 x 3.130	8.3:1	35-60
	6-250	1 bbl	99 @ 3600	184 @ 1600	3.680 x 3.910	8.0:1	35-60
	8-302	2 bbl	141 @ 4000	242 @ 2000	4.000 x 3.000	8.5:1	35-60
	8-351	2 bbl	164 @ 4000	276 @ 2000	4.000 x 3.500	8.6:1	35-85
	8-351	4 bbl	248 @ 5400	290 @ 3800	4.000 x 3.500	8.0:1	35-85
	8-400	2 bbl	168 @ 4200	297 @ 2200	4.000 x 4.000	8.0:1	35-85
	8-429	4 bbl	205 @ 4400	322 @ 2600	4.362 x 3.590	8.5:1	35-75
'74	6-200	1 bbl	84 @ 3800	151 @ 1800	3.680 x 3.130	8.3:1	35-55
	6-250	1 bbl	88 @ 3200	196 @ 1600	3.680 x 3.910	8.0:1	35-55
	8-302	2 bbl	135, 137, 138 @ 4200	228, 230, 234 @ 2200	4.000 x 3.000	8.0:1	35-55
	8-351	2 bbl	159 @ 4000	260 @ 2400	4.000 x 3.500	8.0:1	50-70
	8-351	4 bbl	246 @ 5400	312 @ 3600	4.000 x 3.500	8.0:1	50-70
	8-400	2 bbl	168 @ 3800	310 @ 2000	4.000 x 4.000	8.0:1	50-70
	8-460	4 bbl	200 @ 4000	342 @ 2000	4.362 x 3.850	8.0:1	35-75

■ Beginning 1972 horsepower and torque are SAE net figures. They are measured at the rear of the transmission with all accessories installed and operating. Since the figures vary when a given engine is installed in different models, some are representative rather than exact.

BATTERY AND STARTER SPECIFICATIONS

Year	Engine Displacement (cu in.)	BATTERY			STARTER						
					Lock Test			No-Load Test			Brush Spring Tension (oz)
		Ampere Hour Capacity	Volts		Amps	Volts	Torque (ft lbs)	Amps	Volts	RPM	
'67-'74	6-170	45④	12	Neg.	460	5	9	50	12	9,500	40
	6-200, 250	45④	12	Neg.	670	5	15.5	70	12	9,500	40
	8-exc. below	55③	12	Neg.	①	5	②	70	12	9,500	40
	8-351 4-BBL.	55③	12	Neg.	①	5	②	70	12	9,500	40
	8-400, 428, 429, 460	68, 73	12	Neg.	670	5	15.5	70	12	9,500	40

① 4½ in. diameter starter—670; 4 in. diameter starter—460
② 4½ in. diameter starter—15.5; 4 in. diameter starter—9.0
③ 68AH battery optional; 73AH battery optional
④ 53AH battery optional

Falcon, 1967 Comet — TUNE-UP SPECIFICATIONS

When analyzing compression test results, look for uniformity among cylinders rather than specific pressures.

	ENGINE		SPARK PLUGS		DISTRIBUTOR		IGNITION TIMING (deg) ▲		VALVES	Fuel	IDLE SPEED (rpm) ▲	
Year	No. Cyl Displacement (cu in.)	hp	Type §	Gap (in.)	Point Dwell* (deg)	Point Gap* (in.)	Man Trans	Auto Trans	Intake Opens ■ (deg) ●	Pump Pressure (psi)	Man Trans	Auto Trans
'67	6-170	105	BF-82	.034	40	.025	6B(5B)	12B(5B)	9	4-5	575	550
	6-200	120	BF-82	.034	40	.025	6B(5B)	12B(5B)	7	4-5	575(700)	550
	8-289	200	BF-42	.034	29	.017	6B(TDC)	6B(TDC)	16	4½-5½	575(625)	475(550)
	8-289	225	BF-42	.034	29	.017	6B(TDC)	6B(TDC)	15	4½-5½	750	650
'68	6-170	100	BF-82	.034	37	.027	6B	6B	9	4½-5½	700	550
	6-200	115	BF-82	.034	37	.027	6B	6B	9	4½-5½	700	550
	8-289	195	BF-42	.034	27	.021	6B	6B	16	4½-5½	625	550
	8-302	230	BF-32	.034	27	.021	6B	6B	16	4½-5½	625	550
'69	6-170	100	BF-82	.034	37	.027	6B	6B	9	4½-5½	750	550
	6-200	115	BF-82	.034	37	.027	6B	6B	9	4½-5½	750	550①
	8-302	220	BF-42	.034	27/29	.021/ .017	6B	6B	16	4½-5½	650	550①
'70	6-200	120	BF-82	.035	37	.027	6B	6B	9	4½-5½	750②	550③
	8-302	220	BF-42	.035	27/29	.021/ .017	6B	6B	16	4½-5½	800/500④	600/500④

* Where two figures are separated by a slash, the first figure is for engines equipped with dual diaphragm distributors, while the second is for engines equipped with single diaphragm distributors

▲ See text for procedure

● Figure in parentheses indicates California engine

■ All figures Before Top Dead Center

§ All spark plug listings are Autolite original equipment numbers

① A/C off

② For air conditioned vehicles, adjust idle speed to 800 rpm with A/C off.

③ For air conditioned vehicles, adjust idle speed to 600 rpm with A/C off

④ First figure is for idle speed with solenoid energized and automatic transmission in Drive, while second figure is for idle speed with solenoid disconnected and automatic transmission in Neutral

B Before Top Dead Center

TDC Top Dead Center

— Not applicable

Maverick, 1971-74 Comet — TUNE-UP SPECIFICATIONS

When analyzing compression test results, look for uniformity among cylinders rather than specific pressures.

	ENGINE		SPARK PLUGS		DISTRIBUTOR		IGNITION TIMING (deg) ▲		VALVES	Fuel	IDLE SPEED (rpm) ▲	
Year	No. Cyl Displacement (cu in.)	hp	Type §	Gap (in.)	Point Dwell* (deg)	Point Gap* (in.)	Man Trans	Auto Trans	Intake Opens ■ (deg) ●	Pump Pressure (psi)	Man Trans	Auto Trans
'70	6-170	105	BF-82	.034	37/39	.027/ .025	6B	6B	9	4½	750	550
	6-200	120	BF-82	.034	37/39	.027/ .025	6B	6B	9	4½	800/500	600/500
	6-250	155	BF-82	.034	37/39	.027/ .025	—	6B	10	4-6	—	550
'71	6-170	100	BRF-82	.034	35/36	.027/ .025	6B	—	9	4-6	750	—
	6-200	115	BRF-82	.034	35/36	.027/ .025	6B	6B	9	4-6	800/500	600/500
	6-250	145	BRF-82	.034	35/36	.027/ .025	6B	6B	10	4-6	750/500	600/500
	8-302	210	BRF-42	.034	26/28	.021/ .017	6B	6B	16	4-6	800/500	600/500
'72	6-170	82	BRF-82	.034	37	.027/	6B	—	9	4-6	750	—
	6-200	91	BRF-82	.034	37	.027	6B	6B	9	4-6	800/500	600/500
	6-250	98	BRF-82	.034	37	.027	6B	6B	10	4-6	750/500	600/500
	8-302	143	BRF-42	.034	28	.017	6B	6B	16	4-6	800/500	600/500

Maverick, 1971-74 Comet — TUNE-UP SPECIFICATIONS, Continued

When analyzing compression test results, look for uniformity among cylinders rather than specific pressures.

	ENGINE		SPARK PLUGS		DISTRIBUTOR		IGNITION TIMING (deg) ▲		VALVES	Fuel	IDLE SPEED (rpm) ▲	
Year	No. Cyl Displacement (cu in.)	hp	Type §	Gap (in.)	Point Dwell* (deg)	Point Gap* (in.)	Man Trans	Auto Trans	Intake Opens ■ (deg) ●	Pump Pressure (psi)	Man Trans	Auto Trans
'73	6-200	91	BRF-82	.034	37	.027/ .025	6B	6B	9	4-6	800/500	600/500
	6-250	98	BRF-82	.034	37	.027/ .025	—	6B	10	4-6	—	600/500
	8-302	143	BRF-42	.034	28	.017	6B	6B	16	4-6	800/500	600/500
'74	6-200	84	BRF-82	.034	37	.024/ .030	6B	6B	28	4½-5½	800/500	650/500
	6-250	88	BRF-82	.034	37	.024/ .030	6B	6B	26	4½-5½	800/500	650/500
	8-302	137	BRF-42	.034	27	.014/ .020	6B	6B	②	4½-5½	800/500	550/500①

* Where two figures are separated by a slash, the first figure is for engines equipped with dual diaphragm distributors and the second figure is for engines equipped with single diaphragm distributors

▲ See text for procedure

■ All figures Before Top Dead Center

● Where two figures are separated by a slash, the first figure is for idle speed with solenoid energized and automatic transmission in Drive, while the second is for idle speed with solenoid disconnected and automatic transmission in Neutral

§ All spark plug listings are Autolite original equipment numbers

B Before Top Dead Center

— Not applicable

① 600/500 with air conditioning

② 16° BTC—manual transmission
20° BTC—automatic transmission

Fairlane, Torino, Montego, Mustang, Cougar — TUNE-UP SPECIFICATIONS

When analyzing compression test results, look for uniformity among cylinders rather than specific pressures.

	ENGINE		SPARK PLUGS		DISTRIBUTOR		IGNITION TIMING (deg) ▲		VALVES	Fuel	IDLE SPEED (rpm) ▲	
Year	No. Cyl Displacement (cu in.)	hp	Type §	Gap (in.)	Point Dwell* (deg)	Point Gap* (in.)	Man Trans	Auto Trans	Intake Opens ■ (deg) ●	Pump Pressure (psi)	Man Trans	Auto Trans
'67	6-200	120	BF-82	.034	39	.025	6B(5B)	12B(5B)	7(9)	4½-5½	575(700)	550②
	8-289	200	BF-42	.034	29	.017	6B(5B)	6B(5B)	15	4½-5½	575(625)	475(550)
	8-289	225	BF-42	.034	29	.017	6B(5B)	6B(5B)	16	4½-5½	600(625)	525(550)
	8-289 H.P.	271	BF-32	.034	32	.020	12B	12B	46	4½-5½	750	650
	8-390	270	BF-42	.034	29	.017	10B(6B)	10B(6B)	13	4½-5½	575(625)	475(550)
	8-390	320	BF-32	.034	29	.017	12B(6B)	12B(6B)	18	4½-5½	600(625)	575(550)
	8-390	335	BF-42	.035	29	.017	12B(6B)	12B(6B)	18	4½-5½	600(625)	525(550)
	8-427	425	BF-82	.030	23	.020	8B	8B	48	4½-5½	800	800
'68	6-200	115	BF-82	.034	38	.027	6B	6B	9	4-6	700	550②
	8-289	195	BF-42	.034	27	.021	6B	6B	15	4-6	700	550
	8-302	210	BF-32	.034	27	.021	6B	6B	15	4-6	625	550②
	8-302	230	BF-32	.034	29(27)①	.017 (.021)①	6B	6B	15	4-6	625	550②
	8-390	265	BF-32	.034	29(27)①	.017 (.021)①	6B	6B	13	4½-6	625	550
	8-390	280	BF-32	.034	27	.021	—	6B	13	4½-6	—	550
	8-390 GT	325	BF-32	.034	29	.016	6B	6B	18	4½-6	700	550
	8-427	390	BF-32	.034	29	.017	—	6B	18	4½-6	—	600
	8-428	335	BF-32	.034	29	.017	—	6B	18	4½-6	—	600

Fairlane, Torino, Montego, Mustang, Cougar

TUNE-UP SPECIFICATIONS, Continued

When analyzing compression test results, look for uniformity among cylinders rather than specific pressures.

Year	ENGINE No. Cyl Displacement (cu in.)	ENGINE hp	SPARK PLUGS Type §	SPARK PLUGS Gap (in.)	DISTRIBUTOR Point Dwell* (deg)	DISTRIBUTOR Point Gap* (in.)	IGNITION TIMING (deg) ▲ Man Trans	IGNITION TIMING (deg) ▲ Auto Trans	VALVES Intake Opens ■ (deg) ●	Fuel Pump Pressure (psi)	IDLE SPEED (rpm) ▲ Man Trans	IDLE SPEED (rpm) ▲ Auto Trans
'69	6-200	115	BF-82	.034	38	.027	6B	6B	9	4½-5½	750	550②
	6-250	155	BF-82	.034	38	.025	6B	6B	10	4½-5½	700 [700/500]	550 [550/450]
	8-302	220	BF-42	.034	29③	.021④	6B	6B	16	4½-5½	650	550②
	8-302	290	BF-32	.035	32	.020	16B	—	40	4½-5½	800/500	—
	8-351	250	BF-42	.034	29	.017	6B	6B	11	4½-5½	650	550
	8-351	290	BF-32	.034	29	.017	6B	6B	11	4½-5½	675	575
	8-390	320	BF-42	.034	29③	.017⑤	6B	6B	16	4½-5½	700	550
	8-428	335	BF-32	.034	27⑥	.021④	6B	6B	18	4½-5½	700	650
'70	6-200	120	BF-82	.035	38	.027	6B	6B	9	4-6	750⑦	550⑤
	6-250	155	BF-82	.035	38	.025	6B	6B	10	4-6	750/500	600/500
	8-302	210	BF-42	.035	27	.021	6B	6B	16	4-6	800/500	600/500
	8-302	290	AF-32	.035	32	.020	16B	—	40	4½-6½	800/500	—
	8-351C	250	AF-42	.035	27	.021	6B	6B	12	5-7	700/500	600
	8-351W	250	BF-42	.035	27	.021	10B	10B	11	5-7	700/500	575 [600/500]
	8-351C	300	BF-32	.035	27	.021	6B	6B	16	5-6	800/500	600 [600/500]
	8-428	335	BF-32	.035	32	.020	6B	6B	18	4½-6½	725	675 [675/500]
	8-429	360	BF-42	.035	27/29	.021/.017	6B	6B	16	5-7	700	600
	8-429CJ	370	AF-32	.035	27/29	.021/.017	10B	10B	16	6½-8½	700 [700/500]	650
	8-429	BOSS	AF-32	.035	27/29	.021/.017	10B	10B	16	6½-8½	650/500	700/500
'71	6-250	145	BRF-82	.034	36	.027/.025	6B	6B	10	4-6	750	600
	8-302	210	BRF-42	.034	27	.021	6B	6B	16	4-6	800/500	575 [600/500]
	8-351C	240	ARF-42	.034	27	.021	6B	6B	12	5-7	700/500	600
	8-351W	240	BRF-42	.034	27	.021	6B	6B	12	5-7	700/500	575 [600/500]
	8-351CJ	280	ARF-42	.034	27	.021	6B	6B	18	5-7	800/500	600
	8-351C	285	ARF-32	.034	27	.021	6B	6B	18	5-7	800/500	600
	8-351	BOSS	ARF-32	.034	27/29	.021/.017	6B	6B	18	4½-5½	800	590
	8-429	360	BRF-42	.034	27/29	.021/.017	4B	4B	16	5-7	700	600 [600/500]
	8-429CJ	370	ARF-42	.034	25	.020	10B	10B	32	4½-6½	700	650 [650/500]
	8-429	SCJ	ARF-42	.034	28	.020	10B	10B	40½	4½-6½	650/500	700/500
'72	6-250	95	BRF-82	.034	37	.027	6B	6B	10(16)	4½-6½	750/500	600/500
	8-302	140	BRF-42	.034	28	.017	6B	6B	16	5½-6½	800/500	575 [600/500]
	8-351C	165	ARF-42	.034	28	.017	6B	6B	12	5½-6½	750/500	575/500⑨
	8-351W	165	BRF-42	.034	28	.017	—	6B	12	5½-6½	—	575 [600/500]

Fairlane, Torino, Montego, Mustang, Cougar

TUNE-UP SPECIFICATIONS, Continued

When analyzing compression test results, look for uniformity among cylinders rather than specific pressures.

	ENGINE		SPARK PLUGS		DISTRIBUTOR		IGNITION TIMING (deg) ▲		VALVES	Fuel	IDLE SPEED (rpm) ▲	
Year	No. Cyl Displacement (cu in.)	hp	Type §	Gap (in.)	Point Dwell* (deg)	Point Gap* (in.)	Man Trans	Auto Trans	Intake Opens ■ (deg) ●	Pump Pressure (psi)	Man Trans	Auto Trans
'72	8-351CJ	266	ARF-42	.034	28	.017⑩	16B	16B⑪	14	5½-6½	1000/500	700/500⑪⑫
	8-351HO	N.A.	ARF-42	.034	28	.020	10B	—	17½	5½-6½	1000/500	—
	8-400	168	ARF-42	.034	28	.017	—	6B	17	4½-5½	—	625/500
	8-429	205	ARF-42	.034	28	.017	—	10B	8	5½-6½	—	600/500
'73	6-250	95	BRF-82	.034	37	.027/.025	6B	6B	16	4½-6½	750/500	600/500
	8-302	140	BRF-42	.034	28	.017	6B	6B	16	5½-6½	800/500	575 [600/500]
	8-351C	165	ARF-42	.034	28	.017	—	6B	12	5½-6½	—	625/500
	8-351W	165	BRF-42	.034	28	.017	—	6B	12	5½-6½	—	575 [600/500]
	8-351CJ	266	ARF-42	.034	28⑬	.017⑩	16B	16B⑪	14	5½-6½	1000/500	800/500⑪
	8-400	168	ARF-42	.034	28	.017	—	6B	17	5½-6½	—	625/500
	8-429	205	ARF-42	.034	28	.017	—	10B	8	5½-6½	—	600/500
'74	8-302	135, 137, 138	BRF-42	.034	28	.017	6B	6B	16⑮	4½-5½	800/500	625/500
	8-351W	154	BRF-42	.034	28	.017	—	6B	15	5½-6½	—	600/500
	8-351C	158, 159	ARF-42	.034	28	.017	—	10B	19.5	5½-6½	—	625/500
	8-351CJ	246	ARF-42	.034	28	.017	—	18B	14	5½-6½	—	800/500
	8-400	168	ARF-42	.044	—	—	—	6B⑭	17	5½-6½	—	625/500
	8-460	200	ARF-52	.044	—	—	—	14B	8	5½-6½	—	650/500

* Where two figures are separated by a slash, the first figure is for engines equipped with dual diaphragm distributors and the second figure is for engines equipped with single diaphragm distributors

▲ See text for procedure

● Figures in parentheses apply to California engines. Figures in brackets are for solenoid equipped vehicles only. In all cases where two figures are separated by a slash, the first is for idle speed with solenoid energized and automatic transmission in Drive, while the second is for idle speed with solenoid disconnected and automatic transmission in Neutral.

■ All figures are in degrees Before Top Dead Center

§ All spark plug listings are Autolite original equipment numbers

① Figure in parentheses applies to thermactor exhaust system

② A/C off

③ Figure is 27 degrees for automatic transmission

④ Figure is .017 for automatic transmission

⑤ Figure is .021 for automatic transmission

⑥ Figure is 29 degrees for automatic transmission

⑦ For air conditioned vehicles, adjust idle speed to 800 rpm with A/C on

⑤ For air conditioned vehicles, adjust idle speed to 600 rpm with A/C on

⑨ Figure is 625/500 for California engines

⑩ Figure is .020 for manual transmission with dual point distributor

⑪ On Cougars with automatic transmission, set ignition timing to 6B and set idle speed to 650 rpm

⑫ Figure is 800/500 for California engines

⑬ Figure is 32°-35° on manual transmission model with dual point distributor with both point sets combined

⑭ 12° BTC for Cougar XR7

⑮ 20° BTC for 302 automatic

B Before Top Dead Center

C Cleveland

CJ Cobra Jet

HO High Output

N.A. Not available

SCJ Super Cobra Jet

W Windsor

— Not applicable

MECHANICAL VALVE LIFTER CLEARANCE

Year	Engine	Intake (Hot) In.	Exhaust (Hot) In.
1967	289 High Performance	.019	.021
1967	427	.025	.025
1969-1970	302 BOSS	.025	.025
1969-1970	429 BOSS	.013 (Cold)	.013 (Cold)
1970-1971	429 SCJ	.019	.019
1971	351 BOSS	.025	.025
1972	351 HO	.025	.025

Fairlane, Falcon, Comet, Maverick, Mustang, Cougar

CAPACITIES

Year	ENGINE No. Cyl. (Cu. In.) Displacement	Engine Crankcase Add 1 Qt For New Filter	TRANSMISSION Pts To Refill After Draining — Manual 3-Speed	Manual 4-Speed	Automatic	Drive Axle (pts)	Gasoline Tank (gals)	COOLING SYSTEM (qts) With Heater	With A/C
'67	FALCON								
	6-170, 200	3.5	2	—	15	2.5	16①	9.5	9.5
	8-289	4	3.5	3.5	17	4	16①	15	15
	COMET, FAIRLANE								
	6-170, 200	3.5	2②	—	15	4	20	9.5	9.5
	8-289	4	3.5	3.5	17	4	20	15	15
	8-390	4	—	3.5	26	5	20	20.5	20.5
	MUSTANG								
	6-200	3.5	2	—	15	2.5	16	9.5	9.5
	8-289	4	3.5	4	17	4	17	15	15
	8-390	4	3.5	4	26	5	16	20.5	20.5
	COUGAR								
	8-289	4	3.5	4	17	4	17	15	15
	8-390	4	3.5	4	26	4	17	15	15
	8-427	5	—	4	—	5	20	19.5	19.5
'68	FALCON								
	6-170, 200	3.5	3.5	—	16	4④	16①	9.5	9.5
	8-289, 302	4	3.5	3.5	18	4	16⑤	15	15
	FAIRLANE								
	6-200	3.5	3.5	—	16	4	20	9.5	9.5
	8-289, 302	4	3.5	3.5	18	4	20	15	15
	8-390, 427, 428	4	3.5	3.5	26	5	20	20.5	20.5
	MUSTANG								
	6-200	3.5	3.5	—	16	2.5	16	9.5	9.5
	MUSTANG, COUGAR								
	8-289,302	4	3.5	4	18	4	16	15	15
	8-390, 427, 428	4	3.5	4	26	5	16	20.5	20.5
	MONTEGO								
	6-200	3.5	3.5	—	16	4	20	9.5	9.5
	8-289, 302	4	3.5	3.5	18	4	20	15	15
	8-390, 427, 428	4	—	3.5	26	5	20	20.5	20.5
'69	FALCON								
	6-170, 200	3.5	3.5	—	16	2.5	16①	9.5	9.5
	8-302	4	3.5	—	18	4	16①	13.5	13.5
	FAIRLANE								
	6-250	3.5	3.5	—	18	4	20	10	10
	8-302	4	3.5	—	—	—	20	—	—
	8-351	4	3.5	4	22	5	20	14.5	16.5
	8-390, 428	4	3.5	4	26	5	20	20	20
	MUSTANG								
	6-200	3.5	3.5	—	16	4	20	9	9
	6-250	3.5	3.5	—	18	4	20	10	10
	8-302, 351	4	3.5	4	18⑥	4⑦	20	13.5	15
	8-390, 428	4	—	4	26	5	20	14.5	16
	MONTEGO								
	6-250	3.5	3.5	—	18	4	20	10	10
	8-302	4	3.5	4	18	4	20	13.5	13.5

Fairlane, Falcon, Comet, Maverick, Mustang, Cougar

CAPACITIES, Continued

Year	ENGINE No. Cyl. (Cu. In.) Displacement	Engine Crankcase Add 1 Qt For New Filter	TRANSMISSION Pts To Refill After Draining Manual 3-Speed	4-Speed	Automatic	Drive Axle (pts)	Gasoline Tank (gals)	COOLING SYSTEM (qts) With Heater	With A/C
'69	COUGAR, MONTEGO								
	8-351	4	3.5	4	22	5	20⑧	14.5	16
	8-390, 428	4	—	4	26	5	20⑧	20	20
'70	FALCON, MAVERICK								
	6-170, 200	3.5	3.5	—	16	2.5	16	9	9
	MAVERICK								
	6-250	3.5	—	—	18	2.5	16	10	10
	FAIRLANE								
	6-250	3.5	3.5	—	18	4	22	11.5	11.5
	FALCON, FAIRLANE								
	8-302	4	3.5	4	18	5	22	15.5	16.5
	FAIRLANE								
	8-351	4	3.5	4	22	5	22	15.5	16.5
	8-429	6⑨	—	4	26	5	22	19.5	19.5
	MUSTANG								
	6-200	3.5	3.5	—	16	2.25	22	9	9
	6-250	3.5	3.5	—	18	4	22	10	10
	8-302	4	3.5	4	18	4	22	13.5	15
	8-351	4	3.5	4	22	5	22	14.5	16
	8-428	4	—	4	26	5	22	19.5	19.5
	MONTEGO								
	6-250	3.5	3.5	—	18	4	22	11.5	11.5
	8-302	3.5	3.5	—	18	4	22	15	15
	MONTEGO, COUGAR								
	8-351	4	3.5	4	22	4	22	15.5	16
	8-429, 428	4⑨	—	4	26	5	22	19.5	19.5
'71	MAVERICK, COMET								
	6-170, 200	3.5	3.5	—	16	2.5	15	9	9
	6-250	3.5	3.5	—	18	2.5	15	9.5	9.5
	8-302	4	3.5	—	18	4	15	13.5	14
	TORINO, MONTEGO								
	6-250	3.5	3.5	—	18	4	20⑩	11	11
	8-302	4	3.5	—	18	4	20⑩	15	15.5
	8-351	4	3.5	4	22	5	20⑩	15.5	16.5
	8-429	6⑨	—	4	26	5	20⑩	19.5	19.5
	MUSTANG								
	6-250	3.5	3.5	—	18	4	20	11	11
	8-302	4	3.5	—	18	4	20	15	15.5
	MUSTANG, COUGAR								
	8-351	4	3.5	4	22	5	20	15.5	16
	8-429	6⑨	—	4	26	5	20	19.5	19.5
'72	MAVERICK, COMET								
	6-170, 200	3.5	3.5	—	16	4	15	9	9
	6-250	3.5	3.5	—	18	4	15	9.5	10.5
	8-302	4	3.5	—	18	4	15	13.5	14.5

Fairlane, Falcon, Comet, Maverick, Mustang, Cougar

CAPACITIES, Continued

Year	ENGINE No. Cyl. (Cu. In.) Displacement	Engine Crankcase Add 1 Qt For New Filter	TRANSMISSION Pts To Refill After Draining Manual 3-Speed	Manual 4-Speed	Automatic	Drive Axle (pts)	Gasoline Tank (gals)	COOLING SYSTEM (qts) With Heater	With A/C
'72	TORINO, MONTEGO								
	6-250	3.5	3.5	—	18	4	22.5⑩	11.5	11.5
	8-302	4	3.5	—	18	4	22.5⑩	15	15
	8-351	4	—	4	20.5⑪	4	22.5⑩	15.5	16
	8-400	4	—	—	26	4	22.5⑩	17.5	17.5
	8-429	4	—	—	26	5	22.5	19	19
	MUSTANG								
	6-250	3.5	3.5	—	18	4	19.5	11	11
	8-302	4	3.5	—	18	4	19.5	15	15.5
	MUSTANG, COUGAR								
	8-351	4	3.5	4	22⑫	5	19.5	16	16
'73	MAVERICK, COMET								
	6-200	3.5	3.5	—	16	4	15	9	9
	6-250	3.5	3.5	—	18	4	15	9.5	10.5
	8-302	4	3.5	—	18	4	15	13.5	14.5
	TORINO, MONTEGO								
	6-250	3.5	3.5	—	18	4	22.5⑩	11.5	11.5
	8-302	4	3.5	—	18	4	22.5⑩	15	15
	8-351	4	—	4	20.5⑪	4	22.5⑩	15.5	16
	8-400	4	—	—	26	4	22.5⑩	17.5	17.5
	8-429	4	—	—	26	5	22.5	19	19
	MUSTANG								
	6-250	3.5	3.5	—	18	4	19.5	11	11
	8-302	4	3.5	—	18	4	19.5	15	15.5
	MUSTANG, COUGAR								
	8-351	4	—	4	22⑫	5	19.5	16	16
'74	MAVERICK, COMET								
	6-200	4	3.5	—	16	4	15	9.0	9.0
	6-250	4	3.5	—	18	4	15	9.7	9.7
	8-302	4	3.5	—	18	4	15	13.4	14.2
	TORINO, MONTEGO								
	8-302	4	3.5	—	⑬	4	26.5⑰	15.2	15.7
	TORINO, MONTEGO, COUGAR								
	8-351	4	—	—	⑭	4⑯	26.5⑰	⑱	⑲
	8-400	4	—	—	25⑮	5	26.5⑰	17.7	18.4
	8-460	6	—	—	25⑮	5	26.5⑰	18.8	19.5

① 20 gals on station wagon
② 3.5 pts on Fairlane
④ 2 pts with 170 cu. in. engine
⑤ 20 gals on station wagon
⑥ 22 pts with 351 engine
⑦ 5 pts with 351 engine
⑧ 17 gals on Cougar
⑨ 429 4 bbl—4 qts
428, 429 CJ, SCJ—6 qts
add 1 qt if equipped with oil cooler
⑩ Less 2 gals—station wagon, Ranchero
⑪ 26 pts for 351 CJ
⑫ Less 1 pt with 4 bbl
⑬ C4—18 pts; FMX—22 pts
⑭ 351 2V with C-4—20 pts; 351-2V with FMX—22pts; 351 2V with C-6—25 pts; 351-4V (C6)—21 pts
⑮ Cougar—21 pts
⑯ Cougar—5 pts
⑰ Station wagon—21.5 gallons
⑱ 351 W 2V—16.3 qts
351 C 2V—15.8 qts
351 C 4V—15.7 qts
⑲ 351 W 2V—16.8 qts
351 C 2V—16.6 qts
351 C 4V—16.3 qts
— Not applicable

TORQUE SPECIFICATIONS

All readings in ft lbs

Year	Engine Displacement (cu in.)	Cylinder Head Bolts*	Rod Bearing Bolts	Main Bearing Bolts	Crankshaft Pulley Bolt	Flywheel to Crankshaft Bolts	Manifold Intake	Manifold Exhaust
'67-'68	6	70-75	19-24	60-70	85-100	75-85	None	13-18
	8-260, 289, 302	65-70	19-24①	60-70	70-90	75-85	20-22	15-20
	8-390, 428	80-90	40-45	95-105	70-90	75-85	32-35	18-24
	8-427	100-110	53-58	95-105	70-90	75-85	32-35	18-24
'69	6	70-75	19-24	60-70	85-100	75-85	—	13-18
	8-302	65-72	19-24	60-70	70-90	75-85	23-25	12-16
	8-351W	95-100	40-45	95-105	70-90	75-85	23-25	18-24
	8-390	80-90	40-45	95-105	70-90	75-85	32-35	18-24
	8-428	80-90	53-58	95-105	70-90	75-85	32-35	18-24
'70-'74	6	70-75	19-24③	60-70	85-100	75-85	—	13-18
	8-302	65-72	19-24④	60-70⑤	70-90	75-85	23-25	12-16
	8-351	95-100②	40-45⑦	95-105⑧	70-90	75-85	23-25 (5/16) 28-32 (3/8) 6-9 (1/4)	12-22
	8-400	95-105⑨	40-45	95-105 (1/2 in.-13) 35-45 (3/8 in.-16)	70-90	75-85	21-25 (5/16) 27-33 (3/8) 6-9 (1/4)	12-16
	8-428	80-90	53-58	95-105	70-90	75-85	32-35	18-24
	8-429, 460	130-140	40-45	95-105⑥	70-90	75-85	25-30	28-33
	8-429 Boss	90-95	85-90	70-80	70-90	75-85	25-30	28-33

① 289 High perf. 40-45
② 351 Boss and HO three steps—40, 80, 120 ft. lbs.
③ 250—21-26
④ 302 Boss—40-45
⑤ 302 Boss—outer bolts 35-40
⑥ 7/16 in. bolts—70-80
⑦ 351 Boss and HO—43-48 ft. lbs.
⑧ 3/8 in. bolts—34-45 ft. lbs.
⑨ Three steps—55, 75, then maximum figure
* Tighten cylinder head bolts in three steps

WHEEL ALIGNMENT SPECIFICATIONS

Year	Model	Caster Range (deg)	Caster Pref Setting (deg)	Camber Range (deg)	Camber Pref Setting (deg)	Toe-in	Steering Axis Inclin.	Wheel Pivot Ratio (deg) Inner Wheel	Wheel Pivot Ratio (deg) Wheel Outer
'67	Comet, Falcon, Fairlane	1N to 0	1/2N	1/4N to 3/4P	1/4P	3/16 to 5/16	7 1/2	20	17 3/4
	Cougar, Mustang	1/4N to 3/4P	1/4P	1/2P to 1 1/2P	1P	1/8 to 1/4	6 3/4	20	18 3/4
'68	Comet, Falcon②, Fairlane, Montego	1 1/2N to 1/2P	1/2N	1/2N to 1P	1/4P	3/16 to 5/16	7	20	18 1/8
	Cougar & Mustang	3/4N to 1 1/4P	1/4P	1/4P to 1 3/4P	1P	3/16 to 5/16	6 3/4	20	18 3/4
'69	Falcon, Torino, Montego	1 3/4N to 1/4P	3/4N	1/2N to 1P	1/4P	1/8 to 1/4	7	20	18 1/8
	Cougar & Mustang	3/4N to 1 1/4P	1/4P	1/4P to 1 3/4P	3/4P	1/8 to 1/4	6 3/4	20	18 3/4
'70-'71	Montego, Falcon, Torino	1 1/4N to 1/4N	3/4N	1/2N to 1P	1/4P	1/8 to 3/8	7 2/3②	20	③
	Cougar & Mustang	1N to 1P	0	0 to 1 1/2P⑤	1P	1/16 to 5/16	6 3/4	20	18 2/3
	Maverick, Comet	1 1/2N to 1/2P	1/2N	1/2N to 1/4P	1/4P	1/16 to 5/16	6 3/4	20	18 3/4④
'72	Torino, Montego	1 1/4N to 2 3/4P	3/4P	1/4N to 1 3/4P	3/4P	1/16 to 7/16	7 2/3	20	17 3/4
	Mustang, Cougar	2N to 2P	0	1/2N to 1 1/2P	1/2P	1/16 to 3/8	6 3/4	20	17 3/4
	Maverick, Comet	2 1/2N to 1 1/2P	1/2N	3/4N to 1 1/4P	1/4P	1/16 to 3/8	6 3/4	20	18 1/2④
'73	Torino, Montego	3/4N to 2 1/4P	3/4P	1/4N to 1 3/4P	3/4P	3/16 to 9/16	7 2/3	20	17.73
	Mustang, Cougar	2N to 2P	0	1/2N to 1 1/2P	1/2P	1/16 to 3/8	6 3/4	20	17.72
	Maverick, Comet	2 1/2N to 1 1/2P	1/2N	3/4N to 1 1/4P	1/4P	1/16 to 3/8	6 3/4	20	18.44④
'74	Torino, Montego, Cougar	1/2P to 3 1/2P	2P	⑥	⑦	0 to 3/8	9	20	17.73
	Maverick, Comet	2 1/2N to 1/2P	1/2N	3/4N to 1 1/4P	1/4P	1/16 to 3/8	6 3/4	20	18.44④

② Falcon—6 2/3
③ Falcon—18°6′; others with manual steering—17°19′; power steering—17°49′
④ 18.2° for power steering.
⑤ 1970 models—1/4P to 1 3/4P
N Negative P Positive
⑥ Left—3/8N to 1 5/8P
Right—7/8N to 1 1/8P
⑦ Left—5/8P
Right—1/8P

PISTON CLEARANCE

Year	Engine	Piston-to-Bore Minimum	Clearance (in.) Maximum
'67-'69	170, 200, 250	0.0014	0.0020
'67-'74	289, 302, 351W	0.0018	0.0026
'67-'69	390, 428	0.0015	0.0023
'67	427 (solid lifter)	0.0042	0.0066
'68	427 (hydraulic lifter)	0.0030	0.0038
'70-'74	170, 200, 250	0.0013	0.0021
'70-'74	351C, 400, 429, 460	0.0014	0.0022
'70	429CJ, 429SCJ	0.0030	0.0038
'71	429CJ, 429SCJ	0.0042	0.0050
'72	351HO (CJ)	0.0034	0.0042

VALVE SPECIFICATIONS

Year	Engine No. Cyl. Displacement (cu in.)	Seat Angle (deg)	Face Angle (deg)	Spring Test Pressure (lbs @ in.)	Spring Installed Height (in.)	STEM TO GUIDE Clearance (in.)		STEM Diameter (in.)	
						Intake	Exhaust	Intake	Exhaust
'67	6-170, 200	45	44	150 @ 1.22	1 9/32	.0008-.0025	.0010-.0027	.3104	.3102
	8-289	45	44	180 @ 1.23	1 21/32	.0010-.0027	.0010-.0027	.3420	.3420
	8-289①	45	44	247 @ 1.31	1 25/32	.0010-.0027	.0010-.0027	.3420	.3420
	8-390	45	44	220 @ 1.38	1 13/16	.0010-.0024	.0010-.0024	.3715	.3715
	8-390②	45	44	268 @ 1.31	1 13/16	.0010-.0024	.0010-.0024	.3715	.3715
	8-427	③	④	268 @ 1.31	1 13/16	.0010-.0024	.0020-.0034	.3715	.3705
'68	6-170, 200	45	44	150 @ 1.22	1 9/32	.0008-.0025	.0010-.0027	.3104	.3102
	8-289, 302	45	44	180 @ 1.23	1 21/32	.0010-.0027	.0015-.0032	.3420	.3415
	8-390	45	44	220 @ 1.38	1 13/16	.0010-.0024	.0015-.0032	.3715	.3710
	8-390②	45	44	268 @ 1.31	1 13/16	.0010-.0024	.0015-.0032	.3715	.3710
	8-427	③	④	268 @ 1.31	1 13/16	.0010-.0024	.0020-.0034	.3715	.3705
'69	6-170, 200	45	44	150 @ 1.22	1 9/32	.0008-.0025	.0010-.0027	.3104	.3102
	6-250	45	44	150 @ 1.22	1 9/32	.0008-.0025	.0010-.0027	.3104	.3102
	8-302	45	44	180 @ 1.23	1 21/32	.0010-.0027	.0015-.0032	.3420	.3415
	8-351	45	44	215 @ 1.34	1 25/32	.0010-.0027	.0015-.0032	.3420	.3415
	8-390	45	44	220 @ 1.38	1 13/16	.0010-.0027	.0015-.0032	.3715	.3710
	8-428	③	④	268 @ 1.31	1 13/16	.0010-.0027	.0015-.0032	.3715	.3710
'70	6-170, 200	45	44	150 @ 1.22	1 9/32	.0008-.0025	.0010-.0027	.3104	.3102
	6-250	45	44	150 @ 1.22	1 9/32	.0008-.0025	.0010-.0027	.3104	.3102
	8-302	45	44	180 @ 1.23	1 21/32	.0010-.0027	.0010-.0027	.3420	.3415
	8-302⑤	45	44	315 @ 1.31	1 13/16	.0010-.0027	.0015-.0032	.3420	.3415
	8-351⑥	45	44	215 @ 1.34	1 25/32	.0010-.0027	.0010-.0027	.3420	.3415
	8-351⑦	45	44	209 @ 1.42	1 13/16	.0010-.0027	.0015-.0032	.3420	.3415
	8-351⑧	45	44	285 @ 1.31	1 13/16	.0010-.0027	.0015-.0032	.3420	.3415
	8-428	③	④	265 @ 1.31	1 13/16	.0015-.0032	.0015-.0032	.3715	.3710
	8-429	45	44	253 @ 1.33	1 13/16	.0010-.0027	.0010-.0027	.3420	.3420
	8-429⑤	③	④	315 @ 1.31	1 13/16	.0010-.0024	.0020-.0034	.3715	.3705
	8-429⑨	③	④	306 @ 1.36	1 13/16	.0010-.0024	.0020-.0034	.3420	.3417
'71	6-170, 200	45	44	150 @ 1.22	1 9/32	.0008-.0025	.0010-.0027	.3104	.3102
	6-250	45	44	150 @ 1.22	1 9/32	.0008-.0025	.0010-.0027	.3104	.3102
	8-302	45	44	180 @ 1.23	1 21/32	.0010-.0027	.0015-.0032	.3420	.3415
	8-302⑤	45	44	315 @ 1.31	1 13/16	.0010-.0027	.0015-.0032	.3420	.3415
	8-351⑥	45	44	215 @ 1.34	1 25/32	.0010-.0027	.0015-.0032	.3420	.3415
	8-351⑦	45	44	210 @ 1.42	1 13/16	.0010-.0027	.0015-.0032	.3420	.3415
	8-351⑧	45	44	285 @ 1.31	1 13/16	.0010-.0027	.0015-.0032	.3420	.3415
	8-429	45	45	229 @ 1.33	1 13/16	.0010-.0027	.0010-.0027	.3420	.3420

VALVE SPECIFICATIONS

Year	Engine No. Cyl. Displacement (cu in.)	Seat Angle (deg)	Face Angle (deg)	Spring Test Pressure (lbs @ in.)	Spring Installed Height (in.)	STEM TO GUIDE Clearance (in.) Intake	Exhaust	STEM Diameter (in.) Intake	Exhaust
'72	6-170, 200	45	44	150 @ 1.22	1 19/32	.0008-.0025	.0010-.0027	.3104	.3102
	6-250	45	44	150 @ 1.22	1 19/32	.0008-.0025	.0010-.0027	.3104	.3102
	8-302	45	44	200 @ 1.23	1 11/16	.0010-.0027	.0015-.0032	.3420	.3415
	8-351⑥	45	44	200 @ 1.34	1 25/32	.0010-.0027	.0015-.0032	.3420	.3415
	8-351⑦	45	44	210 @ 1.42	1 13/16	.0010-.0027	.0015-.0032	.3420	.3415
	8-351⑧	45	44	285 @ 1.23	1 13/16	.0010-.0027	.0015-.0032	.3420	.3415
	8-351⑤	45	44	315 @ 1.23	1 13/16	.0010-.0027	.0015-.0032	.3420	.3415
	8-400	45	44	226 @ 1.39	1 13/16	.0010-.0027	.0015-.0032	.3420	.3415
	8-429	45	45	229 @ 1.33	1 13/16	.0010-.0027	.0010-.0027	.3420	.3420
'73-	6-200	45	44	150 @ 1.22	1 19/32	.0008-.0025	.0010-.0027	.3104	.3102
'74	6-250	45	44	150 @ 1.22	1 19/32	.0008-.0025	.0010-.0027	.3104	.3102
	8-302	45	44	200 @ 1.23	1 11/16	.0010-.0027	.0015-.0032	.3420	.3415
	8-351⑥	45	44	200 @ 1.34	1 25/32	.0010-.0027	.0015-.0032	.3420	.3415
	8-351⑦	45	44	210 @ 1.42	1 13/16	.0010-.0027	.0015-.0032	.3420	.3415
	8-351⑧	45	44	285 @ 1.23	1 13/16	.0010-.0027	.0015-.0032	.3420	.3415
	8-400	45	44	226 @ 1.39	1 13/16	.0010-.0027	.0015-.0032	.3420	.3415
	8-429	45	45	229 @ 1.33	1 13/16	.0010-.0027	.0010-.0027	.3420	.3420
	8-460	45	45	253 @ 1.33	1 13/16	.0010-.0027	.0015-.0032	.3420	.3415

① Hi-Performance
② GT
③ Intake valve seat angle 30°
Exhaust valve seat angle 45°
④ Intake valve face angle 29°
Exhaust valve face angle 44°
⑤ Boss
⑥ Windsor heads
⑦ Cleveland 2 bbl
⑧ Cleveland 4 bbl
⑨ Cobra Jet

CRANKSHAFT AND CONNECTING ROD SPECIFICATIONS

All measurements are given in in.

Year	Engine Displace. (cu in.)	CRANKSHAFT Main Brg. Journal Dia	Main Brg. Oil Clearance	Shaft End-Play	Thrust on No.	CONNECTING ROD Journal Diameter	Oil Clearance	Side Clearance
'67-'74	6-170	2.2482-2.2490	.0005-.0022	.004-.008	3	2.1232-2.1240	.0008-.0024	.003-.010
	6-200	2.2482-2.2490	.0005-.0022	.004-.008	5	2.1232-2.1240	.0008-.0024	.003-.010
	6-250	2.3982-2.3990	.0005-.0022	.004-.008	5	2.1232-2.1240	.0008-.0024	.003-.010
	8-302, 289	2.2482-2.2490	.0005-.0024⑤	.004-.008	3	2.1228-2.1236①	.0008-.0026②	.010-.020
	8-351W	2.2994-3.0002	.0013-.0030	.004-.008	3	2.3103-2.3111	.0008-.0026	.010-.020
	8-351C	2.7484-2.7492	.0009-.0026⑥	.004-.010	3	2.3103-2.3111	.0008-.0026⑦	.010-.020
	8-390	2.7484-2.7492	.0008-.0020	.004-.010	3	2.4380-2.4388	.0008-.0030	.010-.020
	8-400	2.9994-3.0002	.0011-.0028	.004-.008	3	2.3103-2.3111	.0011-.0026	.010-.020
	8-427	2.7484-2.7492	.0010-.0031	.004-.010	3	2.4380-2.4388	.0013-.0032	.010-.020
	8-428	2.7484-2.7492	.0010-.0020	.004-.010	3	2.4380-2.4388	.0010-.0030	.010-.020
	8-429, 460	2.9994-3.0002	.0010-.0020③⑧	.004-.008	3	2.4992-2.5000	.0008-.0028④	.010-.020

① Boss 302—2.1222-2.1230
② Boss 302—.0015-.0025
③ Boss 429—.0010-.0025
④ Boss 429—.0015-.0025
⑤ 302—.001-.0018 No. 1 bearing only
⑥ Boss 351 and 351 HO—.0011-.0015
⑦ Boss 351 and 351 HO—.0011-.0015
⑧ No. 1—.0010-.0015

RING GAP

Year	Engine	Top Compression	Bottom Compression
'67-'74	6-170, 200, 250 8-289, 302, 351, 400, 428, 429, 460	.010-.020	.010-.020
'67-'68	8-390	.010-.031	.010-.020
'67	8-427	.010-.031	.010-.020
'68	8-427	.018-.028	.015-.025

Year	Engine	Oil Control
'67-'74	6-170, 200, 250	.015-.055
'67-'68	8-289	.015-.069
'67-'68	8-390	.015-.066
'67	8-289, 427	.015-.066
'68-'71	8-302, 351	.015-.069
'68	8-427	.015-.055
'69	8-390	.015-.055
'69-'71	8-428, 429	.010-.035
'72-'74	8-302, 351	.015-.055①
'72-'74	8-400	.015-.069
'72-'74	8- 429, 460	.015-.055

① .015-.069 in Cleveland built engine

RING SIDE CLEARANCE

Year	Engine	Top Compression	Bottom Compression
'67	6-200, 8-289	.0019-.0036	.002-.004
'67	8-390	.002-.004	.002-.004
'67	6-170	.0019-.0036	.002-.004
'67	8-427	.0024-.0041	.002-.004
'68-'74	All engines	002-.004	.002-.004

Year	Engine	Oil Control
'67-'74	All engines	Snug

ALTERNATOR AND REGULATOR SPECIFICATIONS

	ALTERNATOR			REGULATOR						
					Field Relay			Regulator		
Year	Part No. or Manufacturer	Field Current @ 12 V	Output (amps)	Part No. or Manufacturer	Air Gap (in.)	Point Gap (in.)	Volts to Close	Air Gap (in.)	Point Gap (in.)	Volts @ 75°
'67-'69	Autolite	2.8-3.3	38	Autolite	—	—	2.5	.049-.056	.017-.022	13.8-14.4
	Autolite	2.9-3.1	42	Autolite	.012-.022	.015-.022	2.5	.049-.056	.017-.022	13.8-14.4
	Autolite	2.9	45	Autolite	.015	—	2.5-4	.052	.019	13.8-14.6
	Autolite	2.9	55	Autolite	.015	—	2.5-4	.052	.019	13.8-14.6
	Leece-Neville	2.9	53	Leece-Neville	.012	.025	7	.047	.019	14.1-14.9
'70	Autolite Purple	2.4	38	Autolite	—	—	2-4.2	—	—	13.5-15.3
	Autolite Orange	2.9	42	Autolite	—	—	2-4.2	—	—	13.5-15.3
	Autolite Red	2.9	55	Autolite	—	—	2-4.2	—	—	13.5-15.3
	Autolite Green	2.9	61	Autolite	—	—	2-4.2	—	—	13.5-15.3
	Autolite Black	2.9	65	Autolite	—	—	2-4.2	—	—	13.5-15.3
'71	Autolite Purple	2.4	38	Autolite	—	—	2.5-4	—	—	13.5-15.3
	Autolite Orange	2.9	42	Autolite	—	—	2.5-4	—	—	13.5-15.3
	Autolite Red	2.9	55	Autolite	—	—	2.5-4	—	—	13.5-15.3
	Autolite Green	2.9	61	Autolite	—	—	2.5-4	—	—	13.5-15.3
	Autolite Black	2.9	65	Autolite	—	—	2.5-4	—	—	13.5-15.3
'72-'74	Motorcraft Purple	2.4	38	Motorcraft	—	—	2.5-4	—	—	13.5-15.4
	Motorcraft Orange	2.9	42	Motorcraft	—	—	2.5-4	—	—	13.5-15.4
	Motorcraft Red	2.9	55	Motorcraft	—	—	2.5-4	—	—	13.5-15.4
	Motorcraft Green	2.9	61	Motorcraft	—	—	2.5-4	—	—	13.5-15.4
	Motorcraft Black	2.9	65	Motorcraft	—	—	2.5-4	—	—	13.5-15.4

— Not Applicable

BRAKE SPECIFICATIONS

Year	Model	Master Cylinder Disc	Master Cylinder Drum	Wheel Cylinder Front Disc	Wheel Cylinder Front Drum	Wheel Cylinder Rear	Brake Disc or Drum Diameter Front Disc	Brake Disc or Drum Diameter Front Drum	Brake Disc or Drum Diameter Rear
'67-'68	6 Falcon Sedan	—	1.0	—	1 1/16	27/32	—	9.0	9.0
	All Falcon and Comet Wag.	.9375①	1.0	—	1 3/32	15/16	11.3	10.0	10.0
	Fairlane Wag.	.9375①	1.0	2.38	1 3/32	15/16	11.3	10.0	10.0
	8 Falcon Sed., 6 Montego, All Fairlane and Comet Sed.	.9375①	1.0	2.38	1 1/8	29/32	11.3	10.0	10.0
	6 Mustang	1.0	1.0	2.38	1 1/16	27/32	—	10.0	10.0
	8 Mustang	1.0	1.0	2.38	1 1/8	7/8	11.3	10.0	10.0
	Cougar (289, 302)	1.0	1.0	2.38	1 1/8	7/8	11.4	—	10.0
	Cougar (390, 427)	1.0	1.0	2.38	1 3/32	13/16	11.4	—	10.0
	8 Montego	.9375①	1.0	2.38	1 3/32	7/8	—	10.0	10.0
'69	6 Falcon (200 cu in.)	.9375①	1.0	2.38	1 1/16	27/32	11.3	9.0	9.0
	6 Mustang	—	1.0	—	1 1/16	27/32	—	9.0	9.0
	Falcon and Fairlane Sta. Wag.	.9375①	1.0	2.38	1 3/32	15/16	11.3	10.0	10.0
	Falcon exc. 6 cyl. 200 and Sta. Wag., Fairlane 250 and 302 exc. Sta. Wag. Mustang V8 302	.9375①	1.0	2.38	1 1/8	7/8	11.3	10.0	10.0
	Fairlane and Montego conv. and pass. with 351, 390, and All Cougar, and all 8 Mustang exc. 302	.9375①	1.0	2.38	1 3/32	7/8	11.3	10.0	10.0
'70	6 Falcon, Maverick, Mustang	—	1.0	—	1 1/16	27/32	—	9.0	9.0
	All Cougar	1.0	1.0	2.38	1 1/8	29/32	11.3	10.0	10.0
	Falcon, Montego, Torino Sta. Wag.	.9375①③	1.0	2.38	1 1/8	31/32	11.3	10.0	10.0
	All Cougar, 8 Falcon Sed., Torino and Montego Sed.	.9375①③	1.0	2.38	1 1/8	29/32	11.3	10.0	10.0
	Mustang 8	1.0	1.0	2.38	1 1/8	7/8④	11.3	10.0	10.0
'71	Cougar	1.0	1.0	2.38	1 1/8	29/32	11.3	10.0	10.0
	6 Mustang	—	1.0	—	1 1/8	29/32	—	9.0	10.0
	8 Mustang	1.0	1.0	2.38	1 1/8	7/8	11.3	10.0	10.0
	6 Maverick	—	1.0	—	1 1/16	27/32	—	9.0	9.0
	8 Maverick	—	1.0	—	1 1/8	7/8	—	10.0	10.0
	6 Comet	—	1.0	—	1 1/16	27/32	—	10.0	10.0
	8 Comet	—	1.0	—	1 1/8	7/8	—	10.0	10.0
	Montego and Torino Sed.	.9375①	1.0	2.38	1 1/8	29/32	11.3	10.0	10.0
	Montego and Torino Sta. Wag.	.9375①	1.0	2.38	1 1/8	31/32	11.3	10.0	10.0
'72-'73	Cougar	1.0⑨	1.0	2.38	1 1/8	29/32⑧	11.3	10.0	10.0
	6 Comet⑥	—	1.0	—	1 1/8	27/32	—	9.0④	9.0④
	8 Comet⑥ (10 in.)	—	1.0	—	1 1/8	27/32	—	10.0	10.0
	Montego, Torino	1.0	1.0	3.10	—	1.0	10.72	—	10.0⑦
	Mustang	1.0⑨	1.0	2.38	1 1/8	7/8⑤	11.3	10.0	10.0
	Maverick⑥	—	1.0	—	1 1/8	27/32	—	9.0④	9.0④
'74	Maverick, Comet	.9380	.9380	2.60	1.125	0.843	11.03	10.0	10.0
	Torino, Montego, Cougar	1.0	1.0	3.10	—	1.0	10.72	—	10.0⑦

① Also applies to all power brakes
③ Torino and Montego only
④ 10″ brakes required for 1972 250 1-V cars equipped with optional D70-14 or DR78-14 tires, and all 1973 models
⑤ 29/32″ on all 1972 V8 equipped cars, and 27/32″ on all 1973 models
⑥ 10″ on 1972 302 V8 equipped cars, and on all 1973 models
⑦ 11″ on Station Wagons with 351, 400 or 429 V8
⑧ 27/32″ all 1973
⑨ .9375 in 1973
— Not applicable

NOTE: 1967-73 Mustang models are covered in this section. Refer to the "Pinto and Mustang II" car section for coverage of 1974 Mustang II models.

CHARGING SYSTEM

All Ford cars from 1967 to the present have used alternating current (AC) charging systems. This system makes use of an AC generator or alternator, a voltage regulator, a charge indicator or ammeter, and, of course, the battery.

Mechanical energy is supplied to the alternator via a drive belt. Attached to the belt-driven pulley is a field coil or rotor which revolves within the alternator housing, producing a magnetic field of alternating current. This alternating current is then converted into usable direct current (DC) by a diode rectifier. The output of the alternator should be sufficient to supply power to the electrical system and recharge the battery. The voltage regulator controls the output of the alternator so that adequate current is supplied without damage to electrical components.

Charging system troubleshooting and repair procedures can be found in the Unit Repair Section under Charging and Starting Systems.

Fuse Link

Since 1970, all Ford products have incorporated a fuse link in the charging system. The fuse link is a short length of insulated wire, several gauge sizes smaller than the system it protects. The fuse link blows out if a booster battery is hooked into the system incorrectly, or if a component of the electrical system is shorted to ground. When the fuse link blows, it leaves an open circuit in the charging system and the alternator will not charge the battery. A blown fuse link can be identified by bare wire ends or bubbled insulation. It is located in the engine wire harness on or near the starter relay and is marked FUSE LINK.

AC Generator (Alternator)

The AC generator is covered in the Unit Repair Section.

Caution Since the AC generator and regulator are designed for use on only one polarity system, the following precautions must be observed:

1. The polarity of the battery, generator and regulator must be matched and considered before making any electrical connections in the system.
2. When connecting a booster battery, be sure to join the negative battery terminals together and the positive battery terminals together.
3. When connecting a charger to the battery, connect the charger positive lead to the battery positive terminal. Connect the charger negative lead to the battery negative terminal.
4. Never operate the AC generator on open circuit. Be sure that all connections in the circuit are clean and tight.
5. Do not short across or ground any of the terminals on the AC generator.
6. Do not attempt to polarize the AC generator.
7. Do not use test lamps of more than 12 volts for checking diode continuity.
8. Avoid long soldering times when replacing diodes or transistors. Prolonged heat is damaging to these units.
9. Disconnect the battery ground terminal when servicing any AC system. This will prevent the possibility of accidental reversing of polarity.

Alternator R & R

1. Disconnect the battery ground cable.
2. Loosen the alternator mounting bolts and remove the adjustment arm to alternator attaching bolt. Disengage the alternator belt.
3. Remove the electrical connectors from the alternator and remove the alternator. On some models it is necessary to remove the alternator mounting bolts and the alternator wiring ground bolt from engine to gain access to the electrical connectors.
4. Reverse above procedure to reinstall.

Voltage Regulator R & R

1. Disconnect the negative battery cable.
2. Remove the regulator mounting screws.
3. Remove the cable quick-disconnect from the old regulator and attach to the new regulator.
4. Place the mounting bracket for the radio suppression capacitor over the hole for the lower regulator's mounting screw and install the screws.
5. Connect the negative battery cable.
6. Test the system for proper voltage regulation.

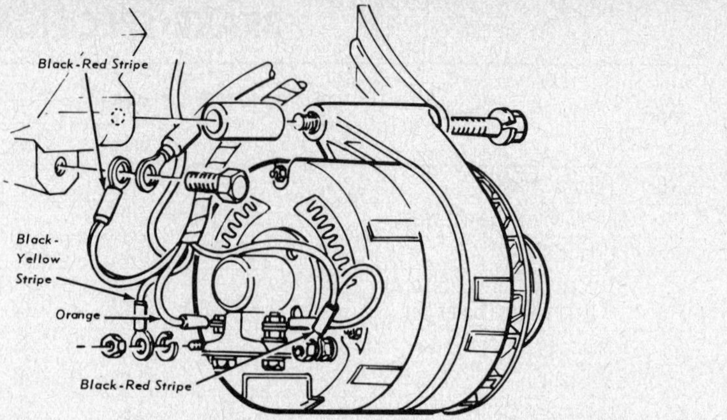

Black-Red Stripe
Black-Yellow Stripe
Orange
Black-Red Stripe

Typical alternator mounting
(© Ford Motor Co)

STARTING SYSTEM

The starter is a four-brush, series-parallel wound unit. The circuit is completed by means of a relay controlled switch which is part of the ignition switch.

Starting system troubleshooting and repair procedures can be found in the Unit Repair Section.

All models, except 1970-74 Torinos, Montegos, Mustangs, and Cougars with the 429 or 460 V8, have a started with a self-contained engagement mechanism. The 429 and 460 V8 engined models use a starter to which is mounted an outboard solenoid. There is no difference in procedures for removing or installing these two types of starters.

Starter R & R

Due to interference of the exhaust inlet pipe on some models, the steering idler arm must be lowered to provide clearance for starter removal.

1. Disconnect the starter cable at the starter terminal, remove the flywheel housing to starter retaining screws. Remove the starter assembly and the rubber dust ring.
2. Position the rubber dust ring on the flywheel housing.
3. Position the starter assembly to the flywheel housing, and begin on the starter retaining screws. On a car with an automatic transmission, the transmission dipstick tube bracket is mounted under the starter side mounting

bolt. Snug all bolts, then tighten to 15 ft. lbs., tightening the middle bolt first.

NOTE: Intermittent starter operation on solenoid starter motor equipped 429 and 460 V8s may be due to the loosening of screws and terminals on the solenoid switch assembly. To remedy this, apply a small amount of Loctite® TL-290 or, its equivalent, as in the illustration.

Starter Drive R & R

Positive Engagement Starters

1. After removing the starter from the engine, loosen and remove the brush cover band and the cover of the starter drive plunger lever.
2. Loosen the thru-bolts enough to facilitate the removal of the drive end housing and plunger lever return spring.
3. Some drive end housings are equipped with needle bearings. If the starter is so equipped, and you are not replacing the bearings, insert a dummy shaft through the housing to prevent the loss of any of the bearing needles.
4. Remove the retaining pivot pin and starter drive plunger lever.
5. Remove the stop-ring and retainer from the end of the armature shaft. Remove the drive gear assembly.
6. Apply a thin coat of white grease to the splines of the armature shaft. Install the drive gear assembly on the armature shaft and also install a new stop-ring.
7. Position the starter gear plunger lever on the starter frame and install the pivot pin. Check to see that the plunger lever properly engages the starter drive assembly.
8. Install a new stop-ring retainer. Remove the dummy shaft from the drive end housing and lightly grease the needle bearings, if so equipped. Position the starter drive plunger lever's return spring and the drive end housing to the starter frame.
9. Tighten the thru-bolts to 55–75 inch pounds (in. lbs).
10. Position the plunger lever cover and brush cover band, with its gasket, on the starter. Tighten the brush cover band retaining screw.

Solenoid-Actuated Starters

See the "Unit Repair Section."

IGNITION SYSTEM

All pre-1974 compact and intermediate Ford cars have used a conventional contact breaker ignition system, consisting of a distributor containing the points and condenser, a coil, and the high voltage wiring to the spark plugs.

There are three different types of distributor used on 1967 models, the vacuum advance, as used with 6-cylinder engines, the dual advance distributor, as used with the V8 standard production engines and the centrifugal advance distributor, used on some of the high performance engines.

In 1968 all models adopted the dual advance distributor to provide more accurately timed ignition and cleaner, smog-free exhaust. Some of these distributors have dual diaphragm vacuum advance mechanisms. These have two vacuum lines to the distributor bellows, one to advance the timing during high speed road use, and one to retard the timing at idle.

All 1973-74 models use a single diaphragm vacuum advance unit on the distributor.

Beginning in 1974, Ford is utilizing a solid state of "breakerless" ignition system on all 200 cu in and larger engines in the state of California, and on all 400 and 460 cu in V8s nationwide. This system is unique in

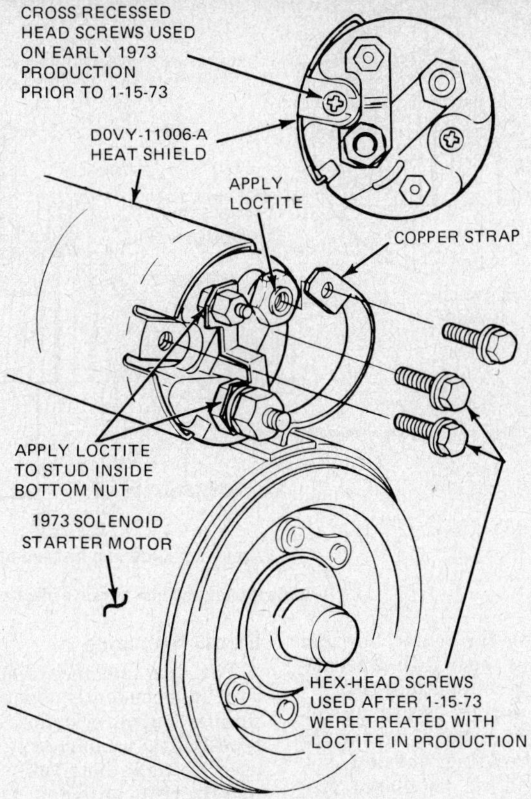
CROSS RECESSED HEAD SCREWS USED ON EARLY 1973 PRODUCTION PRIOR TO 1-15-73
D0VY-11006-A HEAT SHIELD
APPLY LOCTITE
COPPER STRAP
APPLY LOCTITE TO STUD INSIDE BOTTOM NUT
1973 SOLENOID STARTER MOTOR
HEX-HEAD SCREWS USED AFTER 1-15-73 WERE TREATED WITH LOCTITE IN PRODUCTION

Solenoid-actuated starter motor
(© Ford Motor Co)

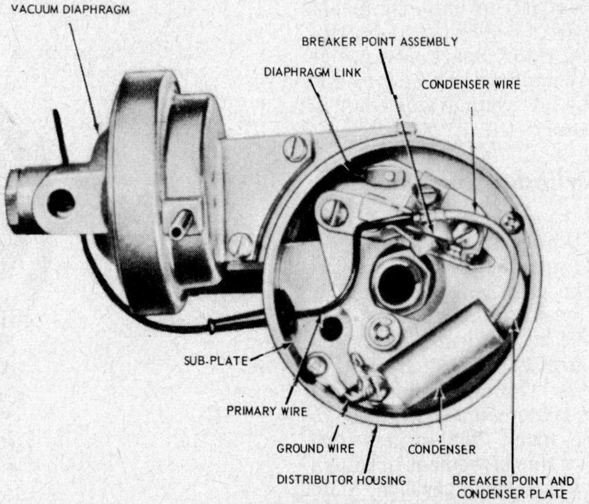
VACUUM DIAPHRAGM
BREAKER POINT ASSEMBLY
DIAPHRAGM LINK
CONDENSER WIRE
SUB-PLATE
PRIMARY WIRE
GROUND WIRE
CONDENSER
DISTRIBUTOR HOUSING
BREAKER POINT AND CONDENSER PLATE

Breaker plate installed—6 cylinder engine, dual diaphragm distributor
(© Ford Motor Co)

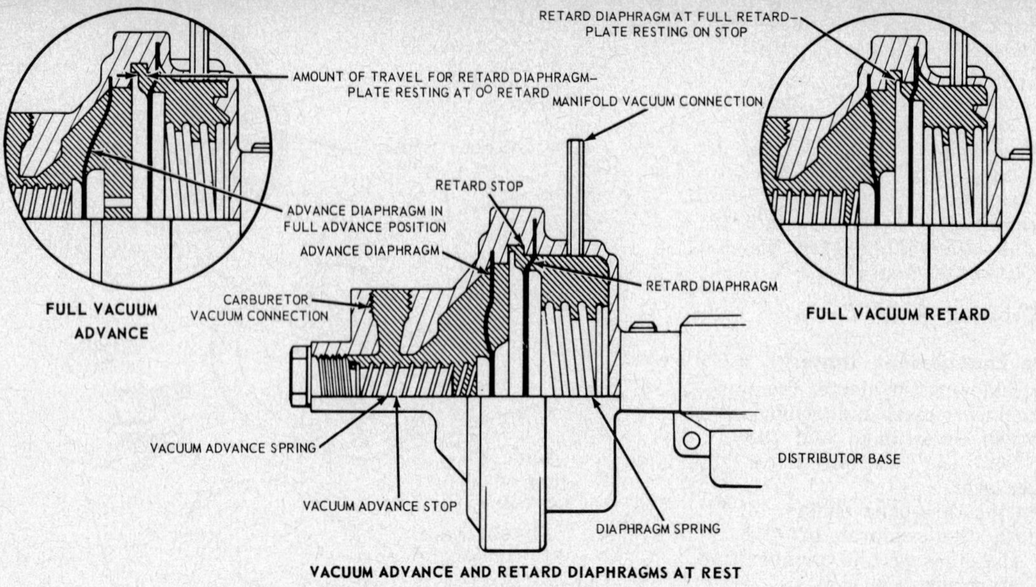
RETARD DIAPHRAGM AT FULL RETARD-PLATE RESTING ON STOP
AMOUNT OF TRAVEL FOR RETARD DIAPHRAGM-PLATE RESTING AT 0° RETARD
MANIFOLD VACUUM CONNECTION
RETARD STOP
ADVANCE DIAPHRAGM IN FULL ADVANCE POSITION
ADVANCE DIAPHRAGM
RETARD DIAPHRAGM
CARBURETOR VACUUM CONNECTION
FULL VACUUM ADVANCE
FULL VACUUM RETARD
VACUUM ADVANCE SPRING
DISTRIBUTOR BASE
VACUUM ADVANCE STOP
DIAPHRAGM SPRING
VACUUM ADVANCE AND RETARD DIAPHRAGMS AT REST

Dual diaphragm vacuum advance mechanism (© Ford Motor Co)

that it eliminates the contact breaker points, replacing them with a permanent magnet low voltage generator.

Briefly, the system works as follows: When the ignition is on and the distributor is rotating, the low voltage generator in the distributor produces alternating current which is then sent to the electronic control module. The module senses the signal from the low voltage generator as the alternating current wave swings from positive to negative each time one of the gear teeth on the armature passes the magnetic field in the coil of the generator. When a gear tooth is directly opposite the magnetic field, the alternating current wave is at crossover (neither negative nor positive). The control module senses this and cuts off electricity (low voltage) to the coil, causing it to fire (high voltage). After the coil fires, the timing circuitry in the module redirects the low tension voltage to the coil.

Other than the low voltage generator and the control module, the rest of the system is conventional in appearance, with a conventional distributor cap and rotor. Spark advance or retard is accomplished by moving the plate for the low voltage generator in the distributor.

1967 6-Cylinder Vacuum Advance

Ignition timing changes are entirely satisfied by the action of the breaker plate. The position of the plate is controlled by a vacuum-actuated diaphragm working against the tension of two accurately calibrated breaker plate springs. The diaphragm moves the breaker plate counterclockwise to advance the spark. The springs tend to counteract this movement to return timing to a retarded position. Cam and rotor rotation are clockwise as viewed from the top.

Dual Advance

The dual advance distributor has two independently operated spark-timing control systems. A governor-type and a vacuum-type control are used on each distributor of standard production engines. Centrifugal weights cause the cam to advance or rotate ahead, relative to the distributor shaft.

The vacuum control mechanism operates through a spring loaded diaphragm and movable breaker plate, about the same as the vacuum advance distributor.

Distributor Removal

1. Remove distributor cap. Disconnect the primary wire at the coil and the vacuum control line at the distributor.
2. Scribe a mark on the distributor body, showing position of the rotor. Then, scribe another mark on the distributor body and engine block, showing the position of the body in the block. These marks can be used to advantage when reassembling the distributor in an undisturbed engine.
3. Remove the screw, lockwasher and hold-down clamp. Pull the distributor out of the block. Do not rotate crankshaft while distributor is out of block because it will then be necessary to retime ignition.

Distributor Installation

1. If the engine was not cranked while the distributor was removed, install the distributor in the engine, aligning the tip of the rotor with the marks that were made on the distributor body and the engine. Proceed to Step 3. If the engine was cranked while the distributor was removed, rotate the crankshaft to bring No. 1 piston to T.D.C. of its compression stroke.

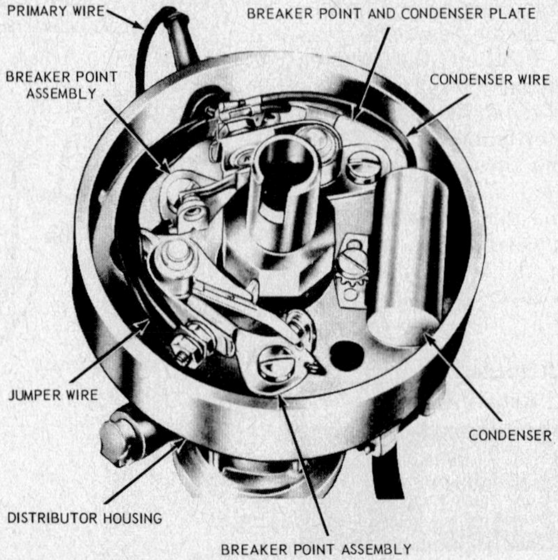
PRIMARY WIRE
BREAKER POINT AND CONDENSER PLATE
BREAKER POINT ASSEMBLY
CONDENSER WIRE
JUMPER WIRE
CONDENSER
DISTRIBUTOR HOUSING
BREAKER POINT ASSEMBLY

Dual-point distributor breaker plate
(© Ford Motor Co)

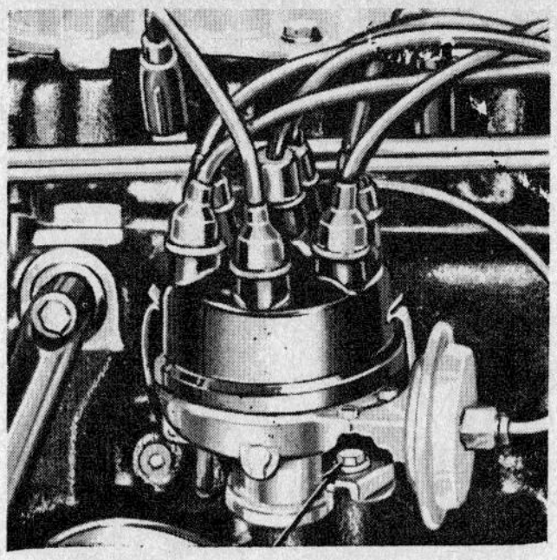

Distributor installation—6 cyl
(© Ford Motor Co)

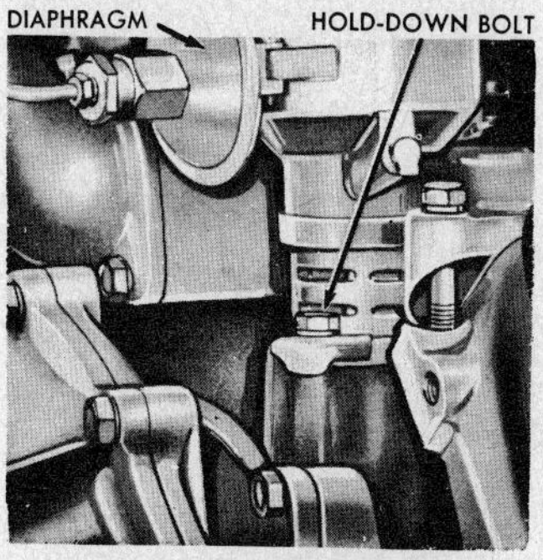
DIAPHRAGM
HOLD-DOWN BOLT

Distributor installation—V8
(© Ford Motor Co)

2. Position distributor in the block with the rotor at No. 1 firing position. Be sure that the oil pump intermediate driveshaft is properly seated in the oil pump.
3. Install, but do not tighten, the distributor retaining clamp and screw.
4. Rotate the distributor body clockwise until the breaker points start to open.
5. Tighten the retaining clamp screw.
6. Install distributor cap.
7. Connect distributor primary wire.
8. Start engine and run long enough to obtain engine operating temperature.
9. Idle engine to 500 rpm. Then, with a timing light, check the timing marks at the front pulley and make necessary corrections.
10. Connect the vacuum control line to the distributor and check advance characteristics with the timing light when the engine is accelerated.

Contact Point Replacement and Adjustment

1. Unsnap the distributor cap retaining clips and position the cap clear of the breaker plate. Remove the rotor by pulling it straight up.
2. Remove the metal point shield, if so equipped.
3. Disconnect the primary lead and condenser wires from the contact point assembly. On dual-point distributors, remove the jumper strap also.
4. Remove the contact point and condenser retaining screws. Lift the contact point assembly and condenser from the distributor.
5. Lightly lubricate the distributor cam with heat-resistant lubricant.
6. Place the new contact point assembly and condenser in the distributor. Install, but do not tighten, the retaining screws.
7. On all pre-1968 six-cylinder engines, position the ground wire under the contact point assembly screw, and connect the primary and condenser wires to the contact point assembly. On all V8 engines, except those equipped with a centrifugal advance distributor, place the ground wire under the contact point assembly screw farthest from the contacts. This ground wire is positioned under the condenser retaining screw on all post-1967 six-cylinder engines.
8. Turn the engine until the rubbing block on the point assembly is resting on the high point of the distributor cam lobe. Insert a feeler gauge of specified thickness between the contact points and adjust the gap. Tighten the retaining screw and remove the feeler gauge.
9. Connect the primary and condenser wires to the contact point assembly in the same order as they were removed. On those distributors with a metal point shield, the wires should be positioned 180 degrees (180°) from each other. Install the shield.
10. Install the rotor and distributor cap.
11. If a dwell meter is available, check to see that the distributor dwell is within specifications.

Ignition Timing

1. Locate the timing marks and pointer on the lower engine pulley and engine's front cover.
2. Clean the marks and apply chalk or bright-colored paint to the pointer.
3. Attach a timing light according to the manufacturer's specifications.
4. Disconnect and plug all vacuum lines leading to the distributor.
5. If the recommended engine idle speed is in excess of 500 rpm, set the idle at 500 rpm for setting the timing. If the recommended idle speed is below 500 rpm, do not alter it.
6. Aim the timing light at the timing mark and pointer on the front of the engine. If the marks align when the timing light flashes, remove the timing light, set the idle to its proper specification, and connect the vacuum lines at the distributor. If the marks do not align when the light flashes, turn the engine off and loosen the distributor hold-down clamp slightly.
7. Start the engine again, and observe the alignment of the timing marks. To advance the timing, turn the distributor counter-clockwise, on six-cylinder engines, or clockwise, for V8 engines. When altering the timing, it is wise to tap the distributor lightly with a wooden hammer handle to move it in the desired direction. Grasping the distributor with your hand may result in a painful electric shock. When the timing marks are aligned, turn the engine off and tighten the distributor hold-down clamp.

FUEL SYSTEM

Data on capacity of the gas tank is in the Capacities table.

Data on fuel pump pressure will be found in the Tune-up Specifications table. Both the above tables can be found in this car section.

Information covering operation and diagnosis of the fuel gauge will be found in the Unit Repair Section.

Fuel Pump

A single-action, permanently sealed Carter fuel pump is used on all models. On 6-cylinder engines the fuel pump is located on the lower, left center of the engine block. The V8 fuel pump is mounted on the left side of the cylinder front cover.

R & R—All Models

1. Remove the inlet and outlet lines from the pump.
2. Remove the fuel pump retaining screws and remove the pump and gasket.
3. Clean all gasket material from the pump mounting surface on the engine, and apply a coat of oil-resistant sealer to the new gasket.
4. Position pump on engine and install retaining screws.
5. Reinstall lines, start engine and check for leaks.

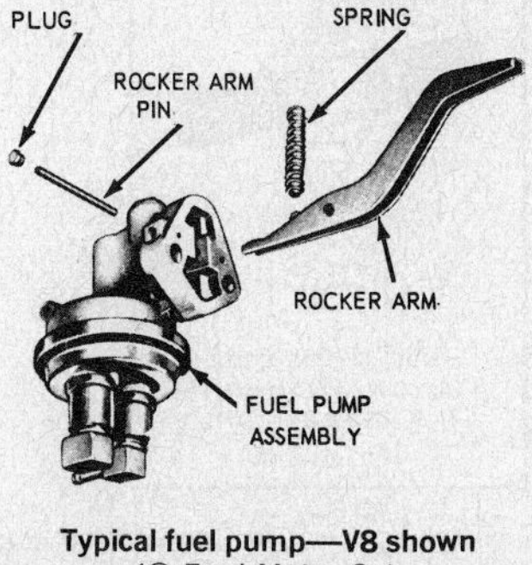
PLUG
ROCKER ARM SPRING
ROCKER ARM PIN
ROCKER ARM
FUEL PUMP ASSEMBLY

Typical fuel pump—V8 shown
(© Ford Motor Co)

NOTE: if resistance is felt while positioning the fuel pump on the block, the camshaft eccentric is in the high position. To ease installation, connect a remote engine starter switch to the engine and "tap" remote switch until resistance fades.

Fuel Filter

All models use a non-serviceable in-line fuel filter which is located at the carburetor fuel inlet.

Fuel Filter R & R

The filter is removed by removing the air cleaner, loosening the hose clamp on the inlet line, and unscrewing the filter. When installing, use a new hose clamp to prevent leakage.

Carburetor

Ford uses eight types of carburetors: Autolite 1100, Carter YF and RBS (1-barrel), Autolite 2100 (2-barrel), Autolite 4100, Autolite 4300, Holley 4150C, and Rochester Quadrajet 4VM (4-barrel).

Idle Speed and Mixture Adjustments

1967: Adjust with air cleaner removed.

1968-74: Adjust with air cleaner installed.

Idle Speed Adjustment

This is the procedure for adjusting all carburetors; any exceptions are listed below.

NOTE: If the following adjustment fails to produce a satisfactory idle, the following items should be checked: vacuum leaks, ignition wiring continuity, spark plug condition, dwell angle, breaker point condition, ignition timing, carburetor float level, PCV valve condition, valve clearance, cylinder compression, and, failing all else, check for an overly lean air fuel mixture with a CO meter of known accuracy.

1. Run engine at fast idle to equalize operating temperature.
2. Make sure the choke plate is fully released.
3. Turn headlights on high beam. On models equipped with an automatic transmission, apply the parking brake and put the transmission selector lever in Drive.
4. If engine is equipped with hot idle compensator valve, make sure it is fully seated in the closed position.
5. Attach tachometer of known accuracy to the engine.
6. On cars equipped with air conditioning, 1967-69 models (except 200 CI 6-cylinder and 302 V8 engines with automatic transmission) set idle speed with air conditioner turned ON. On all 1970 and later models the idle speed is set with the air conditioner turned OFF.
7. On 1967 and later models equipped with a temperature sensing valve in the distributor vacuum line, remove and plug the vacuum hoses from the intake manifold to the valve, at the valve located in the intake manifold. Also plug the intake manifold hose fitting on the valve.

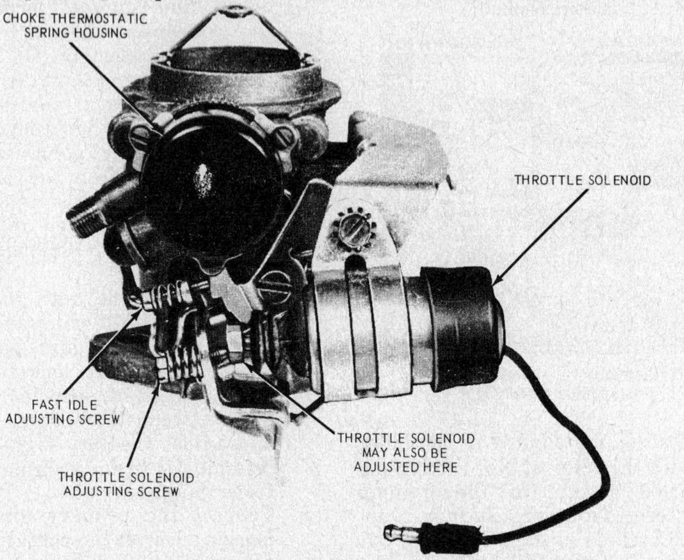
CHOKE THERMOSTATIC SPRING HOUSING
THROTTLE SOLENOID
FAST IDLE ADJUSTING SCREW
THROTTLE SOLENOID MAY ALSO BE ADJUSTED HERE
THROTTLE SOLENOID ADJUSTING SCREW

Carburetor adjustments—solenoid equipped Carter RBS 1V
(© Ford Motor Co)

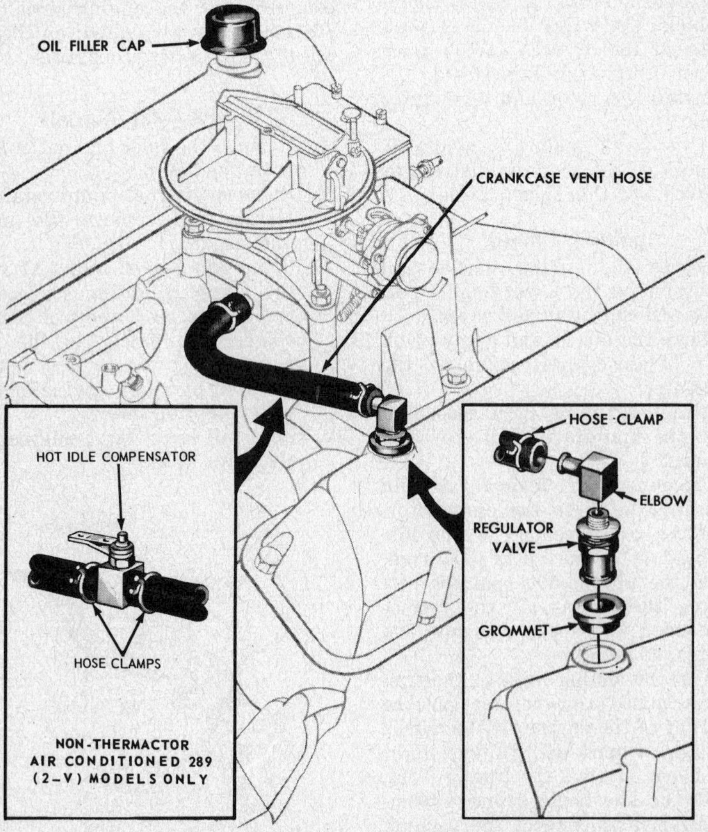
OIL FILLER CAP
CRANKCASE VENT HOSE
HOT IDLE COMPENSATOR
HOSE CLAMPS
NON-THERMACTOR AIR CONDITIONED 289 (2-V) MODELS ONLY
HOSE CLAMP
ELBOW
REGULATOR VALVE
GROMMET

Typical hot idle compensator installation
(© Ford Motor Co)

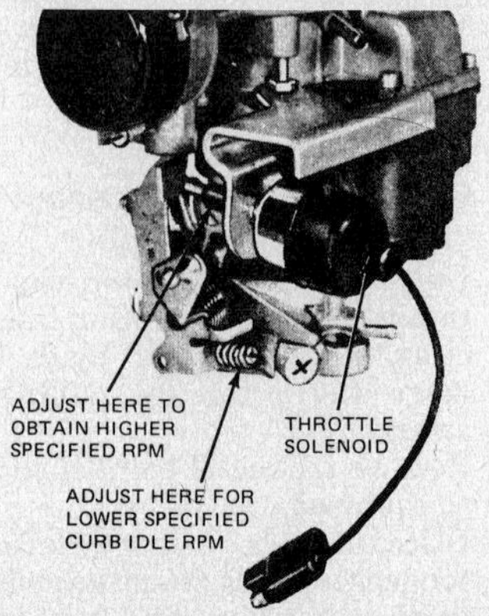
ADJUST HERE TO OBTAIN HIGHER SPECIFIED RPM
THROTTLE SOLENOID
ADJUST HERE FOR LOWER SPECIFIED CURB IDLE RPM

Carburetor adjustments—solenoid equipped Carter YF 1V
(© Ford Motor Co)

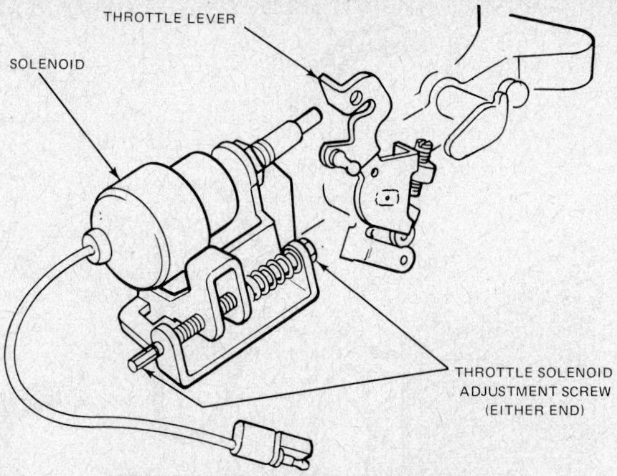
THROTTLE LEVER
SOLENOID
THROTTLE SOLENOID ADJUSTMENT SCREW (EITHER END)
1972-74 throttle solenoid adjustment—Motorcraft 2100-D and 4300 installation shown
(© Ford Motor Co)

8. Make sure the dashpot is working freely and not binding.
9. If it is not possible to adjust the idle speed with the air cleaner installed, the engine idle speed must be rechecked after installing the air cleaner. On cars with vacuum controlled heat ducts in the air cleaner, the vacuum line must be plugged if the carburetor is to be adjusted with the air cleaner removed.
10. On carburetors which do not have an electric throttle solenoid, turn the idle speed adjusting screw inward or outward to obtain the specified idle speed. On 1969–71 models which have a throttle solenoid, turn the solenoid plunger in or out to obtain the higher of the two idle speeds listed in the "Tune-up Specifications" table. On 1972-74 models which are equipped with a throttle solenoid, turn the throttle solenoid adjustment screw inward or outward to obtain the higher of the two idle speeds listed in the "Tune-up Specifications" table.
11. If equipped with a throttle solenoid, disconnect the lead wire from the solenoid and turn the curb idle adjusting screw on the carburetor to obtain the lower of the two idle speeds listed in the "Tune-up Specifications" table. On models equipped with an automatic transmission, place the transmission selector lever in Park or neutral before adjusting the lower idle speed.

NOTE: with the electric solenoid disengaged, the carburetor adjusting screw must make contact with the throttle shaft to prevent the throttle plates from jamming in the throttle bore when the engine is shut off.

Fuel Mixture Adjustment

1. On 1967 models turn the mixture screws clockwise until engine speed begins to drop, then back out until engine reaches highest rpm.
2. On 1968 and later models with idle mixture limiters, adjust by turning the idle mixture adjusting screw(s) inward to obtain the smoothest idle possible *within the range of the idle limiters. Limiter caps should not be removed,* unless a CO meter is available to bring the emissions within the legal limits.

Dashpot Adjustment

Type A Dashpots

1. Adjust throttle to fast idle position and turn dashpot adjusting screw out until it is clear of dashpot plunger assembly.
2. Turn screw in until it contacts plunger. Then turn dashpot adjusting screw in specified number of turns against plunger.

NOTE: Not all engines are equipped with dashpots, and not all are adjusted in this manner. This chart applies only to models mentioned.

Year, Engines and Models	*No. of Turns*
1967 Falcon with 170 six cylinder, automatic and without emission control	3½
1967 Comet, Fairlane, Falcon, and Mustang with 200 six cylinder and automatic and without emission control	3½
1967 Comet, Fairlane, Falcon and Mustang with six cylinder, auto transmission, and emission control	2
1969 Falcon and Mustang 200 six cylinder with automatic	2¼
1969 Falcon and Mustang 200 six cylinder with manual transmission	3¼

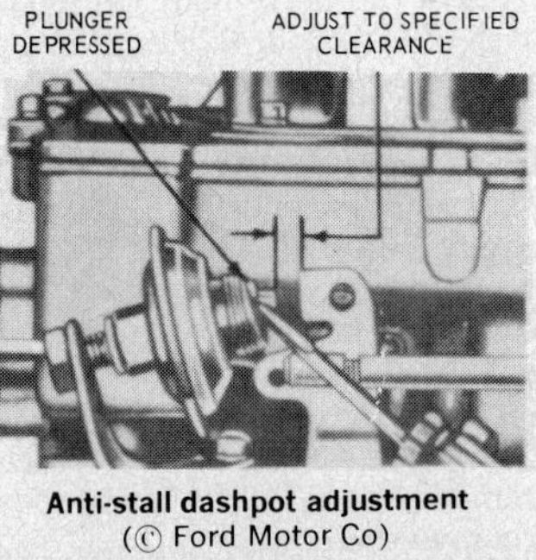
PLUNGER DEPRESSED
ADJUST TO SPECIFIED CLEARANCE
Anti-stall dashpot adjustment
(© Ford Motor Co)

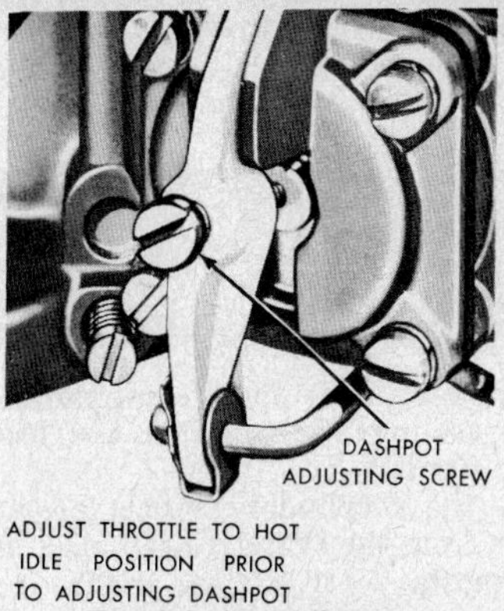
DASHPOT ADJUSTING SCREW
ADJUST THROTTLE TO HOT IDLE POSITION PRIOR TO ADJUSTING DASHPOT
Type A dashpot adjustment
(© Ford Motor Co)

Type B Dashpots

1. With engine idle speed and mixture properly adjusted and with engine at operating temperature, loosen dashpot lock nut.
2. Hold throttle in closed position and depress dashpot plunger. Measure clearance between plunger and cam. Adjust dashpot nut to give proper clearance.

NOTE: Not all engines have dashpots and not all are adjusted in this manner. This chart applies only to models mentioned.

Year, Model and Engine	*Clearance* Manual *(in.)*	Automatic *(in.)*
1967 Falcon with 170 six and emission control		⅛
1967 289 2 V without emission control		0.060-0.090
1967 289 2 V with emission control	0.110-0.140	0.110-0.140
1967 390 2V with emission control when equipped with dashpot	0.080-0.110	0.110-0.140
1967 390 2V without emission control	⅛	⅛
1967 289 4V with emission control	⅛	⅛
1967 390 4V when equipped with dashpot		⅛
1969 Montego, Fairlane and Mustang 250 six except when solenoid equipped	0.080	
1969 302 2V	⅛	⅛
1969 351 Windsor 2V	7/64	
1969 351 Windsor 4V	3/32	
1969 390 4V	⅛	
1969 428 CJ	0.100	0.100
1969 Falcon 170 six	0.100	0.100
1970-71 170 and 200 six cylinder if so equipped	7/64	7/64
1970-71 Montego, Fairlane, and Mustang 250 six		7/32
1970 302 2V without air conditioning		⅛
1970-71 351 Windsor 2V without air conditioning		⅛
1970-71 351 Cleveland 2V without air conditioning		⅛
1970-71 351 Cleveland 4V without air conditioning		0.080
1970 429 4V Montego and Fairlane	0.070	0.070
1970 428 CJ without air conditioning	0.140	0.200

Linkage Adjustments

Linkage adjustment procedures are found in the Automatic Transmission Section.

COOLING SYSTEM

The 6-cylinder and V8 engines employ cooling systems that are basically similar.

In the 6-cylinder engine, coolant flows from the cylinder head, past the thermostat (if it is open) and into the radiator upper tank. In the V8 engine, coolant from each cylinder head flows through water passages in the intake manifold, then past the thermostat (if it is open) and into the radiator upper tank.

The standard thermostat operating temperature is 185°-192°F. However, a low reading thermostat of 157°-162°F is available for use with non-permanent-type anti freeze solutions.

A single water pump assembly is used. The pump has a sealed bearing integral with the water pump shaft. The bearing requires no lubrication. There is a bleed hole in the water pump housing. This is not a lubrication hole.

Some models are equipped with a coolant recovery or "constant full" system. These systems have a non-vented radiator cap that forces coolant expansion into an expansion reservoir. When adding coolant to these systems, add coolant to the reservoir only, not the radiator.

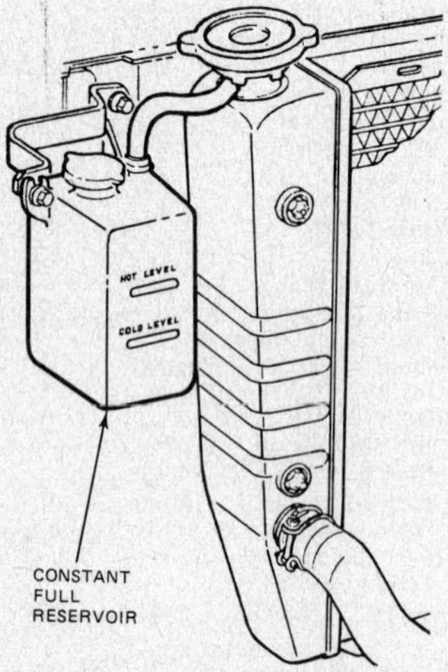
HOT LEVEL
COLD LEVEL
CONSTANT FULL RESERVOIR

Constant-Full cooling system
(© Ford Motor Co)

Radiator

Removal

1. Drain cooling system.
2. Disconnect upper and lower hoses at the radiator.
3. On automatic transmission-equipped cars, disconnect oil cooler lines at radiator.
4. On vehicles equipped with a fan shroud, remove the shroud retaining screws and position the shroud out of the way.
5. Remove radiator attaching bolts and lift out the radiator.

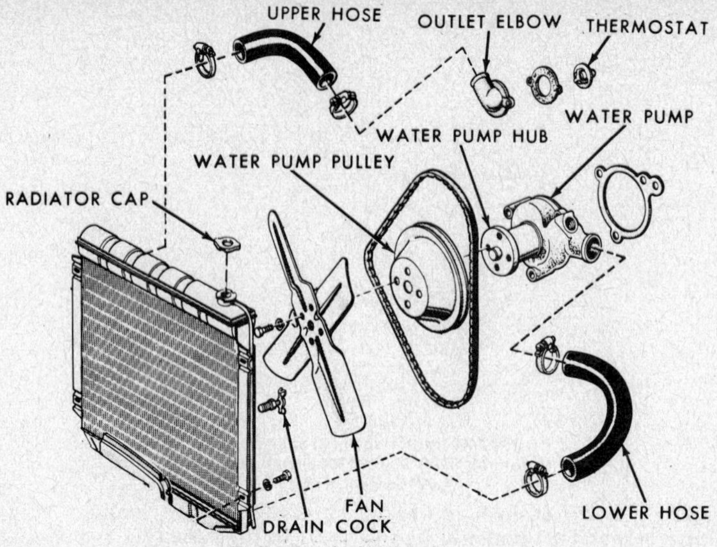
UPPER HOSE
OUTLET ELBOW
THERMOSTAT
WATER PUMP HUB
WATER PUMP
WATER PUMP PULLEY
RADIATOR CAP
FAN
DRAIN COCK
LOWER HOSE

Radiator and related parts
(© Ford Motor Co)

Installation

1. If a new radiator is to be installed, transfer the petcock from the old radiator to the new one. On cars equipped with automatic transmissions, transfer the oil cooler line fittings from the old radiator to the new one.
2. Position the radiator and install, but do not tighten, the radiator support bolts. On cars equipped with automatic transmissions, connect the oil cooler lines. Then tighten the radiator support bolts.
3. On vehicles equipped with a fan shroud, reinstall the shroud.
4. Connect the radiator hoses. Close the radiator petcock. Then fill and bleed the cooling system.
5. Start the engine and bring to operating temperature. Check for leaks.
6. On cars equipped with automatic transmissions, check the cooler lines for leaks and interference. Check transmission fluid level.

Water Pump R & R

1. Drain cooling system.
2. On 351C and 400 V8, disconnect the negative battery cable.
3. On cars with power steering, remove the drive belt. On models with 390, 427, or 428 engines, remove the power steering mounting retaining screws and remove the pump and bracket as an asembly and position it out of the way.
4. If the vehicle is equipped with air conditioning, remove the idler pulley bracket and air conditioner drive belt.
5. On engines with Thermactor, remove the belt; on 1968 models, remove the pump.
6. Disconnect the lower radiator hose and heater hose from the water pump.
7. On cars equipped with a fan shroud, remove the retaining screws and position the shroud rearward.
8. Remove the fan and spacer from the engine, and if the car is equipped with a fan shroud, remove the fan and shroud from the engine as an assembly.
9. Loosen alternator mounting bolts, remove the alternator belt and remove the alternator adjusting arm bracket from the water pump.
10. Loosen bypass hose at water pump.
11. Remove water pump retaining screws and remove pump from engine.
12. Clean any gasket material from the pump mounting surface, and on 429 V8 remove the water pump backing plate and replace the gasket.

NOTE: The 250 6-cylinder engine originally uses a one-piece gasket for the cylinder front cover and water pump. Trim away the old gasket at the edge of the cylinder cover and replace with service gasket.

13. Remove the heater hose fitting from the old pump and install it on the new pump.
14. Coat both sides of the new gasket with a water-resistant sealer, then re-install pump reversing the above procedure.

Thermostat R & R

1. Open the drain cock and drain the radiator so the coolant level is below the coolant outlet elbow which houses the thermostat.
2. Remove the outlet elbow retaining bolts and position the elbow sufficiently clear of the intake manifold or cylinder head to provide access to the thermostat.

3. Remove the thermostat and old gasket. On 1967 six-cylinder and 289 V8 engines, the thermostat must be rotated counterclockwise to remove it. All post-1967 thermostats are removed in the same manner.
4. Clean the mating surfaces of the outlet elbow and the engine to remove all old gasket material and sealer. Coat the new gasket with water-resistant sealer and install it on the engine. Install the thermostat in the outlet elbow. On the above-mention engines (step three), the thermostat must be rotated clockwise to lock it in position.
5. Install the outlet elbow and retaining bolts on the engine. Torque the bolts to 12–15 ft lbs.
6. Refill the radiator. Run the engine at operating temperature and check for leaks. Recheck the coolant level.

EMISSION CONTROLS

All Models

All Ford cars from 1967 to the present have used positive crankcase ventilation (PCV) systems. The PCV system routes a harmful mixture of blow-by gases and condensation vapors, which were formerly dispelled into the atmosphere, through a modulating valve (PCV valve) and into the intake manifold where they combine with the carburetor air fuel mixture and are burned in the combustion chamber. Prior to 1968, this system incorporated an open crankcase with breather cap. From 1968 on, the system is closed to the atmosphere, deriving its fresh air from the air cleaner.

1967

On those 1967 models sold in California, 1968-69 cars with manual transmissions, and 1968-71 high-performance V8 models, the Thermactor (air injection) system was used. This system, which injects fresh air into the exhaust ports to achieve afterburning of raw exhaust fumes, consists of an air pump, a bypass and a check valve, and external air manifolds (not an integral part of the engine exhaust manifolds), and air injector tubes in the exhaust ports.

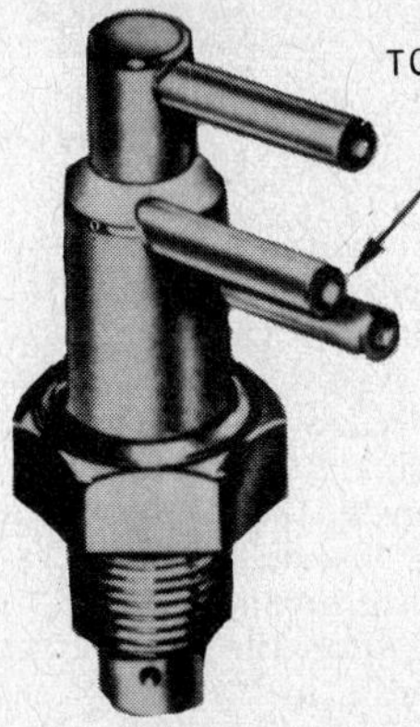
TO DISTRIBUTOR

Distributor vacuum control valve (ported vacuum switch)
(© Ford Motor Co)

1968-69

In order to comply with federal antipollution laws, Ford Motor Company adopted the IMCO (IMproved COmbustion) emission control system in 1968. Rather than burning the exhaust gases in the exhaust manifolds, as in the Thermactor system, the IMCO system reduces carbon monoxide and hydrocarbons through more complete combustion in the combustion chambers. This is accomplished through the use of a heated air intake system which thermostatically supplies air, which has been warmed by the exhaust manifold, as needed, to the air cleaner, as well as idle mixture limiter caps which prevent the air fuel mixture from being adjusted to an overly rich condition at idle, and control of ignition timing by a dual diaphragm vacuum advance mechanism on the distributor and a ported vacuum or temperature override switch (PVS). The outer chamber of the dual vacuum advance is controlled by carburetor vacuum and the inner chamber by intake manifold vacuum. During normal engine operation the outer diaphragm advances ignition timing, while the inner diaphragm retards timing at idle. Three vacuum hoses are attached to the PVS switch; the top hose is connected to the carburetor, the second to the distributor, and the third to the intake manifold. When the engine is operating under normal temperature conditions, vacuum is supplied to the distributor vacuum advance by the carburetor. If the engine should overheat, the PVS switch connects intake manifold vacuum to the distributor which advances ignition timing while the engine is idling, thus speeding up the engine and lowering engine temperature.

In 1969, to further aid in reducing emissions, a distributor vacuum advance (deceleration) control valve and a throttle solenoid were used on some models. The deceleration valve provides maximum intake manifold vacuum to the distributor and subsequent timing advance to prevent backfiring in the exhaust system when the vehicle is slowing down.

The throttle solenoid is located on the side of the carburetor. When the ignition key is turned On, the throttle solenoid plunger extends and contacts the carburetor throttle lever, raising the idle speed of the engine. When the ignition key is turned off, the solenoid lever retracts, allowing the carburetor throttle lever to fall back on the carburetor idle speed adjusting screw. This prevents the engine from running-on when the key is turned off.

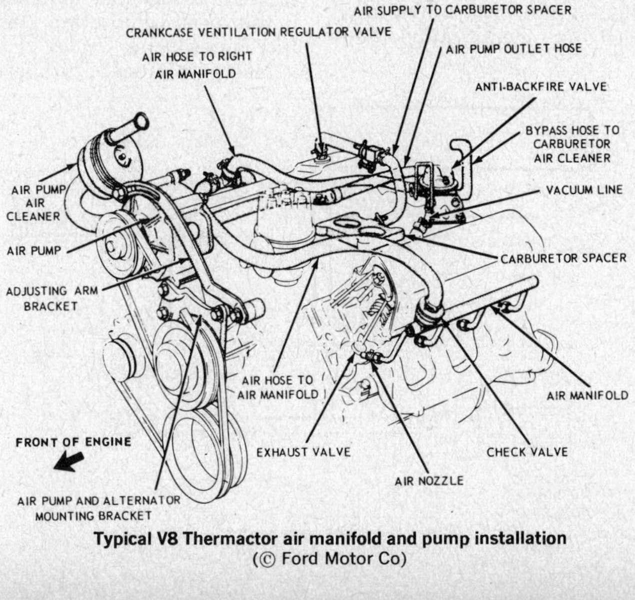
AIR SUPPLY TO CARBURETOR SPACER
CRANKCASE VENTILATION REGULATOR VALVE
AIR HOSE TO RIGHT AIR MANIFOLD
AIR PUMP OUTLET HOSE
ANTI-BACKFIRE VALVE
BYPASS HOSE TO CARBURETOR AIR CLEANER
AIR PUMP AIR CLEANER
VACUUM LINE
AIR PUMP
CARBURETOR SPACER
ADJUSTING ARM BRACKET
AIR HOSE TO AIR MANIFOLD
AIR MANIFOLD
FRONT OF ENGINE
EXHAUST VALVE
CHECK VALVE
AIR NOZZLE
AIR PUMP AND ALTERNATOR MOUNTING BRACKET

Typical V8 Thermactor air manifold and pump installation
(© Ford Motor Co)

1970-71

The fuel evaporative emission control system was used on California models in 1970, and nationwide in 1971. This system eliminates pollution due to evaporating fuel by channeling the breathing of the fuel tank

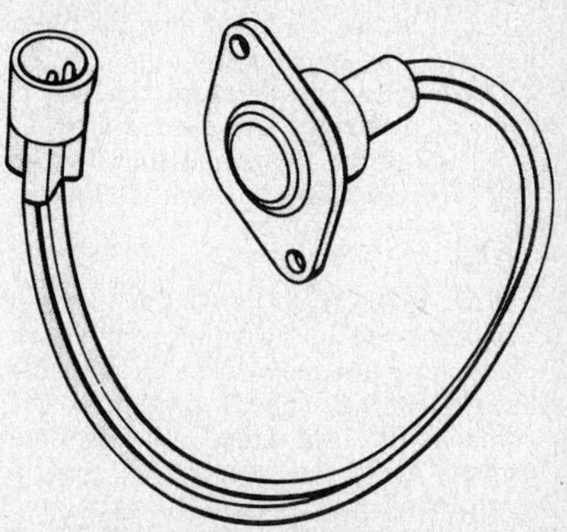

Thermal switch
(© Ford Motor Co)

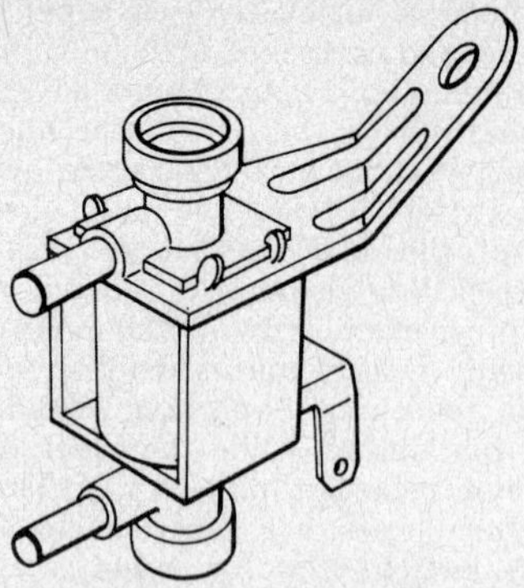

Distributor modulator valve
(© Ford Motor Co)

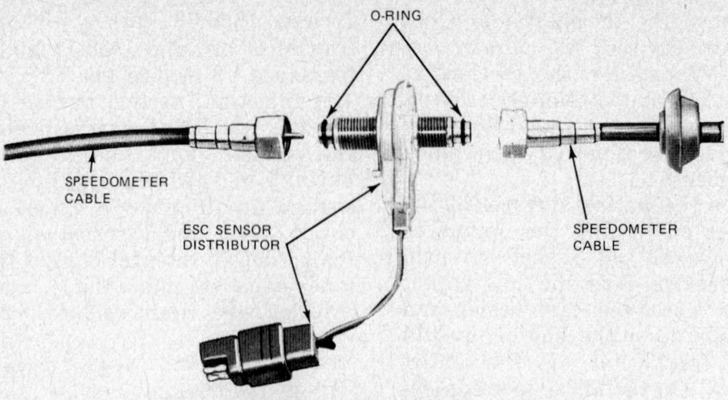
O-RING
SPEEDOMETER CABLE
ESC SENSOR DISTRIBUTOR
SPEEDOMETER CABLE

Speed sensor location
(© Ford Motor Co)

and by the venting of the carburetor float bowl through a canister filled with activated charcoal, condensing the fuel vapors and returning them to the fuel system.

The IMCO system of emission control was further extended in 1970 to become the Distributor Modulator (Dist-O-Vac) System. The Dist-O-Vac system incorporated all of the IMCO features but included three units of equipment which control spark advance in a more sophisticated manner. A speed sensor is located between two sections of the speedometer cable and generates a small current which increases in direct proportion to speed. A thermal switch is located in the right door pillar and activates at outside temperatures of 58° or higher. The impulses of both are fed into the electonic control amplifier. The distributor vacuum advance hose is connected from the carburetor, through the electronic control amplifier, to the distributor. When ambient temperature is above 58°, the contacts in the temperature switch open, and a plunger in the amplifier prevents vacuum from being supplied to the distributor. When vehicle speed reaches approximately 30 mph, the signal from the speed sensor causes the control amplifier to open the vacuum line to the distributor and ignition timing is allowed to advance in the normal manner. When the ambient temperature is below 58°, the temperature switch closes, and normal vacuum is supplied to the distributor regardless of vehicle speed. In the event of engine overheating, the ported vacuum switch (PVS), a carryover from the IMCO system, overrides the electronic control modulator by connecting intake manifold vacuum to the distributor.

1972

For 1972, the Dist-O-Vac system was replaced by two different spark control systems. The Electronic Spark Control (ESC) system is the same as the old Dist-O-Vac system except that the electronic control modulator was separated into two pieces, an amplifier and a distributor modulator valve. The amplifier judges the signals sent to it by the speed and temperature switches and tells the distributor modulator valve when to open and close and thus allow or prevent vacuum to reach the distributor. The Transmission Regulated Spark (TRS) is similar to the ESC system except that the speed sensor is replaced by a transmission switch. The switch is mounted on the side of the transmission and is hydraulically actuated on cars equipped with an automatic transmission and manually actuated on models equipped with a manual transmission. When the ambient temperature is above 55°, the transmission switch is closed whenever the transmission is in any gear other than high gear (manual transmission), or high gear or reverse (automatic transmission). When the transmission switch closes, it signals the distributor modulator valve to close and thus prevents carburetor vacuum from reaching the distributor. As in past systems, neither of these systems is functional below 55–58°, and both are bypassed by the PVS if the engine should overheat.

On some 1972 models, a spark delay valve was inserted into the vacuum advance line to the distributor. The valve closes under hard acceleration, blocking carburetor vacuum to the distributor for a pre-determined period of seconds. The valves are color coded for identification purposes.

1973-74

1973 and later models utilize an Exhaust Gas Recirculation System (EGR) to control oxides of nitrogen. On V8 engines, exhaust gases travel through the exhaust gas crossover passage in the intake manifold. A portion of these gases is diverted into a spacer which is mounted under the carburetor The EGR control valve, which is attached to the rear of the spacer, consists of a vacuum diaphragm with an attached plunger which normally blocks off exhaust gases from entering the intake manifold. On 6 cylinder engine, an external tube carries exhaust manifold gases to the carburetor spacer. On all models except those equipped with a 250 six-cylinder and manual transmission, the EGR valve is controlled by a vacuum line from the carburetor which passes through a ported vacuum switch. The EGR ported vacuum switch provides vacuum to the EGR valve at coolant temperature above 125°F. The vacuum diaphragm then opens the EGR valve permitting exhaust gases to flow through the carburetor spacer and enter the intake manifold where they combine with the fuel mixture and enter the combustion chambers. The exhaust gases are relatively oxygen-free, and tend to dilute the combustion charge. This lowers peak combustion temperature thereby reducing oxides of nitrogen.

Models equipped with a 250 six-

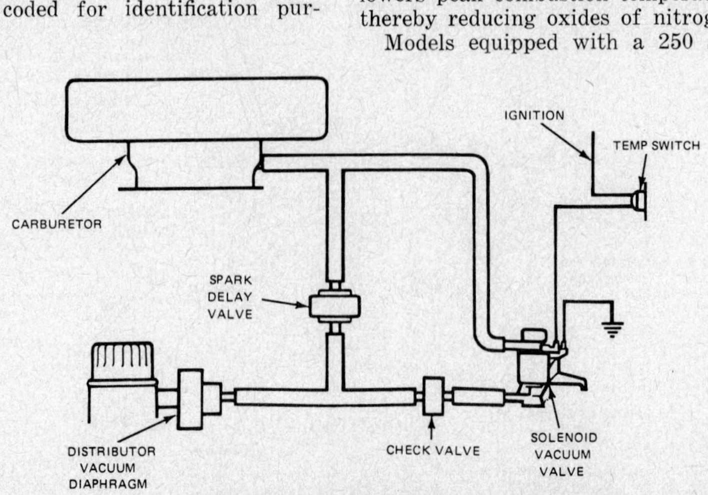
IGNITION
TEMP SWITCH
CARBURETOR
SPARK DELAY VALVE
DISTRIBUTOR VACUUM DIAPHRAGM
CHECK VALVE
SOLENOID VACUUM VALVE

Delay vacuum by-pass system—DVB
(© Ford Motor Co)

cylinder engine and manual transmission have a combined spark control and EGR system called "TRS+1." The spark control portion of this system is identical to the TRS system described under "1972." Operation of the EGR control valve is governed by vacuum from either the distributor vacuum port on the carburetor or the EGR vacuum port. When the TRS system is not in operation, EGR valve vacuum comes from the EGR port on the carburetor. The vacuum passes through a coolant temperature vacuum valve and a three-way solenoid valve. The coolant valve blocks vacuum from the EGR valve until the engine coolant temperature has reached 60°F. The vacuum lines from both the EGR and distributor vacuum ports on the carburetor connect to the three-way solenoid valve. The third line is an outlet line to the EGR valve. When the TRS system is not in operation, the three-way solenoid valve is de-energized. When the TRS system is in operation, the solenoid is energized, blocking the EGR port on the three-way solenoid, and opening the distributor port to the EGR valve. When the transmission is shifted into high gear, the TRS and three-way solenoids are de-energized. This restores normal vacuum to the distributor and the EGR valve.

Models equipped with a 250 six-cylinder engine and automatic transmission use a new system to control distributor spark advance. The system contains a three-way solenoid valve, an ambient temperature switch, and a vacuum bleed line to the air cleaner. The operation of the three-way solenoid valve is identical to the valve described above for 250 manual transmission engines. The only difference is that the output line of the three-way valve is connected to the distributor. When the ambient temperature is above 60°, the contacts in the temperature sensor close and complete the circuit to the three-way solenoid. This energizes the solenoid and connects the EGR vacuum port on the carburetor to the distributor vacuum advance. When the ambient temperature is below 49°, the solenoid is de-energized and the distributor vacuum advance operates in the normal manner.

1973-74 Torino and Montego station wagons equipped with a 302 or 351W V8 and manual transmission and all models that are equipped with a 351C, 400, or 429 V8 use the new Delay Vacuum By-Pass (DVB) spark control system. This system provides two paths by which carburetor vacuum can reach the distributor vacuum advance. The system consists of a spark delay valve, a check valve, a solenoid vacuum valve, and an ambient temperature switch. When the ambient temperature is below 49°F. the temperature switch contacts and the vacuum solenoid are open (de-energized). Under these conditions, vacuum will flow from the carburetor, through the open solenoid, and to the distributor. Since the spark delay valve resists the flow of carburetor vacuum, the vacuum will always flow through the vacuum solenoid when it is open, since this is the path of least resistance. When the ambient temperature rises above 60°F. the contacts in the temperature switch (which is located in the door post) close. This passes ignition switch current to the solenoid, energizing the solenoid. This blocks one of the vacuum paths. All distributor vacuum must now flow through the spark delay valve. When carburetor vacuum rises above a certain level on acceleration, a rubber valve in the spark delay valve blocks vacuum from passing through the valve for 5-30 seconds. After this delay, normal vacuum is supplied to the distributor. When the vacuum solenoid is closed (temperature above 60°), the vacuum line from the solenoid to the distributor is vented to atmosphere. To prevent the vacuum that is passing through the spark delay valve from escaping through the solenoid into the atmosphere, a one-way check valve is installed in the vacuum line from the solenoid to the distributor.

In 1973 and later models, dual diaphragm distributors are not used. Also new on some 1973-74 models is an electric choke heating element. When ambient temperature is above 63°, and the ignition switch is turned on, a heating element in the choke housing raises the temperature of the choke bimetallic spring, thus preventing the choke from engaging.

All 1974 models sold in the state of California are equipped with a Thermactor (air injection) system of emission control to reduce hydrocarbons and carbon monoxide. This system is used in addition to the above mentioned EGR and IMCO systems, which are used to reduce oxides of nitrogen. Refer to the 1967 emission control section for a description of components.

Consult the Unit Repair Section for complete testing and troubleshooting procedures for emission control equipment.

ENGINE

There were three different six-cylinder engines available in compact and intermediate size Ford products from 1967-72: the 170, the 200 and the 250 cu. in. engines. The 170 engine was dropped from production in 1973. These engines are all of the same family, and the only great difference among them is their bore and stroke. One distinguishing characteristic that makes these engines easily identifiable is the fact that the intake manifold is cast as an integral part of the cylinder head.

Optional V8 engines for these models are very numerous, and like the family of six-cylinder engines, there is a great amount of similarity among them.

The most widely used are the 289, and 302 V8s. These are remarkably compact engines with stud-mounted rockers and wedge-shaped combustion chambers. The 289 V8 was discontinued in 1969.

In 1969, Ford Motor Company introduced a longer stroke, higher block version of the 302 engine. This engine is the 351 Windsor engine and features the wedge-shaped combustion chambers and stud-mounted rockers of the small block engine in a new intermediate sized block.

A high-performance version of the 302 engine was also introduced in 1969. Called the Boss 302, this engine featured mechanical valve lifters and large valve—small spark plug cylinder heads similar to the ones that were used on the 1970 and later 351 Cleveland engines.

In 1970, Ford Motor Company added the 351 Cleveland engine. The 351 Cleveland engine has the same bore and stroke as the Windsor engine, and there most of the resemblance ends. It has different main bearing size, larger valves, smaller plugs, and semi-hemispherical combustion chambers. It is used concurrently with the Windsor engine and is found in many of the same models. A longer stroke, 400 cu in. version of the 351 Cleveland V8 was introduced in 1972.

The Boss 302 V8 was eliminated from production in 1971, and it was replaced by a high-performance version of the 351 Cleveland engine. It is designated as the 351 HO (High Output) engine, available on 1971-72 models.

In late 1966, Ford installed the 390 cu. in. V8 in the Cyclone GT and Fairlane GT. This V8 was soon joined by other large V8s, the 427 and the 428 Cobra Jet.

In 1970 some Mercury Montegos and Cyclones and Fairlanes use the 429 V8. This V8 comes in three forms. The first is the 429 4V engine, which is the same as is used in full sized Mercury and Ford cars. The second is the 429 CJ engine which uses stronger rods, big valve heads, smaller 14 mm. plugs, and an ignition governor set at 5,800 rpm. The third is the 429 Super CJ, which is similar to the 429 CJ except for forged pistons, four bolt main caps, solid lifters, and a 6,000 rpm governor. The 429 CJ and SCJ were discontinued after the 1971 model year run.

In 1969 and 1970 Ford released about one thousand Mustangs and Cougars powered by the Boss 429 engine. This engine is based loosely on the 429 engines discussed above, but its features are so individual it must be covered separately. It has modified hemispherical combustion chambers, very large valves and ports, valve seats canted in two planes, rockers with individual rocker shafts, and O-rings and chevron seals in lieu of head gaskets. The heads are of aluminum, the valves take special valve seals, the main bearings have four bolt main caps, and the spark plugs pass through the rocker covers. In short, this is a very special engine that demands special procedures found in this section.

Tool—T60K-6000-A

6 cyl engine lifting hook
(© Ford Motor Co)

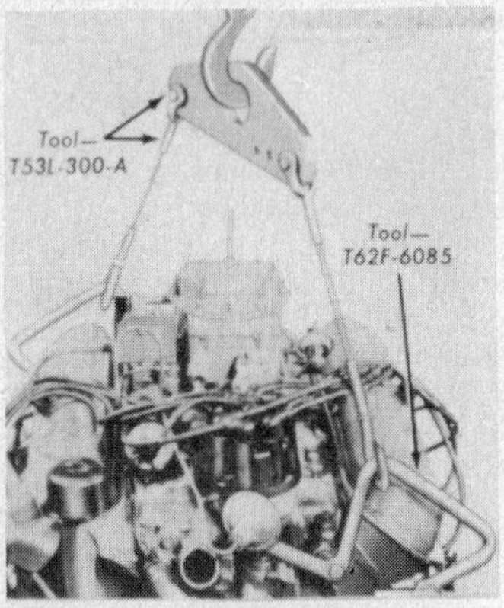
Tool—
T53L-300-A
Tool—
T62F-6085

V8 engine lifting brackets and sling
(© Ford Motor Co)

Engine Removal

1. Scribe the hood hinge outline on the under-hood, disconnect the hood and remove.
2. Drain the entire cooling system and crankcase.
3. Remove the air cleaner, disconnect the battery at the cylinder head. On automatic transmission equipped cars, disconnect oil cooler lines at the radiator.
4. Remove upper and lower radiator hoses and remove radiator. If equipped with air conditioning, unbolt compressor and position compressor out of way with refrigerant lines intact. Unbolt and lay refrigerant radiator forward without disconnecting refrigerant lines.

NOTE: If there is not enough slack in the refrigerant lines to position the compressor out of the way, the refrigerant in the system must be evacuated (using proper safety precautions) before the lines can be disconnected from the compressor.

On some 428 CJ engines and all 429 Super CJ, Boss 302, and Boss 429 engines disconnect inlet and outlet lines from engine oil cooler, remove hold-down bracket and remove cooler.

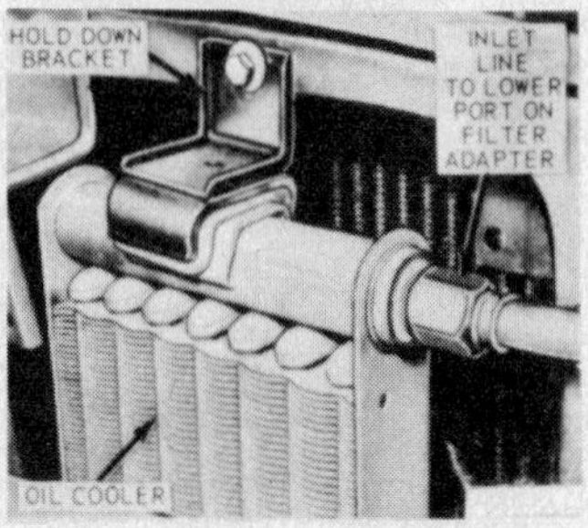
HOLD DOWN
BRACKET
INLET
LINE
TO LOWER
PORT ON
FILTER
ADAPTER
OIL COOLER

Engine oil cooler
(© Ford Motor Co)

5. Remove fan, fan belt and upper pully.
6. Disconnect the heater hoses from the engine.
7. Disconnect the alternator wires at the alternator, the starter cable at the starter, the accelerator rod at the carburetor.
8. Disconnect fuel tank line at the fuel pump and plug the line.
9. Disconnect the coil primary wire at the coil. Disconnect wires at the oil pressure and water temperature sending units.
10. Remove the starter and dust seal.
11. On a car equipped with a manual-shift transmission, remove the clutch retracting spring. Disconnect the clutch equalizer shaft and arm bracket at the underbody rail and remove the arm bracket and equalizer shaft.
12. Raise the car. Remove the flywheel or converter housing upper retaining bolts.
13. Disconnect the exhaust pipe or pipes at the exhaust manifold. Disconnect the right and left motor mount at the underbody bracket. Remove the flywheel or converter housing cover.
14. On a car with manual shift, remove the flywheel housing lower retaining bolts.
15. On a car equipped with automatic transmission, disconnect throttle valve vacuum line at the intake manifold (2 lines on 1973 models) disconnect the converter from the flywheel. Remove the converter housing lower retaining bolts. On a car with power steering, disconnect power steering pump from cylinder head. Put drive belt and wire steering pump out of the way.
16. Lower the car. Support the transmission and fiywheel or converter housing with a jack.
17. Attach an engine lifting hook. Lift the engine up and out of the compartment and onto an adequate workstand.

Engine Installation

1. Place a new gasket over the studs of the exhaust manifold/s.
2. Attach engine sling and lifting device. Lift engine from workstand.
3. Lower the engine into the engine compartment. Be sure the exhaust manifold/s is in proper alignment with the muffler inlet pipe/s, and the dowels in the block engage the holes in the flywheel housing.
   On a car with automatic transmission, start the converter pilot into the crankshaft.
   On a car with manual-shift transmission, start the transmission main drive gear into the clutch disc. If the engine hangs up after the shaft enters, rotate the crankshaft slowly (with transmission in gear) until the shaft and clutch disc splines mesh.
4. Install the fiywheel or converter housing upper bolts.
5. Install engine support insulator to bracket retaining nuts. Disconnect engine lifting sling and remove lifting brackets.
6. Raise front of car. Connect exhaust line/s and tighten attachments.
7. Position dust seal and install starter.
8. On cars with manual-shift transmissions, install remaining flywheel housing-to-engine bolts. Connect clutch release rod. Position the clutch equalizer bar and bracket, and install retaining bolts. Install clutch pedal retracting spring.
9. On cars with automatic transmissions, remove the retainer holding the converter in the housing. Attach the converter to the flywheel. Install the converter housing inspection cover and the remaining converter housing retaining bolts.
10. Remove the support from the transmission and lower the car.
11. Connect engine ground strap and coil primary wire.
12. Connect water temperature gauge wire and the heater hose at coolant outlet housing. Connect accelerator rod at the bellcrank.
13. On cars with automatic transmission, connect the transmission filler tube bracket. Connect the throttle valve vacuum line.
14. On cars with power steering, install the drive belt and power steering pump bracket. Install the bracket retaining bolts. Adjust drive belt to proper tension.
15. Remove plug from the fuel tank line. Connect the flexible fuel line and the oil pressure sending unit wire.

16. Install the pulley, belt, spacer, and fan. Adjust belt tension.
17. Tighten alternator adjusting bolts. Connect generator wires and the battery ground cable.
18. Install radiator. Connect radiator hoses. On air conditioned cars, install compressor and refrigerant radiator. On some 428 CJ engines, and all 429 Super CJ, Boss 302, and Boss 429 engines, install engine oil cooler and hold-down bracket and connect inlet and outlet lines.
19. On cars with automatic transmission, connect oil cooler lines.
20. Install oil filter. Connect heater hose at water pump, after bleeding the system.
21. Bring crankcase to level with correct grade of oil. Run engine at fast idle and check for leaks. Install air cleaner and make final engine adjustments.
22. Install and adjust hood.
23. Road-test car.

Intake Manifold R & R
6 Cylinder

170, 200 and 250 cu. in. sixes have intake manifolds that are integral with the cylinder head and cannot be removed.

289, 302, 351W, 390, 427, 428, 429, 429CJ, 429SCJ, and 460

1. Drain the cooling system.
2. Disconnect the upper radiator hose from the thermostat housing and the bypass hose from the manifold.
3. Remove the air cleaner and ducts.
4. Remove the distributor cap and wires from the engine. Mark the position of the distributor rotor in relationship to the intake manifold, remove the primary wire from the coil, then remove the distributor hold-down bolt and the distributor.
5. Remove all vacuum lines from the intake manifold and remove the temperature sending unit wire.
6. Disconnect the fuel line and any vacuum lines from the carburetor.
7. Remove all carburetor linkage and kickdown linkage that attaches to the intake manifold.
8. On 390, 427 and 428 engines, remove the valve covers, the rocker arm assemblies and the pushrods. The rocker arms should be removed by backing off each of the four bolts two turns in sequence from front to back. Keep pushrods in order so that they can be installed in their original position.
9. Remove the manifold attaching bolts and remove the manifold. If it is necessary to pry the manifold to loosen it from the engine, use care not to damage any gasket sealing surfaces.
10. Clean all gasket surfaces and firmly cement new gaskets in place. The gaskets should be securely locked in place before attempting to install the manifold.
11. Reverse above procedure to reinstall.

302 Boss, 351C, 351 HO and 400 V8

1. Drain cooling system and remove air cleaner. On Boss 302 engine, disconnect Thermactor air hose from check valve at rear of intake manifold and loosen hose clamp at hose bracket. Remove air hose and Thermactor air by-pass valve from bracket and position out of way.
2. Disconnect accelerator linkage and accelerator downshift linkage, if so equipped, and position out of way. On Boss 302, disconnect choke cable from carburetor.
3. Disconnect high tension lead and wires from coil. Disconnect engine wire loom and position out of way.
4. Disconnect spark plug wires

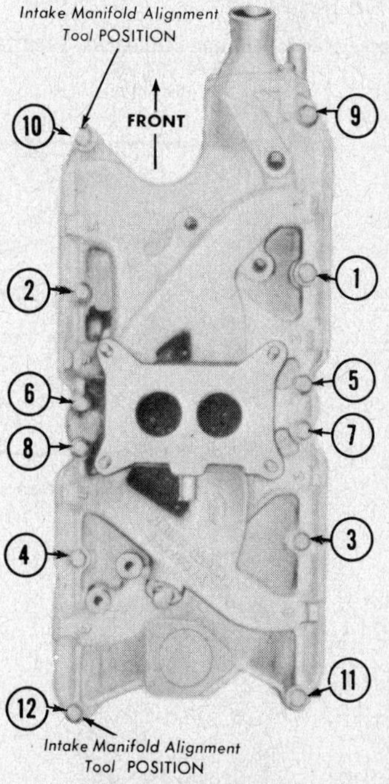
Intake Manifold Alignment Tool POSITION
FRONT
10
9
2
1
6
5
8
7
4
3
12
11
Intake Manifold Alignment Tool POSITION

Intake manifold torque sequence—1967 289 V8
(© Ford Motor Co)

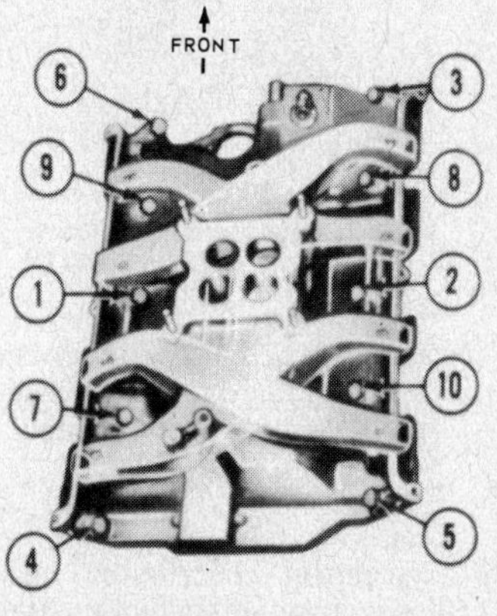
FRONT
6
3
9
8
1
2
7
10
4
5

Intake manifold torque sequence—390, 427 and 428 V8
(© Ford Motor Co)

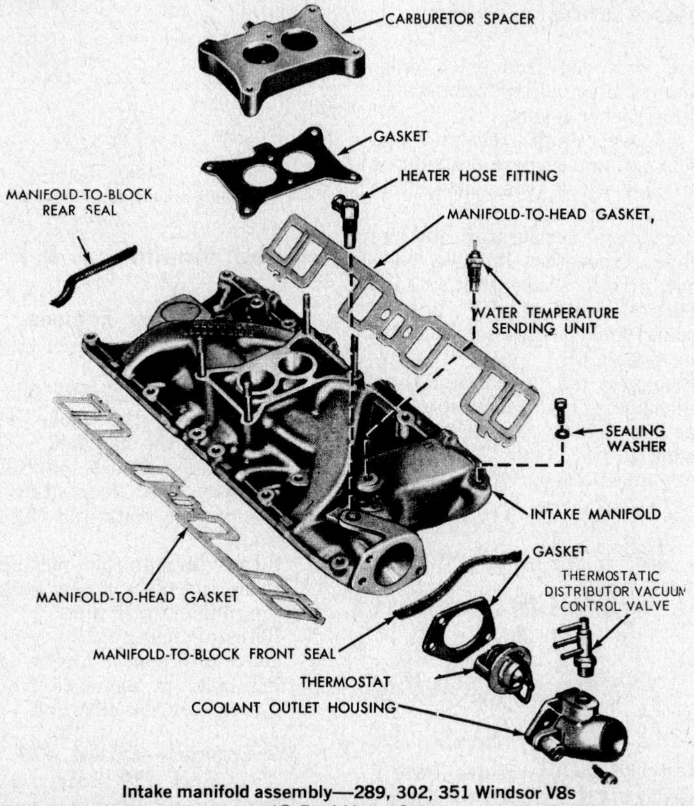
CARBURETOR SPACER
GASKET
HEATER HOSE FITTING
MANIFOLD-TO-BLOCK REAR SEAL
MANIFOLD-TO-HEAD GASKET,
WATER TEMPERATURE SENDING UNIT
SEALING WASHER
INTAKE MANIFOLD
GASKET
THERMOSTATIC DISTRIBUTOR VACUUM CONTROL VALVE
MANIFOLD-TO-HEAD GASKET
MANIFOLD-TO-BLOCK FRONT SEAL
THERMOSTAT
COOLANT OUTLET HOUSING

Intake manifold assembly—289, 302, 351 Windsor V8s
(© Ford Motor Co)

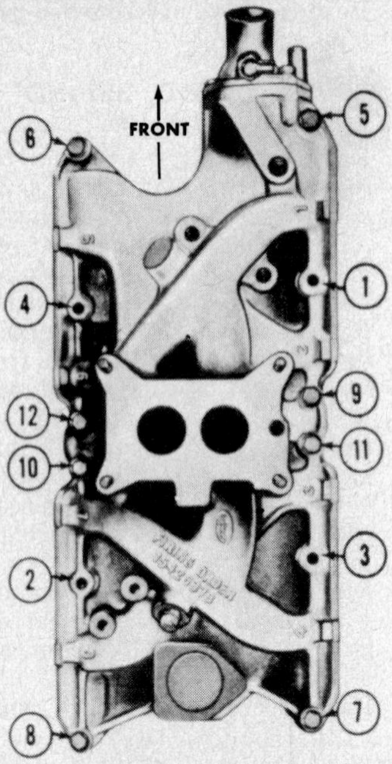
FRONT
6
5
4
1
12
9
10
11
2
3
8
7

Intake manifold torque sequence—1968 289, 1968-74 302 V8
(© Ford Motor Co)

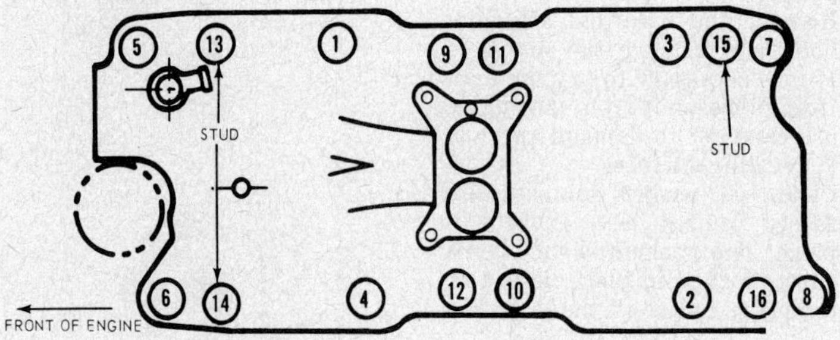
5
13
1
9
11
3
15
7
STUD
STUD
FRONT OF ENGINE
6
14
4
12
10
2
16
8

Intake manifold torque sequence—1969-74 351W V8
(© Ford Motor Co)

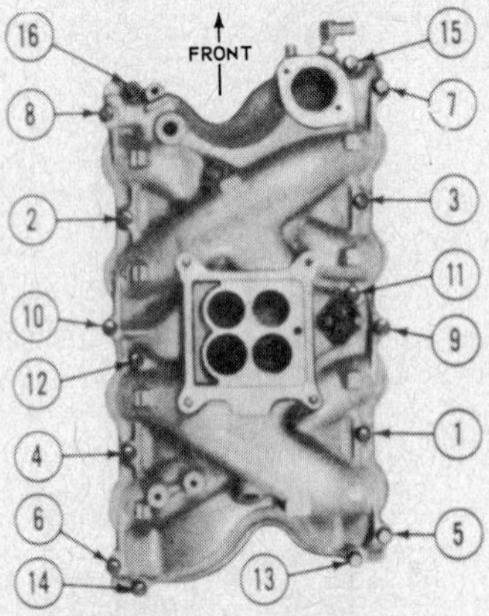
16
FRONT
15
8
7
2
3
11
10
9
12
4
1
6
5
14
13

Intake manifold torque sequence—1970-74 429, 1973-74 460PI V8
(© Ford Motor Co)

from spark plugs by grasping, twisting, and pulling molded cap only. Remove distributor cap and wire assembly.

5. Remove carburetor fuel inlet line.
6. Disconnect distributor vacuum hoses from distributor. Remove hold-down bolt and remove distributor.
7. Disconnect radiator upper hose from coolant outlet housing and disconnect temperature sender wire.
8. Loosen clamp on water pump by-pass hose at coolant outlet housing and slide hose off outlet housing.
9. Disconnect crankcase vent hose (PCV) at rocker cover.
10. If vehicle is air conditioned, remove compressor to intake manifold brackets.
11. Remove intake manifold and carburetor as an assembly. Discard all used gaskets and clean all mating surfaces.
12. Reverse procedure to install.

Boss 429 V8

1. Disconnect battery.
2. Drain cooling system.
3. Disconnect heater hose from manifold.
4. Disconnect positive crank case ventilation (PCV) hose from right-hand rocker cover. Disconnect and tag all vacuum lines from rear of intake manifold.
5. Twist and pull the molded spark plug wire cap from each plug. Remove plug wires from brackets on rocker covers.
6. Disconnect high tension lead from coil and remove distributor cap and wires from distributor as an assembly.
7. Disconnect accelerator linkage from carburetor. Remove bolts that attach accelerator linkage bellcrank. Disconnect linkage spring and position linkage to one side.
8. Disconnect all distributor vacuum lines from carburetor and vacuum control valves and tag them.
9. Disconnect carburetor fuel line.

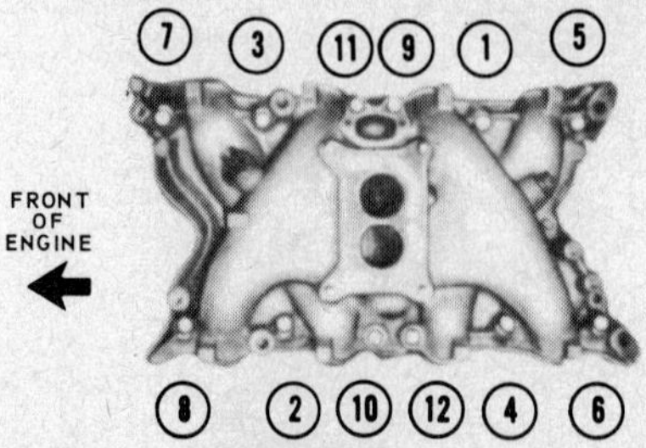
7
3
11
9
1
5
FRONT OF ENGINE
8
2
10
12
4
6

Intake manifold torque sequence—351C and 400 V8
(© Ford Motor Co)

10. Disconnect wiring harness from coil battery terminal, temperature sender unit, oil pressure sending unit, and other connections as necessary. Disengage wiring harness from retaining clips at left rocker cover bolts. Move harness out of way.
11. Disconnect Thermactor air bypass valve from mounting bracket and place it to one side.
12. Remove coil and bracket assembly.
13. Disconnect manifold heat inlet and outlet tubes from rear of manifold and from exhaust pipe.
14. Remove distributor from engine.
15. Remove intake manifold attaching bolts.
16. Remove manifold and carburetor as an assembly. Discard used gaskets.
17. To install intake manifold, reverse above procedure—the manifold should be torqued in place as shown in the illustration.

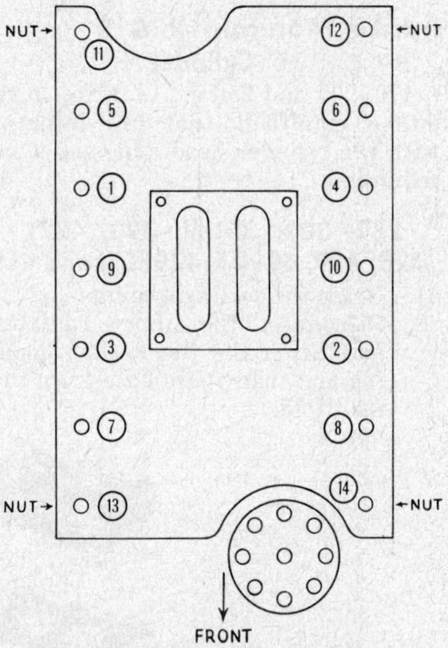
NUT
12
NUT
11
5
6
1
4
9
10
3
2
7
8
14
NUT
13
NUT
FRONT

Tightening procedure—Boss 429

Exhaust Manifold R & R

6 Cylinder Engines

1. Remove the air cleaner and heat duct body.
2. Disconnect the muffler inlet pipe and remove the choke hot air tube from the manifold.
3. Bend the exhaust manifold attaching bolt lock tabs back, remove the bolts and the manifold.
4. Clean all manifold mating surfaces and place a new gasket on the muffler inlet pipe.
5. Reinstall manifold by reversing above procedure, torque attaching bolts in sequence from the centermost bolt outward.

V8 Engines—Except 428 CJ and 429 Boss

1. On right exhaust manifold,

remove the air cleaner, automatic choke heat tube and air cleaner heat ducts.
2. Disconnect the exhaust manifold(s) from the muffler inlet pipe(s).
3. Remove the manifold attaching bolts and remove the manifold(s).
4. Reverse above procedure to reinstall, using new inlet pipe gaskets.

NOTE: To remove the left side exhaust manifold from a car equipped with a 351 C, or 400 engine, it is necessary to remove the oil filter and the transmission selector cross-shaft or clutch linkage and equalizer shaft bracket, depending on transmission type.

429 Boss Engine

1. Remove the battery ground cable.
2. Remove the valve covers.
3. Disconnect the Thermactor air manifolds from the check valves.
4. Remove the air manifolds from the exhaust manifolds.
5. With the car on a hoist, remove the 8 exhaust manifold attaching bolts and disconnect the muffler inlet pipes.
6. Disconnect the clutch linkage and equalizer bracket from the engine.
7. Work the manifolds rearward and remove them through the engine compartment.
8. Clean all gasket surfaces and install new gaskets on the muffler inlet pipes.
9. Reinstall the manifold, working them into position from under the vehicle.

428 CJ Engine

This procedure is for removing both manifolds. If only one manifold is to be removed, do not remove any equipment located on or near the opposite side of the engine.

1. Remove the air cleaner, heat tubes, choke and vacuum lines from the manifold.
2. Remove the air cleaner heat tube mounting studs and the three forward attaching bolts from the right-side manifold.
3. Raise the car on a hoist, and remove the idler arm bracket from the frame.
4. Disconnect the starter cable and remove the starter motor.
5. Remove the remaining right-side manifold attaching bolts.
6. Disconnect all exhaust system hangers and lower the exhaust system.
7. Remove the inlet pipes from the manifolds.
8. On vehicles with manual transmission, remove the clutch linkage and equalizer bracket from the engine.
9. Disconnect the Pitman arm from the steering sector shaft and, on vehicles with power steering, remove the steering control valve bracket from the frame.
10. Lower the car, disconnect the steering shaft flex joint, unbolt and remove the steering gear box assembly from the frame.
11. Raise the car again and disconnect and remove both motor mounts and the rear crossmember support attaching bolts.
12. Position a jack under the engine and, using a piece of wood under the oil pan, raise the engine slightly.
13. Remove remaining manifold attaching bolts and remove the manifolds.
14. Clean all gasket surfaces and, using new inlet pipe gaskets, reverse above procedure to reinstall manifolds.

Valve System

The 6-cylinder engines are equipped with tubular pushrods and barrel type tappets. Valve lash is controlled by self locking adjusting screws.

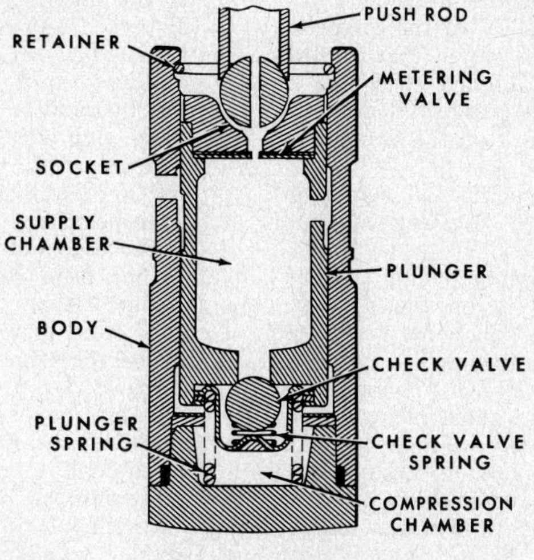
PUSH ROD
RETAINER
METERING VALVE
SOCKET
SUPPLY CHAMBER
PLUNGER
BODY
CHECK VALVE
PLUNGER SPRING
CHECK VALVE SPRING
COMPRESSION CHAMBER

Hydraulic tappet
(© Ford Motor Co)

V8 engines, except the 289, 427 high performance, 429 SCJ, and Boss 302, 351, and 429, use hydraulic tappets. The pushrods in the V8s also transfer oil under pressure to the friction areas of the rocker arms.

Preliminary Valve Adjustment

6-Cylinder

1. Crank the engine until the TDC mark on the crankshaft damper is aligned with timing pointer on the cylinder front cover, and no. 1 piston is on its compression stroke.
2. Scribe a mark on the damper at this point.
3. Scribe two more marks on the damper, each equally spaced from the first mark, dividing the damper into thirds.
4. With the engine on TDC of the compression stroke, (mark A aligned with the pointer) back off the rocker arm adjusting nut until there is end-play in the pushrod. Tighten the adjusting nut until all clearance is removed, then tighten the adjusting nut one additional turn on 1969 and later models and 3/4 of a turn on all 1967-68 models. To determine when all clearance is removed from the rocker arm, turn the pushrod with the fingers. When the pushrod can no longer be turned, all clearance has been removed.
5. Repeat this procedure for each valve, turning the crankshaft 1/3 turn to the next mark each time and following the engine firing order of 1-5-3-6-2-4.

289 and 1968-69 302 V8

NOTE: This procedure for the 289 and early 302 V8 engines is designed for engines in which the rocker arm mounting studs do not incorporate a positive stop shoulder on the mounting stud. These engines were originally equipped with this kind of stud. However, due to production differences, it is possible some 289 or early 302 engines may be encountered that are equipped with positive stop rocker arm mounting studs. Before following this procedure, verify that the rocker arm mounting studs do not incorporate a positive stop shoulder. On studs without a positive stop, the shank portion of the stud that is exposed just above the cylinder head is the same diameter as the threaded portion, at the top of the stud, to which the rocker arm retaining nut attaches. If the shank portion of the stud is of greater diameter than the threaded portion, this identifies it as a positive stop rocker arm stud and the procedure for the 351 engine should be followed.

1. Crank the engine until no. 1 cylinder is at TDC of the compression stroke and the timing

pointer is aligned with the mark on the crankshaft damper.
2. Scribe a mark on the damper at this point.
3. Scribe three more marks on the damper, dividing the damper into quarters.
4. With mark A aligned with the timing pointer, adjust the valves on no. 1 cylinder by backing off the adjusting nut until the pushrod has free play in it. Then, tighten the nut until there is no free play in the pushrod. This can be determined by turning the pushrod while tightening the nut; when the pushrod can no longer be turned, all clearance has been removed. After the clearance has been removed tighten the nut an additional 3/4 of a turn.
5. Repeat this procedure for each valve, turning the crankshaft 1/4 turn to the next mark each time and following the engine firing order of 1-5-4-2-6-3-7-8.

351, 400, 429, 460 and All 1970-74 302 V8

1. Crank the engine until no. 1 cylinder is at TDC of the compression stroke and the timing pointer is aligned with the 0 mark on the crankshaft damper.
2. Scribe a mark on the damper at this point.
3. Scribe two additional marks on the damper, dividing it into thirds.
4. With the timing pointer aligned with mark A on the damper, tighten the following valves to the specified torque:
   302 and 429–No. 1, 7 and 8 Intake; No. 1, 5 and 4 exhaust
   351 and 400– No. 1, 4 and 8 Intake; No. 1, 3 and 7 Exhaust
5. Rotate the crankshaft 180° to point B and tighten the following valves:
   302 and 429– No. 5 and 4 Intake; No. 2 and 6 Exhaust
   351 and 400– No. 3 and 7 Intake; No. 2 and 6 Exhaust
6. Rotate the crankshaft 270° to point C and tighten the following valves:
   302 and 429– No. 2, 3 and 6 Intake; No. 7, 3 and 8 Exhaust
   351 and 400– No. 2, 5 and 6 Intake; No. 4. 5 and 8 Exhaust
7. Rocker arm tighten specifications are: 302 and 351W—tighten nut until it contacts the rocker shoulder, then torque to 18–20 ft lbs.; 351C and 400—tighten bolt to 18-25 ft lbs.; 429, 460—tighten nut until it contacts rocker shoulder, then torque to 18-22 ft lbs.

390, 428 and 1968 427

1. Position the left rocker arm and oil deflector assembly on the head, making sure the oversize bolt is installed in the second rocker arm stand from the front of the engine.
2. Install each rocker arm stand attaching bolt finger tight, then, working from the front of the engine back, tighten each bolt two turns at a tine until the rocker arm is mounted on the head.
3. Torque the bolts to 40-45 ft lbs.
4. Position the right rocker arm and oil deflector assembly on the head, making sure the oversize bolt is installed in the third rocker arm stand from the front of the engine.
5. Repeat Steps 2 and 3 on the right side, this time working from the rear of the engine forward.

289 HP, Boss 302, Boss 351 and Boss 429, 429SCJ and 1967 427

1. Make primary valve adjustment in the following manner, and continue to install rocker covers and fill cooling system.

NOTE: Tappets must be adjusted while on the low radius of the cam.

2. If the distributor has not been disturbed and ignition timing is reasonably correct, proceed as follows: rotate crankshaft until the distributor rotor points to No. 1 plug wire tower of the distributor cap. Adjust valves in cylinder firing order according to rotor position.
3. If the distributor is out of time or has been removed from the engine: turn the crankshaft until No. 1 piston is at the top of its compression stroke. (intake valve of No. 6 cylinder just beginning to open), and the crankshaft damper is on T.D.C. Make three chalk marks on the crankshaft damper, 120° apart, starting with T.D.C. These marks will divide crankshaft travel into three parts, or six segments, of each engine cycle. Valve adjustment can then be made in firing sequence, beginning with No. 1 on TDC and progressing through the regular order of firing by advancing one chalk mark (120 crankshaft degrees) at a time.

V8 Mechanical Valve Lifter Final Adjustment

1. Run engine to bring to operating temperature.
2. Remove rocker covers.
3. Insert a feeler gauge of specified thickness between the rocker arm and valve, and with engine running, adjust rocker arm to obtain desired clearance.
4. Reinstall rocker cover.

Disassembly of Cylinder Heads

1. Remove cylinder heads.
2. Compress valve springs using valve spring compressor.
3. Remove valve locks or keys.
4. Release valve springs.
5. Remove valve springs, retainers, oil seals, and valves. On Boss 302 and Boss 429 engines, remove valve spring seals also.

NOTE: if a valve does not slide out of the guide easily check end of stem for mushrooming or heading over. If the stem is mushroomed, file off excess, remove and discard valve. If valve is not mushroomed, lubricate

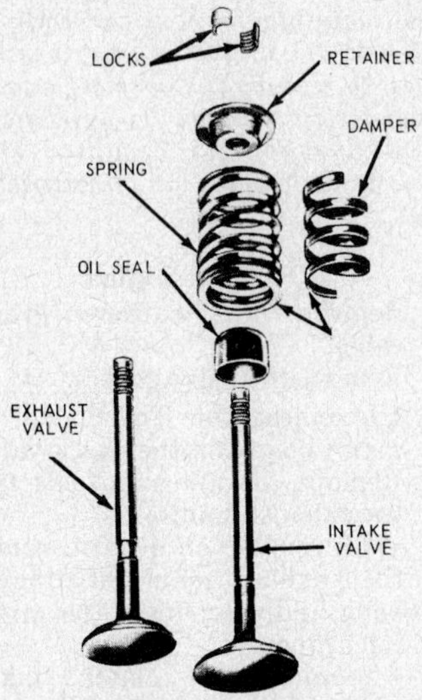
LOCKS
RETAINER
DAMPER
SPRING
OIL SEAL
EXHAUST VALVE
INTAKE VALVE

Valve assembly—351 Cleveland V8
(© Ford Motor Co)

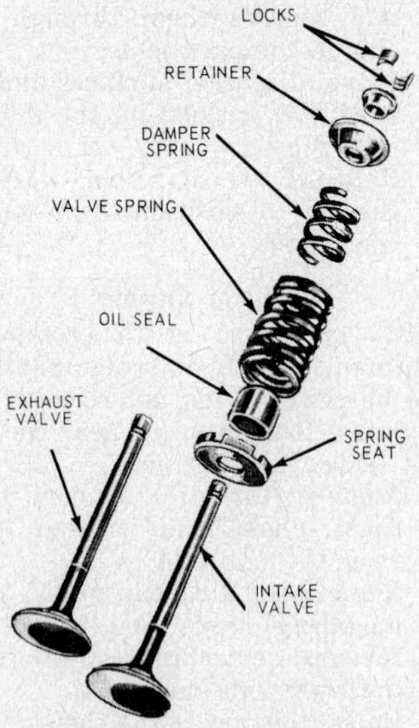
LOCKS
RETAINER
DAMPER SPRING
VALVE SPRING
OIL SEAL
EXHAUST VALVE
SPRING SEAT
INTAKE VALVE

Valve assembly—Boss 302 V8
(© Ford Motor Co)

system of valve, remove, and check for stem wear or damage.

Valve Seals—Boss 429

The Boss 429 uses special valve seals which require special handling. To remove, grasp bottom edge of valve seal with Perfect Circle tool No. VSIT-1 or equivalent and pull seal from valve. To install, place plastic installation cap that comes with seal kit over valve stem. Start seal carefully over cap. Push seal down until jacket touches top of guide.

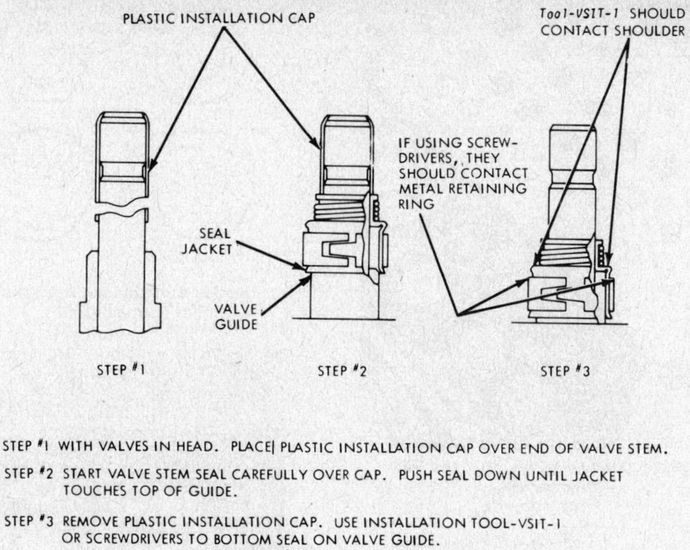
PLASTIC INSTALLATION CAP
Tool-VSIT-1 SHOULD CONTACT SHOULDER
IF USING SCREW-DRIVERS, THEY SHOULD CONTACT METAL RETAINING RING
SEAL JACKET
VALVE GUIDE
STEP #1
STEP #2
STEP #3
STEP #1 WITH VALVES IN HEAD. PLACE PLASTIC INSTALLATION CAP OVER END OF VALVE STEM.
STEP #2 START VALVE STEM SEAL CAREFULLY OVER CAP. PUSH SEAL DOWN UNTIL JACKET TOUCHES TOP OF GUIDE.
STEP #3 REMOVE PLASTIC INSTALLATION CAP. USE INSTALLATION TOOL-VSIT-1 OR SCREWDRIVERS TO BOTTOM SEAL ON VALVE GUIDE.

Installing valve stem seals—Boss 429
(© Ford Motor Co)

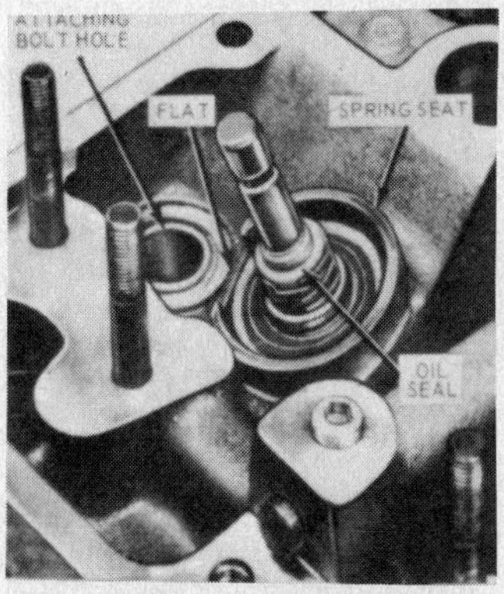
FLAT
SPRING SEAT
OIL SEAL

Valve spring seal and oil seal location —Boss 429
(© Ford Motor Co)

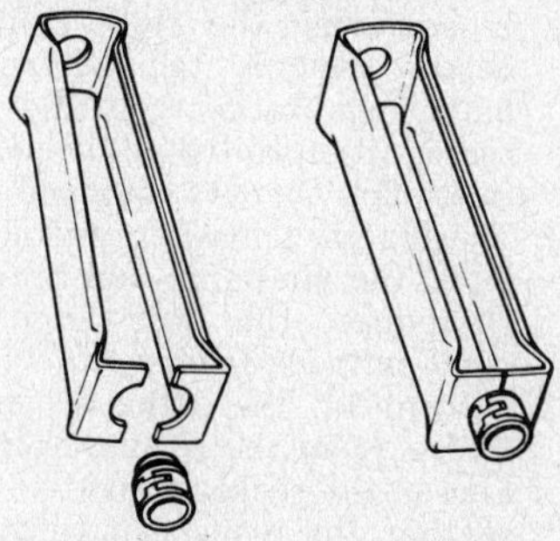

Boss 429 valve stem seal tool
(© Ford Motor Co)

Remove plastic installation cap. Grasp valve seal with Perfect Circle tool and push seal on to valve guide until it bottoms. If tool is not available, place two small screwdrivers about 90° from gap in metal retaining ring and push seal downward until it bottoms.

Valve Guides

Ford Motor Company engines use integral valve guides. Mercury and Ford dealers offer valves with oversize stems for worn guides. To fit these, enlarge valve guide bores with valve guide reamers to an oversize that cleans up wear. If a large oversize is required it is best to approach that size in stages by using a series of reamers of increasing diameter. This helps to maintain the concentricity of the guide bore with the valve seat. The correct valve guide to stem clearance is at front of this section. As an alternative, some local automotive machine shops will fit replacement guides that use standard stem valves.

Cylinder Head

6 Cylinder Removal

1. Drain cooling system, remove the air cleaner and disconnect the battery cable at the cylinder head.

Removing rocker arm assembly—6 cyl
(© Ford Motor Co)

2. Disconnect exhaust pipe at the manifold end, spring the exhaust pipe down and remove the flange gasket.
3. Disconnect the fuel and vacuum lines from the carburetor. Disconnect the intake manifold line at the intake manifold.
4. Disconnect the accelerator and retracting spring at the carburetor.
5. Disconnect the carburetor spacer outlet line at the spacer. Disconnect the radiator upper hose and the heater hose at the water outlet elbow. Disconnect the radiator lower hose and the heater hose at the water pump.
6. Disconnect the distributor vacuum control line at the distributor. Disconnect the gas filter line on the inlet side of the filter.
7. Disconnect the spark plug wires and remove the plugs.
8. Remove the rocker arm cover.
9. Back off all of the tappet adjusting screws to relieve tension on the rocker shaft. Loosen the rocker arm shaft attaching bolts and remove the rocker arm and shaft assembly. Remove the valve pushrods, in order, and keep them that way.
10. Remove one cylinder-head bolt from each end of the head (at opposite corners) and install cylinder head guide studs. Remove the remaining cylinder head bolts and lift off the cylinder head.

To help in removal and installation of cylinder head, two 6 in. x 7/16—14 bolts with heads cut off and the head end slightly tapered and slotted for installation and removal, with a screwdriver, will reduce the possibility of damage during head replacement. These guide studs make a handy tool during head removal and gasket and head replacement.

6-Cylinder Installation

1. Clean the cylinder head and block surfaces. Be sure of flatness and no surface damage.
2. Apply cylinder head gasket sealer to both sides of the new gasket and slide the gasket down over the two guide studs in the cylinder block.

NOTE: apply gasket sealer only to steel shim head gaskets. Steel-asbestos composite head gaskets are to be installed without any sealer.

3. Carefully lower the cylinder head over the guide studs. Place the exhaust pipe flange on the manifold studs (new gasket).
4. Coat the threads of the end bolts for the right side of the cylinder head with a small amount of water-resistant sealer. Install, but do not tighten, two head bolts at opposite ends to hold the

head gasket in place. Remove the guide studs and install the remaining bolts.

5. Cylinder head torquing should proceed in three steps and in prescribed order. Tighten to 55 ft. lbs., then give them a second tightening to 65 ft. lbs. The final step is to 75 ft. lbs., at which they should remain undisturbed.
6. Lubricate both ends of the pushrods and install them in their original locations.
7. Apply a petroleum jelly-type lubricant to the rocker arm pads and the valve stem tips and position the rocker arm shaft assembly on the head. Be sure the oil holes in the shaft are in a down position.
8. Tighten all the rocker shaft retaining bolts to 30-35 ft. lbs. and do a preliminary valve adjustment (make sure there are no tight valve adjustments).
9. Hook up the exhaust pipe.
10. Reconnect the heater and radiator hoses.
11. Reposition the distributor vacuum line, the carburetor gas line and the intake manifold vacuum line on the engine. Hook them up to their respective connections and reconnect the battery cable to the cylinder head.
12. Connect the accelerator rod and retracting spring. Connect the choke control cable and adjust the choke.
13. Reconnect the vacuum line at the distributor. Connect the fuel inlet line at the fuel filter and the intake manifold vacuum line at the vacuum pump. Connect the windshield wiper vacuum line to the other side of the vacuum pump.
14. Lightly lubricate the spark plug threads, install them and torque to 25 ft. lbs. Connect spark plug wires and be sure the wires are all the way down in their sockets.
15. Fill the cooling system and bleed. Run the engine to stabilize all engine parts temperatures.
16. Adjust engine idle speed and idle fuel-air adjustment.

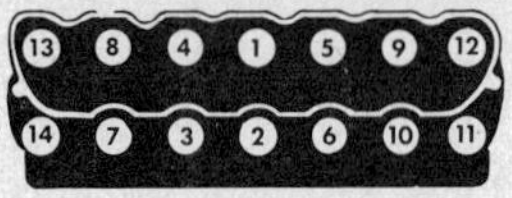
13 8 4 1 5 9 12
14 7 3 2 6 10 11

170, 200, 250 cu in. 6 cyl

17. Coat one side of a new rocker cover gasket with oil-resistant sealer. Lay the treated side of the gasket on the cover and install the cover. Be sure the gasket seals evenly all around the cylinder head.

All V8 Except 390, 427, 428 and Boss 429

1. Remove the valve covers and disconnect the negative battery cable.

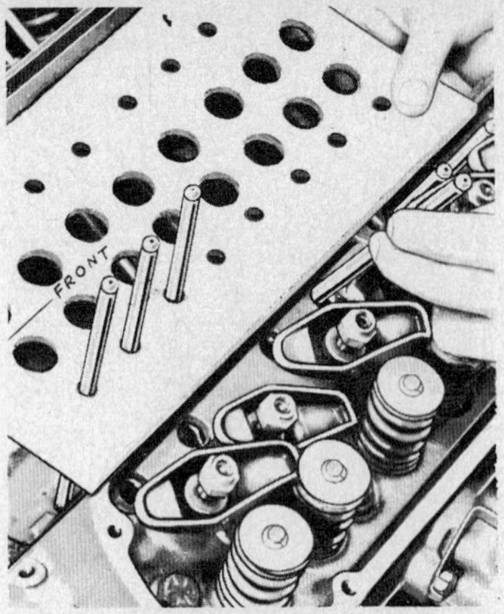
FRONT

Pushrod removal—289, 302, and 351 Windsor V8s
(© Ford Motor Co)

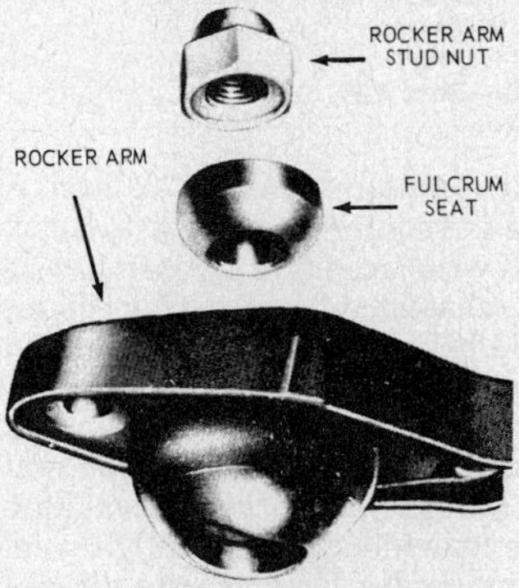
ROCKER ARM STUD NUT
ROCKER ARM
FULCRUM SEAT

289, 302, and 351 Windsor rocker arm assembly
(© Ford Motor Co)

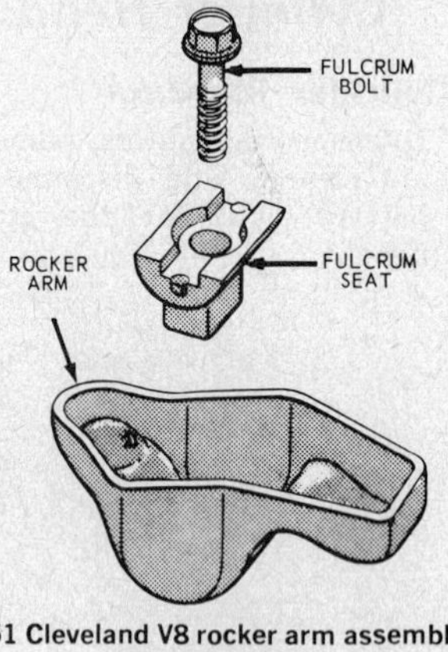
FULCRUM BOLT
ROCKER ARM
FULCRUM SEAT

351 Cleveland V8 rocker arm assembly
(© Ford Motor Co)

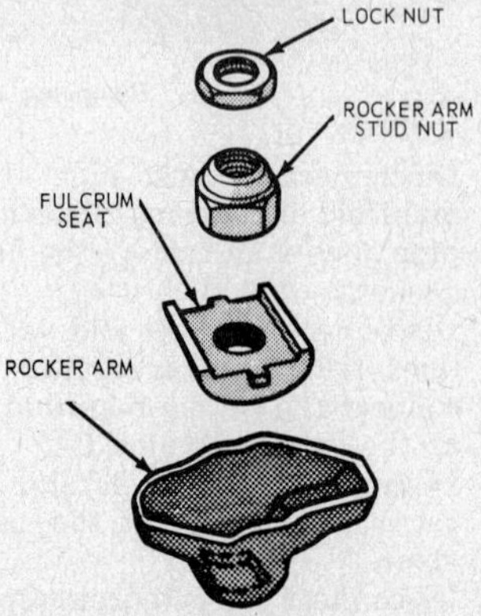
LOCK NUT
ROCKER ARM STUD NUT
FULCRUM SEAT
ROCKER ARM

Boss 302 rocker arm assembly
(© Ford Motor Co)

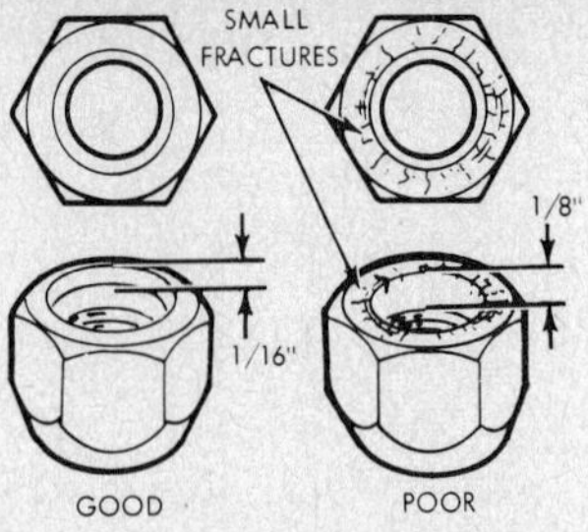
SMALL FRACTURES
1/8"
1/16"
GOOD
POOR

Rocker arm stud nut inspection
(© Ford Motor Co)

Removing push rods—351 Cleveland V8
(© Ford Motor Co)

2. Remove the intake manifold and carburetor assembly.
3. On cars equipped with air conditioning, remove the compressor from the engine and position it to one side, *without disconnecting the refrigerant lines.*
4. If removing the left cylinder head, on cars equipped with power steering, remove the pump, bracket, and drive belt and position to one side *without disconnecting the lines.* On cars with Thermactor emission control system, disconnect the hose from the air manifold on the left cylinder head.
5. If removing the right cylinder head, remove the alternator mounting bracket bolt and spacer, ignition coil, and air cleaner inlet duct. On cars equipped with Thermactor emission control, remove the air pump and bracket. Disconnect the hose from the right cylinder head.
6. Disconnect the exhaust manifold/s from the exhaust pipe/s.
7. Loosen the rocker arm stud nuts so that the arms can rotate to the side to clear the pushrods. Remove the pushrods.
8. Remove the cylinder head bolts and lift off the cylinder head. On some 351 engines, it may be necessary to remove the exhaust manifold to gain access to the lower cylinder head bolts.
9. Reverse the above procedures for

9 5 1 3 7
10 6 2 4 8

289, 302, 302 Boss, 351W, 351C, 400 V8 shown, 390, 427, 428, 429, 429 Boss (similar bolt pattern) V8.

installation taking care to follow the specified torque sequence as per the diagrams. Perform a preliminary valve adjustment before starting the engine.

390, 427, and 428 V8

1. Remove the intake manifold assembly as previously described.
2. Remove any remaining accessories that may obstruct removal.
3. Disconnect the exhaust manifold/s from the exhaust pipe/s.
4. Unbolt and remove heads.
5. Reverse above procedure for installation taking care to follow the specified torque sequence as per the diagrams.

Boss 429 Removal

1. Disconnect battery.
2. Remove cap that connects crankcase ventilation hose (PCV) to left rocker cover.
3. Remove air cleaner.

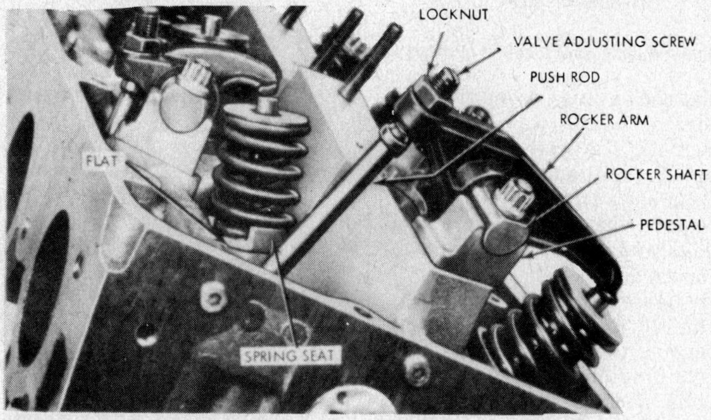
LOCKNUT
VALVE ADJUSTING SCREW
PUSH ROD
ROCKER ARM
ROCKER SHAFT
PEDESTAL
FLAT
SPRING SEAT

4. If removing right head, remove crankcase ventilation hose.
5. Lift each plug wire from bracket.
6. Disconnect wires from spark plugs by twisting and pulling on molded duct caps.
7. If removing left head, disconnect brake master cylinder from booster and move it to one side to provide clearance.
8. Remove rocker cover attaching nuts and bolts.
9. Lift rocker covers from heads.
10. Clean gasket material from covers and heads.
11. Remove intake manifold.
12. Back off all rocker arm adjusting screws.
13. Remove all rocker shaft attaching nuts from rocker shafts.

NOTE: each rocker on a Boss 429 engine has its own individual rocker shaft.

14. Remove rocker arms, shafts and pedestals. Keep them in sequence so that they can be installed in their original position.
15. Lift pushrods from cylinder head. Keep them in sequence to install into their original bores.
16. Disconnect exhaust head pipe from exhaust manifold.
17. Disconnect air hose from Thermactor check valve on head being removed.
18. Remove ten cylinder head bolts. Connect lifting sling to lifting eye at each end of cylinder head, and lift cylinder head from block with hoist.
19. Remove all rubber and steel gaskets from head and block.
20. Clean cylinder block and head mating surfaces.

Boss 429 Installation

1. Wipe head and block surfaces with chlorathane or a similar solvent.
2. Coat upper end of cylinder head and block with silicone rubber primer (Dow Corning A-4094 or equivalent). Coat gasket counter bores with quick drying adhesive sealer to prevent dropping gaskets while installing head.
3. Position four combustion chamber gaskets in counter bores with tabs seated down. Locate tabs by rotating gasket between finger and thumb to feel tabs.
4. Press four ¼ in. ID gaskets into cylinder head counter bores with stepped side facing up.
5. Press seventeen ½ in. ID gaskets into cylinder head counter bores with stepped side facing up.
6. Apply a continuous strip of sealant along top edge of cylinder head.
7. Install guide pin at each end of cylinder block.
8. Lower cylinder head into place over guide pins. Take care not to drop any gaskets.
9. Install but do not tighten eight attaching bolts and flat washers.
10. Remove two guide pins and install two remaining bolts and washers.
11. Torque attaching bolts in sequence shown at front of section to 55-60 ft. lbs. Then torque to 75-80 ft. lbs. Finally torque to 90-95 ft. lbs.
12. Connect Thermactor air to check valve.
13. Connect lead pipe to exhaust manifold.
14. Lubricate both ends of pushrods and install.
15. Lubricate rocker arms and shafts with engine oil and install with loosened adjusting screws. Do not torque shafts down at this time.
16. Rotate crank shaft damper until No. 1 piston is at TDC at end of compression stroke.
17. Install distributor in cylinder block with rotor at No. 1 firing position and points just beginning to open. Install hold-down clamp and bolt.
18. Torque rocker shaft nuts on No. 1 cylinder intake and exhaust to 12-15 ft. lbs. If engine is equipped with a solid lifter camshaft, adjust valve clearance to specification (cold) using feeler gauge or valve gapper between rocker arm and valve stem tip. Torque adjusting screws in place. If engine is equipped with an hydraulic lifter camshaft, loosen locknut and turn in adjusting screw on No. 1 cylinder intake and exhaust rocker until all clearance is removed. Rotate pushrod with fingers while tightening adjusting screw to determine point when clearance is removed. Tighten adjusting screws 1/16 turn further. Hold adjusting screws in place and torque locknuts to 20-30 ft. lbs.
19. Rotate crankshaft 90° to position No. 5 piston at TDC and repeat step 18 for No. 5 intake and exhaust rockers.
20. Rotate crank shaft 90° and repeat procedure in Step 18 for each cylinder in firing order (1-5-4-2-6-3-7-8).
21. Remove distributor.
22. Coat one side of new rocker cover gasket with oil resistant sealer and lay cemented side in place on cover.
23. Install cover. Make sure gasket seats evenly all around cover.
24. Tighten cover attaching bolts evenly and alternately in two steps. Then torque cover bolts to 12-15 ft. lbs. Wait two minutes and retorque to 12-15 ft. lbs.
25. Install intake manifold.
26. Connect each spark plug wire to its respective plug. Insert plug wires into brackets on valve cover.
27. Install cap and crank case ventilation hose (PCV) on valve cover.
28. If installing left head, install master cylinder on booster.
29. Install air cleaner and connect battery.

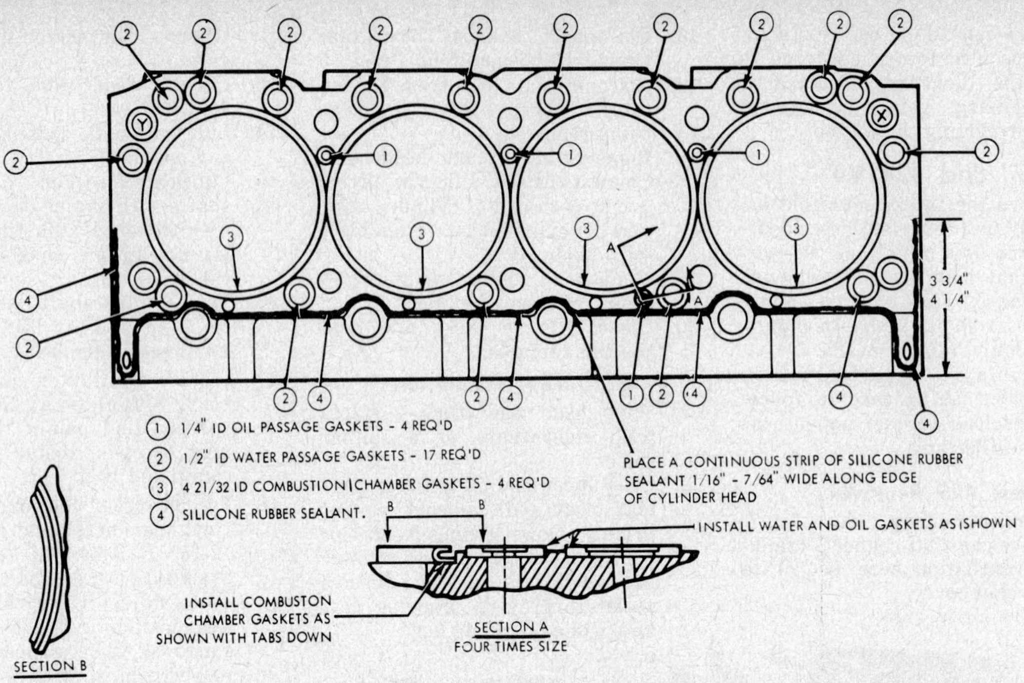
1/4" ID OIL PASSAGE GASKETS - 4 REQ'D
1/2" ID WATER PASSAGE GASKETS - 17 REQ'D
4 21/32 ID COMBUSTION CHAMBER GASKETS - 4 REQ'D
SILICONE RUBBER SEALANT.
PLACE A CONTINUOUS STRIP OF SILICONE RUBBER SEALANT 1/16" - 7/64" WIDE ALONG EDGE OF CYLINDER HEAD
INSTALL WATER AND OIL GASKETS AS SHOWN
INSTALL COMBUSTON CHAMBER GASKETS AS SHOWN WITH TABS DOWN
SECTION A
FOUR TIMES SIZE
SECTION B
3 3/4"
4 1/4"

Boss 429 cylinder head gasket location (© Ford Motor Co)

Chilton's

TIME SAVER

Frequently valves become bent or warped or their seats become blocked with carbon or other material. Left unattended, this can cause burnt valves, damaged cylinder heads and other expensive troubles. To detect leaking valves early, perform this test whenever the cylinder head is removed.

1. **After removing head, replace spark plugs. Removing spark plugs before removing heads eliminates breakage.**
2. **Place head on bench with valves, springs, retainers and keys installed and combustion chambers up.**
3. **Pour enough gasoline in each combustion chamber to completely cover both valves. Watch combustion chambers for two minutes for any leakage.**

Timing Cover, Chain, and Camshaft

6-Cylinder Cover and Chain

Removal

1. Drain the cooling system and crankcase.
2. Disconnect the upper radiator hose from the intake manifold and the lower hose from the water pump. On cars with automatic transmission, disconnect the cooler lines from the radiator.
3. Remove the radiator, fan and pulley, and engine drive belts. On models with air conditioning, remove the condenser retaining bolts and position the condenser forward. *Do not disconnect the refrigerant lines.*
4. On 170 and 200 cu. in. engines remove the cylinder front cover retaining bolts and front oil pan bolts and gently pry the cover away from the block. On 250 engines, it is necessary to remove the oil pan before removing the front cover.
5. Remove the crankshaft pulley bolt and use a puller to remove the vibration damper.

Tool

Crankshaft damper removal (© Ford Motor Co)

6. With a socket wrench of the proper size on the crankshaft pulley bolt, gently rotate the crankshaft in a clockwise direction until all slack is removed from the left side of the timing chain. Scribe a mark on the engine block parallel to the present position of the left side of the chain. Next, turn the crankshaft in a counterclockwise direction to remove all the slack from the right side of the chain. Force the left side of the chain outward with the fingers and measure the distance between the reference point and the present position of the chain. If the distance exceeds ½ inch, replace the chain and sprockets.

REFERENCE POINT

Checking timing chain deflection (© Ford Motor Co)

7. Crank the engine until the timing marks are aligned as shown in the illustration. Remove the bolt, slide sprocket and chain forward and remove as an assembly.

Installation

1. Position the sprockets and chain on the engine, making sure that the timing marks are aligned, dot to dot.
2. Reinstall the front cover, applying oil resistant sealer to the new gasket.

NOTE: on 170 and 200 engines, trim away the exposed portion of the old oil pan gasket flush with front of the engine block. Cut and position the required portion of a new gasket to the oil pan, applying sealer to both sides of it.

3. On 250 engines, reinstall the oil pan.
4. Install the fan, pulley and belts. Adjust belt tension.

5. Install the radiator, connect the radiator hoses and transmission cooling lines. If equipped with air conditioning, install the condenser.
6. Fill the crankcase and cooling system. Start the engine and check for leaks.

V8 Cover and Chain

Removal

1. Drain cooling system, remove air cleaner and disconnect the battery.
2. Disconnect radiator hoses and remove the radiator.
3. Disconnect heater hose at water pump. Slide water pump by-pass hose clamp toward the pump.
4. Loosen generator mounting bolts at the generator. Remove the generator support bolt at the water pump. Remove Thermactor pump on 428 CJ, 429 Super CJ, Boss 302, and Boss 429 engines.
5. Remove the fan, spacer, pulley, and drive belt.
6. Remove pulley from crankshaft pulley adapter. Remove cap screw and washer from front end of crankshaft. Remove crankshaft pulley adapter with a puller.
7. Disconnect fuel pump outlet line at the pump. Remove fuel pump retaining bolts and lay the pump to the side.
8. Remove the front cover attaching bolts. On the 351C and 400 engines, it is necessary to remove the oil pan before the front cover can be removed.
9. Remove the crankshaft oil slinger if so equipped.
10. Check timing chain deflection, using the procedure outlined in Step 6 of the six cylinder cover and chain removal.
11. Crank engine until sprocket timing marks are aligned as shown in valve timing illustration.

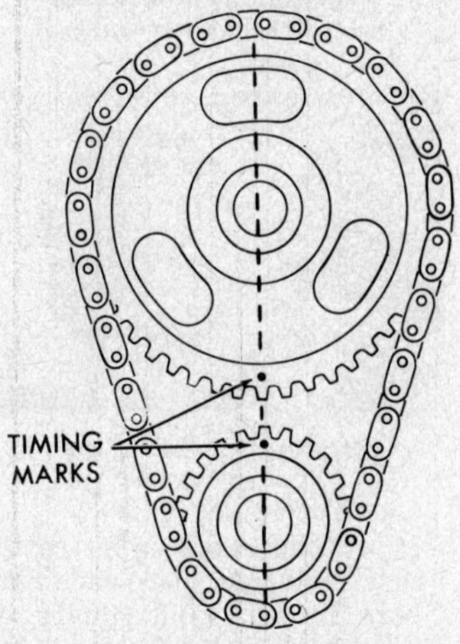
TIMING
MARKS

Timing mark alignment

12. Remove crankshaft sprocket cap screw, washers, and fuel pump eccentric. Slide both sprockets and chain forward and off as an assembly.

Installation

1. Position sprockets and chain on the camshaft and crankshaft with both timing marks dot to dot on a centerline. Install fuel pump eccentric, washers and sprocket attaching bolt. Torque the sprocket attaching bolt to 30–35 ft lbs.
2. Install crankshaft front oil slinger.
3. Clean front cover and mating surfaces of old gasket material.
4. Coat a new cover gasket with sealer and position it on the block.

NOTE: On all except 351C and 400 engines, trim away the exposed portion of the oil pan gasket flush with the cylinder block. Cut and position the required portion of a new gasket to the oil pan, applying sealer to both sides of it. On 351C and 400 engines, after installing the cylinder front cover, install the oil pan using a new gasket.

5. Install front cover, using a crankshaft-to-cover alignment tool. Torque attaching bolts to 12-15 ft. lbs.
6. Install fuel pump, torque attaching bolts to 23-28 ft. lbs., connect fuel pump outlet tube.
7. Install crankshaft pulley adapter and torque attaching bolt to 70-90 ft. lbs. Install crankshaft pulley.
8. Install water pump pulley, drive belt, spacer and fan.
9. Install generator support bolt at the water pump. Tighten generator mounting bolts. Adjust drive belt tension. Install Thermactor pump if so equipped.
10. Install radiator and connect all coolant and heater hoses. Connect battery cables.
11. Refill and bleed cooling system.
12. Start engine and operate at fast idle to operating temperature.
13. Check for leaks, install air cleaner. Adjust ignition timing and make all final adjustments.

6 & 8 Cylinder Cover Seal R & R

It is a recommended practice to replace the cover seal any time the front cover is removed.

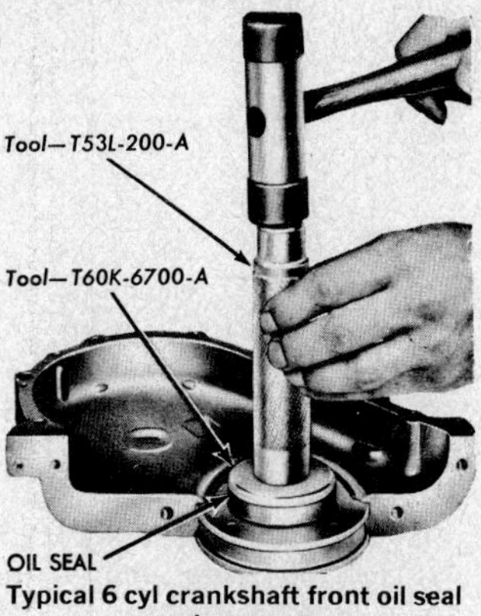
Tool—T53L-200-A
Tool—T60K-6700-A
OIL SEAL

Typical 6 cyl crankshaft front oil seal replacement
(© Ford Motor Co)

1. With the cover removed from the car, drive the old seal from the rear of cover with a pinpunch. Clean out the recess in the cover.
2. Coat the new seal with grease and drive it into the cover until it is fully seated. Check the seal after installation to be sure the spring is properly positioned in the seal.

Camshaft R & R

6 Cylinder Engines

1. Remove the cylinder head as directed in that section.
2. Remove the cylinder front cover, timing chain and sprockets as outlined in the preceding section.
3. Disconnect and remove the grille. On Mustang models, remove the gravel deflector.
4. Using a magnet, remove the valve lifters and keep them in order so that they can be installed in their original positions.
5. Remove the camshaft thrust plate and remove the camshaft by pulling it from the front of the engine. Use care not to damage the camshaft lobes or journals while removing the cam from the engine.
6. Before installing the camshaft, coat the lobes with Lubriplate and the journals and all valve parts with heavy oil.
7. Reverse above procedure to install, following recommended torque settings and tightening sequences. Perform a preliminary valve adjustment before starting the engine.

V8 Engines

1. Remove the intake manifold as outlined previously.
2. Remove the cylinder front cover, timing chain and sprockets as directed previously.
3. Remove the grille, and, on models with air conditioning, remove the condenser retaining bolts and position it out of the way. *Do not disconnect refrigerant lines.*
4. Remove the rocker arm covers.
5. On 390, 427 and 428 engines it is necessary to remove the rocker arm shafts to remove the intake manifold. On all other engines with individually mounted rocker arms, loosen the rocker arm fulcrum bolts and rotate the rocker arms to the side.
6. Remove the pushrods and lifters and keep them in order so that they can be installed in their original positions.
7. Remove the camshaft thrust plate and washer if so equipped. Remove the camshaft from the front of the engine. Use care not to damage camshaft lobes or journals while removing the cam from the engine.

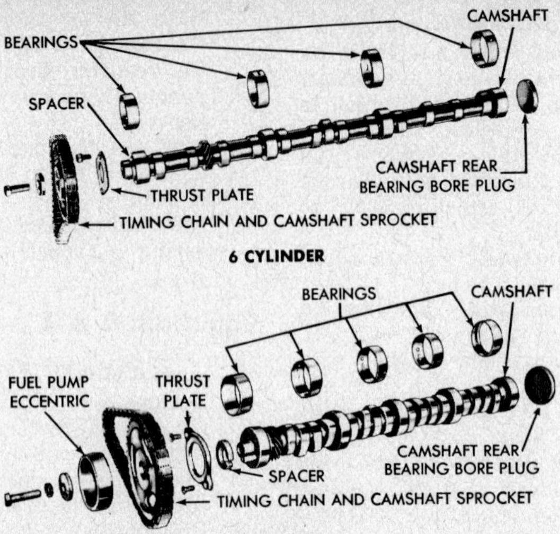

CAMSHAFT
BEARINGS
SPACER
CAMSHAFT REAR BEARING BORE PLUG
THRUST PLATE
TIMING CHAIN AND CAMSHAFT SPROCKET
6 CYLINDER
BEARINGS
CAMSHAFT
FUEL PUMP ECCENTRIC
THRUST PLATE
CAMSHAFT REAR BEARING BORE PLUG
SPACER
TIMING CHAIN AND CAMSHAFT SPROCKET

8 CYLINDER
Camshaft and related parts
(© Ford Motor Co)

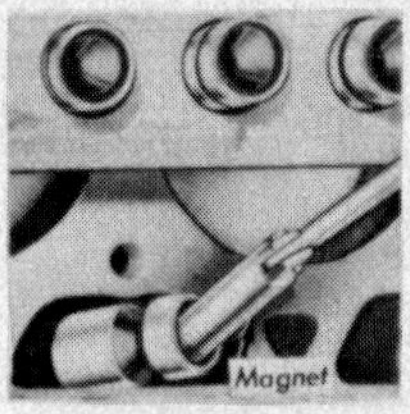

Magnet

Tappet removal
(© Ford Motor Co)

8. Before installing the camshaft, coat the lobes with Lubriplate and the journals and valve parts with heavy oil.
9. Reverse above procedure to install.

NOTE: on engines with individually mounted rocker arms, it is necessary to perform a preliminary valve adjustment before starting the engine.

Connecting Rods and Pistons

Removal

1. Drain crankcase and remove oil pan. Remove oil baffle tray if so equipped.

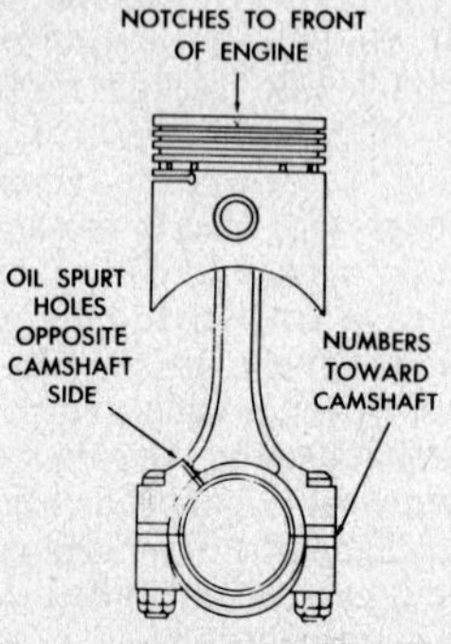

NOTCHES TO FRONT OF ENGINE
OIL SPURT HOLES OPPOSITE CAMSHAFT SIDE
NUMBERS TOWARD CAMSHAFT

Piston and rod assembly—6 cyl
(© Ford Motor Co)

2. Drain cooling system and remove cylinder head or heads.
3. Remove any ridge and/or deposits from the upper end of cylinder bores with a ridge reamer.

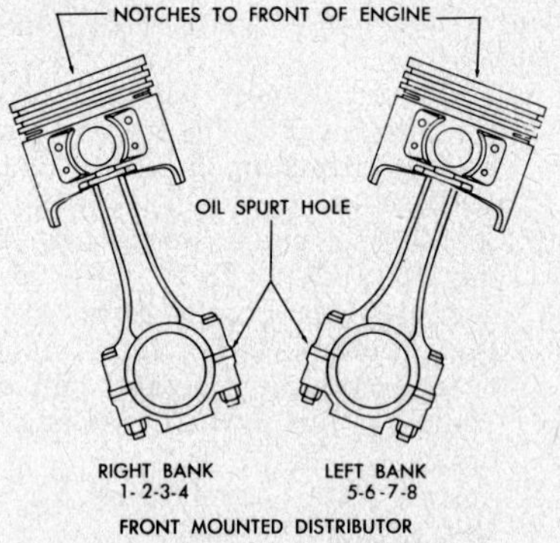

NOTCHES TO FRONT OF ENGINE
OIL SPURT HOLE
RIGHT BANK
1-2-3-4
LEFT BANK
5-6-7-8
FRONT MOUNTED DISTRIBUTOR

Piston and rod assembly—V8 289 cu in.

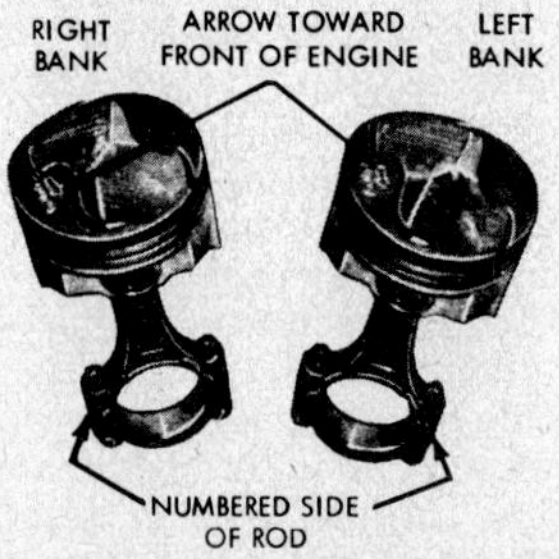

RIGHT BANK
ARROW TOWARD FRONT OF ENGINE
LEFT BANK
NUMBERED SIDE OF ROD

Piston and rod assembly—351 Cleveland and Boss 302 V8s
(© Ford Motor Co)

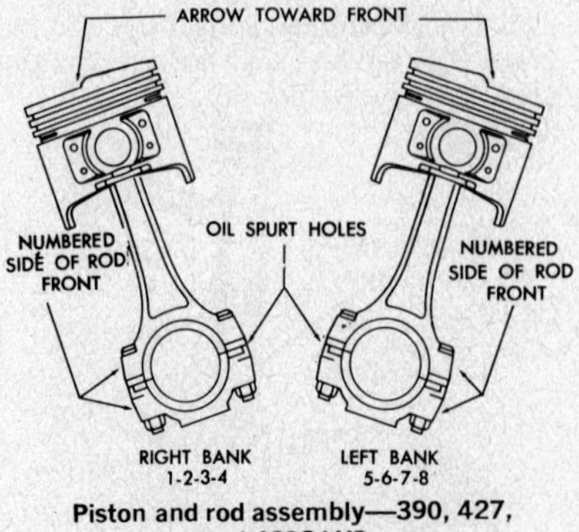

ARROW TOWARD FRONT
NUMBERED SIDE OF ROD FRONT
OIL SPURT HOLES
NUMBERED SIDE OF ROD FRONT
RIGHT BANK
1-2-3-4
LEFT BANK
5-6-7-8

Piston and rod assembly—390, 427, and 428CJ V8s
(© Ford Motor Co)

4. Check rods and pistons for identification numbers and, if necessary, number them.
5. Remove connecting rod cap nuts and caps. Push the rods away from the crankshaft and install caps and nuts loosely to their respective rods.
6. Push piston and rod assemblies up and out of the cylinders.

Installation

1. Lightly coat pistons, rings and cylinder walls with light engine oil.
2. With bearing caps removed, install pieces of protective rubber hose on bearing cap bolts.
3. Install each piston in its respective bore, using thread guards on each assembly. Guide the rod bearing into place on the crankcase journal.
4. Remove thread guards from connecting rods and install lower half of bearing and cap. Check clearances.
5. Install oil pan.
6. Install cylinder head.
7. Refill crankcase and cooling system.
8. Start engine, bring to operating temperature and check for leaks.

Piston Ring Replacement

Before replacing rings, inspect cylinder bores.

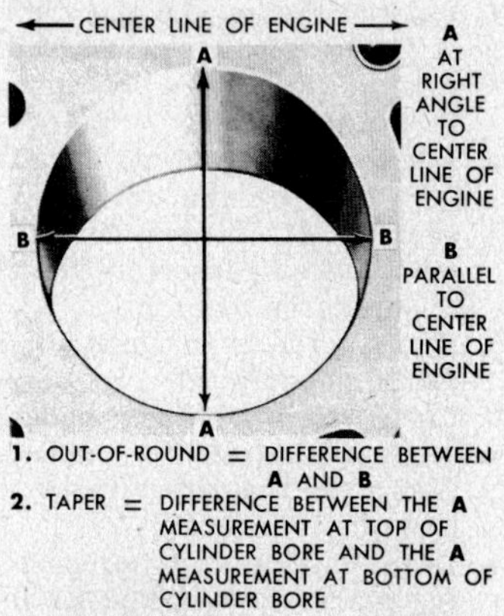

CENTER LINE OF ENGINE
A AT RIGHT ANGLE TO CENTER LINE OF ENGINE
B PARALLEL TO CENTER LINE OF ENGINE
A
B
B
A
1. OUT-OF-ROUND = DIFFERENCE BETWEEN A AND B
2. TAPER = DIFFERENCE BETWEEN THE A MEASUREMENT AT TOP OF CYLINDER BORE AND THE A MEASUREMENT AT BOTTOM OF CYLINDER BORE

Taper and out of roundness
(© Ford Motor Co)

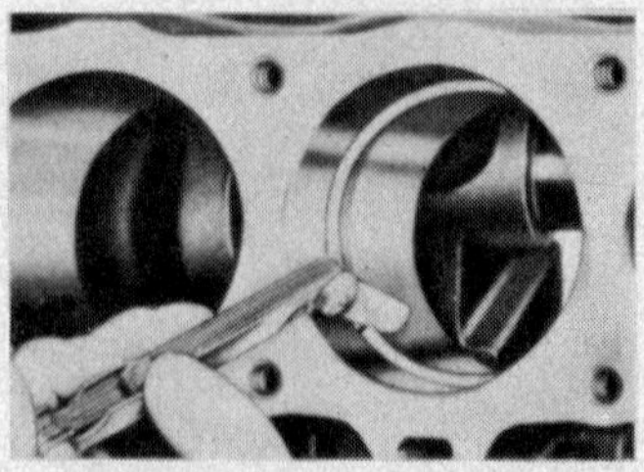

Measuring piston ring gap
(© Ford Motor Co)

1. If cylinder bore is in satisfactory condition, place each ring in bore in turn and square it in bore with head of piston. Measure ring gap. If ring gap is greater than limit, get new ring. If ring gap is less than limit, file end of ring to obtain correct gap.

Measuring ring side clearance
(© Ford Motor Co)

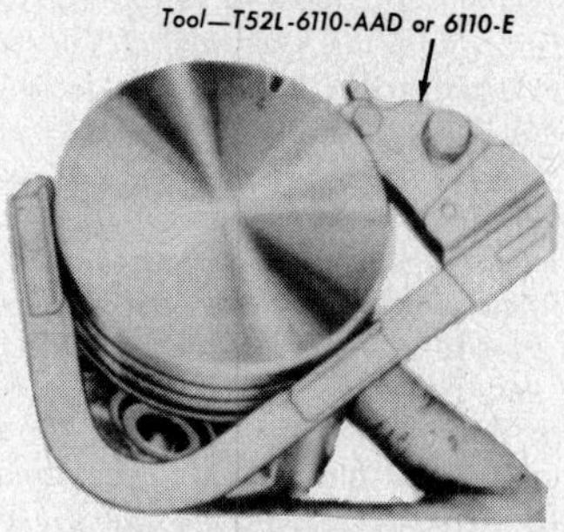
Tool—T52L-6110-AAD or 6110-E

Cleaning ring grooves
(© Ford Motor Co)

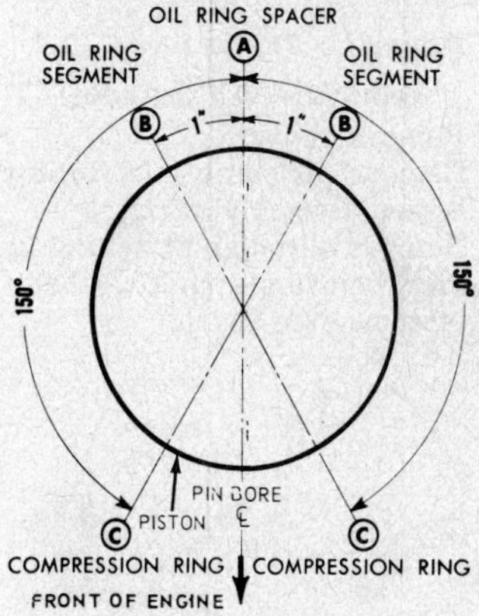
OIL RING SPACER
A
OIL RING SEGMENT
OIL RING SEGMENT
B
B
1°
1°
150°
150°
PIN BORE
℄
PISTON
C
C
COMPRESSION RING
COMPRESSION RING
FRONT OF ENGINE

Ring gap spacing
(© Ford Motor Co)

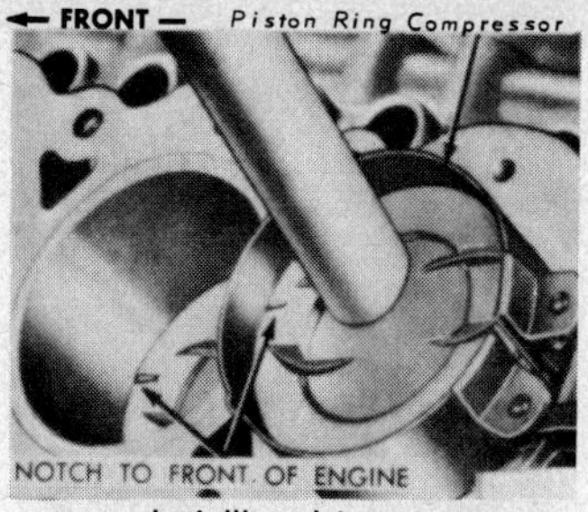
← FRONT —
Piston Ring Compressor
NOTCH TO FRONT OF ENGINE

Installing piston
(© Ford Motor Co)

2. Check ring side clearance by installing rings on piston, and inserting feeler gauge of correct dimension between ring and lower land. Gauge should slide freely around ring circumference without binding. Any wear will form a step on lower land. Replace any pistons having high steps. Before checking ring side clearance be sure ring grooves are clean and free of carbon, sludge, or grit.
3. Space ring gaps at equidistant intervals around piston circumference. Be sure to install piston in its original bore. Install short lengths of rubber tubing over connecting rod bolts to prevent damage to rod journal. Install ring compressor over rings on piston. Lower piston rod assembly into bore until ring compressor contacts block. Using wooden handle of hammer, push piston into bore while guiding rod onto journal.

Lubrication

All engines are equipped with full-flow-type oil filters to condition the oil before it reaches the main bearings. The filter is equipped with an internal, relief, by-pass valve as a safety precaution.

Oil Pan R & R

NOTE: on certain engine-chassis combinations, interference will be encountered between the oil pan and oil pump while attempting to remove the oil pan. If this occurs, lower the oil pan and reach inside it and remove the two bolts retaining the oil pump and pickup tube to the engine block.

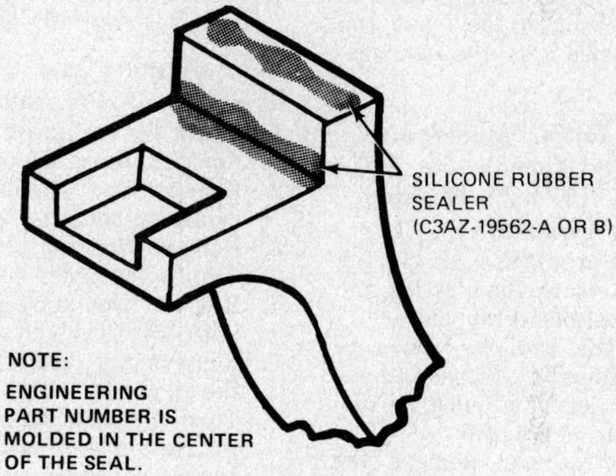
SILICONE RUBBER SEALER (C3AZ-19562-A OR B)
NOTE:
ENGINEERING PART NUMBER IS MOLDED IN THE CENTER OF THE SEAL.

Old style oil pan gasket seal
(© Ford Motor Co)

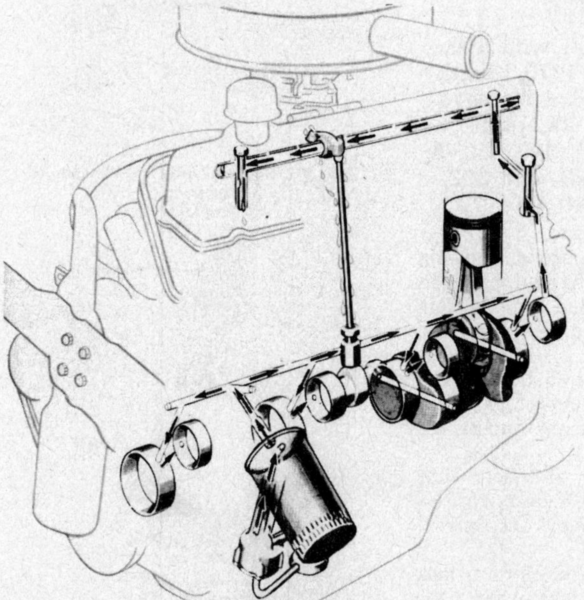

6 cyl engine lubrication
(© Ford Motor Co)

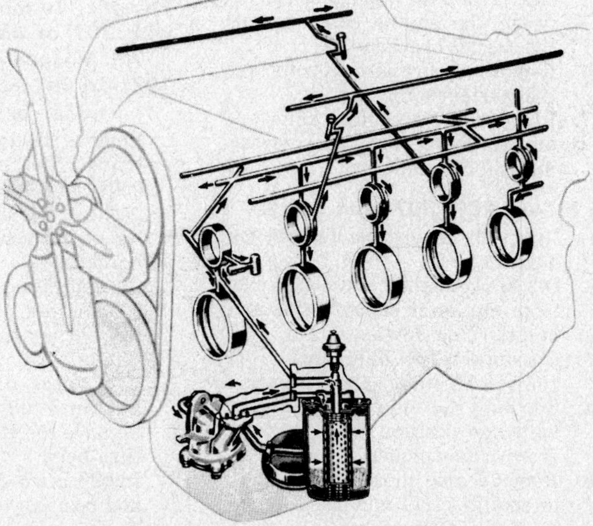

390, 427, and 428CJ V8s engine lubrication
(© Ford Motor Co)

Lower the pump and pickup tube assembly into the pan and remove it with the pan. To ensure proper gasket sealing, the oil pan retaining bolts should be tightened from the center outward.

1967-70 170, 200, and 250 6 Cylinder—All Models

1. Drain the crankcase. Remove the dipstick and the flywheel inspection plate.
2. In Mustangs and Cougars, disconnect the stabilizer bar and pull downward, out of the way.
3. Remove one bolt, loosen the other and swing no. 2 crossmember out of the way.
4. Remove the retaining bolts and oil pan. Reverse the above procedure to install.

1971-74 Maverick and Comet with 170 and 200 6 Cylinder

1. Drain the crankcase. Remove the dipstick and the flywheel inspection plate.
2. Remove the retaining bolts and oil pan. Reverse the above procedures to install, taking care to place the tabs of the front and rear oil seals over the pan gasket.

1971-74 Torino, Montego, Maverick, and Comet with 250 6 Cylinder, 1971-73 Mustang 6 Cylinder

1. Drain the crankcase and cooling system. Remove the dipstick and the flywheel inspection plate.
2. Remove the radiator. On cars with automatic transmissions, the oil cooler lines must be disconnected and plugged.
3. Raise the vehicle. Remove the stabilizer bar.
4. Remove the engine support thru-bolts and nuts.
5. Raise the engine with a jack and place two 2 in. wooden blocks between the engine supports and the chassis brackets.
6. Remove the retaining bolts and the starter motor.
7. Remove the retaining bolts and oil pan. Reverse the above procedures for installation.

1967-69 289, 302, and 351 V8

1. Drain the crankcase. Remove the dipstick.
2. Disconnect the stabilizer bar from the lower control arms and pull the ends down.
3. Disconnect the idler arm from 1967-68 Mustangs and Cougars.
4. Remove the oil pan retaining bolts and position the pan on the front crossmember.
5. Remove one oil inlet tube bolt, loosen the other and position the tube out of the way.
6. Turn the crankshaft as required for clearance to remove the pan.
7. Install in the reverse order from above.

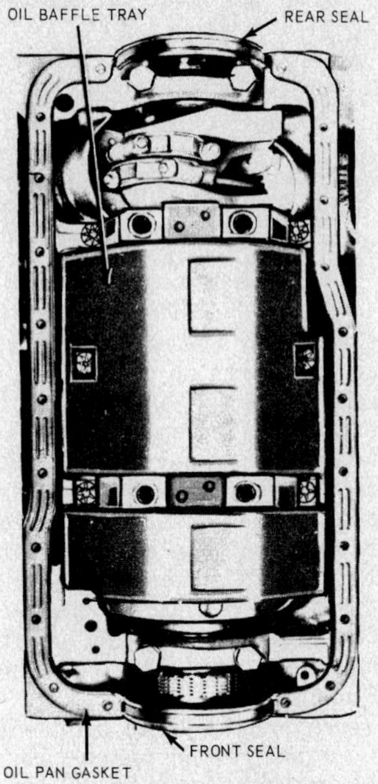

OIL BAFFLE TRAY
REAR SEAL
OIL PAN GASKET
FRONT SEAL

Oil baffle tray—Boss 302
(© Ford Motor Co)

1970 Mustang and Cougar 302, Boss 302, 351W, and 351C V8

1. Drain the crankcase. Remove the dipstick. Raise the vehicle.
2. Remove the stabilizer-to-frame retaining bolts.
3. Remove the two bolts retaining the crossmember to the chassis.
4. Remove the starter from cars with 351 Cleveland engines.
5. Remove the retaining bolts and the oil pan.
6. Turn the crankshaft as required for clearance to remove the pan.
7. Install in the reverse order from above.

1967-69 All models with 390, 427, or 428 V8; 1970 Falcon, Fairlane, Torino, and Montego with 302 or 351 V8; 1970-74 All Models with 429, 460 V8; 1971-74 All models with 302, 351, or 400 V8

1. Remove the dipstick.
2. Remove the fan shroud retaining bolts, on models so equipped, and position the shroud over the fan.
3. Raise the vehicle and drain the crankcase.
4. On vehicles with 351C, 400, and 429 engines, disconnect the negative battery cable and remove the starter.
5. Disconnect the stabilizer bar links and pull the ends down.
6. Remove the engine front support thru-bolts.
7. Install a wooden block on a jack and position the jack beneath the leading edge of the pan.
8. Raise the engine and place 1–1 ½ in. wood blocks between the engine supports and the chassis. Remove the jack from beneath the engine.
9. Remove the oil pan retaining bolts and lower the pan to the crossmember.
10. If the car is equipped with an automatic transmission, position the oil cooler lines out of the way.
11. Turn the crankshaft as required to obtain clearance to remove the pan.
12. Install in reverse of above.

NOTE: Oil leakage from the rear section of the oil pan gasket (not the rear main seal) has been a problem on some 429 and 460 Police Interceptor V8's. Ford has remedied the situation with a new style seal. However, if the neoprene seal is of the old type, the seal may be prevented from leaking by the application of silicone rubber sealer to the corners of the rear main bearing cap saddle, as shown, prior to installation. Once the silicone sealer is applied, install the oil pan immediately, as the sealer will begin to harden.

Oil Pump

Removal—All Engines

1. Remove oil pan.
2. Remove oil pump inlet tube and screen assembly.
3. Remove oil pump attaching bolts and remove oil pump gasket and intermediate shaft.

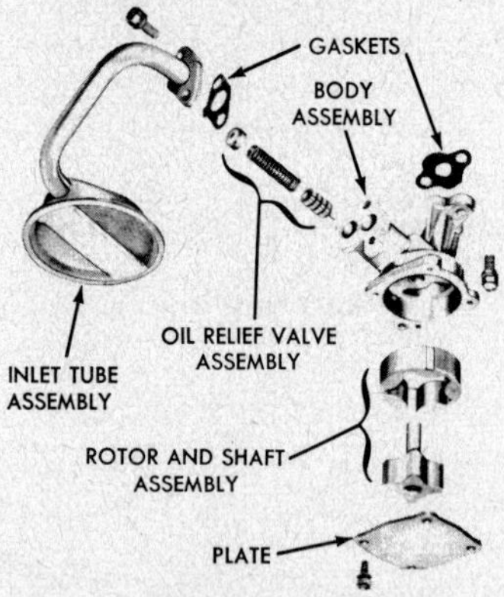

GASKETS
BODY ASSEMBLY
OIL RELIEF VALVE ASSEMBLY
INLET TUBE ASSEMBLY
ROTOR AND SHAFT ASSEMBLY
PLATE

289, 302, Boss 302, and 351 Windsor V8 oil pump
(© Ford Motor Co)

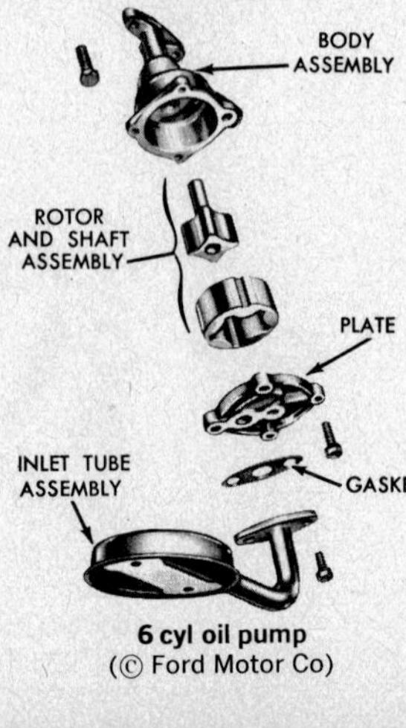

BODY ASSEMBLY
ROTOR AND SHAFT ASSEMBLY
PLATE
INLET TUBE ASSEMBLY
GASKET

6 cyl oil pump
(© Ford Motor Co)

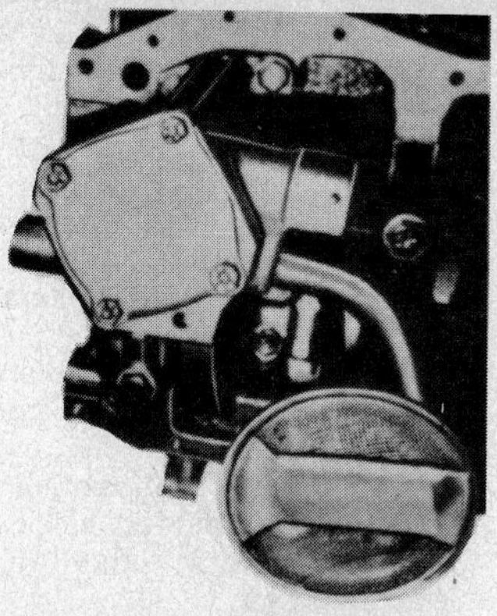

Oil pump and inlet tube installed —351 Cleveland V8 (© Ford Motor Co)

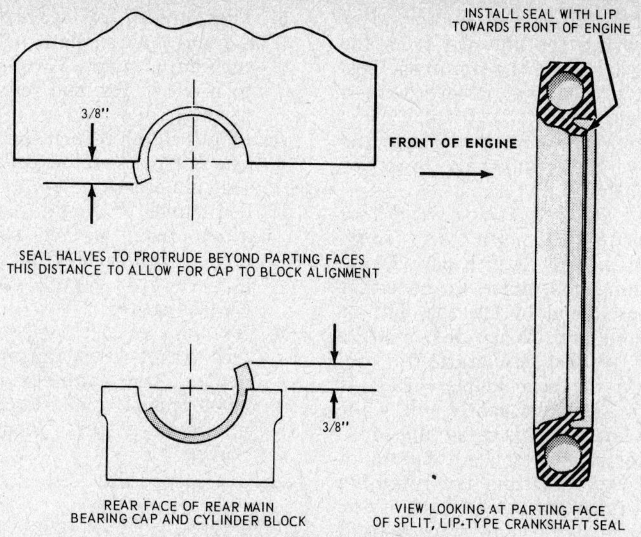
INSTALL SEAL WITH LIP
TOWARDS FRONT OF ENGINE
3/8"
FRONT OF ENGINE
SEAL HALVES TO PROTRUDE BEYOND PARTING FACES
THIS DISTANCE TO ALLOW FOR CAP TO BLOCK ALIGNMENT
3/8"
REAR FACE OF REAR MAIN
BEARING CAP AND CYLINDER BLOCK
VIEW LOOKING AT PARTING FACE
OF SPLIT, LIP-TYPE CRANKSHAFT SEAL

Installing split lip type rear oil seal (© Ford Motor Co)

Installation—All Engines

1. Prime oil pump by filling inlet and outlet port with engine oil and rotating shaft of pump to distribute it.
2. Position intermediate drive shaft into distributor socket.
3. Position new gasket on pump body and insert intermediate drive shaft into pump body.
4. Install pump and intermediate shaft as an assembly.

NOTE: do not force pump if it does not seat readily. The drive shaft may be misaligned with the distributor shaft. To align rotate intermediate drive shaft into a new position.

5. Install and torque oil pump attaching screws to 12-15 ft. lbs. on six cylinder, 20-25 ft. lbs. on V8s.
6. Install oil pan.

Rear Crankshaft Oil Seal R & R

1967-69 390, 427, and 428 All 1970-74 Engines

NOTE: the rear oil seal installed in these engines is a rubber type seal.

1. Remove the oil pan, and, if required, the oil pump.
2. Loosen all main bearing caps allowing the crankshaft to lower slightly.

NOTE: the crankshaft should not be allowed to drop more than 1/32 in.

3. Remove the rear main bearing cap and remove the seal from the cap and block.
4. Carefully clean the seal grooves in the cap and block with solvent.
5. Soak the new seal halves in clean engine oil.
6. Install the upper half of the seal in the block with the undercut side of the seal toward the front of the engine. Slide the seal around the crankshaft journal until 3/8 in. protrudes beyond the base of the block.
7. Repeat above procedure on lower seal, allowing an equal length of the seal to protrude beyond the opposite end of the bearing cap.
8. Install rear bearing cap and torque all main bearings to specifications. Apply sealer only to the rear of the seals.
9. Dip the bearing cap side seals in oil, then immediately install them. Do not use any sealer on the side seals. Tap the seals into place and do not clip the protruding ends.
10. Install the oil pump and pan. Fill the crankcase with oil, start engine check for leaks.

All Other Engines

NOTE: The rear oil seal originally installed in these engines is a rope (fabric) type seal. However, all service replacements are of the rubber type. To remove the rope type seal and install the rubber type, the following procedure is used.

1. Drain the crankcase and remove the oil pan.
2. Remove the lower half of the

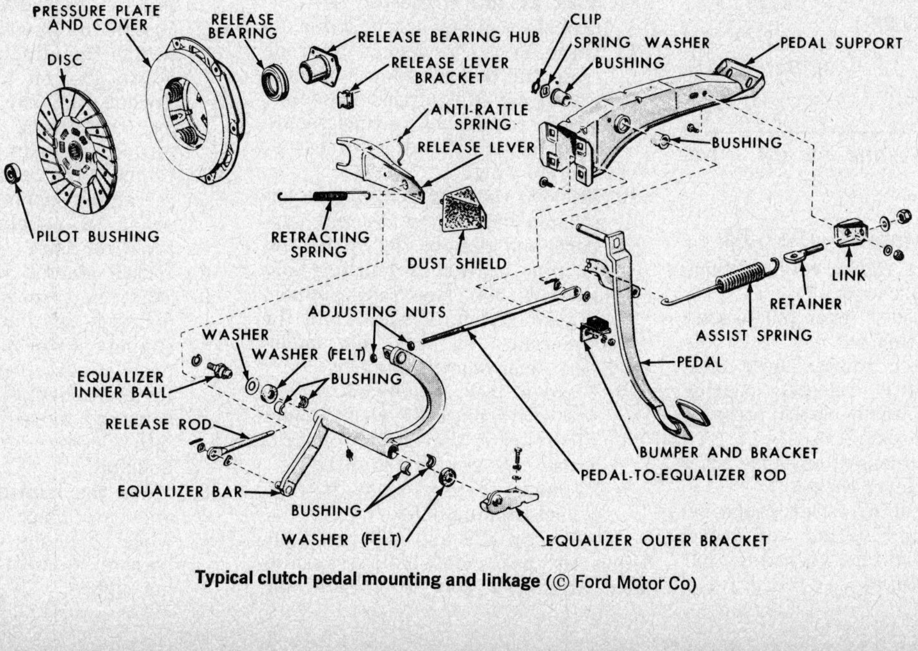
PRESSURE PLATE
AND COVER
RELEASE
BEARING
RELEASE BEARING HUB
CLIP
SPRING WASHER
PEDAL SUPPORT
DISC
RELEASE LEVER
BRACKET
BUSHING
ANTI-RATTLE
SPRING
RELEASE LEVER
BUSHING
PILOT BUSHING
RETRACTING
SPRING
DUST SHIELD
LINK
RETAINER
ADJUSTING NUTS
ASSIST SPRING
WASHER
WASHER (FELT)
EQUALIZER
INNER BALL
BUSHING
PEDAL
RELEASE ROD
BUMPER AND BRACKET
PEDAL-TO-EQUALIZER ROD
EQUALIZER BAR
BUSHING
WASHER (FELT)
EQUALIZER OUTER BRACKET

Typical clutch pedal mounting and linkage (© Ford Motor Co)

rear main bearing cap and, after removing the old seal from the cap, drive out the pin in the bottom of the seal groove with a punch.
3. Loosen all main bearing caps and allow the crankshaft to lower slightly.

NOTE: The crankshaft should not be allowed to drop more than 1/32 in.

4. With a 6 in. length of 3/16 in. brazing rod, drive up on either exposed end of the top half of the oil seal. When the opposite end of the seal starts to protrude, have a helper grasp it with pliers and gently pull, while the driven end is being tapped.
5. After removing both halves of the rope seal and the retaining pin from the lower half of the bearing cap, follow steps 4–10 of the above procedure for 1970-74 engines to install the rubber seal.

CLUTCH

The clutch is a single dry disc type and is mechanically engaged. Centrifugal weights are used to increase pressure plate grip at high rpm.

Clutch Pedal Adjustment

Year and Engine	*Clearance* (in.)*	*Free Travel (in.)*
1967 Six	0.178	$\frac{3}{4}$-$1\frac{1}{8}$
1967 V8	0.128	$\frac{3}{4}$-$1\frac{1}{8}$
1968 except 390, 427, 428	0.136	$\frac{3}{4}$-$1\frac{1}{8}$
1968 390, 427 and 428	0.178	$\frac{3}{4}$-$1\frac{1}{8}$
1969-71 except 390, 428 and 429	0.136	$\frac{7}{8}$-$1\frac{1}{8}$
1969-71 390, 428 and 429	0.178	$\frac{7}{8}$-$1\frac{1}{8}$
1972-74 Torino, Montego, Cougar and 1972-73 Mustang	0.194	$\frac{7}{8}$-$1\frac{1}{8}$
1972-74 Comet and Maverick	0.136	$\frac{7}{8}$-$1\frac{1}{8}$

* Between adjusting nut and swivel sleeve

Pedal Adjustment—1967-74

1. Disconnect clutch return spring from release lever.
2. Loosen release lever rod locknut and adjusting nut.
3. Move clutch release lever rearward until release bearing lightly contacts clutch pressure plate release fingers.
4. Adjust rod length until rod seats in release lever pocket.
5. Insert specified feeler gauge between adjusting nut and swivel sleeve. Tighten adjusting nut against gauge.
6. Tighten lock nut against adjusting nut, taking care not to disturb adjustment. Torque locknut to 15-20 ft. lbs. and remove feeler gauge.
7. Install clutch return spring.
8. Check free travel at pedal. Readjust if necessary to obtain specified travel. Moving adjusting nut away from swivel sleeve increases travel. Moving adjusting nut toward swivel sleeve decreases travel.
9. As final check, measure pedal free travel with transmission in neutral and engine running at 3,000 rpm. If pedal travel is not minimum of $\frac{1}{2}$ in., readjust free travel.

Chilton's TIME SAVER

If a problem is encountered with clutch adjustment rods bending, check the clutch equalizer shaft. A bent or distorted equalizer shaft will allow the clutch pedal to travel too far, which will bend the adjustment rod.

Clutch and/or Transmission Removal

1. Disconnect and remove starter and dust ring, if the clutch is to be removed. On floor-shift models, remove the boot retainer and shifter lever.
2. Raise the car.
3. Disconnect the driveshaft at the rear universal joint and remove the driveshaft.
4. Disconnect the speedometer cable at the transmission extension. On cars with transmission regulated spark, disconnect the lead wire at the connector. Disconnect the seat belt sensor wires.
5. Disconnect the gear shift rods from the transmission shift levers. If car is equipped with four speed, remove bolts that secure shift control bracket to extension housing.
6. Remove the bolt holding the extension housing to the rear support, and remove the muffler inlet pipe bracket to housing bolt.
7. Remove the two rear support bracket insulator nuts from the underside of the crossmember. Remove crossmember.
8. Place a jack (equipped with a protective piece of wood) under the rear of the engine oil pan. Raise the engine, slightly.
9. Remove transmission - to - flywheel-housing bolts.

NOTE: on 429 and 460 cu in. engines the upper left-hand transmission attaching bolt is a seal bolt. Carefully note its position so that it may be reinstalled in its original position.

10. Slide the transmission back and out of the car.
11. To remove the clutch, remove release lever retracting spring and disconnect pedal at the equalizer bar.
12. Remove bolts that secure engine rear plate to front lower part of bellhousing.
13. Remove bolts that attach bell housing to cylinder block and remove housing and release lever as a unit.
14. Loosen six pressure plate cover attaching bolts evenly to release spring pressure. Mark cover and flywheel to facilitate reassembly in same position.
15. Remove six attaching bolts while holding pressure plate cover. Remove pressure plate and clutch disc.

Caution Do not depress the clutch pedal while the transmission is removed.

Clutch and/or Transmission Installation

1. To install the clutch, first wash flywheel surface with alcohol.
2. Attach the clutch disc and pressure plate assembly to the flywheel with the bolts finger tight.
3. Align the clutch disc with the pilot bushing. Torque cover bolts to 12-20 ft. lbs. on 1967-74 vehicles.
4. Lightly lubricate the release lever fulcrum ends. Install the release lever in the flywheel housing and install the dust shield.
5. Apply very little lubricant on the release bearing retainer journal. Attach the release bearing and hub on the release lever.
6. Install the flywheel housing and torque the attaching bolts to 40-50 ft. lbs. on all 1967-74 V8s. Torque 1967-74 sixes to 23-33 ft. lbs. Install the dust cover and torque the bolts to 17-20 ft. lbs.
7. Connect the release rod and the retracting spring. Connect the pedal - to - equalizer - rod at the equalizer bar.
8. Install starter and dust ring.
9. Start the transmission extension housing up and over the rear support. After moving the transmission back just far enough for the pilot shaft to clear the clutch housing, move it upward and into position on the flywheel housing.
10. Move the transmission forward and into place against the flywheel housing, and install the transmission attaching bolts finger-tight.

11. Tighten the transmission bolts to 37-42 ft. lbs. on all cars.
12. Slowly lower the engine onto the crossmember.
13. Install and torque the insulator-to-crossmember nuts to 25-35 ft. lbs. on all 1967-69 vehicles except 1968-69 390, 427 and 428 CJ Cougars and Mustangs. Torque 1968-69 390, 427 and 428 CJ Cougars and Mustangs to 30-42 ft. lbs. Torque 1970-74 Torinos, Montegos, Mavericks and Comets to 30-50 ft. lbs. and 1970-74 Cougars and 1970-73 Mustangs to 25-35 ft. lbs.
14. Connect gear shift rods and the speedometer cable. On transmission regulated spark equipped cars, connect the lead wire at the connector.
15. Hook up the drive shaft.
16. Refill transmission to proper level. On floor-shift models, install the boot retainer and shift lever.

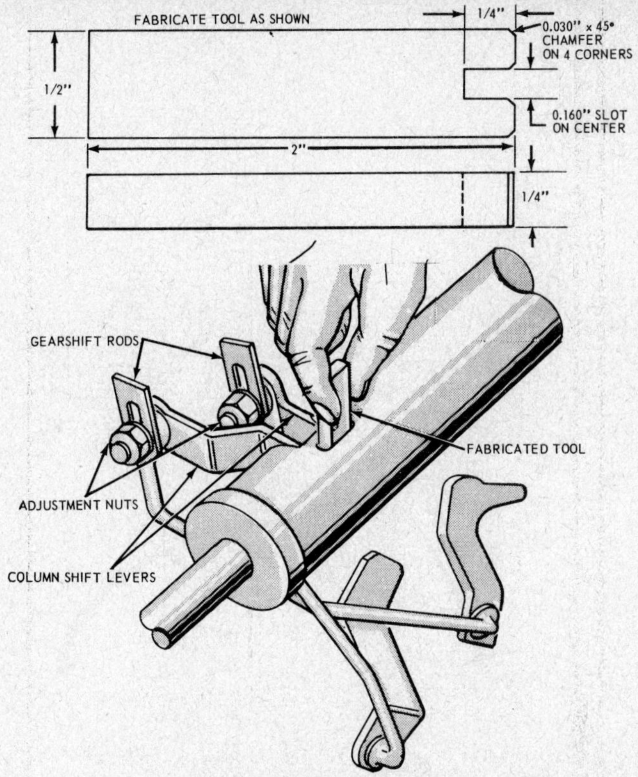

FABRICATE TOOL AS SHOWN
1/4"
0.030" x 45° CHAMFER ON 4 CORNERS
1/2"
0.160" SLOT ON CENTER
2"
1/4"
GEARSHIFT RODS
FABRICATED TOOL
ADJUSTMENT NUTS
COLUMN SHIFT LEVERS

Manual transmission column shift adjustment—1967
(© Ford Motor Co)

MANUAL TRANSMISSION

There are four manual transmissions used during the 1967-74 period: (1) a light duty, top cover, three speed with a non-synchromesh low gear used on 1967 six cylinders, (2) a heavy duty, top cover, fully synchromesh three speed used on 1967 V8s and on all 1968-74 three speed applications, (3) a medium duty, top cover, overdrive transmission with non-synchromesh low gear used on some 1967 Fairlane 289 2V V8s, (4) a heavy duty, top cover, fully synchromesh, Ford-built four speed used on 1967-74 V8s.

Three-Speed Column Shift Linkage Adjustment

With the transmission in neutral, the shift lever should be in a horizontal plane and parallel to the instrument panel line. Corrective adjustments should be made at the gear shift rods.

1967

1. Place lever in neutral.
2. Loosen two gear shift rod adjustment nuts.
3. Insert locally fabricated tool in slot provided in lower steering column. See figure for manufacturing dimensions of tool. Align levers to insert tool.
4. Tighten gear shift rod adjustment nuts, and remove tool.
5. Check gear lever for smooth crossover.

1968-74

1. Place lever in neutral.
2. Loosen two gear shift rod adjustment nuts.
3. Insert 3/16 in. diameter alignment pin through first and reverse gear shift lever and second and third gear shift lever. Align levers to insert pin.
4. Tighten gear shift rod adjustment nuts, and remove pin.
5. Check gear lever for smooth crossover.

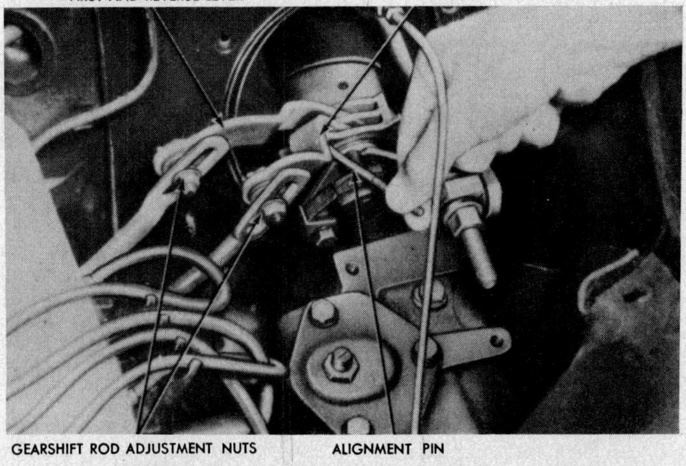

FIRST AND REVERSE LEVER
SECOND AND THIRD LEVER
GEARSHIFT ROD ADJUSTMENT NUTS
ALIGNMENT PIN

Manual transmission column shift adjustment—1968-70 (© Ford Motor Co)

Three Speed Floor and Console Shift Linkage

1. Loosen three shift linkage adjustment nuts.
2. Install a $\frac{1}{4}$ in. diameter alignment pin through control bracket and levers.
3. Tighten three shift linkage adjustment nuts and remove alignment pin.
4. Check gear lever for smooth crossover.

Four-Speed Linkage

1. Place shifter lever in neutral position, then raise car on a hoist.
2. Insert a $\frac{1}{4}$ in. rod into the alignment holes of the shift levers.
3. If the holes are not in exact alignment, check for bent connecting rods or loose lever lock nuts at the rod ends. Make replacements or repairs, then adjust as follows.
4. Loosen the three rod-to-lever retaining lock nuts and move the levers until the $\frac{1}{4}$ in. gauge rod will enter the alignment holes. Be sure that the transmission shift

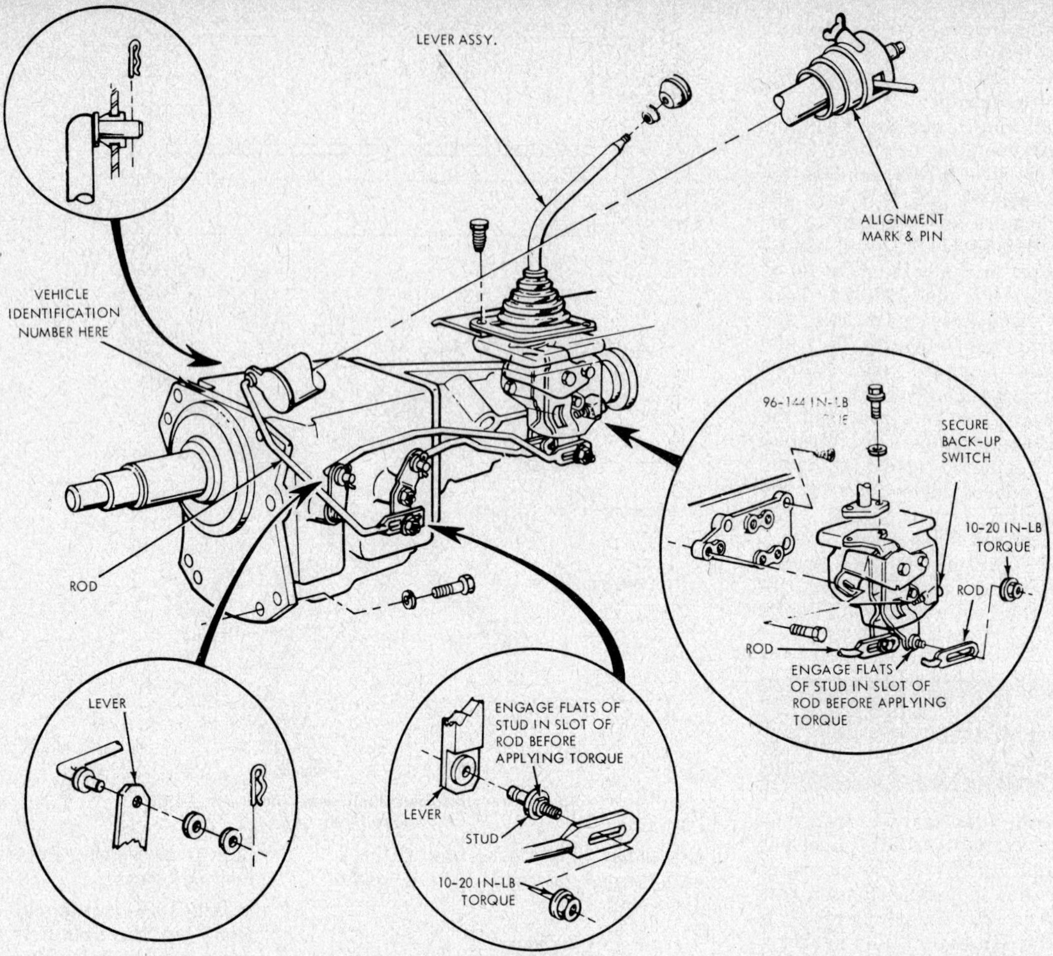
LEVER ASSY.
ALIGNMENT
MARK & PIN
VEHICLE
IDENTIFICATION
NUMBER HERE
ROD
SECURE
BACK-UP
SWITCH
10-20 IN-LB
TORQUE
ROD
ROD
ENGAGE FLATS
OF STUD IN SLOT OF
ROD BEFORE APPLYING
TORQUE
LEVER
ENGAGE FLATS OF
STUD IN SLOT OF
ROD BEFORE
APPLYING TORQUE
LEVER
STUD
10-20 IN-LB
TORQUE

Three-speed floor mounted shift linkage and lock rod (© Ford Motor Co)

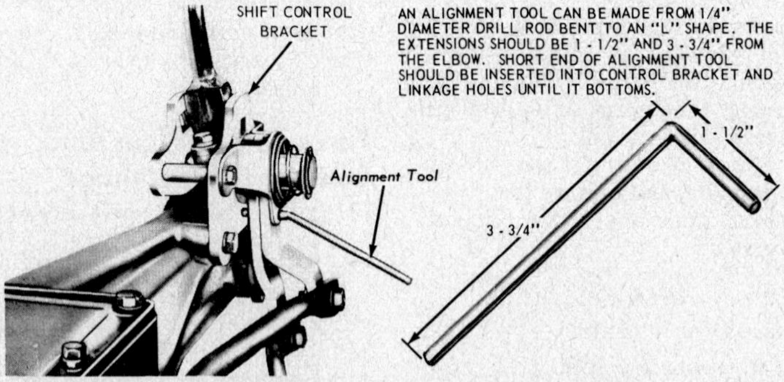
SHIFT CONTROL
BRACKET
AN ALIGNMENT TOOL CAN BE MADE FROM 1/4" DIAMETER DRILL ROD BENT TO AN "L" SHAPE. THE EXTENSIONS SHOULD BE 1 - 1/2" AND 3 - 3/4" FROM THE ELBOW. SHORT END OF ALIGNMENT TOOL SHOULD BE INSERTED INTO CONTROL BRACKET AND LINKAGE HOLES UNTIL IT BOTTOMS.
Alignment Tool
1 - 1/2"
3 - 3/4"

Manual transmission floor or console shift adjustment
(© Ford Motor Co)

levers are in neutral and the reverse shifter lever is in the neutral detent.

5. Install the shift rods and torque the lock nuts to 18-23 ft. lbs.
6. Remove the ¼ in. gauge rod.
7. Operate the shift levers to assure correct shifting.
8. Lower the car and road test.

Transmission Lock Rod Adjustment

1970 and later models with floor or console mounted shifters and manual transmissions incorporate a transmission lock rod which prevents the shifter from being moved from the reverse position when the ignition lock is in the OFF position. The lock rod connects the shift tube in the steering column to the transmission reverse lever. The lock rod cannot be properly adjusted until the manual linkage adjustment is correct.

1. With the transmission selector lever in the neutral position, loosen the lock rod adjustment nut on the transmission reverse lever.
2. Insert a .180 in. diameter rod (No. 15 drill bit) in the gauge pin hole located at the 6 o'clock position on the steering column socket casting, directly below the ignition lock.
3. Manipulate the pin until the casting will not move with the pin inserted.
4. Torque the lock rod adjustment rod to 10-20 ft. lbs.
5. Remove the pin and check the linkage operation.

Transmission Removal

See Clutch and/or Transmission Removal.

AUTOMATIC TRANSMISSION

Three different automatic transmissions are used in Ford compact and intermediate cars: a C4, a C6, and a FMX. The C4 is a light duty transmission used on six cylinder and small block V8 engines. The FMX is an intermediate duty transmission used on medium duty V8s. The C6 is a heavy duty transmission used on high-performance and large displacement V8 engines. A semi-automatic version of the C4, the C4S, has been available on the Maverick.

C4 Three-Speed Automatic

Throttle Linkage Adjustment

Initial Adjustments—All Models

1. Apply parking brake and place selector lever at N.
2. Run engine at normal idle speed. If engine is cold, run engine at fast idle speed (about 1200 rpm) until it reaches normal operating temperature. When engine is warm, slow it down to normal idle speed.
3. Connect tachometer to engine.
4. Adjust engine idle speed to specified rpm with transmission selector lever at D or D_1 or D_2.
5. The carburetor throttle lever must be against hot idle speed adjusting screw at specified idle speed in D or D_1 or D_2.

1967-69 Mustang and Cougar Sixes and V8s, 1967-68 Comet, Montego, and Fairlane Sixes and 1967-69 Falcon Sixes and V8s—Final Adjustments

1. With engine off, check accelerator pedal for height of 4½ in. measured from top of pedal at pivot point to floor pan. To obtain correct pedal height, adjust accelerator connecting link at point A in figure.
2. With engine off disconnect downshift control cable at point B from accelerator shaft lever.
3. With carburetor choke in off position, depress accelerator to floor. Block pedal to hold it in wide open position.
4. Rotate downshift lever C counter clockwise to place it against internal stop.
5. With lever held in this position, and all slack removed from

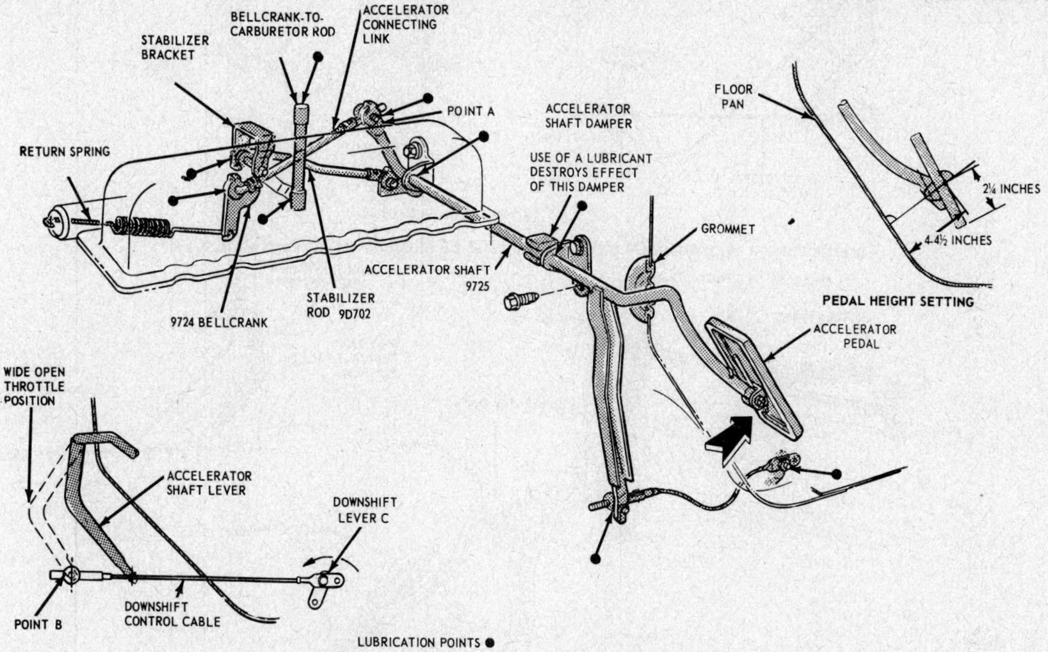

BELLCRANK-TO-CARBURETOR ROD
ACCELERATOR CONNECTING LINK
STABILIZER BRACKET
POINT A
ACCELERATOR SHAFT DAMPER
FLOOR PAN
RETURN SPRING
USE OF A LUBRICANT DESTROYS EFFECT OF THIS DAMPER
2¼ INCHES
GROMMET
4-4½ INCHES
ACCELERATOR SHAFT 9725
STABILIZER ROD 9D702
9724 BELLCRANK
PEDAL HEIGHT SETTING
ACCELERATOR PEDAL
WIDE OPEN THROTTLE POSITION
ACCELERATOR SHAFT LEVER
DOWNSHIFT LEVER C
POINT B
DOWNSHIFT CONTROL CABLE
LUBRICATION POINTS ●

Throttle linkage adjustment C4 transmission 1967-68 Montego, Comet, and Fairlane, and 1967-69 Falcon with six cylinder (© Ford Motor Co)

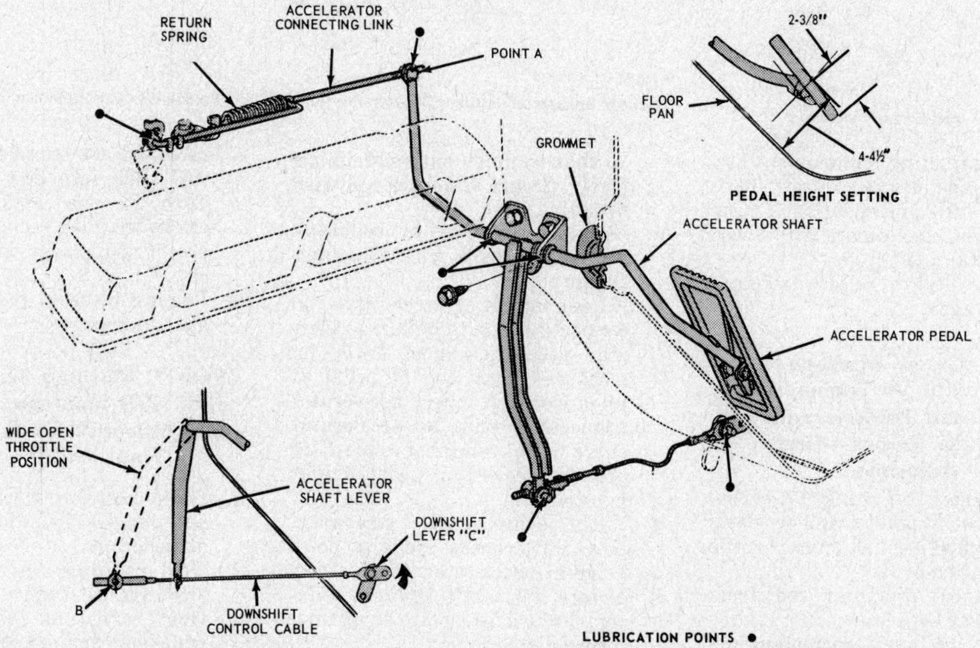

RETURN SPRING
ACCELERATOR CONNECTING LINK
POINT A
2-3/8"
FLOOR PAN
GROMMET
4-4½"
PEDAL HEIGHT SETTING
ACCELERATOR SHAFT
ACCELERATOR PEDAL
WIDE OPEN THROTTLE POSITION
ACCELERATOR SHAFT LEVER
DOWNSHIFT LEVER "C"
B
DOWNSHIFT CONTROL CABLE
LUBRICATION POINTS ●

Throttle linkage adjustment C4 transmission 1967-68 Cougar and Mustang V8 (© Ford Motor Co)

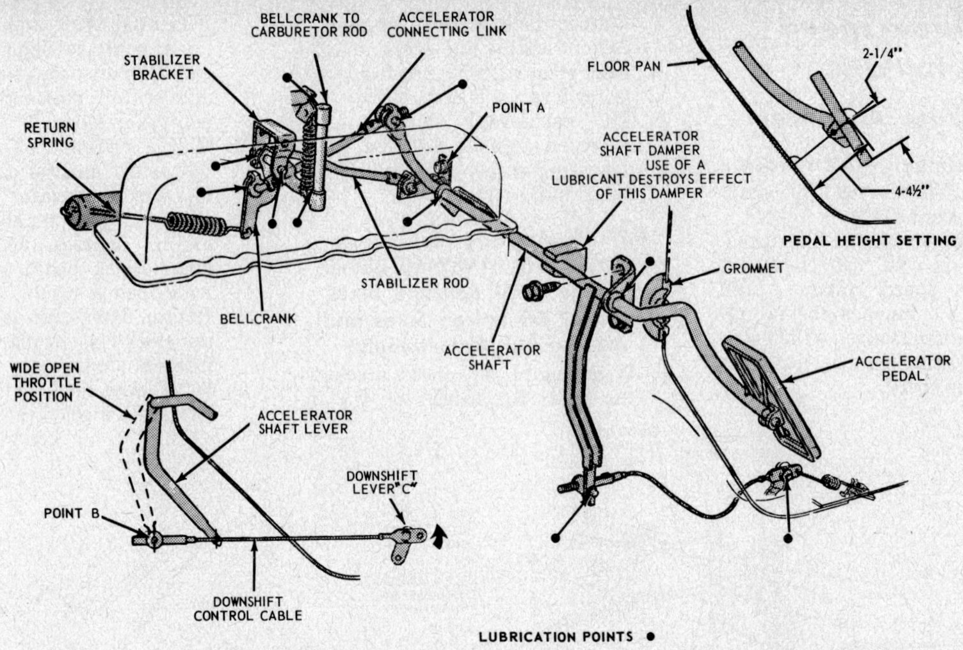
BELLCRANK TO CARBURETOR ROD
ACCELERATOR CONNECTING LINK
STABILIZER BRACKET
RETURN SPRING
POINT A
FLOOR PAN
2-1/4"
4-4½"
PEDAL HEIGHT SETTING
ACCELERATOR SHAFT DAMPER USE OF A LUBRICANT DESTROYS EFFECT OF THIS DAMPER
GROMMET
STABILIZER ROD
BELLCRANK
ACCELERATOR SHAFT
ACCELERATOR PEDAL
WIDE OPEN THROTTLE POSITION
ACCELERATOR SHAFT LEVER
DOWNSHIFT LEVER "C"
POINT B
DOWNSHIFT CONTROL CABLE
LUBRICATION POINTS ●

Throttle linkage adjustment C4 transmission 1967-68 Mustang six (© Ford Motor Co)

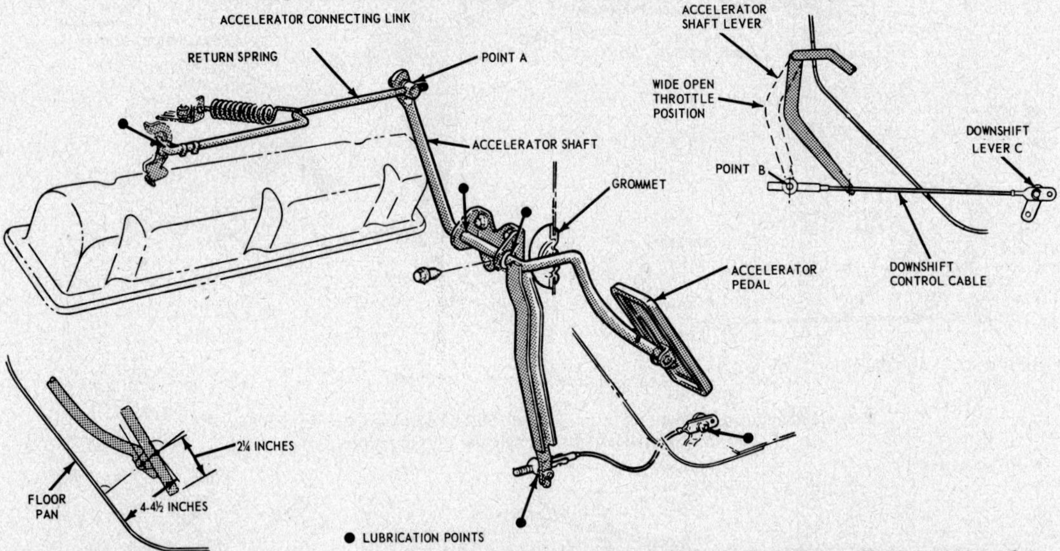
ACCELERATOR CONNECTING LINK
RETURN SPRING
POINT A
ACCELERATOR SHAFT LEVER
WIDE OPEN THROTTLE POSITION
ACCELERATOR SHAFT
GROMMET
POINT B
DOWNSHIFT LEVER C
ACCELERATOR PEDAL
DOWNSHIFT CONTROL CABLE
2¼ INCHES
FLOOR PAN
4-4½ INCHES
● LUBRICATION POINTS
PEDAL HEIGHT SETTING

Throttle linkage adjustment C4 transmission 1967-69 Falcon V8 (© Ford Motor Co)

cable, adjusting trunnion so that it will slide into accelerator shaft lever. Turn one additional turn clockwise, then secure it to lever with retaining clip.

6. Remove block to release carburetor linkage.

1967-69 Comet, Montego, and Fairlane with V8 Engine, 1969 Montego and Fairlane with Six Cylinder Engine—Final Adjustment

1. Disconnect bellcrank to carburetor rod at point C and accelerator connecting link from throttle shaft at point B.
2. Disconnect stabilizer rod from stabilizer at point B.
3. Insert ¼ inch diameter pin through stabilizer and bracket.
4. Adjust length of stabilizer rod so that trunnion enters stabilizer freely. Secure stabilizer rod with retaining clip.
5. Secure carburetor to bellcrank rod to bell crank with attaching clip at point C.
6. Adjust length of accelerator rod connecting link to obtain accelerator pedal height of 4-4½ in. measured from top of pedal at pivot point. Connect accelerator connecting link to accelerator shaft with retaining clip after proper accelerator pedal height is obtained.
7. With engine off, disconnect downshift control cable at point D from accelerator shaft lever.
8. Rotate downshift lever E counter clockwise to place it against internal stop.
9. With lever held in this position, and all slack removed from cable, adjust trunnion so that it will slide into downshift lever. Turn it one additional turn clockwise, then secure it to accelerator shaft lever with retaining clip.
10. Remove block to release accelerator linkage.

1969-70 Mustang Six Cylinder, and 1970 Montego, Fairlane, and Maverick Six Cylinder—Final Adjustments

1. Disconnect throttle return spring and remove trunnion and cable at bellcrank.
2. Hold transmission in full downshift against stop.
3. Hold carburetor throttle lever wide open against stop.
4. Adjust trunnion at bellcrank until ball stud on shaft and ball

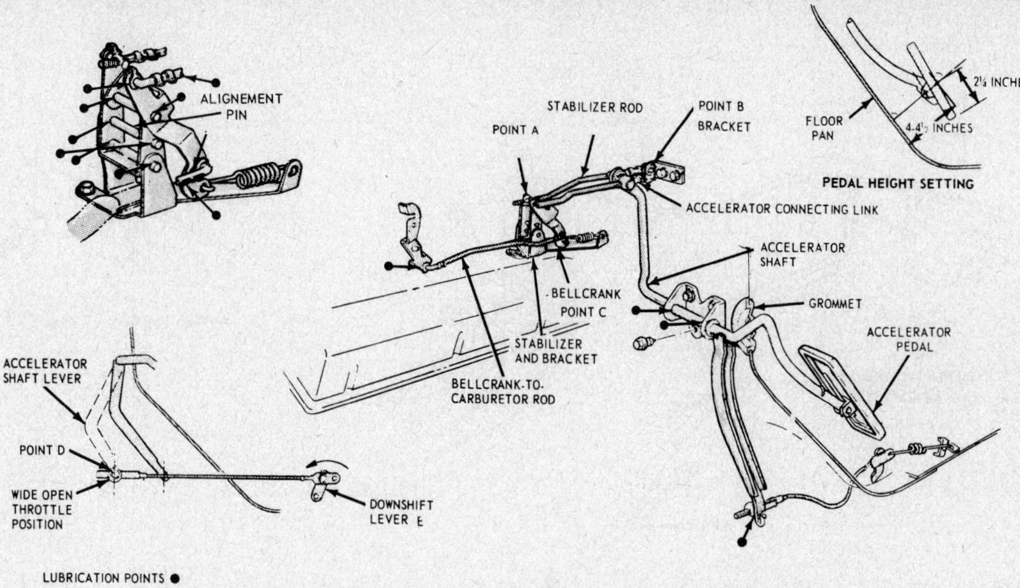
ALIGNEMENT PIN
STABILIZER ROD
POINT B
BRACKET
POINT A
FLOOR PAN
2¼ INCHES
4-4½ INCHES
PEDAL HEIGHT SETTING
ACCELERATOR CONNECTING LINK
ACCELERATOR SHAFT
BELLCRANK
POINT C
GROMMET
STABILIZER AND BRACKET
ACCELERATOR PEDAL
BELLCRANK-TO-CARBURETOR ROD
ACCELERATOR SHAFT LEVER
POINT D
WIDE OPEN THROTTLE POSITION
DOWNSHIFT LEVER E
LUBRICATION POINTS ●

Throttle linkage adjustment C4 transmission 1967-69 Montego, Comet, Falcon, and Fairlane
(© Ford Motor Co)

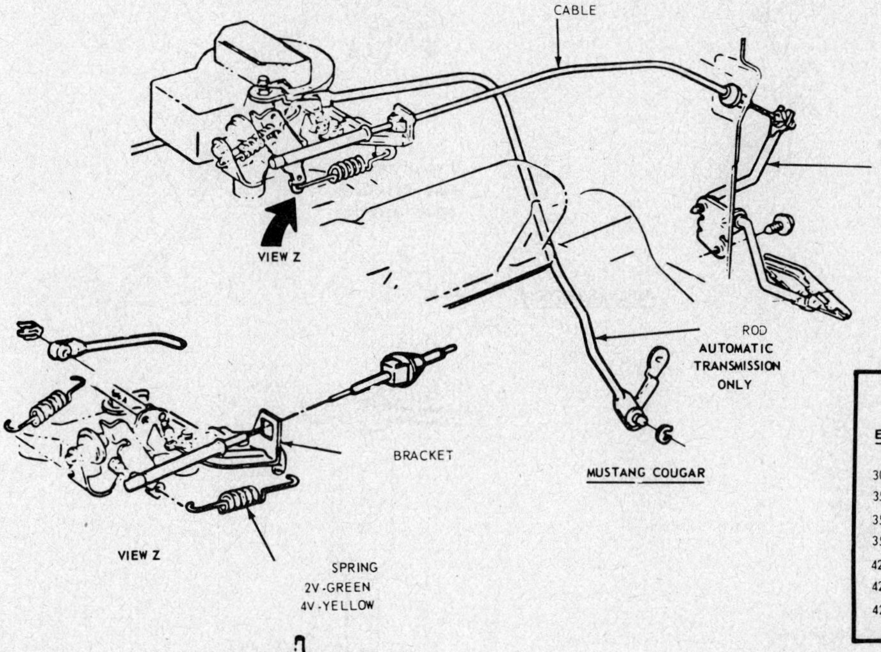
CABLE
PEDAL
VIEW Z
ROD
AUTOMATIC TRANSMISSION ONLY
BRACKET
MUSTANG COUGAR
VIEW Z
SPRING
2V-GREEN
4V-YELLOW

MUSTANG/COUGAR/FAIRLANE/MONTEGO			
ENG.	TRANS.	COLOR CODE	COLOR STRIP
302-2V	C-4	GOLD	BROWN
351-2V	C-4	GOLD	WHITE
351-2V	FMX	GOLD	RED
351-4V	FMX	GOLD	BLUE
428-4V	C-6	GOLD	GREEN
429-4V	C-6	GOLD	BLACK
429–CJ	C-6	GOLD	VIOLET

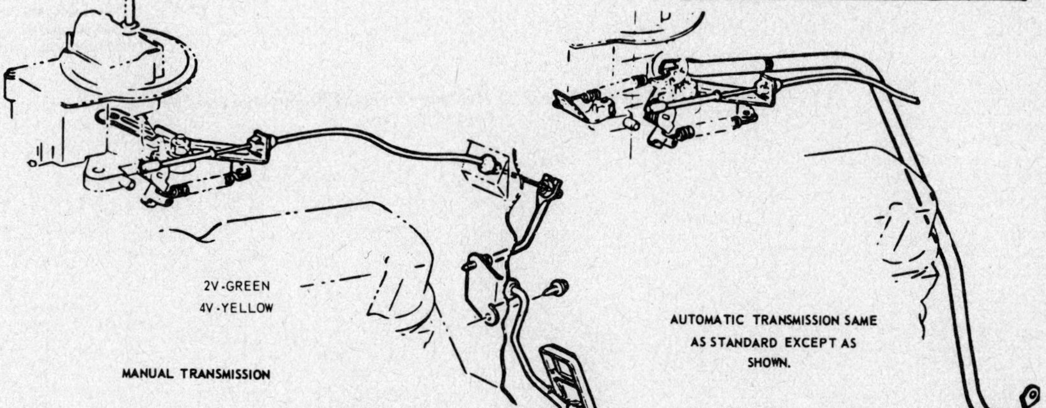
2V-GREEN
4V-YELLOW
MANUAL TRANSMISSION
AUTOMATIC TRANSMISSION SAME AS STANDARD EXCEPT AS SHOWN.
FAIRLANE/MONTEGO

Throttle linkage adjustment—1969-72 Cougar and Mustang V8s, and 1972 Montego and Fairlane V8s (© Ford Motor Co)

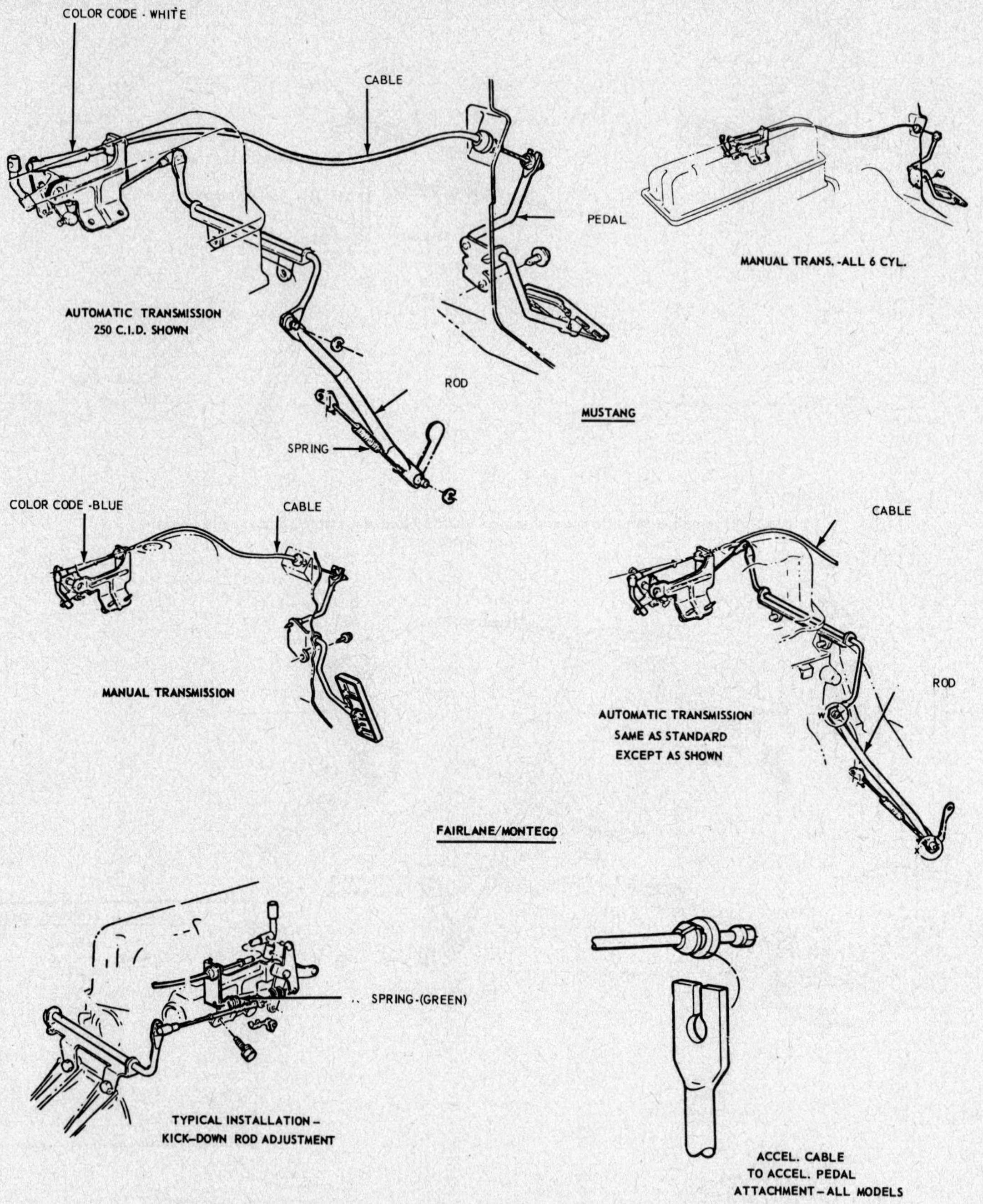
COLOR CODE - WHITE
CABLE
PEDAL
MANUAL TRANS.-ALL 6 CYL.
AUTOMATIC TRANSMISSION
250 C.I.D. SHOWN
ROD
MUSTANG
SPRING
COLOR CODE -BLUE
CABLE
CABLE
MANUAL TRANSMISSION
ROD
AUTOMATIC TRANSMISSION
SAME AS STANDARD
EXCEPT AS SHOWN
FAIRLANE/MONTEGO
SPRING-(GREEN)
TYPICAL INSTALLATION –
KICK-DOWN ROD ADJUSTMENT
ACCEL. CABLE
TO ACCEL. PEDAL
ATTACHMENT – ALL MODELS

Throttle linkage adjustment 1969-70 Mustang six and 1970 Montego and Fairlane Six
(© Ford Motor Co)

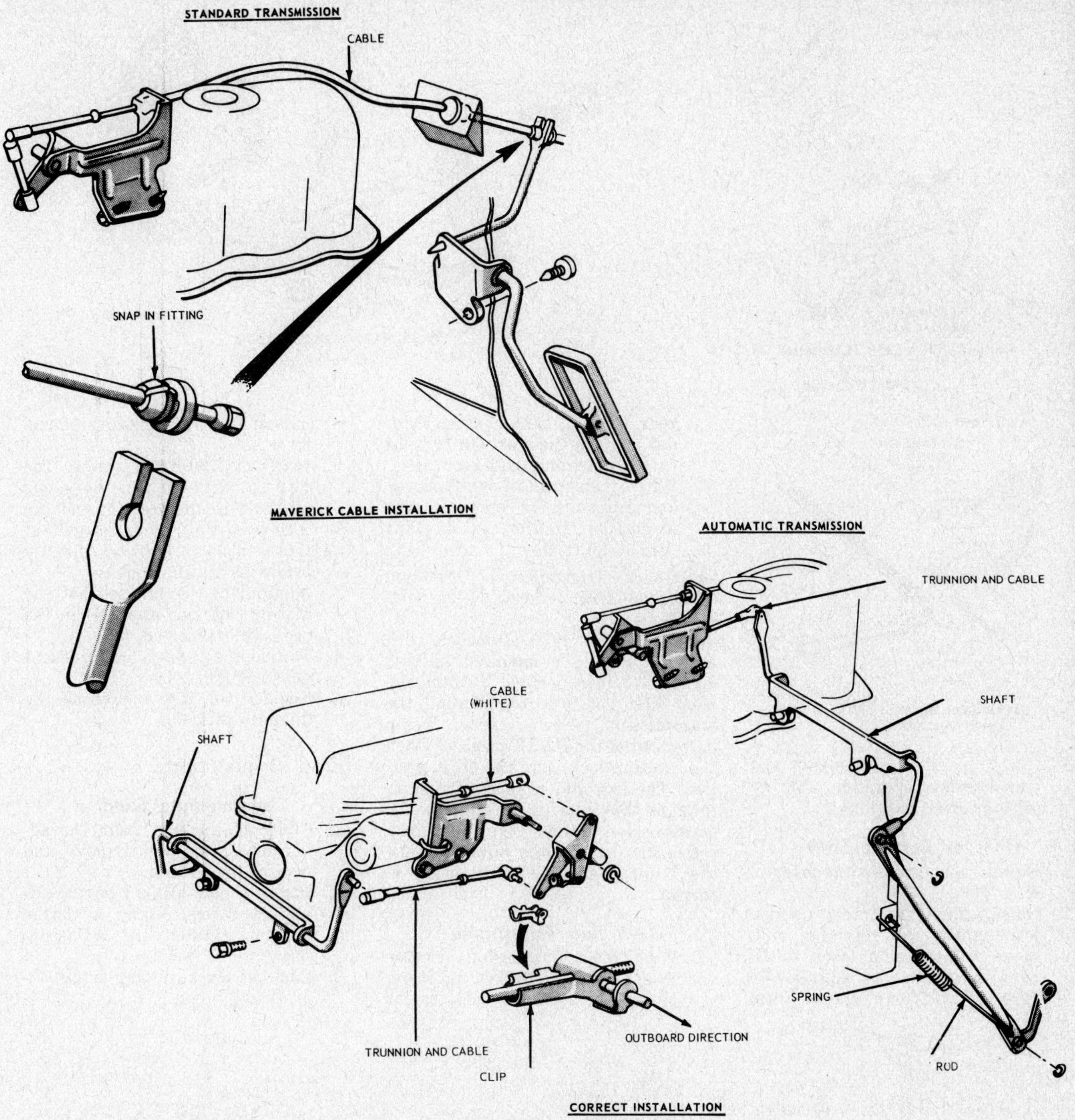
STANDARD TRANSMISSION
CABLE
SNAP IN FITTING
MAVERICK CABLE INSTALLATION
AUTOMATIC TRANSMISSION
TRUNNION AND CABLE
SHAFT
CABLE (WHITE)
SHAFT
SPRING
OUTBOARD DIRECTION
TRUNNION AND CABLE
CLIP
ROD
CORRECT INSTALLATION

Throttle linkage adjustment—1969-70 Maverick (© Ford Motor Co)

stud receiver on cable align. Then turn trunnion one full additional turn to increase length.
5. Release transmission and carburetor to normal free position.
6. Install throttle return spring.

1969-74 Cougar and 1969-73 Mustang V8s, and 1970-74 Montego and Torino V8s—Final Adjustments

1. Disconnect throttle and downshift return springs.
2. Hold carburetor throttle lever in wide open position against stop.
3. Hold transmission in full downshift position against internal stop.
4. Turn adjustment screw on carburetor downshift lever to within 0.040-0.080 in. on 1971 and earlier models, 0.050–0.070 in. on 1972 models, and 0.010–0.080 on 1973-74 models, of contacting pickup surface of carburetor throttle lever.
5. Release transmission and carburetor to normal free positions.
6. Install throttle and downshift return springs.

Manual Linkage Adjustment

1967-74 Column Shift

1. With engine stopped, loosen clamp at shift lever at point A so that shift rod is free to slide in clamp. On vehicles equipped with a shift cable, remove the nut at point A and at manual lever stud.
2. Place transmission shift lever into D or D_1 (large dot) position. On Maverick with semi-automatic transmission, place lever in Hi.
3. Shift manual lever at transmission into D, D_1, or Hi. On 1967-71 transmissions, D of Hi is third detent from rear. On 1972-74 transmissions, D is the second detent from the rear.
4. Tighten clamp on shift rod at point A to 10-20 ft. lbs. On vehicles equipped with a shift cable, position the cable end on the transmission manual lever stud, aligning the flats. Start the adjusting nut.

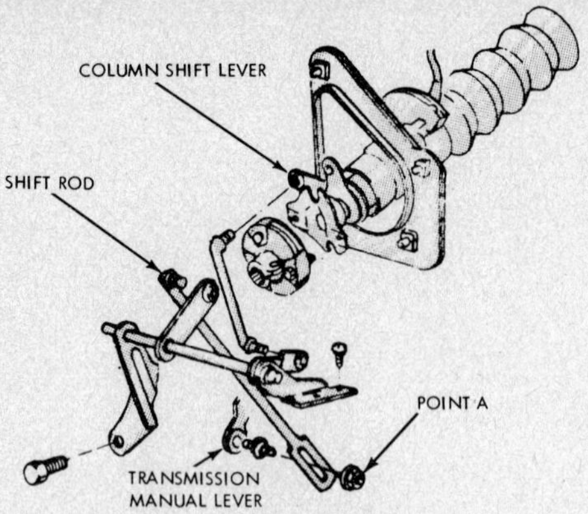
COLUMN SHIFT LEVER
SHIFT ROD
POINT A
TRANSMISSION
MANUAL LEVER

Column shift—1970-74 Maverick, 1971-74 Comet
(© Ford Motor Co)

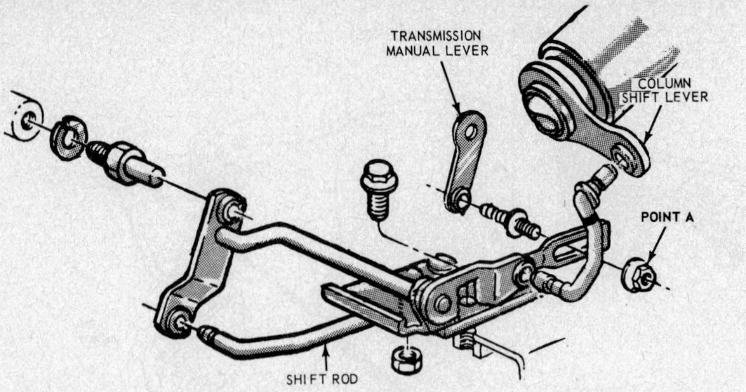
TRANSMISSION
MANUAL LEVER
COLUMN
SHIFT LEVER
POINT A
SHIFT ROD

Typical column shift 1969-70
(© Ford Motor Co)

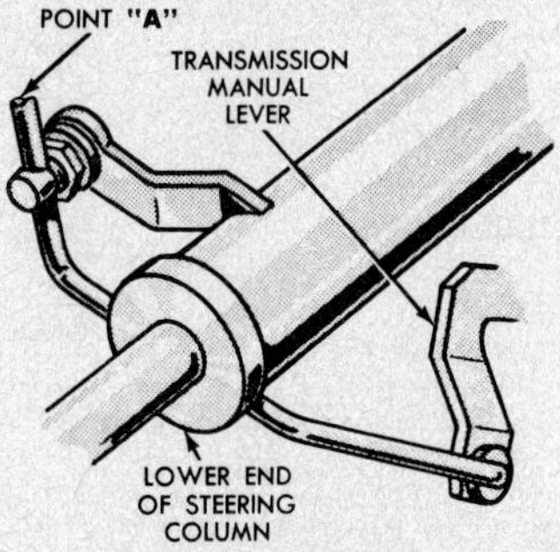
POINT "A"
TRANSMISSION
MANUAL
LEVER
LOWER END
OF STEERING
COLUMN

Typical column shift 1967-68
(© Ford Motor Co)

5. Check pointer alignment and transmission operation for all selector lever positions.

Floor or Console Shift

1. Place transmission shift lever in D.
2. Raise vehicle and loosen manual lever shift rod retaining nut. Move transmission lever to D_1 or D position. On all 1967-70 cars, D is fourth detent from rear. On 1971 cars, D is the third detent from the rear. On 1972-74 cars, D is second from rear.
3. With transmission shift lever and transmission manual lever in position, tighten nut at point A to 10-20 ft. lbs.
4. Check transmission operation for all selector lever detent positions.

NOTE: since 1970, all models with a floor or console mounted selector lever have incorporated a transmission lock out rod to prevent the transmission selector from being moved out of the PARK position when the ignition lock is in the OFF position. The lock rod connects the shift tube in the steering column to the transmission manual lever. The lock rod cannot be properly adjusted until the manual linkage adjustment is correct.

Lock Rod Adjustment

1. With the transmission selector lever in the DRIVE position, loosen the lock rod adjustment nut on the transmission manual lever.
2. Insert a .180 in. diameter rod (No. 15 drill bit) in the gauge pin hole in the steering column socket casting, it is located at the 6 o'clock position directly below the ignition lock.
3. Manipulate the pin so that the casting will not move when the pin is fully inserted.
4. Torque the lock rod adjustment nut to 10-20 ft. lbs.
5. Remove the pin and check the linkage operation.

Band Adjustment

Intermediate Band

1. Clean all the dirt from the adjusting screw and remove and discard the locknut.
2. Install a new locknut on the adjusting screw. Using a torque wrench, tighten the adjusting screw to 10 ft lbs.
3. Back off the adjusting screw *exactly 1¾ turns.*

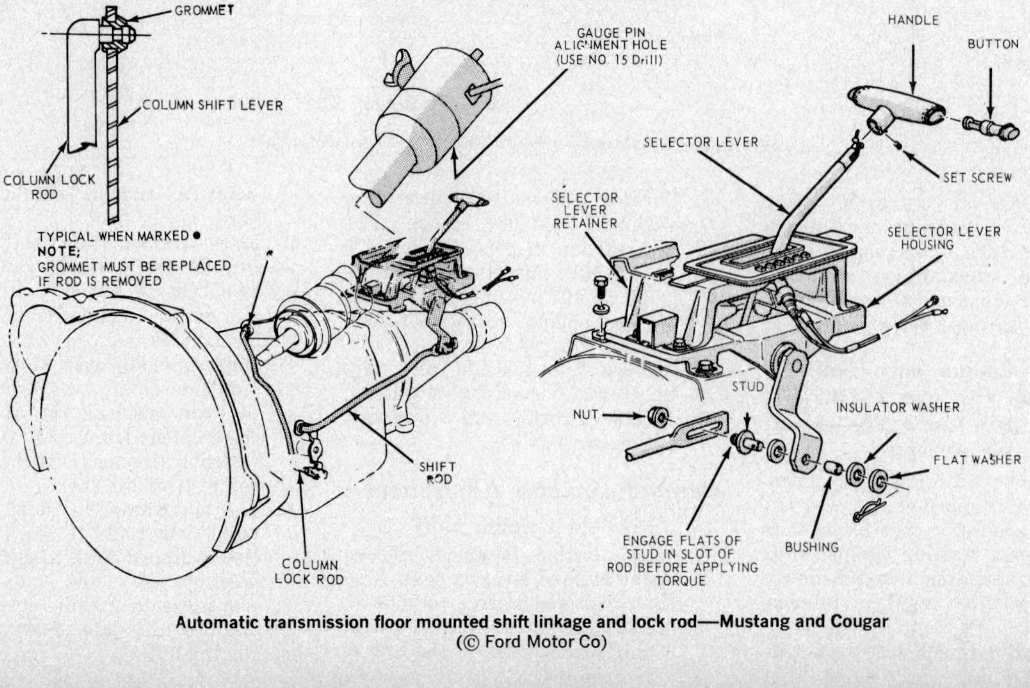
GROMMET
COLUMN SHIFT LEVER
COLUMN LOCK
ROD
TYPICAL WHEN MARKED ●
NOTE;
GROMMET MUST BE REPLACED
IF ROD IS REMOVED
GAUGE PIN
ALIGNMENT HOLE
(USE NO. 15 Drill)
SHIFT
ROD
COLUMN
LOCK ROD
HANDLE
BUTTON
SELECTOR LEVER
SET SCREW
SELECTOR
LEVER
RETAINER
SELECTOR LEVER
HOUSING
STUD
NUT
INSULATOR WASHER
FLAT WASHER
ENGAGE FLATS OF
STUD IN SLOT OF
ROD BEFORE APPLYING
TORQUE
BUSHING

Automatic transmission floor mounted shift linkage and lock rod—Mustang and Cougar
(© Ford Motor Co)

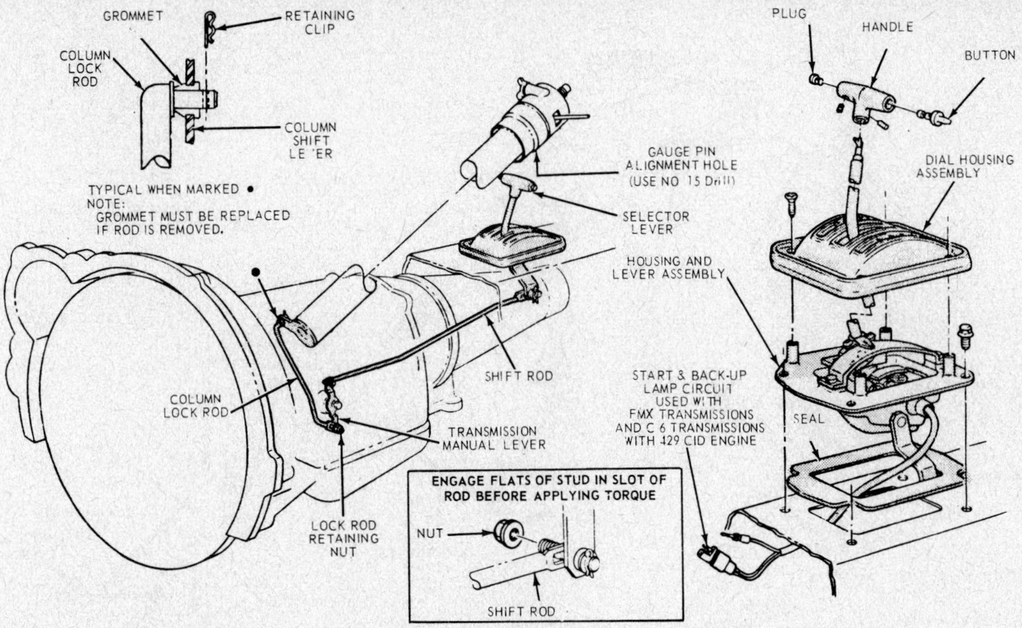
GROMMET
RETAINING CLIP
COLUMN LOCK ROD
COLUMN SHIFT LEVER
TYPICAL WHEN MARKED •
NOTE:
GROMMET MUST BE REPLACED IF ROD IS REMOVED.
GAUGE PIN ALIGNMENT HOLE (USE NO 15 Drill)
SELECTOR LEVER
HOUSING AND LEVER ASSEMBLY
SHIFT ROD
COLUMN LOCK ROD
TRANSMISSION MANUAL LEVER
LOCK ROD RETAINING NUT
ENGAGE FLATS OF STUD IN SLOT OF ROD BEFORE APPLYING TORQUE
NUT
SHIFT ROD
PLUG
HANDLE
BUTTON
DIAL HOUSING ASSEMBLY
START & BACK-UP LAMP CIRCUIT USED WITH FMX TRANSMISSIONS AND C 6 TRANSMISSIONS WITH 429 CID ENGINE
SEAL

Automatic transmission floor mounted shift linkage and lock rod—Fairlane and Montego
(© Ford Motor Co)

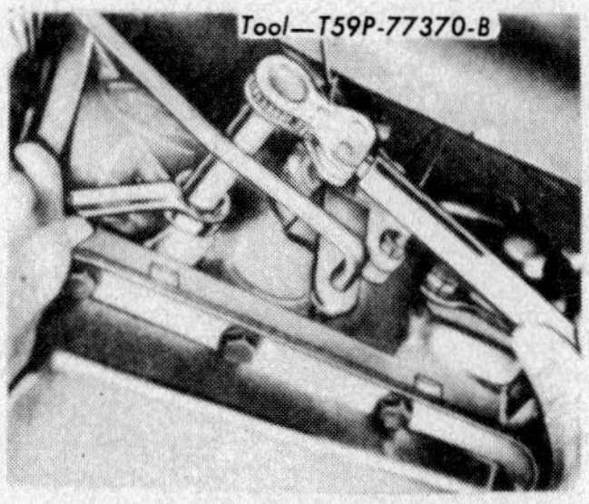
Tool—T59P-77370-B

C-4 Intermediate band adjustment
(© Ford Motor Co)

4. Hold the adjusting screw steady and tighten the locknut to the proper torque.

Low-Reverse Band

1. Clean all dirt from around the band adjusting screw, and remove and discard the locknut.
2. Install a new locknut on the adjusting screw. Using a torque wrench, tighten the adjusting screw to 10 ft lbs.
3. Back off the adjusting screw *exactly 3 full turns.*
4. Hold the adjusting screw steady and tighten the locknut to the proper torque.

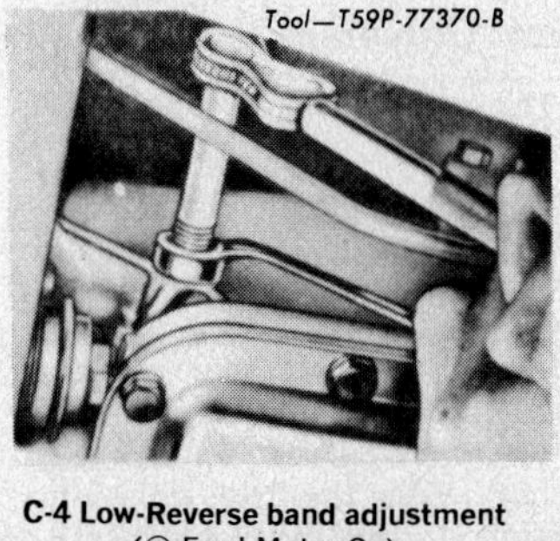
Tool—T59P-77370-B

C-4 Low-Reverse band adjustment
(© Ford Motor Co)

C6 Three-Speed Automatic

Throttle and Downshift Linkage

Initial Adjustments

See C4 three speed automatic.

1967-74 Montego, Comet, and Fairlane with 390, 427 Engines —Final Adjustments

1. Disconnect bellcrank to carburetor rod at point C and accelerator rod from throttle shaft at point B.
2. Disconnect stabilizer rod from stabilizer at point A.
3. Insert 1/4 in. diameter pin through stabilizer and bracket.
4. Adjust length of stabilizer rod so that trunnion enters stabilizer freely. Secure stabilizer rod with retaining clip.
5. Secure carburetor to bellcrank rod to bellcrank with attaching clip at point C.
6. Adjust length of accelerator rod to obtain accelerator pedal height of 4-4 1/2 in. measured at pedal.
7. Connect accelerator rod to accelerator shaft with retaining clip after proper accelerator pedal height has been established.
8. With engine off, disconnect downshift rod from lever at point D.
9. With carburetor choke in off position, depress accelerator pedal to floor; block pedal to hold it in open position.
10. Rotate downshift lever on transmission in counter clockwise direction to place it against internal stop.
11. Adjust trunnion at point D so that it enters downshift lever freely.
12. Turn it one additional turn counter clockwise to lengthen rod. Secure it to lever with retaining clip.
13. Remove block from accelerator pedal.

1967-68 Cougar and Mustang with 390, 427 Engines— Final Adjustments

1. With engine off, check accelerator pedal for height of 4 1/2 in. measured from top of pedal at pivot point to floor pan. To obtain correct pedal height, adjust accelerator connecting link at point A.
2. With engine off, disconnect downshift control cable at point B and from accelerator shaft lever.
3. With carburetor choke in off position, depress accelerator pedal to floor. Block pedal to hold it in wide open position.
4. Rotate downshift lever C counter clockwise to place it against internal stop.
5. With lever held in this position, and with all slack removed from cable, adjust trunnion so that it will slide into accelerator shaft lever. Turn it one turn clockwise, then secure it to lever with retaining clip.
6. Remove block to release accelerator linkage.

1969-74 All Models—Final Adjustments

See C4 Three Speed Automatic under 1969-74 Cougar V8.

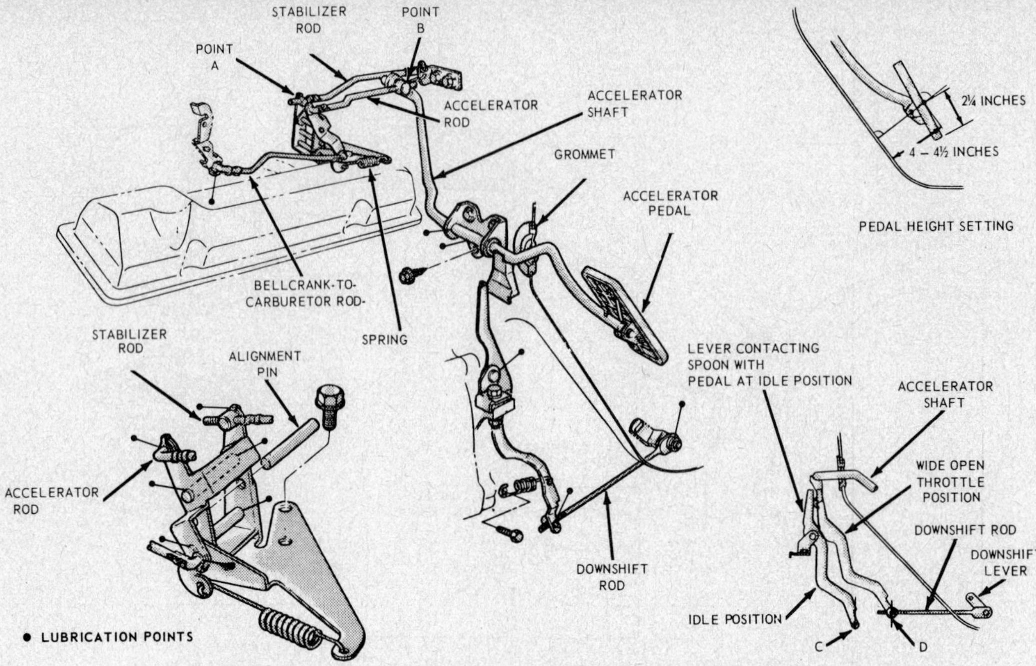
STABILIZER ROD
POINT B
POINT A
ACCELERATOR ROD
ACCELERATOR SHAFT
GROMMET
ACCELERATOR PEDAL
BELLCRANK-TO-CARBURETOR ROD
SPRING
STABILIZER ROD
ALIGNMENT PIN
ACCELERATOR ROD
LEVER CONTACTING SPOON WITH PEDAL AT IDLE POSITION
ACCELERATOR SHAFT
WIDE OPEN THROTTLE POSITION
DOWNSHIFT ROD
DOWNSHIFT LEVER
DOWNSHIFT ROD
IDLE POSITION
C
D
2¼ INCHES
4 – 4½ INCHES
PEDAL HEIGHT SETTING
● LUBRICATION POINTS

Throttle linkage adjustment—C6 transmission 1967-68 Montego, Comet and Fairlane with 390, 427 (© Ford Motor Co)

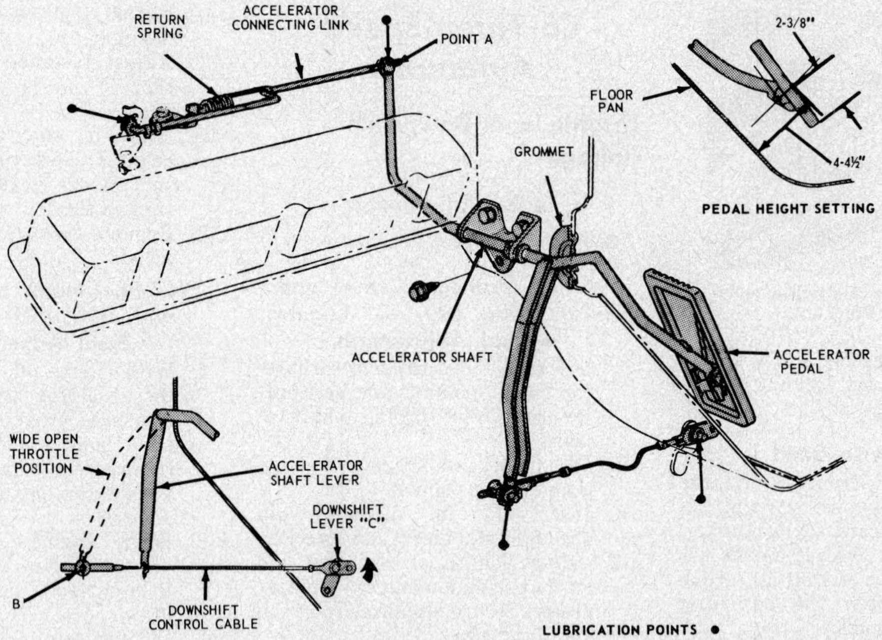
RETURN SPRING
ACCELERATOR CONNECTING LINK
POINT A
2-3/8"
FLOOR PAN
GROMMET
4-4½"
PEDAL HEIGHT SETTING
ACCELERATOR SHAFT
ACCELERATOR PEDAL
WIDE OPEN THROTTLE POSITION
ACCELERATOR SHAFT LEVER
DOWNSHIFT LEVER "C"
B
DOWNSHIFT CONTROL CABLE
LUBRICATION POINTS ●

Throttle linkage adjustment—C6 transmission 1967-68 Cougar and Mustang with 390, 427 (© Ford Motor Co)

Manual Linkage Adjustment, Transmission Lock Rod Adjustment

See C4 Three Speed Automatic.

C6 Band Adjustment

Intermediate Band Adjustment

1. Raise the car on a hoist or place it on jackstands.
2. Clean the threads of the intermediate band adjusting screw.
3. Loosen the adjustment screw lock nut.
4. Tighten the adjusting screw to 10 ft lbs and back the screw off *exactly 1½ turns.* Tighten the adjusting screw locknut.

FMX Automatic Transmission

Since 1969, the FMX transmission has been used in some intermediate size Fords. It is usually used in conjunction with the 351 V8 engine. The throttle and downshift linkage adjustments are the same as used with the C4 transmission.

FMX Band Adjustment

See Ford section.

U-JOINTS

Rear Universal Joint Removal

The rear universal joint has two pillow blocks which are bolted to the pinion shaft flange.

Take out the four bolts that hold the bearing blocks to the pinion shaft and gently tap off the bearing blocks.

Lower the back end of the drive shaft and the front end can be slid out of the back of the transmission together with the transmission yoke portion of the front universal joint.

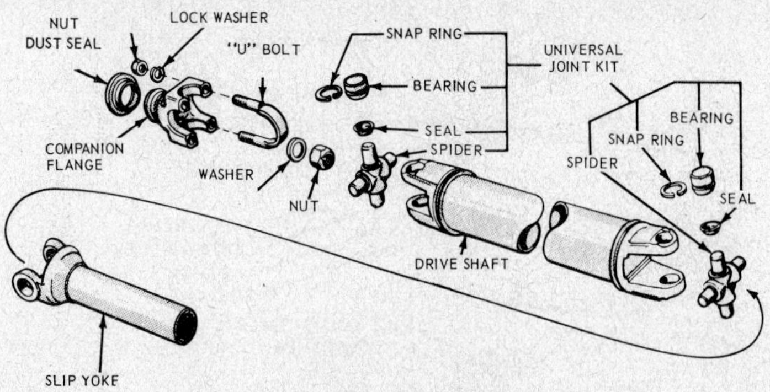
NUT
DUST SEAL
LOCK WASHER
"U" BOLT
SNAP RING
UNIVERSAL JOINT KIT
BEARING
SEAL
SPIDER
COMPANION FLANGE
WASHER
NUT
BEARING
SNAP RING
SPIDER
SEAL
DRIVE SHAFT
SLIP YOKE

Driveshaft and universal joint assembly
(© Ford Motor Co)

Carry the assembly—the front universal joint complete, the driveshaft and the rear universal joint—to the bench and remove the cross from the rear universal joint by taking out the lock rings from the inner side of the bearings. Using a large punch or an arbor press, drive one of the bearings in toward the center, which will force out the opposite bearing.

When it is pressed out far enough to grip it with a pair of pliers, grip it and pull it out of the driveshaft yoke.

Now drive the cross in the opposite direction until the opposite bearing has been driven far enough out for gripping with a pair of pliers.

When both bearings have been taken out, the cross can be lifted from between the two yokes.

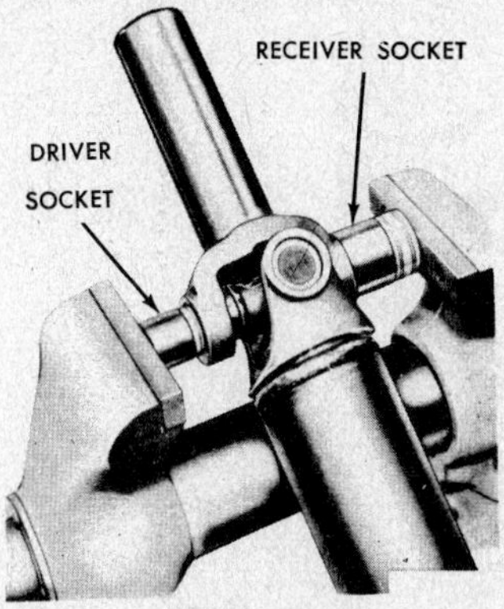
RECEIVER SOCKET
DRIVER SOCKET

U-joint removal
(© Ford Motor Co)

Front Universal Joint Removal

Follow the procedure given above for the rear universal joint but leave the rear universal joint cross in place on the driveshaft if it is not to be removed.

Remove the lock rings from the inner side of two opposite bearings and press on the outer side of one of the bearings, forcing the cross over, which will force the bearing on the opposite side out of its yoke.

Remove the bearing which was forced out of the yoke and then press the cross in the opposite direction to press the other bearing out.

Repeat this procedure on the third and fourth bearings.

When installing the new bearings in the universal joint yoke, it is possible to put them in with a driver of some type, but it is recommended that this work be done in an arbor press since a heavy jolt on the needle bearings can very easily misalign them, which will greatly shorten their life.

JACKING, HOISTING

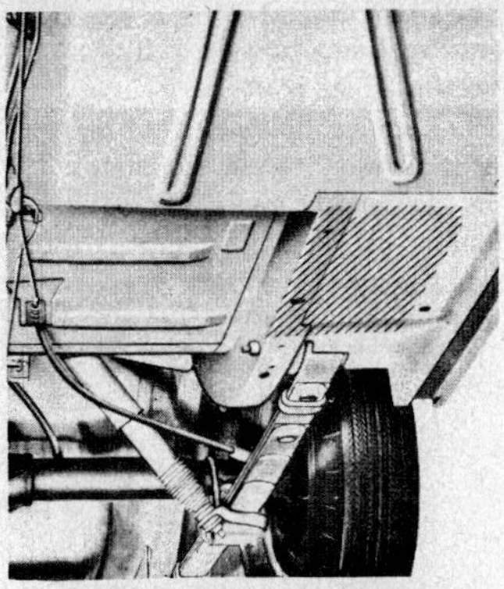

Hoist contact area—rear
(© Ford Motor Co)

Hoist contact area—front
(© Ford Motor Co)

Jack car at front under spring seat of lower control arm. Jack car at rear axle housing close to differential case.

Twin post lifts—front adapters must be carefully placed, large enough to cover entire spring seat area. On models with leaf spring rear suspension, rear adapters or forks must be placed under axle not more than one in. outboard from welds near differential housing. Do not allow the lifts to contact the steering linkage.

On 1972-74 Torinos and Montegos, as well as 1974 Cougars, *do not* position the fork lifts outboard of the rear suspension lower arms. Place the forklifts under the axle housing inboard of the suspension arm brackets.

Frame contact lifts—on all except 1972-74 Torino and Montego and 1974 Cougar, place adapters as shown in diagram. Be sure that pads cover at least 12 sq. in. in area.

FRONT SUSPENSION

On all compact and intermediate Ford Products, except the 1972-74 Torino and Montego and 1974 Cougar, the front coil springs are mounted on top of the upper control arm to a tower in the sheet metal of the body. This type of mounting provides good stability. The lower arm and stabilizing strut substitute for the conventional A frame and serve to guide the lower part of the spindle through its cycle of up-and-down movement. The rod-type stabilizing strut is mounted between two rubber buffer pads at the front end to cushion fore and aft thrust of suspension. The effective length of this rod is variable and must be considered in maintenance. Ball joints are of the usual steel construction.

On 1972-74 Torinos and Montegos and 1974 Cougars, the front coil springs are mounted between the upper and lower control arm. This type of mounting, used on standard-sized Fords for many years, aids cornering ability by lowering the roll center.

Front end alignment procedures are given in the Unit Repair Section. **Figures covering the caster, camber, toe-in, kingpin inclination, and turning radius can be found in the** Front Wheel Alignment table of this section.

Coil Spring on Upper Arm

Shock Absorber

Removal

1. Raise the hood and remove the three shock absorber-to-spring tower attaching bolts.
2. Raise the front of the vehicle and place jackstands under the lower control arms.
3. Remove the shock absorber lower attaching nuts, washers, and insulators.
4. Lift the shock absorber and upper bracket from the spring

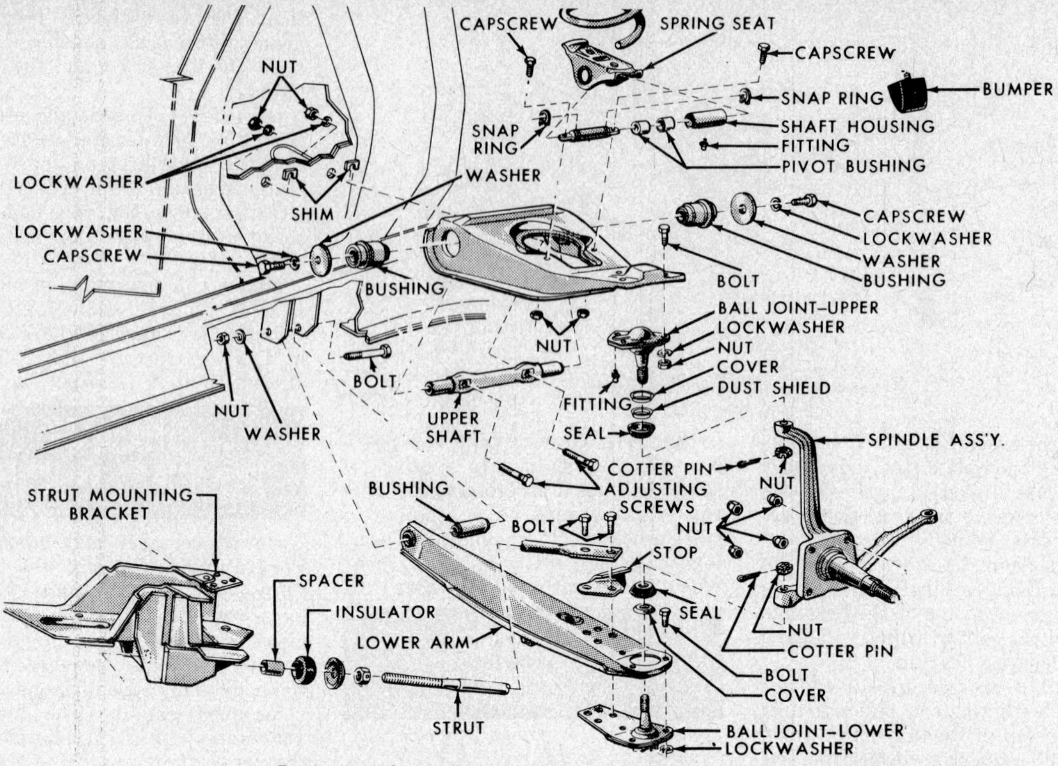
CAPSCREW
SPRING SEAT
CAPSCREW
BUMPER
NUT
SNAP RING
SNAP RING
SHAFT HOUSING
FITTING
PIVOT BUSHING
LOCKWASHER
WASHER
SHIM
LOCKWASHER
CAPSCREW
CAPSCREW
LOCKWASHER
WASHER
BUSHING
BUSHING
BOLT
BALL JOINT–UPPER
LOCKWASHER
NUT
NUT
COVER
BOLT
DUST SHIELD
NUT
FITTING
WASHER
UPPER SHAFT
SEAL
SPINDLE ASS'Y.
COTTER PIN
NUT
ADJUSTING SCREWS
STRUT MOUNTING BRACKET
BUSHING
BOLT
NUT
STOP
SPACER
INSULATOR
SEAL
LOWER ARM
NUT
COTTER PIN
BOLT
COVER
STRUT
BALL JOINT–LOWER
LOCKWASHER

Front suspension—spring on upper arm (© Ford Motor Co)

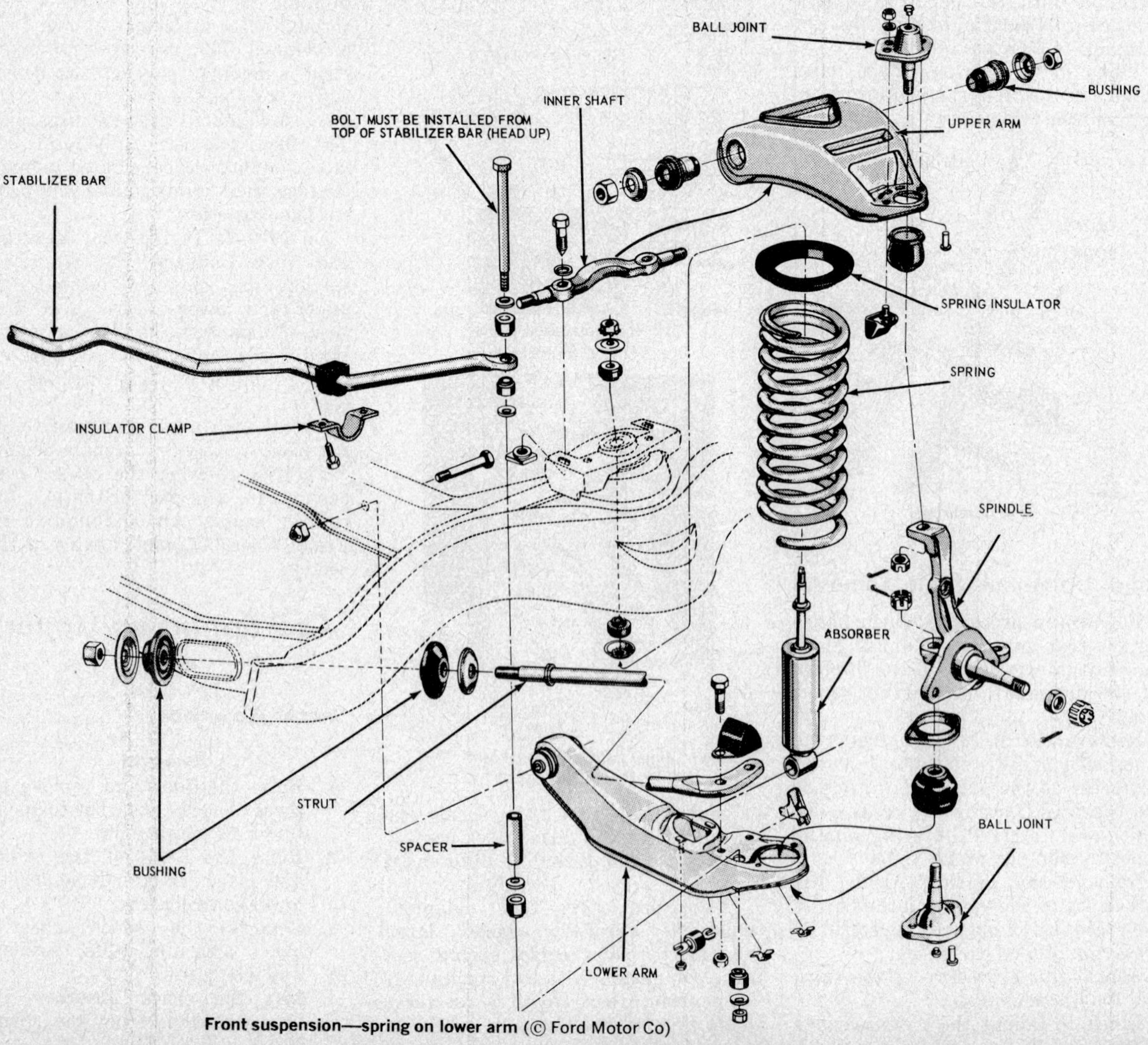
BALL JOINT
BUSHING
INNER SHAFT
BOLT MUST BE INSTALLED FROM TOP OF STABILIZER BAR (HEAD UP)
UPPER ARM
STABILIZER BAR
SPRING INSULATOR
SPRING
INSULATOR CLAMP
SPINDLE
ABSORBER
STRUT
BALL JOINT
SPACER
BUSHING
LOWER ARM

Front suspension—spring on lower arm (© Ford Motor Co)

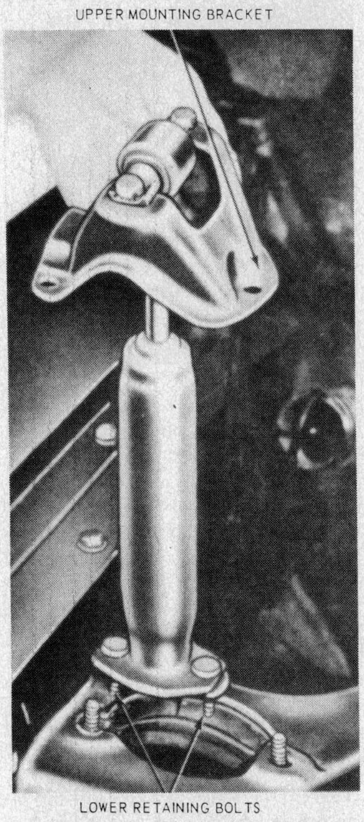
UPPER MOUNTING BRACKET
LOWER RETAINING BOLTS
Removing shock absorber and bracket assembly—spring on upper arm
(© Ford Motor Co)

tower and remove the bracket from the shock absorber. Remove the insulators from the lower attaching studs.

Installation

1. Install the upper mounting bracket on the shock absorber. Install the insulators on the lower attaching studs.
2. Place the shock absorber and upper bracket assembly in the spring tower, making sure that the shock absorber lower studs are in the pivot plate holes.
3. Install the two washers and attaching nuts on the lower studs of the shock absorbers.
4. Install the three shock absorber upper mounting bracket attaching nuts.
5. Remove the jackstands and lower the vehicle.

Front Spring

Removal

1. Raise hood and remove shock absorber upper mounting bracket bolts.
2. Raise front of vehicle, and place safety stands under inboard ends of lower control arms.
3. Remove shock absorber lower attaching nuts, washers and insulators.
4. Lift shock absorber and upper bracket from spring tower.
5. Remove wheel cover on hub cap.
6. Remove grease cap, cotter pin, nut lock, adjusting nut, and outer bearing.
7. Pull wheel, tire and hub and drum off spindle as an assembly.
8. Install spring compressor as shown in figures.
9. Compress spring until all tension is removed from control arms.
10. Remove two upper control arm attaching nuts and swing control arm out board.
11. Release spring compressor and remove.
12. Remove spring.

Installation

1. Place upper spring insulator on spring and secure in place with tape.
2. Position spring in spring tower and compress with spring compressor.
3. Swing upper control arm in board and install attaching nuts.
4. Release spring pressure and guide spring into upper arm spring seat. The end of the spring must be not more than ½ in. from tab on spring seat.
5. Remove spring compressor and position wheel, tire, and hub and drum on spindle.
6. Install bearing, washer and adjusting nut.
7. On disc brake cars, loosen adjusting nut three turns, and rock wheel hub and rotor assembly in and out to push disc brake pads away from rotor.
8. While rotating wheel, hub and drum assembly, torque adjusting nut to 17-25 ft. lbs. to seat bearing.
9. With 1⅛ in. box wrench back off adjusting nut ½ turn, and tighten nut to 10-15 in. lbs. or finger tight.
10. Position lock on adjusting nut and install new cotter pin. Bend ends of pin around castellated flange of nut lock.
11. Check front wheel rotation and install grease cap and hub cap.
12. Install shock absorber and upper bracket assembly, making sure shock absorber lower studs have insulators and are in pivot plate holes.
13. Install nuts and washers on lower studs and torque to 8-12 ft. lbs. on 1970 and later models and 12-17 ft. lbs. on 1967-69 models.
14. Install nuts on shock absorber upper bracket.
15. Lower car.

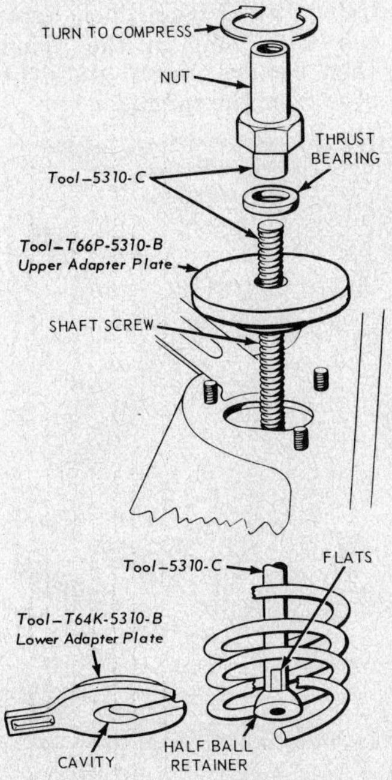
TURN TO COMPRESS
NUT
THRUST BEARING
Tool–5310-C
Tool–T66P-5310-B
Upper Adapter Plate
SHAFT SCREW
Tool–5310-C
FLATS
Tool–T64K-5310-B
Lower Adapter Plate
CAVITY
HALF BALL RETAINER
Spring compressor—spring on upper arm
(© Ford Motor Co)

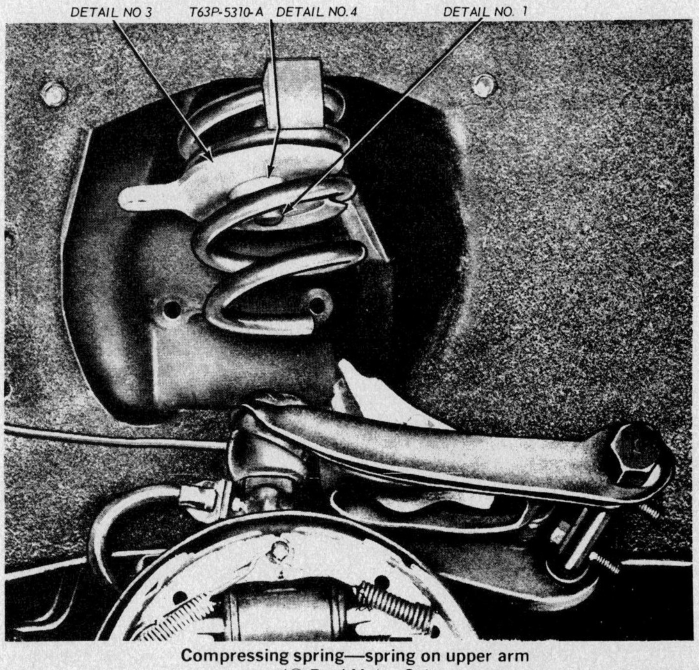
DETAIL NO 3
T63P-5310-A
DETAIL NO. 4
DETAIL NO. 1
Compressing spring—spring on upper arm
(© Ford Motor Co)

Lower Ball Joint

On all intermediate size Ford cars which have the coil springs mounted on the upper control arm, the lower ball joint is an integral part of the lower control arm. If the lower ball joint is defective the entire lower control arm must be replaced.

Inspection

1. Raise the vehicle on a hoist or floor jack so that the front wheel falls to the full down position.
2. Have an assistant grasp the bottom of the tire and move the wheel in and out.
3. As the wheel is being moved, observe the lower control arm where the spindle attaches to it.
4. Any movement between the lower part of the spindle and the lower control arm indicates a bad control arm which must be replaced.

NOTE: during this check, the upper ball joint will be unloaded and may move; this is normal and not an indication of a bad ball joint. Also, do not mistake a loose wheel bearing for a worn ball joint.

Replacement

1. Position an upper control arm support between the upper arm and side rail as shown in the illustration.
2. Raise the vehicle, position jack stands and remove the wheel and tire.
3. Remove the stabilizer bar to link attaching nut and disconnect the bar from the link.
4. Remove the link bolt from the lower arm.
5. Remove the strut bar to lower attaching nuts and bolts.
6. Remove the lower ball joint cotter pin and back off the nut. Using a suitable tool, loosen the ball joint stud in the spindle.
7. Remove the nut from the arm and lower the arm.
8. Remove the lower arm to underbody cam attaching parts and remove the arm.
9. To install, position the lower arm in the underbody and install the ball joint and cam attaching parts loosely.
10. Install the stabilizer and strut and torque the attaching parts to specifications.
11. Torque the lower arm pivot and ball joint stud to specifications.
12. Lower the car and remove the upper arm support.
13. Front end alignment must be rechecked.

Upper Ball Joint

Inspection

1. Raise the vehicle on a hoist or floor jack so that the front wheels hang in full down position.

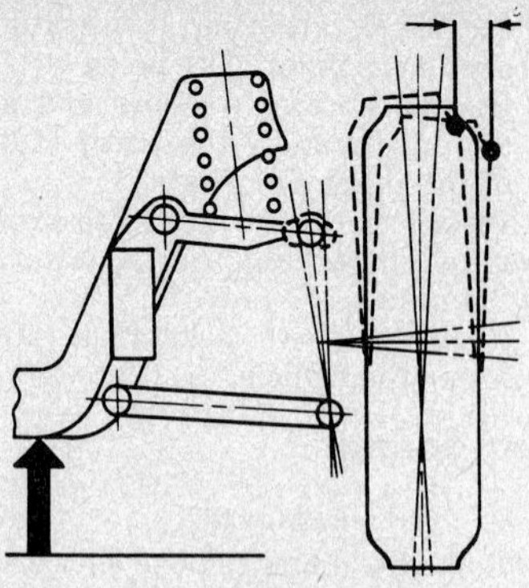

Measuring upper ball joint radial play —spring on upper arm
(© Ford Motor Co)

2. Have an assistant grasp the wheel top and bottom and apply alternate in and out pressure to the top and bottom of the wheel.
3. Radial play of ¼ in. is acceptable measured at the inside of the wheel adjacent to the upper arm.

NOTE: this radial play measurement is multiplied at the outer circumference of the tire and should not be measured here. Measure only at the inside of the wheel.

Replacement

1. Position support between the upper arm and frame rail as shown in illustration.
2. Raise the vehicle and remove the tire and wheel.
3. Remove the upper ball joint cotter pin and loosen the nut.
4. Using a suitable tool, loosen the ball joint in the spindle.
5. Remove the three ball joint retaining viets using a large chisel.
6. Remove the nut from the ball joint stud and remove the ball joint.
7. Clean and remove all burrs from the ball joint mounting area of the control arm before installing new ball joint.

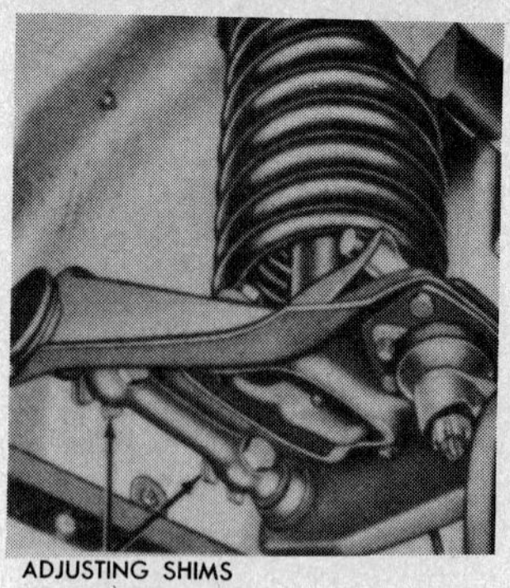
ADJUSTING SHIMS

Upper control arm assembly —spring on upper arm
(© Ford Motor Co)

8. Install the ball joint in the upper arm using the service part nuts and bolts. Do not attempt to rivet a new ball joint to the arm.
9. Install and torque the ball joint stud nut and install the cotter pin.
10. Lubricate the new joint with a hand type grease gun only, using an air pressure gun may loosen the ball joint seal.
11. Install wheel, lower vehicle and remove upper arm support.
12. Check front end alignment.

Upper Control Arm

Replacement

1. Remove the shock absorber and upper mounting bracket from the car as an assembly.
2. Raise the vehicle and remove the wheel and tire as an assembly.
3. Install spring compressor tool.
4. Place a safety stand under the lower arm.
5. Remove the cotter pin from the upper ball joint stud and loosen the nut.
6. Using a suitable tool, loosen the ball joint in the spindle, then, remove the nut and lift the stud from the spindle.

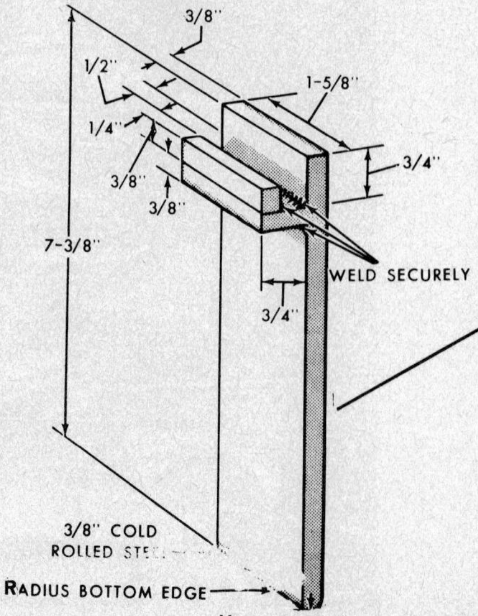
3/8"
1/2"
1-5/8"
1/4"
3/4"
3/8"
3/8"
7-3/8"
WELD SECURELY
3/4"
3/8" COLD
ROLLED
RADIUS BOTTOM EDGE

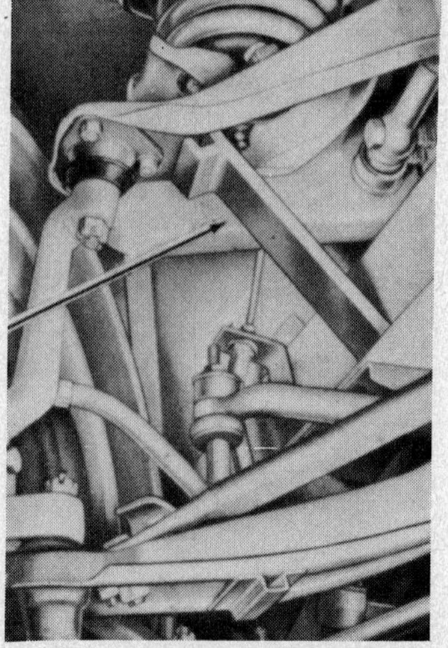

Upper control arm support—spring on upper arm
(© Ford Motor Co)

7. Remove the upper arm attaching nuts from the engine compartment, and remove the upper arm.
8. To install the arm, position it on the mounting bracket and install the attaching nuts on the inner shaft attaching bolts.

NOTE: the original equipment keystone-type lockwashers must be used with the inner shaft attaching nuts and bolts.

9. Install the upper ball joint stud in the spindle and tighten the nut to specifications. Install a new cotter pin.
10. Remove spring compressor and position spring on upper arm. Install wheel and check front end alignment.

Chilton's TIME SAVER

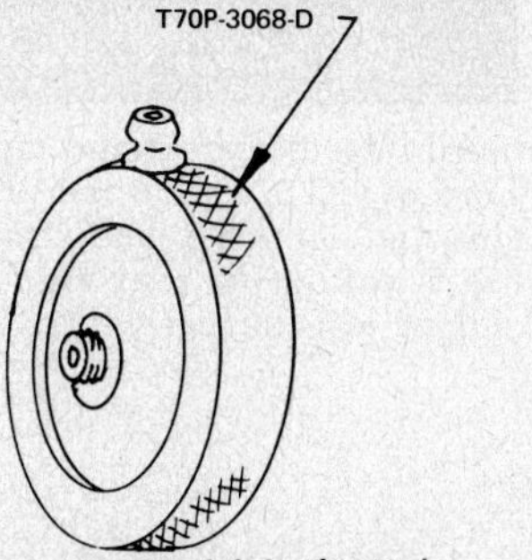
T70P-3068-D
Upper control arm lubricating tool
(© Ford Motor Co)

When upper control arm bushings become low on lubrication, they become very noisy. This can often be corrected by lubrication and it is not necessary to replace the bushings. On early models that do not contain grease plugs it is necessary to drill and tap the bushing to accept a grease fitting. On later models with grease plugs it is difficult to remove the plug and grease the bushing with conventional tools. Ford Motor Co. has available through its dealers an upper A-arm lubrication kit which greatly eases the performance of this operation.

Coil Spring on Lower Arm

Shock Absorber

Removal and Replacement

1. Remove the nut, washer, and bushing from the upper end of the shock absorber.
2. Raise the vehicle and install jackstands under the frame rails.
3. Remove the two bolts securing the shock absorber to the lower control arm and remove the shock absorber.
4. Install a new bushing and washer on the top of the shock absorber and position the unit inside the front spring. Install the two lower attaching bolts and torque them to 8–15 ft lbs.
5. Remove the jackstands and lower the vehicle.
6. Place a new bushing and washer on the shock absorber top stud and install the attaching nut. Torque to 22–30 ft lbs.

Coil Spring and Lower Control Arm R & R

1. Raise car and support it with stands placed in back of lower arms.
2. If equipped with drum type brakes, remove the wheel and brake drum as an assembly. Remove the brake backing plate attaching bolts and remove the backing plate from the spindle. Wire the assembly back out of the way.
3. If equipped with disc brakes, remove the wheel from the hub. Remove the bolts and washers that hold the caliper and brake hose bracket to the spindle. Remove the caliper from the rotor and wire it back out of the way. Then, remove the hub and rotor from the spindle.
4. Disconnect lower end of the shock absorber and push it up to the retracted position.

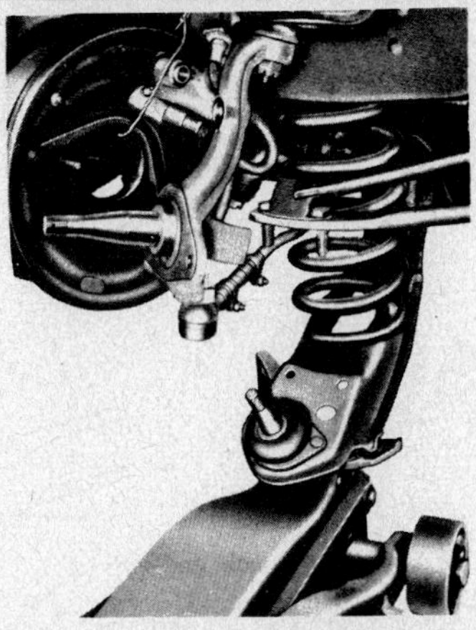
Coil spring and lower arm replacement —spring on lower arm
(© Ford Motor Co)

5. Disconnect stabilizer bar link from the lower arm.
6. Remove cotter pins from the upper and lower ball joint stud nuts.
7. Remove two bolts and nuts holding the strut to the lower arm.
8. Loosen the lower ball joint stud nut two turns. Do not remove this nut.
9. Install a spreader tool between the upper and lower ball joint studs.
10. Expand the tool until the tool exerts considerable pressure on the studs. Tap the spindle near the lower stud with a hammer to loosen the stud in the spindle. Do not loosen the stud with tool pressure only.
11. Position floor jack under the lower arm and remove the lower ball joint stud nut.
12. Lower floor jack and remove the spring and insulator.
13. Remove the A-arm to crossmember attaching parts, and remove the arm from the car.
14. Reverse above procedure to install. If lower control arm was replaced because of damage, check front end alignment.

Lower Ball Joint

Inspection

1. Raise the vehicle by placing a floor jack under the lower arm; or, raise the vehicle on a hoist and place a jack stand under the lower arm and lower the vehicle onto it to remove the preload from the lower ball joint.

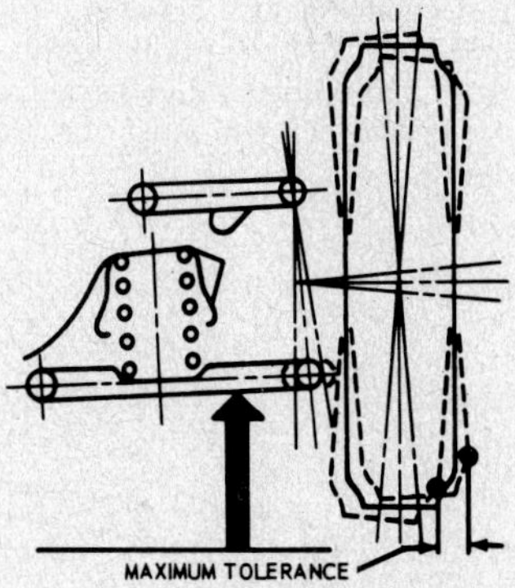
MAXIMUM TOLERANCE
Measuring lower ball joint radial play —spring on lower arm
(© Ford Motor Co)

2. Have an assistant grasp the wheel top and bottom and apply alternate in and out pressure to the top and bottom of the wheel.
3. Radial play of $1/4$ in. is acceptable measured at the inside of the wheel adjacent to the lower arm.

NOTE: this radial play is multiplied at the outer circumference of the tire and should be measured only at the inside of the wheel.

Replacement

1. Raise the vehicle on a hoist and allow the front wheels to fall to their full down position.
2. Drill a 1/8 in. hole completely through each ball joint attaching rivet.
3. Use a $3/8$ in. drill in the pilot hole to drill off the head of the rivet.
4. Drive the rivets from the lower arm.
5. Place a jack under the lower arm and lower the vehicle about 6 in.
6. Remove the lower ball joint stud cotter pin and attaching nut.

7. Using a suitable tool, loosen the ball joint from the spindle and remove the ball joint from the lower arm.
8. Clean all metal burrs from the lower arm and install the new ball joint, using the service part nuts and bolts to attach the ball joint to the lower arm. Do not attempt to rerivet the ball joint once it has been removed.
9. Check front end alignment.

Upper Ball Joint

Inspection

1. Raise the vehicle by placing a floor jack under the lower arm. Do not allow the lower arm to hang freely with the vehicle on a hoist or bumper jack.
2. Have an assistant grasp the bottom of the tire and move the wheel in and out.
3. As the wheel is being moved, observe the upper control arm where the spindle attaches to it. Any movement between the upper part of the spindle and the upper ball joint indicates a bad ball joint which must be replaced.

NOTE: During this check the lower ball joint will be unloaded and may move; this is normal and not an indication of a bad ball joint. Also, do not mistake a loose wheel bearing for a defective ball joint.

Replacement

1. Raise the vehicle on a hoist and allow the front wheels to fall to their full down position.
2. Drill a 1/8 in. hole completely through each ball joint attaching rivet.
3. Using a large chisel, cut off the head of each rivet and drive them from the upper arm.
4. Place a jack under the lower arm and lower the vehicle about 6 in.
5. Remove the cotter pin and attaching nut from the ball joint stud.
6. Using a suitable tool, loosen the ball joint stud from the spindle and remove the ball joint from the upper arm.
7. Clean all metal burrs from the upper arm and install the new ball point, using the service part nuts and bolts to attach the ball joint to the upper arm. Do not attempt to rerivet the ball joint once it has been removed.
8. Check front end alignment.

Upper Control Arm

Replacement

1. Raise the vehicle on a hoist.
2. If equipped with drum brakes remove the tire, wheel and brake drum as an assembly. If equipped with disc brakes, remove the tire and wheel.
3. Remove the cotter pin and attaching nut from the ball joint stud.
4. Using a suitable tool, loosen the upper ball joint from the spindle.
5. Place a jack under the lower arm and lower the vehicle about 6 in.
6. Remove the upper arm inner shaft attaching bolts and remove the arm and shaft from the chassis as an assembly.
7. Reverse above procedure to install.
8. Adjust front end alignment.

REAR SUSPENSION

All intermediate and compact-sized Ford products, except the 1972-74 Torino and Montego, and 1974 Cougar use a leaf-spring rear suspension. A pair of leaf springs support the axle

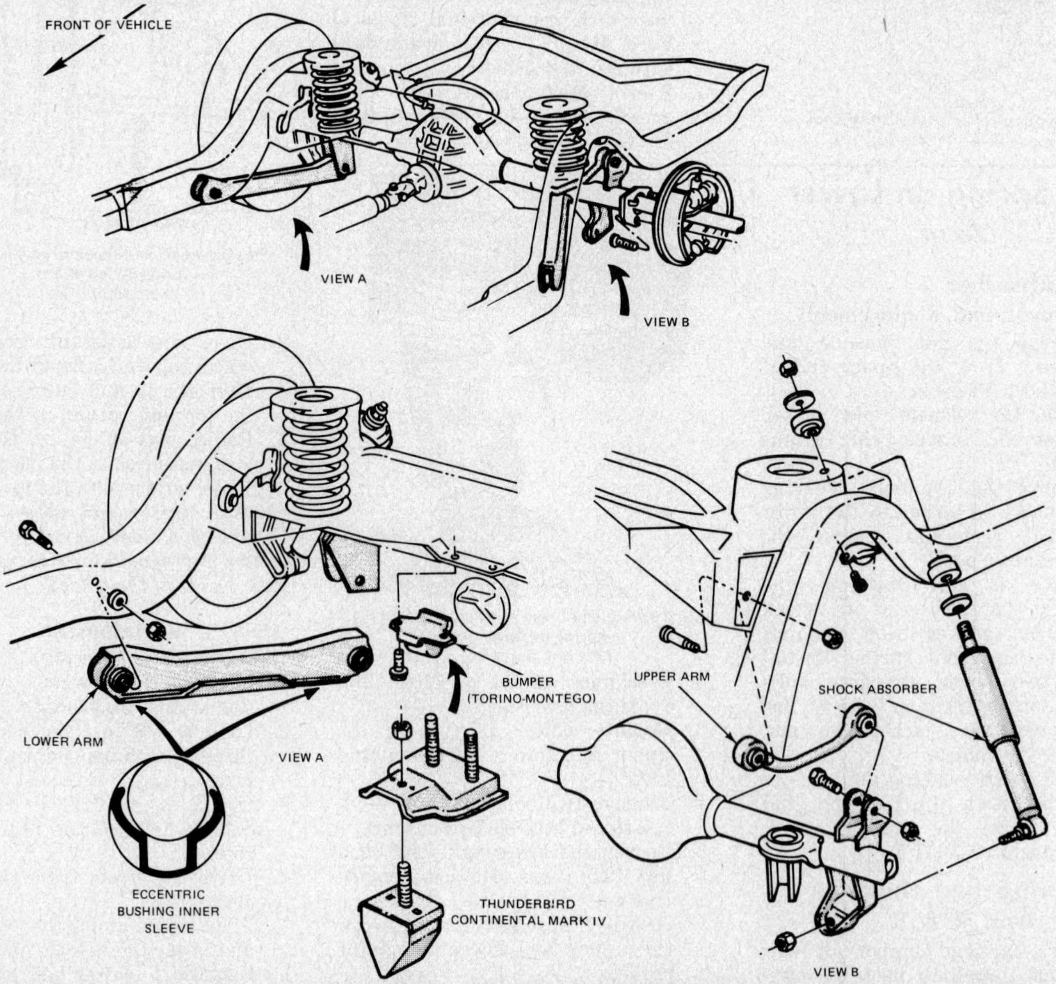
FRONT OF VEHICLE
VIEW A
VIEW B
LOWER ARM
VIEW A
ECCENTRIC
BUSHING INNER
SLEEVE
BUMPER
(TORINO-MONTEGO)
THUNDERBIRD
CONTINENTAL MARK IV
UPPER ARM
SHOCK ABSORBER
VIEW B

Coil spring rear suspension (© Ford Motor Co)

housing, which is secured to the springs by two U-bolts and retaining plates. Each spring is suspended from the underbody side rails by a hanger at the front and a shackle at the rear. The shock absorbers are mounted between the leaf spring retaining plates and brackets bolted to the crossmember. Some 1969-71 high-performance models are equipped with staggered rear shock absorbers.

1972-74 Torinos and Montegos and 1974 Cougars utilize a coil spring, rear suspension. The axle housing is suspended from the frame by an upper and lower trailing arm, and a shock absorber at each side of the vehicle. These arms pivot in the frame members and the rear axle housing brackets. Each coil spring is mounted between a lower seat which is welded to the axle housing and an upper seat integral with the frame. The shock absorbers are bolted to the spring upper seats at the top and brackets mounted on the axle housing at the bottom. A rear stabilizer, bar attached to the frame side rail brackets and the two axle housing brackets, is available as optional equipment.

Leaf Spring Suspension

Spring R & R

1. Raise the vehicle and place supports beneath the underbody and axle.
2. Disconnect the lower end of the shock absorber from the spring clip plate and position it out of the way. Remove the supports from under the axle.
3. Remove the spring plate nuts from the U-bolt and remove the spring plate. With a jack, raise the rear axle just enough to remove the weight of the housing from the spring.
4. Remove the two rear shackle attaching nuts, the shackle bar, and the two inner bushings.
5. Remove the rear shackle assembly and the two outer bushings.
6. Remove the nut from the spring mounting bolt and tap the bolt out of the bushing at the front hanger. Lift out the spring assembly.

NOTE: all used attaching components (nuts, bolts, etc.) must be discarded and replaced with new ones prior to assembly.

7. Position the leaf spring under the axle housing and insert the shackle assembly into the rear hanger bracket and the rear eye of the spring.
8. Install the shackle inner bushings, the shackle plate, and the locknuts. Hand-tighten the locknuts.
9. Position the spring eye in the front hanger, slip the washer on the front hanger bolt, and, from the inboard side, insert the bolt through the hanger and eye. Install the locknut on the hanger bolt finger-tight.
10. Lower the rear axle housing so that it rests on the spring. Place the spring plate on the U-bolt and tighten the nuts.
11. Attach the lower end of the shock absorber to the spring plate using a new nut.
12. Place jackstands under the rear axle. Lower the vehicle until the spring is in the approximate curb load position, and tighten the front hanger locknut.
13. Tighten the rear shackle locknuts. Close the hole in the inner rail with a body plug.
14. Remove the jackstands and lower the vehicle.

Shock Absorber R & R

1967-73 Mustang and Cougar

1. Disconnect the shock absorber at the spring plate.
2. Remove the shock absorber access cover from the trunk. Remove the rear seat from 1969–73 convertibles to reach the access cover.
3. Remove the shock absorber upper retaining nut.
4. Compress and remove the shock absorber. Remove all bushings and washers from the unit.
5. Place new inner bushings and washers on the shock absorber studs.
6. Connect the upper stud to the mounting. Install a new outer bushing, washer, and nut on the stud. Install the access cover.
7. Connect the lower stud to the spring plate. Install a new outer bushing, washer, and nut on the stud. Be sure that the spring plate is free of burrs.

1967 Comet, 1967-70 Falcon and Fairlane, 1968-71 Torino and Montego, All Models Except Convertible

1. Remove the spare from the trunk. On station wagons, remove the access cover from the opening in the seat riser over the shock absorber. On Rancheros, remove the attaching screws and remove the forward half of the floor panel, then remove the access cover from the opening in the floor pan. On all other models, fold back the trunk floor mat and remove the access cover.
2. Remove the nut, outer washer, and rubber bushing from the top of the shock absorber.
3. Raise the vehicle and remove the attaching nut, outer washer, and bushing from the shock absorber at the spring plate. Compress and remove the shock absorber. Remove all bushings and washers from the unit.
4. Position a new inner washer and bushing on each shock absorber stud.
5. Place the shock absorber between the spring plate and the mounting in the floor pan. Install a new outer bushing, washer, and nut on the lower stud. Make sure that the spring plate is free of burrs. Lower the vehicle.
6. Install the new outer bushing, washer, and nut on the upper stud.
7. On station wagon models, replace the retaining screws and floor bed panel. On Rancheros, install the access cover and the forward half of the bed. On all other models, install the access cover and secure the spare in the trunk.

1967 Comet, 1967-70 Fairlane, and 1968-71 Torino and Montego Convertibles

1. Remove the rear seat.
2. Raise the vehicle and install jackstands. Have an assistant hold the shock absorber from underneath the car and remove the nut, washer, and bushing from the top of the shock absorber.
3. Remove the lower shock absorber nut, washer, and bushing. Compress and remove the shock absorber. Remove the inner bushings and washers from the unit.
4. Place the new inner washers and bushings on the shock absorber. Secure the shock absorber at its lower attachment by installing the new outer bushing, washer, and nut on the lower mounting stud.
5. Lower the vehicle and install the new outer bushing, washer, and nut on the top of the shock absorber.
6. Install the rear seat.

1970-74 Maverick and 1971-74 Comet

1. Remove the lower end of the shock absorber from the spring plate.
2. Remove the nut retaining the upper end of the shock absorber to the mounting bracket underneath the car.
3. Compress and remove the shock absorber.
4. Transfer the washers and bushings to the new shock absorber. Insert the upper stud through the mounting bracket, and install the attaching nut finger-tight.
5. Compress and install the shock absorber to the spring plate. Install the washers, bushings, and attaching nuts.
6. Tighten the upper and lower attaching nuts.

Coil Spring Suspension

Spring R & R

1. Place a jack under the rear axle housing. Raise the vehicle and place jackstands under the frame side rails.
2. Disconnect the lower studs of the shock absorbers from the mounting brackets on the axle housing.
3. Lower the axle housing until the springs are fully released.
4. Remove the springs and insulators from the vehicle.
5. Place the insulators in each upper seat and position the springs between the upper and lower seats.
6. With the springs in position, raise the axle housing until the lower studs of the rear shock absorbers reach the mounting brackets on the axle housing. Connect the lower studs and install the attaching nuts.
7. Remove the jackstands and lower the vehicle.

Shock Absorber R & R

1. Raise the vehicle and install jackstands.
2. Remove the shock absorber outer attaching nut, washer and insulator from the stud at the top side of the spring upper seat. Compress the shock sufficiently to clear the spring seat hole, and remove the inner insulator and washer from the upper attaching stud.
3. Remove the locknut and disconnect the shock absorber lower stud at the mounting bracket on the axle housing. Remove the shock absorber.
4. Position a new inner washer and insulator on the upper attaching stud. Place the upper stud in the hole in the upper spring seat. While maintaining the shock in this position, install a new outer insulator, washer, and nut on the stud from the top side of the spring upper seat.
5. Extend the shock absorber. Locate the lower stud in the mounting bracket hole on the axle housing and install the locknut.

BRAKES

Single-anchor, internal-expanding hydraulic brakes are standard on all models.

An independent parking brake operates the rear wheel brake shoes through a mechanical cable linkage. Brake shoe or pad replacement and adjustment procedures as well as wheel cylinder and master cylinder overhaul and brake bleeding procedures can be found in the Unit Repair Section.

Self-Adjusting Brakes

The self-adjusting brake mechanism consists of a cable, cable guide, adjuster lever, and adjuster spring. The cable is hooked over the anchor pin at the top and is connected to the lever at the bottom. The cable is connected to the secondary brake shoe by means of the cable guide. The adjuster spring is hooked to the primary brake shoe and to the lever.

The automatic adjuster operates only when the brakes are applied while the car is moving rearward.

With the car moving rearward and the brakes applied, the wrapping action of the shoes following the drum forces the upper end of the primary shoe against the anchor pin. Action of the wheel cylinder moves the upper end of the secondary shoe away from the anchor pin. Movement of the secondary shoe causes the cable to pull the adjusting lever upward and against the end of a tooth on the adjusting screw star wheel. Upward travel of the lever increases as lining wear increases. When the lever can move far enough upward to pass over the end of the tooth, the adjuster spring pulls the lever downward causing the star wheel to turn and expand the shoes. The star wheel is turned one tooth at a time as the linings progressively wear.

Disc Brakes

Since 1967, disc brakes have been available on front wheels of some models. Complete Service Procedures are covered in the Unit Repair Section.

Master Cylinder

Since 1967, a tandem-type (dual) master cylinder has been used on all models. This design divides the brake hydraulic system into two independent and hydraulically separated

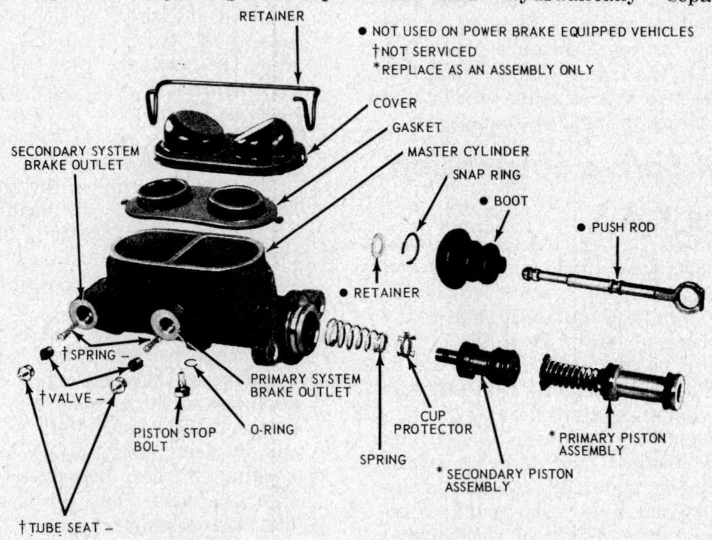
RETAINER
● NOT USED ON POWER BRAKE EQUIPPED VEHICLES
†NOT SERVICED
*REPLACE AS AN ASSEMBLY ONLY
COVER
GASKET
MASTER CYLINDER
SECONDARY SYSTEM BRAKE OUTLET
SNAP RING
● BOOT
● PUSH ROD
● RETAINER
†SPRING
†VALVE
PRIMARY SYSTEM BRAKE OUTLET
PISTON STOP BOLT
O-RING
CUP PROTECTOR
SPRING
* PRIMARY PISTON ASSEMBLY
* SECONDARY PISTON ASSEMBLY
†TUBE SEAT

Dual master cylinder—drum brakes (© Ford Motor Co)

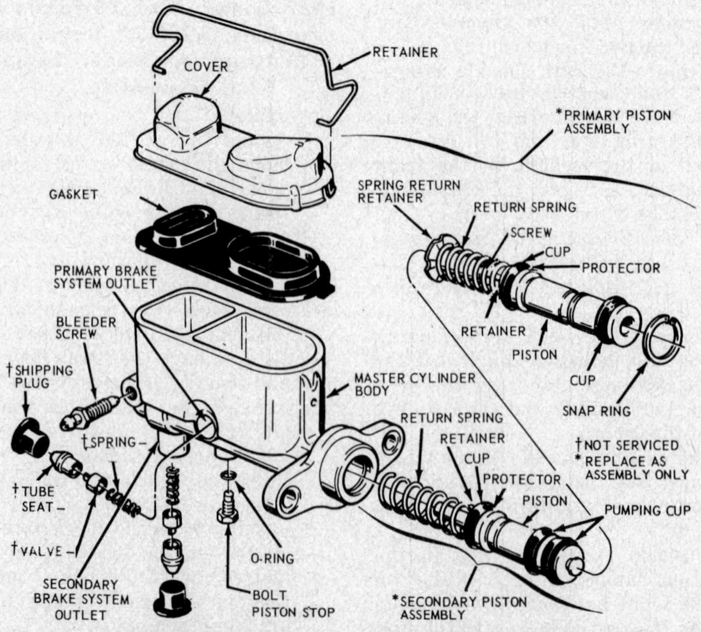
RETAINER
COVER
*PRIMARY PISTON ASSEMBLY
GASKET
SPRING RETURN RETAINER
RETURN SPRING
SCREW
CUP
PROTECTOR
PRIMARY BRAKE SYSTEM OUTLET
BLEEDER SCREW
RETAINER
PISTON
†SHIPPING PLUG
MASTER CYLINDER BODY
CUP
SNAP RING
†SPRING
RETURN SPRING
RETAINER
CUP
†NOT SERVICED
* REPLACE AS ASSEMBLY ONLY
PROTECTOR
†TUBE SEAT
PISTON
PUMPING CUP
†VALVE
O-RING
SECONDARY BRAKE SYSTEM OUTLET
BOLT PISTON STOP
*SECONDARY PISTON ASSEMBLY

Dual master cylinder—disc brakes (© Ford Motor Co)

halves. In the event of a single hydraulic failure, 50% braking efficiency is maintained.

Dual Master Cylinder R & R

Standard Brakes

1. Working under the dash, disconnect the master cylinder pushrod from the brake pedal. The pushrod cannot be removed from the master cylinder.
2. Disconnect the stoplight switch wires and remove the switch from the brake pedal, using care not to damage the switch.
3. Disconnect the brake lines from the master cylinder.
4. Remove the attaching screws from the firewall and remove the master cylinder from the car.
5. Reinstall in reverse of above order, leaving the brake line fittings loose at the master cylinder.
6. Fill the master cylinder, and with the brake lines loose, slowly bleed the air from the master cylinder using the foot pedal.

Power Brakes

1. Disconnect the brake line from the master cylinder.
2. Remove the two nuts and lockwashers that attach the master cylinder to the brake booster.
3. Remove the master cylinder from the booster.
4. Reverse above procedure to reinstall.
5. Fill master cylinder and bleed entire brake system.
6. Refill master cylinder.

Power Brakes

Power Unit Removal

1. Working inside the car below the instrument panel, disconnect booster valve operating rod from the brake pedal assembly.
2. Open the hood, and disconnect the wires from the stop light switch at the brake master cylinder.
3. Disconnect the brake line at the master cylinder outlet fitting.
4. Disconnect manifold vacuum hose from the booster unit.
5. Remove the four bracket-to-dash panel attaching bolts.
6. Remove the booster and bracket assembly from the dash panel, sliding the valve operating rod out from the engine side of the dash panel.

Power Unit Installation

1. Mount the booster and bracket assembly to the dash panel by sliding the valve operating rod in through the hole in the dash panel, and installing the attaching bolts.
2. Connect manifold vacuum hose to the booster.
3. Connect the brake line to the master cylinder outlet fitting.
4. Connect stop light switch wires.
5. Working inside the car below the instrument panel, install the rubber boot on the valve operating rod at the passenger side of the dash panel.
6. Connect the valve operating rod to the brake pedal with the bushings, eccentric shoulder bolt, and nut.

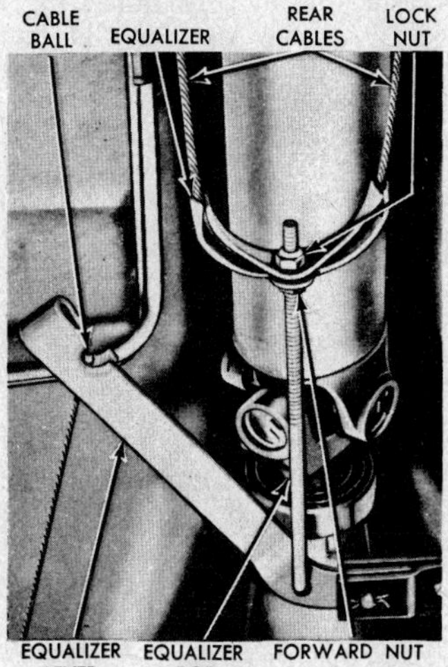
CABLE BALL
EQUALIZER
REAR CABLES
LOCK NUT
EQUALIZER LEVER
EQUALIZER ROD
FORWARD NUT

Parking brake linkage
(© Ford Motor Co)

Parking Brake Adjustment

In most cases, a rear brake shoe adjustment will provide satisfactory parking brake action. However, if parking brake cables are excessively loose after releasing the handbrake, proceed as follows:

1. On handle-actuated systems pull up the handle to the third notch. On pedal-actuated systems, depress the parking brake pedal one notch from its normal released position.
2. Loosen locknut on equalizer rod under the car. Then loosen the nut in front of the equalizer, several turns.
3. Turn the locknut forward against the equalizer until the cables are tight enough so that the rear wheels cannot be turned by hand. Then, back off the adjustment until the rear wheels turn freely.
4. When cables are properly adjusted, tighten both nuts against the equalizer.
5. Release the handle and feel for freeness of rear wheels.

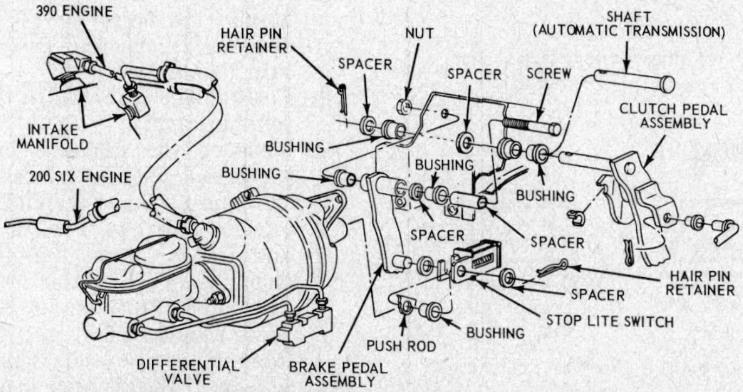
390 ENGINE
HAIR PIN RETAINER
NUT
SHAFT (AUTOMATIC TRANSMISSION)
SPACER
SPACER
SCREW
CLUTCH PEDAL ASSEMBLY
INTAKE MANIFOLD
BUSHING
BUSHING
BUSHING
200 SIX ENGINE
BUSHING
SPACER
SPACER
HAIR PIN RETAINER
SPACER
STOP LITE SWITCH
BUSHING
PUSH ROD
DIFFERENTIAL VALVE
BRAKE PEDAL ASSEMBLY

Vacuum brake booster installation (© Ford Motor Co)

STEERING

The manual steering gear is of the worm and recirculating ball type. The sector shaft is straddle-mounted in the cover above the gear and a housing-mounted roller bearing below the gear. The steering linkage consists of a Pitman arm, a steering (Pitman) arm to idler arm rod, an idler arm and tie-rods.

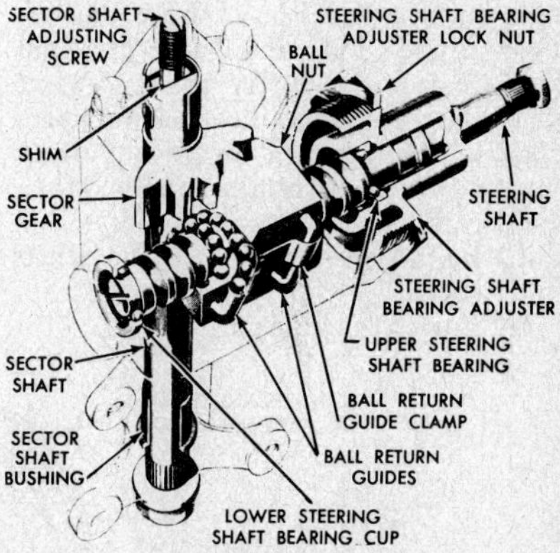
SECTOR SHAFT ADJUSTING SCREW
STEERING SHAFT BEARING ADJUSTER LOCK NUT
BALL NUT
SHIM
SECTOR GEAR
STEERING SHAFT
STEERING SHAFT BEARING ADJUSTER
UPPER STEERING SHAFT BEARING
SECTOR SHAFT
BALL RETURN GUIDE CLAMP
SECTOR SHAFT BUSHING
BALL RETURN GUIDES
LOWER STEERING SHAFT BEARING CUP

Recirculating ball type steering
(© Ford Motor Co)

Power steering is available as an option. On all compact and intermediate Ford products, except the 1971–73 Mustang and Cougar, 1972-74 Torino and Montego and the 1974 Cougar, the power steering system is the Bendix nonintegral type. The Bendix system utilizes the manual worm and recirculating ball steering gear. Hydraulic assist is provided externally to the steering linkage via a power steering pump, power cylinder, and control valve. The 1972-73 Mustangs and Cougars use the Saginaw integral system, while the 1972-74 Torinos and Montegos and 1974 Cougars use the Ford integral system. On both types, hydraulic assist is directly applied to the steering gear, eliminating all hoses and hardware which were previously mounted under the chassis.

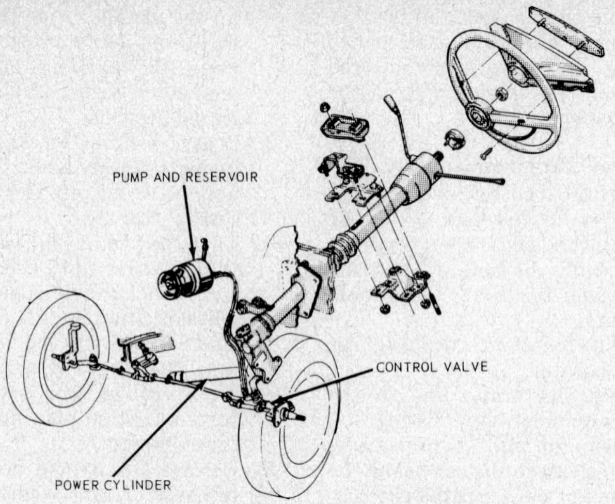
PUMP AND RESERVOIR
CONTROL VALVE
POWER CYLINDER

Bendix non-integral power steering system
(© Ford Motor Co)

Wheel Bearing Adjustment

1. Raise the front of the vehicle.
2. Remove the wheel cover and grease cap.
3. Remove the cotter pin and nut lock.
4. Back off the adjusting nut and retighten the nut to 17–25 ft. lbs. Back off the adjusting nut again ½ turn. Retighten the nut to 10–15 in. lbs. Install the nut lock so that the castellations are aligned with the cotter pin hole. Install the cotter pin and bend the ends around the castellations of the nut lock to prevent interference with the radio static collector in the grease cap.
5. Install the grease cap and wheel cover.
6. Lower the vehicle.

Power Steering Pump R & R—All Models

1. Drain the fluid from the pump reservoir by disconnecting the fluid return hose at the pump. Then, disconnect the pressure hose from the pump.
2. Remove the mounting bolts from the front of the pump. On eight cylinder engines, there is a nut on the rear of the pump that must be removed. After removal, move the pump inward to loosen the belt tension and remove the belt from the pulley. Then, remove the pump from the car.
3. To reinstall the pump, position on mounting bracket and loosely install the mounting bolts and nuts. Put the drive belt over the pulley and move the pump outward against the belt until the proper belt tension is obtained. Measure the belt tension with a belt tension gauge for the proper adjustment. Only in cases where a belt tension gauge is not available should the belt deflection method be used.
4. Tighten the mounting bolts and nuts.

Control Valve R & R (Non-integral type)

1. Raise the car. If a post hoist is used, be sure to place the hoist adapters under the front suspension steering arms. *Do not allow the hoist adapters to contact the steering linkage.*
2. Disconnect the four fluid line fittings at the control valve and drain the fluid from the lines. Turn the front wheels back and forth to force all the fluid from the system.

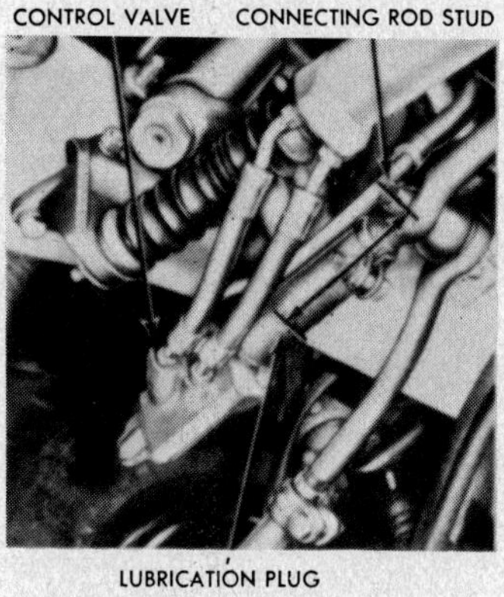
CONTROL VALVE
CONNECTING ROD STUD
LUBRICATION PLUG

Control valve installation measurements
(© Ford Motor Co)

3. Loosen the clamping nut and bolt at the right end of the sleeve.
4. Remove the roll pin from the steering arm-to-idler arm rod through the slot in the sleeve.
5. Remove the control valve ball stud nut.
6. Remove the ball stud from the sector shaft arm using puller.
7. After turning the front wheels fully to the left, unthread the control valve from the center link steering arm-to-idler arm rod.
8. To install the control valve, thread the valve on the center link until about four threads are still visible.
9. Position the ball stud in the sector shaft arm.
10. Measure the distance between the grease plug in the sleeve and the stud at the inner end of the left tie rod. For Ford Mustang and Cougar cars, the distance should be 4 ⅞ in. For Montego, Falcon and Fairlane cars, the distance should be 5 ⅝ in. 1970 and later Maverick and Comet are 5 ⅞ in. If the distance is not correct, disconnect the ball stud

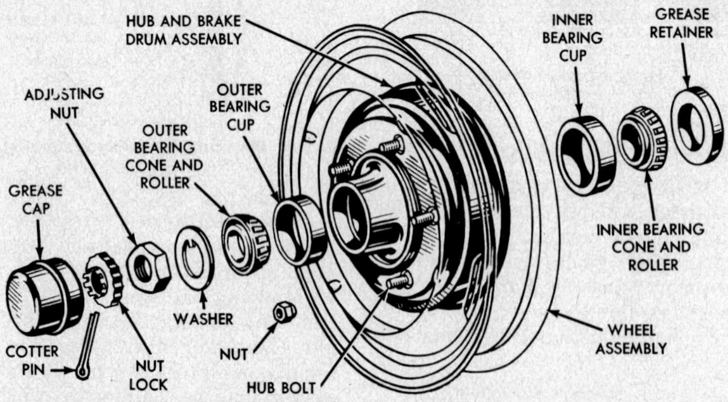
HUB AND BRAKE DRUM ASSEMBLY
INNER BEARING CUP
GREASE RETAINER
ADJUSTING NUT
OUTER BEARING CUP
OUTER BEARING CONE AND ROLLER
GREASE CAP
INNER BEARING CONE AND ROLLER
WASHER
WHEEL ASSEMBLY
COTTER PIN
NUT
NUT LOCK
HUB BOLT

Front hub, bearings, and grease retainers—drum brakes shown, disc brakes similar
(© Ford Motor Co)

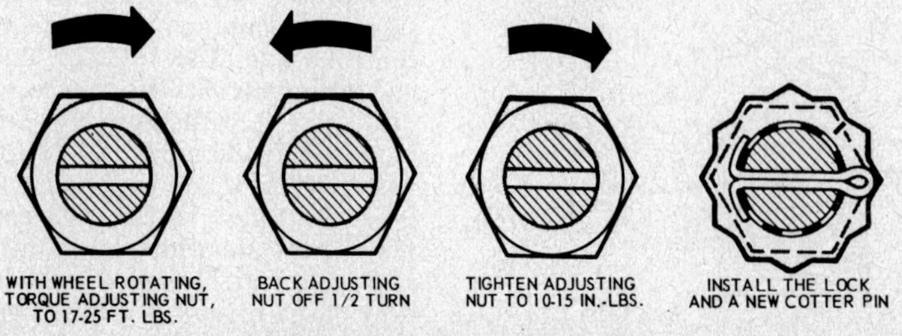
WITH WHEEL ROTATING, TORQUE ADJUSTING NUT, TO 17-25 FT. LBS.
BACK ADJUSTING NUT OFF 1/2 TURN
TIGHTEN ADJUSTING NUT TO 10-15 IN.-LBS.
INSTALL THE LOCK AND A NEW COTTER PIN

Adjusting wheel bearings (© Ford Motor Co)

from the sector shaft arm and turn the valve on the center link until the correct distance is obtained.

11. When the distance is correct and the ball stud is positioned in the sector shaft arm, align the hole in the steering arm-to-idler arm rod with the slot near the end of the valve sleeve. Install the roll pin in the rod hole to lock the valve in place on the rod.
12. Tighten the valve sleeve clamp bolt to the proper torque: 18-42 in. lbs. for all Ford Motor Co. applications.
13. Install the ball stud nut and tighten to the proper torque. Install a new cotter pin.
14. Connect all fluid lines to the control valve and tighten all fittings securely. Do not over-tighten.
15. Fill the fluid reservoir with power steering fluid to the full mark on the dipstick.
16. Start the engine and run it for a few minutes to warm the fluid in the power steering system. Turn the steering wheel back and forth to the stops and check the system for leaks.
17. Increase the engine speed to about 1000 rpm, turn the steering wheel back and forth several times, and stop the engine. Check the control valve and hose connections for leaks.
18. Recheck the fluid level and add fluid if necessary.
19. Start the engine again, and check the position of the steering wheel when the front wheels are straight ahead. *Do not make any adjustments until toe-in is checked.*
20. With engine running, check toe-in (see Front Wheel Alignment section).
21. Check steering wheel turning effort which should be equal in both directions.

Power Cylinder R & R (Non-integral type)

1. Disconnect the two fluid lines from the power cylinder and drain the fluid.
2. Remove the pal nut, attaching nut, washer and the insulator from the end of the power cylinder rod. Remove the cotter pin and castellated nut holding the power cylinder stud to the center link.
3. Disconnect the power cylinder stud from the center link.
4. Remove the insulator sleeve and washer from the end of the power cylinder.
5. Inspect the tube fittings and seats in the power cylinder for nicks, burrs, or other damage. Replace the seats or tubes if damaged.
6. Install the washer, sleeve and the insulator on the end of the power cylinder rod.
7. Extend the rod as far as possible, insert the rod in the bracket on the frame and compress the rod so the stud may be inserted in the center link. Secure the stud with the castellated nut and a new cotter pin.
8. Install the insulator, washer, nut, and a pal nut on the power cylinder rod.
9. Connect the two fluid lines to their proper ports on the power cylinder.
10. Fill the reservoir with power steering fluid to the full mark on the dipstick. Start the engine and run for a few minutes to warm the fluid. Turn the steering wheel back and forth to the stops to fill the system. Stop the engine.
11. Recheck the fluid level and add fluid if necessary. Check for fluid leaks.
12. Start the engine again, turn the steering wheel back and forth, and check for leaks while the engine is running.

Steering Wheel R & R

1. Open the hood and disconnect the negative cable from the battery.
2. On post-1967 models with safety crash pads, remove the crash pad attaching screws from the underside of the steering wheel spoke and remove the pad. On all models equipped with a horn button, remove the horn button or ring by pressing down evenly and turning it counterclockwise approximately 20° and then lifting it from the steering wheel. Disconnect the horn wires from the crash pad on models so equipped.
3. Remove the nut from the end of the shaft. Install a steering wheel puller on the end of the shaft and remove the wheel.

PULLER

Steering wheel removal
(© Ford Motor Co)

Caution The use of knock-off type steering wheel puller or the use of a hammer on the steering shaft will damage the column bearing, on collapsible columns, the column itself may be damaged.

4. Lubricate the upper surface of the steering shaft upper bushing with white grease. Transfer all serviceable parts to the new steering wheel.
5. Position the steering wheel on the shaft so that the alignment marks line up. Install a locknut and torque it to 20–30 ft lbs. Connect the horn wires.
6. Install the horn button or ring by turning it clockwise or install the crash pad on 1968 and later models.

Turn Signal Switch R & R

1. Open the hood and disconnect the negative battery cable.
2. Remove the steering wheel.
3. Unscrew the turn signal handle from the side of the column. Remove the emergency flasher retainer and knob, if so equipped.
4. On pre-1968 and earlier models, disconnect the two wire connector blocks at the dash panel above the steering column. On post-1967 models, remove the wire assembly cover and disconnect the wire connector plugs. Record the location and color code of each wire and tape the wires together. Make sure that the horn wires are disconnected. Remove the plastic cover from the wiring harness. Attach a piece of heavy cord to the switch wires to pull them through the column during installation.
5. Remove the retaining clips and attaching screws from the turn signal switch and pull the switch and wire assembly from the top of the column.
6. Tape the ends of the new switch wires together and transfer the pull cord to these wires.
7. Pull the wires down through the column with the cord and attach the new switch to the column hub.
8. Connect the wiring plugs to their mating plugs at the lower end of the column and install the plastic cover at the harness.
9. Install all retaining clips and wire assembly covers that were removed and install the turn signal handle. Install the emergency flasher retainer and knob, if so equipped.
10. Install the steering wheel and retaining nut.
11. Connect the negative battery cable.

INSTRUMENT PANEL

Ignition Lock Cylinder Replacement

1967-69

1. Insert key and turn to Acc. position.

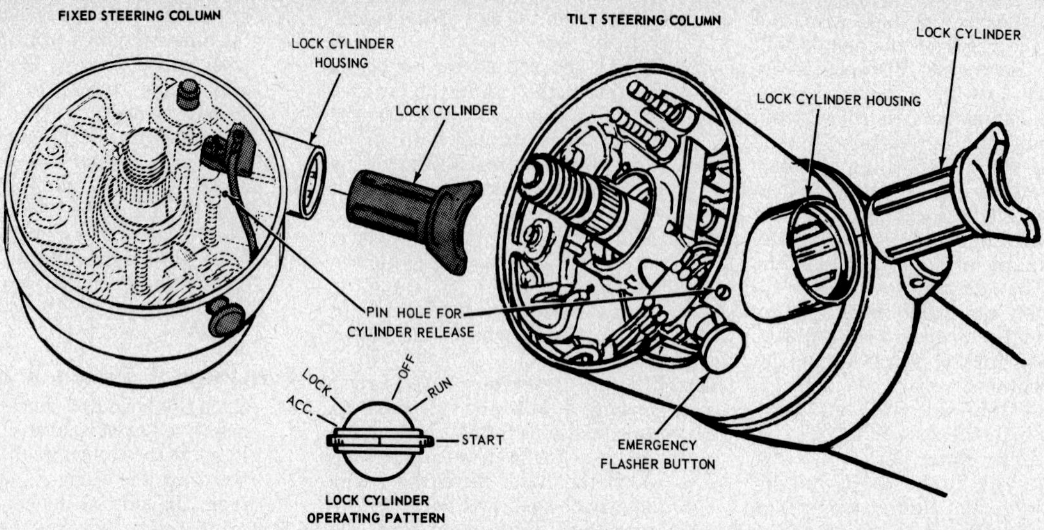
FIXED STEERING COLUMN
TILT STEERING COLUMN
LOCK CYLINDER HOUSING
LOCK CYLINDER
LOCK CYLINDER
LOCK CYLINDER HOUSING
PIN HOLE FOR CYLINDER RELEASE
LOCK
OFF
RUN
ACC.
START
LOCK CYLINDER OPERATING PATTERN
EMERGENCY FLASHER BUTTON

Lock cylinder replacement with locking column (© Ford Motor Co)

2. With stiff wire in hole, depress lock pin and rotate cylinder counterclockwise, then pull out cylinder.

1970-74

1. Disconnect the negative battery cable.
2. On cars with a fixed steering column, remove the steering wheel trim pad and the steering wheel. Insert a stiff wire into the hole located in the lock cylinder housing. On cars with a tilt steering wheel, this hole is located on the outside of the steering column near the emergency flasher button and it is not necessary to remove the steering wheel.
3. Place the gear shift lever in Reverse on standard shift cars and in Park on cars with automatic transmission, and turn the ignition key to the ON or RUN position.
4. Depress wire and remove lock cylinder and wire.
5. Insert new cylinder into housing and turn to the OFF position. This will lock the cylinder into position.
6. Reinstall steering wheel and pad.
7. Connect negative battery cable.

Ignition Switch Replacement

1967-69

1. Remove cylinder as above.
2. Press in on rear of switch and rotate the switch one-eighth turn counterclockwise. Remove the bezel, switch and spacer.
3. Remove nut from back of switch. Remove the accessory and gauge feed wires from accessory terminal. Pull insulated plug from rear of switch.
4. Install in reverse of above.

1970-74

1. Disconnect the negative battery cable.
2. Remove shrouding from the steering column, and detach and lower the steering column from the brake support bracket.
3. Disconnect the switch wiring at the multiple plug.
4. Remove the two nuts that retain the switch to steering column.
5. On models with a steering column-mounted gearshift lever, disconnect the ignition switch plunger from the ignition switch actuator rod and remove the ignition switch. On models with a floor mounted gearshift lever, remove the pin that connects the switch plunger to the switch actuator and remove the switch.
6. To re-install the switch, place both locking mechanism at top of column and switch itself in lock position for correct adjustment. To hold column in lock position, place automatic shift lever in PARK or manual shift lever in reverse, and turn to LOCK and remove the key. New switches are held in lock by plastic shipping pins. To pin existing switches, pull the switch plunger out as far as it will go and push back in to first detent. Insert 3/32 in. diameter wire into locking hole in the top of the switch.
7. Connect the switch plunger to the switch actuator rod.
8. Position the switch on the column and install the attaching nuts. Do not tighten them.
9. Move the switch up and down to locate the mid-position of rod lash, and then tighten the nuts.
10. Remove the locking pin or wire.
11. Attach the steering column to the brake support bracket and install the shrouding.

Headlight Switch Replacement

1. Disconnect the negative battery cable.
2. Remove the headlight switch control knob and shaft after depressing the release button on the rear of the switch. Some models require special procedures to gain access to the release button. They are:
   a. On 1967–71 Mustangs and Cougars, remove the two screws that attach the parking brake mechanism to the dash panel and lower the brake control with the vent cable attached to it.
   b. On 1970–74 Mavericks and Comets equipped with air conditioning, disconnect the left A/C duct from the duct-to-register connector, loosen the two nuts that retain the left register to the utility shelf and remove the connector from the register.
   c. On 1972–73 Mustangs and Cougars, insert a screwdriver through the hole in the bottom of the instrument panel beneath the headlight switch and depress the headlight switch release button with the screwdriver.

KNOB RELEASE BUTTON

Headlight switch (© Ford Motor Co)

3. After pulling the switch shaft and knob from the switch, remove the bezel nut that attaches the switch to the instrument panel.
4. Lower the switch and disconnect the lead wires from the switch.
5. On models equipped with headlight doors, disconnect the vacuum hoses from the headlight switch.
6. Reverse the above procedure to

install the new switch. When installing the new switch, insert the control knob and shaft into the switch until a distinct click is heard, signifying that the shaft is locked in place.

Neutral Safety and Back-Up Light Switch Assembly—Automatic Transmission

1967-74

Ford small cars throughout this period have used the same neutral switches and back up switches as full sized Fords.

See Ford section for a complete breakdown of years, transmissions, and adjustments.

Back-Up Light Switch—Manual Transmission

The back-up light switch may be located in either one of two places. The back-up light switch location, on cars with column shift selector and linkage controls, is at the bottom of the column.

The back-up light switch location, on cars with consoles and floor shift selector, is on the left side of the transmission back at the shift control bracket.

WINDSHIELD WIPERS

Motor R & R

1967-69 Montego, Comet, Falcon, Fairlane, and Torino

1. Disconnect wiper motor wire connector.
2. Remove wiper arm and blade assemblies.
3. Remove cowl top grille panel retaining screws and remove cowl top grille.
4. Remove wiper link retaining clip from wiper motor arm.
5. Remove four wiper motor retaining bolts and remove wiper motor and mounting bracket.
6. To install position wiper motor and mounting bracket against dash panel and install four retaining bolts.
7. Place wiper link on motor drive arm and install retaining clip.
8. Install cowl top grille panel.
9. Connect wiper motor wiring connectors.
10. Check motor operation.

1967-68 Cougar and Mustang

1. Disconnect battery.
2. Remove courtesy light. If car is air conditioned, lower air conditioner to floor.
3. Disconnect wiper motor plug connector.
4. Remove nut retaining pivot arm and wiper arms to motor.
5. Remove bolts and star washers retaining motor to mounting bracket, and remove motor.
6. To install motor, attach motor to mounting bracket with bolts and star washers.
7. Position pivot arm and wiper arms on motor and install retaining nut.
8. Connect motor wire plug and battery.
9. Check motor operation and install courtesy light and air conditioner.

1969-70 Cougar and Mustang

1. Remove wiper arm and blade assemblies from pivot shafts and disconnect left side washer hose at T fitting on cowl grille.
2. Remove eight screws and remove cowl top grille.
3. Motor is located inside left fresh air plenum chamber. Disconnect motor ground wire by removing one screw at forward edge of plenum chamber.
4. Disconnect motor wire at plug and push it back into plenum chamber.
5. Disconnect linkage drive arm from motor output arm crank pin by removing retaining clip.
6. Remove three bolts that retain motor to mounting bracket, rotate motor output arm 180 degrees, and remove motor.
7. Before installing motor, rotate output arm 180 degrees. Before connecting linkage drive arm to motor, turn ignition to ACC position to allow motor to go to park position.

1970-71 Montego, Falcon, Fairlane, and Torino; 1972-74 Torino and Montego with Non-Depressed Wipers; 1971-73 Mustang and 1971-74 Cougar

1. Disconnect battery and wiper motor connector.
2. Remove cowl top left vent screen by removing four retaining drive pins.
3. Remove wiper link retaining clip from wiper motor arm.
4. Remove three wiper motor retaining bolts, and remove wiper motor and mounting bracket.
5. To install motor, place wiper motor and mounting bracket against dash panel and install three retaining bolts.
6. Position wiper link on motor

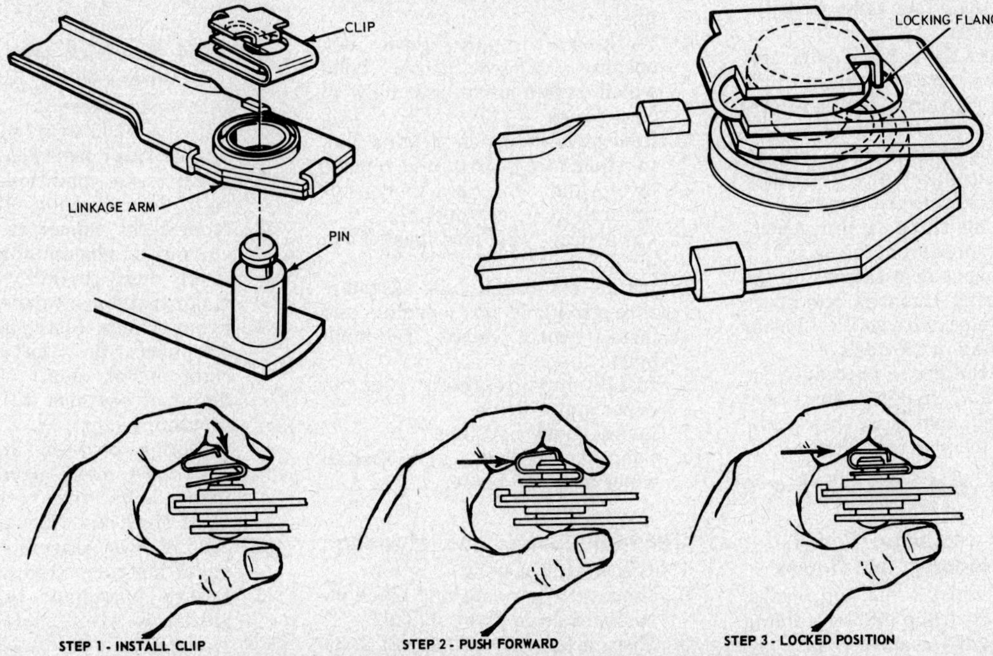
CLIP
LINKAGE ARM
PIN
LOCKING FLANGE
STEP 1 - INSTALL CLIP
STEP 2 - PUSH FORWARD
STEP 3 - LOCKED POSITION

Installation of windshield wiper connecting clips (© Ford Motor Co)

drive arm, and install connecting clip. Be sure to force clip locking flange into locked position as shown in figure.
7. Install cowl top vent screen and secure with four drive pins.
8. Check motor operation and connect wiring plugs.

1970-74 Maverick and Comet

1. Remove instrument cluster.
2. If air conditioned, remove center connector and duct assembly. Remove mounting bracket screw behind center duct, disconnect assembly from plenum chamber and left duct, and pull center connector and duct assembly out through cluster opening.
3. Working through cluster opening, disconnect two pivot shaft links from motor drive arm by removing retaining clip.
4. Disconnect wiring plug at motor, remove three retaining bolts, and remove motor through cluster opening.
5. To install motor, bolt motor to mounting plate with three retaining bolts.
6. Connect right pivot shaft link to motor and then connect left pivot shaft link. Lock clip as shown.
7. On air conditioned vehicles, insert end of center connector and duct assembly near mounting bracket into left duct and opposite end into plenum chamber.
8. Secure assembly with mounting bracket screw.
9. Install instrument cluster, and check operation of wiper motor.

1972-74 Torino and Montego (Depressed Park)

1. Disconnect the negative battery cable.
2. Remove the wiper arms from the pivot shafts.
3. Disconnect the linkage drive arm from the motor output arm crankpin by removing the retaining clip.
4. From the engine side of the dash, disconnect the two wire connectors from the motor.
5. Remove the three retaining bolts and the motor from the dash.
6. If the output arm catches on the dash during removal, hand-turn the arm clockwise so it will clear the opening in the dash.
7. Reverse the above procedure for installation, making sure that the output arm is in the "park" position prior to installation.

Pivot Shaft and Linkage R & R

1967-69 Montego, Comet, Falcon, Fairlane, and Torino

1. Remove wiper arms and blades.
2. Remove cowl top grille retaining screws and remove cowl top grille.
3. Remove clip retaining drive arm to pivot.
4. Remove three retaining screws from each pivot and remove pivot shaft and link assembly.
5. To install, position pivot shaft and link assembly in the cowl and install pivot shaft retaining screws.
6. Place left link on motor drive arm and install retaining clip.
7. Install wiper arms and blades, and check wiper operation.
8. Install cowl top grille panel.

1967-68 Cougar and Mustang—Left Side

1. Disconnect battery.
2. Remove wiper arm and blade assembly.
3. Remove four screws that retain heater control to instrument panel and move heater control outward.
4. Remove clip that retains link to motor drive.
5. Working through heater control opening, remove three pivot shaft retaining bolts.
6. Remove pivot and link out through heater control opening.
7. To install, put a new gasket on pivot.
8. Install pivot through heater control opening, and install three retaining bolts.
9. Install clip that retains link to motor drive.
10. Install heater control assembly.
11. Install arm and blade assembly.

1967-68 Cougar and Mustang—Right Side

1. Disconnect battery.
2. Remove wiper arm and blade assembly.
3. Remove glove box liner retaining screws and remove glove box liner.
4. Working through glove box opening, remove three bolts which retain pivot assembly to cowl panel.
5. Remove clip which retains link to wiper motor drive and remove pivot and link assembly out through glove box opening.
6. To install, put new gasket on pivot.
7. Install pivot and link assembly through glove box opening and install three pivot retaining bolts.
8. Install link retaining clip on wiper motor drive.
9. Install glove box liner.
10. Connect battery and install wiper arm and blade.

1969-70 Cougar and Mustang

1. Disconnect battery.
2. Remove wiper arm and blade assemblies from pivot shafts.
3. Disconnect washer hose at T fitting on cowl grille.
4. Remove eight screws and remove cowl top grille.
5. Disconnect linkage drive arm from motor output arm crank pin by removing retaining clip.
6. Remove clip and disconnect right link from right arm and pivot shaft assembly.
7. Remove three retaining screws and remove right arm and pivot shaft assembly.
8. Remove three screws retaining left arm and pivot shaft.
9. Lift out pivot shaft and arm, left link, and linkage drive arm as one assembly. Assembly comes out to right.
10. When installing pivot shaft assemblies, tighten retaining bolts to 3-7 ft. lbs. Install left pivot shaft and linkage first. Be sure linkage connecting clips are forced into locked position as shown in figure.

1970-74 Maverick and 1971-74 Comet—Left Side

1. Remove instrument cluster.
2. Remove wiper arm and blade assembly from pivot shaft.
3. Working through cluster opening, disconnect both pivot shaft links from motor drive arm by removing retaining clip.
4. Remove three bolts that retain left pivot shaft assembly to cowl and take left pivot shaft assembly out through cluster opening.
5. Before installing, cement new gasket on pivot shaft mounting flange. Tighten retaining bolts to 3-7 ft. lbs. After installing pivot shaft and link assembly to cowl connect right pivot shaft link to motor drive arm first, and then connect left link. Be sure connecting clip is locked as shown in figure.

1970-74 Maverick and 1971-74 Comet—Right Side

1. Disconnect battery.
2. Remove wiper arm and blade assembly from pivot shaft.
3. If car is air conditioned, remove right duct assembly. Unclip duct from right connector, slide left end out of plenum chamber, and lower duct assembly out from under instrument panel.
4. From under instrument panel, disconnect first left and then right pivot shaft link from motor drive arm by removing remaining clip.
5. Reaching between utility shelf and instrument panel, remove three bolts that retain right pivot shaft and link assembly to cowl. Lower assembly out from under instrument panel.
6. Before installing, cement new gasket to pivot shaft mounting flange. After installing pivot shaft and link assembly to cowl,

be sure right pivot shaft link is connected to motor drive arm before left pivot shaft link. Be sure connecting clip is in locked position as shown in figure.

1971-74 Torino, Montego, and Cougar, and 1971-73 Mustang

1. Disconnect the negative battery cable.
2. Remove the wiper arms from the pivot shafts.
3. Remove the four retaining drive pins and the cowl top vent screen.
4. Remove the drive arm-to-pivot retaining clip.
5. Remove the three retaining screws from each pivot and remove the pivot shaft and link assembly.
6. Transfer the right pivot, if necessary, by removing the connecting clip.
7. Position the pivot shaft and link assembly in the cowl, and install the pivot shaft retaining screws.
8. Position the left link on the motor drive arm and install the connecting clip.
9. Install the wiper arms.
10. Connect the negative cable and test wiper operation.
11. Install the cowl top vent screen.

RADIO

Removal and Replacement

1967 Comet, Falcon and Fairlane

1. Disconnect negative cable from battery.
2. Pull radio control knobs off and remove nuts and washers that attach radio to instrument panel.
3. Disconnect antenna lead at right side of radio (at back of AM-FM radio).
4. Disconnect speaker lead.
5. Disconnect radio lead wire and dial light wire from quick disconnects.
6. Remove radio support bracket.
7. Remove radio from instrument panel.
8. To install, position radio in instrument panel and install washers and attaching nuts at knob shafts. Be sure radio mounting stud enters support bracket.
9. Install radio support bracket.
10. Connect antenna lead to radio.
11. Connect radio speaker lead.
12. Connect radio power lead and dial light lead.
13. Install radio control knobs.
14. Connect battery.
15. Check radio operation.

1967-68 Cougar and Mustang without Console

1. Disconnect battery.
2. Remove rear support bracket attaching nut.
3. Remove four screws that attach bezel and receiver to instrument panel.
4. Move receiver rearward away from instrument panel.
5. Disconnect antenna, speaker, and power leads and remove receiver from instrument panel.
6. To install, position radio under instrument panel and connect speaker, antenna, and power leads.
7. Secure receiver to instrument panel with attaching screws.
8. Secure rear support bracket to receiver with attaching nut.
9. Connect battery.
10. Check operation of radio.

1967-68 Cougar and Mustang with Console

1. Disconnect battery.
2. Remove two screws attaching right and left supports to support bracket.
3. Remove console assembly.
4. Disconnect radio wiring and antenna lead.
5. Remove control knobs from radio.
6. Remove two nuts and washers from radio shafts and remove radio.
7. To install, position radio in opening and install nuts and washers on control shafts.
8. Install control knobs.
9. Connect radio wires and antenna lead cable.
10. Install console assembly.
11. Install two screws attaching right and left support to support bracket.
12. Connect battery.

1968-74 Montego, Fairlane, Torino, and Falcon

1. Disconnect battery.
2. Pull radio control knobs off shafts.
3. Remove radio support to instrument panel attaching screw.
4. Remove two bezel nuts from radio control shafts.
5. Lower radio and disconnect antenna, speaker, and power leads. Remove radio.
6. To install, connect antenna, speaker and power leads to radio.
7. Position radio in instrument panel and install two bezel nuts. Torque bezel nuts to 30-35 in. lbs.
8. Install radio support bracket to instrument panel attaching screw and torque to 30-35 in. lbs.
9. Connect battery.
10. Adjust antenna trimmer, if necessary.
11. Install radio control knobs and set push buttons for desired stations.

1969-71 Cougar and Mustang

1. Disconnect battery.
2. Pull control knobs, discs, and sleeve from radio control shafts.
3. Remove radio applique from instrument panel.
4. Remove right and left finish panels.
5. Remove two mounting plate attaching screws.
6. Pull radio out of instrument panel and disconnect wires from radio.
7. Remove mounting plate and rear support from radio.
8. Remove radio.
9. To replace, install mounting plate and rear support on radio.
10. Position radio near opening and connect wires to radio.
11. Install jumper wire to ground radio to instrument panel.
12. Connect battery and check operation of radio.
13. Adjust antenna trimmer.
14. Disconnect battery and remove jumper cable.
15. Insert radio and wires into panel opening. Be sure radio rear support slips over instrument panel reinforcement.

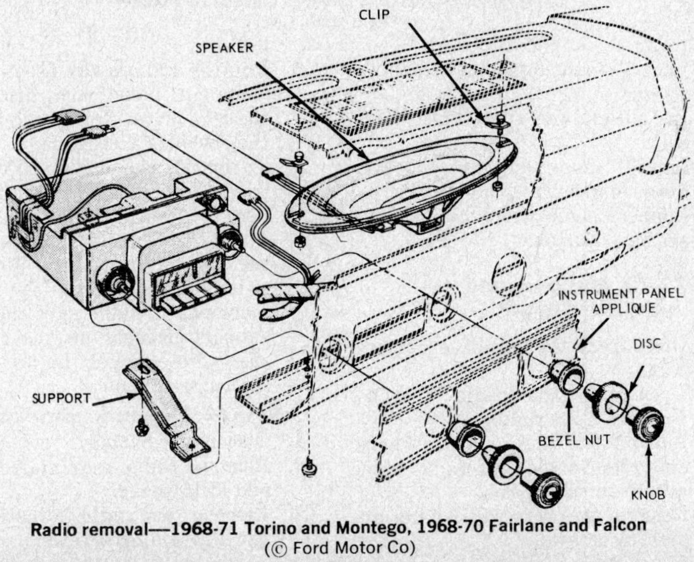
CLIP
SPEAKER
INSTRUMENT PANEL APPLIQUE
DISC
SUPPORT
BEZEL NUT
KNOB

Radio removal—1968-71 Torino and Montego, 1968-70 Fairlane and Falcon
(© Ford Motor Co)

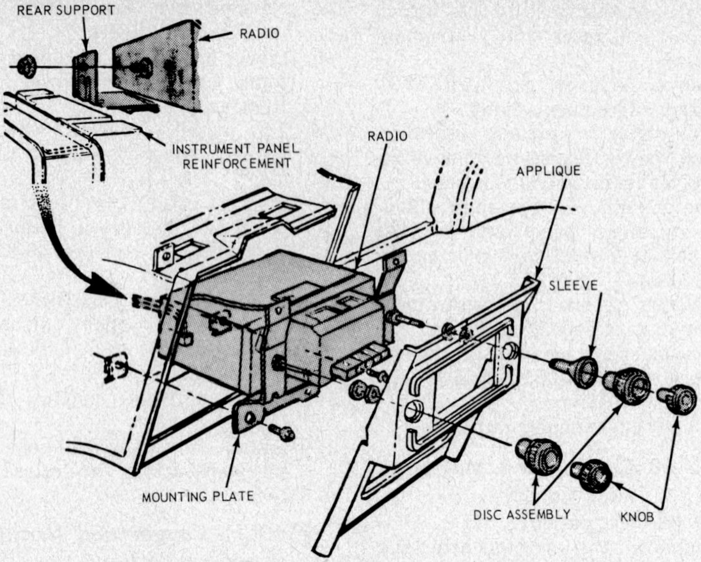
REAR SUPPORT
RADIO
INSTRUMENT PANEL REINFORCEMENT
RADIO
APPLIQUE
SLEEVE
MOUNTING PLATE
DISC ASSEMBLY
KNOB

Radio removal—1969-70 Cougar and Mustang
(© Ford Motor Co)

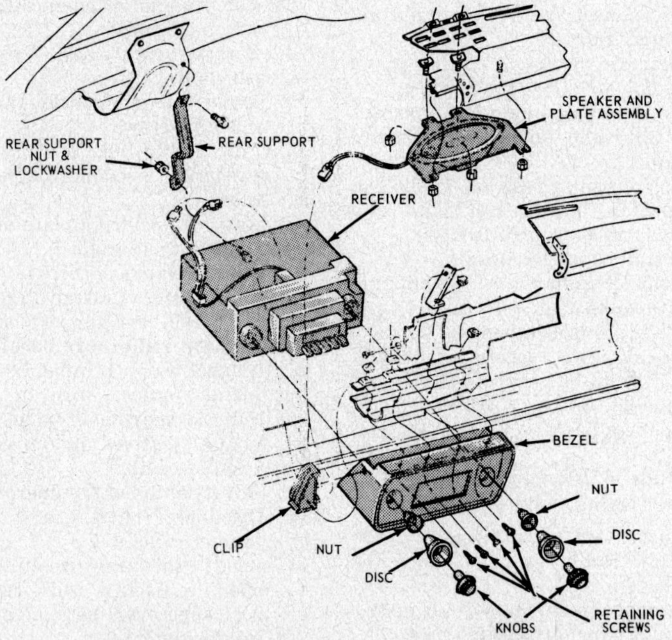
SPEAKER AND PLATE ASSEMBLY
REAR SUPPORT NUT & LOCKWASHER
REAR SUPPORT
RECEIVER
BEZEL
NUT
DISC
CLIP
NUT
DISC
KNOBS
RETAINING SCREWS

Radio removal—1970-74 Maverick and 1971-74 Comet
(© Ford Motor Co)

16. Install mounting plate attaching screws.
17. Install left and right finish panels.
18. Install radio applique, sleeve, discs, and control knobs.
19. Connect radio ground cable and set push buttons.

1972-73 Mustang and 1972-74 Cougar

1. Disconnect the negative battery cable.
2. Disconnect the radio antenna wire from the radio.
3. Pull off the radio control knobs and remove the two radio bezel nuts from the radio.
4. Remove the four radio bezel attaching screws.
5. Pull the radio away from the instrument panel and disconnect the lead wires from the radio as they become accessible.
6. To install the radio, position it on the instrument panel and connect the lead wires to it.
7. To complete installation, reverse the removal procedure. When positioning the radio in the instrument panel, make sure the radio support bracket on the rear of the radio engages the tab on the instrument panel.

1970-74 Maverick and Comet

1. Disconnect battery.
2. Remove radio rear support nut and lock washer.
3. Remove four radio to instrument panel retaining screws.
4. Pull radio from instrument panel and disconnect antenna, speaker, and power leads.
5. Remove radio.
6. Remove knob and disc assemblies from radio shafts.
7. Remove two bezel retaining nuts and remove bezel.
8. To install radio, position bezel on radio and install two bezel retaining nuts.
9. Install disc and knob assemblies on radio shafts.
10. Connect antenna, speaker, and power connectors.
11. Position radio so that rear support mounting bolt enters hole in rear support mounting bracket.
12. Install four radio to instrument panel retaining screws.
13. Install radio rear support nut and lock washer.
14. Place speaker and power wire harnesses in clip on bezel.
15. Connect battery and check operation of radio.
16. Adjust selector buttons for desired stations.

HEATER

Vehicles without Air Conditioning

Heater R & R

1969-70 Cougar and Mustang

1. Disconnect battery and drain coolant.
2. Remove instrument panel pad.
3. Remove glove compartment liner and door.
4. Remove air distribution duct from heater.
5. Disconnect control cables from heater assembly.
6. Disconnect wires from blower motor resistor.
7. Remove right courtesy light located on underside of instrument panel, if so equipped.
8. Remove heater support to dash panel retaining screw.
9. Disconnect vacuum hoses and remove power air vent duct, if so equipped.
10. Remove blower motor ground wire grounding screw.
11. Disconnect heater hoses from heater at dash panel.
12. Working in engine compartment, remove five heater assembly retaining nuts.
13. Remove instrument panel to cowl attaching screws.
14. Remove instrument panel right side brace.
15. Pull heater assembly and right side of instrument panel rearward, and remove heater assembly. Reverse procedure to install.

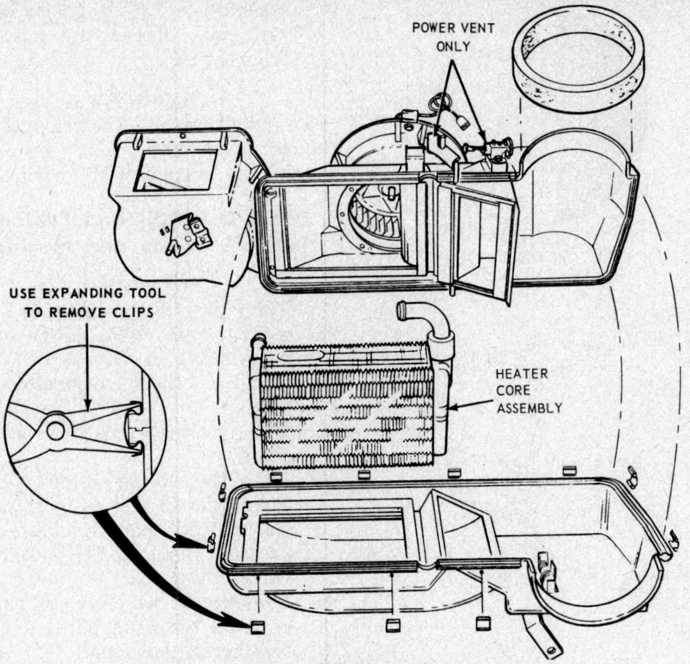
POWER VENT ONLY
USE EXPANDING TOOL TO REMOVE CLIPS
HEATER CORE ASSEMBLY

Heater core removal—1969-73 Cougar and Mustang
(© Ford Motor Co)

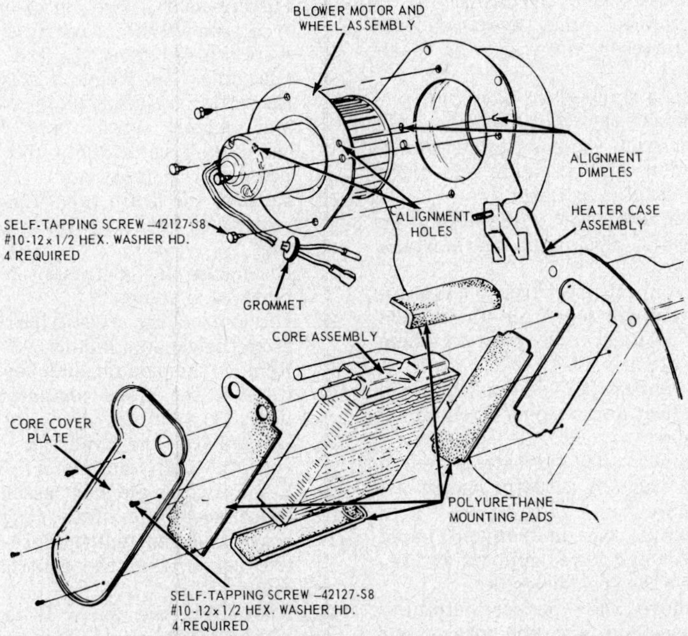
BLOWER MOTOR AND WHEEL ASSEMBLY
ALIGNMENT DIMPLES
SELF-TAPPING SCREW –42127-S8 #10-12 x 1/2 HEX. WASHER HD. 4 REQUIRED
ALIGNMENT HOLES
HEATER CASE ASSEMBLY
GROMMET
CORE ASSEMBLY
CORE COVER PLATE
POLYURETHANE MOUNTING PADS
SELF-TAPPING SCREW –42127-S8 #10-12 x 1/2 HEX. WASHER HD. 4 REQUIRED

Heater, blower motor and core assemblies—1967 Comet, 1967-70 Fairlane and Falcon, and 1968-74 Montego and Torino
(© Ford Motor Co)

1967 Comet, 1967-70 Falcon and Fairlane, 1968-74 Torino and Montego

1. Drain coolant.
2. Disconnect both heater hoses at dash.
3. Remove nuts retaining heater assembly to dash.
4. Disconnect temperature and defroster cables at heater.
5. Disconnect wires from resistor, and disconnect blower motor wires and clip retaining heater assembly to defroster nozzle.
6. Remove glove box.
7. Remove bolt and nut right air duct control to instrument panel. Remove nuts retaining right air duct and remove duct assembly.
8. Remove heater assembly to bench.

1967-68 Cougar and Mustang

1. Disconnect battery and drain coolant.
2. Disconnect heater hoses at engine.
3. Loosen screws at choke housing and position hose out.
4. Remove nuts retaining heater to dash.
5. Remove screw retaining ground wire at dash and disconnect two wires. Remove glove box liner.
6. Disconnect defroster hoses, temperature control cable, defroster control cable, and heat control cable.
7. Remove screw retaining heater to air intake.
8. Remove heater assembly from vehicle pulling hose through dash.

1970-74 Maverick and 1971-74 Comet

1. Drain the cooling system and disconnect the negative battery cable.
2. Disconnect the blower ground wire (black) from the fender apron.
3. Disconnect the heater hoses from the engine block.
4. Remove the five heater assembly to firewall attaching bolts from the firewall.
5. Working inside the car, remove the ignition switch and plate from the package tray and remove the tray from the dash.
6. Remove the right kick panel and remove the package tray bracket.
7. Disconnect the heater control cables from the heater.
8. Disconnect the defroster air duct from the top of the heater.
9. Disconnect the heater blower motor lead wires from the resistor at the bottom of the heater.
10. Remove the one screw from the bracket that mounts the heater to the dash.
11. Remove the heater from the car by pulling the heater hoses through the firewall, then disconnecting them from the heater.

Heater Core R & R

1967-68 Mustang and Cougar

1. Remove heater as above.
2. Remove clips retaining housing halves and separate the halves.
3. Lift core from housing chamber.
4. Install in reverse of above.

1969-70 Cougar and Mustang 1970-74 Maverick and Comet

1. Remove heater assembly.
2. Remove air inlet seal from heater assembly.
3. Remove eleven clips from heater assembly flange and separate heater assembly housing.
4. Remove heater core from heater assembly housing. Reverse procedure to install.

1967-74 Montego, Fairlane, Torino, Falcon, 1967 Comet, and 1971-73 Mustang and 1971-74 Cougar

The heater core is located in the heater case in a diagonal position. It is serviced through an opening in the

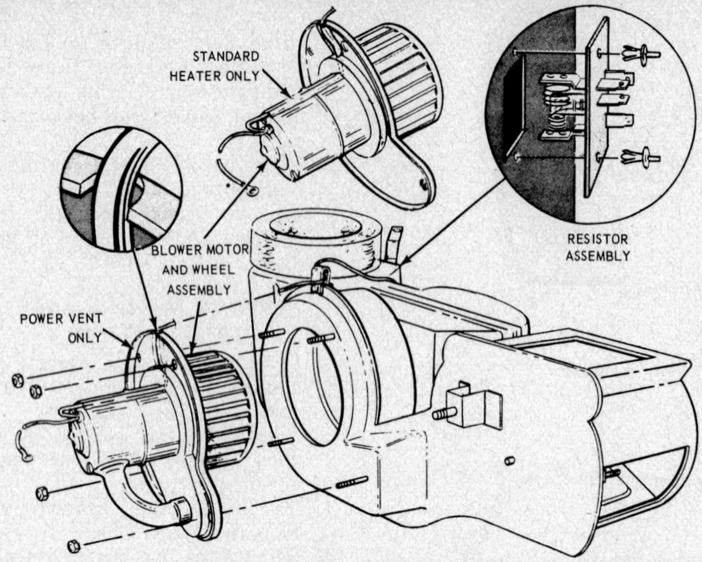
STANDARD
HEATER ONLY
BLOWER MOTOR
AND WHEEL
ASSEMBLY
POWER VENT
ONLY
RESISTOR
ASSEMBLY

Heater blower and motor installation—1969-73 Mustang, 1969-74 Cougar, 1970-74 Maverick and 1971-74 Comet
(© Ford Motor Co)

back plate. With the heater assembly removed from the vehicle, remove heater core cover and pad and remove core. Reverse procedure to install.

Blower Motor R & R

The blower motor on all models is located inside the heater assembly. To replace the blower motor, remove the heater assembly from the car following the steps in the above procedures. Once the heater assembly is removed, it is a simple operation to remove the motor attaching bolts and remove the motor. On all models, the motor and cage are removed as an assembly.

Vehicles with Integral Heater-Air Conditioning

NOTE: removal of the heater-air conditioner housing requires evacuation of the air conditioner refrigerant. This operation requires special tools and training. Failure to follow proper safety precautions may cause personal injury.

Heater-Air Conditioner Housing R & R

1967 Comet, Falcon and Fairlane with Selectaire

Removal

NOTE: to remove the core, it is necessary to remove the entire evaporator assembly.

1. Partially drain the cooling system.
2. Purge the system of refrigerant.
3. Disconnect the heater hoses at the dash and remove the weather seal gasket.
4. Unwrap the insulation from the sensing bulb. Unclamp the bulb.
5. Disconnect the receiver-to-evaporator hose at the dash panel. Leave the expansion valve attached to the hose. Remove the weather seal at the dash.
6. Disconnect the evaporator-to-compressor hose at the dash panel.
7. Take out the glove box liner.
8. Take out the right hand fresh air duct from the cowl upper panel. Remove the vacuum line from the vacuum actuator.
9. Disconnect the wires from the resistor block and thermostatic switch.
10. Disconnect the three plenum-to-instrument panel air ducts from the plenum and position them out of the way.
11. Disconnect the vacuum line from the heat-defrost door vacuum actuator.
12. Remove the defroster plenum and vacuum actuator as an assembly.
13. Remove the instrument panel upper and lower support and remove the speaker grille.
14. Remove the speaker retaining screws and move the speaker out of the way.
15. Remove the defroster nozzle.
16. Remove the evaporator case drain case hose clamp and drain hose at the dash.
17. Cover the floor mats and remove the four nuts holding the heater-air conditioner assembly to the dash. Pull the assembly from the dash and rest it on the car floor.
18. Disconnect the wire from the thermostatic switch.
19. Disconnect the temperature-blend door actuating bowden cable and the vacuum line at the air condition-heat door vacuum actuator.
20. Position the front seat all the way back; turn the bottom of the assembly toward the rear of the car and remove the assembly from the car.

Installation

To install, reverse the removal procedure. Evacuate, leak test and charge the system with refrigerant.

1968-70 Falcon and Fairlane, 1968-71 Torino and Montego

Removal

NOTE: to remove the core, it is necessary to remove the entire evaporator assembly.

1. Remove the carburetor air cleaner.
2. Disconnect the battery ground cable.
3. Drain the cooling system.
4. Purge the system of refrigerant.
5. Disconnect the high and low pressure lines at the expansion valve.
6. Remove the two piece seal retainer from the dash panel and the refrigerant hose seal.
7. Disconnect the three heater hoses at the dash panel.
8. Disconnect the two clutch wires from the vacuum switch at the water valve mounting plate.
9. Disconnect the vacuum hoses at the water valves, clutch switch and vacuum supply tank. Push the hose-wire harness into the passenger compartment.
10. Remove the drain tube hose and seal from the evaporator housing.
11. Disengage the defroster nozzle from the plenum.
12. Disconnect the red-stripe hose from the vacuum motor.
13. Remove the plenum chamber.
14. Remove the glove compartment liner.
15. Disconnect the vacuum hose from the right vent motor.
16. Remove the right vent assembly.
17. Disconnect the four vacuum hoses and the temperature control cable from the control assembly.
18. Disconnect the wires from the blower resistor and icing switch.
19. Disconnect the flexible hoses from the center air duct.
20. Remove the center air duct.
21. Remove the defroster nozzle.
22. Remove the evaporator retaining nuts and remove the assembly.

Installation

To install, reverse the removal procedure. Evacuate, leak test, and charge the system with refrigerant.

1969-70 Mustang and Cougar

Removal

NOTE: to remove the core, it is necessary to remove the entire evaporator assembly.

1. Remove the carburetor air cleaner.

2. Disconnect the battery ground cable.
3. Drain the cooling system.
4. Purge the system of refrigerant.
5. Remove the heat shield from the expansion valve.
6. Disconnect the low pressure hose and service valve from the compressor.
7. Disconnect the high pressure hose at the quick disconnect.
8. Remove the straps retaining the refrigerant hoses to the dash-to-fender apron supports.
9. Disconnect the heater hoses from the heater core. Remove the upper and lower seal retainers and remove the hose seal.
10. Remove the evaporator housing and blower housing nuts from the engine side of dash panel.
11. Remove the instrument panel pad.
12. Remove the glove box assembly and support.
13. Remove the instrument cluster assembly.
14. Disconnect all vacuum hoses.
15. Disconnect the control cable from the temperature blend door, wires from the A/C thermostat switch.
16. Disconnect air ducts from the plenum chamber, remove the air ducts.
17. Remove the A/C defrost plenum chamber.
18. Remove the instrument right side brace, evaporator housing upper rear support.
19. Move the blower housing to the left away from the evaporator housing.
20. Cover carpet and pull drain tube from hole in floor pan.
21. Remove the instrument panel lower finish cover from around the steering column.
22. Remove nuts and bolts retaining the instrument panel to steering column support.
23. Position the instrument panel back and remove the evaporator housing from the vehicle.

Installation

To install, reverse the removal procedure, Evacuate. Leak test. Charge the system.

1970-74 Maverick and 1971-74 Comet

Removal

NOTE: to facilitate installation, tag vacuum lines and electrical wires, as to their proper location, before disassembling unit. To remove the core, it is necessary to remove the entire evaporator assembly.

1. Disconnect the battery and remove the air cleaner.
2. Drain the cooling system.
3. Connect a manifold gauge set to the compressor, and discharge the system.
4. Remove the expansion valve and disconnect the heater hoses from the heater core. Tape over openings to avoid entry of dirt.
5. Remove the utility shelf and bracket from the lower edge of the instrument panel, and remove the right cowl trim panel and radio.
6. Disconnect the right and left A/C register air ducts from the plenum chamber.
7. Remove the floor distribution duct from the blower housing.
8. Remove the center register from the instrument panel. Then pull the plenum chamber part way through the register opening to disengage it from the blower housing. Disconnect the (blue) hose from the (7) door motor on the plenum chamber.
9. Disconnect the vacuum hoses from the doormotors.
10. Disconnect the vacuum harness multiple connector from the control assembly.
11. Disconnect the temperature control cable from the evaporator housing, and disconnect the vacuum hoses from the adjacent water valve vacuum switch.
12. Move A/C assembly rearward and away from the dash panel.
13. Remove any remaining hoses and disconnect wires from the blower resistor, the de-icing switch and the blower motor ground wire.
14. Remove the evaporator and blower housing assembly from the vehicle.

Installation

1. Install assembly into the vehicle by reversing the removal procedures, being careful to correctly connect the vacuum holes. When making connections to the water valve vacuum switch, connect the purple hose to the nipple closest to the switch plunger and attach the green hose to the water valve motor.
2. After installation, adjust the temperature control cable and, if neccessary, the water valve vacuum switch.
3. Evacuate, leak test and charge the system.

1971-73 Mustang and 1971-74 Cougar

Removal

NOTE: to remove the core, it is necessary to remove the entire evaporator assembly.

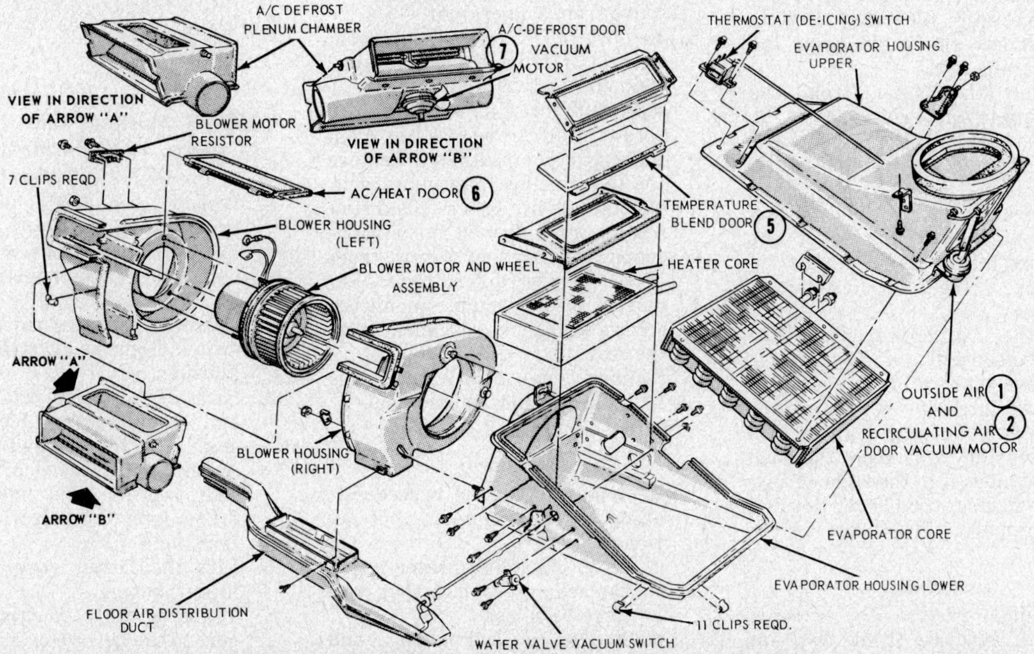
A/C DEFROST PLENUM CHAMBER
A/C-DEFROST DOOR VACUUM MOTOR
7
THERMOSTAT (DE-ICING) SWITCH
EVAPORATOR HOUSING UPPER
VIEW IN DIRECTION OF ARROW "A"
BLOWER MOTOR RESISTOR
VIEW IN DIRECTION OF ARROW "B"
7 CLIPS REQD
AC/HEAT DOOR
6
TEMPERATURE BLEND DOOR
5
BLOWER HOUSING (LEFT)
BLOWER MOTOR AND WHEEL ASSEMBLY
HEATER CORE
ARROW "A"
OUTSIDE AIR
1
AND
RECIRCULATING AIR
2
DOOR VACUUM MOTOR
BLOWER HOUSING (RIGHT)
ARROW "B"
EVAPORATOR CORE
EVAPORATOR HOUSING LOWER
FLOOR AIR DISTRIBUTION DUCT
11 CLIPS REQD.
WATER VALVE VACUUM SWITCH

Heater-air conditioner assembly—1970-74 Maverick, 1971-74 Comet

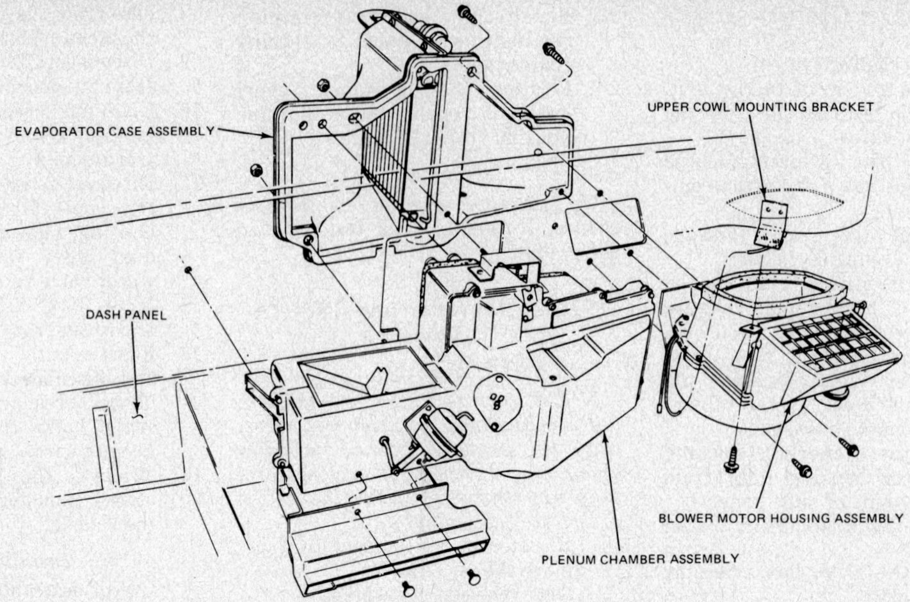
EVAPORATOR CASE ASSEMBLY
UPPER COWL MOUNTING BRACKET
DASH PANEL
BLOWER MOTOR HOUSING ASSEMBLY
PLENUM CHAMBER ASSEMBLY

Heater-air conditioner assembly—1972-74 Torino and Montego

1. Remove the carburetor air cleaner.
2. Disconnect the battery.
3. Drain the cooling system.
4. Purge the system of refrigerant.
5. Disconnect the evaporator tubes from the expansion valve, disconnect the heater hoses.
6. Remove the housing-to-dash panel mounting stud nuts.
7. Remove the glove box and map light from the lower edge, right side of instrument panel.
8. Disconnect the vacuum hoses at the motor.
9. Disconnect the two hoses from the water valve vacuum switch, and disengage the hoses from the slip at the top of the housing.
10. Disconnect the wires from the thermostatic (de-icing) switch.
11. Disconnect the cable from the door crank arm.
12. Remove the motor from the housing to allow clearance at the lower edge of the instrument panel, and remove the motor bracket.
13. Remove the motor to allow clearance at the right side of the housing during removal.
14. Remove the housing-to-cowl bracket.
15. Pull the drain hose from the hole in the floor pan.
16. Remove the two blower housing-to-cowl attaching screws, lower the blower housing slightly. Pull the housing away from the dash panel, move it to the right to separate it from the blower housing and remove it from the vehicle.

Installation

To install, reverse the removal procedure. Evacuate, Leak test, and Charge the refrigerant system.

1972-74 Torino and Montego

Removal

NOTE: to remove the core, it is necessary to remove the entire assembly.

1. Discharge system as outlined under instructions referring to units with six cylinder compressor.
2. Disconnect the heater hoses, and position them so coolant will not escape.
3. Disconnect liquid line to expansion valve, low pressure line to STV valve, and STV valve equalizer line.
4. Remove insulation around capillary tube, and remove tube from suction line. Remove expansion valve from evaporator.
5. Remove STV valve by disconnecting it from the evaporator.
6. Remove the two mounting flange nuts and three mounting flange screws that can be reached from the engine compartment. Remove the sheet metal mounting screws, plenum right lower mounting screws, and blower housing-to-evaporator housing screw from under the instrument panel. Remove the plenum mounting screws and move the plenum to the rear.
7. Remove the evaporator case from the engine compartment.

Installation

1. Reverse the removal procedures, observing the following precautions:
   a. After installing heater hoses, replace any coolant that may have been lost.
   b. Evacuate, leak test, and charge the system.

Heater Core R & R

1967 Comet, 1967-70 Falcon and Fairlane, 1968-71 Torino and Montego

1. Remove the heater-air conditioner assembly.
2. Separate the heater housing from the plenum.
3. Slip the heater core out of the plenum.
4. Transfer the old heater core seal to the new core.
5. Slip the new core with seal into the plenum.
6. Install the heater housing to the plenum. Connect the wires at the resistor block, and install the seal and retainer at the evaporator tubes.
7. Install the heater-air conditoner assembly.

1969-73 Mustang and 1969-74 Cougar, 1970-74 Maverick, 1971-74 Comet

1. Remove the heater-air conditioner assembly.
2. Remove the flange clips and upper half of the housing assembly.
3. Remove the water valve vacuum switch from the lower half of the housing.
4. Remove the screw, retaining clip and temperature blend door shaft, the four screws and door upper frame, the door, and the four screws and door lower frame from the lower half of the housing.
5. Lift the heater core from the lower housing.
6. Transfer the pads from the old core to the new core.
7. Reverse the above procedures to

install. Leak-test, evacuate and charge the regrigeration system.

1972-74 Torino and Montego

1. Drain the cooling system and disconnect the heater hoses at the core.
2. Remove the glove box.
3. Remove the two snap clips and the heater air outlet register from the plenum.
4. Remove the temperature control cable assembly mounting screw, and disconnect the end of the cable from the blend door crank arm.
5. Remove the blue and red vacuum hoses from the high-low door vacuum motor; the yellow hose from the panel-defrost door motor, and the brown hose from the inline tee connector.
6. Disconnect the wires at the resistor block.
7. Remove the ten screws and the rear half of the plenum.
8. Remove the mounting nut from the heater core tube support bracket.
9. Reverse the above procedures to install, taking care to apply body sealer around the case flanges to insure a positive seal.

1967-68 Mustang and Cougar

Removal

NOTE: to remove the core, it is necessary to disassemble the entire evaporator assembly.

1. Drain the coolant.
2. Purge the system of refrigerant.
3. Disconnect the heater hoses and refrigerant lines at the dash seal and retainer.
4. Take off the vacuum supply tank.
5. Take off the two evaporator case stud mounting stud nuts and the one blower housing stud nut on the engine side of the dash panel.
6. Open the glove box.
7. Disconnect the vacuum hoses from the reheat and outside-recirculating vacuum motors.
8. Disconnect the control cable from the temperature-blend door.
9. Disconnect the wiring from the thermostat switch.
10. Take out the evaporator rear support bracket screw.
11. Take out the blower housing support-to-cowl screw.
12. Position the blower housing to the left, away from the evaporator case.
13. Pull up the drain tube.
14. Move the evaporator case rearward and downward under the instrument panel.
15. Disconnect the vacuum hoses from the A/C heat and the A/C defrost vacuum motors.
16. Disconnect the wiring from the A/C clutch switch blower motor resistor and blower motor.
17. Take off the blower housing and A/C defrost penum chamber assembly down toward the right side and remove them from the car.
18. Take off the twelve upper-to-lower case flange caps.
19. Take out the A/C thermostat switch capillary tube.
20. Take out the dash panel stud mounting bracket screws.
21. Take out the evaporator core from the upper case.
22. Remove the rubber grommet from the core tubes.
23. Remove the water valve vacuum switch, two retaining screws, and remove the switch.
24. Remove the upper frame and temperature blend door screws, shaft and lever assembly, and retaining clip.
25. Remove the lower frame four retaining screws and remove the lower frame.
26. Remove the retaining clip on the reheat-door lever, position the motor arm out of the way and remove the shaft and lever assembly, and the reheat door.
27. Remove the heater core.

Installation

To install, reverse the removal procedure. Evacuate, leak test, and charge the system with refrigerant.

Blower Motor R & R

1967 Comet, 1967-70 Falcon and Fairlane, 1968-74 Torino and Montego

Removal

1. Take out the glove box.
2. On 1971 and earlier models, take out the right hand fresh air duct. On 1972 and later models, remove recirculating air duct.
3. Disconnect the vacuum line from the actuator and move it out of the way.
4. Disconnect the plug from the resistor block and lift out the resistor block.
5. On 1971 and earlier models, take off the blower motor cover and lift out the motor and the blower wheel. On 1972 and later models, remove all blower housing flange screws, separate blower housing halves, and unscrew and remove blower assembly.
6. Remove the blower wheel.

Installation

1. Install the blower wheel on the motor.
2. Install the motor and shell and ground wire in the case.
3. On 1971 and earlier models, install the blower cover. On 1972 and later models, install blower assembly into lower housing, and reassemble housing.
4. Connect the wires.
5. Fasten the resistor block to the plenum.
6. Install the fresh air duct on earlier models, recirculating air duct on 1972 and later models.
7. Install the glove box.

1967-68 Mustang and Cougar

1. Disconnect the battery ground cable.
2. Drain the cooling system.
3. Disconnect the heater hoses at the engine.
4. Loosen the screws at the choke housing and move the hose away.
5. Take off the nuts holding the heater to the dash.
6. Take out the screw holding the ground wire to the dash and disconnect the two wires.
7. Take out the screw holding the heater to the air intake. Lower the heater to the floor, pulling the hose through the dash.
8. Take out the nuts holding the motor mounting plate to the heater.
9. Lift out the motor and blower assembly.
10. Reverse above procedures to install.

1969-70 Mustang and Cougar

Removal

1. Disconnect battery ground cable, and drain cooling system.
2. Remove instrument panel pad, glove compartment liner, and glove compartment door.
3. Remove the heater air distribution duct.
4. Disconnect the control cables, and the wires from the blower motor resistor.
5. Remove the right side courtesy light, if applicable.
6. Remove the heater support mounting screw from the dash.
7. Disconnect the vacuum hoses. If the vehicle is equipped with a power ventilation system, remove the power vent air duct.
8. Disconnect the heater hoses at the dash panel.
9. From the engine compartment, remove the blower motor ground screw, and the five heater assembly retaining nuts.
10. Remove the screws which hold the instrument panel to the cowl, and the instrument panel right side brace. Pull the right side of the instrument panel rearward, and remove the heater assembly.
11. Disconnect blower motor wires where they connect at the resistor.
12. Remove the four mounting plate nuts, and remove the blower and motor assembly.

Installation

1. To install, reverse the procedures, being careful to properly adjust the control cables.

1970-74 Maverick, 1971-74 Comet

Removal

1. Remove the radio assembly.
2. Remove the utility shelf, and air ducts from the plenum chamber.
3. Remove the air duct from the bottom of the blower housing.
4. Remove the blower housing mounting stud nut and lock plate.
5. Rotate the blower housing from the evaporator housing.
6. Disconnect the vacuum hoses, resistor and ground wires, and remove the housing.
7. Separate the left and right halves.

Installation

1. Set the motor in place.
2. Install the motor attaching nuts.
3. Set the blower fan on the motor shaft.
4. Install the blower motor and fan assembly.
5. Set the blower housing in place.
6. Install the blower housing attaching nuts, washers, and screws.
7. Install the water valve.

1971-73 Mustang and 1971-74 Cougar

Removal

1. Remove the blower housing mounting bracket stud nut (engine side of the dash panel.)
2. Remove the two blower housing-to-instrument panel support mounting screws.
3. Disconnect the blower motor ground wire (black) from the resistor.
4. Disconnect the blower motor lead wire (orange-black) from the resistor.
5. Rotate the blower housing to a diagonal position. Remove the blower motor mounting screws, and remove the blower motor and wheel as an assembly.

Installation

1. Position the assembly and secure the mounting screws.
2. Connect the blower motor lead and ground wires.
3. Position the blower motor on the blower housing and install the mounting bracket.

SEAT BELTS

Seat Belt/Starter Interlock System—1974

Starting with 1974 models, a new starter interlock system is employed consisting of a warning light, buzzer, seat sensors, switches in the outboard belt retractors, and an electronic logic module. Basically, the starter will not engage unless the driver and other front seat passenger sit in the seat and pull out the seat belt. Unless the driver or passenger has remained seated and buckled, the sequence must be repeated every time the engine is started. Leaving the belts pulled all the way out also will prevent the engine from being started, as the belts must be retracted and buckled each time the engine is started. In the event of a starter interlock system failure, or to permit the use of a remote starter switch when working under the hood, a starter interlock by-pass switch is located in the engine compartment, thereby eliminating the need to perform the buckling sequence.

NOTE: Each time the by-pass switch is operated, the buckling sequence may be eliminated once and once only. The system may not be permanently by-passed.

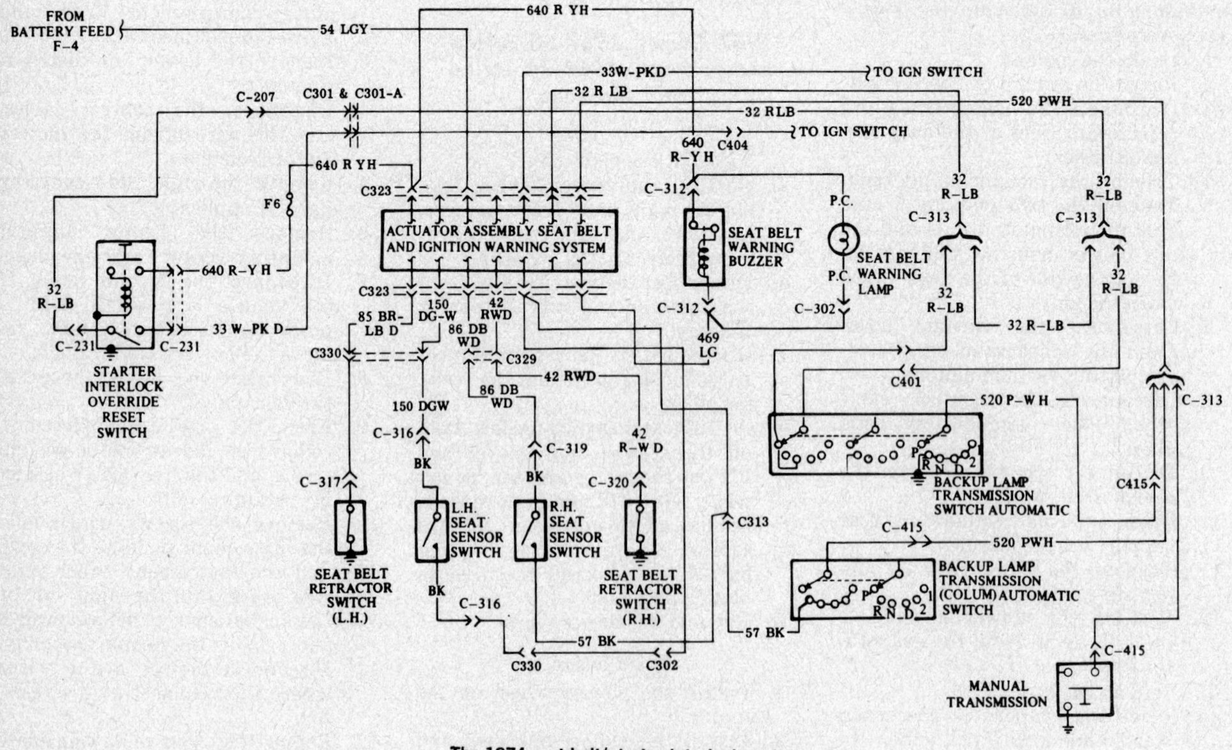
FROM BATTERY FEED F-4
54 LGY
640 R YH
33W-PKD
TO IGN SWITCH
32 R LB
520 PWH
C-207
C301 & C301-A
32 RLB
TO IGN SWITCH
640 R-Y H
C404
640 R YH
F6
C323
C-312
P.C.
ACTUATOR ASSEMBLY SEAT BELT AND IGNITION WARNING SYSTEM
SEAT BELT WARNING BUZZER
SEAT BELT WARNING LAMP
C-313
32 R-LB
640 R-Y H
33 W-PK D
C-231
STARTER INTERLOCK OVERRIDE RESET SWITCH
85 BR-LB D
150 DG-W
42 RWD
86 DB WD
C330
C329
469 LG
C-302
C401
150 DGW
C-316
86 DB WD
42 RWD
C-319
42 R-W D
BK
C-317
C-320
520 P-W H
BACKUP LAMP TRANSMISSION SWITCH AUTOMATIC
C415
L.H. SEAT SENSOR SWITCH
R.H. SEAT SENSOR SWITCH
C313
C-415
SEAT BELT RETRACTOR SWITCH (L.H.)
SEAT BELT RETRACTOR SWITCH (R.H.)
BACKUP LAMP TRANSMISSION (COLUM) AUTOMATIC SWITCH
57 BK
C302
MANUAL TRANSMISSION

The 1974 seat belt/starter interlock system

Firebird • Tempest GTO • Ventura II LeMans • Grand Am

Front Suspension C479, U121

Fuel System C448, U194

Heater C489

Ignition System C446, U178

Instrument Panel C486, U281

Manual Transmission C472, U4

Jacking and Hoisting C479

Radio C488

Rear Suspension C482

Seat Belts C491

Specifications

Starting System C446, U127

Steering C484, U81, U92

Windshield Wipers C488

YEAR IDENTIFICATION

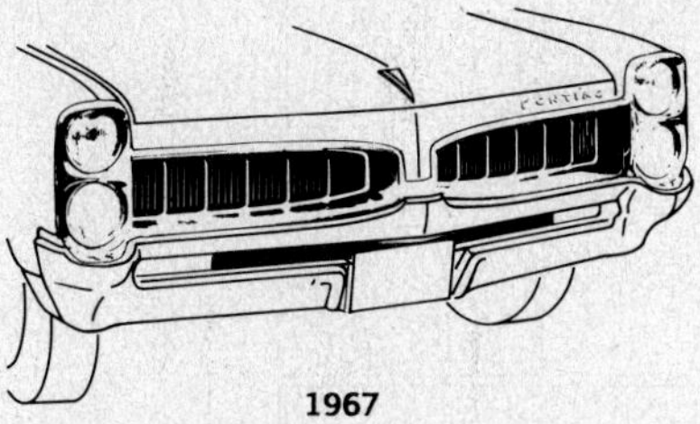
1967

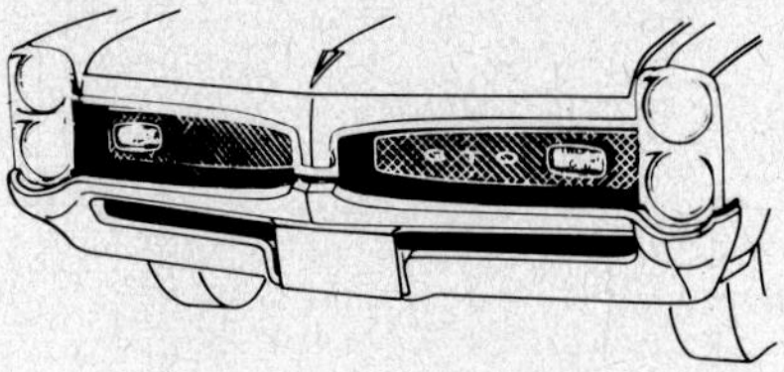
1967 GTO

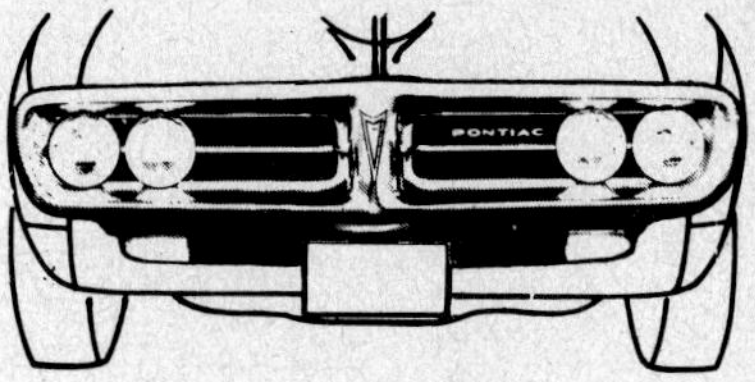
1967 Firebird

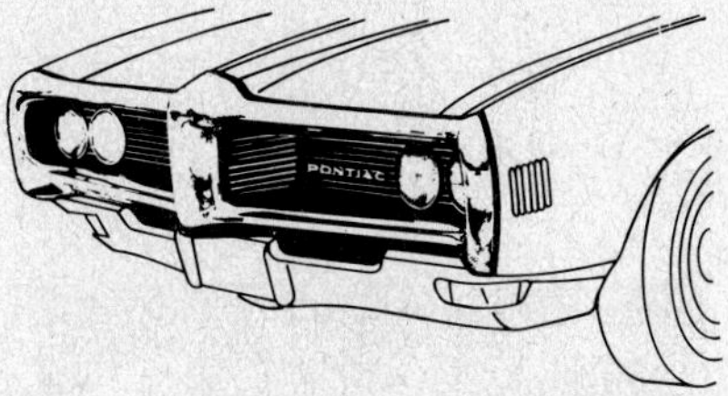
1968

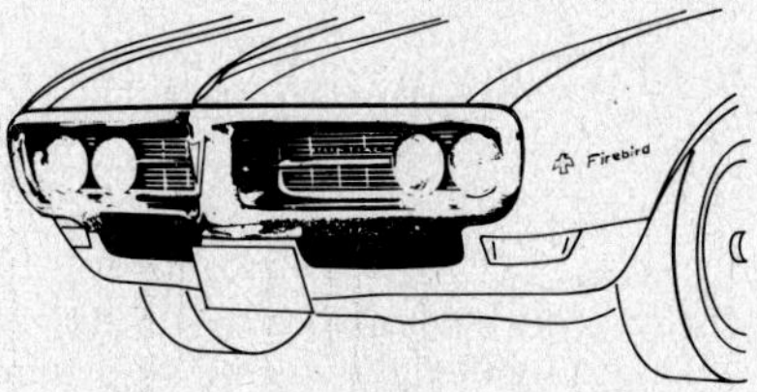
1968 Firebird

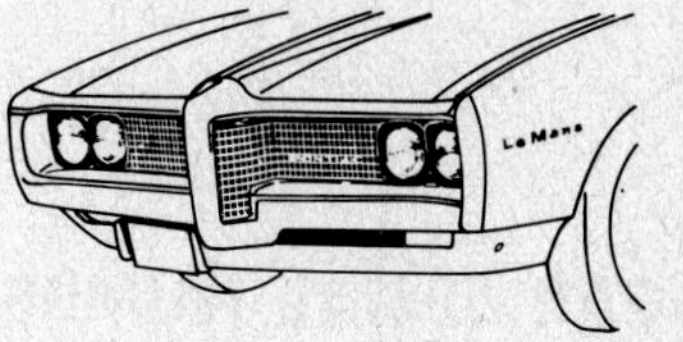
1969

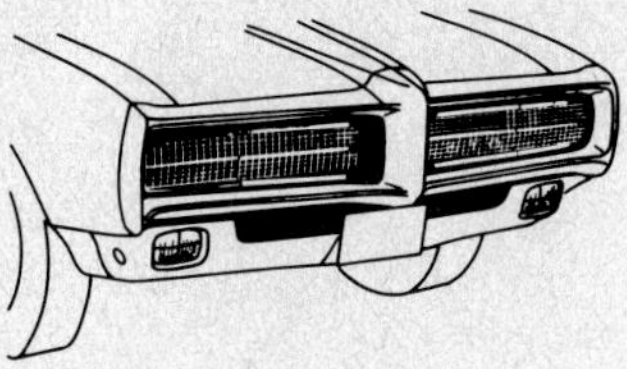
1969 GTO

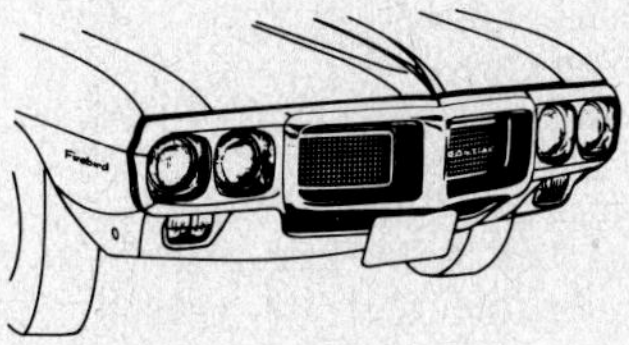
1969 Firebird

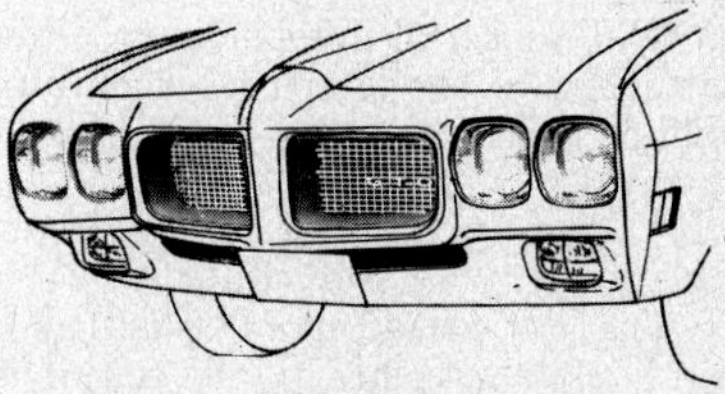
1970 GTO

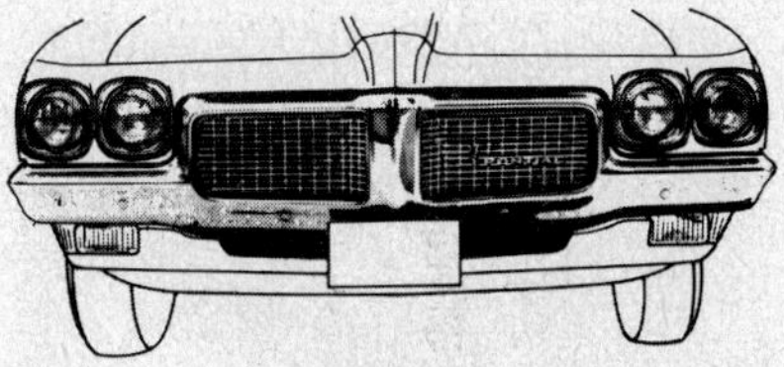
1970 Tempest

1970-71 Firebird

1971 Tempest

1971 GTO

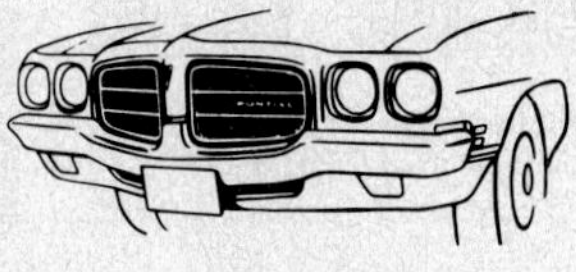
1972 Tempest

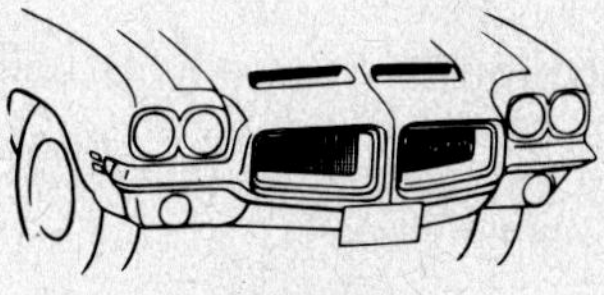
1972 GTO

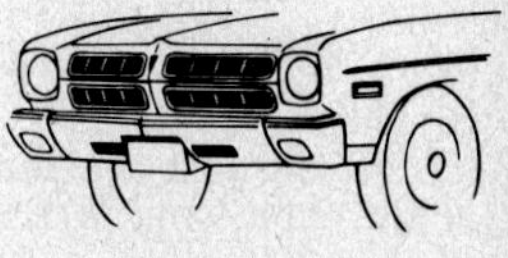
1971-72 Ventura II

1973 LeMans

1973 Firebird

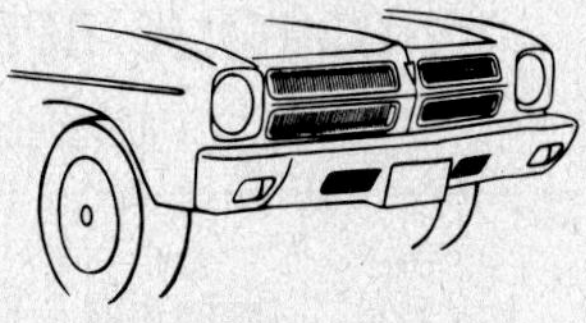
1973 Ventura II

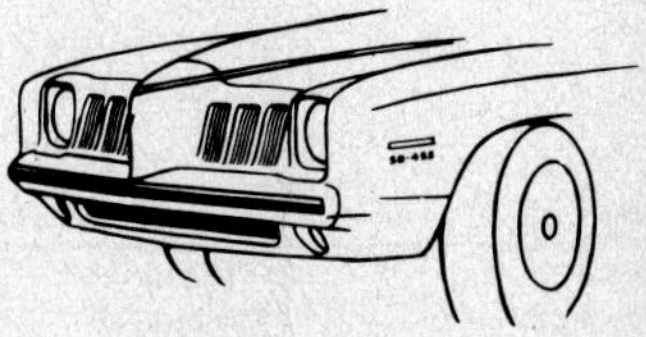
1973 Grand Am

1974 Firebird

1974 Ventura II

1974 LeMans

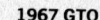

1974 Grand Am

FIRING ORDER

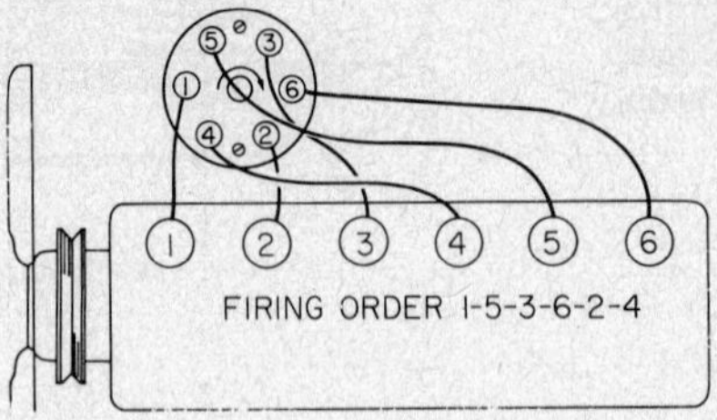
FIRING ORDER 1-5-3-6-2-4

1967-74 6 cyl
(© Pontiac Div., G.M. Corp)

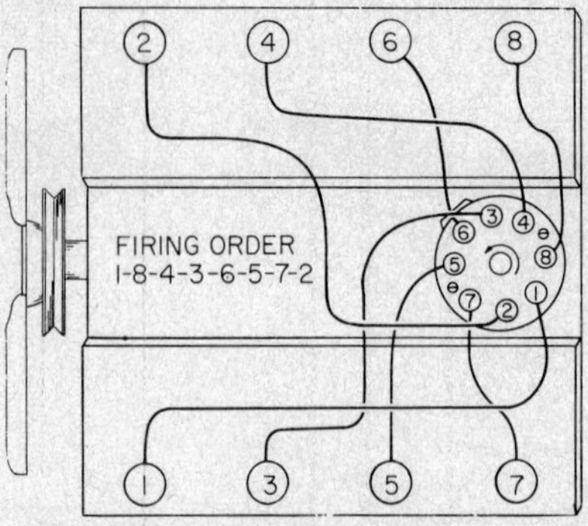
FIRING ORDER
1-8-4-3-6-5-7-2

1967-74 V8 except 307
(© Pontiac Div., G.M. Corp)

CAR SERIAL NUMBER LOCATION

1967

The car serial number is on a plate attached to the left front door hinge pillar. The number is interpreted below:

1968-74

The car serial number is located on a plate attached to the top of the instrument panel, left-hand side, visible through the windshield. The number is interpreted as follows:

1967-74

First digit: Car division
Second and third digits: Series number
Fourth and fifth digits: Body style code
Sixth digit: Year manufactured
Seventh digit: Plant
Eighth digit: Engine used.
Ninth to thirteenth digits—sequential serial number

Engine Identification

The engine number, on V8 engines, is located on a machined pad on the right-hand bank of the engine block. The engine production code is stamped immediately below this number.

On six cylinder engines, the engine code is stamped on the cylinder head-to-block contact surface behind the oil filler pipe.

On 1972-74 six cylinder engines, the code is stamped on the distributor mounting pad (right side of block).

Use the following charts to find your engine and its special equipment.

6-cyl engine number location
(© Pontiac Div., G.M. Corp)

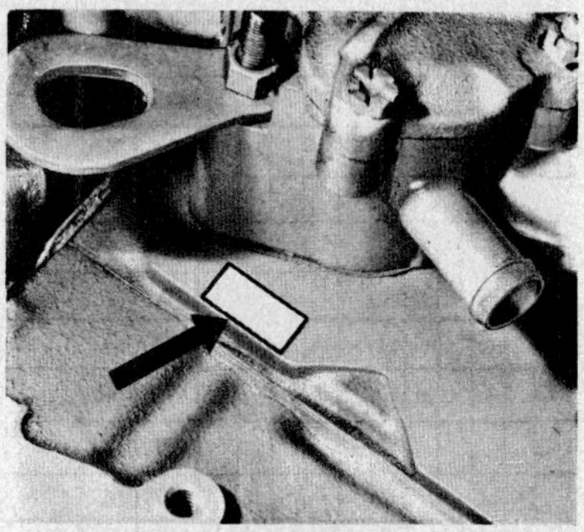

Engine number and code location—1967-68 V8 engines
(© Pontiac Div., G.M. Corp)

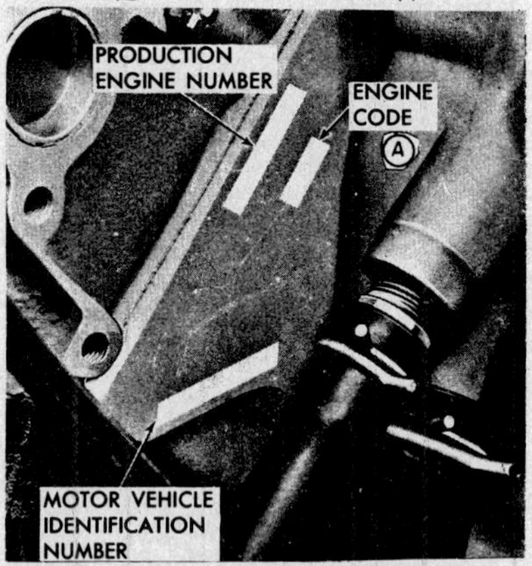
PRODUCTION
ENGINE NUMBER
ENGINE
CODE
A
MOTOR VEHICLE
IDENTIFICATION
NUMBER

Engine number and code location—1970-74 V8 engines
(© Pontiac Div., G.M. Corp)

TORQUE SPECIFICATIONS

All readings in ft lbs

Year	Engine Displacement (cu in.)	Cylinder Head Bolts	Rod Bearing Bolts	Main Bearing Bolts	Crankshaft Pulley Bolt	Flywheel to Crankshaft Bolts	MANIFOLD Intake	MANIFOLD Exhaust
'67-'69	6	85-100	30-35	60-70	Pressed on	60-70	25-40	15-25
	8	85-100	40-46	90-110▲	130-190	85-100	20-35	30-45
'70-'74	6	95	35	65	Pressed on	60	25-30①	25
	8 P	95	43②	90-110	160	95	40	30
	8-307 C ('71-'72)	65	45	75	60	60	30	25

▲ Rear main—120 ft. lbs.
C Chevrolet engine used in Ventura II
P Pontiac engine

① End bolts 15-20 ft. lbs.
② 63 ft lbs on 455 S.D. engine

Firebird, Tempest, GTO, Ventura II, LeMans, Grand Am GENERAL ENGINE SPECIFICATIONS

Year	Engine Cu. In. Displacement	Carburetor Type	Advertised Horsepower @ rpm ■	Advertised Torque @ rpm (ft lbs) ■	Bore and Stroke (in.)	Advertised Compression Ratio	Oil Pressure @ 2050 rpm
'67	6-230 OHC	1 bbl	165 @ 4700	216 @ 2600	3.8762 x 3.250	9.0:1	31①
	6-230 OHC	4 bbl	215 @ 5200	240 @ 3800	3.8762 x 3.250	10.5:1	31①
	8-326	2 bbl	250 @ 4600	333 @ 3800	3.7199 x 3.750	9.2:1	35
	8-326 HO	4 bbl	285 @ 5000	359 @ 3200	3.7199 x 3.750	10.5:1	35
	8-400	4 bbl	325 @ 4800	410 @ 3400	4.1222 x 3.750	10.75:1	58
	8-400 Ram Air	4 bbl	325 @ 5200	410 @ 3600	4.1222 x 3.750	10.75:1	58
	8-400	4 bbl	360 @ 5100	438 @ 3600	4.1222 x 3.750	10.75:1	58
	8-400 Ram Air	4 bbl	360 @ 5400	438 @ 3800	4.1222 x 3.750	10.75:1	58
'68	6-250 OHC	1 bbl	175 @ 4800	240 @ 2600	3.8762 x 3.530	9.0:1	31①
	6-250 OHC	4 bbl	215 @ 5200	255 @ 3800	3.8762 x 3.530	10.5:1	31①
	8-350	2 bbl	265 @ 4600	355 @ 2800	3.8762 x 3.750	9.2:1	35
	8-350 HO	4 bbl	320 @ 5100	380 @ 3200	3.8762 x 3.750	10.5:1	35
	8-400	2 bbl	265 @ 4600	397 @ 2400	4.1212 x 3.750	8.6:1	58
	8-400	4 bbl	330 @ 4800	430 @ 3300	4.1212 x 3.750	10.75:1	58
	8-400 Ram Air	4 bbl	335 @ 5300	430 @ 3600	4.1212 x 3.750	10.75:1	58
	8-400	4 bbl	350 @ 5000	445 @ 3000	4.1212 x 3.750	10.75:1	58
	8-400 HO	4 bbl	360 @ 5100	445 @ 3600	4.1212 x 3.750	10.75:1	58
	8-400 Ram Air	4 bbl	360 @ 5400	445 @ 3800	4.1212 x 3.750	10.75:1	58
'69	6-250 OHC	1 bbl	175 @ 4800	240 @ 2600	3.8762 x 3.530	9.0:1	31①
	6-250 OHC	4 bbl	215 @ 5200	255 @ 3500	3.8762 x 3.530	10.5:1	31①
	6-250 OHC	4 bbl	230 @ 5400	260 @ 3600	3.8762 x 3.530	10.5:1	31①
	8-350	2 bbl	265 @ 4600	325 @ 2800	3.8762 x 3.750	9.2:1	35
	8-350	4 bbl	325 @ 5100	380 @ 3200	3.8762 x 3.750	10.5:1	35
	8-350	4 bbl	330 @ 5100	380 @ 3200	3.8762 x 3.750	10.5:1	35
	8-400	2 bbl	265 @ 4600	397 @ 2400	4.1212 x 3.750	8.6:1	35
	8-400	4 bbl	330 @ 4800	430 @ 3300	4.1212 x 3.750	10.75:1	58
	8-400 HO	4 bbl	335 @ 5000	430 @ 3400	4.1212 x 3.750	10.75:1	58
	8-400 Ram Air	4 bbl	345 @ 5400	430 @ 3700	4.1212 x 3.750	10.75:1	58
	8-400 Ram Air	4 bbl	366 @ 5100	445 @ 3600	4.1212 x 3.750	10.75:1	58
	8-400 Ram Air IV	4 bbl	370 @ 5500	445 @ 3900	4.1212 x 3.750	10.75:1	58
'70	6-250	1 bbl	155 @ 4200	235 @ 1600	3.876 2x 3.530	8.5:1	53②
	8-350	2 bbl	255 @ 4600	355 @ 2800	3.8762 x 3.750	8.8:1	35
	8-400	2 bbl	265 @ 4600	397 @ 2400	4.1212 x 3.750	8.8:1	35
	8-400	4 bbl	330 @ 4800	430 @ 3000	4.1212 x 3.750	10.25:1③	35
	8-400 Ram Air	4 bbl	345 @ 5000	430 @ 3400	4.1212 x 3.750	10.5:1	35
	8-400	4 bbl	350 @ 4800	445 @ 2900	4.1212 x 3.750	10.0:1	35
	8-400	4 bbl	366 @ 5100	445 @ 3600	4.1212 x 3.750	10.5:1	35
	8-400	4 bbl	370 @ 5500	445 @ 3900	4.1212 x 3.750	10.5:1	35
	8-455	4 bbl	360 @ 4600	500 @ 3100	4.1522 x 4.210	10.25:1	35
'71	6-250	1 bbl	145 @ 4200	230 @ 1600	3.8750 x 3.530	8.5:1	38④
	8-307	2 bbl	200 @ 4600	300 @ 2400	3.8750 x 3.250	8.5:1	40②
	8-350	2 bbl	250 @ 4400	350 @ 2400	3.8762 x 3.750	8.0:1	35
	8-400	2 bbl	265 @ 4400	400 @ 2400	4.1212 x 3.750	8.2:1	58
	8-400	4 bbl	300 @ 4800	400 @ 3600	4.1212 x 3.750	8.2:1	58
	8-455	4 bbl	325 @ 4400	455 @ 3200	4.1522 x 4.210	8.2:1	35
	8-455 HO	4 bbl	335 @ 4800	480 @ 3600	4.1522 x 4.210	8.4:1	35

GENERAL ENGINE SPECIFICATIONS, Continued

Year	Engine Cu. In. Displacement	Carburetor Type	Advertised Horsepower @ rpm ■	Advertised Torque @ rpm (ft lbs) ■	Bore and Stroke (in.)	Advertised Compression Ratio	Oil Pressure @ 2050 rpm
'72	6-250	1 bbl	110 @ 3800	185 @ 1600	3.8750 x 3.530	8.5:1	40②
	8-307	2 bbl	130 @ 4400	230 @ 2400	3.8750 x 3.250	8.5:1	40②
	8-350	2 bbl	160 @ 4400	270 @ 2000	3.8762 x 3.750	8.2:1	35
	8-400	2 bbl	175 @ 4000	310 @ 2400	4.1212 x 3.750	8.2:1	35
	8-400	4 bbl	200 @ 4000	295 @ 2800	4.1212 x 3.750	8.2:1	35
	8-400	4 bbl	250 @ 4400	325 @ 3200	4.1212 x 3.750	8.2:1	35
	8-455	4 bbl	250 @ 3600	375 @ 2400	4.1522 x 4.210	8.2:1	35
	8-455	4 bbl	300 @ 4000	415 @ 3200	4.1522 x 4.210	8.4:1	35
'73	6-250	1 bbl	100 @ 3600	175 @ 1600	3.8750 x 3.530	8.2:1	50-65②
	8-350 SE	2 bbl	150 @ 4000	270 @ 2000	3.8762 x 3.750	7.6:1	55-60
	8-350 DE	2 bbl	175 @ 4400	280 @ 2400	3.8782 x 3.750	7.6:1	55-60
	8-400 SE	2 bbl	170 @ 3600	320 @ 2000	4.1212 x 3.750	8.0:1	55-60
	8-400 DE	2 bbl	185 @ 4000	320 @ 2400	4.1212 x 3.750	8.0:1	55-60
	8-400 DE	4 bbl	230 @ 4400	325 @ 3200	4.1212 x 3.750	8.0:1	55-60
	8-455 DE	4 bbl	250 @ 4000	370 @ 2800	4.1522 x 4.210	8.0:1	55-60
	8-455S.D. DE	4 bbl	310 @ 4000	390 @ 3600	4.1522 x 4.210	8.4:1	75-80
'74	6-250	1 bbl	100 @ 3600	175 @ 1600	3.8750 x 3.530	8.2:1	50-65②
	8-350 SE	2 bbl	155 @ 4000	275 @ 2400	3.8762 x 3.750	7.6:1	55-60
	8-350 DE	2 bbl	170 @ 4400	290 @ 2400	3.8782 x 3.750	7.6:1	55-60
	8-350 SE	4 bbl	170 @ 4000	280 @ 2000	3.8762 x 3.750	7.6:1	55-60
	8-350 DE	4 bbl	200 @ 4000	295 @ 2800	3.8762 x 3.750	7.6:1	55-60
	8-400 SE	2 bbl	175 @ 3600	315 @ 2000	4.1212 x 3.750	8.0:1	55-60
	8-400 DE	2 bbl	190 @ 4000	330 @ 2400	4.1212 x 3.750	8.0:1	55-60
	8-400 DE	4 bbl	225 @ 4000	330 @ 2800	4.1212 x 3.750	8.0:1	55-60
	8-455 SE	4 bbl	215 @ 3600	355 @ 2400	4.1522 x 4.210	8.0:1	55-60
	8-455 DE	4 bbl	250 @ 4000	380 @ 2800	4.1522 x 4.210	8.0:1	55-60
	8-455S.D. DE	4 bbl	290 @ 4000	395 @ 3200	4.1522 x 4.210	8.4:1	75-80

■ Beginning 1972 horsepower and torque are SAE net figures. They are measured at the rear of the transmission with all accessories installed and operating. Since the figures vary when a given engine is installed in different models, some are representative, rather than exact.

① Oil pressure at 2800 rpm

② Oil pressure at 2000 rpm

③ For vehicles equipped with automatic transmissions, advertised compression ratio is 10.0:1

④ Oil pressure at 1500 rpm

HO High Output

OHC Overhead Cam

SE Single Exhaust

DE Dual Exhaust

BATTERY AND STARTER SPECIFICATIONS

Year	Engine Displacement (cu in.)	BATTERY: Ampere Hour Capacity	BATTERY: Volts	BATTERY: Terminal Grounded	STARTER Lock Test: Amps	STARTER Lock Test: Volts	STARTER Lock Test: Torque (ft lbs)	STARTER No-Load Test: Amps	STARTER No-Load Test: Volts	STARTER No-Load Test: RPM	Brush Spring Tension (oz)
'67-'69	6	44①	12	Neg.				49-76	10.6	6,200-9,600	35
	8-326, 350	53①	12	Neg.				65-100	10.6	3,600-5,100	35
	8-400	61	12	Neg.				Not Recommended			35
'70-'74	6	45①	12	Neg.				Not Recommended			35
	6-Ventura II	45	12	Neg.				50-80	9	5,500-10,500	35
	8-Ventura II (307—1971-72)	61	12	Neg.				50-80	9	5,500-10,500	35
	8-350 P	53①	12	Neg.				Not Recommended			35
	8-400, 455	61	12	Neg.				Not Recommended			35

① 61 amp battery used w/AC or H.D. battery option.

P Pontiac engine

ALTERNATOR AND REGULATOR SPECIFICATIONS

	ALTERNATOR			REGULATOR						
					Field Relay			Regulator		
Year	Part No. or Manufacturer	Field Current @ 12 V	Output (amps)	Part No. or Manufacturer	Air Gap (in.)	Point Gap (in.)	Volts to Close	Air Gap (in.)	Point Gap (in.)	Volts @ 75°
'67-'69	1100761	2.2-2.6	37	1119515②	.015	.030	1.5-3.2	.067	.014	13.5-16.0
	1100704	2.2-2.6	37	1119515	.015	.030	1.5-3.2	.067	.014	13.5-16.0
	1100832③	4.0-4.5	37	1119515	.015	.030	1.5-3.2	.067	.014	13.5-16.0
	1100830③	4.0-4.5	37	1119515	.015	.030	1.5-3.2	.067	.014	13.5-16.0
	1100700	2.2-2.6	55	1119515	.015	.030	1.5-3.2	.067	.014	13.5-16.0
	1100760	2.2-2.6	55	1119515	.015	.030	1.5-3.2	.067	.014	13.5-16.0
'70	1100704	2.2-2.6	37	1119515②	.015	.030	1.5-3.2	.067	.014	13.5-16.0
	1100888	2.2-2.6	55	1119515	.015	.030	1.5-3.2	.067	.014	13.5-16.0
	1100905	2.2-2.6	37	1119515	.015	.030	1.5-3.2	.067	.014	13.5-16.0
	1100700	2.2-2.6	55	1119515	.015	.030	1.5-3.2	.067	.014	13.5-16.0
	1100891	2.2-2.6	55	1119515	.015	.030	1.5-3.2	.067	.014	13.5-16.0
	1100892	2.2-2.6	55	1119515	.015	.030	1.5-3.2	.067	.014	13.5-16.0
	1100906	2.2-2.6	55	1119515	.015	.030	1.5-3.2	.067	.014	13.5-16.0
	1100895	2.2-2.6	61	1119515	.015	.030	1.5-3.2	.067	.014	13.5-16.0
'71-'74	1100550	4.0-4.5	37	1119515	.015	.030	1.5-3.2	.067	.014	13.8-14.8
	1100834	4.0-4.5	37	1119515	.015	.030	1.5-3.2	.067	.014	13.8-14.8
	1100927	4.0-4.5	37	Integral with Alternator						
	1100566④	4.0-4.5	37	1119515	.015	.030	1.5-3.2	.067	.014	13.8-14.8
	1100836④	4.0-4.5	37	1119515	.015	.030	1.5-3.2	.067	.014	13.8-14.8
	1100920	4.0-4.5	55	Integral with Alternator						
	1100928	4.0-4.5	55	Integral with Alternator						
	1100843④	4.0-4.5	61	1119515	.015	.030	1.5-3.2	.067	.014	13.8-14.8
	11001015	4.0-4.5	80	Integral with Alternator						
	1100497	4.0-4.9	37	Integral with Alternator						

① w/Transistor ignition
② Transistor regulator 1116368 optional equipment until 1970
③ Integrated Circuit Generator (C.S.I.—no external regulator) optional on 1969 Firebird
④ Used only on Ventura II
—— Not applicable

1967

ENGINE IDENTIFICATION CODES

No. Cyls.	Cu. In. Displ.	Type	Code	No. Cyls.	Cu. In. Displ.	Type	Code
6	230	AT, 1 BBL	ZG	8	326	AT, 2 BBL w/Ex. Em.	XF
6	230	3 Spd, MT, 1 BBL	ZK	8	326	AT, 4 BBL w/Ex. Em.	XG
6	230	AT, 4 BBL w/Ex. Em.	ZL	8	400	AT, 2 BBL w/Ex. Em.	XL
6	230	AT, 1 BBL	ZM	8	400	AT, 2 BBL	XM
6	250	AT, 1 BBL	ZN	8	400	AT, 4 BBL	XP
6	230	MT, 4 BBL w/Ex. Em.	ZR	8	326	MT, 4 BBL w/Ex. Em.	XR
6	230	3 Spd, MT, 1 BBL	ZS	8	400	MT, 4 BBL	XS
8	400	3 Spd, MT, 4 BBL	WT	8	400	AT, 4 BBL w/Ex. Em.	YI
8	400	4 BBL w/Ex. Em.	WV	8	400	AT, 4 BBL w/Ex. Em.	YQ
8	400	MT, 4 BBL w/Ex. Em.	WW	8	400	MT, 4 BBL w/Ex. Em.	YR
8	326	3 Spd, MT, 2 BBL w/Ex. Em.	WX	8	400	AT, 4 BBL (335 HP)	YS
8	326	3 Spd, MT, 2 BBL	WP	8	400	AT, 4 BBL (360 HP)	YZ
8	326	3 Spd, MT, 4 BBL	WR	6	230	3 Spd, MT, 4 BBL	ZD
8	400	3 Spd, MT, 4 BBL	WS	6	230	AT, 4 BBL	ZE
8	400	AT, 4 BBL w/Ex. Em.	XE	6	230	3 Spd, MT, 1 BBL	ZF

1968 FIREBIRD ENGINE IDENTIFICATION

DISPLACEMENT	HORSEPOWER	ENGINE CODE	TRANS. MANUAL	TRANS. AUTOMATIC	CARB. 1-BBL	CARB. 2-BBL	CARB. QUADRAJET	COMP. RATIO 9.0	COMP. RATIO 9.2	COMP. RATIO 10.5	COMP. RATIO 10.75	CAMSHAFT 9777254	CAMSHAFT 9779066	CAMSHAFT 9779067	CAMSHAFT 9779068	CAMSHAFT 9785744	CAMSHAFT 9790826	CAMSHAFT 9792539	STANDARD DISTRIBUTOR 1110430	STANDARD DISTRIBUTOR 1110431	STANDARD DISTRIBUTOR 1111281	STANDARD DISTRIBUTOR 1111282	STANDARD DISTRIBUTOR 1111447	STANDARD DISTRIBUTOR 1111270	STANDARD DISTRIBUTOR 1111449	VALVE SPRINGS SINGLE	VALVE SPRINGS STD. TWO	VALVE SPRINGS H.D. TWO (SPEC.)	VALVE SPRINGS RAM AIR
250 Cu. In. (six)	175	ZK	X		X			X									X		X							X			
	175	ZN		X	X			X									X		X							X			
	215	ZD	X				X			X								X		X							X		
	215	ZE		X			X			X								X		X							X		
350 Cu. In. (V8)	265	WC	X			X			X			X									X						X		
	265	YJ		X		X			X			X									X						X		
	320	WK	X				X			X			X										X				X		
	320	YM		X			X			X			X									X					X		
400 Cu. In. (V8)	335	XN		X			X				X				X									●					X
	335	WQ	X				X				X				X										●			X	
	335	WI	X				X				X					X									●				X
	335	WZ	X				X				X			X											●			X	
	330	YW		X			X				X			X										●			X		
	330	YT		X			X				X			X										●			X		

● With 60 PSI Oil Pump Spring
All Cars Use CCS

1969 FIREBIRD ENGINE IDENTIFICATION

	HORSEPOWER	ENGINE CODE	DISPLACEMENT 250	DISPLACEMENT 350	DISPLACEMENT 400	TRANS. MANUAL	TRANS. AUTOMATIC	CARB. 1 BBL (MV)	CARB. 2 BBL (2GV)	CARB. 4 BBL (4MV)	COMP. RATIO 9.0:1	COMP. RATIO 9.2:1	COMP. RATIO 10.5:1	COMP. RATIO 10.75:1	CAMSHAFT 9790826	CAMSHAFT 9792539	CAMSHAFT 9796327	CAMSHAFT 9777254	CAMSHAFT 9779067	CAMSHAFT 9779068	CAMSHAFT 9794041	DISTRIBUTOR 1110474	DISTRIBUTOR 1110475	DISTRIBUTOR 1111941 (b)	DISTRIBUTOR 1111942	DISTRIBUTOR 1111945	DISTRIBUTOR 1111946 (b)	DISTRIBUTOR 1111952 (b)	DISTRIBUTOR 1111960	VALVE SPRINGS SINGLE	VALVE SPRINGS STD.-DUAL	VALVE SPRINGS H. D.-DUAL	VALVE SPRINGS H. D. SPEC.-DUAL	VALVE SPRINGS RAM AIR IV-DUAL	CYL. HEAD SMALL VALVE	CYL. HEAD LARGE VALVE
	175	(a)ZK ZC	X			X		X			X				X								X							X					X	
	175	(a)ZN ZF	X				X	X			X				X								X							X					X	
	230	(a)ZD ZH	X			X				X			X				X					X									X				X	
	215	(a)ZE ZL	X				X			X			X			X						X									X				X	
	265	(a)WC WM		X		X			X			X						X											X			X			X	
	265	(a)XL XB		X			X		X			X						X							X							X			X	
(c)	265	(a)YJ YE		X			X		X			X						X							X							X			X	
	325	WN		X		X				X			X							X								(e)					X			X
	325	XC		X			X			X			X						X								(d)						X			X
	330	WZ			X	X				X				X					X									X					X			X
	330	YT			X		X			X				X					X								X					X				X
	335	WQ			X		X			X				X						X								X					X			X
	335	YW			X					X				X					X								X					X				X
	345	WH			X					X				X							X			X										X		X
	345	XN			X		X			X				X							X			X										X		X

(a) Early production (small valve) engines with 30° intake valve seat angle. Later production (small valve) engines use 45° intake valve seat. NOTE: all large valve engines use 30° intake valve seat.

(b) Uses hardened drive gear for use with 60 psi oil pump and high tension distributor points.

(c) Two speed (M31) if equipped with A/C; Turbo-Hydramatic (M38) optional without A/C.

(d) Uses distributor 1111965

(e) Uses distributor 1111966

1970 FIREBIRD ENGINE IDENTIFICATION

		DISPLACEMENT			TRANS.		CARB.			COMP. RATIO					CAMSHAFT					DISTRIBUTOR									VALVE SPRING					CYL. HEAD	
HORSEPOWER	ENGINE CODE	250	350	400	MANUAL	AUTOMATIC	1 BBL. (MV)	2 BBL. (2GV)	4 BBL. (4MV)	8.5:1	8.8:1	10.0:1	10.25:1	10.5:1	3864897	9777254 (U)	9779067 (P)	9779068 (S)	9794041 (T)	1110463	1110464	1111148$	1111176$	1112007	1112008	1112009$	1112013*	1112024$	SINGLE	STD.-DUAL	H.D.-DUAL	H.D. SPEC.-DUAL	SUPER DUTY-DUAL	SMALL VALVE	LARGE VALVE
155	ZB	X			X		X			X					X					X									X					X	
155	ZG	X				X	X			X					X						X								X					X	
255	WU		X		X			X			X					X									X					X				X	
255	YU		X			X		X			X					X									X					X				X	
265	XX			X		X		X			X					X								X						X				X	
330	WT			X	X				X				X				X						X									X			X
330	YS			X		X			X			X					X					X								X					X
345	WS ¶			X	X				X					X				X										X				X			X
345	YZ ¶			X		X			X					X				X								X						X			X
370	WH §			X	X				X					X					X								X						X		X
370	XN §			X		X			X					X					X								X						X		X

¶ RAM AIR III

§ RAM AIR SUPER DUTY

* Uses cadmium gear for use with R.A. Super Duty only.

$ Uses hardened drive gear.

1971 FIREBIRD ENGINE IDENTIFICATION

			Model Usage	Displacement				Transmission			Carburetor			Cylinder Heads											Camshaft					Valve Lifter			Distributor								
														Compression Ratio				Rocker Arm Stud		Valve Spring			Valve Size																		
ENGINE CODE	Engine No. (Last Two Digits)	HORSEPOWER	"F" SERIES	250 L-6	350 V-8	400 V-8	455 V-8	MANUAL (3-Speed)	MANUAL (4-Speed)	AUTOMATIC	MV (1 Bbl.)	2GV (2 Bbl.)	4MV (4 Bbl.)	8.5:1	8.0:1	8.2:1	8.4:1	PRESSED-IN	THREADED	SINGLE	DUAL (STD.)	DUAL (H.D.)	SMALL	LARGE	3864897	483555 (W)	9779066 (N)	9779067 (P)	9779068 (S)	HIGH-BALL (STD.)	HIGH-BALL*	LOW-BALL	1110489	1112069	1112068	1112070	1112072	1112073	1112083	1112089	1112090
CAA	51	145	X	X				X			X			X				X		X			X		X					X			X								
CAB	52	145	X	X						X	X			X				X		X			X		X					X			X								
WR	94	250	X		X			X				X			X			X			X		X			X				X									X		
WN	90	250	X		X			X				X			X			X			X		X			X				X											X
WU	92	250	X		X				X			X			X			X			X		X			X				X									X		
YP	98	250	X		X				X			X			X			X			X		X			X				X											X
YU	96	250	X		X					**		X			X			X			X		X			X				X					X						
WP	97	250	X		X					**		X			X			X			X		X			X				X											X
XR	95	250	X		X					**		X			X			X			X		X				X			X				X							
YN	99	250	X		X					**		X			X			X			X		X				X			X											X
WT	78	300	X			X		X					X			X			X			X		X				X			X					X					
WK	74	300	X			X			X				X			X			X			X		X				X			X					X					
XX%	73	265	X			X			X				X			X			X			X		X					X		X					X					
YX	71	265	X			X				X		X				X		X			X		X			X				X										X	
YS	79	300	X			X				X			X			X			X		X			X				X		X						X					
WL†	18	335	X				X	X					X				X		X		X			X					X			X						X			
WC†	15	335	X				X		X				X				X		X		X			X					X			X						X			
YC+	19	325	X				X			X			X			X		X			X			X				X		X							X				
YE†	16	335	X				X			X			X				X		X		X			X					X			X						X			

* Lifter Body with Cast-Iron Foot

** "YU" is used with M35 transmission; "XR" is used with M38 transmission.

† 455 H.O. Engine

%Man. Trans. Models use WS engine code

+ Man. Trans. Models use WJ engine code

& Man. Trans. Models use WG engine code

1968 TEMPEST ENGINE IDENTIFICATION

DISPLACEMENT	HORSEPOWER	ENGINE CODE	TRANS.		CARB.			COMP. RATIO					CAMSHAFT						STANDARD DISTRIBUTOR								VALVE SPRINGS			
			MANUAL	AUTOMATIC	1-BBL	2-BBL	QUADRAJET	8.6	9.0	9.2	10.5	10.75	9777254	9779067	9779068	9785744	9790826	9792539	1110430	1110431	1111281	1111282	1111447	1111272	1111270	1111449	SINGLE	STD. TWO	H.D. TWO (SPEC.)	RAM AIR
250 Cu. In. (six)	175	ZK	X		X				X								X		X								X			
	175	ZN		X	X				X								X		X								X			
	215	ZO	X				X				X							X		X								X		
	215	ZE		X			X				X							X		X								X		
350 Cu. In. (V8)	265	WD	X			X				X			X								X							X		
	265	YN		X		X				X			X								X							X		
	320	WR	X				X				X		X										X					X		
	320	YP		X			X				X		X									X						X		
	265	XM		X		X		X					X											X				X		
400 Cu. In. (V8)	360	WT	X				X					X		X												●			X	
	350	YS		X			X					X		X											●			X		
	360	WS	X				X					X				X										●			X	
	350	YZ		X			X					X		X											●			X		
	360	XS	X				X					X				X										●				X
	360	XP		X			X					X			X										●					X

● With 60 PSI Oil Pump Spring

All Cars Use CCS

1969 TEMPEST ENGINE IDENTIFICATION

	HORSEPOWER	ENGINE CODE	DISPLACE-MENT			TRANS.		CARB.			COMP. RATIO					CAMSHAFT								DISTRIBUTOR								VALVE SPRINGS					CYL. HEAD	
			250	350	400	MANUAL	AUTOMATIC	1 BBL (MV)	2 BBL (2GV)	4 BBL (4MV)	8.6:1	9.0:1	9.2:1	10.5:1	10.75:1	9790826	9792539	9796327	9777254	9785744	9779067	9779068	9794041	1110474	1110475	1111940	1111946 (b)	1111942	1111952 (b)	1111941 (b)	1111960	SINGLE	STD.-DUAL	H. D.-DUAL	H. D. SPEC.-DUAL	RAM AIR IV-DUAL	SMALL VALVE	LARGE VALVE
	175	(a)ZK ZC	X			X		X				X				X									X							X					X	
	175	(a)ZN ZF	X				X	X				X				X									X							X					X	
	230	(a)ZD ZH	X			X				X				X				X						X									X				X	
	215	(a)ZE ZL	X				X			X				X			X							X									X				X	
	265	(a)XR XS		X			X		X				X						X									X						X			X	
(c)	265	(a)YN YU		X			X		X				X						X									X						X			X	
	265	(a)WP WU		X		X			X				X						X												X			X			X	
	330	XU		X			X			X				X							X						(d)								X		X	
	330	WV		X		X				X				X								X							(e)						X		X	
	350	YS			X		X			X					X						X						X							X				X
	350	WT			X	X				X												X							X					X				X
	366	YZ			X		X			X					X							X					X								X			X
	366	WS			X	X				X					X					X									X						X			X
	265	(a)XM XX			X		X		X		X								X							X								X			X	
	370	XP			X		X			X					X								X							X						X		X
	370	WW			X	X				X					X								X							X						X		X

(a) Early production (small valve) engines with 30° intake valve seat angle. Later production (small valve) engines use 45° intake valve seat. NOTE: all large valve engines use 30° intake valve seat.

(b) Uses hardened drive gear for use with 60 psi oil pump and high tension distributor points.

(c) Two speed (M31) if equipped with A/C; Turbo-Hydramatic (M38) optional without A/C.

(d) Uses distributor 1111965

(e) Uses distributor 1111966

1970 TEMPEST ENGINE IDENTIFICATION

HORSEPOWER	ENGINE CODE	DISPLACEMENT				TRANS.		CARB.			COMP. RATIO					CAMSHAFT					DISTRIBUTOR									VALVE SPRINGS				CYL. HEAD	
		250	350	400	455	MANUAL	AUTOMATIC	1 BBL. (MV)	2 BBL. (GV)	4 BBL. (4MV)	8.5:1	8.8:1	10.0:1	10.25:1	10.5:1	9777254 (U)	9779066 (N)	9779067 (P)	9779068 (S)	9794041 (T)	1110463	1110464	1112008	1112007	1111148 ④	1111176 ④	1112009 ④	1112012 ④	1112011*	SINGLE	STD.—DUAL	H.D. SPEC.-DUAL	RAM-AIR IV-DUAL	SMALL VALVE	LARGE VALVE
155	ZB①	X				X		X			X										X									X				X	
155	ZG①	X					X	X			X											X								X				X	
255	WU		X			X			X			X				X							X								X			X	
255	YU		X				X		X			X				X							X								X			X	
366	WS②			X		X				X					X				X								†					X			X
350	WT			X		X				X				X				X								X						X			X
370	WW③			X		X				X					X					X									X				X		X
370	XP③			X			X			X					X					X									X				X		X
265	XX			X			X		X			X				X								X							X			X	
330	XV			X			X			X			X				X							X							X			X	
350	YS			X			X			X			X					X							X						X				X
366	YZ②			X			X			X					X				X								X					X			X
370	WA				X	X				X				X					X									X			X				X
370	YC				X		X			X				X				X										X			X				X

①L-6 camshaft usage is 3864897 for both manual and automatic transmissions.
† WS Engine uses 1112024 Distributor.
②Ram Air III
③Ram Air IV
④Uses hardened drive gear for use with 60 psi oil pump and high tension distributor points.
*Uses cadmium gear for use with R.A. IV only.

1971 TEMPEST ENGINE IDENTIFICATION

ENGINE CODE	Engine No. (Last Two Digits)	HORSEPOWER	Model Usage	Displacement				Transmission			Carburetor			Cylinder Heads: Compression Ratio				Cylinder Heads: Rocker Arm Stud		Cylinder Heads: Valve Spring			Cylinder Heads: Valve Size		Camshaft					Valve Lifter			Distributor								
			"A" SERIES	250 L-6	350 V-8	400 V-8	455 V-8	MANUAL (3-Speed)	MANUAL (4-speed)	AUTOMATIC	MV (1Bbl.)	2GV (2 Bbl.)	4MV (4 Bbl.)	8.5:1	8.0:1	8.2:1	8.4:1	PRESSED-IN	THREADED	SINGLE	DUAL (STD.)	DUAL (H.D.)	SMALL	LARGE	3864897	483555 (W)	9779066 (N)	9779067 (P)	9779068 (S)	HIGH-BALL (STD.)	HIGH-BALL*	LOW-BALL	1110489	1112069	1112068	1112070	1112072	1112073	1112083	1112089	1112090
ZB	63	145	X	X				X			X			X				X		X			X		X					X			X								
ZG	64	145	X	X						X	X			X				X		X			X		X					X			X								
WR	94	250	X		X			X				X			X			X			X		X			X				X									X		
WN	90	250	X		X			X				X			X			X			X		X			X				X											X
WU	92	250	X		X				X			X			X			X			X		X			X				X									X		
YP	98	250	X		X				X			X			X			X			X		X			X				X											X
YU	96	250	X		X					**		X			X			X			X		X			X				X				X							
WP	97	250	X		X					**		X			X			X			X		X			X				X											X
XR	95	250	X		X					**		X			X			X			X		X				X			X				X							
YN	99	250	X		X					**		X			X			X			X		X				X			X											X
WT	78	300	X			X		X					X			X			X			X		X				X			X					X					
WK	74	300	X			X			X				X			X			X			X		X				X			X					X					
XX%	73	265	X			X				X		X				X		X			X		X			X				X					X						
YX	71	265	X			X				X		X				X		X			X		X			X				X										X	
YS	79	300	X			X				X			X			X			X		X			X				X		X						X					
WL†	18	335	X				X	X					X				X		X		X			X					X			X						X			
WC†	15	335	X				X		X				X				X		X		X			X					X			X						X			
YC+	19	325	X				X			X			X			X		X			X			X				X		X							X				
YE†	16	335	X				X			X			X				X		X		X			X					X			X						X			

*Lifter Body with Cast-Iron Foot
**"YU" is used with M35 transmission; "XR" is used with M38 transmission.
†455 H.O. Engine
%Man. Trans. Models use WS engine code
+ Man. Trans. Models use WJ engine code
& Man. Trans. Models use WG engine code

1971 VENTURA ENGINE IDENTIFICATION

		DISPLACEMENT		TRANSMISSION		CARBURETOR		CYLINDER HEADS				CAMSHAFT		VALVE LIFTER	DISTRIBUTOR		
								COMP. RATIO	ROCKER ARM STUD	VALVE SPRING							
ENGINE CODE	HORSEPOWER	250 L-6	307 V-8	MANUAL	AUTOMATIC	MV	2GV	8.5:1	PRESSED—IN	SINGLE	DUAL	3864897	3896929	HIGH BALL	1110489	1112005	1112039
CAA	145	X		X		X		X	X	X		X		X	X		
CAB	145	X			X	X		X	X	X		X		X	X		
CCA	200		X	X			X	X	X		X		X	X		X	
CCC	200		X		X		X	X	X		X		X	X			X

1972-'74 Engine Identification Codes

The second letter in the vehicle identification number is the engine code.

TYPE	DISPLACEMENT	ALL SERIES CARBURETOR	EXHAUST	CODE
L6	250	1BBL.	Single	D
V8	307②	2BBL.	Single	F
V8	350	2BBL.	Single	M
V8	350	2BBL.	Dual	N
V8	400	2BBL.	Single	R
V8	400	2BBL.	Dual	P
V8	400	4BBL.	Single	S

TYPE	DISPLACEMENT	ALL SERIES CARBURETOR	EXHAUST	CODE
V8	400	4BBL.	Dual	T
V8	455	2BBL.	Single	V
V8	455	2BBL.	Dual	U
V8	455	4BBL.	Single	W
V8	455	4BBL.	Dual	Y
V8	455H.O.①	4BBL.	Dual	X

① —SD in 1973.
② —1972 only.

WHEEL ALIGNMENT SPECIFICATIONS

Year	Model	CASTER Range (deg)	CASTER Pref Setting (deg)	CAMBER Range (deg)	CAMBER Pref Setting (deg)	Toe-in (in.)	Steering Axis Inclin.	WHEEL PIVOT RATIO (deg) Inner Wheel	WHEEL PIVOT RATIO (deg) Wheel Outer
'67-'69	Exc. Firebird	2N to 1N	1½N	¼N to ¾P	¼P	0 to ⅛	9	20	18.25
'67-'69	Firebird	0 to 1P	½P	¼N to ¾P	¼P	⅛ to ¼	8.25 to 9.25	20	——
'70-'71	Tempest, LeMans	1N to 2N	1½N	¼N to ¾P	¼P	0 to ⅛	9	20	22
	Station Wagon	1½N to 2½N	2N	¼N to ¾P	¼P	0 to ⅛	9	20	22
	Firebird	½N to 1½N	1N	¼P to 1¼P	¾P	⅛ to ¼	8.25 to 9.25	20	22
'71-'72	Tempest, LeMans	2N to 1N	1½N	½N to ½P	0	1/16 to 3/16	9	20	22
	Firebird	½N to ½P	0	½P to 1½P	1P	⅛ to ¼	8.25 to 9.25	20	22
	Ventura II	0 to 1P	½P	¼ to ¾P	¼P	⅛ to ¼	N.A.	20	22
'73-'74	LeMans, Grand Am	③	④	①	②	0 to ⅛	N.A.	20	22
	Firebird	½N to ½P	0	½P to 1½P	1P	⅛ to ¼	10.35	20	22
	Ventura II	0 to 1P	½P	¼N to ¾P	¼P	⅛ to ¼	8.5 to 9.5	20	22

N Negative P Positive

① LH: ½P to 1½P; RH: 0 to 1P
② LH: 1P; RH: ½P
③ Manual steering—1½N to ½N
Power steering—½N to ½P
④ Manual steering—1N
Power steering—0

Tempest, GTO, LeMans, Grand Am

TUNE-UP SPECIFICATIONS

When analyzing compression test results, look for uniformity among cylinders rather than specific pressures.

	ENGINE		SPARK PLUGS		DISTRIBUTOR		IGNITION TIMING (deg) ▲		VALVES	Fuel	IDLE SPEED (rpm) ▲	
Year	No. Cyl Displacement (cu in.)	hp	Type §	Gap (in.)	Point Dwell (deg)	Point Gap (in.)	Man Trans	Auto Trans	Intake Opens ■ (deg) ●	Pump Pressure (psi)	Man Trans	Auto Trans
'67	6-230 OHC	140	44N	.035	32½	.019	58(TDC)①	5B(TDC)①	7	4-5½	600(700)	500(600)
	6-230 OHC	215	44N	.035	32½	.019	6B	6B	14	4-5½	600(700)	500(600)
	8-326	250	45S	.035	30	.019	6B	6B	22	5-6½	600②(700)	500②(600)
	8-326	285	45S	.035	30	.019	6B	6B	22	5-6½	600②(700)	500②(600)
	8-400	255	45S	.035	30	.019	6B	6B	22	5-6½	600②(700)	500②(600)
	8-400	335	45S	.035	30	.019	6B	6B	23/30	5-6½	600②(700)	500②(600)
	8-400	360	44S	.035	30	,019	6B	6B	31	5-6½	700	600
	8-400 Ram Air	360	44S	.035	30	,019	6B	6B	38	5-6½	700	600
'68	6-250 OHC	175	44N	.035	32½	.019	TDC	TDC	14	4-5½	700①/500	600①/500
	6-250 OHC	215	44N	.035	30	.019	5B	5B	14	4-5½	800①/600	600①/500
	8-350	265	45S	.035	30	.019	9B	9B	22	5-6½	700①/500	600①/500
	8-350	320	45S	.035	30	.019	9B	9B	23/30	5-6½	850①/650	650①/500
	8-400	265	44S	.035	30	.019	9B	9B	22	5-6½	800/500①	600①/500
	8-400	350	44S	.035	30	.019	9B	9B	31/23	5-6½	850①/650	650①/500
	8-400	360	44S	.035	30	.019	9B	9B	31/23	5-6½	1000①/650	650①/500
	8-400 Ram Air	360	44S	.035	30	.019	9B	9B	38/31	5-6½	1000①/650	650①/500
'69	6-250 OHC	175	R-44NS	.035	32½	.019	TDC	TDC	14	4-5½	700①/500	600①/500
	6-250 OHC	215	R-44NS	.035	32½	.019	5B	5B	22/14	4-5½	850①/600	600①/500
	6-250 OHC	230	R-44NS	.035	32½	.019	5B	5B	22/14	4-5½	850①/600	600①/500
	8-350	265	R-46S	.035	30	.019	9B	9B	22	5-6½	850	650
	8-350	330	R-45S	.035	30	.019	9B	9B	38/23	5-6½	1000	650
	8-400	265	R-46S	.035	30	.019	9B	9B	22	5-6½	850	650
	8-400	330	R-45S	.035	30	.019	9B	9B	23	5-6½	1000	650
	8-400	350	R-45S	.035	30	.019	9B	9B	23	5-6½	1000	650
	8-400 Ram Air	366	R-45S	.035	30	.019	9B	9B	23	5-6½	1000①/650	650/500①
	8-400 Ram Air	370	R-44S	.035	30	.019	15B	15B	42	5-6½	1000①/650	650/500①
'70	6-250	155	R-46T	.035	32½	.019	TDC	4B	16	4-5	830/750①	630/600①
	8-350	255	R-46S	.035	30	.019	9B	9B	22	5-6½	800	650
	8-400	265	R-46S	.035	30	.019	9B	9B	22	5-6½	800	650
	8-400	330	R-45S	.035	30	.019	9B	9B	30	5-6½	950	650
	8-400	350	R-46S	.035	30	.019	9B	9B	23	5-6½	950	650
	8-400 Ram Air	366	R-46S	.035	30	.019	9B	9B	31	5-6½	950	650
	8-400 Ram Air	370	R-46S	.035	30	.019	15B	15B	40	5-6½	1000①/650	750①/500
	8-455	360	R-46S	.035	30	.019	9B	9B	31/23	5-6½	950	650
'71	6-250	145	R-46TS	.035	32½	.019	4B	4B	16	4-5	850/550①	650/500①
	8-350	250	R-47S	.035	30	.019	12B	12B	26/30	5-6½③	800	600
	8-400	265	R-47S	.035	30	.019	—	8B	26	5-6½③	—	600
	8-400	300	R-46S	.035	30	.019	12B	12B	23	5-6½③	1000/600①	700
	8-455	325	R-46S	.035	30	.019	—	12B	23	5-6½③	—	650
	8-455	335	R-46S	.035	30	.019	12B	12B	31	5-6½③	1000/600①	700
'72	6-250	110	R-45T	.035	32½	.019	4B	4B	16	4-5	700/450①	600/450①
	8-350	160	R-46TS	.035	30	.019	8B	10B	26/30④	5-6½	800	625
	8-400	175	R-46TS	.035	30	.019	—	10B	23/26④	5-6½	—	625
	8-400	200	R-46TS	.035	30	.019	8B	10B	23	5-6½	1000/600①	700/500①
	8-455	250	R-45TS	.035	30	.019	—	10B	23	5-6½	—	650/500①
	8-455	300	R-45TS	.035	—	—	8B	10B	31	5-6½	1000/600①	700/500①

Tempest, GTO, LeMans, Grand Am

TUNE-UP SPECIFICATIONS

When analyzing compression test results, look for uniformity among cylinders rather than specific pressures.

Year	ENGINE No. Cyl Displacement (cu in.)	hp	SPARK PLUGS Type §	Gap (in.)	DISTRIBUTOR Point Dwell (deg)	Point Gap (in.)	IGNITION TIMING (deg) ▲ Man Trans	Auto Trans	VALVES Intake Opens ■ (deg) ●	Fuel Pump Pressure (psi)	IDLE SPEED (rpm) ▲ Man Trans	Auto Trans
'73	6-250	100	R-46TS	.040	32½	.019	6B	6B	16	4-5	700/450①	600
	8-350 SE	150	R-46TS	.040	30	.019	10B	12B	26/30④	5-6½	900/600①	650
	8-350 DE	175	R-46TS	.040	30	.019	10B	12B	26/30④	5-6½	900/600①	650
	8-400 SE	170	R-46TS	.040	30	.019	10B	12B	26	5-6½	—	650
	8-400 DE	185	R-46TS	.040	30	.019	10B	12B	23/30④	5-6½	—	650
	8-400 DE	230	R-45TS	.040	30	.019	10B	12B	23/30④	5-6½	1000/600①	650
	8-455 DE	250	R-45TS	.040	30	.019	10B	12B	23	5-6½	—	650
	8-455 S.D. DE	310	R-44TS	.040	30	.019	10B	12B	42	5-6½	1000/600①	750/500①
'74	6-250	all	R-46TS	.040	32½	.019	6B	6B	16	4-5	700/450①	600
	8-350	all	R-46TS	.040	30	.019	10B	12B⑤	26/30④	5-6½	900/600①	650
	8-400 2 bbl	all	R-46TS	.040	30	.019	10B	12B⑤	26	5-6½	900/600①	650
	8-400 4 bbl	all	R-45TS	.040	30	.019	10B	12B⑤	23/30④	5-6½	1000/600①	650
	8-455	all	R-45TS	.040	30	.019	10B	12B⑤	23	5-6½	1000/600①	650
	8-455 S.D.	all	R-45TS	.040	30	.019	10B	12B⑤	42	5-6½	1000/600①	750/500①

SE Single Exhaust
DE Dual Exhaust
▲ See text for procedure
● Figure in parentheses indicates California engine
■ All figures are in degrees Before Top Dead Center. Where two figures appear, the first represents timing with manual transmission, the second with automatic transmission.
§ All spark plug listings are A.C. original equipment numbers

① Lower figure indicates idle speed with solenoid disconnected
② Adjust idle on air conditioned 100 rpm higher with A/C off, except on California vehicles
③ 6½-8 with A/C
④ Lower figure represents manual transmission models; higher figure indicates automatic transmission.
⑤ 10 B on California engines
B Before Top Dead Center
TDC Top Dead Center
— Not applicable

BRAKE SPECIFICATIONS

Year	Model	MASTER CYLINDER Disc	Drum	WHEEL CYLINDER Front Disc	Front Drum	Rear	BRAKE DISC OR DRUM DIAMETER Front Disc	Front Drum	Rear
'67-'68	Tempest, Le Mans, GTO	1.125	1.0	2.062	1.125	.875	11.0	9.5	9.5
	Firebird	1.125	1.0	2.062	1.125	.875	11.0	9.5	9.5
'69-'72	Tempest, Le Mans, GTO	1.125	1.0	2.938	1.125	.875	11.0	9.5	9.5
'73-'74	LeMans, Grand Am	1.0	—	2.938	—	.875②	11.0	—	9.5③
'69	Firebird	1.125	1.0	2.938	1.125	.875	11.0	9.5	9.5
'70-'74	Firebird	1.0①	—	2.938	—	.875	11.0	—	9.5
'71-'74	Ventura II	1.125	1.0	2.938	1.125	.875	11.0	9.5	9.5

① 1.125—with power brakes
② .9375 in. on station wagon
③ 11.0 in. on station wagon
— Not applicable

Firebird

TUNE-UP SPECIFICATIONS

When analyzing compression test results, look for uniformity among cylinders rather than specific pressures.

	ENGINE		SPARK PLUGS		DISTRIBUTOR		IGNITION TIMING (deg) ▲		VALVES	Fuel	IDLE SPEED (rpm) ▲	
Year	No. Cyl Displacement (cu in.)	hp	Type §	Gap (in.)	Point Dwell (deg)	Point Gap (in.)	Man Trans	Auto Trans	Intake Opens ■ (deg) ●	Pump Pressure (psi)	Man Trans	Auto Trans
'67	6-230 OHC	165	44N	.035	32½	.019	5B(TDC)	5B(TDC)	7	4-5½	600(700)	500(600)
	6-230 OHC	215	44N	.035	32½	.019	6B	6B	14	4-5½	600(700)	500(600)
	8-326	250	45S	.035	30	.019	6B	6B	22	5-6½	600②(700)	500②(600)
	8-326	285	45S	.035	30	.019	6B	6B	22	5-6½	600②(700)	500②(600)
	8-400	325	45S	.035	30	.019	6B	6B	22/30	5-6½	600②(700)	500②(600)
	8-400 Ram Air	325	45S	.035	30	.019	6B	6B	22/30	5-6½	600②(700)	500②(600)
'68	6-250 OHC	175	44N	.035	32½	.019	TDC	TDC	14	4-5½	700①/500	600①/500
	6-250 OHC	215	44N	.035	30	.019	5B	5B	14	4-5½	800①/600	600①/500
	8-350	265	45S	.035	30	.019	9B	9B	22	5-6½	700①/500	600①/500
	8-350	320	45S	.035	30	.019	9B	9B	23/30	5-6½	850①/650	650①/500
	8-400	330	44S	.035	30	.019	9B	9B	31/23	5-6½	850①/650	650①/500
	8-400	335	44S	.035	30	.019	9B	9B	31/23	5-6½	850①/650	650①/500
	8-400 Ram Air	335	44S	.035	30	.019	9B	9B	38/31	5-6½	1000①/650	650①/500
'69	6-250 OHC	175	R-44NS	.035	32½	.019	TDC	TDC	14	4-5½	700①/500	600①/500
	6-250 OHC	215	R-44NS	.035	32½	.019	5B	5B	22/14	4-5½	850①/600	600/500①
	6-250 OHC	230	R-44NS	.035	32½	.019	5B	5B	22/14	4-5½	850/600①	600/500①
	8-350	265	R-46S	.035	30	.019	9B	9B	22	5-6½	850	650
	8-350	325	R-45S	.035	30	.019	9B	9B	38/23	5-6½	1000	650
	8-400	330	R-45S	.035	30	.019	9B	9B	23	5-6½	1000	650
	8-400	335	R-45S	.035	30	.019	9B	9B	23	5-6½	1000	650
	8-400 Ram Air	345	R-44S	.035	30	.019	9B	9B	31/38	5-6½	1000/650①	650/500①
'70	6-250	155	R-46T	.035	32½	.019	TDC	4B	16	4-5½	850/500①	650/500①
	8-350	255	R-46S	.035	30	.019	9B	9B	22	5-6½	800	650
	8-400	265	R-46S③	.035	30	.019	9B	9B	22	5-6½	800	650
	8-400	330	R-45S	.035	30	.019	9B	9B	30	5-6½	950	650
	8-400 Ram Air	345	R-44S	.035	30	.019	9B	9B	30	5-6½	950	650
	8-400 Ram Air	370	R-44S	.035	30	.019	15B	15B	30	5-6½	1000/650①	750/500①
'71	6-250	145	R-46TS	.035	32½	.019	4B	4B	16	4-5	850/550①	650/500①
	8-350	250	R-47S	.035	30	.019	12B	12B	26/30⑤	④5-6½	800	600
	8-400	265	R-47S	.035	30	.019	—	8B	26	④5-6½	—	600
	8-400	300	R-46S	.035	30	.019	12B	12B	23	④5-6½	1000/600①	700
	8-455	325	R-46S	.035	30	.019	—	12B	23	④5-6½	—	650
	8-455	335	R-46S	.035	30	.019	12B	12B	31	④5-6½	1000/600①	700
'72	6-250	110	R-45T	.035	32½	.019	4B	4B	16	4-5	700①/450	600①/450
	8-350	160	R-46TS	.035	30	.019	8B	10B	26/30⑤	5-6½	800	625
	8-400	175	R-46TS	.035	30	.019	—	10B	23/26⑤	5-6½	—	625
	8-400	250	R-45TS	.035	30	.019	8B	10B	23	5-6½	1000/600①	700/500①
	8-455	300	R-45TS	.035	30	—	8B	10B	31	5-6½	1000/600①	700/500①
'73	6-250	100	R-46TS	.040	32½	.019	6B	6B	16	4-5	700/450①	600
	8-350 SE	150	R-46TS	.040	30	.019	10B	12B	26/30⑤	5-6½	900/600①	650
	8-350 DE	175	R-46TS	.040	30	.019	10B	12B	26/30⑤	5-6½	900/600①	650
	8-400 SE	170	R-46TS	.040	30	.019	10B	12B	26	5-6½	—	650
	8-400 DE	230	R-45TS	.040	30	.019	10B	12B	23/30⑤	5-6½	1000/600①	650
	8-455 DE	250	R-45TS	.040	30	.019	10B	12B	23	5-6½	1000/600①	650
	8-455 S.D. DE	310	R-44TS	.040	30	.019	10B	12B	42	5-6½	1000/600①	750/500①

CAPACITIES

Year	ENGINE No. Cyl. (Cu. In.) Displacement	Engine Crankcase Add 1 Qt For New Filter	TRANSMISSION Pts To Refill After Draining Manual 3-Speed	4-Speed	Automatic ●	Drive Axle (pts)	Gasoline Tank (gals)	COOLING SYSTEM (qts) With Heater	With A/C
'67	6-230 OHC	5	2.8	2.5	15	3	18.5	12.1	12.7
	8-326	5	2.8	2.5	15	3	18.5	18.6	20.2
	8-400	5	2.8	2.5	19	3	18.5	12.8	19.4
'68	6-250 OHC	5	3.5	3.5	15	3	18.5	12.1	12.7
	8-350	5	3.5	2.8	15	3	18.5	18.6	20.2
	8-400	5	3.5	2.8	19	3	18.5	17.8	19.4
'69	6-250 OHC	5	3.5	3.5	15④	3	21.5	11.9	12.3
	8-350	5	3.5①	2.5	15④	3	21.5	19.9	20.3
	8-400	5	2.8	2.5	19	3②	21.5	18.3	18.7
'70	6-250	4	3.5	—	6	3②	19.5③	13	—
	8-350	5	3.5①	2.5	6	3②	19.5③	19.9	19.9
	8-400	5	2.5	2.5	7.5	3②	19.5③	18.3	18.3
	8-455	5	2.5	2.5	7.5	3②	19.5③	17.5	17.5
'71	6-250	4	3.5	—	6	4.25	17	12	12.4
	8-350	5	3.5①	2.5	6	4.25	17	20	20.5
	8-400	5	2.8	2.5	7.5	4.25	17	18.6	18.7
	8-455	5	2.8	2.5	7.5	4.25	17	17.9	16.8
'72	6-250	4	3.5	—	6	4.25	17	12	12.4
	8-350	5	3.5	2.5	6	4.25	17	20	20.5
	8-400	5	2.8	2.5	7.5	4.25	17	18.6	18.7
	8-455	5	—	2.5	7.5	4.25	17	17.9	19
'73	6-250	4	3.5	—	7.5	4.25	18	12.5	—
	8-350	5	3.5	2.5	7.5	4.25	18	22.4	22.7
	8-400	5	—	2.5	7.5	4.25	18	22.4	22.7/23.5④
	8-455	5	—	2.5	7.5	4.25	18	20.9	21.8
'74	6-250	4	3.5	—	7.5	4.25	21.5	13.5	—
	8-350	5	3.5	2.5	7.5	4.25	21.5	22.1	22.7
	8-400	5	—	2.5	7.5	4.25	21.5	21.9	22.7/23.5④
	8-455	5	—	2.5	7.5	4.25	21.5	21.9	22

● '70 and later specifications do not include torque converter
① 2.8 pts with heavy duty 3-speed transmission
② 4 pts with heavy duty axle
③ California cars—18.5 gals
④ Lower figure indicates 2 bbl model; higer figure indicates 4 bbl engine
OHC Overhead camshaft
— Not applicable

RING SIDE CLEARANCE

Year	Engine	Top Compression	Bottom Compression
'67-'69	6-230, 250	.0015-.0050	.0015-.0050
'70-'74	6-250, 8-307 ('71-'72)	.0012-.0027	.0012-.0032
'67-'74	8-350, 400, 455	.0015-.0050	.0015-.0050

Year	Engine	Oil Control
'67-'69	6-230, 250	.0015-.0050
'70-'74	6-250	.0001-.0050
'71-'72	8-307	.002-.007
'67-'74	8-350, 400, 455	.0015-.0050

Firebird

TUNE-UP SPECIFICATIONS

When analyzing compression test results, look for uniformity among cylinders rather than specific pressures.

	ENGINE		SPARK PLUGS		DISTRIBUTOR		IGNITION TIMING (deg) ▲		VALVES	Fuel	IDLE SPEED (rpm) ▲	
Year	No. Cyl Displacement (cu in.)	hp	Type §	Gap (in.)	Point Dwell (deg)	Point Gap (in.)	Man Trans	Auto Trans	Intake Opens ■ (deg) ●	Pump Pressure (psi)	Man Trans	Auto Trans
'67	6-230 OHC	165	44N	.035	32½	.019	5B(TDC)	5B(TDC)	7	4-5½	600(700)	500(600)
	6-230 OHC	215	44N	.035	32½	.019	6B	6B	14	4-5½	600(700)	500(600)
	8-326	250	45S	.035	30	.019	6B	6B	22	5-6½	600②(700)	500②(600)
	8-326	285	45S	.035	30	.019	6B	6B	22	5-6½	600②(700)	500②(600)
	8-400	325	45S	.035	30	.019	6B	6B	22/30	5-6½	600②(700)	500②(600)
	8-400 Ram Air	325	45S	.035	30	.019	6B	6B	22/30	5-6½	600②(700)	500②(600)
'68	6-250 OHC	175	44N	.035	32½	.019	TDC	TDC	14	4-5½	700①/500	600①/500
	6-250 OHC	215	44N	.035	30	.019	5B	5B	14	4-5½	800①/600	600①/500
	8-350	265	45S	.035	30	.019	9B	9B	22	5-6½	700①/500	600①/500
	8-350	320	45S	.035	30	.019	9B	9B	23/30	5-6½	850①/650	650①/500
	8-400	330	44S	.035	30	.019	9B	9B	31/23	5-6½	850①/650	650①/500
	8-400	335	44S	.035	30	.019	9B	9B	31/23	5-6½	850①/650	650①/500
	8-400 Ram Air	335	44S	.035	30	.019	9B	9B	38/31	5-6½	1000①/650	650①/500
'69	6-250 OHC	175	R-44NS	.035	32½	.019	TDC	TDC	14	4-5½	700①/500	600①/500
	6-250 OHC	215	R-44NS	.035	32½	.019	5B	5B	22/14	4-5½	850①/600	600/500①
	6-250 OHC	230	R-44NS	.035	32½	.019	5B	5B	22/14	4-5½	850/600①	600/500①
	8-350	265	R-46S	.035	30	.019	9B	9B	22	5-6½	850	650
	8-350	325	R-45S	.035	30	.019	9B	9B	38/23	5-6½	1000	650
	8-400	330	R-45S	.035	30	.019	9B	9B	23	5-6½	1000	650
	8-400	335	R-45S	.035	30	.019	9B	9B	23	5-6½	1000	650
	8-400 Ram Air	345	R-44S	.035	30	.019	9B	9B	31/38	5-6½	1000/650①	650/500①
'70	6-250	155	R-46T	.035	32½	.019	TDC	4B	16	4-5½	850/500①	650/500①
	8-350	255	R-46S	.035	30	.019	9B	9B	22	5-6½	800	650
	8-400	265	R-46S③	.035	30	.019	9B	9B	22	5-6½	800	650
	8-400	330	R-45S	.035	30	.019	9B	9B	30	5-6½	950	650
	8-400 Ram Air	345	R-44S	.035	30	.019	9B	9B	30	5-6½	950	650
	8-400 Ram Air	370	R-44S	.035	30	.019	15B	15B	30	5-6½	1000/650①	750/500①
'71	6-250	145	R-46TS	.035	32½	.019	4B	4B	16	4-5	850/550①	650/500①
	8-350	250	R-47S	.035	30	.019	12B	12B	26/30⑤	④5-6½	800	600
	8-400	265	R-47S	.035	30	.019	—	8B	26	④5-6½	—	600
	8-400	300	R-46S	.035	30	.019	12B	12B	23	④5-6½	1000/600①	700
	8-455	325	R-46S	.035	30	.019	—	12B	23	④5-6½	—	650
	8-455	335	R-46S	.035	30	.019	12B	12B	31	④5-6½	1000/600①	700
'72	6-250	110	R-45T	.035	32½	.019	4B	4B	16	4-5	700①/450	600①/450
	8-350	160	R-46TS	.035	30	.019	8B	10B	26/30⑤	5-6½	800	625
	8-400	175	R-46TS	.035	30	.019	—	10B	23/26⑤	5-6½	—	625
	8-400	250	R-45TS	.035	30	.019	8B	10B	23	5-6½	1000/600①	700/500①
	8-455	300	R-45TS	.035	30	—	8B	10B	31	5-6½	1000/600①	700/500①
'73	6-250	100	R-46TS	.040	32½	.019	6B	6B	16	4-5	700/450①	600
	8-350 SE	150	R-46TS	.040	30	.019	10B	12B	26/30⑤	5-6½	900/600①	650
	8-350 DE	175	R-46TS	.040	30	.019	10B	12B	26/30⑤	5-6½	900/600①	650
	8-400 SE	170	R-46TS	.040	30	.019	10B	12B	26	5-6½	—	650
	8-400 DE	230	R-45TS	.040	30	.019	10B	12B	23/30⑤	5-6½	1000/600①	650
	8-455 DE	250	R-45TS	.040	30	.019	10B	12B	23	5-6½	1000/600①	650
	8-455 S.D. DE	310	R-44TS	.040	30	.019	10B	12B	42	5-6½	1000/600①	750/500①

Firebird

TUNE-UP SPECIFICATIONS

When analyzing compression test results, look for uniformity among cylinders rather than specific pressures.

	ENGINE		SPARK PLUGS		DISTRIBUTOR		IGNITION TIMING (deg) ▲		VALVES	Fuel	IDLE SPEED (rpm) ▲	
Year	No. Cyl Displacement (cu in.)	hp	Type §	Gap (in.)	Point Dwell (deg)	Point Gap (in.)	Man Trans	Auto Trans	Intake Opens ■ (deg) ●	Pump Pressure (psi)	Man Trans	Auto Trans
'74	6-250	all	R-46TS	.040	32½	.019	6B	6B	16	4-5	700/450①	600
	8-350 SE	all	R-46TS	.040	30	.019	10B	12B⑥	26/30⑤	5-6½	900/600①	650
	8-400 2 bbl	all	R-46TS	.040	30	.019	10B	12B⑥	26	5-6½	900/600①	650
	8-400 4 bbl	all	R-45TS	.040	30	.019	10B	12B⑥	23/30⑤	5-6½	1000/600①	650
	8-455	all	R-45TS	.040	30	.019	10B	12B⑥	23	5-6½	1000/600①	650
	8-455 S.D.	290	R-45TS	.040	30	.019	10B	12B⑥	42	5-6½	1000/600①	750/500①

SE Single Exhaust
DE Dual Exhaust
▲ See text for procedure
● Figure in parentheses indicates California engine
■ All figures are in degrees Before Top Dead Center. Where two figures appear, the first represents timing with manual transmission, the second with automatic transmission.
§ All spark plug listings are A.C. original equipment numbers
B Before Top Dead Center
TDC Top Dead Center
— Not applicable

① Lower figure indicates idle speed with solenoid disconnected
② Adjust idle on air conditioned 100 rpm higher with A/C off, except on California vehicles
③ AC-R-45S with automatic transmission.
④ 6½-8 with A/C
⑤ Lower figure represents manual transmission models; higher figure indicates automatic transmission.
⑥ 10B on California engines

Ventura II

TUNE-UP SPECIFICATIONS

When analyzing compression test results, look for uniformity among cylinders rather than specific pressures.

	ENGINE		SPARK PLUGS		DISTRIBUTOR		IGNITION TIMING (deg) ▲		VALVES	Fuel	IDLE SPEED (rpm) ▲	
Year	No. Cyl Displacement (cu in.)	hp	Type §	Gap (in.)	Point Dwell (deg)	Point Gap (in.)	Man Trans	Auto Trans	Intake Opens ■ (deg) ●	Pump Pressure (psi)	Man Trans	Auto Trans
'71	6-250	145	R-46TS	.035	31-34	.019	4B	4B	16	4-5	500	500
	8-307	200	R-45TS	.035	29-31	.019	4B	8B	28	5½-7½	600	550
'72	6-250	110	R-46TS	.035	31-34	.019	4B	4B	16	4-5	700①/450	600①/450
	8-307	130	R-45TS	.035	29-31	.019	4B	8B	28	5½-7½	900①/450	600①/450
	8-350	160	R-46TS	.035	29-31	.019	10B	10B	16	5-6½	800	625
'73	6-250	110	R-46TS	.035	31-34	.019	6B	6B	16	4-5	700/450①	600
	8-350 SE	150	R-46TS	.040	29-31	.019	10B	12B	16	5-6½	900/600①	650
	8-350 DE	175	R-46TS	.040	29-31	.019	10B	12B	16	5-6½	900/600①	650
'74	6-250	all	R-46TS	.040	32½	.019	6B	6B	16	4-5	700/450①	600
	8-30	all	R-46TS	.040	30	.019	10B	12B②	26/30③	5-6½	900/600①	650

SE Single Exhaust
DE Dual Exhaust
▲ See text for procedure
■ All figures Before Top Dead Center
§ All spark plug listings are A.C. original equipment numbers

① Lower figure indicates idle speed with solenoid disconnected
② 10 B on California engines
③ Lower figure represents manual transmission models; Higher figure indicates automatic transmission.
B Before Top Dead Center

Tempest, GTO, LeMans, Grand Am

CAPACITIES

Year	ENGINE No. Cyl. (Cu. In.) Displacement	Engine Crankcase Add 1 Qt For New Filter	TRANSMISSION Pts To Refill After Draining: Manual 3-Speed	Manual 4-Speed	Automatic ●	Drive Axle (pts)	Gasoline Tank (gals)	COOLING SYSTEM (qts) With Heater	With A/C
'67	6-230 OHC	5	2.8	2.5	15	3	21.5	12.1	12.7
	8-326	5	2.8	2.5	15	3	21.5	18.6	20.2
	8-400	6	2.8	2.5	19	3	21.5	17.8	19.4
'68	6-250 OHC	5	3.5	3.5	15	3	21.5	12.1	12.7
	8-350	5	3.5	2.8	15	3	21.5	18.6	20.2
	8-400	5	3.5	2.8①	19	3	21.5	17.8	19.4
'69	6-250 OHC	5	3.5	3.5	13⑤	3	21.5②	11.9	12.3
	8-350	5	3.5③	2.5	15⑤	3	21.5②	19.9	21.3
	8-400	5	2.8	2.5	19	3④	21.5②	18.3	19.7
'70	6-250	4	3.5	—	6	3④	20②	13	—
	8-350	5	3.5③	2.5	6	3④	20②	19.9	19.9
	8-400	5	2.5	2.5	7.5	3④	20②	18.3	18.3
	8-455	5	2.5	2.5	7.5	3④	20②	17.5	17.5
'71	6-250	4	3.5	—	6	3④	19	13	12.4
	8-350	5	3.5③	2.5	6	3④	19	20	20.5
	8-400	5	2.8	2.5	7.5	3④	19	18.6	20.8
	8-455	5	2.8	2.5	7.5	3④	19	17.9	16.8
'72	6-250	4	3.5	—	6	3④	20②	13	12.4
	8-350	5	3.5	2.5	6	3④	20②	20	20.5
	8-400	5	2.8	2.5	7.5	3④	20②	18.6	20.8
	8-455	5	—	2.5	7.5	3④	20②	17.9	19
'73	6-250	4	3.5	—	7.5	4.25	21.8	13.3	—
	8-350	5	3.5	2.5	7.5	4.25⑦	21.8⑧	22.0	23.1
	8-400	5	2.8/3.5⑥	2.5	7.5	4.25⑦	21.8⑧⑨	22.0/23.0⑩	23.1/24.0⑩
	8-455	5	—	2.5	7.5	4.25⑦	21.8⑨	21.1	22.2
'74	6-250	4	3.5	—	7.5	4.25	21.8	13.5	—
	8-350	5	3.5	2.5	7.5	4.25⑦	21.8⑧	22.0	23.1
	8-400	5	2.8/3.5⑥	2.5	7.5	4.25⑦	21.8⑧⑨	22.0/23.0⑩	23.1/24.0⑩
	8-455	5	—	2.5	7.5	4.25⑦	21.5⑨	22.1	22.2

● '70 and later specifications do not include torque converter
① GTO close ratio 4-speed transmission—2.5 pts
② Station wagons: '69—20 gals, '70—22.5 gals, '72—23 gals less 1 gal for California cars—'70
③ 2.8 pts with heavy duty 3-speed transmission
④ 5 pts with 8.875 in. ring gear
⑤ 16 pts with 3-speed transmission
⑥ Lower figure represents 3-speed Muncie transmission; higher figure indicates 3-speed Saginaw transmission
⑦ 5.25 pts with 8.875 in. ring gear (station wagon)
⑧ 22 gals station wagon
⑨ 25 gals Grand Am
⑩ Lower figure indicates 2 bbl engine; higher figure indicates 4 bbl engine
OHC Overhead cam engine
— Not applicable

Firebird

CAPACITIES

Year	ENGINE No. Cyl. (Cu. In.) Displacement	Engine Crankcase Add 1 Qt For New Filter	TRANSMISSION Pts To Refill After Draining: Manual 3-Speed	Manual 4-Speed	Automatic ●	Drive Axle (pts)	Gasoline Tank (gals)	COOLING SYSTEM (qts) With Heater	With A/C
'67	6-230 OHC	5	2.8	2.5	15	3	18.5	12.1	12.7
	8-326	5	2.8	2.5	15	3	18.5	18.6	20.2
	8-400	5	2.8	2.5	19	3	18.5	12.8	19.4
'68	6-250 OHC	5	3.5	3.5	15	3	18.5	12.1	12.7
	8-350	5	3.5	2.8	15	3	18.5	18.6	20.2
	8-400	5	3.5	2.8	19	3	18.5	17.8	19.4
'69	6-250 OHC	5	3.5	3.5	15④	3	21.5	11.9	12.3
	8-350	5	3.5①	2.5	15④	3	21.5	19.9	20.3
	8-400	5	2.8	2.5	19	3②	21.5	18.3	18.7
'70	6-250	4	3.5	—	6	3②	19.5③	13	—
	8-350	5	3.5①	2.5	6	3②	19.5③	19.9	19.9
	8-400	5	2.5	2.5	7.5	3②	19.5③	18.3	18.3
	8-455	5	2.5	2.5	7.5	3②	19.5③	17.5	17.5
'71	6-250	4	3.5	—	6	4.25	17	12	12.4
	8-350	5	3.5①	2.5	6	4.25	17	20	20.5
	8-400	5	2.8	2.5	7.5	4.25	17	18.6	18.7
	8-455	5	2.8	2.5	7.5	4.25	17	17.9	16.8
'72	6-250	4	3.5	—	6	4.25	17	12	12.4
	8-350	5	3.5	2.5	6	4.25	17	20	20.5
	8-400	5	2.8	2.5	7.5	4.25	17	18.6	18.7
	8-455	5	—	2.5	7.5	4.25	17	17.9	19
'73	6-250	4	3.5	—	7.5	4.25	18	12.5	—
	8-350	5	3.5	2.5	7.5	4.25	18	22.4	22.7
	8-400	5	—	2.5	7.5	4.25	18	22.4	22.7/23.5④
	8-455	5	—	2.5	7.5	4.25	18	20.9	21.8
'74	6-250	4	3.5	—	7.5	4.25	21.5	13.5	—
	8-350	5	3.5	2.5	7.5	4.25	21.5	22.1	22.7
	8-400	5	—	2.5	7.5	4.25	21.5	21.9	22.7/23.5④
	8-455	5	—	2.5	7.5	4.25	21.5	21.9	22

● '70 and later specifications do not include torque converter
① 2.8 pts with heavy duty 3-speed transmission
② 4 pts with heavy duty axle
③ California cars—18.5 gals
④ Lower figure indicates 2 bbl model; higer figure indicates 4 bbl engine
OHC Overhead camshaft
— Not applicable

RING SIDE CLEARANCE

Year	Engine	Top Compression	Bottom Compression
'67-'69	6-230, 250	.0015-.0050	.0015-.0050
'70-'74	6-250, 8-307 ('71-'72)	.0012-.0027	.0012-.0032
'67-'74	8-350, 400, 455	.0015-.0050	.0015-.0050

Year	Engine	Oil Control
'67-'69	6-230, 250	.0015-.0050
'70-'74	6-250	.0001-.0050
'71-'72	8-307	.002-.007
'67-'74	8-350, 400, 455	.0015-.0050

Ventura II

CAPACITIES

Year	ENGINE No. Cyl. (Cu. In.) Displacement	Engine Crankcase Add 1 Qt For New Filter	TRANSMISSION Pts To Refill After Draining: Manual 3-Speed	Manual 4-Speed	Automatic ●	Drive Axle (pts)	Gasoline Tank (gals)	COOLING SYSTEM (qts) With Heater	With A/C
'71	6-250	4	3	—	6	3.75	16	12	—
	8-307	4	3	—	6①	3.75	16	15	16
'72	6-250	4	3	—	6	3.75	16	12	16
	8-307	4	3	—	6①	3.75	16	15	16
	8-350	5	—	—	5	3.75	16	19.4	20.3
'73	6-250	4	3.5	—	6	4.25	21.5	12.1	—
	8-350	5	3.5	2.5	5	4.25	21.5	12.1	12.1
'74	6-250	4	3.5	—	6	4.25	21.5	13.5	—
	8-350	5	3.5	2.5	7.5	4.25	21.5	19.1	19.2

● Specifications do not include torque convertor
① 5 pts with 3-speed transmission
— Not applicable

CRANKSHAFT AND CONNECTING ROD SPECIFICATIONS

All measurements are given in in.

Year	Engine Displace. (cu in.)	CRANKSHAFT Main Brg. Journal Dia	Main Brg. Oil Clearance	Shaft End-Play	Thrust on No.	CONNECTING ROD Journal Diameter	Oil Clearance	Side Clearance
'67	6	2.30	.0003-.0019	.002-.006	7	2.000	.0007-.0027③	.0085-.0135
	8-326	3.00	.0002-.0017	.0035-.0085	4	2.250	.0005-.0025	.006-.011①
	8-400	3.00	.0002-.0017	.0035-.0085	4	2.250	.0005-.0026	.006-.011①
'68	6	2.30	.0003-.0019	.002-.006	7	2.000	.0007-.0027③	.0085-.0135
	8-350	3.00	.0002-.0017	.0035-.0085	4	2.250	.0005-.0025	.006-.011①
'69	8-400	3.00	.0002-.0017	.0035-.0085	4	2.250	.0005-.0026	.006-.011①
	6	2.30	.0003-.0019	.002-.006	7	2.000	.0007-.0027③	.0085-.0135
	8-350	3.00	.0002-.0017④	.0035-.0085	4	2.250	.0005-.0025	.006-.011①
	8-400	3.00	.0002-.0017④	.0035-.0085	4	2.250	.0005-.0026⑤	.006-.011①
'70	6	2.30	.0003-.0029	.002-.006	7	2.000	.0007-.0027	.009-.013
	8-350	3.00	.0002-.0017	.0035-.0085	4	2.250	.0005-.0025	.012-.017①
	8-400	3.00	.0002-.0017⑥	.0035-.0085	4	2.250	.0005-.0026⑤	.012-.017①
	8-455	3.25	.0005-.0021	.0035-.0085	4	2.250	.0010-.0031	.012-.017①
'71-'74	6	2.30	.0003-.0029	.002-.006	7	2.000	.0007-.0027	.009-.014⑩
	8-307 ('71-'72)	⑦	⑧	.002-.006	5	2.099-2.100	.0013-.0035	.002-.006①
	8-350	3.00	.0002-.0017	.003-.009	4	2.250	.0005-.0025	.012-.017①
	8-400	3.00	.0002-.0017	.003-.009	4	2.250	.0005-.0026	.012-.017①
	8-455	3.25	⑨⑪	.003-.009	4	2.250	.0010-.0031⑫	.012-.017①⑬

① Total for 2 connecting rods
② .0005-.0026 in 1966
③ .0007-.0028 on 6 Cyl. 4-BBL. engine option
④ .0012-.0028 on Ram Air IV engine option
⑤ .0015-.0031 on Ram Air IV engine option
⑥ No.'s 1, 2, 3, 4 on Ram Air IV option—.0007-.0023
No.'s 1, 2, 3, 4 on Ram Air IV option—.0012-.0028
No. 5 on Ram Air IV option—.0007-.0022
⑦ No.'s 1, 2, 3, 4—2.4484-2.4493
No. 5—2.4479-2.4488
⑧ No. 1—.0008-.0020
No.'s 2, 3, 4—.0011-.0023
⑨ w/small valve—.0003-.0019
w/large valve—.0005-.0021
⑩ .007-.016 in 1973-74
⑪ 1973-74—.0005-.0021 (455); .0010-.0026 (455 S.D.)
⑫ .0015-.0031 in 455 S.D. engine
⑬ .019-.027 in 455 S.D. engine

Tempest, GTO, LeMans, Grand Am

VALVE SPECIFICATIONS

Year	Engine No. Cyl. Displacement (cu in.)	Seat Angle (deg) ■	Face Angle (deg) ●	Spring Test Pressure▲ (lbs @ in.)	Spring Installed Height (in.)	STEM TO GUIDE Clearance (in.) Intake	STEM TO GUIDE Clearance (in.) Exhaust	STEM Diameter (in.) Intake	STEM Diameter (in.) Exhaust
'67	6-230 1 bbl	30	29	97 @ 1.58	1 37/64	.0016-.0033	.0021-.0038	.34	.34
	6-230 4 bbl	30	29	62 @ 1.58	1 37/64	.0016-.0033	.0021-.0038	.34	.34
	8-326	30	29	62 @ 1.59	1 19/32	.0016-.0033	.0021-.0038	.34	.34
	8-400	30	29	62 @ 1.59	1 19/32	.0016-.0033	.0021-.0038	.34	.34
	8-400 R.A.	30	29	104 @ 1.59	1 19/32	.0016-.0033	.0021-.0038	.34	.34
'68	6-250 1 bbl	30	29	98 @ 1.63	1 5/8	.0016-.0033	.0021-.0038	.3416	.3416
	6-250 4 bbl	30	29	65 @ 1.63	1 5/8	.0016-.0033	.0021-.0038	.3416	.3411
	8-350	30	29	63 @ 1.58	1 37/64	.0016-.0033	.0021-.0038	.3416	.3411
	8-400 2 bbl	30	29	63 @ 1.58	1 37/64	.0016-.0033	.0021-.0038	.3416	.3411
	8-400①4 bbl	30	29	66 @ 1.56	1 9/16	.0016-.0033	.0021-.0038	.3416	.3411
	8-400 R.A.	30	29	76 @ 1.71	1 23/36	.0016-.0033	.0021-.0038	.3416	.3411
'69	6-250 1 bbl	45	44	98 @ 1.63	1 5/8	.0016-.0033	.0021-.0038	.3416	.3411
	6-250 4 bbl	45	44	65 @ 1.63	1 5/8	.0016-.0033	0021-.0038	.3416	.3411
	8-350 2 bbl	45	44	63 @ 1.58	1 37/64	.0016-.0033	.0021-.0038	.3416	.3411
	8-350 4 bbl	45	44	83 @ 1.59	1 19/32	.0016-.0033	.0021-.0038	.3416	.3411
	8-400 2 bbl	30	29	63 @ 1.58	1 37/64	.0016-.0033	.0021-.0038	.3416	.3411
	8-400 4 bbl	30	29	66 @ 1.56	1 5/8	.0016-.0033	.0021-.0038	.3416	.3411
	8-400 R.A.	30	29	83 @ 1.59	1 19/32	.0016-.0032	.0021-.0038	.3416	.3411
	8-400 R.A. IV	30	29	75 @ 1.82	1 53/64	.0016-.0033	.0021-.0038	.3416	.3411
'70	6-250 1 bbl	46④	45⑤	60 @ 1.66	1 21/32	.0010-.0027	.0021-.0027	.3414	.3414
	8-350 2 bbl	45	44	63 @ 1.58	1 37/64	.0010-.0033	.0021-.0038	.3416	.3416
	8-400 2 bbl	45	44	63 @ 1.58	1 37/64	.0016-.0033	.0021-.0038	.3416	.3411
	8-400② 4 bbl	30	29	61 @ 1.59	1 19/32	.0016-.0033	.0021-.0038	.3416	.3411
	8-400③ 4 bbl	30	29	66 @ 1.56	1 9/16	.0016-.0033	.0021-.0038	.3416	.3416
	8-400 R.A. IV	30	29	76 @ 1.82	1 13/16	.0016-.0033	.0021-.0038	.3416	.3411
	8-455	30	29	66 @ 1.56	1 9/16	.0016-.0033	.0021-.0038	.3416	.3411
'71	6-250 1 bbl	46②	45②	61 @ 1.66	1 21/32	.0010-.0027	.0010-.0027	.3414	.3414
	8-350 2 bbl	45	44	61 @ 1.59	1 19/32	.0016-.0033	.0012-.0038	.3416	.3411
	8-400⑥	30	29	60 @ 1.60	1 19/32	.0016-.0033	.0021-.0038	.3416	.3411
	8-400 2 bbl	45	44	61 @ 1.59	1 19/32	.0016-.0033	.0021-.0038	.3416	.3411
	8-400 4 bbl	30	29	65 @ 1.57	1 9/16	.0016-.0033	.0021-.0038	.3416	.3411
	8-455	30	29	65 @ 1.57	1 9/16	.0016-.0033	.0021-.0038	.3416	.3416
	8-455 H.O.	30	29	66 @ 1.56	1 9/16	.0016-.0033	.0021-.0038	.3416	.3416
'72	6-250	46②	45②	60 @ 1.66	1 21/32	.0010-.0027	.0010-.0027	.3414	.3414
	8-350	45	44	61 @ 1.59	1 19/32	.0016-.0033	.0021-.0038	.3416	.3411
	8-400⑥	30	29	60 @ 1.60	1 19/32	.0016-.0033	.0021-.0038	.3416	.3411
	8-400 2 bbl	45	44	61 @ 1.59	1 19/32	.0016-.0033	.0021-.0038	.3416	.3411
	8-400 4 bbl	30	29	65 @ 1.57	1 9/16	.0016-.0033	.0021-.0038	.3416	.3411
	8-455	30	29	64 @ 1.57	1 9/16	.0016-.0033	.0021-.0038	.3416	.3416
	8-455 H.O.	30	29	66 @ 1.56	1 9/16	.0016-.0033	.0021-.0038	.3416	.3416
'73	6-250	46	45	60 @ 1.66	1 21/32	.0010-.0027	.0010-.0027	.3414	.3414
	8-350	45	44	61 @ 1.59	1 19/32	.0016-.0033	.0021-.0038	.3416	.3411
	8-400 4 bbl	30	29	60 @ 1.60	1 19/32	.0016-.0033	.0021-.0038	.3416	.3411
	8-400 2 bbl	45	44	61 @ 1.59	1 19/32	.0016-.0033	.0021-.0038	.3416	.3411
	8-400 4 bbl auto.	30	29	65 @ 1.57	1 9/16	.0016-.0033	.0021-.0038	.3416	.3411
	8-455	30	29	64 @ 1.57	1 9/16	.0016-.0033	.0021-.0038	.3416	.3411
	8-455 S.D.	45	44	70 @ 1.82	1 9/16	.0016-.0033	.0021-.0038	.3416	.3416

Tempest, GTO, LeMans, Grand Am

VALVE SPECIFICATIONS

Year	Engine No. Cyl. Displacement (cu in.)	Seat Angle (deg) ■	Face Angle (deg) ●	Spring Test Pressure▲ (lbs @ in.)	Spring Installed Height (in.)	STEM TO GUIDE Clearance (in.) Intake	Exhaust	STEM Diameter (in.) Intake	Exhaust
'74	6-250	46	45	60 @ 1.66	1 21/32	.0010-.0027	.0010-.0027	.3414	.3414
	8-350	45	44	61 @ 1.59	1 19/32	.0016-.0033	.0021-.0038	.3416	.3411
	8-400 4 bbl	30	29	60 @ 1.60	1 19/32	.0016-.0033	.0021-.0038	.3416	.3411
	8-400 2 bbl	45	44	61 @ 1.59	1 19/32	.0016-.0033	.0021-.0038	.3416	.3411
	8-400 4 bbl auto.	30	29	65 @ 1.57	1 9/16	.0016-.0033	.0021-.0038	.3416	.3411
	8-455	30	29	64 @ 1.57	1 9/16	.0016-.0033	.0021-.0038	.3416	.3411
	8-455 S.D.	45	44	70 @ 1.82	1 9/16	.0016-.0033	.0021-.0038	.3416	.3416

■ Intake valve seat angles are shown. All exhaust valve seat angles are 45° unless otherwise indicated.
● Intake valve face angles are shown. All exhaust valve face angles are 44° unless otherwise indicated.
① Applies to HO also
② Standard and Ram Air GTO with manual transmission
③ Standard GTO with automatic transmission
④ Exhaust valve seat angle 46°
⑤ Exhaust valve face angle 45°
⑥ All 400 cu in. engines with manual transmission

▲INNER SPRING TEST PRESSURE

'67	6-230 4 bbl	31 @ 1.56
	8-326	31 @ 1.57
	8-400	31 @ 1.57⑦
'68	6-250 4 bbl	34 @ 1.59
	8-350	35 @ 1.54
	8-400 2 bbl	35 @ 1.54
	8-400⑧ 4 bbl	38 @ 1.52⑨
	8-400 RA	43 @ 1.64
'69	6-250 4 bbl	34 @ 1.59
	8-350 2 bbl	35 @ 1.54
	8-350 4 bbl	45 @ 1.64
	8-400 2 bbl	35 @ 1.54
	8-400 4 bbl	38 @ 1.52
	8-400 RA IV	45 @ 1.52⑩
'70	8-350 2 bbl	35 @ 1.54
	8-400 2 bbl	35 @ 1.54
	8-400⑪ 4 bbl	57 @ 1.52
	8-400⑫ 4 bbl	38 @ 1.52
	8-400 RA IV	40 @ 1.75
	8-455	38 @ 1.52
'71	8-350 2 bbl	33 @ 1.55
	8-400⑬	56 @ 1.53
	8-400 2 bbl	33 @ 1.55
	8-450 4 bbl	36 @ 1.53
	8-455	37 @ 1.53
	8-455 HO	38 @ 1.52
'72	8-350	33 @ 1.55
	8-400⑬	56 @ 1.53
	8-400 2 bbl	33 @ 1.55
	8-400 4 bbl	36 @ 1.53
	8-455	37 @ 1.53
	8-455 HO	38 @ 1.52
'73	8-350	33 @ 1.55
	8-400 4 bbl	56 @ 1.53
	8-400 2 bbl	33 @ 1.55
	8-400 4 bbl auto.	36 @ 1.53
	8-455	37 @ 1.53
	8-455 S.D.	40 @ 1.75
'74	8-350	33 @ 1.55
	8-400 4 bbl	56 @ 1.53
	8-400 2 bbl	33 @ 1.55
	8-400 4 bbl auto.	36 @ 1.53
	8-455	37 @ 1.53
	8-455 S.D.	40 @ 1.75

⑦ With manual trans.—50 @ 1.57
⑧ Applies to HO also
⑨ With manual trans.—68 @ 1.52
⑩ With manual trans.—38 @ 1.52
⑪ Standard GTO with manual transmission and all Ram Air
⑫ Standard GTO with automatic transmission
⑬ All 400 cu in. engines with manual transmission

RING GAP

Year	Engine	Top Compression	Bottom Compression
'67-'69	6-230, 250	.005-.025	.005-.025
'67-'69	All 8 cylinders	.010-.030	.010-.030
'71-'72	8-307	.010-.020	.010-.020
'70-'74	8-350, 400	.009-.029	.005-.025
'70-'74	8-455	.011-.031	.005-.025
'70-'74	6-250	.010-.020	.010-.020

Year	Engine	Oil Control
'67-'74	All engines	.015-.005

VALVE SPECIFICATIONS

Year	Engine No. Cyl. Displacement (cu in.)	Seat Angle (deg) ■	Face Angle (deg) ●	Spring Test Pressure▲ (lbs @ in.)	Spring Installed Height (in.)	STEM TO GUIDE Clearance (in.) Intake	Exhaust	STEM Diameter (in.) Intake	Exhaust
'67	6-230 1 bbl	30	29	97 @ 1.58	1 37/64	.0016-.0033	.0021-.0058	.3400	.3400
	6-230 4 bbl	30	29	62 @ 1.58	1 37/64	.0016-.0033	.0021-.0038	.3400	.3400
	8-326	30	29	62 @ 1.59	1 19/32	.0016-.0033	.0021-.0038	.3400	.3400
	8-400 4 bbl	30	29	62 @ 1.59	1 19/32	.0016-.0033	.0021-.0038	.3400	.3400
	8-400 Ram Air	30	29	102 @ 1.59	1 19/32	.0016-.0033	.0021-.0038	.3400	.3400
'68	6-250 1 bbl	30	29	98 @ 1.63	1 5/8	.0016-.0033	.0021-.0038	.3416	.3411
	6-250 4 bbl	30	29	65 @ 1.63	1 5/8	.0016-.0033	.0021-.0038	.3416	.3411
	8-350	30	29	63 @ 1.58	1 37/64	.0016-.0033	.0021-.0038	.3416	.3411
	8-400① 4 bbl	30	29	66 @ 1.56	1 9/16	.0016-.0033	.0021-.0038	.3416	.3411
	8-400 Ram Air	30	29	76 @ 1.71	1 23/32	.0016-.0033	.0021-.0038	.3416	.3411
'69	6-250 1 bbl	45	44	97 @ 1.63	1 5/8	.0016-.0033	.0021-.0038	.3416	.3411
	6-250 4 bbl	45	44	65 @ 1.63	1 5/8	.0016-.0033	.0021-.0038	.3416	.3411
	8-350 2 bbl	45	44	63 @ 1.58	1 37/64	.0016-.0033	.0021-.0038	.3416	.3411
	8-350 4 bbl	45	44	83 @ 1.59	1 19/32	.0016-.0033	.0021-.0038	.3416	.3411
	8-400 4 bbl	30	29	66 @ 1.56	1 5/8	.0016-.0033	.0021-.0038	.3416	.3411
	8-400 Ram Air	30	29	83 @ 1.59	1 19/32	.0016-.0033	.0021-.0038	.3416	.3411
	8-400 Ram Air II	30	29	75 @ 1.82	1 53/64	.0016-.0033	.0021-.0038	.3416	.3411
'70	6-250 1 bbl	46④	45④	60 @ 1.66	1 21/32	.0010-.0027	.0010-.0027	.3414	.3414
	8-350 2 bbl	45	44	63 @ 1.58	1 37/64	.0016-.0033	.0021-.0038	.3416	.3416
	8-400 2 bbl	45	44	63 @ 1.58	1 37/64	.0016-.0033	.0021-.0038	.3416	.3411
	8-400② 4 bbl	30	29	61 @ 1.59	1 19/32	.0016-.0033	.0021-.0038	.3416	.3411
	8-400③ 4 bbl	30	29	66 @ 1.56	1 9/16	.0016-.0033	.0021-.0038	.3416	.3416
	8-400 Ram Air	30	29	61 @ 1.59	1 19/32	.0016-.0033	.0021-.0038	.3416	.3411
'71	6-250 1 bbl	46④	45④	61 @ 1.66	1 21/32	.0010-.0027	.0010-.0027	.3414	.3414
	8-307 2 bbl	46④	45④	80 @ 1.70	1 45/64	.0010-.0027	.0010-.0027	.3414	.3414
	8-350 2 bbl	45	44	61 @ 1.57	1 19/32	.0016-.0033	.0021-.0058	.3416	.3411
	8-400②	30	29	60 @ 1.60	1 19/32	.0016-.0033	.0021-.0038	.3416	.3411
	8-400 2 bbl	45	44	61 @ 1.59	1 19/32	.0016-.0033	.0021-.0038	.3416	.3411
	8-400 4 bbl	30	29	65 @ 1.57	1 9/16	.0016-.0033	.0021-.0038	.3416	.3411
	8-455	30	29	65 @ 1.57	1 9/16	.0016-.0033	.0021-.0038	.3416	.3416
	8-455 H.O.	30	29	66 @ 1.56	1 9/16	.0016-.0033	.0021-.0038	.3416	.3416
'72	6-250 1 bbl	46④	45④	60 @ 1.66	1 21/32	.0010-.0027	.0010-.0027	.3414	.3414
	8-307 2 bbl	46④	45④	81 @ 1.70	1 45/64	.0010-.0027	.0010-.0027	.3414	.3414
	8-350⑤ 2 bbl	46④	45④	60 @ 1.66	1 21/32	.0010-.0027	.0010-.0027	.3414	.3414
	8-350⑥ 2 bbl	45	44	61 @ 1.59	1 19/32	.0016-.0033	.0021-.0038	.3414	.3411
	8-400②	30	29	60 @ 1.60	1 19/32	.0016-.0033	.0021-.0038	.3416	.3411
	8-400 2 bbl	45	44	61 @ 1.59	1 19/32	.0016-.0033	.0021-.0038	.3416	.3411
	8-400 4 bbl	30	29	65 @ 1.57	1 9/16	.0016-.0033	.0021-.0038	.3416	.3411
	8-455 H.O.	30	29	66 @ 1.56	1 9/16	.0016-.0033	.0021-.0038	.3416	.3416
'73	6-250 1 bbl	46④	45④	60 @ 1.66	1 21/32	.0010-.0027	.0010-.0027	.3414	.3414
	8-350 2 bbl	45	44	61 @ 1.59	1 19/32	.0016-.0033	.0021-.0038	.3414	.3411
	8-400②	30	29	60 @ 1.60	1 19/32	.0016-.0033	.0021-.0038	.3416	.3411
	8-400 2 bbl	45	44	61 @ 1.59	1 19/32	.0016-.0033	.0021-.0038	.3416	.3411
	8-400 4 bbl	30	29	65 @ 1.57⑦	1 9/16	.0016-.0033	.0021-.0038	.3416	.3411
	8-455	30	29	66 @ 1.56⑧	1 9/16	.0016-.0033	.0021-.0038	.3416	.3411⑨

VALVE SPECIFICATIONS

Year	Engine No. Cyl. Displacement (cu in.)	Seat Angle (deg) ■	Face Angle (deg) ●	Spring Test Pressure▲ (lbs @ in.)	Spring Installed Height (in.)	STEM TO GUIDE Clearance (in.)		STEM Diameter (in.)	
						Intake	Exhaust	Intake	Exhaust
'74	6-250 1 bbl	46④	45④	60 @ 1.66	$1\frac{21}{32}$	.0010-.0027	.0010-.0027	.3414	.3414
	8-350 2 bbl	45	44	61 @ 1.59	$1\frac{19}{32}$	.0016-.0033	.0021-.0038	.3414	.3411
	8-400②	30	29	60 @ 1.60	$1\frac{19}{32}$	.0016-.0033	.0021-.0038	.3416	.3411
	8-400 2 bbl	45	44	61 @ 1.59	$1\frac{19}{32}$	.0016-.0033	.0021-.0038	.3416	.3411
	8-400 4 bbl	30	29	65 @ 1.57⑦	$1\frac{9}{16}$	.0016-.0033	.0021-.0038	.3416	.3411
	8-455	30	29	66 @ 1.56⑧	$1\frac{9}{16}$	.0016-.0033	.0021-.0038	.3416	.3411⑨

- ■ Intake valve seat angles are shown. All exhaust valve seat angles are 45° unless otherwise indicated.
- ● Intake valve face angles are shown. All exhaust valve face angles are 44° unless otherwise indicated.

① Applies to H.O. also
② Manual transmission with 400 cu in. engine
③ Automatic transmission with 400 cu in. engine
④ Exhaust valve seat and face angles are the same as intake valve seat and face angles
⑤ Ventura II only
⑥ Firebird only
⑦ 59 @ 1.50 with manual transmission
⑧ 70 @ 1.82 for 455 S.D. engine
⑨ .3416 in. for 455 S.D. engine

▲INNER SPRING TEST PRESSURE (lbs @ in.)

Year	Engine No. Cyl Displacement (cu in.)	Test Pressure
'67	6-230 4 bbl	31 @ 1.56
	8-326 2 bbl	31 @ 1.57
	8-326 4 bbl	31 @ 1.57
	8-440 4 bbl	31 @ 1.57①
'68	6-250 4 bbl	34 @ 1.59
	8-350	35 @ 1.54
	8-400 4 bbl	38 @ 1.52②
	8-400 Ram Air	43 @ 1.64
'69	6-250 4 bbl	34 @ 1.59
	8-350 2 bbl	35 @ 1.54
	8-350 4 bbl	45 @ 1.52
	8-400 4 bbl	38 @ 1.32
	8-400 Ram Air II	45 @ 1.52③
'70	8-350 2 bbl	35 @ 1.54
	8-400 2 bbl	35 @ 1.54
	8-400 4 bbl	57 @ 1.52④
	8-400 4 bbl	45 @ 1.52⑤
	8-400 Ram Air	57 @ 1.52
'71	8-350 2 bbl	33 @ 1.55
	8-400	56 @ 1.53④
	8-400 2 bbl	33 @ 1.55
	8-400 4 bbl	36 @ 1.53
	8-455	37 @ 1.53
	8-455 H.O.	38 @ 1.52
'72	8-400	56 @ 1.53④
	8-400 2 bbl	33 @ 1.55
	8-400 4 bbl	36 @ 1.53
	8-455 H.O.	38 @ 1.52
'73	8-350	33 @ 1.55
	8-400	56 @ 1.53④
	8-400 2 bbl	33 @ 1.55
	8-400 4 bbl	36 @ 1.53
	8-455	36 @ 1.53⑥
'74	8-350	33 @ 1.55
	8-400	56 @ 1.53④
	8-400 2 bbl	33 @ 1.55
	8-400 4 bbl	36 @ 1.53
	8-455	36 @ 1.53⑥

① With manual transmission: 50 @ 1.57
② With manual transmission: 57 @ 1.52
③ With manual transmission: 38 @ 1.52
④ 400 cu in. engine with manual transmission
⑤ 400 cu in. engine with automatic transmission
⑥ 40 @ 1.75 for 455 S.D.

PISTON CLEARANCE

Year	Engine	Piston-to-Bore Clearance (in.)
'67	6-230 OHC	.0022-.0028
	8-326, 400	.0022-.0028
'68	6-250 OHC	.0022-.0028
	8-350, 400	.0025-.0031
'69	6-250 OHC	.0022-.0028
	8-350, 400	.0025-.0031
	8-400 Ram Air	.0055-.0061
'70	6-250	.0005-.0015
	8-350, 400	.0025-.0033
	8-400 Ram Air	.0055-.0061
'71	6-250	.0005-.0015
	8-350, 400	.0025-.0033
	8-307	.0005-.0011
'72	6-250	.0005-.0015
	8-350, 400, 455	.0025-.0033
	8-307	.0005-.0011
'73-'74	6-250	.0005-.0015
	8-350, 400	.0029-.0037
	8-455	.0025-.0033
	8-455 S.D.	.0060-.0068

CHARGING SYSTEM

An alternating-current (AC) generator is used. This unit is the Delco-Remy, Delcotron, or Transistor C.S.I. unit. Trouble shooting and repair of these charging systems is covered in the "Unit Repair Section" of this manual.

Caution Since the Delcotron and regulator are designed for use on only one polarity system, the following precautions must be observed:

1. The polarity of the battery, generator and regulator must be considered before making any electrical connections with the system.
2. When connecting a booster battery, be sure to connect the negative battery terminals respectively, and the positive battery terminals respectively.
3. When connecting a charger to the battery, connect the charger positive lead to the battery positive terminal. Connect the charger negative lead to the battery negative terminal.
4. Never operate the Delcotron on open circuit. Be sure that all connections in the circuit are clean and tight.
5. Do not short across or ground any of the terminals on the Delcotron regulator.
6. Do not attempt to polarize the Delcotron.
7. Do not use test lamps of more than 12 volts for checking diode continuity.
8. Avoid long soldering times when replacing diodes or transistors. Prolonged heat is damaging to these units.
9. Disconnect the battery ground terminal when servicing any AC system. This will prevent the possibility of accidental reversal of polarity.

Alternator R & R 1967-74

1. Disconnect positive battery cable.
2. Remove alternator wires or connector.
3. Loosen adjusting bolt.
4. Remove V-belt. On power steering six, loosen A. I. R. pump.
5. Remove alternator retaining bolts or thru bolt.
6. Remove alternator.
7. To install, reverse removal procedure. Tighten bracket bolt on non-A/C cars to 10-25 ft. lbs., all other bolts to 25-35 ft. lbs.

Voltage Regulator R&R 1967-70

Removal

1. Disconnect the battery cables.
2. Disconnect the wiring from the voltage regulator.
3. Remove the screws holding the regulator to the firewall or front bulkhead, depending on the car.

Installation

1. Reverse the removal procedures for installation.

Voltage Regulator R&R 1971-74

The voltage regulator is inside the alternator. For R&R procedures see the "Starting and Charging Systems" in the "Unit Repair Section."

STARTING SYSTEM

Starter

The starter circuit consists of the battery, battery cables, starting motor, starter motor solenoid switch, ignition-starter switch and the neutral safety switch, (used on cars with automatic transmission).

The starting motor and solenoid assembly is mounted on the flywheel housing.

The solenoid switch closes the circuit between the battery and the starting motor. It also operates the shift lever that moves the drive pinion into mesh with the flywheel ring gear.

Starter motor, solenoid, and starter drive repair procedures can be found in the "Charging and Starting Systems" section of the "Unit Repair Section."

Starter Removal—Six

1. Disconnect positive battery cable.
2. Disconnect solenoid wires.
3. Disconnect starter brace, if so equipped.
4. Remove starter-to-engine bolts and starter.

Starter Removal—V8

1. Jack up car and support on axle stands.
2. Follow Steps 1-4 of six-cylinder procedure, working from underneath car.

Starter Drive R & R

1. Disconnect the field straps from the solenoid and remove the starter through bolts.
2. Remove the commutator end frame, field frame, and armature from the drive housing.
3. To remove the overrunning clutch from the armature shaft:
   a. Slide the thrust collar from the end of the armature shaft.
   b. Slide a standard ½ in. pipe coupling (or an old pinion of suitable size) onto the armature shaft so that it butts against the snap-ring retainer. Tap the end of the pipe with a hammer, driving the retainer off of the snap-ring.

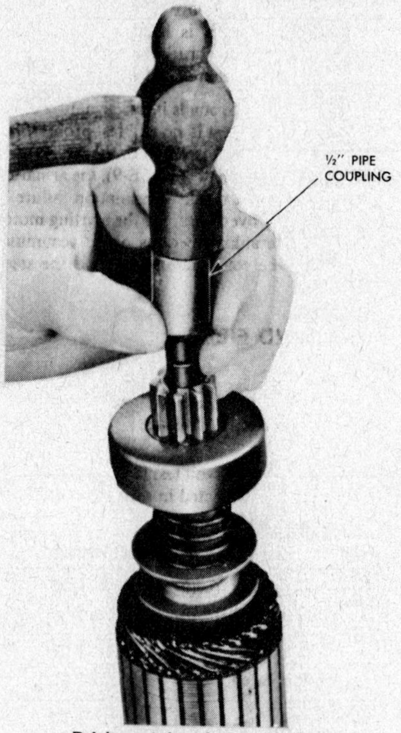
½" PIPE
COUPLING

Driving retainer from snap-ring
(© Pontiac Div., G.M. Corp)

   c. Remove the snap-ring from the groove in the armature shaft.
   d. Slide the retainer and clutch from the armature shaft.
4. To reassemble, reverse the above procedure, being sure to:
   a. Slide the snap-ring, after it has been forced onto the armature shaft, past the grease groove to the snap-ring groove.
   b. Use two pairs of pliers at the same time, on opposite sides of the armature shaft, and grip the retainer and thrust collar and squeeze until the retainer is forced over the snap-ring.

IGNITION SYSTEM

Three types of distributors are used: a 12 volt aluminum internal point adjustment distributor used on six-cylinder engines, a 12 volt aluminum external point adjustment distributor used on eight-cylinder engines, and a 12 volt aluminum unitized transistor ignition distributor.

All the units perform the same function. They induce a high voltage surge into the coil and time these surges with regard to piston movements. They use centrifugal and vacuum ignition timing advance mechanisms to time the surges. They then direct these high-voltage surges through the distributor rotor, distributor cap, and high-tension wiring to the spark plugs.

Distributor Removal

1. Disconnect distributor primary wire from the coil.
2. Remove distributor cap. (Unlatch the cap by using a screwdriver to disengage the latches.)
3. Make reference marks on the block and the distributor housing that align with the tip of the rotor. Do not crank the engine after these marks have been made.
4. Disconect vacuum line at distributor.
5. Remove distributor clamp screw and hold-down clamp.
6. Lift out distributor and distributor-to-block gasket. Notice the slight rotation of the rotor as the distributor is removed from the block.

Distributor Installation

Installation procedure is the reverse of the removal procedure. It should be noted, however, that while inserting the distributor into the block, the rotor should be moved slightly to one side. This is necessary because of the helical cut of the distributor and camshaft gears. As the distributor seats in its bore, the rotor will turn slightly so the reference marks will once again be in line.

Installation—If Engine Has Been Disturbed

1. With No. 1 piston coming up on compression stroke, continue cranking the engine until the pulley timing mark indexes with the zero (0) mark on the engine timing scale.
2. Replace the distributor-to-block gasket.
3. Install the distributor in the block so that the vacuum diaphragm faces the left side of the engine on V8 engines, and to the front of the engine on six-cylinder engines. The rotor should point toward the contact in the cap for no. 1 cylinder. Move the rotor slightly to the side because, as the distributor is pressed into its bore, it will turn a small amount.

Rotor in No. 1 position—6 cyl
(© Pontiac Div., G.M. Corp)

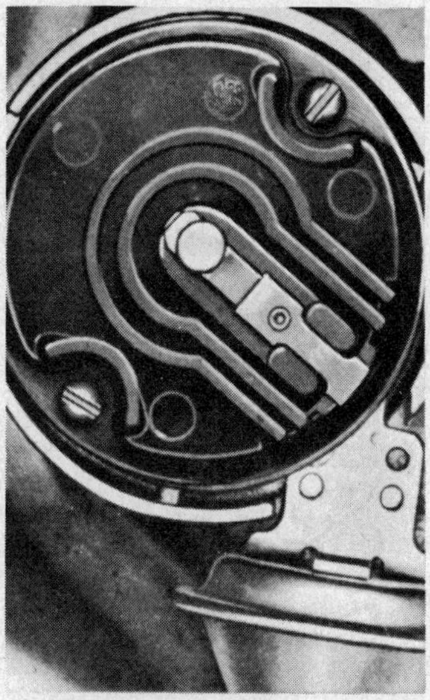

Rotor in No. 1 position—V8
(© Pontiac Div., G.M. Corp)

4. Reverse the removal procedure to complete installation.

Contact Point Replacement and Adjustment

1. Remove the distributor cap and the rotor.
2. Remove the radio frequency interference (R.F.I.) shield, if so equipped.
3. Remove the screws holding the points in place.

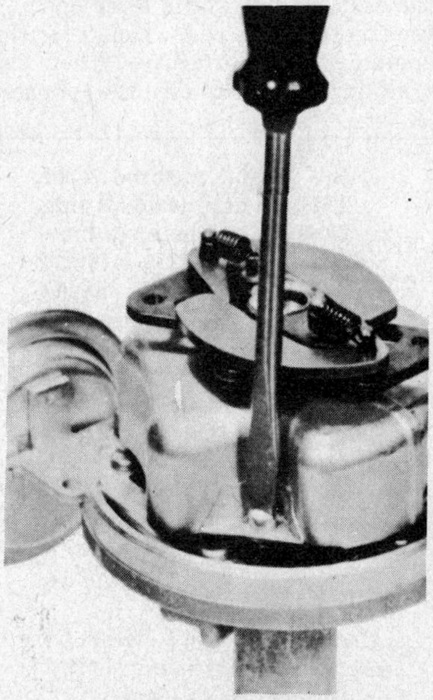

RFI shield 1970-74
(© Pontiac Div., G.M. Corp)

4. Remove the condenser lead and ignition primary lead from the points.
5. Install a new set of points and tighten the attaching screws.
6. Connect the condenser and primary leads to the points.
7. Apply a very small amount of grease to the distributor breaker cam.
8. Install the R.F.I. shield. (The half covering the points should be installed first.)
9. Install the rotor and distributor cap.
10. Set the dwell using a dwell meter, or set the point gap by rotating the engine until the fiber rubbing block of the point set is on a high point of the breaker cam. (The cap, rotor, and R.F.I. shield must be removed to set the points.) Using a ⅛ in. allen wrench, rotate the adjusting screw until the cap meets the specification. Replace the cap, rotor, and R.F.I. shield.

Ignition Timing

Timing marks are located on the front engine cover and harmonic balancer.

1. Disconnect and plug the distributor vacuum advance hose.
2. Make sure that the breaker point gap is adjusted to specifications.

NOTE: it may be necessary to put a small amount of white paint or chalk on the timing marks to make them more visible.

3. Connect a timing light to no. 1 spark plug.
4. Loosen the distributor hold-down clamp.
5. Start the engine and rotate the distributor until the correct mark on the cover lines up with the harmonic balancer mark. Tighten the distributor clamp, and recheck the timing.

Transistor Ignition

This system consists of a special distributor and a special ignition coil. The distributor is similar in external appearance to the standard V8 distributor, but the internal construction bears little resemblance to the contact-point unit. An iron timer core replaces the breaker cam. This eight-lobed timer rotates inside a magnetic pick-up assembly, which replaces the contact points and condenser. The magnetic pick-up assembly consists of a ceramic permanent magnet, a steel pole piece, and a pick-up coil.

The magnetic pick-up assembly is mounted over the distributor shaft bearing, and is rotated by the vacuum advance unit to provide automatic spark advance. Centrifugal advance is provided by the rotating timer core, which is attached to normal advance weights.

Removal, installation, and timing procedures are the same as those given for conventional distributors with the exception of disconnecting the primary lead wires. On models with a transistorized distributor, disconnect the primary wires at the push-on connector.

Trouble shooting of the transistorized ignition system can be found in the "Unit Repair Section" under "Electronic Ignition Systems."

FUEL SYSTEM

Information covering operation and troubles of the fuel gauge will be found in the Unit Repair Section.

Fuel Pump

The fuel pump is of the single action diaphragm-type and is equipped with a pulsation dampening chamber for stabilizing fuel flow.

A vapor diverter is incorporated into the fuel pumps used on air conditioned V8 and 4-BBL. models. The fuel pump is not repairable and must be replaced as a unit if defective.

Fuel Pump R & R—1967-73

1. Disconnect fuel inlet, outlet and vapor return lines at pump and plug pump inlet line.
2. Remove two pump mounting bolts and lockwashers; remove pump and gasket.
3. On Ventura II V8 engines, if rocker arm pushrod is to be removed: take out the two adapter bolts and lockwashers and remove adapter and gasket.
4. Install pump with new gasket coated with sealer. Coat mounting bolt threads with sealer and tighten bolts.

NOTE: on Ventura II V8 engines, mechanical fingers or heavy grease can be used to hold pump pushrod in place during installation. Coat pipe plug threads or adapter gasket with sealer if pushrod was removed.

5. Connect inlet and outlet lines, start engine and check for leaks.

Fuel Filter

Paper and Bronze Types—1967-74

1. Disconnect fuel line connection at inlet of carburetor.
2. Remove inlet fuel filter nut from carburetor using a box wrench.
3. Remove filter element and spring.
4. If a bronze element, blow through cone end—element should allow air to pass freely.
5. Install element spring and new element into carburetor. Bronze elements are installed with small section of cone facing outward.
6. Install new gasket on fitting nut and install nut.
7. Install fuel line and tighten securely. Start engine and check for leaks.

Idle Stop Solenoid

The idle stop solenoid is used on some pre-1973 six-cylinder and 4 bbl V8 engines and all 1973 with manual transmission to prevent after-run when the ignition is turned off. After-run is caused largely by today's higher engine operating temperatures and wider throttle plate openings which are necessary for emission controls. Ordinarily, when the ignition is shut off the loss of spark is enough to stop the engine. However, if the engine has sufficiently high cylinder temperatures, enough air-fuel mixture can pass the wide throttle plate opening and be ignited without the spark plug and the engine will continue running even after the key is turned off. The idle solenoid is attached to the carburetor to solve this problem. The solenoid has an adjustable plunger and is electrically operated. When the ignition is turned on, the plunger is extended and contacts the carburetor throttle lever opening the throttle plate wide enough for the engine to idle properly. When the ignition is turned off, the plunger retracts and the throttle lever falls back on the lever stop. When the throttle lever is on its stop, the throttle plate opening is very small and will not allow enough air-fuel mixture to pass to run the engine with the ignition turned off.

Hot Idle Compensator

The hot idle compensator is used with automatic transmissions. Its purpose is to offset the enrichening effects caused by changes in air density and fuel vapors generated during hot engine operation. It is in a chamber on the float bowl casting. The compensator is a temperature-sensitive unit which opens and closes a passage leading from the atmosphere to an orifice below the throttle valve. At normal operating temperatures, the valve is closed, blocking the passage. During very hot engine operation, low air density and excessive fuel vapors in the carburetor enter the engine manifold causing a rich mixture and attendent rough idling and stalling. At a predetermined temperature, the compensator opens and allows enough air to offset the rich mixture and maintain a smooth idle. When the engine cools, the compensator closes and operation returns to normal.

Idle Speed and Mixture Adjustments

1967 (BV, 2GC, AFB, 4MV, Tri-Power)

Adjust with air cleaner installed.

1. Turn in idle mixture screw/s until lightly seated, then back out 2 turns for 1967 4MV, $1\frac{1}{2}$ turns for others.
2. Set parking brake, place transmission in Neutral, connect a tachometer.
3. Start engine and allow it to warm up to normal operating temperature. Choke must be open and engine off fast idle.
4. Depress hot idle compensator pin on six-cylinder models with A/C and all V8 with automatic transmission. Place transmission in Neutral for manual, Drive for automatic.
5. Adjust idle speed screw to obtain specified idle speed, making sure hot idle compensator is still depressed.

NOTE: only center carb needs adjustment on GTO Tri-Power 389.

6. Adjust mixture screw/s to obtain highest idle speed with best quality idle. "Missing" usually means mixture is too lean; "loping," too rich.
7. Reset idle speed screw to obtain specified idle speed.
8. Adjust idle speed-up device on six-cylinder A/C models as follows:
   a. Turn on A/C.

Chilton's TIME SAVER

Ventura II 307 cu. in.

When replacing a fuel pump on a 307 or 350 cu. in. engine, considerable time can be saved as follows:

1. **Before removing the old pump, remove the upper bolt from the engine's right front mounting boss. This bolt hole is in direct alignment with the fuel pump pushrod. The threaded bolt hole continues into the pump pushrod bore. The bolt acts as an oil plug.**
2. **Temporarily insert a longer bolt, (about $\frac{3}{8}$—16 x 2 in.) into the hole. Screw the bolt into the bore until it bottoms against the pump pushrod. (Don't tighten the bolt with a wrench or the rod can be damaged.)**
3. **The mechanic is now free to remove and install the fuel pump without worrying about fuel pump pushrod misalignment.**

CAUTION: don't forget to reinstall original motor bolt.

b. Adjust diaphragm plunger screw to obtain 500 rpm (1967 auto. without A.I.R.), 600 rpm (1967 auto. with A.I.R. and manual without A.I.R.), or 700 rpm (1967 manual with A.I.R.).

1968-69

Adjust with air cleaner installed.

V8 Engines

1. Turn in idle mixture screws until lightly seated, then back out 4 turns (2-BBL.) or 6 turns (4-BBL.).
2. Connect a tachometer, start engine and allow it to warm up to normal operating temperature. On automatic transmisison, A/C cars, turn off A/C.
3. Place automatic in Drive, manual in Neutral. With idle stop solenoid energized, adjust mixture screws for best lean idle speed.
4. Adjust idle stop solenoid screw to obtain specified idle speed for all 1968 and only 1969 Ram Air; use idle screw for all other 1969 cars.
5. Disconnect idle stop solenoid, then adjust idle speed screw on carburetor to obtain 650 rpm idle for manual transmission 4-BBL., 500 rpm for all others.

NOTE: do not re-adjust mixture screws.

6. Place fast idle lever on top step of cam and adjust fast idle speed.

L-6 Engines

1. Turn in mixture screws until they lightly seat, then back out 5 turns.
2. Start engine, connect tachometer, and allow engine to warm up to normal operating temperature. On automatic transmission cars, place selector in Drive and turn off A/C, if so equipped.
3. Adjust idle stop solenoid screw to obtain 610 rpm for auto. transmission (1-BBL. and 4-BBL.), 730 rpm for manual transmission 1-BBL., 830 rpm for 1968 manual transmission 4-BBL., or 880 rpm for 1969 manual transmission 4-BBL.
4. Turn mixture screws clockwise to obtain 600 rpm for auto. transmission (1-BBL. and 4-BBL.), 700 rpm for manual transmission 1-BBL., 800 rpm for 1968 manual transmission 4-BBL., or 850 rpm for 1969 manual transmission 4-BBL.
5. Disconnect idle stop solenoid and adjust idle speed screw on carburetor to obtain 600 rpm for manual transmission 4-BBL., 500 rpm for all others.

NOTE: don't disturb idle mixture screws or stop solenoid after this point.

6. Reconnect solenoid and adjust fast idle speed.

1970

Adjust with air cleaner installed.

1. On California cars, remove fuel filler cap.
2. Disconnect and plug distributor vacuum advance hose.
3. Plug hot idle compensator on all automatic transmission V8's with Quadrajet (4 MV) carburetor *except* Ram Air III and IV. Also plug compensator on all L-6 and V8 2-BBL. with automatic and A/C.
4. With automatic in Drive, manual in Neutral, adjust curb idle speed as follows:

L-6 and Ram Air IV

a. With idle stop solenoid energized, adjust solenoid screw to obtain 830 rpm for L-6, 1,000 rpm for R.A. IV, 630 rpm for automatic L-6, and 750 rpm for automatic R.A. IV.

b. Adjust mixture screws equally to obtain lean best idle at 1,000 rpm for manual R.A. IV, 750 rpm for automatic R.A. IV, 750 rpm for manual L-6, and 600 rpm for automatic L-6.

c. Disconnect solenoid wire and adjust carburetor idle speed screw to obtain 400 rpm for L-6, 500 rpm for R.A. IV automatic, and 650 rpm for R.A. IV manual.

350, 400, 455 Engines

a. Back out mixture screws 3-5 turns from lightly seated positions.

b. Adjust carburetor idle speed screw to obtain 850 rpm for manual 350 and 400 2-BBL., 1,050 rpm for manual 400 and 455 4-BBL., or 675 rpm for all automatic 350, 400, 455 engines.

c. Lean mixture screws equally (turn in) to obtain 800 rpm for manual 350 and 400 2-BBL., 950 rpm for manual 400 and 455 4-BBL., or 650 rpm for all automatic 350, 400, 455 engines.

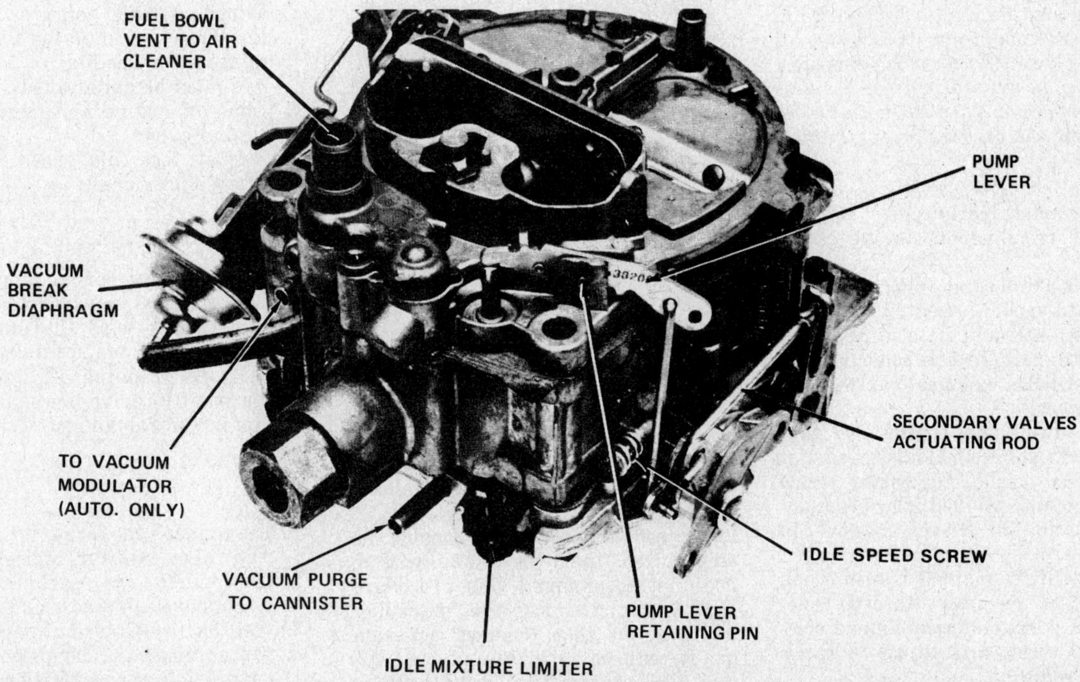
FUEL BOWL
VENT TO AIR
CLEANER
PUMP
LEVER
VACUUM
BREAK
DIAPHRAGM
SECONDARY VALVES
ACTUATING ROD
TO VACUUM
MODULATOR
(AUTO. ONLY)
IDLE SPEED SCREW
VACUUM PURGE
TO CANNISTER
PUMP LEVER
RETAINING PIN
IDLE MIXTURE LIMITER

Rochester 4 bbl (© Pontiac Div., G.M. Corp)

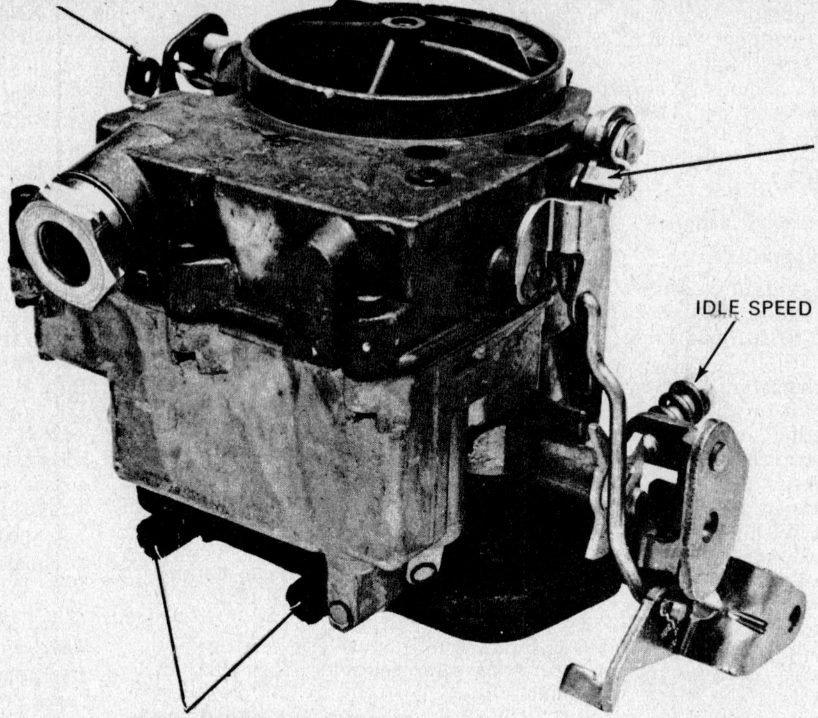
CHOKE ROD GUAGE NOTCH
FAST IDLE LEVER
IDLE SPEED SCREW
IDLE MIXTURE LIMITERS

Carter 2 bbl (© Pontiac Div., G.M. Corp)

1971-72

Adjust with air cleaner installed.

On some models, the idle stop solenoid is no longer used, having been replaced by the combination emission control valve. This valve is energized through the transmission to increase idle speed under conditions of high gear deceleration and to provide full vacuum spark advance during high gear operation. The valve is de-energized at curb idle and in the lower gears to provide a retarded spark under these conditions, the result of which is lower hydrocarbon emission. *The valve need not be adjusted unless the solenoid or throttle body is removed, or the carburetor overhauled.*

V-8 Idle Speed

1. Disconnect carburetor "EVAP" hose from vapor storage canister.
2. Disconnect and plug carburetor-to-vacuum (distributor vacuum) solenoid hose at solenoid. Disconnect throttle solenoid wire on 4-BBL. manual transmission engines.
3. Set dwell and timing (in that order) at specified idle speed.
4. Adjust carburetor speed screw to obtain specified idle speed, automatic in Drive, manual in Neutral.
5. On 4-BBL. manual transmission models, reconnect throttle solenoid wire, manually extend solenoid screw and adjust to specified idle rpm.
6. Place automatic in Park, manual in Neutral and check fast idle speed with screw on top step of cam. Adjust fast idle screw to obtain 1,700 rpm.

NOTE: 2-BBL. carburetors are not adjustable for fast idle.

7. Reconnect distributor vacuum and vapor storage hoses.

6 Cyl. Idle Speed

1. Disconnect fuel tank "EVAP" hose from vapor storage canister.
2. Disconnect and plug distributor vacuum advance hose.
3. Set dwell and timing (in that order) at specified idle speed.
4. Adjust carburetor idle speed screw to obtain 550 rpm for manual, 500 rpm for automatic (in Drive). Do not adjust solenoid screw.
5. Place automatic in Park and manual in Neutral, then place fast idle tang on top step of fast idle cam and check fast idle speed. Adjust to obtain 2,400 rpm.

V-8 and 6 Cyl. Idle Mixture

If the carburetor has been overhauled, or the plastic locks removed from the mixture screws, the following procedure must be used to adjust idle speed and mixture. It must be emphasized that the manufacturer does not recommend this procedure as a substitute for the preceding methods, in that exhaust emission quality can be adversely affected unless the proper test equipment is available.

1. Turn in mixture screw/s until lightly seated, then back out 3½ turns.
2. Start engine and adjust carburetor idle speed screw to obtain a speed 25 rpm above specified idle (automatic), 75 rpm higher for L-6 and 2-BBL. V8 (manual), or 100 rpm higher for 4-BBL. V8 (manual).
3. Turn mixture screw/s in equally until specified idle speed is obtained. At this point, a CO meter should be employed to adjust mixture. A reading of 1.0% or less must be maintained.
4. Shut off engine and install new limiter caps
5. Adjust fast idle speed, as described previously.

1973-74

The idle stop solenoid is used on cars with manual transmission. Make all adjustments with the engine at normal operating temperatures, choke open, air conditioning off, automatic transmission in drive, manual transmission in neutral, and parking brake on.

Idle Speed

1. Disconnect the evap hose from the vapor canister, and plug it.
2. Disconnect the carburetor to vacuum solenoid hose and plug it.
3. Set the dwell and timing.
4. On automatic transmission cars, set the idle to specifications using the idle speed screw.

5. On manual transmission cars, set the idle speed with the idle stop solenoid plunger extended. Using the hex head bolt on the end of the plunger, set the idle speed to the higher idle speed figure.
6. Disconnect the wire from the idle stop solenoid. Set the idle speed, using the idle speed screw, to the lower idle speed figure.
7. Unplug the vacuum hoses and reconnect them.

COOLING SYSTEM

The cooling system consists of the radiator cap, radiator, hoses, water pump, cooling fan, thermostat, and passages for water circulation in the block.

Radiator—1967-74 Tempest, Firebird, GTO and Ventura II

A cross-flow radiator is used instead of a conventional down-flow and center type. With the cross-flow design, coolant flows horizontally through the core and the tanks are located on each side.

Advantages of the cross-flow radiator are improved cooling capability, more effective cooling surface area, and a low silhouette.

Automatic transmission radiators have oil coolers built into the right-hand tank, air-conditioned and high-performance models have greater cooling capacity than standard. The drain cock is located at the inside, lower left-hand corner of the radiator.

Radiator R&R—1967-74 Tempest, GTO, Ventura II and Grand Am

1. Drain coolant.
2. Remove fan shield assembly.
3. Disconnect upper and lower hoses.
4. Disconnect and plug oil cooler lines, if equipped with automatic transmission.

NOTE: on 1969 Tempest models remove fan blade, then remove entire radiator and shroud as an assembly.

5. Remove fan shroud, if installed.
6. Lift radiator straight up and out of car.
7. To install, reverse removal procedure, making sure lower cradles are properly located and automatic transmission is full.

Radiator R & R—1967-74 Firebird

1. Disconnect battery.
2. Drain coolant, then disconnect upper and lower hoses.
3. Disconnect and plug oil cooler lines, if equipped with automatic transmission.
4. Remove upper fan shield (six cylinder) or upper shroud bracket (V8).
5. Remove radiator hold-down bolts and lift radiator and shroud assembly from car.
6. To install, reverse removal procedure, making sure automatic transmission fluid level is correct. Tighten hold-down bolts to 12 ft. lbs.

Water Pump R & R

This is a centrifugal-type waterpump. It is die cast, with sealed bearings and is pressed together. Therefore, it is serviced as a unit.

All Engines 1967-74

1. Disconnect the battery and drain the radiator.
2. Loosen the generator and remove the fan belt.
3. Remove the power steering and air conditioning belts, if so equipped.
4. Remove the fan and water pump pulley.
5. Remove the front generator bracket.
6. Remove the heater hose and radiator hose at the pump

WATER JACKETS
QUENCH AREA
FLAME TRAVEL
QUENCH ARE.
WATER JACKETS

Cylinder quench area (© Pontiac Div., G.M. Corp)

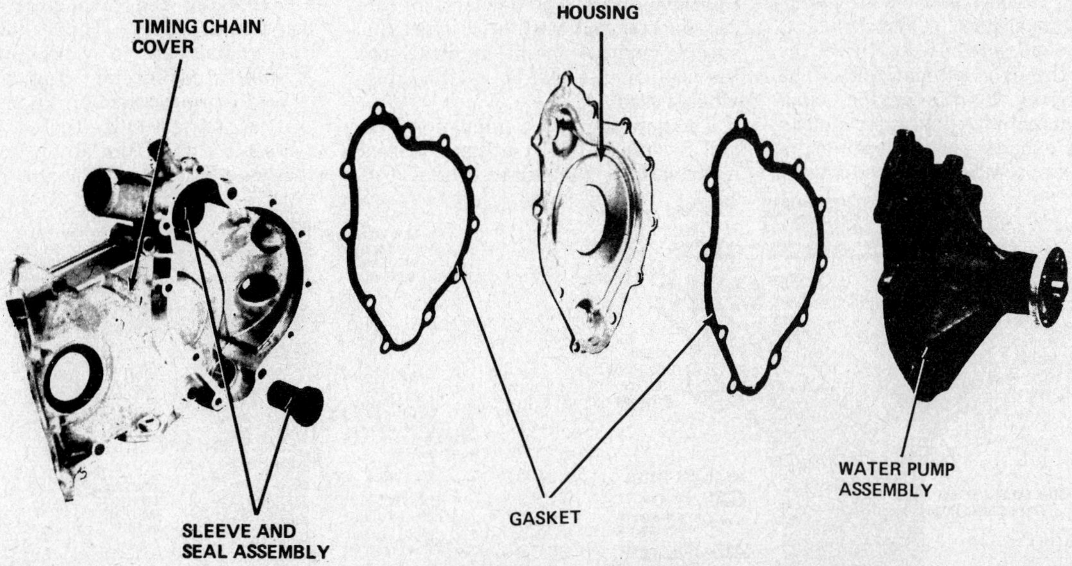
TIMING CHAIN COVER
HOUSING
SLEEVE AND SEAL ASSEMBLY
GASKET
WATER PUMP ASSEMBLY

V8 (except 307) water pump assembly (© Pontiac Div., G.M. Corp)

NOTE: remove the upper front timing cover and the two accessory drive housing bolts on OHC six engines.

7. Remove the water pump retaining bolts and the pump.
8. Install the pump by reversing the above steps. Make sure that all gasket surfaces are clean and smooth. Always use a gasket sealer on both sides of the gasket. Torque the retaining bolts to 20 ft lbs on six-cylinder engines, 30 ft lbs on the 307, and 15 ft lbs on all other V8 engines.

Thermostat R & R

1. Drain coolant to below thermostat level.
2. Disconnect upper hose and remove water outlet assembly.
3. Replace by reversing the above steps. Torque attaching bolts to 20-30 ft. lbs. Clean the gasket surfaces and use a gasket sealer and a new gasket.
4. Refill to 3 in. below filler neck and bleed cooling system.

EMISSION CONTROLS

There are three types of emissions to be controlled: crankcase emissions, carburetor and gas tank gas vapor emissions, and exhaust emissions. See the "Unit Repair Section" for troubleshooting and repair information.

1967

Pontiac controlled crankcase emissions in 1967 with the positive crankcase ventilation (PCV) system. The PCV system connects the crankcase to the intake manifold. Crankcase gases are returned to the intake manifold to be reburned.

The Air Injection Reactor (A.I.R.) system was used to treat exhaust emissions. It consists of an air pump, a special air cleaner, a by-pass valve, and tubes and hoses used to inject the air into the exhaust manifolds. The pump, driven by the engine, compresses, distributes, and injects clean air at the exhaust port for each cylinder. The air combines in the exhaust manifolds with the unburned hydrocarbons and carbon monoxide to produce a low-emission exhaust.

A dual diaphragm vacuum advance mechanism is used with the A.I.R. system. It is located on the distributor and takes the place of the single diaphragm unit. The outer diaphragm functions as a normal vacuum advance unit at any engine speed above idle. Vacuum for this diaphragm is supplied from a port above the carburetor throttle plate, since, at higher engine speeds, intake manifold vacuum is low and carburetor vacuum is high.

The inner diaphragm is used to retard the spark at idle. Vacuum is supplied to the diaphram from a port below the throttle because, at idle vacuum, conditions are reversed. Retarding the spark at idle combined with leaner mixtures gives cleaner exhaust at idle.

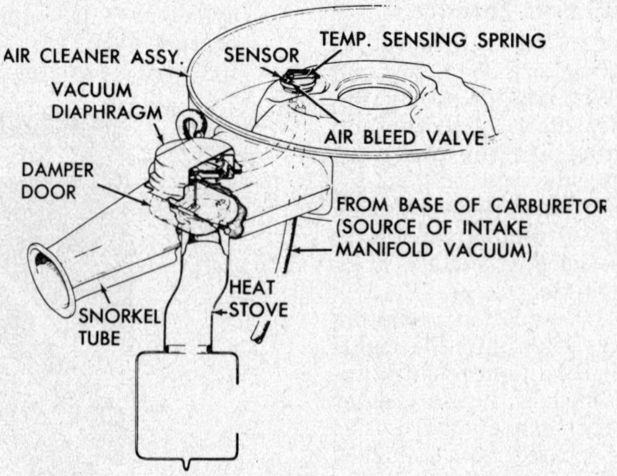
AIR CLEANER ASSY.
SENSOR
TEMP. SENSING SPRING
VACUUM DIAPHRAGM
AIR BLEED VALVE
DAMPER DOOR
FROM BASE OF CARBURETOR (SOURCE OF INTAKE MANIFOLD VACUUM)
HEAT STOVE
SNORKEL TUBE

Auto-Therm air cleaner (© Pontiac Div., G.M. Corp)

1968-69

The General Motors Corporation had elected to adopt a special system of terminal exhaust treatment. This plan supersedes (in most cases) the method used to conform to 1966–67 California laws. The new system cancels out (except with stick shift and special purpose engine applications) the use of the A.I.R. method previously used.

The new concept, Combustion Control System (C.C.S.) utilizes engine modification. Essentially the C.C.S. increases combustion efficiency through carburetor and distributor calibrations and by increasing engine operating temperature.

Carburetors are calibrated leaner and initial ignition timing is retarded. Another carburetor feature is the idle fuel mixture limiting orifice. It is located at the base of the idle mixture screw and makes sure that, even if the idle mixture screw is turned too far, the fuel enrichment will not greatly affect exhaust emissions.

The C.C.S. also incorporates a higher engine operating temperature. A 195° thermostat is used. Engines that run hotter provide a more complete vaporation of the fuel and reduce quench area in the combustion chamber. Quench area is the relatively cool area near the cylinder wall and combustion chamber surfaces. Fuel in these areas does not burn properly because of the lower temperatures. This increases emissions.

The C.C.S. uses a thermostatically controlled air cleaner called the Auto-Therm air cleaner. It is designed to keep the temperature of the air entering the carburetor at approximately 100°. This allows the lean carburetor to work properly, minimizes carburetor icing, and improves engine warm-up characteristics. A sensor unit located on the clean air side of the air filter senses the temperature of the air passing

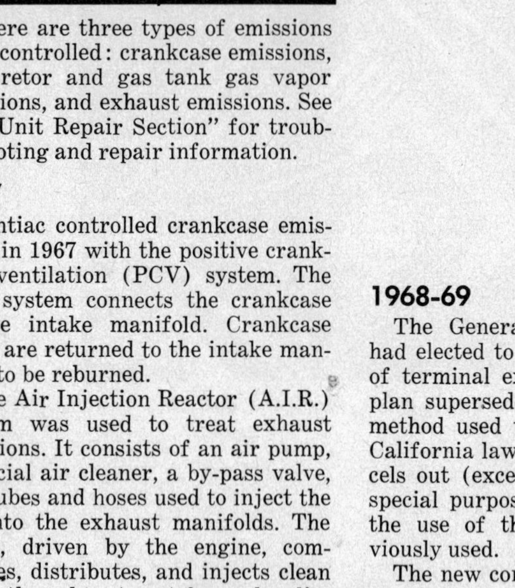
AIR PUMP
AIR DISTRIBUTOR TO EACH CYLINDER
AIR INTAKE
AIR DISTRIBUTOR TO EACH CYLINDER
PISTON EXHAUST STROKE AFTER COMBUSTION
KEY TO A.I.R. SYSTEM
FILTERED AIR
HYDROCARBONS & CARBON MONOXIDE
TREATED EXHAUST (TO ATMOSPHERE THROUGH EXHAUST PIPE)

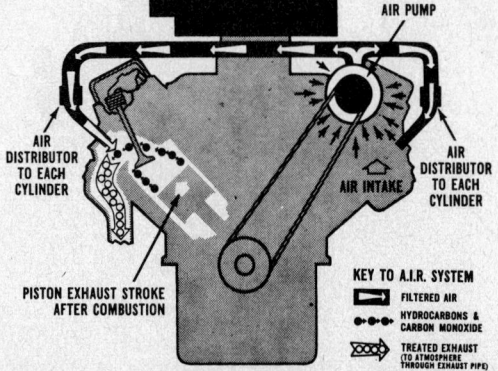

Air Injection Reaction system (© Pontiac Div., G.M. Corp)

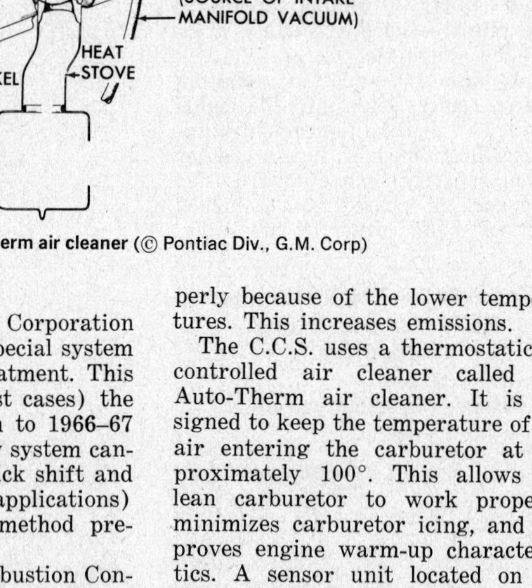
NEW CARBURETOR LEAN MIXTURES, ENGINE IDLE INCREASED
THERMOSTATICALLY CONTROLLED INTAKE AIR
SPARK TIMING CHANGED
HIGH TEMPERATURE THERMOSTAT FOR ENGINE COOLANT
KEY TO C.C.S. SYSTEM
HEATED UNDERHOOD AIR
UNDERHOOD AIR
HOT EXHAUST
HEAT EXCHANGED FROM EXHAUST MANIFOLD TO UNDERHOOD AIR FLOW

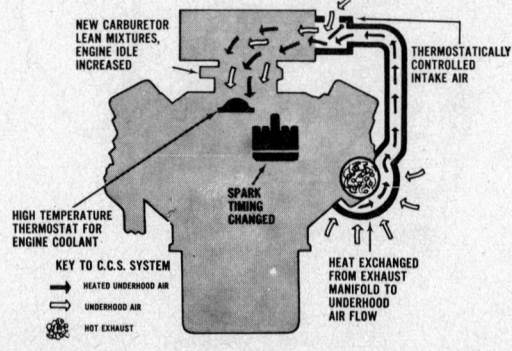

Controlled combustion system (© Pontiac Div., G.M. Corp)

over it and regulates the vacuum supplied to a vacuum diaphragm in the inlet tube of the air cleaner. The colder the air, the greater the amount of vacuum supplied to the vacuum diaphragm. The vacuum diaphragm, depending on the vacuum supplied to it, opens or closes a damper door in the inlet tube of the air cleaner. If the door is open, it allows air from the engine compartment to go to the carburetor. If the door is closed, air flows from the heat stove located on the exhaust manifold into the carburetor. In this way, heated air is supplied to the carburetor on cold days, and when first starting the engine and warming it up.

Since 1968, all car manufacturers have posted idle speeds and other pertinent data relative to the specific engine-car application in a conspicuous place in the engine compartment.

1970

The more stringent 1970 laws require tighter control of emissions. Crankcase emissions are controlled by the Positive Crankcase Ventilation System, and exhaust emissions by the engine Controlled Combustion System (C.C.S.), in conjunction with the new Transmission Controlled Spark System (T.C.S.)

In addition, cars sold in California are equipped with an Evaporation Control System that limits the amount of gasoline vapor discharged into the atmosphere (usually from the carburetor and fuel tank).

The T.C.S. system consists of a transmission switch, a solenoid valve, and a temperature switch. Under normal conditions, the system permits the vacuum distributor (spark) advance to operate only in high gear (both manual and automatic transmissions) and reverse.

The transmission switch is located on the transmission and senses when the transmission is in one of the lower gears. When it is in a lower gear, the switch activates the vacuum solenoid valve. This valve is located in the vacuum line that runs from the carburetor to the distributor and it shuts off vacuum to the distributor advance when it is activated. There is also an engine-temperature sensing switch which overrides the transmission switch. It will allow vacuum advance in the lower gears when engine temperature is below 85° or above 220°. There is always vacuum advance in high gear and reverse.

1971

In 1971, the Combination Emission Control System (C.E.C.), was introduced. It uses the C.C.S. of 1968–69 and incorporates several, but not all, of the features in the T.C.S. of 1970. Although distributor vacuum advance is eliminated in the lower gears, as in the T.C.S. system, it is eliminated in a different manner. A C.E.C. solenoid valve is used to regulate distributor vacuum advance.

The C.E.C. solenoid valve is mounted on the carburetor. Vacuum from the intake manifold passes through a port at the base of the solenoid before it reaches the distributor. When the solenoid receives an electrical signal, the plunger extends, opening the port, which allows vacuum to the distributor. At the same time, the plunger head contacts the carburetor throttle lever increasing the idle speed. When the solenoid is de-energized, the spring-loaded plunger returns to its unextended position closing the port and allowing the throttle lever to rest against the idle speed adjusting screw.

The switch is energized by two switches and one relay.

The time-delay relay is used to energize the C.E.C. solenoid and provide vacuum advance for the first 15 seconds after the ignition is turned on. This happens regardless of engine temperature. After the 15 seconds, the solenoid is again regulated by the temperature switch and the transmission switch.

One of the controlling switches is an engine temperature switch. It allows vacuum advance in all gears, by energizing the C.E.C. solenoid, when the engine temperature is below 82° or above 220°. In between 82° and 220°, this switch will allow no vacuum advance and the solenoid will be de-energized.

The other switch is the transmission switch. When the transmission is in the lower gears, this switch keeps the C.E.C. solenoid in the de-energized position eliminating vacuum

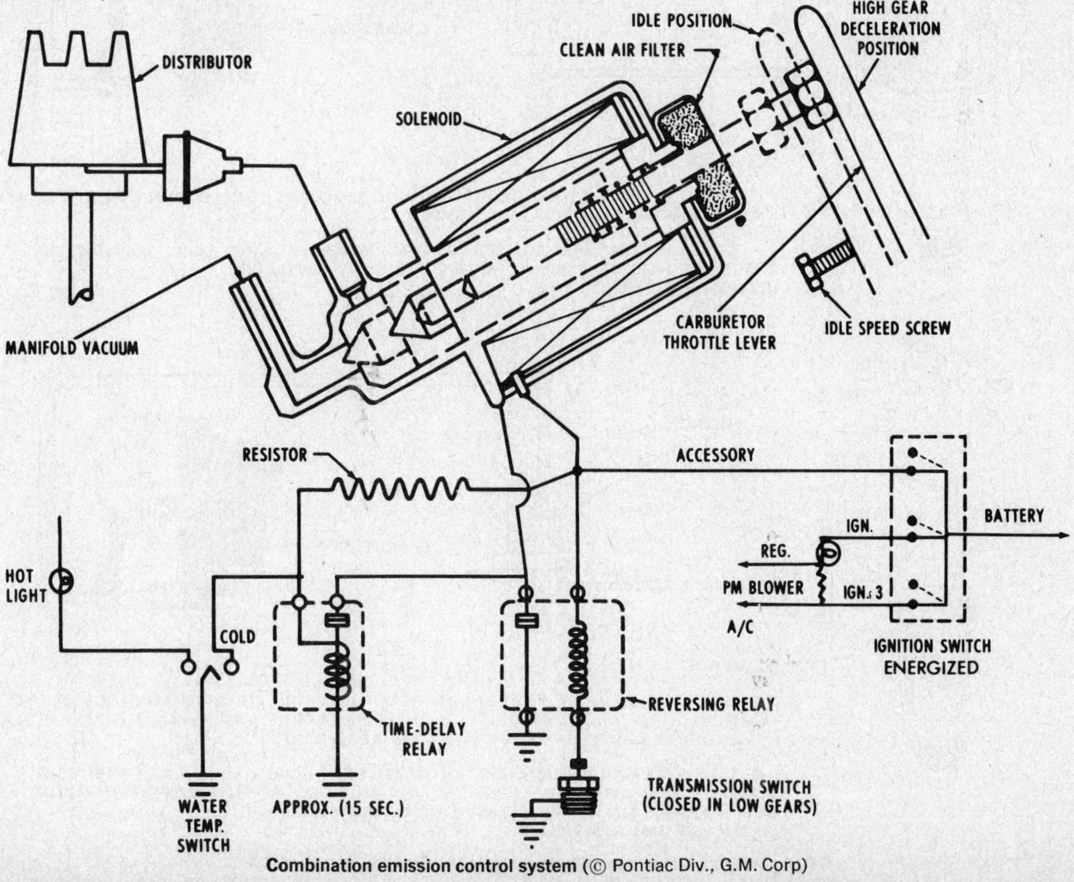
IDLE POSITION
HIGH GEAR DECELERATION POSITION
CLEAN AIR FILTER
DISTRIBUTOR
SOLENOID
MANIFOLD VACUUM
CARBURETOR THROTTLE LEVER
IDLE SPEED SCREW
RESISTOR
ACCESSORY
BATTERY
IGN.
REG.
PM BLOWER
IGN. 3
A/C
IGNITION SWITCH ENERGIZED
HOT LIGHT
COLD
TIME-DELAY RELAY
REVERSING RELAY
WATER TEMP. SWITCH
APPROX. (15 SEC.)
TRANSMISSION SWITCH (CLOSED IN LOW GEARS)

Combination emission control system (© Pontiac Div., G.M. Corp)

advance. In high gear, the solenoid is energized by current from the battery and vacuum advance is supplied.

Engine dieseling is controlled by use of lower throttle plate openings (lower carburetor idle speeds).

On air-conditioned (A/C), automatic transmission cars, a solid-state time device engages the A/C compressor for about three seconds after the ignition is turned off. The load from the compressor effectively stalls the engine and prevents dieseling or overrun.

The evaporation control system was added to all cars in 1971. This system limits the amount of gasoline vapor discharged into the air from the gas tank and carburetor. The fuel tank has a non-vented cap. As vapors are generated in the fuel tank, they flow through a liquid vapor separator to a canister where they are stored. From the canister, the vapors are routed to the carburetor where they are burned when the engine is running.

1972

All six-cylinder models with manual transmissions, and all models with a 307 V8—regardless of type of transmission—use the C.E.C. system. A description of this system can be found under the above 1971 head. All six-cylinder models with automatic transmissions use the A.I.R. system. A description of this system can be found under the above 1968 head. All V8s equipped with a manual four-speed transmission use the T.C.S. system which is described under the above 1970 head. All V8 models equipped with a three-speed manual transmission or an automatic transmission use the new Speed Control Spark System (S.C.S.).

Every engine/transmission combination uses the Auto-Therm air cleaner, P.C.V. system, and the evaporation control system of 1971.

The Speed Controlled Spark (S.C.S.), system uses a solenoid valve in the vacuum line running between the carburetor and the distributor. This valve is the same as the transmission-controlled spark valve. The difference in this system is that the valve is regulated by vehicle speed using a speed control spark switch. The S.C.S. solenoid valve is energized below 38 mph in any gear, under normal operating temperature, allowing no vacuum advance. Above 38 mph, in any gear, or any time engine temperature is higher or lower than normal operating temperature, the solenoid valve is de-energized allowing full vacuum advance to the distributor.

Normal S.C.S. engine operating temperatures range from 95° to 230°. An engine-temperature sensing switch is located in the head and de-energizes the solenoid until operating temperature is reached regardless of vehicle speed.

1973

The Controlled Combustion System (C.C.S.) is standard on all engines. The C.E.C./E.G.R. (Exhaust Gas Re-circulation) system is used on all 6 cyl engines with manual transmission. The Air Injection Reactor (A.I.R.) is used on all 6 cyl, 350 with manual transmission, and 350/400 California engines. A combination of the Transmission Controlled Spark and Exhaust Gas Re-circulation (E.G.R.) is found on all V8 engines.

E.G.R. is a system used to reduce nitrous oxide (NO_x) emissions. It functions by allowing a small amount of exhaust gas into the air fuel mixture in the intake manifold, under certain conditions.

The EGR TCS system consists of a temperature switch which senses

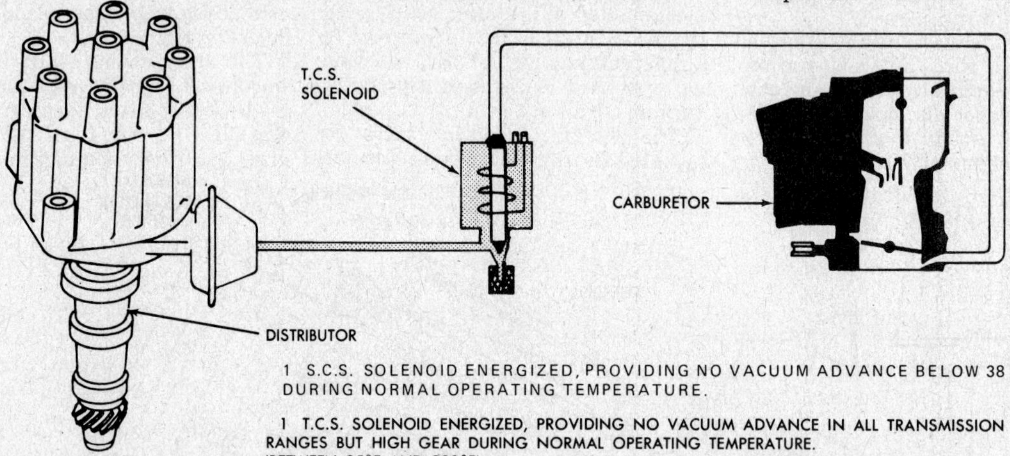
T.C.S.
SOLENOID
CARBURETOR
DISTRIBUTOR

1 S.C.S. SOLENOID ENERGIZED, PROVIDING NO VACUUM ADVANCE BELOW 38 MPH DURING NORMAL OPERATING TEMPERATURE.

1 T.C.S. SOLENOID ENERGIZED, PROVIDING NO VACUUM ADVANCE IN ALL TRANSMISSION RANGES BUT HIGH GEAR DURING NORMAL OPERATING TEMPERATURE. (BETWEEN 85°F AND 220°F)

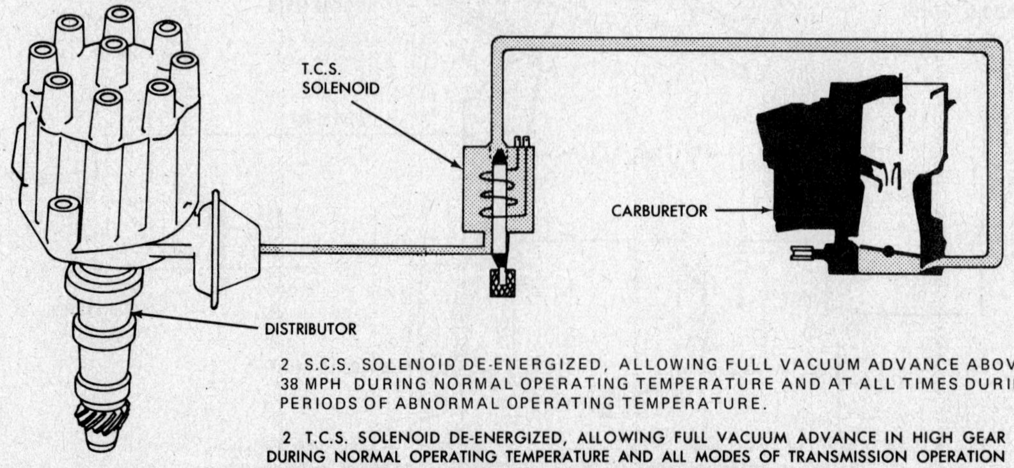
T.C.S.
SOLENOID
CARBURETOR
DISTRIBUTOR

2 S.C.S. SOLENOID DE-ENERGIZED, ALLOWING FULL VACUUM ADVANCE ABOVE 38 MPH DURING NORMAL OPERATING TEMPERATURE AND AT ALL TIMES DURING PERIODS OF ABNORMAL OPERATING TEMPERATURE.

2 T.C.S. SOLENOID DE-ENERGIZED, ALLOWING FULL VACUUM ADVANCE IN HIGH GEAR DURING NORMAL OPERATING TEMPERATURE AND ALL MODES OF TRANSMISSION OPERATION DURING PERIODS OF ABNORMAL ENGINE OPERATING TEMPERATURE. (BELOW 85°F AND ABOVE 220°F)

S.C.S. and T.C.S solenoid and vacuum routing (© Pontiac Div., G.M. Corp)

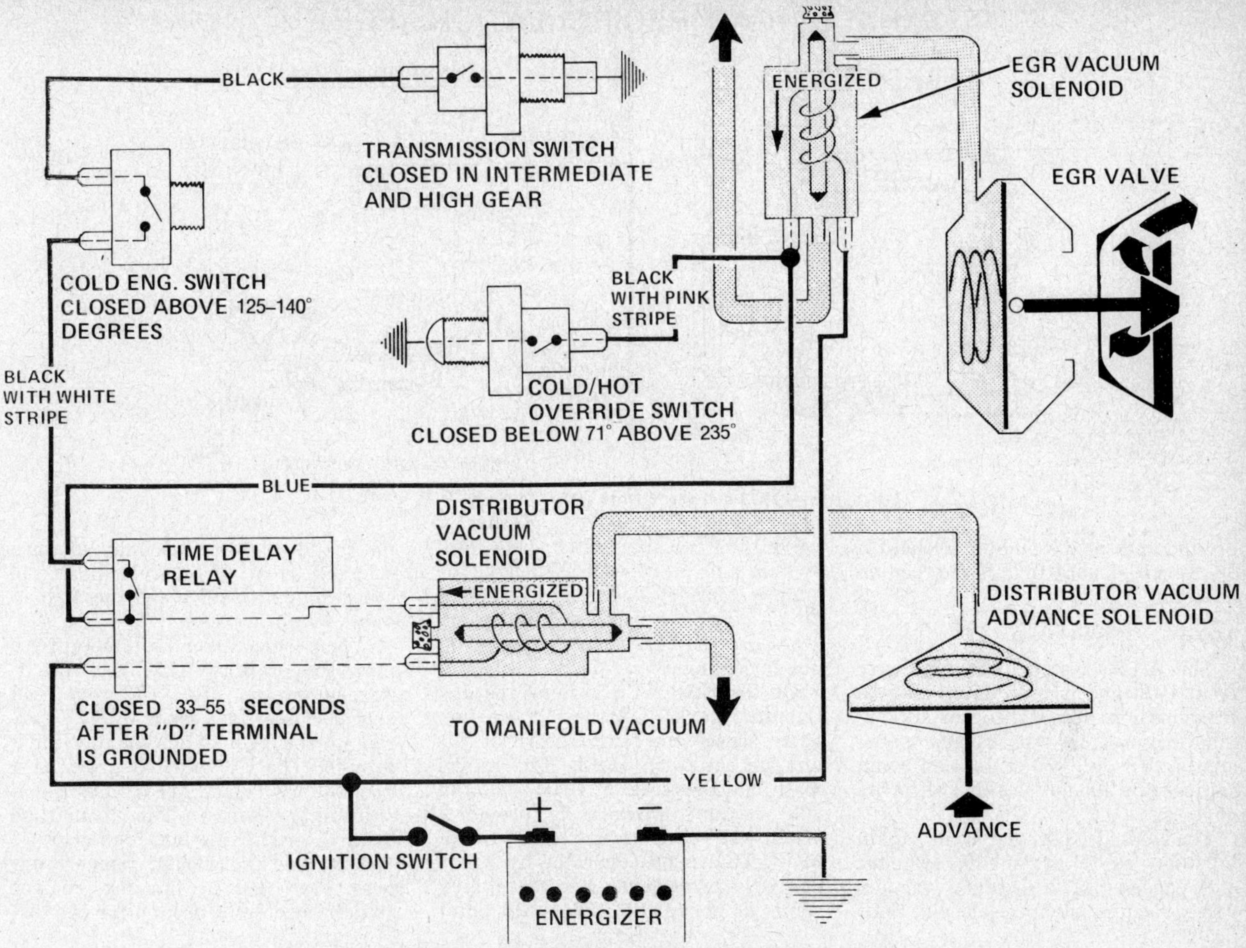
BLACK
TRANSMISSION SWITCH
CLOSED IN INTERMEDIATE
AND HIGH GEAR
ENERGIZED
EGR VACUUM
SOLENOID
EGR VALVE
COLD ENG. SWITCH
CLOSED ABOVE 125–140°
DEGREES
BLACK
WITH PINK
STRIPE
BLACK
WITH WHITE
STRIPE
COLD/HOT
OVERRIDE SWITCH
CLOSED BELOW 71° ABOVE 235°
BLUE
DISTRIBUTOR
VACUUM
SOLENOID
TIME DELAY
RELAY
ENERGIZED
DISTRIBUTOR VACUUM
ADVANCE SOLENOID
CLOSED 33–55 SECONDS
AFTER "D" TERMINAL
IS GROUNDED
TO MANIFOLD VACUUM
YELLOW
+
−
ADVANCE
IGNITION SWITCH
ENERGIZER

1973 combined TCS and EGR system (© Pontiac Div., G.M. Corp)

when the engine temperature is under 71° or over 230°, a second temperature switch sensing engine temperature between 140° and 230°, an EGR solenoid, a vacuum advance solenoid, a transmission switch, and a time delay relay.

The under 71° and over 230° switch is mounted on the left cyl head. The 140° to 230° switch is mounted in the right cyl head. The time delay relay is mounted on the vacuum advance solenoid.

The 71° to 230° switch grounds the circuit for the solenoids below 71° and above 230°. The 140° switch passes current to the transmission switch when engine temperature is between 140° and 230°. The transmission switch then grounds the circuit for the solenoids in first gear only. Between 71° and 140° the temperature switches are both open and the solenoids are in the normal positions.

The vacuum advance solenoid is normally closed, allowing no vacuum advance. The EGR solenoid is normally open, allowing exhaust gas recirculation.

Below 71° there is a complete circuit and both solenoids are energized, allowing vacuum advance and cutting off EGR.

From 71° to 140° there is an open circuit, the solenoids return to their normal positions, and vacuum advance is cut off and EGR is allowed.

From 140° to 230°, in first gear, there is an open circuit and the solenoids are in their normal positions. The time delay relay maintains the open circuit for 33 to 55 seconds after the transmission shifts into second gear. However, after the time delay in second and third gear, the solenoids are energized to allow vacuum advance and cut off EGR.

Over 235° the solenoids are energized and vacuum advance occurs and there is no EGR.

The C.E.C. system operates as for 1971, except that the time-delay relay now provides 20 seconds of vacuum advance before the solenoid is de-energized, and the engine temperature switch provides vacuum advance when engine coolant temperature is below 93°F.

1973½

A mid-year redesign of the emission control system was necessitated by newly-announced Federal standards. On cars equipped with A.I.R., A.I.R. is not supplied to nos. 3 and 6 cylinders. This is done by internal changes in the cylinder heads. Mid-year A.I.R. cylinder heads can usually be identified by the absence of a drilled passage and metal sealing ball at the nos. 3 and 6 cylinder locations.

The new engines have a relocated vacuum source for the air cleaner. Vacuum is supplied through a tee in the hose feeding vacuum to the distributor vacuum spark thermal valve.

The mid-year EGR system operates basically on the same principle as the 1973 system, except for two major differences:

1. The EGR and TCS systems now work completely independent from each other.
2. A new EGR thermal vacuum valve is used to sense the temperature of the intake manifold coolant. Below 95°F, no EGR; above 95°F, ported EGR.

In the TCS system, full vacuum advance is provided below 62°F. When the temperature rises above 62°F, the distributor vacuum spark thermal valve closes and from this point on the distributor solenoid must be energized to get vacuum advance. The upper temperature limit for vacuum advance cut-in is now 240°F.

The Start-Up Relay Switch gives full advance (ported for manual transmission) in any gear for 20 seconds after all engine starts. After the 20 seconds has elapsed, the switch breaks

EXHAUST GAS RECIRCULATION (EGR)

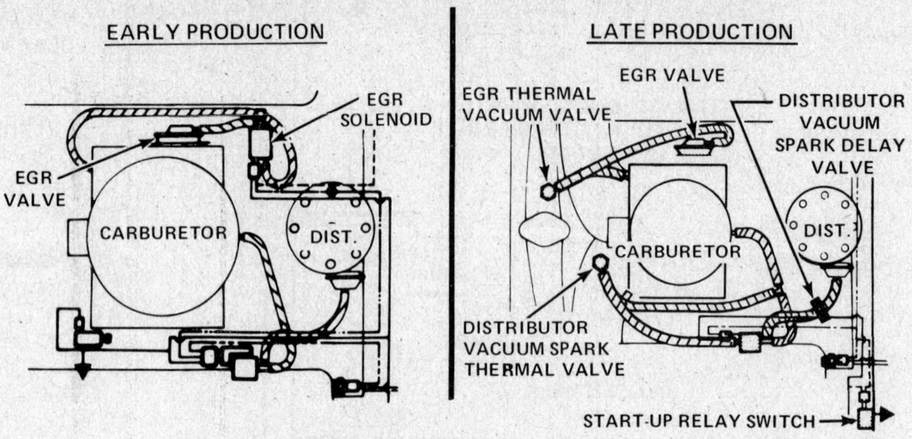
EARLY PRODUCTION
EGR SOLENOID
EGR VALVE
CARBURETOR
DIST.
LATE PRODUCTION
EGR VALVE
EGR THERMAL VACUUM VALVE
DISTRIBUTOR VACUUM SPARK DELAY VALVE
CARBURETOR
DIST.
DISTRIBUTOR VACUUM SPARK THERMAL VALVE
START-UP RELAY SWITCH

EGR system—1973 mid-year changes (© Pontiac Div, G.M. Corp)

ground and the distributor solenoid is de-energized, shutting off the vacuum advance.

1974

The A.I.R. system is carried over from 1973 and is used on all manual transmission and California six-cylinder engines, 350 2 bbl manual transmission V8s, all 350 cu in. California engines and 400 cu in. 2 bbl California engines.

The EGR/TCS system is once again together, as in pre-1973½ systems, and consists of a thermal vacuum valve, vacuum advance solenoid, EGR valve, hot coolant switch, cold feed switch and a time-delay relay for engine starting. The system is found on all V8s. Pontiac six-cylinder engines use the Chevrolet system without any changes.

On the EGR/TCS system, the distributor spark-EGR thermal vacuum valve senses the temperature of the air/fuel mixture inside the intake manifold. Below 62°F, EGR is off and full vacuum advance is provided. When the temperature rises above 62°F, EGR is on (operated by a port above the throttle blade, so that it only comes on above idle). From this point on the distributor vacuum advance solenoid must be energized by the other components and switches to provide vacuum advance.

When the cylinder head metal temperature goes above 125°, 140°, 155°F (depending on use), the cold feed switch closes. This sends the 12V current to the TCS switch looking for a ground. The TCS switch provides a ground only when the transmission shifts into high gear. There is no time delay after shifting into high gear.

Any time the coolant temperature goes over 240°F, the hot coolant switch provides a ground for the dis-

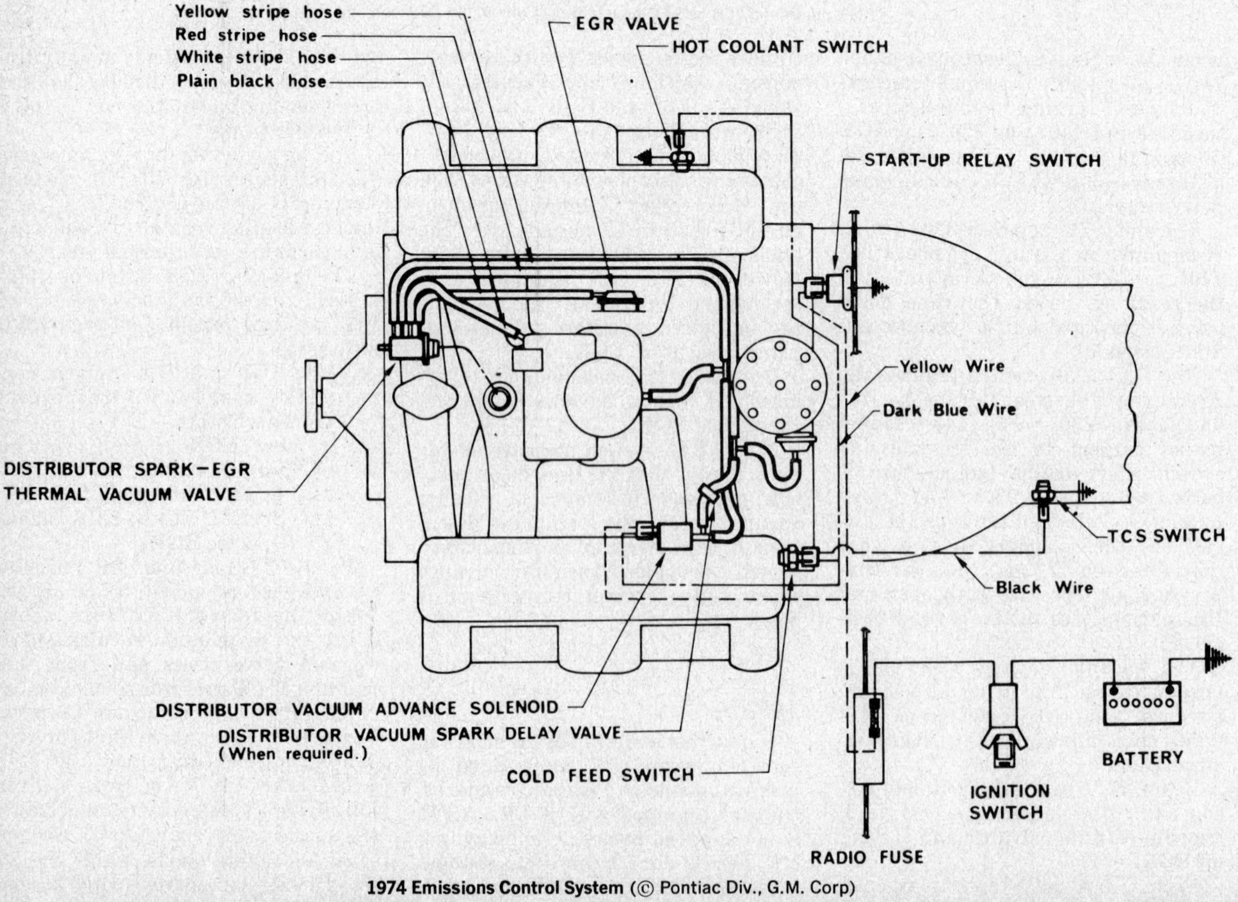
Yellow stripe hose
Red stripe hose
White stripe hose
Plain black hose
EGR VALVE
HOT COOLANT SWITCH
START-UP RELAY SWITCH
Yellow Wire
Dark Blue Wire
DISTRIBUTOR SPARK—EGR THERMAL VACUUM VALVE
TCS SWITCH
Black Wire
DISTRIBUTOR VACUUM ADVANCE SOLENOID
DISTRIBUTOR VACUUM SPARK DELAY VALVE (When required.)
COLD FEED SWITCH
BATTERY
IGNITION SWITCH
RADIO FUSE

1974 Emissions Control System (© Pontiac Div., G.M. Corp)

tributor solenoid. Since the hot coolant switch will ground whether the TCS switch does or not, vacuum advance will be supplied to the distributor in any gear when the coolant temperature reaches 240°F or above.

There is a distributor vacuum spark delay valve on some models, between the distributor solenoid and the distributor acting as a restrictor on vacuum supplied to the distributor. This merely slows down the rate vacuum as initially supplied to the distributor. Full vacuum is eventually supplied.

The function of the start-up relay switch is identical to 1973½. See Pontiac section for further details.

ENGINE

Six-Cylinder Engine

1967-69

A belt-driven, overhead cam engine of 230 or 250 cu in. displacement, was offered from 1966 to 1969. It uses a cast iron block and head, and was available with a 4 bbl carburetor. A unique feature was the accessory drive housing assembly located on the front, right-hand side of the engine containing the oil pump and filter, fuel pump, and distributor. The assembly is driven by the cam belt.

1970-74

The overhead cam six-cylinder engine was replaced by an overhead valve, 250 cu. in., six-cylinder engine in 1970. It has a cast iron block and cylinder head, uses hydraulic valve lifters, and is similar in construction to the Chevrolet engine.

V8 Engine

In 1967, the two 326 cu. in. V8's were kept in the engine lineup, but the old 389 was replaced by three versions of the new 400 cu. in. V8. In 1968 and 1969, the 400 engine was retained, although the Ram Air version of this engine was given four-bolt main caps due to the increased performance. In 1968, an all-new 350 cu. in. engine of Pontiac design was introduced. This engine is used as the standard base engine up to the present.

In 1970, the 400 cu. in. engine was available in two Ram Air versions for use in the GTO—the Ram Air III and IV. For the first time, a high output version of the 455 cu. in. engine, also with four-bolt main caps, was made available in the GTO. This engine was used in the Trans Am Firebird and GTO Judge in 1971, and in the LeMans and Grand Am in 1973.

The 1971 Ventura II has, as an option, a 307 cu. in. V8 of Chevrolet design. This engine was supplemented in 1972 by the two-barrel Pontiac 350 cu. in V8. The 307 cu. in V8 was dropped in 1973.

Engine R & R

1967-74 6 Cylinder and 1967-74 V8

1. Disconnect battery.
2. Drain cooling system.
3. Scribe alignment marks on hood and remove hood from hinges.
4. Disconnect the engine wiring harness and ground straps, alternator wires, and the engine-temperature and oil-pressure sending-unit wires.
5. Remove air cleaner and fan shield or shroud.
6. Disconnect radiator and heater hoses.
7. If equipped with manual transmission, remove radiator.
8. Remove fan and fan pulley.

NOTE: if equipped with power steering and/or air conditioning, disconnect and swing aside pump/compressor *without* disconnecting hoses.

9. Disconnect accelerator linkage and support bracket.
10. Disconnect automatic transmission vacuum modulator line and power brake vacuum line at carburetor.

NOTE: on Firebird models up to 1969 with air conditioning, remove wiper motor.

11. Jack up front of car and drain engine oil.
12. Disconnect fuel lines at pump.
13. Disconnect exhaust pipes.
14. Disconnect the starter wires and remove the starter on six-cylinder models.
15. If equipped with automatic transmission, remove converter cover and crank the engine and three converter retaining bolts, then slide converter to the rear.
16. If equipped with manual transmission, disconnect clutch linkage and remove clutch cross-shaft.

NOTE: remove starter and lower flywheel cover on 1970-72 V8s and L-6 from 1971.

17. Remove four lower bellhousing bolts (two per side).
18. Disconnect transmission filler tube support (automatic) and starter wire shield from cylinder heads.
19. Remove two front motor mount-to-frame bracket bolts.
20. Lower car to floor then, using a jack and a wood block, support the transmission.
21. Remove two remaining bellhousing bolts.
22. Raise transmission slightly, using the jack and wood block, then, using a chain hoist, remove the engine.
23. To install, reverse removal procedure. Install the two upper bellhousing bolts first (with jack still under transmission).

NOTE: do not lower engine completely until jack and wood block are removed.

Manifolds

Intake Manifold R & R

1967-74 V8 Except Ventura II 307

1. Drain radiator and block.

NOTE: there are petcocks on each side of block; jack up rear of car 15-18 in. to drain completely.

2. Remove air cleaner and upper radiator hose.
3. Disconnect heater hose.
4. Disconnect temperature gauge wire, then remove two spark plug wire brackets from manifold.
5. Disconnect power brake vacuum and distributor vacuum lines.

NOTE: vacuum retard line is located at lower rear of vacuum unit on some exhaust emission distributors.

6. Disconnect fuel line at carburetor.
7. Disconnect crankcase vent hose and accelerator linkage.
8. Remove bolts that secure accelerator linkage bracket, then remove intake manifold bolts and nuts. If the intake manifold will not clear the distributor, remove the distributor after noting the position of the rotor and the distributor housing.
9. Remove manifold and gasket.

CAUTION: make sure O-ring between intake manifold and timing chain cover is in place.

10. To install, reverse removal procedure, tightening timing chain cover to manifold bolts to 10-20 ft. lbs., manifold hold-down bolts and nuts evenly to 40-45 ft. lbs.

Intake Manifold R & R—

1971-72 Ventura II 307 V8

1. Drain water from radiator and both sides of block.

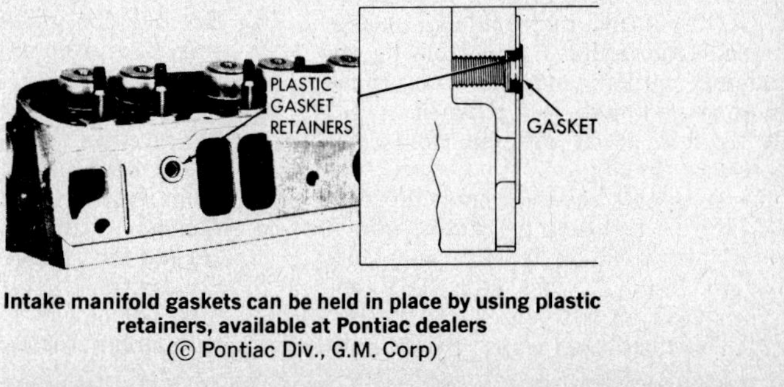
PLASTIC
GASKET
RETAINERS
GASKET

Intake manifold gaskets can be held in place by using plastic retainers, available at Pontiac dealers
(© Pontiac Div., G.M. Corp)

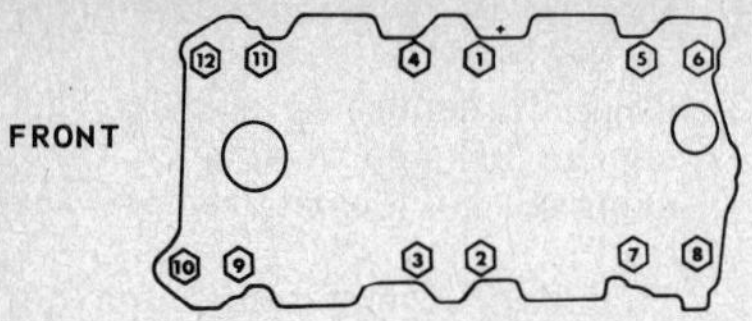
FRONT
12
11
4
1
5
6
10
9
3
2
7
8

307 intake manifold torque sequence
(© Pontiac Div., G.M. Corp)

2. Disconnect battery cables, upper radiator hose, accelerator linkage, carburetor fuel line, coil and temperature sender wires.
3. Disconnect power brake hose at carburetor base and spark advance hose at distributor.
4. Disconnect PCV hoses, then remove distributor cap and matchmark rotor and housing.
5. Remove distributor hold-down clamp and pull out distributor.
6. Remove upper alternator bracket and coil.
7. Remove manifold-to-head bolts, then remove manifold from engine.
8. To install, reverse removal procedure. Stick manifold end seals in position with sealer and tighten manifold bolts to 30 ft. lbs.

6 Cylinder Intake and Exhaust Manifold R & R

1967-74

1. Remove air cleaner.
2. Disconnect accelerator linkage and return spring.
3. Disconnect fuel and vacuum lines at carburetor; disconnect choke rod.

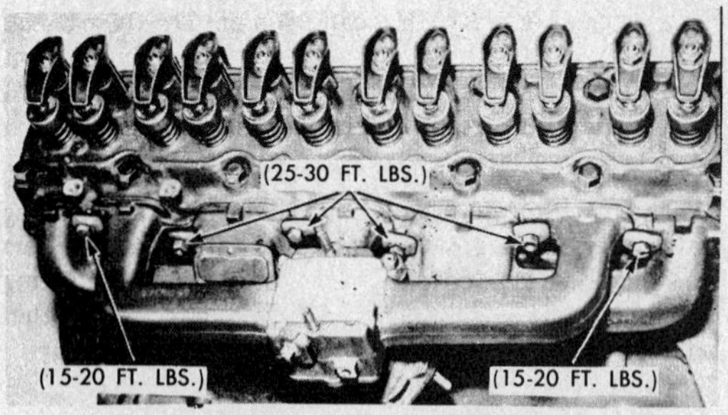
(25-30 FT. LBS.)
(15-20 FT. LBS.)
(15-20 FT. LBS.)

6 cyl manifold torque values
(© Pontiac Div., G.M. Corp)

4. Disconnect exhaust pipe at manifold flange.
5. Remove manifold bolts and clamps, then remove manifolds.

NOTE: intake manifold can be separated from exhaust manifold by removing one bolt and two nuts. These fasteners should be tightened to 15-30 ft. lbs. after the manifolds are bolted to the engine.

6. To install, reverse removal procedure, tightening center clamp bolts to 25-30 ft. lbs., end bolts to 15-20 ft. lbs. (for OHV engines), or all bolts to 30 ft. lbs. (for OHC engines).

V8 Right-Side Exhaust Manifold

Removal

1. On 307 engines, disconnect the battery ground cable.
2. On 307 engines, remove the air cleaner pre-heater stove.
3. Disconnect the exhaust pipe from the manifold.
4. Straighten the tabs on the manifold bolts and remove the manifold bolts, manifold, and gasket.

Installation

1. Clean the gasket surfaces.
2. Replace the exhaust manifold, using a new gasket; the holes in the end of the gasket are slotted.

NOTE: the installation of the gasket may be simplified by first installing the manifold using only the front and rear bolts to retain the manifold. Allow clearance of about 3/16 in. between the cylinder head and the exhaust manifold. After inserting the gasket between the head and the manifold, the remaining bolts may be installed.

3. On the 307 engine, torque the center bolts to 30 ft lbs, and the end bolts to 20 ft lbs. On all other engines, torque all bolts evenly to 30 ft lbs.
4. Bend the tabs against the bolt heads.
5. Attach the exhaust pipe, using a new gasket.
6. Connect the battery ground cable on the 307 (only).
7. Install air cleaner pre-heater stove on the 307 (only).

V8 Left-Side Exhaust Manifold

Removal

1. Remove the generator belt, generator, and mounting bracket as an assembly.
2. Remove the spark plugs from 307 engines.
3. Disconnect the exhaust pipe from the manifold.
4. Remove the air pre-heater shroud from 307 engines.
5. Straighten the tabs on the manifold bolt locks and remove the bolts and manifold.

Installation

1. Clean the gasket surfaces.
2. Reverse the removal procedures for installation.

Valve System

Valve Guides

Pontiac engines have integral valve guides. Pontiac offers valves with oversize stems for worn guides (0.001, 0.003 and 0.005 in. being available for most engines). To fit these, enlarge valve guide bores with valve guide reamers to an oversize that cleans up wear. If a large oversize is required, it is best to approach that size in stages by using a series of reamers of increasing diameter. This helps to maintain the concentricity of the guide bores with the valve seats. The correct valve stem to guide clearance is given in the Valve Specifications table at the beginning of this section.

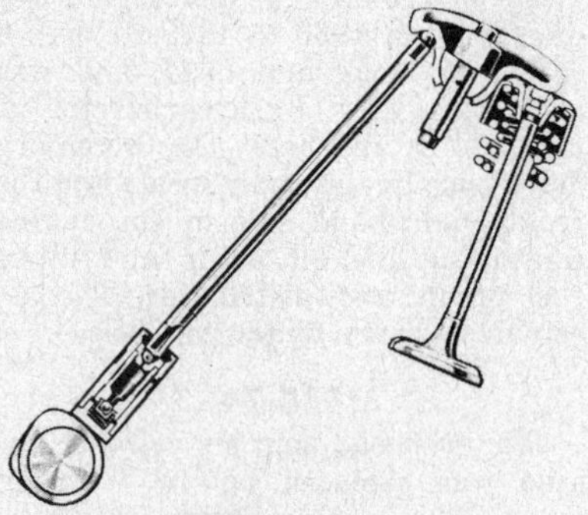

V8 valve train
(© Pontiac Div., G.M. Corp)

As an alternate procedure, some local automotive machine shops fit replacement guides that use standard stem valves.

Rocker Arm R&R

1. Remove the valve covers.
2. Remove the rocker arm nut and rocker arm ball.
3. Lift the rocker arm off the rocker arm stud. Always keep the rocker arm assemblies together and assemble them on the same stud.
4. Remove the pushrod from its bore. Make sure the rods are returned to their original bores, with the same end in the block.
5. Reverse the removal procedure to install the rocker arms and adjust the valve on any rocker arm that was removed before installing the valve cover.

Hydraulic Valve Lifter Disassembly

Disassemble lifters for cleaning only; no repairs are permitted.

1. Grasp lock ring with needle nose pliers and remove. (Depress plunger to gain clearance.)
2. Remove pushrod cup, metering valve disc, and upper metering

disc (if any). Do not bend metering disc.
3. Remove plunger assembly and plunger spring.
4. Remove spring, check valve retainer and check valve from plunger.
5. Clean all parts in solvent (lacquer thinner) and reassemble.

NOTE: internal parts are **not** interchangeable between lifters.

Valve Adjustment

1967-69 6 Cylinder OHC

This engine is equipped with hydraulic valve lash adjusters. These adjusters are located in the cylinder head and serve as a fulcrum of the rocker arms, and locate the rocker arms accurately with the camshaft lobes. This lash adjuster is identical to that of a lifter used in a conventional pushrod engine. However, the lash adjuster remains stationary to maintain adjustment at all times.

These adjusters are to be serviced in the same manner as conventional hydraulic tappets.

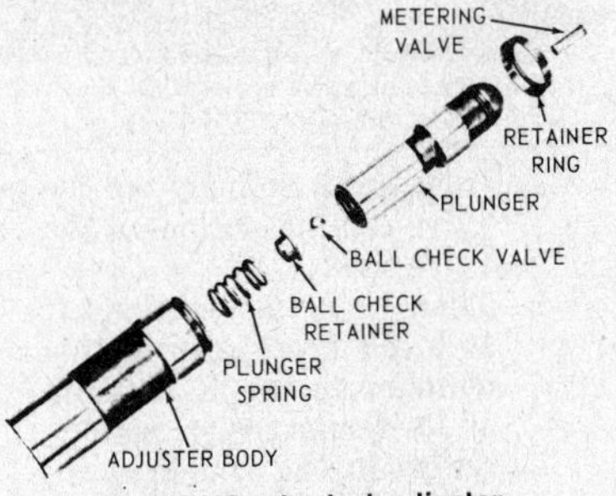
METERING VALVE
RETAINER RING
PLUNGER
BALL CHECK VALVE
BALL CHECK RETAINER
PLUNGER SPRING
ADJUSTER BODY

6 cyl OHC valve lash adjuster
(© Pontiac Div., G.M. Corp)

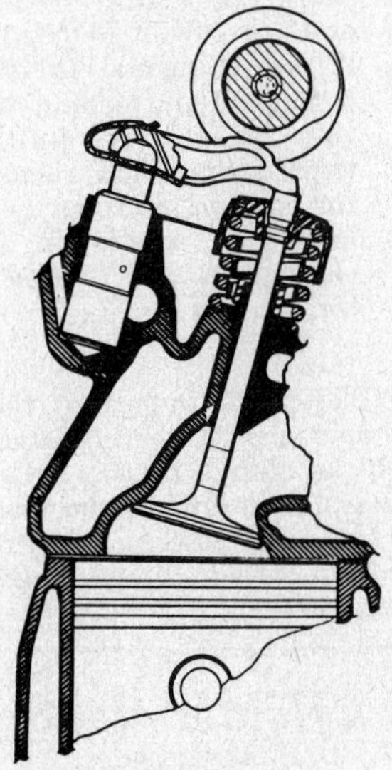

6 cyl OHC valve train
(© Pontiac Div., G.M. Corp)

R & R

1. Remove rocker cover assembly.
2. Remove rocker arm and hydraulic lash adjuster assemblies, keeping them in proper order for correct installation in original positions.
3. If lash adjuster sticks in its bore, proceed as follows:
   a. Remove rocker arm.
   b. Fill vent hole adjacent to lifter with SAE 30 oil.
   c. Insert a 4 in. length of 3/16 in. diameter rod into the vent hole and strike the end of the rod sharply with a hammer.

NOTE: the hydraulic pressure generated in this operation should be sufficient to dislodge even the most stubborn adjuster.

4. To install, reverse removal procedure, with the exception of Step 3.

1970-74 6 Cylinders and All V8s

The purpose of the hydraulic valve lifter is to maintain zero clearance in the valve train. It does this by expanding to take up additional clearance created as the lifter moves onto the base circle of its camshaft lobe. To perform properly, the lifter must be adjusted half-way between its fully extended position and its collapsed position. If the lifter is adjusted too loosely, the valve will not open fully; if adjusted too lightly, any number of major mechanical failures may result.

When a rocker arm is loosened or removed, the lifter will expand to its fully extended position. Upon reassembly, it is necessary to be sure that the lifter is on its camshaft lobe base circle before adjusting the lifter. This is the purpose of the preliminary valve adjustment. Perform the final valve adjustment after the engine is running.

Preliminary Valve Adjustment

1. Rotate the crankshaft until no. 1 piston is at TDC on the compression stroke and the distributor rotor points to no. 1 spark plug wire cap tower. The timing mark should be aligned with zero (0°) on the timing cover.
2. Tighten the adjusting nut until the play just disappears. Adjust both valves. On Ram Air and Super Duty engines, adjust the valves to obtain a 0.008 in. clearance between the rocker arms and valve stems, then tighten the adjusting nut an additional ⅛ turn and tighten the locknut.
3. On V8s, rotate the crankshaft 90°, in the normal direction of rotation, to bring the next piston in firing order to TDC on the compression stroke. Repeat step two until all of the valves are done. On six-cylinder engines, bring each cylinder to TDC on its compression stroke and repeat step two.

Final Valve Adjustment

1. Start the engine and retighten the rocker arm on any valve that is clattering. Tighten until the noise disappears.
2. Allow the engine to run until normal operating temperature is reached, then loosen each rocker arm adjusting nut until clattering begins. Retighten the nut until the noise disappears. On all V8s, except the 307, tighten the nut, very slowly, to 20 ft lbs. On the 307 and 1970–72 six-cylinder engines, tighten the nut ½-1 revolution further, very slowly.

NOTE: the purpose of tightening the adjusting nut slowly is to give the lifter time to adjust its height.

Rocker Arm Stud R & R

1970-74 OHV 6 Cylinder

1. Remove rocker cover and rocker arm.
2. File two slots 3/32-1/8 in. deep on opposite sides of stud. Bottom of slots should be ½ in. from top of stud hole.
3. Place spacer washer (or tool J-6392-3) over stud, then position a stud remover (or tool J-6392-1) on stud and tighten securely.
4. Place a spacer (socket or J-6392-2) over the stud remover, then thread a 7/8 in. nut on stud remover and turn in until stud pulls from head.

Rocker stud height—OHV 6 cyl
(© Pontiac Div., G.M. Corp)

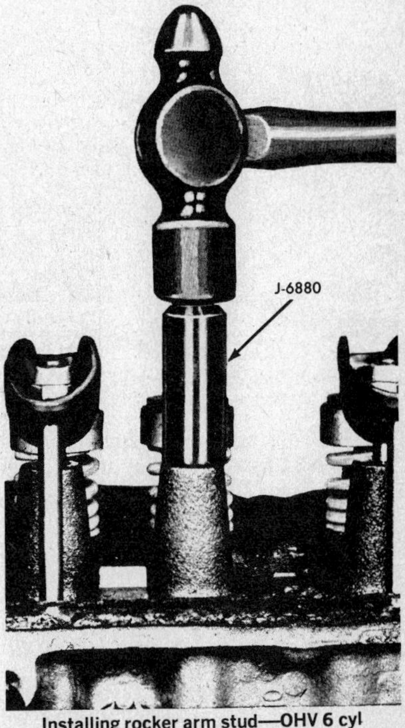
J-6880

Installing rocker arm stud—OHV 6 cyl
(© Pontiac Div., G.M. Corp)

5. If an oversize stud is to be used (0.003 and 0.013 in. oversize studs are available), ream stud hole to proper size.
6. To install, coat press-fit area of stud with axle lube, then press or hammer into place.

NOTE: the factory recommends that tool J-6880 be used for this job. This tool is simply a sleeve that is held in place with an Allen screw—it protects the threads from damage. Any homemade tool similar to the one illustrated will work if care is exercised. Do not hammer directly on the stud, because it is hardened to the point where it will fracture if subjected to shock.

1967-74 V8 Except GTO and Ventura II

Caution This procedure can be used **only** on engines with pressed-in rocker studs. GTO and some special high performance engines have screwed-in rocker studs which are easily identified by their hex head lower portion. Another common stud-securing procedure on standard engines is "pinning" pressed-in studs by drilling through the stud boss and stud and inserting an interference-fit roll pin. Make sure any such pins are removed before attempting the following procedure.

1. Disconnect battery and drain cooling system.
2. Remove rocker cover.
3. Pack oily rags around stud holes and engine openings.
4. Remove rocker arm and pushrod, then file two slots 3/32-1/8 in. deep on opposite sides of the stud. The top of the slots should be ¼-3/8 in. below thread travel.

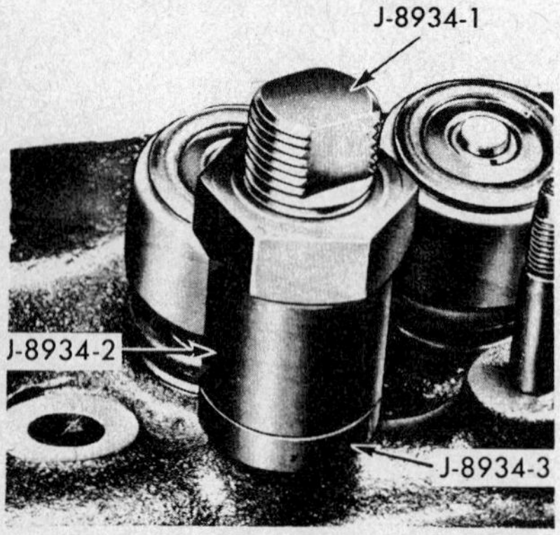
J-8934-1
J-8934-2
J-8934-3

Removing rocker arm stud—V8
(© Pontiac Div., G.M. Corp)

5. Place a spacer washer (or tool J-8934-3) over the stud, then position stud remover (or tool J-8934-1) on stud and tighten Allen screws.
6. Place a spacer (socket or J-8934-2) over the remover, then thread a 7/8 in. nut on stud remover and turn in until stud pulls from head.
7. If an oversize stud is to be used (0.003 in. oversize studs are available), ream stud hole to the proper size, then clean chips from area.
8. To install, refer to Step 6 of OHV 6 cylinder stud replacement procedure, substituting factory tool number J-23342 for J-6880.

NOTE: valve adjustment for Ram Air IV engines is covered later in this section.

GTO Screwed-In Rocker Studs

1. Remove rocker cover.
2. Remove rocker arm and nut.
3. Remove stud, using a deep socket.
4. Install new stud, tightening to 50 ft. lbs.

1971-74 Ventura II V8

1. Remove rocker cover.
2. Place a stack of ⅜ in. washers over stud so that about 8-10 threads show.
3. Thread a ⅜—24 nut onto stud and turn it down with a wrench until stud begins to move. It will be necessary to remove nut and add more washers as the stud comes out.

NOTE: Stud can be rethreaded to ⅜—16 if it's stripped.

4. To install, coat the stud with hypoid lube, then press in using tool J-6880, as for OHV six.

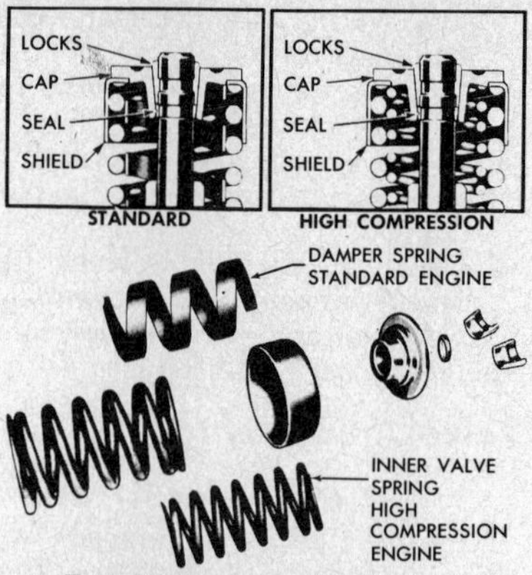
LOCKS
CAP
SEAL
SHIELD
STANDARD
LOCKS
CAP
SEAL
SHIELD
HIGH COMPRESSION
DAMPER SPRING STANDARD ENGINE
INNER VALVE SPRING HIGH COMPRESSION ENGINE

Typical valve spring assemblies
(© Pontiac Div., G.M. Corp)

J 22263-1
J 22263-2

Compressing valve spring OHC 6 cyl
(© Pontiac Div., G.M. Corp)

Chilton's TIME SAVER

The following is a method for replacing valve springs, oil seals or spring retainers without removing the cylinder head.

1. **Obtain a spark plug hole airchuck adapter from an auto parts store.**
2. **To this adapter add an airchuck so that the hose from an air compressor can be attached. This assembly will be used later to pressurize the cylinder.**
3. **Remove the valve rocker cover. Remove the rocker arm from the valve to be worked on.**
4. **Remove the spark plug from the cylinder to be worked on.**
5. **Turn the crankshaft to bring the piston of this cylinder down, away from possible contact with the valve head. Sharply tap the valve retainer to loosen the valve lock.**
6. **Then turn the crankshaft to bring the piston in this cylinder to the Exact Top of its Compression Stroke.**
7. **Screw in the chuck-equipped tool.**
8. **Hook up an air hose to the chuck and turn on the pressure (about 200 lbs.).**
9. **With a strong and constant supply of air holding the valve closed, compress the valve spring and remove the lock and retainer.**
10. **Make the necessary replacements and reassemble.**

NOTE: it is important that the operation be performed exactly as stated, in this order. The piston in the cylinder must be on exact top-center to prevent air pressure from turning the crankshaft.

1²¹⁄₃₂"
TO
1²³⁄₃₂"

Checking valve spring height—6 cyl
(© Pontiac Div., G.M. Corp)

Cylinder Head

1967-69 6 Cylinder OHC

Removal

1. Drain cooling system and remove air cleaner.
2. Disconnect accelerator pedal cable at bellcrank on manifold, and fuel and vacuum lines at carburetor.
3. Disconnect exhaust pipe at mani-

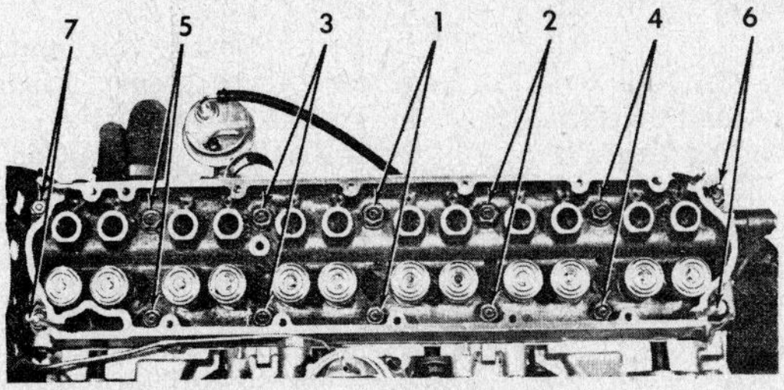
7
5
3
1
2
4
6
Cylinder head torque sequence—OHC 6 cyl
(© Pontiac Div., G.M. Corp)

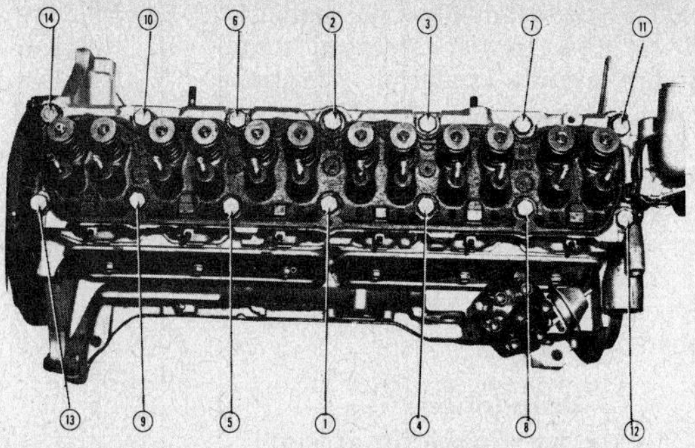
14
10
6
2
3
7
11
13
9
5
1
4
8
12
Cylinder head torque sequence—1970-74 OHV 6 cyl
(© Pontiac Div., G.M. Corp)

fold flange, then remove manifold bolts and clamps and remove manifolds and carburetor as an assembly.

4. Remove timing belt top front cover.
5. Align timing marks, remove belt tension then remove belt from camshaft sprocket.
6. Remove rocker arm cover assembly.
7. Remove timing belt upper front cover mounting support bracket and rear lower cover.
8. Disconnect spark plug wires.
9. Remove rocker arms and hydraulic valve lash adjusters. Keep rocker arms and hydraulic lash adjusters in proper sequence for exact location for installation.
10. Remove cylinder head bolts and gasket.
11. Clean gasket surfaces and carbon from cylinder head and block.

Installation

When installing new head, transfer all serviceable parts to new head using new seals on intake and exhaust valves and new intake and exhaust manifold gaskets.

1. Place new cylinder head gasket in position over dowels in cylinder block.
2. Guide cylinder head into place over dowels and gasket.
3. Start all cylinder head bolts in threads.

NOTE: bolts are of two different lengths. When inserted into proper holes, all bolts will project an equal distance from the head. Do not use sealer of any kind on threads.

4. Tighten cylinder head a little at a time with a torque wrench. Tighten center bolts and then the end bolts. Final torque should be 90-100 ft. lbs. Tighten the bolts to specifications in three stages.
5. Reverse Steps 1-9 of removal to complete installation procedure.

1970-74 6 Cylinder

Removal

1. Drain cooling system, remove air cleaner. Disconnect radiator hoses.
2. Disconnect accelerator pedal rod at bellcrank, fuel and vacuum lines at carburetor. Disconnect exhaust pipe at manifold flange.
3. Remove manifold-to-cylinder head attaching bolts and manifolds.
4. Remove rocker arm cover assembly, temperature sender and coil wires.
5. Loosen rocker arm nuts and rotate rocker arms so the pushrods can be removed.
6. Remove pushrods and store them so they can be installed in their original locations.
7. Disconnect spark plug wires.
8. Remove cylinder head bolts.
9. Lift off the head.
10. Remove cylinder head gasket.

Installation

1. Position new cylinder head gasket on block, on locating dowels.
2. Place cylinder head in position.
3. Install cylinder head attaching bolts. Torque to 95 ft. lbs. Tighten to specifications in three stages.
4. Install pushrods in original location and position.
5. Position rocker arms and torque rocker arm nuts to 20 ft. lbs., further tighten until valve train play is removed. Adjust the valve lash as given in the previous section.
6. Install rocker arm cover.
7. Install manifold-to-cylinder head bolts and torque to 30 ft. lbs. (center) and 15-20 ft. lbs. (end).
8. Install pushrod cover and crankcase breather outlet pipe.
9. Connect all wires, hoses and linkage; fill cooling system and check for leaks.
10. Connect spark plug wires.

1967-74 V8

Removal

NOTE: drain the cooling system, including the block.

1. Remove intake manifold, valley cover, and rocker arm cover.
2. Loosen all rocker arm retaining nuts and pivot rockers off pushrods.
3. Remove pushrods and place in order.

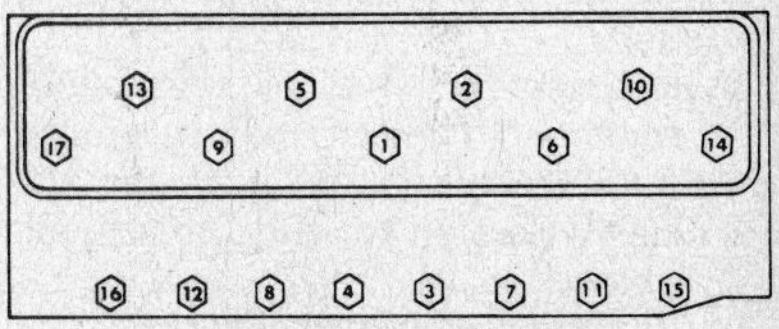
13
5
2
10
17
9
1
6
14
16
12
8
4
3
7
11
15
Cylinder head torque sequence—1971-72 307 V8
(© Pontiac Div., G.M. Corp)

4. On all but the left head of the 455 S.D. engine, remove the exhaust pipe-to-manifold attaching bolts. In order to remove the left head of the 455 S.D., it is necessary to remove the exhaust manifold attaching nuts and drop the manifold. Remove the inner panel of the carburetor heat stove from the two center cylinder head bolts.

NOTE: on 1968-70 air-conditioned Firebird models, remove compressor hold-down bolts and move compressor aside *without* disconnecting hoses.

5. Remove battery ground strap and engine ground strap on left head; engine ground strap and automatic transmission oil filler tube bracket on right head.
6. Remove cylinder head bolts and head, with exhaust manifold attached.

13
10
2
4
7
14
11
1
5
8
12
9
3
6
Cylinder head torque sequence—all V8 except 307
(© Pontiac Div., G.M. Corp)

NOTE: left head must be maneuvered to clear power steering and power brake units except on Ventura II.

NOTE: on 1968-70 air-conditioned Firebird models, the right motor mount-to-frame bolt must be removed and the engine jacked up about 2 in. to gain access to the right rear rocker arm cover bolt and cylinder head bolt.

Installation

1. Check head surface for straightness, then place a new head gasket on block.

CAUTION: on 1968-70 air-conditioned Firebird models, install right rear head bolt into head *before* placing head on block.

NOTE: bolts are of three different lengths on all V8s. When bolts are properly installed, they will project an equal distance from head.

2. Install all bolts and tighten evenly to specified torque. Tighten the bolts to specifications in three stages.
3. Install pushrods in original positions.
4. Position rocker arms over pushrods and tighten ball retaining nuts to 20 ft. lbs. and see the Valve Section for the adjustment procedure.
5. Replace rocker arm cover.
6. Replace valley cover.
7. Replace ground straps, oil filler tube bracket, intake manifold, and right motor mount bolt (on A/C Firebird models).
8. Install exhaust pipe flange nuts. On 455 S.D. engine, install left head exhaust manifold, with new gasket.

NOTE: most left and right cylinder heads are interchangeable within a single year, large- and small-valve heads should not be used on the same engine.

Cylinder Head Disassembly

1. Remove cylinder heads, as previously described.
2. Compress valve springs, using valve spring compressor.
3. Remove valve locks or keys.
4. Release valve springs.
5. Remove valve springs, retainers, oil seals, and valves.

NOTE: if a valve does not slide out of the guide easily, check end of stem for mushrooming or heading over. If head is mushroomed, file off excess material, remove and discard valve. If valve is not mushroomed, lubricate stem, remove valve and check guide for galling.

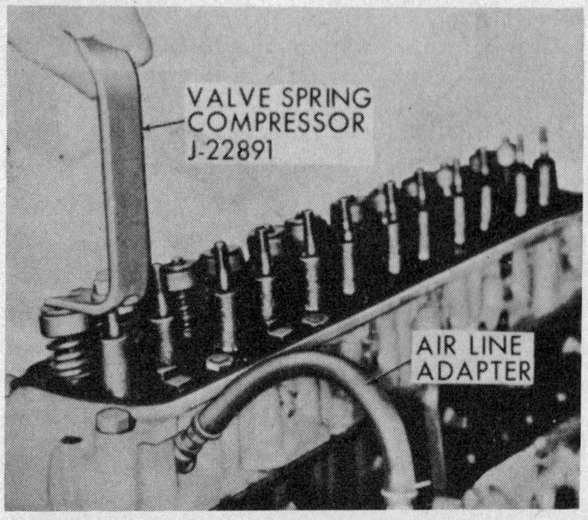
VALVE SPRING
COMPRESSOR
J-22891
AIR LINE
ADAPTER

Timing Case

Timing Gear Cover and Oil Seal R & R

1970-74 OHV 6 Cylinder

1. Drain cooling system and disconnect radiator hoses at radiator.
2. Remove fan and water pump pulley.
3. Remove radiator and fan belt.
4. Remove harmonic balancer, using a puller.
5. Loosen oil pan bolts and allow pan to rest against front crossmember.

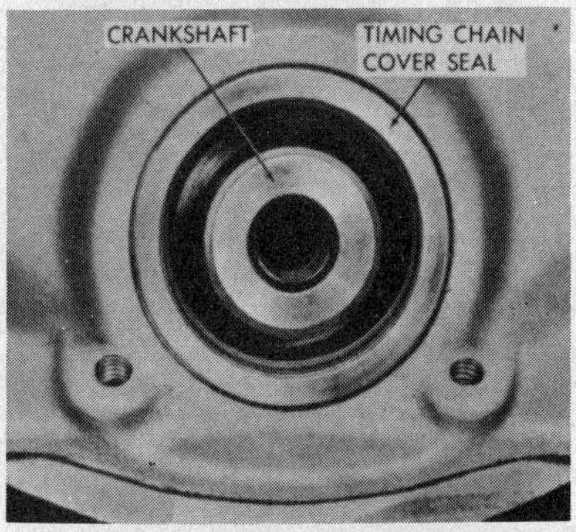
CRANKSHAFT
TIMING CHAIN
COVER SEAL

Timing chain cover oil seal
(© Pontiac Div., G.M. Corp)

6. Remove timing gear cover bolts, then remove cover and gasket.
7. Pry out oil seal using a screwdriver.

NOTE: seal can be replaced with cover installed.

8. Install new seal, with lip toward inside of cover. Drive it into place, using proper seal installer or an old wheel bearing outer race.
9. Inspect oil nozzle for damage and replace if necessary, then clean all gasket surfaces.
10. Install cover and gasket (stick gasket to block with Vaseline or wheel bearing grease), making sure cover is centered properly on crankshaft end.
11. Tighten cover bolts to 7 ft. lbs., then install oil pan and harmonic balancer.

1967-74 V8 Except 307

1. Drain radiator and cylinder block.
2. Loosen alternator adjusting bolts.
3. Remove fan, fan pulley, and accessory drive belts.
4. Disconnect radiator hoses.
5. Remove fuel pump.

NOTE: not necessary if only seal is being replaced.

6. Remove harmonic balancer bolt and washer.
7. Remove harmonic balancer.

NOTE: do not pry on rubber-mounted balancers. Seal can be removed, using a screwdriver, at this point. Install new seal with lip inward.

8. Remove front four oil pan to timing cover bolts.
9. Remove timing cover bolts and nuts and cover to intake manifold bolt.
10. Pull cover forward and remove.
11. Remove O-ring from recess in intake manifold, then clean all gasket surfaces.
12. To replace seal, pry it out of the cover using a screwdriver. Install the new seal with lip inwards.

NOTE: seal can be replaced with cover installed.

13. To install, reverse removal procedure, making sure all gaskets are replaced. Tighten four oil pan bolts to 12 ft. lbs., harmonic balancer bolt to 160 ft. lbs., and fan pulley bolts to 20 ft. lbs.

1971-74 Ventura II 307 V8

NOTE: Removal is similar to other V8 engines with the exceptions noted.

1. Remove oil pan, as outlined in the Lubrication Section.
2. Lower engine back onto motor mounts.
3. Remove harmonic balancer, using a puller.
4. Remove water pump, as outlined previously.
5. Remove timing cover bolts and cover.
6. Install by reversing removal procedure. Tighten cover bolts to 80 in. lbs.

Timing Belt, Crankshaft Sprocket, or Lower Crankcase Cover Seal R & R—1967-69 OHC 6 Cylinder

Radiator removal, at this point, is a distinct advantage for this operation.

1. Remove upper front timing cover.
2. Align timing marks.

NOTE: there are three sets of timing marks that must be aligned. One set is located on the harmonic balancer and the lower front belt cover. A second set is located on the accessory drive housing pulley and the lower front belt cover. The third set is the camshaft pulley set.

The mark on the harmonic balancer must be aligned with zero (0°) on the cover with the no. 1 cylinder on TDC of the compression stroke. The mark on the drive pulley should point toward the water pump and align with its mark on the belt cover. The mark on the camshaft pulley, in 1967–68, aligns with a mark on the cover behind the pulley. In 1969, the camshaft pulley mark aligns with a mark on a bolt head located directly below the camshaft pulley.

All three sets of marks must be aligned at the same time when replacing the camshaft drive belt.

3. Remove fan and water pump pulley.
4. Remove harmonic balancer.
5. Remove timing belt lower front cover.
6. Loosen accessory drive mounting bolts to provide slack in timing belt.
7. Remove timing belt.
8. Remove crankshaft timing belt flange and sprocket.
9. Carefully remove seal from crankcase cover.
10. Install new seal, with lip of seal inward.
11. Replace crankshaft timing belt sprocket and flange.
12. Align timing marks and replace timing belt.
13. Replace timing belt lower cover and harmonic balancer.
14. Adjust timing belt tension.
15. Replace water pump pulley and fan.
16. Replace timing belt upper front cover.

Front Crankcase Cover and Gasket R & R—1967-69 OHC 6 Cylinder

1. Remove timing belt sprocket, as described above.
2. Remove four front oil pan-to-crankcase cover retaining bolts.
3. Loosen remaining oil pan bolts, as necessary, to provide clearance between crankcase cover and oil pan.
4. Remove five front crankcase cover attaching bolts.
5. Remove front crankcase cover and gasket, clean off the old gasket.
6. Inspect cover seal for wear or distortion.
7. Using new gasket installed over dowels and, if ncecessary, new seal, reverse removal procedures, torque oil pan and crankcase cover bolts to 10-15 ft. lbs.

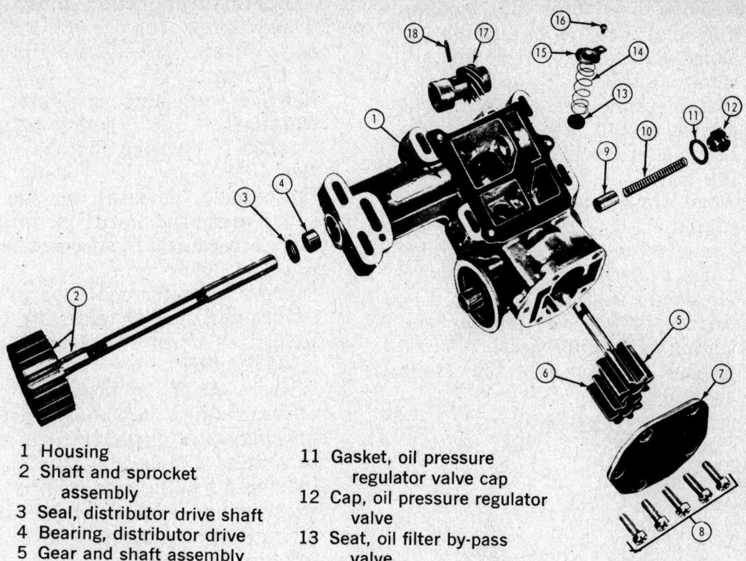

1 Housing
2 Shaft and sprocket assembly
3 Seal, distributor drive shaft
4 Bearing, distributor drive
5 Gear and shaft assembly oil pump drive
6 Gear, oil pump driven cover, oil pump
7 Cover, oil pump
8 Bolt, oil pump cover to housing
9 Valve, oil pressure regulator
10 Spring, oil pressure regulator
11 Gasket, oil pressure regulator valve cap
12 Cap, oil pressure regulator valve
13 Seat, oil filter by-pass valve
14 Spring, oil filter by-pass valve
15 Retainer, oil filter by-pass valve
16 Screw, oil filter by-pass valve retainer
17 Gear and eccentric
18 Pin, distributor oil and fuel pump gear and eccentric

OHC 6 cyl oil pump housing and distributor drive assembly
(© Pontiac Div., G.M. Corp)

Accessory Drive Housing Assembly, Oil Pump, Distributor and Fuel Pump—1967-69 OHC 6 Cylinder

The housing is unique, and consists of the oil pump, distributor and the fuel pump. The oil filter is also attached to this housing. The housing carries the drive sprocket for the above units and is used as a tensioner for the timing belt.

Oil Pressure Regulator R & R

1. Remove cap washer and spring from housing assembly.
2. Using magnet, remove valve from housing assembly.
3. Install valve on spring and install as an assembly.
4. Install cap washer.

Oil Pump R & R

1. Remove oil pump cover and gasket.
2. Remove drive gear and driven gear.
3. Install gears.
4. Replace cover using new gasket. Torque attaching bolts to 20 ft. lbs.

Housing Assembly R & R

1. Remove timing belt top front cover.
2. Align timing marks.
3. Loosen six housing assembly retaining bolts from cylinder block.
4. Remove timing belt from camshaft sprocket and distributor drive.
5. Disconnect fuel lines from fuel pump.

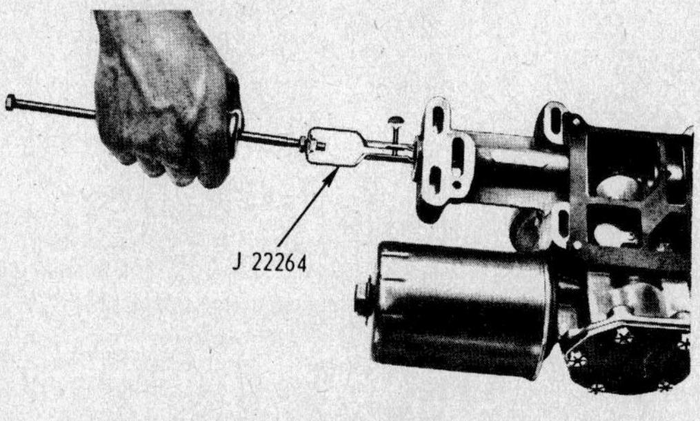
J 22264

Removing seal from OHC 6 distributor and oil pump drive housing
(© Pontiac Div., G.M. Corp)

6. Remove distributor cap, vacuum lines and wires from distributor.
7. Remove housing by removing six retaining bolts.
8. Install, using a new gasket, and loosely install housing assembly to cylinder block with six retaining bolts.
9. Align timing marks and install timing belt.
10. Connect fuel lines to fuel pump.
11. Replace distributor cap, vacuum lines and wires.
12. Adjust timing belt tension, see timing belt adjustment.
13. Replace timing belt top front cover.

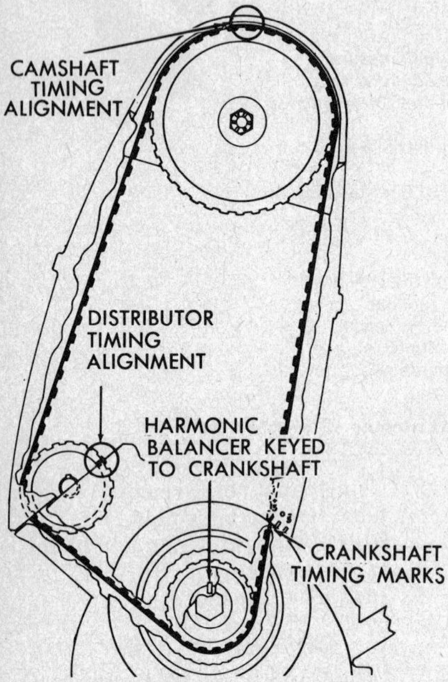
CAMSHAFT
TIMING
ALIGNMENT
DISTRIBUTOR
TIMING
ALIGNMENT
HARMONIC
BALANCER KEYED
TO CRANKSHAFT
CRANKSHAFT
TIMING MARKS

OHC 6 cyl timing mark alignment

1967-69 OHC Timing Belt Adjustment

1. Remove timing belt top front cover.
2. Using J-22232-2 calibration bar, set the pointer of timing belt tension fixture J-22232-1 to zero.

NOTE: this calibration must be performed before each use of J-22232 fixture to insure an accurate timing belt adjustment.

3. Remove camshaft sprocket to camshaft bolt and install J-22232-1 (tension fixture) on the belt with the rollers on the outside (smooth) surface of belt. Thread the fixture mounting bolt into camshaft sprocket bolt location, finger-tight.
4. Squeeze indicator end (upper) of fixture and quickly release so the fixture assumes released or relaxed position.
5. With J-22232-1 installed, as above, adjust accessory drive housing up or down, as required, to obtain a tension adjustment indicator reading centered in the green range, with drive housing mounting bolts torqued to 15 ± 3 ft. lbs.
6. Remove tension fixture and install sprocket retaining bolt, making sure bolt threads and washers are free of dirt.
7. Install upper front timing belt cover.

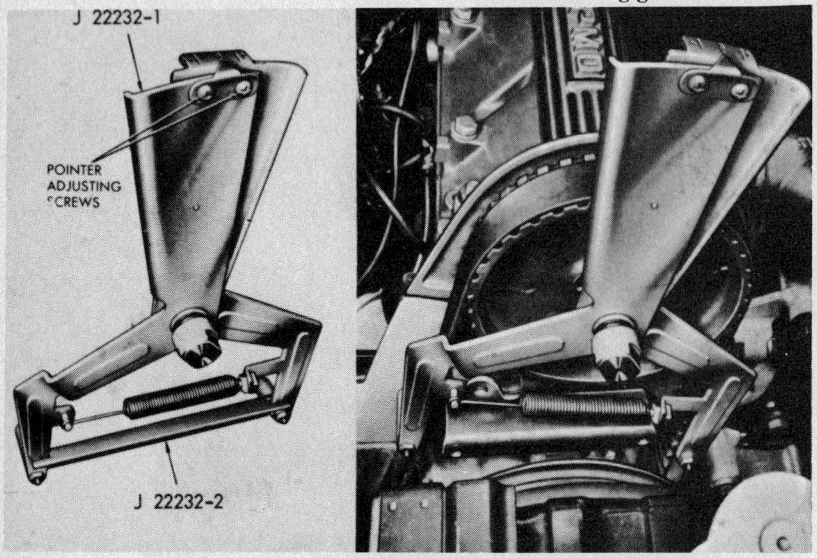
J 22232-1
POINTER
ADJUSTING
SCREWS
J 22232-2

OHC 6 cyl timing belt adjustment with tool j-22232 (© Pontiac Div., G.M. Corp)

Camshaft R & R

1970-74 OHV 6 Cylinder

1. Drain cooling system.
2. Remove radiator, fan, and water pump pulley.
3. Remove grill.
4. Remove valve cover and gasket, then loosen rocker arm nuts and pivot rockers out of the way.
5. Remove pushrods.
6. Remove distributor, fuel pump, and spark plugs.
7. Remove coil, pushrod (tappet gallery) covers and gasket; reach in and remove tappets, keeping them in order.
8. Remove harmonic balancer, then loosen oil pan bolts and allow pan to drop.
9. Remove timing gear cover.
10. Remove two camshaft thrust plate bolts by rotating cam gear holes to gain clearance.
11. Remove the camshift by pulling it straight forward.

NOTE: do not wiggle the camshaft; cam bearings could be dislodged.

12. If cam gear is to be replaced, press it from the shaft using an arbor press.

CAUTION: thrust plate must be positioned so that Woodruff key does not damage it during removal.

13. New cam gear must be pressed onto the shaft, with the shaft supported in back of the front bearing journal.

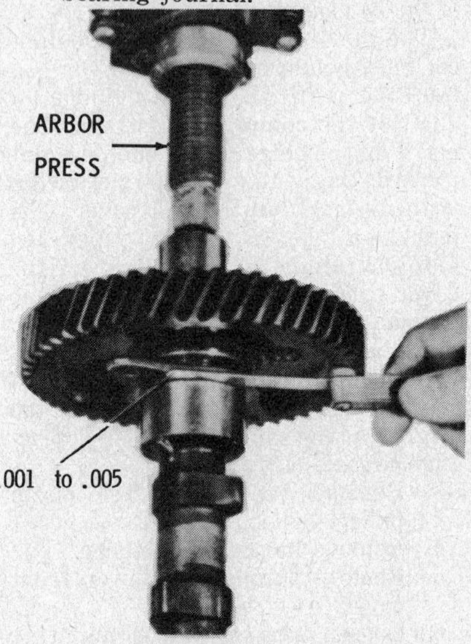
ARBOR
PRESS
.001 to .005

Installing OHV 6 camshaft gear and checking thrust plate end-play
(© Pontiac Div., G.M. Corp)

NOTE: the thrust plate end-play should be 0.001-0.005 in. If less than 0.001 in., replace spacer ring; if greater than 0.005 in., replace thrust plate.

14. Carefully install the camshaft into the engine, then turn crankshaft and camshaft so that timing marks coincide; tighten thrust plate bolts to 5-8 ft. lbs.
15. Check camshaft and crankshaft gear runout using a dial indicator. Cam gear runout should not exceed 0.004 in., crank gear should not exceed 0.003 in.

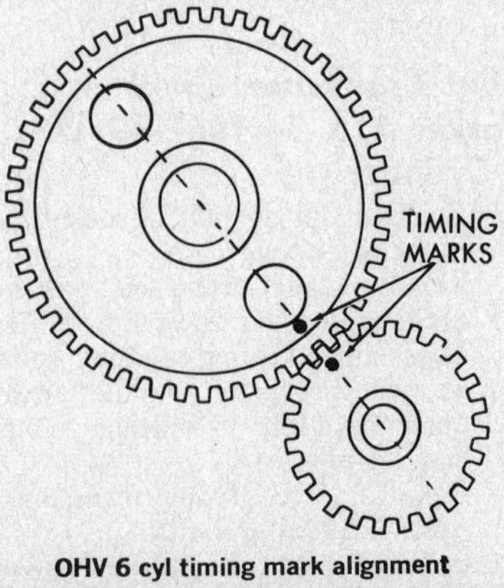
TIMING
MARKS

OHV 6 cyl timing mark alignment

Checking OHV 6 camshaft gear runout
(© Pontiac Div., G.M. Corp)

Checking OHV 6 camshaft gear backlash
(© Pontiac Div., G.M. Corp)

NOTE: if runout is excessive, remove gear and clean burrs from shaft.

16. Check gear backlash using a dial indicator; it should not exceed 0.006 in. and should not be less than 0.004 in.
17. To complete installation, reverse Steps 1-9.

NOTE: install distributor with No. 1 piston at TDC on compression stroke so that vacuum diaphragm faces forward and rotor points to No. 1 spark plug wire cap tower. Make sure oil pump drive shaft is properly indexed with distributor drive shaft.

1967-74 V8 Except 307

1. Drain cooling system and remove air cleaner.
2. Disconnect all water hoses, vacuum lines and spark plug wires. Remove the radiator.
3. Disconnect accelerator linkage, temperature gauge wire, and fuel lines.
4. Remove hood latch brace.
5. Remove PCV hose, then remove rocker covers.

NOTE: on air-conditioned models, remove alternator and bracket.

6. Remove distributor, then remove intake manifold.
7. Remove valley cover.
8. Loosen rocker arm nuts and pivot rockers out of the way.
9. Remove pushrods and lifters (keep them in proper order).
10. Remove harmonic balancer, fuel pump, and four oil pan to timing cover bolts.
11. Remove timing cover and gasket, then remove fuel pump eccentric and bushing.
12. Align timing marks, then remove timing chain and sprockets.
13. Remove camshaft thrust plate.
14. Remove camshaft by pulling straight forward, being careful not to damage cam bearings in the process.

NOTE: it may be necessary to jack up the engine slightly to gain clearance, especially if motor mounts are worn.

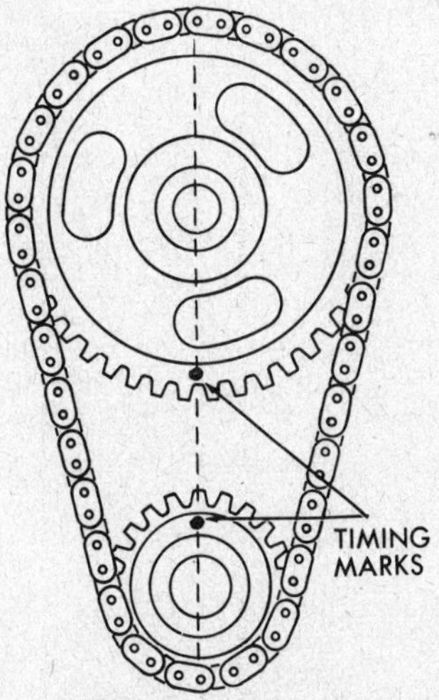
TIMING
MARKS

V8 timing mark alignment
(© Pontiac Div., G.M. Corp)

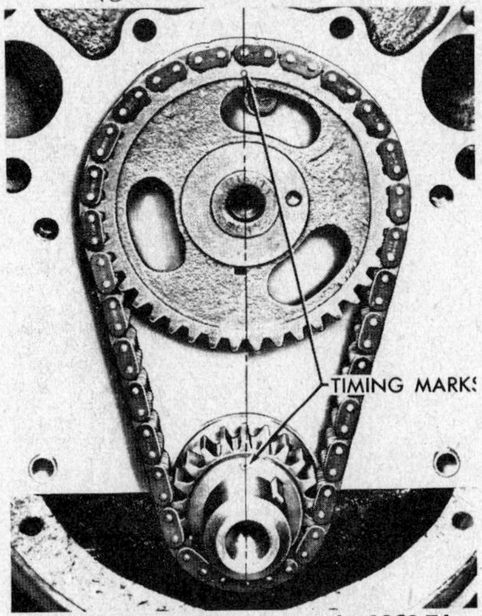
TIMING MARKS

V8 timing gear alignment marks 1969-74
(© Pontiac Div., G.M. Corp)

15. Install new camshaft, with lobes and journals coated with heavy (SAE 50-60) oil, into the engine, being careful not to damage cam bearings.

NOTE: most specialty cams come with a special "break-in" lubricant for the lobes and journals; if such lubricant is available, use it instead of heavy oil.

16. Install camshaft thrust plate and tighten bolts to 20 ft. lbs.
17. To install, reverse Steps 1-12, tightening sprocket bolts to 40 ft. lbs., timing cover bolts and nuts to 30 ft. lbs., oil pan bolts to 12 ft. lbs., and harmonic balancer bolt to 160 ft. lbs.

1971-72 Ventura II 307 V8

1. Remove intake manifold, valve lifters and timing chain cover (requires oil pan removal).
2. Remove the two center bolts and the one lower bolt that secure the hood latch support. This will give adequate clearance for the cam. Remove radiator.
3. Remove fuel pump and pump pushrod.
4. Remove camshaft sprocket bolts, sprocket and timing chain. A light blow to the lower edge of a tight sprocket should free it (use a plastic mallet).
5. Install two 5/16—18 x 4 in. bolts in cam bolt holes and pull cam from block.
6. To install, reverse removal procedure, aligning timing marks as illustrated.

NOTE: cam lobes must be lubricated with Molykote or equivalent before installation. All cam journals are the same diameter, so make sure cam bearings are not dislodged during installation.

1967-69 OHC 6 Cylinder

1. Remove camshaft sprocket and seal.
2. Remove rocker cover assembly.
3. Using an adapter and a slide hammer, drive camshaft to the rear. Make sure bearing surfaces are not damaged during this operation.
4. Disconnect slide hammer and remove camshaft from rear of rocker cover.
5. Remove thrust washer, retaining washer, and bolt from rear of camshaft.
6. Clean and inspect all parts for wear or damage, then inspect

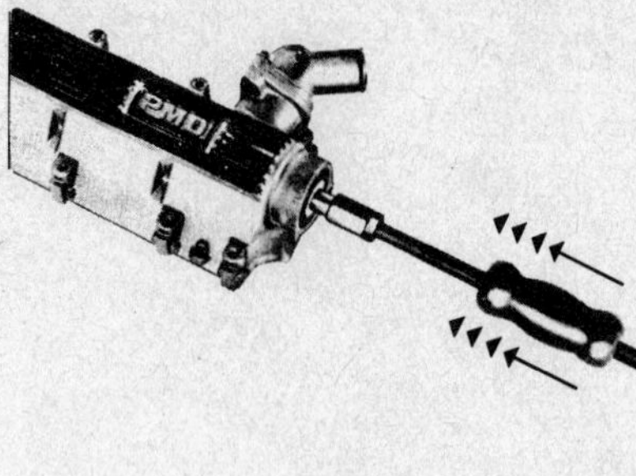

Removing camshaft with slide hammer—OHC 6
(© Pontiac Div., G.M. Corp)

INDEX THRUST WASHER
TANG IN HOLE IN ROCKER
ARM COVER

Camshaft thrust washer position—OHC 6
(© Pontiac Div., G.M. Corp)

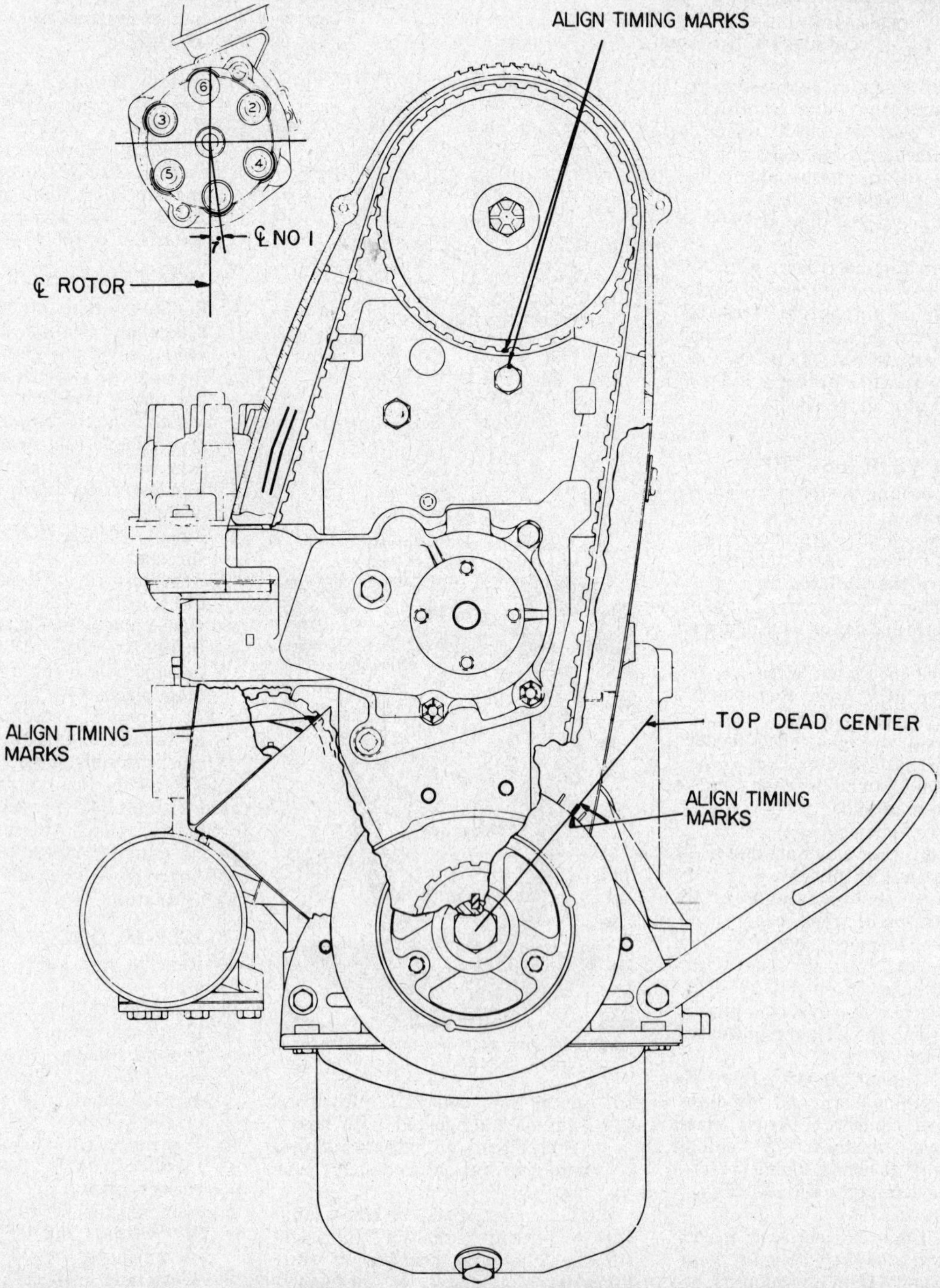
ALIGN TIMING MARKS
℄ NO 1
℄ ROTOR
ALIGN TIMING
MARKS
TOP DEAD CENTER
ALIGN TIMING
MARKS

Timing marks OHC 6 cyl—1969 (© Pontiac Div., G.M. Corp)

bearing surfaces for wear or scoring.
7. Clean camshaft oil passages.
8. To install, reverse removal procedure making sure thrust washer is installed as illustrated. Tighten retaining bolt to 40 ft. lbs.
9. Check camshaft end-play, using a dial indicator on the front sprocket; end-play should be 0.003-0.009 in. and is controlled by the camshaft bore plug.

NOTE: lubricate camshaft lobes and rockers with special lubricant, available at Pontiac dealers. Tighten rocker cover bolts and nuts to 15 ft. lbs. from center outward.

Piston and Connecting Rod 1967-69 OHC 6 Cylinder

Removal

1. Remove the rocker arm cover.
2. Disconnect the fuel and vacuum lines from the carburetor.
3. Remove the cylinder head, and the intake and exhaust manifold as an assembly.
4. Remove the ring ridge, using an appropriate cutter.
5. Remove the oil pan.
6. Mark the connecting rod and piston assembly to make sure they go into the same cylinder and that the same piston face is pointing toward the front of the engine upon reassembly. Do not reverse the bearing caps on the end of the connecting rods.
7. Remove the bearing cap and carefully push the piston and rod from its bore. Do not allow the piston and rod assembly to be scratched, nicked, or struck against a hard surface.

Piston Ring Replacement

1. Remove the old piston rings.
2. Clean any carbon, varnish, or other deposits from the surfaces of the piston. The ring grooves may be cleaned with a suitable tool. A piece of broken ring may be used by scraping the ring

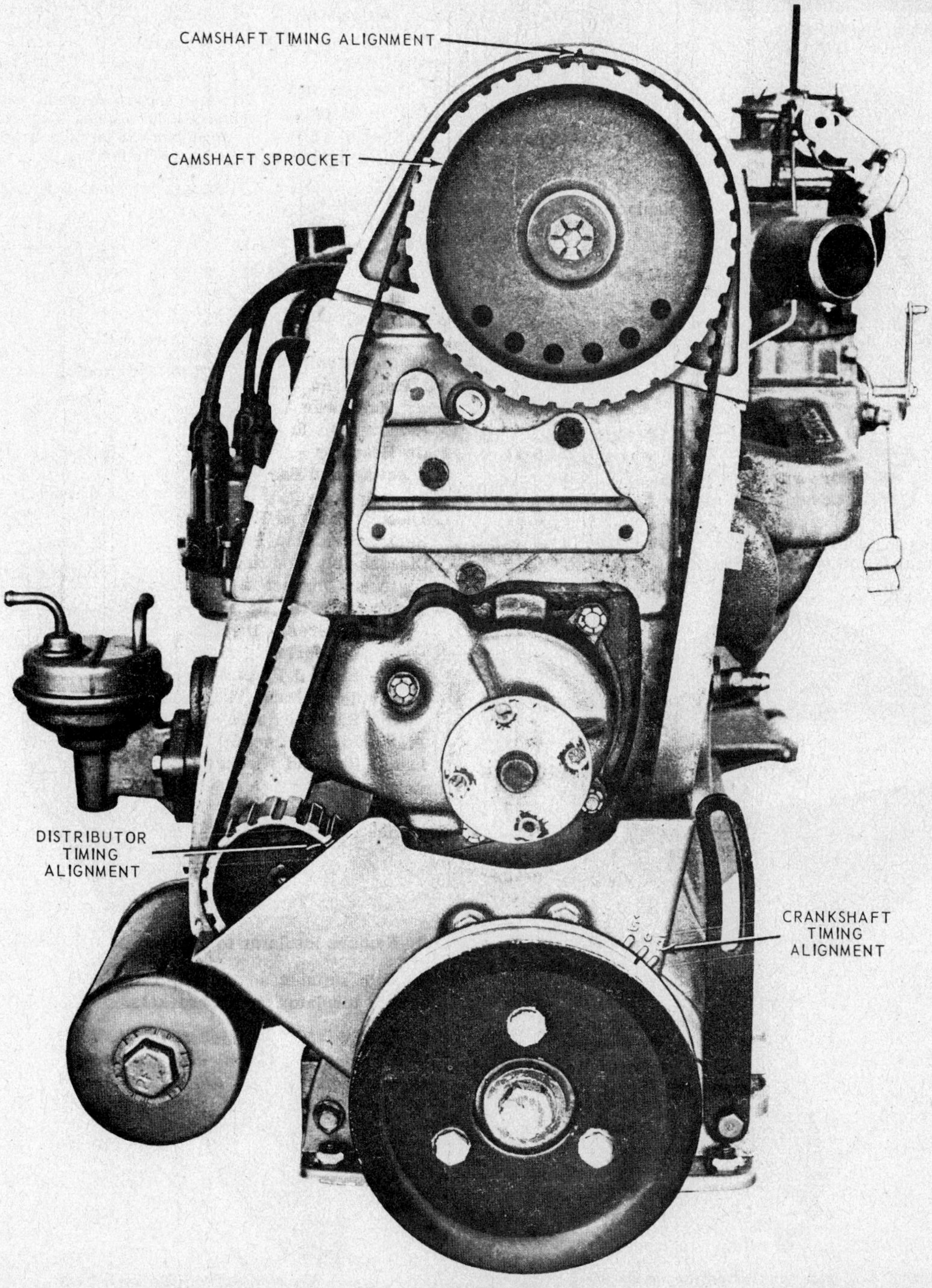

CAMSHAFT TIMING ALIGNMENT
CAMSHAFT SPROCKET
DISTRIBUTOR TIMING ALIGNMENT
CRANKSHAFT TIMING ALIGNMENT

Timing marks OHC 6 cyl—1967-68 (© Pontiac Div., G.M. Corp)

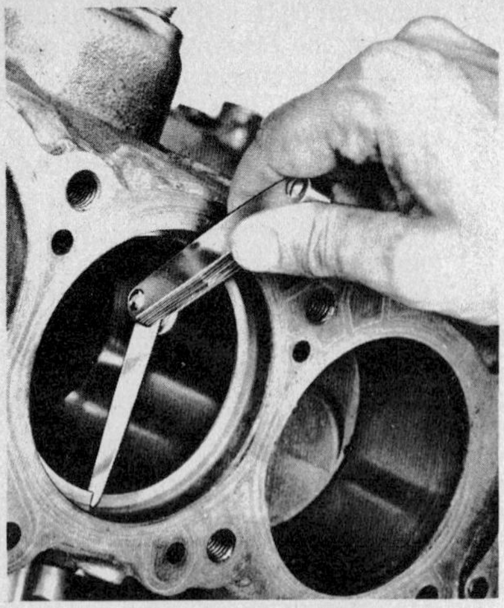

Checking ring end-gap
(© Pontiac Div., G.M. Corp)

Checking ring side clearance
(© Pontiac Div., G.M. Corp)

groove with the sharp edge of the broken ring.

3. Place the ring at the bottom of the bore in that portion that is traveled by the rings. Measure the gap between the ends of the ring. Refer to the "Ring Gap" chart for correct specifications. Grind the ends of the ring to get the proper clearance. Check the end-gap on each ring.
4. Install the rings of the piston. Make sure they are installed in the proper order. Do not spread the ring excessively as the rings are very brittle and will break.
5. Measure the side clearance. Refer to "Ring Side Clearance" chart for correct specifications. If side clearance is excessive, replace the piston.

Piston and Rod Installation

1. Using a piston ring compressor, insert the rod and piston assembly into its bore. Make sure all parts are assembled facing in the correct direction.
2. From under the engine, pull the assembly into place against the crankpin, install the bearing cap, and torque it to 33 ft lbs.
3. Install the oil pan.
4. Install the cylinder head assembly.
5. Connect the fuel and vacuum lines.
6. Install the rocker arm cover.

Piston and Connecting Rod 1967-74 V8

Removal

1. Remove the oil pan, oil baffle, and oil pump.
2. Remove the intake manifold, exhaust manifolds, and cylinder heads.
3. Rotate the crankshaft so the crankpin carrying the connecting rod to be removed projects straight down.
4. Remove the ring ridge, using a suitable cutter.

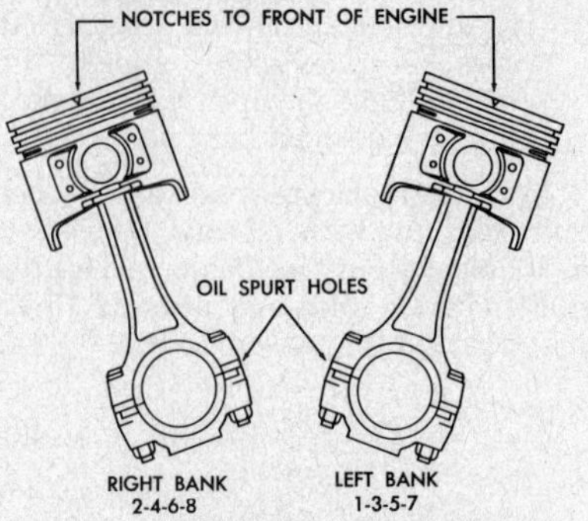
NOTCHES TO FRONT OF ENGINE
OIL SPURT HOLES
RIGHT BANK
2-4-6-8
LEFT BANK
1-3-5-7

V8 piston and rod assembly, except 1971-72 Ventura II 307 V8. See "Camaro" section for small-block V8 piston and rod assembly
(© Pontiac Div., G.M. Corp)

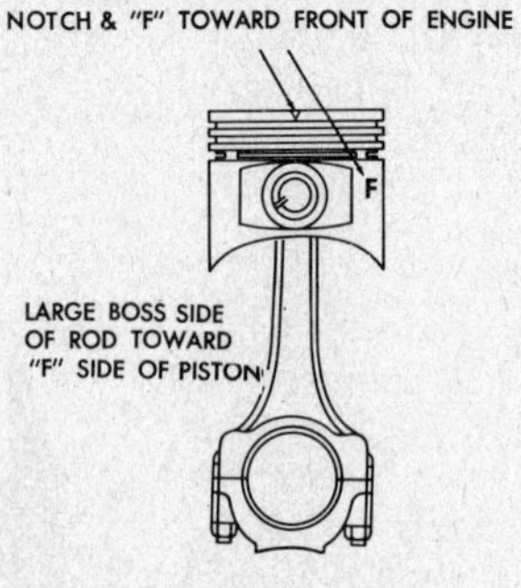
NOTCH & "F" TOWARD FRONT OF ENGINE
F
LARGE BOSS SIDE
OF ROD TOWARD
"F" SIDE OF PISTON

Piston and rod assembly—6 cyl
(© Pontiac Div., G.M. Corp)

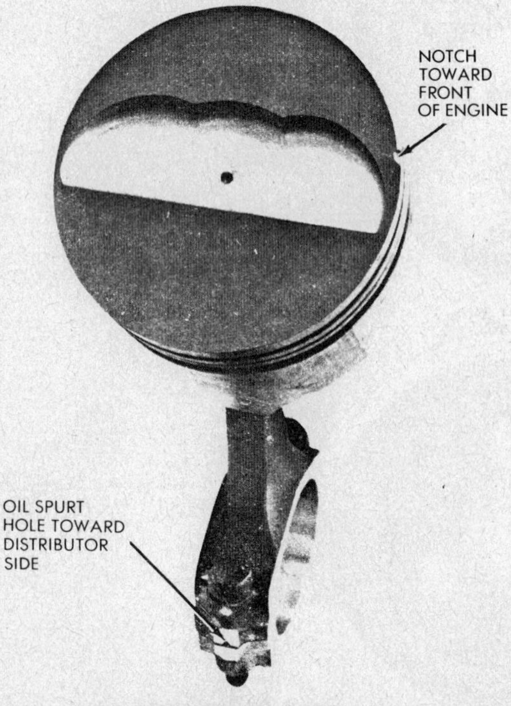
NOTCH
TOWARD
FRONT
OF ENGINE
OIL SPURT
HOLE TOWARD
DISTRIBUTOR
SIDE

OHC 6 cyl piston and rod position in block
(© Pontiac Div., G.M. Corp)

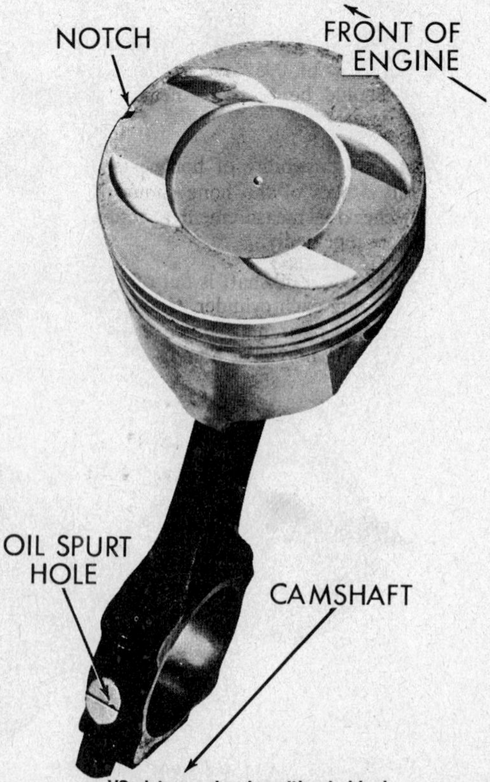
NOTCH
FRONT OF
ENGINE
OIL SPURT
HOLE
CAMSHAFT

V8 piston and rod position in block
(© Pontiac Div., G.M. Corp)

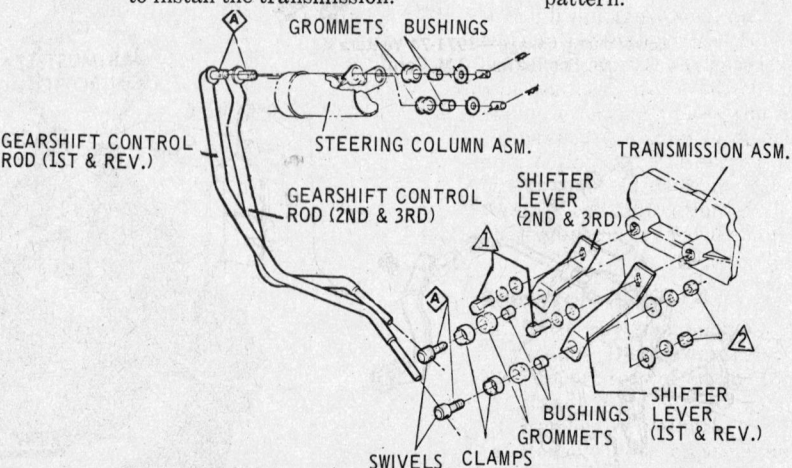

5. Remove the bearing cap. Place a section of rubber tubing on the connecting rod bolts for protection.
6. Push the assembly from its bore.

Piston Ring Replacement

The procedure is the same as for the OHC six-cylinder, but the clearances are different.

Piston and Connecting Rod Installation

Installation is the reverse of removal.

1970-74 OHV 6 Cylinder

Piston R&R and Piston Ring R&R are the same as for the OHC six-cylinder engine. However, ring clearances are different.

Lubrication

A spur, gear-type oil pump circulates the oil under pressure. Maximum oil pressure is regulated by a spring-loaded, ball-type, pressure regulator valve. Oil is supplied to the crankshaft, connecting rods, camshaft bearings and to the valve train, under pressure. There are also metering jets for each cylinder wall, timing chain, and sprocket.

Oil Pan R & R

1967-70 V8 and 1971 Tempest with Manual Transmission

1. Remove engine from car.
2. Remove oil pan bolts.
3. Remove oil pan.

NOTE: 1970 Tempest V8 oil pan can be removed, in some cases, in a manner similar to 1968-69 Firebird V8.

1968-69 Firebird V8

1. Disconnect battery cable at battery.
2. Remove distributor cap and fan shield.
3. Remove fan and fan pulley on air-conditioned models.
4. Disconnect engine ground straps.
5. On air-conditioned models, remove compressor and swing it out of the way without disconnecting hoses.
6. Jack up front of car and drain engine oil.
7. Disconnect steering idler arm from frame.
8. Remove exhaust crossover pipe on single exhaust cars; disconnect exhaust pipes at manifold flanges on dual exhaust cars.
9. Remove starter motor, starter motor bracket, and flywheel cover.
10. Support engine with a chain hoist, then remove motor mounts and loosen rear transmission mount.

NOTE: it may be necessary, in individual cases, to remove the rear transmission mount.

11. Remove oil pan bolts, raise engine about 4½ in., and move engine forward about 1½ in.
12. Remove oil pan by rotating clockwise (to clear oil pump) and pulling down.
13. To install, reverse removal procedure.

1970½ Firebird and All 1971-74 V8 Models

1. Rotate engine until timing mark is at 2:00 o'clock position.
2. Disconnect battery cables.
3. Remove fan. On Ventura II V8, remove only the fan shroud and tilt power steering pump out of the way.
4. Move all water hoses and wiring out of the way.
5. Raise car and drain engine oil. Disconnect idler arm from frame and pitman arm from shaft on Firebird starting 1970½.
6. Disconnect exhaust pipe/s at manifold.
7. Remove starter and bracket, then remove flywheel inspection cover.
8. Support engine with a wood-padded jack.
9. Remove both frame-to-motor mount bolts.
10. Jack up engine for clearance, then remove oil pan bolts and pan.
11. To install, reverse removal procedure. Tighten pan bolts to 12 ft. lbs.

1970-74 OHV 6 Cylinder

1. Remove upper radiator shield assembly.
2. Disconnect positive battery cable.
3. Jack up front of car and drain engine oil.
4. Disconnect exhaust pipe at manifold flange.
5. Remove starter motor and flywheel cover.
6. Raise engine slightly, using a chain hoist, then remove both front motor mount to frame bolts and right motor mount.
7. Remove oil pan bolts, then raise engine and remove oil pan.
8. To install, reverse removal procedure.

NOTE: bolts into timing gear cover should be installed last. They are installed at an angle and holes line up after rest of oil pan bolts are tightened finger-tight.

1967-69 6 Cylinder OHC Removal

1. Disconnect battery.
2. Remove air cleaner assembly.
3. On air conditioned cars, remove compressor from mounting brackets and position to one side.
4. Inspect all water hoses and wiring harness for routing and possible interference. (Engine is raised at least 4½ in. on Tempest, 2 in. on Firebird.)

NOTE: Before raising the car, prop the hood open at least 6 in. to ensure enough clearance between timing belt cover and inner hood panel.

5. Raise car and drain crankcase.
6. Remove starter assembly and flywheel cover.
7. Reroute or disconnect any wiring between bellhousing and floor pan to insure against damage when bellhousing contacts pan.
8. Loosen transmission insulator to crossmember retaining bolts.
9. Remove right and left engine insulator to frame bracket through-bolts.
10. Rotate harmonic balancer until timing mark is at bottom. (This properly positions crankshaft counterweights.)
11. With suitable equipment, raise engine until insulators clear frame brackets.
12. Remove oil pan bolts.
13. Raise engine. Apply a rearward force on the engine-transmission assembly until oil pan clears the flywheel housing. Then, remove the oil pan.
14. Reverse the removal procedure to install the oil pan.

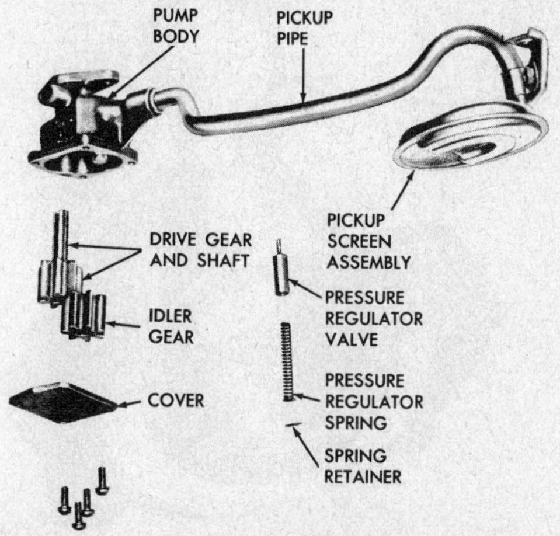
PUMP BODY
PICKUP PIPE
PICKUP SCREEN ASSEMBLY
DRIVE GEAR AND SHAFT
IDLER GEAR
PRESSURE REGULATOR VALVE
PRESSURE REGULATOR SPRING
COVER
SPRING RETAINER

1970-74 OHV 6 oil pump
(© Pontiac Div., G.M. Corp)

Oil Pump R & R

V8 and 6 Cylinder Engines Except 6 Cylinder OHC

1. Remove engine oil pan. (See previous procedure.)
2. Remove pump attaching screws and carefully lower the pump, while removing the pump drive shaft.
3. Reinstall in reverse order.

NOTE: OHC 6 cylinder oil pump R & R is covered earlier in this section.

Rear Main Bearing Oil Seal

1967-74 All 6 Cylinder Engines

Always replace both upper and lower seal halves. It is not necessary to remove the crankshaft to install the seal.

1. Remove the engine oil pan.
2. Remove the rear main bearing cap.
3. Remove the oil seal from the groove in the cap by prying from the bottom with a small screwdriver.
4. Insert a new seal, well lubricated with engine oil, into the bearing cap groove.
5. Remove the upper half of the seal. Use a small hammer and brass pin and tap one end of the oil seal until it protrudes far enough to be removed with pliers.
6. Install a new seal with the lip toward the front of the engine.
7. Install the bearing cap and torque it to specifications.

1967-74 V8 Except 307

1. Remove the oil pan, baffle, and oil pump.
2. Remove the rear main bearing cap.
3. Make a seal tool as illustrated.
4. Insert the tool against one end of the oil seal in the block and drive the seal gently into the groove a distance of 3/4 in. Repeat on the other end of the seal.
5. Form a new seal in the cap. Cut four 3/8 in. long pieces from this seal.
6. Work two of the pieces into each of the gaps which have been made at the end of the seal in the block. Do not cut off any material to make them fit.
7. Form a new seal in the bearing cap.
8. Apply a 1/16 in. bead of sealer from the center of the seal across to the external cork groove.
9. Reassemble the cap and torque to specifications.

307 Engine

1. Remove the oil pan, baffle, oil pump, and rear main bearing cap.
2. Remove the upper half of the seal with a hammer and brass punch.
3. Install a new upper seal.
4. Remove the lower seal half from the bearing cap.
5. Install a new lower seal in the bearing cap.
6. Install the bearing cap and torque it to specifications.

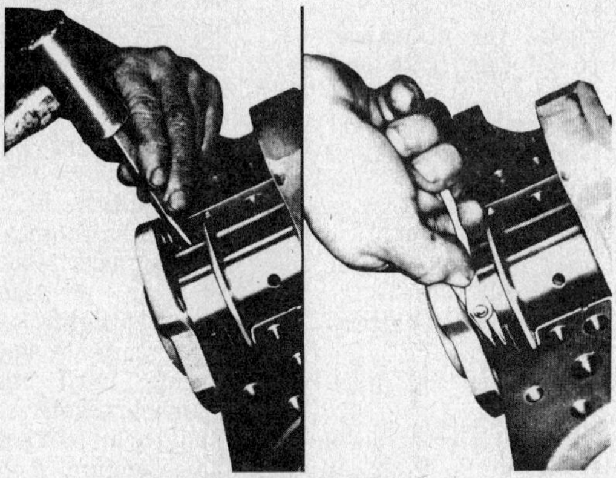

Front oil seal removal—upper half
(© Pontiac Div., G.M. Corp)

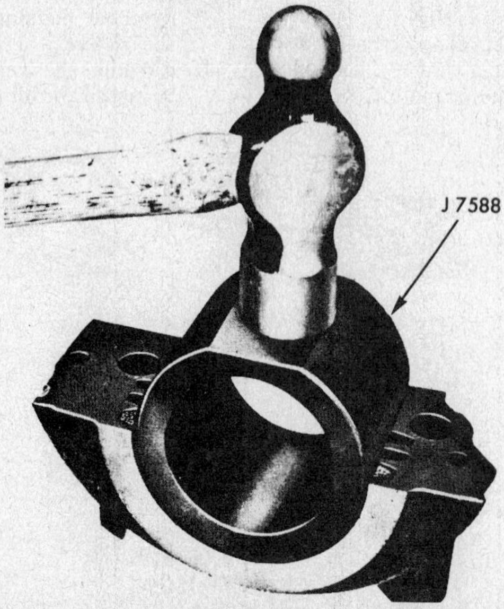
J 7588

Forming new front oil seal
(© Pontiac Div., G.M. Corp)

CLUTCH

A single-plate, dry-disc, diaphragm-spring clutch is used on all Tempest, Firebird, GTO and Ventura II models. The clutch assembly consists of the driven plate, the pressure plate, and the release mechanism. Grooves on both sides of the driven plate prevent the plate's sticking to the flywheel and pressure plate due to vacuum.

Two types of diaphragm type pressure plates are used—a bent finger type, for the high performance OHC six-cylinder and V8s of more than 350 cu. in. displacement, and a flat finger type, for low performance V8s and six-cylinder standard engines. The diaphragm spring design is such that no overcenter spring is required.

The clutch release mechanism consists of a ball thrust (throwout) bearing and various linkage configurations (for the various models) to control this bearing. The throwout bearing slides on the front transmission extension housing (nose piece), which is concentric with and encloses the transmission main drive gear. When pedal pressure is applied, the clutch fork pivots on its ball socket, through linkage action, and the inner end of the fork forces the throwout bearing against the release levers.

A clutch safety switch prevents engine cranking unless the clutch is disengaged (on 1969-74 models). The only periodic clutch service required, other than adjustment for normal wear, is the lubrication of all linkage pivot points every 6,000 miles.

Removal—1967-74

1. Raise car and support on jackstands. Disconnect the battery.
2. Support rear of engine with jackstand.
3. Remove driveshaft.
4. Remove rear crossmember bolts from frame and transmission mounts, and remove crossmember.

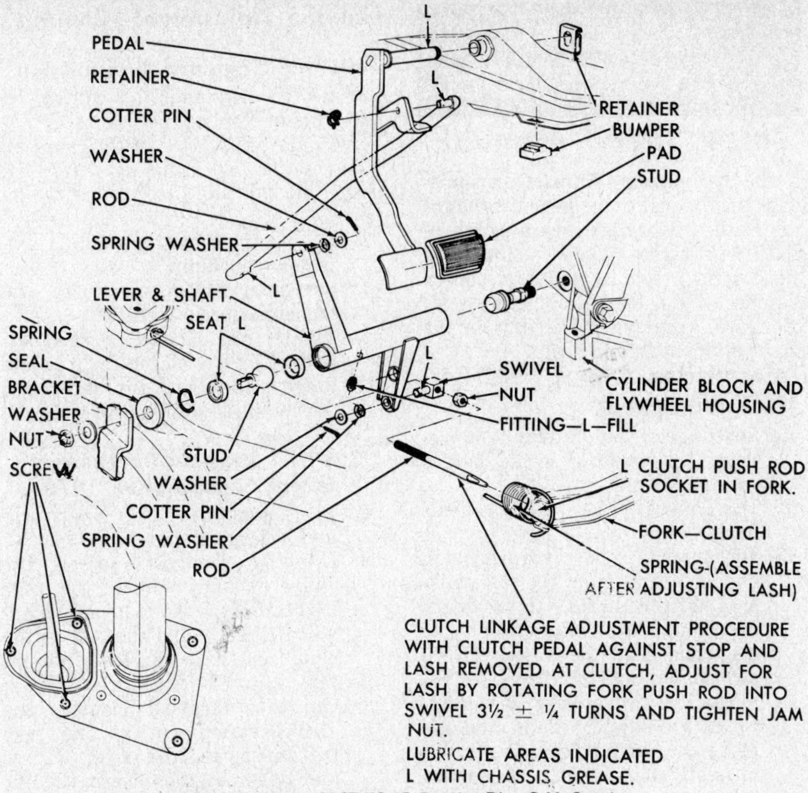

L
PEDAL
RETAINER
L
COTTER PIN
RETAINER
BUMPER
PAD
WASHER
STUD
ROD
SPRING WASHER
L
LEVER & SHAFT
SPRING
SEAT L
SEAL
BRACKET
WASHER
NUT
SCREW
L
SWIVEL
NUT
CYLINDER BLOCK AND FLYWHEEL HOUSING
FITTING—L—FILL
STUD
WASHER
COTTER PIN
SPRING WASHER
ROD
L CLUTCH PUSH ROD SOCKET IN FORK.
FORK—CLUTCH
SPRING-(ASSEMBLE AFTER ADJUSTING LASH)
CLUTCH LINKAGE ADJUSTMENT PROCEDURE WITH CLUTCH PEDAL AGAINST STOP AND LASH REMOVED AT CLUTCH, ADJUST FOR LASH BY ROTATING FORK PUSH ROD INTO SWIVEL 3½ ± ¼ TURNS AND TIGHTEN JAM NUT.
LUBRICATE AREAS INDICATED L WITH CHASSIS GREASE.

Clutch linkage—1967-72 (© Pontiac Div., G.M. Corp)

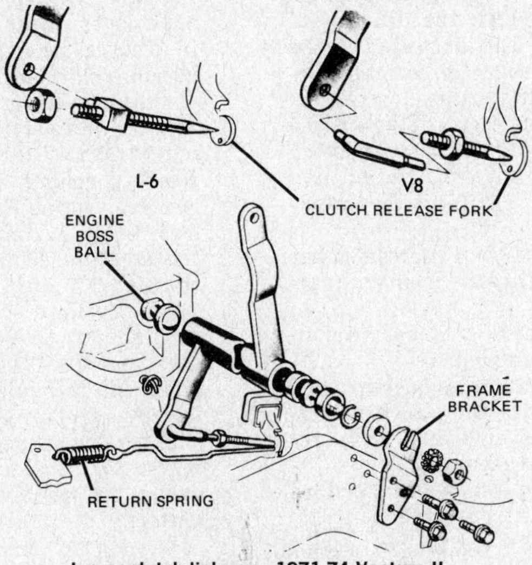

L-6
V8
CLUTCH RELEASE FORK
ENGINE BOSS BALL
FRAME BRACKET
RETURN SPRING

Lower clutch linkage—1971-74 Ventura II
(© Pontiac Div., G.M. Corp)

NOTE: see transmission removal procedure for procedure variations.

5. Disconnect transmission shift linkage, speedometer cable and clutch return spring. Clutch fork pushrod will now hang free.
6. Remove clutch housing cover plate screws and let plate hang from starter gear housing.
7. Lower engine enough to gain access to clutch housing bolts at engine block, then remove all but uppermost bolt.
8. Hold transmission and clutch housing assembly against block over dowel pins while removing last bolt. Remove transmission and clutch housing as an assembly.
9. Matchmark pressure plate and flywheel with paint to make sure correct balance is maintained.
10. Loosen the six cover plate attaching screws, a little at a time, until clutch diaphragm spring tension is released. Remove bolts, clutch assembly and pilot tool.

Installation—1967-74

1. The pilot bearing is an oil-impregnated type bearing pressed into the crankshaft. Inspect and renew, if necessary.
2. Install clutch disc with long hub forward (toward flywheel).
3. Install pressure plate and cover assembly, then align clutch disc by inserting pilot tool, or old transmission mainshaft, into splines. Align mark on clutch cover with mark on flywheel, then align nearest bolt holes.
4. Install bolts in every other hole in cover and tighten alternately. Then, install remaining three bolts, tighten all six to 25 ft. lb. (35 for Ventura II).
5. Remove clutch pilot tool and check to see that it can be reinserted and moved freely.
6. Install clutch fork and dust boot into clutch housing. Lubricate throwout bearing with graphite grease.

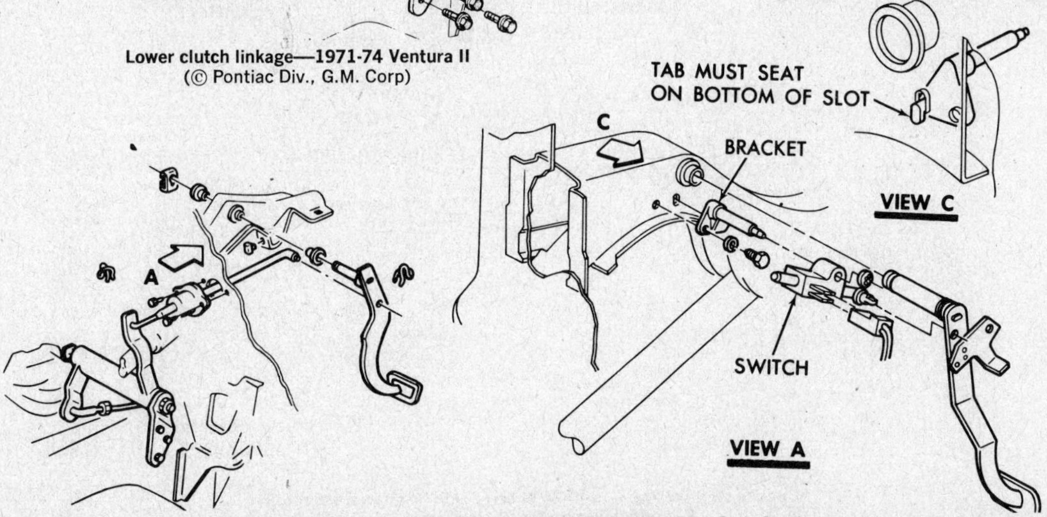

TAB MUST SEAT ON BOTTOM OF SLOT
VIEW C
C
BRACKET
A
SWITCH
VIEW A

Upper clutch linkage—1971-74 Ventura II (© Pontiac Div., G.M. Corp)

7. Complete the reassembly of clutch housing and transmission by reversing removal method. Tighten housing bolts to 40 ft. lbs. (30 for Ventura II).
8. Adjust shifter and clutch release linkage.

Pilot Bearing and Flywheel Replacement—1967-74

1. Remove transmission and clutch.
2. Using a small cold chisel, remove stake marks which hold pilot bearing in the flywheel.
3. Pull the old bearing out of the flywheel, using a slide hammer if necessary.
4. With new bearing held in place, shielded side toward transmission, gently tap on bearing until it enters the flywheel until flush. Stake in at least two places, using a prick punch.
5. If flywheel is removed, make sure to matchmark the flywheel and crankshaft flange.
6. To install, reverse removal procedure, tightening flywheel bolts to 95 ft. lbs.

NOTE: flywheel bolts do not need lockwashers.

Clutch Pedal Adjustment —1967-74

1. Disconnect return spring.
2. With pedal against stop, loosen locknut to allow adjusting rod to be turned out of swivel (V8), or pushrod (6 cyl.), until the throwout bearing contacts the release fingers in the pressure plate.
3. Turn adjusting rod into swivel or pushrod 3½ turns (3 turns for Ventura II); tighten locknut to 8–12 ft. lbs. for 1967–68, 30 ft. lbs. for 1969-72. On 1973-74, tighten locknut to 12.5 ft. lbs. on Grand Am and LeMans, 10 ft. lbs. on Firebird and Ventura.
4. Install return spring and check pedal lash; it should be approximately 1 in.

MANUAL TRANSMISSION

Three Speed Manual

The Saginaw and Muncie transmissions use helical drive gears throughout, with all forward gears synchronized. While the Muncie is similar to the Saginaw, it has a 3¼ in. center distance (3 in. for the Saginaw), an iron case, and larger bearings, input shaft, mainshaft, and gears.

Transmission R & R 1967-74 All Three-Speed

1. Disconnect the battery and release the parking brake before raising the car.
2. Disconnect the speedometer cable.
3. Disconnect the transmission shifter levers from the transmission shifter shafts. On six-cylinder engines, disconnect the electrical lead from the T.C.S. switch. On floor-shift models, remove the two shifter assembly-to-shifter support bolts and remove the shifter from the transmission. If it is not necessary to remove the shifter from the car, it may be left hanging from its floor seal. Mark the differential flange and the driveshaft yoke to assure proper reassembly. Remove the driveshaft.
4. Support the rear of the engine and remove the transmission mount. Do not dent the oil pan severely as it will hit the crankshaft.
5. Remove the four crossmember bolts and slide the member rearward.
6. Remove the four transmission-to-bell housing bolts.
7. Slide the transmission rearward until it clears the clutch assembly and bell housing, then remove the transmission.
8. Reverse the removal procedure to install the transmission.

Linkage Adjustment—Column

1967-68 Saginaw Transmission

1. Set the transmission control levers in Neutral.

NOTE: align the shift levers in Neutral by inserting a 0.185 in. gauge pin through the holes in the levers.

2. Loosen the screw on each adjusting swivel clamp.
3. Set both shift levers on the transmission in Neutral.
4. Tighten the screws on each adjusting swivel clamp to 20 ft lbs.
5. Remove the gauge pin and check the complete shift pattern.

1969-74 Saginaw Transmission, Except Firebird from 1970

1. Place gearshift lever in Reverse and lock ignition.
2. On the Tempest, loosen the swivel clamp bolt at the rear transmission shift lever (First and Reverse) and the bolt at the equalizer shaft and lever assembly.
3. On the Firebird, loosen the swivel clamp nut at the rear transmission shift lever (First and Reverse) then loosen the nut (D) at the idler lever.
4. Position the front transmission shift lever (Second and Third) in Neutral and the rear transmission shift lever (First and Reverse) in Reverse.
5. Tighten the swivel clamp bolt or nut to 20 ft lbs, then unlock the steering column and shift into Neutral. On the Firebird, tighten both swivel clamp nuts, unlock the steering column, and check the complete shift pattern.
6. Align the lower gearshift levers (on column) in Neutral position, then insert a 0.185 in. diameter gauge pin through the hole in the lower control levers.
7. Tighten the swivel clamp bolt or nut to 20 ft lbs, then remove the gauge pin and check the shift pattern.

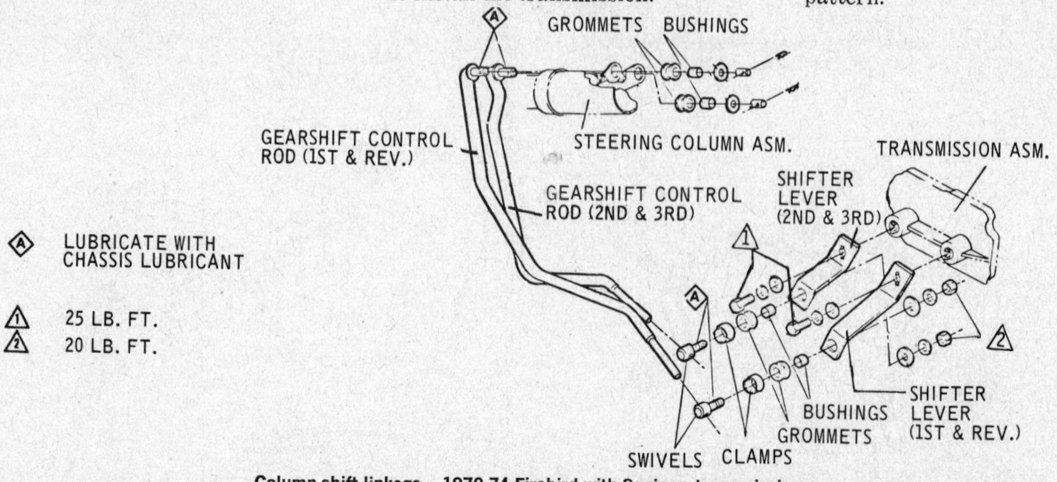
GROMMETS
BUSHINGS
GEARSHIFT CONTROL ROD (1ST & REV.)
STEERING COLUMN ASM.
TRANSMISSION ASM.
GEARSHIFT CONTROL ROD (2ND & 3RD)
SHIFTER LEVER (2ND & 3RD)
LUBRICATE WITH CHASSIS LUBRICANT
25 LB. FT.
20 LB. FT.
SHIFTER LEVER (1ST & REV.)
BUSHINGS
GROMMETS
SWIVELS
CLAMPS

Column shift linkage—1970-74 Firebird with Saginaw transmission
(© Pontiac Div., G.M. Corp)

1967-68 H.D. Dearborn Transmission

1969 and 1970-74 Saginaw and H.D. Dearborn Transmission

1. Place gearshift lever in Neutral.
2. Loosen swivel clamp on gearshift control rod.
3. Loosen trunnion locknuts on 1st-Reverse and 2nd-3rd transmission control rods.
4. Insert a 1/4 in. drill rod into shifter assembly.
5. If gearshift lever is not properly aligned with floor opening:
   a. *Console*—loosen two shifter to support bolts and align shifter. Tighten bolts.
   b. *Without console*—loosen two shifter to support bolts and center shifter in boot; tighten bolts.
6. Position both transmission shift levers in Neutral and tighten locknuts to 30 ft. lbs. (25 ft. lbs. 1971-72; 20 ft. lbs. 1973-74).
7. Remove gauge pin and check shift pattern.
8. Place gearshift lever in Reverse, then place steering column lower lever in Lock position and lock ignition.
9. Push up (pull down—Ventura II) on gearshift control rod to take up lash in column lock mechanism, then tighten adjusting swivel clamp to 20 ft. lbs.

1970-74 H.D. Muncie Transmission

Procedure is the same as Saginaw and H.D. Dearborn transmission linkage adjustment. Tighten swivel clamp nuts to 20 ft. lbs. (Tempest) and 25 ft. lbs. (Firebird). On all 1973-74 models, tighten swivel clamp nuts to 20 ft. lbs.

NOTE: the 1970 Saginaw transmission is not available with floorshift, except on Firebird models.

1970-74 Firebird with Saginaw Transmission

1. Place lever in Reverse and lock ignition.
2. Loosen both swivel clamp nuts.
3. Place front transmission shift lever in Neutral.
4. Place rear transmission lever in Reverse.
5. Tighten both swivel clamp nuts to 20 ft. lbs., unlock column and check shift pattern.

1971-74 Ventura II

1. Follow Steps 1-3 of Firebird procedure.
2. Pull down slightly on 1st-Rev rod to remove slack, then tighten swivel clamp nut at 1st-Rev lever to 20 ft. lbs.
3. Unlock steering column and shift into Neutral. Align column levers and insert a .185-.186 in. gauge pin through alignment holes.
4. Position 2nd-3rd transmission lever in Neutral, then tighten swivel clamp nut to 20 ft. lbs.
5. Remove gauge pin and check shift pattern and ignition lock. With lever in Reverse, key must move to LOCK freely. This should not be possible in any other gear.

Linkage Adjustment—Floor

1967-68 Saginaw Transmission

1. Place gearshift lever in Neutral.
2. Loosen two swivel nut assemblies.
3. Insert a 1/4 in. drill rod into bracket and lever assembly and align shift levers in Neutral position.
4. Position transmission shift levers in Neutral position.
5. Tighten swivel nut assemblies to 30 ft. lbs.
6. Remove gauge pin and check shift pattern.

Four-Speed Manual Transmission

The Saginaw four-speed is an optional floor-shift model and is used with the smaller engines. The four-speed Muncie is an optional model used on the 400 and 455 cu in. engines. Both transmissions are fully synchronized in all forward gears.

Transmission R & R 1967-74 All Four Speed

The R&R procedures for the four-speed transmissions are the same as the R&R procedures for the three-speed transmissions.

Linkage Adjustment—Floor

1967-68 All

1. Place gearshift lever in Neutral.
2. Loosen three swivel nut assemblies.
3. Insert a 1/4 in. drill rod into gauge pin hole in shifter.
4. Position transmission shift levers in Neutral.
5. Install swivel assemblies, adjusting length so that they fit into transmission shift levers without binding; tighten swivel nuts to 30 ft. lbs.
6. Remove gauge pin and check shift pattern.

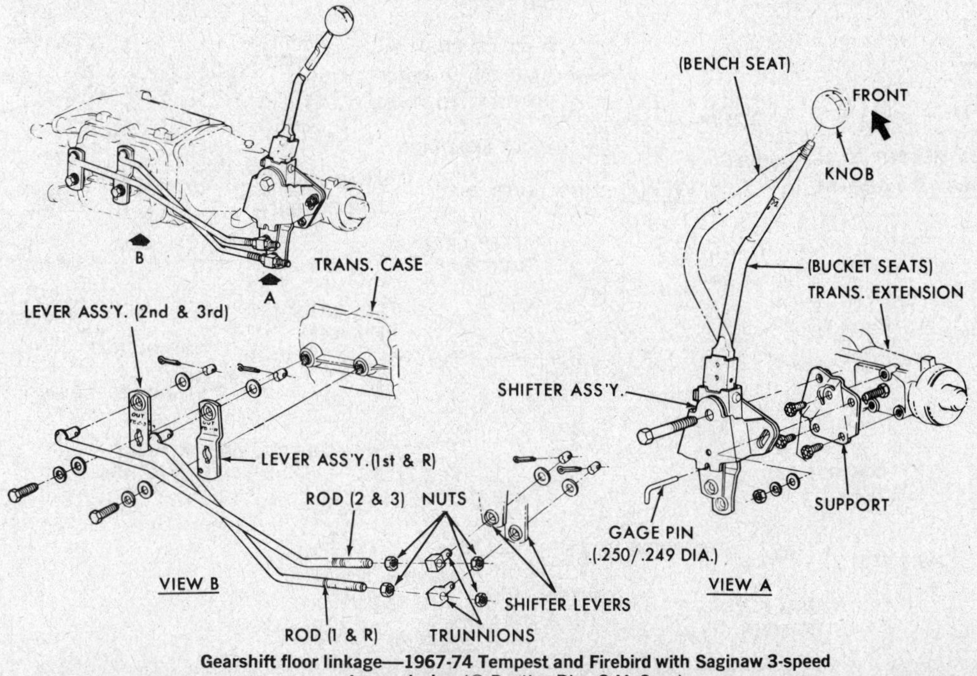

B
A
TRANS. CASE
LEVER ASS'Y. (2nd & 3rd)
LEVER ASS'Y. (1st & R)
ROD (2 & 3)
NUTS
VIEW B
ROD (1 & R)
TRUNNIONS
SHIFTER LEVERS
(BENCH SEAT)
FRONT
KNOB
(BUCKET SEATS)
TRANS. EXTENSION
SHIFTER ASS'Y.
GAGE PIN
(.250/.249 DIA.)
SUPPORT
VIEW A

Gearshift floor linkage—1967-74 Tempest and Firebird with Saginaw 3-speed transmission (© Pontiac Div., G.M. Corp)

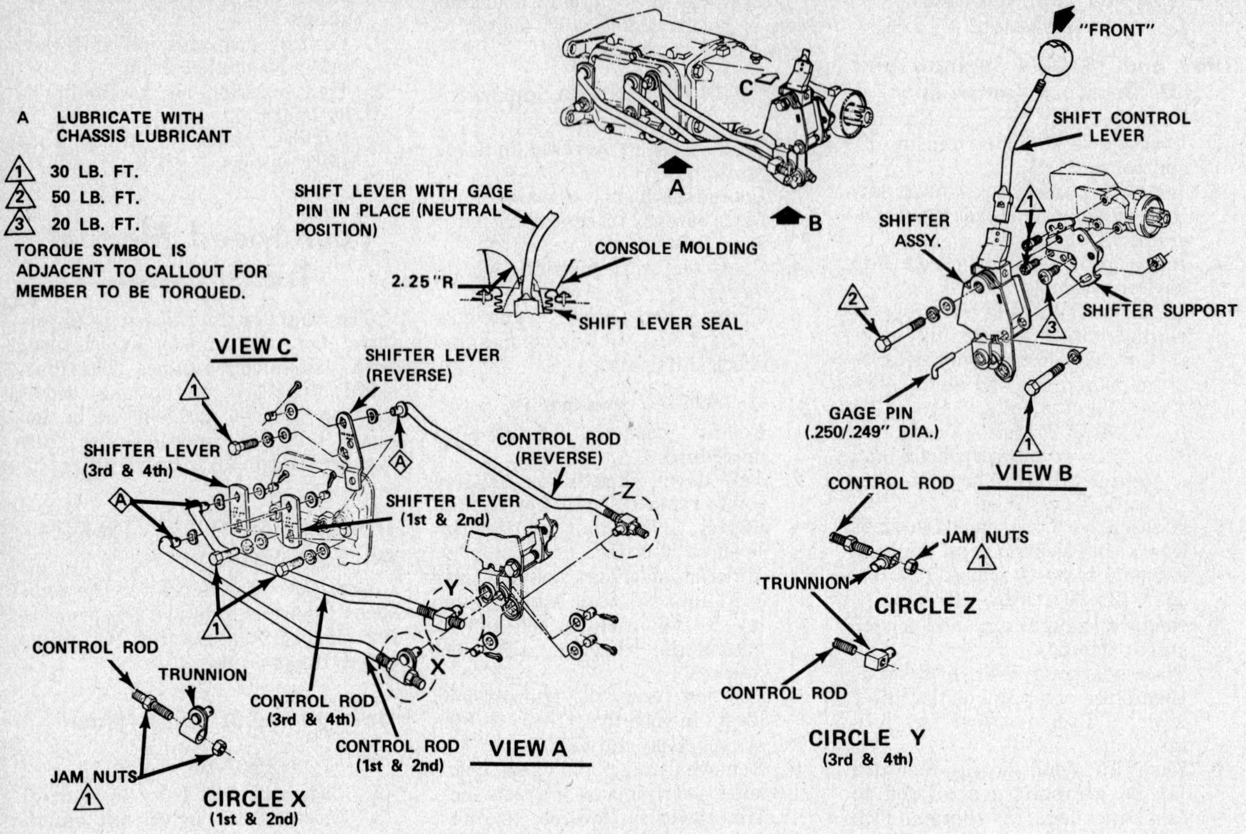
A LUBRICATE WITH CHASSIS LUBRICANT
1 30 LB. FT.
2 50 LB. FT.
3 20 LB. FT.
TORQUE SYMBOL IS ADJACENT TO CALLOUT FOR MEMBER TO BE TORQUED.
"FRONT"
SHIFT CONTROL LEVER
C
A
B
SHIFT LEVER WITH GAGE PIN IN PLACE (NEUTRAL POSITION)
CONSOLE MOLDING
2.25"R
SHIFT LEVER SEAL
SHIFTER ASSY.
SHIFTER SUPPORT
GAGE PIN (.250/.249" DIA.)
VIEW B
VIEW C
SHIFTER LEVER (REVERSE)
CONTROL ROD (REVERSE)
SHIFTER LEVER (3rd & 4th)
SHIFTER LEVER (1st & 2nd)
Z
Y
X
CONTROL ROD
TRUNNION
CONTROL ROD (3rd & 4th)
CONTROL ROD (1st & 2nd)
VIEW A
JAM NUTS
CIRCLE X (1st & 2nd)
JAM NUTS
CIRCLE Z
CIRCLE Y (3rd & 4th)

Gearshift floor linkage—typical Saginaw 4-speed transmission (© Pontiac Div., G.M. Corp)

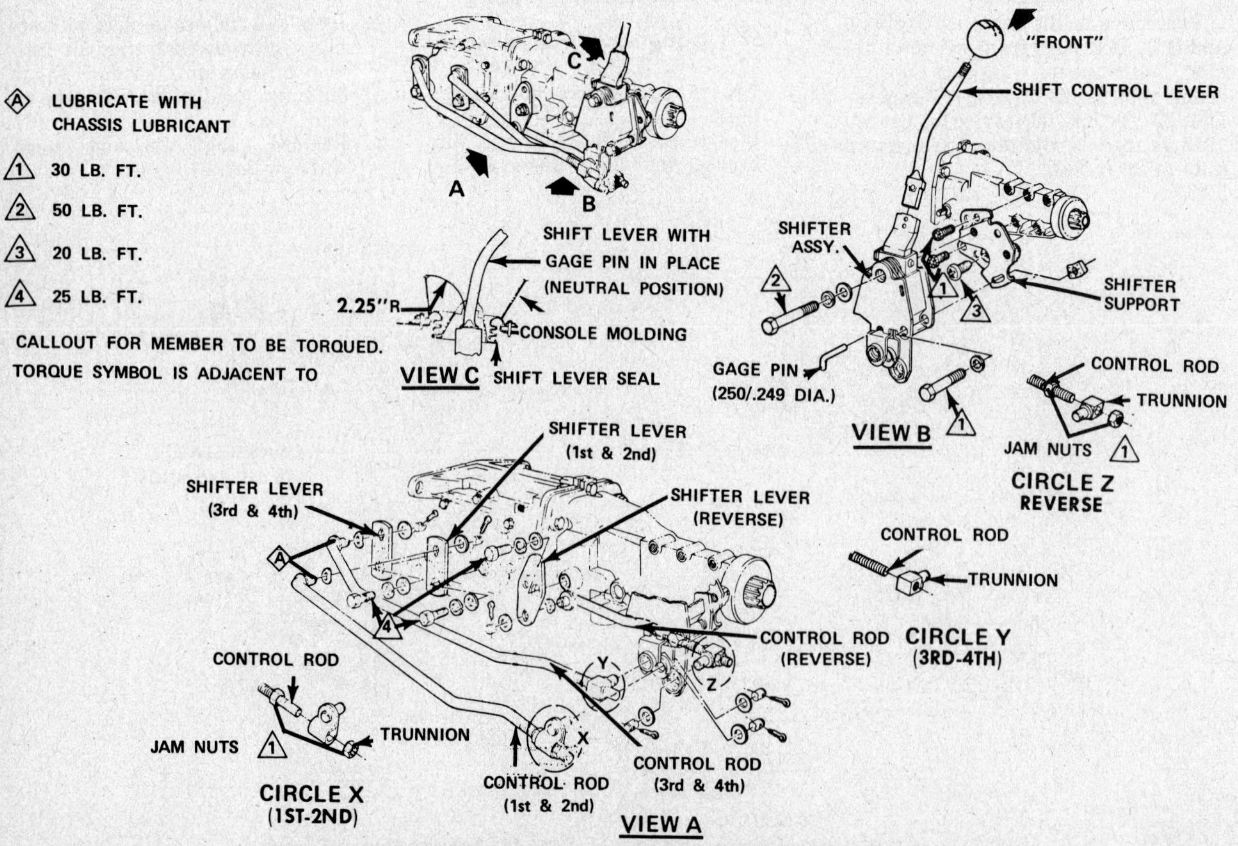
A LUBRICATE WITH CHASSIS LUBRICANT
1 30 LB. FT.
2 50 LB. FT.
3 20 LB. FT.
4 25 LB. FT.
CALLOUT FOR MEMBER TO BE TORQUED.
TORQUE SYMBOL IS ADJACENT TO
"FRONT"
SHIFT CONTROL LEVER
C
A
B
SHIFT LEVER WITH GAGE PIN IN PLACE (NEUTRAL POSITION)
2.25"R
CONSOLE MOLDING
VIEW C
SHIFT LEVER SEAL
SHIFTER ASSY.
SHIFTER SUPPORT
GAGE PIN (250/.249 DIA.)
VIEW B
CONTROL ROD
TRUNNION
JAM NUTS
CIRCLE Z REVERSE
SHIFTER LEVER (1st & 2nd)
SHIFTER LEVER (3rd & 4th)
SHIFTER LEVER (REVERSE)
CONTROL ROD (REVERSE)
CIRCLE Y (3RD-4TH)
Y
Z
X
CONTROL ROD
JAM NUTS
TRUNNION
CIRCLE X (1ST-2ND)
CONTROL ROD (1st & 2nd)
CONTROL ROD (3rd & 4th)
VIEW A

Gearshift floor linkage—Muncie 4-speed transmission (© Pontiac Div., G.M. Corp)

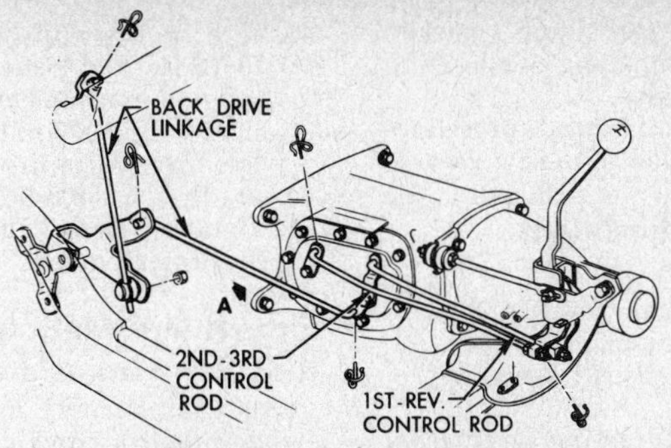
BACK DRIVE
LINKAGE
A
2ND-3RD
CONTROL
ROD
1ST-REV.
CONTROL ROD

Floorshift adjustment—Ventura II
(© Pontiac Div., G.M. Corp)

1969-74 Muncie and 1969 Saginaw Transmission

1. Place gearshift lever in Neutral.
2. Loosen adjusting swivel clamp on gearshift control rod.
3. For 1969 Saginaw, loosen trunnion locknuts on 1st-2nd and Reverse shift rods, then disconnect trunnion from lever. Loosen locknuts for Muncie-equipped 1969 up Tempest, GTO, Firebird.
4. Insert a 1/4 in. drill rod into gauge pin hole in shifter.
5. If gearshift lever is not properly aligned with floor opening:
   a. *Console*—loosen two shifter to support bolts and align shifter. Tighten bolts.
   b. *Without console*—loosen two shifter to support bolts and center shifter in boot; tighten bolts.
6. Place transmission shift levers in Neutral and tighten locknuts to 30 ft. lbs. for 1969 Saginaw.
7. Align trunnion with hole in 3rd-4th shifter lever, insert trunnion and secure with washer and cotter pin for 1969 Saginaw. Tighten locknuts to 20 ft. lbs. for 1969 up Muncie.
8. Remove gauge pin and check shift pattern.
9. Place gearshift lever in Reverse, set steering column lower lever in Lock position and lock ignition.
10. Push up on gearshift control rod to take up lash in steering column lock mechanism, then tighten adjusting swivel clamp nut to 20 ft. lbs.

AUTOMATIC TRANSMISSION

Intermediate size Pontiacs use three types of automatic transmissions. The M-35 two-speed (G.M. Type 300) automatic was used from 1967-69 and was replaced by the M-35 two-speed Powerglide in 1970. From 1968, the Turbo-Hydramatic M-38 (G.M. Type 350) has been used and in 1969 Pontiac introduced the Turbo-Hydramatic M-40 (G.M. Type 400) which is currently in use.

Oil Pan and Strainer R&R Three-Speed (M-40, M-38), Two-Speed (M-35)

1. Raise the car and drain the oil pan.
2. Remove the oil pan bolts, pan, and gasket.
3. Remove the oil strainer-to-valve body screws and the strainer.
4. Clean the oil pan and strainer.
5. Reverse the removal procedure for installation, Use a new gasket. Check the fluid level.

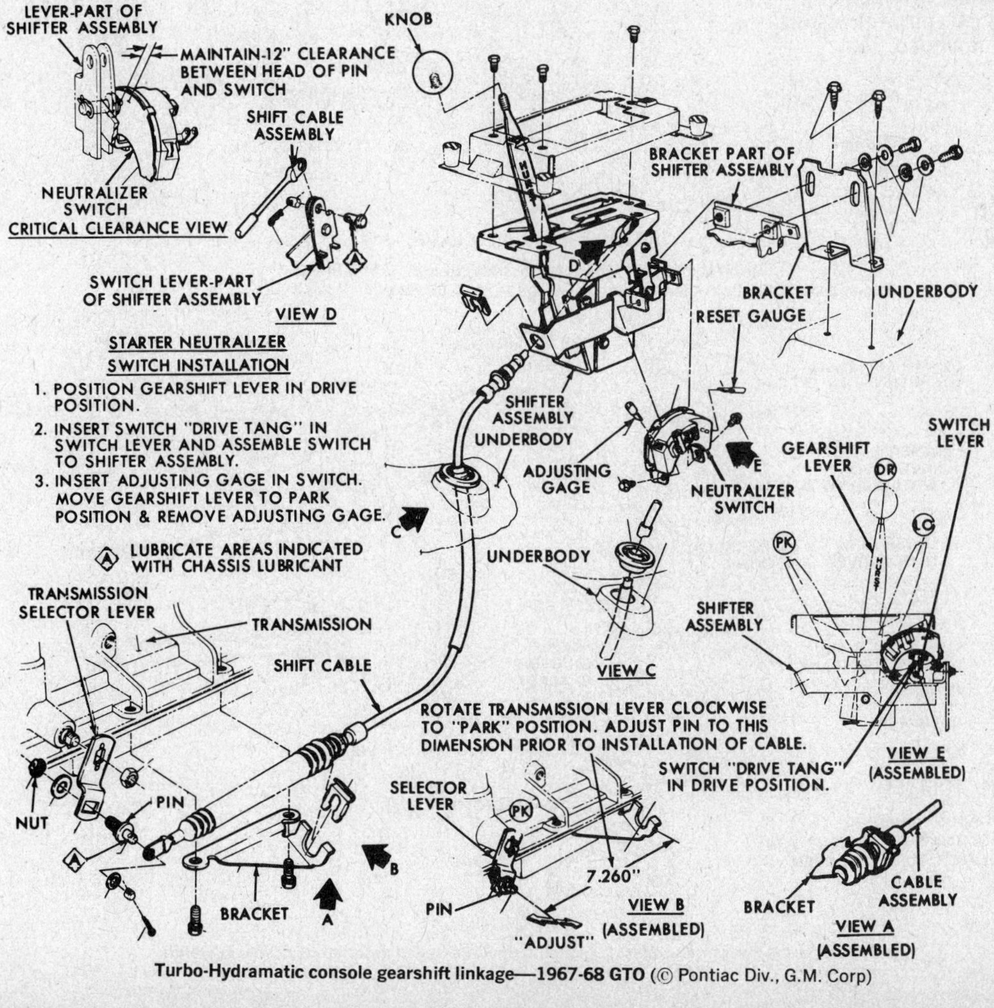
LEVER-PART OF
SHIFTER ASSEMBLY
MAINTAIN .12" CLEARANCE
BETWEEN HEAD OF PIN
AND SWITCH
NEUTRALIZER
SWITCH
CRITICAL CLEARANCE VIEW
SHIFT CABLE
ASSEMBLY
SWITCH LEVER-PART
OF SHIFTER ASSEMBLY
VIEW D
STARTER NEUTRALIZER
SWITCH INSTALLATION
1. POSITION GEARSHIFT LEVER IN DRIVE POSITION.
2. INSERT SWITCH "DRIVE TANG" IN SWITCH LEVER AND ASSEMBLE SWITCH TO SHIFTER ASSEMBLY.
3. INSERT ADJUSTING GAGE IN SWITCH. MOVE GEARSHIFT LEVER TO PARK POSITION & REMOVE ADJUSTING GAGE.
LUBRICATE AREAS INDICATED
WITH CHASSIS LUBRICANT
KNOB
HURST
D
BRACKET PART OF
SHIFTER ASSEMBLY
BRACKET
UNDERBODY
RESET GAUGE
SHIFTER
ASSEMBLY
UNDERBODY
ADJUSTING
GAGE
NEUTRALIZER
SWITCH
E
C
GEARSHIFT
LEVER
SWITCH
LEVER
DR
PK
LG
UNDERBODY
VIEW C
SHIFTER
ASSEMBLY
VIEW E
(ASSEMBLED)
TRANSMISSION
SELECTOR LEVER
TRANSMISSION
SHIFT CABLE
ROTATE TRANSMISSION LEVER CLOCKWISE
TO "PARK" POSITION. ADJUST PIN TO THIS
DIMENSION PRIOR TO INSTALLATION OF CABLE.
SWITCH "DRIVE TANG"
IN DRIVE POSITION.
NUT
PIN
BRACKET
A
B
SELECTOR
LEVER
PK
7.260"
PIN
"ADJUST"
VIEW B
(ASSEMBLED)
BRACKET
CABLE
ASSEMBLY
VIEW A
(ASSEMBLED)

Turbo-Hydramatic console gearshift linkage—1967-68 GTO (© Pontiac Div., G.M. Corp)

Vacuum Modulator R&R

Three-Speed (M-40, M-38), Two-Speed (M-35) 1967-69

1. Disconnect the vacuum hose from the modulator.
2. Remove the modulator bolt and retainer.
3. Slide the modulator out of the case.
4. Reverse the removal procedure to install. Use a new O-ring seal and check the fluid level.

Two-Speed (M-35) 1970-74

1. Remove the oil pan and strainer.
2. Unscrew the vacuum modulator assembly from the case and remove the modulator, gasket, plunger, dampening spring, and modulator valve.
3. Reverse the removal procedure for installation. Use new gaskets in all cases.

Low Band Adjustment Two-Speed (M-35)

1. Place the shifter lever in Neutral and raise the vehicle.
2. Remove the adjusting screw protecting cap.
3. Loosen the adjusting screw locknut 1/4 turn.

Caution Be sure to hold the adjusting screw locknut at 1/4 turn loose during the adjusting procedure.

4. Tighten the adjusting screw to 70 ft lbs and then back off *exactly* four complete turns for a band with 6,000 miles or more of use, three turns for a band with less than 6,000 miles of use.
5. Tighten the locknut and install the protective cap.

Turbo Hydra-Matic M-38, M-40 Band Adjustment

Band adjustments must be made during overhaul and cannot be accomplished without partial disassembly of the transmission. Varying the length of the band apply pin in the servo assemblies determines band adjustment.

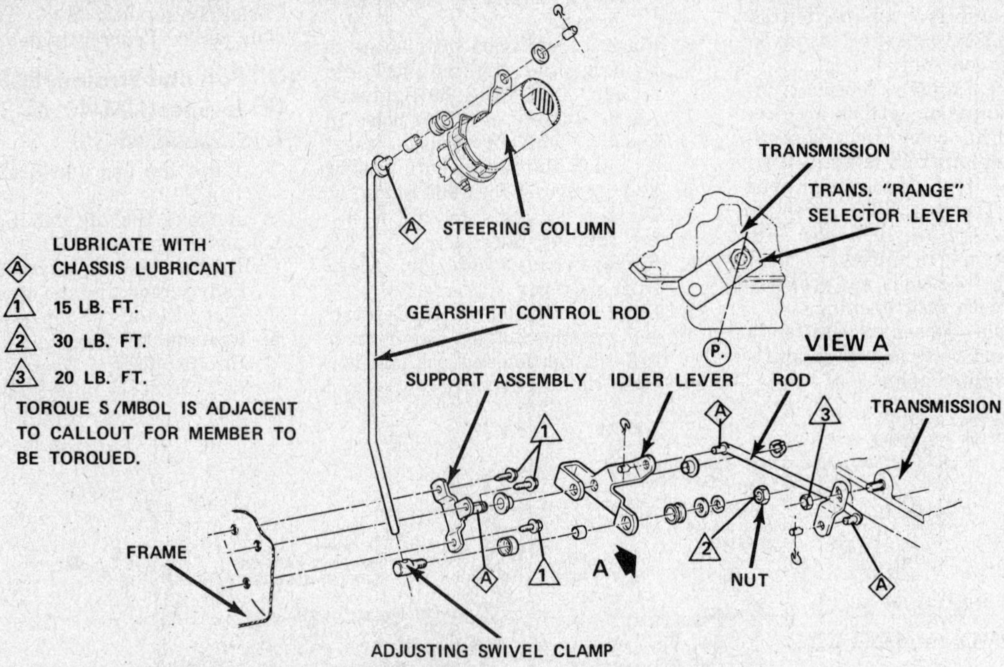
TRANSMISSION
TRANS. "RANGE" SELECTOR LEVER
STEERING COLUMN
LUBRICATE WITH CHASSIS LUBRICANT
15 LB. FT.
30 LB. FT.
20 LB. FT.
TORQUE SYMBOL IS ADJACENT TO CALLOUT FOR MEMBER TO BE TORQUED.
GEARSHIFT CONTROL ROD
VIEW A
SUPPORT ASSEMBLY
IDLER LEVER
ROD
TRANSMISSION
FRAME
NUT
ADJUSTING SWIVEL CLAMP

Turbo-Hydramatic column gearshift linkage—1969 Firebird
Two-speed automatic column gearshift linkage—1969 Firebird (© Pontiac Div., G.M. Corp)

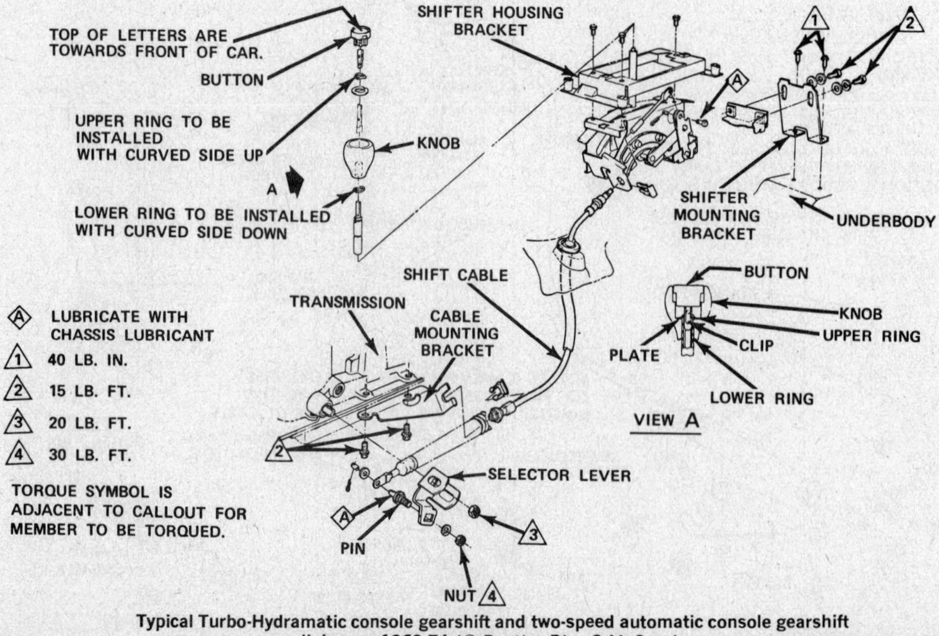
TOP OF LETTERS ARE TOWARDS FRONT OF CAR.
BUTTON
UPPER RING TO BE INSTALLED WITH CURVED SIDE UP
KNOB
LOWER RING TO BE INSTALLED WITH CURVED SIDE DOWN
SHIFTER HOUSING BRACKET
SHIFTER MOUNTING BRACKET
UNDERBODY
SHIFT CABLE
TRANSMISSION
CABLE MOUNTING BRACKET
LUBRICATE WITH CHASSIS LUBRICANT
40 LB. IN.
15 LB. FT.
20 LB. FT.
30 LB. FT.
TORQUE SYMBOL IS ADJACENT TO CALLOUT FOR MEMBER TO BE TORQUED.
SELECTOR LEVER
PIN
NUT
BUTTON
KNOB
UPPER RING
PLATE
CLIP
LOWER RING
VIEW A

Typical Turbo-Hydramatic console gearshift and two-speed automatic console gearshift linkage—1969-74 (© Pontiac Div., G.M. Corp)

Shift Linkage Adjustment

1967-68
Column Shift

1. Loosen the nut on the adjusting swivel clamp.
2. Set the transmission selector lever in the Drive detent.
3. Set the shift lever into the Drive position.
4. Tighten the nut on the adjusting swivel clamp.
5. Check the shifting pattern.

Console Shift

1. Disconnect the cable at the transmission.
2. With the gearshift lever in the Park position, adjust the pin as shown in the 1967–68 console gearshift linkage illustrations.
3. Tighten the pin nut and connect the cable.

All Turbo-Hydramatic Column —1969-74

Two-Speed (M-35) Column —1969-74

1. Loosen screw (nut on Firebird) on adjusting swivel clamp.
2. Place gearshift lever in Park and lock ignition.
3. Place transmission shift lever in Park detent.
4. Push up on gearshift control rod until lash is taken up in steering column lock mechanism, then tighten screw or nut on swivel clamp to 20 ft. lbs. (30 ft. lbs. on 1969 Firebird).
5. Readjust the transmission neutralizer switch if necessary.

Turbo-Hydramatic Console —1969-74

1. Disconnect shift cable from transmission shift lever by removing nut from pin.
2. Adjust back drive linkage (as in Step 4, above).
3. Unlock ignition and rotate transmission shift lever counterclockwise two detents.
4. Place console lever in Neutral and move against forward Neutral stop.
5. Assemble shift cable and pin to transmission shift lever so that no binding exists, then tighten nut to 30 ft. lbs. (20 ft. lbs.—1970-74).
6. Readjust the transmission neutralizer switch if necessary.

Two-Speed (M-35) Console —1969-74

1. Place console lever in Park and lock ignition.
2. Disconnect shift cable from transmission shift lever pin. Loosen the screw on the adjusting swivel at the shaft lever.
3. Rotate transmission shift lever clockwise to Park position and push up on control rod to take up slack.
4. Tighten swivel to 30 ft. lbs. (20 ft. lbs. 1970-74).
5. Unlock ignition and rotate range lever on transmission counterclockwise two positions.
6. Place shift lever in Neutral and move forward against Neutral stop.
7. Assemble shift cable and pin to transmission lever (free fit) and tighten pin nut to 30 ft. lbs. up to 1969 (20 ft. lbs. 1970-74).
8. Readjust the transmission neutralizer switch if necessary.

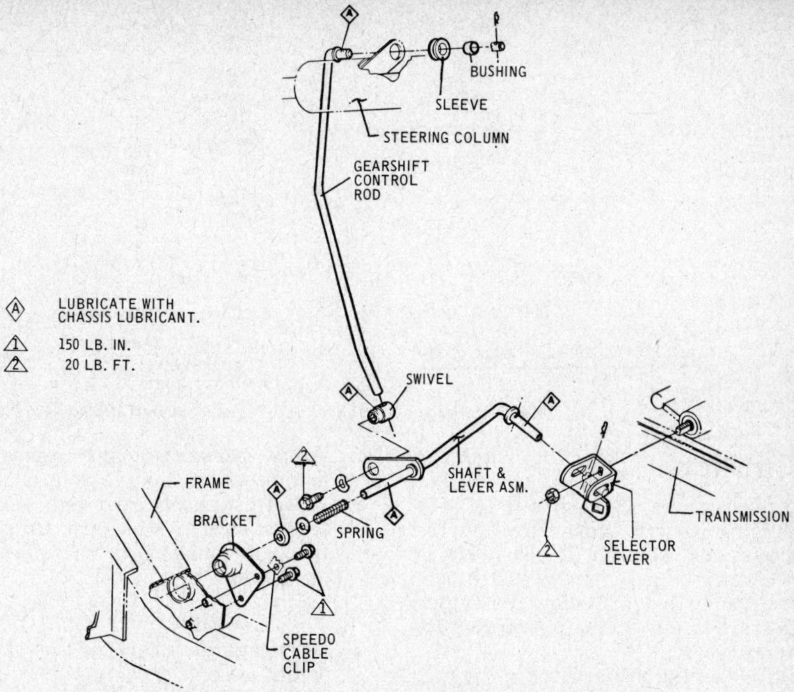
BUSHING
SLEEVE
STEERING COLUMN
GEARSHIFT CONTROL ROD
LUBRICATE WITH CHASSIS LUBRICANT.
150 LB. IN.
20 LB. FT.
SWIVEL
SHAFT & LEVER ASM.
FRAME
BRACKET
SPRING
TRANSMISSION
SELECTOR LEVER
SPEEDO CABLE CLIP
Turbo-Hydramatic column linkage—1970-74 Firebird. M-35 linkage is similar
(© Pontiac Div., G.M. Corp)

Turbo-Hydramatic (M-38) Console —1971-74 Ventura II

NOTE: the letters in the procedure refer to the letters in the accompanying illustration.

1. Loosen both swivel nuts (B and C) on control rod (E).
2. Place transmission lever (F) in Drive.
3. Set pawl rod (K) into Drive notch.
4. Apply load (Y) on actuating lever (D) until pawl rod (K) contacts detent at (Z).
5. Place a 0.094 in. spacer between nut (B) and swivel. Run in nut (B) until it hits spacer, then release load Y and tighten nut (C) to 40 in. lbs.
6. Place transmission shift lever (F) in Park and lock ignition.
7. Loosen nut (H) at idler lever (J), then remove play by rotating shift lever downward. Tighten nut (H) to 20 ft. lbs.

Neutral Safety Switch Adjustment

Column-Mounted Switch

NOTE: the neutral safety switch on 1967-68 console shifters is located on the shifter, not on the steering column.

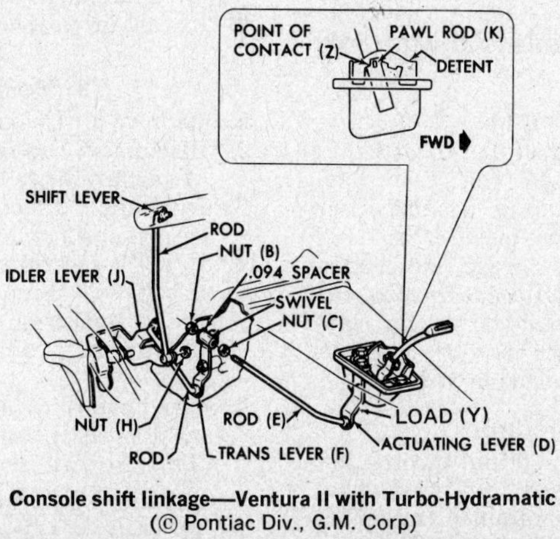
POINT OF CONTACT (Z)
PAWL ROD (K)
DETENT
FWD
SHIFT LEVER
ROD
NUT (B)
.094 SPACER
IDLER LEVER (J)
SWIVEL
NUT (C)
NUT (H)
ROD (E)
LOAD (Y)
ROD
TRANS LEVER (F)
ACTUATING LEVER (D)
Console shift linkage—Ventura II with Turbo-Hydramatic
(© Pontiac Div., G.M. Corp)

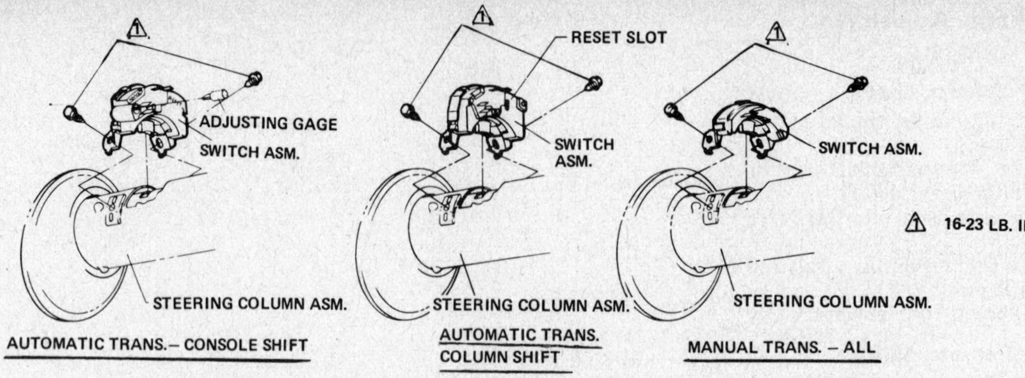
RESET SLOT
ADJUSTING GAGE
SWITCH ASM.
SWITCH ASM.
SWITCH ASM.
16-23 LB. IN.
STEERING COLUMN ASM.
STEERING COLUMN ASM.
STEERING COLUMN ASM.
AUTOMATIC TRANS.– CONSOLE SHIFT
AUTOMATIC TRANS. COLUMN SHIFT
MANUAL TRANS. – ALL

Neutral switch column shift 1967-74, console shift 1969-74 (© Pontiac Div., G.M. Corp)

Caution After the switch has been adjusted, but before starting the engine to test the shifting pattern, make sure that the brakes are securely locked. This is necessary because a misadjusted neutralizer switch will allow the engine to start in any of the forward or reverse gears.

1. Place the shifter lever in Park.
2. Loosen the switch retaining screws. Make sure that the switch drive tang is engaged in the shifter tube slot and that it stays engaged during adjustment.
3. Rotate the switch in its slot until it is in the Park position and then tighten the screws.
4. After observing the above caution, check the shifter pattern by placing the shifter lever in Neutral. If the transmission does not shift into Neutral, place the lever back in Park and rotate the switch slightly until the shift pattern is correct.
5. If it is possible to move the shift lever a large distance without having the transmission respond, check for a worn switch drive tang or bad electrical contacts inside the switch. In either case, replace the switch.

Shifter-Mounted Switch

The adjustment procedures are the same as for the column-mounted switch.

Downshift Cable Adjustment —1969-74

Tempest

1. With engine off and throttle butterflies closed (off fast idle), position retainer against insert on cable (from inside car).
2. To adjust, grasp accelerator pedal lever adjacent to downshift cable and pull carburetor cable to wide open throttle position. Check for full cable travel.

Firebird

1. With engine off and throttle butterflies closed (off fast idle), position the retainer (under the hood) rearward against washer and insert (or Snap Lock up).
2. To adjust, push carburetor extension lever to wide open throttle position and check for full cable travel.

Ventura II

1. Disengage the Snap Lock on the detent cable.
2. Place carburetor lever at wide open position, against stop.
3. With detent cable through detent, push Snap Lock downward until its top is flush with the cable.

Throttle Valve (TV) Linkage Adjustment—Two-Speed (M-35) 1970-74

6 Cylinder Models

1. Remove air cleaner.
2. Disconnect TV control rod swivel and clip from carburetor lever, then disconnect TV return spring from bellhousing.
3. Push TV control rod rearward until transmission TV lever is against internal transmission stop.
4. Holding TV control rod in this position, hold carburetor lever in wide open throttle position and adjust TV control rod swivel so that pin freely enters hole in carburetor lever without binding.
5. Secure swivel, connect return spring and check linkage action for binding.
6. Install air cleaner.

V8 Models

1. Remove air cleaner.
2. Disconnect accelerator linkage at carburetor.
3. Disconnect throttle and TV rod return springs.
4. Pull TV rod forward until transmission is through detent, hold in this position and open carburetor butterflies to wide open position.
5. The butterflies must reach wide open position at the same time that the ball stud contacts end of slot in upper TV rod (± 1/32 in.).
6. If necessary, adjust swivel end of upper TV rod.
7. Connect linkage and springs, then check linkage for binding.
8. Install air cleaner.

U-Joint

A splined yoke and universal assembly and a rear universal joint are used to accommodate changes in length and orientation of the driveshaft as the car moves over bumps.

Driveshaft R&R

1. Mark the driveshaft rear yoke and the differential flange to assure correct alignment upon reassembly.
2. Remove the U-bolts and nuts from the differential flange.
3. Remove the driveshaft assembly by first sliding the driveshaft sufficiently forward to disengage the differential flange, then slide the shaft downward and rearward to disengage the front splined yoke from the transmission output shaft.
4. Installation is the reverse of removal. Be sure to align the match mark made before disassembly.

U-Joint R&R All Front and Single Cardan Rear U-Joints

Removal

1. Remove the driveshaft.

NOTE: the universal may have snap-rings that are used to retain the bearing cups in the yokes. These snap-rings may be located at the outside of each yoke or in a groove at the base or open end of each bearing cap. In both cases, there are four snaprings for each universal joint and they must be removed before proceeding further.

2. Support the splined yoke (front universal) or the journal (rear universal) in a manner that will allow the fixed yoke on the driveshaft to be moved. Support the opposite end so that the driveshaft will be in a horizontal position.

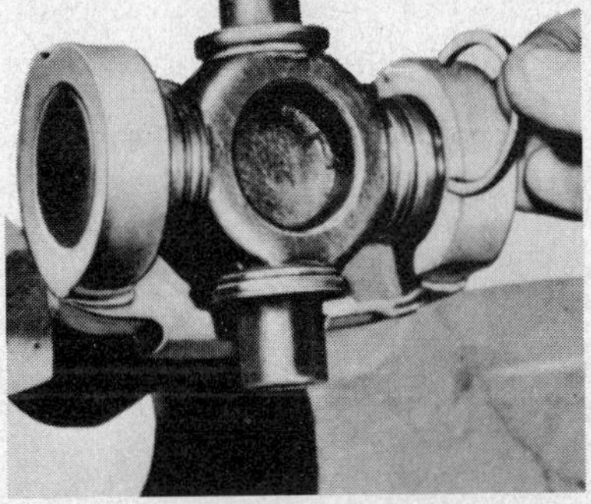

Installing snap-ring
(© Pontiac Div., G.M. Corp)

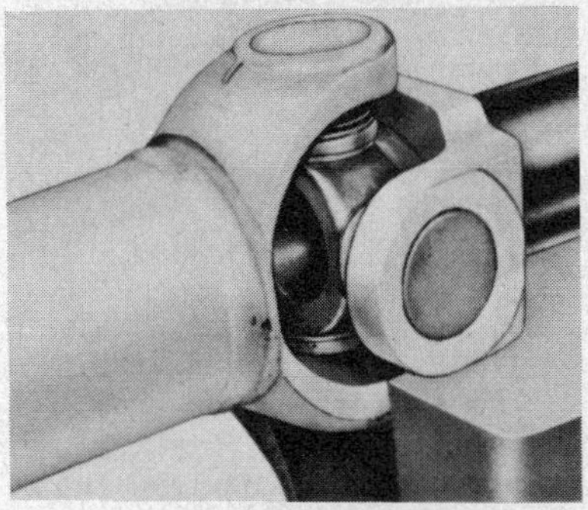

Supporting splined yoke
(© Pontiac Div., G.M. Corp)

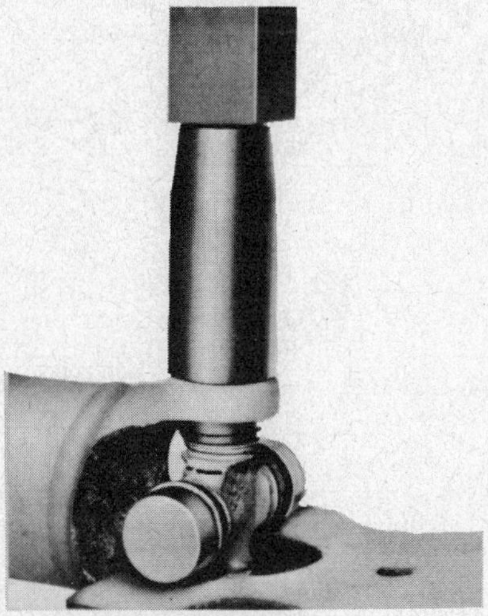

Bearing removal
(© Pontiac Div., G.M. Corp)

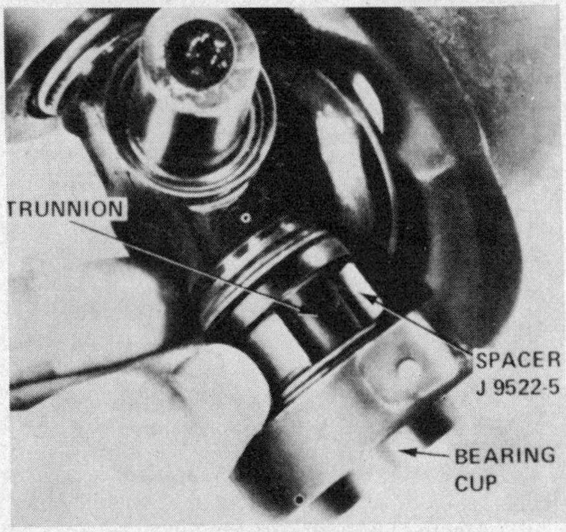
TRUNNION
SPACER
J 9522-5
BEARING
CUP

Using spacer to remove U-joint bearing cup
(© Pontiac Div., G.M. Corp)

3. Using a piece of pipe, or a similar tool with a large enough diameter, apply force to the fixed yoke until the bearing is almost completely pushed out of the yoke and into the pipe. Remove the bearing completely by inserting a spacer (tool #J9522-5) between the seal and the bearing cup and finish pressing the bearing out of its yoke, or by tapping around the circumference of the exposed portion of the bearing with a punch and small hammer.

NOTE: The plastic which retains the bearing will be sheared when the bearing cup is pressed out. Be sure to remove the remains of the plastic retainer from the ears of the yoke. It is easier to remove the remains if a small pin or punch is first driven through the injection holes in the yoke. Failure to remove all of the plastic remains may prevent the bearing cups from being pressed into place and the bearing retainers from being properly seated.

4. Remove the rest of the bearings following the same procedure.

Installation

1. Install a bearing one-quarter of the way into one side of the splined yoke (front universal) or fixed yoke (rear universal).
2. Insert the journal into the yoke so that an arm of the journal seats into the bearing.
3. Press in the bearing the remaining distance.
4. Install the opposite bearing. Do not allow the bearing rollers to jam. Continually check for free movement of the journal in the bearings as they are pressed into the yoke.
5. Install the rest of the bearings in the same manner.

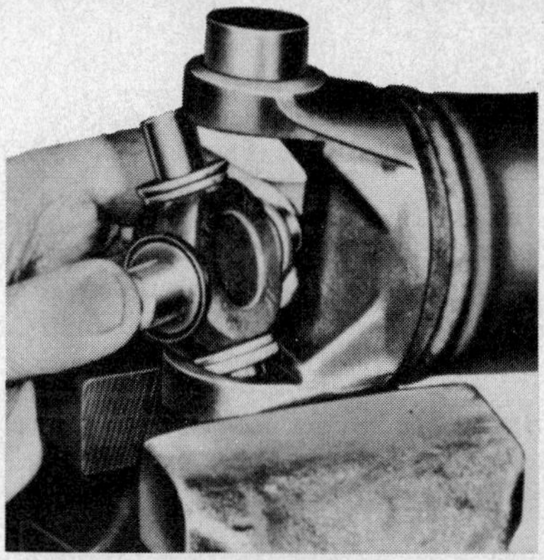

Installing journal
(© Pontiac Div., G.M. Corp)

JACKING, HOISTING

Jack car at front spring seats of lower control arms. Jack car at rear under axle housing, or under a frame member.

FRONT SUSPENSION

Ball joints, located at the outer ends of the upper and lower control arms, act as pivot points for both the vertical movement of the wheel and rotation of the steering knuckle. The spherical joints have a fixed boot grease seal to protect against dirt and water. Steering knuckles and spindles are one-piece forgings.

Rubber bushings at the upper inner control arm ends pivot on shafts attached to the frame. By varying shim thickness at this point, caster and camber adjustments are accomplished. The inner ends of the lower control arms are also rubber mounted, and are attached to the front crossmember through brackets.

The upper ends of the coil springs are seated in the frame, while the lower ends rest on the lower control arms. Double-action shock absorbers are located inside the coil springs, the rubber insulated upper end of each unit being fastened to the frame, the similarly insulated lower end to the lower control arm.

For increased roll stability, a stabilizer bar is rubber mounted to the frame and is connected to the lower control arms via links at each end.

The Ventura II front suspension is similar to the Tempest, the main difference being that the stabilizer bar mounting brackets are located by two clamps and sleeves mounted to the inboard ends. The gap between the sleeve and bracket never should exceed ⅛ in.

The front suspension of the Grand Am is basically similar to the LeMans, except for the use of harder

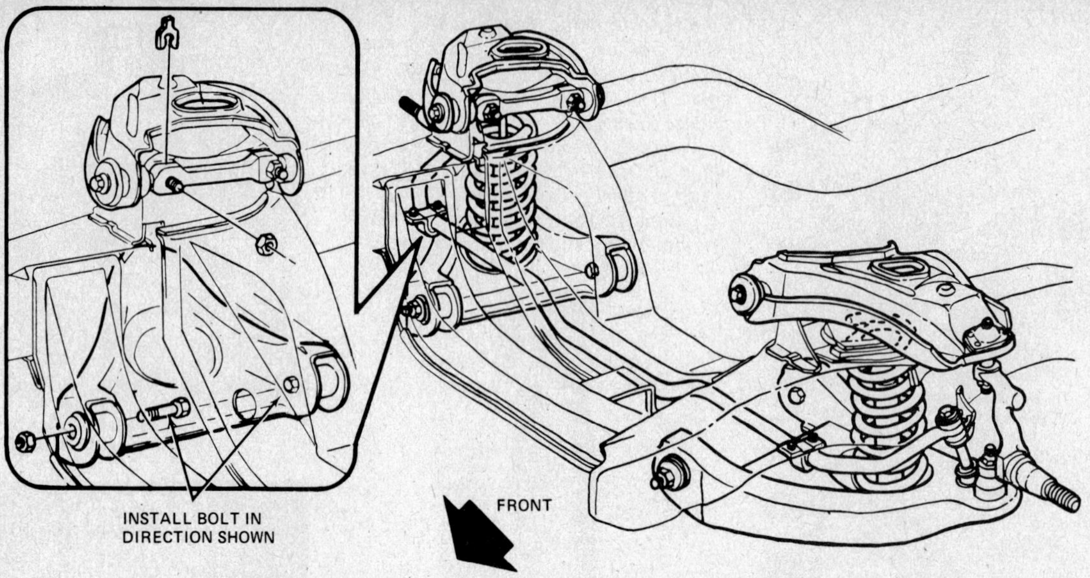
INSTALL BOLT IN
DIRECTION SHOWN
FRONT

Front suspension—1971-74 Ventura II (© Pontiac Div., G.M. Corp)

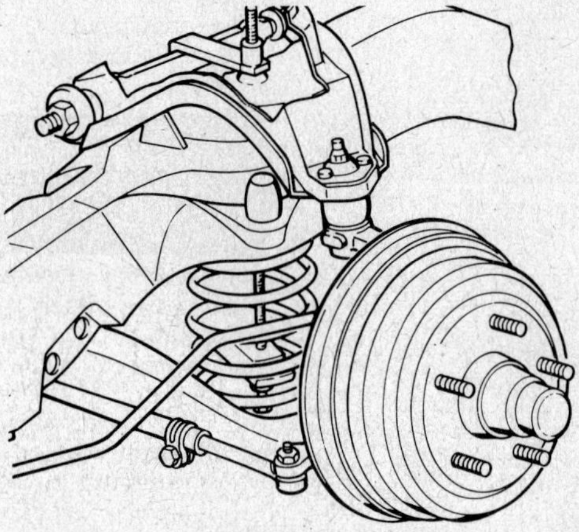

Typical front suspension—1967-74
(© Pontiac Div., G.M. Corp)

suspension bushings to reduce ride firmness and the 1.12 in. stabilizer bar mounted into 1.22 in. diameter plastic grommets for more effective stabilization without increasing bar size. The Grand Am shock absorbers consist of a plastic air cell to separate the air and fluid in the shock reservoir. This eliminates aeration of the fluid and enables the shocks to retain their firmness over rough road conditions. See the Unit Repair Section for wheel alignment procedures.

Front Shock Absorber R&R

Removal

1. Remove the nut, retainer, and grommet which are attached to the upper end of the shock absorber and seat against the frame bracket.

NOTE: it may be necessary to hold the shock absorber shaft to remove the nut. This may be done with a wrench on the end of the shaft.

2. Raise the car to allow the shock to be dropped from the lower control arm.
3. Remove the two shock absorber lower attaching screws and lower the shock from the control arm.

Installation

1. Install the shock absorber by reversing the removal steps.
2. Make sure all grommets are in the correct position.
3. The upper stud nut must be tightened until it bottoms at the end of the threads.

Coil Spring R & R—1967-68 Tempest and GTO

1. Jack up car to allow lower control arm to hang free. Support car on jack stands under the frame side rails.
2. Remove wheel and brake drum.
3. Remove shock absorber.
4. Disconnect stabilizer bar from lower control arm.
5. Insert a spring compressing tool through the shock absorber mounting holes and compress the coil spring until it lifts from its seat.

NOTE: a spring compressor can be fabricated using a length of threaded rod, a support plate and a support hook.

6. Remove backing plate and swing it out of the way.
7. Disconnect lower ball joint stud and swing steering knuckle out of the way.
8. Pull lower control arm down far enough to remove spring.
9. To install, reverse removal procedure.

NOTE: spring must be compressed before installation.

Coil Spring R & R—1967-74 Firebird, 1969-74 Tempest, GTO, and Ventura II

1. Jack up car and support on jack stands at frame side rails.
2. Remove shock absorber.
3. Disconnect stabilizer bar at lower control arm.
4. Support lower control arm with a hydraulic floor jack, then remove the two inner control arm to front crossmember bolts.
5. Carefully lower the control arm, allowing the spring to relax.

Caution Allow the spring to completely expand before attempting to remove it.

6. Reach in and remove spring.
7. To install, reverse the removal procedure.

Upper Control Arm Removal

1. Support car weight at outer end of lower control arm.
2. Remove wheel and tire.
3. Remove cotter pin and nut from upper control arm ball stud.
4. Remove the stud from the knuckle with a pry bar, while tapping with a hammer.
5. Remove two nuts that hold the upper control arm cross-shaft to

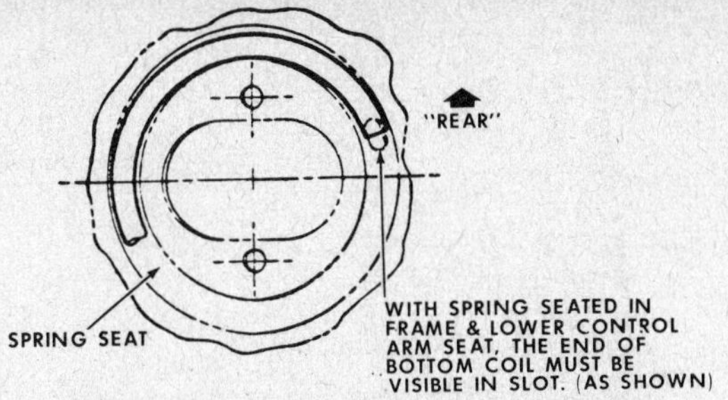
"REAR"
SPRING SEAT
WITH SPRING SEATED IN FRAME & LOWER CONTROL ARM SEAT, THE END OF BOTTOM COIL MUST BE VISIBLE IN SLOT. (AS SHOWN)

Front coil spring position on lower control arm—all except Firebird
(© Pontiac Div., G.M. Corp)

front crossmember. Count number of shims at each bolt.

NOTE: on V8 Firebird models up to 1969 with air conditioning, swing compressor out of the way.

Ball Joint Inspection

NOTE: before performing this inspection, make sure the wheel bearings are adjusted correctly and that the A arm bushings are in good condition.

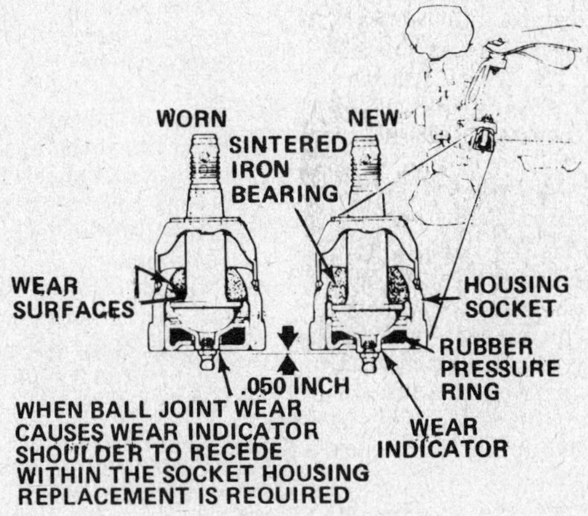
WORN
NEW
SINTERED IRON BEARING
WEAR SURFACES
HOUSING SOCKET
RUBBER PRESSURE RING
.050 INCH
WHEN BALL JOINT WEAR CAUSES WEAR INDICATOR SHOULDER TO RECEDE WITHIN THE SOCKET HOUSING REPLACEMENT IS REQUIRED
WEAR INDICATOR

Lower ball joint wear indicator
(© Pontiac Div., G.M. Corp)

1. Jack the car up under the front lower control arm at the spring seat.
2. Raise the car until there is 1–2 in. of clearance under the wheel.
3. Insert a bar under the wheel and pry upward. If the wheel raises more than 1/8 in., the ball joints are worn. Determine whether the upper or lower ball joint is worn by visual inspection while prying on the wheel.

NOTE: due to the distribution of forces in the suspension, the lower ball joint is usually the defective joint.

Alternate Ball Joint Inspection Method

Upper—Tension Type

1. Disengage the ball stud from the steering knuckle, the weight of the car being supported by a jack under the spring seat on the side being checked.
2. Install the stud nut onto the stud and check the torque required to rotate the ball stud.
3. If the torque is less than 1/2 ft lb, the joint must be replaced.

Lower—Compression Type

1. Place a jack under the lower control arm spring seat and jack up the car.
2. Pry the wheel and tire up and down (or remove the wheel and hub to eliminate wheel bearing play) and measure the play in the joint using a dial indicator or a standard inspection station ball joint checking device.
3. If play exceeds 0.050 in., the ball joint must be replaced.

Lower—Tension Type

1. Place a jack under the lower control arm spring seat and jack up the car.
2. Remove the grease fitting from the lower ball joint.
3. Remove the hub and backing plate, or caliper assembly.
4. Separate the lower ball stud from the steering knuckle using a pry bar and hammer.

NOTE: Make sure that the seal is not damaged.

5. Place the probe of the dial indicator into the grease fitting hole until it touches the base of the ball joint.
6. Preload and zero the indicator, then pull up and down on the threaded portion of the stud and measure the play.
7. If the play exceeds 0.050 in., the ball joint must be replaced.

Upper Ball Joint Removal

1. Prickpunch the center of the four rivets.
2. Drill through the heads of these rivets.
3. Chisel off rivet heads and tap out rivets with a punch.

Upper Ball Joint Installation

1. Install new ball joint against top side of upper control arm. Secure joint to control arm with the four special alloy bolts and nuts furnished with the replacement part.
2. Torque these bolts and nuts to 10-12 ft. lbs. (9 ft. lbs.—1969-74).

NOTE: use special bolts only.

Upper Control Arm Installation

1. Install bolts through holes and install upper control arm to crossmember.
2. Secure two nuts and washers to the bolts holding the upper control arm shaft to front crossmember. Install same number of shims as removed at each bolt. Torque bolts to 50 ft. lbs. on all 1967-71 models and 1972-74 Ventura. On 1972-74 Firebird, LeMans and Grand Am, tighten the bolts to 80 ft lbs.
3. Lubricate ball joint with chassis lube.
4. Install ball joint stud through knuckle. Install nut, and torque to 50 ft. lbs. (40 ft. lbs.—1972-74). Insert cotter pin.

Caution Care should be taken to insure that the steering knuckle hole, ball stud, and nut are free of dirt and grease before tightening the nut. Turn the nut only in the tightening direction to align the slot with the hole to insert the cotter pin. DO NOT BACK OFF THE NUT. Maximum torque to align the slot with the hole should not exceed 70 ft lbs.

5. Install wheel and tire assembly.
6. Lower car to floor.
7. Bounce car to neutralize front end suspension and torque pivot shaft nuts to 50 ft. lbs.
8. Be sure to recheck caster and camber.

Lower Control Arm and Ball Joint R & R

1. Remove coil spring and lower control arm inner bolts.
2. Separate lower ball joint from steering knuckle by prying, while hammering sharply on steering knuckle.
3. Press lower ball joint from lower control arm using suitable arbors and a large bench vise.
4. To install, reverse removal procedure, tightening lower ball joint stud nut to 85-90 ft. lbs. (70 ft. lbs—1972-74).

NOTE: if only ball joint is to be removed, remove brake caliper or hub and backing plate, with jack under lower arm. Begin with Step 2.

Wheel Bearing Inspection and Adjustment

Inspection

1. Raise the car and support it under the front lower control arm.
2. Spin the wheel to check for any unusual noise. Bad wheel bearings sometimes squeal or sound as though there is sand in the bearing.
3. If bearings are noisy or loose, they should be cleaned, inspected, and repacked before adjustment.
4. To check for loose bearings, grip the tire at top and bottom and move the wheel in and out. Movement greater than 0.005 in. indicates improper adjustment or excessive wear.

Adjustment

1. Lift the wheel off the ground by jacking under the lower control arm.
2. Remove the dust cap from the hub.
3. Remove the cotter pin and discard it.
4. Snug up the spindle nut to seat the bearings. Then back off the nut ¼–½ turn.
5. Retighten the nut by hand until it is finger-tight.
6. Loosen the nut until the nearest hole in the spindle lines up with a slot in the spindle nut and then insert a new cotter pin. When the bearing is properly adjusted, there will be 0.001-0.008 in. endplay.

NOTE: under no circumstances is the final bearing nut adjustment to be even finger-tight.

7. Replace the dust cover and lower the car.

REAR SUSPENSION

1967-74 Tempest, GTO, LeMans and Grand Am

The rear wheels are fastened to axle shafts within a Salisbury-type, solid axle housing. The axle housing is connected to the frame by a four-link suspension system, consisting of two upper and two lower control arms pivoted in rubber at each end. These control arms locate the axle laterally and axially with relation to the frame, and oppose torque reaction under acceleration and braking.

Two coil springs are mounted between seats in the frame and axle housing to carry the load of the vehicle. A steel stabilizer bar is mounted on some GTO and LeMans models, and all Grand Ams, to improve side roll stability. This bar attaches to the lower control arms and is positioned under the axle housing.

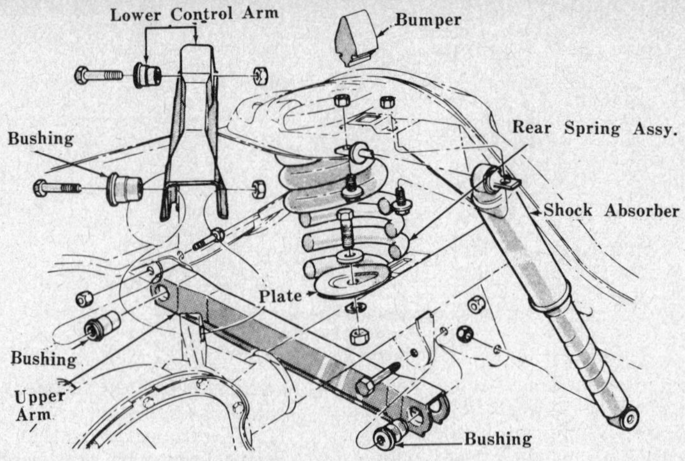
Lower Control Arm
Bumper
Bushing
Rear Spring Assy.
Shock Absorber
Plate
Bushing
Upper Arm
Bushing

Coil spring rear suspension—1967-74
(© Pontiac Div., G.M. Corp)

Shock absorbers are direct double-action hydraulic units and are mounted between the lower control arms and frame. The Grand Am uses the gas cell shock absorber described in the "Front Suspension" section.

1967-74 Firebird and 1971-74 Ventura II

Firebird models use dual multiple-leaf springs and two hydraulic shock absorbers mounted between the lower spring seats and the floor pan. The shocks are staggered, the right shock in front of, and the left shock behind, the axle tubes to reduce spring wind-up under acceleration and braking.

A steel stabilizer bar is used on Formula and Trans Am models to improve side roll stability. This bar is mounted in rubber and is supported by brackets under each shock and spring anchor plate. Two strut supports connect the bar to the frame side rails.

The Ventura II suspension is similar to that used on the Firebird, except that single leaf rear springs are utilized. These springs have a dampener strapped ten inches behind the front spring eye to lessen oscillations under loading.

Shock Absorber R&R

1. Raise the car at the axle housing.
2. Remove the nut, retainer, and grommet, or nut, and lockwasher, as equipped, which attach the lower end of the shock absorber to its mounting.
3. Remove the two shock absorber upper attaching screws and the shock absorber.
4. Reverse the removal procedures to install. Tighten the lower nut to 65 ft lbs. on LeMans and Grand Am, to 10 ft lbs. on Firebird and to 55 ft lbs. on Ventura.

Rear Spring R&R Coil Spring

1. Raise the rear of the car and support it solidly on the frame rails.
2. Remove the clip that attaches the brake hose to its bracket on the frame crossmember.
3. Support the rear axle with a jack.
4. Remove the nut and lockwasher from the shock absorber and disconnect the shock from the axle. It may be necessary to adjust the height of the jack to disconnect the shock.
5. Carefully lower the jack until the spring is free and remove the spring. Note the position of the spring and replace it with the lower coil pointing in the same direction.
6. Reverse the removal steps to install the spring.

Rear Spring R&R Leaf Spring

Removal

1. Jack up the car at the rear axle. Then support the major portion of the weight of the car on the frame rails, leaving the jack in place under the axle. At this point the jack should be supporting the axle only; there should be no tension on the spring.
2. Disconnect the shock at the axle and move it out of the way.
3. Remove the spring and shock absorber anchor plate nuts and remove the anchor plate and lower spring cushion pad.
4. Raise the axle with the jack and remove the upper spring cushion pad.
5 Loosen the upper and lower spring shackle pin nuts.
6. Loosen the front spring eye bolt.
7. Remove the screws securing the spring front mounting bracket to the floor pan and carefully let the spring swing down.
8. Remove the lower shackle pin from the rear of the spring and remove the spring from the car.

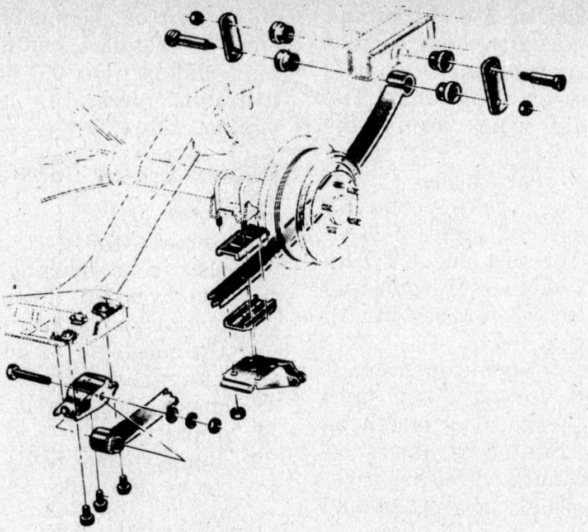

Rear spring installation—Ventura II
(© Pontiac Div., G.M. Corp)

Installation

Caution Torque values must be used as specified during reassembly to assure proper retention. Always replace any worn parts, especially bolts and nuts.

1. Install the front spring mounting bracket on the front spring eye and loosely insert the bolt and nut. Do not tighten the spring eyebolt until the weight of the car is on the springs.
2. Place the spring into the shackles at the rear of the car and loosely install the lower shackle pin and nut. Do not tighten them.
3. Raise the front end of the spring and install the spring mounting bracket to the floor pan and torque the bolts to 25 ft lbs. Make sure the tab on the spring mounting bracket is indexed in the slot in the floor pan and that the parking brake cables are on the top side of the spring.
4. Place the upper spring cushion pan on the spring and lower the axle onto spring.
5. Install the lower spring cushion and shock absorber anchor plate and torque the anchor plate nuts to 40 ft lbs.
6. Install the shock absorber.
7. Put the weight of the car on the springs and torque the shackle pin nuts to 50 ft lbs. Tighten front eyebolt to 75 ft lbs.

BRAKES

Standard brakes are of the duo-servo, self-adjusting type. The self-adjusting feature operates only when the brakes are applied with car moving in reverse.

Metallic brake linings, used on some early high-performance models, never should be installed on cars equipped with standard brake drums unless the drums are radius ground and honed to a special finish. See the Unit Repair Section of this manual for more information on metallic brake linings.

Since 1967, a dual-type master cylinder has been used. For detailed information on this type cylinder, see Unit Repair Section.

The parking brake uses a foot-operated control lever, enclosed cables, rear wheel brake shoe levers and struts to the rear wheel shoes.

Information on brake adjustments, lining replacement, bleeding procedure, master and wheel cylinder overhaul can be found in the Unit Repair Section.

Disc Brakes

From 1967, single-piston, sliding-caliper disc brakes have been available as optional equipment on most models (standard with high performance packages and Firebird starting 1970 and on all models except Ventura since 1971). These brakes have a vented, cast-iron rotor with two braking surfaces.

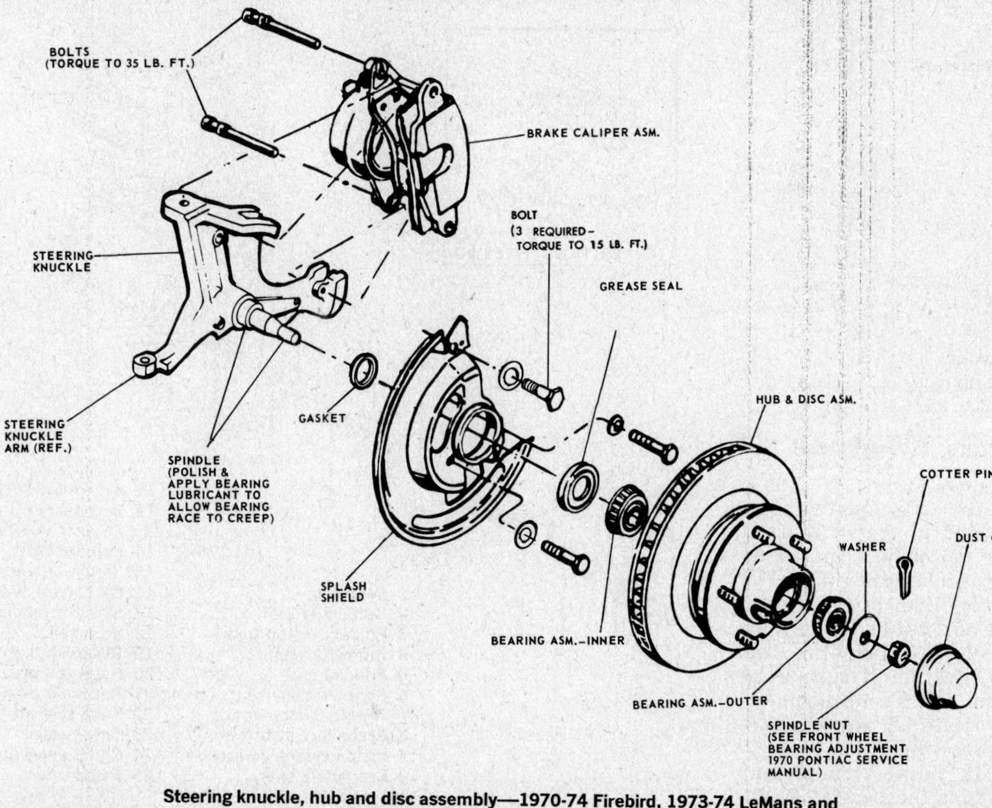
BOLTS
(TORQUE TO 35 LB. FT.)
BRAKE CALIPER ASM.
BOLT
(3 REQUIRED-
TORQUE TO 15 LB. FT.)
STEERING
KNUCKLE
GREASE SEAL
HUB & DISC ASM.
STEERING
KNUCKLE
ARM (REF.)
GASKET
SPINDLE
(POLISH &
APPLY BEARING
LUBRICANT TO
ALLOW BEARING
RACE TO CREEP)
COTTER PIN
WASHER
DUST CAP
SPLASH
SHIELD
BEARING ASM.-INNER
BEARING ASM.-OUTER
SPINDLE NUT
(SEE FRONT WHEEL
BEARING ADJUSTMENT
1970 PONTIAC SERVICE
MANUAL)

Steering knuckle, hub and disc assembly—1970-74 Firebird, 1973-74 LeMans and Grand Am (© Pontiac Div., G.M. Corp)

Disc brakes need no adjustment because, during operation, the application and release of hydraulic pressure causes the piston and caliper to move only slightly. In the released position, the pads do not move very far from the rotor thus, as pads wear down, the piston simply moves farther out of the caliper bore and the caliper repositions itself on its mounting bolts to maintain proper pad-to-rotor clearance.

A metering valve in the front brake circuit prevents the discs from operating until about 75 psi exists in the system. This enables the rear drum brakes to operate in synchronization with the front discs and reduces the possibility of unequal brake application and premature front brake lock-up. A proportioning valve in the rear brake circuit of some models limits the amount of hydraulic pressure that can be applied to the rear brakes, preventing the rear brakes from locking up. Starting 1971, a two- or three-function combination valve replaces the separate units used previously. The pressure required to operate front brakes is now 110-150 psi. Disc brake pads should be examined for wear every 12,000 miles. 1974 Pontiacs employ a lining wear indicator. As the lining material wears down, a steel sensor approaches the rotor. When enough lining material has worn away, the sensor makes contact with the rotor causing noise which is audible to the driver. See the Unit Repair Section of this manual for service procedures.

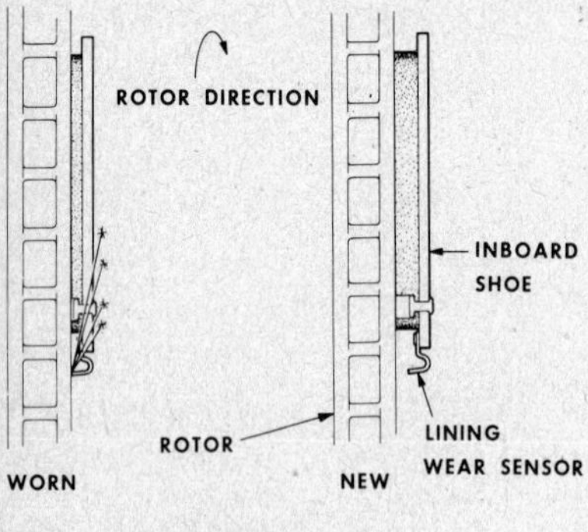
ROTOR DIRECTION
INBOARD SHOE
ROTOR
LINING WEAR SENSOR
WORN
NEW
LEFT FRONT

1974 disc brake lining wear indicator
(© Pontiac Div, G.M. Corp)

Parking Brake Adjustment —1967-74

The automatic self-adjusting feature incorporated in the rear brake mechanism normally maintains proper parking brake adjustment. For this reason, the rear brake adjustment must be checked before any adjustment of the parking brake cables is done. Check the parking brake mechanism and cables for free movement and lubricate all working surfaces before proceeding.

Caution It is very important that the parking brake cables are not too tight. If the cables are too tight, they create a drag and position the secondary shoes so that the self-adjusters continue to operate in compensation for drag wear. The result is rapidly worn rear brake linings.

1. Jack up both rear wheels.
2. Push parking brake pedal 5-7 notches from full release position (for Tempest and GTO up to 1970), 2 notches (Firebird up to 1970), or 4-8 notches for all series starting 1971.
3. Loosen rear equalizer locknut and adjust forward nut until light rear brake drag is felt as wheels are rotated by hand.
4. Tighten locknut and release parking brake pedal; no drag should be felt.

Master Cylinder R & R

1967-74

1. Disconnect hydraulic line/s at master cylinder; disconnect clevis at pedal.
2. Remove the two retaining nuts and lockwashers that hold cylinder to firewall.
3. Remove the master cylinder, gasket and rubber boot.
4. Position master cylinder on firewall; reconnect pushrod clevis to brake pedal.
5. Install nuts and lockwashers.
6. Install hydraulic line/s, then check brake pedal free play.
7. Bleed brakes, as described in Unit Repair Section.

NOTE: cars having disc brakes do not have a check valve in the front outlet port of the master cylinder. If one is installed, front discs will immediately wear out due to residual hydraulic pressure holding pads against rotor.

Power Brake Boosters R&R 1967-74

1. Remove the vacuum hose from the front housing and discard the grommet. Remove the master cylinder and position away from the booster. It is not necessary to disconnect the lines from the master cylinder if it is not to be repaired.
2. Remove the clevis pin retainer from the brake pedal inside the car.
3. Remove the nuts from the vacuum cylinder studs under the dash and remove the vacuum power section.
4. Reverse the removal procedure to install the booster.

STEERING

The steering system consists of a steering wheel, steering column, universal joint (except Ventura), intermediate steering shaft (except Ventura), flexible coupling, manual or power steering gear, and steering linkage.

The manual steering gear is the recirculating-ball nut type. The steering shaft, worm shaft, and worm nut are all in line. The steering shaft and worm shaft are separated by a flexible coupling. This coupling permits

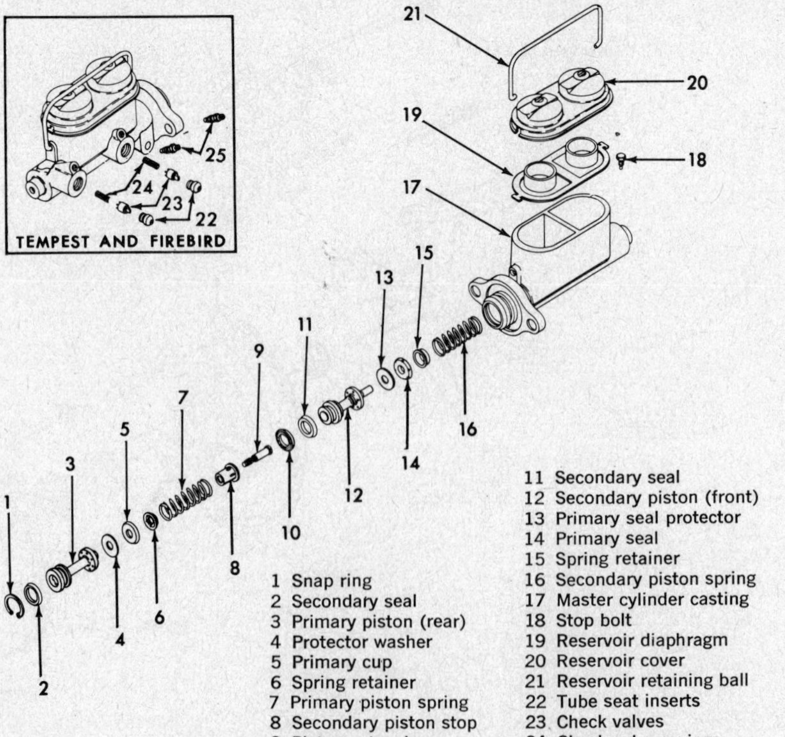
TEMPEST AND FIREBIRD

1 Snap ring
2 Secondary seal
3 Primary piston (rear)
4 Protector washer
5 Primary cup
6 Spring retainer
7 Primary piston spring
8 Secondary piston stop
9 Piston extension screw
10 Secondary seal
11 Secondary seal
12 Secondary piston (front)
13 Primary seal protector
14 Primary seal
15 Spring retainer
16 Secondary piston spring
17 Master cylinder casting
18 Stop bolt
19 Reservoir diaphragm
20 Reservoir cover
21 Reservoir retaining ball
22 Tube seat inserts
23 Check valves
24 Check valve springs
25 Bleed valves

Dual master cylinder (© Pontiac Div., G.M. Corp)

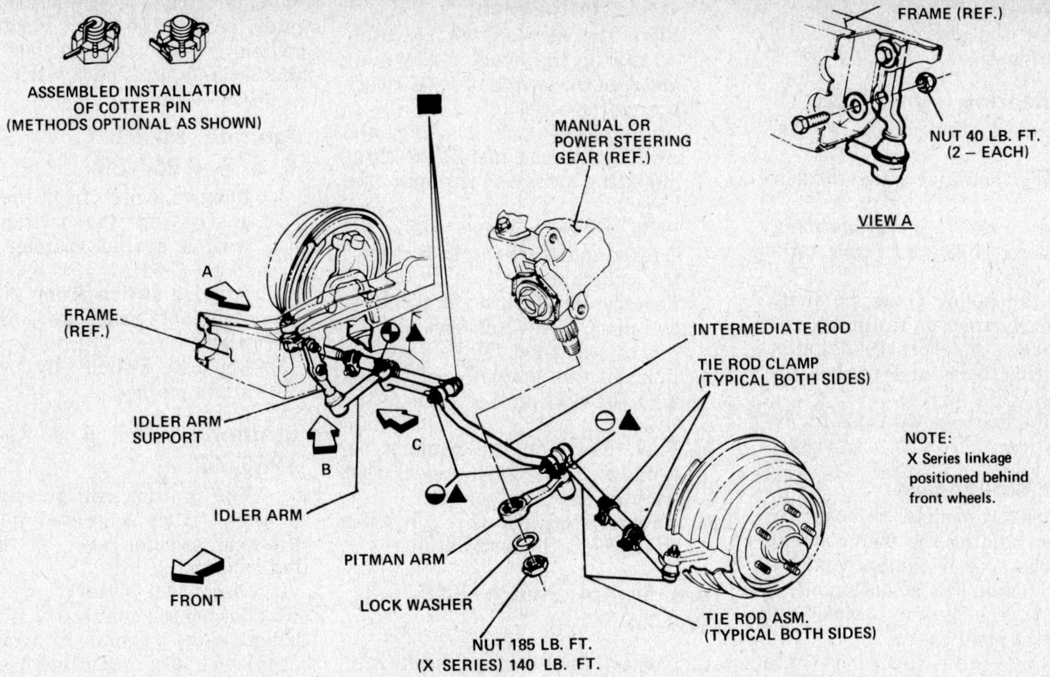
ASSEMBLED INSTALLATION
OF COTTER PIN
(METHODS OPTIONAL AS SHOWN)
FRAME (REF.)
NUT 40 LB. FT.
(2 – EACH)
VIEW A
MANUAL OR
POWER STEERING
GEAR (REF.)
A
FRAME
(REF.)
INTERMEDIATE ROD
TIE ROD CLAMP
(TYPICAL BOTH SIDES)
NOTE:
X Series linkage
positioned behind
front wheels.
IDLER ARM
SUPPORT
B
C
IDLER ARM
PITMAN ARM
FRONT
LOCK WASHER
TIE ROD ASM.
(TYPICAL BOTH SIDES)
NUT 185 LB. FT.
(X SERIES) 140 LB. FT.

Steering linkage (© Pontiac Div., G.M. Corp)

the gear to be removed independently of the steering shaft and steering column.

All Pontiacs use a variable-ratio power steering gear. The gear is the recirculating-ball type, incorporating a wormshaft and a rack-piston. A rotary valve is contained in the gear housing, eliminating the need for individually mounted valve and cylinder assemblies.

Hydraulic pressure for the power steering is provided by a constant displacement vane-type pump. It is located on the left front of the engine and is belt-driven by the engine crankshaft pulley.

Tie Rod End Inspection

1. Raise the car under the lower control arm.
2. Make sure that the control arm ball joints are good and that the wheel bearings are adjusted. Grasp the tire on either side and move the tire from side to side. If excessive play is present (more than 1/16 in.), visually inspect the linkage as the tire is moved.

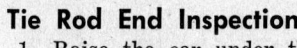

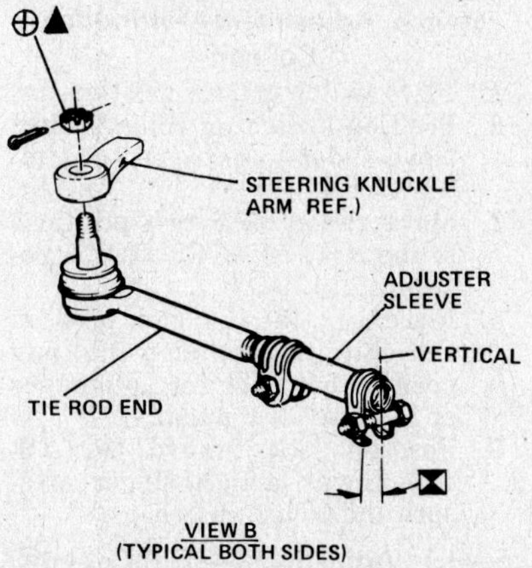
STEERING KNUCKLE
ARM REF.)
ADJUSTER
SLEEVE
VERTICAL
TIE ROD END
VIEW B
(TYPICAL BOTH SIDES)

Tie rod assembly—typical
(© Pontiac Div., G.M. Corp)

Tie Rod End R&R

1. Loosen the tie rod adjuster sleeve clamp nuts.
2. Remove the tie rod stud nut cotter pin and nut.
3. Remove the tie rod stud from the steering arm or intermediate rod. This is a taper fit. Removal is accomplished using a ball joint removal tool or by hitting the tie rod stud sharply with a hammer. If the ball joint is to be reused, the removal tool must be used.
4. Unthread the tie rod from the adjuster sleeve. Outer tie rods have right-hand threads and inner tie rods have left-hand threads. Count the number of turns the tie rod must be rotated to remove it from the adjusting sleeve. This will allow a reasonably accurate realignment upon reassembly.
5. Reverse the removal procedures for installation. Clean all rust and dirt from the threads. Check the alignment and adjust if necessary.

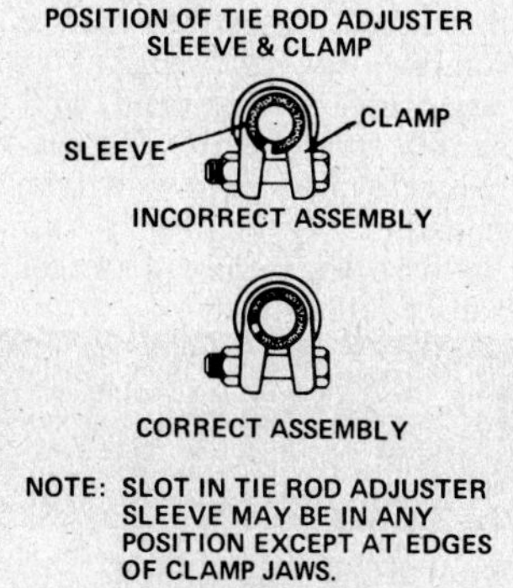
POSITION OF TIE ROD ADJUSTER
SLEEVE & CLAMP
SLEEVE
CLAMP
INCORRECT ASSEMBLY
CORRECT ASSEMBLY
NOTE: SLOT IN TIE ROD ADJUSTER
SLEEVE MAY BE IN ANY
POSITION EXCEPT AT EDGES
OF CLAMP JAWS.

Clamp installation
(© Pontiac Div., G.M. Corp)

Intermediate Rod R&R

1. Remove the left and right-side inner tie rod ends from the intermediate rod. These are taper fits; remove them as described in the tie rod section.
2. Remove the intermediate rod studs from the idler and pitman arms. These are taper fits.
3. Remove the intermediate rod.
4. Reverse the above steps for installation.

Pitman Arm R&R

1. Remove the intermediate rod stud from the pitman arm. This is a taper fit; remove it as described in the tie rod section.
2. Remove the pitman arm nut and lockwasher from the pitman shaft.
3. Remove the pitman arm from the pitman shaft using a puller. Do not hammer on the end of the puller or serious internal damage will be done to the steering gear box.
4. Reverse the above steps to install.

Idler Arm R&R

1. Remove the intermediate arm stud. This is a taper fit; see the tie rod section for the removal procedures.
2. Remove the two bolts attaching the idler arm to the frame.

3. Remove the idler arm.
4. Reverse the above steps for installation.

Power Steering Pump R&R

1. Disconnect the hoses at the pump.
2. Remove the drive pulley attaching nut.
3. Loosen the bracket-to-pump mounting bolts and remove the drive belt.
4. Slide the pulley from the shaft. Do not hammer on the pulley.
5. Remove the bracket-to-pump mounting bolts and remove the pump.
6. Reverse the removal steps for installation.

Steering Wheel R&R

1. On deluxe models, remove the screws holding the trim cover to the wheel, or if equipped with a horn button, lift the button off.
2. Remove the steering wheel nut from the steering shaft.
3. Position the wheels in the straight-ahead position and make match marks on the steering shaft and steering wheel.
4. Using a puller, remove the steering wheel.
5. Disconnect the horn wire insulator by rotating the insulator counterclockwise to the unlock position and then pull up.
6. Reverse the removal procedures for installation. Make sure the match marks are lined up when installing the wheel.

Turn Signal Switch R&R 1967-68

Removal

Caution Make sure the steering column is supported at all times as the column is extremely easy to bend.

1. Remove the bolts holding the column bracket.
2. Remove the wire protector, wire clip, and cover.
3. Remove the steering wheel.
4. Slide the preload springs and turn signal cancelling cam of the steering shaft.
5. Remove the turn signal lever screw and lever.
6. Push the hazard warning knob in and remove the knob.
7. Remove the snap-ring from the steering shaft.
8. Loosen the three switch mounting screws until the cover assembly can be rotated counterclockwise. Remove the cover assembly.
9. Remove the three switch attaching screws entirely and remove the old switch.

NOTE: these three screws hold the entire assembly together. Carefully note the position and orientation of these parts to aid reassembly.

Installation

1. Place the new switch assembly on top of the housing assembly and feed the switch wires through the switch cover.
2. Align the switch housing and cover holes, and install the three mounting screws through the holes.
3. Slide three springs onto the screws and start the screws into the lockplate.
4. Run the wires through the bowl and place the switch assembly on top of the bowl. Make sure the tangs of the lockplate are aligned with the slots on the inside of the bowl.
5. Push down on the housing assembly and turn clockwise. Tighten the three screws.
6. Reverse steps one through seven to complete the installation.

Turn Signal Switch R&R 1969-74

1. Remove the steering wheel.
2. Remove the three cover screws and lift the cover off the shaft. Do not remove the screws completely.

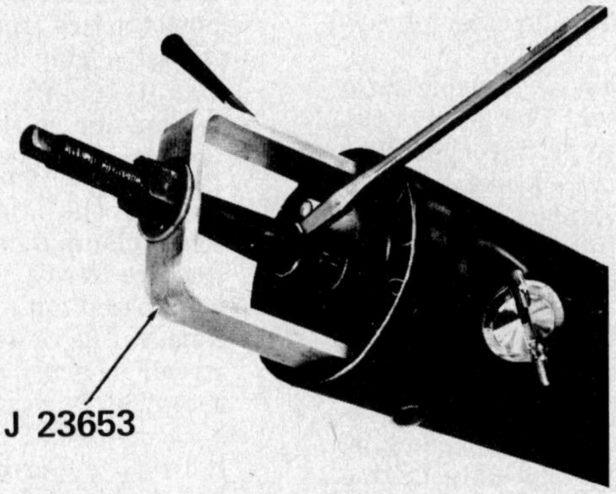
J 23653

Snap-ring removal
(© Pontiac Div., G.M. Corp)

3. Depress the lockplate and remove the snap-ring.
4. Slide the upper bearing spring and turn signal cam off the shaft.
5. Remove the turn signal lever screw and lever.
6. Push the hazard warning switch in and remove the knob.
7. Lower the steering column and disconnect the switch wiring.
8. Remove the turn signal switch mounting screws and pull the switch straight up with the wire protector and remove it from the housing.
9. Reverse the removal procedures for installation.

INSTRUMENT PANEL

The instrument cluster includes the speedometer head, the generator charge indicator, the oil pressure indicator and the temperature indicator. Also, the fuel gauge, light switch, wiper and washer switch, starter and ignition switch and the cigarette lighter.

Ignition Switch R & R—1967-68

1. Remove switch from the dash by unscrewing the switch ferrule with a special spanner wrench, tool J-5893-A.
2. Remove switch from back of instrument panel and disconnect wires.
3. Replace switch by reversing above method.

Ignition Switch R & R—1969-74

The ignition and steering wheel locking switch is located just below the gear selector lever on the steering column.

1. Disconnect battery.
2. Loosen toe pan screws.
3. Remove column to panel nuts, lower steering column, and disconnect switch wire connectors.
4. Remove switch attaching screws and switch.
5. To install, move key lock to OFF-LOCK position.
6. Move actuator rod hole in switch to OFF-LOCK position.
7. Install switch, with rod in hole, then reverse removal procedure.

Switch Adjustment—Standard Column

1. Place switch in OFF position.
2. Position switch on column, then move slider to extreme left (toward wheel).
3. Move slider back two positions to the right of ACCESSORY position.
4. Place key in any run position and shift transmission into any position but Park for automatics or Reverse for manual.
5. Position lock toward ACCESSORY with a light finger pressure and secure switch.

Switch Adjustment—Tilt Column

1. Place key in ACCESSORY position; leave key in lock.

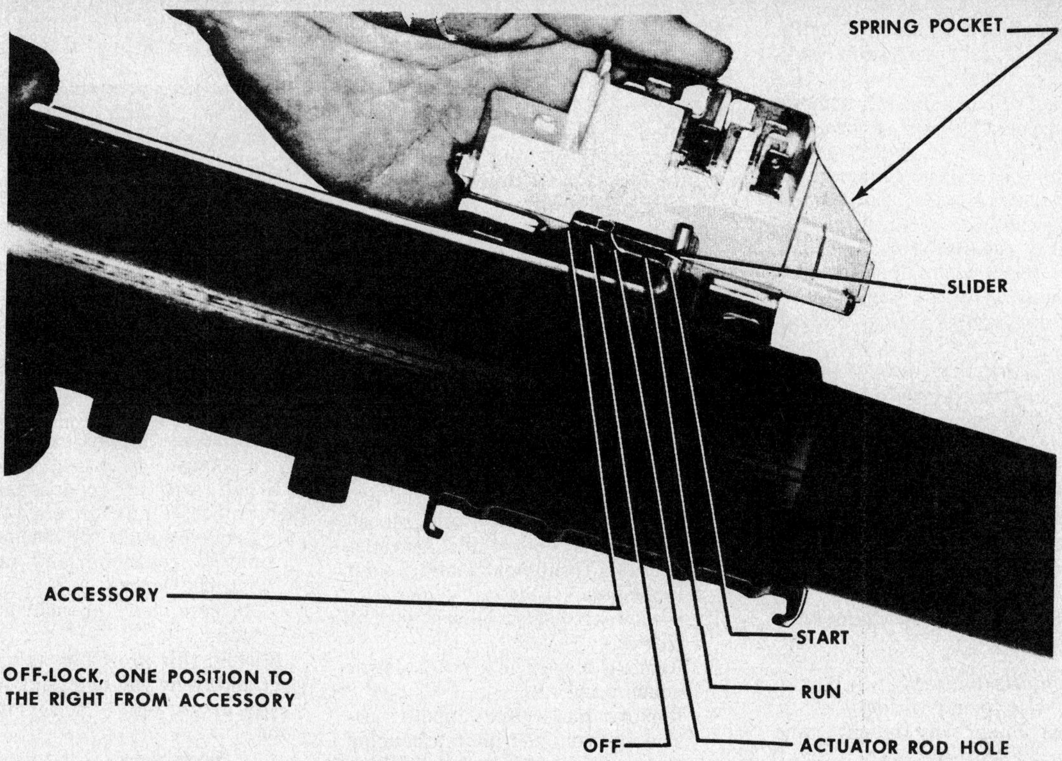
SPRING POCKET
SLIDER
ACCESSORY
OFF-LOCK, ONE POSITION TO THE RIGHT FROM ACCESSORY
START
RUN
OFF
ACTUATOR ROD HOLE

1969-74 ignition lock switch (© Pontiac Div., G.M. Corp)

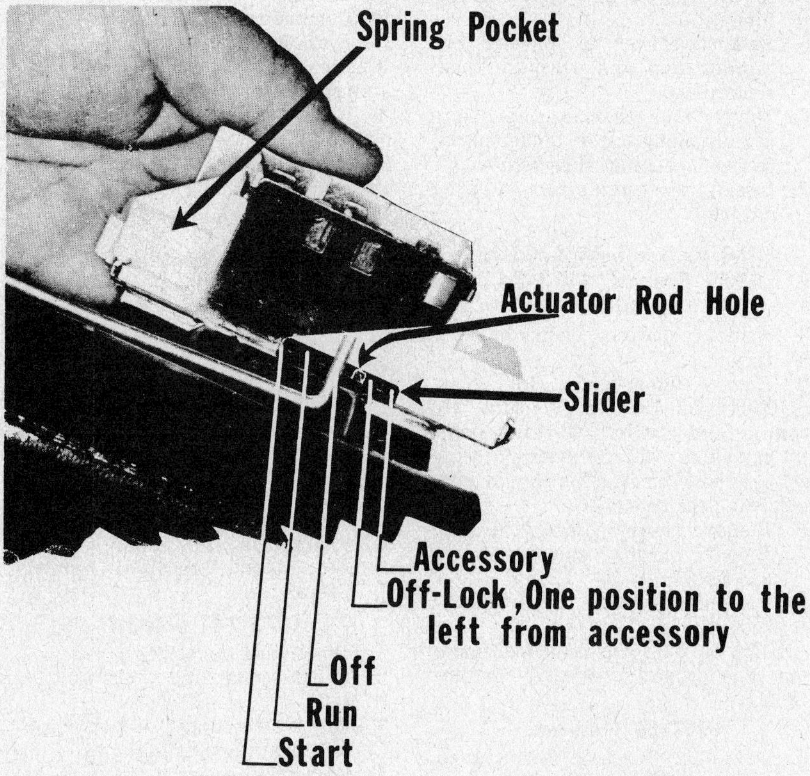
Spring Pocket
Actuator Rod Hole
Slider
Accessory
Off-Lock, One position to the left from accessory
Off
Run
Start

Adjusting ignition switch—1969-72 tilt column (© Pontiac Div., G.M. Corp)

2. Loosen switch mounting screws.
3. Push switch upward toward wheel to make certain it is in ACCESSORY detent.
4. Hold key in full counter clockwise ACCESSORY position and tighten switch mounting screws.
5. Switch is properly adjusted if: it will go into ACCESSORY position, the key can be removed when in lock, and switch will go into START position.

Lock Cylinder Replacement—1967-68

1. Disconnect battery, then insert key.
2. Remove lock cylinder by placing in off position and inserting wire into small hole in cylinder face. While pushing in on wire, continue to turn cylinder counterclockwise, then pull cylinder from case.

Lock Cylinder Replacement—1969-74

1. Remove steering wheel.
2. Pull turn signal switch up far enough to allow access to spring latch slot.
3. Place key in RUN position, insert a thin screwdriver into the slot next to the switch mounting screw boss and depress spring latch.

NOTE: there is a casting flash over this slot if the lock has never before been removed. It is necessary sometimes to use substantial force to break it. Be careful not to damage anything beneath the flashing when penetrating the slot.

4. Remove lock from housing.

Depressing lock cylinder spring latch (© Pontiac Div., G.M. Corp)

5. To install, first hold lock cylinder sleeve and rotate knob clockwise against stop.
6. Lay a 1/16 in. drill on housing surface next to housing bore.

NOTE: the 1/16 in. drill prevents forcing the lock cylinder inward beyond its normal latched position. The buzzer switch and spring latch can hold the lock cylinder too far inward. Complete disassembly of the upper bearing housing is necessary to release an improperly installed lock cylinder.

7. Insert cylinder into housing bore, aligning keyway, and push in to abutment.
8. Rotate knob counterclockwise, pushing in slightly, until cylinder mates with sector.
9. Push in until spring latch pops into groove, then remove drill.

Lighting Switch Replacement —1967-74

1. Disconnect battery.
2. Pull knob to on position.
3. Reach under instrument panel and depress the switch shaft retainer (see illustration), then remove knob and shaft assembly.

NOTE: disconnect vacuum hose on vacuum-operated headlamp models.

4. Remove retaining ferrule nut.
5. Remove switch from instrument panel.
6. Disconnect multi-plug connector from switch.
7. Install in reverse of above. (In checking lights before installation, switch must be grounded to test dome lights on some models).

WINDSHIELD WIPERS

Motor R & R

1967-74

1. Remove hoses and wire terminals that are connected to wiper unit.
2. Remove clip that secures wiper crank to wiper transmission arm.

NOTE: this clip is under leaf screen on depressed-park motors, and accessible only after firewall bolts are removed on some standard motors. On some models, the wiper arm must be removed to facilitate motor removal.

3. Remove screws that secure wiper assembly to firewall.
4. Install a gasket on the motor.
5. Position wiper assembly on firewall and secure.
6. Connect wire terminals and hoses.
7. Connect wiper crank with wiper transmission arm.
8. Reverse the removal procedures for installation.

Wiper Transmission R & R

1967-74

1. Remove arm and blade assemblies.
2. Remove fresh air intake grille.
3. Remove wiper transmission retaining screws.
4. Loosen, but do not remove, wiper transmission crank to linkage nuts.
5. Remove wiper transmissions and linkage, through cowl opening.
6. To install, reverse above procedure. Make sure wiper blades are in park position after they are installed.

1967 Tempest & GTO

1. Disconnect battery. On six cylinder models, loosen and reposition battery to provide clearance between front fender and fender inner panel.
2. Disconnect heater blower wire at blower.
3. Remove blower motor to blower housing bolts.
4. Remove motor and impeller assembly from the blower housing and position with impeller facing toward engine below right hood hinge.
5. Remove blower to impeller retaining nut and washer, then separate.
6. Move motor, then impeller, separately along top of fender panel to front opening, then remove.
7. Install by reversing removal procedure.

1968-69 Tempest & GTO, 1969 Firebird, 1971-74 Ventura II

1. Remove battery and battery tray.
2. Remove inner fender skirt.

NOTE: on 1971-72 Ventura II, remove fender skirt attaching bolts and pry skirt away far enough to insert a wooden block. This should give sufficient clearance.

3. Remove blower power wire.
4. Remove blower retaining screws and blower.
5. To install, reverse removal procedure.

NOTE: if duct was removed, make sure it is properly sealed during installation.

1967-68 Firebird

1. Disconnect battery cables, then remove battery and battery tray.
2. Unclip heater hoses from fender skirt.
3. Scribe alignment marks at hood hinges, then remove hood.
4. Remove right front fender and skirt as an assembly.
5. Disconnect blower power wire.
6. Remove blower screws and blower.
7. To install, reverse removal procedure.

NOTE: if duct was removed, make sure it is properly sealed during installation.

RADIO

Radio R & R

1967-70

1. Disconnect antenna and power leads, remove tape deck and multiplex.
2. Loosen hex screws and remove knobs.
3. Remove escutcheon retaining nuts.
4. Remove screw that holds receiver to panel bracket, then remove ash tray.

NOTE: with air conditioner, outlet duct and bezel must be removed.

5. Remove speaker by disconnecting output connector and mounting bracket screws.
6. Reverse above procedure to reinstall.

NOTE: this procedure is very general, and some combinations of accessories may require slight modifications.

1970½-74 Firebird

1. Disconnect battery.
2. Remove glove box, glove box door and lower right A/C duct.
3. Remove radio knobs, nuts and trim plate.
4. Disconnect antenna and power lines.
5. Disconnect speaker leads, then remove radio bracket and radio from passenger side of dashboard.
6. To install, reverse removal procedure.

1971-72 Tempest, GTO and Ventura II—1971-74

1. Disconnect battery. Remove lower A/C duct on Tempest.
2. Remove radio knobs, bezels and hex nuts.
3. Remove support bracket bolt.
4. Disconnect electrical and antenna leads; remove radio from under dash.
5. To install, reverse removal procedure.

1973-74 LeMans

1. Disconnect the battery.
2. Remove the radio knobs and bezels.
3. Remove the upper and lower instrument panel trim plates.
4. Remove the two radio side retaining screws.
5. Remove the radio from the panel opening, disconnecting the electrical connections and the antenna lead.
6. To install, reverse the removal procedure. If the radio is to be replaced, remove the bushing from the rear of the radio and install it on the replacement radio.

1973-74 Grand Am

1. Disconnect the battery.
2. Remove the radio knobs and bezels and the retaining hex nut from the right-hand radio tuning shaft.
3. Remove the four retaining screws and the trim plate.
4. Remove the two side retaining screws and the mounting bracket screw.
5. Remove the radio and the mounting bracket from the dash, disconnecting the electrical connections and the antenna lead.
6. To install, reverse the removal procedure.

HEATER

Heater Blower R & R—Except Air-Conditioned Cars

1970-74 Tempest, Firebird, & GTO

1. Jack up front of car and remove right front wheel.
2. Cut access hole along stamped outline on right fender skirt, using an air chisel.
3. Disconnect blower power wire.
4. Remove blower.
5. To install, reverse removal procedure, covering access hole with a metal plate secured with sealer and sheet metal screws.

1973-74 LeMans & Grand Am

1. Disconnect the blower motor feed wire and the ground wire.
2. Remove the blower motor retaining screws and remove the motor and transfer impeller.
3. To replace, reverse the removal procedure.

1971-74 Ventura II

1. Disconnect the battery.
2. Detach the heater hoses from the clips on the right front fender skirt.
3. Raise the car and remove all fender skirt attaching bolts except those which attach the skirt to the radiator support.
4. Pull down on the skirt and block the skirt to all clearance for removal of the blower motor.
5. Disconnect the electrical wiring from the motor.
6. Remove the attaching screws and remove the blower motor. Pry the motor flange gently if the sealer acts as an adhesive.
7. Remove the blower impeller retaining nut and separate the motor from the impeller.
8. To replace, reverse the removal procedure.

Heater Core R & R—Except Air-Conditioned Cars

1967 Tempest & GTO

1. Drain radiator and remove glove compartment.
2. Disconnect heater hoses at the heater.
3. Disconnect heater control cables at heater.
4. Remove front wheel.
5. Remove wire connector from resistor at top left side of heater air outlet by prying connector up with a screwdriver.
6. Cut a one inch hole in the skirt.
7. Remove six nuts from the heater to air inlet duct and remove heater.
8. Install by reversing removal procedure.
9. Patch the skirt hole.

1968 Tempest and GTO

1. Disconnect heater hoses at heater.
2. Remove glove compartment.
3. Remove five nuts which secure heater to firewall.
4. Pull case from firewall, then disconnect cables and wire connector from resistor.

1967-74 Firebird, 1969-74 Tempest & GTO

1. Drain radiator.
2. Disconnect heater hoses at air inlet assembly.

NOTE: the water pump hose goes to top heater core pipe, the other hose (from rear of right cylinder head on V8, center of block on 6) goes to the lower heater core pipe.

3. Remove nuts from core studs on firewall (under hood).

NOTE: on 1970-74 Firebird, remove glove box and door, then remove heater outlet from case. Remove defroster duct screw on all 1971-74 models.

4. From inside the car, pull the heater assembly from the firewall.
5. Disconnect control cables and wires, then remove heater assembly.
6. To remove core, unhook retaining springs.
7. To install, reverse removal procedure, making sure core is properly sealed during installation.

1971-74 Ventura II

1. Disconnect battery.
2. Drain radiator, disconnect heater hoses at core and plug core tubes.
3. Remove nuts from core case studs on firewall.
4. Remove glove box and glove box door.

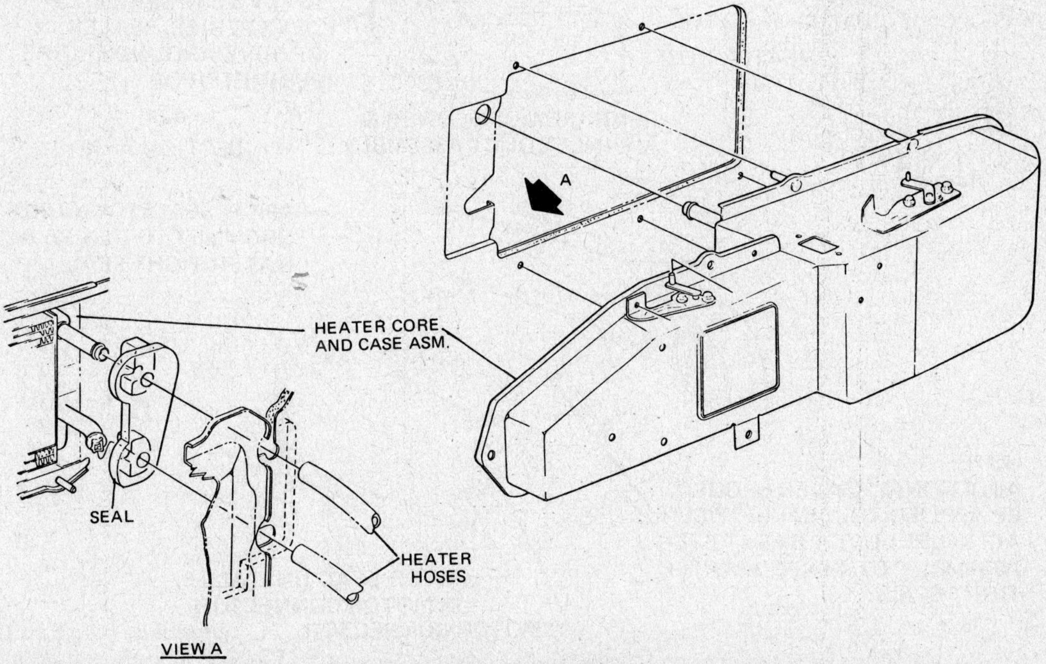
A
HEATER CORE
AND CASE ASM.
SEAL
HEATER
HOSES
VIEW A

Heater core—Firebird and Tempest (© Pontiac Div., G.M. Corp)

5. From inside car, drill out lower right hand heater case stud with 1/4 in. drill.
6. Pull entire heater case, with core, from firewall.
7. Disconnect Bowdin cables and blower resistor connector, then remove case from car.
8. Remove core from case.
9. To install, reverse removal procedure. Use sealer around core and replace drilled stud with new screw and Pal nut.

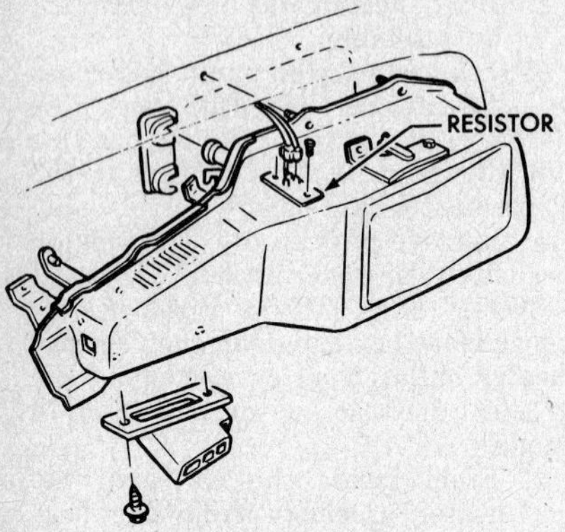
RESISTOR
Heater core—Ventura II
(© Pontiac Div., G.M. Corp)

Heater Blower R&R—Air-Conditioned Cars

Tempest and GTO 1967

1. Remove the inner skirt of the right front fender.
2. Scribe alignment marks on the hood and hood hinge.
3. Support hood and remove the hood hinge.
4. Remove the blower motor lead and ground wire at the blower motor.
5. Remove the five blower motor attaching screws.
6. Remove the blower motor from beneath fender.
7. Reverse the above steps for installation.

Firebird, Tempest and GTO 1968-69

1. Remove the fender brace, battery, and tray.
2. Scribe alignment marks and remove hood.
3. Remove the right front fender and skirt as an assembly.
4. Disconnect the motor wire and cooling tube from the motor.
5. Remove the motor attaching screws and the motor.
6. Reverse the above steps for installation.

Firebird, Tempest and GTO 1970-74

1. Raise the car and remove the right front wheel.
2. Cut an access hole along the outline stamped in the right-hand fender skirt.
3. Disconnect the blower wire, remove the blower attaching bolts, and remove the blower.
4. Reverse the above steps for installation.

Ventura II 1971-74

1. Disconnect the battery.
2. Detach the heater hoses from the clips on the right front fender skirt.
3. Raise the car and remove all of the fender skirt attaching bolts, except those attaching the skirt to the radiator support.
4. Pull out then down on the skirt and block the skirt to allow clearance for removal of the blower motor.
5. Disconnect the cooling line and wire from the motor.
6. Remove the blower motor attaching screws and remove the blower motor.
7. Reverse the above steps for installation.

Heater Core and Case R&R—Air-Conditioned Cars

Tempest, GTO 1967-69 Firebird 1967-70

1. Remove the glove box.
2. Remove the lower instrument panel air-conditioning duct and outlet assembly by removing the five attaching screws and retainer.
3. Lower the duct and outlet assembly after disconnecting the right and left-side nozzle connections.
4. Disconnect the temperature control cable and vacuum hose.
5. Drain the cooling system and remove the two water hoses attached to the heater core.
6. Remove the six heater core-to-cowl attaching nuts. It is necessary to cut a 1 in. diameter hole in the right-hand fender skirt to remove the lower nut.
7. Remove two screws from the heater core and case evaporator housing seal and remove the seal and retainer.
8. Remove the core and case assembly.
9. Mark the heater cam and bracket assembly to ensure proper reinstallation and remove the heater cam and bracket.

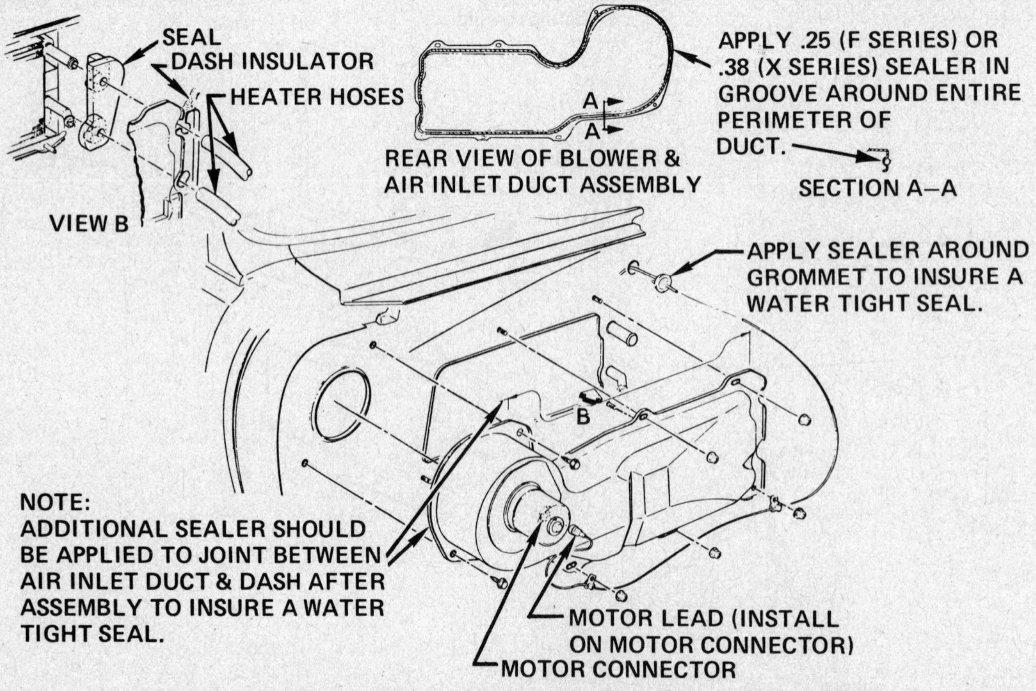
SEAL
DASH INSULATOR
HEATER HOSES
VIEW B
A
A
REAR VIEW OF BLOWER & AIR INLET DUCT ASSEMBLY
APPLY .25 (F SERIES) OR .38 (X SERIES) SEALER IN GROOVE AROUND ENTIRE PERIMETER OF DUCT.
SECTION A—A
APPLY SEALER AROUND GROMMET TO INSURE A WATER TIGHT SEAL.
B
NOTE:
ADDITIONAL SEALER SHOULD BE APPLIED TO JOINT BETWEEN AIR INLET DUCT & DASH AFTER ASSEMBLY TO INSURE A WATER TIGHT SEAL.
MOTOR LEAD (INSTALL ON MOTOR CONNECTOR)
MOTOR CONNECTOR
Blower motor—Firebird and Ventura II (© Pontiac Div., G.M. Corp)

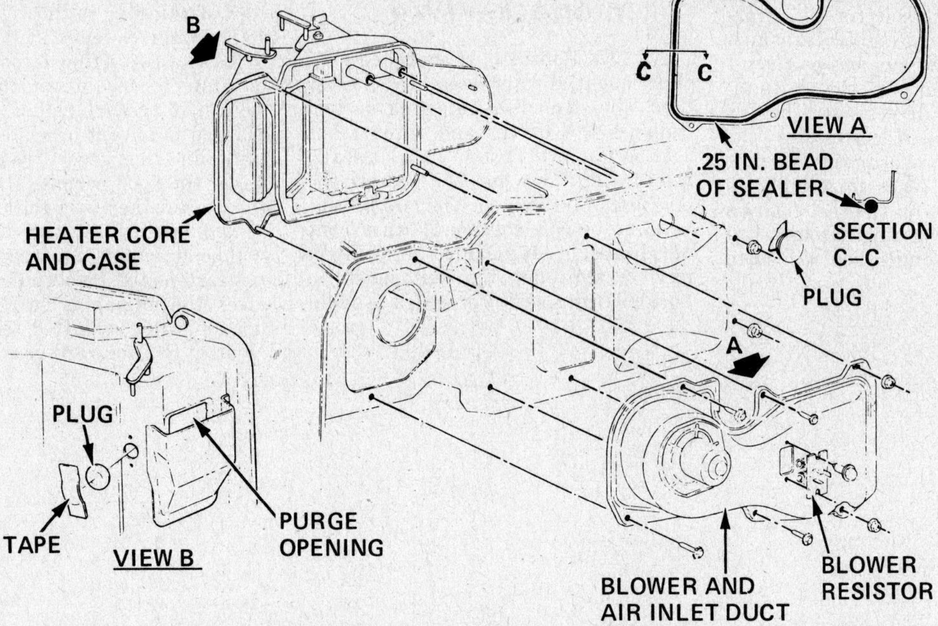
B
C
C
VIEW A
.25 IN. BEAD
OF SEALER
SECTION
C–C
PLUG
HEATER CORE
AND CASE
A
PLUG
TAPE
VIEW B
PURGE
OPENING
BLOWER AND
AIR INLET DUCT
BLOWER
RESISTOR

Blower motor—LeMans and Grand Am (© Pontiac Div., G.M. Corp)

10. Remove the front case-to-rear case attaching screws and separate the cases.
11. Remove the heater core retaining screws and core.
12. Reverse the above steps for installation.

Tempest 1970, LeMans 1970-74 & Grand Am 1973-74

1. Drain the coolant.
2. Disconnect the water hoses at the heater core tubes to prevent spilling coolant during removal.
3. Remove the glove compartment.
4. Remove the cold air duct and heater outlet.
5. Remove the defroster duct attaching screw.
6. Remove the screws and nuts which retain the case to the dash. Remove the blower motor resistor to gain access to the upper retaining nut inside the evaporator case.
7. Move the core and case assembly rearward to free the attaching studs from the cowl and remove the core and case assembly.
8. Disconnect the temperature cable and vacuum hoses from the core and case assembly.
9. Remove the core and case assembly from the car.
10. Remove the heater core retaining screws and core.
11. Reverse the above steps for installation.

Firebird 1970½-74

1. Drain the coolant.
2. Remove the glove box and door.
3. Remove the cold air duct on the lower right-hand side.
4. Remove the left and center lower A/C ducts.
5. Raise the car and remove the rocker panel trim on the right side and remove the screws holding the forward trim brackets.
6. Remove the three lower fender bolts at rear of the fender.
7. Remove the four fender-to-skirt bolts at the rear of the wheel opening.
8. Remove the two fender skirt bolts near the blower motor area.
9. Pry the rear portion of the fender out at the bottom to gain access to the hose clamp on the water valve-to-core hose and disconnect the hose at the heater core.
10. Disconnect the water pump hose at the heater core.
11. Remove the two heater case retaining nuts under the hood at the dash.
12. Remove the two heater case retaining bolts inside the car.
13. Remove the console and tape player if equipped.
14. Disconnect the temperature cable at the heater case.
15. Remove the heater outlet duct.
16. Remove the lower defroster duct screw.
17. Remove the right kick panel, and the heater core and case as an assembly.
18. Disconnect the vacuum hoses from the heater case and remove the core from the case.
19. Reverse the above steps for installation.

Ventura II 1971-74

1. Disconnect the battery and drain the coolant.
2. Disconnect the upper heater hose at the core pipe and remove the accessible heater core and case assembly attaching nuts.
3. Remove the right front fender skirt bolts and lower the skirt to gain access to the lower heater hose clamp. Loosen the clamp and disconnect the hose.
4. Remove the lower right-hand heater core and case assembly attaching nut.
5. Remove the glove compartment and door.
6. Remove the recirculation vacuum diaphragm at the right-hand kick panel.
7. Remove the heater outlet and cold air distributor duct.
8. Remove the heater case extension screws and separate the extension from the heater case.
9. Disconnect the heater cables and electrical connectors, and remove the case and core as an assembly.
10. Separate the core from the case.
11. Reverse the above steps for installation.

SEAT BELTS

Buzzer System—1973

The front seat belt warning system consists of a switch in each belt retractor, a sensor switch in the seat cushion on the passenger side, a reminder light, and a warning buzzer. The circuit wiring is routed through the ignition switch and parking brake warning switch on manual transmission models or through the ignition switch and transmission switch on models equipped with automatic transmissions.

With the ignition switch on and the

parking brake released on cars equipped with manual transmissions, or with the shift selector in a forward position on automatic transmission models, the warning circuit (light and buzzer) is closed (activated) until the driver's seat belt is extended to open (de-activate) the circuit. The seat sensor on the passenger side will react to weights in excess of 0-47 lbs on the seat cushion and close the warning circuit. Extending the passenger belt will open the circuit.

Seat Belt/Starter Interlock—1974

All 1974 Pontiacs are equipped with the sequential interlock seat belt system. The sequential interlock system requires the driver and right front seat occupant to first sit in their seats, then fasten their seat belts before the engine can be started. The middle seat position, on cars equipped with a front bench seat, is not included in the interlock system, but the belt must be buckled if this seat is occupied to avoid activating the familiar buzzer and warning light system. The seat sensors are similar to those found in the 1973 buzzer systems.

Engine restarting is possible without interference from the interlock system if the driver has not left his seat. In the event of system malfunction, an emergency by-pass switch under the hood permits starting when the ignition key is in the ON position.

The buzzer/warning light system will be activated if a front seat belt is not fastened at an occupied front seat after the engine is started and the transmission is shifted from Park or Neutral to a forward gear.

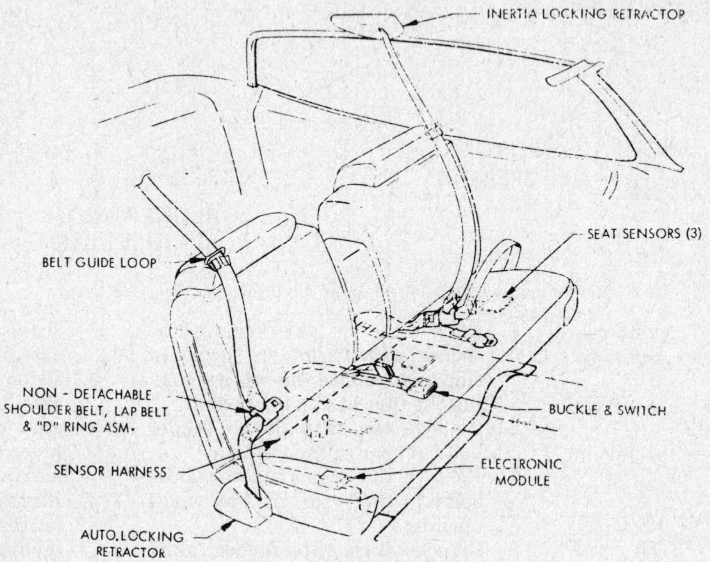
INERTIA LOCKING RETRACTOR
SEAT SENSORS (3)
BELT GUIDE LOOP
NON - DETACHABLE SHOULDER BELT, LAP BELT & "D" RING ASM.
BUCKLE & SWITCH
SENSOR HARNESS
ELECTRONIC MODULE
AUTO.LOCKING RETRACTOR

1974 Seat Belt/starter system
(© Pontiac Div., G.M. Corp)

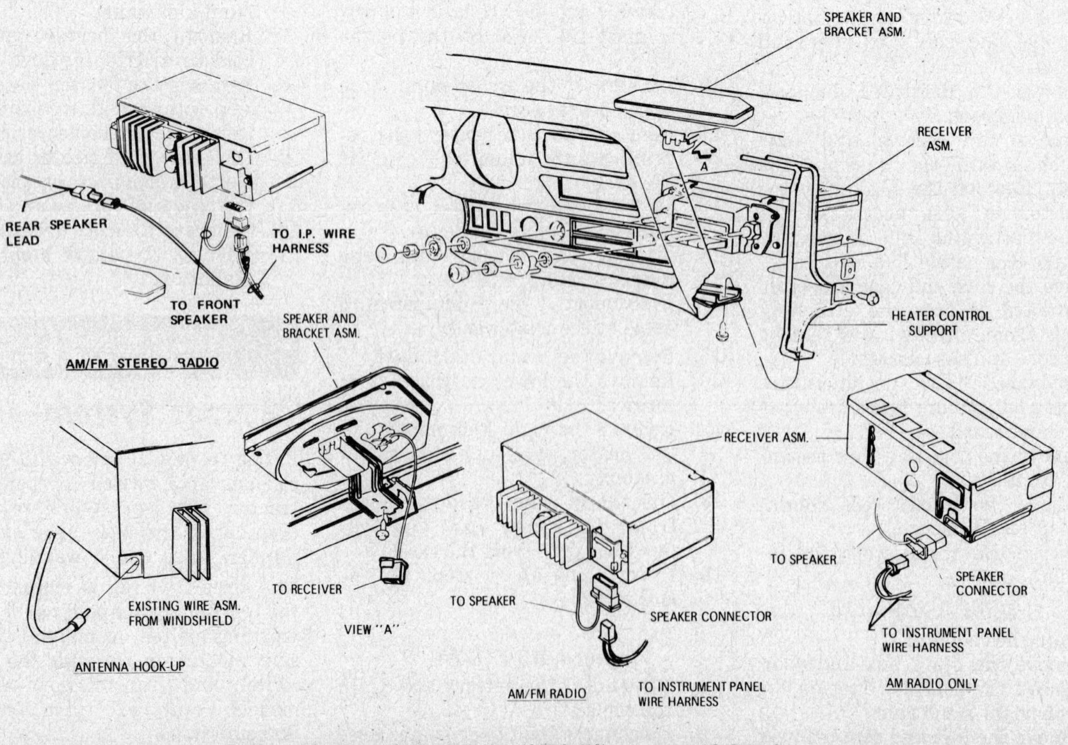
SPEAKER AND BRACKET ASM.
RECEIVER ASM.
A
REAR SPEAKER LEAD
TO I.P. WIRE HARNESS
TO FRONT SPEAKER
HEATER CONTROL SUPPORT
AM/FM STEREO RADIO
SPEAKER AND BRACKET ASM.
RECEIVER ASM.
TO SPEAKER
SPEAKER CONNECTOR
EXISTING WIRE ASM. FROM WINDSHIELD
TO RECEIVER
VIEW "A"
TO SPEAKER
SPEAKER CONNECTOR
TO INSTRUMENT PANEL WIRE HARNESS
ANTENNA HOOK-UP
AM/FM RADIO
TO INSTRUMENT PANEL WIRE HARNESS
AM RADIO ONLY

Radio and front speaker installation (1971–74)—Lemans (© G.M. Corp)

INDEX

Ford • Mercury • Thunderbird

YEAR IDENTIFICATION

FORD

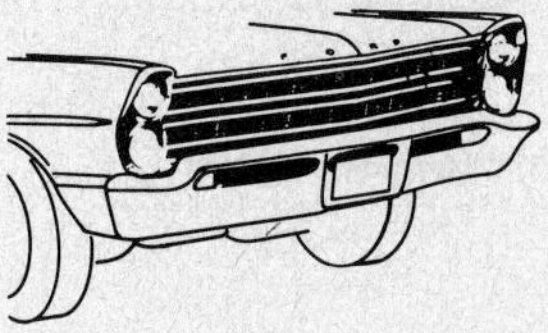
1967

1968

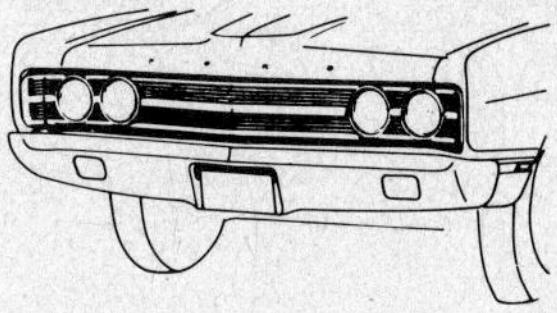
1969

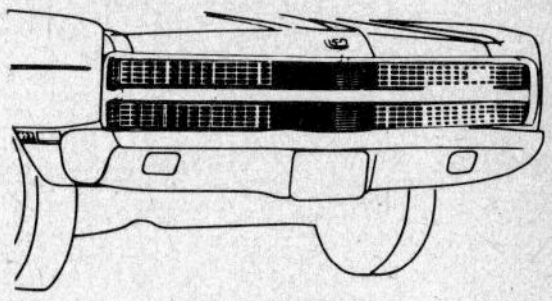
1969 LTD

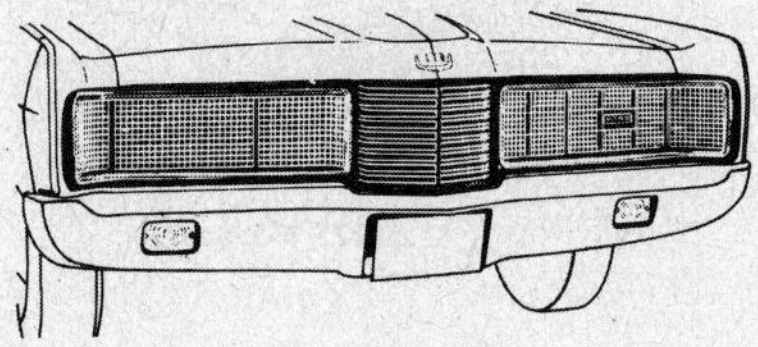
1970 LTD

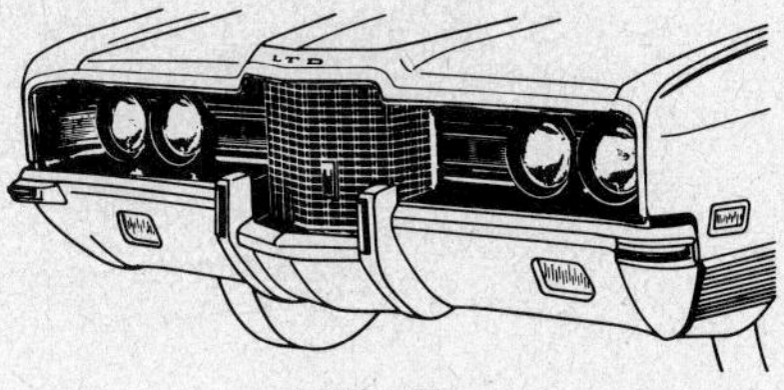
1971 LTD

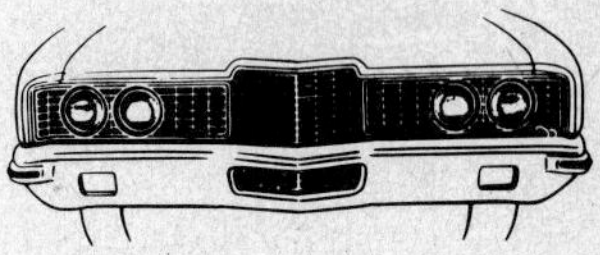
1972 Galaxie

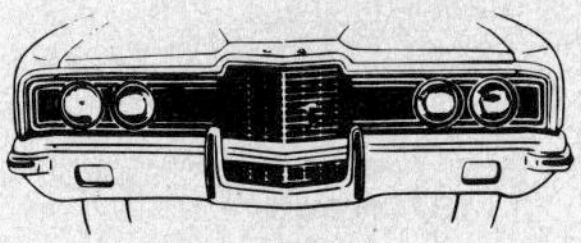
1972 LTD

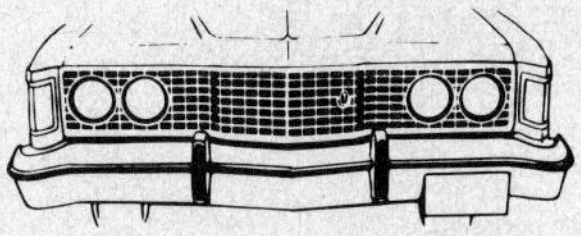
1973 Galaxie

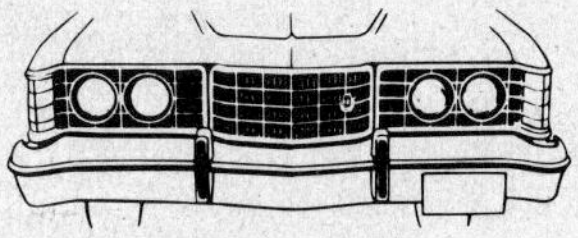
1973 LTD

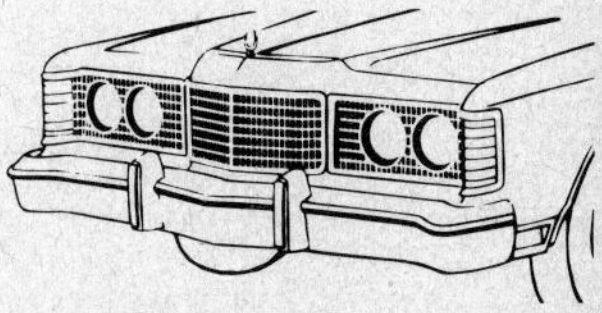
1974 LTD

THUNDERBIRD

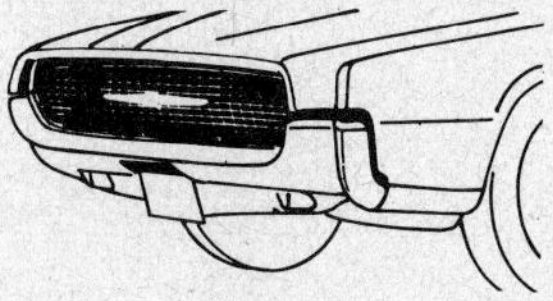
1967

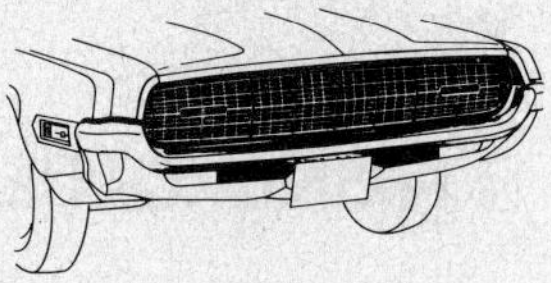
1968

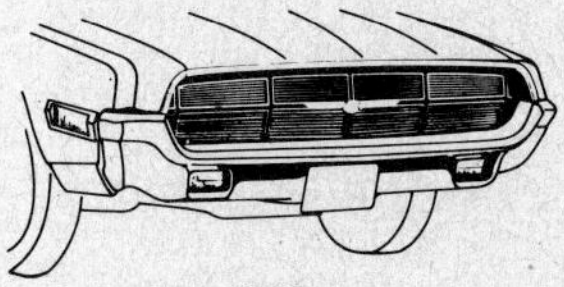
1969

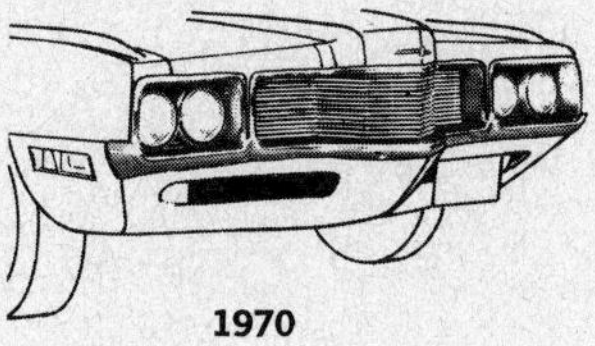
1970

1972

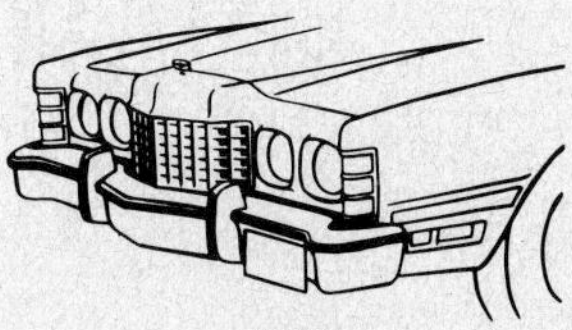
1973

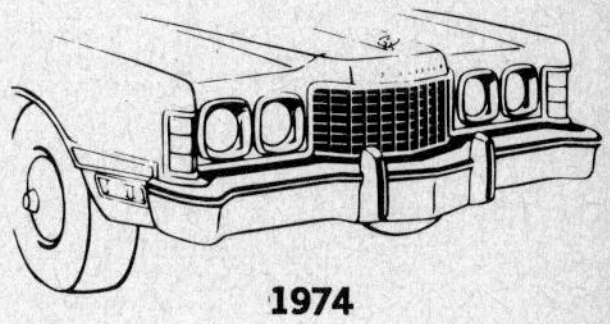
1974

MERCURY

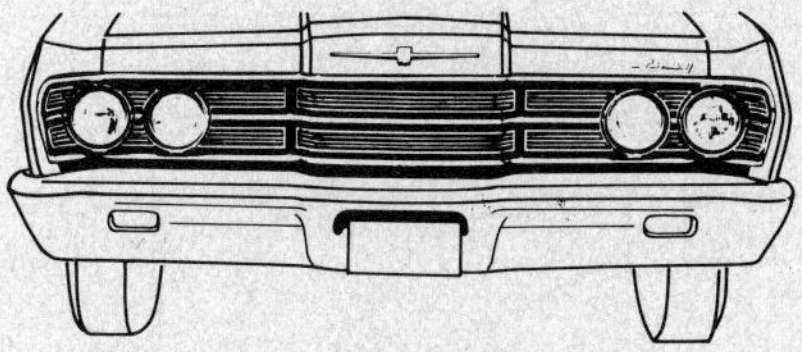
1967

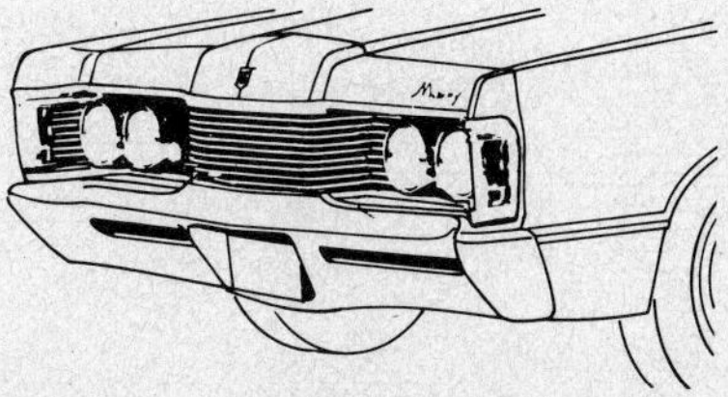
1968

1969

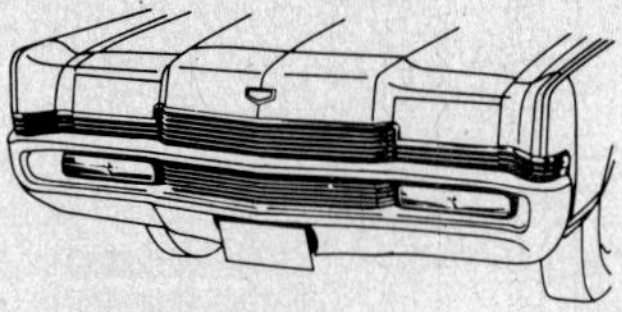

1969 Marquis

1970 Monterey

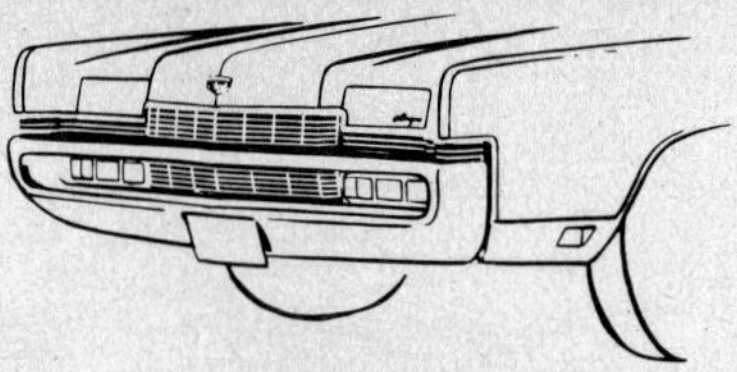

1970 Marquis Brougham

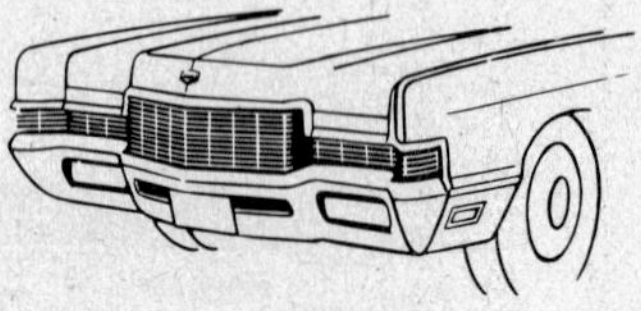

1971

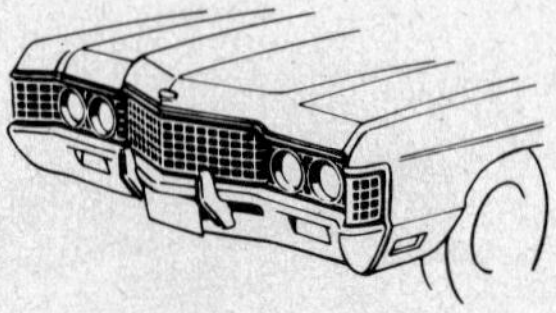

1972 Monterey

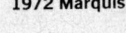

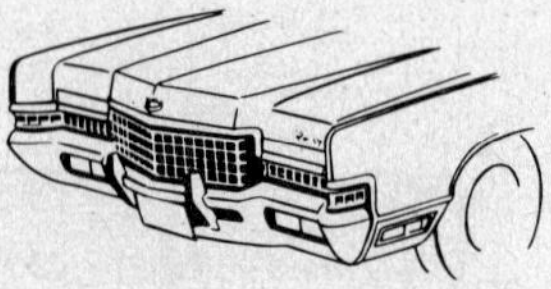

1972 Marquis

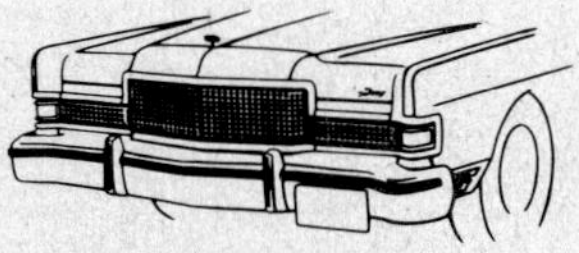

1973 Marquis

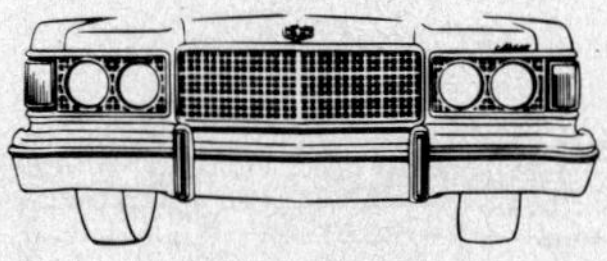

1974 Monterey

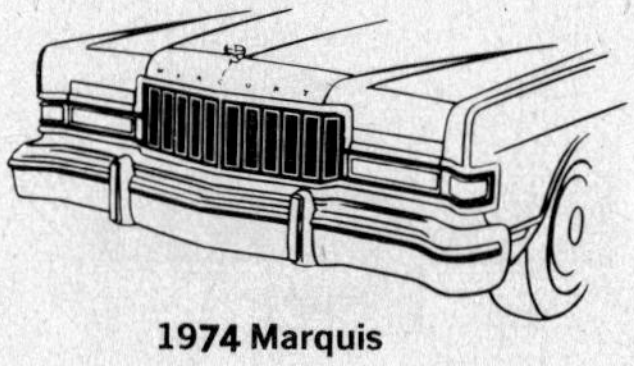

1974 Marquis

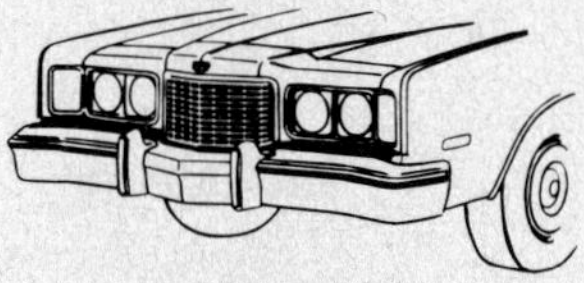

1974 Montego

FIRING ORDER

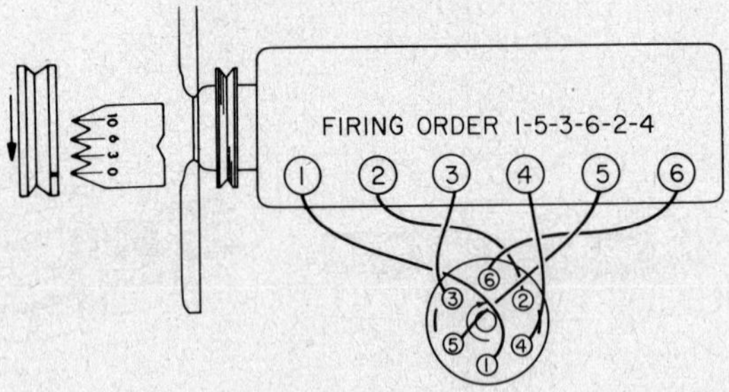
FIRING ORDER 1-5-3-6-2-4
1 2 3 4 5 6

240 cu. in. 6 cyl.

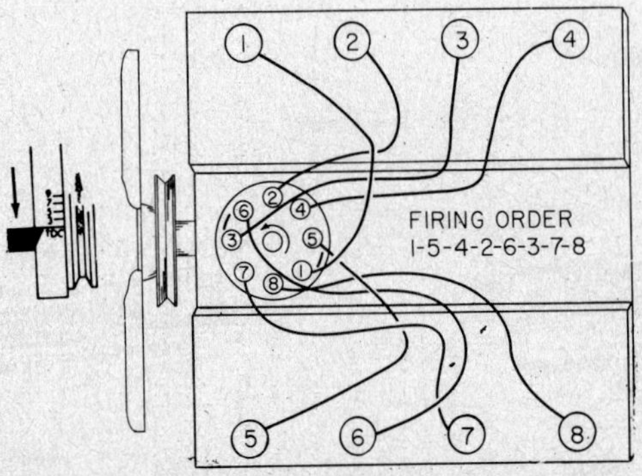
FIRING ORDER
1-5-4-2-6-3-7-8
1 2 3 4
5 6 7 8

V8 except 351, 400 cu. in.

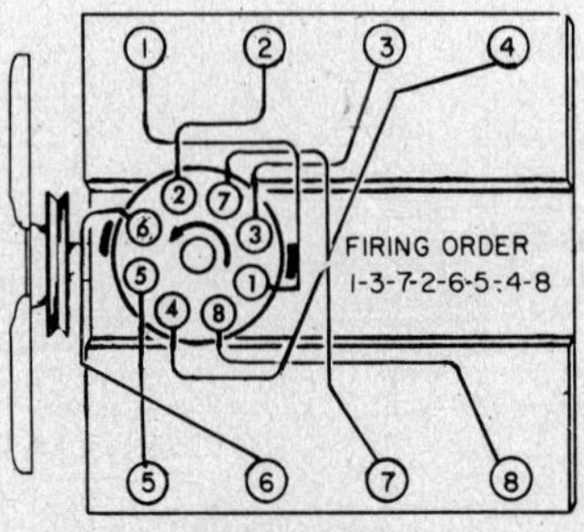
FIRING ORDER
1-3-7-2-6-5-4-8
1 2 3 4
5 6 7 8

V8 351, 400 cu. in.

CAR SERIAL NUMBER LOCATION AND ENGINE IDENTIFICATION

1967

Engine is identified through car serial number. Serial numbers, and other pertinent information, are on a plate riveted to the rear edge of the left front door pillar.

The engine number is stamped on the top surface of the engine block near the crankcase breather pipe, front left side.

The car serial number is composed of eleven digits, interpreted as illustrated. The production year code is the last digit of the model year in which the vehicle was produced. (For example, "9" = 1969). The fifth digit, a letter, represents the engine identification code. (See table.)

1968-74

The serial number can be found on a plate attached to the top of the instrument panel, visible through the windshield. Information for identification remains essentially the same as for 1967 models.

Vehicle Certification Label

1970-74

The label is located on the rear of the driver's door. The upper portion contains the name of the manufacturer, the month and year of manufacture, and the certification statement. The lower portion of the label is interpreted in the illustration.

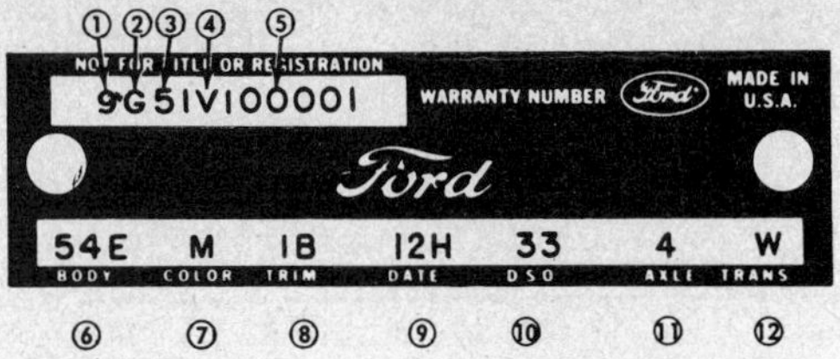
1 2 3 4 5
NOT FOR TITLE OR REGISTRATION
9G51V100001
WARRANTY NUMBER
MADE IN U.S.A.
Ford
54E M 1B 12H 33 4 W
BODY COLOR TRIM DATE DSO AXLE TRANS
6 7 8 9 10 11 12

1 Model year code
2 Assembly plant code
3 Body serial code
4 Engine code
5 Consecutive unit number
6 Body type code
7 Color code
8 Trim code
9 Date code
10 District—special equipment code
11 Rear axle code
12 Transmission code

Ford
9Y83N100001
Ford

Typical vehicle identification number (VIN) tab

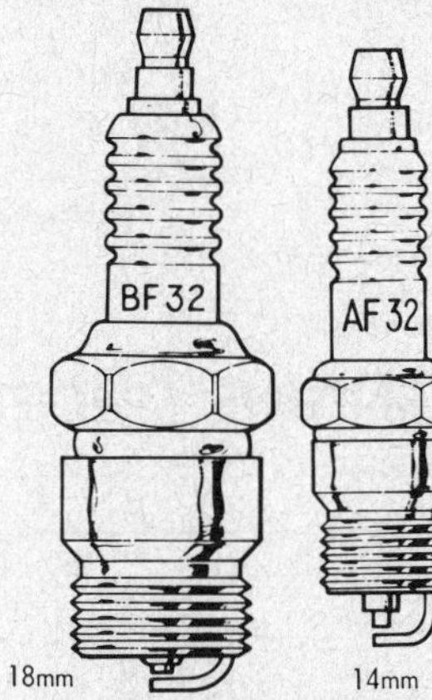
BF 32
AF 32
18mm
14mm

Left—Windsor spark plug
Right—Cleveland spark plug

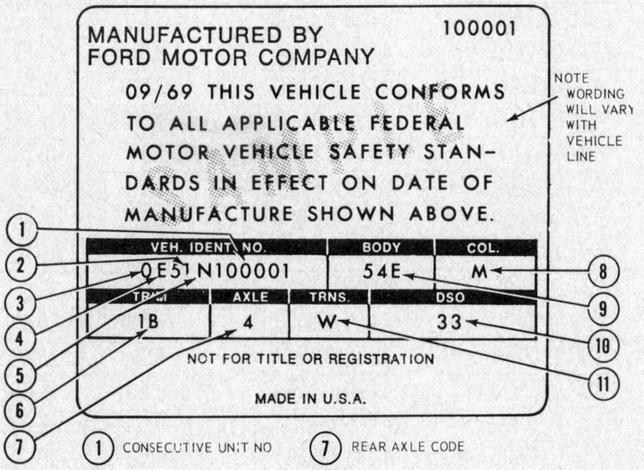
MANUFACTURED BY
FORD MOTOR COMPANY
100001
09/69 THIS VEHICLE CONFORMS
TO ALL APPLICABLE FEDERAL
MOTOR VEHICLE SAFETY STAN-
DARDS IN EFFECT ON DATE OF
MANUFACTURE SHOWN ABOVE.
NOTE WORDING WILL VARY WITH VEHICLE LINE
VEH. IDENT. NO.
BODY
COL.
0E51N100001
54E
M
TRIM
AXLE
TRNS.
DSO
1B
4
W
33
NOT FOR TITLE OR REGISTRATION
MADE IN U.S.A.
1 2 3 4 5 6 7 8 9 10 11

1. CONSECUTIVE UNIT NO
2. BODY SERIAL CODE
3. MODEL YEAR CODE
4. ASSEMBLY PLANT CODE
5. ENGINE CODE
6. TRIM CODE
7. REAR AXLE CODE
8. COLOR CODE
9. BODY TYPE CODE
10. DISTRICT SPEC EQUIP CODE
11. TRANSMISSION CODE

Vehicle Certification Label

TRANSMISSION CODES

1967-68

1.	Three speed manual
2.	Overdrive
3.	Three speed manual
5.	Four speed manual
W.	Automatic C4
U.	Automatic C6
X.	Automatic FX
Y.	Automatic MX
Z.	Automatic C6 (XPL Special)—Police and trailer towing

1969-71

1.	Three speed manual
5.	Four speed manual—wide ratio
6.	Four speed manual—close ratio
W.	Automatic C4
U.	Automatic C6
X.	Automatic FMX
Y.	Automatic MX
Z.	Automatic C6 special—Police and trailer towing

1972-74

W.	Automatic C4
U.	Automatic C6
X.	Automatic FMX
#.	Automatic CW
Z.	Automatic C6 Special—Police trailer towing

The CW transmission is a Borg-Warner unit used on 1973-74 400 cid equipped Ford sedans only.

Ford, Mercury, Thunderbird

ENGINE CODE

The engine code designation is the 5th digit of the vehicle identification number (V.I.N.). The V.I.N. is stamped on a plate located at the rear edge of the left front door on 1967 models and located at the left side of the instrument panel, visible through the windshield, on 1968-74 models.

Disp	Bbl	Hp	'67	'68	'69	'70	'71	'72	'73	'74
6-Cylinder Models										
240	1	103 (net)						V		
240	1	140					V			
240	1	150	V	V	V	V				
8-Cylinder Models										
289	2	200	C							
302	2	140 (net)						F		
302	2	210		F	F	F	F			
351 W	2	153 (net)						H	H	H
351 C	2	154, 159 (net)*								H
351 C	2	163 (net)						H	H	
351	2	240					H			
351	2	250				H				
390	2	255					Y			
390	2	265			Y	Y				
390	2	270	H,Y	Y		Y				
390	2	280	X	X						
390	4	315	Z	7						

Disp	Bbl	Hp	'67	'68	'69	'70	'71	'72	'73	'74
400	2	168 (net)								S
400	2	172 (net)						S	S	
400	2	260					S			
410	4	330	M							
427	8	425	R							
428	4	340		Q						
428	4	345	Q							
428 PI	4	360	P	P	P	P				
429	4	208, 212 (net)*						N	N	
429 PI	4	N.A.						P		
429	4	320			K	K	K			
429	4	360		N	N	N	N			
429 PI	4	370					P			
460	4	200, 208, 212 (net)*						A	A	A
460 PI	4	267, 274 (net)*							C	C

* Net horsepower rating varies with model application

PI Police Interceptor

Ford, Mercury, Thunderbird

GENERAL ENGINE SPECIFICATIONS

Year	Engine No. Cyl. Displacement Cu. In.	Carburetor Type	Advertised Horsepower @ rpm ■	Advertised Torque @ rpm (ft lbs) ■	Bore and Stroke (in.)	Advertised Compression Ratio	Oil Pressure @ 2050 rpm
'67	6-240	1 bbl	150 @ 4000	234 @ 2200	4.000 x 3.180	9.2:1	35-60
	8-289	2 bbl	200 @ 4400	282 @ 2400	4.000 x 2.870	9.3:1	35-55
	8-390	2 bbl	265 @ 4400	401 @ 2600	4.050 x 3.784	9.5:1	35-65
	8-390①	2 bbl	275 @ 4400	405 @ 2600	4.050 x 3.784	9.5:1	35-65
	8-390	4 bbl	315 @ 4600	427 @ 2800	4.050 x 3.784	10.5:1	35-65
	8-410	4 bbl	330 @ 4600	444 @ 2800	4.050 x 3.980	10.5:1	35-65
	8-427	4 bbl	410 @ 5600	476 @ 3400	4.233 x 3.781	11.1:1	40-55
	8-427	2 x 4 bbl	425 @ 6000	480 @ 3700	4.233 x 3.781	11.1:1	40-55
	8-428	4 bbl	345 @ 4600	462 @ 2800	4.130 x 3.984	10.5:1	35-65
	8-428①	4 bbl	360 @ 5400	459 @ 3200	4.130 x 3.984	10.5:1	45-70
'68	6-240	1 bbl	150 @ 4000	234 @ 2200	4.000 x 3.180	9.2:1	35-60
	8-302	2 bbl	210 @ 4400	295 @ 2400	4.000 x 3.000	9.5:1	35-60
	8-390	2 bbl	270 @ 4400	390 @ 2600	4.050 x 3.784	9.5:1	35-60
	8-390	2 bbl	280 @ 4400	403 @ 2600	4.050 x 3.784	10.5:1	35-60
	8-390	4 bbl	315 @ 4600	427 @ 2800	4.050 x 3.784	10.5:1	35-60
	8-428	4 bbl	345 @ 4600	462 @ 2800	4.130 x 3.984	10.5:1	35-60
	8-428①	4 bbl	360 @ 5400	459 @ 3200	4.130 x 3.984	10.5:1	35-60
	8-429	4 bbl	360 @ 4600	480 @ 2800	4.360 x 3.590	10.5:1	35-60
'69	6-240	1 bbl	150 @ 4000	234 @ 2200	4.000 x 3.180	9.2:1	35-60
	8-302	2 bbl	210 @ 4400	295 @ 2400	4.000 x 3.000	9.5:1	35-60
	8-390	2 bbl	270 @ 4400	390 @ 2600	4.050 x 3.784	9.5:1	35-60
	8-390	2 bbl	280 @ 4400	430 @ 2600	4.050 x 3.784	10.5:1	35-60
	8-428①	4 bbl	360 @ 5400	459 @ 3200	4.130 x 3.984	10.5:1	35-60
	8-429	2 bbl	320 @ 4400	460 @ 2200	4.360 x 3.590	10.5:1	35-60
	8-429	4 bbl	360 @ 4600	476 @ 2800	4.360 x 3.590	11.0:1	35-60

Ford, Mercury, Thunderbird

GENERAL ENGINE SPECIFICATIONS

Year	Engine No. Cyl. Cu. In. Displacement	Carburetor Type	Advertised Horsepower @ rpm ■	Advertised Torque @ rpm (ft lbs) ■	Bore and Stroke (in.)	Advertised Compression Ratio	Oil Pressure @ 2050 rpm
'70	6-240	1 bbl	150 @ 4000	234 @ 2200	4.000 x 3.180	9.2:1	35-60
	8-302	2 bbl	210 @ 4400	295 @ 2400	4.000 x 3.000	9.5:1	35-60
	8-351	2 bbl	250 @ 4600	355 @ 2600	4.000 x 3.500	9.5:1	35-60
	8-390	2 bbl	270 @ 4400	390 @ 2600	4.050 x 3.784	9.5:1	35-60
	8-428①	4 bbl	360 @ 5400	459 @ 3200	4.130 x 3.984	10.5:1	35-60
	8-429	2 bbl	320 @ 4400	460 @ 2200	4.360 x 3.590	10.5:1	35-60
	8-429	4 bbl	360 @ 4600	476 @ 2800	4.360 x 3.590	11.0:1	35-60
'71	6-240	1 bbl	140 @ 4000	230 @ 2200	4.000 x 3.180	8.9:1	35-60
	8-302	2 bbl	210 @ 4600	296 @ 2600	4.000 x 3.000	9.0:1	35-60
	8-351	2 bbl	240 @ 4600	350 @ 2600	4.000 x 3.500	8.9:1	35-60
	8-390	2 bbl	255 @ 4400	376 @ 2600	4.050 x 3.784	9.5:1	35-60
	8-400	2 bbl	260 @ 4400	400 @ 2200	4.000 x 4.000	9.0:1	50-70
	8-429	2 bbl	320 @ 4400	460 @ 2200	4.360 x 3.590	10.5:1	35-75
	8-429	4 bbl	360 @ 4600	480 @ 2800	4.360 x 3.590	10.5:1	35-75
	8-429①	4 bbl	370 @ 5400	450 @ 3400	4.360 x 3.590	11.0:1	35-75
'72	6-240	1 bbl	103 @ 3800	170 @ 2200	4.000 x 3.180	8.5:1	35-60
	8-302	2 bbl	140 @ 4000	239 @ 2000	4.000 x 3.000	8.5:1	35-60
	8-351 W	2 bbl	153 @ 3800	266 @ 2000	4.000 x 3.500	8.3:1	35-60
	8-351 C	2 bbl	163 @ 3800	277 @ 2000	4.000 x 3.500	8.6:1	35-60
	8-400	2 bbl	172 @ 4000	298 @ 2200	4.000 x 4.000	8.4:1	50-70
	8-429	4 bbl	208 @ 4400	322 @ 2800	4.362 x 3.590	8.5:1	35-75
	8-429	4 bbl	212 @ 4400	327 @ 2600	4.362 x 3.590	8.5:1	35-75
	8-460	4 bbl	200 @ 4400	326 @ 2800	4.362 x 3.850	8.5:1	35-75
	8-460	4 bbl	212 @ 4400	342 @ 2800	4.362 x 3.850	8.5:1	35-75
'73	8-351 W	2 bbl	153 @ 3800	266 @ 2000	4.000 x 3.500	8.3:1	35-60
	8-351 C	2 bbl	163 @ 3800	277 @ 2000	4.000 x 3.500	8.6:1	35-60
	8-400	2 bbl	172 @ 4000	298 @ 2200	4.000 x 4.000	8.4:1	50-70
	8-429	4 bbl	208 @ 4400	322 @ 2800	4.362 x 3.590	8.5:1	35-75
	8-429	4 bbl	212 @ 4400	327 @ 2600	4.362 x 3.590	8.5:1	35-75
	8-460	4 bbl	200 @ 4400	326 @ 2800	4.362 x 3.850	8.5:1	35-75
	8-460	4 bbl	212 @ 4400	342 @ 2800	4.362 x 3.850	8.5:1	35-75
'74	8-351 W	2 bbl	154, 158 @ 3800	256, 264 @ 2400	4.000 x 3.500	8.0:1	35-60
	8-351 C	2 bbl	159 @ 4000	260 @ 2400	4.000 x 3.500	8.0:1	35-60
	8-400	2 bbl	168 @ 3800	310 @ 2000	4.000 x 4.000	8.0:1	35-60
	8-460	4 bbl	202, 208 @ 4400	330, 338 @ 2800	4.362 x 3.850	8.0:1	35-75

■ Beginning 1972, horsepower and torque are SAE net figures. They are measured at the rear of the transmission with all accessories installed and operating. Since the figures vary when a given engine is installed in different models, some are representative rather than exact.

① Police Interceptor
W Windsor Built
C Cleveland Built

Ford

TUNE-UP SPECIFICATIONS

When analyzing compression test results, look for uniformity among cylinders rather than specific pressures.

	ENGINE		SPARK PLUGS		DISTRIBUTOR		IGNITION TIMING (deg) ▲		VALVES	Fuel	IDLE SPEED (rpm) ▲	
Year	No. Cyl Displacement (cu in.)	hp	Type §	Gap (in.)	Point Dwell (deg)	Point Gap (in.)	Man Trans	Auto Trans	Intake Opens ■ (deg) ●	Pump Pressure (psi)	Man Trans *	Auto Trans
'67	6-240	150	BTF-42	.034	37-42	.025	6B(TDC)	10B(4B)	12	4-6	550(600)	525(500)
	8-289	200	BF-42	.034	26-31	.017	6B(TDC)	6B(TDC)	16	4-6	625(635)	525(575)
	8-390	270	BF-42	.034	26-31	.017	10B(6B)	10B(6B)	16	4½-6½	600(635)	525(550)
	8-390	315	BF-42	.034	26-31	.017	10B(6B)	10B(6B)	16	4½-6½	600(635)	500(550)
	8-427①	425	BF-32	.034	22-24	.020	8B	—	48	4½-6½	750	—
	8-428	345	BF-42	.034	26-31	.017	10B(6B)	10B(6B)	16	4½-6½	575(625)	475(550)
	8-428PI	360	BF-32	.030	26-31	.017	12B	12B	18	4½-6½	600(625)	600(550)
'68	6-240	150	BF-42	.034	35-40	.027	6B	6B	12	4-6	600	500
	8-302	210	BF-32	.034	24-29	.021	6B	6B	16	4-6	625	550②
	8-390	270	BF-32	.034	24-29③	.021③	6B	6B	13	4½-6½	625	550
	8-390	315	BF-32	.034	24-29③	.021③	6B	6B	16	4½-6½	625	550
	8-428	345	BF-32	.034	24-29③	.021③	6B	6B	16	4½-6½	625	550
	8-428PI	360	BF-32	.034	26-31	.017	—	6B	18	4½-6½	—	600
'69	6-240	150	BF-42	.034	35-40	.027	6B	6B	12	4-6	775/550	550
	8-302	210	BF-42	.034	24-29③	.021③	6B	6B	16	4½-6½	650	550②
	8-390	270	BF-42	.034	24-29③	.021③	6B	6B	13	4½-6½	650	550
	8-428PI	360	BF-32	.034	24-29③	.021③	—	6B	18	4½-6½	—	600
	8-429	320	BF-42	.034	26-31	.017	—	6B	16	4½-6½	—	550
	8-429	360	BF-42	.034	24-29③	.021③	6B	6B	16	4½-6½	650	550
'70	6-240	150	BF-42	.034	35-40	.027	6B	6B	12	4-6	800/500	500
	8-302	210	BF-42	.034	24-29	.021	6B	6B	16	4-6	575 [800/500]	575 [600/500]
	8-351	250	BF-42	.034	24-29	.021	10B	10B	11	5-7	575 [700/500]	575 [600/500]
	8-390	270	BF-42	.034	24-29③	.021③	6B	6B	13	5-7	750/500	600/500
	8-428PI	360	BF-32	.034	24-29	.021	—	6B	18	4½-6½	—	600/500
	8-429	320	BRF-42	.034	24-29③	.021③	—	6B	16	5-7	—	600/500
	8-429	360	BRF-42	.034	24-29③	.021③	6B	6B	16	5-7	700/500	600/500
'71	6-240	140	BRF-42	.034	33-38	.027	6B	6B	18	4-6	800/500	600/500
	8-302	210	BRF-42	.034	24-29	.021	6B	6B	16	4-6	575 [800/500]	575 [650/500]
	8-351W	240	BRF-42	.034	24-29	.021	6B	6B	11	5-7	575 [775/500]	575 [600/500]
	8-351C	240	ARF-42	.034	24-29	.021	—	6B	12	5-7	—	625/550
	8-390	255	BRF-42	.034	24-29	.021	—	6B	13	5-7	—	600/475
	8-400	260	ARF-42	.034	26-31	.017	—	10B(6B)	17	5-7	—	625/500
	8-429PI	370	ARF-42	.034	27½-29½	.020	—	10B	32	5-7	—	650/500
	8-429	320	BRF-42	.034	24-29③	.021③	—	4B	16	5-7	—	600
	8-429	360	BRF-42	.034	24-29③	.021③	4B	4B	16	5-7	700	600
'72	6-240	103	BRF-42	.034	35-39	.027	—	6B	18	4-6	—	500
	8-302	140	BRF-42	.034	26-30	.017	—	6B	16	5-7	—	575 [600/500]
	8-351W	153	BRF-42	.034	26-30	.017	—	6B	11	5-7	—	575 [600/500]
	8-351C	163	ARF-42	.034	26-30	.017	—	6B	12	5-7	—	600/500
	8-400	172	ARF-42	.034	26-30	.017	—	6B	17	5-7	—	625/500
	8-429	208	BRF-42	.034	26-30	.017	—	10B	8	5-7	—	600/500
	8-429PI	N.A.	ARF-42	.034	26-30	.017	—	10B	32	4½-6½	—	650/500

Ford — TUNE-UP SPECIFICATIONS

When analyzing compression test results, look for uniformity among cylinders rather than specific pressures.

ENGINE			SPARK PLUGS		DISTRIBUTOR		IGNITION TIMING (deg) ▲		VALVES	Fuel	IDLE SPEED (rpm) ▲	
Year	No. Cyl Displacement (cu in.)	hp	Type §	Gap (in.)	Point Dwell (deg)	Point Gap (in.)	Man Trans	Auto Trans	Intake Opens ■ (deg) ●	Pump Pressure (psi)	Man Trans *	Auto Trans
'73	8-351W	153	BRF-42	.034	26-30	.017	—	6B	11	5-7	—	575 [600/500]
	8-351C	163	ARF-42	.034	26-30	.017	—	6B	12	5-7	—	600/500
	8-400	172	ARF-42	.034	26-30	.017	—	6B	17	5-7	—	625/500
	8-429	208	BRF-42	.034	26-30	.017	—	10B	8	5-7	—	600/500
	8-429PI	N.A.	ARF-42	.034	26-30	.017	—	10B	32	4½-6½	—	650/500
'74	8-351W	154,158	BRF-42	.034④	26-30	.014-.020	—	6B	15	4-6	—	[600/500]
	8-351C	159	ARF-42	.034④	26-30	.014-.020	—	14B	19½	5½-6½	—	[700/500]
	8-400	168	ARF-42	.034④	—	—	—	12B	17	5½-6½	—	[625/500]
	8-460	202, 208	ARF-52	.044	—	—	—	14B	8	5½-6½	—	[650/500]⑤
	8-460 PI	N.A.	ARF-52	.044	—	—	—	10B	18	Electric	—	[700/500]

▲ See text for procedure
● Figure in parentheses indicates California engine
■ All figures Before Top Dead Center
* Figures in brackets are for solenoid equipped vehicles only. In all cases where two figures are separated by a slash, the first is for idle speed with solenoid energized and the automatic transmission in Drive, while the second is for idle speed with solenoid disconnected and automatic transmission in Neutral.
§ All spark plug listings are Autolite original equipment numbers
① Adjust mechanical lifters, intake and exhaust, to .025 inch with engine hot
② A/C off
③ For engines equipped with single diaphragm distributors, adjust point dwell to 26-31 degrees and point gap to .017 inch
④ .044 on California models
⑤ 675/500 for California engines
B Before Top Dead Center
C Cleveland
N.A. Not available
PI Police Interceptor
TDC Top Dead Center
W Windsor
— Not applicable

Mercury — TUNE-UP SPECIFICATIONS

When analyzing compression test results, look for uniformity among cylinders rather than specific pressures.

ENGINE			SPARK PLUGS		DISTRIBUTOR		IGNITION TIMING (deg) ▲		VALVES	Fuel	IDLE SPEED (rpm) ▲	
Year	No. Cyl Displacement (cu in.)	hp	Type §	Gap (in.)	Point Dwell * (deg)	Point Gap * (in.)	Man Trans	Auto Trans	Intake Opens ■ (deg) ●	Pump Pressure (psi)	Man Trans	Auto Trans
'67	8-390	270	BF-42	.034	28	.017	10B(6B)	10B(6B)	13	5-6	575(625)	475(550)
	8-410	330	BF-42	.034	28	.017	10B(6B)	10B(6B)	16	5-6	575(625)	475(550)
	8-428	345	BF-42	.034	28	.017	10B(6B)	10B(6B)	16	5-6	575(625)	475(550)
	8-428	360	BF-42	.034	28	.017	12B	12B	18	5-6	600(625)	600(550)
'68	8-390	265	BF-32	.030	27	.017	6B	6B	13	4½-6½	625	550
	8-390	280	BF-32	.030	27	.017	—	6B	16	4½-6½	—	550
	8-390	315	BF-32	.030	27	.017	6B	6B	16	4½-6½	625	550
	8-428	340	BF-32	.030	27	.017	6B	6B	16	4½-6½	625	550
	8-428PI	360	BF-32	.030	27	.017	—	6B	18	4½-6½	—	600
'69	8-390	265	BF-42	.034	29	.017	6B	6B	13	4½-6½	650	550
	8-390	280	BF-42	.030	27	.021	—	6B	13	4½-6½	—	550
	8-428PI	360	BF-42	.034	29	.016	—	6B	18	4½-6½	—	600
	8-429	320	BF-42	.034	29	.017	6B	6B	16	4½-6½	650	550
	8-429	360	BF-42	.034	29	.017	6B	6B	16	4½-6½	650	550
'70	8-390	265	BF-42	.034	27	.021	10B	10B	13	5½-6½	750/500	575
	8-428PI	360	BF-32	.034	27	.021	—	6B	13	5-6	—	600
	8-429	320	BF-42	.034	27	.021	6B	6B	18	5½-6½	850/500	600
	8-429	360	BF-42	.034	27	.021	6B	6B	16	5½-6½	850/500	600

Mercury

TUNE-UP SPECIFICATIONS

When analyzing compression test results, look for uniformity among cylinders rather than specific pressures.

ENGINE			SPARK PLUGS		DISTRIBUTOR		IGNITION TIMING (deg) ▲		VALVES	Fuel	IDLE SPEED (rpm) ▲	
Year	No. Cyl Displacement (cu in.)	hp	Type §	Gap (in.)	Point Dwell * (deg)	Point Gap * (in.)	Man Trans	Auto Trans	Intake Opens ■ (deg) ●	Pump Pressure (psi)	Man Trans	Auto Trans
'71	8-351C	240	ARF-42	.034	27	.021	6B	6B	12	5½-6½	700/500	600 [600/500]
	8-351W	240	BRF-42	.034	27	.021	6B	6B	11	5½-6½	775/500	575 [600/500]
	8-400	260	ARF-42	.034	27/29	.021/ .017	—	10B(6B)	17	5½-6½	—	600/500
	8-429	320	BRF-42	.034	27/29	.021/ .017	—	6B	16	5½-6½	—	590 [600/500]
	8-429	360	BRF-42	.034	27/29	.021/ .017	4B	4B	16	5½-6½	700	650
	8-429PI	370	AF-32	.034	27/29	.021/ .017	10B	10B	32	5½-6½	700 [700/500]	650 [650/500]
'72	8-351C	163	ARF-42	.034	28	.017	6B	6B	12	5½-6½	750/500	575/500①
	8-400	172	ARF-42	.034	28	.017	—	8B(6B)	17	5½-6½	—	625/500
	8-429	208	BRF-42	.034	28	.017	—	10B	8	5½-6½	—	650/500
	8-429PI	N.A.	ARF-42	.034	28	.020	—	10B	32	5½-6½	—	650/500
	8-460	200	BRF-42	.034	28	.017	—	10B(6B)②	8	5½-6½	—	625/500
'73	8-351C	163	ARF-42	.034	28	.017	—	6B	12	5½-6½	—	650/500
	8-400	172	ARF-42	.034	28	.017	—	6B	17	5½-6½	—	650/500
	8-429	208	BRF-42	.034	28	.017	—	10B	8	5½-6½	—	650/500
	8-429PI	N.A.	ARF-42	.034	28	.020	—	10B	32	5½-6½	—	650/500
	8-460	200	BRF-42	.034	28	.017	—	6B	8	5½-6½	—	625/500
'74	8-351C	159	ARF-42	.034③	28	.017	—	14B	19½	5½-6½		[600/500]
	8-400	168	ARF-42	.034③	—	—	—	12B	17	5½-6½		[625/500]
	8-460	202, 208	ARF-52	.044	—	—	—	10B	8	5½-6½		[625/500]

* Where two figures are separated by a slash, the first figure is for engines equipped with dual diaphragm distributors, while the second is for engines equipped with single diaphragm distributors

▲ See text for procedure

● Figure in parentheses indicates California engine

■ All figures Before Top Dead Center

□ Figures in brackets are for solenoid equipped vehicles only. In all cases where two figures are separated by a slash, the first figure is for idle speed with solenoid energized and automatic transmission in Drive, while the second is for idle speed with solenoid disconnected and automatic transmission in Neutral.

§ All spark plug listings are Autolite original equipment numbers

① Figure is 625/500 for California engines

② For all vehicles with 3.00 axles, figure is 6B

③ .044 on California models

B Before Top Dead Center

C Cleveland

N.A. Not available

PI Police Interceptor

W Windsor

— Not applicable

Thunderbird

TUNE-UP SPECIFICATIONS

When analyzing compression test results, look for uniformity among cylinders rather than specific pressures.

ENGINE			SPARK PLUGS		DISTRIBUTOR		IGNITION TIMING (deg) ▲		VALVES	Fuel	IDLE SPEED (rpm) ▲	
Year	No. Cyl Displacement (cu in.)	hp	Type §	Gap (in.)	Point Dwell (deg)	Point Gap (in.)	Man Trans	Auto Trans	Intake Opens ■ (deg) ●	Pump Pressure (psi)	Man Trans	Auto Trans
'67	8-390		BF-42	.034	26-31	.017	—	10B(6B)	16	4½-6½	—	475(550)
	8-428		BF-42	.034	26-31	.017	—	10B(6B)	16	4½-6½	—	475(550)
'68	8-390		BF-42	.034	26-31	.017	—	6B	16	4½-6½	—	550
	8-429		BF-42	.034	26-31	.017	—	6B	16	4½-6½	—	550

Thunderbird — TUNE-UP SPECIFICATIONS

When analyzing compression test results, look for uniformity among cylinders rather than specific pressures.

Year	ENGINE No. Cyl Displacement (cu in.)	ENGINE hp	SPARK PLUGS Type §	SPARK PLUGS Gap (in.)	DISTRIBUTOR Point Dwell (deg)	DISTRIBUTOR Point Gap (in.)	IGNITION TIMING (deg) ▲ Man Trans	IGNITION TIMING (deg) ▲ Auto Trans	VALVES Intake Opens ■ (deg) ●	Fuel Pump Pressure (psi)	IDLE SPEED (rpm) ▲ Man Trans	IDLE SPEED (rpm) ▲ Auto Trans
'69	8-429		BF-42	.034	26-31	.017	—	6B	16	4½-6½	—	550
'70	8-429		BRF-42	.034	26-31	.017	—	6B	16	5½-6½	—	600
'71	8-429		BRF-42	.034	26-31	.017	—	4B	16	5½-6½	—	600
'72	8-429		BRF-42	.034	26-30	.020	—	10B	8	5½-6½	—	650/500①
	8-460		BRF-42	.034	26-30	.020	—	10B(6B)	8	5½-6½	—	650/500①
'73	8-429		BRF-42	.034	26-30	.020	—	10B	8	5½-6½	—	650/500①
	8-460		BRF-42	.034	26-30	.020	—	6B	8	5½-6½	—	650/500①
'74	8-460		ARF-52	.044	—	—	—	14B	8	5½-6½	—	[650/500]②

▲ See text for procedure
● Figure in parentheses indicates California engine
■ All figures Before Top Dead Center
§ All spark plug listings are Autolite original equipment numbers
— Not applicable

① First figure is for idle speed with solenoid energized and automatic transmission in Drive, while the second figure is for idle speed with solenoid disconnected and automatic transmission in Neutral
② 675/500 for California engines
B Before Top Dead Center

Ford — CAPACITIES

Year	ENGINE No. Cyl. (Cu. In.) Displacement	Engine Crankcase Add 1 Qt For New Filter	TRANSMISSION Pts To Refill After Draining Manual 3-Speed	Manual 4-Speed	Automatic	Drive Axle (pts)	Gasoline Tank (gals) ■	COOLING SYSTEM (qts) With Heater	With A/C
'67	6-240	4	3.5	—		5	25	13	13
	8-289	4	3.5	—		5	25	15	15
	8-390	4	3.5	4.0		5	25	20.5	20.5
	8-427	5	—	4.0		5	25	20.5	20.5
	8-428	4	—	4.0		5	25	20.5	20.5
'68	6-240	4	3.5	—		5	25	13	13
	8-302	4	3.5	—		5	25	13.7	13.7
	8-390	4	3.5	4.0		5	25	20.2	20.2
	8-427	5	—	4.0		5	25	20.6	20.6
	8-428	4	—	4.0		5	25	19.4	19.4
'69	6-240	4	3.5	—		5	24.5	14.3	14.3
	8-302	4	3.5	—		4.5	24.5	15.4	15.6
	8-390	4	3.5	—		4.5	24.5	20.1	20.5
	8-428P	4	—	—		4.5	24.5	19.7	19.7
	8-429	4	—	4.0		4.5	24.5	20.5	21.5
'70	6-240	4	3.5	—		5	24.5	14.4	14.4
	8-302	4	3.5	—		4.5	24.5	15.4	15.6
	8-351	4	3.5	—		4.5	24.5	16.5	16.9
	8-390	4	3.5	—		4.5	24.5	20.1	20.5
	8-428P	4	—	—		4.5	24.5	19.7	19.7
	8-429	4	—	—		4.5	24.5	18.6	19.0
'71	6-240	4	3.5	—		5	22.5	14.1	14.1
	8-302	4	3.5	—		4.5	22.5	15.2	15.6
	8-351	4	3.5	—		4.5	22.5	16.3	16.7
	8-390	4	—	—		4.5	22.5	20.3	26.3
	8-400	4	—	—		4.5	22.5	17.6	17.6
	8-429	4	—	—		4.5	22.5	18.8	18.8

Ford

CAPACITIES

Year	ENGINE No. Cyl. (Cu. In.) Displacement	Engine Crankcase Add 1 Qt For New Filter	TRANSMISSION Pts To Refill After Draining Manual 3-Speed	Manual 4-Speed	Automatic	Drive Axle (pts)	Gasoline Tank (gals) ■	COOLING SYSTEM (qts) With Heater	With A/C
'72	6-240	4	—	—		4	22	14.2	14.2
	8-302	4	—	—		4.5	22	15.2	15.2
	8-351	4	—	—		4.5	22	16.3	16.3
	8-400	4	—	—		5	22	17.7	18.3
	8-429	4	—	—		5	22	18.8	19.5
'73	8-351	4	—	—		4.5	22	16.3	16.3
	8-400	4	—	—		5	22	17.7	18.3
	8-429	4	—	—		5	22	18.8	19.5
'74	8-351	4	—	—	See	4.5	22	16.3	①
	8-400	4	—	—	chart	5	22	18.0	18.0
	8-460	4	—	—	below	5	22	19.4	19.4

① 351W—17.1 qts.; 351C—16.3 qts
■ Station wagons:
'67 to '70—20 gals
'71—22 gals
'72-'74—21 gals
P Police
— Not applicable

AUTOMATIC TRANSMISSION REFILL CAPACITIES (Pts)

Year	Code▲	Capacities
'67-'72	X, Y	22
'67-'72	W	20.5
'67-'69	U, Z	26
'70-'74	U, Z	25.5

▲ Transmission code can be found on the serial number plate or the vehicle certification label.

Mercury

CAPACITIES

Year	ENGINE No. Cyl. (Cu. In.) Displacement	Engine Crankcase Add 1 Qt For New Filter	TRANSMISSION Pts To Refill After Draining Manual 3-Speed	Manual 4-Speed	Automatic	Drive Axle (pts)	Gasoline Tank (gals) ●	COOLING SYSTEM (qts) With Heater	With A/C
'67	8-390	4	3.5	—	26①	5	25	20.5	21.2
	8-410	4	—	4	26	5	25	20.5	21.2
	8-428	4	—	4	26	5	25	20.5	21.2
'68	8-390	4	3.5	—	26	5	25	20.5	21.5
	8-428	4	—	—	26	5	25	20.5	21.5
'69	8-390	4	3.5	—	26	5	24.5	20.1	20.5
	8-428	4	—	—	26	5	24.5	19.7	19.7
	8-429	4	—	—	26	5	24.5	20.5	21.5
'70	8-390	4	3.5	—	25.5	5	24.5	20.1	20.5
	8-428	4	—	—	25.5	5	24.5	19.7	19.7
	8-429	4	—	—	25.5	5	24.5	20.5	21.5
'71	8-351	4	3.5	—	22	5	23	16.3	16.7
	8-400	4	—	—	25	5	23	17.6	17.6
	8-429	4	—	—	25	5	23	18.8	18.8
'72	8-351	4	—	—	22	4	22	15.8	16.3
	8-400	4	—	—	25.5	5	22	17.7	18.3
	8-429	4	—	—	25.5	5	22	18.8	19.5
'73-'74	8-351	4	—	—	22	4	22	15.8	16.3
	8-400	4	—	—	25.5	5	22	17.7	18.3
	8-429	4	—	—	25.5	5	22	18.8	19.5
	8-460	4	—	—	26	5	22	19.5	19.5

● Station wagons:
'67 to '69—20 gals
'70 to '71—22 gals
'72 to '74—21 gals

① Merc-o-matic, 3-speed transmission—22 pts
— Not applicable

Thunderbird

CAPACITIES

Year	ENGINE No. Cyl. (Cu. In.) Displacement	Engine Crankcase Add 1 Qt For New Filter	TRANSMISSION Pts To Refill After Draining Manual 3-Speed	Manual 4-Speed	Automatic	Drive Axle (pts)	Gasoline Tank (gals)	COOLING SYSTEM (qts) With Heater	With A/C
'67	8-390, 428	4	—	—	26.6	5	24	20.5	22.7
'68	8-390	4	—	—	26.6	5	24	20.5	22.7
	8-429	4	—	—	26.6	5	24	18.9	19.2
'69	8-429	4	—	—	26	5	24	18.5	19.0
'70	8-429	4	—	—	26	5	24①	19.4	19.4
'71	8-429	4	—	—	26	5	22.5	19.4	19.4
'72	8-429	4	—	—	26	5	22.5	18.8	18.8
	8-460	4	—	—	26	5	22.5	20	20
'73-'74	8-429	4	—	—	26	5	22.5	18.8	18.8
	8-460	4	—	—	26	5	22.5	20	20

① With evaporative emission controls—22.5 gals
— Not applicable

RING GAP

All measurements are given in inches

Year	Engine	Top Compression	Bottom Compression
'67-'74	6-240, 8-289, 302 351, 429, 400, 460	.010-.020	.010-.020
'67-'68	8-390, 410, 427	.010-.031	.010-.020
'69-'71	8-390	.010-.020	.010-.020
'67-'70	8-428	.010-.020	.010-.020

Year	Engine	Oil Control
'67-'72	6-240	.015-.055
'67-'71	8-302	.015-.069
'67	8-289	.015-.055
'72	8-302	.015-.055
'70-'74	8-351, 351W	.015-.069
'72-'74	8-351C	.015-.055
'67-'68	8-390, 410	.015-.066
'67	8-390, 410	.015-.069
'69-'71	8-390	.015-.055
'70-'74	8-400	.015-.069
'67	8-427	.015-.066
'67-'68	8-428	.015-.066
'69-'70	8-428, 429	.010-.035
'71-'74	8-429, 460	.015-.055

PISTON CLEARANCE

Year	Engine	Piston-to-Bore Clearance (in.)
'67-'72	240 Six	.0014-.0022
'67-'74	289, 302, 351W V8	.0018-.0026
'67-'71	390, 410, 428 V8	.0015-.0023
'67	427 (solid lifter)	.0042-.0066
'68	427 (hyd. lifter)	.0030-.0038
'70-'74	351C, 400, 429, 460 V8	.0014-.0022

RING SIDE CLEARANCE

All measurements are given in inches

Year	Engine	Top Compression	Bottom Compression
'67-'74	All engines except 8-289	.002-.004	.002-.004
'67	8-289	.0019-.0036	.0019-.0036

Year	Engine	Oil Control
'67-'74	All engines	Snug

All measurements given in inches

VALVE SPECIFICATIONS

Year	Engine No. Cyl. Displacement (cu in.)	Seat Angle (deg)	Face Angle (deg)	Spring Test Pressure (lbs @ in.)	Spring Installed Height (in.)	STEM TO GUIDE Clearance (in.) Intake	STEM TO GUIDE Clearance (in.) Exhaust	STEM Diameter (in.) Intake	STEM Diameter (in.) Exhaust
'67	6-240	45	44	197 @ 1.30	1 11/16	.0010-.0027	.0010-.0027	.3420	.3420
	8-289	45	44	175 @ 1.23	1 21/32	.0010-.0027	.0010-.0027	.3420	.3420
	8-390	45	44	220 @ 1.38	1 13/16	.0010-.0024	.0010-.0024	.3715	.3715
	8-410	45	44	220 @ 1.38	1 13/16	.0010-.0024	.0010-.0024	.3715	.3715
	8-427	①	②	268 @ 1.31	1 13/16	.0010-.0024	.0020-.0034	.3715	.3705
	8-428	45	44	220 @ 1.38	1 13/16	.0010-.0024	.0010-.0024	.3715	.3715
'68	6-240	45	44	197 @ 1.30	1 11/16	.0010-.0027	.0010-.0027	.3420	.3420
	8-302	45	44	180 @ 1.23	1 21/32	.0010-.0027	.0015-.0032	.3420	.3415
	8-390	45	44	220 @ 1.38	1 13/16	.0010-.0024	.0015-.0032	.3715	.3710
	8-427	①	②	268 @ 1.31	1 13/16	.0010-.0024	.0020-.0034	.3715	.3705
	8-428	45	44	220 @ 1.38	1 13/16	.0010-.0024	.0015-.0032	.3715	.3710
	8-429	45	44	253 @ 1.33	1 13/16	.0010-.0027	.0010-.0027	.3420	.3420
'69	6-240	45	44	197 @ 1.30	1 11/16	.0010-.0027	.0010-.0027	.3420	.3420
	8-302	45	44	180 @ 1.23	1 21/32	.0010-.0027	.0015-.0032	.3420	.3415
	8-390	45	44	220 @ 1.38	1 13/16	.0010-.0027	.0015-.0032	.3715	.3710
	8-429	45	44	251 @ 1.33	1 13/16	.0010-.0027	.0010-.0027	.3420	.3420
'70	6-240	45	44	197 @ 1.30	1 11/16	.0010-.0027	.0010-.0027	.3420	.3420
	8-302	45	44	180 @ 1.23	1 21/32	.0010-.0027	.0015-.0032	.3420	.3415
	8-351	45	44	215 @ 1.34	1 25/32	.0010-.0027	.0010-.0027	.3420	.3415
	8-390	①	44	220 @ 1.38	1 13/16	.0010-.0027	.0015-.0032	.3715	.3710
	8-429	45	44	253 @ 1.33	1 13/16	.0010-.0027	.0010-.0027	.3420	.3420
'71	6-240	45	44	197 @ 1.30	1 11/16	.0010-.0027	.0010-.0027	.3420	.3420
	8-302	45	44	180 @ 1.23	1 21/32	.0010-.0027	.0015-.0032	.3420	.3415
	8-351③	45	44	215 @ 1.34	1 25/32	.0010-.0027	.0015-.0032	.3420	.3415
	8-351④	45	44	210 @ 1.42	1 13/16	.0010-.0027	.0015-.0032	.3420	.3415
	8-390	①	44	220 @ 1.38	1 13/16	.0010-.0027	.0015-.0032	.3715	.3710
	8-400	45	44	226 @ 1.39	1 13/16	.0010-.0027	.0015-.0032	.3420	.3415
	8-429	45	45	253 @ 1.33	1 13/16	.0010-.0027	.0015-.0032	.3420	.3415
'72	6-240	45	44	197 @ 1.30	1 11/16	.0010-.0027	.0010-.0027	.3420	.3420
	8-302	45	44	200 @ 1.31	1 11/16	.0010-.0027	.0015-.0032	.3420	.3415
	8-351③	45	44	200 @ 1.34	1 25/32	.0010-.0027	.0015-.0032	.3420	.3415
	8-351④	45	44	210 @ 1.42	1 13/16	.0010-.0027	.0015-.0032	.3420	.3415
	8-400	45	44	226 @ 1.39	1 13/16	.0010-.0027	.0015-.0032	.3420	.3415
	8-429	45	45	229 @ 1.33	1 13/16	.0010-.0027	.0010-.0027	.3420	.3420
	8-460	45	45	229 @ 1.33	1 13/16	.0010-.0027	.0010-.0027	.3420	.3420
'73-	8-351③	45	44	200 @ 1.34	1 25/32	.0010-.0027	.0015-.0032	.3420	.3415
'74	8-351④	45	44	210 @ 1.42	1 13/16	.0010-.0027	.0015-.0032	.3420	.3415
	8-400	45	44	226 @ 1.39	1 13/16	.0010-.0027	.0015-.0032	.3420	.3415
	8-429	45	45	229 @ 1.33	1 13/16	.0010-.0027	.0010-.0027	.3420	.3420
	8-460	45	45	229 @ 1.33	1 13/16	.0010-.0027	.0010-.0027	.3420	.3420

① Intake valve seat angle 30°
Exhaust valve seat angle 45°

② Intake valve face angle 29°
Exhaust valve face angle 44°

③ Windsor heads

④ Cleveland heads

CRANKSHAFT AND CONNECTING ROD SPECIFICATIONS

All measurements are given in in.

Year	Engine No. Cyl. Displacement (cu in.)	CRANKSHAFT				CONNECTING ROD		
		Main Brg. Journal Dia	Main Brg. Oil Clearance	Shaft End-Play	Thrust on No.	Journal Diameter	Oil Clearance	Side Clearance
'67	6-240	2.3986-2.3990	.0008-.0024	.004-.008	5	2.1228-2.1236	.0006-.0026	.006-.013
	8-289	2.2482-2.2490	.0005-.0022	.004-.008	3	2.1228-2.1236	.0007-.0028	.010-.020
	8-390, 410	2.7484-2.7492	.0005-.0025	.004-.010	3	2.4380-2.4388	.0007-.0028	.014-.020
	8-427	2.7484-2.7492	.0007-.0031	.004-.010	3	2.4380-2.4388	.0013-.0032	.014-.020
	8-428	2.7484-2.7492	.0008-.0012	.004-.010	3	2.4380-2.4388	.0008-.0022	.014-.020
'68	6-240	2.3986-2.3990	.0008-.0024	.004-.008	5	2.1232-2.1246	.0007-.0028	.014-.020
	8-302	2.2486-2.2490	.0005-.0024	.004-.008	3	2.1232-2.1246	.0007-.0028	.014-.020
	8-390, 427, 428, 429	2.7488-2.7492	.0008-.0012	.004-.008	3	2.4384-2.4388	.0007-.0028	.014-.020
'69	6-240	2.3982-2.3990	.0005-.0015	.004-.008	5	2.1228-2.1236	.0008-.0015	.006-.013
	8-302	2.2482-2.2490	.0005-.0015	.004-.008	3	2.1228-2.1236	.0008-.0015	.010-.020
	8-390	2.7484-2.7492	.0013-.0025	.004-.010	3	2.4380-2.4388	.0008-.0015	.010-.020
	8-428	2.7484-2.7492	.0010-.0020	.004-.010	3	2.4380-2.4388	.0020-.0030	.010-.020
	8-429	2.9994-3.0002	.0005-.0015	.004-.008	3	2.4992-2.5000	.0008-.0015	.010-.020
'70	6-240	2.3982-2.3990	.0005-.0015	.004-.008	5	2.1228-2.1236	.0008-.0026	.006-.013
	8-302	2.2482-2.2490	.0005-.0015	.004-.008	3	2.1228-2.1236	.0008-.0026	.010-.020
	8-351	2.9994-2.3002	.0013-.0025	.004-.008	3	2.3103-2.3111	.0008-.0026	.010-.020
	8-390	2.7484-2.7492	.0005-.0025	.004-.008	3	2.4380-2.4388	.0008-.0026	.010-.020
	8-428	2.7484-2.7492	.0008-.0020	.004-.008	3	2.4380-2.4388	.0008-.0026	.010-.020
	8-429	2.9994-3.0002	.0005-.0025	.004-.008	3	2.4992-2.5000	.0008-.0026	.010-.020
'71	6-240	2.3982-2.3990	.0005-.0022	.004-.008	5	2.1228-2.1236	.0008-.0026	.006-.013
	8-302	2.2482-2.2490	.0005-.0024①	.004-.008	3	2.1228-2.1236	.0008-.0026	.010-.020
	8-351W	2.9994-3.0002	.0013-.0030	.004-.008	3	2.3103-2.3111	.0008-.0026	.010-.020
	8-351C	2.7484-2.7492	.0009-.0026	.004-.010	3	2.3103-2.3111	.0008-.0026	.010-.020
	8-390	2.7484-2.7492	.0008-.0020	.004-.008	3	2.4380-2.4388	.0010-.0030	.010-.020
	8-400	2.9994-3.0002	.0009-.0026	.004-.010	3	2.3103-2.3111	.0008-.0026	.010-.020
	8-429	2.9994-3.0002	.0005-.0025	.004-.008	3	2.4992-2.5000	.0008-.0028	.010-.020
'72	6-240	2.3982-2.3990	.0005-.0022	.004-.008	5	2.1228-2.1236	.0008-.0026	.006-.013
	8-302	2.2482-2.2490	.0005-.0024①	.004-.008	3	2.1228-2.1236	.0008-.0026	.010-.020
	8-351W	2.9994-3.0002	.0008-.0026	.004-.008	3	2.3103-2.3111	.0008-.0026	.010-.020
	8-351C	2.7484-2.7492	.0011-.0028	.004-.010	3	2.3103-2.3111	.0011-.0026	.010-.020
	8-400	2.9994-3.0002	.0011-.0028	.004-.010	3	2.3103-2.3111	.0011-.0026	.010-.020
	8-429	2.9994-3.0002	.0010-.0020②	.004-.008	3	2.4992-2.5000	.0008-.0028	.010-.020
	8-460	2.9994-3.0002	.0010-.0020②	.004-.008	3	2.4992-2.5000	.0008-.0026	.010-.020
'73-'74	8-351W	2.9994-3.0002	.0008-.0026	.004-.008	3	2.3103-2.3111	.0008-.0026	.010-.020
	8-351C	2.7484-2.7492	.0011-.0028	.004-.010	3	2.3103-2.3111	.0011-.0026	.010-.020
	8-400	2.9994-3.0002	.0011-.0028	.004-.010	3	2.3103-2.3111	.0011-.0026	.010-.020
	8-429	2.9994-3.0002	.0010-.0020②	.004-.008	3	2.4992-2.5000	.0008-.0028	.010-.020
	8-460	2.9994-3.0002	.0010-.0020②	.004-.008	3	2.4992-2.5000	.0008-.0026	.010-.020

① #1—.0001-.0018

② #1—.010-.015

TORQUE SPECIFICATIONS

All readings in ft lbs

Year	Engine No. Cyl. Displacement (cu in.)	Cylinder Head Bolts	Rod Bearing Bolts	Main Bearing Bolts	Crankshaft Pulley Bolt	Flywheel to Crankshaft Bolts	MANIFOLD Intake	MANIFOLD Exhaust
'67-'68	6-240	70-75	40-45	60-70	130-145	75-85	25	25
	8-289, 302	65-70	19-24	60-70	70-90	75-85	21	15½
	8-390, 410, 428, 429	80-90	40-45	95-105	70-90	75-85	33½	15½
	8-427	100-110	53-58	95-105	70-90	75-85	33½	15½
'69	6-240	70-75	40-45	60-70	130-150	75-85	25	25
	8-302	65-72	19-24	60-70	70-90	75-85	24	14
	8-390, 428	80-90	40-45	95-105	70-90	75-85	33½	21
	8-429	130-140	40-45	95-105	70-90	75-85	27½	30½
'70	6-240	70-75	40-45	60-70	130-150	75-85	25	25
	8-302	65-72	19-24	60-70	70-90	75-85	24	14
	8-351	95-100	40-45	95-105	70-90	75-85	23-25	18-24
	8-390	80-90	③	95-105	70-90	75-85	32-35	18-24
	8-429	130-140	40-45	95-105	70-90	75-85	27½	30½
'71	6-240	70-75	40-45	60-70	130-150	75-85	25	25
	8-302	65-72	19-24	60-70	70-90	75-85	24	14
	8-351	95-100	40-45	95-105	70-90	75-85	23-25	18-24④
	8-390	80-90	40-45	95-105	70-90	75-85	32-35	18-24
	8-400	95-105	40-45	95-105	70-90	75-85	27-33	12-16
	8-429	130-140	40-45	95-105	70-90	75-85	27½	30½
'72	6-240	70-75	40-45	60-70	130-150	75-85	23-28	23-28
	8-302	65-72	19-24	60-70	70-90	75-85	23-25	12-16
	8-351W	105-112	40-45	95-105	100-130	75-85	23-25	18-24
	8-351C, 400	95-105⑤	40-45⑥	⑦	70-90	75-85	⑧	12-16
	8-429, 460	130-140	40-45	95-105	70-90	75-85	25-30	28-33
'73-'74	8-351W	105-112	40-45	95-105	100-130	75-85	23-25	18-24
	8-351C, 400	95-105⑤	40-45⑥	⑦	70-90	75-85	⑧	12-16
	8-429, 460	130-140	40-45	95-105	70-90	75-85	25-30	28-33

③ 390—40-45; 428—53-58
Tighten cylinder head bolts in 3 steps: the first 20 ft. lbs. less than maximum torque, the second 10 ft. lbs. less than maximum torque, and the third maximum torque
④ 351C engine—12-16
⑤ 351 HO—120
⑥ 351 HO—40-45
⑦ ½ x 13 in. bolt—95-105
⅜ x 16 in. bolt—35-45
⑧ ⁵⁄₁₆ in. bolt—21-25
⅜ in. bolt—27-23
¼ in. bolt—6-9

BATTERY AND STARTER SPECIFICATIONS

Year	Engine No. Cyl. Displacement (cu in.)	BATTERY Ampere Hour Capacity	BATTERY Volts	BATTERY Terminal Grounded	STARTER Lock Test Amps	STARTER Lock Test Volts	STARTER Lock Test Torque (ft lbs)	STARTER No-Load Test Amps	STARTER No-Load Test Volts	STARTER No-Load Test RPM	Brush Spring Tension (oz)
'67	6	45	12	Neg.	670	5	15.5	70	12	9,500	40
	8-289, 390	45①	12	Neg.	670	5	15.5	70	12	9,500	40
	8-428	80	12	Neg.	670	5	15.5	70	12	9,500	40
'68-'69	6	45	12	Neg.	670	5	15.5	70	12	9,500	40
	8-302	55②	12	Neg.	670	5	15.5	70	12	9,500	40
	8-390	45③	12	Neg.	670	5	15.5	70	12	9,500	40
	8-428	80	12	Neg.	670	5	15.5	70	12	9,500	40
	8-429	80	12	Neg.	700	5	15.5	70	12	9,500	40

BATTERY AND STARTER SPECIFICATIONS

		BATTERY			STARTER						
					Lock Test			No-Load Test			
Year	Engine No. Cyl. Displacement (cu in.)	Ampere Hour Capacity	Volts	Terminal Grounded	Amps	Volts	Torque (ft lbs)	Amps	Volts	RPM	Brush Spring Tension (oz)
'70	6	45	12	Neg.	670	5	15.5	70	12	9,500	40
	8-302, 351	55②	12	Neg.	670	5	15.5	70	12	9,500	40
	8-390	45③	12	Neg.	670	5	15.5	70	12	9,500	40
	8-428, 429	80	12	Neg.	700	5	15.5	70	12	11,000	40
'71	6	45④	12	Neg.	670	5	15.5	70	12	9,500	40
	8-302	45④	12	Neg.	670	5	15.5	70	12	9,500	40
	8-351	45③	12	Neg.	670	5	15.5	70	12	9,500	40
	8-390	55②	12	Neg.	670	5	15.5	70	12	9,500	40
	8-400	70⑤	12	Neg.	700	5	15.5	70	12	11,000	40
	8-429	80	12	Neg.	700	5	15.5	70	12	11,000	40
'72	6	45	12	Neg.	670	5	15.5	70	12	9,500	40
	8-302	45	12	Neg.	670	5	15.5	70	12	9,500	40
	8-351	45③	12	Neg.	670	5	15.5	70	12	9,500	40
	8-400	70⑤	12	Neg.	670	5	15.5	70	12	9,500	40
	8-429	80	12	Neg.	700	5	15.5	70	12	11,000	40
	8-460	85	12	Neg.	700	5	15.5	70	12	11,000	40
'73-'74	8-351	55③	12	Neg.	670	5	15.5	70	12	9,500	40
	8-400	70⑤	12	Neg.	670	5	15.5	70	12	9,500	40
	8-429	80⑥	12	Neg.	700	5	15.5	70	12	11,000	40
	8-460	85⑥	12	Neg.	700	5	15.5	70	12	11,000	40

• Starter specifications in table are for 4½ in. starter. Starter specifications for all models with a 4 in. diameter starter are: 460 5 9 70 12 — 40

① 55 Amp. with automatic transmission or air conditioning
② 70 Amp. with air conditioning
③ 70 Amp. with air conditioning
④ 55 Amp. with air conditioning
⑤ 80 Amp. with air conditioning
⑥ 77 Amp. side terminal standard on Thunderbird

BRAKE SPECIFICATIONS

All measurements given in in.

		MASTER CYLINDER		WHEEL CYLINDER			BRAKE DISC OR DRUM DIAMETER		
				Front			Front		
Year	Model	Disc	Drum	Disc	Drum	Rear	Disc	Drum	Rear
'67	Ford and Mercury	1.0①	1.0①	1.938	1.094	.938	11.87	11.03	11.03
	Thunderbird	1.0	—	1.938	—	.938	11.87	—	11.03
'68	Ford and Mercury	1.0	1.0	2.750	1.094	.938	11.72	11.03	11.03
	Thunderbird	1.0	—	2.750	—	.938	11.72	—	11.03
'69	Ford and Mercury Sedan	1.0	1.0	2.750	1.125	.938	11.72	11.03	11.03
	Ford and Mercury Wagon	1.0	1.0	2.750	1.094	.938	11.72	11.03	11.03
	Thunderbird	1.0	—	2.750	—	.938	11.72	—	11.03
'70-'71	Ford and Mercury	1.0	1.0	2.750	1.125	.938	11.72	11.03	11.03
	Thunderbird	1.0	—	2.750	—	.938	11.72	—	11.03
'72	Ford and Mercury	1.0	1.0	2.750	1.125	.938	11.72	11.03	11.03
	Thunderbird	1.0	—	3.100	—	.938	11.72	—	11.03
'73-'74	Ford, Mercury and Thunderbird	1.0	—	3.100	—	1.0	11.72	—	11.03

① With power brakes—.937
— Not applicable

ALTERNATOR AND REGULATOR SPECIFICATIONS

	ALTERNATOR			REGULATOR						
					Field Relay			Regulator		
Year	Part No. or Manufacturer	Field Current @ 12 V	Output (amps)	Part No. or Manufacturer	Air Gap (in.)	Point Gap (in.)	Volts to Close	Air Gap (in.)	Point Gap (in.)	Volts @ 75°
'67	Autolite	2.5	38	Autolite	.014	—	2.5-4	—	—	13.9-14.9
	Autolite	2.9	42	Autolite	.014	—	2.5-4	—	—	13.9-14.9
	Autolite	2.9	45	Autolite	.014	—	2.5-4	—	—	13.9-14.9
	Autolite	2.9	55	Autolite	.014	—	2.5-4	—	—	13.9-14.9
	Autolite	4.6	60	Autolite②	①	①	2.5-4	①	①	13.9-14.9
	Leece-Neville	2.9	53	Leece-Neville③	.010	.019	1.6-2.6	.050	.019	13.9-14.9
	Leece-Neville	2.9	65	Leece-Neville④	.012	.025	6.2-7.2	.050	.019	13.9-14.9
'68	Autolite C6AF10300C	2.9	42	Autolite	①	①	4.2-9.0	①	①	13.5-15.3
	Autolite C6AF10300G	2.9	55	Autolite	①	①	4.2-9.0	①	①	13.5-15.3
	Autolite C6TF10300F	2.9	65	Autolite	①	①	4.2-9.0	①	①	13.5-15.3
	Leece-Neville	2.9	65	Leece-Neville	.012	.025	6.2-7.2	.047	.019	13.9-14.9
'69	Autolite	2.9	42	Autolite	①	①	4.2-9.0	①	①	13.5-15.3
	Autolite	2.9	55	Autolite	①	①	4.2-9.0	①	①	13.5-15.3
	Autolite	2.9	65	Autolite	①	①	4.2-9.0	①	①	13.5-15.3
	Leece-Neville	2.9	65	Leece-Neville	.012	.025	6.2-7.2	.047	.019	13.9-14.9
'70-'74	Autolite⑤	2.9	42	Autolite	①	①	2.0-4.2	①	①	13.5-15.3
	Autolite	2.9	55	Autolite	①	①	2.0-4.2	①	①	13.5-15.3
	Autolite	2.9	61	Autolite	①	①	2.0-4.2	①	①	13.5-15.3
	Autolite	2.9	65	Autolite	①	①	2.0-4.2	①	①	13.5-15.3
	Autolite	2.9	70	Motorcraft	①	①	2.5-4.0	①	①	13.5-15.3
	Leece-Neville	2.9	65	Leece-Neville	.012	.025	6.2-7.2	.047	.019	13.9-14.9

① Transistorized regulator—not adjustable
② Autolite Transistor
③ Leece-Neville 53 Amp only
④ Leece-Neville 53 and 65 Amp
⑤ Beginning 1974, the name Autolite has been changed to Motorcraft

WHEEL ALIGNMENT SPECIFICATIONS

		CASTER		CAMBER				WHEEL PIVOT RATIO (deg)	
Year	Model	Range (deg)	Pref Setting (deg)	Range (deg)	Pref Setting (deg)	Toe-in	Steering Axis Inclin. (deg)	Inner Wheel	Wheel Outer
'67	Ford, Mercury	$\frac{1}{2}$P to $1\frac{1}{2}$P	1P	$\frac{1}{4}$N to $1\frac{1}{4}$P	$\frac{3}{4}$P	$\frac{1}{16}$ to $\frac{3}{16}$	$7\frac{3}{4}$	20	$18\frac{1}{8}$
	T-Bird	$\frac{1}{2}$N to $1\frac{1}{2}$P	$\frac{1}{2}$P	$\frac{1}{2}$P to $1\frac{1}{2}$P	1P	$\frac{1}{8}$ to $\frac{1}{4}$	$7\frac{3}{4}$	20	$18\frac{1}{8}$
'68-'69	Ford, Mercury	0 to 2P	1P	$\frac{1}{4}$N to $1\frac{1}{4}$P	$\frac{3}{4}$P	$\frac{1}{8}$ to $\frac{1}{4}$	$7\frac{3}{4}$	20	$18\frac{1}{8}$
	T-Bird	0 to 2P	1P	$\frac{1}{4}$N to $1\frac{1}{4}$P	$\frac{1}{2}$P	$\frac{1}{16}$ to $\frac{5}{16}$	$7\frac{3}{4}$	20	$18\frac{1}{4}$
'70-'71	Ford, Mercury	0 to 2P	1P	$\frac{1}{4}$N to $1\frac{1}{4}$P	$\frac{1}{2}$P	$\frac{1}{16}$ to $\frac{5}{16}$	$7\frac{3}{4}$	20	$19\frac{4}{25}$
	T-Bird	0 to 2P	1P	$\frac{1}{4}$N to $1\frac{1}{4}$P	$\frac{1}{2}$P	$\frac{1}{16}$ to $\frac{5}{16}$	$7\frac{3}{4}$	20	$19\frac{8}{25}$
'72	Ford, Mercury	1N to 3P	1P	$\frac{1}{2}$N to $1\frac{1}{2}$P	$\frac{1}{2}$P	$\frac{1}{16}$ to $\frac{7}{16}$	$7\frac{3}{4}$	20	$19\frac{4}{25}$
	T-Bird	1N to 3P	1P	$\frac{1}{4}$N to $1\frac{3}{4}$P	$\frac{3}{4}$P	$\frac{1}{16}$ to $\frac{7}{16}$	$7\frac{3}{4}$	20	$17\frac{37}{50}$
'73	Ford, Mercury	0 to 4P	2P	1N to 1P	0	$\frac{1}{16}$ to $\frac{7}{16}$	$7\frac{3}{4}$	20	$18\frac{3}{4}$
	T-Bird	$\frac{1}{2}$N to $3\frac{1}{2}$P	$1\frac{1}{2}$P	$\frac{1}{4}$N to $1\frac{3}{4}$P	$\frac{3}{4}$P	$\frac{1}{16}$ to $\frac{7}{16}$	$7\frac{3}{4}$	20	$17\frac{3}{4}$
'74	Ford, Mercury	0 to 4P	2P	①	②	$\frac{1}{16}$ to $\frac{7}{16}$	$7\frac{3}{4}$	20	$18\frac{3}{4}$
	T-Bird	$\frac{1}{2}$N to $3\frac{1}{2}$P	2P	$\frac{1}{4}$N to $1\frac{3}{4}$P	$\frac{3}{4}$P	$\frac{1}{16}$ to $\frac{7}{16}$	$7\frac{3}{4}$	20	$17\frac{3}{4}$

N Negative P Positive

① Left wheel—$\frac{1}{2}$N to $1\frac{1}{2}$P, right weel—$\frac{3}{4}$N to $1\frac{1}{4}$P

② Left wheel—$\frac{1}{2}$P, right weel—$\frac{1}{4}$P

CHARGING SYSTEM

All Ford cars to the present have used alternating-current (AC) charging systems. This system makes use of an AC generator or alternator, a voltage regulator, a charge indicator or ammeter, and, of course, the battery.

Mechanical energy is supplied to the alternator via a drive belt. Attached to the belt-driven pulley is a field coil or rotor which revolves within the alternator housing thus producing a magnetic field of alternating current. This alternating current is then converted into usable, direct current by a diode rectifier. The output of the alternator should be sufficient to supply power to the electrical system and also recharge the battery. The voltage regulator controls the output of the alternator so that adequate current is supplied without injury to electrical components. Charging system troubleshooting and repairs may be found in the Unit Repair Section under Charging and Starting Systems.

This charging system requires certain precautions.

1. Reversing battery connections will cause damage to the one-way electrical valves, the rectifiers.
2. Booster battery connections must be made as follows: the negative terminal of the booster battery must be connected to the negative terminal of the car battery. The positive terminal of the booster battery must be connected to the positive terminal of the car battery.
3. Fast chargers should never be used as boosters to start AC circuit-equipped cars.
4. When servicing the battery with a fast charger, always disconnect car battery cables.
5. Never attempt to polarize an AC generator.

Complete alternator servicing data is in the Unit Repair Section.

Alternator R & R

1. Disconnect the negative battery cable.
2. Loosen the alternator mounting bolts, remove the alternator to adjusting arm bolt and remove the belt.
3. Remove the alternator mounting bolt and spacer, position the alternator so that the wire connectors can be disconnected and remove the alternator.

NOTE: on alternators with integral regulators mounted on the back of the alternator housing, press the sides of the retainer clip and remove the wire from the regulator.

4. Reverse above procedure to reinstall, applying pressure only to the front of the alternator housing when tightening the drive belt.

Regulator R & R

1. Disconnect the negative battery cable. On 1969 and later Fords the regulator is located behind the battery and it is necessary to remove the battery to remove the regulator.
2. Remove the regulator mounting screws and wires, then remove the regulator.
3. On vehicles with integral regulator, remove the alternator to adjusting arm bolt and the drive belt.
4. Swing the alternator down, remove the terminal covers from the regulator and remove the regulator attaching nuts.
5. Press the sides of the retainer clip and remove the retaining clip and supply wire. Remove the regulator.
6. Reverse above procedure to reinstall.

Fuse Link

Since 1970, all Ford products have incorporated a fuse link in the charging system. The fuse link is a short length of insulated wire, several gauge sizes smaller than the system it protects. The fuse link blows out if a booster battery is hooked into the system incorrectly, or if a component of the electrical system is shorted to ground. When the fuse link blows, it leaves an open circuit in the charging system and the alternator will not charge the battery. A blown fuse link can be indentified by bare wire ends or bubbled insulation. It is located in the engine wire harness on or near the starter solenoid and is marked FUSE LINK.

STARTING SYSTEM

The starter is a four-brush, series-parallel wound unit. The circuit is completed by means of a relay-controlled switch which is energized by the ignition switch. When the starter is energized, the starting motor pinion is placed into mesh with the engine flywheel ring gear, thus cranking the engine. When the engine starts, the pinion is disengaged from the flywheel to protect the armature in the starter from turning at an excessive speed.

All models, except 1970 and later 429 and 460 V8 engined Thunderbirds, Fords and Mercurys, used positive engagement starters. These medium-duty starters feature a self-contained engagement mechanism. The above mentioned 429 and 460 V8 engined cars are equipped with heavy-duty, solenoid-actuated starters, to which an outboard solenoid is mounted. There is no difference in procedures for removing or installing these two types of starters.

Starting system troubleshooting and repairs may be found in the Unit Repair Section under Charging and Starting Systems.

Starter R & R

1. Disconnect the negative battery cable.
2. Disconnect the starter cable from the starter.
3. Remove the starter mounting bolts.
4. Manipulate the starter so that it can be lowered through the steering linkage. On some engine/chassis combinations this can be done by turning the steering wheel all the way to the right; on others it will be necessary to remove the idler arm bracket attaching bolts and lower the assembly away from the engine.
5. Reverse above procedure to reinstall.

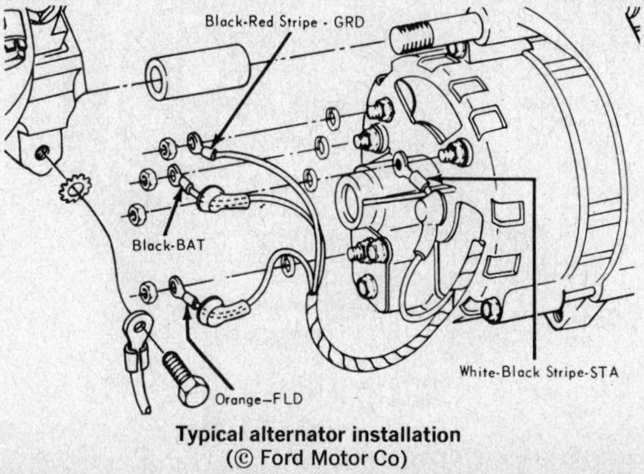
Black-Red Stripe - GRD
Black-BAT
Orange—FLD
White-Black Stripe-STA

Typical alternator installation
(© Ford Motor Co)

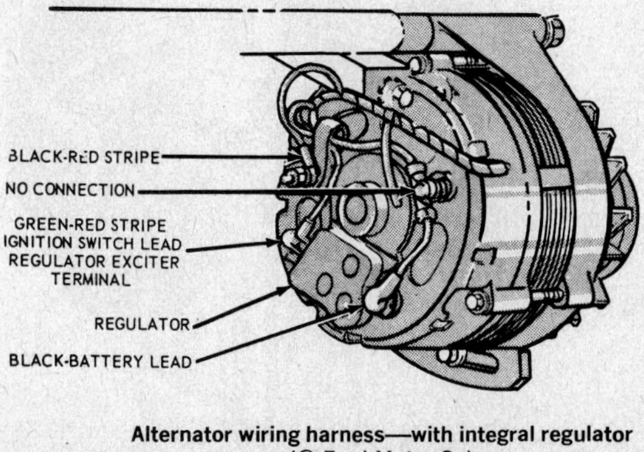
BLACK-RED STRIPE
NO CONNECTION
GREEN-RED STRIPE
IGNITION SWITCH LEAD
REGULATOR EXCITER
TERMINAL
REGULATOR
BLACK-BATTERY LEAD

Alternator wiring harness—with integral regulator
(© Ford Motor Co)

Starter Drive R & R

Positive Engagement Starters

1. Loosen and remove the brush cover band and the starter drive plunger lever cover.
2. Loosen the thru-bolts enough to facilitate the removal of the drive end housing and plunger lever return spring.
3. Some drive end housings are equipped with needle bearings. If yours is so equipped, and you are not replacing the bearings, insert a dummy shaft through the housing to prevent the loss of any of the bearing needles.
4. Remove the retaining pivot pin and starter drive plunger lever.
5. Remove the stop-ring and retainer from the end of the armature shaft. Remove the drive gear assembly.
6. Apply a thin coat of Lubriplate to the armature shaft splines. Install the drive gear assembly on the armature shaft and install a new stop-ring.
7. Position the starter gear plunger lever on the starter frame and install the pivot pin. Check to see that the plunger lever properly engages the starter drive assembly.
8. Install a new stop-ring retainer. Remove the dummy shaft from the drive end housing and lightly grease the needle bearings, if so equipped. Position the starter drive plunger lever return spring and the drive end housing to the starter frame.
9. Tighten the thru-bolts to 55–75 inch pounds (in. lbs).
10. Position the plunger lever cover and brush cover band, with its gasket, on the starter. Tighten the brush cover band retaining screw.

Solenoid-Actuated Starters

See "Unit Repair Section."

IGNITION SYSTEM

Distributor R & R

All Models

Remove the distributor cap and mark the position of tip of the rotor in relation to the body of the distributor and the engine block. Disconnect the ignition primary wires, the vacuum line(s) then take out the hold-down bolt that holds the distributor down in the block and lift it up out of the block.

Do not disturb the engine after the distributor has been removed. If the engine is cranked with the distributor removed, the engine will have to be retimed.

Ignition Retiming

If the timing relationship has been disturbed, proceed to retime the ignition as follows: bring No. 1 cylinder up into the firing position. This can be checked by removing the spark plug, placing your thumb in the spark plug hole, then cranking the engine until the compression attempts to blow by your thumb. Now, slowly bring the crankshaft around until the T.D.C. mark on the crankshaft pulley lines up with the pointer. This is the approximate firing position for No. 1 cylinder.

Scribe a mark on the engine that corresponds with the position of the no. 1 spark plug wire in the distributor cap. Remove the distributor and reinstall it so that the tip of the rotor aligns with the mark on the engine.

Viewed from above, rotation of distributor for six cylinder engine is clockwise; for eight cylinder, counterclockwise.

Contact Point Replacement and Adjustment

1. Unsnap the distributor cap retaining clips and position the cap clear of the breaker plate. Remove the rotor by pulling it straight up.
2. Remove the metal point shield, if so equipped.
3. Disconnect the primary lead and condenser wires from the contact point assembly. On dual-point distributors, remove the jumper strap also.
4. Remove the contact point and condenser retaining screws. Lift the contact point assembly and condenser from the distributor.
5. Lightly lubricate the distributor cam with heat-resistant lubricant.
6. Place the new contact point assembly and condenser in the distributor. Install, but do not tighten, the retaining screws.
7. On all 1967 six-cylinder engines, position the ground wire under the contact point assembly screw and connect the primary and condenser wires to the contact point assembly. On all V8 engines, except those equipped with a centrifugal advance distributor, place the ground wire under the contact point assembly screw farthest from the contacts. On all post-1967 six-cylinder engines, this ground wire is positioned under the condenser retaining screw.
8. Turn the engine until the rubbing block on the point assembly is resting on the high point of the distributor cam lobe. Insert a feeler gauge of specified thickness between the contact points and adjust the gap. Tighten the retaining screw and remove the feeler gauge.
9. Connect the primary and condenser wires to the contact point assembly in the same order in which they were removed. On distributors equipped with a metal point shield, the wires should be positioned 180 degrees

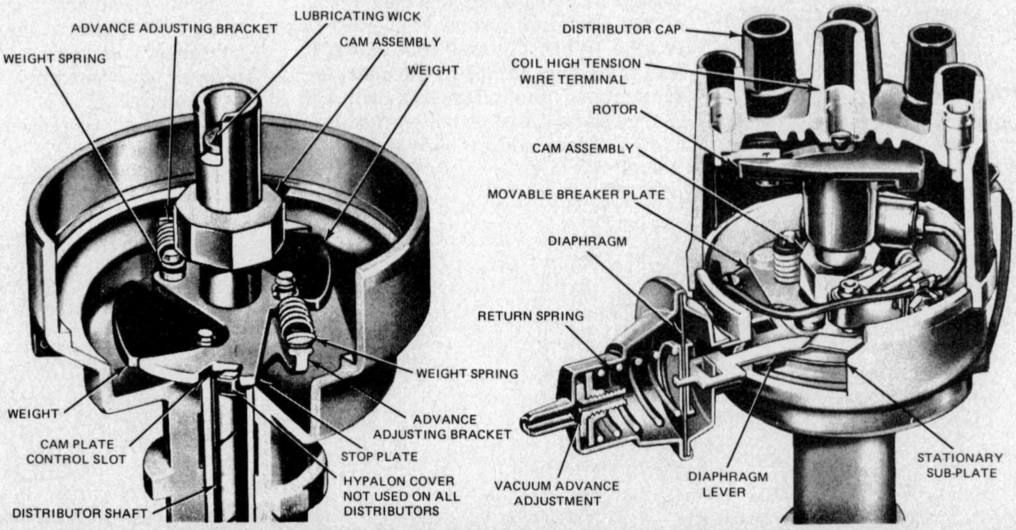
ADVANCE ADJUSTING BRACKET
LUBRICATING WICK
CAM ASSEMBLY
WEIGHT SPRING
WEIGHT
WEIGHT SPRING
WEIGHT
ADVANCE ADJUSTING BRACKET
CAM PLATE CONTROL SLOT
STOP PLATE
HYPALON COVER NOT USED ON ALL DISTRIBUTORS
DISTRIBUTOR SHAFT
DISTRIBUTOR CAP
COIL HIGH TENSION WIRE TERMINAL
ROTOR
CAM ASSEMBLY
MOVABLE BREAKER PLATE
DIAPHRAGM
RETURN SPRING
VACUUM ADVANCE ADJUSTMENT
DIAPHRAGM LEVER
STATIONARY SUB-PLATE

Dual advance distributor with single vacuum diaphragm (© Ford Motor Co)

(180°) from each other, then install the shield.
10. Install the rotor and distributor cap.
11. If a dwell meter is available, check to see that the distributor dwell is within specifications.

Ignition Timing

1. Locate the timing marks and pointer on the lower engine pulley and engine front cover.
2. Clean the marks and apply chalk or bright-colored paint to the pointer.
3. Attach a timing light according to the manufacturer's specifications.
4. Disconnect and plug all vacuum lines leading to the distributor.
5. If the recommended engine idle speed is in excess of 500 rpm, set the idle at 500 rpm for setting the timing. If the recommended idle speed is below 500 rpm, do not alter it.
6. Aim the timing light at the timing mark and pointer on the front of the engine. If the marks align when the timing light flashes, remove the timing light, set the idle to its proper specification, and connect the vacuum lines at the distributor. If the marks do not align when the light flashes, loosen the distributor hold-down clamp slightly.
7. Start the engine again, and observe the alignment of the timing marks. To advance the timing, turn the distributor counterclockwise on six-cylinder engines and clockwise on V8 engines. When altering the timing, it is wise to tap the distributor lightly with a wooden hammer handle in order to move it in the desired direction. Grasping the distributor with your hand may result in a painful electric shock. When the timing marks are aligned, turn the engine off and tighten the distributor hold-down clamp.

Solid State Ignition

Beginning 1974, Ford is utilizing a solid state or "breakerless" ignition system on all 351 cubic inch and larger engines in the state of California, and on all 400 and 460 cubic inch V8s nationwide. This system is unique in that it eliminates the contact breaker points, replacing them with a permanent magnet, low voltage generator.

Briefly, the system works as follows; When the ignition is on and the distributor is rotating, the low voltage generator in the distributor produces alternating current which is then sent to the electronic control module. The module senses the signal from the low voltage generator as the alternating current wave swings from positive to negative each time one of the gear teeth on the armature passes the magnetic field in the coil of the generator. When a gear tooth is directly opposite the magnetic field, the alternating current wave is at crossover (neither negative nor positive). The control module senses this and cuts off electricity (low voltage) to the coil, causing it to fire (high voltage). After the coil fires, the timing circuitry in the module redirects the low tension voltage to the coil.

Other than the low voltage generator and the control module, the rest of the system is conventional in appearance, with a conventional distributor cap and rotor. Spark advance or retard is accomplished by moving the plate for the low voltage generator in the distributor.

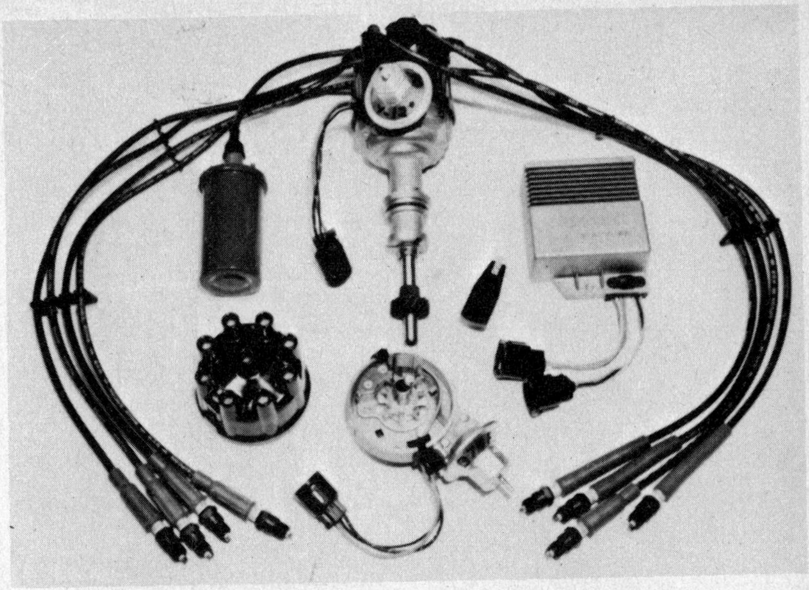

Solid state "breakerless" ignition system components (© Ford Motor Co)

FUEL SYSTEM

Fuel Pump

A single-action, permanently sealed Carter fuel pump is used on all models. On 6-cylinder engines, the fuel pump is located on the lower left center of the engine block. The V8 fuel pump is mounted on the left side of the cylinder front cover.

R&R—All Models

1. Remove the inlet and outlet lines from the pump.
2. Remove the fuel pump retaining screws and remove the pump and gasket.
3. Clean all gasket material from the pump mounting surface on the engine, and apply a coat of oil-resistant sealer to the new gasket.
4. Position pump on engine and install retaining screws.
5. Reinstall lines, start engine and check for leaks.

NOTE: if resistance is felt while positioning the fuel pump on the block, the camshaft eccentric is in the high position. To ease installation, connect a remote engine starter switch to the engine and "tap" remote switch until resistance fades.

Fuel Filter

All models use a non-serviceable inline fuel filter which is located at the carburetor fuel inlet.

Fuel Filter R & R

1. Remove the air cleaner.
2. Loosen the hose clamp at the fuel inlet hose connection.
3. Unscrew the filter from the carburetor.
4. Disconnect the filter from the hose and discard the hose clamp.
5. Reverse the above procedure to install, using a new hose clamp. After installation, start the engine and check for fuel leakage.

Carburetor

Ford uses seven types of carburetors: Autolite (Motorcraft) 1100, Carter YF and RBS (1-barrel), Autolite (Motorcraft) 2100 (2-barrel), Autolite (Motorcraft) 4300, and Holly 4150 and 4150C (4-barrel).

Idle Speed Adjustment

1967: Adjust with air cleaner removed.

1968-74: Adjust with air cleaner installed.

This is the procedure for adjusting all carburetors, any exceptions are listed below.

1. Run engine at fast idle to equalize operating temperature.
2. Make sure the choke plate is fully released.
3. Turn headlights on high beam.
4. If engine is equipped with hot idle compensator valve, make

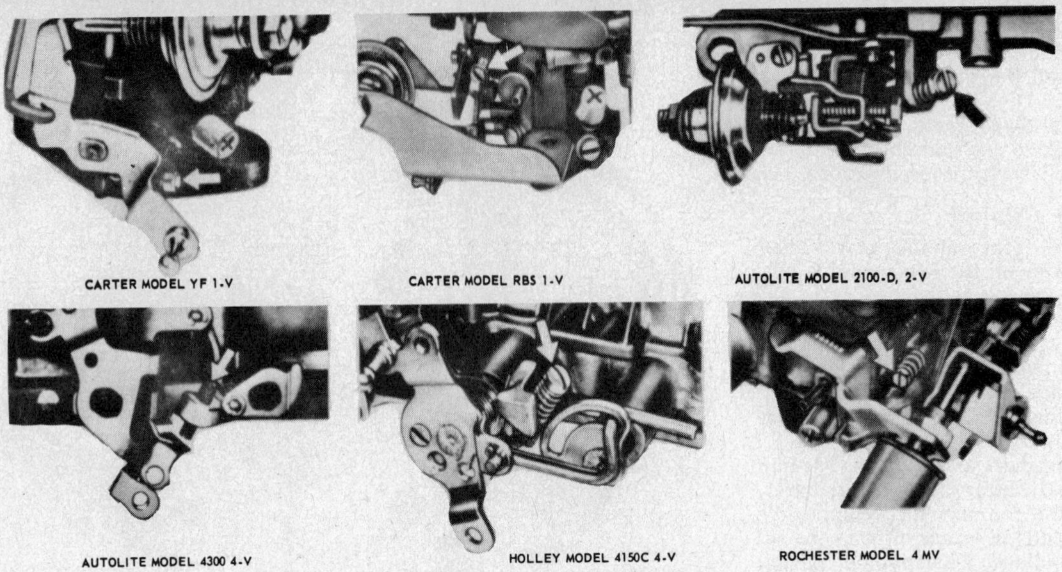
CARTER MODEL YF 1-V
CARTER MODEL RBS 1-V
AUTOLITE MODEL 2100-D, 2-V
AUTOLITE MODEL 4300 4-V
HOLLEY MODEL 4150C 4-V
ROCHESTER MODEL 4 MV

Idle speed adjusting screws (© Ford Motor Co)

sure it is fully seated in the closed position.

5. Attach tachometer of known accuracy to the engine.
6. On cars equipped with air conditioning, 1967-69 models (except 302 V8 engines with automatic transmission) set idle speed with air conditioner turned ON. On all 1970 and later models the idle speed is set with the air conditioner turned OFF.
7. On models equipped with a temperature sensing valve in the distributor vacuum line, remove and plug the vacuum hoses from the distributor to the valve and from the intake manifold to the valve, at the valve located in the intake manifold.
8. Make sure the dashpot is working freely and not binding.
9. If it is not possible to adjust the idle speed with the air cleaner installed, the engine idle speed must be rechecked after installing the air cleaner. On cars with vacuum controlled heat ducts in the air cleaner, the vacuum line must be plugged if the carburetor is to be adjusted with the air cleaner removed.
10. On 1969–71 model cars for which the specifications list two idle speeds, the first speed listed is obtained by turning the plunger on the electric solenoid. On 1972-74 models equipped with an electric solenoid, the higher idle speed is adjusted by turning the adjusting screw in the solenoid mounting bracket. On all models with a solenoid, the lower idle speed is obtained by putting the transmission in Park or Neutral, disconnecting the solenoid and adjusting the carburetor idle screw in the normal manner.

NOTE: with the electric solenoid disengaged, the carburetor adjusting screw must make contact with the throttle shaft to prevent the throttle plates from jamming in the throttle bore when the engine is shut off.

Fuel Mixture Adjustment

1. On 1967 models, turn the mixture screws clockwise until engine speed begins to drop, then back out until engine reaches highest rpm.
2. On 1968 and later models with idle mixture limiters, adjust to obtain the highest rpm possible. Limiter caps should not be removed.

Dashpot Adjustment 1967 Six Cylinder

1. Adjust throttle position to fast idle position and turn dashpot adjusting screw out until it is clear of dashpot plunger assembly.
2. Turn in screw until it contacts plunger. Then turn in screw

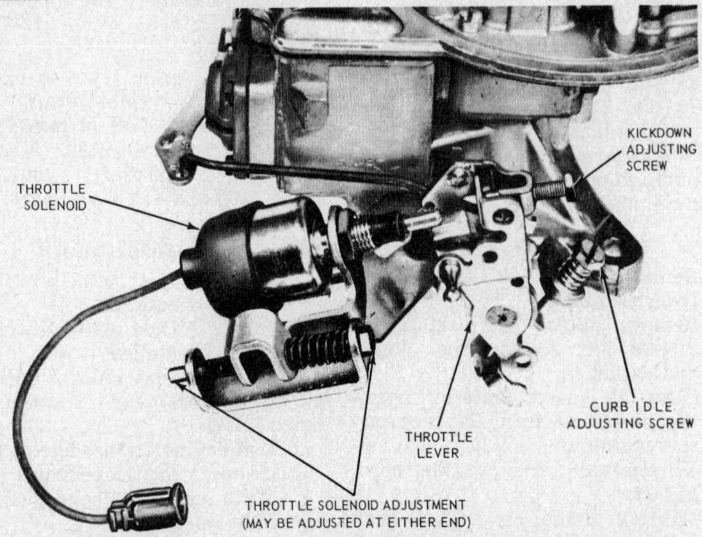
THROTTLE SOLENOID
KICKDOWN ADJUSTING SCREW
CURB IDLE ADJUSTING SCREW
THROTTLE LEVER
THROTTLE SOLENOID ADJUSTMENT (MAY BE ADJUSTED AT EITHER END)

Throttle solenoid adjusting locations—Motorcraft 2100 shown; Motorcraft 4300 similar.
(© Ford Motor Co)

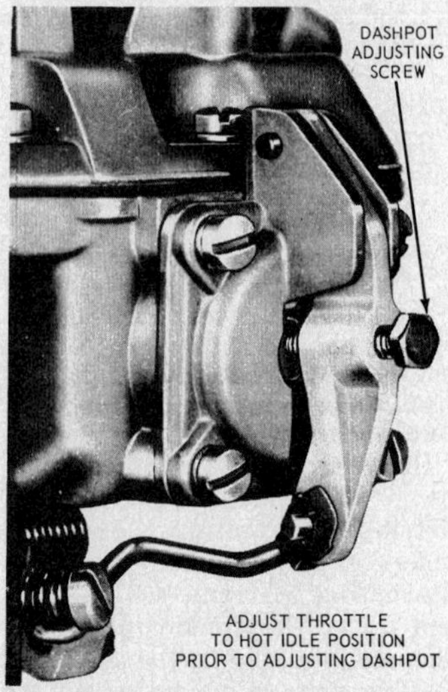
DASHPOT ADJUSTING SCREW
ADJUST THROTTLE TO HOT IDLE POSITION PRIOR TO ADJUSTING DASHPOT

Dashpot—1967 6 cylinder
(© Ford Motor Co)

specified number of turns against plunger.

Models	*Number of Turns*
1967 240 six	
without emission control	6
with emission control	2

3. Check accelerator pump setting.

Dashpot Adjustment—All Others

1. With engine idle speed and mixture properly adjusted and with engine at operating temperature, loosen dashpot locknut.
2. Hold throttle in closed position and depress dashpot plunger. Measure clearance between plunger and cam. Adjust dashpot adjusting nut to give proper clearance.
3. Tighten locknut and check setting of accelerator pump.

Dashpot Adjustment

Model	*Manual*	*Clearance (in.) Automatic*
1967 289 2V with emission control		0.110 - 0.140
1967 390 2V with emission control		0.080 - 0.110
1967 390 4V with emission control		⅛
1967 428 4V with emission control		⅛
1967 428 Police with emission control		⅛
1968 240 Six without thermactor pump		0.080
1968 240 Six with thermactor pump		0.100
1968 302 2V		0.125
1968 390 2V		0.125
1968 390 4V		0.093
1968 428 4V		0.093
1968 428 Police with thermactor pump		0.109
1969 240 six	0.080	0.080
1969 302 2V	⅛	⅛
1969 351 2V	7/64	—
1969 351 4V	3/32	—
1969 390 2V	⅛	⅛
1969 390 4V	⅛	—
1969 428 Police	—	7/64
1969 429 2V	—	⅛
1969 429 4V	3/32	—
1970 240 1V		7/64
1971 240 1V		0.100
1970-72 302, 351, 400, 429 2V		⅛
1970-71 429 4V		0.100
1972 240 1V		7/64

NOTE: many models are equipped with a solenoid instead of a dashpot.

COOLING SYSTEM

Both the 6-cylinder and V8 engines employ cooling systems that are basically similar.

In the 6-cylinder engine, coolant flows from the cylinder head, past the thermostat (if it is open) and into the radiator upper tank. In the V8 engine, coolant from each cylinder head flows through water passages in the intake manifold, then past the thermostat (if it is open) and into the radiator upper tank.

The standard thermostat operating temperature is 185°–192°F. However, a low reading thermostat of 157°–162°F is available for use with nonpermanent-type anti freeze solutions.

A single water pump assembly is used. The pump has a sealed bearing integral with the water pump shaft. The bearing requires no lubrication. There is a bleed hole in the water pump housing. This is not a lubrication hole.

Radiator R & R

1. Drain the cooling system.
2. Remove the upper and lower radiator hoses from the radiator.
3. On models with a fan shroud, remove the shroud attaching screws and move the shroud rearward to gain clearance.
4. If equipped with automatic transmission, remove the cooler lines from the radiator.
5. Remove radiator attaching screws and remove radiator from the car.
6. Reverse above procedure to install.
7. Fill cooling system, run engine at fast idle and check for leaks.

Water Pump R & R

1. Drain the cooling system.
2. On 351C and 400 V8, disconnect the negative battery cable.
3. On cars with power steering, remove the drive belt; models with 390, 427 and 428 engine, remove the power steering mounting retaining screws and remove the pump and bracket as an assembly and position it out of the way.
4. If vehicle is equipped with air conditioning, remove the idler pulley and drive belt from the engine.
5. Disconnect the lower radiator hose, heater hose and bypass hose from the water pump.
6. On cars with a fan shroud, remove the shroud retaining screws and position the shroud rearward over the fan.
7. Remove the fan attaching screws and remove the fan, fan spacer and shroud from the engine compartment.
8. Loosen the alternator mounting bolts and remove the belt.
9. Remove any accessory mounting brackets from the water pump.
10. Remove the water pump mounting bolts and remove the pump from the engine.
11. Clean all gasket surfaces, and on 429 and 460 V8 remove the water pump backing plate and replace the gasket.

NOTE: the 240 6-cylinder engine originally had a one-piece gasket for the cylinder front cover and the water pump. Trim away the old gasket at the edge of the cylinder cover and replace with service gasket.

12. Remove the water pump fitting from the old pump and install it in the new pump.
13. Coat both sides of the new gasket with water resistant sealer, then install pump by reversing above procedure.

Thermostat R & R

1. Open the drain cock and drain the radiator so that the coolant level is below the coolant outlet elbow which houses the thermostat.
2. Remove the outlet elbow retaining bolts and position the elbow clear of the intake manifold or cylinder head sufficiently to provide access to the thermostat.
3. Remove the thermostat and old gasket. On 1967 cars with either six-cylinder or 289 V8 engines, the thermostat must be rotated counterclockwise for removal. All post-1967 thermostats are removed in the same manner.
4. Clean the mating surfaces of the outlet elbow and the engine to remove all old gasket material and sealer. Coat the new gasket with water-resistant sealer and install it on the engine. Install the thermostat in the outlet elbow. On the above mentioned 1967 engines, and all 1968 and later engines, the thermostat

must be rotated clockwise to lock it in position.

5. Install the outlet elbow and retaining bolts on the engine. Torque the bolts to 12–15 ft lbs.
6. Refill the radiator. Run the engine at operating temperature and check for leaks. Recheck the coolant level.

EMISSION CONTROLS

All Models

All Ford cars use positive crankcase ventilation (PCV) systems. The PCV system routes a harmful mixture of blow-by gases and condensation vapors, which were formerly dispelled into the atmosphere, through a modulating valve (PCV valve) and into the intake manifold where they combine with the carburetor air/fuel mixture and are burned in the combustion chamber. Prior to 1968, this system incorporated an open crankcase with breather cap. From 1968 on, the system is closed to the atmosphere, deriving its fresh air from the air cleaner.

1967-71

On 1967 models sold in California, 1968-69 cars with manual transmissions, and 1968-71 high-performance V8 models, the Thermactor (air injection) system was used. This system, which injects fresh air into the exhaust ports to achieve afterburning of raw exhaust fumes, consists of an air pump, a bypass and a check valve, and external air manifolds (not an integral part of the engine exhaust manifolds).

1968-69

In order to comply with stringent, federal antipollution laws, Ford Motor Company adopted the IMCO (IMproved COmbustion) emission control system in 1968. Rather than burning the exhaust gases in the exhaust manifolds, as in the Thermactor system, the IMCO system reduces carbon monoxide and hydrocarbons through more complete combustion in the combustion chambers. This is accomplished through the use of a heated air intake system which thermostatically supplies air, which has been heated by the exhaust manifold, as needed, to the air cleaner, as well as idle mixture limiter caps which prevent the air/fuel mixture from being adjusted to an overly rich condition at idle, and control of ignition timing by a dual diaphragm vacuum advance mechanism on the distributor and a ported vacuum or temperature override switch (PVS). The outer chamber of the vacuum advance is controlled by carburetor vacuum and the inner chamber by intake manifold vacuum. During normal engine operation the outer diaphragm advances ignition timing, while the inner diaphragm retards timing at idle. Three vacuum hoses are attached to the PVS switch, the top hose is connected to the carburetor, the second to the distributor, and the third to the intake manifold. When the engine is operating under normal temperature conditions, vacuum is supplied to the distributor vacuum advance by the carburetor. If the engine should overheat, the PVS switch connects intake manifold vacuum to the distributor which advances ignition timing while the engine is idling, thus speeding up the engine and lowering engine temperature.

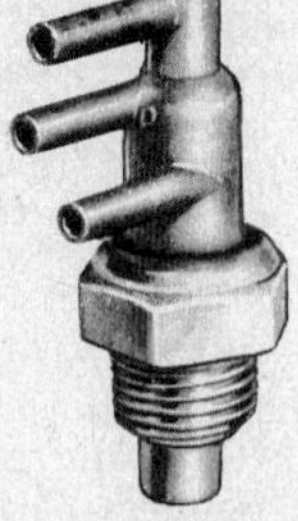

Ported Vacuum Switch (PVS)
(© Ford Motor Co)

In 1969, to further aid in reducing emissions, a distributor vacuum advance (deceleration) control valve and a throttle solenoid were used on some models. The deceleration valve provides maximum intake manifold vacuum to the distributor and subsequent timing advance to prevent backfiring in the exhaust system when the vehicle is slowing down. The throttle solenoid is located on the side of the carburetor. When the ignition key is turned on, the throttle solenoid plunger extends and contacts the carburetor throttle lever, raising the idle speed of the engine. When the ignition key is turned off, the solenoid lever retracts, allowing the carburetor throttle lever to fall back on the carburetor idle speed adjusting screw. This prevents the engine from running on when the key is turned off.

1970-71

The fuel evaporative emission control system was introduced on California models in 1970, and nationwide in 1971. This system eliminates pollution due to evaporating fuel by channeling the breathing of the fuel tank and by the venting of the carburetor float bowl through a canister filled with activated charcoal, condensing the fuel vapors and returning them to the fuel system.

The IMCO system of emission control was further extended in 1970 to become the Distributor Modulator (Dist-O-Vac) System. The Dist-O-Vac system incorporated all of the IMCO features but included three units of equipment which control spark advance in a more sophisticated manner. A speed sensor is located between two sections of the speedometer cable and generates a small current which increases in direct proportion to speed. A thermal switch is located in the right door pillar and activates at outside temperatures of 58°F or higher. The impulses of both are fed into the electronic control amplifier.

The distributor vacuum advance hose is connected from the carburetor, through the electronic control amplifier, to the distributor. When ambient temperature is above 58°F, the contacts in the temperature switch open and a plunger in the amplifier prevents vacuum from being supplied to the distributor. When vehicle speed reaches approximately 30 mph, the signal from the speed sensor causes the control amplifier to open the vacuum line to the distributor and ignition timing is allowed to advance in the normal manner. When the ambient temperature is below 58°F, the temperature switch closes, and normal vacuum is supplied to the distributor regardless of vehicle speed. In the event of engine overheating, the ported vacuum switch (PVS), a carryover from the IMCO system overrides the electronic control modulator by connecting intake manifold vacuum to the distributor.

1972

For 1972, the Dist-O-Vac stystem was replaced by two different spark control systems. The Electronic Spark Control (ESC) system is the same as the old Dist-O-Vac system except that the electronic control modulator was separated into two pieces, an amplifier and a distributor modulator valve. The amplifier judges the signals sent to it by the speed and temperature switches and tells the distributor modulator valve when to open and close and thus allow or prevent vacuum to reach the distributor. The Transmission Regulated Spark (TRS) is similar to the ESC system except that the speed sensor is replaced by a transmission switch. The switch is mounted on the side of the transmission and is hydraulically actuated on cars equipped with an automatic transmission and manually actuated on models equipped with a manual transmission. When the ambient temperature is above 55°F, the transmission switch is closed whenever the transmission is in any gear other than high gear (manual transmission), or high gear or reverse (automatic transmission).

When the transmission switch closes, it signals the distributor modulator valve to close and thus prevent carburetor vacuum from reaching the distributor. As in past systems, neither of these systems is functional below 55–58°F, and both are bypassed by the PVS if the engine should overheat.

On some 1972 models, a spark delay valve has been inserted into the vacuum advance line to the distributor. The valve closes under hard acceleration, blocking carburetor vacuum to the distributor for a predetermined period of a few seconds. The valves are color coded for identification purposes.

1973-74

1973-74 models use an Exhaust Gas Recirculation System (EGR) to control oxides of nitrogen. On V8 engines, exhaust gases travel through the exhaust gas crossover passage in the intake manifold. A portion of these gases is diverted into a spacer which is mounted under the carburetor. The EGR control valve, which is attached to the rear of the spacer, consists of a vacuum diaphragm with an attached plunger which normally blocks off exhaust gases from entering the intake manifold. The EGR valve is controlled by a vacuum line from the carburetor which passes through a ported vacuum switch. The EGR ported vacuum switch provides vacuum to the EGR valve at coolant temperatures above 125°F. The vacuum diaphragm then opens the EGR valve permitting exhaust gases to flow through the carburetor spacer and enter the intake manifold where they combine with the fuel mixture and enter the combustion chambers. The exhaust gases are relatively oxygen-free and tend to dilute the combustion charge. This lowers peak combustion temperature thereby reducing oxides of nitrogen.

All models that are equipped with a 351C, 400, 429, or 460 V8 use the new Delay Vacuum By-Pass (DVB) spark control system. This system provides two paths by which carburetor vacuum can reach the distributor vacuum advance. The system consist of a spark delay valve, a check valve, a solenoid vacuum valve, and an ambient temperature switch. When the ambient temperature is below 49°F, the temperature switch contacts are open and the vacuum solenoid is open (de-energized). Under these conditions, vacuum will flow from the carburetor, through the open solenoid, and to the distributor. Since the spark delay valve resist the flow of carburetor vacuum, the vacuum will always flow through the vacuum solenoid when it is open, since this is the path of least resistance. When the ambient temperature rises above 60°F, the contacts in the temperature switch (which is located in the door post) close. This passes ignition switch current to the solenoid, energizing the solenoid. This blocks one of the two vacuum paths. All distributor vacuum must now flow through the spark delay valve. When carburetor vacuum rises above a certain level on acceleration, a rubber valve in the spark delay valve blocks vacuum from passing through the valve for from 5 to 30 seconds. After this time delay has elapsed, normal vacuum is supplied to the distributor. When the vacuum solenoid is closed, (temperature above 60°), the vacuum line from the solenoid to the distributor is vented to atmosphere. To prevent the vacuum that is passing through the spark delay valve from escaping through the solenoid into the atmosphere, a one-way check valve is installed in the vacuum line from the solenoid to the distributor.

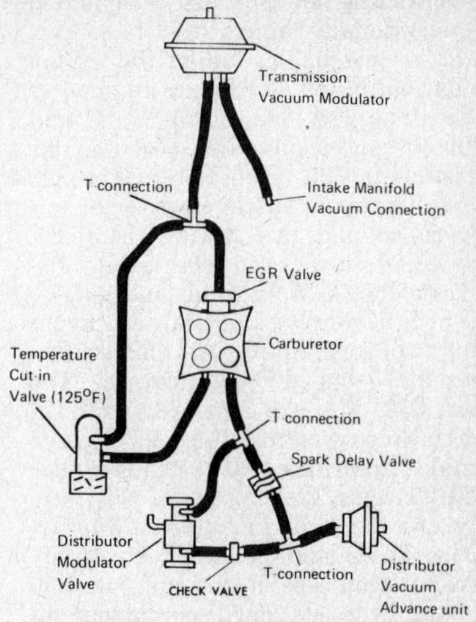
Transmission
Vacuum Modulator
T connection
Intake Manifold
Vacuum Connection
EGR Valve
Carburetor
Temperature
Cut-in
Valve (125°F)
T connection
Spark Delay Valve
Distributor
Modulator
Valve
CHECK VALVE
T-connection
Distributor
Vacuum
Advance unit

Typical vacuum hose schematic with EGR (© Ford Motor Co)

In order to meet 1974 California emission control standards, all 1974 Ford cars sold in that state will be equipped with a Thermactor (air injection) system to control hydrocarbons and carbon monoxide. The EGR and IMCO systems are retained, as in 1973, to control oxides of nitrogen.

Starting in 1973, dual diaphragm distributors are not used. Consult the "Unit Repair Section" for complete testing and troubleshooting procedures of emission control equipment.

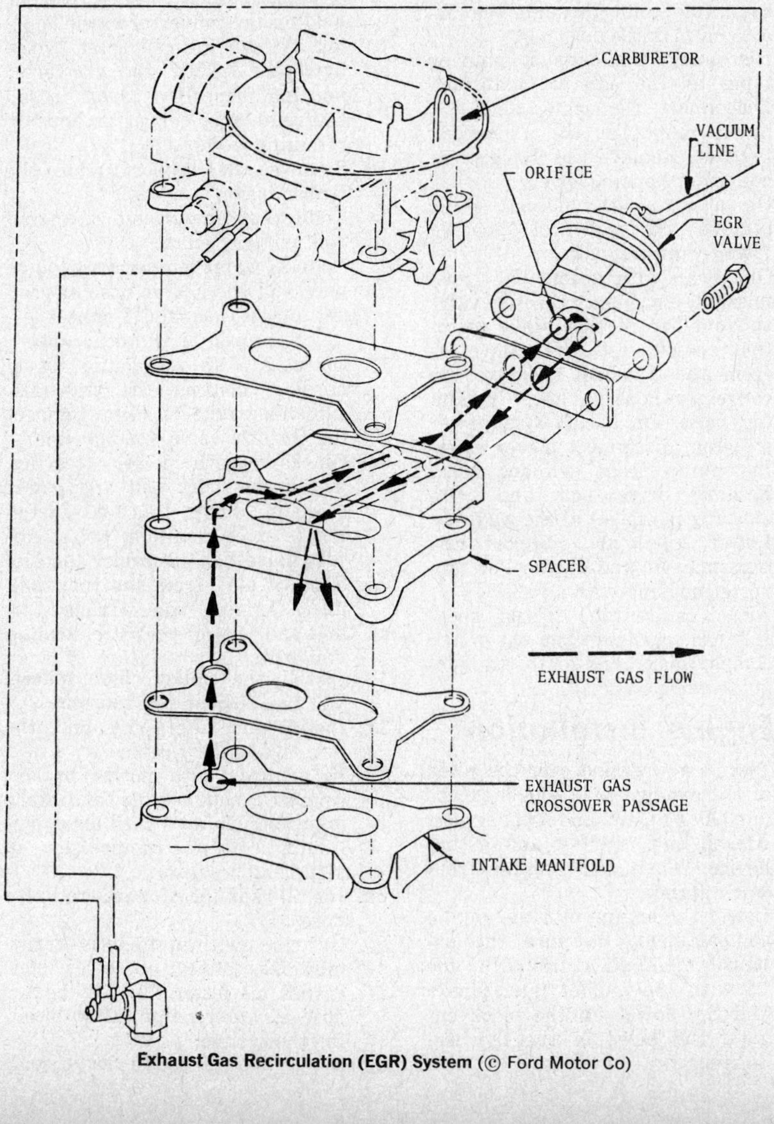
CARBURETOR
VACUUM
LINE
ORIFICE
EGR
VALVE
SPACER
EXHAUST GAS FLOW
EXHAUST GAS
CROSSOVER PASSAGE
INTAKE MANIFOLD

Exhaust Gas Recirculation (EGR) System (© Ford Motor Co)

ENGINE

The only 6-cylinder engine available on full sized 1967-72 Fords is the 240 cu. in. version. The intake manifolding on this six is mounted conventionally on the right-hand side and is detachable, unlike the intake manifolding on Ford sixes in smaller cars. The 289, 302, 351W, 351C and 400 V8 engines are the most popular engines in full sized Fords. The 289 and 302 are identical in exterior appearance and are notably compact, about 20 in. across. The larger displacement 351W is wider and bulkier although nearly identical in layout and conformation. All have trapezoidal shaped valve covers. The 352, 390, 410, 427 and 428 family of engines is recognizable by its unusual intake manifold that extends under valve covers. The engines of this family are identical in exterior appearance. These engines have been widely used in full size Fords and the 390 engine was standard equipment in Thunderbirds through 1968, with the 428 as an option in 1967.

The 429 engine was the first of a new series of big block Ford engines. It has been available in two-barrel and four-barrel versions. The engine is identifiable by its great bulk, and by the tunnel port configuration noticeable in the shape of its intake manifold. A similar 460 V8 is available on the 1972-74 Thunderbird and Mercury and the 1974 Ford. The 240 Six and 302 V8 were discontinued in 1973 Fords, the 351 engine becoming standard equipment. The 429 V8 was dropped after the 1973 model run.

Engine Removal

1. Scribe the hood hinge outline on the underside of the hood, disconnect the hood and remove.
2. Drain the entire cooling system and oil from engine oil pan.
3. Remove the air cleaner, disconnect the battery at the cylinder head. On automatic transmission-equipped cars, disconnect oil cooler lines at the radiator.
4. Remove the upper and lower radiator hoses from the engine and, if the engine is equipped with a fan shroud, disconnect the shroud from the radiator and position it rearward. Remove the radiator from the car.
5. Remove the fan attaching screws and remove the fan, fan spacer and shroud from the engine as an assembly. Loosen and remove all drive belts.
6. Disconnect the heater hoses from the engine. If the vehicle is equipped with power steering, remove the pump from the engine and position it out of the way.
7. Remove the alternator mounting bolts and ground wire from the block and remove the alternator. Disconnect the carburetor and kickdown linkage from the engine.
8. On models with power brakes, remove the vacuum line from the engine. On cars with air conditioning, remove the compressor mounting bracket from the engine and position the compressor out of the way without disconnecting the refrigerant lines.

NOTE: if the compressor lines do not have enough slack to move the compressor out of the way without disconnecting the refrigerant lines, the air conditioning system must be evacuated, using the required tools, before the refrigerant lines can be disconnected.

9. Disconnect fuel tank line at the fuel pump and plug the line.
10. Disconnect the coil primary wire at the coil. Disconnect wires at the oil pressure and water temperature-sending units.
11. Remove the starter and dust seal.
12. On a car equipped with a manual-shift transmission, remove the clutch retracting spring. Disconnect the clutch equalizer shaft and arm bracket at the underbody rail and remove the arm bracket and equalizer.
13. Raise the car. Remove the flywheel or converter housing upper retaining bolts through the access holes in the floor pan.
14. Disconnect the exhaust pipe or pipes at the exhaust manifold. Disconnect the right and left motor mount at the underbody bracket. Remove the flywheel or converter housing cover.
15. On a car with manual shift, remove the flywheel housing lower retaining bolts.
16. On a car with automatic transmission, disconnect throttle valve vacuum line at the intake manifold, disconnect the converter from the flywheel. Remove the converter housing lower retaining bolts. On a car with power steering, disconnect power steering pump from cylinder head. Remove drive belt and wire steering pump out of the way.
17. Lower the car. Support the transmission and flywheel or converter housing with a jack.
18. Attach an engine lifting hook. Lift the engine up and out of the compartment and onto an adequate work stand.

Engine Installation

1. Place a new gasket over the studs of the exhaust manifold/s except on 390, 410, 427 and 428 engines.
2. Attach engine sling and lifting device. Then lift engine from work stand.
3. Lower the engine into the engine compartment. Be sure the exhaust manifold/s properly line up with the muffler inlet pipe/s and the dowels in the block engage the holes in the flywheel housing.

   On a car with automatic transmission, start the converter pilot into the crankshaft.

   On a car with manual-shift transmission, start the transmission main drive gear into the clutch disc. If the engine hangs up after the shaft enters, rotate the crankshaft slowly (with transmission in gear) until the shaft and clutch disc splines mesh.
4. Install the flywheel or converter housing upper bolts.
5. Install engine support insulator to bracket retaining nuts. Disconnect engine lifting sling and remove lifting brackets.
6. Raise front of car. Connect exhaust line/s and tighten attachments.
7. Position dust seal and install starter.
8. On cars with manual-shift transmissions, install remaining flywheel housing-to-engine bolts. Connect clutch release rod. Position the clutch equalizer bar and bracket and install retaining bolts. Install clutch pedal retracting spring.
9. On cars with automatic transmissions, remove the retainer holding the converter in the housing. Attach the converter to the flywheel. Install the converter housing inspection cover. Install the remaining converter housing retaining bolts.
10. Remove the support from the transmission and lower the car.
11. Connect engine ground strap and coil primary wire.
12. Connect water temperature gauge wire and the heater hose at coolant outlet housing. Connect accelerator rod at the bellcrank.
13. On cars with automatic transmission, connect the transmission filler tube bracket. Connect the throttle valve vacuum line.
14. On cars with power steering, install the drive belt and power steering pump bracket. Install the bracket retaining bolts. Adjust drive belt to proper tension.
15. Remove plug from the fuel tank line. Connect the flexible fuel line and the oil pressure sending unit wire.
16. Install the pulley, belt spacer, and fan. Adjust belt tension.
17. Install the alternator and the negative battery cable.
18. In vehicles with power brakes, connect vacuum line at intake manifold. On cars with air conditioning, install compressor on mounting bracket.
19. Install radiator. Connect radiator hoses.
20. On cars with automatic transmissions, connect oil cooler lines.
21. Install oil filter. Connect heater hose at water pump, after bleeding the system.
22. Bring crankcase to level with

correct grade of oil. Run engine at fast idle and check for leaks. Install air cleaner and make final engine adjustments.
23. Install and adjust hood.
24. Road test car.

Engine Manifolds

Intake and Exhaust Manifold Removal—All 6-Cylinder

1. Remove the air cleaner. Remove the carburetor linkage and kick down linkage from the engine.
2. Disconnect the fuel line from the carburetor and all vacuum lines from the manifolds.

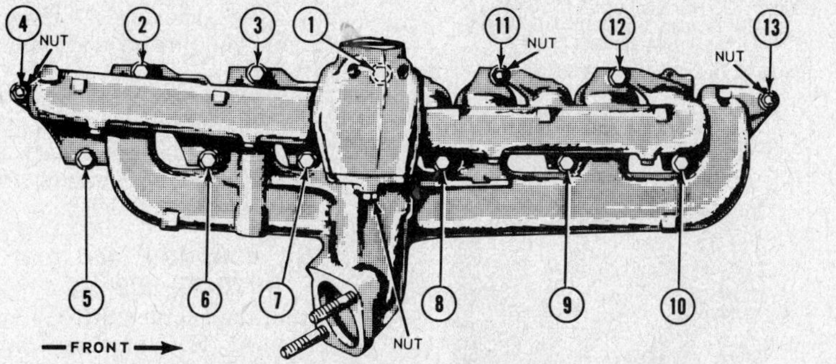
4
NUT
2
3
1
11
NUT
12
13
NUT
5
6
7
8
9
10
FRONT
NUT
Intake and exhaust manifold torque sequence—240 six cyl. (© Ford Motor Co)

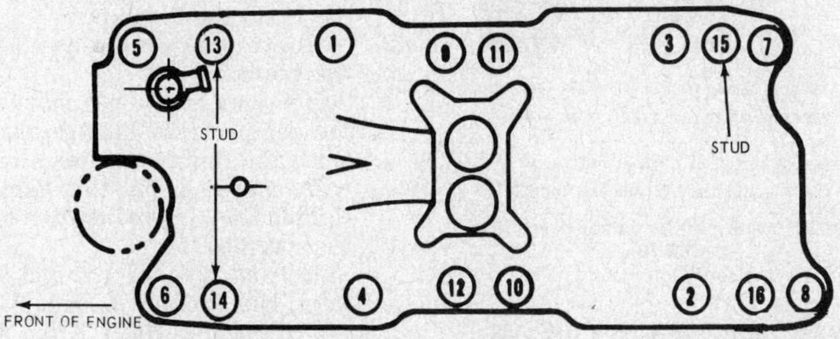
5
13
1
9
11
3
15
7
STUD
STUD
6
14
4
12
10
2
16
8
FRONT OF ENGINE
Intake manifold torque sequence—351W V8 (© Ford Motor Co)

3. Remove the negative battery cable, then remove the alternator mounting bolts and remove the alternator from the engine with the wires attached.
4. Disconnect the muffler inlet pipe from the engine.
5. Remove the manifold attaching parts from the engine, and remove the two manifolds as an assembly.
6. To separate the manifolds, remove the carburetor and then remove the nuts that secure the manifolds together.
7. Clean all gasket areas and reverse above procedure to install; using all new gaskets.

Intake Manifold Removal—All V8

1. Drain the cooling system.
2. Disconnect the upper radiator hose from the thermostat housing and the bypass hose from the manifold.
3. Remove the air cleaner and ducts.
4. Remove the distributor cap and wires from the engine. Mark the position of the distributor rotor in relationship to the intake manifold, remove the primary wire from the coil, then remove the distributor hold-down bolt and the distributor.
5. Remove all vacuum lines from the intake manifold and remove the temperature sending unit wire.
6. Disconnect the fuel line and any vacuum lines from the carburetor.
7. Remove all carburetor linkage and kickdown linkage that attaches to the intake manifold.
8. On 390, 410, 427 and 428 engines, remove the valve covers, the rocker arm assemblies and the pushrods. The rocker arms should be removed by backing off each of the four bolts two turns in sequence from front to back. Keep pushrods in order so that they can be installed in their original position.
9. Remove the manifold attaching bolts and remove the manifold. If it is necessary to pry the manifold to loosen it from the engine, use care not to damage any gasket sealing surfaces.
10. Clean all gasket surfaces and firmly cement new gaskets in place. The gaskets should be securely locked in place before attempting to install the manifold.
11. Reverse above procedure to reinstall.

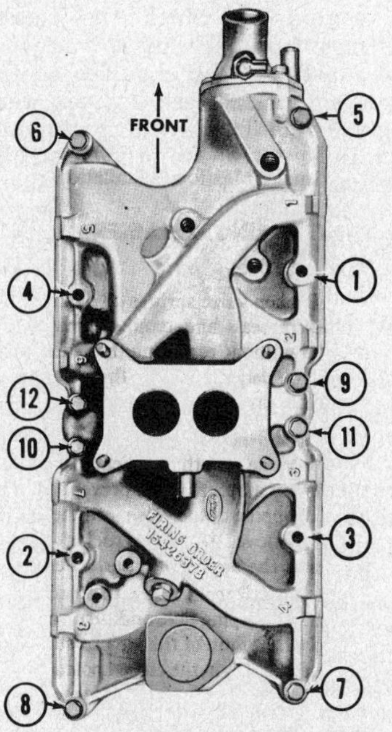
FRONT
6
5
4
1
9
12
11
10
2
3
8
7
Intake manifold torque sequence—all 302 and 1967 289 V8 (© Ford Motor Co)

Exhaust Manifold Removal—All V8

1. If the right-side manifold is to be removed, disconnect the choke heat tube, remove the air cleaner and ducts.
2. On models with 427 V8, to remove the left manifold, remove the clutch linkage and brackets from the engine block.
3. If the right side is to be removed, disconnect and lower the idler arm, and remove the motor support attaching nuts and raise the engine several inches.
4. On vehicles with 351C and 400 V8s, to remove the left manifold, remove the oil filter. If equipped with an automatic transmission remove the transmission selector lever cross-shaft from the engine block. If equipped with a manual transmission, disconnect the equalizer shaft bracket and clutch linkage from the engine.
5. Disconnect the manifolds from the muffler inlet pipes.
6. If the manifold attaching bolts are installed with locking washers, bend back the tabs on the washers.
7. Remove the manifold to cylinder head attaching bolts, and remove the manifolds from the car.
8. Clean all gasket surfaces, and reverse above procedure to install; using all new gaskets.

Valve System

All engines used in full-size Ford products, with the exception of the 1967 427 V8, are equipped with hydraulic valve lifters. Valve systems with hydraulic valve lifters operate with zero clearance in the valve train, and because of this the rocker arms are nonadjustable. The only means by which valve system clearances can be altered is by installing .060 in. over- or undersize pushrods; but, because of the hydraulic lifter's natural ability to compensate for slack in the valve train, all components of the valve system should be checked for wear if there is excessive play in the system.

When a valve in the engine is in the closed position, the valve lifter is resting on the base circle of the camshaft lobe and the pushrod is in its lowest position. To remove this additional clearance from the valve train, the valve lifter expands to maintain zero clearance in the valve system. When a rocker arm is loosened or removed from the engine, the lifter expands to its fullest travel. When the rocker arm is reinstalled on the engine, the proper valve setting is obtained by tightening the rocker arm to a specified limit. But with the lifter fully expanded, if the camshaft lobe is on a high point it will require excessive torque to compress the lifter and obtain the proper setting. Because of this, when any component of the valve system has been removed, a preliminary valve adjustment procedure must be followed to ensure that when the rocker arm is reinstalled on the engine and tightened, the camshaft lobe for that cylinder is in the low position.

Preliminary Valve Adjustment

6-Cylinder

1. Crank the engine until the TDC mark on the crankshaft damper is aligned with timing pointer on the cylinder front cover.
2. Scribe a mark on the damper at this point.
3. Scribe two more marks on the damper, each equally spaced from the first mark (see illustration).
4. With the engine on TDC of the compression stroke, (mark A aligned with the pointer) back off the rocker arm adjusting nut until there is end-play in the pushrod. Tighten the adjusting nut until all clearance is removed, then tighten the adjusting nut one additional turn on 1969 and later models and 3/4 of a turn on all 1967-68 models. To determine when all clearance is removed from the rocker arm, turn the pushrod with the fingers. When the pushrod can no longer be turned, all clearance has been removed.
5. Repeat this procedure for each valve, turning the crankshaft 1/3 turn to the next mark each time and following the engine firing order of 1-5-3-6-2-4.

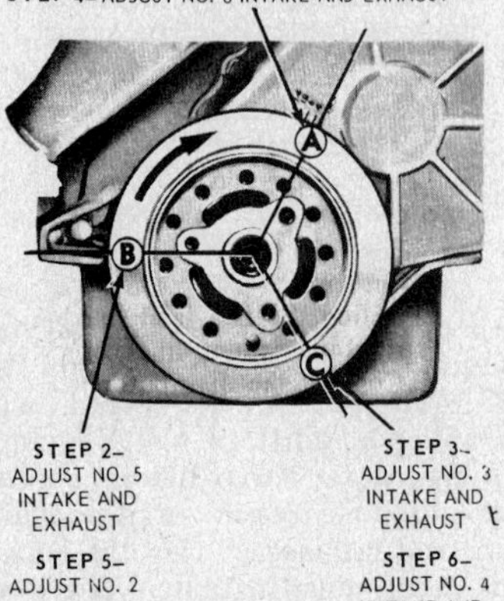
STEP 1–SET NO. 1 PISTON ON T.D.C. AT END OF COMPRESSION STROKE ADJUST NO. 1 INTAKE AND EXHAUST
STEP 4–ADJUST NO. 6 INTAKE AND EXHAUST
A
B
C
STEP 2–ADJUST NO. 5 INTAKE AND EXHAUST
STEP 3–ADJUST NO. 3 INTAKE AND EXHAUST
STEP 5–ADJUST NO. 2 INTAKE AND EXHAUST
STEP 6–ADJUST NO. 4 INTAKE AND EXHAUST

Position of crankshaft for valve adjustment —6 cylinder
(© Ford Motor Co)

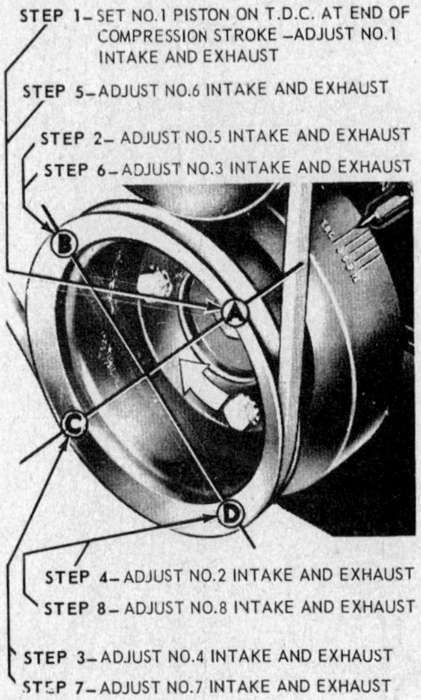
STEP 1–SET NO.1 PISTON ON T.D.C. AT END OF COMPRESSION STROKE –ADJUST NO.1 INTAKE AND EXHAUST
STEP 5–ADJUST NO.6 INTAKE AND EXHAUST
STEP 2–ADJUST NO.5 INTAKE AND EXHAUST
STEP 6–ADJUST NO.3 INTAKE AND EXHAUST
A
B
C
D
STEP 4–ADJUST NO.2 INTAKE AND EXHAUST
STEP 8–ADJUST NO.8 INTAKE AND EXHAUST
STEP 3–ADJUST NO.4 INTAKE AND EXHAUST
STEP 7–ADJUST NO.7 INTAKE AND EXHAUST

Position of crankshaft for valve adjustment —289 V8
(© Ford Motor Co)

289 and 1968-69 302 V8

NOTE: this procedure for the 289 and early 302 V8 engines is designed for engines in which the rocker arm mounting studs do *not* incorporate a positive stop shoulder on the mounting stud. These engines were originally equipped with this kind of stud. However, due to production differences, it is possible some 289 or early 302 engines may be encountered that *are* equipped with positive stop rocker arm mounting studs. Before following this procedure, verify that the rocker arm mounting studs do not incorporate a positive stop shoulder. On studs without a positive stop, the shank portion of the stud that is exposed just above the cylinder head is the same diameter as the threaded portion, at the top of the stud, to which the rocker arm retaining nut attaches. If the shank portion of the stud is of greater diameter than the threaded portion, this identifies it as a positive stop rocker arm stud and the procedure for the 351 engine should be followed.

1. Crank the engine until #1 cylinder is at TDC of the compression stroke and the timing pointer is aligned with the mark on the crankshaft damper.
2. Scribe a mark on the damper at this point.
3. Scribe three more marks on the damper, dividing the damper into quarters (see illustration).
4. With mark A aligned with the timing pointer, adjust the valves on #1 cylinder by backing off the adjusting nut until the pushrod has free play in it. Then, tighten the nut until there is no free play in the rocker arm. This can be determined by turning the pushrod while tightening the nut; when the pushrod can no longer be turned, all clearance has been removed. After the clearance has been removed, tighten the nut an additional 3/4 of a turn.
5. Repeat this procedure for each valve, turning the crankshaft 1/4 turn to the next mark each time and following the engine firing order of 1-5-4-2-6-3-7-8.

351, 400, 429, 460 and 1970-72 302 V8

1. Crank the engine until #1 cylinder is at TDC of the compression stroke and the timing pointer is aligned with the mark on the crankshaft damper.
2. Scribe a mark on the damper at this point.
3. Scribe two additional marks on the damper (see illustration).
4. With the timing pointer aligned with mark A on the damper, tighten the following valves to the specified torque:
   302 and 429- No. 1, 7 and 8 Intake; No. 1, 5 and 4 Exhaust
   351 and 400- No. 1, 4 and 8 Intake; No. 1, 3 and 7 Exhaust
5. Rotate the crankshaft 180° to point B and tighten the following valves:
   302 and 429- No. 5 and 4 Intake; No. 2 and 6 Exhaust
   351 and 400- No. 3 and 7 Intake; No. 2 and 6 Exhaust
6. Rotate the crankshaft 270° to point C and tighten the following valves:
   302 and 429- No. 2, 3 and 6 Intake; No. 7, 3 and 8 Exhaust
   351 and 400- No. 2, 5 and 6 Intake; No. 4, 5 and 8 Exhaust
7. Rocker arm tighten specifications are: 302 and 351W—tighten nut until it contacts the rocker shoulder, then torque to 18-20 ft. lbs.; 351C and 400—tighten bolt to 18-25 ft. lbs.; 429—tighten nut until it contacts rocker shoulder, then torque to 18-22 ft. lbs.

390, 410, 428 and 1968 427

1. Position the left rocker arm and oil deflector assembly on the head, making sure the oversize bolt is installed in the second rocker arm stand from the front of the engine.

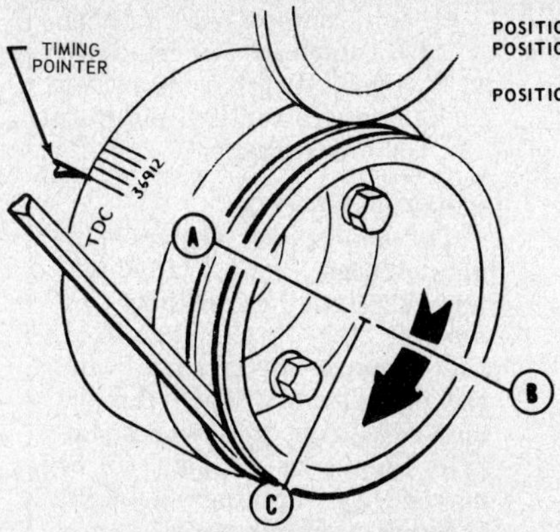
With No. 1 at TDC at end of compression stroke make a chalk mark at points B and C approximately 90 degrees apart.
TIMING POINTER
TDC
A
B
C
POSITION A – No. 1 at TDC at end of compression stroke.
POSITION B – Rotate the crankshaft 180 degrees (one half revolution) clockwise from POSITION A.
POSITION C – Rotate the crankshaft 270 degrees (three quarter revolution) clockwise from POSITION B.

Position of crankshaft for valve adjustment—302, 351, 400 and 429 V8 (© Ford Motor Co)

2. Install each rocker arm stand attaching bolt finger tight, then, working from the front of the engine back, tighten each bolt two turns at a time until the rocker arm is mounted on the head.
3. Torque the bolts to 40-45 ft. lbs.
4. Position the right rocker arm and oil deflector assembly on the head, making sure the oversize bolt is installed in the third rocker arm stand from the front of the engine.
5. Repeat Steps 2 and 3 on the right side, this time working from the rear of the engine forward.

Mechanical Adjustable Valve Adjustment—Primary Step

1. Make primary valve adjustment in the following manner, and continue to install rocker covers and fill cooling system.

NOTE: tappets must be adjusted while on the low radius of the cam.

2. If the distributor has not been disturbed and ignition timing is reasonably correct, proceed as follows: rotate crankshaft until the distributor rotor points to No. 1 plug wire tower of the distributor cap. Adjust valves in cylinder firing order according to rotor position.
3. If the distributor is out of time or has been removed from the engine: turn the crankshaft until No. 1 piston is at the top of its compression stroke, (intake valve of No. 6 cylinder just beginning to open), and the crankshaft damper is on T.D.C. Make three chalk marks on the crankshaft damper, 120° apart, starting with T.D.C. These marks will divide crankshaft travel into three parts, or six segments, of each engine cycle. Valve adjustment can then be made in firing sequence, beginning with No. 1 on T.D.C. and progressing through the regular order of firing by advancing one chalk mark, (120 crankshaft degrees) at a time.

Mechanical Adjustable Valve Adjustment—Final Step

NOTE: be sure engine is at regular operating temperature by running at least thirty minutes.

1. With engine idling, check valve clearance with a feeler gauge. Adjust clearance, if necessary, to .016 in. (hot) for both intake and exhaust.

Valve Guides

Valve guides on all engines are an integral part of the cylinder head casting. If valve guides become worn, they can be reamed oversize or bronze replacement bushings can be installed. Oversize valves are available with stem diameters .003, .015, and .030 in. larger than standard. If the guides are to be reamed more than .003 in. oversize, they must be reamed in steps starting with .003 in. and progressing until the desired diameter is achieved.

NOTE: when valve guides become worn, the excessive clearance between the valve and the head can allow the valve to tap on the cylinder head and emit a noise very similar to the noise a defective valve lifter emits. When checking the valve system to locate a noise, and the lifters are not defective and no excessive clearances exist in the valve train, the valve guides should be checked for wear.

Valve stem seal removal
(© Ford Motor Co)

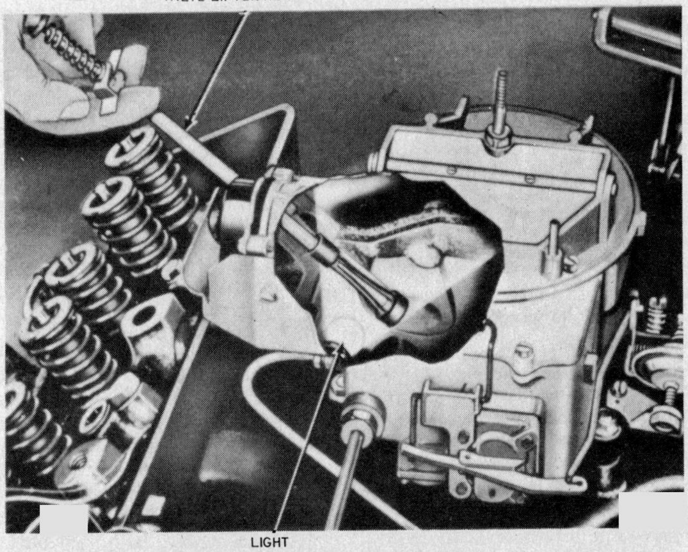
VALVE LIFTER REMOVER
LIGHT

Removing valve lifter—intake manifold installed (© Ford Motor Co)

Chilton's TIME SAVER

Frequently valves become bent or warped, or their seats become blocked with carbon or other material. Left unattended, these situations can cause burnt valves, damaged cylinder heads and other expensive trouble. To detect leaking valves early, perform this test whenever the cylinder head is removed.

1. **After removing head, replace spark plugs. Removing spark plugs before removing heads eliminates breakage.**
2. **Place head on bench with valves, springs, retainers, and keys installed—combustion chambers up.**
3. **Pour enough gasoline into each combustion chamber to completely cover both valves. Watch combustion chambers for two minutes for any leakage.**

Tappet Removal

To remove and replace tappets from 390, 410, 427 and 428 engines without removing the intake manifold, first remove rocker covers and rocker assembly. Then remove pushrods from their bores. Locate tappet or tappets to be moved by shining a light through pushrod bores. Use a magnet or claw tool to seize tappet and withdraw it through pushrod bore. It may be necessary on some tappets to move them over and draw them through a larger adjoining pushrod bore, but tappets should always be replaced in their original holes.

Cylinder Head

6-Cylinder Head Removal

1. Drain coolant and remove air cleaner. Disconnect battery cable at cylinder head.
2. Disconnect exhaust pipe at manifold.
3. Disconnect accelerator retracting spring, choke control cable and accelerator rod at carburetor.
4. Disconnect fuel line and distributor control vacuum line at the carburetor.
5. Disconnect coolant tubes from carburetor spacer. Disconnect coolant and heater hoses.
6. Disconnect distributor control vacuum line at distributor and fuel inlet line at the filter. Remove lines as an assembly.
7. On an engine equipped with positive crankcase ventilation, disconnect the emission exhaust tube.
8. Disconnect spark plug wires at the plugs and the small wire from the temperature-sending unit. On an engine equipped with a Thermactor exhaust emission control system, disconnect the air pump hose at the air manifold assembly. Unscrew the tube nuts and remove the air manifold. Disconnect the anti-backfire valve air and vacuum lines at the intake manifold. On a car equipped with power brakes, disconnect the brake vacuum line at the intake manifold.
9. Remove rocker arm cover.
10. Loosen the rocker arm stud nut so that the rocker arm can be rotated to one side. Remove valve pushrods and keep them in sequence.
11. Remove one cylinder-head bolt from each end and install two

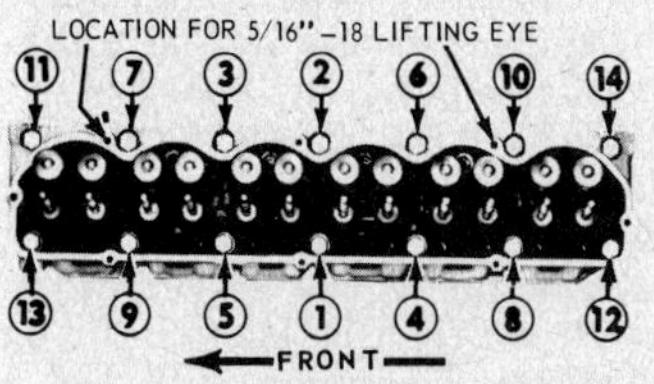

LOCATION FOR 5/16"–18 LIFTING EYE
11
7
3
2
6
10
14
13
9
5
1
4
8
12
FRONT

Cylinder head torque sequence—240 six cyl.
(© Ford Motor Co)

7/16 in. x 14 guide studs.

12. Remove remaining cylinder head bolts, then remove cylinder head.

6-Cylinder Head Installation

1. Clean head and block surfaces.
2. Apply sealer to both sides of head gasket. Position gasket over guide studs or dowel pins.

NOTE: apply gasket sealer only to steel shim head gaskets. Steel-asbestos composite head gaskets are to be installed without any sealer.

3. Install new gasket on the exhaust pipe flange.
4. Lift the cylinder head over the guide studs and slide it carefully into place while guiding the exhaust manifold studs into the exhaust pipe flange.
5. Coat cylinder-head attaching bolts with water-resistant sealer and install (but do not tighten), the head bolts.
6. Torque the head, in proper sequence, and in three progressive steps to 75 ft. lbs.
7. Lubricate both ends of the pushrods and insert them in their original bores and sockets.
8. Lubricate valve stem tips and rocker arm pads.
9. Position the rocker arms and tighten the stud nuts enough to hold the pushrods in position. Adjust valve lash, as outlined later.
10. Do a preliminary, cold, valve lash adjustment.
11. Install exhaust pipe-to-manifold nuts and lockwashers. Torque to 17-22 ft. lbs.
12. Connect radiator and heater hoses. Connect coolant tubes at the carburetor spacer.
13. Connect distributor vacuum line and the carburetor fuel line. Connect battery cable to cylinder head.
14. On engines equipped with positive crankcase ventilation, clean components thoroughly and install.

NOTE: on engines equipped with a Thermactor exhaust emission control system, install the air manifold assembly on the cylinder head. Connect the air pump outlet hose to the air manifold. Connect the anti-backfire valve, air and vacuum lines to the intake manifold.

15. Connect accelerator rod pull-back spring. Connect choke control cable and the accelerator rod at the carburetor.
16. Connect distributor control vacuum line at distributor. Connect carburetor fuel line at fuel filter.
17. Connect temperature - sending unit wire at sending unit. Connect spark plug wires.
18. Completely fill and bleed the cooling system.
19. Run engine for a minimum of 30 minutes at 1200 rpm to stabilize engine temperature. Then, check for coolant and oil leaks.
20. Adjust engine idle mixture and speed. Check valve lash and adjust, if necessary.
21. Install valve rocker arm cover, then the air cleaner.

V8 Heads, 390, 410, 427 428, Removal

1. Remove intake manifold as previously described.
2. Remove any remaining accessories.
3. Disconnect the muffler inlet pipes from the manifolds.
4. Unbolt and remove heads.

V8 Heads, 289, 302, 351, 400, 429, and 460 cu. in., Removal

1. Remove the intake manifold and carburetor as an assembly.
2. Remove rocker arm covers.
3. On cars equipped with air conditioning, isolate and remove the compressor.
4. If the left cylinder head is involved on a car with power steering, remove the steering pump and bracket and remove the drive belt. Tie assembly out of the way.
5. If the left cylinder head is involved on a car equipped with a Thermactor exhaust emission control system, disconnect the hose from the air manifold on the left cylinder head.

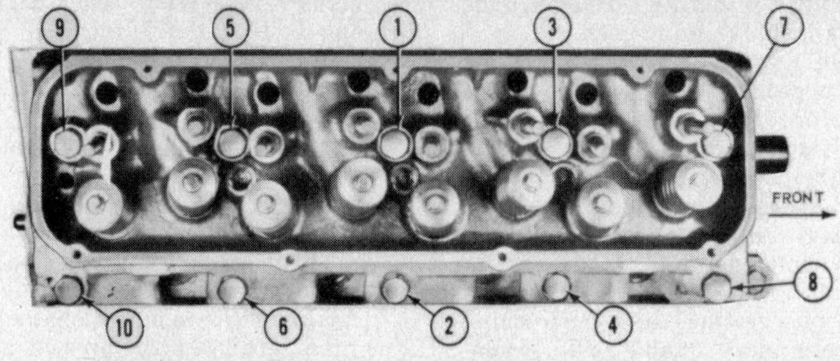
FRONT
Cylinder head torque sequence—all V8 (© Ford Motor Co)

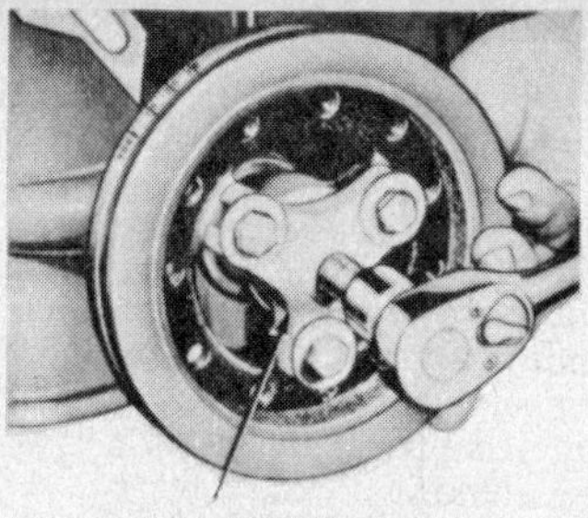
Removing crankshaft damper
(© Ford Motor Co)

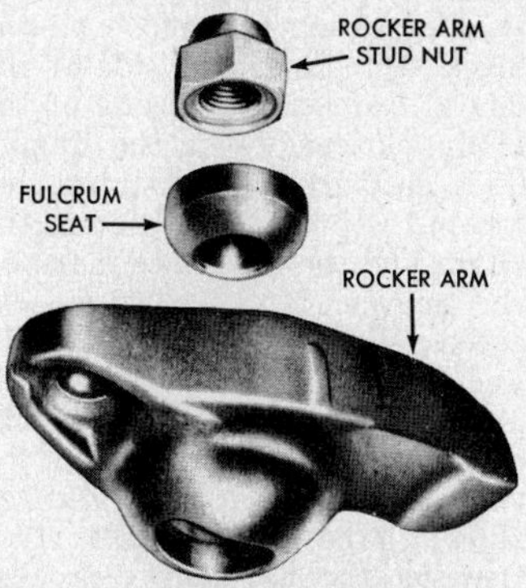
ROCKER ARM STUD NUT
FULCRUM SEAT
ROCKER ARM
Rocker arm—1967-69 6 cyl. and 289 cu. in. V8; 302 and 351W V8 similar
(© Ford Motor Co)

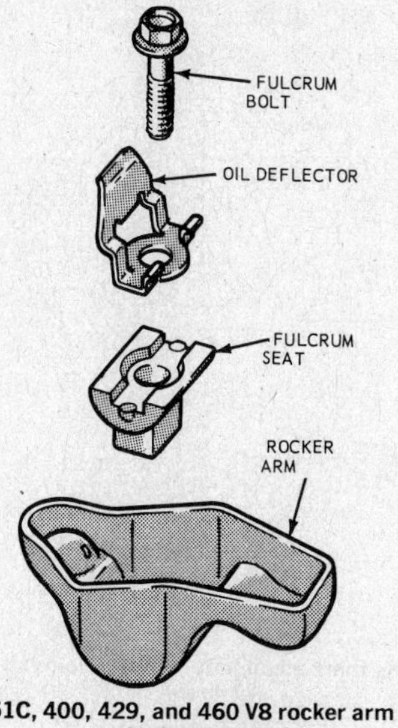
FULCRUM BOLT
OIL DEFLECTOR
FULCRUM SEAT
ROCKER ARM
351C, 400, 429, and 460 V8 rocker arm and related parts
(© Ford Motor Co)

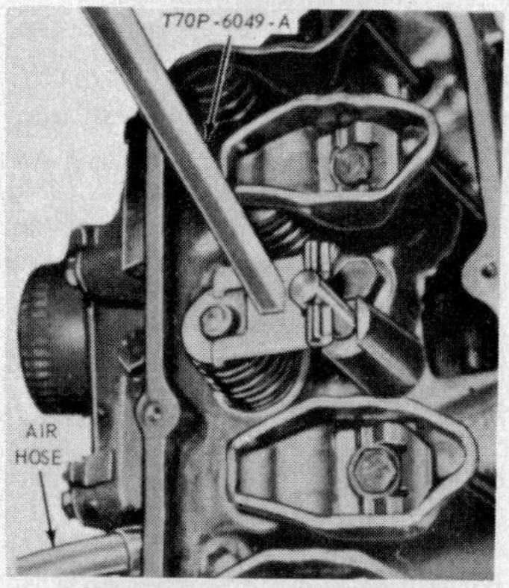
AIR HOSE
Compressing valve spring with cylinder head installed
(© Ford Motor Co)

6. If the right head is involved, remove the alternator mounting bracket bolt and spacer, ignition coil and air cleaner inlet duct from the right cylinder head.
7. If the right cylinder head is to be removed on an engine equipped with a Thermactor exhaust emission control system, remove the air pump and bracket. Disconnect the hose from the right cylinder head.
8. Disconnect the exhaust manifold/s at the exhaust pipe/s.
9. Loosen rocker arm stud nuts so that the arms can rotate to the side to clear the pushrods. Remove the pushrods. On 351 engines, remove exhaust manifold to get access to lower cylinder head bolts.
10. Remove cylinder-head bolts and lift off cylinder head.

V8 Heads Installation

Reverse above procedure, (see valve lash adjustment under Valve System, in the following paragraphs).

Timing Case

Timing Gear Cover Removal

6-Cylinder Engines

1. Drain the cooling system and the crankcase.
2. Remove the radiator from the car.
3. Loosen and remove all engine drive belts.
4. On vehicles with power steering, disconnect the pump mounting bracket from the cylinder front cover and position the pump and bracket out of the way.
5. On models with air conditioning, remove the condenser mounting bolts and position the condenser out of the way. *Do not disconnect the refrigerant lines.*
6. Disconnect and remove the fan and fan spacer.
7. Remove any accessory drive pulleys from the crankshaft damper. Remove the capscrew and washer from the crankshaft end; then, using a puller, remove the crankshaft damper.
8. Remove the alternator adjusting arm bolt and position the arm out of the way.
9. Remove the starter cable and attaching bolts, and remove the starter.
10. Remove the engine front support insulator to intermediate support bracket nuts on both supports. Remove the engine rear support insulator to crossmember bolt and insulator to transmission extension housing bolts. Raise the transmission and remove the support insulator. Lower the transmission to the crossmember.
11. Raise the engine and place 2 in. thick blocks of wood between both supports and brackets.
12. Remove the oil pan bolts, and lower the oil pan. Reach inside the oil pan and remove the two oil pump to block bolts, and lower the pump and screen into the pan. Turn the crankshaft as required to gain clearance and remove the oil pan.
13. Remove the front cover attaching bolts and remove the cover from the engine.
14. Reverse above procedure to install.

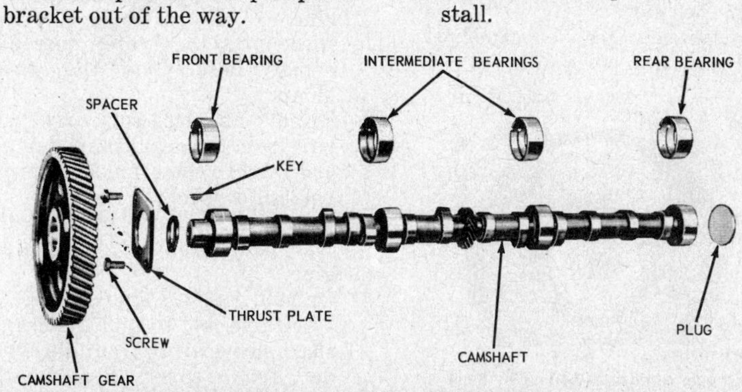
FRONT BEARING
INTERMEDIATE BEARINGS
REAR BEARING
SPACER
KEY
THRUST PLATE
SCREW
CAMSHAFT
PLUG
CAMSHAFT GEAR
Camshaft and related parts—240 cu. in. 6 cyl. (© Ford Motor Co)

Timing Gear and/or Camshaft Replacement

6-Cylinder

1. Remove the timing case cover.
2. Mark the location of the grille center support and hood lock assembly in relation to the radiator support. Remove the grille, center support, and hood lock as an assembly.
3. Remove the air cleaner and valve cover.
4. Disconnect the fuel pump outlet line and remove the fuel pump from the engine.
5. Loosen the rocker arm nuts and position the rocker arms to the side so the pushrods can be removed. Keep the pushrods in order so that they can be returned to their original location in the engine.
6. Remove the pushrod cover from the side of the engine, and, using a magnet, remove the lifters from their bores. Keep the lifters in order so they can be returned to their original location in the engine.
7. Rotate the engine until the timing marks are aligned on the timing gears.

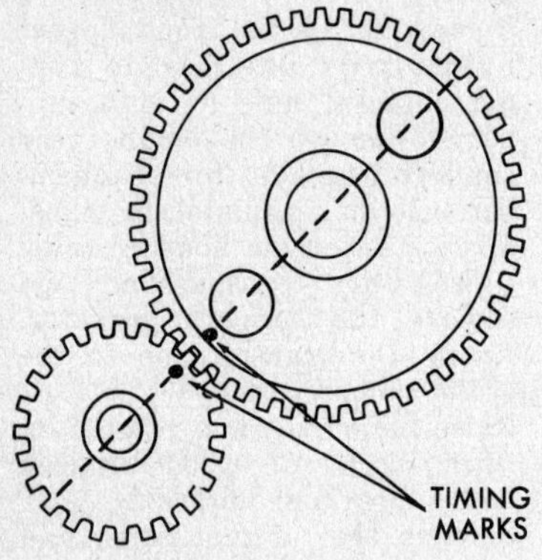
TIMING
MARKS

Timing mark alignment—240 6 cyl.

8. Remove the camshaft thrust plate screws.
9. Remove the camshaft by pulling it out the front of the engine. Use care not to damage the camshaft lobes or journals while removing the cam from the engine.
10. Place the camshaft/gear assembly in a press and press the cam from the gear.
11. Position new gear on camshaft and press into position.

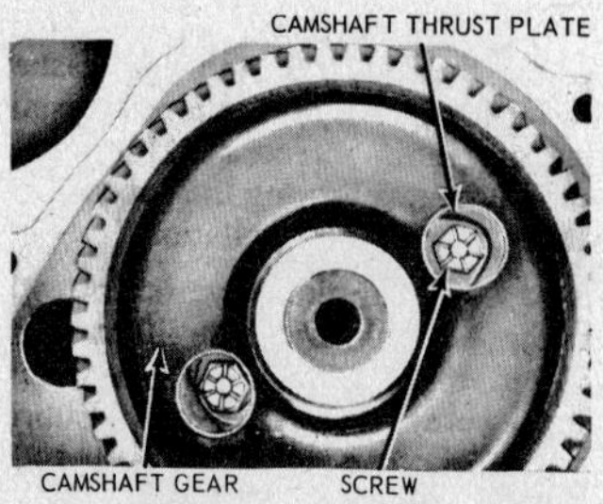
CAMSHAFT THRUST PLATE
CAMSHAFT GEAR
SCREW

Camshaft gear removal—240 cu. in. 6 cyl.
(© Ford Motor Co)

12. Using a puller, remove the crankshaft timing gear.
13. Using a suitable tool, press the new gear onto the crankshaft.
14. Before installing the camshaft in the engine, coat the lobes with Lubriplate and the journals and all valve train components with heavy oil.
15. Reverse above procedure to install, following recommended torque settings and performing preliminary valve adjustment before starting engine.

Tool–T64T-6306-A
Tool–T65L-6306-A

Camshaft gear installation—240 cu. in. 6 cyl.
(© Ford Motor Co)

V8 Cover and Chain

Removal

1. Drain the cooling system and crankcase.
2. Disconnect the negative battery cable.
3. If equipped with a fan shroud, disconnect it from the radiator and position it rearward.
4. Remove the radiator. Remove the fuel pump.
5. Remove the fan attaching bolts, remove the fan, fan spacer and shroud from the engine.
6. Loosen and remove all engine drive belts.
7. Remove the power steering pump mounting bracket and position the pump and bracket out of the way.
8. If equipped with air conditioning, remove the compressor and condenser and position them out of the way. *Do not disconnect the refrigerant lines.*
9. Disconnect the alternator adjusting arm from the engine and position it out of the way.
10. If equipped with Thermactor, remove the pump from the engine.
11. Disconnect the heater hose and bypass hose from the water pump.
12. Remove any accessory drive pulleys from the crankshaft damper and remove the crankshaft front bolt and washer.
13. Using a puller, remove the crankshaft damper from the engine.
14. On 390, 410, 427 and 428 V8, use a suitable tool to pull the crankshaft sleeve away from the cylinder front cover. Remove the sleeve from the engine.
15. Remove the front cover attaching bolts and the front oil pan bolts.
16. Remove the cover from the engine.
17. Remove the crankshaft front oil slinger.
18. To check timing chain free play, rotate the crankshaft in a clockwise direction until all slack is removed from the left side of the chain. Scribe a mark on the engine parallel to the present position of the chain. Next, rotate the crankshaft in a counterclockwise direction to remove all the slack from the right side of the chain. Force the left side of the chain outward with the fingers and measure the distance between the present position of the chain and the reference mark on the engine. If the distance exceeds ½ in., replace the chain and sprockets.
19. To replace the chain and sprockets, crank the engine until the timing marks are aligned as shown in the illustration.
20. Remove the camshaft sprocket attaching bolt and remove the chain and sprockets from the engine by sliding them forward as an assembly.

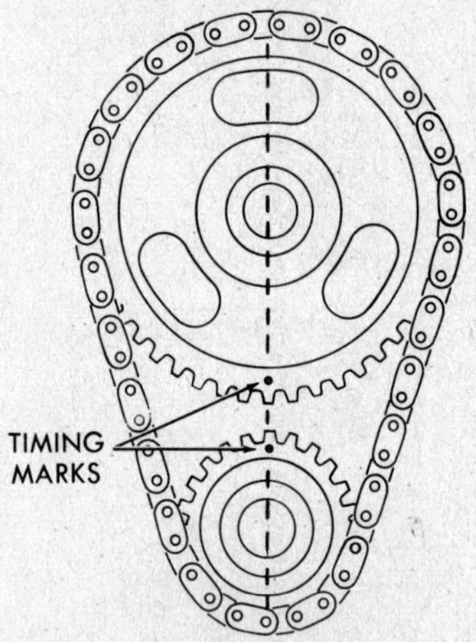
TIMING
MARKS

Timing mark alignment—V8 front mounted distributor

Installation

1. Position the chain and sprockets on the engine, making sure that the timing marks on the sprockets are aligned.
2. Clean all gasket surfaces. Trim away the exposed portion of the oil pan gasket flush with the front of the block.
3. Cut and position the required portion of a new gasket to the oil pan, applying sealer to both sides of it.
4. Reinstall the front cover, applying oil resistant sealer to the new gasket.
5. Install the components that were removed from the engine by reversing the removal procedure.

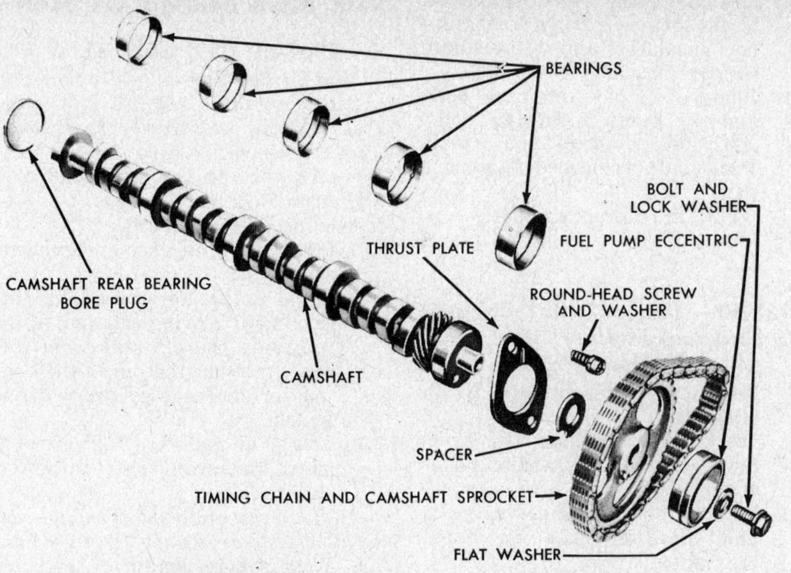
BEARINGS
BOLT AND
LOCK WASHER
FUEL PUMP ECCENTRIC
THRUST PLATE
CAMSHAFT REAR BEARING
BORE PLUG
ROUND-HEAD SCREW
AND WASHER
CAMSHAFT
SPACER
TIMING CHAIN AND CAMSHAFT SPROCKET
FLAT WASHER
V8 camshaft and related parts (© Ford Motor Co)

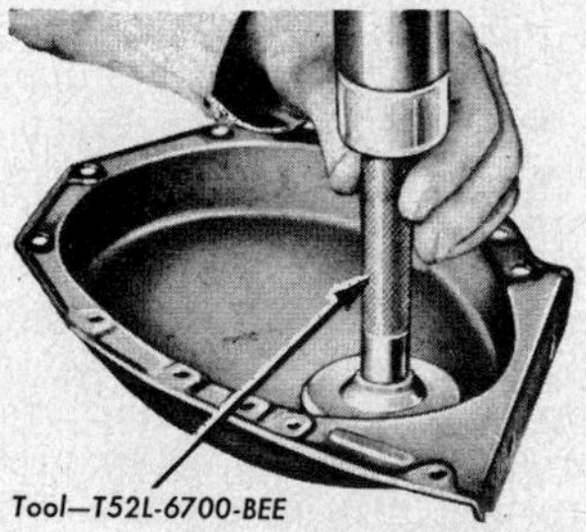
Tool—T52L-6700-BEE
Timing case oil seal installation—6 cyl. (© Ford Motor Co)

Timing Case Oil Seal Replacement

All Models

To replace the oil seal, it is necessary to take off the timing case cover and drive the seal out with a pin punch. Clean out the recess in the cover and install a new seal using a special driving tool.

Coat the new seal with grease to reduce friction when installing and starting the car.

V8 Camshaft Replacement

1. Remove the intake manifold.
2. Remove the cylinder front cover, timing chain and sprockets as outlined previously.
3. Remove the rocker arm covers.
4. On 390, 410, 427 and 428 engines it is necessary to remove the rocker arm shafts to remove the intake manifold. On all other engines with individual rocker arms, loosen the rocker arm fulcrum bolts and rotate the rocker arms to the side.
5. Remove the pushrods and lifters and keep them in order so that they can be installed in their original location.
6. Remove the camshaft thrust plate and washer if so equipped. Remove the camshaft from the front of the engine. On certain engine/chassis combinations it may be necessary to remove the grille to gain adequate clearance to remove the camshaft. Use care not to damage the camshaft lobes or journals while removing the cam from the engine.
7. Before installing the camshaft in the engine, coat the lobes with Lubriplate and the journals and all valve train components with heavy oil.
8. Reverse above procedure to install.
9. On all engines with individually mounted rocker arms, a preliminary valve adjustment must be performed before starting the engine.

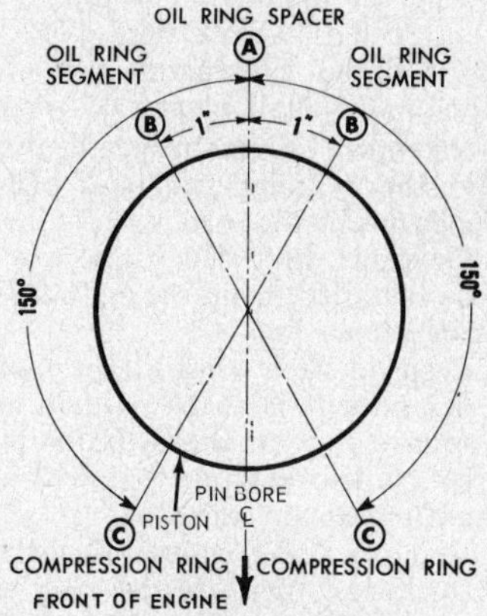
OIL RING SPACER
OIL RING
SEGMENT
OIL RING
SEGMENT
A
B
B
1"
1"
150°
150°
PIN BORE
PISTON
C
C
COMPRESSION RING
COMPRESSION RING
FRONT OF ENGINE
Piston ring spacing (© Ford Motor Co)

Connecting Rods and Pistons

Piston Ring Replacement

Each piston is fitted with 3 piston rings: an upper and lower compression ring which seals the combustion chamber of the engine so that the expanding gases of the power stroke do not escape, and an oil control ring which prevents cylinder wall lubricating oil from entering the combustion chamber. Due to the great amount of pressure and high temperature present in the piston area dur-

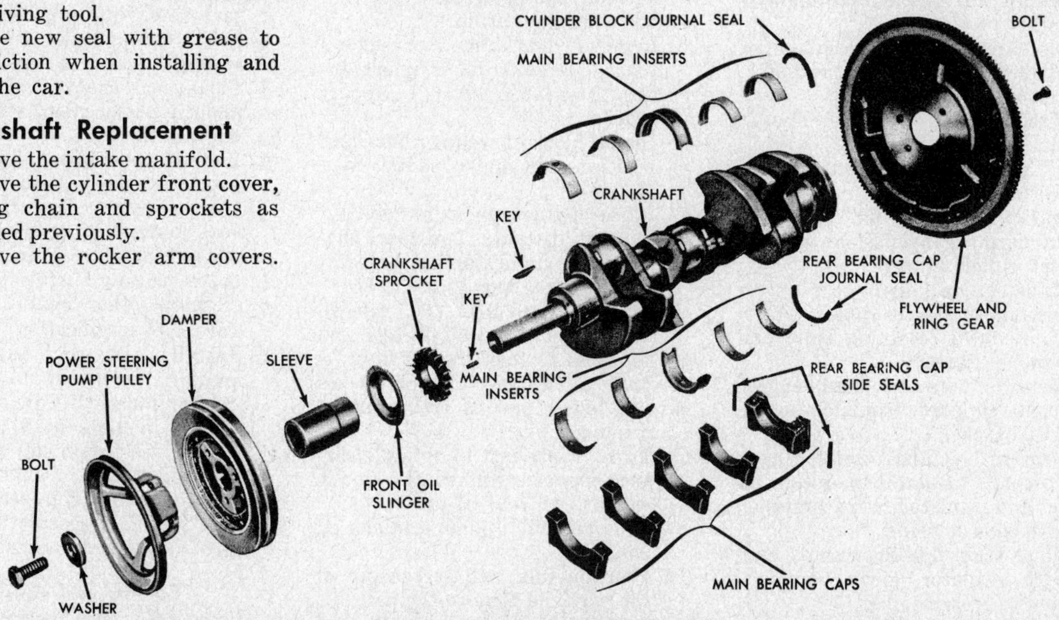
CYLINDER BLOCK JOURNAL SEAL
BOLT
MAIN BEARING INSERTS
CRANKSHAFT
KEY
CRANKSHAFT
SPROCKET
KEY
REAR BEARING CAP
JOURNAL SEAL
FLYWHEEL AND
RING GEAR
DAMPER
POWER STEERING
PUMP PULLEY
SLEEVE
MAIN BEARING
INSERTS
REAR BEARING CAP
SIDE SEALS
BOLT
FRONT OIL
SLINGER
WASHER
MAIN BEARING CAPS
V8 crankshaft and related parts (© Ford Motor Co)

ing combustion, piston ring clearances are very critical. Before replacing piston rings, piston and cylinder wall dimensions must first be checked; for even new piston rings cannot seal a piston or cylinder wall that is worn beyond specifications.

1. Using an internal micrometer, measure cylinder wall taper and out-of-roundness.
2. Measure piston outside diameter and subtract this measurement from the cylinder bore diameter obtained in above step. The result of this subtraction will give piston to wall clearance which also must be within specification.
3. If the cylinder wall and piston measurements are within specifications, and new rings are to be installed, hone the cylinder to the proper finish.
4. Position each ring in the cylinder bore it is to be used in and square it with the cylinder wall by gently pushing it downward with an inverted piston.
5. Using a feeler gauge of correct thickness, measure the ring end gap. If it exceeds specifications, try another ring, if it is less than specifications file the end of the ring to correct.
6. Install the rings on the pistons and measure piston ring-to-piston side clearance.

NOTE: before installing piston rings, the ring grooves on the piston should be thoroughly cleaned of all foreign material.

7. Space ring gaps on piston as shown in illustration.

Engine Lubrication

Oil Pan Removal

1967-72—6 Cylinder All

1. Drain crankcase and cooling system.
2. Disconnect upper hose at outlet elbow and lower hose at radiator. Remove radiator.
3. Disconnect flexible fuel line at fuel pump.
4. With automatic transmission, disconnect kickdown rod at bellcrank assembly. On car with standard transmission, disconnect clutch linkage.
5. Raise car on hoist.
6. Disconnect starter cable at starter. Remove retaining bolts and remove starter.
7. Remove nuts on both engine front support insulator-to-support bracket.
8. Remove bolt and insulator, rear support insulator-to-crossmember and insulator-to-transmission extension housing.
9. Raise transmission, remove support insulator, lower transmission to crossmember.
10. Raise engine with transmission jack and place 3-in. thick wood blocks between both front support insulators and intermediate support brackets.
11. Remove oil pan retaining bolts and oil pump mounting bolts. With oil pump in pan, rotate crankshaft as needed to remove pan.
12. Install in reverse of above.

1967-69—289, 302, 351 Cu. In. V8 Ford and Mercury, 1967 390, 428 Thunderbird

1. Remove oil level dipstick. Drain oil pan.
2. Disconnect stabilizer bar from lower control arms, and pull ends down.
3. Remove oil pan attaching bolts and position pan on front cross-member.
4. Remove one oil inlet tube bolt and loosen the other to position tube out of way to remove pan.
5. Turn crankshaft as required for clearance to remove pan.
6. Install in reverse of above.

1967-74 All V8s Except Those Listed in Above Procedure

1. Raise car and place safety stands in position. Drain oil from crankcase. On 429 V8s, disconnect the negative battery cable. On 1970–71 429 V8s, remove bolt attaching vacuum line retaining clip to upper right side of converter housing.
2. Disconnect stabilizer bar links and pull ends down. On models equipped with a fan shroud, remove the shroud from the radiator and position it rearward over the fan. On automatic transmission equipped cars, position oil cooler lines aside.
3. Remove nuts and lockwashers from engine front support insulator-to-intermediate support bracket.
4. Install block of wood on jack and position jack under leading edge of pan.
5. Raise engine approximately 1¼ in. and insert a 1-in. block between insulators and crossmember. Remove floor jack. On 351C, 400, 429, and 460 V8s, remove the starter. On 1972-74 429 and 460 V8s remove the oil filter.
6. Remove oil pan attaching screws and lower pan to frame crossmember.
7. Turn crankshaft to obtain clearance between crankshaft counterweight and rear of pan.
8. Remove oil pump attaching bolts.
9. Position tube and screen out of the way and remove the pan.
10. Install in reverse of above.

Rear Main Bearing Oil Seal

1967-69 289, 302, 351W

NOTE: the rear oil seal originally installed in these engines is a rope (fabric) type seal. However, all service replacements are of the rubber type. To remove the rope type seal and install the rubber type, the following procedure is used.

1. Drain the crankcase and remove the oil pan.
2. Remove the lower half of the rear main bearing cap and, after removing the old seal from the cap, drive out the pin in the bottom of the seal groove with a punch.
3. Loosen all main bearing caps and allow the crankshaft to lower slightly.

NOTE: the crankshaft should not be allowed to drop more than 1/32 in.

4. With a 6 in. length of 3/16 in. brazing rod, drive up on either exposed end of the top half of the oil seal. When the opposite end of the seal starts to protrude, have a helper grasp it with pliers and gently pull while the driven end is being tapped.
5. After removing both halves of the rope seal and the retaining pin from the lower half of the bearing cap, follow steps four through 10 of the below procedure for 1970-74 engines to install the rubber seal.

1967-69 390, 410, 427, 428 and All 1970-74

NOTE: the rear oil seal installed in these engines is a rubber type seal.

1. Loosen all main bearing cap bolts, lowering crankshaft slightly but not more than 1/32 in.
2. Remove rear main cap, and remove upper and lower halves of seal. On block half of seal, use seal removing tool or insert a small metal screw into end of seal with which to draw it out.
3. Clean seal grooves with solvent and dip replacement seal in clean engine oil.
4. Install upper seal half in its groove in block with lip toward front of engine by rotating it on seal journal of crankshaft until approximately 3/8 in. protrudes below parting surface.
5. Tighten other main caps and torque to specification.
6. Install lower seal half in rear main cap with lip to front and approximately 3/8 in. of seal protrudes to mate with upper seal.
7. Install rear main cap and torque.
8. Dip side seals in engine oil and install them. Tap seals in last half inch if necessary. Do not cut protruding ends of seals.

1967-69 6-Cylinder

If the rear main bearing oil seal

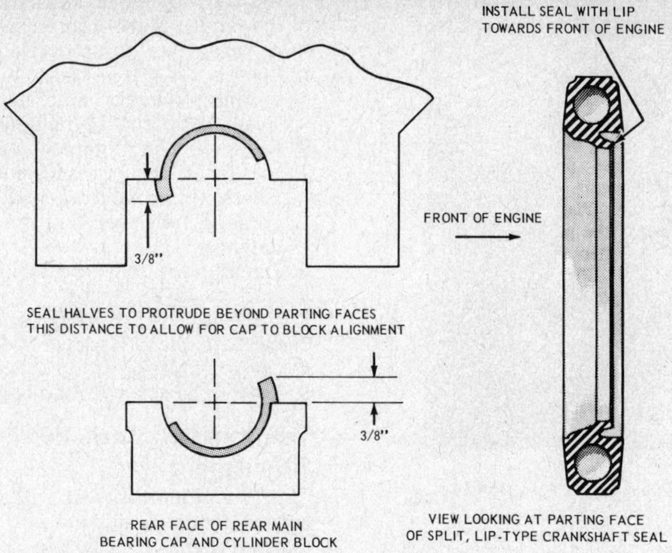
INSTALL SEAL WITH LIP
TOWARDS FRONT OF ENGINE
3/8"
FRONT OF ENGINE
SEAL HALVES TO PROTRUDE BEYOND PARTING FACES
THIS DISTANCE TO ALLOW FOR CAP TO BLOCK ALIGNMENT
3/8"
REAR FACE OF REAR MAIN
BEARING CAP AND CYLINDER BLOCK
VIEW LOOKING AT PARTING FACE
OF SPLIT, LIP-TYPE CRANKSHAFT SEAL

Installing split-lip type rear main oil seal (© Ford Motor Co)

is the only operation involved, it can be replaced in the car according to the following procedure.

NOTE: if the oil seal is being replaced in conjunction with a rear main bearing replacement, the engine must be removed from the car.

1. Remove the starter.
2. On cars equipped with automatic transmissions, remove the transmission. On cars equipped with manual shift transmissions, remove the transmission, clutch, flywheel and engine rear cover plate.
3. With an awl, punch holes in the main bearing oil seal, on opposite sides of the crankshaft and just above the bearing cap to cylinder block split line. Insert a sheet metal screw in each hole. With two large screwdrivers, pry the oil seal out.
4. Clean the oil recess in the cylinder block, main bearing cap and the crankshaft sealing surface.
5. Lubricate the entire oil seal. Then, install and drive the seal into its seat .005 in. below the face of the cylinder block with tool T-65L-6701-A.
6. The remaining procedure is the reverse of removal.

CLUTCH

Clutch Pedal Adjustment

1. Disconnect the clutch return spring from the release lever.
2. Loosen the release lever adjusting nut and locknut.
3. Move the clutch release lever rearward until the throwout bearing can be felt to lightly contact the pressure plate fingers.
4. Adjust the rod length until the rod seats in the pocket in the release lever.
5. Insert a feeler gauge of specified thickness between the adjusting nut and swivel sleeve. Tighten the nut against the feeler gauge. Correct feeler gauge thicknesses are: 1967—0.206 in., 1968—0.120 in., 1969-71—0.194 in.
6. Tighten the locknut against the adjusting nut, being careful not to disturb the adjustment.
7. Connect the clutch return spring.
8. Make a final check with the engine running at 3000 rpm, and transmission in neutral. Under this condition, centrifugal weights on release fingers may reduce the clearance. Readjust, if necessary, to obtain at least ½in. free-play while maintaining the 3000 rpm to prevent fingers contacting release bearing. This is important.

Clutch and/or Transmission R & R

1. Raise the vehicle on a hoist.
2. Disconnect the driveshaft from the rear U-joint flange and slide the front yoke from the transmission.
3. Insert a cap or rag in the transmission extension housing to prevent fluid leakage.
4. Disconnect the speedometer cable and shifter linkage from the transmission. On models with a four-speed transmission, remove the shifter mounting bracket from the extension housing.
5. On models with a three-speed transmission, disconnect the transmission mount from the crossmember. If equipped with a four-speed transmission, remove the front parking brake cable from the crossmember and remove the crossmember from the car.
6. Remove the bolts that mount the transmission to the bellhousing. On 429 V8s, the upper left-hand transmission attaching bolt is a seal bolt. Carefully note its location so that it may be returned to its original position.
7. Move the transmission rearward until the input shaft clears the bellhousing and lower it from the car.
8. Disconnect the clutch release lever return spring.
9. If equipped with a one-piece aluminum bellhousing, remove the starter and remove the bellhousing from the engine. If equipped with a cast iron bellhousing, remove only the inspection cover from the bottom of the bellhousing.
10. Loosen the 6 pressure plate attaching bolts evenly to release spring pressure, and remove the clutch assembly from the car.
11. To install, position clutch assembly on flywheel and install each pressure plate attaching bolt finger tight.
12. Insert a transmission pilot shaft or other suitable tool to align the clutch disc with the flywheel and alternately tighten the pressure plate attaching bolts until the plate is secured to the flywheel.
13. Reverse above procedure to install transmission and driveshaft.

MANUAL TRANSMISSION

Manual Transmission Linkage Adjustment

Column Mounted

1. Place the gear shift lever in the Neutral position.
2. Loosen the two gear shift adjustment nuts on the shift linkage.
3. Insert a 3/16 in. alignment tool through the first and reverse lever, the second and third gear shift lever, and the two holes in the lower casing. An alignment tool can be fabricated from 3/16 in. rod bent to an L shape. The extension that is to be inserted into the levers should be 1 in. in length from the elbow.
4. Manipulate the levers so the alignment tool will move freely through the alignment holes.
5. Tighten the two gear shift rod adjustment nuts.
6. Remove the tool and check linkage operation.

Floor Mounted

1. Place hand shifter lever in neutral position, then raise car on a hoist.
2. Insert a ¼ in. rod into the alignment holes of the shift levers.
3. If the holes are not in exact alignment, check for bent connecting

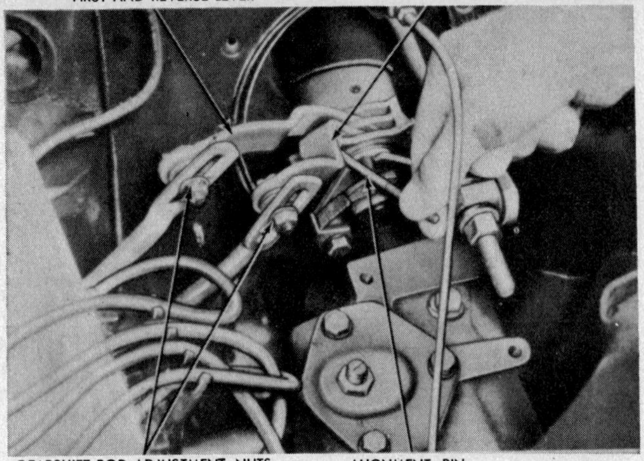
FIRST AND REVERSE LEVER
SECOND AND THIRD LEVER
GEARSHIFT ROD ADJUSTMENT NUTS
ALIGNMENT PIN

Gearshift linkage adjustment 3-speed transmission (© Ford Motor Co)

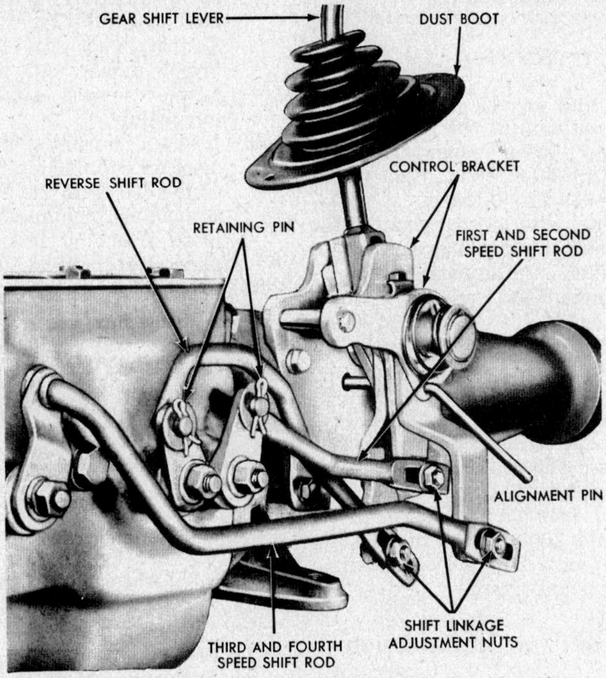
GEAR SHIFT LEVER
DUST BOOT
CONTROL BRACKET
REVERSE SHIFT ROD
RETAINING PIN
FIRST AND SECOND SPEED SHIFT ROD
ALIGNMENT PIN
SHIFT LINKAGE ADJUSTMENT NUTS
THIRD AND FOURTH SPEED SHIFT ROD

Adjusting shift linkage, 4-speed transmission (© Ford Motor Co)

rods or loose lever locknuts at the rod ends. Make replacements or repairs, then adjust as follows.

4. Loosen the three rod-to-lever retaining locknuts and move the levers until the 1/4 in. gauge rod will enter the alignment holes. Be sure that the transmission shift levers are in neutral, and the reverse shifter lever is in the neutral detent.
5. Install shift rods and torque locknuts to 18–23 ft. lbs.
6. Remove the 1/4 in. gauge rod.
7. Operate the shift levers to assure correct shifting.
8. Lower the car and road-test.

Transmission Lock Rod Adjustment

1970 and later models with floor or console mounted shifters and manual transmissions incorporate a transmission lock rod which prevents the shifter from being moved from the reverse position when the ignition lock is in the OFF position. The lock rod connects the shift tube in the steering column to the transmission reverse lever. The lock rod cannot be properly adjusted until the manual linkage adjustment is correct.

1. With the transmission selector lever in the neutral position, loosen the lock rod adjustment nut on the transmission reverse lever.
2. Insert a .180 in. diameter rod (No. 15 drill bit) in the gauge pin hole located at the 6 o'clock position on the steering column socket casting, directly below the ignition lock.
3. Manipulate the pin until the casting will not move with the pin inserted.
4. Torque the lock rod adjustment nut to 10-20 ft. lbs.
5. Remove the pin and check the linkage operation.

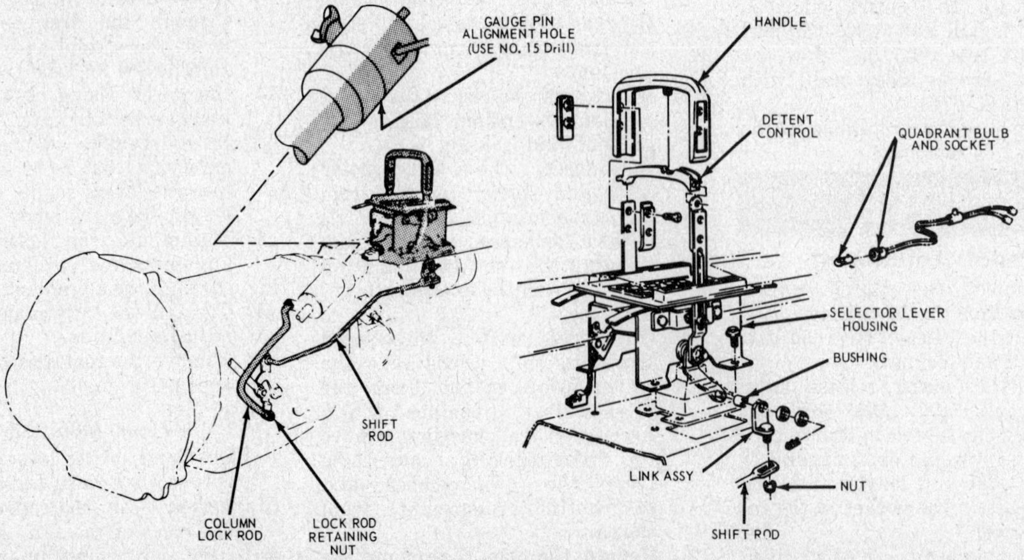
GAUGE PIN ALIGNMENT HOLE (USE NO. 15 Drill)
HANDLE
DETENT CONTROL
QUADRANT BULB AND SOCKET
SELECTOR LEVER HOUSING
BUSHING
SHIFT ROD
LINK ASSY
NUT
COLUMN LOCK ROD
LOCK ROD RETAINING NUT
SHIFT ROD

Floor mounted automatic transmission linkage (© Ford Motor Co)

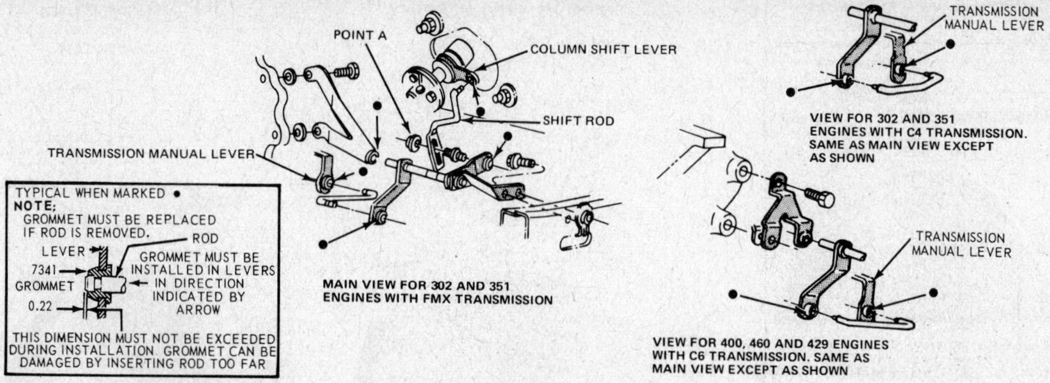
POINT A
COLUMN SHIFT LEVER
SHIFT ROD
TRANSMISSION MANUAL LEVER
TYPICAL WHEN MARKED •
NOTE;
GROMMET MUST BE REPLACED IF ROD IS REMOVED.
ROD
LEVER
7341
GROMMET
0.22
GROMMET MUST BE INSTALLED IN LEVERS IN DIRECTION INDICATED BY ARROW
THIS DIMENSION MUST NOT BE EXCEEDED DURING INSTALLATION. GROMMET CAN BE DAMAGED BY INSERTING ROD TOO FAR
MAIN VIEW FOR 302 AND 351 ENGINES WITH FMX TRANSMISSION
TRANSMISSION MANUAL LEVER
VIEW FOR 302 AND 351 ENGINES WITH C4 TRANSMISSION. SAME AS MAIN VIEW EXCEPT AS SHOWN
TRANSMISSION MANUAL LEVER
VIEW FOR 400, 460 AND 429 ENGINES WITH C6 TRANSMISSION. SAME AS MAIN VIEW EXCEPT AS SHOWN

1971-74 Ford and Mercury column shift manual linkage (© Ford Motor Co)

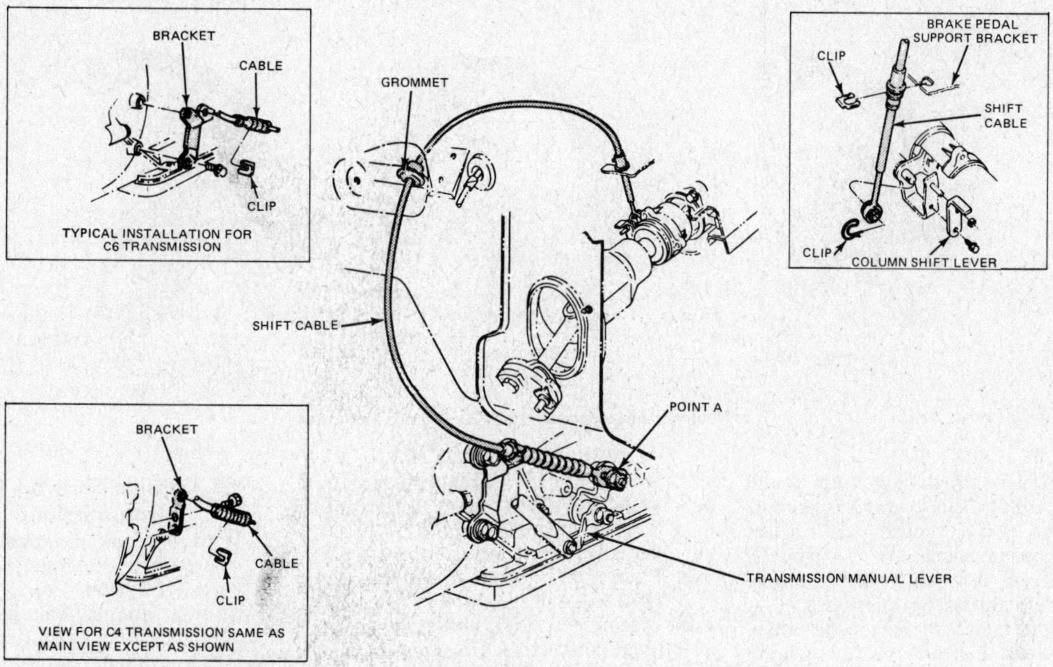
BRACKET
CABLE
CLIP
TYPICAL INSTALLATION FOR C6 TRANSMISSION
GROMMET
BRAKE PEDAL SUPPORT BRACKET
CLIP
SHIFT CABLE
CLIP
COLUMN SHIFT LEVER
SHIFT CABLE
POINT A
BRACKET
CABLE
CLIP
VIEW FOR C4 TRANSMISSION SAME AS MAIN VIEW EXCEPT AS SHOWN
TRANSMISSION MANUAL LEVER

1972-74 Thunderbird column shift manual linkage (© Ford Motor Co)

AUTOMATIC TRANSMISSION

Manual Linkage Adjustment

1. With engine off, loosen clamp at shift lever so shift rod is free to slide.

   On models with a shift cable, remove the nut from the transmission manual lever and disconnect the cable from the transmission.
2. Position selector lever in D1 position (large green dot) on dual range transmissions. On select shift transmission (P R N D 2 1) position lever in D position tightly against the D stop.
3. Shift lever at transmission into D1 detent position on dual range transmissions or into D position on select shift transmissions.

NOTE: D1 position is second from rear on all dual range transmissions.

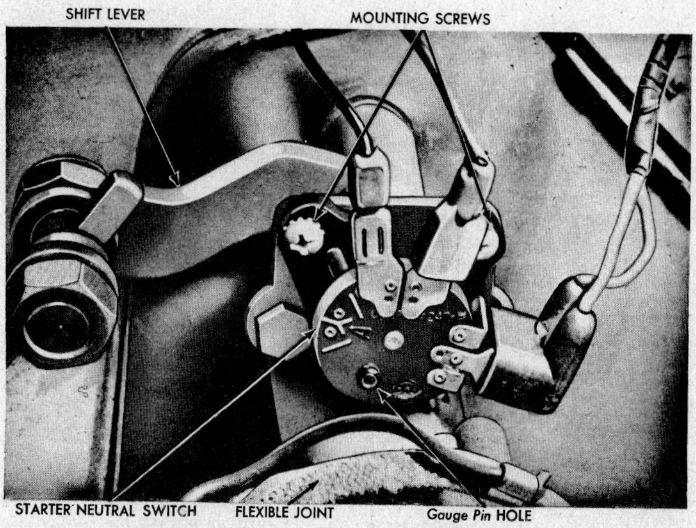
SHIFT LEVER
MOUNTING SCREWS
STARTER NEUTRAL SWITCH
FLEXIBLE JOINT
Gauge Pin HOLE

Neutral start switch—column-mounted C4 and C6 1967 (© Ford Motor Co)

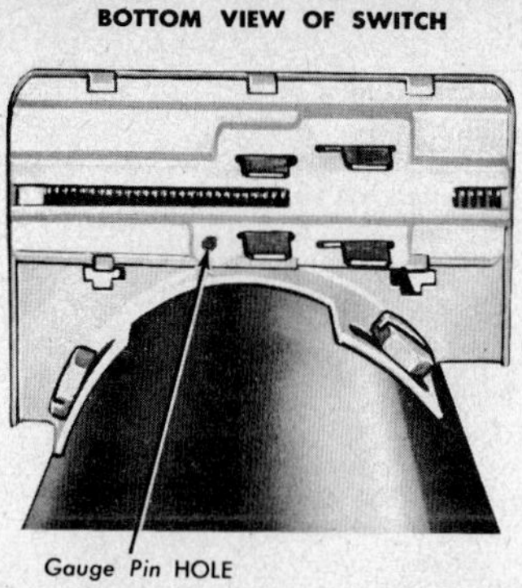
BOTTOM VIEW OF SWITCH
Gauge Pin HOLE

Neutral start switch—1967 Ford and Mercury with C6 Column Shift (© Ford Motor Co)

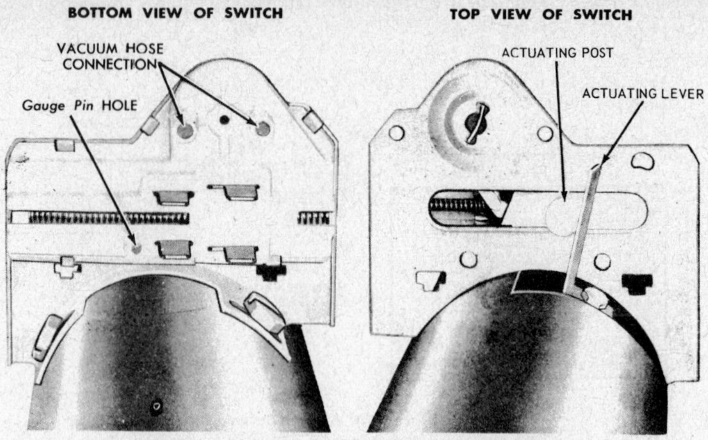
BOTTOM VIEW OF SWITCH
TOP VIEW OF SWITCH
VACUUM HOSE CONNECTION
Gauge Pin HOLE
ACTUATING POST
ACTUATING LEVER

Neutral start switch—1967 T-Bird (© Ford Motor Co)

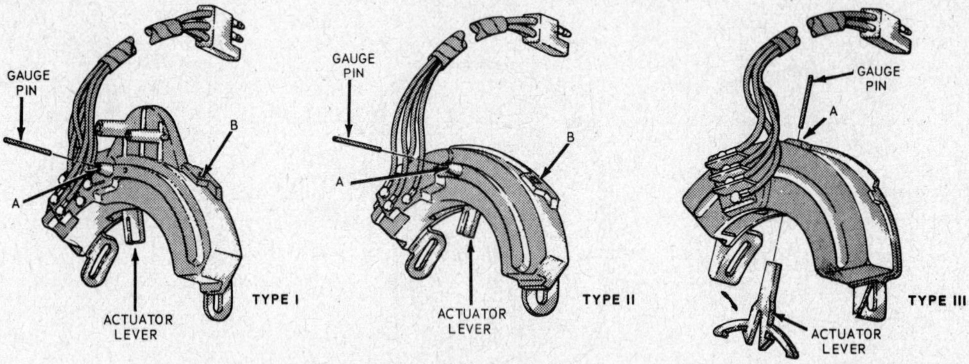
GAUGE PIN
A
B
ACTUATOR LEVER
TYPE I
TYPE II
TYPE III

Neutral start switches—1968-70 (© Ford Motor Co)

D position is third from rear on all column shift select shift transmissions and 1967-68 console shift select shift transmissions. D position is fourth from rear on 1969-72 console shift select shift transmissions.

4. Tighten clamp and torque nut to 8-13 ft. lbs. on 1967-68 column shifts and 10–20 ft. lbs. on 1969-74 column shifts. Torque 1967-68 console shift nuts to 20–25 ft. lbs. and 1969–72 console shift nuts to 10–20 ft. lbs.

Neutral Start Switch Adjustment

1967 Column Shift Cruise-O-Matics and All 1967 Console Shifts

1. With manual linkage properly adjusted, try to engage starter in each position on quadrant.

Starter should engage only in Park and Neutral positions.

2. To adjust, loosen screws that locate switch on steering column.
3. Place shift lever in neutral detent.
4. Rotate switch until gauge pin (No. 43 drill) can be inserted in gauge pin hole a full 31/64 in.
5. Tighten down locating screws and check starter engagement in each position as in Step 1.

Column Shift 1968-71

1. With manual linkage properly adjusted, try to engage starter in each position on quadrant. Starter should engage only in neutral or park position.
2. Place shift lever in neutral detent.
3. Disconnect start switch wires at plug connector. Disconnect vacuum hoses, if any. Remove screws securing neutral start switch to steering column and remove switch. Remove actuator lever along with Type III switches.
4. With switch wires facing up, move actuator lever fully to the left and insert gauge pin (No. 43 drill) into gauge pin hole at point A. See accompanying figure. On Type III switch, be sure gauge pin is inserted a full ½ in.
5. With pin in place, move actuator lever to right until positive stop is engaged.
6. On Type I and Type II switches, remove gauge pin and insert it at point B. On Type III switches, remove gauge pin, align two holes in switch at point A and reinstall gauge pin.
7. Reinstall switch on steering column. Be sure shift lever is engaged in neutral detent.
8. Connect switch wires and vacuum hoses and remove gauge pin.
9. Check starter engagement as in Step 1.

1967 Console Shift C4 and C6 Transmissions

1. With manual linkage properly adjusted, try to engage starter in each position on quadrant. Starter should engage only in Neutral or Park position.
2. Remove handle from shift lever and chrome trim panel from top of console.
3. Place lever in Neutral, remove quadrant retaining screws and indicator light, and lift quadrant from console.
4. Loosen switch attaching screws, and move shift lever back and forth until gauge pin (No. 43 drill) can be inserted into gauge pin holes.
5. Place shift lever in neutral position, and slide switch back and forward until switch actuating lever contacts shift lever.
6. Reassemble shift quadrant in console.
7. Check starter engagement as in Step 1.

Console Shift 1968-71

1. With manual linkage properly adjusted, try to engage starter at each position on quadrant. Starter should engage only in Neutral and Park positions.
2. Remove shift handle from shift lever, and console from vehicle.
3. Loosen switch attaching screws, and move shift lever back and

forward until gauge pin (No. 43 drill) can be inserted fully.
4. Place shift lever firmly against neutral detent stop and slide switch back and forward until switch lever contacts shift lever.
5. Tighten switch attaching screws, and check starter engagement as in Step 1.
6. Reinstall console and shift linkage.

Column Shift 1972-74

1972–74 models which are equipped with a column mounted shift lever are not equipped with neutral start switch. Instead, an ignition lock cylinder-to-shift lever interlock prevents these models from being started in any gear other than Park or Neutral.

Lock Rod Adjustment

From 1970–71, all models with a floor or console mounted selector lever incorporated a transmission lock rod to prevent the transmission selector from being moved out of the Park position when the ignition lock is in the Off position. The lock rod connects the shift tube in the steering column to the transmission manual lever. The lock rod cannot be properly adjusted until the manual linkage adjustment is correct.

1. With the transmission selector lever in the Drive position, loosen the lock rod adjustment nut on the transmission manual lever.
2. Insert a .180 in. diameter rod (No. 15 drill bit) in the gauge pin hole in the steering column socket casting, it is located at the 6 o'clock position directly below the ignition lock.
3. Manipulate the pin so that the casting will not move when the pin is fully inserted.
4. Torque the lock rod adjustment nut to 10-20 ft. lbs.
5. Remove the pin and check the linkage operation.

Throttle Linkage Adjustments

All 1967-68 Throttle and Downshift Linkage

1. Apply the parking brake and place selector lever in N.
2. Run engine at fast idle until it reaches normal operating temperature. Then, slow it down to normal idle.
3. Connect a tachometer to the engine.
4. Adjust engine to specified idle speed with selector in D1 or D2. Due to the vacuum parking brake release (if so equipped), the parking brake will not hold while selector is in D1 or D2. Keep service brake applied.
5. When satisfied that idle speed is correct, stop engine and adjust dashpot clearance. Check clearance between dashpot plunger and throttle lever.
6. With engine stopped, disconnect carburetor return spring from throttle lever and loosen accelerator cable conduit attaching clamp.
7. With accelerator pedal to floor and throttle lever wide open, slide cable conduit to rear (to left on six cylinder engine) to remove slack from cable. Tighten clamp.
8. Disconnect downshift lever return spring and hold throttle lever wide open. Depress downshift rod to "through detent stop". Set downshift lever adjusting screw against throttle lever.
9. Connect carburetor return spring and downshift lever return spring.

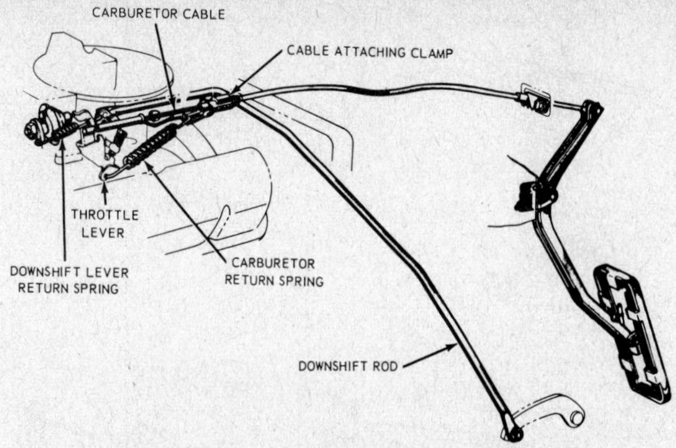
CARBURETOR CABLE
CABLE ATTACHING CLAMP
THROTTLE LEVER
DOWNSHIFT LEVER RETURN SPRING
CARBURETOR RETURN SPRING
DOWNSHIFT ROD

Throttle linkage—V8 1967-69 (© Ford Motor Co)

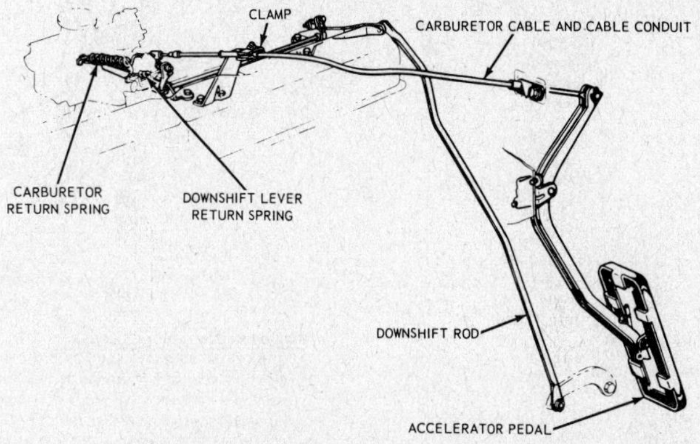
CLAMP
CARBURETOR CABLE AND CABLE CONDUIT
CARBURETOR RETURN SPRING
DOWNSHIFT LEVER RETURN SPRING
DOWNSHIFT ROD
ACCELERATOR PEDAL

Throttle linkage—6 cyl. 1967-69 (© Ford Motor Co)

All Beginning 1969

1. Disconnect downshift lever return spring.
2. Hold throttle shaft lever wide open, and hold downshift rod against "through detent stop".
3. Adjust downshift screw to provide 0.050-0.070 in. clearance between screw and throttle shaft lever on 1969–72 models and 0.010-0.080 in. on 1973-74 models. On 240 cu. in. engine, tighten locknut.
4. Connect downshift lever return spring.

C-4 Band Adjustment

Intermediate Band

1. Clean all the dirt from the adjusting screw and remove and discard the locknut.
2. Install a new locknut on the adjusting screw using a torque wrench, tighten the adjusting screw to 10 ft lbs.
3. Back off the adjusting screw *exactly 1¾ turns.*
4. Hold the adjusting screw steady and tighten the locknut to the proper torque.

Low-Reverse Band

1. Clean all dirt from around the band adjusting screw, and remove and discard the locknut.
2. Install a new locknut of the adjusting screw. Using a torque wrench, tighten the adjusting screw to 10 ft lbs.
3. Back off the adjusting screw *exactly three full turns.*
4. Hold the adjusting screw steady and tighten the locknut to the proper torque.

C-6 Band Adjustment

Intermediate Band Adjustment

1. Raise the car on a hoist or place it on jack stands.
2. Clean the threads of the intermediate band adjusting screw.
3. Loosen the adjustment screw locknut.

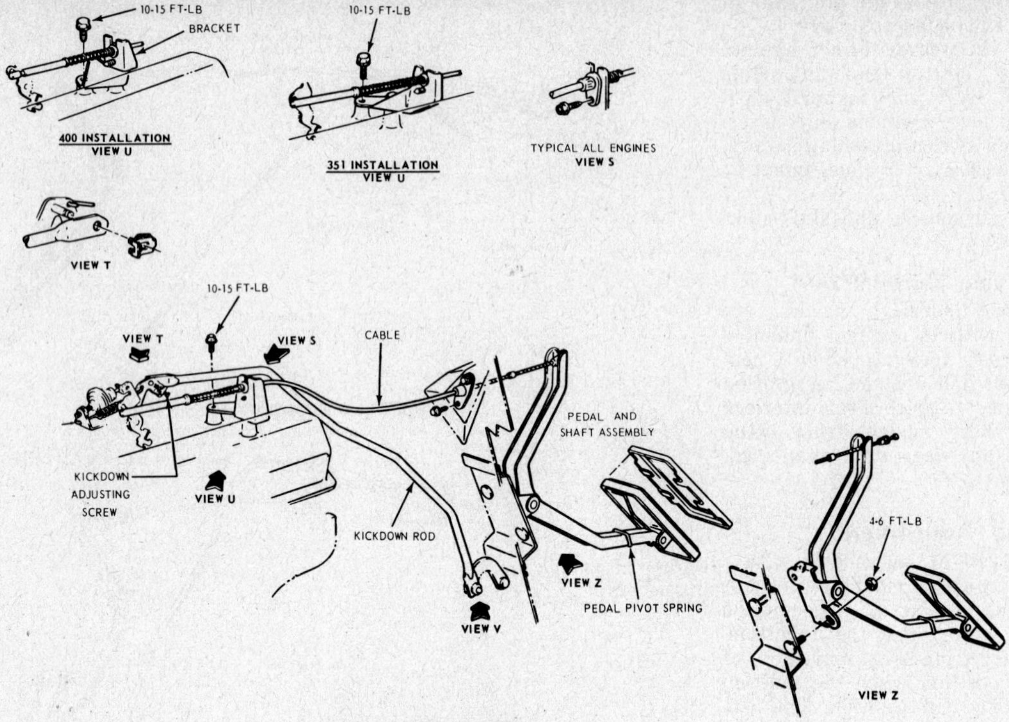
10-15 FT-LB
BRACKET
400 INSTALLATION
VIEW U
10-15 FT-LB
351 INSTALLATION
VIEW U
TYPICAL ALL ENGINES
VIEW S
VIEW T
10-15 FT-LB
VIEW T
VIEW S
CABLE
PEDAL AND
SHAFT ASSEMBLY
KICKDOWN
ADJUSTING
SCREW
VIEW U
KICKDOWN ROD
4-6 FT-LB
VIEW Z
PEDAL PIVOT SPRING
VIEW V
VIEW Z

KICK-DOWN CONTROL ADJUSTMENT

A. WITH THE CARBURETOR HELD AT W.O.T. POSITION AND THE KICKDOWN ROD HELD DOWNWARD AGAINST THE "THROUGH DETENT" STOP, ADJUST THE KICKDOWN LEVER ADJUSTING SCREW ON CARBURETOR TO OBTAIN .01 TO .08 CLEARANCE BETWEEN ADJUSTING SCREW AND THROTTLE ARM SHAFT LEVER TAB.

B. RETURN SYSTEM TO IDLE–NEUTRAL

1973-74 Ford and Mercury throttle/downshift linkage adjustment (© Ford Motor Co)

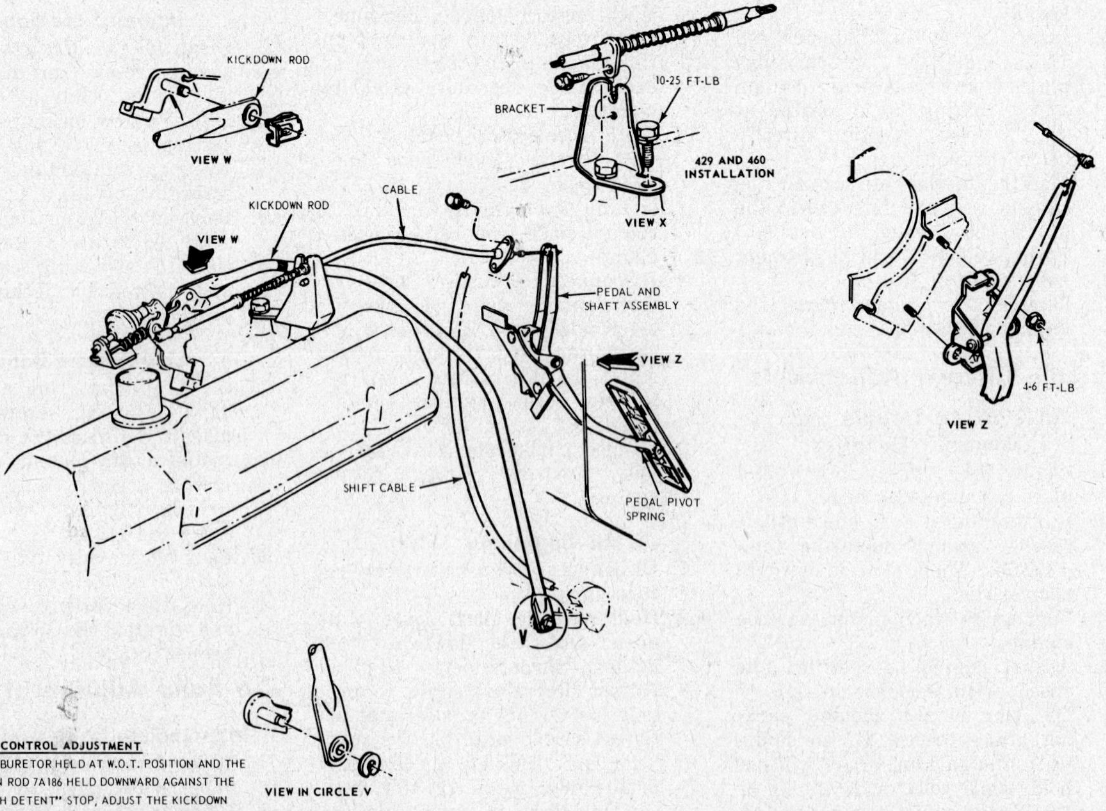
KICKDOWN ROD
VIEW W
10-25 FT-LB
BRACKET
429 AND 460
INSTALLATION
VIEW X
CABLE
KICKDOWN ROD
VIEW W
PEDAL AND
SHAFT ASSEMBLY
VIEW Z
SHIFT CABLE
PEDAL PIVOT
SPRING
V
4-6 FT-LB
VIEW Z
VIEW IN CIRCLE V

KICK-DOWN CONTROL ADJUSTMENT

A. WITH CARBURETOR HELD AT W.O.T. POSITION AND THE KICKDOWN ROD 7A186 HELD DOWNWARD AGAINST THE "THROUGH DETENT" STOP, ADJUST THE KICKDOWN ADJUSTING SCREW TO OBTAIN .01 TO .08 CLEARANCE BETWEEN SCREW AND THROTTLE ARM.

B. RETURN SYSTEM TO IDLE–NEUTRAL.

1972-74 Thunderbird throttle/downshift linkage adjustment (© Ford Motor Co)

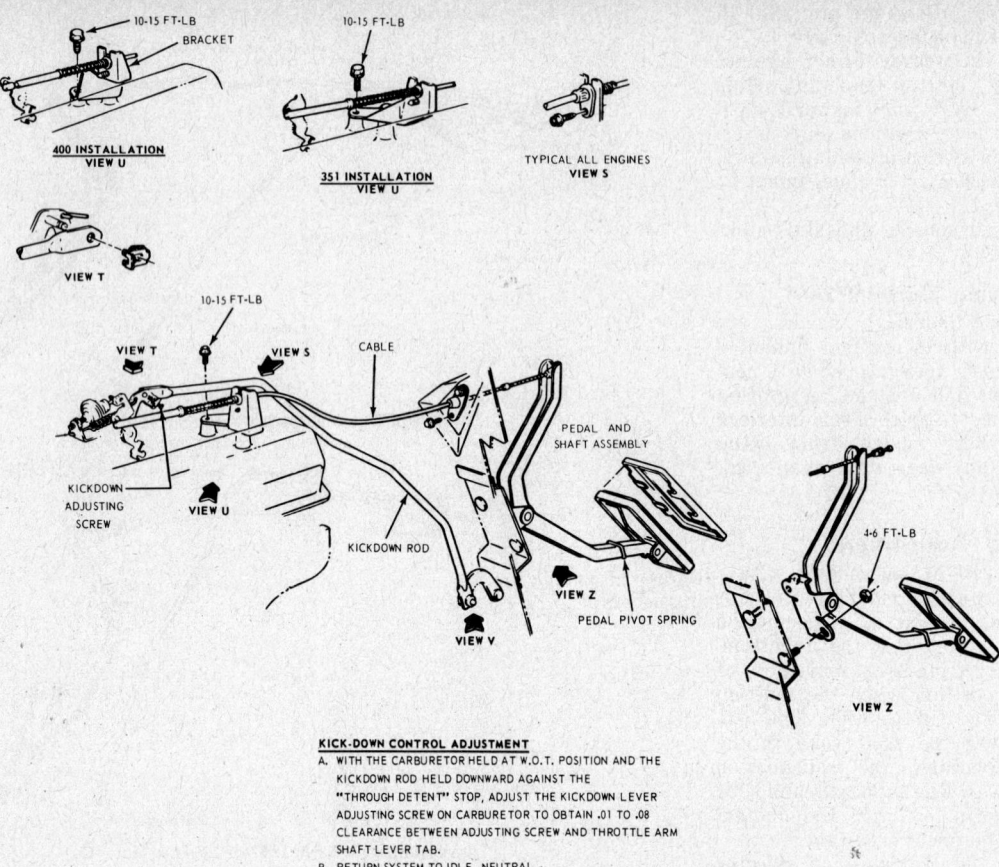

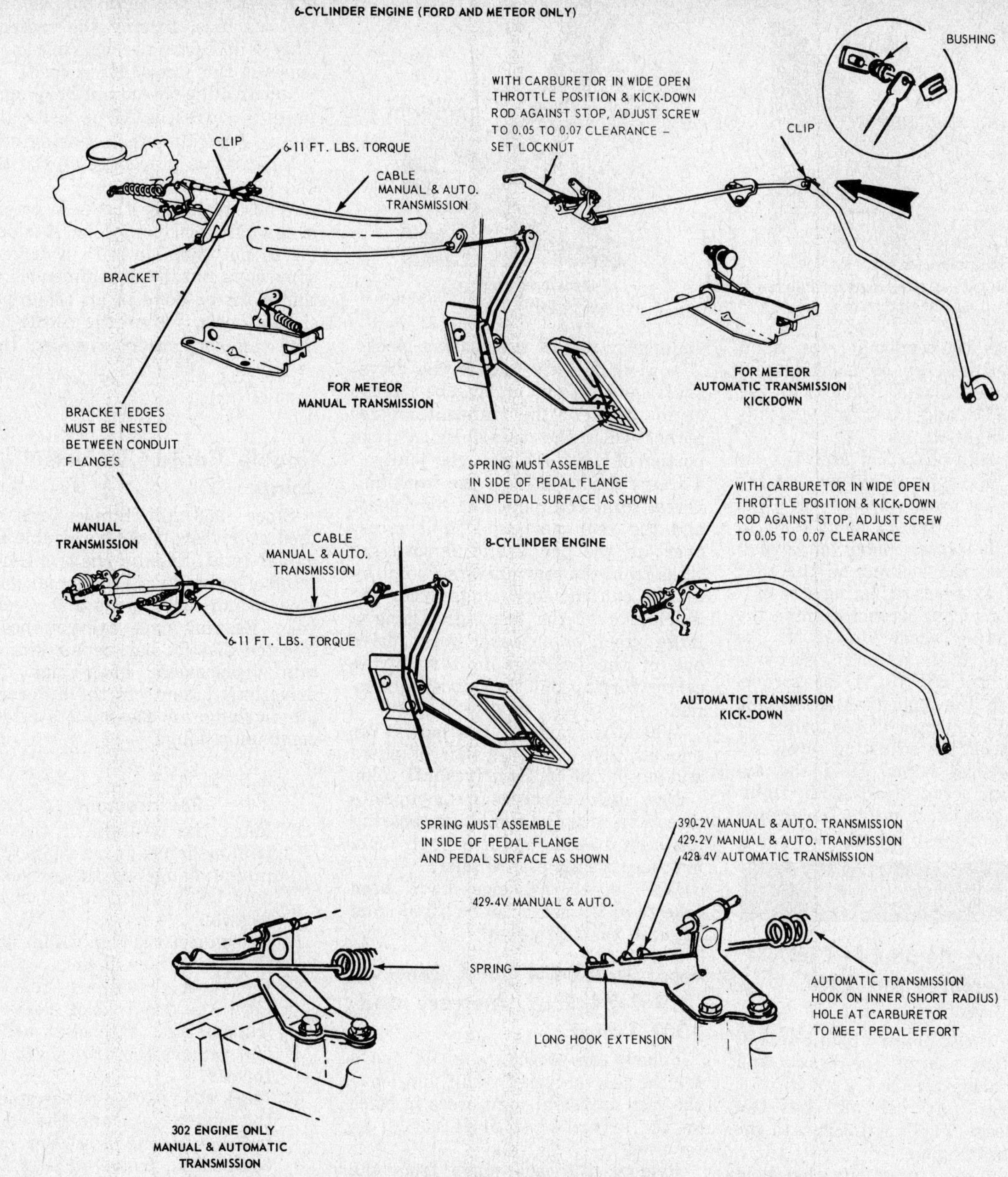
6-CYLINDER ENGINE (FORD AND METEOR ONLY)
BUSHING
WITH CARBURETOR IN WIDE OPEN THROTTLE POSITION & KICK-DOWN ROD AGAINST STOP, ADJUST SCREW TO 0.05 TO 0.07 CLEARANCE – SET LOCKNUT
CLIP
CLIP
6-11 FT. LBS. TORQUE
CABLE MANUAL & AUTO. TRANSMISSION
BRACKET
FOR METEOR MANUAL TRANSMISSION
FOR METEOR AUTOMATIC TRANSMISSION KICKDOWN
BRACKET EDGES MUST BE NESTED BETWEEN CONDUIT FLANGES
SPRING MUST ASSEMBLE IN SIDE OF PEDAL FLANGE AND PEDAL SURFACE AS SHOWN
WITH CARBURETOR IN WIDE OPEN THROTTLE POSITION & KICK-DOWN ROD AGAINST STOP, ADJUST SCREW TO 0.05 TO 0.07 CLEARANCE
MANUAL TRANSMISSION
CABLE MANUAL & AUTO. TRANSMISSION
8-CYLINDER ENGINE
6-11 FT. LBS. TORQUE
AUTOMATIC TRANSMISSION KICK-DOWN
SPRING MUST ASSEMBLE IN SIDE OF PEDAL FLANGE AND PEDAL SURFACE AS SHOWN
390-2V MANUAL & AUTO. TRANSMISSION
429-2V MANUAL & AUTO. TRANSMISSION
428 4V AUTOMATIC TRANSMISSION
429-4V MANUAL & AUTO.
SPRING
AUTOMATIC TRANSMISSION HOOK ON INNER (SHORT RADIUS) HOLE AT CARBURETOR TO MEET PEDAL EFFORT
LONG HOOK EXTENSION
302 ENGINE ONLY MANUAL & AUTOMATIC TRANSMISSION

Throttle linkage adjustment—1969-70 Ford and Mercury (© Ford Motor Co)

4. Tighten the adjusting screw to 10 ft lbs and back the screw off *exactly 1½ turns*. Tighten the adjusting screw locknut.

FMX, MX, and CW Band Adjustment

Front Band Adjustment

1. Drain the transmission fluid and remove the oil pan, fluid filter screen, and clip.
2. Clean the pan and filter screen and remove the old gasket.
3. Loosen the front servo adjusting screw locknut.
4. Pull back the actuating rod and insert a ¼ in. spacer bar between the adjusting screw and the servo piston stem. Tighten

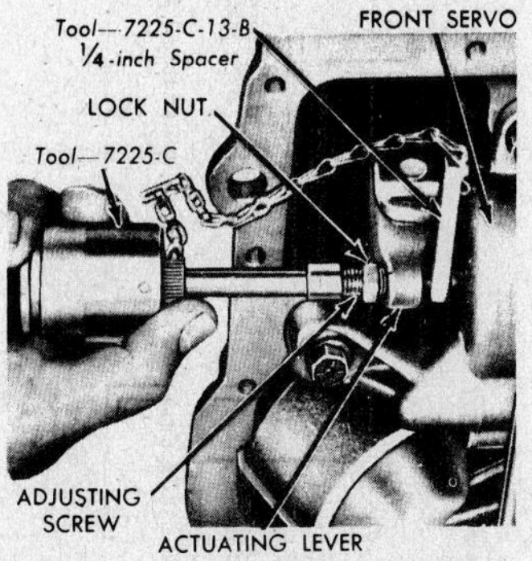
Tool—7225-C-13-B
¼-inch Spacer
FRONT SERVO
LOCK NUT
Tool—7225-C
ADJUSTING SCREW
ACTUATING LEVER

CW, FMX, and MX front band adjustment (© Ford Motor Co)

the adjusting screw to 10 in. lbs torque. Remove the spacer bar and tighten the adjusting screw *an additional ¾ turn*. Hold the adjusting screw fast and tighten the locknut securely (20-25 ft lbs).
5. Install the transmission fluid filter screen and clip. Install pan with a new pan gasket.
6. Refill the transmission to the mark on the dipstick. Start the engine, run for a few minutes, shift the selector lever through all positions, and place it in Park. Recheck the fluid level and add fluid if necessary.

Rear Band Adjustments

On certain cars with a console floor shift, the entire console, shift lever and linkage will have to be removed to gain access to the rear band external adjusting screw.

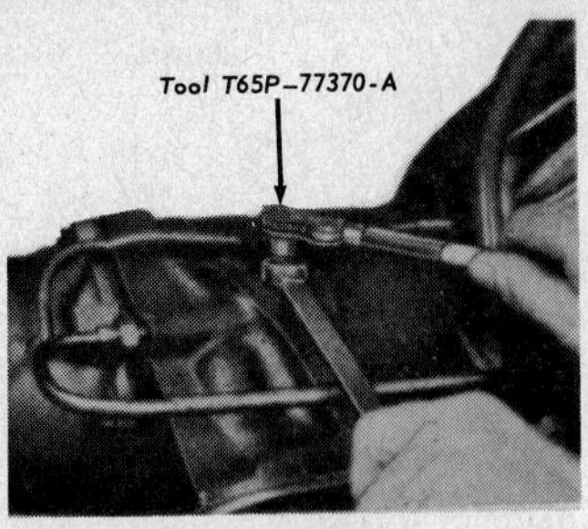
Tool T65P-77370-A

CW, FMX, and MX rear band external adjustment
(© Ford Motor Co)

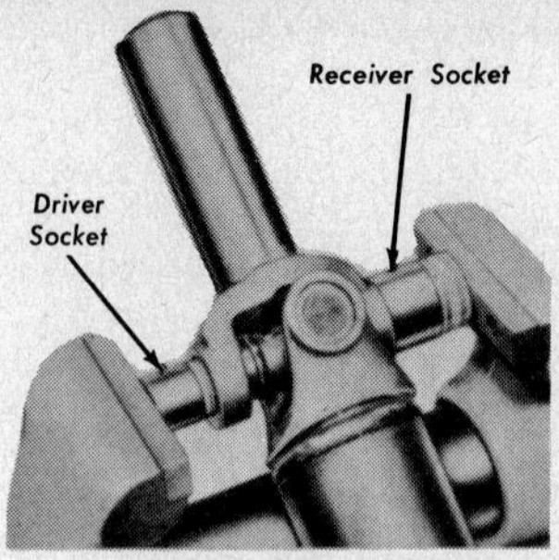
Receiver Socket
Driver Socket

U-joint removal
(© Ford Motor Co)

1. Locate the external rear band adjusting screw on the transmission case, clean all dirt from the threads, and coat the threads with light oil.

NOTE: the adjusting screw is located on the upper right side of the transmission case. Access is often through a hole in the front floor to the right of center under the carpet.

2. Loosen the locknut on the rear band external adjusting screw.
3. Using torque wrench tighten the adjusting screw to 10 ft lbs torque. If the adjusting screw is tighter than 10 ft lbs torque, loosen the adjusting screw and retighten to the proper torque.
4. Back off the adjusting screw *exactly 1½ turns*. Hold the adjusting screw steady while tightening the locknut to the proper torque (35–40 ft lbs).

U-JOINTS

Rear Joint Removal—1967-74 Ford, Mercury and 1967 T-Bird

The universal joints on all Fords in this section are of the cross- and needle-bearing-type.

The rear universal joint has two pillow blocks which are bolted to the pinion shaft flange.

Take out the four bolts that hold the bearing blocks to the pinion shaft and gently tap off the bearing blocks.

Lower the back end of the driveshaft and the front end can be slid out of the back of the transmission together with the transmission yoke portion of the front universal joint.

Carry the assembly—the front universal joint complete, the driveshaft and the rear universal joint crossover—to the bench and remove the cross from the rear universal joint by taking out the lock rings from the inner side of the bearings. Using a large punch or an arbor press, drive one of the bearings in toward the center forcing out the opposite bearing.

When the bearing is pressed out far enough, grip it with a pair of pliers and pull it out of the driveshaft yoke.

Now, drive the cross in the opposite direction until the remaining bearing has been driven out far enough for a purchase with a pair of pliers.

When both bearings have been taken out, the cross can be lifted from between the two yokes.

Front Universal Joint Removal—1967-74 Ford, Mercury and 1967 T-Bird

Follow the procedure given above for the rear universal joint, but leave the rear universal joint cross in place on the driveshaft if it is not to be removed.

Remove the lock rings from the inner side of two opposite bearings and press on the outer side of one of the bearings, forcing the crossover. This will force the bearing on the opposite side out of its yoke.

Remove the forced-out bearing and press the cross in the opposite direction to force the other bearing out.

Repeat this procedure on the third and fourth bearings.

When installing the new bearings in the universal joint yoke, it is possible to put them in with a driver of some type, but it is recommended that this work be done in an arbor press since a heavy jolt on the needle bearings can very easily misalign them.

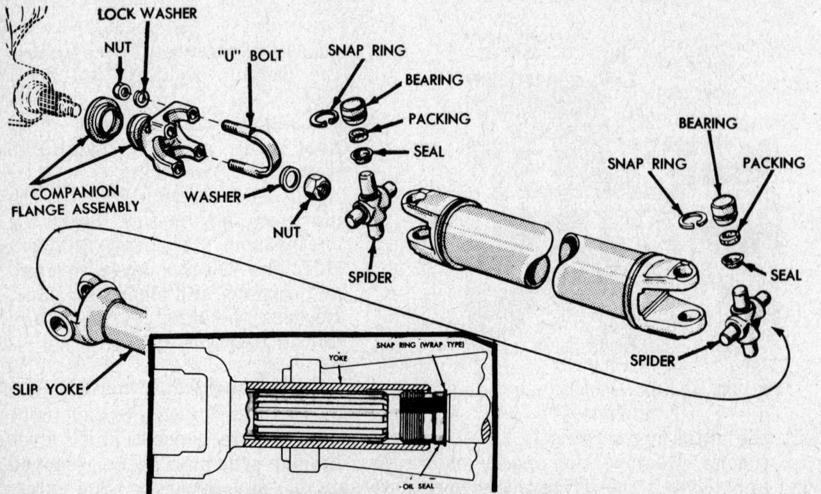
LOCK WASHER
NUT
"U" BOLT
SNAP RING
BEARING
PACKING
SEAL
COMPANION FLANGE ASSEMBLY
WASHER
NUT
SPIDER
BEARING
SNAP RING
PACKING
SEAL
SPIDER
SLIP YOKE
SNAP RING (WRAP TYPE)
YOKE
OIL SEAL

Driveshaft and universal joint (© Ford Motor Co)

Double Cardan Universal Joints

Since 1968, all Thunderbirds have used a driveshaft with a double Cardan U-Joint. Each of the two Cardan joints consist of two universal joints, a centering socket yoke and a center yoke. Bearing cups are retained by injected plastic; but, repair kits contain replacement snap-rings. This driveshaft mounts to the differential pinion flange by means of a circular companion flange.

Replacement

1. Mark the position of the companion flange in relation to the pinion flange so the driveshaft may be returned to its original location.
2. Disconnect the companion flange from the pinion flange.
3. Pull the driveshaft rearward until the front yoke clears the transmission extension housing and remove the driveshaft from the car.
4. Mark the position of the spiders, the center yoke and the centering socket yoke in relation to the companion flange. *The spiders must be assembled with the bosses in their original position to provide proper clearance.*
5. If the universal joints have been previously replaced and are retained with snap-rings, remove the snap-rings.
6. Using a press or large punch, drive one of the bearing caps on the U-Joint to be replaced toward the center of the driveshaft. Remove the bearing cap opposite the cap being driven as it emerges from the driveshaft. Repeat this procedure until all the bearing caps have been removed, then, remove the spider.
7. To disassemble the ball socket from the yoke, insert a screwdriver into the centering ball socket and pry out the rubber seal. Remove the retainer, three piece ball seat, washer and

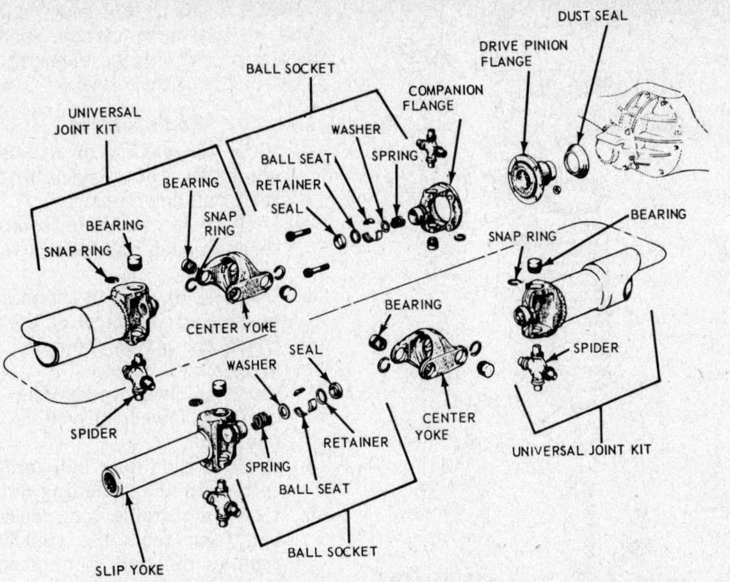
DUST SEAL
DRIVE PINION FLANGE
BALL SOCKET
COMPANION FLANGE
UNIVERSAL JOINT KIT
WASHER
BALL SEAT
SPRING
RETAINER
BEARING
SEAL
SNAP RING
BEARING
BEARING
SNAP RING
SNAP RING
CENTER YOKE
BEARING
SEAL
WASHER
SPIDER
SPIDER
CENTER YOKE
RETAINER
SPRING
UNIVERSAL JOINT KIT
BALL SEAT
BALL SOCKET
SLIP YOKE

Driveshaft with double Cardan universal joints (© Ford Motor Co)

spring from the ball socket.

8. Reverse above procedure to install, making sure all parts are mounted in their original location.

JACKING, HOISTING

Ford, Mercury and T-Bird

1. Jack car at front spring seats of lower control arms, and at rear axle housing close to differential case.
2. To lift at frame, use adapters so that contact will be made at points shown. Adapters should support at least 12 sq. in.

FRONT SUSPENSION

Shock Absorber R & R

All Models

1. Remove the nut, washer, and bushing from the upper end of the shock absorber.
2. Raise the vehicle and install jackstands under the frame rails.
3. Remove the two bolts securing the shock absorber to the lower control arm and remove the shock absorber.
4. Install a new bushing and washer on the top of the shock absorber and position the unit inside the front spring. Install the two lower attaching bolts.
5. Remove the jackstands and lower the vehicle.
6. Place a new bushing and washer on the shock absorber top stud and install the attaching nut.

Coil Spring and Lower Control Arm R & R

All Models

1. Raise car and support with stands placed back of lower arms.
2. If equipped with drum type brakes, remove the wheel and brake drum as an assembly. Remove the brake backing plate attaching bolts and remove the backing plate from the spindle. Wire the assembly back out of the way.
3. If equipped with disc brakes, remove the wheel from the hub. Remove two bolts and washers that hold the caliper and brake hose bracket to the spindle. Remove the caliper from the rotor and wire it back out of the way. Then, remove the hub and rotor from the spindle.
4. Disconnect lower end of the shock absorber and push it up to the retracted position.
5. Disconnect stabilizer bar link from the lower arm.
6. Remove cotter pins from the upper and lower ball joint stud nuts.
7. Remove two bolts and nuts holding the strut to the lower arm.
8. Loosen the lower ball joint stud nut two turns. Do not remove this nut.
9. Install spreader tool between the upper and lower ball joint studs.
10. Expand the tool until the tool

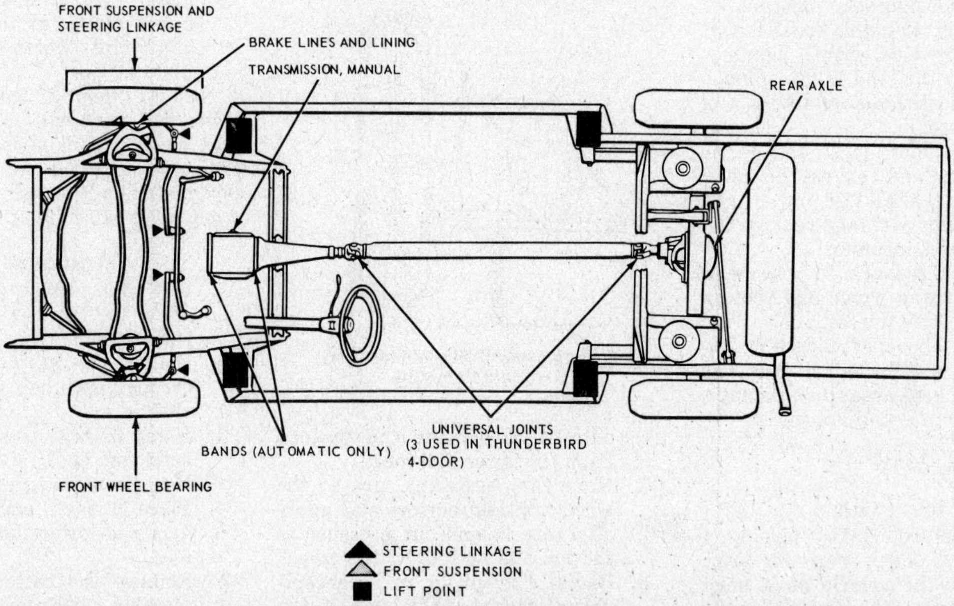
FRONT SUSPENSION AND STEERING LINKAGE
BRAKE LINES AND LINING
TRANSMISSION, MANUAL
REAR AXLE
UNIVERSAL JOINTS (3 USED IN THUNDERBIRD 4-DOOR)
BANDS (AUTOMATIC ONLY)
FRONT WHEEL BEARING
STEERING LINKAGE
FRONT SUSPENSION
LIFT POINT

Ford hoist lifting positions (© Ford Motor Co)

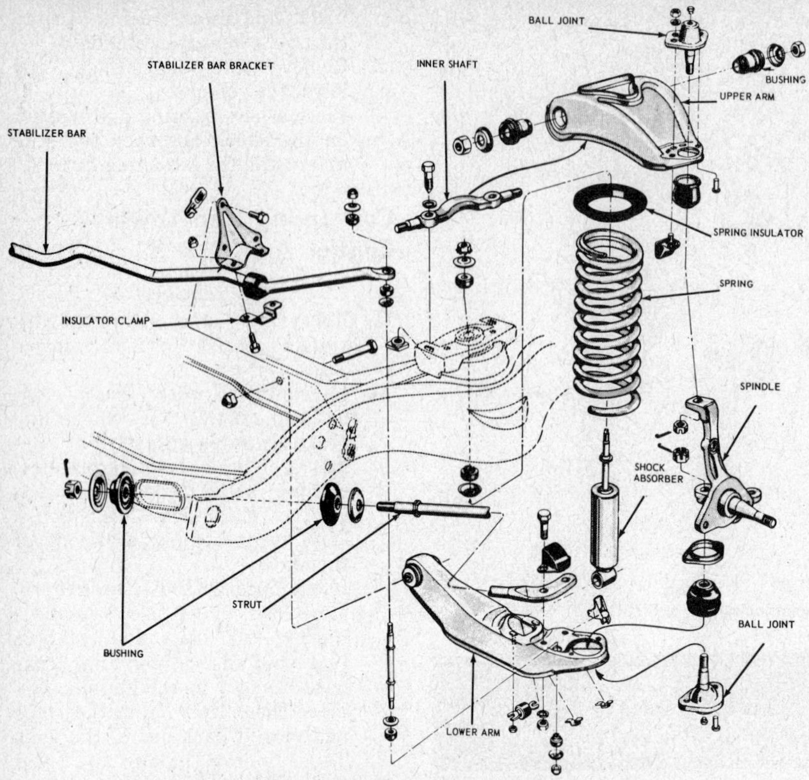

BALL JOINT
STABILIZER BAR BRACKET
INNER SHAFT
BUSHING
UPPER ARM
STABILIZER BAR
SPRING INSULATOR
SPRING
INSULATOR CLAMP
SPINDLE
SHOCK ABSORBER
STRUT
BALL JOINT
BUSHING
LOWER ARM

Typical front suspension—1967-70 (© Ford Motor Co)

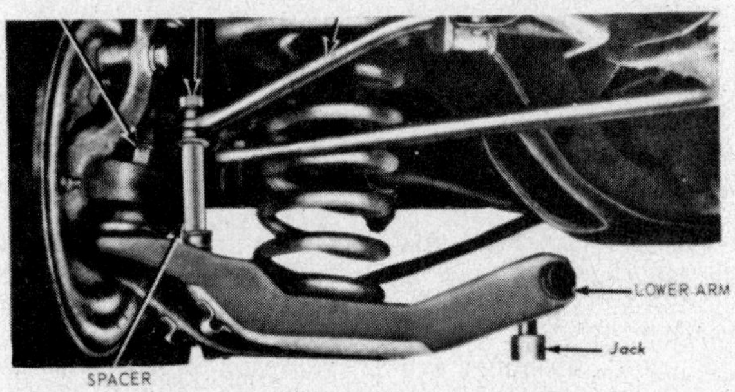

LOWER ARM
Jack
SPACER

Removing front coil spring (© Ford Motor Co)

exerts considerable pressure on the studs. Tap the spindle near the lower stud with a hammer to loosen the stud in the spindle. Do not loosen the stud with tool pressure only.

11. Position floor jack under the lower arm and remove the lower ball joint stud nut.
12. Lower floor jack and remove the spring and insulator.
13. Remove the A-arm to crossmember attaching parts, and remove the arm from the car.
14. Reverse above procedure to install. If lower control arm was replaced because of damage, check front end alignment.

Lower Ball Joint

Inspection

1. Raise the vehicle by placing a floor jack under the lower arm; or, raise the vehicle on a hoist and place a jack stand under the lower arm and lower the vehicle onto it to remove the preload from the lower ball joint.
2. Have an assistant grasp the wheel top and bottom and apply alternate in and out pressure to the top and bottom of the wheel.
3. Radial play of 1/4 in. is acceptable measured at the inside of the wheel adjacent to the lower arm.

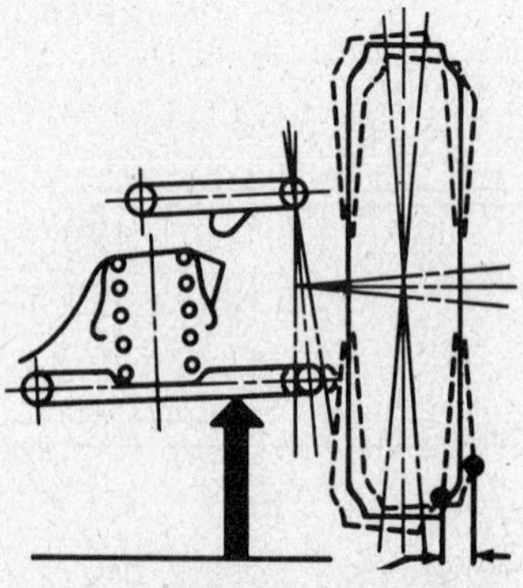

Measuring lower ball joint radial play (© Ford Motor Co)

NOTE: this radial play is multiplied at the outer circumference of the tire and should be measured only at the inside of the wheel.

Replacement

1. Raise the vehicle on a hoist and allow the front wheels to fall to their full down position.
2. Drill a 1/8 in. hole completely through each ball joint attaching rivet.
3. Use a 3/8 in. drill in the pilot hole to drill off the head of the rivet.
4. Drive the rivets from the lower arm.
5. Place a jack under the lower arm and lower the vehicle about 6 in.
6. Remove the lower ball joint stud cotter pin and attaching nut.
7. Using a suitable tool, loosen the ball joint from the spindle and remove the ball joint from the lower arm.
8. Clean all metal burrs from the lower arm and install the new ball joint, using the service part nuts and bolts to attach the ball joint to the lower arm. Do not attempt to rerivet the ball joint once it has been removed.
9. Check front end alignment.

Upper Ball Joint

Inspection

1. Raise the vehicle by placing a floor jack under the lower arm. Do not allow the lower arm to hang freely with the vehicle on a hoist or bumper jack.
2. Have an assistant grasp the bottom of the tire and move the wheel in and out.
3. As the wheel is being moved, observe the upper control arm where the spindle attaches to it. Any movement between the upper part of the spindle and the upper ball joint indicates a bad ball joint which must be replaced.

NOTE: during this check the lower ball joint will be unloaded and may move; this is normal and not an indication of a bad ball joint. Also, do not mistake a loose wheel bearing for a defective ball joint.

Replacement

1. Raise the vehicle on a hoist and allow the front wheels to fall to their full down position.
2. Drill a 1/8 in. hole completely through each ball joint attaching rivet.
3. Using a large chisel, cut off the head of each rivet and drive them from the upper arm.
4. Place a jack under the lower arm and lower the vehicle about 6 in.
5. Remove the cotter pin and attaching nut from the ball joint stud.

6. Using a suitable tool, loosen the ball joint stud from the spindle and remove the ball joint from the upper arm.
7. Clean all metal burrs from the upper arm and install the new ball joint, using the service part nuts and bolts to attach the ball joint to the upper arm. Do not attempt to rerivet the ball joint once it has been removed.
8. Check front end alignment.

Upper Control Arm

Replacement

1. Perform steps 1-12 of the above "Coil Spring and Lower Control Arm R&R" procedure.
2. Remove the upper arm inner shaft attaching bolts and remove the arm and shaft from the chassis as an assembly.
3. Reverse above procedure to install.
4. Adjust front end alignment.

REAR SUSPENSION

The rear suspension is a coil-link design. Large, low-rate coil springs are mounted between rear axle pads and frame supports. Parallel lower arms extend forward of the spring seats to rubber frame anchor to accommodate driving and breaking forces. A third link is mounted between the axle and the frame to control torque reaction forces from the rear wheels.

Lateral (side sway) motion of the rear axle is controlled by a rubber bushed rear track bar, linked laterally between the axle and frame.

Rear Springs R & R

1. Place car on hoist and lift under rear axle housing. Place jack stands under frame side rails.
2. Disconnect track bar at the rear axle housing bracket.
3. Disconnect rear shock absorbers from the rear axle housing brackets.
4. Disconnect hose from axle housing vent.
5. Lower hoist with axle housing until coil springs are released.
6. Remove spring lower retainer with bolt, nut, washer and insulator.
7. Remove spring with large rubber insulator pads from car.
8. Install in reverse of above.

Rear Shock Absorber Replacement

Rear shock absorbers on all Fords are straddle-mounted and are held to rubber bushings at both the top and bottom connections. Simply remove the nuts from the top and bottom of the shock absorber and lift the shock absorber off the car.

BRAKES

All models have single anchor, internal expanding, self adjusting shoe brakes on the rear wheels. On models without disc brakes, the front brakes are identical to the rear brakes with the exception of parking brake hardware. Front disc brakes have been available as an option since 1967. 1967 disc brakes have dual piston, anchored calipers. 1968 and later vehicles have single piston, floating calipers. All 1967 and later cars have dual reservoir master cylinders and brake systems in which the front and rear brake hydraulic systems are separate and independent of each other.

NOTE: procedure for brake shoe or pad replacement and adjustment as well as wheel and master cylinder overhaul, and brake bleeding can be found in the "Unit Repair Section."

Master Cylinder

1967-74 Dual Master Cylinder R&R

Standard Brakes

1. Working under the dash, disconnect the master cylinder pushrod from the brake pedal. The pushrod cannot be removed from the master cylinder.
2. Disconnect the stoplight switch wires and remove the switch from the brake pedal, using care not to damage the switch.
3. Disconnect the brake lines from the master cylinder.
4. Remove the attaching screws from the firewall and remove the master cylinder from the car.
5. Reinstall in reverse of above order, leaving the brake line fittings loose at the master cylinder.
6. Fill the master cylinder, and with the brake lines loose, slowly

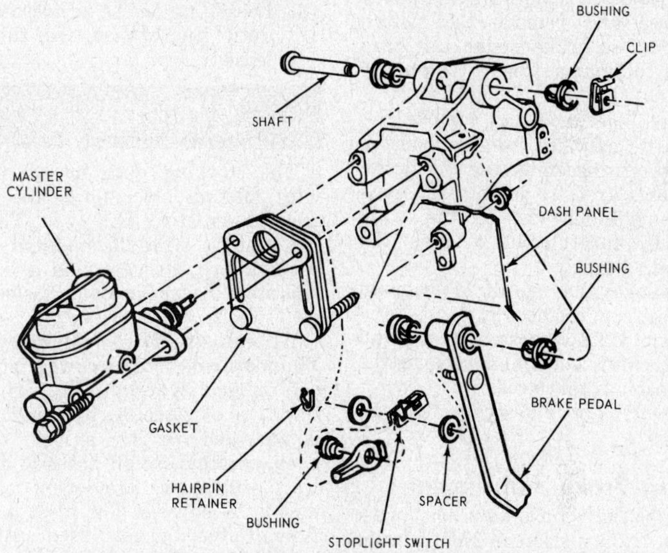
BUSHING
CLIP
SHAFT
MASTER CYLINDER
DASH PANEL
BUSHING
BRAKE PEDAL
GASKET
HAIRPIN RETAINER
BUSHING
SPACER
STOPLIGHT SWITCH

Master cylinder and brake pedal installation—non-power brakes—1969-71 Ford and Mercury installation shown
(© Ford Motor Co)

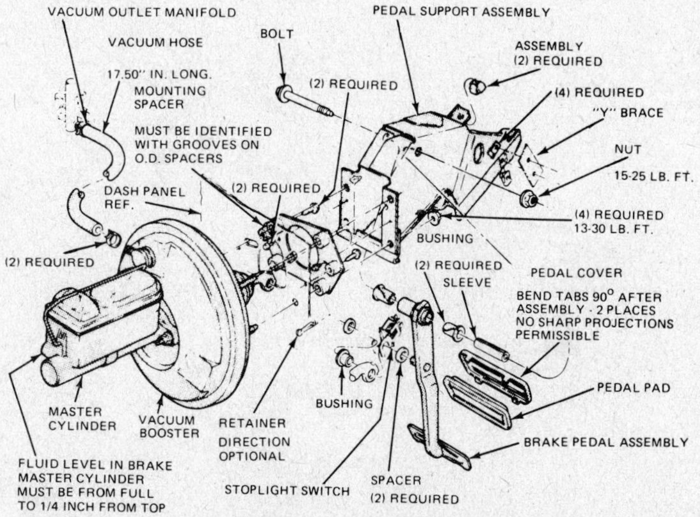
VACUUM OUTLET MANIFOLD
VACUUM HOSE
17.50" IN. LONG.
MOUNTING SPACER
MUST BE IDENTIFIED WITH GROOVES ON O.D. SPACERS
DASH PANEL REF.
(2) REQUIRED
BOLT
(2) REQUIRED
(2) REQUIRED
PEDAL SUPPORT ASSEMBLY
ASSEMBLY (2) REQUIRED
(4) REQUIRED
"Y" BRACE
NUT
15-25 LB. FT.
(4) REQUIRED
13-30 LB. FT.
BUSHING
(2) REQUIRED
SLEEVE
PEDAL COVER
BEND TABS 90° AFTER ASSEMBLY - 2 PLACES NO SHARP PROJECTIONS PERMISSIBLE
PEDAL PAD
BUSHING
BRAKE PEDAL ASSEMBLY
MASTER CYLINDER
VACUUM BOOSTER
RETAINER DIRECTION OPTIONAL
FLUID LEVEL IN BRAKE MASTER CYLINDER MUST BE FROM FULL TO 1/4 INCH FROM TOP
STOPLIGHT SWITCH
SPACER (2) REQUIRED

Master cylinder and vacuum booster installation—power brakes—1972-74 Thunderbird installation shown
(© Ford Motor Co)

bleed the air from the master cylinder using the foot pedal.

Power Brakes

1. Disconnect the brake line from the master cylinder.
2. Remove the two nuts and lockwashers that attach the master cylinder to the brake booster.
3. Remove the master cylinder from the booster.
4. Reverse above procedure to reinstall.
5. Fill master cylinder and bleed entire brake system.
6. Refill master cylinder.

Brake Booster R & R

1. Working from inside the car, beneath the instrument panel, remove the booster pushrod from the brake pedal.
2. Disconnect the stop light switch wires and remove the switch from the brake pedal. Use care not to damage the switch during removal.
3. Raise the hood and remove the master cylinder from the booster without disconnecting the brake lines. Carefully position the master cylinder out of the way, being careful not to kink the brake lines.
4. Remove the manifold vacuum hose from the booster.
5. Remove the booster to firewall attaching bolts and remove the booster from the car.
6. Reverse above procedure to reinstall.

Parking Brake Adjustment

1. Raise the vehicle on a hoist with the transmission in Neutral and the parking brake fully released.

Chilton's TIME SAVER

Rear Brake Drum Removal

Occasional cases of rear wheel drums, frozen to the rear axle flange, require much time and effort to remove without damage.

If a rear drum resists normal efforts to remove by tapping, try the following method:

1. **Drive two or three of the serrated hub bolts out of the drum and into the brake shoe area.**
2. **With an old screwdriver or other suitable wedge forced between the drum and axle flange through these bolt holes, tap and wedge the drum from the axle flange.**
3. **After the drum is removed, the bolts can be recovered and returned to their respective places in the axle flange.**

Any damage to the drum can usually be corrected by a few taps with a hammer.

2. Tighten the adjusting nut against the cable equalizer until the rear brakes drag when the wheels are turned.
3. Loosen up on the adjustment nut until the brakes are fully released.

STEERING

The steering gear on all models with manual steering is the worm and recirculating ball type. The sector shaft is straddle mounted in the cover above the gear and a housing mounted roller bearing below the gear.

All full-size Fords, Mercurys and Thunderbirds with power steering use integral type power steering. On this type of steering, hydraulic assist is provided directly to the steering gear, eliminating all hoses and hardware which was previously mounted under the chassis. The most common type of steering gear used with integral power steering is the Ford torsion bar model. The torsion bar type power steering unit includes a worm and one-piece rack piston, which is meshed with the gear teeth on the steering sector shaft. In certain limited applications a Saginaw Rotary Valve type power steering unit is used. In this unit, the rack-piston nut is of one piece design and is geared to the steering sector shaft.

All adjustment and overhaul operations are contained in the Unit Repair Section of this book; listed under manual steering and power steering respectively.

Wheel Bearing Adjustment

1. Raise the front of the vehicle.
2. Remove the wheel cover and grease cap.
3. Remove the cotter pin and nut lock.
4. Back off the adjusting nut and retighten the nut to 17–25 ft. lbs. Back off the adjusting nut again ½ turn. Retighten the nut to 10–15 in. lbs. Install the nut

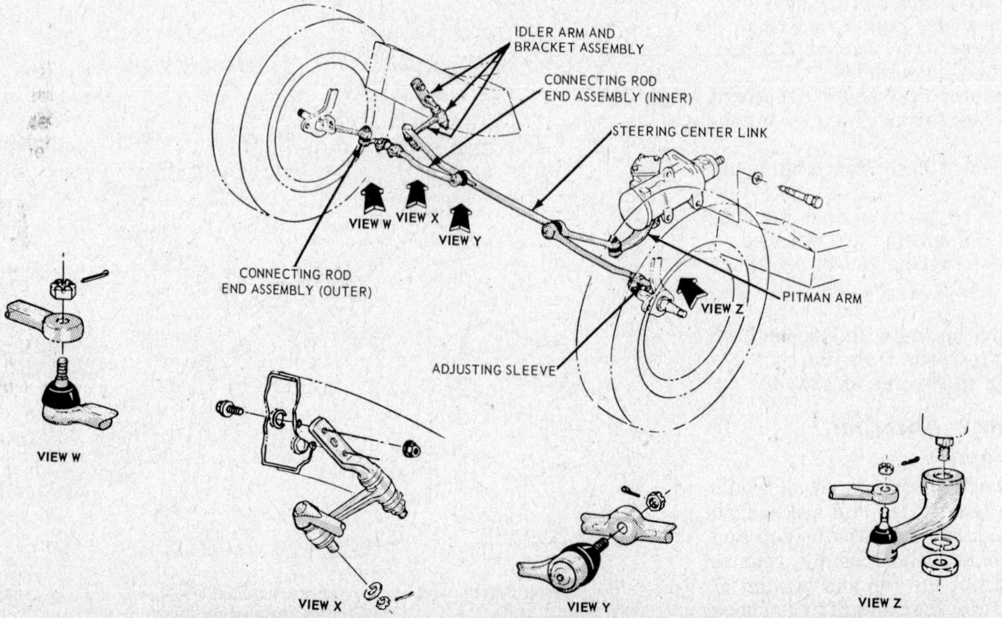
IDLER ARM AND
BRACKET ASSEMBLY
CONNECTING ROD
END ASSEMBLY (INNER)
STEERING CENTER LINK
VIEW W
VIEW X
VIEW Y
CONNECTING ROD
END ASSEMBLY (OUTER)
PITMAN ARM
VIEW Z
ADJUSTING SLEEVE
VIEW W
VIEW X
VIEW Y
VIEW Z

1969-74 Ford and Mercury manual or power steering linkage (© Ford Motor Co)

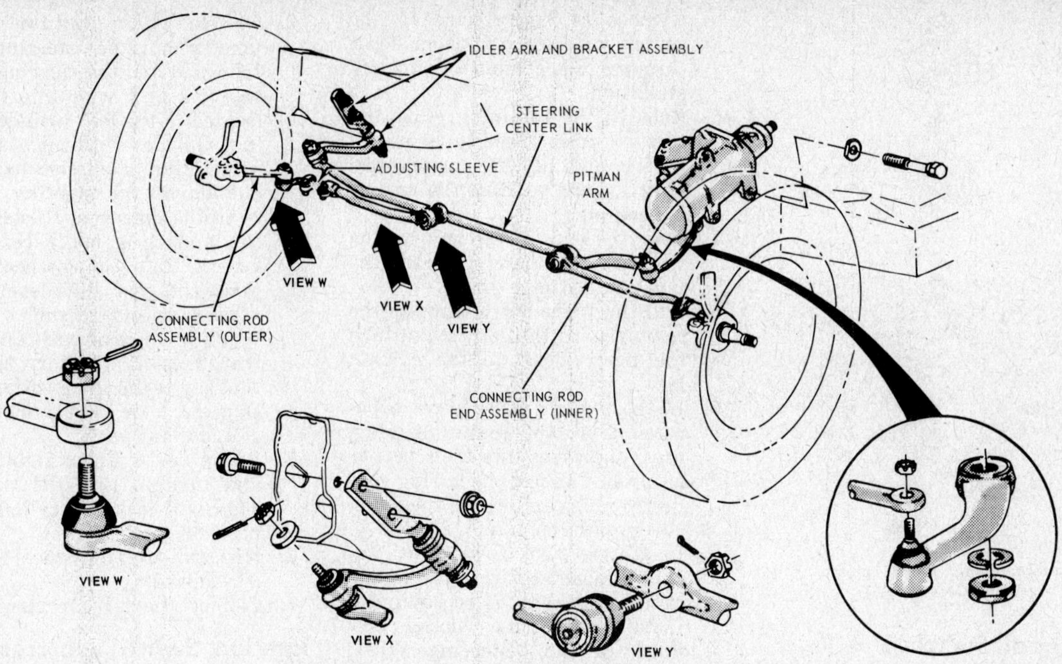
IDLER ARM AND BRACKET ASSEMBLY
STEERING CENTER LINK
ADJUSTING SLEEVE
PITMAN ARM
VIEW W
VIEW X
VIEW Y
CONNECTING ROD ASSEMBLY (OUTER)
CONNECTING ROD END ASSEMBLY (INNER)
VIEW W
VIEW X
VIEW Y

1972-74 Thunderbird power steering linkage (© Ford Motor Co)

lock so that the castellations are aligned with the cotter pin hole. Install the cotter pin and bend the ends around the castellations of the nut lock to prevent interference with the radio static collector in the grease cap.

5. Install the grease cap and wheel cover.
6. Lower the vehicle.

Power Steering Pump R & R

1. Drain the fluid from the pump reservoir by disconnecting the fluid return hose at the pump. Then, disconnect the pressure hose from the pump.
2. Remove the mounting bolts from the front of the pump. On eight cylinder engines, there is a nut on the rear of the pump that must be removed. After removal, move the pump inward to loosen the belt tension and remove the belt from the pulley. Then, remove the pump from the car.
3. To reinstall the pump, position on mounting bracket and loosely install the mounting bolts and nuts. Put the drive belt over the pulley and move the pump outward against the belt until the proper belt tension is obtained. Measure the belt tension with a belt tension gauge for the proper adjustment. Only in cases where a belt tension gauge is not available should the belt deflection method be used. If the belt deflection method is used, be sure to check with a belt tension gauge as soon as possible, since deflection method is not accurate.
4. Tighten the mounting bolts and nuts.

Steering Wheel R & R

1. Disconnect the negative battery cable.
2. Remove the horn ring or hub cap by pushing it down and rotating it counterclockwise. On post-1967 models, remove the retaining screws (from underside of steering wheel) and the crash pad. On both 1967-69 Thunderbirds and 1969–70 Fords and Mercurys with speed control, the switch bezels must be pried up with a thin knife blade and the center trim plate removed to gain access to the crash pad retaining screws. On later models with speed control, the switches simply snap into plastic retainers inside the crash pad. Disconnect the horn and speed control wires.
3. Remove the steering wheel nut. Install a steering wheel puller on the end of the shaft and remove the wheel.

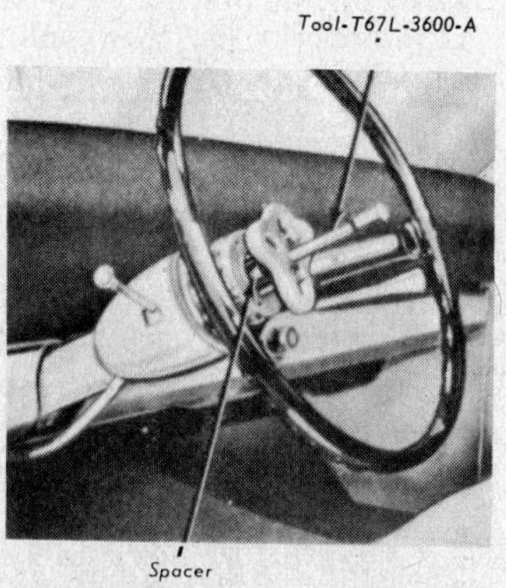
Tool-T67L-3600-A
Spacer

Removing steering wheel with puller (© Ford Motor Co)

Caution The use of a knock-off type steering wheel puller or the use of a hammer on the steering shaft will damage the column bearing and, on collapsible columns, the column itself may be damaged.

4. Lubricate the steering shaft bushing with white grease. Transfer all serviceable parts to the new steering wheel.
5. With the front wheels pointing in a straight-ahead direction, and with the alignment marks on steering wheel and the steering shaft lined up, install the steering wheel and locknut.
6. Connect the horn and speed control wires and install the horn ring or hub cap. On post-1967 models, install the crash pad and retaining screws.
7. Connect the negative battery cable.

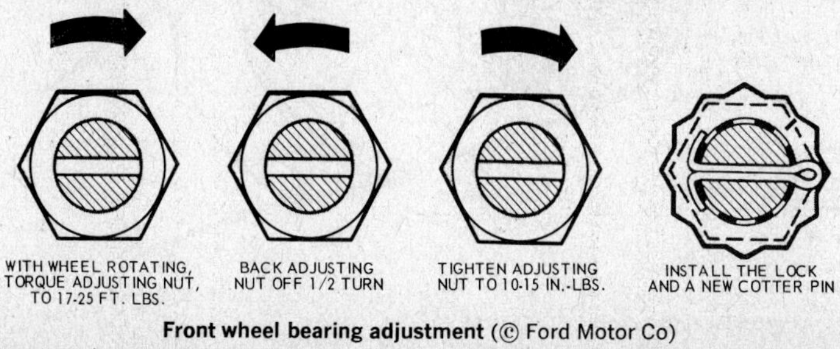
WITH WHEEL ROTATING, TORQUE ADJUSTING NUT, TO 17-25 FT. LBS.
BACK ADJUSTING NUT OFF 1/2 TURN
TIGHTEN ADJUSTING NUT TO 10-15 IN.-LBS.
INSTALL THE LOCK AND A NEW COTTER PIN

Front wheel bearing adjustment (© Ford Motor Co)

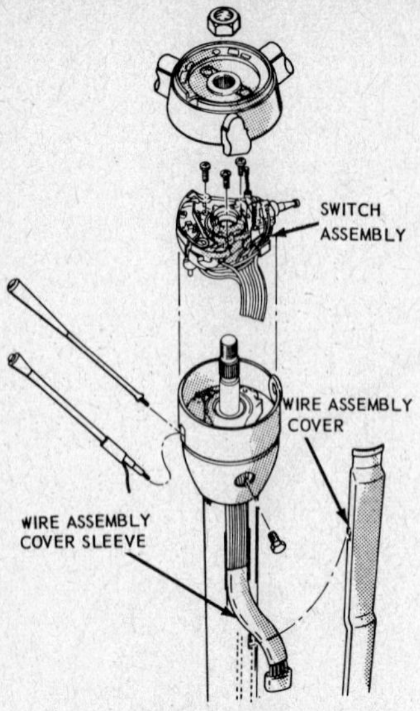
SWITCH ASSEMBLY
WIRE ASSEMBLY COVER
WIRE ASSEMBLY COVER SLEEVE

Turn signal switch—fixed column
(© Ford Motor Co)

Turn Signal Switch R & R

1. Disconnect the negative battery cable.
2. Remove the steering wheel as outlined in the "Steering Wheel R&R" section.
3. Unscrew the turn signal lever from the side of the column. Remove the emergency flasher retainer and knob, if so equipped.
4. Locate and remove the finish cover on the steering column and disconnect the wiring connector plugs.
5. On all 1967-68 models, all 1969–70 Thunderbirds, and all 1969-74 models with a tilt steering column, it is necessary to separate the wires from the connector plug in order to remove the switch and wires. First note the location and color code of each wire, prior to removal, with the wire terminal removal tool. Remove the plastic cover from the wiring harness. Attach a piece of heavy cord to the switch wires to pull them down through the column during installation.
6. Remove the retaining clips and screws from the turn signal switch and lift the switch and wire assembly from the top of the column.
7. Tape the ends of the new switch wires together and transfer the pull cord to these wires.
8. Pull the wires down through the column with the cord and attach the new switch to the column hub.
9. If the switch wires were separated from the connector plug, press the wires into their proper location. Connect the wiring connector plugs and install the finish cover on the column.
10. Install the turn signal lever. Install the emergency flasher retainer and knob, if so equipped.
11. Install the steering wheel as outlined in the "Steering Wheel R&R" section.
12. Connect the negative battery cable and test the operation of the turn signals, horn, emergency flashers, and speed control, if so equipped.

INSTRUMENT PANEL

Ignition Lock Cylinder Replacement

1967-69

1. Insert key and turn to Acc. position.
2. With stiff wire in hole, depress lock pin and rotate cylinder counterclockwise, then pull out cylinder.

1970-74

1. Disconnect the negative battery cable.
2. On cars with a fixed steering column, remove the steering wheel trim pad and the steering wheel. Insert a stiff wire into the hole located in the lock cylinder housing. On cars with a tilt steering wheel, this hole is located on the outside of the steering column near the emergency flasher button and it is not necessary to remove the steering wheel.
3. Place the gear shift lever in Reverse on standard shift cars and in Park on cars with automatic transmission, and turn the ignition key to the ON position.
4. Depress wire and remove lock cylinder and wire.
5. Insert new cylinder into housing and turn to the OFF position. This will lock the cylinder into position.
6. Reinstall steering wheel and pad if removed.
7. Connect negative battery cable.

Ignition Switch Replacement

1967-69

1. Remove cylinder as above.
2. Unscrew the bezel from the ignition switch and remove switch from panel.
3. Remove insulated plug from rear of switch.
4. Install in reverse of above.

1970-74

1. Disconnect the negative battery cable.
2. Remove the shrouding from the steering column, and detach and lower the steering column from the brake support bracket.
3. Disconnect the switch wiring at the multiple plug.
4. Remove the two nuts that retain the switch to the steering column.
5. On vehicles with column mounted gearshift lever, detach the switch plunger from the switch

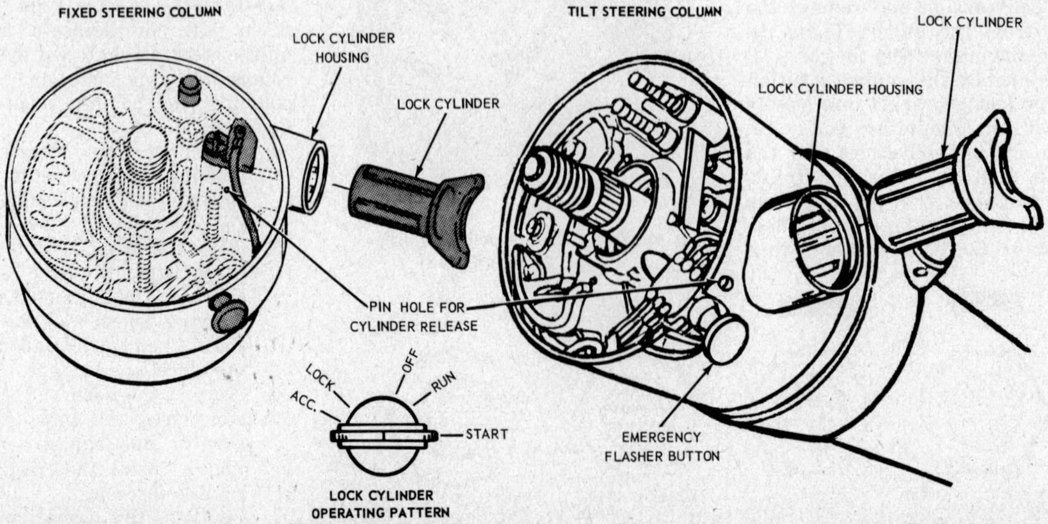
FIXED STEERING COLUMN
TILT STEERING COLUMN
LOCK CYLINDER HOUSING
LOCK CYLINDER
LOCK CYLINDER HOUSING
LOCK CYLINDER
PIN HOLE FOR CYLINDER RELEASE
LOCK
OFF
ACC.
RUN
START
EMERGENCY FLASHER BUTTON
LOCK CYLINDER OPERATING PATTERN

Post-1970 lock cylinder replacement (© Ford Motor Co)

actuator rod and remove the switch. On vehicles with console mounted gearshift lever, remove the pin connecting the plunger to the actuator and remove the switch.

6. To re-install the switch, place both the lock mechanism at the top of the column and the switch itself in lock position for correct adjustment. To hold the column in the lock position, place the automatic shift lever in PARK or manual shift lever in reverse, and turn to LOCK and remove the key. New switches are held in lock by plastic shipping pins. To pin existing switches, pull the switch plunger out as far as it will go and push it back into the first detent. Insert a 3/32 in. diameter wire in the locking hole in the top of the switch.
7. Connect the switch plunger to the switch actuator rod.
8. Position the switch on the column and install the attaching nuts. Do not tighten them.
9. Move the switch up and down to locate mid-position of rod lash, and then tighten the nuts.
10. Remove the locking pin or wire.
11. Attach the steering column to the brake support bracket and install the shrouding.

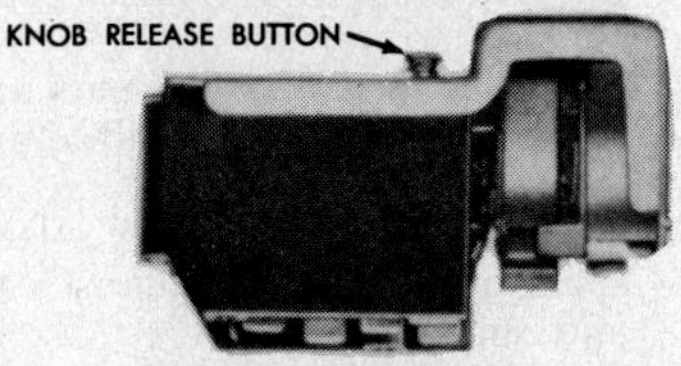
KNOB RELEASE BUTTON

Typical headlight switch
(© Ford Motor Co)

Headlight Switch R & R

All Except 1970 Mercury and 1972-74 Thunderbird

1. Disconnect the negative battery cable.
2. On 1971-74 Ford and 1971 and 1974 Mercury, remove the instrument panel pad, and instrument cluster. (See Instrument Cluster R&R.) On 1972 Mercurys, remove the instrument panel pad only.
3. Pull the headlight switch control knob to the full ON position and press the release knob on the switch. With the knob depressed, pull the knob and shaft from the switch.
4. Remove the wire connector from the back of the switch and, if equipped with headlight doors, remove the vacuum hoses. On 1967-69 Mercury, remove the wire harness bracket.
5. Remove the bezel retaining nut and remove the switch from the dash. On 1971-72 Fords and 1971 Mercurys, the switch is attached to the dash with three screws instead of a bezel nut.
6. Reverse above procedure to reinstall. When installing the headlight switch control knob and shaft, turn the shaft in the switch until a distinct click is heard, locking the shaft in place.

1970 Mercury

1. Remove the battery ground cable.
2. Working under the dash, remove the wire connector from the back of the headlight switch. If equipped with headlight doors, remove the vacuum hoses from the switch.
3. Remove the four switch retaining screws and remove the switch from the dash.
4. Reverse above procedure to install.

1972-74 Thunderbird

1. Disconnect the negative battery cable.
2. Remove the cluster trim panel.
3. Remove the headlight switch mounting plate.
4. Remove the bezel nut and disconnect the multiple connector.
5. Remove the switch.
6. Reverse the above procedure to install.

WINDSHIELD WIPERS

Motor R & R

Ford, and Mercury 1967-74, Thunderbird 1972-74

1. Disconnect the negative battery cable.
2. Remove the wiper arm and blade assemblies from the pivot shafts.
3. On 1967-70 models, remove the cowl grille. On 1971-72 Fords and Mercurys, remove the left side cowl grille.
4. Disconnect the wiper links at the wiper output pin by removing the retaining clip.
5. Disconnect the wire leads from the motor. On 1967-68 models the leads are located under the hood; and, on 1969-74 cars they are located under the dash.
6. On 1967-68 models, remove the motor and bracket attaching bolts from the engine side of the firewall and remove the motor from the car. On 1969-74 models, remove the motor attaching bolts from under the dash and remove the motor.
7. Reverse above procedure to install.

NOTE: before installing the wiper arms and blades, operate the wiper motor to ensure the pivot shafts are in the park position when the arms and blades are installed.

Thunderbird, 1967-71 Except 1970

This motor works by hydraulic pressure taken from the power steering system. During wiper operation, a part of the fluid supply is bypassed through the wiper motor by a valve on the motor.

1. Remove wiper arm and blade assemblies, pivot shaft nuts and bezels.
2. Remove the cowl top panel.
3. Disconnect both pivot shaft links at the wiper motor.
4. Remove carburetor air cleaner.

Caution If the engine has been running recently, watch out for hot fluid in the wiper system.

5. Disconnect the lines at the wiper motor.
6. Remove wiper motor mounting screws.
7. Disconnect the control cable from the motor, then remove the motor.
8. If replacing the wiper motor, transfer all fittings.
9. Position motor to the bracket area, connect and adjust the control cable.
10. Start the lines in the fittings, position the motor on its mount and install attaching screws. Tighten fittings.
11. Connect the links to the wiper motor arm.
12. Start engine and check operation of wiper motor. Stop engine and bring power steering reservoir to level.
13. Reinstall cowl top panel.
14. Install bezels, nuts and wiper arm assemblies. Install the air cleaner.

Thunderbird, 1970

1970 Thunderbirds used electric, two-speed wipers instead of the usual hydraulic type.

1. Disconnect the negative battery cable.
2. Disconnect the windshield washer hose. Remove the three retaining bolts and pull the cowl grille from under the two clips.
3. Disconnect the wiper motor leads from the engine side of the firewall and push the wiring and insulating grommet through the hole in the firewall.
4. Remove the four motor to dash retaining bolts.
5. Lift the wiper motor out and, at the same time, pull the wiper arm and blade assembly to the left to gain access to the wiper output pin.
6. Remove the clip and disconnect the wiper links from the motor.
7. Remove the three motor-to-mounting plate bolts and remove the motor.
8. To reinstall, first position the wire harness and grommet in the hole in the firewall, then reverse above procedure.

Transmission or Linkage R & R

1967-74 All Models

1. Disconnect the battery ground cable.
2. Remove the wiper arms and blades from the pivots as an assembly. On Thunderbird be sure to remove the tension arm retaining clip from the stud on the left pivot.
3. Remove the cowl grille from the car.
4. Disconnect the linkage arm from the drive arm by removing the clip.
5. Remove the pivot attaching screws from the cowl and remove the pivot from the cowl.

NOTE: on 1969-72 Fords and Mercurys, to remove the left wiper transmission, it is first necessary to loosen the attaching screws on the right wiper arm pivot.

RADIO

Removal and Installation

1967 Ford and Mercury

1. Disconnect battery.
2. Remove cigarette lighter and radio knobs.
3. Remove instrument cluster retaining screws and instrument cluster.
4. Remove radio support nut and two bolts which retain radio in cluster.
5. Move radio out of cluster and disconnect antenna, speaker and power leads.
6. Reverse procedure to install radio.

1967-69 Thunderbird

1. Disconnect battery.
2. Remove inspection cover plate beneath steering wheel.
3. If necessary remove vacuum motor on inboard tilt swing column to provide clearance. Place shift lever in any position but Park before removing motor.
4. Remove two knobs and discs from radio.
5. Remove sleeve or fader control and two hex mounting nuts from radio shafts.
6. Remove radio rear support bracket.
7. Slide radio forward and down toward inspection hole.
8. Disconnect all leads and remove radio.
9. Reverse procedure to install radio.

1968 Ford

1. Disconnect battery.
2. Remove mouldings from windshield pillars.
3. Unsnap mouldings from right side of instrument panel pad.
4. Remove two pop off access covers from cluster area.
5. Remove four screws attaching right half of pad to instrument panel.
6. Remove two screws attaching left side of pad to instrument panel above cluster.
7. Remove one screw attaching each end of instrument panel lower pad to upper pad and remove upper pad from vehicle.
8. Pull all knobs from radio control shafts.
9. Remove ten retaining buttons and remove lens and mask from instrument cluster.
10. Remove two screws from blackout cover at right of speedometer and remove cover.
11. Remove four screws attaching radio front plate to instrument cluster.
12. Pull radio out and disconnect leads.
13. Reverse procedure to install radio.

1968 Mercury

1. Disconnect the negative battery cable.
2. Pull the radio control knobs from the radio.
3. Remove the four screws attaching the bezel around the speedometer and remove the bezel.
4. Pull the windshield wiper control knob off the shaft.
5. Remove the clock and heater knobs.
6. Remove the nut attaching the radio to the rear support.
7. Remove the four screws attaching the cluster right finish cover and remove the cover.
8. Remove the four screws attaching the radio and mounting plate to the instrument panel. Pull the radio out from the instrument panel and disconnect the radio leads from the radio.
9. Remove the mounting plate from the radio. Reverse above procedure to install.

1969-70 Mercury

1. Disconnect battery.
2. Remove radio knobs and remove nut from radio shaft.
3. Remove radio rear support nut and nut retaining radio to instrument panel.
4. Lower radio and disconnect antenna, radio, power, and speaker lead wires.
5. Remove radio. Reverse procedure to install radio.

1969-70 Ford

1. Remove radio knobs and wiper and washer knobs.
2. Remove lighter and pull off heater switch knobs.
3. Remove ten screws retaining instrument panel trim cover assembly and remove.
4. Remove lower rear radio support bolt.
5. Remove three nuts retaining radio in instrument panel and pull radio halfway out.
6. Disconnect all leads and remove radio.
7. Reverse procedure to install radio.

1970-71 Thunderbird

Use procedure under 1970-71 Mark III.

1971-74 Ford and Mercury

1. Disconnect the negative battery cable.
2. Remove the radio knobs and the nuts retaining the radio cover bezel.
3. Remove the bezel and the nut retaining the fader control to the bezel.
4. Remove the upper and lower radio support brackets and bolts.
5. Disconnect all leads from the radio.
6. Remove the two nuts retaining the radio to the instrument panel and remove the radio.
7. Reverse above procedure to install.

1972-74 Thunderbird

1. Disconnect the negative battery cable.
2. Remove the knobs from the radio shafts.
3. Remove the radio shaft nuts and the rear support attaching screw.
4. Disconnect the power lead, speaker wires and antenna lead, and remove the radio.
5. Reverse the above procedure to install.

HEATER

Vehicles Without Air Conditioning

Heater Core R & R

1967-74 Ford and Mercury

1. Partially drain cooling system.
2. Remove heater hoses at core.

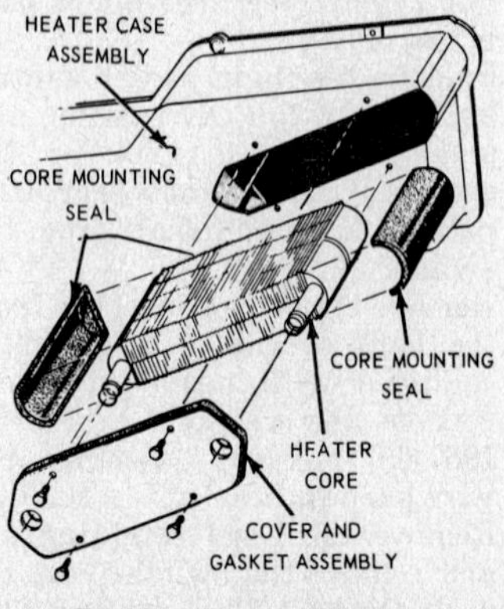
HEATER CASE ASSEMBLY
CORE MOUNTING SEAL
CORE MOUNTING SEAL
HEATER CORE
COVER AND GASKET ASSEMBLY

Ford heater core installation
(© Ford Motor Co)

3. Remove retaining screws, core cover and seal from plenum.
4. Remove core from plenum.
5. Install in reverse of above, applying a thin coat of silicone to the pads.

Thunderbird 1967-71

1. Remove the hood and air cleaner.
2. Drain the cooling system.
3. Remove the heater hoses and position the hoses and hot water valve out of the way.
4. Disconnect the vacuum hose from the top of the heater case and position it out of the way.
5. Remove the transmission dip stick and tube assembly from the transmission.
6. Disconnect the blower motor lead wires.
7. Remove the heater core case cover and remove the core from the case.
8. Reverse above procedure to install.

1972-74 Thunderbird

1. Drain the coolant and disconnect the hoses from the heater core.
2. Remove the glove box and the heater air outlet register.
3. Remove the mounting screw and disconnect the temperature cable at the blend door crank arm.
4. Remove the blue and red vacuum hoses from the high-low door vacuum motor, the yellow hose from the panel-defrost door motor, and the brown hose at the tee connector to the temperature bypass door motor.
5. Disconnect the wiring connector from the resistor.
6. Remove the 10 retaining screws and the rear half of the plenum case.
7. Remove the heater core tube support bracket mounting nut.
8. Reverse the above procedure to install, taking care to reseal the plenum case halves.

Blower Motor R & R

1967-71 Thunderbird

1. Working inside the car, remove the right kick panel cover.
2. Remove the screws attaching the fresh air duct and remove the duct from the car.
3. Reach inside the cowl panel and disconnect the blower motor wire leads.
4. Still working inside the cowl panel, remove the one screw attaching the blower motor to the mounting plate. Rotate the motor mounting plate clockwise to disengage it from the heater case.
5. Remove the blower motor and wheel assembly from the car by guiding it out of the opening in the cowl panel.

1972-74 Thunderbird

1. Remove the glovebox and recirc air register and duct assembly.
2. Remove the two, blower lower housing retaining screws.
3. Disconnect the white hose from the outside recirc air door vacuum motor, and remove the vacuum motor from the blower lower housing. Leave the motor actuator connected to the door crank arm.
4. Disconnect the orange lead wire and black ground wire from the blower motor.
5. Remove the six flange screws and separate the blower lower housing from the upper housing. Remove the lower housing from the car.
6. Remove the blower motor and wheel assembly from the lower housing.
7. Reverse the above procedure to install.

1967 Ford and Mercury

1. Open the hood and mark the location of the hood hinges on the hood. Remove the hood attaching bolts and remove the hood.
2. Remove the retaining nut and bolt and remove the right hood hinge support.
3. Remove the retaining bolts and remove the right hood hinge and support as an assembly.
4. Disconnect the heater motor wires.
5. Remove the heater motor mounting screws and on 1967 models remove the motor from the car.
6. Reverse above procedure to install.

1968-72 Ford and Mercury

1. Disconnect the negative battery cable.
2. Disconnect the blower motor wire leads under the hood.
3. Remove any parts mounted on the inside of the right fender apron.
4. Raise the vehicle on a hoist and remove the right front wheel.
5. Remove the fender apron-to-fender attaching bolts and lower the fender apron.
6. Insert a block of wood between the apron and the fender to gain working space.
7. Reach inside the fender apron and remove the blower motor mounting plate attaching screws.
8. Remove the blower motor, wheel and mounting plate from inside the fender as an assembly.
9. Reverse above procedure to install.

1973-74 Ford and Mercury

1. Disconnect the blower motor lead wire. This is an orange wire located at the rear of the right hood hinge.
2. Remove the mounting screw from the black ground wire located at the upper cowl. Remove both wires from the clip.
3. Remove the right front tire and wheel.
4. In order to get to the blower motor, an access hole must be cut out in the right front fender apron. The pattern for this hole has been outlined on the apron by the factory. It appears as a beaded line.
5. A small indentation or drill dimple is present 1/2 in. from the centerline of the bead. Drill a 1 in. diameter hole at this drill dimple. Be careful not to damage the heater case by overdrilling.
6. Using aircraft snips, cut along the bead to create the opening. Do not use a saber saw.
7. Remove the blower motor mounting plate screws and disconnect the cooler tube from the motor.
8. Remove the motor and wheel assembly out of the heater case and out through the access hole.
9. To install, reverse the removal procedure. Apply rope sealer to the motor mounting plate. Obtain a cover plate from your local Ford parts department, drill 8, 1/8 in. holes in the fender apron and install the cover plate.

Vehicles With Integral Heater-Air Conditioner Assembly

Heater Core R & R

1967-68 Ford and Mercury

1. Drain the cooling system and raise the front of the vehicle.
2. Remove the right front wheel and tire.
3. To gain access to the core, remove the two upper bolts and the bolts around the wheel well retaining the inner fender apron. Pull the apron down and block it in this position.
4. Disconnect the heater hoses.
5. Remove the water valve retaining screws and position the valve to one side.
6. Remove the core housing-to-dash retaining screws and the core housing from the car.
7. Remove the core from the housing by removing the retaining screws and separating the housing halves.
8. Reverse the above procedure to install, taking care to seal the housing halves together.

1969-72 Ford and Mercury

1. Drain the cooling system.
2. Remove the carburetor air cleaner.
3. Remove the two screws retaining the vacuum manifold to the dash.

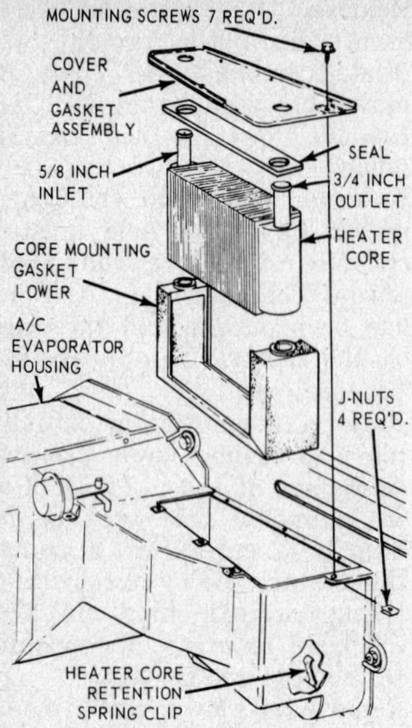
MOUNTING SCREWS 7 REQ'D.
COVER AND GASKET ASSEMBLY
SEAL
5/8 INCH INLET
3/4 INCH OUTLET
HEATER CORE
CORE MOUNTING GASKET LOWER
A/C EVAPORATOR HOUSING
J-NUTS 4 REQ'D.
HEATER CORE RETENTION SPRING CLIP

1969-72 Ford and Mercury heater-air conditioner assembly—heater core removal (© Ford Motor Co)

Disconnect the vacuum hoses as necessary, taking note of their placement, and move the manifold to one side of the heater core cover.

4. Disconnect the heater hoses.
5. Remove the seven attaching screws and the heater core cover.
6. Remove the heater core and pad from the housing.
7. Reverse above procedure to install.

1973-74 Ford and Mercury

1. Drain the cooling system.
2. Disconnect the heater hoses at the heater core tubes.

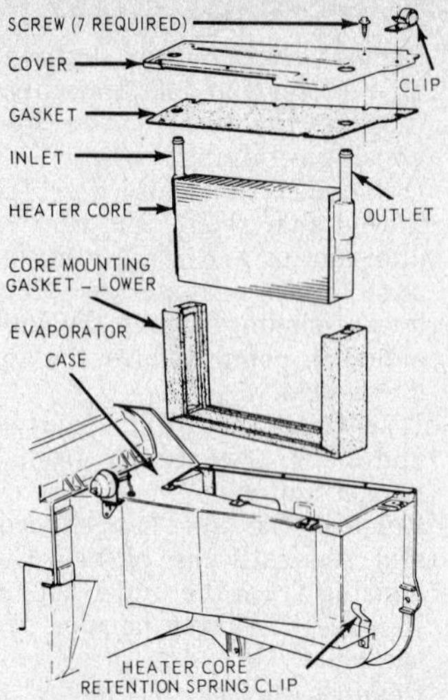
SCREW (7 REQUIRED)
COVER
CLIP
GASKET
INLET
HEATER CORE
OUTLET
CORE MOUNTING GASKET – LOWER
EVAPORATOR CASE
HEATER CORE RETENTION SPRING CLIP

Heater core removal—1973-74 Ford and Mercury (© Ford Motor Co)

3. Remove the seven screws which retain the core cover plate to the core housing and lift off the plate.
4. Pull the heater core and mounting gasket up out of the case. Remove the core mounting gasket.
5. Reverse the above procedure to install, taking care to ensure that the core and gasket seat firmly forward of the core retention spring in the case. Fill the cooling system with the recommended mixture of water and anti-freeze (coolant).

1967-71 Thunderbird

1. Drain the cooling system.
2. Remove the air cleaner. Scribe the outline of the hinges on the hood and remove the hood.
3. On models equipped with hydraulic wipers, disconnect and plug the hydraulic lines at the motor.
4. Disconnect the heater hoses.
5. Disconnect the vacuum supply hose from the top of the housing and remove the oil pressure sender unit from the engine.
6. Remove the transmission dipstick and tube assembly.
7. Disconnect the icing switch multiple connector.
8. Remove the heater-air conditioner housing front cover.
9. Remove the glove compartment liner, and disconnect the electrical and vacuum junction blocks from the inner dash panel.
10. Remove two evaporator stud nuts and remove the heater core case cover.
11. Remove the core retaining bracket and core.
12. Reverse above procedure to install.

1972-74 Thunderbird

See heater core R&R for non-air-conditioned 1972-74 Thunderbirds.

Blower Motor R & R

1967-68 Ford and Mercury

1. Take off the protective cover from the engine firewall.
2. Take out the mounting plate-to-evaporator housing attaching screws.
3. Disconnect the motor wires.
4. Lift out the motor assembly.
5. Reverse above procedure to install.

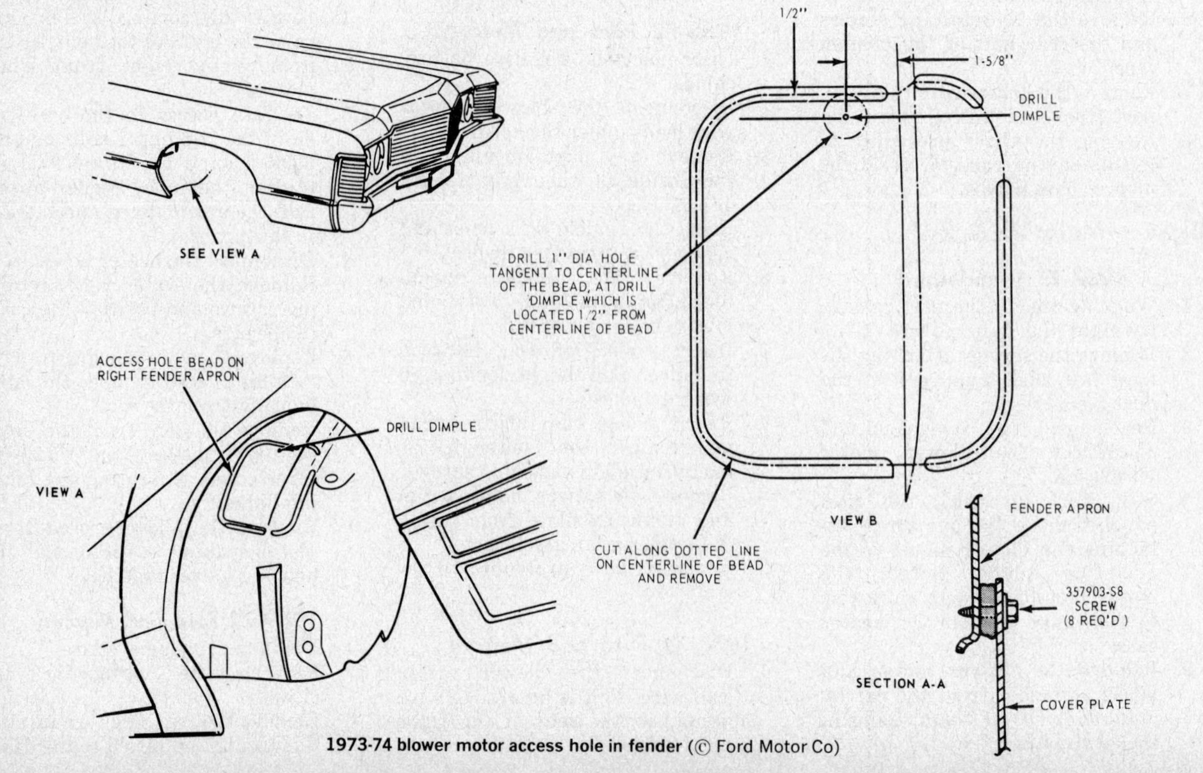
SEE VIEW A
1/2"
1-5/8"
DRILL DIMPLE
DRILL 1" DIA HOLE TANGENT TO CENTERLINE OF THE BEAD, AT DRILL DIMPLE WHICH IS LOCATED 1/2" FROM CENTERLINE OF BEAD
ACCESS HOLE BEAD ON RIGHT FENDER APRON
DRILL DIMPLE
VIEW A
CUT ALONG DOTTED LINE ON CENTERLINE OF BEAD AND REMOVE
VIEW B
FENDER APRON
357903-S8 SCREW (8 REQ'D)
SECTION A-A
COVER PLATE

1973-74 blower motor access hole in fender (© Ford Motor Co)

1969-72 Ford and Mercury

1. Remove the battery.
2. Remove the right front wheel.
3. Remove the vacuum tank bolts and fender apron bolts.
4. Move the fender apron inboard.
5. Remove the blower motor attaching screws and vent hose.
6. Pry upward on the hood hinge and remove the blower.
7. Reverse the above procedure to install.

1973-74 Ford and Mercury

For air-conditioned cars, follow the same procedure outlined under "Blower Motor R & R" for non-air-conditioned 1973-74 Ford and Mercury.

1967-71 Thunderbird

1. Disconnect the ground cable from the battery.
2. Take out the courtesy light from the lower edge of the instrument panel.
3. Take out the glove box liner.
4. Take off the right cowl side of the trim panel.
5. Take out the six duct mounting flange screws. Reach through the recirculating door opening and take the vacuum hose from the vacuum motor and take out the duct assembly.
6. Disconnect the lead wire from the blower motor.
7. Lift out the motor and wheel assembly through the opening in the cowl side panel.
8. Take out the screw from the motor mounting plate.
9. Rotate the motor mounting plate counter-clockwise until unlocked, then lift out.
10. Reverse the above procedure to install.

1972-74 Thunderbird

See "Blower Motor R&R" for non-air-conditioned 1972-74 Thunderbirds.

SEAT BELTS

Seat Belt—Starter Interlock System

Starting with 1974 models, a new starter interlock system is employed consisting of a warning light, buzzer, seat sensors, switches in the outboard belt retractors, and an electronic logic module. The starter will not engage unless the driver and right front seat passenger sit on their seats and pull out their seat belts. Unless the driver and passesger have remained seated and buckled, the sequence must be repeated every time the engine is started. Leaving the belts pulled all the way out will also prevent the engine from being started, as the belts must be retracted and buckled each time the engine is started. In the event of a starter interlock system failure, or to permit the use of a remote starter switch when working under the hood, a starter interlock by-pass switch is located in the engine compartment, eliminating the need to perform the buckling sequence.

NOTE: Each time the by-pass switch is operated the buckling sequence may be eliminated one time only. The system may not be permanently by-passed.

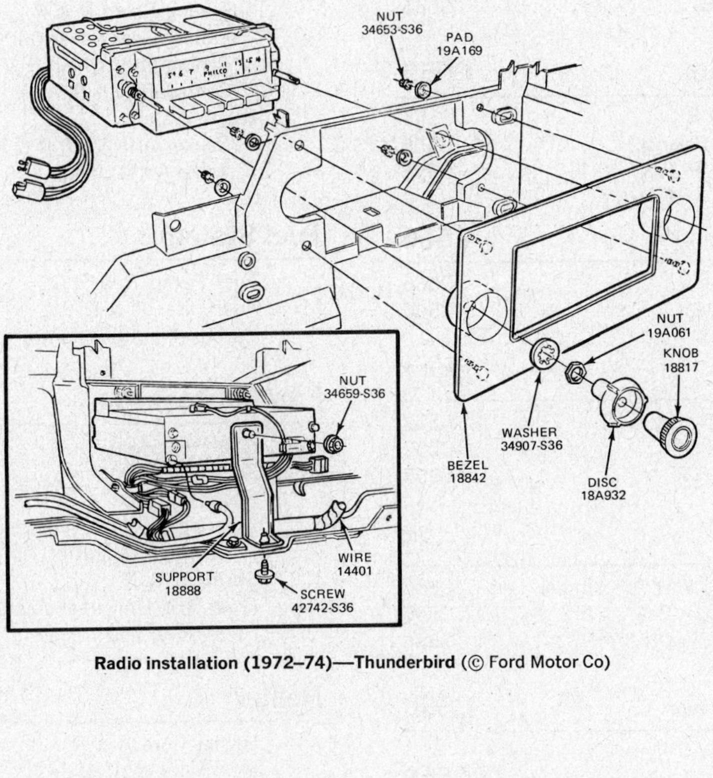
NUT
34653-S36
PAD
19A169
NUT
19A061
KNOB
18817
WASHER
34907-S36
BEZEL
18842
DISC
18A932
NUT
34659-S36
WIRE
14401
SUPPORT
18888
SCREW
42742-S36

Radio installation (1972–74)—Thunderbird (© Ford Motor Co)

INDEX

Jeep

MODEL IDENTIFICATION

CJ-6 Universal Jeep

Jeepster

Jeepster Commando

Jeepster Convertible

Wagoneer

CJ-5 Universal Jeep

1974 Cherokee

Vehicle Serial Number

The vehicle serial number is on a metal plate mounted on the firewall under the hood. It is on the left side for models CJ-5, CJ-5A, CJ-6, CJ-6A, DJ-5, DJ-6, and the Jeepster. The serial number plate is on the left front door body hinge pillar on the Wagoneer and Cherokee.

Axle and Transmission Identifying Numbers

Axles on Jeep vehicles have a model number cast into the axle differential housing near or on one of the reinforcing webs. A tag installed under one of the gear cover screw heads lists the number of teeth on the gear and also on the pinion. In some cases, the axle ratio is also listed.

Manual transmissions are identified by the manufacturer's model number on a metal plate attached to the transmission case cover. Starting 1972, automatic transmissions have a serial number on a plate on the right side.

ENGINE IDENTIFICATION CODE

The engine identification code is located: at the front of the block above the water pump on 1967-71 four cylinder engines; stamped on a boss between the No. 2 and No. 3 spark plugs on 1967-74 232 and 258 sixes; at the right block deck between the front two spark plugs on 1967-71 225 V6 engines; on the alternator bracket on 1967-68 327 V8 engines; and stamped on a tab on the right valve cover on 1971-74 304, 360, and 401 V8 engines. Beginning 1972, the engine code is the eighth digit of the vehicle identification number.

Disp	Bbl	Hp	'67	'68	'69	'70	'71	'72	'73	'74
4-Cylinder—(Kaiser)										
134	1	75	4J	4J	4J	SF	F			
6-Cylinder—(Buick)										
225	1	155	NH	PH						
225	2	160	NH	PH	RH	SH	HC			
6-Cylinder—(AMC)										
232	1	100 (net)						E	E	E
232	1	145	9L	1L	1L	3L	E			
258	1	110 (net)						A	A	A
258	1	150					A			
8-Cylinder—(AMC)										
304	2	150 (net)						H	H	H
304	2	210					H			
327	2	250	E	E						
327	4	270	E	E						
8-Cylinder—(Buick)										
350	2	230		KPO	KRO	KSO	KTO			
8-Cylinder—(AMC)										
360	2	175 (net)						N	N	N
360	2	245					N			
360	4	195 (net)							P	P
401	4	225 (net)								Z

FIRING ORDER AND ROTATION

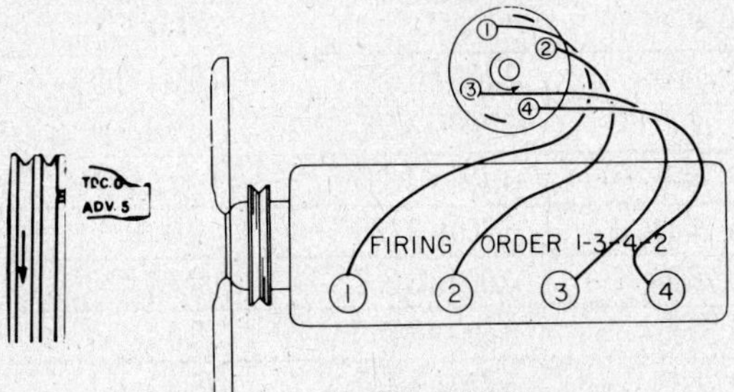
TDC 0
ADV. 5
FIRING ORDER 1-3-4-2

4 cyl F-head (134 cu in.)

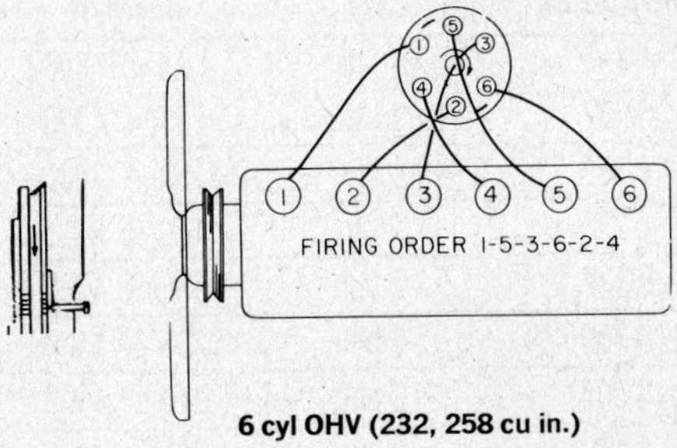
FIRING ORDER 1-5-3-6-2-4

6 cyl OHV (232, 258 cu in.)

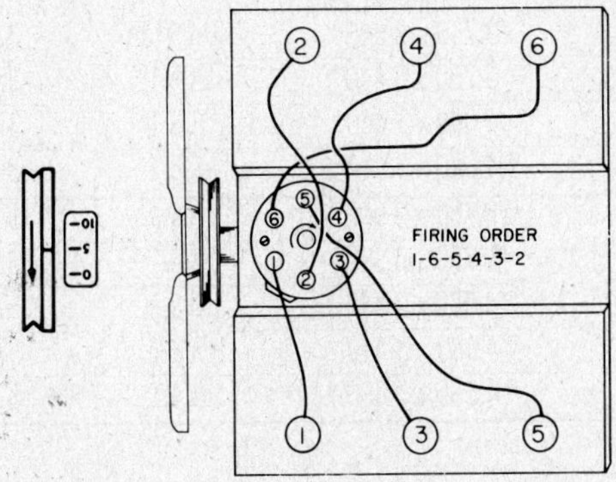
FIRING ORDER
1-6-5-4-3-2

V6 225 cu in.

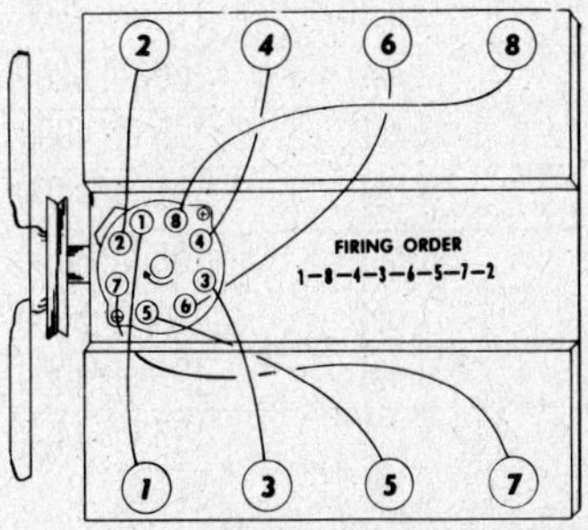
FIRING ORDER
1-8-4-3-6-5-7-2

V8 350 cu in.

Clockwise @ Rotor
1-8-4-3-6-5-7-2

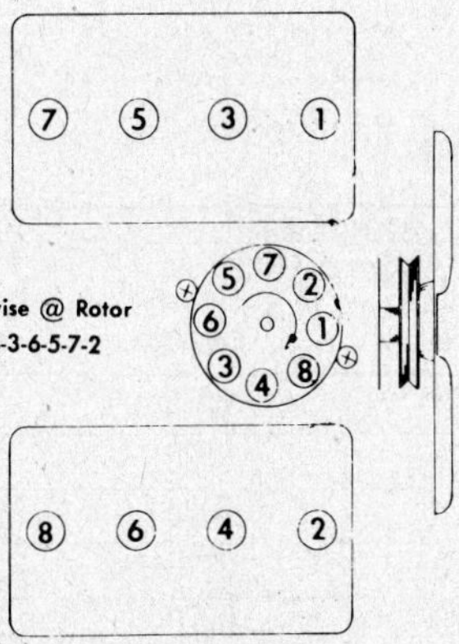

V8 (304, 360, 401 cu in.)

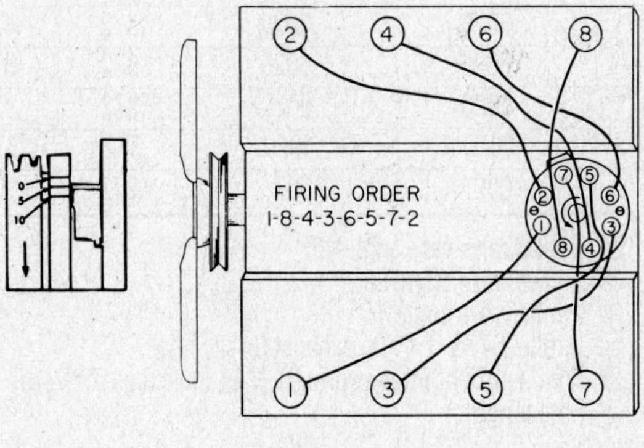
FIRING ORDER
1-8-4-3-6-5-7-2

V8 327 cu in.

PISTON CLEARANCE

(All measurements are in inches)

Engine No. Cyl. Displacement (cu. in.)	Piston to Bore Clearance
4-134	.0025
6-225	①
6-232	.0009-.0017②
6-258	.0009-.0017
8-304	.0010-.0018
8-327	③
8-350	④
8-360	.0012-.0020
8-401	.0010-.0018

① Top Land—.0265 in.-.0345 in.
Skirt Top—.0005 in.-.0011 in.
Skirt Bottom—.0005 in.-.0021 in.

② Skirt Bottom

③ Top Land—.028 in.-.032 in.
Skirt Top—.0009 in.-.0025 in.
Skirt Bottom—.0009 in.-.0015 in.

④ Top Land—.0270 in.-.0360 in.
Skirt Top—.0008 in.-.0014 in.
Skirt Bottom—.0013 in.-.0029 in.

GENERAL ENGINE SPECIFICATIONS

Year	Engine Cu In. Displacement	Carburetor Type	Advertised Horsepower @ rpm ■	Advertised Torque @ rpm (ft lbs) ■	Bore and Stroke (in.)	Advertised Compression Ratio	Oil Pressure @ 30 mph (psi)
'67-'71	4-134	1 bbl	75 @ 4000	114 @ 2000	3.125 x 3.375	7.4:1/6.9:1/7.8:1	35
'67-'71	6-232	1 bbl	145 @ 4300	215 @ 1600	3.750 x 3.500	8.5:1	50
'71	6-258	1 bbl	150 @ 3800	240 @ 1800	3.750 x 3.895	8.0:1/7.6:1	37
'67-'71	6-225	2 bbl	160 @ 4200	235 @ 2400	3.750 x 3.400	9.0:1	33
'67-'69	8-327	2 bbl	250 @ 4700	340 @ 2600	4.000 x 3.250	8.7:1	55
'69-'71	8-350	2 bbl	230 @ 4400	350 @ 2400	3.800 x 3.850	9.0:1	37
'71	8-304	2 bbl	210 @ 4400	300 @ 2600	3.750 x 3.440	8.4:1	37
'71	8-360	2 bbl	245 @ 4400	365 @ 2600	4.080 x 3.440	8.5:1	37
'72-'73	6-232	1 bbl	100 @ 3600	185 @ 1800	3.750 x 3.500	8.0:1/7.6:1	37
'72-'73	6-258	1 bbl	110 @ 3500	195 @ 2000	3.750 x 3.895	8.0:1/7.6:1	37
'72-'74	8-304	2 bbl	150 @ 4200	245 @ 2500	3.750 x 3.440	8.4:1	37
'72-'73	8-360	2 bbl	175 @ 4000	285 @ 2400	4.080 x 3.440	8.5:1	37
'72-'73	8-360	4 bbl	195 @ 4400	295 @ 2900	4.080 x 3.440	8.5:1	37
'74	6-232	1 bbl	100 @ 3500	185 @ 1800	3.750 x 3.500	8.0:1	37
	6-258	1 bbl	110 @ 3500	195 @ 2000	3.750 x 3.900	8.0:1	37
	8-360	2 bbl	175 @ 4000	285 @ 2400	4.080 x 3.440	8.3:1	37
	8-360	4 bbl	195 @ 4400	295 @ 2900	4.080 x 3.440	8.3:1	37
	8-401	4 bbl	225 @ 4600	345 @ 3300	4.165 x 3.680	8.4:1	37

■ Beginning in 1972, horsepower and torque are SAE net figures. They are measured at the rear of the transmission with all accessories installed and operating. Since the figures vary when a given engine is installed in different models, some are representative rather than exact.

VALVE SPECIFICATIONS

Year	Engine No. Cyl. Displacement (cu in.)	Seat Angle (deg) •	Face Angle (deg) ■	Spring Test Pressure (lbs @ in.)	Spring Installed Height (in.)	STEM TO GUIDE Clearance (in.)		STEM Diameter (in.)	
						Intake	Exhaust	Intake	Exhaust
'67-'71	4-134	45①	46②	73 @ 1 27/32	⑥	.0014	.0035	.373	.371
	6-232	45③	45③	90 @ 1 13/16	2 13/64⑦	.0020	.0020	.373	.373
	6-258	45③	44	195 @ 1 7/16	—	.0020	.0020	.372	.372
	6-225	45④	45④	⑤	1 23/32	.0020	.0025	.3407	.3407
'67-'69	8-327	45③	45③	88 @ 1 13/16	2 13/64⑦	.0020	.0020	.372	.372
	8-350	45④	45④	75 @ 1 11/16	1 23/32	.0025	.0025	.372	.372
'71	8-304	45	44½	195 @ 1 7/16	—	.0020	.0020	.372	.372
	8-360	45	44½	195 @ 1 7/16	—	.0020	.0020	.372	.372
'72-'74	6-232	44½	44	100 @ 1 13/16	—	.0020	.0020	.372	.372
	6-258	44½	44	100 @ 1 13/16	—	.0020	.0020	.372	.372
	8-304	44½	44	84 @ 1 13/16	—	.0020	.0020	.372	.372
	8-360	44½	44	84 @ 1 13/16	—	.0020	.0020	.372	.372
'74	8-401	44½	44	84 @ 1 13/16	—	.002	.002	.372	.372

• Exhaust valve seat angle given; all intake valve seat angles are 30° unless otherwise noted
■ Exhaust valve face angle given: all intake valve face angles are 29° unless otherwise noted
— Not applicable
① Intake valve seat angle 45°
② Intake valve face angle 46°
③ Intake valve angle 30°
④ Intake valve angle 45°
⑤ Intake: 64 @ 1 11/16; exhaust 64 @ 1 5/8
⑥ Free length of intake spring 1 31/32 in.; exhaust 2½ in.
⑦ Free length

TUNE-UP SPECIFICATIONS

When analyzing compression test results, look for uniformity among cylinders rather than specific pressures.

Year	ENGINE No. Cyl Displacement (cu. in.)	hp	SPARK PLUGS Type §	Gap (in.)	DISTRIBUTOR Point Dwell (deg)	Point Gap (in.)	IGNITION TIMING (deg) ▲	VALVES Intake Opens (deg) ■	Fuel Pump Pressure (psi)	IDLE SPEED (rpm) • Man Trans	Auto Trans
'67-'71	4—134	75	Ch J8	.030	40	.020	5B	9	3	600	N.A.
'67-'71	6—232	140	Ch N-14Y	.035	32	.016	①	12½	5	650⑤	700⑤
'71	6—258	150	Ch N-14Y	.035	32	.016	5B	12½	4-5½	600	700
'67-'71	6—225	160	AC 44S	.035	30	.016	5B	24	5	550	N.A.
'67-'69	8—327	250	Ch H-14Y	.035	30	.016	②	12½	4½	550③	500③
'69-'71	8—350	230	Ch H-14Y	.035	30	.016	④	24	5	650⑤	700⑤
'71	8—304	210	Ch N-12Y	.035	30	.016	2½B	18½	4-5½	650	700
'71	8—360	245	Ch N-12Y	.035	30	.016	2½B	18½	4-5½	650	750
'72	6—232	100	Ch N-12Y	.035	32	.016	5B⑥	12½	4-5	700	600
'72	6—258	110	Ch N-12Y	.035	32	.016	3B⑥	12½	4-5	700	600
'72	8—304	150	Ch N-12Y	.035	30	.016	5B⑥	14¾	5-6½	750	650
'72	8—360	175	Ch N-12Y	.035	30	.016	5B⑥	14¾	5-6½	750	650
'73-'74	6—232	100	Ch N-12Y	.035	32	.016	5B⑥	12½	4-5	700⑦	—
'73-'74	6—258	258	Ch N-12Y	.035	32	.016	3B⑥	12½	4-5	700⑦	550
'73-'74	8—304	150	Ch N-12Y	.035	30	.016	5B⑥	14¾	5-6½	750	700
'73-'74	8—360	175	Ch N-12Y	.035	30	.016	5B⑥	14¾	5-6½	750	700
'73-'74	8—360	195	Ch N-12Y	.035	30	.016	5B⑥	14¾	5-6½	750	700
'74	8—401	225	Ch N-12Y	.035	30	.016	5B⑥	25½	5-6½	700	700

▲ With vacuum advance disconnected
■ All figures before TDC (BTDC)
• With manual transmission in Neutral and automatic transmission in Drive
B Before top dead center (BTDC)
① W/o emission control, 5B on dist. model 1110340, 0 on dist. model 110444, 0 w/ emission control
② 5B w/o emission control, 0 w/ emission control
③ 650/700 rpm w/o emission control
④ 0 on dist. model 1111330, 1111474, and 1111938, 5B on model 11116964
⑤ 100 rpm less w/o emission control
⑥ At 550 rpm
⑦ 700 rpm for CJ, 600 rpm Commando and Wagoneer
§ original equipment

CAPACITIES

Model	Engine Crankcase (add 1 qt for new filter)	TRANSMISSIONS Manual (add 1 pt for overdrive) 3-Speed	4-Speed	Automatic (pts) •	Front Drive Axle (pts)	Transfer Case (pts)	Rear Drive Axle (pts)	Gas Tank (gal)	Cooling System (qts) With Heater
4—134①	4	1½	—	22	—	—	2	15	12
4—134②	4	3	—	22	2½	3½	3	15	12
6—225	4	2½	6½	19	2½	3¼	3	20	13
8—327	5	2½	6½	22	2½	3¼	3	—	19
8—350	4	2½	6½	22	2½	3....	3	—	15
6—232	5	2½	6½	22	2½	3¼	3	16④	10½
6—258	5	2½	6½	22	2½	3¼③	3	16④	10½
8—304	4	2¾	6½	22	2½	3¼③	3	16④	14
8—360	4	2¾	6½	22	2½	3¼③	3	22④	13
8—401	4	—	—	22	2½	⑤	3	22	13

• Includes torque converter
① 2-wheel drive
② 4-wheel drive
③ 3.5 pts with Quadra-Trac and 1 pt more with reduction unit
④ 1972-74—22 gals Wagoneer and Cherokee; 15.5 gals CJ

GENERATOR AND REGULATOR SPECIFICATIONS

Make	GENERATORS—6 VOLT Model No.	Output Amps	Brush Spring Tension (oz)	REGULATORS—6 VOLT Model No.	Regulated Voltage	Regulated Amperage	Cutout Relay Closing Voltage
Auto-Lite	GDZ4817	35	35-53	VRP-6003	7.1-7.3	49	6.3-6.8 @ 1000 rpm
	GDZ6001	35	35-53	VRP-4007 VBO-4601			
	GGW4801	45	35-53	VBO-4601C	7.1-7.3	49	6.3-6.8 @ 1000 rpm
	GGW7404	45	18-36				
Delco-Remy	1102811		28	1972063	6.9-7.4	42-47	5.9-6.7

Make	GENERATORS—12 VOLT Model No.	Output Amps	Brush Spring Tension (oz)	REGULATORS—12 VOLT Model No.	Regulated Voltage	Regulated Amperage	Cutout Relay Closing Voltage
Auto-Lite	GJC-7002	30	18-36	VRX-6009	14.3-14.7	39	12.6-13.6 @ 1325 rpm
	GJP-7202	35	18-36	VBO-4201E-4A	14.3-14.7	39	12.6-13.6 @ 1325 rpm
	GJP-7402A	35	18-36				
	GJP-7401A	35	18-36				
Delco-Remy	1102096	35	28	1972029	14.2-14.4	36	11.8-13.5
Prestolite	GJP-7402B	35	18-36	VBO-4201 E-4A	14.2-14.4	36	12.6-13.6 @ 1325 rpm

ALTERNATOR AND REGULATOR SPECIFICATIONS

Make	ALTERNATOR Model No.	Field Current Draw @ 12 V-Amps	Output (Amps)	REGULATOR Model No.	Type	Regulated Voltage	Regulated Amperage
Motorola	A12NW528 A12NW526	1.2-1.7	35	R2K1	Transistorized	14.2-14.6	35
Motorola	A12NAM453 A12NAM451-S A12NW526 A12NW525 A12NW527	1.2-1.7	35	TVR-12-W14	Transistorized	14.2-14.6	35
Motorola	ALK6312	2.4-2.5	35	VSC-62437	Transistorized	14.2	35
	A12NAM460	2.0-2.6	35	R2AM4	Transistorized	15.0	35
	A12NAM555	1.8-2.4	55	R2AM4	Transistorized	15.0	55
Motorola	—	1.8-2.5	37/51	8RD-2001	Transistorized	14.2	37/51

BRAKE SPECIFICATIONS

(All measurements are given in inches)

Year	Model	MASTER CYLINDER Disc	Drum	WHEEL CYLINDER Front Disc	Drum	Rear	BRAKE DISC OR DRUM DIAMETER Front Disc	Drum	Rear
'67-'71	CJ	—	1	—	1	13/16	—	10	10
'72	CJ	—	1	—	1 1/8	15/16	—	10	10
'67-'71	Wagoneer	—	1	—	1 1/8	1	—	11	11
'72-'73	Wagoneer	—	1	—	1 1/8	15/16	—	11	11
'67-'71	Jeepster	—	1	—	1	13/16	—	10①	10①
'72-'73	Commando	—	1	—	1 1/8	15/16	—	11	11
'73-'74	CJ	—	1	—	1 1/8	15/16	—	11	11
'74	Wagoneer, Cherokee	1 1/8	1	2 3/4	1 1/8	15/16	12	11	11

① 11 in. with Bendix brakes

BATTERY AND STARTER SPECIFICATIONS

Model	Battery: Ampere Hour Capacity	Battery: Volts	Battery: Terminal Grounded	Starter Lock Test: Amps	Lock Test: Volts	Lock Test: Torque (ft lbs)	No-Load Test: Amps	No-Load Test: Volts	No-Load Test: RPM	Brush Spring Tension (oz)
Universal, Dispatcher 4 Cyl	100	6	Neg.	335	2.0	6.0	65	5.0	4,300	42-53
			Neg.	600	3.0	15.0	60	5.0	6.000	24
Universal, Dispatcher 4 Cyl	50	12	Neg.	170/280	4.0	1.5/6.2	50	10.0	4,400/5,300	31-47
			Neg.	435	5.8	10.5	75	10.3	6,900	35
Jeepster 4 Cyl	50	12	Neg.	405	—	9.0	50	10.0	5,300	32-40
232 6 Cyl (to 1971)	50/70	12	Neg.	405	4.0	9.0	60	10.0	4,200	32-40
V6	50	12	Neg.	—	—	—	75	10.6	6,200	32-40
327V8	60	12	Neg.	405	4.0	9.0	60	10.0	4,200	32-40
350V8	60/70	12	Neg.	300-360	3.5	9.0	65-100	10.6	3,600-5,100	35
232, 258 6 Cyl ('72-'74)	50	12	Neg.	600	4.3	6.5	65	12.0	9,250	40
304V8	50/70	12	Neg.	600	3.4	—	65	12.0	9,250	40
360V8	60/70	12	Neg.	600	3.4	—	65	12.0	9,250	40

CRANKSHAFT AND CONNECTING ROD SPECIFICATIONS

All measurements are given in inches

Engine No. Cyl. Displacement (cu in.)	Crankshaft: Main Brg. Journal Dia	Crankshaft: Main Brg. Oil Clearance	Crankshaft: Shaft End-Play	Crankshaft: Thrust on No.	Connecting Rod: Journal Diameter	Connecting Rod: Oil Clearance	Connecting Rod: Side Clearance
4-134	2.333	.0019	.005	1	1.9375	.0014	.007
6-225	2.4995	.0009	.006	2	2.0000	.0021	.010
6-232	2.4988	.0012	.005	3	2.0952	.0008	.009
6-258	2.4986-2.5001	.001-.002	.002-.007	3	2.0934-2.0955	.001-.002	.003-.010①
8-327	2.4991	.0018	.005	1	2.2486	.0015	.010
8-350	2.9995	.0010	.006	3	2.0000	.0012	.010
8-304	2.7489-2.7474②	.001-.002③	.003-.008	3	2.0945	.001-.002	.006-.018
8-360	2.7489-2.7474②	.001-.002③	.003-.008	3	2.0945	.001-.002	.006-.018
8-401	2.7489-2.7474②	.001-.002③	.003-.008	3	2.2470	.001-.002	.006-.018

① .005-.014 1972 and 1973
② Rear main, 2.7479-2.7464
③ Rear Main, .002-.003

WHEEL ALIGNMENT

Model	Caster Pref. Setting (deg)	Camber Pref. Setting (deg)	Toe-In (in.)	King-Pin Inclination (deg)	Wheel Pivot Ratio: Inner Wheel	Wheel Pivot Ratio: Outer Wheel
CJ-5, CJ-6, DJ-5, DJ-6, CJ-5A, CJ-6A	3	1°30′	3/64-3/32	7½	20	20
Jeepster, Commando	3	1°30′	3/64-3/32	7½	—	—
Wagoneer, Cherokee	3	1°30′	3/64-3/32	7½	—	—

RING GAP

All measurements are given in in.

Engine	Top Compression	Bottom Compression	Oil Control
4-134	.007-.015①	.007-.015①	.007-.015①
6-225	.010-.020	.010-.020	.015-.035
6-232	.010-.020	.010-.020	.010-.025②
6-258	.010-.020	.010-.020	.010-.025②
8-327	.010-.020	.010-.020	.015-.055
8-350	.010-.020	.010-.020	.015-.035
8-304	.010-.020	.010-.020	.010-.025
8-360	.010-.020	.010-.020	.015-.045
8-360	.010-.020	.010-.020	.015-.055

① The maximum ring gap for the 4-134 engine with standard bore can be as high as .045 in.
② Ring gap for oil control ring in 1973-74 is .015-.055

RING SIDE CLEARANCE

All measurements are given in in.

Engine	Top Compression	Bottom Compression	Oil Control
4-134	.002-.004	.0015-.0035	.001-.0025
6-225	.002-.0035	.003-.0035	.0015-.0085
6-232	.0015-.003	.0015-.003	.001-.008
6-258	.0015-.003	.0015-.003	.001-.008
8-304	.0015-.0035	.0015-.0035	.0011-.008
8-327	.002-.004	.002-.004	.000-.005
8-350	.003-.005	.003-.005	.0035-.0095
8-360	.0015-.003	.0015-.0035	.000-.007
8-401	.0015-.003	.0015-.0035	.000-.007

TORQUE SPECIFICATIONS

All readings in ft lbs

Engine No. Cyl. Displacement (cu in.)	Cylinder Head Bolts	Rod Bearing Bolts	Main Bearing Bolts	Crankshaft Pulley Bolt	Flywheel to Crankshaft Bolts	MANIFOLD Intake	MANIFOLD Exhaust
4-134	60-70	35-45	65-75	60-70	35-41	29-35	29-35
6-232, 258	95-115	26-30	75-85	18-28	95-120	37-47	20-30
6-225	65-80	30-40	95-120	140-160	50-65	25-35	15-20
8-327	58-62	46-50	①	70-80	100-110	20-25	20-25
8-350	②	35	110	140-180	60	50	18
8-304, 360	100-120	26-30	90-105	18-28	95-120	37-47	20-30
8-401	100-120	35-40	90-105	18-28	95-120	37-47	20-30

① 80-85; rear only 50-55
② Metal gasket 75; composition 80

CYLINDER HEAD BOLT TIGHTENING SEQUENCE

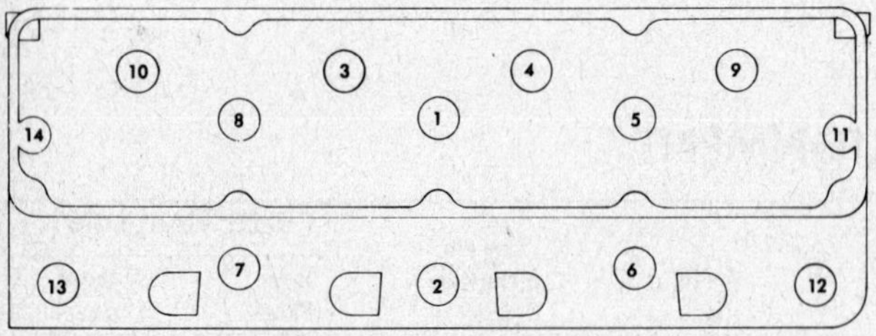
10 3 4 9
14 8 1 5 11
13 7 2 6 12

V8 (304, 360, and 401 cu in.)

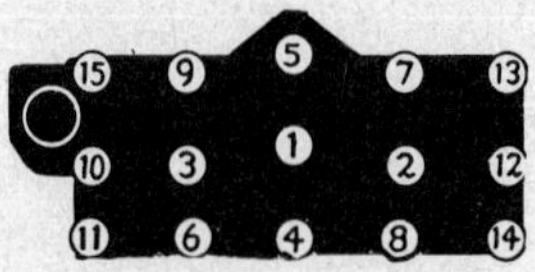
15 9 5 7 13
10 3 1 2 12
11 6 4 8 14

4 cyl F-head (134 cu in.)

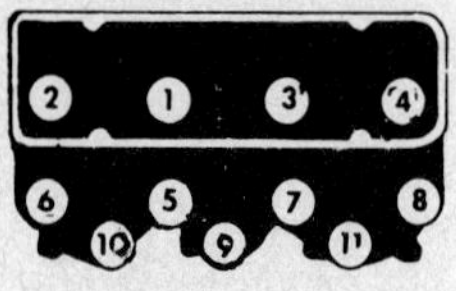
2 1 3 4
6 5 7 8
10 9 11

V6 225 cu in.

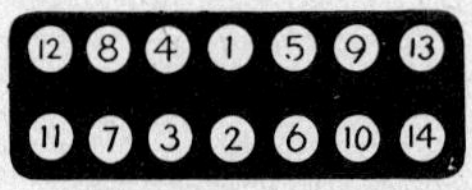
12 8 4 1 5 9 13
11 7 3 2 6 10 14

6 cyl 232 and 258 cu in.

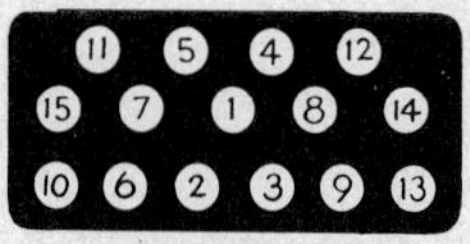
11 5 4 12
15 7 1 8 14
10 6 2 3 9 13

V8 327 cu in.

9 3 1 6 8
7 5 2 4 10

V8 350 cu in.

NOTE: Jeep vehicles have, in the past, used a variety of engines made by other manufacturers. The only engines covered in detail in this section are the F4 and the American Motors 327 V8. For specific procedures concerning the 225 V6 and the 350 V8, refer to the Buick Special section. For specific procedures concerning the 232 and 258 in-line sixes and the 304, 360, and 401 V8, refer to the American Motors section. Specifications for all of the engines are given at the beginning of this section.

CHARGING SYSTEM

CAUTION: Since the AC generator and regulator are designed for use on only one polarity system, the following precautions must be observed:

a. The polarity of the battery, generator and regulator must be matched and considered before making any electrical connections in the system.

b. When connecting a booster battery, be sure to connect the negative battery terminals together and the positive battery terminals together.

c. When connecting a charger to the battery, connect the charger positive lead to the battery positive terminal. Connect the charger negative lead to the battery negative terminal.

d. Never operate the AC generator on open circuit. Be sure that all connections in the circuit are clean and tight.

e. Do not short across or ground any of the terminals on the AC generator.

f. Do not attempt to polarize the AC generator.

g. Do not use test lamps of more than 12 V for checking diode continuity.

h. Avoid long soldering times when replacing diodes or transistors. Prolonged heat is damaging to these units.

i. Disconnect the battery ground terminal when servicing any AC system. This will prevent the possibility of accidentally reversing polarity.

DC Generator Polarity

CAUTION: Whenever the circuits to the generator, the regulator or the battery have been disconnected, it is best to apply the following procedure:

Before the engine is started, momentarily short the Bat to the Gen terminals of the regulator with a screwdriver. This gives a momentary surge of current from the battery to the generator and correctly polarizes the generator with regard to the battery.

Failure to polarize the generator before starting the engine may severely damage the regulator because reversed polarity causes vibration, arcing, and burning of the relay points.

Alternator R & R

Unfasten the bolt holding the tension bar to the alternator. Push the alternator in toward the engine to release the drive belt. Unfasten the mounting bolt to release the alternator from the engine.

When reinstalling, adjust the drive belt to allow ½ in. play on the longest run between pulleys.

Regulator R & R

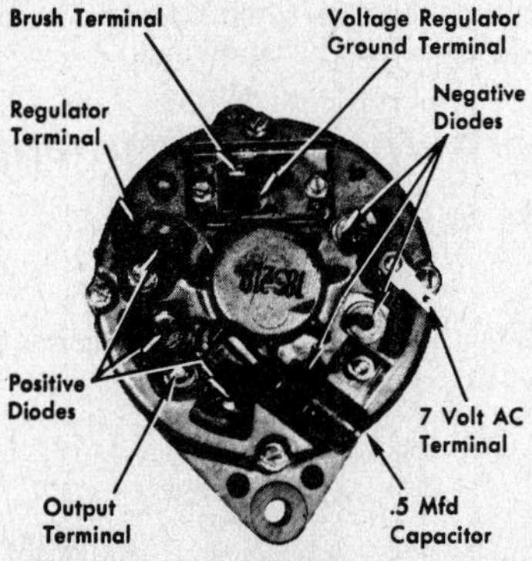
Brush Terminal
Voltage Regulator Ground Terminal
Regulator Terminal
Negative Diodes
Positive Diodes
7 Volt AC Terminal
Output Terminal
.5 Mfd Capacitor

Wire locations for alternator hook-up
(© Kaiser Willys Corp)

232, 258, 304, 327, 360 and 401 Engines

Disconnect the plug from the regulator. Remove the attaching sheet metal screws and lift off the regulator. Install in the reverse of removal.

STARTING SYSTEM

Starter Removal

232 and 258 Engines

Remove the oil filler pipe and disconnect the battery and solenoid leads from the starter. From underneath the vehicle, remove the bolts that attach the starter to the bellhousing and lift out the starter.

Install in the reverse of removal.

327V8, 304V8, 360V8, 401V8

Disconnect the battery lead and solenoid lead from the starter. From underneath the vehicle, remove the attaching bolts and lift out the starter. Install in the reverse of removal.

Starter Drive R & R

F4

The starter drive on the F4 starter is not to be removed. If it is defective, the whole starter unit must be replaced.

IGNITION SYSTEM

Distributor Removal

F4

The distributor assembly on all Jeep 4 cylinder inline engines is located on the right side of the engine.

To remove it, take off the distributor cap and wire assembly and bend it out of the way. Remove the ignition primary wire from the side of the distributor and take off the vacuum lines to the carburetor. Mark the distributor housing and the engine crankcase to ensure correct reinstallation. Note the position of the rotor. Remove the bolt that holds the distributor down into the block and lift it off the engine.

Distributor Installation

F4

If the crankshaft has not been rotated, simply match the marks made on removal and reinstall the rotor as noted on removal.

If the crankshaft has been rotated, turn the crankshaft until no. one cylinder is at the top of the compression stroke as indicated by air being forced out from no. one spark plug opening. Install the distributor with the rotor pointing toward no. one spark plug wire on the distributor cap and the points just opening. Start the engine and finish the timing procedure with a timing light.

Contact Point Replacement and Adjustment

F4

1. Pry the distributor cap hold-down clips loose from the cap and remove the cap and rotor.
2. Loosen the nut which holds the condenser lead and spring arm of the points assembly and remove the lead.
3. Remove the condenser and points assembly hold-down screws and remove the assembly and condenser from the distributor.
4. Install the new points assembly and condenser in the reverse order of removal.
5. Turn the engine until the fiber block on the breaker arm is resting on one of the cam lobes at the highest point.
6. Loosen the lock screw and turn the adjusting eccentric until the proper gap is obtained. Tighten the lock screw.
7. Replace the rotor and cap and start the engine to check the ignition timing and point dwell. Make any necessary adjustments to obtain the correct timing and dwell.

327 V8

1. Remove the distributor cap, condenser, and primary leads which are attached to the nylon terminal.
2. Loosen the two base screws and remove the points and condenser.
3. When installing the points, make sure the pilot hole is properly positioned over the hole in the breaker plate.
4. Install the new condenser, then attach the primary and condenser leads to the nylon terminal.
5. Reverse the lubricator and make sure that the terminal leads will not touch the rotor.
6. Install the rotor, making sure that the round and square holes are lined up with their respective dowels.
7. Adjust the point dwell to specifications by turning the allen screw on the point assembly through the window in the side of the cap.

Ignition Timing

F4

1. Hook up a timing light to the distributor, following the manufacturer's instructions, and make the timing marks on the front crankshaft pulley and the timing gear cover visible.
2. Loosen the distributor mounting bolt just enough so that the distributor can be turned with resistance.
3. Start the engine and allow it to reach operating temperature.
4. With the timing light operating and aimed at the timing marks on the front pulley and timing gear cover, adjust the timing by turning the distributor.
5. Tighten the distributor mounting bolt and accelerate the engine to see if the vacuum advance is working properly by watching the movement of the timing mark.

327 V8

The 327 V8 ignition timing is adjusted in the same manner as all of the other American Motors V8s. Refer to the American Motors section for ignition timing procedures.

FUEL SYSTEM

Fuel Pump Removal and Installation

1. Disconnect the fuel lines leading to the carburetor and from the fuel tank.
2. Remove the two attaching bolts that hold the fuel pump to the engine and lift the fuel pump off of the engine.
3. Before installing the fuel pump, make sure that all of the mating surfaces are clean.
4. Cement a new gasket to the mating surface of the fuel pump.
5. Position the fuel pump on the cylinder block so that the cam lever of the pump rests on the camshaft.
6. Secure the pump to the engine with the two bolts and lock washers.
7. Connect the fuel lines to the fuel pump.

Fuel Filter Removal and Installation

The fuel filter is located in the fuel pump bowl. The bowl is either attached to the side or to the bottom of the fuel pump. The element may be replaced by unscrewing the bail wire and removing the cartridge.

Carburetor Adjustments

Idle Mixture Adjustment

F4

Turn the idle adjustment screw 3/4 to 1 3/4 turns open from the fully closed position for normal adjustment setting.

For a richer mixture, turn this screw out. For a leaner mixture, turn this screw in.

Turn the screw until highest rpm is reached and the engine is idling smoothly.

327 V8

1. With the air cleaner installed, connect a tachometer to the engine.
2. Gently seat both mixture screws, then back them out exactly one turn.

NOTE: All adjustments of dual mixture screws must be made equally.

3. Start the engine and allow it to warm up to operating temperature.
4. Adjust the throttle stop screw to obtain 600 rpm for 1967 models, keeping both manual and automatic transmissions in Neutral. On A/C cars, set the speed to 600 rpm, with the A/C turned on.

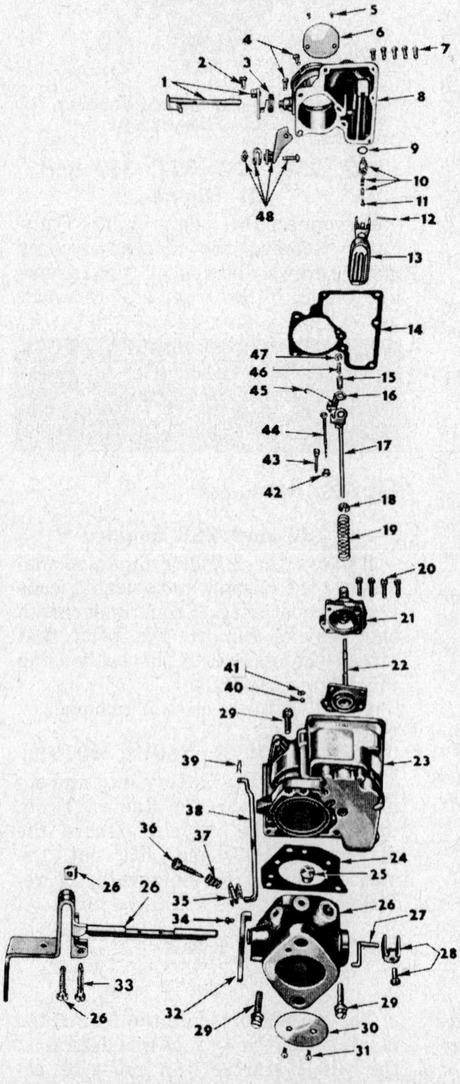

1—Choke shaft and lever
2—Screw
3—Choke lever spring
4—Screw and washer
5—Choke valve screw
6—Choke valve
7—Screw and washer
8—Air horn
9—Needle seat gasket
10—Needle spring and seat
11—Needle pin
12—Float pin
13—Float
14—Gasket
15—Pump spring
16—Metering rod arm
17—Pump link
18—Pump spring retainer
19—Vacuum diaphragm spring
20—Screw and washer
21—Diaphragm housing
22—Diaphragm
23—Body
24—Gasket
25—Idle port plug
26—Throttle body lever and shaft assembly
27—Pump link connector
28—Throttle shaft arm
29—Screw and washer
30—Throttle valve
31—Throttle valve screw
32—Fast idle arm
33—Adjusting screw
34—Body flange plug
35—Clevis clip
36—Idle adjusting screw
37—Idle screw spring
38—Fast idle connector rod
39—Pin spring
40—Ball check valve
41—Ball check valve retainer ring
42—Metering rod jet
43—Low speed jet
44—Metering rod
45—Metering rod spring
46—Inner pump spring
47—Pump spring retainer
48—Bracket and clamp assembly (choke and throttle)

An exploded view of the F-head 4 cyl carburetor (© Kaiser Willys Corp)

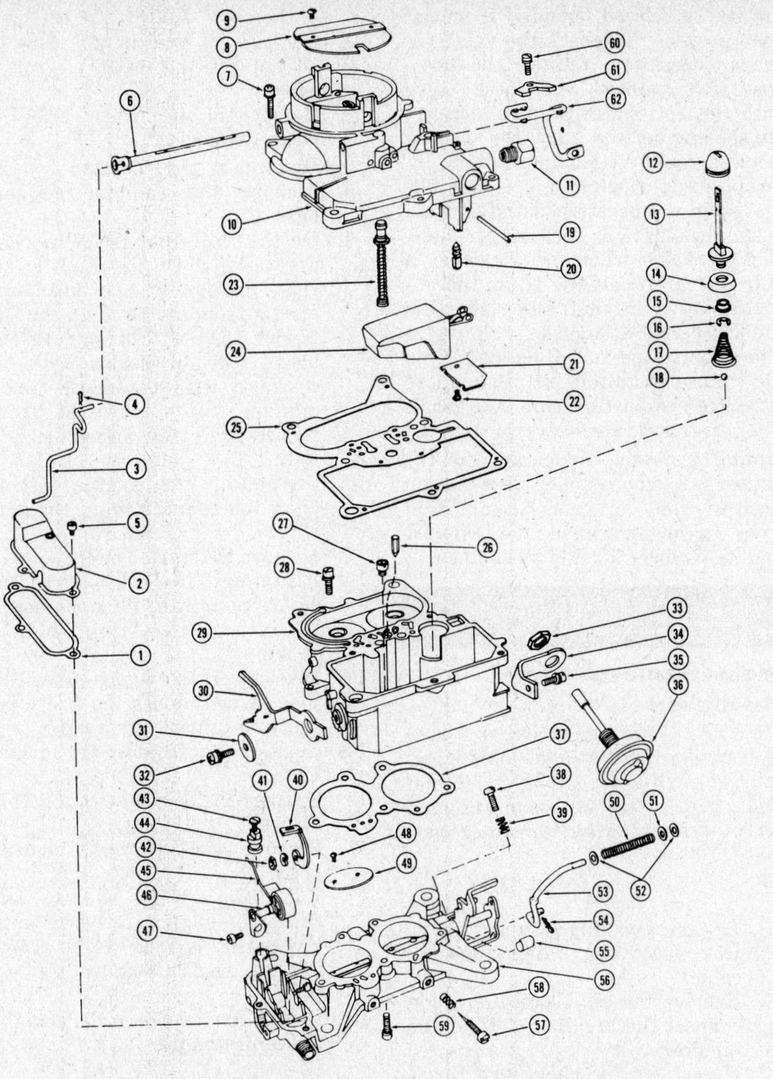

An exploded view of the 8-327 cu in. two barrel carburetor (© Kaiser Willys Corp)

1—Thermostat housing cover gasket
2—Thermostat cover and guide assembly
3—Choke rod
4—Choke rod retainer
5—Thermostat housing cover screw
6—Choke shaft and lever assembly
7—Air horn-to-main body screw
8—Choke plate
9—Choke plate screw
10—Air horn and plugs assembly
11—Fuel inlet fitting
12—Acceleration pump stem seal
13—Acceleration pump assembly
14—Acceleration pump cup
15—Acceleration pump cup liner
16—Acceleration pump cup retainer
17—Acceleration pump return spring
18—Acceleration pump inlet valve
19—Float hinge pin
20—Fuel inlet needle assembly
21—Fuel bowl baffle
22—Fuel bowl baffle screw
23—Power valve piston assembly
24—Float assembly
25—Main body gasket
26—Pump discharge valve
27—Main jet
28—Throttle body-to-main body screw and lockwasher
29—Main body and plugs assembly
30—Fast idle cam
31—Fast idle cam washer
32—Fast idle cam screw
33—Dashpot nut
34—Dashpot bracket
35—Dashpot bracket screw and lockwasher
36—Dashpot assembly
37—Throttle body gasket
38—Throttle stop screw
39—Throttle stop screw spring
40—Fast idle and dechoke lever
41—Lockwasher
42—Nut
43—Choke piston screw
44—Choke piston
45—Choke piston link
46—Choke thermostat assembly
47—Choke thermostat assembly lock screw
48—Throttle plate screw
49—Throttle plate
50—Pump drive spring
51—Pump link washer
52—Pump drive spring retainer
53—Pump operating link
54—Pump operating link retainer
55—Throttle shaft bearing ribbon
56—Throttle body and shaft assembly
57—Idle adjusting needle
58—Idle adjusting needle spring
59—Throttle body to main body screw and lockwasher
60—Clamp retainer screw
61—Pump rod clamp
62—Pump rod

5. Turn the mixture screws counterclockwise until the engine speed drops off, then slowly turn the screws equal amounts clockwise until the speed picks up. Continue past this point until the speed begins to fall off again, then back out the screws to again obtain the fastest idle. This mid-range adjustment is called the "lean best idle" speed.
6. Readjust the idle stop screw, if necessary, to obtain the specified idle. If the idle speed changed more than 50 rpm during mixture adjustment, readjust the mixture.
7. Disconnect the tachometer.

Dashpot Adjustment

Some carburetors are equipped with a dashpot to prevent stalling. The dashpot adjustment procedure for these carburetors is as follows:

1. Be sure that the throttle valves are closed tightly and that the diaphragm stem is fully depressed.
2. Measure the clearance between the dashpot stem and the throttle lever with a feeler gauge.
3. If the clearance is not correct, adjust it by loosening the locknut and rotating the dashpot until the proper clearance is obtained. Tighten the locknut.

On the 327 V8 engine with the Holley 4 bbl carburetor, the dashpot is adjusted to 5/32 in. clearance on the model 2209 and 3/32 in. on the model 4160.

COOLING SYSTEM

Radiator Removal and Installation

1. Drain the radiator by opening the drain cock and removing the radiator pressure cap.
2. Remove the upper and lower hose clamps and hose at the radiator. On vehicles with an automatic transmission, disconnect the oil cooler lines. Plug the lines to prevent dirt from entering the transmission oil.
3. Remove the cap screws, lock washers, and flat washers that hold the radiator to the radiator support.
4. Remove the radiator.
5. Install the radiator in the reverse order of removal.

Water Pump Removal and Installation

F4

1. Drain the coolant from the system by opening the petcock.
2. Remove the fan belt, fan, and fan pulley.

3. Remove the bolts which attach the water pump to the block and remove the pump.
4. Install the pump in the reverse order of removal, using a new gasket.

327 V8

1. Open the petcock and drain the radiator.
2. Remove the radiator fan shroud by removing the two attaching bolts and nuts.
3. Loosen the alternator at the support.
4. Remove the fan belt.
5. Remove the fan, fan hub, and the fan pulley which are attached by four capscrews and lockwashers.
6. Remove the four nuts and lockwashers from the water pump mounting studs in the timing chain cover.
7. Remove the water pump and its gasket.
8. Install the water pump in the reverse order of removal, using a new gasket.

Thermostat Removal and Installation

F4

The thermostat is located in a housing on the top front of the cylinder head. To remove it, drain the cooling system, unscrew and remove the two bolts which hold the housing to the head, lift the housing, and remove the thermostat. Remove the gasket and replace it with a new one, installing the thermostat in the reverse order of removal.

327 V8

The thermostat is located in the water outlet manifold, enclosed by the thermostat housing. Remove it in the same manner as for the F4.

EMISSION CONTROLS

F4 and 327 V8

The F4 and 327 V8 have an AIR (air injection reactor) type exhaust emission control system along with a closed PCV (positive crankcase ventilation) system.

The AIR system consists of a belt driven air pump which directs compressed air through connecting hoses to a steel distribution manifold into stainless steel injection tubes in the exhaust port adjacent to each exhaust valve stem. This air, with its normal oxygen content, reacts with the hot but incompletely burned exhaust gases and permits further combustion in the exhaust port or manifold.

Between the air pump and the injection manifold on the F4, there is an anti-backfire diverter valve. The valve remains closed except when the throttle is closed rapidly from an open position. To check the valve for proper operation, remove the large hose that connects the check valve with the anti-backfire valve, accelerate the engine, and allow the throttle to close rapidly. If a momentary interuption of rushing air is audible, the valve is operating satisfactorily.

On the 327 V8, there is an anti-backfire valve which is known as a gulp valve. It differs from the diverter valve in that when there is sudden deceleration, the gulp valve allows extra air to be "gulped" into the intake manifold so that more complete combustion can take place. The diverter valve diverts the air coming from the air pump into the atmosphere when sudden deceleration occurs. This prevents combustion from taking place in the exhaust manifold where it could do damage.

ENGINE

Engine Removal and Installation

NOTE: This operation requires discharging the air conditioning system. This requires special tools and skills. For safety reasons, it should not be attempted by untrained persons.

F4

1. Drain the cooling system.
2. Disconnect the battery ground cable.
3. Remove the air cleaner and disconnect the breather hose at the oil filter.
4. Disconnect the choke and throttle controls.
5. Disconnect the fuel line and windshield wiper hose at the fuel pump.
6. Remove the radiator stay bar, if so equipped.
7. Remove the radiator and heater hoses.
8. Remove the fan blades, fan hub, radiator, and shroud.
9. Remove the starter motor.
10. Disconnect:
    a. The alternator or generator.
    b. The ignition primary wire at coil.
    c. The oil pressure and temperature sending units.
    d. The exhaust pipe from manifold.
    e. The engine ground strap.
11. Attach a lifting device to the engine. Unbolt and remove the front engine supports.
12. Remove the flywheel housing bolts.
13. Pull the engine forward until the clutch clears the flywheel housing. Lift the engine from the vehicle.
14. Install the engine by reversing the removal procedure.

V6

1. Remove the hood if necessary.
2. Disconnect the battery ground cable.
3. Remove the air cleaner.
4. Drain the coolant.
5. Disconnect the radiator hoses.
6. Remove the radiator support bars.
7. On the Universal series, remove the radiator. On the Jeepster series, disconnect the headlamp wiring from the block on the left fender, the horn wiring from the horn, the oil cooler lines if equipped with automatic transmission, and remove the front fenders, radiator, and grille as a unit.
8. Disconnect the engine wiring from the connectors on the firewall.
9. Remove the starter motor.
10. Disconnect the fuel hoses at the right frame rail. Plug the hoses.
11. Disconnect the throttle and choke.
12. Disconnect the exhaust pipes.
13. Place a jack under the transmission and support the weight.
14. Remove the front motor mount bolts.
15. Support the engine with a lifting device.
16. Remove the flywheel housing bolts.
17. Raise the engine slightly and slide the engine forward until the engine is free of the transmission shaft. Remove the engine.
18. Install in reverse order of the above procedure.

327 and 350 V8

1. Remove the hood.
2. Remove the air cleaner.
3. Drain the radiator and cylinder block.
4. Disconnect the radiator and heater hoses.
5. If equipped with an automatic transmission, disconnect the oil cooler lines at the radiator. Remove the radiator.
6. Remove the fan, belt, and hub.
7. Drain the engine oil and remove the filter.
8. Disconnect the temperature-sender lead, pressure-sender lead, coil, starter solenoid, and alternator and distributor leads.
9. Disconnect the accelerator cable at the carburetor throttle shaft lever and at the cable support bracket.
10. Disconnect the heater system vacuum valve hose at the intake manifold.
11. Disconnect the flexible fuel line from the frame-to-crankcase at the frame end. Plug the end of the hose.
12. Disconnect the exhaust pipes at both manifolds.

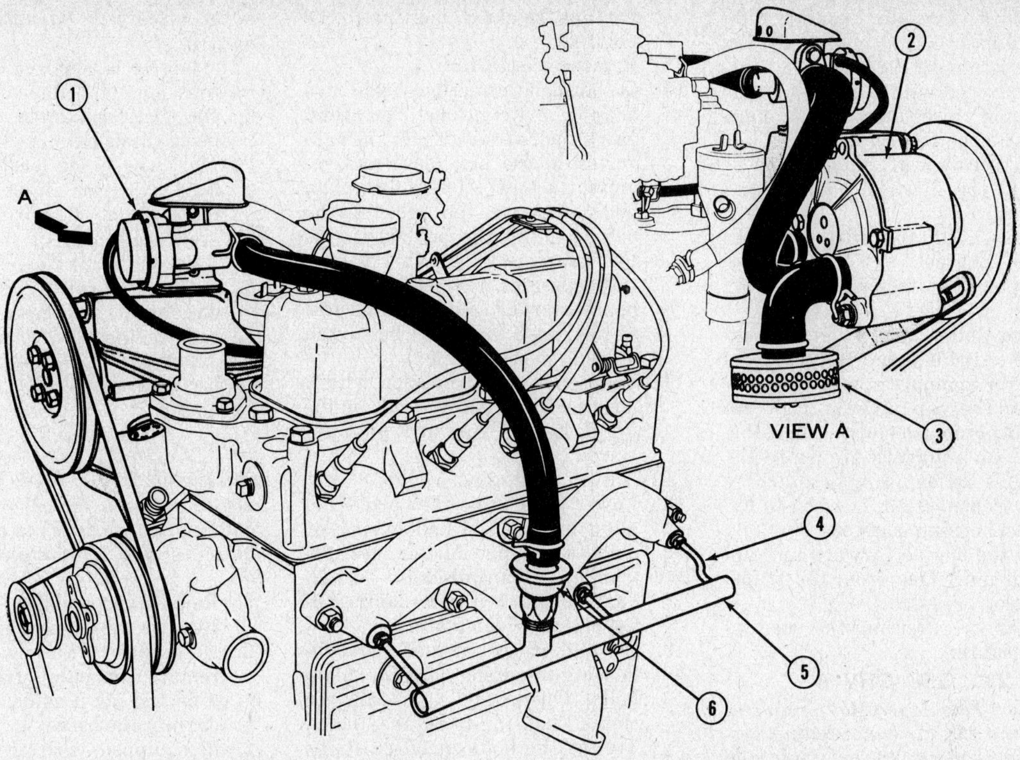
A
VIEW A
1
2
3
4
5
6

Exhaust emission control system for the F-head 4 cyl engine (© Kaiser Willys Corp)

1—Anti-backfire diverter valve
2—Air pump
3—Pump air filter
4—Air injection tube(s)
5—Air delivery manifold
6—Check valve

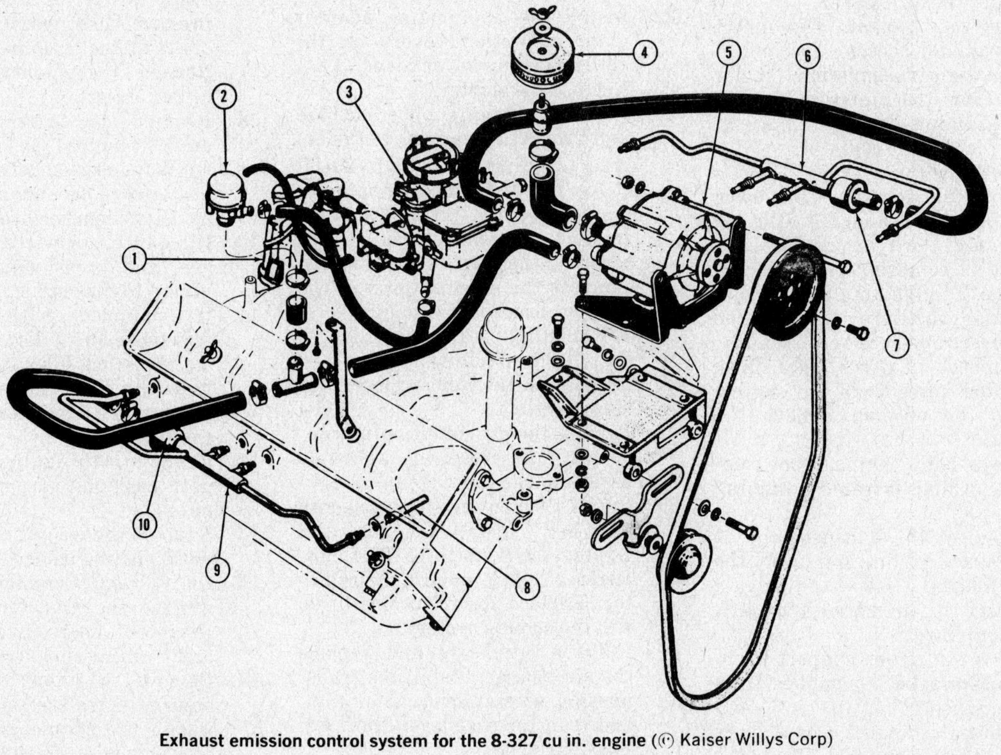
1
2
3
4
5
6
7
8
9
10

Exhaust emission control system for the 8-327 cu in. engine (© Kaiser Willys Corp)

1—Distributor
2—Anti-backfire (gulp) valve
3—Carburetor
4—Filter
5—Air pump
6—Air delivery distribution manifold (left)
7—Check valve
8—Air injection tube(s)
9—Air delivery distribution manifold (right)
10—Check vave

13. Remove the air conditioning compressor (if so equipped). Do not disconnect the hoses.
14. If equipped with a manual transmission, disconnect the linkage at the clutch. Disconnect the clutch cross-shaft support brackets at the flywheel housing and frame.
15. Install a suitable lifting fixture on the engine.
16. Support the transmission on a jack.
17. Remove the nuts from the engine-to-front support brackets.
18. With a manual transmission, remove the cap screws from the transmission-to-clutch housing. With an automatic transmission, remove the cap screws attaching the transmission housing-to-flywheel housing adaptor.
19. Pull the engine forward and upward until free from the transmission or clutch.
20. Install by reversing the removal procedure.

232, 258 OHV 6

NOTE: This operation requires discharging the air conditioning system. This requires special tools and skills for safety reasons. It should not be attempted by untrained persons.

1. Remove the hood after marking the hinge locations. The hood need not be removed on the CJ series.
2. Remove the air cleaner.
3. Drain the coolant. Disconnect the radiator hoses. Disconnect automatic transmission cooler lines from the radiator. If there is a radiator shroud, remove it, then remove the radiator.
4. Remove the fan.
5. Remove and set aside the power steering pump and belt. Do not disconnect the hydraulic lines.
6. Bleed the compressor refrigerant charge. See the note at the start of this procedure. Remove the condenser and receiver assembly.
7. Disconnect all wires, lines, linkage, and hoses from the engine.
8. Drain the oil and remove the filter.
9. Remove both engine front support cushion-to-frame retaining nuts.
10. Disconnect the exhaust pipe at the support bracket and the manifold.
11. Support the engine with the lifting equipment.
12. Remove the front support cushion and bracket assemblies from the engine.
13. Remove the transfer case lever boot, the floor mat, and the transmission access cover.
14. On automatic transmissions, remove the upper bolts holding the bellhousing to the engine adaptor plate. On manual transmissions, remove the upper bolts holding the clutch housing to the engine.
15. Remove the starter.
16. On automatics, remove the two adaptor plate inspection covers. Mark the relationship of the converter to the flex plate and remove the converter-to-flex plate bolts. Remove the rest of the bolts holding the bellhousing to the adaptor plate. On manual transmissions, remove the clutch housing lower cover and the rest of the bolts holding the clutch housing to the engine.
17. Support the transmission with a floor jack and remove the engine by pulling it forward and upward.

To install the engine:

18. Lower the engine into place and align it with the bellhousing or clutch housing. Make sure the manual transmission clutch shaft aligns with the splines of the clutch driven plate.
19. On automatics, install the bellhousing-to-engine adaptor plate bolts. On manuals, install the clutch housing-to-engine bolts. Torque the bolts to 25–28 ft lbs at the top and 40–45 ft lbs at the bottom.
20. Remove the floor jack.
21. Align the marks made in step 16 and install the converter-to-flex plate bolts, torquing them to 21–23 ft lbs.
22. Install the two engine adaptor plate inspection covers or the clutch housing lower cover.
23. Replace the starter.
24. Install the front support cushion and bracket assemblies to the engine, torquing the bolts to 25–30 ft lbs. Lower the engine onto the frame supports. Install the front support cushion retaining nuts, torquing them to 25–30 ft lbs.
25. Connect the exhaust pipe at the support bracket and manifold. A new manifold seal is advisable.
26. Install the oil filter.
27. Replace all the items removed in step seven.
28. Replace the air conditioning condenser and receiver assembly and recharge the system.
29. Replace the power steering pump and belt. Install the fan and tighten the bolts to 15–25 ft lbs.
30. Replace and reconnect the radiator. Replace the oil cooler lines. Fill the cooling system.
31. Fill the crankcase and replace the air cleaner. Install the transmission access cover, floor mat, and transfer case lever boot. Replace the hood.

304, 360 and 401 V8

NOTE: This operation requires discharging the air conditioning system. This requires special tools and skills. For safety reasons, it should not be attempted by untrained persons.

The engine is removed without the transmission and bellhousing.

1. On the Commando and Wagoneer, the hood must be removed. Mark the hinge locations at the hood panel for alignment during installation. Remove the hood from the hinges.
2. Remove the air cleaner assembly.
3. Drain the cooling system and disconnect the upper and lower radiator hoses. If equipped with automatic transmission, disconnect the cooler lines from the radiator.

NOTE: If the vehicle is equipped with a radiator shroud, it is necessary to separate the shroud from the radiator to facilitate removal and installation of the radiator and engine fan.

4. Remove the radiator.
5. Remove the engine fan.
6. If equipped with power steering, remove the pump from the engine and lay it aside. Do not disconnect the hoses.
7. If equipped with air conditioning, turn both service valves clockwise to the front seated position. Bleed the compressor refrigerant charge by slowly loosening the service valve fittings. Disconnect the condenser and evaporator lines from the compressor. Disconnect the receiver outlet at the disconnect coupling. Remove the condenser and receiver assembly.
8. Remove the battery and tray only if required.
9. On Wagoneer models, remove the heater core housing and charcoal canister from the firewall.
10. Disconnect all wires, lines, linkage, and hoses which are connected to the engine.
11. If equipped with automatic transmission, disconnect the transmission filler tube bracket from the right cylinder head. Do not remove the filler tube from the transmission.
12. Remove both engine front support cushion-to-frame retaining nuts.
13. Support the weight of the engine with a lifting device.
14. On CJ and Commando models, remove the transfer case shift lever boot, floor (if so equipped), and transmission access cover.
15. Remove the upper bolts which secure the transmission bellhousing to the engine adapter plate on vehicles equipped with automatic transmission. If equipped with manual transmission, remove the upper bolts which secure the clutch housing to the engine.
16. Disconnect the exhaust pipes at

the exhaust manifolds and support bracket.

17. Remove the starter motor.
18. Support the transmission with a floor jack.
19. If equipped with automatic transmission, remove the two engine adapter plate inspection covers. Mark the assembled position of the converter and flex plate and remove the converter-to-flex plate cap screws. Remove the remaining bolts which secure the transmission bellhousing to the engine adapter plate.
20. If equipped with manual transmission, remove the clutch housing lower cover and the remaining bolts which secure the clutch housing to the engine.
21. Remove the engine by pulling upward and forward.

NOTE: If equipped with power brakes, care must be taken to avoid damaging the power unit while removing the engine.

To install the engine:

22. Lower the engine slowly into the engine compartment and align with the transmission bellhousing (automatic transmission) or clutch housing (manual transmission). On manual transmissions, make certain the clutch shaft is aligned properly with the splines of the clutch driven plate.
23. Install the transmission bellhousing-to-engine adapter plate bolts (automatic transmission) or the clutch housing to engine bolts (manual transmission). Tighten the bolts to the specified torque. Remove the floor jack which was used to support the transmission.
24. If equipped with automatic transmission, align the marks previously made on the converter and flex plate, install the converter-to-flex plate cap screws and tighten to the specified torque.
25. Install the two engine adapter plate inspection covers (automatic transmission) or the clutch housing lower cover (manual transmission).
26. Install the starter motor.
27. Lower the engine onto the frame supports, remove the lifting device and install the front support cushion retaining nuts. Tighten the nuts to the specified torque.
28. Connect the exhaust pipes at the exhaust manifolds and support bracket.
29. If equipped with automatic transmission, connect the transmission filler tube bracket to the right cylinder head.
30. On Wagoneer models, install the heater core housing and charcoal canister to the firewall.
31. If removed, install the battery and tray.
32. Connect all wires, lines, linkage and hoses which were previously disconnected from the engine.
33. If removed, install the air conditioning condenser and receiver assembly. Connect the receiver outlet to the disconnect coupling. Connect the condenser and evaporator lines to the compressor. Purge the compressor of air.

Caution Both service valves must be open before the air conditioning system is operated.

34. If equipped with power steering, connect the power steering pump to the engine.
35. Install the engine fan and tighten the retaining bolts to the specified torque.
36. Install the radiator and connect the upper and lower hoses. If equipped with automatic transmission, connect the cooler lines.
37. Fill the cooling system to the specified level.
38. Install the air cleaner assembly.
39. Start the engine. Check all connections for leaks. Stop the engine.
40. If removed, install and align the hood assembly.
41. If removed, install the transmission access cover, floor mat and transfer case shift lever boot.

Manifolds

F4

The intake manifold is cast as an integral part of the cylinder head.

The exhaust manifold is removed by removing the five nuts from the manifold studs, removing the two bolts that hold the manifold to the exhaust pipe, and lifting the manifold off of the mounting studs. Remove the center and two end gaskets from the cylinder block. Install in the reverse order of removal, using new gaskets.

NOTE: On engines with the AIR exhaust emission control devices, the rubber hose leading from the air pump to the air injection manifold must be disconnected in order to remove the exhaust manifold.

Intake Manifold Removal and Installation

327 V8

1. Disconnect the water outlet tube and remove the distributor.
2. Take off the air cleaner.
3. Disconnect all throttle linkage at the carburetor.
4. Disconnect the vacuum lines, the coil, and the ignition primary leads.
5. Remove the bolts which hold the intake manifold to both the cylinder heads and lift off the manifold.
6. Remove all gaskets and replace with new ones.
7. Replace the intake manifold in the reverse order of removal.

Exhaust Manifold Removal and Installation

327 V8

Disconnect the exhaust pipe at the flange, remove the bolts which hold the manifold to the cylinder head, and lift off the manifold.

Install in the reverse order of removal.

Valve System

F4

The intake valves are located in the cylinder head and are operated by the gear driven camshaft through push rods and rocker arms. The exhaust valves are located in the block, stems down, and are operated directly by the tappets. The intake valves are adjusted by adjusting nuts on the rocker arms and the exhaust valves are adjusted by adjusting screws on the tappets. Both the intake and exhaust valve guides are replaceable.

327 V8

The valve arrangement is an overhead type operated by a camshaft through pushrods and rocker arms. The valves are not adjustable. The valve guides are replaceable.

Rocker Arm Shaft Removal and Installation

1. Remove the cap screws which hold the valve cover in place and remove the valve cover and the gasket.
2. On the F4, remove the nuts which hold the rocker arm shaft to the mounting studs and lift off the rocker arm shaft. On the 327 V8, remove the rocker arm retaining cap screws and remove the rocker arm shafts.
3. If the pushrods are removed, replace them in the same positions from which they were removed.
4. Install the rocker arm shafts in the reverse order of removal, using a new gasket under the valve covers.

Valve Adjustment

Only the F4 engine requires periodic valve adjustments. All the others have self-adjusting hydraulic lifters. Valve clearance can be properly adjusted only when the lifter is on the heel or low portion of the cam. The exhaust valves (in the block) are adjusted by turning the adjusting screw in or out of the lifter to obtain the proper clearance between the end of the adjusting screw and the stem of the valve. The intake valves (in the head) are adjusted by turning the rocker arm screw at the pushrod end

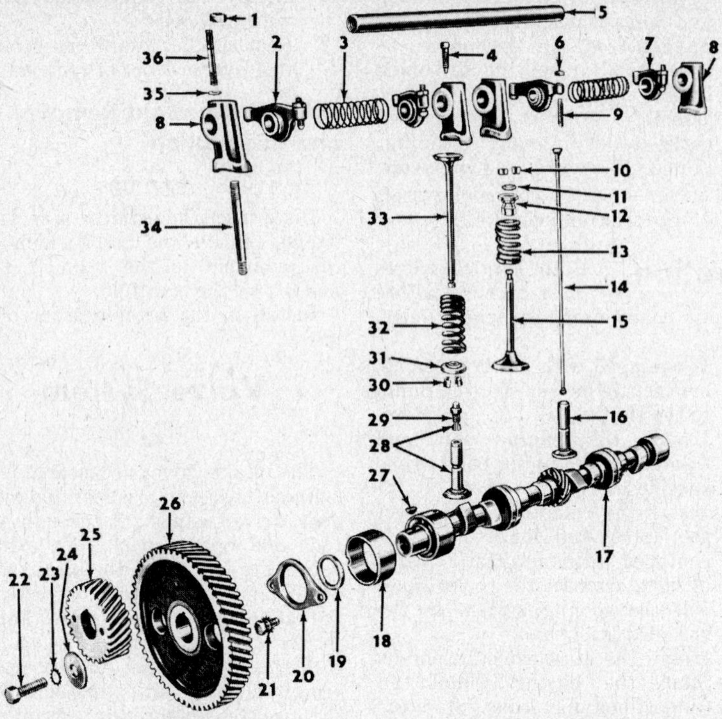
1
2
3
4
5
6
7
8
9
10
11
12
13
14
15
16
17
18
19
20
21
22
23
24
25
26
27
28
29
30
31
32
33
34
35
36

Valve system for the F-head 4 cyl engine (© Kaiser Willys Corp)

1—Nut
2—Left rocker arm
3—Rocker arm shaft spring
4—Rocker shaft lock screw
5—Rocker shaft
6—Nut
7—Right rocker arm
8—Rocker arm shaft bracket
9—Intake valve tappet adjusting screw
10—Intake valve upper retainer lock
11—Oil seal
12—Intake valve spring upper retainer
13—Intake valve spring
14—Intake valve push rod
15—Intake valve
16—Intake valve tappet
17—Camshaft
18—Camshaft front bearing
19—Camshaft thrust plate spacer
20—Camshaft thrust plate
21—Bolt and lock washer
22—Bolt
23—Lock washer
24—Camshaft gear washer
25—Crankshaft gear
26—Camshaft gear
27—Woodruff key No. 9
28—Exhaust valve tappet
29—Tappet adjusting screw
30—Spring retainer lock
31—Roto cap assembly
32—Exhaust valve spring
33—Exhaust valve
34—Rocker shaft support stud
35—Washer
36—Rocker arm cover stud

to obtain the proper clearance between the rocker arm and the valve stem. The engine must be cold for proper valve adjustment.

Cylinder Head

Cylinder Head Removal and Installation

F4

1. Drain the coolant.
2. Remove the upper radiator hose. Remove the carburetor.
3. On early engines, remove the bypass hose from the front of the cylinder head.
4. Remove the rocker arm cover.
5. Disconnect the oil line.
6. Remove the rocker arm attaching stud nuts and rocker arm shaft assembly.
7. Remove the cylinder head bolts. One head bolt is located below the carburetor mounting, inside the intake manifold.
8. Lift off the cylinder head.
9. Remove the pushrods and valve lifters.
10. Reverse the procedure for installation.

327 V8

The cylinder heads have two holes to assist head location. Maximum out-of-true is 0.006 in. for the entire length of head; 0.001 in. every 1 in. Make sure the rear rocker arm bolts are properly installed, otherwise no oil will get to the rockers.

1. Remove the oil filler tube, rocker covers, power steering pump, alternator, exhaust manifolds, and air conditioner. Swing the air conditioner out of the way without disconnecting its hoses.
2. Remove the rockers and pushrods.
3. Disconnect the water hoses, fuel lines, wiring, vacuum lines; remove the distributor and intake manifold.
4. Remove the cylinder head bolts and lift off the heads carefully, making sure all ground straps, etc. have been disconnected.

There are two locating dowels on the cylinder block to assist in gasket alignment during installation. Apply a commercial sealing compound to both sides of the head gasket. The word "top" and "A.M." should always face upward when installing the gasket. Tighten the head bolts to 58-62 ft lbs in three steps in the sequence illustrated. The rest of installation is the reverse of removal.

Timing Cover, Gear/Chain, and Camshaft

Timing Cover Removal and Installation

F4

1. To remove the timing gear cover, it is necessary to remove the radiator, fan, and the pulleys.
2. Remove the bolts, nuts, and lockwashers from the timing gear cover.
3. Remove the cover, timing pointer, and cover gasket from the engine. Discard the gasket.
4. Install in the reverse order of removal, using a new cover gasket.

327 V8

The timing chain cover on the 327 V8 is a cast iron affair that contains the water pump. Remove the timing chain cover as follows:

1. Drain the cooling system and remove the radiator and shroud. Remove the fan and pulley.
2. Remove the nut which secures the vibration damper to the crankshaft and remove the damper. Use a new cork washer when reinstalling the vibration damper.
3. Remove the heater hose from the hose adapter going into the housing.
4. Unscrew the cap screws which hold the timing chain cover to the block.
5. Remove the cover and gasket.
6. Replace in the reverse order of removal, using a new gasket.

Timing Gear Cover Oil Seal Removal and Installation

F4

1. The timing gear cover has to be removed from the engine to replace the oil seal.
2. Pry out the old seal with a screwdriver.
3. Install the new seal by tapping it gently into place.
4. Install the timing gear cover in the reverse order of removal, using a new gasket.

327 V8

The timing chain cover oil seal can be replaced without removing the whole cover assembly from the engine. This is accomplished through the use of a special threaded tool that fits over the crankshaft and threads the seal onto it. When the tool is pushed down against the crankshaft, the seal pops out. The new seal is placed over the crankshaft, into position, and then tapped into place.

If the tool is not available, the timing chain cover has to be removed and the seal replaced in the manner outlined for the F4.

Timing Gear/Chain Removal and Installation

F4

1. Remove the timing gear cover.
2. Remove the oil slinger and spacer from the crankshaft.
3. Using a gear puller, remove the timing gears and the woodruff keys.
4. Install the gears in the reverse order of removal, lining up the alignment marks on both gears and using a new cover gasket.

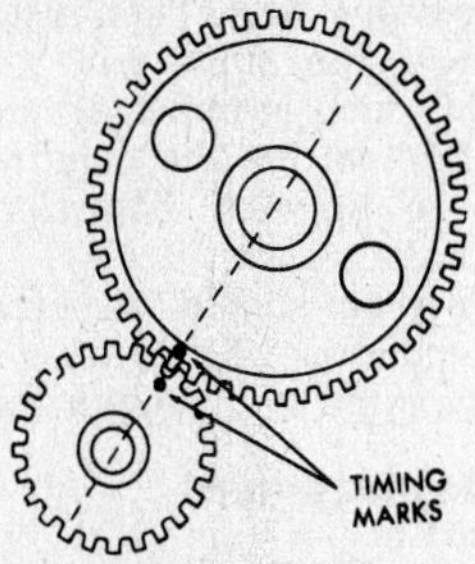
TIMING MARKS

Aligning timing marks—4 cyl
(© Willys Corp)

327 V8

To remove the timing chain, the fuel pump has to be removed.

1. Remove the timing chain cover and gasket.
2. Remove the crankshaft oil slinger from the crankshaft.
3. Remove the fuel pump eccentric from the face of the camshaft sprocket by removing the retaining bolt, lockwasher, and flat washer.
4. Pry the camshaft sprocket and crankshaft sprocket forward a little at a time until the camshaft sprocket is free of the camshaft.
5. Remove the timing chain from both sprockets.
6. Continue prying the crankshaft sprocket forward until it is free from the crankshaft.
7. Install the timing chain and sprockets in the reverse order of removal, making sure that the alignment marks on the sprockets are aligned.

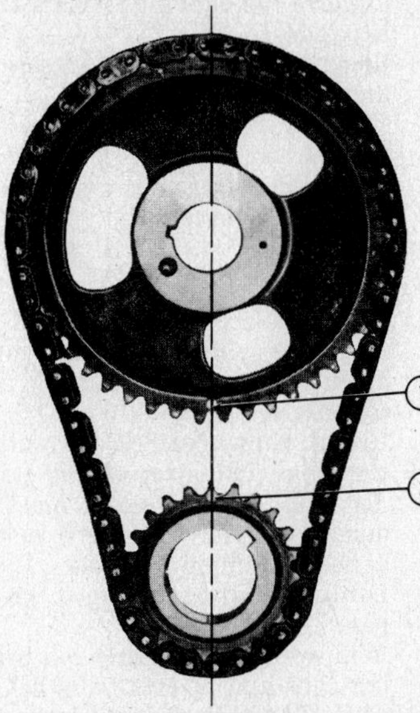

Timing chain sprocket alignment marks
(© Kaiser Willys Corp)

1—Camshaft sprocket timing mark
2—Crankshaft sprocket timing mark

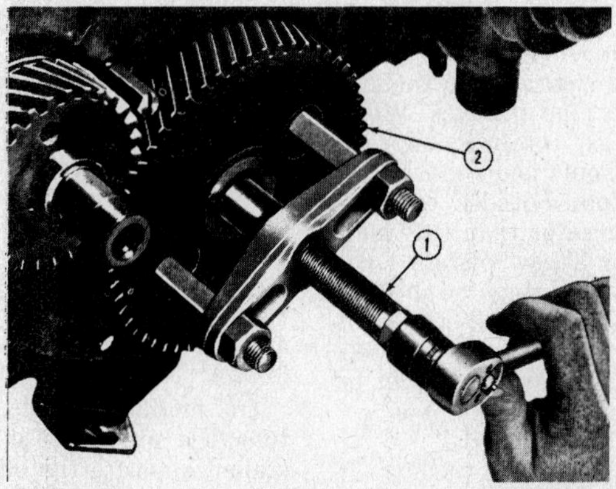

Removing the timing gears with a gear puller—F-Head 4 cyl
(© Kaiser Willys Corp)

1—Puller
2—Camshaft gear

Camshaft Removal and Installation

F4

1. Remove the timing gear cover, the timing gears, and the camshaft thrust plate.
2. Remove the cylinder head, pushrods, and exhaust valves.
3. Remove the distributor and the oil pump.
4. Lift the valve tappets off of the camshaft and use common, clip type clothes pins on the shank of each lifter to hold them up off of the camshaft.
5. Remove the camshaft thrust plate attaching screws and remove the thrust plate and spacer.
6. Pull the camshaft forward out of the cylinder block, using care to prevent damage to the bearing surfaces.
7. Before installing the camshaft, lubricate it generously with clean engine oil.
8. Carefully slide the camshaft into place. Do not allow the rear of the camshaft to strike sharply against the expansion plug installed in the rear end of the bore.
9. Install the camshaft thrust plate. Slide the thrust plate spacer onto the end of the camshaft with the beveled inner edge of the spacer facing the camshaft.
10. Install the timing gears.
11. Turn the crankshaft until the marks on the timing gears are aligned.
12. With a new gasket installed, and the wider side of the shaft on top (nearer the top of the cylinder block) insert the oil pump into the opening on the left side of the block.
13. Insert a long bladed screwdriver into the distributor hole and engage the slot in the end of the oil pump shaft. Turn the shaft until the slot is positioned at what would be roughly the nine-thirty position on a clock face.
14. Remove the screwdriver and, looking down into the distributor hole, observe the position of the slot in the end of the oil pump shaft to make certain it is properly positioned.
15. Replace the screwdriver and, while turning the screwdriver clockwise to guide the oil pump driveshaft gear into engagement with the camshaft gear, press against the oil pump to force it into place.
16. Remove the screwdriver and again observe the position of the slot. If the installation was properly made, the slot will be in a position roughly equivalent to 11 o'clock on a clock face with the wider side of the shaft still on the top. If the slot is improperly positioned, remove the oil pump assembly and repeat the operation.
17. Replace the oil pump attaching screws.
18. Replace the distributor, the valves, and the cylinder head.
19. Replace the timing gear cover.

327 V8

1. Detach the battery cable.

2. Drain the radiator and both banks of the cylinder block. Remove the radiator, the hoses, and the thermostat housing.
3. Remove the distributor, complete with spark plug wires and the coil, from the intake manifold.
4. Remove the intake manifold as a complete assembly.
5. Take off the valve cover and take out the valve train, including the hydraulic tappets.

NOTE: Keep the valve train components in proper order. They must be returned to their original place during assembly.

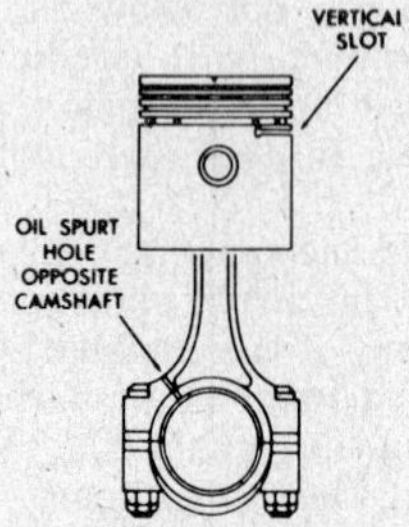
VERTICAL SLOT
OIL SPURT HOLE OPPOSITE CAMSHAFT

Piston to rod assembly—F4

6. Remove the power steering pump from its bracket, without disconnecting the hoses. Set it out of the way.
7. Remove the fan assembly and then the fuel pump. Unfasten the heater hose at the water pump.
8. Unbolt the alternator bracket and set it out of the way, complete with the alternator. Do not disconnect the alternator wiring.
9. Remove the crankshaft pulley and the vibration damper.
10. Remove the water pump and the cylinder head water distribution manifold.
11. With the timing marks in vertical alignment, remove the front cover, distributor/oil pump drive gear, fuel pump eccentric, sprockets, and the timing chain.
12. Unfasten the hood latch upper support bracket attachment screws. Move the bracket, as necessary, to permit withdrawal of the camshaft.
13. Use care during camshaft removal, so that the journal bearings are not damaged.
14. Inspect all parts for wear and damage. Replace them as required.

Installation of the cam is the reverse of removal. Install the timing chain and cover as outlined above. Adjust the belt tension and fill up the cooling system.

NOTE: Lubricate the camshaft, tappets, and the valve train with a suitable engine oil supplement. Add the remaining supplement to the crankcase, and leave it in the engine for at least the first 1000 miles. It does not require draining until the next regular oil change.

Piston Removal

F4

1. Remove the cylinder head and the oil pan.
2. Remove the ridge from the tops of the cylinder bores, using a ridge reamer.
3. Remove the oil pan and, one at a time, remove the connecting rod caps and push the piston assemblies out the top of the block. Number all pistons, connecting rods, and caps on removal.
4. Remove the old rings with a ring expander.
5. Release the piston pin lockscrews and force out the pins.
6. Check the cylinder bores for distortion, taper, and other evidence of excessive wear. Bore and hone as necessary.

327 V8

1. Drain the cooling system and remove the cylinder head assembly as outlined in the applicable section above.
2. Use a ridge reamer to remove the ridge at the top of the cylinder wall. Each cylinder must be done separately with the piston at the bottom of its stroke.
3. Drain the oil and remove the oil pan.
4. Remove the connecting rod bearing caps and inserts from below.

NOTE: The rods and caps have the number of the cylinder to which they were assembled stamped on them. It is important that they be kept in the order in which they were removed.

5. Withdraw the piston and connecting rod assemblies through the *top* of the cylinder bore. Use care not to scratch the connecting rod journals or the cylinder walls with the rod bolts.

Piston Ring Replacement

F4

When new rings are installed without reboring the cylinders, the cylinder wall glaze should be broken by honing.

New piston rings should be checked for end-gap and clearance in the cylinder bores and ring grooves. When fitting new rings, compression ring side-clearance should be no more than 0.006 in. for four-cylinder engines. Any clearance greater than this indicates a need for a new piston. End-gap of compression rings is checked by pushing the ring to the bottom of the bore in which it will operate. Compression ring end-gap should be at least 0.007 in. for four-cylinder engines.

Piston pins should be a push-fit. If they are excessively loose, the piston must be replaced.

When assembling the rod and piston assemblies to the four-cylinder engine, the T-slot in the piston should be on the left side. The oil spurt hole should face to the right, away from the camshaft and the T-slot.

327 V8

1. Clean the carbon from the oil ring grooves, the oil drain openings and the pin boss. Use care not to remove any metal from the ring grooves or lands, as this will change clearance.
2. Measure the ring clearances and the cylinder bore taper as outlined in the "Engine Rebuilding" section.
3. Remove the glaze from the cylinder bore wall with an *expanding* hone. Ten strokes (down and return) are sufficient to clean the walls; more than ten will change clearances.

Caution Never use a rigid hone to remove cylinder glaze; it will destroy cylinder taper.

4. Install the oil control rings on the pistons, first. Then install the compression rings with the top side (which is marked) up. Use a ring tool on the compression ring to prevent distortion and breakage.

Piston rings should be arranged with the end gaps 120° apart, with no gap being placed over the pin boss.

Piston Replacement

F4

1. Assemble the piston to the rod by pushing in and locking the pin.
2. Using a ring expander, install the piston rings. Install the bottom (oil) ring first, center ring second, and top ring last.
3. Coat all the bearing surfaces and rings, and the piston skirt, with engine oil.
4. Turn down the crankpin of the cylinder being worked on.
5. Make sure that the gaps in the rings are not in line.
6. Using a ring compressor, install the piston and rod assembly into the cylinder and carefully tap down until the rod bearing is solidly seated on the crankpin.
7. Install the cap and lower bearing shell. Torque to the specified figure.
8. Install all piston assemblies in the same manner.
9. Install the cylinder head and oil pan.

327 V8

On engines using split-skirt pistons, the slit in the skirt must be installed opposite the oil squirt hole in the connecting rod. Solid skirt pistons are assembled so that the boss, or dimple, (and, in some instances, the letter F) at the top of the piston is on the same side of the connecting rod as the boss. This will be found on the connecting rod channel about halfway up the rod.

The piston and rod assemblies are united to the engine from the top and the dimple, or dot, on the top of the piston goes toward the front. On those engines having split-skirt pistons, the slit in the skirt of the piston goes to the left side of the engine.

Piston pins are a press fit in the connecting rod, hand fit in the piston at 68°F. Before assembly, clean the ring grooves using a broken ring or commercial groove cleaner. Piston-to-cylinder bore clearance at top land should be 0.028-0.032 in.; at skirt top 0.0009-0.0025 in.; at skirt bottom 0.0009-0.0015 in.

Lubrication System

Oil Pan Removal and Installation

Due to the variety of engines used in Jeep vehicles, oil pan removal and installation procedures range from simply removing the attaching bolts to removing the front end components for access. On the Commando and CJ series with the 232 or 258 OHV 6, the engine right support must be unbolted from the block and the engine raised by means of a jack under the bellhousing.

Oil Pump Removal and Installation

F4

1. Set No. 1 piston at TDC for reference for reinstalling the oil pump without greatly disturbing the ignition timing.
2. Remove the distributor cap and note the position of the distributor rotor. If the distributor is already removed, sight through the distributor hole before removing the oil pump. The slot should be near the vertical position.
3. Remove the capscrews and lockwashers which attach the oil pump to the engine.
4. Carefully slide the oil pump and its drive shaft out of the cylinder block.
5. Check the clearance between the lobes of the rotors: it should be 0.010 in. Check the clearance between the outer rotor and the pump housing; it should be 0.012 in.
6. Remove the gasket, clean the mating surfaces, and install a new gasket.
7. If the distributor was left in the engine and was not disturbed, install the oil pump, engaging the distributor shaft without disturbing the position of the rotor. If the distributor was removed along with the oil pump, refer to the "Camshaft Removal and Installation" procedure for exact details on installing the oil pump and distributor.

327 V8

The oil pump is driven by the distributor drive shaft. Oil pump removal and installation does not, however, affect distributor timing because the drive gear remains in mesh with the camshaft gear.

1. Drain the oil and remove the oil pan.
2. Unfasten the oil pump attachment screws. Withdraw the pump and gasket from the engine block.
3. Remove the pump cover by unfastening the attachment screws.

With a straightedge across the pump body and gears, clearance should be 0.000-0.004 in. (gears should project above body). Do not disturb the location of the tube in the pump body if possible. Now, measure the clearance between gears and wall of gear cavity opposite point of gear mesh; should be 0.008 in. The oil pressure relief valve is set at the factory to 60 psi and is not adjustable.

Installation is the reverse of removal.

Rear Main Seal Removal and Installation

F4

1. Drain the oil from the engine and remove the oil pan.
2. Remove the screws and lockwashers that attach the rear main bearing cap to the cylinder block.
3. Remove the bearing cap with a lifting bar to pry the cap off of the mounting dowels. Do not apply too much pressure to the cap. Lift the cap off a little at a time from one side to the other until the cap is removed.
4. Remove the two pieces of rear main bearing cap packing out of position between the side of the

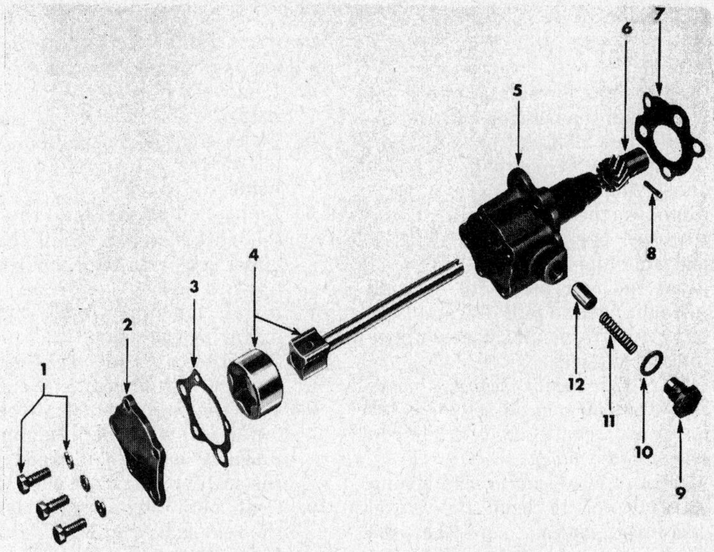

1
2
3
4
5
6
7
8
9
10
11
12

An exploded view of an F-head 4 cyl oil pump (© Kaiser Willys Corp)

1—Cover screw
2—Cover
3—Cover gasket
4—Shaft and rotors
5—Body assembly
6—Driven gear
7—Pump gasket
8—Gear retaining pin
9—Relief valve retainer
10—Relief valve retainer gasket
11—Relief valve spring
12—Relief valve plunger

Checking the clearance between the rotors of an F-head 4 cyl oil pump (© Kaiser Willys Corp)

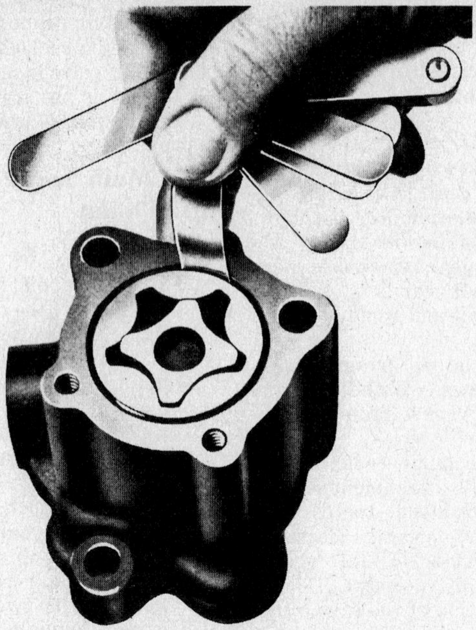

Checking the clearance between the outer rotor and the housing—F-head 4 cyl
(© Kaiser Willys Corp)

bearing cap and the cylinder block.

5. Remove the lower half of the oil seal from the bearing cap and install a new half.

NOTE: Coat the seal with oil to facilitate installation.

6. Remove the upper half of the seal by pushing it out with a suitable tool.
7. Coat the new seal with oil and, using a wire to pull it around the crankshaft, install the new upper half of the seal.

NOTE: For better sealing, make the joints of the seal off-set from the joints of the rear main bearing cap and the cylinder block.

8. Reinstall the bearing cap, being careful not to bend the dowel pins and making sure that the seal is inserted correctly. Tighten to the correct torque.
9. Reinstall the oil pan and fill the crankcase with the correct amount of oil.

327 V8

On this engine, a packing type rear main bearing seal is used. The replacement seal kit, however, contains a neoprene seal.

1. Drain the engine oil and remove the oil pan.
2. Remove the rear main bearing cap.
3. With a 6 in. length of 3/16 in. brazing rod, drive up on either exposed end of the top half of the oil seal. When the opposite end of the seal starts to protrude, grasp it with pliers and pull gently while the driven end is being tapped.

NOTE: Check to see if the bearing cap has a small pin in it to retain the old wick-type seal; if one is present, remove it. Failure to do so will result in damage to the neoprene seal.

4. Remove and discard the lower half of the seal.
5. Clean the main cap, then loosen all of the remaining main cap bolts.
6. Lightly oil all surfaces, then coat the block-side surface of the new upper seal with soap and the seal lip with SAE 40 engine oil.
7. Install the upper seal with the lip facing the front.
8. Coat the cap and block-side seal surface with Permatex No. 2.
9. Coat the back surface of the new lower seal with soap, the lip with SAE 40 engine oil, and install the seal into the main cap.
10. Coat both chamfered edges of the rear main cap with Permatex No. 2, install the bearing inserts (if removed), and tighten the cap bolts.
11. Cement the oil pan gasket to the block and coat the gasket tongues with Permatex No. 2 where they fit into the rear main cap, as well as the front neoprene seal.
12. Coat the rear pan seal with soap and place it into the proper recess, then install the oil pan bolts and tighten them.

CLUTCH

Removal

All Models Except 350 V8 and 225 V6

1. Remove the transmission.
2. Disconnect the clutch linkage.
3. Mark the clutch pressure plate and engine flywheel so the clutch will be reassembled in the same position.
4. Remove the clutch pressure plate bracket bolts alternately, a little at a time, to prevent distortion.
5. Remove the pressure plate assembly and driven plate from the flywheel.

225 V6 and 350 V8

1. Mark the universal joint and transmission shaft companion flange for proper indexing at the time of installation. Remove the two U-bolts and disconnect the driveshaft at the front joint. Slide the driveshaft rearward as far as possible and tie it to one side.
2. Disconnect the shift linkage from the transmission.
3. Disconnect the speedometer cable at the transmission.
4. Loosen all three exhaust pipe ball joints to permit the transmission and the rear of the engine to be lowered.
5. Remove the two bolts holding the transmission mounting pad to the transmission support. Leave the mounting pad bolted to the transmission.
6. With a padded jack under the engine, raise the unit until the transmission mounting pad just clears the transmission support.
7. Remove the four bolts holding the transmission support to the body members. Remove the support, then lower the jack to allow the transmission to clear the underbody.
8. Remove the upper left transmission-to-flywheel housing bolt and install a guide pin. Remove the lower right bolt and install a guide pin.
9. Remove the other two transmission attaching bolts. Slide the transmission back until the drive gear shaft disengages the clutch disc and clears the flywheel housing. Lower the transmission.
10. Remove the pedal return spring from the clutch fork.
11. Remove the flywheel housing.
12. Remove the throw-out bearing.
13. Disconnect the clutch fork from the ball stud.
14. Mark the clutch cover and flywheel to assure proper balance on reassembly.
15. Loosen the clutch cover-to-flywheel bolts one turn at a time until spring pressure is released.
16. Support the pressure plate and cover assembly while removing the last bolts, then remove the cover assembly and driven plate.

Installation

All Models Except 350 V8 and 225 V6

NOTE: The clutch release bearing is lubricated during assembly and need not be lubricated at any other time.

1. Put a very small amount of light grease in the flywheel pilot bushing. Install the driven plate with short end of hub toward flywheel. Place the pressure plate assembly in position.
2. Using a clutch plate aligning arbor or a spare transmission mainshaft, align the driven plate splines. Tighten the pressure plate screws evenly to 40 ft lbs. Remove the aligning arbor.
3. Assemble the flywheel housing to the engine. Make sure that the clutch release bearing carrier return spring is hooked in place. Reverse the order of the clutch assembly removal procedure to complete installation.

225 V6 and 350 V8

Install the clutch by reversing the removal procedure. Use a clutch aligning pilot or a spare main drive gear through the hub of the driven plate and into the pilot bushing. Be sure to align the clutch cover-to-flywheel index marks.

Pedal Adjustment

Universal (CJ) Series, Jeepster

Adjust the linkage at the turnbuckle on the cable from the clutch fork control lever so that the clutch pedal can be depressed 1 in. before clutch disengagement starts.

Wagoneer

1. Disconnect the adjustable rod from the clutch pedal.
2. Adjust the clutch pedal stop bolt for a positive over-center action. This is done by turning the stop bolt in or out to obtain clutch pedal travel of ¼–½ in. before the over-center spring assists the pedal to the floorboard. The pedal need not be the same height as the brake pedal.
3. Adjust the rod from the brake pedal to the cross-shaft so that proper angle is obtained between the arm of the cross-shaft and the top of the left frame rail. For the 350 V8, the correct angle is 30°. For the 327 V8 and the 232 OHV 6, the correct angle is 49°. This angle may be measured with a protractor.
4. Adjust the cross-shaft to throw-out lever link so that the clutch pedal can be depressed 1 in. before clutch engagement starts.

1972 and Later Models

All vehicles equipped with 232, 258 OHV6, 304V8, 360 and 401 V8 engines are utilizing a new cable-actuated linkage. To adjust the cable, follow this procedure:

1. Lift the clutch pedal up against the support bracket stop.
2. Disconnect the clutch fork return spring.
3. Loosen the ball adjusting nut for some cable slack.
4. Turn the ball adjusting nut until slack is taken up and the clutch throw-out bearing contacts the pressure plate fingers.
5. Back off adjusting nut ¾ turn to provide proper free-play and then tighten the jam nut.
6. Connect the clutch fork return spring.

If the clutch cable adjustment does not provide satisfactory disengagement, the pedal height may be adjusted by following these steps:

1. Lift the pedal up against the support bracket stop.
2. Adjust the stop to provide 7 in. clearance between the pedal and the floorpan by turning the stop-screw located on top of the support bracket directly behind the instrument cluster.
3. Readjust the clutch control cable.

MANUAL TRANSMISSION

Transmission Removal and Installation

The transmission and transfer case can be removed as a unit. These instructions apply to both three and four-speed transmissions, and also generally to two-wheel drive models which have no transfer case.

Universal (CJ) Series

1. Drain the transmission and transfer case.
2. Remove the floor pan inspection plate.

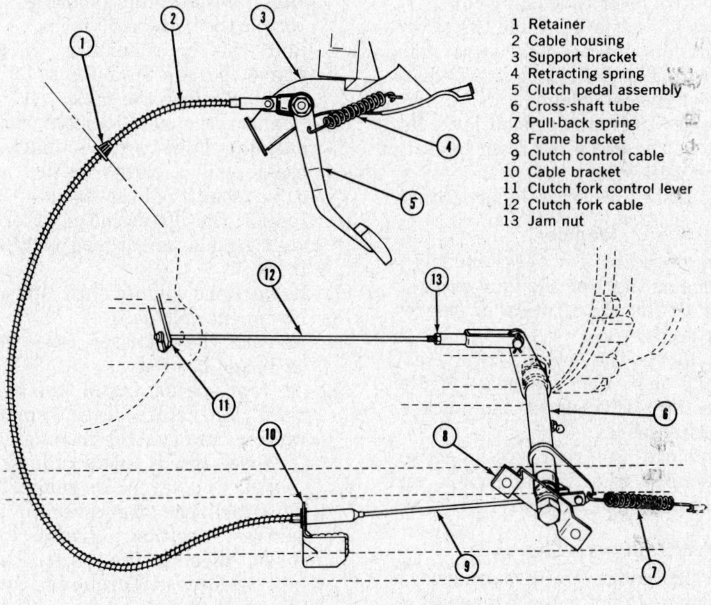
1 Retainer
2 Cable housing
3 Support bracket
4 Retracting spring
5 Clutch pedal assembly
6 Cross-shaft tube
7 Pull-back spring
8 Frame bracket
9 Clutch control cable
10 Cable bracket
11 Clutch fork control lever
12 Clutch fork cable
13 Jam nut

Clutch linkage—Jeepster (© Willys Corp)

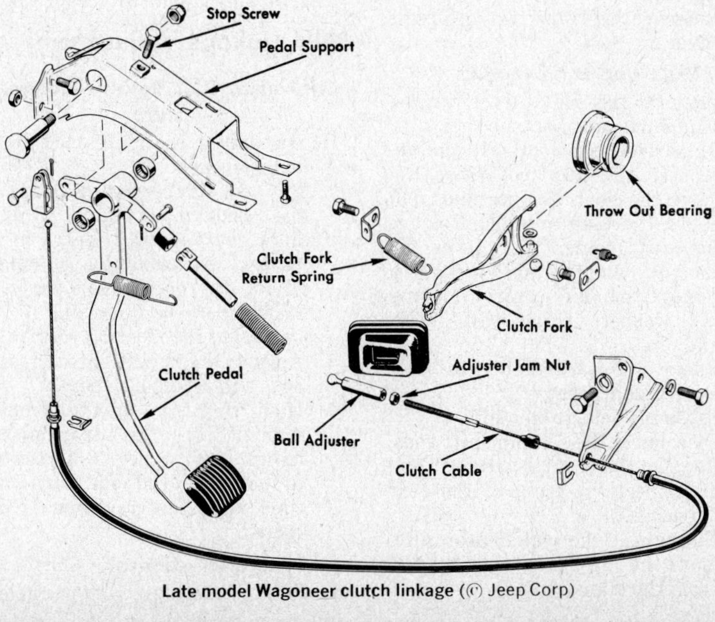
Stop Screw
Pedal Support
Throw Out Bearing
Clutch Fork
Return Spring
Clutch Fork
Adjuster Jam Nut
Clutch Pedal
Ball Adjuster
Clutch Cable

Late model Wagoneer clutch linkage (© Jeep Corp)

3. Remove the shift lever and housing, or disconnect the remote control rods, depending on the model.
4. If the vehicle has a power take-off, remove the shift lever.
5. Disconnect the front and rear driveshafts from the transfer case. Disconnect the power take-off driveshaft.
6. Disconnect the speedometer cable.
7. Disconnect the handbrake cable.
8. Disconnect the clutch release cable or rod.
9. Place the jacks under the engine and transmission, protecting the oil pan with a wooden block.
10. Remove the rear crossmember.
11. Unbolt the transmission from the flywheel housing.
12. Force the transmission to the right to disengage the clutch control lever tube ball joint.
13. Lower the jacks. Slide the transmission and transfer case rearward until the clutch shaft clears the flywheel housing.
14. Lower the transmission jack. Remove the assembly from beneath the vehicle.
15. To install, reverse the procedure.

Jeepster

The procedure for these models is the same as that for the Universal series, with the substitution of the following steps:

2. Remove the right front seat, floor mat, and floorboard center section. Disconnect the back-up switch wires.
10. Remove the rear crossmember. Remove the transmission and transfer case stabilizer brackets.

Wagoneer, Cherokee

The procedure for these models is the same as that for the Universal series, with the substitution of the following step:

2. Remove the transmission access cover.

1972 and Later Models

1. Remove the shift lever knobs, trim rings, and boots.
2. On three-speed floorshift models, remove the floor covering. Remove the floor pan section from above the transmission. Remove the shift control and lever assembly. On four-speed models, remove the shift control housing cap, washer, spring, shift lever, and pin.
3. Remove the transfer case shift lever and bracket.
4. Raise the vehicle on a lift.
5. Disconnect the column shift rods.
6. Remove the front driveshaft and disconnect the front of the rear driveshaft.
7. Disconnect the clutch cable. Remove the cable mounting bracket from the transfer case.
8. Disconnect the speedometer cable and back-up light switch. Disconnect the parking brake cable if it is connected to the crossmember.
9. Support the transmission with a floor jack.
10. Unbolt the crossmember from the frame. Unbolt the transmission from the clutch housing.
11. Lower the transmission slightly and move it to the rear to disengage the clutch shaft. Remove the unit.

To replace the transmission:

12. Place the wave washer and throw-out bearing and sleeve assembly in the fork. Center the bearing over the release levers.
13. Slide the transmission into place, being careful to align the transmission splines with those on the clutch plate. Bolt the transmission to the clutch housing and torque the bolts to 55 ft lbs.
14. Bolt the crossmember to the frame. Torque the bolts to 30–35 ft lbs. Remove the jack.
15. Connect the speedometer cable, back-up light switch, parking brake cable, clutch cable, and cable mounting bracket.
16. Install the driveshafts. Flange bolts should be torqued to 25–45 ft lbs.
17. Replace the column shift linkage.
18. Lower the vehicle.
19. Replace the transfer case shift lever and bracket.
20. On four-speeds, install the lever pivot pin, shift lever, spring, washer, and control housing cap. On three-speeds, install the shift control and lever assembly. Set the gears and the cover in the neutral position. Install the cover, placing the shift forks into the sleeves. Torque the cover bolts to 8–15 ft lbs.
21. Replace the floor covering, boots, trim rings, and shift lever knobs.

Shift Linkage Adjustment

Universal (CJ) Series—Column Shift

1. Disconnect the shift rods at the transmission.
2. Put the transmission lever in the neutral position. *NOTE: Lock the gearshift levers in the neutral positions by putting a ¼ in. dia rod through the gearshift levers and housing at the bottom of the steering column.*
3. Adjust the length of the shift rods and reconnect them.
4. If shifting from first to second is difficult or the transmission hangs in first gear, shorten the first-reverse rod one turn at a time until the condition is corrected.

Jeepster—Console Shift

1. Remove the plug from the hole in the left side of the console. If there is no hole, cut a 1 1/8 in. dia. hole or remove the console.
2. Lift the shift tower rubber cover and remove the plug in the shift tower. Move the selector lever to the neutral position.
3. Loosen the adjusting nuts at the transmission.
4. Insert a 3/16 in. dia rod through the holes in the console and shift tower, and through the aligning holes in the two shift levers. Check to see that the transmission shift levers are in neutral positions.
5. Torque the adjusting nuts to 15–20 ft lbs.
6. Remove the adjusting rod, replace the plugs, and check the shifting action. If the selector lever interferes with the console, relocate the console.

Wagoneer—Column Shift

1. Put the selector lever in Neutral position.
2. Loosen the shift rod adjusting nuts at the transmission. Place the shift levers in Neutral position.
3. Insert a 3/16 in. dia. rod through the remote control shift levers and housing at the bottom of the steering column.
4. Torque the adjusting nuts to 15–20 ft lbs. Remove the adjusting rod.

Transfer Case Removal

The transfer case can also be removed as a separate unit.

Jeepster

1. Drain the transmission and transfer case.
2. Remove the transfer case shift lever.
3. Disconnect the driveshafts.
4. Disconnect the speedometer cable.
5. Disconnect the brake cable (directly under the transfer case).
6. Disconnect the clutch cables from the cross-shaft.
7. Disconnect the clutch control cross-shaft ball joint at frame.
8. Remove the transfer case stabilizer bracket.
9. Remove the bolts securing the transfer case to the transmission. Slide the transfer case rearward to remove it.
10. Reinstall in the reverse order of the above steps.

Wagoneer, Cherokee

This procedure is the same as that detailed above for the removal of the Jeepster transfer case with the substitution of the following steps:

5. Disconnect the parking brake spring from the fuel tank flange. Remove the clevis pin from the brake cable connnecting bracket.

6. Remove exhaust pipe bracket bolts.
7. Delete Step 7.
8. Delete Step 8.

Universal (CJ) Series

1. Drain the transmission and transfer case.
2. Disconnect the brake cable.
3. Disconnect the driveshafts.
4. Disconnect the speedometer cable.
5. Disconnect the transfer case shift levers.
6. Remove the cover plate on the rear of the transfer case. Remove the cotter key, nut, and washer from the transmission mainshaft.
7. If possible, remove the transfer case main drive gear from the transmission mainshaft.
8. Remove the transfer case mounting bracket bolts and nuts.
9. Unbolt the transmission from the transfer case.
10. Remove the transfer case. If the main drive gear has not been removed in Step 7, proceed as follows: Brace the end of the transmission mainshaft so that it cannot move in the transmission, pull the transfer case to the rear to remove. Be careful that the transmission mainshaft bearing, which bears in both housings, remains in the transmission case.
11. Installation is the reverse of the removal procedure.

Quadra-Trac Models

Complete assembly removal is normally not required except when the front output shaft, front annular bearing, transmission output shaft seals, or the transfer case (front housing) require servicing. To service the chain, drive sprocket, differential unit, diaphragm control system, needle bearing, thrust washer, or the rear output shaft, just the rear case cover has to be removed, not the entire unit.

To remove the transfer case from the vehicle, proceed as follows:

1. Lift and support the vehicle.
2. Mark the front and rear output shaft yokes and universal joints to provide alignment references to be used during assembly. Disconnect the front drive shaft rear universal joint from the transfer case front yoke.
3. Disconnect the rear propeller shaft front universal joint from the transfer case rear yoke.
4. Remove the bolts which attach the exhaust pipe bracket to the transfer case.
5. Mark the diaphragm control vacuum hoses for identification during assembly, then disconnect the diaphragm control vacuum hoses, Lock-Out indicator switch wire, and the speedometer cable.
6. Disconnect the parking brake cable guide from the pivot on the right frame side.
7. Remove the two transfer case-to-transmission bolts which enter from the front side. Install a 7/16-14×5 in. guide pin into the upper hole. Remove the two transfer case-to-transmission bolts which enter from the rear. Install a 7/16-14×5 in. guide pin into the upper hole.
8. Move the transfer case assembly backward until the unit is free of the transmission output shaft and guide pins.
9. Lower the assembly from the vehicle.
10. Remove all gasket material from the rear of the transmission.

To install the complete assembly:

11. Position a new gasket onto the rear of the transmission.
12. Install 7/16-14×5 in. guide pins in the upper threaded holes in the transmission adapter and the transfer case.
13. Lift the transfer case assembly and move it forward to the transmission. The drive hub splines must align with the transmission output shaft. Slight rotation of the transfer case rear output shaft yoke may be necessary. Do not install any attaching bolts until the transfer case assembly is positioned against the transmission gasket.
14. Install the rear and front attaching bolts.
15. Attach the exhaust pipe support bracket to the transfer case.
16. Align and attach the front and rear propeller shafts.
17. Connect the Lock-Out indicator

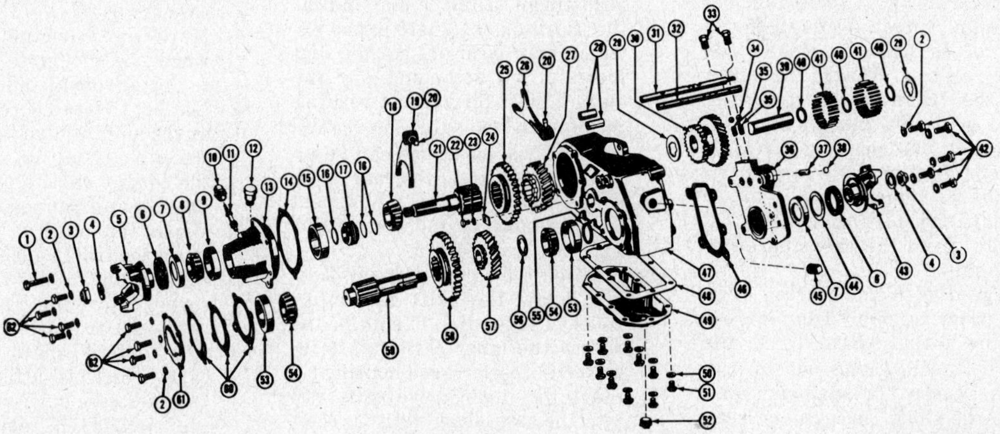

Transfer case (© Willys Corp)

1 Long bolt
2 Lock washer
3 Nut
4 Flat washer
5 Rear propeller shaft yoke
6 Felt seal
7 Yoke oil seal
8 Cone and roller
9 Bearing cup
10 Speedometer driven gear sleeve
11 Speedometer driven gear
12 Breather
13 Rear bearing cap
14 Rear bearing cap gasket
15 Bearing cup
16 Shims
17 Speedometer drive gear
18 Cone and roller
19 Outer shift fork
20 Shift fork bolt
21 Rear output shaft
22 Bolt
23 Lock washer
24 Lock plate
25 Mainshaft sliding gear
26 Inner shift fork
27 Mainshaft gear
28 Shift rod caps
29 Thrust washer
30 Intermediate gear
31 Inner shift rail
32 Outer shift rail
33 Poppet plug
34 Poppet ball
35 Poppet spring
36 Shift rail housing
37 Shift rail interlock
38 Plug
39 Intermediate shaft
40 Bearing spacer
41 Needle bearings
42 Bolt
43 Front propeller shaft yoke
44 Oil seal gasket
45 Oil fill plug
46 Shift rail housing gasket
47 Case
48 Bottom cover gasket
49 Bottom cover
50 Lock washer
51 Bolt
52 Oil drain plug
53 Bearing cup
54 Cone and roller
55 Thrust washer
56 Thrust washer
57 Front output shaft gear
58 Front output shaft sliding gear
59 Front output shaft
60 Shims
61 Cover plate
62 Bolt

switch wire and diaphragm control vacuum hoses.

18. Connect the parking brake cable guide to the pivot bracket on the right frame side.
19. Install the proper type and amount of lubricant and lower the vehicle.

Transfer Case Disassembly

The transfer case can be disassembled as follows:

1. Remove the rear bearing cap assembly.
2. Remove the bottom cover.
3. Remove the lockplate bolt, lockwasher, and lock plate.
4. Drive the intermediate shaft out the rear of the case using a dummy shaft. This tool allows the two sets of needle bearings and three spacers to remain in position as the shaft is withdrawn. The aligner should be centered in the intermediate gear assembly to avoid interference from the thrust washers.
5. Remove the intermediate gear through the bottom of the case.
6. Remove the front output shaft yoke. Remove the felt oil seal, the oil seal gasket and front oil seal.
7. Remove the rear cover. *CAUTION: When removing the rear cover, care should be exercised to avoid damaging the gasket and shim separating the cover plate from the transfer case.*
8. Using a soft-faced hammer, drive the rear bearing cup from the case.
9. Loosen and remove the inner shift fork bolt. Tap the underdrive and direct shift rail to the rear of the case to remove the shift rail cap. Tap the inner rail out the front of the case. The main gear and inner shift fork can then be removed. *NOTE: Front refers to the transmission side of the transfer case.*
10. Remove the shift rail housing assembly from the case and outer shift rail.
11. Wedge the front bearing cone and roller assembly from its seat on the output shaft. Drive the front bearing cone out of the case. Loosen the snap-ring and slide the shaft through the rear of the case. *NOTE: A snap-ring is used on early models only. Current models use a thrust washer on each side of the bearing.*
12. With the shaft removed, the output shaft sliding gear can be lifted from the outer fork. The fork can then be turned and the shift rail fork bolt removed.

Transfer Case Assembly

NOTE: Design changes have been incorporated in the mainshaft, intermediate, and output shaft gears on silent type transfer cases. These late design gears are not interchangeable with early type gears. Should replacement be required, individual gears should be replaced with the identifying numbers on each.

1. Slide the front-wheel drive shift rail partially into the case. Place the front-wheel drive shift fork on the rail with the shift rod fork bolt hole aligned with the countersunk hole on the rail. Replace the shift rail fork bolt and torque to 12–15 ft lbs and replace the safety wire.
2. Place the front-wheel drive shift fork in the proper position in the case. Set the front output shaft sliding gear in the shift fork with the gear facing the front of the transfer case.
3. Install the rear cone and roller on the front output shaft.
4. Hold the output shaft gear in place and insert the output shaft.
5. Install the thrust washer and snap-ring. *NOTE: A snap-ring is used on early models only. Current models use a thrust washer on each side of the bearing.*
6. Install the front cone and roller on the front output shaft.
7. Install the front and rear bearing cup.
8. Install the shift rail housing gasket, shift rail housing, lockwashers, and bolts, and torque to 28–30 ft lbs.
9. Replace the rear cover shim set, rear cover plate, lockwashers, and bolts (28–32 ft lbs).
10. Check the output shaft bearing adjustment using a dial indicator. Position the shaft in the extreme rear position, set the dial indicator on zero, and pry the output shaft forward. A reading of 0.001–0.003 in. should be obtained. This clearance can be altered by changing the rear cover shims. Shims for this adjustment are available as follows: 0.003 in., 0.010 in., 0.031 in.
11. Position the outer shift rail so it will allow the shift rail interlocks to enter the detents in the rod as the inner shift rail is inserted in the shift rod housing.
12. Start the inner drive shift rail into the case along with its shift fork. Place the mainshaft gear on the fork with the gear facing the front of the transfer case. Push the shift rail into the case and through the fork until the countersunk hole on the rod aligns with the shift fork bolt hole. Replace the bolt and torque to 12–15 ft lbs.
13. Place the thrust washers with the tang aligned to the groove in the case. The rear thrust washer can be held in place by just starting the intermediate shaft into the case. The front thrust washer can be held with heavy grease.
14. Position the intermediate gear in the case. Using a soft-faced hammer, drive the intermediate shaft into the intermediate gear. Install the intermediate shaft lockplate, lockwasher, and bolt. Torque to 12–15 ft lbs.
15. Install the rear bearing cap assembly. Torque the long bolt and four short bolts 28–32 ft lbs.
16. Tap the shift rail cups about 3/8 in. into the case.
17. Install the lower cover gasket, the lower cover, lockwashers, and bolts (torque to 12–15 ft lbs).
18. Replace the oil seal gasket and felt oil seal.
19. Install the front and rear propeller shaft yokes (225–250 ft lbs).

Quadra-Trac Rear Case Cover Removal and Disassembly

Most Quadra-Trac components can be serviced without removing the complete unit from the vehicle. To gain access to the rear output shaft, drive sprocket and thrust washer, chain, differential and needle bearing, or the diaphragm control system, just the rear cover has to be removed.

1. Lift and support the vehicle.
2. If the vehicle is equipped with a reduction unit, continue on to the next step for the reduction unit removal procedure. If the vehicle is not equipped with a reduction unit, proceed to Step 7.
3. Loosen all the bolts that attach the reduction unit to the transfer case cover.
4. Move the reduction unit backward just enough to allow the oil to drain from the unit.
5. Loosen the cable retaining bolt at the shift control lever. Loosen the cable clamp bolt and remove the control cable from the clamp bracket and control lever.
6. When the oil has drained, remove the bolts which hold the reduction unit to the transfer case cover. Move the reduction unit rearward to clear the transmission output shaft and pinion cage which is attached to the transfer case drive sprocket. The pinion cage will remain with the transfer case assembly.

NOTE: The pinion cage should not be removed if the transfer case cover assembly is to be removed, but may be removed for inspection or replacement if the transfer case cover assembly is to remain in the vehicle. Removal of the pinion cage involves only removing the snap-ring which holds the cage to the sprocket and sliding the cage backward.

7. Remove the transfer case drain plug and allow the unit to drain.
8. Mark the rear output shaft yoke

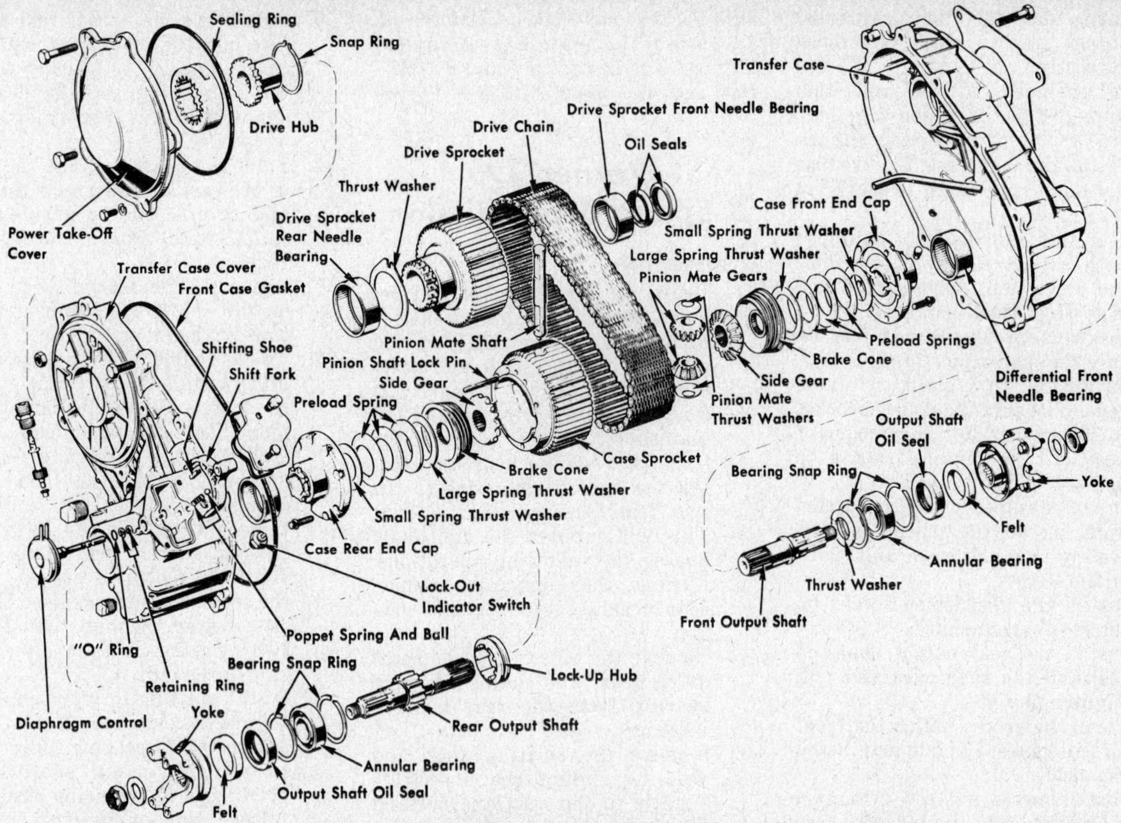

Sealing Ring
Snap Ring
Drive Hub
Power Take-Off Cover
Transfer Case
Drive Sprocket Front Needle Bearing
Drive Chain
Oil Seals
Drive Sprocket
Thrust Washer
Drive Sprocket Rear Needle Bearing
Case Front End Cap
Small Spring Thrust Washer
Large Spring Thrust Washer
Pinion Mate Gears
Transfer Case Cover
Front Case Gasket
Preload Springs
Brake Cone
Shifting Shoe
Pinion Mate Shaft
Pinion Shaft Lock Pin
Shift Fork
Side Gear
Differential Front Needle Bearing
Preload Spring
Pinion Mate Thrust Washers
Output Shaft Oil Seal
Case Sprocket
Bearing Snap Ring
Yoke
Brake Cone
Large Spring Thrust Washer
Felt
Small Spring Thrust Washer
Annular Bearing
Case Rear End Cap
Thrust Washer
Lock-Out Indicator Switch
Front Output Shaft
Poppet Spring And Ball
"O" Ring
Bearing Snap Ring
Lock-Up Hub
Retaining Ring
Yoke
Diaphragm Control
Rear Output Shaft
Annular Bearing
Output Shaft Oil Seal
Felt

Exploded view of a Quadra-Trac transfer case (© Jeep Corp)

and universal joint to provide an alignment reference during reassembly. Disconnect the rear propeller shaft front universal joint from the transfer case rear yoke.

9. Mark the diaphragm control vacuum hoses for identification during reassembly, then disconnect them. Also remove the lock-up indicator switch wire and the speedometer cable. Remove the indicator switch.
10. Disconnect the parking brake cable guide from the pivot on the right frame side.
11. Remove the bolts which attach the case cover assembly to the case (front housing). Carefully slide the cover assembly backward off the front output shaft and the transmission output shaft.
12. To disassemble the unit, remove the rear output shaft yoke.
13. If the unit is *not* equipped with a reduction unit, remove the power take-off cover from the rear of the transfer case cover. Remove the sealing ring from the transfer case cover.
14. Using a piece of wood 2 in. × 4 in. and 6 in. long, position the cover and sprocket.
15. If *not* equipped with a reduction unit, remove the drive hub and sleeve from the drive sprocket rear splines by expanding the internal snap-ring. The ring expanding tabs are accessible through a slot in the outside edge of the drive sleeve.

Quadra-Trac case cover positioned for disassembly
(© Jeep Corp)

If equipped with a reduction unit, remove the pinion cage snap-ring and carrier. Lift the case cover from the drive sprocket and differential. The cover, rear output shaft, bearings and seal, drive sprocket rear needle bearing, and lock-up hub can now be serviced without any further disassembly of other components.

16. Slide the drive sprocket toward the differential unit and remove the chain. The differential unit may now be serviced without any further disassembly of other components.

Quadra-Trac Assembly and Rear Case Cover Installation

1. Position the drive sprocket on a block of wood 2 in. × 4 in. and 6 in. long.
2. Place the differential assembly about 2 in. from the drive sprocket and with the front end of the differential on the bench.

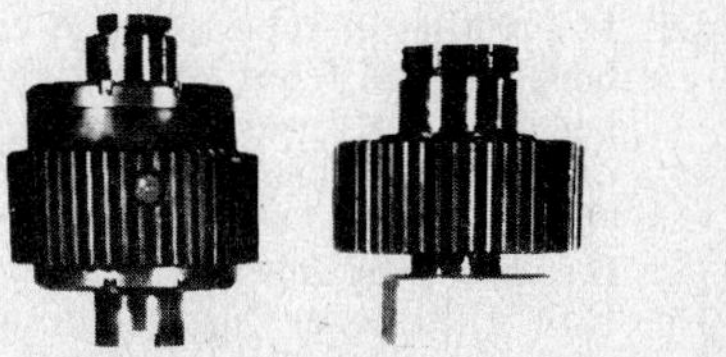

Differential and drive sprockets positioned for chain installation
(© Jeep Corp)

3. Position the drive chain around the drive sprocket and the differential assembly. Be sure that the chain is properly engaged with the sprocket and differential teeth and that the slack is removed from the chain.
4. Insert the rear output shaft into the differential.
5. Shift the lock-up hub rearward in the case cover. Lubricate the drive sprocket thrust washer and insert it in position on the case cover.
6. Carefully align the case cover and position it onto the drive sprocket and differential. The output shaft may have to be slightly rotated to align it with the lock-up hub. Be

Drive chain positioned around the differential and drive sprockets
(© Jeep Corp)

sure that the drive sprocket thrust washer stays positioned correctly.

7. If equipped with a reduction unit, install the pinion cage onto the drive sprocket rear splines. Install the snap-ring. Be sure that the snap-ring seats properly in the groove.

   If the vehicle is *not* equipped with a reduction unit, assemble the drive hub, drive sleeve, and snap-ring, then install them onto the drive sprocket rear splines. Be sure the snap-ring seats properly.
8. Rotate the drive sleeve or pinion cage to be sure the drive sprocket thrust washer did not come out of position. No binding should be present.
9. If *not* equipped with a reduction unit, install the power take-off sealing ring and cover and tighten the screws.
10. Install the speedometer gear on the rear output shaft.
11. Install the rear output shaft oil seal and the rear yoke and nut. Tighten the nut.
12. Clean the groove which the front oil seal gasket fits into and install the seal.
13. Install two 3/8 in.-16 × 2 in. long pilot studs into the transfer case front cover housing.
14. Insert the oil tube into the case bore at the front output shaft bearing boss. Insert a 6 in. length of 5/16 in. rod into the tube. The rod will be used as a pilot to align the tube with the case cover.
15. Lift the cover assembly and align the tube pilot with the hole in the cover. Move the assembly forward over the pilot studs.
16. Move the cover assembly forward to mesh with the front output shaft and transmission output shaft. It may be necessary to rotate the rear output shaft slightly to allow the two sets of splines to engage.
17. After the cover assembly has been moved forward and is evenly touching the front half of the case, remove the pilot studs and install the rear cover attaching bolts. Tighten the bolts alternately and evenly.
18. Install the Lock-Out indicator switch and connect the Lock-Out switch wire, diaphragm control vacuum hoses, and the speedometer cable.
19. Install the rear drive shaft.
20. Install the parking brake cable guide to the pivot on the right frame side.
21. Install the reduction unit, if so equipped.
22. Install the proper type and amount of lubricant and lower the vehicle.

NOTE: Use 8 oz of limited slip differential lubricant additive mixed with SAE 30 non-detergent motor oil. 3.5 pints of the mixture is required to fill the transfer case without a reduction unit, 4.5 pints with a reduction unit.

Warner T96 3 Speed Transmission

Disassembly

1. Drain the transmission and remove the top cover and gasket.
2. Remove the clutch shaft bearing retainer and the shaft and bearing snap-rings.
3. Loop a piece of wire around the mainshaft, to the rear of the first-speed sliding gear, and fasten the ends of the wire to the two front transmission screws. This will support the mainshaft during the following operations.
4. Remove the companion flange, rear bearing retainer, and gasket.
5. Remove the oil seal, speedometer drive gear, and mainshaft rear bearing from the rear bearing retainer.
6. Remove the shifting fork and shoe by sliding the mainshaft slightly to the rear and cocking the shaft away from the fork.
7. Remove the countershaft and idler shaft lockplate.
8. With a dummy shaft and soft hammer, drive the countershaft out of the case. Let the countergear assembly rest in the bottom of the case.
9. Remove the clutch shaft and bearing from the front of the case.
10. Remove the small and large snap-rings and the mainshaft rear bearing from the mainshaft.
11. Remove the blocker ring, clutch hub, and synchronizer assembly.
12. Remove the low and reverse sliding gears and the constant-mesh gear and mainshaft as a unit, through the top.
13. Remove the countershaft gears from the top.
14. Drive the reverse idler shaft out through the rear, then remove the idler gear.

Assembly

1. With the reverse idler gear in place, tap the idler shaft into place.
2. Assemble the countershaft gear by inserting a dummy shaft and the tubular bearing spacer into the countergear. Grease both ends of the gear bore and insert 20 bearing rollers into each end. Add a roller bearing spacer washer to each end of the gear and place the assembly in the bottom of the case, large end of gear forward.
3. Install the mainshaft rear bearing onto the mainshaft with the closed side of the bearing facing the front. Replace the bearing snap-ring and the mainshaft snap-ring.
4. Start the shaft through the rear of the case and assemble the low and reverse sliding gear on the shaft, fork groove toward the rear.
5. Assemble the second-speed gear on the shaft, synchronizer teeth toward the front.
6. To assemble the synchronizer unit, install the two springs in the high and intermediate clutch hub. These springs must be installed with the spring tension opposed. Install the three synchronizer shifting plates into the three slots in the hub, with the smooth side of the plates out. With the plates in position, slip the second and third-speed clutch sleeve over the hub. Install the two blocking rings, one on each side of the hub.
7. Install shifting fork and shoe.
8. Grease the clutch shaft pilot bore and install 13 bearing rollers.
9. Install the clutch shaft main drive gear and bearing assembly (closed side of bearing toward inside of case).
10. Enter the mainshaft bearing in the case and assemble the shaft in position.
11. Install the front bearing retainer.
12. Invert the transmission, then line up the countergear bore with the countershaft bore in the case. Enter the countershaft into the case from the rear and entirely displace the dummy shaft.
13. Install the countershaft idler shaft lockplate.
14. Install the rear bearing snap-ring and bearing onto the shaft.
15. Attach the rear bearing retainer and gasket to the case.
16. Install speedometer drive gear onto the shaft with the shoulder of the gear front. Replace the rear oil seal if necessary.
17. Install the companion flange and check the operation of the transmission.
18. Fill with lubricant to level, then install the transmission case cover.

Warner T14(A), T15(A) 3 Speed Transmission

Transmission Disassembly

1. Separate the transfer case by removing the five capscrews.
2. Remove the cover and gasket. Disassemble the floorshift housing cover by removing the shift rails, poppet balls, springs, and shift forks.

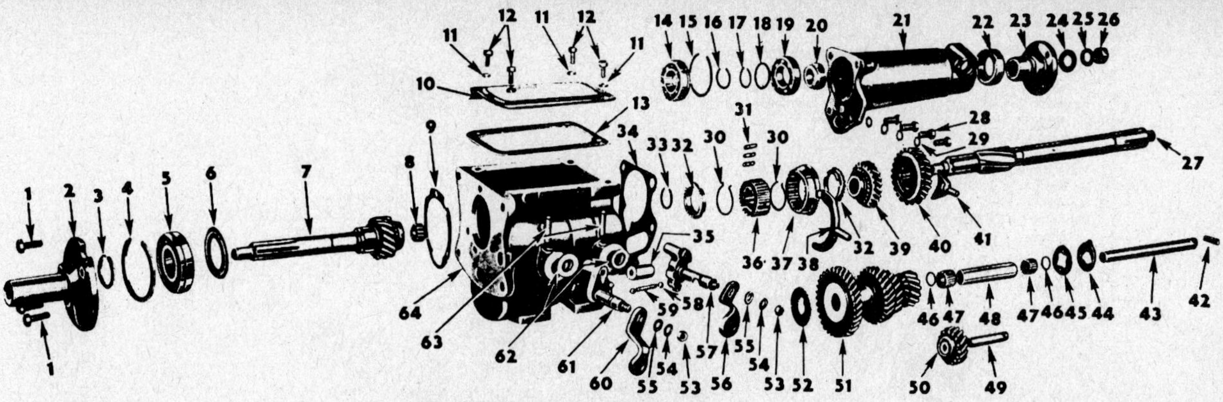

Warner T-96 three-speed transmission—two-wheel drive (© Willys Corp)

1 Main bearing retainer bolt
2 Main bearing retainer
3 Main drive gear snap-ring
4 Bearing snap-ring
5 Main drive gear bearing
6 Oil baffle
7 Main drive gear
8 Pilot bearing rollers
9 Bearing retainer gasket
10 Case cover
11 Case cover bolt gasket
12 Case cover bolt
13 Case cover gasket
14 Rear main shaft bearing
15 Rear bearing snap-ring
16 Mainshaft snap-ring
17 Rear bearing snap-ring
18 Rear bearing washer
19 Rear mainshaft bearing
20 Speedometer drive gear
21 Rear bearing retainer
22 Mainshaft oil seal
23 Coupling flange
24 Mainshaft washer
25 Mainshaft nut lockwasher
26 Mainshaft nut
27 Mainshaft
28 Rear bearing retainer bolt
29 Retainer bolt lockwasher
30 Synchronizer spring
31 Synchronizer shifting plate
32 Blocking ring
33 Clutch hub snap-ring
34 Rear bearing retainer gasket
35 Interlock sleeve
36 Clutch hub
37 Clutch sleeve
38 High and intermediate shift fork
39 Second speed gear
40 Low and reverse gear
41 Low and reverse shift fork
42 Idler and countershaft lock-plate
43 Countershaft
44 Thrust washer
45 Thrust washer
46 Countershaft bearing shift spacer
47 Countershaft bearing rollers
48 Countershaft bearing long spacer
49 Reverse idler gear shaft
50 Reverse idler gear
51 Countershaft gear
52 Thrust washer
53 Control lever to shaft nut
54 lever-to-shaft lockwasher
55 Lever-to-shaft washer
56 Low and reverse control lever
57 Low and reverse shift lever
58 Poppet ball
59 Poppet spring
60 High and intermediate control lever
61 High and intermediate shift lever
62 Shift shaft oil seal
63 Shift lever shaft pin
64 Transmission case

3. Remove the nut, flat washer, transfer case drive gear, adaptor, and spacer.
4. Remove the main drive gear bearing retainer and gasket.
5. Remove the main drive gear and mainshaft bearing snap-rings.
6. Pull out the main drive gear and mainshaft bearings.
7. Remove the main drive gear.
8. Remove the mainshaft assembly through the cover opening.
9. On remote-shift models, remove the roll pins from the lever shafts and housing. From inside the case, slide the levers and interlock assembly out. Remove the forks and lever assemblies.
10. Remove the lockplate from the slots in the reverse idler shaft and countershaft.
11. Drive the countershaft out to the rear with a dummy shaft. Remove the countergear and the two thrust washers. Remove the spacer washers, rollers, and spacer from the gear.
12. Drive the reverse idler shaft out to the rear. Remove the gear, washers, and roller bearings.
13. Remove the clutch hub snap-ring and the second-third synchronizer assembly.
14. Remove second and reverse gears.
15. Remove the clutch hub snap-ring and the low synchronizer assembly.
16. Remove low gear.

Synchronizer Disassembly and Assembly

1. Remove the springs. The low synchronizer has only one spring; second-third, two.
2. Mark the sleeve and hub before separating.
3. Remove the hub.
4. Remove the three shifter plates from hub.
5. Inspect all parts for wear.
6. Assemble in the reverse order of disassembly. On the second-third unit, make sure that the spring openings are 120° from each other, with spring tension opposed.

NOTE: if a synchronizer assembly is replaced on a floor-shift unit, the shift fork operating the synchronizer being replaced must have the letter "A" just under the shaft hole on the side opposite the pin.

Inspection

1. Wash all parts in solvent.
2. Air dry.
3. Check the case bearing and shaft bores. Check for cracks or burrs.
4. Check all gears and bronze blocking rings for cracks, and chipped, worn, or cracked teeth If any gears are replaced, also replace the meshing gears.
5. Check all bearings and bushings for wear or damage.
6. Check to see that the synchronizer sleeves slide freely on the clutch hubs.

Transmission Assembly

1. Place the reverse idler gear with the dummy shaft, roller bearing, and thrust washers in the case. Install the reverse idler shaft.
2. Assemble the countershaft center spacer, four bearing spacers, and bearing rollers in the countershaft gear.
3. Install the large countergear thrust washer in front of case. Position the small thrust washer on the countergear hub with the lip facing the groove in the case. Holding the countergear in position, push in the countershaft from the rear.
4. Install the lockplate in the slots of the reverse idler shaft and the countershaft.
5. Install to mainshaft:
   a. low gear.
   b. bronze blocking ring.
   c. low synchronizer assembly.
   d. largest snap-ring that fits in groove.
   e. second gear.
   f. bronze blocking ring.
   g. second-third synchronizer assembly.
   h. largest snap-ring that fits in groove.
   i. reverse gear.
6. Install the mainshaft assembly through the top of the case.
7. Install the bronze blocking ring to the second-third synchronizer assembly.
8. On remote-shift units, install new O-rings on the shifter lever shafts and install the shafts into the case.

NOTE: T-15 interlock levers are marked as to location. T-14 levers have no marks and are interchangeable.

9. Depress the interlock lever while installing the shift fork into the shift lever and synchronizer

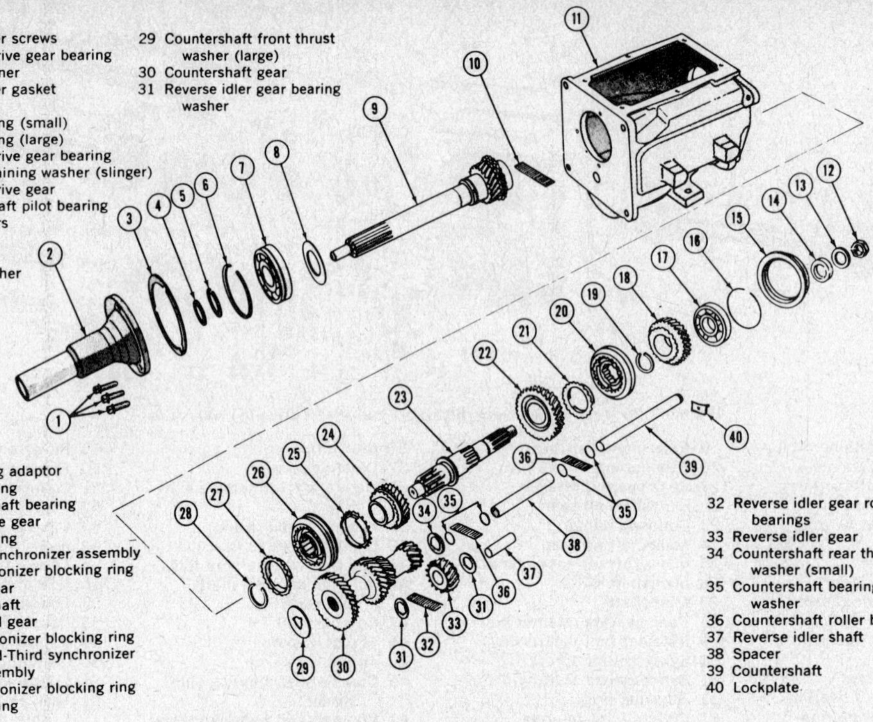

1 Retainer screws
2 Main drive gear bearing retainer
3 Retainer gasket
4 Oil seal
5 Snap-ring (small)
6 Snap-ring (large)
7 Main drive gear bearing
8 Oil Retaining washer (slinger)
9 Main drive gear
10 Mainshaft pilot bearing rollers
11 Case
12 Nut
13 Flatwasher
14 Spacer
15 Bearing adaptor
16 Snap-ring
17 Mainshaft bearing
18 Reverse gear
19 Snap-ring
20 Low synchronizer assembly
21 Synchronizer blocking ring
22 Low gear
23 Mainshaft
24 Second gear
25 Synchronizer blocking ring
26 Second-Third synchronizer assembly
27 Synchronizer blocking ring
28 Snap-ring
29 Countershaft front thrust washer (large)
30 Countershaft gear
31 Reverse idler gear bearing washer
32 Reverse idler gear roller bearings
33 Reverse idler gear
34 Countershaft rear thrust washer (small)
35 Countershaft bearing spacer washer
36 Countershaft roller bearings
37 Reverse idler shaft
38 Spacer
39 Countershaft
40 Lockplate

T-14 or T-15 transmission—exploded view (© Kaiser Jeep Corp)

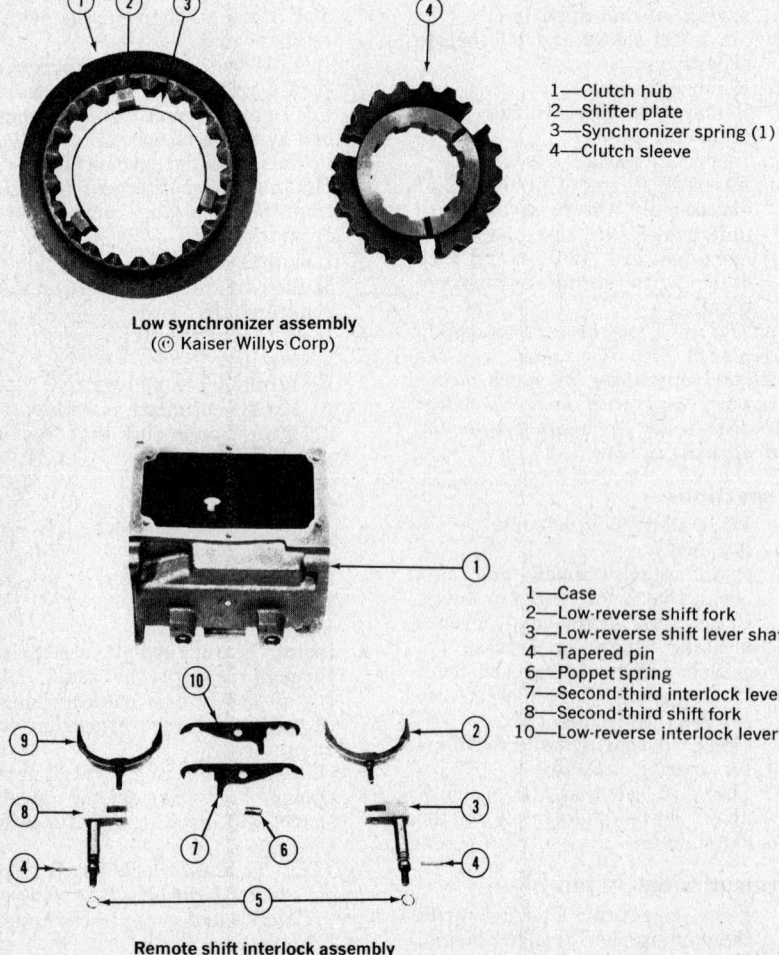

1—Clutch hub
2—Shifter plate
3—Synchronizer spring (1)
4—Clutch sleeve

Low synchronizer assembly
(© Kaiser Willys Corp)

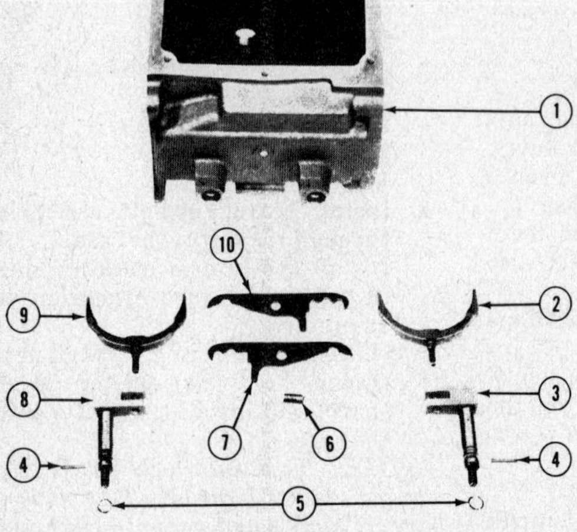

1—Case
2—Low-reverse shift fork
3—Low-reverse shift lever shaft
4—Tapered pin
6—Poppet spring
7—Second-third interlock lever
8—Second-third shift fork
10—Low-reverse interlock lever

Remote shift interlock assembly
(© Kaiser Willys Corp)

clutch sleeve. Install the poppet spring. Install the tapered pins securing the shafts in the case.

10. Install the main drive gear roller bearings.
11. Install the main drive gear and oil slinger into the case with cutaway portion of the gear toward the countergear. Install the main drive gear to the mainshaft.
12. Using the bearing installer and thrust yoke tool, install the main drive gear and mainshaft bearings. Drive the bearings into position. The thrust yoke is needed to prevent damage to the synchronizer clutch.
13. Install the main drive gear and mainshaft bearing snap-rings. The mainshaft bearing snap-ring is 0.010 in. thicker than the main drive gear bearing snap-ring.
14. Install the mainshaft rear bearing adaptor, spacer, transfer case drive gear, flat washer, and nut. Torque the nut to 130–170 ft lbs.
15. Replace the main drive gear bearing retainer oil seal. Install the retainer and gasket. Align the oil drain holes in the retainer and gasket.
16. Install the case cover gasket. On remote-shift units, install the cover gasket with the vent holes to the left side.
17. Position the gear train and floor-shift assembly in neutral. Insert the shifter forks into the clutch sleeves. Install and torque the bolts to 8–15 ft lbs.

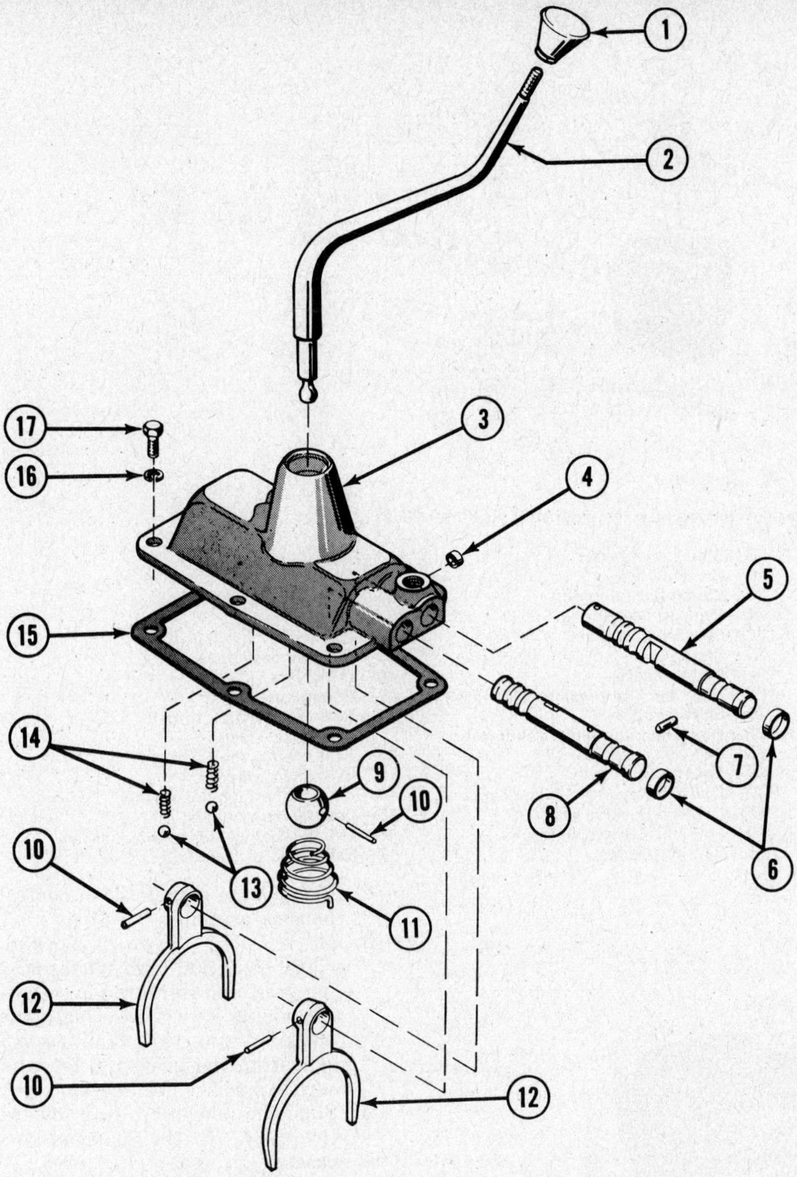
1
2
3
4
5
6
7
8
9
10
11
12
13
14
15
16
17

Floor shift control housing assembly (© Kaiser Willys Corp)

1—Shift lever knob
2—Shift lever
3—Control housing
4—Plug
5—Shift rail (second-third)
6—Shift rail cap
7—Interlock plunger
8—Shift rail (low-reverse)
9—Shift lever fulcrum ball
10—Pin
11—Shift lever support spring
12—Shift fork
13—Poppet ball
14—Poppet spring
15—Gasket
16—Lockwasher
17—Bolt

Warner T86 and T90 3 Speed Transmission

Disassembly

1. Drain the lubricant and flush out the case.
2. If a transfer case is involved, remove its rear cover.
3. If a power take-off is involved, remove the shift unit which replaces the cover.
4. Remove the cotter pin, nut, and washer, and remove the transfer case main drive gear.
5. Remove the transmission shift cover.
6. Loop a piece of wire around the mainshaft just back of the second-speed gear. Twist the wire and attach one end to the right front cover screw, the other end to the left cover screw. Tighten the wire to prevent the mainshaft from pulling out of the case when the transfer case is removed. Should the mainshaft come out, the synchronizer parts will drop into the bottom of the case.
7. Remove the five screws holding the transfer case to the rear face of the transmission.
8. Support the transfer case, then tap lightly on the end of the transmission mainshaft to separate the two units. The transmission mainshaft bearing should slide out of the transfer case and stay with the transmission.
9. Remove the three screws and washers in the front main drive gear bearing retainer, then remove the retainer and gasket.
10. Remove the two hollow-head screws that support the oil collector.
11. Remove the lockplate from the reverse idler shaft and the countershaft at the rear of the case.
12. Drive the countershaft out the rear of the case with a dummy shaft and a brass drift.
13. Remove the loop of wire previously twisted around the mainshaft for support.
14. Remove the mainshaft rear bearing adaptor, then remove the mainshaft assembly from the case. The assembly may be removed through the rear opening of the case. Remove the main drive gear.
15. Remove the countershaft gear set and three thrust washers from the bottom of the case, then dismantle the countershaft gear assembly.
16. Remove the reverse idler shaft and gear by driving the shaft out with a brass drift.
17. On column-shift models, check the clearance between the ends of the interlock sleeve and the notched surface of each shift lever. The correct clearance is 0.001–0.007 in. Several sizes of interlock sleeves are available for adjustment.

Assembly

Assemble the transmission in the reverse order of disassembly, giving the following points particular attention.

1. The countershaft gear set, when assembled in the case, should have 0.012–0.018 in. end-play. This clearance is controlled by the selective thickness of the rear steel thrust washer.
2. Assemble the large bronze washer at the front of the case with the lip entered in the slot in the case.
3. The bronze-faced steel washer is placed next to the gear at the rear end, and the steel washer next to the case.
4. To assemble the countershaft bearing rollers, use a dummy shaft. Use grease and a loading sleeve to facilitate reassembly of the countershaft gear components.
5. In assembling the mainshaft gears, low and reverse gear is installed with the shift shoe groove toward the front.

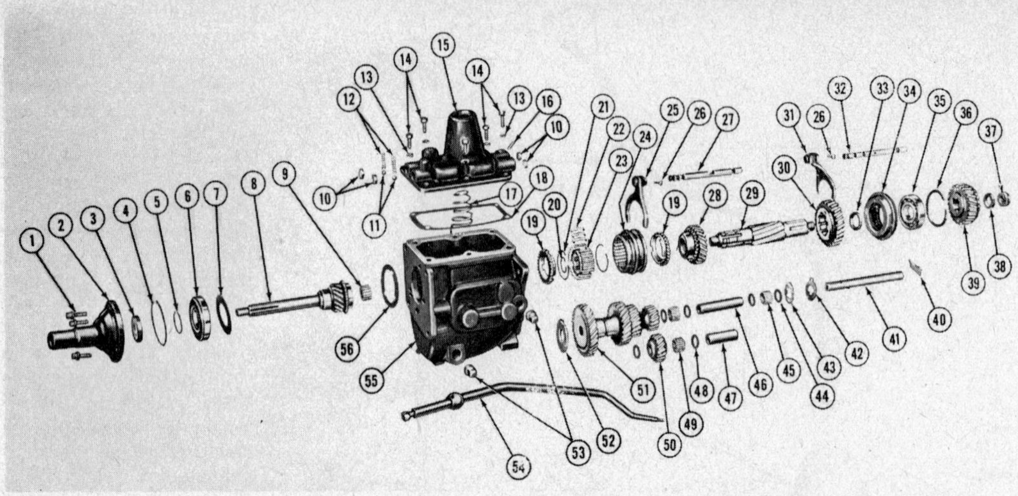

T-90, T-86 three-speed transmissions, floor shift (© Kaiser Willys Corp)

1—Bearing retainer screws
2—Main drive gear bearing retainer
3—Bearing retainer oil seal
4—Bearing snap-ring
5—Main drive gear snap ring
6—Main drive gear bearing
7—Front bearing oil retaining washer
8—Main drive gear
9—Pilot roller bearing
10—Shift rail cap
11—Poppet ball
12—Poppet spring
13—Lock washer
14—Shift housing bolt
15—Control housing
16—Interlock punger
17—Shift lever spring
18—Shift tower gasket
19—Blocking ring
20—Clutch hub snap ring
21—Synchronizer spring
22—Synchronizer plate
23—Clutch hub
24—Clutch sleeve
25—High and intermediate clutch fork
26—Shift fork pin
27—High and intermediate shift rail
28—Second speed gear
29—Main shaft
30—Low and Reverse sliding gear
31—Low and Reverse shift fork
32—Low and Reverse shift rail
33—Bearing spacer
34—Rear bearing adapter
35—Rear bearing
36—Rear bearing snap ring
37—Nut
38—Washer
39—Transfer case drive gear
40—Lock plate
41—Countershaft
42—Rear countershaft thrust washer (steel)
43—Rear countershaft thrust washer (bronze)
44—Countershaft bearing washer
45—Countershaft bearing
46—Countershaft center bearing spacer
47—Reverse idler gear shaft

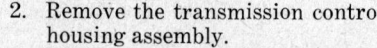

Measuring the interlock sleeve clearance
(© Kaiser Willys Corp)

6. In assembling the synchronizer unit, install the two springs in the high and intermediate clutch hub with spring tension opposed. Place the right, lipped end of a spring in the slot of the hub and place the spring in the hub. Turn the hub around and make the same installation with the other spring, starting with the same slot. Install the three synchronizer shifting plates into the three slots in the hub, with the smooth sides of the plates out. Hold the plate in position and slip the second and direct clutch sleeve over the hub, with the long beveled edge toward the long part of the clutch hub. Install the completed assembly onto the mainshaft with the beveled edge of the clutch sleeve toward the front end of the shaft.
7. When installing the mainshaft, be sure the bearing rollers are in place in the pilot bore of the clutch gear.
8. Be sure that the countershaft and reverse idler shaft lockplate are in position and completely recessed into the indents of the transfer case.

Warner T98, T18 4 Speed Transmission

Disassembly

1. Remove the transmission transfer case adaptor plate and gasket.
2. Remove the transmission control housing assembly.
3. Mark the two blocking rings, third and high synchronizing gear, and third and high synchronizing sleeve. Also mark the blocking ring, low and second synchronizing gear, and low and second synchronizer sleeve.
4. Slide the low-speed gear toward the rear of the transmission case.
5. Disengage the reverse gearshift arm from the reverse idler gear and remove the reverse gearshift arm from the reverse mounting pin.
6. Move the low-speed gear back into neutral position.
7. Remove the rear bearing retainer. Remove the snap-ring from the main drive pinion (clutch shaft) and the outer race of the drive pinion ball bearing.
8. Remove the main drive pinion ball bearing and oil slinger.
9. Remove the snap-ring from the outer bearing race of the transmission mainshaft ball bearing, then, with a bearing puller, pull the bearing.
10. Separate the mainshaft assembly from the main drive pinion.
11. Lift the mainshaft assembly from the case.
12. Remove the main drive pinion from the case.
13. Remove the mainshaft pilot rollers from the drive pinion.

14. Mark the relation between the synchronizer gears and splines on the mainshaft.
15. Disassemble the mainshaft by removing the snap-ring holding the third and high synchronizer assembly onto the mainshaft.
16. Remove the snap-ring holding the second-speed synchronizer onto the mainshaft.
17. Slide the second-speed synchronizer and second-speed gear from the mainshaft.
18. Remove the two remaining snap-rings, spacer, and thrust washer from the mainshaft.
19. Remove the two large lockrings and push the synchronizer gear out of the sleeve.
20. If the second-speed synchronizer assembly is to be disassembled, wrap the assembly in a cloth to prevent losing the lock balls and springs. Push the gear out of the sleeve in a direction opposite the shift fork groove. Remove the cloth and lift the balls, springs, and plates out of the gear.
21. Remove the lockplate for the countershaft and the reverse idler gear shaft.
22. With a pry bar in the slot of the reverse idler gear shaft, loosen the shaft. Slip the reverse idler shaft out of the housing and gear. Lift the reverse idler gear from the case.
23. To remove the countershaft, use a dummy shaft, (1⅛ x 9.850 in.) to displace the countershaft and keep the countergear components intact. After the countershaft has been pushed entirely out of the countergear and case, remove the gear.
24. Completely disassemble the countergear assembly.
25. To disassemble the reverse idler gear assembly, remove one of the snap-rings and tap out the washer, both sets of bearing rollers, center spacer, and sleeve. Remove the remaining snap-ring.

Assembly

Assemble in the reverse order of disassembly. Pay particular attention to the following:

1. Install the countershaft from the rear, with the bronze front thrust washer and the steel-backed bronze rear thrust washer installed with the lugs engaged in the notches in the end of the gear cluster. Do not seat the countershaft until the reverse idler gear and shaft have been installed.
2. Install the reverse idler shaft until the lockplate slot is adjacent to the countershaft slot. Insert the lock-plate and tap the shafts together.

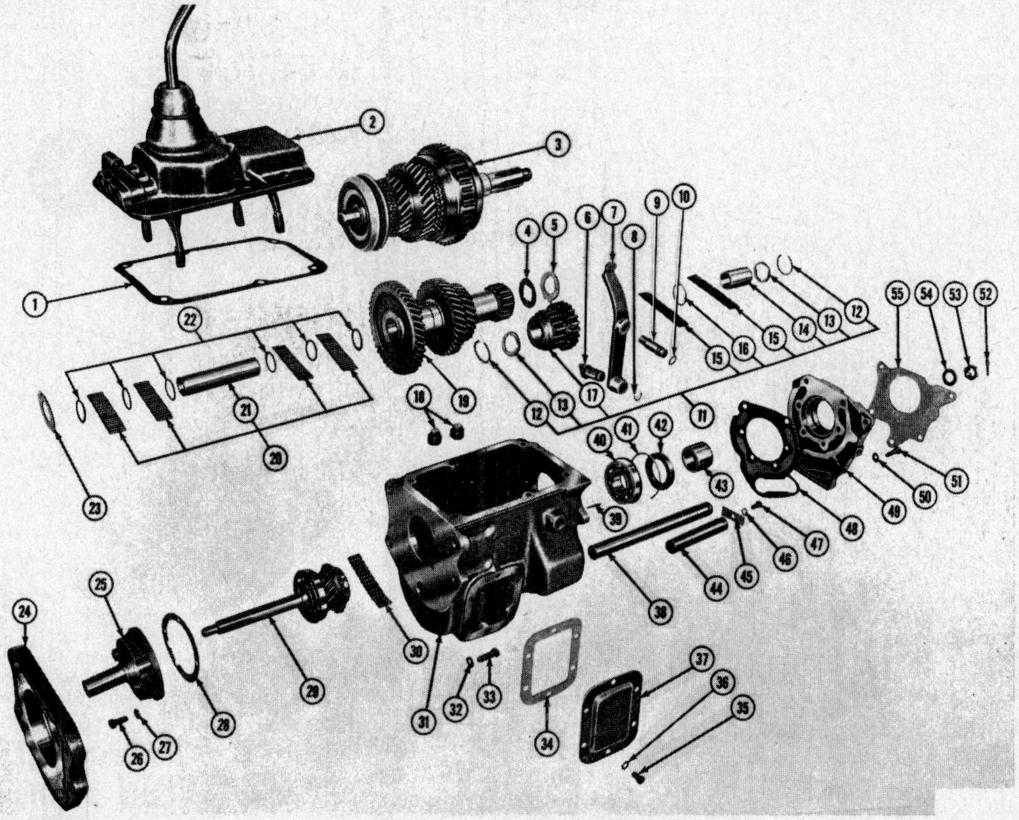

Warner T-18 and T-98 transmission (© Kaiser Willys Corp)

1—Control housing gasket
2—Control housing assembly
3—Mainshaft assembly
4—Thrust washer
5—Thrust washer
6—Reverse shifting shoe
7—Reverse shifting arm
8—C-washer
9—Reverse shifting arm pivot
10—O-ring
11—Reverse idler gear assembly
12—Snap-ring
13—Thrust washer
14—Sleeve
15—Bearing rollers
16—Spacer
17—Reverse idler gear
18—Pipe plug
19—Countershaft gears
20—Bearing rollers
21—Spacer
22—Spacer
23—Thrust washer
24—Bellhousing-to-transmission adapter plate
25—Bearing retainer
26—Bearing retainer bolt
27—Bearing retainer lockwasher
28—Bearing retainer gasket
29—Main drive gear
30—Bearing rollers
31—Transmission case
32—Adapter plate lockwasher
33—Adapter plate capscrew
34—Side opening cover gasket
35—Side opening cover bolt
36—Side opening cover lockwasher
37—Side opening cover
38—Countershaft
39—Shifting arm pivot taper pin
40—Bearing
41—Snap-ring
42—Oil seal
43—Spacer
44—Reverse-idler gear shaft
45—Lock plate
46—Lock plate lockwasher
47—Lock plate bolt
48—Gasket
49—Adapter plate
50—Adapter plate lockwasher
51—Adapter plate bolt
52—Cotter key
53—Nut
54—Washer
55—Gasket

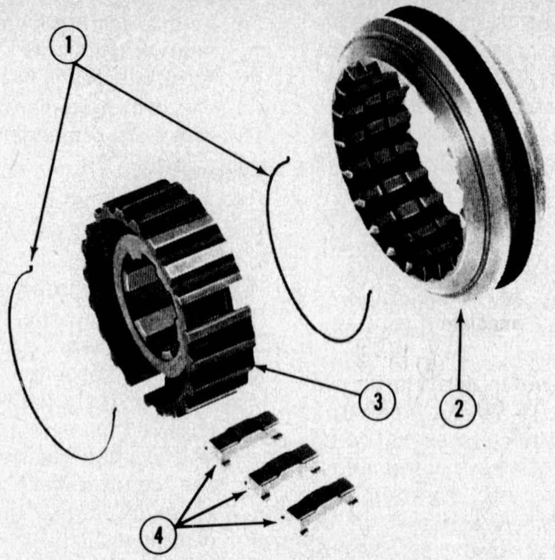
1
2
3
4

Second and third gear synchronizer assembly
(© Kaiser Willys Corp)

1—Synchronizer spring (2)
2—Clutch hub
3—Cutch sleeve
4—Shifter plate

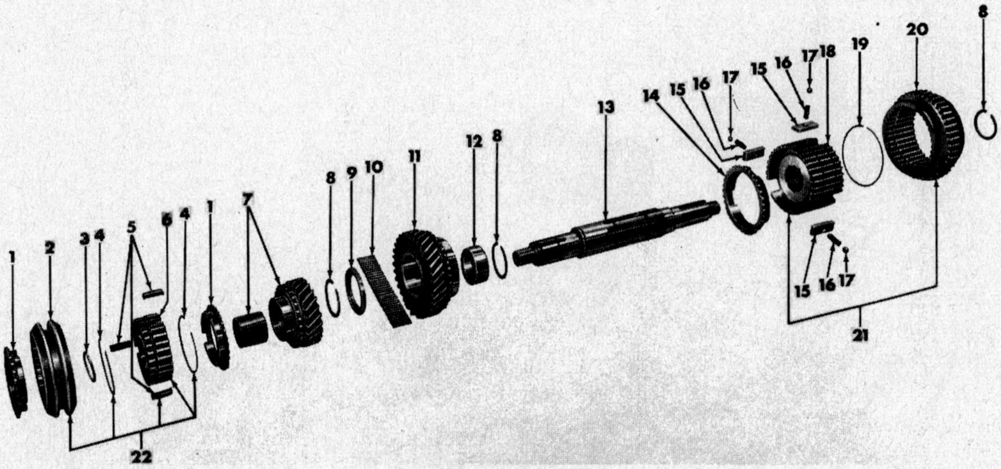
1
2
3 4
5
6 4
1
7
8
9
10
11
12
8
13
14
15
16
17
15
16
17
18
19
20
8
15
16
17
21
22

Four-speed main shaft assembly (© Kaiser Willys Corp)

1—Blocking ring
2—Direct and third clutch sleeve
3—Snap ring
4—Spring
5—Shifting plate
6—Direct and third clutch hub
7—Third speed gear assembly
8—Snap ring
9—Thrust washer
10—Bearing rollers
11—Second speed gear
12—Spacer
13—Mainshaft
14—Blocking ring
15—Shifting plate
16—Poppet spring
17—Ball
18—Low and second clutch hub
19—Retaining ring
20—Low and second speed gear
21—Second speed synchronizer assembly
22—Direct and third synchronizer assembly

3. Assemble the second-speed synchronizer by installing the low-second hub into low-second gear. Install the retaining ring in the gear. Slide the hub out of the gear until the holes in the hub are clear of the gear. Install the shifter plates and springs. Push the hub back into the gear. Push a shifter plate toward the center of the gear while installing the ball. Repeat for the other two balls. Push the hub into the gear until the balls snap into position.
4. Assemble the third-fourth synchronizer by installing the springs with the tension opposed. Place the right, lipped end of one spring in a hub slot. Place the spring in hub. Turn the hub around and repeat the operation with the other spring. Install the three synchronizer shifting plates in the hub with the smooth side of the plates out. Slip the clutch sleeve over the hub with the long beveled edge toward the long part of the hub. Install the two blocking rings.
5. Assemble the mainshaft, placing the threaded end up. Install the snap-ring and thrust washer with the recessed side covering the snap-ring. Install the bearing rollers around the shaft and hold them with a rubber band. Install the spacer. Install the second gear, tapered shoulder up. Install the snap-ring and blocking ring. Install the second-speed synchronizer and snap-ring. Install third gear, tapered shoulder to front. Install the third-fourth synchronizer assembly and snap-ring.
6. Install the main drive gear assembly and bearings in front of the case and mainshaft assembly through the top of the case. Temporarily install the bearing retainer.
7. Install the mainshaft bearing snap-ring; press the bearing into the case. Remove the bearing retainer. Install the oil slinger and snap-ring. Press the main drive gear bearing into the case. Use the thickest snap-ring that will fit in the groove.
8. Measure the space between the main drive gear bearing retainer and the case. Install a gasket 0.003–0.005 in. thicker than this measurement.

Warner T85 3 Speed Transmission

Disassembly

1. With the transmission drained and mounted in an adequate stand, remove the cap screws, washers, and side cover assembly of the transmission.
2. Remove the four cap screws and washers which hold the mainshaft rear bearing retainer extension to the case and move the extension away from the case about ½ in. Then rotate the retainer to expose the countershaft end and lock key.
3. From the front of the transmission, drive the countershaft to

1—Bearing retainer
2—Snap ring
3—Washer
4—Snap ring
5—Bearing
6—Washer
7—Main drive gear
8—Roller
9—Gasket
10—Pipe plug
11—Case
12—Spacer
13—Snap ring
14—Blocking ring
15—Synchronizer spring
16—Clutch hub, high and intermediate
17—Clutch sleeve, high and intermediate
18—Second speed gear
19—Sliding gear, low and reverse
20—Mainshaft
21—Bearing adapter
22—Bearing
23—Snap ring
24—Washer
25—Nut
26—Seal
27—Woodruff key
28—Countershaft
29—Thrust washer, steel
30—Thrust washer, rear
31—Washers
32—Spacer
33—Rollers
34—Woodruff key
35—Shaft
36—Reverse idler gear
37—Countershaft gears
38—Thrust washer, front
39—Synchronizer shifting plate
40—Gasket
41—Shift shoe, low and reverse
42—Shift lever, low and reverse
43—Side cover (control housing)
44—Lockwasher
45—Bolt
46—Washer
47—Lockwasher
48—Hex nut
49—Control lever, low and reverse
50—Control lever, high and intermediate
51—Interlock sleeve
52—Interlock pin
53—Poppet spring
54—Poppet ball
55—Oil seal
56—Shift lever, high and intermediate
57—Shift fork, high and intermediate
58—Cap screw

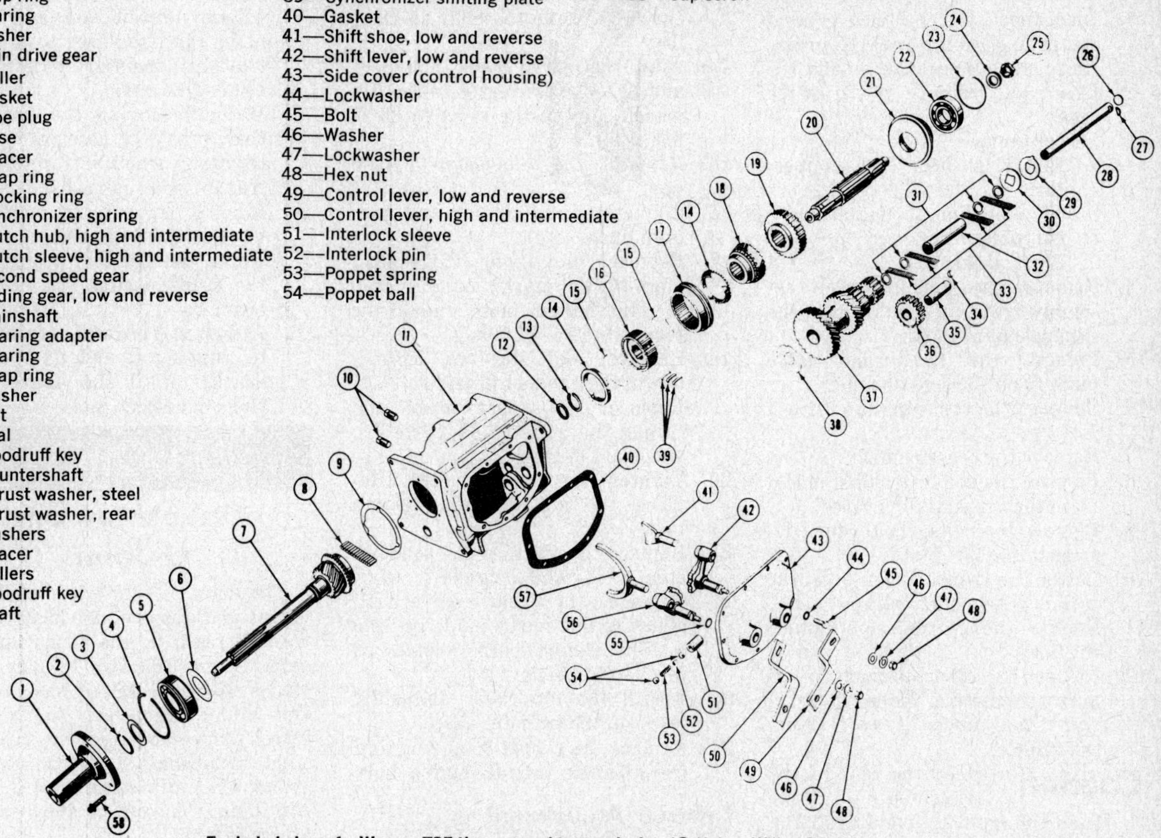

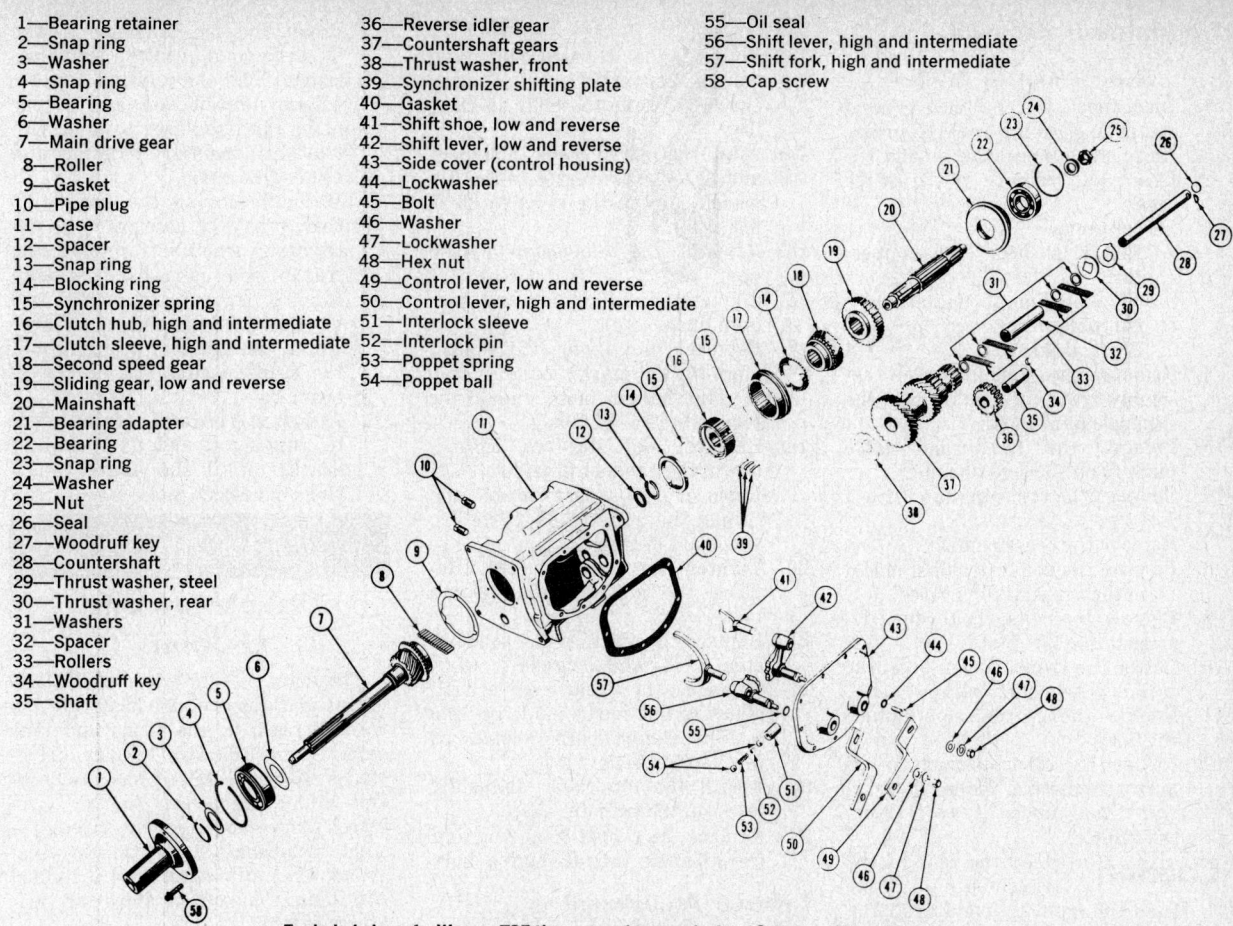

Exploded view of a Warner T85 three speed transmission (© Kaiser Willys Corp)

the rear, using a countershaft dummy.

4. Work the countershaft all the way out of the cluster, end spacers, rollers and roller bearing spacer.
5. Leave the dummy shaft in place in the countershaft gear cluster to keep the bearings and spacers in location.
6. Lower the countergear cluster down into the bottom of the case, then remove the rear bearing retainer extension, gasket, and mainshaft assembly from the transmission case.
7. Remove the mainshaft front bearing rollers from inside the main drive gear.
8. Remove the bearing spacing washer from the front end of the mainshaft.
9. Remove the attaching cap screws and washers, then the main drive gear bearing retainer from front of the case.
10. Remove the main drive gear bearing snap-ring from the front side of the main drive gear bearing.
11. With the transmission case upended (front up) press the main drive gear out of the bearing.
12. Remove the oil retainer from the main drive gear.
13. Tap the main drive gear bearing out through the front of the case and remove the main drive gear bearing snap-ring from the shaft.
14. Using a brass drift, drive the reverse idler shaft to the rear of the case to clear the lock key.
15. Remove the lock key and, from the rear of the case, drive the idler gear shaft into the case, then remove the idler gear and shaft from the case.
16. Lift out the countergear, dummy shaft, and washers from the case.
17. Remove the synchronizing ring from the front side of the second and third-speed clutch. Remove the clutch hub retaining snap-ring from the front end of the mainshaft.
18. Remove the second- and third-speed clutch sleeve from the clutch hub, then remove the clutch hub from the mainshaft.
19. Remove the two clutch key springs and three clutch keys from the clutch hub.
20. Remove the rear synchronizer ring and second-speed gear from the mainshaft.
21. Remove the first and reverse sliding gear from the mainshaft.
22. Remove the speedometer driven gear lock plate-to-extension bolt and lock washer, then remove the lock plate.
23. Insert a screwdriver in the lock-plate slot in the fitting and pry the fitting and shaft from the extension.
24. Remove the mainshaft rear bearing front snap-ring from the rear bearing retainer extension and tap the mainshaft and rear bearing out of the retainer extension.
25. Remove the snap-ring from the rear of the speedometer drive gear.
26. Remove the speedometer drive gear, detent ball and speedometer gear front snap-ring.
27. Remove the mainshaft rear bearing rear snap-ring.
28. Using a press, press the mainshaft rear bearing toward the rear of the shaft until loose and remove it.
29. Remove the seal from the rear bearing retainer.

Assembly

1. Assemble by reversing the above procedure.

AUTOMATIC TRANSMISSION

All current Jeep vehicles use the General Motors Turbo Hydra-Matic 400 automatic transmission. The 327 V8 used a Borg Warner AS-8F unit.

Transmission Removal

Models Prior to 1972

1. Disconnect the battery ground strap. Release the parking brake. Raise and support the vehicle.
2. Drain and remove the transfer case.
3. Disconnect:
   a. Electrical lead case connector.
   b. Vacuum line at modulator.
   c. Oil cooler lines.
   d. Shift linkage.
4. Remove the exhaust pipe assembly from the muffler and the exhaust manifolds.
5. Remove the handbrake cable plate from the crossmember.
6. Support the transmission with a jack.
7. Remove the crossmember.
8. Remove the converter dust shield from the transmission case.
9. Remove the bolts, the torque coverter to the flex plate.
10. Lower the transmission until the jack is barely supporting it.
11. Remove the transmission mounting bolts.
12. Raise the transmission to its normal position, slide it rearward, and lower it away from the vehicle.

Caution Keep the rear of the transmission lower than the front to avoid dropping the converter.

13. Installation is the reverse of removal.

1972 and Later Models

1. Remove the bolt holding the transmission dipstick tube to the engine.
2. Remove the shift lever carpet trim ring.
3. Remove the top cover and lever on the transfer case.
4. Remove the rear driveshaft after making chalk marks so that it can be replaced in the same position.
5. Remove the exhaust pipe clamp bolt, shift lever, downshift wire, and speedometer cable.
6. Place a jack under the transmission.
7. Remove the rear crossmember.
8. Remove the exhaust pipe.
9. Disconnect the transfer case end of the front driveshaft after making chalk marks so that it can be replaced in the same position.
10. Detach the oil cooler lines and the vacuum line.
11. Remove the converter housing splash pan. Mark the relationship between the converter and the flywheel and unbolt the converter from the flywheel.
12. Unbolt the converter housing from the engine and remove the transmission.

To install:

13. Replace the transmission and bolt the converter housing to the engine. Torque the bolts to 28 ft lbs.
14. Align the marks made in step 11 and bolt the converter to the flywheel. Torque the bolts to 33 ft lbs.
15. Replace the converter splash pan.
16. Connect the oil cooler and vacuum lines.
17. Replace the front driveshaft, aligning the marks made in step 9. The flange bolts should be torqued to 25–45 ft lbs.
18. Replace, but do not tighten down, the exhaust pipe.
19. Replace the crossmember and torque the bolts to 30–35 ft lbs. Remove the jack.
20. Tighten the exhaust pipe. Replace the exhaust pipe clamp bolt.
21. Replace the shift lever, speedometer cable, and downshift wire.
22. Replace the rear driveshaft, aligning the marks made in Step 4. The flange bolts should be torqued to 25-45 ft lbs.
23. Install the top cover and shift lever on the transfer case.
24. Replace the carpet trim ring and the dipstick tube-to-engine bolt.

Linkage Adjustment

Cable-Operated Linkage

1. Disconnect the control cable at the transmission lever and place the transmission shift lever in Neutral.
2. Place the control lever in neutral position.
3. Loosen the two nuts at the upper end of the control cable housing and move the housing up or down until the cable exactly matches the position of the lever on the transmission.
4. Lock the nuts on the housing and connect the cable to the lever.

Rod-Operated Linkage

1. Remove the adjusting block from the transmission shift lever.
2. Make sure that the transmission lever is in Neutral position.
3. Place the selector lever in the Neutral position and hold firmly against the stop.
4. Loosen the locknuts on the adjusting block. Install the block on the transmission lever. Tighten the locknuts to 6–12 ft lbs.
5. Check the shifting operation. If the console interferes with the shift selector lever, reposition the console.

Neutral Safety Switch Adjustment

1. Make certain the shift linkage is correctly adjusted.
2. Set the handbrake and the footbrake. Put the handlever on the steering column in the Drive position. Hold the ignition key (or starter button) on and slowly move the handlever toward neutral until the starter cranks and the engine runs.
3. Without moving the lever further, press the accelerator to determine whether or not the transmission is really in neutral.
4. If all is correct, the engine will have started when the handlever got to the Neutral position, and the transmission will not be in gear.
5. Adjust the neutral safety switch by turning it and its mounting bracket until the above conditions have been met.

U-JOINTS

Driveshaft and U-Joints

The drive of four-wheel drive Universal and Jeepster models from the transfer case to the front and rear axles is through two tubular driveshafts. Each driveshaft has two cross and roller universal joints. Two-wheel drive models drive through a single driveshaft with two universal joints. Each driveshaft has a splined slip joint at one end to allow for variations in length.

Jeepster V6 models have a front driveshaft made up of two shafts with three universal joints and one slip joint. The shorter of the two shafts, directly ahead of the transfer case, has a shaft support bearing.

Wagoneer models use several types and sizes of driveshafts, depending upon various transmission and equipment options. These are divided into two basic types. The first is that with two cross and roller joints and a slip joint. The second has a cross and roller joint at one end, and a ball and trunnion universal joint at the other end. Automatic transmission Wagoneer models have the slip joint end of the front driveshaft at the axle rather than at the transfer case, as on all other models.

Cross and Roller Universal Joint

Snap-Ring Type Disassembly and Repair

1. Remove the snap-rings.
2. Press on the end of one bearing until the opposite bearing is pushed from the yoke arm.
3. Turn the joint over. Press the first bearing back out of the arm by pressing on the exposed end of the journal shaft. Repeat this operation for the other two bearings, then lift out the journal assembly by sliding it to one side.

1 Grease cover
2 Gasket
3 Thrust washer
4 Spring washer
5 Centering button
6 Bearing ball
7 Bearing roller
8 Universal joint body
9 Trunnion pin
10 Clamp
11 Dust cover
12 Clamp
13 Breather
14 Ballhead
15 Tube
16 Tube yoke
17 Seal retainer
18 Bearing seal
19 Cross
20 Bearing cup
21 Bearing roller
22 Cup retainer ring
23 Roller retainer
24 Tie link
25 Bearing block retainer

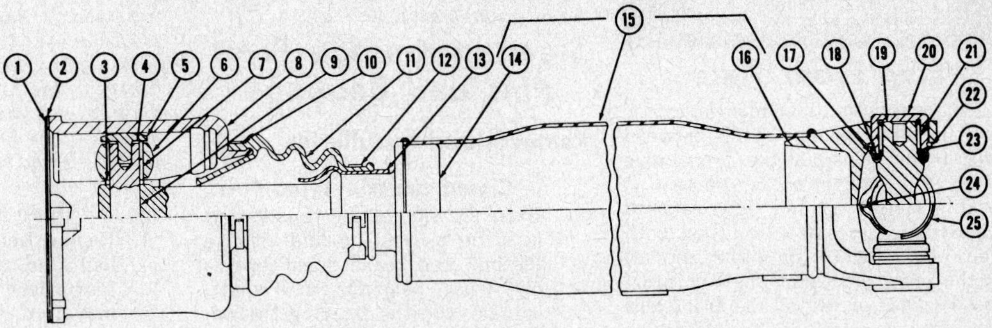

Rear driveshaft shaft—ball and trunnion type (© Willys Corp.)

4. Wash all parts in solvent and inspect for wear. Replace all worn parts.
5. Install new gaskets on the journal assembly. Make certain that the grease channel in each journal trunnion is open.
6. Pack the bearing cones one-third full of grease and install the rollers.
7. Assemble in the reverse order of disassembly. If the joint binds when assembled, tap the arms lightly to relieve any pressure on the bearings at the end of the journal.

U-Bolt Type Disassembly and Repair

Remove the attaching U-bolts to release one set of bearing races. Slide the driveshaft into the yoke flange to remove the races. The rest of the disassembly and repair procedure is the same as that given above for the snap-ring type of cross and roller joint. The correct U-bolt torque is 15–20 ft lbs.

Ball and Trunnion Universal Joint

Disassembly and Repair

1. Clamp the shaft firmly in a vise.
2. Bend the grease cover lugs away from the universal joint body. Remove the cover and gasket.
3. Remove the two clamps from the dust cover. Push the joint body toward the driveshaft tube. Remove two each: centering buttons, spring washers, ball and roller bearings, and thrust washers, from the trunnion pin.
4. Press the trunnion pin from ballhead.
5. If the ballhead is bent out of alignment or if the trunnion pin bore is worn or damaged, replace the driveshaft.

To reassemble:

6. Secure the larger end of the dust cover to the joint body with the larger of two clamps. Install the smaller clamp. Fit the cover over the ballhead shaft.
7. Push the universal joint cover toward the driveshaft tube. Press the trunnion pin into the centered position. If the trunnion pin is not centered, imbalance will result.
8. Install the thrust washers, ball and roller bearings, spring washer, and centering buttons on the trunnion pin. Compress the centering buttons. Move the joint body to hold the buttons in place.
9. Insert the breather between the dust cover and the ballhead shaft, along the length of the shaft. The breather must extend no more than ½ in. beyond the dust cover. Tighten the clamp screw to secure the cover to the shaft. Cut away any portion of dust cover protruding under the clamps.
10. Pack the raceways around the ball and roller bearings with about 2 oz of universal joint grease.
11. Position the gasket and grease cover on the body. Bend the lugs of the cover into the notches of the body. Move the body back and forth to distribute grease in the raceways.

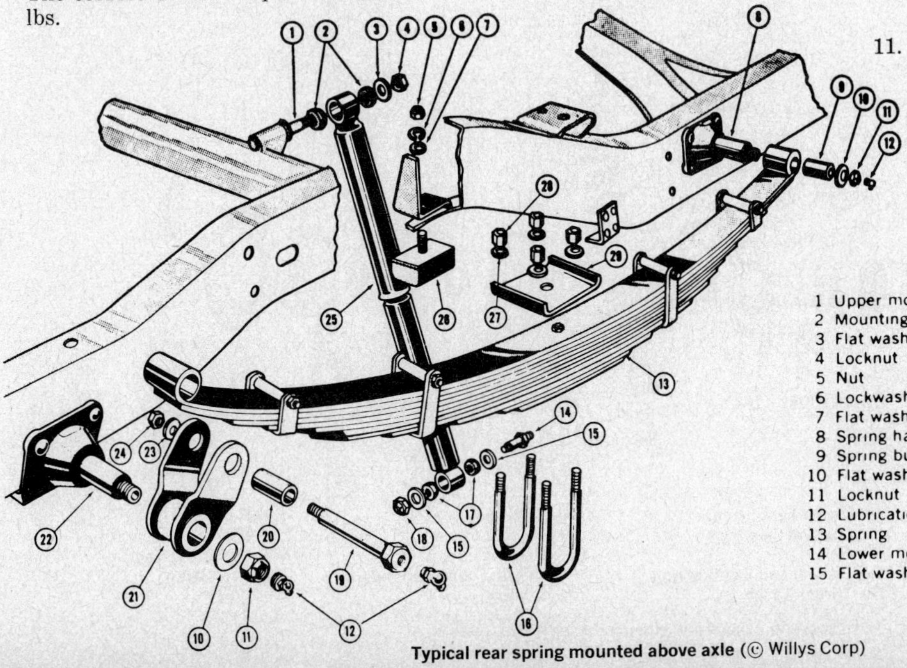

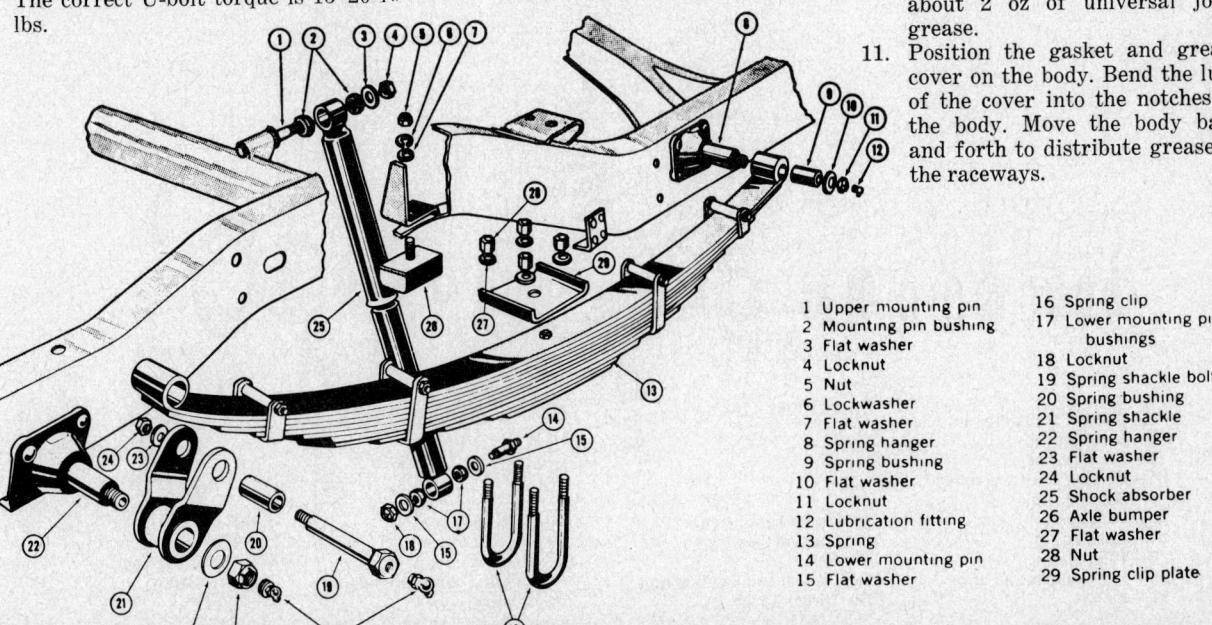

1 Upper mounting pin
2 Mounting pin bushing
3 Flat washer
4 Locknut
5 Nut
6 Lockwasher
7 Flat washer
8 Spring hanger
9 Spring bushing
10 Flat washer
11 Locknut
12 Lubrication fitting
13 Spring
14 Lower mounting pin
15 Flat washer
16 Spring clip
17 Lower mounting pin bushings
18 Locknut
19 Spring shackle bolt
20 Spring bushing
21 Spring shackle
22 Spring hanger
23 Flat washer
24 Locknut
25 Shock absorber
26 Axle bumper
27 Flat washer
28 Nut
29 Spring clip plate

Typical rear spring mounted above axle (© Willys Corp)

FRONT SUSPENSION

Live Front Axle

On four-wheel drive models, caster is adjusted by placing shims between the spring pads on the front axle housing and the top of the spring.

This method should only be used where it is necessary to adjust both sides of the vehicle the same amount. In the event the caster angle is incorrect because of sag of the front leaf springs, it is advisable to replace the springs rather than use caster wedges. Camber cannot be adjusted.

Solid Front Axle

Universal models with two-wheel drive have a solid front axle. The axle may be either of tubular construction or a forged I-beam. Springs may be slung either under or over the axle. Standard caster and camber are built into the front axle. Camber cannot be changed, but caster can be adjusted by placing tapered shims between the springs and spring seats.

Shock Absorber Removal and Installation

1. Raise the vehicle.
2. Remove the lock nuts and washers (cotter pins on older models) that hold the upper and lower mounting eyes to the mounting pins.
3. Pull the shock absorber eyes and the rubber bushings from the mounting pins.
4. To install the shock absorber, first install the rubber bushings and shock absorber eyes, then install the washers and locknuts or cotter pins.
5. Tighten the locknuts securely.

NOTE: If a shock absorber is removed from the vehicle and turned upside down, it will lose its prime and become inoperative.

Steering Knuckle Pivot Pins and Bearings

Removal and Installation

Closed Knuckle Type

1. Raise the side of the vehicle that is to be worked on and remove the hub and brake drum assembly, wheel bearings, axle shaft, spindle, and the steering tie-rod.
2. Remove the eight screws that hold the oil seal retainer in place.
3. Remove the four screws that hold the lower pivot pin bearing cap.
4. Remove the four screws that hold the upper bearing cap and remove the bearing cap.
5. The steering knuckle can now be removed from the axle.
6. Lift out the bearings and inspect, clean, and replace all worn parts.
7. Install in the reverse order of removal.

NOTE: When installing the steering knuckle, sufficient shims must be placed under the top bearing cap to obtain the correct preload on the bearing. The preload should be 12-16 lbs and checked with a spring scale hooked in the hole in the knuckle arm for the tie-rod socket.

Open Knuckle Type

1. Replacement of the ball joints, or ball stud, as they will be called from here on, requires the removal of the steering knuckle. To remove the steering knuckle, first remove the wheel, brake drum, and hub as an assembly. Remove the brake assembly from the spindle. Position the brake assembly on the front axle in a convenient place. Remove the snap-ring from the axle shaft.
2. Remove the spindle and bearing assembly. It may be necessary to tap the spindle with a soft mallet to disengage it from the steering knuckle.

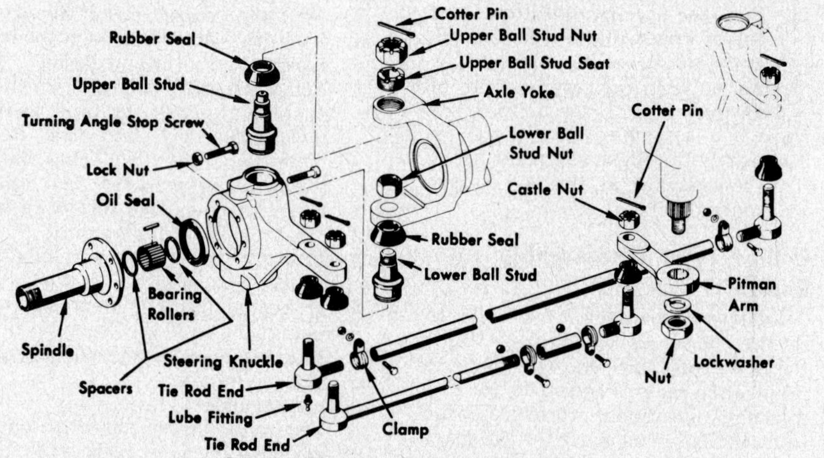

Cotter Pin
Rubber Seal
Upper Ball Stud Nut
Upper Ball Stud Seat
Upper Ball Stud
Axle Yoke
Turning Angle Stop Screw
Cotter Pin
Lower Ball Stud Nut
Lock Nut
Oil Seal
Castle Nut
Rubber Seal
Lower Ball Stud
Bearing Rollers
Pitman Arm
Spindle
Steering Knuckle
Lockwasher
Nut
Spacers
Tie Rod End
Lube Fitting
Clamp
Tie Rod End

Open knuckle front axle, Commando and CJ
(© Jeep Corp)

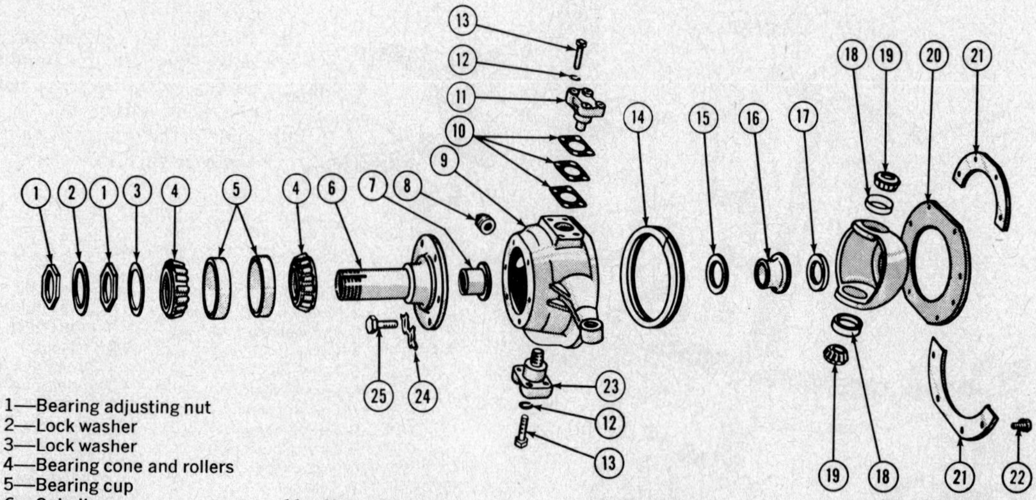

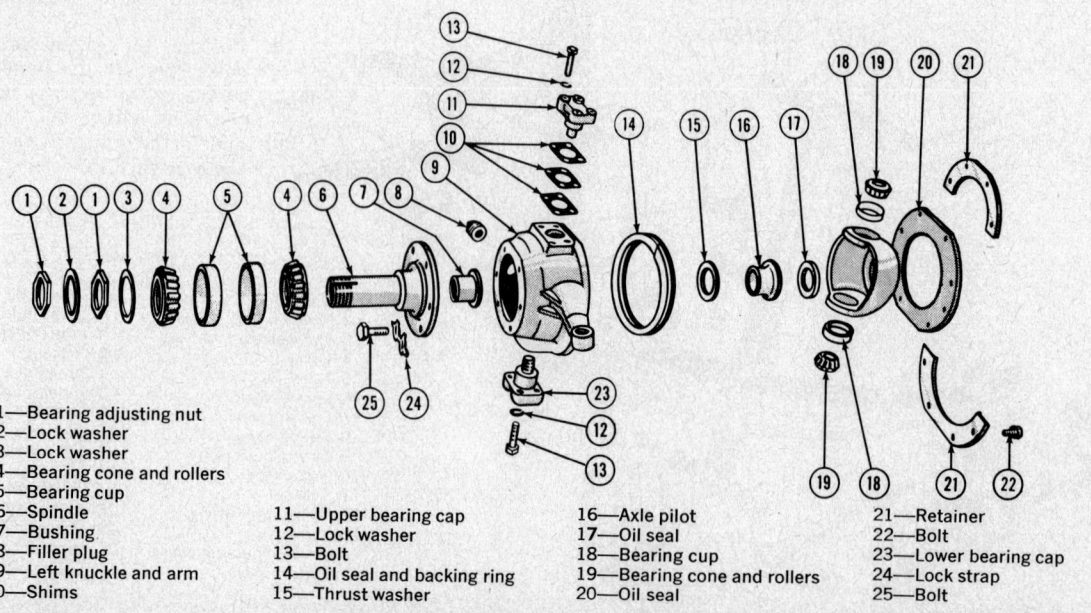

1—Bearing adjusting nut
2—Lock washer
3—Lock washer
4—Bearing cone and rollers
5—Bearing cup
6—Spindle
7—Bushing
8—Filler plug
9—Left knuckle and arm
10—Shims
11—Upper bearing cap
12—Lock washer
13—Bolt
14—Oil seal and backing ring
15—Thrust washer
16—Axle pilot
17—Oil seal
18—Bearing cup
19—Bearing cone and rollers
20—Oil seal
21—Retainer
22—Bolt
23—Lower bearing cap
24—Lock strap
25—Bolt

Closed knuckle front axle (© Kaiser Willys Corp)

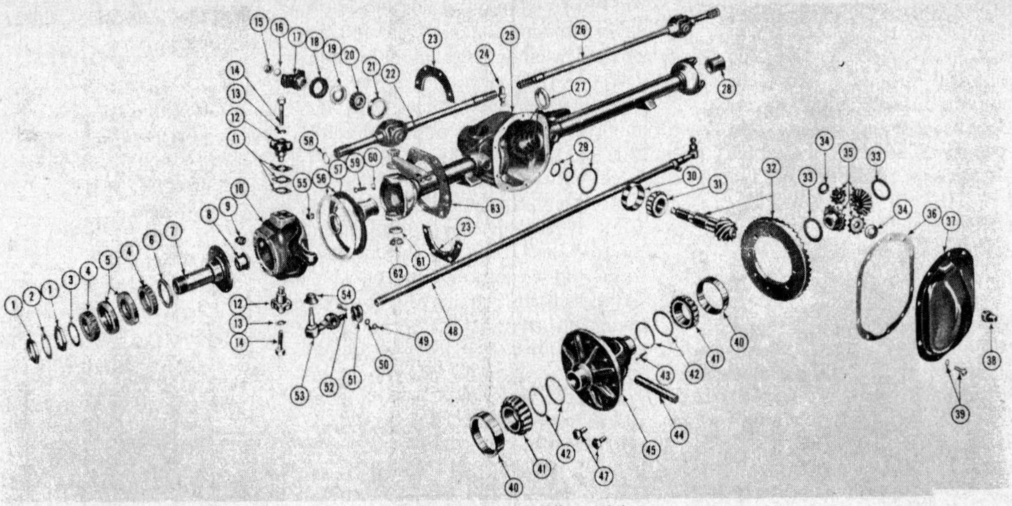

Live front axle and differential
(© Kaiser Willys Corp)

1—Nut
2—Lock washer
3—Bearing lock washer
4—Wheel bearing cap
5—Cone and rollers
6—Oil seal
7—Spindle
8—Spindle bushing
9—Filter plug
10—Right knuckle and arm
11—Shims
12—Pivot pin
13—Lock washer
14—Cap screw
15—Nut
16—Washer
17—Universal joint yoke
18—Oil seal
19—Oil slinger
20—Cone and rollers
21—Bearing cup
22—Right axle shaft with universal joint
23—Knuckle oil seal retainer
24—Housing breather
25—Front axle housing
26—Axle shaft with universal joint
27—Oil seal
28—Axle shaft guide
29—Shim pack
30—Bearing cup
31—Cone and rollers
32—Ring gear and pinion
33—Thrust washer
34—Thrust washer
35—Differential gears
36—Housing cover gasket
37—Housing cover
38—Fill plug
39—Screw and lock washer
40—Bearing cup
41—Cone and rollers
42—Shims
43—Lock pin
44—Pinion shaft
45—Differential case
47—Bolts
48—Steering tie-rod
49—Tie-rod clamp nut
50—Lock washer
51—Tie-rod socket clamp
52—Screw
53—Tie-rod socket
54—Dust cover
55—Nut
56—Oil seal and backing ring
57—Thrust washer
58—Snap-ring
59—Stop bolt
60—Nut
61—Bearing cup
62—Cone and rollers
63—Gasket

3. Slide the axle shaft out through the steering knuckle.
4. Disconnect the steering rods from the knuckle arm.
5. Remove the lower ball stud nut.
6. Remove the cotter pin from the upper stud. Loosen the upper stud until the top edge of the nut is flush with the top end of the stud.
7. Use a lead hammer to unseat the upper and lower studs from the yoke. Remove the upper nut and the knuckle assembly.
8. Remove the ball stud seat from the upper hole in the axle yoke. It is threaded in the hole. There are special wrenches available for removing the seat.
9. Securely clamp the knuckle assembly in a vise with the upper ball stud pointed down.
10. Using a large socket or drift, of approximately the same size as the ball stud, and a mallet, drive the lower stud out of the knuckle.

NOTE: Throughout this procedure, where a ball stud is either removed or installed, a hydraulic press or a two-jawed gear puller can be used and, if at all possible, should be used to make the job easier. However it is possible to complete the job using a mallet, a drift, and a large socket the same size as the ball studs.

11. Place the socket on the bottom surface of the upper ball stud. Place the drift through the hole where the lower ball stud was and place it on the socket. Drive the upper ball stud out of the knuckle with a mallet.
12. Before installing the lower ball stud, run the lower ball stud nut onto the stud just far enough so the head of the stud is flush with the top edge of the nut.
13. Invert the knuckle in the vise. Position the lower ball stud in the knuckle with the nut in place. Place the same size socket over the nut and drive the ball stud into place with the drift and mallet.
14. Use the same procedure for installing the upper ball stud. The drift will not be needed to install the upper ball stud.
15. Install the upper ball stud seat into the axle yoke. Use a new one if the old one shows evidence of wear. The top of the seat should be flush with the top of the yoke.
16. Install the knuckle assembly onto the axle yoke. Install the lower stud nut. Tighten it to 70-90 ft lbs.
17. Install the upper stud nut and tighten it to 100 ft lbs. Install the cotter pin. If the cotter pin holes do not align, tighten the nut until the pin can be installed. Do not loosen the nut to align the holes.
18. Install the axle shaft, spindle and bearing assembly, and brake assembly. Connect the steering rods. Install the drum and hub, and wheel assembly. Adjust the wheel bearings. Check the turning angle. Adjust the stop screw to permit the proper turning angle of 31°.

Springs

Removal and Installation

Prior to 1972

1. Raise the vehicle with a jack under the axle and place a jackstand under the frame side rail. Then lower the axle jack so that the load is relieved from the spring and the wheels rest on the floor.
2. Remove the nuts which secure the spring clip bolts. Remove the spring plate and clip bolts. Free the spring from the axle by raising the axle jack.
3. Remove the pivot bolt nut and drive out the pivot bolt. Disconnect the shackle either by removing the lower nuts and bolts on the rubber-bushed shackles, or by removing the threaded bushings on the U-shackles.
4. To replace, first install the pivot bolt. Then, connect the shackle using the following procedures.
5. On bronze-bushed pivot bolts, install the bolt and nut and tighten the nut. Then back it off two cotter pin slots and install the cotter pin. The nut must be drawn

up tightly but must be sufficiently loose to allow the spring to pivot freely. Otherwise the spring might break.

6. On rubber-bushed pivot bolts and locknuts (or lockwasher and nut), only tighten the bolt enough to hold the bushings in position until the vehicle is lowered from the jack.
7. Connect the shackle. On rubber-bushed shackles install the bolts as in Step 6 above. For U-shackles, insert the shackle through the frame bracket and eye of the spring. Holding the U-shackle tightly against the frame, start the upper bushing on the shackle, taking care that when it enters the thread in the frame it does not cross-thread. Screw the bushing on the shackle tightly against the spring eye and thread the bushing in approximately half way. Then, alternately from top bushing to lower bushing, turn them in until the head of the bushing is snug against the frame bracket and the bushing in the spring eye is 1/32 in. away from the spring as measured from the inside of the hexagon head to the spring. Lubricate the bushing and then try the flex of the shackle, which must be free. If a shackle is tight, rethread the bushings on the shackle.
8. Move the axle into position on the spring by lowering or raising the axle jack. Install the spring clip bolts, spring plate, lockwashers, and nuts. Torque the nuts to 50-55 ft lbs. Avoid over-tightening. Be sure the spring is free to move at both ends.
9. Remove both jacks. On rubber bushed shackles and pivot bolts, allow the weight of the vehicle to seat the bushings in their operating positions. Then torque the nuts to 27-30 ft lbs.

1972 and Later

1. Raise the vehicle with a jack under the axle. Place a jackstand under the frame side rail. Then lower the axle jack so the load is relieved from the spring and the wheels rest slightly on the floor.
2. Disconnect the shock absorber from the spring clip plate.
3. Remove the nuts which secure the spring clips (U-bolts). Remove the spring plate and spring clips. Free the spring from the axle by raising the axle.
4. Remove the pivot bolt nut and drive out the pivot bolt. Disconnect the shackle from the shackle bracket by removing the lock nut, lock nut and bolt or nut, or lockwasher and bolt.
5. With the spring removed, the spring shackle and/or shackle plate may be removed from the spring by removing the lock nut, lock nut and shackle bolt or nut, or lockwasher and shackle bolt.
6. Inspect the bushings in the eye of the main spring leaf and the bushings of the spring shackle for excessive wear. Replace if necessary.
7. The spring can be disassembled, for replacing an individual spring leaf, by removing the clips and the center bolt.
8. To install the spring on the vehicle with the bushings in place and the spring shackle attached to the springs, position the spring in the pivot hanger and install the pivot bolt and lock nut. Only tighten the lock nut enough to hold the bushings in position until the vehicle is lowered from the jack.
9. Position the spring and install the shackle, shackle bolts, shackle plate if applicable, lockwasher, and nut. Only finger tighten the nuts at this time.
10. Move the axle into position on the spring by lowering the axle jack. Place the spring center bolt in the axle saddle hole. Install the spring clips, spring plate, lockwashers and nuts. Torque the 7/16 in. nuts to 36-42 ft lbs and the ½ in. nuts to 45-65 ft lbs.

NOTE: Be sure that the center bolt is properly centered in the axle saddle.

11. Connect the shock absorber.
12. Remove the axle and allow the weight of the vehicle to seat the bushings in their operating positions. Then torque the 7/16 in. spring pivot bolt nuts and spring shackle nuts to 25-40 ft lbs. Torque the ⅝ in. shackle nuts to 55-75 ft lbs.

Front Axle Universal Joints

Three types of constant velocity universal joints are used on Jeep four-wheel drives. The first is the Bendix type universal joint, the second the Rzeppa type, and the third the Spicer type.

Removal

1. Remove the wheel.
2. Remove the hub dust cap.
3. Remove the axle shaft driving flange bolts.
4. Apply and hold the foot brakes. Remove the axle shaft flange with a puller.
5. Release the lip on the lockwasher, remove the outer nut, lockwasher, adjusting nut, and bearing lockwasher. Use a special wrench for these nuts.
6. Remove the wheel hub and drum assembly with the bearings.
7. Remove the hydraulic brake tube, backing plate screws, spindle, axle shaft and universal joint assembly.
8. Install in the reverse order of removal.

Repair

Bendix Joint

The factory no longer supplies replacement component parts for the Bendix universal joint. Rebuilding these universals requires complex shop equipment and is economically unfeasible. However, the complete universal joint assembly may be replaced.

If the assembly falls apart upon removal from the vehicle, reassemble as follows:

1. Place the differential half of the axle shaft in a vise, with the ground portion above the jaws.

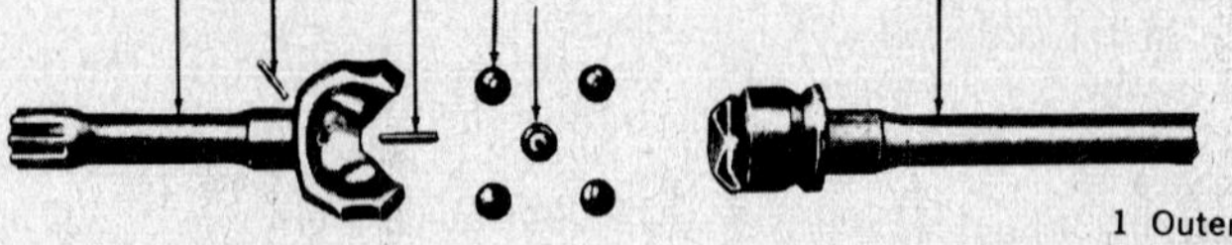

1
2
3
4
5
6

1 Outer shaft
2 Lock pin
3 Center ball pin
4 Universal joint ball
5 Center ball
6 Inner shaft

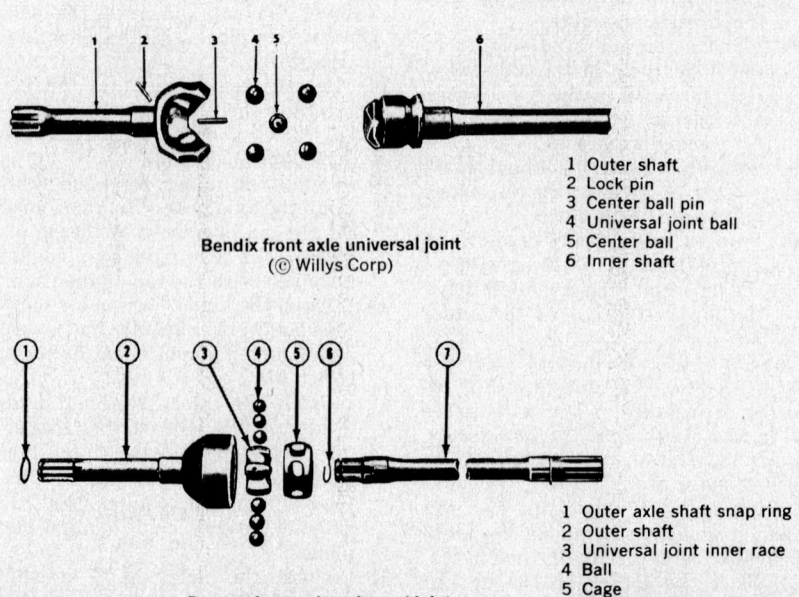

Bendix front axle universal joint
(© Willys Corp)

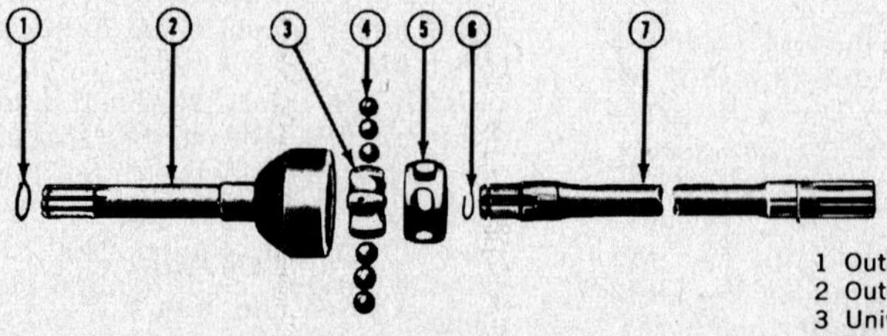

1
2
3
4
5
6
7

1 Outer axle shaft snap ring
2 Outer shaft
3 Universal joint inner race
4 Ball
5 Cage
6 Axle shaft retainer snap ring
7 Inner shaft

Rzeppa front axle universal joint
(© Willys Corp)

2. Install the center ball in the socket in the shaft, with the hole and groove toward you.
3. Drop the center ball pin into the drilled passage in the wheel half of the shaft.
4. Place the wheel half of the shaft on the center ball. Then slip three balls into the raceways.
5. Turn the center ball until the groove lines up with the raceway for the remaining ball. Slip the ball into the raceway and straighten up the wheel end of the shaft.
6. Turn the center ball until the center ball pin drops into the hole in the ball.
7. Install the retainer pin and prick punch both ends to lock it in place.
8. After reassembly, grasp both ends of the shaft and twist the ends back and forth. Should excessive wear be indicated by backlash or lost motion, the assembly should be replaced.

Rzeppa Joint

1. To dismantle the Rzeppa joint, remove the three screws (some axles have no screws) that hold the front axle shaft to the joint itself, and pull the shaft out of the splined inner race. To take out the axle shaft retainer, remove the retainer ring on the shaft. Push down on the various points of the inner race and cage until the balls can be removed with the help of a small screwdriver.

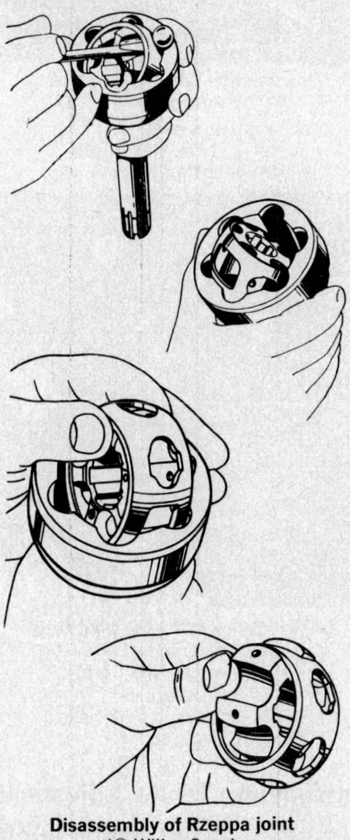

Disassembly of Rzeppa joint
(© Willys Corp)

2. There are two large elongated holes in the cage. Turn the cage so that the two bosses in the spindle shaft will drop into the elongated holes in the cage. The cage can then be lifted out.
3. To remove the inner race, turn it so that one of the bosses will drop into an elongated hole in this cage, then shift the race to one side and lift it out.
4. Reverse the procedure to reassemble.

Spicer Joint

The Spicer universal joint is a cross and roller unit with needle bearings. It is quite similar in design to the Spicer driveshaft universal joint. Disassembly is as follows:

1. Remove the snap-rings.
2. Press on the end of one bearing until the opposite bearing is pushed from the yoke arm.

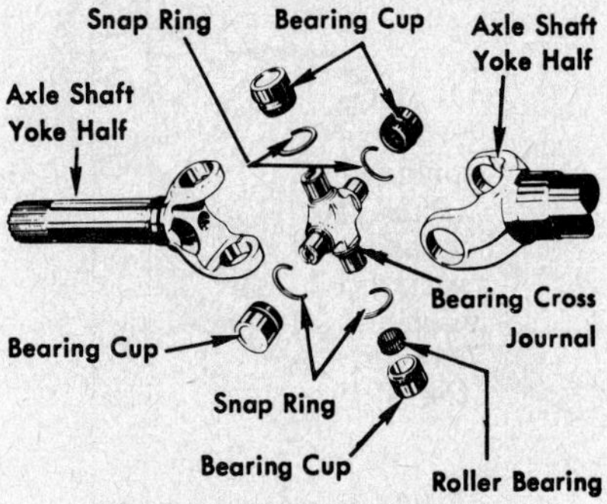
Snap Ring
Bearing Cup
Axle Shaft Yoke Half
Axle Shaft Yoke Half
Bearing Cross Journal
Bearing Cup
Snap Ring
Bearing Cup
Roller Bearing

Spicer front axle universal joint
(© Willys Corp)

3. Turn the joint over. Press the first bearing back out of the arm by pressing on the exposed end of the journal shaft. Repeat this operation for the other two bearings, then lift out the journal assembly by sliding it to one side.
4. Wash all parts in solvent and inspect for wear. Replace all worn parts.
5. Install new gaskets on the journal assembly. Make certain that the grease channel in each journal trunnion is open.
6. Pack the bearing cones one-third full of grease and install the rollers.
7. Assemble in the reverse order of disassembly. If the joint binds when assembled, tap the arms lightly to relieve any pressure on the bearings at the end of the journal.

DRIVE AXLES

NOTE: The following procedures apply to both front and rear drive axles.

Axle Shaft End-Play Adjustment

1. Remove the wheel and tire and, using a puller, remove the brake drum from the tapered shaft. (Do not use a knock-off puller, as the bearing or other parts may be damaged.)
2. Disconnect the brake line from the wheel cylinder.
3. Remove the backing plate.
4. To reduce the axle play, remove the shims; to increase end-play, add shims.

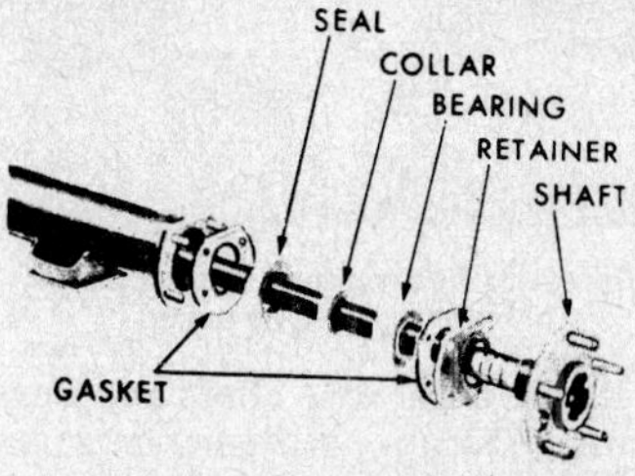
SEAL
COLLAR
BEARING
RETAINER
SHAFT
GASKET

Adjusting axle shaft end-play

5. To measure the results, reinstall the backing plate and thoroughly tighten the retaining bolts. A dial gauge can be set up to ascertain exact bearing play.
6. Reconnect the brake line and bleed air from the brake system.
7. Reinstall the hub and drum, wheel and tire.
8. Recommended end-play is 0.012–0.020 in.

On this construction, with the tapered roller bearing, end-play adjustment is accomplished by adding or removing shims from behind the backing plate.

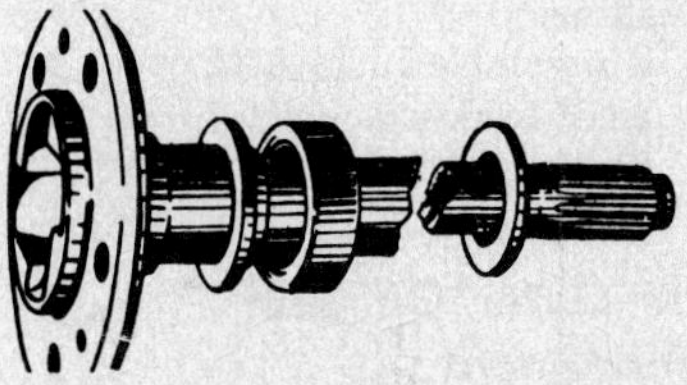

Rear axle shaft, showing arrangement of oil seals

Axle Shaft and/or Bearing Replacement

1. Remove the wheel and tire and, using a puller, remove the brake drum from the tapered shaft. (Do not use a knock-off puller, as the bearing or other parts may be damaged.)
2. Disconnect the brake line from the wheel cylinder.
3. Remove the backing plate. Note the thickness of the shims used, to aid in reassembly.

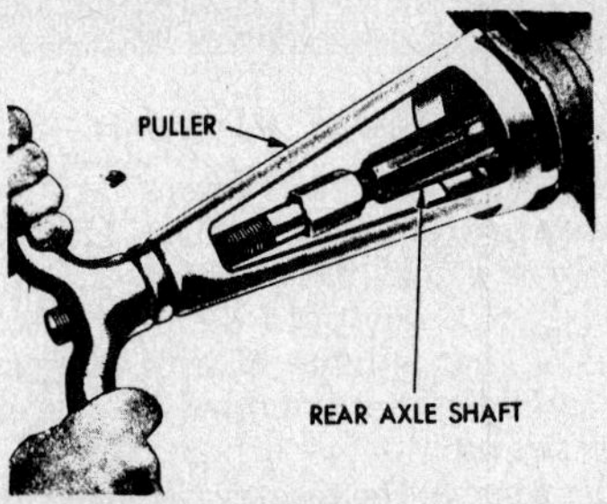
PULLER
REAR AXLE SHAFT

Removing rear axle shaft and bearing, using screw-type puller

1
2
3

Removing bearing cone from rear axle, using screw-type puller

4. Remove the axle shaft and bearing. (Drum, without axle key and nut on about halfway, may be used as an inertia puller.)
5. Press off the old and press on the new bearing cone.
6. Install a new seal, as required.
7. Place the axle shaft in the proper position and drive in the cone. Do not use a hammer and punch to locate the cone, as damage may occur.
8. Check axle shaft end-play. A dial gauge can be set up to measure the clearance. It is necessary that the axle shaft be entirely against the center block or a false reading will be obtained.
9. To reduce axle play, remove shims. To increase end-play, add shims.
10. Reassemble in reverse order and bleed brakes as needed.
11. Recommended end-play is 0.012–0.020 in.

Axle Outer Oil Seal Replacement

1. Remove the wheel and tire and, using a puller, remove the brake drum from the tapered shaft. (Do not use a knock-off puller, as bearing or other parts may be damaged.)
2. Disconnect the brake line from the wheel cylinder.
3. Remove the backing plate.
4. These backing plate bolts also hold the oil seal, which can now be replaced. Replace the shims, as removed, unless bearing is to be adjusted at the same time.
5. Reinstall in the reverse order of above.

BRAKES

Master Cylinder

All Jeep brake systems are actuated hydraulically through either a single or a dual master cylinder. Some models are equipped with a power booster that is integral with the master cylinder and mounted on the engine firewall.

To remove the master cylinder, disconnect and plug the brake lines, disconnect the wires from the stoplight switch, remove the attaching nuts, and lift out the assembly.

Installation is the reverse of the removal procedure. Make certain that all parts are clean. Bleed the brakes.

Power Booster

Power-assisted brakes are optional on some Jeep models. A Bendix single-diaphragm unit is used and it operates by utilizing manifold vacuum and atmospheric pressure to reduce pedal travel and effort. Free-play is factory set and not adjustable.

Removal

1. Clean the master cylinder and booster unit.
2. Remove the cotter and clevis pins securing the booster pushrod to the pedal linkage.
3. Disconnect the vacuum hose from the booster check valve.

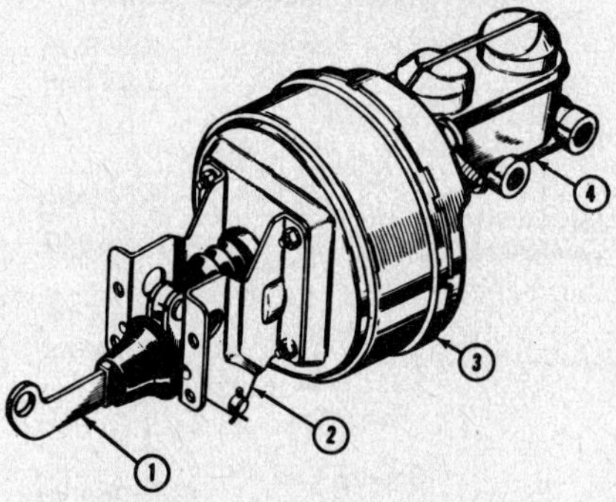
1
2
3
4

Brake booster unit and master cylinder
(© Willys Corp)

1 Pedal link
2 Mounting bracket
3 Power section
4 Master cylinder

4. Disconnect the fluid lines from the master cylinder. Plug the ends and catch any escaping fluid. *Do not reuse brake fluid.*
5. Disconnect the stoplight wires from the switch.
6. Remove the attaching nuts, booster unit assembly, and block spacers.
7. Remove the attaching nuts and separate the master cylinder from the booster.

Installation

To install the booster unit, reverse the removal procedure and bleed the brakes.

CAUTION: Do not pressure-bleed power-assisted brake systems.

Parking Brakes

The parking brake is operated by a foot pedal and a hand release lever. When the pedal is depressed, the rear brakes are actuated via an adjustable cable.

Some J-series vehicles may be equipped with a transmission brake mounted at the rear output bearing housing on the transfer case.

1
2

Master cylinder brake line outlets
(© Willys Corp)

1 Primary outlet—to front wheel brakes
2 Secondary outlet—to rear wheel brakes

Parking Brake Adjustment

1. Make certain the service brakes are in adjustment.
2. Raise the rear wheels.
3. Disengage the parking brake pedal.
4. Loosen the locknut on the brake cable adjusting rod.
5. Spin the wheels and tighten the rod until the brakes drag slightly.
6. Back off the adjustment until the wheels spin freely.
7. Tighten the locknut.

1
2
3

Transmission brake adjustment
(© Kaiser Willys Corp)

1—Ball nut
2—3/32 in. clearance
3—Adjusting screw

1
2
3
4

Brake bleeding and adjusting fixtures, models prior to 1972
(© Kaiser Willys Corp)

1—Adjusting cam
2—Brake hydraulic hose
3—Bleeder screw
4—Adjusting cam

Transmission Brake Adjustment

1. Release the transmission brake pedal.

2. Rotate the transmission brake drum until the holes line up with the adjusting screws.
3. Turn the adjusting screws until the shoes are snug in the drum.
4. Back off the adjustment screws seven notches.
5. Make certain there is 3/32 in. clearance between the drum backing plate and the operating lever.

NOTE: If the clearance is incorrect, remove the drum and adjust the ball nut on the operating link until correct clearance is obtained.

STEERING

Steering Connecting Rod

The steering connecting rod is of the ball and socket type. All ball seat springs are identical except for their location. The ball joints must be loose enough to allow free movement, yet tight enough to prevent end-play.

1 Steering knuckles
2 Ball joint assembly
3 Front axle housing
4 Ball joint
5 Steering arm
6 Steering gear
7 Drag link
8 Tie rod ends
9 Bellcrank assembly
10 Tie rod
11 Connecting rod

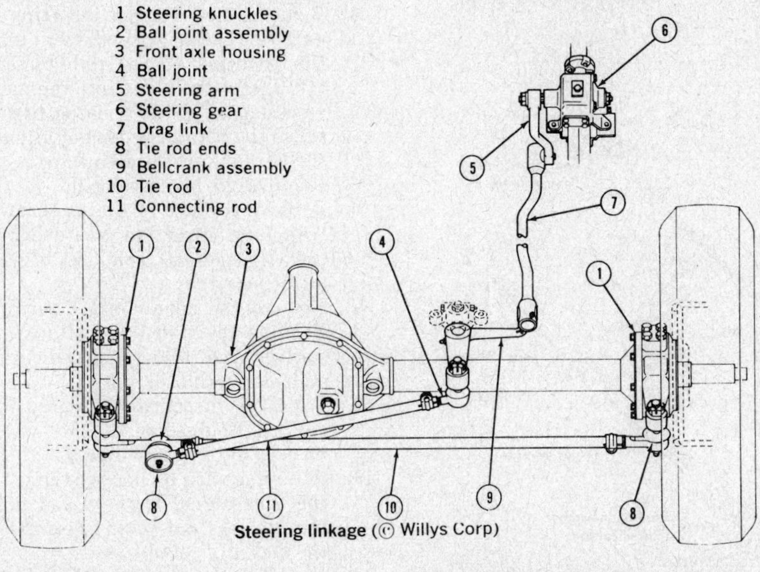

Steering linkage (© Willys Corp)

Removal

1. Remove the cotter pins and nuts from both ends.
2. Remove the rod.
3. Inspect all parts and replace them as necessary. NOTE: Ball joints on late-model vehicles cannot be disassembled for service or inspection.
4. Locate wheels in the straight-ahead position.
5. Locate the steering arm parallel to the centerline of the vehicle.
6. Align the steering arm and gearshaft at the high point and then install the steering connecting rod with nuts and new cotter pins.

Tie Rods

The tie rods are a three-piece construction consisting of the rod and two ball and socket assemblies. Right-hand and left-hand threads on the rods provide toe-in adjustment without removing the rod.

NOTE: Early production F4-134 4×2 vehicles are equipped with a divided type tie rod connecting the steering knuckles. On these vehicles, each wheel must be adjusted independently.

Tie Rod Removal

1. Remove cotter pins and nuts at both ends.
2. Using a puller or expansion fork, remove the tie rods from the steering knuckle arms.
3. Separate the joint seals and remove the socket assembly by loosening the clamp bolt nuts and unscrewing the unit.
4. Inspect all parts and replace as necessary.
5. Install by reversing the removal procedure. Use new seals and cotter pins, then torque the nuts to 38–42 ft lbs. If the steering arm was removed, torque the nut to 70–90 ft lbs for models with drag link steering, and 110–140 ft lbs for all others.

Power Steering Pump Removal and Installation

Before working on the power steering pump, clean the exterior of the pump and the reservoir assembly.

1. Loosen the drive belt tension adjustment bolt and remove the belt.
2. Place a receptacle under the pump/reservoir assembly and disconnect the pressure and return hoses from the pump. Fluid will drain out of the pump and hoses. Lay the ends of the hoses up higher than the steering gear to prevent all of the fluid from draining out. Cover the ends of the hoses to prevent dirt from entering.
3. Remove either the bolts that hold the pump to the mounting bracket or the bolts that hold the bracket and pump to the engine, whichever is easiest. Remove the pump from the engine.
4. Install the pump in the reverse order of removal and install the correct type and amount of fluid.

Steering Wheel Removal and Installation

CJ Models

1. Disconnect the negative battery cable.
2. Locate the front tires to a straight ahead position.
3. Remove the horn button by pulling it from the center of the steering wheel.
4. Remove the steering wheel nut and the horn button contact cup.
5. Scribe a line mark on the steering wheel and the steering shaft. Release the turn signal assembly from the steering post.
6. Using a puller, remove the steering wheel and spring, if present.
7. Install the steering wheel in the reverse order of removal. Line up the marks that were scribed on the steering wheel and the steering shaft.

Commando

1. Disconnect the negative battery cable.
2. Pull the horn button from the center of the steering wheel.
3. Remove the steering wheel nut and washer.
4. Remove the three attaching screws in the wheel cavity and remove the horn button receiver bushing, receiver, and spring.
5. Scribe a line mark on the steering wheel and the steering shaft and use a puller to remove the steering wheel.
6. Replace the steering wheel in the reverse order of removal, aligning the marks that were scribed.

Wagoneer, Cherokee

1. Disconnect the negative battery cable.
2. Remove the steering wheel spoke horn cover attaching screws from the under side of the steering wheel spoke and remove the horn cover.
3. Disconnect the horn wire from the switch in the steering wheel cavity by gently pulling and wiggling the quick disconnect connector.
4. Remove the steering wheel nut and washer.
5. Scribe a line mark on the steering wheel and the steering shaft and use a puller to remove the steering wheel.
6. Install the steering wheel in the reverse order of removal, aligning the scribe marks.

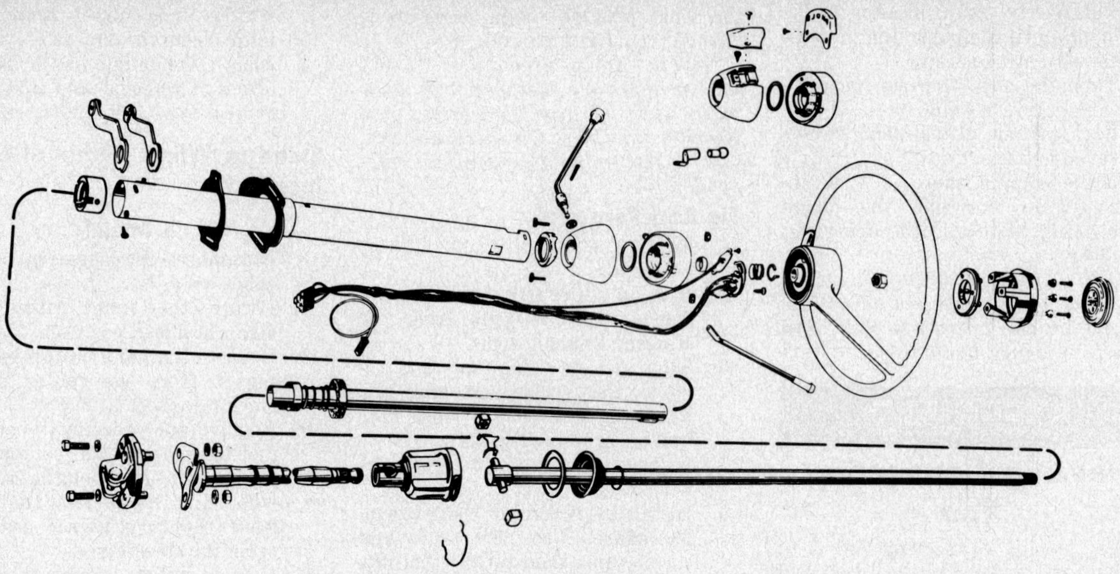

Exploded view of a Wagoneer steering column (© Jeep Corp)

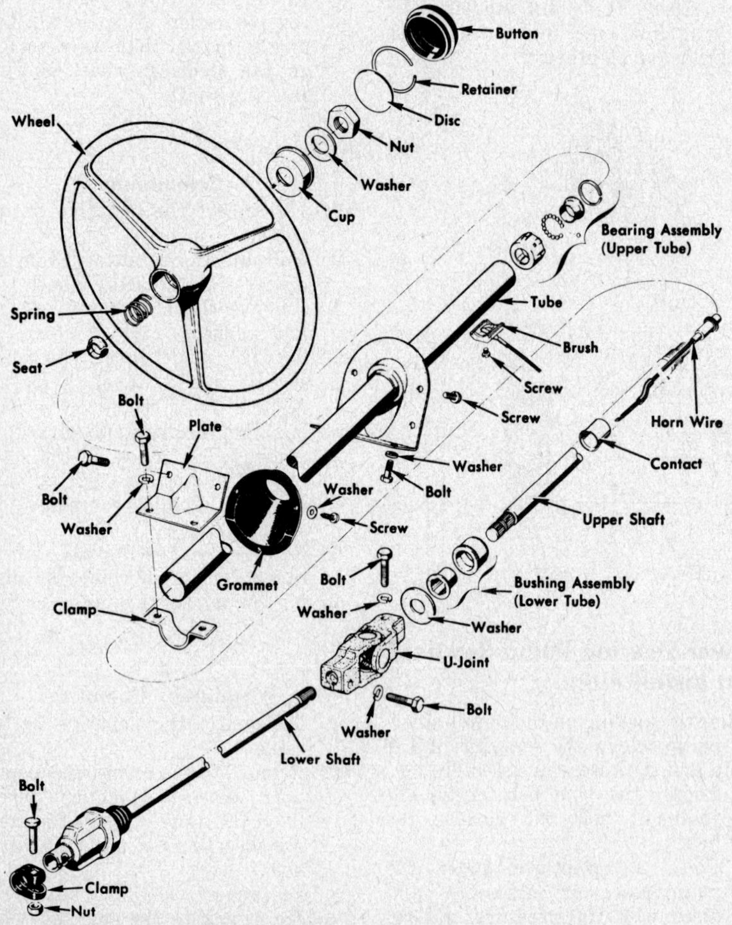
Button
Retainer
Disc
Nut
Washer
Cup
Wheel
Bearing Assembly
(Upper Tube)
Tube
Spring
Seat
Brush
Screw
Screw
Horn Wire
Bolt
Plate
Contact
Washer
Bolt
Bolt
Washer
Washer
Screw
Upper Shaft
Grommet
Bolt
Bushing Assembly
(Lower Tube)
Clamp
Washer
Washer
U-Joint
Bolt
Washer
Lower Shaft
Bolt
Clamp
Nut

Exploded view of a CJ steering column (© Jeep Corp)

INSTRUMENT PANEL

Turn Signal Switch Removal and Installation

CJ

The turn signal switch unit is secured to the steering column with two Allen head screws. To remove the unit, remove the Allen head screws. Replace in reverse order of removal.

Commando

1. Remove the steering wheel.
2. Remove the direction signal lever.
3. Disconnect the direction signal harness from the frame harness and remove the wires from each plastic connector.
4. Remove the wires by inserting a narrow blade screwdriver into the terminal end of the connector. Insert the blade into the narrowest part of the opening to depress the retaining tang and pull the wire out of the connector.
5. Remove the harness loom.
6. Remove the two retaining screws from the direction switch and the two screws from the 4-way flasher switch.
7. Pry out the horn contact button.
8. Remove the two bowl attaching screws and allow the bowl to slide down the column.
9. Tape the disconnected wires together. Fold some of the wires back to flatten the bulge.
10. Attach a wire or heavy string to the turn signal harness and pull the harness out from the top of the steering column.
11. Install in the reverse order of removal.

Wagoneer, Cherokee

1. Disconnect the battery and remove the steering wheel.
2. Loosen the anti-theft cover retaining screws and lift the cover from the column. It is not necessary to completely remove the screws.
3. Depress the lock plate and pry the round wire snap ring from the steering shaft groove. Remove the snap ring, lock plate, directional signal canceling cam, upper bearing preload spring, and the thrust washer from the steering shaft.
4. Place the directional signal actuating lever in the right turn position and remove the lever.
5. Depress the hazard warning light switch and remove the but-

ton by turning it counterclockwise.

6. Remove the direction signal wire harness connector block from its mounting bracket on the side of the steering column. On vehicles with automatic transmissions, use a stiff wire to depress the lock tab which retains the shift quadrant light wire in the connector block.
7. Remove the direction signal switch retaining screws and pull the switch and wire harness from the column.
8. Install in the reverse order of removal.

Ignition Switch Removal and Installation

Wagoneer, Cherokee

1. Disconnect the battery.
2. Remove the steering wheel.
3. Loosen the anti-theft cover retaining screws and lift the cover from the column.
4. Depress the lock plate and remove the round wire snap ring from the steering shaft groove.
5. Remove the lock plate, direction signal cancelling cam, upper bearing preload spring, and thrust washer from the steering shaft.
6. Place the direction signal actuating lever in the right turn position and remove the lever.
7. Depress the 4-way flasher switch and remove the button by turning it in a counterclockwise direction.
8. Place the automatic transmission shift lever in the Park position. Remove the shift lever by driving out the pivot pin with a 1/4 in. punch.
9. Remove the direction signal wire harness connector block from its mounting bracket on the right side of the lower column. Use a stiff wire, such as a paper clip, to depress the lock tab which retains the shift quadrant light wire in the connector block.
10. Remove the direction signal switch retaining screws and pull the direction signal switch and wire harness from the column.
11. Use a small wire with a right angle bend to remove the buzzer switch and clip as an assembly. Place the lock in the RUN position. Hook the bend of the wire into the loop of the clip at the top of the switch at the base of the housing and pull up and out on the clip.
12. Place the key in the LOCK position and using a small flat screwdriver, depress the lock cylinder retaining tab.
13. Remove the lock cylinder.
14. To remove the ignition switch, remove the two mounting screws and disconnect the switch from the remote rod. Remove the harness connector and remove the switch from the vehicle.
15. To install the switch with the actuator rod disconnected, position the switch on the column and move the slider to extreme left (Accessory position). The left side of the switch is toward the steering wheel.
16. Install the actuator rod in the slider and install the switch to the steering column being careful not to move the slider out of position.
17. Tighten the retaining screws.
18. Reassemble and install the lock cylinder and the steering column in the reverse order of removal.

CJ and Commando

1. Press the main switch body toward the instrument panel, compressing the spring until the notched bezel is free to be turned counterclockwise and removed.
2. Pull back the main switch body and lower it from under the instrument panel so that the wiring harness plug can be removed from the prong connection.
3. Install the switch in the reverse order of removal with the key installed in the OFF position and pointing straight up and down. The word STARTER should be at the top when the switch is installed in the dash.

Head Light Switch Removal and Installation

To replace the old push-pull type head light switch, use an allen wrench to loosen the set screw and remove the knob. Remove the retaining nut and remove the switch through the back of the instrument panel. Install in reverse order.

To replace the new style push-pull switch, first disconnect the wire connector plug from the switch. Pull the control knob out to the second position. From behind the instrument panel, depress the knob release button and pull the knob out of the switch. Remove the retaining nut and bezel and remove the switch through the back of the panel. Replace in reverse order.

To replace the two-position rocker type switch found in the Commandos, first disconnect one of the battery cables. Remove the control panel by depressing the clip springs located on each side of the panel while at the same time, pushing away from the panel. Remove the circuit breaker and the attached wires. Remove the screws which hold the switch to the panel and remove the switch. Replace in reverse order.

WINDSHIELD WIPERS

Vacuum Operated Wiper, CJ

Motor Removal and Installation

On the early CJ models, the windshield wiper motor was vacuum actuated and mounted at the top of the windshield. To remove it, disconnect the vacuum hose, remove the wiper arm assembly, remove the attaching bolts, and remove the motor assembly from the windshield. Replace in the reverse order.

Electric Wiper Motor

CJ

1. Remove the plastic hole plug at the extreme left of the bottom of the windshield frame air duct and disconnect the drive link from the motor crank.
2. Disconnect the wires from the back of the control switch.
3. Remove the motor cover then remove the motor.
4. Install the wiper motor in the reverse order of the removal procedure.

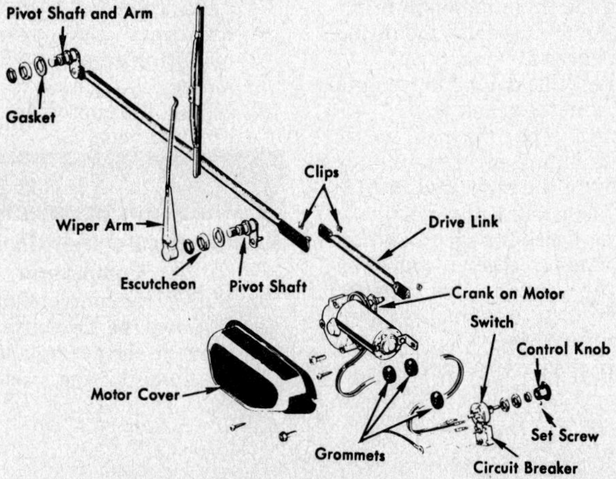

Pivot Shaft and Arm
Gasket
Clips
Wiper Arm
Drive Link
Escutcheon
Pivot Shaft
Crank on Motor
Switch
Control Knob
Motor Cover
Set Screw
Grommets
Circuit Breaker

Windshield wiper components for late model CJs
(© Jeep Corp)

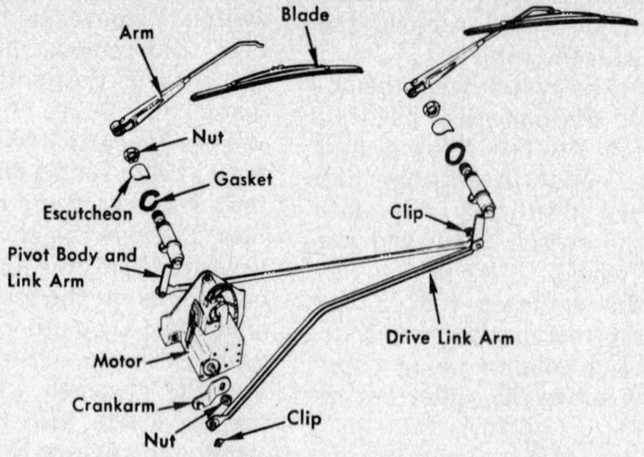
Blade
Arm
Nut
Gasket
Escutcheon
Clip
Pivot Body and
Link Arm
Drive Link Arm
Motor
Crankarm
Clip
Nut

Windshield wiper components for late model Commandos
(© Jeep Corp)

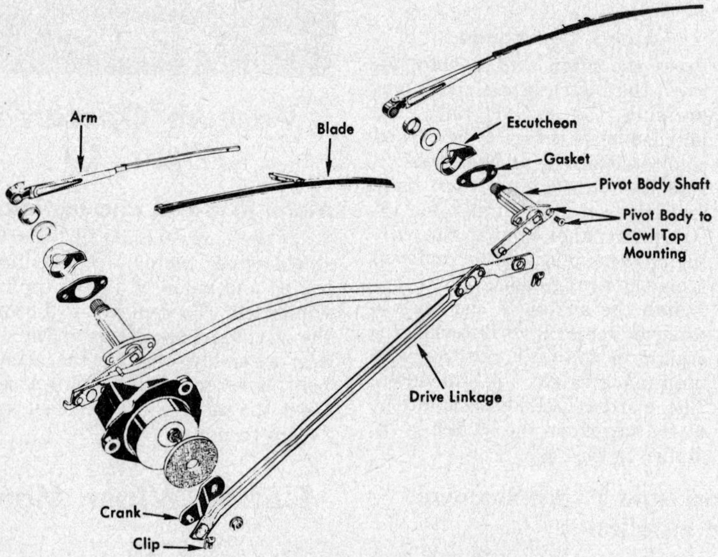
Arm
Blade
Escutcheon
Gasket
Pivot Body Shaft
Pivot Body to
Cowl Top
Mounting
Drive Linkage
Crank
Clip

Windshield wiper components for late model Wagoneers
(© Jeep Corp)

Commando

1. Disconnect the wire harness plug and the speedometer cable from the instrument cluster.
2. Remove the instrument cluster from the instrument panel by depressing the retainer springs at each corner.
3. Remove the three motor-to-brake and clutch pedal mounting bracket screws.
4. Disconnect the wiper drive link from the motor crank.
5. Disconnect the washer hoses from the pump, pivot the motor assembly to the right and drop it below the instrument panel.
6. Mark the wires for identification and disconnect the wire harness from the motor and washer pump.
7. Remove the motor.
8. Install in the reverse order.

Wagoneer, Cherokee

1. Disconnect the wiper drive link from the crank under the instrument panel.
2. Mark the wires for identification at the motor under the hood.
3. Disconnect the motor and washer pump wires at the motor under the hood.
4. Remove the motor-to-dash mounting screws and remove the motor.
5. Install the motor in the reverse order of removal.

RADIO

Removal and Installation

Commando

1. Pull off the control knobs.
2. Remove the two attaching nuts.
3. Remove the antenna lead.
4. Disconnect the rear support strap from the radio, push the radio back far enough to clear the back of the instrument panel and lower the radio far enough to disconnect the speaker leads.
5. Remove the fused wire and remove the radio. Replace the radio in the reverse order of removal.

Wagoneer, Cherokee

1. Open the glove box door and remove the liner and lock striker.
2. Remove the antenna lead.
3. Disconnect the fused wire from the fuse panel.
4. Disconnect the rear support bracket from the radio.
5. Pull off the radio control knobs and remove the radio attaching nuts.
6. Push the radio back to clear the dash panel and remove the radio through the glove box.

HEATER

Heater Core Removal and Installation

CJ

1. Drain the cooling system.
2. Remove the screws that hold the two halves of the duct together and separate the two halves.
3. Remove the screws that hold the heater core to the duct and remove the core.
4. Install the core in the reverse order of removal.

Wagoneer, Cherokee

1. Drain the cooling system.
2. Disconnect the temperature control cable at the heater unit.
3. Remove the heater hoses at the heater unit.
4. Disconnect the heater resistor.
5. Remove the nuts that hold the heater core and duct to the firewall and remove the core and duct assembly.

NOTE: Two of the nuts are located on the inside of the vehicle.

6. Remove the screws that hold the two halves of the duct together and remove the heater core from the duct.
7. Assemble and install the heater core and duct in the reverse order of removal and disassembly.

Blower Motor Removal and Installation

The blower motor is removed from the vehicle simply by removing the attaching screws that hold it to the heater housing and lifting out the motor and fan assembly. Install the blower assembly in the reverse order of removal.

Lincoln Continental Mark III • Mark IV

YEAR IDENTIFICATION

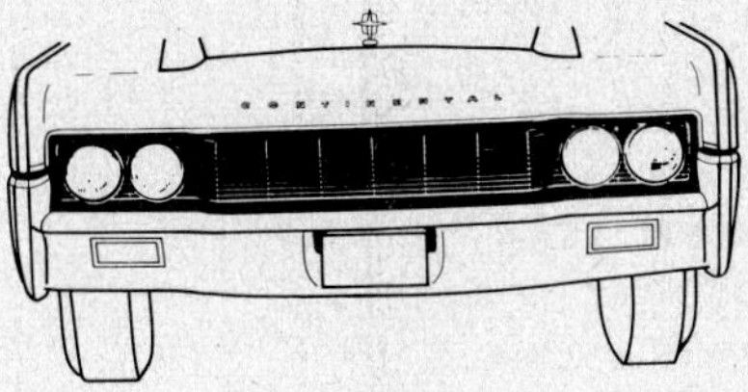
1967

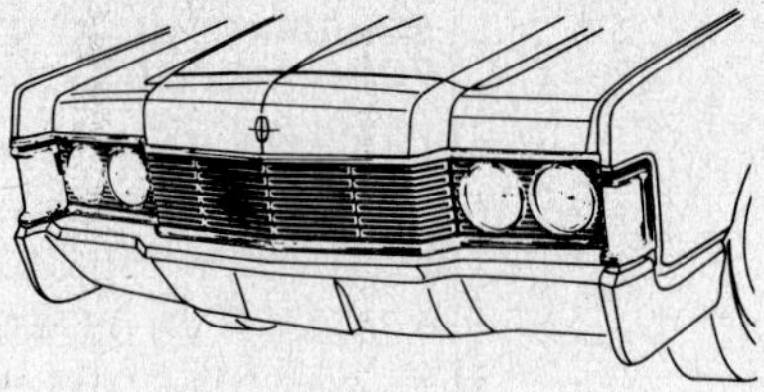
1968

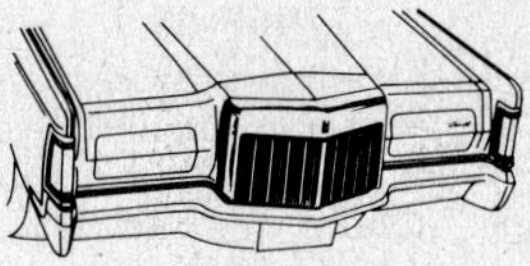
1969 Mark III

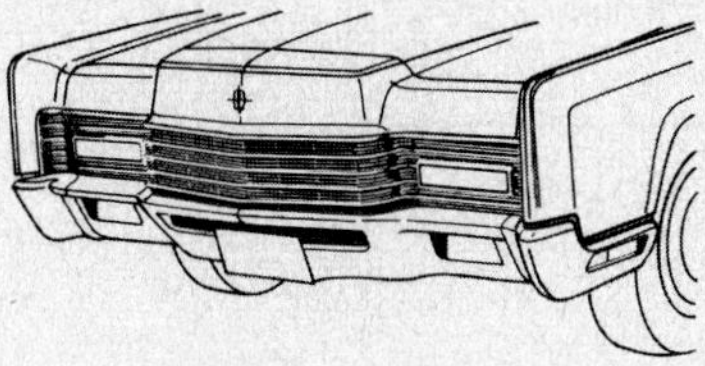
1970 Continental

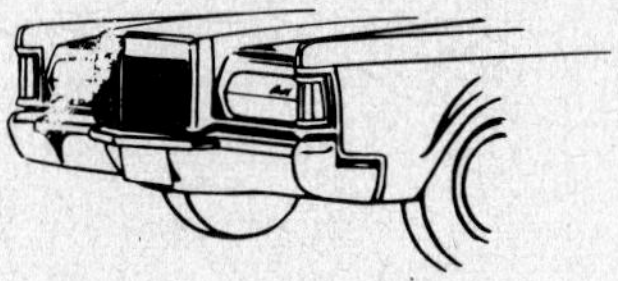
1970-71 Continental Mark III

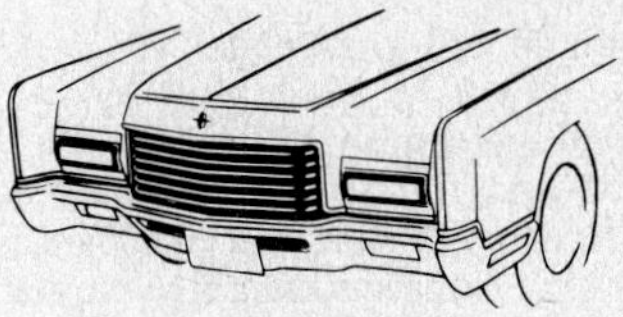
1971 Continental

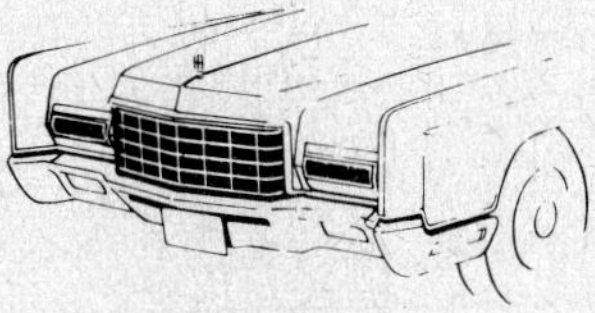
1972 Continental

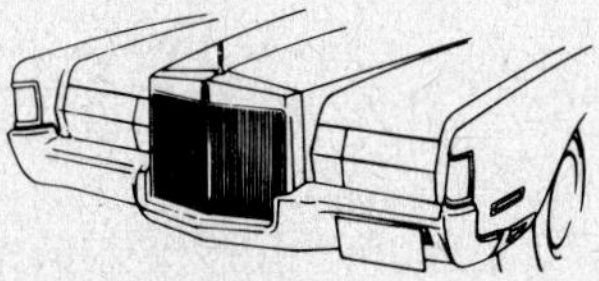
1973 Continental Mark IV

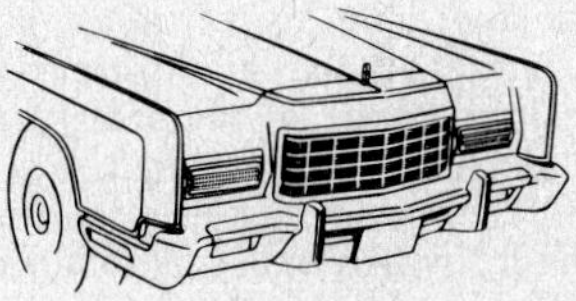
1973 Continental

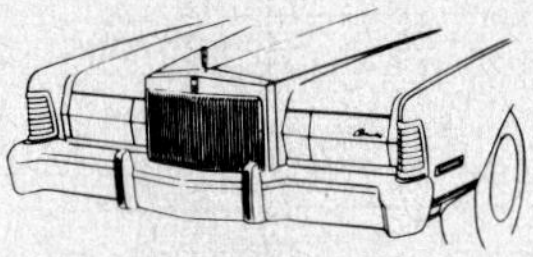
1973 Continental Mark IV

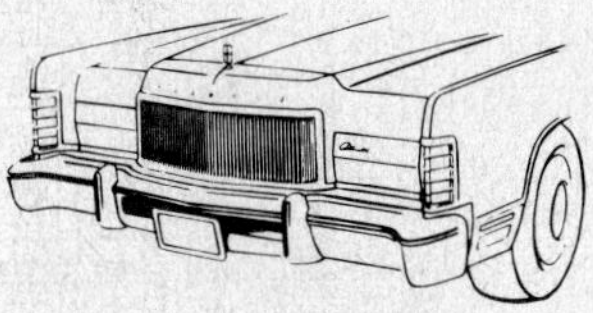
1974 Continental

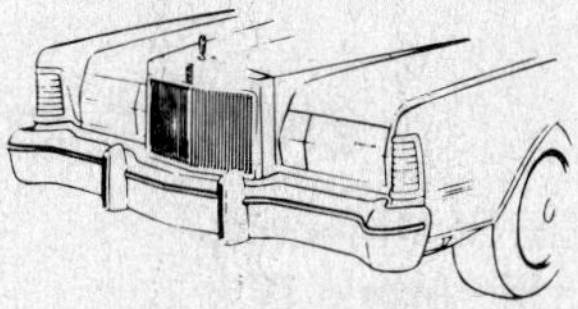
1974 Continental Mark IV

FIRING ORDER

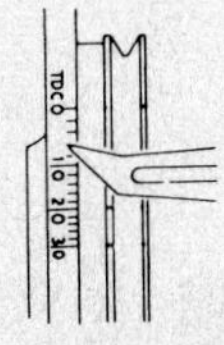
TDC 0
10
20
30
1967 timing marks
(© Ford Motor Co)

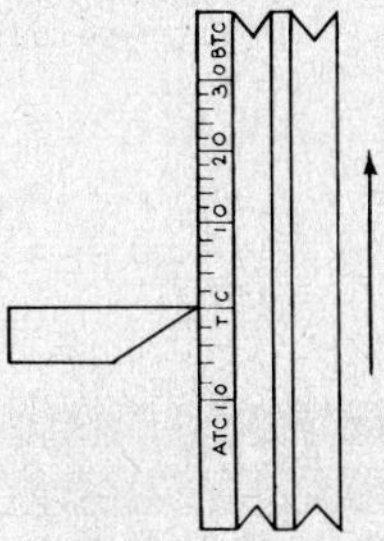
30 BTC
20
10
TC
10 ATC
1968-74 timing marks

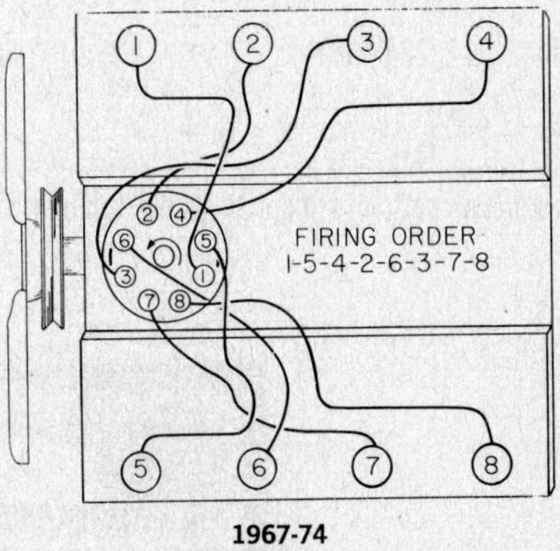
1
2
3
4
FIRING ORDER
1-5-4-2-6-3-7-8
5
6
7
8
1967-74
(© Ford Motor Co)

CAR SERIAL NUMBER LOCATION

1967-68

The vehicle number is stamped on a plate attached to the left front door hinge post. The engine number and vehicle number are identical.

1969-74

The vehicle number is stamped on an aluminum tab riveted to the top of the instrument panel, visible through the driver's side windshield. The serial number contains eleven digits. They are interpreted as follows:

First: Model year code. (9 = 1969, 0 = 1970, 1 = 1971, 2 = 1972)
Second: Assembly plant code.
Third and fourth: Body serial code.
Fifth: Engine code. (A = 460 cu. in.)
Last six: Consecutive unit number.

Vehicle Certification Label

1970-74

The vehicle certification label is attached to the left-hand door jamb. This label has, on its upper portion, the name of the manufacturer, the month and year of manufacture, and the certification statement. The label also shows the vehicle identification number, which must match that on the dashboard. See the illustration for interpretation of the label.

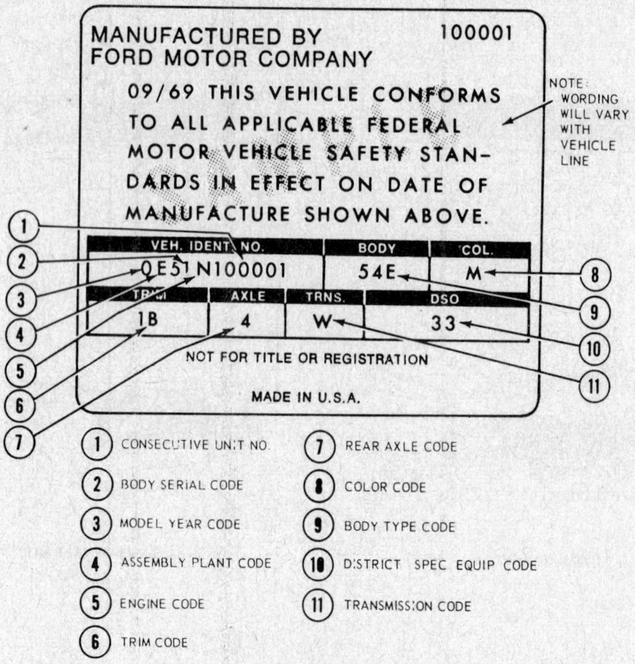
MANUFACTURED BY
FORD MOTOR COMPANY
100001
09/69 THIS VEHICLE CONFORMS TO ALL APPLICABLE FEDERAL MOTOR VEHICLE SAFETY STANDARDS IN EFFECT ON DATE OF MANUFACTURE SHOWN ABOVE.
NOTE: WORDING WILL VARY WITH VEHICLE LINE
VEH. IDENT. NO.
BODY
COL.
0E51N100001
54E
M
TRIM
AXLE
TRNS.
DSO
1B
4
W
33
NOT FOR TITLE OR REGISTRATION
MADE IN U.S.A.
1 CONSECUTIVE UNIT NO.
2 BODY SERIAL CODE
3 MODEL YEAR CODE
4 ASSEMBLY PLANT CODE
5 ENGINE CODE
6 TRIM CODE
7 REAR AXLE CODE
8 COLOR CODE
9 BODY TYPE CODE
10 DISTRICT SPEC EQUIP CODE
11 TRANSMISSION CODE

Vehicle certification label—1970-74
(© Ford Motor Co)

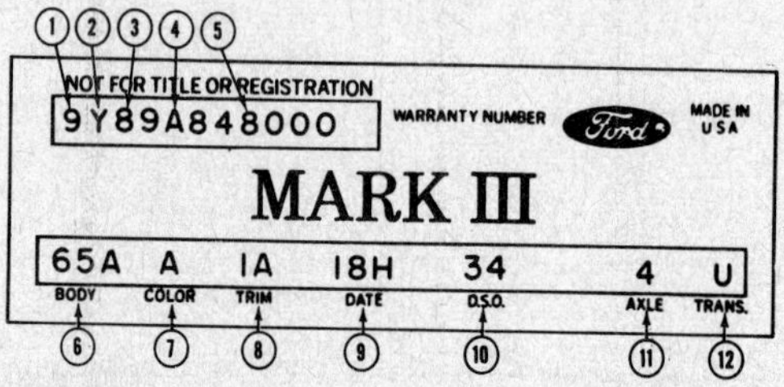
NOT FOR TITLE OR REGISTRATION
9Y89A848000
WARRANTY NUMBER
MADE IN USA
MARK III
65A A IA 18H 34 4 U
BODY COLOR TRIM DATE D.S.O. AXLE TRANS.

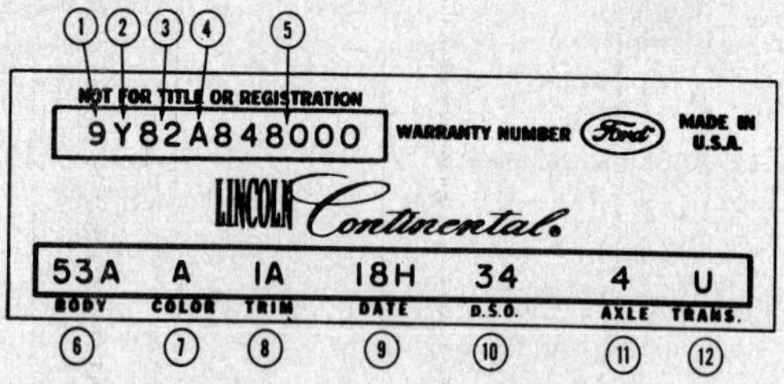
NOT FOR TITLE OR REGISTRATION
9Y82A848000
WARRANTY NUMBER
MADE IN U.S.A.
LINCOLN Continental
53A A IA 18H 34 4 U
BODY COLOR TRIM DATE D.S.O. AXLE TRANS.

1 Model year code
2 Assembly plant code
3 Body serial code
4 Engine code
5 Consecutive unit number
6 Body type code
7 Color code
8 Trim code
9 Date code
10 District—special equipment code
11 Rear axle code
12 Transmission code

ENGINE CODE

Lincoln Continental, Mark III, Mark IV

The engine code designation is the 5th digit of the vehicle identification number (V.I.N.). The V.I.N. is stamped on a plate located at the rear edge of the left front door on 1967 models and located at the left side of the instrument panel visible through the windshield on 1968-74 models.

Disp	Bbl	Hp	'67	'68	'69	'70	'71	'72	'73	'74
8-Cylinder Models										
460	4	202, 208, 219 (net)*							A	A
460	4	212, 224 (net)*						A		
460	4	365		A	A	A	A			
462	4	340	G	G						

* Net horsepower rating varies with model application

9Y83N100001

GENERAL ENGINE SPECIFICATIONS

Year	Engine Cu. In. Displacement	Carburetor Type	Advertised Horsepower @ rpm ■	Advertised Torque @ rpm (ft lbs) ■	Bore and Stroke (in.)	Advertised Compression Ratio	Oil Pressure @ 2050 rpm
'67	8-462	4 bbl	340 @ 4600	485 @ 2800	4.380 x 3.830	10.25:1	54
'68	8-460	4 bbl	365 @ 4600	500 @ 2800	4.362 x 3.850	10.50:1	55
	8-462	4 bbl	340 @ 4600	485 @ 2800	4.380 x 3.830	10.25:1	54
'69	8-460	4 bbl	365 @ 4600	500 @ 2800	4.362 x 3.850	10.50:1	55
'70	8-460	4 bbl	365 @ 4600	500 @ 2800	4.362 x 3.850	10.50:1	55
'71	8-460	4 bbl	365 @ 4600	500 @ 2800	4.362 x 3.850	10.50:1	35-75
'72	8-460	4 bbl	224 @ 4400	357 @ 2800	4.362 x 3.850	8.50:1	35-75
	8-460 Mark IV	4 bbl	212 @ 4400	342 @ 2800	4.362 x 3.850	8.50:1	35-75
'73	8-460 Continental	4 bbl	224 @ 4400	357 @ 2800	4.362 x 3.850	8.5:1	35-65
	8-460 Mark IV	4 bbl	212 @ 4400	342 @ 2800	4.362 x 3.850	8.5:1	35-65
'74	8-460 Continental	4 bbl	224 @ 4400	357 @ 2800	4.362 x 3.850	8.5:1	35-65
	8-460 Mark IV	4 bbl	212 @ 4400	342 @ 2800	4.362 x 3.850	8.5:1	35-65

■ Beginning 1972, horsepower and torque are SAE net figures. They are measured at the rear of the transmission with all accessories installed and operating. Since the figures vary when a given engine is installed in different models, some are representative rather than exact.

TUNE-UP SPECIFICATIONS

	ENGINE		SPARK PLUGS		DISTRIBUTOR		IGNITION TIMING (deg) ▲		VALVES	Fuel	IDLE SPEED (rpm) ▲	
Year	No. Cyl Displacement (cu in.)	hp	Type §	Gap (in.)	Point Dwell (deg)	Point Gap (in.)	Man Trans	Auto Trans	Intake Opens ■ (deg) ●	Pump Pressure (psi)	Man Trans	Auto Trans
'67	8-462	340	BTF-42	.034	26-31	.017	—	10B	20	4½-6½	—	475(500)
'68	8-460	365	BF-42	.034	26-31	.017	—	10B	16	4½-6½	—	550
	8-462	340	BTF-42	.034	26-31	.017	—	10B	20	4½-6½	—	550①
'69	8-460	365	BF-42	.034	26-31	.017	—	10B	16	4½-6½	—	550①
'70	8-460	365	BF-42	.034	26-31	.017	—	10B	16	5-7	—	600
'71	8-460	365	BRF-42	.034	26-31	.017	—	4B	16	5-7	—	600
'72	8-460	224	BRF-42	.034	26-30	.017	—	10B(6B)	16	5-7	—	625/500②
'73	8-460	224	ARF-42	.034	26-30	.017	—	6B	16	5-7	—	625/500②
'74	8-460	224	ARF-42	.034	Electronic		—	6B	16	5-7	—	625/500②

▲ See text for procedure
● Figure in parentheses indicates California engine
■ All figures Before Top Dead Center
§ All spark plug listings are Autolite original equipment numbers
① A/C on
② First figure is for idle speed with solenoid energized and automatic transmission in Drive, while second figure is for idle speed with solenoid disconnected and automatic transmission in Neutral
B Before Top Dead Center
— Not applicable

CAPACITIES

Year	ENGINE No. Cyl. (Cu. In.) Displacement	Engine Crankcase Add 1 Qt For New Filter	TRANSMISSION Pts To Refill After Draining Manual 3-Speed	4-Speed	Automatic	Drive Axle (pts)	Gasoline Tank (gals)	COOLING SYSTEM (qts) With Heater	With A/C
'67	8-462	5	—	—	27	5	25	23	23
'68	8-460	4	—	—	27	5	25	19.3	19.3
	8-462	5	—	—	27	5	25	22.1	22.1
'69	8-460	4	—	—	26	5	25②	19.5④	19.5④
'70	8-460	4	—	—	26①	5	③	19.5④	19.5④
'71	8-460	4	—	—	26①	5	23	19.4	19.4
'72	8-460	4	—	—	26①	5	22.5	19.4	19.4
'73	8-460	4	—	—	26	5	22⑤	19.5⑥	19.5⑥
'74	8-460	4	—	—	26	5	26.5	19.5⑥	19.5⑥

① Mark III—25.5 pts
② Mark III—24 gals
③ Without evaporative emission controls:
Continental—24.5 gals
Mark III—24.1 gals
with evaporative emission controls:
Continental—23.1 gals
Mark III—22.5 gals
④ Mark III—19.4 qts
⑤ Mark IV—22.5 gals
⑥ Mark IV—20.5 qts
— Not applicable

RING GAP

All measurements are given in in.

Year	Engine	Top Compression	Bottom Compression
'67-'68	8-462	.010-.031	.010-.020
'68	8-460	.010-.031	.010-.031
'69-'73	8-460	.010-.020	.010-.020
'74	8-460	.010-.020	.010-.020

Year	Engine	Oil Control
'67-'68	8-460, 462	.015-.066
'69-'70	8-460	.010-.035
'71-'73	8-460	.015-.055
'74	8-460	.015-.055

RING SIDE CLEARANCE

All measurements are given in in.

Year	Engine	Top Compression	Bottom Compression
'67-'68	8-462	.0020-.0035	.0020-.0035
'68-'73	8-460	.002-.004	.002-.004
'74	8-460	.002-.004	.002-.004

Year	Engine	Oil Control
'67-'73	All engines	Snug
'74	8-460	Snug

PISTON CLEARANCE

Year	Engine	Piston to bore clearance (in.)
'67-'68	462	.0014-.0022
'69-'74	460	.0014-.0022

CRANKSHAFT AND CONNECTING ROD SPECIFICATIONS

All measurements are given in in.

Year	Engine Displace. (cu in.)	CRANKSHAFT Main Brg. Journal Dia	Main Brg. Oil Clearance	Shaft End-Play	Thrust on No.	CONNECTING ROD Journal Diameter	Oil Clearance	Side Clearance
'67-'68	462	2.8994-2.9002	.0016	.006	3	2.5992-2.6001	.0016	.006
'68-'74	460	2.9994-3.0002	.0005-.0025	.004-.008	3	2.4992-2.5000	.0008-.0026	.010-.020

TORQUE SPECIFICATIONS

All readings in ft lbs

Year	Engine Displacement (cu in.)	Cylinder Head Bolts	Rod Bearing Bolts	Main Bearing Bolts	Crankshaft Pulley Bolt	Flywheel to Crankshaft Bolts	MANIFOLD Intake	Exhaust
'67-'68	462	135-145	40-45	95-105	75-90	75-85	23-28	15-21
'68-'74	460	130-140①	40-45	95-105	70-90	75-85	25-30	28-33

① In three steps:
Step 1—70-80
Step 2—100-110
Step 3—130-140

VALVE SPECIFICATIONS

Year	Engine No. Cyl. Displacement (cu in.)	Seat Angle (deg)	Face Angle (deg)	Spring Test Pressure (lbs @ in.)	Spring Installed Height (in.)	STEM TO GUIDE Clearance (in.) Intake	Exhaust	STEM Diameter (in.) Intake	Exhaust
'67	8-462	45	45	70 @ 1.65	1 21/32	.0008-.0025	.0010-.0027	.3714	.3712
'68	8-460	45	46	80 @ 1.81	1 13/16	.0010-.0027	.0010-.0027	.3420	.3420
	8-462	45	45	70 @ 1.65	1 21/32	.0008-.0025	.0010-.0027	.3714	.3412
'69	8-460	45	46	80 @ 1.81	1 13/16	.0010-.0027	.0010-.0027	.3420	.3420
'70	8-460	45	46	80 @ 1.81	1 13/16	.0010-.0027	.0010-.0027	.3420	.3420
'71	8-460	45	46	80 @ 1.81	1 13/16	.0010-.0027	.0010-.0027	.3420	.3420
'72	8-460	45	46	80 @ 1.81	1 13/16	.0010-.0027	.0010-.0027	.3420	.3420
'73	8-460	45	44	170 @ 1.39	1 13/16	.0010-.0027	.0010-.0027	.3420	.3420
'74	8-460	45	44	170 @ 1.39	1 13/16	.0010-.0027	.0010-.0027	.3420	.3420

BATTERY AND STARTER SPECIFICATIONS

Year	Engine Displacement (cu in.)	BATTERY Ampere Hour Capacity	Volts		STARTER Lock Test Amps	Volts	Torque (ft lbs)	No-Load Test Amps	Volts	RPM	Brush Spring Tension (oz)
'67-'69	462, 460	85	12	Neg.	670	5	15.5	70	12	9,500	40
'70-'72	460	85	12	Neg.	Not Recommended			70	12	—	40
'73	460	77①	12	Neg.	Not Recommended			70	12	—	40
'74	460	77	12	Neg.	Not Recommended			70	12	—	40

①Side Terminal

ALTERNATOR AND REGULATOR SPECIFICATIONS

	ALTERNATOR			REGULATOR						
					Field Relay			Regulator		
Year	Part No. or Manufacturer	Field Current @ 12 V	Output (amps)	Part No. or Manufacturer	Air Gap (in.)	Point Gap (in.)	Volts to Close	Air Gap (in.)	Point Gap (in.)	Volts @ 75°
'67	Autolite	4.4-4.8	60	Autolite	.014	—	2.5-4	.052	.020	13.8-14.6
'68-'69	Autolite	2.9-3.1	55	Autolite	.018	.019	2.5-4	.052	.020	13.3-15.3
'70-'71	Autolite① DOLF-10300	2.9-3.1	55	Autolite		③		—	—	13.3-14.6
	Autolite② DOAF-10300	2.8-3.3	65	Autolite		③		—	—	13.8-15.3
'72-'74	Motorcraft D2AF-10300-CA	2.9	61	Motorcraft	—	—	2.5-4	—	—	13.5-15.3
	Motorcraft D2OF-10300-AA	2.9	64④	Motorcraft	—	—	2.5-4	—	—	13.5-15.3
	Motorcraft D2SF-10300-AA	2.9	55	Motorcraft	—	—	2.5-4	—	—	13.5-15.3
	Motorcraft D2OF-10300-CB	2.9	61	Motorcraft	—	—	2.5-4	—	—	13.5-15.3
	Motorcraft D3VF-10300-AA	2.9	90	Motorcraft	—	—	2.5-4	—	—	13.5-15.3

① Integral regulator
② Opt.; required with heated back window
③ Transistor type
④ 70 amp—1973

BRAKE SPECIFICATIONS

		MASTER CYLINDER		WHEEL CYLINDER			BRAKE DISC OR DRUM DIAMETER		
				Front			Front		
Year	Model	Disc	Drum	Disc	Drum	Rear	Disc	Drum	Rear
'67-'69	All exc. Mark III	1.0	—	$1\frac{15}{16}$	—	$\frac{15}{16}$	11.96	—	11.09①
'68-'69	Mark III	1.0	—	$2\frac{3}{4}$	—	$\frac{15}{16}$	11.72	—	11.03②
'70-'72	All exc. Mark III, IV	1.0	—	$1\frac{15}{16}$	—	$\frac{15}{16}$	11.72	—	11.03
	Mark III, IV	1.0	—	2.755	—	$\frac{15}{16}$	11.72	—	11.03
'73	All Models	1.0	—	3.1	—	1.0	11.72	—	11.03
'74	All Models	1.0	—	3.1	—	1.0	11.72	—	11.03

① Refinishing Limit—11.150
② Refinishing Limit—11.090
— Not applicable

All measurements are given in in.

WHEEL ALIGNMENT SPECIFICATIONS

		CASTER		CAMBER				WHEEL PIVOT RATIO (deg)	
Year	Model	Range (deg)	Pref Setting (deg) ■	Range (deg)	Pref Setting (deg) ▲	Toe-in (in.)	Steering Axis Inclin.	Inner Wheel	Wheel Outer
'67-'69	Continental	$2\frac{1}{4}$N to $\frac{3}{4}$N	$1\frac{1}{2}$N	0 to $\frac{3}{4}$P	$\frac{1}{2}$P	$\frac{1}{16}$ to $\frac{3}{16}$	$7\frac{3}{4}$	20	$17\frac{3}{4}$
'68-'70	Mark III	$\frac{1}{2}$P to $1\frac{1}{2}$P	1	0 to 1P	$\frac{1}{2}$P	$\frac{1}{8}$ to $\frac{1}{4}$	$7\frac{3}{4}$	20	19.3
'70	Continental	$2\frac{1}{4}$N to $\frac{3}{4}$N	$1\frac{1}{2}$N	$\frac{1}{8}$P to $\frac{5}{8}$P	$\frac{1}{2}$P	0 to $\frac{1}{16}$	$7\frac{3}{4}$	20	$18\frac{1}{2}$
'71	Continental	$2\frac{1}{2}$N to $\frac{1}{2}$N	$1\frac{1}{2}$N	$\frac{1}{4}$N to $1\frac{1}{4}$N	$\frac{1}{2}$P	0 to $\frac{1}{4}$	$7\frac{7}{8}$	20	$18\frac{1}{2}$
	Mark III	0 to 2P	1	$\frac{1}{4}$N to $1\frac{1}{4}$P	$\frac{1}{2}$P	$\frac{1}{16}$ to $\frac{5}{16}$	$7\frac{3}{4}$	20	$19\frac{1}{4}$
'72	Continental	$\frac{1}{2}$N to $2\frac{1}{2}$P	$1\frac{1}{2}$P①	$\frac{1}{2}$N to $1\frac{1}{2}$P	$\frac{1}{2}$P②	0 to $\frac{1}{4}$	$7\frac{3}{4}$	20	$18\frac{7}{16}$
'72-'74	Mark IV	0 to 2P	1P①	$\frac{1}{4}$N to $1\frac{1}{4}$P	$\frac{1}{2}$P③	$\frac{1}{16}$ to $\frac{5}{16}$	$7\frac{3}{4}$	20	$17\frac{3}{4}$
'73-'74	Continental	$\frac{1}{2}$N to $2\frac{1}{2}$P	1P	$\frac{1}{4}$N to $1\frac{1}{4}$P	$\frac{1}{2}$P	0 to $\frac{1}{4}$	$7\frac{3}{4}$	20	$17\frac{3}{4}$

■ Not to vary more than $\frac{1}{2}$ degree from one side to the other unless otherwise noted
▲ Not to vary more than $\frac{1}{4}$ degree from one side to the other unless otherwise noted
N Negative P Positive

① Maximum caster difference between wheels should not exceed 1°
② Maximum camber difference between wheels should not exceed 1°
③ Maximum camber difference between wheels should not exceed $\frac{3}{4}$°

CHARGING SYSTEM

General information on alternator and regulator repair and troubleshooting is in the Unit Repair Section under the heading Charging and Starting Systems.

Alternator

Cars are equipped with alternating current generators. This charging system is different from the DC circuit, and requires certain precautions.

1. Reversing battery connections will cause damage to the one-way electrical valves, the rectifiers.
2. Booster battery connections must be made as follows: the negative terminal of the booster battery must be connected to the negative terminal of the car battery. The positive terminal of the booster battery must be connected to the positive terminal of the car battery.
3. Fast charges should never be used as boosters to start AC circuit equipped cars.
4. When servicing the battery with a fast charger, always disconnect car battery cables.
5. Never attempt to polarize an AC generator.
   Complete alternator servicing data is in the Unit Repair Section.

Alternator R & R

1. Disconnect the negative battery cable.
2. Loosen the alternator mounting bolts, remove the alternator to adjusting arm bolt and remove the belt.
3. Remove the alternator mounting bolt and spacer, position the alternator so that the wire connectors can be disconnected and remove the alternator.

NOTE: on alternators with integral regulators mounted on the back of the alternator housing, press the sides of the retainer clip and remove the wire from the regulator.

4. Reverse above procedure to reinstall, applying pressure only to the front of the alternator housing when tightening the drive belt.

Regulator R & R

1. Disconnect the negative battery cable.
2. Remove the regulator mounting screws and wires, then remove the regulator.
3. On vehicles with integral regulator, remove the alternator to adjusting arm bolt and the drive belt.
4. Swing the alternator down, remove the terminal covers from the regulator and remove the regulator attaching nuts.
5. Press the sides of the retainer clip and remove the retaining clip and supply wire. Remove the regulator.
6. Reverse above procedure to reinstall.

Fuse Link

Since 1970, all Ford products have incorporated a fuse link in the charging system. The fuse link is a short length of insulated wire, several gauge sizes smaller than the system it protects. The fuse link blows out if a booster battery is hooked into the system incorrectly, or if a component of the electrical system is shorted to ground. When the fuse link blows, it leaves an open circuit in the charging system and the alternator will not charge the battery. A blown fuse link can be identified by bare wire ends or bubbled insulation. It is located in the engine wire harness on or near the starter relay and is marked FUSE LINK.

STARTING SYSTEM

Prior to 1968, the Lincoln Continental featured a starter with a self-contained engagement mechanism. From 1968 to the present, all Lincoln and Continental models have used a starter to which is mounted an outboard solenoid. There is no difference in procedures for removing or installing these two types of starters.

Starter R & R

Disconnect starter cable, raise car, turn front wheels fully to the right. Remove the two bolts attaching the steering idler arm, remove starter mounting bolts. Remove starter.

Solenoid R & R

Since the entire starter must be removed from the car prior to removing the solenoid, this procedure may be found in the "Unit Repair Section."

Starter Drive R & R

See "Unit Repair Section."

IGNITION SYSTEM

Distributor Removal

The distributor is located at the front of the engine between the cylinder banks.

Remove the carburetor air cleaner,

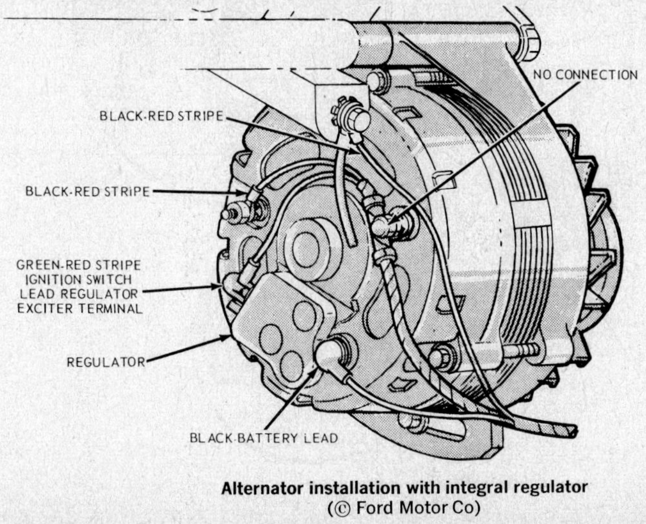
NO CONNECTION
BLACK-RED STRIPE
BLACK-RED STRIPE
GREEN-RED STRIPE
IGNITION SWITCH
LEAD REGULATOR
EXCITER TERMINAL
REGULATOR
BLACK BATTERY LEAD

Alternator installation with integral regulator
(© Ford Motor Co)

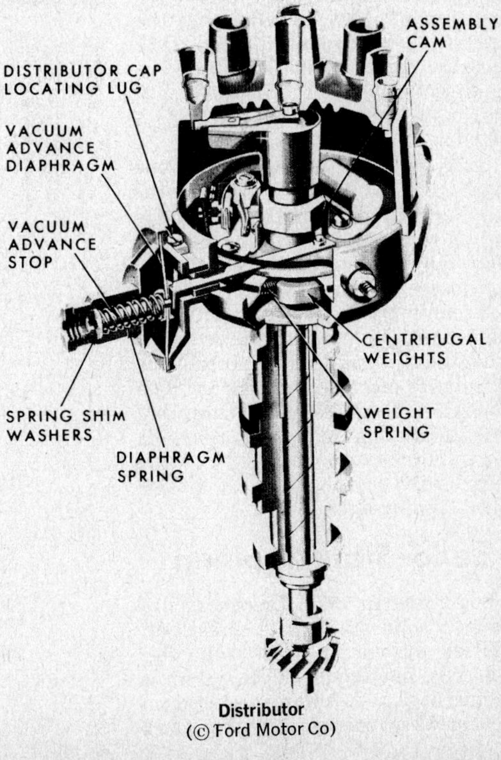
ASSEMBLY CAM
DISTRIBUTOR CAP LOCATING LUG
VACUUM ADVANCE DIAPHRAGM
VACUUM ADVANCE STOP
CENTRIFUGAL WEIGHTS
SPRING SHIM WASHERS
WEIGHT SPRING
DIAPHRAGM SPRING

Distributor
(© Ford Motor Co)

take off the ignition primary lead and the vacuum advance lead. Carefully mark the position of the rotor in relation to the body of the distributor, and mark the position of the body of the distributor relative to the chamber cover. Remove the hold-down bolt and lift out distributor. The marks are made so that the distributor can be reinstalled without having to retime the ignition.

Ignition Timing

1. Locate the timing mark and pointer. Mark the pointer and timing mark according to the timing specifications of your car.
2. Install a stroboscopic type timing light according to the manufacturer's specifications.
3. Disconnect the vacuum line(s) to the distributor and plug them. Loosen the distributor hold-down slightly.
4. Start the engine. If the engine idle speed is above 500 rpm, it should be brought down to approximately 500 rpm before timing is attempted.
5. Check the timing mark and pointer alignment with the timing light. To advance the timing, turn the distributor clockwise.
6. Stop the engine, tighten the distributor hold-down, start the car, and check the timing.

Ignition Retiming

If the timing relationship has been disturbed, retime the ignition as follows: bring No. 1 cylinder up to the firing position. This can be checked by removing the spark plug, placing your thumb in the spark plug hole and then cranking the engine until the compression attempts to blow by your thumb. Now, slowly bring the crankshaft around until the T.D.C. mark on the crankshaft pulley lines up with the pointer. This is the approximate firing position for No. 1 cylinder.

Note the placement of the no. one spark plug wire on the distributor cap. Scribe a mark on the distributor body directly below the no. one spark plug wire. Remove the distributor cap, loosen the distributor hold-down, and move the distributor until the mark that you made is directly beneath the tip of the rotor. Install the distributor cap and, working counterclockwise, check to make sure that the installation of the spark plug wires corresponds with the firing order of the engine. Check the timing with a timing light.

Solid State Ignition

Beginning in 1974, Lincoln is utilizing a solid state or "breakerless" ignition system on both 460 cubic inch V8s, nationwide. This system is unique in that it eliminates the contact breaker points, replacing them with a permanent magnet low voltage generator.

Briefly, the system works as follows: When the ignition is on and the distributor is rotating, the low voltage generator in the distributor produces alternating current which is then sent to the electronic control module. The module senses the signal from the low voltage generator as the alternating current wave swings from positive to negative each time one of the gear teeth on the armature passes the magnetic field in the coil of the generator. When a gear tooth is directly opposite the magnetic field, the alternating current wave is at crossover (neither negative nor positive). The control module senses this and cuts off electricity (low voltage) to the coil, causing it to fire (high voltage). After the coil fires, the timing circuitry in the module redirects the low tension voltage to the coil.

Other than the low voltage generator and the control module, the rest of the system is conventional in appearance, with a standard distributor cap and rotor. Spark advance or retard is accomplished by moving the plate for the low voltage generator in the distributor.

FUEL SYSTEM

Fuel Pump Removal

1967-68

The fuel pump is mounted on the top portion of the engine front cover.

To remove the pump, disconnect the fuel and vapor discharge connections. The pump can then be unbolted and lifted off.

On power-steering models, the bolts are accessible from under the car.

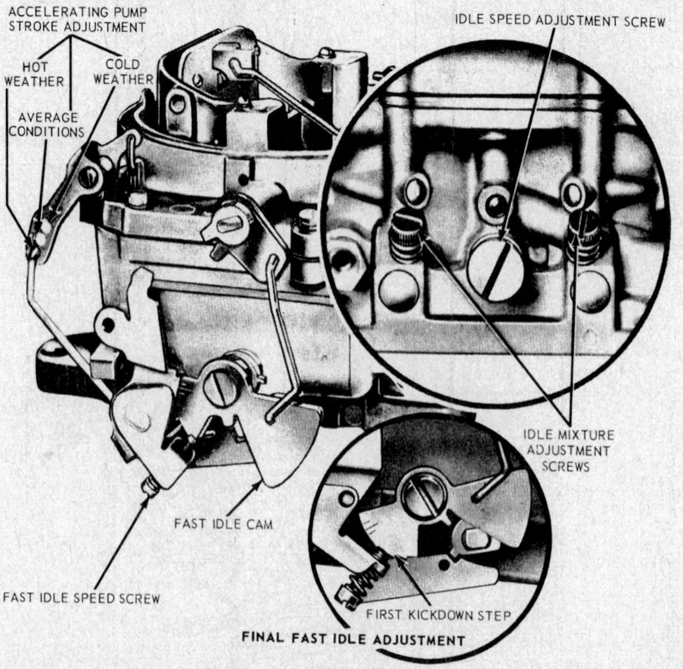
ACCELERATING PUMP STROKE ADJUSTMENT
HOT WEATHER
COLD WEATHER
AVERAGE CONDITIONS
IDLE SPEED ADJUSTMENT SCREW
IDLE MIXTURE ADJUSTMENT SCREWS
FAST IDLE CAM
FAST IDLE SPEED SCREW
FIRST KICKDOWN STEP
FINAL FAST IDLE ADJUSTMENT

Carter carburetor adjustments
(© Ford Motor Co)

1968-74 460 Engine

The fuel pump is mounted on the left side of the cylinder front cover.

A separate in-line fuel filter is used. The filter cannot be serviced. Renew it in case of obstruction. This pump is spring loaded in opposition to camshaft eccentric lobe action, and is conventional.

The pump is Carter-built and cannot be serviced.

Carburetor

Two different carburetors have been used on Lincoln engines: the 462 V8s are equipped with a Carter carburetor, while the 460 V8 uses a model 4300 Autolite carburetor.

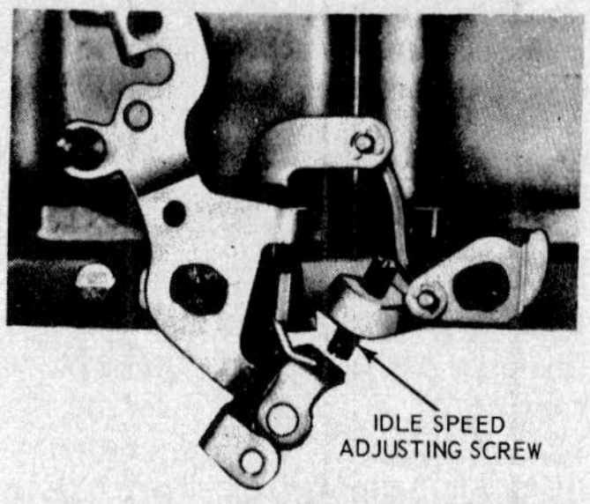
IDLE SPEED ADJUSTING SCREW

Autolite carburetor idle speed adjustment
(© Ford Motor Co)

Idle Speed Adjustment

1. 1967-68 Carter Carburetor: *Adjust with air cleaner removed.* 1968-74 4300 Carburetor: *Adjust with air cleaner installed.* If it is not possible to adjust carburetor idle speed with the air cleaner installed, the engine idle speed must be rechecked after installing the air cleaner. On models with vacuum controlled heat ducts in the air cleaner, the

vacuum line must be plugged if the carburetor is to be adjusted with the air cleaner removed.
2. Run engine at fast idle to equalize operating temperature.
3. Make sure the choke plate is fully released.
4. Turn headlights on high beam.
5. Tape hot idle compensator so that it is fully seated in the closed position.
6. On vehicles equipped with air conditioning, all models EXCEPT 1969, set the idle speed with the air conditioner turned OFF. 1969 models, set the idle speed with the air conditioner turned ON.
7. Remove and plug the vacuum line to the parking brake release, then, set the parking brake and put the transmission in the Drive position.
8. Attach a tachometer of known accuracy to the engine.
9. Adjust the idle speed screw or solenoid to obtain specified rpm. On Carter carburetors, turn the idle speed adjusting screw in to decrease speed and out to increase engine speed. On Autolite carburetors, turn the idle adjusting screw in to increase speed and out to decrease speed. On 1967-71 carburetors with an electric solenoid, turn the solenoid plunger to the right to increase idle speed and to the left to decrease it. On 1972-74 carburetors with an electric solenoid, turn the adjusting screw in the solenoid mounting bracket to adjust the idle speed.

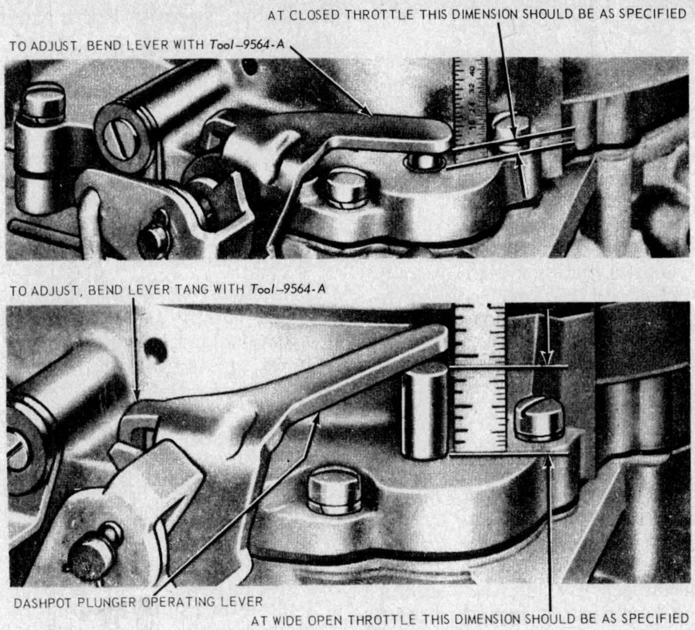
AT CLOSED THROTTLE THIS DIMENSION SHOULD BE AS SPECIFIED
TO ADJUST, BEND LEVER WITH Tool–9564-A
TO ADJUST, BEND LEVER TANG WITH Tool–9564-A
DASHPOT PLUNGER OPERATING LEVER
AT WIDE OPEN THROTTLE THIS DIMENSION SHOULD BE AS SPECIFIED

Carter carburetor anti-stall dashpot adjustments
(© Ford Motor Co)

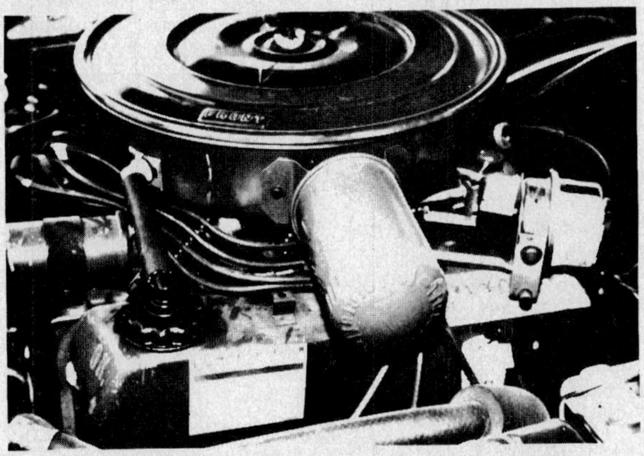

The device that looks like an oil filter attached to the air cleaner is actually a canister designed to prevent an air cleaner "hoot" noise. It may be found on engines beginning 1973

NOTE: There are two engine idle speeds listed for cars with solenoid equipped carburetors. The first or higher speed is adjusted as explained above, the second is adjusted with the solenoid electrical lead disconnected, and the transmission in Park or Neutral, by turning the adjustment screw on the side of the carburetor.

With the solenoid disconnected, the idle adjusting screw must contact the throttle shaft or the throttle plates may become jammed in the throttle bores of the carburetor when the engine is shut off.

Fuel Mixture Adjustment

1. On engines with Carter carburetors, turn the mixture screws clockwise until engine idle becomes rough, then, back out adjustment screws until engine reaches highest rpm.
2. On Autolite carburetors with idle mixture limiter caps, follow the same procedure, but, final adjustment must be made with the caps installed.
3. If adjusting the idle mixture has altered engine idle speed, reset idle speed to specification.

Dashpot Adjustment

Carter Carburetor

1. With the carburetor idle speed adjusted to specification, measure the distance between the dashpot lever and the top surface of the carburetor. If the distance is not within specs bend the dashpot lever to correct.
2. With the carburetor in the full open position, measure the distance between the dashpot lever and the top surface of the carburetor. If the distance is not within specs, bend the rear end of the dashpot lever to correct.

Autolite Carburetor

1. With the carburetor idle speed adjusted to specification, depress the plunger of the dashpot with a screwdriver. Measure the distance between the tip of the plunger and the carburetor throttle lever. If the distance is not within specs, loosen the dashpot locknut and turn the dashpot to adjust.

Dashpot Adjustments

Carter Carburetor	#1 setting	#2 setting
1967	1/8 in.	7/16 in.
Autolite Carburetor		
1968-69	3/32 in.	
1970-71	1/10 in.	

COOLING SYSTEM

All models prior to 1968 featured a radiator supply tank in their cooling systems, which is attached to the intake manifold. The purpose of this tank is to control the surging of the coolant. On these models, the surge tank houses the thermostat.

Beginning in 1968, the radiator supply tank was eliminated in favor of a new type of radiator with enlarged tanks provided on both sides of the core.

On this new type of radiator, a cold fill reference mark is stamped into the metal about 2 in. below the filler cap. This radiator must be checked for fluid level when the engine is cold and not running.

Radiator Removal

1. Drain the cooling system.
2. Disconnect the upper and lower radiator hoses from the radiator.
3. Disconnect the transmission cooler lines from the radiator.
4. If the air conditioner condenser attaches to the radiator, remove the retaining bolts and position the condenser out of the way. *Do not disconnect the refrigerant lines.*
5. If equipped with a fan shroud, disconnect it from the radiator and position it rearward over the fan.
6. Remove the radiator mounting bolts, and remove the radiator from the car.
7. Reverse above procedure to install.

Water Pump Removal

462 Engine

1. Drain cooling system and disconnect battery.
2. On air conditioned cars, remove fan drive clutch, fan, and compressor drive pulley as an assembly.
3. Remove radiator supply tank.
4. If not air conditioned, remove fan and spacer.
5. Loosen clamp securing bypass hose.
6. Remove alternator splash shield.
7. Loosen alternator adjusting bracket and mounting bracket bolts. Push alternator inward and remove bolts.
8. Disconnect radiator outlet and heater hose at water pump.
9. Remove water pump retaining bolts. Position dip stick tube bracket and power steering pump bracket to allow clearance.
10. Remove water pump.

460 Engine

1. Drain cooling system.
2. Remove bolts retaining fan assembly to water pump.
3. Remove radiator shroud and fan.
4. On air conditioned cars, loosen compressor drive belt.
5. Loosen alternator mounting bolts and remove alternator drive belt.
6. Remove water pump pulley.
7. Disconnect radiator lower hose, heater hose, and bypass hose at water pump.
8. Remove water pump bolts and remove water pump.

Radiator Supply Tank and Thermostat R & R

All 1967 Models

1. Disconnect the negative battery cable.
2. Drain the coolant to a level below that of the supply tank.
3. Disconnect the primary and secondary wires from the ignition coil.
4. Remove the bolts which attach the supply tank to the intake manifold. Remove the tank, gasket, and thermostat.
5. Position the new thermostat within the intake manifold with the copper element toward the engine. Coat the radiator supply tank gasket with water-resistant sealer and install it on the intake manifold.
6. Connect the primary and secondary wires to the ignition coil, close the radiator drain cock, and connect the ground cable to the battery.
7. Fill the supply to its required level with coolant, install the pressure cap, start the engine, and check the system for leaks.

All 1968-74 Models

1. Drain the radiator so that the coolant level is below the thermostat.
2. Remove the coolant outlet housing retaining bolts, pull the elbow away from the manifold, and remove the thermostat and its gasket.
3. Clean the coolant outlet housing and manifold gasket surfaces. Coat a new gasket with water-resistant sealer, and position the gasket on the manifold.
4. Install the thermostat into the outlet with the bridge section facing the outlet. Turn the thermostat clockwise until it locks into position against the flats which are cast into the intake elbow.
5. Position the coolant outlet elbow against the intake manifold. Install the retaining bolts, and torque them to specifications.
6. Fill the radiator to the cold fill level, install the cap, start the engine, and check the system for leaks.

EMISSION CONTROLS

All Models

Regardless of what other emission controls have been featured from year to year on Lincoln cars, all 1967-74 models have featured positive crankcase ventilation (PCV) for purposes of burning the crankcase fumes, which on earlier cars had been dispelled through the road draft tube. Prior to 1968 this feature had been incorporated into an open crankcase (with breather cap). From 1968 on, a closed crankcase has been used.

1967

On all 1967 models, the Thermactor (air injection) system of emission controls was employed. Composed of an air pump, a bypass and a check valve, and external air manifolds (not an integral part of the engine exhaust manifolds), the system injects fresh air into the exhaust ports to achieve afterburning of raw exhaust fumes—hence more complete combustion of fuel than had been previously possible.

In addition to the Thermactor System, the 1967 models also feature a heated air intake system for purposes of improved cold-weather operation and faster engine warm-up. A metal shroud around the exhaust manifold channels manifold-warmed air through a heat-sensitive unit in the air cleaner and into the carburetor. As the engine becomes warmer, the supply of manifold-warmed air is reduced. This system has been standard on every Lincoln model since 1967. All carburetors from 1968 on are equipped with idle speed and mixture limiter caps, in order to prevent rich carburetor adjustments.

1968-69

All Lincoln cars from 1968 to the present feature a distributor vacuum control valve, which is also known as a temperature sensing valve or a ported vacuum switch (PVS). This valve is installed in the coolant outlet elbow and features three ports which are connected by hoses to a carburetor, the intake manifold, and the distributor vacuum advance diaphragm. This valve operates during periods of higher-than-normal operating temperatures (usually associated with prolonged idle periods) to supply added vacuum from the intake manifold to the distributor, thus advancing the timing, increasing idle speed, and enhancing the operation of the cooling system.

During the 1968–69 model years, the Thermactor System was not used on Lincolns.

Most 1969 and later carburetors are equipped with an electrically controlled throttle solenoid, which raises engine idle speeds and reduces terminal exhaust pollutants.

1970-71

Lincoln cars returned to the Thermactor System in 1970, this time in combination with the other, aforementioned, improvements which are grouped together into what is called the IMCO (IMproved COmbustion) system. The only change in the Thermactor system for 1970 is that its air manifolds are cast as an integral part of the engine's exhaust manifolds. The Thermactor System continued to be used on all 1971 models and on those 1972 cars designed for California.

Beginning in 1970, some Lincoln cars were equipped with an Evaporative Emisson Control System, a further extension of the IMCO system. This component channels the breathing of the fuel tank and the venting of the carburetor float bowl through a canister filled with activated charcoal, with the result that pollution due to evaporating of fuel is eliminated. The Evaporative Emission Control System became standard on all models in 1971.

1972

1972 California cars are equipped with an addition to the IMCO System, an Electronic Spark Control (ESC) system. This system is composed of an electronic control amplifier, a three-way distributor modulator valve, a speed sensor (found between two sections of the speedometer cable), and a thermal switch (located in the right door pillar of the Lincoln Continental and in the left door pillar of the Continental Mark IV).

The three-way distributor modulator valve is found within the vacuum line connecting the previously discussed ported vacuum switch and the carburetor. It is vented to the atmosphere. The thermal switch is designed to react to a critical temperature range of 50–58° F (outside air temperature). The speed sensor reacts to speeds in excess of 40 mph. The thermal switch dominates over the speed sensor. The impulses from both are fed into the electronic control amplifier.

When the ambient temperature is below 49°F, the ESC system does not operate. When the outside temperature rises above 65°F, the contacts in the temperature switch close. This causes the temperature switch to pass current from the ignition switch to the amplifier. The amplifier then signals the distributor modulator to close and prevent vacuum from reaching the distributor. When the vehicle reaches a speed of 40 mph, the signal from the speed sensor causes the modulator to open and restore normal vacuum advance to the engine. If the engine should overheat at idle, the ported vacuum switch overrides the ESC system and connects intake manifold vacuum to the distributor.

1973-74

The 1973 emission control system consists of a new Exhaust Gas Recirculation (EGR) system, and a Delayed Vacuum Bypass (DVB) spark advance control system.

The DVB system provides two paths by which carburetor vacuum can reach the distributor vacuum advance. The system consists of a spark delay valve, a check valve, a solenoid vacuum valve, and an ambient temperature switch. When the ambient temperature is below 49°F, the temperature switch contacts are open and the vacuum solenoid is open (de-energized). Under these conditions, vacuum will flow from the carburetor, through the open solenoid, and to the distributor. Since the spark delay valve resists the flow of carburetor vacuum, the vacuum will always flow through the vacuum solenoid when it is open, since this is the path of least resistance. When the ambient temperature rises above 60°F, the contacts in the temperature switch (which is located in the door post) close. This passes ignition switch current to the solenoid, energizing the solenoid. This blocks one of the two vacuum paths. All distributor vacuum must now flow through the spark delay valve. When carburetor vacuum rises above a certain level on acceleration, a rubber valve in the spark delay valve blocks vacuum from passing through the valve for from 5 to 30 seconds. After this time delay has elapsed, normal vacuum is supplied to the distributor. When the vacuum solenoid is closed (temperature above 60°), the vacuum line from the solenoid to the distributor is vented to atmosphere. To prevent the vacuum that is passing through the spark delay valve from escaping through the solenoid into the atmosphere, a one-way check valve is installed in the vacuum line from the solenoid to the distributor.

The EGR system consists of a control valve, a temperature-controlled vacuum switch, and a special carburetor mounting spacer. A hole that is drilled in the carburetor flange on the intake manifold passes exhaust gases from the manifold crossover passage into the carburetor spacer. A plunger which is attached to the EGR valve normally prevents the exhaust gases from entering the engine. When the engine coolant temperature reaches 125°F, the EGR vacuum valve opens and connects carburetor vacuum to the EGR valve. Under high carburetor vacuum conditions, the EGR valve opens and recirculates exhaust gases into the engine. This lowers peak combustion temperature and reduces oxides of nitrogen.

The spark delay is connected into the distributor vacuum line and closes on hard acceleration to prevent carburetor vacuum from reaching the distributor. After a predetermined number of seconds, the spark delay valve opens and carburetor vacuum is again connected to the distributor.

To meet the standards of the revised California emission controls, all California engines for 1974 will be equipped with the Ford Thermactor system, Exhaust Gas Recirculation (EGR) and the Ford Improved Combustion (IMCO) system.

The new Thermactor system keeps hydrocarbon and carbon monoxide emissions at the required level, while the EGR and IMCO systems are designed to reduce oxides of nitrogen.

See the "Unit Repair Section" for troubleshooting procedures for all emission control equipment.

ENGINE

Lincoln Engines—1967-1974

The 1967 Lincoln Continental was equipped with a massive V8 engine of 4.380 in. bore and 3.830 in. stroke for a total displacement of 462 cu in. Despite its bulk, the engine proved admirably suited for use in a car of this size. Outstanding features of the engine were its comparatively short stroke, deep Y-block construction, and cylinder heads with flat mating surfaces and no indentations for the combustion chambers. Mounted on the block at approximately 60° to the axis of the bore, these cylinder heads with flat mating surfaces topped combustion chambers which were formed by the angle between head and piston in the top of the bore. This engine continued in use through 1968.

During 1968 the 460 cu. in. engine was introduced. Throughout that year it was mixed indiscriminately with the 462 engine in Lincoln production, only the new Mark III used the 460 exclusively. Because of this mixing and because the bore, 4.36 in., and stroke, 3.85 in., and displacement are close to those of the older engine, many people confuse the two. The new engine differs substantially. It has canted valves, stud mounted rocker arms, semi-hemispherical combustion chambers, tunnel ports, a block split at crankshaft centerline, an intake manifold that replaces the valley cover, and a much lighter weight. Since 1969 this engine has been used exclusively.

Engine Removal

1967-74

Engine R & R is for the engine only, without the transmission attached.

1. Raise the hood, and cover or mask all parts of the car that could be scratched during R & R procedures.
2. Set the parking brake and raise the car. Put stands beneath the underbody front crossmember.
3. Drain the engine cooling system and the engine oil pan.
4. Scribe the hinge outline on the underside of the hood. Remove hood.
5. If the engine is equipped with an exhaust emission control system, remove the crankcase vent filter from the air cleaner. Remove carburetor air cleaner and air inlet duct assembly. Disconnect the battery ground.

6. Remove both engine radiator hoses.
7. Disconnect heater hoses at intake manifold and water pump. Disconnect power brake and power booster line from the intake manifold connection and position it to one side.
8. Disconnect heater vacuum hose from the intake manifold.
9. Disconnect automatic transmission vacuum line at the intake manifold.
10. Remove transmission tube slotted bracket from the right rear exhaust manifold mounting stud.
11. Disconnect battery ground strap at cylinder block.
12. Disconnect primary wires at the coil. Disconnect wires from temperature-sending unit and the fast idle solenoid (air-conditioned cars).
13. Disconnect wire from oil pressure-sending unit. Detach wiring loom from valve rocker arm cover and position it out of the way.
14. Disconnect transmission fluid lines at the radiator. Remove transmission fluid filter from underbody side member (if car is so equipped).
15. Remove fuel hose mounting bracket from radiator. Remove heat shield from fuel pump. Disconnect hoses from fuel pump.
16. On air-conditioned cars, remove fan drive clutch to water pump pulley retaining bolts. Remove fan drive clutch, fan and compressor pulley from the car as a unit.
17. Remove fan blade and spacer assembly from water pump pulley.
18. On vehicles equipped with air conditioning, disconnect the compressor electrical lead and remove the compressor mounting bracket attaching bolts. Remove the compressor from the engine and position it out of the way without disconnecting the refrigerant lines.

Caution If the compressor refrigerant lines do not have enough slack to position the compressor out of the way without disconnecting the refrigerant lines, the air conditioning system will have to be evacuated by a trained air conditioning serviceman. Under no circumstances should an untrained person attempt to disconnect the air conditioning refrigerant lines.

19. Remove the alternator mounting bolts and position the alternator out of the way without disconnecting the wires.
20. Disconnect the transmission and accelerator linkage at the bellcrank. Secure the linkage to the dash panel for engine clearance purposes.
21. Remove access cover from the converter housing. Remove underbody splash shield at lower front of transmission.
22. Remove resonator inlet pipes from the exhaust manifolds.
23. Remove the power steering pump mounting bracket from the engine and position the pump and bracket out of the way.
24. Remove the nuts and washers that hold the engine front support insulators to the underbody side members.
25. Remove the starter attaching bolts. Remove the starter.
26. Detach the oil cooler inlet and outlet transfer line retaining clip from the cylinder block.
27. Remove the flywheel to converter retaining nuts.
28. Remove lower converter housing to cylinder block retaining bolts.
29. Install a transmission support under the transmission.
30. Remove the upper converter housing to cylinder block retaining bolts.
31. Attach engine lifting eyes to the exhaust manifolds.
32. Install lifting sling and attach to chain hoist. With plenty of help, carefully raise and remove engine from car.
33. Install by reversing removal procedure.

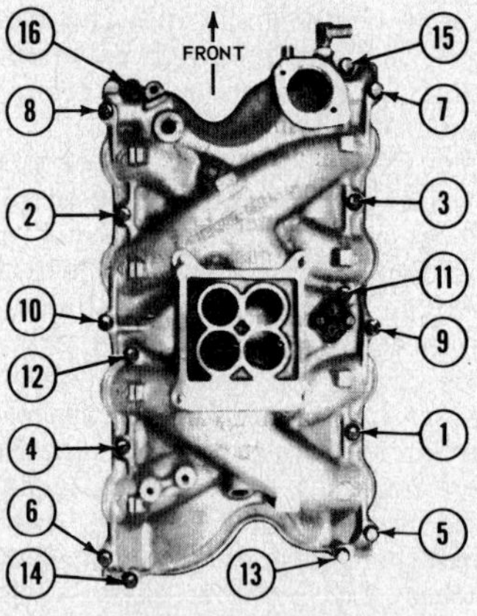
FRONT
16
15
8
7
2
3
11
10
9
12
4
1
6
5
14
13
Intake manifold torque sequence
(© Ford Motor Co)

Intake and Exhaust Manifold(s)

Intake Manifold R & R

1. Drain the cooling system.
2. Disconnect the upper radiator hose from the thermostat housing and the bypass hose from the intake manifold. On 462 V8, disconnect and remove the radiator surge tank from the intake manifold.
3. Remove the air cleaner and ducts from the engine.
4. Disconnect the spark plug wires from the spark plugs and remove the distributor cap and wires from the engine as an assembly. On models equipped with a 460 V8, mark the position of the distributor rotor in relation to the intake manifold, remove the primary wire from the coil and the distributor hold-down bolt, then, remove the distributor from the engine.
5. Remove all vacuum lines from the intake manifold and the wire from the temperature sending unit.
6. Disconnect all fuel and vacuum lines from the carburetor.
7. Remove all carburetor and kick-down linkage that attaches to the intake manifold.
8. Remove the manifold attaching bolts and remove the manifold. If it is necessary to pry the manifold to loosen it from the engine, use care not to damage any gasket sealing surfaces.
9. Clean all gasket surfaces and cement new gaskets firmly in place. The gaskets should be firmly locked in place before attempting to install the manifold.
10. Reverse above procedure to install.

Exhaust Manifold Removal—462 Engines

1. Remove air cleaner and air inlet duct assembly. Block rear wheels and set parking brake. Raise front of car and install safety stands.
2. Disconnect the exhaust manifold/s at the resonator inlet pipe/s.
3. Detach the engine front support insulators from the underbody side members.
4. Place a jack under the front edge of the oil pan. Raise the front of the engine about 2 in. to make clearance for removal of the exhaust manifold/s.

Caution When raising the engine, use care to prevent forcing the engine against the automatic temperature control case (if so equipped) in the engine compartment. Position 2 in. wood blocks between the front support insulators and underbody side members. Remove the jack and let the engine rest on the wood blocks.

5. Unlock and remove the manifold lower retaining bolts. Remove safety stands and lower the car.
6. Remove the two automatic choke tubes from the right exhaust manifold.
7. If the engine is equipped with an exhaust emission control system, remove the air hose/s from the air manifold/s.
8. Unlock and remove the exhaust manifold retaining nuts, manifold/s and gasket/s.
9. Install by reversing the above procedure.

Exhaust Manifold Removal—460 Engine

1. Remove air cleaner and warm air duct assembly to remove right exhaust manifold.
2. Disconnect manifolds at exhaust pipe.
3. Remove retaining bolts and washers, and remove manifolds and lifting brackets.

Valve System

Description

See Ford section.

Preliminary Valve Adjustment

462 V8s

See Ford section, under 352 V8.

1968 460 V8

See Ford section, under 289 V8.

1967-74 460 V8

See Ford section, under 429 V8.

Chilton's TIME SAVER

The following is a method for replacing valve springs, oil seals or spring retainers without removing the cylinder head.

1. **Purchase an air chuck with a spark plug hole adaptor.**
2. **Remove the valve rocker cover. Remove the rocker arm from the valve to be worked on.**
3. **Remove the spark plug from the cylinder to be worked on.**
4. **Turn the crankshaft to bring the piston of this cylinder down, away from possible contact with the valve head. Sharply tap the valve retainer to loosen the valve lock.**
5. **Then turn the crankshaft to bring the piston in this cylinder to the Exact Top of its Compression Stroke.**
6. **Screw the air chuck fitting into the spark plug hole.**
7. **Hook up an air hose to the chuck and turn on the pressure (about 200 lbs.).**
8. **With a strong and constant supply of air holding the valve closed, compress the valve spring and remove the lock and retainer.**
9. **Make the necessary replacements and reassemble.**

NOTE: it is important that the operation be performed exactly as stated, in this order. The piston in the cylinder must be on exact top-center to prevent air pressure from turning the crankshaft.

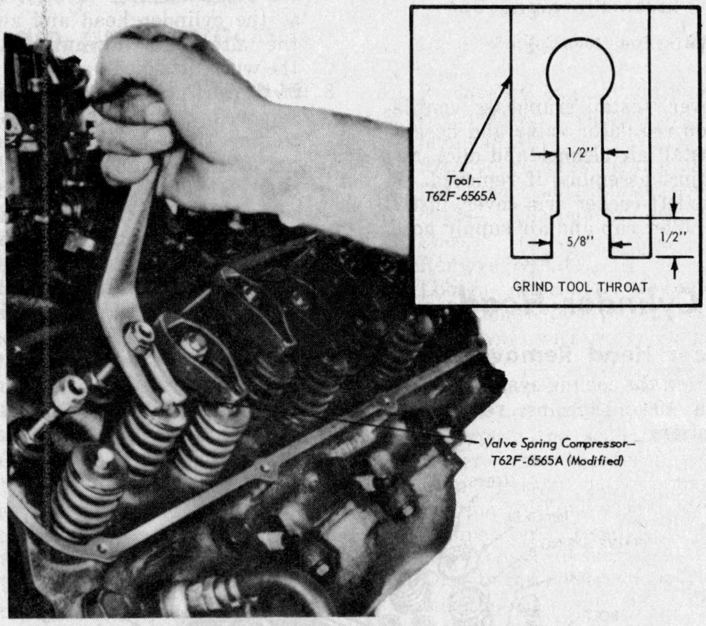
Tool—
T62F-6565A
1/2"
5/8"
1/2"
GRIND TOOL THROAT
Valve Spring Compressor—
T62F-6565A (Modified)
Compressing valve spring (© Ford Motor Co)

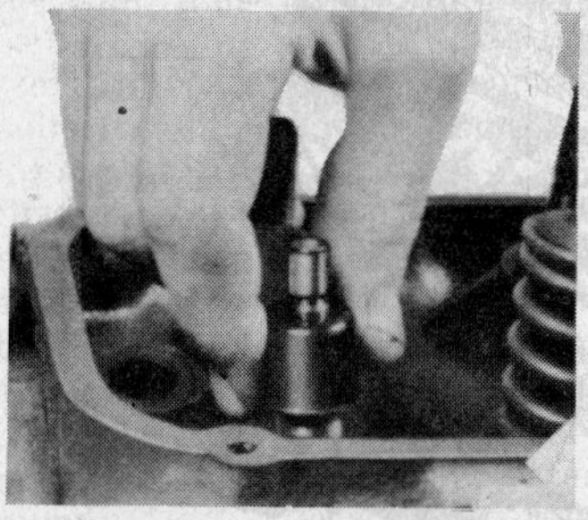
Replacing valve stem seal (© Ford Motor Co)

Valve Guides

Lincolns use integral valve guides. Lincoln dealers offer valves with oversize stems for worn guides. To fit these, enlarge valve guide bores with valve guide reamers to an oversize that cleans up wear. If a large oversize is required, it is best to approach that size through stages by using a series of reamers of increasing diameters. This helps to maintain the concentricity of the guide bore with the valve seat. The correct valve guide to stem clearance is in front of this section. As an alternative, some local automotive machine shops will fit replacement guides that use standard stem valves.

Rocker Assembly Removal—462 Engines

1. Raise the hood and remove the carburetor air cleaner. Disconnect the ignition wires where they cross over the rocker cover. Remove the rocker cover and carefully scrape off its gasket.
2. Now, working a little at a time, loosen the bolts that hold the rocker brackets to the cylinder head so that the tension of the valve springs will be left off, a little at a time. Once the tension is released, remove the screws and lift the rocker assemblies up off the cylinder head.
3. If the rockers are to be disassembled, they should be laid out carefully on a bench, disassembled and marked so that they can be reassembled in the same position as before. Rocker assemblies are installed in reverse order of removal, following procedure under Preliminary Valve Adjustment.

1968-74—460 Engine Rocker Assemblies

These rocker arms are of the pedestal-mounted-type and are removable, one at a time.

Removal

1. If removing a rocker arm assembly from the right cylinder head, partially drain the cooling system and disconnect heater water tubes at the water pump and intake manifold. Remove tube assembly retaining bolts and move tube assembly out of the way. Remove crankcase ventilation regulator valve and hose from valve rocker arm cover. Remove air cleaner and duct assembly. If removing an arm assembly from the left side, take off oil filler cap and air supply hose from valve rocker cover.
2. Disconnect plug wires at spark plugs. Twist, then pull, on molded

mounting gasket and install the gasket on the oil pump.

5. Insert the intermediate shaft into the distributor shaft hex bore. Make sure that the intermediate shaft is properly seated. Do not attempt to force the pump into position if it does not seat readily, as the intermediate shaft hex may be misaligned with the distributor shaft. To align, rotate the intermediate shaft until it can be seated. Secure the oil pump to the cylinder block and torque the screws to 20–25 ft lbs. As you secure the oil pump, make certain that the gasket is properly installed; leakage resulting from improper gasket installation could cause loss of oil pressure and subsequent engine damage.
6. Install the oil pan and its related parts.

Rear Main Bearing Oil Seal

1967-69

The rear main oil seal originally installed in these engines is a rope (or fabric) type seal. All service replacements, however, are of the rubber type. To remove the rope type seal and install the rubber type, the following method is used:

1. Drain the crankcase and remove the oil pan.
2. Remove the lower half of the rear main bearing cap and, after removing the old seal from the cap, drive out the pin in the bottom of the seal groove with a punch.
3. Loosen all main bearing caps, and allow the crankshaft to lower slightly. This lowering should not exceed 1/32 in.
4. Using a 6 in. length of 3/16 in. brazing rod, drive up on either exposed end of the top half of the oil seal. When the opposite end of the seal begins to protrude, grasp it with a pair of pliers and pull while continuing to tap the driven end.
5. After removing both halves of the rope seal and the retaining pin from the lower half of the bearing cap, install the new rubber seal by following steps 4-10 of the procedure for 1970-74 engines.

Rear Crankshaft Oil Seal R & R

1970-74

1. Remove the oil pan, and, if required, the oil pump.
2. Loosen all main bearing caps allowing the crankshaft to lower slightly.

NOTE: the crankshaft should not be allowed to drop more than 1/32 in.

3. Remove the rear main bearing cap and remove the seal from the cap and block.
4. Carefully clean the seal grooves in the cap and block with solvent.
5. Soak the new seal halves in clean engine oil.
6. Install the upper half of the seal in the block with the undercut side of the seal toward the front of the engine. Slide the seal around the crankshaft journal until ⅜ in. protrudes beyond the base of the block.
7. Repeat above procedure on lower seal, allowing an equal length of the seal to protrude beyond the opposite end of the bearing cap.
8. Install rear bearing cap and torque all main bearings to specifications. Apply sealer only to the rear of the seals.
9. Dip the bearing cap side seals in oil, then immediately install them. Do not use any sealer on the side seals. Tap the seals into place and do not clip the protruding ends.
10. Install the oil pump and pan. Fill the crankcase with oil, start engine, check for leaks.

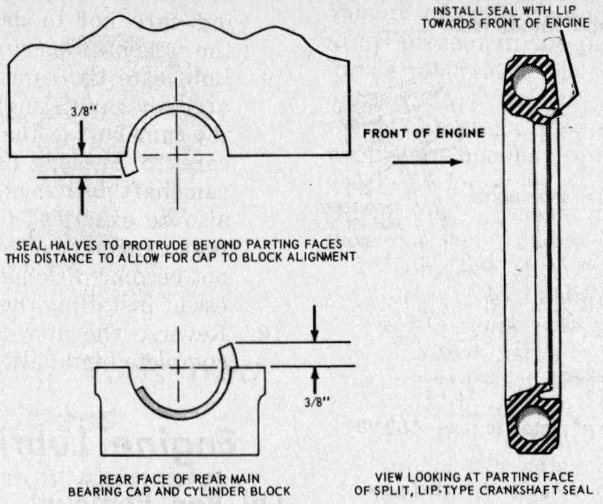
INSTALL SEAL WITH LIP TOWARDS FRONT OF ENGINE
3/8"
FRONT OF ENGINE
SEAL HALVES TO PROTRUDE BEYOND PARTING FACES THIS DISTANCE TO ALLOW FOR CAP TO BLOCK ALIGNMENT
3/8"
REAR FACE OF REAR MAIN BEARING CAP AND CYLINDER BLOCK
VIEW LOOKING AT PARTING FACE OF SPLIT, LIP-TYPE CRANKSHAFT SEAL

1970-71 rear main seal installation (© Ford Motor Co)

AUTOMATIC TRANSMISSION

All 1967-74 Lincolns and Continentals use a Ford C6 automatic transmission. This heavy-duty three-speed unit is capable of providing automatic upshifts and downshifts through the three forward gear ratios, in addition to offering manual selection of first and second gears.

Only one band—the intermediate band—is used in this transmission. This band, along with the forward clutch, is used to obtain the intermediate gear. The adjustment of this band is the only adjustment required for the C6 transmission.

Prior to 1973, Lincoln automatic transmissions featured a single-diaphragm transmission modulator valve. 1973-74 cars (because of the inclusion of the exhaust gas recirculation system within the emission controls) are equipped with a dual-diaphragm transmission modulator valve.

Neutral Safety and Back-Up Light Switch Adjustment

1967

1. With manual linkage properly adjusted, try to engage starter in each position on quadrant. Starter should engage only in park and neutral positions.
2. To adjust loosen screws that locate switch on steering column.

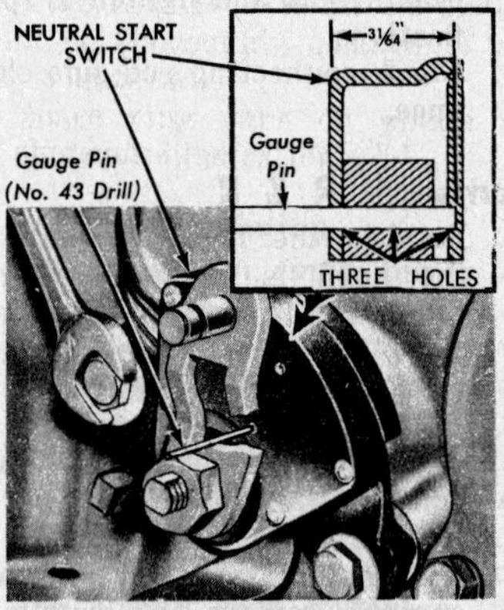
NEUTRAL START SWITCH
Gauge Pin (No. 43 Drill)
Gauge Pin
THREE HOLES

Neutral start switch—1967 (© Ford Motor Co)

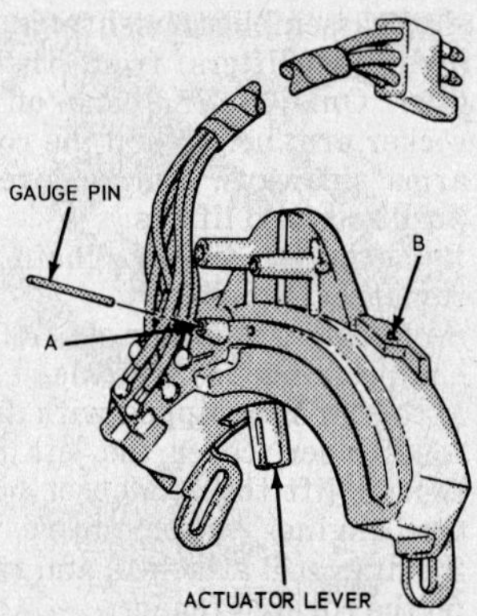
GAUGE PIN
A
B
ACTUATOR LEVER

Neutral start switch—1968-74 (© Ford Motor Co)

Exhaust Manifold Removal—460 Engine

1. Remove air cleaner and warm air duct assembly to remove right exhaust manifold.
2. Disconnect manifolds at exhaust pipe.
3. Remove retaining bolts and washers, and remove manifolds and lifting brackets.

Valve System

Description

See Ford section.

Preliminary Valve Adjustment

462 V8s

See Ford section, under 352 V8.

1968 460 V8

See Ford section, under 289 V8.

1967-74 460 V8

See Ford section, under 429 V8.

Chilton's TIME SAVER

The following is a method for replacing valve springs, oil seals or spring retainers without removing the cylinder head.

1. **Purchase an air chuck with a spark plug hole adaptor.**
2. **Remove the valve rocker cover. Remove the rocker arm from the valve to be worked on.**
3. **Remove the spark plug from the cylinder to be worked on.**
4. **Turn the crankshaft to bring the piston of this cylinder down, away from possible contact with the valve head. Sharply tap the valve retainer to loosen the valve lock.**
5. **Then turn the crankshaft to bring the piston in this cylinder to the Exact Top of its Compression Stroke.**
6. **Screw the air chuck fitting into the spark plug hole.**
7. **Hook up an air hose to the chuck and turn on the pressure (about 200 lbs.).**
8. **With a strong and constant supply of air holding the valve closed, compress the valve spring and remove the lock and retainer.**
9. **Make the necessary replacements and reassemble.**

NOTE: it is important that the operation be performed exactly as stated, in this order. The piston in the cylinder must be on exact top-center to prevent air pressure from turning the crankshaft.

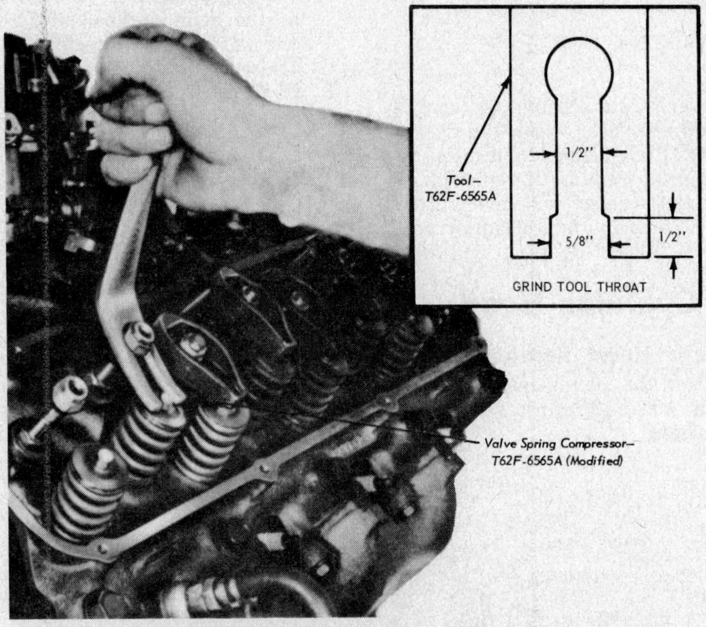
Tool—
T62F-6565A
1/2"
5/8"
1/2"
GRIND TOOL THROAT
Valve Spring Compressor—
T62F-6565A (Modified)

Compressing valve spring (© Ford Motor Co)

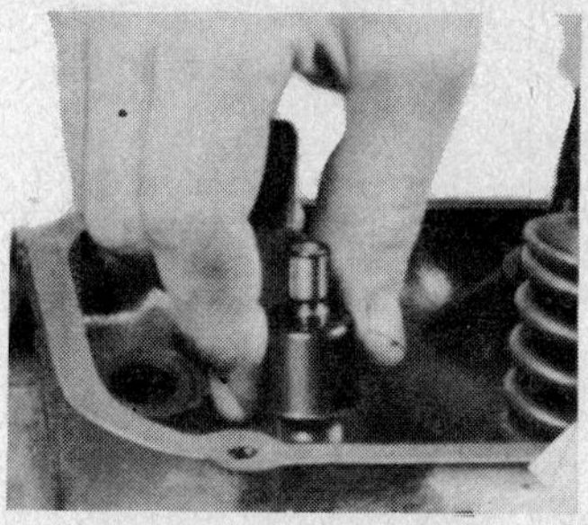

Replacing valve stem seal (© Ford Motor Co)

Valve Guides

Lincolns use integral valve guides. Lincoln dealers offer valves with oversize stems for worn guides. To fit these, enlarge valve guide bores with valve guide reamers to an oversize that cleans up wear. If a large oversize is required, it is best to approach that size through stages by using a series of reamers of increasing diameters. This helps to maintain the concentricity of the guide bore with the valve seat. The correct valve guide to stem clearance is in front of this section. As an alternative, some local automotive machine shops will fit replacement guides that use standard stem valves.

Rocker Assembly Removal—462 Engines

1. Raise the hood and remove the carburetor air cleaner. Disconnect the ignition wires where they cross over the rocker cover. Remove the rocker cover and carefully scrape off its gasket.
2. Now, working a little at a time, loosen the bolts that hold the rocker brackets to the cylinder head so that the tension of the valve springs will be left off, a little at a time. Once the tension is released, remove the screws and lift the rocker assemblies up off the cylinder head.
3. If the rockers are to be disassembled, they should be laid out carefully on a bench, disassembled and marked so that they can be reassembled in the same position as before. Rocker assemblies are installed in reverse order of removal, following procedure under Preliminary Valve Adjustment.

1968-74—460 Engine Rocker Assemblies

These rocker arms are of the pedestal-mounted-type and are removable, one at a time.

Removal

1. If removing a rocker arm assembly from the right cylinder head, partially drain the cooling system and disconnect heater water tubes at the water pump and intake manifold. Remove tube assembly retaining bolts and move tube assembly out of the way. Remove crankcase ventilation regulator valve and hose from valve rocker arm cover. Remove air cleaner and duct assembly. If removing an arm assembly from the left side, take off oil filler cap and air supply hose from valve rocker cover.
2. Disconnect plug wires at spark plugs. Twist, then pull, on molded

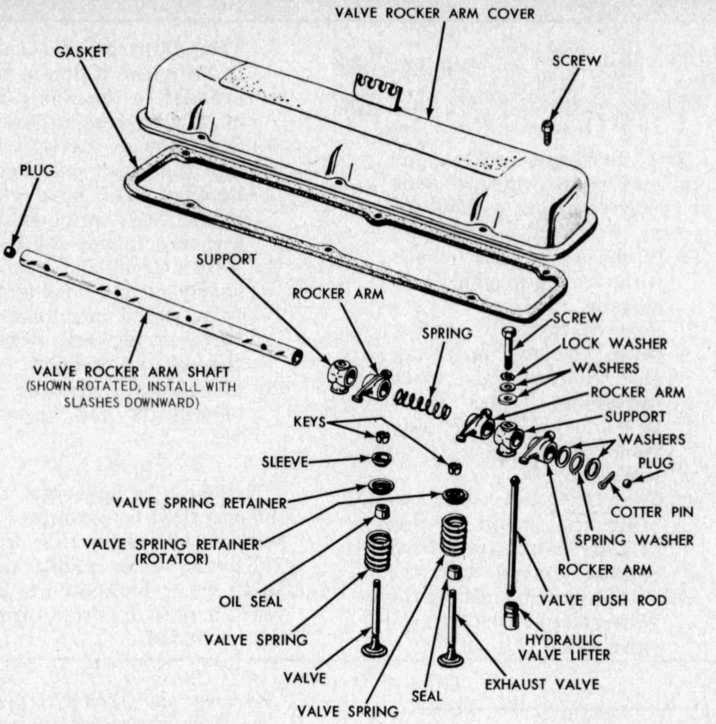
VALVE ROCKER ARM COVER
GASKET
SCREW
PLUG
SUPPORT
ROCKER ARM
SCREW
SPRING
LOCK WASHER
WASHERS
ROCKER ARM
VALVE ROCKER ARM SHAFT
(SHOWN ROTATED, INSTALL WITH
SLASHES DOWNWARD)
SUPPORT
KEYS
WASHERS
SLEEVE
PLUG
VALVE SPRING RETAINER
COTTER PIN
VALVE SPRING RETAINER
(ROTATOR)
SPRING WASHER
ROCKER ARM
OIL SEAL
VALVE PUSH ROD
VALVE SPRING
HYDRAULIC
VALVE LIFTER
VALVE
EXHAUST VALVE
SEAL
VALVE SPRING

Rocker shaft and valve components—462 V8 (© Ford Motor Co)

cap of wire only. Do not pull the wire. Remove wires from bracket on the valve rocker arm covers and pull wires out of the way.

3. Remove rocker arm covers.
4. Remove rocker arm stud nut, fulcrum seat, and rocker arm.

NOTE: rocker arm studs that are broken, or have bad threads, should be replaced.

If the stud is broken, flush with the head, drill and use an easy-out.

When installing the new stud, lubricate the threads, then torque to 65-75 ft. lbs.

Installation

1. Apply lubriplate to top of valve stem.
2. Lubriplate fulcrum seat and socket. Install rocker arm, fulcrum seat and stud nut. Perform preliminary valve adjustment.
3. Adjust valve clearance according to recommendations.
4. Clean rocker arm covers and cylinder head gasket surfaces.
5. Apply oil-resistant sealer to one side of new cover gaskets. Apply cemented side of gaskets in rim of covers.
6. Position covers on cylinder heads. Install and torque cover bolts to 2½-4 ft. lbs. Two minutes later, retorque attaching bolts to same specifications.
7. Route spark plug wires in brackets on valve rocker covers. Reconnect plug wires.
8. Install heater tube assembly, if disconnected, and fill cooling system.
9. On the right valve rocker arm cover, install crankcase ventilation regulator valve and hose.
10. Install air cleaner and duct, and adjust assembly, if removed. On the left rocker arm cover, install oil filler cap and air supply hose.

Cylinder Head

Cylinder Head Removal

1. Drain the cooling system.
2. On 1967 Lincolns, remove the battery.
3. If the right side cylinder head is to be removed from a 462 engine, remove the horns and mounting brackets and support the transmission filler tube support brace.
4. On vehicles equipped with a 462 V8, disconnect the spark plug wires from the spark plugs, and remove distributor cap and wires from the engine as an assembly. Mark the position of the distributor rotor in relation to the intake manifold, disconnect the distributor primary wire from the coil, remove the distributor hold-down bolt and remove the distributor from the engine.
5. Remove the intake manifold from the engine, following the procedure outlined under Intake Manifold R&R.
6. On 462 engines, remove the pushrod chamber cover from the engine.
7. If the right cylinder head is to be removed, disconnect the negative battery cable, loosen the alternator mounting bolts, remove the bolt attaching the alternator to the cylinder head and swing the alternator downward with the wires attached.
8. If the left cylinder head is to be removed, remove the air conditioning compressor and mounting bracket from the head and position them out of the way without disconnecting the refrigerant lines. Remove the power steering pump and mounting bracket from the head and position them out of the way without disconnecting the lines.
9. Remove the valve covers. On 462 engine remove the rocker arm assemblies from the engine. On 460 engine, loosen each rocker

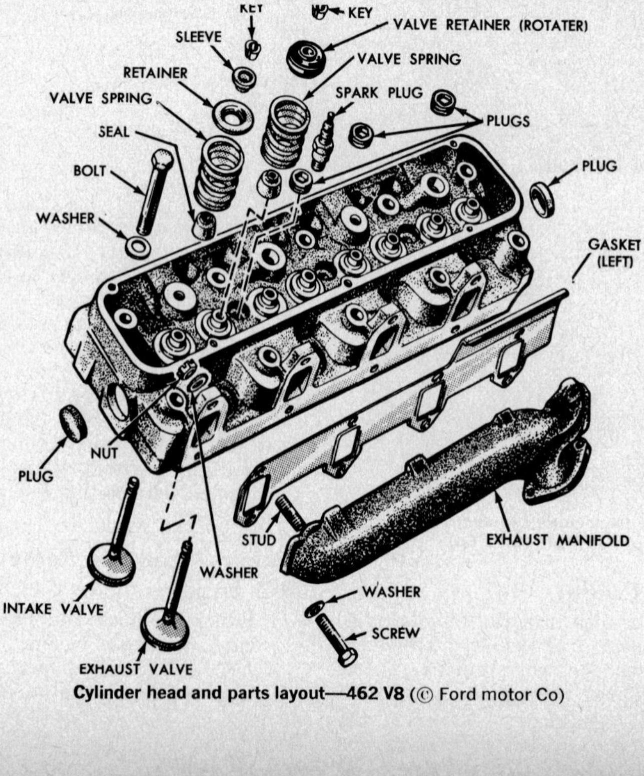
KEY
KEY
VALVE RETAINER (ROTATER)
SLEEVE
VALVE SPRING
RETAINER
SPARK PLUG
VALVE SPRING
PLUGS
SEAL
BOLT
PLUG
WASHER
GASKET
(LEFT)
NUT
PLUG
STUD
EXHAUST MANIFOLD
WASHER
WASHER
INTAKE VALVE
SCREW
EXHAUST VALVE

Cylinder head and parts layout—462 V8 (© Ford motor Co)

arm and turn them to the side.

10. Remove the pushrods from the engine and keep them in order so they can be returned to their original locations in the engine.
11. Remove the exhaust manifold to resonator inlet pipe attaching bolts.
12. Remove the cylinder head attaching bolts and remove the head(s) from the engine.
13. Reverse above procedure to install, tightening the head bolts to specification in three steps and performing a preliminary valve adjustment before starting engine.

9
5
1
3
7
10
8
6
2
4

Cylinder head torque sequence
(© Ford Motor Co)

Timing Case Cover, Chain and Sprockets

Timing Case Cover Removal

462 Engines

1. Drain entire engine cooling system. Remove the hood.
2. Disconnect all radiator hoses and the overflow pipe from the coolant supply tank.
3. Remove the bolt securing the supply tank brace, engine ground strap and battery ground cable to the water pump. Remove supply tank thermostat and gasket. Loosen coolant by-pass hose at water pump.
4. On a car equipped with air-conditioning, loosen the compressor support bracket bolts. Remove the drive belt, then, remove the fan drive clutch and fan assembly and the compressor drive pulley as a unit.
5. Loosen the alternator, remove the fan and alternator drive belts. Remove the fan blade assembly, spacer and mounting bolts from the water pump pulley as a unit.
6. Disconnect the dipstick tube bracket at the water pump. Remove the steering pump reservoir bracket from the water pump and loosen the remaining bracket mounting bolts to allow clearance for removal of the water pump.
7. Remove the water pump. Remove the crankshaft damper attaching bolt. Remove the damper.
8. Disconnect power steering lines at the pump and plug the lines. Remove bolts holding the power steering reservoir to the front cover.
9. Remove the crankshaft damper key and remove the power steering pump.
10. Remove the shield from the fuel pump, fuel lines from the pump; remove the pump. Remove the cup-type plug from the top of the cylinder front cover by using a long punch. Remove the fuel pump pushrod.
11. Remove the oil pan.
12. If timing chain is to be replaced, perform Steps 16-18 under 460.

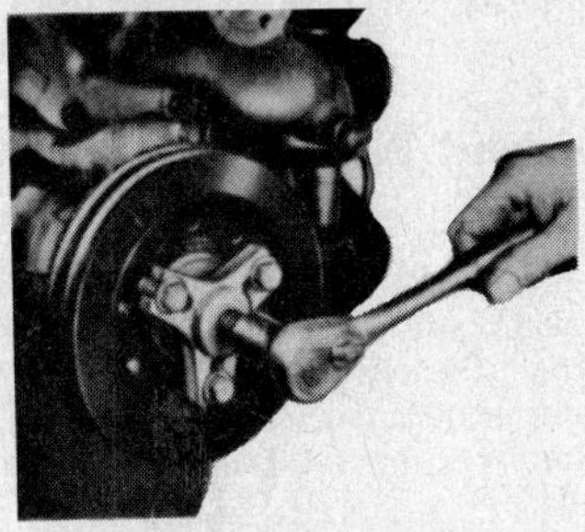

Removing crankshaft vibration damper
(© Ford Motor Co)

460 Engine Removal

1. Drain cooling system and crankcase.
2. Remove oil pan and oil pump.
3. Remove fan blades from water pump shaft.
4. Remove radiator (fan) shroud.
5. Disconnect all radiator hoses at engine. Disconnect oil cooler lines.
6. Remove radiator.
7. Loosen alternator. Loosen air conditioner idler pulley. Remove drive belts with water pump pulley.
8. Remove air conditioner compressor (do not open compressor lines to expose the sealed air-conditioner system to atmosphere).
9. Remove crankshaft pulley attaching bolt and washer. Remove damper and remove Woodruff key from crankshaft.
10. Disconnect power steering pressure line at pump. Drain fluid.
11. Remove steering pump.
12. Loosen by-pass hose at water pump. Disconnect heater hose at pump.
13. Disconnect and plug fuel inlet line at fuel pump. Disconnect fuel line at carburetor fuel pump. Remove fuel pump.
14. Remove front cover-to-block attaching bolts. Remove front cover and water pump as an assembly. Discard gasket.
15. If a new front cover is to be installed, change the water pump at this time.
16. Check timing chain deflection, at this time, by rotating crankshaft in a clockwise direction enough to take up the slack on the right hand side of the chain (as facing the open chain). Establish a reference mark on the block and measure from this point to the left side of the chain. This measurement when deflected should not exceed ½ in. If deflection is more than ½ in., replace chain and both sprockets.
17. If chain and sprockets are being removed, crank the engine until timing marks on the sprockets are at their closest related points and on a center line with both crankshaft and camshaft centers.
18. Remove camshaft sprocket capscrew, washer, and fuel pump eccentric. Slide off timing chain, sprockets and chain as an assembly.

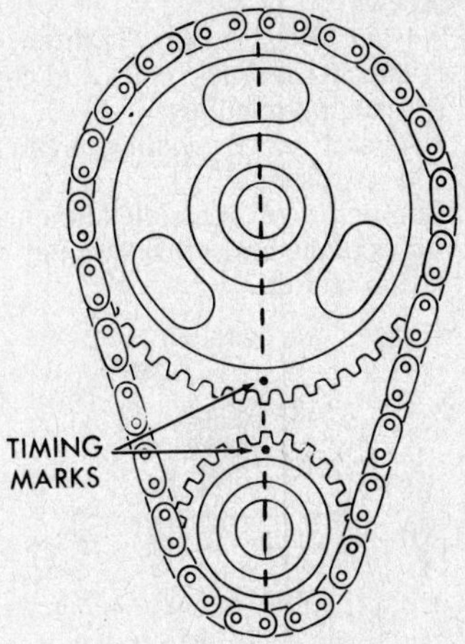
TIMING
MARKS

Valve timing alignment marks

460 Engine Installation

1. Install chain and sprockets as an assembly with sprocket timing marks directly toward each other and on a centerline with the crankshaft and camshaft.
2. Install fuel pump eccentric, washer, and attaching cap screw. Torque camshaft sprocket attaching screw to 40-45 ft. lbs. Lubricate chain and sprockets with engine oil.
3. After cleaning mating surfaces, coat the areas with oil-resistant sealer and position gasket on cylinder block.
4. Position cover over crankshaft and slide cover on against cylinder block. Coat cover retaining screws with oil-resistant sealer and install screws. Torque attaching screws to 10-13 ft. lbs.
5. Apply lubriplate to oil seal rubbing surface of steering pump inner hub. Apply mixture of white lead and oil to crankshaft stub in preparing damper installation. Install power steering pump.
6. Install crankshaft damper Woodruff key and press on crankshaft damper. Do not hammer damper into place. Install damper retainer screw and washer. Torque to 75-90 ft. lbs.
7. Coat new fuel pump gasket with oil-resistant sealer and place on

fuel pump. Install fuel pump. Connect fuel lines to fuel pump.
8. Install oil pump and oil pan.
9. Install air-conditioner compressor and water pump.
10. Install water pump pulley and all drive belts.
11. Position radiator to lower support, position upper support to radiator retaining bolts. Connect air coolant hoses. Connect oil cooler lines.
12. Place fan assembly inside radiator shroud and set in position on water pump hub. Install shroud to radiator screws and tighten. Insert and tighten fan attaching screws.
13. Adjust belt tension. Tighten alternator retaining bolts and compressor idler pulley.
14 Fill and bleed cooling system. Fill crankcase.
15. Run engine at fast idle and check for coolant and oil leaks. Set ignition timing.

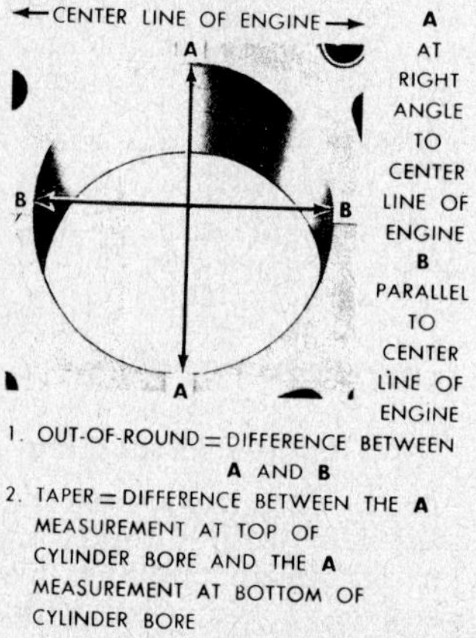
← CENTER LINE OF ENGINE →
A
B
B
A
A AT RIGHT ANGLE TO CENTER LINE OF ENGINE
B PARALLEL TO CENTER LINE OF ENGINE
1. OUT-OF-ROUND = DIFFERENCE BETWEEN A AND B
2. TAPER = DIFFERENCE BETWEEN THE A MEASUREMENT AT TOP OF CYLINDER BORE AND THE A MEASUREMENT AT BOTTOM OF CYLINDER BORE

Cylinder bore out of roundness and taper
(© Ford Motor Co)

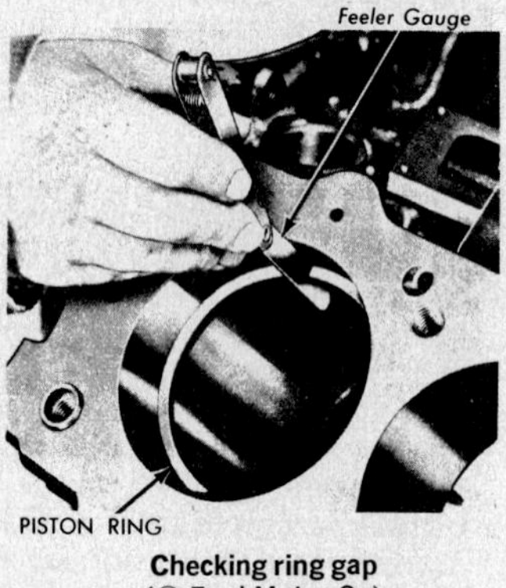
Feeler Gauge
PISTON RING

Checking ring gap
(© Ford Motor Co)

Checking ring side clearance
(© Ford Motor Co)

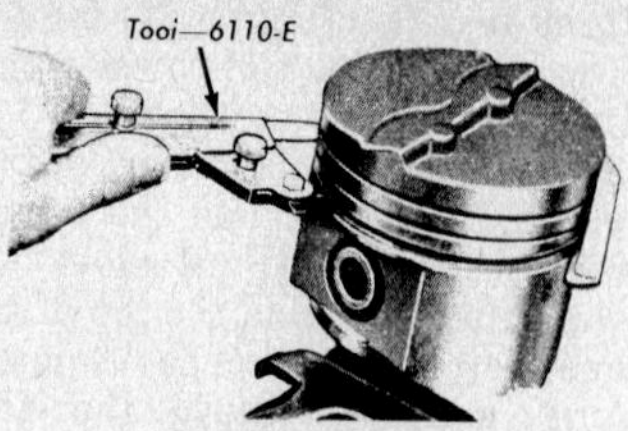
Tool—6110-E

Cleaning ring grooves
(© Ford Motor Co)

Connecting Rods and Pistons

Rod and Piston Assembly

Removal

On all Lincoln Continental and Mark III and IV models, the rod and piston assemblies are removed through the top of the block.

Remove the oil pan and cylinder heads.

Start with any pistons that are down and remove the ring ridge from the top of the cylinder wall with a ring ridge reamer or a bearing scraper.

From underneath the car, take off the lower half of the connecting rod on those rods from which the cylinder ridge has been removed. Carefully mark the cap so that it can be replaced in the same position on the same rod, or install the cap on the rod immediately.

Push the upper half of the rod and piston assembly up out of the top of the block.

Repeat on the rest of the cylinders and piston assemblies.

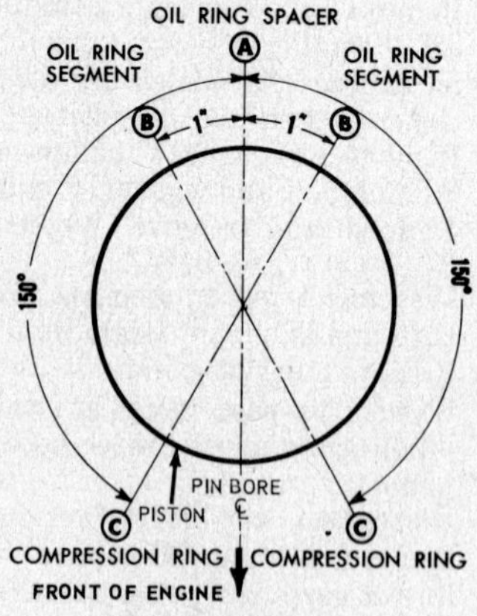
OIL RING SPACER
A
OIL RING SEGMENT
OIL RING SEGMENT
B
B
1°
1°
150°
150°
PIN BORE
℄
PISTON
C
C
COMPRESSION RING
COMPRESSION RING
FRONT OF ENGINE

Spacing piston rings
(© Ford Motor Co)

Piston Rings

Replacement

Each piston is fitted with 3 piston rings: an upper and lower compression ring which seals the combustion chamber of the engine so that the expanding gases of the power stroke do not escape, and an oil control ring which prevents cylinder wall lubricating oil from entering the combustion chamber. Due to the great amount of pressure and high temperature present in the piston area during combustion, piston ring clearances are very critical. Before replacing piston rings, piston and cylinder wall dimensions must first be checked; for even new piston rings cannot seal a piston or cylinder wall that is worn beyond specifications.

1. Using an internal micrometer, measure cylinder wall taper and out-of-roundness.
2. Measure piston outside diameter and subtract this measurement from the cylinder bore diameter obtained in above step. The result of this subtraction will give piston to wall clearance which also must be within specification.
3. If the cylinder wall and piston measurements are within specifications, and new rings are to be installed, hone the cylinder to the proper finish.
4. Position each ring in the cylinder bore it is to be used in and square it with the cylinder wall by gently pushing it downward with an inverted piston.
5. Using a feeler gauge of correct thickness, measure the ring end gap. If it exceeds specifications, try another ring, if it is less than specifications file the end of the ring to correct.
6. Install the rings on the pistons and measure piston ring to piston side clearance.

NOTE: before installing piston rings, the ring grooves on the piston should be thoroughly cleaned of all foreign material.

7. Space ring gaps on piston as shown in illustration.

Installation

1. Coat the piston, rings, and cylinder wall with light engine oil.
2. With bearing caps removed, install pieces of protective rubber hose on each bearing cap bolt to prevent them from scoring any internal engine parts during installation.
3. Using a piston ring compressor tool, install each piston in the bore it was removed from.

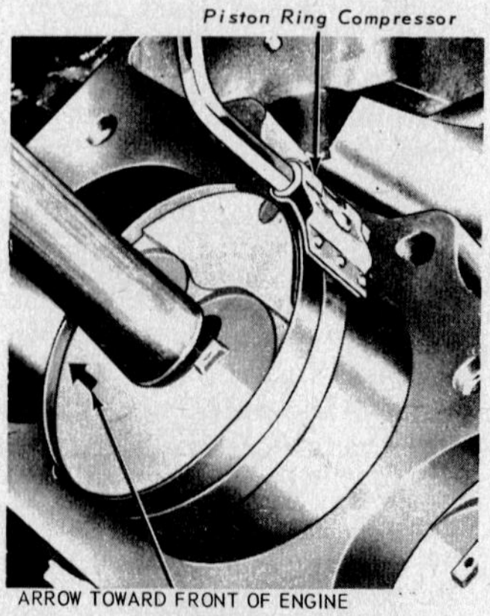
Piston Ring Compressor
ARROW TOWARD FRONT OF ENGINE

Piston installation
(© Ford Motor Co)

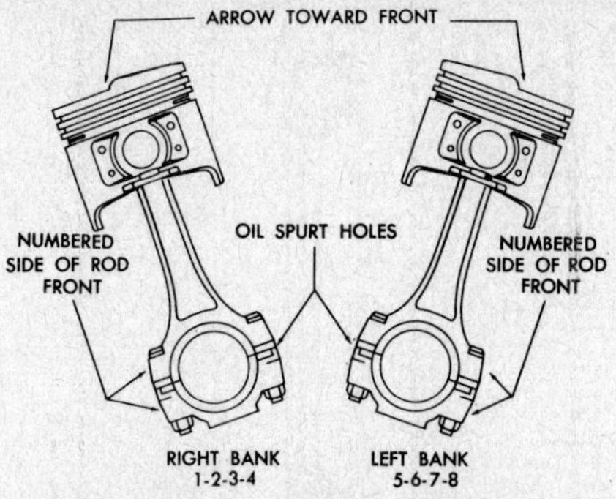
ARROW TOWARD FRONT
NUMBERED SIDE OF ROD FRONT
OIL SPURT HOLES
NUMBERED SIDE OF ROD FRONT
RIGHT BANK 1-2-3-4
LEFT BANK 5-6-7-8

Correct relation of piston to rod—462 V8

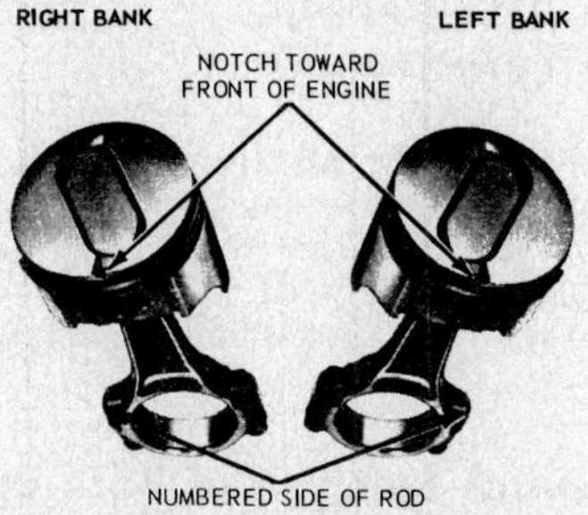
RIGHT BANK
LEFT BANK
NOTCH TOWARD FRONT OF ENGINE
NUMBERED SIDE OF ROD

Correct piston and rod positions for 460 engines
(© Ford Motor Co)

4. Remove the thread guards from the connecting rods, position the upper bearing insert on the rod, and carefully guide the rod onto the crankshaft journal.
5. Install the lower half of the bearing cap and tighten to specifications.
6. Check connecting rod side clearance.

Camshaft R & R

1. Remove the hood assembly. If the hood is properly aligned, index the hinges to the hood prior to removing the hood, in order to simplify installation.
2. Remove the intake manifold, referring to the procedure under "Intake Manifold R&R."
3. On 462 V8 engines, remove the push rod chamber covers. On all engines, remove the distributor and the valve covers.
4. Remove the valve rocker arm shaft assemblies, push rods, and hydraulic lifters from the engine. On 460 V8, back off the rocker arm bolts, turn the rocker arms sideways, and remove the push rods and lifters.
5. Remove the timing chain and camshaft sprocket.
6. Remove the radiator. In 460 V8 engines, remove the grille.
7. If the car is equipped with an air conditioner, cover the left front fender, lift the condenser out of the engine compartment with the lines still attached, and rest it on the covered fender.
8. Remove the camshaft from the front of the cylinder block, taking care not to damage any of the camshaft bearing surfaces.
9. Lubricate the camshaft journals and lobes with engine oil. Install the camshaft in the engine, using care to prevent damage to the camshaft bearings. Care should also be exercised to see that the rear camshaft bearing plug does not become dislodged in the process of installing the camshaft.
10. Reverse the above procedure to complete installation.

Engine Lubrication

Oil Pan Removal

462 Engines

1. Position No. 1 piston to 15° B.T.D.C. Remove the oil dipstick.
2. Disconnect the fan shroud and place it over the fan.
3. Set the parking brake, then raise the car. The car must be supported in a manner that will not interfere with the lowering of the pan.
4. Drain crankcase.
5. Remove generator splash shield. Disconnect engine lateral restrictor.
6. To provide clearance, remove engine front support insulator to underbody side member retaining nuts. With a block of wood on a floor jack under the front edge of the oil pan, raise the engine about an inch. Insert a ½ in. block of wood between the insulators and the underbody side members. Remove the floor jack.
7. Remove the end attachments of the front stabilizer bar and rotate the ends of the bar downward to position the center of the bar up away from the oil pan.
8. Remove oil pan attaching bolts. Free the oil pan from the cylinder block. Remove the two bolts that hold the oil pump pick-up tube and screen assembly to the oil pump, and allow the tube and screen to drop into the oil pan. Remove the oil pan.
9. Install the oil pan by reversing the removal procedure.

1968-69 460 Engine

1. Disconnect radiator shroud.
2. Raise car on a hoist and drain crankcase.
3. Disconnect idler arm from underbody.
4. Loosen starter mounting bolts.
5. Remove cylinder block to converter housing bolts.
6. Disconnect engine front support insulators from underbody crossmember. Place floor jack under front of oil pan (block of wood between jack and oil pan). Raise engine just enough to insert 1 in. wood blocks between insulators and underbody side members. Remove floor jack.
7. Remove end attachments of front stabilizer bar and rotate ends of bar down to raise center of bar. Remove oil filter.
8. Remove oil pan mounting bolts and lower oil pan to underbody crossmember. Remove splash shield from right side of oil pan.
9. Disconnect pressure line at power steering pump. Remove bolts holding the pump to cylinder front cover and rotate pump to clear the oil pan. Remove the oil pan.
10. Install oil pan in reverse order of removal and torque attaching bolts to 6-9 ft. lbs. Torque oil pump-to-cylinder block bolts to 20-25 ft. lbs.

1970-74 460 Engine

1. Disconnect the negative battery cable.
2. Disconnect the fan shroud from the radiator and position it rearward over the fan.
3. Drain the crankcase and remove the oil filter.
4. On Mark III and Mark IV models, disconnect the oil cooler lines from the radiator. Remove the bolt that attaches the oil cooler line bracket to the cylinder block.
5. Remove the end attachments of the front stabilizer bar and rotate the ends downward.
6. Remove the starter attaching bolts.
7. Remove the motor mount to chassis attaching bolts and raise the engine several inches.
8. Place blocks of wood between the motor mounts and the chassis.
9. Remove the converter housing to engine block support bracket bolts and remove the brackets.
10. Remove the oil pan attaching bolts and remove the pan from the engine. On Mark III models, it will be necessary to move the oil cooler lines out of position to remove the pan.
11. Clean all gasket mounting surfaces and reverse above procedure to install.

Oil Pump R & R

1. Remove the oil pan, referring to the procedure for "Oil Pan R&R."
2. Remove the oil pump mounting bolts and remove the pump from the cylinder block.
3. Prime the oil pump by filling either the inlet or outlet port with clean engine oil. Rotate the pump shaft so that the oil is evenly distributed within the pump body.
4. Install the distributor intermediate shaft within the oil pump rotor shaft. Apply oil-resistant sealer to the new oil pump

mounting gasket and install the gasket on the oil pump.

5. Insert the intermediate shaft into the distributor shaft hex bore. Make sure that the intermediate shaft is properly seated. Do not attempt to force the pump into position if it does not seat readily, as the intermediate shaft hex may be misaligned with the distributor shaft. To align, rotate the intermediate shaft until it can be seated. Secure the oil pump to the cylinder block and torque the screws to 20–25 ft lbs. As you secure the oil pump, make certain that the gasket is properly installed; leakage resulting from improper gasket installation could cause loss of oil pressure and subsequent engine damage.
6. Install the oil pan and its related parts.

Rear Main Bearing Oil Seal

1967-69

The rear main oil seal originally installed in these engines is a rope (or fabric) type seal. All service replacements, however, are of the rubber type. To remove the rope type seal and install the rubber type, the following method is used:

1. Drain the crankcase and remove the oil pan.
2. Remove the lower half of the rear main bearing cap and, after removing the old seal from the cap, drive out the pin in the bottom of the seal groove with a punch.
3. Loosen all main bearing caps, and allow the crankshaft to lower slightly. This lowering should not exceed 1/32 in.
4. Using a 6 in. length of 3/16 in. brazing rod, drive up on either exposed end of the top half of the oil seal. When the opposite end of the seal begins to protrude, grasp it with a pair of pliers and pull while continuing to tap the driven end.
5. After removing both halves of the rope seal and the retaining pin from the lower half of the bearing cap, install the new rubber seal by following steps 4-10 of the procedure for 1970-74 engines.

Rear Crankshaft Oil Seal R & R

1970-74

1. Remove the oil pan, and, if required, the oil pump.
2. Loosen all main bearing caps allowing the crankshaft to lower slightly.

NOTE: the crankshaft should not be allowed to drop more than 1/32 in.

3. Remove the rear main bearing

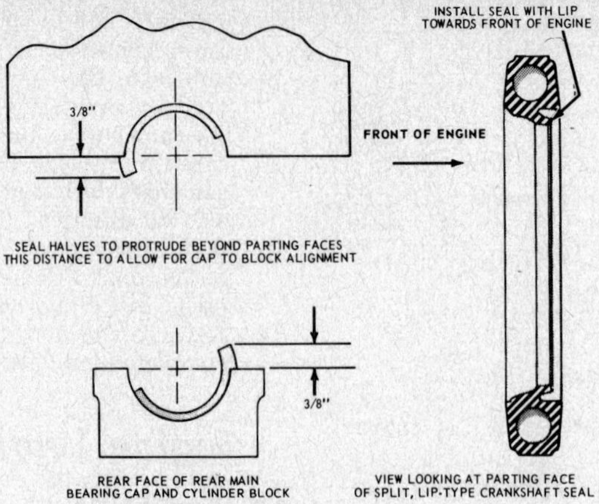
INSTALL SEAL WITH LIP TOWARDS FRONT OF ENGINE
3/8"
FRONT OF ENGINE
SEAL HALVES TO PROTRUDE BEYOND PARTING FACES THIS DISTANCE TO ALLOW FOR CAP TO BLOCK ALIGNMENT
3/8"
REAR FACE OF REAR MAIN BEARING CAP AND CYLINDER BLOCK
VIEW LOOKING AT PARTING FACE OF SPLIT, LIP-TYPE CRANKSHAFT SEAL

1970-71 rear main seal installation (© Ford Motor Co)

cap and remove the seal from the cap and block.

4. Carefully clean the seal grooves in the cap and block with solvent.
5. Soak the new seal halves in clean engine oil.
6. Install the upper half of the seal in the block with the undercut side of the seal toward the front of the engine. Slide the seal around the crankshaft journal until $3/8$ in. protrudes beyond the base of the block.
7. Repeat above procedure on lower seal, allowing an equal length of the seal to protrude beyond the opposite end of the bearing cap.
8. Install rear bearing cap and torque all main bearings to specifications. Apply sealer only to the rear of the seals.
9. Dip the bearing cap side seals in oil, then immediately install them. Do not use any sealer on the side seals. Tap the seals into place and do not clip the protruding ends.
10. Install the oil pump and pan. Fill the crankcase with oil, start engine, check for leaks.

AUTOMATIC TRANSMISSION

All 1967-74 Lincolns and Continentals use a Ford C6 automatic transmission. This heavy-duty three-speed unit is capable of providing automatic upshifts and downshifts through the three forward gear ratios, in addition to offering manual selection of first and second gears.

Only one band—the intermediate band—is used in this transmission. This band, along with the forward clutch, is used to obtain the intermediate gear. The adjustment of this band is the only adjustment required for the C6 transmission.

Prior to 1973, Lincoln automatic transmissions featured a single-diaphragm transmission modulator valve. 1973-74 cars (because of the inclusion of the exhaust gas recirculation system within the emission controls) are equipped with a dual-diaphragm transmission modulator valve.

Neutral Safety and Back-Up Light Switch Adjustment

1967

1. With manual linkage properly adjusted, try to engage starter in each position on quadrant. Starter should engage only in park and neutral positions.
2. To adjust loosen screws that locate switch on steering column.

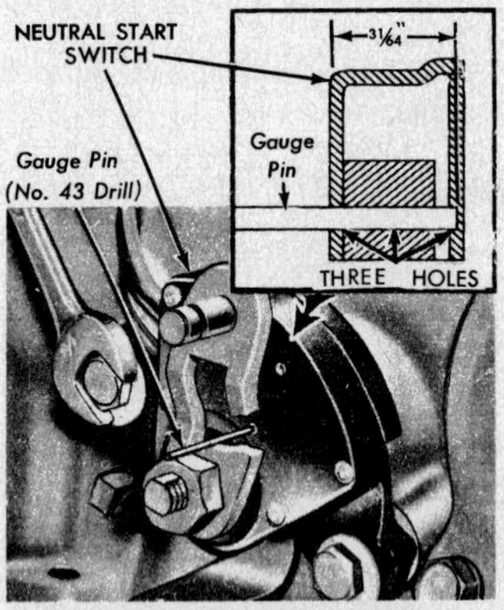
NEUTRAL START SWITCH
Gauge Pin (No. 43 Drill)
Gauge Pin
THREE HOLES

Neutral start switch—1967 (© Ford Motor Co)

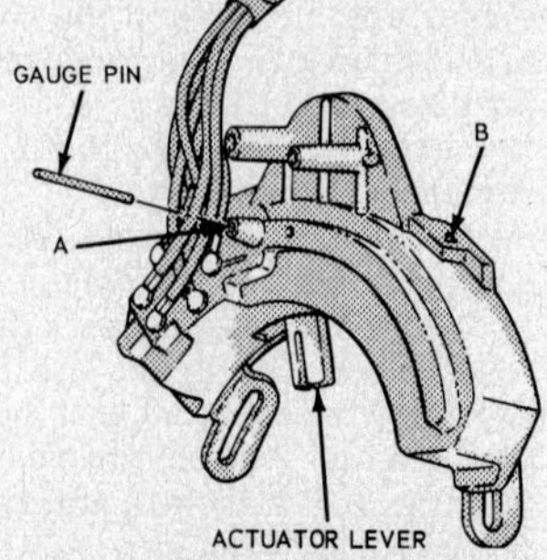
GAUGE PIN
B
A
ACTUATOR LEVER

Neutral start switch—1968-74 (© Ford Motor Co)

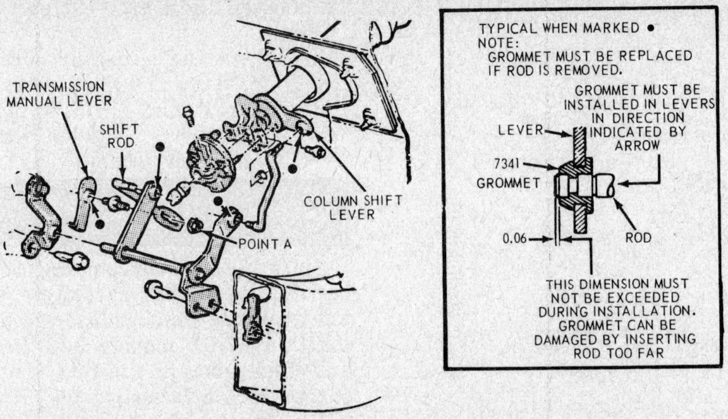
TRANSMISSION MANUAL LEVER
SHIFT ROD
COLUMN SHIFT LEVER
POINT A
TYPICAL WHEN MARKED •
NOTE:
GROMMET MUST BE REPLACED IF ROD IS REMOVED.
GROMMET MUST BE INSTALLED IN LEVERS IN DIRECTION INDICATED BY ARROW
LEVER
7341 GROMMET
ROD
0.06
THIS DIMENSION MUST NOT BE EXCEEDED DURING INSTALLATION. GROMMET CAN BE DAMAGED BY INSERTING ROD TOO FAR

Transmission manual linkage—Lincoln Continental (© Ford Motor Co)

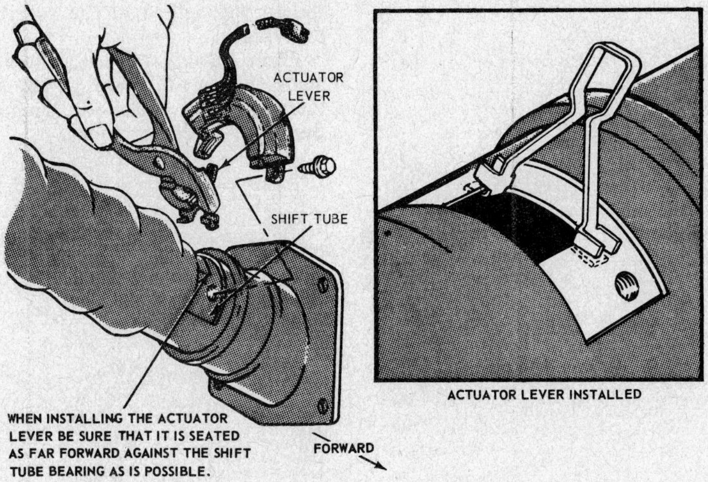
ACTUATOR LEVER
SHIFT TUBE
WHEN INSTALLING THE ACTUATOR LEVER BE SURE THAT IT IS SEATED AS FAR FORWARD AGAINST THE SHIFT TUBE BEARING AS IS POSSIBLE.
FORWARD
ACTUATOR LEVER INSTALLED

Removing or installing switch actuator—1968-70 (© Ford Motor Co)

3. Place shift lever in neutral detent.
4. Rotate switch until gauge pin (No. 43 drill) can be inserted into gauge pin hole $^{31}/_{64}$ in.
5. Tighten down locating screws and check starter engagement in each position as in step one.

1968-74

1. With manual linkage properly adjusted, try to engage starter in each position on quadrant. Starter should engage only in park or neutral positions.
2. Place shift lever in neutral detent.
3. Disconnect start switch wires at plug connector. Disconnect vacuum hoses if any. Remove screws securing neutral start switch to steering column and remove switch. Remove actuator lever along with Type III switches.
4. With switch wires facing up move actuator lever fully to the left and insert gauge pin (No. 43 drill) into gauge pin hole at point A. See accompanying figure. On Type III switch, be sure gauge pin is inserted a full $^1/_2$ in.
5. With pin in place, move actuator lever to right until positive stop is engaged.
6. On Type I and Type II switches remove gauge pin and insert it at point B. On Type III switches remove gauge pin, align two holes in switch at point A and reinstall gauge pin.
7. Reinstall switch on steering column. Be sure shift lever is engaged in neutral detent.
8. Connect switch wires and vacuum hoses and remove gauge pin.
9. Check starter engagement as in Step 1.

Manual Linkage Adjustment

1. If the car is equipped with a tilt wheel steering, position the column up as far as possible. With the engine off, place the selector lever against the stop in the D1 (large dot) position. Raise the car, and remove linkage splash shield.

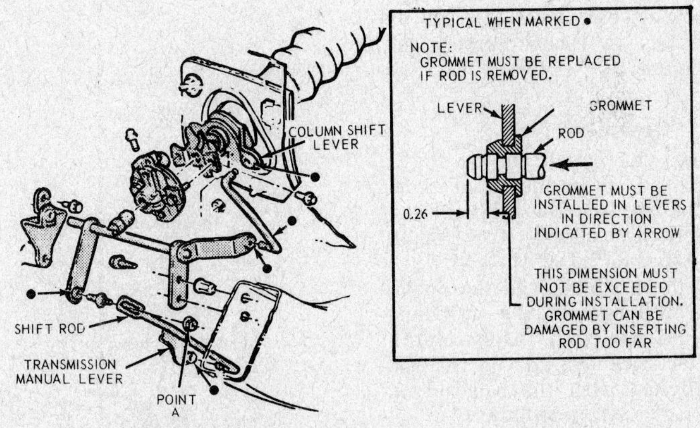
TYPICAL WHEN MARKED •
NOTE:
GROMMET MUST BE REPLACED IF ROD IS REMOVED.
LEVER
GROMMET
ROD
0.26
GROMMET MUST BE INSTALLED IN LEVERS IN DIRECTION INDICATED BY ARROW
THIS DIMENSION MUST NOT BE EXCEEDED DURING INSTALLATION. GROMMET CAN BE DAMAGED BY INSERTING ROD TOO FAR
COLUMN SHIFT LEVER
SHIFT ROD
TRANSMISSION MANUAL LEVER
POINT A

Transmission manual linkage—Mark III (© Ford Motor Co)

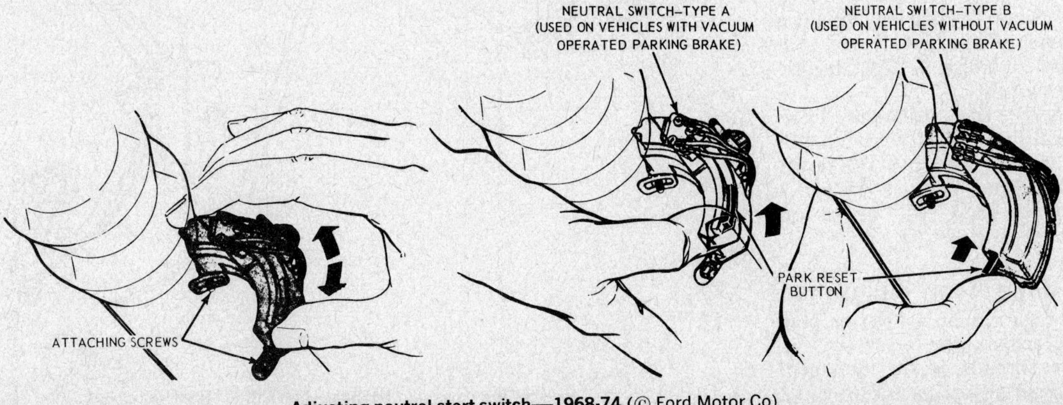
NEUTRAL SWITCH–TYPE A
(USED ON VEHICLES WITH VACUUM OPERATED PARKING BRAKE)
NEUTRAL SWITCH–TYPE B
(USED ON VEHICLES WITHOUT VACUUM OPERATED PARKING BRAKE)
PARK RESET BUTTON
ATTACHING SCREWS

Adjusting neutral start switch—1968-74 (© Ford Motor Co)

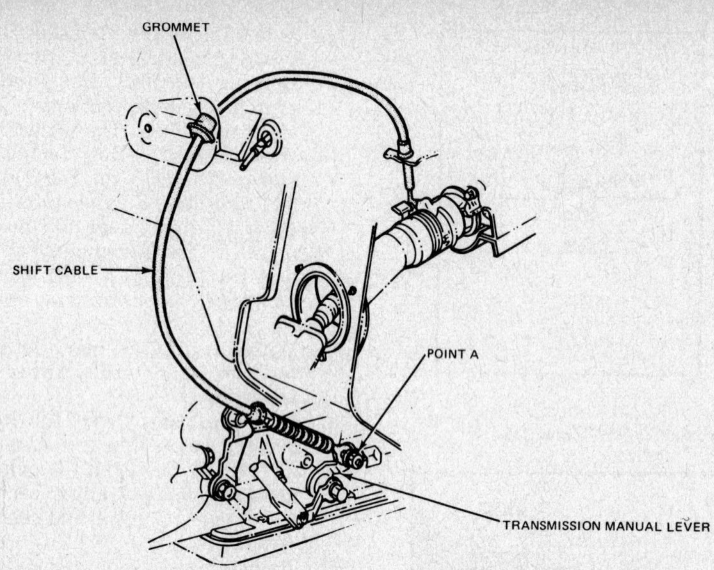
GROMMET
SHIFT CABLE
POINT A
TRANSMISSION MANUAL LEVER

Transmission manual linkage—Mark IV (© Ford Motor Co)

2. Disconnect the adjustable link from the transmission manual shift lever on the transmission.
3. Be sure the transmission shift is fully engaged in D1, the second detent from the bottom. The bottom detent is L (low).
4. Loosen locknut on adjustable link, then pull down on the link to hold the selector lever against the D1 stop. Adjust the link by turning the lower end until the hole in the link aligns with the stud on the transmission manual lever. Connect it to the transmission shift lever.
5. Check selector lever through all positions to secure correct adjustment.

Downshift Rod

1. Loosen the locknut on the downshift rod. Disconnect rod from the ballstud on the bellcrank assembly by sliding the spring clip off the end of the rod.
2. Pull upward and hold the downshift rod against the transmission internal stop. Adjust length of rod until the hole in the rod is aligned with the ballstud on the bellcrank assembly.
3. Lengthen the downshift rod one turn and position it on the ballstud. Slide the spring clip over the end of the rod to lock the rod to the ballstud. Tighten locknut securely.
4. Be sure the bellcrank outer bracket is against the stop pin. If it is not, lengthen the downshift rod one turn. If the rod is too long, there will be no upshift.

Intermediate Band Adjustment

1. Raise the car on a hoist or place it on jack stands.
2. Clean threads of the intermediate band adjusting screw.
3. Loosen adjusting screw locknut.
4. Tighten the adjusting screw to 10 ft. lbs., and back the screw off exactly 1 turn (1971-74 models, 1 1/2 turns). Tighten the adjusting screw locknut.

U-JOINTS

Since 1967, all Lincoln models have been equipped with Cardan universal joints at the front end of the driveshaft. 1967-69 models had Cardan universal joints at the rear of driveshaft which attached to the differential by means of a conventional pinion flange. In 1970 a companion flange was added to the rear of the driveshaft.

Each Cardan universal joint consists of two universal joints, a centering socket yoke or companion flange, and a center yoke.

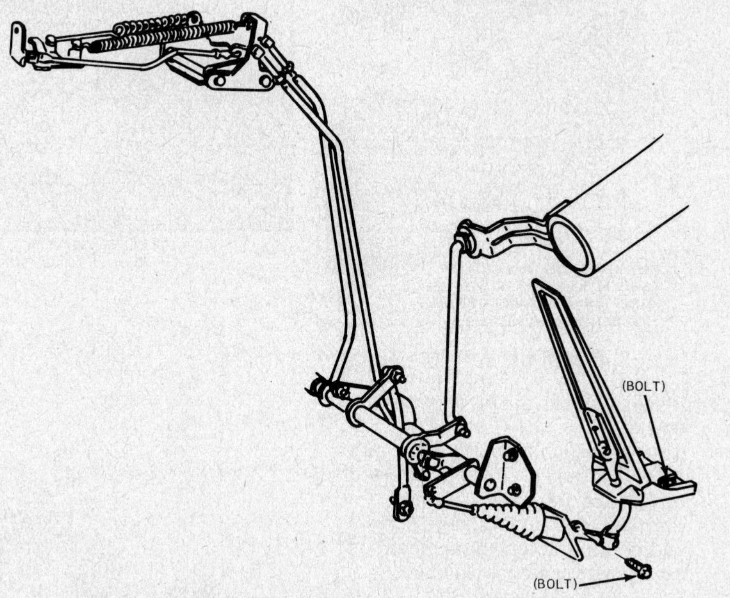
(BOLT)
(BOLT)

Throttle and downshift linkage—1967-70 Continental (© Ford Motor Co)

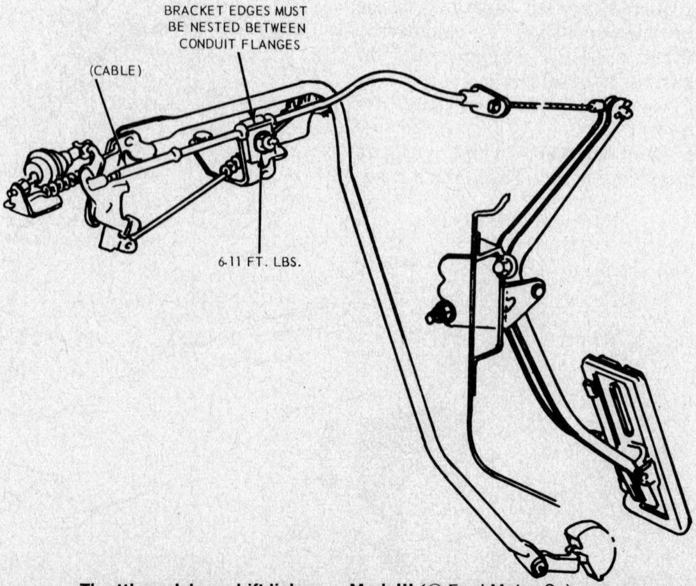
BRACKET EDGES MUST
BE NESTED BETWEEN
CONDUIT FLANGES
(CABLE)
6-11 FT. LBS.

Throttle and downshift linkage—Mark III (© Ford Motor Co)

Tool-T71P-77370-D
Tool-T71P-77370-H

Intermediate band adjustment
(© Ford Motor Co)

Driveshaft and Universal Joint R & R

1. Mark the position of the centering socket yoke or companion flange in relation to the pinion flange so the driveshaft can be returned to its original location.
2. Disconnect the centering socket yoke or companion flange from the pinion flange.
3. Pull the driveshaft rearward until it clears the transmission extension housing and remove the driveshaft from the car.
4. Mark the position of the spiders, the center yoke, and the centering socket or companion flange. *The spiders must be assembled with the bosses in their original location to provide proper clearance.*
5. Remove the snap-rings that retain the spider bearing caps.
6. Using a suitable tool, drive one of the bearing caps on the U-joint to be replaced toward the center of the driveshaft. If the bearing cannot be driven all the way out of the yoke, pull it from the driveshaft using lock-pliers; or, position the protruding bearing cap in the jaws of a vise and, using a soft hammer, drive the center yoke away from the bearing cap.
7. Repeat Step 6 until all bearing caps have been removed, then, remove the spiders.
8. To remove the centering socket or companion flange, pull it from its mounting stud and remove the rubber seal.

Caution When removing a universal joint that mounts to the driveshaft proper, use care when driving the universal joint out of the center yoke. If the universal joint is driven too far, the oil slinger on the front of the driveshaft yoke will be driven against the inside of the center yoke, damaging the oil slinger.

JACKING, HOISTING

Drive-On Hoist

Care should be exercised when driving the car on to a hoist because the body may contact the upright flanges on the hoist with subsequent damage. The approach ramp should be built up slightly if the angle of approach is too steep.

Rail-Type Hoist

The forks which contact the rear axle must be carefully positioned to avoid damage to the shock absorbers.

Forklift Hoist

The rear post fork, if not adjustable to width, may require special adapters to avoid damaging the rear shock absorbers.

Frame Contact Hoist

Particular care must be exercised when using a frame contact hoist. Specific areas marked on the underbody are designated as hoisting areas.

The lifting areas at the front of the vehicle are clearly designated by corrugated metal plates. These plates are bolted to the underbody midway between the front edge of the door and the rear edge of the front fender wheel opening. The front hoist pads or adapter arms, must be positioned on these corrugated plates.

The lifting areas at the rear of the vehicle are located at the edge of the underbody approximately 15 in. forward of the front edge of the rear wheel opening cover panel. The rear hoist pads, or adapter arms, must not be positioned forward of this point.

Floor Jack (Support)

Various acceptable jacking locations are available when it is necessary to raise any one portion of the vehicle. However, when jacking against sheet metal, a wood block 2 x 4 of suitable length should be placed between the jack and the sheet metal to prevent damaging or deforming the metal. Do not attempt to raise one entire side of the body by placing a jack midway between the front and rear wheels. This procedure will probably result in permanent damage.

Jacking at the Front

Each wheel can be raised inde-

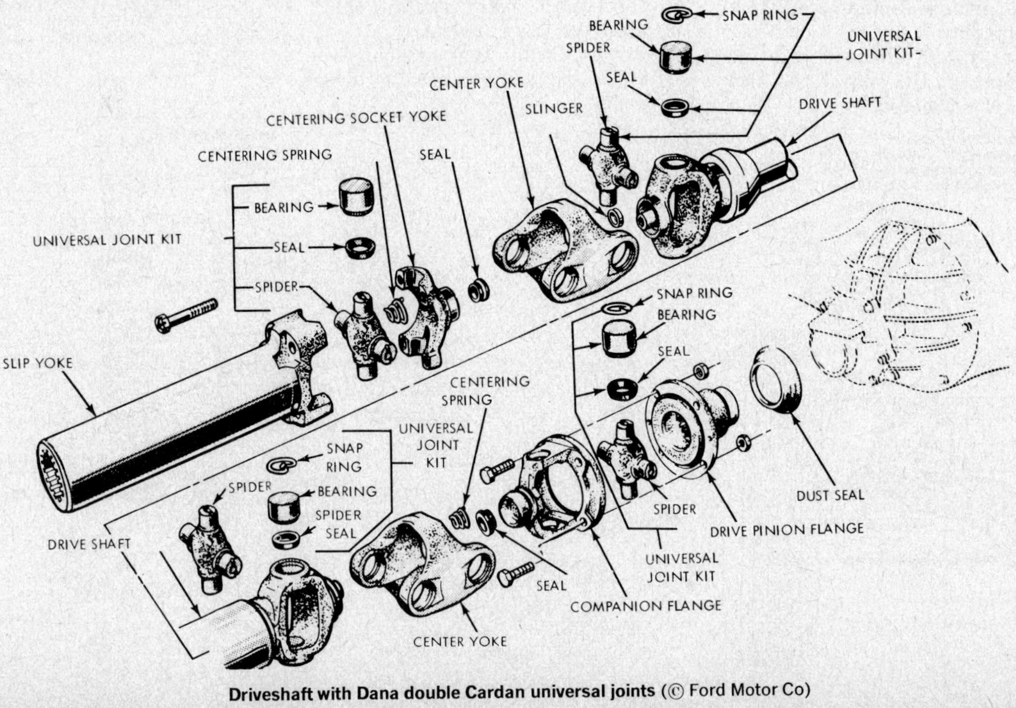
SNAP RING
BEARING
UNIVERSAL JOINT KIT
SPIDER
SEAL
CENTER YOKE
DRIVE SHAFT
SLINGER
CENTERING SOCKET YOKE
CENTERING SPRING
SEAL
BEARING
UNIVERSAL JOINT KIT
SEAL
SPIDER
SNAP RING
BEARING
SLIP YOKE
SEAL
CENTERING SPRING
UNIVERSAL JOINT KIT
SNAP RING
SPIDER
BEARING
SPIDER SEAL
DRIVE SHAFT
DUST SEAL
SPIDER
DRIVE PINION FLANGE
UNIVERSAL JOINT KIT
SEAL
COMPANION FLANGE
CENTER YOKE

Driveshaft with Dana double Cardan universal joints (© Ford Motor Co)

pendently by placing a floor jack under the spring seat pocket in the lower suspension arm.

Jacking at the Rear

Each wheel can be raised independently by placing a floor jack under the rear axle housing.

Bumper Jack

The bumper jack lifting points are similar to those specified in previous models. There is a mounting bracket at the underside edge at the front and rear bumpers for a bumper jack.

FRONT SUSPENSION

Since 1967, all Lincolns and Continentals have incorporated a front suspension system in which the coil springs are supported on the lower suspension member. Each side of this independent front suspension uses two ball joints—upper and lower. Shock absorbers are positioned within the coil springs and are affixed to the lower suspension me..ber and the top of the spring tower.

Front Spring and Lower Arm R & R

1967-69 Except Mark III

1. Raise the car. Place a support under each underbody side rail to the rear of the lower arm, in the lifting pad area.
2. Remove wheel and tire assembly, then, remove the hub and drum. On disc brake-equipped cars: remove two bolts and washers that attach the caliper to the spindle. Remove the caliper from the rotor and wire it to the underbody. Remove the hub and rotor from the spindle.
3. Loosen splash shield to provide clearance at the end of the arm when it is lowered.
4. Remove the shock absorber, and disconnect the stabilizing strut from the lower arm. Disconnect the stabilizer bar from the suspension bar.
5. Remove the cotter pin and loosen the castellated nut attaching the lower ball joint to the spindle.
6. Place a box wrench over the lower end of the ball joint remover tool between the two spindle pivot points. (The tool should seat firmly against the ends of both studs, and not against the lower stud nut.)
7. Turn the wrench until both studs are under tension, then, rap the spindle near the lower stud to loosen the stud from the spindle. Do not loosen the stud with tool pressure alone.
8. Place a jack under the outer end of the lower arm and raise the arm several inches.
9. Install spring compressor tool inside the spring with the jaws of the tool toward the center of the car.
10. Remove the nut from the ball joint stud. Lower the jack until the spindle and spring are free, and remove the spring and insulators.
11. Remove the lower arm to crossmember nut, bolt, washers, and spacer, then remove arm.
12. Install by reversing the removal procedure.

Front Spring Removal—1969-71 Mark III, 1972-74 Mark IV and 1970-74 Continental

1. Raise vehicle and support front end of frame with jack stands.
2. Place jack under lower arm to support it.
3. Disconnect lower end of shock absorber from lower arm.
4. Remove bolts that attach strut and rebound bumper to lower arm.
5. Disconnect lower end of sway bar stud from lower arm
6. Remove nut and bolt that secures inner end of lower arm to crossmember.
7. Lower jack slowly to relieve spring pressure on lower arm then remove spring.

Ball Joints

See Ford section.

Shock Absorber R & R

1967-69 Except Mark III

1. Remove the stud nut which is located at the upper eye of the shock absorber. Remove the upper eye stud bracket to crossmember attaching bolt and remove the stud bracket.
2. Remove the shock absorber-to-suspension lower arm attaching bolts. Lower and remove the shock absorber.
3. Examine the shock absorber unit and the rubber bushings. Replace any parts that are defective, deteriorated, or worn.
4. Fully extend the shock absorber. Position it inside the coil spring. Connect the lower end of the shock absorber to the suspension lower arm and torque the attaching nuts to 22–28 ft lbs.
5. Insert the upper bracket stud through the bushing in the shock absorber upper eye. Install the stud bracket-to-crossmember at-

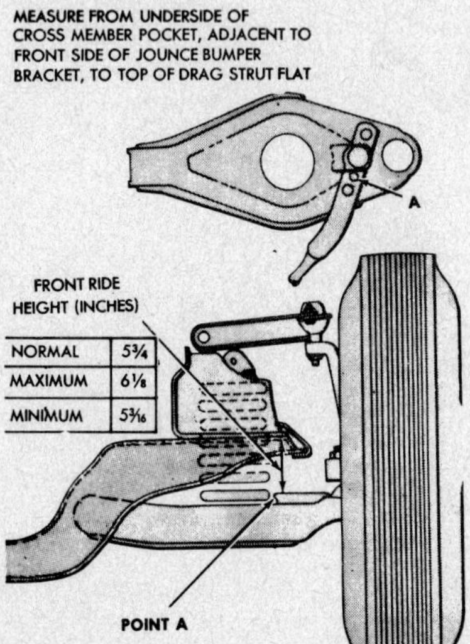
MEASURE FROM UNDERSIDE OF CROSS MEMBER POCKET, ADJACENT TO FRONT SIDE OF JOUNCE BUMPER BRACKET, TO TOP OF DRAG STRUT FLAT
A
FRONT RIDE HEIGHT (INCHES)
NORMAL 5¾
MAXIMUM 6⅛
MINIMUM 5 5/16
POINT A

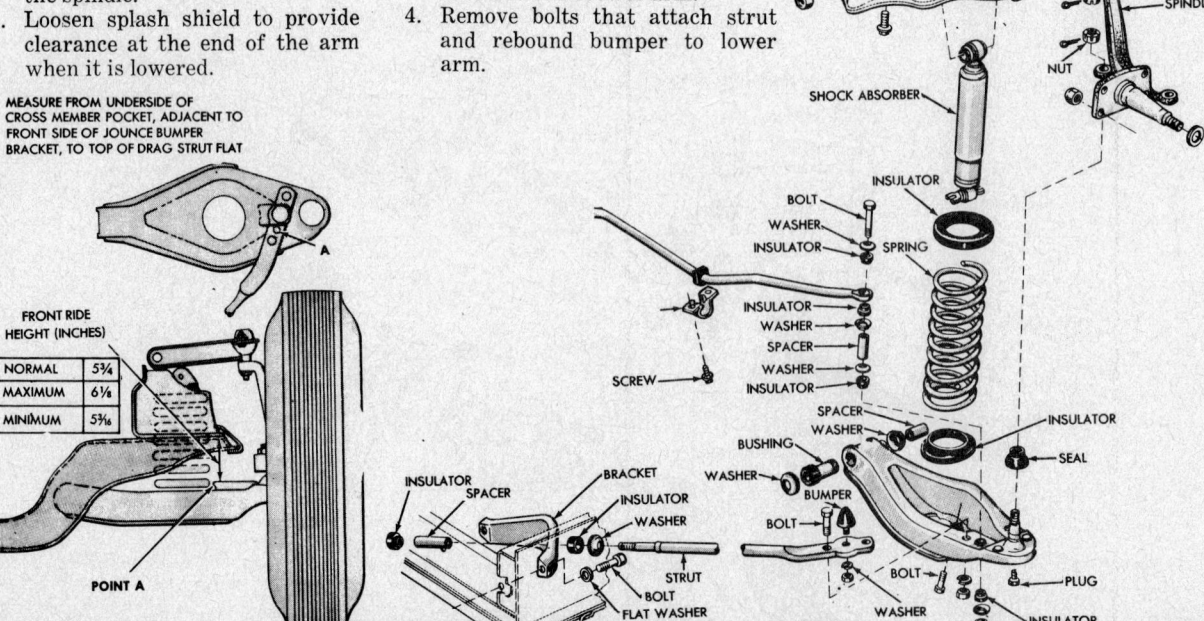

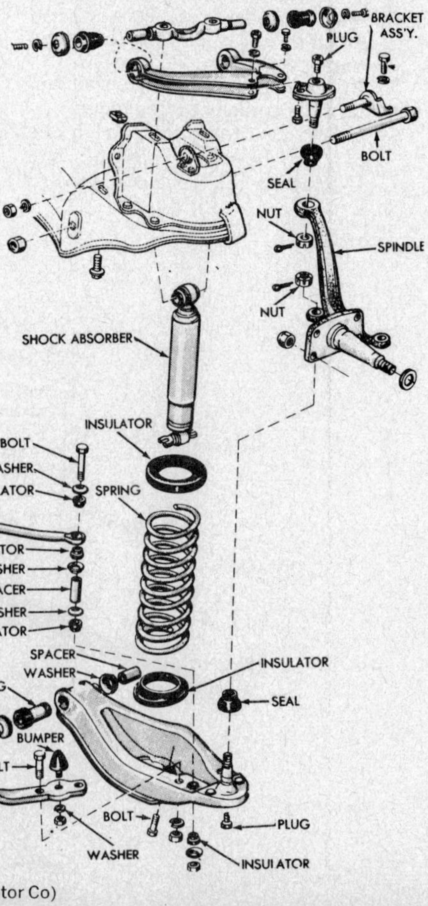
BRACKET ASS'Y.
PLUG
BOLT
SEAL
NUT
SPINDLE
NUT
SHOCK ABSORBER
INSULATOR
BOLT
WASHER
INSULATOR
SPRING
INSULATOR
WASHER
SPACER
WASHER
INSULATOR
SCREW
SPACER
WASHER
INSULATOR
BUSHING
SEAL
WASHER
BUMPER
BOLT
BOLT
WASHER
PLUG
INSULATOR

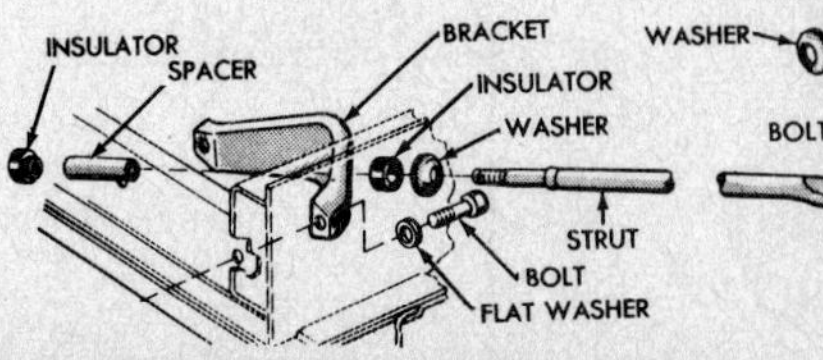
INSULATOR
SPACER
BRACKET
INSULATOR
WASHER
STRUT
BOLT
FLAT WASHER

Front suspension—1967-69 except Mark III (© Ford Motor Co)

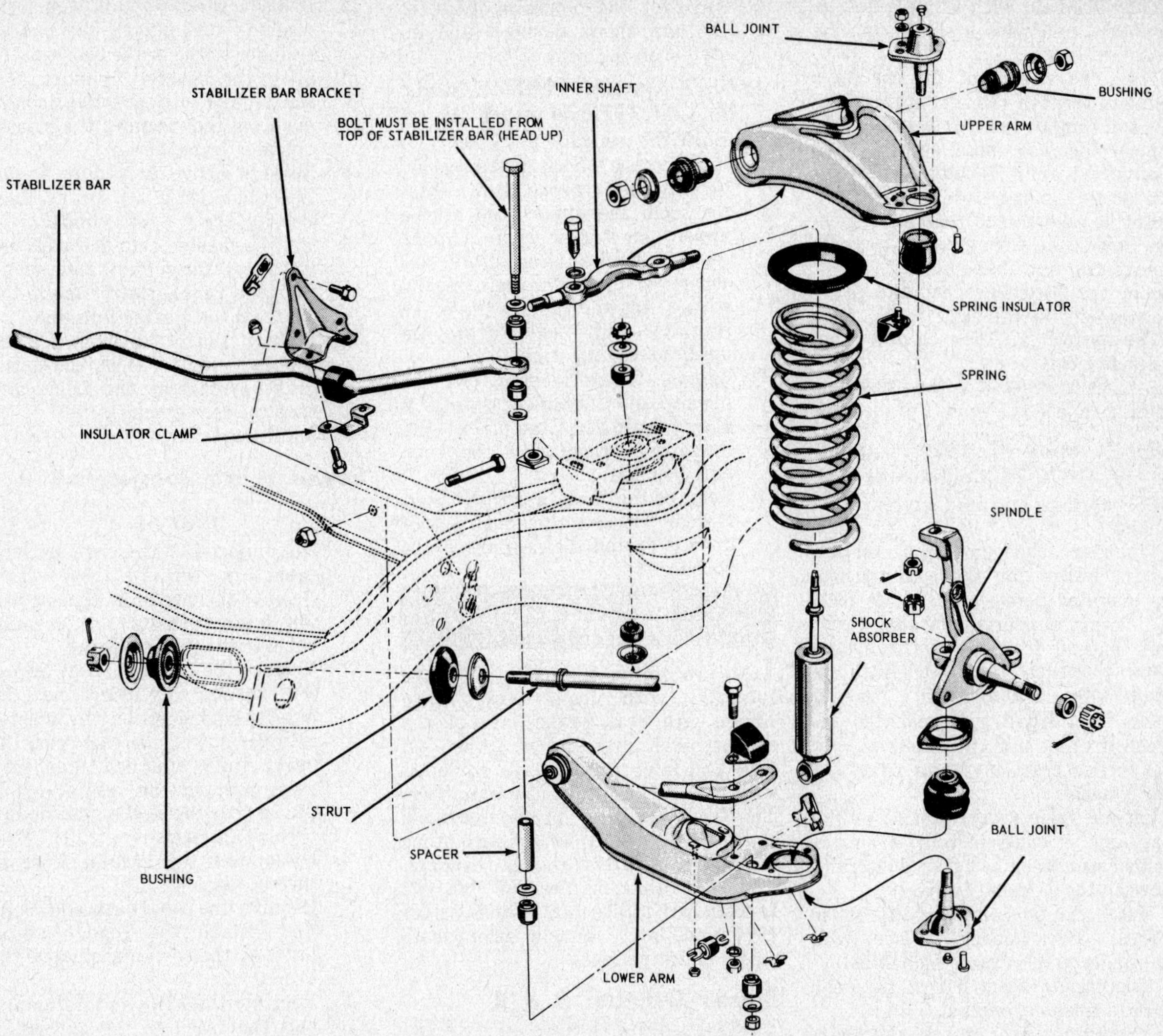
BALL JOINT
BUSHING
UPPER ARM
STABILIZER BAR BRACKET
INNER SHAFT
BOLT MUST BE INSTALLED FROM TOP OF STABILIZER BAR (HEAD UP)
STABILIZER BAR
SPRING INSULATOR
SPRING
INSULATOR CLAMP
SPINDLE
SHOCK ABSORBER
STRUT
BALL JOINT
SPACER
BUSHING
LOWER ARM

Front suspension—1970-74 Lincoln Continental, 1969-71 Mark III, and 1972-74 Mark IV
(© Ford Motor Co)

taching bolt, but do not tighten the bolt at this time.

6. Install the upper eye bracket stud nut. Torque the nut to 40–55 ft lbs.
7. Torque the stud bracket-to-crossmember attaching bolt to 20–30 ft lbs.

1970-74 Lincoln Continental, 1969-71 Mark III, and 1972-74 Mark IV

1. Remove the nut, washer, and bushing from the shock absorber upper end.
2. Raise the vehicle and install safety stands.
3. Remove the two bolts which affix the shock absorber to the lower arm. Remove the shock absorber.
4. Place a washer and bushing on the shock absorber top stud and position the shock absorber within the coil spring. Install the two lower attaching bolts, and torque them to 8–15 ft lbs.
5. Remove the safety stands and lower the vehicle.
6. Place a bushing and washer on the shock absorber top stud and install the attaching nut. Torque this fitting to 20–28 ft lbs.

REAR SUSPENSION

Up to and including the 1969 model year, the Lincoln Continental rear suspension system featured semi-elliptic leaf springs. In 1969, the newly introduced Continental Mark III came equipped with rear coil springs, and from 1970 to 1974 all Lincolns, Mark III, and Mark IV have used coil springs.

Rear Spring R & R

1967-69 except Mark III

Longitudinal leaf springs are used on these models.

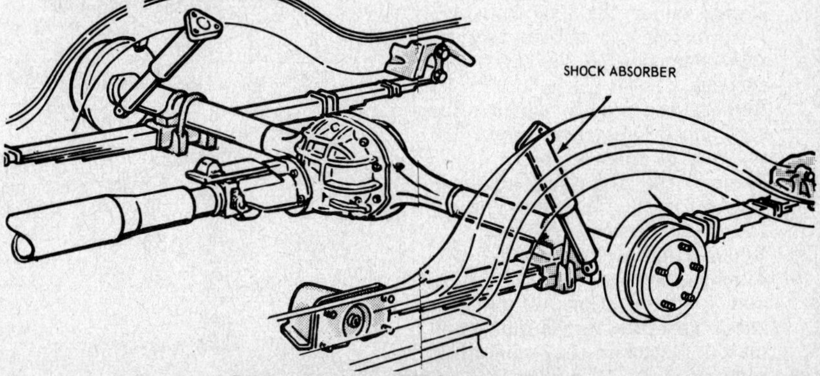
SHOCK ABSORBER

Rear suspension—1967-69 except Mark III

They are held with a single bolt at the front, and with a shackle at the back.

Take the weight of the car on a frame in front of the rear spring. Unbolt and remove the rear shackle. Disconnect the rear shock absorber and remove the four U-bolts from each side of the spring saddle where the spring is held to the rear axle housing. Lower the spring to the ground, remove the nut that holds the front pin in the frame bracket and drive the front spring pin out.

The spring can then be slid from under the car.

Replace in reverse of the procedure which removed it.

1969-71 Mark III, 1972-74 Mark IV, 1970-74 Continental

Coil springs are used at rear suspension.

The rear suspension is a coil-link design. Large, low-rate coil springs are mounted between rear axle pads and frame supports. Parallel lower arms extend forward of the spring seats to rubber frame anchor to accommodate driving and braking forces. A third link is mounted between the axle and the frame to control torque reaction forces from the rear wheels.

Lateral (side sway) motion of the rear axle is controlled by a rubber bushed rear track bar, linked laterally between the axle and frame.

1. Place car on hoist and lift under rear axle housing. Place jack stands under frame side rails.
2. Disconnect track bar at the rear axle housing bracket.
3. Disconnect rear shock absorbers from the rear axle housing brackets.
4. Disconnect hose from axle housing vent.
5. Lower hoist with axle housing until coil springs are released.
6. Remove spring lower retainer with bolt, nut, washer and insulator.
7. Remove spring with large rubber insulator pads from car.
8. Install in reverse of above.

Shock Absorber R & R

1967-69 except Mark III

1. Lift the car and place support stands under the axle housing. Position the car with a jack to relieve tension on the shock absorbers.
2. Remove the screws which affix the shock absorber mounting plate to the crossmember.
3. Remove the attaching nut and washers from the lower end of the shock absorber.
4. Remove the shock absorber.
5. Remove the nut, outer washer, and insulator that attach the shock absorber to the mounting plate. Remove the mounting plate.
6. Transfer the mounting plate to the new shock absorber and install it on the car.

1970-74 Lincoln, 1969-71 Mark III, and 1972-74 Mark IV

1. Raise the vehicle.
2. Remove the shock absorber attaching nut, washer, and insulator from the upper stud at the upper side of the spring upper seat. Compress the shock absorber to clear the hole in the spring seat and remove the inner insulator and washer from the upper attaching stud.
3. Remove the self-locking attaching nut and disconnect the shock absorber lower stud from the mounting bracket on the rear axle housing.
4. Remove the shock absorber from the car. Reverse the above procedure to install the new shock absorber.

BRAKES

All Lincoln models, from 1967, are equipped with front power disc brakes. All rear brakes are of the conventional shoe design. Also, all 1967 and later vehicles are equipped with dual reservoir master cylinders. The front and rear brake hydraulic systems are independent of each other on vehicles with dual master cylinders. The disc brake calipers on 1967-69 Lincoln cars utilize dual pistons, while 1970 and later models incorporate single piston calipers.

Master Cylinder R & R

1967-74

1. Disconnect the brake lines from the master cylinder.
2. Remove the two nuts and lockwashers that attach the master cylinder to the brake booster.
3. Slide the master cylinder forward until it clears the booster pushrod, then remove the master cylinder from the car.
4. Reverse above procedure to install; but, leave the brake lines loose on the master cylinder.
5. Fill the master cylinder with extra-heavy duty fluid and, using the foot pedal, slowly bleed the air from the master cylinder.
6. Tighten the brake lines, fill the master cylinder, then, bleed the brake system at the front and then the rear wheels.
7. Refill master cylinder.

Power Brake Booster R & R

1967-68

1. Disconnect the negative battery cable.
2. Remove the two bolts that attach the brake pressure differential valve to the fender apron.
3. Remove the two nuts that attach the master cylinder to the booster and position the master cylinder out of the way with the brake lines attached. Use care when moving the master cylinder so that the brake lines do not become kinked.
4. Disconnect the vacuum hose at the booster.
5. Remove the two nuts and bolts that attach the fender apron brace to the cowl and remove the brace.
6. Remove the clip and attaching bolt that secures the air conditioning hose to the hood latch and position the air conditioning hose out of the way.

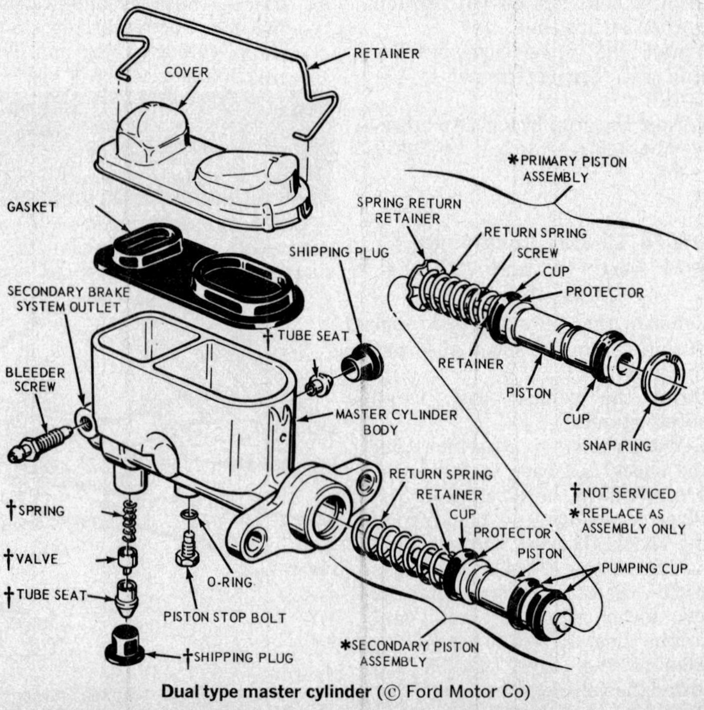
RETAINER
COVER
*PRIMARY PISTON ASSEMBLY
GASKET
SPRING RETURN RETAINER
RETURN SPRING
SHIPPING PLUG
SCREW
CUP
PROTECTOR
SECONDARY BRAKE SYSTEM OUTLET
†TUBE SEAT
RETAINER
BLEEDER SCREW
PISTON
CUP
SNAP RING
MASTER CYLINDER BODY
RETURN SPRING
RETAINER
CUP
PROTECTOR
PISTON
PUMPING CUP
†NOT SERVICED
*REPLACE AS ASSEMBLY ONLY
†SPRING
†VALVE
†TUBE SEAT
O-RING
PISTON STOP BOLT
†SHIPPING PLUG
*SECONDARY PISTON ASSEMBLY

Dual type master cylinder (© Ford Motor Co)

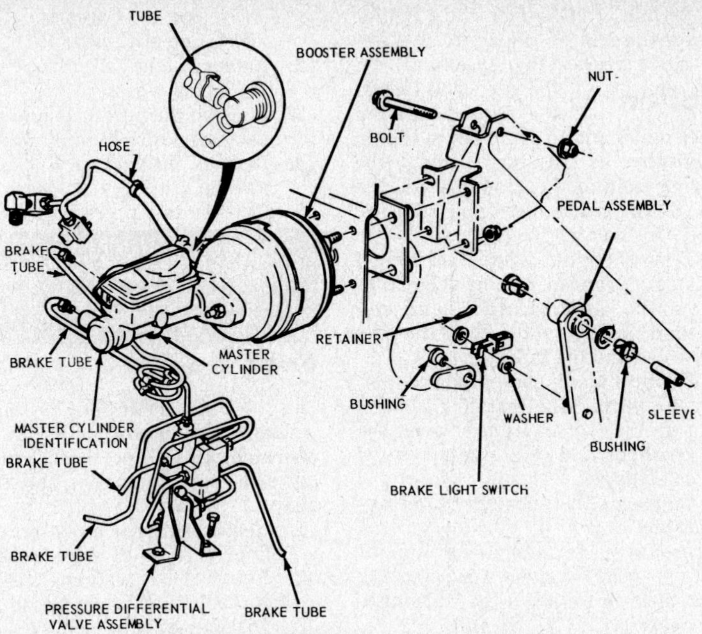
TUBE
BOOSTER ASSEMBLY
NUT
BOLT
HOSE
PEDAL ASSEMBLY
BRAKE TUBE
RETAINER
BRAKE TUBE
MASTER CYLINDER
BUSHING
WASHER
SLEEVE
BUSHING
MASTER CYLINDER IDENTIFICATION
BRAKE TUBE
BRAKE LIGHT SWITCH
BRAKE TUBE
PRESSURE DIFFERENTIAL VALVE ASSEMBLY
BRAKE TUBE

Brake pedal and booster installation (© Ford Motor Co)

7. Working under the dash, disconnect and remove the stop light switch and pushrod from the brake pedal. Use care not to damage the stop light switch during removal.
8. Remove the nuts that retain the booster to the firewall from the interior side of the firewall.
9. Remove the booster from under the hood.
10. Reverse above procedure to install.

1969-74

1. Disconnect the vacuum hose from the booster.
2. Remove the two nuts and lockwashers that mount the master cylinder to the booster and move the master cylinder out of the way with the lines attached. Use care not to kink the brake lines.
3. Working under the dash, disconnect and remove the stop light switch and pushrod from the brake pedal. Use care not to damage the switch during removal.
4. Remove the four booster to firewall attaching nuts from the interior side of the firewall.
5. Remove the booster from under the hood.
6. Reverse above procedure to install.

Parking Brake Cable Adjustment

1. Fully release the parking brake pedal.
2. Raise the car on a hoist.
3. Adjust the pedal cable to about 10 in., measured from the cable attachment at the crossmember to the cable adjusting nut.
4. Depress the parking brake pedal one notch from normal, released position.
5. Loosen locknut on equalizer rod and turn the forward nut inward toward the front of the car until a moderate drag is felt when turning the rear wheels.
6. Holding forward nut in position, tighten locknut. Lock the adjustment at the equalizer.
7. Release parking brake, and make sure that the brake shoes return to the fully released position.

Other Brake System Service

Procedures for brake adjustment, shoe replacement, bleeding of the system, and the overhaul of wheel cylinders, calipers, and master cylinders may be found in the "Unit Repair Section."

STEERING

All Lincoln cars use a torsion-bar type of hydraulically assisted power steering system. This system furnishes assist to reduce the amount of effort required at the steering wheel to turn the car, while it reduces road shock and vibrations.

Three different types of power steering pumps have been used on Lincolns and Continentals since 1967. A roller-type hydraulic pump was standard on 1967-69 cars. In 1970-71, a Ford-Thompson slipper type power steering pump was used, and a constant-displacement vane type pump is the unit found on all 1972–74 Lincoln Continentals and the Continental Mark IV.

Steering Gear Assembly Removal

1967

1. Disconnect pressure and return line from steering gear. Cap each line and plug inlets in steering gear.
2. Remove ground strap from steering gear housing.
3. Remove bolt that attaches flex coupling to steering gear.
4. Remove bolt that attaches left brace to torque box. Loosen bolt that secures brace to side rail and swing brace to one side.
5. Remove pitman arm from sector shaft.
6. Remove pipe between manifold and resonator.
7. Disconnect linkage rod from equalizer shaft. Remove equalizer stud from side rail. Move equalizer shaft up and out of way. Do not lose stud or bushings.
8. Remove bolt from lower end of fender splash shield. Move splash shield to one side to gain access to steering gear.
9. Remove three steering gear attaching bolts. Support gear before completely removing last bolt.
10. Move steering gear down to free it from flex joint. Rotate it counterclockwise to provide clearance

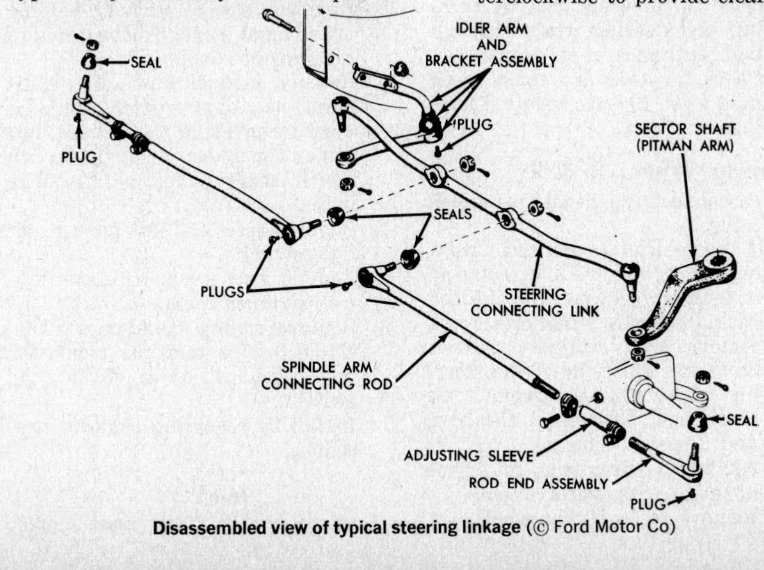
SEAL
PLUG
IDLER ARM AND BRACKET ASSEMBLY
PLUG
SECTOR SHAFT (PITMAN ARM)
SEALS
PLUGS
STEERING CONNECTING LINK
SPINDLE ARM CONNECTING ROD
SEAL
ADJUSTING SLEEVE
ROD END ASSEMBLY
PLUG

Disassembled view of typical steering linkage (© Ford Motor Co)

between side rail and engine.

11. Remove steering gear and remove three pads from gear. Reverse procedure to install.

1968-74

1. Disconnect hydraulic lines from the steering gear. Plug lines and ports to protect from leaking and the entry of dirt.
2. Remove the two bolts that hold the flex coupling to the steering gear and to the column.
3. Raise the car and remove the sector shaft attaching nut.
4. Remove pitman arm from the sector shaft.
5. Support steering gear, then remove the three steering gear attaching bolts.
6. Work the steering gear free of the flex coupling and remove it from the car.
7. If the flex coupling stayed on the input shaft, lift it off the shaft at this time.
8. Install by sliding the flex coupling into place on the steering shaft. Turn steering wheel so that the spokes are in the horizontal position.
9. Center the steering gear input shaft.
10. Slide the steering gear input shaft into the flex coupling and into place on the frame side rail. Install the three attaching bolts and torque them to specifications.
11. Be sure that the front wheels are in a straight ahead position, then install the pitman arm on the sector shaft. Install and tighten the sector shaft to pitman arm attaching nut to 150-225 ft. lbs.
12. Move the flex coupling into place on the input shaft and steering column shaft, install and tighten attaching bolts.
13. Connect and tighten the fluid pressure and the return lines to the steering gear.
14. Fill the power steering pump and cycle the steering gear by turning the steering wheel through both extremes of its travel.
15. Check for leaks and again check fluid level. Be sure required level is maintained.

Steering Wheel R & R

1. Disconnect the negative battery cable.
2. If the vehicle is equipped with a horn ring, remove it by rotating it counterclockwise. If equipped with a steering wheel crash pad, remove the retaining screws from the underside of the steering wheel and then remove the crash pad. Disconnect the horn and speed control (if so equipped) wires from the inside of the steering wheel center.
3. Remove the steering wheel nut, install a steering wheel puller on the end of the shaft, and remove the steering wheel.

Caution The use of a knock-off type steering wheel puller and a hammer is highly inadvisable, as they may damage the steering column bearing or (in the case of the collapsible-type steering wheel) the column itself.

4. With the front wheels positioned straight ahead, line up the marks on the steering wheel and column and install the steering wheel and the locknut.
5. Connect the horn and speed control wires and install the horn ring if so equipped and the crashpad and retaining screws if so equipped.
6. Connect the negative battery cable.

Procedures for the overhaul of steering gear and power steering pump may be found in the "Unit Repair Section."

INSTRUMENT PANEL

Ignition Lock R & R

See Ford section

Ignition Switch R & R

See Ford Section.

Light Switch Replacement

Except Mark III and Mark IV

1. Disconnect battery.
2. Remove knob and shaft by pressing release knob button on switch housing and with knob in full on position.
3. Remove moulding nut from switch.
4. Remove junction block from switch.
5. Install in reverse of above.

Mark III

1. Disconnect battery ground cable.
2. Remove seven screws holding lower finish panel to lower side of instrument panel.
3. Remove control knob and shaft from headlight switch. This is done by pressing the release button on the underside of the switch (with shaft pulled all the way out).
4. Remove bezel and nut from headlight switch.
5. Remove two screws from switch-to-instrument panel.
6. Remove switch from panel. Disconnect wire multiple connector and vacuum hoses from the switch.
7. Install by reversing removal procedure.

Mark IV

1. Remove the instrument cluster trim panel, as explained under "Instrument Cluster R&R."
2. Remove the lighting switch mounting plate.
3. Remove the bezel nut and disconnect the multiple connector.
4. Remove the vacuum lines and the switch.
5. Reverse this procedure to install.

WINDSHIELD WIPERS

Motor R & R

1967-69

The wiper motor is hydraulically operated by oil pressure from the power steering pump via the steering gear.

1. Remove washer coordinator hose from bottom of wiper motor.
2. Remove oil return, feed and control lines from wiper motor.
3. Disconnect wiper control cable at the wiper motor.
4. Remove two screws holding the wiper motor to the auxiliary drive mounting plate. Remove wiper motor.
5. Install motor by reversing the removal procedure.
6. Refill the power steering system and bleed the lines.

1970-74 Continental and 1972-74 Mark IV

1. Disconnect battery.
2. Remove wiper arm and blade assemblies from pivot shafts.
3. Remove left cowl screen for access.
4. Disconnect linkage drive arm from motor output arm crank pin by removing retaining clip.
5. Disconnect two push on wire connectors from the motor.
6. From engine side of dash, remove three bolts that retain motor and remove motor. Reverse procedure to install.

1970 Mark III

1. Disconnect battery.
2. Disconnect washer hose, remove three retaining bolts, and pull cowl top grille out from under two clips.
3. Disconnect connector plugs from wiring harness at engine side of dash panel. Push wiring and plugs along with grommet through hole in dash.
4. Remove four motor to cowl retaining bolts. Lift motor out, and at the same time pull wiper arm and blade assembly to left for access to motor crank pin clip. Remove clip and disconnect drive link from motor crank pin. Remove three retaining bolts and separate motor from mounting plate and cover and wiring harness assembly. Reverse procedure to install.

1971 Mark III

See 1971 Thunderbird.

Transmission R & R

1967-69

Auxiliary Drive

1. Remove both wiper arms and blades from the pivot assemblies.
2. Remove the ventilation grille and screen.
3. Remove both washer nozzles.
4. Disconnect the pivot shaft drive arm from the auxiliary drive.
5. Remove the four screws and the auxiliary drive assembly.
6. To install, reverse the removal procedure.

Wiper Pivot

1. Remove the windshield wiper arms and blades.
2. Remove the cowl top ventilation grille and screen.
3. Right hand: disconnect the drive arm from the pivot shaft assembly.
4. Left hand: disconnect the drive arm from the right hand pivot assembly and the drive arm from the auxiliary drive assembly.
5. Remove the pivot shaft retaining capscrews and nuts.
6. Remove the pivot shaft and housing from the car.
7. To install, reverse the removal procedure.

1970-74 Continental

1. Disconnect battery.
2. Remove wiper arm and blade assemblies from pivot shafts.
3. Remove cowl screens for access.
4. Disconnect left linkage arm from drive arm by removing clip.
5. Remove three bolts retaining left pivot shaft assembly through cowl opening.
6. Disconnect linkage drive arm from motor crank pin by removing clip.
7. Remove three bolts that connect drive arm pivot shaft assembly to cowl. Remove pivot shaft drivearm and right arm as an assembly. Reverse procedure to install.

1970 Mark III

1. Disconnect battery.
2. Disconnect washer hose, remove three retaining bolts, and pull cowl top grille out from under two clips.
3. Remove wiper arm and blade assemblies.
4. To remove left pivot shaft, loosen right pivot shaft retaining bolts, and remove left pivot shaft retaining bolts. Remove connecting clip, and disconnect left pivot shaft link from right pivot shaft crank pin. Work left pivot shaft and link assembly toward right and out through cowl opening.
5. To remove right pivot shaft, remove three retaining bolts and disconnect linkage from crank pin by removing clip. Lift pivot shaft assembly from cowl. Reverse procedure to install.

1971 Mark III, and 1972-74 Mark IV

1. Remove the wiper arm and blade assemblies. Be sure to remove the tension arm retaining clip from the tension arm retaining stud on the left pivot assembly.
2. Remove the retaining screws and remove the cowl grille. Disconnect the washer hoses.
3. Remove the clip retaining the link assembly to the motor.
4. Remove the screws that attach the pivot shaft and link assembly to the cowl and remove the pivot shaft and link assembly.
5. Reverse above procedure to install.

RADIO

Radio R & R

1967-69 Except Mark III

1. Disconnect battery.
2. Remove eight screws in the lower control housing.
3. Disconnect lead from the speaker/s.
4. Disconnect power antenna lead.
5. Disconnect lead to the foot operated switch for AM-FM radios on cars so equipped.
6. Disconnect one two-way disconnect for power and pilot light.
7. Remove the two knobs and two bezels on the selector shafts. Remove the two nuts and two retainers on the selector shafts.
8. Remove the two screws holding the radio bracket to the lower reinforcement on the instrument panel.
9. Remove the two nuts and washers from the selector shafts. Disconnect the antenna lead and remove the radio.
10. To install, reverse the above.

1969-71—Mark III

Removal

1. Disconnect ground from battery.
2. Pull knobs off the control shafts.
3. Remove the cover plate located below the steering column.
4. Remove nut from the right radio control shaft.
5. Remove six screws and the trim applique from in front of the radio.
6. Remove the nut and washer from the right radio control shaft.
7. Remove screw attaching the front left side of the radio to the instrument panel.
8. Remove the radio support attaching screw.
9. Disconnect the radio power wires and speaker wires at the connectors.
10. Disconnect the antenna lead-in cable and remove the radio.

Installation

1. Connect the power, speaker, and antenna leads to the radio.
2. Position radio to instrument panel and install the attaching screw at the left front side of the radio.
3. Install the washer and nut on the radio right control shaft.
4. Install radio rear support attaching screw.
5. Position the trim applique to the instrument panel and install the six attaching screws.
6. Install the nut on the radio right control shaft.
7. Install the discs, felt washer and knobs on the radio control shafts.
8. Install cover plate below the steering column.
9. Connect the ground cable to the battery.
10. Check operation of radio and set the push buttons.

1970-74 Continental

1. Disconnect battery.
2. Remove map light assembly.
3. Remove right and left inspection covers.
4. Remove lower instrument panel pad.
5. Remove glove box, open ashtray, and leave it open.
6. Remove glove box switch.
7. Through glove box opening remove two nuts retaining radio finish panel to instrument panel.
8. Remove radio knobs.
9. Remove two screws at top of finish panel. Position panel out and disconnect cigar lighter and light from right panel.
10. Through glove box opening remove nut from lower right corner of center finish panel.
11. Remove radio top support nut and three mounting screws. Pull radio out. Disconnect power leads and antenna cable. Remove radio. Reverse procedure to install.

1972-74 Mark IV

1. Disconnect the negative battery cable.
2. Pull the radio control knobs off the radio shafts.
3. Remove the nuts from both radio control shafts.
4. Remove the radio rear support to panel attaching screw.
5. Disconnect the radio power wires. Disconnect the speaker wires at the connectors.
6. Disconnect the antenna lead and remove the radio.
7. Reverse the above procedure to install.

HEATER

Heater Core Removal

1967-69 Continental

1. Disconnect battery, remove air cleaner, and drain coolant from system.
2. Disconnect hoses at heater core.
3. Remove harness clamp on top of evaporator-heater case.
4. Remove temperature blender door variable actuator.
5. Remove heater core cover plate retaining screws and cover plate.
6. Lift out heater core. Reverse procedure to install.

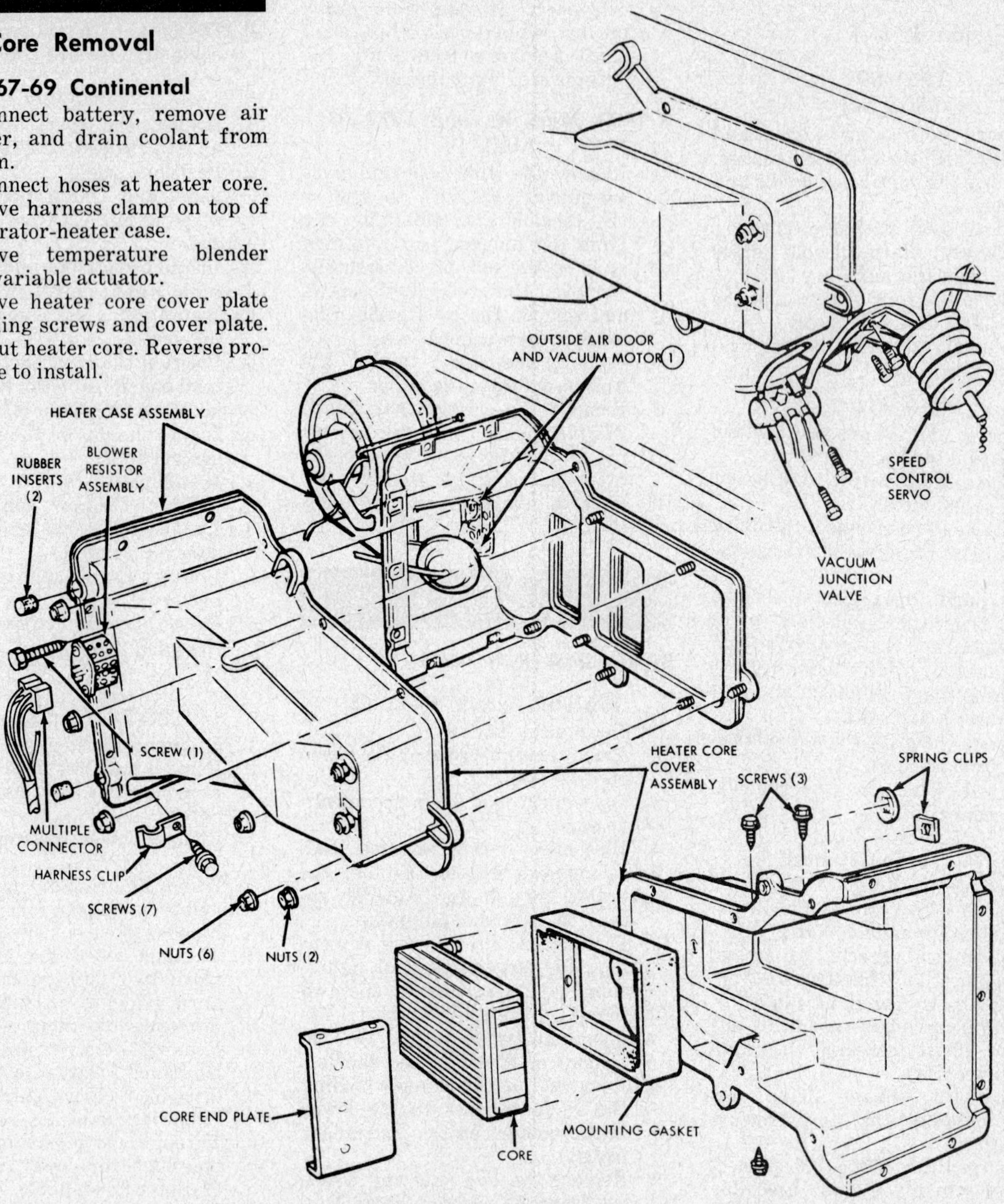
OUTSIDE AIR DOOR AND VACUUM MOTOR (1)
HEATER CASE ASSEMBLY
RUBBER INSERTS (2)
BLOWER RESISTOR ASSEMBLY
SPEED CONTROL SERVO
VACUUM JUNCTION VALVE
SCREW (1)
HEATER CORE COVER ASSEMBLY
SPRING CLIPS
SCREWS (3)
MULTIPLE CONNECTOR
HARNESS CLIP
SCREWS (7)
NUTS (6)
NUTS (2)
CORE END PLATE
MOUNTING GASKET
CORE

Heater core removal—1970-74 Lincoln Continental (© Ford Motor Co)

1969-71 Mark III

1. Remove hood and air cleaner and drain engine coolant.
2. Disconnect both hydraulic lines at wiper motor and position them to one side on 1969 Mark III.
3. Disconnect heater hoses at heater core and position hoses and water valve away from housing.
4. Disconnect vacuum supply hose on top of housing and remove oil pressure sending unit from back of engine.
5. Remove transmission dip stick and tube assembly.
6. Disconnect multiple connector leading to icing switch.
7. Remove evaporator housing front cover. On air-conditioned cars, remove the glove compartment liner and disconnect the electrical and vacuum junction blocks on the inner dash panel.
8. Remove heater core housing cover.
9. Remove heater core retaining bracket and remove heater core. Reverse procedure to install.

1970-74 Continental

1. Drain engine coolant.
2. Disconnect vacuum junction valve from dash panel and move valve and vacuum hoses away from case.
3. Disconnect speed control servo and bracket assembly if so equipped from dash panel and move it away from case.
4. Disconnect multiple connector from blower resistor and remove harness from clip on case.
5. Disconnect heater hoses from heater case and remove hose support clamp from case. Move hoses and water valve away from case.
6. Remove seven case cover to case flange attaching screws and wire harness clip.
7. Remove six cover to back plate stud nuts.
8. Remove one upper case to dash panel mounting screw.
9. Remove two case to dash panel mounting stud nuts, one on inboard mounting flange and one below case on lower flange.
10. Carefully move heater core assembly forward to clear mounting

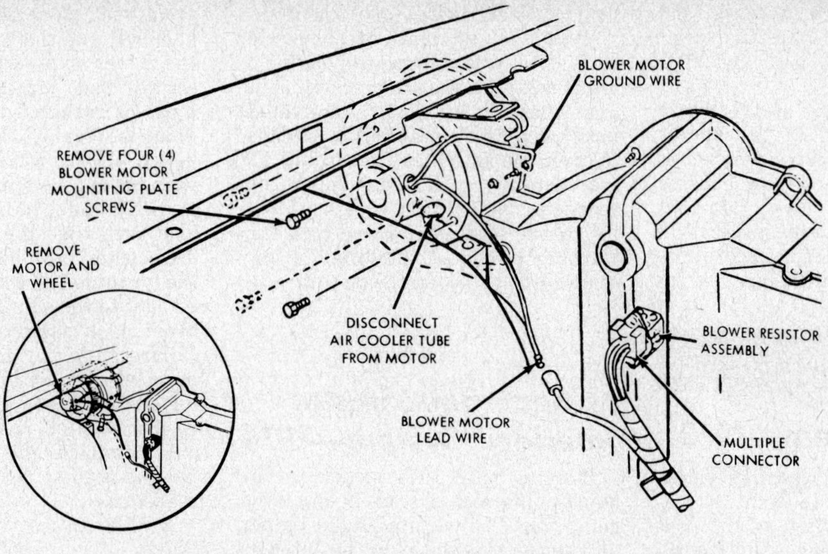
BLOWER MOTOR
GROUND WIRE
REMOVE FOUR (4)
BLOWER MOTOR
MOUNTING PLATE
SCREWS
REMOVE
MOTOR AND
WHEEL
DISCONNECT
AIR COOLER TUBE
FROM MOTOR
BLOWER RESISTOR
ASSEMBLY
BLOWER MOTOR
LEAD WIRE
MULTIPLE
CONNECTOR

Heater blower removal—1970-74 Lincoln Continental (© Ford Motor Co)

studs and lift it up and out of vehicle.

11. Remove two spring clips from core tubes on front of core cover.
12. Remove three screws from core end plate and remove plate.
13. Remove heater core and mounting gasket assembly from core cover and remove gasket from core. Reverse procedure to install.

1972-74 Mark IV

1. Drain the engine coolant and disconnect the heater hoses from the heater core.
2. Remove the glove box.
3. Remove the heater air outlet register from the plenum assembly. It is held in position by two snap-rings.
4. Remove the temperature control cable assembly mounting screw, and disconnect the end of the cable from the blend door crank arm by removing the spring nut.
5. Remove the blue and red vacuum hoses from the high-low door vacuum motor, and the brown hose at the in-line tee connector to the temperature bypass door motor.
6. Disconnect the wire connector from the resistor.
7. Remove 10 screws from around the flange of the plenum case and remove the rear case half of the plenum.
8. Remove the mounting nut from the heater core tube support bracket.
9. Reinstall in the reverse procedure. To provide a positive seal between the front and rear case halves, apply body sealer around the case flanges prior to installation. Be certain that the core mounting gasket is properly installed. Reverse procedure to install.

Heater Blower Removal

1967-69 Continental

The blower motor is mounted in the right fender well.

1. Remove right fender splash shield secured with six bolts.
2. Remove four screws retaining blower motor to housing.
3. Disconnect electrical leads and remove motor.
4. Remove four nuts retaining motor housing to air door assembly and remove one nut through motor opening.
5. Remove housing and disassemble boot.
6. From inside car, remove right cowl trim panel and remove three screws retaining air door assembly to cowl.
7. From under fender remove screw at top.
8. Disconnect vacuum hose and remove air door assembly. Reverse procedure to install.

1969-71 Mark III

1. Remove right cowl side trim panel.
2. Remove screws retaining duct to cowl side panel and sound baffle and remove duct.
3. Disconnect lead wire to blower motor.
4. Remove one screw from motor mounting plate, rotate motor mounting plate clockwise to unlock plate from case and remove motor and wheel assembly through opening in cowl side of panel. Reverse procedure to install.

1970-74 Continental

1. Remove hood.
2. Remove right hood hinge and right fender inner support brace as an assembly.
3. Disconnect blower motor air cooling tube from motor.
4. Disconnect motor lead wire from harness and ground wire from dash panel.
5. Disconnect rear section of right front fender panel apron from fender around wheel opening and remove two lower fender to cowl mounting screws.
6. Separate fender apron from fender wheel opening so that apron can be pushed downward away from blower motor.
7. Remove four blower motor plate screws. Move motor and wheel forward out of blower scroll and remove assembly through opening while applying pressure to fender apron to enlarge opening at hinge area. Reverse procedure to install.

1972-74 Mark IV

1. Remove the glove box for access.
2. Remove the recirculation air register and duct assembly from the blower assembly.
3. Remove the two screws that attach the blower lower housing to the dash panel.
4. Disconnect the white hose from the outside-recirc air door vacuum motor and remove the vacuum motor from the blower lower housing. It is held in place by two screws. Leave the motor actuator connected to the door crank arm.
5. Disconnect the orange blower motor lead wire from the harness connector, and disconnect the black motor ground wire.
6. Remove the six upper-to-lower blower housing flange screws.
7. Separate the blower lower housing and motor assembly from the upper housing and remove it from beneath the instrument panel.

8. Remove the blower motor and wheel assembly from the lower housing. It is held by four screws.
9. The upper flange of the recirc duct is retained to the blower upper housing with two S-clips that remained on the housing during removal. Be certain that the duct is properly installed in the two clips during reinstallation. Reverse procedure to install.

SEAT BELTS

Buzzer System—1973

The front seat belt warning system consists of a switch in each belt retractor, a sensor switch in the seat cushion on the passenger side, a reminder light and a warning buzzer. The circuit wiring is routed through the ignition switch and transmission neutral safety switch on all models.

With the automatic transmission shift selector in a forward position on all models, the warning circuit (light and buzzer) is closed (activated) until the driver's seat belt is extended to open (de-activate) the circuit. The seat sensor on the passenger side reacts to weights in excess of 0-47 lbs. on the seat cushion and closes the warning circuit. Extending the passenger belt will open the circuit.

Seat Belt/Starter Interlock System—1974

Starting with 1974 models, a new starter interlock system is employed, consisting of a warning light, buzzer, seat sensors, switches in the outboard belt retractors, and an electronic logic module. The starter will not operate unless the driver and right front seat passenger sit on the seat and pull out their seat belts. Unless the driver or passenger has remained seated and buckled, the sequence must be repeated every time the engine is started. Leaving the belts pulled all the way out will also prevent the engine from being started as the belts must be retracted and buckled each time the engine is started. The center seat belt is connected to the warning light and buzzer system, but not to the starter interlock. In the event of a starter interlock system failure or to permit the use of a remote starter switch when working under the hood, a starter interlock by-pass switch is located in the engine compartment, thereby eliminating the need to perform the buckling sequence.

NOTE: Each time the by-pass switch is operated the buckling sequence may be eliminated only once. The system may not be permanently by-passed.

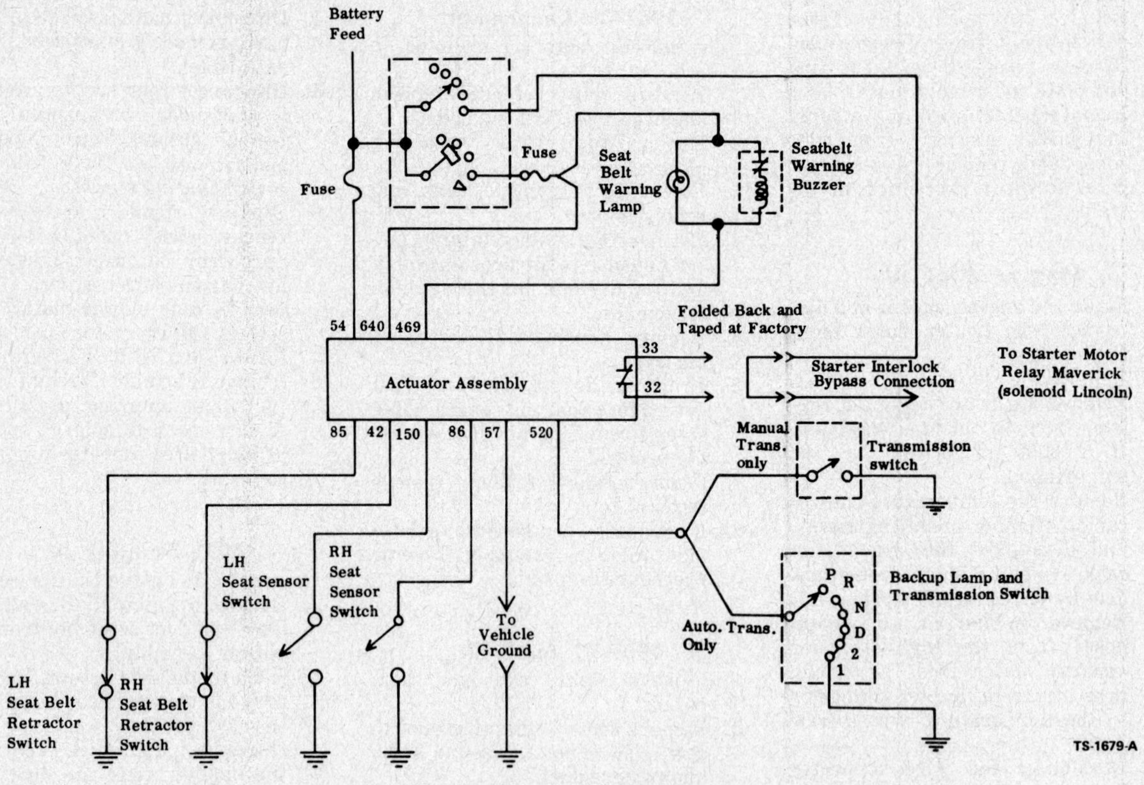

Battery Feed
Fuse
Fuse
Seat Belt Warning Lamp
Seatbelt Warning Buzzer
54
640
469
Folded Back and Taped at Factory
33
32
Actuator Assembly
Starter Interlock Bypass Connection
To Starter Motor Relay Maverick (solenoid Lincoln)
85
42
150
86
57
520
Manual Trans. only
Transmission switch
LH Seat Sensor Switch
RH Seat Sensor Switch
To Vehicle Ground
Backup Lamp and Transmission Switch
P
R
N
D
2
1
Auto. Trans. Only
LH Seat Belt Retractor Switch
RH Seat Belt Retractor Switch
TS-1679-A

Late 1973 Lincolns (and Mavericks) have the 1974 seat belt/starter interlock system components and wiring. The interlock parts of the system are not connected, since only a light and buzzer warning system was required for 1973. (© Ford Motor Co)

Oldsmobile • F-85 • Omega

YEAR IDENTIFICATION

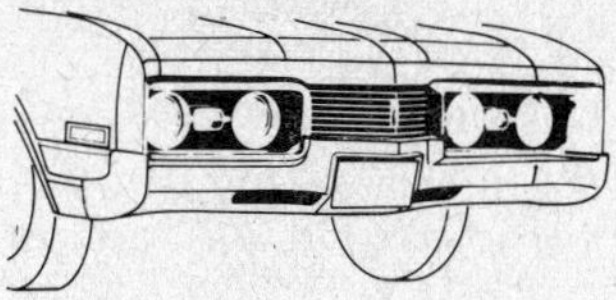

1967 Delta 88

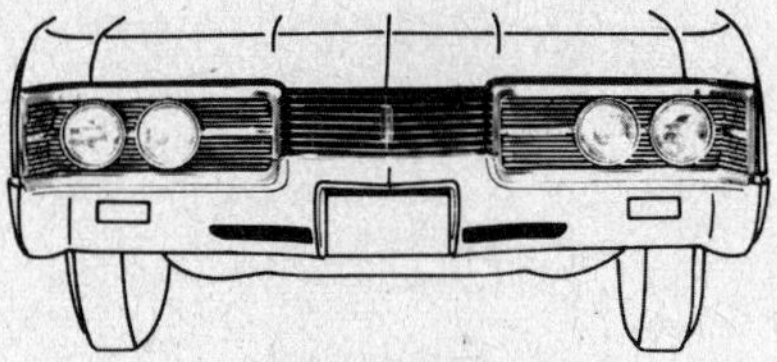

1967 Delmont

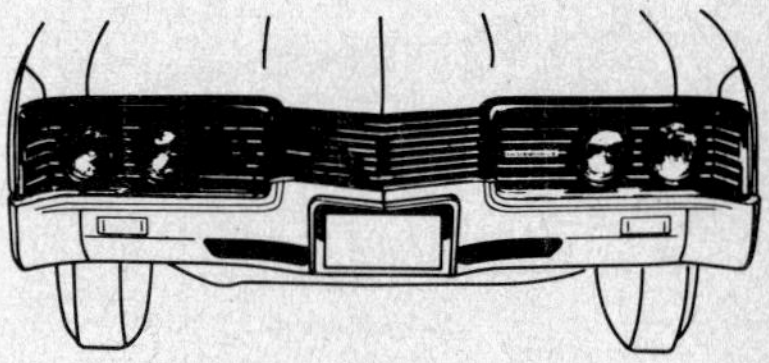

1967 98

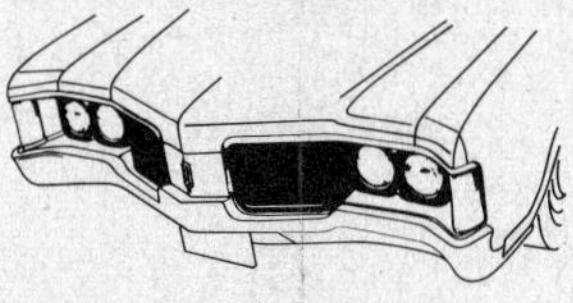

1966 88-98

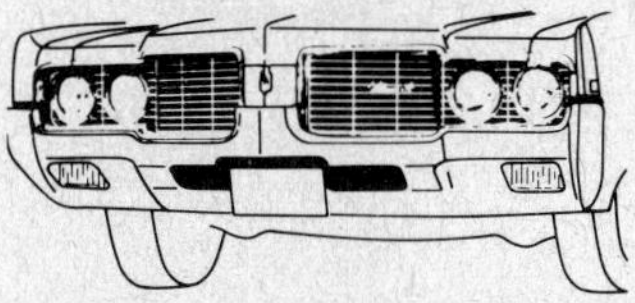

1969 88

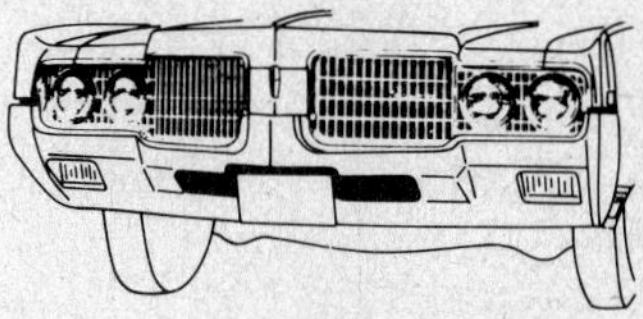

1969 98

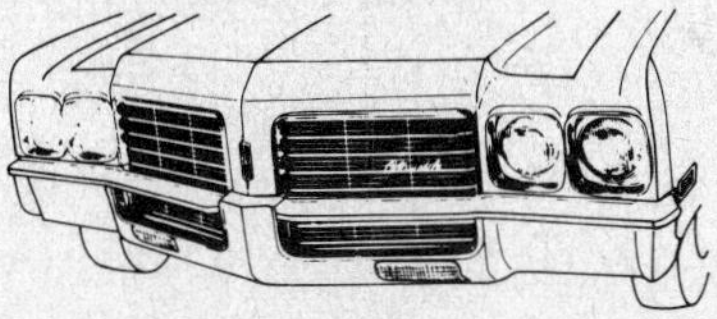

1970 98 Series

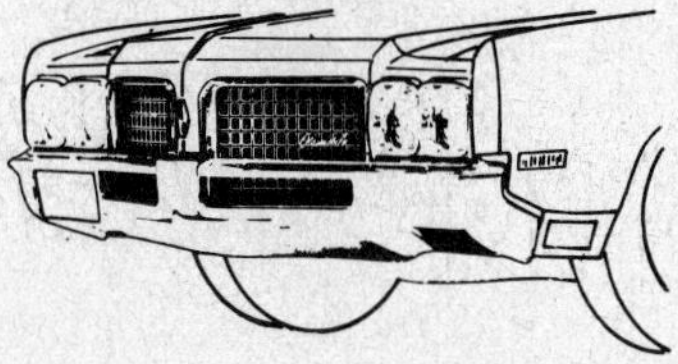

1970 Delta 88

1971 Delta 88

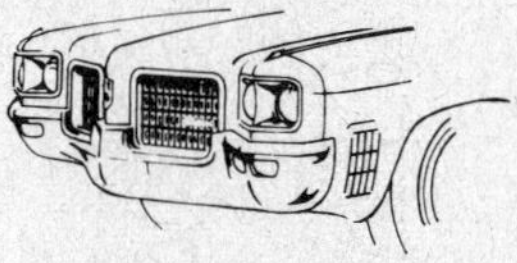

1971 98

1972 Delta 88

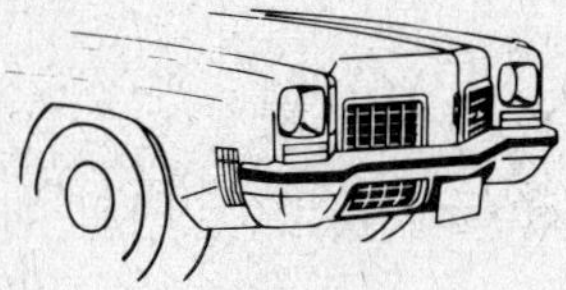

1972 98

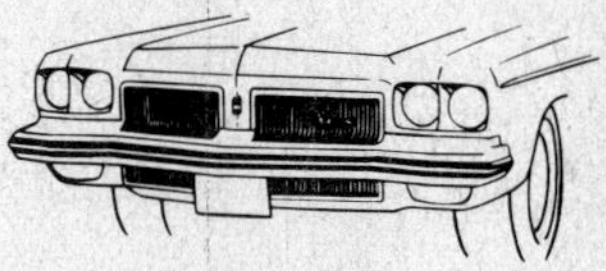

1973 Delta 88

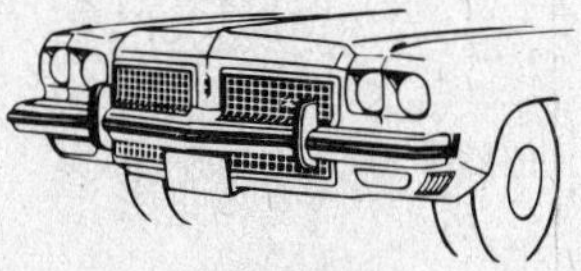

1973 98

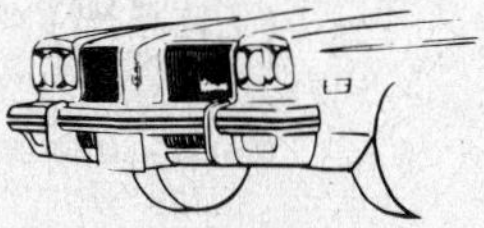

1974 Delta 88

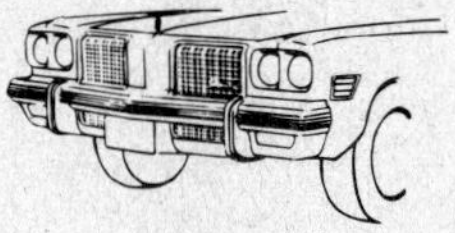

1974 98

F85

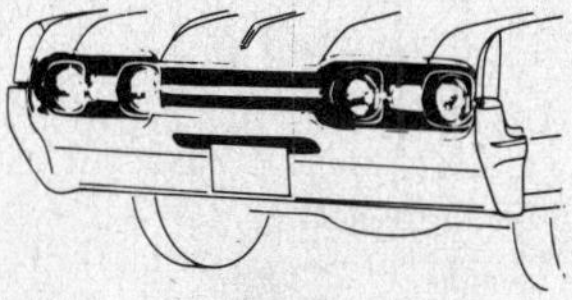

1967 F85

1968 F85

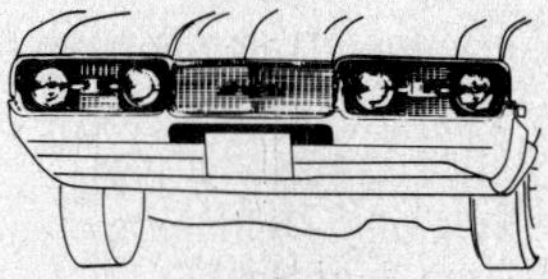

1968 442

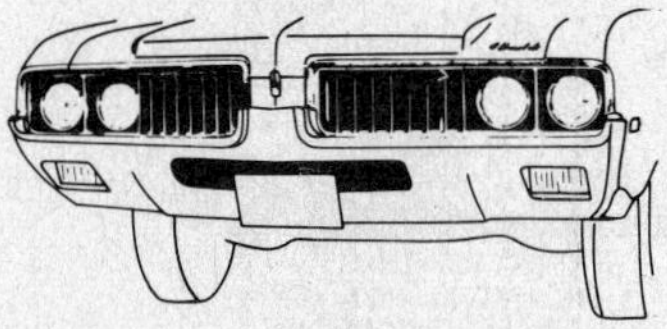

1969 F85

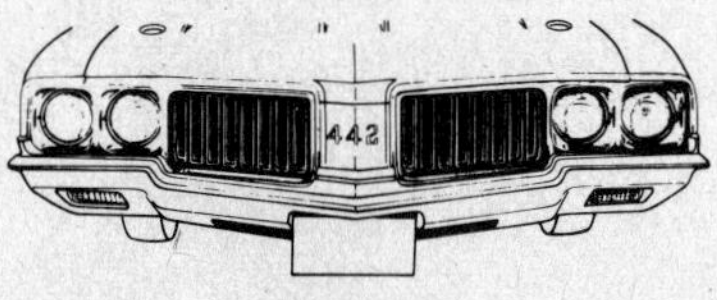

1970 4-4-2

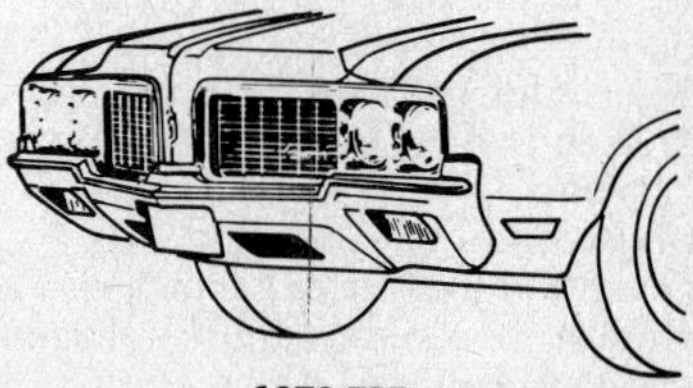

1970 F85

YEAR IDENTIFICATION

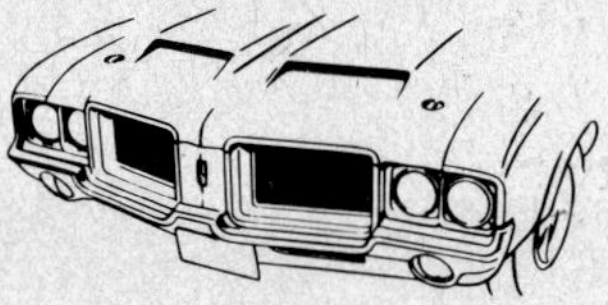
1971 4-4-2

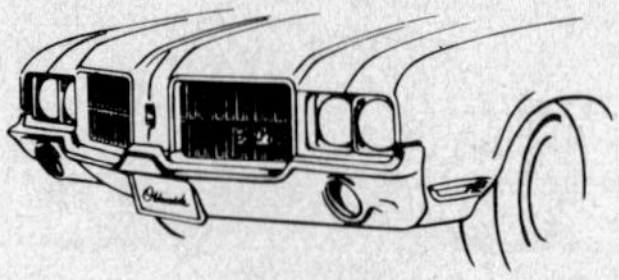
1971 Cutlass Supreme

1972 Cutlass S

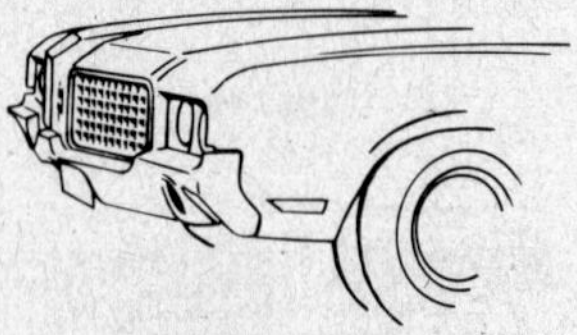
1972 Cutlass Supreme

1973 Cutlass S

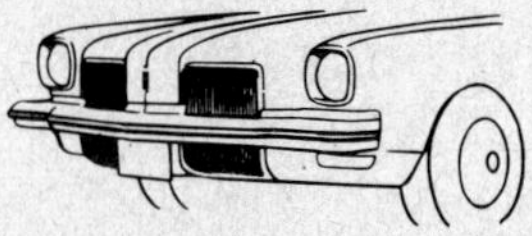
1973 Cutlass Supreme

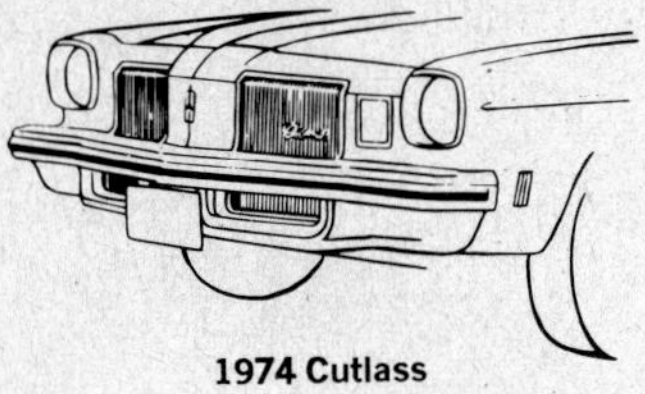
1974 Cutlass

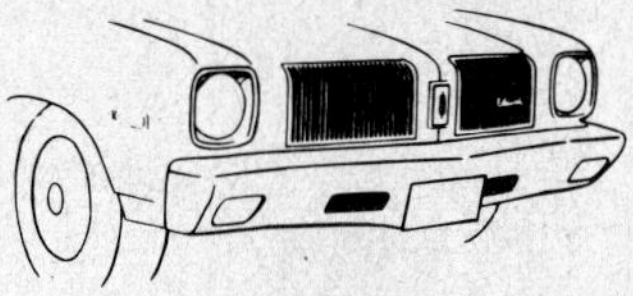
1973 Omega

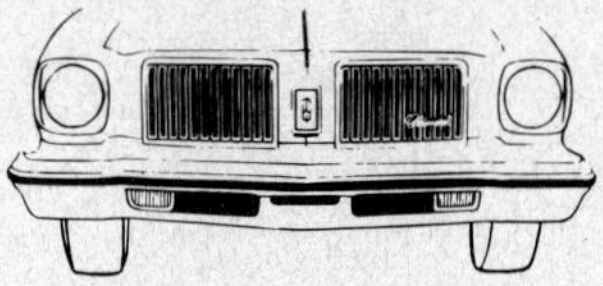
1974 Omega

FIRING ORDER

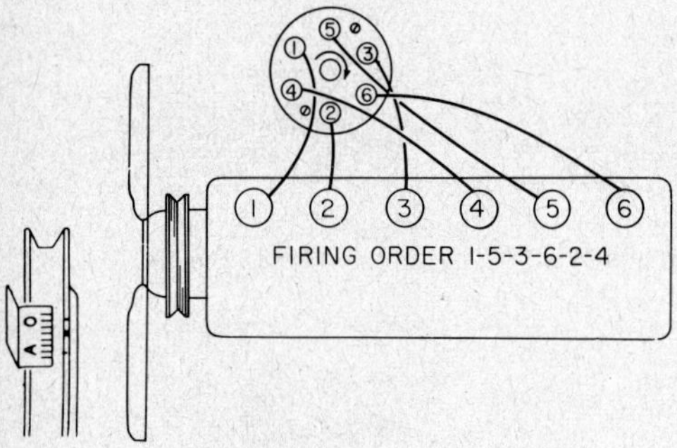
FIRING ORDER 1-5-3-6-2-4
OHV 6 cyl.

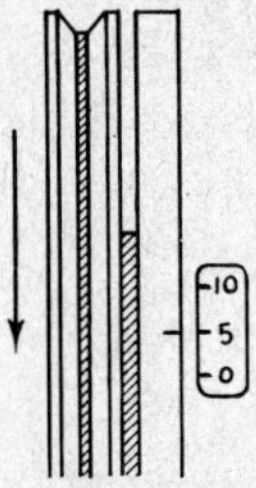
10
5
0
Timing mark—V8

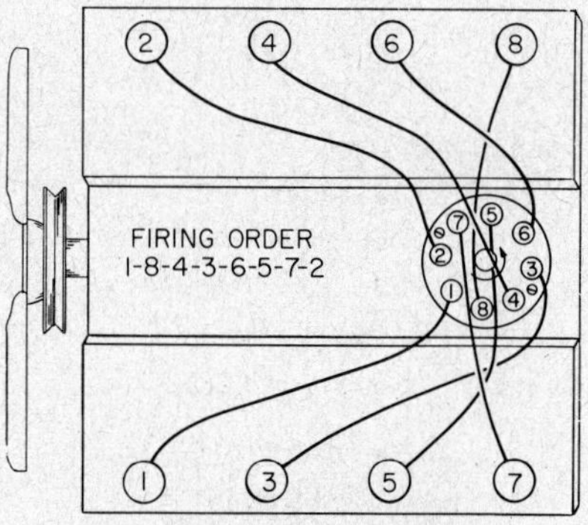
FIRING ORDER
1-8-4-3-6-5-7-2
330, 350, 400, 425, 455 V8

CAR SERIAL NUMBER LOCATION

1967

Located on left front door hinge pillar.

1968-74

Left side of instrument panel, visible through windshield.

1967-74

First digit—Oldsmobile Division
Second digit indicates series
Third digit or letter indicates engine
Fourth and fifth digits indicate body type
Sixth digit indicates year
Seventh digit (letter) indicates plant
Eighth to tenth digits—sequential serial number

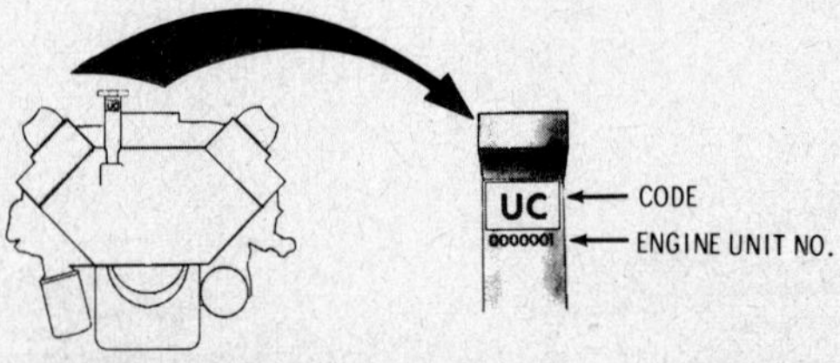
UC
000001
CODE
ENGINE UNIT NO.
V8 engine identification code location—1968-74

ENGINE IDENTIFICATION NUMBER
S200001
NUMBER ON THIS SURFACE IS NOT ENGINE IDENTIFICATION NUMBER
V8 engine identification code location—1967

ENGINE IDENTIFICATION CODE

The engine identification code is stamped on a machined pad located at the front of the right cylinder head on 1967 V8 models, on the right side of the cylinder block directly behind the distributor on 1967-71 six cylinder models, and located on tape attached directly to the front of the oil filler tube on all 1968-74 V8 models and 1973-74 six cylinder models.

Disp	Bbl	Hp	'67	'68	'69	'70	'71	'72	'73	'74
6-Cylinder Models										
250	1	100 (net)							CCA CCB CCC CCD	CCA CCB CCC CCD
250	1	145					VB VF			
250	1	155	F	VA VB VE VF	VA VB VE VF	VB VF				
8-Cylinder Models										
330	2	250	W							
330	2	260	X							
330	4	320	WG XG							
350	2	145 (net)							QS QT	
350	2	160 (net)						QA QB QC	QN QQ QP QQ QS QT	
350	4	160, 180, 200# (net)							QB QC QD QL QO QU QW TB TC TL TO	
350	4	180 (net)						QD QE QJ QK	QA QB QD QE QJ QK QL	
350	2	240					QA QI QJ TC TD TE			
350	2	250		QA QB QI QS TB TD TL	QA QB QI QJ TB TC TD TL	QA QI QJ TC TD TL				
350	2	260			QB QN QO QP					
350	4	300		TN						

Disp	Bbl	Hp	'67	'68	'69	'70	'71	'72	'73	'74
8-Cylinder Models										
350	4	310		QN QP QV QX	QN QP QV	QN QP QV				
350	4	325			QX	QD QX				
400	2	290		QI						
400	2	300	V							
400	4	325		QR QS QW	QR QS QW					
400	4	350	VG	QU	QU					
400	4	360		QT	QT					
425	2	300	PL							
425	2	310	P							
425	4	365	R							
425	4	375	RS							
455	4	210 (net)								UA UB UC UD UL UU UW VA VB VC VD VL
455	4	225, 250 (net)						US UT UU UV	UA UB UD US UT	
455	4	230 (net)							UV UX	
455	4	270 (net)						UA UB UD UE		
455	2	280					UC UD UE			
455	4	300 (net)						UL UN UO		
455	2	310		UC UD UJ	UC UD UJ	UC UD UJ				
455	2	320		UA UB		TX TY				
455	4	320					TD TN TQ TU TV TW UN UO			
455	4	340					TB			

ENGINE IDENTIFICATION CODE

Disp	Bbl	Hp	'67	'68	'69	'70	'71	'72	'73	'74
8-Cylinder Models										
455	4	340					TL			
							TS			
							TT			
455	4	350					US			
							UT			
455	4	365		UN	UN	TP				
				UO	UO	TQ				
						TU				
						TV				
						TW				
						UN				
						UO				
						TS				
						TT				
455	4	370								
455	4	390			UL					

With dual exhaust

PISTON CLEARANCE

Year	Engine	Piston-to-Bore Clearance (in.)
'67	L6-250	.0025
	V8-330, 400, 425	.0075-.0125
'68	L6-250	.0025
	V8-350, 400, 455	.0075-.0125
'69	L6-250	.0025
	V8-350	.0075-.0125
	V8-400, 455	.0010-.0020
'70-'74	L6-250	.0025
	V8-350, 455	.0010-.0020①

① 1972 W-30 (option 455 cu in. V8)—.0025-.0035 in.

Olds & F-85 GENERAL ENGINE SPECIFICATIONS

Year	Engine Cu. In. Displacement	Carburetor Type	Advertised Horsepower @ rpm ■	Advertised Torque @ rpm (ft lbs) ■	Bore and Stroke (in.)	Advertised Compression Ratio	Oil Pressure @ 2050 rpm
'67	6-250	1 bbl	155 @ 4200	240 @ 2000	3.875 x 3.530	8.50:1	30-45
	8-330	2 bbl	250 @ 4800	335 @ 2800	3.938 x 3.385	9.00:1	35-45
	8-330	2 bbl	260 @ 4800	355 @ 2800	3.938 x 3.385	10.25:1	35-45
	8-330	4 bbl	310 @ 5200	340 @ 3600	3.938 x 3.385	9.00:1	35-45
	8-330	4 bbl	320 @ 5200	360 @ 3600	3.938 x 3.385	10.25:1	35-45
	8-400	2 bbl	300 @ 4600	425 @ 3000	4.000 x 3.975	10.25:1	35-50
	8-400	4 bbl	350 @ 5000	440 @ 3600	4.000 x 3.975	10.05:1	35-50
	8-425	2 bbl	300 @ 4400	430 @ 2400	4.126 x 3.975	9.00:1	30-45
	8-425	2 bbl	310 @ 4400	450 @ 2400	4.126 x 3.975	10.25:1	30-45
	8-425	4 bbl	365 @ 4800	470 @ 3200	4.126 x 3.975	10.25:1	30-45
	8-425	4 bbl	375 @ 4000	470 @ 3200	4.126 x 3.975	10.50:1	30-45
'68	6-250	1 bbl	155 @ 4200	240 @ 2000	3.875 x 3.530	8.50:1	30-45
	8-350	2 bbl	250 @ 4400	355 @ 2600	4.057 x 3.385	9.00:1	35-45
	8-350	4 bbl	300 @ 4800	390 @ 3600	4.057 x 3.385	10.25:1	35-45
	8-350	4 bbl	310 @ 4800	390 @ 3600	4.057 x 3.385	10.25:1	35-45
	8-400	2 bbl	290 @ 4600	425 @ 2400	3.870 x 4.250	9.00:1	35-50
	8-400	4 bbl	325 @ 4600	440 @ 3200	3.870 x 4.250	10.50:1	35-50
	8-400	4 bbl	350 @ 4800	440 @ 3200	3.870 x 4.250	10.50:1	35-50
	8-400	4 bbl	360 @ 5400	440 @ 3600	3.870 x 4.250	10.50:1	35-50
	8-455	2 bbl	310 @ 4200	490 @ 2400	4.126 x 4.250	9.00:1	30-45
	8-455	2 bbl	320 @ 4200	500 @ 2400	4.126 x 4.250	10.25:1	30-45
	8-455	4 bbl	365 @ 4600	510 @ 3000	4.126 x 4.250	10.25:1	30-45
'69	6-250	1 bbl	155 @ 4200	240 @ 2000	3.875 x 3.530	8.50:1	30-45
	8-350	2 bbl	250 @ 4400	355 @ 2600	4.057 x 3.385	9.00:1	30-45
	8-350	4 bbl	310 @ 4800	390 @ 3200	4.057 x 3.385	10.25:1	30-45
	8-350	4 bbl	325 @ 5400	360 @ 3600	4.057 x 3.385	10.50:1	30-45
	8-400	4 bbl	325 @ 4600	440 @ 3000	3.870 x 4.250	10.50:1	35-50
	8-400	4 bbl	350 @ 4800	440 @ 3200	3.870 x 4.250	10.50:1	35-50
	8-400	4 bbl	360 @ 5400	440 @ 3600	3.870 x 4.250	10.50:1	35-50
	8-455	2 bbl	310 @ 4200	490 @ 2400	4.126 x 4.250	9.00:1	30-45
	8-455	4 bbl	365 @ 4600	510 @ 3000	4.126 x 4.250	10.25:1	30-45
	8-455	4 bbl	390 @ 5000	500 @ 3200	4.126 x 4.250	10.25:1	30-45

GENERAL ENGINE SPECIFICATIONS

Year	Engine Cu. In. Displacement	Carburetor Type	Advertised Horsepower @ rpm ■	Advertised Torque @ rpm (ft lbs) ■	Bore and Stroke (in.)	Advertised Compression Ratio	Oil Pressure @ 2050 rpm
'70	6-250	1 bbl	155 @ 4200	240 @ 2000	3.875 x 3.530	8.50:1	30-45
	8-350	2 bbl	250 @ 4400	355 @ 2600	4.057 x 3.385	9.00:1	30-45
	8-350	4 bbl	310 @ 4800	390 @ 3200	4.057 x 3.385	10.25:1	30-45
	8-350	4 bbl	325 @ 5400	360 @ 3600	4.057 x 3.385	10.50:1	30-45
	8-455	2 bbl	310 @ 4200	490 @ 2400	4.125 x 4.250	9.00:1	30-45
	8-455	2 bbl	320 @ 4200	500 @ 2400	4.126 x 4.250	10.25:1	30-45
	8-455	4 bbl	365 @ 4600	510 @ 3000	4.126 x 4.250	10.25:1	35-45
	8-455	4 bbl	365 @ 5000	500 @ 3200	4.126 x 4.250	10.50:1	35-50
	8-455	4 bbl	370 @ 5200	500 @ 3600	4.126 x 4.250	10.50:1	35-50
	8-455	4 bbl	390 @ 5000	500 @ 3200	4.126 x 4.250	10.25:1	30-45
'71	6-250	1 bbl	145 @ 4200	230 @ 2000	3.875 x 3.530	8.00:1	30-45
	8-350	2 bbl	240 @ 4200	350 @ 2400	4.057 x 3.385	8.50:1	30-45
	8-350	4 bbl	260 @ 4600	360 @ 3200	4.057 x 3.385	8.50:1	30-45
	8-455	2 bbl	280 @ 4000	445 @ 2000	4.126 x 4.250	8.50:1	30-45
	8-455	4 bbl	320 @ 4400	460 @ 2800	4.126 x 4.250	8.50:1	30-45
	8-455	4 bbl	340 @ 4600	460 @ 3200	4.126 x 4.250	8.50:1	30-50
	8-455	4 bbl	350 @ 4700	460 @ 3200	4.126 x 4.250	8.50:1	30-50
'72	8-350	2 bbl	160 @ 4000	275 @ 2400	4.057 x 3.385	8.50:1	30-45
	8-350①	2 bbl	175 @ 4000	295 @ 2600	4.057 x 3.385	8.50:1	30-45
	8-350	4 bbl	180 @ 4000	275 @ 2800	4.057 x 3.385	8.50:1	30-45
	8-350①	4 bbl	200 @ 4400	300 @ 3200	4.057 x 3.385	8.50:1	30-45
	8-455	4 bbl	225 @ 3600	360 @ 2600	4.126 x 4.250	8.50:1	30-50
	8-455①	4 bbl	250 @ 4200	370 @ 2800	4.126 x 4.250	8.50:1	30-50
	8-455	4 bbl	270 @ 4400	370 @ 3200	4.126 x 4.250	8.50:1	30-50
	8-455	4 bbl	300 @ 4700	410 @ 3200	4.126 x 4.250	8.50:1	30-50
'73	6-250	1 bbl	100 @ 3600	175 @ 1600	3.875 x 3.530	8.50:1	30-45
	8-350	2 bbl	160 @ 3800	275 @ 2400	4.057 x 3.385	8.50:1	30-45
	8-350	4 bbl	180 @ 3800	275 @ 2800	4.057 x 3.385	8.50:1	30-45
	8-455	4 bbl	225 @ 3600	360 @ 2600	4.126 x 4.250	8.50:1	30-50
	8-455	4 bbl	250 @ 4000	370 @ 2800	4.126 x 4.250	8.50:1	30-50
'74	6-250	1 bbl	100 @ 3600	175 @ 1600	3.875 x 3.530	8.50:1	30-45
	8-350	2 bbl	N.A.	N.A.	4.057 x 3.385	8.50:1	30-45
	8-350	4 bbl	160 @ 3800	275 @ 2400	4.057 x 3.385	8.50:1	30-45
	8-350	4 bbl	180 @ 3800	275 @ 2800	4.057 x 3.385	8.50:1	30-45
	8-350①	4 bbl	200 @ 4200	300 @ 3200	4.057 x 3.385	8.50:1	30-45
	8-455	2 bbl	N.A.	N.A.	4.126 x 4.250	8.50:1	30-50
	8-455	4 bbl	210 @ 3600	350 @ 2400	4.126 x 4.250	8.50:1	30-50
	8-455①	4 bbl	230 @ 4000	370 @ 2800	4.126 x 4.250	8.50:1	30-50

■ Beginning 1972, horsepower and torque are SAE net figures. They are measured at the rear of the transmission with all accessories installed and operating. Since the figures vary when a given engine is installed in different models, some are representative rather than exact.

① Dual exhaust

F-85, Cutlass, Omega, Vista Cruiser, 442

TUNE-UP SPECIFICATIONS

When analyzing compression test results, look for uniformity among cylinders rather than specific pressures.

	ENGINE		SPARK PLUGS		DISTRIBUTOR		IGNITION TIMING (deg) ▲			VALVES	Fuel	IDLE SPEED (rpm) ▲	
Year	No. Cyl Displacement (cu in.)	hp	Type §	Gap (in.)	Point Dwell (deg)	Point Gap (in.)	Man Trans	‡	Auto Trans	Intake Opens ■ (deg) ●	Pump Pressure (psi)	Man Trans	Auto Trans
'67	6-250	155	46N	.035	31-34	.019	4B		4B	62	3½-4½	500(700)①	500①
	8-330	250	45S	.030	28-32	.016	7½B		7½B	12	7¾-9	600(650)①	575(600)①
	8-330	320	44S	.030	28-32	.016	7½B		7½B	21	7¾-9	600(650)	500(600)
	8-400	300	44S	.030	28-32	.016	7½B		7½B	21	7¾-9	600(650)	550(600)
	8-400	350	44S	.030	28-32	.016	7½8		7½B	21②	7¾-9	600(650)	550(600)
'68	6-250	155	46N	.035	31-34	.019	TDC		4B	16	3½-4½	725	600-400
	8-350	250	45S	.030	28-32	.016	5B		5B	16	5½-7	675	575
	8-350	310	44S	.030	28-32	.016	7½B		7½B	16	5½-7	675	575
	8-400	290	45S	.030	28-32	.016	—		5B	21	5½-7	—	575
	8-400	325	44S	.030	28-32	.016	—		2½B	21	5½-7	—	575
	8-400	350	44S	.030	28-32	.016	7½B		7½B	21	5½-7	700	500
	8-400	360	44S	.030	28-32	.016	12½B		12½B	56	5½-7	750	750
'69	6-250	155	R-46N	.035	31-34	.019	TDC		4B	16	3½-4½	775/400	625/400
	8-350	250	R-45S	.030	28-32	.016	6B		6B	16	5½-7	675/400	600/400
	8-350	310	R-44S	.030	28-32	.016	8B		8B	16	5½-7	675	575
	8-350	325	R-44S	.030	28-32	.016	12B		—	40	5½-7	850	—
	8-400	325	R-44S	.030	28-32	.016	—		8B	21	5½-7	—	550
	8-400	350	R-44S	.030	28-32	.016	2B		—	50	5½-7	750	—
	8-400	360	R-43S	.030	28-32	.016	14B		14	56	5½-7	850	650
'70	6-250	155	R-46T	.035	31-34	.019	TDC		4B	16	4-5	830-750	630-600
	8-350	250	R-46S	.030	28-32	.016	10B		10B	16	5½-6½	750	575
	8-350	310	R-45S	.030	28-32	.016	10B		10B	16	5½-6½	650	575
	8-350	325	R-43S	.030	28-32	.016	14B		14B	40	5½-6½	750	625
	8-455	320	R-45S	.030	28-32	.016	—		8B	20	5½-6½	—	575
	8-455	365③	R-44S	.030	28-32	.016	—		12½	20	5½-6½	—	600
	8-455	365④	R-45S	.030	28-32	.016	—		8B	24	5½-6½	—	575
	8-455	365⑤	R-44S	.030	28-32	.016	12B		12B	24②	5½-6½	700	650
	8-455	370⑤	R-44S	.030	28-32	.016	8B		8B	56	5½-6½	700	650
'71	6-250	145	R-46TS	.035	31-34	.019	4B		4B	16	4-5	600⑧	575⑧
	8-350	240	R-46S	.040	28-32	.016	10B		10B	14	5½-6½	750	600
	8-350	260	R-45S⑥	.040	28-32	.016	10B		12B	14②	5½-6½	750	600
	8-455	280	R-46S	.040	28-32	.016	—		8B	20	5½-6½	—	600
	8-455	320	R-46S	.040	28-32	.016	—		8B	20	5½-6½	—	600
	8-455	340	R-45S	.040	28-32	.016	10B		10B	24②	5½-6½	750	600
	8-455	350	R-45S	.040	28-32	.016	12B		10B	56	5½-6½	750	600
'72	8-350	160	R-46S	.040	28-32	.016	8B		8B(6B)	16(22)	5½-6½	750	650/550
	8-350	180	R-46S	.040	28-32	.016	8B		12B	16(22)	5½-6½	750	600
	8-455	250	R-46S	.040	28-32	.016	10B		8B	30⑦	5½-6½	750	600
	8-455	270	R-46S	.040	28-32	.016	10B		8B	30⑦	5½-6½	750	600
	8-455	300	R-45S	.040	28-32	.016	12B		10B	56	5½-6½	750	650
'73	6-250	100	R-46TS	.035	33	.019	6B		6B	16	4-5	700/450	600/450
	8-350	160	R-46S	.040	30	.016	—		14B	22	5½-6½	—	650/550
	8-350	180	R-46S	.040	30	.016	—		12B	22	5½-6½	—	650/550
	8-350	180	R-45S	.040	30	.016	12B		—	22	5½-6½	1000/600	—
	8-455	225	R-45S	.040	30	.016	10B		8B	28	5½-6½	1000/750	650/550

F-85, Cutlass, Omega, Vista Cruiser, 442 TUNE-UP SPECIFICATIONS

When analyzing compression test results, look for uniformity among cylinders rather than specific pressures.

Year	ENGINE No. Cyl Displacement (cu in.)	ENGINE hp	SPARK PLUGS Type §	SPARK PLUGS Gap (in.)	DISTRIBUTOR Point Dwell (deg)	DISTRIBUTOR Point Gap (in.)	IGNITION TIMING (deg) ▲ Man Trans	‡	IGNITION TIMING (deg) ▲ Auto Trans	VALVES Intake Opens ■ (deg) ●	Fuel Pump Pressure (psi)	IDLE SPEED (rpm) ▲ Man Trans	IDLE SPEED (rpm) ▲ Auto Trans
'74	6-250	100	R-46TS	.035	33	.019	8B		8B	16	4-5	850/450	600/450
	8-350	N.A.	R-46S	.040	30	.016	—		14B	22	5½-6½	—	700/450
	8-350	160, 180	R-46S	.040	30	.016	—		12B	22	5½-6½	—	650/550
	8-350	200	R-46S	.040	30	.016	—		14B	22	5½-6½	—	650/550
	8-455	N.A.	R-46S	.040	30	.016	—		8B	22	5½-6½	—	650/550
	8-455	210	R-46S	.040	30	.016	—		8B	22	5½-6½	—	650/550
	8-455	230	R-46SX	.080	⑨	⑨	—		8B	22	5½-6½	—	650/550

▲ See text for procedure
■ All figures Before Top Dead Center
● Figure in parentheses indicates California engine
‡ Set timing with carburetor adjusted to the following speeds:

All V8	Without A/C	With A/C
1967-68	850	1250
1969 350 Cu. In.	850	1000
1969 400 Cu. In.	850	1250
1970-74	1100	850

§ All spark plug listings are A.C. original equipment numbers
① A/C on
② Figure is 30 degrees for manual transmission
③ Cutlass
④ Vista Cruiser
⑤ 442
⑥ AC-R-46S for automatic transmission
⑦ Figure is 44 degrees for manual transmission
⑧ Without A/C
550—automatic transmission
500—manual transmission
⑨ Electronic ignition
B Before Top Dead Center
TDC Top Dead Center
— Not applicable
N.A. Not Available

Delta 88 Delmont, 88, 98 TUNE-UP SPECIFICATIONS

When analyzing compression test results, look for uniformity among cylinders rather than specific pressures.

Year	ENGINE No. Cyl Displacement (cu in.)	ENGINE hp	SPARK PLUGS Type §	SPARK PLUGS Gap (in.)	DISTRIBUTOR Point Dwell (deg)	DISTRIBUTOR Point Gap (in.)	IGNITION TIMING (deg) ▲ Man Trans	‡	IGNITION TIMING (deg) ▲ Auto Trans	VALVES Intake Opens ■ (deg) ●	Fuel Pump Pressure (psi)	IDLE SPEED (rpm) ▲ Man Trans	IDLE SPEED (rpm) ▲ Auto Trans
'67	8-330	250	45S	.030	28-32	.016	7½B		7½B	12	7¾-9	600(650)	575(600)
	8-330	260	44S	.030	28-32	.016	7½B		7½B	12	7¾-9	600(650)	575(600)
	8-330	320	44S	.030	28-32	.016	7½B		7½B	21	7¾-9	600(650)	575(600)
	8-425	300	45S	.030	28-32	.016	7½B		7½B	21	7¾-9	575(600)	575
	8-425	310	44S	.030	28-32	.016	5B		5B	21	7¾-9	575(600)	575
	8-425	365	44S	.030	28-32	.016	7½B		7½B	21	7¾-9	575(600)	575
	8-425	375	44S	.030	28-32	.016	7½B		7½B	21	7¾-9	575(600)	575
'68	8-350	250	45S	.030	28-32	.016	5B		5B	16	5-7	675	575
	8-350	300	44S	.030	28-32	.016	7½B		7½B	16	5-7	675	575
	8-455	310	45S	.030	28-32	.016	5B		5B	20	5-7	675	575
	8-455	320	44S	.030	28-32	.016	7½B		7½B	20	5-7	675	575
	8-455	365	44S	.030	28-32	.016	7½B		7½B	20	5-7	675	575
'69	8-350	250	45S	.030	28-32	.016	6B		6B	16	5-7	675/400	600/400
	8-455	310	45S	.030	28-32	.016	6B		6B	20	5-7	675/400	600/400
	8-455	365	44S	.030	28-32	.016	—		8B	20	5-7	—	575
	8-455	390	43S	.030	28-32	.016	—		10B	24	5½-6½	—	575
'70	8-350	250	R-46S	.030	28-32	.016	8B		8B	16	5½-6½	675	575
	8-455	310	R-46S	.030	28-32	.016	8B		8B	20	5½-6½	675	575
	8-455	365	R-45S	.030	28-32	.016	—		8B	20	5½-6½	—	575
'71	8-350	240	R-46S	.040	28-32	.016	—		10B	14	5½-6½	—	600
	8-455	280	R-46S	.040	28-32	.016	—		8B	20	5½-6½	—	600
	8-455	320	R-46S	.040	28-32	.016	—		8B	20	5½-6½	—	600

Delta 88 Delmont, 88, 98 TUNE-UP SPECIFICATIONS

When analyzing compression test results, look for uniformity among cylinders rather than specific pressures.

Year	ENGINE No. Cyl Displacement (cu in.)	ENGINE hp	SPARK PLUGS Type §	SPARK PLUGS Gap (in.)	DISTRIBUTOR Point Dwell (deg)	DISTRIBUTOR Point Gap (in.)	IGNITION TIMING (deg) ▲ Man Trans	‡	IGNITION TIMING (deg) ▲ Auto Trans	VALVES Intake Opens ■ (deg) ●	Fuel Pump Pressure (psi)	IDLE SPEED (rpm) ▲ Man Trans	IDLE SPEED (rpm) ▲ Auto Trans‡
'72	8-350	160	R-46S	.040	28-32	.016	—		8B	16	5½-6½	—	650/600
	8-350	180	R-46S	.040	28-32	.016	—		12B	22	5½-6½	—	600
	8-455	225	R-46S	.040	28-32	.016	—		8B	20	5½-6½	—	650/600
'73	8-350	160	R-46S	.040	30	.016	—		12B	16	5½-6½	—	700/550
	8-455	225	R-46S	.040	30	.016	—		8B	20	5½-6½	—	650/550
'74	8-350	180	R-46S	.040	30	.016	—		12B	16	5½-6½	—	650/550
	8-455	N.A.	R-46S	.040	30	.016	—		8B	20	5½-6½	—	700/550
	8-455	210	R-46S	.040	30	.016	—		8B	20	5½-6½	—	650/550
	8-455	230	R-46SX	.080	①	①	—		8B	20	5½-6½	—	650/550

▲ See text for procedure

‡ Set timing with carburetor adjusted to the following speeds:

Year	Without A/C	With A/C
1967-1969	850	1250
1970-1974	1100	850

■ All figures are in degrees Before Top Dead Center

● Figures in parentheses apply to California engines. Where two figures appear separated by a slash, the first is idle speed with solenoid energized, the second is idle speed with solenoid disconnected.

§ All spark plug listings are A.C. original equipment numbers

B Before Top Dead Center

— Not applicable

① Electronic ignition

N.A. Not Available

Oldsmobile CAPACITIES

Year	ENGINE No. Cyl. Displacement (Cu. In.)	Engine Crankcase Add 1 Qt For New Filter	TRANSMISSION Pts To Refill After Draining Manual 3-Speed	TRANSMISSION Manual 4-Speed	TRANSMISSION Automatic ●	Drive Axle (pts)	Gasoline Tank (gals)	COOLING SYSTEM (qts) With Heater	COOLING SYSTEM (qts) With A/C
'67	8-330	4	4.9	—	5	3	25	16.5	17
	8-425	4	4.9	—	8	4.6①	25	17.5	18
'68	8-350	4	4.9	—	5	3.7	20	17.5	18
	8-455	4	4.9	—	8	5.3	25	17.5	18
'69	8-350	4	4.9	—	6	3.7	25	17.5	18
	8-455	4	4.9	—	6	5.3	25	17.5	18
'70	8-350	4	4.9	—	6	3.7	25	17.5	18
	8-455	4	4.9	—	6	5.3	25	17.5	18
'71	8-350	4	—	—	6	4.3	24②	17.5	18
	8-455	4	—	—	6	5.4	24②	17.5	18
'72	8-350	4	—	—	6	4.3	24③	16.2	16.7
	8-455	4	—	—	6	5.4	24③	17	17.5
'73	8-350	4	—	—	6	4.3	26	16.2⑤	16.2⑤
	8-455	4	—	—	6	5.4	26④	17.0⑥	17.5⑥
'74	8-350	4	—	—	6	4.3	26	21⑥	21⑥
	8-455	4	—	—	6	5.5	26④	21⑦	21.5④

● Specifications do not include torque converter

① 5.3 pts with limited slip

② 22.7 gals with station wagon

③ 23 gals on station wagon

④ 22 gals on station wagon

⑤ With heavy duty cooling system—21.5 qts

⑥ With heavy duty cooling system—22.5 qts

⑦ With heavy duty cooling system—23.5 qts

— Not applicable

Oldsmobile F-85, Cutlass, Vista Cruiser, Omega CAPACITIES

Year	ENGINE No. Cyl. Displacement (Cu. In.)	Engine Crankcase Add 1 Qt For New Filter	TRANSMISSION Pts To Refill After Draining Manual 3-Speed	Manual 4-Speed	Automatic ●	Drive Axle (pts)	Gasoline Tank (gals)	COOLING SYSTEM (qts) With Heater	With A/C
'67	6-250	4	3.5	2.25	5	3①	20③	11.7	11.7
	8-330	4	3.5	2.25	5	3①	20③	15.2	15.7
	8-400	4	3.5	2.25	5	3①	20③	15.2	15.7
'68	6-250	4	3.5	2.25	5	3.7	20	12.2	12.2
	8-350	4	3.5	2.25	5	3.7	20	15.2	15.7
	8-400	4	3.5	—	5	3.7	20	15.2	15.7
'69	6-250	4	3.5	—	6	3.7	20④	12.2	12.2
	8-350	4	3.5	2.25	6	3.7	20④	15.2	15.7
	8-400	4	3.5	—	8	3.7	23	15.2	15.7
'70	6-250	4	3.5	—	6	3.7	20④	12.2	12.2
	8-350	4	3.5	2.25	6	3.7	20④	15.2	15.7
	8-455	4	3.5	2.25	6	3.7	20④	17.5	18
'71	6-250	4	3.5	—	6	4.25	20⑤	12.2	12.2
	8-350	4	3.5	2.25	6	4.25	20⑤	15.2	15.7
	8-455	4	3.5	—	6	4.25	20⑤	17.5	18
'72	8-350	4	3.5	2.25	6	4.25②	20④	15.2	15.7
	8-455	4	—	—	6	4.25②	23	17	17.5
'73	6-250	4	3.5	—	6	4.25	21	12.5	—
	8-350	4	3.5	2.25	6	4.25②⑦	22⑥	15.9⑨	⑧⑨
	8-455	4	—	2.25	6	4.25②⑦	22	17.0⑩	18⑩
'74	6-250	4	3.5	—	6	4.25	21	15.5	—
	8-350	4	—	—	6	4.25⑦	22⑥	20.0⑪	20.0⑫
	8-455	4	—	—	6	5.50	22	21.0⑬	21.5⑬

● Specifications do not include torque converter
① Limited slip differential—3.69 pts
② Limited slip differential—5.4 pts
③ Station wagon 24 gals
④ Station wagon 23 gals
⑤ Station wagon 22 gals
⑥ Omega 21 gals
⑦ Vista Cruiser—5.5 pts
⑧ Omega—16.5 qts
Cutlass—16 qts
⑨ Heavy duty cooling—21 qts
⑩ Heavy duty cooling—22 qts
⑪ Omega—18.5 qts
⑫ Omega—19.5 qts
⑬ Heavy duty cooling—22.5 qts
— Not applicable

Oldsmobile 442 CAPACITIES

Year	ENGINE No. Cyl. Displacement (Cu. In.)	Engine Crankcase Add 1 Qt For New Filter	TRANSMISSION Pts To Refill After Draining Manual 3-Speed	Manual 4-Speed	Automatic ●	Drive Axle (pts)	Gasoline Tank (gals)	COOLING SYSTEM (qts) With Heater	With A/C
'67	8-400	4	4.9	2.25	8	3	20	16.2	16.7
'68	8-400	4	4.9	2.25	8	3.69	20	16.2	17.2
'69	8-400	4	4.9	2.25	8	3.69	20	16.2	17.2
'70	8-455	4	5	2.25	8	3.69	20	16.2	17.2
'71	8-455	4	4.5	2.5	6	4.26	20	16.2	17.2

● Specifications do not include torque converter

CRANKSHAFT AND CONNECTING ROD SPECIFICATIONS

All measurements are given in in.

Year	Engine Displace. (cu in.)	CRANKSHAFT Main Brg. Journal Dia	Main Brg. Oil Clearance	Shaft End-Play	Thrust on No.	CONNECTING ROD Journal Diameter	Oil Clearance	Side Clearance
'67	L6-250	2.2988	.0003-.0029	.002-.006	7	1.999-2.000	.0007-.0040	.0085-.0135
	8-330	2.4990	.0015-.0031	.004-.008	3	2.1238-2.1248	.0015-.0030	.002-.013
	8-400, 425	3.0000	.0015-.0031②	.004-.008	3	2.4988-2.5003	.0008-.0018	.002-.013
'68-'69	L6-250	2.2988	.0003-.0029	.002-.006	7	1.999-2.000	.0007-.0040	.0085-.0135
	8-350	2.4990	.0005-.0021①	.004-.008	3	2.1238-2.1248	.0009-.0031③	.002-.013
	8-400, 455	2.9998	.0005-.0021②	.004-.008	3	2.4988-2.4998	.0004-.0033	.002-.013
'70-'74	L6-250	2.3004	.0003-.0029	.002-.006	7	1.999-2.000	.0007-.0027	.007-.016
	8-350	2.4990⑥	.0005-.0021①	.004-.008	3	2.1238-2.1248	.0004-.0033⑦	④
	8-455	2.9998⑥	.0005-.0021②	.004-.008	3	2.4988-2.4998	.0004-.0033	④⑤

① No. 5—.0015-.0031
② No. 5—.0020-.0034
③ 1969—.0005-.0026
④ 1970—.002-.013; 1971—.002-.011; 1972-'74 -.006-.020
⑤ 1970-73 W-30—.002-.021
⑥ 1973-'74—2.50 in.
⑦ 1973-'74—.0005-.0026

ALTERNATOR AND REGULATOR SPECIFICATIONS

Year	ALTERNATOR Part No. or Manufacturer	Field Current @ 12 V	Output (amps)	REGULATOR Part No. or Manufacturer	Field Relay Air Gap (in.)	Field Relay Point Gap (in.)	Field Relay Volts to Close	Regulator Air Gap (in.)	Regulator Point Gap (in.)	Volts @ 75°
'67-'70	1100767	2.2-2.6	37	1119515	.015	.030	6.3-8.3	.060	.014	13.5-14.4
	1100880	2.2-2.6	37	Transistor type, integral with alternator, no adjustment						
	1100734	2.2-2.6	42	1119515	.015	.030	6.3-8.3	.060	.014	13.5-14.4
	1100878	2.2-2.6	42	1119515	.015	.030	6.3-8.3	.060	.014	13.5-14.4
	1100907	2.2-2.6	55	1119515	.015	.030	6.3-8.3	.060	.014	13.5-14.4
'71-'72	1100566	2.2-2.6	37	1119515	Not Adjustable					13.5-14.4
	1102440	2.2-2.6	37	1119515	Not Adjustable					13.5-14.4
	1100888	2.2-2.6	37	1119515	Not Adjustable					13.5-14.4
	1100934	2.2-2.6	37	Transistor type, integral with alternator, no adjustment						
	1100567	2.2-2.6	42	1119515	Not Adjustable					13.5-14.4
	1102439	2.2-2.6	55	1119515	Not Adjustable					13.5-14.4
	1100568	2.2-2.6	55	1119515	Not Adjustable					13.5-14.4
	1100569	2.2-2.6	55	1119515	Not Adjustable					13.5-14.4
	1100935	2.2-2.6	55	Transistor type, integral with alternator, no adjustment						
	1100570	2.2-2.6	61	1119515	Not Adjustable					13.5-14.4
	1100553	2.2-2.6	63	1119515	Not Adjustable					13.5-14.4
	1102435	2.2-2.6	42	1119515	Not Adjustable					13.5-14.4
	1102437	2.2-2.6	55	1119515	Not Adjustable					13.5-14.4
	1102463	2.2-2.6	61	1119515	Not Adjustable					13.5-14.4
'73-'74	1100497	2.2-2.6	37	Transistor type, integral with alternator, no adjustment						
	1100934	2.2-2.6	37	Transistor type, integral with alternator, no adjustment						
	1102367	2.2-2.6	55	Transistor type, integral with alternator, no adjustment						
	1100537	2.2-2.6	42	Transistor type, integral with alternator, no adjustment						
	1102368	2.2-2.6	61	Transistor type, integral with alternator, no adjustment						

VALVE SPECIFICATIONS

Year	Engine No. Cyl. Displacement (cu in.)	Seat Angle (deg)	Face Angle (deg)	Spring Test Pressure (lbs @ in.)	Spring Installed Height (in.)	STEM TO GUIDE Clearance (in.) Intake	STEM TO GUIDE Clearance (in.) Exhaust	STEM Diameter (in.) Intake	STEM Diameter (in.) Exhaust
'67	6-250	46	45	186 @ 1.27	1 21/32	.0010-.0027	.0010-.0027	.3414	.3414
	8-330	45	46	187 @ 1.27	1 21/32	.0010-.0027	.0015-.0032	.3429	.3424
	8-400	①	①	187 @ 1.27	1 21/32	.0010-.0030	.0010-.0030	.3429	.3424
	8-425	45	45	187 @ 1.27	1 21/32	.0010-.0030	.0010-.0030	.3429	.3424
'68	6-250	46	45	186 @ 1.27	1 21/32	.0010-.0027	.0010-.0027	.3414	.3414
	8-350	45	46	187 @ 1.27	1 21/32	.0010-.0027	.0015-.0032	.3429	.3424
	8-400②	45	46	187 @ 1.27	1 21/32	.0010-.0027	.0015-.0032	.3429	.3424
	8-400③	①	④	187 @ 1.27	1 21/32	.0010-.0027	.0015-.0032	.3429	.3424
	8-455	45	46	187 @ 1.27	1 21/32	.0010-.0027	.0015-.0032	.3429	.3424
'69	6-250	46	45	186 @ 1.27	1 21/32	.0010-.0027	.0010-.0027	.3414	.3414
	8-350	45	46	187 @ 1.27	1 21/32	.0010-.0027	.0015-.0032	.3429	.3424
	8-400	①	④	187 @ 1.27	1 21/32	.0010-.0027	.0015-.0032	.3429	.3424
	8-455	45	46	187 @ 1.27	1 21/32	.0010-.0027	.0015-.0032	.3429	.3424
'70	6-250	46	45	186 @ 1.27	1 21/32	.0010-.0027	.0010-.0027	.3414	.3414
	8-350	45	46	187 @ 1.27	1 21/32	.0010-.0027	.0015-.0032	.3429	.3424
	8-455	45	46	187 @ 1.27	1 21/32	.0010-.0027	.0015-.0032	.3429	.3424
	8-455⑧	①	④	187 @ 1.27⑤	1 21/32	.0010-.0027	.0015-.0032	.3429	.3424
'71	6-250	46	45	186 @ 1.27	1 21/32	.0010-.0027	.0010-.0027	.3414	.3414
	8-350	45	46	187 @ 1.27	1 21/32	.0010-.0027	.0015-.0032	.3424	.3424
	8-455	45	46	187 @ 1.27	1 21/32	.0010-.0027	.0015-.0032	.3429	.3424
	8-455⑧	①	④	187 @ 1.27⑤	1 21/32	.0010-.0027	.0015-.0032	.3429	.3424
'72	8-350	⑥	⑦	187 @ 1.27	1 21/32	.0010-.0027	.0015-.0032	.3429	.3424
	8-350⑨	45	46	198 @ 1.23	1 21/32	.0010-.0027	.0015-.0032	.3429	.3424
	8-455⑩	⑥	46	187 @ 1.27	1 21/32	.0010-.0027	.0015-.0032	.3429	.3424
	8-455	①	④	206 @ 1.19	1 21/32	.0010-.0027	.0015-.0032	.3429	.3424
'73	6-250	46	45	186 @ 1.27	1 21/32	.0010-.0027	.0010-.0027	.3413	.3413
	8-350	⑫	⑬	187 @ 1.27	1 21/32	.0010-.0027	.0015-.0032	.3429	.3424
	8-455⑩⑪	⑫	⑮	187 @ 1.27	1 21/32	.0010-.0027	.0015-.0032	.3429	.3424
	8-455⑭	⑮	⑯	206 @ 1.19	1 21/32	.0010-.0027	.0015-.0032	.3429	.3424
'74	6-250	46	45	186 @ 1.27	1 21/32	.0010-.0027	.0010-.0027	.3413	.3413
	8-350	⑫	⑬	187 @ 1.27	1 21/32	.0010-.0027	.0015-.0032	.3429	.3424
	8-455⑩⑪	⑫	⑮	187 @ 1.27	1 21/32	.0010-.0027	.0015-.0032	.3429	.3424
	8-455⑭	⑮	⑯	206 @ 1.19	1 21/32	.0010-.0027	.0015-.0032	.3429	.3424

① Intake 30°, exhaust 45°
② 2 bbl carburetor
③ 4 bbl carburetor
④ Intake 30°, exhaust 46°
⑤ With air induction—302 @ 1.17
⑥ Intake 45°, exhaust 30°
⑦ Intake 46°, exhaust 30°
⑧ 4-4-2
⑨ California cars only
⑩ Oldsmobile 98
⑪ Oldsmobile 88
⑫ Intake 45°, exhaust 59°
⑬ Intake 46°, exhaust 60°
⑭ Cutlass
⑮ Intake 60°, exhaust 45°
⑯ Intake 60°, exhaust 46°

BATTERY AND STARTER SPECIFICATIONS

Year	Engine Displacement (cu in.)	BATTERY Ampere Hour Capacity	BATTERY Volts	BATTERY Terminal Grounded	STARTER Lock Test Amps	STARTER Lock Test Volts	STARTER Lock Test Torque (ft lbs)	STARTER No-Load Test Amps	STARTER No-Load Test Volts	STARTER No-Load Test RPM	STARTER Brush Spring Tension (oz)
'67-'74	6	44	12	Neg.	Not Recommended			50-80	9-10.5	6,000-10,000	35
	8-350	62	12	Neg.	Not Recommended			50-80	9-10.5	5,000-6,000	35
	8-400, 425, 455	70, 73, 75	12	Neg.	Not Recommended			50-80	9-10.5	5,000-6,000	35

BRAKE SPECIFICATIONS

Year	Model	Master Cylinder Disc	Master Cylinder Drum	Wheel Cylinder Front Disc	Wheel Cylinder Front Drum	Wheel Cylinder Rear	Brake Disc or Drum Diameter Front Disc	Brake Disc or Drum Diameter Front Drum	Brake Disc or Drum Diameter Rear
'67	Cutlass Std. Sta. Wag.	—	1.0	—	1 1/16	7/8	—	9 1/2	9 1/2
	Vista Cruiser	—	1.0	—	1 1/16	15/16	—	9 1/2	9 1/2
	F-85, 442	1 1/8	1.0	2 1/16	1 1/16	13/16①	11	9 1/2	9 1/2
	88, 98 Series	1 1/8	1.0②	1 15/16	1 1/8③	1.0	11 7/8	11	11
'68	All except 88, 98 Series	1 1/8	1.0	2 1/16	1 1/8	15/16④	11	9 1/2	9 1/2
	88, 98 Series	1 1/8	1.0	1 15/16	1 3/16	1.0	11 7/8	11	11
'69	All except 88, 98 Series	1 1/8	1.0	2 15/16	1 1/8	15/16⑤	10 29/32	9 1/2	9 1/2
	88, 98 Series	1 1/8	1.0	2 15/16	1 3/16	1.0	11 13/16	9 1/2	9 1/2⑥
'70	All except 88, 98 Series	1 1/8	1.0	2 15/16	1 1/8	7/8④⑦	11	9 1/2	9 1/2
	88, 98 Series	1 1/8	1.0	2 15/16	1 3/16	15/16	11 29/32	11	11
'71-'74	F-85/Cutlass, 442, Std. Sta. Wag., Vista Cruiser, Omega	⑧	1.0	2 15/16	1 1/8	7/8⑤	11	9 1/2	9 1/2
	88, 98 Series	1 1/8	—	2 15/16	—	15/16	11 29/32	—	11
	Custom Cruiser	1 1/8	—	2 15/16	—	1.0	11 29/32	—	12

① 7/8 on F-85 without disc brakes
1.0 on 442 without disc brakes
② 7/8 on 98 Series with metallic lining
③ 1 3/16 on 98 Series with metallic lining
④ 13/16 on F-85, 442 with disc brakes
⑤ 1.0 on Vista Cruiser
⑥ 11 with disc brakes
⑦ 15/16 on Std. Sta. Wagon
⑧ Manual disc brakes—1.0 in.; power disc brakes 1 1/8 in.
— Not applicable

WHEEL ALIGNMENT SPECIFICATIONS

Year	Model	Caster Range (deg)	Caster Pref Setting (deg)	Camber Range (deg)	Camber Pref Setting (deg)	Toe-in (in.)	Steering Axis Inclin.	Wheel Pivot Ratio (deg) Inner Wheel	Wheel Pivot Ratio (deg) Wheel Outer
'67	F-85 Series	1/2N to 2N	1 1/2N	1/4N to 1/2P	1/4P	1/8 to 3/16	9	20	18 3/5
	88 & 98 Series	1/2N to 1 1/2N	1/2N	1/4N to 1/2P	1/4P	1/8 to 3/16	11	20	18 3/10④
'68-'69	F-85 Series	1/2N to 2N	1 1/4N①	1/4N to 1/2P	1/8P	1/8 to 3/16	9	20	18 3/5
	88 & 98 Series	1/2N to 1 1/2N	1 1/4N①	1/4N to 1/2P	1/8P	1/8 to 3/16	11	20	18 3/10④
'70	F-85 Series	1/2N to 2N	1 1/4N①	1/4N to 1/2P	1/8P	1/8 to 3/16	9	20	18 3/5
	88 & 98 Series	1/2N to 1 1/2N	1 1/4N①	1/4N to 1/2P	1/8P	1/8 to 3/16	11	20	18 3/10④
'71-'72	F-85 Series	3/4N to 1 3/4N	1 1/4N	3/4N to 3/4P*	1/4P*	1/16N to 1/16P	8	20	19②
	88 & 98 Series	1/2P to 1 1/2P	1P	3/4N to 3/4P*	1/4P*	1/16N to 1/16P	10 1/2③	20	18 1/2
'73-'74	Omega	1/2N to 1 1/2P	1/2P	1/2N to 1P	1/2P	1/16 to 5/16	9	N.A.	N.A.
	Cutlass	3/4N to 1 3/4N	1 1/4N	⑤	⑤	1/16	10 1/2	20	19②
	88 & 98 Series	0 to 2P	1P	3/4N to 3/4P*	1/4P*	1/16 to 1/16	9 1/2	20	18 1/2

* Left side camber to be 1/2° more positive than right side
① Power steering—3/4N
② Power steering—18
③ 9.6 for 1972 88 & 98 Series
④ 17 7/10 for power steering
⑤ 1°P—LH; 1/2°N—RH: ± 3/4°
N Negative P Positive
N.A. Not available

RING SIDE CLEARANCE

Year	Engine	Top Compression	Bottom Compression
'67-'71	6-250	.0020-.0038	.0020-.0038
'67-'71	All 8 cylinder	.0018-.0033	.0018-.0038
'72-'74	8-350, 455	.0020-.0040	.0020-.0040
'73-'74	6-250	.0012-.0027	.0012-.0032

Year	Engine	Oil Control
'67-'74	6-250	.000-.005
'67-'69	8-330, 350	.0001-.0051
'67	8-400, 425	.0021-.0081
'68-'69	8-400	.0006-.0096
'70-'74	8-350	.0006-.0096
'68-'74	8-455	.0021-.0031

RING GAP

Year	Engine	Top Compression	Bottom Compression
'67-'71	6-250, 8-330, 350	.010-.020	.010-.020
'67	8-400, 425	.013-.023	.013-.023
'68-'69	8-400	.010-.020	.010-.020
'68-'71	8-455	.013-.023	.013-.023
'72-'74	8-350, 455	.010-.023	.010-.023
'73-'74	6-250	.010-.020	.010-.020

Year	Engine	Oil Control
'67-'74	All engines	.015-.055

TORQUE SPECIFICATIONS

All readings in ft lbs

Year	Engine	Cylinder Head Bolts	Rod Bearing Bolts	Main Bearing Bolts	Crankshaft Pulley Bolt	Flywheel to Crankshaft Bolts	MANIFOLD Intake	MANIFOLD Exhaust
'67-'74	6-All	95	35	65	Press fit	60	25	30④
	8-All	80①⑤	42	120②	160 min	③	35①⑥	25

① To obtain accurate torque readings, all bolts must be clean and lightly coated with engine oil
②8-330, 350—80 on No. 1-4, 120 on No. 5
③ A.T. 60 ft lbs.; M.T. 90 ft lbs. (1970-73), 80 ft lbs. (1966-69)
④ This refers to those bolts holding the exhaust manifold to the cylinder head
⑤ 1973-'74 -85 ft lbs
⑥ 1973-'74 -40 ft lbs
min minimum

CHARGING SYSTEM

The charging system consists of the Delco-Remy Delcotron AC generator and a conventional relay-type regulator. Starting in 1969, the Delcotron offered as standard equipment in the 442 model was equipped with a built in transistorized regulator unit. This regulator is a completely electronic sealed unit and cannot be adjusted. A capacitor mounted in the end frame keeps down high voltages and suppresses radio noise. All 1973-74 models have this integral alternator/regulator as standard equipment.

See "Charging and Starting Systems" in the Unit Repair Section for charging system test and component overhaul procedures.

Caution Since the Delcotron and regulator are designed for use on only one polarity system, the following precautions must be observed:

1. The polarity of the battery, generator, and regulator must be matched and considered before making any electrical connections in the system.
2. When connecting a booster battery, be sure to connect the negative battery terminals together and the positive battery terminals together.
3. When connecting a charger to the battery, connect the charger positive lead to the battery positive terminal. Connect the charger negative lead to the battery negative terminal.
4. Never operate the Delcotron on open circuit. Be sure that all connections in the circuit are clean and tight.
5. Do not short across or ground any of the terminals on the Delcotron regulator.
6. Do not attempt to polarize the Delcotron.
7. Do not use test lamps of more than 12 volts for checking diode continuity.
8. Avoid long soldering times when replacing diodes or transistors. Prolonged heat is damaging to these units.
9. Disconnect the battery ground terminal when servicing any A.C. system. This will prevent the possibility of accidental reversing of polarity.

Alternator

Removal

NOTE: Before removing the alternator, disconnect the battery ground cable.

1. Disconnect the wiring from the alternator.
2. Remove the mounting bolts and drive belt.
3. Lift out the alternator.

Installation

To install, reverse the removal procedure, connect the battery ground cable and tighten the alternator belt. Determine belt tension at a point halfway between the pulleys by pressing on the belt with moderate thumb pressure. If the distance between the pulleys (measured at the pulley center) is 13–16 in., the belt should deflect ½ in. at the halfway point or ¼ in. if the distance is 7–10 in. If the deflection is found to be too little or too much, make the proper adjustments.

Regulator

All 4-4-2 models from 1969 to and including 1971 and all 1973-74 models are equipped with a generator containing a built-in transistorized regulator. This is a completely sealed unit that cannot be adjusted or disassembled. All other models are equipped with a conventional, externally mounted regulator which should be removed and installed in the following manner:

Removal

1. Disconnect the electrical connector from the regulator.
2. Remove the attaching screws and the regulator.

Installation

To install, reverse the removal procedure.

STARTING SYSTEM

Specifications on the battery and starter are in the Battery and Starter Specifications table.

See "Charging and Starting Systems" in the Unit Repair Section for starter motor service procedures, including overhaul and starter drive replacement.

Starter R & R

1967-69 Except 400 Cu. In. Engine

1. Disconnect battery.
2. Noting positions of wires, disconnect starter wiring.
3. If equipped with manual transmission, remove flywheel cover.
4. Remove upper support attaching bolt.
5. Remove two mounting bolts and remove starter. If equipped with dual exhausts, it may be necessary to remove the left-hand exhaust pipe.
6. Install by reversing the above procedure.

1967-69 400 Cu. In. Engine

1. Disconnect battery.
2. Disconnect clutch return spring at clutch release yoke.
3. Disconnect exhaust pipe from left manifold.
4. Loosen upper and remove lower starter to block brace bolts.
5. Remove two starter to brace block bolts.
6. Move starter forward and downward, then disconnect wires from three starter terminals. In 4-4-2 models equipped with automatic transmissions, it may be necessary to remove the flywheel housing cover.
7. Remove starter.
8. Install by reversing the above procedure.

1970-74

1. Disconnect battery and carefully hoist car.
2. Remove upper support attaching bolts.
3. Remove flywheel housing cover.
4. Remove two starter mounting bolts.
5. Lower starter, disconnect wiring, and remove starter. If equipped with dual exhausts, it may be necessary to remove the left-hand exhaust pipe.
6. Install by reversing the above procedure.

IGNITION SYSTEM

Distributors on V8 engines have a window in the cap so that the point gap (dwell angle) may be adjusted with an Allen wrench while the engine is running. When installing a new contact point set, only the gap is adjusted; the spring tension and point alignment are pre-adjusted.

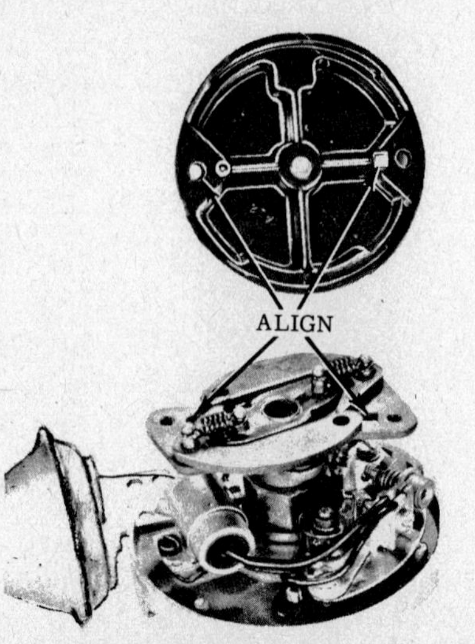
ALIGN

Rotor installation
(© Oldsmobile Div, G.M. Corp)

Distributor Removal

All Engines

1. Remove distributor cap, primary wire and vacuum line at the distributor.
2. Scribe a mark on the distributor body, locating the position of the rotor, and scribe another mark on the distributor body and engine block, showing the position of the body in the block.
3. Remove the hold-down screw and lift the distributor out of the block.

Note: Do not crank the engine with the distributor removed; this will change the timing.

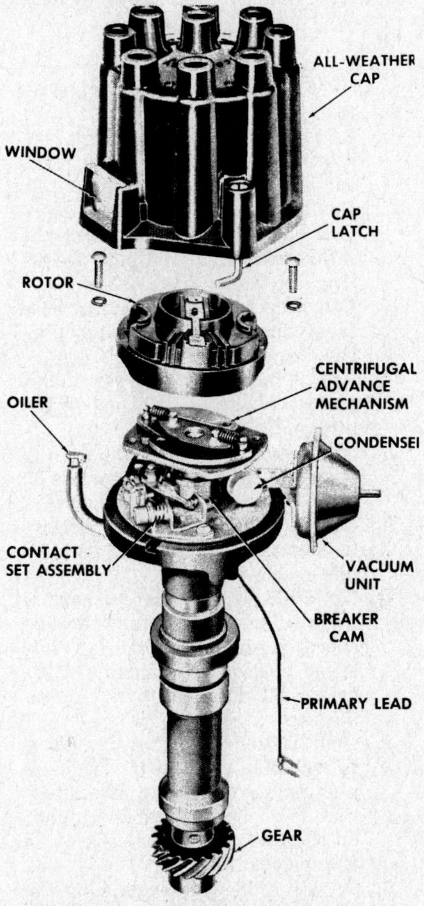
ALL-WEATHER CAP
WINDOW
CAP LATCH
ROTOR
CENTRIFUGAL ADVANCE MECHANISM
OILER
CONDENSER
CONTACT SET ASSEMBLY
VACUUM UNIT
BREAKER CAM
PRIMARY LEAD
GEAR

Distributor details, externally adjusted type
(© Oldsmobile Div, G.M. Corp)

Distributor Installation

If engine has *not* been disturbed (cranked) after removing the distributor, perform the following procedure for installation:

1. Turn the rotor clockwise until it is about 1/8 turn past the locating mark previously made on the distributor housing.
2. Push the distributor down into the block. It may be necessary to turn the rotor slightly until the shaft engages in the block. The mark on the distributor housing must line up with the mark made on the engine block.
3. Tighten the hold-down bolt until it is snug and then connect the vacuum advance line.
4. Connect the primary wire to the coil and install the distributor cap.
5. Check the timing and adjust it as necessary. Tighten the hold-down bolt.

If engine has been disturbed (cranked) after removing distributor, perform the following procedure for installation:

1. Crank the engine until no. one piston is at the top of its compression stroke. The compression stroke can be determined by removing the spark plug from the no. one cylinder and placing your thumb over the hole while an assistant slowly cranks the engine. Crank until compression is felt at the hole and then continue cranking slowly until the timing mark on the crankshaft pulley lines up with the 0° timing mark.
2. Position the distributor in the block but do not allow it to engage with its drive gear. Observe the position of the vacuum control unit on the distributor. If the distributor is located correctly, the vacuum unit will be positioned normally so that the vacuum hose can be easily connected to it.
3. Position the distributor rotor so that it aligns with the no. one spark plug in the distributor cap.
4. Press firmly downward on the distributor housing while an assistant kicks the starter over a few times. This will assure the distributor shaft engaging the oil pump shaft, thereby allowing the distributor to fully contact the engine block.
5. Install the hold-down clamp and tighten the bolt until it is snug.
6. Turn the distributor slightly until the points just open, then tighten the bolt.
7. Install the distributor cap.
8. Attach all wires and the vacuum advance hose.
9. Check the timing and adjust it as necessary.

Contact Point Replacement

1. Remove the distributor cap and rotor.
2. Beginning with 1970 models, V8 distributors were equipped with a two-piece metal shield to suppress radio static. Remove the two attaching screws and the shield.
3. Remove the two wiring terminals from the retainer.
4. Remove the mounting screws and lift out the contact points and condenser.
5. Install the new contact points and condenser and tighten the mounting screws.
6. Install the primary and condenser wire terminals in the retainer. If the replacement point set has a snap-lock type retainer, the terminals can be pushed in to provide plenty of clearance between the shield (if so equipped) and the terminals to prevent accidental short circuiting. If the contact points have a screw type retainer, insufficient clearance may exist between the terminals and the shield, possibly causing a short circuit. To prevent this possibility, insert terminals in the retainer and bend them slightly toward the distributor cam. Make sure the wiring does not interfere with the other components.
7. Inspect the cam lubricator wick and replace or rotate it if it is worn out or dry. Using a feeler gauge, check and adjust the point gap.
8. If so equipped, install the two-piece shield and tighten the mounting screws.
9. Install the rotor, making sure that the round peg goes in the round hole and the square peg into the square hole.
10. Install the distributor cap.
11. Set the points to specifications with a dwell meter while the engine is running.

Ignition Timing

1. Disconnect vacuum advance hose from the distributor and plug it.
2. Remove the air cleaner and tape over the vaccum hose fitting (if so equipped) on the manifold.
3. Connect the tachometer and adjust the engine speed to specifications.

NOTE: If the car is equipped with electronic ignition and a tachometer, the in-tachometer wire (usually purple) going to the coil must be disconnected before connecting an external tachometer.

4. Connect a timing light, loosen the distributor mounting bolt, and turn the distributor until the specified timing is obtained. See the "Tune-Up" specifications chart for the proper engine speed for checking timing.
5. The six-cylinder (L-6) timing indicator has an "0" marking signifying TDC and an "A" signifying 10° BTDC. The marks in between the two represent 2, 4, 6, and 8° before TDC. The V8 indicator has four V-shaped slots each representing 4°.
6. Tighten the mounting bolt and recheck timing to see if it changed during tightening.
7. Unplug the vacuum advance hose and connect it to the distributor.
8. Remove the tape from the vacuum hose fitting and install and connect the hose, if so equipped.
9. Install the air cleaner.

FUEL SYSTEM

Gas tank capacities may be found in the Capacities table at the beginning of this section. See "Dash Gauges and Indicators" in the Unit Repair Section for a discussion of fuel gauge operation.

Fuel Pump Removal

1. Disconnect the fuel and vacuum lines.
2. Remove the two mounting bolts.
3. Remove the pump and gasket.

Installation is the reverse of removal.

Fuel Filter

All carburetors have a fuel filter which is integral with the carburetor body. To replace the filter element, remove the fuel inlet line, then remove the inlet fitting and pull out the filter element. Be careful when tightening the brass fitting because the threads are easily stripped.

Idle Speed and Mixture Adjustments

1967 All Engines

Adjust only with the air cleaner removed.

1. Set the parking brake, block the front wheels, then start the engine and allow it to warm up.
2. With the engine warm and the choke fully open, place the automatic transmission in Drive or the standard transmission in Neutral.
3. If equipped with factory air conditioning, the hot idle compensator located on the carburetor must be held closed.
4. Adjust the idle screw to the engine speed specified in the tune-up chart. After adjusting the idle, hand-operate the throttle once or twice and allow it to return to idle. Observe the tachometer reading; once rpm is stabilized, readjust as necessary.
5. With the tachometer or manifold vacuum gauge connected, turn in each mixture adjusting screw until it lightly seats.
6. Turn out each screw to obtain the highest steady rpm or vacuum reading and then turn in each screw 1/4 turn. Readjust the slow idle to specifications.
7. Install the air cleaner and look for an idle change. Readjust as necessary.

1968-70 1-bbl

Adjust only with the air cleaner removed.

1. Run the engine to attain the normal operating temperature and remove the air cleaner. Disconnect the air vacuum hose from the base of the carburetor and plug the fitting.
2. Disconnect the vacuum advance hose from the distributor and plug the end of the hose. Plug the carburetor hot idle compensator so it is closed.
3. Apply the parking brake and set blocks in front of the rear wheels.
4. If so equipped, turn off the air conditioner.
5. If the car has an automatic transmission, place the selector lever in Drive, or in neutral if it has a manual transmission.
6. The choke must be fully opened and the fast idle cam follower must be off the cam.
7. The solenoid wire must be connected and the throttle stop screw should not touch the throttle lever.
8. Adjust the idle mixture to obtain the highest rpm possible. Adjust the throttle solenoid plunger to obtain an idle speed 25 rpm above the higher of the two idle speeds in the tune-up specifications.
9. Turn the idle mixture screw inward to lower the idle speed to the correct rpm.
10. Disconnect the solenoid wire and adjust the throttle stop screw to obtain the lower of the two idle speeds in the specifications.

1971 and 1973-74 1-bbl

NOTE: These models are equipped with a CEC solenoid. This solenoid does not function as an idle speed solenoid and it should not be adjusted during a routine carburetor adjustment.

1. Run the engine to the normal operating temperature, making sure that the choke is fully open.
2. Set the parking brake and block the drive wheels.
3. Disconnect the fuel tank hose from the vapor canister.
4. Disconnect the distributor vacuum hoses from the CEC solenoid and plug the hose leading to the carburetor.
5. Set the dwell and timing.
6. Turn off the air conditioner and place automatic transmissions in Drive and manual transmissions in Neutral.
7. Connect a tachometer to the engine and, on 1971 models, turn the idle speed adjusting screw to obtain the correct speed.
8. On 1973-74 Omegas with a six cylinder engine, turn the *throttle* solenoid plunger inward or outward to obtain the higher of the two idle speeds listed in the specifications tables. Disconnect the lead wire from the solenoid and insert a small allen wrench into the end of the solenoid to obtain the lower of the two idle speeds listed. On models with an automatic transmission, this shut-off speed adjustment should be made with the transmission in Park.
9. Idle mixture is set at the factory and should not require adjustment.

1968-69 2-bbl

Adjust only with the air cleaner removed.

1. Run the engine to the normal operating temperature. Plug the carburetor hot idle compensator.
2. Remove the air cleaner, disconnect the vacuum hose from the intake manifold, and plug the fitting.
3. Disconnect the vacuum hose from the distributor and plug the hose.
4. Apply the parking brake, block the drive wheels, and turn off the air conditioning.
5. Make sure that the choke is fully open and the fast idle screw is on the clearance step of the cam.
6. Adjust the idle mixture screws to obtain the highest possible idle speed.
7. On 1968–69 models without a throttle solenoid, adjust the idle speed screw to obtain an idle speed that is 25 rpm above the figure listed in the tune-up specifications.
8. On 1968–69 models with a throttle solenoid, adjust the solenoid plunger to obtain an idle speed that is 25 rpm above the higher of the two idle speeds listed in the specifications.
9. On all 1968–69 models turn the idle mixture screws inward to lower the idle speed to the correct rpm.
10. On all 1968–69 models equipped with a throttle solenoid, discon-

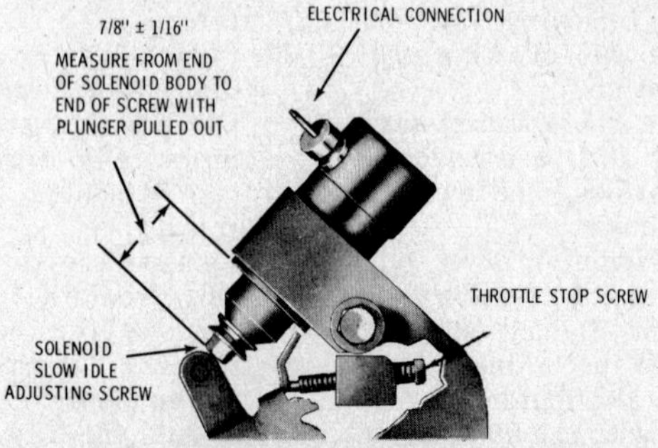
7/8" ± 1/16"
MEASURE FROM END OF SOLENOID BODY TO END OF SCREW WITH PLUNGER PULLED OUT
ELECTRICAL CONNECTION
THROTTLE STOP SCREW
SOLENOID SLOW IDLE ADJUSTING SCREW

Adjusting throttle closing solenoid—1-bbl
(© Oldsmobile Div, G.M. Corp)

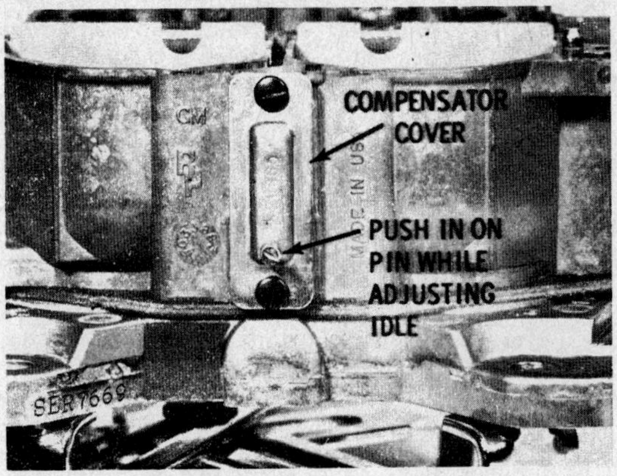
COMPENSATOR
COVER
PUSH IN ON
PIN WHILE
ADJUSTING
IDLE

4 bbl compensator cover (1968-72)
(© Oldsmobile Div, G.M. Corp)

nect the solenoid wire and adjust the throttle stop screw to obtain the lower of the two idle speeds listed in the tune-up specifications.

1968-69 4-bbl

Adjust only with the air cleaner removed.

1. Remove the air cleaner and the air cleaner vacuum hose.
2. Disconnect and plug the vacuum hose from the distributor.
3. Run engine to the normal operating temperature. Tape the carburetor hot idle compensator closed.
4. Apply the parking brake and block the drive wheels.
5. If so equipped, turn off the air conditioner.
6. Make sure the choke is opened fully and the fast idle cam follower is off the cam steps. Place the car in Drive (automatic) or neutral (manual).
7. Adjust the idle mixture screws to obtain highest possible rpm.
8. Adjust the idle speed screw to obtain idle speed 25 rpm higher than figure in tune-up specifications table.
9. Turn the idle mixture screws inward to lower the idle speed to the correct rpm.

1970-74 2-bbl and 4-bbl

Adjust with air cleaner removed.

1. Warm up engine and leave it running.
2. Remove air cleaner, disconnect air cleaner hose at the intake manifold and plug the fitting.
3. Make sure the choke is open and the air conditioner is off. Set the parking brake and block the drive wheels.
4. Disconnect the hoses from the vapor canister and the EGR valve, depending on equipment. Plug the hoses, except on 1970-72 models which are equipped with 4-bbl carburetors. On 1973-74 4-bbl models, plug the hoses.
5. Disconnect the distributor vacuum hose at the distributor and plug the hose.
6. Set the dwell and timing.
7. On models without a throttle solenoid or vacuum actuator, turn the idle speed adjusting screw inward or outward to obtain the idle speed listed in the specifications.
8. On models with a throttle solenoid or vacuum actuator, turn the solenoid plunger inward or outward to obtain the higher of the two idle speeds listed in the tune-up specifications. After this adjustment has been made, disconnect the electric lead from the solenoid or the vacuum hose from the vacuum actuator. Plug the vacuum hose after disconnecting it. On models with an automatic transmission, place the transmission in Park. Adjust the throttle stop screw to obtain an idle speed which corresponds with the lower of the two idle speeds listed in the specifications.

A double throttle return spring is a 1974 federal safety requirement

NOTE: idle mixture screws have been preset at the factory and capped. Remove the caps only in the case of major overhaul, throttle body removal or when all other possible causes of poor idle condition have been thoroughly checked.

9. To adjust the idle mixture, stop the engine, connect a CO (carbon monoxide) meter to the exhaust system and turn the idle mixture screws until they are lightly seated. Back out the idle mixture screws 6 full turns, then start engine and adjust the screws equally to obtain a good idle at the specified rpm with a maximum CO reading of 0.6 percent on the 1971 2-barrel models and 0.3 percent on 1972-73 models, and 0.3 percent on 1971-74 4-barrel. Temporarily install the air cleaner and check that the CO concentration does not exceed the specified level, readjusting idle mixture screws if necessary.
10. Install new idler limiter caps.
11. Reinstall and reconnect everything which was removed or disconnected in Steps 1 through 5.

COOLING SYSTEM

Detailed information on cooling system capacity is in the Capacities table.

Information on the water temperature gauge is in the Unit Repair Section.

Radiator R & R

1. Drain the cooling system.
2. Remove the upper radiator baffle and slide the shroud back over the fan, if so equipped.
3. Unfasten the upper and lower hoses from the radiator.
4. Disconnect the overflow hose and the optional coolant recovery system hose, if so equipped.
5. On models equipped with an automatic transmission, disconnect and cap the lines which run to the oil cooler.
6. Unfasten the radiator's securing bolts and withdraw the radiator upward to disengage it from its supports. Remove the radiator from the car.

NOTE: It may be necessary to rotate the fan blades in order to keep them out of the way.

Installation is performed in the reverse order of removal. Refill the cooling system.

Water Pump R & R

1. Drain the cooling system.
2. Unfasten the heater, bypass, and lower radiator hoses from the pump.
3. Loosen the drive belts. Remove the fan and pulley, complete with the fan clutch, if so equipped.

NOTE: Keep the fan in an upright position during removal to prevent the silicone fluid from leaking out of the fan clutch.

4. Unfasten the bolts which secure the water pump and remove it.

NOTE: On six-cylinder engines, pull the pump straight out, to prevent impeller damage.

Installation is performed in the following order:

1. Apply a thin coating of sealer to the pump housing gasket mounting surface.

2. Place a *new* gasket on the housing.
3. Install the pump assembly. Lightly oil the self-tapping bolts and tighten them to 13 ft lbs.
4. Torque the 5/16 in. bolts to the following specifications:
   1967-69—25 ft lbs
   1970-74—10 ft lbs
5. Install the fan assembly and tighten the bolts which secure it to the pump to 20 ft lbs.

NOTE: On 1970-74 models which have a clutch-operated fan, torque the bolt to 15 ft lbs.

6. Install the drive belts and adjust their tension.
7. Refill the cooling system.

Thermostat R & R

1. Remove the hoses from the thermostat.
2. Remove the water outlet and gasket from the thermostat housing.
3. Install the new thermostat and gasket in the engine. The thermostat may be etched with the word "front"; if so, "front" must face the radiator.
4. Connect the hoses and refill the cooling system.

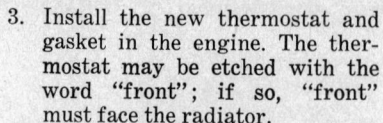

EMISSION CONTROLS

NOTE: See "Emission Control Systems" in the Unit Repair Section, for testing and adjustment of the various system components.

1967

Crankcase Ventilation

The Positive Crankcase Ventilation system used on all 1967 Oldsmobiles is designed to reburn crankcase blowby vapors by utilizing manifold vacuum to draw them through a hose connected between the valve cover and the base of the carburetor. This feeds the vapors back into the combustion chambers.

The hose contains a spring loaded PCV valve, which ensures proper operation of the engine at the two extremes of operation—full throttle, and idle. When the engine is idling, the very high manifold vacuum draws the PCV valve plunger, against spring tension, toward the front of the valve, enabling it to restrict the flow of gases through the system. Thus, the blowby vapors and air remain a very small part of the mixture flow, permitting efficient combustion, in spite of the tremendous vacuum available to draw material from the crankcase. When the throttle is opened all the way, negligible vacuum is available, and so the tension of the spring forces the rear of the valve plunger to seal off against the back of the valve, thus keeping fuel vapors from entering the crankcase.

On California systems, the crankcase vent cap is sealed off, and connected through a hose to the air cleaner. Thus the vapors which would normally escape to the atmosphere at full throttle are drawn into the carburetor with the inrushing air.

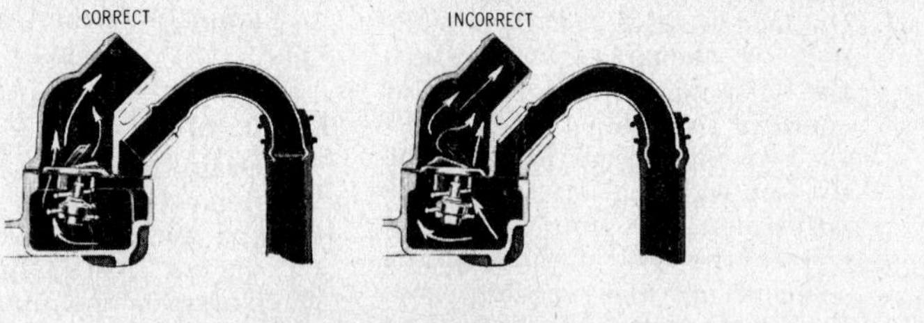
CORRECT
INCORRECT
Proper thermostat installation direction
(© Oldsmobile Div, G.M. Corp)

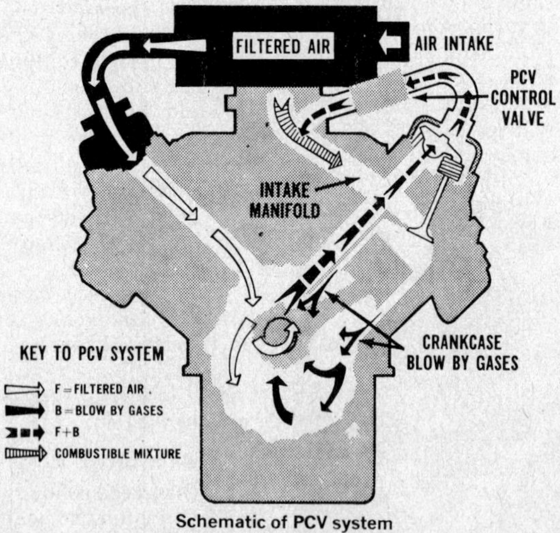
FILTERED AIR
AIR INTAKE
PCV CONTROL VALVE
INTAKE MANIFOLD
CRANKCASE BLOW BY GASES
KEY TO PCV SYSTEM
F = FILTERED AIR
B = BLOW BY GASES
F+B
COMBUSTIBLE MIXTURE
Schematic of PCV system
(© Oldsmobile Div, G.M. Corp)

Air Injection Reactor System

This system reduces air pollution by using an engine-driven compressor to force filtered air into the exhaust port of each cylinder. Here it combines with the unburned hydrocarbons and carbon monoxide and, during high temperatures, a chemical reaction is created resulting in a cleaner exhaust emission. Those 400 cu in. and 425 cu in. engines equipped with air conditioning use a thermostatic vacuum switch to advance ignition timing thereby lowering high coolant temperatures occurring during idle.

The AIR air pump (compressor) takes in air through a silencer and a filter and compresses it. Pump pressure is regulated through a relief valve located on the outer pump body. The pump forces air through a check valve and then into each engine ex-

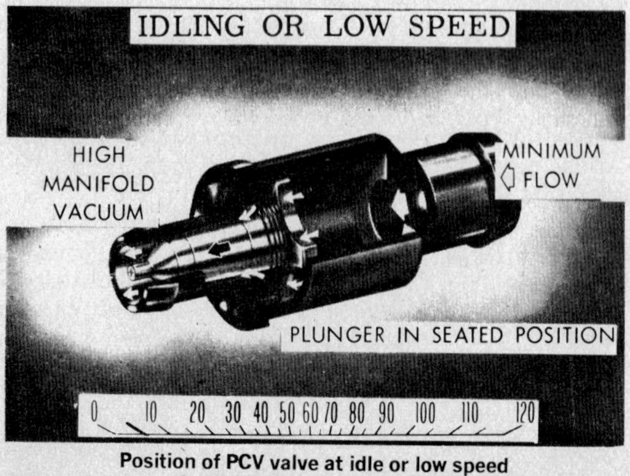
IDLING OR LOW SPEED
HIGH MANIFOLD VACUUM
MINIMUM FLOW
PLUNGER IN SEATED POSITION
0 10 20 30 40 50 60 70 80 90 100 110 120
Position of PCV valve at idle or low speed
(© Oldsmobile Div, G.M. Corp)

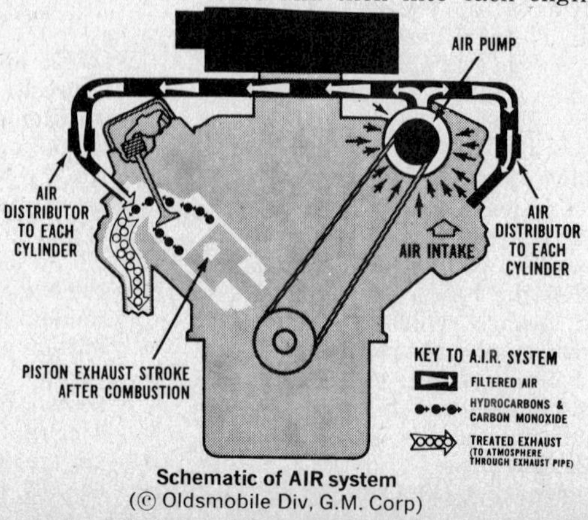
AIR PUMP
AIR DISTRIBUTOR TO EACH CYLINDER
AIR INTAKE
AIR DISTRIBUTOR TO EACH CYLINDER
PISTON EXHAUST STROKE AFTER COMBUSTION
KEY TO A.I.R. SYSTEM
FILTERED AIR
HYDROCARBONS & CARBON MONOXIDE
TREATED EXHAUST
Schematic of AIR system
(© Oldsmobile Div, G.M. Corp)

haust port. The check valve closes only when exhaust manifold pressure is greater than pump pressure. This prevents any backflow of exhaust through the system if the pump fails or the pump belt breaks. When decelerating, exhaust backfires are prevented by an air intake bleed valve. This valve injects air into the intake manifold as the throttle is closed. During deceleration, the mixture in the intake manifold is too rich to burn but ignites when combined with this injected air. At idle, a control valve (not present on six-cylinder engines) prevents this air from going to the bleed valve creating a lean mixture and a rough idle.

The AIR system is used only on cars sold in California.

1968-69

In 1968, emission control devices increased in number with the addition of CCS and the throttle closing solenoid. For the first time, their use was required on all cars made for sale in the USA, not only on those cars sold in California. These devices were continued in 1969.

Crankcase Ventilation System

Crankcase ventilation systems for 1968 and 1969, used a closed oil filler cap and PCV valve as did the closed (California) system of 1967. Operation is also the same as the earlier closed system.

Thermostatic Vacuum Switch

A thermostatic vacuum switch was available on 1968 and 1969 models equipped with air conditioning or on 400 and some 455 cu in. engines. This switch, the same used on 1967 California models, advances ignition timing when coolant temperatures rise above 220° F thereby allowing the engine to run cooler. For details on switch operation, see "Cooling System."

Controlled Combustion System (CCS)

The Controlled Combustion System was used for the first time in 1968. Standard equipment for all engines, this system consists of a special air cleaner assembly including a temperature sensor, vacuum motor (actually a spring-operated diaphragm), control damper assembly, and vacuum hoses. This system improves engine warm-up and fuel economy by directing heated air from the exhaust manifold into the air cleaner when engine compartment temperatures are 85° F or below. When the temperature inside the air cleaner reaches 100° F, a temperature sensor shuts off vacuum to the vacuum motor and the control damper opens, allowing underhood air to mix with the heated air to keep air temperature at a constant 100° F. When the car is undergoing full throttle operation, only outside air enters the air cleaner. On 4-4-2 models with the W-30 engine, there is no temperature sensor in the left air cleaner snorkle. It is controlled by manifold vacuum instead. This left snorkle stays closed until full throttle when vacuum drops to a reading of 6–8 in. Hg.

Throttle Closing Solenoid

In 1968 and 1969, all one-barrel carburetors were equipped with a throttle closing solenoid to prevent engine run-on once the ignition is turned off. Some two-barrels were so equipped but no four-barrels. The solenoid plunger extends when the ignition switch is turned on to raise engine idle speed and retracts when the switch is turned off to prevent the engine from running on.

1970

In 1970, the list of emission control devices grew with the addition of TCS and the evaporative control system.

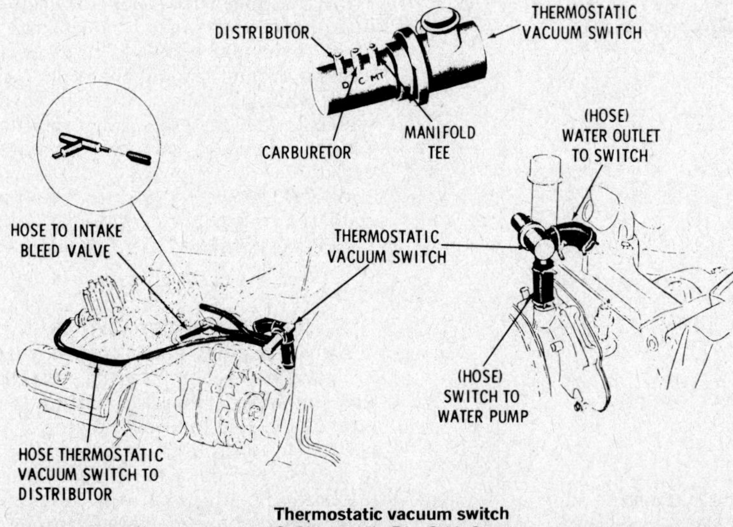

DISTRIBUTOR
THERMOSTATIC VACUUM SWITCH
D C MT
CARBURETOR
MANIFOLD TEE
(HOSE) WATER OUTLET TO SWITCH
HOSE TO INTAKE BLEED VALVE
THERMOSTATIC VACUUM SWITCH
(HOSE) SWITCH TO WATER PUMP
HOSE THERMOSTATIC VACUUM SWITCH TO DISTRIBUTOR

Thermostatic vacuum switch
(© Oldsmobile Div, G.M. Corp)

Crankcase Ventilation System

For 1970, the crankcase ventilation system remains unchanged from preceding years.

Thermostatic Vacuum Switch

All F-85 models (including 4-4-2) equipped with the 455 cu in. engine (except some W-30 cars) used a thermostatic vacuum switch to advance engine timing for cooling engine operation during idle. For details on this switch, see "Cooling System."

Controlled Combustion System (CCS)

This system remains unchanged from 1968 and 1969 models.

Throttle Closing Solenoid

Remains unchanged from 1969. Continued as standard equipment on all one-barrel carburetors but no longer used on two-barrels.

Transmission-Controlled Spark (TCS)

TCS is new for 1970, consisting of a temperature switch (6 cyl only), a solenoid valve, and a transmission switch. This system allows vacuum-controlled spark advance to the distributor only when the transmission is in high gear or when a six-cylinder's engine temperature is below 85°F or above 220° F. A vacuum line runs from the carburetor to the TCS solenoid (mounted on the intake manifold) and on to the vacuum advance unit on the distributor. A pressure-sensitive switch is located on the side of the transmission case (automatic transmission) and is electrically connected to the TCS solenoid at the intake manifold.

When the transmission is in any other gear than high gear, the transmission switch is closed and the circuit to the TCS solenoid is complete. This causes the solenoid to close and prevents carburetor vacuum from reaching the distributor. When the transmission enters high gear, hydraulic pressure opens the transmission switch, and the circuit to the solenoid opens. This permits carburetor vacuum to pass to the distributor and advance the spark. On six-cylinder engines, the temperature sending switch is electrically connected to the solenoid through a relay. At engine temperatures below 85° F or above 220° F, this switch opens up and stops current from reaching the solenoid, thereby permitting vacuum to pass through to the distributor and advancing the spark. The system used on models that are equipped with a manual transmission is identical, except that the transmission switch is manually actuated by the transmission linkage.

Evaporative Control System

California law requires that all 1970 model cars sold in that state be equipped with an evaporative control system as a means of preventing fuel vapor loss to the atmosphere. The system consists of a special fuel tank, a liquid/vapor separator, a carbon canister, and a special gas cap. A gas tank baffle limits tank capacity by 1 gal to provide room for expansion of fuel. The liquid/vapor separator is mounted to the underbody near the tank. Its purpose is to separate the liquid fuel from the vapors.

A vapor line connects to the separator output and runs to the front of the car where it attaches to a carbon-filled canister mounted on the front fender inner panel. Fuel vapors from the separator are stored here and then withdrawn by manifold vacuum through a hose to the intake manifold where they are reburned.

Caution The pressure/vacuum cap used with this system cannot be replaced by a cap of any other design.

1971

The distributor vacuum control switch (replaces thermostatic vacuum switch) and limiter caps for the idle mixture screws are new for 1971. The other equipment is carried on from 1970.

Distributor Vacuum Control Switch

This switch combines the functions of a TCS solenoid with those of a thermostatic vacuum switch. All cars having air conditioning, heavy-duty cooling systems, and all F-85 models (Cutlass, 4-4-2) equipped with the 455 cu in. engine use this switch assembly, while all other models use a TCS solenoid. This vacuum control switch allows vacuum to reach the distributor when the transmission is in third or fourth gear or when coolant temperatures are high at idle. Operating the car in first or second gear energizes the solenoid which raises the solenoid plunger to block off port C thereby shutting off the vacuum supply from the carburetor. By blocking off port C, port V (vent) is opened to the atmosphere to drain any vacuum that might be present in the vacuum advance unit. In third or fourth gear, the transmission switch opens and current to the solenoid stops and the solenoid plunger drops to seal off the vent port (V). This allows vacuum from the carburetor to enter the switch at port C and out port D (distributor) to the distributor vacuum advance. When coolant temperatures reaches 210° F, expansion within the intake manifold moves the plunger upward to seal off the vent (V) port and opening up the manifold (MT) port to manifold vacuum. At 218–224° F, full manifold vacuum is directed to port D (distributor) and on to the vacuum advance unit on the distributor. This advances the spark and cools coolant temperatures, regardless of transmission position.

Limiter Caps

Beginning in 1971, limiter caps (plastic caps) were placed over the idle mixture screws on the carburetor. Mixture is pre-set at the factory and no further adjustment is required.

Evaporative Control System

In 1971, this system was standard for all models, not just California cars. The system remains basically the same as that used in 1970.

1972

1972 cars contain the same emission control equipment as 1971 cars with the following exceptions:

Transmission-Controlled Spark Solenoid

For 1972, this switch is used only on Cutlass models equipped with 350 cu in. two-barrel engines and no air conditioning. On all other models equipped with TCS, the vacuum cut-off solenoid is contained in the distributor vacuum control switch.

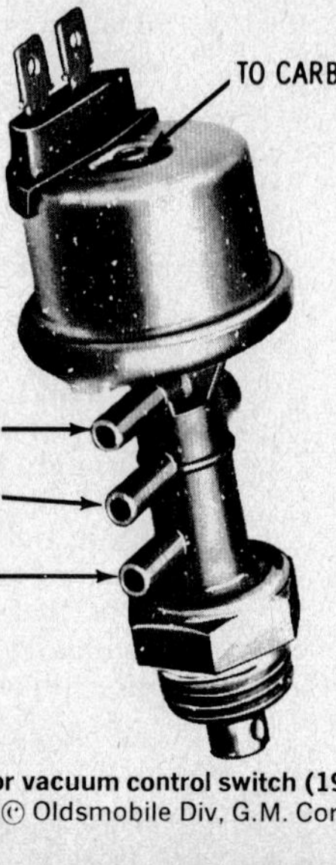
TO CARBURETOR (PORT C)
VENT (PORT V)
TO DISTRIBUTOR (PORT D)
TO MANIFOLD (PORT MT)

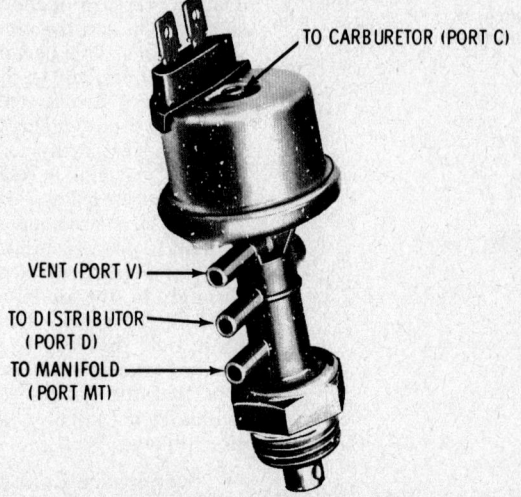

Distributor vacuum control switch (1971 shown)
(© Oldsmobile Div, G.M. Corp)

Idle Solenoid

The two-barrel and four-barrel carburetors are now equipped with an idle solenoid or a vacuum actuator. Both controls help to create a higher idle speed as a means of reducing emissions.

1973

Exhaust Gas Recirculation

All 1973 models are equipped with Exhaust Gas Recirculation (EGR). This system routes a portion of the engine exhaust gases back into the engine to dilute the incoming air/fuel mixture. By reducing the amount of combustible material in the combustion chamber, peak combustion temperature and the corresponding formation of oxides of Nitrogen (NO_x) are lowered.

An internal intake manifold passage conducts gases from the intake manifold crossover passage to the air/fuel passages in the manifold on V8 engines. In 6-cylinder engines, an external tube carries the exhaust gases to the intake manifold. The EGR control valve is attached to the intake manifold and normally blocks the exhaust gases from entering the engine. The EGR valve contains a spring-loaded diaphragm which is controlled by carburetor vacuum. The EGR valve vacuum hose contains a low-temperature cut-off valve which blocks carburetor vacuum from the control valve until the ambient temperature around the intake manifold has reached 50–60°F. The black and white plastic cut-off valve must always be installed with the side marked "EGR" facing the EGR valve.

Models equipped with a 350 2-bbl engine use the same port on the carburetor as a source for both EGR and distributor vacuum.

Cars made on or after 15 March 1973 have a black plastic cover over the EGR low temperature cut-off valve, so that the valve is dependent upon engine, rather than air, temperature. Engines with 4-bbl carburetors and automatic transmissions have a large cover which is held in place by a strap around the oil filler tube. All other engines have a smaller cover which is held in place by a retainer fastened under a bolt on the water outlet.

NOTE: If the retainer is removed, coat the threads of the bolt with sealer and torque it to 20 ft lbs upon installation.

Thermal Vacuum Switch

All V8 engines are equipped with a Thermal Vacuum Switch (TVS). Vacuum hoses from the carburetor, intake manifold, and distributor connect to this switch which is controlled by engine coolant temperature. During normal engine operation, vacuum from the carburetor passes through the TVS to the distributor. If the engine should overheat while idling, the TVS connects intake manifold vacuum to the distributor which helps to lower the coolant temperature.

On models equipped with a 350 2-bbl engine, the intake manifold vacuum hose to the TVS contains a vacuum reducing valve. The purpose of this valve is to limit the amount of vacuum supplied to the distributor by the intake manifold to 9 in. Hg. This valve is required on this engine because of the fact that the distributor and EGR valve normally share the same vacuum port on the carburetor. Since the vacuum from this source is divided between two sources, the distributor is calibrated to operate on a maximum of about 7 in. Hg.

Thermal Check and Delay Valve

All 350 and 455 cu in. 4-bbl carburetor engines, except for the 350 engine equipped with manual transmission, have a thermal check and delay valve. This valve is in the vacuum line which runs between the carburetor spark port and the TVS.

When the underhood (or engine block) temperature is below 50°F full carburetor-ported vacuum is supplied to the distributor vacuum unit. Above 50°F, the valve blocks full vacuum for up to 40 seconds.

If ported vacuum drops, the valve opens, causing the distributor vacuum advance to be retarded. As vacuum increases, the valve closes, blocking full vacuum again.

Cars made from 15 March 1973 have a cover over the valve so that it is more dependent upon engine block temperature. For a description of the cover, see the section which describes the EGR system, above.

Air Injection Reactor

All six-cylinder engines are equipped with Air Injection Reactor (AIR). A description of this system is provided above under "1967."

Combined Emission Controls

All Omegas equipped with a six-cylinder engine and a manual transmission are equipped with a CEC valve. This system is basically a Transmission Controlled Spark (TCS) system. The CEC solenoid is mounted on the side of the carburetor and the carburetor vacuum line to the distributor passes through it. This switch, which is normally closed, is energized to allow vacuum advance only under the following conditions: when engine coolant temperature is below 93° F, for a period of 20 seconds after the engine is started, or when the transmission is in third gear. When any of the above conditions exist, a complete circuit is made from the ignition switch through either the temperature switch, time-delay relay, or transmission switch to the CEC solenoid. This energizes the solenoid and causes its plunger to extend, uncovering the carburetor vacuum port to the distributor and raising the idle speed of the engine.

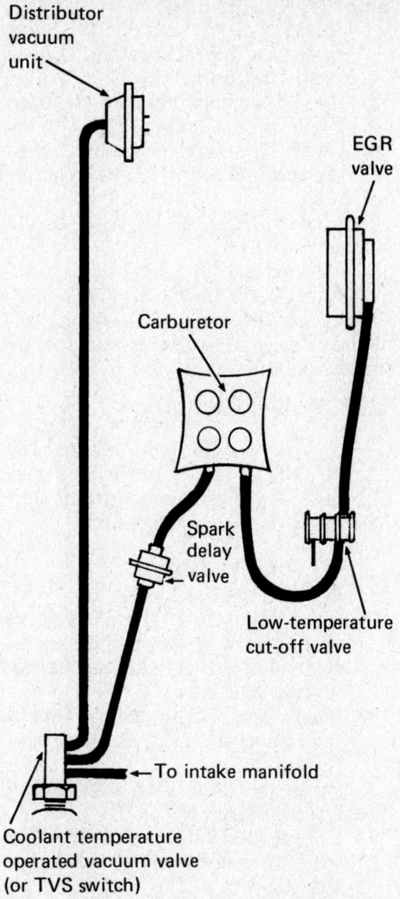

Distributor vacuum unit
EGR valve
Carburetor
Spark delay valve
Low-temperature cut-off valve
To intake manifold
Coolant temperature operated vacuum valve (or TVS switch)

1973 350 4 bbl and 455 V8 emission controls
(© Oldsmobile Div, G.M. Corp)

Controlled Combustion System

All 1973 models are equipped with the Controlled Combustion System (CCS). This system is described above under "1968–69."

1974

Exhaust Gas Recirculation

The 1974 exhaust gas recirculation (EGR) system remains basically the same as that used on cars made after 15 March 1973 (see above). However, a backpressure transducer valve (BPV) has been added to the EGR system used on V8 engines which are sold in California.

The bottom of the BPV diaphragm is open to exhaust pressure. At idle, the lack of exhaust backpressure allows the spring above the diaphragm to open an air bleed, which prevents vacuum from reaching the EGR valve. When there is backpressure in the exhaust system, i.e., above idle, the diaphragm is forced up against the spring, closing the air bleed, which allows the EGR valve to get normal vacuum.

By preventing EGR from occurring at idle, the idle quality is improved on California cars, which have a greater amount of exhaust gases recirculating than cars made for the rest of the nation.

Distributor Vacuum Valve

A distributor vacuum valve (DVV) is used on all 350 and 455 cu in. engines sold in California and on some of the 455 cu in. engines which are sold nationally.

The DVV switches the distributor vacuum advance unit's vacuum source from the carburetor spark port to the EGR port. Below 7 in. Hg, the vacuum unit operates from the spark port. Above 7 in. Hg, the vacuum supply is switched by the DVV from the spark port to the EGR port.

Other Emission Control Systems

The rest of the emission control systems used on 1974 Oldsmobile V8 engines remain the same as those described above for 1973.

All of the emission controls used on six-cylinder Omega models remain unchanged for 1974. See the "1973" section above for their description.

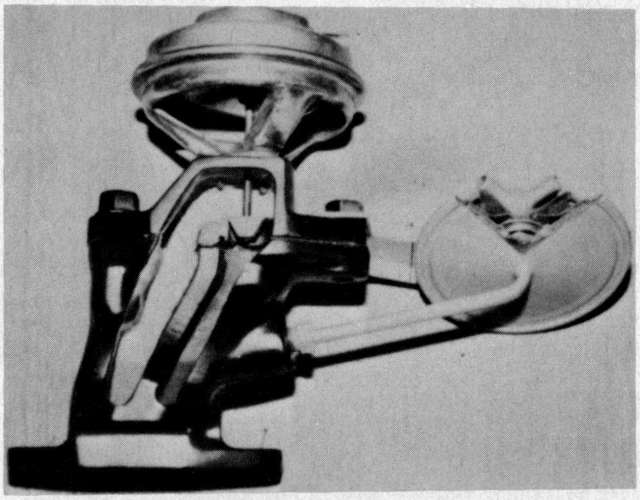

1974 EGR valve with back pressure transducer valve (BPV) is used on California V8s

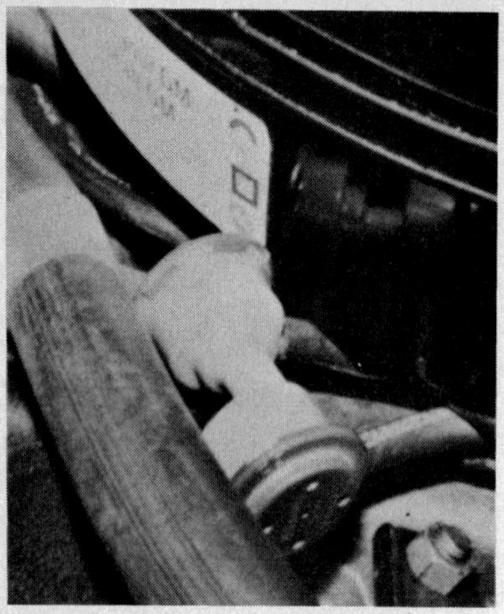

The distributor vacuum valve (DVV) is used on some V8s in 1974

AIR System Component R & R

Air Injection Pump

1. Unfasten the air supply hose(s) from the pump.
2. Compress the pump drive belt to keep the pump pulley from rotating.
3. Unfasten the pulley securing bolts and remove the drive belt, together with the pulley.
4. Remove the bolts which secure the pump to its mounting bracket.
5. Withdraw the pump assembly from the bracket.

Caution Never clamp the pump in a vise or pry on the pump housing. The housing is made of aluminum and distorts easily.

Installation of the pump is performed in the following order:

1. Install the pump on its mounting bracket, but do not tighten the mounting bolts.
2. Install the pulley and finger-tighten its mounting bolts.
3. Install and adjust the drive belt. Do not pry on the pump housing during adjustment.
4. Keep the pump pulley from turning by compressing the drive belt and tighten the pulley bolts to 9 ft lbs.
5. Connect the hose(s) to the pump.
6. Tighten the pump mounting bolts to 25 ft lbs and recheck belt tension.

Diverter (By-Pass) Valve

1. Disconnect the vacuum signal line from the diverter valve.
2. Unfasten the valve exhaust hose(s).
3. Loosen the securing screws and remove the valve from the air pump or elbow.

Installation is performed in the reverse order of removal. Use a new gasket and tighten the valve attaching screws to 7 ft lbs.

EGR Valve R & R

1. Unfasten the vacuum signal hose from the top of the EGR valve.
2. On V8 models, remove the two EGR valve securing bolts.
3. On L6 models, remove the clamping bolt and clamp from the manifold.
4. Remove the EGR valve from the manifold.
5. Discard the old gasket.

Installation of the EGR valve is performed in the reverse order of removal. Use a new gasket and torque the valve securing bolt(s) to 25 ft lbs.

EGR Valve Cleaning

Caution Do not clamp the EGR valve in a vise or wash it in solvents; permanent damage to the valve will result.

6-Cyl Engines

1. Remove the EGR valve.
2. Clean the base of the EGR valve with a wire brush, being sure to remove all of the exhaust deposits from the base.
3. Insert the valve portion into a regular spark plug cleaning machine.
4. Clean the valve with a 30 second blast of abrasive.
5. Unseat the valve by depressing the diaphragm spring and repeat step 4.
6. Repeat steps 4 and 5 until all of the deposits have been removed from the valve.
7. Use compressed air to remove any abrasive material which may remain on the EGR valve.
8. Install the valve on the manifold.

V8 Engines

1. Remove the EGR valve.
2. Tap lightly on the sides and end of the EGR valve with a plastic hammer while holding the valve in your hand. Remove all exhaust deposits from the valve seat in this manner.
3. Use a wire wheel to buff the exhaust deposits from around the valve mounting surfaces.
4. Remove any exhaust deposits from the valve outlet area with a screwdriver.
5. Check the EGR valve to be sure that all of the deposits have been removed and install it on the manifold.

Thermostatically Controlled Air Cleaner

Vacuum Motor R & R

1. Remove the air cleaner assembly from the carburetor.
2. Detach the line from the vacuum motor.
3. Drill out the two retaining strap spot welds with a 1/16 in. drill.
4. Remove the retaining strap. Enlarge the holes, if necessary to do so.

NOTE: Use care not to damage the air cleaner snorkel.

5. Cock the motor to one side to un-

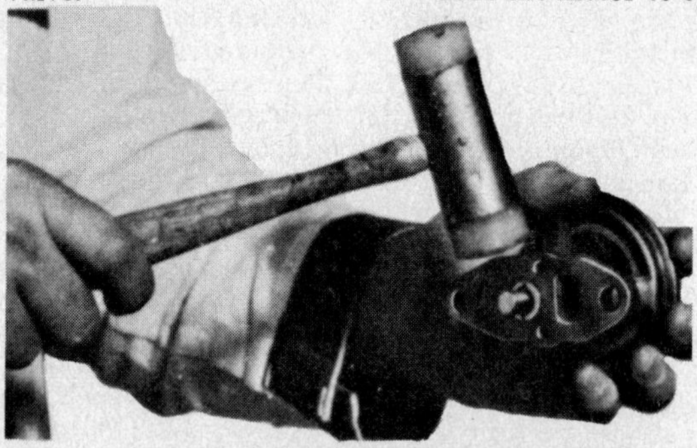

Cleaning the EGR valve used on the V8 engines
(© Oldsmobile Div, G.M. Corp)

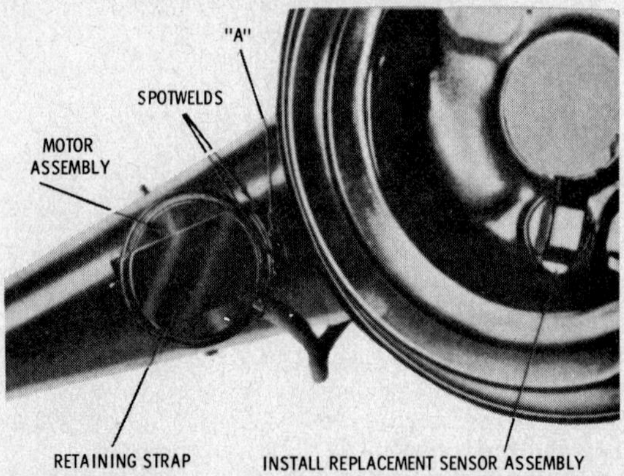
"A"
SPOTWELDS
MOTOR ASSEMBLY
RETAINING STRAP
INSTALL REPLACEMENT SENSOR ASSEMBLY IN SAME POSITION AS ORIGINAL ASSEMBLY

Thermostatically controlled air cleaner component replacement—"A" indicates 7/16 in. hole
(© Oldsmobile Div, G.M. Corp)

hook its linkage from the air door and lift the motor out.

Installation of a new motor is performed in the following order:

1. Drill a 7/64 in. hole at a point midway between the two holes previously drilled for the spot welds.
2. Connect the vacuum motor linkage to the air door assembly.
3. Secure the vacuum motor with the sheet metal screw and strap supplied with the motor service package.

NOTE: Once the sheet metal screw has been installed in the 7/64 in. hole, be sure that it does not interfere with the air door assembly. Use a shorter screw or shorten the existing one, as required.

4. Connect the vacuum line to the motor and install the air cleaner assembly on the carburetor.

NOTE: Be sure that the vacuum hose is not pinched during installation.

Thermal Sensor R & R

1. Remove the air cleaner assembly from the carburetor.
2. Detach the vacuum lines from the sensor.
3. Pry the tabs up on the sensor retaining clip and remove the sensor and gasket.

NOTE: Be careful to note the position of the sensor.

Sensor installation is performed in the reverse order of removal. Be sure to install the sensor in its original position.

ENGINE

Engine Removal

All Models

1. Disconnect the negative battery cable.
2. Scribe the outline of the hood hinges on the hood and remove the hood.
3. Drain the cooling system and disconnect the radiator and heater hoses from the engine.
4. Disconnect the engine ground strap from the cylinder head. Remove the fan shroud.
5. Disconnect and tag all vacuum lines and electrical leads from the engine.
6. Disconnect the throttle linkage. Disconnect the fuel line from the fuel pump. Remove clutch equalizer on M/T Omegas.
7. If the car is equipped with an automatic transmission, disconnect the cooler lines from the radiator. If equipped with power steering or air conditioning, remove the pump and bracket or compressor and bracket from the engine *without disconnecting the lines.*

Caution Disconnecting the air conditioner lines could result in personal injury or damage to the A/C system.

8. Remove the radiator. Raise the car.
9. Disconnect the exhaust pipes from the exhaust manifolds. Remove the motor mount thru–bolts. Remove the starter.
10. On models equipped with an automatic transmission, remove the torque converter cover. Turn the crankshaft pulley to gain access to the three torque converter-to-flywheel attaching bolts and remove the bolts.
11. Remove the transmission or clutch housing-to-engine bolts, place a jack under the transmission, and raise the transmission several inches.
12. Attach a chain hoist to the engine and remove the engine from the car.
13. Reverse the above procedure to install the engine.

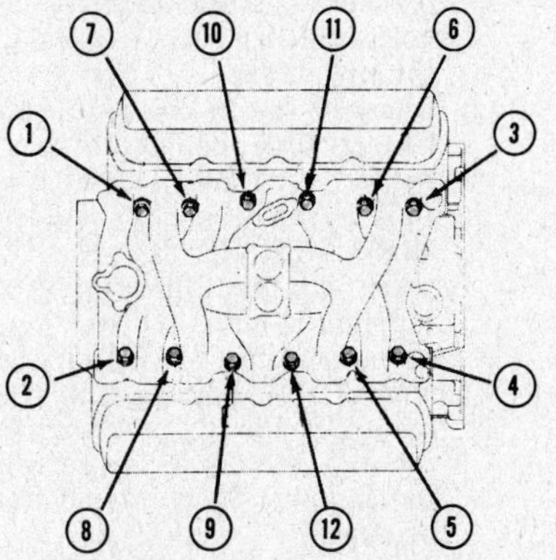

7
10
11
6
1
3
2
4
8
9
12
5

Intake manifold bolt tightening sequence—V8
(© Oldsmobile Div, G.M. Corp)

Engine Manifolds

Intake Manifold Removal

All V8 Models

1. Remove the carburetor air cleaner, drain the radiator.
2. Disconnect the upper radiator hose and heater hose from the manifold.
3. Disconnect the throttle linkage, vacuum and gas lines from the carburetor.
4. Remove the bolts that hold the intake manifold to the two cylinder heads.
5. The coil can be left on the intake manifold if the wires are disconnected.
6. Remove the generator and air conditioning compressor brackets if necessary.

Caution Do not disconnect the A/C lines. Severe personal injury or damage to the A/C system could result.

7. Disconnect the temperature gauge wire.

NOTE: On the 400 and 425 cu. in. engines it may be necessary to remove the distributor to provide clearance for manifold removal. On the 455 cu. in. engine it will be necessary to remove the oil filler tube.

Install in the reverse order of removal, tightening all bolts first to 15 ft. lbs., then to the figure specified in the torque chart, in the sequence illustrated. Coat all gasket surfaces with sealer.

Exhaust Manifold Removal

All V8 Models

1. Disconnect the negative battery cable.
2. Remove the bolts from the exhaust manifold flanges on both sides and take off the crossover pipe.
3. On the right side, remove generator and bracket.
4. Remove the hot air pipe and shroud if so equipped.
5. Disconnect the exhaust pipe from the manifold.
6. Remove the bolts that hold the exhaust manifold to the cylinder head and lift off the exhaust manifolds.

On some models with the 455 cu. in. engine, the starter will have to be removed to work on the left-hand exhaust manifold. On air-conditioned models with the 455 cu in. and 350 cu in (1971-74) engines, the front wheel will have to be removed in order to gain access to the right-hand manifold through the opening in the fender inner panel. When installing, tighten the manifold-to-head attaching bolts to 25 ft. lbs. torque, tightening those in the center first.

Combination Manifold

OHV 6 Models

This engine uses a combined intake and exhaust manifold, equipped with thermostatic heat-riser valve.

1. Remove the air cleaner assembly.
2. Detach the throttle cable and lever at the bellcrank. Unfasten the throttle return spring.
3. Detach the fuel and vacuum lines from the carburetor.
4. Remove the PCV hose and valve from the grommet on the valve cover. Disconnect the air supply hose from the check valve on the air injection manifold (right-hand side of engine), if so equipped.
5. Detach the downpipe from the exhaust manifold flange. Discard the old packing.
6. Unfasten the manifold securing bolts and remove the clamps.
7. Remove the manifold assembly and throw the old gasket away.
8. If it is necessary to separate the manifolds, unfasten the single

bolt and two nuts at the center of the assembly.

Installation is performed in the reverse order of removal.

Before reinstalling the manifold, thoroughly clean out the ports to prevent turbulence, particularly in the intake manifold. Use a new gasket and packing during installation.

Valve System

Hydraulic lifters are used on all engines. These lifters are not interchangeable. To remove hydraulic lifters, first remove intake manifold and rocker assemblies, then pull out lifters.

Hydraulic lifters operate normally under conditions of zero valve lash. See Rocker Shaft Removal for valve lash adjustment.

Rocker arm lubrication is provided by means of oil feed through the pushrods on V8 engines.

Valve guides are not replaceable, but may be reamed to 0.003 in., 0.005 and 0.013 in. oversize. Occasionally a valve guide bore will be oversize as manufactured. These are marked on the inboard side of the cylinder heads on the machined surface just above the intake manifold. To ream a 0.010 in. oversize valve guide bore, use the 0.013 in. oversize reamer. Service valves are available in five different stem diameters: Standard, 0.003 oversize, 0.005 oversize, 0.010 oversize and 0.013 oversize.

Rocker Arm Replacement

V8

Remove the valve covers. Remove the two bolts that attach the rocker arm pivot to the cylinder head. Remove the rocker arms in pairs. Install the pairs of rocker arms for each cylinder only when the lifters are off the cam lobe and the valves are closed. Lubricate all pivot and rocker arm wear points with white grease. Torque the hardened flanged retaining bolts to 25 ft. lbs.

6 Cylinder

1. Remove the valve cover.
2. Remove the attaching nut from the rocker arm to be removed, and lift the rocker arm nut, ball, and the rocker arm from the engine.
3. If more than one rocker arm is being removed, repeat step two until all the arms have been removed. Keep the nuts, balls, and arms in order when they are removed so they can be installed in their original location.
4. Install the rocker arm and ball on their stud after coating wear points with white grease.
5. Make sure the pushrod is installed in the lifter and the end of the rocker arm, and tighten the rocker arm attaching nut finger-tight.
6. Adjust the valves.

Valve Adjustment

V8

These valves cannot be adjusted. If there is excessive clearance in the valve train, look for worn pushrods, rocker arms, valve springs, or collapsed or stuck valve lifters.

6 Cylinder

1. Remove the distributor cap from the distributor and crank the engine until no. 1 piston is at top dead center (TDC). TDC can be determined in the following manner:
   a. Remove the spark plug from no. 1 cylinder.
   b. Place your thumb over the spark plug hole while an assistant cranks the engine.
   c. When no. 1 piston begins its compression stroke, compression at the spark plug hole will try to force your thumb outward.
   d. Observe the crankshaft pulley and turn the engine (preferably by hand) until the timing mark on the pulley aligns with the "0" (TDC) mark on the indicator. No. 1 piston is now at TDC.
   e. At this time, look at the rotor. The pointer on the rotor should be pointing to the no. 1 cylinder tower in the cap and the points should be open.
2. The valves on no. 1 cylinder can now be adjusted. Loosen the rocker arm adjusting nut until the pushrod can be rotated (lash) and then tighten the nut until all lash is removed and the pushrod can't be rotated. Tighten the adjusting nut an additional full turn to center the lifter plunger.
3. Using a socket wrench, turn the crankshaft pulley $\frac{1}{4}$ turn in the direction of engine rotation (counterclockwise when viewed from the rear). By turning the crankshaft, piston no. 5 is now at TDC and its valves can be adjusted. After adjusting no. 5, turn the crankshaft another $\frac{1}{4}$ turn to bring piston no. 3 to TDC and adjust its valves. Follow the firing order (1-5-3-6-2-4, from front to rear) and adjust the valves for cylinder no. 6 and then no. 2 and no. 4, making sure that the crankshaft is turned $\frac{1}{4}$ turn after each cylinder is adjusted.
4. Install the distributor cap and the rocker arm cover.

Cylinder Head

Caution Do not disconnect the A/C lines. Severe personal injury or system damage could result.

V8

1. Drain the cooling system.
2. Remove the intake manifold and carburetor as an assembly.
3. Remove exhaust manifolds.
4. Loosen or remove any accessory brackets which interfere.
5. Remove the valve cover. Loosen any accessory brackets which are in the way.
6. On V8 engines, remove rocker arm bolts, pivots, rocker arms and pushrods. Scribe the pivots and identify the rocker arms and pushrods so that they may be installed in their original locations.

NOTE: On some F-85 models equipped with a 455 cu in. engine and air conditioning, disconnect the right motor mount and jack up the right front corner of the engine to remove the no. 8 pushrod. When the above models are also equipped with power brakes, it is necessary to disconnect the booster and turn it sideways to remove no. 7 pushrod.

7. Remove cylinder head bolts and cylinder head(s).
8. Install in the reverse order of removal. It is recommended that the head gasket be coated on both sides with sealer. Dip head bolts in oil before installing. Tighten all head bolts in the correct sequence to 60-70 ft. lbs., then again in sequence to the specified torque. See Specifications at the beginning of this section for correct head bolt torque. Retorque the bolts after engine is warmed-up.

OHV 6 Engine

1. Drain cooling system (including block) and remove manifold assembly and valve mechanism.
2. Remove fuel and vacuum line from retaining clip and disconnect wires from temperature sending units.
3. Disconnect upper radiator hose and battery ground strap.
4. Remove coil.

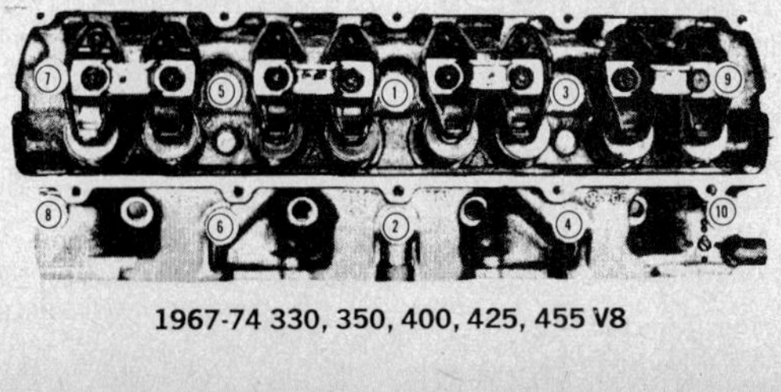
7
5
1
3
9
8
6
2
4
10

1967-74 330, 350, 400, 425, 455 V8

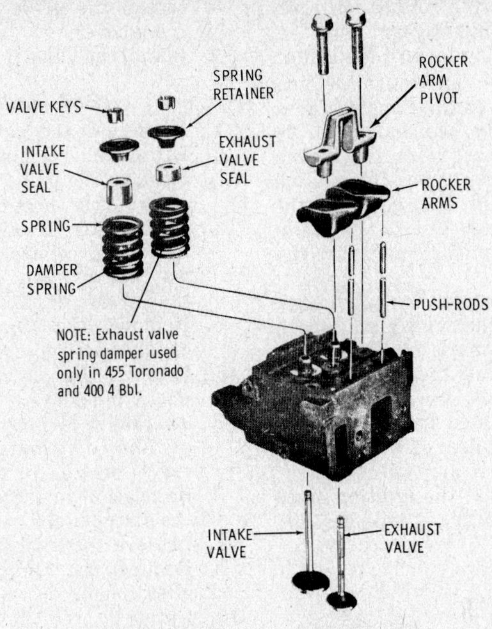
VALVE KEYS
SPRING RETAINER
ROCKER ARM PIVOT
INTAKE VALVE SEAL
EXHAUST VALVE SEAL
ROCKER ARMS
SPRING
DAMPER SPRING
PUSH-RODS
NOTE: Exhaust valve spring damper used only in 455 Toronado and 400 4 Bbl.
INTAKE VALVE
EXHAUST VALVE

Valve and cylinder head assembly—V8
(© Oldsmobile Div, G.M. Corp)

5. Remove cylinder head bolts, then head and gasket.

NOTE: Place the cylinder head on two blocks of wood, so that it is not damaged.

Install in the reverse order of removal. See Specifications at the beginning of this section for correct head bolt torque and tightening sequence. Use sealer on the head bolts prior to installation. Do not use gasket sealer when using a composition steel-asbestos head gasket. Retorque the head bolts after the engine has warmed up.

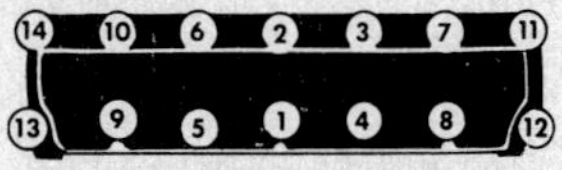
14 10 6 2 3 7 11
13 9 5 1 4 8 12

1967-71 and 1973-74 OHV 6 cyl.

1. Drain the cooling system and disconnect the radiator and heater hoses, remove the radiator core, the fan blades and pulley.
2. Remove the vibration damper and crankshaft pulley.
3. Place a jack under the engine, take a light load on the jack and remove the two bolts that attach the front of the engine to the frame.

Chilton's TIME SAVER

Field experience indicates the need for quick replacement data on worn, loose or thread damaged valve rocker arm studs.

1. **Place a thin-walled socket and a flat washer over the bad stud.**
2. **Turn the stud nut on until the stud pulls free of the cylinder head.**
3. **Unless the bad stud was loose, a standard stud can be replaced. If the stud was loose in the head, oversize studs and appropriate reamers are available from the dealer.**
4. **While cleaning or reconditioning the hole, chill the new stud (in the household refrigerator or the soda dispenser).**
5. **Run the engine until it is warm, then lightly tap the new stud into the cylinder head stud hole.**

NOTE: carefully measure the exposed length of the corresponding studs. If the new stud is inserted to a greater depth than necessary, it may damage the head.

Timing Case and Camshaft

Front Cover R & R

V8 Engines

The timing case cover and the water pump housing are a one-piece casting.

4. Drain the oil and remove the oil pan (see Engine Lubrication section).
5. Remove the front cover attaching bolts and remove the cover, timing indicator and water pump from the front of the engine.
6. Install in the reverse order of removal using a new gasket with sealing compound. Tighten self-tapping water pump attaching screws to 13 ft. lbs., 5/16 in. front cover attaching bolts to 25 ft. lbs. and the four bottom bolts (cover plate) to 35 ft. lbs. Torque the pulley hub bolt to 160 ft lbs, crankshaft pulley bolts to 20 ft lbs (10 ft lbs for 1972), and fan bolts to 20 ft lbs.

1967-71, and 1973-74 OHV 6 Models

1. Remove the crankshaft pulley. Remove the oil pan.
2. Remove the timing case cover attaching bolts.
3. Remove the cover and gasket. Pry the old seal out of the front side of the cover with a large screwdriver.
4. Install the new seal so that the open end of the seal is toward the inside of the cover. When reinstalling, be careful that cover is positioned to center seal on the shaft.
5. Tighten the screws and the two bolts inside the engine to 6-7½ ft. lbs.

Front Cover Oil Seal —All Engines

Removal and Installation (Cover not removed)

1. Remove belts.
2. Remove pulley and hubs.
3. Carefully pry out old seal with screwdriver or thin punch, using care not to damage shaft surface.
4. Coat outside diameter of new seal with proper sealer.
5. Drive in seal with proper tool, using care not to distort it nor damage mating surfaces or shaft.
6. Reinstall removed parts and adjust belts.

Timing Gear Replacement

6 Cylinder Engine

Timing gears are arranged so that (unless deliberately disturbed) the valve timing will remain as set at the factory. Unless the gears are badly worn or seriously damaged, the valve timing will remain constant within reasonable limits.

If it becomes necessary to remove the timing gear, proceed in the following order:

1. Remove the camshaft.
2. Place the camshaft and gear assembly in an arbor press. Using an adapter, press the camshaft from the gear.

Caution The thrust plate should be positioned so that the Woodruff key and shaft do not damage it during removal.

3. If the crankshaft gear requires replacement, remove it with a gear puller. Replace it using a drift of the proper size.

Installation is performed in the reverse order of removal. The clearance

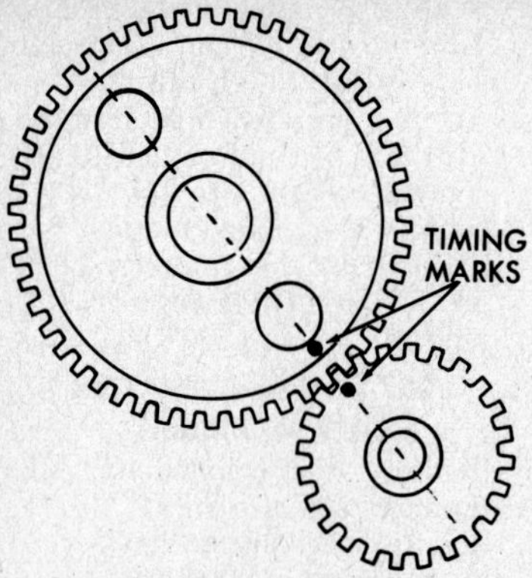
TIMING
MARKS

Timing marks—OHV 6

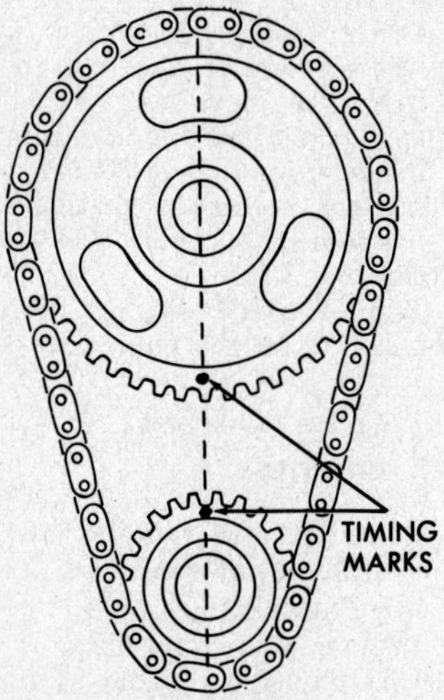
TIMING
MARKS

Timing marks—except OHV 6

between the camshaft and the thrust plate should be 0.001-0.005 in. Install the camshaft as outlined below.

Timing Chain Replacement and Valve Timing

V8

On all Oldsmobile engines, except the L6, a chain is used to drive the camshaft. The construction is such that the chain can be worn even badly without seriously affecting the valve timing. If the chain is worn badly enough to cause the timing to jump or it becomes necessary to replace either the chain or the sprockets or both, proceed as follows:

1. Remove the timing case cover and take off the camshaft gear.

NOTE: the fuel pump operating cam is bolted to the front of the camshaft sprocket and the sprocket is located on the camshaft by means of a dowel.

2. Remove the oil slinger, timing chain, and the camshaft sprocket. If the crankshaft sprocket is to be replaced, remove it also at this time.
3. Reinstall the crankshaft sprocket being careful to start it with the keyway in perfect alignment since it is rather difficult to correct for misalignment after the gear has been started on the shaft. Turn the timing mark on the crankshaft gear until it points directly toward the center of the camshaft. Mount the timing chain over the camshaft gear and start the camshaft gear up on to its shaft with the timing marks as close as possible to each other and in line between the shaft centers. Rotate the camshaft to align the shaft with the new gear.

A dowel pin is used for alignment. Secure the camshaft gear and check to see that the mark on the crankshaft sprocket and the mark on the camshaft sprocket are as described above. Valves timed in this manner are correct regardless of which piston is at top center. It may be necessary, however, to retime the ignition since there is a possibility it will be 180° out of position.

Camshaft R & R

L6 Engine

1. Remove the valve lifters and the crankcase front cover.
2. Remove the grille from the front of the car.
3. Remove the fuel pump.
4. Align the timing gear marks on the crankshaft and the camshaft gears, then remove the thrust plate bolts.
5. Remove the camshaft and gear assembly from the engine. Support the shaft during removal to prevent damage to the camshaft bearing.
6. Check the camshaft journals with a micrometer to determine if they are out-of-round. If the journals exceed .001 in. out-of round, replace the camshaft. Check the assembly for signs of wear or damage.
7. Insert the camshaft and gear assembly in the engine, being careful not to damage the shaft.
8. Turn the crankshaft and camshaft gears so that the valve timing marks align. Push the camshaft into position and install and torque the thrust plate bolts to 80 in. lbs (1967), or 7 ft lbs (1968-74).
9. Check camshaft and crankshaft gear run-out with a dial indicator. Camshaft gear run-out should not exceed .004 in. and crankshaft gear run-out should not be above .003 in.
10. If run-out is excessive, clean off any burrs from the shaft and make another measurement. If run-out is still excessive, replace the gear.
11. Using a dial indicator, check the backlash at several points between the camshaft and crankshaft gear teeth. Backlash should be .004–.006 in.
12. Install the fuel pump.
13. Install the grille and crankcase front cover.
14. Install the valve lifters.

1967-70 V8

1. Disconnect the battery.
2. Drain and remove the radiator.
3. Remove the grille and any other obstructing sheet metal.
4. If the car is air conditioned, move the condenser out of the way but *do not disconnect any of the refrigerant lines.*
5. Remove the fuel pump and crankcase front cover.
6. Remove the oil slinger, timing chain and gears.
7. To facilitate proper installation of the distributor, mark the exact location of the distributor in relation to the block. Remove the distributor.
8. Remove the intake manifold.
9. Remove the rocker arm assemblies, pushrods, and lifters.
10. Carefully remove the camshaft from the block.
11. Inspect the camshaft assembly for excessive wear or damage.
12. Liberally coat camshaft with heavy engine oil prior to installation.
13. Carefully insert the camshaft into the engine.
14. Install the lifters, pushrods, rocker arm assemblies, and valve covers.
15. Install the intake manifold.
16. Install the timing chain and gears, oil slinger, and front cover.
17. Install the fuel pump, radiator, air conditioning condenser, and any front-end sheet metal that may have been removed.
18. Install the distributor to agree with the location markings made before removal.

1971-74 V8

1. Disconnect the battery.
2. Drain and remove the radiator.
3. Disconnect the fuel line at the fuel pump.
4. Disconnect the throttle cable.
5. Remove the generator belt, loosen the generator bolts, and move the generator to one side.
6. Remove the power steering pump from its brackets and move it out of the way.
7. Remove the air conditioning compressor from its brackets and move the compressor out of the way *without disconnecting the lines.*
8. Disconnect the hoses from the water pump.
9. Disconnect the electrical and vacuum connections.
10. Mark the distributor as to location in the block. Remove the distributor.
11. Raise the car and drain the oil pan.

12. Remove the exhaust crossover pipe and starter motor.
13. Disconnect the exhaust pipe at the manifold.
14. Remove the harmonic balancer and pulley.
15. Support the engine and remove the front motor mounts.
16. Remove the flywheel inspection cover.
17. Remove the engine oil pan.
18. Support the engine by placing wooden blocks between the exhaust manifolds and the front crossmember.
19. Remove the engine front cover.
20. Remove the valve covers.
21. Remove the intake manifold, oil filler pipe, and temperature sending switch.
22. Mark the lifters, pushrods, and rocker arms as to location so that they may be installed in the same position. Remove these parts.
23. If the car is equipped with air conditioning, remove the condenser attaching bolts and move the condenser to one side.

NOTE: Do not remove the A/C lines from the condenser.

24. Remove the fuel pump eccentric, camshaft gear, oil slinger, and timing chain.
25. Carefully remove the camshaft from the engine.
26. Inspect the shaft for signs of excessive wear or damage.
27. Liberally coat camshaft and bearings with heavy-weight engine oil and insert them into the engine.
28. Align the timing marks on the camshaft and crankshaft gears. See "Timing Chain Replacement and Valve Timing" for details.
29. Install the distributor using the locating marks made during removal. If any problems are encountered, see "Distributor Installation" in the "Ignition" Section.
30. To install, reverse the removal procedure but pay attention to the following points:
    a. Install the timing indicator before installing the power steering pump bracket.
    b. Install the flywheel inspection cover after installing the starter.
    c. Replace the engine oil and radiator coolant.

Connecting Rods and Pistons

Piston Assembly Removal

1. Remove cylinder head.
2. Remove oil pan.
3. Examine cylinder bores for top ridge. If ridge exists, remove it before taking pistons out.
4. Number all the pistons, connecting rods and caps. Starting at the front, the right bank is numbered 2-4-6-8. The left bank is numbered, 1-3-5-7.

The OHV in-line 6 engine has an order of 1-2-3-4-5-6.

5. With No. 4 crankpin straight down, remove cap and bearing shell from No. 1 connecting rod. Install connecting rod bolt guides to hold upper half of the bearing shell in place.
6. Push piston and rod assembly up out of the cylinder. Then remove bolt guides and reinstall cap and bearing shell on the rod.
7. Remove the remaining rod and piston assemblies in the same manner.

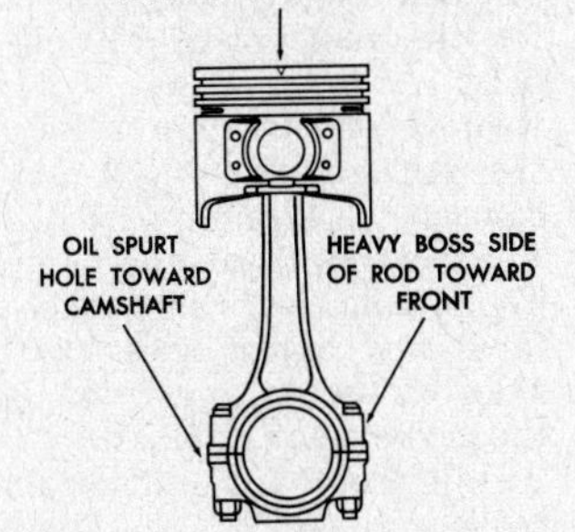
NOTCH TO FRONT OF ENGINE
OIL SPURT HOLE TOWARD CAMSHAFT
HEAVY BOSS SIDE OF ROD TOWARD FRONT

Piston and rod assembly—OHV 6

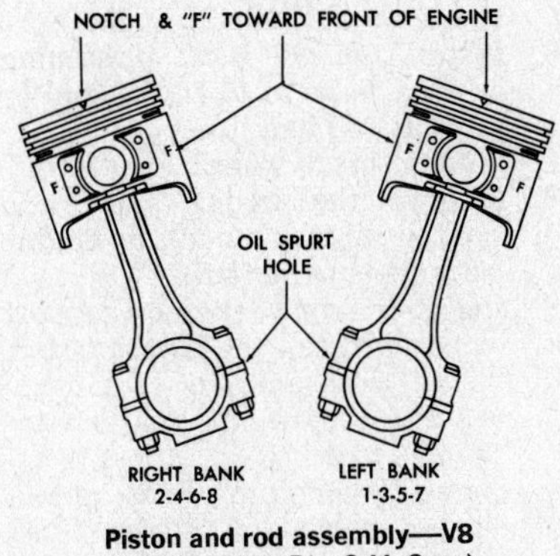
NOTCH & "F" TOWARD FRONT OF ENGINE
OIL SPURT HOLE
RIGHT BANK 2-4-6-8
LEFT BANK 1-3-5-7

Piston and rod assembly—V8
(© Oldsmobile Div, G.M. Corp)

8. Carefully remove oil rings with piston ring expander.
9. Carefully press out the old pin.

NOTE: check the cylinder bores for out-of-round, taper or other damage. Any cylinders requiring attention may be bored or honed the same as any conventional cast iron cylinder block. Maximum allowable taper is .010 in.

Fitting Rings and Pins

1. When new rings are installed without reboring the cylinders, cylinder wall glaze should be broken. This can be done by using the finest grade stones in a cylinder hone.
2. New piston rings must be checked for clearance in piston grooves and for cap in cylinder bores.
3. When fitting new rings to new pistons the side clearance for compression rings should be checked.
4. Check end gap of compression rings by placing them in the bore in which they will operate. Then push them to the bottom of the bore with a piston. Now measure the end gap in each ring. The end gap should be no less than .015 in.
5. If piston pin bosses are worn out of round or oversize, the piston and pin should be replaced. Oversize pins are not practical because the pin is a press fit in the connecting rod. Piston pins must fit the piston with an easy finger push at 70°F.
6. In assembling the piston to the connecting rod, a press is ideal. However, substitutes are available that will serve the purpose.
7. If the rod assembly is to go into the left bank, the boss on the rod and cap go toward the rear of the engine. If the rod assembly is to go into the right bank, the boss on the rod and cap go toward the front of the engine. In both cases, the connecting rod bearing oil spurt holes point up.

Piston Assembly Installation

1. Carefully assemble the piston to the connecting rod (press in the pin).
2. Remove piston and rod from the press. Rock the piston on the pin to be sure pin or piston boss was not damaged during the pressing operation.
3. Install ring expander in lower ring groove. Position the ends of the expander above the piston pin where groove is not slotted. The ends of the expander must butt together.
4. Install oil ring rails over expander with gaps up on same side of piston as oil spurt hole in connecting rod.
5. Install compression rings, (with a ring expander) in top and center groove.
6. Coat all bearing surfaces, rings and piston skirt with engine oil.
7. Position the crankpin of the cylinder being worked on, down.
8. Remove connecting rod bearing cap and with upper bearing shell correctly seated in the rod, install connecting rod bolt guides.
9. Make sure the gaps in the two oil ring rails are up toward the center of the engine. Make sure the gaps of the compression rings are not in line with each other or the oil ring rails. Be sure the ends of the oil ring spacer-expander are butted and not overlapped.
10. With a good ring compressor, install the piston and rod assembly into the cylinder bore and carefully tap down until the rod

bearing is solidly seated on the crankpin.

11. Remove the connecting rod bolt guides and install cap and lower bearing shell. Torque to specifications.
12. Install other piston and rod assemblies in the same manner. When the assemblies are all installed, the oil spurt holes will be up. The rib on the edge of the rod cap will be on the same side as the conical boss on the connecting rod web. These marks will be toward the other connecting rod on the same crankpin.
13. Accumulated end clearance between rod bearings on any crankpin should be as specified.
14. Install oil screen and oil pan.
15. Install cylinder heads.

NOTE: before starting a new or reconditioned engine, it is advisable to pack the oil pump with petroleum jelly to insure pump priming for immediate lubrication.

Engine Lubrication

Oil Pan R & R

All 1967-70 Olds and F-85 with 350, 425, and 455 Cu In. Engines All 1970-74 F-85, Cutlass, and Omega Except 1970-72 455 Cutlass

1. Disconnect the negative battery cable and remove the dipstick.
2. On 1968-74 88 and 98 models, remove the upper radiator support and fan shroud attaching screws.
3. Raise the car on a hoist and drain the crankcase.
4. On F-85, Cutlass, 442 and Vista Cruiser models, disconnect the exhaust pipe from the right exhaust manifold. On 88 and 98 models lower the relay rod by disconnecting the idler arm or pitman arm.
5. Disconnect the engine mounts and carefully jack the front of the engine up as far as possible using a suitable tool. The special lifting tool bolts to the front of the block.
6. Remove crossover pipe and starter.
7. Remove oil pan attaching bolts, rotate the crankshaft until the No. 1 crankshaft throw is up, then remove the oil pan.
8. When installing, apply sealer to both sides of pan gasket and install on block. Install the front and rear (rubber) seals. Install the pan, tightening 5/16 in. bolts to 15 ft. lbs. and 1/4 in. bolts to 10 ft. lbs.
9. Reverse Steps 1 through 6 to complete installation.

1969 400 Cu. In. 1970-72 F-85 Cutlass—455 Cu. In.

1. Disconnect the negative battery cable and disconnect the fan shroud.
2. Raise the car on a hoist and drain the crankcase.
3. Remove the driveshaft.
4. Disconnect the exhaust pipe and starter.
5. Install a rear engine support bar and remove the flywheel housing inspection cover.
6. Disconnect modulator line, speedometer cable, oil cooler lines, solenoid wire and linkage.
7. Remove transmission crossmember, transmission and flywheel.
8. Raise the front of the engine.
9. Remove the right engine mount and raise the engine 2 in. Install a wedge block.
10. Loosen the left engine mount-to-block bolts enough to allow for the removal of the oil pan bolts.
11. Remove the oil pan bolts, free the pan from the block and disconnect the oil pump.
12. Remove the oil pan and pump.
13. To install, clean all gasket surfaces and apply sealer to both sides of the pan gaskets. Install the gaskets on the block.
14. Install front and rear (rubber) seals.
15. Hold the oil pan in approximate position and install the oil pump, tightening bolts to 35 ft. lbs.
16. Install the oil pan, tightening 5/16 in. bolts to 15 ft. lbs. and 1/4 in. bolts to 10 ft. lbs.
17. Install the flywheel.
18. Remove the wedge block and tighten engine mount to engine block bolts to 50 ft. lbs.
19. Remove front engine support tool and install the transmission.
20. Install transmission crossmember and remove the rear engine support tool.
21. Connect modulator lines, speedometer cable, oil cooler lines, solenoid wire and linkage.
22. Connect the starter and exhaust pipe.
23. Install the driveshaft.
24. Lower car and fill the crankcase.
25. Connect the fan shroud and connect the battery negative cable.

1967-68 400 Cu. In.

1. Disconnect the battery negative cable and remove the upper radiator baffle.
2. Remove driveshaft, transmission crossmember, transmission and flywheel.
3. Disconnect the left exhaust pipe and the starter.
4. Disconnect the right engine mount. Raise both the front and rear of the engine, tilting it to the left and using the left engine mount as a pivot.
5. Install a rear engine support bar, inserting a 1 in. block between the bar and the right rear corner on the oil pan to obtain additional lift on the right side.
6. Raise the front of the engine. The engine must rock when raised.
7. Raise the right side of the engine approximately 2½ in. and insert a block between the upper and lower right engine mounts.
8. Remove the support bar from the rear of the engine.
9. Remove oil pan attaching bolts and remove oil pan toward the rear of the engine. No. 1 and No. 2 connecting rod journals should be at 4 or 7 o'clock position as viewed from the front of the engine.
10. To install, follow Step 8 of the 350, 425, and 455 cu. in. engine procedure and reverse Steps 1 through 8 above.

6 Cylinder Engine

1. Disconnect battery positive cable, fuel flex line at the fuel pump and starter leads at the starter. On 1967-69 models, to remove the pan the engine must be removed, so refer to engine removal procedures.
2. Remove upper radiator support and bracket to upper hose. On cars with air conditioning, remove the fan and clutch assembly.
3. Remove front motor mount bracket to motor mount bolts.
4. Raise the car on a hoist and drain crankcase.
5. Disconnect automatic transmission linkage and remove flywheel cover and starter.
6. Disconnect exhaust pipe at the manifold.
7. Position timing mark notch at the 6 o'clock position.
8. Raise the engine with a jack at the crankshaft damper and remove the right engine mount with bracket.
9. Remove the oil pan attaching bolts and the oil pan. It may be necessary to raise the engine further to get the pan out. Be careful not to damage cowl mounted parts.
10. To install, reverse the above procedure. Use new gaskets.

Oil Pump

On all engines, the oil pump is mounted to the bottom of the block and is accessible only by removing the oil pan.

On V8 engines, remove the oil pan, then unbolt and remove the oil pump and screen as an assembly. On the OHV 6 the pickup tube has a bolt-attached bracket.

Rear Main Bearing Oil Seal

V8 Engine

The crankshaft need not be removed to replace the rear main bearing upper oil seal.

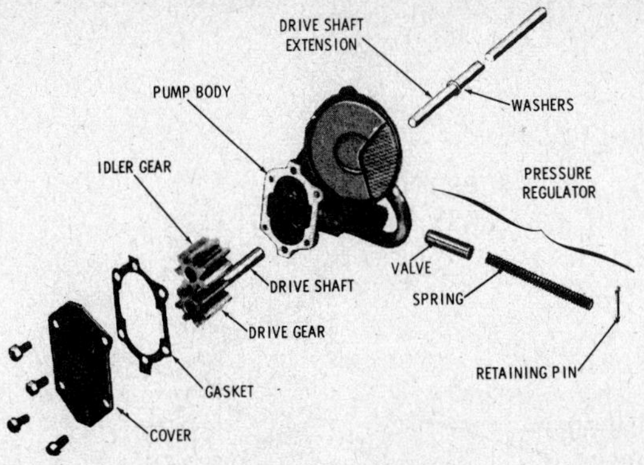
DRIVE SHAFT EXTENSION
PUMP BODY
WASHERS
IDLER GEAR
PRESSURE REGULATOR
VALVE
DRIVE SHAFT
SPRING
DRIVE GEAR
RETAINING PIN
GASKET
COVER

Oil pump—V8
(© Oldsmobile Div, G.M. Corp)

1. Drain the crankcase and remove the oil pan and rear main bearing cap.
2. Using a blunt-ended tool, drive the upper seal into its groove on each side until it is tightly packed. This is usually ¼-¾ in.
3. Cut pieces of new seal 1/16 in. longer than required to fill the grooves and install, packing into place.
4. Carefully trim any protruding seal, being sure not to scratch or damage the bearing surface.
5. Install a new seal in the bearing cap and install cap, tightening bolts to 120 ft. lbs. Install the oil pan.

6 Cylinder Engine

The rear main bearing oil seal is of moulded design and can be replaced (both halves) without removal of the crankshaft.

NOTE: always replace both halves as a unit. Install with the lip facing toward front of the engine.

1. With oil pan and pump removed, remove the rear main bearing cap.
2. Remove oil seal from the groove by lifting the end tab, then clean seal groove.
3. Lubricate the lip and O.D. of a new seal with engine oil. Keep oil off the parting line surface.
4. Insert seal into cap and roll into place with fingers. Use light pressure on the seal to prevent cutting the O.D. of the seal with the sharp edges of the groove. Be sure the tabs of the seal are properly located in the cross grooves.
5. To remove upper half of seal, use a small hammer to tap a brass pin punch on one end of seal until it protrudes far enough to be removed with pliers.
6. Lubricate the lip and O.D. of a new seal with engine oil. Keep oil off parting line surface. Gradually push with a hammer handle, while turning crankshaft, until seal is rolled into place. Be careful that seal bead on O.D. of seal is not cut.
7. Install rear main bearing cap (with new seal) and torque to specifications. Be sure cross seal tabs are in place and properly seated.

CLUTCH

Clutch Pedal Adjustment

1967-72

The clutch pedal should be adjusted so that there is ¾ to 1 in. free-play at the clutch pedal before the throwout bearing engages the clutch fingers. This adjustment is made under the car at the adjustable clutch rod just in front of the throwout fork. Loosen the jam nut and turn the adjusting screw until the desired clearance is obtained, then tighten the jam nut.

1973-74

The clutch pedal free-play should be adjusted to the following specifications, which are measured from the center of the clutch pedal pad:

Cutlass—¾-1 in.
Omega—⅞-1½ in.

To adjust free-play, proceed in the following manner:

1. Loosen the locknut on the push rod swivel.
2. Detach the pedal return spring.
3. Turn the equalizer assembly until the clutch pedal seats against the rubber bumper on the dash brace.
4. Push the outer end of the clutch fork rearward, so that the throwout bearing just contacts the clutch plate.
5. Remove the retaining clip from the lower push rod swivel and install the swivel in the *upper* gauge hole. Install the retaining clip.
6. Lengthen the push rod until there is no lash.
7. Remove the retaining clip and reinstall the swivel in the *lower* hole on the equalizer lever.
8. Tighten the locknut against the swivel. Be sure that the rod length remains unchanged.
9. Install the pedal return spring and check pedal free-play.

Clutch R & R

1. Remove the transmission.
2. Detach the clutch return spring and clutch release rod assembly.
3. Withdraw the throwout bearing.
4. Without removing the starter from the engine, remove the flywheel housing.

NOTE: The release yoke, boot and ball stud will remain in the housing.

5. Scribe a mark opposite the "X" mark on the flywheel cover.
6. Loosen the pressure plate evenly, one turn at a time.

Clutch installation is performed in the following order:

Caution Do not lubricate the splines as the lubricant will be forced on to the damper, resulting in clutch rattle.

1. Install the clutch disc/cover assembly and finger-tighten its securing bolts.

NOTE: Align the mark made during removal with the "X" mark on the flywheel cover.

2. Use a clutch arbor or an old input shaft to align the disc by inserting it through the disc and into the pilot bearing.
3. Tighten every other bolt until the cover assembly is within ¼ in. of the flywheel.
4. Repeat step 3 for the three remaining bolts.
5. Tighten the first three bolts to the torque figure given below and then tighten the remaining three bolts to the same figure.
   1967-70—17 ft lbs
   1971-74—30 ft lbs
6. Remove the arbor. Lubricate the inside groove of the throwout bearing and the release yoke ball stud with wheel bearing grease.
7. Install the throwout bearing.
8. Install the flywheel housing and the transmission. Adjust clutch free-play as outlined above.

MANUAL TRANSMISSION

See the Capacities Table at the beginning of this section for manual transmission refill capacities. For manual transmission overhaul procedures, see the Unit Repair Section.

Transmission Removal

1. Disconnect throttle linkage and raise car. If applicable, disconnect T.C.S. switch.
2. Remove driveshaft.
3. Install engine support bar with appropriate adapter.
4. On console equipped floorshifts, disconnect shifter assembly at transmission, allowing this unit to remain in car. On regular floorshifts, remove floor pan seal. Insert a feeler gauge between the shift lever and its point of

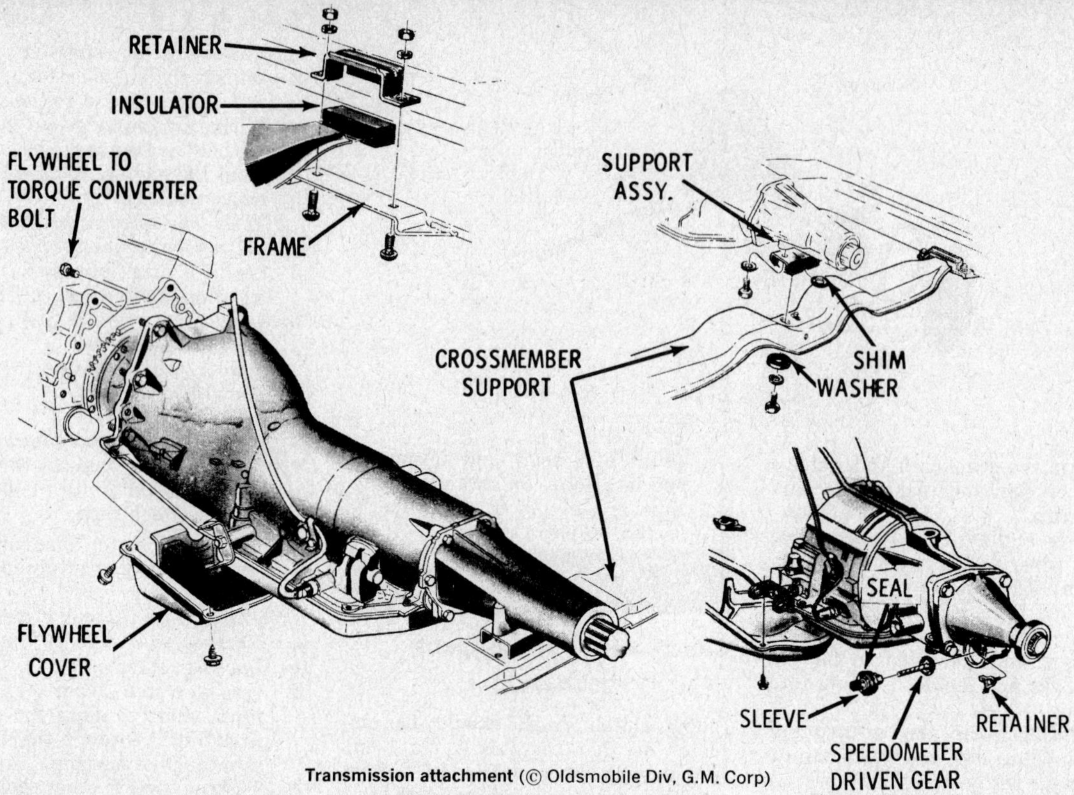
RETAINER
INSULATOR
FLYWHEEL TO TORQUE CONVERTER BOLT
FRAME
SUPPORT ASSY.
CROSSMEMBER SUPPORT
SHIM
WASHER
SEAL
FLYWHEEL COVER
SLEEVE
RETAINER
SPEEDOMETER DRIVEN GEAR

Transmission attachment (© Oldsmobile Div, G.M. Corp)

attachment. This will release a pin allowing the lever to be removed. Remove the shifter with transmission.

5. Disconnect parking brake cables and remove cross support bar.
6. Disconnect speedometer cable.
7. Remove transmission upper and lower bolts.

Caution During removal, use aligning studs to support the transmission, otherwise distortion of the clutch driven plate will result.

8. Slide transmission rearward and remove. On models equipped with dual exhaust, it may be necessary to disconnect left exhaust pipe at the manifold.
9. Install by reversing procedure above.

Shift Linkage Adjustment

1967-68 3-Speed Column Shift

1. With transmission in neutral, loosen the swivel nuts on the shift rods at the transmission. Make sure that the shift rods are free to move in the swivels.
2. Insert a 3/16 in. rod through the shift levers and into the upper hole of the column bracket.
3. With transmission levers in neutral, tighten the swivel nuts to 23 ft. lbs.
4. Remove the 3/16 in. rod and check that the column shift levers are exactly in line, adjusting one of them if necessary.
5. Check the operation of the shift linkage.

1969-74 3-Speed Column Shift

1. With the transmission in reverse and the car raised on a hoist, loosen the swivel bolts on the shift rods at the transmission.
2. Check that the shift rods move freely in the swivels, then push up on the reverse shift rod until the detent in the column is felt and tighten the swivel bolt for the first-reverse rod to 20 ft. lbs.
3. With transmission in neutral, insert a 3/16 in. rod through the second-third shift lever and into the alignment hole. Tighten the swivel bolt for the second-third shift lever to 20 ft. lbs.
4. Lower the car and check the shift operation.
5. Place transmission in Reverse and the ignition in LOCK position. Check that the key can be removed, the wheel not turned and the transmission will not shift out of Reverse.
6. Turn the ignition to RUN position and place the transmission in second gear. Check that the ignition key cannot be removed and that the steering wheel will turn.

Cutlass 3- and 4-Speed Floor Shift

The linkage adjustment procedure is the same as that described above for the column shift type, with the exception that the shift levers are aligned with a ¼ in. rod.

Omega 3-Speed Floorshift

1. Place the shift lever in Neutral and raise the car with a hoist.
2. Loosen the swivel nuts on the shift rods and detach the rods from the shifter assembly.
3. Insert a ¼ in. pin in the locating gauge hole on the shifter.
4. Adjust the swivel so that free pin length is obtained.
5. Tighten the swivel nuts and attach the shift rods back to the shifter.
6. Position the shift lever in Reverse and turn the ignition key to LOCK.
7. Loosen the equalizer clamp screw and pull the backdrive rod down lightly against the stop.
8. Torque the clamp screw to 23 ft lbs.
9. Lower the car and perform steps 5-6 of the "1969-74 3-Speed Column Shift" adjustment above.

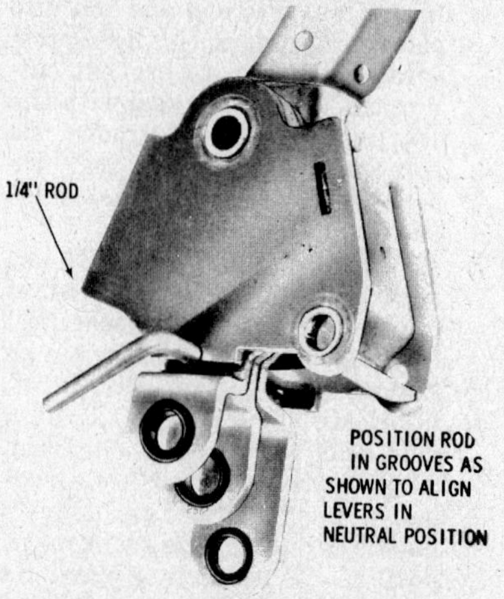
1/4" ROD
POSITION ROD IN GROOVES AS SHOWN TO ALIGN LEVERS IN NEUTRAL POSITION

Adjusting shift linkage—4-speed (© Oldsmobile Div, G.M. Corp)

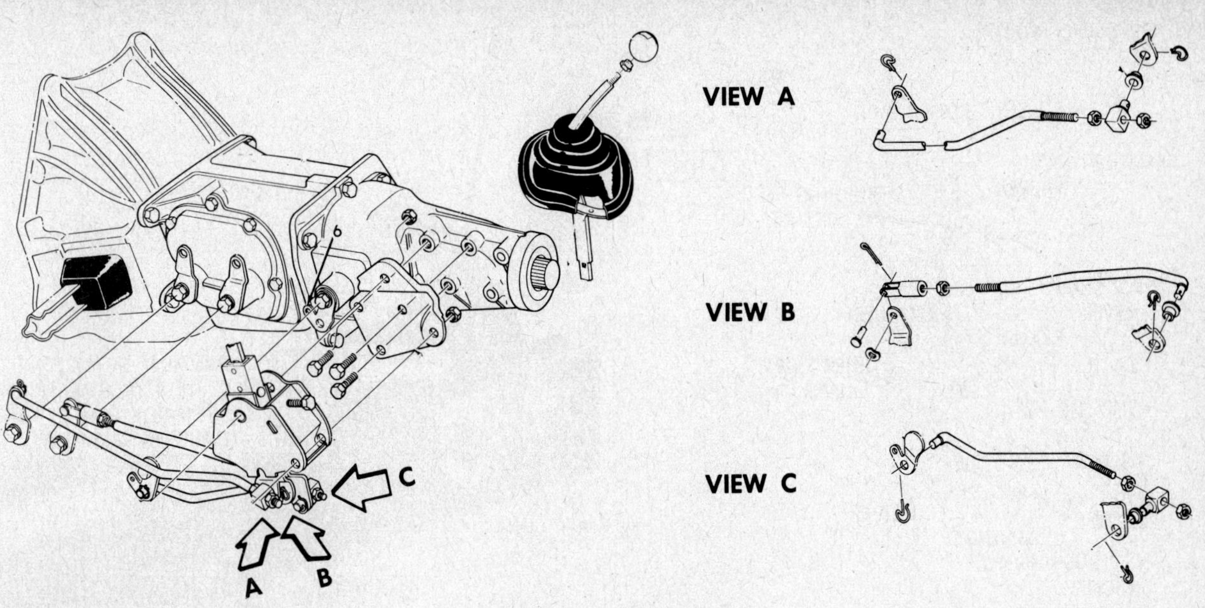
VIEW A
VIEW B
VIEW C
C
A
B

Floor shift control linkage details

AUTOMATIC TRANSMISSION

Shift Linkage Adjustment

Turbo Hydra-Matic and Jetaway

The proper linkage adjustment is obtained by positioning the shift lever in the D or Drive position at the column or console, whichever the case, and positioning the manual lever in the D detent at the transmission. See the illustrations for procedure.

Neutral Safety Switch

1967-74 Column-Mounted Switch
1971-74 Console-Mounted Switch

1. Place the gear selector in the appropriate range:
   1967-70 Column—Drive (D)
   1971-74 Column—Neutral (N)
   1971-74 Console—Park (P)
2. Loosen the switch securing screws.

NOTE: Remove the center console first, if necessary.

3. Fit a 0.090 in. gauge pin into the outer hole on the switch cover.
4. Move the switch until the gauge pin drops into the alignment hole on the inner slide.

Tighten the switch securing screws; then remove the gauge pin.

NOTE: Do not overtighten the switch securing screws (20 in. lbs maximum).

1967-70 Console-Mounted Switch

1. Remove the center console assembly.
2. Position the gear selector lever

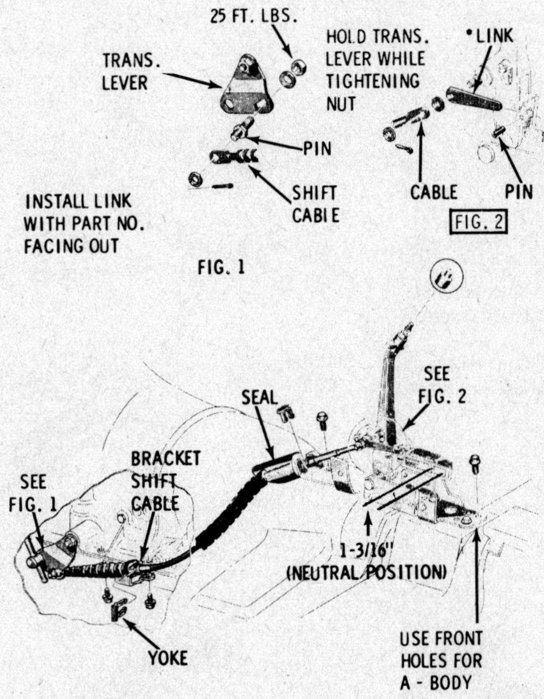
25 FT. LBS.
TRANS. LEVER
HOLD TRANS. LEVER WHILE TIGHTENING NUT
•LINK
PIN
SHIFT CABLE
INSTALL LINK WITH PART NO. FACING OUT
FIG. 1
CABLE
PIN
FIG. 2
SEE FIG. 2
SEAL
BRACKET SHIFT CABLE
SEE FIG. 1
1-3/16" (NEUTRAL POSITION)
YOKE
USE FRONT HOLES FOR A - BODY

SHIFT CABLE ADJUSTMENT

1. Loosen shift rod clamp screw, loosen pin in transmission manual lever.
2. Place shift lever in "P" position, place transmission manual lever in "P" position and ignition key in lock position.
3. Pull shift rod lightly against lock stop and tighten clamp screw.
4. Move pin in manual transmission lever to give "free pin" fit and tighten attaching nut.
5. Check Operation:
   A. Move shift handle into each gear position and see that transmission manual lever is also in detent position.
   B. With key in "run" position and transmission in "reverse," be sure that key cannot be removed and that steering wheel is not locked.
   C. With key in "lock" position and transmission in "park," be sure that key can be removed and that steering wheel is locked.

Console shift linkage adjustment for Turbo Hydra-Matic transmission
(© Oldsmobile Div, G.M. Corp)

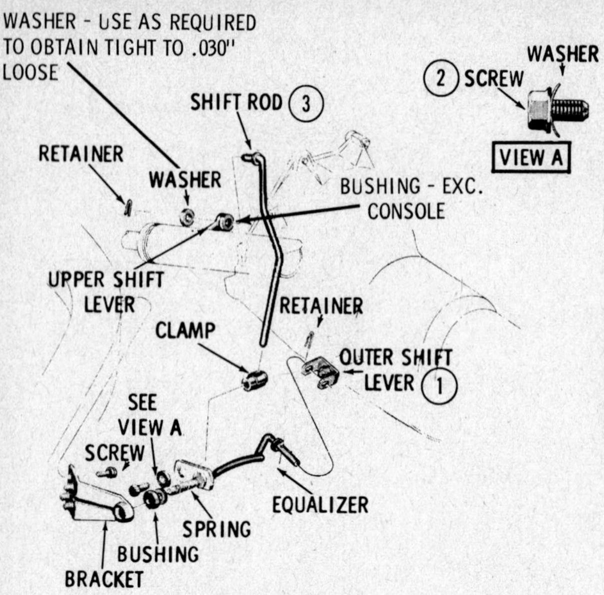
WASHER - USE AS REQUIRED
TO OBTAIN TIGHT TO .030"
LOOSE
WASHER
2 SCREW
VIEW A
SHIFT ROD 3
RETAINER
WASHER
BUSHING - EXC.
CONSOLE
UPPER SHIFT
LEVER
RETAINER
CLAMP
OUTER SHIFT
LEVER 1
SEE
VIEW A
SCREW
EQUALIZER
SPRING
BUSHING
BRACKET

Column shift linkage adjustment for Turbo Hydra-matic transmission
(© Oldsmobile Div, G.M. Corp)

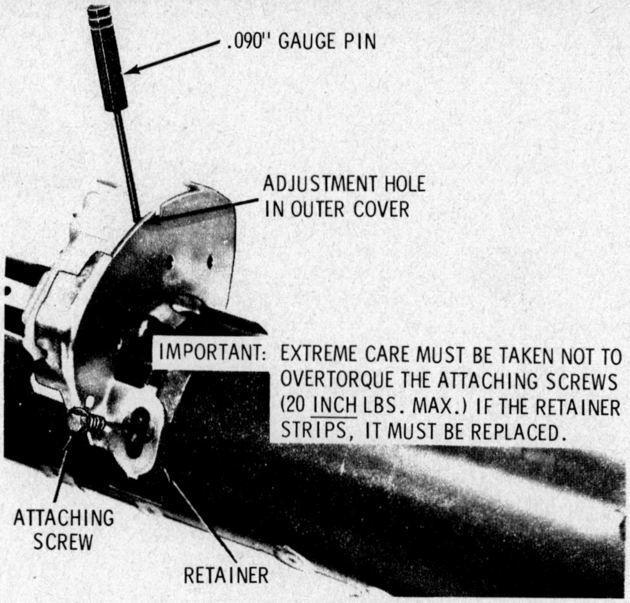
.090" GAUGE PIN
ADJUSTMENT HOLE
IN OUTER COVER
IMPORTANT: EXTREME CARE MUST BE TAKEN NOT TO
OVERTORQUE THE ATTACHING SCREWS
(20 INCH LBS. MAX.) IF THE RETAINER
STRIPS, IT MUST BE REPLACED.
ATTACHING
SCREW
RETAINER

Neutral safety switch adjustment (© Oldsmobile Div, G.M. Corp)

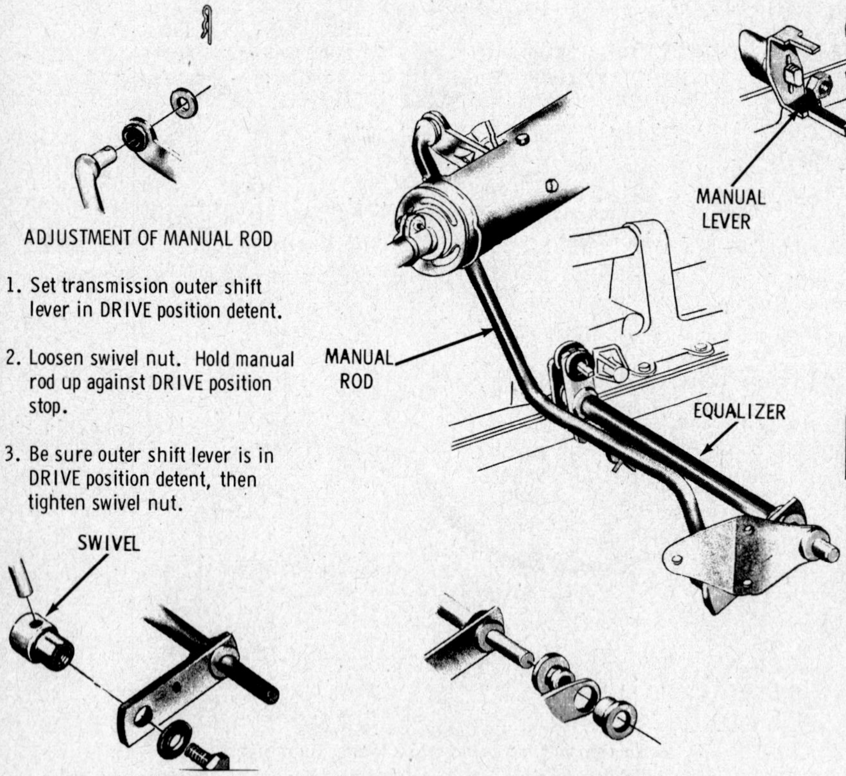
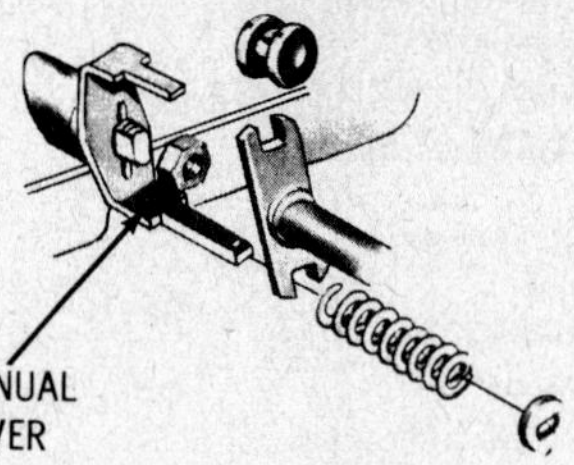
ADJUSTMENT OF MANUAL ROD
1. Set transmission outer shift lever in DRIVE position detent.
2. Loosen swivel nut. Hold manual rod up against DRIVE position stop.
3. Be sure outer shift lever is in DRIVE position detent, then tighten swivel nut.
SWIVEL
MANUAL
ROD
MANUAL
LEVER
EQUALIZER

Column shift linkage adjustment for Jetaway transmission (© Oldsmobile Div, G.M. Corp)

SHIFT ROD ADJUSTMENT

1. Set transmission outer lever in drive position.
2. Hold upper shift lever against drive position stop in upper steering column (do not raise lever).
3. Tighten screw in clamp on lower end of shift rod to specified torque.
4. Check Operation:
   A. With key in "run" position and transmission in "reverse" be sure that key cannot be removed and that steering wheel is not locked.
   B. With key in "lock" position and shift lever in "park," be sure that key can be removed, that steering wheel is locked, and that the transmission remains in park when the steering column is locked.

Shift rod adjustment

against the neutral stop.

3. Adjust the switch so that the car will start only when the gear selector lever is in Park (P) or Neutral (N).

U-JOINTS

Cross and bearing-type universals are used on all Oldsmobile models.

Driveshaft and Universal Joint Removal

1. Mark the companion flange and the driveshaft so they can be installed in the same position. Remove the four bolts that hold the rear universal filler blocks to the pinion shaft flange and pry the universal joint off the pinion flange, lowering the back end of the shaft to the floor.
2. Tape the bearing blocks to the universal joints so that they don't get lost or dirty.
3. The front end of the shaft can then be slid off the back of the transmission shaft and carried to the bench.
4. The bearings are held into the yokes by two lock plates, one on each side.
5. Take out the nut that holds the lock plate in position and lift off the lock plate. The bearing can then be driven from one side

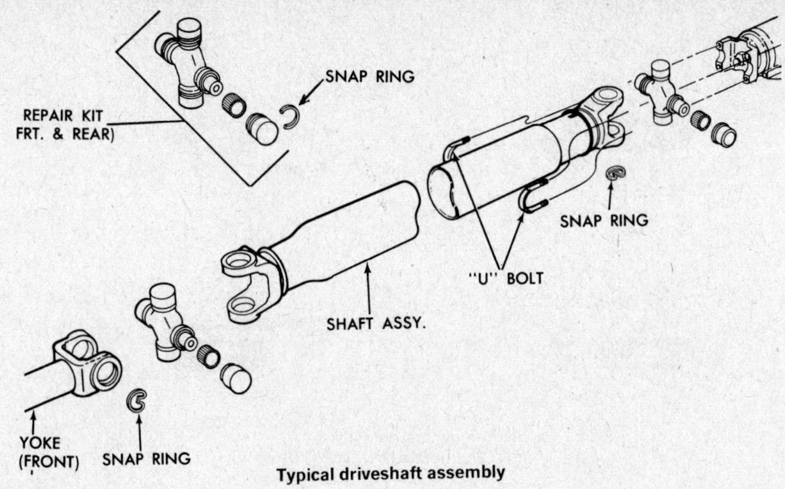
SNAP RING
REPAIR KIT
FRT. & REAR)
SNAP RING
"U" BOLT
SHAFT ASSY.
YOKE
(FRONT)
SNAP RING

Typical driveshaft assembly

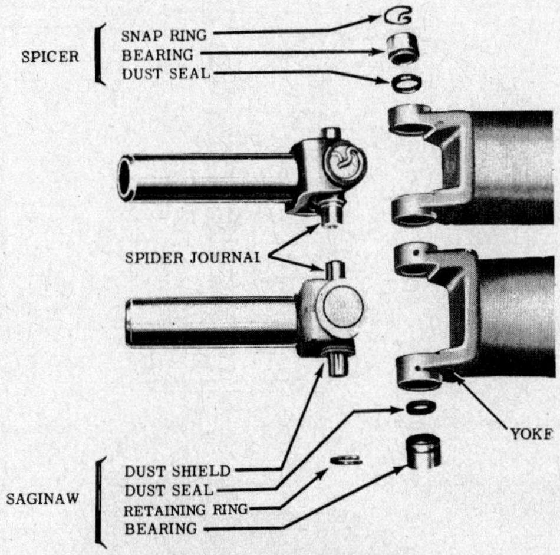
SPICER
SNAP RING
BEARING
DUST SEAL
SPIDER JOURNAL
YOKE
SAGINAW
DUST SHIELD
DUST SEAL
RETAINING RING
BEARING

NOTE: RETAINING RINGS ARE USED ON SAGINAW WITH SERVICE REPLACEMENT BEARINGS ONLY.

Driveshaft identification

across to the other which will drive the opposite side bearing out. Once the opposite side bearing has been removed, drive on the cross, itself, to drive out the first bearing.

6. It is recommended, when reinstalling bearings, that an arbor press or a very heavy C-clamp be used, because driving on them distorts the outer race of the needle bearings.

Drive Shaft Torque

U-bolts 16 ft. lbs. Center bearing to body 14 ft. lbs. Slip yoke nut 50-75 ft. lbs.

Constant Velocity Joint

This joint consists of two universal joints closely coupled with a coupling yoke. There is a centering ball socket between the two joints which maintains their relative position. On pre-1973 models the ball is integral with the shaft and, if damaged, the entire driveshaft must be replaced. On 1973-74 models the centering ball is a press-fit and can be replaced. The ball socket is integral with the flange yoke. The spring loaded ball seats are replaceable.

To disassemble the C.V. joint, first mark the relation of the flange yoke and driveshaft yoke, coupling ball support tube yoke. The cross bearing cups are pressed out in the usual manner, but they must be disassembled in the following sequence: rear of coupling yoke (2), differential flange yoke (2), front end of the coupling yoke (2) and driveshaft (2). Reassemble in the reverse of this order.

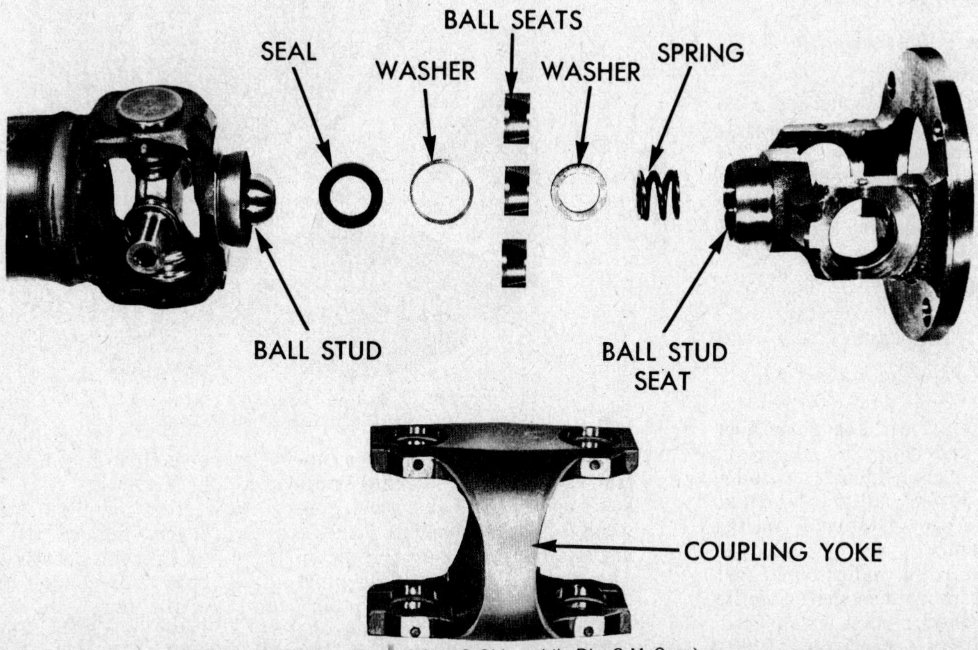
BALL SEATS
SEAL
WASHER
WASHER
SPRING
BALL STUD
BALL STUD
SEAT
COUPLING YOKE

Constant velocity joint (© Oldsmobile Div, G.M. Corp)

JACKING, HOISTING

When supporting car on floor jack or floor stand, the car should be supported at the suspension points only. Under no condition should the car be supported at extreme ends of frame or side rail.

When using a frame contact lift on an Omega, place the contact pads on the front sub-frame just behind the center body mounts and on the rear leaf spring's front attachment bracket.

Never use a bumper jack other than that provided with car.

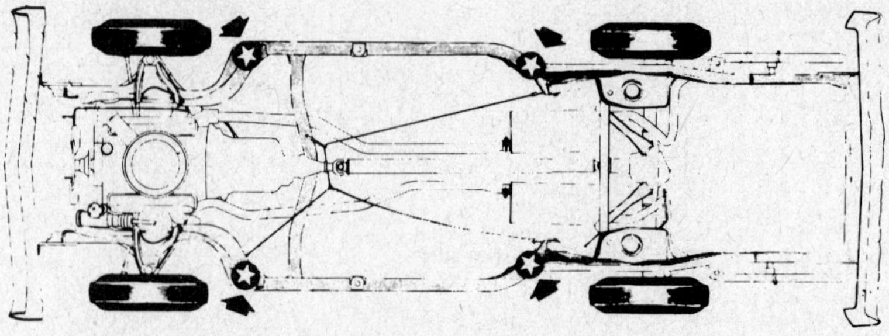

Hoist contact point
(© Oldsmobile Div, G.M. Corp)

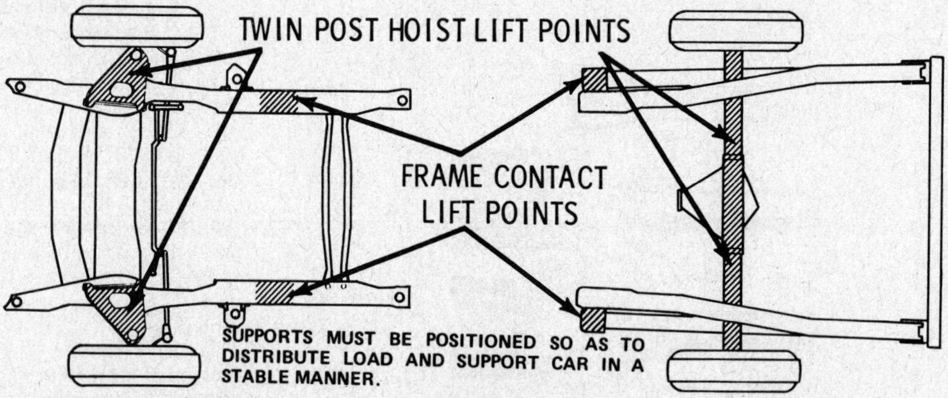
TWIN POST HOIST LIFT POINTS
FRAME CONTACT LIFT POINTS
SUPPORTS MUST BE POSITIONED SO AS TO DISTRIBUTE LOAD AND SUPPORT CAR IN A STABLE MANNER.

Omega hoisting points (© Oldsmobile Div, G.M. Corp)

FRONT SUSPENSION

Front wheel alignment procedures, ball joint checks, wheel bearing and seal replacement procedures can be found in the Unit Repair Section.

Front Shock Absorber R & R —All Models

1. Remove the two bolts and lockwashers securing the shock to the lower control arm.
2. Remove the upper nut, retainer, and grommet from the shock.
3. To install, reverse the removal procedure.

Lower Ball Joint

Inspection

1967-73 Cutlass and F-85
1967-72 88 and 98

1. Jack up the car and place floor stands under the left and right control arms as near as possible to the lower ball joints. Make sure the car sits steadily on the floor stands.
2. Position a dial indicator so that its button contacts the inside lip of the wheel rim.
3. Place a 2 x 4 (about 6 in. tall) vertically between the lower control arm and the steering knuckle. Insert a pry bar between the wood and the steering knuckle nut and pry gently up and down. The dial indicator reading must not exceed .125 in. and there should be no deflection on the 1971-72 88 and 98 models. Repeat this procedure for the other side.
4. After completing this vertical check, remove the wood block and reposition the dial indicator button to contact the outer lip of the wheel rim.
5. Push in on the top of the tire while pulling out on the bottom

J-8001
J-6126
BRAKE DRUM

Ball joint horizontal check
(© Oldsmobile Div, G.M. Corp)

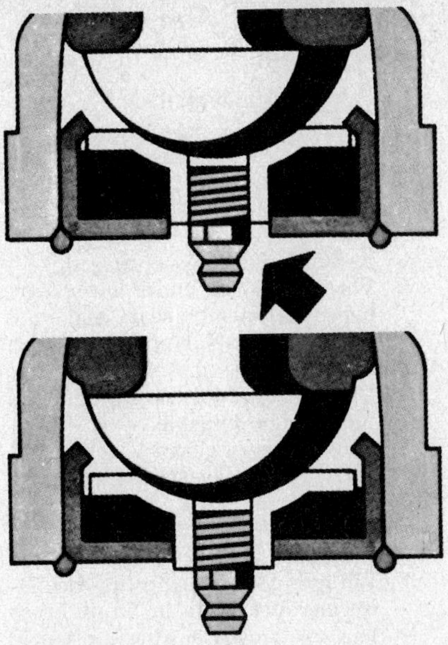

1973-74 Oldsmobile ball joint wear indicator

and observe the dial indicator reading. Reverse this push-pull procedure and check the reading. This procedure (horizontal check) enables you to check both upper and lower ball joints. The gauge reading should not exceed .125 in.

6. Do the same on the other side.

1973-74 88 and 98, 1974 Cutlass

These lower ball joints contain a visual wear indicator. The lower ball joint grease plug screws into the wear indicator which protrudes from the bottom of the ball joint housing. As long as the wear indicator extends out of the ball joint housing, the ball joint is not worn. If the tip of the wear indicator is parallel with, or recessed into the ball joint housing, the ball joint is defective.

Omega

NOTE: The lower ball joint used on the Omega is not internally preloaded but rather, is seated by the car's weight. Therefore, some looseness may be apparent when the lower control arm is raised with a jack; this looseness does not necessarily mean that the joint is defective or worn.

1. Use a jack placed underneath the lower control arm to support vehicle weight.
2. Measure the distance between the grease fitting and the threaded stud.
3. Raise the tire by means of a lever, to seat the ball stud, and measure the distance again.
4. If the difference between the two measurements is greater than 1/16 in., the ball joint is worn and should be replaced.
5. Shake the wheel and observe the end of the stud or the nut on the knuckle boss for *excessive* looseness. Replace any parts which are defective.

R & R

1. Raise car and support the frame with floor stands.
2. Remove the tire and wheel.
3. Place a floor jack under the control arm spring seat.
4. Remove the cotter pin from the ball joint stud and, using an appropriate tool, separate the ball joint from the steering knuckle.
5. Raise the control arm to relieve tension and remove the stud nut.
6. If the backing plate blocks removal of the ball joint, loosen the backing plate bolts to obtain the necessary clearance.
7. Hold the brake assembly out of way by placing a wooden block between the frame and the upper control arm.
8. Using a screwdriver or chisel, remove the ball joint seal.
9. Using a suitable tool, remove the ball joint.
10. Press in a new ball joint until it bottoms on the lower control arm.

NOTE: On disc brake cars, make sure the grease purge on the seal faces away from the brakes.

11. On 1967-72 Cutlass and F-85 models, install the ball joint stud into the steering knuckle, torque the nut to 40 ft lbs (1967-69) or 70 ft lbs (1970-72), and install the cotter pin.
12. On cars other than 1967-72 Cutlass and F-85 models, reassemble the suspension and torque the ball joint stud nut to 70 ft lbs

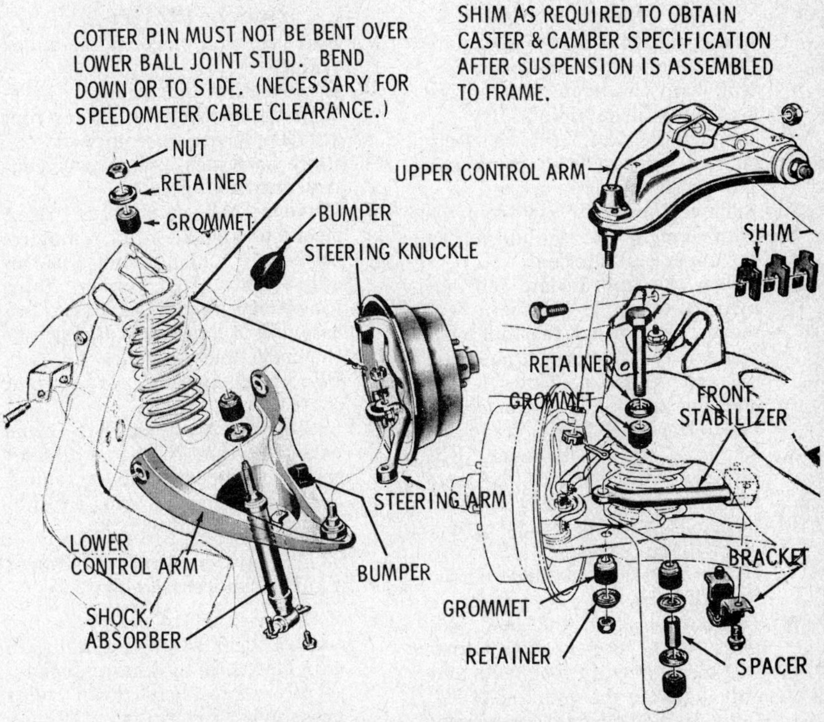
COTTER PIN MUST NOT BE BENT OVER LOWER BALL JOINT STUD. BEND DOWN OR TO SIDE. (NECESSARY FOR SPEEDOMETER CABLE CLEARANCE.)
SHIM AS REQUIRED TO OBTAIN CASTER & CAMBER SPECIFICATION AFTER SUSPENSION IS ASSEMBLED TO FRAME.
NUT
RETAINER
GROMMET
BUMPER
STEERING KNUCKLE
UPPER CONTROL ARM
SHIM
RETAINER
GROMMET
FRONT STABILIZER
STEERING ARM
LOWER CONTROL ARM
BUMPER
SHOCK ABSORBER
BRACKET
GROMMET
RETAINER
SPACER

1967-74 front suspension—except F85 (© Oldsmobile Div, G.M. Corp)

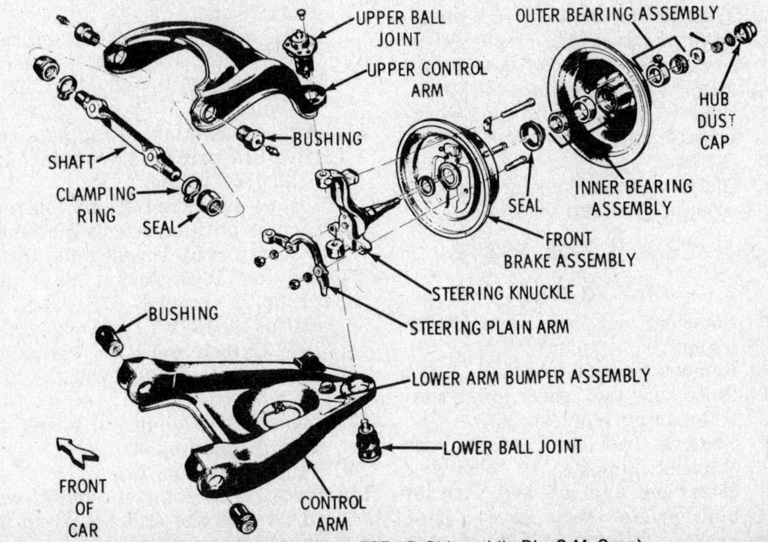
UPPER BALL JOINT
UPPER CONTROL ARM
OUTER BEARING ASSEMBLY
HUB DUST CAP
BUSHING
SHAFT
CLAMPING RING
SEAL
SEAL
INNER BEARING ASSEMBLY
FRONT BRAKE ASSEMBLY
STEERING KNUCKLE
STEERING PLAIN ARM
BUSHING
LOWER ARM BUMPER ASSEMBLY
LOWER BALL JOINT
FRONT OF CAR
CONTROL ARM

1967-74 front suspension—F85 (© Oldsmobile Div, G.M. Corp)

(1967-70) or 90 ft lbs (1971-74). Install the cotter pin and bend it to the side of the nut. On the Omega tighten the nut to 80 ft lbs.

13. If applicable, tighten the backing plate bolts.
14. Install the ball joint fitting and lube until grease appears at the seal.
15. Install the tire and wheel assembly.

Upper Ball Joint

Inspection

To inspect the upper ball joints, follow steps 4-6 of the "1967-73 Cutlass and F85/1967-72 88 and 98" lower ball joint inspection procedure.

R & R

1. Raise the front of car and place floor stands under the lower control arm between the spring seats and the ball joints.
2. Remove the wheel and the speedometer cable (if so equipped) from the steering knuckle.
3. Remove the cotter pin from the upper ball joint stud and loosen the upper ball joint nut.
4. Using the appropriate tool (if available, use a ball joint remover tool), break the stud loose and remove the nut and pull stud out of knuckle. Support the steering knuckle to prevent damage to the brake line.
5. Using a 1/8 in. diameter drill bit, drill into each of the four rivet heads a depth of 1/4 in.
6. Drill off the rivet heads with a 1/2 in. diameter bit.
7. Punch out the rivets and remove the ball joint.
8. To install, place the new ball joint in the upper control arm and secure it with four bolts and nuts. Tighten the nuts to 8 ft lbs.
9. Connect the ball joint-to-steering knuckle. Torque the nut to 40 ft lbs minimum.

NOTE: When replacing ball joints, use only high-quality replacement parts and bolts and nuts specified to be strong enough to endure the stress.

10. Install the grease fitting and lubricate until grease appears at the seal.
11. Install the speedometer cable (if so equipped) and the wheel.

Upper Control Arm R & R

1967-70 F-85

1. Raise car and place stands under frame.
2. Remove tire and wheel.
3. Place floor jack under lower control arm spring seat.
4. Remove ball joint stud from steering knuckle, by removing cotter pin and nut and with an appropriate tool, press joint loose from knuckle. For left-side arm removal, it may be necessary to move the steering gear out of the way. When installing a gear, torque bolts to 70 ft lbs.
5. Support hub assembly and remove upper arm by sliding shaft off end of bolts.

NOTE: mark or locate alignment shims for easier reassembly.

6. Attach arm assembly to frame using original shims. Torque to 55 ft lbs for 1967-70 models.
7. Install ball joint. Torque nut to 40 ft lbs (minimum). Install a grease fitting and lubricate.
8. Install hub, drum and wheel assembly and lower car to floor.

Except 1967-70 F-85 and All Models 1971-74

1. Raise car and place stands under frame.
2. Remove tire and wheel.
3. Remove speedometer cable from knuckle where so equipped.
4. Place floor jack under lower control arm spring seat.
5. Remove ball joint stud from steering knuckle, by removing cotter pin and nut and with an appropriate tool, press joint loose from knuckle. Support hub assembly to prevent damage to the brake line.
6. Disconnect ground strap from control arm.
7. Loosen the pivot shaft-to-frame nuts and remove the alignment shims. Support hub assembly and remove upper arms by sliding shaft off end of bolts.

NOTE: mark or locate alignment shims for easier reassembly.

8. It is necessary to remove upper control arm attaching bolts to gain clearance to remove arm assembly. Tap bolt down with brass drift. Pry bolt up with box wrench. Using a suitable pry bar and block of wood, pry bolts from frame.
9. Remove control arm from car.
10. To reinstall, position bolts loosely in frame and install pivot shaft on bolts.
11. Install lock washers and nuts and with brass drift, drive attaching bolts into frame.
12. Install alignment shims, placing them in position from which they were removed. Torque nuts, 105 ft lbs for 1967 cars, 75 ft lbs (1968-71 except F-85) and 85 ft lbs for all 1972-74 models except 1972 Cutlass and F-85. Torque to 50 ft lbs for 1971-72 Cutlass and F-85 models.
13. Connect ball joint and torque to 40 ft lbs minimum.
14. Attach ground strap.
15. Install speedometer cable and wheel and tire and lower car to floor.

Lower Control Arm and/or Front Spring R & R

All Models

1. Raise front of car and support by stands under frame.
2. Remove tire and wheel.
3. Disconnect stabilizer link from lower arm.
4. Remove shock absorber.
5. Place floor jack under lower arm, between spring seat and ball joint. Using a spring compressor, compress spring.
6. Disconnect lower control arm ball joint from knuckle.
7. Slowly lower floor jack until spring is fully extended and remove spring.
8. To reinstall, tape insulator to top of spring.
9. While holding spring and insulator against pilot in front cross bar, tilt spring so it will pivot in lower arm. Rotate spring so bottom coil will index with edge of hole in arm spring seat. Spring should not cover any portion of hole.
10. With floor jack positioned between seat and ball joint, raise arm until ball joint is tight in knuckle. Install ball joint nut and tighten to 90 ft lbs, except for Omega, which should be tightened to 80 ft lbs.
11. Install shock absorber.
12. Connect stabilizer link.
13. Install wheel and lower car.

Wheel Bearings

The front wheel bearings must be correctly adjusted. Cones should slip-fit into the spindle. The inside diameter of the cone must be lubricated and the spindle nut should be free-running on its threads.

Adjustment

1. Tighten the adjusting nut to 30 ft lbs.
2. Back off on the nut 1/2 of a turn.
3. Finger-tighten the nut and install the cotter pin or the retaining ring.

NOTE: If the retaining ring or cotter pin cannot be installed, back off on the nut until the tabs on the clip align with the serrations on the nut. Do not back off on the nut more than 1/24 of a turn.

4. Once adjusted, the front wheel bearings should have 0.001-0.008 in. of end-play.

REAR SUSPENSION

Rear Shock Absorber Replacement

All—Except Omega

To replace the rear shock absorber, first raise the car and support the rear axle to prevent stretching of the brake hose. Then remove the nut from the lower end of the shock and tap the shock free from the bracket. To disconnect the shock at the top, remove the bolt or bolts and remove the shock.

NOTE: on extended station wagons, a retainer and grommet will be removed with the nut at the top.

Omega

1. Raise the vehicle and support the rear axle housing.
2. Remove the lower shock mounting bolt from the shock absorber eye.
3. Unfasten the upper mounting bracket bolts and withdraw the shock.

Intallation is performed in the reverse order of removal, except that the upper attaching bolts should remain loose while the lower (eye) bolt is being tightened.

Upper bolts and nuts—18 ft lbs
Lower stud nut—45 ft lbs

Rear Coil Spring Replacement

1. Disconnect the shock absorber link and raise the car enough to take the pressure off the coil spring and, reaching down through the coil spring, remove the bolt that holds the bottom of the spring to the insulating pad on the rear axle.
2. Working through the coil spring upward, take out the upper bolt that holds the spring to the frame at the top.
3. If the car has been raised sufficiently, the spring can be lifted out.

Leaf Spring Replacement

1. Lift the rear of the car by the axle housing and support the car on the floor stands.
2. Loosen the tailpipe and resonator if you are removing the right-side spring.
3. Remove the lower shock absorber nut and move the shock out of the way.
4. Relax the springs by lowering the lift or jack. Leave the jack under the housing for support.
5. Remove the bolts and shackles from the rear of the spring.
6. Remove the U-bolt attaching nuts.
7. Remove ONLY the nut from the front spring attachment and, while holding the spring up, remove the bolt from the front of the spring and remove the spring.
8. Remove the insulators from the spring.
9. To install, reverse the removal procedure.

NOTE: When making rear suspension repairs, replace all bolts and nuts with the specified replacement bolts.

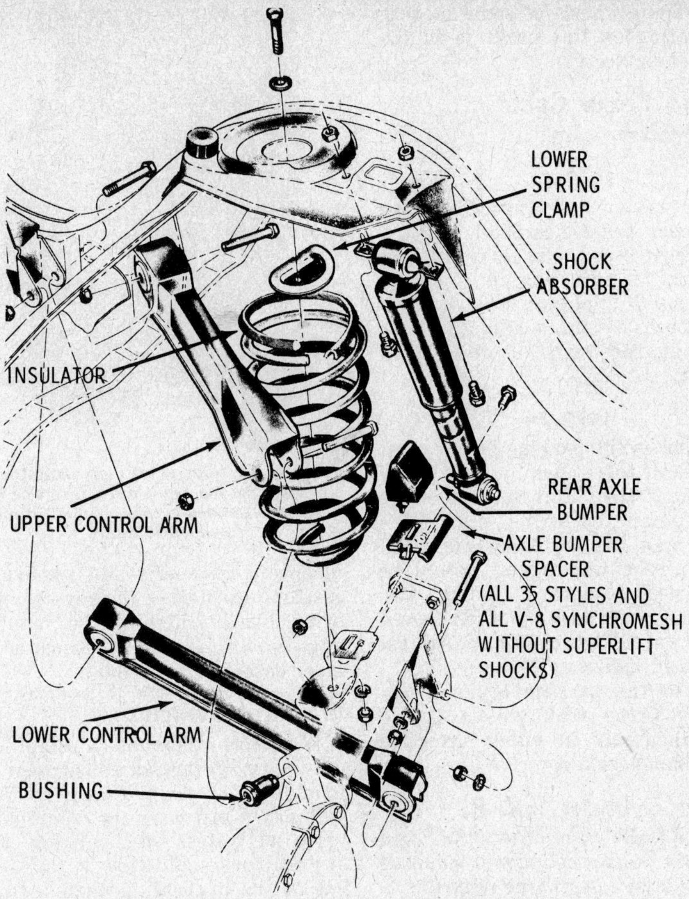
LOWER
SPRING
CLAMP
SHOCK
ABSORBER
INSULATOR
REAR AXLE
BUMPER
UPPER CONTROL ARM
AXLE BUMPER
SPACER
(ALL 35 STYLES AND
ALL V-8 SYNCHROMESH
WITHOUT SUPERLIFT
SHOCKS)
LOWER CONTROL ARM
BUSHING

1967-74 coil spring rear suspension (© Oldsmobile Div, G.M. Corp)

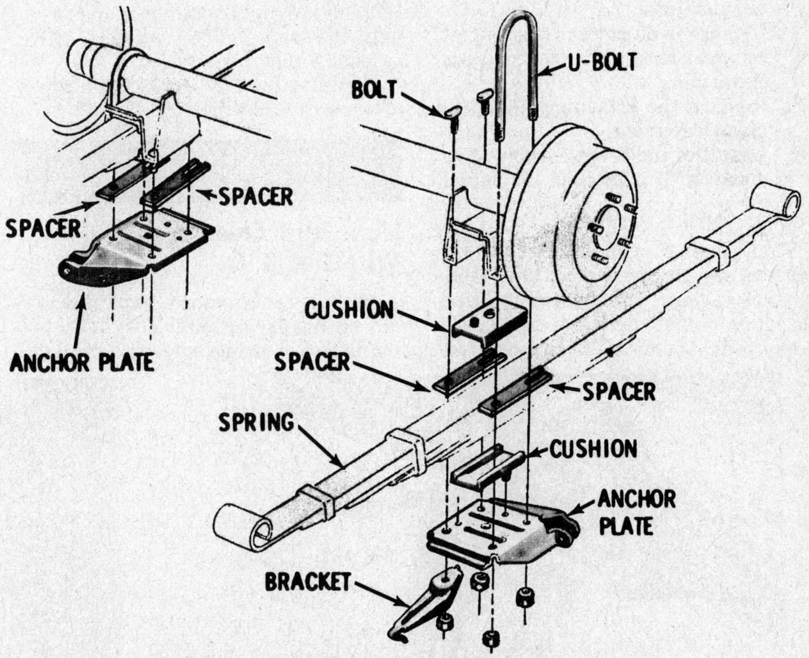
U-BOLT
BOLT
SPACER
SPACER
ANCHOR PLATE
CUSHION
SPACER
SPACER
SPRING
CUSHION
ANCHOR
PLATE
BRACKET

Omega leaf spring rear suspension—Custom Cruiser similar (© Oldsmobile Div, G.M. Corp)

BRAKES

Information on brake adjustments, lining replacement, bleeding procedure, master and wheel cylinder overhaul is in the Unit Repair Section.

Information on the grease seal replacement is in the Unit Repair Section.

Beginning in 1967, a dual-type master cylinder is used. For detailed information on this type cylinder, see Unit Repair Section.

1969-74

A single-cylinder disc brake is used

on the front wheels of some models. Information on this brake is in the Unit Repair Section.

Parking Brake Cable Adjustment

1967-71

1. Release parking brake. Check for proper pedal clearance.
2. Adjust rear cables by tightening equalizer adjusting nut to obtain heavy drag at rear brakes.
3. Loosen equalizer adjusting nut seven full turns. Tighten locknut.

1972-74

1. Depress the parking brake pedal exactly three clicks.
2. Loosen the nut at the rear of the equalizer adjusting nut. Then tighten the adjusting nut until the rear wheels can barely be turned backward (using two hands) but lock up when moved forward. Tighten the nut against the adjusting nut.
3. With the parking brake disengaged the rear wheels should turn freely in either direction with *no brake drag.*

Master Cylinder R & R

NOTE: Be sure that the area where the master cylinder is mounted is clean, before beginning removal.

1. Disconnect and cap or plug hydraulic lines.
2. If there is no power booster unit, remove the pushrod-to-pedal clevis pin.
3. Remove the attaching bolts and master cylinder.
4. Install in the reverse order of removal. Fill with fluid and bleed.

Power Brake Unit

The master cylinder and power booster are removed as a unit. Disconnect vacuum and hydraulic lines. Disconnect the pushrod from the brake pedal. Remove the vacuum unit mounting stud nuts and remove the assembly. Install in the reverse order of removal, tightening the mounting nuts to 28 ft. lbs. Fill the master cylinder reservoir with fluid.

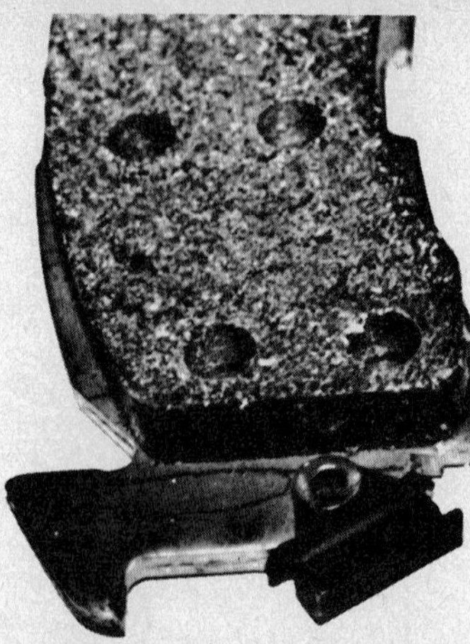

A brake pad with a warning indicator that squeals when the pad is worn to service limits has been extended for use on all 1974 models with disc brakes

Warning Switch

Whenever there is a significant difference in pressure between the front disc or drum and rear drum systems, a piston in the combination valve activates the warning light switch, thus indicating a failure in one of the hydraulic systems. In the event of combination valve malfunction, no attempt should be made to repair the valve. The complete valve assembly must be replaced.

NOTE: Bleed the hydraulic system after switch replacement.

STEERING

Horn and Steering Wheel R & R

Round center horn caps are removed by prying out. The horn pad on deluxe steering wheels is removed by either pulling down and out or by removing screws from underneath. Disconnect the battery when working on the horn.

Extreme caution must be exercised when removing the steering wheel: the energy absorbing column is held rigid by plastic fasteners which easily shear or loosen when abnormal pressure is applied. Use a steering wheel pulling tool. Carefully torque steering wheel retaining nut to 35 ft. lbs. when installing.

Turn Signal Switch Replacement Except Tilt and Telescopic

1967-68

1. Disconnect the battery.
2. Remove the steering wheel.
3. Disconnect the switch connector.
4. Hold the column against the support assembly and remove the bracket assembly to expose the wiring.
5. Pry out the wiring clip. *Do not pry against the wires.*
6. With the wiring hanging outside the jacket, install the bracket, tightening the nuts finger-tight.
7. Remove the turn signal canceling cam and spring from the upper steering shaft.
8. Remove the turn signal lever.
9. Unscrew the four-way flasher knob.
10. Remove the C-ring, thrust washer, and wave washer from the upper steering shaft.
11. Loosen the switch mounting screws. Turn the cover assembly counterclockwise and remove it from the top of the jacket.
12. Cut the turn signal wiring harness at the bottom of the cover.
13. Mark the position of the cover and lockplate for reassembly reference.
14. Remove the switch mounting screws. Do not lose the springs.
15. Remove the turn signal switch.

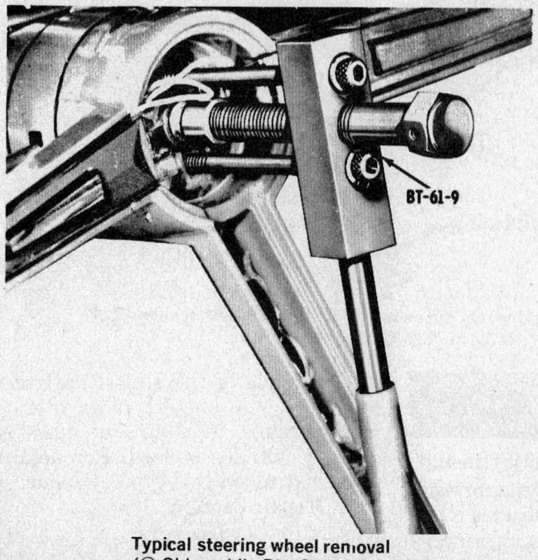
BT-61-9

Typical steering wheel removal
(© Oldsmobile Div, G.M. Corp)

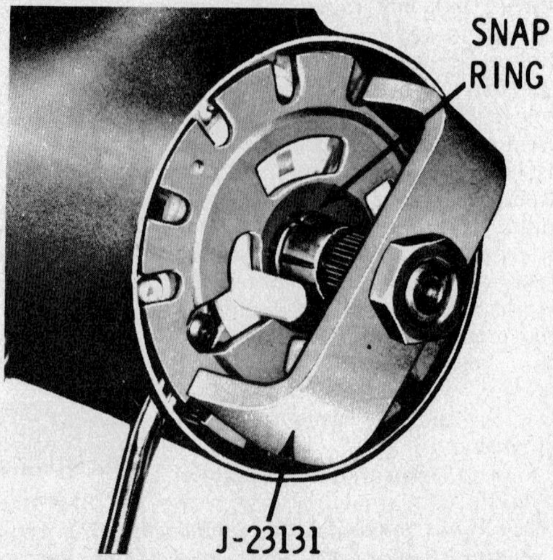
SNAP RING
J-23131

Compressing the lockplate for removing or installing the snap-ring
(© Oldsmobile Div, G.M. Corp)

16. To install, reverse the removal procedure.

1969-74

1. Disconnect the battery.
2. Remove the steering wheel.
3. Remove the cover from the shaft. Plastic keepers under the cover are not necessary for installation.
4. Depress the lockplate and remove the snap-ring from the shaft with an appropriate tool.
5. Remove the lockplate and cancelling cam.
6. Remove the upper bearing preload spring.
7. Remove the turn signal lever.
8. Remove the four-way flasher knob.
9. Remove the three screws from the switch.
10. Disconnect the turn signal connector from the wiring harness.
11. Tape the turn signal wires at the connector and carefully remove the turn signal switch, wiring, and protector from the column as a unit.
12. To install, reverse the removal procedure using a new shaft snap-ring. To aid in installation of the snap-ring, use the lockplate compressing tool used during the removal procedure. When replacing screws (especially cover screws), make sure they are of the same size.

Turn Signal Switch Replacement Tilt and Telescopic Column

1967-68

1. Disconnect the battery ground cable.
2. Disconnect the wiring from the turn signal and cornering light.
3. Remove the steering wheel.
4. Remove the four-way flasher knob, turn signal, and tilt levers.
5. Remove the cover.
6. Remove the bolts from the column support bracket assembly and remove the bracket assembly.
7. Pry the clip or protector from the wires.
8. Move the wiring outside the bracket and reinstall the bracket with bolts finger-tight.
9. Remove C-ring and horn contact carrier assembly.
10. Remove the upper bearing spring.
11. Cut the turn signal and cornering light wiring as close as possible to the turn signal switch.
12. Remove the turn signal switch assembly.
13. Reverse the removal procedure to install, making sure that the wires are connected correctly.

1969-74

1. Disconnect negative battery cable.
2. Remove the steering wheel.
3. Remove the screws and lift the cover from the shaft. Plastic keepers are not necessary for installation.
4. Compress the lockplate with a suitable tool and pry the wire snap-ring from shaft.
5. Remove the lockplate and cancelling cam.
6. Remove the upper bearing preload spring.
7. Remove the turn signal lever and the four-way flasher knob.
8. Lift up on the tilt lever and position the housing in its central position.
9. Remove the switch attaching screws.
10. Remove the lower trim cap from the instrument panel and disconnect the turn signal connector from the harness.
11. Remove the four bolts securing the bracket assembly to the jacket.
12. On cars with automatic transmissions, loosen the screw holding the shift indicator needle and disconnect the clip from the link.
13. Remove the two nuts from the column support bracket while holding the column in position. Remove the bracket assembly and wire protector from the wiring, then loosely install the bracket-to-support column.
14. Tape the turn signal wires at the connector to keep them flat and parallel.
15. Carefully remove the turn signal switch and wiring from the column.
16. To install, reverse the removal procedure, making sure that screws of the same size are used.

Steering Linkage

On all models two short tie-rods are attached to either end of a central relay rod. The pitman shaft has a vertical axis and the pitman arm rotates through a horizontal plane. The tie-rods have ball studs at each end and have an adjustable middle section which is secured with clamps.

Use a suitable puller to remove the pitman arm from the pitman shaft. When assembling, install the pitman arm with the front wheels in the straight-ahead position and the steering wheel centered. Tighten the pitman arm retaining nut to 180 ft lbs.

Whenever the tie-rod end is assembled to the tie-rod, make sure that an equal number of threads are exposed at each end of the tie rod sleeve. Tighten tie-rod clamp bolts to 19-24 ft. lbs. When disconnecting a linkage joint, never pry a wedge between the joint and the attached part. Always use a puller. When removing a tie-rod from a steering arm, loosen the ball stud nut, then tap the end of the steering arm with a hammer to free the tie-rod. Always use new seals when reassembling. Tighten tie-rod joint nuts to 45 ft. lbs.

Toe-in and steering wheel spoke alignment is obtained by turning the adjusting sleeves on the tie-rods which in turn lengthen or shorten the tie-rod assemblies.

Power Steering Pump Removal

Remove and cap the two hoses that run through the pump, loosen the clamp bolts so that the pump can be slid along its adjusting slot and take the belt off. Remove the three bolts that hold the pump bracket to the cylinder heads and lift off the pump.

INSTRUMENT PANEL

Ignition Switch and/or Lock Cylinder Replacement

1967-68

1. Disconnect battery.
2. Place switch in off position and insert a paper clip in small hole in cylinder face. While pushing in on wire turn cylinder counterclockwise and pull cylinder from case.
3. To remove the ignition switch, remove nut from passenger side of dash.
4. Pull switch from under dash and remove wiring connector. If the car is equipped with air conditioning it will be necessary to remove some ducting.
5. To remove theft resistant connector, where used, switch must be out from under dash. With screwdriver, depress tangs and separate the connector.
6. Install in reverse order of above.

1969-74 Ignition Switch

1. Disconnect negative battery cable.
2. Place ignition switch in "ACC" position (1969), "RUN" position (1970) or "OFF-UNLOCKED" (1971-74).
3. Remove toe pan cover (if applicable) and loosen toe clamp bolts.
4. Remove lower instrument panel trim and toe pan trim panel.
5. Remove automatic transmission shift indicator needle.
6. Remove steering column dash bracket and let steering wheel rest on the driver's seat.
7. Remove two switch attaching screws and lift switch off actuator rod.
8. Disconnect wiring.

9. To install, check that lock cylinder is still in "ACC" (1969), "RUN" (1970) or "OFF-UNLOCKED" (1971-74) position and move sliding portion of switch until switch hole is positioned as illustrated. Hold the switch in this position with a 0.090 in. pin as illustrated.
10. Connect the wiring to the switch.
11. Position switch over actuator rod, install attaching screws (tighten to 3 ft. lbs.) and remove the 0.090 in. pin.
12. Reverse Steps 1 through 6 to complete installation.

1969-74 Lock Cylinder

1. Disconnect the negative battery cable.
2. Remove the steering wheel.
3. On models equipped with a tilt and travel steering column, pry up the three tabs on the plastic lock cover.
4. On models with a standard or tilt column remove the three screws that attach the lock cover and remove it. The plastic keepers on the underside of the cover can be discarded after the cover is removed.
5. Depress the steering wheel lock plate and pry the snap-ring from the steering shaft.
6. Remove the lock plate, cancelling cam, and upper bearing spring.
7. Position the turn signal lever in the right turn position and unscrew the turn signal lever.
8. Push the hazard warning knob in and unscrew the knob.
9. Remove the turn signal switch retaining screws and pull the switch up out of the way.
10. On 1969-70 models, insert the ignition key into the cylinder and turn it to the "Acc" position. On 1971-74 models, turn the key to the "Run" position.
11. Insert a long thin screwdriver into the slot in the upper bearing housing and depress the release tab while pulling the cylinder from the column.
12. Insert the new lock cylinder into the column after aligning the key on the cylinder with the keyway in the column.
13. Press inward on the cylinder while turning it clockwise.
14. Reverse the above procedure to complete installation.

Headlight Switch Replacement

1967-68

1. Disconnect battery.
2. Pull knob out to on position.
3. Reach under instrument panel, depress the switch shaft retainer, and remove knob and shaft assembly.
4. Remove retaining ferrule nut.
5. Remove switch from instrument panel.
6. Disconnect the multi-plug connector from the switch.
7. Install in reverse of above. (In checking lights before installation, switch must be grounded to test dome lights).

1969-74

1. Disconnect the battery.
2. On 1971-73 88 and 98 models and 1973-74 Cutlass models remove the left-hand control panel from the dash.
3. Pull the switch to "ON" position, then depress the spring-loaded button on the switch body and pull knob out of the switch.
4. Remove the escutcheon.

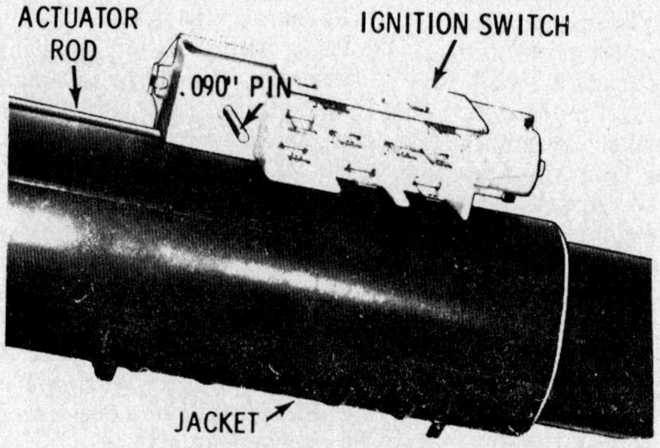
ACTUATOR ROD
IGNITION SWITCH
.090" PIN
JACKET
Holding ignition switch in position—1969-71
(© Oldsmobile Div, G.M. Corp)

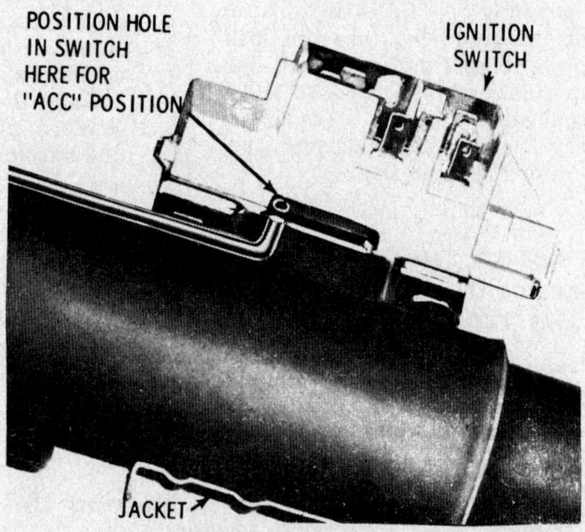
POSITION HOLE IN SWITCH HERE FOR "ACC" POSITION
IGNITION SWITCH
JACKET
Ignition switch in "ACC" position—1969
(© Oldsmobile Div, G.M. Corp)

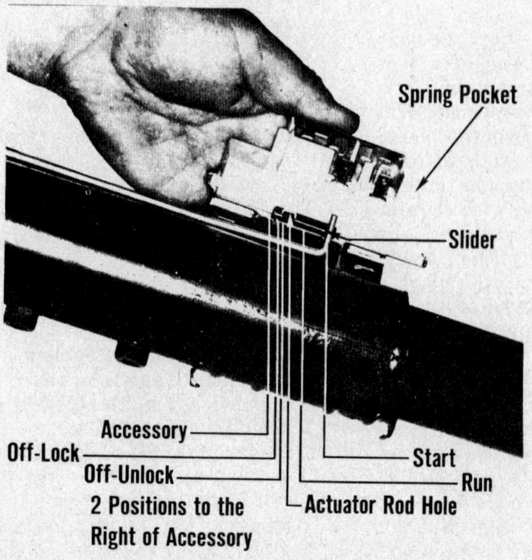
Spring Pocket
Slider
Accessory
Off-Lock
Off-Unlock
2 Positions to the Right of Accessory
Start
Run
Actuator Rod Hole
Ignition switch in "Off-Unlocked" position—1971-72
(© Oldsmobile Div, G.M. Corp)

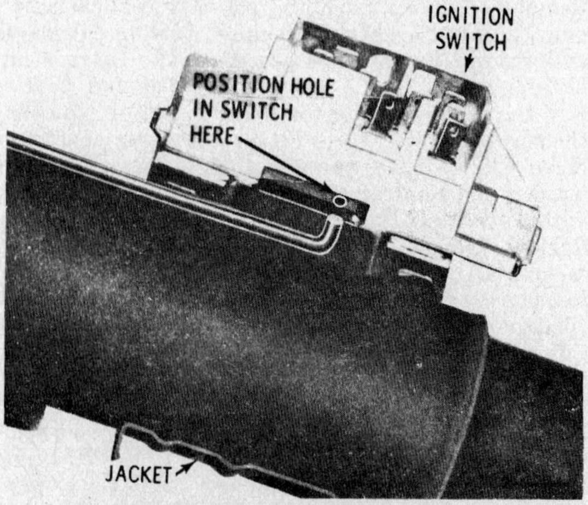
IGNITION SWITCH
POSITION HOLE IN SWITCH HERE
JACKET
Ignition switch in "RUN" position—1970
(© Oldsmobile Div, G.M. Corp)

5. Remove the switch from behind the panel and disconnect the multiple connector.
6. Install in the reverse order of the above procedure.

WINDSHIELD WIPERS

Motor R & R

1967 F-85 and Oldsmobile

1. Disconnect the wiring and windshield washer hoses, if equipped.
2. Remove the access hole cover in the upper cowl.
3. Loosen the two transmission-to-crankarm attaching nuts until the ball will slip from its socket. It is not necessary to remove the screws completely.
4. Reverse the above steps for installation.

1968-69 F-85

1. Disconnect the wiring and the windshield washer hoses.
2. Remove the wiper blade and arm assembly attached to the motor.
3. Remove the attaching screws.
4. Lift the left rear edge of the vent screen and loosen the two nuts securing the transmission to the crankarm.
5. Remove the motor.
6. Reverse the above steps to install. Make sure the wiper arm assemblies are installed properly.

1968-70 Oldsmobile

1. Disconnect the wiring and the washer hoses.
2. Remove the three motor attaching screws and the access hole plug.
3. Loosen the two, transmission crankarm attaching nuts through the access hole.
4. Hold the motor with one hand and, with the other hand, move the wiper arm halfway through its travel. This will center the crankarm in the hole in the dash.
5. Remove the motor, guiding the crankarm through the hole.
6. Reverse the above steps to install.

1970 F-85

1. Remove the three cowl screen attaching screws from the left side of the cowl screen and lift the screen.
2. Loosen the two nuts securing the transmission crankarm to the pivot arm through the cowl opening.
3. Disconnect the wiring and washer hoses.
4. Remove the three motor securing screws and, guiding the crankarm through the hole in the dash, remove the motor.
5. Reverse the above steps to install.

1971-74—All Models

1. Remove the cowl screen.
2. Loosen the transmission drive link-to-crankarm attaching nuts, and remove the link from the arm.
3. Disconnect the wiring and washer hoses.
4. Remove the three motor attaching screws, guide the crankarm through the hole in the dash, and remove the motor.
5. Reverse the above steps to install.

RADIO

Removal and Installation

1967-72 F-85 and Cutlass
1967-70 88 and 98
1973-74 Omega

1. Disconnect battery.
2. If equipped with air conditioning, remove cool air manifold.
3. Remove defroster manifold if necessary.
4. Remove radio knobs, washers or rear speaker control.
5. Remove radio attaching nuts and escutcheons.
6. Disconnect all wiring and antenna lead-in.
7. Remove radio support bracket attaching screw(s), if applicable.
8. Remove radio from rear of instrument panel.
9. Install by reversing removal procedure.

1971-74 88 and 98

1. Disconnect the negative battery cable.
2. Unfasten the nut which secures the radio to its mounting brace.
3. Detach the speaker and antenna leads from the radio.
4. Unfasten the radio ground strap screw.
5. Use a thin-bladed screwdriver to carefully pry out the map and flood light lens assembly.
6. Unfasten the four right-hand control panel securing screws. Withdraw the control panel from the dash.
7. Turn the radio knobs until the notch at the base of the knob appears. Insert a pointed object under the retainer and release it. Pull the knobs off the shafts.
8. Remove the inside knobs and nuts from the shafts.
9. Unfasten the nut which secures the radio attaching brace to the control panel.

Installation is the reverse of removal.

1973-74 Cutlass

1. Detach the cable from the negative battery terminal.
2. Remove the four screws which secure the steering column and separate it from the instrument panel.
3. Pull the knobs off the radio.
4. Unfasten the nuts from the front of the radio.
5. Remove its four retaining screws and then gently pull the right-hand control panel up and out.
6. Unfasten the radio support bracket screw.
7. Remove the four ashtray housing screws and take the housing off the tie-bar.
8. Disconnect the antenna and speaker wiring from the radio.
9. Withdraw the radio from behind the control panel.

Installation is the reverse of removal.

HEATER

Blower Motor and Heater Core R & R For Cars without Air Conditioning

1967 F-85, Cutlass

To remove the blower and inlet assembly, remove the right front wheel and disconnect the motor wiring. Remove the attaching nuts and screws. The lower outboard nut can be removed by drilling a $\frac{3}{4}$ in. hole through the fender panel at the dimple provided in the fender filler panel. When finished with the job, plug the hole with a rubber grommet. Remove the assembly and remove the blower motor from the assembly.

To remove the heater core and case, disconnect the heater hoses and remove the five attaching nuts. Remove the lower outboard nut as described in the preceding paragraph. Disconnect the wiring, control cables and remove the case. To remove the core, remove the retainer and pry the clip on the other side. Installation is the reverse of the removal procedure.

1967-69 All Other Models

To remove the heater case and core, remove the glove box. Disconnect the wiring, vacuum lines and defroster hoses from the heater case. Drain the radiator enough so that the heater hoses and gasket may be removed. Remove the blower assembly attaching screws and nuts and, from inside the car, remove the heater case. Remove the heater core from the case. Install in the reverse order of the above procedure.

To remove the blower assembly, disconnect the blower feed wire. To reach the upper sheet metal screw, construct a 3 foot length of $\frac{3}{8}$ drive extensions and a 7/16 socket, then feed the tool through the opening between the fender filler and the fender forward of the right front wheel. Use sealing compound to hold the screw when removing or installing. Remove the remaining attaching nuts and screws. Push the heater case studs back until the studs do not protrude through the dash. Remove the fender to dash panel attaching screw just over the blower assembly case and remove the two bolts from the bottom rear of the fender. Keep track of the shims. Push down on the inner fender panel and remove the blower assembly. The blower motor may be removed from the blower assembly at this point. Install in reverse order of the removal procedure.

1970 88 and 98 1973-74 Omega

To remove the heater case and core, remove the glove box. Disconnect the wiring, vacuum lines and defroster hoses from the heater case. Drain the radiator enough so that the heater hoses can be disconnected. Remove the blower assembly attaching screws and remove the heater case from inside the car. Remove the heater core from the case. Install in the reverse of the above procedure.

To remove the blower motor, disconnect the blower feed wire. Remove the fender filler panel bolts and move the filler panel forward and inward. Remove the blower assembly attaching nuts and screws. Push the heater case studs back so that they do not protrude through the dash. Push down on the inner fender panel and remove the blower assembly. Remove the blower motor attaching screws and remove the blower. When installing, use a bead of sealer around the heater inlet.

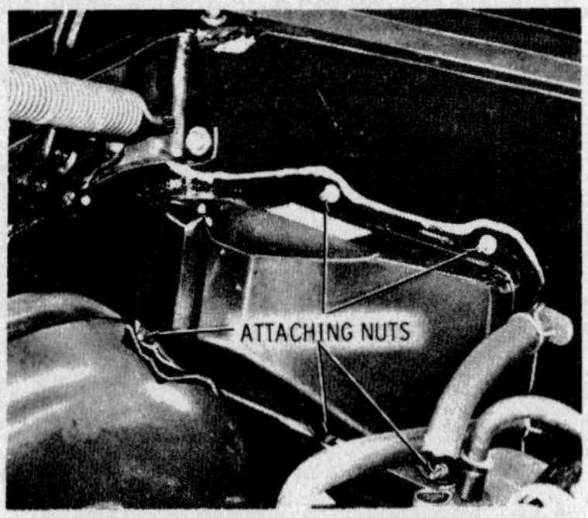
ATTACHING NUTS
Blower and air inlet attachment
(© Oldsmobile Div, G.M. Corp)

1971-74 88 and 98

To remove the heater case and core, disconnect the battery and remove the four heater case to dash panel attaching nuts. Drain the radiator enough so that the heater hoses may be disconnected. Disconnect the control cables and vacuum hose. Remove the defroster duct to case attaching screw and the right half of the right hand dash trim panel. Remove the heater case from the car. The heater core may now be removed from the case. Install in reverse order of removal.

To remove the blower motor, disconnect the battery and remove the right front wheel. Remove the canister or battery. Remove the three filler plate to radiator support screws, the filler plate to wheelhouse attaching screws and the filler plate. Remove the blower attaching screws and the connector. Remove the blower. Installation is the reverse of the removal procedure.

1968-74 F-85 Cutlass and 442, Vista-Cruiser

To remove the heater blower and inlet assembly, remove the right front fender filler panel. Disconnect the blower motor wiring. Remove the attaching nuts and screws and remove the heater assembly. The blower motor may be removed from the inlet assembly by removing the attaching screws. Installation is the reverse of the removal procedure.

To remove the core from the heater case, drain the radiator, disconnect the heater hoses and remove the five attaching nuts. On 1968-72 models to gain access to the lower nut it will be necessary to disconnect the right fender at the bottom and wedge it away from the body. Disconnect the wiring and the three control cables and remove the case assembly from the dash. Remove the core retainer and core. Install in reverse of the above procedure.

Blower Motor R & R for Cars with Air Conditioning

1967 F-85 and Oldsmobile

1. Remove the blower-to-evaporator duct. It is held in place by seven screws and it splits in half.
2. Remove the nuts and screws holding the blower case to the firewall.
3. Disconnect the wiring.
4. Remove the blower case and then remove the blower from the case.
5. Reverse the above steps to install.

1968-74 F-85 Cutlass and 1968-70 Oldsmobile

1. Disconnect the wiring.
2. Remove the five screws securing the motor to the case.
3. Remove the motor.
4. Reverse the above steps to install.

1971-74 88 and 98

1. Raise the car and remove the right front wheel and tire.
2. Remove the charcoal canister.
3. Unfasten the bolts which attach the radiator supports to the filler panel.
4. Remove the wheel arch securing bolts.
5. Take the right-hand wheel arch filler panel off.
6. Unfasten the blower motor mounting screws, remove the motor and disconnect its wiring.

Installation is performed in the reverse order of removal.

1973-74 Omega

The blower motor removal procedure for A/C equipped Omega models is similar to that for those models without A/C. For blower motor R & R, see "Blower Motor and Heater Core Removal for Cars without Air Conditioning", above.

NOTE: The heater core removal procedure is different for Omegas with A/C, however, than for those without it. See below for details.

Heater Core R & R for Cars with Air Conditioning

1967 F-85 and Oldsmobile

1. Working inside the passenger compartment, remove the rear retainer and seal located at the extreme right of the heater box assembly. It is held in place by three screws and a metal tab at the top.
2. Remove the roughly cylindrical distribution manifold which is attached to the heater box. It is secured by two screws.
3. Remove the defroster manifold from the heater box.
4. Disconnect the cables and wiring from the heater box.

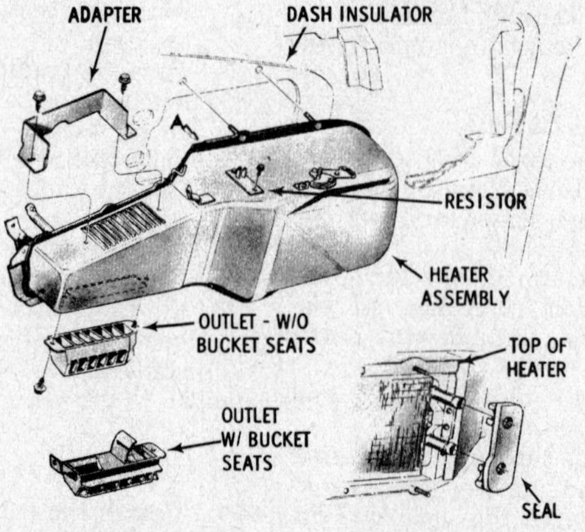
ADAPTER
DASH INSULATOR
RESISTOR
HEATER ASSEMBLY
OUTLET - W/O BUCKET SEATS
TOP OF HEATER
OUTLET W/ BUCKET SEATS
SEAL
Heater assembly
(© Oldsmobile Div, G.M. Corp)

5. Working outside the passenger compartment, drain the radiator.
6. Remove the heater core hoses.
7. Remove the nuts from the heater box studs. Some of the nuts may also secure the blower case as well. Look for screws inside the car.
8. Remove the heater box. Remove the core from the heater box.
9. Reverse the above steps to install.

1968-70 Oldsmobile

1. Working inside the car, remove the right and left duct hoses from the heater box. The hoses are sometimes stapled into place with three staples and there are tabs that snap into holes in the hoses.
2. Remove the manifold assembly from the front of the heater box.
3. Disconnect the wiring and vacuum hoses.
4. Remove the screws and/or nuts securing the heater box to the firewall. Fasteners may be located on both sides of the firewall.
5. Drain the radiator and disconnect the heater hoses from the heater core.
6. Remove the heater box and remove the core from the box by removing the top half of the heater box.
7. Reverse the above steps to install.

1971-74 Oldsmobile

1. Working inside the car, remove the air distribution hoses from the heater box. Hoses are sometimes held in place by staples. There are also tabs that snap into holes in the end of the hoses.
2. Remove the manifold from the front of the heater box. It is held in place by two screws and a tab.
3. Disconnect the wiring, vacuum hoses, and cables.
4. Disconnect the defroster manifold from the top of the heater box.
5. Working from outside the car, drain the radiator and disconnect the heater hoses.
6. Remove the heater box stud nuts and remove the heater box from the firewall.
7. Remove the heater core from the heater box.
8. Reverse the above steps to install.

1968-74 F-85 Cutlass

1. Working inside the car, remove the defroster adaptor from the upper right side of the heater box.
2. Remove the manifold attached to the front of the heater box. It is secured by two screws and a metal tab.
3. Disconnect the vacuum hoses, cables, and wiring.
4. Working outside the car, drain the radiator and disconnect the heater hoses from the heater core.
5. Remove the nuts from the heater box studs and remove the heater box.
6. Remove the heater core from the heater box.
7. Reverse the above steps to install.

1973-74 Omega

1. Disconnect the battery and drain the cooling system.
2. Detach the upper heater hose at the core tube.
3. Remove all accessible heater core and case securing nuts.
4. Unfasten the right-hand front fender filler panel bolts and lower the panel, in order to gain access to the lower heater hose clamp.
5. Unfasten the hose clamp and detach the hose from the lower heater core tube.
6. Unfasten the lower nut which secures the right-hand heater case/core assembly.
7. Plug both of the core tubes to prevent coolant from leaking.
8. Remove the glovebox and its door.
9. Take the vacuum diaphragm assembly off the right-hand kick-panel.
10. Remove the outlet from the bottom of the heater case.
11. Separate the cold air duct from the heater case.
12. Unfasten the screws which secure the extension to the heater case. Remove the extension from the case.
13. Detach the cables and the wiring from the case. Remove the core and case as an assembly.
14. Remove the core from the case.

Installation is performed in the reverse order of removal.

SEAT BELTS

Warning System

1972-73

The seat belt warning system consists of lap belt retractor switches, a pressure-sensitive switch underneath the right-hand front passenger's seat, a warning lamp and a buzzer.

On manual transmission-equipped cars the circuit is wired through the ignition switch, the parking brake warning light switch and a relay, which is located between the instrument cluster wiring and the switch on the parking brake. A diode is used to prevent feedback into the parking brake warning circuit.

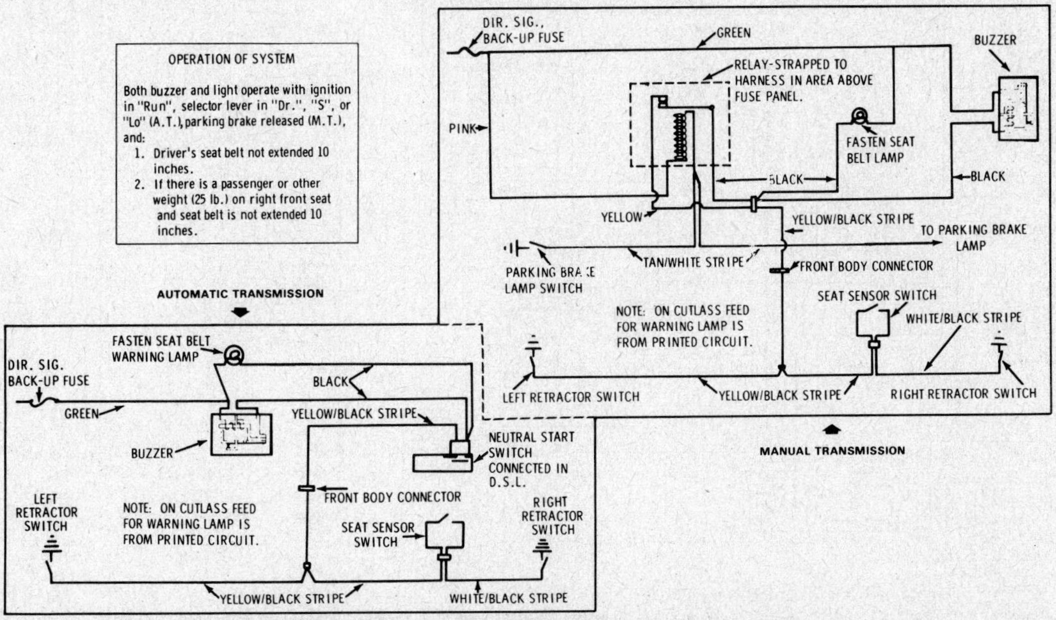
OPERATION OF SYSTEM
Both buzzer and light operate with ignition in "Run", selector lever in "Dr.", "S", or "Lo" (A.T.), parking brake released (M.T.), and:
1. Driver's seat belt not extended 10 inches.
2. If there is a passenger or other weight (25 lb.) on right front seat and seat belt is not extended 10 inches.
AUTOMATIC TRANSMISSION
FASTEN SEAT BELT WARNING LAMP
DIR. SIG. BACK-UP FUSE
GREEN
BLACK
YELLOW/BLACK STRIPE
BUZZER
NEUTRAL START SWITCH CONNECTED IN D.S.L.
FRONT BODY CONNECTOR
LEFT RETRACTOR SWITCH
NOTE: ON CUTLASS FEED FOR WARNING LAMP IS FROM PRINTED CIRCUIT.
SEAT SENSOR SWITCH
RIGHT RETRACTOR SWITCH
YELLOW/BLACK STRIPE
WHITE/BLACK STRIPE
DIR. SIG., BACK-UP FUSE
GREEN
BUZZER
RELAY-STRAPPED TO HARNESS IN AREA ABOVE FUSE PANEL.
PINK
FASTEN SEAT BELT LAMP
BLACK
BLACK
YELLOW
YELLOW/BLACK STRIPE
TO PARKING BRAKE LAMP
TAN/WHITE STRIPE
FRONT BODY CONNECTOR
LAMP SWITCH
SEAT SENSOR SWITCH
NOTE: ON CUTLASS FEED FOR WARNING LAMP IS FROM PRINTED CIRCUIT.
WHITE/BLACK STRIPE
LEFT RETRACTOR SWITCH
YELLOW/BLACK STRIPE
RIGHT RETRACTOR SWITCH
MANUAL TRANSMISSION

Seat belt warning system wiring (© Oldsmobile Div, G.M. Corp)

On cars having automatic transmissions, the seat belt warning circuit is wired through the ignition switch and the combination back-up lamp/neutral safety switch.

With the ignition key in the "RUN" position, a weight of 40-50 lbs on the seat (pressure-sensitive switch), energizes the circuit when the parking brake is released (M/T) or the gear selector placed in a forward drive range (A/T).

A warning light will glow and a buzzer will sound with the circuit energized, until the seat belts are withdrawn from the retractors and fastened over the laps of the two outboard front seat occupants.

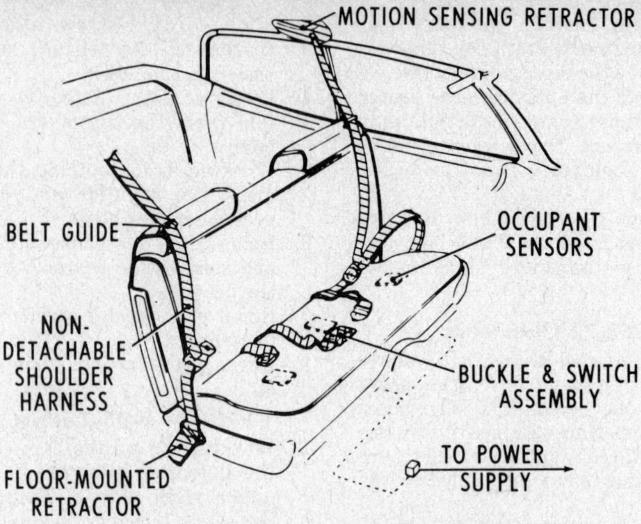
MOTION SENSING RETRACTOR
BELT GUIDE
OCCUPANT SENSORS
NON-DETACHABLE SHOULDER HARNESS
BUCKLE & SWITCH ASSEMBLY
TO POWER SUPPLY
FLOOR-MOUNTED RETRACTOR

Components of the 1974 seat belt/starter interlock system (© G.M. Corp)

Seat Belt/Starter Interlock System

1974

As required by law, all 1974 Oldsmobile passenger cars cannot be started until the front seat occupants sit down and then fasten their seat belts. If the proper sequence is not followed, e.g., the occupants fasten the seat belts and then sit on them, the car cannot be started.

If, after the car is started, the seat belts are unfastened, a warning buzzer and light will be activated in a similar manner to that described above for 1972-73 models.

The shoulder harness and lap belt are permanently fastened together, so that they both must be worn. The shoulder harness uses an inertia-lock reel to allow freedom of movement under normal driving conditions.

NOTE: This type of reel locks up when the car decelerates rapidly, as during a crash.

The lap belts use the same ratchet-type retractors that the 1972-73 models use.

The switches for the interlock system have been removed from the lap belt retractors and placed in the belt buckles. The seat sensors remain the same as those used in 1972-73, except that two more have been added.

For ease of service, the car may be started from outside, by reaching in and turning the key but without depressing the seat sensors.

In case of system failure, an override switch is located under the hood. This is a "one start" switch and it must be reset each time it is used.

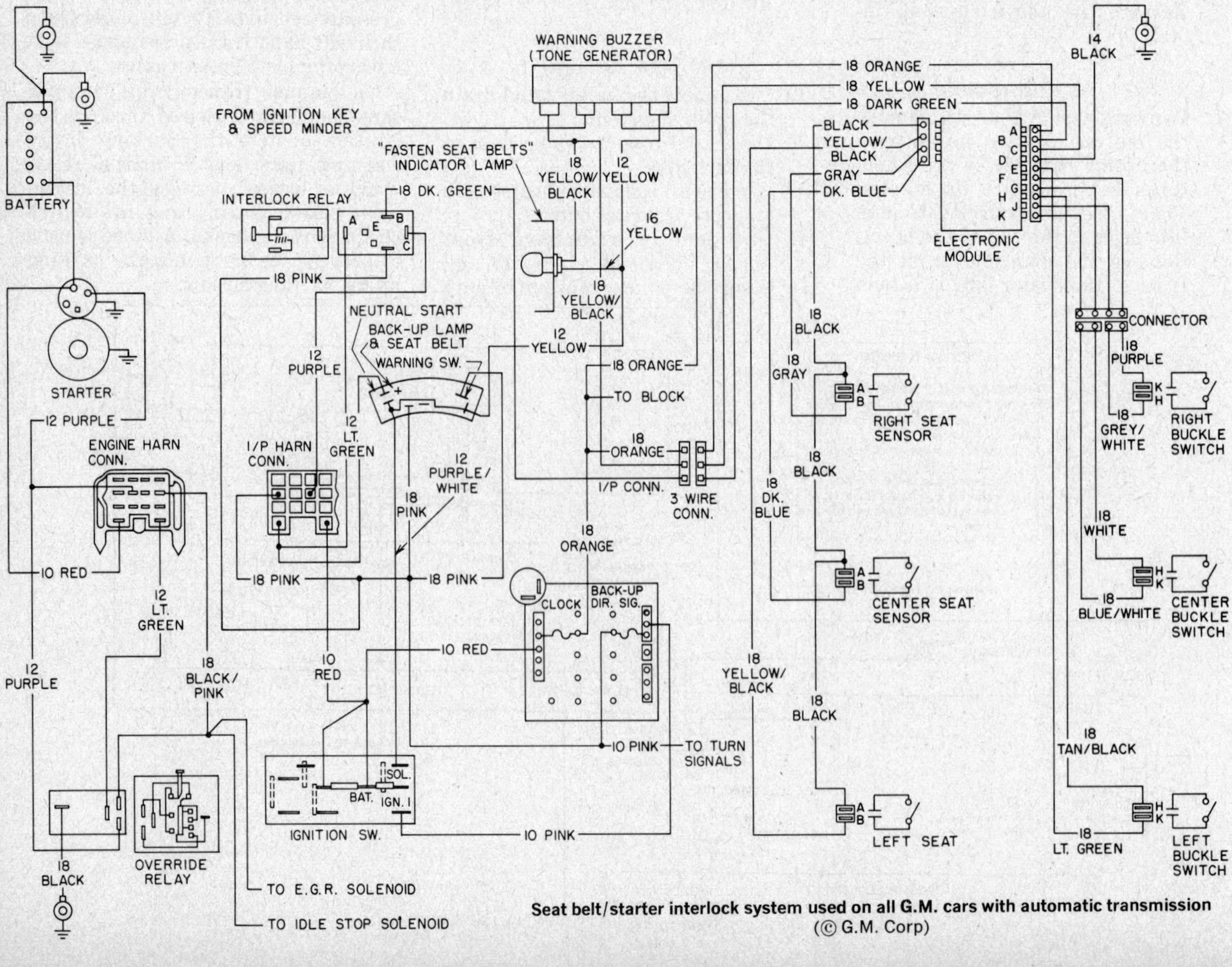
WARNING BUZZER (TONE GENERATOR)
BATTERY
FROM IGNITION KEY & SPEED MINDER
"FASTEN SEAT BELTS" INDICATOR LAMP
18 DK. GREEN
18 YELLOW/BLACK
12 YELLOW
16 YELLOW
INTERLOCK RELAY
18 PINK
NEUTRAL START BACK-UP LAMP & SEAT BELT WARNING SW.
12 PURPLE
12 LT. GREEN
STARTER
ENGINE HARN CONN.
I/P HARN CONN.
12 PURPLE/WHITE
18 PINK
10 RED
12 LT. GREEN
18 BLACK/PINK
10 RED
CLOCK
BACK-UP DIR. SIG.
10 PINK
TO TURN SIGNALS
IGNITION SW.
SOL.
BAT.
IGN. I
18 BLACK
OVERRIDE RELAY
TO E.G.R. SOLENOID
TO IDLE STOP SOLENOID
18 ORANGE
18 YELLOW
18 DARK GREEN
BLACK
YELLOW/BLACK
GRAY
DK. BLUE
ELECTRONIC MODULE
14 BLACK
TO BLOCK
I/P CONN.
3 WIRE CONN.
18 GRAY
RIGHT SEAT SENSOR
18 DK. BLUE
CENTER SEAT SENSOR
18 YELLOW/BLACK
LEFT SEAT
CONNECTOR
18 PURPLE
18 GREY/WHITE
RIGHT BUCKLE SWITCH
18 WHITE
18 BLUE/WHITE
CENTER BUCKLE SWITCH
18 TAN/BLACK
18 LT. GREEN
LEFT BUCKLE SWITCH

Seat belt/starter interlock system used on all G.M. cars with automatic transmission (© G.M. Corp)

Oldsmobile Toronado

YEAR IDENTIFICATION

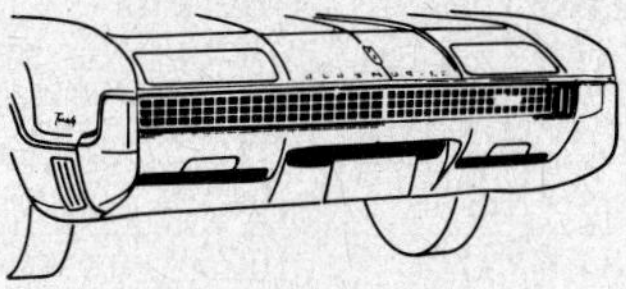
1967

1968

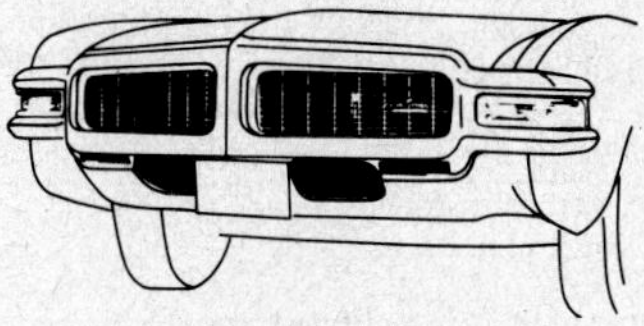
1969

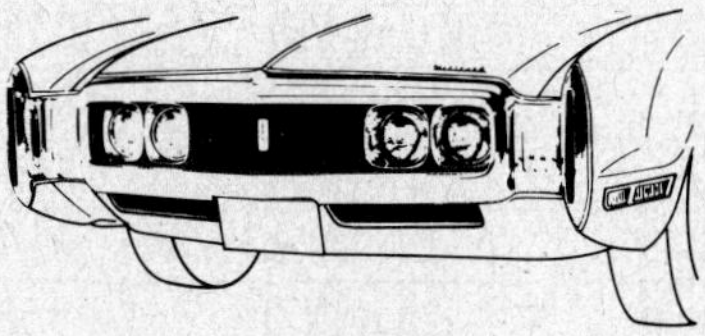
1970

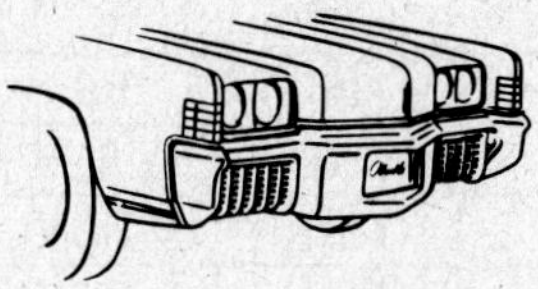
1971

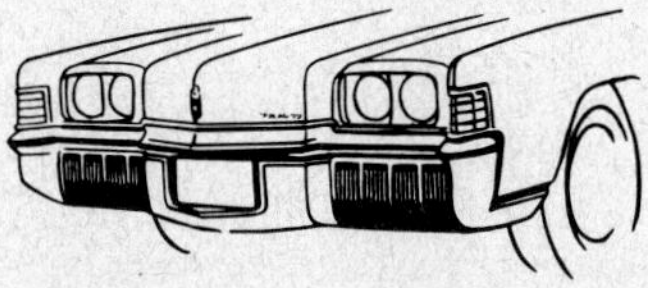
1972

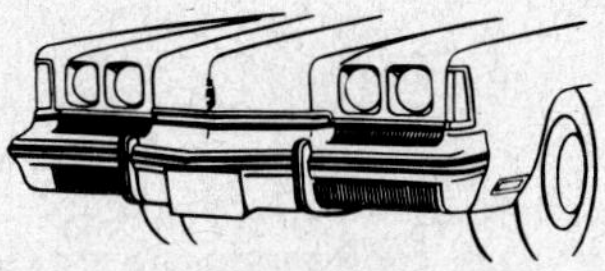
1973

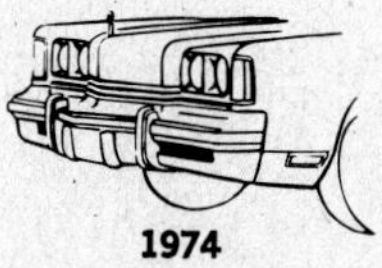
1974

FIRING ORDER

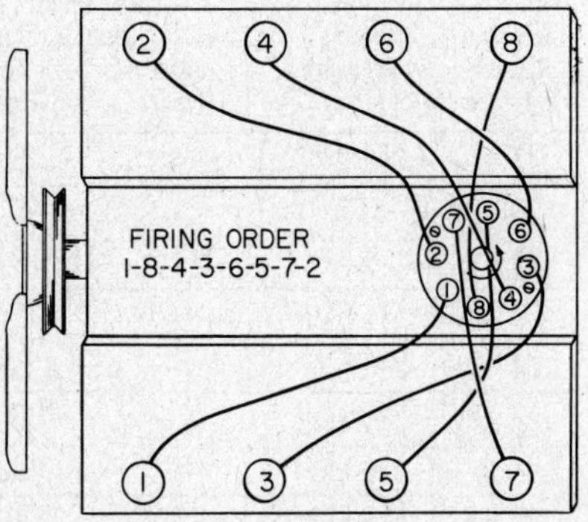
FIRING ORDER
1-8-4-3-6-5-7-2

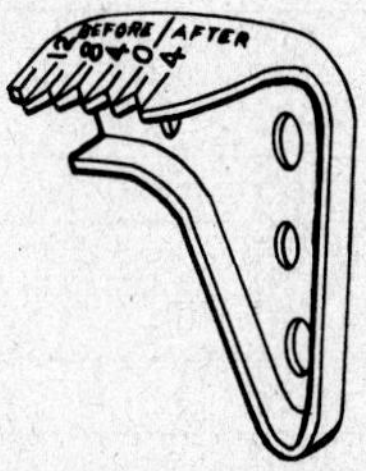
BEFORE
AFTER
Timing marks—1969-74
(© Oldsmobile Div, G.M. Corp)

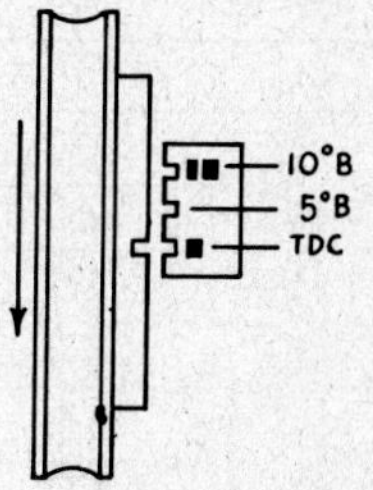
10°B
5°B
TDC
Timing marks—1967

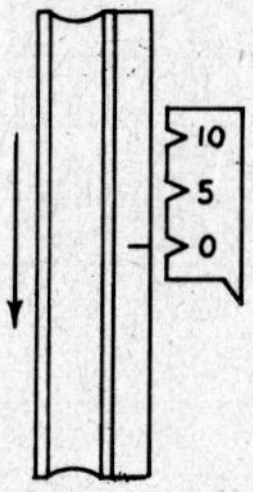
10
5
0
Timing marks—1968

CAR SERIAL NUMBER LOCATION AND ENGINE IDENTIFICATION

Vehicle Identification Number

1967

The plate is located on the left front door pillar. All Toronado models, Series 39687, are built in the Lansing plant in these years. Starting serial numbers for the standard Toronado and Deluxe Toronado are 394877M-600001 and 396877M600002 respectively (for 1967 models).

1968-71

The identification plate is located on the dashboard, and can be seen through the left-hand side of the windshield.

1972-74

The vehicle identification plate is located on the left side of the dashboard, visible through the windshield.

Engine Identification

1967

The engine identification number is stamped on a pad on the front of the right cylinder head. All engines are 425 cu. in. displacement.

1968-74

The engine identification number is found on a tape attached to the oil breather tube. All engines are 455 cu. in. displacement.

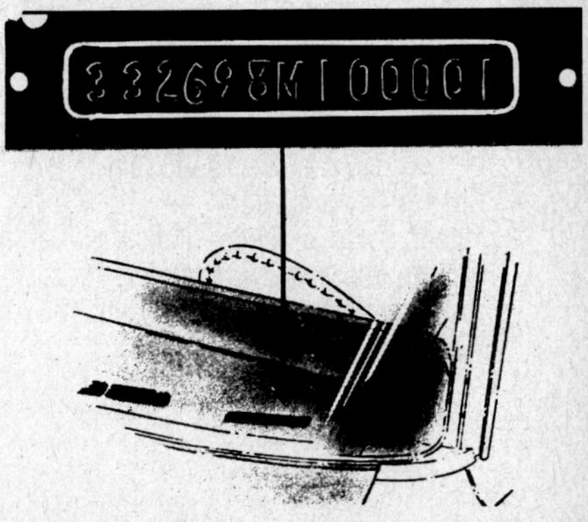
332698M100001
Vehicle identification number plate—1968-74
(© Oldsmobile Div, G.M. Corp)

GENERAL ENGINE SPECIFICATIONS

Year	Engine No. Cyl. Cu. In. Displacement	Carburetor Type	Advertised Horsepower @ rpm ■	Advertised Torque @ rpm (ft lbs) ■	Bore and Stroke (in.)	Advertised Compression Ratio	Oil Pressure @ 2050 rpm
'67	8-425	4 bbl	385 @ 4800	475 @ 3200	4.126 x 3.975	10.50:1	38
'68	8-455	4 bbl	375 @ 4600	510 @ 3000	4.126 x 4.250	10.25:1	38
	8-455	4 bbl	400 @ 4800	500 @ 3200	4.126 x 4.250	10.25:1	38
'69	8-455	4 bbl	375 @ 4600	510 @ 3000	4.126 x 4.250	10.25:1	38
	8-455	4 bbl	400 @ 4800	500 @ 3200	4.126 x 4.250	10.25:1	38
'70	8-455	4 bbl	375 @ 4600	510 @ 3000	4.126 x 4.250	10.25:1	38
	8-455	4 bbl	400 @ 3200	500 @ 3200	4.126 x 4.250	10.25:1	38
'71	8-455	4 bbl	350 @ 4400	465 @ 2800	4.126 x 4.250	8.50:1	38
'72	8-455	4 bbl	265 @ 4200	375 @ 2800	4.126 x 4.250	8.50:1	38
'73	8-455	4 bbl	250 @ 4000	375 @ 2800	4.126 x 4.250	8.50:1	38
'74	8-455	4 bbl	230 @ 3800	370 @ 2800	4.125 x 4.259	8.50:1	38

■ Beginning 1972, horsepower and torque are SAE net figures. They are measured at the rear of the transmission with all accessories installed and operating. Since the figures vary when a given engine is installed in different models, some are representative rather than exact.

TUNE-UP SPECIFICATIONS

When analyzing compression test results, look for uniformity among cylinders rather than specific pressures.

ENGINE			SPARK PLUGS		DISTRIBUTOR		IGNITION TIMING (deg) ▲		VALVES	Fuel	IDLE SPEED (rpm) ▲	
Year	No. Cyl Displacement (cu in.)	hp	Type §	Gap (in.)	Point Dwell (deg)	Point Gap (in.)	Man Trans †	Auto Trans	Intake Opens (deg) ●	Pump Pressure (psi)	Man Trans	Auto Trans
'67	8-425	385	44S	.030	28-32	.016	—	7½B	21	7¾-9	—	500
'68	8-455	375	44S	.030	28-32	.016	—	7½B	20	5-7	—	575
	8-455	400①	44S	.030	28-32	.016	—	10B	20	5-7	—	575
'69	8-455	375	44S	.030	28-32	.016	—	8B	20	5½-6½	—	575
	8-455	400①	44S	.030	28-32	.016	—	10B	24	5½-6½	—	575
'70	8-455	375	45S	.030	28-32	.016	—	8B	22	5½-6½	—	600
	8-455	400①	44S	.030	28-32	.016	—	12B	24	5½-6½	—	600
'71	8-455	350	46S	.040	28-32	.016	—	10B	22	5½-6½	—	600
'72	8-455	265	46S	.040	28-32	.016	—	8B	20	5½-6½	—	650/550
'73	8-455	250	R46S	.040	30	.016	—	8B	N.A.	5½-6½	—	650/550
'74	8-455	250	R46S	.040	30	.016	—	10B	N.A.	5½-6½	—	650/550
'74	8-455	230	R46SX	.080	Electronic		—	10B	N.A.	5½-6½	—	650/550

† Set timing with carburetor adjusted to the following speeds:
1967-1969 850 rpm
1970-1974 1100 rpm

▲ See text for procedure

● Figure in parentheses indicates California engine. Where two figures appear separated by a slash, the first is idle speed with solenoid energized, the second is idle speed with solenoid disconnected.

§ All spark plug listings are A.C. original equipment numbers

① Air Injection Reactor System

B Before Top Dead Center

— Not applicable

CAPACITIES

Year	ENGINE No. Cyl. (Cu. In.) Displacement	Engine Crankcase Add 1 Qt For New Filter	TRANSMISSION Pts To Refill After Draining Manual 3-Speed	Manual 4-Speed	Automatic ●	Drive Axle (pts)	Gasoline Tank (gals)	COOLING SYSTEM (qts) With Heater	With A/C
'67	8-425	5	—	—	5.5	4.5	24	17.5	18
'68	8-455	5	—	—	5.5	4.5	24	18	18.5
'69	8-455	5	—	—	8	4	24	18	18.5
'70	8-455	5	—	—	8	4	24	18	18.5
'71	8-455	5	—	—	8	4	24	18	18.5
'72	8-455	5	—	—	8	4	25	19.5	20
'73	8-455	5	—	—	8	4	26	19.5	20
'74	8-455	5	—	—	8	4	26	21	21

● Does not include torque converter
— Not applicable

VALVE SPECIFICATIONS

Year	Engine No. Cyl. Displacement (cu in.)	Seat Angle (deg)	Face Angle (deg)	Spring Test Pressure (lbs @ in.)	Spring Installed Height (in.)	STEM TO GUIDE Clearance (in.) Intake	Exhaust	STEM Diameter (in.) Intake	Exhaust
'67	8-425	①	②	187 @ 1.27	1 21/32	.0010-.0027	.0015-.0032	.3424	.3424
'68	8-455	①	②	187 @ 1.27	1 21/32	.0010-.0027	.0015-.0032	.3429	.3424
'69	8-455	①	②	187 @ 1.27	1 21/32	.0010-.0027	.0015-.0032	.3429	.3424
'70	8-455	45	46	187 @ 1.27	1 21/32	.0010-.0027	.0015-.0032	.3429	.3424
'71	8-455	45	46	187 @ 1.27	1 21/32	.0010-.0027	.0015-.0032	.3429	.3424
'72	8-455	45	46	197 @ 1.23	1 21/32	.0010-.0027	.0015-.0032	.3429	.3424
'73	8-455	45	46	197 @ 1.23	1 21/32	.0010-.0027	.0015-.0032	.3429	.3424
'74	8-455	45	46	197 @ 1.23	1 21/32	.0010-.0027	.0015-.0032	.3429	.3424

① Intake valve seat angle 30°
Exhaust valve seat angle 45°

② Intake valve face angle 30°
Exhaust valve face angle 46°

RING GAP

All measurements are given in in.

Year	Engine	Top Compression	Bottom Compression
'67-'71	8-425, 455	.013-.023	.013-.023
'72-'74	8-455	.010-.023	.010-.023

Year	Engine	Oil Control
'67-'74	All engines	.015-.055

RING SIDE CLEARANCE

All measurements are given in in.

Year	Engine	Top Compression	Bottom Compression
'67-'71	All engines	.0018-.0033	.0018-.0038
'72-'74	8-455	.0020-.0040	.0020-.0040

Year	Engine	Oil Control
'67	8-425	.0021-.0081
'68-'74	8-455	.0021-.0031

CRANKSHAFT AND CONNECTING ROD SPECIFICATIONS

All measurements are given in in.

Year	Engine No. Cyl. Displacement (cu in.)	CRANKSHAFT				CONNECTING ROD		
		Main Brg. Journal Dia	Main Brg. Oil Clearance	Shaft End-Play	Thrust on No.	Journal Diameter	Oil Clearance	Side Clearance
'67	425	2.9998	.0015-.0031①	.004-.008	3	2.4988-2.5003	.0008-.0018	.002-.013
'68-'74	455	2.9998	.0005-.0021①	.004-.008	3	2.4988-2.4998	.0004-.0033	②③

① No. 5—.0020-.0034
② 1968-70—.002-.013; 1971—.002-.011; 1972—.006-.020
③ 1970-72 W-30—.002-.021

TORQUE SPECIFICATIONS

All readings in ft lbs

Year	Engine No. Cyl. Displacement (cu in.)	Cylinder Head Bolts	Rod Bearing Bolts	Main Bearing Bolts	Crankshaft Pulley Bolt	Flywheel to Crankshaft Bolts	MANIFOLD	
							Intake	Exhaust
'67	425	80	42	120	160	60	35	25
'68-'74	455	80	42	120	160	60	35	25

BATTERY AND STARTER SPECIFICATIONS

Year	Engine Displacement (cu in.)	BATTERY			STARTER						Brush Spring Tension (oz)
					Lock Test			No-Load Test			
		Ampere Hour Capacity	Volts	Terminal Grounded	Amps	Volts	Torque (ft lbs)	Amps	Volts	RPM	
'67	425	73	12	Neg.	Not Recommended			70-105	10.6	3,800	35
'68-'69	455	75	12	Neg.	Not Recommended			70-105	10.6	3,800	35
'70-'71	455	74	12	Neg.	Not Recommended			—	—	—	35
'72-'74	455	73	12	Neg.	Not Recommended			—	—	—	35

ENGINE IDENTIFICATION CODE

The engine identification code is stamped on a machined pad located at the front of the right cylinder head on 1967 models; and located on tape attached directly to the front of the oil filler tube on all 1968-74 models.

Disp	Bbl	Hp	'67	'68	'69	'70	'71	'72	'73	'74
425	4	385	RT							
455	4	230 (net)							UQ UV VO VP	
455	4	250 (net)							UU UV	
455	4	265 (net)						UU UV		
455	4	350					US UT			
455	4	375		US UT UV	US UT UV	US UT				
455	4	400		UW	UW	UV UW				

PISTON CLEARANCE

Year	Engine	Piston-to-bore Clearance (in.)
'67	425	.00075-.00125
'68	455	.00075-.00125
'69-'74	455	.001-.002

ALTERNATOR AND REGULATOR SPECIFICATIONS

	ALTERNATOR			REGULATOR						
					Field Relay			Regulator		
Year	Part No. or Manufacturer	Field Current @ 12 V	Output (amps)	Part No. or Manufacturer	Air Gap (in.)	Point Gap (in.)	Volts to Close	Air Gap (in.)	Point Gap (in.)	Volts @ 75°
'67	1100734	2.2-2.6	42	1119515	.015	.030	6.3-8.3	.060	.014	13.5-14.4
'68-'69	1100734	2.2-2.6	42	1119515	Not Adjustable					13.5-14.4
	1100777	2.2-2.6	55	1119515	Not Adjustable					13.5-14.4
'70	1100878	2.2-2.6	42	1119515	Not Adjustable					13.5-14.4
	1100907	2.2-2.6	55	1119515	Not Adjustable					13.5-14.4
'71	1100567	2.2-2.6	42	1119515	Not Adjustable					13.5-14.4
	1100570	2.2-2.6	61	1119515	Not Adjustable					13.5-14.4
'72-'74	1100573	2.2-2.6	42	Transistor type, integral with alternator, no adjustment						
	1100597	2.2-2.6	61	Transistor type, integral with alternator, no adjustment						

BRAKE SPECIFICATIONS

All measurements given in in.

		MASTER CYLINDER		WHEEL CYLINDER			BRAKE DISC OR DRUM DIAMETER		
				Front			Front		
Year	Model	Disc	Drum	Disc	Drum	Rear	Disc	Drum	Rear
'67-'68	All	1.0	1.0	2.06	1 1/8	7/8	11.30	11.0	11.0
'69	All	1 1/8	1.0	2 15/16	1 1/8	7/8	10.9	11.0	11.0
'70-'73	All	1 1/8	—	2 15/16	—	15/16	10.88	—	11.0
'74	All	1 1/8	—	2 15/16	—	15/16	11.00	—	11.0

— Not applicable

WHEEL ALIGNMENT SPECIFICATIONS

		CASTER		CAMBER				WHEEL PIVOT RATIO (deg)	
Year	Model	Range (deg)	Pref Setting (deg)	Range (deg)	Pref Setting (deg)	Toe-in (in.)	Steering Axis Inclin.	Inner Wheel	Wheel Outer
'67	All	1 1/2N to 2 1/2N	2N	1/4N to 1/2P	1/8P	0 to 1/16	11	20	18 1/5
'68-'69	All	1 1/2N to 2 1/2N	2N	1/4N to 1/2P	1/8P	0 to 1/16	11	20	18 1/5
'70	All	1 1/2N to 2 1/2N	2N	1/4N to 1/2P	1/8P	0 to 1/16	11	20	18 1/5
'71-'74	All	1 1/2N to 2 1/2N	2N	1/4N to 3/4P ① 3/4N to 1/4P ②	1/4P ① 1/4N ②	0 to 1/16	11	—	—

N Negative P Positive

① Left side (to be 1/2P more than right side)
② Right side

NOTE: Service procedures for the Charging System, Starting System, Ignition System, Fuel System, Cooling System, Emission Controls, and Seat Belt/Starter Interlock System on the Toronado can be found in the Oldsmobile, F-85 and Omega section.

ENGINE

Toronados in 1967 used a 425 cu. in. engine, but moved to the 455 cu in. series in 1968, which remains unchanged to the present. The 425 cu in. engine is rated at 385 hp at 4800 rpm for 1967. With the advent of the 455, a great many horsepower options were offered over the years. For information regarding specifications on these engines, consult the beginning of this section.

1973-74 cars are equipped with an Exhaust Gas Recirculation (EGR) valve. This valve is located on the intake manifold and consists of a spring-loaded diaphragm and plunger that protrudes into the manifold. A vacuum line runs fom the carburetor to a temperature sensor and then to the EGR valve. When ambient underhood temperatures rise above 60° F., the temperature sensor opens and allows vacuum to pass from the carburetor to the EGR valve. When carburetor vacuum becomes strong enough, the plunger in the EGR valve opens thereby permitting exhaust gases to flow to the intake manifold and then into the combustion chamber where they can be reburned.

Engine R & R

1. Drain radiator.
2. Remove hood, marking hinge for reassembly.
3. Disconnect battery.
4. Disconnect radiator hoses and cooler lines, heater hoses, vacuum hoses, engine to body ground strap, fuel hose from fuel line, wiring and accelerator cable. Remove air conditioner compressor and power steering pump without disconnecting lines and set them aside.
5. Remove coil, throttle control switch bracket, radiator support and radiator. Remove air cleaner.
6. Raise the car.
7. Disconnect exhaust pipes at manifold. Loosen, but do not remove, upper left flywheel cover attaching bolt (this will require 30 in. of wrench extension).
8. Disconnect wires and remove starter.
9. Remove torque converter cover and remove three bolts securing the converter to flywheel. Scribe marks on converter and flywheel for reassembly.
10. Attach a final drive supporting tool (BT-6322) to support final drive assembly.
11. Remove two attaching bolts from right output shaft support bracket and one through bolt attaching final drive to engine block on the left side. Scribe around the washers for correct reassembly.
12. Remove engine mount to crossmember nuts and front engine mount nuts.
13. Lower the car.
14. Support engine by using a lifting fixture (BT-6606).
15. Remove six bolts, transmission to engine.
16. Using suitable lifting device, lift engine from car.

Caution If car is to be moved, install converter holding tool (J-21654).

17. To install, reverse removal procedure.

Manifolds

Intake Manifold Removal and Installation

1. Remove the air cleaner. Drain the cooling system. Disconnect the upper radiator hose, the thermostat-bypass hose, and the heater hose at the rear of the intake manifold.
2. Remove the throttle cable and all fuel and vacuum lines.
3. Disconnect the ignition coil mounting bracket and the alternator and air conditioning brackets.

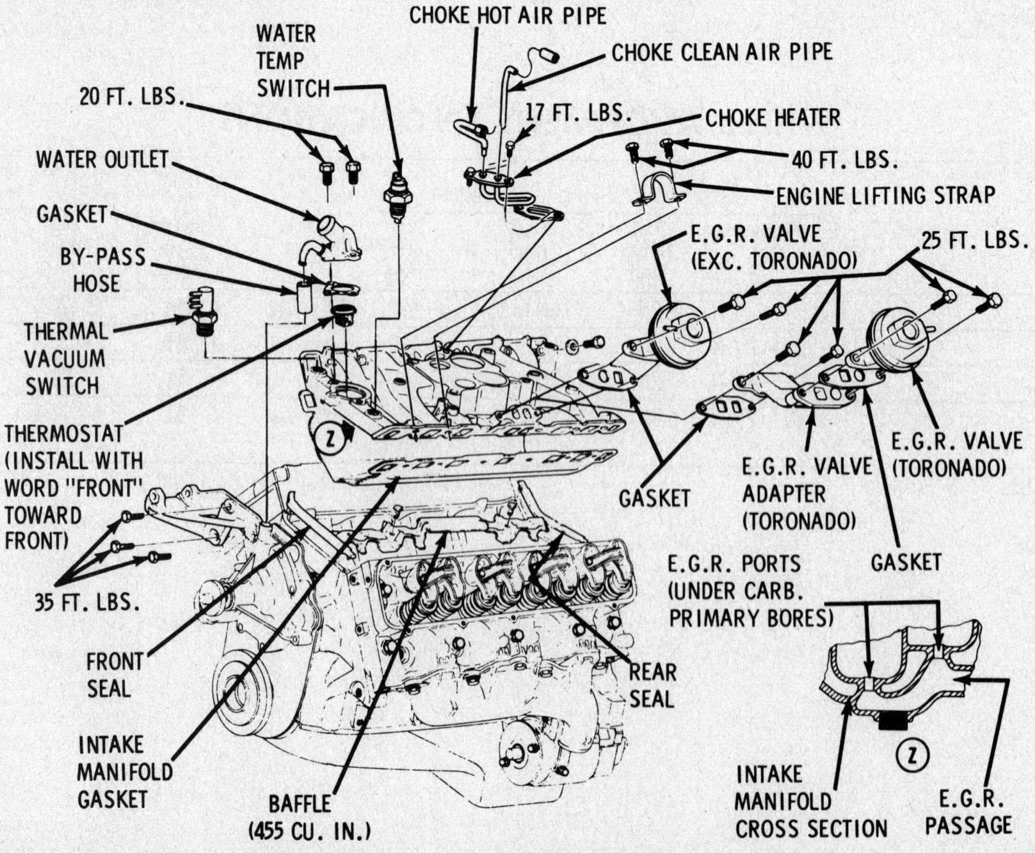
CHOKE HOT AIR PIPE
WATER TEMP SWITCH
CHOKE CLEAN AIR PIPE
20 FT. LBS.
17 FT. LBS.
CHOKE HEATER
40 FT. LBS.
WATER OUTLET
ENGINE LIFTING STRAP
GASKET
E.G.R. VALVE (EXC. TORONADO)
25 FT. LBS.
BY-PASS HOSE
THERMAL VACUUM SWITCH
THERMOSTAT (INSTALL WITH WORD "FRONT" TOWARD FRONT)
E.G.R. VALVE (TORONADO)
E.G.R. VALVE ADAPTER (TORONADO)
GASKET
35 FT. LBS.
E.G.R. PORTS (UNDER CARB. PRIMARY BORES)
GASKET
FRONT SEAL
REAR SEAL
INTAKE MANIFOLD GASKET
BAFFLE (455 CU. IN.)
INTAKE MANIFOLD CROSS SECTION
E.G.R. PASSAGE

Intake manifold components (© Oldsmobile Div, G.M. Corp)

NOTE: Position the alternator and air conditioning compressor out of the way and secure them. Do not disconnect any refrigerant lines.

4. Before removing the intake manifold bolts, disconnect the temperature gauge electrical lead. Remove the manifold bolts and lift off the manifold with the carburetor attached.

NOTE: It is necessary to remove the oil filler tube to add clearance when removing the manifold.

5. Before installation, clean the mating surfaces of the manifold.
6. Position the intake manifold gasket correctly on the heads, making certain that the ports in the head align with the holes in the gasket.
7. Install the end gaskets with the ends placed under the cylinder head.
8. Lower the intake manifold onto the engine using caution that the gaskets do not slip.
9. Connect the thermostat bypass hose to the water pump and install the manifold bolts after they have been cleaned and oiled.
10. Torque the manifold bolts to 15 ft lbs using the correct torque sequence. Then re-torque to 40 ft lbs.
11. Install the mounting brackets for the ignition coil, air conditioning and the alternator.
12. Connect the temperature gauge lead and all fuel and vacuum lines.
13. Install all disconnected hoses, spark plug wires, throttle linkage and air cleaner. Fill the cooling system.

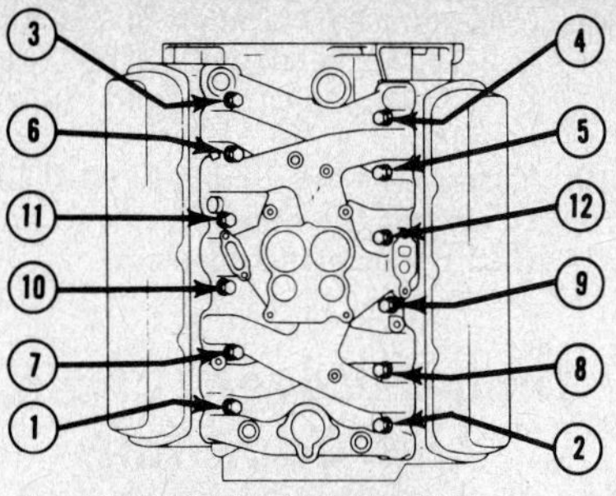
3
4
6
5
11
12
10
9
7
8
1
2
1. LUBRICATE ENTIRE BOLT IN ENGINE OIL.
2. TORQUE ALL BOLTS IN SEQUENCE SHOWN TO 15 FT. LBS.
3. RE-TORQUE IN SEQUENCE SHOWN TO 40 FT. LBS.

Intake manifold torque sequence (© Oldsmobile Div, G.M. Corp)

Exhaust Manifold Removal and Installation

Left Side

1. Remove the air cleaner and the carburetor heat box on the manifold.
2. Remove the lower alternator bracket; raise the front of the car and support it securely.
3. Remove the front exhaust pipes.
4. Lower the car and remove the manifold attaching bolts. Remove the manifold from above.
5. To install, reverse the removal procedure using the correct torque for the manifold attaching bolts. (See illustration for the correct torque specifications.)

Right Side

1. Raise the car and support it securely.
2. Remove the exhaust pipe and the right front wheel.
3. Remove the attaching bolts and lower the manifold down and out from under the vehicle.
4. To install, reverse the removal procedure.

Valve System

The Toronado uses camshaft-operated hydraulic lifters. Lubricant is supplied through the pushrods to the rocker arm assembly.

Toronado engines use non-replaceable valve guides. Should the guides become worn, they must be reamed to the next oversize and larger diameter valves installed.

Valves are available in standard size, .003 in. oversize, .005 in. oversize, .010 in. oversize and .013 in. oversize. When the guides are reamed, use caution to keep the reamer straight in the valve guide bore.

Rocker Arm Assembly Removal and Installation

Remove the valve cover, rocker flange bolts, rocker pivot and the rocker arms. Remove each set of rocker arms as a unit. To install, position the rocker arm assemblies and lubricate the wear points. Install the rocker pivots. Install the flange bolts and tighten to 25 ft lbs.

Cylinder Head

Cylinder Head Removal and Installation

1. Drain the radiator and the engine block.

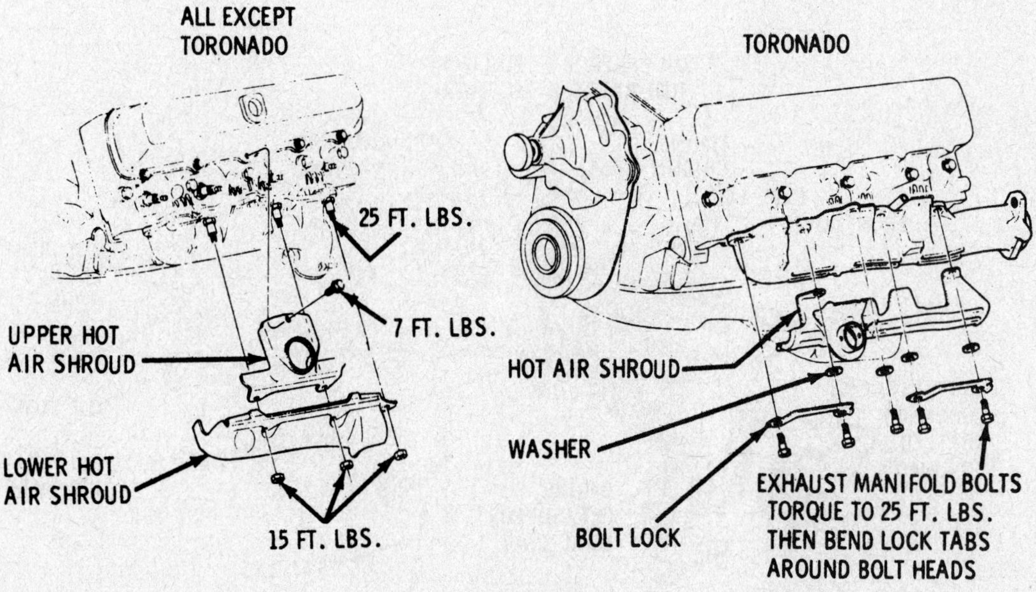
ALL EXCEPT TORONADO
TORONADO
25 FT. LBS.
7 FT. LBS.
UPPER HOT AIR SHROUD
LOWER HOT AIR SHROUD
15 FT. LBS.
HOT AIR SHROUD
WASHER
BOLT LOCK
EXHAUST MANIFOLD BOLTS TORQUE TO 25 FT. LBS. THEN BEND LOCK TABS AROUND BOLT HEADS

Exhaust manifold components and torque requirements (© Oldsmobile Div, G.M. Corp)

2. Remove the intake and exhaust manifolds. (see Manifolds)
3. Remove the valve covers.

NOTE: It may be necessary to remove some accessory brackets which are in the way.

4. Remove the engine ground strap, which is attached to the right cylinder head.
5. Pull out the push rods, noting the location of each.
6. Remove the rocker arm bolts, rocker pivots, and rocker arms.

Caution The rocker arms, rocker pivots and push rods must be replaced in their original positions.

7. Remove the cylinder head bolts and lift off the heads.
8. Before installation, the head gasket should be coated with sealer on both sides.
9. Position the cylinder heads and install the head bolts after they have been cleaned and lubricated.
10. Torque the head bolts to 60 ft lbs following the sequence given and then re-torque to 85 ft lbs.

Timing Cover, Chain, and Camshaft

Timing Cover Removal and Installation

1967-70

1. Drain the cooling system. Disconnect the upper and lower radiator, heater and bypass hoses.
2. Remove the radiator, belts, fan and fan pulley, crankshaft pulley and the harmonic balancer.
3. Drain the oil and remove the oil pan.
4. Remove the timing cover attaching bolts and pull off the cover. Also, remove the timing pointer and the water pump.
5. Before assembly, remove all old gaskets and install a new timing cover gasket.
6. Position the front cover, timing pointer and the water pump.
7. Lubricate the attaching bolts and install.
8. Install the harmonic balancer on the crankshaft after lubrication. Torque to 160 ft lbs.
9. Connect all cooling hoses.
10. Install the crankshaft pulley.
11. Install the fan and the fan pulley. Torque the attaching bolts to 20 ft lbs.
12. Install the drive belts and adjust.
13. Install the oil pan, fill the crankcase and the radiator.
14. Run the engine and check for leaks.

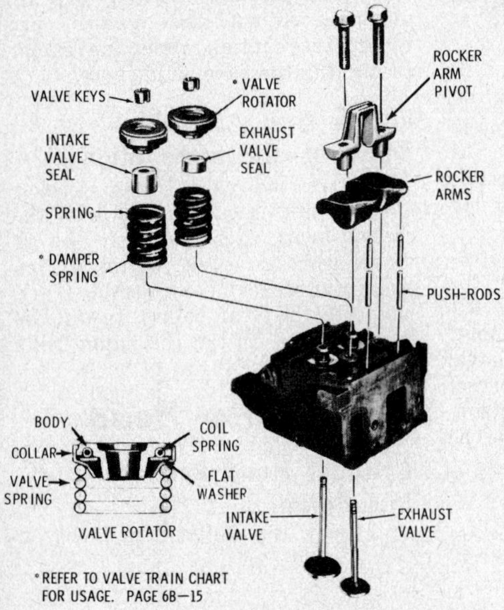
VALVE KEYS
* VALVE ROTATOR
ROCKER ARM PIVOT
INTAKE VALVE SEAL
EXHAUST VALVE SEAL
SPRING
ROCKER ARMS
* DAMPER SPRING
PUSH-RODS
BODY
COLLAR
COIL SPRING
VALVE SPRING
FLAT WASHER
VALVE ROTATOR
INTAKE VALVE
EXHAUST VALVE
* REFER TO VALVE TRAIN CHART FOR USAGE. PAGE 6B—15

Cylinder head and valve assembly
(© Oldsmobile Div, G.M. Corp)

7
5
1
3
9
8
6
2
4
10

Cylinder head torque chart
(© Oldsmobile Div, G.M. Corp)

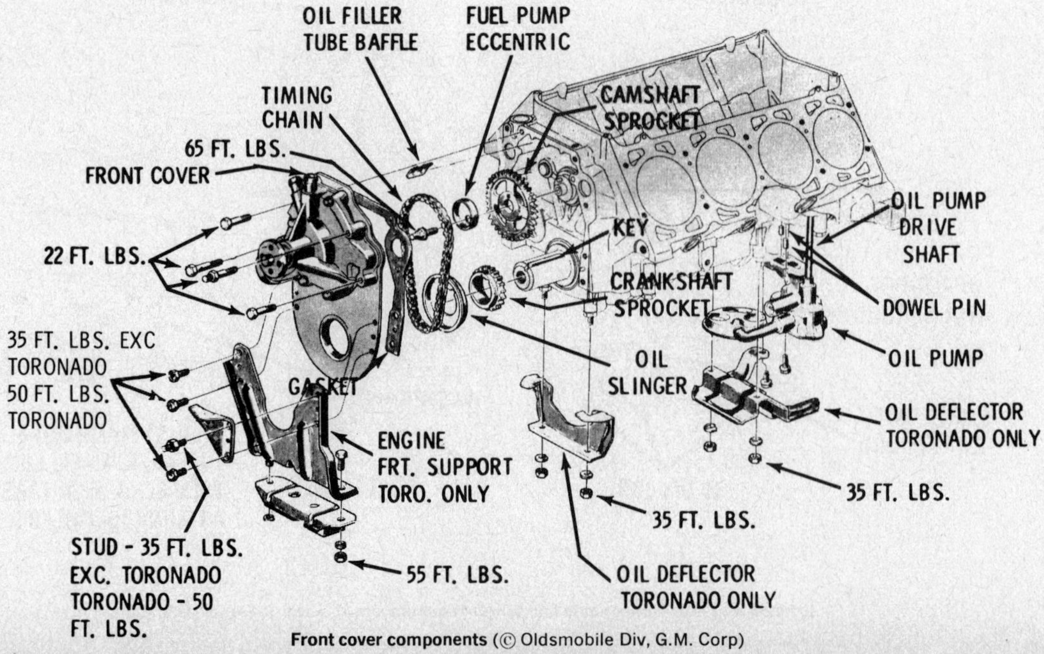
OIL FILLER TUBE BAFFLE
FUEL PUMP ECCENTRIC
TIMING CHAIN
CAMSHAFT SPROCKET
65 FT. LBS.
FRONT COVER
OIL PUMP DRIVE SHAFT
KEY
22 FT. LBS.
CRANKSHAFT SPROCKET
DOWEL PIN
35 FT. LBS. EXC TORONADO
50 FT. LBS. TORONADO
OIL SLINGER
OIL PUMP
GASKET
OIL DEFLECTOR TORONADO ONLY
ENGINE FRT. SUPPORT TORO. ONLY
35 FT. LBS.
35 FT. LBS.
STUD - 35 FT. LBS. EXC. TORONADO TORONADO - 50 FT. LBS.
55 FT. LBS.
OIL DEFLECTOR TORONADO ONLY

Front cover components (© Oldsmobile Div, G.M. Corp)

1971-74

In order to remove the front cover, the engine must be removed from the car.

Timing Cover Oil Seal Removal and Installation

1. Remove all drive belts, crankshaft pulley and pulley hub.
2. Using an inside puller, remove the seal.
3. Before installing a new seal, apply sealer to the outside of the seal.
4. Install the seal making sure that it is installed straight and the sealing surface is not damaged.
5. Position the pulley hub and the crankshaft pulley and adjust the drive belts.

Timing Chain Removal and Installation

NOTE: 1971-74 models require that the engine be removed before performing the chain removal procedure.

1. Remove the front engine cover.
2. Remove the fuel pump eccentric, oil slinger, cam gear and timing chain.
3. Remove the key from the crankshaft keyway and then the crankshaft gear, if necessary.

NOTE: If it is necessary to remove the crankshaft gear, it will be necessary to use a puller.

4. To install, align the camshaft and crankshaft gears. The camshaft gear aligning mark must be in the 6 o'clock position while the crankshaft gear must be in the 12 o'clock position.
5. Position the fuel pump eccentric with the flat side against the gear. Using a brass hammer, place the key against the gear until it bottoms.
6. Install the oil slinger and torque the attaching nut to 160 ft lbs.

Camshaft Removal and Installation

NOTE: The removal and installation of the camshaft on 1971-74 models requires the removal of the engine since the oil pan and the front cover must be removed.

1. Remove the oil pan, front cover and the distributor.

NOTE: Before removing the distributor, position the No. 1 piston at top dead center of its compression stroke.

2. Remove the valve covers and the intake manifold.
3. Remove the water temperature sensor and the oil filler tube.
4. Remove the rocker arm assemblies, the push rods and the lifters.

Caution It is important that the lifters, the push rods, and the rocker arm assemblies be replaced in their original positions.

5. Remove the fuel pump eccentric, camshaft gear, oil slinger and the timing chain.
6. Remove the camshaft by carefully withdrawing it from the front of the engine. Use caution not to damage the camshaft bearings during this procedure. Keep the camshaft parallel with the crankshaft as it is removed.
7. Before installing the camshaft, coat both the cam lobes and the bearings with camshaft grease. Install the camshaft and align the timing marks on the camshaft and crankshaft gears as outlined in the Timing Chain Removal and Installation section.
8. Install the distributor. (See Distributor Installation.)
9. Reverse the removal procedure to complete the installation.

FRONT SEAL
TOOL BT-6406
Removing the front oil seal
(© Oldsmobile Div, G.M. Corp)

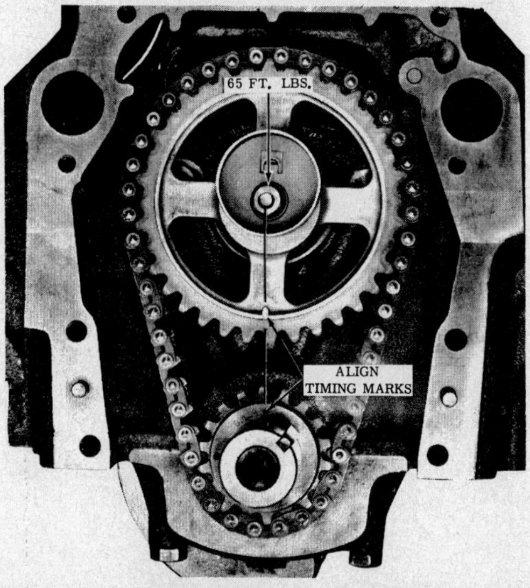
65 FT. LBS.
ALIGN
TIMING MARKS
Camshaft and crankshaft gear alignment
(© Oldsmobile Div, G.M. Corp)

Engine Lubrication

Oil Pan R & R

1967

1. Remove engine assembly.
2. Remove dipstick.
3. Drain oil and remove filter assembly.
4. Remove mount from front cover.
5. Remove oil pan attaching bolts and remove oil pan.
6. Apply a good sealer to both sides of pan gaskets and install on block.
7. Install front and rear seal.
8. Wipe lubricant on seal area and install pan. Torque 5/16 in. bolts to 15 ft. lbs. and 1/4 in. bolts to 10 ft. lbs.
9. Reinstall mount to front cover and oil filter assembly.
10. Reinstall engine and fill crankcase as explained in charts.

1968-70

1. Disconnect battery and remove dipstick.
2. Remove upper radiator support screws and fan shroud screws.

3. Hoist car and drain oil.
4. Disconnect engine mounts and jack front of engine up as far as possible.
5. Remove crossover pipe and starter.
6. Remove oil pan attaching bolts and remove oil pan.
7. Install in reverse order of removal, using new gaskets with sealer on both sides.

1971-74

The engine must be removed from the vehicle in order to remove the oil pan. Follow the procedure described for 1967 models above.

Oil Pump R & R

Remove the oil pan as described above. Remove the oil baffle. Remove the oil pump to rear main bearing cap attaching bolts, then remove the pump and drive shaft extension.

Rear Main Oil Seal Replacement

Whether or not the engine must be removed from the vehicle in order to replace the rear main bearing oil seal depends upon the removal of the oil pan. See "Oil Pan R & R" above. Remove the oil pan and rear main bearing cap. Using a blunt-ended tool, drive the upper seal into its groove on each side until it is tightly packed. This is usually ¼—¾ in. Cut pieces of the old lower bearing cap seal 1/16 in. longer than the distance each side of the upper seal was compressed. Install these pieces into each side of the upper seal seat, packing them into place. Carefully trim any protruding seal, being sure not to scratch or damage the bearing surface. Install a new seal in the bearing cap and install the cap, tightening bolts to 120 ft. lbs. Install the oil pan.

AUTOMATIC TRANSMISSION

The Turbo-Hydramatic transmission used on the Toronado is a fully automatic transmission used for front-wheel drive applications. It consists primarily of a three element hydraulic torque converter, dual sprocket and link assembly, compound planetary gear set, three multiple disc clutches, a sprag clutch, a roller clutch, two band assemblies and hydraulic control system.

Linkage Adjustments

See illustration for manual linkage adjustment.

Kick-down Adjustment

1. Push forward on the switch contact so that it is flush with the switch housing.
2. Place the accelerator pedal to the wide open position. This will set the switch.
3. If there is any doubt whether the switch is working, it may be checked with a test light across the two connector poles.

Automatic Transmission Removal

1. Disconnect battery.
2. Disconnect oil cooler lines at transmission and speedometer cable at governor.
3. Install engine support bar.
4. Remove nut D and bolts A, B and C as in illustration. A special wrench, such as MAC S-147, must be used to remove nut D on 1967 models.
5. Remove bolts A, B, C and D as in illustrations.
6. Loosen flywheel cover plate bolt A. (See illustration.)
7. Raise the car on a hoist.
8. Disconnect starter wiring, then remove starter.
9. Remove bolts B, C and D from flywheel cover plate.
10. Remove flywheel to converter bolt E. Rotate flywheel until all bolts are removed.
11. Disconnect vacuum modulator line and stator wiring.
12. Install transmission lift.
13. Remove shift linkage.
14. Remove bolts E, F, G and nut from H. (See illustration.)

NOTE: When the last three transmission to final drive bolts are removed, a quantity of oil will be lost.

15. Remove bolts A and B. (See illustration.)
16. Remove the two upper engine mount brackets to transmission bolts A and B. (See illustration.)
17. Remove the four brackets to engine mount bolts.
18. Slide transmission rearward and down. Engine mount bracket will follow transmission down. Install converter holding tool J-21654.
19. After transmission is removed from car, the link assembly cover insulator can be removed or installed.

Automatic Transmission Installation

When installing the transmission, the motor mount bracket must be positioned loosely on the link assembly cover until the transmission is in place. Then reverse removal procedure. Torque the bolts as follows:

Engine to torque converter housing—30 ft. lbs.
Engine bracket to transmission—55 ft. lbs.
Engine bracket to rubber mount—55 ft. lbs.
Oil cooler lines to transmission—30 ft. lbs.
Final drive to transmission nuts and bolts—25 ft. lbs.
Torque converter to flywheel bolts—30 ft. lbs.
Flywheel housing cover—5 ft. lbs.
Starter to transmission—30 ft. lbs.

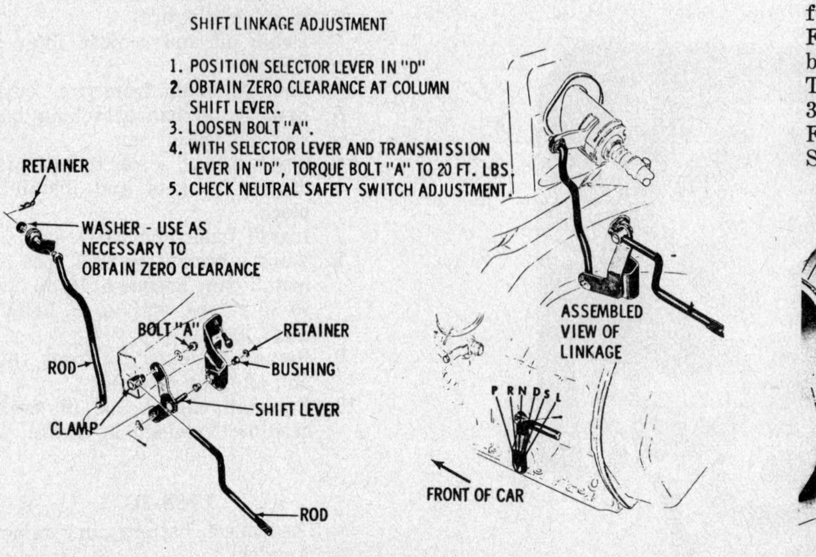
SHIFT LINKAGE ADJUSTMENT
1. POSITION SELECTOR LEVER IN "D"
2. OBTAIN ZERO CLEARANCE AT COLUMN SHIFT LEVER.
3. LOOSEN BOLT "A".
4. WITH SELECTOR LEVER AND TRANSMISSION LEVER IN "D", TORQUE BOLT "A" TO 20 FT. LBS.
5. CHECK NEUTRAL SAFETY SWITCH ADJUSTMENT.
RETAINER
WASHER - USE AS NECESSARY TO OBTAIN ZERO CLEARANCE
BOLT "A"
RETAINER
ROD
BUSHING
SHIFT LEVER
CLAMP
ROD
ASSEMBLED VIEW OF LINKAGE
P R N D S L
FRONT OF CAR

Shift linkage adjustments
(© Oldsmobile Div, G.M. Corp)

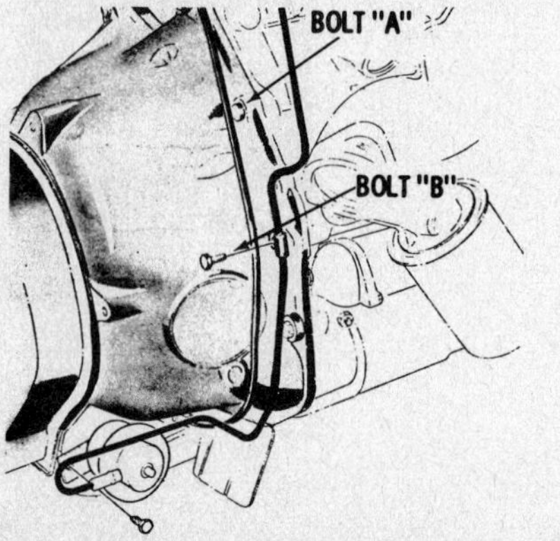
BOLT "A"
BOLT "B"

Transmission to engine attachment
(© Oldsmobile Div, G.M. Corp)

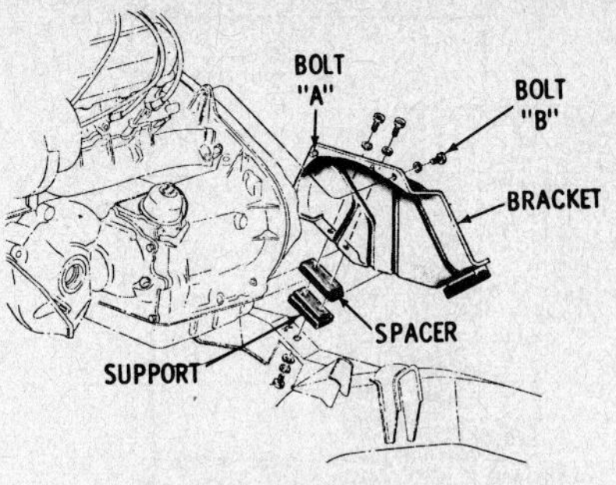
BOLT "A"
BOLT "B"
BRACKET
SPACER
SUPPORT

Engine mount attachment
(© Oldsmobile Div, G.M. Corp)

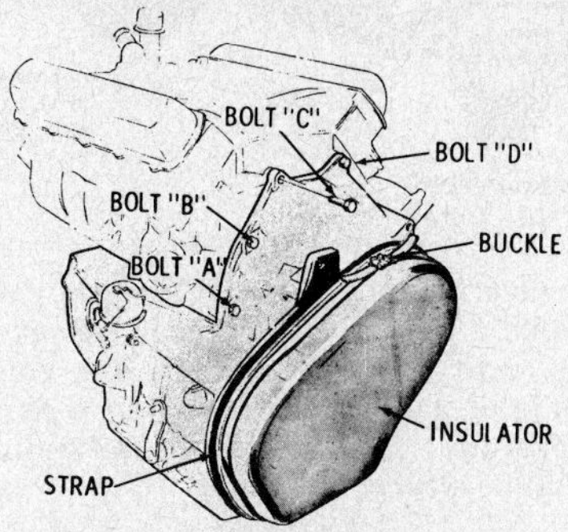
BOLT "C"
BOLT "D"
BOLT "B"
BOLT "A"
BUCKLE
INSULATOR
STRAP

Transmission to engine attachment
(© Oldsmobile Div, G.M. Corp)

After the transmission is installed, check transmission oil level. Refer to capacity chart at the beginning of this car section.

Drive and Driven Sprockets for the Transmission Drive

If it should be necessary to replace either the drive sprocket, chain, or driven sprocket, the three unit combination must be replaced as a set. They are matched and are not to be serviced separately.

Removal

1. Remove cover housing attaching bolts.
2. Remove cover housing and gasket. Discard the gasket.
3. Install J-4646 snap-ring pliers into sprocket bearing retaining snap-rings located under the drive and driven sprockets, then remove snap-rings from retaining grooves in support housings.

NOTE: Do not remove snap-rings from beneath the sprockets. Leave them in a loose position between the sprockets and the bearing assemblies.

4. Remove drive and driven sprockets, link assemblies, bearings and shaft simultaneously by alternately pulling upward on the drive and driven sprockets until the bearings are out of the drive and driven support housings.

NOTE: It may be necessary to pry up on the sprockets. Use care.

Caution Do not pry on the guide links or the aluminum case. Pry only on the sprockets.

5. Remove link assembly from drive and driven sprockets.
6. Remove two hook-type oil seal rings from turbine shaft.
7. Inspect drive and driven sprocket bearing assemblies for rough or defective bearings.

NOTE: Do not remove bearing assemblies from drive or driven sprockets unless they need replacement.

8. If removal of bearing assembly from drive and/or driven sprockets is necessary, proceed as follows:
   A. Remove sprocket to bearing assembly retaining snap-ring using tool J-5589 (snap-ring pliers).
   B. Mount sprocket with turbine or input shaft placed in hole in work bench on two 2 x 4 x 10 in. pieces of wood.
   C. With a hammer and brass rod, drive the inner race alternately through each of the access openings until the bearing assembly is removed from the sprocket hub. Drive the sprocket, then turbine shaft and link assembly.

Inspection

1. Inspect drive sprocket teeth for nicks, burrs, scoring, galling and excessive wear.
2. Inspect drive sprocket to ball bearing retaining snap-ring for damage.
3. Inspect drive sprocket ball bearing inner race mounting surface for damage.
4. Inspect turbine shaft for open lubrication passages. Run a tag wire through the passages to make sure they are open.
5. Inspect spline for damage.
6. Inspect the ground bushing journals for damage.
7. Inspect the two hook-type oil seal grooves for damage or excessive wear.
8. Inspect the turbine shaft for cracks or distortion.
9. Inspect the link assembly for damage or loose links.

NOTE: Take particular notice of the guide links. They are the wide outside links on each side of the link assembly.

Installation

Install by reversing removal procedures.

Driven Sprocket at Input Shaft Inspection

1. Inspect driven sprocket teeth for nicks, burrs, scoring, galling and excessive wear.
2. Inspect sprocket to ball bearing retaining snap-ring for damage.
3. Inspect ball bearing inner race mounting surface for damage.
4. Inspect input shaft for open lubrication holes. Run a tag wire through the holes to make sure they are open.
5. Inspect spline for damage.
6. Inspect ground bushing journals for damage.

Sprocket Bearing Installation

1. Turn sprocket so that turbine or input shaft is pointing upward.
2. Install new sprocket bearing as follows:
   A. Install snap-ring, letter side down to shaft.
   B. Assemble bearing assembly on turbine or input shaft.
   C. Using drift (J-6133-A), drive the bearing assembly onto the hub of the sprocket until it is resting on the bearing seat of the sprocket.
   D. Install sprocket to bearing assembly retaining snap-ring into groove sprocket hub.
3. Install two hook-type oil seal rings onto turbine shaft.

Front Unit End-Play Check

1. Install front unit end-play checking tool, (J-22241), into driven sprocket housing so that the urethane on the tool can engage the splines and the forward clutch housing. Let the tool bottom on the main-shaft, then withdraw it approximately $^1/_{16}$-$^1/_8$ in.
2. Remove two of the 5/16—18 bolts from the driven support housing.
3. Install 5/16—18 threaded slide hammer bolt with jam nut into

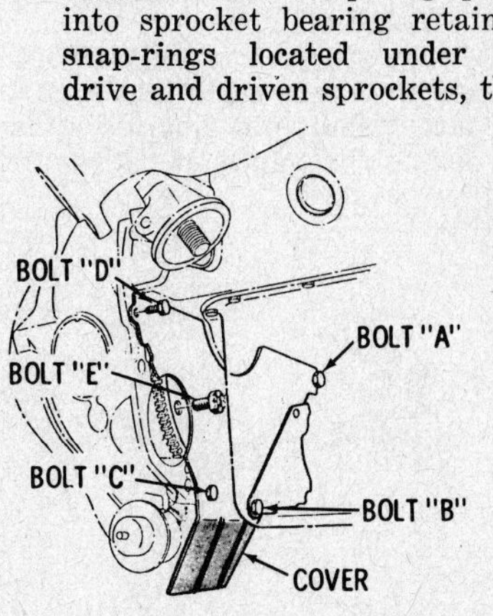
BOLT "D"
BOLT "A"
BOLT "E"
BOLT "C"
BOLT "B"
COVER

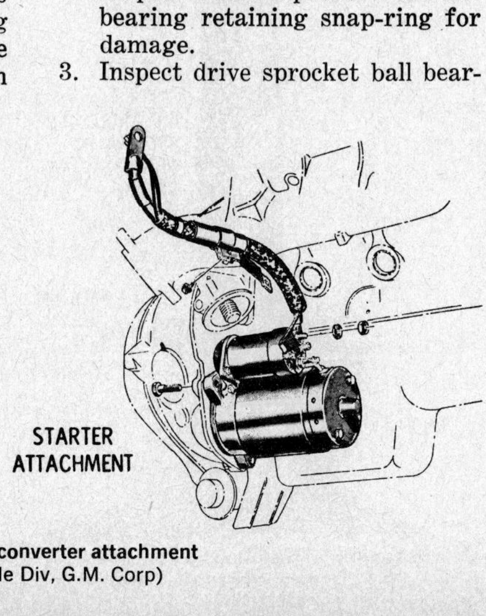
STARTER
ATTACHMENT

Transmission to converter attachment
(© Oldsmobile Div, G.M. Corp)

REMOVE BOLT
END PLAY CHECKING TOOL J-22241
BOLT REMOVED
HOLD REAR UNIT UP
END PLAY .003" TO .024"

Checking front unit end-play
(© Oldsmobile Div, G.M. Corp)

one bolt hole in driven support housing.

NOTE: Do not thread slide hammer bolt deep enough to interfere with forward clutch travel.

4. Mount dial indicator on rod and index indicator to register with the forward clutch drum which can be reached through second bolt removed from driven support housing.
5. Push end-play tool down to remove slack.
6. Push and hold output flange outward. Place a screwdriver in case opening at parking pawl area and push upward on output carrier.

THICKNESS	COLOR
.060 - .064	Yellow
.071 - .075	Blue
.082 - .086	Red
.093 - .097	Brown
.104 - .108	Green
.115 - .119	Black
.126 - .130	Purple

Front unit end-play selective washer thickness

7. Place another screwdriver between the metal lip of the end-play tool and the drive sprocket housing. Now, push upward on the metal lip of the end-play tool and read the resulting end-play. This should be .003-.024 in. The selective washer controlling this end-play is the phenolic thrust washer located between the driven support housing and the forward clutch housing. If more or less washer thickness is required to bring the end-play within specifications, select the proper washer from the chart.

Differential

Planetary-Type

1967

This type differential replaces the conventional spider and beveled axle drive pinions with a planetary gear set to distribute torque to the respective drive axles.

Engine torque is transmitted from the power train, to the main drive pinion and ring gear, to the differential housing. Torque is then applied through the planetary and sun gear mechanism to both drive axles at variable speed requirements.

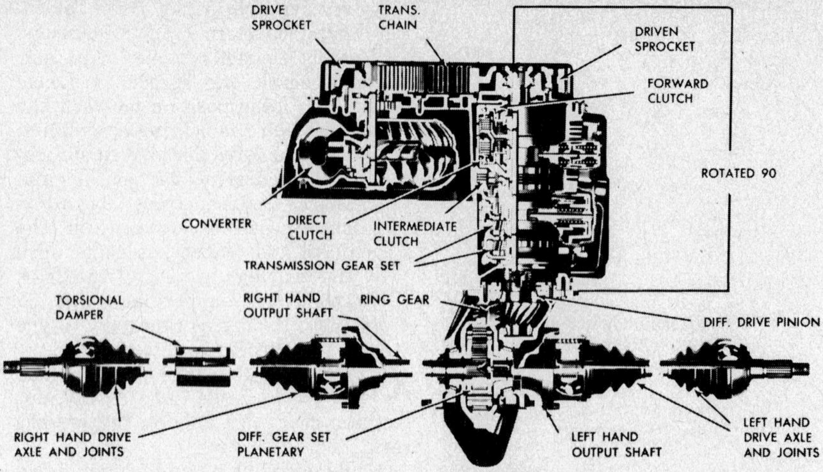

DRIVE SPROCKET
TRANS. CHAIN
DRIVEN SPROCKET
FORWARD CLUTCH
ROTATED 90
CONVERTER
DIRECT CLUTCH
INTERMEDIATE CLUTCH
TRANSMISSION GEAR SET
TORSIONAL DAMPER
RIGHT HAND OUTPUT SHAFT
RING GEAR
DIFF. DRIVE PINION
RIGHT HAND DRIVE AXLE AND JOINTS
DIFF. GEAR SET PLANETARY
LEFT HAND OUTPUT SHAFT
LEFT HAND DRIVE AXLE AND JOINTS

Power train cross-section—1967
(© Oldsmobile Div, G.M. Corp)

While the car is moving straight ahead, the planetary gears are fixed and rotate with the differential case and ring gear, as a unit. However, when turning, the planetary gears revolve upon their individual axes with differential action, allowing the drive axles to rotate at different speeds.

This unit is not a controlled or limited slip differential.

Bevel Gear-Type

1968-74

Since 1968, a bevel gear-type differential is used on all front-wheel drive models. This design supersedes the original planetary gear-type final drive. While unit removal and installation procedures are typical, the assembly is not interchangeable with the 1967 design.

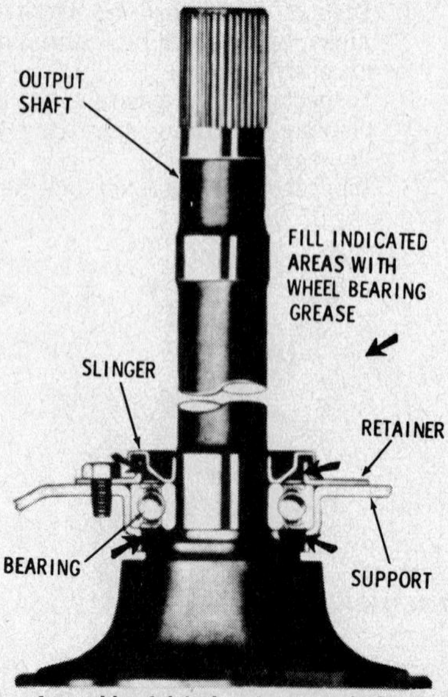

OUTPUT SHAFT
FILL INDICATED AREAS WITH WHEEL BEARING GREASE
SLINGER
RETAINER
BEARING
SUPPORT

Assembly of right-hand output shaft
(© Oldsmobile Div, G.M. Corp)

Overhauling the differential assembly is not encouraged. However, reconditioning procedures are given in later paragraphs of this final drive coverage. Differences in procedure will be clearly indicated.

Output Shafts, Bearings and Seals

Right Side Removal

1. Disconnect battery.
2. Hoist car.
3. Remove engine oil filter.
4. Disconnect right-hand drive axle.
5. Disconnect support from engine and brace.
6. Remove output shaft assembly.
7. If seal is to be removed, install seal remover J-943 into seal and drive seal out with a hammer.
8. If output shaft bearing is to be removed, use a press.

Right Side Installation

1. If output bearing was removed, assemble parts as illustrated.
2. Position assembly in a press and install bearing until seated.
3. Pack area between bearing and retainer with wheel bearing grease, then install slinger.
4. If seal was removed, it can now be installed.
5. Apply special seal lubricant to output shaft seal, then install output shaft into final drive, indexing the splines of both units.

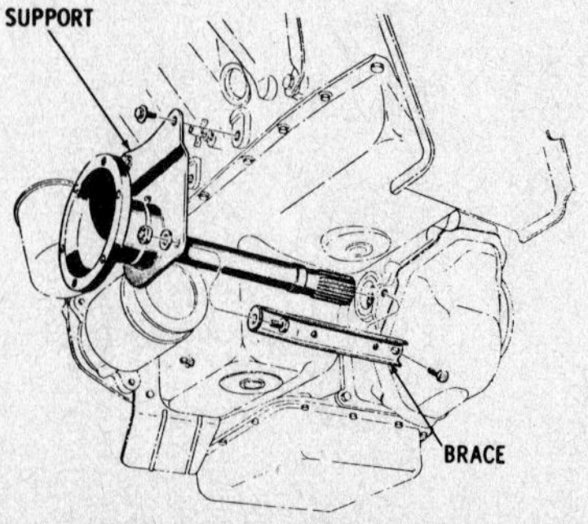

SUPPORT
BRACE

Right-hand output shaft
(© Oldsmobile Div, G.M. Corp)

6. Install support to engine and brace bolts.
7. Connect drive axle to output shaft.
8. Install engine oil filter.
9. Connect battery, check engine oil level and check for oil leaks.

Left Side Removal

The left-hand output shaft can normally be removed only after removing the final drive assembly from the car. However, if the left-hand axle assembly has been removed for any reason, the output shaft and seal can be removed as follows:

1. Remove left hand drive axle assembly, as described above.
2. Using a 9/16 in. socket, remove left-hand output shaft retaining bolt and left-hand shaft.
3. Install left-hand output shaft tool J-943 into seal and drive out with a hammer.

Left Side Installation

1. If seal was removed, install new seal.
2. Apply special seal lubricant to seal, then insert output shaft into final drive assembly, indexing splines of output shaft with splines of final drive.
3. Install left-hand output shaft retaining bolt and torque to 45 ft. lbs.
4. Install left-hand axle as described above.

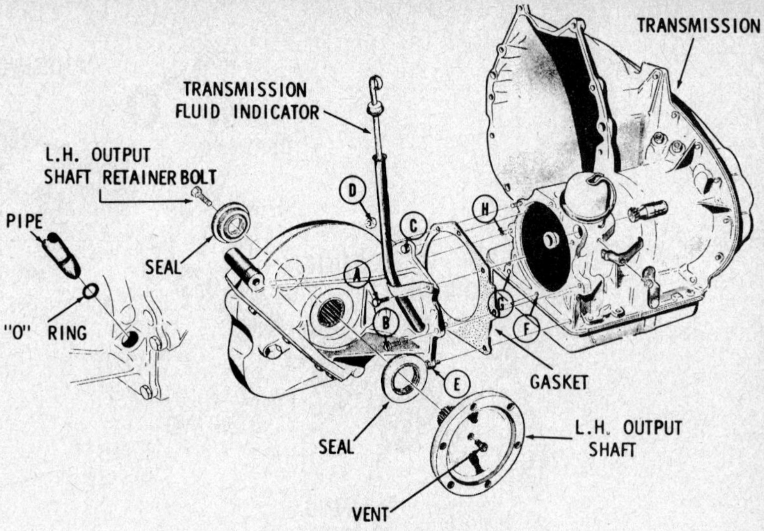
TRANSMISSION
TRANSMISSION FLUID INDICATOR
L.H. OUTPUT SHAFT RETAINER BOLT
PIPE
SEAL
"O" RING
D
C
H
A
B
G
F
E
GASKET
SEAL
L.H. OUTPUT SHAFT
VENT
Transmission attachment bolts
(© Oldsmobile Div, G.M. Corp)

Final Drive

Removal

1. Disconnect battery.
2. See illustration. Remove bolts A, B, and C. Nut D must be removed with a special wrench, such as MAC S-147.

NOTE: it may be necessary to remove the transmission filler tube to gain clearance.

3. Hoist the car. If a two post hoist is used, the car must be supported with floor stands at the front frame rails and the front post lowered.
4. Disconnect right and left drive axles from the output shafts.
5. Remove engine oil filter.
6. Disconnect brace from final drive, then disconnect right-hand output shaft assembly from engine.
7. Remove output shaft assembly from final drive.
8. See illustration. Remove bolt X and loosen bolts Y and Z.
9. Remove final drive cover and allow lubricant to drain.
10. Position transmission lift with adapter for final drive. Install an anchor bolt through final drive housing and lift pad.
11. See illustration. Remove bolts E, F, and G, and nut from H.
12. Move transmission lift toward front of car to disengage final drive splines from transmission.
13. Lower transmission lift and remove final drive from lift.
14. Using a 9/16 in. socket, remove the left output shaft retainer bolt, then pull output shaft from final drive.
15. Remove transmission to final drive gasket.

Installation

1. Apply special seal lubricant to both output shaft seals.
2. Install the left output shaft into the final drive. Retain with bolt and torque to 45 ft. lbs.
3. Position final drive on transmission lift and install an anchor bolt through the housing and lift pad.
4. Apply a thin film of special seal lubricant on the transmission side of the new final drive to transmission gasket. Then position gasket on the transmission.
5. Raise the transmission lift. Align the two bolt studs D and H on the transmission with their mating holes in the final drive. Move final drive until it mates with the transmission.

Caution It may be necessary to rotate the left output shaft to align the splines on the final drive with the splines of the transmission output shaft.

6. Install bolts E, F, and G and nut H finger tight.
7. Install bolt X and torque to 75 ft. lbs. Tighten and torque bolts Y and Z to 50 ft. lbs.
8. Loosen and remove lift from final drive.
9. Position a new cover gasket on the final drive, then install cover. Torque cover bolts to 30 ft. lbs.
10. Install right output shaft into final drive, indexing splines of output shaft with splines of final drive. Install mounting bracket and brace bolts and tighten.
11. Connect drive axles to output shafts.

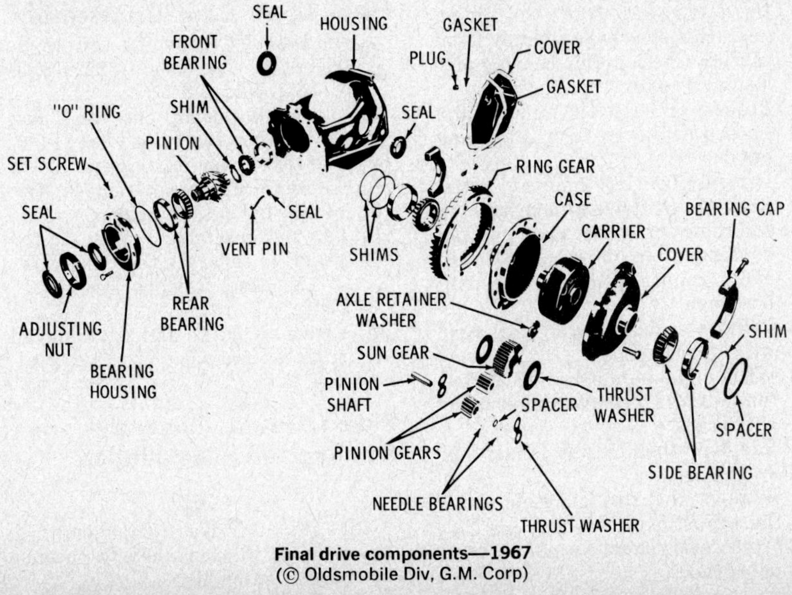
SEAL
HOUSING
GASKET
FRONT BEARING
PLUG
COVER
GASKET
"O" RING
SHIM
SEAL
PINION
SET SCREW
RING GEAR
SEAL
SEAL
CASE
BEARING CAP
VENT PIN
SHIMS
CARRIER
COVER
REAR BEARING
ADJUSTING NUT
AXLE RETAINER WASHER
SHIM
BEARING HOUSING
SUN GEAR
PINION SHAFT
THRUST WASHER
SPACER
SPACER
PINION GEARS
SIDE BEARING
NEEDLE BEARINGS
THRUST WASHER
Final drive components—1967
(© Oldsmobile Div, G.M. Corp)

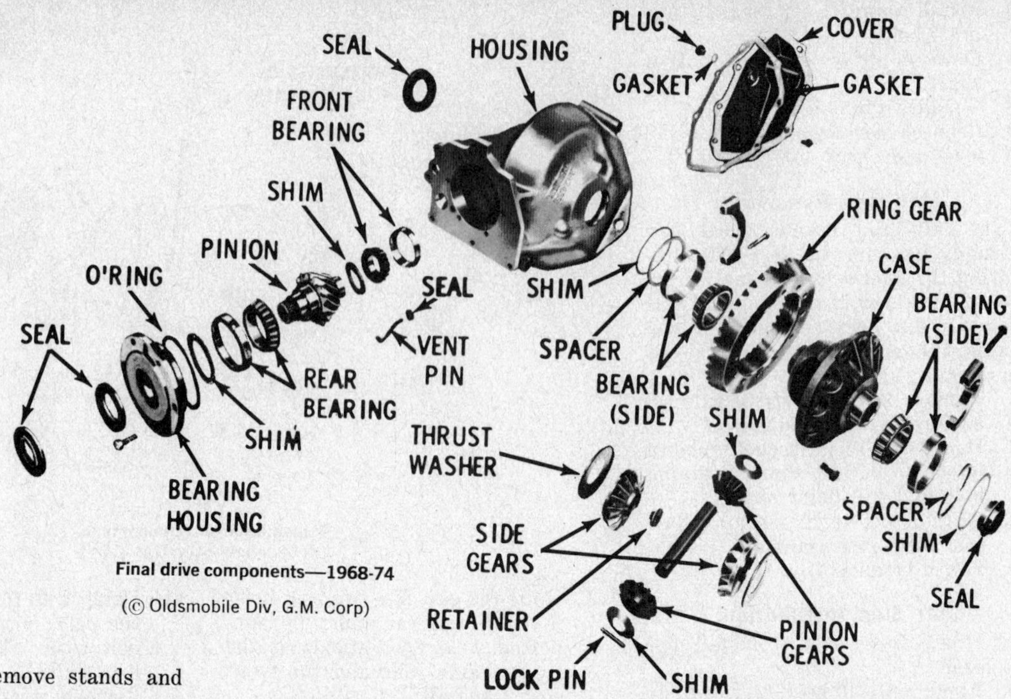
PLUG
COVER
SEAL
HOUSING
GASKET
GASKET
FRONT BEARING
SHIM
RING GEAR
PINION
CASE
O'RING
SEAL
SHIM
BEARING (SIDE)
SEAL
VENT PIN
SPACER
REAR BEARING
BEARING (SIDE)
SHIM
SHIM
THRUST WASHER
BEARING HOUSING
SIDE GEARS
SPACER
SHIM
RETAINER
SEAL
PINION GEARS
LOCK PIN
SHIM

Final drive components—1968-74

(© Oldsmobile Div, G.M. Corp)

12. Install oil filter.
13. Raise hoist, remove stands and lower car.
14. If filler tube was removed, attach a new O-ring and install filler tube.
15. Install bolts A, B, and C and nut D. Torque all final drive to transmission bolts to 25 ft. lbs. Torque nuts to about 25 ft. lbs.
16. Connect battery.
17. Fill final drive with four and one-half pints of lubricant, part No. 1050015.
18. Check engine oil level. Start engine and check transmission fluid level.
19. Check for any oil leaks.

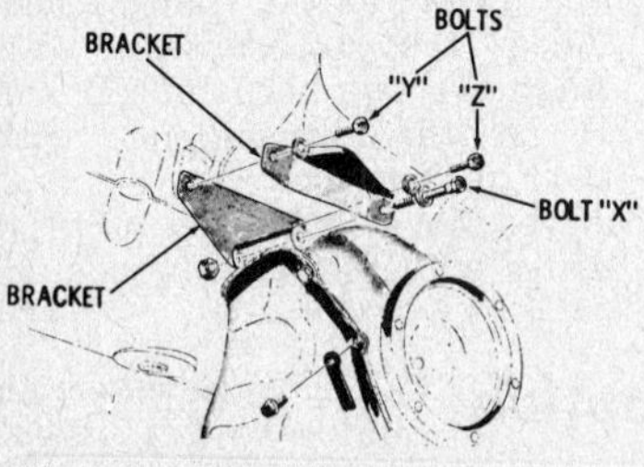
BRACKET
BOLTS
"Y"
"Z"
BOLT "X"
BRACKET

Disconnecting final drive from engine
(© Oldsmobile Div, G.M. Corp)

Drive Unit Disassembly

Adequate facilities are a must for this service.

1. If available, install adapter J-22296-1 onto differential holding fixture J-3289. Differential holding fixture must be modified to obtain clearance between fixture and final drive housing. Mount final drive in holding fixture.
2. Use a drain pan under the assembly. Remove the drain plug. Then, remove the cover attaching screws and cover.
3. Rotate final drive until pinion points down, then check ring gear to pinion backlash with a dial indicator. Record backlash for reassembly. Check pinion and side bearing pre-load with tools, J-22208-1 and J-22208-2, with the help of a torque wrench. Record pre-load reading.
4. Remove side bearing caps.

NOTE: Side bearing caps are of different size and can only be installed in one position.

5. Install spreader J-22196 onto final drive, indexing the two guides on the spreader with the two holes on the carrier.
6. Turn the spreader screw to expand the spreader until the spacer and shims can be removed from between the small side of the bearing and the carrier.
7. Remove spreader from the carrier.
8. Remove the spacer and shims, then slide the case assembly to the left, away from the pinion gear. Remove case assembly from carrier. Check pinion bearing preload and record the reading.
9. Rotate carrier so the pinion is up.
10. Loosen set screw from adjusting nut.
11. Remove bearing housing bolts. Remove the drive pinion housing and remove the adjusting nut and housing from drive pinion. Remove rubber seal from bearing housing.
12. Remove rubber seal and vent wire from carrier.
13. With slide hammer J-2619 and tool J-22201, remove pinion front outer race.
14. Remove the output shaft oil seals.
15. Remove the two oil seals from the adjustment nut.
16. If necessary, remove pinion rear outer race.

Pinion Bearing Removal

1. Remove the pinion front bearing and selective shim. Bearing can be removed with a press.
2. Remove the pinion rear bearing.

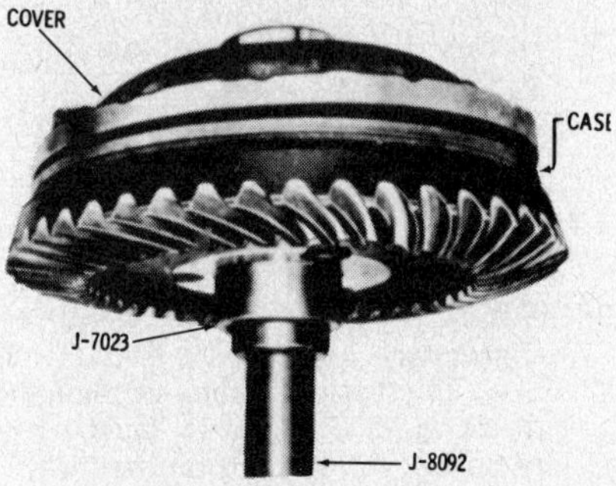
COVER
CASE
J-7023
J-8092

Separating case halves
(© Oldsmobile Div, G.M. Corp)

Final Drive Case Disassembly

1. If the side bearings are to be removed, use tools J-22229-1, J-8433-1, and J-8416-1.
2. Mark ring gear, case and case cover, then remove all but two of the case cover to ring gear bolts. Loosen, but do not remove, two of the bolts 180° apart.
3. Jar the assembly lightly on the bench to separate the two halves of the case. Remove pinion carrier.
4. Clean all parts and examine all surfaces for wear or other damage.

Pinion Gears, Planetary-Type Removal and Installation

1967

(See Final Drive Components)

1. Support the planetary pinion carrier assembly.

2. Press or drive the pinion pins out of the carrier.
3. Remove the pinion thrust washers, spacer, needle bearings, sun gear and thrust washers.

NOTE: The sun gear can be removed from only one opening of the carrier. This opening can be identified by the thinner wall at the carrier opening.

4. After removing the sun gear, the left axle retainer washer can be removed from the carrier.
5. Install by installing loading tool J-22210 into planet pinion. Position a spacer washer over the loading tool, then install 24 needle bearings on each side of the spacer washer.
6. If the axle retainer washer was removed, install it at this time.
7. Position a thrust washer on each side of the sun gear, then insert the sun gear into carrier through large opening.
8. Position a thrust washer on each side of the planet pinion, then insert planet pinion into carrier.
9. Using a deep socket as a receiver, press pinion pin into carrier, until it bottoms.
10. Place a large punch in a vise, to be used as an anvil, and stake the opposite end of the pinion pin in three places.

Pinion Gears, Bevel-Type Removal and Installation

1. After ring gear has been removed, drive lock pin from pinion shaft.
2. Push pinion shaft out of case.
3. Rotate one pinion gear and shim toward access hole in case, then remove.

NOTE: Keep corresponding shims and pinion gear together for correct assembly.

4. Remove the other pinion and shim.
5. Remove side gears and thrust washers, keeping gears and washers in proper relationship for correct installation.

NOTE: The left-side gear has the threaded retainer that secures the (short) left output shaft. If threaded retainer is to be removed, use a brass drift to prevent trouble.

6. Upon assembling pinion and side gears into the case, lubricate components with a quality extreme pressure lubricant.
7. Place side gear thrust washers over the side gear hubs and install side gears into case. Gear with threaded retainer belongs in left side of case.
8. Position one pinion (without shims) between side gears, then rotate gears until pinion is directly opposite from loading opening in case. Place other pinion between side gears so that the pinion shaft holes are in line; then rotate gears to make sure holes in pinions line up with holes in case.
9. If holes line up, rotate pinions back to loading opening just enough to permit insertion of the pinion gear shims.
10. Install pinion shaft. Drive pinion shaft retaining lock pin into position.

Checking Pinion Depth

1. Install pinion front outer race. Drive race in until it bottoms.
2. Lubricate front bearing with final drive lubricant and install into front outer race.

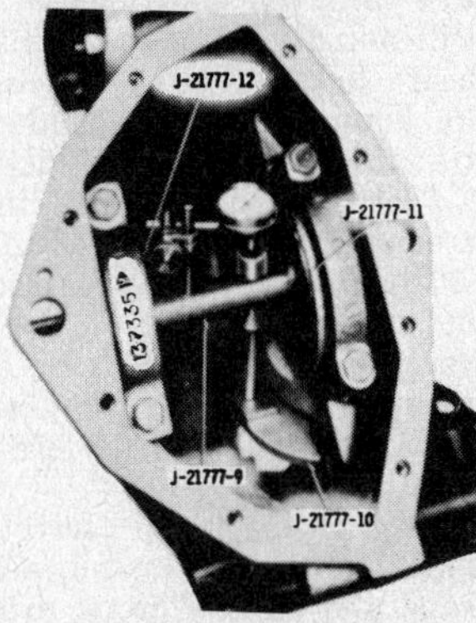
J-21777-12
J-21777-11
J-21777-9
J-21777-10

Checking pinion depth
(© Oldsmobile Div, G.M. Corp)

3. Position tool J-21777-10 on the front bearing. Install tool J-21579 onto final drive housing and retain with two bolts. Thread screw J-21777-13 into J-21579 until tip of screw engages tool J-21777-10. Torque tool J-21777-13 to 20 in. lbs. to pre-load the bearing.
4. Remove dial indicator post from tool J-21777-9 and install discs J-21777-11 and J-21777-12. Reinstall dial indicator post.
5. Place the gauging discs in the side bearing bores and install the side bearing caps.
6. Position the dial indicator on the mounting post of the gauge shaft with the contact button touching the indicator pad. Set dial indicator to zero, then depress the dial indicator until the needle rotates three-quarters of a turn clockwise. Tighten dial indicator.
7. Position the gauge shaft assembly in the carrier so that the dial indicator contact rod is directly over the gauging area of the gauge block, and the discs are seated fully in the side bearing bores.
8. Position gauge shaft so that the indicator rod contacts the gauging area. Rotate gauge rod back and forth until the indicator reads the greatest deflection. At the point of greatest deflection, set the indicator to zero. Repeat the rocking action to verify the zero setting.
9. After zero setting is obtained, rotate gauge shaft until the indicator rod does not touch the gauging area. Read the pinion depth directly from the dial indicator.
10. Select the correct pinion shim to be used during assembly on the following basis:
    A. If a service pinion is being used, or a production pinion with no marking, the correct shim will have a thickness equal to the indicator gauge reading found in Step 9.
    B. If a production pinion is being used and it is marked + or —, the correct shim will be determined as follows:
    If the pinion is marked +, the shim thickness indicated by the dial indicator on the pinion setting gauge must be increased by the amount etched on the pinion. If the pinion is marked —, the shim thickness indicated on the dial must be decreased by the amount etched on the pinion.
11. Remove pinion depth checking tools and front bearing from carrier.

Final Drive Case Assembly

1. Install the pinion carrier into the case.
2. With the case and cover alignment marks indexed, insert four ring gear attaching bolts through case and cover. Align mark on ring gear with alignment marks on case and cover, then install ring gear onto case. Tighten the six attaching bolts alternately. Torque bolts to 85 ft. lbs.
3. If side bearings were removed, they can be installed now. Drive bearing on until it bottoms.
4. Install pinion rear bearing.
5. Position correct shim on drive pinion and install the drive pinion front bearing with tool J-21022 and a press.
6. Lubricate pinion bearings and install pinion into carrier.
7. Install seals into adjusting nut.
8. Install O-ring and vent pin onto face of carrier. Torque attaching nuts to 35 ft. lbs.
9. Install seal protector J-22236 over drive pinion, then install the adjusting nut over the seal protector and thread into the housing.
10. Assemble tools, as illustrated, and adjust pinion bearing preload. The preload is 2-10 in. lbs. for new bearings, and 2-3 in. lbs. for used bearings. Adjust new bearing preload to 4 in. lbs. while rotating the pinion and checking preload. Adjust until preload remains constant. When correct preload is obtained, tighten the set screw. Record preload reading as it will be used when mak-

ing side bearing preload adjustment. Leave the tools on pinion for side bearing preload adjustment.

Side Bearing Preload Adjustment

Differential side bearing preload is adjusted by means of shims located between the side bearings and the carrier. One spacer is used on the right side only. Shims are used on both sides and come in thickness increments of .002 in. from .036 to .070 in. By changing the thickness of both side shims equally, ring gear and pinion backlash will not change.

1. Lubricate the side bearings with final drive lubricant.
2. Place differential in position in the carrier.
3. If the original ring gear and pinion are being used, subtract the reading obtained in Step 8 from the reading obtained in Step 3 of the Final Drive Disassembly procedure. This determines the original side bearing preload and will aid in determining whether thicker or thinner shims are needed to bring the side bearing preload to specifications.
4. Install original shim onto left side and spacer onto the right side.
5. Install the carrier spreader and apply just enough tension to allow the shim to be installed between the spacer and the carrier.
6. Release tension on the spreader, install side bearing caps, then check preload. Preload should be 15-20 in. lbs. for new bearings and 5-7 in. lbs. for old bearings over the pinion bearing preload obtained in Step 11, Final Drive Case Assembly.
7. If pre-load is not within specifications, select thicker or thinner shims to bring preload within limits.

Backlash Adjustment

1. Rotate differential case a few times to seat bearings, then mount dial indicator in order to read movement at the outer edge of one of the ring gear teeth.

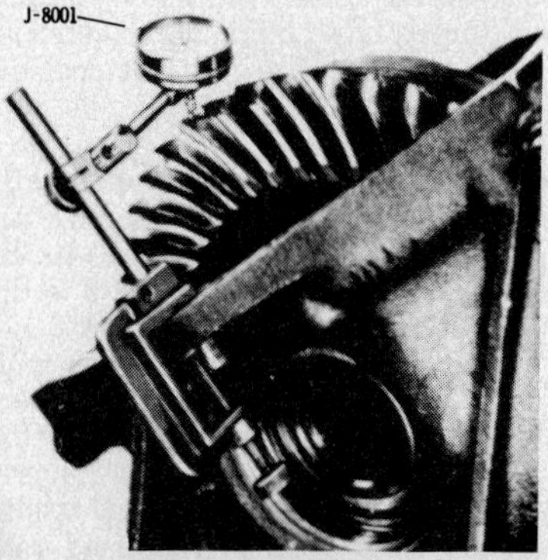
J-8001

Checking backlash
(© Oldsmobile Div, G.M. Corp)

2. Check backlash at three points around the ring gear. Lash must not vary more than .002 in.
3. Backlash at the minimum point should be .006-.008 in. for all new gears. If original ring gear and pinion were installed, backlash should be set at the same reading obtained in Step 3 of Final Drive Disassembly procedure, if reading was within specifications.
4. If backlash was not within limits, correct by increasing thickness of one differential shim and decreasing thickness of other side shim the same amount. This will not disturb differential side bearing preload. For each .001 in. change in backlash desired, transfer .002 in. shim thickness. To decrease backlash .001 in., decrease thickness of right shim .002 in. and increase thickness of left shim .002 in. To increase backlash .002 in. increase thickness of right shim .004 in. and decrease thickness of left shim .004 in.
5. When backlash is correct, remove spreader. Install bearing caps and bolts. Torque to 65 ft. lbs.
6. Install new output shaft seals.
7. Install new gasket onto housing. Install cover, torque cover attaching bolts to 30 ft. lbs. Fill final drive to correct level.

DRIVE AXLES

Drive axles are a complete flexible assembly and consist of an axle shaft with an inner and outer constant velocity joints. Right axle shaft has a torsional damper mounted in the center. The inner constant velocity joint has complete flexibility, plus inward and outward movement. The outer constant velocity joint has complete flexibility but doesn't allow for inward and outward movement.

Beginning in 1967, Tri-pot inboard drive joints replace the ball spline Rzeppa joints of earlier production. These joints consist of a three-pronged trunnion spider, needle bearing mounted balls, a universal housing, axle shaft, and rubber boot. This joint combines constant velocity universal action with axial slip motion.

Drive Axle Removal —Right Side

1. Hoist car under lower control arms.
2. Remove drive axle cotter pin, nut and washer.
3. Remove oil filter.
4. Remove inner constant velocity joint attaching bolts.
5. Push inner constant velocity joint outward enough to disengage the right-hand final drive output shaft, then move rearward.
6. Remove right-hand output shaft bracket bolts to engine and final drive.
7. Remove right-hand output shaft and drive axle assembly.

Caution Care must be exercised so that constant velocity joints do not turn to full extremes, and that seals are not damaged against shock absorber or stabilizer bar.

Drive Axle Installation —Right Side

1. Carefully place righthand drive axle assembly into lower control arm and enter outer race splines into knuckle.
2. Lubricate final drive output shaft seal, with special seal lubricant part No. 1050169.
3. Install right-hand output shaft into final drive and attach the support bolts to engine and brakes. Torque the bolts to 50 ft. lbs.
4. Move right-hand drive axle assembly toward front of car and align with right-hand output shaft. Install attaching bolts and torque to 65 ft. lbs.
5. Install oil filter.
6. Install washer and nut on drive axle. Torque to 150 ft. lbs. on 1967-74 models, then insert cotter pin.
7. Remove floor stands and lower hoist.
8. Check engine oil. Add if necessary.

Drive Axle Removal —Left Side

1. Hoist car under lower control arms.
2. Remove wheel and, if equipped with drum brakes, remove drum.

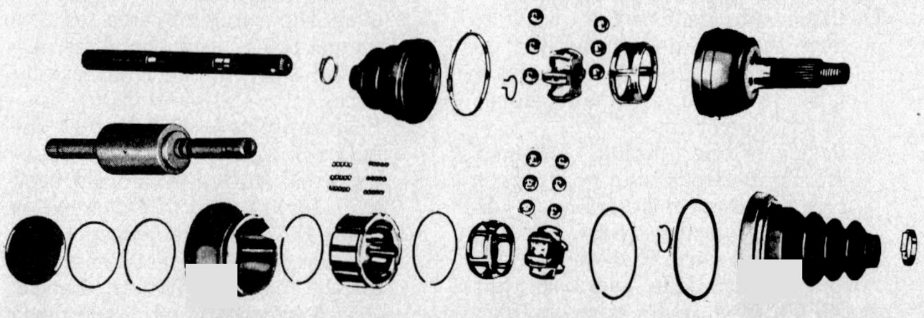

Drive axle assembly

If equipped with disc brakes, remove disc.
3. Remove drive axle cotter pin, nut and washer.
4. On 1967-69 models only, position access slot in hub assembly so that each of the attaching bolts can be removed. It will be necessary to push aside adjuster lever to remove one of the bolts.
5. On 1967-69 models only, install a slide hammer with adapter on the hub.

joint from knuckle. Care must be exercised so that ball joint does not damage drive axle seal.
13. Remove knuckle and support, so that brake hose is not damaged.
14. Carefully guide drive axle assembly outboard.

NOTE: Care must be exercised so that constant velocity joints do not turn to full extremes and that seals are not damaged against shock absorber or stabilizer bar.

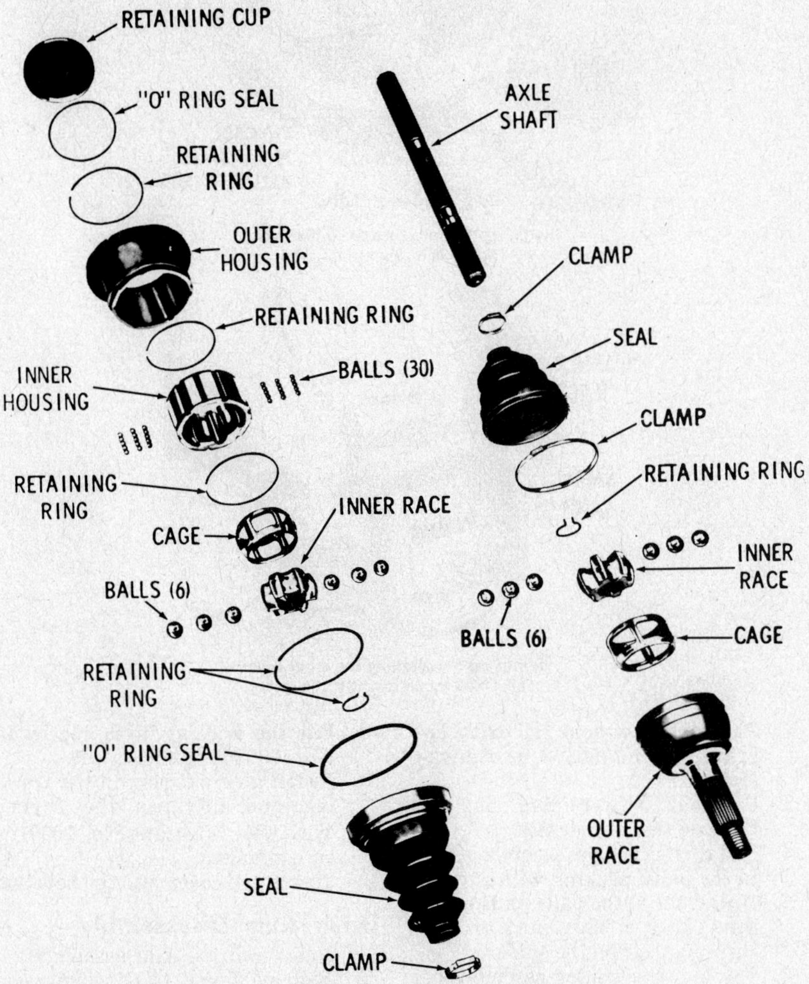
RETAINING CUP
"O" RING SEAL
RETAINING RING
OUTER HOUSING
RETAINING RING
BALLS (30)
INNER HOUSING
RETAINING RING
CAGE
INNER RACE
BALLS (6)
RETAINING RING
"O" RING SEAL
SEAL
CLAMP
AXLE SHAFT
CLAMP
SEAL
CLAMP
RETAINING RING
INNER RACE
BALLS (6)
CAGE
OUTER RACE

Left-hand drive axle assembly
(© Oldsmobile Div, G.M. Corp)

6. On 1967-69 models only, remove hub assembly. It will again be necessary to push aside adjuster lever for clearance for hub assembly.
7. Remove tie-rod end cotter pin and nut.
8. Remove the tie-rod end from the knuckle with a puller.
9. Remove bolts from drive axle assembly and left output shaft. Insert a spacer between the axle shaft and lower control arm.
10. Remove upper control arm ball joint cotter pin and nut.
11. Using hammer and brass drift, drive on knuckle until upper ball joint stud is free.
12. Using puller, remove lower ball

Drive Axle Installation —Left Side

1. Carefully guide left-hand drive axle assembly onto lower control arm and into position on spacer.
2. Insert lower control ball joint stud into knuckle and attach nut. Do not torque.
3. Center left-hand drive axle assembly in opening of knuckle and insert upper ball joint stud.
4. Place brake hose clip over upper ball joint stud and install nut. Do not torque.
5. Insert tie-rod end stud into knuckle and attach nut. Torque to 45 ft. lbs. on 1967-69 models and 35 ft lbs. on 1970-74 models. Install cotter pin and crimp.
6. On 1967-69 models, lubricate hub assembly bearing O.D. with E.P. grease and install. Torque to 65 ft. lbs.
7. Align inner constant velocity joint with output shaft and install attaching bolts. Torque to 65 ft. lbs.
8. Torque upper and lower ball joint stud nuts to 40 ft. lbs. Install cotter pins and crimp.

NOTE: Upper ball joint cotter pin must be crimped toward upper control arm to prevent interference with outer constant velocity joint seal.

9. Install drive axle washer and nut. Torque to 60 ft. lbs. on 1967-69 models and 150 ft. lbs. on 1970-74 models. Install cotter pin and crimp.
10. Install drum, if applicable, and wheel.
11. Remove floor stands and lower hoist.
12. Check camber, caster and toe-in and adjust if necessary. Refer to Front End Alignment.

Constant Velocity Joint (Out of Car)

The constant velocity joints are to be replaced as a unit and are only disassembled for repacking and replacement of seals.

Outer C. V. Joint Disassembly

1. Insert axle assembly into vise. Hold by the mid-portion of the axle shaft.
2. Remove inner and outer seal clamps.
3. Slide seal down axle shaft to gain access to C. V. joint.
4. Using snap-ring pliers, spread retaining ring until C. V. joint can be removed from axle spline.
5. Remove retaining ring.
6. Slide seal from axle shaft.
7. Remove grease from constant velocity joint.
8. Holding constant velocity joint with one hand, tilt cage and inner race so that one ball can be removed. Continue until all six balls are removed.
9. Turn cage 90° and, with large slot in cage aligned with land in inner race, lift out.
10. With cage and inner race assembly, turn inner race 90° in line with large hole in cage. Lift land on inner race up through large hole in cage and turn up and out to separate parts.

Outer C. V. Joint Assembly

1. Insert land of inner race into large hole in cage and pivot to install into cage.
2. Align inner race and pivot inner race 90° to align in outer race.
3. Insert balls into outer race one at a time until all six balls are installed. Inner race and cage will have to be tilted so that each ball can be inserted.

4. Pack constant velocity joint full of lubricant, part No. 1050530.
5. Pack inside of seal with the same lubricant, until folds of seal are full.
6. Place small keystone clamp on axle shaft.
7. Install seal onto axle shaft.
8. Install retaining ring into inner race.
9. Insert axle shaft into splines of outer constant velocity joint until retaining ring secures shaft.
10. Position seal in slot of outer race.
11. Install large keystone clamp over seal and secure.

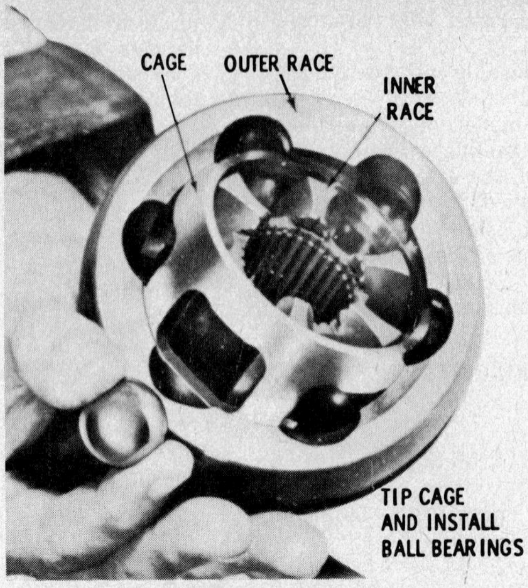
CAGE
OUTER RACE
INNER RACE
TIP CAGE AND INSTALL BALL BEARINGS

Installing the balls into the outer race
(© Oldsmobile Div, G.M. Corp)

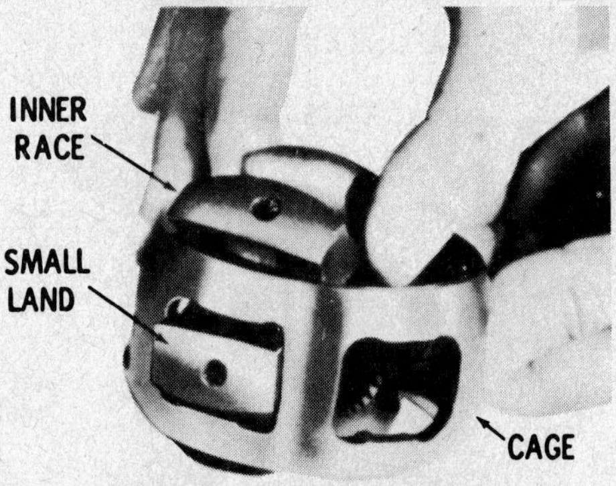
INNER RACE
SMALL LAND
CAGE

Removing or installing the inner race
(© Oldsmobile Div, G.M. Corp)

1967-74 Inner C. V. Joint Disassembly

1. Place axle in a vise, clamping on the mid-portion of the axle shaft.
2. Remove the small seal clamp.
3. Remove the large end of the seal from C. V. joint with a hammer and chisel.
4. Carefully slide the seal down the axle shaft.
5. Carefully lift the housing assembly from the spider assembly and remove the O-ring from the housing outer surface. Use a rubber band to hold the three balls on the spider.

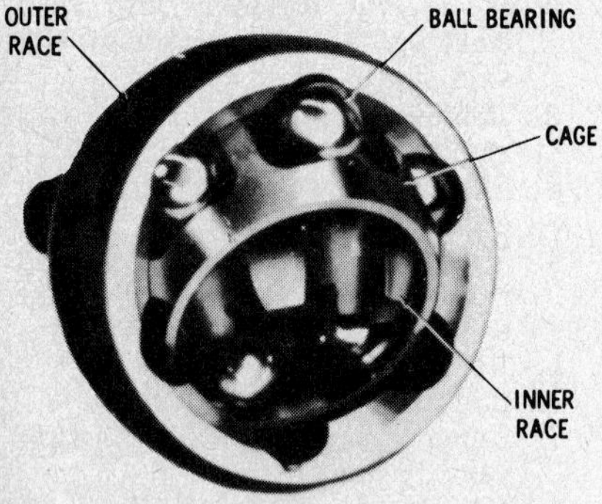
OUTER RACE
BALL BEARING
CAGE
INNER RACE

Removing the balls from the outer race
(© Oldsmobile Div, G.M. Corp)

6. Remove the retaining ring from the end of the axle shaft.
7. Slide the spider assembly from the shaft.
8. Remove the inner retaining ring from the axle shaft.
9. Slide the seal off the axle shaft.
10. Remove the cover from the housing, prying with a screwdriver.
11. Remove the O-ring from the housing.
12. Remove the three balls from the spider, being careful not to lose the needle bearings. There are 53 needles per ball.

1967-74 Inner C. V. Joint Assembly

1. Slide a new seal clamp onto the axle shaft, to be installed after the seal is positioned.
2. Pack the new seal full with lubricant No. 1050802 or equivalent.
3. Position the retaining ring on the axle shaft inner slot.
4. Install the needle bearings (53) in the balls, packing with grease.
5. Install the three balls on the spider. Use a rubber band to hold them in place on the spider.
6. Position the spider assembly on the axle shaft and install the retaining ring.
7. Install a new O-ring in the outer groove in the housing.
8. Remove the rubber band from the spider assembly and push the spider assembly into the housing.
9. Lubricate the housing outer groove O-ring with seal lubricant No. 1050169 or equivalent and slide the seal into position, lightly tapping it into place with a soft hammer and staking in six evenly spaced places. Be careful not to cut the O-ring with the metal portion of the seal.
10. Position seal into groove on the axle shaft and install the clamp.
11. Extend the axle shaft until the seal is at maximum length.
12. Fill the housing with lubricant No. 1050802 or equivalent.
13. Install a new O-ring in the housing and lubricate the O-ring with seal lubricant No. 1050169 or equivalent.
14. Install the cover into the housing.

Drive Axle Disassembly

1. Remove drive axle assembly.
2. Remove outer C. V. joint seal clamps.
3. Remove inner C. V. joint seal by prying out peened spots and driving off seal.
4. Slide seals inboard on shaft.

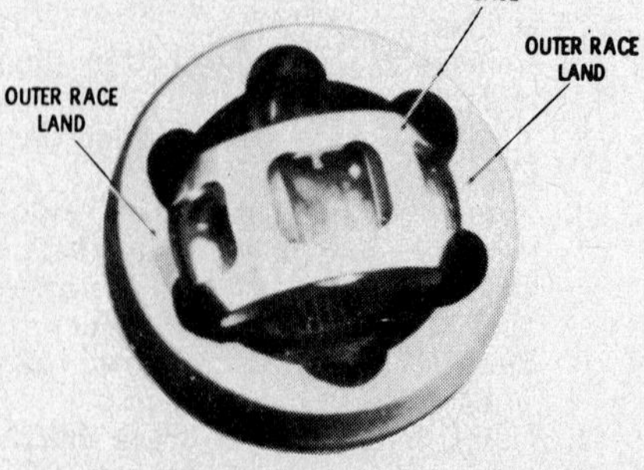
CAGE
OUTER RACE LAND
OUTER RACE LAND

Positioning the cage
(© Oldsmobile Div, G.M. Corp)

5. Using snap-ring pliers, spread retaining rings until both C. V. joints can be removed from axle shaft.
6. Remove seals from axle.

Drive Axle Assembly

1. Pack seals with lubricant, part No. 1050530.
2. Place outer C. V. joint seal on axle, with keystone clamps in position on seal.
3. Insert axle into outer C. V. joint until retaining ring locks axle into position.
4. Position seal and clamps and secure keystone clamps.
5. Place inner C. V. joint seal on axle with keystone clamp in position on seal.
6. Insert axle into inner C. V. joint until retaining ring locks axle into position.
7. Place axle assembly into press. Press seal into position and peen to secure.
8. Secure small keystone clamp with seal in position.
9. Install drive axle assembly.

FRONT SUSPENSION

The front suspension consists of control arms, stabilizer bar, shock absorbers and a right and left torsion bar. Torsion bars are used in place of conventional coil springs. The front end of the torsion bar is attached to the lower control arm. The rear of torsion bar is mounted into an adjustable arm at the torsion bar crossmember. The carrying height of the car is controlled by this adjustment.

Wheel Hub (Front) Removal and Installation

1. Carefully pull drum from hub assembly.
2. Remove drive axle cotter pin, nut and washer. Remove disc, if so equipped.
3. Position access slot in hub assembly so each of the attaching bolts can be removed.
4. Position spacer tool (J-22237) and install front hub puller (J-21579) and slide hammer (J-2619).
5. Remove hub assembly.
6. To install, reverse removal procedure.

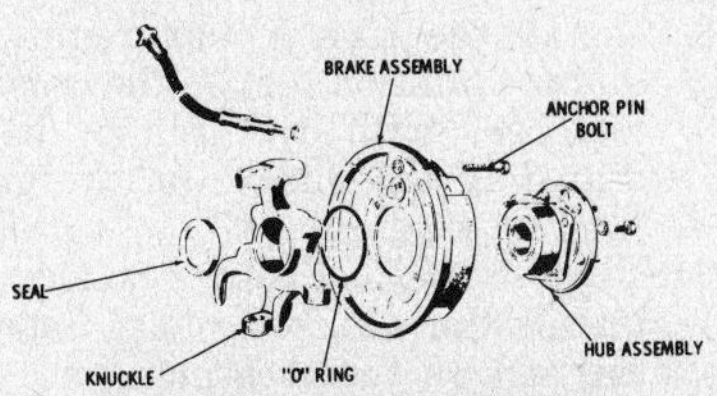
BRAKE ASSEMBLY
ANCHOR PIN BOLT
SEAL
KNUCKLE
"O" RING
HUB ASSEMBLY

Front hub assembly—1967-69
(© Oldsmobile Div, G.M. Corp)

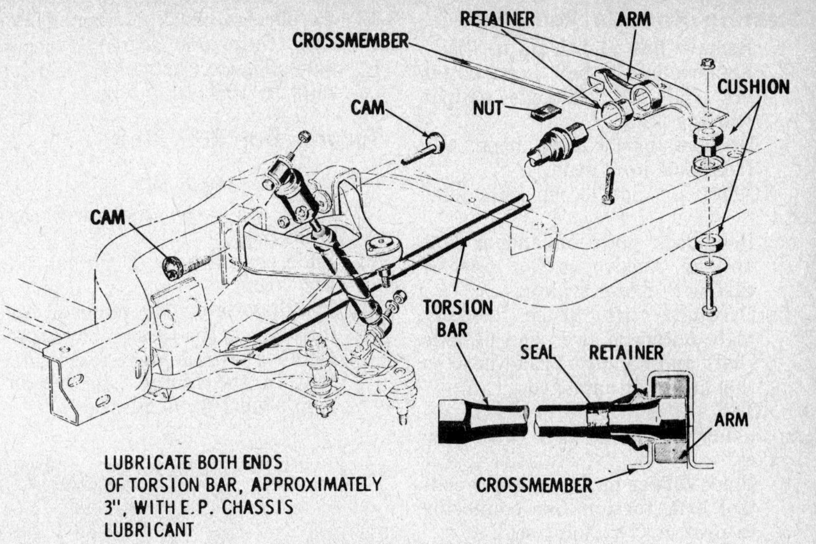
RETAINER
ARM
CROSSMEMBER
CUSHION
CAM
NUT
CAM
TORSION BAR
SEAL
RETAINER
ARM
CROSSMEMBER
LUBRICATE BOTH ENDS
OF TORSION BAR, APPROXIMATELY
3", WITH E.P. CHASSIS
LUBRICANT

Front suspension—1967-74
(© Oldsmobile Div, G.M. Corp)

NOTE: O.D. of bearing must be lubricated with E.P. chassis lubricant. Use care when installing hub assembly over drive axle splines.

Disc R & R

1970-74

1. Siphon off about two-thirds of the fluid in the front reservoir of the master cylinder. Do not empty the reservoir or it will be necessary to bleed the system.
2. Hoist the car and remove the wheel.
3. Position piston compressor tool on the caliper and tighten the screw until the piston bottoms and the shoes are backed off the disc.
4. Remove the two caliper to knuckle attaching bolts and carefully lift the caliper from the disc. Support it so that the hose is not kinked or stretched.
5. Mark the hub and disc so that they will be correctly positioned when installed, then pull evenly on the disc to remove.
6. To install, reverse the above procedure. Make sure that the disc is positioned according to the marks made during removal. Tighten the caliper attaching bolts to 35 ft. lbs. and the wheel nuts to 115 ft. lbs. Fill the front reservoir of the master cylinder and check the action of the brakes.

Steering Knuckle O-Ring Seal

1967-68

Replacement of seal with wheel removed.

1. Remove hub and drum.
2. Remove upper ball joint cotter pin and nut.
3. Remove brake line hose clip from ball joint stud.

NOTE: Do not loosen ball joint stud.

4. Bend lock plate on anchor bolt up and remove anchor bolt.
5. Carefully lift brake backing plate outboard over end of axle shaft and support brake hose so that it is not damaged.
6. Remove O-ring seal.
7. To install, reverse removal procedure.

Knuckle Seals—1969-74

Right-Hand Seal Removal

1. Hoist car under lower control arms.
2. Remove drive axle cotter pin, nut and washer.
3. Remove oil filter element.
4. Remove inner C. V. joint attaching bolts and push joint outward and rearward to disengage from output shaft.
5. Remove output shaft.
6. Remove drive axle assembly.
7. Pry seal from knuckle.

Left-Hand Seal Removal

1. Hoist car under lower control arms.
2. Remove wheel and drum.
3. Remove drive axle cotter pin, nut and washer.
4. Remove tie-rod end cotter pin and nut.
5. Split tie-rod.
6. Place support block between drive axle and lower control arm.
7. Remove upper control arm ball joint cotter pin and nut. Remove brake hose clip from ball joint stud.
8. Using hammer and brass drift, drive on knuckle until ball joint stud is free.
9. Install spacer between lower ball joint seal and knuckle.
10. Remove lower ball joint from knuckle, using a puller.
11. Remove knuckle.
12. Pry seal from knuckle.

Steering Knuckle Removal

1. Remove hub and drum or disc.
2. Remove upper ball joint cotter pin and nut. Remove caliper starting 1969.
3. Remove brake line hose clip from ball joint stud.

NOTE: Do not loosen ball joint stud.

4. Bend lock plate on anchor bolt up and remove anchor bolt of cars with drum brakes.
5. Carefully lift brake backing plate outboard over end of axle shaft and support brake hose so that it is not damaged.

NOTE: It is not necessary to remove dust shield on cars with disc brakes.

6. Place rubber pad over lower control arm torsion bar connector to protect C.V. joint seal.
7. Using a brass drift and hammer loosen upper ball joint stud.
8. Remove cotter pin and nut from tie-rod end.
9. Using brass drift and hammer, remove tie-rod end from knuckle.
10. Remove cotter pin and nut from lower ball joint.
11. Carefully place ball joint puller adapter between ball joint seal and knuckle.
12. Remove lower ball joint from knuckle.
13. Remove knuckle.
14. Knuckle seal can be pried from the knuckle at this time.

Steering Knuckle Installation

1. Using seal installer, install seal into knuckle. Seal should be packed with chassis grease.
2. Install lower ball joint stud into knuckle and attach nut. Do not tighten nut at this time.
3. Install tie-rod and stud into knuckle and attach nut. Do not tighten nut at this time.
4. Install upper ball joint stud into knuckle and attach nut. Do not tighten nut at this time.
5. Install backing plate onto knuckle with anchor bolt and lock plate. Do not tighten nut at this time.
6. Remove upper ball joint attaching nut and install brake line hose clip.
7. Torque ball joint nuts to a minimum of 40 ft. lbs. up to 1969, 85 ft. lbs. starting 1970. Never back off to install cotter pins.

NOTE: Cotter pin on upper ball joint must be bent up, only, to prevent interference with C. V. joint seal.

8. Torque tie-rod end to 30 ft. lbs. and install cotter pin.
9. Torque anchor bolt to 135 ft. lbs. on drum brake models, and bend lock plate onto flat of bolt head.
10. Install drum or disc and wheel; install drive axle nut.
11. Remove floor stand and lower car.
12. Be sure to check camber, caster and toe-in, and adjust if necessary. Tighten drive axle and lug nuts to 105-110 ft. lbs.

Torsion Bar Removal

1967-68

1. Hoist car under the lower control arms.
2. Slide seal at rear of torsion bar forward.
3. Install torsion bar remover and installer on the torsion bar crossmember. Position the tool center bolt in the dimple on the torsion adjusting arm.
4. Turn the torsion adjusting bolt counter-clockwise, counting the number of turns necessary to remove it.
5. Remove the torsion adjusting nut, and turn the center bolt of the removal and installation tool until the torsion bar is completely relaxed.
6. Slide the torsion bar forward until it bottoms in the control arm. The adjusting arm will drop out.
7. Remove the bolt from the crossmember on the side from which you are removing the torsion bar.
8. Raise the crossmember and twist it rearward until the torsion bar is free.
9. Support the frame horns with stands, and lower the hoist until the control arms are hanging freely.
10. Remove the lower control arm rear bushing bolt.
11. Pry the lower control arm downward until the torsion bar can be pulled out.

1969-74

1. Hoist car and support at lift points.
2. Place torsion bar remover and installer so that center screw is seated in dimple of torsion adjusting arm.
3. Remove torsion bar adjusting bolt, counting number of turns necessary.
4. Turn center screw of tool until torsion bar is completely relaxed.
5. Disconnect stabilizer link.
6. Disconnect shock absorber from lower control arm.
7. Remove bolts from lower control arm to frame.
8. Pry lower control arm from frame and move forward until torsion bar and adjusting arm can be removed.

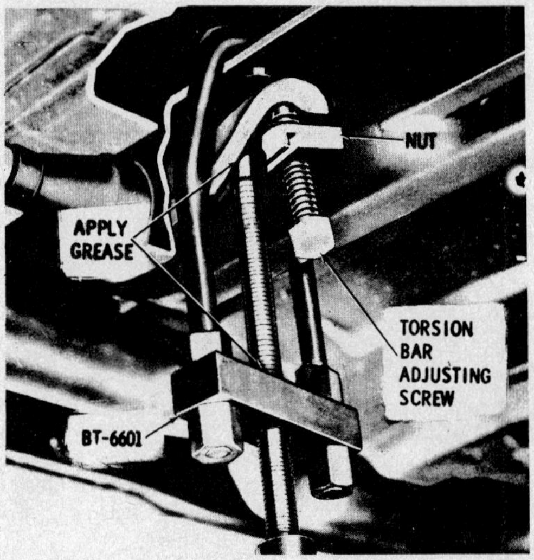
NUT
APPLY GREASE
TORSION BAR ADJUSTING SCREW
BT-6601

Torsion bar removal
(© Oldsmobile Div, G.M. Corp)

Torsion Bar Installation

1967-68

1. Lubricate both ends of the torsion bar (approximately 3 in.) with extreme pressure chassis lubricant.
2. Install the torsion bar in the lower control arm, pushing it forward until it bottoms.
3. Pry the crossmember back, and align the torsion bar with the hole in the crossmember.
4. Position the lower control arm, and install the bolt and nut. Do not torque.
5. Raise the hoist, and remove the frame stands.
6. Install the torsion bar adjusting arm in the crossmember, and pull the torsion bar rearward until fully seated in the arm.
7. Install the crossmember bolt and torque to 40 ft. lbs.
8. Install the torsion bar removal and installation tool on the crossmember, with the center bolt seated in the dimple on the adjusting arm.
9. Tighten the tool center bolt, and install the adjusting nut under the arm in the crossmember.
10. Lubricate the adjusting bolt

threads with extreme pressure chassis lubricant, and install the same number of turns that it was backed out.

11. Lower the car to the ground, and torque the control arm bolt to 80 ft. lbs.

1969-74

1. Lubricate both ends of torsion bar for approximately 3 in. with extreme pressure chassis lubricant.
2. Position adjusting arm into crossmember, insert torson bar into adjusting arm and lower control arm, then position lower control arm into frame brackets and install nuts and bolts loosely.
3. Connect shock to lower control arm, tightening nut to 80 ft. lbs.
4. Connect stabilizer bar to lower control arm. Torque nut to 15 ft. lbs. and cut off bolt ¼ in. below nut.
5. Place torsion bar remover and installer over crossmember and tighten center screw.
6. Raise hoist under lower control arms.
7. Torque lower control arm bushing nuts to 90 ft. lbs.
8. Check ride height and adjust if necessary.

Upper Control Arm Removal

NOTE: The upper control arm is serviced as an assembly, less bushings.

1. Hoist car and remove wheel.
2. Remove upper shock attaching bolt.
3. Remove cotter pin and nut on upper ball joint.
4. Disconnect brake hose clamp from ball joint stud.
5. Separate upper ball joint stud from steering knuckle.
6. Remove upper control arm cam assemblies and remove control arm from car by guiding shock absorber through access hole in arm.

Upper Control Arm Installation

1. Guide upper control arm over shock absorber and install bushing ends into frame horns.
2. Install cam assemblies.

NOTE: Front cam is mounted up, rear cam is mounted down.

3. Install ball joint stud into knuckle.
4. Install brake hose clip onto ball joint stud.
5. Install ball joint nut. Torque to 50 ft. lbs. and insert cotter pin, crimp.

NOTE: Cotter pin must be crimped toward upper control arm to prevent interference with outer C. V. joint seal.

6. Install upper shock, attaching bolt and nut. Torque to 75 ft. lbs, 90 ft. lbs for 1972-74 models.
7. Install wheel.
8. Lower hoist.
9. Check camber, caster and toe-in, and adjust if necessary.

Upper Control Arm Bushing Removal (On the Car)

NOTE: The upper control arm bushings can be removed and installed on or off the car.

1. Hoist car under lower control arms and remove wheel.
2. Disconnect upper shock absorber attaching bolt.
3. Remove cam assemblies from control arms.
4. Move control arms out of frame horns and attach bushing removal tools.

Upper Control Arm Bushing Installation (On the Car)

1. Install tools and press bushings into control arm.
2. Move control arm into frame horns and install cam assemblies. Front cam is installed with the bolt in the lower position. Rear cam is installed with the bolt in the upper position.
3. Connect upper shock attaching bolt. Torque to 75 ft. lbs, 90 ft. lbs on 1972-74 models.
4. Replace wheel and lower car.
5. Align front wheels.

Lower Control Arm Removal —Right Side 1967-68

1. Remove drive axle assembly.
2. Hoist car and place floor stands under frame horns.
3. Relax the torsion bar. Refer to Torsion Bar Removal.
4. Remove wheel.
5. Remove shock absorber.
6. Disconnect stabilizer bar from lower control arm. Discard the bolt.
7. Place a spacer between stabilizer bar and tie rod.
8. Remove cotter pin and nut from lower ball joint stud.
9. Remove the ball joint stud from spindle.
10. Remove lower control arm bushing bolts and, with the aid of a helper, remove lower control arm and torsion bar, as an assembly. Torsion bar arm will drop out at this time.
11. Carefully slide torsion bar from lower control arm and store in a safe clean place.

Lower Control Arm Installation —Right Side 1967-68

1. Lubricate both ends of torsion bar for approximately 3 in., with extreme pressure chassis lubricant.
2. Install torsion bar into nut of lower control arm.
3. With the aid of a helper, lift torsion bar and lower control arm assembly up until torsion

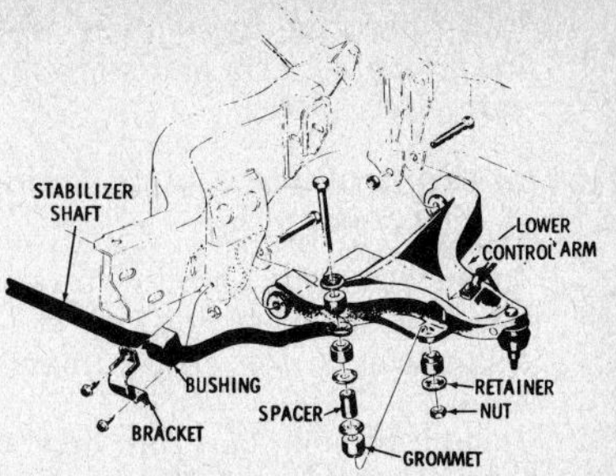
STABILIZER SHAFT
LOWER CONTROL ARM
BUSHING
RETAINER
NUT
SPACER
BRACKET
GROMMET

Lower control arm and related components
(© Oldsmobile Div, G.M. Corp)

bar will engage arm in crossmember and bushing ends of lower control arm engage frame horn.

NOTE: Make sure daub of paint on torsion bar is in the same position as when removed.

4. Install lower control arm bushing bolts and nuts. Do not torque.
5. Install lower control arm ball joint stud into knuckle. Install and torque to 40 ft. lbs.
6. Remove spacer from between stabilizer bar and tie rod.
7. Using a new bolt, connect stabilizer bar to lower control arm. Torque to 14 ft. lbs. Cut bolt off ¼ in. below nut.
8. Install shock absorber. Torque upper bolts to 75 ft. lbs., lower nut to 75 ft. lbs.
9. Install wheel.
10. Position torsion bar removal and installation tool over torsion bar crossmember and tighten center bolt until adjustment nut can be positioned through crossmember. Lubricate adjuster bolt with E. P. chassis lubricant and turn in the same number of turns noted during removal.
11. Raise hoist under lower control arms and remove floor stands.
12. Install right-hand drive axle assembly.
13. Torque lower control arm bushing bolts to 75 ft. lbs.
14. Check caster, camber and toe-in.

Lower Control Arm Removal —Left Side 1967-68

1. Remove drive axle assembly. Refer to Drive Axle Assembly Removal—Left Hand.
2. Place floor stands under frame horns.
3. Lower hoist slowly until floor stands are seated and hoist is still under lower control arm.
4. Remove shock absorber and bolt from stabilizer bar to lower control arm. Discard the bolt.
5. Completely relax the torsion bar. Refer to Torsion Bar Removal.
6. Lower front hoist to floor.
7. With the aid of a helper, remove lower control arm attaching bolts and carefully lower control arm and torsion bar as an assembly. Torsion bar arm will drop out at this time.

8. Carefully slide torsion bar from lower control arm and store in a safe clean place.

Lower Control Arm Installation —Left Side 1967-68

1. Lubricate both ends of torsion bar with extreme pressure chassis lubricant for approximately 3 in.
2. Install torsion bar into nut of lower control arm.
3. With the aid of a helper, lift torsion bar and lower control arm assembly until torsion bar will engage arm in crossmember and bushing ends of lower control arm engage frame horn.

NOTE: Make sure daub of paint on torsion bar is in the same position as when removed.

4. Install lower control arm bushing bolts and nuts. Do not torque.
5. Position torsion bar removal and installation tool over torsion bar crossmember and tighten center bolt until lower control arm is in a horizontal plane.
6. Install drive axle. Refer to Drive Axle Installation—Left Side.
7. Install shock absorber. Torque upper bolt to 75 ft. lbs., lower nut to 75 ft. lbs.
8. Using a new bolt, connect stabilizer bar to lower control arm. Refer to illustration for correct sequence of grommets, retainers and spacer. Torque to 14 ft. lbs. Cut bolt off 1/4 in. below nut.
9. Continue to tighten center bolt of tool until adjustment nut can be positioned through crossmember. Lubricate adjuster bolt with E. P. chassis lubricant and turn in the same amount of turns noted during removal.
10. Install drum and wheel.
11. Remove floor stands and lower hoist.
12. Torque lower control arm bushing bolt to 75 ft. lbs.
13. Check caster, camber and toe-in.

Lower Control Arm R & R —1969-74

1. Hoist car and support at lift points. Remove wheel assembly.
2. Place torsion bar remover and installer over crossmember so that center screw is seated in dimple of torsion adjusting arm.
3. Remove torsion bar adjusting bolt and nut, counting the number of turns necessary.

NOTE: This number of turns will be used when installing, to obtain initial carrying height.

4. Turn center screw of tool until torsion bar is completely relaxed.
5. Disconnect shock absorber and stabilizer link from lower control arm.
6. Remove drive axle nut.
7. Remove cotter pin and nut from lower ball joint stud.
8. Remove ball joint stud from knuckle, using puller.
9. Push drive axle in and pull knuckle outward to gain clearance, then remove lower control arm from knuckle and torsion bar.
10. Install by reversing removal procedure. Check and adjust ride height if necessary.

Lower Control Arm Bushing Removal

1. Hoist car on a two post lift.
2. Disconnect upper shock attaching bolt.
3. Remove stabilizer link bolt and discard the bolt.
4. Place floor stands under frame horns. Lower front lift to floor.

NOTE: On 1971-74 models, the frame brace must be unbolted and moved away from the lower control arm mounts.

5. Install torsion bar removal and installation tool.
6. Remove lower control arm bushing bolts and lower control arm until free of frame horns.
7. Install bolts through rear bushing and press out bushing.

NOTE: Because of the torsion bar nut attachment to the lower control arm, it will be necessary to use a hardened 1/2-20 nut, to remove the front bushing.

Lower Control Arm Bushing Installation

1. Install tools and press rear bushing into lower control arm.

NOTE: Because of the torsion bar nut attachment to the lower control arm, it will be necessary to use a hardened 1/2-20 nut, to install the front bushing.

2. Raise lower control arm into frame horns and install bushing bolts and nuts. Do not torque.
3. Turn center bolt of tool into dimple of torsion bar arm until adjusting nut can be inserted through center frame support. Turn adjusting bolt clockwise the same number of turns needed to remove. Remove tool.
4. Raise front lift under lower control arms, and remove floor stands.
5. Connect upper shock attaching bolt and nut. Torque to 75 ft. lbs.
6. Using a new bolt, attach stabilizer link bolt to lower control arm. Torque to 14 ft. lbs.
7. Lower car and torque lower control arm bushing bolts to 75 ft. lbs. 90 ft lbs for 1972 cars. The frame brace on 1971-74 cars should be torqued to 55 ft lbs.

Ball Joint Vertical Check

1967-72

1. Raise the car and position floor stands under the left and right lower control arm, as near as possible to each lower ball joint. Car must be stable and should not rock on floor stands.
2. Position dial indicator to register vertical movement at wheel hub.
3. Place a pry bar between the lower control arm and the outer race of the C.V. joint and pry down on the bar. Care must be used so that the drive axle seal is not damaged. The vertical reading must not exceed .125 in.

Ball Joint Horizontal Check

1967-72

1. Place car on floor stands, as outlined in Step 1 in the Vertical Check.
2. Position dial indicator at the rim of the wheel, to indicate side play.
3. Grasp wheel with the hands, top and bottom, and push in on the bottom of the tire while pulling out at the top. Read gauge, then reverse the push-pull procedure. Horizontal deflection on the gauge should not exceed .125 in. at the wheel rim. This procedure checks both the upper and lower ball joints.

1973-74

1973-74 lower ball joints contain a visual wear indicator. The lower ball joint grease plug screws into the wear indicator which protrudes from the bottom of the ball joint housing. As long as the wear indicator extends out of the ball joint housing, the ball joint is not worn. If the tip of the wear indicator is parallel with, or recessed into the ball joint housing, the ball joint is defective.

Lower Control Arm Ball Joint Removal

1. Remove knuckle.
2. Using hack saw, saw the three rivet heads off.
3. Using a 7/32 in. bit, drill side rivets 3/16 in. deep.
4. Using hammer and punch, drive center rivet out of the control arm.

Lower Control Arm Ball Joint Installation

1. Install service ball joint into control arm and torque bolts and nut. Side bolts are torqued to 25 ft lbs while the upper nut is tightened to 45 ft lbs.
2. Install knuckle.

Lower Control Arm Ball Joint Seal Removal

The lower ball joint seal can be installed with lower control arm either in or out of the car.

1. Remove steering knuckle. Refer to Knuckle Removal.

2. Using hammer and chisel, drive seal from ball joint.
3. Wipe grease from ball joint and stud.

Lower Control Arm Ball Joint Seal Installation

1. Position new seal over ball joint stud.
2. Lubricate jaws of seal installer and carefully slide jaw between seal and retainer.
3. Tap lightly with hammer on center bolt of tool until retainer is fully seated.
4. Install knuckle.
5. Lubricate the ball joint fitting until grease appears from seal.

Stabilizer Bar Removal

1. Remove link bolts, nuts, grommets, spacers and retainers from lower control arm. Discard bolts.
2. Remove two bolts which attach dust shield to frame, both sides.
3. Remove bracket to frame attaching bolts and remove stabilizer bar from front of car.

Stabilizer Bar Installation

Reverse removal procedure.

NOTE: New link bolts are torqued to 14 ft. lbs., then cut off $\frac{1}{4}$ in. from nut.

Torsion Bar Crossmember Removal

1. Raise car on a two post hoist and place floor stand under front torque boxes. Lower front hoist.
2. Disconnect parking brake cable and equalizer, and clip at torsion bar crossmember. Pull cable through the crossmember.
3. Relax torsion bars. Refer to Torsion Bar Removal.
4. Remove torsion bar with a torsion bar removal and installation tool.
5. Slide both torsion bars forward until they bottom in lower control arm nut.
6. Remove bolts from torsion bar crossmember to frame.
7. Raise torsion bar crossmember, remove rubber cushions from frame horns.
8. Disconnect hangers at muffler and tail pipes.
9. Move torsion bar crossmember to the right or left side until member clears frame, then remove.

Torsion Bar Crossmember Installation

1. Insert torsion bar crossmember above frame on right side of car and position left side over frame horn.
2. Raise crossmember so that rubber cushions can be installed.
3. Lubricate ends of torsion bars with extreme pressure chassis lubricant for about 3 in.
4. Raise crossmember up and toward rear of car. Raise torsion bars until they enter hole provided for them in crossmember.
5. Install adjuster arms into crossmember and slide torsion bars toward the rear of car until fully seated against rear edge of crossmember.
6. Install rebound cushions, bolts, washers and nuts through frame and crossmember. Torque to 40 ft. lbs.
7. Position torsion bar installation and removal tool over crossmember and tighten center bolt until nut can be inserted through crossmember.
8. Lubricate adjuster bolt with extreme pressure chassis lubricant and turn the same number of turns required to remove it.
9. Remove tool.
10. Install seals over retainers at rear of torsion bars.
11. Insert parking brake cable through crossmember. Install clip at crossmember.
12. Connect parking brake cable to equalizer.
13. Connect and tighten muffler and tail pipe hangers.
14. Hoist car and remove floor stands.
15. Lower car.
16. Check parking brake cable adjustment. Adjust as necessary.

Front End Alignment

Carrying height is controlled by the adjustment setting of the torsion bar adjusting bolt. Clockwise rotation of the bolt increases the front height. It is very important that this height be considered and made correct before further steering geometry is established. Car must be on a level surface, gas tank full or a compensating weight added. Front seat must be all the way to the rear and tires inflated properly. All doors must be closed and no passengers or additional weight should be in the car or trunk.

1. Check rocker panel to ground dimension, as illustrated. Front and rear reading to ground should be as follows. Front to rear and side to side should be within $\frac{3}{4}$ in.

	Front	*Rear*
1967-68	8 in.	$8\frac{1}{4}$ in.
1969-70	8 in.	8 in.
1971-74	$8\frac{3}{4}$ in.	9 in.

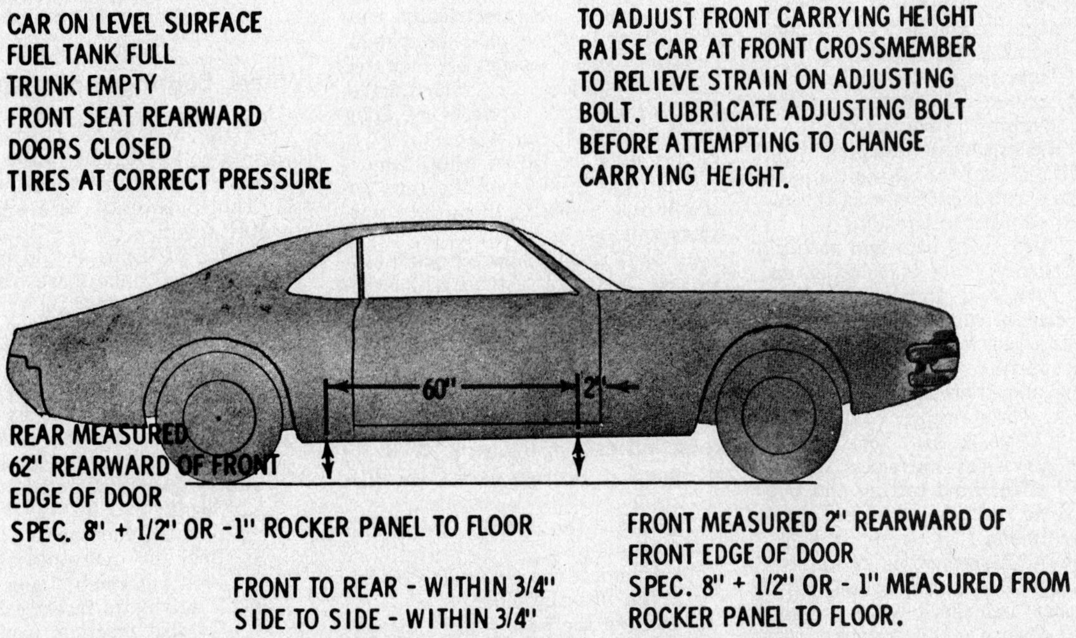
CAR ON LEVEL SURFACE
FUEL TANK FULL
TRUNK EMPTY
FRONT SEAT REARWARD
DOORS CLOSED
TIRES AT CORRECT PRESSURE
TO ADJUST FRONT CARRYING HEIGHT RAISE CAR AT FRONT CROSSMEMBER TO RELIEVE STRAIN ON ADJUSTING BOLT. LUBRICATE ADJUSTING BOLT BEFORE ATTEMPTING TO CHANGE CARRYING HEIGHT.
60"
2"
REAR MEASURED 62" REARWARD OF FRONT EDGE OF DOOR
SPEC. 8" + 1/2" OR -1" ROCKER PANEL TO FLOOR
FRONT MEASURED 2" REARWARD OF FRONT EDGE OF DOOR
SPEC. 8" + 1/2" OR - 1" MEASURED FROM ROCKER PANEL TO FLOOR.
FRONT TO REAR - WITHIN 3/4"
SIDE TO SIDE - WITHIN 3/4"

Adjusting carrying height—1967-70 (© Oldsmobile Div, G.M. Corp)

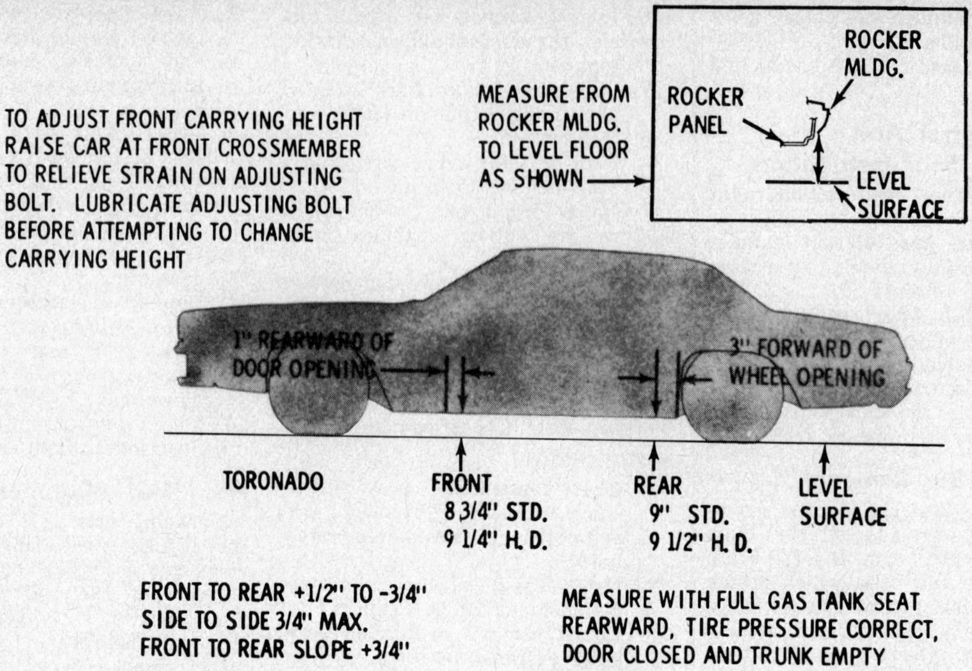
TO ADJUST FRONT CARRYING HEIGHT RAISE CAR AT FRONT CROSSMEMBER TO RELIEVE STRAIN ON ADJUSTING BOLT. LUBRICATE ADJUSTING BOLT BEFORE ATTEMPTING TO CHANGE CARRYING HEIGHT
MEASURE FROM ROCKER MLDG. TO LEVEL FLOOR AS SHOWN
ROCKER MLDG.
ROCKER PANEL
LEVEL SURFACE
1" REARWARD OF DOOR OPENING
3" FORWARD OF WHEEL OPENING
TORONADO
FRONT
8 3/4" STD.
9 1/4" H.D.
REAR
9" STD.
9 1/2" H.D.
LEVEL SURFACE
FRONT TO REAR +1/2" TO -3/4"
SIDE TO SIDE 3/4" MAX.
FRONT TO REAR SLOPE +3/4"
MEASURE WITH FULL GAS TANK SEAT REARWARD, TIRE PRESSURE CORRECT, DOOR CLOSED AND TRUNK EMPTY

Adjusting carrying height—1971-74 (© Oldsmobile Div, G.M. Corp)

2. Align car on wheel alignment equipment as follows:
3. Raise front end and check wheel runout. Set and center the runout, then lower the car.
4. Loosen nuts on inboard side of upper control arm cam bolts.
5. Check camber and adjust if necessary with rear cam bolt.
6. Take the caster reading. Use camber reading scale for making this adjustment.
   A. Turn rear bolt so camber reading is ¼° more than original setting, for every 1° of caster change needed for correct reading. Turn to plus side of camber if caster is negative and to negative camber if caster is positive.
   B. Turn the front cam bolts so camber will return to the original proper setting.
   C. Recheck caster reading.

NOTE: If a problem exists, and you should run out of cam in the attempt to gain correct reading:
   A. Turn front cam bolt so high part of cam is pointing up.
   B. Turn rear cam bolt so high part of cam is pointing down.

This is a location to start from and a correct setting should be obtainable with the above procedure.

NOTE: Torque upper control arm cam nuts to 95 ft. lbs.; hold head of bolt securely. Any movement of the cam will affect final setting and you will have to recheck caster and camber adjustment.

7. Toe-in adjustment is as follows.
   A. Center steering wheel, raise car and check wheel runout.
   B. Loosen tie rod end nuts, and adjust to proper setting.
   C. Tighten tie rod end nuts. Torque nuts 20 ft. lbs. Position tie rod clamps so openings of clamps are facing up. This is a very necessary setting. Interference and possible trouble with front end linkage could occur if clamps snag anything while turning.

REAR SUSPENSION

Some 1971-74 models are equipped with True-Track Braking (JL9 option). This is an electrically controlled rear brake equalizing system. The wheel speed sensors are mounted under the spindles, each with a driveshaft which runs through the spindle to attach to the grease cap.

Care must be taken when removing the rear spindle or the rear assembly not to break the sensor wiring or damage the sensor unit.

An illustration of the axle and sensor may be found in the Cadillac Eldorado Section.

All 1971-74 models have a straight tubular axle housing instead of the I-beam drop axle used on 1967-70 models.

Rear Wheel Spindle R & R

1. Support the rear of the car with stands.
2. Remove the wheel, drum and hub assembly.
3. Disconnect the brake line fitting at the wheel cylinder.
4. Remove the four spindle attaching bolts and tie the backing plate out of the way.
5. On 1971-74 models, pull the spindle with a slide hammer.
6. On 1967-70 models, place a jack under the axle and remove the four bolts from the center spring clamp assembly. Remove the rubber insulator and lower the axle enough with the jack to provide working room for the spindle removal. Either drive the spindle out from behind or use a pulling tool.
7. To install, reverse the removal procedure. Install spindle with the keyway up, tightening the four bolts progressively one turn at a time. Adjust the rear wheel bearing.

Wheel Bearing Adjustment

For the rear wheel tapered roller bearings to be correctly adjusted, the following precautions should be taken:

1. The cones must be a slip fit on the spindle.
2. Inside of cones should be lubricated to make sure the cone creeps on the spindle.
3. Spindle nut must be a free-running fit on the threads.
4. Adjustment of rear wheel bearings should be made by continuously revolving the wheel while torquing the nut as follows:
   A. Torque adjusting nut to 25-30 ft. lbs. to seat all components thoroughly.
   B. Back off nut one-half turn, then retighten finger tight.
   C. If unable to insert cotter pin at this position, back off to nearest castellation.

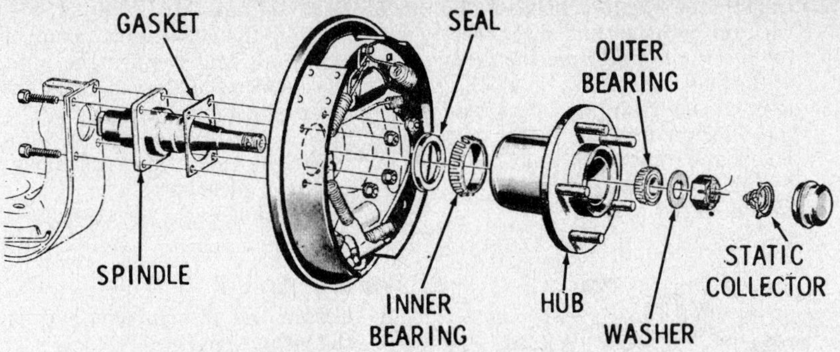
GASKET
SEAL
OUTER
BEARING
SPINDLE
INNER
BEARING
HUB
WASHER
STATIC
COLLECTOR

Rear hub assembly—1967-74
(© Oldsmobile Div, G.M. Corp)

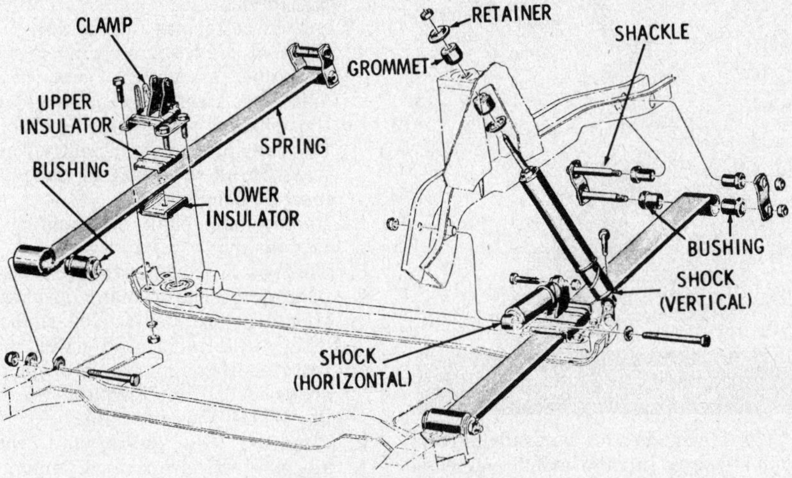
CLAMP
RETAINER
GROMMET
SHACKLE
UPPER
INSULATOR
SPRING
BUSHING
LOWER
INSULATOR
BUSHING
SHOCK
(VERTICAL)
SHOCK
(HORIZONTAL)

Rear suspension—1967-70
(© Oldsmobile Div, G.M. Corp)

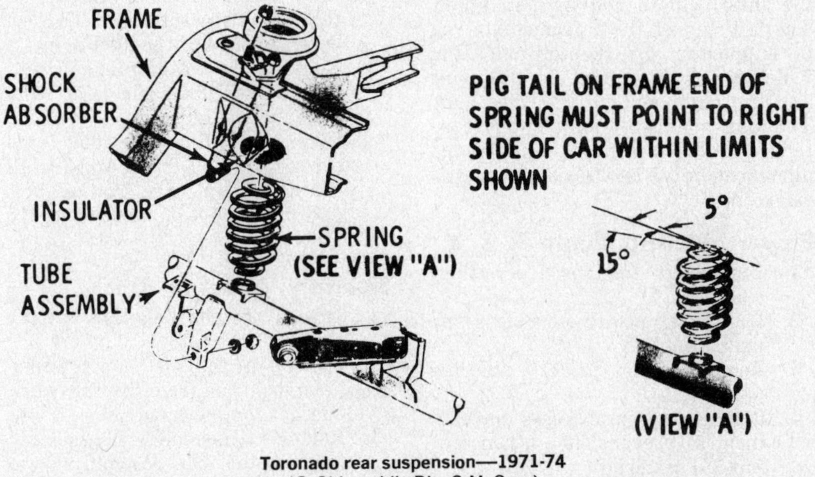
FRAME
SHOCK
ABSORBER
INSULATOR
SPRING
(SEE VIEW "A")
TUBE
ASSEMBLY
PIG TAIL ON FRAME END OF
SPRING MUST POINT TO RIGHT
SIDE OF CAR WITHIN LIMITS
SHOWN
5°
15°
(VIEW "A")

Toronado rear suspension—1971-74
(© Oldsmobile Div, G.M. Corp)

Rear Leaf Spring Removal

1967-70

1. Raise car and support on frame pad. With jack under axle, remove wheel.
2. Remove nut only from front of rear spring.
3. Remove two attaching nuts on rear shackle (outer). Remove rear shackle (outer).
4. Remove four attaching bolts on center clamp assembly.
5. Lift center clamp up, shock will hold it in position.
6. On 1967 models, remove resonator bracket attaching bolts to frame and allow resonator to hang loose.
7. Lower jack until axle is free from spring.
8. Remove shackle assembly from spring and body.
9. Remove bolt from front of rear spring and remove spring.
10. If spring bushing is worn, remove and replace it.

Rear Leaf Spring Installation

1967-70

To install, reverse removal procedure.

A. Front bushing is a press fit. Replacement will require an arbor press.
B. Torque resonator bracket attaching bolts to 14 ft. lbs.
C. Torque four spring center clamp assembly bolts to 30 ft. lbs.
D. Install wheel, torque to 115 ft. lbs.
E. Remove all supports and, with car on the ground, torque rear shackle bolts to 40 ft. lbs. and front spring bolt to 75-80 ft. lbs.

Rear Coil Spring R & R

1971-74

1. With the car supported with floor stands, position a hoist under the tube assembly and raise it enough to relieve the tension on the shock absorber.
2. Disconnect the shock absorbers at the tube assembly.
3. Carefully lower the tube assembly until the springs are fully extended.

Caution Do not stretch the brake hydraulic hose.

4. Remove the springs and insulators.
5. When installing, place the insulator on top of the spring and install the spring with the identification tag next to the tube assembly.
6. Hoist the tube assembly and connect the shock absorber, tightening the lower nut to 65 ft. lbs.

BRAKES

Brake adjustment, brake lining replacement, hydraulic cylinder overhaul and bleeding procedures can be found in the Unit Repair Section. Power brake overhaul procedures can be found in the Unit Repair Section.

On 1967 and 1968 models, the 4-piston Delco Moraine power front disc brake became available as an option. In 1969 it was replaced by the single piston disc brake. On 1970-74 models, the single piston Delco Moraine power front disc brakes are standard equipment. Beginning in 1967, a dual hydraulic system is used. A distributor assembly actuates a warning light switch whenever there is a failure in one of the hydraulic systems. Up to 1970, a balance valve in the rear system is used to proportion the hydraulic pressure to the rear wheels when more than 310 psi is required at the front (disc brake) wheels. On 1971-74 models, the distributor and balance functions are integrated in the combination valve assembly. Service procedures for the Delco Moraine single cylinder disc brake are found in the Unit Repair Section.

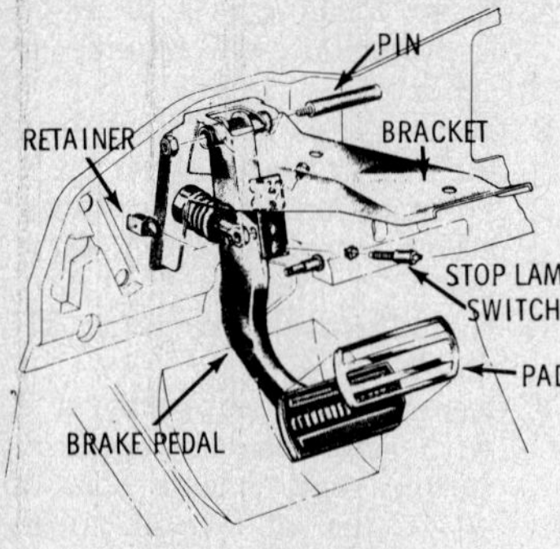
PIN
RETAINER
BRACKET
STOP LAMP SWITCH
PAD
BRAKE PEDAL

Brake pedal assembly
(© Oldsmobile Div, G.M. Corp)

Brake Pedal Travel

Maximum allowable brake pedal travel on 1967-70 models is 1⅞ in. On 1971-74 models maximum allowable travel is 2½ in. To bring pedal travel within specifications, adjust self-adjusting brakes by driving the car backward and forward alternately and applying the brakes. If pedal travel does not decrease, either the linings are excessively worn or the self-adjusting mechanism is frozen.

Parking Brake Adjustment

1. Release the parking brake.
2. Check hydraulic brake pedal travel, adjusting if necessary.
3. Tighten the equalizer adjusting nut until heavy resistance is felt when rotating the rear wheels forward, then back off the adjusting nut seven full turns.

Parking Brake Outer Cable R & R

1. Disconnect the cable at the connector.
2. Remove the conduit bracket retainer.
3. Remove the rear wheel and brake drum.
4. Disconnect the cable from the actuating lever and install a corbin type hose clamp over the conduit retainer fingers.
5. Tap on the conduit lightly to remove it from the backing plate.
6. Install in the reverse order of removal.

Master Cylinder R & R

1. Disconnect and plug hydraulic lines, and drain the cylinder.
2. Remove the attaching nuts and remove the master cylinder from the power unit.

Power Cylinder Removal

1. From inside the car, detach the brake pushrod from the brake pedal.
2. Detach the vacuum hose at the vacuum cylinder and disconnect the hydraulic line from the front of the slave cylinder.
3. Remove the four nuts that hold the vacuum unit up to the toeboard and remove the unit.
4. Install in reverse order of removal. Bleed system.

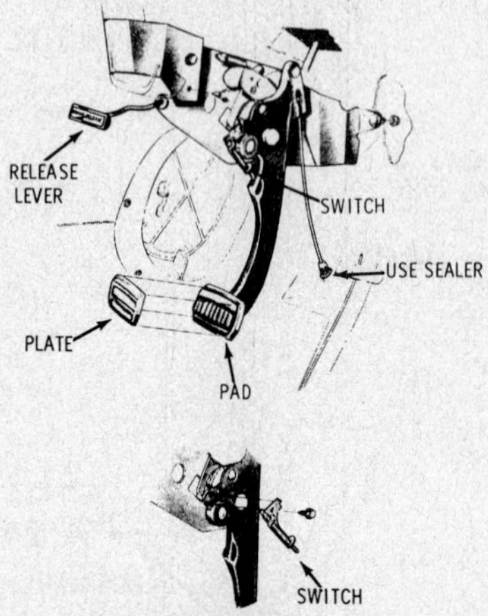
RELEASE LEVER
SWITCH
USE SEALER
PLATE
PAD
SWITCH

Parking brake assembly
(© Oldsmobile Div, G.M. Corp)

STEERING

The Toronado uses a parallelogram type steering linkage which connects both front wheels to the steering gear through the pitman arm. The right and left tie rods are attached to the steering arms at the wheels and to the intermediate rod by ball studs. The left end of the intermediate rod is supported by the pitman arm which is driven by the steering gear and the right end by the idler arm. The idler arm pivots on a support attached to the frame. The pitman and idler arms must be always parallel to each other.

Power Steering Pump R & R

1. Disconnect the positive battery cable.
2. Loosen the power steering pump pulley nut.
3. Remove the power steering pump belt.
4. Remove the pump hoses and seal them to prevent the entrance of foreign material.
5. Remove the pump assembly from the engine with the link attached.

NOTE: If the model is equipped with a power steering cooler, disconnect the return hose at the cooler—not at the steering gear.

6. Remove the hoses and link from the pump.

Tie Rod R & R

NOTE: Any time the tie rods are replaced, the front end alignment must be checked and reset to specifications.

1. Raise the car.
2. Remove the cotter pins from the ball studs and remove the nuts.
3. Disconnect the tie rod from the steering arm with a puller.
4. Loosen the clamp bolts and unscrew the tie-rod end assemblies from the adjuster tubes.
5. Installation is the reverse of removal.

Pitman Arm R & R

1. Loosen the pitman arm nut on the pitman shaft.
2. Remove the flexible coupling bolt at the gear side of the coupling.
3. Disconnect the pitman arm from the intermediate rod by removing the cotter pin and the nut.
4. Remove the three steering gear-to-frame attaching bolts and raise the steering gear to clear the pitman arm stud. Position the steering gear sufficiently forward to allow access to the pitman arm shaft nut.
5. Remove the shaft nut and the pitman arm.
6. To install reverse the removal procedure. The pitman shaft nut should be torqued to 200 ft lbs. The pitman arm stud should be inserted through the intermediate rod. The nut torque is 45 ft lbs. Install the cotter pin.
7. Readjust the toe-in and the steering wheel spoke alignment.

Idler Arm R & R

1. Remove the bolt and nut from the bracket which is attached to the frame crossmember. This secures one end of the idler arm.
2. Remove the cotter pin and nut. Remove the idler arm joint from the intermediate rod.
3. When installing the idler arm torque it to 40 ft lbs and install the cotter pin. The bracket bolt and nut should be torqued to 110 ft lbs.

Steering Wheel R & R

1. Disconnect the negative battery cable.
2. Pull up on the horn cap retainer assembly and remove the horn contact components.
3. Remove the contact assembly and remove the assembly from the wheel.
4. Remove the steering wheel nut. Using a puller carefully remove the wheel.
5. If the car is equipped with a tilt and telescope wheel use the following procedure.
   a. After removing the horn pad, disconnect the bayonet connector of the horn wire.
   b. Push the locking lever counterclockwise to the full release position.
   c. Scribe marks on the plate assembly in the area of the at-

taching screws. Remove the screws.
d. Remove the plate assembly.
e. Release the nut and remove the wheel.

Turn Signal Switch R & R

1. Disconnect the negative battery cable.
2. Remove the steering wheel. (See "Steering Wheel R&R.")
3. Remove the lower trim cap on the instrument panel and disconnect the turn signal connector from the harness. Wrap the connector with tape to prevent damage when removing the switch.
4. Remove the four bolts which fasten the jacket assembly to the bracket.
5. Remove the shift indicator.
6. Remove nuts A and B in the illustration from the bracket assembly while holding the column in position. Remove the bracket assembly and the wire protector from the turn signal wiring and then reinstall the nuts loosely.
7. Remove the plastic cover.
8. Using the correct puller remove the C-ring.
9. Using needle-nose pliers, remove the lockplate and the carrier assembly.
10. Release the upper bearing spring.
11. Place the signal lever in the right turn position and remove the lever. Position the tilt wheel in the center position.
12. Depress the hazard warning knob and then remove the knob.
13. Loosen and remove the three screws which fasten the switch and then carefully pull the switch and wiring from the top end of the column.

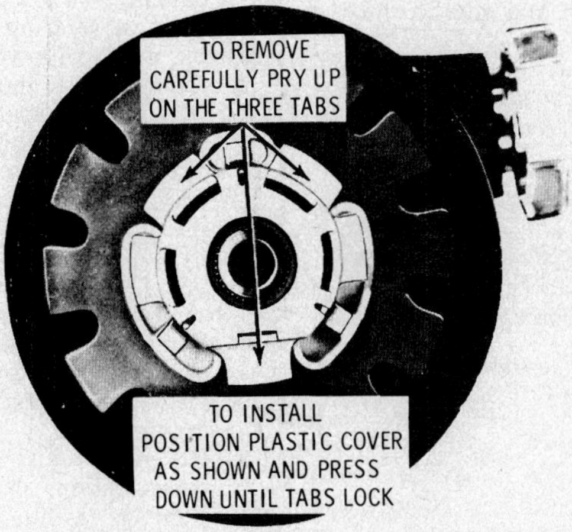
TO REMOVE
CAREFULLY PRY UP
ON THE THREE TABS
TO INSTALL
POSITION PLASTIC COVER
AS SHOWN AND PRESS
DOWN UNTIL TABS LOCK

Plastic cover
(© Oldsmobile Div, G.M. Corp)

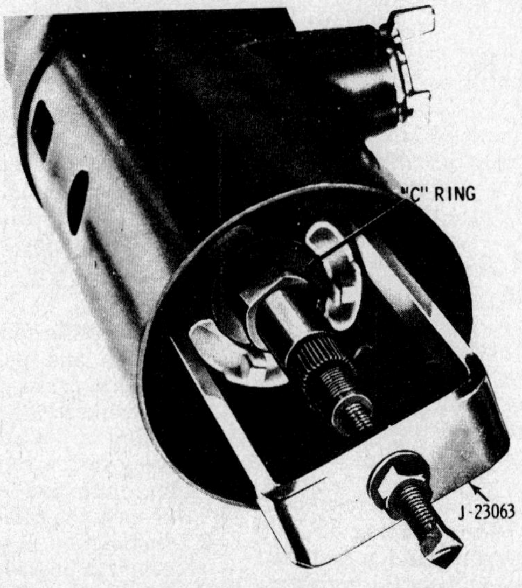
"C" RING
J-23063

Removing the C-ring
(© Oldsmobile Div, G.M. Corp)

INSTRUMENT PANEL

Ignition Switch R & R Standard Column

1967-68

1. Remove control panel.
2. Turn switch to Acc. position.
3. Insert a paper clip into the small hole in the front side of the switch and depress, while turning the key counterclockwise. The lock should pop out.
4. Remove escutcheon.
5. Remove switch from backside of instrument panel and remove wiring connector.
6. Install by reversing above procedure.

1969-74

1. Disconnect the negative battery cable.
2. Place the ignition switch in "ACC" position (1969), "RUN" position (1970) or "OFF-UNLOCKED" (1971-74).
3. Remove the toe pan cover (if applicable) and loosen the toe clamp bolts.
4. Remove the lower instrument panel trim and toe pan trim panel.
5. Remove the automatic transmission shift indicator needle.
6. Remove the steering column dash bracket and let the steering wheel rest on the driver's seat.
7. Remove the two switch attaching screws and lift the switch off the actuator rod.
8. Disconnect the wiring.
9. To install, check that the lock cylinder is still in "ACC" (1969), "RUN" (1970) or "OFF-UNLOCKED" (1971-74) position and move the sliding portion of the switch until the switch hole is positioned as illustrated. Hold the switch in this position with a 0.090 in. pin as illustrated.
10. Connect the wiring to the switch.
11. Position the switch over the actuator rod, install the attaching screws (tighten to 3 ft. lbs.) and remove the 0.090 in. pin.
12. Reverse Steps 1 through 6 to complete installation.

Ignition Lock Cylinder R & R Tilt and Telescope Column

1. Follow the complete procedure for the "Turn Signal Switch R&R."
2. Place the lock assembly in the "run" position and then insert a long, thin screwdriver into the slot as shown and pull outward on the lock assembly to remove it.

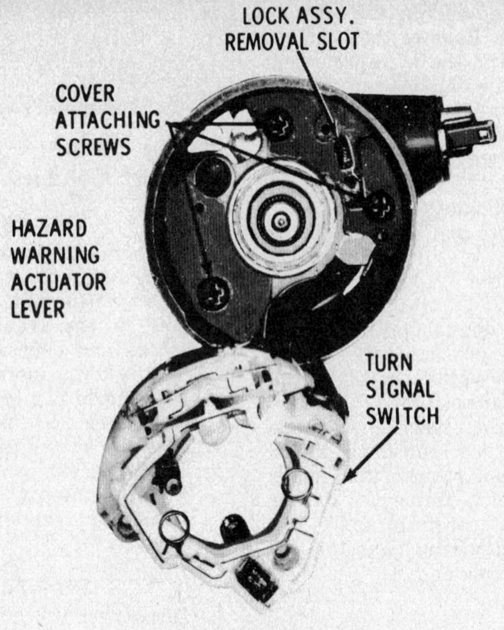
LOCK ASSY.
REMOVAL SLOT
COVER
ATTACHING
SCREWS
HAZARD
WARNING
ACTUATOR
LEVER
TURN
SIGNAL
SWITCH
Ignition lock removal
(© Oldsmobile Div, G.M. Corp)

Headlight Switch R & R

1967-70

1. Remove lower left-hand trim panel.
2. Remove knob by first pulling the knob out to the headlight position, then depressing the spring-loaded button on switch body. Then, pull knob out of switch assembly.
3. Remove escutcheon nut.
4. Remove headlamp switch from rear of control panel.
5. Disconnect wiring and vacuum hoses.
6. Installation is the reverse of removal.

1971-74

The left hand control panel must be removed in order to remove the headlight switch.

1. Disconnect the battery.
2. Pry the floor lamp lens and lamp assembly out with a thin screwdriver.
3. Remove the screws from the left side of the lower steering trim and from the left hand trim panel.
4. Remove the nut and screw from the temperature cable on the bottom of the air conditioner or heater control.
5. Remove the ground wire attaching screw from the left hand panel lower brace.
6. Remove the four control panel attaching screws and remove the panel.
7. Remove the multiple connector from the headlight switch.
8. Pull the switch to "ON" position and push in on the small button on the switch, then pull the switch knob and shaft from the switch.
9. Remove the escutcheon from the switch and remove switch.
10. Install in reverse order of removal.

WINDSHIELD WIPERS

The windshield wiper system consists of the wiper motor and transmission assembly.

Motor R & R

1. Raise the hood and remove the cowl screen or grille.
2. Loosen the wiper transmission drive link attaching nuts which attach to the motor crankarm. Disconnect the drive link.
3. Disconnect the wiring and the washer hoses.
4. Remove the three motor attaching screws.
5. Remove the motor while guiding the crankarm through the hole.
6. To install the unit reverse the removal procedure.

Transmission R & R

1. Remove the wiper arms and blades.
2. Remove the cowl screen or grille.
3. Loosen the transmission drive link where it connects to the motor crankarm and then disconnect the drive link from the crankarm.
4. Remove the right and left transmission-to-body attaching screws and lift the transmission and the linkage assembly out through the cowl plenum chamber opening.
5. To install the unit, place the transmission and linkage assembly in the plenum chamber and install the transmission mounting screws loosely.
6. Connect the transmission drive link to the motor crankarm and then tighten the securing nuts.

NOTE: During installation, the motor must be in the "park" position.

7. The transmission assemblies must be aligned before the body attaching screws are tightened.
8. Reinstall the cowl screen, wiper arms, and the blades. Check the wiper pattern and park position of the arms.

RADIO

R & R

1967-70

1. Disconnect battery.
2. Remove both lower cluster panels.
3. Remove steering column attaching nuts and lower bracket.
4. Remove shift indicator needle.
5. Disconnect speedometer cable.
6. Remove attaching nuts from cluster lower brackets, leaving brackets attached to the instrument panel.
7. Remove two upper instrument panel screws and lay cluster assembly on steering column.
8. Remove radio knobs, washers or rear seat speaker control.
9. Remove radio attaching nuts and escutcheons.
10. Disconnect all wiring and antenna lead-in.
11. Remove lower radio support bracket attaching nut.
12. Remove radio from instrument panel.
13. Install by reversing the removal procedure.

1971-74

1. Loosen the ground strap at the lower tie bar and tape the edge of the instrument panel to prevent scratching.
2. Remove the radio support bracket nut at the rear of the radio.
3. Disconnect the three lights from the bezel.
4. Remove the four bezel attaching screws and pull the bezel forward as far as possible.
5. Disconnect all wiring from the radio.
6. Remove the radio knobs, attaching nuts and escutcheons, then remove the radio.
7. Installation is the reverse of the removal procedure. The antenna trimmer must be adjusted when the radio is installed.

HEATER

Blower Assembly R & R (1967-69)

1. Remove the blower feed wire.
2. Using a long extension and a 7/16 in. socket, remove the sheet metal screw which holds the heater inlet to the dash. The socket can be inserted through the opening in the fender filler plate forward of the right front wheel.
3. Remove all the remaining nuts and push the heater case studs back until they no longer come through the dash.
4. Remove three of the bolts which hold the front fender. These bolts are situated at the rear of the front fender. The removal of these should allow the fender to be moved outward and upward slightly.
5. Remove the blower motor screws and remove the motor from the heater inlet. These should be removed separately from beneath the fender.
6. Reverse the removal procedure to install. Apply sealer to the heater inlet before installation.

Heater-Blower R & R (1970)

1. Disconnect blower feed and resistor wiring.
2. Disconnect vacuum hoses from the air inlet and forced vent diaphragms.
3. Disconnect temperature cable from temperature door lever.
4. Disconnect heater hoses. Keep open ends of hoses above engine coolant level to prevent loss of coolant.
5. Remove heater assembly attaching screws.
6. Remove heater assembly from the cowl.
7. If heater core is to be removed, it can be removed at this time.
8. To install, reverse the removal procedure. Be sure to apply sealer to the mounting face of the heater assembly.

Blower Motor R & R (1971-74)

1. Remove the right front fender filler panel.
2. Disconnect the blower electrical wiring.
3. Remove the five nuts and two screws which secure the inlet assembly to the dash.
4. Remove the inlet assembly and the blower motor. The fan may be removed from the shaft by releasing the nut and lockwasher.
5. To install, reverse the removal procedure.

Heater Case and Core R & R (1967-70)

1. Remove the glove box.
2. Disconnect the wiring, vacuum lines, and the defroster hoses from the heater case.
3. Drain the radiator below the level of the heater. Remove the heater hoses and gasket.
4. Remove the blower assembly screws and also the heater case from inside the car.
5. Separate the heater core from the case.
6. To install, reverse the removal procedure.

Heater Case and Core R & R (1971-74)

1. Drain the radiator and disconnect the heater hoses.
2. Remove the five attaching nuts.

NOTE: In order to gain access to one of the nuts, it will be necessary to disconnect the right front fender at the bottom and block the fender away from the body so that the nut may be removed through the opening.

3. Disconnect the wiring and the three control cables.
4. The case assembly may be removed from under the dash. The core may be separated from the case if it is defective.

INDEX

Pinto • Mustang II

YEAR IDENTIFICATION

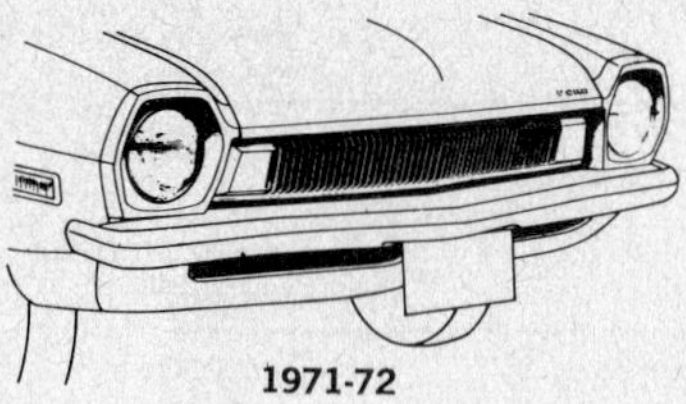
1971-72

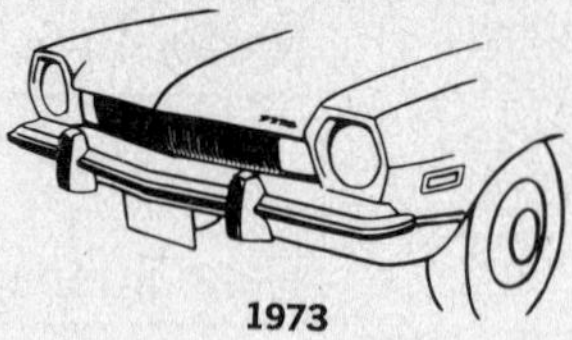
1973

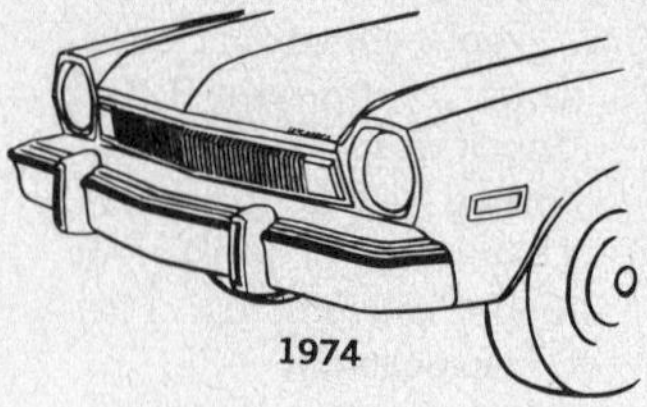
1974

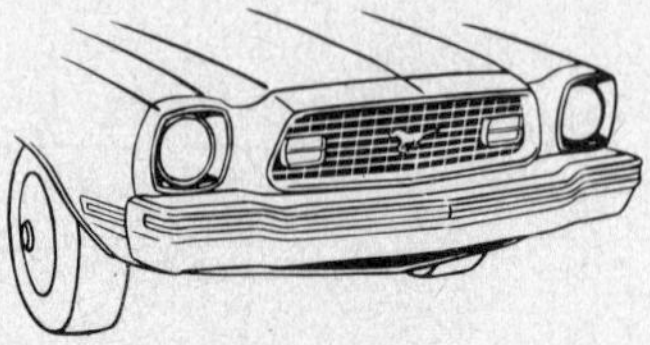
1974 Mustang II

FIRING ORDER

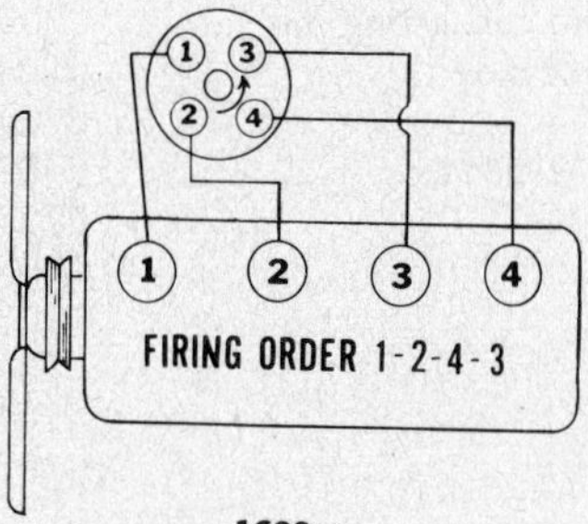
1
3
2
4
1
2
3
4
FIRING ORDER 1-2-4-3
1600 cc

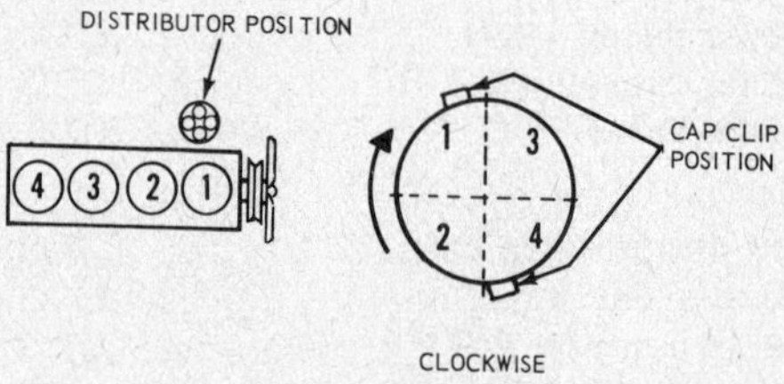
DISTRIBUTOR POSITION
4
3
2
1
CAP CLIP POSITION
1
3
2
4
CLOCKWISE
FIRING ORDER –1–3–4–2

2000 and 2300 cc

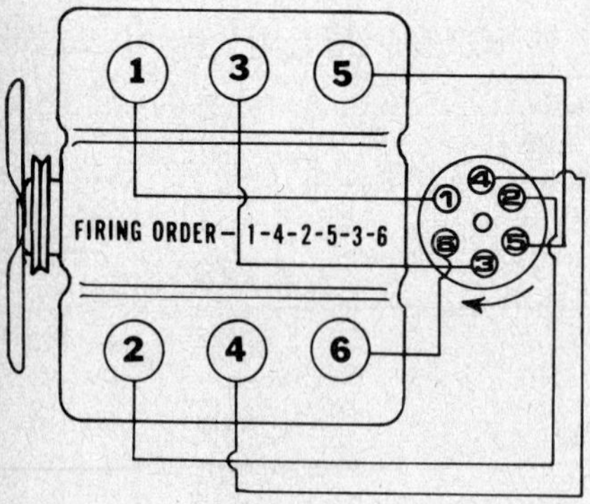
1
3
5
FIRING ORDER–1-4-2-5-3-6
2
4
6
2800 cc V6

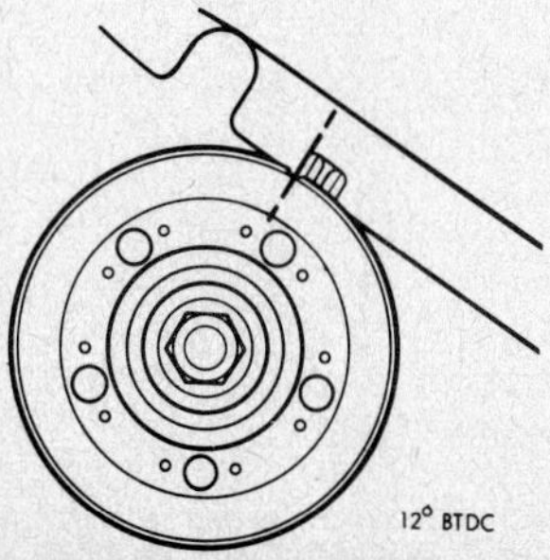
12° BTDC
Timing marks—1600 cc engine

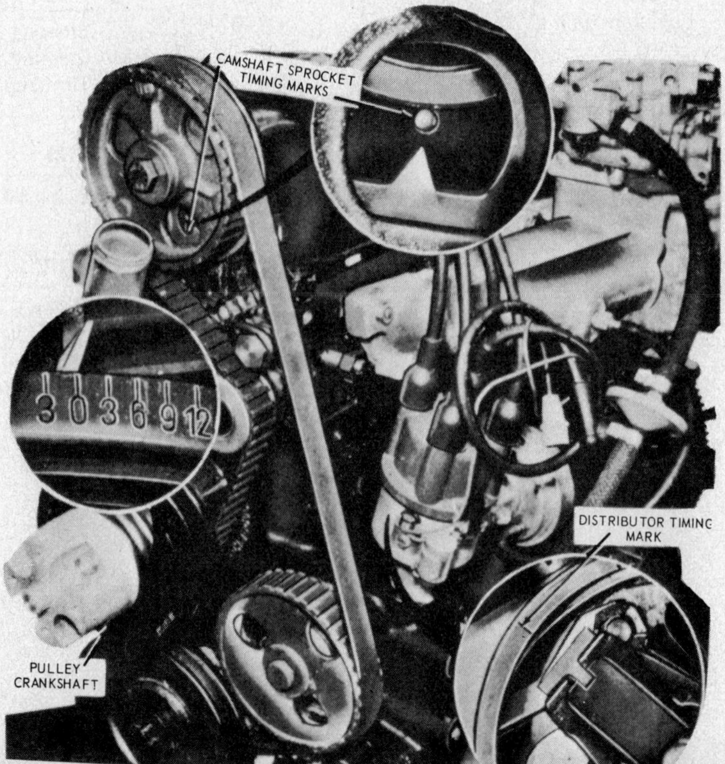
CAMSHAFT SPROCKET TIMING MARKS
3 0 3 6 9 12
DISTRIBUTOR TIMING MARK
PULLEY CRANKSHAFT
Timing Marks—2000 cc. engine

CAR SERIAL NUMBER LOCATION AND ENGINE IDENTIFICATION

Vehicle Identification Number

The Vehicle Identification Number is located on a tab mounted on the upper left-hand corner of the dashboard, visible through the windshield. The VIN also appears on the Vehicle Certification Label, and is interpreted according to the illustration of this label.

Vehicle Certification Label

The Vehicle Certification Label is located on the rear edge of the driver's door. Alteration or removal of this label will result in its destruction, or the appearance of the word VOID.

ISIOX100001

Vehicle identification number plate

1. CONSECUTIVE UNIT NO.
2. BODY SERIAL CODE
3. MODEL YEAR CODE
4. ASSEMBLY PLANT CODE
5. ENGINE CODE
6. TRIM CODE
7. REAR AXLE CODE
8. COLOR CODE
9. BODY TYPE CODE
10. DISTRICT - SPECIAL EQUIPMENT CODE
11. TRANSMISSION CODE

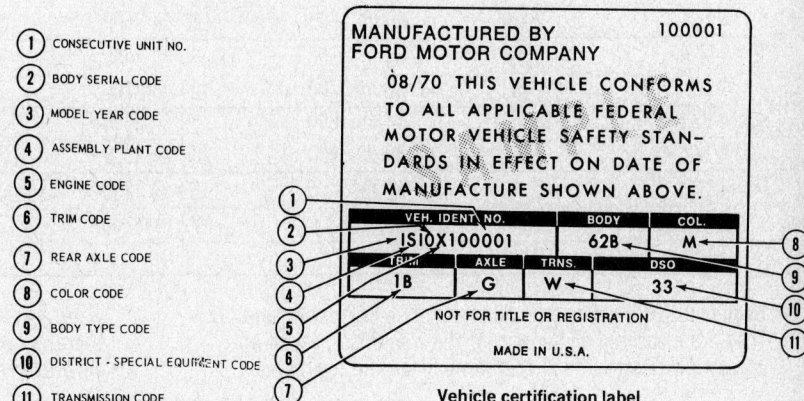

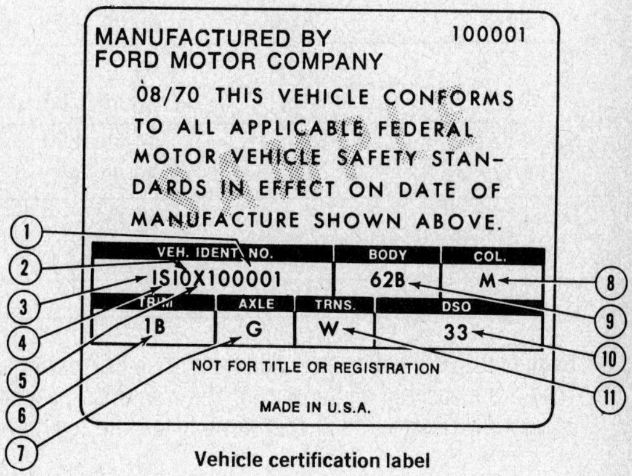
MANUFACTURED BY
FORD MOTOR COMPANY
100001
08/70 THIS VEHICLE CONFORMS TO ALL APPLICABLE FEDERAL MOTOR VEHICLE SAFETY STANDARDS IN EFFECT ON DATE OF MANUFACTURE SHOWN ABOVE.
VEH. IDENT. NO.
BODY
COL.
ISIOX100001
62B
M
TRIM
AXLE
TRNS.
DSO
1B
G
W
33
NOT FOR TITLE OR REGISTRATION
MADE IN U.S.A.
1
2
3
4
5
6
7
8
9
10
11

Vehicle certification label

TORQUE SPECIFICATIONS

All readings in ft lbs

Year	Engine No. Cyl. Displacement (cu in.)	Cylinder Head Bolts	Rod Bearing Bolts	Main Bearing Bolts	Crankshaft Pulley Bolt	Flywheel to Crankshaft Bolts	MANIFOLD Intake	MANIFOLD Exhaust
'71-'74	97.6 (1600cc)	65-70	30-35	65-70	24-28	50-55	12-15	15-18
	122.0 (2000 cc)	65-80	29-34	65-75	39-43	47-51	12-15	12-15
	170.8 (2800 cc)	65-80	22-26	65-75	32-36	45-50	15-18	15-18

ENGINE CODE

Pinto, Mustang II

The engine code designation is the 5th digit of the vehicle identification number (V.I.N.). The V.I.N. is stamped on a plate located at the left side of the instrument panel visible through the windshield on all models.

Disp	Bbl	Hp	'71	'72	'73	'74
4-Cylinder Models						
98 (1600cc)	1	54 (net)		W	W	
98 (1600cc)	1	75	W			
122 (2000cc)	2	83 (net)			X	
122 (2000cc)	2	85, 86 (net)*		X	X	
122 (2000cc)	2	100	X			
140 (2300cc)	2	102 (net)				—
6-Cylinder Models						
171 (2800cc)	2	140 (net)				—

* Net horsepower rating varies with model application

PISTON CLEARANCE

Year	Engine	Piston-to-Bore Clearance (in.)
'71-'73	4-1600 cc	.0016-.0022* .0019-.0025**
'71-'74	4-2000 cc	.0010-.0020
'74	4-2300 cc	.0014-.0022
'74	6-2800 cc	.0009-.0021

* No. 1, 2, and 3
** No. 4

GENERAL ENGINE SPECIFICATIONS

Year	Engine No. Cyl. Cu. In. Displacement	Carburetor Type	Advertised Horsepower @ rpm ■	Advertised Torque @ rpm (ft lbs) ■	Bore and Stroke (in.)	Advertised Compression Ratio	Oil Pressure @ 2050 rpm
'71	4-97.6	1 bbl	75 @ 5000	96 @ 3000	3.188 x 3.056	8.0:1	38
	4-122	2 bbl	100 @ 5600	120 @ 3600	3.575 x 3.029	8.6:1	50①
'72	4-97.6	1 bbl	54 @ 4600	80 @ 2400	3.188 x 3.056	8.0:1	38
	4-122	2 bbl	86 @ 5400	103 @ 3200	3.575 x 3.029	8.2:1	50①
'73	4-97.6	1 bbl	54 @ 4600	80 @ 2400	3.188 x 3.056	8.0:1	38
	4-122	2 bbl	86 @ 5400	103 @ 3200	3.575 x 3.029	8.2:1	50①
'74	4-122	2 bbl	86 @ 5400	103 @ 3200	3.575 x 3.029	8.2:1	50①
	4-140	2 bbl	102 @ 5200	122 @ 3200	3.781 x 3.126	8.4:1	50
	6-170.8	2 bbl	—	—	3.660 x 2.700	8.2:1	40-55①

■ Beginning 1972, horsepower and torque are SAE net figures. They are measured at the rear of the transmission with all accessories installed and operating. Since the figures vary when a given engine is installed in different models, some are representative rather than exact.

① Oil pressure at 1500 rpm.

TUNE-UP SPECIFICATIONS

When analyzing compression test results, look for uniformity among cylinders rather than specific pressures.

	ENGINE		SPARK PLUGS		DISTRIBUTOR		IGNITION TIMING (deg) ▲		VALVES	Fuel	IDLE SPEED (rpm) ▲	
Year	No. Cyl Displacement	hp (cu in.)	Type §	Gap (in.)	Point Dwell (deg)	Point Gap (in.)	Man Trans	Auto Trans	Intake Opens ■ (deg)	Pump Pressure (psi)	Man Trans	Auto Trans
'71	97.6	(1600 cc)	AGR-22	.030	40	.025	12B	—	17	3½-5½	800/500③	—
'71	122	(2000 cc)	BRF-32①	②	40	.025	6B-10B	6B-10B	24	3½-5½	750/500③	650/500③
'72	97.6	(1600 cc)	AGR-22	.030	40	.025	12B	—	17	3½-5½	800/500③	—
'72	122	(2000 cc)	BRF-42	.034	40	.025	6B-10B	6B-10B	24	3½-5½	750/500③	650/500③
'73	97.6	(1600 cc)	AGR-32	.034	40	.025	12B	—	17	3½-5½	800/500③	—
	122	(2000 cc)	BRF-42	.034	40	.025	6B-10B	6B-10B	24	3½-5½	750/500③	650/500③
'74	122	(2000 cc)	BRF-42	.034	39	.025	6B④	6B④	24	3½-4½	750	650
	140	(2300 cc)	AGRF-52	.034	39	.025	6B	6B	22	3½-4½	750	650
	170.8	(2800 cc)	AGR-42	.034	38	.025	12B	12B	20	3½-4½	750	650

▲ See text for procedure

■ All figures Before Top Dead Center

§ All spark plug listings are Autolite original equipment numbers

① BRF-42 recommended service plug

② For BRF-32, set gap to .025 inches and for BRF-42, set gap to .034 inches

③ First figure is for idle speed with solenoid energized and automatic transmission in Drive, while the second figure is for idle speed with solenoid disconnected and automatic transmission in Neutral. Cars without a solenoid use lower figure.

④ See engine compartment sticker for timing on California engines

B Before Top Dead Center

— Not applicable

VALVE SPECIFICATIONS

Year	Engine No. Cyl. Displacement (cu in.)	Seat Angle (deg)	Face Angle (deg)	Spring Test Pressure (lbs @ in.)	Spring Installed Height (in.)	STEM TO GUIDE Clearance (in.) Intake	Exhaust	STEM Diameter (in.) Intake	Exhaust
'71	4-97.6	45	45	47 @ 1.26	1 17/64	.0008-.0030	.0017-.0039	.3100	.3100
	4-122	45	45	67 @ 1.42	1 13/32	.0015-.0015	.0015-.0025	.3149	.3149
'72	4-97.6	45	45	50 @ 1.26	1 17/64	.0008-.0027	.0017-.0036	.3102	.3093
	4-122	45	46	69 @ 1.42	1 13/32	.0008-.0025	.0018-.0035	.3163	.3153
'73	4-97.6	45	44	47 @ 1.263	1 17/64	.0008-.0027	.0017-.0036	.3102	.3093
	4-122	45	44	69 @ 1.418	1 13/32	.0008-.0025	.0018-.0035	.3163	.3153
'74	4-122	45	46	69 @ 1.418	1 13/32	.0008-.0025	.0018-.0035	.3163	.3153
	4-140	45	46	75 @ 1.560	1 9/16	.0006-.0023	.0006-.0023	.3424	.3415
	6-170.8	45	45	64 @ 1.585	1 37/64	.0008-.0025	.0018-.0035	.3162	.3153

CAPACITIES

Year	ENGINE No. Cyl. (Cu. In.) Displacement	Engine ■ Crankcase Add 1 Qt For New Filter	TRANSMISSION Pts To Refill After Draining Manual 3-Speed	Manual 4-Speed	Automatic	Drive Axle (pts)	Gasoline Tank (gals)	COOLING SYSTEM (qts) With Heater	With A/C
'71-'72	4-98 (1600cc)	3	—	2.5	—	2.2	11①	7.75	—
	4-122 (2000cc)	4	—	2.5	16	2.2	11①	8.50	8.50
'73	4-98.6 (1600cc)	3	—	2.8	—	2.2	11①	7.80	—
	4-122 (2000cc)	4	—	2.8	16	2.2	11①	8.50	8.50
'74	4-122 (2000 cc)	4	—	2.8	16	2.2	11①	8.50	8.50
	4-140 (2300 cc)	4	—	2.8	16	2.2	11①②	8.80	9.29
	6-170.8 (2800 cc)	4.5	—	2.8	16	2.2	13	12.5	12.8

■ ½ quart for 1600cc
— Not applicable
① Wagon—12 gals
② Mustang II—13 gals

CRANKSHAFT AND CONNECTING ROD SPECIFICATIONS

All measurements are given in in.

Year	Engine No. Cyl. Displacement (cu in.)	CRANKSHAFT Main Brg. Journal Dia	Main Brg. Oil Clearance	Shaft End-Play	Thrust on No.	CONNECTING ROD Journal Diameter	Oil Clearance	Side Clearance
'71	97.6 (1600cc)	2.1253-2.1261	.0004-.0018	.003-.011	3	1.9368-1.9376	.0004-.0024	.004-.010
	122.0 (2000cc)	2.2432-2.2440	.0005-.0015	.004-.008	3	2.0464-2.0472	.0006-.0026	.004-.010
'72-'73	97.6 (1600cc)	2.1253-2.1261	.0005-.0016	.003-.011	3	1.9368-1.9376	.0004-.0024	.004-.010
	122.0 (2000cc)	2.2432-2.2440	.0006-.0016	.003-.011	3	2.0464-2.0472	.0006-.0026	.004-.010
'74	122.0 (2000 cc)	2.2441	.0006-.0016	.003-.011	3	2.0472	.0006-.0026	.004-.010
	140.0 (2300 cc)	2.3990	.0008-.0026	.004-.008	3	2.0472	.0008-.0024	.0035-.0105
	170.8 (2800 cc)	2.2437	.0006-.0019	.004-.008	3	2.1252-2.1260	.0016-.0021	.004-.011

RING GAP

All measurements are given in in.

Year	Engine	Top Compression	Bottom Compression
'71-'73	1600 cc	.009-.014	.009-.014
'71-'72	2000 cc	.019-.021	.019-.021
'73-'74	2000 cc	.015-.023	.015-.023
'74	2300 cc	.010-.035	.010-.020
'74	2800 cc	.015-.023	.015-.023

Year	Engine	Oil Control
'71-'73	1600 cc	.009-.014
'71-'74	2000 cc	.016-.055
'74	2300 cc	.010-.035
'74	2800 cc	.010-.035

RING SIDE CLEARANCE

All measurements are given in in.

Year	Engine	Top Compression	Bottom Compression
'71-'73	4-1600 cc	.0016-.0036	.0016-.0036
'71-'74	4-2000 cc	.0019-.0038	.0019-.0038
'74	2300 cc	.0020-.0040	N.A.
'74	2800 cc	.0020-.0033	N.A.

Year	Engine	Oil Control
'71-'73	1600 cc	.0018-.0038
'71-'74	2000 cc	Snug

BRAKE SPECIFICATIONS

All measurements given in in.

Year	Model	Master Cylinder Disc	Master Cylinder Drum	Wheel Cylinder Front Disc	Wheel Cylinder Front Drum	Wheel Cylinder Rear	Brake Disc or Drum Diameter Front Disc	Brake Disc or Drum Diameter Front Drum	Brake Disc or Drum Diameter Rear
'71-'73	All Models	.9375	.9375	2.125	1.000	.7187①	9.3	9.0	9.0
'74	All Models	.9375	—	2.600	—	.8750	9.3	—	9.0

① .8750 on station wagons

WHEEL ALIGNMENT SPECIFICATIONS

Year	Model	Caster Range (deg)	Caster Pref Setting (deg)	Camber Range (deg)	Camber Pref Setting (deg)	Toe-in (in.)	Steering Axis Inclin.	Wheel Pivot Ratio (deg) Inner Wheel	Wheel Pivot Ratio (deg) Wheel Outer
'71	All models	1P to 2P	1½P	0 to 1½P	¾P	0 to ¼	8.968	20	18.95
'72	All models	½N to 3½P	1½P	¼N to 1¾P	¾P	1/16 to 7/16	8.968	20	18.94
'73	All models	1N to 3P	1P	¼N to 1¾P	¾P	0 to ¼	8.968	20	18.94
'74	Mustang II	1N to 3P	1P	0 to 1½P	¾P	0 to ¼	9.763	—	—
'74	Pinto	¾N to 3P	1¼P	¼N to 1¾P	¾P	¼ to ⅜	10.018	—	—

N Negative P Positive

BATTERY AND STARTER SPECIFICATIONS

Year	Engine Displacement (cu in.)	Battery Ampere Hour Capacity	Battery Volts	Battery Terminal Grounded	Starter Lock Test Amps	Starter Lock Test Volts	Starter Lock Test Torque (ft lbs)	Starter No-Load Test Amps	Starter No-Load Test Volts	Starter No-Load Test RPM	Brush Spring Tension (oz)
'71-'74	All Models	41, 45, 54	12	Neg.	460	5	9	70	12	180-250	40

ALTERNATOR AND REGULATOR SPECIFICATIONS

Year	Alternator Part No. or Manufacturer	Alternator Field Current @ 12 V	Alternator Output (amps)	Regulator Part No. or Manufacturer	Field Relay Air Gap (in.)	Field Relay Point Gap (in.)	Field Relay Volts to Close	Regulator Air Gap (in.)	Regulator Point Gap (in.)	Regulator Volts @ 75°
'71	D0ZF-B	2.4	38	D0AF-A	Not Adjustable		2.5-4.0	Not Adjustable		13.5-15.3
	D0AF-G	2.9	42	D0AF-A	Not Adjustable		2.5-4.0	Not Adjustable		13.5-15.3
'72	D2ZF-AA	2.4	38	D2AF-AA	Not Adjustable		2.5-4.0	Not Adjustable		13.5-15.3
	D2AF-AA	2.9	42	D2AF-AA	Not Adjustable		2.5-4.0	Not Adjustable		13.5-15.3
	D2SF-AA	2.9	55	D2AF-AA	Not Adjustable		2.5-4.0	Not Adjustable		13.5-15.3
	D2AF-CA	2.9	61	D2AF-AA	Not Adjustable		2.5-4.0	Not Adjustable		13.5-15.3
	D2OF-AA	2.9	65	D2AF-AA	Not Adjustable		2.5-4.0	Not Adjustable		13.5-15.3
'73	D2ZF-AC	2.4	38	D3AF-AA	Not Adjustable		2.5-4.0	Not Adjustable		13.5-15.3
	D2OF-DB	2.9	42	D3AF-AA	Not Adjustable		2.5-4.0	Not Adjustable		13.5-15.3
	D2OF-CB	2.9	61	D3AF-AA	Not Adjustable		2.5-4.0	Not Adjustable		13.5-15.3
	D2ZF-BA	2.9	61	D3AF-AA	Not Adjustable		2.5-4.0	Not Adjustable		13.5-15.3
	D2ZF-AB	2.9	70	D3TF-AA	Not Adjustable		2.5-4.0	Not Adjustable		13.5-15.3
'74	All	—	38	All	Not adjustable		2.5-4.0	Not Adjustable		13.5-15.3
	All	—	61	All	Not adjustable		2.5-4.0	Not Adjustable		13.5-15.3
	All	—	70	All	Not adjustable		2.5-4.0	Not Adjustable		13.5-15.3

NOTE: The 1974 Mustang II is covered in this section. Mustang models from 1967 through 1973 appear in the Fairlane, Falcon, Mustang, Comet, Cougar, Montego, Maverick, Torino car section.

CHARGING SYSTEM

The charging system consists of the battery, the alternator, the regulator and the wires and cables required to connect these units. Repair and testing of the alternator and regulator are covered in the "Unit Repair Section."

Caution Precautions that should be taken into consideration when working on this, or any other, AC charging system are as follows:

1. Never switch battery polarity.
2. When installing a battery, always connect the grounded terminal first.
3. Never disconnect the battery while the engine is running.
4. If the molded connector is disconnected from the alternator, do not ground the hot wire.
5. Never run the alternator with any charging system component disconnected.
6. Never electric weld around the car without disconnecting the alternator.
7. Never apply any voltage in excess of 12 volts during testing.
8. Never "jump" a battery for starting purposes with more than 12 volts.

Alternator Removal

1. Disconnect the battery negative cable.
2. Disconnect the alternator connectors.
3. Loosen the three mounting bolts and tilt the alternator in towards the engine.
4. Remove the fanbelt, then remove the mounting bolts and the alternator.

Alternator Installation

1. Position the alternator and loosely install the mounting bolts.
2. Install fanbelt, pry on the front of the alternator so as to place tension on the belt (1/4 in. deflection at belt midpoint), then tighten mounting bolts.
3. Connect alternator wires and the battery cable.

Regulator R & R

NOTE: The regulator is preset at the factory and is not adjustable.

1. Disconnect the battery ground cable.
2. Remove the wiring harness from the regulator.
3. Remove the regulator retaining screws and remove the regulator.
4. Position the regulator on the car and install the retaining screws.
5. Attach the wiring to the regulator and connect the ground cable.

STARTING SYSTEM

The engine is equipped with an Motor craft positive engagement starter. Internal starter repair procedures can be found in the Unit Repair Section.

R&R

1. Raise the vehicle on a hoist.
2. Disconnect the starter cable from the starter motor.
3. Remove the starter attaching bolts and move the starter forward and remove it from the car.
4. Reverse above procedure to install. Tighten the retaining bolts to 15–20 ft lbs.

IGNITION SYSTEM

Distributor

The 1600 cc engine uses an Autolite distributor which is mounted on the right side of the engine and rotates

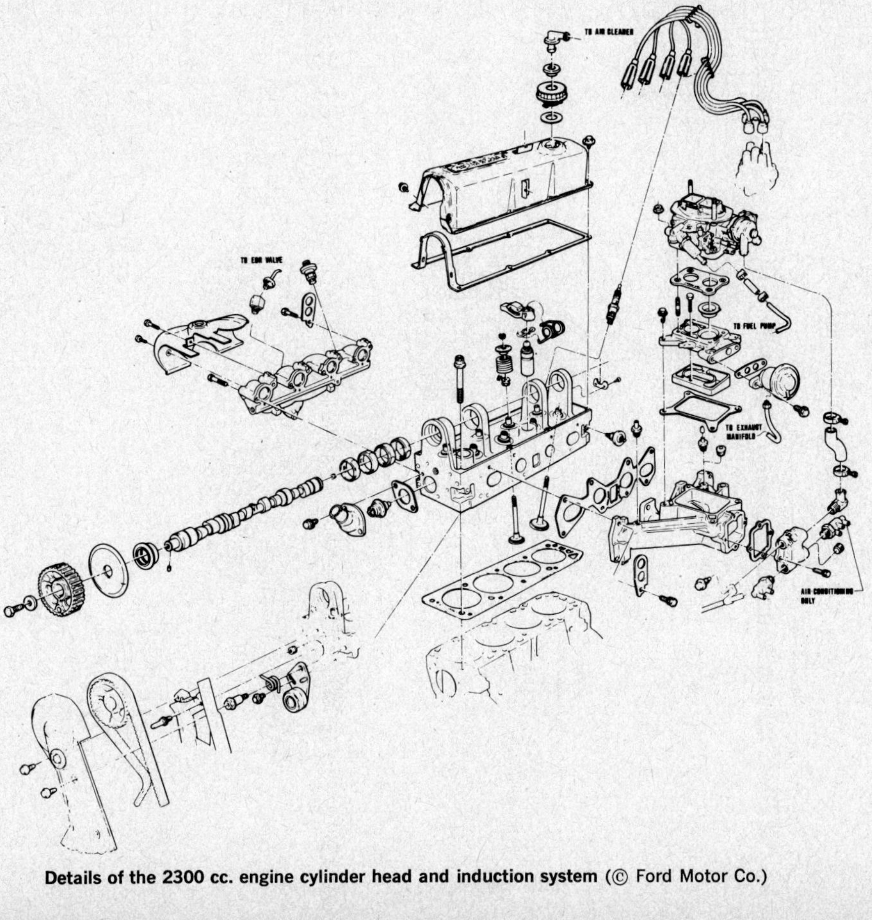
TO AIR CLEANER
TO EGR VALVE
TO FUEL PUMP
TO EXHAUST MANIFOLD
AIR CONDITIONING ONLY

Details of the 2300 cc. engine cylinder head and induction system (© Ford Motor Co.)

counterclockwise. The 2000 cc and V6 engines are equipped with a Bosch distributor driven by an auxiliary shaft. The distributor is located on the left side of the engine and rotates in a clockwise direction. Both distributors are the dual advance type; that is, they have both centrifugal and vacuum advance. Some models are equipped with a vacuum retard mechanism which retards ignition timing during deceleration and idling.

Removal

1. Unsnap the two clips and remove the distributor cap.
2. Note their positioning, and then disconnect the vacuum lines from the distributor.
3. Matchmark the distributor housing and the engine block, then scribe another mark on the housing to indicate the rotor position.
4. Remove the bolt that holds the distributor, then carefully pull out the unit.

Installation

1. Align matchmarks, if engine has not been disturbed, and install distributor.

NOTE: keep in mind that the helical gear will tend to rotate the distributor as it is pushed down.

2. If engine has been disturbed, turn crankshaft until No. 1 piston is at TDC on compression stroke and timing marks are aligned. Place the cap on the distributor and scribe the location of no. one spark plug tower. Install the distributor so that the rotor points toward no. one. Tighten the hold-down bolt.
3. Tighten the hold-down bolt and connect the primary and high-tension wires. Adjust contact breaker points and ignition timing. Connect the vacuum line(s).

Contact Point Replacement and Adjustment

1600 cc

1. Remove the distributor cap. Remove the screw that retains the primary and condenser wires to the point set.
2. Remove the two retaining screws and lift out the point set. It is best to replace the condenser and point set at the same time.
3. Lubricate the cam with silicone cam lube. Place the point set on the breaker plate, making sure the tab on the bottom engages the indentation in the plate. Tighten the retaining screw.
4. Install the primary and condenser wires to the point set, making sure that the connectors are parallel to each other and to the ground when tightened.
5. Turn the engine to bring the point set rubbing block onto one of the cam's high points. Insert a feeler gauge, thickness equal to the point gap specified in the "Tune-Up Specifications" chart, between the contacts.
6. Adjust the gap if the feeler gauge does not fit between the contacts with just a slight drag. Partially loosen the retaining screws and insert a screwdriver in the breaker plate notch at the top of the points. Twist the screwdriver until the correct gap is obtained, and then tighten the retaining screws.
7. Install the distributor cap, aligning the tab in the cap with the notch in the distributor. Check

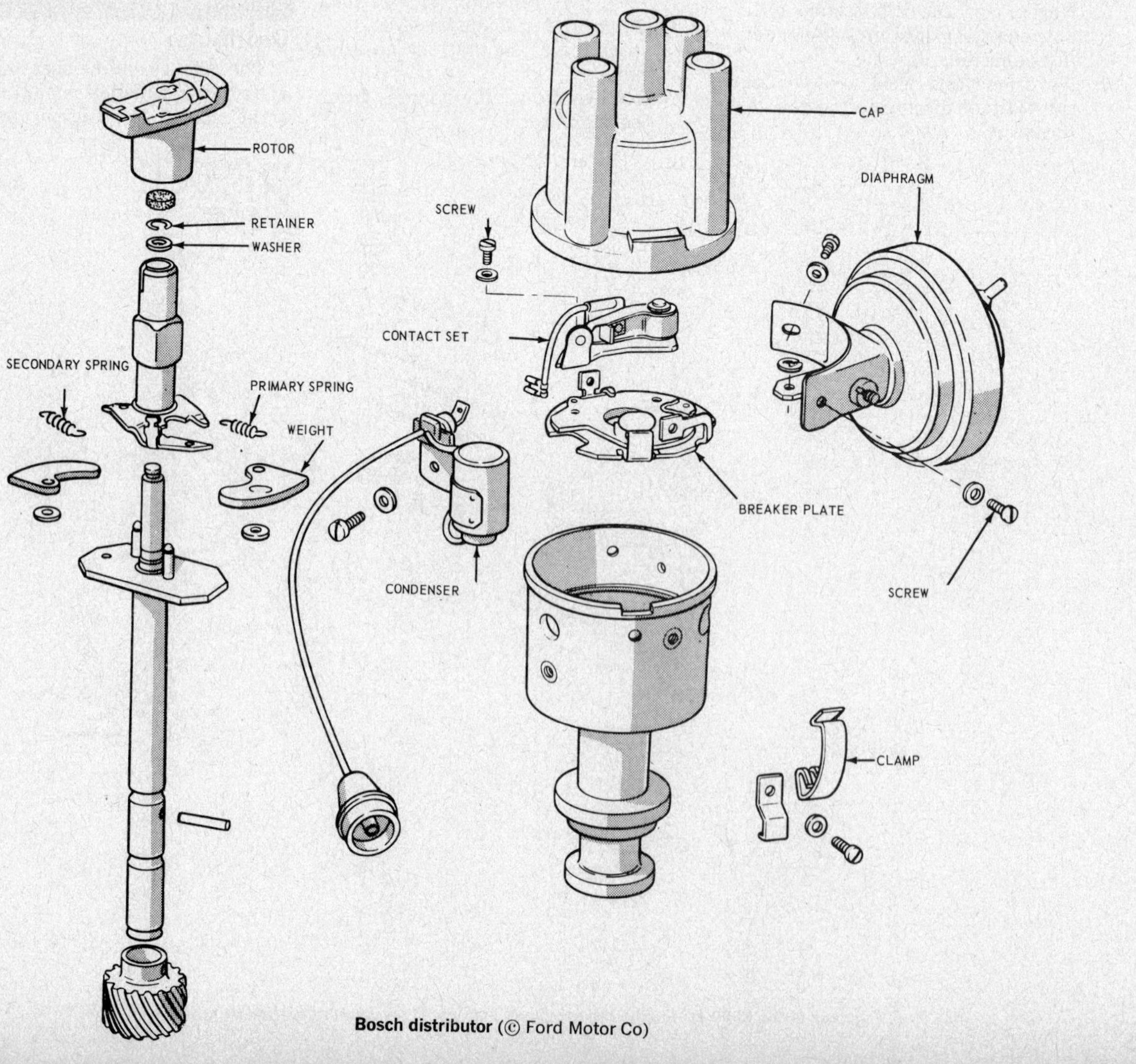
CAP
ROTOR
DIAPHRAGM
SCREW
RETAINER
WASHER
CONTACT SET
SECONDARY SPRING
PRIMARY SPRING
WEIGHT
BREAKER PLATE
CONDENSER
SCREW
CLAMP

Bosch distributor (© Ford Motor Co)

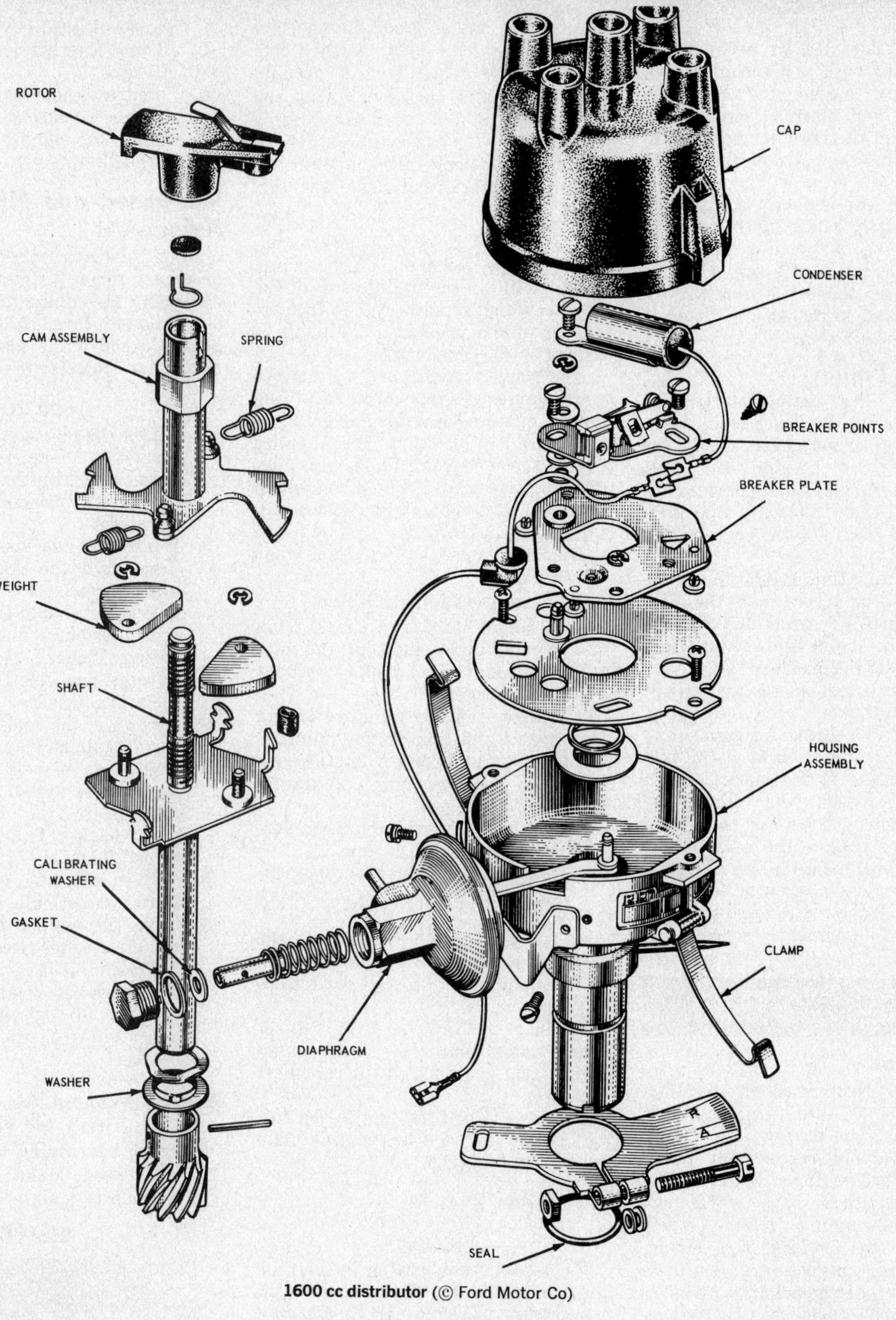
ROTOR
CAP
CONDENSER
CAM ASSEMBLY
SPRING
BREAKER POINTS
BREAKER PLATE
WEIGHT
SHAFT
HOUSING ASSEMBLY
CALIBRATING WASHER
GASKET
CLAMP
DIAPHRAGM
WASHER
SEAL

1600 cc distributor (© Ford Motor Co)

the dwell angle with a meter, if one is available.

2000 cc, 2800 cc V6

1. Remove the distributor cap. Pull the breaker point wire from the condenser connector near the outside edge of the distributor body.
2. Remove the single retaining screw and lift out the point set.
3. To replace the condenser: remove the attaching screw, grasp the condenser and wire, and work the rubber grommet out of the distributor body. Disconnect the ignition wire connector from the coil and disconnect the coil wire from the condenser.
4. To install the condenser: place the condenser and wire assembly on the side of the distributor and work the grommet into the distributor body. Install the retaining screw and position the end of the wire attached to the condenser on the "dist" coil post. Install the ignition wire on the coil post over the condenser wire.
5. Position the point set on the breaker plate and tighten the retaining screw. Connect the breaker point wire to the condenser. Lubricate the cam with silicone cam lube.
6. Turn the engine to bring the point set rubbing block onto one of the cam's high points. Insert a feeler gauge, the thickness of which is equal to the point gap specified in the "Tune-Up Specifications" chart, between the contacts.

Caution When rotating the engine manually, never turn the pulley counterclockwise or the camshaft drive belt may slip and alter the timing.

7. Adjust the gap if the feeler gauge does not fit between the contacts with just a slight drag. Slightly loosen the retaining screw and insert a screwdriver between the boss on the breaker plate and the notch on the points. Twist the screwdriver until the correct gap is obtained, and then tighten the retaining screw.
8. Install the distributor cap, aligning the tab in the cap with the notch in the distributor. Check the dwell angle with a meter if one is available.

Ignition Timing

1. Locate the timing marks and pointer on the lower engine pulley and front cover. Clean the marks and pointer, and then scribe the mark and pointer with chalk. (See "Tune-Up Specifications" chart for the correct timing.)
2. Hook up a timing light to no. one spark plug according to the manufacturer's instructions. Disconnect the one or two vacuum lines and plug the open end (s).
3. Attach a tachometer and adjust the engine idle speed to 600 rpm. (See "Idle Speed Adjustment".)
4. Aim the timing light at the pulley marks. If the marks do not align, loosen the distributor hold-down screw or bolt and slowly rotate the distributor until the marks align. Tighten the hold-down screw or bolt.
5. Recheck the timing, and then adjust the engine to normal idle speed.

FUEL SYSTEM

Carburetor

The carburetor used on the 1600 cc engine is an Autolite single-barrel downdraft unit having idle, main, power valve, and accelerator pump systems. Cars equipped with exhaust emission controls have a tamper-proof slow-running volume screw that limits the rich mixture setting.

All other engines are equipped with an Autolite model 5200 carburetor. The 5200 model is a two stage, two venturi carburetor. The primary stage venturi bore is of smaller diameter than the secondary stage venturi bore. The secondary stage is actuated by mechanical linkage when the primary throttle plates reach an opening of approximately 45°. The primary stage includes a curb idle system, accelerator pump system, idle transfer system, main metering system and power enrichment system.

The secondary stage includes a transfer system, main metering system and power system. Both stages share a common fuel bowl.

On both carburetors, the automatic choke is mounted on the carburetor housing. It has a bimetallic thermostatic coil which winds up when cold and unwinds when hot. A vacuum diaphragm and spring controls the initial operation of the choke. Engine coolant flowing through a choke water cover heats the bimetal coil and controls the final choke opening.

Fuel Pump

The 1600 cc engine uses a diaphragm-type mechanical fuel pump, mounted on the right-hand side of the engine, which supplies fuel to the carburetor under pressure. The pump is driven by the camshaft.

The 2000cc, 2300cc and V6 engines use a diaphragm-type mechanical fuel pump, mounted on the left-front of the cylinder block, which supplies fuel to the carburetor under pressure. The pump is actuated by a rod which is driven by an eccentric on the auxiliary shaft. Both fuel pumps are sealed and must be replaced when defective.

Removal and Installation

1. Disconnect the fuel lines from the fuel pump and plug the inlet line from the gas tank to prevent gas leakage.
2. Remove the fuel pump retaining screws and remove the pump.
3. On 2000 and 2300 cc engines, remove the fuel pump actuating rod.
4. Clean all gasket mounting surfaces.
5. On 2000 and 2300 cc engines, install the fuel pump actuating rod.
6. Apply oil-resistant sealer to the fuel pump, position the pump on the engine and install the retaining screws.

NOTE: On 1600 cc and V6 engines, make sure the fuel pump rocker arm is riding on the camshaft eccentric.

7. Connect the fuel lines to the fuel pump, start the engine and check for leaks.

Fuel Filter R & R

1600 cc

The fuel filter is located in the fuel line beneath the battery; therefore, it is necessary to remove the battery to replace the filter.

1. Disconnect the battery cables. Remove the hold-down retaining nut and remove the battery.

Caution Be careful not to spill electrolyte from the battery as you are removing it.

2. Loosen the filter clamps, remove the lines from the old filter, and install the replacement filter.
3. Tighten the filter clamps and replace the battery.

2000 cc and 2800 cc

The fuel filter is located in the fuel line between the fuel pump and the carburetor.

1. Squeeze the tabs on the fuel filter clamps together and remove the old filter.
2. Compress the clamp tabs and install the replacement filter, positioning the clamps near the ends of the filter.

Idle Speed and Mixture Adjustment

The following prerequisites are necessary for adjustment on all models: bring the engine to normal operating temperature, switch on the high beams, remove the air cleaner, and attach a tachometer to the engine.

1600 cc

1. Check the idle speed. If it is necessary to make an adjustment, turn the nut on the bottom of the carburetor solenoid to correct the speed.
2. When the idle speed is correct, disconnect the solenoid at the quick-disconnect.
3. Idle speed should equal the lower figure in the "Tune-Up Specifications" chart. Turn the carburetor idle screw if an adjustment is necessary.
4. Reconnect the solenoid. Open the throttle slightly and check to see that the solenoid plunger extends. Idle speed should be increased to the higher figure given in the "Tune-Up Specifications" chart.
5. Adjust the idle mixture screw until a smooth idle is obtained.
6. Turn the engine off and install the air cleaner. Recheck the idle speed and, if it is not correct, remove the air cleaner and readjust the idle speed. Repeat this operation until the idle speed is correct.

2000 cc Without Air Conditioning and all V6

1. Start the engine and check the idle speed. Make this check on automatic-equipped cars with the

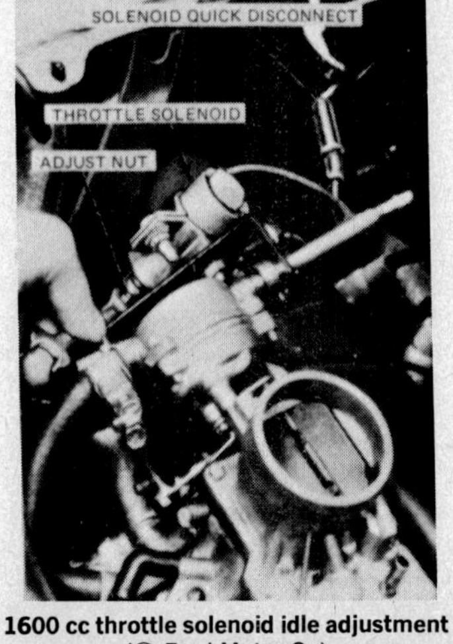
SOLENOID QUICK DISCONNECT
THROTTLE SOLENOID
ADJUST NUT

1600 cc throttle solenoid idle adjustment
(© Ford Motor Co)

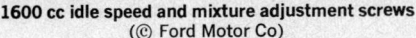

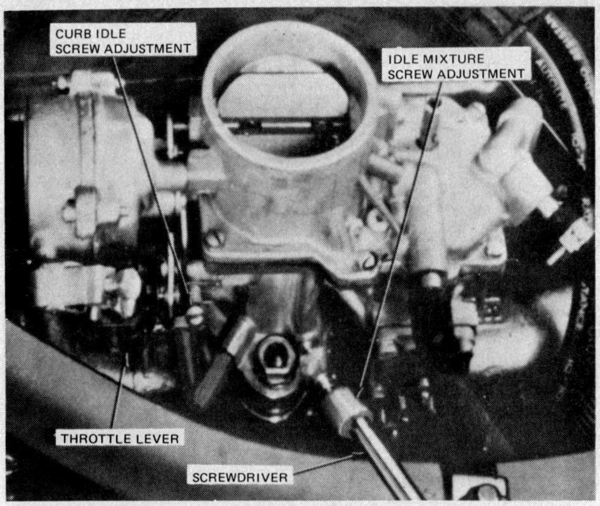
CURB IDLE
SCREW ADJUSTMENT
IDLE MIXTURE
SCREW ADJUSTMENT
THROTTLE LEVER
SCREWDRIVER
1600 cc idle speed and mixture adjustment screws
(© Ford Motor Co)

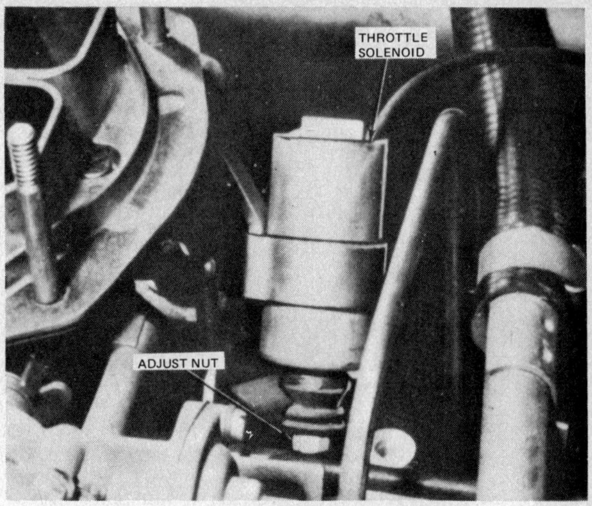
THROTTLE
SOLENOID
ADJUST NUT
Throttle solenoid adjustment
(© Ford Motor Co)

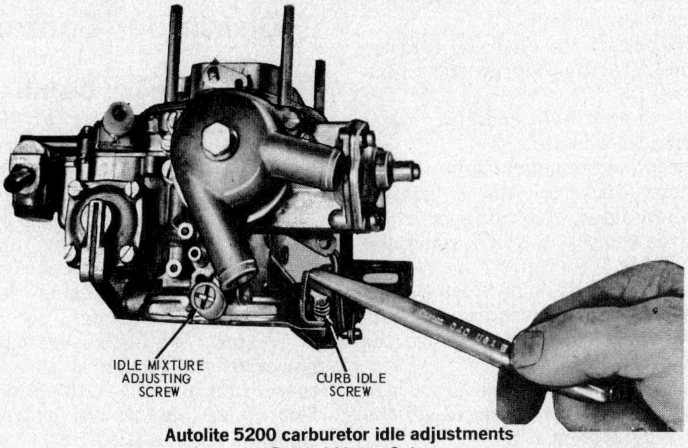
IDLE MIXTURE
ADJUSTING
SCREW
CURB IDLE
SCREW
Autolite 5200 carburetor idle adjustments
(© Ford Motor Co)

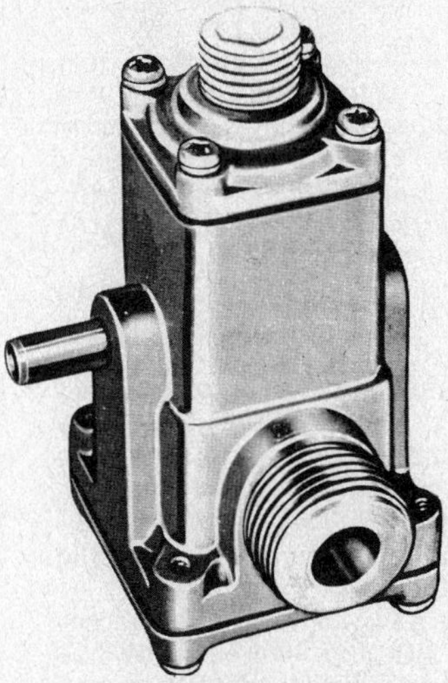
Deceleration valve
(© Ford Motor Co)

selector in Drive and the wheels blocked.

2. Turn the carburetor curb idle screw in or out as necessary to correct the idle speed to the figure in the "Tune-Up Specifications" chart.
3. Adjust the carburetor idle mixture adjusting screw to obtain the smoothest idle.
4. Turn off the engine and install the air cleaner. Restart the engine and check the idle speed. If the idle speed has changed, remove the air cleaner and readjust the idle speed. Repeat this operation until the idle speed is correct.

2000 cc With Air Conditioning

1. Turn the air conditioner on and, if equipped with automatic transmission, block the wheels and place the selector in Drive.
2. Check the idle speed and, if it isn't equal to the higher figure given in the "Tune-up Specifications" chart, turn the adjusting nut on the bottom of the carburetor solenoid to correct it.
3. Disconnect the solenoid at the quick-disconnect. Turn the air conditioner off and, on automatic-equipped cars, put the selector in neutral.
4. Check the idle speed. If it does not conform with the lower figure in the "Tune-Up Specifications" chart, adjust the carburetor curb idle screw to correct it.
5. Reconnect the solenoid. Open the throttle slightly and check to see that the solenoid plunger extends. The idle speed should be increased to the higher figure listed in the "Tune-Up Specifications" chart.
6. Turn the carburetor idle mixture screw until the smoothest idle is obtained.
7. Turn the engine off and install the air cleaner. Restart the engine and check the idle speed (A/C on, automatic transmission in Drive). If an adjustment is necessary, turn the engine off and remove the air cleaner. Start the engine and adjust the idle speed. Repeat this operation as many times as necessary.

Decel Valve Adjustment

The following tools are necessary to adjust the decel valve: a tachometer a vacuum gauge, and a watch. Ignition timing must be correct before performing this adjustment.

1. Attach a tachometer to the engine. Disconnect and plug the air-fuel hose that runs from the carburetor to the deceleration valve.
2. Remove a vacuum hose from the intake manifold and connect a vacuum gauge to that fitting.
3. Start the engine and adjust the carburetor idle mixture screw for the highest possible vacuum reading.

NOTE: This reading must not exceed 18.5 in. Hg for cars with dual-diaphragm distributors or 19.5 in. Hg

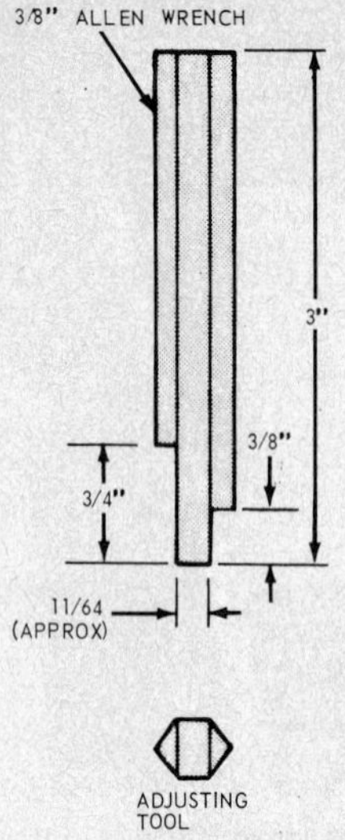
3/8" ALLEN WRENCH
3"
3/8"
3/4"
11/64
(APPROX)
ADJUSTING
TOOL

Deceleration valve adjustment tool
(© Ford Motor Co)

for cars with single-diaphragm distributors. The deceleration valve will not function properly if the vacuum exceeds these values. If the vacuum is too high, readjust the carburetor idle mixture adjusting screw to obtain the specified engine vacuum.

4. Adjust the engine idle speed to specification as previously described.
5. Reconnect the vacuum hose removed for the installation of the vacuum gauge. Insert a "T" fitting into the air-fuel line between the carburetor and the deceleration valve and connect the vacuum gauge to the fitting.
6. Have an assistant raise the engine speed to 3000 rpm for five seconds. While observing the vacuum gauge and the second hand of the watch, have your assistant quickly release the throttle.
7. It the gauge shows a reading for two seconds and then returns to zero, the valve is functioning properly and requires no adjustment.
8. If the reading on the gauge remained for more than two seconds, the adjusting screw on the top of the deceleration valve must be turned in. If the reading remained for less than two seconds, turn the adjusting screw out. An adjustment tool can be fabricated from a 3/8 in. allen wrench by grinding it to the specifications shown in the figure.

NOTE: Later model valves have a cover on the top of the valve which must be pried off for access to the adjusting screw.

9. After adjusting the valve, repeat steps six, seven, and eight to check the operation of the valve. If an adjustment will not bring it within specifications, the valve must be overhauled or replaced.

COOLING SYSTEM

The cooling system consists of the water pump, fan, thermostat, radiator, and connecting lines. Coolant is circulated from the bottom of the radiator up through the water pump and into the cylinder block and cylinder head to the thermostat. If the engine is at operating temperature (or hotter), the coolant is returned to the radiator top tank, from where it flows down through the radiator tubes to be cooled by air. If the engine is cold, the coolant flows through a bypass hose to allow the coolant in the block and head to warm up quickly.

Radiator R & R

1. Remove the radiator cap and drain the coolant.
2. Disconnect the charcoal canister line from the clip on the radiator.
3. Disconnect the radiator hoses from the radiator.
4. Disconnect the transmission oil cooler lines from the bottom of the radiator, if so equipped.
5. Place a block of wood under the radiator for support and remove the mounting bolts. Position the fan shroud, if so equipped, rearward over the fan. Remove the radiator.
6. Reverse the removal procedure to install the radiator. Refill the cooling system.

Water Pump

1. Drain the cooling system.
2. Disconnect the lower radiator hose and heater hose from the water pump.
3. Loosen the alternator retaining and adjusting bolt, and remove the drive belt.
4. Remove the fan and water pump pulley. On 2000 and 2300 cc engines, remove the camshaft drive belt cover.
5. Remove the water pump retaining bolts and remove the pump from the engine.
6. Clean all mating surfaces and install the pump with a new gasket coated with sealer. If a new pump is being installed, transfer the heater hose fitting from the old pump.
7. Reverse the removal steps to install the pump. Refill the cooling system.

Thermostat R & R

1. Drain the cooling system.
2. Remove the thermostat housing attaching bolts.
3. On 1600 cc and V6 engines, lift the thermostat housing from the engine and remove the thermostat and gasket.
4. On 2000 cc engines, remove the retaining clip, thermostat, thermostat seal, and gasket from the housing.
5. Clean the gasket mating surfaces and the thermostat housing.
6. Install the thermostat, gasket, seal, and retaining clip (2000 cc only) in the thermostat housing. Coat the gasket with sealer.
7. Install the attaching bolts and tighten them to 12–15 ft lbs.
8. Refill the cooling system.

EMISSION CONTROLS

Testing and diagnosis of emission control equipment that is not covered in this section is included in the "Emission Control" section of the "Unit Repair Section."

Distributor Controls

Dual-Diaphragm Distributor

Certain models use a dual-diaphragm distributor. This distributor has a normal set of centrifugal advance weights and vacuum diaphragm advance, with the addition of another diaphragm controlled by manifold vacuum. This second diaphragm acts to retard the spark under deceleration and idle, when manifold vacuum is greatest. While this decreases the power of the engine at these times, there is an increase in the braking effect of the engine and hydrocarbon emissions are reduced.

Coolant Temperature Control Valve

Certain models use a coolant temperature control valve which screws into the water jacket. Vacuum lines connect it to the carburetor, outer distributor vacuum chamber (advance), and the intake manifold. This valve helps prevent overheating by connecting intake manifold vacuum to the distributor and allowing vacuum advance during idling when the coolant temperature reaches a certain point.

Spark Delay Valve

Some models utilize a spark delay in the vacuum line to the vacuum advance chamber of the distributor. This valve cuts off vacuum advance during certain heavy throttle applications for a period of seconds.

Electronic Spark Control

This system blocks carburetor vacuum to the distributor vacuum advance mechanism under certain speed and temperature conditions. It consists of a temperature sensor, a speed sensor, an amplifier, and a distributor modulator vacuum valve. This system prevents ignition advance by blocking carburetor vacuum from the distributor advance mechanism until the car reaches 35 mph when the ambient temperature is over 65°F.

The temperature sensor monitors outside air temperature and relays this information to the amplifier. The amplifier controls the distributor modulator vacuum valve, which is connected into the carburetor-to-distributor vacuum line and is normally open. When the temperature is over 65°F, the sensor sends a signal to the amplifier which relays the signal to the distributor vacuum modulator. The modulator closes, cutting off ignition advance, until vehicle speed reaches 35 mph as signaled by the speed sensor in the speedometer cable. When the ambient temperature is below 49° the system does not function.

Exhaust Gas Recirculation

Some models utilize an Exhaust Gas Recirculation System (EGR) to control oxides of nitrogen. On V6 engines, exhaust gases travel through the exhaust gas crossover passage in the intake manifold. A portion of these gases are diverted into a spacer which is mounted under the carburetor. The EGR control valve, which is attached to the rear of the spacer, consists of a vacuum diaphragm with an attached plunger which normally block off exhaust gases from entering the intake manifold. On 4 cylinder engines, an external tube carries exhaust manifold gases to the carburetor spacer. The EGR valve is controlled by a vacuum line from the carburetor.

The vacuum diaphragm opens the EGR valve permitting exhaust gases to flow through the carburetor spacer and enter the intake manifold where they combine with the fuel mixture and enter the combustion chambers. The exhaust gases are relatively oxygen-free, and tend to dilute the combustion charge. This lowers peak combustion temperature thereby reducing oxides of nitrogen.

Thermactor

Some 1974 models are equipped with an air injection system. The thermactor system consists of an air pump, check valves, anti-backfire valve, and air distribution and injection tubes. The belt driven air pump injects air into the exhaust manifold near the cylinder head. The air combines with the gases leaving the cylinders and burns off some of the harmful exhaust gases.

Fuel System Controls

Carburetors

Carburetors are calibrated for leaner mixtures to decrease unburned hydrocarbon emissions. Idle mixture adjusting screws are equipped with limiter caps to prevent their being adjusted for excessively rich air-fuel mixtures at idle. The 1600 cc engine and 2000 cc engines equipped with air conditioning have a throttle positioning solenoid, which raises the idle speed when energized and retracts from the throttle lever when de-energized to prevent dieseling.

Deceleration Valve

1971-72 All Models; 1973 2000 cc With Manual Transmission

This valve is a vacuum-actuated valve which is attached to the intake manifold and connected to the carburetor with an air-fuel line. High vacuum during deceleration opens the valve and draws a metered air-fuel mixture through the hose from the carburetor. This enters the intake manifold and then the combustion chamber, where it is burned. This extra mixture slows the engine's deceleration rate and reduces the usually high exhaust emissions during slow-down. Decel valve adjustment is outlined under carburetor adjustments. Tests and parts replacement procedures follow. A malfunctioning deceleration valve can be caused by one of three things: a leaking diaphragm, a defective poppet valve, or improper adjustment.

Diaphragm Test

With the engine running, cover the small hole in the base of the valve. If the engine idle smoothes out or the speed decreases, the diaphragm is leaking and must be replaced.

Poppet Valve Test

If the engine idles excessively high, and it is not caused by improper carburetor adjustment, throttle linkage bind, or throttle plate bind, the poppet valve in the decel valve may be defective. With the engine running, disconnect the air-fuel line from the carburetor to the decel valve at the decel valve. Seal the opening where the line was disconnected. If the engine speed decreases noticeably, the poppet valve is hanging open and must be replaced.

NOTE: see "Fuel System" for decel valve adjustment.

Decel Valve R & R

1. Disconnect the air-fuel hose from the decel valve.
2. Loosen the union nut that attaches the decel valve to the intake manifold.
3. Reverse the removal steps to install the valve.

Poppet Valve R & R

1. While holding the decel valve cover, loosen the four retaining screws.
2. Remove the screws and gradually release the spring pressure from the cover.
3. Remove the cover and invert the valve to remove the poppet valve and spring.
4. Install the new valve using a reverse of the removal procedure.

Diaphragm R & R

1. Remove the bottom cover from the decel valve.
2. Remove the diaphragm and spring retainer.
3. Install the replacement diaphragm and spring retainer into the bottom of the housing.
4. Install the bottom cover on the decel valve.

Heated Air Intake Air Cleaner

The Pinto air cleaner is equipped with a thermostatically controlled door in the air cleaner snorkel. When the underhood temperature is under 90°F, the door is closed, blocking off cooler underhood air from the air cleaner and allowing heated air from a shroud over the exhaust manifold to enter. When the temperature is over 130°F, the door opens allowing the cooler underhood air to enter the air cleaner.

Evaporative Emission Control System

All models are equipped with a fuel vapor control system. The system has four major components—the fuel tank, the vapor separator, the three-way control valve, and the vapor absorbing charcoal canister. The fuel tank is equipped with a non-vented filler cap and has the vapor separator welded to its top side. The vapor separator cannot be serviced separately if defective—the entire fuel tank must be replaced.

. The tank fuel filler neck is double-sealed and, in addition to fulfilling its primary function of receiving fuel, vents air through a secondary chamber and indicates fuel level.

The vapor separator (see illustration) serves to prevent the entry of liquid fuel into the three-way control valve supply line.

The three-way control valve has three internal valves—a check valve to regulate fuel control (0.3-0.65 psi), a safety pressure relief valve to permit vapor blow-off in case of a plugged vapor line, and a vacuum relief air valve to replace air in the tank as fuel is consumed (to prevent tank collapse).

Crankcase Emission Controls

Crankcase emission control equipment consists of an oil separator (mounted on the side of the engine block), a positive crankcase ventilation (PCV) valve (mounted on the top of the oil separator), a closed oil filler cap, and connecting hoses.

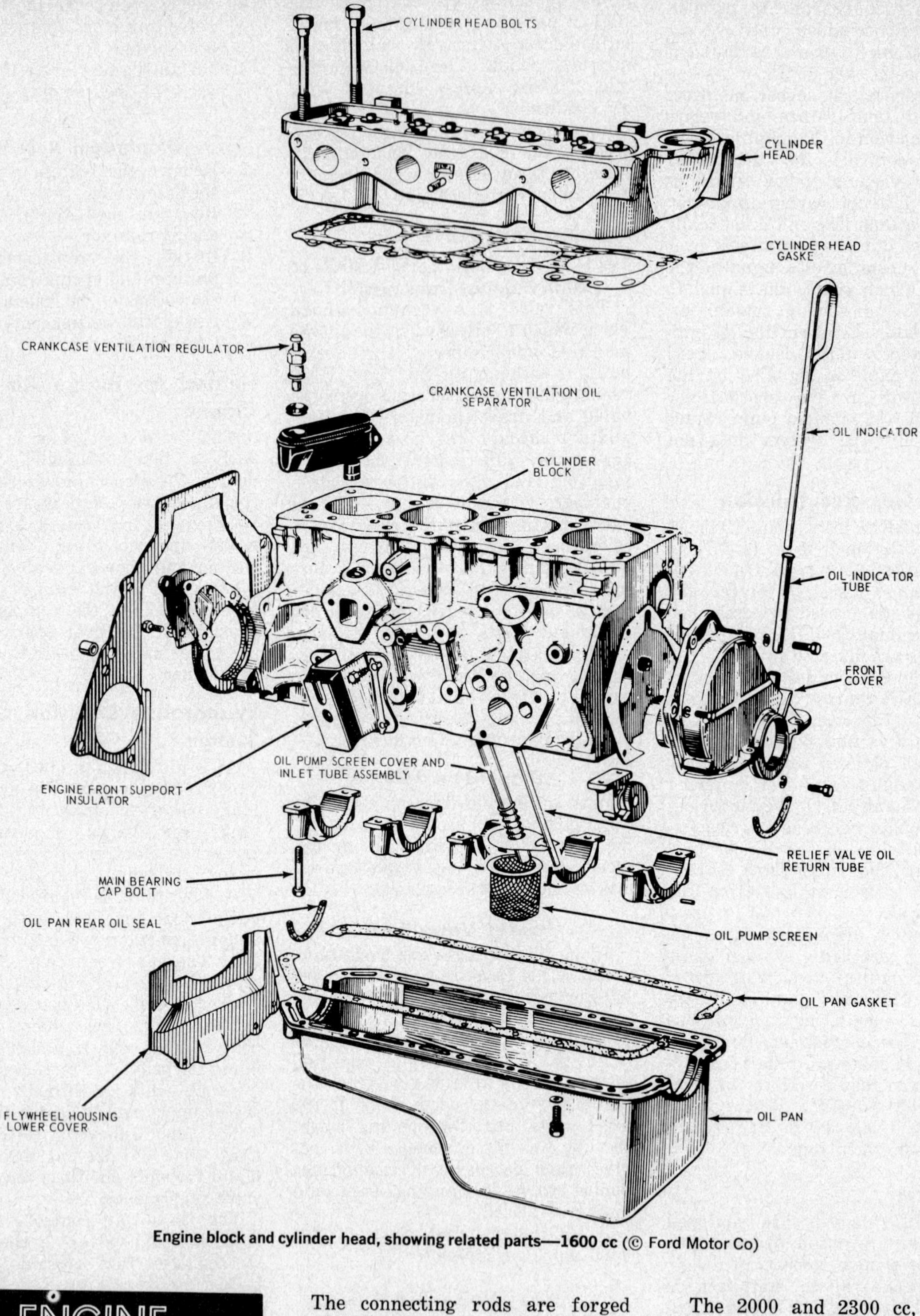
CYLINDER HEAD BOLTS
CYLINDER HEAD
CYLINDER HEAD GASKE
CRANKCASE VENTILATION REGULATOR
CRANKCASE VENTILATION OIL SEPARATOR
OIL INDICATOR
CYLINDER BLOCK
OIL INDICATOR TUBE
FRONT COVER
OIL PUMP SCREEN COVER AND INLET TUBE ASSEMBLY
ENGINE FRONT SUPPORT INSULATOR
RELIEF VALVE OIL RETURN TUBE
MAIN BEARING CAP BOLT
OIL PAN REAR OIL SEAL
OIL PUMP SCREEN
OIL PAN GASKET
FLYWHEEL HOUSING LOWER COVER
OIL PAN

Engine block and cylinder head, showing related parts—1600 cc (© Ford Motor Co)

ENGINE

The standard engine used in the Pinto through 1973 is a 1600 cc, four-cylinder, inline overhead valve unit having a cross-flow cylinder head and piston-shaped combustion chambers. The cylinder bores are machined in the cast-iron block and cooled by full-length water jackets.

The crankshaft is made of cast iron and runs in five main bearings. End-play is controlled by half thrust washers on each side of the center main bearing.

The connecting rods are forged steel and pistons are solid skirt aluminum alloy with two compression rings and one oil ring. Piston pins are full-floating.

The camshaft is driven in a conventional manner, at one-half engine speed, by a single-row roller chain. A helical gear on the cam drives the distributor and oil pump, while an eccentric operates the fuel pump.

The cast-iron cylinder head has integral valve guides; although guide replacement is possible and sleeves are available. Intake valves are aluminum coated, and cannot be refaced.

The 2000 and 2300 cc, overhead camshaft, four-cylinder engine is of cast-iron construction. The crankshaft is supported by five main bearings and the camshaft by three bearings. The camshaft is belt driven by the crankshaft. Belt tension is adjusted by a spring loaded idler pulley.

The pistons are made from an aluminum alloy and forged steel connecting rods are used.

The 2800 cc engine is a V6 overhead valve design. The cylinder heads and engine block are made of cast iron. Four main bearings support the crankshaft. The distributor and the

METRIC THREADS

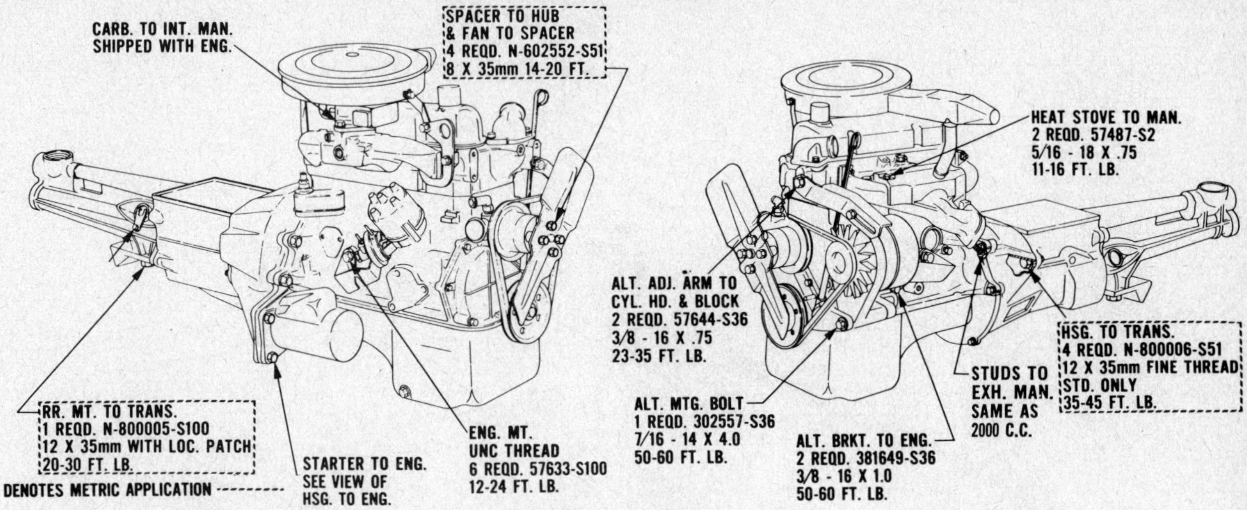
CARB. TO INT. MAN.
SHIPPED WITH ENG.
SPACER TO HUB
& FAN TO SPACER
4 REQD. N-602552-S51
8 X 35mm 14-20 FT. LB.
HEAT STOVE TO MAN.
2 REQD. 57487-S2
5/16 - 18 X .75
11-16 FT. LB.
ALT. ADJ. ARM TO
CYL. HD. & BLOCK
2 REQD. 57644-S36
3/8 - 16 X .75
23-35 FT. LB.
HSG. TO TRANS.
4 REQD. N-800006-S51
12 X 35mm FINE THREAD
STD. ONLY
35-45 FT. LB.
STUDS TO
EXH. MAN.
SAME AS
2000 C.C.
ALT. MTG. BOLT
1 REQD. 302557-S36
7/16 - 14 X 4.0
50-60 FT. LB.
ALT. BRKT. TO ENG.
2 REQD. 381649-S36
3/8 - 16 X 1.0
50-60 FT. LB.
RR. MT. TO TRANS.
1 REQD. N-800005-S100
12 X 35mm WITH LOC. PATCH
20-30 FT. LB.
ENG. MT.
UNC THREAD
6 REQD. 57633-S100
12-24 FT. LB.
STARTER TO ENG.
SEE VIEW OF
HSG. TO ENG.
DENOTES METRIC APPLICATION

1600 cc. ENGINE

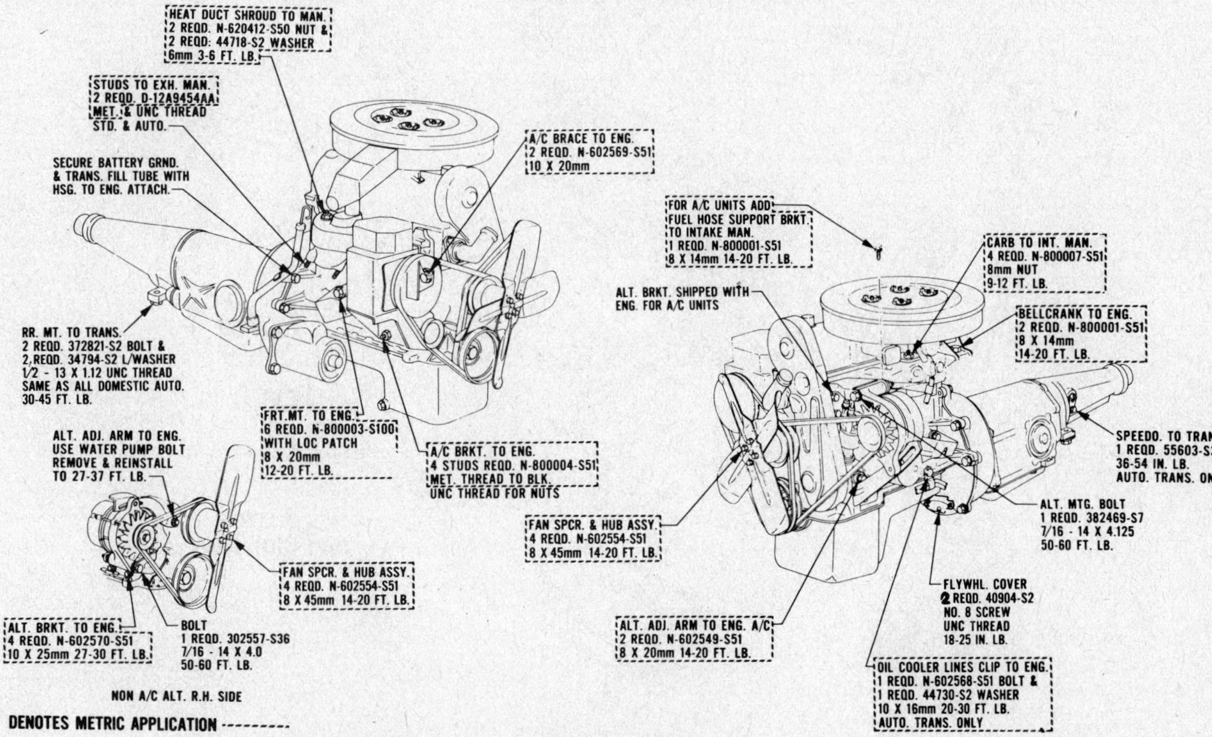
HEAT DUCT SHROUD TO MAN.
2 REQD. N-620412-S50 NUT &
2 REQD. 44718-S2 WASHER
6mm 3-6 FT. LB.
STUDS TO EXH. MAN.
2 REQD. D-12A9454AA
MET. & UNC THREAD
STD. & AUTO.
SECURE BATTERY GRND.
& TRANS. FILL TUBE WITH
HSG. TO ENG. ATTACH.
A/C BRACE TO ENG.
2 REQD. N-602569-S51
10 X 20mm
FOR A/C UNITS ADD
FUEL HOSE SUPPORT BRKT.
TO INTAKE MAN.
1 REQD. N-800001-S51
8 X 14mm 14-20 FT. LB.
CARB TO INT. MAN.
4 REQD. N-800007-S51
8mm NUT
9-12 FT. LB.
ALT. BRKT. SHIPPED WITH
ENG. FOR A/C UNITS
BELLCRANK TO ENG.
2 REQD. N-800001-S51
8 X 14mm
14-20 FT. LB.
RR. MT. TO TRANS.
2 REQD. 372821-S2 BOLT &
2 REQD. 34794-S2 L/WASHER
1/2 - 13 X 1.12 UNC THREAD
SAME AS ALL DOMESTIC AUTO.
30-45 FT. LB.
FRT. MT. TO ENG.
6 REQD. N-800003-S100
WITH LOC PATCH
8 X 20mm
12-20 FT. LB.
A/C BRKT. TO ENG.
4 STUDS REQD. N-800004-S51
MET. THREAD TO BLK.
UNC THREAD FOR NUTS
SPEEDO. TO TRANS.
1 REQD. 55603-S36
36-54 IN. LB.
AUTO. TRANS. ONLY
ALT. ADJ. ARM TO ENG.
USE WATER PUMP BOLT
REMOVE & REINSTALL
TO 27-37 FT. LB.
FAN SPCR. & HUB ASSY.
4 REQD. N-602554-S51
8 X 45mm 14-20 FT. LB.
ALT. MTG. BOLT
1 REQD. 382469-S7
7/16 - 14 X 4.125
50-60 FT. LB.
FAN SPCR. & HUB ASSY.
4 REQD. N-602554-S51
8 X 45mm 14-20 FT. LB.
FLYWHL. COVER
2 REQD. 40904-S2
NO. 8 SCREW
UNC THREAD
18-25 IN. LB.
ALT. BRKT. TO ENG.
4 REQD. N-602570-S51
10 X 25mm 27-30 FT. LB.
BOLT
1 REQD. 302557-S36
7/16 - 14 X 4.0
50-60 FT. LB.
ALT. ADJ. ARM TO ENG. A/C
2 REQD. N-602549-S51
8 X 20mm 14-20 FT. LB.
OIL COOLER LINES CLIP TO ENG.
1 REQD. N-602568-S51 BOLT &
1 REQD. 44730-S2 WASHER
10 X 16mm 20-30 FT. LB.
AUTO. TRANS. ONLY
NON A/C ALT. R.H. SIDE
DENOTES METRIC APPLICATION

2000 cc. ENGINE

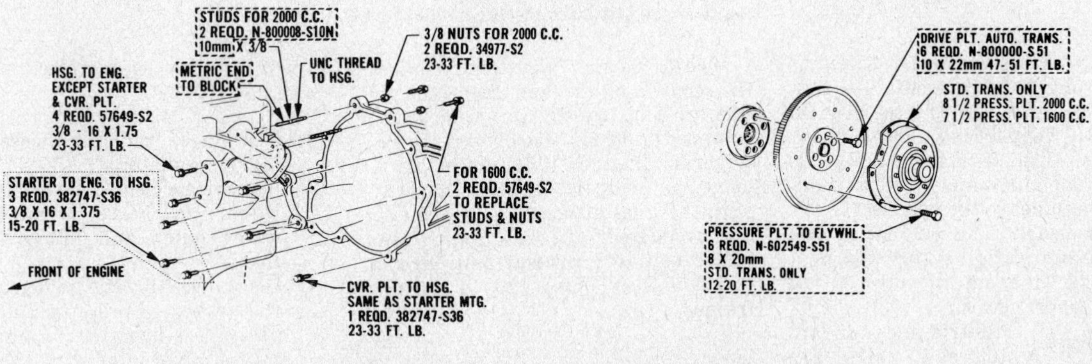
STUDS FOR 2000 C.C.
2 REQD. N-800008-S100
10mm X 3/8
3/8 NUTS FOR 2000 C.C.
2 REQD. 34977-S2
23-33 FT. LB.
METRIC END
TO BLOCK
UNC THREAD
TO HSG.
HSG. TO ENG.
EXCEPT STARTER
& CVR. PLT.
4 REQD. 57649-S2
3/8 - 16 X 1.75
23-33 FT. LB.
STARTER TO ENG. TO HSG.
3 REQD. 382747-S36
3/8 X 16 X 1.375
15-20 FT. LB.
FOR 1600 C.C.
2 REQD. 57649-S2
TO REPLACE
STUDS & NUTS
23-33 FT. LB.
FRONT OF ENGINE
CVR. PLT. TO HSG.
SAME AS STARTER MTG.
1 REQD. 382747-S36
23-33 FT. LB.
DRIVE PLT. AUTO. TRANS.
6 REQD. N-800000-S51
10 X 22mm 47- 51 FT. LB.
STD. TRANS. ONLY
8 1/2 PRESS. PLT. 2000 C.C.
7 1/2 PRESS. PLT. 1600 C.C.
PRESSURE PLT. TO FLYWHL.
6 REQD. N-602549-S51
8 X 20mm
STD. TRANS. ONLY
12-20 FT. LB.

HOUSING TO ENGINE– 1600 C.C. AND 2000 C.C.

Metric bolt location (© Ford Motor Co)

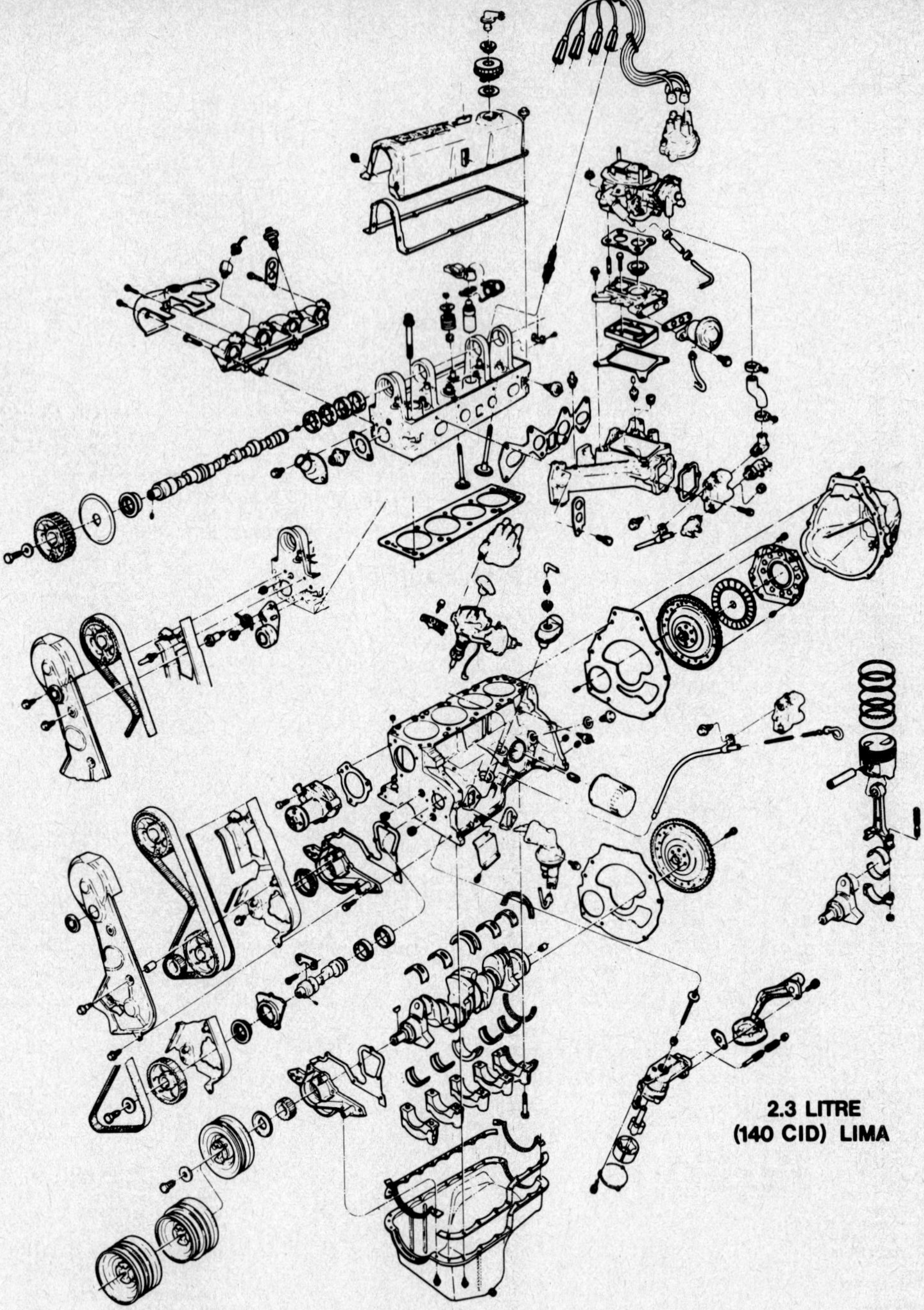
2.3 LITRE
(140 CID) LIMA

Exploded view of 2300 cc engine (© Ford Motor Co)

oil pump are driven by an eccentric at the front of the camshaft. The connecting rods are forged steel with replaceable copper-lead alloy insert bearings. The intake manifold is made from aluminum and has individual passages to the openings in the cylinder heads. The V6 has a full pressure lubrication system fed by a rotor type oil pump mounted at the rear of the crankcase.

Caution

Metric and standard thread bolts are mixed throughout the 1600 and 2000cc engine and transmission. Only metric tools should be used to remove metric bolts. See accompanying illustration for location of metric bolts.

If any repair operation requires the removal of a component of the air conditioning system (on vehicles so equipped), do not disconnect the refrigerant lines. If it is impossible to move the component out of the way with the lines attached, have the system evacuated. Air conditioning systems contain pressurized Freon, which is very dangerous to the untrained.

Engine Removal—1600 cc

1. Remove hood, after scribing matchmarks around hinges.
2. Disconnect battery cables.
3. Drain the cooling system.

NOTE: drain engine block as well as radiator.

4. Disconnect radiator hoses and remove radiator.
5. Remove air cleaner assembly.
6. Disconnect heater hoses from water pump and intake manifold.
7. Disconnect throttle linkage.
8. Disconnect oil pressure and temperature sender wires, then disconnect alternator wires. Disconnect the carburetor solenoid and coil battery wires.

NOTE: it is a good idea to tag these wires.

9. Disconnect exhaust pipe from manifold and remove hot air tubes.
10. Disconnect fuel inlet line at fuel pump.

NOTE: plug the line so that gas does not siphon from tank.

11. Disconnect coil wires, then remove spark plug wires and distributor cap.
12. Jack up the front of the car and support on axle stands.
13. Disconnect starter wires, remove starter and oil pan shield.
14. Remove clutch cover. Drain the oil.
15. Lower the car to the floor.
16. Remove clutch housing-to-engine bolts, then install lifting brackets and chain hoist.
17. Disconnect the front motor mounts, while supporting engine with chain hoist.
18. Place an axle stand or wooden block under the transmission.
19. Raise the engine slightly, while pulling forward to separate the transmission input shaft from the clutch: lift engine out of car.

Engine Installation—1600 cc

1. Position the engine assembly in the engine compartment and start the input shaft into the clutch disc. It may be necessary to adjust the position of the transmission if the input shaft doesn't enter the clutch disc properly. If the engine won't move after the shaft enters the clutch, turn the crankshaft pulley slowly with the transmission in gear until the splines on the input shaft align with those on the clutch disc.
2. Slide the engine rearward, making sure the flywheel upper cover plate engages the dowels on the clutch housing. Align the front motor mounts and the exhaust manifold with the exhaust pipe.
3. Install the front motor mount nuts and tighten them to 20–30 ft lbs.
4. Install and tighten the upper clutch housing-to-engine attaching bolts. Make sure that the engine ground strap is secured by the upper left bolt.
5. Install the distributor cap and wires. Connect the fuel line to the fuel pump.
6. Connect the oil pressure water temperature sending unit wires. Connect the carburetor solenoid and distributor battery wires.
7. Connect the alternator wires.
8. Connect the exhaust pipe to the exhaust manifold and install the heat duct on the manifold.
9. Connect the throttle linkage to the carburetor.
10. Connect the heater hoses to the engine.
11. Install the radiator and connect the hoses.
12. Install the air cleaner.
13. Jack the front of the car up and support it with stands.
14. Install the starter and connect the cable.
15. Install the lower clutch housing cover.
16. Install the oil pan drain plug and the cooling system drain plug in the block. Close the radiator petcock.
17. Remove the jack stands and lower the car.
18. Fill the engine with oil and the cooling system with coolant.
19. Connect the negative battery cable.
20. Start the engine and allow it to idle. Check for leaks and perform any necessary adjustments.
21. Install the hood.

Engine Removal—2000 and 2300 cc

1. Drain the engine of coolant and oil. Remove the hood.
2. Remove the air cleaner and the exhaust manifold shroud.
3. Disconnect the battery ground cable.
4. Remove the upper and lower hoses from the radiator.
5. Remove the radiator and fan.
6. Disconnect the heater hose from the water pump and carburetor choke fitting.
7. Disconnect the wires from the alternator and starter. It is good practice to tag these wires to prevent confusion during installation.
8. Disconnect the carburetor accelerator cable. If the vehicle is equipped with air conditioning, remove the compressor from the mounting bracket and lay it aside.

NOTE: leave the refrigerant lines attached.

9. Disconnect the flexible fuel line from the fuel tank line and plug the fuel tank line.
10. Disconnect the coil primary wire and the water temperature and oil temperature sending units.
11. Jack up vehicle and remove the starter.
12. Remove the flywheel (or converter housing) upper mounting bolts.

NOTE: Two 10 mm × 3/8 in. studs are used to attach the upper housing to the engine. If the studs are removed, make sure they are reinstalled with the metric threads in the engine block.

13. Disconnect the exhaust pipe at the exhaust manifold. Unbolt the engine right and left mount at the underbody bracket. Remove the flywheel (or converter housing) cover.
14. On vehicles equipped with manual transmissions, remove the flywheel housing lower mounting bolts. On automatic transmission vehicles, disconnect the converter from the flywheel and remove the converter housing lower mounting bolts. It is necessary to turn the crankshaft pulley to gain access to the four converter - to - flywheel attaching nuts.
15. Lower the vehicle and support the transmission or converter housing with a hydraulic jack.
16. Attach the engine lifting apparatus and carefully pull the engine from the engine compartment.
17. On automatic transmission-equipped vehicles, match-mark the flywheel and the torque converter so they can be rejoined correctly.

Engine Installation—2000 and 2300 cc

1. Place a new gasket over the exhaust pipe.
2. Carefully, lower the engine into the engine compartment. Be sure that the exhaust manifold studs are aligned with the holes in the exhaust pipe flange. On a vehicle with automatic transmission, start the converter pilot shaft into the crankshaft. On manual transmission cars, start the transmission drive gear into the clutch disc. It may be necessary to adjust the position of the transmission with relation to the engine if the input shaft fails to enter the clutch disc. If the engine hangs up after the shaft enters, turn the crankshaft slowly with the transmission in gear, until the input shaft splines mesh with the clutch disc splines.
3. Remove the lifting apparatus and install the flywheel (or converter housing) upper mounting bolts.
4. Remove the jack from the transmission and jack up vehicle.
5. Install the flywheel (or converter housing) lower mounting bolts. On an automatic transmission car, attach the converter to the flywheel and torque to 23-28 ft. lbs.
6. Install the flywheel (or converter housing) dust cover.
7. Install the engine left and right mounting brackets to the underbody.
8. Unplug the fuel tank line and connect it to the flexible line. Tighten the exhaust pipe and exhaust manifold.
9. Lower the vehicle and connect the water and oil temperature sending units, coil primary wire and accelerator cable.
10. Install and connect the starter. Connect the alternator wires, and heater hose to the water pump and carburetor choke fitting.

11. Install the fan pulley, fan and drive belt. On vehicles equipped with air conditioning, install the compressor on the mounting bracket and adjust the belt tension. Drive belt should sag approximately ½ in. under thumb pressure at the middle of the longest side.
12. Install the radiator and connect the upper and lower hoses. Fill and bleed the cooling system. Fill the engine with the proper amount and grade of engine oil.
13. Connect the battery ground cable and operate the engine at fast idle, checking all gaskets and hoses for leaks.
14. On automatic transmission vehicles, adjust the transmission control linkage.
15. Install the air cleaner and connect the crankcase ventilation hose.
16. Install the hood.

Engine Manifolds

Intake Manifold Removal

All 4 Cylinder Models

1. Drain the cooling system.
2. Remove the air cleaner and disconnect the throttle shaft at the carburetor throttle lever.
3. Disconnect the fuel line and vacuum line from the carburetor. Disconnect the carburetor solenoid wire at the quick-disconnect.
4. Remove the choke thermostatic spring and water housing.
5. Disconnect the water outlet hose and crankcase ventilation hose from the intake manifold.
6. Disconnect the decel-to-carburetor hose at the carburetor.
7. Remove the intake manifold attaching bolts and remove the manifold.
8. Remove all gasket material.
9. If the intake manifold is to be replaced, transfer all necessary components to the new manifold. Loosen the union fitting on the manifold and remove the decel valve from the intake manifold. Remove the decel valve adaptor from the manifold by inserting a large allen wrench into the adaptor and turning the adaptor out of the manifold.

Intake Manifold Installation

All 4 Cylinder Models

1. Clean the cylinder head and intake manifold mating surfaces thoroughly.
2. Carefully coat the mating surfaces with sealer and position a new gasket on the studs. Install the manifold and torque the nuts alternately and evenly to 15–18 ft lbs (1600 cc), or 12–15 ft lbs (2000 cc).
3. Further installation is the reverse of removal.

Intake Manifold Removal and Installation

2800 cc

1. Remove the air cleaner assembly and disconnect the battery.
2. Disconnect the throttle cables.
3. Drain the cooling system. Disconnect and remove the hose from the water outlet to the radiator and the hoses and line from the water outlet to the water pump.
4. Remove the distributor cap and spark plug wires as an assembly. Disconnect the distributor wire and the vacuum line.
5. Mark the position of the distributor and remove it.
6. Remove the fuel line and filter between the fuel pump and the carburetor and then remove the rocker arm covers.
7. Remove the intake manifold bolts and nuts. Tap the manifold lightly with a plastic hammer to break the gasket seal, and then lift off the manifold.
8. Remove all the gasket material and dirt from the manifold and cylinder heads.
9. Apply sealing compound to the joining surfaces. Place the manifold gasket in place. (Make sure that the tap on the right bank of the cylinder head gasket fits into the cutout of the manifold gasket.)
10. Install the intake manifold. Tighten the attaching bolts until they are hand tight, and then torque them, in sequence, to 15-18 ft lbs.

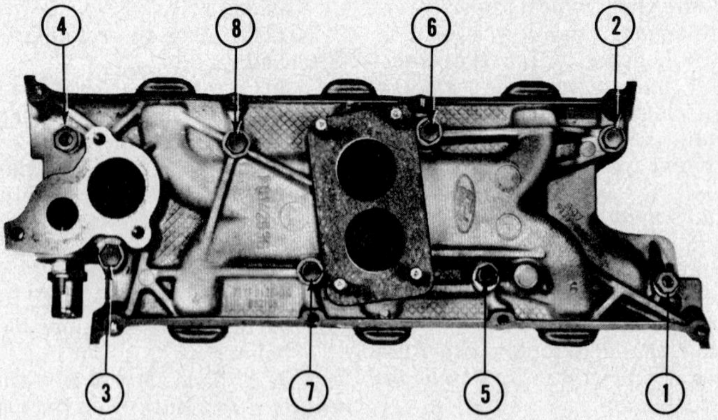
4
8
6
2
3
7
5
1

V6 intake manifold tightening sequence
(© Ford Motor Co)

NOTE: Tightening bolt no. 7 with a torque wrench will require an attachment called a "crow's foot."

11. Install the distributor so the rotor is pointing to the mark made previously.
12. Connect the distributor wire and vacuum line.
13. Install the carburetor, fuel line, fuel filter, and the rocker arm covers.
14. Install the distributor cap and wires.
15. Install and adjust the carburetor linkage.
16. Install the air cleaner assembly and air cleaner tube to the carburetor. Connect the battery.
17. Adjust the ignition timing.

Exhaust Manifold R & R

1600 cc

1. Remove the air cleaner.
2. Place a block of wood under the front of the exhaust pipe and disconnect the exhaust pipe from the manifold.
3. Remove the exhaust manifold attaching nuts and bolts, and remove the manifold.
4. If a new manifold is to be installed, remove the heat shroud from the old manifold and install it on the new manifold.
5. Clean the exhaust manifold and cylinder head mating surfaces.
6. Install a new gasket over the center studs on the cylinder head.
7. Position the exhaust manifold near the cylinder head and install the end exhaust manifold gaskets between the manifold and the head.
8. Install the attaching nuts and bolts and tighten them to 15–18 ft lbs.
9. Connect the exhaust pipe to the manifold, remove the wood support, and install the air cleaner.

2000 and 2300 cc

1. Remove the air cleaner. Remove the heat shroud from the exhaust manifold.
2. Place a block of wood under the exhaust pipe, and then disconnect it from the manifold.
3. Remove the attaching nuts and remove the manifold from the head.
4. Install a light coat of graphite grease on the exhaust manifold mating surface and position the manifold on the cylinder head.
5. Install the attaching nuts and tighten them to 12–15 ft lbs.

6. Connect the exhaust pipe to the manifold and remove the wood support from under the pipe.
7. Install the air cleaner.

2800 cc

1. Remove the air cleaner.
2. Remove the four attaching nuts from the exhaust manifold shroud (right side only).
3. Disconnect the attaching nuts from the muffler inlet pipe.
4. Remove the exhaust manifold attaching nuts and remove the manifold.
5. These manifolds do not use gaskets. When installing the manifold, smear a light coat of graphite grease on the mating surfaces.
6. Position the manifold on the studs and install the bolts hand-tight then torque them evenly to 15-18 ft lbs.
7. Install a new inlet pipe gasket and the attaching nuts.
8. Position the exhaust manifold shroud on the manifold and install the attaching nuts (right side).
9. Install the air cleaner.

Valve System

1600 cc

The valves are mounted vertically in the cylinder head, the intake valve heads being larger than the exhaust valve heads. The exhaust valves are stellite-coated for better heat and wear resistance, while the intake valves are coated with diffused aluminum for the same reason. *The factory does not recommend grinding the intake valves or lapping the intake valve seats, because the grinding operation removes the coating and shortens the life of the valve.* Exhaust valves, on the other hand, may be ground if necessary.

Valve stems are phosphate-coated for better wear resistance. Valve guides are cast integral with the head, although sleeves are available if guides become worn. In addition, valves are available with 0.003 and 0.015 in. oversize stem diameters.

The valve keepers do not grip the stem, allowing the valves to rotate freely during operation.

Valve Removal

1. Remove cylinder head, as previously described.
2. Compress valve springs, using valve spring compressor.
3. Remove valve locks or keys.
4. Release valve springs.
5. Remove valve springs, retainers, oil seals, and valves. Check valve spring squareness—5/64 in. is maximum permissible tolerance.

NOTE: if a valve does not slide out of the guide easily, check end of stem for mushrooming or heading over. If head is mushroomed, file off

Chilton's TIME SAVER

The following is a method for replacing valve springs, oil seals or spring retainers without removing the cylinder head.

1. **Obtain an air hose spark plug hole adaptor.**
2. **Remove the valve rocker cover.**
3. **Remove the rocker arm from the valve to be worked on.**
4. **Remove the spark plug from the cylinder to be worked on.**
5. **Turn the crankshaft to bring the piston of this cylinder down, away from possible contact with the valve head. Sharply tap the valve retainer to loosen the valve lock.**
6. **Then turn the crankshaft to bring the piston in this cylinder to the Exact Top of its Compression Stroke.**
7. **Screw in the spark plug hole adaptor.**
8. **Hook up an air hose to the chuck and turn on the pressure.**
9. **With a strong and constant supply of air holding the valve closed, compress the valve spring and remove the lock and retainer.**
10. **Make the necessary replacements and reassemble.**

NOTE: it is important that the operation be performed exactly as stated, in this order. The piston in the cylinder must be on exact top-center to prevent air pressure from turning the crankshaft.

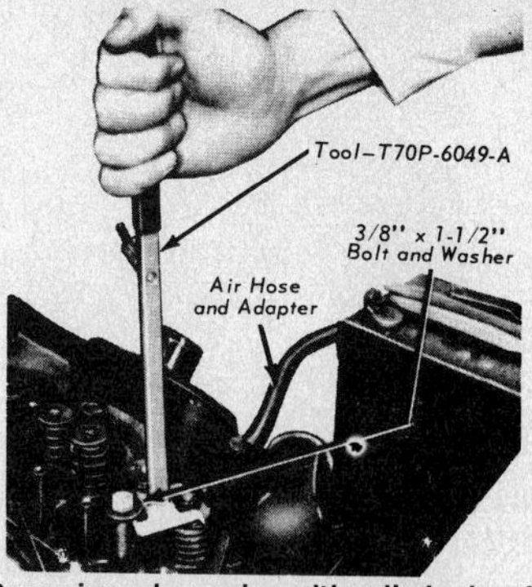
Tool—T70P-6049-A
3/8" x 1-1/2" Bolt and Washer
Air Hose and Adapter

Removing valve spring with cylinder head installed—1600 cc
(© Ford Motor Co)

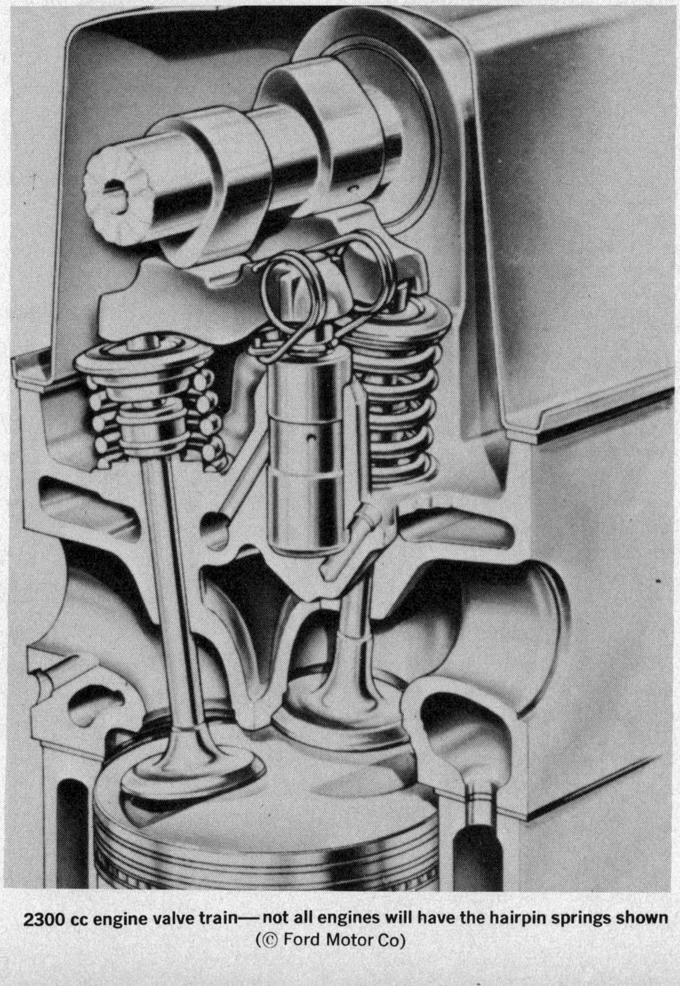

2300 cc engine valve train—not all engines will have the hairpin springs shown
(© Ford Motor Co)

WRENCH
ADJUSTING SCREW
FEELER GAUGE

Adjusting valve clearance—1600 cc
(© Ford Motor Co)

excess material, remove and discard valve. If valve is not mushroomed, lubricate stem, remove valve and check guide for galling. Valve seat width (minimum and desirable) is 1/16 in. for intakes, 5/64 in. for exhausts.

Valve Adjustment

1600 cc

Valves are set with the engine at normal operating temperature and turned off.

1. Remove the air cleaner. Disconnect the carburetor solenoid wire at the connector near the rear of the valve cover.
2. Remove the throttle cable retaining screw, pry the end of the throttle cable off the carburetor stud, and position the cable out of the way.
3. Remove the valve cover. Identify the spark plug wires and disconnect them.
4. Turn the engine to depress the proper valves by turning the crankshaft pulley.

Valve Clearance Adjustment

1600 cc Engine—Set Hot

Valve Depressed	*Valves to Adjust to .010*	*.017*
No. 1	No. 3	No. 8
No. 2	No. 7	No. 5
No. 3	No. 6	No. 1
No. 6	No. 2	No. 4

5. Insert a feeler gauge of the specified thickness between the tip of the rocker arm and the top of the valve. If an adjustment is necessary, turn the adjusting screw in or out as necessary.
6. Install the removed or disconnected components in a reverse order of removal. Tighten the valve cover retaining screws to 2.5–3.5 ft lbs.

2000 cc

Valves are set with engine cold.

1. Remove the air cleaner. Identify the spark plug wires and remove them, positioning them out of the way.
2. On non-air-conditioned models, move the heater hose attached to the carburetor choke housing off the valve cover and out of the way. On air-conditioned models, disconnect the carburetor choke heater hose from the heater hot water valve and position it out of the way.
3. Remove the valve cover retaining screw (note the position of the screws with rubber coated washers) and remove the valve cover.
4. Turn the crankshaft pulley to depress the valves specified in the chart.

Caution Never turn the pulley in a counterclockwise direction, as the camshaft drive belt may slip and alter the timing.

5. Check clearance according to the following chart:

Valve Clearance Adjustment

2000 cc Engine—Set Cold

Valve Depressed	*Valves to Adjust to .008*	*.010*
No. 1	No. 6	No. 7
No. 2	No. 8	No. 3
No. 3	No. 2	No. 5
No. 5	No. 4	No. 1

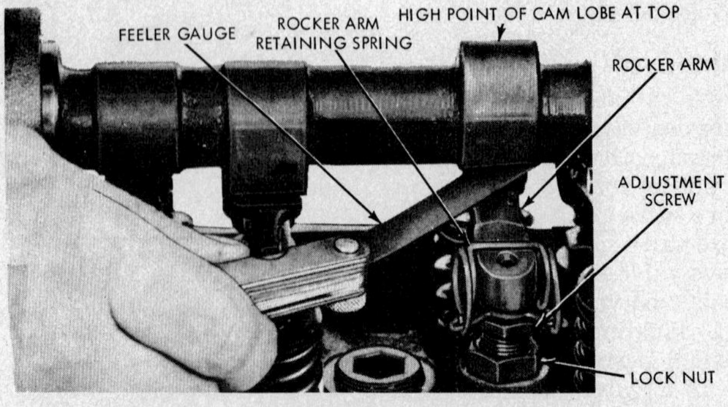
FEELER GAUGE
ROCKER ARM RETAINING SPRING
HIGH POINT OF CAM LOBE AT TOP
ROCKER ARM
ADJUSTMENT SCREW
LOCK NUT

Checking valve clearance—2000 cc
(© Ford Motor Co)

Clearance is checked between the rocker arm and the cam. Use a screwdriver to snap the retaining spring off the rocker arm until it hangs loose. Use a feeler gauge of the specified thickness to check the clearance.

6. If an adjustment is necessary, loosen the locknut and turn the adjusting screw in or out as necessary. When the adjustment is correct, tighten the locknut and snap the retaining spring back into place.
7. Replace the removed or disconnected components in a reverse order of removal. Tighten the rear valve cover cap screws to 4–6 ft lbs. from the back forward, the two vertical cap screws to 1–2 ft lbs, the two lateral cap screws to 4–6 ft lbs, and retighten the two vertical cap screws to 4–6 ft lbs.

2300 cc

This engine uses hydraulic lash adjusters. Thus, no routine valve adjustment is required.

2800 cc

Valve clearance on this engine should be measured cold. Clearances are .014 in. for intake valves and .016 in. for exhaust valves.

Rocker Arm or Shaft R & R

1600 cc

1. Remove the valve cover as described under "Valve Adjustment." Disconnect the spark plug wires and move them out of the way.
2. Loosen each rocker shaft attaching bolt one turn at a time until all the bolts are loose.
3. Remove the rocker shaft.
4. To install, position the rocker shaft on the head and align the pushrods with the rocker arm adjusting screws.
5. Starting from the front of the engine and working back, tighten each bolt one turn at a time until the shaft is mounted on the head. Finally, tighten each bolt to 25-30 ft lbs.

2000 cc

1. Remove the valve cover as described under "Valve Adjustment."
2. Rotate the crankshaft in a clockwise direction until the cam lobe for the rocker arm that is to be removed is pointing straight up.
3. Remove the retaining spring from the rocker arm.

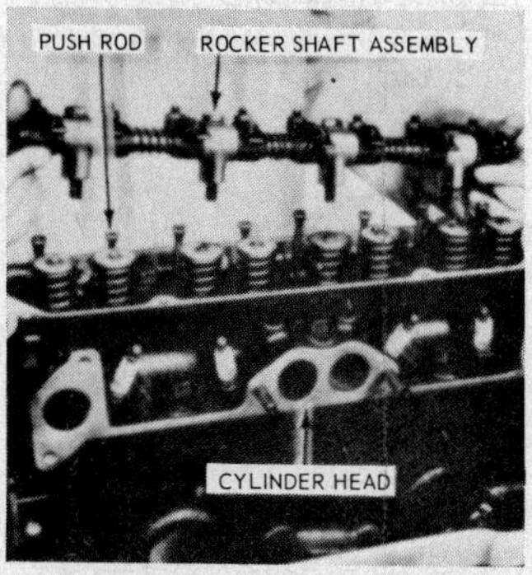
PUSH ROD
ROCKER SHAFT ASSEMBLY
CYLINDER HEAD

Removing rocker arm assembly—1600 cc
(© Ford Motor Co)

4. Depress the valve spring that corresponds to the rocker arm that is to be removed just enough to remove the rocker arm.
5. To install, position the rocker arm on the valve and adjusting screw and install the rocker arm retaining spring.
6. Adjust the valve clearance as previously described.
7. Install the valve cover, air cleaner, and any other components that were removed or disconnected in a reverse order of removal.

Cylinder Head

Removal—1600 cc

1. Remove the air cleaner, then disconnect the fuel line at the pump and the carburetor.
2. Drain the cooling system.
3. Disconnect spark plug wires, then disconnect heater and vacuum hoses from the intake manifold and choke housing.
4. Disconnect temperature sender wire, then disconnect exhaust pipe at manifold flange.
5. Disconnect throttle linkage and distributor vacuum line at carburetor. Disconnect the carburetor solenoid wire.

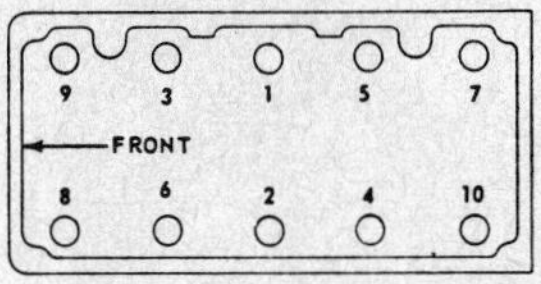
9
3
1
5
7
FRONT
8
6
2
4
10

1600 cc cylinder head bolt tightening sequence

6. Remove thermostat housing and thermostat.
7. Remove rocker arm cover and gasket, then remove the rocker shaft bolts, evenly, and the rocker shaft assembly.
8. Remove pushrods and place them aside in proper order for correct installation.
9. Remove cylinder head bolts, head, and gasket.

Installation—1600 cc

1. Place a new head gasket on the block.
2. Position the cylinder head and install the bolts. Tighten evenly in sequence (see illustration under *Torque Specifications* table) to proper torque.

NOTE: manifolds may be installed prior to placing head on block.

3. Install pushrods in correct order, then place rocker arms and shaft assembly on head and locate pushrods in rocker arm screws. Tighten rocker arm bolts to 25-30 ft. lbs.
4. Adjust valve clearance, then install rocker arm cover and gasket.
5. Continue installation by reversing Steps 1-6 of removal procedure.

Removal—2000 cc

NOTE: This procedure can be adapted to the 2300 cc engine.

1. Drain the cooling system.
2. Remove the air cleaner and the valve rocker cover.
3. Remove the intake and exhaust manifolds. The intake manifold, decel valve and carburetor can be removed as an assembly.
4. Remove the camshaft drive belt cover.
5. Loosen the drive belt tensioner and remove the drive belt.
6. Remove the water outlet from the cylinder head.
7. Remove the cylinder head bolts evenly, and remove the cylinder head.

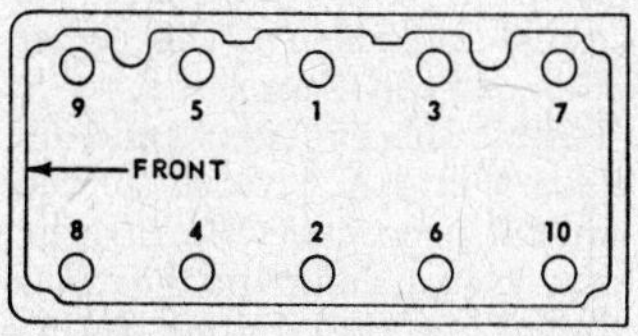
9
5
1
3
7
FRONT
8
4
2
6
10

Cylinder head bolt tightening sequence — 2000 cc

NOTE: A special 12-point allen wrench is necessary to remove the head bolts.

Installation—2000 cc

1. Position a new cylinder head gasket on the block.
2. Position the cylinder head and camshaft assembly on the block. Install the bolts finger tight, then torque according to specifications.

NOTE: If difficulty in positioning the head on the block is encountered, guide pins may be fabricated by cutting the heads off two extra cylinder head bolts.

3. Set the crankshaft at TDC and be sure that the camshaft drive gear and distributor are positioned correctly.
4. Install the camshaft drive belt and release the tensioner. Rotate the crankshaft two full turns to remove all slack from the belt. The timing marks should again be aligned. Tighten the tensioner lockbolt and pivot bolt.
5. Install the camshaft drive belt cover.
6. Apply sealer to the water outlet and new gasket, and install.
7. Install the intake and exhaust manifolds.
8. Adjust the valve clearance.
9. Install a new valve cover gasket and install the valve cover.
10. Install the air cleaner and crankcase ventilation hose.
11. Refill the cooling system.

Removal and Installation—2800 cc

1. Remove the air cleaner assembly and disconnect the battery and accelerator linkage. Drain the cooling system.
2. Remove the distributor cap with the spark plug wires attached. Remove the distributor vacuum line and distributor. Remove the hose from the water pump to the water outlet which is on the carburetor.
3. Remove the valve covers, fuel line and filter, carburetor, and the intake manifold.
4. Remove the rocker arm shaft and oil baffles. Remove the pushrods, keeping them in the proper sequence for installation.
5. Remove the exhaust manifold, referring to the appropriate procedures.
6. Remove the cylinder head retaining bolts and remove the cylinder heads and gaskets.

Caution do not lay the cylinder head flat on its surface.

7. Remove all gasket material and carbon from the engine block and cylinder heads.
8. Place the head gaskets on the engine block.

NOTE: The left and right gaskets are not interchangeable.

9. Install guide studs in the engine block. Install the cylinder head assemblies on the engine block one at a time. Tighten the cylinder head bolts in sequence, and in steps, to 65-80 lbs.
10. Install the intake and exhaust manifolds.

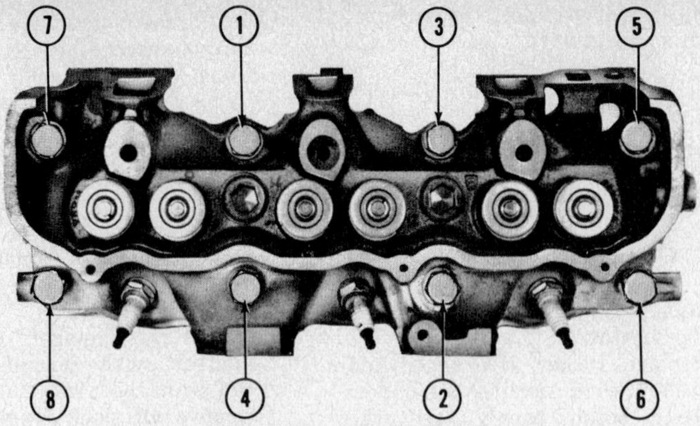
7
1
3
5
8
4
2
6

V6 cylinder head tightening sequence
(© Ford Motor Co)

11. Install the pushrods in the proper sequence. Install the oil baffles and the rocker arm shaft assemblies. Adjust the valve clearances.
12. Install the valve covers with new gaskets.
13. Install the distributor and set the ignition timing.
14. Install the carburetor and the distributor cap with the spark plug wires.
15. Connect the accelerator linkage, fuel line, with fuel filter installed, and distributor vacuum line to the carburetor. Fill the cooling system.

Timing Cover, Chain, and Camshaft—1600 cc

Timing Cover and Chain R & R

1. Drain coolant.
2. Disconnect radiator hoses at the engine, then remove radiator.
3. Remove fanbelt, fan, and water pump pulley.
4. Remove the water pump.
5. Remove the crankshaft pulley, using a puller only.
6. Remove the front cover.

NOTE: cover is secured by four oil pan bolts as well.

Perform steps 7 through 13 to remove and install the timing chain.

TIMING CHAIN TENSIONER
TIMING CHAIN

Timing chain tensioner—1600 cc
(© Ford Motor Co)

7. With the transmission in neutral, have an assistant tap the starter to align the cam and crankshaft sprockets.
8. Remove the timing chain tensioner.
9. Remove the timing chain sprocket attaching bolts.

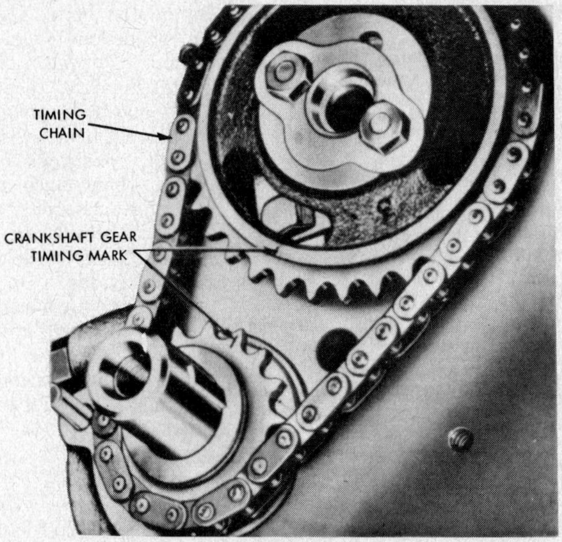
TIMING CHAIN
CRANKSHAFT GEAR
TIMING MARK

Valve timing mark alignment—1600 cc
(© Ford Motor Co)

10. Slide the timing chain and the camshaft sprocket off the engine as an assembly.

NOTE: The timing chain tensioner pad is designed so that two grooves are gradually worn into it. Do not alter the grooves. Replace the chain and tensioner as a unit.

11. Install the replacement timing chain on the camshaft and crankshaft sprockets and align the timing marks.
12. Position the sprockets and timing chain on the engine. Be sure that the timing marks on the sprockets are aligned as shown in the figure.
13. Install the camshaft sprocket attaching bolts.
14. Coat the front cover gasket with sealer and position it and the cover on the engine.
15. Using a large socket wrench or other suitable tool to center the cover on the engine, install the cover attaching bolts.
16. Tighten the bolts to 5–7 ft lbs and remove the centering tool.
17. Install the four front oil pan bolts and tighten them to 7–9 ft lbs.
18. Install the lower engine pulley and the water pump. Adjust the engine drive belts.
19. Install the radiator and fill the cooling system.

Camshaft and Valve Lifter R & R

The 1600 cc engine utilizes mushroom lifters, i.e., the bottom diameter is larger than the top diameter. For this reason, it is necessary to remove the engine, remove most of its external components, and invert it to remove the camshaft and/or lifters.

1. Remove the engine from the car and mount it securely on a stand.
2. Remove the fuel and oil pumps.
3. Remove the distributor.
4. Remove the valve cover, rocker shaft, and pushrods.
5. Remove the front cover and timing chain.
6. Place a pan under the engine and invert it on the stand.
7. Remove the oil pan.
8. Remove the camshaft thrust plate and remove the camshaft.
9. Remove the lifters.
10. Install the camshaft and/or lifters using a reverse of the removal procedure. Be sure to utilize the specific instructions on installing the timing chain and distributor. Adjust the valve clearance as previously described.

Camshaft, Auxiliary Shaft and Timing Belt —2000 cc and 2300 cc

Improper installation of the camshaft drive belt can result in poor engine performance. The engine will run if the belt is displaced by one or two teeth. A quick visual check can be employed to verify camshaft timing. Turn the engine over until the two round locating holes in the camshaft pulley are visible from the left rear of the engine, parallel to the ground. When these holes are parallel to the ground, the timing pointer should point to TDC. If the drive belt is mislocated, the crankshaft damper will be retarded or advanced 19° per tooth.

Camshaft timing on the 2300 cc engine can be checked by removing a rubber plug from the front cover. The camshaft sprocket mark and timing pointer can then be seen through the hole.

Timing Belt R & R

1. Remove the camshaft drive belt cover.
2. Remove the distributor cap from the distributor and position it out of the way.
3. Turn the engine clockwise until:
   a. The timing pointer is aligned with the "0" mark on the pulley.
   b. The pointer on the camshaft sprocket is aligned with the ball in the belt guide plate.
   c. The distributor rotor is aligned with the timing mark on the upper lip of the distributor housing.

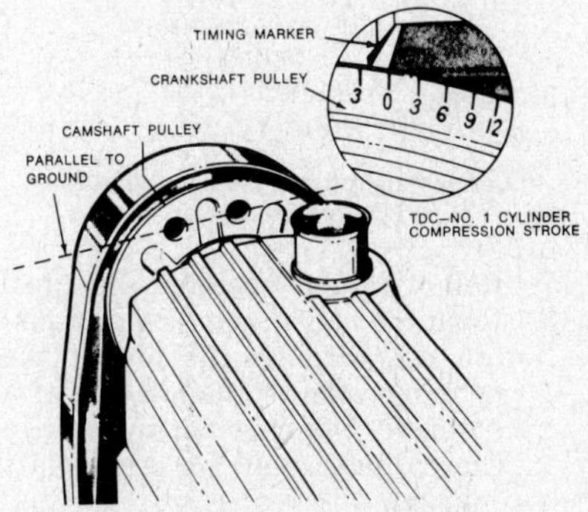
TIMING MARKER
CRANKSHAFT PULLEY
3 0 3 6 9 12
CAMSHAFT PULLEY
PARALLEL TO GROUND
TDC—NO. 1 CYLINDER COMPRESSION STROKE

Checking camshaft timing
(© Ford Motor Co)

4. Loosen the drive belt tensioner bolt and move the tensioner as far left as possible. Tighten the tensioner adjustment bolt.
5. Remove the belt from the pulleys.
6. Preconditions should be as in step three. Install the belt on the three sprockets, making sure that the cogs in the belt engage the slots in the sprockets.
7. Loosen the tensioner adjustment bolt and allow the full spring pressure of the tensioner to force the tensioner against the belt.
8. Turn the crankshaft pulley clockwise two complete turns to remove all slack from the belt.
9. Continue to turn the pulley until the marks described in step three are aligned. If the belt has slipped, remove the belt and repeat the installation procedure.
10. Position the drive belt tensioner so there is no free-play in the drive belt and tighten the tensioner adjustment bolt. Be careful not to overtighten the belt.

Camshaft R & R

1. Remove the cylinder head as previously described.
2. Remove the rocker arms.
3. Remove the camshaft drive gear attaching bolt and washer, and remove the gear and belt guide plate.
4. Carefully slide the camshaft out of the rear of the cylinder head.
5. Reverse the removal procedure to install the camshaft and cylinder head.

Auxiliary Shaft R & R

1. Remove the camshaft drive belt cover.
2. Remove the drive belt. Follow the steps under "Timing Belt R&R." Remove the auxiliary shaft sprocket. A puller may be necessary to remove the sprocket.
3. Remove the distributor and fuel pump. Follow all steps under "Distributor R&R."

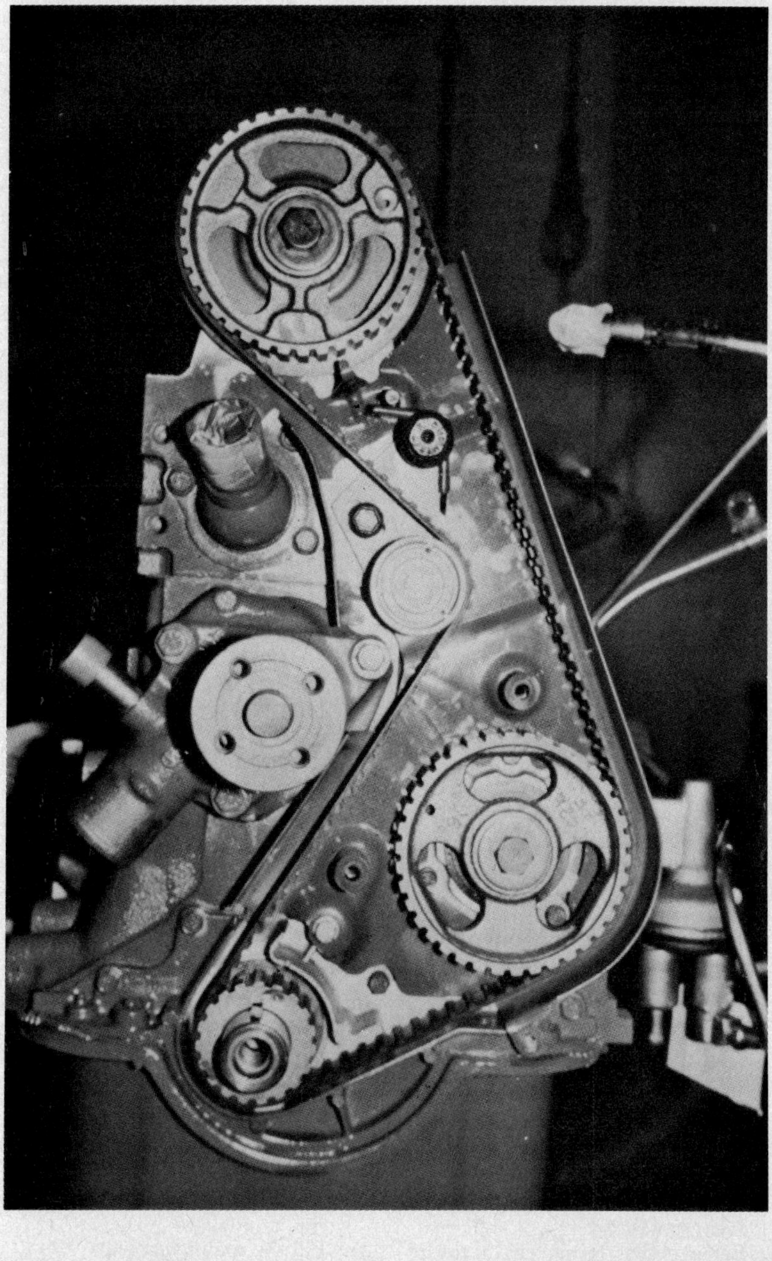

4. Remove the auxiliary shaft cover and thrust plate.
5. Withdraw the auxiliary shaft from the block.
6. Slide the auxiliary shaft into the housing and insert the thrust plate to hold the shaft.
7. Install a new gasket and auxiliary shaft cover.
8. Fit a new gasket into the fuel pump and install the pump.
9. Insert the distributor and install the auxiliary shaft sprocket. Follow all steps under "Distributor R&R."
10. Align the timing marks and install the drive belt. Follow all steps under "Timing Belt R&R."
11. Install the drive belt cover.
12. Check the ignition timing.

Timing Case and Camshaft—V6

Front Cover Removal and Installation

1. Remove the oil pan as described in the following section.
2. Remove the radiator and any other necessary parts to allow clearance.
3. Remove the alternator and drive belts. Remove the water pump and water lines.
4. Remove the fan.
5. Remove the crankshaft pulley with a puller and, if necessary, remove the guide sleeves from the cylinder block.
6. Remove the front cover retaining bolts and remove the front cover. If the front cover plate gasket needs replacement, remove the two screws and the plate to replace the gasket.
7. To install, reverse the procedures, cleaning all surfaces of gasket material and installing new gaskets and sealing compound.

NOTE: If the guide sleeves were removed, install them with new seal rings but do not use sealing compound.

Camshaft Removal and Installation

1. Drain the cooling system.
2. Remove the radiator.
3. Remove the distributor cap with the spark plug wires attached. Remove the distributor vacuum line, distributor, alternator, rocker arm covers, fuel line and filter, carburetor, and intake manifold.
4. Remove the rocker arm and shaft assemblies. Lift out the pushrods and mark them so they can be replaced in the same location.
5. Remove the oil pan. (See the following sections.)
6. Remove the timing chain cover.
7. Remove the camshaft gear retaining bolt and slide the gear off the camshaft. Remove the camshaft thrust plate.
8. Remove the valve lifters from the engine block with a magnet. Lifters should be identified to permit installation in the same location.
9. Carefully pull the camshaft from the engine block, avoiding damage to the camshaft bearings. Remove the key and spacer ring.
10. Coat the camshaft with a moly cam lubricant or SAE 90 gear oil.
11. Install the camshaft, carefully avoiding damage to the bearings.

NOTE: When installing the camshaft, do not push it hard into the engine. There is an oil plug at the rear of the engine block called the "bore plug." (See the illustration of the camshaft assembly.) If the camshaft is installed too far into the engine or forced into the engine, it could push this plug out, resulting in oil leaking on the clutch and pressure plate and causing serious damage.

12. Install the spacer ring with the worn side toward the engine. Insert the camshaft key. Install the thrust plate.
13. Install the camshaft timing gear and align the timing marks. Install the retaining washer and bolt.
14. Install the valve lifters.
15. Install the timing cover.
16. Install the belt drive pulley and secure it with the washer and retaining bolt.
17. Install the oil pan.

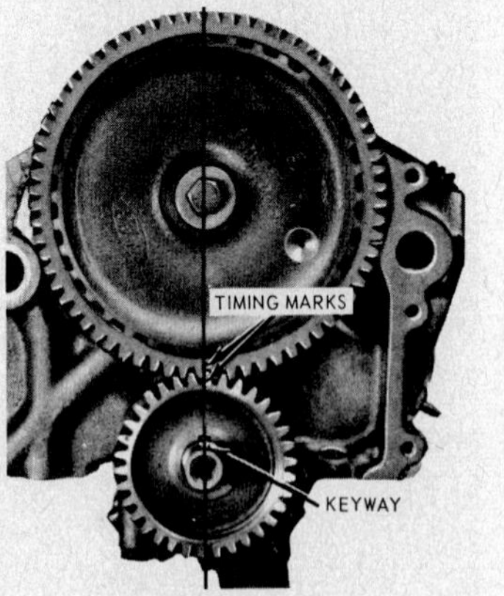
TIMING MARKS
KEYWAY

V6 timing gear installation
(© Ford Motor Co)

18. Install the pushrods in the same locations from which they were removed. Install the intake manifold.
19. Install the oil baffles and rocker arm shaft assemblies. Adjust the valves to the cold setting.
20. Install the carburetor, fuel line and filter, alternator, distributor cap, and wires.
21. FIll the cooling system.
22. Install the rocker arm covers but not permanently. Run the engine, check for leaks, and set the ignition timing.
23. Set the valves at their hot setting. Install the valve covers permanently.

Pistons and Rings

Piston R & R and Piston Ring Replacement

1. Drain the cooling system and the crankcase.
2. Remove the cylinder head and manifolds as an assembly.
3. Remove the oil pan and oil pump.
4. Turn the crankshaft until the piston to be removed is at the bottom of its stroke.
5. Place a cloth on the head of the piston to be removed and, using a ridge reamer, remove the deposits from the upper end of the cylinder bore.

NOTE: never remove more than 1/32 in. from the ring travel area when removing the ridges.

6. Mark all connecting rod bearing caps so they may be returned to their original location in the engine.

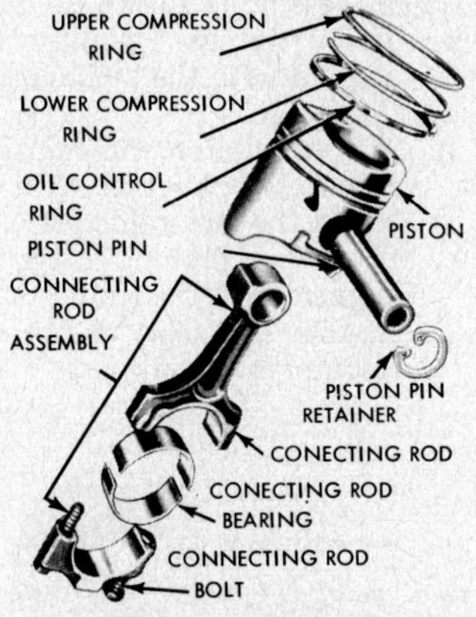
UPPER COMPRESSION RING
LOWER COMPRESSION RING
OIL CONTROL RING
PISTON PIN
CONNECTING ROD ASSEMBLY
PISTON
PISTON PIN RETAINER
CONECTING ROD
CONECTING ROD BEARING
CONNECTING ROD BOLT

Connecting rod and piston assembly
(© Ford Motor Co)

7. Remove the connecting rod caps.
8. Push the connecting rod and piston out through the top of the cylinder with the handle end of a hammer. Use care not to damage the cylinder wall or crankshaft journal.
9. Using internal micrometer, measure bores both across thrust faces of cylinder and parallel to axis of crankshaft at minimum of four locations equally spaced. The bore must not be out of round by more than 0.005 in. and it must not "taper" more than 0.010 in. "Taper" is the difference in wear between two bore measurements in any cylinder.
10. If cylinder bore is in satisfactory condition, place each ring in bore in turn and square it in

bore with head of piston. Measure ring gap. If ring gap is greater than limit, get new ring. If ring gap is less than limit, file end of ring to obtain correct gap.

11. Check ring side clearance by installing rings on piston, and inserting feeler gauge of correct dimension between ring and lower land. Gauge should slide freely around ring circumference without binding. Any wear will form a step on lower land. Replace any pistons having high steps. Before checking ring side clearance be sure ring grooves are clean and free of carbon, sludge, or grit.
12. Space ring gaps at equidistant intervals around piston circumference. Be sure to install piston in its original bore. Install short lengths of rubber tubing over connecting rod bolts to prevent damage to rod journal. Install ring compressor over rings on piston. Lower piston, and rod assembly into bore until ring compressor contacts block. Using wooden handle of hammer, push piston into bore while guiding rod onto journal.

NOTE: arrows on pistons must point forward.

Engine Lubrication

Oil Pan R&R

1. Drain the crankcase.
2. Remove the oil dipstick.
3. On 1600 cc engines, disconnect the negative battery cable, remove the starter motor retaining bolts and remove the starter from the engine.
4. Disconnect the steering shaft connection from the rack and pinion.
5. Disconnect the rack and pinion from the crossmember and move it forward to provide clearance.

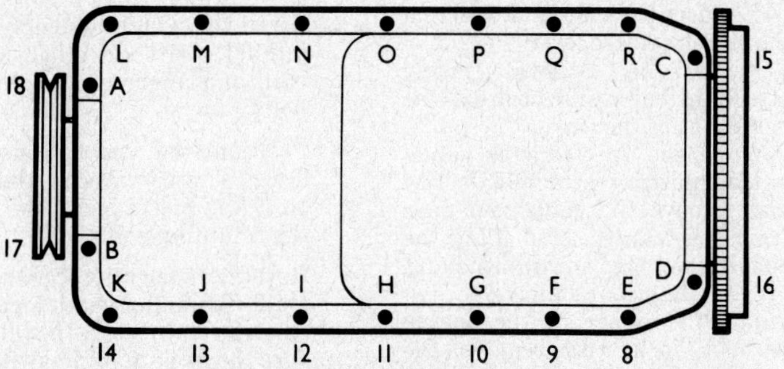
1
2
3
4
5
6
7
L
M
N
O
P
Q
R
C
15
18
A
17
B
K
J
I
H
G
F
E
D
16
14
13
12
11
10
9
8

1600 cc oil pan bolt tightening sequence
(© Ford Motor Co)

6. Remove the flywheel housing inspection cover.
7. Remove the oil pan attaching bolts and remove the pan.
8. Clean the gasket mounting surface of the block and the pan.
9. Coat the block surface and the oil pan gasket with oil resistant sealer and position the gasket on the block.
10. Coat the oil pan front oil seal and the cylinder front cover with oil resistant sealer and position the seal on the front cover, making sure the ends of the seal contact the oil pan gasket.
11. Coat the rear oil pan seal with oil resistant sealer and install it in the rear main bearing cap.
12. Position the pan on the block and tighten the bolts to specification. On 1600 cc engines tighten the bolts to a torque of 6–8 ft. lbs., and on 2000 cc engines to 4-6 ft. lbs.
13. Reverse steps 1-6 to complete installation.

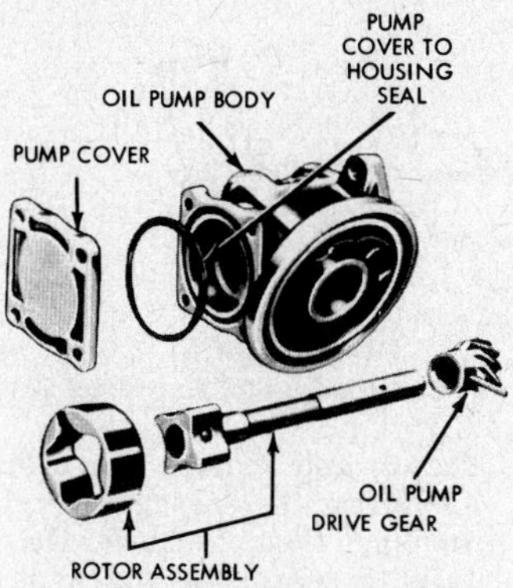
PUMP COVER TO HOUSING SEAL
OIL PUMP BODY
PUMP COVER
OIL PUMP DRIVE GEAR
ROTOR ASSEMBLY

Eccentric bi-rotor oil pump
(© Ford Motor Co)

Oil Pump—1600

The oil pump and filter assembly is bolted to the left side of the block and can be serviced with the engine installed in the car.

Two types of oil pump have been installed during production—an eccentric bi-rotor type and a sliding vane type. These pumps are readily identified by their end covers—the eccentric bi-rotor type has four recesses cast into its cover while the sliding vane type has a flat cover. These two pumps are interchangeable, although their internal parts are not.

Removal and Installation

1. Lift the hood and place a drain pan under the oil pump.
2. Remove the three bolts which hold the pump and filter assembly.

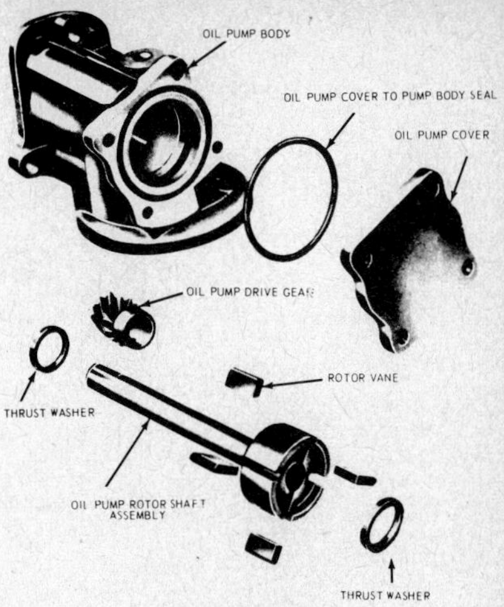
OIL PUMP BODY
OIL PUMP COVER TO PUMP BODY SEAL
OIL PUMP COVER
OIL PUMP DRIVE GEAR
ROTOR VANE
THRUST WASHER
OIL PUMP ROTOR SHAFT ASSEMBLY
THRUST WASHER

Sliding vane oil pump
(© Ford Motor Co)

NOTE: tighten these bolts to 13-15 ft. lbs. when installing pump.

3. Remove filter from pump.
4. To install, reverse removal procedure.

Oil Pump—2000, 2300

The oil pump, of bi-rotor design, is mounted to the bottom of the cylinder block, inside the oil pan. To remove the pump, remove the oil pan and remove the two bolts that mount the oil pump to the block.

Crankshaft Rear Main Oil Seal R & R

1. Remove the transmission, clutch and flywheel. Place a support under the engine to hold it when the transmission is removed.
2. On 1600 cc engines, remove the oil pan and unbolt the oil seal carrier from the rear of the crankshaft.
3. On 2000 cc engines, remove the seal from the rear of the crankshaft by turning a sheet metal screw into the seal and pulling the seal from the crankshaft.
4. Using a seal installation tool, drive a new seal into place. On 1600 cc engines, install the seal carrier and the oil pan.
5. Install the flywheel, clutch and transmission.

CLUTCH

Adjustment

Cars Built Before 10/1/70

1. From under the car, pull the clutch cable toward the front of the vehicle until the C-clip can be removed from the cable. Remove the clip.
2. Continue to pull the cable toward the front of the vehicle until all free movement has been eliminated from the clutch release bearing.

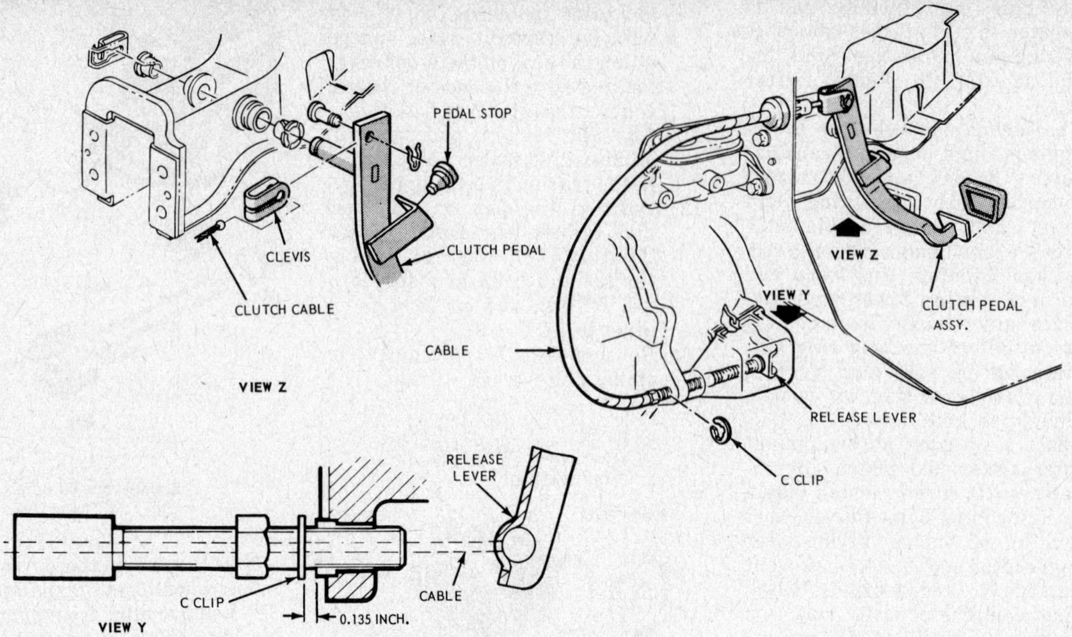
PEDAL STOP
CLEVIS
CLUTCH PEDAL
CLUTCH CABLE
VIEW Z
VIEW Y
CLUTCH PEDAL ASSY.
CABLE
RELEASE LEVER
C CLIP
VIEW Z
RELEASE LEVER
C CLIP
CABLE
0.135 INCH.
VIEW Y

Clutch linkage (© Ford Motor Co)

3. While holding the cable in the zero free play position, insert a 0.135 in. spacer against the flywheel boss on the engine side and install the C-clip in the closest possible groove next to the spacer.
4. Remove the spacer and release the cable.

Cars Built After 10/1/70

1. Working under the car, loosen the clutch adjusting nut, the front locknut and the rear locknut (if so equipped).
2. Pull the clutch cable toward the front of the car until all freeplay is removed from the clutch release lever.
3. Holding the cable in this position, place a 1/4 in. spacer against the engine side of the flywheel housing and tighten the adjusting nut finger-tight against the spacer.
4. Hold the adjusting nut so that it maintains its position and tighten the front locknut against the adjusting nut.
5. Remove the spacer and tighten the rear locknut (if so equipped) against the transmission side of the flywheel housing.

Clutch, Clutch Housing, and Transmission R&R

Removal

1. Place the gearshift lever in the neutral position. Raise the car and remove the back-up light switch from the transmission extension housing.
2. Loosen the shift lever locknut. Remove the knob and the locknut from the shift lever. Remove the four rubber boot attaching screws and remove the boot.
3. Compress the corrugated rubber spring, then remove the retaining snap-ring and slide the spring upward on the lever.
4. Bend the shift lever locktabs up, then thread the plastic dome nut from the extension housing.
5. Lift the shift lever from the extension housing.
6. Working from under the hood, remove the upper flywheel housing-to-engine attaching bolts.
7. Raise the vehicle and matchmark the driveshaft and the rear axle pinion.
8. Disconnect and remove the driveshaft. Place rags in the extension housing to prevent loss of lubricant.
9. Remove the clutch release lever dust cover.
10. Disconnect the clutch cable from the clutch release lever.
11. Remove the starter motor attaching bolts and position the motor out of the way.
12. Remove the speedometer cable-to-transmission attaching screw and remove the cable and gear from the transmission. Plug the opening in the transmission to prevent lubricant spillage.
13. Support the rear of the engine with a jack and remove the crossmember-to-body attaching bolts.
14. Remove the bolts that attach the crossmember to the transmission extension housing and remove the crossmember from the car.
15. Lower the engine to gain working room, and remove the remaining flywheel housing-to-engine attaching bolts.
16. Slide the transmission rearward and remove it from the car.
17. If the clutch is to be removed loosen the six pressure plate attaching bolts evenly to release spring pressure gradually. If the same pressure plate and cover are to be reused, mark the position of the pressure plate and flywheel so they can be returned to their original location.
18. Remove the pressure plate attaching bolts and remove the pressure plate and clutch from the car.

Installation

1. Position the clutch and pressure plate on the flywheel and install the attaching bolts loosely.

NOTE: the three dowel pins on the flywheel must be aligned with the pressure plate.

2. Align the clutch assembly, using a pilot shaft or other suitable tool, and alternately tighten the bolts.
3. Position the transmission and flywheel assembly on the studs on the cylinder block and install the retaining bolts.
4. Reverse removal procedure to install remaining equipment. The shift lever must be installed before the back-up light switch.

MANUAL TRANSMISSION

Transmission R&R

See *Clutch, Clutch Housing, and Transmission R&R* in this car section.

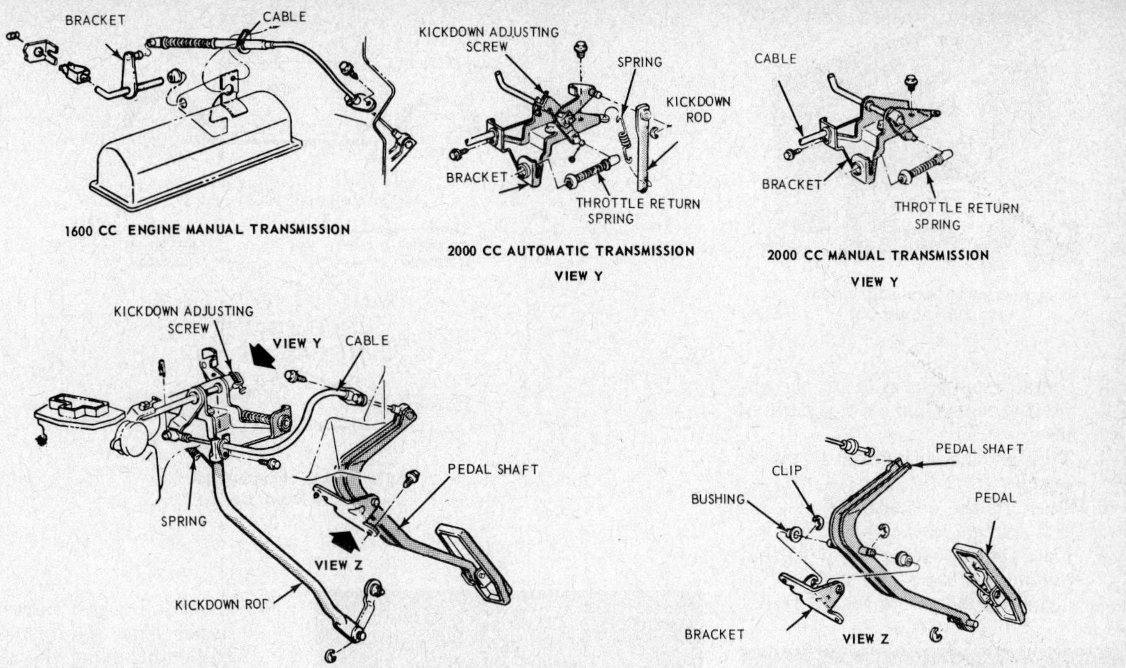
BRACKET
CABLE
1600 CC ENGINE MANUAL TRANSMISSION
KICKDOWN ADJUSTING SCREW
SPRING
KICKDOWN ROD
BRACKET
THROTTLE RETURN SPRING
2000 CC AUTOMATIC TRANSMISSION
VIEW Y
CABLE
BRACKET
THROTTLE RETURN SPRING
2000 CC MANUAL TRANSMISSION
VIEW Y
KICKDOWN ADJUSTING SCREW
VIEW Y
CABLE
PEDAL SHAFT
SPRING
VIEW Z
KICKDOWN ROD
PEDAL SHAFT
CLIP
BUSHING
PEDAL
BRACKET
VIEW Z
Throttle linkage (© Ford Motor Co)

AUTOMATIC TRANSMISSION

NOTE: Perform these adjustments in the order listed here.

Downshift Linkage Adjustment

1. Disconnect the downshift lever return spring.
2. Hold the throttle shaft lever in the wide open position. Hold the downshift rod against the through detent stop. Adjust the downshift screw to obtain 0.050-0.070 in. clearance between the screw tip and the throttle shaft lever tab.
3. Connect the downshift lever return spring.

Manual Linkage Adjustment

1. Place the transmission selector lever in the Drive position.
2. Raise the vehicle and loosen the manual linkage shift rod at the selector lever.
3. Move the transmission manual lever to the Drive position (fourth detent position from the rear of the transmission).
4. Tighten the nut on the manual linkage shift rod to 10-20 ft. lbs.
5. Lower the car and check transmission operation.

Neutral Start Switch Adjustment

1. Place the transmission selector lever in the Neutral position.
2. Raise the vehicle on a hoist and loosen the two bolts that attach the neutral switch to the transmission.
3. Rotate the switch until a gauge pin (shank end of a #43 drill bit) can be inserted through the gauge pin holes in the switch. The gauge pin must be inserted a full 31/64 in. into the switch, through all three holes in the switch.
4. Tighten the switch retaining bolts to 50-75 in. lbs. and remove the pin.

Neutral Switch Replacement

1. Raise the car, with the transmission in neutral, and disconnect the downshift linkage.
2. Remove the neutral switch attaching bolts and remove the switch and disconnect the wires.

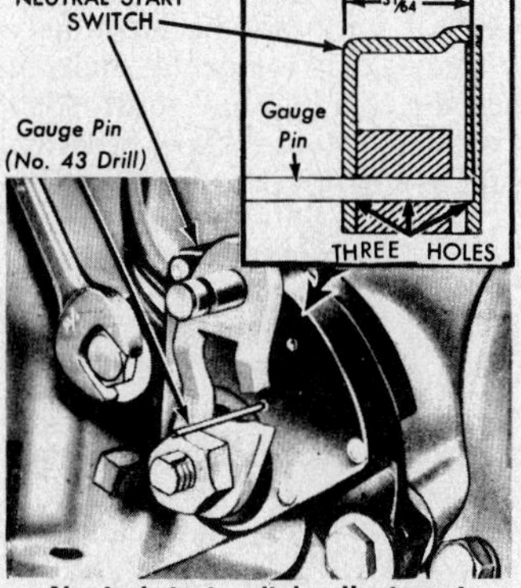
NEUTRAL START SWITCH
Gauge Pin (No. 43 Drill)
31/64"
Gauge Pin
THREE HOLES
Neutral start switch adjustment
(© Ford Motor Co)

3. Install the replacement switch and adjust it as described above.
4. Install the downshift outer lever.
5. Connect the downshift linkage rod to the downshift lever.

Band Adjustments

Caution The torque figures and numbers of turns given in these procedures must be exactly correct to prevent transmission damage.

Intermediate Band

1. Wipe clean the area around the adjusting screw on the side of the transmission, near the left-front corner of the transmission.
2. Remove the adjusting screw locknut and discard it.

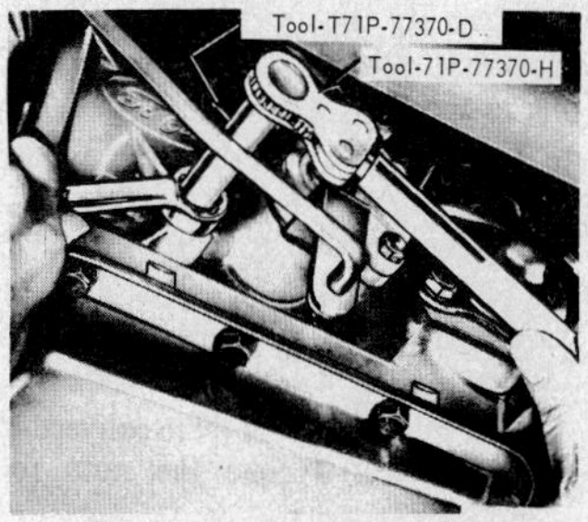
Tool-T71P-77370-D
Tool-71P-77370-H
Intermediate band adjustment
(© Ford Motor Co)

3. Install a new locknut on the adjusting screw but do not tighten it.
4. Tighten the adjusting screw to *exactly 10 ft lbs.*
5. Back off the adjusting screw *exactly 1¾ turns.*
6. Hold the adjusting screw so that it *does not turn* and tighten the adjusting screw locknut to 35–45 ft lbs.

Low-Reverse Band

1. Wipe clean the area around the adjusting screw on the side of the transmission, near the right-rear corner.
2. Remove the adjusting screw locknut and discard it.

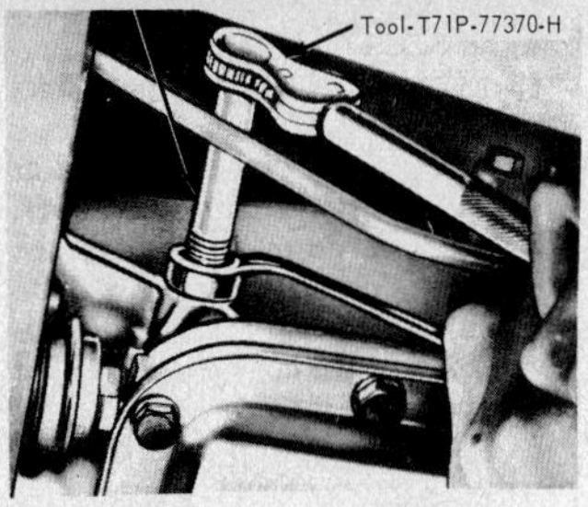
Tool-T71P-77370-H

Low-reverse band adjustment
(© Ford Motor Co)

3. Install a new locknut on the adjusting screw but do not tighten it.
4. Tighten the adjusting screw to *exactly 10 ft lbs.*
5. Back off the adjusting screw *exactly 3 full turns.*
6. Hold the adjusting screw so that it *does not turn* and tighten the adjusting screw to 35–45 ft lbs.

U-JOINTS

U-Joint R&R

1. Raise the vehicle.
2. Mark the position of the rear driveshaft yoke in relation to the pinion flange so the driveshaft can be returned to its original location.
3. Disconnect the rear U-Joint from the pinion flange and remove the loose bearing caps.

   Pull the driveshaft rearward until it clears the transmission extension housing. Remove the driveshaft from the car.
4. Place the driveshaft in a vise and remove the snap-rings from the U-Joint to be removed.
5. Using a suitable tool, drive one of the bearing caps on the U-Joint to be removed toward the center of the driveshaft.
6. Remove the opposite bearing cap from the one being driven as it emerges from the driveshaft.
7. Repeat Step 6 until all bearing caps have been removed.
8. Remove the U-Joint spider from the driveshaft.
9. To install, position the spider in the driveshaft and drive the bearing caps onto the spider.
10. Install the snap-rings in the driveshaft.
11. Reinstall the driveshaft using a reverse of the removal procedure. Make sure that the yoke and pinion flange marks are aligned.

JACKING, HOISTING

Lift and jacking points are shown in the figure.

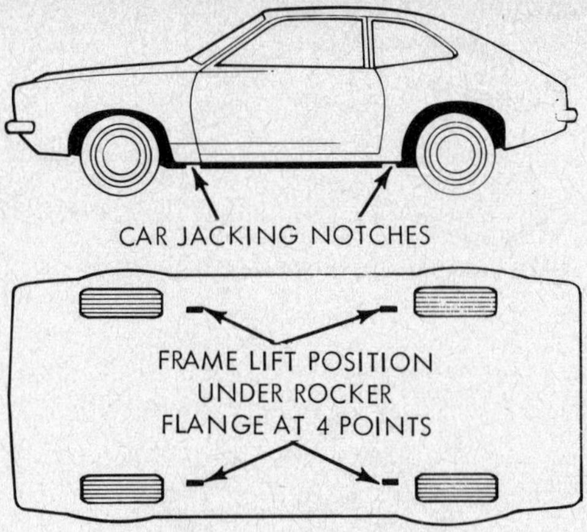
CAR JACKING NOTCHES
FRAME LIFT POSITION
UNDER ROCKER
FLANGE AT 4 POINTS

Lifting and jacking points
(© Ford Motor Co)

FRONT SUSPENSION

Upper Ball Joint

Inspection

1. Raise the vehicle by placing a floor jack under the lower arm. Do not allow the lower arm to hang freely with the vehicle on a hoist or bumper jack.
2. Have an assistant grasp the bottom of the tire and move the wheel in and out.
3. As the wheel is being moved, observe the upper control arm where the spindle attaches to it. Any movement between the upper part of the spindle and the upper ball joint indicates a bad ball joint which must be replaced.

NOTE: during this check the lower ball joint will be unloaded and may move; this is normal and not an indication of a bad ball joint. Also, do not mistake a loose wheel bearing for a defective ball joint.

Replacement

1. Raise the vehicle and allow the front wheels to fall into their full down position.
2. Drill a 1/8 in. hole completely through each ball joint attaching rivet.
3. Using a large chisel, cut off the head of each rivet and drive them from the upper arm.
4. Place a jack under the lower arm and lower the vehicle about 6 in.
5. Remove the cotter pin and attaching nut from the ball joint stud.
6. Using a suitable tool, loosen the ball joint stud from the spindle and remove the ball joint from the upper arm.
7. Clean all metal burrs from the upper arm and install the new ball joint, using the service part nuts and bolts to attach the ball joint to the upper arm. Do not attempt to re-rivet the ball joint once it has been removed.
8. Check front end alignment.

Lower Ball Joint

Inspection

1. Raise the vehicle by placing a floor jack under the lower arm; or, raise the vehicle on a hoist and place a jack stand under the lower arm and lower the vehicle onto it to remove the preload from the lower ball joint.
2. Have an assistant grasp the wheel top and bottom and apply alternate in and out pressure to the top and bottom of the wheel.
3. Radial play of ¼ in. is acceptable measured at the inside of the wheel adjacent to the lower arm.

NOTE: this radial play is multiplied at the outer circumference of the tire and should be measured only at the inside of the wheel.

Replacement

1. Raise the vehicle and allow the front wheels to fall to their full down position.
2. Drill a ⅛ in. hole completely through each ball joint attaching rivet.
3. Use a ⅜ in. drill in the pilot hole to drill off the head of the rivet.
4. Drive the rivets from the lower arm.
5. Place a jack under the lower arm and lower the vehicle about 6 in.
6. Remove the lower ball joint stud cotter pin and attaching nut.
7. Using a suitable tool, loosen the ball joint from the spindle and remove the ball joint from the lower arm.

8. Clean all metal burrs from the lower arm and install the new ball joint, using the service part nuts and bolts to attach the ball joint to the lower arm. Do not attempt to re-rivet the ball joint once it has been removed.
9. Check front end alignment.

Upper Control Arm

Replacement

1. Raise the vehicle on a hoist.
2. If equipped with drum brakes, remove the tire, wheel and brake drum as an assembly. If equipped with disc brakes, remove the tire and wheel, remove the caliper attaching bolts and position the caliper out of the way with the brake hose attached. Remove the rotor and hub from the spindle.
3. Disconnect the lower control arm and remove the coil spring.
4. Remove the cotter pin and attaching nut from the ball joint stud.
5. Using a suitable tool, loosen the upper ball joint from the spindle.
6. Remove the upper arm inner shaft attaching bolts and remove the arm and shaft from the chassis as an assembly.
7. Reverse above procedure to install.
8. Adjust front end alignment.

Lower Control Arm R & R

1. Raise the car and support it with stands placed back of the lower arms.
2. If equipped with drum type brakes, remove the wheel and brake drums as an assembly. Remove the brake backing plate attaching bolts and remove the backing plate from the spindle. Wire the assembly back out of the way.
3. If equipped with disc brakes, remove the wheel from the hub. Remove the caliper from the rotor and wire it back out of the way. Remove the hub and rotor from the spindle.
4. Disconnect the shock absorber and remove it.
5. Remove the cotter pins from the upper and lower ball joint stud nuts.
6. Remove the two bolts and nuts holding the strut to the lower arm.
7. Loosen the lower ball joint stud nut two turns. Do not remove this nut.
8. Install a spreader tool between the upper and lower ball joint studs.
9. Expand the tool until the tool exerts considerable pressure on the studs. Tap the spindle near the lower stud with a hammer to loosen the stud in the spindle. Do not loosen the stud with tool pressure only.
10. Position a floor jack under the lower arm and remove the lower ball joint and nut.
11. Lower the floor jack and remove the spring and insulator.
12. Remove the A arm-to-crossmember attaching parts, and remove the arm from the car.
13. Reverse the above procedure to install. If the lower control arm was replaced because of damage, have front-end alignment checked.

Spring R & R

1. Jack up the front of the car and support it with jackstands.
2. Remove the shock absorber.
3. Disconnect the strut bar from the lower control arm.
4. Place a floor jack under the lower control arm.
5. Remove the nut and bolt that attach the lower control arm to the front crossmember.
6. Carefully lower the jack, slowly, to relieve the spring pressure from the lower arm.
7. Remove the spring and upper insulator.
8. Place the upper insulator on the spring and secure it in place with tape.
9. Position the spring on the lower control arm. Make sure that the bottom of the spring properly engages the seat on the lower control arm.
10. Raise the lower control arm with the floor jack and guide the lower control arm and the top of the spring into place. Install the lower control arm attaching bolt and nut. Tighten the lower control arm attaching bolt to 75–110 ft lbs.
11. Install the shock absorber after removing the jack.
12. Remove the jack stands and lower the car.

Shock Absorber R & R

1. Remove the nut, washer, and bushing from the upper end of the shock. If the shaft of the shock absorber turns while you are attempting to remove the nut, hold the shaft in place with an adjustable wrench while removing the nut.
2. Raise the front end of the car and install jackstands.
3. Disconnect the bottom of the shock absorber from the lower control arm. It may be necessary to raise the lower arm to remove the bottom bolt.
4. Remove the shock absorber from under the car.
5. Position the replacement shock absorber on the lower control arm and install the attaching bolts.
6. Remove the jackstands and lower the car.
7. Connect the top of the shock absorber to the upper spring pad.

Wheel Bearing Adustment

1. Jack the front of the car up and support it with jackstands.
2. Remove the dust cap and spindle nut cotter pin. Slide the nut lock off. Discard the pin.
3. Tighten the adjusting nut to 17–25 ft lbs while turning the wheel. Back the nut off one-half turn.
4. Tighten the nut to 10–15 in. lbs.
5. Install the nut lock on the adjusting nut so that two of the slots align with the hole in the spindle.
6. Install a new cotter pin and bend back its ends.
7. Install the dust cap and lower the car.

REAR SUSPENSION

The rear suspension consists of conventional three-leaf, longitudinal, semi-elliptic springs, located asymmetrically to the rear axle carrier and fastened by U-bolt clamps. Standard telescopic shock absorbers control vertical rebound.

Rear Shock Absorber R & R

1. Disconnect the lower end of the shock absorber from the spring plate.
2. Remove the three bolts retaining the shock absorber mounting bracket at the upper end of the shock.
3. Compress and remove shock from car.
4. Transfer mounting bracket to new shock.
5. Position shock absorber on car and install attaching parts.

Rear Spring R & R

1. Disconnect the lower end of the shock absorber from the spring plate and position the shock out of the way.
2. Raise the vehicle on a hoist and place supports under the axle and the underbody.
3. Remove the spring plate attaching nuts from the U-bolts. Remove the spring plate.
4. Disconnect and remove the rear shackle from the spring.
5. Remove the front hanger bolt and nut from the eye of the spring. Remove the spring from the car.
6. Reverse above procedure to install.

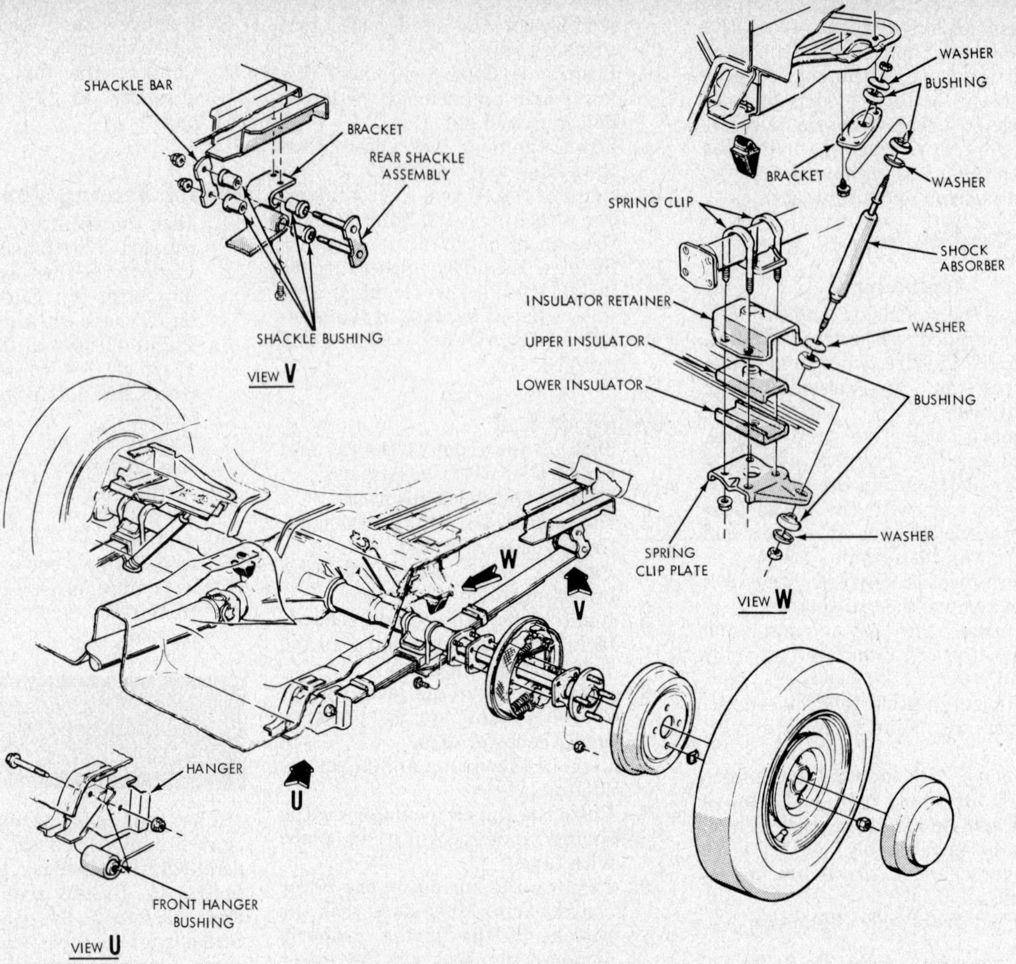
SHACKLE BAR
BRACKET
REAR SHACKLE ASSEMBLY
SHACKLE BUSHING
VIEW V
WASHER
BUSHING
BRACKET
WASHER
SPRING CLIP
SHOCK ABSORBER
INSULATOR RETAINER
WASHER
UPPER INSULATOR
LOWER INSULATOR
BUSHING
WASHER
SPRING CLIP PLATE
VIEW W
W
V
HANGER
U
FRONT HANGER BUSHING
VIEW U

Pinto rear suspension (© Ford Motor Co)

NOTE: all used attaching parts must be discarded and replaced with new parts.

BRAKES

The drum brake system incorporates single anchor, internal expanding and self adjusting brake assemblies. The brake hydraulic system employs a dual reservoir master cylinder, a pressure differential valve and a single cylinder, dual piston wheel cylinder mounted on each backing plate. Front disc brakes are available as an option.

The parking brake is operated through a floor-mounted lever located between the front seats. Pulling the lever transmits force through a two cable linkage to operate the rear drum brakes. A self-adjusting feature operates when there is excessive clearance between the brake shoes and drums.

Replacement and overhaul procedures are included in the "Unit Repair Section."

Master Cylinder Removal

1. Working under the dash, disconnect the stop light switch wires from the stop light switch and remove the switch and master cylinder pushrod from the brake pedal. Use care not to damage the stop light switch during removal.
2. Raise the hood and remove the brake lines from the master cylinder.
3. Remove the capscrews and lockwashers that attach the master cylinder to the firewall and remove the master cylinder.
4. Reverse above procedure to install, but, leave the brake lines loose on the master cylinder.
5. Fill the master cylinder with Extra Heavy Duty Brake Fluid.
6. Bleed the master cylinder by slowly depressing the foot pedal.
7. Refill master cylinder and bleed the front, then the rear, brakes.

Parking Brake Adjustment

1. Fully release the parking brake.

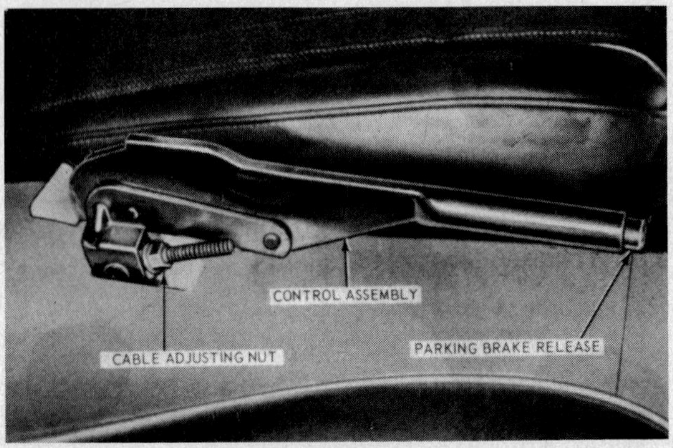
CONTROL ASSEMBLY
CABLE ADJUSTING NUT
PARKING BRAKE RELEASE

Parking brake adjustment (© Ford Motor Co)

2. Place the transmission in Neutral and raise the rear of the vehicle until the rear wheels clear the floor.
3. Tighten the adjusting nut, located under the rear of the lever boot, until the rear brakes drag when the rear wheels are turned.
4. Loosen the adjusting nut until the rear wheels can be turned without the rear brakes dragging.
5. Lower the rear of the vehicle and check the operation of the parking brake.

STEERING

The steering gear is of the rack and pinion type. The gear input shaft is connected to the steering shaft by means of a flexible cable. A pinion gear, machined on the input shaft, engages the rack and rotation of the input shaft pinion causes the rack to move laterally.

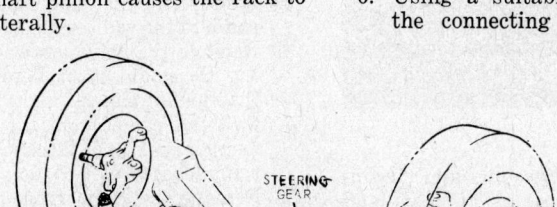

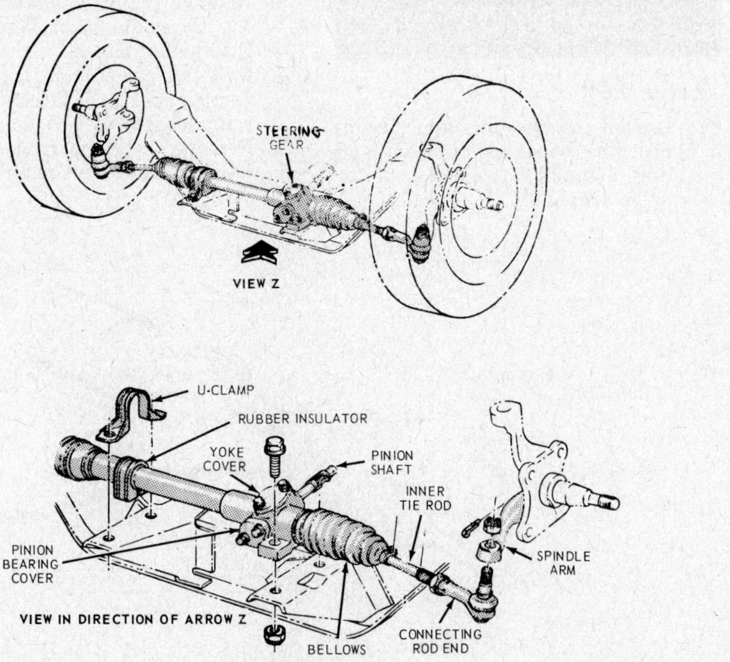
STEERING GEAR
VIEW Z
U-CLAMP
RUBBER INSULATOR
YOKE COVER
PINION SHAFT
INNER TIE ROD
PINION BEARING COVER
SPINDLE ARM
VIEW IN DIRECTION OF ARROW Z
CONNECTING ROD END
BELLOWS

Rack and pinion steering
(© Ford Motor Co)

The tie-rod is attached at each end of the rack joint. This allows the tie-rods to move with the front suspension. The gear is sealed at each end with rubber bellows. The steering gear is filled with approximately 5 oz. of SAE-90 E.P. type oil at initial assembly and checking or refilling is not required unless fluid leakage is evident or repairs become necessary.

Couplings attaching the tie-rods are retained on the rack, are pinned and cannot be disassembled in service. Replacement of inner tie-rods, rack, housing, or upper pinion bearing requires installation of a new steering gear assembly.

Caution When the front wheels of the vehicle are suspended completely off the ground, do not turn the wheels quickly or forcefully from lock to lock. This could cause a build-up of hydraulic pressure within the steering gear which could damage or blow out the bellows.

Steering Gear R & R

1. Position the steering wheel in the straight ahead position and raise the front of the car.
2. Remove the bolts retaining the flexible coupling to the pinion shaft.
3. Remove the four nuts and bolts that retain the steering gear to the mounting pad on the crossmember.
4. Remove the U-clamp. Remove the U-clamp attaching bolts.
5. Remove the cotterpins and loosen the nuts securing the connecting rod ends to the spindle arms.
6. Using a suitable tool, separate the connecting rods from the spindle arms and remove the nuts from the rod ends.
7. Remove the steering gear from the left-side of the vehicle.
8. Before installing the steering gear, make sure that the front wheels and the steering wheel are in the straight-ahead position.
9. Obtain a .050 in. shim having bite-in teeth on both sides. Position the shim on the bolt shanks.
10. File off the bite-in teeth around the two gear mounting holes in the left-side crossmember mounting bracket.
11. Install the steering gear on the mounting bracket so that the shim is between the steering and the mounting bracket.
12. Install two new cones and tighten them to 50–65 ft lbs.
13. Install the rubber insulator and U-clamp on the right side of the steering gear.
14. Install the connecting rod ends in the spindle ends and tighten the attaching nuts to 18–30 ft lbs. Install a new cotter pin in the spindle end.
15. Make sure the steering gear is centered. When the gear is centered, the bottom bolt which attaches the flexible coupling to the pinion shaft should be straight up and down with the bottom of the bolt pointing downward.
16. Connect the flexible coupling to the pinion shaft and tighten the attaching bolt.

Steering Wheel R & R

1. Disconnect the battery ground cable.
2. On models with a small horn button, remove the horn button by pushing down and turning it counterclockwise.
3. On deluxe steering wheels, remove the pad by removing the two screws from behind the steering wheel. Disconnect the horn wires from the pad.
4. Remove the steering wheel attaching nut and, using a puller, remove the steering wheel.
5. Align the mark on the hub with the mark on the shaft and install the wheel on the shaft.
6. Install the attaching nut and tighten it to 30–40 ft lbs.
7. Install the horn button or pad.

Turn Signal and Flasher Switch R & R

1. Remove the steering wheel as previously outlined.
2. Remove the turn signal lever by unscrewing it from the steering column.
3. Snap off the lower steering column shroud.
4. Disconnect the steering column wiring connectors from the steering column by lifting up on the tabs and removing the connectors from the brackets.
6. Remove the three screws that attach the head of the switch to the top of the steering column.
7. Pull the switch and wire assembly up and out of the steering column. A thin wire attached to the connector will make it easy to pull it down through the column.
8. To install the switch, position it and the wires in the steering column and work the wires down the steering column.
9. Secure the wires and connectors to the base of the steering column.

10. Connect the wire connectors at the base of the column.
11. Install the switch head attaching screws.
12. Install the turn signal lever and steering wheel.

INSTRUMENT PANEL

Headlight Switch R & R

1. Disconnect the battery ground cable.
2. Remove the instrument cluster.
3. Remove the headlight switch control knob, shaft and retaining nut.
4. Disconnect the multiple connector from the switch and remove the switch from instrument cluster opening.
5. Reverse above procedure to install.

Ignition Switch

Removal

1. To gain access to the switch, remove the steering column shroud and disconnect and lower the steering column from the brake support bracket.
2. Disconnect the negative battery cable.
3. Disconnect the switch wiring at the multiple connector.
4. Remove the two nuts that retain the ignition switch to the steering column.
5. Remove the pin that connects the switch plunger to the actuating rod and remove the switch.

Installation

1. When installing the ignition switch, both the switch and the ignition lock must be in the LOCK position. The manual parts can be held in place by turning the ignition lock cylinder to the LOCK position with the transmission in PARK (automatic transmission) or REVERSE (standard transmission). To hold the switch in the LOCK position, insert a pin in the hole on the top of the switch, after manually moving the switch to the lock position.
2. Position the hole in the end of the switch plunger to the hole in the actuator and install the connecting pin.
3. Position the ignition switch on the steering column, and install, but do not tighten the retaining nuts.
4. Move the switch up and down on the steering column to find the mid-point of the actuating rod lash, then tighten the switch retaining nuts.
5. Remove the locking pin from the switch and install the steering column and shroud.

Ignition Lock Cylinder R & R

1. Disconnect the negative battery cable.
2. Remove the steering wheel as described under "Steering." Insert a stiff wire into the hole located in the lock cylinder housing.
3. Place the gearshift lever in reverse on standard shift cars and in Park on cars with an automatic transmission, and turn the ignition key to the "on" position.
4. Depress the wire and remove the lock cylinder and wire.
5. Insert the new cylinder into housing and turn it to the "off" position. This will lock the cylinder into position.
6. Reinstall the steering wheel and pad.
7. Connect the negative battery cable.

WINDSHIELD WIPERS

Motor R&R

1. Loosen the two nuts and disconnect the wiper pivot shaft and link assembly from the motor drive arm ball.

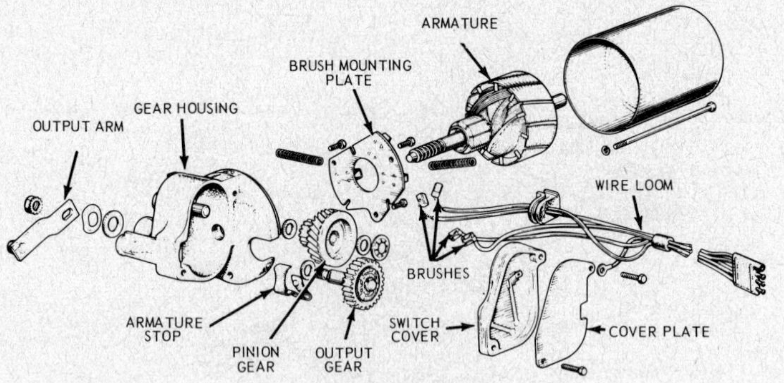
ARMATURE
BRUSH MOUNTING PLATE
GEAR HOUSING
OUTPUT ARM
WIRE LOOM
BRUSHES
ARMATURE STOP
PINION GEAR
OUTPUT GEAR
SWITCH COVER
COVER PLATE

Wiper motor disassembled
(© Ford Motor Co)

2. Remove the three motor attaching screws and lower the motor away from the left side of the dash.
3. Disconnect the wiper motor wires and remove the wires.
4. To install, position the motor under the dash and install the wires. Operate the motor to ensure it is in Park position.
5. Position the motor to the dash and install the retaining screws.
6. Position the wiper pivot shaft and link assembly to the motor drive arm ball and tighten the two nuts.

Wiper Blade Pivot R & R

1. Remove the windshield wiper arms and blades from the pivot shafts.
2. Loosen the two nuts retaining the wiper pivot shaft and link assembly to the motor drive arm ball.
3. Remove the three screws attaching each pivot shaft.
4. Remove the pivot shaft and link assembly from under the left side of the dash.
5. Reverse above procedure to install. Operate the wiper motor before installing the wiper blades to ensure the pivots are in Park.

RADIO

R&R

1. Disconnect the negative battery cable.
2. Remove the bolt that mounts the radio to the radio support.
3. Remove the four screws attaching the radio cover bezel to the instrument panel.
4. Pull the radio from the instrument panel and disconnect the radio lead wires.
5. Remove the radio from the car.
6. Reverse above procedure to install.

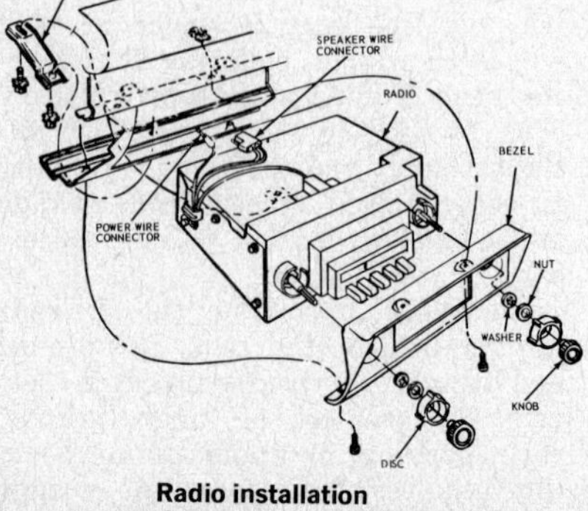
REAR SUPPORT
SPEAKER WIRE CONNECTOR
RADIO
BEZEL
POWER WIRE CONNECTOR
NUT
WASHER
KNOB
DISC

Radio installation
(© Ford Motor Co)

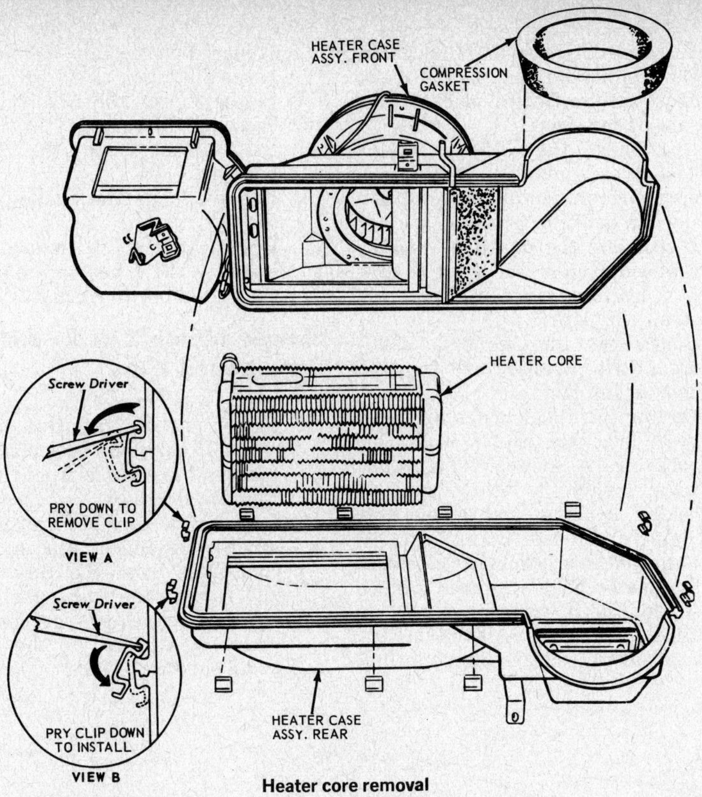
HEATER CASE ASSY. FRONT
COMPRESSION GASKET
HEATER CORE
Screw Driver
PRY DOWN TO REMOVE CLIP
VIEW A
Screw Driver
PRY CLIP DOWN TO INSTALL
VIEW B
HEATER CASE ASSY. REAR

Heater core removal
(© Ford Motor Co)

HEATER

Heater Assembly R & R, Non-Air Conditioned Cars

1. Drain the cooling system and disconnect the negative battery cable.
2. Disconnect the blower motor ground wire (black) at the engine side of the dash panel.
3. Disconnect the heater hoses at the engine block.
4. Remove the four nuts that attach the heater assembly to the dash, from the engine side of the dash.
5. Working inside the car, remove the glove box.
6. Disconnect the control cables from the heater.
7. Remove the snap-rivet that attaches the forward side of the defroster air duct to the heater assembly. Move the air duct back into the defroster nozzle and disengage it from the tabs on the heater box. Tilt the forward edge of the duct up and forward to disengage it from the nozzle, and remove it from the left side of the heater assembly.
8. Remove the heater assembly to dash panel support bracket mounting screw and remove the heater assembly. At the same time, pull the heater hoses through the dash panel. Then, disconnect the hoses from the heater core in the case.

Blower Motor R & R, Non-Air Conditioned Cars

1. Remove the heater assembly.
2. Disconnect the blower motor lead wire from the resistor. Remove the four blower motor mounting plate attaching nuts and remove the motor and wheel.

Heater Core R & R, Non-Air Conditioned Cars

1. Remove the heater assembly.
2. Remove the compression gasket from the cowl air inlet and remove the eleven clips from the case. Separate the case and remove the heater core.

Heater Assembly R & R, Air Conditioned Cars

1971-72

NOTE: This procedure requires evacuation of the air conditioning refrigerant. Failure to exercise proper safety precautions could cause personal injury.

1. Disconnect the negative battery cable and drain the cooling system.
2. Evacuate the air conditioning system.
3. Disconnect the heater hose from the heater housing.
4. Remove the expansion valve from the evaporator core and tape the openings on the core closed.
5. Disconnect the green and brown vacuum hoses from the hot water valve and remove the two screws that attach the hot water valve and vacuum motor to the firewall.
6. Remove the three heater housing attaching nuts from the engine side of the firewall.
7. Remove the glove box door and the glove box. On models equipped with a console, remove the console.
8. Remove the radio and the kick panel from under the right side of the instrument panel.
9. Remove the three bolts that attach the right pillar brace to the lower edge of the instrument panel.
10. Disconnect the temperature control cable from the heater housing, and the purple and green vacuum hoses from the water valve vacuum switch on the heater housing.
11. Disconnect the white hose from the vacuum motor and the electrical leads from the blower motor resistor.
12. Disconnect the blower motor ground wire from the cowl and the red and yellow vacuum hoses from the vacuum motor above the heater blower motor.
13. Remove the cover plate from the bottom of the defroster duct that runs out of the blower motor.
14. Remove the two screws that attach the air distribution duct to the blower motor and remove the duct.
15. Reach through the opening left by the removal of the air distribution duct and remove the nut and lock plate that attaches the blower housing to the heater housing.
16. Turn the blower housing counterclockwise to disconnect it from the heater housing. Position the blower housing out of the way on the transmission tunnel.
17. Remove the drain hose from the heater housing and remove the screw that attaches the right side of the heater housing to the cowl upper support.
18. Remove the heater housing from under the instrument panel.
19. Reverse the above procedure to install the heater housing. After installation, charge the refrigerant system.

1973-74

NOTE: This procedure requires evacuation of the air conditioning refrigerant. Failure to exercise proper safety precautions could cause personal injury.

1. Disconnect the negative battery cable and drain the cooling system.
2. Evacuate the air conditioning system.
3. Disconnect the heater hoses from the heater core tubes.
4. Disconnect the expansion valve from the evaporator core tubes and plug the openings in the core tubes.
5. Remove the three nuts that attach the heater assembly to the firewall.
6. Remove the glove box and disconnect the right and left air ducts from the heater housing.
7. Disconnect the blue vacuum hose from the A/C-defroster distribution housing. Open the access door in the bottom of the housing and remove the two screws that attach the housing to the instrument panel defroster ducts. Remove the housing from the top of the blower motor housing.
8. Disconnect the red and the yellow vacuum hoses from the A/C-heat door vacuum motor (upper left side of housing).
9. Disconnect the white vacuum hose from outside recirculation door vacuum motor (upper right side of housing).
10. Disconnect the multiple vacuum connector from the rear of the A/C-heater control on the instrument panel.
11. Disconnect the control cable from the temperature control door crank arm.
12. Disconnect the purple and the green vacuum hoses from the water valve switch. The water valve switch is located on the heater housing just above the temperature door crank arm.
13. Remove the bracket that attaches the heater housing to the underside of the instrument panel.
14. Move the heater assembly rearward until it clears its mounting studs, then detach the vacuum hoses that are taped or clipped to the top of the housing.
15. Tag and disconnect the wiring that attaches to the heater housing.
16. Remove the heater housing from the car.
17. Reverse the above procedure to install the heater housing. Charge the refrigerant system.

Blower Motor R & R, Air Conditioned Cars

1971-72

1. Disconnect the negative battery cable. If equipped with a console, remove the console from the car.
2. Remove the radio.
3. Remove the fuse panel attaching screw, disconnect the multiple connector from the fuse panel and remove the fuse panel from the fuse panel support bracket which is attached to the brake pedal support bracket.

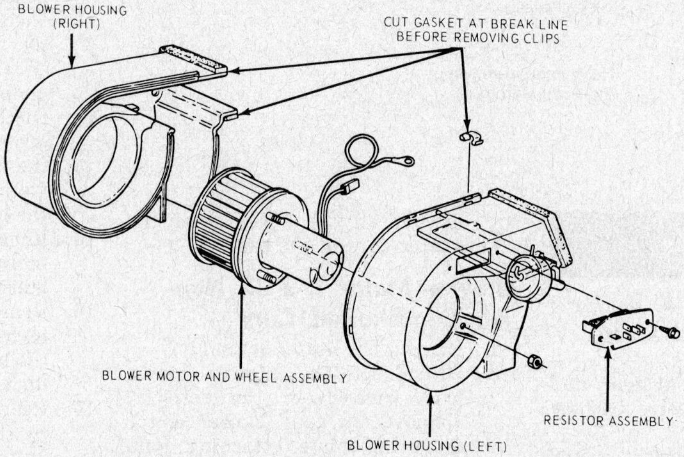
BLOWER HOUSING (RIGHT)
CUT GASKET AT BREAK LINE BEFORE REMOVING CLIPS
BLOWER MOTOR AND WHEEL ASSEMBLY
RESISTOR ASSEMBLY
BLOWER HOUSING (LEFT)

1973 Heater blower motor removal (© Ford Motor Co)

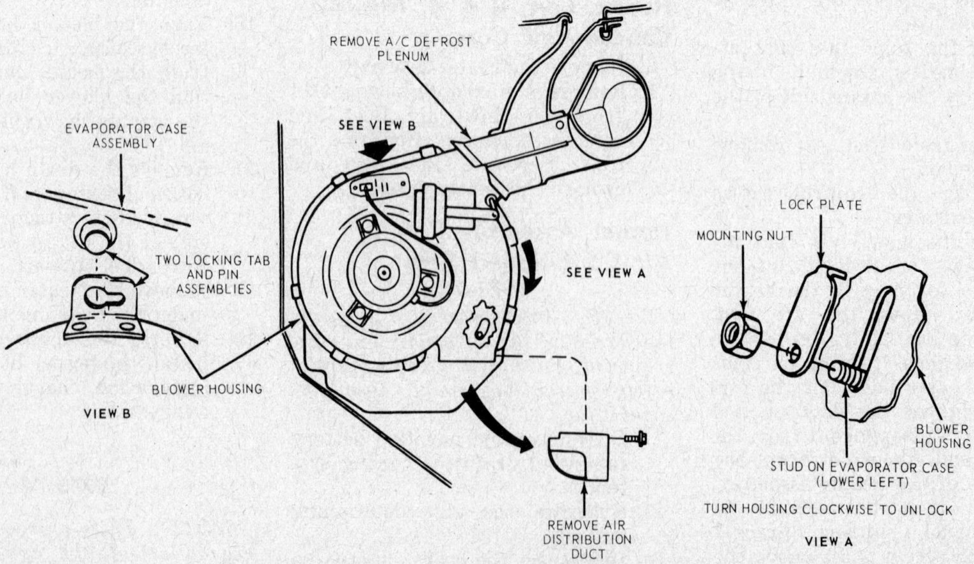
REMOVE A/C DEFROST PLENUM
SEE VIEW B
EVAPORATOR CASE ASSEMBLY
TWO LOCKING TAB AND PIN ASSEMBLIES
SEE VIEW A
BLOWER HOUSING
VIEW B
REMOVE AIR DISTRIBUTION DUCT
LOCK PLATE
MOUNTING NUT
BLOWER HOUSING
STUD ON EVAPORATOR CASE (LOWER LEFT)
TURN HOUSING CLOCKWISE TO UNLOCK
VIEW A

1973 Heater blower motor and housing removal (© Ford Motor Co)

4. Remove the fuse panel support bracket from the brake pedal support bracket and position it out of the way.
5. Remove the instrument panel-to-cowl brace and position the fuse panel on the lower edge of the instrument panel.
6. Disconnect the lead wires from the blower motor resistor and the blower motor ground wire from the cowl.
7. Remove the red and yellow vacuum hoses from the vacuum motor over the blower motor.
8. Remove the cover plate from the bottom of the defroster outlet duct of the blower motor.
9. Remove the two screws that attach the air distribution duct to the blower motor housing.
10. Reach through the opening left by the removal of the air distribution duct and remove the nut and lock plate that attaches the blower motor housing to the heater housing.
11. Turn the blower motor counterclockwise to disconnect it from the heater housing and position the blower motor on the transmission tunnel.
12. Remove the steering column-to-instrument panel brace. It may be necessary to move the blower housing slightly rearward to gain access to the upper brace attaching bolt.
13. Cut the blower housing-to-heater housing gasket at the break in the two blower housing pieces.
14. Disconnect the A/C-heat door rod from the A/C-heat door.
15. Remove the seven clips and separate the two halves of the blower housing.
16. Remove the left half of the blower housing with the blower motor attached.
17. Remove the three blower motor mounting nuts and remove the blower motor and wheel.
18. Reverse the above procedure to install the blower motor.

1973-74

1. Disconnect the negative battery cable.
2. Remove the two screws that attach the hot air distribution duct to the bottom of the blower housing and remove the duct.
3. Open the access door in the bottom of the A/C-defroster distribution housing and remove the two screws that attach the distribution housing to the instrument panel defroster ducts.
4. Working through the opening left by removal of the bottom heat distribution duct, remove the nut and lock plate that attaches the blower housing to the heater housing.
5. Turn the blower motor housing clockwise to disengage the two locking tabs on the blower housing from the pin on the heater housing.
6. Remove the blower housing from the car.
7. Cut the blower outlet gasket at the blower housing seams.
8. Remove the clips that secure the two halves of the blower housing, and separate the housing.
9. Remove the three blower motor attaching nuts and the motor.

Heater Core R & R, Air Conditioned Cars

1971-74

1. Remove the heater housing and remove the rubber seal from the housing.
2. Remove the eleven clips that hold the two halves of the heater housing together and separate the housing.
3. Remove the A/C thermostatic de-icing switch from the top of the housing.
4. Remove four screws and remove the evaporator core from the upper housing.
5. Remove four screws and the temperature blend door upper frame.
6. Remove the spring clip and crank arm and remove the temperature blend door from the housing.
7. Remove four screws and the temperature blend door lower frame.
8. Remove the heater core and gasket from the lower housing.

SEAT BELTS

Seat Belt/Starter Interlock System—1974

All Ford vehicles are equipped with the Federally-required starter interlock system. The purpose of this system is to force the wearing of seat belts.

The system includes a warning light and buzzer (as in late 1972 and 1973), weight sensors in the front seats, switches in the outboard front seat belt retractors, and an electronic control module. The center front seat is tied into the warning light and buzzer system, but not into the starter interlock.

The electronic control module requires that the driver and right front passenger first sit down, then pull out their seat belts. If this is not done, the starter will not operate, but the light and buzzer will. The sequence must be followed each time the engine is started unless the driver and passenger have remained seated and buckled. If the seat belts have been pulled out and left buckled, the engine will not start. The switches in the retractors must be cycled for each start. If the belts are released after the start, the light and buzzer will operate.

If the system should fail, preventing starting, the interlock by-pass switch under the hood can be used. This switch permits one start without interference from the interlock system. This by-pass switch can also be used for servicing purposes.

INDEX

Pontiac · Grand Prix

YEAR IDENTIFICATION

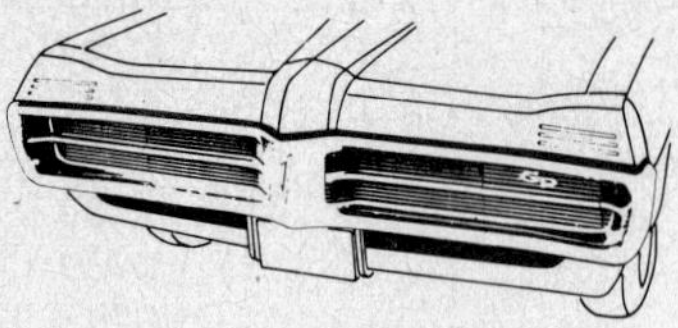

1967 Grand Prix

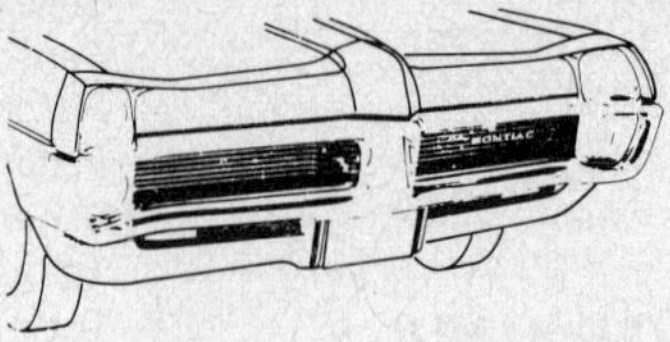

1967

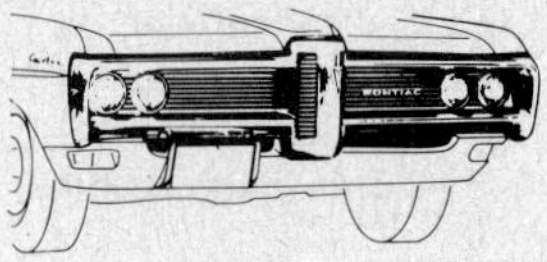

1968

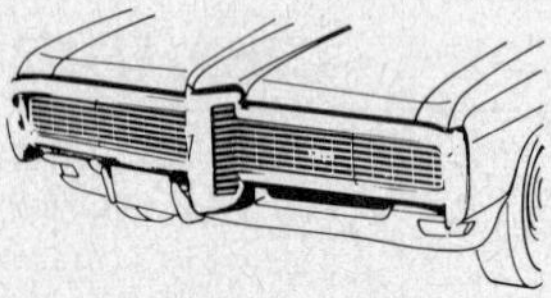

1968 Grand Prix

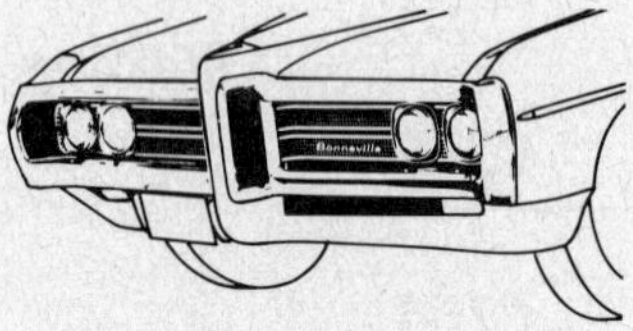

1969

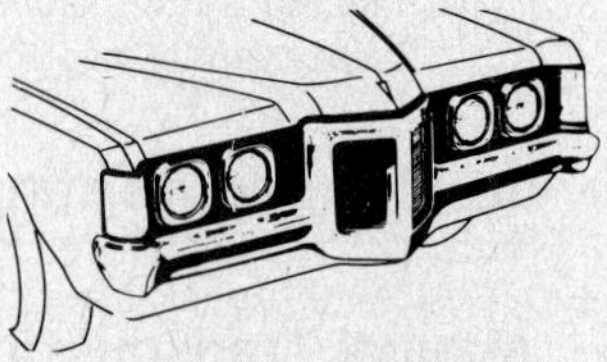

1969 Grand Prix

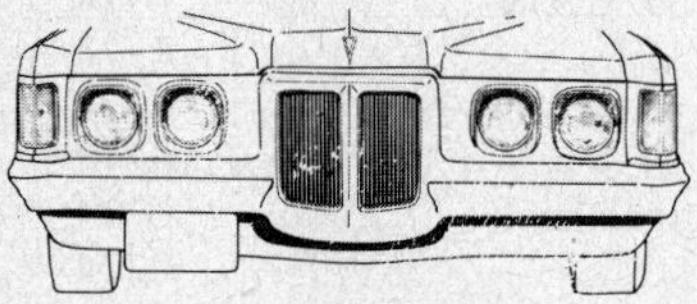

1970 Grand Prix

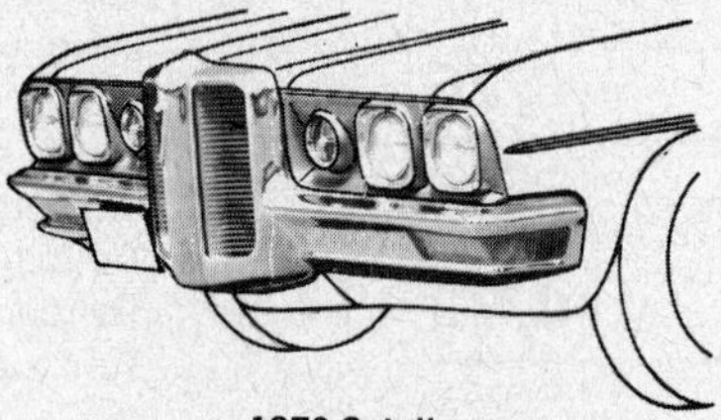

1970 Catalina

1971

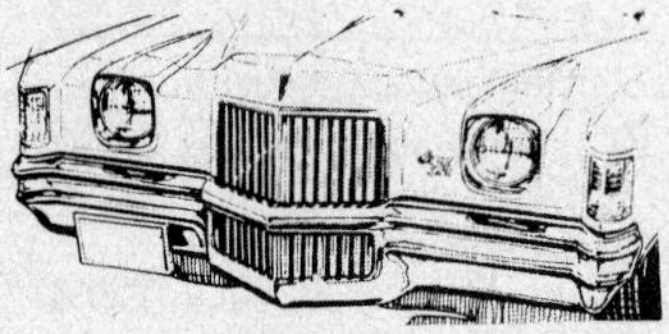

1971 Grand Prix

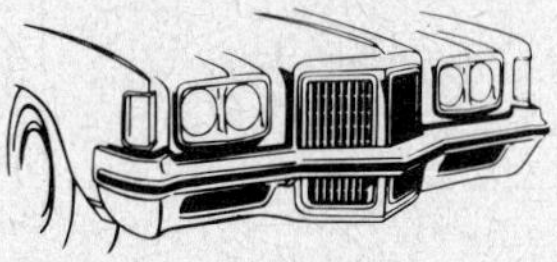

1972

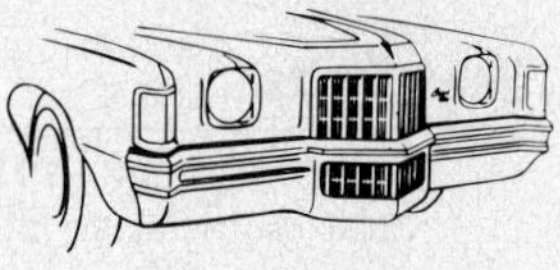

1972 Grand Prix

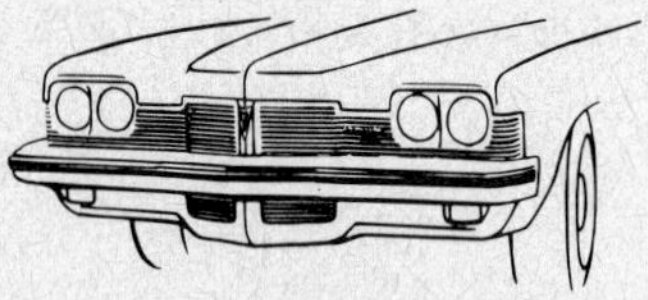

1973 Catalina

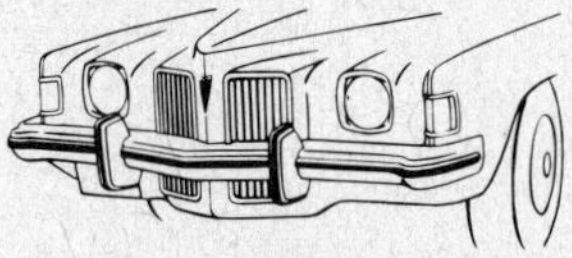

1973 Grand Prix

1974 Catalina

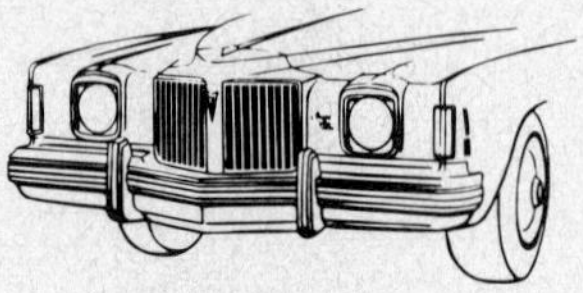

1974 Grand Prix

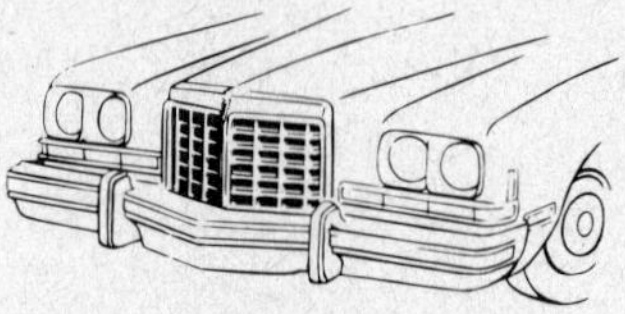

1974 Grand Ville

FIRING ORDER

Ignition timing marks—1967-74
(© Pontiac Div, G.M. Corp)

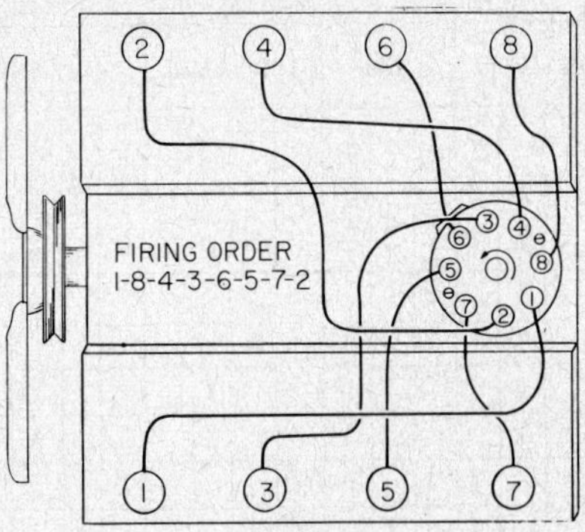
FIRING ORDER
1-8-4-3-6-5-7-2

1967-74 V8
(© Pontiac Div, G.M. Corp)

CAR SERIAL NUMBER LOCATION

1967

Car serial number is on the left front door pillar. This number is interpreted below.

1968-74

Car serial number is located on the upper left-hand side of the instrument panel, visible through the windshield. The number is interpreted as follows:

1967-74

First digit: Car division
Second and third digits: Series number
Fourth and fifth digits: Body style code
Sixth digit: Year manufactured
Seventh digit: Plant
Eighth digit: Engine used (1 = V8; 6 = 6 cyl.)
Ninth to thirteenth digits—sequential serial number

ENGINE IDENTIFICATION

1967-74

The engine production number is found on the front of the right bank of cylinders, stamped into the block.

The engine production code is stamped on a machined pad just beneath this number. Refer to the charts for engine code interpretation.
First digit: Pontiac Division.
Second and third digit: Model series.
Fourth and fifth digit: Body style.
Sixth digit: Year manufactured.
Seventh digit: Plant.

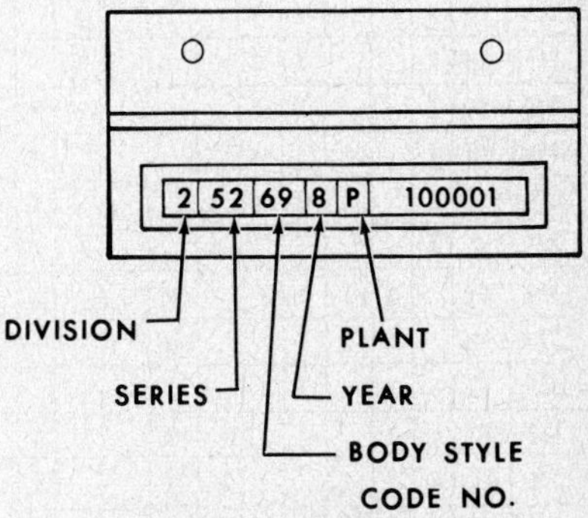
2 52 69 8 P 100001
DIVISION
SERIES
PLANT
YEAR
BODY STYLE CODE NO.

Typical vehicle serial number

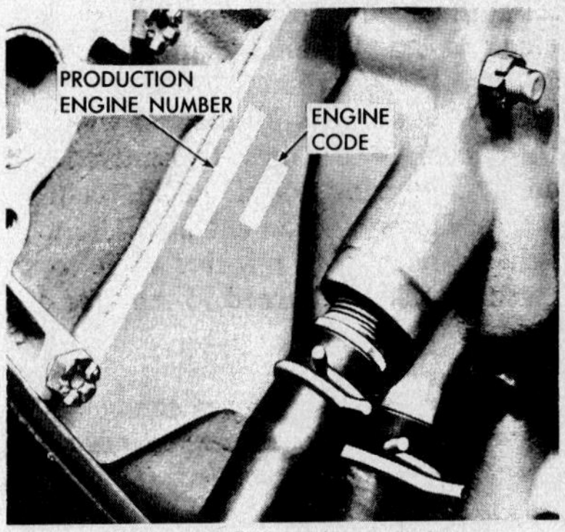
PRODUCTION ENGINE NUMBER
ENGINE CODE

Engine serial number location

TORQUE SPECIFICATIONS

All readings in ft lbs

Year	Engine Displacement (cu in.)	Cylinder Head Bolts	Rod Bearing Bolts	Main Bearing Bolts	Crankshaft Pulley Bolt	Flywheel to Crankshaft Bolts	MANIFOLD Intake	MANIFOLD Exhaust
'67-'74	All Series	80-95	35-45③	85-95①②	160	90-95	40	30

① Rear main—120
② 1968-74—100
③ 63 ft lbs on 455 S.D. engine

1967 ENGINE CODES AND SPECIAL EQUIPMENT

HORSEPOWER	ENGINE CODE	DISP.		TRANS		CARB.			COMP. RATIO				CAMSHAFT				STANDARD DISTRIBUTOR										BREAKER LESS				VALVE SPRINGS			AIR COND.	A.I.R. SYSTEM	C.C.S.	SPECIAL EXHAUST MANIFOLDS
		400	428	MANUAL	AUTOMATIC	2-BBL	4-BBL	QUADRAJET	7.9	8.6	10.5	10.75	9779254(U)	9779066(N)	9779067(P)	9779068(S)	1111250	1111254	1111237	1111253	1111242	1111183	1111252	1111261	1111243	1111244	1111245	1111251	1111180	1111255	STD. TWO	H.D. TWO	H.D. SPECIAL				
265	WA	X		X		X				X			X								X										X						
265	WB	X		X		X				X			X								X										X						
333	WD	X		X			X				X				X			X													X				X		
333	WE	X		X			X				X				X					X										0	X						
260	XB	X			X	X			X				X								X										X						
293	XC	X			X		X		X					X							X										X						
350	XH	X			X		X				X			X											X		0				X						
350	XJ	X			X		X				X			X											X		0				X			X			
350	XY	X		X			X				X				X											X					X				X		
350	XZ	X		X			X				X				X										X		0				X						
265	YA	X			X	X				X			X								X										X						
265	YB	X			X	X				X			X											X							X					X	
290	YC	X			X	X					X		X							X										0	X						
290	YD	X			X	X					X		X							X										0	X			X			
325	YE	X			X		X				X			X						X										0	X						
325	YF	X			X		X				X			X						X										0	X			X			
360	WG		X	X	X			X			X				X							X							0			X					
376	WJ		X	X				X				X				X	●					X						●	0				X				X
376	Y3		X		X			X				X				X	●					X						●	0			X					X
360	Y2		X		X			X			X				X							X							0			X					
376	XK		X	X				X				X				X			X				●										X		X		X
360	YH		X		X			X			X				X							X							0			X					
376	YK		X		X			X				X				X	●					X						●	0			X					X
360	YY		X	X				X							X				X													X			X		

● With 60 PSI oil pump spring
0 Optional

ALTERNATOR AND REGULATOR SPECIFICATIONS

Year	ALTERNATOR Part No. or Manufacturer	ALTERNATOR Field Current @ 12 V	ALTERNATOR Output (amps)	REGULATOR Part No. or Manufacturer	Field Relay Air Gap (in.)	Field Relay Point Gap (in.)	Field Relay Volts to Close	Regulator Air Gap (in.)	Regulator Point Gap (in.)	Regulator Volts @ 75°
'67-'69	1100699	1.9-2.3	42	1119511	.015	.030	2.3-3.7	.057	.015	13.5-14.4
	1100700	1.9-2.3	55	1119511	.015	.030	2.3-3.7	.057	.015	13.5-14.4
	1100800	1.9-2.3	55	1119511	.015	.030	2.3-3.7	.057	.015	13.5-14.4
	1100801	1.9-2.3	42	1119511	.015	.030	2.3-3.7	.057	.015	13.5-14.4
'70	1100704	2.2-2.6	37	1119515	.015	.030	2.3-3.7	.057	.015	13.5-14.4
	1100700	2.2-2.6	55	1119515	.015	.030	2.3-3.7	.057	.015	13.5-14.4
	1100895	2.2-2.6	61	1119515	.015	.030	2.3-3.7	.057	.015	13.5-14.4
	1117765	4.1-4.6	62	1116368	Transistorized Regulator					
'71-'74	1100927	4-4.5	37	—	Transistorized Regulator					
	1100928	4-4.5	55	—	Transistorized Regulator					
	1101015	4-4.5	80	—	Transistorized Regulator					

— Not applicable

1968 ENGINE CODES AND SPECIAL EQUIPMENT

Displacement	Horsepower	Engine Code	Trans-mission: Manual	Automatic	Carburetor: 2-BBL.	Quadrajet	Compression Ratio: 8.6	10.5	10.75	Camshaft: 9777254	9779066	9779067	9779068	Standard Distributor: 1111272	1111270	1111449	1111300	1111448	1111435	1111450	Valve Springs: Std. Two	H.D. Two (Spec.)	Special Exhaust Manifolds
400 Cu. In. Engine	290	WA	X		X			X			X							X			X		
	290	WB	X		X			X			X							X			X		
	265	YA		X	X		X			X				X							X		
	290	YC		X	X			X				X		X							X		
	340	YE		X		X		X			X						X				X		
	350	XZ	X			X		X				X					X				X		
	350	XH		X		X		X			X						X				X		
428 Cu. In. Engine	375	WG	X			X		X					X							X	X		
	390	WJ	X			X			X			X				●						X	X
	375	YH		X		X		X				X							X		X		
	390	YK		X		X			X			X			●						X		X

• With 60 psi oil pump spring. All cars use CCS

1969 ENGINE CODES AND SPECIAL EQUIPMENT

Displace-ment: 400	428	Horsepower	Engine Code	Trans-mission: Manual	Automatic	Carburetor: 2-BBL. (2GV)	4-BBL. (4MV)	Compression Ratio: 8.6:1	10.5:1	10.75:1	Camshaft: 9777254	9779066	9779067	9779068	Distributor: 1111253	1111940	1111946 (e)	1111952 (e)	1111960	1111959	Valve Springs: H.D.—Dual	H.D. Spec.—Dual	Cylinder Head: Small Valve	Large Valve
X		290	(a) WA WD	X		X			X			X						X			X		X	
X		265	(a) YA YB		X	X		X			X					X					X		X	
X		290	(a) WB WE	X		X			X			X						X			X		X	
X		290	(a) YC YD		X	X			X		X				X						X		X	
	X	360	WG	X			X		X				X						X		X			X
	X	360	(a) YL YH		X		X		X			X								X	X		X	
	X	390	WJ	X			X			X				X				X				X		X
	X	360	(b) XK		X		X		X				X							X	X			X
	X	360	(a) XE (c) XJ		X		X		X				X							X	X		X	
	X	390	YK		X		X			X			X				X				X			X
X		350	(d) WX	X			X		X				X					X			X			X
X		350	(d) XH		X		X		X			X			X						X			X
	X	370	(d) WF	X			X		X				X						X		X			X
	X	370	(d) XF		X		X		X			X								X	X			X
	X	390	(d) WL	X			X			X				X				X				X		X
	X	390	(d) XG		X		X			X			X				X				X			X
X		265	(d) YF		X	X		X			X					X					X		X	
X		340	XZ.		X		X		X		X				X						X		X	

(a) Early production (small valve) engines with 30° intake valve seat angle. Later production (small valve) engines use 45° intake valve seat. NOTE: All large valve engines use 30° intake valve seat.

(b) Police Freeway Enforcer.
(c) Police Highway Patrol
(d) Grand Prix
(e) Uses special hardened drive gear. (With 60 psi oil pump)

1970 ENGINE CODES AND SPECIAL EQUIPMENT

HORSEPOWER	ENGINE CODE	USAGE: PONTIAC	USAGE: GRAND PRIX	DISPLACEMENT: 350	DISPLACEMENT: 400	DISPLACEMENT: 455	TRANS: MANUAL	TRANS: AUTOMATIC	CARB: 2 BBL (2GV)	CARB: 4 BBL (4MV)	COMP. RATIO: 8.8:1	COMP. RATIO: 10.0:1	COMP. RATIO: 10.25:1	CAMSHAFT: 9777254 (U)	CAMSHAFT: 9779066 (N)	CAMSHAFT: 9779067 (P)	CAMSHAFT: 9779068 (S)	DISTRIBUTOR: 1112008	DISTRIBUTOR: 1112007	DISTRIBUTOR: 1111148 *	DISTRIBUTOR: 1111176 *	DISTRIBUTOR: 1111105	DISTRIBUTOR: 1112012 *	VALVE SPRINGS: STD.-DUAL	CYL. HEAD: SMALL VALVE	CYL. HEAD: LARGE VALVE
225	W7	X		X			X		X		X			X				X						X	X	
255	X7	X		X				X	X		X			X				X						X	X	
290	WE	X			X		X		X			X			X			X						X	X	
350	WX		X		X		X			X			X			X					X			X		X
350	XH		X		X			X		X			X		X					X				X		X
330	XZ	X			X			X		X		X			X				X					X	X	
265	YB	X	X		X			X	X		X			X					X					X	X	
290	YD	X			X			X	X			X		X					X					X	X	
370	WG	X	X			X	X			X			X				X						X	X		X
370	XF	X	X			X		X		X			X			X							X	X		X
360	YH	X				X		X		X		X				X						X		X	X	

* Uses hardened drive gear for use with 60 psi oil pump and high tension distributor points

1971 ENGINE CODES AND SPECIAL EQUIPMENT

ENGINE CODE	HORSEPOWER	MODEL USAGE: "B" SERIES	MODEL USAGE: "G" SERIES	DISPLACEMENT: 250 L-6	DISPLACEMENT: 350 V-8	DISPLACEMENT: 400 V-8	DISPLACEMENT: 455 V-8	TRANSMISSION: MANUAL (3 Speed)	TRANSMISSION: MANUAL (4 Speed)	TRANSMISSION: AUTOMATIC	CARBURETOR: MV (1 Bbl.)	CARBURETOR: 2GV (2 Bbl.)	CARBURETOR: 4MV (4 Bbl.)	CYLINDER HEADS: Compression Ratio: 8.5:1	CYLINDER HEADS: Compression Ratio: 8.0:1	CYLINDER HEADS: Compression Ratio: 8.2:1	CYLINDER HEADS: Compression Ratio: 8.4:1	CYLINDER HEADS: Rocker Arm Stud: PRESSED-IN	CYLINDER HEADS: Rocker Arm Stud: THREADED	CYLINDER HEADS: Valve Spring: SINGLE	CYLINDER HEADS: Valve Spring: DUAL (STD.)	CYLINDER HEADS: Valve Spring: DUAL (H.D.)	CYLINDER HEADS: Valve Size: SMALL	CYLINDER HEADS: Valve Size: LARGE	CAMSHAFT: 3864897	CAMSHAFT: 483555 (W)	CAMSHAFT: 9779066 (N)	CAMSHAFT: 9779067 (P)	CAMSHAFT: 9779068 (S)	VALVE LIFTER: HIGH-BALL (STD.)	VALVE LIFTER: HIGH-BALL*	VALVE LIFTER: LOW-BALL	DISTRIBUTOR: 1110489	DISTRIBUTOR: 1112069	DISTRIBUTOR: 1112068	DISTRIBUTOR: 1112070	DISTRIBUTOR: 1112071	DISTRIBUTOR: 1112072	DISTRIBUTOR: 1112073	DISTRIBUTOR: 1112083
WR	250	X			X			X				X			X			X			X		X			X				X										X
YU	250	X			X					**		X			X			X			X		X			X				X				X						
XR	250	X			X					**		X			X			X			X		X				X			X				X						
WT	300		X			X		X					X			X			X			X		X					X			X					X			
WK	300		X			X			X				X			X			X			X		X					X			X					X			
XX%	265	X				X				X		X				X		X			X		X			X				X					X					
YS	300	X	X			X				X			X			X			X		X			X				X		X						X				
YC+	325	X	X				X			X			X			X		X			X			X				X		X								X		
YG &	280	X					X			X		X				X		X			X		X				X			X							X			

* Lifter Body with Cast-Iron Foot

** "YU" is used with M35 transmission; "XR" is used with M38 transmission

% Man. Trans. Models use WS engine code

\+ Man. Trans. Models use WJ engine code

& Man. Trans. Models use WG engine code

1972-73 ENGINE CODES

The second letter of the vehicle identification number is the engine identity.

TYPE	DISPLACEMENT	CARBURETOR	EXHAUST	CODE
L6	250	1 BBL.	Single	D
V8	307②	2 BBL.	Single	F
V8	350	2 BBL.	Single	M
V8	350	2 BBL.	Dual	N
V8	400	2 BBL.	Single	R
V8	400	2 BBL.	Dual	P
V8	400	4 BBL.	Single	S
V8	400	4 BBL.	Dual	T

TYPE	DISPLACEMENT	CARBURETOR	EXHAUST	CODE
V8	455	2 BBL.	Single	V
V8	455	2 BBL.	Dual	U
V8	455	4 BBL.	Single	W
V8	455	4 BBL.	Dual	Y
V8	455 H.O. ①	4 BBL.	Dual	X

① S.D. in 1973-74

② 1972 only

GENERAL ENGINE SPECIFICATIONS

Year	Engine No. Cyl. Displacement Cu. In.	Carburetor Type	Advertised Horsepower @ rpm ■	Advertised Torque @ rpm (ft lbs) ■	Bore and Stroke (in.)	Advertised Compression Ratio	Oil Pressure @ 2050 rpm
'67	8-400	2 bbl	265 @ 4600	397 @ 2400	4.1222 x 3.750	8.6:1	35
	8-400	2 bbl	290 @ 4600	428 @ 2500	4.1222 x 3.750	10.5:1	35
	8-400	4 bbl	325 @ 4800	445 @ 2900	4.1222 x 3.750	10.5:1	35
	8-400	4 bbl	333 @ 5000	445 @ 3000	4.1222 x 3.750	10.5:1	35
	8-400	4 bbl	350 @ 4800	440 @ 3000	4.1222 x 3.750	10.5:1	35
	8-428	4 bbl	360 @4600	472 @ 3200	4.1222 x 4.000	10.5:1	35
	8-428	4 bbl	376 @ 5100	462 @ 3400	4.1222 x 4.000	10.75:1	35
'68	8-400	2 bbl	265 @ 4600	397 @ 2400	4.1222 x 4.000	8.6:1	35
	8-400	2 bbl	290 @ 4600	428 @ 2500	4.1212 x 3.750	10.5:1	35
	8-400	4 bbl	340 @ 4800	445 @ 2900	4.1212 x 3.750	10.5:1	35
	8-400	4 bbl	350 @ 5000	445 @ 3000	4.1212 x 3.750	10.5:1	35
	8-428	4 bbl	375 @ 4800	472 @ 3200	4.1212 x 4.000	10.5:1	35
	8-428	4 bbl	390 @ 5200	465 @ 3400	4.1212 x 4.000	10.75:1	35
'69	8-400	2 bbl	265 @ 4600	397 @ 2400	4.1212 x 3.750	8.6:1	35
	8-400	2 bbl	290 @ 4600	428 @ 2500	4.1212 x 3.750	10.5:1	35
	8-400	4 bbl	340 @ 4800	445 @ 2900	4.1212 x 3.750	10.5:1	35
	8-428	4 bbl	360 @ 4600	472 @ 3200	4.1212 x 4.000	10.5:1	35
	8-428	4 bbl	390 @ 5200	465 @ 3400	4.1212 x 4.000	10.75:1	35
'70	8-350	2 bbl	255 @ 4600	355 @ 2800	3.8762 x 3.750	8.8:1	35
	8-400	2 bbl	265 @ 4600	397 @ 2400	4.1212 x 3.750	8.8:1	35
	8-400	2 bbl	290 @ 4600	428 @ 2500	4.1212 x 3.750	10.0:1	35
	8-400	4 bbl	330 @ 4800	445 @ 2900	4.1212 x 3.750	10.0:1	35
	8-455	4 bbl	360 @ 4300	500 @ 2700	4.1522 x 4.210	10.0:1	35
	8-455 HO	4 bbl	370 @ 4600	500 @ 3100	4.1522 x 4.210	10.25:1	35
'71	8-350	2 bbl	250 @ 4400	350 @ 2400	3.8762 x 3.750	8.0:1	35
	8-400	2 bbl	265 @ 4400	400 @ 2400	4.1212 x 3.750	8.2:1	35
	8-400	4 bbl	300 @ 4800	400 @ 3600	4.1212 x 3.750	8.2:1	35
	8-455	2 bbl	280 @ 4400	455 @ 2000	4.1522 x 4.210	8.2:1	35
	8-455	4 bbl	325 @ 4400	455 @ 3200	4.1522 x 4.210	8.2:1	35
'72	8-400	2 bbl	175 @ 4000	310 @ 2400	4.1212 x 3.750	8.2:1	35
	8-400 DE	2 bbl	200 @ 4000	325 @ 2400	4.1212 x 3.750	8.2:1	35
	8-400	4 bbl	200 @ 4000	295 @ 2800	4.1212 x 3.750	8.2:1	35
	8-400 DE	4 bbl	250 @ 4400	325 @ 3200	4.1212 x 3.750	8.2:1	35
	8-455	2 bbl	185 @ 4000	350 @ 2000	4.1522 x 4.210	8.2:1	35
	8-455 DE	2 bbl	200 @ 4000	370 @ 2000	4.1522 x 4.210	8.2:1	35
	8-455	4 bbl	220 @ 3600	350 @ 2400	4.1522 x 4.210	8.2:1	35
	8-455 DE	4 bbl	250 @ 3600	370 @ 2400	4.1522 x 4.210	8.2:1	35
'73	8-350 SE	2 bbl	150 @ 4000	270 @ 2000	3.8762 x 3.750	7.6:1	55-60
	8-350 DE	2 bbl	175 @ 4400	280 @ 2400	3.8762 x 3.750	7.6:1	55-60
	8-400 SE	2 bbl	170 @ 3600	320 @ 2000	4.1212 x 3.750	8.0:1	55-60
	8-400 DE	2 bbl	185 @ 4000	320 @ 2400	4.1212 x 3.750	8.0:1	55-60
	8-400 SE	4 bbl	200 @ 4000	310 @ 2400	4.1212 x 3.750	8.0:1	55-60
	8-400 DE	4 bbl	230 @ 4400	325 @ 3200	4.1212 x 3.750	8.0:1	55-60
	8-455 SE	4 bbl	215 @ 3600	350 @ 2400	4.1522 x 4.210	8.0:1	55-60
	8-455 DE	4 bbl	250 @ 4000	370 @ 2800	4.1522 x 4.210	8.0:1	55-60
	8-455S.D. DE	4 bbl	310 @ 4000	390 @ 3600	4.1522 x 4.210	8.4:1	75-80

GENERAL ENGINE SPECIFICATIONS

Year	Engine No. Cyl. Displacement (Cu. In.)	Carburetor Type	Advertised Horsepower @ rpm ■	Advertised Torque @ rpm (ft lbs) ■	Bore and Stroke (in.)	Advertised Compression Ratio	Oil Pressure @ 2050 rpm
'74	8-350 SE	2 bbl	155 @ 4000	275 @ 2400	3.8762 x 3.750	7.6:1	55-60
	8-350 DE	2 bbl	170 @ 4400	292 @ 2400	3.8762 x 3.750	7.6:1	55-60
	8-400 SE	2 bbl	175 @ 3600	315 @ 2000	4.1212 x 3.750	8.0:1	55-60
	8-400 DE	2 bbl	190 @ 4000	330 @ 2400	4.1212 x 3.750	8.0:1	55-60
	8-400 SE	4 bbl	200 @ 4000	320 @ 2400	4.1212 x 3.750	8.0:1	55-60
	8-400 DE	4 bbl	225 @ 4400	330 @ 2800	4.1212 x 3.750	8.0:1	55-60
	8-455 SE	4 bbl	215 @ 3600	355 @ 2400	4.1522 x 4.210	8.0:1	55-60
	8-455 DE	4 bbl	250 @ 4000	380 @ 2800	4.1522 x 4.210	8.0:1	55-60
	8-455 S.D. DE	4 bbl	290 @ 4000	395 @ 3600	4.1522 x 4.210	8.4:1	75-80

■ Beginning 1972, horsepower and torque are SAE net figures. They are measured at the rear of the transmission with all accessories installed and operating. Since the figures vary when a given engine is installed in different models, some are representative rather than exact.

HO High output
SE Single exhaust
DE Dual exhaust
S.D. Super Duty

Pontiac

CAPACITIES

Year	ENGINE No. Cyl. (Cu. In.) Displacement	Engine Crankcase Add 1 Qt For New Filter	TRANSMISSION Pts To Refill After Draining: Manual 3-Speed	Manual 4-Speed	Automatic ●	Drive Axle (pts)	Gasoline Tank (gals)	COOLING SYSTEM (qts): With Heater	With A/C
'67	8-400	6	2.8	2.5	19	4.5	26.5③	18	18②
	8-428	6	2.8	2.5	19	4.5	26.5③	17.2	17.2
'68	8-400	5	5	2.5	19	4.5	26.5③	18	18②
	8-428	5	5	2.5	19	4.5	26.5③	17.2	17.2
'69	8-400	5	2.8	—	19	4.5	26.5③	18	18
	8-428	5	2.8	—	19	4.5	26.5③	17.2	17.2
'70	8-350	5	2.8	—	6	4.5	26③	19.6	19.6
	8-400	5	2.8	—	7.5	4.5	26③	18	18
	8-455	5	2.8	—	7.5	4.5	26③	17.2	17.2
'71	8-350	5	2.8	—	6	4.5	23.5④	20.2	21
	8-400	5	2.8	2.5	7.5	4.5	23.5④	18.6	19.6
	8-455	5	2.8	—	7.5	4.5	23.5④	17.9	19
'72	8-400	5	—	—	7.5	5.5	25⑤	18.6	19.6
	8-455	5	—	—	7.5	5.5	25⑤	17.9	19
'73	8-350	5	—	—	7.5	4.25	25.8⑥	22.0	23.1
	8-400	5	—	—	7.5	4.25	25.8⑥	22.0	23.1/24.0①
	8-455	5	—	—	7.5	4.25	25.8⑥	21.1	22.2
'74	8-350	5	—	—	7.5	4.25	25.8	21.6	23.1
	8-400	5	—	—	7.5	4.25	25.8	21.6	23.1/24.0①
	8-455	5	—	—	7.5	4.25	25.8	21.6	22.2

● '70 and later specifications do not include torque convertor
① Lower figure indicates 2 bbl engine; higher figure indicates 4 bbl engine
② 18.6 qts on Grand Prix
③ Station wagon—24 gals
④ Station wagon—22.5 gals
⑤ Station wagon—23 gals
⑥ Station wagon—22 gals
—— Not applicable

Grand Prix

CAPACITIES

Year	ENGINE No. Cyl. (Cu. In.) Displacement	Engine Crankcase Add 1 Qt For New Filter	TRANSMISSION Pts To Refill After Draining Manual 3-Speed	Manual 4-Speed	Automatic •	Drive Axle (pts)	Gasoline Tank (gals)	COOLING SYSTEM (qts) With Heater	With A/C
'67	8-400	6	2.8	2.5	19	4.5	26.5	18.6	18.6
	8-421	6	2.8	2.5	19	4.5	26.5	17.2	17.2
'68	8-400	5	5	2.5	19	4.5	26.5	18.6	18.6
	8-428	5	5	2.5	19	4.5	26.5	17.2	17.2
'69	8-400	5	2.8	—	19	4.5	21.5	18.7	18.7
	8-428	5	2.8	—	19	4.5	21.5	17.5	17.5
'70	8-400	5	2.8	—	7.5	3①	24.5	18.7	21.1
	8-455	5	2.8	—	7.5	3①	24.5	17.5	19.9
'71	8-400	5	2.8	2.5	7.5	3①	23.5	18.6	19.6
	8-455	5	2.8	—	7.5	3①	23.5	17.9	19
'72	8-400	5	—	—	7.5	3①	26	18.7	18
	8-455	5	—	—	7.5	3①	26	19.7	19.2
'73	8-400	5	—	—	7.5	4.25	25	23.1	23.1
	8-455	5	—	—	7.5	4.25	25	23.1	23.1
'74	8-400	5	—	—	7.5	4.25	25	21.6	23.1
	8-455	5	—	—	7.5	4.25	25	23.1	23.1

• '70 and later specifications do not include torque convertor
① 5 pts with 8.875 in. ring gear
—— Not applicable

BATTERY AND STARTER SPECIFICATIONS

Year	Model	BATTERY Ampere Hour Capacity	Volts	Terminal Grounded	STARTER Lock Test Amps	Volts	Torque (ft lbs)	No-Load Test Amps	Volts	RPM	Brush Spring Tension (oz)
'67-'68	with Synchromesh	53	12	Neg.	Not Recommended			100	10.6	4,350	35
	with Hydramatic	61	12	Neg.	Not Recommended			120	10.6	4,350	35
	Hvy. Duty Opt.	70	12	Neg.	Not Recommended			Not Recommended			35
'69	Std.	61	12	Neg.	Not Recommended			Not Recommended			35
	H.D.②	70	12	Neg.	Not Recommended			Not Recommended			35
	Grand Prix	61	12	Neg.	Not Recommended			Not Recommended			35
'70	350 Std.	53	12	Neg.	Not Recommended			Not Recommended			35
	400 Std.; 350, 400 Opt.①	61	12	Neg.	Not Recommended			Not Recommended			35
	455 Std.; 350, 400 Opt. H.D.②	62	12	Neg.	Not Recommended			Not Recommended			35
	455 H.D. ②	76	12	Neg.	Not Recommended			Not Recommended			35
'71	350 Std.	53	12	Neg.	Not Recommended			Not Recommended			35
	400 Std.; 350, 400 Opt.①	61	12	Neg.	Not Recommended			Not Recommended			35
	455 Std.; 350, 400 H.D.①	62	12	Neg.	Not Recommended			Not Recommended			35
	455 H.D. ②	76	12	Neg.	Not Recommended			Not Recommended			35
'72-'74	350 Std.	53	12	Neg.	Not Recommended			Not Recommended			35
	400 Std.	61	12	Neg.	Not Recommended			Not Recommended			35
	455 Std.; 400 H.D.	62	12	Neg.	Not Recommended			Not Recommended			35
	455 H.D.	73	12	Neg.	Not Recommended			Not Recommended			35
	455 Eng.③	80	12	Neg.	Not Recommended			Not Recommended			35

① Standard w/AC and/or rear window defogger
② Heavy Duty option
③ Maintenance free; Std. Grand Prix SJ

H.D. Heavy Duty
Std. Standard
Opt. Optional
Eng. Energizer

VALVE SPECIFICATIONS

Year	Engine No. Cyl. Displacement (cu in.)	Seat Angle (deg) ■	Face Angle (deg) ●	Spring Test Pressure▲ (lbs @ in.)	Spring Installed Height (in.)	STEM TO GUIDE Clearance (in.) Intake	Exhaust	STEM Diameter (in.) Intake	Exhaust
'67	8-400	30	29	62 @ 1.59	1 19/32	.0016-.0033	.0021-.0038	.34	.34
	8-428	30	29	62 @ 1.59	1 19/32	.0016-.0033	.0021-.0038	.34	.34
'68	8-400①	30	29	63 @ 1.58	1 37/64	.0016-.0033	.0021-.0038	.3416	.3411
	8-400②	30	29	66 @ 1.56	1 33/64	.0016-.0033	.0021-.0038	.3416	.3411
	8-428	30	29	66 @ 1.56	1 33/64	.0016-.0033	.0021-.0038	.3416	.3411
'69	8-400	45	44	63 @ 1.58	1 37/64	.0016-.0033	.0021-.0038	.3416	.3411
	8-428③	30	29	63 @ 1.58	1 37/64	.0016-.0033	.0021-.0038	.3416	.3411
	8-428④	45⑥	44	66 @ 1.56	1 9/16	.0016-.0033	.0021-.0038	.3416	.3411
	8-428⑤ HO	30	29	83 @ 1.59	1 19/32	.0016-.0033	.0021-.0038	.3416	.3411
'70	8-350	45	44	63 @ 1.58	1 37/64	.0016-.0033	.0021-.0038	.3416	.3411
	8-400	45	44	63 @ 1.58	1 37/64	.0016-.0033	.0021-.0038	.3416	.3416
	8-455⑦	30	29	63 @ 1.58	1 37/64	.0016-.0033	.0021-.0038	.3416	.3411
	8-455⑧	45	44	66 @ 1.56	1 9/16	.0016-.0033	.0021-.0038	.3416	.3411
	8-455 HO	30	45	66 @ 1.56	1 9/16	.0016-.0033	.0021-.0038	.3416	.3411
'71	8-350	45	44	61 @ 1.59	1 19/32	.0016-.0033	.0021-.0038	.3416	.3411
	8-400 2 bbl	45	44	61 @ 1.59	1 19/32	.0016-.0033	.0021-.0038	.3416	.3411
	8-400 4 bbl	30	29	65 @ 1.57	1 9/16	.0016-.0033	.0021-.0038	.3416	.3411
	8-455 2 bbl	45	44	61 @ 1.59	1 19/32	.0016-.0033	.0021-.0038	.3416	.3411
	8-455 4 bbl	30	29	65 @ 1.57	1 9/16	.0016-.0033	.0021-.0038	.3416	.3411
'72	8-400 2 bbl	45	44	61 @ 1.59	1 19/32	.0016-.0033	.0021-.0038	.3416	.3411
	8-400 4 bbl	30	29	65 @ 1.57	1 9/16	.0016-.0033	.0021-.0038	.3416	.3411
	8-455 2 bbl	45	44	61 @ 1.59	1 19/32	.0016-.0033	.0021-.0038	.3416	.3411
	8-455 4 bbl	30	29	65 @ 1.57	1 9/16	.0016-.0033	.0021-.0038	.3416	.3411
'73	8-350	45	44	61 @ 1.59	1 19/32	.0016-.0033	.0021-.0038	.3416	.3411
	8-400 2 bbl	45	44	61 @ 1.59	1 19/32	.0016-.0033	.0021-.0038	.3416	.3411
	8-400 4 bbl	30	29	65 @ 1.57	1 9/16	.0016-.0033	.0021-.0038	.3416	.3411
	8-455 2 bbl	45	44	61 @ 1.59	1 19/32	.0016-.0033	.0021-.0038	.3416	.3411
	8-455 4 bbl	30	29	65 @ 1.57	1 9/16	.0016-.0033	.0021-.0038	.3416	.3411
	8-455 S.D.	45	44	70 @ 1.82	1 9/16	.0016-.0033	.0021-.0038	.3416	.3416
'74	8-350	45	44	61 @ 1.59	1 19/32	.0016-.0033	.0021-.0038	.3416	.3411
	8-400 2 bbl	45	44	61 @ 1.59	1 19/32	.0016-.0033	.0021-.0038	.3416	.3411
	8-400 4 bbl	30	29	65 @ 1.57	1 9/16	.0016-.0033	.0021-.0038	.3416	.3411
	8-455 2 bbl	45	44	61 @ 1.59	1 19/32	.0016-.0033	.0021-.0038	.3416	.3411
	8-455 4 bbl	30	29	65 @ 1.57	1 9/16	.0016-.0033	.0021-.0038	.3416	.3411
	8-455 S.D.	45	44	70 @ 1.82	1 9/16	.0016-.0033	.0021-.0038	.3416	.3416

■ Intake valve seat angles are shown. All exhaust valve seat angles are 45° unless otherwise indicated.
● Intake valve face angles are shown. All exhaust valve face angles are 44° unless otherwise indicated.
① All 400 2 bbl and 400 4 bbl with automatic transmission except Grand Prix
② 400 with manual transmission and Grand Prix
③ With automatic transmission only
④ Standard 428 with manual transmission and 428 HO with automatic
⑤ 428 HO with manual transmission only
⑥ 428 HO with automatic transmission—
intake valve seat angle 30°
intake valve face angle 29°
⑦ With manual transmission
⑧ With automatic transmission
HO High output
S.D. Super Duty

▲INNER SPRING TEST PRESSURE

'67	8-400	31 @ 1.57
	8-428	31 @ 1.57
'68	8-400⑨	35 @ 1.54
	8-400⑩	38 @ 1.52
	8-428	38 @ 1.52
'69	8-400	35 @ 1.54
	8-428⑪	35 @ 1.54
	8-428⑫	38 @ 1.52
	8-428⑬ HO	45 @ 1.52
'70	8-350	35 @ 1.54
	8-400	35 @ 1.54
	8-455⑭	35 @ 1.54
	8-455⑮	38 @ 1.52
'70	8-455 HO	38 @ 1.52
'71	8-350	33 @ 1.55
	8-400 2 bbl	33 @ 1.55
	8-400 4 bbl	37 @ 1.53
	8-455 2 bbl	33 @ 1.55
	8-455 4 bbl	37 @ 1.53
'72	8-400 2 bbl	33 @ 1.55
	8-400 4 bbl	37 @ 1.53
'73	8-350	33 @ 1.55
	8-400 2 bbl	33 @ 1.55
	8-400 4 bbl	37 @ 1.53
	8-455	37 @ 1.53
	8-455 S.D.	40 @ 1.75
'74	8-350	33 @ 1.55
	8-400 2 bbl	33 @ 1.55
'74	8-400 4 bbl	37 @ 1.53
	8-455	37 @ 1.53
	8-455 S.D.	40 @ 1.75

⑨ All 400 2 bbl and 8-400 4 bbl with automatic transmission except Grand Prix
⑩ 400 with manual transmission and Grand Prix
⑪ With automatic only
⑫ Standard 428 with manual transmission and 428 HO with automatic transmission
⑬ 428 HO with manual transmission only
⑭ With manual transmission
⑮ With automatic transmission

PISTON CLEARANCE

Year	Engine	Piston-to-Bore Clearance (in.)
'67	8-400	.0022-.0028
	8-428	.0030-.0036
'68-'69	8-400	.0025-.0031
	8-428	.0030-.0036
'70-'72	8-350	.0025-.0033
	8-400	.0025-.0033
	8-455	.0025-.0033
	8-400 Ram Air	.0055-.0061
'73-'74	8-350	.0029-.0037
	8-400	.0029-.0037
	8-455	.0025-.0033
	8-455 S.D.	.0060-.0068

TUNE-UP SPECIFICATIONS

When analyzing compression test results, look for uniformity among cylinders rather than specific pressures.

Year	ENGINE No. Cyl Displacement	ENGINE hp (cu in.)	SPARK PLUGS Type §	SPARK PLUGS Gap (in.)	DISTRIBUTOR Point Dwell (deg)	DISTRIBUTOR Point Gap (in.)	IGNITION TIMING (deg) ▲ Man Trans	IGNITION TIMING (deg) ▲ Auto Trans	VALVES Intake Opens ■ (deg) ●	Fuel Pump Pressure (psi)	IDLE SPEED (rpm) ▲ Man Trans	IDLE SPEED (rpm) ▲ Auto Trans
'67	8-400	265	45S	.035	28-32	.019	6B	6B	22	5-6½	600(700)	500②(600)
	8-400	333	45S	.035	28-32	.019	6B	6B	23/30	5-6½	600②(700)	500②(600)
	8-400	350	45S	.035	28-32	.019	6B	6B	23/30	5-6½	600②(700)	500②(600)
	8-428	360	44S	.035	28-32	.019	6B	6B	23/30	5-6½	700	600(700)
	8-428	376	44S	.035	28-32	.019	6B	6B	31	5-6½	700	600(700)
'68	8-400	265	45S	.035	28-32	.019	9B	9B	22	5-6½	800/500①	600①/500
	8-400	290	45S	.035	28-32	.019	9B	9B	30/22	5-6½	800/500①	600①/500
	8-400	340	45S	.035	28-32	.019	9B	9B	23/30	5-6½	850/650①	600①/500
	8-400	350	45S	.035	28-32	.019	9B	9B	23/30	5-6½	850/650①	600①/500
	8-428	375	44S	.035	28-32	.019	9B	9B	23	5-6½	850/650①	650①/500
	8-428	390	44S	.035	28-32	.019	9B	9B	31/23	5-6½	850/650①	650①/500
'69	8-400	265	R-46S	.035	28-32	.019	9B	9B	22	5-6½	850	650
	8-400	290	R-46S	.035	28-32	.019	9B	9B	30/22	5-6½	850	650
	8-400	340	R-46S	.035	28-32	.019	9B	9B	30/22	5-6½	1000	650
	8-428	360	R-45S③	.035	28-32	.019	9B	9B	23/30	5-6½	1000	650
	8-428	390	R-44S	.035	28-32	.019	9B	9B	23/30	5-6½	1000	650
'70	8-350	255	R-46S	.035	28-32	.019	9B	9B	22	5-6½	800	650
	8-400	265	R-46S④	.035	28-32	.019	9B	9B	30/22	5-6½	800	650
	8-400	290	R-46S④	.035	28-32	.019	9B	9B	30/22	5-6½	800	650
	8-400	330	R-46S	.035	28-32	.019	9B	9B	30	5-6½	950	650
	8-455	360	R-45S	.035	28-32	.019	9B	9B	31/23	5-6½	950	650
	8-455	370	R-45S	.035	28-32	.019	9B	9B	23	5-6½	950	650
'71	8-350	250	R-47S	.035	28-32	.019	12B	12B	26B/30B	5-6½⑤	800	600
	8-400	265	R-47S	.035	28-32	.019	—	8B	26B	5-6½⑤	—	600
	8-400	300	R-46S	.035	28-32	.019	12B	12B	23B	5-6½⑤	1000/600①	700
	8-455	280	R-46S	.035	28-32	.019	—	12B	30B	5-6½⑤	—	650
	8-455	325	R-46S	.035	28-32	.019	—	12B	23B	5-6½⑤	—	650
	8-455	335	R-46S	.035	28-32	.019	12B	12B	31B	5-6½⑤	1000/600①	700
'72	8-400	175	R-46TS	.035	28-32	.019	—	10B	26	5-6½	—	625
	8-400	200	R-45TS	.035	28-32	.019	8B	10B	23	5-6½	1000/600①	700/500①
	8-400	250	R-45TS	.035	28-32	.019	10B	10B	23	5-6½	1000/600①	700/500①
	8-455	185	R-45TS	.035	28-32	.019	—	10B	30	5-6½	—	625
	8-455	200	R-45TS	.035	28-32	.019	—	10B	23	5-6½	—	625
	8-455	220	R-45TS	.035	28-32	.019	—	10B	23	5-6½	—	650/500①
	8-455	250	R-45TS	.035	28-32	.019	—	10B	23	5-6½	—	650/500①
'73	8-350	150	R-46TS	.040	28-32	.016	—	12B	26/30⑦	5-6½	—	650
	8-350	175	R-46TS	.040	28-32	.016	—	12B	26/30⑦	5-6½	—	650
	8-400	170	R-46TS	.040	28-32	.016	—	12B	26	5-6½	—	650
	8-400	185	R-46TS	.040	28-32	.016	—	12B	26	5-6½	—	650
	8-400	200	R-45TS	.040	28-32	.016	—	12B	26	5-6½	—	650
	8-400	230	R-45TS	.040	28-32	.016	—	12B	26	5-6½	—	650
	8-455	215	R-45TS	.040	28-32	.016	—	12B	23	5-6½	—	650
	8-455	250	R-45TS	.040	28-32	.016	—	12B	23	5-6½	—	650
	8-455 S.D.	310	R-45TS	.040	28-32	.016	—	12B	23	5-6½	—	750/600①

TUNE-UP SPECIFICATIONS

When analyzing compression test results, look for uniformity among cylinders rather than specific pressures.

Year	ENGINE No. Cyl Displacement (cu in.)	ENGINE hp	SPARK PLUGS Type §	SPARK PLUGS Gap (in.)	DISTRIBUTOR Point Dwell (deg)	DISTRIBUTOR Point Gap (in.)	IGNITION TIMING (deg) ▲ Man Trans	IGNITION TIMING (deg) ▲ Auto Trans	VALVES Intake Opens ■ (deg) ●	Fuel Pump Pressure (psi)	IDLE SPEED (rpm) ▲ Man Trans	IDLE SPEED (rpm) ▲ Auto Trans
'74	8-350 All	155	R-46TS	.040	28-32	.016	—	12B⑥	26/30⑦	5-6½	—	650
	8-400 2 bbl	175	R-46TS	.040	28-32	.016	—	12B⑥	26	5-6½	—	650
	8-400 4 bbl	200	R-45TS	.040	28-32	.016	—	12B⑥	23/30⑦	5-6½	—	650
	8-455 All	215	R-45TS	.040	28-32	.016	—	12B⑥	24	5-6½	—	650
	8-455 S.D.	290	R-44TS	.040	28-32	.016	—	12B⑥	42	5-6½	—	750/500①

▲ See text for procedure
● Figure in parentheses indicates California engine
■ All figures are in degrees Before Top Dead Center. Where two figures appear, the first represents timing with manual transmission, the second with automatic transmission.
§ All spark plug listings are A.C. original equipment numbers
① Lower figure indicates idle speed with solenoid disconnected
② Adjust idle on air conditioned 100 rpm higher with A/C off, except on California vehicles
③ AC-R-44S with manual transmission
④ AC-R-45S with automatic transmission
⑤ 6½-8 with A/C
⑥ 10B on California engines
⑦ Lower figure represents manual trans. model; higher figure indicates automatic trans.
B Before Top Dead Center
— Not applicable
S.D. Super Duty

CRANKSHAFT AND CONNECTING ROD SPECIFICATIONS

All measurements are given in in.

Year	Engine Displace. (cu in.)	CRANKSHAFT Main Brg. Journal Dia	CRANKSHAFT Main Brg. Oil Clearance	CRANKSHAFT Shaft End-Play	CRANKSHAFT Thrust on No.	CONNECTING ROD Journal Diameter	CONNECTING ROD Oil Clearance	CONNECTING ROD Side Clearance
'67-'69	8-400	3.000	.0018	.006	4	2.250	.0015	.009
	8-428	3.250	.0018	.006	4	2.250	.0015	.009
'70	8-350	3.000	.0002-.0017	.0035-.0085	4	2.250	.0005-.0025	.012-.017②
	8-400	3.000	.0002-.0017	.0035-.0085	4	2.250	.0005-.0025	.012-.017
	8-455	3.250	.0005-.0021	.0035-.0085	4	2.250	.0005-.0026	.012-.017
'71-'74	8-350	3.000	.0002-.0017	.0035-.0085④	4	2.250	.0005-.0025	.012-.017
	8-400	3.000	.0002-.0017	.0035-.0085④	4	2.250	.0005-.0026	.012-.017
	8-455	3.250	.0005-.0021③	.0035-.0085④	4	2.250	.0010-.0031⑤	.012-.017⑥

① Bearing No. 1—.0015
② Total for two rods
③ 455 cu in. with small valve on No. 1 cylinder—.0003-.0019
④ 1972-74 models—0.003-0.009 in.
⑤ .0015-.0031 in 455 S.D. engine
⑥ .019-.027 in 455 S.D. engine
Exc. Except

RING GAP

All measurements are given in inches

Year	Engine	Top Compression	Bottom Compression
'67-'69	All engines	.010-.030	.010-.030
'70-'74	8-350, 400	.009-.029	.005-.025
'70-'74	8-455	.011-.031	.005-.025

Year	Engine	Oil Control
'67-'74	All engines	.015-.055

RING SIDE CLEARANCE

All measurements are given in inches

Year	Engine	Top Compression	Bottom Compression
'67-'74	All engines	.0015-.0050	.0015-.0050

Year	Engine	Oil Control
'67-'74	All engines	.0015-.0050

BRAKE SPECIFICATIONS

Year	Model	Master Cylinder		Wheel Cylinder			Brake Disc or Drum Diameter		
				Front		Rear	Front		Rear
		Disc	Drum	Disc	Drum		Disc	Drum	
'67	Catalina, Executive, Bonneville	1.00	1.0	1.19	1.19	.94	11.00	11.00	11.0
	Grand Prix	1.00	1.0	1.19	1.19	.94	11.00	11.80	11.0
'68	All	1.12	1.0	2.06	1.12	.94	11.12	11.00	11.0
'69	Catalina, Executive, Bonneville	1.12	1.0	2.94	1.12	.94	11.68	11.00	11.0
	Grand Prix	1.00	—	1.12	—	.94	10.90	—	11.0
'70	Catalina, Executive, Bonneville	1.12	1.0	2.94	1.12	.94	11.75	11.00	11.0
	Grand Prix	1.12	—	2.94	—	.88	11.00	—	9.5
'71-'74	Catalina, Grand Ville, Bonneville	1.12	—	2.94	—	.94	11.75②	—	11.0
	Grand Prix	1.12	—	2.94	—	.88	11.00	—	9.5
	Station Wagons	1.12	—	2.94	—	.94①	11.75②	—	12.0

— Not applicable
① 1973-74—1.0
② 1973-74—11.86

WHEEL ALIGNMENT SPECIFICATIONS

Year	Model	Caster Range (deg)	Caster Pref Setting (deg)	Camber Range (deg)	Camber Pref Setting (deg)	Toe-in (in.)	Steering Axis Inclin.	Wheel Pivot Ratio (deg) Inner Wheel	Wheel Pivot Ratio (deg) Wheel Outer
'67-'68	All Series	1N to 2N	1½N	¼N to ¾P	¼P	0 to ⅛	8½	20	18
'69-'70	All Series	1N to 2N	1½N	0 to ½P	¼P	0 to ⅛	8½	20	18
'71	Grand Prix	1N to 2N	1½N	½N to ½P	0	1/16 to 3/16	8½	20	18
	Catalina, Grand Ville & Bonneville	½P to 1½P	1P	¼P to 1¼P	¾P	⅛ to ¼	8½	20	18
'72	Grand Prix	1N to 2N	1½N	¼N to ¾P	¼P	0 to ⅛	9	20	18
	Catalina, Grand Ville & Bonneville	1N to 2N	1½N	¼N to ¾P	¼P	0 to ⅛	8½	20	18
'73-'74	Grand Prix	2½P to 3½P	3P	½P to 1½P (LH)	1P	0 to ⅛	—	20	18
				0 to 1P (RH)	½P				
	Pontiac	½P to 1½P	1P	½P to 1½P (LH)	1P	0 to ⅛	—	20	18
				0 to 1P (RH)	½P				

N Negative P Positive
LH lefthand side RH righthand side

CHARGING SYSTEM

1967-1974

The Delco-Remy Delcotron is used. The purpose of this unit is to satisfy the increase in electrical loads that have been imposed upon the car battery by modern conditions of traffic and driving patterns.

Alternator

Troubleshooting and repair procedures can be found in the Charging and Starting Systems section of the "Unit Repair Section."

Since the Delcotron and regulator are designed for use on only one polarity system, the following precautions must be observed:

1. The polarity of the battery, generator and regulator must be matched and considered before making any electrical connections to the system.
2. When connecting a booster battery, be sure to connect the negative battery terminals respectively, and the positive battery terminals respectively.
3. When connecting a charger to the battery, connect the charger positive lead to the battery positive terminal. Connect the charger negative lead to the battery negative terminal.
4. Never operate the Delcotron on open circuit. Be sure that all connections in the circuit are clean and tight.
5. Do not short across or ground any of the terminals on the Delcotron regulator.
6. Do not attempt to polarize the Delcotron.
7. Do not use test lamps of more than 12 volts for checking diode continuity.
8. Avoid long soldering times when replacing diodes or transistors. Prolonged heat is damaging to these units.
9. Disconnect the battery ground terminal when servicing any AC system. This will prevent the possibility of accidental reversal of polarity.

Series 10-S.I. (Integrated Circuit) AC Generator

See Charging and Starting Systems Section in Unit Repair Section for service and test procedures.

Alternator R & R

1. Disconnect positive battery cable.
2. Remove two terminal plug leads from alternator.
3. Loosen adjusting bolts.
4. Remove V-belt and through-bolt.
5. Remove alternator.
6. To install, reverse removal procedure. Tighten all bolts to 30 ft. lbs., except slotted adjuster bolt (20 ft. lbs.).

Voltage Regulator R & R 1967-70

Removal

1. Disconnect the battery cables.
2. Disconnect the wiring from the voltage regulator.
3. Remove the screws holding the regulator to the firewall or front bulkhead depending on the car.

Installation

1. Reverse the removal procedures to install.

Voltage Regulator R & R 1971-74

The voltage regulator is inside the alternator. For R&R procedures see "Starting and Charging Systems" in the "Unit Repair Section."

STARTING SYSTEM

All starters are 12 volt with the shift lever mechanism and solenoid plunger enclosed in the drive housing. The solenoid is attached to the housing.

A more detailed discussion of starters and their troubles can be found in the Unit Repair Section under Starting and Charging Systems.

Starter R & R

1. Disconnect starter motor cable from battery.
2. Raise front of car and support on stands.
3. Pull cable and wire loom down to hang free.
4. Disconnect brace, starting 1971.
5. Remove mounting screws and starter motor with cable and solenoid wires.
6. Remove wires from starter.
7. To reinstall reverse the above, first installing the wires to solenoid.

Starter Drive R & R

1. Disconnect the field straps from the solenoid and remove the starter through bolts.
2. Remove the commutator end frame, field frame and armature from the drive housing.
3. To remove the overrunning clutch from the armature shaft:
   a. Slide the thrust collar from the end of the armature shaft.
   b. Slide a standard ½ in. pipe coupling (or an old pinion of suitable size) onto the armature shaft so that it butts against the snap-ring retainer. Tap the end of the pipe with a hammer, driving the retainer off of the snap-ring.
   c. Remove the snap-ring from the groove in the armature shaft.
   d. Slide the retainer and clutch from the armature shaft.
4. To reassemble, reverse the above procedure, being sure to:
   a. Slide the snap-ring, after it has been forced onto the armature shaft, past the grease groove to the snap-ring groove.
   b. Use two pairs of pliers at the same time, on opposite sides of the armature shaft, and grip the retainer and the thrust collar and squeeze until the retainer is forced over the snap-ring.

IGNITION SYSTEM

Distributor

An external adjustment distributor is used. The cap has a window for adjusting dwell time (cam angle) with the cap in place.

Adjustment of dwell is made on the car while the engine is operating or may be set statically with a feeler gauge.

The point set has the breaker lever spring tension and point alignment pre-set and is serviced as an assembly. Only the dwell angle requires adjustment after replacement.

Under part throttle operation, manifold vacuum is enough to actuate the vacuum control diaphragm. This causes the movable plate to advance the spark and aid fuel economy. During acceleration, or on a heavy pull, the vacuum is insufficient to move the plate. The plate is spring-loaded, through the vacuum control diaphragm, and remains in the retarded position.

The centrifugal advance is conventional and operates through two spring-loaded weights.

On 1970-74 Pontiacs, the radios are more sensitive to ignition interference due to the antenna in the windshield. To combat this all distributors have a Radio Frequency Interference Shield (R.F.I.) covering the circuit breaker plate assembly. Shield must be removed to install points or condenser, but dwell angle may be set through an opening in the shield.

Transistor Ignition

This system consists of a special distributor, and a special ignition coil. The distributor is similar in external appearance to the standard V8 distributor, but the internal construction bears little resemblance to the contact-point unit. An iron timer core

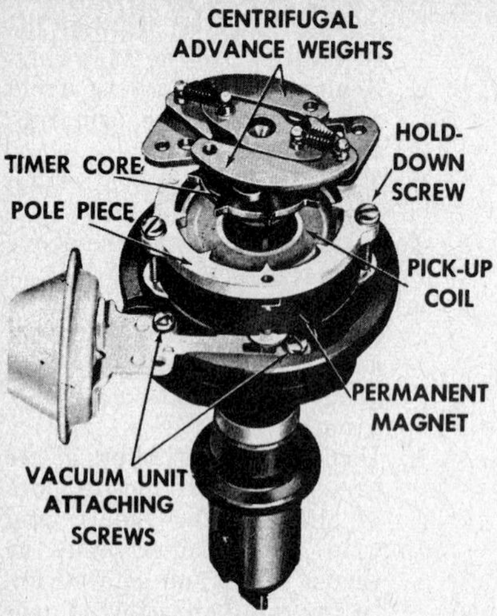
CENTRIFUGAL ADVANCE WEIGHTS
HOLD-DOWN SCREW
TIMER CORE
POLE PIECE
PICK-UP COIL
PERMANENT MAGNET
VACUUM UNIT ATTACHING SCREWS

Transistor ignition distributor
(© Pontiac Div, G.M. Corp)

replaces the breaker cam. This eight-lobed timer rotates inside a magnetic pick-up assembly, which replaces the contact points and condenser. The magnetic pick-up assembly consists of a ceramic permanent magnet, a steel pole piece, and a pick-up coil.

The magnetic pick-up assembly is mounted over the distributor shaft bearing, and is rotated by the vacuum advance unit to provide automatic spark advance. Centrifugal advance is provided by the rotating timer core, which is attached to normal advance weights. Troubleshooting is found in the Unit Repair Section.

Removal

1. Disconnect pick-up coil connector.
2. Remove distributor cap.
3. Crank engine so that rotor points to No. 1 cylinder plug tower and timing mark on crankshaft pulley are indexed with pointer.

NOTE: Observe the position of the rotor and make marks on the distributor housing and on the block that line up with tip of the rotor. Make sure these marks line up upon reassembly. If the engine is disturbed, these marks can be used for reassembly.

4. Remove distributor vacuum line.
5. Remove distributor hold-down bolt and clamp. Do not disturb the engine after the distributor has been removed.
6. Lift the distributor out of its bore. Notice the slight rotation of the rotor as the distributor is removed from the block.

Installation

Installation procedure is the reverse of the removal procedure. However, before inserting the distributor into the block, the rotor should be moved slightly to one side. This is necessary because of the helical cut of the gears. As the distributor seats in its bore, the rotor will rotate slightly so that the reference marks will once again be in line. Retime the engine with a timing light.

Installation If Engine Has Been Disturbed

1. With no. 1 piston on the compression stroke, rotate the crankshaft until the pulley timing mark indexes with the stationary mark at TDC.
2. Replace the distributor to block gasket.
3. Install the distributor in the block so that the vacuum diaphragm faces the left side of the engine. The rotor should point toward the contact in the cap for no. 1 cylinder. Move the rotor slightly to the side because as the distributor is pressed into its bore it will rotate a small amount.
4. Install the distributor clamp and clamp bolt.
5. Install the vacuum line, rotor, cap, and coil wire.
6. It is necessary to retime the engine with a timing light.

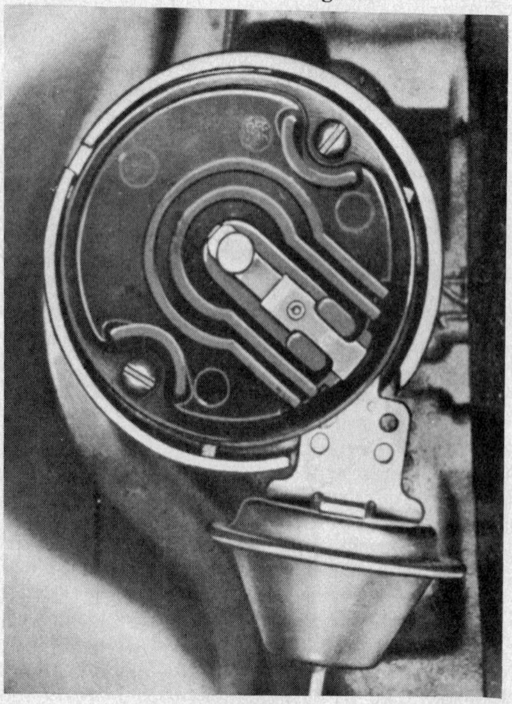

V8 distributor in no. 1 firing position
(© Pontiac Div, G.M. Corp)

Ignition Timing

Timing marks are located on the front engine cover and on the harmonic balancer.

1. Disconnect the distributor vacuum advance hose from the distributor.
2. Make sure the point gap is adjusted. Using a dwell meter is an alternate method of setting the gap.

NOTE: It may be necessary to put a small amount of white paint or chalk on the timing marks to make them more visible.

3. Connect a timing light to no. 1 cylinder.
4. Loosen the distributor clamp.
5. Start the engine and rotate the distributor until the correct marks line up. Tighten the distributor clamp and recheck the timing.
6. Reconnect the vacuum hose.

Contact Point Replacement and Adjustment

1. Remove the distributor cap and the rotor.
2. Remove the R.F.I. shield, if so equipped.
3. Remove the screws holding the points in place.
4. Remove the condenser lead and primary lead from the points.
5. Install a new set of points and tighten the attaching screws.
6. Connect the condenser and primary leads, to the points.
7. Apply a very small amount of grease to the breaker cam.
8. Install the R.F.I. shield; the half covering the points should be installed first.
9. Install the rotor and distributor cap.
10. Set the dwell using a dwell meter, or set the point gap by rotating the engine until the point arm rubbing block is on a high point of the breaker cam. (The cap, rotor, and R.F.I. shield must be removed to set the points.) Using an 1/8 in. allen wrench, rotate the adjusting screw until the gap meets the specification. Replace the cap, rotor, and R.F.I. shield.

Unitized Ignition System—1971-74

A new unitized ignition system is optional on late 1971 and all 1972-74 Grand Prix SJ, Grand Ville and Grand Safari models having the 455 cu. in. V8 with four-barrel carburetor. This system replaces the ignition coil, distributor, amplifier, wiring and spark plug wires used with previous transistorized systems. The conventional contact points and condenser have been eliminated in this system, thus making it unnecessary to perform any tune-up jobs other than spark plug replacement, ignition timing adjustment and idle speed adjustment. Removal, installation, and timing procedures are the same as those given for conventional distributors with the exception of disconnecting the primary lead wires. On models with a transistorized distributor, disconnect the primary wires at the push-on connector.

Troubleshooting of the Transistorized Ignition System can be found in the "Unit Repair Section" under "Electronic Ignition Systems."

FUEL SYSTEM

Since 1967, a disposable-type fuel pump has been used. When a fuel pump failure is noted, a pump assembly replacement is in order.

The fuel pump is of the single-action diaphragm type and is equipped with a pulsation dampening chamber for stabilizing fuel flow.

Information covering operation and troubles of the fuel gauge will be found in the Unit Repair Section.

Fuel Pump Removal

1971-74

1. From the left front side of the engine, disconnect the input and output lines from the fuel pump.
2. Remove the bolts which hold the fuel pump to the timing case cover and lift off the pump.

NOTE: on models equipped with power steering it is possible, but somewhat difficult, to reach the mounting bolts with the steering pump in place. It may pay to slack off on the power steering pump, remove its mounting bolts and, with it still connected to its lines, lift it up out of the way.

Fuel Filter

Paper and Bronze Types—1967-74

1. Disconnect fuel line connection at inlet of carburetor.
2. Remove inlet fuel filter nut from carburetor using a box wrench.
3. Remove filter element and spring.
4. If a bronze element, blow through cone end—element should allow air to pass freely.
5. Install element spring and new element into carburetor. Bronze elements are installed with small section of cone facing outward.
6. Install new gasket on fitting nut and install nut.
7. Install fuel line and tighten securely. Start engine and check for leaks.

Idle Stop Solenoid

The idle stop solenoid is used on all 4 bbl V8 engines to prevent after-run when the ignition is turned off. After-run is caused largely by today's higher engine operating temperatures and wider throttle plate openings necessary for emission controls. Ordinarily, when the ignition is shut off, the loss of spark is enough to stop the engine. However, if the engine has high enough cylinder temperatures, enough air-fuel mixture can pass the wide throttle plate opening and be ignited without the spark plug, and the engine will continue running even after the key is turned off. The idle solenoid is attached to the carburetor to solve this problem. The solenoid has an adjustable plunger and is electrically operated. When the ignition is turned on, the plunger is extended and contacts the carburetor throttle lever, opening the throttle plate wide enough for the engine to idle properly. When the ignition is turned off, the plunger retracts and the throttle lever falls back on the lever stop. When the throttle lever is on its stop the throttle plate opening is very small and will not allow enough air-fuel mixture to pass to run the engine with the ignition off.

Hot Idle Compensator

The hot idle compensator is used with automatic transmissions. Its purpose is to offset the enrichening effects caused by changes in air density and fuel vapors generated during hot engine operation. It is in a chamber on the float bowl casting. The compensator is a temperature-sensitive device which opens and closes a passage leading from the atmosphere to an orifice below the throttle valve.

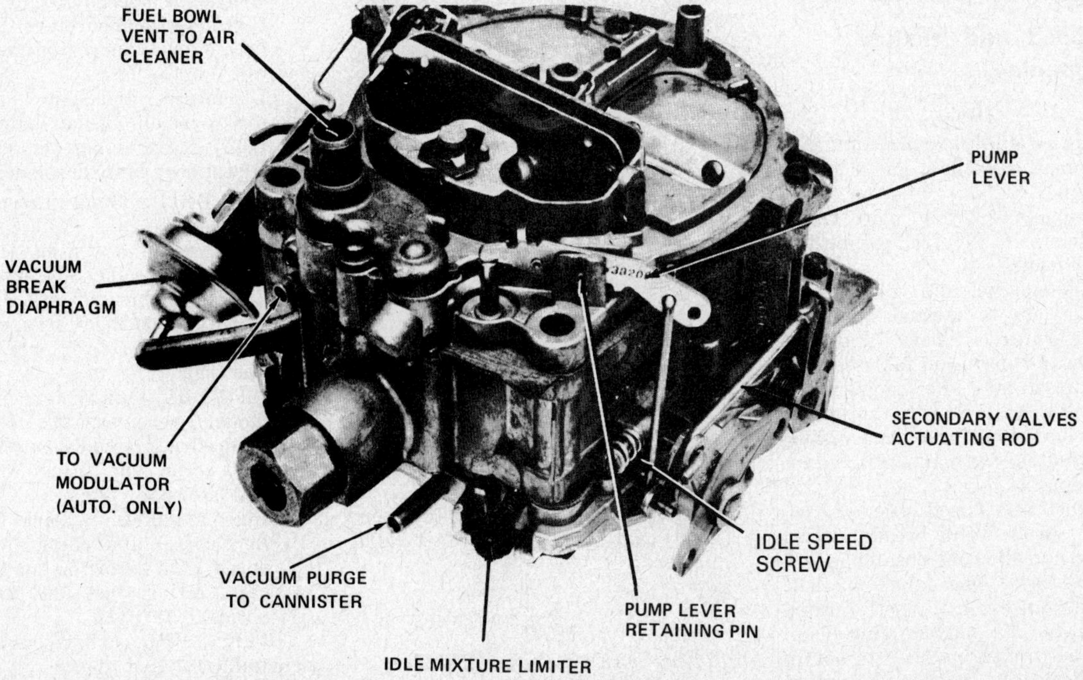
FUEL BOWL
VENT TO AIR
CLEANER
PUMP
LEVER
VACUUM
BREAK
DIAPHRAGM
SECONDARY VALVES
ACTUATING ROD
TO VACUUM
MODULATOR
(AUTO. ONLY)
IDLE SPEED
SCREW
VACUUM PURGE
TO CANNISTER
PUMP LEVER
RETAINING PIN
IDLE MIXTURE LIMITER

4 bbl carburetor idle mixture and idle speed screws (© Pontiac Div, G.M. Corp)

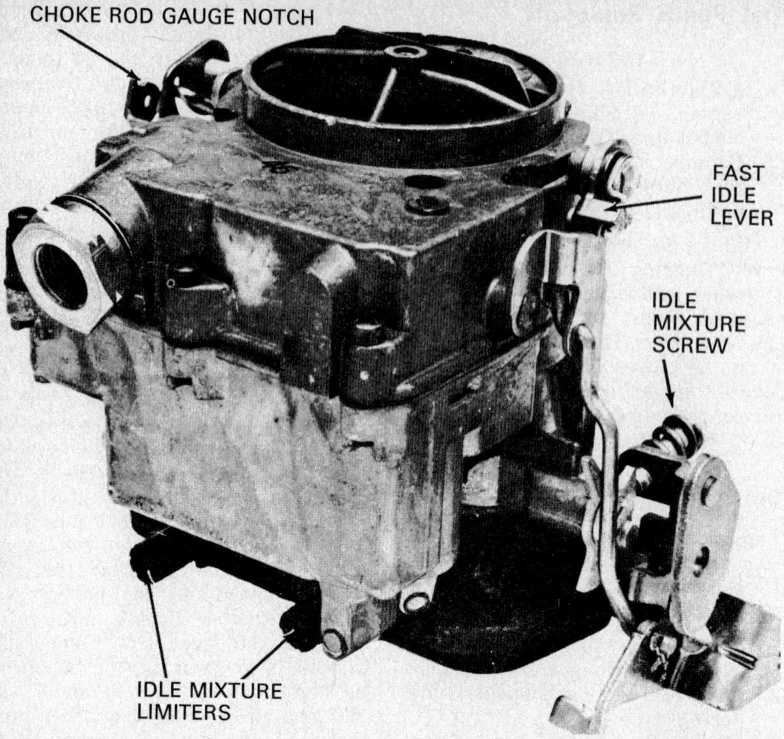
CHOKE ROD GAUGE NOTCH
FAST IDLE LEVER
IDLE MIXTURE SCREW
IDLE MIXTURE LIMITERS

2 bbl carburetor idle mixture and idle speed screws (© Pontiac Div, G.M. Corp)

2. Disconnect and plug distributor vacuum advance hose.
3. Plug hot idle compensator on all automatic transmission V8's with Quadrajet (4MV). Also plug compensator on all V8 2-BBL. with automatic and A/C.
4. With automatic in Drive, Manual in Neutral, adjust curb idle speed as follows:
5. Back out mixture screws 3-5 turns from lightly seated positions.
6. Adjust carburetor idle speed screw to obtain 850 rpm for manual 350 and 400 2-BBL., 1,050 rpm for manual 400 and 455 4-BBL., or 675 rpm for all automatic 350, 400, 455 engines.
7. Lean mixture screws equally (turn in) to obtain 800 rpm for manual 350 and 400 2-BBL., 950 rpm for manual 400 and 455 4-BBL., or 650 rpm for all automatic 350, 400, 455 engines.

At normal operating temperatures the valve is closed blocking the passage. During very hot engine operation, low air density and excessive fuel vapors in the carburetor enter the engine manifold causing a rich mixture and attendant rough idling and stalling. At a predetermined temperature the compensator opens and allows enough air to enter the carburetor to offset the rich mixture and maintain a smooth idle. When the engine cools the compensator closes and operation returns to normal.

Idle Speed and Mixture Adjustments

1967

Adjust with air cleaner installed.

1. Connect a vacuum gauge to the engine.
2. Set parking brake, place transmission in Neutral, connect a tachometer.
3. Start engine and allow it to warm up to normal operating temperature. Choke must be open and engine off fast idle.
4. Depress hot idle compensator pin on all V8 with automatic transmission. Place transmission in Neutral for manual, Drive for automatic.
5. Adjust idle speed screw to obtain specified idle speed, making sure hot idle compensator is still depressed. One and one-half turns out from a lightly seated position is a good starting place.
6. Adjust mixture screws to obtain highest idle speed and vacuum with best quality idle. "Missing" usually means mixture is too lean; "loping", too rich. Turn the screws in to lean out the mixture.
7. Reset idle speed screw to obtain specified idle speed.
8. It may be necessary to reset the mixture screws again.

1968-69

Adjust with air cleaner installed.

1. Turn in idle mixture screws until lightly seated, then back out 4 turns (2-BBL.) or 6 turns (4-BBL.).
2. Connect a tachometer, start engine and allow it to warm up to normal operating temperature.
3. Place automatic in Drive, manual in Neutral. Turn on A/C if so equipped. With idle stop solenoid energized, adjust mixture screws for best lean idle speed.
4. Adjust idle stop solenoid screw to obtain specified idle speed for all 1968 models; use idle screw for all 1969 cars.
5. Disconnect idle stop solenoid, then adjust idle speed screw on carburetor to obtain 650 rpm idle for manual transmission 4-BBL., 500 rpm for all others.

NOTE: do not re-adjust mixture screws.

6. Place fast idle lever on top step of cam and adjust fast idle speed.

1970

Adjust with air cleaner installed.

1. On California cars, remove fuel filler cap.

1971-74

Adjust with air cleaner installed.

The Combination Emission Control (C.E.C.) valve was introduced in 1971. This valve is energized through the transmission switch to increase idle speed under conditions of high gear deceleration and to provide full vacuum spark advance during high gear operation. The valve is de-energized at curb idle and in the lower gears to prevent carburetor vacuum from reaching the distributor and advancing ignition timing under these conditions, the result of which is lower exhaust emission. *The valve need not be adjusted unless the solenoid or throttle body is removed, or the carburetor overhauled.*

1. Disconnect carburetor "EVAP" hose from vapor storage canister.
2. Disconnect and plug carburetor-to-vacuum (distributor vacuum) solenoid hose at solenoid. Disconnect throttle solenoid wire on 4-BBL. manual transmission engines.
3. Set dwell and timing (in that order) at specified idle speed.
4. Adjust carburetor speed screw to obtain specified idle speed, automatic in Drive, manual in Neutral.
5. On 4-BBL. manual transmission models, reconnect throttle solenoid wire, manually extend solenoid screw and adjust to specified idle rpm.
6. Place automatic in Park, manual in Neutral and check fast idle speed with screw on top step of cam. Adjust fast idle screw to obtain 1,700 rpm.

NOTE: 2 BBL. carburetors are not adjustable for fast idle.

7. Reconnect distributor vacuum and vapor storage hoses.

Idle Mixture If Carburetor Is Rebuilt

If the carburetor has been overhauled, or the plastic locks removed from the mixture screws, the following procedure must be used to adjust idle speed and mixture.

1. Turn in mixture screws until lightly seated, then back out 3½ turns ('73-'74—6 turns)
2. Start engine and adjust carburetor idle speed screw to obtain a speed 25 rpm above specified idle (automatic), 75 rpm higher for 2-BBL. V8 (manual), or 100 rpm higher for 4-BBL. V8 (manual).
3. Turn mixture screws in equally until specified idle speed is obtained. At this point a CO meter should be employed to adjust mixture. A reading of 0.2% or less must be maintained.
4. Shut off engine and install new limiter caps, with tabs against full rich stops.
5. Adjust fast idle speed, as described previously.

1973-74

The idle stop solenoid is used on cars with manual transmission. Make all adjustments with the engine at normal operating temperatures, choke open, air conditioning off, automatic transmission in drive, manual transmission in neutral, and parking brake on.

Idle Speed

1. Disconnect the evaporative hose from the vapor canister and plug it.
2. Disconnect the carburetor to distributor vacuum solenoid hose and plug it.
3. Set the dwell and timing.
4. On automatic transmission cars, set the idle to specifications using the idle speed screw.
5. On manual transmission cars, set the idle speed with the idle stop solenoid plunger extended. Using the hex head bolt on the end of the plunger, set the idle speed to the higher idle speed figure.
6. Disconnect the wire from the idle stop solenoid. Set the idle speed, using the idle speed screw, to the lower idle speed figure.
7. Unplug the vacuum hoses and reconnect them.

Throttle Linkage Adjustment

The throttle linkage is the flexible cable type, and there is no adjustment in this system. If any binding is present, check for correct routing of the cable or pedal interference.

COOLING SYSTEM

The cooling system consists of the radiator cap, radiator, hoses, water-pump, cooling fan, thermostat, and passages for water circulation in the block.

A cross-flow radiator is used instead of a conventional down-flow and center type. With the cross-flow design, coolant flows horizontally through the core and the tanks are located on each side.

Advantages of the cross-flow radiator are improved cooling capability, more effective cooling surface area, and a low silhouette.

Automatic transmission radiators have oil coolers built into the right-hand tank, air-conditioned and high-performance models have greater cooling capacity than standard. The drain cock is located at the inside, lower left-hand corner of the radiator.

Radiator R & R

1. Drain the radiator.
2. On Grand Prix, remove the fan.
3. Disconnect the upper and lower radiator hoses.
4. If equipped with automatic transmission, disconnect the cooling lines and plug them to prevent excessive fluid loss.
5. Remove the radiator upper bracket bolts and remove the bracket.
6. Remove the radiator and shroud assembly by lifting straight up.
7. Reverse the above steps to install the radiator.

Water Pump R & R

This is a centrifugal type water-pump. It is die cast, with sealed bearings, and is pressed together. Therefore, it is serviced as a unit.

NOTE: It is sometimes more convenient to remove the radiator than to leave it in place. This depends on the working space available and the options on the car such as air conditioning and power steering.

1. Disconnect the battery and drain the radiator.
2. Loosen the generator and remove the fan belt.
3. Remove the power steering and air conditioning belts, if so equipped.
4. Remove the fan and water pump pulley.
5. Remove the front generator bracket.
6. Remove the heater hose and radiator hose at the pump.
7. Remove the water pump retaining bolts and remove the pump.
8. Install the pump by reversing above steps. Make sure the gasket surfaces are clean and smooth. Always use a gasket sealer on both sides of the gasket. Torque the retaining bolts to 15 ft lbs.

Thermostat R & R

1. Drain coolant to below thermostat level.
2. Disconnect the upper hose and remove water outlet assembly.
3. Replace by reversing the above steps. Clean gasket surfaces and use a gasket sealer and a new gasket. Torque attaching bolts to 20-30 ft. lbs.
4. Refill to 3 in. below filler neck and bleed cooling system.

EMISSION CONTROLS

There are three types of emissions to be controlled: crankcase emissions, carburetor and gas tank gas vapor emissions, and exhaust emissions. See the "Unit Repair Section" for troubleshooting and repair information.

1967

Pontiac controlled crankcase emissions with the positive crankcase ventilation system. The PCV system connects the crankcase to the intake manifold. Crankcase gases are returned to the intake manifold to be reburned.

The Air Injector Reactor (A.I.R.) system was used to treat exhaust emissions. It consists of an air pump, a special air cleaner, a bypass valve, and tubes and hoses used to inject the air into the exhaust manifolds. The pump, driven by the engine, compresses, distributes, and injects clean air at the exhaust port for each cylinder. In the exhaust manifolds, the air combines with the unburned hydrocarbons and carbon monoxide to produce a low-emission exhaust.

A dual-diaphragm vacuum advance mechanism is used with the A.I.R. system. It is located on the distributor and takes the place of the single-diaphragm unit. The outer diaphragm functions as a normal vacuum advance unit at any engine speed above idle. Vacuum for this diaphragm is supplied from a port above the carburetor plate, since at higher engine speeds intake manifold vacuum is low and carburetor vacuum is high.

The inner diaphragm is used to retard the spark at idle. Vacuum is supplied to the diaphragm from a port below the carburetor throttle plates, because at idle vacuum conditions are reversed. Retarding the spark at idle combined with leaner mixtures gives cleaner exhaust at idle.

1968-69

General Motors elected to adopt a special system of terminal exhaust treatment. This plan supersedes the method used to conform to 1967 California laws. The new system cancels out, except in special-purpose applications, the use of the A.I.R. method previously used.

The new concept, Combustion Control System, (C.C.S.), utilizes engine modifications. Essentially the C.C.S. increases combustion efficiency through carburetor and distributor calibrations and by increasing engine operating temperature.

Carburetors are calibrated leaner and initial ignition timing is retarded. Another carburetor feature is the idle fuel mixture limiting orifice. It is located at the base of the idle mixture screw and makes sure that, even if the idle mixture screw is turned out too far, the fuel enrichment will not greatly affect exhaust emissions.

The C.C.S. also incorporates a higher engine operation temperature. A 195° thermostat is used. Engines with higher operating temperatures provide more complete vaporation of the fuel and reduce quench area in the combustion chamber. Quench area is the relatively cool area near the cylinder wall and combustion chamber surfaces. Fuel in these areas does not burn properly because of the lower temperatures. This incomplete burning increases emissions.

The C.C.S. uses a thermostatically controlled air cleaner called the Auto-Therm air cleaner. It is designed to keep the temperature of the air entering the carburetor at approximately 100°. This allows the lean carburetor to work properly, minimizes carburetor icing, and improves engine warm-up characteristics. A sensor unit located on the clean air side of the air filter senses the temperature of the air passing over it and regulates the vacuum supplied to a vacuum diaphragm in the inlet tube of the air cleaner. The colder the air, the greater the amount of vacuum supplied to the vacuum diaphragm. The vacuum diaphragm, depending on the vacuum supplied to it, opens or closes a damper door in the inlet tube of the air cleaner. If the door is open it allows air from the engine compartment to go to the carburetor. If the door is closed, air flows from the heat stove located on the exhaust manifold into the carburetor, in this way heated air is supplied to the carburetor during cold days and when first starting the engine and warming it up.

1970

The more stringent 1970 laws require tighter control of emissions. Crankcase emissions are controlled by the Closed Positive Crankcase Ventilation System, and exhaust emissions by the engine Controlled Combustion System (C.C.S.), in conjunction with the new Transmission Controlled Spark System (T.C.S.).

In addition, cars sold in California are equipped with an Evaporation Control System that limits the amount of gasoline vapor discharged into the atmosphere (usually from the carburetor and fuel tank).

The T.C.S. system consists of a transmission switch, a solenoid valve, and a temperature switch. Under normal conditions, the system permits the vacuum distributor (spark) advance to operate only in high gear (both manual and automatic transmissions) and reverse.

The transmission switch is located on the transmission and senses when the transmission is in one of the lower gears. When in a lower gear, the switch activates the vacuum solenoid valve. This valve is located in the vacuum line that runs from the carburetor to the distributor, and it prevents vacuum from going to the distributor advance when it is activated. There is also an engine-temperature sensing switch which overrides the transmission switch. It will allow vacuum advance in the lower gears when engine temperature is below 85° or above 220°. There is always vacuum advance in high gear and reverse.

1971

In 1971, the Combination Emission Control System (C.E.C.) was introduced. It uses the C.C.S. of 1968-69 and incorporates several but not all of the features in the T.C.S. of 1970. Although distributor vacuum advance is eliminated in the lower gears, as in the T.C.S. system, it is eliminated in a different manner. A C.E.C. solenoid valve is used to regulate distributor vacuum advance and the T.C.S. valve is eliminated.

The C.E.C. solenoid valve is mounted on the carburetor. Vacuum from the intake manifold passes through a port at the base of the solenoid before it reaches the distributor. When the solenoid receives an electrical signal from the transmission or temperature switches, the plunger extends, opening the solenoid's vacuum port, which allows vacuum to the distributor. At the same time the plunger head contacts the carburetor throttle lever increasing engine speed. When the solenoid is de-energized the spring-loaded plunger returns to its unextended position closing the vacuum port and allowing the throttle lever to rest against the idle speed adjusting screw.

The C.E.C. solenoid valve is energized by two switches and one relay.

The time delay relay is used to energize the C.E.C. solenoid and provide vacuum advance for the first 15 seconds after the ignition is turned on. This happens regardless of engine temperature. After the 15 seconds, the solenoid is again regulated by the temperature switch and the transmission switch.

One of the controlling switches is an engine temperature switch. It allows vacuum advance in all gears, by energizing the C.E.C. solenoid, when engine temperature is below 82° or above 220°. Between these temperatures, the C.E.C. solenoid is controlled by the transmission switch.

The other switch is the transmission switch. When the transmission is in the lower gears, this switch keeps the C.E.C. solenoid in the de-energized position eliminating vacuum advance. In high gear, the solenoid is energized by the transmission switch, and vacuum advance is supplied.

Engine dieseling is controlled by use of lower throttle plate openings (lower idle speeds).

On A/C, automatic transmission cars, a solid-state timing device engages the A/C compressor for about three seconds after the ignition is turned off. The load from the compressor effectively stalls the engine and prevents dieseling or over-run.

An evaporation control system was added to all cars in 1971. This system limits the amount of gasoline vapor discharged into the air from the gas tank and carburetor. The fuel tank has a non-vented cap. As vapors are generated in the fuel tank, they flow through a liquid vapor separator to a canister where they are stored. From the canister the vapors are routed to the carburetor where they are burned when the engine is running.

1972

All models use the new Speed Control Spark System, (S.C.S.).

Every engine and transmission combination uses the Auto-therm air cleaner, P.C.V. system, and the evaporation control system of 1971.

The S.C.S. system uses a solenoid valve in the vacuum line running between the carburetor and the distributor. This valve is the same as the Transmission Controlled Spark Valve used in 1970. The difference in this system is that the valve is regulated by vehicle speed using a speed control spark switch, instead of by a transmission switch. The S.C.S. solenoid valve is energized below 38 mph in any gear, under normal operating temperature, allowing no vacuum advance. Above 38 mph, in any gear, or any time engine temperature is higher or lower than normal operating temperature, the solenoid valve is de-energized allowing full vacuum advance to the distributor.

Normally S.C.S. engine operating temperatures range from 95° to 230°. An engine temperature sensing switch is located in the head and de-energizes the solenoid until operating temperature is reached regardless of vehicle speed.

1973

The Controlled Combustion System (C.C.S.) is standard on all engines. The Air Injection Reactor (A.I.R.) is used on all 350 engines with manual transmissions and 350/400 California engines. A combination of the

Transmission Controlled Spark and Exhaust Gas Re-Circulation (E.G.R.) is found on all V8 engines.

E.G.R. is a system used to reduce nitrous oxide (NO_X) emissions. It functions by allowing a small amount of exhaust gas into the air fuel mixture in the intake manifold, under certain conditions.

The EGR-TCS system consists of a temperature switch which senses when the engine temperature is under 71° or over 230°, a second temperature switch sensing engine temperature between 140° and 230°, an EGR solenoid, a vacuum advance solenoid, a transmission switch, and a time delay relay.

The under 71° and over 230° switch is mounted on the left cylinder head. The 140° to 230° switch is mounted in the right cylinder head. The time delay relay is mounted on the vacuum advance solenoid.

The 71° to 230° switch grounds the circuit for the solenoids below 71° and above 230°. The 140° switch passes current to the transmission switch when engine temperature is between 140° and 230°. The transmission switch then grounds the circuit for the solenoids in first gear only. Between 71° and 140° the temperature switches are both open and the solenoids are in the normal positions.

The vacuum advance solenoid is normally closed, allowing no vacuum advance. The EGR solenoid is normally open, allowing exhaust gas recirculation.

Below 71° there is a complete circuit and both solenoids are energized, allowing vacuum advance and cutting off EGR.

From 71° to 140° there is an open circuit, the solenoids return to their normal positions and vacuum advance is cut off and EGR is allowed.

From 140° to 230°, in first gear, there is an open circuit and the solenoids are in their normal positions. The time delay relay maintains the open circuit for 33 to 55 seconds after the transmission shifts into second gear. However, after the time delay in second and third gear, the solenoids are energized to allow vacuum advance and cut off EGR.

Over 235° the solenoids are energized, vacuum advance occurs and there is no EGR.

1973½

A mid-year redesign of the emission control system was necessitated by newly-announced Federal standards. On cars equipped with A.I.R., A.I.R. is not supplied to nos. 3 and 6 cylinders. This is done by internal changes in the cylinder heads. Mid-year A.I.R. cylinder heads can usually be identified by the absence of a drilled passage and metal sealing ball at the nos. 3 and 6 cylinder locations.

The new engines have a relocated vacuum source for the air cleaner. Vacuum is supplied through a tee in the hose feeding vacuum to the distributor vacuum spark thermal valve.

The mid-year EGR system operates basically on the same principle as the 1973 system, except for two major differences:

1. The EGR and TCS systems now work completely independent of each other.
2. A new EGR thermal vacuum valve is used to sense the temperature of the intake manifold coolant. Below 95°F, no EGR; above 95°F, ported EGR.

In the TCS system, full vacuum advance is provided below 62°F. When the temperature rises above 62°F, the distributor vacuum spark thermal valve closes and from this point on the distributor solenoid must be energized to get vacuum advance. The upper temperature limit for vacuum advance cut-in is now 240°F.

The Start-Up Relay Switch gives full advance (ported for manual transmission) in any gear for 20 seconds after all engine starts. After the 20 seconds has elapsed, the switch breaks ground and the distributor solenoid is de-energized, shutting off the vacuum advance.

1974

The A.I.R. system is carried over from 1973 and is used on all manual transmission and California six-cylinder engines, 350 2 bbl manual transmission V8s, all 350 cu in California engines and 400 cu in 2 bbl California engines.

The EGR/TCS system is once again together, as in pre-1973½ systems, and consists of a thermal vacuum valve, vacuum advance solenoid, EGR valve, hot coolant switch, cold feed switch and a time-delay relay for engine starting. The system is found on all V8s. Pontiac six-cylinder engines use the Chevrolet system without any changes.

On the EGR/TCS system, the distributor spark-EGR thermal vacuum valve senses the temperature of the air/fuel mixture inside the intake manifold. Below 62°F, EGR is off and full vacuum advance is provided. When the temperature rises above 62°F, EGR is on (operated by a port above the throttle blade, so that it only comes on above idle). From this point on the distributor vacuum advance solenoid must be energized by the other components and switches to provide vacuum advance.

When the cylinder head metal temperature goes above 125°, 140°, 155°F (depending on use), the cold feed switch closes. This sends the 12V current to the TCS switch looking for a ground. The TCS switch provides a ground only when the transmission shifts into high gear. There is no time delay after shifting into high gear.

Any time the coolant temperature goes over 240°F, the hot coolant switch provides a ground for the distributor solenoid. Since the hot coolant switch will ground whether the TCS switch does or not, vacuum advance will be supplied to the distributor in any gear when the coolant temperature reaches 240°F or above.

There is a distributor vacuum spark delay valve on some models, between the distributor solenoid and the distributor acting as a restrictor on vacuum supplied to the distributor. This merely slows down the rate vacuum is initially supplied to the distributor. Full vacuum is eventually supplied.

The function of the start-up relay switch is identical to 1973½.

ENGINE

In 1967, Pontiac increased the bore of both V8s, increasing the 389 to 400 cu. in. and the 421 to 428 cu. in. At the same time, Pontiac introduced a new cylinder head with larger ports and valves and larger combustion chambers than used previously.

In 1970 Pontiac increased the displacement of its largest engine again by bringing the bore and stroke of its 428 engine out to 4.15 in. by 4.21 in. for 455 cu. in., and then introduced a small bore 350 cu. in. version of their 400 V8 for their base Catalina engine. In 1971, Pontiac retained the 1970 engines, modifying them to operate on low-lead fuel. No premium-fuel engines have been offered by Pontiac since 1970.

Engine Removal and Installation

1967-74

1. Disconnect battery cables and remove battery.
2. Drain cooling system.
3. Scribe alignment marks around hood hinges and remove hood.
4. Disconnect engine wiring and all ground straps.
5. Remove air cleaner and fan shroud, then disconnect radiator and heater hoses.
6. Remove the radiator.
7. Remove power steering pump and A/C compressor from brackets and swing units aside without disconnecting hoses.

Caution If the compressor refrigerant lines do not have enough slack to position the compressor out of the way without disconnecting the refrigerant lines, the air conditioning system will have to be removed by a trained air-conditioning specialist. Under no conditions should an untrained person attempt to disconnect the air conditioning refrigerant lines. These lines contain pressurized Freon, which can be

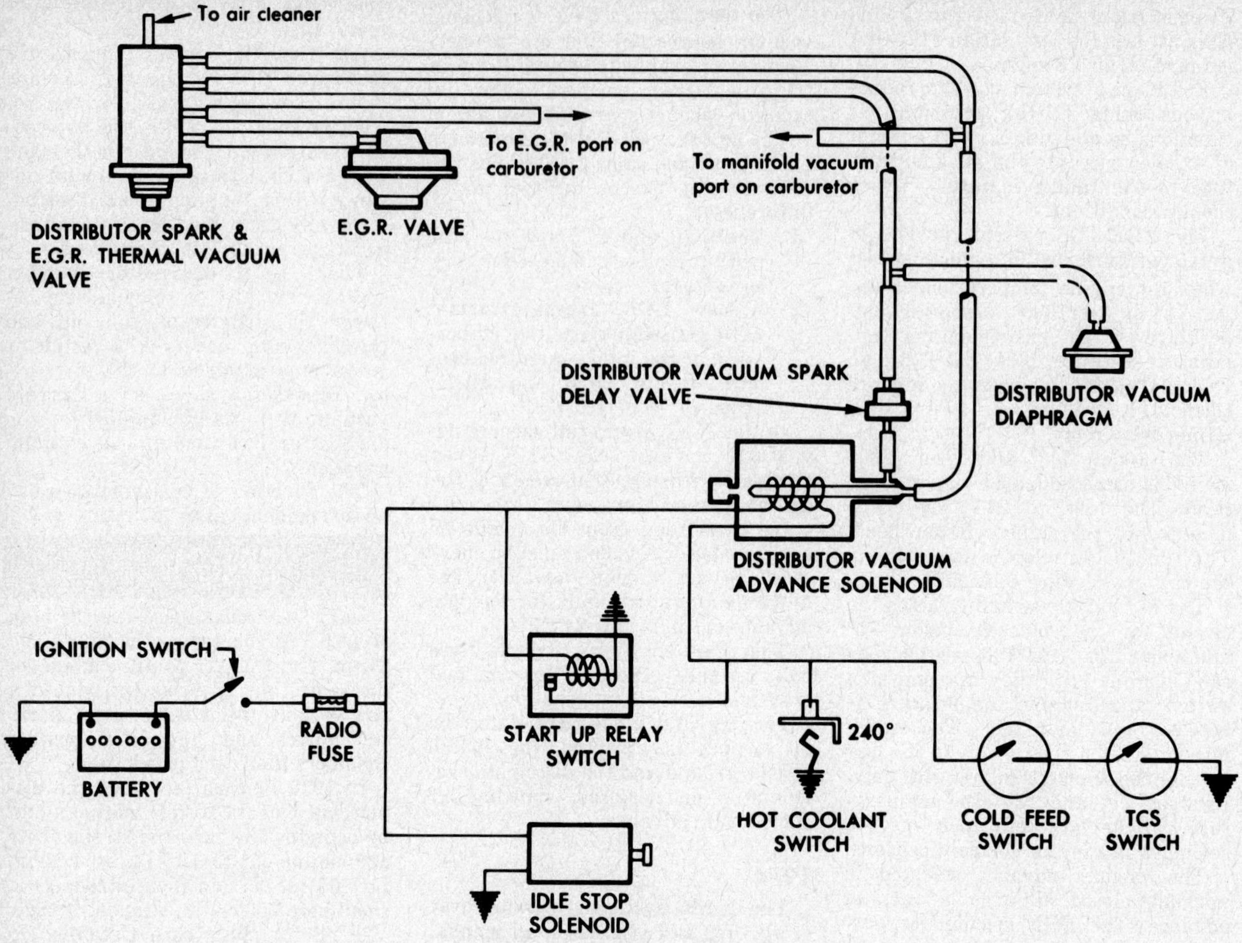

To air cleaner
To E.G.R. port on carburetor
To manifold vacuum port on carburetor
DISTRIBUTOR SPARK & E.G.R. THERMAL VACUUM VALVE
E.G.R. VALVE
DISTRIBUTOR VACUUM SPARK DELAY VALVE
DISTRIBUTOR VACUUM DIAPHRAGM
DISTRIBUTOR VACUUM ADVANCE SOLENOID
IGNITION SWITCH
BATTERY
RADIO FUSE
START UP RELAY SWITCH
240°
HOT COOLANT SWITCH
COLD FEED SWITCH
TCS SWITCH
IDLE STOP SOLENOID

1974 emissions control system—schematic diagram
(© Pontiac Div., G.M. Corp)

extremely dangerous to the untrained.

8. Remove fan and fan pulley.
9. Disconnect accelerator linkage or cable and remove bracket.
10. Disconnect transmission vacuum modulator line (automatic) and power brake vacuum line.
11. Jack up car and support on axle stands.
12. Drain engine oil, disconnect fuel lines at pump and exhaust pipes from manifolds.
13. Disconnect starter wires and remove starter motor on manual transmission cars.
14. If equipped with automatic transmission: remove converter cover and three converter retaining bolts. Slide converter rearward.
15. If equipped with manual transmission: disconnect clutch linkage and remove cross-shaft and flywheel housing cover.
16. Remove four lower bellhousing bolts—two per side.
17. Disconnect auto transmission filler tube support and starter wire shield.
18. Remove the two front motor mount bolts, then lower car to floor.
19. Support auto transmission with a wood-padded jack, then remove the two remaining bellhousing bolts from above.
20. Jack up auto transmission slightly, attach a chain hoist and remove the engine.
21. To install, reverse removal procedure. Note that there are dowel pins in the block that have matching holes in the bellhousing. These dowel pins must be in almost perfect alignment with their holes before the engine and bellhousing will go together. Do not lower the engine completely while the jack is supporting the transmission.

Manifolds

Exhaust Manifold Removal

Tab locks are used on front and rear pairs of bolts on each exhaust manifold. When removing bolts, straighten tabs from beneath car using long handled screw driver. When installing tab locks, bend tabs against sides of bolt not over top of bolt.

Left-Side Manifold

1. If the car is equipped with power steering, disconnect the power steering pump but leave it attached to its hoses and pull it up out of the way.
2. Remove the generator belt, the generator and the mounting bracket as an assembly.
3. From underneath the vehicle, disconnect the exhaust crossover pipe flange.
4. If the car is equipped with power brakes, the rear bolts of the manifold are difficult to reach but they can be removed with a box wrench.
5. Remove the bolts that hold the manifold to the left cylinder head and take off the manifold.

Right-Side Manifold

From underneath the vehicle, disconnect the upper flange from the right manifold. This is the upper flange where the cross manifold, exhaust pipe and right manifold join.

From underneath the vehicle, remove the bolts that hold the manifold to the head on the back two flanges. The front flange can be removed from the top of the car with a box wrench.

Intake Manifold Removal

All Models

1. Drain coolant from petcocks on radiator and on each side of block.

NOTE: most of the coolant can be drained from block through radiator drain by raising rear end of car approximately 15-18 in. off floor.

2. Remove air cleaner.
3. Remove water outlet fitting bolts and position fitting out of way, leaving radiator hose attached.
4. Disconnect heater hose from fitting.
5. Disconnect wire from thermo-gauge unit.
6. Remove spark plug wire brackets from manifold.
7. On cars equipped with power brakes, remove power brake vacuum pipe from carburetor.
8. Disconnect distributor to carburetor vacuum hoses.
9. Disconnect fuel line connecting carburetor and fuel pump.
10. Disconnect crank case vent hose from intake manifold.
11. Disconnect throttle rod from carburetor.
12. Remove screws retaining throttle control bracket assembly.
13. Remove intake manifold retaining bolts and nuts, and remove manifold and gaskets. Make sure that O-ring seal between intake manifold and timing chain cover is retained and installed during assembly.
14. Reverse procedure to install. Use plastic gasket retainers, as shown, to prevent manifold gaskets from slipping out of place.

lifter is to maintain zero clearance in the valve train. It does this by expanding to take up additional clearance created as the lifter moves onto the base circle of its camshaft lobe. To perform properly, the lifter must be adjusted halfway between its fully extended position and its collapsed position. If the lifter is adjusted too loosely, the valve will not open fully, if adjusted too tightly any number of major mechanical failures will result. When a rocker arm is loosened or removed, the lifter will expand to its fully extended position. Upon reassembly, it is necessary to be sure the lifter is on its camshaft lobe base circle before adjusting the lifter. This is the purpose of the preliminary valve adjustment. Perform the final valve adjustment after the engine is running.

Preliminary Valve Adjustment

1. Rotate the crankshaft until no. 1 piston is at TDC on the compression stroke and the distributor rotor points to no. 1 spark plug wire cap tower. The timing mark should be aligned with 0° on the timing cover.
2. Tighten the adjusting nut until the play disappears. Adjust both valves.
3. Rotate the crankshaft 90°, in the normal direction of rotation, to bring the next piston in the firing order to TDC on the compression stroke. Repeat step two until all valves are done.

Final Valve Adjustment

1. Start the engine and retighten the rocker arm on any valve that is clattering. Tighten until the noise disappears.
2. Allow the engine to run until normal operating temperature is reached. Loosen each rocker arm adjusting nut until clattering begins. Retighten the nut until the noise disappears. On all V8s, tighten the nut further to 20 ft lbs, tighten very slowly.

NOTE: The purpose of tightening the adjusting nut slowly is to give the lifter time to adjust its height as the adjusting nut is turned down.

Cylinder Head Disassembly

1. Remove cylinder heads.
2. Compress valve springs, using valve spring compressor.
3. Remove valve locks or keys.
4. Release valve springs.
5. Remove valve springs, retainers, oil seals, and valves.

NOTE: if a valve does not slide out of the guide easily, check end of stem for mushrooming or heading over. If head is mushroomed, file off excess material, remove and discard valve. If valve is not mushroomed, lubricate stem, remove valve and check guide for galling.

Valve Guides

Pontiac engines have integral valve guides. Pontiac offers valves with oversize stems for worn guides (0.001, 0.003 and 0.005 in. being available for most engines). To fit these, enlarge valve guide bores with valve guide reamers to an oversize that cleans up wear. If a large oversize is required, it is best to approach that size in stages by using a series of reamers of increasing diameter. This helps to maintain the concentricity of the guide bores with the valve seats.

As an alternate procedure, some local automotive machine shops fit replacement guides that use standard stem valves.

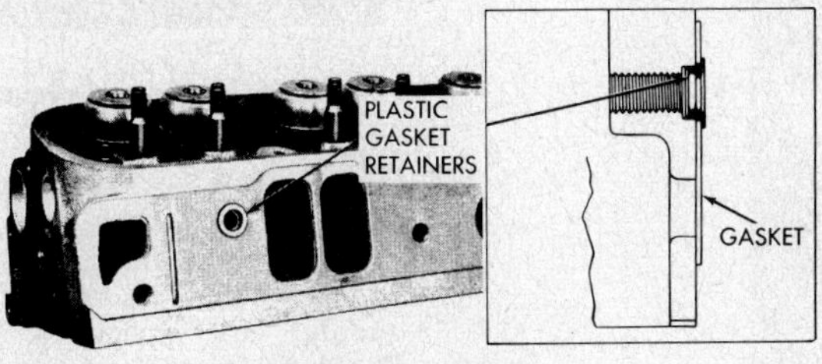
PLASTIC
GASKET
RETAINERS
GASKET

Plastic manifold retainers
(© Pontiac Div, G.M. Corp)

Hydraulic lifter
(© Pontiac Div, G.M. Corp)

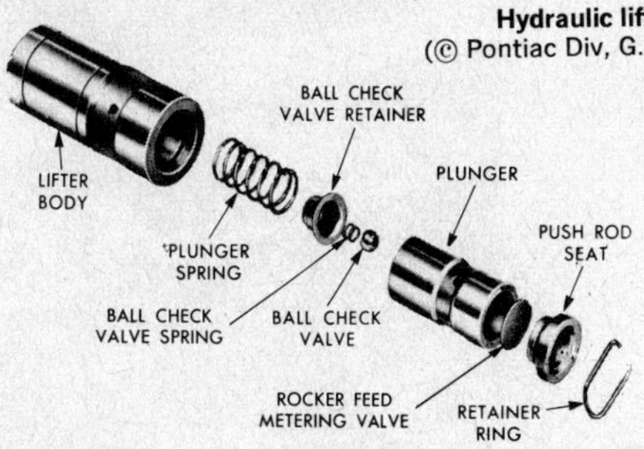
BALL CHECK
VALVE RETAINER
LIFTER
BODY
PLUNGER
PLUNGER
SPRING
PUSH ROD
SEAT
BALL CHECK
VALVE SPRING
BALL CHECK
VALVE
ROCKER FEED
METERING VALVE
RETAINER
RING

Valve System

All V8 engines use a ball pivot type valve train and hydraulic valve lifters.

Rocker Arm R & R

1. Remove the valve covers.
2. Remove the rocker arm nut and rocker arm ball.
3. Lift the rocker arm off the rocker arm stud. Always keep the rocker arm assemblies together and assemble them on the same stud.
4. Remove the pushrod from its bore. Make sure the rods are returned to their original bore, with the same end in the block.
5. Reverse the removal procedure to install the rocker arms and adjust the valve on any rocker arm removed before installing the valve cover.

Valve Lifters

The purpose of the hydraulic valve

Valve Springs

All Models

In order to check on the condition of the valve springs, lay all of the springs on a flat surface and carefully measure across the top of the intake springs with a straightedge to see that all are the same height. If all are the same height, it may safely be assumed that they are all in good condition because it is very unlikely that they will all collapse an equal amount. Do the same with exhaust valve springs.

If one or more are found to be a different height from the rest of the springs, it is a good idea to get one new spring and carefully measure all the old springs against the new one. Those which come up to the same height as the new spring may be considered to be in good condition. Those which do not should be replaced.

Where regular spring testing equipment is not available, this is generally

Chilton's TIME SAVER

The following is a method for replacing valve springs, oil seals or spring retainers without removing the cylinder head.

1. **Obtain a spark plug hole air chuck adaptor from an auto parts store.**
2. **To this adaptor add an air chuck so that the hose from an air compressor can be attached. This assembly will be used later to pressurize the cylinder.**
3. **Remove the valve rocker cover. Remove the rocker arm from the valve to be worked on.**
4. **Remove the spark plug from the cylinder to be worked on.**
5. **Turn the crankshaft to bring the piston of this cylinder down, away from possible contact with the valve head. Sharply tap the valve retainer to loosen the valve lock.**
6. **Then turn the crankshaft to bring the piston in this cylinder to the Exact Top of its Compression Stroke.**
7. **Screw in the chuck-equipped tool.**
8. **Hook up an air hose to the chuck and turn on the pressure (about 200 lbs.).**
9. **With a strong and constant supply of air holding the valve closed, compress the valve spring and remove the lock and retainer.**
10. **Make the necessary replacements and reassemble.**

NOTE: it is important that the operation be performed exactly as stated, in this order. The piston in the cylinder must be on exact top-center to prevent air pressure from turning the crankshaft.

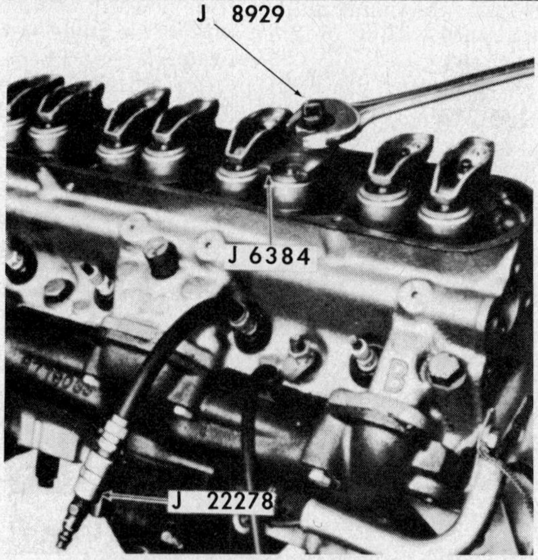
J 8929
J 6384
J 22278
Compressing valve spring—air chuck method
(© Pontiac Div, G.M. Corp)

considered to be a good, safe way to check the condition of the valve springs.

Hydraulic Valve Lifter Removal

Remove the rocker cover and the intake manifold, then take off the pushrod cover. Loosen the rocker arm ball nut and lift the rocker arm off the pushrod. The pushrods can be pulled up through the cylinder head and the lifters can then be pulled up out of their bores. Tool J-3049 (hydraulic valve lifter remover) may facilitate removal of the lifters. The lifters must be returned to the bores from which they were taken.

Caution The hydraulic lifter is a complete assembly, matchmated at the factory, and the bore of one lifter positively cannot be used in the body of another. These parts should not be mixed.

NOTE: the rear-most pushrod on the left bank cannot be lifted out on cars equipped with a defroster unit. However, the pushrod can be lifted up far enough to permit removal of the hydraulic lifter.

Cylinder Head

Cylinder Head Removal

1. Drain the cooling system including the block. Remove intake manifold, valley cover, and rocker arm cover.
2. Loosen all rocker arm retaining nuts and pivot rockers off pushrods.
3. Remove pushrods and place in order. The pushrods must be replaced in the same position with the same end in the block.
4. On all but the left head of the 455 S.D. engine, remove the exhaust pipe-to-manifold attaching bolts. In order to remove the left head of the 455 S.D., it is necessary to remove the exhaust manifold attaching nuts and drop the manifold. Remove the inner panel of the carburetor heat stove from the two center cylinder head bolts.
5. Remove battery ground strap and engine ground strap on left head; engine ground strap and automatic transmission oil filler tube bracket on right head.
6. Remove cylinder head bolts and head, with exhaust manifold attached.

NOTE: left head must be maneuvered to clear power steering and power brake units.

Cylinder Head Installation

1. Check head surface for straightness, then place a new head gasket on block.

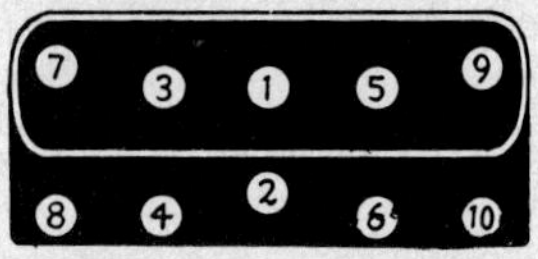
7
3
1
5
9
8
4
2
6
10
V8 cylinder head tightening sequence

NOTE: bolts are of three different lengths on all V8s. When bolts are properly installed, they will project an equal distance from head.

2. Install all bolts and tighten evenly to specified torque. Tighten to specifications in three stages.
3. Install pushrods in original positions.
4. Position rocker arms over pushrods and adjust valves as given in the "Hydraulic Valve Lifter" section.
5. Replace rocker arm cover.
6. Replace valley cover.
7. Replace ground straps, oil filler tube bracket, intake manifold.
8. Install exhaust pipe flange nuts. On 455 S.D. engine, install left head exhaust manifold, with new gasket.

NOTE: Large and small valve heads should not be used on the same engine.

Stud Removal

Pressed-in Studs

Caution This procedure can be used *only* on engines with pressed-in rocker studs. Some special high performance engines have screwed-in rocker studs which are easily identified by their hex head

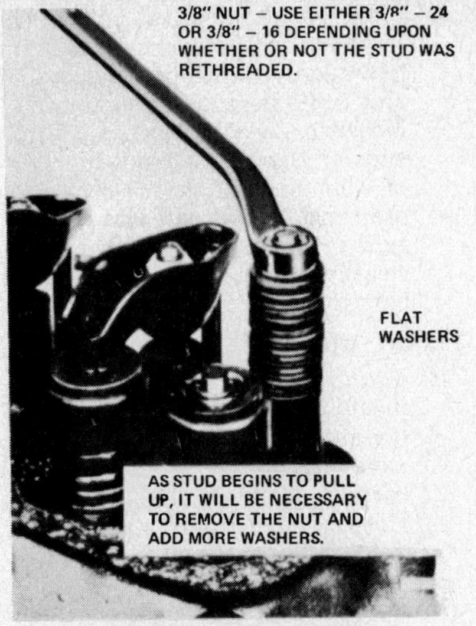
3/8" NUT – USE EITHER 3/8" – 24 OR 3/8" – 16 DEPENDING UPON WHETHER OR NOT THE STUD WAS RETHREADED.
FLAT WASHERS
AS STUD BEGINS TO PULL UP, IT WILL BE NECESSARY TO REMOVE THE NUT AND ADD MORE WASHERS.

Rocker arm stud removal
(© Pontiac Div, G.M. Corp)

lower portion. Another common stud-securing procedure on standard engines is "pinning" pressed-in studs by drilling through the stud boss and stud and inserting an interference-fit roll pin. Make sure any such pins are removed before attempting the following procedure.

1. Disconnect battery and drain cooling system.
2. Remove rocker cover.
3. Pack oily rags around stud holes and engine openings.
4. Remove rocker arm and push-rod, then file two slots 3/32-1/8 in. deep on opposite sides of the stud. The top of the slots should be ¼-⅜ in. below thread travel.
5. Place a spacer washer (or tool J-8934-3) over the stud, then position stud remover (or tool J-7934-1) on stud and tighten Allen screws.
6. Place a spacer (socket or J-8934-2) over the remover, then thread a 7/8 in. nut on stud remover and turn in until stud pulls from head.
7. If an oversize stud is to be used (0.005 in. oversize studs are available), ream stud hole to the proper size, then clean chips from area.
8. To install, coat press-pit area of stud with axle lube, then press or hammer into place. If possible use Pontiac Tool J-23342. Cool the stud in dry ice to facilitate installation.

Timing Cover, Chain, and Camshaft

Timing Case Cover R & R and Seal Replacement

1. Drain radiator and cylinder block.
2. Loosen alternator adjusting bolts.
3. Remove fan, fan pulley, and accessory drive belts.
4. Disconnect radiator hoses.
5. Remove fuel pump.
6. Remove harmonic balancer bolt and washer.
7. Remove harmonic balancer.

NOTE: do not pry on rubber-mounted balancers. If only seal is to be replaced, proceed to Step 12.

8. Remove front four oil pan to timing cover bolts.
9. Remove timing cover bolts and nuts and cover to intake manifold bolt.
10. Pull cover forward and remove.
11. Remove O-ring from recess in intake manifold, then clean all gasket surfaces.
12. To replace seal, pry it out of the cover using a screwdriver. Install the new seal with lip inwards.

NOTE: seal can be replaced with cover installed.

13. To install, reverse removal procedure, making sure all gaskets are replaced. Tighten four oil pan bolts to 12 ft. lbs., harmonic balancer bolt to 160 ft. lbs., and fan pulley bolts to 20 ft. lbs.

Timing Chain and Sprocket R & R

1. Remove the timing case cover and fuel pump cam.
2. Turn the crank and camshaft (if the chain is broken) until the two timing marks are in line between the shaft centers.
3. Using a puller, draw the sprocket off the front of the camshaft.
4. Arrange the new chain on the sprocket and set the sprocket up over the camshaft by looping the chain over the crank sprocket. That way, when the cam sprocket engages its key, the timing marks are nearest each other and in line between the shaft centers.
5. Secure the camshaft sprocket in this position, with pump cam in place.

NOTE: when reassembling the timing case cover, extra care should be taken to make sure that the oil seal between the bottom of the timing case cover and the front of the oil pan is still a good one. Plenty of gasket cement should be used, at this point, to prevent oil leaks.

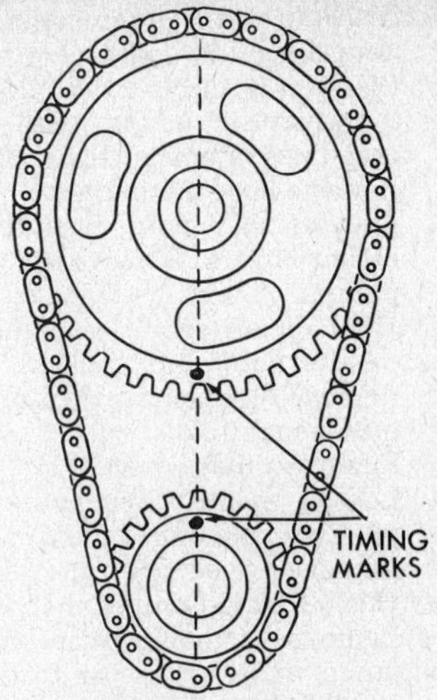
TIMING MARKS

Valve timing marks 1967-68
(© Pontiac Div, G.M. Corp)

Camshaft R & R

1. Drain cooling system and remove air cleaner.

TIMING MARKS

V8 timing marks 1969-74
(© Pontiac Div, G.M. Corp)

2. Disconnect all water hoses, vacuum lines and spark plug wires.
3. Disconnect accelerator linkage, temperature gauge wire, and fuel lines. Remove the radiator.
4. Remove hood latch brace.
5. Remove PCV hose, then remove rocker covers. Remove the water pump.

NOTE: on air-conditioned models, remove alternator and bracket.

6. Remove distributor, then remove intake manifold.
7. Remove valley cover.
8. Loosen rocker arm nuts and pivot rockers out of the way.
9. Remove pushrods and lifters (keep them in proper order).
10. Remove harmonic balancer, fuel pump, and four oil pan to timing cover bolts.
11. Remove timing cover and gasket, then remove fuel pump eccentric and bushing.
12. Align timing marks, then remove timing chain and sprockets.
13. Remove camshaft thrust plate.
14. Remove camshaft by pulling straight forward, being careful not to damage cam bearings in the process.

NOTE: it may be necessary to jack up the engine slightly to gain clearance, especially if motor mounts are worn.

15. Install new camshaft, with lobes and journals coated with heavy (SAE 50-60) oil, into the engine, being careful not to damage cam bearings.

NOTE: most specialty cams come with a special "break-in" lubricant for the lobes and journals; if such lubricant is available, use it instead of heavy oil.

16. Install camshaft thrust plate and tighten bolts to 20 ft. lbs.
17. To install, reverse steps 1-12, tightening sprocket bolts to 40 ft. lbs., timing cover bolts and nuts to 30 ft. lbs., oil pan bolts to 12 ft. lbs., and harmonic balancer bolt to 160 ft. lbs.

Piston and Connecting Rod Removal

Slipper skirt tin-plated aluminum pistons with steel struts are used.

All three rings are located above the wrist pin. The letter F, or the depression in the edge of the piston, goes to the front of the engine in all cases.

1. Remove the oil pan, oil baffle, and oil pump.
2. Remove the intake manifold, exhaust manifolds, and cylinder heads.
3. Rotate the crankshaft so the crank pin carrying the connecting rod to be removed projects straight down.
4. Remove the ring ridge, using a suitable cutter.
5. Remove the bearing cap. Place a section of rubber tubing on the connecting rod bolts for protection.
6. Push the assembly from its bore. Note which side of the piston faces the front of the engine and which bank and cylinder the piston and rod assembly came from.

Piston Ring Replacement

1. Remove the old piston rings.
2. Clean any carbon, varnish, and any other deposits from piston surfaces. The ring grooves may be cleaned with a suitable tool. A piece of broken ring may be used by scraping the ring groove with the sharp edge of the broken ring.
3. Place the a ring at the bottom of the bore in that portion that is traveled by the rings. Square the ring in its bore with a piston top. Measure the gap between the ends of the ring. Grind the ends of the ring to get the proper clearance. Check the end-gap on each ring. Measure the side-clearance. If side-clearance is excessive, replace the piston.

Piston and Rod Installation

1. Using a piston ring compressor, insert the rod and piston assembly into its bore. Make sure all parts are assembled facing in the correct direction. Lubricate the rings, rod bearings, and bore with oil.

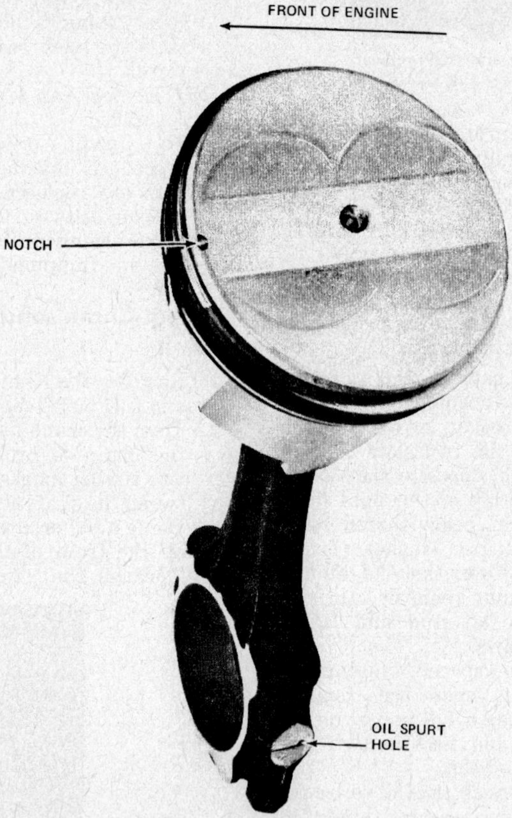
FRONT OF ENGINE
NOTCH
OIL SPURT HOLE

Piston and rod assembly
(© Pontiac Div, G.M. Corp)

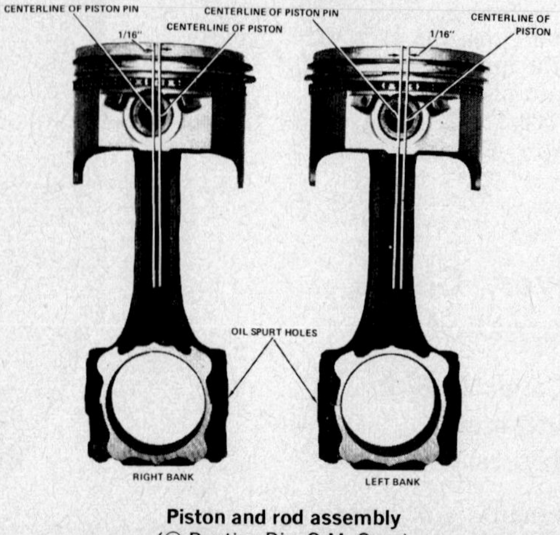
CENTERLINE OF PISTON PIN
CENTERLINE OF PISTON
1/16"
CENTERLINE OF PISTON PIN
1/16"
CENTERLINE OF PISTON
OIL SPURT HOLES
RIGHT BANK
LEFT BANK

Piston and rod assembly
(© Pontiac Div, G.M. Corp)

2. From under the engine, pull the assembly into place against the crankpin and install the bearing cap. Torque to 43 ft lbs (455 S.D.—63 ft lbs). Do not reverse the bearing cap on the end of the connecting rod.
3. Install the oil pan.
4. Install the cylinder head assembly and adjust the valves.
5. Connect the fuel and vacuum lines.
6. Install the rocker arm cover.

Lubrication

A spur, gear type oil pump circulates the oil under pressure. Maximum oil pressure is regulated by a spring-loaded, ball type pressure regulator valve. Oil is supplied to the crankshaft, connecting rods, camshaft bearings, and valve train, under pressure. There are also metering jets for each cylinder wall, timing chain, and sprockets.

Oil Pan Removal and Installation

1967-74

1. Disconnect battery cables.
2. Remove fan shroud and the power steering belt, then tilt the steering pump upward.
3. On A/C cars up to 1969, and all cars starting 1970, remove fan and pulley.
4. Disconnect engine ground straps. Drain radiator starting 1970.
5. On A/C cars, remove compressor from brackets and swing aside WITHOUT DISCONNECTING HOSES.
6. Check all wiring, fuel lines and water hoses for clearance—engine must be raised some 4½ in. Disconnect radiator hose at water pump starting 1970.
7. Jack up car and drain engine oil.
8. Disconnect steering idler arm from frame on all cars up to 1970. On Grand Prix models starting 1971, both this operation and the removal of the Pitman arm from the steering box are necessary.
9. Remove exhaust crossover pipe on single-exhaust cars; disconnect manifold flanges on dual-exhaust cars. Wire pipes out of the way to gain working room.
10. Remove flywheel housing cover, starter motor, and motor bracket (on 1969 and later models).
11. Attach a hoist to the front of the engine.
12. Support engine on hoist and remove front motor mount bolts and mounts.
13. Loosen rear motor mount at transmission or, better still, remove it entirely and allow extension housing to rest on crossmember.
14. Remove oil pan bolts, then raise engine straight up about 4½ in. until top of transmission is hitting floor pan. On some 1969 and later models, it also helps to move engine forward about 1½ in.
15. Rotate oil pan forward to clear oil pump, then remove oil pan.
16. Place wood blocks between engine and motor mount brackets for safety.

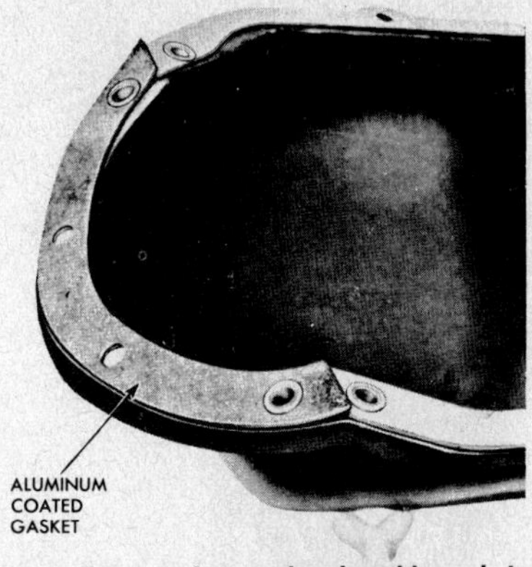
ALUMINUM
COATED
GASKET

Front oil pan gasket overlapping side gaskets
(© Pontiac Div, G.M. Corp)

17. To install, reverse removal procedure. Clean all gasket surfaces thoroughly. Use gasket cement and a new gasket.

Rear Main Bearing Oil Seal R & R

1. Remove the oil pan, baffle, and oil pump.
2. Remove the rear main bearing cap.
3. Make a seal tool as illustrated.

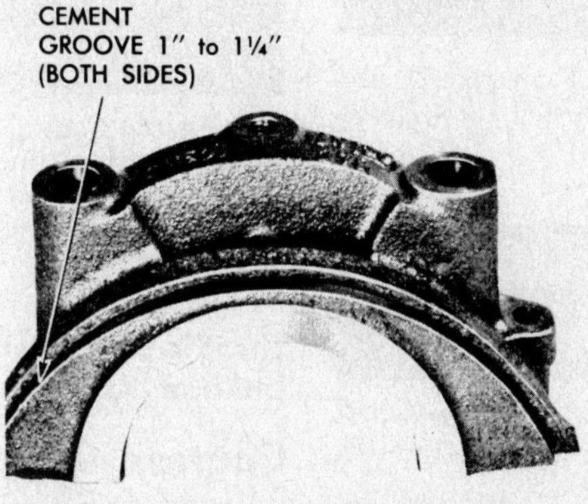
CEMENT
GROOVE 1″ to 1¼″
(BOTH SIDES)

Rear main bearing oil seal positioned in bearing cap
(© Pontiac Div, G.M. Corp)

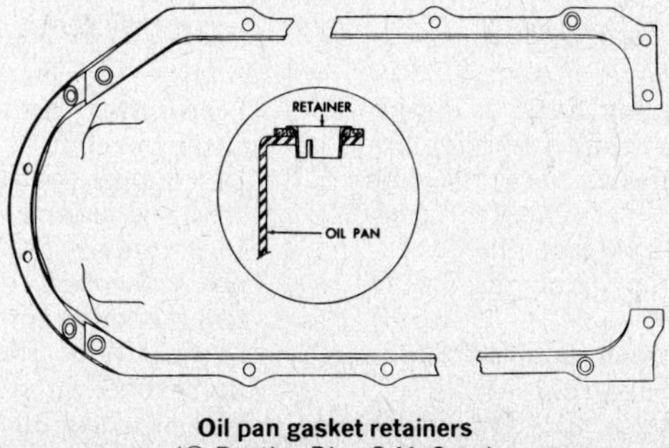
RETAINER
OIL PAN

Oil pan gasket retainers
(© Pontiac Div., G.M. Corp)

4. Insert the tool against one end of the oil seal in the block and drive the seal gently into the groove ¾ in. Repeat on the other end of the seal.
5. Form a new seal in the cap. Cut four pieces ⅜ in. long from this seal.
6. Work two of the pieces into each of the gaps which have been made at the end of the seal in the block. Do not cut off any material to make them fit.

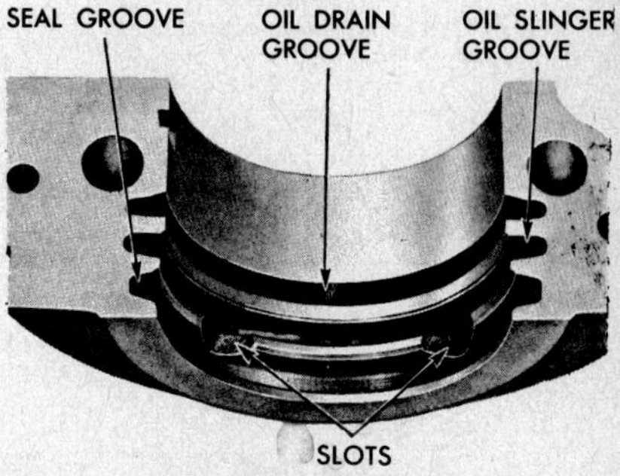
SEAL GROOVE
OIL DRAIN GROOVE
OIL SLINGER GROOVE
SLOTS

Rear main bearing cap
(© Pontiac Div., G.M. Corp)

7. Form a new seal in the bearing cap.
8. Apply a 1/16 in. bead of sealer from the center of the seal across to the external cork groove.
9. Reassemble the cap and torque to specifications.

Oil Pump R & R

1. Remove engine oil pan.
2. Remove pump attaching screws and carefully lower the pump, while removing the pump drive shaft.
3. Reinstall in reverse order.

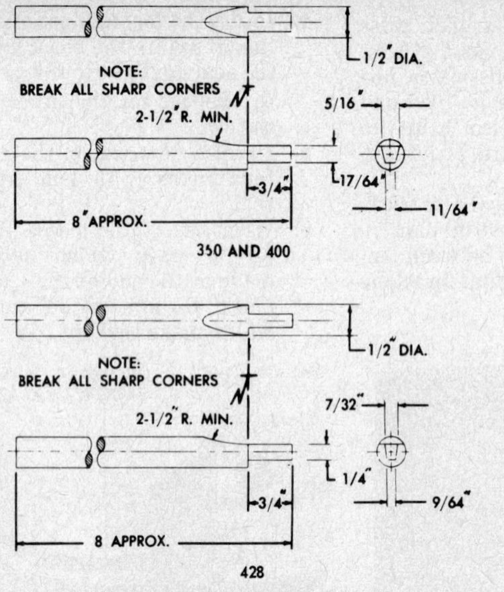
NOTE:
BREAK ALL SHARP CORNERS
2-1/2" R. MIN.
1/2" DIA.
5/16"
17/64"
11/64"
3/4"
8" APPROX.
350 AND 400
NOTE:
BREAK ALL SHARP CORNERS
2-1/2" R. MIN.
1/2" DIA.
7/32"
1/4"
9/64"
3/4"
8 APPROX.
428

Upper rear main bearing seal tool
(© Pontiac Div., G.M. Corp)

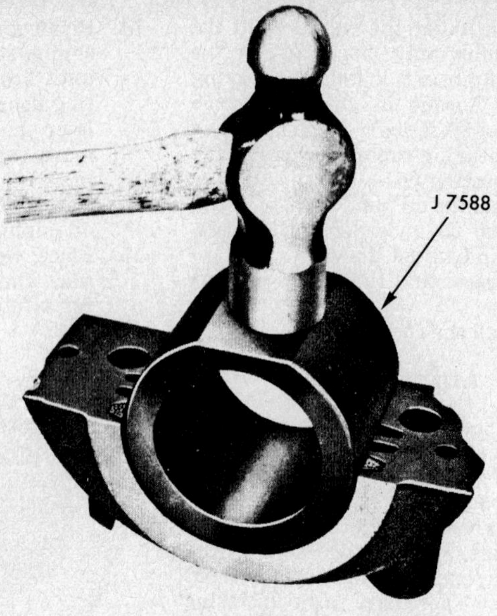
J 7588

Forming a new crankshaft seal
(© Pontiac Div., G.M. Corp)

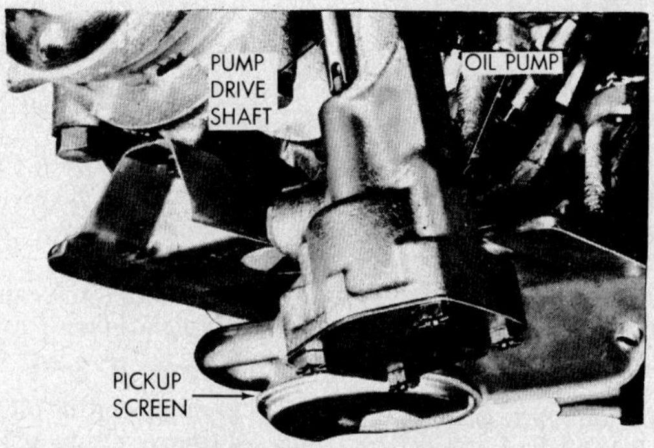
PUMP
DRIVE
SHAFT
OIL PUMP
PICKUP
SCREEN

Oil pump and pump drive shaft
(© Pontiac Div, G.M. Corp)

CLUTCH

See the Firebird Tempest GTO section for adjustment and R&R Procedures.

MANUAL TRANSMISSION

See the Firebird, Tempest, GTO section for R&R and linkage adjustment.

Step-by-step repair procedures are covered in the Unit Repair Section.

Muncie Four Speed

1. Put selector lever in neutral.
2. Loosen trunnion nuts on transmission gear shift control rods.
3. Put transmission bracket and lever assembly in neutral position and install gauge pin.
4. Put levers on transmission in neutral.
5. Torque trunnion nuts to 30 ft. lbs. (20 ft. lbs.—1971-74).
6. Remove gauge pin and check complete shift pattern.

AUTOMATIC TRANSMISSION

Full sized Pontiacs use three types of automatic transmission. From 1967 to the present two Turbo-Hydramatic transmissions (M-38 and M-40) plus a two-speed automatic (M-35) are used.

Throttle Valve (TV) Linkage Adjustments

Caution Satisfactory linkage operation can not prevail if binding or excessive wear exists.

1970-72 M-35 Two-Speed

1. Remove air cleaner.
2. Disconnect accelerator linkage at carburetor.
3. Disconnect return spring and T.V. rod return spring.
4. Pull upper T.V. rod forward until through detent. At same time, open throttle at carburetor to W.O.T. position. W.O.T. must be reached at the same time the ball stud contacts end of slot in upper T.V. rod.
5. If necessary, adjust upper swivel. Tolerance is ± 1/32 in.
6. Reconnect return springs and linkage, then install air cleaner.

Selector Lever Linkage Adjustment

1967-68 Turbo-Hydramatic

See illustrations.

All Turbo-Hydramatic and M-35 Two-Speed Column—1969-74

1. Loosen screw on adjusting swivel clamp.
2. Place gearshift lever in Park and lock ignition.
3. Place transmission shift lever in Park detent (rotate clockwise, see illustrations).
4. Push up on gearshift control rod until lash is taken up in steering column lock mechanism, then tighten screw on swivel clamp to 20 ft. lbs.

All Turbo-Hydramatic Console—1969-74

1. Disconnect shift cable from transmission shift lever by removing nut from pin.
2. Adjust back drive linkage (as in Step 4, above).
3. Unlock ignition and rotate transmission shift lever counterclockwise two detents.
4. Place console lever in Neutral and move against forward Neutral stop.
5. Assemble shift cable and pin to transmission shift lever so that no binding exists, then tighten nut to 30 ft. lbs. (20 ft. lbs.—1970-74).

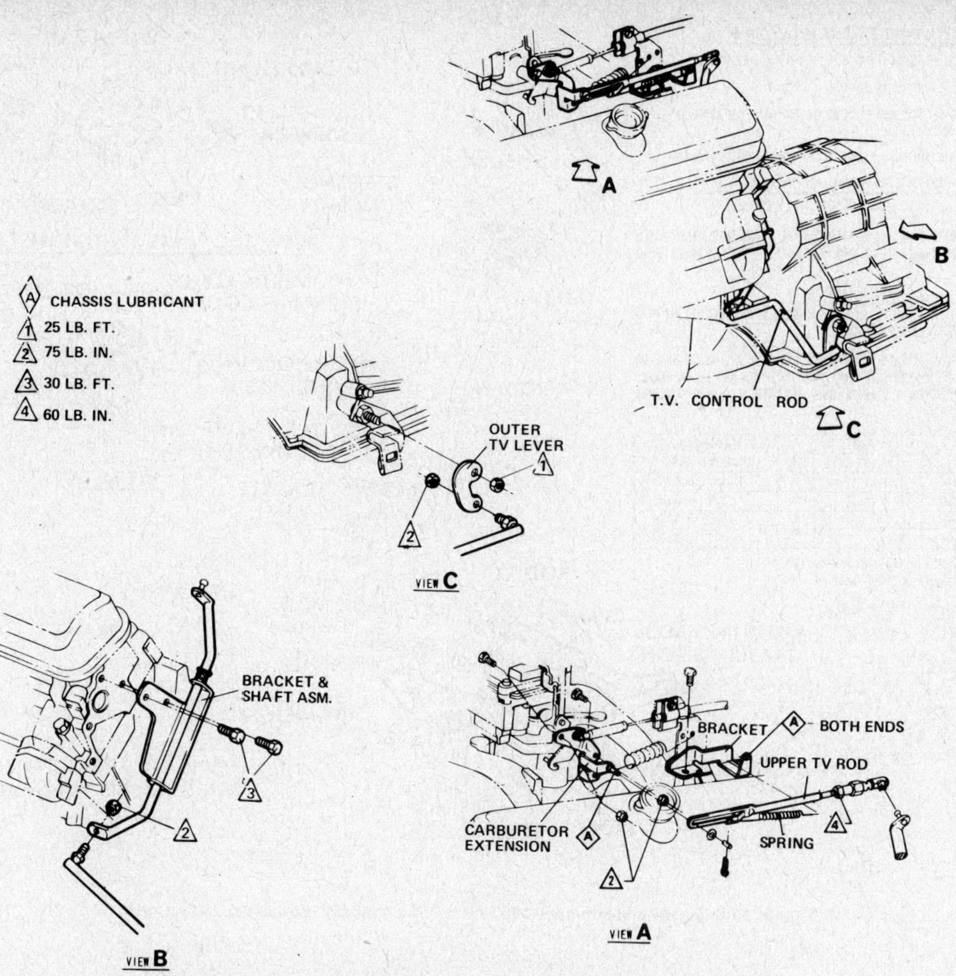
A
B
C
CHASSIS LUBRICANT
25 LB. FT.
75 LB. IN.
30 LB. FT.
60 LB. IN.
T.V. CONTROL ROD
OUTER
TV LEVER
VIEW C
BRACKET &
SHAFT ASM.
VIEW B
BRACKET
BOTH ENDS
UPPER TV ROD
CARBURETOR
EXTENSION
SPRING
VIEW A

Throttle valve linkage adjustment—1970-72 Catalina with M-35 transmission
(© Pontiac Div., G.M. Corp)

Downshift Cable Adjustment —1969-74

1. With engine off and throttle butterflies closed (off fast idle), position retainer against insert (from inside car).
2. To adjust, grasp accelerator pedal lever to wide open throttle position. Check for full cable travel.

Neutral Start Switch Adjustment

1967-68

See illustrations.

NOTE: The neutral safety switch on 1967-68 console shifters is located on the shifter, not on the steering column.

1969-74

Caution After the switch has been adjusted, before starting the engine to test the shifting pattern, make sure the brakes are securely locked. This is necessary because a misadjusted neutralizer switch will allow the engine to start in any of the forward or reverse gears.

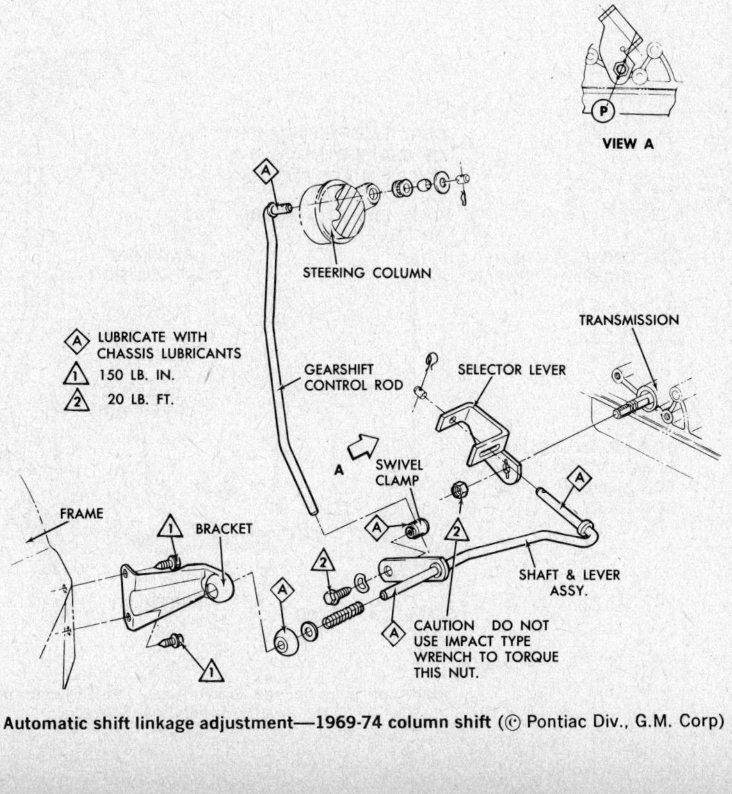
P
VIEW A
STEERING COLUMN
LUBRICATE WITH
CHASSIS LUBRICANTS
150 LB. IN.
20 LB. FT.
GEARSHIFT
CONTROL ROD
SELECTOR LEVER
TRANSMISSION
A
SWIVEL
CLAMP
FRAME
BRACKET
SHAFT & LEVER
ASSY.
CAUTION DO NOT
USE IMPACT TYPE
WRENCH TO TORQUE
THIS NUT.

Automatic shift linkage adjustment—1969-74 column shift (© Pontiac Div., G.M. Corp)

CONTROL ADJUSTMENT PROCEDURE

SET TRANSMISSION SELECTOR LEVER IN DRIVE DETENT. (SEE VIEW B)

SET SHIFT LEVER IN DRIVE. (SEE VIEW A)

PULL DOWN ON SHIFT ROD AND PUSH UP ON END OF LEVER ASSEMBLY TO TAKE UP SLACK IN SYSTEM.

TIGHTEN SCREW ON ADJUSTING SWIVEL CLAMP TO SPECIFIED TORQUE.

STARTER NEUTRALIZER SWITCH INSTALLATION

1. POSITION GEARSHIFT LEVER IN DRIVE POSITION. (SEE VIEW "A")
2. INSERT SWITCH "DRIVE TANG" IN SHIFTER TUBE SLOT AND ASSEMBLE SWITCH TO STEERING COLUMN JACKET USING TWO (2) #8-32 x 7/32" WASHER HEAD TAPPING SCREW.

ADJUSTMENT

1. INSERT NOMINAL ADJUSTING GAGE IN SWITCH. MOVE GEAR SELECTOR TO PARK POSITION AND REMOVE ADJUSTING GAGE.
2. THE STARTER SHOULD OPERATE ONLY WHEN IGNITION KEY IS TURNED TO "START" POSITION WITH SHIFT LEVER IN "PARK" POSITION AND IN "NEUTRAL" SHIFT POSITION. HOWEVER, IF STARTER DOES OPERATE IN OTHER POSITIONS USE THE FOLLOWING TESTS.

SWITCH ADJUSTED	STARTS IN				RESET* AND RETEST USING THIS GAGE
	PK.	REV.	N	DR.	
USING NOMINAL GAGE	X	X	X		#1 + GAGE
USING #1 + GAGE	X	X	X		#2 + GAGE
USING NOMINAL GAGE	X		X	X	#1 − GAGE
USING #1 − GAGE	X		X	X	#2 − GAGE

*Insert blade of nominal adjusting gage in reset slot. Move gearshift lever slowly to "LOW" position.

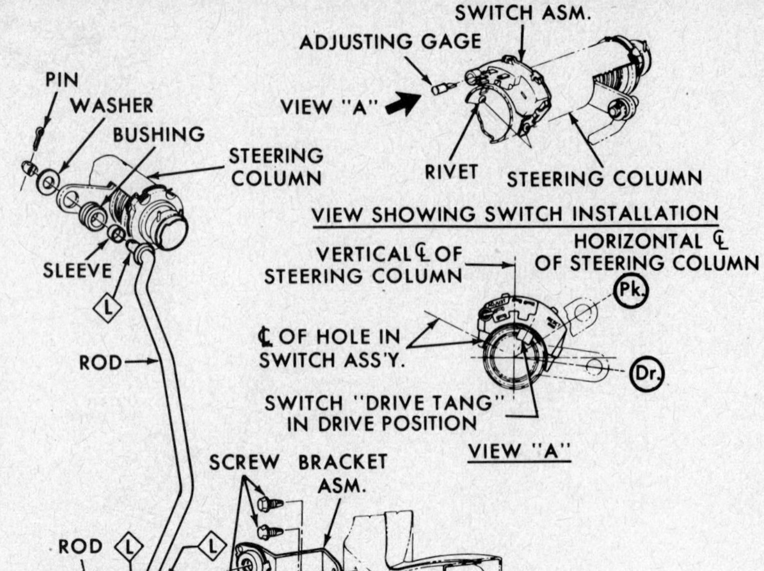
SWITCH ASM.
ADJUSTING GAGE
VIEW "A"
PIN
WASHER
BUSHING
STEERING COLUMN
RIVET
STEERING COLUMN
VIEW SHOWING SWITCH INSTALLATION
VERTICAL ℄ OF STEERING COLUMN
HORIZONTAL ℄ OF STEERING COLUMN
SLEEVE
L
Pk.
℄ OF HOLE IN SWITCH ASS'Y.
ROD
Dr.
SWITCH "DRIVE TANG" IN DRIVE POSITION
VIEW "A"

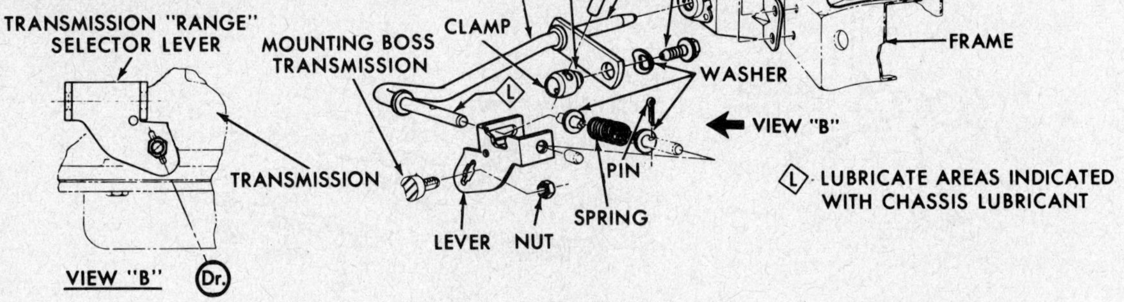
SCREW
BRACKET ASM.
ROD
L
L
CLAMP
TRANSMISSION "RANGE" SELECTOR LEVER
MOUNTING BOSS TRANSMISSION
FRAME
WASHER
L
VIEW "B"
TRANSMISSION
PIN
L LUBRICATE AREAS INDICATED WITH CHASSIS LUBRICANT
SPRING
LEVER
NUT
VIEW "B"
Dr.

Automatic shift linkage adjustment—1967-68 column shift (© Pontiac Div., G.M. Corp)

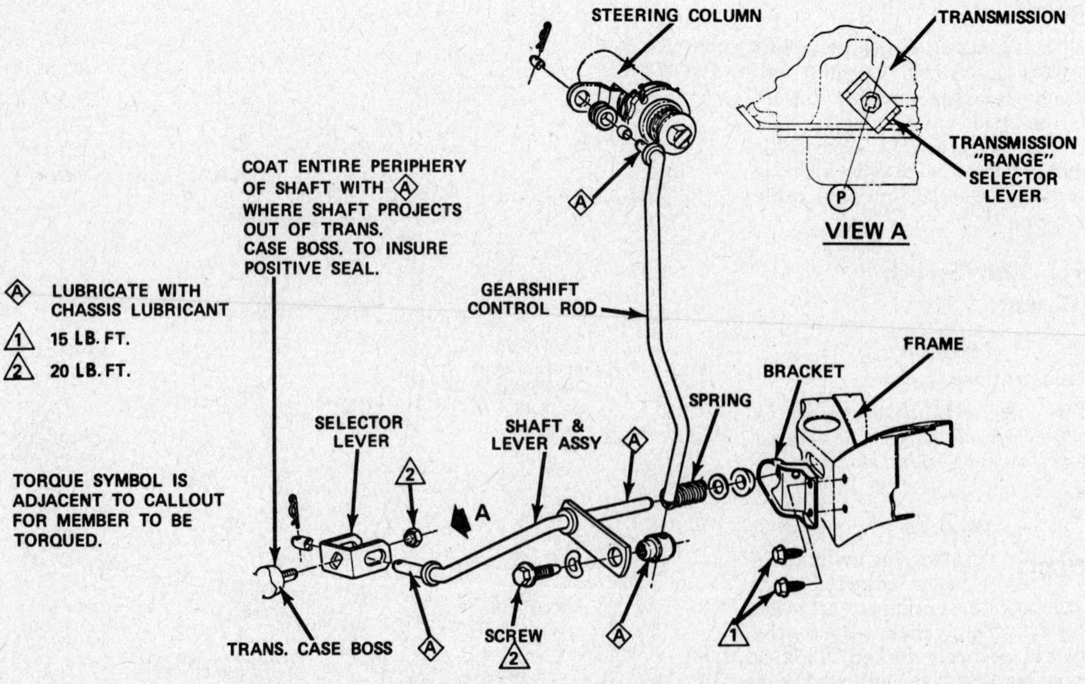
STEERING COLUMN
TRANSMISSION
TRANSMISSION "RANGE" SELECTOR LEVER
P
VIEW A
COAT ENTIRE PERIPHERY OF SHAFT WITH A WHERE SHAFT PROJECTS OUT OF TRANS. CASE BOSS. TO INSURE POSITIVE SEAL.
A
A LUBRICATE WITH CHASSIS LUBRICANT
1 15 LB. FT.
2 20 LB. FT.
GEARSHIFT CONTROL ROD
FRAME
BRACKET
SPRING
SELECTOR LEVER
SHAFT & LEVER ASSY
A
2
A
TORQUE SYMBOL IS ADJACENT TO CALLOUT FOR MEMBER TO BE TORQUED.
TRANS. CASE BOSS
A
SCREW
2
A
1

Automatic shift linkage adjustment—1969-74 column shift Grand Prix
(© Pontiac Div., G.M. Corp)

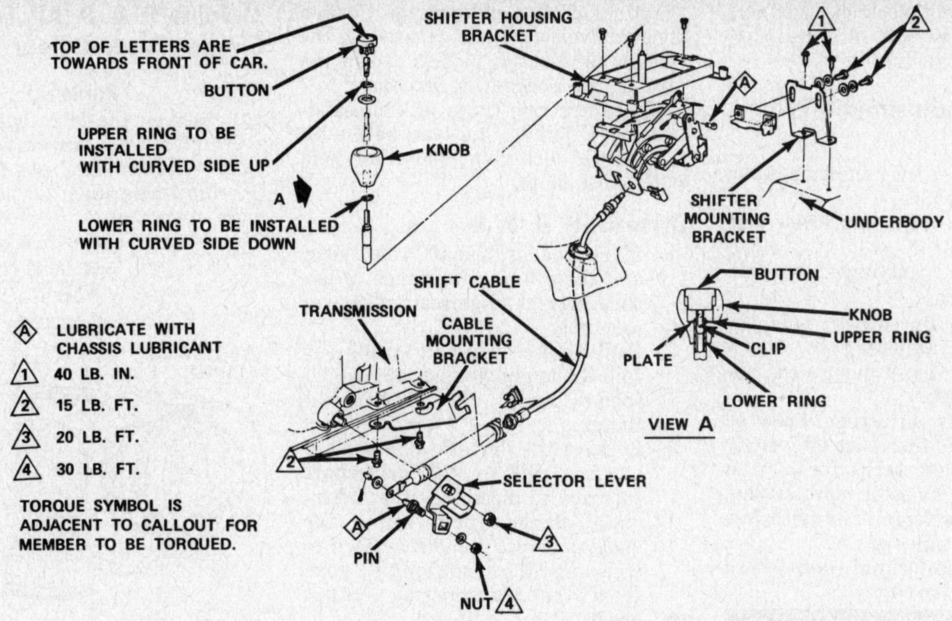
TOP OF LETTERS ARE TOWARDS FRONT OF CAR.
BUTTON
UPPER RING TO BE INSTALLED WITH CURVED SIDE UP
KNOB
A
LOWER RING TO BE INSTALLED WITH CURVED SIDE DOWN
SHIFTER HOUSING BRACKET
SHIFTER MOUNTING BRACKET
UNDERBODY
SHIFT CABLE
TRANSMISSION
CABLE MOUNTING BRACKET
LUBRICATE WITH CHASSIS LUBRICANT
1 40 LB. IN.
2 15 LB. FT.
3 20 LB. FT.
4 30 LB. FT.
TORQUE SYMBOL IS ADJACENT TO CALLOUT FOR MEMBER TO BE TORQUED.
SELECTOR LEVER
PIN
NUT
BUTTON
KNOB
UPPER RING
CLIP
PLATE
LOWER RING
VIEW A

Automatic shift linkage adjustment—1969-74 console shift Grand Prix
(© Pontiac Div., G.M. Corp)

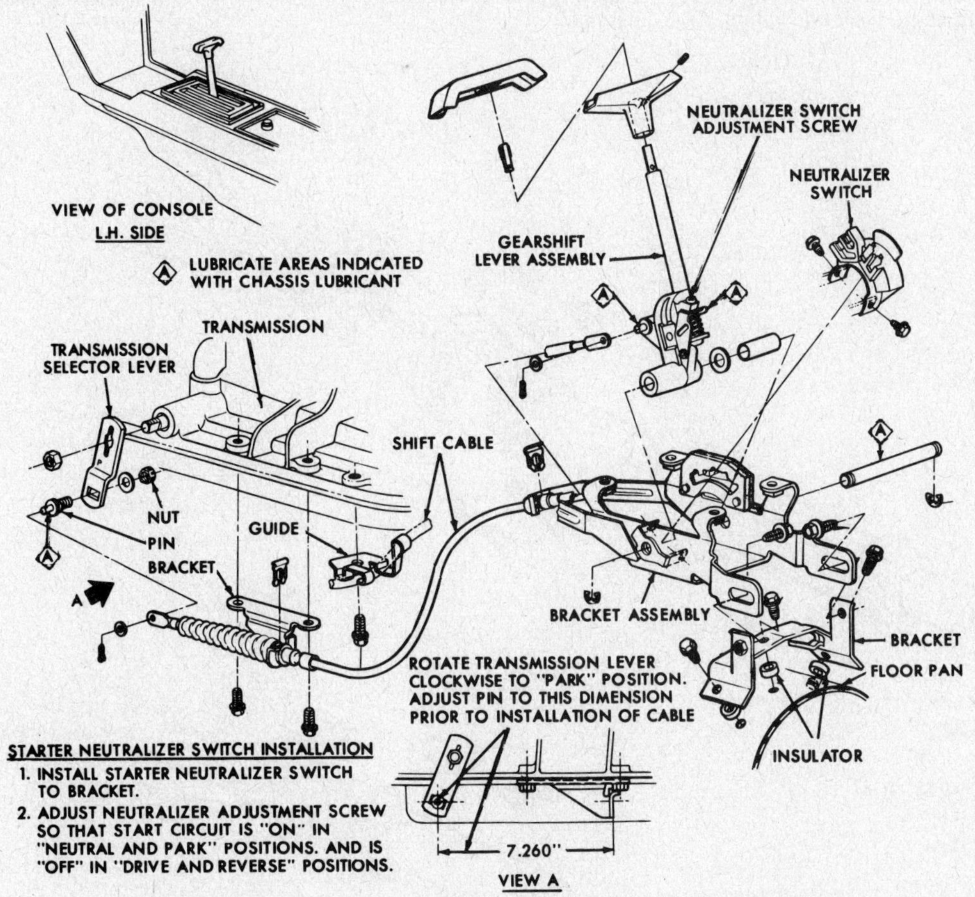
VIEW OF CONSOLE L.H. SIDE
LUBRICATE AREAS INDICATED WITH CHASSIS LUBRICANT
NEUTRALIZER SWITCH ADJUSTMENT SCREW
NEUTRALIZER SWITCH
GEARSHIFT LEVER ASSEMBLY
TRANSMISSION
TRANSMISSION SELECTOR LEVER
SHIFT CABLE
NUT
PIN
GUIDE
BRACKET
A
BRACKET ASSEMBLY
BRACKET
FLOOR PAN
ROTATE TRANSMISSION LEVER CLOCKWISE TO "PARK" POSITION. ADJUST PIN TO THIS DIMENSION PRIOR TO INSTALLATION OF CABLE
INSULATOR
STARTER NEUTRALIZER SWITCH INSTALLATION
1. INSTALL STARTER NEUTRALIZER SWITCH TO BRACKET.
2. ADJUST NEUTRALIZER ADJUSTMENT SCREW SO THAT START CIRCUIT IS "ON" IN "NEUTRAL AND PARK" POSITIONS. AND IS "OFF" IN "DRIVE AND REVERSE" POSITIONS.
7.260"
VIEW A

Neutral start switch adjustment—1967-74 console shift (© Pontiac Div., G.M. Corp)

1. Place the shifter lever in Park.
2. Loosen the switch retaining screws. Make sure the switch drive tang is engaged in the shifter tube slot and that it stays engaged during adjustment.
3. Rotate the switch in its slot until it is in the Park position and tighten the screws.
4. After observing the above caution, check the shifter pattern by placing the shifter lever in neutral. If the transmission does not shift into neutral, place the lever back in Park and rotate the switch slightly until the shift pattern is correct.
5. If it is possible to move the shift lever a large distance without having the transmission respond, check for a worn switch drive

tang or bad electrical contacts inside the switch. In either case replace the switch.

Low Band Adjustment Two Speed (M-35)

1. Place shifter lever in neutral and raise the vehicle.
2. Remove the adjusting screw protecting cap.
3. Loosen the adjusting screw locknut 1/4 turn.

Caution Be sure to hold the adjusting screw locknut ¼ turn loose during the adjusting procedure.

4. Tighten the adjusting screw to 70 ft lbs and then back off exactly four complete turns for a band with 6,000 miles or more of use; three turns for a band with less than 6,000 miles of use.
5. Tighten the locknut, and install the protective cap.

U-JOINTS

Two basic designs are used; one is a typical solid shaft with two joints. Starting 1971, a new double Cardan constant velocity joint is used at the rear on all Pontiac models except the Grand Prix and station wagons.

There are two types of cross-and-bearing U-joints. One type held with a C-shaped lock ring; the other held with a lock plate.

Driveshaft R & R

1. Mark the driveshaft rear yoke and the differential flange to assure correct alignment upon reassembly.
2. Remove the bolts and straps (or four bolts on double cardan U-joint) from the differential flange.
3. Remove the driveshaft assembly by first sliding the driveshaft forward to disengage the differential flange, then sliding the shaft downward and rearward to disengage the front splined yoke from the transmission output shaft.
4. Installation is the reversal of removal. Be sure to align the match mark made before disassembly.

U-Joint R & R All Front and Single Cardan Rear U-Joints

Removal

1. Remove the driveshaft.

NOTE: The universal may have snap-rings that are used to retain the bearing cups in the yokes. These snap-rings may be located at the outside of each yoke or in a groove at the

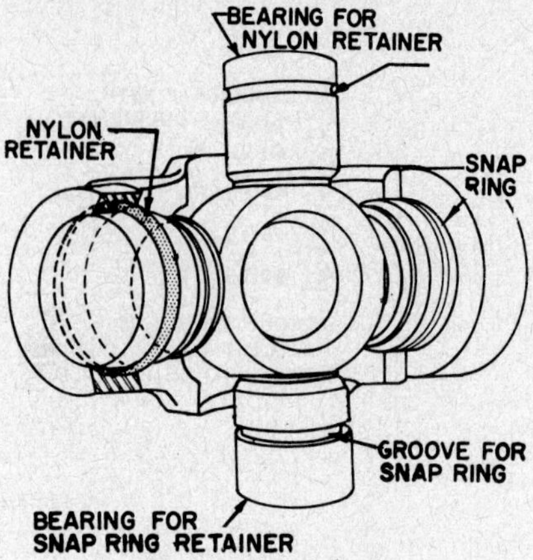
BEARING FOR
NYLON RETAINER
NYLON
RETAINER
SNAP
RING
GROOVE FOR
SNAP RING
BEARING FOR
SNAP RING RETAINER

U-joint locking methods
(© Pontiac Div., G.M. Corp)

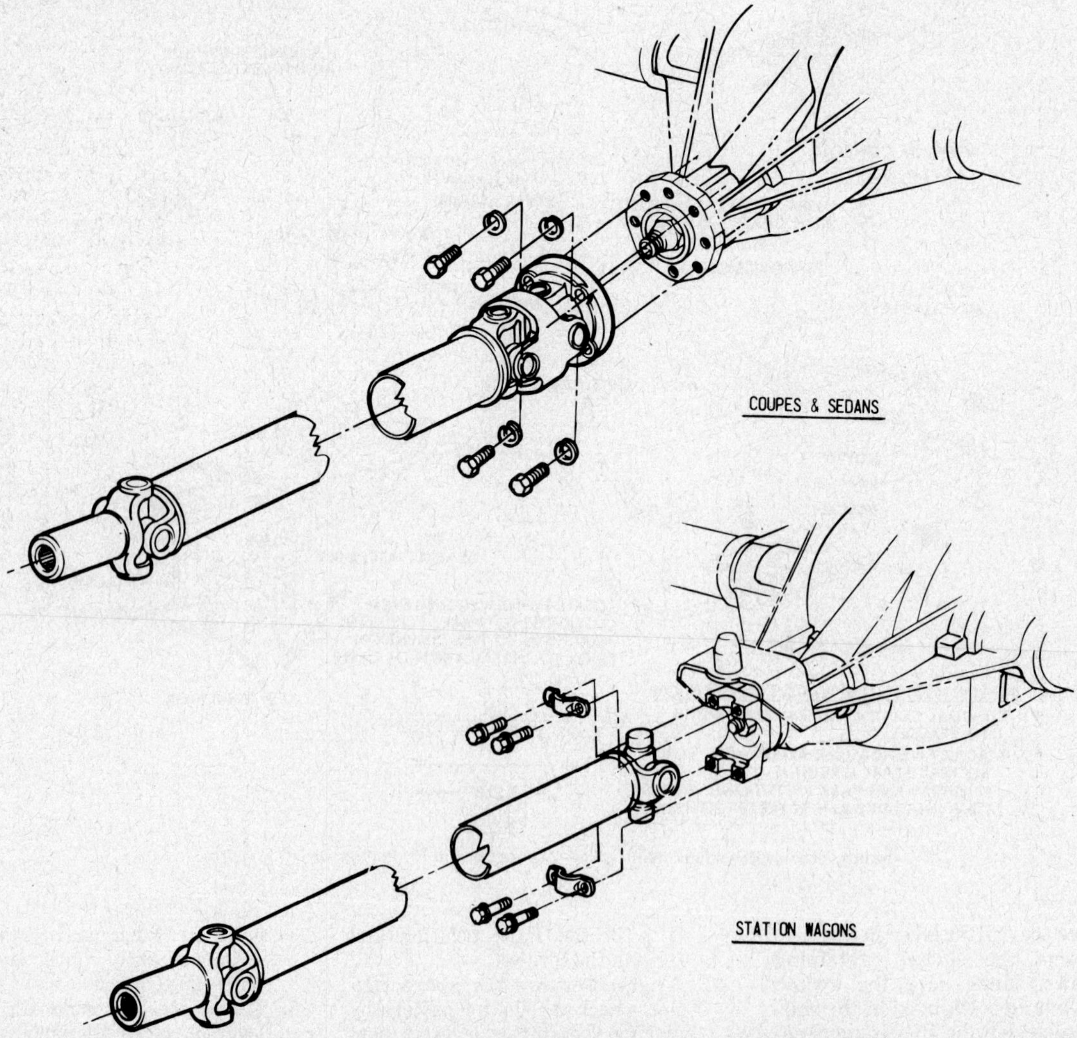
COUPES & SEDANS
STATION WAGONS

1971-74 Pontiac U-joint and driveshaft construction. Grand Prix similar to station wagon
(© Pontiac Div., G.M. Corp)

base or open end of each bearing cap. In both cases, there are four snap-rings for each universal joint and they must be removed before proceeding further.

2. Support the splined yoke (front universal) or the journal (rear universal) in such a manner that will allow the fixed yoke on the driveshaft to be moved. Support the opposite end so that the driveshaft will be in a horizontal position.
3. Using a piece of pipe or similar tool with a large enough diameter, apply force to the fixed yoke until the bearing is almost completely pushed out of the yoke and into the pipe. Remove the bearing completely by inserting a spacer (tool # J9522-5) between the seal and the bearing cup and finish pressing the bearing out of its yoke, or by tapping around the circumference of the exposed portion of the bearing with a punch and small hammer.

NOTE: The plastic which retains factory-installed bearings will be sheared when the bearing cup is pressed out. Be sure to remove the remains of the plastic retainer from the ears of the yoke. It is easier to remove the remains if a small pin or punch is first driven through the injection holes in the yoke. Failure to remove all of the plastic remains may prevent the bearing cups from being pressed into place and the bearing retainers from being properly seated.

4. Remove the rest of the bearings following the same procedure.

Installation

1. Install a bearing ¼ of the way into one side of the splined yoke (front universal) or fixed yoke (rear universal).
2. Insert the journal into the yoke so that an arm of the journal seats into the bearing.
3. Press the bearing in the remaining distance and snap the bearing retainer into place.
4. Install the opposite bearing. Do not allow the bearing rollers to jam. Continually check for free movement of the journal in the bearings as they are pressed into the yoke.

Installing snap-ring retainer
(© Pontiac Div., G.M. Corp)

5. Install the rest of the bearings in the same manner.

Double Cardan Constant-Velocity Rear U-Joint R & R

Removal

1. Using a punch, mark the link yoke and the adjoining yokes before disassembly to ensure proper reassembly and driveshaft balance.

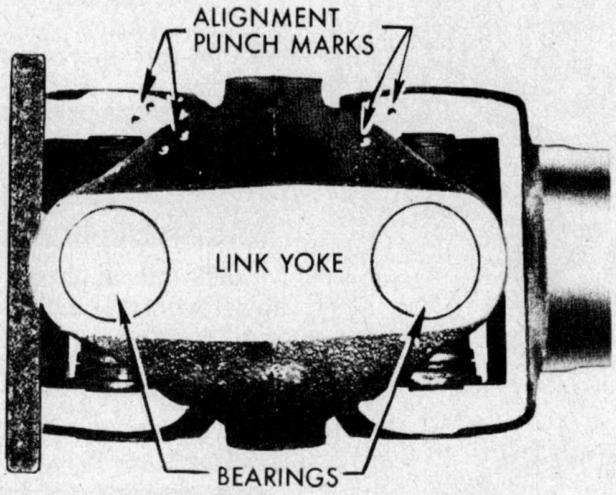
ALIGNMENT
PUNCH MARKS
LINK YOKE
BEARINGS

Match marks for double cardan joint
(© Pontiac Div., G.M. Corp)

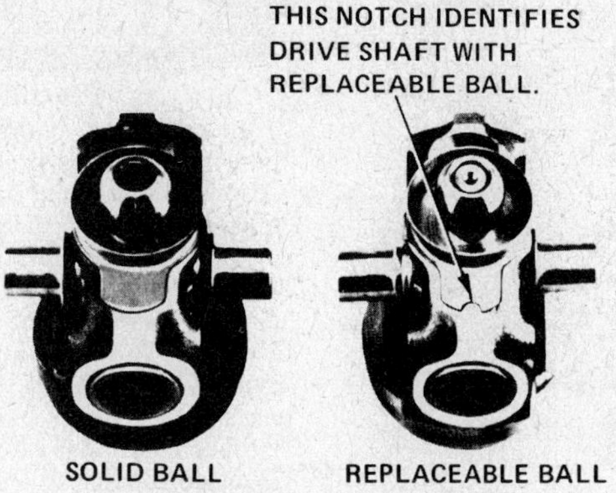
THIS NOTCH IDENTIFIES
DRIVE SHAFT WITH
REPLACEABLE BALL.
SOLID BALL
REPLACEABLE BALL

Solid and replaceable U-joint balls
(© Pontiac Div., G.M. Corp)

NOTE: It is easier to remove the universal joint bearings from the flange yoke first. The first pair of flange yoke universal joint bearings to be removed is the pair in the link yoke.

2. With the driveshaft in a horizontal position, solidly support the link yoke (a 1 7/8 in. pipe will do).
3. Apply force to the bearing cup on the opposite side with a 1⅛ in. pipe or a socket the size of the bearing cup. Use a hammer, vise, or press to apply force. Force the cup inward as far as possible.

NOTE: In the absence of a press, a heavy vise may be used, but make sure that the universal to be removed is at a right angle to the jaws of the vise. Do not cock the bearing cups in their bores.

4. Remove the pieces of pipe and complete the removal of the protruding bearing cup by tapping around the circumference of the exposed portion of the bearing with a small hammer.
5. Reverse the position of the pieces of pipe and apply force to the exposed journal end. This will force the other bearing cup out of its bore and allow removal of the flange.

NOTE: There is a ball joint located between the two universals. The ball portion of this joint is on the inner end of the flange yoke. Prior to 1973, the ball was not replaceable. In 1973-74, the ball, as well as the ball seat parts, is replaceable. Care must be taken not to damage the ball. The ball portion of this joint is on the driveshaft. To remove the seat, pry the seal out with a screwdriver.

6. To remove the journal from the flange, use steps two through five.
7. Remove the universal joint bearings from the driveshaft using the steps from two through five. The first pair of bearing caps that should be removed is the pair in the link yoke.

Installation

1. Examine the ball stud seat and ball stud for scores or wear. Worn seats can be replaced with a kit. A worn ball, however, requires the replacement of the entire propeller shaft yoke and flange assembly. Clean the ball

seat cavity and fill it with grease. Install the spring, washer, ball seats, and spacer, if removed.

2. Install the universal joints opposite the order in which they were disassembled.

Journal installation
(© Pontiac Div., G.M. Corp)

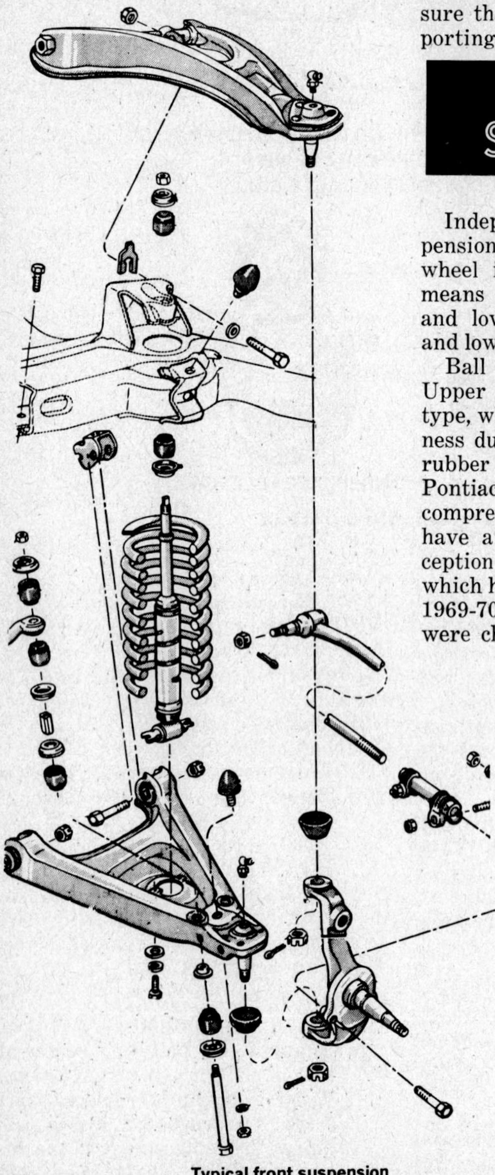

Typical front suspension
(© Pontiac Div., G.M. Corp)

3. Install a bearing $\frac{1}{4}$ of the way into one side of the yoke.
4. Insert the journal into the yoke so that an arm of the journal seats into the bearing.
5. Press the bearing in the remaining distance and install its snap-ring.
6. Install the opposite bearing. Do not allow the bearing rollers to jam. Continually check for free movement of the journal in the bearings as they are pressed into the yoke.
7. Install the rest of the bearings in the same manner.

JACKING, HOISTING

Jack car at front spring seats of lower control arms and, at rear, at axle housing.

When using frame lift, use side rails at points shown on diagram. Be sure that adapters are properly supporting these designated areas.

FRONT SUSPENSION

Description

Independent, coil-spring front suspension is used on all models. Each wheel is attached to the frame by means of a steering knuckle, upper and lower control arms, and upper and lower ball joints.

Ball joints are of two basic types. Upper ball joints are of the tension type, which normally display no looseness due to their being preloaded by rubber cushions. Lower ball joints on Pontiac models up to 1970 are of the compression type, which normally have a built-in "looseness". An exception to this is the Grand Prix, which has tension type lower joints in 1969-70. In 1971, all lower ball joints were changed to the tension type.

Shock Absorber R & R

1. Remove the nut, retainer and grommet which attach the upper end of the shock absorber to the frame bracket.

NOTE: The shock absorber stud may turn while loosening the nut. If necessary, use pliers or a wrench to hold the top of the stud while removing the nut, do not grasp the shaft as any marks on the shaft will cause rapid failure of the shock.

2. Raise the car to allow removal of the shock down through the lower control arm.
3. Remove the two shock absorber lower attaching screws and remove the shock through the lower control arm.
4. Reverse the above steps to install. Make sure all grommets and washers are in the correct position. Tighten the stud nut until it bottoms at the end of the threads.

Ball Joint Inspection

1967-72

NOTE: Before performing this inspection, make sure the wheel bearings are adjusted correctly and that the A-arm bushings are in good condition.

1. Jack the car up under the front lower control arm at the spring seat.
2. Raise the car until there is 1-2 in. of clearance under the wheel.
3. Insert a bar under the wheel and pry upward. If the wheel raises more than $\frac{1}{8}$ in. the ball joints are worn. Determine if the upper or lower ball joint is worn by visual inspection while prying on the wheel.

NOTE: Due to the distribution of forces in the suspension, the lower ball joint is usually the defective joint.

1973-74

1973-74 lower ball joints contain a visual wear indicator. The lower ball joint grease plug screws into the wear indicator which protrudes from the bottom of the ball joint housing. As long as the wear indicator extends out of the ball joint housing, the ball joint is not worn. If the tip of the wear indicator is parallel with, or recessed into the ball joint housing, the ball joint is defective.

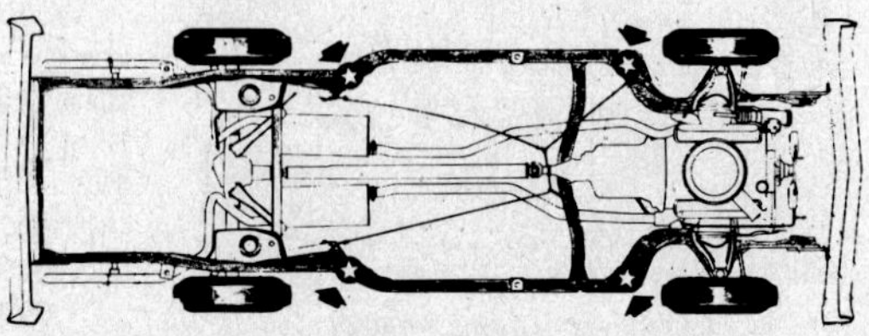

Hoist contact lifting points

Alternate Ball Joint Inspection Method

Upper—Tension Type

1. Disengage the ball stud from the steering knuckle, weight of car being supported by a jack under the spring seat on the side being checked.
2. Install stud nut onto stud and check torque required to rotate ball stud.
3. If torque is less than ½ ft. lb., the joint must be replaced.

Lower—Compression Type

1. Place a jack under lower control arm spring seat and jack up car.
2. Pry wheel and tire up and down (or remove wheel and hub to eliminate wheel bearing play) and measure play in joint using a dial indicator or a standard inspection station ball joint checking device.
3. If play exceeds 0.050 in., the ball joint must be replaced.

Lower—Tension Type

1. Place a jack under the lower control arm spring seat and jack up car.
2. Remove grease fitting from lower ball joint.
3. Remove hub and backing plate, or caliper, assembly.
4. Separate lower ball stud from steering knuckle using a pry bar and hammer.

NOTE: make sure seal is not damaged.

5. Place probe of dial indicator into grease fitting hole until it touches base of ball joint.
6. Preload and zero indicator, then pull up and down on threaded portion of stud and measure play.
7. If play exceeds 0.050 in., the ball joint must be replaced.

Ball Joint Replacement

Ball joints are riveted to the control arms at the factory except on 1969-74 Grand Prix and all 1971-74 models.

The service joint comes with specially hardened bolts and nuts that replace the rivets. It is extremely important that only these special fasteners are installed—standard bolts are not strong enough for this application. Tighten service bolts to 9 ft. lbs. for upper joints, 16 ft. lbs. for lower joints. Upper ball stud nuts must be tightened to a minimum torque of 50 ft. lbs. (80 ft. lbs. is allowable in order to line up cotter pin holes). Lower ball stud nuts must be tightened to a minimum torque of 85-90 ft. lbs. (120 ft. lbs. maximum) for 1969-74 Grand Prix and all 1971-74, 50 ft. lbs. for all others.

All 1971-74 and 1969-74 G.P. models have their lower ball joints pressed into the control arms. The entire control arm can be removed and the joint pressed out using various spacers and a large bench vise, or the old joint can be pressed from the arm while in the car using a screw-type remover. The new joint must be pressed into place, in any case, to avoid damage.

Upper Ball Joint R & R

Removal

1. Raise the car and support the lower control arm.
2. Remove the ball joint stud nut and cotter pin. Using a ball joint removing tool, break the taper holding the steering knuckle to the ball joint stud and move the steering knuckle out of the way.
3. Remove the rivets securing the ball joint to the control arm by chiseling or drilling the rivet heads and drive out the rivets with a punch.
4. Remove the ball joint from the control arm.

Installation

1. Install the new ball joint assembly using the special bolts supplied with the ball joint. Torque to 9 ft lbs.
2. Insert the ball stud in the steering knuckle and tighten the nut to 40 ft lbs. Insert a new cotter pin.
3. Install the wheel and tire.
4. Lower the car.

NOTE: It may be necessary to adjust the wheel alignment after installing a new ball joint.

Lower Ball Joint R & R All 1967-70 Except 1969-70 Grand Prix

Removal

NOTE: Jack the car securely under the lower control arm.

1. Remove the hub and backing plate assembly or, if equipped with disc brakes, hub and brake caliper.
2. Remove the ball joint stud from the steering knuckle using a ball joint removal tool.
3. Remove the ball joint assembly from the lower control arm by chiseling or drilling the rivet heads and drive out the rivets with a punch.

Installation

1. Installation is the same as the upper ball joint installation procedures.

Lower Ball Joint R & R All 1971-74 and Grand Prix 1969-74

Removal

1. Raise the car under the lower control arm.
2. Remove the hub and backing plate or, if equipped with disc brakes, the rotor and caliper assembly, remove the stud nut and cotter pin.
3. Remove the ball joint stud from the steering knuckle using a ball joint removal tool.
4. Pry the ball joint seal and retainer off the joint.
5. Press the ball joint out of the lower control arm. This is a very heavy press fit.

Installation

1. Press, do not hammer, a new ball joint into place and reverse steps 1 to 4 to install.

Front Spring R & R

1967-74

1. Jack up car and support on jack stands at frame side rails.
2. Remove shock absorber.
3. Disconnect stabilizer bar at lower control arm.
4. Support lower control arm with a hydraulic floor jack, then remove the two inner control arm to front crossmember bolts.
5. Carefully lower the control arm, allowing the spring to relax.
6. Reach in and remove spring.
7. To install, reverse removal procedure. Tighten pivot bolts to 110 ft. lbs., nuts to 80 ft. lbs. (1972-74—bolts to 120 ft lbs; nuts to 90 ft lbs), with car resting on wheels.

Wheel Bearing Inspection and Adjustment

Inspection

1. Raise the car and support it under the front lower control arm.
2. Spin the wheel to check for unusual noise. Bad wheel bearings sometimes squeal or sound as though there is sand in the bearing.
3. If the bearings are noisy or loose, they should be cleaned, inspected, and repacked before adjustment.
4. To check for loose bearings, grip the tire at top and bottom and move the wheel in and out. Movement greater than 0.005 in. indicates improper adjustment or excessive wear.

Adjustment

1. Lift the wheel off the ground by jacking under the lower control arm.
2. Remove the dust cap from the hub.
3. Remove the cotter pin and discard.
4. Snug up the spindle nut to seat the bearings. Then back off the nut ¼–½ turn.

5. Retighten the nut by hand until it is finger-tight.
6. Loosen the nut until the nearest hole in the spindle lines up with a slot in the spindle nut, and insert a new cotter pin. When the bearing is properly adjusted there will be 0.001-0.008 in. end-play.

NOTE: Under no circumstances is the final bearing nut adjustment to be even finger-tight.

7. Replace the dust cover and lower the car.

REAR SUSPENSION

The rear wheels are fastened to the axle shafts within a solid axle housing. The axle housing is connected to the frame by a four-link suspension system, consisting of two upper and two lower control arms pivoted in rubber at each end. These control arms locate the axle with relation to the frame and oppose torque reaction under acceleration and braking.

Two coil springs are mounted be-

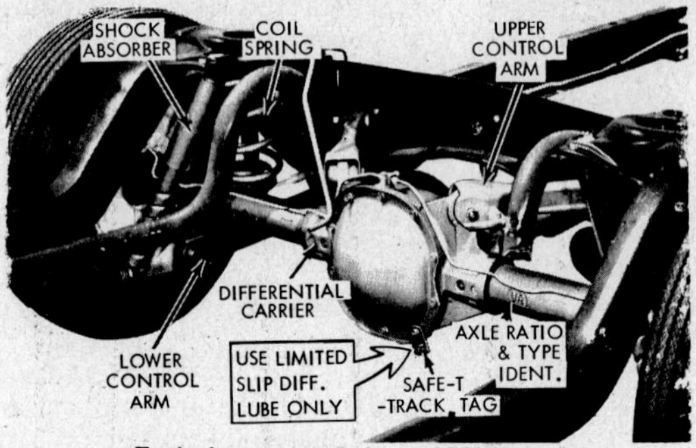
SHOCK ABSORBER
COIL SPRING
UPPER CONTROL ARM
DIFFERENTIAL CARRIER
AXLE RATIO & TYPE IDENT.
LOWER CONTROL ARM
USE LIMITED SLIP DIFF. LUBE ONLY
SAFE-T -TRACK TAG

Typical rear suspension—1969-70
(© Pontiac Div., G.M. Corp)

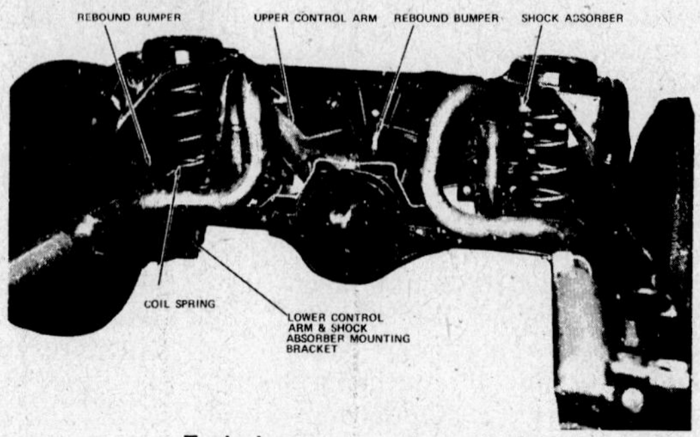
REBOUND BUMPER
UPPER CONTROL ARM
REBOUND BUMPER
SHOCK ABSORBER
COIL SPRING
LOWER CONTROL ARM & SHOCK ABSORBER MOUNTING BRACKET

Typical rear suspension—1971-74
(© Pontiac Div., G.M. Corp)

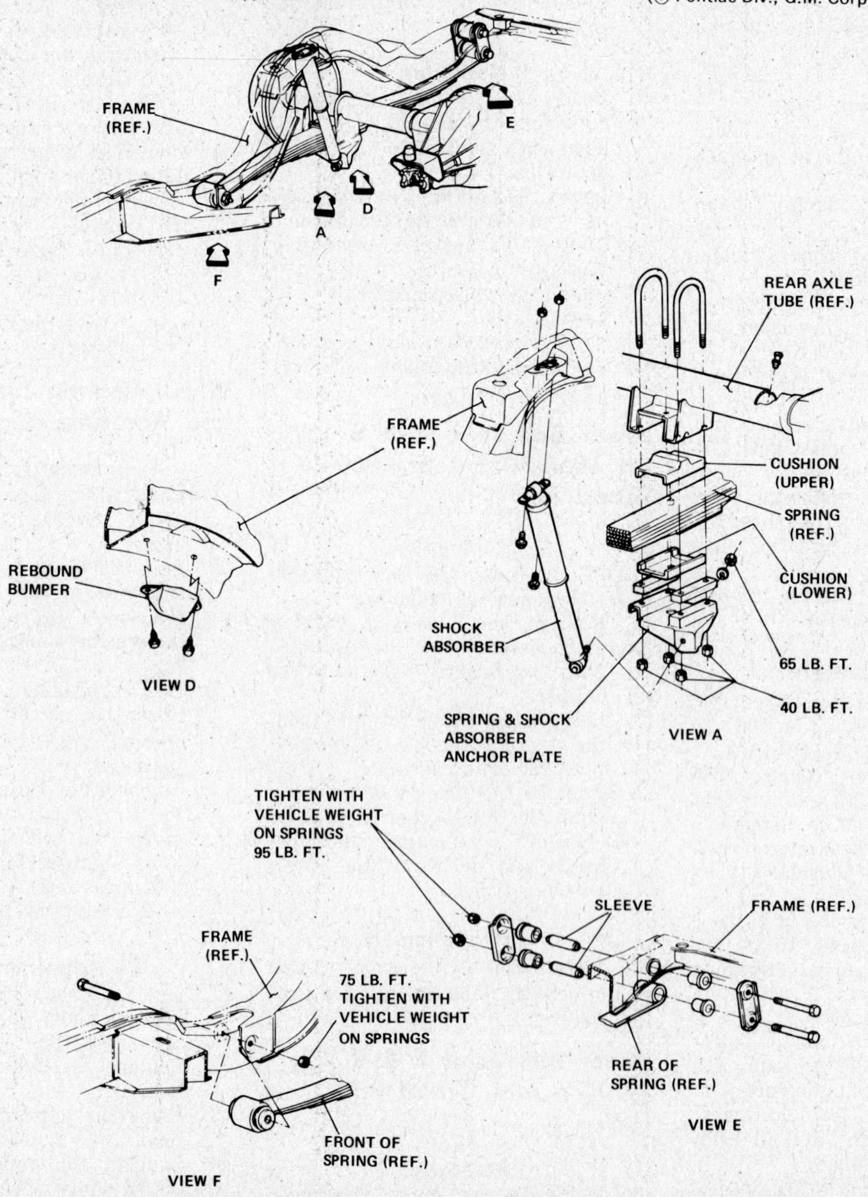
FRAME (REF.)
E
A
D
F
REAR AXLE TUBE (REF.)
FRAME (REF.)
CUSHION (UPPER)
SPRING (REF.)
REBOUND BUMPER
CUSHION (LOWER)
SHOCK ABSORBER
65 LB. FT.
VIEW D
40 LB. FT.
SPRING & SHOCK ABSORBER ANCHOR PLATE
VIEW A
TIGHTEN WITH VEHICLE WEIGHT ON SPRINGS 95 LB. FT.
SLEEVE
FRAME (REF.)
FRAME (REF.)
75 LB. FT. TIGHTEN WITH VEHICLE WEIGHT ON SPRINGS
REAR OF SPRING (REF.)
VIEW E
FRONT OF SPRING (REF.)
VIEW F

1971-74 Pontiac station wagon leaf spring rear suspension (© Pontiac Div., G.M. Corp)

tween seats in the frame and on the axle housing. Shock absorbers are direct double-action hydraulic units and are mounted between the lower control arms and the frame.

Rubber bumpers are mounted near the outer ends of the axle housing and at the center of the frame cross member to prevent metal-to-metal contact during bottoming of the suspension.

Shock Absorber R & R

1. Raise the car at the axle housing.
2. Remove the nut, retainer, and grommet, or nut, and lock washer, as equipped, which attach the lower end of the shock absorber to its mounting.
3. Remove the two shock absorber upper attaching screws and remove the shock absorber.
4. Reverse the removal procedures to install.

Rear Leaf Spring Replacement —1971-74 Station Wagon

1. Jack up car at axle housing. Make sure you don't crush exhaust pipe.
2. Support car at both frame side rails, using axle stands.
3. Remove nut and lockwasher from lower shock stud.
4. Move shock out of the way.
5. Remove spring anchor plate nuts, then remove anchor plate and cushion.
6. Jack axle housing up and remove upper cushion.
7. Loosen upper and lower spring shackle nuts.
8. Loosen front spring eye bolt.
9. Remove front eye bolt and carefully lower spring.
10. Support spring and remove lower shackle pin.
11. Remove spring.
12. To install, reverse removal procedure. Tighten front eye bolt to 75 ft. lbs., shackle nuts to 95 ft. lbs., and lower shock nut to 65 ft. lbs.

Rear Coil Spring Replacement

1. Jack up the back of the car and support both sides on stand jacks on the frame, in front of the rear axle. Disconnect shock absorber.
2. Place a jack under the lower trailing arm and remove the bolts which hold the trailing arm to the rear axle housing.

NOTE: spring can often be removed without disconnecting lower control arm.

3. Slowly, and very carefully, let the trailing arm come down until the tension is released from the rear coil spring. Then, take off the coil spring. Note the direction the end of the last coil is pointing. Reinstall the spring in the same position.
4. When starting a new coil spring, make certain that the bottom of the coil is properly inserted into the socket in the frame and into the form plate on the trailing arm.
5. Jack the trailing arm into place and reinstall the trailing arm rear bolt.

BRAKES

Information on brake adjustment, lining replacement, bleeding procedure, master and wheel cylinder overhaul can be found in the Unit Repair Section.

Standard brakes are of the duo-servo, self-adjusting type.

Metallic brake linings, used on some early high-performance models, never should be installed on cars equipped with standard brake drums unless the drums are radius ground and honed to a special finish. See the Unit Repair Section of this manual for more information on metallic brake linings.

Disc Brakes

From 1967, single-piston, sliding caliper disc brakes have been available as optional equipment on most models (standard with high performance packages). These brakes have a vented, cast-iron rotor with two braking surfaces. For 1971-74, power disc brakes are standard on all Grand Prix and full-size Pontiac models. Drum brakes are no longer available on the front wheels.

Disc brakes need no adjustment because, during operation, the application and release of hydraulic pressure causes the piston and caliper to move only slightly. In the released position, the pads do not move very far from the rotor; thus, as pads wear down, the piston simply moves farther out of the caliper bore and the caliper repositions itself on its mounting bolts to maintain proper pad-to-rotor clearance.

A metering valve in the front brake circuit prevents the discs from operating until about 75 psi exists in the system. This enables the rear drum brakes to operate in synchronization with the front discs and reduces the possibility of unequal brake application and premature lock-up. A proportioning valve in the rear brake circuit of some models accomplishes the same. Starting 1971, all functions of the two separate valves are performed by either a two- or three-element combination valve. The two-function valve is used on all wagons and sedans except Grand Prix, which uses a three-function valve. Disc brake pads should be examined for wear every 12,000 miles. 1974 Pontiacs employ a disc brake pad wear indicator. As the lining material wears down, a steel sensor approaches the rotor. When enough lining material has worn away, the sensor makes contact with the rotor causing noise which is audible to the driver. See the Unit Repair Section of this manual for service procedures.

Master Cylinder Removal

The master cylinder is located in the engine compartment just above the steering column.

The master cylinder is a sealed unit. A sealing diaphragm covers the reservoir, hermetically sealing the system from contamination.

From under the dash, disconnect the brake pedal from the master cylinder on Bendix power brakes and non-power brakes. Delco power booster pushrods are not connected to the master cylinder. From under the hood, disconnect the hydraulic lines and the stoplight wire.

Remove the bolts which hold the master cylinder to the cowl panel and lift off the master cylinder.

The unit is installed in reverse order of removal. Bleed the brakes after installation.

Power Brake Booster R & R 1967-74

1. Remove the vacuum hose from the front housing and discard the grommet. Remove the master cylinder and position it away from the booster. It is not necessary to disconnect the lines from the master cylinder if it is not to be repaired.
2. Remove the clevis pin retainer from the brake pedal inside the car.
3. Remove the nuts from the vacuum cylinder studs under the dash and remove the vacuum power section.
4. Reverse the removal procedure to install the booster.

Parking Brake Adjustment

1. Jack up both rear wheels.
2. Apply parking brake, five notches from full release.
3. Loosen equalizer rear locknut. Adjust forward nut until a light to moderate drag is felt when rear wheels are rotated.
4. Tighten the locknut.
5. Fully release the parking brake and rotate rear wheels; no drag should be felt.

Parking Brake Lever Removal

A foot-operated parking brake is used on these models.

Remove the clevis which holds the cable to the foot-brake lever, then disconnect the bolts that hold the lever assembly to the bracket. Let the assembly come down sufficiently to get at the bolts which hold the cable conduit to the bracket assembly.

Disconnect the release lever at the dash and move the entire assembly out from under the vehicle.

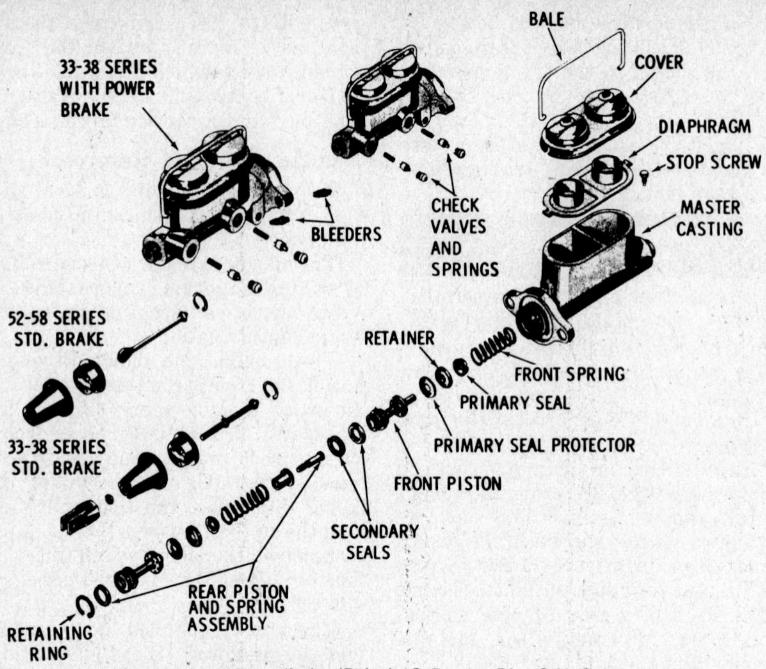
BALE
COVER
33-38 SERIES WITH POWER BRAKE
DIAPHRAGM
STOP SCREW
CHECK VALVES AND SPRINGS
MASTER CASTING
BLEEDERS
52-58 SERIES STD. BRAKE
RETAINER
FRONT SPRING
PRIMARY SEAL
33-38 SERIES STD. BRAKE
PRIMARY SEAL PROTECTOR
FRONT PISTON
SECONDARY SEALS
REAR PISTON AND SPRING ASSEMBLY
RETAINING RING

Dual type master cylinder (Delco) (© Pontiac Div., G.M. Corp)

STEERING

The steering system consists of a steering wheel, steering column, universal joint, intermediate steering shaft, flexible coupling, manual or power steering gear, and steering linkage.

The manual steering gear is the recirculating ball nut type. The steering shaft, worm shaft, and worm nut are all in line. The steering shaft and worm shaft are separated by a flexible coupling. This coupling permits the gear to be removed independently of the steering shaft and steering column.

All Pontiacs use a variable-ratio power steering gear. The gear is the recirculating ball type incorporating a wormshaft and a rack-piston. A rotary valve is contained in the gear housing, eliminating the need for separately mounted valve and cylinder assemblies.

Hydraulic pressure for the power steering is provided by a constant-displacement vane type pump. It is located on the left front of the engine and is belt-driven off the engine crankshaft pulley.

See the "Unit Repair Section" for rebuilding procedures.

Tie-Rod End Inspection

1. Raise the car under the lower control arm.
2. Make sure the control arm ball joints are good and that the wheel bearings are adjusted. Grasp the tire on either side and move the tire from side to side. If excessive play is present, more than 1/16 in., visually inspect the linkage as the tire is moved.

Tie-Rod End R & R

1. Loosen the tie-rod adjuster sleeve clamp nuts.
2. Remove the tie-rod stud nut cotter pin and nut.
3. Remove the tie-rod stud from the steering arm or intermediate rod. This is a taper fit. Removal is accomplished by using a ball joint removal tool or by hitting the tie rod stud sharply with a hammer. If the ball joint is to be reused the removal tool must be used.
4. Unthread the tie rod from the adjuster sleeve. Outer tie rods have right-hand threads and inner tie rods have left-hand threads. Count the number of turns the tie rod must be rotated to remove it from the adjusting sleeve. This will allow a reasonably accurate realignment upon reassembly.
5. Reverse the removal procedures to install. Clean rust and dirt from the threads. Check the alignment and adjust if necessary.

Intermediate Rod R & R

1. Remove the left and right-side inner tie-rod ends from the intermediate rod. These are taper fits, remove them as described in the tie rod section.
2. Remove the intermediate rod studs from the idler and pitman arms. These are taper fits.
3. Remove the intermediate rod.
4. Reverse the above steps to install.

Pitman Arm R & R

1. Remove the intermediate rod stud from the pitman arm. This is a taper fit, remove it as described in the tie rod section.
2. Remove the pitman arm nut and lockwasher from the pitman shaft.
3. Remove the pitman arm from the pitman shaft using a puller. Do not hammer on the end of the puller or serious internal damage will be done to the steering gear box.
4. Reverse the above steps to install.

Idler Arm R & R

1. Remove the intermediate arm stud. This is a taper fit, see the tie-rod section for removal.
2. Remove the two bolts attaching the idler arm to the frame.
3. Remove the idler arm.
4. Reverse the above steps to install.

Power Steering Pump R & R

1. Disconnect the hoses at the pump.
2. Remove the drive pulley attaching nut.
3. Loosen the bracket-to-pump mounting bolts and remove the drive belt.
4. Slide the pulley from the shaft. Do not hammer on the pulley.
5. Remove the bracket-to-pump mounting bolts and remove the pump.
6. Reverse the removal steps to install.

Steering Wheel R & R

1. On deluxe models, remove the screws holding the trim cover to the wheel or, if equipped with a horn button, lift the button off.
2. Remove the steering wheel nut from the steering shaft.
3. Position the wheels in the straight-ahead position and make match marks on the steering shaft and steering wheel.
4. Using a puller, remove the steering wheel.
5. Disconnect the horn wire insulator by rotating the insulator counterclockwise to unlock position and then pull up.
6. Reverse the removal procedures to install. Make sure the match marks are lined up when installing the wheel.

Turn Signal Switch R & R 1967-68

Removal

Caution Make sure the steering column is supported at all times as the column is extremely easy to bend.

1. Remove the bolts holding the column bracket.

2. Remove the wire protector, wire clip, and cover.
3. Remove the steering wheel.
4. Slide the preload springs and turn signal cancelling cam off the steering shaft.
5. Remove the turn signal lever screw and lever.
6. Push the hazard warning knob in and remove the knob.
7. Remove the snap-ring from the steering shaft.
8. Loosen the three switch mounting screws until the cover assembly can be rotated counterclockwise. Remove the cover assembly.
9. Remove the three switch attaching screws entirely and remove the old switch.

NOTE: These three screws hold the entire assembly together. Carefully note the position and orientation of these parts to aid reassembly.

Installation

1. Place the new switch assembly on top of the housing assembly and feed the switch wires through the switch cover.
2. Align the switch housing and cover holes and install the three mounting screws through the holes.
3. Slide three springs onto the screws and start the screws into the lockplate.
4. Run the wires through the bowl and place the switch assembly on top of the bowl. Make sure the tangs of the lockplate are aligned with the slots on the inside of the bowl.
5. Push down on the housing assembly and turn clockwise. Tighten the three screws.
6. Reverse steps one through seven to complete the installation.

Turn Signal Switch R & R 1969-74

1. Remove the steering wheel.
2. Loosen the three cover screws and lift cover off the shaft. Do not remove the screws completely.
3. Depress the lockplate downward and remove the snap-ring.
4. Slide the upper bearing spring and turn signal cam off the shaft.
5. Remove the turn signal lever screw and lever.
6. Push the hazard warning switch in and remove the knob.
7. Lower the steering column and disconnect the switch wiring.
8. Remove the turn signal switch mounting screws and pull the switch straight up with the wire protector and remove it from the housing.
9. Reverse the removal procedures to install.

INSTRUMENT PANEL

Ignition Switch Replacement

1967-68

1. Remove ignition lock.
2. Remove bezel retaining switch to dash. Take care not to destroy fiber optic light.
3. Remove wire connector from ignition switch.
4. Remove switch.
5. Reverse procedure to install.

1969-74

1. Disconnect battery.
2. Loosen toe pan screws on steering column.
3. Remove column to instrument panel attaching nuts.
4. Lower column and disconnect switch wire connectors.
5. Remove switch attaching screws and remove switch.
6. To replace move key lock to OFF- LOCK position.
7. Move actuator rod hole in switch to OFF-LOCK position.
8. Install switch with rod in hole.
9. Position and reassemble steering column in reverse of disassembly procedure.

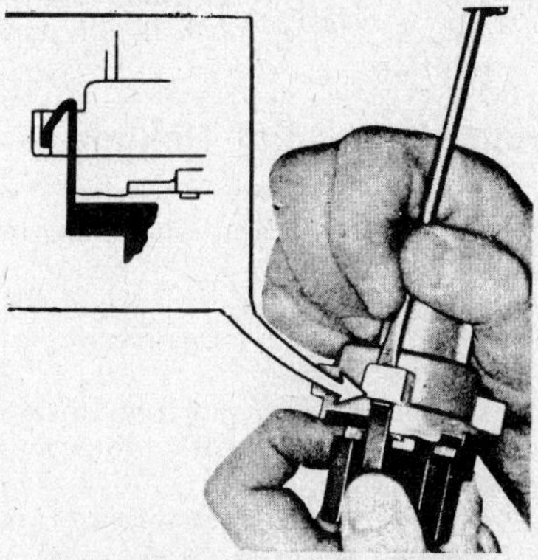

Unlocking ignition switch connector
(© Pontiac Div., G.M. Corp)

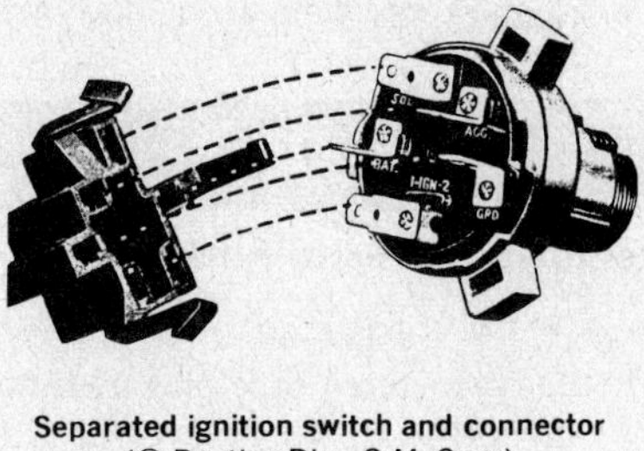

Separated ignition switch and connector
(© Pontiac Div., G.M. Corp)

Switch Adjustment—Standard Column

1. Place switch in OFF position.
2. Position switch on column, then move slider to extreme left (toward wheel).
3. Move slider back two positions to the right of ACCESSORY positon.
4. Place key in any run position and shift transmission into any position but Park for automatics or Reverse for manual.
5. Position lock toward ACCESSORY with a light finger pressure and secure switch.

Switch Adjustment—Tilt Column

1. Place key in ACCESSORY positon; leave key in lock.
2. Loosen switch mounting screws.
3. Push switch upward toward wheel to make certain it is in ACCESSORY detent.
4. Hold key in full counter clockwise ACCESSORY position and tighten switch mounting screws.
5. Switch is properly adjusted if: it will go into ACCESSORY position, the key can be removed when in lock, and switch will go into START position.

Lock Cylinder Replacement

1967-68

1. Disconnect the battery, then insert the key.
2. Remove the lock cylinder by placing it in the "off" position and inserting a wire into the small hole in the cylinder face. While pushing in on the wire, continue to turn the cylinder counterclockwise, then pull the cylinder from the case.

1969-74

1. Remove steering wheel.
2. Pull turn signal switch up far enough to allow access to spring latch slot.
3. Place key in RUN position, insert a thin screwdriver into the slot next to the switch mounting screw boss and depress spring latch.
4. Remove lock from housing. Thin flash of metal over slot is easily broken.
5. To install, first hold lock cylinder sleeve and rotate knob clockwise against stop.

Caution If lock cylinder is forced beyond its normal latched position, complete disassembly of upper bearing assembly will be necessary to free it.

6. Lay a 1/6 in. drill on housing surface next to housing bore.
7. Insert cylinder into housing bore, aligning keyway, and push in to abutment.
8. Rotate knob counterclockwise, pushing in slightly, until cylinder mates with sector.
9. Push in until spring latch pops into groove, then remove drill.

Headlight Switch Replacement

1967

1. Disconnect battery.
2. Pull switch knob to ON position, push latch button on side of

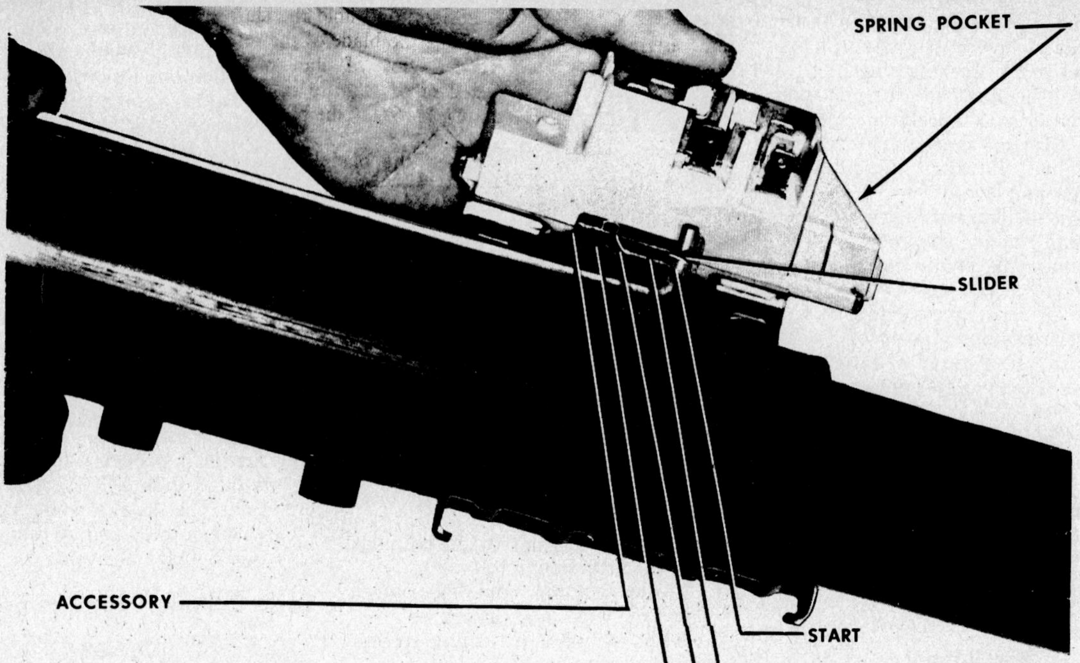
SPRING POCKET
SLIDER
ACCESSORY
START
OFF-LOCK, ONE POSITION TO THE RIGHT FROM ACCESSORY
RUN
OFF
ACTUATOR ROD HOLE

Installing ignition switch (© Pontiac Div., G.M. Corp)

switch to ON position and pull out switch knob.
3. Unscrew bushing from switch and remove switch.
4. Remove push on connector with leads from light switch and connect to new switch.
5. On Grand Prix models remove vacuum connectors and connect new switch.
6. Position new switch in instrument panel, and start bushing through ferrule into switch. Tighten bushing securely.
7. Insert knob into switch until end of knob engages catch.
8. Connect battery.

1968-74

1. Depress button on switch and remove knob and shaft.
2. Remove retaining nut.
3. Remove wire connector from switch and remove switch.
4. On vacuum operated headlight models, remove vacuum connector.
5. Reverse procedure to install.

WINDSHIELD WIPERS

Motor R & R

1. Disconnect electrical and hose connections at wiper.
2. Disconnect wiper crank from wiper transmission linkage, through cowl opening.
3. Remove wiper motor mounting screws, then remove the motor from the firewall.
4. Install by reversing removal procedure. Motor must be in park position.

Transmission and Linkage R & R

1. Remove arm and blade assemblies.
2. Remove fresh air intake grille.
3. Remove wiper transmission retaining screws.
4. Loosen retainer holding linkage which connects with wiper motor crank.
5. Remove wiper transmission and linkage.
6. Install by reversing removal procedure. Be sure wiper blades are in park position after they are installed.

RADIO

Removal & Installation

1967-68

1. Remove stereo tape player, if so equipped.
2. Remove knobs, springs, nuts, and bezels from control bushings.
3. If car is air conditioned, remove three Phillips head screws holding bottom air conditioning air duct and remove duct.
4. Disconnect stereo multiplex plug from radio, if so equipped.
5. Remove antenna lead-in and speaker connector.
6. Remove hex head screw holding right side of radio to brace.
7. Disconnect dial light socket and lower radio to floor.
8. Remove multiplex adapter if so equipped.
9. Reverse procedure to install.

1969-70

1. Disconnect battery.
2. Remove lower air conditioning duct if equipped.
3. Remove two radio control knobs and hex nuts.
4. Remove ash tray and bracket.
5. Remove upper air conditioning duct, if so equipped.
6. Disconnect all radio connections.
7. Remove screws holding radio brace to lower edge of instrument panel and remove radio.
8. Reverse procedure to install.

1971-74 Pontiac

1. Disconnect battery, then remove radio knobs and hex nuts.
2. Remove upper and lower instrument panel trim plates and lower front radio bracket.
3. Remove glove box and disconnect radio connections.
4. Loosen side brace screw and slide radio toward front seat.
5. To install, reverse removal procedure.

1971-72 Grand Prix

1. Disconnect battery and remove lower A/C duct.
2. Remove control knobs and hex nuts, then remove support bracket bolt.

3. Disconnect electrical leads and remove radio.
4. To install, reverse removal procedure.

1973-74 Grand Prix

1. Remove the lower instrument panel trim cover.
2. Disconnect the battery.
3. Remove the knobs from the radio.
4. Remove the two side retaining screws and the radio mounting bracket retaining screw (below radio).
5. Remove radio and bracket as an assembly; disconnect radio connections and antenna lead-in while radio is pulled out.
6. Reverse the above steps to install.

HEATER

Cars w/o A/C

1967 Pontiac and Grand Prix

Heater Blower, Impeller and Inlet Duct R & R

1. Disconnect wires at connector to blower.
2. Disconnect water hoses and plug openings.
3. Disconnect vacuum hose at air inlet duct diaphragm.
4. Remove nuts and screws that hold air inlet and remove assembly.
5. Remove large motor retaining ring from motor.
6. Remove motor and impeller assembly.
7. Install in reverse of above.

Heater Core R & R

1. Drain radiator.
2. Disconnect inlet and outlet hoses at heater.
3. Disconnect temperature control cable at top of heater core and case.
4. Disconnect vacuum hose from defroster and air inlet diaphragms.
5. Remove wire connector from resistor assembly at top of air outlet duct by prying up with flat blade screwdriver.
6. Remove nuts and screws securing heater to air inlet duct assembly.
7. Remove heater core and case assembly.
8. Remove heater core.
9. Install in reverse of above.
10. Adjust temperature control cable.

1968 Pontiac and Grand Prix

Heater Blower Motor, Impeller and Duct R&R

1. Remove hood hinge to fender retaining bolts.
2. Prop hood and rest hinge on plenum.
3. Remove blower motor or duct retaining screws as desired.
4. Remove motor electrical lead.
5. Remove motor or duct as desired.
6. Reverse procedure to install.

Heater Core R & R

1. Drain radiator.
2. Disconnect inlet and outlet hoses at heater.
3. Disconnect temperature control cable at top of heater core and case.
4. Disconnect vacuum hose from defroster and air inlet diaphragms.
5. Remove wire connector from resistor assembly at top of air outlet duct by prying up with flat blade screwdriver.
6. Remove nuts and screws securing heater to air inlet duct assembly.
7. Remove heater core and case assembly.
8. Remove heater core.
9. Install in reverse of above.
10. Adjust temperature control cable.

1969 Except G.P.

Blower Motor R & R

1. Remove fender skirt.
2. Disconnect power lead.
3. Remove retaining screws.
4. Remove motor.
5. To install, reverse removal procedure.

Heater Core R & R

Same as 1970-74 Pontiac.

1970-74 Except G.P.

Blower Motor and Impeller

1. Jack up front of car and remove right front wheel.
2. Cut access hole along stamped outline on right fender skirt, using an air chisel.
3. Disconnect blower power wire.
4. Remove blower.
5. To install, reverse removal procedure, covering access hole with a metal plate secured with sealer and sheet metal screws.

Heater Core R & R

1. Drain radiator.
2. Disconnect heater hoses at air inlet assembly.

NOTE: the water pump hose goes to right-hand heater core pipe, the other hose (from rear of right cylinder head) goes to the left-hand heater core pipe.

3. Remove nuts from core studs on firewall (under hood).
4. From inside the car, pull the heater assembly from the firewall.
5. Disconnect control cables, vacuum hoses and wires, then remove heater assembly.
6. To remove core, unhook retaining springs.
7. To install, reverse removal procedure, making sure core is properly sealed during installation.

1969-74 Grand Prix

Blower Motor R & R

1. Disconnect power wire.
2. Remove motor retaining screws.
3. Remove motor.
4. To install, reverse removal procedure.

Heater Core R & R

Same as 1970-74 Pontiac.

Cars With A/C

1967-69 Pontiac and Grand Prix

Blower

1. Remove the hoses from the inner fender panel.
2. Remove the rocker molding.
3. Loosen the lower rear fender retaining screws to allow the bottom of the fender to move.
4. Remove the inner panel.
5. Remove the blower motor or inlet duct retaining screws.
6. Remove the motor feed wire and cooling tube.
7. Remove the motor and impeller.
8. Reverse the above steps to install.

Heater Core and Case Assembly

1. Drain the coolant.
2. Remove the heater case-to-cowl attaching nuts. It may be necessary to drill a 1 in. hole in the fender skirt to gain access to the lower nut.
3. Remove the two water hoses attached to the heater core.
4. Remove the lower duct and outlet assembly.
5. Remove the glove box.
6. Remove the defroster duct attaching screw.
7. Remove the screws retaining case to the dash.
8. Remove the core and case assembly.
9. Disconnect the cables and wires.
10. Match-mark the heater cam and bracket and remove as an assembly.
11. Remove the case half screws and separate the case halves.
12. Remove the core screws and remove the core.
13. Reverse the above steps to install.

1970-74

Blower—Grand Prix

1. Working under the hood, disconnect the blower motor feed wire.
2. Remove the blower motor or duct retaining screws as required.
3. Remove the motor or duct.
4. Reverse the above steps to install.

1973 Grand Prix w/o V.I.R.

On some 1973 Grand Prix models without the V.I.R. (Valves In Receiver) system, removal and replacement of the blower motor may be hindered by the position of the POA valve-to-compressor tube. If this tube is positioned so that the blower motor cannot be removed:

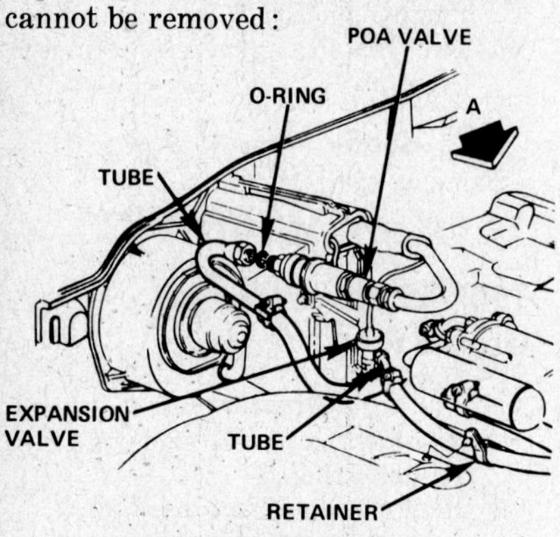
POA VALVE
O-RING
A
TUBE
EXPANSION VALVE
TUBE
RETAINER

POA valve location
(© Pontiac Div., G.M. Corp.)

1. Disconnect the blower motor feed wire and cooling tube.
2. Remove the six blower retaining screws.
3. Loosen the fitting on the POA valve-to-compressor tube at the POA valve just enough to allow the tube to be turned (approx. ¼ to ½ turn).

Caution This procedure should be done only by a trained air-conditioning specialist. Escaping refrigerant (Freon) could cause severe injury, even blindness.

4. Reposition the lower portion of the tube to allow clearance when removing the blower motor. Retighten the fiting to 20-33 ft lb.
5. Remove the blower motor and impeller.
6. To install, reverse the removal procedure.

Blower—Pontiac

1. Remove the right-hand front wheel.
2. Cut an access hole ¾ of the way along the outline stamped in the right inner fender panel.
3. Disconnect the blower feed wire.
4. Remove the blower motor.
5. Plug the hole in the inner fender panel and reverse the above steps to install.

Heater Core—Pontiac and Grand Prix

1. Drain the radiator.
2. Disconnect the heater hoses.
3. Remove the retaining nuts from the core case studs on the engine side of the dash.
4. Remove the glove box.
5. Remove the defroster duct retaining screw from the heater case and pull the heater assembly from the firewall.
6. Disconnect the heater control cables and wires.
7. Remove the core tube seal and core assembly retaining strips and remove the core.
8. Reverse the above steps to install.

SEAT BELTS

Buzzer System—1973

The front seat belt warning system consists of a switch in each belt retractor, a sensor switch in the seat cushion on the passenger side, a reminder light and a warning buzzer. The circuit wiring is routed through the ignition switch and parking brake warning switch on manual transmission models or through the ignition switch and transmission switch on models equipped with automatic transmissions.

With the ignition switch on and the parking brake released with manual transmissions or with the shift selector in a forward position on automatic transmission models, the warning circuit (light and buzzer) is closed (activated) until the driver's seat belt is extended to open (de-activate) the circuit. The seat sensor on the passenger side will react to weights in excess of 0-47 lbs. on the seat cushion and close the warning circuit. Extending the passenger belt will open the circuit.

Seat Belt/Starter Interlock System—1974

All 1974 Pontiacs are equipped with the sequential interlock seat belt system. The sequential interlock system requires the driver and right front seat occupant to first sit in their seats, then fasten their seat belts before the engine can be started. The middle seat position on cars equipped with a front bench seat is not included in the interlock system, but the belt must be buckled if this seat is occupied to avoid activating the familiar buzzer and warning light system. The seat sensors are similar to those found in the 1973 buzzer systems.

Engine restarting is possible without interference from the interlock system if the driver has not left his seat. In the event of system malfunction, an emergency by-pass switch under the hood permits starting when the ignition key is in the ON position.

The buzzer/warning light system will be activated if a front seat belt is not fastened at an occupied front seat after the car is started and moved into forward gear.

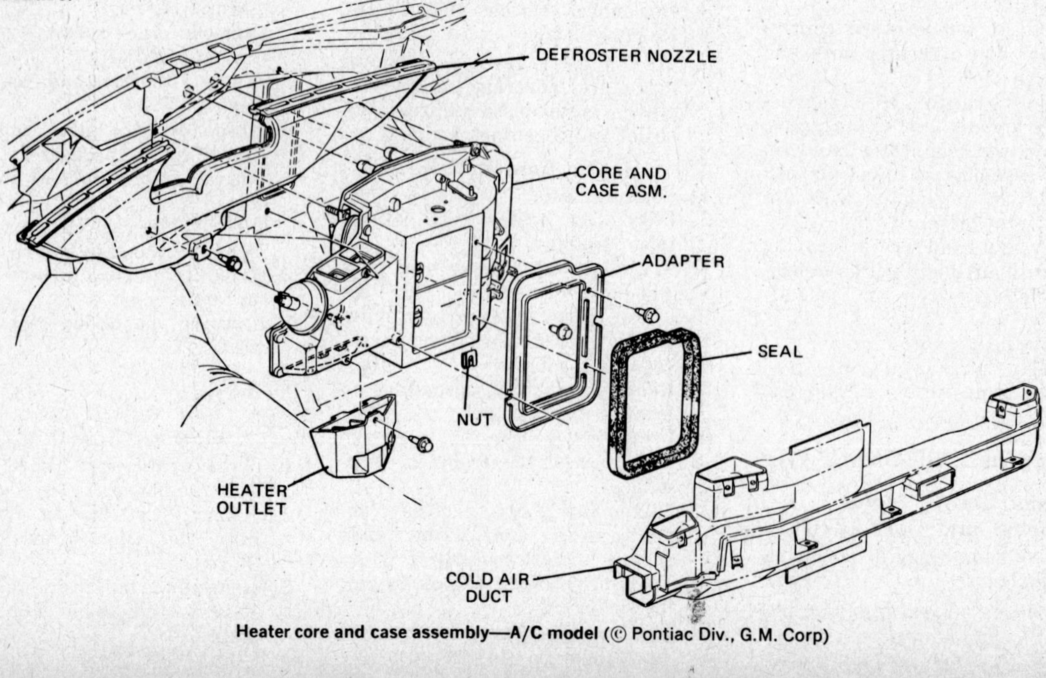
DEFROSTER NOZZLE
CORE AND CASE ASM.
ADAPTER
SEAL
NUT
HEATER OUTLET
COLD AIR DUCT

Heater core and case assembly—A/C model (© Pontiac Div., G.M. Corp)

Rambler • Javelin • AMX • Hornet • Gremlin

YEAR IDENTIFICATION

SERIES 10, REBEL AND MATADOR

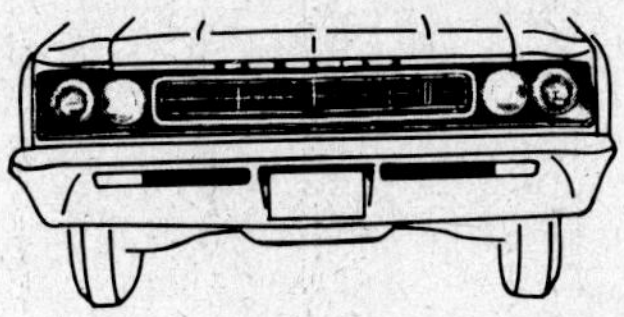
1967 Rebel

1968 Rebel

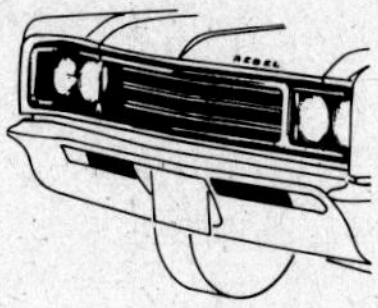
1969 Rebel

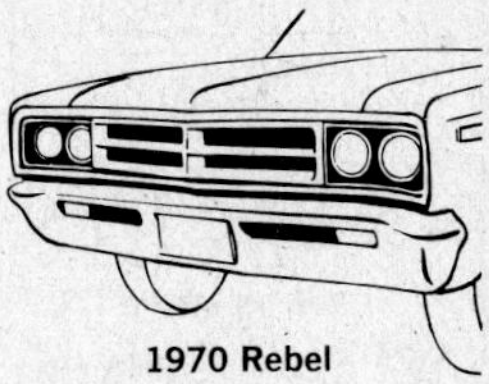
1970 Rebel

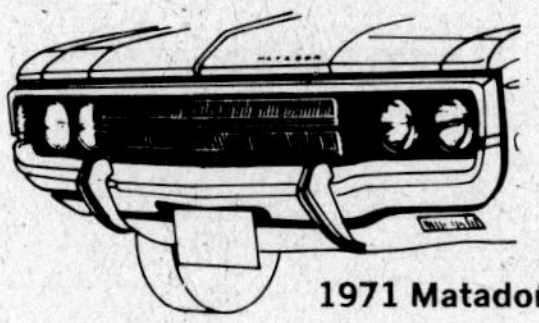
1971 Matador

1972 Matador

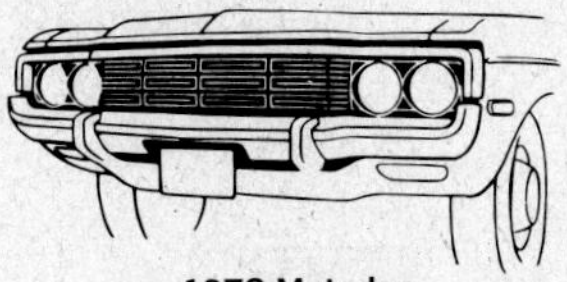
1973 Matador

1974 Matador

SERIES 80, AMBASSADOR

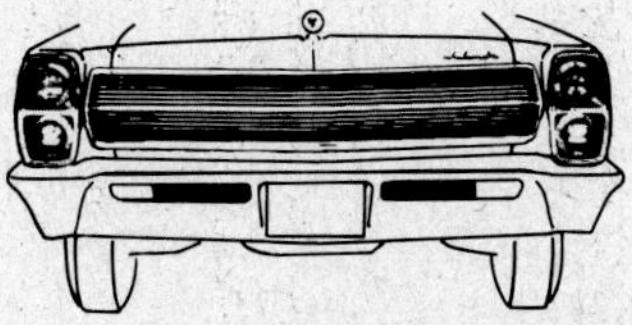
1967

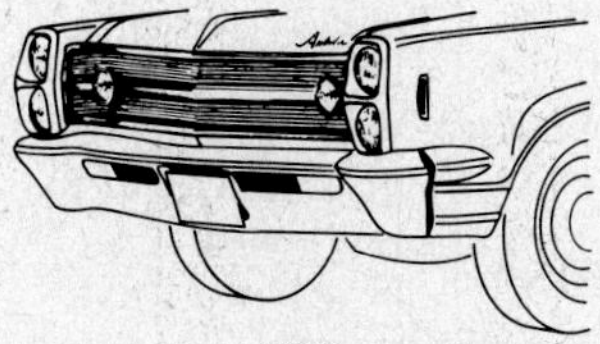
1968

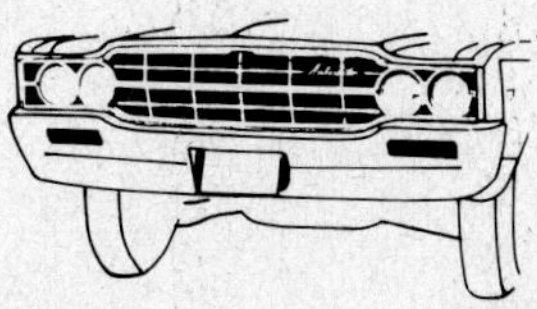
1969

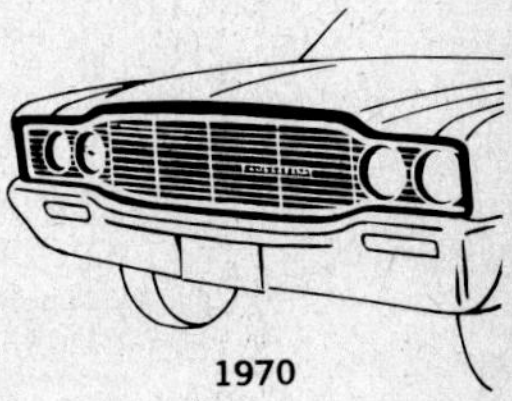
1970

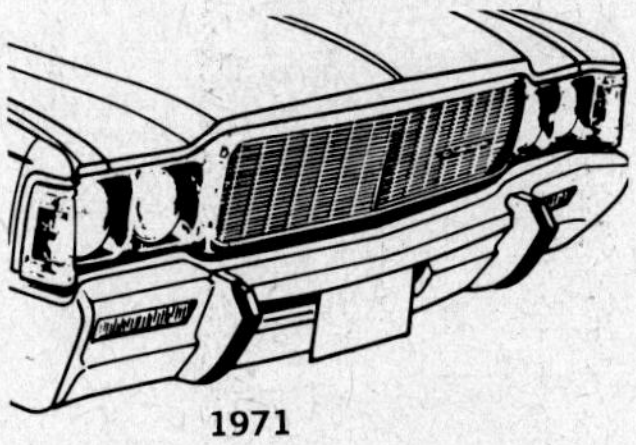
1971

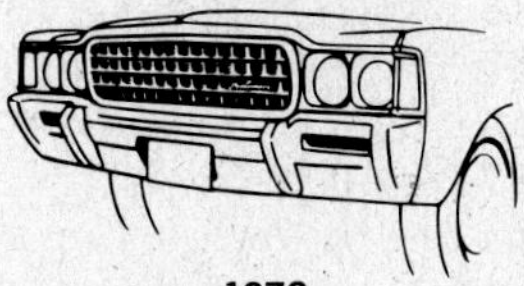
1972

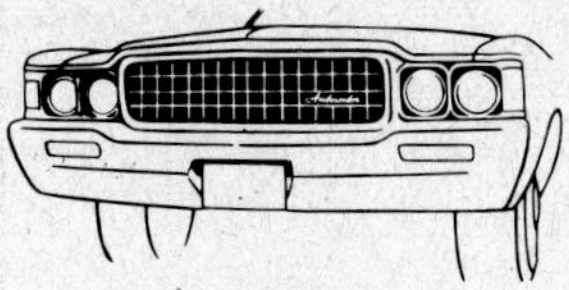
1973

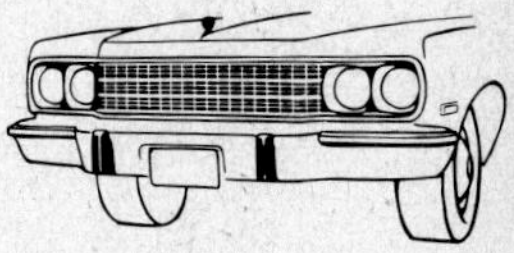
1974

SERIES 01 AND 40

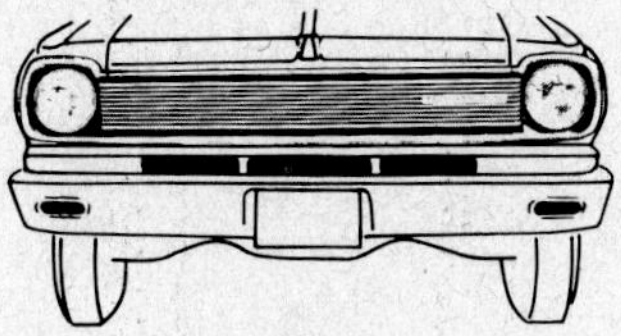
1967 American

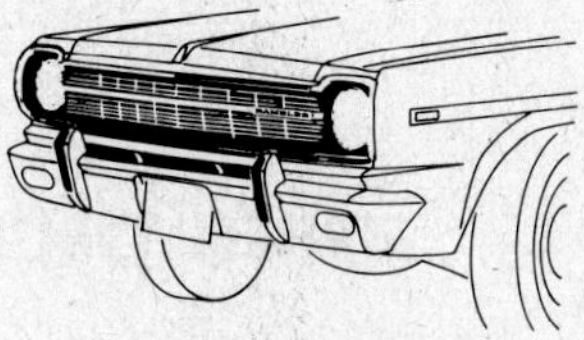
1968-69 American

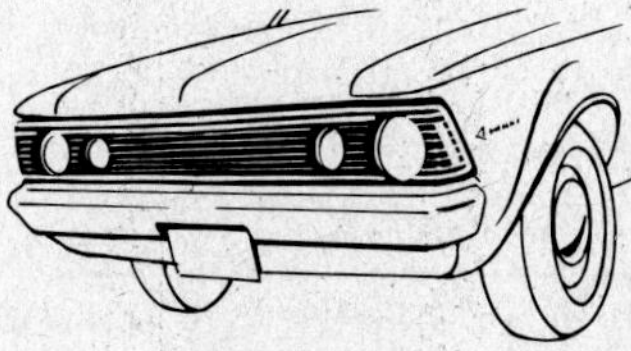
1970-72 Hornet

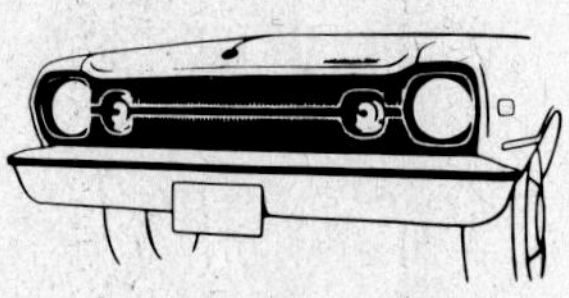
1973 Hornet

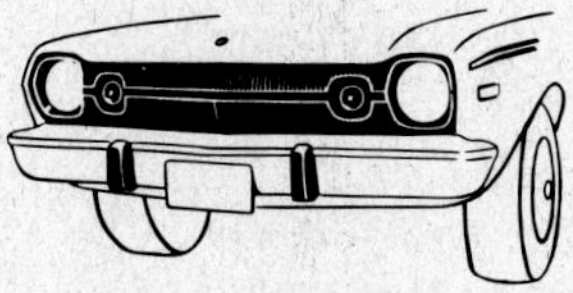
1974 Hornet

1970 Gremlin

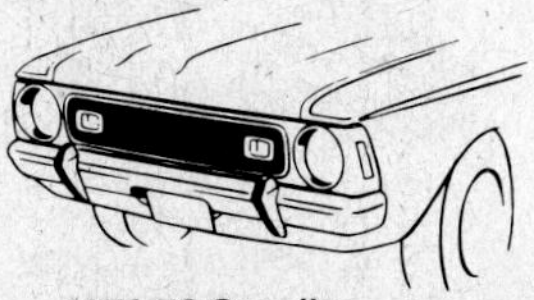
1971-72 Gremlin

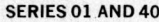

1973 Gremlin

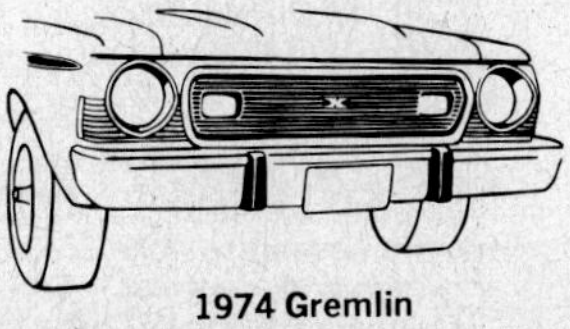
1974 Gremlin

SERIES 50, MARLIN

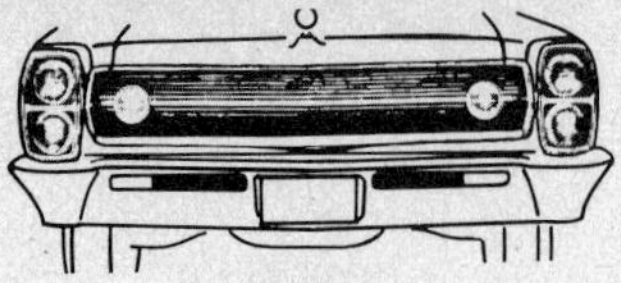

1967

SERIES 70, JAVELIN

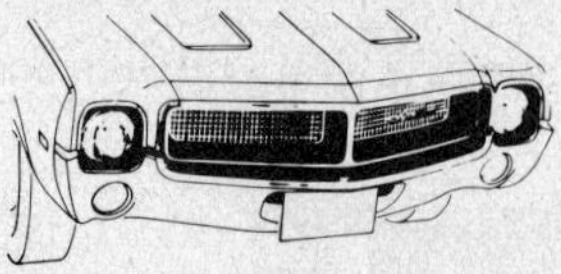

1968

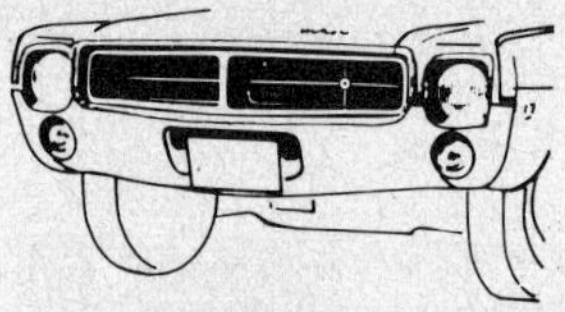

1969

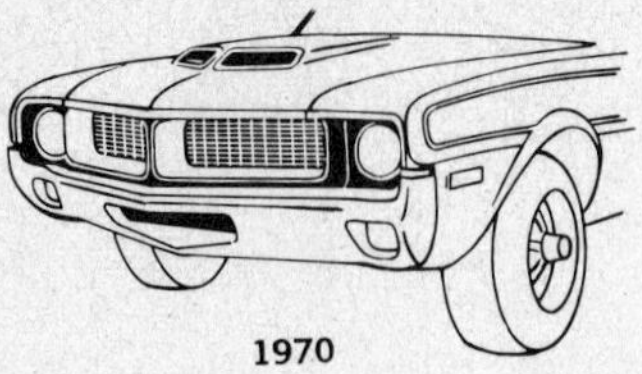

1970

1971 Javelin SST

1972 Javelin SST

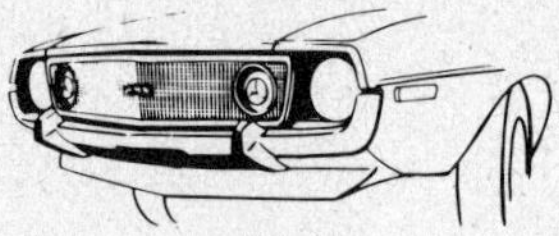

1973 Javelin

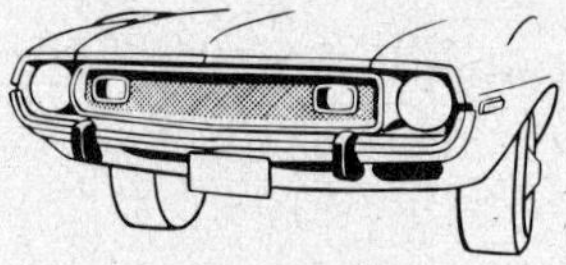

1974 Javelin

SERIES 30, AMX

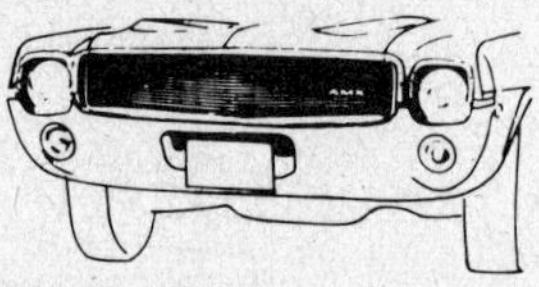

1968-69 AMX

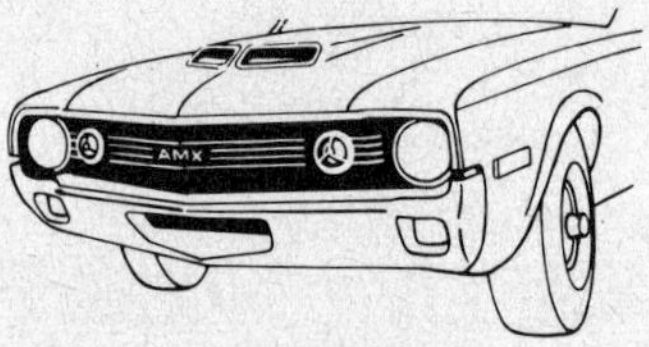

1970 AMX

1971 Javelin AMX

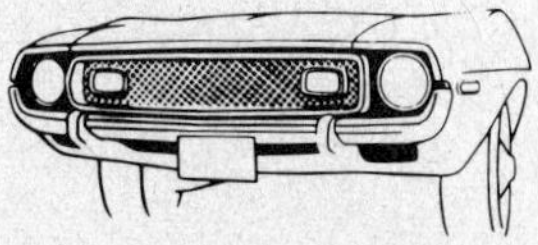

1972 Javelin AMX

1973 AMX

1974 AMX

FIRING ORDER

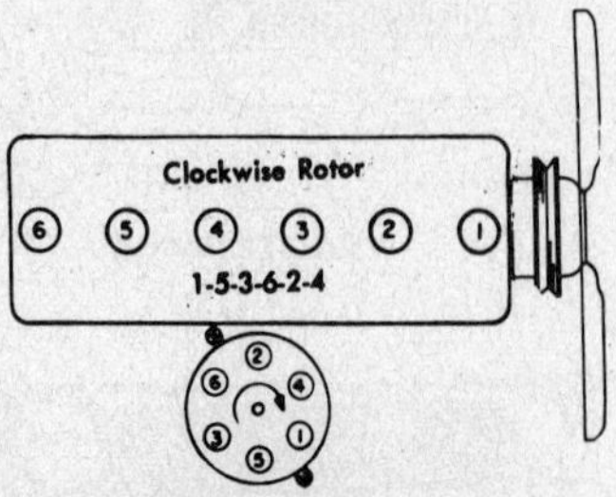
Clockwise Rotor
6 5 4 3 2 1
1-5-3-6-2-4

6 cylinder OHV 199, 232 and 258—1967-74
(© American Motors Corp)

Ignition timing marks—199, 232, 258
6 cylinder engines
(© American Motors Corp)

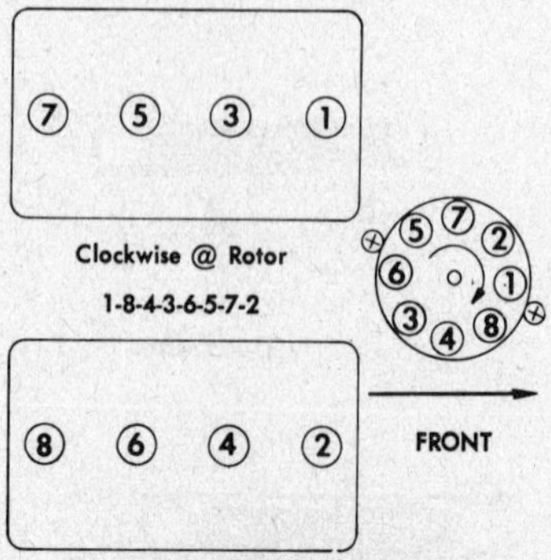
7 5 3 1
Clockwise @ Rotor
1-8-4-3-6-5-7-2
8 6 4 2
FRONT

290, 304, 343, 360, 390 and 401—V8
(© American Motors Corp)

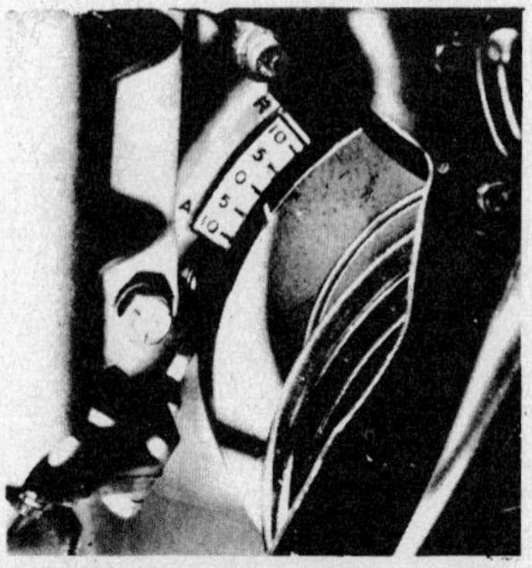

Timing marks—290, 304, 343, 360, 390, and 401 V8
(© American Motors Corp)

CAR SERIAL NUMBER LOCATION

1967-68

The car serial number is found on a plate attached to the right front wheelwell, under the hood.

1969-74

The thirteen digit car serial number is stamped on the left top of the dashboard, visible through the windshield. On 1970-74 vehicles, this number also can be found on a non-removable sticker on the front, left-side door pillar.

Engine Identification Code

Six—199, 232, 258—Stamped on right upper side of block.

V8—290, 304, 343, 360, 390, 401—Stamped on a tag attached to right-hand front of valve cover. *NOTE: From 1967, all V8 engines have their cubic inch displacement cast into block, on both banks, between the first and second core plugs. This is the best way to tell engine displacement, because valve covers are interchangeable between engines.*

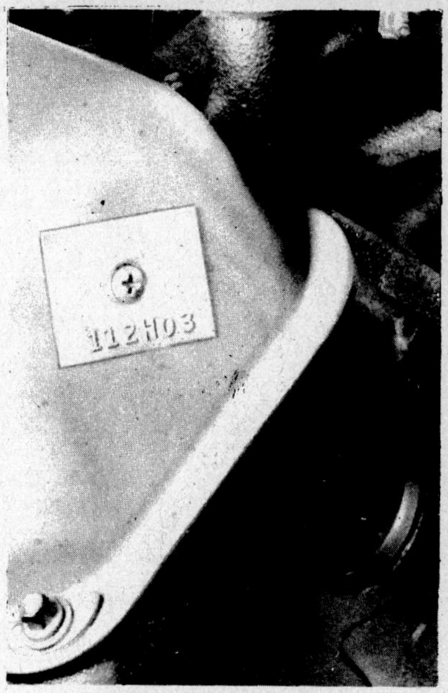
112H03

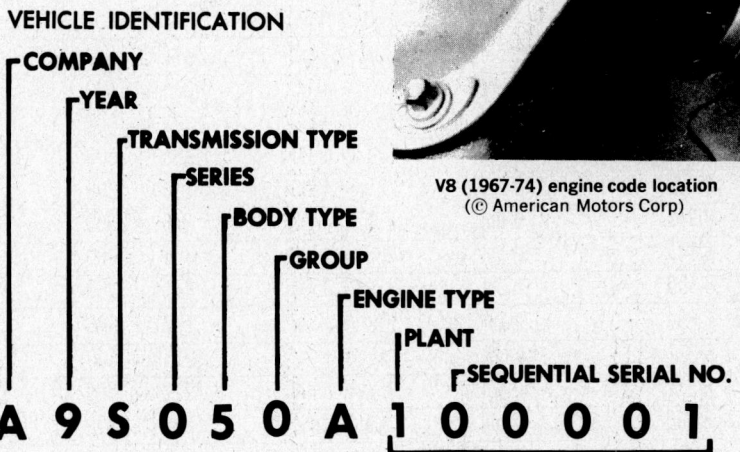

V8 (1967-74) engine code location
(© American Motors Corp)

VEHICLE IDENTIFICATION

COMPANY
YEAR
TRANSMISSION TYPE
SERIES
BODY TYPE
GROUP
ENGINE TYPE
PLANT
SEQUENTIAL SERIAL NO.

A 9 S 0 5 0 A 1 0 0 0 0 1

809L27

6 cyl. engine code location

ENGINE CODE

Rambler, Javelin, AMX, Hornet, Gremlin

The engine code is the 4th digit of the engine build code stamped on a machined surface of the cylinder block between No. 2 and No. 3 cylinders on 6 cylinder engines and stamped on a tag attached to the right bank valve cover on V8 engines. In addition, the engine code is the 7th digit of the Vehicle Identification Number. (V.I.N.) The V.I.N. is stamped on a plate located at the left side of the instrument panel visible through the windshield on 1970-74 models.

Disp	Bbl	Hp	'67	'68	'69	'70	'71	'72	'73	'74
6-Cylinder Models										
199	1	128	J	J	J	A				
232	1	100 (net)						E	E	E
232	1	135					E			
232	1	145	L	L	L	E				
232	2	155	L	L	L	G				
258	1	110 (net)						A	A	A
258	1	150					A			

Disp	Bbl	Hp	'67	'68	'69	'70	'71	'72	'73	'74
8-Cylinder Models										
290	2	200	H	H	H					
290	4	225	N	N	N					
304	2	150 (net)						H	H	H
304	2	210				H	H			
343	2	235	S	S	S					
343	4	280	Z	Z	Z					
360	2	175 (net)						N	N	N
360	4	195, 220# (net)						P	P	P
360	2	245				N	N			
360	4	290				P	P			
390	4	315		X	X					
390	4	325				X				
390	4	340				Y				
401	4	225 (net)						Z	Z	Z
401	4	330					Z			

With dual exhaust

GENERAL ENGINE SPECIFICATIONS

Year	Engine No. Cyl. Displacement Cu. In.	Carburetor Type	Advertised Horsepower @ rpm ■	Advertised Torque @ rpm (ft lbs) ■	Bore and Stroke (in.)	Advertised Compression Ratio	Oil Pressure @ 2050 rpm
'67	6-199	1 bbl	128 @ 4400	182 @ 1600	3.750 x 3.000	8.5:1	46
	6-232	1 bbl	145 @ 4300	215 @ 1600	3.750 x 3.500	8.5:1	46
	6-232	2 bbl	155 @ 4400	222 @ 1600	3.750 x 3.500	8.5:1	46
	8-290	2 bbl	200 @ 4600	285 @ 2800	3.750 x 3.280	9.0:1	46
	8-290	4 bbl	225 @ 4700	300 @ 3200	3.750 x 3.280	10.0:1	46
	8-343	2 bbl	235 @ 4400	345 @ 2600	4.080 x 3.280	9.0:1	46
	8-343	4 bbl	280 @ 4800	365 @ 3000	4.080 x 3.280	10.2:1	46
'68	6-199	1 bbl	128 @ 4400	182 @ 1600	3.750 x 3.000	8.5:1	46
	6-232	1 bbl	145 @ 4300	215 @ 1600	3.750 x 3.500	8.5:1	46
	6-232	2 bbl	155 @ 4400	222 @ 1600	3.750 x 3.500	8.5:1	46
	8-290	2 bbl	200 @ 4600	285 @ 2800	3.750 x 3.280	9.0:1	46
	8-290	4 bbl	225 @ 4700	300 @ 3200	3.750 x 3.280	10.0:1	46
	8-343	2 bbl	235 @ 4400	345 @ 2600	4.080 x 3.280	9.0:1	46
	8-343	4 bbl	280 @ 4800	365 @ 3000	4.080 x 3.280	10.2:1	46
	8-390	4 bbl	315 @ 4600	425 @ 3200	4.165 x 3.574	10.2:1	46
'69	6-199	1 bbl	128 @ 4400	182 @ 1600	3.750 x 3.000	8.5:1	46
	6-232	1 bbl	145 @ 4300	215 @ 1600	3.750 x 3.500	8.5:1	46
	6-232	2 bbl	155 @ 4400	222 @ 1600	3.750 x 3.500	8.5:1	46
	8-290	2 bbl	200 @ 4600	285 @ 2800	3.750 x 3.280	9.0:1	46
	8-290	4 bbl	225 @ 4700	300 @ 3200	3.750 x 3.280	10.0:1	46
	8-343	2 bbl	235 @ 4400	345 @ 2600	4.080 x 3.280	9.0:1	46
	8-343	4 bbl	280 @ 4800	365 @ 3000	4.080 x 3.280	10.2:1	46
	8-390	4 bbl	315 @ 4600	425 @ 3200	4.165 x 3.754	10.2:1	46
'70	6-199	1 bbl	128 @ 4400	182 @ 1600	3.750 x 3.000	8.5:1	46
	6-232	1 bbl	145 @ 4300	215 @ 1600	3.750 x 3.500	8.5:1	46
	6-232	2 bbl	155 @ 4400	222 @ 1600	3.750 x 3.500	8.5:1	46
	8-304	2 bbl	210 @ 4400	305 @ 2800	3.750 x 3.440	9.0:1	46
	8-360	2 bbl	245 @ 4400	365 @ 2400	4.080 x 3.440	9.0:1	46
	8-360	4 bbl	290 @ 4800	395 @ 3200	4.080 x 3.440	10.0:1	46
	8-390	4 bbl	325 @ 5000	420 @ 3200	4.165 x 3.574	10.0:1	46
	8-390	4 bbl	340 @ 5100	430 @ 3600	4.165 x 3.574	10.0:1	46
'71	6-232	1 bbl	135 @ 4000	210 @ 1600	3.750 x 3.500	8.0:1	46
	6-258	1 bbl	150 @ 3800	240 @ 1800	3.750 x 3.900	8.0:1	46
	8-304	2 bbl	210 @ 4400	300 @ 2600	3.750 x 3.444	8.4:1	46
	8-360	2 bbl	245 @ 4400	365 @ 2600	4.080 x 3.444	8.5:1	46
	8-360	4 bbl	285 @ 4800	330 @ 5000	4.080 x 3.444	8.5:1	46
	8-401	4 bbl	330 @ 5000	430 @ 3400	4.650 x 3.680	9.5:1	46
'72	6-232	1 bbl	100 @ 3600	185 @ 1800	3.750 x 3.500	8.0:1	46
	6-258	1 bbl	110 @ 3500	195 @ 2000	3.750 x 3.900	8.0:1	46
	8-304	2 bbl	150 @ 4200	245 @ 2500	3.750 x 3.440	8.4:1	46
	8-360	2 bbl	175 @ 4000	285 @ 2400	4.080 x 3.440	8.5:1	46
	8-360	4 bbl	195 @ 4400	295 @ 2900	4.080 x 3.440	8.5:1	46
	8-401	4 bbl	255 @ 4600	345 @ 3300	4.165 x 3.680	8.5:1	46

GENERAL ENGINE SPECIFICATIONS

Year	Engine No. Cyl. Displacement Cu. In.	Carburetor Type	Advertised Horsepower @ rpm ■	Advertised Torque @ rpm (ft lbs) ■	Bore and Stroke (in.)	Advertised Compression Ratio	Oil Pressure @ 2050 rpm
'73	6-232	1 bbl	100 @ 3600	185 @ 1800	3.750 x 3.500	8.0:1	46
	6-258	1 bbl	110 @ 3500	195 @ 2000	3.750 x 3.900	8.0:1	46
	8-304	2 bbl	150 @ 4200	245 @ 2500	3.750 x 3.440	8.3:1	46
	8-360	2 bbl	175 @ 4000	285 @ 2400	4.080 x 3.440	8.3:1	46
	8-360	4 bbl	195 @ 4400	295 @ 2900	4.080 x 3.440	8.3:1	46
	8-360①	4 bbl	220 @ 4400	315 @ 3100	4.080 x 3.440	8.3:1	46
	8-401	4 bbl	255 @ 4600	345 @ 3300	4.165 x 3.680	8.5:1	46
'74	6-232	1 bbl	100 @ 3600	185 @ 1800	3.750 x 3.500	8.0:1	46
	6-258	1 bbl	110 @ 3500	195 @ 2000	3.750 x 3.900	8.0:1	46
	8-304	2 bbl	150 @ 4200	245 @ 2500	3.750 x 3.440	8.4:1	46
	8-360	2 bbl	175 @ 4000	285 @ 2400	4.080 x 3.440	8.5:1	46
	8-360	4 bbl	195 @ 4400	295 @ 2900	4.080 x 3.440	8.5:1	46
	8-360①	4 bbl	220 @ 4400	315 @ 3100	4.080 x 3.440	8.5:1	46
	8-401	4 bbl	255 @ 4600	345 @ 3300	4.165 x 3.680	8.5:1	46

■ Beginning 1972, horsepower and torque are SAE net figures. They are measured at the rear of the transmission with all accessories installed and operating. Since the figures vary when a given engine is installed in different models, some are representative rather than exact.

① Dual exhaust

CRANKSHAFT AND CONNECTING ROD SPECIFICATIONS

All measurements are given in in.

Year	Engine No. Cyl.	CRANKSHAFT				CONNECTING ROD		
		Main Brg. Journal Dia	Main Brg. Oil Clearance	Shaft End-Play	Thrust on No.	Journal Diameter	Oil Clearance	Side Clearance
'67-'69	6	2.4986-2.5001	.001-.002	.0015-.007	3	2.0934-2.0955	.001-.002	.008-.010
	8, All	①	.001-.002②	.003-.008	3	③	.001-.002	.009-.015
'70-'74	6	2.4986-2.5001	.001-.002	.0015-.007⑤	3	2.0934-2.0955	.001-.002	.008-.010⑥
	8, All	①	.001-.002②	.003-.008	3	④	.001-.002	.009-.015

① Nos. 1-4—2.7474-2.7489; No. 5—2.7464-2.7479
② Rear main—.002-.003
③ 8-290, 343—2.0934-2.0955; 8-390—2.2471-2.2492
④ 1970 390, All 401—2.2471-2.2485; 304, 360—2.0934-2.0955
⑤ 1972-74—.0015-.0065
⑥ 1972-74—.005-.014

RING GAP

All measurements are given in in.

Year	Engine	Top Compression	Bottom Compression
'67-'74	All engines	.010-.020	.010-.020

Year	Engine	Oil Control
'67-'71	All engines	.015-.055
'72-'74	6-232, 258, 8-304	.010-.025
'72-'74	8-360	.015-.045
'72-'74	8-401	.015-.055

RING SIDE CLEARANCE

All measurements are given in in.

Year	Engine	Top Compression	Bottom Compression
'67-'71	6-199, 232, 258	.0015-.0035	.0015-.0035
'67-'71	8-287, 290, 327, 343, 390, 304, 360, 401	.002-.004	.002-.004
'72-'74	All engines	.0015-.0035	.0015-.0035

Year	Engine	Oil Control
'67-'71	All engines	.000-.005
'72-'74	6-232, 258, 8-304	.001-.008
'72-'74	8-360, 401	.000-.007

Rambler, American, Hornet, Gremlin, Rebel, Ambassador, Matador

TUNE-UP SPECIFICATIONS

When analyzing compression test results, look for uniformity among cylinders rather than specific pressures.

	ENGINE		SPARK PLUGS		DISTRIBUTOR		IGNITION TIMING (deg) ▲		VALVES	Fuel	IDLE SPEED (rpm) ▲	
Year	No. Cyl Displacement (cu in.)	hp	Type §	Gap (in.)	Point Dwell (deg)	Point Gap (in.)	Man Trans ●	Auto Trans	Intake Opens ■ (deg) ●	Pump Pressure (psi)	Man Trans	Auto Trans
'67	6-199	128	N-14Y	.035	33	.016	10B(TDC)	10B(TDC)	12½	4-5½	600	600
	6-232	145	N-14Y	.035	33	.016	5B(TDC)	5B(TDC)	12½	4-5½	600	600
	6-232	155	N-14Y	.035	33	.016	5B(TDC)	5B(TDC)	12½	4-5½	600	600
	8-290	200	N-12Y	.035	30	.016	TDC	TDC	18½	4-5½	600	600
	8-290	225	N-12Y	.035	30	.016	3B	3B	18½	4-5½	600	600
	8-343	235	N-12Y	.035	30	.016	TDC	TDC	18½	4-5½	600	600
	8-343	280	N-12Y	.035	30	.016	TDC	TDC	18½	4-5½	600	600
'68	6-199	128	N-14Y	.035	33	.016	TDC	5B	12½	4-5½	600	525
	6-232	145	N-14Y	.035	33	.016	TDC	TDC①	12½	4-5½	600	525②
	6-232	155	N-14Y	.035	33	.016	TDC	TDC①	12½	4-5½	600	525②
	8-290	200	N-12Y	.035	30	.016	TDC	TDC	18½	4-5½	650	550
	8-290	225	N-12Y	.035	30	.016	TDC	TDC	18½	4-5½	650	550
	8-343	235	N-12Y	.035	30	.016	TDC	TDC	18½	4-5½	650	550
	8-343	280	N-12Y	.035	30	.016	TDC	TDC	18½	4-5½	650	550
	8-390	315	N-12Y	.035	30	.016	TDC	TDC	18½	4-5½	650	550
'69	6-199	128	N-14Y	.035	33	.016	TDC	5B	12½	4-5½	600	525
	6-232	145	N-14Y	.035	33	.016	TDC	TDC①	12½	4-5½	600	525
	6-232	155	N-14Y	.035	33	.016	TDC	TDC①	12½	4-5½	600	525
	8-290	200	N-12Y	.035	30	.016	TDC	TDC	18½	4-5½	650	550
	8-290	225	N-12Y	.035	30	.016	TDC	TDC	18½	4-5½	650	550
	8-343	235	N-12Y	.035	30	.016	TDC	TDC	18½	4-5½	650	550
	8-343	280	N-12Y	.035	30	.016	TDC	TDC	18½	4-5½	650	550
	8-390	315	N-12Y	.035	30	.016	TDC	TDC	18½	4-5½	650	550
'70	6-199	128	N-14Y	.035	33	.016	3B	3B	12½	4-5½	600	550
	6-232	145	N-14Y	.035	33	.016	—	3B	12½	4-5½	—	550
	6-232	155	N-14Y	.035	33	.016	—	3B	12½	4-5½	—	550
	8-304	210	N-12Y	.035	30	.016	—	5B	18½	4-5½	—	600
	8-360	245	N-12Y	.035	30	.016	5B	5B	18½	4-5½	650	600
	8-360	290	N-12Y	.035	30	.016	5B	5B	18½	4-5½	650	600
	8-390	325	N-12Y	.035	30	.016	5B	5B	18½	4-5½	650	600
	8-390	340	N-12Y	.035	30	.016	5B	5B	18½	4-5½	650	600
'71	6-232	135	N-12Y	.035	33	.016	3B	5B	12½	4-5½	700	600
	6-258	150	N-12Y	.035	33	.016	5B	5B	12½	4-5½	700	600
	8-304	210	N-12Y	.035	30	.016	2½B	2½B	14¾	4-5½	750	650
	8-360	245	N-12Y	.035	30	.016	2½B	2½B	14¾	4-5½	750	650
	8-360	285	N-12Y	.035	30	.016	2½B	2½B	14¾	4-5½	750	650
	8-401	330	N-12Y	.035	30	.016	2½B	2½B	25½	4-5½	750	650
'72	6-232	100	N-12Y	.035	33	.016	5B(3B)	5B(3B)	12	4-5½	600(700)	550(600)
	6-258	110	N-12Y	.035	33	.016	5B(3B)	5B(3B)	12	4-5½	600(700)	550(600)
	8-304	150	N-12Y	.035	30	.016	5B	5B	14¾	4-5½	750	650(700)
	8-360	175	N-12Y	.035	30	.016	5B	5B	14¾	4-5½	750	700
	8-360	195	N-12Y	.035	30	.016	5B	5B	14¾	4-5½	750	700
	8-401	255	N-12Y	.035	30	.016	5B	5B	25½	4-5½	750	650(700)

Rambler, American, Hornet, Gremlin, Rebel, Ambassador, Matador

TUNE-UP SPECIFICATIONS

When analyzing compression test results, look for uniformity among cylinders rather than specific pressures.

ENGINE			SPARK PLUGS		DISTRIBUTOR		IGNITION TIMING (deg) ▲ ●		VALVES	Fuel	IDLE SPEED (rpm) ▲	
Year	No. Cyl Displacement (cu in.)	hp	Type §	Gap (in.)	Point Dwell (deg)	Point Gap (in.)	Man Trans	Auto Trans	Intake Opens ■ (deg) ●	Pump Pressure (psi)	Man Trans	Auto Trans
'73	6-232	100	N-12Y	.035	33	.016	5B(3B)	5B(3B)	12	4-5½	700	600
	6-258	110	N-12Y	.035	33	.016	5B(3B)	5B(3B)	12	4-5½	700	600
	8-304	150	N-12Y	.035	30	.016	5B	5B	14¾	4-5½	750	700
	8-360	175	N-12Y	.035	30	.016	5B	5B	14¾	4-5½	750	700
	8-360	195	N-12Y	.035	30	.016	5B	5B	14¾	4-5½	750	700
	8-401	255	N-12Y	.035	30	.016	5B	5B	25½	4-5½	750	700
'74	6-232	100	N-12Y	.035	33	.016	5B(3B)	5B(3B)	12	4-5½	700	600
	6-258	110	N-12Y	.035	33	.016	5B(3B)	5B(3B)	12	4-5½	700	600
	8-304	150	N-12Y	.035	30	.016	5B	5B	14¾	4-5½	750	700
	8-360	175	N-12Y	.035	30	.016	5B	5B	14¾	4-5½	750	700
	8-360	195	N-12Y	.035	30	.016	5B	5B	14¾	4-5½	750	700
	8-401	255	N-12Y	.035	30	.016	5B	5B	25½	4-5½	750	700

▲ See text for procedure
● Figure in parentheses indicates California engine
■ All figures Before Top Dead Center
§ All spark plug listings are Champion original equipment numbers
① For Rogue model, figure is 5 degrees Before Top Dead Center Center
② Set in Neutral
B Before Top Dead Center
TDC Top Dead Center
— Not applicable

AMX-Javelin

TUNE-UP SPECIFICATIONS

When analyzing compression test results, look for uniformity among cylinders rather than specific pressures.

ENGINE			SPARK PLUGS		DISTRIBUTOR		IGNITION TIMING (deg) ▲		VALVES	Fuel	IDLE SPEED (rpm) ▲	
Year	No. Cyl Displacement (cu in.)	hp	Type §	Gap (in.)	Point Dwell (deg)	Point Gap (in.)	Man Trans	Auto Trans	Intake Opens ■ (deg) ●	Pump Pressure (psi)	Man Trans	Auto Trans
'68	6-232	145	N-14Y	.035	31-34	.016	TDC	TDC	12½	4-5½	600	525
	8-290	200	N-12Y	.035	29-31	.016	TDC	TDC	18½	4-5½	650	550
	8-290	225	N-12Y	.035	29-31	.016	TDC	TDC	18½	4-5½	650	550
	8-343	280	N-12Y	.035	29-31	.016	TDC	TDC	18½	5-6½	650	550
	8-390	315	N-12Y	.035	29-31	.016	TDC	TDC	18½	5-6½	650	550
'69	6-232	145	N-14Y	.035	31-34	.016	TDC	TDC	12½	4-5½	600	525
	8-290	200	N-12Y	.035	29-31	.016	TDC	TDC	18½	5-6½	650	550
	8-290	225	N-12Y	.035	29-31	.016	TDC	TDC	18½	5-6½	650	550
	8-343	280	N-12Y	.035	29-31	.016	TDC	TDC	18½	5-6½	650	550
	8-390	315	N-12Y	.035	29-31	.016	TDC	TDC	18½	5-6½	650	550
'70	6-232	145	N-14Y	.035	31-34	.016	3B	3B	12½	4-5½	600	550
	8-304	210	N-12Y	.035	29-31	.016	5B	5B	18½	5-6½	650	600
	8-360	245	N-12Y	.035	29-31	.016	5B	5B	18½	5-6½	650	600
	8-360	290	N-12Y	.035	29-31	.016	5B	5B	18½	5-6½	650	600
	8-390	325	N-12Y	.035	29-31	.016	TDC①	TDC①	18½	5-6½	650	600

AMX-Javelin

TUNE-UP SPECIFICATIONS

When analyzing compression test results, look for uniformity among cylinders rather than specific pressures.

Year	ENGINE No. Cyl Displacement (cu in.)	ENGINE hp	SPARK PLUGS Type §	SPARK PLUGS Gap (in.)	DISTRIBUTOR Point Dwell (deg)	DISTRIBUTOR Point Gap (in.)	IGNITION TIMING (deg) ▲ Man Trans	IGNITION TIMING (deg) ▲ Auto Trans	VALVES Intake Opens ■ (deg) ●	Fuel Pump Pressure (psi)	IDLE SPEED (rpm) ▲ Man Trans	IDLE SPEED (rpm) ▲ Auto Trans
'71	6-232	135	N-12Y	.035	31-34	.016	3B	5B	12½	4-5½	700	600
	6-258	150	N-12Y	.035	31-34	.016	—	5B	12½	4-5½	—	600
	8-304	210	N-12Y	.035	29-31	.016	2½B	2½B	14¾	5-6½	750	650
	8-360	245	N-12Y	.035	29-31	.016	2½B	2½B	14¾	5-6½	750	650
	8-360	285	N-12Y	.035	29-31	.016	2½B	2½B	14¾	5-6½	750	650
	8-401	330	N-12Y	.035	29-31	.016	2½B	2½B	25½	5-6½	750	650
'72	6-232	100	N-12Y	.035	31-34	.016	5B	5B	12½	4-5½	600(700)	550(600)
	6-258	110	N-12Y	.035	31-34	.016	—	3B	12½	4-5½	—	550(600)
	8-304	150	N-12Y	.035	29-31	.016	5B	5B	14¾	5-6½	750	650(700)
	8-360	175	N-12Y	.035	29-31	.016	—	5B	14¾	5-6½	—	700
	8-360	195	N-12Y	.035	29-31	.016	5B	5B	14¾	5-6½	750	700
	8-401	255	N-12Y	.035	29-31	.016	5B	5B	25½	5-6½	750	650(700)
'73	6-232	100	N-12Y	.035	31-34	.016	5B	5B	12½	4-5½	700	600
	6-258	110	N-12Y	.035	31-34	.016	—	3B	12½	4-5½	—	600
	8-304	150	N-12Y	.035	29-31	.016	5B	5B	14¾	5-6½	750	700
	8-360	175	N-12Y	.035	29-31	.016	—	5B	14¾	5-6½	—	700
	8-360	190	N-12Y	.035	29-31	.016	5B	5B	14¾	5-6½	750	700
	8-401	255	N-12Y	.035	29-31	.016	5B	5B	25½	5-6½	750	700
'74	6-232	100	N-12Y	.035	31-34	.016	5B	5B	12½	4-5½	600(700)	550(600)
	6-258	110	N-12Y	.035	31-34	.016	—	3B	12½	4-5½	—	550(600)
	8-304	150	N-12Y	.035	29-31	.016	5B	5B	14¾	5-6½	750	650(700)
	8-360	175	N-12Y	.035	29-31	.016	—	5B	14¾	5-6½	—	700
	8-360	220	N-12Y	.035	29-31	.016	5B	5B	14¾	5-6½	750	700
	8-401	255	N-12Y	.035	29-31	.016	5B	5B	25½	5-6½	750	650(700)

▲ See text for procedure
■ All figures Before Top Dead Center
● Figure in parentheses indicates California engine
§ All spark plug listings are Champion original equipment numbers

① For vehicles prior to engine code No. 209X26, adjust ignition timing to 5 degrees Before Top Dead Center
B Before Top Dead Center
TDC Top Dead Center
— Not applicable

WHEEL ALIGNMENT SPECIFICATIONS

Year	Model	CASTER Range (deg)	CASTER Pref Setting (deg)	CAMBER Range (deg)	CAMBER Pref Setting (deg)	Toe-in (in.)	Steering Axis Inclin.	WHEEL PIVOT RATIO (deg) Inner Wheel	WHEEL PIVOT RATIO (deg) Wheel Outer
'67-'68	American, Javelin, AMX	½N to ½P▲	0	3/8N to 3/8P	0	1/16 to 3/16	6½	25	25
	Rebel	½N to ½P▲	0	3/8N to 3/8P	0	1/16 to 3/16	6½	25	25
	Marlin	½N to ½P▲	0	3/8N to 3/8P	0	1/16 to 3/16	6⅛	25	25
	Ambassador	½N to ½P▲	0	3/8N to 3/8P	0	1/16 to 3/16	6⅛	25	25
'69	Series 01, 30, 70	½N to ½P▲	0	3/8N to 3/8P	0	1/16 to 3/16	6½	25	22
	Series 10, 80	0 to 1N	½N	3/8N to 3/8P	0	1/16 to 3/16	6½	25	22
'70-'71	All Series	½P to 1½P	1P	3/8N to 3/8P	0	1/16 to 3/16	7¾	25	22
'72-'74	All Series	½P to 1½P	1P③	①	②	1/16 to 3/16	7¾	25	22

▲ With power steering ½P to 1½P
① Left: ⅛P to ⅝P; Right: 0 to ½P
② Left ⅜P; Right: ⅛P
③ 1973 01-40 Series—0 deg.
N Negative P Positive
PS Power steering

01 American/Hornet
10 Classic/Rebel/Matador
30 AMX
40 Gremlin
70 Javelin
80 Ambassador

CAPACITIES

Year	ENGINE No. Cyl. (Cu. In.) Displacement	Engine Crankcase Add 1 Qt For New Filter	TRANSMISSION Pts To Refill After Draining Manual 3-Speed	Manual 4-Speed	Automatic	Drive Axle (pts)	Gasoline Tank (gals)	COOLING SYSTEM (qts) With Heater	With A/C
'67	6-199	4	1.5	—	18	3	See	10.5	10.5
	6-232	4	1.5	—	18	4②	chart	10.5	10.5
	8-290	4	2.5	3.5	18	4		14	14
	8-343	4	—	3.5	20	4		13	13
'68	6-199	4	1.5	—	18	3		10.5	10.5
	6-232	4	1.5①	—	18	3		10.5	10.5
	8-290	4	3	3.5	18	4		14	14
	8-343	4	—	3.5	20	4		13	13
	8-390	4	—	3.5	20	4		13	13
'69	6-199	4	1.5	—	18.5	3		10.5	10.5
	6-232	4	1.5①	—	18.5	3		10.5	10.5
	8-290	4	3	2.5	18.5	4		14	14
	8-343	4	—	2.5	20	4		13	13
	8-390	4	—	2.5	20	4		13	13
'70	6-199	4	1.5	—	18.5	3		10.5	10.5
	6-232	4	1.5①	—	18.5	3		10.5	10.5
	8-304	4	3	2.5	18.5	4		14	14
	8-360	4	—	2.5	20	4		13	13
	8-390	4	—	2.5	20	4		13	13
'71	6-232	4	1.5①	—	18.5	3③		10.5	10.5
	6-258	4	2.5	—	18.5	3③		10.5	10.5
	8-304	4	2.5	2.5	18.5	4		14	14
	8-360	4	3	2.5	20	4		13	13
	8-401	4	—	2.5	20	4		13	13
'72	6-232	4	1.5①	—	17	3③		10.5	10.5
	6-258	4	2.5	—	17	3③		10.5	10.5
	8-304	4	2.5	2.5	17	4		14	14
	8-360	4	2.5	2.5	19	4		13	13
	8-401	4	2.5	2.5	19	4		13	13
'73	6-232	4	2.5	—	17	3③		10.5	10.5
	6-258	4	2.5	—	17	3③		10.5	10.5
	8-304	4	2.5	2.5	17	4		14	14
	8-360	4	2.5	2.5	19	4		13	14
	8-401	4	2.5	2.5	19	4		13	14
'74	6-232	4	2.5	—	17	3③		10.5	10.5
	6-258	4	2.5	—	17	3③		10.5	10.5
	8-304	4	2.5	2.5	17	4		14	14
	8-360	4	2.5	2.5	19	4		13	14
	8-401	4	2.5	2.5	19	4		13	14

① Fully synchronized transmission 2.25 pts
② American—3 pts
③ 8.875 ring gear—4 pts
— Not applicable

GASOLINE TANK CAPACITIES (gals)

Model	'67	'68	'69	'70	'71	'72	'73	'74
Ambassador	21.5	21.5	21.5	21.5	19.5	19.5	19.5	24.9
American	16	16	16					
AMX		19	19	19				
Javelin		19	19	19	16	16	16	16
Rebel	21.5	21.5	21.5	21.5				
Rambler		16	16	16				
Gremlin					21	21	21	21
Hornet					16	16	16	16
Matador					19.5	19.5	19.5	24.9
Classic								
Marlin	21.5							
3 seat wagons:	'67 to '70—19, '71—17, '72—20, '73—20, '74—20							

PISTON CLEARANCE

Year	Engine	Piston-to-Bore Clearance (in.)
'67	6-199, 232	.0003-.0009
	V8-290, 343	.0012-.0020
'68-'69	6-199, 232	.0005-.0013
	V8-290, 390①	.0010-.0018
	V8-343	.0012-.0020
'70	6-199, 232	.0005-.0013
	V8-304, 390	.0010-.0018
	V8-360	.0012-.0020
'71	6-232, 258	.0005-.0013
	V8-304, 401	.0010-.0018
	V8-360	.0012-.0020
72-'74	6-232, 258	.0009-.0017
	V8-304, 401	.0010-.0018
	V8-360	.0012-.0020

① 390 cu in. engine—1969 only

ALTERNATOR AND REGULATOR SPECIFICATIONS

	ALTERNATOR			REGULATOR						
					Field Relay			Regulator		
Year	Part No. or Manufacturer	Field Current @ 12 V	Output (amps)	Part No. or Manufacturer	Air Gap (in.)	Point Gap (in.)	Volts to Close	Air Gap (in.)	Point Gap (in.)	Volts @ 75°
'67-'68	ALE6305(6)	2.3-2.4	40	R2AM1	Not adjustable, sealed at factory					
	ALK6310	2.4-2.5	35	VSC-62436	Not adjustable, sealed at factory					
	A12NAM453	2.0-2.6	35	R2AM1	Not adjustable, sealed at factory					
	ALK6309	2.4-2.5	35	VSC-62436	Not adjustable, sealed at factory					
	A12NAM552	1.8-2.4	40	R2AM1	Not adjustable, sealed at factory					
	A12NAM455	2.0-2.6	35	R2AM1	Not adjustable, sealed at factory					
	ALK6311(0)	2.4-2.5	35	VSC-6234L	Not adjustable, sealed at factory					
	A12NAM553	1.8-2.4	40	R2AM1	Not adjustable, sealed at factory					
'69-'70	3195534(5)	2.4-2.5	35	3195003	Not adjustable, sealed at factory					
	A12NAM456(7)	2.0-2.6	35	R2AM4	Not adjustable, sealed at factory					
	A12NAM606(2)	1.8-2.4	55	R2AM4	Not adjustable, sealed at factory					
'71	6-70D44186C01①	2.4-2.5	35	8RB2005	Not adjustable, sealed at factory					
	8-70D44187C01①	2.0-2.6	35	8RB2005	Not adjustable, sealed at factory					
	6-70D44188C01② 8-70D44189C01	1.8-2.4	55	8RB2005	Not adjustable, sealed at factory					
'72-'74	8AL2025F	1.8-2.4	37	8RB2005	Not adjustable, sealed at factory					
	8AL2026F③	1.8-2.4	55	8RB2005	Not adjustable, sealed at factory					

① C02 for Matador
② Std. with A/C or rear defogger.
③ Std. All Ambassadors, A/C, rear defogger or "Command-Air"

TORQUE SPECIFICATIONS

All readings in ft lbs

Year	Engine No. Cyl.	Cylinder Head Bolts	Rod Bearing Bolts	Main Bearing Bolts	Crankshaft Pulley Bolt	Flywheel to Crankshaft Bolts	MANIFOLD Intake	MANIFOLD Exhaust
'67-'74	6-All	80⑤	26-30	75-85	50-60	100-110	20-25	20-25
	8-All	①	②	95-105	20-25③	100-110	40-45	30-35

① To 1969—90-100; 1970-73—105-115
② 290, 304, 343, 360—26-30; 390, 401—35-40
③ Pulley-to-damper bolts
④ No. 5 (rear main 55 ft. lbs.)
⑤ 1973-74—105 ft. lbs.

BRAKE SPECIFICATIONS

All measurements given in in.

Year	Model	Master Cylinder Disc	Master Cylinder Drum	Wheel Cylinder Front Disc	Wheel Cylinder Front Drum	Wheel Cylinder Rear	Brake Disc or Drum Diameter Front Disc	Brake Disc or Drum Diameter Front Drum	Brake Disc or Drum Diameter Rear
'67-'69	American, Rebel	1.0	1.0	2.00	1.12②	.94④	11.19	9.0	9.0①③
	Rebel (Wag.)	1.0	1.0	2.00	1.09②	.94	11.19	10.0	10.0
	Marlin-6	1.0	1.0	2.00	1.12	.94⑥	11.19	10.0	10.0
	Marlin-8	1.0	1.0	2.00	1.19	.94⑥	11.19	10.0	10.0
	Ambassador	1.0	1.0	2.00	1.12②	.94⑥	11.19	10.0	10.0
	Javelin	1.0	1.0	2.00	1.19②	.94⑤	11.19	10.0	10.0
	AMX	1.0	—	2.00	—	.88	11.19	—	10.0
'70	Hornet	1.0	1.0	2.00	1.12②	.94	11.19	9.0①	9.0①
	Gremlin	—	1.0	—	1.12	.88	—	9.0	9.0
	Rebel	1.0	1.0	2.00	1.12②	.94⑤	11.19	10.0	10.0
	Rebel (Wag.)	1.0	1.0	2.00	1.09②	.94	11.19	10.0	10.0
	Ambassador	1.0	1.0	2.00	1.12②	.94⑥	11.19	10.0	10.0
	Ambassador (Wag.)	1.0	1.0	2.00	1.19	.94	11.19	10.0	10.0
	Javelin	1.0	1.0	2.00	1.19	.94⑤	11.19	10.0	10.0
	AMX	1.0	—	2.00	—	.88	11.19	—	10.0
'71-'74	Hornet, Gremlin-6	⑦	1.0	2.75	1.12	.88⑪	11.00	9.0	9.0③
	Hornet, Gremlin-8	⑦	1.0	2.75	1.19	.88	11.00	10.0	10.0
	Matador⑫	⑦	1.0	2.75	1.09⑧	.94⑩	11.00	10.0	10.0
	Ambassador	⑦	1.0	2.75	1.19	.94⑩	11.00	10.0	10.0
	Javelin-6	⑦	1.0	2.75	1.12	.88⑨	11.00	9.0	9.0③
	Javelin, AMX-8	⑦	1.0	2.75	1.19	.88⑨	11.00	10.0	10.0

① 10 in. with V8
② 1.19 in. with V8
③ With disc brakes 10 in.
④ 0.91 in. with V8
⑤ 6 cyl disc brakes 1 in.
⑥ Disc brakes 1.12 in.
⑦ Optional disc brakes on Hornet, Gremlin, Javelin, Matador and Ambassador: Hornet, Gremlin, Javelin—1.063 in. man./1.000 in. power; Matador, Ambassador—1.125 in. power (no man.). Starting in 1973, power disc brakes became standard on Ambassador and Javelin.
⑧ 6 cyl std. models; V8 models use 1.19 in. bores
⑨ 0.94 in. rear bores with front discs
⑩ 1.00 in rear bores on wagons with disc brakes
⑪ Gremlin-6: 0.81 in.
⑫ Disc brakes standard on 1974 Matador coupe.
Wag. Station wagon
Man. Manual
Std. Standard
— Not applicable

BATTERY AND STARTER SPECIFICATIONS

Year	Engine No. Cyl. Displacement (cu in.)	Battery Ampere Hour Capacity	Battery Volts	Battery Terminal Grounded	Starter Lock Test Amps	Starter Lock Test Volts	Starter Lock Test Torque (ft lbs)	Starter No-Load Test Amps	Starter No-Load Test Volts	Starter No-Load Test RPM	Brush Spring Tension (oz)
'67-'69	6	50	12	Neg.	290	4.3	6.5	63	10.6	7,850	35
	8	60	12	Neg.	500	4.5	9	70	12	9,500	40
	8 (opt.)	70	12	Neg.	500	4.5	10	70	12	9,500	40
'70-'74	6, 8-304	50	12	Neg.	600①	3.4	13	65	12	9,250	40
	8-360, 401	60	12	Neg.	600①	3.4	13	65	12	9,250	40
	All (opt.)	70	12	Neg.	600①	3.4	13	65	12	9,250	40

① 1970—500 @ 4.5

VALVE SPECIFICATIONS

Year	Engine No. Cyl. Displacement (cu in.)	Seat Angle (deg) ■	Face Angle (deg) ●	Spring Test Pressure (lbs @ in.)	Spring Installed Height (in.)	STEM TO GUIDE Clearance (in.) Intake	Exhaust	STEM Diameter (in.) Intake	Exhaust
'67	6-199	45	44	155 @ 1.44	1 13/16	.0010-.0030	.0010-.0030	.3720	.3720
	6-232	45	44	155 @ 1.44	1 13/16	.0010-.0030	.0010-.0030	.3720	.3720
	8-290	45	44	195 @ 1.41	1 13/16	.0010-.0030	.0010-.0030	.3720	.3720
	8-343	45	44	195 @ 1.41	1 13/16	.0010-.0030	.0010-.0030	.3720	.3720
'68	6-199	45	44	195 @ 1.44	1 13/16	.0010-.0030	.0010-.0030	.3720	.3720
	6-232	45	44	195 @ 1.44	1 13/16	.0010-.0030	.0010-.0030	.3720	.3720
	8-290	45	44	195 @ 1.41	1 13/16	.0010-.0030	.0010-.0030	.3720	.3720
	8-343	45	44	195 @ 1.41	1 13/16	.0010-.0030	.0010-.0030	.3720	.3720
	8-390	45	44	195 @ 1.41	1 13/16	.0010-.0030	.0010-.0030	.3720	.3720
'69	6-199	44	44	195 @ 1.44	1 13/16	.0010-.0030	.0010-.0030	.3720	.3720
	6-232	44	44	195 @ 1.44	1 13/16	.0010-.0030	.0010-.0030	.3720	.3720
	8-290	45	44.5	200 @ 1.39	1 13/16	.0010-.0030	.0010-.0030	.3720	.3720
	8-343	45	44.5	200 @ 1.39	1 13/16	.0010-.0030	.0010-.0030	.3720	.3720
	8-390	45	44.5	200 @ 1.39	1 13/16	.0010-.0030	.0010-.0030	.3720	.3720
'70	6-199	44	44	195 @ 1.44	1 13/16	.0010-.0030	.0010-.0030	.3720	.3720
	6-232	44	44	195 @ 1.44	1 13/16	.0010-.0030	.0010-.0030	.3720	.3720
	8-304	45	44.5	200 @ 1.39	1 13/16	.0010-.0030	.0010-.0030	.3720	.3720
	8-360	45	44.5	200 @ 1.39	1 13/16	.0010-.0030	.0010-.0030	.3720	.3720
	8-390	45	44.5	200 @ 1.39	1 13/16	.0010-.0030	.0010-.0030	.3720	.3720
	8-390①	45	44.5	189 @ 1.39	1 13/16	.0010-.0030	.0010-.0030	.3720	.3720
'71	6-232	44.5	44	195 @ 1.44	1 13/16	.0010-.0030	.0010-.0030	.3720	.3720
	6-258	44.5	44	195 @ 1.44	1 13/16	.0010-.0030	.0010-.0030	.3720	.3720
	8-304	45	44.5	189 @ 1.39	1 13/16	.0010-.0030	.0010-.0030	.3720	.3720
	8-360	45	44.5	189 @ 1.39	1 13/16	.0010-.0030	.0010-.0030	.3720	.3720
	8-401	45	44.5	189 @ 1.39	1 13/16	.0010-.0030	.0010-.0030	.3720	.3720
'72	6-232	44.5	44	195 @ 1.44	1 13/16	.0010-.0030	.0010-.0030	.3720	.3720
	6-258	44.5	44	195 @ 1.44	1 13/16	.0010-.0030	.0010-.0030	.3720	.3720
	8-304	45	44.5	218 @ 1.39	1 13/16	.0010-.0030	.0010-.0030	.3720	.3720
	8-360	45	44.5	218 @ 1.39	1 13/16	.0010-.0030	.0010-.0030	.3720	.3720
	8-401	45	44.5	218 @ 1.39	1 13/16	.0010-.0030	.0010-.0030	.3720	.3720
'73	6-232	44.5	44	195 @ 1.44	1 13/16	.0010-.0030	.0010-.0030	.3720	.3720
	6-258	44.5	44	195 @ 1.44	1 13/16	.0010-.0030	.0010-.0030	.3720	.3720
	8-304	44.5	44	218 @ 1.39	1 13/16	.0010-.0030	.0010-.0030	.3720	.3720
	8-360	44.5	44	218 @ 1.39	1 13/16	.0010-.0030	.0010-.0030	.3720	.3720
	8-401	44.5	44	218 @ 1.39	1 13/16	.0010-.0030	.0010-.0030	.3720	.3720
'74	6-232	44.5	44	195 @ 1.44	1 13/16	.0010-.0030	.0010-.0030	.3720	.3720
	6-258	44.5	44	195 @ 1.44	1 13/16	.0010-.0030	.0010-.0030	.3720	.3720
	8-304	45	44.5	218 @ 1.39	1 13/16	.0010-.0030	.0010-.0030	.3720	.3720
	8-360	45	44.5	218 @ 1.39	1 13/16	.0010-.0030	.0010-.0030	.3720	.3720
	8-401	45	44.5	218 @ 1.39	1 13/16	.0010-.0030	.0010-.0030	.3720	.3720

■ Exhaust valve face angles are shown
All intake valve seat angles are 30°

● Exhaust valve seat angles are shown
All intake valve face angles are 29°

① Rebel

CHARGING SYSTEM

General information on generator and regulator repair and troubleshooting can be found in the Unit Repair Section.

Regulator Removal

Disconnect plug to the regulator. Remove the metal screws which hold the regulator to the sheet metal and lift off the regulator.

Alternator R & R

1. Disconnect battery cables.
2. Disconnect alternator wires or plug, then loosen adjusting bolt.
3. Remove V-belt, mounting bolts and alternator.
4. To install, reverse removal procedure. V8 brackets have a hole to use as a tensioner bar fulcrum.

Alternator Precautions

Caution Since the alternator and regulator are designed for use on only one polarity system, the following precautions must be observed:

1. The polarity of the battery, generator and regulator must be matched and considered before making any electrical connections in the system.
2. When connecting a booster battery, be sure to connect the negative battery terminals respectively and the positive battery terminals respectively.
3. When connecting a charger to the battery, connect the charger positive lead to the battery positive terminal. Connect the charger negative lead to the battery negative terminal.
4. Never operate the alternator on open circuit. Be sure that all connections in the circuit are clean and tight.
5. Do not short across or ground any of the terminals on the alternator regulator.
6. Do not attempt to polarize the alternator.
7. Do not use test lamps of more than 12 volts for checking diode continuity.
8. Avoid long soldering times when replacing diodes or transistors. Prolonged heat is damaging to these units.
9. Disconnect the battery ground terminal when servicing any AC system. This will prevent the possibility of accidental reversing of polarity.
10. If electronic welding equipment is used on the car, be sure to completely disconnect the alternator.

STARTING SYSTEM

American Motors cars made between 1967-74 are equipped with two different types of starter motors. 1967-68 sixes have a starter motor that uses an enclosed shift lever with an overriding clutch drive. The solenoid is attached to the drive end housing.

The second type of starter motor, which is used on V8 engines in 1967–68 and on all engines from 1969 onward, has an integral positive engagement drive and a separate starter relay.

Starter repair procedures can be found in the Unit Repair Section.

Starter Removal

6 Cylinder

Remove the oil filler pipe, disconnect the battery lead from the starter and the solenoid lead from the starter. From underneath the vehicle, remove the bolts which hold the starter to the bell housing and lift off the starter.

V8

Disconnect the battery wire and the solenoid wire at the starter. From underneath the vehicle, remove the bolts which hold the starter to the flywheel housing and lift off the starter.

IGNITION SYSTEM

On all cars with emission control systems, the distributor uses a cam lubricator. The lubricator should be rotated one-half turn every 12,000 miles and replaced at 24,000 mile intervals. Never oil the lubricator; always replace it at the proper interval. It is a good idea, however, to apply a small amount of high-melting-point lubricant to the breaker cam itself, when the points are replaced.

A transmission-controlled spark (TCS) is used on 1971–72 models equipped with 304 and 360 cu in. V8 engines, with automatic transmissions and on all cars sold in California. In 1973-74, it is used on all cars, except those with 401 cu in. engines. For details of this system, see the section on emission controls.

Distributor Removal

6-Cylinder Models

The distributor is mounted on the side of the engine. Remove the distributor cap and mark the position of the rotor relative to the distributor body, then mark the distributor body relative to the block. Remove the distributor hold-down screw, disconnect the ignition primary wire and the vacuum advance tube. Lift the distributor out of the block.

V8 Models

1. Remove the distributor cap, mark the position of the rotor relative to the distributor body and mark the body relative to the block. Remove the carburetor air cleaner, the distributor primary wire and the distributor vacuum lines.
2. Remove the hold-down bolt and take the distributor up out of the block.

The rotor and body are marked so that they can be returned to the position from which they were removed. Do not turn the engine after the distributor has been taken off.

Distributor Installation

Engine Not Disturbed—Timing Retained

Install the distributor in the re-

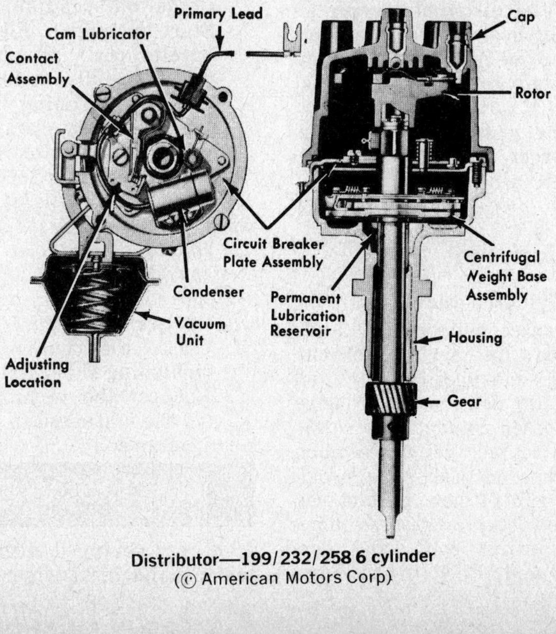
Primary Lead
Cam Lubricator
Contact Assembly
Cap
Rotor
Circuit Breaker Plate Assembly
Centrifugal Weight Base Assembly
Condenser
Permanent Lubrication Reservoir
Vacuum Unit
Housing
Adjusting Location
Gear

Distributor—199/232/258 6 cylinder
(© American Motors Corp)

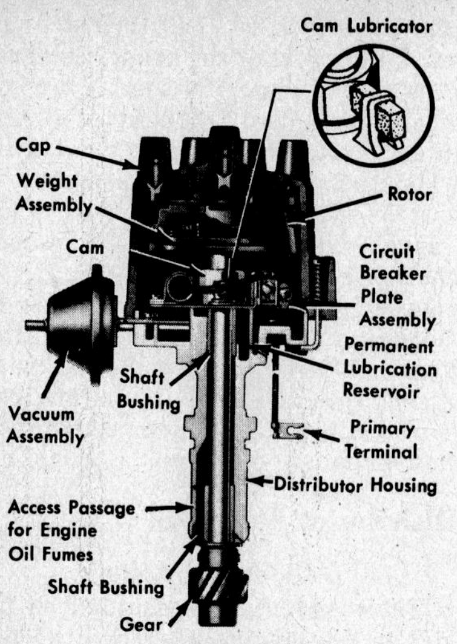
Cam Lubricator
Cap
Weight Assembly
Rotor
Cam
Circuit Breaker Plate Assembly
Permanent Lubrication Reservoir
Shaft Bushing
Vacuum Assembly
Primary Terminal
Distributor Housing
Access Passage for Engine Oil Fumes
Shaft Bushing
Gear

Distributor—all V8
(© American Motors Corp)

verse order of removal. Be sure that the rotor and distributor are installed with the marks, which were made during removal, in alignment. Adjust the timing as required.

Engine Disturbed—Timing Lost

If the rotor position was not noted during removal, or if the engine was cranked with the distributor out, install it as follows:

1. Remove the spark plug from the no. one cylinder and position a compression gauge or a thumb over the spark plug hole.
2. Slowly crank the engine, until compression pressure starts to build up.
3. Continue cranking the engine so that the timing mark or pointer aligns with the TDC mark.

Caution The timing and TDC marks will also align with the no. six cylinder on its exhaust stroke. Hence, it is important that the no. one cylinder is in its compression stroke when the distributor is installed.

4. Install the distributor with its drive meshed, so that the rotor points to the no. one terminal on the distributor with engine at TDC.
5. Complete installation in the reverse order of removal and adjust the timing as required.

Point Replacement

6-Cylinder Models

The condenser and primary leads are retained by spring tension. Remove the distributor rotor and cap, release the tension and remove the leads. Loosen contact base screw and remove contact point assembly. Install a new condenser, set approximate point gap of new contact set, lubricate cam lobes or reverse lubricator and install rotor and cap. Check dwell and adjust if necessary.

V8 Models

Remove the distributor cap, condenser and primary leads which are attached to the nylon terminal. Loosen the two base screws and remove points. When installing points, make sure pilot hole is properly positioned over hole in breaker plate. Install new condenser, then attach primary and condenser leads to nylon terminal. Reverse lubricator and check that terminal leads will not touch rotor. Install rotor, making sure round and square holes are lined up with their respective dowels. Adjust point dwell to specification by turning Allen screw on point set through window in side of cap.

Ignition Timing

A scale located on the timing chain cover and a notch milled into the vibration damper are used as references to set ignition timing.

1967

1. Set the engine idle to the proper specification.
2. Connect a timing light in accordance with the manufacturer's instructions.
3. Loosen the distributor clamp and rotate the distributor to adjust the timing to the proper setting.
4. After tightening the distributor, check the timing again to be sure that it still falls within specification.

1968-74

1. On the 1970-74 models, disconnect the vacuum hose(s), at the distributor vacuum unit on six-cylinder engines, or at the carburetor on V8 engines. Plug the vacuum return line to prevent leakage.
2. Connect a timing light and a tachometer in accordance with the manufacturer's instructions. If the timing light has an advance control, be sure that it is in the "off" position.
3. Start the engine. Adjust the carburetor curb idle screw so that the engine idles at 500 rpm.
4. Adjust the timing by loosening the distributor clamp and rotating the distributor. Set the timing to the proper specification.

NOTE: A white paint mark is applied to the scale for the specified, initial timing setting. Do not mistake this mark for TDC. Serious engine damage could result, as the engine will run overadvanced, if this is done.

5. Check the timing again after tightening the distributor clamp.
6. Connect the vacuum hoses and set the idle speed to normal specifications.

FUEL SYSTEM

On cars equipped with vacuum-operated windshield wipers (1967-71), a double-action, vacuum booster fuel pump is used. If the car is equipped with an electric wiper motor, a conventional single-action fuel pump is fitted.

Emission controls are covered in the selections which deal with them, except when their service is part of the carburetor adjustment. In this case, their adjustment is covered in this section.

Fuel Pump R & R

Disconnect both gas lines from the fuel pump, disconnect the vacuum line, if it is a vacuum pump. Remove the two bolts which hold it to the block and lift off the pump.

Installation is the reverse of removal.

Fuel Filter R & R

Up to 1969, fuel filters are located on the fuel pump inside a bowl. The bowl is attached either to the side or the bottom of the pump, and the element can be replaced (12,000 miles) by unscrewing the bail wire and removing the cartridge.

Starting 1969, an inline fuel filter is located in the carburetor inlet. To change these filters (24,000 miles), unscrew the gas line at the carburetor, remove the element and install a new element. Do not try to clean these elements.

In 1970, the inline filter was changed to a 15 micron paper element unit. The filter assembly is located in the carburetor fuel intake line and secured to it by means of clamps and two short lengths of rubber hose. It should be replaced every 12,000 miles on 1970-72 models or every 15,000 miles, starting in 1973.

Carburetor Adjustments

1967—Except 232 Six

Adjust with air cleaner installed.

1. Connect a tachometer to the engine.
2. On 2-BBL. and 4-BBL. carburetors, gently seat both mixture screws, then back out exactly one turn.

NOTE: all adjustments of dual mixture screws must be made equally.

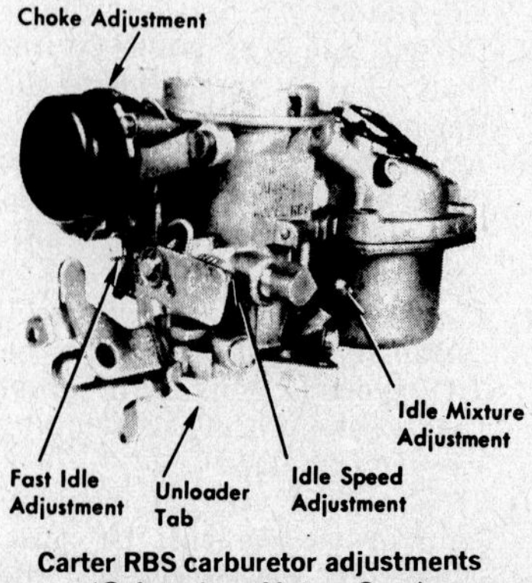
Choke Adjustment
Idle Mixture Adjustment
Fast Idle Adjustment
Unloader Tab
Idle Speed Adjustment

Carter RBS carburetor adjustments
(© American Motors Corp)

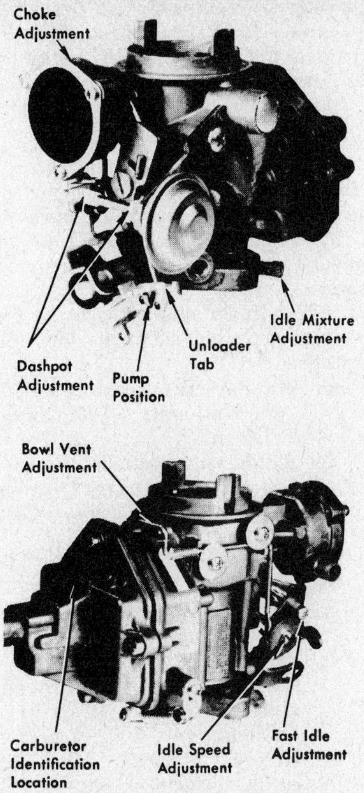
Choke Adjustment
Dashpot Adjustment
Pump Position
Unloader Tab
Idle Mixture Adjustment
Bowl Vent Adjustment
Carburetor Identification Location
Idle Speed Adjustment
Fast Idle Adjustment
Holley 1931 carburetor adjustments
(© American Motors Corp)

3. Start engine and allow it to warm up to normal operating temperature.
4. Adjust throttle stop screw to obtain 600 rpm for 1967 (except 1967 232), models, both manual and automatic transmissions in Neutral. On A/C cars, set speed to 600 rpm for 1967, with A/C turned *on*.
5. Turn mixture screw/s counterclockwise until engine speed drops off, then slowly turn screw/s (equal amounts) clockwise until speed picks up. Continue past this point until speed begins to fall off again, then back out screw/s to again obtain the fastest idle. This mid-range adjustment is called the "lean best idle" speed.
6. Readjust idle stop screw, if necessary, to obtain specified idle. If idle speed changed more than 50 rpm during the mixture adjustment, readjust the mixture.
7. Disconnect tachometer.

1967 232 Six-Cylinder

Adjust with air cleaner installed.

1. Connect a tachometer to the engine.
2. Turn idle mixture screw/s clockwise until gently seated, then back out 3 turns (engine off).
3. Start engine and allow it to warm up to normal operating temperature.
4. With both manual and automatic transmissions in Neutral, A/C on, adjust throttle stop screw to obtain 600 rpm.
5. Turn idle mixture screw/s counterclockwise (out) until no further increase in engine idle speed is obtained, then turn screw/s inward (equally) until a 20 rpm drop is noted.
6. Turn mixture screw/s outward again until original idle speed is just regained.
7. At this point, idle speed should be 600 rpm. If not, reset idle speed screw to achieve this figure, then readjust mixture until 600 rpm is obtained without requiring further mixture adjustment.
8. Disconnect tachometer.

1968 199/232 Six-Cylinder (1-BBL. and 2-BBL.) and 290/343 V8 (4-BBL. Manual)

Adjust with air cleaner installed.

1. Turn in mixture screw/s until gently seated, then back out one turn. Connect a tachometer.
2. Start engine and set idle speed to 550 rpm (manual six), 475 rpm (auto six) with auto transmission in Drive, or 650 rpm V8 4-BBL. (manual).

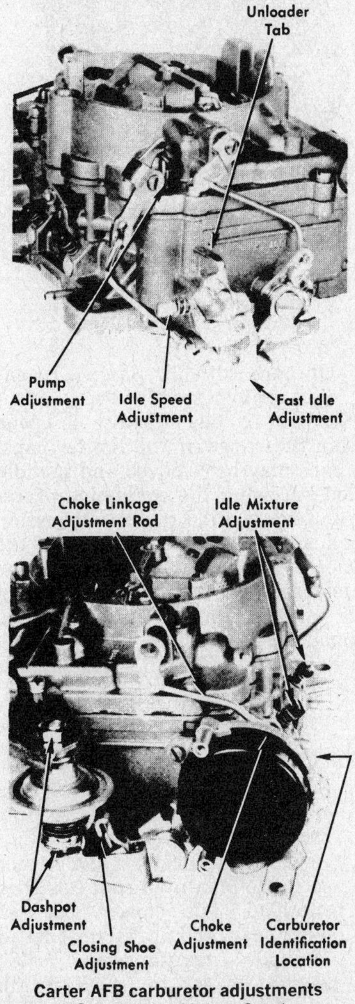
Unloader Tab
Pump Adjustment
Idle Speed Adjustment
Fast Idle Adjustment
Choke Linkage Adjustment Rod
Idle Mixture Adjustment
Dashpot Adjustment
Closing Shoe Adjustment
Choke Adjustment
Carburetor Identification Location
Carter AFB carburetor adjustments
(© American Motors Corp)

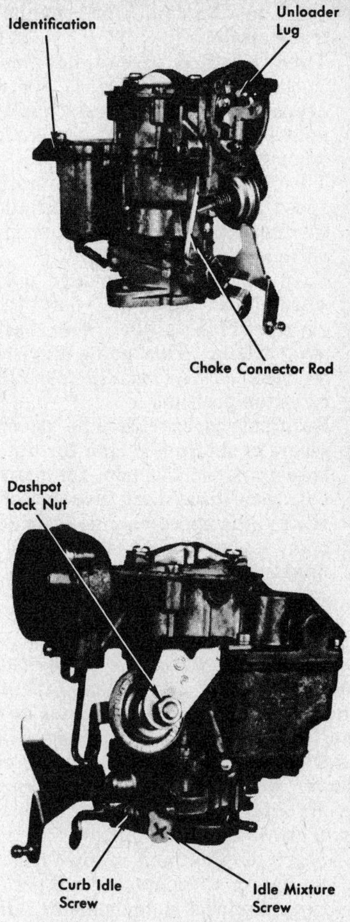
Identification
Unloader Lug
Choke Connector Rod
Dashpot Lock Nut
Curb Idle Screw
Idle Mixture Screw
Carter YF carburetor adjustments
(© American Motors Corp)

3. Turn mixture screw/s counterclockwise until engine speed drops off slightly. On 2-BBL. and 4-BBL. carburetors, turn both mixture screws equally unless the engine definitely demands otherwise.
4. Turn mixture screw/s (equally) inwards until speed is regained, then continue inwards until speed just begins to fall off again.
5. Turn mixture screw/s outwards until speed is regained. This is the "lean best idle" setting.
6. Readjust idle speed screw to obtain 600 rpm for manual, 525 rpm for auto.
7. Disconnect tachometer. If any idle speed change over 30 rpm is noticed, readjust idle mixture screws.

1968 290/343 V8 (Automatic 2-BBL. and 4-BBL.) and 290/343 V8 (Manual 2-BBL.)

Adjust with air cleaner installed.

1. Connect a tachometer.
2. Starting from a counterclockwise mixture stop position, turn mixture screws inward ½ turn each.
3. Start engine and adjust idle speed screw to obtain 500 rpm in Drive for auto transmission, 650

rpm in Neutral for manual transmission.

4. Turn mixture screws counterclockwise until engine speed drops off, moving screws equally unless the engine demands otherwise.
5. Turn screws clockwise until speed is regained, then continue turning screws until speed drops off again.
6. Turn both screws equally outward until speed is just regained. This is the "lean best idle" setting. This point may be reached at the maximum full rich stop position.
7. Readjust carburetor idle speed screw to obtain 550 rpm for auto transmission, 650 rpm for manual, then disconnect tachometer. If any idle speed change over 30 rpm is noticed, readjust idle mixture screws.

1969-71

Adjust with air cleaner installed. NOTE: Do not allow the engine to idle for more than three minutes at a time. If the idle mixture adjustment is not completed at the end of three minutes, run the engine at 2000 rpm for one minute. Continue the adjustments at the specified rpm.

1. Start engine and allow it to warm up to operating temperature. Connect a tachometer. *On engine with air pumps, disconnect air bypass hose at valve.*
2. Adjust carburetor idle speed screw to obtain 600 rpm for 6-cylinder manual, 525 rpm for 1969 6-cylinder automatic (in Drive), 550 rpm for 1970 6-cylinder automatic (in Drive), 650 rpm for V8 manual, 550 rpm for 1969 V8 automatic (in Drive), or 600 rpm for 1970 V8 automatic (in Drive), 700 rpm for six-cylinder manual, 600 rpm for 1971 six-cylinder automatic, 750 rpm for the 1971 V8 manual, and 650 rpm for the 1971 V8 automatic.
3. Starting from full rich stop/s (or two turns from seated on 4-BBL. manual V8) turn mixture screw/s clockwise until engine speed drops off.
4. Turn mixture screw/s counterclockwise until engine speed picks up to former level. The highest idle speed obtainable within the range of the limiter caps (or between the rich drop-off and lean drop-off points for 4-BBL. manual V8) is the "lean best idle setting." Both mixture screws should be turned equally unless the engine definitely demands otherwise.
5. If idle speed changes more than 30 rpm during mixture adjustment, reset carburetor idle speed screw and readjust mixture.

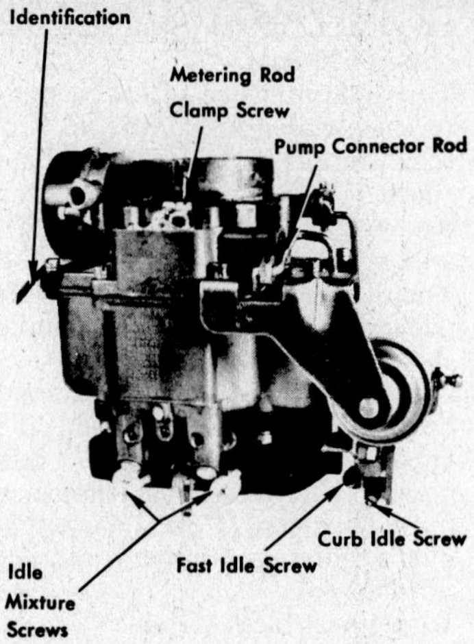
Identification
Metering Rod
Clamp Screw
Pump Connector Rod
Curb Idle Screw
Fast Idle Screw
Idle
Mixture
Screws

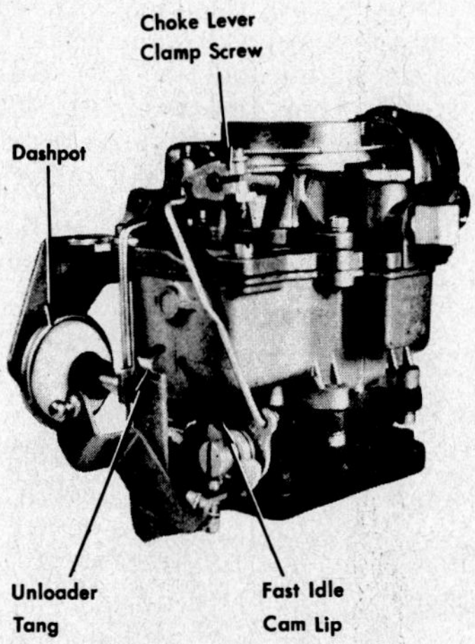
Choke Lever
Clamp Screw
Dashpot
Unloader
Tang
Fast Idle
Cam Lip

WCD carburetor adjustments
(© American Motors Corp)

6. On cars with air pumps, reconnect air bypass valve hose.

NOTE: if idle quality is poor within the range of the limiter caps, the caps may be removed and the idle speed set using the corrective procedure. Keep in mind that a combustion gas analyzer is necessary to meet the critical federal exhaust emission standards. All cars should have a 14:1 air/fuel ratio except 4-BBL. manual transmission V8's, which should be set up at 13.5:1 (air bypass hose disconnected).

Idle Quality Corrective Procedure

1. Remove idle limiter caps by inserting a sheet metal screw into the center of the cap.
2. Adjust carburetor idle speed screw to obtain 50 rpm less than specified idle speed for all 6-cylinder, and all V8 automatic. Manual transmission V8's should be set to specified idle speed.
3. Adjust mixture as described under *1968 199/232 Six-Cylinder and 290/343 V8 4-BBL. Manual.*
4. Install new service idle limiter caps with ears against full rich stops.

1972

The basic procedure for adjusting the 1972 emission control carburetors is the same as that for 1969–71, above. There are, however, some variations.

1. Six-cylinder engines use the following rpm settings for idle speed:
   a. Manual transmissions — 600 rpm/National; 700 rpm/California.
   b. Automatic transmissions — 500 rpm (in Drive)/National; 600 rpm (in Drive)/California.
2. V8 engines use the following idle settings:
   a. Manual transmissions — 750 rpm/all engines.
   b. Automatic transmissions — set the 304 and 401 cu in. engines at 650 rpm (in Drive)/National; at 700 rpm (in Drive)/California. The 360 cu in. engine is set at 700 rpm/National and California.
3. On 360 and 401 cu in. V8 engines, with automatic transmissions, set the idle speed by adjusting the throttle stop solenoid, if so equipped, to the specified figure. Then adjust the engine idle to 500 rpm with the idle stop solenoid disconnected. Reconnect the solenoid.

Caution When adjusting the idle speed on a car equipped with an automatic transmis-

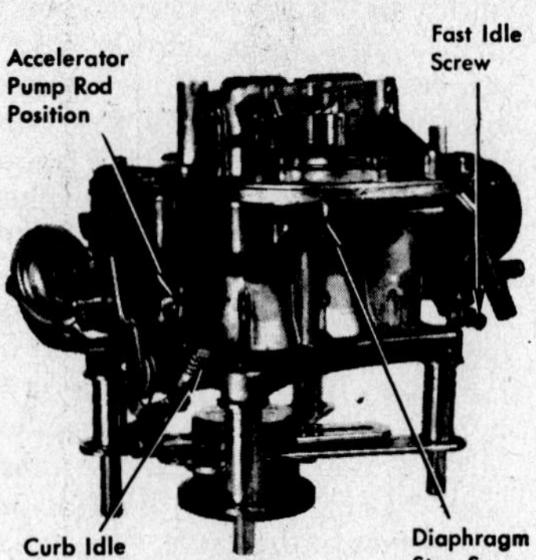
Accelerator
Pump Rod
Position
Fast Idle
Screw
Curb Idle
Screw
Diaphragm
Stop Screw

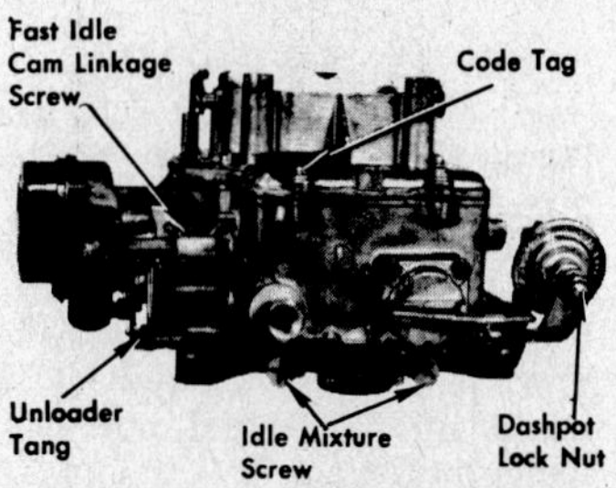
Fast Idle
Cam Linkage
Screw
Code Tag
Unloader
Tang
Idle Mixture
Screw
Dashpot
Lock Nut

Autolite 2100 carburetor adjustments
(© American Motors Corp)

sion, set in the Drive range, be sure that the parking brake is firmly on and that the front wheels are blocked.

1973-74

Adjust with air cleaner installed.

NOTE: Do not allow the engine to idle more than three minutes at a time. If the idle/mixture adjustment is not completed by the end of three minutes, run the engine for one minute at 2,000 rpm. Return to specified rpm and continue the adjustment.

1. Remove the idle limiter cap(s) by inserting a screw in its center. Turn the cap clockwise to remove it.
2. Discard the old cap(s).
3. Start the engine and allow it to reach normal operating temperature.
4. Install a tachometer of known accuracy, in accordance with its manufacturer's instructions.
5. Adjust the idle speed to 30 rpm above the speed specified in the "Tune-Up Specifications" chart.

NOTE: On V8, automatic transmission equipped cars, adjust the idle speed by turning the hex screw on the throttle stop solenoid.

6. Turn the mixture screws until they are seated against their full-rich stops.
7. Then turn the mixture screws clockwise (leaner) until a drop in engine idle speed is noted.
8. Turn the mixture screws counterclockwise from this position until the highest rpm is obtained.

NOTE: When adjusting the idle mixture on a carburetor which has two mixture screws, turn both screws equally unless satisfactory idle cannot be obtained in this manner.

9. If the idle speed changes more than 30 rpm during the mixture adjusting procedure, set the idle to 30 rpm above specification and repeat steps 6-8 again.
10. After completing steps 1-9 satisfactorily, turn the mixture screws clockwise until the engine idle speed drops the amount specfied below:

Engine/Transmission	*RPM*
6 cyl/manual	35
6 cyl/automatic	20
V8/All	40

11. Install new service idle limiter caps.

Caution When adjusting the idle speed/mixture on a car with its automatic transmission set in Drive range, be sure that the parking brake is firmly on and that the front wheels are blocked.

Dashpot Adjustment

Some carburetors are equipped with a dashpot to prevent stalling. The dashpot adjustment procedure for these carburetors is as follows:

1. Be sure that the throttle valves are closed tightly and that the diaphragm stem is fully depressed.
2. Measure the clearance between the dashpot stem and the throttle lever with a feeler gauge. For the proper clearance specification see the chart below.
3. If the clearance is not correct, adjust it by loosening the locknut and rotating the dashpot until the proper clearance is obtained. Tighten the locknut.

Year	*Carburetor*		*Clearance (Gauge size in.)*
1968	WCD (2-V)	All	0.080
	AFB (4-V)	4467S	0.215
		4468S	0.190
		4469S	0.140
1969	RBS (1-V)	All	0.095
	6200 (2-V)	All	0.140
	AFB (4-V)	All	0.160-0.170
1970	YF (1-V)	4768S	0.120
		4770S	0.095
	WCD (2-V)	All	0.095
	2100 (2-V)	All	0.125
	4300 (4-V)	All	0.125
1971	YF (1-V)	All	0.110
	2100 (2-V)	All	0.125
	4300 (4-V)	1TM4	0.065
		1TA4	0.125
1972-73	YF (1-V)	All	0.095
	2100 (2-V)	2DM2	0.110
		2DA2, 3DM2	0.140
	4300 (4-V)	All	0.140

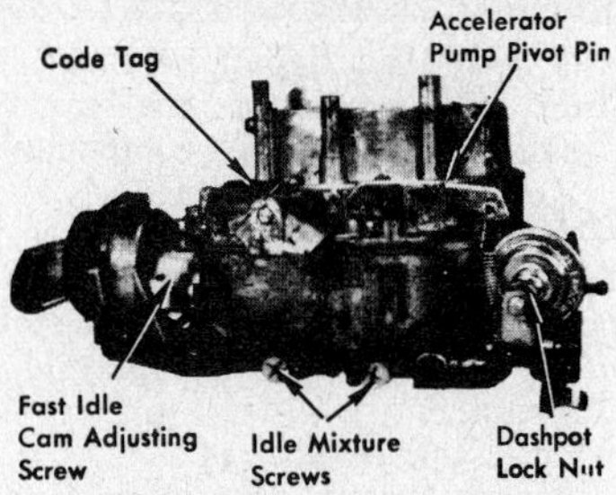
Code Tag
Accelerator Pump Pivot Pin
Fast Idle Cam Adjusting Screw
Idle Mixture Screws
Dashpot Lock Nut

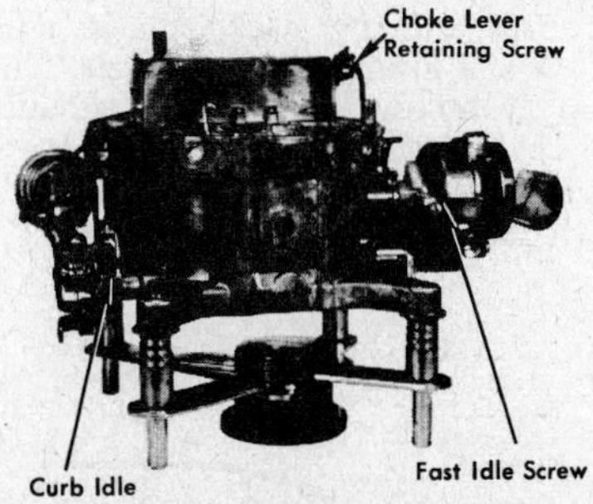
Choke Lever Retaining Screw
Curb Idle
Fast Idle Screw

Autolite 4300 carburetor adjustments
(© American Motors Corp)

COOLING SYSTEM

American Motors cars are equipped with a conventional cooling system which utilizes a vertical flow radiator, a water pump, and a thermostat. An internal by-pass port is used on the six-cylinder engine, which allows water to flow through the engine when the thermostat is closed. The V8 engine uses an external hose to perform the same function.

Information on the water temperature gauge can be found in the Unit Repair Section.

Radiator Removal

Raise the hood, drain the radiator, remove the upper and lower radiator hose. Take out the bolts which hold the radiator to its cradle and, if the car is fitted with an oil cooler for the transmission, disconnect the oil cooler lines and lift the core up and out.

Water Pump Removal

The water pump is a centrifugal unit having a non-adjustable packless seal. It is non-serviceable and must be replaced if defective—no maintenance is required.

6 Cylinder

1. Drain the cooling system.
2. Unfasten the radiator and the heater hoses at the pump.
3. Loosen the adjustment bolts from the alternator and the power steering pump (if so equipped).
4. Unfasten the fan ring securing bolts. Remove the fan and pump pulley assembly. Withdraw the fan ring.
5. Remove the securing bolts from the water pump. Withdraw the pump along with its gasket.

Installation is the reverse order of removal. Always use a new pump gasket. Bleed the radiator by running the engine and opening the heater control valve. Run the engine long enough so that the thermostat opens. Check the coolant level.

The water pump securing bolts should be tightened to 10–15 ft lbs.

V8

1. Drain the cooling system at the radiator. Remove the upper hose from the radiator.
2. Take the air cleaner off the carburetor.
3. Detach the fan shroud. Remove the fan and hub assembly by withdrawing the attaching bolts.
4. If the car is equipped with power steering, remove the pump assembly from its bracket.
5. If the car is equipped with an emission control air pump, unfasten the three cap screws from the bracket at the cylinder head, and withdraw the pump, complete with bracket.
6. Loosen the bolts attaching the alternator bracket. Leave one bolt in position, so that the alternator may be snug to one side. Do not detach the wires from the alternator.
7. Unfasten the heater hose at the water pump.

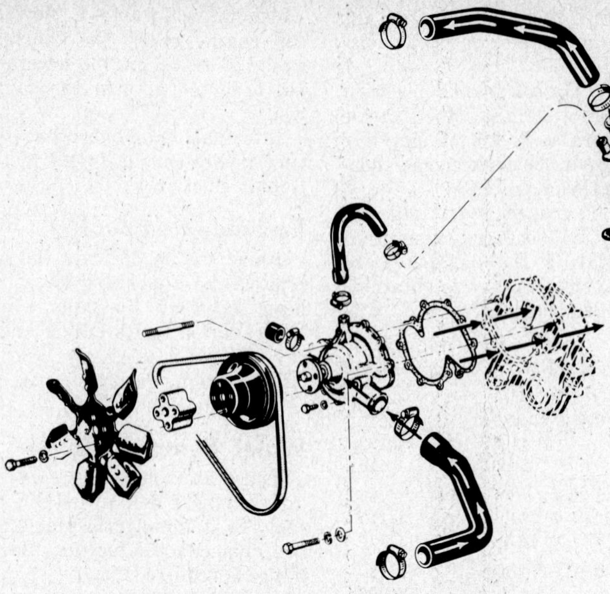

Water pump components and coolant flow 1967-74 V8
(© American Motors Corp)

8. On cars equipped with A/C, unfasten the compressor bracket and set it and the compressor out of the way.

Caution Do not discharge the compressor or unfasten the hoses from it. If this is done, the system must be recharged. Also, a burn could result from the escaping coolant coming in contact with the skin.

9. Remove the by-pass and the lower radiator hoses from the pump.
10. Withdraw the pump and clean the gasket areas.

Installation is the reverse of removal. Always install a new pump gasket. Tighten the pump bolts to 40–50 in. lbs. Bleed the cooling system by starting the engine and opening the heater valve. Leave it open until the thermostat opens. Check the coolant level.

Chilton's TIME SAVER

On V8 engines, water pumps have two different shaft lengths depending on application. Long-shaft pumps can be used in short-shaft applications if the flange on the pump shaft is pressed further down towards the pump (using an axle press) and the fan spacer drilled to receive the longer shaft.

Thermostat Removal

The thermostat is located in the water outlet housing at the top of the cylinder head, or on V8 models in front of the manifold.

Disconnect the upper radiator hose and remove the bolts which hold the water outlet neck to the engine. Remove the thermostat.

EMISSION CONTROLS

See the "Unit Repair Section" for testing and repair of the various emission control system components.

1967 California Models

An air injection system (Air-Guard) was used to meet the emission requirements of all cars sold in California.

This system consists of:

1. A belt-driven, vane-type pump which feeds air through a manifold and into each exhaust port via a stainless steel nozzle. The air mixes with the hot exhaust gases and aids in burning them completely in the exhaust manifold.
2. A carburetor with a different flow characteristic and a dashpot which is used to control throttle closing speed (except on six-cylinder models with automatic transmissions).
3. A distributor with a different advance curve and a special cam lubricator.
4. A positive crankcase ventilation system (PCV) retained from earlier models.

The air injection and the modifications were used on all but the 232 cu in. six. This engine used a new system of engine modifications to meet California emission standards.

These engine modifications consist of:

1. A composition head gasket to replace the steel head gasket.
2. An emission-calibrated carburetor, equipped with idle limiter caps to prevent the fuel/air mixture from being set over rich.
3. A distributor with a centrifugal advance curve designed to retard the timing only at idle speed, while still retaining normal performance characteristics.
4. A positive crankcase ventilation system (PCV) retained from earlier models.

1968-69 All Models

In 1968 all cars made for sale in the U.S. were required to have emission control systems similar to those used in California in 1967. American Motors cars adapted the engine modification system which had been used on the 232 cu in. six in California, the year before. Only V8 engines equipped with manual transmissions retained the air injection system.

Additionally added engine modifications consist of:

1. A "low-quench" combustion chamber on six-cylinder engines.
2. A thermostatically controlled air cleaner (TAC) on all V8s, except

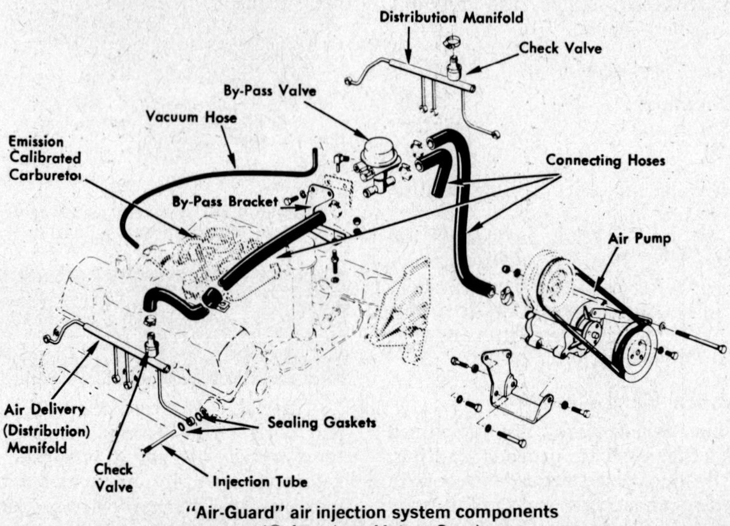
Distribution Manifold
Check Valve
By-Pass Valve
Vacuum Hose
Emission Calibrated Carburetor
Connecting Hoses
By-Pass Bracket
Air Pump
Air Delivery (Distribution) Manifold
Sealing Gaskets
Check Valve
Injection Tube

"Air-Guard" air injection system components
(© American Motors Corp)

those equipped with a 2V carburetor and manual transmission. The TAC allows only air heated by a stove on the exhaust manifold to enter the air cleaner when the under-hood temperature is less than 120° F. When the air is above this temperature, the valve opens, allowing under-hood air to be drawn through the air cleaner snorkle, in a conventional manner.

The 1968 modifications were carried over to the 1969 model year.

1970 All Models

All of the 1968–69 emission controls have been carried over to 1970. In addition, the following controls are added:

1. A deceleration valve is added to the 199, 232, and 390 cu. in. engines when equipped with manual transmissions. When the car is decelerating and intake manifold pressure rises to a specific value, the valve closes off the vacuum spark port opening. Direct intake manifold vacuum is supplied to the advance diaphragm (dual-diaphragm distributor). This permits maximum ignition timing advance, to prevent afterburning in the engine exhaust system.
2. A dual-diaphragm distributor is used on all engines equipped with a deceleration valve and on the 304 and 360 cu in. V8 engines. It is not used on the 232 or 390 cu in. engines with automatic transmissions. It has a retard (secondary) diaphragm in addition to the advance (primary) diaphragm. The secondary diaphragm permits additional timing retardation during closed throttle deceleration and idle, thus reducing hydrocarbon emissions.

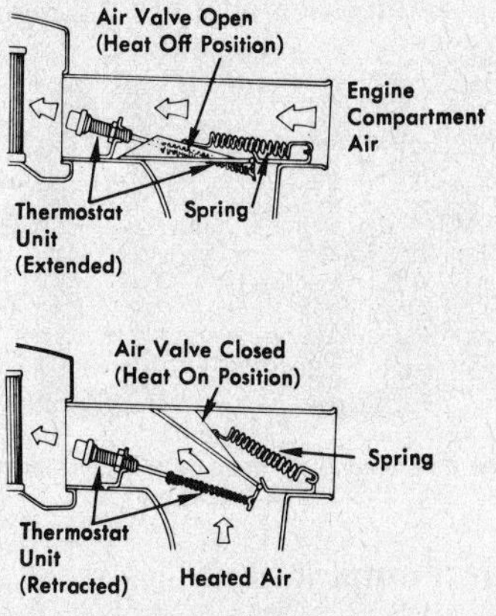
Air Valve Open
(Heat Off Position)
Engine
Compartment
Air
Thermostat
Unit
(Extended)
Spring
Air Valve Closed
(Heat On Position)
Spring
Thermostat
Unit
(Retracted)
Heated Air

Thermostatically controlled air cleaner (TAC) —6 cylinder application
(© American Motors Corp)

1970 California Models

In addition to the above modifications, all cars sold in California, starting with 1970 models, have to be equipped with an evaporative emission control system (EEC).

The American Motors EEC System consists of:

1. A fuel expansion tank that is integral with the fuel tank.
2. A closed vent system on the fuel tank.
3. A fuel check valve used to prevent the flow of *liquid* fuel through the closed vent system (not used on Gremlin models).
4. A special pressure and vacuum relief filler cap.

The EEC system routes raw fuel vapor into the PCV system, where it is burned along with regular crankcase emissions and the fuel-air mixture.

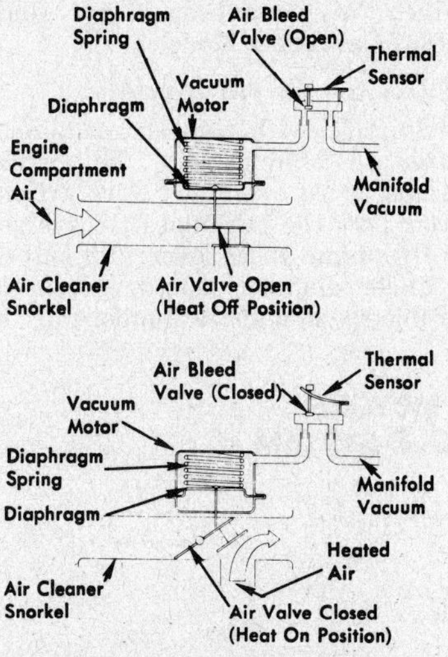
Diaphragm
Spring
Air Bleed
Valve (Open)
Thermal
Sensor
Vacuum
Motor
Diaphragm
Engine
Compartment
Air
Manifold
Vacuum
Air Cleaner
Snorkel
Air Valve Open
(Heat Off Position)
Air Bleed
Valve (Closed)
Thermal
Sensor
Vacuum
Motor
Diaphragm
Spring
Manifold
Vacuum
Diaphragm
Heated
Air
Air Cleaner
Snorkel
Air Valve Closed
(Heat On Position)

Thermostatically controlled air cleaner (TAC) —V8 engine application
(© American Motors Corp)

1971 All Models

The use of the evaporative emission control (EEC) system has been extended to the nationwide emission control package. All other systems have been retained, except for the dual-diaphragm distributor and the deceleration valve.

In addition, a charcoal canister has been added to the EEC system, on V8 engines equipped with automatic transmissions. The canister is used for fuel vapor storage.

1971 California

To meet oxides of nitrogen (NO_x) emission standards for California, a transmission-controlled spark (TCS) has been adapted, in addition to the other emission control systems. The TCS system is also used nationally on the 304 and 360 cu in. V8 engines, when equipped with an automatic transmission.

The TCS system functions to lower peak combustion temperature and pressures, thus reducing exhaust emissions of oxides of nitrogen.

The TCS system consists of:

1. A transmission control switch which opens or closes, depending upon car speed and the gear selected.
2. A solenoid vacuum valve that is activated by the transmission switch. It vents ported vacuum into the atmosphere, resulting in no distributor vacuum advance, when it is energized.
3. A temperature override switch, mounted on the front crossmember, is used to complete the circuit to the battery if the ambient temperature is more than 63° F. If the temperature is lower than this, the TCS system does not function.

The TCS system prevents vacuum advance from occurring when the car is in a low or intermediate gear and the ambient temperature is above 63° F. When the car is in high gear (or above 34 mph—automatic transmission) or the temperature is higher than 63° F, full vacuum advance is supplied to the distributor.

1972 All Models

The 1972 emission controls have remained similar to those used in 1971. Several detail improvements have been incorporated. These consist of:

1. A charcoal canister is used on the EEC system of all V8 models with automatic transmissions, for fuel vapor storage. A "purge valve" is used to empty the canister into the PCV system at normal cruising speed.
2. The thermostatically controlled air cleaner (TAC) is extended in use to all engines in 1972. The TAC used on the V8 engines has a vacuum assist motor to operate the door in the air cleaner snorkle. The six-cylinder engine TAC works by spring tension against a thermostatically controlled door.

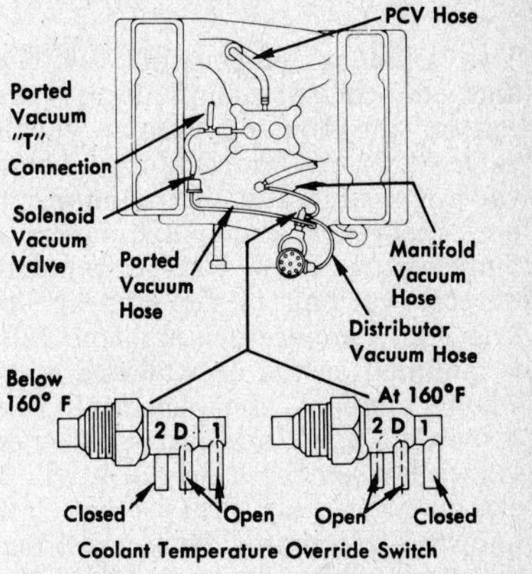
PCV Hose
Ported
Vacuum
"T"
Connection
Solenoid
Vacuum
Valve
Ported
Vacuum
Hose
Manifold
Vacuum
Hose
Distributor
Vacuum Hose
Below
160° F
At 160°F
2 D 1
2 D 1
Closed
Open
Open
Closed
Coolant Temperature Override Switch

TCS hose routing, when equipped with a coolant temperature override switch
(© American Motors Corp)

3. A coolant temperature operated vacuum valve is used on cars equipped with V8 engines and automatic transmissions. If the coolant temperature is above 160° F, intake manifold vacuum

is blocked off and carburetor ported vacuum is sent through a hose to the distributor advance diaphragm, thus decreasing the amount of vacuum advance. On cars equipped with TCS, the distributor vacuum advance is controlled by the TCS system once 163° F is reached.

1973 All Models

All six cylinder models are equipped with TCS. A description of this system can be found above under "1972 California."

New in 1973 is an Exhaust Gas Recirculation (EGR) system which is used on all V8s and six cylinder Matadors. This system directs a portion of the exhaust gases back into the intake manifold where they combine with the incoming mixture. This diluting of the mixture lowers peak combustion temperatures and reduces NO_x. The EGR valve, which is controlled by carburetor vacuum, controls the amount of exhaust gas, if any, that is recycled into the engine.

1973 AMERICAN MOTORS EXHAUST GAS RECYCLE SYSTEM

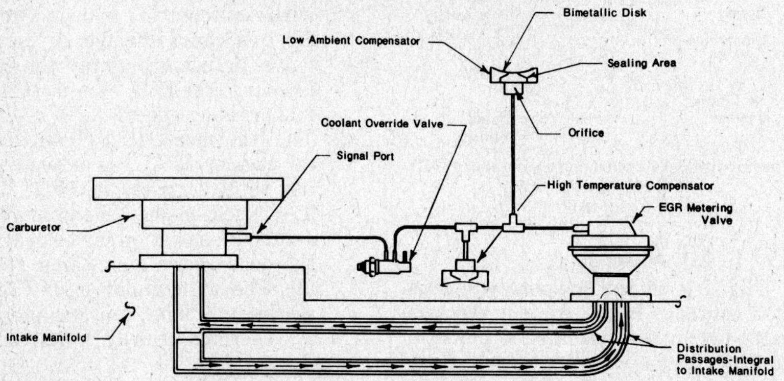
Bimetallic Disk
Low Ambient Compensator
Sealing Area
Coolant Override Valve
Orifice
Signal Port
High Temperature Compensator
EGR Metering Valve
Carburetor
Intake Manifold
Distribution Passages-Integral to Intake Manifold

Two ambient temperature switches and one coolant temperature valve control the flow of vacuum to the valve. The low temperature ambient valve is mounted in the radiator support, near the grille, and opens at temperatures below 60°F to vent carburetor vacuum to the atmosphere. The high temperature ambient valve is mounted on the firewall and opens when ambient temperature rises above 115°F. When either of these valves is open the EGR valve will be closed, preventing exhaust gas from entering the engine. The coolant temperature valve is mounted in either the intake manifold or engine block and is closed to block vacuum when coolant temperature is below 115°F (160° on 304 V8 with manual transmssion).

Also new for 1973 is an electrically-assisted automatic choke used on V8 models equipped with 4-bbl carburetors.

Once under-hood temperatures reach 95°F (± 15°F), a bimetallic switch located in the choke cap closes, allowing a ceramic heating element to draw power from a special tap on the alternator.

This causes the choke valve to open faster than normal, thus reducing CO emission during engine warm-up.

After the engine is shut off, the bimetallic switch remains closed until under-hood temperature drops below 65°F. Thus, if the engine is turned off for only a short time or if the ambient temperature is above 65°F, the choke will function for only a limited period of time.

All Matador wagons and all V8s are equipped with an AIR pump which is described above under "1967 California Models."

1973½–74 All Models

Starting with vehicles made on or after 15 March 1973, the ambient temperature overrides were dropped from both the TCS and EGR systems.

Dropping these overrides on six-cylinder engines caused driveability problems, so a spark temperature override was added. This override provides normal vacuum advance below a coolant temperature of 160°F. Addition of the spark temperature override meant that the EGR coolant temperature override had to be dropped from the six-cylinder engines.

At the same time these changes were made, a new transmission controlled spark (TCS) was incorporated on all models equipped with automatic transmissions.

NOTE: The new TCS switch was used on Kenosha-built cars after VIN A3AXXXX229935 and on Brampton-built cars after VIN A3AXXXX723815 (6 cyl) or VIN A3AXXXX726274 (V8).

An adjustable TCS solenoid control switch, which is operated by transmission governor oil pressure, is mounted at the right rear of the block on sixes or at the rear of the right-hand valve cover on V8s. The switch is present at the factory and should not normally require adjustment. If adjustment becomes necessary, the procedure for it may be found in the emission control unit repair section.

For 1974, most of the changes made in March are retained, except that the EGR coolant temperature override has been returned to the six-cylinder engines.

In addition, 1974 cars also have the following:

1. A back pressure sensing device to prevent EGR from occurring during idle, is used on all California six-cylinder engines when equipped with EGR valves, and V8s with automatic transmissions (except for the 401 cu in. V8).

The back pressure sensing device used on some 1974 California engines when equipped with EGR

2. Exhaust gas recirculation (EGR) has been extended to all six-cylinder engines, as well as V8s, except for the following:
   232 cu in. six—all Hornet sedans, Hornet hatchback, and Gremlin.
   258 cu in. six—Hornet 2-door sedan, Hornet hatchback, and Gremlin.
3. A new style diverter valve is used with air injection. The relief valve is now part of the diverter valve, rather than being mounted on the pump.
4. All engines for 1974 use a charcoal canister which is purged through the air cleaner snorkel. There is no purge valve on the canister.
5. The electrically assisted choke is retained on all 4-bbl V8 engines.

New diverter valves used with "Air Guard" on 1974 AMC cars

Air Pump R & R

Caution Never place the pump in a vise or attempt to dismantle it. The pump has no internal parts that are replaceable and it is serviced as a unit. Never pry or hammer on the pump housing.

1. Loosen the bolts on the pump pulley.
2. Loosen the air pump attachment

bracket. On V8 models with air conditioning, loosen the power steering pump to aid in drive belt removal.

3. Detach the air supply hoses at the pump. On models made prior to 1968, detach the separate air filter.
4. Remove the drivebelt and pulley from the hub.
5. Unfasten the bolts on the bracket and withdraw the pump.

Installation is performed in the following order:

1. Place the pump on its mounting bracket and install, but do not tighten, the attachment bolts.
2. With the rotor shaft used as a center, fit the pulley into the hub and install the drive belt over the pulley.
3. Tighten the pulley attachment bolts, using care not to snap them off.
4. Adjust the pump until the belt is secure. Tighten the mounting bolts and the adjusting screw to 18–22 ft. lbs; do not overtighten.
5. Attach the hoses and clamps.

Air Pump Relief Valve R & R

NOTE: 1973 air pumps do have a relief valve mounted on them. It is part of the diverter valve.

1. Use a gear puller and a steel bridge to remove the relief valve from the pump.
2. Remove the pressure plug from the new relief valve assembly (if so equipped).
3. Insert the relief valve into its housing mounting hole.
4. Place a block of wood over the valve. Use a hammer to tap the valve until it lightly registers against the housing. Use care not to distort the housing.
5. Press the pressure plug into the center of the relief valve.

Air pump relief valve removal
(© American Motors Corp)

1968-74 Centrifugal Filter Fan R & R

NOTE: Never attempt to clean the filter fan. It is impossible to remove the fan without destroying it.

1. Remove the air pump from the car, as detailed above.
2. Gently pry the outer disc off and pull off the remaining portion. Be careful that no fragments from the fan enter the pump air intake.

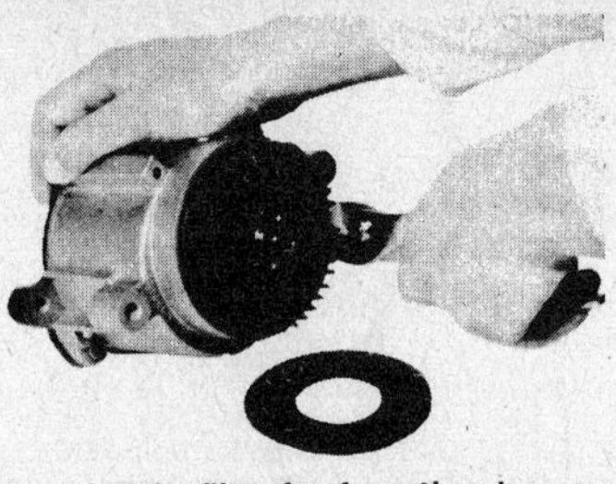

Removing the filter fan from the air pump
(© American Motors Corp)

3. Install a new filter fan pulling it into place with the pump pulley and attaching bolts.
4. Alternately torque the bolts so that the fan is drawn down *evenly*. Be sure that the outer edge of the fan fits into the pump housing.

Caution Never hammer or press the fan into place; damage to it and the pump will result.

5. Install the pump on the car.

NOTE: For the first 20-30 miles of operation, the fan may squeal until its lip has worn in. This is normal and does not indicate a damaged pump.

Exhaust Tube R & R

1. Remove the exhaust tube by grasping *it* (never the pump body) in a vise or a pair of pliers. Pull the tube out with a gentle twisting motion.
2. Install the new exhaust tube by tapping it into the hole with a hammer and a wooden block. Be careful not to damage its end.
3. Tap it until 7/8 in. of the tube remains above the pump cover.

NOTE: Do not clamp the pump in a vise while installing the exhaust tube.

By-Pass (Diverter) Valve R & R

1. Disconnect the hoses from the valve.
2. Remove the screws that attach the valve bracket to the engine. Withdraw the valve and bracket assembly.
3. Installation is the reverse of removal.

Air Injection Manifold and Check Valve Assembly R & R

6 Cylinder

1. Remove the intake/exhaust manifold assembly, after disconnecting the hoses from the air injection manifold.
2. Place the assembly in a vise and unfasten the retaining nuts on the air injection manifold at each cylinder exhaust port.
3. Lightly tap the injection tubes, then pull the injection manifold away from the exhaust manifold.
4. If the tubes have become fused to the injection manifold, remove them by applying heat while rotating them with pliers.

Installation of the injection manifold and tubes is performed as follows:

1. Insert new air injection tubes into the exhaust manifold.

NOTE: the shorter tubes go into the no. three and four cylinders.

2. Using a new gasket, assemble the exhaust/intake manifold to the engine.
3. Using new gaskets, install the air injection manifold on to the exhaust manifold in the reverse order of removal.

V8

1. Detach the air delivery hose at the check valve.
2. Unfasten the air injection manifold attachment nuts from the cylinder head. Carefully, ease the air injection manifold away from the head.

NOTE: on some models it may be necessary to lower the bottom steering shaft clamp to gain access to the left rear mounting bolt; or to disconnect the right engine support and raise the engine to remove the right air injection manifold assembly.

3. On newer cars, the air injection tubes and the manifold are removed as an assembly.
4. On older models, or if the tubes are hard to remove, use an "easy-out" to twist the tube out gradually.

NOTE: Some interference may be encountered because of the normal carbon buildup on the tubes. Injection tubes which are removed with an "easy-out" must be replaced with new ones.

Installation is the reverse of removal.

PCV Valve R & R

The PCV valve must be replaced at periodic intervals or if it becomes inoperative. It cannot be cleaned or repaired.

1. Remove the PCV valve from the grommet on the intake manifold on V8 engines or the valve cover on the sixes.
2. Unfasten the hose from the valve.
3. Installation is the reverse of removal.

EGR Valve R & R

1. Remove the air cleaner assembly from the carburetor.
2. Unfasten the vacuum line from the top of the EGR valve.
3. Loosen and remove the two screws which secure the valve to the manifold.
4. Withdraw the EGR valve, complete with its gasket.

Installation of the EGR valve is the reverse of its removal. Always use a new gasket. Tighten the valve securing bolts to 13 ft lbs.

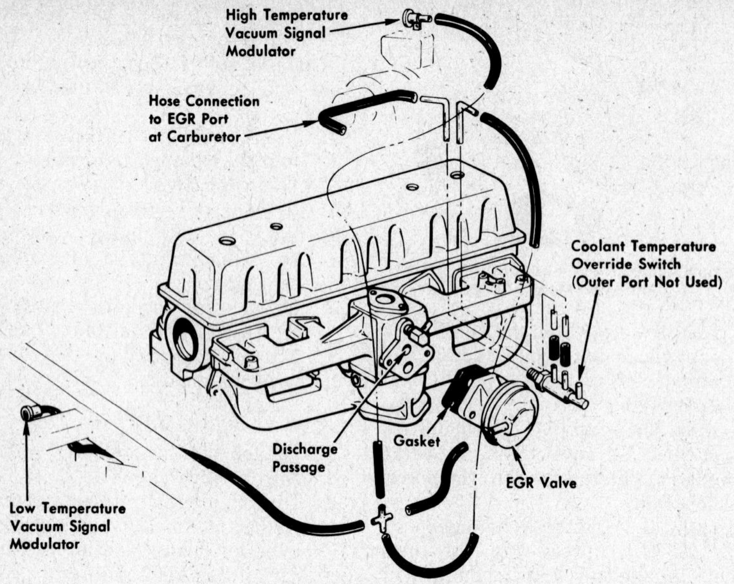
High Temperature Vacuum Signal Modulator
Hose Connection to EGR Port at Carburetor
Coolant Temperature Override Switch (Outer Port Not Used)
Discharge Passage
Gasket
EGR Valve
Low Temperature Vacuum Signal Modulator

EGR valve installation and hose routing—6 cylinder
(© American Motors Corp)

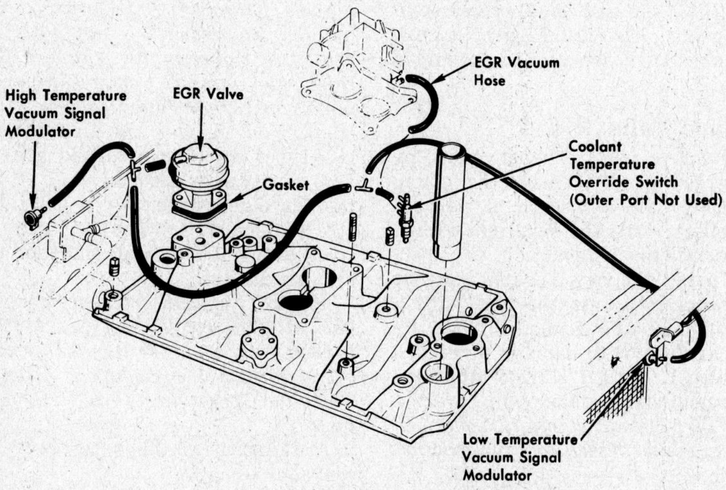
EGR Vacuum Hose
High Temperature Vacuum Signal Modulator
EGR Valve
Gasket
Coolant Temperature Override Switch (Outer Port Not Used)
Low Temperature Vacuum Signal Modulator

EGR valve installation and hose routing—V8
(© American Motors Corp)

EGR Valve and Passage Cleaning

1. Remove the EGR valve.
2. Use a wire brush to clean all of the deposits from the stainless steel pintle.
3. Press down on the pintle to open the EGR valve and then release it to close the valve. Replace the valve assembly if it will not close fully.
4. Inspect the manifold passages. If necessary, clean them with a spiral wire brush.

NOTE: On six-cylinder engines, deposits will build up most rapidly in the upper passage. If the deposits cannot be removed with the wire brush, use a 9/16 in. drill bit. Rotate the drill by hand, after coating it with heavy grease.

5. Install the EGR valve with a new gasket.

ENGINE

In 1967, two new 290 cu. in. V8s, one having 200 horsepower and the other 225 (depending on carburetion), were introduced. In the same year, two 343 cu. in. engines having 235 and 280 horsepower were available. In 1969, a 390 cu. in. V8, based on the 343, was introduced. This engine had a forged steel crankshaft and was rated at 315 horsepower.

In 1970, the 290 became a 304 and the 343 a 360. Horsepower figures increased by ten, except for the 300 horsepower, four-barrel 360. The 390 power rating was increased to 335 horsepower the same year. In 1971, the 390 engine was replaced by the similar 401 cu. in. unit.

From 1967-70, the seven-main-bearing six was offered in either a 199 or a 232 cu in. displacement version. The 232 cu in. engine was available with a 1V or a 2V carburetor. In 1970 a 258 cu in. engine was added to the six-cylinder line-up. The 199 cu in. engine was dropped in 1972, and the 232 became the base six-cylinder engine. The sixes are now available only with a 1V carburetor; the 2V carb having been dropped at the end of the 1971 production run.

Engine R & R

All 1967-74 6-Cylinder

1. Remove hood; mark hinge position for easy assembly.
2. Remove battery and air cleaner.
3. Drain engine oil and cooling system.
4. On automatic transmission equipped cars: drain transmission oil and remove cooler lines (if so equipped).
5. Remove power steering pump, smog pump and air conditioner compressor and condenser (if so equipped).

Caution Do *not* disconnect air conditioner or power steering lines.

6. Disconnect all hoses, tubes and wiring connecting engine and radiator to body and chassis. Remove radiator and starter motor for extra clearance in some models.
7. Disconnect exhaust pipe at manifold.
8. Disconnect speedometer cable and shift linkage.
9. Support engine and transmission and remove rear engine crossmember.
10. Either disconnect rear U-joint and pull driveshaft from transmission, or:
11. Disconnect front motor mounts at engine, then lift engine and transmission forward and out through hood opening, while allowing slip joint to pull out of extension housing.

Installation is the reverse of removal.

1967-74 V8—All Models

1. Follow Steps 1-6, inclusive, of six-cylinder procedure, then continue as follows:
2. Disconnect exhaust pipes from manifolds.
3. Support engine with chain hoist.
4. Remove engine rear crossmember.
5. Disconnect speedometer cable at transmission.
6. Disconnect automatic transmission shift linkage or standard transmission shift rods at transmission. If equipped with American Motors four-speed shifter, remove boot from floor pan and pull the two bolts that hold shift lever to shift mechanism; the mechanism can remain attached. If equipped with Hurst linkage, the shift lever should be removed

from transmission for adequate clearance (see illustration).

7. Disconnect front motor mounts and pull engine forward and upward, while supporting driveshaft as slip joint is removed from extension housing.

NOTE: if desirable, remove entire driveshaft beforehand by splitting rear U-joint.

Installation procedure is the reverse of removal.

Engine Manifolds

Intake Manifold R & R

6 Cylinder

The intake manifold is mounted on the left-hand side of the engine and bolted to the cylinder head. A gasket is used between the intake manifold and the head, none is required for the exhaust manifold. The manifold on the Rogue 232 incorporates an internal water tube to supply carburetor heat; it is secured with a tapered fitting.

1. Remove air cleaner, carburetor linkage, and PCV hose. Remove the TCS solenoid and bracket, if so equipped.
2. On Rogue 232 engines, remove coolant hoses from intake manifold and plug the ends.
3. Disconnect the exhaust pipe at the manifold flange. Remove the securing bolts from the A/C compressor bracket and set the compressor out of the way.

Caution Do not discharge the compressor or disconnect the A/C lines.

4. Remove manifold hold-down bolts and separate the intake and exhaust manifold from the head as a unit. Always use a new gasket when installing manifolds.

Installation is performed in the following order:

1. Always use a new intake manifold gasket. Install the manifold assembly.
2. Tighten the manifold securing bolts in the proper sequence (see illustrations) and tighten them to 25 ft lbs.
3. Fit the flange gasket and attach the exhaust pipe to the flange.
4. Install the carburetor and its linkages.
5. Install the A/C compressor and the bracket to the intake manifold (if so equipped).
6. If the TCS solenoid vacuum valve and bracket were removed, install them on the manifold.
7. Attach the PCV hose and install the air cleaner.

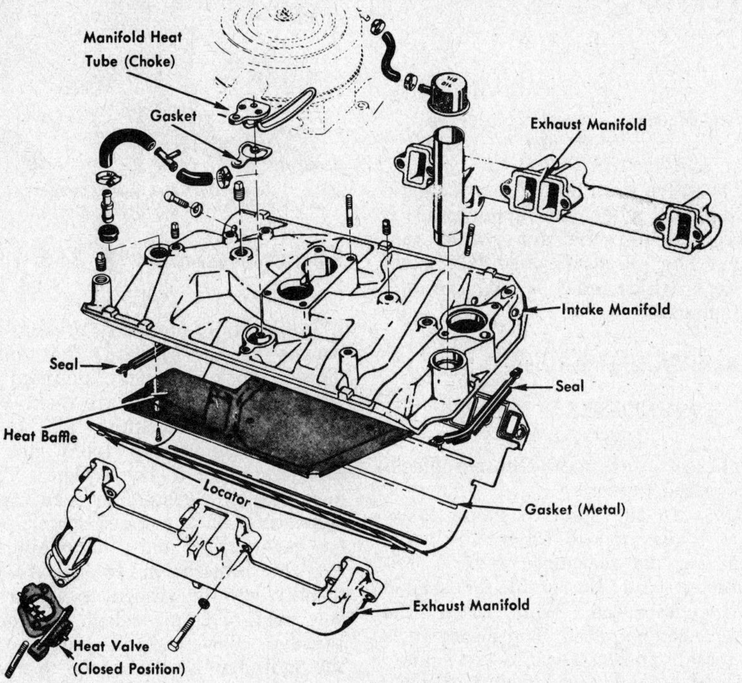
Manifold Heat Tube (Choke)
Gasket
Exhaust Manifold
Intake Manifold
Seal
Seal
Heat Baffle
Locator
Gasket (Metal)
Exhaust Manifold
Heat Valve (Closed Position)

Two-barrel intake manifold—V8
(© American Motors Corp)

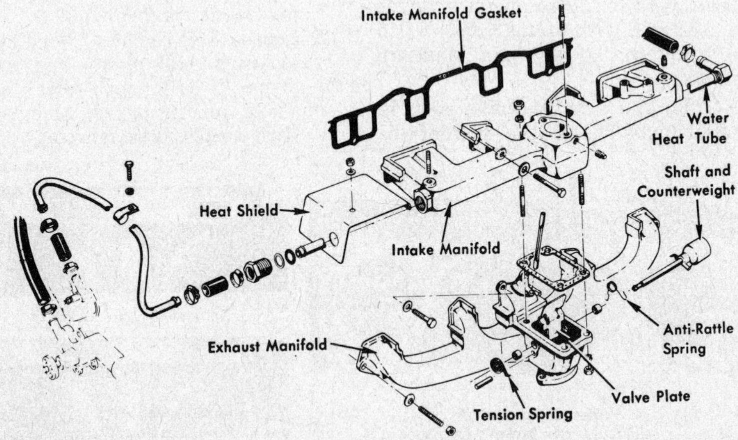
Intake Manifold Gasket
Water Heat Tube
Shaft and Counterweight
Heat Shield
Intake Manifold
Anti-Rattle Spring
Exhaust Manifold
Valve Plate
Tension Spring

6 cylinder intake and exhaust manifold
(© American Motors Corp)

V8 Engines

The cast iron manifold completely encloses and seals the tappet valley between the cylinder heads. The manifold contains water passages, a crankcase vent passage, exhaust crossover and induction passages. A one-piece metal gasket seals the intake manifold to cylinder head joint and also serves as an oil baffle. The left-hand carburetor bores supply cylinders No. 1, 7, 4 and 6; the right-hand bores cylinders No. 3, 5, 2 and 8.

1. Drain the cooling system.
2. Remove the air cleaner assembly from the carburetor.
3. Mark and remove the spark plug wires.
4. Remove the spark plug wire guides from the cylinder head cover, ignition coil and by-pass valve brackets.
5. Detach the radiator upper hose and the by-pass hoses from their fittings on the intake manifold.
6. Remove the ignition coil and bracket. Set the coil/bracket assembly out of the way.
7. Remove the TCS solenoid, if so equipped, from the right-hand valve cover.
8. Unfasten any of the emission control wiring or hoses as necessary.
9. Disconnect the throttle linkage and fuel and vacuum lines from the carburetor.
10. On cars equipped with air injection, remove the by-pass (diverter) valve bracket. Set the valve assembly (with hoses) out of the way, forward of the engine.
11. If the car is equipped with "Cruise Command" (automatic speed control), remove the vacuum servo mounting bracket and set the servo assembly aside.
12. Remove the carburetor assembly from the manifold.
13. Withdraw the intake manifold

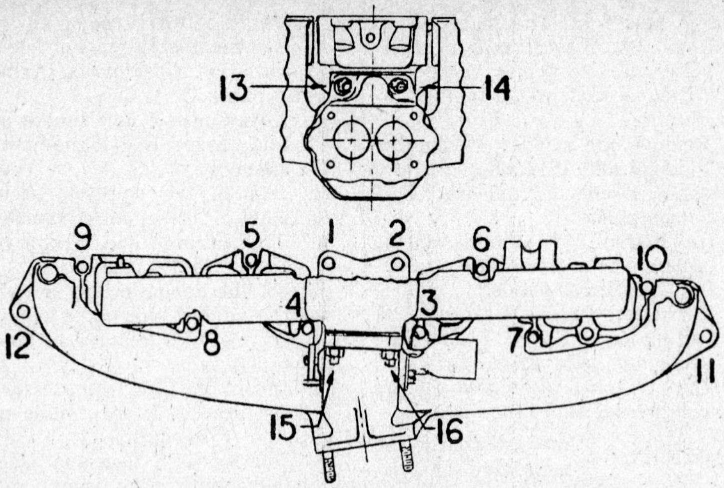
13
14
9
5
1
2
6
10
4
3
12
8
7
11
15
16

Intake manifold torque sequence—OHV 232 and 258 6 cylinder
(© American Motors Corp)

assembly complete with gasket and seals.

Always use a new gasket when installing the intake manifold. Use a good commercial sealer on both sides of the metal gasket and on the rubber end seals. Align the gasket at the rear first, then at the front.

The rest of the installation procedure is the reverse of removal. Torque the manifold bolts to 40-45 ft lbs, evenly.

Exhaust Manifold R & R

V8 Models

NOTE: The mating surfaces of both the exhaust manifold and the cylinder head are machined smooth, thus eliminating any need for a gasket between them.

1. Detach the wires from the spark plugs after marking them for firing order.
2. On models equipped with air injection, detach the air delivery hoses from the injection manifold. Remove the injection manifold and nozzles from the exhaust manifold.
3. Unfasten the downpipe from the exhaust manifold flange.
4. Remove the bolts and washers used to retain the manifold.
5. Remove the shields from the spark plugs.
6. Withdraw the exhaust manifold from the cylinder head.
7. Clean the machined surfaces of the manifold and head. Installation is the reverse of removal.

6 Cylinder

Exhaust manifold is removed along with *intake* manifold; see previous instructions.

Valve System

American Motors cars use hydraulic tappets; thus, no mechanical valve adjustment is necessary. The valve guides are integral with the head on all engines.

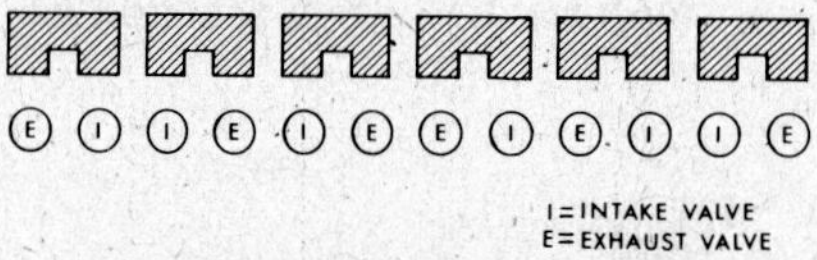
E I I E I E E I E I I E
I=INTAKE VALVE
E=EXHAUST VALVE

Valve sequence—OHV 6 199/232/258 —bottom view
(© American Motors Corp)

The valve stem oil deflectors should be replaced whenever valve service is performed on the six-cylinder engines. The V8 engines use valve stem oil seals which must be replaced only if damaged.

Valve Guide Service

199/232/258 6 Cylinder 1967-74 V8

These engines do not have replaceable valve guides.

Measure the stem to guide clearance in one of two ways. The valve stem can be measured with a micrometer and the guide measured using calibrated pilots, then the difference computed. The best way is to install the valve into the guide, without spring, and measure the lateral movement using a dial indicator. If stem to guide clearance is excessive, guides must be reamed to the proper oversize. Three oversize valves are available with stems 0.003, 0.015 and 0.030 in. larger than standard diameter.

NOTE: the exhaust valve stem is tapered 0.0005-0.001 in., smaller diameter toward valve head. Proper stem to guide clearance is 0.001-0.003 in. for both intake and exhaust valves.

No provision is made for adjustment of hydraulic tappet travel. Tappets having various thicknesses of push rod seats are available and can be installed to get a standard center travel position under normal operating conditions.

J21931-1
J21931-2

Removing valve spring keepers
(© American Motors Corp)

Rocker Assembly R & R

V8

Individually mounted, pressed steel rocker arms operate the valves. These rockers are mounted on threaded studs and are held by a pivot ball and locknut. The hollow pushrods conduct oil from each hydraulic tappet to the rockers. There is a metering system in each tappet, consisting of a stepped lower pushrod cap surface and a flat plate. Any loss of lubrication to the rockers usually can be traced to failure of this part, or to a blocked pushrod oil passage. The pushrods rub against the cylinder head during operation and serve to maintain the correct rocker to valve stem angle.

1. Remove valve covers, after first removing any accessories and the air cleaner preheat tube.
2. Loosen and remove the retaining locknuts, ball pivots and rocker arms. It is a good idea to lay them out in order, along with their respective pushrods.

1
1
2
2

Valve sequence V8
(© American Motors Corp)
1 Exhaust valves
2 Intake valves

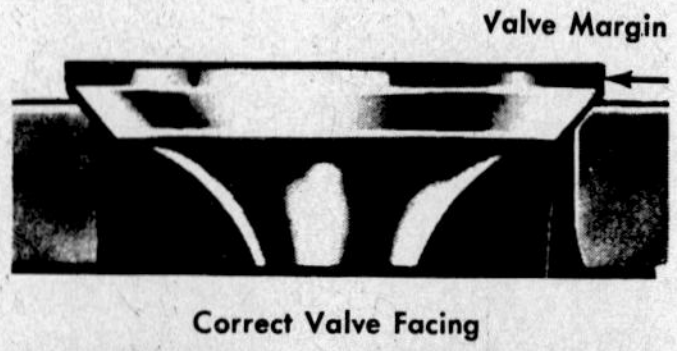
Valve Margin

Correct Valve Facing

Incorrect Valve Facing
(© American Motors Corp)

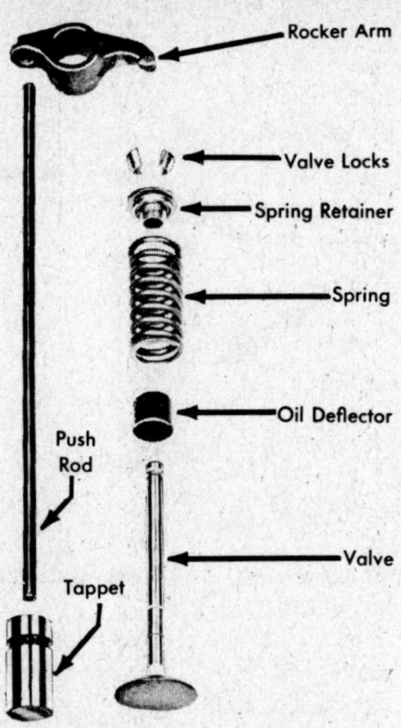
Rocker Arm
Valve Locks
Spring Retainer
Spring
Oil Deflector
Push Rod
Valve
Tappet

Valve assembly sequence—OHV 6 cylinder
(© American Motors Corp)

3. Installation is the reverse of removal.

NOTE: when installing new threaded studs, make sure hex nut is fully seated and tightened to 65-70 ft. lbs. Retaining locknuts are tightened to 20-25 ft. lbs.

6 Cylinder

The rocker shaft assembly is secured to the cylinder head with six cap bolts. Oil pressure for rocker lubrication is supplied via No. 3 camshaft bearing from the main oil gallery to No. 5 rocker support. Rocker shaft is 0.8575-0.8585 in. diameter; oil clearance is 0.003-0.005 in.

1. Remove valve cover.
2. Unbolt cap bolts and remove rockers and shaft.
3. Installation is the reverse of removal.

NOTE: hold rockers in place using large rubber bands.

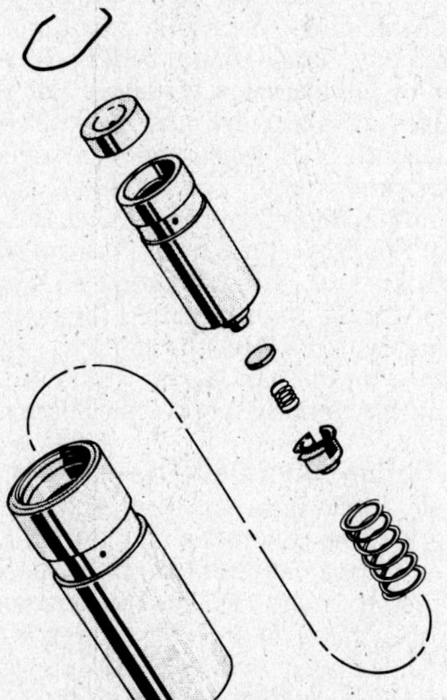

Sectional view of hydraulic tappet (metering disc not shown)
(© American Motors Corp)

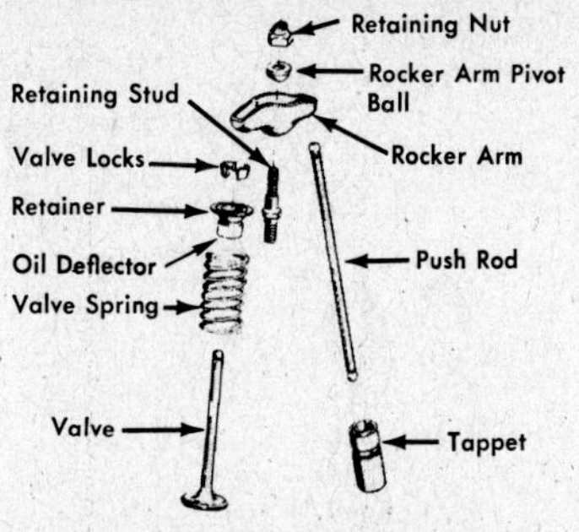
Retaining Nut
Rocker Arm Pivot Ball
Retaining Stud
Valve Locks
Rocker Arm
Retainer
Oil Deflector
Push Rod
Valve Spring
Valve
Tappet

OHV V8 rocker arm assembly
(© American Motors Corp)

Cylinder Head R & R

All 6 Cylinder

1. Drain the cooling system. Disconnect throttle linkage, fuel lines, water hoses, spark plug wires and vacuum line. Remove the air cleaner, PCV hose, and the temperature sender.
2. Remove the valve cover and its gasket. Remove the rocker arm/shaft assembly and the pushrods. Keep the pushrods in order.
3. Remove the intake and exhaust manifold assembly from the head.
4. Detach the spark plug wires and remove the plugs.
5. Unfasten the battery ground cable, the coil, and the coil bracket from the head.
6. Unfasten the bolts and remove the cylinder head from the block.
7. Clean the gasket surfaces of both the head and the block. Remove the carbon deposits from the top of each piston and from the combustion chambers.
8. Check the head for straightness. If the head (or the block) is 0.008 in. out of true over its entire length, 0.001 in. in 1 in., or 0.003 in. in 6 in., the head requires resurfacing.

Installation of the cylinder head is performed in the following order:

1. Use a new head gasket and coat both of its sides with sealer. The word "top," on the gasket, faces upward.
2. Tighten the head bolts in three stages and proper sequence, see the illustration below, to the proper torque specification.
3. The rest of installation is the reverse of the removal. Remember to refill the cooling system when completed.

V8

The cylinder heads have two holes to assist head location. Maximum out of true is 0.006 in. for the entire length of head; 0.001 in every 1 in. Make sure the rear rocker arm bolts are properly installed, otherwise no oil will get to the rockers.

1. Remove oil filler tube, rocker covers, power steering pump, alternator, exhaust manifolds and air conditioner. Swing air condi-

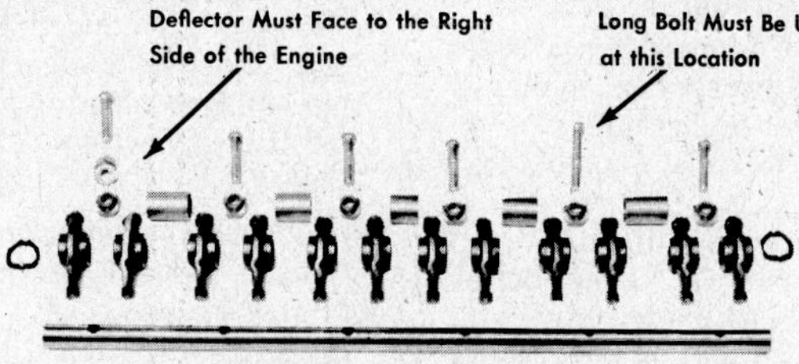
Deflector Must Face to the Right Side of the Engine
Long Bolt Must Be Used at this Location

OHV 199/232/258 6 cylinder rocker arm assembly
(© American Motors Corp)

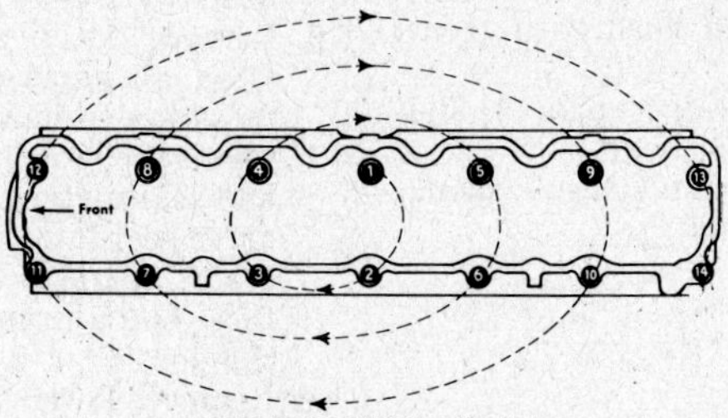
Front

199, 232, 258 6 cylinder

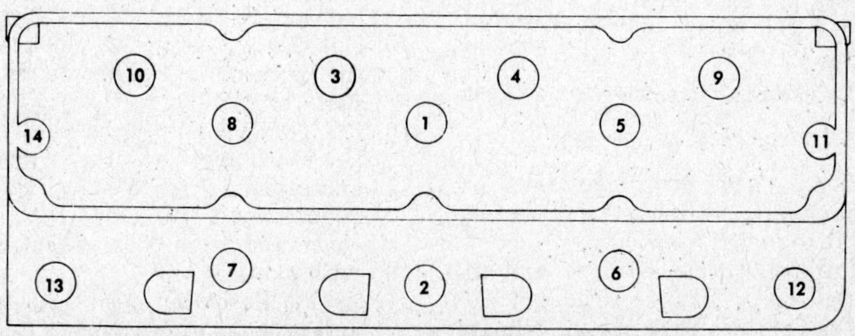
10
3
4
9
14
8
1
5
11
13
7
2
6
12

290, 304, 343, 360, 390, and 401 V8

tioner out of the way without disconnecting its hoses.

2. Drain the cooling system. Remove rockers and pushrods.
3. Disconnect water hoses, fuel lines, wiring, vacuum lines; remove distributor and intake manifold.
4. Remove cylinder head bolts and lift off heads carefully, making sure all ground straps, etc. have been disconnected.

There are two locating dowels on the cylinder block to assist in gasket alignment during installation. Apply a commercial sealing compound to both sides of the head gasket. The word "top" and "A.M." should always face upward when installing the gasket. Tighten the head bolts to specifications in three steps in the sequence illustrated. The rest of removal is the reverse of installation.

Timing Cover, Chain, and Camshaft

Vibration Damper Removal

All Models

Remove the radiator core and the fan. Remove the nut from the center of the pulley and, using a puller, remove the pulley from the front of the crankshaft.

Timing Case Cover R&R

6 Cylinder

The timing chain cover has a seal and oil slinger to prevent oil leakage past the crankshaft pulley hub.

1. Remove all V-belts, fan blades and pulley.
2. Remove vibration damper.
3. Remove oil pan to cover bolts and cover to block bolts.
4. Raise cover and pull oil pan front seal up far enough to extract the tabs from the holes in cover.
5. Remove cover gasket from block; cut off seal tab flush with front face of block.
6. Clean all mating surfaces and remove oil seal.
7. Install new front oil seal, using proper size arbor.

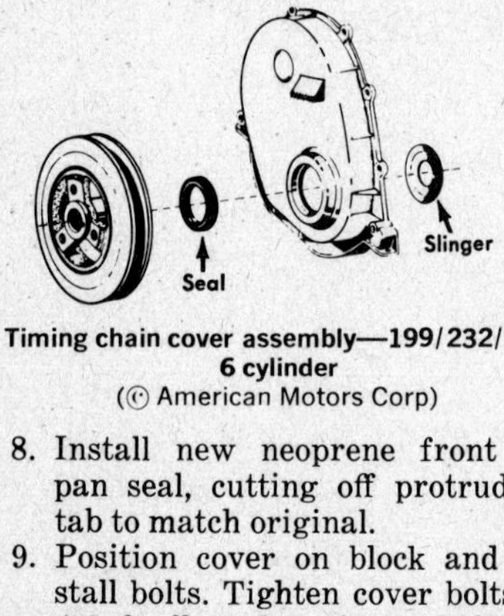
Seal
Slinger

Timing chain cover assembly—199/232/258 6 cylinder
(© American Motors Corp)

8. Install new neoprene front oil pan seal, cutting off protruding tab to match original.
9. Position cover on block and install bolts. Tighten cover bolts to 4-6 ft. lbs.; four lower bolts to 10-12 ft. lbs.

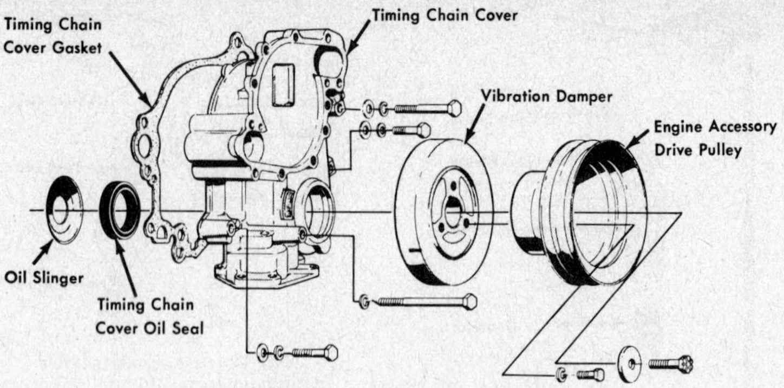
Timing Chain Cover Gasket
Timing Chain Cover
Vibration Damper
Engine Accessory Drive Pulley
Oil Slinger
Timing Chain Cover Oil Seal

Timing chain cover assembly—1967-74 V8
(© American Motors Corp)

10. Install vibration damper, tightening bolt to 50-60 ft. lbs.

NOTE: front oil seal can be installed with cover in place only if proper tool or duplicate is available.

V8

The die-cast timing cover incorporates an oil seal at the vibration damper hub. This seal must be installed from the rear; therefore the cover must be removed from engine in every case to replace front seal.

1. Drain coolant and remove hoses from cover.
2. Remove distributor, fuel pump, alternator drive belt, accessory drive belts, fan and hub assembly.
3. Remove the vibration damper bolt, then pull off the damper.
4. Remove air conditioner compressor and power steering pump, if so equipped, and swing them out of the way *without* disconnecting hoses.

NOTE: Do not discharge the compressor or remove the hoses. Injury could result.

5. Remove the two front oil pan bolts from beneath the car, then remove the eight 9/16 in. hex head cover bolts.
6. Remove cover from block, then clean all parts and mating surfaces and remove oil seal.
7. Coat new seal lips with Vaseline and seal surface with sealer, then drive seal into cover bore until it seats against the outer cover face. Use a proper size arbor for this job.
8. Remove lower dowel pin from cylinder block; this must be replaced when cover is in position but before bolts are installed.
9. Cut the oil pan gasket flush with the block on both sides of the oil pan.
10. Cut corresponding pieces of gasket from another oil pan gasket and cement them to cover. Install neoprene oil pan front seal into cover and align cork gasket tabs with pan seal.
11. Apply Permatex No. 2 to gaskets, then position cover. Install oil pan bolts and tighten evenly until cover lines up with upper dowel pin.
12. Install lower dowel pin, then cover to block bolts; tighten to 20-30 ft. lbs.
13. Install all removed pieces and adjust ignition timing.

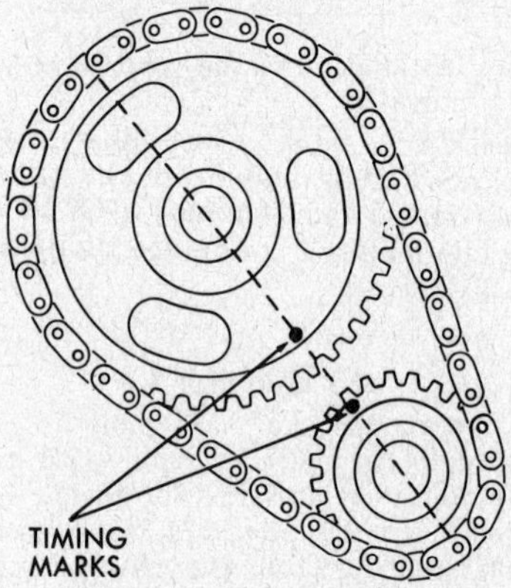
TIMING MARKS

Six-cylinder timing chain and sprockets

Timing Chain Check—all 6 Cylinder

To check valve timing, remove valve cover and spark plugs, then rotate crankshaft until No. 6 piston is at TDC on compression stroke. Compression stroke can be determined by holding a finger in the No. 6 spark plug hole while turning the engine by hand—finger will be forced out by compression pressure. Set the valves of No. 1 cylinder to 0.003 in. clearance and rock the crankshaft back and forth. The exhaust valve should open before the TDC mark on the pulley lines up with the pointer—measure the actual distance. The intake valve should open the same distance *past* the pointer—if it varies more than ½ in., remove the timing cover and inspect the chain.

Timing Chain Check—all V8

To check the valve timing, remove the rocker covers and spark plugs, then rotate the crankshaft until No. 6 piston is at TDC on compression stroke. This places No. 1 piston on TDC exhaust overlap. Rotate the crankshaft counterclockwise 90° (¼ turn) and install a dial indicator on No. 1 intake rocker pushrod end. Crank the engine in the normal di-

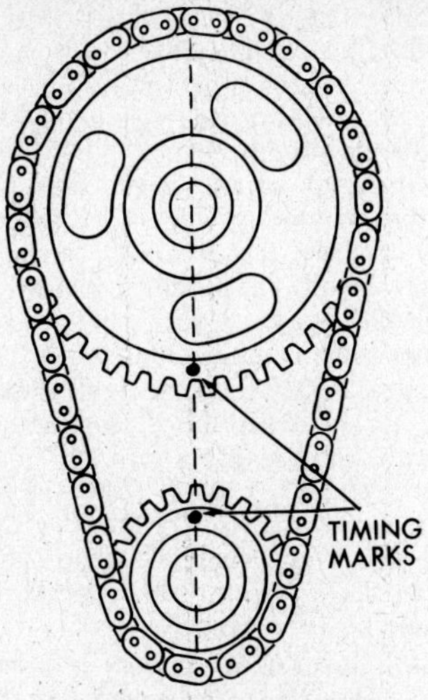
TIMING
MARKS

V8 timing chain and sprockets

rection of rotation until the pushrod moves, as indicated on the dial by a ± 0.020 in. pointer movement. In this position, the timing pointer should align with TDC mark on 1967-74 engines. If this varies more than about ¼ in., remove timing cover for chain inspection.

Camshaft R & R

6 Cylinder—All

1. Drain the cooling system and remove the radiator.
2. If the car is equipped with air conditioning, remove the condenser and the receiver unit as a *charged assembly*, only.

NOTE: do not discharge the A/C system; personal injury or damage to the system could result.

3. Remove the valve cover and gasket.
4. Remove the rocker arm/shaft assembly and withdraw the cylinder head complete with gaskets. Remove the tappets.

NOTE: pushrods and tappets should be kept in the proper order They must be returned to their original places during assembly.

5. Remove the drivebelt(s), fan assembly, accessory pulley(s), vibration damper, and the timing chain cover.
6. Remove the fuel pump. Take off the distributor assembly, including spark plug wires.
7. Turn the crankshaft until the "0" timing mark on the crankshaft sprocket is nearest to, on a centerline with, and aligns with the timing pointer on the camshaft sprocket.
8. Remove the sprockets and the timing chain as an assembly.
9. Remove the front bumper and/or grille as necessary. Withdraw the camshaft through the opening.
10. Inspect the bearing journals, distributor drive, cam lobes, and tappets for wear or damage. Replace parts, as required.

Camshaft installation is performed in the following order:

1. Use a generous amount of a suitable engine oil supplement on the camshaft. Install it in the block, using care not to damage any surfaces.
2. Install the timing chain and sprocket assembly as outlined above.
3. Install the timing chain cover and a new oil seal, as outlined above.
4. Fit the vibration damper and the accessory drive pulley(s).
5. Install the engine fan assembly and the drive belt(s). Tighten the belts to the proper tension.
6. Install the fuel pump.
7. With the number one piston at TDC of its compression stroke, fit the distributor so that the rotor is aligned with the no. one terminal on the cap (distributor fully seated on the block). Install the cap and the spark plug wires.
8. Install the tappets, cylinder head, its gasket, valve train (pushrods in the same order, as removed), valve cover and its gasket.

NOTE: All valve train components must be lubricated with engine oil supplement. The supplement must remain in the engine for at least the first 1000 miles. It does not require draining until the next regular oil change.

9. Install the air conditioner receiver and condenser, without discharging any coolant (if so equipped).
10. Install the radiator and top up the cooling system.
11. Install the front bumper and/or grille.

V8s—All

1. Detach the battery cable.
2. Drain the radiator and both banks of the cylinder block. Remove the radiator, the hoses, and the thermostat housing.
3. Remove the distributor, complete with spark plug wires and the coil from the intake manifold.
4. Remove the intake manifold as a complete assembly.
5. Take off the valve cover and take out the valve train, including the hydraulic tappets.

NOTE: Keep the valve train components in proper order. They must be returned to their original place during assembly.

6. Remove the power steering pump from its bracket, without disconnecting the hoses. Set it out of the way.
7. Remove the fan assembly and then the fuel pump. Unfasten the heater hose at the water pump.
8. Unbolt the alternator bracket and set it out of the way, complete with the alternator. Do not disconnect the alternator wiring.
9. Remove the crankshaft pulley and the vibration damper.
10. With the timing marks in vertical alignment, remove the front cover, distributor/oil pump drive gear, fuel pump eccentric, sprockets, and the timing chain.
11. Unfasten the hood latch upper support bracket attachment screws. Move the bracket, as necessary, to permit withdrawal of the camshaft.
12. Use care during camshaft removal, so that the journal bearings are not damaged.
13. Inspect all parts for wear and damage. Replace them as required.

Installation of the cam is the reverse of removal. Install the timing chain and cover as outlined above. Adjust the belt tension and fill up the cooling system.

NOTE: Lubricate the camshaft, tappets, and the valve train with a suitable engine oil supplement. Add the remaining supplement to the crankcase, and leave it in the engine for at least the first 1000 miles. It does not require draining until the next regular oil change.

Timing Chain R&R

All Models

1. Remove the timing case cover and turn the engine until the mark on the crankshaft sprocket points upwards, and the mark on the camshaft sprocket points downwards. Marks should be near each other and in line between the shaft centers.
2. Remove the bolts which hold the camshaft sprocket to the camshaft and start a puller over the crank gear.
3. Pull the crank gear off the front of the crankshaft.
4. On the bench, arrange the new chain over the sprockets so that the marks are nearest each other and in line between their own centers, then carry this to the engine. Start the crank gear up on its key and arrange the camshaft so that, when the three bolts line up, the marks are between shaft centers.

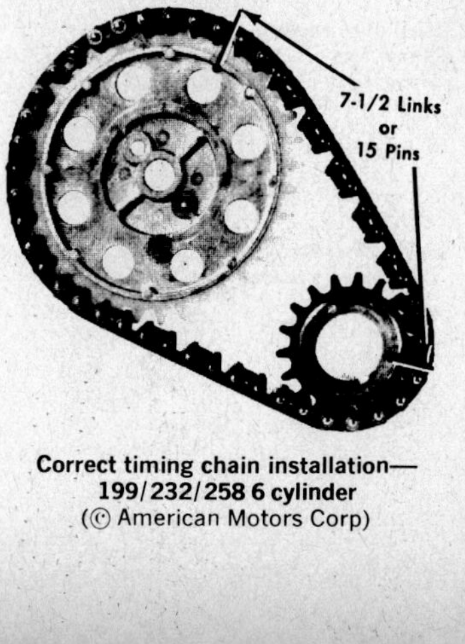
7-1/2 Links
or
15 Pins

Correct timing chain installation—
199/232/258 6 cylinder
(© American Motors Corp)

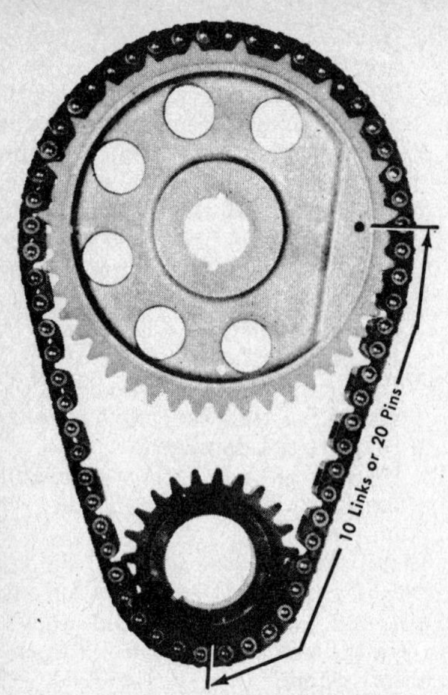
10 Links or 20 Pins

Correct timing chain installation—V8
(© American Motors Corp)

NOTE: on 6 cylinder engines, locate the marked cam tooth at one o'clock position; mark on crank should be approximately at point of mesh. Count the number of links between the marks; 15 pins or 7½ links for OHV 199/232/258 engine.

On all V8 engines, locate the marked cam tooth on a horizontal line at three or nine o'clock position; mark on crank at point of mesh. Count the number of links between marks; should be 20 pins or 10 links.

5. Secure the cam gear to the camshaft and force the crankshaft gear all the way on the shaft.
6. Reassemble the front of the engine.

Piston Removal

All Engines

1. Drain the cooling system and remove the cylinder head assembly as outlined in the applicable section above.

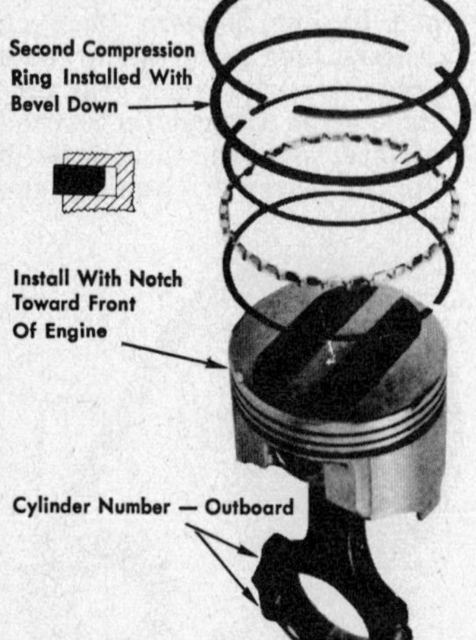
Second Compression Ring Installed With Bevel Down
Install With Notch Toward Front Of Engine
Cylinder Number — Outboard
Squirt Hole — Inboard

390 V8 piston assembly
(© American Motors Corp)

2. Use a ridge reamer to remove the ridge at the top of the cylinder wall. Each cylinder must be done separately with the piston at the bottom of its stroke.
3. Drain the oil and remove the oil pan.
4. Remove the connecting rod bearing caps and inserts from below.

NOTE: The rods and caps have the number of the cylinder, to which they were assembled, stamped on them. It is important that they be kept in the order in which they were removed.

5. Withdraw the piston and connecting rod assemblies through the *top* of the cylinder bore. Use care not to scratch the connecting rod journals or the cylinder walls with the rod bolts.

Ring Replacement

All Engines

1. Clean the carbon from the oil ring grooves, the oil drain openings and the pin boss. Use care not to remove any metal from the ring grooves or lands, as this will change clearance.
2. Measure the ring clearances and the cylinder bore taper as outlined in the "Engine Rebuilding" section.
3. Remove the glaze from the cylinder bore wall with an *expanding* hone. Ten strokes (down and return) are sufficient to clean the walls; more than ten will change clearances.

Caution Never use a rigid hone to remove cylinder glaze; it will destroy cylinder taper.

4. Install the oil control rings on the pistons, first. Then install the compression rings with the top side (which is marked) up. Use a ring tool on the compression ring to prevent distortion and breakage.

Rod and Piston Assembly Installation

On engines using split-skirt pistons, the slit in the skirt must be installed opposite the oil squirt hole in the connecting rod. Solid skirt pistons are assembled so that the boss, or dimple, (and, in some instances, the letter F) at the top of the piston is on the same side of the connecting rod as the boss. This will be found on the connecting rod channel about halfway up the rod.

The piston and rod assemblies are united to the engine from the top and the dimple, or dot, on the top of the piston goes toward the front. On those engines having split-skirt pistons, the slit in the skirt of the piston goes to the left side of the engine.

V8 Engines

The piston pins are a press fit in the connecting rod, hand fit in piston at 68°F; they must be removed and installed using an arbor press. The connecting rod is centered on the piston pin ± 0.030 in.; piston pin to piston bore clearance is 0.0003-0.0005 in. at room temperature.

Ring end gap is measured at the bottom of the cylinder bore near the end of ring travel area; push ring down using an inverted piston and measure gap with feeler gauge. Compression rings—0.010-0.020 in.; oil ring—0.015-0.055 in. (rail gap).

Prior to installing piston and connecting rod assembly into 1967-74 engines, except 1968-69 390, arrange ring gaps with No. 1 180° from No. 2 and No. 3 at least 90° from No. 2. Each rail gap on oil control ring should be 30° apart.

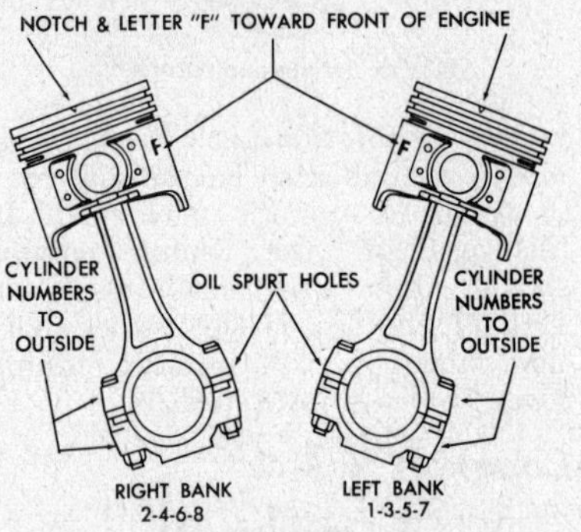
NOTCH & LETTER "F" TOWARD FRONT OF ENGINE
CYLINDER NUMBERS TO OUTSIDE
OIL SPURT HOLES
CYLINDER NUMBERS TO OUTSIDE
RIGHT BANK 2-4-6-8
LEFT BANK 1-3-5-7

Piston and rod assembly—V8 engines

On 1968-69 390 engine, arrange No. 1 gap 180° from No. 2; oil control expander spacer tangs must be installed in drilled holes above piston pin and oil control rails must be 180° apart.

6 Cylinder Engines

Pistons of the 199 engine can be identified by their flat head and two notches; 232 and 258 pistons have a concave head with one notch.

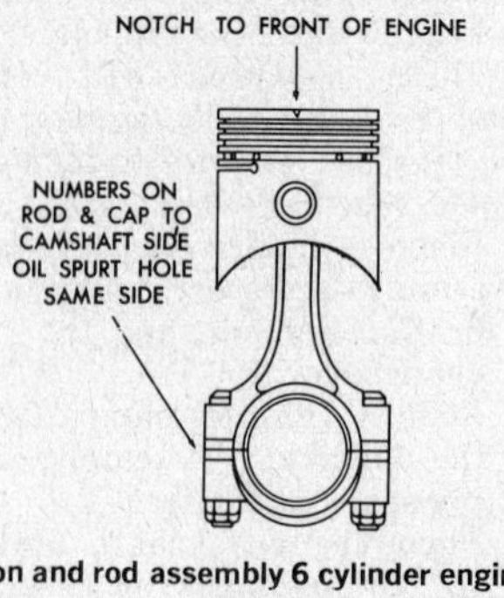
NOTCH TO FRONT OF ENGINE
NUMBERS ON ROD & CAP TO CAMSHAFT SIDE OIL SPURT HOLE SAME SIDE

Piston and rod assembly 6 cylinder engine

Engine Lubrication

Full pressure lubrication is used throughout the engine, except for the piston pins. The piston pins receive lubrication by means of squirt holes in the connecting rods, as well as, oil "throw-off."

A positive pressure, gear-type pump supplies oil pressure. The pump is mounted on a boss which is next to the number four main bearing, on the six-cylinder engines.

Oil Pan R & R

NOTE: it is far easier to remove the engine in most cases.

1967 All 6 Cylinder Engines

1. Support weight of front of car, and remove front springs.
2. Support front of engine from above the engine compartment, then remove the engine support-cushion attaching nuts at the mounting bracket.
3. Disconnect idler arm.
4. If equipped, remove front stabilizer bar.
5. Remove attaching bolts from front crossmember and pry crossmember down to gain clearance. To assist in holding crossmember down, install wood spacer blocks between the crossmember and body side sill.
6. Remove flywheel dust cover.
7. Drain oil and turn crankshaft so No. 1 piston is on upstroke, and remove pan.
8. To install, reverse the removal procedure.

1968-74 All 6 Cylinder Engines

1. Disconnect front cushions from engine bracket and remove right bracket from engine.
2. Disconnect ground strap.
3. Remove valve cover and air cleaner.
4. If equipped, remove fan shroud.
5. Raise engine as far as possible.
6. Disconnect idler arm from side sill.
7. If equipped, disconnect stabilizer bar.
8. Loosen strut rod bolts at lower control arms.
9. Remove bolts retaining crossmember, and, with weight of car on wheels, pry down crossmember and insert wooden blocks to hold it down.
10. Drain oil and remove pan.
11. To install, reverse removal procedure.

1967 V8 Engines

1. Remove front springs. (See Front Suspension.) Support weight of front of car.
2. Support front of engine from above, and take away support cushion at engine.
3. Remove idler arm and piston rod from bracket on power steering models.
4. Remove sway bar.
5. Remove front suspension cross member from side sills.
6. Pry crossmember down to get clearance for pan. Use of wooden blocks between crossmember and side sills will aid.
7. Remove flywheel dust cover.
8. Drain oil and remove pan.
9. To install, reverse the removal procedure.

All 1968-74 V8 Engines

1. Turn crankshaft until mark on damper is 180° from cover marks.
2. Disconnect engine cushion mounts from crossmember; remove fan shroud, if so equipped.
3. Disconnect ground strap; disconnect cushion mount brackets from block on American.
4. Remove starter motor.
5. Remove idler arm, except on 1969 Ambassador.
6. Ambassador sway bar: disconnect at side sills. American, Javelin, AMX, Rebel, Matador, Gremlin, Hornet sway bar: loosen links at lower control arms as far as possible.
7. Disconnect shock absorbers at lower control arms on all 1969 except Ambassador.
8. Attach chain hoist or lifting fixture and raise engine as far as possible.
9. Remove cushion mounts and brackets from American.
10. Loosen strut rod bolts at lower control arms; remove crossmember side sill bolts.
11. With car weight on front wheels, pry crossmember down far enough for clearance. Use wood blocks for support between crossmember and side sills.
12. Remove oil pan bolts and oil pan.
13. Reverse the removal procedure to install the oil pan.

Oil Pump Service

6 Cylinder

The oil pump is driven by the distributor drive shaft. Oil pump R&R does not, however, affect distributor timing because the drive gear remains in mesh with the camshaft gear.

1. Drain the oil and remove the oil pan.
2. Unfasten the oil pump attachment screws. Withdraw the pump and gasket from the engine block.
3. Remove the pump cover by unfastening the attachment screws.

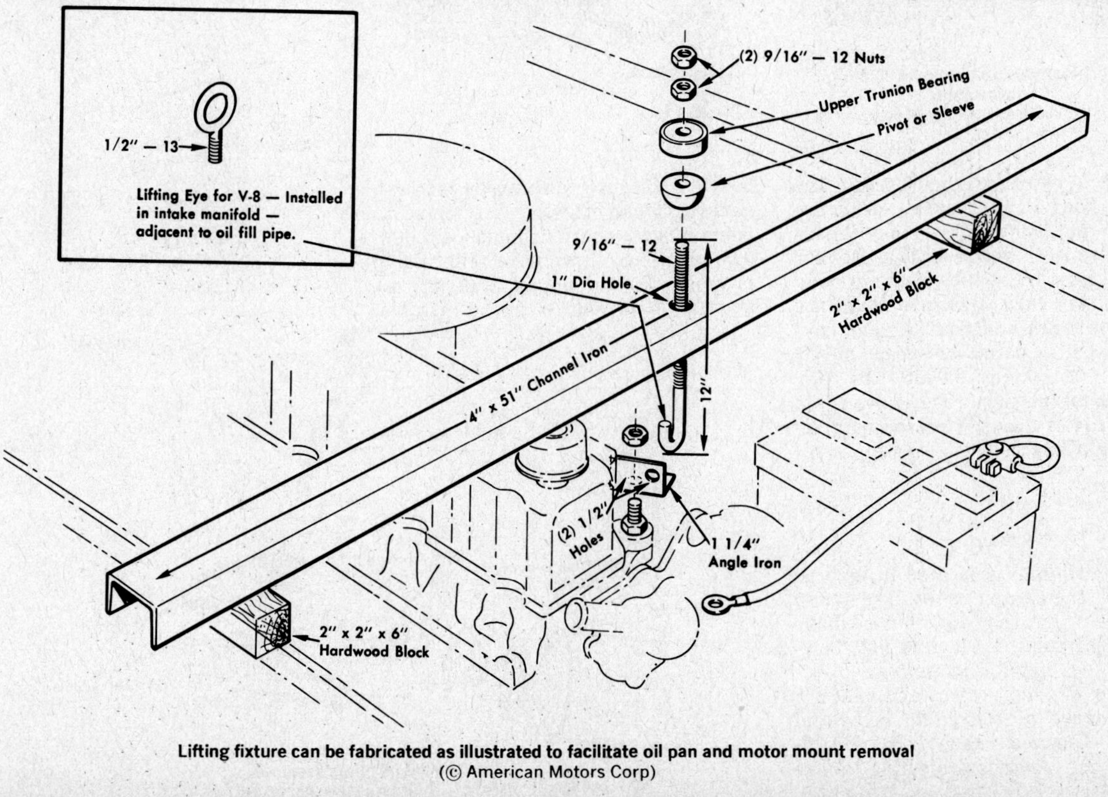
1/2" — 13
Lifting Eye for V-8 — Installed in intake manifold — adjacent to oil fill pipe.
(2) 9/16" — 12 Nuts
Upper Trunion Bearing
Pivot or Sleeve
9/16" — 12
1" Dia Hole
2" x 2" x 6" Hardwood Block
4" x 51" Channel Iron
12"
(2) 1/2" Holes
1 1/4" Angle Iron
2" x 2" x 6" Hardwood Block

Lifting fixture can be fabricated as illustrated to facilitate oil pan and motor mount removal
(© American Motors Corp)

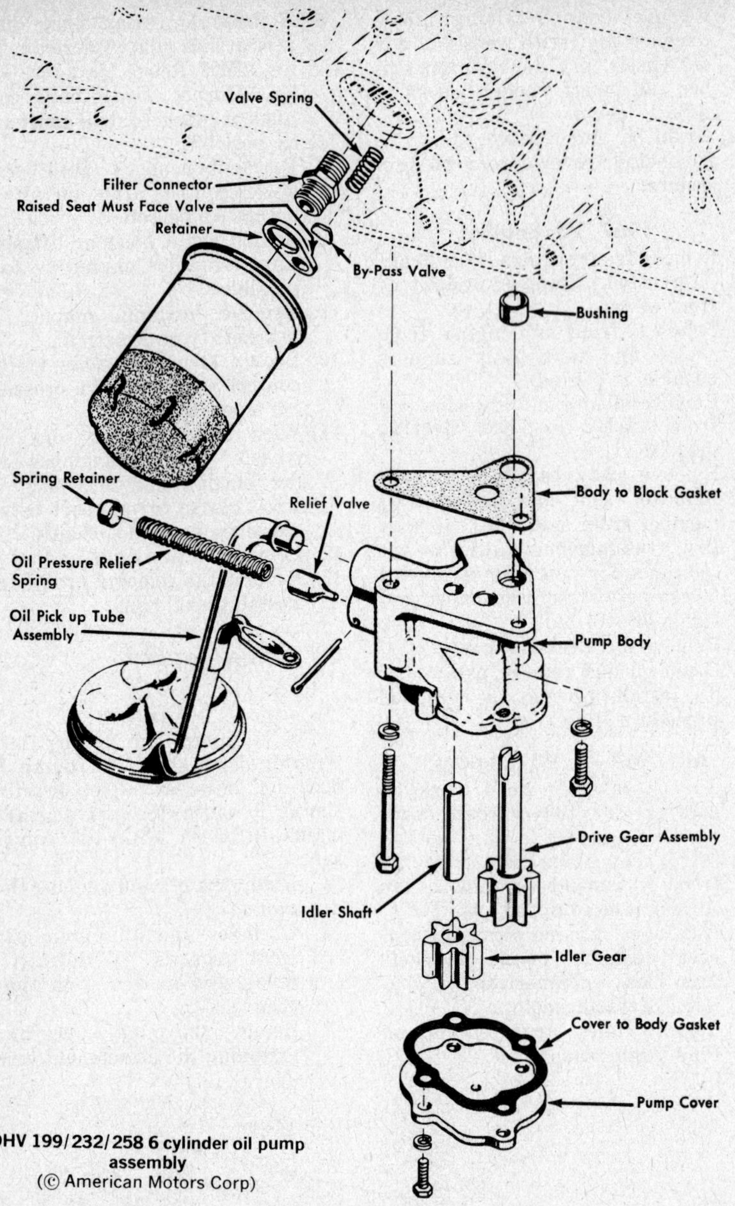
Valve Spring
Filter Connector
Raised Seat Must Face Valve
Retainer
By-Pass Valve
Bushing
Spring Retainer
Relief Valve
Body to Block Gasket
Oil Pressure Relief Spring
Oil Pick up Tube Assembly
Pump Body
Drive Gear Assembly
Idler Shaft
Idler Gear
Cover to Body Gasket
Pump Cover

OHV 199/232/258 6 cylinder oil pump assembly
(© American Motors Corp)

With a straightedge across the pump body and gears, clearance should be 0.000-0.004 in. (gears should project above body). Do not disturb location of tube in pump body if possible. Now, measure clearance between gears and wall of gear cavity opposite point of gear mesh; should be 0.0005-0.0025 in. for six. The oil pressure relief valve is set at the factory and is not adjustable.

Installation is the reverse of removal.

V8

The oil pump is located in, and as part of, the timing cover. The pump is driven by the distributor drive shaft. Oil pump R&R does not, however, affect distributor timing.

Remove pump cover and place a straightedge across pump body and gears. Clearance should be 0.0025-0.0065 in. (gears projecting above body). Measure clearance between gears and wall of gear cavity opposite point of gear mesh; should be 0.002-0.004 in. The oil pressure relief valve is set to 75 psi up to 1969, 85 psi starting 1970, and is not adjustable.

Checking oil pump gear end clearance
(© American Motors Corp)

Checking oil pump gear to body clearance
(© American Motors Corp)

Rear Main Bearing Oil Seal R & R

6 Cylinder Engines

To remove and replace the neoprene seal used on 199/232/258 engines:

1. Remove oil pan, as previously described.
2. Scrape clean all gasket surfaces, then remove rear main cap.

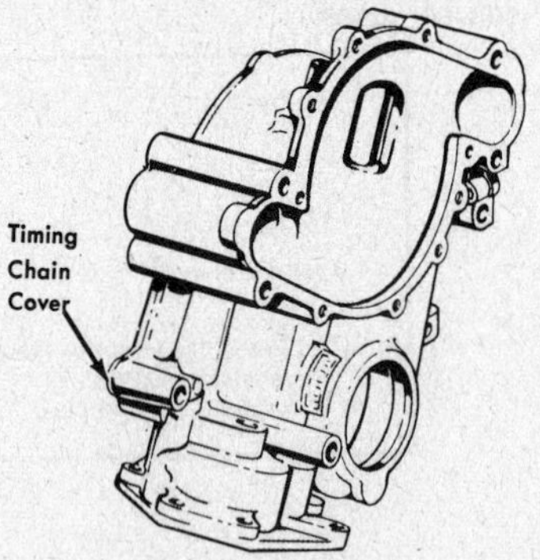
Timing Chain Cover

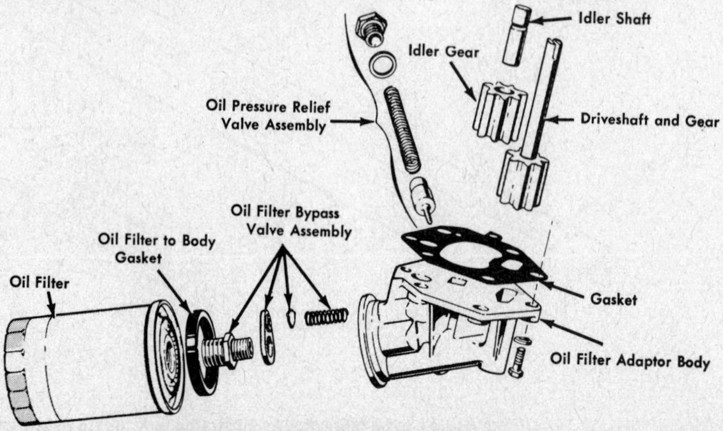
Idler Shaft
Idler Gear
Oil Pressure Relief Valve Assembly
Driveshaft and Gear
Oil Filter Bypass Valve Assembly
Oil Filter to Body Gasket
Oil Filter
Gasket
Oil Filter Adaptor Body

V8 oil pump assembly
(© American Motors Corp)

3. Discard lower portion of seal; drive out upper portion, using a brass drift, until it can be grasped with pliers.
4. Clean main cap, then *loosen* all remaining main cap bolts.
5. Lightly oil all surfaces, then coat the block-side surface of the new upper seal with soap and the seal lip with SAE 40 engine oil.
6. Install upper seal portion with the lip facing the front.
7. Coat the cap and block-side seal surface with Permatex No. 2.
8. Coat the back surface of new lower seal with soap, the lip with SAE 40 engine oil. Install lower seal firmly into main cap.
9. Coat both chamfered edges of rear main cap with Permatex No. 2, install bearing inserts (if removed) and tighten cap bolts to 75-80 ft. lbs.
10. Cement oil pan gasket to block; coat gasket tongues with Permatex No. 2 where they fit into rear main cap, as well as front neoprene seal.
11. Coat rear pan seal with soap and place into proper recess, then install oil pan bolts ($\frac{1}{4}$ in.—5-8 ft. lbs.; 5/16 in.—10-12 ft. lbs).

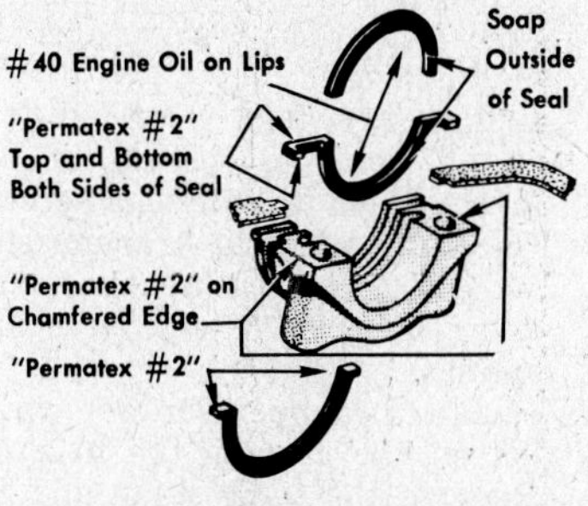
Soap
Outside
of Seal
#40 Engine Oil on Lips
"Permatex #2"
Top and Bottom
Both Sides of Seal
"Permatex #2" on
Chamfered Edge
"Permatex #2"

Rear main bearing oil seal—199/232/258 6 cylinder and all V8
(© American Motors Corp)

V8 Engines

A neoprene seal, consisting of two pieces, is used. Procedure is identical to that used for the 199/232/258 6 cylinder, except that main cap bolts are tightened to 95-105 ft. lbs.

CLUTCH

Standard Clutch

The clutch is a single-plate, dry-disc, coil spring type (except for the S-type in 1967 Ambassador, Classic, Marlin and Rebel models with the 232 cu. in. six). A semi-centrifugal clutch assembly is used with the 4-speed transmission V8, three rollers (six with 390) being equally spaced between the three clutch levers. These rollers are forced outward by centrifugal force and supply additional force to the pressure plate to prevent clutch slippage. The driven plate is spring-cushioned and has riveted linings. The throwout bearing is a ball bearing, pre-packed with grease at the factory.

No adjustment for wear is provided in the clutch itself, although an adjustment is built into the clutch cover to allow the release lever height to be varied. These adjusting nuts normally are not disturbed unless the clutch pressure plate is removed for overhaul.

Pedal travel decrease due to normal wear of the linings can be compensated for by adjusting the clutch pedal free-play (as described later).

S-type Clutch

1967

In 1967, a self-adjusting clutch system was introduced as standard equipment on the Rebel, Ambassador, Marlin and Rambler Classic series. It is smoother in action, needs less pedal pressure, and is self-adjusting throughout its service life.

Linkage design utilizes an enclosed cable to transmit motion between the clutch pedal and the main lever. The lever oscillates on a sealed, oilite bushing, or needle bearings (depending upon engine application) and is supported on a fulcrum pin attached to the engine, or clutch housing. The main lever transmits motion through an automatic wear adjuster to the fork, then to the cover assembly. This engages and releases the clutch. The cable assembly absorbs the effect of engine motion on clutch actuation.

Pressure plate load is obtained from an externally mounted spring, one end of which is attached to the engine and transmission assembly. The other end is attached to the main lever. Spring load acts on the main lever through the wear compensator (adjuster) fork and cover assembly, applying the pressure plate load required to carry the engine torque.

The automatic wear adjuster is located between the main spring and the cover assembly.

The adjuster senses and maintains a specific angular travel of the main lever. As the clutch facing wears, the travel of the main lever increases causing the actuating arm on the lever to contact a spring. The spring acts as a one-way clutch on a threaded push rod. The actuating arm, pushing on the spring when the clutch is released, rotates the rod and increases the overall length of the adjuster. The actuating arm also repositions the spring on the rod when the clutch is engaged. This sequence of events reduces the travel of the main lever to the desired arc and continues throughout clutch life. An annular contact ball bearing is used to carry the load between fork and cover assembly levers. This bearing is under load at all times.

NOTE: crankshaft end-play has an effect on light torque chatter. Therefore, if this type of chatter does exist, it is recommended that crankshaft end-play be held to .006 in. maximum. The light bearing loads (of the type S system) at initial engagement are insufficient to prevent crankshaft end flutter until about 20% of engagement is reached.

Pedal Clearance Adjustment

Adjust the free-play of the clutch pedal to $\frac{1}{2}$-$\frac{3}{4}$ in. for 1967, $\frac{7}{8}$-$1\frac{1}{8}$ in. thereafter. This is done by changing the length of the link between the throwout lever and the clutch lever.

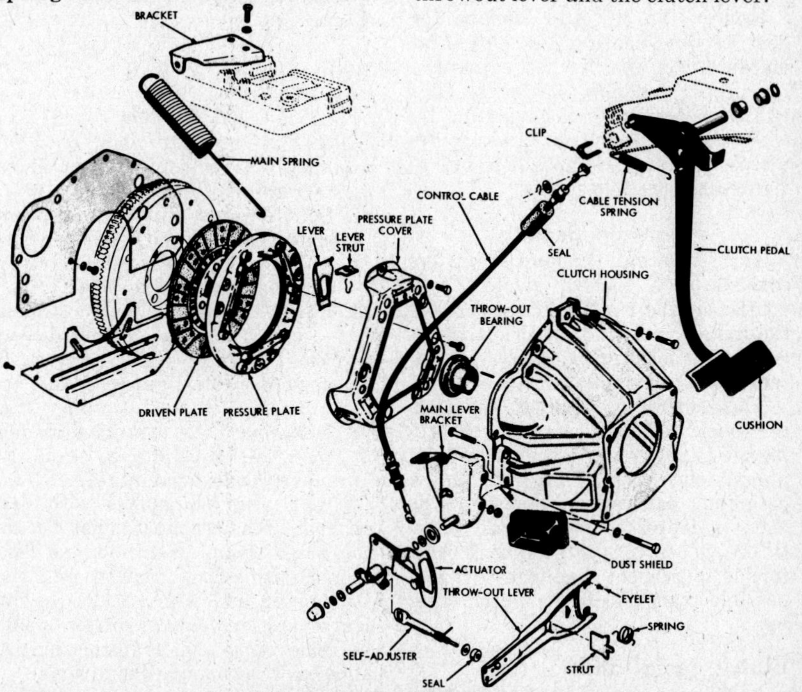
BRACKET
MAIN SPRING
CLIP
CONTROL CABLE
CABLE TENSION SPRING
PRESSURE PLATE COVER
LEVER
LEVER STRUT
SEAL
CLUTCH PEDAL
CLUTCH HOUSING
THROW-OUT BEARING
DRIVEN PLATE
PRESSURE PLATE
MAIN LEVER BRACKET
CUSHION
DUST SHIELD
ACTUATOR
THROW-OUT LEVER
EYELET
SPRING
SELF-ADJUSTER
STRUT
SEAL

S-type clutch and linkage assembly
(© American Motors Corp)

NOTE: adjust clutch pedal to floor clearance to 6½ in. for models with 199 cu. in. engine. On 232, 258 and all V8 models, adjust clutch pedal height by inserting a 5/16 in. x 4½ in. long pin into the alignment holes in the pedal bracket. Adjust pedal height so that pin slides freely.

Clutch Removal

Remove the transmission as outlined later (place wood-padded jack under oil pan instead of clutch housing), then disconnect the clutch linkage at the release lever and remove the capscrews that hold the bellhousing (clutch housing) to the engine. It may be necessary to move the rear of the engine up or down to gain wrench clearance.

NOTE: any shims between the housing and engine must be replaced in exactly the same place to prevent misalignment.

Matchmark the clutch cover, pressure plate and flywheel before removal to ensure proper balance. Loosen each clutch cover capscrew a few turns at a time until spring tension is released, then remove the cover, pressure plate, and disc.

Pilot Bushing

Check the pilot bushing in the end of the crankshaft for scoring or looseness. If it is necessary to replace the bushing, use either an expanding-end slidehammer or a suitable tap. Screwing the tap into the bore until it bottoms will force the bushing out.

Lubricate the bushing with wheel bearing grease or Molykote before installing the clutch.

Flywheel

Inspect the flywheel surface for heat cracks, scoring, or blue heat marks. Check the flywheel capscrews for proper torque (105 ft. lbs.). It will be necessary to lock-up the flywheel ring gear with a block or flywheel holding clamp tool before tightening these capscrews.

Throwout Bearing

The throwout (release) linkage consists of a forked, pivoted lever contacting the bearing at one end and the linkage pushrod on the other. A return spring keeps the lever in contact with the ball pivot.

The throwout bearing itself is pre-lubricated and cannot be repacked if dry. Failure is evidenced by uneven clutch pedal pressure and a grinding, rattling noise when the pedal is depressed. Replace any noisy throwout bearings as soon as is practicable to prevent disintegration and possible transmission or clutch damage.

Clutch Installation

Slide the new clutch disc onto the transmission input shaft to check for binding. Remove any burrs from either the splines or hub using sandpaper, then clean with gasoline and lubricate the splines and hub with Molykote. Place the clutch disc against the flywheel and secure it by inserting a dummy pilot shaft (such shafts, made of wood, are available from automotive jobbers) or an old transmission input shaft.

Place the new pressure plate (it's always good policy to replace the pressure plate when installing a new disc) in position, after first making sure that the clutch disc is facing the proper direction (flywheel side is so marked), and that matchmarks are aligned if old pressure plate is used.

Install all the capscrews finger-tight. Tighten the screws a little at a time, working around the pressure plate to avoid distorting it, to 40 ft. lbs. Remove the pilot shaft.

NOTE: do not depress clutch pedal until transmission is installed or throwout bearing will fall out.

Install the clutch housing, throwout bearing and transmission. Hook up clutch linkage and check adjustment.

MANUAL TRANSMISSION

American Motors cars use Borg-Warner manual transmissions. For specific details of transmission overhaul, see the "Unit Repair Section."

An identification tag, containing Borg-Warner and American Motors part numbers, is located at the rear of the transmission. These numbers are important when ordering replacement parts, so always see that the tag is installed when the transmission is overhauled.

Transmission R & R

All Models

NOTE: Open the hood to avoid damage to it, when the rear crossmember is removed.

1. Split the rear universal joint and slide the driveshaft off the back of the transmission. (See Universal Joints and Drive Lines.)
2. Remove shift mechanism linkage to the transmission, and disconnect the clutch linkage and speedometer cable. Support the engine.
3. Disconnect the overdrive mechanism (if so equipped) and remove the rear mounts.

NOTE: on V8 models with dual exhaust, exhaust pipes must be disconnected from manifolds so that rear crossmember can be removed. On Javelin and AMX models having Hurst shifter, entire shifter should be removed so that transmission can slide back far enough for removal.

4. Take out the transmission support crossmember, remove the two studs which hold the transmission to the bell housing and replace these two studs with two long pilot studs.
5. Take out the two bottom studs and slide the transmission assembly along the pilot studs and out of the car.

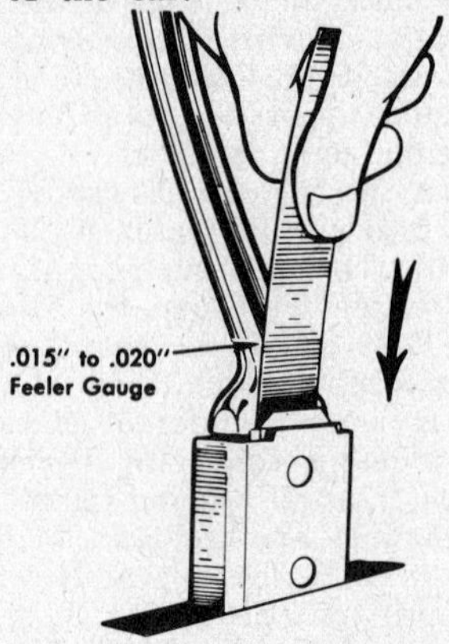

.015" to .020"
Feeler Gauge

Removing lever from Hurst shifter
(© American Motors Corp)

Installation of the manual transmission is performed in the following order:

1. Fit the throwout bearing and the sleeve assembly in the clutch fork. Center the bearing over the clutch lever.
2. Install two pilot studs in the clutch housing, instead of the lower clutch housing cap screws.
3. Carefully slide the transmission into place. Be careful not to damage the clutch driven plate splines.
4. Install the upper screws, which attach the case to the housing. Remove the pilot studs and install the lower cap screws.
5. If the car is equipped with a floor shift, install the shift mechanism.
6. Attach the speedometer cable, back-up light switch wires and the transmission controlled spark (TCS) wire (if so equipped).
7. Raise the transmission. Attach the rear crossmember and support to the transmission. Fasten the crossmember to the side sills.
8. Attach the exhaust pipes to the exhaust manifolds, on V8 engines, if they were removed.
9. Install the front U-joint yoke on the transmission, as detailed elsewhere. Do the same for the rear U-joint at the differential.
10. Connect the shift rods on the column shift transmissions and the reverse lock-up rod (if so equipped) on the floor shift transmission. Check the transmission oil level and add lubricant, as needed.
11. Remove the supports and lower the car.
12. Install the shift lever, the boot, the bezel, and the retainer, if the

car is equipped with a floor-shift transmission.

13. Adjust the shift linkage, as detailed below.

Shift Lever Adjustment

Column Shift—1967-69

Loosen the trunnion locknuts on the shift rods, then position the two operating levers in the center of the jacket tube cut-out. Insert a 3/16 in. drill through any existing aligning holes in the shift levers, shift gate and bracket. With the levers in neutral, adjust the trunnions for a free fit, without binding, in the levers. Lock the trunnions in this position, then check the shift lever positions for binding.

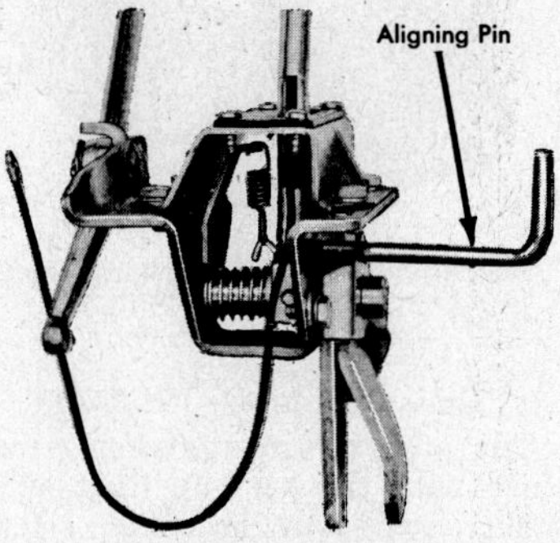
Aligning Pin
Aligning shift levers
(© American Motors Corp)

Column Shift—1970-74

1. Detach the shift rods from the shift levers. Insert a 3/16 in. drill through the column shift lever holes.
2. Shift into Reverse and lock the column with the ignition key. Position the First/Reverse shift lever in Reverse.
3. Adjust the shift rod trunnion to a free pin fit in the outer shift lever. Tighten the trunnion locknuts.
4. Unlock the column and move the gearshift to Neutral. Both of the transmission outer shift levers should be in the Neutral detent.
5. Repeat step three for the Second/Third shift rod trunnion.
6. Withdraw the drill from the column levers. Shift through all

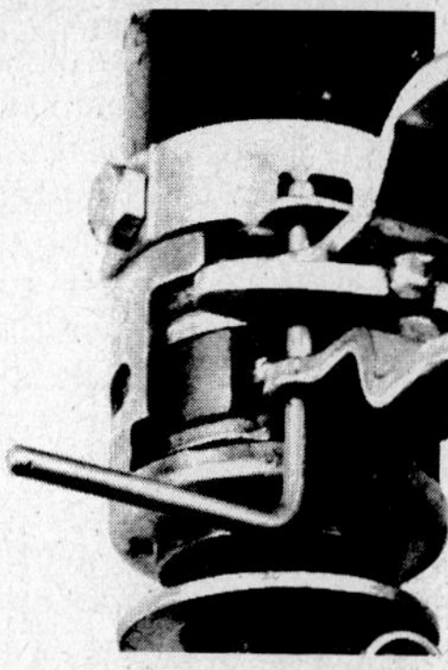
Aligning shift levers column shift models with gauge hole
(© American Motors Corp)

gears and check for a free cross-over into Neutral.

7. Shift into Reverse and lock the column. The column should lock without any binding.

Three-Speed Floorshift—Through 1969

Place the transmission shift levers in neutral. Loosen the 2-3 transmission lever attaching nut and adjustment bolt. With the 1-R shift rod in neutral position, align the 2-3 rod so the shift notch is exactly aligned with the 1-R shift rod notch. Tighten the adjustment bolt and attaching nut. Operate the shift lever to make sure there is no binding in the 1-2 shift.

To adjust the back-up light switch, loosen the two jam nuts and slide the switch forward or backward.

Three-Speed Floorshift—1970-71

Loosen the reverse lock rod trunnion locknuts about ½ in. Shift into reverse and lock the steering column. It may be necessary to move the lower column lever upward until it is in the locked position.

Tighten the lower trunnion locknut until it contacts the trunnion. Tighten the upper locknut while holding the trunnion centered in the column lever. Unlock the steering column, shift in neutral, and check that

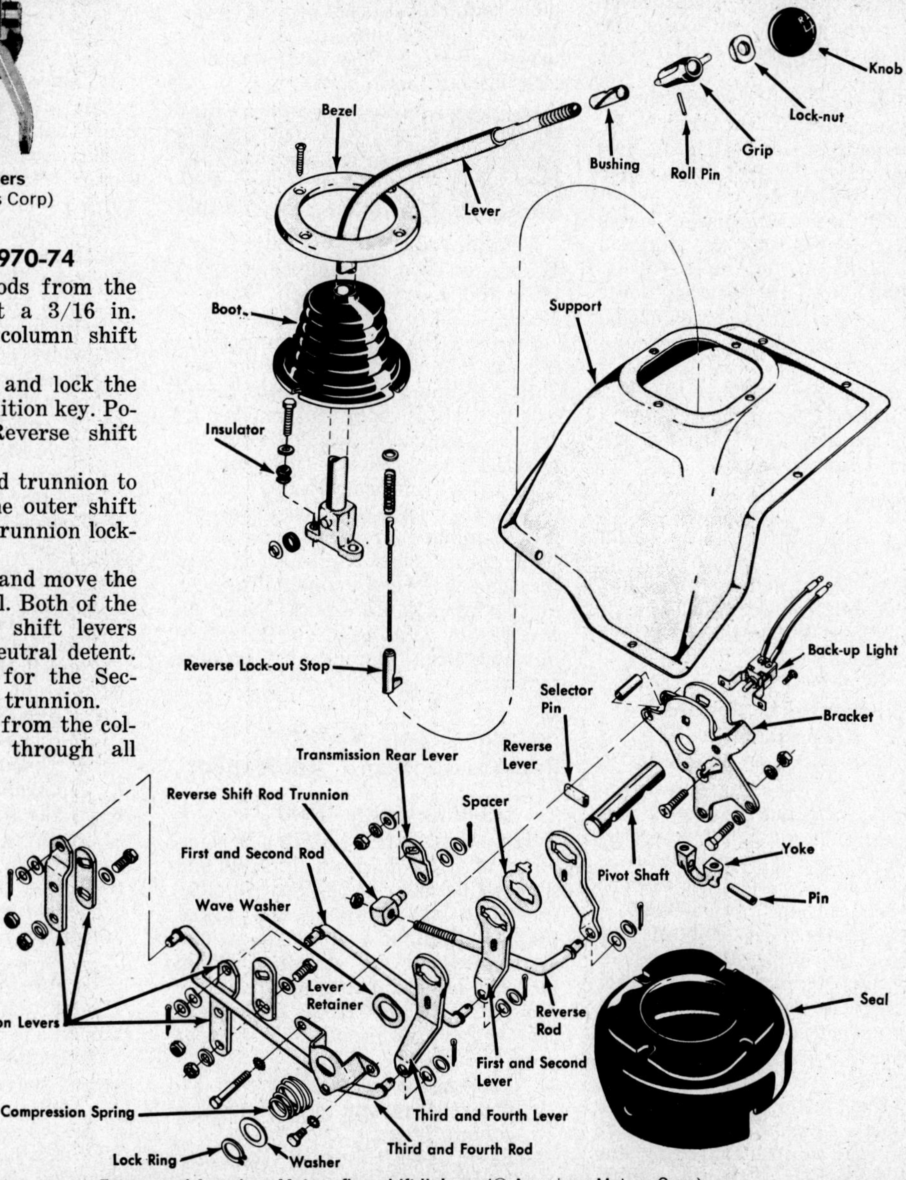
Knob
Lock-nut
Grip
Roll Pin
Bushing
Bezel
Lever
Support
Boot
Insulator
Reverse Lock-out Stop
Back-up Light
Bracket
Selector Pin
Reverse Lever
Transmission Rear Lever
Reverse Shift Rod Trunnion
Spacer
Yoke
Pivot Shaft
Pin
First and Second Rod
Wave Washer
Lever Retainer
Reverse Rod
Seal
Transmission Levers
First and Second Lever
Compression Spring
Third and Fourth Lever
Lock Ring
Washer
Third and Fourth Rod
Four-speed American Motors floorshift linkage (© American Motors Corp)

the transmission shift levers are in their neutral positions.

Loosen the 2-3 transmission lever attaching nut and adjustment bolt. With the 1-R shift rod in the neutral position, align the 1-R and 2-3 shift rod notches. Tighten the adjustment bolt and attaching nut.

Shift through the gears, checking for binding in the 1-2 shift in particular. Shift into reverse and lock the column—this operation should be smooth with no binding.

Three-Speed Floorshift—1972-74

For the correct standard steering column adjustment procedure, refer to "Three-Speed Floorshift—Through 1969," above.

If the car is equipped with an adjustable steering column, refer to the 1970–71 floor-mounted shift linkage adjustment procedures, to obtain correct adjustment details.

Four-Speed AM Floorshift—Through 1969

Loosen the transmission shift lever nuts (two per lever) and loosen the locknuts on the reverse shift rod at the trunnion.

Install a 1/4 in. drill through the selector lever retainer, through the levers, spacer plate and aligning hole in the mounting bracket (this is the neutral position).

Place all three transmission levers in neutral, then adjust the trunnion on the reverse shift rod so that it enters freely into the reverse lever without binding. Lock the nuts on the reverse rod and install washer and cotter pin.

Tighten the lower nuts on the shift levers, making sure the outer levers stay in position, then tighten the upper nut to approximately 10 ft. lbs.

Caution Do not overtighten these nuts, otherwise the shift shafts might break.

Remove the 1/4 in. drill rod, then lubricate the shift rod ends with chassis grease and check operation of shifter in all gears.

Four-Speed Hurst Floorshift—Starting 1969

NOTE: It may be necessary to lower the rear of the transmission to install the shift lever aligning pin. Before lowering the transmission, open the hood and remove the air cleaner. Then disconnect the exhaust system and the rear crossmember.

Remove the boot assembly or plug and loosen the lower nuts and bolts on the two transmission forward speed shift levers. Loosen the two self-locking nuts at the center of the shift levers. Loosen the two locknuts on the reverse shift rod trunnion.

With the shifter in neutral position, insert a 1/4 in. diameter aligning pin into the shifter housing and through the center of the three shifter levers. Make sure that the pin enters the notch in the far side of the housing. Check that the transmission levers are in their neutral positions. Remove and reinsert the aligning pin. The pin should slide in freely. If it does not, the shifter is not correctly aligned in the neutral position.

Tighten the lower bolts and nuts at the transmission forward speed shift levers. Tighten the self-locking nuts to 10 ft. lbs. Make sure the transmission reverse lever is in the neutral position. Tighten the trunnion nuts, being careful not to bind the trunnion in the reverse lever, then remove the aligning pin.

NOTE: on 1970-74 models, loosen the steering column reverse lock-up rod trunnion locknuts about 1/2 in. each. Shift into reverse and lock the column. It may be necessary to move the lower column lever upward until it is in the locked position. Tighten the lower trunnion locknut until it contacts the trunnion. Tighten the upper locknut while holding the trunnion centered in the column lever. Unlock the column and check for proper shifting. The column should lock without binding.

AUTOMATIC TRANSMISSION

The Borg-Warner automatic transmission is used through model year 1971 and is called either Flash-O-Matic or Shift Command, depending on whether the transmission upshifts can be manually controlled or not. Shift-Command transmissions use a modified valve body to enable the driver to manually select a gear and hold the transmission in that gear.

In 1972, American Motors elected to use Chrysler Corporation Torqueflite automatic transmissions in all their cars. These transmissions are the same as the equivalent Chrysler units, the only differences being in case design required by the difference in American Motors' bell-housing configuration and driveshafts.

Neutral Safety Switch Replacement and Adjustment

Column Shift—1967-71

The neutral safety switch is combined with the back-up light switch, thus, adjustment of the neutral safety switch will automatically adjust the back-up light switch. The switch is mounted in the steering column jacket, below the instrument panel.

NOTE: engage the parking brake fully before beginning adjustment procedures.

1. Loosen the two screws that attach the switch to the steering column jacket.
2. Select Neutral with the gear lever.
3. Insert a 3/32 in. punch in the hole on the switch face. Turn the switch until the pin freely enters the hole in the toggle.
4. Tighten the two mounting screws. Withdraw the punch. Be sure that the switch tang entered the channel on the operating shaft, *before* tightening the screws. Check the switch for proper operation.
5. To remove the switch, remove the mounting screws completely and withdraw it.

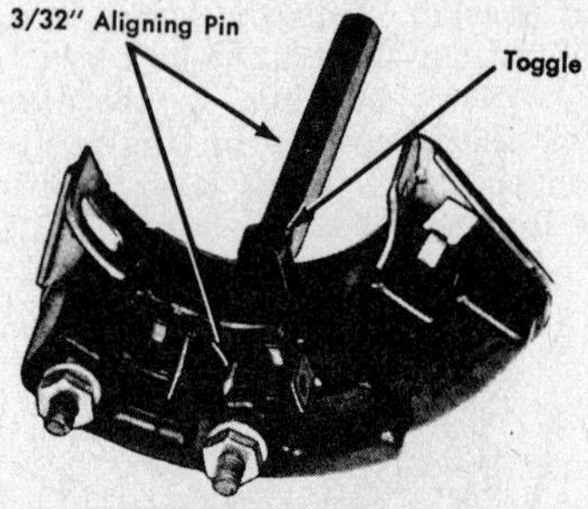
3/32" Aligning Pin
Toggle

Steering column mounting neutral safety switch adjustment—1967-71
(© American Motors Corp)

Console Shift—1967-71

The neutral safety switch is combined with the back-up light switch and is located in the center console. Before starting adjustment procedures be sure that the parking brake is firmly set.

1. Place the selector in Neutral.
2. Take the selector knob off the shift lever, except on 1971 Javelin models.
3. Remove the attachment screws from the console, raise it up and over the selector lever.
4. On the 1971 Javelin models, remove the console cover attaching screws and slide the cover up the selector lever.
5. Loosen the two switch attaching screws.
6. Insert a 3/32 in. punch in the hole in the face of the switch. Move the switch as necessary to freely fit the punch through the hole in the toggle.
7. Tighten the two screws and withdraw the punch. Check for proper switch operation. The car should only start in Park or Neutral.
8. If the switch is to be completely removed, take out the screws and withdraw the switch.
9. When adjustments are completed, assemble the console and shift selector.

All Models—1972-74

On all 1972-74 American Motors cars, a combination back-up light/-neutral safety switch is mounted on the left side of the transmission case. This switch cannot be adjusted; failure means replacement.

To test the switch, proceed in the following manner:

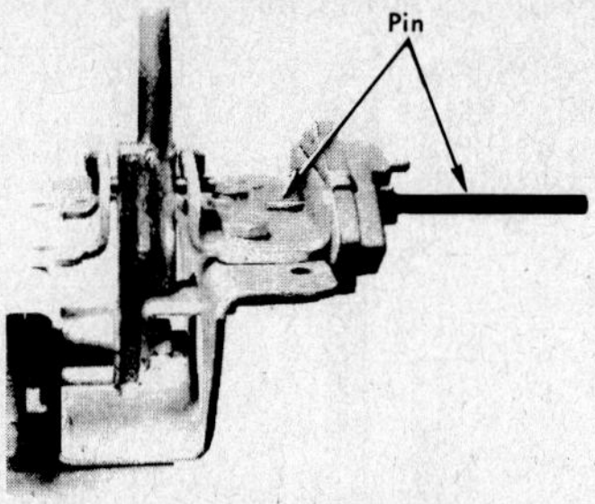
Pin
Console mounted neutral safety switch adjustment—1967-71
(© American Motors Corp)

1. Unfasten the wiring connector from the switch.
2. Use a 12V test lamp to check for continuity between the center pin of the switch and the transmission case. The lamp should only light in Park or Neutral.
3. If the lamp lights up in other positions, check the transmission linkage adjustments before replacing the switch.
4. To test the back-up light function of the switch repeat step two, by bridging the outside pins to test continuity. The light should only light in Reverse. No continuity should be present from either of the pins to the case.

To remove the switch, proceed as follows:

1. Place a container under the switch to catch transmission fluid. Unscrew the switch.
2. Select Park and then Neutral while checking to see that the operating fingers for the switch are centered in the case opening.
3. Screw a new switch and a *new* seal into the transmission. Tighten the switch to 24 ft. lbs.
4. Retest continuity. Replenish the transmission fluid, as required.

Manual Linkage Adjustment

Column Shift—1967

1. Turn off ignition switch.
2. Place selector in Neutral.
3. Disconnect manual lever from transmission outer lever.
4. Move outer lever to extreme rear notch (Low).
5. Move lever forward three notches to Neutral.
6. With lever linkage held against Neutral stop, adjust for free pin fit.
7. Connect linkage and check action, then test drive car.

Floorshift (Shift-Command)—1967

1. Place selector in Neutral.
2. Disconnect linkage rod from shift lever.
3. Move transmission outer lever to extreme forward notch (1).
4. Move lever three notches to rear (Neutral).
5. Adjust for free pin fit.
6. Connect linkage and check action, then test drive car.

1968-71

1. Place selector in Neutral.

NOTE: range 1 for American series.

2. Push shift rod against Neutral stop on shift gate.
3. Push selector lever forward to remove free play, then adjust clevis for free pin fit.
4. Connect linkage and check action, then test drive car.
5. On 1970 and 1971 models, place selector in Park and check column lock operation.

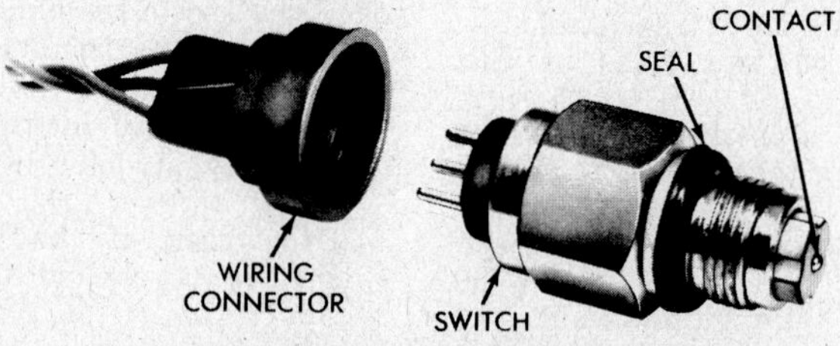
CONTACT
SEAL
WIRING CONNECTOR
SWITCH
Torque-Command neutral safety switch—1972-74
(© Chrysler Corp)

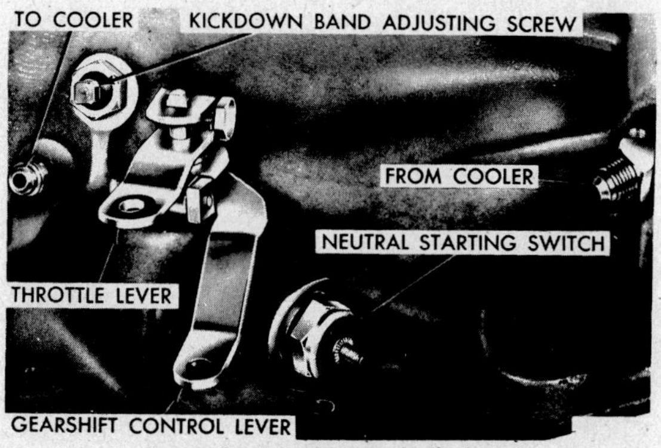
TO COOLER
KICKDOWN BAND ADJUSTING SCREW
FROM COOLER
NEUTRAL STARTING SWITCH
THROTTLE LEVER
GEARSHIFT CONTROL LEVER
Torque-Command external adjustments
(© Chrysler Corp)

Console Shift—1970-71

1. Loosen park lockup rod trunnion locknuts.
2. Place console lever in Neutral.
3. Place transmission shift lever in neutral position.
4. Adjut shift rod for a free pin fit.
5. Place console lever in Park. Lock the steering column. It may be necessary to move the lower column lever upward until it is in the locked position.
6. Tighten the lower trunnion locknut until it contacts the trunnion. Tighten the upper locknut while holding the trunnion centered in the column lever.

Torque-Command—1972-74

1. With the engine off, place the selector in Park and the transmission shifting lever in the Park detent.
2. Adjust the shift rod, as necessary, for a free pin fit.
3. See that the steering column lock and the neutral safety switch operate properly.

Kick Down Band Adjustment

Torque-Command—1972-74

The adjustment screw for the kick-down band is located on the left side of the transmission, above the throttle and manual linkage levers.

1. Loosen the locknut. Back off the screw five turns.
2. Using a torque wrench tighten the screw to 72 in. lbs.
3. Back off two turns on the adjustment screw on the 904 and 988 series transmission.
4. Back off two and one-half turns with the 360 cu in. engines or two turns with the 401 cu in. engine when used with the 727 series transmission.
5. Hold the adjusting screw and tighten the locknut to 29 ft lbs.

Downshift Solenoid R & R

Shift-Command—1967-71

1. Drain the oil and remove oil pan, then disconnect solenoid wire from transmission case terminal.
2. Push in on the solenoid, while twisting, to detach it from the control valve.

Caution do not lose downshift valve spring.

3. To install, reverse the removal procedure, using a new O-ring.

Oil Pan R & R

1967-71 All

1. Jack up the car and disconnect the oil filler tube at the transmission, then drain the transmission oil.
2. Remove oil pan screws and lockwashers, then remove oil pan and gasket.

3. Remove Alnico magnet from the head of the rear servo hold-down bolt, then remove inlet oil screen.

NOTE: do not use air pressure, or any solvents other than ATF, to clean.

4. To install, reverse removal procedure, tightening oil pan screws to 15 ft. lbs.

Torque-Command—1972-74

1. Raise the car on a lift.
2. Place a container with a large mouth under the pan.
3. Unfasten the pan retaining bolts. Tap the pan at one corner in order to break it loose. Allow the fluid to drain from the transmission, then completely withdraw the oil pan.
4. Clean the pan before installing it. Always use a *new* gasket. Tighten the oil pan bolts to 151 in. lbs.
5. Add DEXRON transmission fluid.

Band Adjustments

Front Band—1967-71

1. Drain transmission fluid and remove oil pan.
2. Check for debris, "scorched" smelling fluid, and loose parts.
3. Check pick up screen for clogging, then check that all valve body cap screws and servo bolts are tight (do not overtighten).
4. Check that oil delivery tubes are in place and snug.
5. To adjust, insert a $\frac{1}{4}$ in. gauge block between the front servo, adjusting screw and the piston rod, then tighten adjusting screw to 9 in. lbs. for 1967 transmissions, 10 in. lbs. for 1968-71 transmissions.

Caution The adjusting screw on M11, M11B and M12 transmissions has a left-hand thread.

6. For 1969-71 only: inspect the adjuster wire for proper clearance —one screw thread must be exposed between the wire and the servo actuating lever.
7. Clean and install the oil pan, using a new gasket, then install proper quantity of approved fluid.

Rear Band—1967-71

1. Place a hydraulic jack under the transmission, then remove the four crossmember fasteners and the crossmember.

NOTE: Not necessary to remove crossmember on most Ambassador models. On AMX and Javelin equipped with power steering, lift the hood before lowering transmission to keep the power steering fluid reservoir wingnut from hitting the hood.

2. Lower the transmission, then loosen the rear band adjusting screw locknut and tighten the adjusting screw to 10 ft. lbs. for 1967 and later transmissions.
3. Back off adjusting screw $\frac{3}{4}$ turn for M36, M37, M40, M43, and M44 transmissions, $1\frac{1}{4}$ turns for M11, M11B, and M12 transmissions. Tighten locknut to 28 ft. lbs.
4. Raise transmission and replace crossmember.

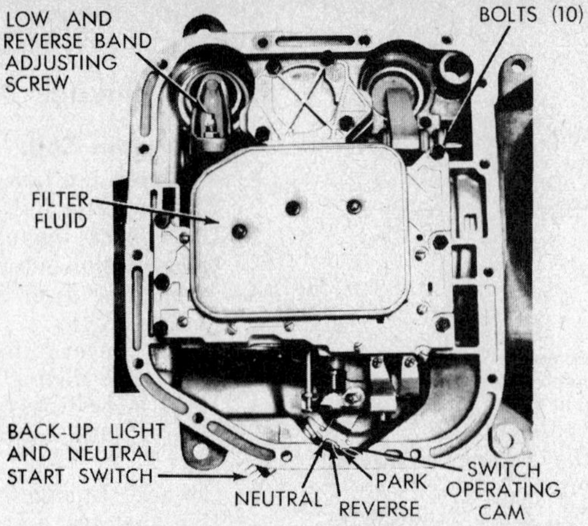
LOW AND REVERSE BAND ADJUSTING SCREW
BOLTS (10)
FILTER FLUID
BACK-UP LIGHT AND NEUTRAL START SWITCH
NEUTRAL
REVERSE
PARK
SWITCH OPERATING CAM
Torque-Command adjustments with the oil pan removed
(© Chrysler Corp)

Low and Reverse Band—1972-74

1. Remove the oil pan, as outlined above.
2. Loosen the locknut on the adjustment screw and back the screw off five turns.
3. Tighten the screw to 72 in. lbs.
4. Make the following adjustments:
   a. Series 904 transmission—back off three and one-quarter turns on the screw
   b. Series 998 transmission—back off four turns on the screw
   c. Series 727 transmission—back off two turns on the screw
5. Hold the adjusting screw while tightening the locknut to 35 ft. lbs.
6. Install the oil pan and a new gasket. Refill the transmission with Type "A" (DEXRON) fluid.

Oil Filter R & R

Torque-Command—1972-74

1. With the oil pan removed, unfasten the screws which secure the filter to the valve body. Withdraw the filter.
2. Inspect the filter for metal particles and chips. If these are present, the transmission has worn or damaged parts.
3. Install a new filter. Tighten the filter securing screws to 28 in. lbs.
4. Clean the oil pan and install it. Always use a new gasket. Fill the transmission with Type "A" (DEXRON) fluid.

U-JOINTS

1967-74 Open Drive Line

A one-piece, tubular driveshaft is used on these models. Some rear yokes are held to the pinion shaft by a bolt, others by the pinion nut. Do not loosen this nut.

Removal and Installation

1. Split rear U-joint by removing nuts.
2. Drop rear of driveshaft and slide front yoke out of transmission.

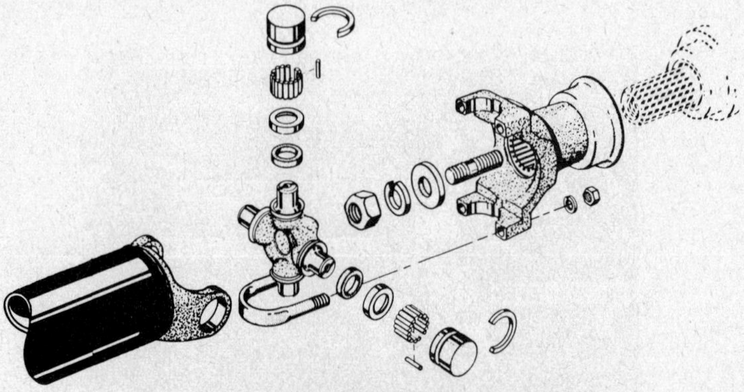

Rear U-joint assembly—1967-74 American and Hornet illustrated
(© American Motors Corp)

9/16" Socket
1-1/8" Socket

Removing end bearing from the yoke

9/16" Socket

Installing end bearing

3. To install, reverse removal procedure, tightening U-joint bolts to 18-22 ft lbs.—1967 and 15 ft lbs.—1968-74.

Universal Joint Repairs

1. Remove the lock rings from the inner side of two opposite bearings and press on the outer side of one of the bearings, forcing the crossover. This will force the bearing on the opposite side out of its yoke.
2. Remove the bearing which was forced out of the yoke, then press the cross in the opposite direction to force the other bearing out.

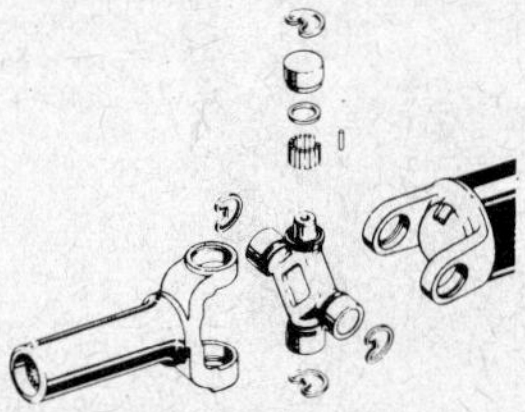

Front universal joint exploded view

3. Repeat this procedure on the third and fourth bearing.
4. When installing the new bearings in the universal joint yoke, it is possible to put them in with a driver of some type, but it is recommended that this work be done in an arbor press because a heavy jolt on the needle bearings can very easily misalign them, and greatly shorten their life.

JACKING, HOISTING

1. Jack car, at front, under lower support arms and, at rear, under rear axle housing.
2. To lift, contact car at rear lift pads marked lift just forward of rear wheels. Front lift points are on underbody sill just to the rear of strut rod-to-sill mounting bracket.

FRONT SUSPENSION

The front suspension on all models is an independent linked type with the coil springs located between seats in the wheelwell panels and seats in the upper control arms. Rubber insulators between the springs and seats reduce noise transmission to the body.

Direct acting, telescopic shock absorbers are located inside the coil springs and the control arms are attached to the body via rubber bushings.

Up to 1969, the lower control arm contained a single ball joint which attached to the steering knuckle, while the upper portion of the knuckle was attached to a trunnion. In 1970, this system was replaced by a double ball joint design, both upper and lower control arms each having one joint.

On all models, strut rods serve to support the lower control arms. Stabilizer bars are used on some models.

Shock Absorber R & R

1970-74

1. Unfasten the two lower shock absorber attachment nuts. Remove the washers and the grommets.
2. Unfasten the upper mounting bracket nuts and bolts from the wheel arch panel.
3. Withdraw the bracket, complete with shock.
4. Remove the upper attachment nut and separate the shock from the mounting bracket.

Install the shock as follows:

1. Fit the grommets, washers, upper mounting bracket and nut on the shock, in the reverse order of removal. Tighten the nut to 30 ft lbs.
2. Fully extend the shock and install two grommets on the lower mounting studs.
3. Lower the shock through the hole in the wheel arch. Fit the lower attachment studs through the lower spring seat.
4. Install the grommets, washers, and nuts. Tighten the nuts to 8 ft lbs.
5. Secure the upper mounting bracket with its attachment nuts and bolts. Tighten them to 20 ft lbs.

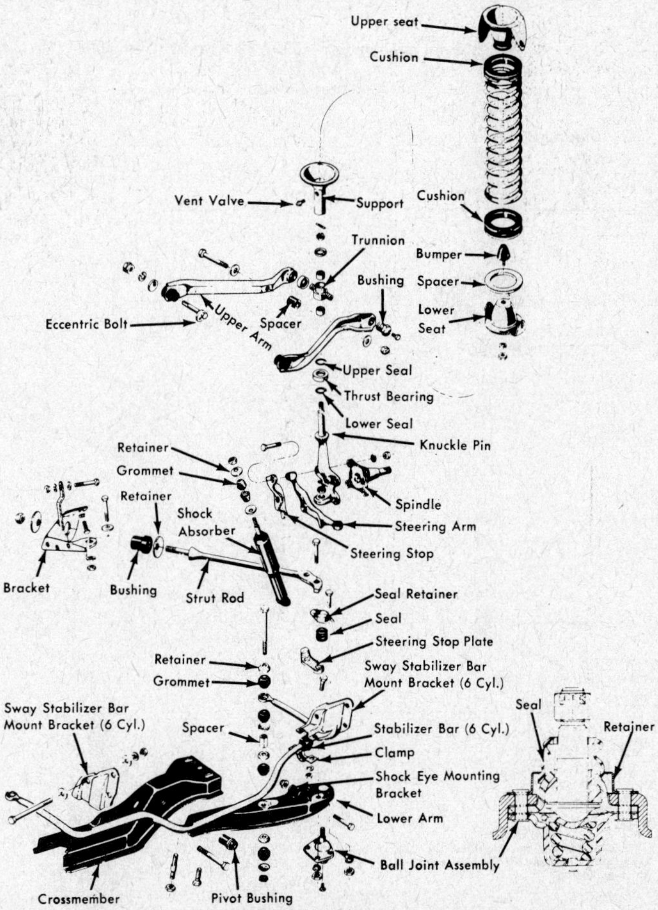
Upper seat
Cushion
Vent Valve
Support
Cushion
Trunnion
Bumper
Bushing
Spacer
Eccentric Bolt
Upper Arm
Spacer
Lower Seat
Upper Seal
Thrust Bearing
Lower Seal
Knuckle Pin
Retainer
Grommet
Retainer
Shock Absorber
Spindle
Steering Arm
Steering Stop
Bracket
Bushing
Strut Rod
Seal Retainer
Seal
Steering Stop Plate
Retainer
Grommet
Sway Stabilizer Bar Mount Bracket (6 Cyl.)
Sway Stabilizer Bar Mount Bracket (6 Cyl.)
Spacer
Seal
Retainer
Stabilizer Bar (6 Cyl.)
Clamp
Shock Eye Mounting Bracket
Lower Arm
Ball Joint Assembly
Crossmember
Pivot Bushing

Typical front suspension—1967-69 Ambassador, Rebel, Classic and Marlin
(© American Motors Corp)

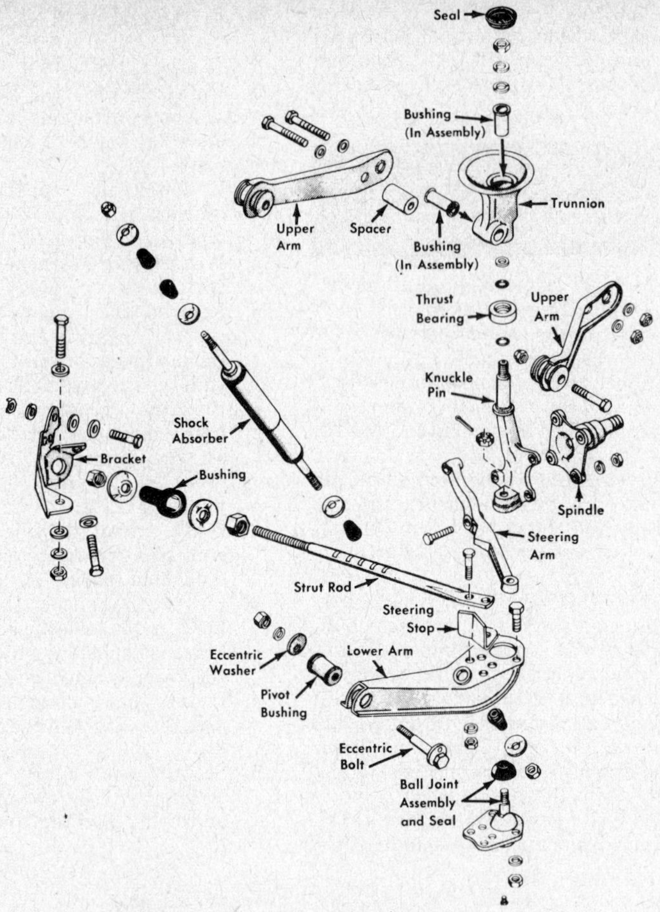
Seal
Bushing (In Assembly)
Trunnion
Upper Arm
Spacer
Bushing (In Assembly)
Thrust Bearing
Upper Arm
Knuckle Pin
Shock Absorber
Bracket
Bushing
Spindle
Steering Arm
Strut Rod
Steering Stop
Eccentric Washer
Lower Arm
Pivot Bushing
Eccentric Bolt
Ball Joint Assembly and Seal

Typical front suspension—1967-69 American, Javelin and AMX
(© American Motors Corp)

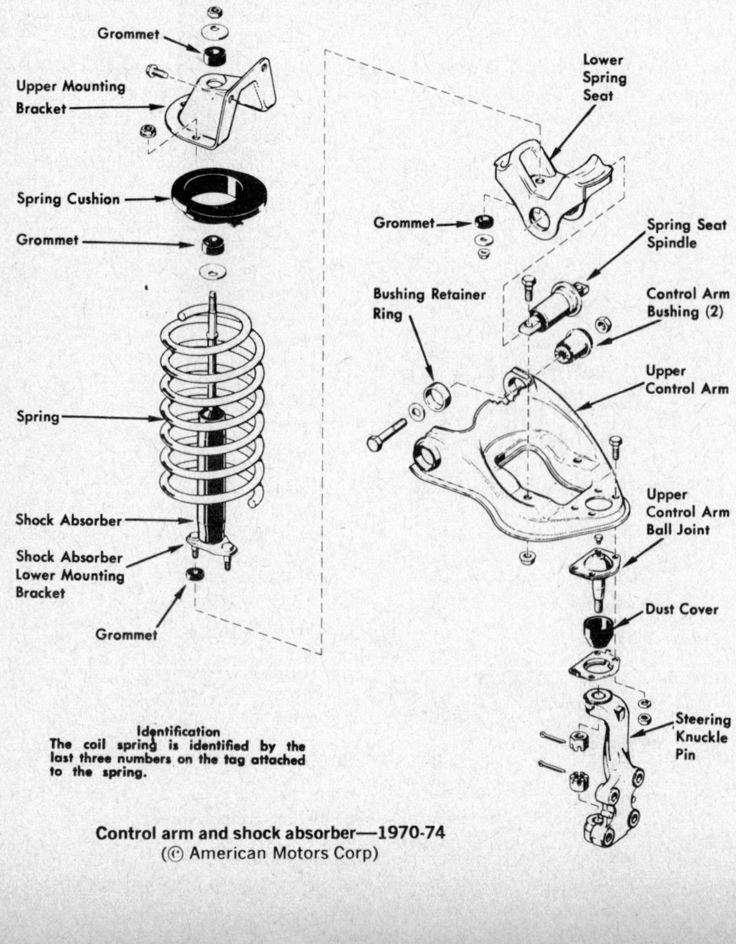
Grommet
Upper Mounting Bracket
Spring Cushion
Grommet
Spring
Shock Absorber
Shock Absorber Lower Mounting Bracket
Grommet
Lower Spring Seat
Grommet
Spring Seat Spindle
Bushing Retainer Ring
Control Arm Bushing (2)
Upper Control Arm
Upper Control Arm Ball Joint
Dust Cover
Steering Knuckle Pin
Identification
The coil spring is identified by the last three numbers on the tag attached to the spring.

Control arm and shock absorber—1970-74
(© American Motors Corp)

Front Spring Removal and Installation

1967-69

Raise rear of car at diagonal corner from front spring to be removed. Install hooks in holes provided in spring seats while compressed. Release load and lower rear corner. This allows spring removal from car.

To install new spring, compress it by means of hydraulic press or jack with seats in place. Be sure holes in seats are aligned. Install hooks to hold spring in compression while placing in position. Reversing the above removal procedures will control position to release hooks when spring is in place.

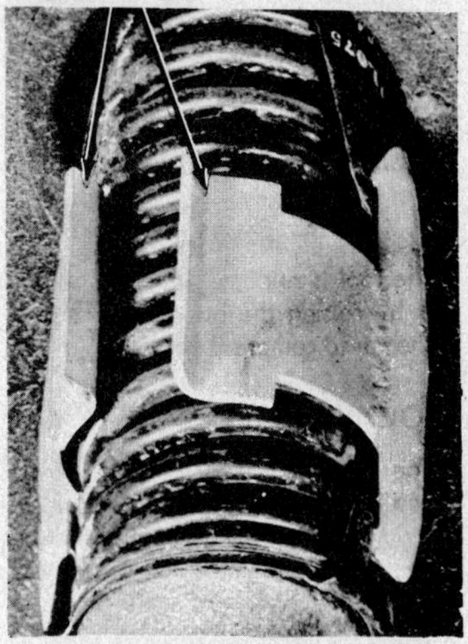

Front coil spring removal tools in place (arrows)
(© American Motors Corp)

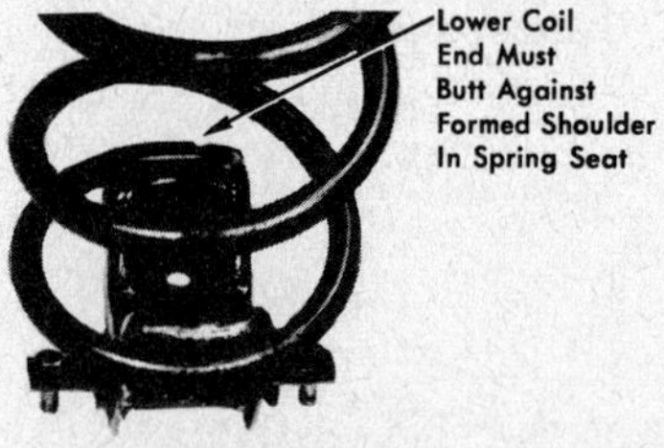
Lower Coil End Must Butt Against Formed Shoulder In Spring Seat

Lower spring seat installation—1970-74 front coil springs
(© American Motors Corp)

1970-74

Jack up the car far enough to reach the two lower shock absorber nuts. Remove the nuts, washers and grommets, then remove the upper mounting bracket screws and bolts from the wheelwell. Lift the bracket and shock absorber from the panel.

Lower the car to the floor, then install a spring compressor through the upper spring seat opening and bolt it to the lower spring seat using the lower shock absorber mounting holes. Remove the lower spring seat spindle retaining nuts, then tighten the compressor tool to compress the spring about 1 in.

Jack up the front of the car and support it on axle stands at the subframe (allowing the control arms to hang free). Remove the front wheel and pull the lower spring seat out away from the car, then slowly release the spring tension and remove the coil spring and lower spring seat.

To install, place the spring compressor through the coil spring and tape the rubber spring cushion to the small-diameter end of the spring (upper). Place the lower spring seat against the spring with the end of the coil against the formed shoulder in the seat. The shoulder and coil end face inwards, toward the engine, when the spring is installed.

Place the spring up against the upper seat, then align the lower spring seat pivot so that the retaining studs will enter the holes in the upper control arm. Compress the coil spring and install the spring, then install the wheel and tire and lower the car to the floor (to place weight on suspension). Install and tighten lower spring seat spindle retaining nuts and tighten them to 35 ft. lbs. Remove the spring compressor and install the shock absorber.

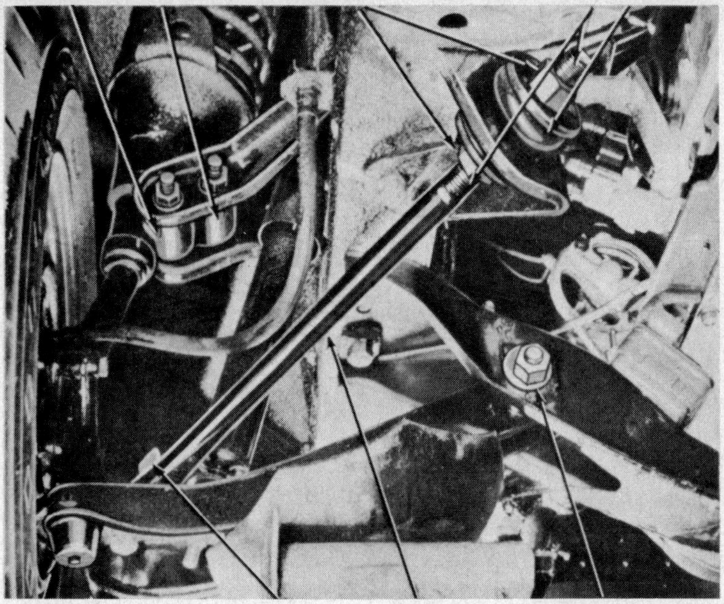
Upper Trunnion
Spacer
Caster Adjustment Nuts
Threaded Strut Rod
Rubber Bushing
Ball Joint
Steering Stop
Strut Rod
Camber Adjustment Eccentric

Rear view of front suspension—models to 1969
(© American Motors Corp)

Control Arm R & R

Upper-Control Arm—1967-69

1. Remove front spring as described above.
2. Remove front or rear arm by disconnecting it at the trunnion, at wheelhouse panel mounting bolt, and the control arm spacer. Upon reassembly, torque spacer bolt nut to 80-90 ft. lbs.
3. Both front and rear arms may be removed as an assembly by disconnecting them from the mounting bracket. Remove lower spring seat support, lock pin and nut from the knuckle pin.

NOTE: to facilitate caster and camber adjustments upon reassembly, mark position of eccentric washers before disassembly.

Upper Control Arm—1970-74

Remove the shock absorber and compress the coil spring approximately 2 in., using the procedure outlined earlier under Front Spring Removal and Installation—1970-74.

Jack up the front of the car and support the body on jackstands placed under the subframes (allow the control arms to hang free). Remove the wheel and the upper ball joint cotter pin and retaining nut. Separate the ball joint stud from the steering knuckle using two hammers—one as a brace and the other to apply shock to the knuckle. Remove the inner pivot bolts from the panel, then remove the control arm.

To install, reverse the removal procedure. Do not tighten the pivot bolt nuts until the full weight of the car is on the wheels. The ball joint stud nut must be tightened to 45 ft. lbs., the lower spring seat pivot retaining nuts to 35 ft. lbs., and the control arm inner pivot bolts to 60 ft. lbs.

NOTE: it may be necessary to align the front end.

Lower Control Arm—1967-74

The inner end of the lower control arm is attached to a removable crossmember. The outer end is attached to the steering knuckle pin and ball joint assembly.

NOTE: on 1967-69 models, it is recommended that the coil spring be removed.

To remove, jack up the car and support it on axle stands under the subframes. Remove the brake drum or caliper and rotor from the spindle, then disconnect the steering arm from the knuckle pin. Remove the lower ball joint stud cotter pin and nut. Separate the ball joint from the knuckle pin using two hammers—one as a brace and the other to apply shock to the knuckle.

Disconnect the sway bar from the control arm, then unbolt the strut rod. Remove the inner pivot bolt and the control arm.

To install, reverse the removal procedure; do not tighten inner pivot bolt until car weight is on wheels. Tighten ball joint retaining nut to 45 ft. lbs., strut rod bolts to 70 ft. lbs., sway bar bolts to 8 ft. lbs., steering arm bolts to 70 ft. lbs., and control arm inner pivot bolt to 95-100 ft. lbs.

Ball Joint Check and Replacement

Jack up the front of the car under the front crossmember or at the subframe jacking points. The control arms must hang free to get an accurate check. Grasp the wheel and tire and lift up and down and pull in and out while observing the lower ball joint. If there is measurable vertical or lateral free-play, the joint is worn enough to warrant replacement.

To check the upper ball joint on 1970-74 models, where a degree of looseness is normal, use a pry bar under the wheel to move tire vertically. If play is more than 0.080 in., the upper joint must be replaced.

To replace the ball joint, the rivets that hold it to the control arm must be drilled out or chiseled away. Remove the rivets and the strut rod mounting bolts if the lower joint is being worked on. In addition, place a punch of suitable size in the bottom open end of the lower control arm to keep the control arm from distorting while pressing the bushing. Remove the steering arm and stud nut, then separate the ball joint from the knuckle pin using two hammers, one as a brace against the knuckle pin and the other to shock the tapered stud loose.

The new ball joint has special 5/16 in. hardened bolts that replace the rivets. Use only these bolts to secure the joint—standard bolts are not strong enough. Tighten nuts to 25 ft. lbs.

Wheel Bearings

Inspection

Check to see that the inner cones of the bearings are free to "creep" on the spindle. Polish and lubricate the spindle to allow "creeping" movement and to keep rust from forming.

Adjustment

1. With the tire and wheel removed and the car supported by a suita-

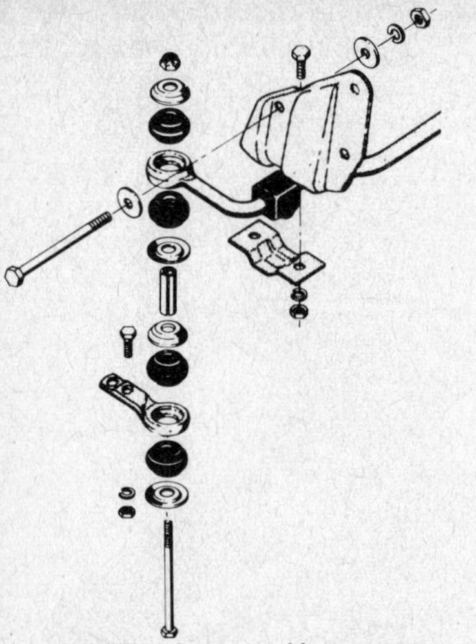

Front stabilizer bar assembly sequence—American, Javelin and AMX to 1969
(© American Motors Corp)

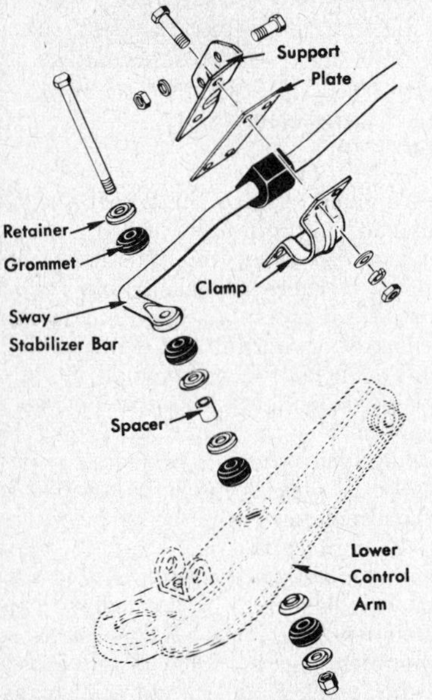
Support
Plate
Retainer
Grommet
Clamp
Sway
Stabilizer Bar
Spacer
Lower
Control
Arm

Front stabilizer bar assembly sequence—Rebel, Marlin and Ambassador to 1969
(© American Motors Corp)

ble and safe means, remove the dust cover from the spindle.
2. Remove the cotter pin and nut retainer.
3. Rotate the wheel while tightening the spindle nut to 20-25 ft lbs.
4. Loosen the spindle nut ⅓ of a turn.
5. Rotate the wheel while tightening the spindle nut to 10 in. lbs torque.
6. Fit the nut retainer over the spindle and align the slots in it with the cotter pin hole. Insert the cotter pin.
7. Install the dust cover.

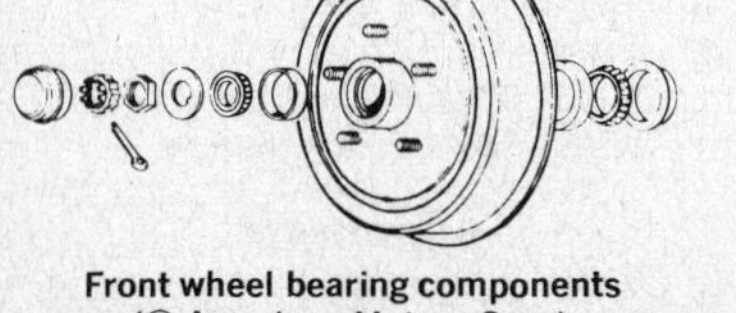

Front wheel bearing components
(© American Motors Corp)

REAR SUSPENSION

All 1967-74 American, Javelin, Hornet, Gremlin and AMX models use a four or five-leaf semi-elliptic spring, Hotchkiss drive rear suspension. Shock absorbers are mounted at their lower ends to studs and are bayonet type at their upper ends. Upper shock nuts are accessible by removing cover plates or by removing trunk floormat; except for AMX models. The upper ends of the shocks in the AMX are mounted to bolted-on brackets, which must be removed in order to remove the shocks.

The rear suspension on Rebel, Ambassador, Matador and Marlin models was changed starting 1967 to a four-trailing arm, coil spring type. The two lower control arms are attached to the outer ends of the axle tubes and to the body side sills, while the two upper control arms are attached to the differential housing and to a rear crossmember. Rubber bushings are used on the lower arms and on the crossmember ends of the upper arms. The lower ends of the upper arms are attached to pressed in bushings in ears on the differential case. Shock absorbers are accessible at their upper ends by removing cover plates in the body or by removing brackets from underneath the car.

Shock Absorber R & R

1. Support the rear axle with jacks or a lift; this allows the weight of the car to compress the rear spring.
2. Unfasten the nut which secures the eye of the shock to the stud.
3. Remove the access plate on the rear underbody panel and unfasten the upper securing nut. It may be necessary to hold the top of the shock while unfastening the nut.

NOTE: Some models do not have an access plate. On these cars, remove the upper attachment plate complete as an assembly.

4. Withdraw the shock from under the car.
5. Installation is the reverse of removal.

Rear Spring R & R

1967-74 American, Javelin, Hornet, and Gremlin

1. Raise the car. Support the rear axle with jacks or a lift to take the load off the rear springs.
2. Detach the rear shock from the lower mounting stud. Lower the axle so that the rear springs hang free.
3. Unfasten the spring hangers.
4. Remove the nut from the bolt which attaches the eye of the spring to the front mount.
5. Unfasten the bolts from the rear shackle.
6. Installation is the reverse of removal.

1967-74 Classic, Marlin, Ambassador, and Matador

1. Raise the rear of the car and support the rear axle with jacks or a lift to take the load off the rear springs.
2. Detach the shock from the axle tube. Lower the axle to the fullest extent of its travel (limited by the control arms).
3. Pull down the axle tube to completely release the spring.
4. Reverse the above to install the spring.

BRAKES

All American Motors cars come equipped with dual tandem master cylinders. This allows one set of brakes to operate, should the other set fail. A switch in the system, connected to a warning light on the instrument panel, indicates a difference in pressure between the front and rear brake lines, thus indicating the failure of one brake system. Repair procedures for both the master cylinder and the switch are found in the "Unit Repair Section."

All drum brakes have automatic brake adjusters. These automatically compensate for lining wear, by operating when the brakes are applied while the car is backing up. The automatic mechanism is attached to the star wheel adjuster, which it works through.

Information on brake adjustments, lining replacement, bleeding procedure, master and wheel cylinder overhaul can be found in the Unit Repair Section.

Master Cylinder R & R

1. Detach the front and rear brake lines from the master cylinder. On cars equipped with drum brakes, the check valves will keep the fluid from draining out of the cylinder. If the car is equipped with disc brakes, one or both of the outlets must be plugged, to prevent fluid loss.
2. Remove the nuts which attach the master cylinder to the firewall or the power brake booster (if so equipped).
3. On cars that have manual brakes, detach the pedal push rod from the brake pedal.
4. Withdraw the master cylinder from the car.

Installation is the reverse of removal. Remember to bleed the brake system once the master cylinder has been installed. (See the "Unit Repair Section.")

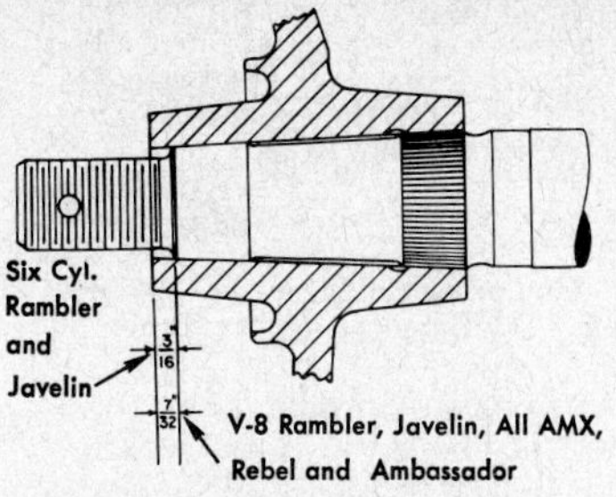
Six Cyl. Rambler and Javelin
3/16
7/32
V-8 Rambler, Javelin, All AMX, Rebel and Ambassador

Rear hub installation—1967-69
(© American Motors Corp)

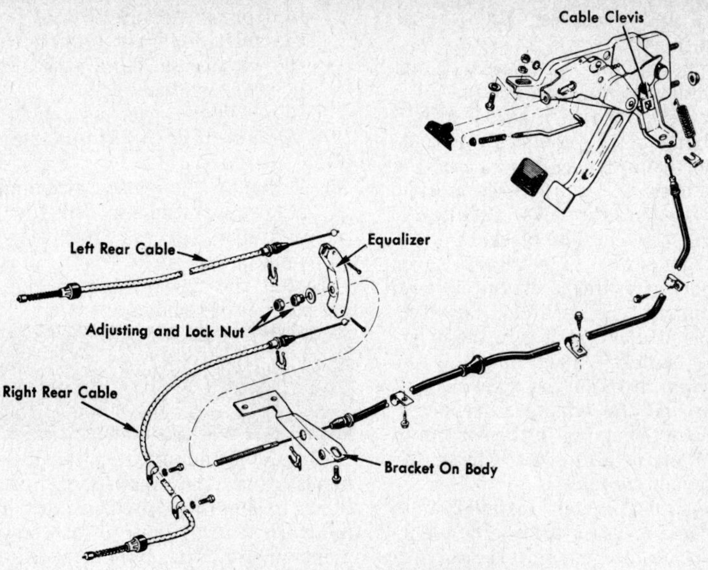
Cable Clevis
Left Rear Cable
Equalizer
Adjusting and Lock Nut
Right Rear Cable
Bracket On Body

Typical foot pedal type parking brake linkage
(© American Motors Corp)

Rear Wheel Hub Installation

1967-74

The rear axle splines cut serrations into the inner diameter of the rear wheel hub. If the hub is to be removed, match mark the hub to the axle so that the job of aligning the serrations and splines will be easier. If this is not done, the axle will cut new splines which may be so near the old that the hub will move on the axle with resultant damage to the hub, axle and differential gears.

When a new hub is installed, the serrations will be cut in the hub as it is installed on the shaft.

If a new axle shaft is installed, a new hub, without serrations, must be installed. An old shaft with a new hub also is an allowable combination.

Slide the hub onto the axle shaft, aligning the serrations of the hub with those of the shaft. Now, install the nut and tighten the hub onto the shaft until the face of the hub is the specified distance from the outer taper of the shaft. Nut must be torqued to 250 ft. lbs.

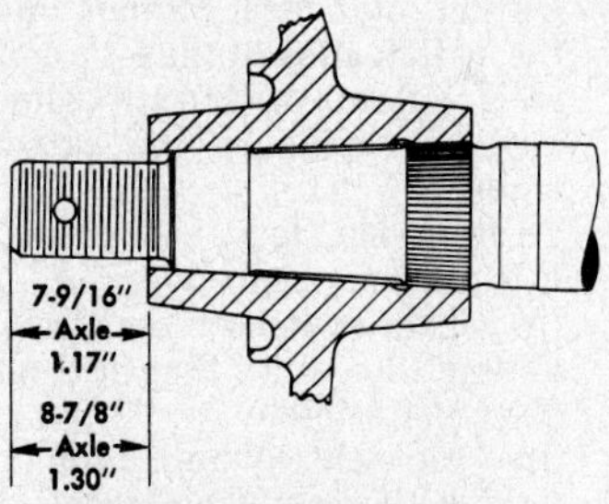
7-9/16"
Axle
1.17"
8-7/8"
Axle
1.30"

Rear hub installation—1970-74
(© American Motors Corp)

Power Brake Unit R & R

Remove the clevis pin from the power-unit operating rod. Disconnect the vacuum line and the hydraulic lines from the power unit, remove the stop light wires, remove the mounting bolts and lift off the power cylinder.

Installation is the reverse order of the above.

Parking Brake Cable Replacement

All Models

1. Disconnect the lower end of the cable at the cross-shaft or equalizer, disconnect it at the hand-brake end.
2. Remove the brackets which retain it to the body and firewall and thread it out of the vehicle.

When a new cable is to be installed, it is always a good idea to tie the new one to the end of the old one so that it will thread through in the same route as the old cable. This, sometimes, will require the service of a helper to guide it.

Parking Brake Cable Adjustment

1967-74

NOTE: before adjusting the parking brake, adjust the service brakes, as outlined in the "Unit Repair Section."

1. On cars that have a foot-operated parking brake lever, set the lever on the first notch from the released position.
2. If the car has an umbrella handle under the dashboard, set it on the fifth notch from the released position.
3. Tighten the cable at the equalizer so that the wheels are locked in forward rotation.
4. Release the parking brake and check for rear brake drag. The wheels should rotate freely with the parking brake off.

STEERING

Power Steering Pump R & R

1. Remove the fan belt.
2. Place a container under the pump to catch fluid.
3. Detach the hoses and cap the outlets, so that the power steering unit does not loose fluid.
4. Unbolt the pump bracket and remove the pump assembly.

Installation is performed in the following manner:

1. Place the pump assembly on the engine and secure it with the attaching bolts.
2. Connect the hoses, being sure that the fittings are tightened evenly.
3. Position the filler neck of the reservoir upright, by loosening the attachment screw and rotating it to the correct position. Tighten the screw to 15–20 ft lbs.
4. Fill the reservoir to the proper level with automatic transmission fluid and adjust the belt tension.

Steering Wheel R & R

1. Remove the horn button by one of the following methods:
   a. 1967-74 center button—lift upward.
   b. 1967-74 trim cover—unfasten the screws, which hold the cover on, from the rear. On "rim-blow" wheels, unfasten the center contact.
2. Unfasten the steering wheel center nut. Before removing the wheel, note the position of the index marks on the wheel and the steering shaft.
3. Remove the wheel with a suitable puller.

Installation is the reverse of removal. Tighten the steering wheel nut to 20 ft lbs.

Turn Signal Switch R & R

1967-69

1. Detach the ground cable at the battery and remove the steering wheel as detailed above.
2. Withdraw the cancelling cam and the spring.
3. If the car is equipped with an adjustable steering wheel, remove the turn signal and the release levers.
4. Push the hazard warning knob

in and remove it (if so equipped).

5. Remove the automatic shift quadrant (if so equipped).
6. Unfasten the turn signal switch wiring at the connector by cutting it on the switch side of the connector. On 1968–69 models, do not cut the wire, unfasten it from the terminal block.
7. Remove the turn signal cover and the switch securing screws.
8. Remove the switch, however, first attach a string to the original switch wiring and pull the string through the steering column as the wiring is removed. Leave the string in the column to aid in installing the wiring for the new switch.

Turn-signal switch installation is the reverse of removal. The new wiring must be inserted into the connector by color code, after switch installation.

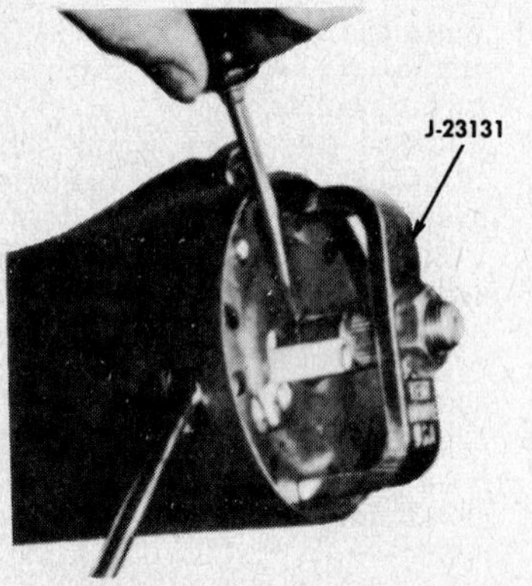
J-23131

Using the special lockplate removal tool
(© American Motors Corp)

1970-74

1. Detach the ground cable from the battery. Remove the steering wheel as outlined above.
2. Unfasten the anti-theft cover attachment screws and remove the cover from the column. Do not remove the screws from the cover; they are attached to it with plastic retainers.
3. To remove the lockplate, a special compressor is required (see illustration). Depress the lockplate and pry the snap-ring from the groove in the steering shaft. Withdraw the tool, snap-ring, plate, turn signal cam, upper bearing preload spring, and the thrust washer from the shaft.
4. Place the turn signal lever in the right turn position and remove it.
5. Depress the hazard warning switch button and remove it, by rotating it counterclockwise.
6. Unfasten the wire harness connector block at its mounting bracket, which is located on the right side of the lower column.
7. If the car is equipped with a column-mounted automatic transmission selector, use a paper clip to depress the locktab that holds the shift quadrant light wire in the connector block (the grey wire at terminal "D").

NOTE: This is not necessary on 1974 Matador and Ambassador models.

8. Unfasten the switch attachment screws. Withdraw the switch and wire harness from the column.

Install the new switch in the reverse order of removal.

INSTRUMENT PANEL

Current is supplied to the instruments and the instrument panel lights through a printed circuit which is attached to the rear of the instrument cluster. The disconnect plug is part of the panel wiring harness and connects to pins attached to the printed circuit. A keyway located on the printed circuit board insures that the plug is always mounted correctly.

Caution Never pry under the plug to remove it, or damage to the printed circuit will result.

An instrument voltage regulator is wired in series with the gauges to supply a constant five volts to them. On the Hornet and Gremlin it is integral with the temperature gauge; on other models it is a separate unit.

Ignition Switch R & R

1967-69

Two types of ignition switch and mountings are used on American Motors products to 1969. Removal and installation of each type follows:

1969 Rebel and Ambassador

1. Disconnect battery.
2. Disconnect switch wires.
3. Remove escutcheon nut and remove switch toward rear of panel.
4. With switch removed, turn key to Acc. position and insert wire (paper clip) in small hole in housing. Depress retainer while turning and pulling out cylinder.
5. Install in reverse of above.

Cylinder Release Hole

Ignition switch assembly—1969 Rebel and Ambassador
(© American Motors Corp)

All Other 1967-69 Models

1. Disconnect battery.
2. Depress switch and turn counterclockwise.
3. Remove switch through rear of panel and bevel from front.
4. Remove wires from switch.

Ignition switch assembly—1967-69
(© American Motors Corp)

5. Remove cylinder as in Step 4 of the above.
6. Install in reverse of above.

1970-71

The ignition switch on all models is mounted on the lower steering column tube and is connected to the lock cylinder via a lock rod.

1. Place key in "OFF-LOCK".
2. Remove switch mounting screws.
3. Disconnect lock rod, remove harness connector and switch.
4. To install, first place both key and switch slide in "OFF-LOCK" positions.
5. Insert a 3/32 in. drill bit into switch alignment hole.
6. With drill in place, hook up lock rod and remove all slack by sliding switch toward steering wheel.
7. Install mounting bolts and tighten securely. Remove drill and hook up wires.

1972-74

Removal of the 1972-74 column mounted ignition switch is the same as for the 1970–71 models, above. However, installation is slightly different:

1. On the standard column, move the switch slide to the left, as far as it will go. On the tilt-column, push the slide to the extreme right.
2. Position the lock rod into the hole on the switch slide.
3. Install the switch on the steering column. Be sure that the slide stays in its detent.
4. On the tilt-column, do not tighten the mounting screws. Instead, push the switch down the column, away from the steering wheel. This will remove any slack from the lock rod.
5. Tighten the switch mounting screws.

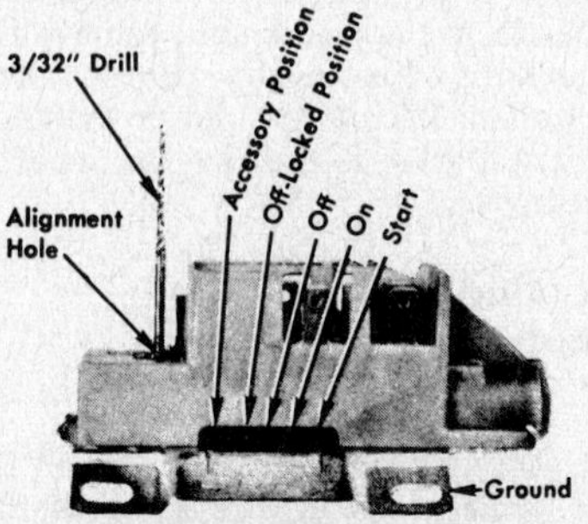
3/32" Drill
Alignment Hole
Accessory Position
Off-Locked Position
Off
On
Start
Ground

Ignition switch positions—1970-74
(© American Motors Corp)

Lock Cylinder R & R—1970-74

1. Loosen anti-theft cover screws and remove cover from column. Remove steering wheel.
2. Depress lock plate as far as possible, using a spacer and steering wheel nut.
3. Remove wire snap-ring from shaft groove, then remove compressor tool, snap-ring, lock plate, turn signal cam, upper bearing preload spring and thrust washer.
4. Place turn signal lever in "right turn" position and remove lever.
5. Depress hazard warning switch and remove button by turning CCW.

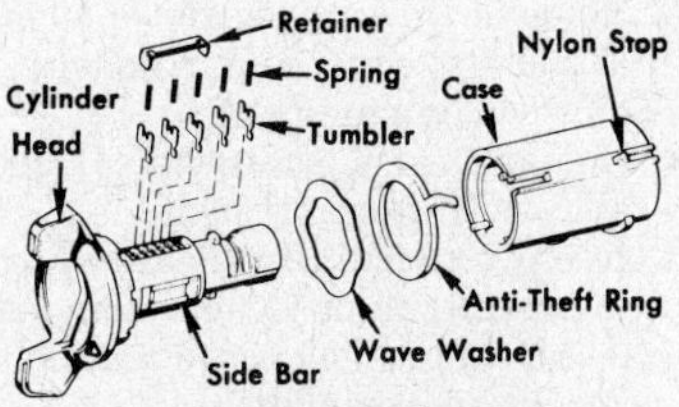
Retainer
Spring
Tumbler
Cylinder Head
Nylon Stop
Case
Anti-Theft Ring
Wave Washer
Side Bar

Ignition key lock—1970-74
(© American Motors Corp)

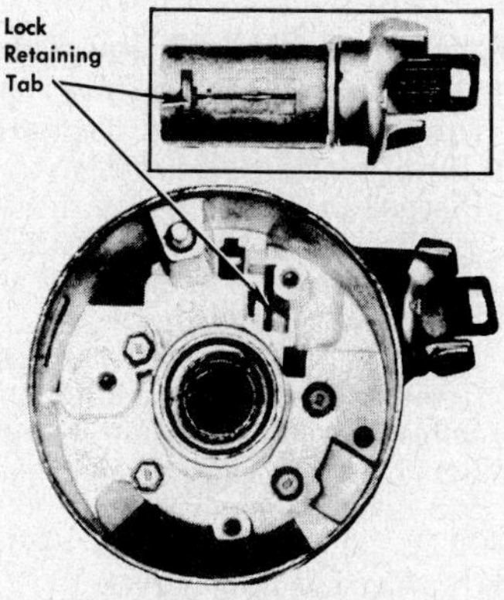
Lock Retaining Tab

Lock cylinder removal—1970-74
(© American Motors Corp)

6. Place automatic in Park, manual in Reverse.
7. Drive out shift lever pin with a ¼ in. punch, then remove shift lever.
8. Remove turn signal wiring block from steering column (lower), then depress shift quadrant light wire lock tab with a paper clip (terminal D) and remove the wire.

NOTE: This is not necessary on 1974 Matador and Ambassador models.

9. Remove turn signal switch retaining screws and pull switch and wires out of column.
10. Place key in "IGN" position and lift key warning buzzer switch from housing.
11. Place key in "LOCK" position, then depress lock cylinder retaining tab and remove cylinder.
12. To install, reverse removal procedure.

Headlight Switch R & R

1967-74 All Other Models

Light switches are similar in all models. Some variation occurs in the shape and position of the nut mounting the switch to dash.

1. Disconnect battery.
2. With switch in "OFF" (up to 1968), "ON" (from 1969), position press the release button and remove the knob and shaft.
3. Remove screws, attaching switch or bracket to panel.
4. Reverse for installation, positioning switch so that the shaft is lined up properly before tightening the bracket screws.

1971-74 Javelin

1. Remove the toggle switch knob by inserting a screwdriver in the groove on its left side. Pry upward, toward the knob, to release the spring clip that retains the knob.
2. Remove the screws that secure the lower cover to the steering column and withdraw the cover.
3. Unfasten the wire connectors and the retaining screws from the switch. Remove the switch.
4. Install the switch in the reverse order of removal.

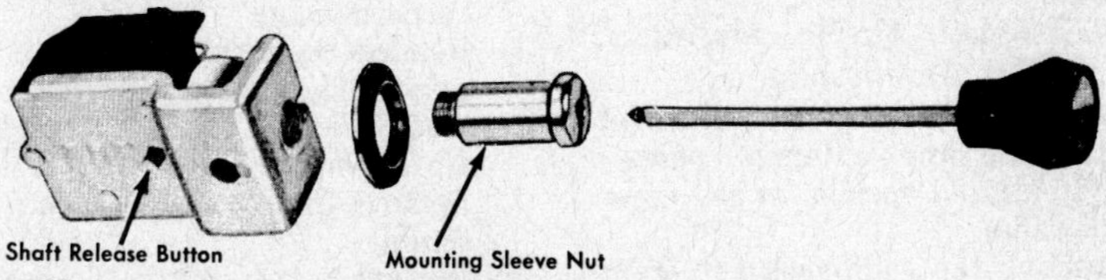
Shaft Release Button
Mounting Sleeve Nut

Light switch assembly
(© American Motors Corp)

WINDSHIELD WIPERS

Motor R & R

1967-74 American, Javelin, AMX, Hornet, and Gremlin

The wiper motor is mounted on the engine side of the firewall and is easily accessible from under the hood.

1. Remove four screws that hold motor to firewall.
2. Remove hose and control cable, if equipped with vacuum wipers.
3. Unplug harness plug under dash, if equipped with electric wipers.
4. Disconnect motor link and remove motor.
5. To install, reverse removal procedure.

1967-74 Rebel, Marlin, Matador, and Ambassador

1. Remove wiper arms and blades and the cowl air intake cover.
2. Slide the link-to-motor retainer clip off of the motor arm stud. Remove the link from the motor.
3. Disconnect control cable and vacuum hose or wiring harness from the motor.
4. Remove the motor and mounting plate-to-dash screws, and the motor assembly.
5. Install by reversing removal procedure.

Transmission R & R

1967-74 American, Javelin, AMX, Hornet, and Gremlin

To remove the pivot shaft body and link assembly after the link has been disconnected from the motor:

1. Remove pivot shaft spacer mounting nut, spacer and gaskets.
2. Disconnect washer hose.
3. Remove cowl ventilator air intake cover fastened to the cowl top by one screw at the front on each side and a retainer pin in the rear center of the cover.
4. The retainer pin is welded to the cover and inserted into a rubber grommet in the cowl top which serves as a retainer.
5. After the air intake cover is removed, the pivot shaft body retaining nuts are accessible for removal. The pivot shaft body and link assembly can then be removed from inside the body.

1967-74 Rebel, Marlin, Matador, and Ambassador

1. Remove the wiper arm and blade assembly and pivot shaft to cowl top nut and spacer.
2. Disconnect the link end from the motor arm, after removing cowl air intake.
3. Close hood and remove two capscrews that hold each pivot shaft body. Remove assembly through cowl opening.
4. Install by reversing removal procedure

RADIO

The following precautions should be observed when working on a car radio:

1. Always observe the proper polarity of the power connections; i.e., positive (+) goes to the power source and negative (—) to ground (negative ground electrical system).
2. Never run the radio without a speaker; damage to the output transistors will result. If a replacement speaker is used, be sure that it is the correct imped-

ance (ohms) for the radio. The proper impedance is stamped on the case of American Motors radios.

3. If a new antenna or antenna cable is used, adjust the antenna trimmer for the best reception of a weak AM station around 1400kc; the trimmer is located either behind the tuning knob or on the bottom of the radio case.

Removal and Installation

1967-69 American

1. Detach the battery ground lead.
2. Unfasten the antenna, power, and speaker wires from the radio.
3. Remove the radio bracket from the dash panel flange.
4. Pull the control knobs off and unfasten the control shaft bushing retainer nuts. Remove the ash tray assembly, if necessary.
5. Slide the radio back and down to remove it from underneath the instrument panel.

NOTE: if equipped with A/C, remove the glovebox and withdraw the radio through its opening.

Installation is the reverse of removal.

1967-73 Rebel, Marlin, Matador, and Ambassador

1. Detach the battery ground cable.
2. Unfasten the antenna, power, ground, and speaker wires from the radio.
3. Remove the radio bracket from the dash panel flange.
4. Remove the cluster overlay.
5. Unfasten the radio mounting screws and withdraw the radio.

Installation is the reverse of removal.

1968-70 Javelin and AMX

1. Disconnect the battery ground cable.
2. Remove the ash tray. Remove the bolt from inside the ash tray which attaches to the radio (if so equipped).
3. Unfasten the radio knobs and remove the shaft retaining nuts. Remove the bezel retaining screws and the bezel on 1970 Javelin/AMX models.
4. Detach all of the leads from the radio.
5. Tip the back of the radio up, toward the toe board. Withdraw it from the rear edge of the center instrument panel pad.

NOTE: if equipped with A/C, remove the discharge duct to gain clearance for radio removal.

Installation is the reverse of removal.

1970-74 Hornet and Gremlin

1. Disconnect the battery ground cable.
2. Remove the ash tray. Remove the chrome ash tray bezel, by unfastening the screw located underneath it. Remove the ash tray bracket, if required.
3. Pull off the radio knobs and unfasten the shaft retaining nuts.
4. Remove the six retaining screws from the center bezel. Remove the center bezel, carefully, by working it free of the rest of the panel.
5. Detach the speaker, antenna, and power leads. Withdraw the radio.

Installation is the reverse of removal.

1971-74 Javelin

1. Disconnect the battery ground lead.
2. Remove the six upper crash pad retaining screws, which are located next to the windshield.
3. Open the passenger-side door and remove the two panel securing screws from the door pillar area.
4. Remove the five securing screws from the upper flange of the instrument cluster bezel.
5. Unfasten the molding attachment screws and the passenger assist handle.
6. Remove the map light to gain access to the crash pad mounting stud which is located behind it. Unfasten the nut from the stud.
7. Remove the entire crash pad assembly.
8. Remove the three speaker mounting plate screws. Remove the speaker.
9. Slide the radio rearward and lift it up, in order to unfasten the speaker and light bulb leads.

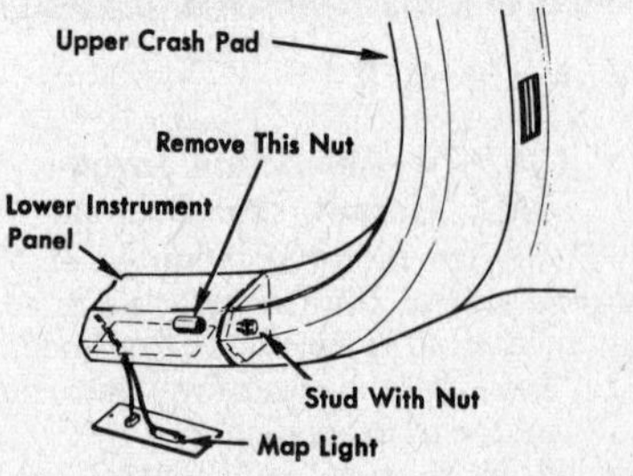

Upper Crash Pad
Remove This Nut
Lower Instrument Panel
Stud With Nut
Map Light

The lower retaining nut for the crash pad is hidden under the map light on the 1971-74 Javelin
(© American Motors Corp)

10. Unfasten the radio power lead at the fuse block. Tie a string to the power lead, to aid in pulling it back through to the fuse block during assembly.
11. Withdraw the radio, complete with power lead.

Installation is the reverse of removal. Be sure to install the upper radio attachment screws and the speaker bracket mounting bolts, as these are part of the ground system.

HEATER

Caution When servicing A/C equipped cars, do not discharge the A/C lines or the evaporator. Damage to the system or personal injury could result.

Heater Core R & R

Rebel, Marlin, Matador and Ambassador—1967-74

1. Disconnect hoses from core and plug hoses and tubes. It will not be necessary to drain entire cooling system. On A/C equipped cars, detach vacuum hoses at damper vacuum motor.
2. Remove lower blower housing attaching nuts and washers in engine compartment.
3. Remove glove compartment door and glove compartment.
4. Remove remaining heater housing screws in passenger compartment, and remove core and housing as an assembly.
5. Slide core from housing.
6. Install in reverse of above.

American—1967-69 Javelin and AMX—1968-74

1. Drain 1½ qts. (2 qts. beginning '70) of coolant from system.
2. Disconnect hoses from heater core tubes in engine compartment. Install corks in hoses and tubes.
3. Disconnect blower motor wires.
4. Remove housing attaching nuts at blower motor opening in dash.
5. Remove glove compartment door and glove compartment.

NOTE: on Javelin and AMX, remove glove box hinge bracket.

6. Disconnect air and defroster cables from damper levers.
7. Remove assembly.
8. Remove the core, defroster, and blower housing assembly from the car.
9. Remove the core from the housing assembly.

Installation is the reverse of removal.

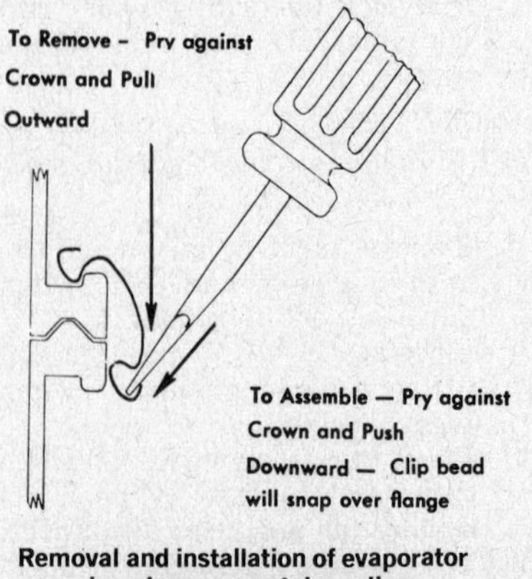

To Remove – Pry against Crown and Pull Outward
To Assemble — Pry against Crown and Push Downward — Clip bead will snap over flange

Removal and installation of evaporator housing cover retainer clip
(© American Motors Corp)

Gremlin and Hornet—1970-74

1. Open heater valve and drain 2 qts. of coolant.
2. Disconnect heater hoses and plug hoses and core fittings.
3. Disconnect blower wires and remove motor and fan assembly.
4. Remove package shelf, if so equipped.
5. Disconnect wire at resistor, located below glove box.
6. Remove instrument panel center bezel, air outlet and duct.
7. Disconnect air and defroster cables from damper levers.
8. Remove right-side windshield pillar molding, the instrument panel upper sheet metal screws and the capscrew at the right door post.
9. Remove right kick panel and heater housing screws.
10. Pull right side of instrument panel outward slightly and remove housing.
11. Remove core, defroster and blower housing.
12. Remove core from housing.

Installation is the reverse of removal.

Heater Blower R & R

Rebel, Marlin, Matador, Ambassador—1967-74

1. Remove water valve from blower housing. It is not necessary to disconnect hoses and control cable.
2. Remove nuts, washers and screws attaching blower housing to dash panel in engine compartment.
3. Remove motor and fan, then separate fan from motor.
4. Install in reverse of above.

Mounting Screws and Nuts

Blower housing attachment
(© American Motors Corp)

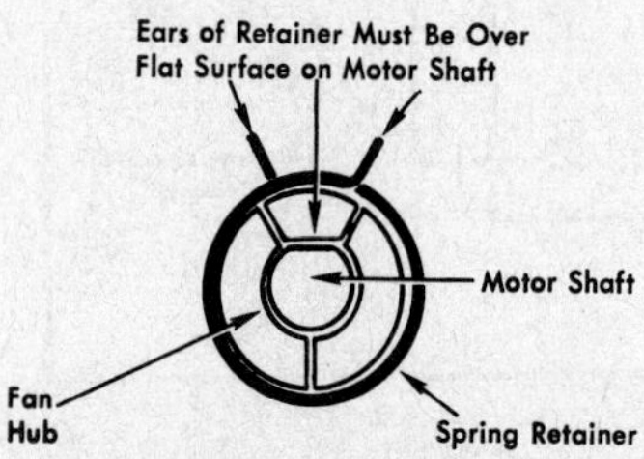
Ears of Retainer Must Be Over Flat Surface on Motor Shaft
Motor Shaft
Fan Hub
Spring Retainer

Blower retaining clip installation
(© American Motors Corp)

Javelin, AMX, American, Hornet and Gremlin—1967-74

1. Disconnect blower wires.
2. Remove three retaining nuts for scroll cover and remove motor and fan assembly.
3. To install, reverse removal procedure.

SEAT BELTS

Warning System 1972-73

Operation

A red light flashes and a buzzer sounds to warn the driver and/or outboard front seat passenger to fasten his/their seat belt(s), under the following conditions:

1. When the ignition is on.
2. When the outboard front seat is occupied (pressure-sensitive switch closed).
3. When the seat belt(s) is/are not fastened.
4. When the automatic transmission selector is placed in any drive range (Forward or Reverse).
5. When the parking brake is released on manual transmission-equipped cars.

The light and buzzer will cease to function as soon as the seat belts are extended from the retractor and fastened over the laps of the driver and/or front seat passenger.

NOTE: If a package, handbag, etc., is placed on the right-hand front seat, the warning system might function even if there is no one sitting in the passenger's seat.

Warning Buzzer and Lamp

To replace the buzzer, which is located under the instrument panel to the left of the instrument cluster, remove the sheetmetal screws (or tape), unfasten the multiconnector and withdraw the buzzer.

Installation is the reverse of removal.

On all series except the Javelin, pry the lamp assembly out of the instrument panel, working from the front, with a penknife or other suitable tool.

NOTE: Be careful not to scratch the painted surface of the instrument panel.

Disconnect the lamp connector and replace the lamp assembly as a complete unit.

On Javelin models, the two seat belt warning lamps are replaced like any other instrument panel warning lamp.

Seat Belt Retractor Switches

If the seat belt retractor switches fail, the entire seat belt assembly must be replaced, as these are not individually serviced components.

The switches are of the normally closed type.

Passenger Seat Sensing Switch

The pressure-sensitive switch used in the outboard front passenger seat is normally opened. It requires between 8-40 lbs pressure to close the warning circuit.

If the switch is overly sensitive, it can be adjusted in the following manner:

Depress the seat cushion above the switch location by applying your full weight on one knee.

This will cause seat cushion to bottom fully, thus bending the metal switch contract strips.

Repeat this procedure until proper sensitivity is attained.

NOTE: The switch used in bucket seats is not adjustable in this manner.

Relay

On some models, a relay is used to control the ground circuit of the warning buzzer and lamp. The relay is normally closed and it completes

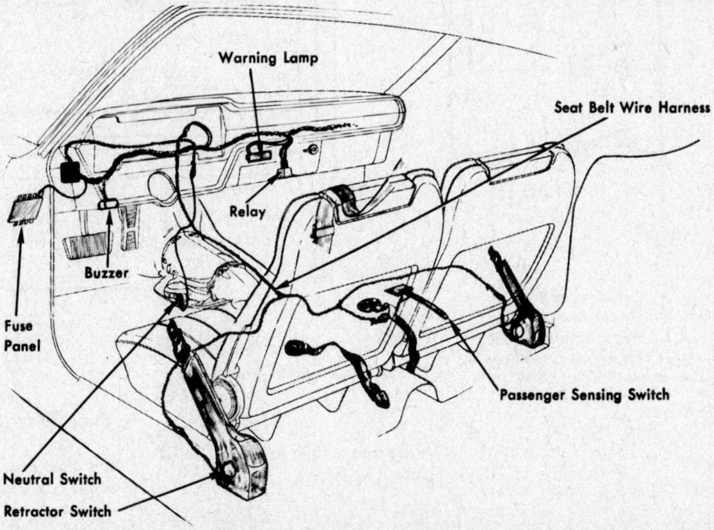
Warning Lamp
Seat Belt Wire Harness
Relay
Buzzer
Fuse Panel
Passenger Sensing Switch
Neutral Switch
Retractor Switch

Typical seat belt warning system component layout
(© American Motors Corp)

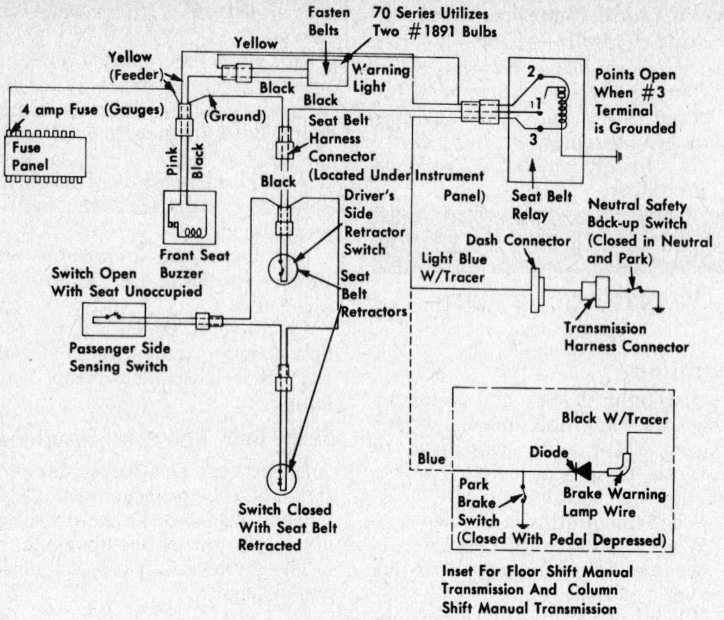
Fasten Belts
70 Series Utilizes Two #1891 Bulbs
Yellow
Yellow (Feeder)
Warning Light
Black
Black
4 amp Fuse (Gauges)
(Ground)
Fuse Panel
Pink
Black
Seat Belt Harness Connector (Located Under Instrument Panel)
Points Open When #3 Terminal is Grounded
Black
Driver's Side Retractor Switch
Seat Belt Relay
Neutral Safety Back-up Switch (Closed in Neutral and Park)
Front Seat Buzzer
Dash Connector
Light Blue W/Tracer
Switch Open With Seat Unoccupied
Seat Belt Retractors
Passenger Side Sensing Switch
Transmission Harness Connector
Black W/Tracer
Blue
Diode
Park Brake Switch
Brake Warning Lamp Wire
(Closed With Pedal Depressed)
Switch Closed With Seat Belt Retracted
Inset For Floor Shift Manual Transmission And Column Shift Manual Transmission

Schematic for seat belt warning system
(© American Motors Corp)

the ground circuit through its case. Grounding the number 3 terminal will cause the points to open, thus breaking the ground circuit for the warning system.

An improperly grounded relay case will cause the seat belt warning system not to function at all, while a burned-out relay could cause the warning system to function all of the time regardless of seat belt position. The relay is located below the lower left-hand instrument panel either next to the courtesy lamp or the brake pedal support bracket.

Diode

On manual transmission-equipped cars, a diode is used between the parking brake warning lamp and the pressure-sensitive switch to prevent feedback between the seat belt warning circuit and the parking brake warning circuit.

Failure of this diode will cause the parking brake warning light to remain lighted at all times.

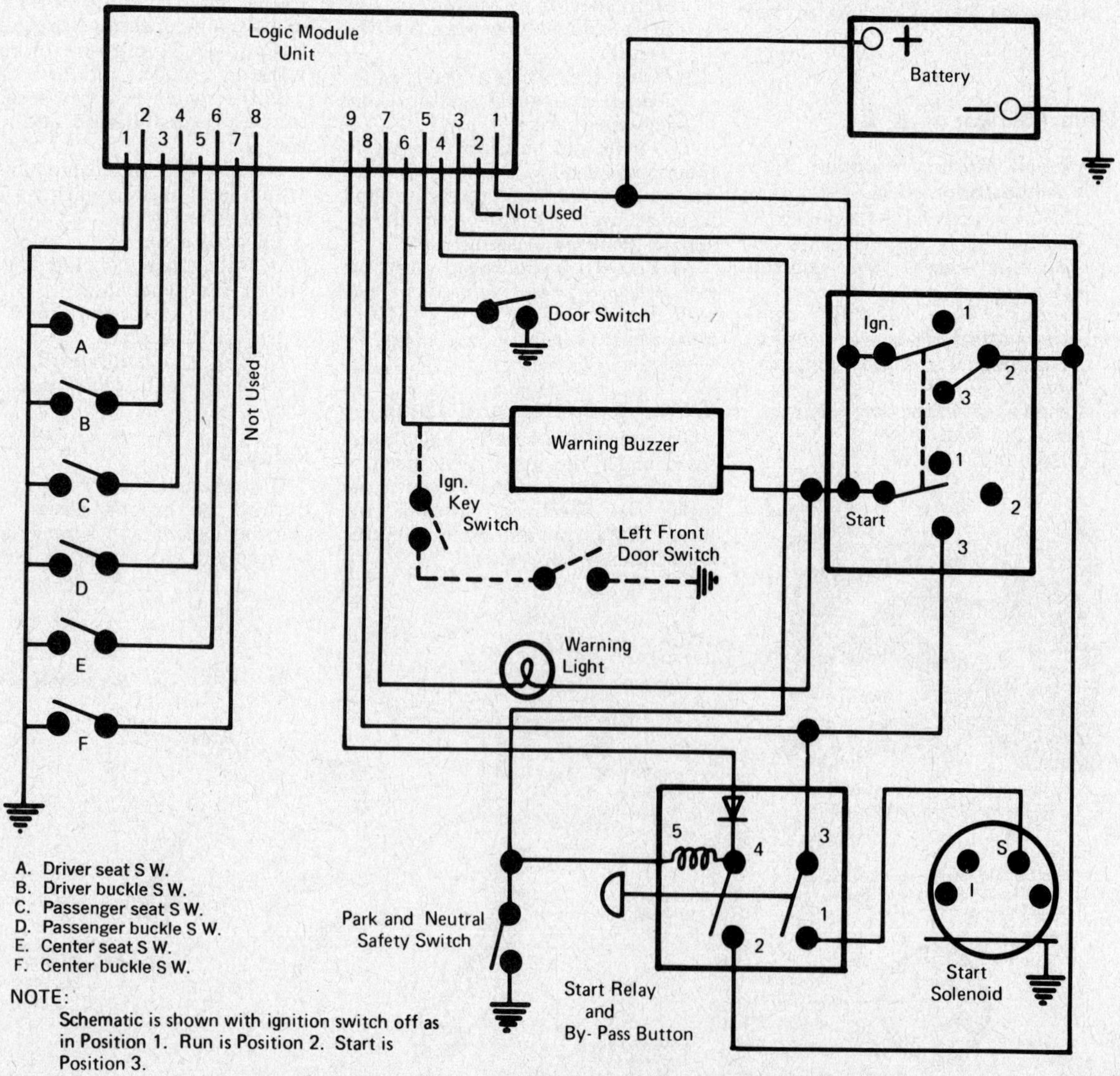
Logic Module Unit
2 4 6 8
1 3 5 7
9 7 5 3 1
8 6 4 2
Not Used
Battery
Door Switch
Ign.
Not Used
Warning Buzzer
Ign. Key Switch
Start
Left Front Door Switch
Warning Light
A
B
C
D
E
F
Park and Neutral Safety Switch
Start Relay and By-Pass Button
Start Solenoid
S
I
A. Driver seat S W.
B. Driver buckle S W.
C. Passenger seat S W.
D. Passenger buckle S W.
E. Center seat S W.
F. Center buckle S W.
NOTE:
Schematic is shown with ignition switch off as in Position 1. Run is Position 2. Start is Position 3.

Schematic diagram for seat belt/starter interlock system on 1974 AMC cars with automatic transmissions (© American Motors Corp)

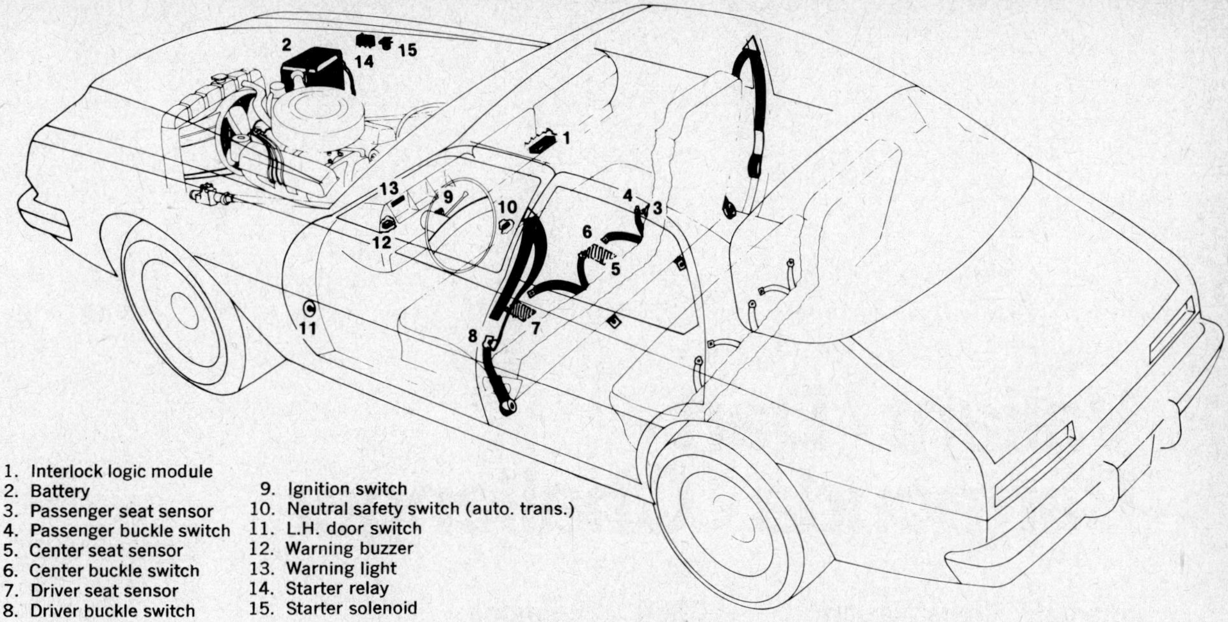

1. Interlock logic module
2. Battery
3. Passenger seat sensor
4. Passenger buckle switch
5. Center seat sensor
6. Center buckle switch
7. Driver seat sensor
8. Driver buckle switch
9. Ignition switch
10. Neutral safety switch (auto. trans.)
11. L.H. door switch
12. Warning buzzer
13. Warning light
14. Starter relay
15. Starter solenoid

Component location for the 1974 seat belt/starter interlock system
(© American Motors Corp)

Seat Belt/Starter Interlock System—1974

Operation

In addition to the light and buzzer used in 1972-73, a starter interlock has been incorporated into the seat belt warning system for 1974.

The car cannot be started unless the seat belts are fastened in a specific order. The driver (and front seat passenger) must get into the car, close the door(s), sit down, and then fasten the seat belts). If the seat belts are not fastened, or if they are fastened before the driver (and passenger) sit down, the car will not start. This prevents the belts from being permanently fastened and shoved behind the seats.

In case of a system failure and to make it easier for mechanics working on a car, a manual by-pass button is located under the hood. Pushing this button allows one "free start," i.e., without fastening the seat belt; each additional free start requires that the button be pushed again.

In addition to the components used for the 1972-73 warning system, a logic module (transistorized), a starter relay/by-pass button and two additional pressure-sensitive seat switches are used. The sensor switches that determine if the seat belt is fastened have been moved from the retractors to the seat belt buckles.

Component Location & Repair

The logic module is located under the center of the instrument panel. The starter relay/by-pass switch is mounted under the hood, next to the starter solenoid on the right-hand inner fender panel. The additional pressure-sensitive switches are mounted in the front seat, beneath the driver and center passenger (bench seat). The warning light and buzzer remain in the same locations as in 1972-73.

Repair of the components is limited to replacement.

INDEX

Valiant • Dart • Barracuda • Challenger

YEAR IDENTIFICATION

VALIANT

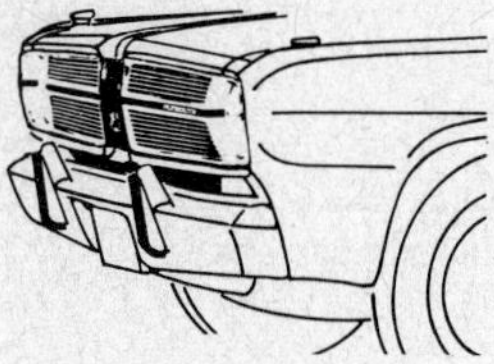
1967

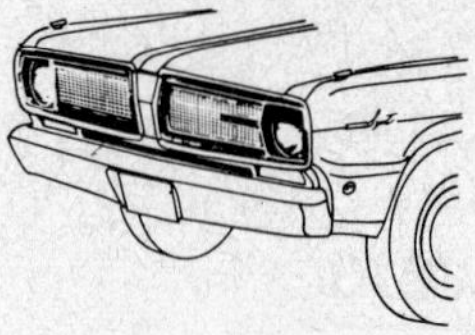
1968

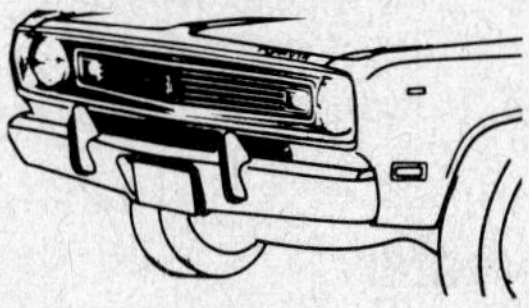
1969

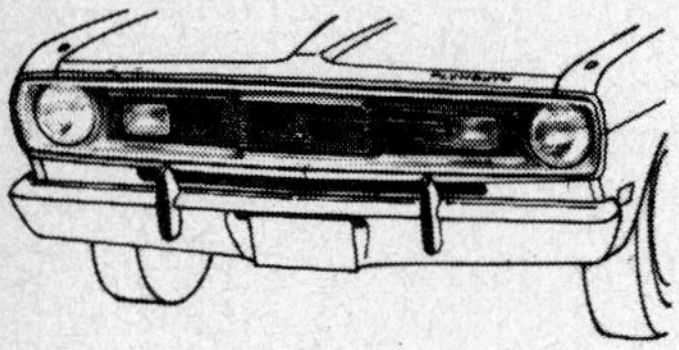
1970-72

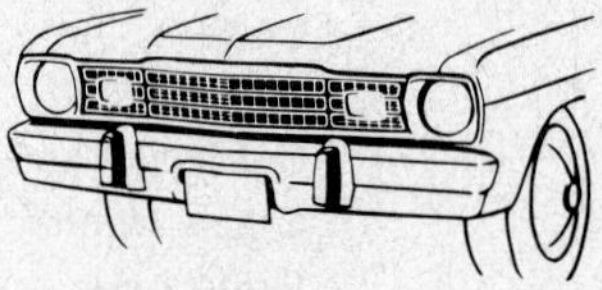
1973

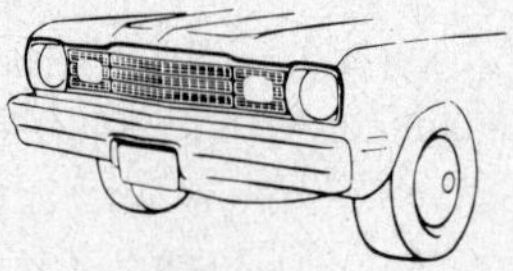
1974

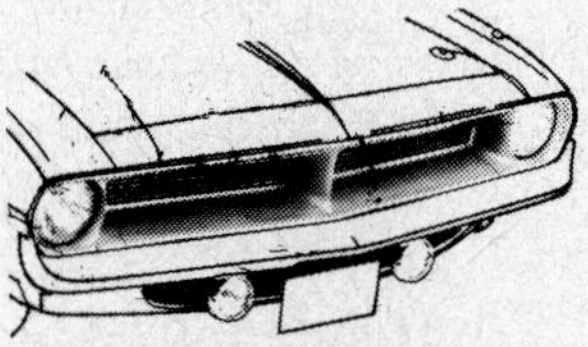
1970 Plymouth Cuda

1971 Cuda

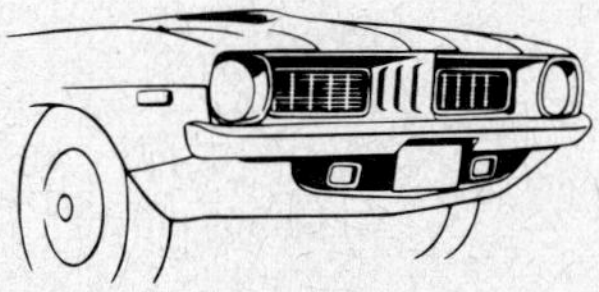
1972 Cuda

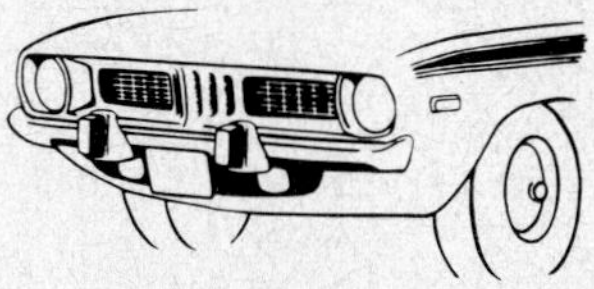
1973 Cuda

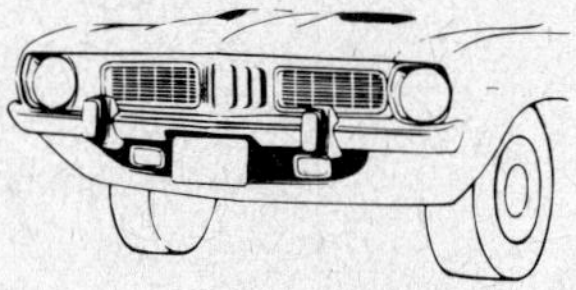
1974 Cuda

DART

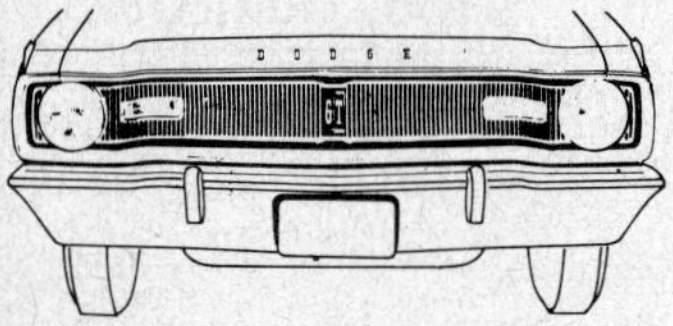
1967

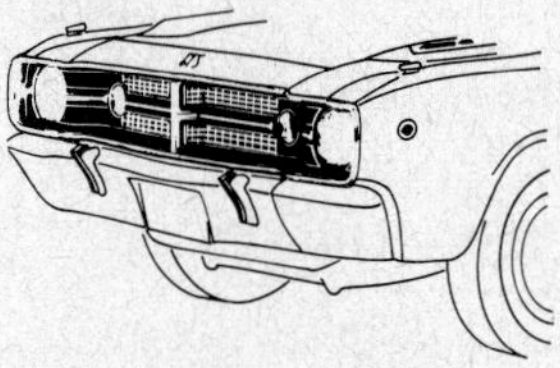
1968

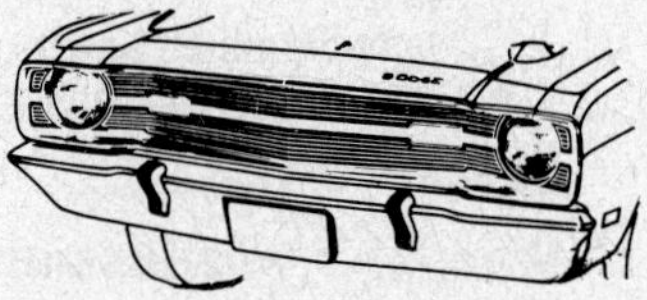
1969

1970 Dart

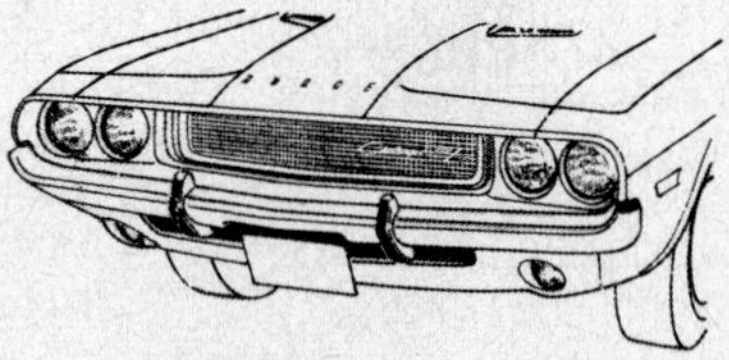
1971 Challenger

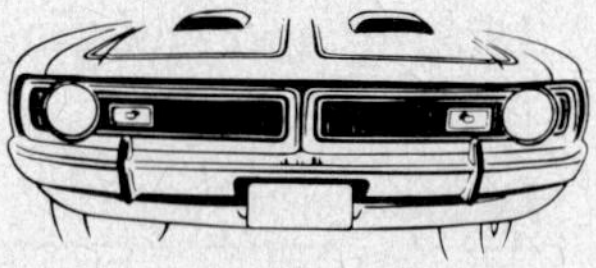
1971 Demon

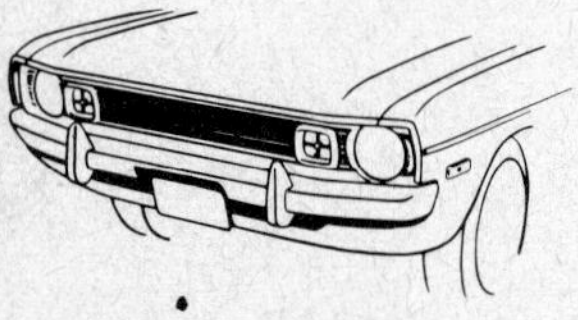
1972 Dart

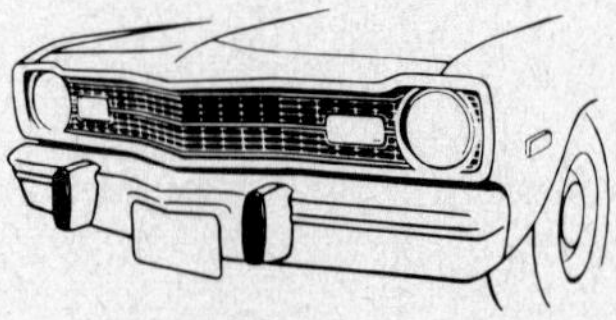
1973 Dart

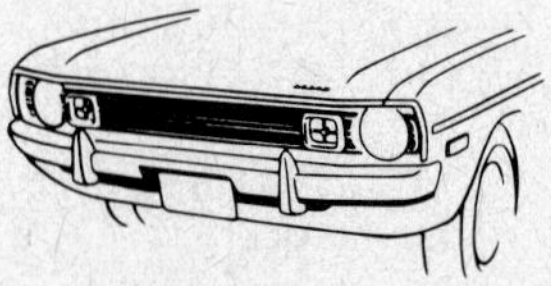
1972 Demon

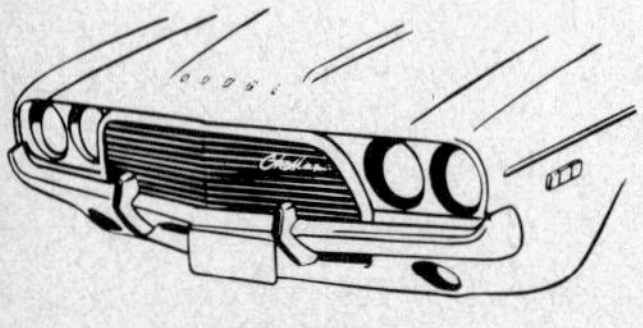
1972 Challenger

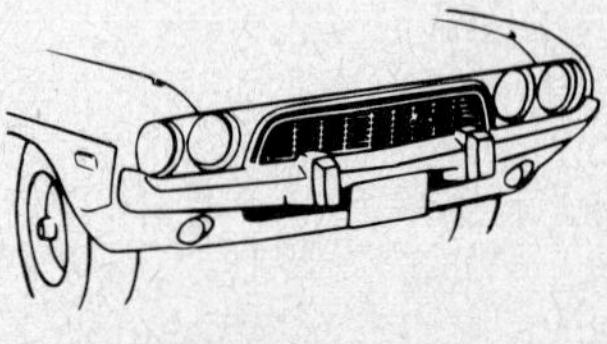
1973 Challenger

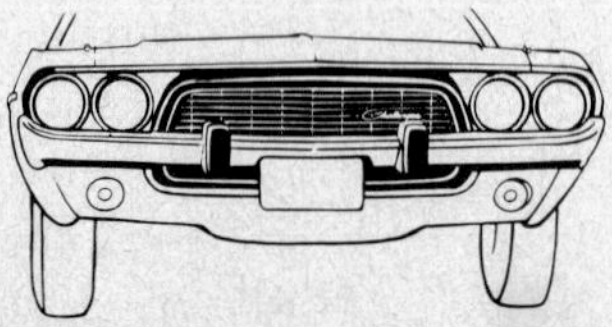
1974 Challenger

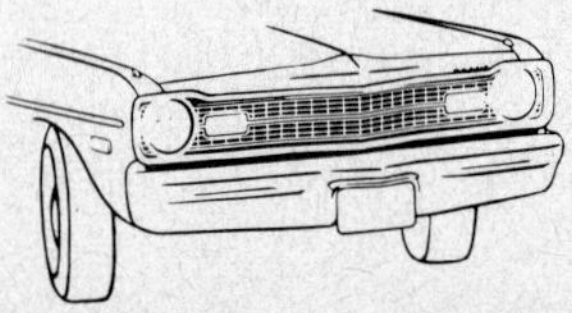
1974 Dart

FIRING ORDER

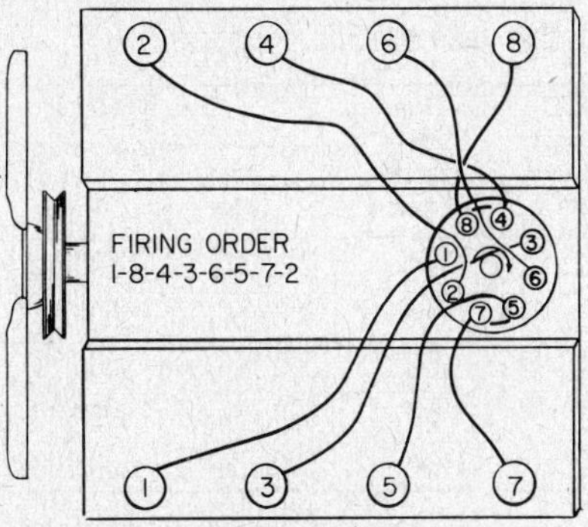
FIRING ORDER
1-8-4-3-6-5-7-2

273, 318, 340, 360 cu. in.
(© Chrysler Corp)

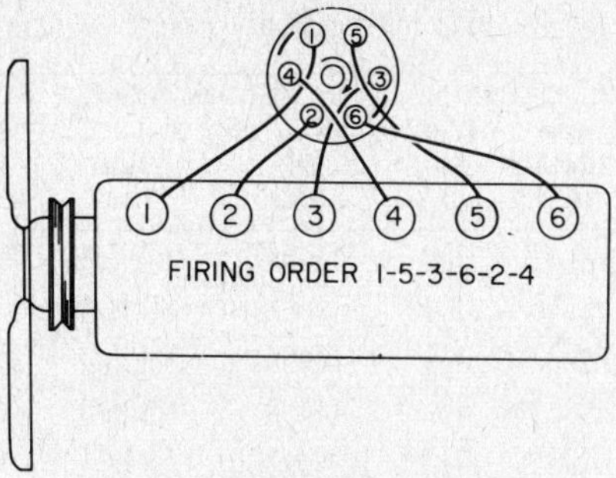
FIRING ORDER 1-5-3-6-2-4

170, 198, 225 cu. in.
(© Chrysler Corp)

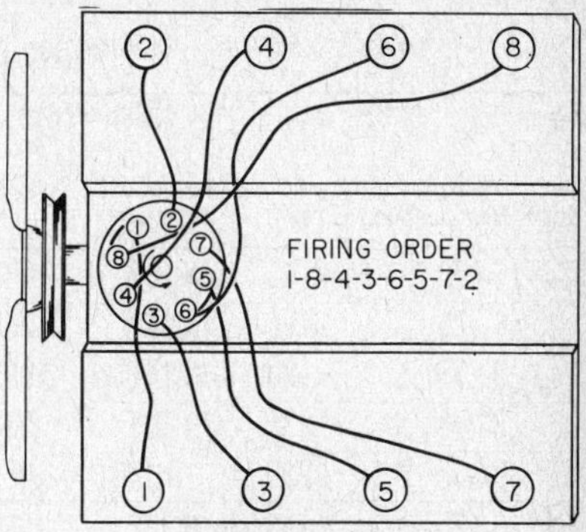
FIRING ORDER
1-8-4-3-6-5-7-2

383, 426 , 440 cu. in.
(© Chrysler Corp)

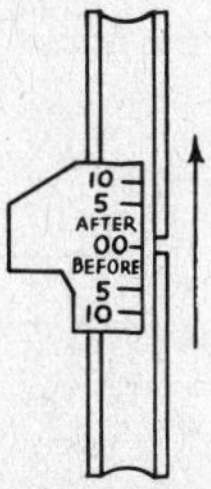
10
5
AFTER
OO
BEFORE
5
10

Timing marks—1967-74 6 cylinder
(© Chrysler Corp)

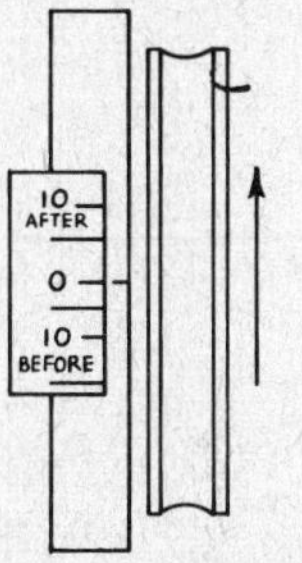
10
AFTER
O
10
BEFORE

Timing marks—1967-74 V8
(© Chrysler Corp)

CAR SERIAL NUMBER LOCATION AND ENGINE IDENTIFICATION

Engine Number Location

170, 198 and 225 cu. in. six engines . . . stamped on joint face of block, next to No. 1 cylinder.

273, 318, 340, and 360 cu. in. V8 engines . . . stamped on front of block, just below left cylinder head.

383, 426 and 440 cu. in. V8 engine . . . stamped on cylinder block pan rail, at left rear corner below starter opening.

C318 7-6

Engine code location—273, 318, 340, 360
(© Chrysler Corp)

C383
7-6

Engine code location—383, 440
(© Chrysler Corp)

ENGINE CODE

Valiant, Dart, Barracuda, Challenger

The engine code designation is the 5th digit of the vehicle identification number (V.I.N.). The V.I.N. is stamped on a plate located at the left front door hinge pillar on 1967 models, located at the left side of the instrument panel visible through the windshield on 1968-74 models, and located to the rear of the right engine mount on the oil pan rail on 1969-74 models.

Disp	Bbl	Hp	'67	'68	'69	'70	'71	'72	'73	'74
6-Cylinder Models										
170	1	115	A	A	A					
198	1	95 (net)							B	B
198	1	100 (net)						B		
198	1	125				B	B			
225	1	105 (net)							C	C
225	1	110 (net)						C		
225	1	145	B	B	B	C	C			
8-Cylinder Models										
273	2	180	D	D	D					
273	4	235	E							
318	2	150 (net)						G	G	G
318	2	230		F	F	G	G			
340	4	240 (net)						H	H	
340	4	275		P	P	H	H			
360	4	240 (net)								
383	2	275					L			
383	4	280	G							
383	2	290				L				
383	4	300	G				N			
383	4	330			H	L				
383	4	335				N				
426	8	425				R	R			
440	4	375				U				
440	6	385					V			
440	6	390				V				

Valiant and Dart

TUNE-UP SPECIFICATIONS

When analyzing compression test results, look for uniformity among cylinders rather than specific pressures.

ENGINE			SPARK PLUGS		DISTRIBUTOR		IGNITION TIMING (deg) ▲		VALVES	Fuel	IDLE SPEED (rpm) ▲	
Year	No. Cyl Displacement (cu in.)	hp	Type §	Gap (in.)	Point Dwell (deg)	Point Gap (in.)	Man Trans	Auto Trans	Intake Opens ■ (deg) ●	Pump Pressure (psi)	Man Trans	Auto Trans
'67	6-170	115	N-14Y	.035	40-45	.020	5B(5A)	5B(5A)	10	3½-5	550(700)①	550(650)①
	6-225	145	N-14Y	.035	40-45	.020	5B(TDC)	5B(TDC)	10	3½-5	550(650)①	550(650)①
	8-273	180	N-14Y	.035	28-32	.017	5B(5A)	10B(5A)	14	5-7	500(700)①	500(650)①
	8-273	235	N-10Y	.035	27-31②	.017	10B(5A)	10B(5A)	14	5-7	600(700)①	600(650)①
	8-383	280③	J-13Y	.035	28-32	.017	12½B(TDC)	12½B(5B)	16	3½-5	500(650)①	500(600)①
'68	6-170	115	N-14Y	.035	40-45	.020	5B(5A)	5B(2½)A	10	3½-5	550(650)①	550(650)①
	6-225	145	N-14Y	.035	40-45	.020	5B(TDC)	5B(TDC)	10	3½-5	550(650)①	550(650)①
	8-273	190	N-14Y	.035	28-33	.017	5A	2½A	10	5-7	700	650
	8-318	230	N-14Y	.035	28-33	.017	5B(5A)	10B(2½A)	10	5-7	650	600
	8-340	275③	N-9Y	.035	27-32④	.017	TDC	5B	26⑤	3½-5	700	650
	8-383	300③	J-11Y	.035	28-33	.017	TDC	5B	18	3½-5	650	600
'69	6-170	115	N-14Y	.035	42-47	.020	5A	2½A	10	3½-5	750	750
	6-225	145	N-14Y	.035	42-47	.020	TDC	TDC	10	3½-5	700	650
	8-273	190	N-14Y	.035	30-35	.017	2½A	2½A	10	5-7	700	650
	8-318	230	N-14Y	.035	30-35	.017	TDC	TDC	10	5-7	700	650
	8-340	275	N-9Y	.035	27-32④	.017	TDC	5B	22	5-7	750	700
	8-383	330③	J-11Y	.035	27-32④	.017	TDC	5B	21	3½-5	700	650
'70	6-198	125	N-14Y	.035	41-46	.020	2½B	TDC	10	3½-5	750	750①
	6-225	145	N-14Y	.035	41-56	.020	TDC	TDC	10	3½-5	700	650①
	8-318	230	N-14Y	.035	30-34	.017	TDC	TDC	10	5-7	750	700
	8-340	275	N-9Y	.035	27-32④	.017	5B	5B	22	5-7	900	900
'71	6-198	125	N-14Y	.035	41-46	.020	2½B	2½B	16	3½-5	800	800
	6-225	145	N-14Y	.035	41-46	.020	TDC(2½B)	TDC(2½B)	16	3½-5	750	750
	8-318	230	N-14Y	.035	30-34	.017	TDC	TDC	10	5-7	750	700
	8-340	275	N-9Y	.035	27-32④	.017	5B	5B	22	5-7	900	900
'72	6-198	100	N-14Y	.035	41-46	.020	2½B	2½B	16	2½-5	800(700)	800(700)
	6-225	110	N-14Y	.035	41-46	.020	TDC(2½B)	TDC(2½B)	16	2½-5	750(700)	750(700)
	8-318	150	N-13Y	.035	30-34	.017	TDC	TDC	10	5-7	750	750(700)
	8-340	240	N-9Y	.035	30-34	.017	TDC(2½B)	2½B	22	5-7	900(850)	750
'73	6-198	95	N-14Y	.035	Electronic		2½B	2½B	16	4-5½	800	750
	6-225	105	N-14Y	.035	Electronic		TDC	TDC	16	4-5½	750	750
	8-318	150	N-13Y	.035	Electronic		2½B	TDC	10	6-7½	750	700
	8-340	240	N-9Y	.035	Electronic		5B	2½B	22	6-7½	850	850
'74	6-198	95	N-14Y	.035	Electronic		2½B	2½B	16	3½-5	800	750
	6-225	105	N-14Y	.035	Electronic		TDC	TDC	16	5-7	800	750
	8-318	150	N-13Y	.035	Electronic		TDC	TDC	10	5-7	750	750
	8-360	185	N-12Y	.035	Electronic		5B(2½B)	5B	22	5-7	850	850

MECHANICAL VALVE LIFTER CLEARANCE

Year	Engine	Intake (Hot) In.	Exhaust (Hot) In.
1967-74	All six cylinder	.010	.020
1967	273 V8	.013	.021

▲ See text for procedure
■ All figures Before Top Dead Center
● Figure in parentheses indicates California engine

§ All spark plug listings are Champion original equipment numbers
① A/C on
② Adjust both sets of points to this figure. With both sets connected, total reading should be 36-40 degrees.
③ Dart only
④ Adjust both sets of points to this figure. With both sets connected, total reading should be 37-42 degrees.
⑤ Figure is 22 degrees for automatic transmission
A After Top Dead Center
B Before Top Dead Center
TDC Top Dead Center

Barracuda, Challenger TUNE-UP SPECIFICATIONS

When analyzing compression test results, look for uniformity among cylinders rather than specific pressures.

	ENGINE		SPARK PLUGS		DISTRIBUTOR		IGNITION TIMING (deg) ▲		VALVES	Fuel	IDLE SPEED (rpm) ▲	
Year	No. Cyl Displacement (cu in.)	hp	Type §	Gap (in.)	Point Dwell (deg)	Point Gap (in.)	Man Trans	Auto Trans	Intake Opens ■ (deg) ●	Pump Pressure (psi)	Man Trans	Auto Trans
'67	6-225	145	N-14Y	.035	43	.020	5B(TDC)	5B(TDC)	10	3½-5	550(650)	550(650)
	8-273	180	N-14Y	.035	30	.017	5B(5A)	10B(5A)	14	5-7	500(750)	500(650)
	8-273	235	N-10Y	.035	29①	.017	10B(5A)	10B(5A)	14	5-7	600(700)	600(650)
	8-383	280	J-13Y	.035	28-33	.017	TDC	5B	16		650	600
'68	6-225	145	N-14Y	.035	43	.020	5B(TDC)	5B(TDC)	10	3½-5	550(650)②	550(650)②
	8-318	230	N-14Y	.035	31	.017	5B(5A)	10B(2½A)	10	5-7	650	600
	8-340	275	N-9Y	.035	30③	.017	TDC	5B	26④	3½-5	700	650
	8-383	300	J-11Y	.035	31	.017	TDC	5B	18	3½-5	650	600
'69	6-225	145	N-14Y	.035	45	.020	TDC	TDC	10	3½-5	700	650
	8-318	230	N-14Y	.035	33	.017	TDC	TDC	10	5-7	700	650
	8-340	275	N-9Y	.035	30③	.017	TDC	5B	22	5-7	750	700
	8-383	330	J-11Y	.035	30③	.017	TDC	5B	21	3½-5	700	650
'70	6-225	145	N-14Y	.035	44	.020	TDC	TDC	10	3½-5	700	650
	8-318	230	N-14Y	.035	32	.017	TDC	TDC	10	5-7	750	700
	8-340	275	N-9Y	.035	30③	.017	5B	5B	22	5-7	900	900
	8-383	290	J-14Y	.035	30½	.019	TDC	2½B	18	3½-5	750	650
	8-383	330	J-11Y	.035	30½	.019	TDC	2½B	18	3½-5	750	700
	8-383	335	J-11Y	.035	30½	.019	TDC	2½B	21	3½-5	750	750
	8-426	425	N-10Y	.035	30③	.017	TDC	2½B	36	7-8½	900	900
	8-440	375	J-11Y	.035	30½	.019	TDC	2½B	21	3½-5	900	800
	8-440	390	J-11Y	.035	30③	.017	5B	5B	21	6-7½	900	900
'71	6-198	125	N-14Y	.035	44	.020	2½B	2½B	16	3½-5	800	800
	6-225	145	N-14Y	.035	44	.020	TDC(2½B)	TDC(2½B)	16	3½-5	750	750
	8-318	230	N-14Y	.035	32	.017	TDC	TDC	10	5-7	750	700
	8-340	275	N-9Y	.035	32③	.017	5B	5B	22	5-7	900	900
	8-383	275	J-14Y	.035	30½	.019	TDC	2½B	18	3½-5	750	700
	8-383	300	J-11Y	.035	30½	.019	TDC	2½B	21	3½-5	900	800
	8-426	425	N-10Y	.035	30	.017	TDC	2½B	36	7-8½	900	900
	8-440	385	J-11Y	.035	30	.017	21	6-7½	950	950	5B	5B
'72	6-225	110	N-14Y	.035	44	.020	TDC(2½B)	TDC(2½B)	16	2½-5	750(700)	750(700)
	8-318	150	N-13Y	.035	32	.017	TDC	TDC	10	5-7	750	750(700)
	8-340	240	N-9Y	.035	Electronic		TDC(2½B)	2½B	22	5-7	900(850)	750
'73	8-318	150	N-13Y	.035	Electronic		2½B	TDC	10	6-7½	750	700
	8-340	240	N-9Y	.035	Electronic		5B	2½B	22	6-7½	850	850
'74	8-318	150	N-13Y	.035	Electronic		TDC	TDC	10	5-7	750	750
	8-360	185	N-12Y	.035	Electronic		5B(2½B)	5B	22	5-7	850	850

▲ See text for procedure
● Figure in parentheses indicates California engine
■ All figures Before Top Dead Center
§ All spark plug listings are Champion original equipment numbers
① Adjust both sets of points to this figure. With both sets connected, the total reading should be 38 degrees.
② A/C on
③ Adjust both sets of points to this figure. With both sets connected, the total reading should be 40 degrees.
④ For vehicles with automatic transmission, adjust to 22 degrees Before Top Dead Center
A After Top Dead Center
B Before Top Dead Center
TDC Top Dead Center
— Not applicable

MECHANICAL VALVE LIFTER CLEARANCE

Year	Engine	Intake (Hot) In.	Exhaust (Hot) In.
1967-74	All 6 cylinder	.010	.020
1967	273 V8	.013	.021

GENERAL ENGINE SPECIFICATIONS

Year	Engine No. Cyl. Cu. In. Displacement	Carburetor Type	Advertised Horsepower @ rpm ■	Advertised Torque @ rpm (ft lbs) ■	Bore and Stroke (in.)	Advertised Compression Ratio	Oil Pressure @ 2050 rpm
'67	6-170	1 bbl	115 @ 4400	155 @ 2400	3.406 x 3.125	8.5:1	55
	6-225	1 bbl	145 @ 4000	215 @ 2400	3.406 x 4.125	8.4:1	55
	8-273	2 bbl	180 @ 4200	260 @ 1600	3.625 x 3.310	8.8:1	55
	8-273	4 bbl	235 @ 5200	280 @ 4000	3.625 x 3.310	10.5:1	55
	8-383	4 bbl	280 @ 4200	400 @ 2400	4.250 x 3.375	10.0:1	55
'68	6-170	1 bbl	115 @ 4400	155 @ 2400	3.406 x 3.125	8.5:1	55
	6-225	1 bbl	145 @ 4000	215 @ 2400	3.406 x 4.125	8.4:1	55
	8-273	2 bbl	190 @ 4400	260 @ 2000	3.625 x 3.310	9.0:1	55
	8-318	2 bbl	230 @ 4400	340 @ 2400	3.910 x 3.310	9.2:1	55
	8-340	4 bbl	275 @ 5000	340 @ 3200	4.040 x 3.310	10.5:1	55
	8-383	4 bbl	300 @ 4400	400 @ 2400	4.250 x 3.375	10.0:1	55
'69	6-170	1 bbl	115 @ 4400	155 @ 2400	3.406 x 3.125	8.5:1	55
	6-225	1 bbl	145 @ 4000	215 @ 2400	3.406 x 4.125	8.4:1	55
	8-273	2 bbl	190 @ 4400	260 @ 2000	3.625 x 3.310	9.0:1	55
	8-318	2 bbl	230 @ 4400	340 @ 2400	3.910 x 3.310	9.2:1	55
	8-340	4 bbl	275 @ 5000	340 @ 3200	4.040 x 3.310	10.5:1	55
	8-383	4 bbl	330 @ 5200	410 @ 3600	4.250 x 3.375	10.0:1	55
'70	6-198	1 bbl	125 @ 4400	180 @ 2000	3.406 x 3.640	8.4:1	55
	6-225	1 bbl	145 @ 4000	215 @ 2400	3.406 x 4.125	8.4:1	55
	8-318	2 bbl	230 @ 4400	320 @ 2000	3.910 x 3.310	8.8:1	55
	8-340	4 bbl	275 @ 5000	340 @ 3200	4.040 x 3.310	10.5:1	55
	8-383	2 bbl	290 @ 4400	390 @ 2800	4.250 x 3.375	8.7:1	55
	8-383	4 bbl	330 @ 5000	425 @ 3200	4.250 x 3.375	9.5:1	55
	8-383 HP	4 bbl	335 @ 5200	425 @ 3400	4.250 x 3.375	10.5:1	55
	8-426 Hemi	2 x 4 bbl	425 @ 5000	490 @ 4000	4.250 x 3.750	10.2:1	55
	8-440 HP	4 bbl	375 @ 4600	480 @ 3200	4.320 x 3.750	9.7:1	55
	8-440 Six Pack	3 x 2 bbl	390 @ 4700	490 @ 3200	4.320 x 3.750	10.5:1	55
'71	6-198	1 bbl	125 @ 4400	180 @ 2000	3.406 x 3.640	8.4:1	55
	6-225	1 bbl	145 @ 4000	215 @ 2400	3.406 x 4.125	8.4:1	55
	8-318	2 bbl	230 @ 4400	320 @ 2000	3.910 x 3.310	8.6:1	55
	8-340	4 bbl	275 @ 5000	340 @ 3200	4.040 x 3.310	10.3:1	55
	8-340	3 x 2 bbl	290 @ 5000	340 @ 3200	4.040 x 3.310	10.3:1	55
	8-383	2 bbl	275 @ 4400	375 @ 2800	4.250 x 3.375	8.5:1	55
	8-383 HP	4 bbl	300 @ 4800	410 @ 3400	4.250 x 3.375	8.5:1	55
	8-426 Hemi	4 bbl	425 @ 5000	490 @ 4000	4.250 x 3.750	10.2:1	55
	8-440 Six Pack	2 x 4 bbl	385 @ 4700	490 @ 3200	4.320 x 3.750	10.3:1	55
'72	6-198	1 bbl	100 @ 4400①	160 @ 2400②	3.406 x 3.640	8.4:1	55
	6-225	1 bbl	110 @ 4000③	185 @ 2000④	3.406 x 4.125	8.4:1	55
	8-318	2 bbl	150 @ 4000	260 @ 1600	3.910 x 3.310	8.6:1	55
	8-340	4 bbl	240 @ 4800	290 @ 3600	4.040 x 3.310	8.5:1	55
'73	6-198	1 bbl	95 @ 4000	155 @ 1600	3.406 x 3.640	8.4:1	55
	6-225	1 bbl	105 @ 4000	185 @ 1600	3.406 x 4.125	8.4:1	55
	8-318	2 bbl	150 @ 3600	265 @ 2000	3.910 x 3.310	8.6:1	55
	8-340	4 bbl	240 @ 4800	295 @ 3600	4.040 x 3.310	8.5:1	55

GENERAL ENGINE SPECIFICATIONS

Year	Engine No. Cyl. Cu. In. Displacement	Carburetor Type	Advertised Horsepower @ rpm ■	Advertised Torque @ rpm (ft lbs) ■	Bore and Stroke (in.)	Advertised Compression Ratio	Oil Pressure @ 2050 rpm
'74	6-198	1 bbl	95 @ 4000	150 @ 1600	3.406 x 3.640	8.4:1	55
	6-225	1 bbl	105 @ 4000	185 @ 1600	3.406 x 4.125	8.4:1	55
	8-318	2 bbl	150 @ 3600	265 @ 2000	3.910 x 3.310	8.6:1	55
	8-360	4 bbl	185 @ 4000	285 @ 4000	4.000 x 3.580	8.4:1	55

■ Beginning 1972, horsepower and torque are SAE net figures. They are measured at the rear of the transmission with all accessories installed and operating. Since the figures vary when a given engine is installed in different models, some figures are representative rather than exact.

① For California vehicles, advertised horsepower is 94 @ 4400 rpm

② For California vehicles, advertised torque is 158 @ 2400 rpm

③ For California vehicles, advertised horsepower is 97 @ 4000 rpm

④ For California vehicles, advertised torque is 180 @ 2000 rpm

HP High Performance

CRANKSHAFT AND CONNECTING ROD SPECIFICATIONS

All measurements are given in in.

Year	Engine No. Cyl. Displacement (cu in.)	CRANKSHAFT Main Brg. Journal Dia	CRANKSHAFT Main Brg. Oil Clearance	CRANKSHAFT Shaft End-Play	CRANKSHAFT Thrust on No.	CONNECTING ROD Journal Diameter	CONNECTING ROD Oil Clearance	CONNECTING ROD Side Clearance
'67-'74	6-170, 198, 225	2.7495-2.7505	.0005-.0015	.002-.007	3	2.1865-2.1875	.0005-.0015	.006-.012
'67-'68	8-273, 318, 340	2.4495-2.5005	.0005-.0015	.002-.007	3	2.124-2.125	.0005-.0025	.006-.014
'69-'74	8-273, 318, 340, 360	2.4495-2.5005	.0005-.0015	.002-.007	3	2.124-2.125	.0005-.0025	.009-.017
'67-'71	8-383	2.6245-2.6255	.0005-.0015	.002-.007	3	2.3740-2.3750	.0005-.0015	.009-.017
'70-'71	8-440	2.7495-2.7505	.0005-.0015	.002-.007	3	2.3740-2.3750	.0010-.0020	.009-.017
'70	8-426 Hemi	2.7495-2.7505	.0015-.0025	.002-.007	3	2.374-2.375	.0015-.0025	.009-.017
'71	8-426 Hemi	2.7490-2.7500	.0015-.0030	.002-.007	3	2.3738-2.3745	.0015-.0025	.013-.017

TORQUE SPECIFICATIONS

All readings in ft lbs

Year	Engine No. Cyl. Displacement (cu in.)	Cylinder Head Bolts	Rod Bearing Bolts	Main Bearing Bolts	Crankshaft Pulley Bolt	Flywheel to Crankshaft Bolts	MANIFOLD Intake	MANIFOLD Exhaust
'67-'74	6-All	70	45	85	Press fit	55	10①	10
'67-'74	8-273, 318, 340, 360	95	45	85	②	65	40	30
'67-'71	8-383, 440	70	45	85	②	55	40	30
'70-'71	8-426 Hemi	75	75	100③	135	70	④	35

① Intake to exhaust bolts—20 ft. lbs.

② Vibration damper bolts—15 ft. lbs. for 1966-69, 9 ft. lbs. for 1970-74. End of crankshaft bolt (except 1971 with 318 or 340 engine) 135 ft. lbs., 1971 with 318 or 340 engine—100 ft. lbs.

③ Cross bolt mains—45 ft. lbs.

④ Torque the four center bolts on either side to 6 ft. lbs., all others to 4 ft. lbs.

CAPACITIES

Year	ENGINE No. Cyl. (Cu. In.) Displacement	Engine Crankcase Add 1 Qt For New Filter	TRANSMISSION Pts To Refill After Draining Manual 3-Speed	4-Speed	Automatic	Drive Axle (pts)	Gasoline Tank (gals)	COOLING SYSTEM (qts) With Heater	With A/C
'67	6-170	4	6.5	—	16	2	18	12	13
	6-225	4	6.5	—	16	2	18	13	14
	8-273	4	6.5	8	16	2	18	19	20
	8-383	4	—	8	18.5	4	18	17	18
'68	6-170	4	6.5	—	16	2	18	12	13
	6-225	4	6.5	—	16	2	18	13	14
	8-273	4	6	8.5	16	2	18	19	20
	8-318	4	6.5	8.5	16	2④	18	18⑨	19⑨
	8-340	4	—	8.5	17.5	4	18	18	19
	8-383	4	—	8.5	17.5	4	18	17	18
'69	6-170	4	6.5	—	16	2	18	12	14
	6-225	4	6.5	—	16	2	18	13	15
	8-273	4	6.5	7.5	16	2⑤	18	17	19
	8-318	4	6	7.5	16	2④	18	17	19
	8-340	4	—	7.5	16	4	18	16	16
	8-383	4	—	7.5	16	4	18	16	16
'70	6-198	4	6.5①	—	17	2	18	13	14
	6-225	4	6.5①	—	17	2	18	13	14
	8-318	4	4.75	7.5	16	4	18	16	17
	8-340	4	4.75	7	16	4	18	15.5	15.5
	8-383	4	4.75	7.5	19③	4	18	14.5	15
	8-426	6	—	7.5	17	5.5	18	17	—
	8-440	6	—	7.5	19	5.5	18	17	—
'71	6-198	4	6.5①	—	17	2⑥	17⑦	13	14
	6-225	4	6.5①	—	17	2⑥	17⑦	13	14
	8-318	4	4.75	—	17	4.5	17⑦	16	17.5
	8-340	4	4.75	7	16.3	4.5	17⑦	15.5	15.5
	8-383	4	4.75	7.5	19③	4.5	18	14.5	15
	8-426	6	—	7.5	16.3	5.5	18	17	—
	8-440	6	—	7.5	19	5.5	18	15.5	17
'72	6-198	4	6.5	—	17	2	16	13	14
	6-225	4	6.5①	—	17	2	16⑧	13	14
	8-318	4	4.75	—	17	4.5	16⑧	16	17
	8-340	4	4.75	7②	16.3	4.5	16⑧	15	15
'73	6-198	4	6.5	—	17	2	16	13	13
	6-225	4	6.5	—	17	2	16	13	14
	8-318	4	4.75	—	17	4.5	16⑧	16	17.5
	8-340	4	4.75	7②	16.3	4.5	16⑧	15.5⑨	15.5
'74	6-198	4	6.5	—	16.5	2	16	13	—
	6-225	4	6.5	—	16.5	2	16	13	14.0
	8-318	4	4.75	7.0	16.5	4.5	16	16	17.5
	8-360	4	4.75	7.0	16.1	4.5	16	16	16.0

① Barracuda, Challenger—4.75 pts
② Barracuda, Challenger—7.5 pts
③ Hi-performance—16 pts
④ Manual transmission—4 pts
⑤ 4-speed transmission—4 pts
⑥ Barracuda, Challenger—4.5 pts
⑦ Barracuda, Challenger—18 gals
⑧ Barracuda—16.5 gals, Challenger—18 gals
— Not applicable
⑨ Barracuda, Challenger—15 qts

VALVE SPECIFICATIONS

Year	Engine No. Cyl. Displacement (cu in.)	Seat Angle (deg)	Face Angle (deg)	Spring Test Pressure, (lbs @ in.)	Spring Installed Height (in.)	STEM TO GUIDE Clearance (in.)		STEM Diameter (in.)	
						Intake	Exhaust	Intake	Exhaust
'67	6-170	45	④	144 @ 1.31	1 11/16	.0010-.0030	.0020-.0040	.3725	.3715
	6-225	45	④	144 @ 1.31	1 11/16	.0010-.0030	.0020-.0040	.3725	.3715
	8-273②	45	45	144 @ 1.31	1 11/16	.0010-.0030	.0020-.0040	.3275	.3715
	8-273③	45	45	177 @ 1.31	1 11/16	.0010-.0030	.0020-.0040	.3725	.3715
	8-383	45	45	200 @ 1.44	1 7/8	.0010-.0030	.0020-.0040	.3725	.3715
'68	6-170	45	①	144 @ 1.31	1 11/16	.0010-.0030	.0020-.0040	.3725	.3715
	6-225	45	①	144 @ 1.31	1 11/16	.0010-.0030	.0020-.0040	.3725	.3715
	8-273	45	①	177 @ 1.31	1 11/16	.0010-.0030	.0020-.0040	.3725	.3715
	8-318	45	①	177 @ 1.31	1 11/16	.0010-.0030	.0020-.0040	.3725	.3715
	8-340	45	①	242 @ 1.22	1 11/16	.0010-.0030	.0020-.0040	.3725	.3715
	8-383	45	45	230 @ 1.41	1 7/8	.0010-.0030	.0020-.0040	.3725	.3715
'69	6-170	45	①	144 @ 1.31	1 11/16	.0010-.0030	.0020-.0040	.3725	.3715
	6-225	45	①	144 @ 1.31	1 11/16	.0010-.0030	.0020-.0040	.3725	.3715
	8-273	45	①	177 @ 1.31	1 11/16	.0010-.0030	.0020-.0040	.3725	.3715
	8-318	45	①	177 @ 1.31	1 11/16	.0010-.0030	.0020-.0040	.3725	.3715
	8-340	45	①	242 @ 1.22	1 11/16	.0010-.0030	.0020-.0040	.3725	.3715
	8-383	45	45	246 @ 1.36	1 7/8	.0010-.0030	.0020-.0040	.3725	.3715
'70	6-198	45	①	144 @ 1.31	1 11/16	.0010-.0030	.0020-.0040	.3725	.3715
	6-225	45	①	144 @ 1.31	1 11/16	.0010-.0030	.0020-.0040	.3725	.3715
	8-318	45	①	177 @ 1.31	1 11/16	.0010-.0030	.0020-.0040	.3725	.3715
	8-340	45	①	242 @ 1.22	1 11/16	.0015-.0035	.0025-.0045	.3720	.3710
	8-383②	45	45	200 @ 1.44	1 7/8	.0010-.0030	.0020-.0040	.3727	.3717
	8-383③	45	45	246 @ 1.72	1 7/8	.0015-.0032	.0025-.0042	.3722	.3712
	8-426	45	45	310 @ 1.38	1 7/8	.0020-.0040	.0030-.0050	.3090	.3080
	8-440	45	45	310 @ 1.38	1 7/8	.0015-.0032	.0025-.0042	.3725	.3715
'71	6-198	45	①	144 @ 1.31	1 11/16	.0010-.0030	.0020-.0040	.3725	.3715
	6-225	45	①	144 @ 1.31	1 11/16	.0010-.0030	.0020-.0040	.3725	.3715
	8-318	45	①	177 @ 1.31	1 11/16	.0010-.0030	.0020-.0040	.3725	.3715
	8-340	45	①	238 @ 1.31	1 11/16	.0015-.0035	.0025-.0045	.3720	.3710
	8-383②	45	45	200 @ 1.44	1 7/8	.0010-.0030	.0020-.0040	.3727	.3717
	8-383③	45	45	246 @ 1.72	1 7/8	.0015-.0032	.0025-.0042	.3722	.3712
	8-426	45	45	310 @ 1.38	1 7/8	.0020-.0040	.0030-.0050	3090	.3080
	8-440	45	45	200 @ 1.44	1 7/8	.0010-.0030	.0020-.0040	.3727	.3717
'72	6-198	45	①	144 @ 1.31	1 11/16	.0010-.0030	.0020-.0040	.3725	.3715
	6-225	45	①	144 @ 1.31	1 11/16	.0010-.0030	.0020-.0040	.3725	.3715
	8-318	45	①	177 @ 1.31	1 11/16	.0010-.0030	.0020-.0040	.3725	.3715
	8-340	45	①	208 @ 1.31	1 11/16	.0015-.0035	.0025-.0045	.3720	.3710
'73	6-198	45	④	160 @ 1.24	1 21/32	.0010-.0030	.0020-.0040	.3725	.3715
	6-225	45	④	160 @ 1.24	1 21/32	.0010-.0030	.0020-.0040	.3725	.3715
	8-318	45	④	189 @ 1.28	1 21/32	.0010-.0030	.0020-.0040	.3725	.3715
	8-340	45	④	238 @ 1.22	1 21/32	.0015-.0035	.0025-.0045	.3720	.3710
'74	6-198	45	47	160 @ 1.24	1 21/32	.0010-.0030	.0020-.0040	.3725	.3715
	6-225	45	47	160 @ 1.24	1 21/32	.0010-.0030	.0020-.0040	.3725	.3715
	8-318	45	47	189 @ 1.28	1 21/32	.0010-.0030	.0020-.0040	.3725	.3715
	8-360	45	47	238 @ 1.22	1 21/32	.0010-.0030	.0025-.0045	.3725	.3715

① Intake 45°, Exhaust 43°
② 2 bbl carburetor
③ 4 bbl carburetor
④ Intake 45°, Exhaust 47°

BATTERY AND STARTER SPECIFICATIONS

Year	Engine No. cyl Displacement (cu in.)	BATTERY Ampere Hour Capacity	Volts	Terminal Grounded	STARTER Lock Test Amps	Volts	Torque (ft lbs)	No-Load Test Amps	Volts	RPM	Brush Spring Tension (oz)
'67	6-170	38	12	Neg.	380	4	—	90	11	2,950	32-48
	6-225	48	12	Neg.	380	4	—	85	11	1,950	32-48
	8-273①	48	12	Neg.	450	4	—	90	11	2,400	32-48
'68-'69	6-170	38	12	Neg.	380	4	—	90	11	2,950	32-36
	6-225, 273, 318, 340	48	12	Neg.	425	4	—	90	11	2,300	32-36
	8-383	59	12	Neg.	425	4	—	90	11	2,300	32-36
'70	6 & 8-198, 225, 318, 340	46	12	Neg.	400-450	4	—	90	11	1,925-2,600	32-36
	8-383	59	12	Neg.	400-450	4	—	90	11	1,925-2,600	32-36
	8-426, 440	70	12	Neg.	400-450	4	—	90	11	1,925-2,600	32-36
'71	6 & 8-198, 225, 318	46	12	Neg.	400-450	4	—	90	11	1,925-2,600	32-36
	8-340, 383	59	12	Neg.	400-450	4	—	90	11	1,925-2,600	32-36
	8-426, 440	70	12	Neg.	400-450	4	—	90	11	1,925-2,600	32-36
'72-'73	6 & 8-198, 225, 318, 340	46	12	Neg.	400-450	4	—	90	11	1,925-2,600	32-36
	6 & 8-198, 225, 318, 340	59	12	Neg.	400-450	4	—	90	11	1,925-2,600	32-36
	6 & 8-198, 225, 318, 340	70	12	Neg.	400-450	4	—	90	11	1,925-2,600	32-36
'74	6 & 8-198, 225, 318, 360	48	12	Neg.	475-550	4	—	90	11	3,700-4,200	32-36
	6 & 8-198, 225, 318, 360	70	12	Neg.	475-550	4	—	90	11	3,700-4,200	32-36

① 1967 383 engine, refer to 1968 specifications

ALTERNATOR AND REGULATOR SPECIFICATIONS

Year	ALTERNATOR Part No. or Manufacturer	Field Current @ 12 V	Output (amps)	REGULATOR Part No. or Manufacturer	Field Relay Air Gap (in.)	Point Gap (in.)	Volts to Close	Regulator Air Gap (in.)	Point Gap (in.)	Volts @ 75°
'67-'69	6 Cyl Models	2.38-2.75	26	2098300①	.050①	.014	13.8	.050	.015	13.8-14.4
	8 Cyl Std.	2.38-2.75	35	2098300①	.050①	.014	13.8	.050	.015	13.8-14.4
	Heavy Duty, A/C	2.38-2.75	44	2098300①	.050①	.014	13.8	.050	.015	13.8-14.4
	Special Equip.	2.38-2.75	51	2098300①	.050①	.014	13.8	.050	.015	13.8-14.4
'70-'71	6 Cyl Models	2.38-2.75	26	3438150			Not Adjustable			13.8-14.4
	8 Cyl Std.	2.38-2.75	34②	3438150			Not Adjustable			13.8-14.4
	Heavy Duty, A/C	2.38-2.75	45	3438150			Not Adjustable			13.8-14.4
	Special Equip.	2.38-2.75	51	3438150			Not Adjustable			13.8-14.4
'72-'73	6 Cyl Models	2.5-3.1	39	3438150			Not Adjustable			13.8-14.4
	8 Cyl Std.	2.5-3.1	41	3438150			Not Adjustable			13.8-14.4
	Heavy Duty, A/C	2.5-3.1	50	3438150			Not Adjustable			13.8-14.4
	Special Equip.	2.5-3.1	60	3438150			Not Adjustable			13.8-14.4
'74	6 Cyl Models	2.5-3.1	41	3438150			Not Adjustable			13.8-14.4
	8 Cyl Std.	2.5-3.1	50	3438150			Not Adjustable			13.8-14.4
	Special Equipment	2.5-3.1	65	3438150			Not Adjustable			13.8-14.4

① Essex wire regulator, #2444980, used interchangeably. Air gap setting is .032-.042 in., all other dimensions are identical with #2098300

② '71 models use a standard 44 amp alternator

WHEEL ALIGNMENT SPECIFICATIONS

Year	Model	CASTER Range (deg)	CASTER Pref Setting (deg)	CAMBER Range (deg)	CAMBER Pref Setting (deg)	Toe-in (in.)	Steering Axis Inclin. (deg)	WHEEL PIVOT RATIO (deg) Inner Wheel	WHEEL PIVOT RATIO (deg) Wheel Outer
'67-'68	Manual	1N to 0	1/2N	⑤	⑤	3/32 to 5/32	7 1/2	20	17.6
	Power	1/4P to 1 1/4P	3/4P	⑤	⑤	3/32 to 5/32	7 1/2	20	17.6
'69	Manual	1N to 0⑥	1/2N	⑤	⑤	3/32 to 5/32	7 1/2	20	17.6
	Power	1/4P to 1 1/4P⑥	3/4P	⑤	⑤	3/32 to 5/32	7 1/2	20	17.6
'70	Valiant Manual	1/2N ± 1/2	1/2N	①	②	1/8 ± 1/32	7 1/2	20	17.5
	Valiant Power	3/4P ± 1/2	3/4P	①	②	1/8 ± 1/32	7 1/2	20	17.5
	Dart Manual	0 to 1N	1/2N	①	②	1/8 ± 1/32	7 1/2	20	17.6
	Dart Power	1/4P to 1 1/4P	3/4P	①	②	1/8 ± 1/32	7 1/2	20	17.6
	Barracuda Manual	1 5/16N to 15/16N	1N	①	②	3/32 to 5/32	7 1/2	20	17.5
	Barracuda Power	15/16P to 3/8N	1/16N	①	②	3/32 to 5/32	7 1/2	20	17.5
	Challenger Manual	1 5/16N to 15/16N	1N	①	②	3/32 to 5/32	7 1/2	20	17.8
	Challenger Power	15/16P to 3/8N	1/16N	①	②	3/32 to 5/32	7 1/2	20	17.8
'71-'72	Manual	1N to 0	1/2N	①	②	3/8 ± 5/32	7 1/2	20	17.5
	Power	1/4P to 1 1/4P	3/4P	①	②	3/8 ± 5/32	7 1/2	20	17.5
'73	Valiant, Dart, Barracuda, Challenger								
	Manual	0 to 1N	1/2N	③	④	3/32 to 5/32	7 1/2	20	17.5
	Power	1/4P to 1 1/4P	3/4P	③	④	3/32 to 5/32	7 1/2	20	17.5
'74	Valiant, Dart, Barracuda, Challenger								
	Manual	1 3/4N to 1/2P	1 1/4N	⑦	⑧	1/16 to 1/4	7 1/2	20	18.5
	Power	1/2N to 1 3/4P	1 1/4P	⑦	⑧	1/16 to 1/4	7 1/2	20	18.5

① Left wheel—1/2P ± 1/4; Right wheel—1/4P ± 1/4
② Left wheel—1/2P; Right wheel—1/4P
③ Left wheel—1/4P to 3/4P; Right wheel—0 to 1/2P
④ Left wheel—1/2P; Right wheel—1/4P
⑤ Right side—0 to 1/2P, 1/4P preferred; left side—1/4P to 3/4P, 1/2P preferred
⑥ Dart: manual—1/16P to 1 1/16N; power—3/16P to 1 5/16P
⑦ Left wheel—0 to 1P; Right wheel—1/4N to 3/4P
⑧ Left wheel—1/2P; Right wheel—1/2P
N Negative P Positive

FRONT END HEIGHT

Year	Model	Front End Height
'67-'68	All M.S.	2 ± 1/8①
	All P.S.	2 ± 1/8①
'69	All M.S.	2 ± 1/8①
	All P.S.	2 ± 1/8①
'70	M.S.—Valiant, Dart	2 1/8 ± 1/8
	P.S.—Valiant, Dart	2 1/8 ± 1/8
	M.S.—Barracuda, Challenger	1 3/16 ± 1/8
	P.S.—Barracuda, Challenger	1 3/16 ± 1/8

Year	Model	Front End Height
'71-'72	All M.S.	②
	All P.S.	②
'73	All	③
'74	Dart, Valiant,	
	Barracuda,	1 7/8 ± 1/8
	Challenger	1 1/8 ± 1/8

① Barracuda—1 3/8 ± 1/8
② Dart, Valiant 4DR—2 1/8 ± 1/8
Dart, Valiant 2DR—1 5/8 ± 1/8
Barracuda, Challenger—1 ± 1/8
③ Dart, Valiant 4DR—2 1/8 ± 1/8
Dart, Valiant 2DR—1 7/8 ± 1/8
Barracuda, Challenger—1 1/8 ± 1/8

BRAKE SPECIFICATIONS

(All measurements are given in in.)

Year	Model	Master Cylinder: Disc	Master Cylinder: Drum	Wheel Cylinder: Front Disc	Wheel Cylinder: Front Drum	Wheel Cylinder: Rear	Brake Disc or Drum Diameter: Front Disc	Brake Disc or Drum Diameter: Front Drum	Brake Disc or Drum Diameter: Rear
'67	6 cyl exc Barracuda	—	1.00	—	1.00	15/16	—	9.0	9.0
	6 cyl Barracuda	—	1.00	—	1.00	29/32	—	9.0	9.0
	V8 models exc Barracuda	—	1.00	—	1 1/8	15/16	—	10.0	10.0
	V8 Barracuda	—	1.00	—	1 1/8	29/32	—	10.0	10.0
	Models with disc brakes exc Barracuda	1.00	—	1 5/8	—	15/16	10 25/32	—	10.0
	Barracuda with disc brakes	1.00	—	1 41/64	—	15/16	11 7/8	—	10.0
'68	All 6 cyl	—	1.00	—	1.00	13/16	—	9.0	9.0
	All V8	—	1.00	—	1 1/8	15/16	—	10.0	10.0
	All with disc brakes	1.00①	—	②	—	15/16	③	—	10.0
'69	All 6 cyl	—	1.00	—	1.00	13/16	—	9.0	9.0
	All V8	—	1.00	—	1 1/8	15/16	—	10.0	10.0
	All with disc brakes	④	—	⑤	—	15/16	⑥	—	10.0
'70	All Valiant	1.00	1.00	1.638	1.187	.9375	10.79	9.0	9.0
	6 cyl Barracuda and Challenger	1.125	1.00	2.750	1.187	.9375	10.72	10.0	10.0
	V8 Barracuda, Challenger	1.125	1.00	2.750	1.187	.9375	10.72	11.0⑦	11.0
	6 cyl Dart	1.00	1.00	1.638	1.187	.8125	10.79	10.0	9.0
	V8 Dart	1.00	1.00	1.638	1.187	.9375	10.79	10.0	10.0
'71	6 cyl Dart and Valiant	1.03	1.03	1.625	1.00	.8125	11.04	9.0	9.0
	V8 Dart and Valiant, 6 cyl H.D., 6 cyl Barracuda, Challenger	1.03	1.03	1.625	1.187	.9375	11.04	10.0	10.0
	V8 Barracuda, Challenger	1.03⑧	1.03	2.750	1.187	.9375	10.72⑦	11.0	11.0⑦
'72	6 cyl Dart and Valiant	1.03	15/16	1.638	1.00	13/16	10.98	9.0	9.0
	6 cyl H.D., V8 Dart and Valiant, All Barracuda, Challenger	1.03	1.03	2.751	1 3/16	15/16	10.98	10.0	10.0⑨
'73-'74	Valiant, Dart	1.03⑩	15/16	2.6	1 1/16	13/16⑪	10.82	9.0	9.0⑫
	Barracuda, Challenger	1.00⑬	—	2.75	—	15/16	10.84	—	10.0

① Budd—1 1/8 in.
② Kelsey Hayes 1.638 in.
Bendix 2 in.
Budd 2.375 in.
③ Kelsey Hayes 11.04 in.
Bendix 11.19 in.
Budd 11.88 in.
④ Kelsey Hayes 1 in.
Kelsey Hayes (floating caliper) 1 1/8 in.
Bendix 1 7/8 in.
⑤ Kelsey Hayes 1.636 in.
Kelsey Hayes (floating caliper) 2 3/4 in.
Bendix 2 in.
⑥ Kelsey Hayes 11.04 in.
Kelsey Hayes (floating caliper) 11.75 in.
Bendix 11.19 in.
⑦ 318, 340, 383 2 bbl engines—10 in.
⑧ 426 Hemi—1.125 in.
⑨ 11 in. optional on Barracuda and Challenger
⑩ 15/16 in. with power disc brakes
⑪ 15/16 in. rear drums with front disc brakes
⑫ 10 in. rear drums with front disc brakes
⑬ 1.03 in. with power brakes
— Not applicable

RING SIDE CLEARANCE

All measurements are given in inches

Year	Engine	Top Compression	Bottom Compression
'67-'74	All engines	.0015-.0030	.0015-.0030

Year	Engine	Oil Control
'67-'69	6-170	.0015-.0030
'67-'74	6-198, 225, 8-273, 318, 340, 360, 426	.0002-.0050
'67-'71	8-383, 440	.0000-.0050

RING GAP

All measurements are given in inches

Year	Engine	Top Compression	Bottom Compression
'67-'72	6-170, 198, 225 8-273, 318, 340	.010-.020	.010-.020
'67-'71	8-383, 440	.013-.023	.013-.023
'70	8-426	.013-.023	.013-.023
'71	8-426	.013-.025	.013-.025
'73	All engines except 8-340	.010-.020	.010-.020
'73	8-340	.013-.023	.013-.023
'74	6-198, 225 8-318, 360	.010-.020	.010-.020

Year	Engine	Oil Control
'67-'74	All engines except 6-170	.015-.055
'67-'69	6-170	.010-.020

PISTON CLEARANCE

Year	Engine	Piston-to-Bore Clearance (in.)
'67-'69	6-170	0.0005-0.0015
'70-'74	6-198	0.0005-0.0015
'67-'74	6-225	0.0005-0.0015
'67-'69	8-273	0.0005-0.0015
'68-'74	8-318	0.0005-0.0015
'68-'73	8-340	0.0005-0.0015
'67-'71	8-383	0.0003-0.0013
'70-'71	8-426	0.0025-0.0035
'70-'71	8-440	0.0003-0.0013
'74	8-360	0.0005-0.0015

CHARGING SYSTEM

Caution Because alternator design is unique, special care must be taken when servicing the charging system.

1. Battery polarity should be checked before any connections, such as jumper cables or battery charger leads, are made. Reversed battery connections will damage the diode rectifiers. It is recommended that the battery cables be disconnected before connecting a battery charger.
2. The battery must *never* be disconnected while the alternator is running because the regulator will be damaged.
3. Always disconnect the battery ground lead before replacing the alternator.
4. Do not attempt to polarize an alternator.
5. Do not short across or ground any alternator terminals.
6. Always disconnect the battery ground lead before removing the alternator output cable, whether the engine is running or not.
7. If electric arc welding has to be done on the car, first disconnect the battery and alternator cables. Never start the car with the welding unit attached.

NOTE: see Unit Repair Section for charging system troubleshooting and repairs.

Alternator R & R

1. Disconnect battery ground cable.
2. Disconnect BAT and FLD leads from alternator. Disconnect the ground wire.
3. Remove alternator by removing two mounting bolts and belt tensioner bracket bolt.
4. To reinstall, reverse above.

NOTE: never attempt to polarize an alternator, nor short the regulator.

Regulator R & R

1. Disconnect the cables from the battery posts.
2. Disconnect each electrical lead from the voltage regulator.
3. Remove the regulator by withdrawing its securing screws.
4. Installation is the reverse of the above. Be sure that the electrical leads are connected to the correct terminals and that all connections are clean and tight.

STARTING SYSTEM

All models are equipped with either a reduction-gear starter, with a 3.5:1 reduction gear set, or a direct-drive starter. Both types have solenoids which are mounted on the starter assembly.

See the Unit Repair Section for starting system troubleshooting and repair.

Starter R & R

1. Disconnect the ground cable at the battery.
2. Remove the cable from the starter.
3. Disconnect the solenoid leads at their solenoid terminals.
4. Remove the starter securing bolts and withdraw the starter from the engine flywheel housing. On some models with automatic transmissions, the oil cooler tube bracket will interfere with starter removal. In this case, remove the starter securing bolts, slide the cooler tube bracket off the stud, and then withdraw the starter.
5. Installation is the reverse of the above. Be sure that the starter and flywheel housing mating surfaces are free of dirt and oil.

IGNITION SYSTEM

The ignition system used on most models is of conventional design using primary and secondary ignition circuits. A separate ballast resistor unit is wired in the primary circuit between the battery and the coil. This resistor controls the current flow in the primary circuit, according to engine speed, reducing the current flow at low engine speeds and increasing the current flow at higher engine speeds. The ballast resistor is bypassed during starter operation to allow full battery voltage to flow to the ignition primary circuit.

Certain 1971 and 1972 models are equipped with the Chrysler Electronic Inition System. Beginning 1973, electronic ignition is standard on all models. For further details, refer to the section on electronic ignition systems in the "Unit Repair Section."

Distributor Removal

1. Disconnect the vacuum advance line at the distributor.
2. Disconnect the primary wire at the coil.
3. Unfasten the distributor cap retaining clips and lift off the cap.
4. Mark the distributor body and the engine block to indicate the position of the body in the block. Scribe a mark on the edge of the distributor housing to indicate the position of the rotor on the distributor. These marks can be used as guides when installing the distributor in a correctly timed engine.

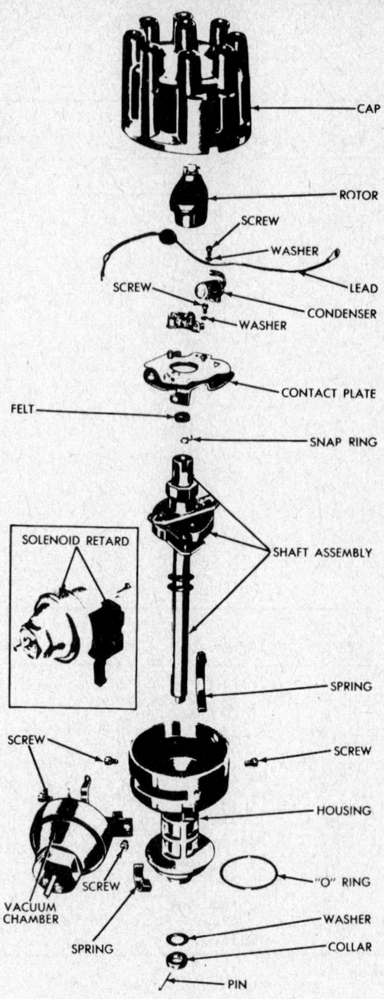
CAP
ROTOR
SCREW
WASHER
LEAD
SCREW
CONDENSER
WASHER
CONTACT PLATE
FELT
SNAP RING
SOLENOID RETARD
SHAFT ASSEMBLY
SPRING
SCREW
SCREW
HOUSING
SCREW
"O" RING
VACUUM CHAMBER
WASHER
SPRING
COLLAR
PIN

Chrysler distributor components
(© Chrysler Corp)

5. Remove the distributor hold-down clamp screw and clamp.
6. Carefully lift the distributor out of the block.

Distributor Installation

If the crankshaft has not been rotated while the distributor was removed from the engine, installation is the reverse of the removal procedure. (See step two or three of the procedure below.) Use the reference marks that were made before removal to correctly position the distributor in the block. Check the point gap and, before connecting the vacuum advance line, adjust the ignition timing.

If the crankshaft has been rotated or otherwise disturbed (as during engine rebuilding) after the distributor was removed, proceed as follows to install the distributor.

1. Bring the no. 1 piston to top dead center (TDC) by removing the no. 1 spark plug and inserting a finger into the hole, while rotating the crankshaft. Compression pressure can be felt as the no. 1 piston approaches TDC. The TDC timing mark on the crankshaft vibration damper

should now be opposite the indicator on the timing chain case.

2. *For six-cylinder engines*: Note the position of the distributor cap (which should be connected to the engine by the spark plug cables). Hold the distributor so that the rotor will be in position *just ahead* of the distributor cap terminal for the no. 1 spark plug when the distributor is installed. Now lower the distributor into its engine block opening, engaging the distributor gear with the camshaft drive gear. Be sure that the rubber O-ring seal is in the groove in the distributor shank. When the distributor is properly seated, the rotor should be under the no. 1 distributor cap terminal with the contact points just opening. Proceed with step four.
3. *For eight-cylinder engines*: Clean the top of the engine block around the distributor opening to ensure a good seal between the distributor base and the block. Note the position of the distributor cap (which should be connected to the engine by the spark plug cables). Hold the distributor so that the rotor will be in position *directly under* the distributor cap terminal for the no. 1 spark plug when the distributor is installed. Now lower the distributor into its engine block opening, engaging the tongue of the distributor shaft with the slot in the distributor and oil pump drive gear. Proceed with step four.
4. Install the distributor hold-down clamp and tighten its retaining screw finger-tight.
5. Check the point gap and refit the distributor cap. Connect the primary wire to the coil.
6. Check and adjust the point dwell and the ignition timing as described below.
7. Connect the vacuum advance line to the distributor.

Contact Point Replacement and Adjustment

Single Point Distributor

Use the procedure described below to remove, install, and adjust a single-contact point set.

1. Pull back the spring clips and lift off the distributor cap. Remove the rotor.
2. Loosen the terminal screw nut and remove the primary and condenser leads.
3. Remove the stationary contact lockscrew and remove the contact point set.
4. Remove the condenser and the retaining screw. Lift out the condenser.
5. Install the new condenser and tighten its retaining screw.
6. Install the point set but do not fully tighten its lockscrew.
7. Connect the condenser and primary leads.
8. If necessary, align the contacts by bending the stationary contact bracket only. *Never bend the movable contact arm to correct alignment.*
9. With the rubbing block of the movable contact arm resting on a peak of the cam lobe, adjust the point gap by inserting a screwdriver in the vee notch of the stationary contact base and using the screwdriver to move the stationary contact.
10. Tighten the lockscrew and recheck the gap setting. Reset if necessary.
11. Install the new rotor and refit the distributor cap.
12. Connect a dwell meter to the engine.
13. Start the engine and run it at idle speed. Note the dwell meter reading. If it is not within specifications, the point gap may be incorrect or the movable contact arm may be distorted. Readjust the contact points and recheck the dwell. Be sure that the correct point set has been installed.

Dual Point Distributor

Removal and installation of dual contact points is the same as for a single point set. However, adjustment of dual points using a dwell meter is slightly different because one set of contacts must be blocked open with a clean insulator while the opposite point set is adjusted to specifications, using the single point set adjustment procedure. When adjusted correctly, tighten the lockscrew. Then block open this contact set and adjust the other set in the same manner as the first. Check the total point dwell. If the contacts have been installed and adjusted correctly, the dwell angle should be as specified for both contact sets.

Ignition Timing

Ignition timing must be checked only when the engine is hot and running at its correct idle speed.

1. Disconnect the vacuum line at the distributor (on all models). On later models with either the ignition retard solenoid or the ignition advance solenoid, the timing must be set with the solenoids connected.
2. Connect a stroboscopic timing light, start the engine, and adjust the idle speed to specification (with the transmission in neutral).
3. Loosen the distributor hold-down screw so the housing can be rotated.
4. Check the ignition timing with the strobe light. If necessary, advance or retard the timing by rotating the distributor housing, until the correct timing is obtained.
5. Tighten the distributor hold-down screw and connect the vacuum line. Stop the engine and disconnect the timing light.

FUEL SYSTEM

Carburetors

Dodge and Plymouth compact and intermediate models have used many different types of carburetors. However, the adjustment procedure for all these carburetors, with a few exceptions, is the same. Some 1967 and all 1968 and later carburetors incorporate modifications to reduce engine exhaust emissions. Carburetor modifications through 1969 are part of Chrysler's Cleaner Air Package, and 1970 and later models are part of the Cleaner Air System. The only carburetor changes used with the Cleaner Air Package are the installation of carburetor mixture limiter stops on the carburetor idle mixture adjustment screws, and leaner carburetor mixtures. With the Cleaner Air System, in addition to the above mentioned changes, faster acting chokes were added and, on some models, solenoid operated throttle stops and distributor retard mechanisms. The throttle stop raises the engine idle speed to reduce engine emissions, but de-energizes when the ignition is shut off to prevent the engine from dieseling. The distributor retard solenoid is activated when the idle speed adjustment screw returns to the curb idle position and contacts a sensor, mounted on the carburetor, which retards ignition timing while the engine is at idle. These carburetors also incorporate an internally mounted hot idle compensator which opens to induct additional air into the carburetor during low speed-high temperature operation.

The 426 Hemi and the 340 and 440 engines were available with multiple carburetor options. The 426 Hemi was equipped with two Carter AFB carburetors. Both carburetors had complete idle systems which must be adjusted and synchronized. The 340 and 440 Six-Pack engines were equipped with three Holley 2300 two-venturi carburetors. Only the center carburetor on these engines was equipped with an idle system and the inboard and outboard carburetors contained no idle adjustments.

Idle Speed and Mixture Adjustments (See Illustrations in Dodge Section)

NOTE: 1967 CAP carburetors can be identified by a green tag attached to the air horn.

1967 Without CAP

Adjust with air cleaner installed.

1. Run engine at fast idle to stabilize engine temperature.
2. Make sure the choke plate is fully released.
3. Attach a tachometer of known accuracy to the engine.
4. If equipped with air conditioning, turn the air conditioner ON.
5. On models wth a six cylinder engine, turn the headlights on high beam.
6. Adjust the carburetor idle speed screw to obtain a curb idle speed of 500 rpm (550 if equipped with air conditioner).
7. Turn the idle mixture screws in or out to obtain the highest rpm possible. After obtaining the highest rpm, turn each idle mixture screw clockwise until the engine speed starts to drop, then turn the mixture screw counterclockwise just enough to regain the lost rpm.
8. If the mixture adjustment procedure has changed the curb idle speed, adjust the idle speed.

1967-74 with CAP or CAS Except 426 Hemi

Adjust with air cleaner installed.

NOTE: this is the basic carburetor adjustment procedure, any specific exceptions are listed below.

1. Run engine at fast idle to stabilize engine temperature.
2. Make sure choke plate is fully released.
3. Attach a tachometer of known accuracy to the engine.
4. Connect an exhaust analyzer to the engine and insert the probe as far into the tailpipe as possible. On vehicles with dual exhaust, insert the probe into the left tailpipe as this is the side without the heat riser valve.
5. Check ignition timing and adjust it as required to conform to specification.
6. If equipped with air conditioning, turn the air conditioner OFF. On models with six-cylinder engines, turn the headlights on high beam.
7. Place the transmission in the Neutral position. Make sure the hot idle compensator valve is fully seated in the closed position.
8. Turn the engine idle speed adjustment screw in or out to adjust idle speed to specification. If equipped with an electric solenoid throttle positioner, turn the solenoid adjusting screw in or out to obtain specified rpm. Then, adjust the curb idle speed screw until it just touches the stop on the carburetor body. Now, back the curb idle speed adjusting screw out one full turn.
9. Turn each idle mixture adjustment screw 1/16 turn richer (counterclockwise). Wait 10 seconds and observe the reading on the exhaust gas analyzer. Continue this procedure until the meter indicates a definite increase in the richness of the mixture.

NOTE: this step is very important. A carburetor that is set too lean will cause the exhaust gas analyzer to give a false reading indicating a rich mixture. Because of this, the carburetor must first be known to have a rich mixture to verify the reading on the exhaust gas analyzer.

10. After verifying the reading obtained on the meter, adjust the mixture screws to get an air/fuel ratio of 14.2:1. Turn the mixture screws clockwise (leaner) to raise the meter reading or counterclockwise (richer) to lower the meter reading.

1968-69 383 and 440 V8

The carburetors used on these engines (Ball & Ball 2V, Carter 4V or Holley 4V) have lead or cup plugs installed over the idle mixture screws and an additional off idle mixture control screw added to the body of the carburetor. When adjusting the carburetor idle speed and mixture, use the off idle adjustment screw to alter the idle speed air /fuel mixture so it conforms to the 14.2:1 ratio specified. If unable to obtain an acceptable engine idle by adjusting this screw, refer to the procedure to correct rough idle and low speed surge.

Rough Idle and Low Speed Surge

Rough idle and low speed surge can be the result of improper balance of the idle mixture adjustment in the right and left carburetor bores. To correct this condition, perform the following operation.

1. On 1968-69 383 or 440 V8, remove the lead plugs from the two limited screws in the base of the carburetor (Ball & Ball or Carter) or the cup plugs from the sides of the primary metering body (Holley). The best way to remove the lead plugs is with a small drill and easy-out. Use a sharp punch to remove cup plugs from a Holley carburetor.
2. On all other models, remove the plastic limiter caps from the idle mixture adjustment screws.
3. Perform Steps 1-8 of the idle speed and mixture adjustment procedure.
4. On 1968-69 383 or 440 V8, turn the single off idle mixture adjustment screw counterclockwise (richer) until it is seated, then turn it clockwise (lean) 3/4 turn. Do not disturb this adjustment during the remainder of this procedure.
5. Turn both idle mixture adjustment screws clockwise until they are lightly seated. On some models, the idle mixture screws have a prevailing torque feature which causes the screws to become more difficult to turn as they approach the seated position.
6. On Ball & Ball carburetors, turn both idle mixture screws 1½ turns counterclockwise. On Carter and Holley carburetors, turn both idle mixture screws 2-3 turns clockwise.
7. Start the engine and perform Steps 9-11 of the idle speed and mixture adjustment procedure.

NOTE: in order to obtain a smooth idle, it is important that both mixture adjustment screws are adjusted an equal number of turns from the fully seated position.

8. Install lead plugs, cup plugs, or plastic caps on the idle mixture screws.

426 Hemi

Because each carburetor is equipped with a complete idle system, accurate carburetor synchronization is very important. After adjusting the idle speed and mixture, it should be rechecked and rebalanced as required in the outside ambient temperature after a road test.

Adjust with air cleaner removed.

1. Run engine at fast idle to stabilize engine temperature.
2. Make sure the choke plate is fully released.
3. Attach a tachometer of known accuracy to the engine.
4. If equipped with a hot idle compensator valve, make sure it is fully seated in the closed position.
5. Place the transmission in the Neutral position.
6. Turn the idle speed adjustment screws in or out to adjust the engine idle speed to specification. If equipped with an electric solenoid throttle positioner, turn the solenoid adjusting screw in or out to obtain specified engine idle speed. Then, turn the curb idle speed adjusting screw clockwise until it just touches the stop on the carburetor throttle body. Next, back the curb idle speed adjusting screw out one full turn.
7. Adjust each idle mixture screw to obtain the highest rpm possible. Repeat this operation until all four mixture adjustment screws have been properly adjusted and balanced.
8. If the idle mixture adjustment procedure has changed the engine idle speed, adjust the idle speed.

Fuel Filter

Removal and Installation

Locate the filter in the fuel line between the fuel pump and the carburetor. Using hose-clamp pliers, remove the attaching clamps and pull the filter off. Reverse this procedure for installation. Be sure that the arrow on the filter is pointing toward the carburetor (direction of fuel flow).

Fuel Pump

The fuel pump used on the six-cylinder and 383 V8 engines are driven by a small cam eccentric cast into the main camshaft. On the 273, 318, 340, and 360 V8 engines, the pump is driven by a pressed steel eccentric secured on the gear end of the camshaft.

On the six-cylinder and 273, 318, 340, and 360 V8 engines, the pump is driven directly by the pump rocker arm pressing on the cam eccentric. On the 383, 426, and 440 big block V8s, there is a pushrod located between the pump rocker arm and the driving eccentric.

Removal and Installation

1. Wipe the pump exterior to remove all dirt and oil.
2. Taking note of positions, remove the pump fuel lines.
3. Remove the bolts securing the pump to the block and remove the pump.
4. Remove all gasket material from machined surfaces. Using a sealer of good quality, coat both sides of the pump gasket.
5. Install the pump to the block. If difficulty is encountered engaging the pump drive, rotate slightly.
6. Connect the fuel lines and tighten the pump bolts. Start the engine and check it for leaks.

COOLING SYSTEM

The cooling system is of conventional design consisting of a radiator, water pump, and thermostat. On those models that are equipped with automatic transmissions, there is a cooler located in the bottom of the radiator tank for the transmission fluid.

Some models are fitted with special cooling fan units which use a silicone fluid coupling device to engage the fan under certain conditions.

One of these fluid coupling units is called Torque Control Drive and it allows the fan to be driven in the normal manner at low engine speeds while limiting the top speed of the fan to a predetermined level at higher engine speeds. The other unit is only used on air-conditioned models and is called Thermal Control Drive. This device is essentially the same as the Torque Control Drive unit except for a thermostatic spring.

Radiator R & R

1. Drain the cooling system.
2. On cars with automatic transmissions, disconnect the fluid cooler lines at the radiator bottom tank. To avoid fluid loss or dirt contamination, plug the cooler lines.
3. Remove the upper and lower radiator hoses.
4. Remove the fan shroud securing screws and separate the shroud from the radiator. Move the shroud toward the engine as far as possible to obtain maximum clearance for removing the radiator.
5. Remove the radiator mounting screws.
6. Lift the radiator out of the engine compartment.

Caution Extreme care should be taken not to damage the radiator cooling fins or water tubes during removal.

7. Reverse the above to install the radiator. Fill the cooling system to 1 ¼ in. below the filler neck with the correct water and antifreeze mixture. Warm up the engine and check the coolant level. On cars with automatic transmissions, check the fluid level after warm-up and add fluid as required.

Water Pump R & R

NOTE: the water pump is serviced only as an assembly. When replacing the water pump, do not install a standard water pump on an air-conditioned car or vice versa.

1. Drain the cooling system.
2. Remove the fan shroud securing screws and move the shroud out of the way.
3. It may be necessary to remove the radiator on some models to obtain the working clearance necessary to remove the water pump.
4. Loosen the alternator mounting bolts. Loosen the mounting bolts for the power steering pump, idler pulley, air conditioning compressor, and air pump (if so equipped). Remove all the accessory belts.
5. Remove the fan, spacer or fluid drive, and the pulley.

Caution For fluid-coupled fan drives, do not position the drive unit with its shaft pointing downward. This will prevent the silicone fluid from draining into the fan-drive bearing and thereby contaminating the grease.

6. On some models, it may be necessary to remove the alternator or compressor mounting bracket bolts from the water pump to swing the alternator or compressor out of the way.
7. Withdraw the bolts which secure the water pump body to its en-

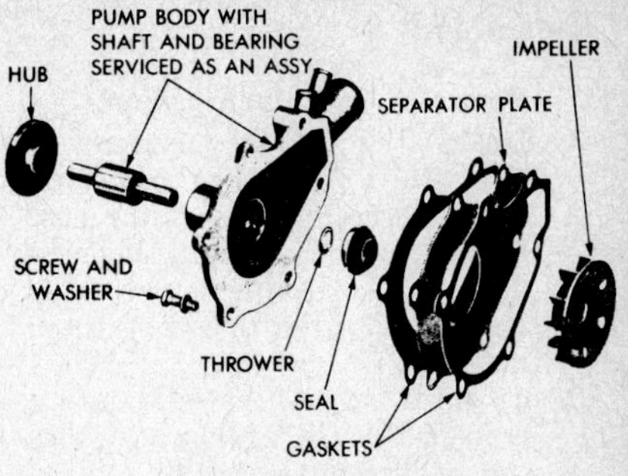
PUMP BODY WITH SHAFT AND BEARING SERVICED AS AN ASSY
HUB
IMPELLER
SEPARATOR PLATE
SCREW AND WASHER
THROWER
SEAL
GASKETS

Water pump—6 cylinder
(© Chrysler Corp)

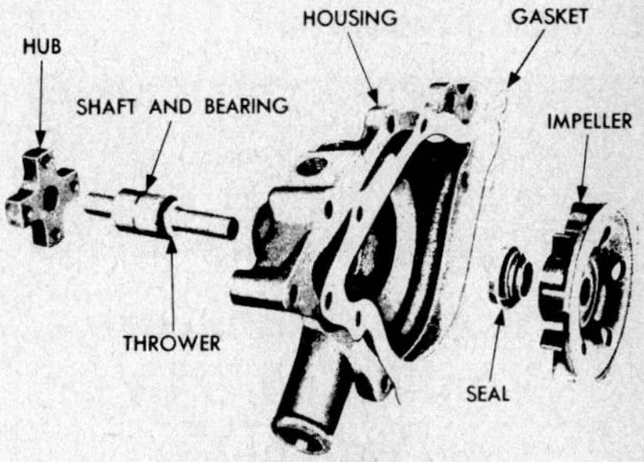
HOUSING
GASKET
HUB
SHAFT AND BEARING
IMPELLER
THROWER
SEAL

Water pump—273 and 318
(© Chrysler Corp)

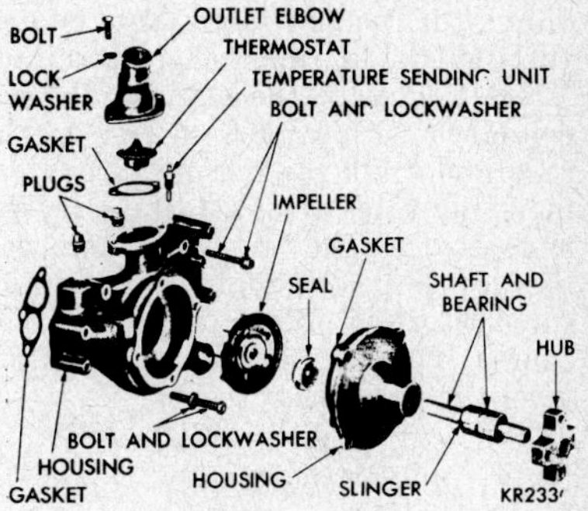
BOLT
OUTLET ELBOW
THERMOSTAT
LOCK WASHER
GASKET
PLUGS
IMPELLER
GASKET
SEAL
SHAFT AND BEARING
HUB
BOLT AND LOCKWASHER
HOUSING
GASKET
HOUSING
SLINGER

Water pump—383
(© Chrysler Corp)

gine block housing. Remove the water pump and discard the gasket.

8. Install the water pump with a new gasket on its housing. Torque its securing bolts to 30 ft lbs.
9. Rotate the pump shaft by hand to be sure that it rotates freely. Refit the alternator or compressor mounting bracket to the pump if either was removed. Install the pulley, spacer or fluid drive, and the fan. Torque their retaining nuts to 15 ft lbs.
10. Refit all the accessory drive belts.
11. Install the radiator if it was removed.
12. Install the fan shroud. Fill the cooling system to 1 ¼ in. below the filler neck with correct water and antifreeze mixture. Warm up the engine and inspect the water pump for any leaks. Check the coolant level and add as required.

Thermostat

Removal and Installation

1. Drain the cooling system to below the level of the thermostat.
2. Remove the upper radiator hose from the thermostat housing flange. Remove the housing bolts and take out the thermostat and housing.
3. To install the thermostat, use a new gasket. On V8s, be sure that the pellet end is facing toward engine. Six-cylinder models must have the vent hole facing up. From this point, reverse the removal procedure.

EMISSION CONTROLS

Positive Crankcase Ventilation (PCV Valve)

All models are equipped with a positive crankcase ventilation system which draws air into the engine through the oil filler cap and circulates it through the engine. The air combines with vapors in the crankcase and exits the engine through a metering valve mounted in the rocker arm cover. The air-vapor mixture then re-enters the engine through the carburetor or intake manifold and passes into the combustion chamber where it is burned.

CAP and CAS

Operation

1967-69 Models

The Cleaner Air Package System is designed to constantly maintain carburetion and ignition timing at the best settings for performance and combustion under all driving requirements and conditions. These adjustments, if maintained, will keep the engine at a good performance level and within the exhaust requirements of federal law.

In the past, normal engines have had comparatively low exhaust emissions at cruise and acceleration attitudes. Excessive emissions occur during deceleration and low-speed operation. Therefore, the CAP system concentrates on reduction of emissions in the idle and deceleration ranges.

The CAP system uses a carburetor and distributor which have been redesigned, and a vacuum advance control valve on cars with manual transmissions.

The carburetor is calibrated to provide leaner mixtures at idle and at low speed. The distributor is designed to give retarded timing at idle. The vacuum advance control valve, in conjunction with the distributor, provides advanced timing during deceleration.

A number of changes have been made that reshape the intake manifold and combustion chamber for more even mixture distribution and better combustion.

CAP idle timing, for all engines, is retarded. Exhaust emission is reduced at idle by using leaner air/fuel mixtures, increased engine speed, and retarded ignition timing. The increased air flow at this idle condition is similar to the distribution and combustion conditions of cruise.

The system operates with late timing during idle, and with conventional spark advance during acceleration and cruise.

The vacuum advance control valve provides additional spark advance during deceleration.

Engine applications involving manual shift transmissions require slightly different handling. They need earlier ignition of the fuel mixture to accomplish efficient combustion and to more completely consume residual fuels.

The vacuum advance control valve is connected by hoses to the carburetor, the intake manifold, and to the distributor vacuum chamber. Carburetor vacuum and manifold vacuum act on the vacuum advance control valve. From these two signals, the vacuum advance control valve senses engine speed and load conditions, and relays a vacuum command to the distributor to modify spark timing when necessary.

Initial, or basic, timing may be retarded as much as fifteen degrees from conventional timing. The vacuum advance control valve does not affect timing at idle because the distributor vacuum chamber receives the same vacuum signal as in the conventional system, namely, carburetor

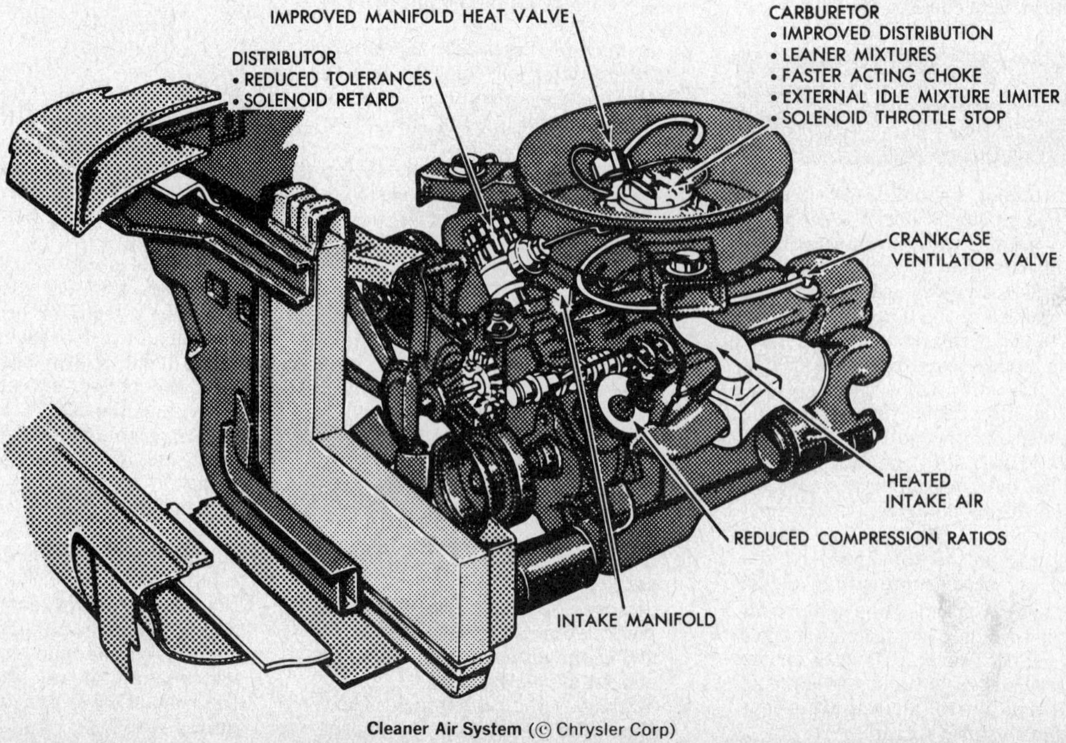
IMPROVED MANIFOLD HEAT VALVE
DISTRIBUTOR
• REDUCED TOLERANCES
• SOLENOID RETARD
CARBURETOR
• IMPROVED DISTRIBUTION
• LEANER MIXTURES
• FASTER ACTING CHOKE
• EXTERNAL IDLE MIXTURE LIMITER
• SOLENOID THROTTLE STOP
CRANKCASE
VENTILATOR VALVE
HEATED
INTAKE AIR
REDUCED COMPRESSION RATIOS
INTAKE MANIFOLD

Cleaner Air System (© Chrysler Corp)

vacuum. This is not strong enough to overcome the distributor vacuum diaphragm spring.

Manifold vacuum acts on the vacuum control valve diaphragm. However, it is not strong enough to overcome the vacuum control spring. The spring holds the vacuum control valve closed to manifold vacuum and open to low carburetor vacuum.

Under acceleration and during normal cruise, the throttle is opened and the increased air flow through the carburetor throat creates carburetor vacuum much greater than under closed throttle conditions.

Manifold vacuum is not enough to overcome the vacuum advance control valve spring. However, the stronger carburetor vacuum overcomes the distributor vacuum diaphragm spring, advancing spark timing.

The conventional system (without exhaust emission control) permits greatest objectionable emissions during deceleration. Carburetor vacuum is too weak to overcome the distributor vacuum advance diaphragm spring.

Manifold vacuum is at its strongest during deceleration. Therefore, the CAP system, when equipped with a vacuum advance control valve, uses manifold vacuum instead of carburetor vacuum to control spark timing. To summarize: during deceleration, manifold vacuum is strong enough to overcome the vacuum advance control valve spring and the distributor vacuum diaphragm spring, moving the spark timing to maximum advance.

1970-74 Models

The CAP system has been improved to CAS, Cleaner Air System. This system utilizes:

1. Heated air intake system;
2. Modified carburetor;
3. Lower compression ratio;
4. Solenoid retarded distributor.

The heated air system is used on all engines except 340, 426 Hemi, 440 Six Pack, and those with the fresh-air scoop option.

When air temperature is between 10 and 100°F, intake air is a mixture of heated and unheated air. The volume of heated and unheated air is regulated by a thermostat, a vacuum diaphragm, and an air control valve in the air cleaner housing. The thermostat regulates the air control valve opening. Under conditions of greatly reduced vacuum such as a sudden burst of acceleration, the vacuum diaphragm overrides the thermostat to open the air control valve fully to unheated air.

Carburetors have leaner mixtures and external idle mixture limiting devices. The automatic choke has been redesigned to release more quickly on engine warmup. An electrical solenoid throttle stop is used on 340, 440, 440 Six Pack, and 426 Hemi engines. These engines use high idle speeds to achieve acceptable emission levels. The solenoid throttle stop de-energizes when the ignition is switched off, allowing the throttle blades to close more completely. This prevents running on.

318, 383, and 440 (except 440 Six Pack) engines have lower compression ratios to reduce hydrocarbon emissions.

Ignition Retard Solenoid

An ignition retard solenoid mounted on the side of the distributor is used on 1971, and some earlier, models. Its function is to retard the ignition timing when the throttle is closed. The solenoid must be operating when the ignition timing is adjusted.

To be sure that the solenoid is working, first check and adjust the ignition timing. Disconnect the ground lead from the solenoid. If the engine idle speed increases noticeably, the solenoid is functioning properly. If the solenoid is defective, it must be replaced with a new unit.

Ignition Advance Solenoid

The ignition retard solenoid was replaced by an ignition advance solenoid in 1972. This solenoid, located on the side of the distributor, is connected to the starter relay and it is designed to advance the ignition timing only while the engine is cranked. When the engine starts, the solenoid ceases to operate, as it is only used as an aid in starting. If the solenoid is not working, starting the engine will be difficult. A defective solenoid may cause the carburetor to "pop" while the engine is cranked.

To check the operation of the solenoid, run the engine at idle speed and connect a jumper wire from the battery to the solenoid lead. If the solenoid is functioning properly, the engine speed will increase noticeably. *Disconnect the jumper wire immediately after checking the operation of the solenoid.* If the solenoid is defective, it must be replaced with a new unit.

ECS

Operation

All 1970 vehicles sold in California and all 1971 and later vehicles have an Evaporation Control System to reduce evaporation losses from the fuel system. The system has an expansion tank in the main fuel tank. This prevents spillage due to expansion of warm fuel. A special filler cap with a two-way relief valve is used. An internal pressure differential, caused by thermal expansion, opens the valve, as does an external pressure differential, caused by fuel usage. Fuel vapors from the carburetor and fuel tank are routed to the crankcase ventilation system. A separator is installed to prevent liquid fuel from entering the crankcase ventilation system.

Evaporation control systems used on 1972 vehicles also include a charcoal canister and an overflow limiting valve.

The limiting valve prevents the fuel tank from being overfilled by trapping fuel in the filler when the tank is full. When pressure in the tank becomes greater than the valve operating pressure, the valve opens and allows the gasoline vapors to flow into the charcoal canister.

The charcoal canister is mounted in the engine compartment. It absorbs vapors and retains them until clean air is drawn through a line from it that runs to the PCV valve. Absorption occurs while the car is parked and cleaning occurs when the car engine is running.

NOx Control System

All 1971 and later vehicles sold in California have a NO_x system to control the emission of oxides of nitrogen. Engines with this system all have a special camshaft and a 185°F thermostat.

Operation

Manual Transmission

The manual transmission NO_x system uses a transmission switch, a thermal switch, and a solenoid vacuum valve. The transmission switch is screwed into the transmission housing and is closed, except in high gear. The thermal switch, mounted on the firewall, is open whenever the ambient temperature is above 70°F. With the transmission in any gear, except high, and the temperature above 70°, the solenoid vacuum valve is energized. This shuts off the distributor vacuum advance line, preventing vacuum advance. Below 70°, the vacuum advance functions normally.

Automatic Transmission

The NO_x system for the automatic transmission is more complex than the manual transmission system. It prevents vacuum advance when the ambient temperature is above 70°F, speed is below 30 mph, or the car is accelerating. The solenoid vacuum valve is interchangeable with that used in the manual transmission system. The speed switch senses the vehicle speed and is driven by the speedometer cable. The control unit is mounted on the firewall. It contains a control module, thermal switch and a vacuum switch. The control unit senses ambient temperature and manifold vacuum.

Air Injection System

Operation

In addition to the CAS, ECS, and

NO_x emission controls systems, an exhaust port air injection system is used on all 1972 six-cylinder models sold in California. This system adds a controlled amount of air, through special passages in the cylinder head, to exhaust gases in the exhaust ports, causing oxidation of the gases and thereby reducing carbon monoxide and hydrocarbon emissions to the required levels.

The air injection system consists of a belt-driven air pump, rubber hose, a check valve to protect the hoses and pump from hot gases, injection tubes, and a combination diverter/pressure relief valve assembly.

Exhaust Gas Recirculation System

Operation

Some models are equipped with an exhaust gas recirculation system in order to reduce the emissions of nitrogen (NO_x). This system permits exhaust gases from the exhaust manifold plenum chamber (six-cylinder engines) or the intake manifold exhaust crossover passage (V8 engines) to pass through an orifice in the intake manifold floor and mix with the incoming air-fuel mixture. The air-fuel mixture is diluted by the exhaust gases which lowers peak flame temperatures, thus restricting the formation of NO_x.

In 1973, Valiant and Dart models have a new exhaust gas recirculation (EGR) system, which is used on all cars sold in the USA, except those equipped with a 340 cu in. 4-bbl V8. The 340 cu in. engine uses only the floor jets, a carryover from 1972.

In addition to the floor jets, all other engines use an EGR control valve. This valve is operated by vacuum and is used to control the flow of exhaust gases combining with the fuel/air mixture. An ambient temperature switch is used to de-activate the EGR system when the outside temperature is below 68°F. Some engines are equipped with a vacuum amplifier which is connected to both the carburetor and the manifold in order to provide enough vacuum to operate the EGR valve.

At idle the valve is closed, thus limiting the flow of exhaust gases into the fuel/air mixture (to prevent stalling). When accelerating, the valve opens, allowing the exhaust gases to flow into the fuel/air mixture.

1973

Starting 15 March 1973, the EGR system ambient temperature sensor was dropped. It has been replaced by a thermostatic valve which is threaded into the top tank of the radiator. A hose runs from one valve nipple to the EGR vacuum amplifier. The other nipple has a filter fitted over it. When the coolant temperature is below 62°F, the valve is opened to the atmosphere, thus preventing the EGR valve diaphragm from getting vacuum. Above 62°F, the valve closes and the EGR valve is allowed to function.

1974

Floor jets have been dropped from all 1974 engines. The EGR temperature switch (mounted in the upper radiator tank), which was introduced in March 1973, has been retained.

NOTE: The thermostatic switch for the EGR system is mounted in the thermostat housing on the 360-4V engine.

Orifice Spark Advance Control Valve

A spark delay valve or orifice spark advance control valve (OSAC) is also used to control emissions of NO_x. The OSAC valve is located in the line that runs from the carburetor vacuum port to the distributor vacuum unit. When the air temperature is above 68°F and the car is accelerating, the OSAC valve delays vacuum advance for approximately 15 seconds (the exact length of time is dependent upon the engine).

1973

Some time after 1 March and before 15 March 1973, the temperature sensor was removed from the OSAC valve, but the general appearance and location of the valve were not changed. The valve can be recognized by a white gasket and a stick-on label with the new part number (3755499).

At the same time, the ignition timing was changed to TDC.

NOTE: See the engine tune-up specifications decal for further timing information.

1974

The OSAC valve has been moved from the firewall to the air cleaner

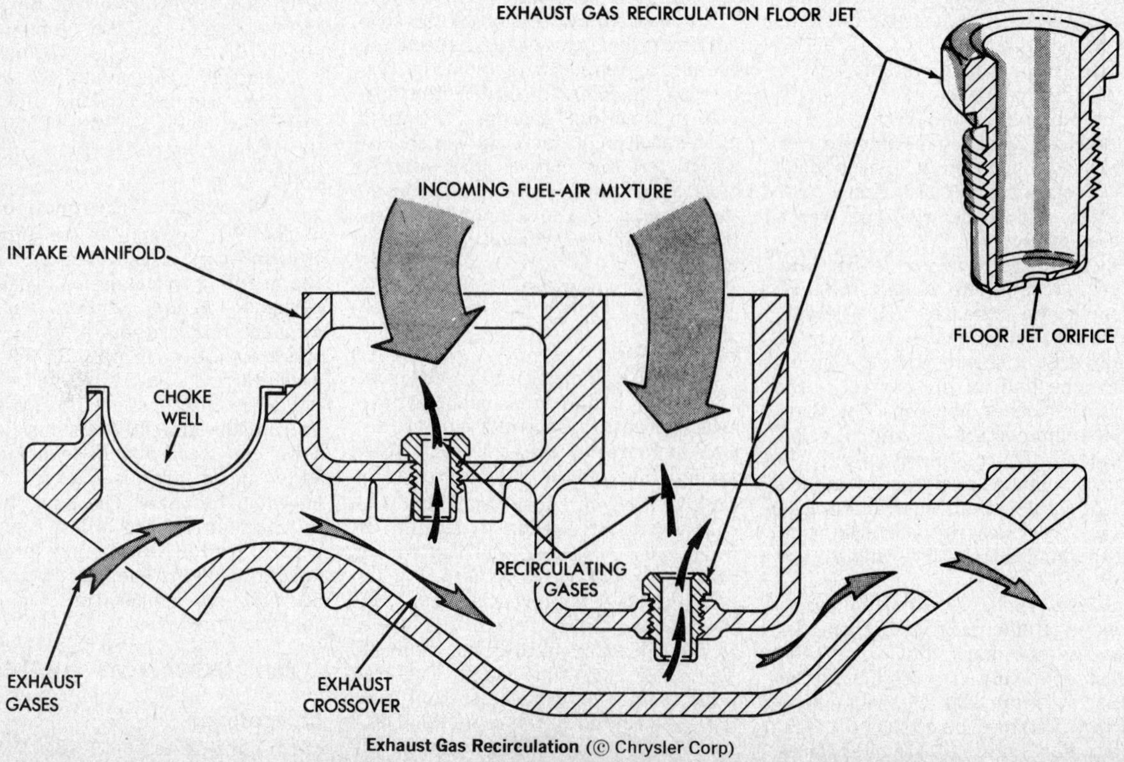
EXHAUST GAS RECIRCULATION FLOOR JET
INCOMING FUEL-AIR MIXTURE
INTAKE MANIFOLD
FLOOR JET ORIFICE
CHOKE WELL
RECIRCULATING GASES
EXHAUST GASES
EXHAUST CROSSOVER

Exhaust Gas Recirculation (© Chrysler Corp)

for 1974, and the temperature control restored. There are six different time delay and operating temperature combinations for the valve. These combinations are identified by a color code tape on the top of the valve. These codes are, as follows:

Color	*Time (sec)*	*Temperature (°F)*
Green	17	58
Red	17	50
Blue	17	①
White	27	58
Orange	27	①
Yellow	27	58

① No temperature control used

Caution Always replace the valve with one having the same color code. Failure to do so could result in poor vehicle performance or lack of compliance with the emission laws.

Electric Assist Choke

An electric assist choke is used to reduce the hydrocarbon and carbon monoxide pollutant levels. When the air temperature is above 68°F, a heater element, located in the automatic choke well, comes on. The heat is applied to the bimetallic choke spring. This reduces the length of the period of air/fuel mixture choke enrichment. The electric choke assist draws three amps while operating.

1974

A two-stage electric assist choke is used for 1974. The two-stage choke may be identified by its external resistor:

Blue resistor 5 ohm—all sixes/V8-318

White resistor 10 ohm— V8-360—

Below 58°F, the heating element gets full, low amperage current from the choke control. Above 58°F, the resistor cuts the current in half. After several minutes of operation above 58°F, the control opens the circuit, so that the heating element gets no current at all.

Most engines use a 20-watt heating element, except for the following, which have 4-bbl carburetors and use a 40-watt choke:

V8-360—All states

V8-360 H.P.—All states

The 40-watt choke has a white paint spot on the choke cover.

Emission Control System Servicing

Due to the complexity of emission control devices, they are designed to be serviced by removal and replacement only. The evaporative control systems' charcoal canister and the air injection pumps' fan filter are the only items that require periodic replacement of parts. In both cases, remove the part in question by extracting its securing screws and replacing the subject part as required. All other parts should be serviced at regular tune-ups (if necessary) as explained in the appropriate section.

ENGINE

The standard equipment engine in most Dodge and Plymouth car models is the slant six. Although this engine has a very long stroke by modern standards (it is/was available in 170, 198, and 225 cu in. versions), it presents a low profile because the entire block is canted 30 degrees to the right.

The 273, 318, 340 and 360 cu in. engines are Chrysler's "A" block series of V8s. Except for the 1967 273 cu in. engine, they all utilize hydraulic tappets. They are of the valve-in-head type, and they vary in compression ratio, piston displacement, camshafts, valve springs, carburetors, intake manifolds, and exhaust systems. Of some interest is the 340 Six Pack high-performance engine. With modified valve train, different heads, and three Holley 2-BBL 2300 carburetors, this engine was Chrysler's hottest small-block offering.

Dodge/Plymouth's "B" block series consists of the 383 and 440 cu in. engines. Actually, these may be divided into two types: the 383 low-block engine and a 440 high-block entry. Basically, the difference is a larger, deeper block on the 440 to accommodate a longer stroke crank. In addition, main journal diameter, connecting rod length, pushrod length, and intake manifolds are different. Otherwise, these engines are similar and many parts will interchange.

In 1968, the 383 found its way into the Barracuda. In 1970, the 440 was added to the option list; it was available in both 4-BBL and 6-BBL versions.

In 1970, the 426 Hemi was added to the Barracuda/Challenger option list. It is basically a "B" series, raised-block engine, but with so many differences that it must be treated as a completely separate engine. It has hemispherical combustion chambers with 2.25 in. intake and 1.95 in. exhaust valves actuated by rocker arms mounted on separate intake and exhaust rocker shafts. The spark plugs are centrally located in the combustion chambers, and aluminum tubes protect the plugs and wires from oil where they pass through the rocker covers. Because of the huge intake ports, there is no room for head bolts on the intake side. Instead studs are mounted in the head which extend down into the valley between the cylinder heads. To reduce piston side thrust, Hemis use longer connecting rods than other raised-block "B" engines, and to strengthen the lower end, the main caps are crossbolted. The Hemi engine was discontinued in 1971 and is no longer available.

Special Engine Markings

Over and undersize engine components are identified by various marks. These marks may be located on top right front engine pads or on the crankshaft counterweights. In addition, some big-block engines may have oversize valve stem markings stamped on cylinder head ends on the untapped boss. For explanation of the meanings of the various markings, consult your local Dodge/Plymouth dealership.

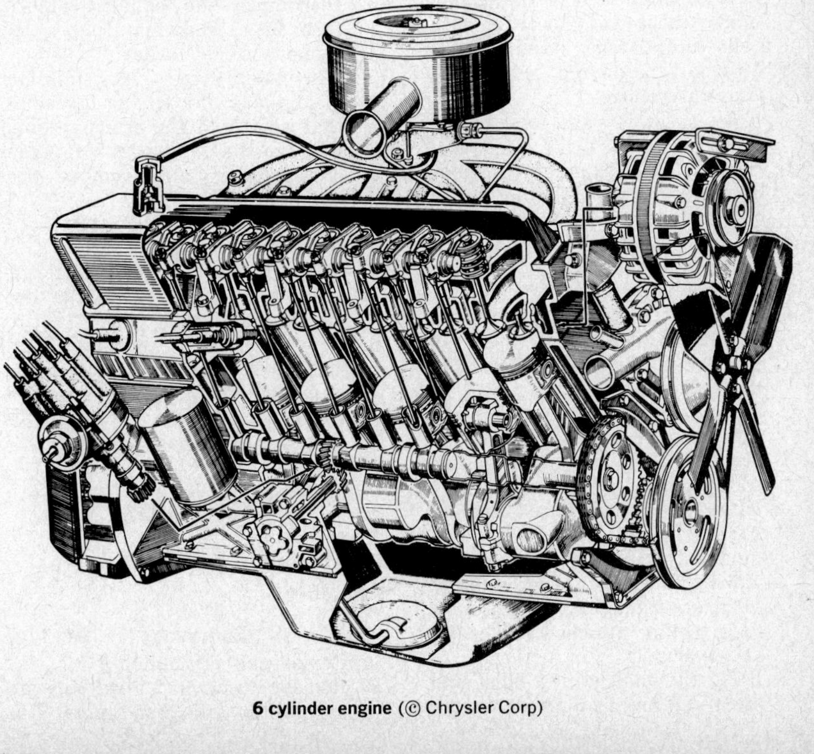

6 cylinder engine (© Chrysler Corp)

Engine R & R

6 Cylinder

1. Scribe the hood hinge outlines on the underside of the hood, then remove the hood.
2. Drain the cooling system, remove the battery and carburetor air cleaner.
3. Remove radiator and heater hoses, then the radiator. Remove PCV and evaporative control system (if so equipped).
4. Remove the outlet vent pipe from the cylinder head cover.
5. Disconnect fuel lines, linkage and wiring to the engine.
6. Disconnect exhaust pipe at exhaust manifold.
7. Raise car on hoist.
8. If equipped with automatic transmission, it must be drained. Remove the oil cooler lines, filler tube and shift cable.
9. Remove the clutch torque shaft, brake cables and rods.
10. Remove the speedometer cable and gear shift rods.
11. Disconnect driveshaft and tie out of the way.
12. Install an engine support fixture to the rear of the engine.
13. Remove the engine rear support crossmember.
14. Remove transmission mounting bolts from clutch housing.
15. Remove the transmission.
16. Lower the car.
17. Position engine lifting fixture onto the engine, and attach chain hoist to the fixture eyebolt.
18. Remove the engine support fixture.
19. Remove the engine front mounting bolts.
20. Lift the engine out of the engine compartment and lower it onto a substantial work stand.
21. To install the engine, reverse the above procedure.

Chilton's TIME SAVER

It is possible to remove the engine without removing the transmission. If the engine is to be removed from the vehicle without removing the transmission, care must be exercised not to allow the weight of the engine to rest on the torque converter hub (automatic transmission) or transmission input shaft (standard transmission).

To remove the engine without removing the transmission, use the following operation. Perform Steps 1-7 and 10 of the removal operation. If the vehicle is equipped with an automatic transmission, attach a remote starter switch to the engine, remove the inspection plate from the bellhousing, crank the engine to gain access to the torque converter-to-driveplate attaching nuts and remove the nuts. If the vehicle is equipped with a manual transmission, disconnect the clutch torque shaft from the engine block and the clutch linkage from the adjustment rod. Remove the bolt that attaches the transmission filler tube to the engine (automatic transmission). Support the transmission and remove the bolts that attach the transmission to the engine or clutch bell housing. When removing the engine, place a block of wood on the lifting point of a floor jack and position the jack under the transmission. As the engine is removed from the vehicle, raise and lower the jack as required so the angle of the transmission duplicates as nearly as possible the angle of the engine.

When installing the engine into a vehicle with an automatic transmission, keep in mind that the crankshaft flange bolt circle, the inner and outer circle of holes in the driveplate, and the four tapped holes in the front face of the converter all have one hole offset. To insure proper engine-torque converter balance, the torque converter must be mounted to the driveplate in the same location it was originally installed.

When installing the engine into a vehicle with a manual transmission, it may be necessary to turn the crankshaft pulley, with the transmission in gear, to get the transmission input shaft spline to mesh with the inner hub on the clutch disc.

V8

1. Scribe the outline of the hood hinge brackets on the bottom of the hood and remove the hood.
2. Drain the cooling system and remove the radiator.
3. Remove the battery.
4. Remove the fuel line from the fuel pump and plug the line.
5. Remove all wires and hoses that attach to the engine.
6. If equipped with air conditioning and/or power steering, remove the unit from the engine and position it out of the way *without disconnecting the lines.*
7. Attach lifting sling to the engine. On models equipped with a 426 Hemi engine, never attempt to remove the engine with the lifting sling attached to the intake manifold.
8. Raise the vehicle on a hoist and install an engine support fixture to support the rear of the engine.
9. On automatic transmission models, drain the transmission. On standard transmission models, disconnect the clutch torque shaft from the engine.
10. Disconnect the exhaust pipe/s from the exhaust manifold/s.
11. Remove the driveshaft.
12. Disconnect the transmission linkage and any wiring or cables that attach to the transmission.
13. Remove the engine rear support crossmember and remove the transmission.
14. Remove the bolts that attach the motor mounts to the chassis.
15. Lower the vehicle and attach a chain hoist or other lifting device to the engine.
16. Raise the engine and carefully remove it from the engine compartment.
17. Reverse the above procedure to install the engine.

Manifolds

6 Cylinder Combination Manifold

Removal

1. Remove air cleaner.
2. Remove vacuum control tube at carburetor and distributor. Remove the EGR line at the carburetor.
3. Remove fuel line and carburetor.
4. Remove three bolts that hold the flange.
5. Remove nuts and washers holding the intake and exhaust manifolds to the cylinder head.
6. Remove the assembly from the head.
7. Remove three bolts holding the intake and exhaust manifolds together.
8. Clean manifold mating and attaching surfaces with a straight edge and feeler gauge. All mating surfaces should be flat and plane within .008 in.

Installation

1. Place a new gasket between intake and exhaust manifolds and install three attaching bolts, loosely.
2. With a new gasket in place, position the complete manifold combination on the cylinder head.
3. Install conical washers (cupped side away from the nut) and nuts. Torque alternately to a final 10 ft. lbs.
4. Now, torque the three intake-to-exhaust manifold nuts to 15 ft. lbs.
5. Connect the exhaust pipe to the manifold flange and torque these two bolts to 30 ft. lbs.

6. Install carburetor and connect line, vacuum line and throttle linkage.
7. Install air cleaner. Start engine and check for intake and exhaust leaks.

V8 Intake Manifold R&R

All Engines Except 426 Hemi

1. Drain the cooling system. Disconnect the negative battery cable.
2. Remove the air cleaner and disconnect the fuel line from the carburetor.
3. Disconnect all vacuum lines that attach to the carburetor or intake manifold.
4. Disconnect the spark plug wires from the plugs and remove the distributor cap and wires as an assembly.
5. Disconnect the wires from the coil and the temperature sending unit.
6. Disconnect the heater hose and bypass hose from the intake manifold.
7. Remove the intake manifold attaching bolts and remove the manifold, carburetor and coil from the engine as an assembly.
8. Clean all gasket mounting surfaces and firmly cement new gaskets to the engine.
9. Reverse above precedure to install.

426 Hemi

See Dodge-Plymouth section.

Exhaust Manifold

V8 Models

Disconnect the exhaust manifold at the pipe flange. Access to these bolts is underneath the vehicle. If so equipped, disconnect the Air Injection nozzles and carburetor heated air stove. Disconnect any components of the EGR system which are in the way. Remove the exhaust manifold by removing the securing bolts and washers. To reach these bolts, it may be necessary to jack the engine slightly off its front mounts. When the exhaust manifold is removed, sometimes the securing studs will come out with the nuts. If this occurs, studs must be replaced with the aid of sealing compound on the coarse thread ends. If this is not done, water leaks may develop at the studs. To install the exhaust manifold, reverse the removal procedure.

Valve System

All valves used in Chrysler engines (except 426 Hemi) are arranged in line in the cylinder head; they ride in guides that are integrally cast with the head. Service valves with oversize stems are available; therefore, valve guides may be reamed if required. Do not attempt to ream guides in one step to their maximum .030 in. oversize; work in .005, .015, and .030 in. steps. This allows the guide to be reamed true in relation to its seat.

All six-cylinder engines used in Chrysler vehicles are equipped with solid (mechanical) lifters. The 1967 273 V8s were also equipped with mechanical lifters; subsequent to the above date, all V8s utilized hydraulic lifters. With the exception of the 340 Six Pack engine and the 426 Hemi, these hydraulic lifters are non adjustable.

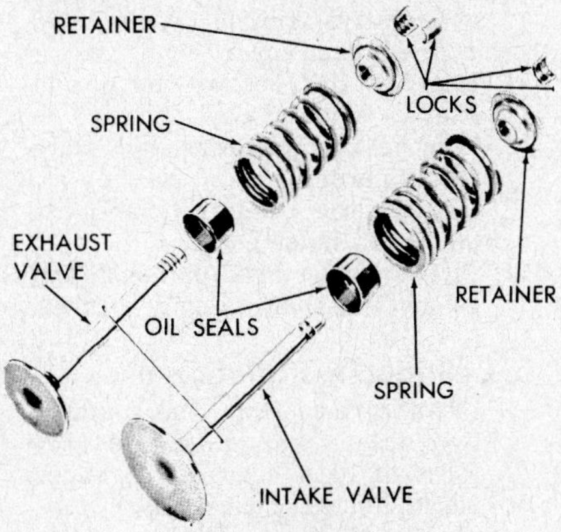
RETAINER
LOCKS
SPRING
EXHAUST VALVE
OIL SEALS
RETAINER
SPRING
INTAKE VALVE
Valve assembly
(© Chrysler Corp)

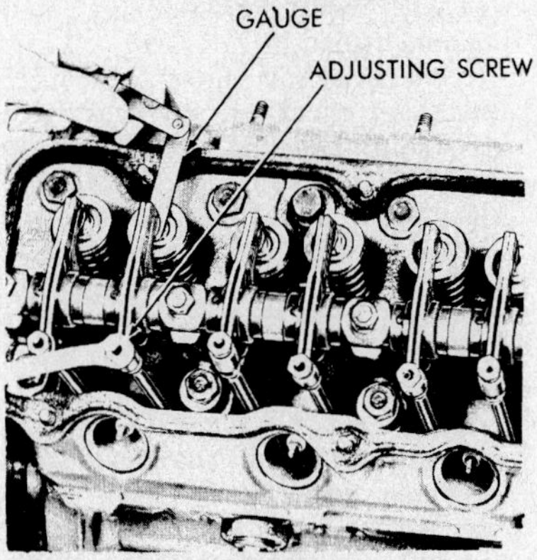
GAUGE
ADJUSTING SCREW
Valve adjustment
(© Chrysler Corp)

Rocker Shaft Removal

All Engines except 426 Hemi

1. Remove closed ventilation system (PCV). On V8s, remove the spark plug wires.
2. Remove valve cover with gasket.
3. Remove rocker shaft bolts with retainers.
4. To replace the rocker arms, reverse the removal procedure. Be sure to torque rocker arm bolts to 25 ft lbs. On engines with adjustable lifters, set the valves. When replacing the valve cover, use a new gasket.

NOTE: when replacing rocker arms, be sure to align the oil holes.

426 Hemi

1. Remove air cleaner, and distributor cap with spark plug cables and secondary coil cable as an assembly.
2. Grasp secondary cables at plastic spark covers and pull covers straight out.
3. Remove spark plugs.
4. On left bank, disconnect brake lines at master cylinder, and remove cotter pin and clevis pin from linkage in back of power brake.
5. Remove four nuts attaching booster to mounting bracket and remove power brake and master cylinder assembly.
6. Remove rocker covers and gaskets.
7. Remove five bolts that attach rocker shafts assembly on each head.

NOTE: these rocker shaft assembly bolts pass through the head and into the block. Anytime rocker shaft assembly is removed, remove that head, fit a new gasket, reassemble and torque.

8. Lift off rocker shafts assembly.
9. To install the rocker arms, reverse removal procedure. Be sure all oil holes are aligned.

Valve Adjustment

170, 198, 225, and 273 Cu. In. Engines

1. Warm up the engine until it reaches its normal operating temperature (water temperature of about 185°F).
2. Set the engine idle speed to 550 rpm and run the engine at this speed for five minutes.
3. Remove the valve cover by withdrawing its securing bolts. Be careful of the hot oil which will splash off the rocker assembly when the cover is removed.

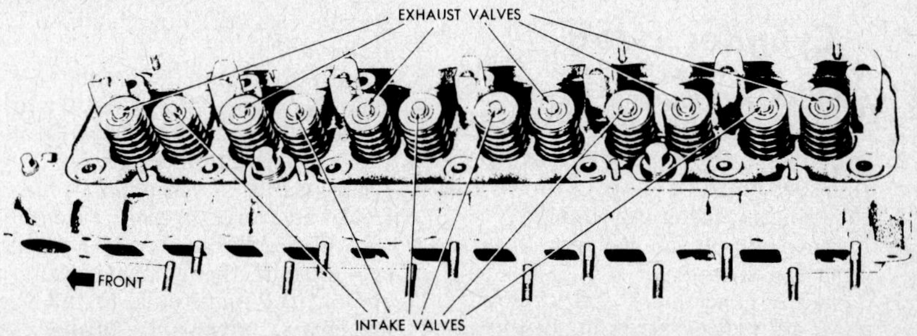
EXHAUST VALVES
FRONT
INTAKE VALVES
Cylinder head, showing valve sequence—170, 198 and 225 engines (© Chrysler Corp)

4. Using the proper thickness feeler gauge, measure the clearance between the valve stem tip and the end of the rocker arm adjusting screw at each valve. If necessary, turn the adjusting screw to obtain the correct valve clearance.
5. After all of the valves have been checked and adjusted, stop the engine and replace the valve cover, using a new gasket between the cover and cylinder head. If much oil was lost during the valve adjustment procedure, check the oil level in the crankcase.

340 Six Pack and 426 Hemi

1. Adjust ignition timing to TDC.
2. Mark crankshaft damper with chalk at TDC and 180° opposite TDC.
3. Rotate crankshaft until No. 1 cylinder is at TDC and points are just opening.
4. Adjust intake tappets on No. 2 and No. 7 cylinders and exhaust tappets on No. 4 and No. 8 cylinders. On 1967-69 engines, adjust the intake valves to have a clearance of .028 in. and the exhaust valves .032 in. with the engine COLD. On 1970–71 engines, adjust the valves to have zero lash, then tighten the adjustment screw an additional 1½ turns. Tighten the locknuts to 25 ft lbs.
5. Rotate crankshaft 180° in normal direction of rotation until points open to fire No. 4 cylinder.
6. Adjust intake tappets on No. 1 and No. 8 cylinders and exhaust tappets on No. 3 and No. 6 cylinders as in Step 4.
7. Rotate crankshaft 180° in normal direction of rotation until points open to fire No. 6 cylinder.
8. Adjust intake tappets on No. 3 and No. 4 cylinders and exhaust tappets on No. 5 and No. 7 cylinders as in Step 4.
9. Rotate crankshaft 180° in normal direction of rotation until points open to fire No. 7 cylinder.
10. Adjust intake tappets on No. 5 and No. 6 cylinders and exhaust tappets on No. 1 and No. 2 cylinders as in Step 4.
11. Set ignition timing to operating specifications and install rocker covers.

Cylinder Head

6 Cylinder Removal

1. Drain the cooling system.
2. Remove carburetor air cleaner and fuel lines.
3. Disconnect accelerator linkage.
4. Remove all of the vacuum lines from the carburetor.
5. Carefully disconnect spark plug wires by pulling straight, in line with plug.
6. Disconnect heater hose and clamp holding the by-pass hose.
7. Disconnect the heat indicator-sending-unit wire.
8. Disconnect exhaust pipe at the exhaust manifold flange. If so equipped, disconnect the diverter valve vacuum line from the intake manifold; also remove the air injection assembly (if applicable).
9. Remove the intake and exhaust manifold and carburetor as an assembly.
10. Remove the outlet vent tube, evaporative control system, and cylinder head cover.
11. Remove the rocker arms and shaft.
12. Remove the pushrods and place them in order.
13. Remove the head bolts and lift off the cylinder head.
14. Place cylinder head on bench and remove the spark plugs and tubes.

6 Cylinder Installation

1. Clean carbon from the combustion area. Clean all gasket surfaces of both head and cylinder block. Install spark plugs (the aluminum plug shields act as satisfactory gasket material between spark plug body and cylinder head.)
2. If there is any cause to suspect leakage, check all surfaces with a straightedge. If out of flatness exceeds 0.00075 times the span length in any direction, replace head or machine head gasket surface. For example, on a 12 in. span the maximum allowable out of flat is 12 x 0.00075 or 0.009 in.
3. Apply a reliable sealer to the new gasket and install the gasket and cylinder head.
4. Install the 14 cylinder head bolts. Starting at the top center, tighten all cylinder head bolts to specification in three steps.
5. Inspect all push rods for bends or wear. Replace if necessary.
6. Insert the pushrods, small ends down into the tappets.
7. Install rocker arms and shaft assembly with flat on the end of the shaft on top and pointing toward the front of the engine. This is necessary to provide lubrication to the rocker assemblies. Torque the attaching bolts to 25 ft. lbs.
8. Loosen the three bolts that connect the intake and exhaust manifolds. (This is necessary to obtain proper alignment.)
9. Position intake and exhaust manifold and carburetor assembly onto the cylinder head. Put the cup side of the conical washers against the manifolds, install the attaching nuts and torque to specifications.
10. Retighten the three intake-to-exhaust manifold bolts to specifications. Be sure to torque the inner bolt first.
11. Connect the heater hose and bypass hose clamp.
12. Connect the heat indicator sending-unit wire, the accelerator linkage and the spark plug wires. If applicable, install vacuum control tube at the carburetor, the air injection assembly, and the diverter valve.
13. Install carburetor vacuum line(s).
14. Connect exhaust pipe to the exhaust manifold.
15. Install the fuel line and carburetor air cleaner.
16. Refill the cooling system.
17. Start the engine and let run until operating temperatures have been reached.
18. Adjust valve tappet clearance to .010 in. (intake) and .020 in. (exhaust.) The adjusting screw in the pushrod end of the rocker arm should have a minimum of 3 ft. lbs. (36 in. lbs.) tension as it is turned. If less, replace the adjusting screw and the rocker arm.
19. Place the new cylinder head cover gasket in position and install cylinder head cover. Torque attaching nuts to 40 in. lbs. (3 1/3 ft. lbs.).
20. Install outlet vent tube, and evaporative control system (if applicable).

273, 318, 340, and 360 V8 Removal

1. Drain cooling system and disconnect battery.
2. Remove alternator, air cleaner and fuel line.
3. Disconnect accelerator linkage.
4. Remove vacuum hose(s) from the carburetor.
5. Remove distributor cap and wires. If removing heads in vehicle, remove plugs to prevent breaking them.
6. Disconnect coil wires, temperature sending wire, heater hoses, and bypass hose.
7. Remove closed ventilation system (PCV), evaporative control system if so equipped, and valve covers.
8. Remove intake manifold, ignition coil, and carburetor as an assembly.
9. Remove exhaust manifolds.
10. Remove rocker arm and shaft assemblies. Remove pushrods and identify to ensure installation in original location.
11. Remove 10 head bolts from each cylinder head and lift off heads.
12. Clean all surfaces.
13. Inspect all surfaces with straight edge if there is any reason to suspect leakage. If out of

flatness exceeds 0.00075 times span length in any direction, replace head or machine mating surface. For example, if span length is 12 in., maximum out of flatness is 12 x 0.00075 or 0.009 in.

14. Reverse procedure to install. Be sure to torque the cylinder head to specifications in three stages.

Chilton's TIME SAVER

If only one head is to be removed, it is possible to leave the intake manifold on the engine while removing the head:

1. **Remove the head bolts from the intake manifold on the side from which the head is to be removed.**
2. **Loosen, but do not remove, the bolts on the opposite side of the manifold 1½-2 turns.**
3. **Perform steps 9-11 above.**
4. **Slip the head out from under the intake manifold.**
5. **Perform steps 12-14 above.**

383 and 440 Wedge V8s and 426 Hemi V8

See Dodge-Plymouth Section.

Disassembly of Cylinder Head

1. Remove cylinder heads.
2. Compress valve springs using valve spring compressor.
3. Remove valve locks or keys.
4. Release valve springs.
5. Remove valve springs, retainers, oil seals, and valves.

NOTE: if a valve does not slide out of the guide easily, check end of stem for mushrooming or heading over. If head is mushroomed, file off excess, remove and discard valve. If valve is not mushroomed, lubricate stem of valve, remove, and check for stem wear or damage.

Cylinder Head Bolt Tightening Sequence

NOTE: torque to specifications in three steps.

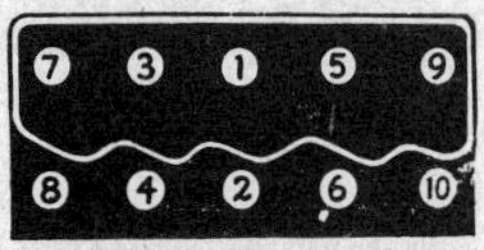

273, 318, 340, 360 cu. in. V8
(© Chrysler Corp)

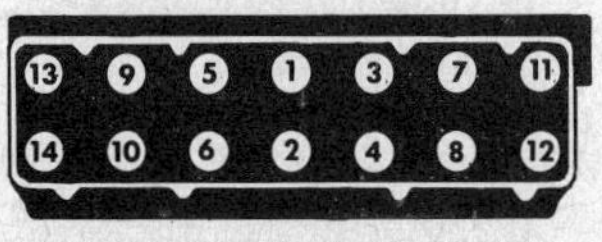

6 cylinder
(© Chrysler Corp)

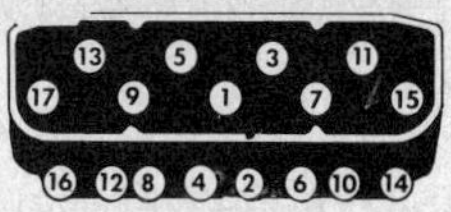

383, 440 cu. in. V8
(© Chrysler Corp)

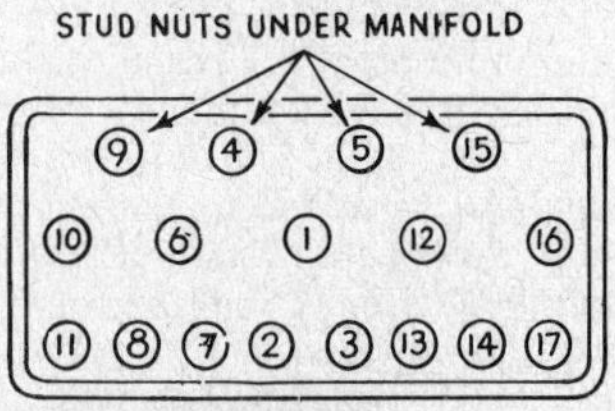
STUD NUTS UNDER MANIFOLD

426 Hemi V8
(© Chrysler Corp)

Chilton's TIME SAVER

Frequently valves become bent or warped or their seats become blocked with carbon or other material. Left unattended, this can cause burnt valves, damaged cylinder heads and other expensive troubles. To detect leaking valves early, perform this test whenever the cylinder head is removed.

1. **After removing head, replace sparkplugs. Removing sparkplugs before removing heads eliminates breakage.**
2. **Place head on bench with valves, springs, retainers and keys installed and combustion chambers up.**
3. **Pour enough gasoline in each combustion chamber to completely cover both valves. Watch combustion chambers for two minutes for any leakage.**

Timing Cover, Chain, and Camshaft

Timing Chain and Cover R & R

1. Drain the cooling system.
2. Disconnect the upper and lower radiator hoses from the engine. Disconnect the transmission cooler lines from the radiator.
3. If equipped with a fan shroud, remove it from the radiator and position it rearward over the fan.
4. Remove the radiator attaching screws and remove the radiator from the vehicle.

NOTE: it may not be necessary to remove the radiator and shroud if there is enough room to work the timing cover out.

5. Remove the bolts that attach the fan to the water pump and remove the fan, fan spacer (if so equipped) and pulley from the engine.
6. Disconnect the negative battery cable. Remove the bolts that attach the alternator mounting bracket to the engine and remove the alternator and bracket from the engine and position them out of the way with the wires attached.
7. If equipped with power steering, remove the bolts that attach the power steering pump mounting bracket to the engine. Remove the pump and bracket from the engine and position them out of the way with the lines attached.
8. Remove the water pump from the engine.
9. Remove the bolt and washer that attach the vibration damper to the crankshaft.
10. Using a puller, remove the vibration damper.
11. Remove the bolts that attach the timing chain cover to the block and the front of the oil pan. Remove the cover from the engine.
12. To check timing chain slack, place a scale next to the timing chain to detect any movement in the chain. Place a torque wrench and socket on the camshaft sprocket attaching bolt. Apply either 30 ft lbs. (if cylinder heads are installed on the engine) or 15 ft lbs. (cylinder heads removed) of force to the bolt and rotate the bolt in the direction of crankshaft rotation to remove all slack from the chain. While applying torque to the camshaft sprocket bolt, the crankshaft should not be allowed to rotate. It may be necessary to block the crankshaft to prevent rotation. Position the scale over the edge of a timing chain link

Removing vibration damper
(© Chrysler Corp)

and apply an equal amount of torque in the opposite direction. If the movement of the chain exceeds 3/16 in., replace the chain.

13. To remove the timing chain, crank the engine until the timing marks on the sprockets are aligned, remove the bolt that attaches the cam sprocket to the camshaft, and slide the chain and both sprockets forward and remove them from the engine as an assembly.
14. Reverse above procedure to install, making sure the timing marks on the camshaft and crankshaft sprockets are aligned when they are installed on the engine.

Timing Gear Cover Seal Replacement

All Engines

1. Using a puller, separate the seal from the retainer.
2. Using fingers and a screwdriver, pull the seal from the case.
3. To install the seal, place it in the case with the rubber side downward.
4. Seat the seal tightly against the cover face. There should be maximum clearance of 0.0014 in. between the seal and the cover. Be certain not to overcompress seal.

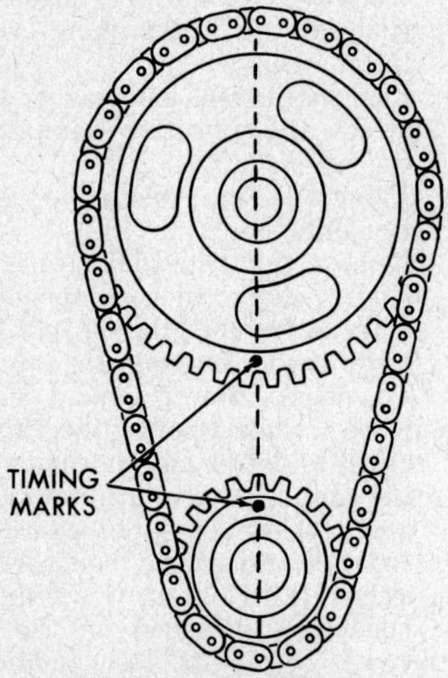
TIMING
MARKS
Alignment of timing marks—V8
(© Chrysler Corp)

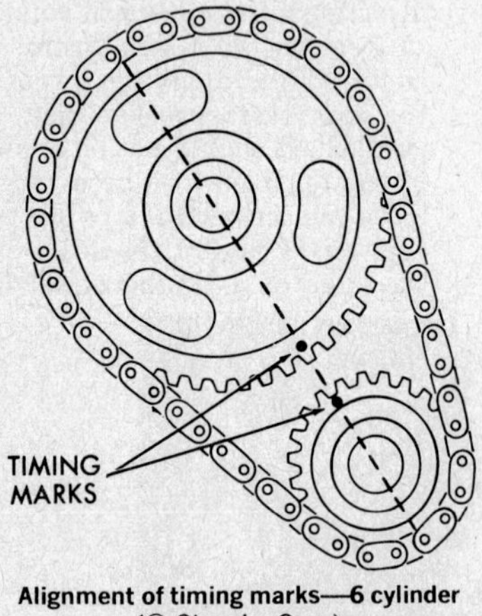
TIMING
MARKS
Alignment of timing marks—6 cylinder
(© Chrysler Corp)

Camshaft Removal and Installation

NOTE: whenever a new camshaft and/or new tappets are installed, the manufacturer recommends that one qt of their engine oil supplement, or equivalent, be added to the engine oil to aid break-in. This oil mixture should be left in the engine for a minimum of 500 miles.

6 Cylinder Engines

1. Remove the timing gear cover, camshaft sprocket, and timing chain.
2. Remove the valve tappets, keeping them in order to ensure installation in their original location.
3. Remove the crankshaft sprocket.
4. Remove the distributor and the oil pump.
5. Remove the fuel pump.
6. Fit a long bolt into the front of the camshaft to facilitate camshaft removal.
7. Remove the camshaft, being careful not to damage the cam bearings with the cam lobes.
8. Lubricate the camshaft lobes and bearing journals with camshaft lubricant. Insert the camshaft into the engine block.
9. Install the fuel pump and oil pump.
10. Install the distributor. (Refer to the "Distributor Installation" procedure.)
11. Inspect the crowns of all the tappet faces with a straightedge. Replace any tappets that have dished or worn surfaces. Install the tappets.
12. Replace the timing gear and timing gear cover.

V8 Engines

1. Remove the timing gear cover, camshaft and crankshaft sprocket, and the timing chain.
2. Remove the valve tappets, keeping them in order to ensure installation in their original location.
3. Remove the distributor and lift out the oil pump and distributor driveshaft.
4. Remove the camshaft thrust plate (is so equipped). Take note of the location of the oil tab.
5. Fit a long bolt into the front of the camshaft and remove the camshaft, being careful not to damage the cam bearings with the cam lobes.
6. Lubricate the camshaft lobes and bearing journals with camshaft lubricant. Insert the camshaft into the engine block within 2 in. of its final position in the block.

TORQUE WRENCH
3/16 INCH
Measuring timing chain stretch
(© Chrysler Corp)

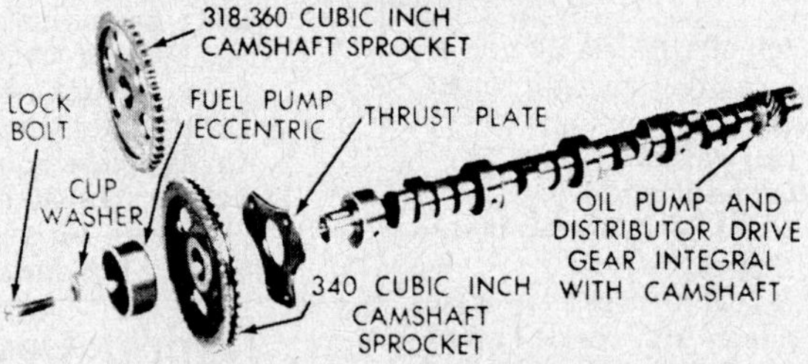
318-360 CUBIC INCH
CAMSHAFT SPROCKET
LOCK
BOLT
FUEL PUMP
ECCENTRIC
THRUST PLATE
CUP
WASHER
OIL PUMP AND
DISTRIBUTOR DRIVE
GEAR INTEGRAL
WITH CAMSHAFT
340 CUBIC INCH
CAMSHAFT
SPROCKET
Camshaft and sprocket assembly
(© Chrysler Corp)

7. Have an assistant support the camshaft with a screwdriver to prevent the camshaft from contacting the freeze plug in the rear of the engine block. Position the screwdriver against the rear side of the cam gear and be careful not to damage the cam lobes.
8. Refit the camshaft thrust plate (if so equipped), and the chain oil tab. Be sure its tang enters the lower right hole in the thrust plate. Tab top edge must be flat against the thrust plate.
9. Install the oil pump and the distributor driveshaft. Install the distributor. (Refer to the "Distributor Installation" procedure.)
10. Inspect the crown of all the tappet faces with a straightedge. Replace any tappets that have dished or worn surfaces. Install the tappets.
11. Install the timing gear and gear cover.

Pistons and Connecting Rods

Piston Removal and Piston Ring Replacement

1. Remove the cylinder heads.
2. Remove the oil pan.
3. Turn the crankshaft until the No. 1 piston is at the bottom of its stroke. Place a rag over the top of the piston, and using a ridge reamer, remove the ridge of carbon from the top of the cylinder wall. Repeat this operation on all cylinders.

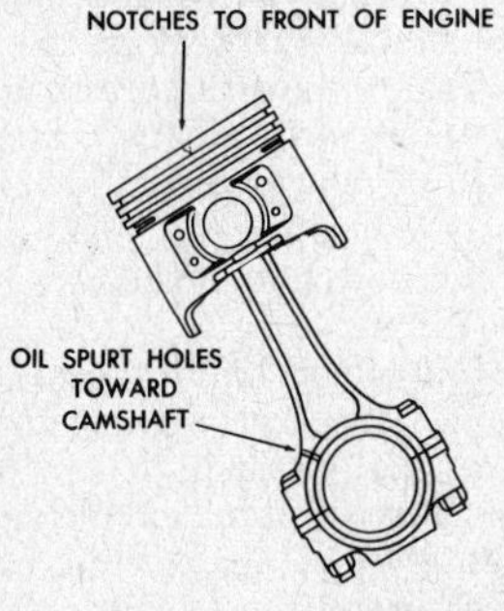
NOTCHES TO FRONT OF ENGINE
OIL SPURT HOLES TOWARD CAMSHAFT

Piston and rod assembly—6 cylinder
(© Chrysler Corp)

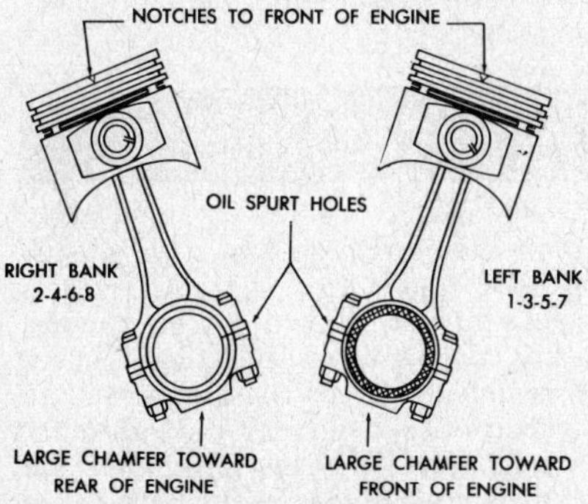
NOTCHES TO FRONT OF ENGINE
OIL SPURT HOLES
RIGHT BANK
2-4-6-8
LEFT BANK
1-3-5-7
LARGE CHAMFER TOWARD REAR OF ENGINE
LARGE CHAMFER TOWARD FRONT OF ENGINE

Piston and rod assembly—V8
(© Chrysler Corp)

4. Remove the connecting rod cap from the No. 1 piston connecting rod. Rotate the engine so the piston and connecting rod assembly are centered in the cylinder bore. Place a block of wood against the bottom of the piston and carefully drive the piston-connecting rod assembly from the cylinder block. Replace the connecting rod cap and bearing half on the connecting rod so they do not become mixed. Repeat this operation until all the pistons have been removed.

NOTE: Number the pistons, rods and caps to aid in identification during assembly.

5. Using a piston ring removal tool remove the piston rings.
6. If cylinder bore is in satisfactory condition, place each ring in bore in turn and square it in bore with head of piston. Measure ring gap. If ring gap is greater than limit, use new ring. If ring gap is less than limit, file end of ring to obtain correct gap.
7. Check ring side clearance by installing rings on piston, and inserting feeler gauge of correct dimension between ring and lower land. Gauge should slide freely around ring circumference without binding. Any wear will form a step on lower land. Replace any pistons having high steps. Before checking ring side clearance be sure ring grooves are clean and free of carbon, sludge, or grit.
8. Space ring gaps at equidistant intervals around piston circumference. Be sure to install piston in its original bore. Install short lengths of rubber tubing over connecting rod bolts to prevent damage to rod journal. Install ring compressor over rings on piston. Lower piston rod assembly into bore until ring compressor contacts block. Using wooden handle of hammer push piston into bore while guiding rod onto journal.

Engine Lubrication

Oil Pan Removal

Slant Six—1967-74 Dart and Valiant 1967-69 Barracuda

1. Disconnect the battery and drain the radiator. Disconnect the upper and lower radiator hoses, and remove the oil dipstick.
2. Remove the radiator shroud attaching screws and position it rearward on the engine (if so equipped).
3. Jack up the vehicle and drain the oil.
4. Remove the steering center link from the steering and idler arms.
5. Position a jack stand at the right front corner of the engine oil pan. Be sure not to support the engine at the crankshaft pulley or vibration damper.
6. Remove the front engine mount bolts. Raise the engine about $1\frac{1}{2}$–2 in.
7. Remove the oil pan bolts, rotate the engine crankshaft to clear the counterweights, and remove the oil pan.
8. Using a new pan gasket set, install the oil pan and torque it to 200 in. lbs.
9. Lower the engine into its original position and install the front engine mount bolts. Torque to specifications.
10. Connect the steering and idler arms to the center link. Torque to specification; be sure to install the cotter pins.
11. If removed, install the radiator hoses and replace the fan shroud.
12. Fill the cooling system, install the dipstick, replace the oil, and check for leaks. Connect the battery and start the vehicle. Run for five minutes, then check again for leaks.

1970-74 Barracuda and Challenger

1. Disconnect the battery and remove the oil dipstick. Jack up the vehicle and drain the oil.
2. Remove the steering center link with the idler arm attached.
3. Disconnect the exhaust pipe from its manifold and secure it out of the way.
4. Remove the oil pan attaching bolts. Rotate the engine crankshaft in order to clear the counterweights. Remove the oil pan.
5. To install the oil pan, reverse the removal procedure. Torque the pan bolts to 200 in. lbs.

273, 318, 340, and 360 V8s

1. Disconnect the battery and remove the dipstick.
2. Jack up the vehicle and drain the oil. If so equipped, remove the torque converter-to-engine left housing strut.
3. Disconnect the steering center link from the steering and idler arms.
4. Disconnect the exhaust pipes from the manifolds and secure them out of the way.
5. Visually check to see if there is sufficient clearance to reach all of the oil pan bolts. If there is not, it will be necessary to raise the engine about $1\frac{1}{2}$–2 in. Do this by loosening the motor mounts and jacking or hoisting the engine until the bolts in question become accessible. Be sure to raise the engine only the minimum amount necessary to reach these bolts. Remove the oil pan

bolts, rotate the engine crankshaft to clear the counterweights, and remove the pan with a twisting motion.

6. When installing the oil pan, be sure that the oil strainer will be parallel with and will contact the pan bottom. Use a new gasket and torque the pan bolts to 200 in. lbs.
7. If it was necessary to jack the engine from its mounts, return it to its proper position at this time. Torque the engine mount bolts to specifications.
8. Install the engine-to-converter housing strut (if so equipped).
9. From this point, reverse the removal procedure.

383, 426, and 440 V8s

1. Disconnect the battery and remove the dipstick.
2. Jack up the vehicle and remove the center steering link from the steering and idler arms.
3. Disconnect the exhaust pipes from the manifolds and secure them out of the way.
4. If there is not sufficient clearance for the oil pan to clear the exhaust pipe, remove the clamp attaching the exhaust pipe to the extension and remove the exhaust pipe.
5. Drain the oil.
6. Remove the dust shield from the torque converter.
7. Extract the oil pan bolts. On some models, it may be necessary to jack the engine off its mounts (1½–2 in.) to reach the oil pan bolts. Do this by loosening the motor mounts and jacking or hoisting the engine. Raise the engine only the minimum amount required to reach the bolts in question. When removing the oil pan, be sure to rotate the crankshaft to clear the counterweights. Remove the pan with a twisting motion.
8. When installing the oil pan, be sure to use a new gasket. Torque the pan bolts to 200 in. lbs.
9. If it was necessary to jack the engine, lower it now and torque the engine mounts to specifications. To proceed, reverse the order of removal. After completion, be sure to start the vehicle and idle for at least five minutes. Check for leaks.

Oil Pump

Six Cylinder Removal

1. Drain radiator, disconnect upper and lower hoses, and remove fan shroud.
2. Raise vehicle on hoist, support front of engine with jack stand placed under right front corner of oil pan, and remove engine mount bolts. Do not support engine at crankshaft pulley or vibration damper.

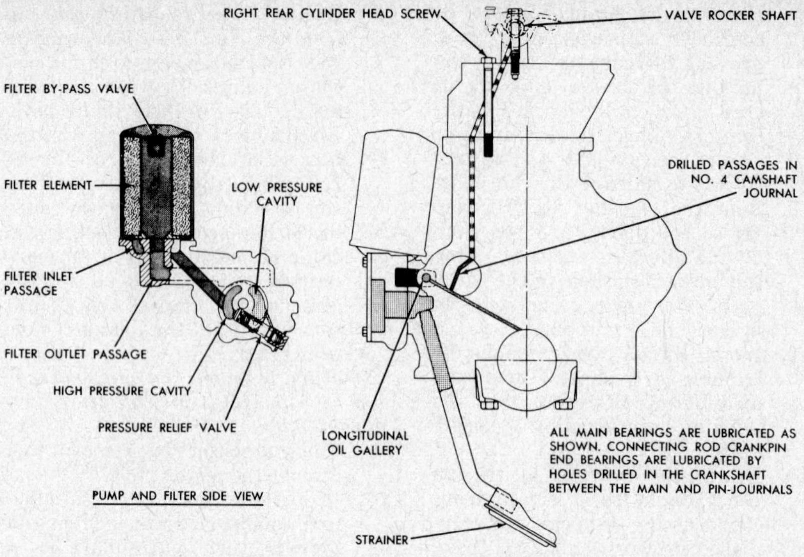
RIGHT REAR CYLINDER HEAD SCREW
VALVE ROCKER SHAFT
FILTER BY-PASS VALVE
FILTER ELEMENT
LOW PRESSURE CAVITY
DRILLED PASSAGES IN NO. 4 CAMSHAFT JOURNAL
FILTER INLET PASSAGE
FILTER OUTLET PASSAGE
HIGH PRESSURE CAVITY
PRESSURE RELIEF VALVE
LONGITUDINAL OIL GALLERY
ALL MAIN BEARINGS ARE LUBRICATED AS SHOWN. CONNECTING ROD CRANKPIN END BEARINGS ARE LUBRICATED BY HOLES DRILLED IN THE CRANKSHAFT BETWEEN THE MAIN AND PIN-JOURNALS
PUMP AND FILTER SIDE VIEW
STRAINER

Oil circuit—6 cylinder (© Chrysler Corp)

3. Raise engine approximately 1½—2 in.
4. Remove oil filter, oil pump attaching bolts, and pump assembly.

273, 318, 340, and 360 Engines

1. Remove oil pan.
2. Remove oil pump from rear main bearing cap.

383, 426, and 440 V8s

1. The oil pump is located on the bottom side of the engine block at the filter.
2. Removal consists of taking out the attaching bolts and removing the pump and filter as an assembly.
3. To install the pump, reverse the removal procedure.

Rear Main Bearing Oil Seal

Service replacement seals are of split rubber type composition. This type of seal makes it possible to replace the upper half of the rear main oil seal without removing the engine from the car. When installing rubber seals, they must be replaced as a set and cannot be combined with the rope type rear main seal. The following procedure is for removing the rope type seal and replacing it with the rubber type seal.

NOTE: on vehicles with a 426 Hemi engine, remove the transmission and vibration damper in addition to the procedure listed below.

Replacement

1. Remove the oil pan.
2. Remove the rear seal retainer and the rear main bearing cap.
3. Remove the lower rope seal by prying from the side with a small screwdriver.
4. To remove the upper rope seal, drive up on either exposed end of the seal with a 6 in. piece of 3/16 in. brazing rod. When the opposite end of the seal starts to protrude from the block, have an assistant grasp it with pliers and gently pull it from the block while the opposite end is being driven.
5. Wipe crankshaft clean and lightly oil crankshaft and new seal before installing seal.
6. Loosen all main bearing caps slightly to lower the crankshaft which will ease installation.

Caution Do not allow the crankshaft to drop enough to permit the main bearings to become displaced on the crankshaft.

7. Hold the seal tightly against the crankshaft with the thumb (with paint stripe to the rear) and install the seal in the block groove. Rotate the crankshaft if necessary while installing the seal in the groove. *Make sure the sharp edges on the block groove do not cut or nick the rear of the seal.*
8. Install lower half of seal (with paint stripe to the rear) into the lower seal retainer.
9. Install rear main bearing cap.
10. Tighten all main bearing caps to specification.

NOTE: make sure all main bearings are located in their proper position before tightening the main bearing caps.

CLUTCH

All models utilize a single, dry plate clutch operated by a pedal suspended under the dash. All models are equipped with a return spring; some models have centrifugal rollers assembled between the pressure plate and cover. Six-cylinder and light-duty V8 models utilize a non-centrifugal clutch; six-cylinder heavy-duty usage and most V8s use a semi-centrifugal type.

Clutch Removal

1967-74

1. Remove the transmission.
2. Remove the clutch housing pan.
3. Disconnect the fork return spring from the clutch housing and release fork.
4. Remove the spring washer fastening the fork rod to the torque shaft lever pin. Remove the pin from the rod and release fork.
5. On models with three-speed transmissions (if this procedure is applicable to vehicle in question) remove the clip and plain washer securing the interlock rod to the torque shaft lever and remove the washers and rod from the torque shaft.
6. Remove the sleeve assembly and clutch release bearing from the clutch release fork.
7. Punch-mark the clutch cover and flywheel so they may be installed in the same relative positions.
8. Loosen the clutch cover attaching screws in two stages to avoid bending the cover flange.
9. Remove the clutch assembly. Be careful not to contaminate the clutch with grease or oil.

Clutch Installation

1. Lightly lubricate the drive pinion bushing in the end of the crankshaft. Use about ½ teaspoonful of long-life chassis grease. Lubricant should be inserted in the radius in back of the bushing.
2. Thoroughly clean the surfaces of the flywheel and pressure plate with fine sandpaper. All oil or grease must be removed at this time.
3. Position the clutch disc, pressure plate, and cover in the mounting position. Springs on disc damper must be facing away from the flywheel. Do not touch the disc facing at any time. Insert a clutch disc aligning arbor or suitable substitute (such as a spare transmission drive pinion) through the disc hub and into the bushing.
4. Align the punch marks that were made at removal. Install the clutch cover bolts but do not tighten them.
5. Tighten all bolts a few turns at a time in an alternate sequence. Torque 5/16 in. bolts to 20 in. lbs. and 3/8 in. bolts to 30 ft lbs. Remove the alignment tool.
6. Pack the bearing sleeve cavity with an appropriate NLGI Grade 2 EP grease. Apply the same lubricant to the release fork pads of the sleeve.
7. Insert the release bearing and sleeve assembly into the clutch housing as far forward as possible. Lightly lubricate the fork fingers and retaining spring.
8. Insert the fork fingers under the clutch sleeve retaining springs. Retaining springs on the sleeve must have lateral freedom.
9. Make sure that the groove in the seal is properly seated in the seal opening flange in the clutch housing. Replace the pedal rod on the torque shaft lever pin and secure it with a spring washer.
10. Insert the threaded end of the fork rod assembly in the opening provided in the end of the release fork rod. Replace the eye end of the fork rod on the torque shaft lever pin and lock it with a spring washer.
11. If applicable, install the fork return spring between the release fork and the clutch housing.
12. If applicable, install the spring and plain washer with interlock rod in the torque shaft lever and lock it in position with a washer and clip.
13. When installing the transmission, be sure not to allow grease to settle on the splines or pilot end of the transmission drive pinion.
14. Install the transmission and adjust the clutch pedal free-play.

Clutch Linkage (Height and Free-Play) Adjustment

1. If the vehicle is equipped with a gearshift interlock rod (six-cylinder models and some light-duty V8s with three speeds after 1967) disconnect it by loosening the rod swivel clamp screw.
2. Adjust the fork rod by rotating the self-locking nut to provide 5/32 in. free-play at the fork end. This adjustment will result in the proper 1 in. free-play at the clutch pedal.
3. If the gearshift interlock was disconnected, refer to its adjustment below.

Gearshift Interlock Adjustment

1. Disconnect the interlock pawl from the clutch rod swivel.
2. Adjust the clutch pedal free-play.
3. With the first-reverse lever on the transmission in the neutral (middle detent) position, the interlock pawl should enter the slot in the first-reverse lever.
4. Loosen the swivel clamp bolt and move the swivel on the rod to enter the pawl. Install the washers with a clip. Hold the interlock pawl forward and torque the swivel clamp bolt to 100–125 in. lbs. The clutch pedal must be in the fully returned position during this adjustment. Under no circumstances should the clutch rod be pulled rearward to engage the pawl swivel.
5. Shift the clutch through all gear positions at least three times. Clutch action should be normal.
6. Disengage the clutch and shift halfway to first or reverse gear. The clutch should be held down by the interlock to within 1–2 in. of the floor.

OLD BEARING
RELEASE BEARING SLEEVE
NEW BEARING

Replacing clutch release bearing (© Chrysler Corp)

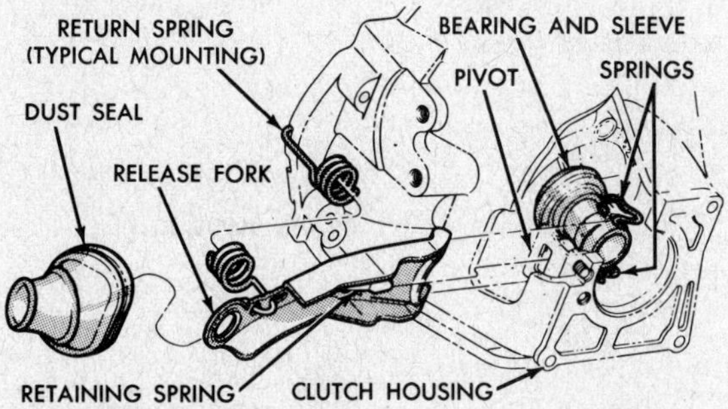
RETURN SPRING (TYPICAL MOUNTING)
BEARING AND SLEEVE
PIVOT
SPRINGS
DUST SEAL
RELEASE FORK
RETAINING SPRING
CLUTCH HOUSING

Clutch release fork, bearing and sleeve (© Chrysler Corp)

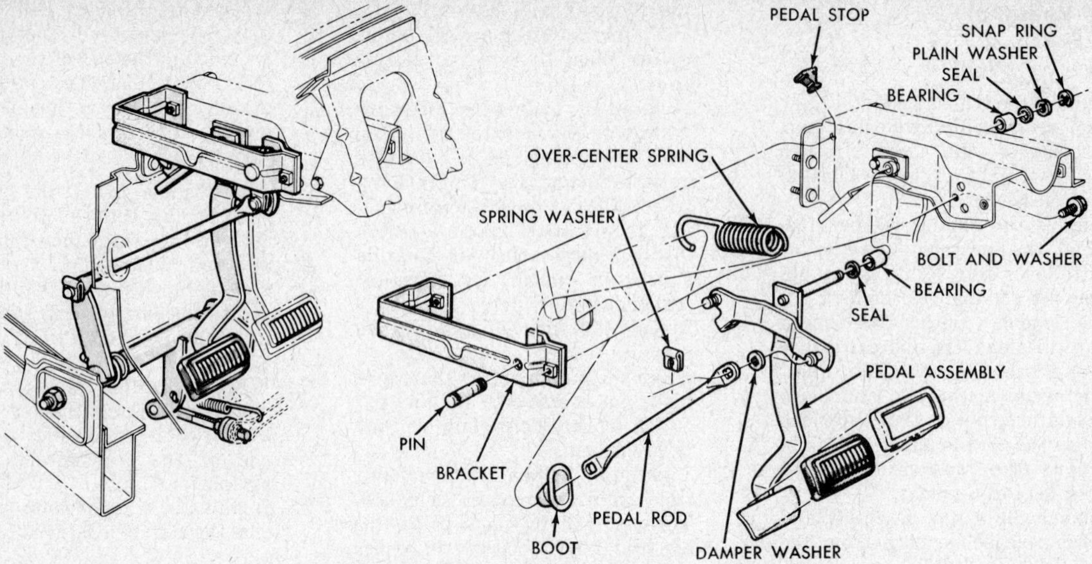
PEDAL STOP
SNAP RING
PLAIN WASHER
SEAL
BEARING
OVER-CENTER SPRING
SPRING WASHER
BOLT AND WASHER
BEARING
SEAL
PEDAL ASSEMBLY
PIN
BRACKET
PEDAL ROD
BOOT
DAMPER WASHER
Typical clutch pedal and linkage (© Chrysler Corp)

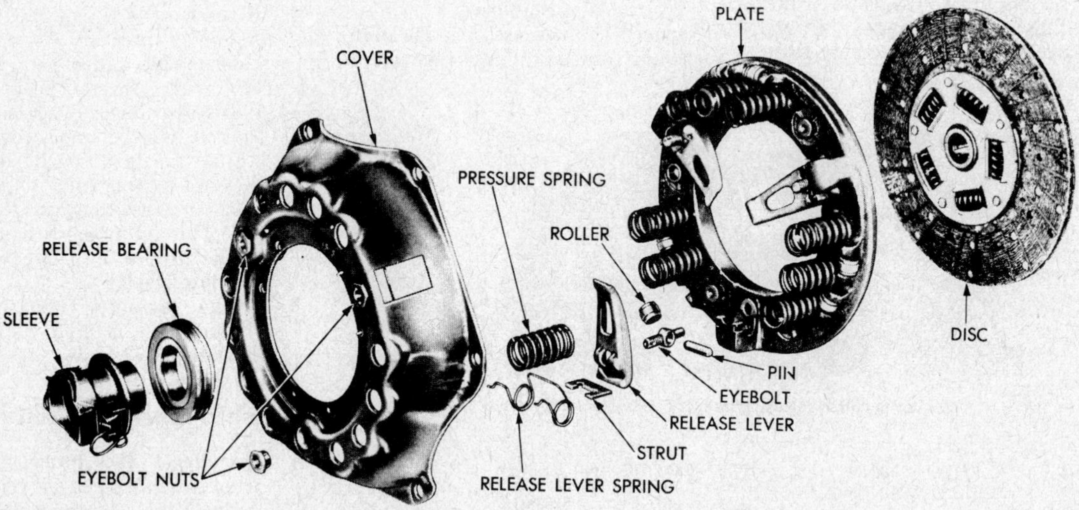
PLATE
COVER
PRESSURE SPRING
ROLLER
RELEASE BEARING
SLEEVE
DISC
PIN
EYEBOLT
RELEASE LEVER
STRUT
EYEBOLT NUTS
RELEASE LEVER SPRING
Chrysler semi-centrifugal clutch (© Chrysler Corp)

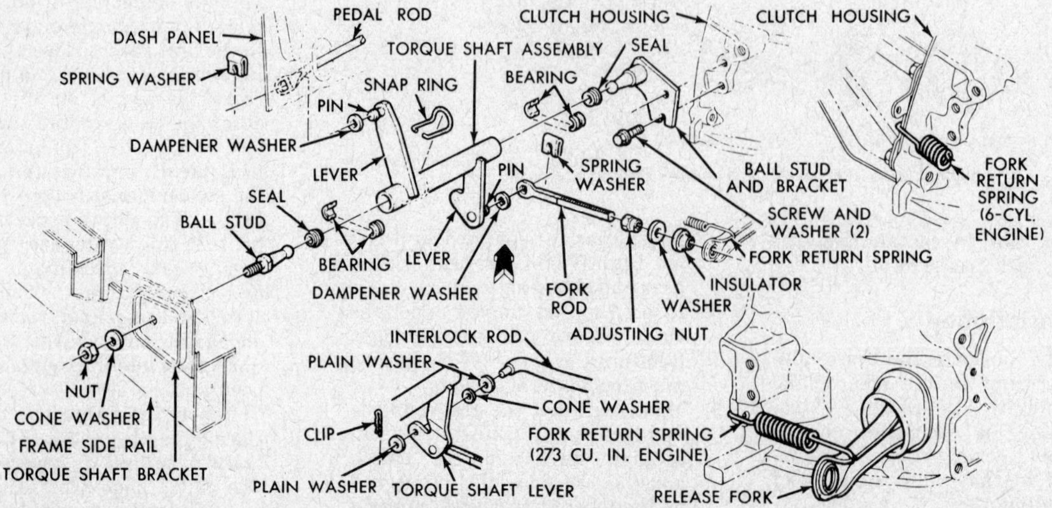
PEDAL ROD
CLUTCH HOUSING
CLUTCH HOUSING
DASH PANEL
TORQUE SHAFT ASSEMBLY
SEAL
SPRING WASHER
SNAP RING
BEARING
PIN
DAMPENER WASHER
LEVER
PIN
SPRING WASHER
BALL STUD AND BRACKET
FORK RETURN SPRING (6-CYL. ENGINE)
SEAL
BALL STUD
SCREW AND WASHER (2)
BEARING
LEVER
FORK RETURN SPRING
DAMPENER WASHER
FORK ROD
INSULATOR
WASHER
ADJUSTING NUT
INTERLOCK ROD
PLAIN WASHER
NUT
CONE WASHER
CONE WASHER
FRAME SIDE RAIL
CLIP
FORK RETURN SPRING (273 CU. IN. ENGINE)
TORQUE SHAFT BRACKET
PLAIN WASHER
TORQUE SHAFT LEVER
RELEASE FORK
Typical clutch linkage (© Chrysler Corp)

MANUAL TRANSMISSION

Dodge and Plymouth have used four synchromesh manual transmissions in recent years. Six cylinders use a three speed, top cover transmission with synchromesh on second and third. V8s up to 1970 use a similar three speed, top cover transmission with synchromesh on second and third. Beginning 1970, V8s use a new fully synchromesh, side cover three speed. All Dodge and Plymouth four speed cars use a fully synchromesh, side cover four speed.

Removal

Top Cover Three Speeds

1. Drain transmission.
2. Disconnect driveshaft at rear universal joint. Carefully pull shaft yoke out of transmission.
3. Disconnect speedometer cable, TCS switch and back up light switch.
4. Install engine support fixture or jack up engine about 1 in. and block in place.
5. Disconnect transmission extension housing from center crossmember.
6. Support transmission with jack and remove crossmember. Remove bolts that attach transmission to clutch housing.
7. Slide transmission rearward until pinion shaft clears clutch disc before lowering transmission.
8. Lower transmission and remove.

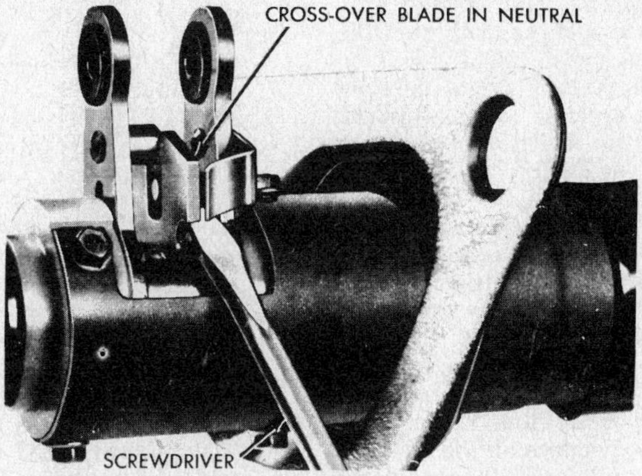
CROSS-OVER BLADE IN NEUTRAL
SCREWDRIVER
Holding cross-over blades in neutral (© Chrysler Corp)

Fully Synchromesh, Side Cover Three Speed

1. Remove shift rods from transmission levers.
2. Drain transmission fluid.
3. Disconnect driveshaft at rear universal joint. Mark both parts for reassembly.
4. Carefully pull yoke out of transmission extension.
5. Disconnect speedometer cable, the TCS switch and back-up lights.
6. Remove part of exhaust if it blocks transmission.
7. Raise engine slightly and block in place.
8. Support transmission with jack, and remove crossmember.
9. Remove transmission to clutch housing bolts.
10. Slide transmission to rear until drive pinion shaft clears clutch disc, lower transmission, and remove from vehicle.

Four Speed

1. Raise vehicle on a hoist and drain transmission.
2. Disconnect all shift controls from transmission levers. Remove three bolts securing shift unit to extension housing.
3. Disconnect driveshaft at rear universal joint. Carefully pull yoke out of transmission extension.
4. Disconnect speedometer cable, TCS switch and back-up light switch leads.
5. Disconnect left exhaust pipe or dual exhausts. Disconnect parking brake cable.
6. Raise engine slightly and block in place.
7. Disconnect transmission extension from crossmember.
8. Remove crossmember.
9. Support transmission with jack. Remove clutch housing to transmission bolts.
10. Slide transmission to rear until drive pinion shaft clears clutch disc.
11. Lower transmission and remove from vehicle.

Manual Transmission Installation

Lightly grease the inner end of the pilot shaft bushing in the flywheel. In addition, grease the pinion bearing retainer pilot at the clutch release shaft.

Position the transmission so that the drive pinion is centered in the clutch housing bore. Push the transmission forward until the pinion shaft enters the clutch disc. Place the transmission in gear. Twist the output shaft until the splines are in alignment. Push the transmission forward until it is seated against the clutch housing.

Caution The transmission must not hang after the pinion is inside the clutch.

Replace the transmission coupling bolts. Torque them to 50 ft lbs. With a drift, align the crossmember bolt holes and install the bolts. Torque them to 40–50 ft lbs. Remove the engine support fixture and hooks. Install the extension housing and bolt in position. If so equipped, tighten the engine mount-to-crossmember bolt. Install and perform the gearshift linkage adjustment. Connect the driveshaft and universal joints. Connect the exhaust system and fill the transmission with an appropriate lubricant. Road-test the vehicle.

Linkage Adjustment

Column Mounted 1967

With the second and third control rod disconnected from the lever on the column, and first and reverse control rod disconnected at the transmission, levers in neutral:

1. Check for axial freedom of the shift levers in the column. If the outer end of the levers move up or down along the column axis over 1/16 in., loosen the two upper bushing screws and rotate the plastic bushing, downward, until all of the axial play is eliminated. Retighten bushing screws.
2. Wedge a screwdriver between the crossover blade and the second and third lever, so that the crossover blade is engaged with both lever crossover pins.
3. Adjust the swivel on the end of second and third control rod until the stub shaft of the swivel enters the hole in the column lever. Install washers and clip. Tighten swivel locknut to 70 in. lbs.
4. Slide the clamp and swivel, on the end of the first and reverse control rod, until the swivel stub shaft enters the hole in the transmission lever. Install washers and clip. Tighten the swivel clamp bolt to 100 in. lbs.

Column Mounted 1968-69

1. Remove both shift rod lever swivels at the transmission levers.
2. Make sure both transmission levers are in the Neutral (middle) position.
3. Adjust the 2nd-3rd shift rod swivel so it will enter the 2nd-3rd (forward) lever at the

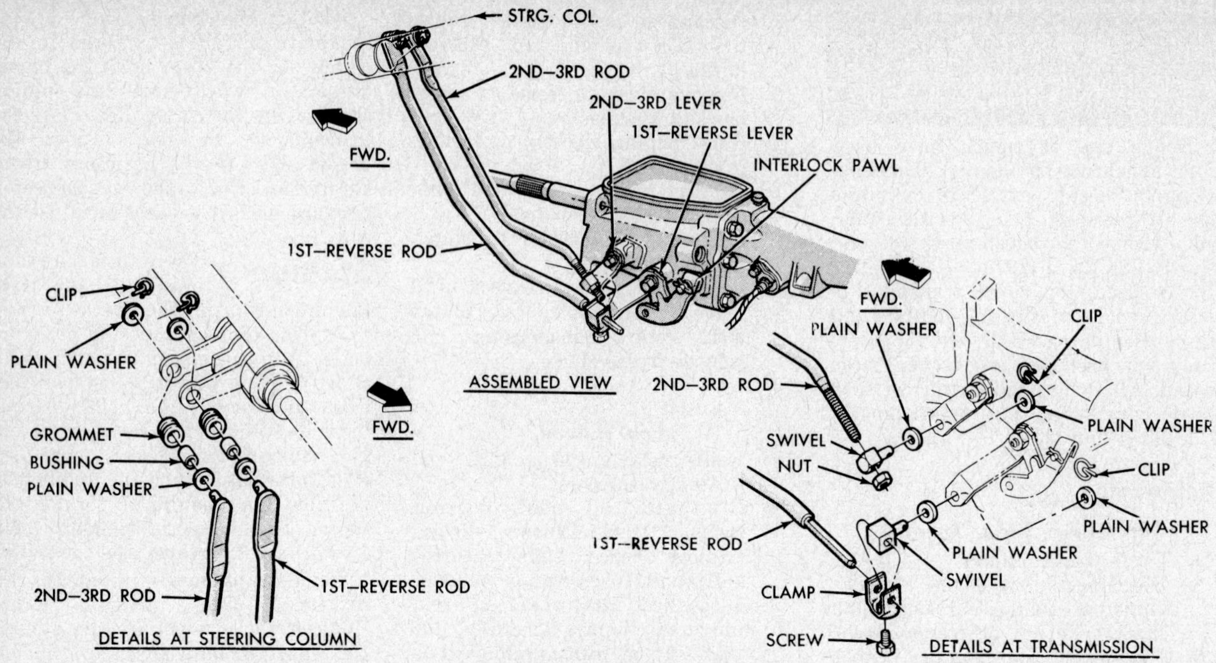
STRG. COL.
2ND–3RD ROD
2ND–3RD LEVER
1ST–REVERSE LEVER
INTERLOCK PAWL
FWD.
1ST–REVERSE ROD
CLIP
PLAIN WASHER
GROMMET
BUSHING
PLAIN WASHER
2ND–3RD ROD
1ST–REVERSE ROD
DETAILS AT STEERING COLUMN
ASSEMBLED VIEW
FWD.
FWD.
PLAIN WASHER
CLIP
2ND–3RD ROD
PLAIN WASHER
SWIVEL
NUT
CLIP
PLAIN WASHER
1ST–REVERSE ROD
PLAIN WASHER
SWIVEL
CLAMP
SCREW
DETAILS AT TRANSMISSION

3-speed shift linkage (© Chrysler Corp)

transmission while the hand lever on the steering column is held 10° above the horizontal (neutral) position. Position the swivel in the lever and install the washer and clip and tighten the attaching nut to 70 in. lbs.

4. Place a screwdriver or other suitable tool between the cross-over blade and the 2nd-3rd lever at the base of the steering column, so that both lever pins are engaged by the cross-over blade.
5. Adjust the 1st-reverse shift rod swivel so it will freely enter the lever on the transmission. Position the swivel in the transmission lever and install the washer and clip and tighten the attaching nut to 100 in. lbs.
6. Remove the tool from the cross-over blade at the steering column and check linkage operation.

Column Mounted 1970-74

1. Remove both shift rod swivels from the transmission.
2. Make sure the transmission levers are in the Neutral (middle) position.
3. Move the shift lever on the steering column to line up the locating slots in the bottom of the steering column housing and bearing housing. Install a suitable tool in the slots and lock the ignition switch.
4. Place a screwdriver between the cross-over blade and the 2nd-3rd lever at the base of the steering column so that both lever pins are engaged by the cross-over blade.
5. Set the 1st-reverse (rear) lever on the transmission to the Reverse (forward) position.
6. Adjust the 1st-reverse rod swivel so it will freely enter the lever on the transmission. Insert the swivel into the lever on the transmission and install the washer and clip and tighten the attaching nut to 100 in. lbs.
7. Remove the tool from the slots in the steering column, unlock the ignition switch and place the shift lever on the column in the Neutral position.
8. Adjust the 2nd-3rd shift rod swivel so it will freely enter the lever on the transmission. Insert the swivel into the lever and install the washer and clip and tighten the attaching nut to 100 in. lbs.
9. Remove the tool from the cross-over blades on the steering column and check linkage operation.

Floor Mounted Three and Four Speed—1967-74

NOTE: this procedure is for Chrysler Corporation linkage only. On models equipped with a Hurst shifter, see the Hurst Shifter section of this manual for adjustment procedure.

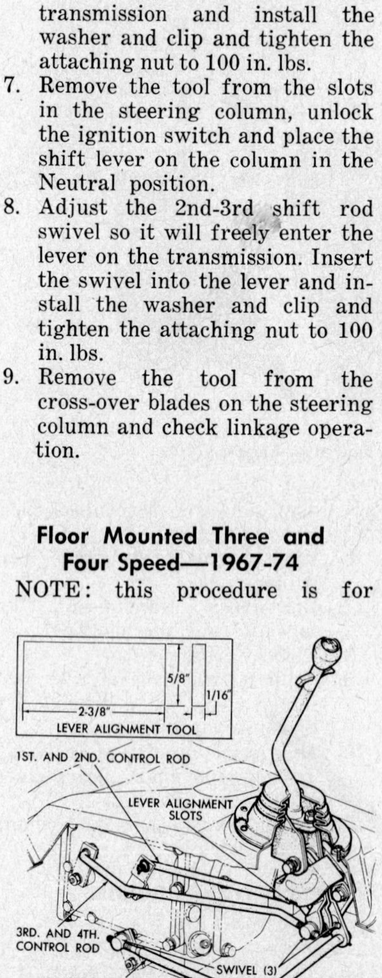
5/8"
1/16"
2-3/8"
LEVER ALIGNMENT TOOL
1ST. AND 2ND. CONTROL ROD
LEVER ALIGNMENT SLOTS
3RD. AND 4TH. CONTROL ROD
SWIVEL (3)
REVERSE CONTROL ROD

1968 4-speed shift linkage
(© Chrysler Corp)

1. Make up a lever aligning tool from 1/16 in. thick metal, as illustrated.
2. With transmission in neutral, disconnect all control rods from the transmission levers.
3. Insert lever aligning tool through the slots in the levers, making sure it is through all the levers and against the back plate.
4. Now that all levers are locked in neutral, adjust length of control rods so they enter the transmission levers freely, without any forward or reverse movement.
5. Install control rod flat washers and retaining clips. Then, remove the aligning tool.
6. Check linkage for ease of shifting into all gears and for cross-over smoothness.

AUTOMATIC TRANSMISSION

Model identification appears in large letters embossed on the lower side of the bell housing. While designs and servicing procedures are similar for all vehicles, internal parts are necessarily different. Therefore, when replacing parts, refer to the seven-digit part number stamped on the left side of the transmission oil flange.

The transmission combines a torque converter and a fully automatic three-speed gear system. The converter housing and transmission case are an integral aluminum casting. The transmission consists of two multiple disc clutches, an overrunning clutch, two servos and bands, and two planetary gear sets to provide three forward ratios and a reverse ratio. The common sun gear of the planetary gear sets is connected to the front clutch by a driving shell splined to the sun gear and to the front clutch retainer. The hydraulic system consists of the oil pump and a single valve body that contains all valves except the governor valve.

Cooling the converter is accomplished by circulating the transmission fluid through an oil-to-water type cooler located in the lower tank of the radiator. The torque converter assembly is a sealed unit that cannot be disassembled.

Draining, Refilling, Filter Service

For most models in normal service, the automatic transmission fluid need not be changed. However, for vehicles used in severe service, and for an extra measure of protection, fluid should be changed at 36,000 mile intervals. If the vehicle is used in competition, or for trailer towing, it is recommended that fluid be changed at 12,000 mile intervals.

To drain the transmission fluid, raise the car on a hoist or jack up the front of the car and support it with suitable stands. Place a container, which has a large opening, under the transmission oil pan. Loosen the pan bolts at one corner, tap the pan to break the seal, and allow the fluid to drain. Remove the oil pan and filter. Remove the access plate from in front of the torque converter, with a socket wrench on the vibration damper bolt, rotate the engine clockwise to bring the converter drain to bottom. Position the container under the converter, withdraw the drainplug, and allow the fluid to drain.

Refit the converter drainplug and torque it to 110 in. lbs. Install the access plate. Place a new filter on the bottom of the valve body and tighten the retaining screws to 35 in. lbs. Clean the oil pan, fit a new gasket, and install the assembly. Torque the pan bolts to 150 in. lbs. Remove the container and lower the car.

Fill the transmission with six qt of Dexron automatic transmission fluid. Start the engine and allow it to idle for at least two minutes. With the parking brake engaged, move the selector lever momentarily to each position, ending in the neutral position. Add enough fluid to bring the level to the mark on the dipstick. Road-test the vehicle to thoroughly warm up the transmission and recheck the fluid level, with the engine idling and the parking brake engaged, after the transmission is at its normal operating temperature. The fluid level should then be between the "full" and "add one pint" marks.

Neutral Start Switch

The neutral switch is mounted in the transmission case on all models.

When the transmission manual lever is placed in either the Park or Neutral position, a cam, which is attached to the transmission throttle lever inside the transmission, contacts the neutral start switch and provides a ground to complete the starter solenoid circuit. On late model compacts and intermediates, the back-up light switch has been incorporated into the neutral switch. The combination neutral and back-up light switch can be identified by the three electrical terminals on the rear of the switch. On this type of switch, the center terminal is for the neutral switch and the two outer terminals are for the back-up lights.

NOTE: in order for the neutral start switch to function properly, the transmission manual linkage must be properly adjusted and the actuator cam in the transmission must be centered in the neutral switch mounting hole in the transmission.

To remove switch, remove all wiring and, with the aid of a wrench, remove switch. Have a container of adequate size at hand to catch draining fluid. When replacing switch, be sure to use a new seal. Torque switch to 24 ft. lbs. Replace fluid.

Shift Linkage Adjustment

1967-69 Column Shift

1. Place the gear shift selector lever in the Park position.
2. Loosen the transmission linkage control rod swivel clamp screw a few turns.
3. Manually move the transmission lever to the Park (rear) position.
4. With the control lever on the transmission in the Park detent and the selector lever in Park, tighten the swivel clamp screw to 100 in. lbs.

1967-69 Console Shift

1. With gearshift selector lever in park position, loosen bolt in lower rod adjusting lever.
2. Move transmission control lever all the way to the rear (park detent.)
3. With control lever in transmission in park position detent, and selector lever in park position, tighten the bolt in the lower rod adjusting lever securely.
4. Reconnect the battery.

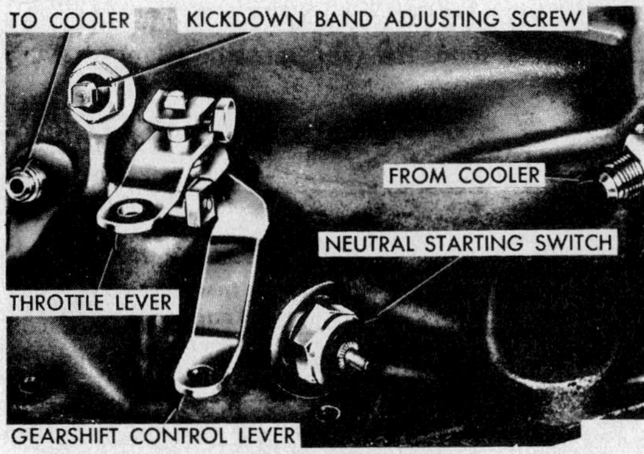
TO COOLER
KICKDOWN BAND ADJUSTING SCREW
FROM COOLER
NEUTRAL STARTING SWITCH
THROTTLE LEVER
GEARSHIFT CONTROL LEVER

Torqueflite external controls
(© Chrysler Corp)

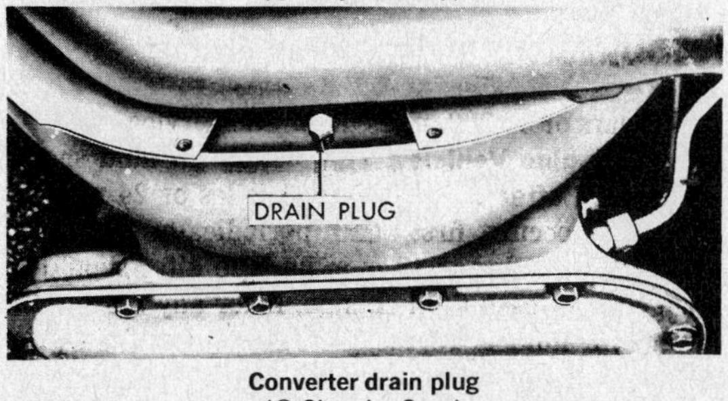
DRAIN PLUG

Converter drain plug
(© Chrysler Corp)

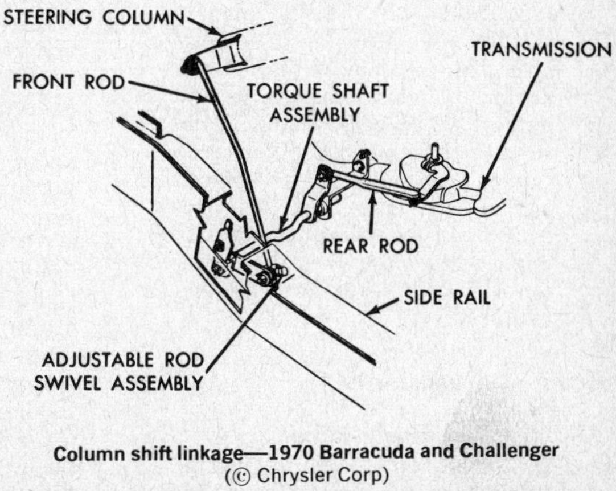
STEERING COLUMN
TRANSMISSION
FRONT ROD
TORQUE SHAFT ASSEMBLY
REAR ROD
SIDE RAIL
ADJUSTABLE ROD SWIVEL ASSEMBLY

Column shift linkage—1970 Barracuda and Challenger
(© Chrysler Corp)

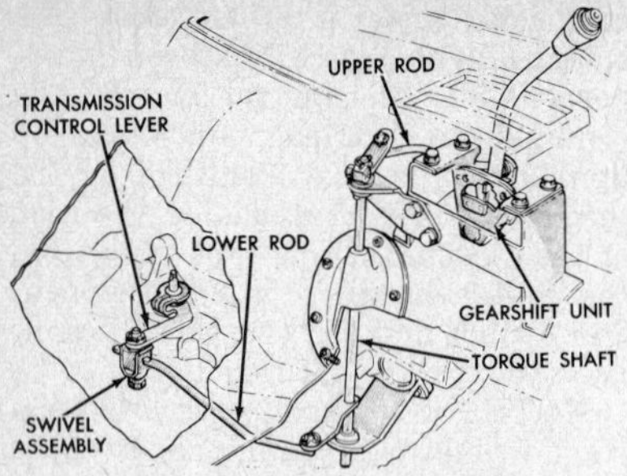
UPPER ROD
TRANSMISSION CONTROL LEVER
LOWER ROD
GEARSHIFT UNIT
TORQUE SHAFT
SWIVEL ASSEMBLY

Automatic console shift linkage
(© Chrysler Corp)

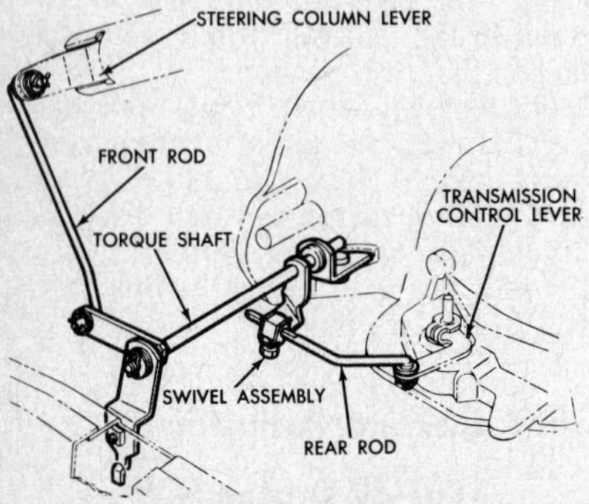
STEERING COLUMN LEVER
FRONT ROD
TRANSMISSION CONTROL LEVER
TORQUE SHAFT
SWIVEL ASSEMBLY
REAR ROD

Automatic column shift linkage—except 1970 Barracuda and Challenger
(© Chrysler Corp)

Gearshift Linkage Adjustment 1970-74

1. On models equipped with a steering column lever, place the gearshift control lever in Park. Lock the steering column. On models equipped with a console-mounted shift lever, at the upper end of the steering column align the locating slots in the bottom of the shift housing and the bearing housing. Install an appropriate tool to hold this alignment and lock the steering column with the ignition key.
2. Move the gearshift control lever (located on the transmission, see neutral start switch illustration) fully rearward (in Park).
3. Position the adjustable rod to the proper length and install it with no load in any direction on the linkage. Tighten the locknut.
4. Check the adjustment by determining that the shift effort is free and the detents engage crisply. Gate stops must be positive. The position of the detents should be close enough to the gate stops in neutral and Drive so that the hand lever will slide into position when placed against the gate and then released. In addition, key starts must occur only when the transmission shift lever is in neutral or Park.

Band Adjustments

Kickdown Band

The kickdown band adjusting screw is located on the left-hand side of the transmission case near the throttle lever shaft.

1. Loosen the locknut and back off about five turns. Be sure the adjusting screw is free in the case.
2. Using an in. lbs torque wrench, torque the adjusting screw to 47–50 in. lbs. If adapter is not used, tighten adjusting screw to 72 in. lbs which is the true torque.
3. Back off the adjusting screw exactly to specification. Keep the screw from turning, and torque the locknut to specification.

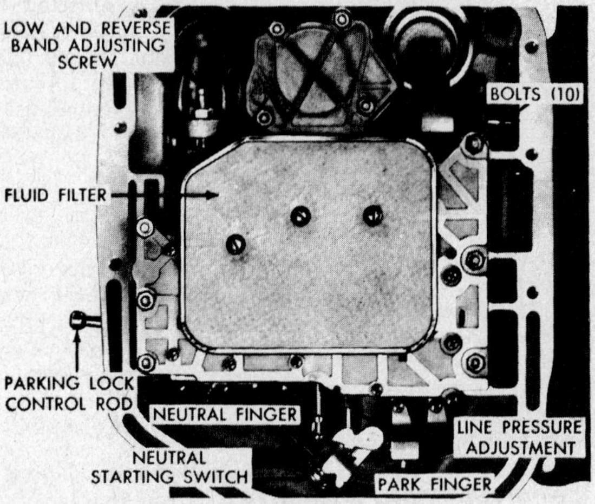
LOW AND REVERSE BAND ADJUSTING SCREW
BOLTS (10)
FLUID FILTER
PARKING LOCK CONTROL ROD
NEUTRAL FINGER
LINE PRESSURE ADJUSTMENT
NEUTRAL STARTING SWITCH
PARK FINGER

Low and reverse band adjusting screw location
(© Chrysler Corp)

Kickdown Band Adjustments

A-904	
1967-70 170 six	2⅝ turns
1967-70 198 and 225 six	2 turns
1967-69 273 V8	2 turns
1968-74 318 V8	2 turns
A-727	
1967-70 sixes and V8 except Hemi	2 turns
1970-71 Hemi V8 and 440-6	1½ turns
1971-74 225 six, 318, 340, 360, 383	2½ turns
1970-71 440 w/dual exhaust	2 turns
A-904 kickdown locknut torque	25 ft. lbs.
A-727 kickdown locknut torque	29 ft. lbs.
A-904 (1971-74) kickdown locknut torque	29 ft. lbs.

Low and Reverse Band

Access to the low and reverse band requires oil pan removal.

1. Raise the car, drain transmission and remove the transmission oil pan.
2. Loosen the band adjusting screw locknut and back off the nut about five turns. Be sure the adjusting screw turns freely in the lever.
3. With the same tools as used on the kickdown band adjustment, tighten the adjusting screw to 47–50 in. lbs. If adapter is not used, torque to 72 in. lbs., the true torque.
4. Back off the adjusting screw exactly to specification. Keep the screw from turning and torque the locknut to specification.
5. Reinstall oil pan, using new gasket, and torque the pan bolts to 150 in. lbs.
6. Refill transmission to prescribed level.

Low and Reverse Band Screw Adjustment

A-904	
1967-74 except 318 V8	3¼ turns
1968-74 318 V8	4 turns
Locknut torque	20 ft. lbs.
Locknut torque (1971-74)	35 ft. lbs.
A-727	
1967-74	2 turns
Locknut torque	35 ft. lbs.

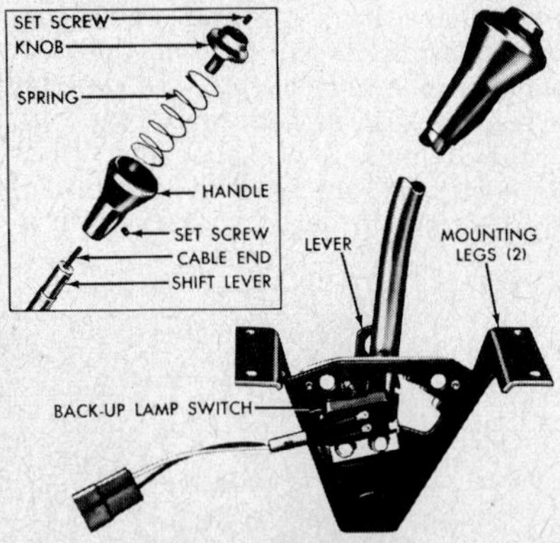
SET SCREW
KNOB
SPRING
HANDLE
SET SCREW
CABLE END
SHIFT LEVER
LEVER
MOUNTING LEGS (2)
BACK-UP LAMP SWITCH

Automatic console shift linkage
(© Chrysler Corp)

U-JOINTS

All Dodge and Plymouth vehicles use a cross and roller universal joint at both the front and rear. Two basic types of driveshafts are used: a solid tube type and a type that incorporates an internal vibration damper inside the tube itself. On certain applications, the driveshaft may be found to incorporate an inertia-type ring at the front universal joint. Servicing of all driveshafts is identical.

U-Joint Replacement

1. Raise the vehicle.
2. Mark the position of the rear driveshaft yoke in relation to the

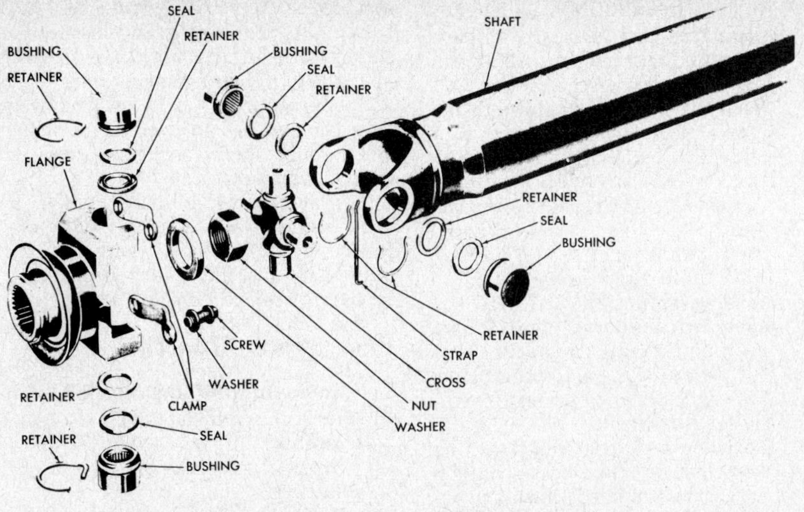
SEAL
RETAINER
BUSHING
RETAINER
BUSHING
SEAL
RETAINER
SHAFT
FLANGE
RETAINER
SEAL
BUSHING
RETAINER
SCREW
STRAP
WASHER
CROSS
RETAINER
CLAMP
NUT
WASHER
RETAINER
SEAL
BUSHING

Rear cross and roller universal joint (© Chrysler Corp)

pinion flange so the driveshaft can be returned to its original location.

3. Disconnect the rear U-Joint from the pinion flange and remove the loose bearing caps. Pull the driveshaft rearward until it clears the transmission extension housing. Remove the driveshaft from the car.
4. Place the driveshaft in a vise and remove the snap-rings from the U-Joint to be removed.
5. Using a suitable tool, drive one of the bearing caps on the U-Joint to be removed toward the center of the driveshaft.
6. Remove the opposite bearing cap from the one being driven as it emerges from the driveshaft.
7. Repeat Step 6 until all bearing caps have been removed.
8. Remove the U-Joint spider from the driveshaft.
9. To install, position the spider in the driveshaft and drive the bearing caps onto the spider.
10. Install the snap-rings in the driveshaft.
11. Reinstall the driveshaft in its original location in the car.

JACKING, HOISTING

Jack car at front control arms and at rear under axle housing.

To lift at frame use adapters, so that contact will be made at points shown. Lifting pads must extend beyond sides of supporting structure.

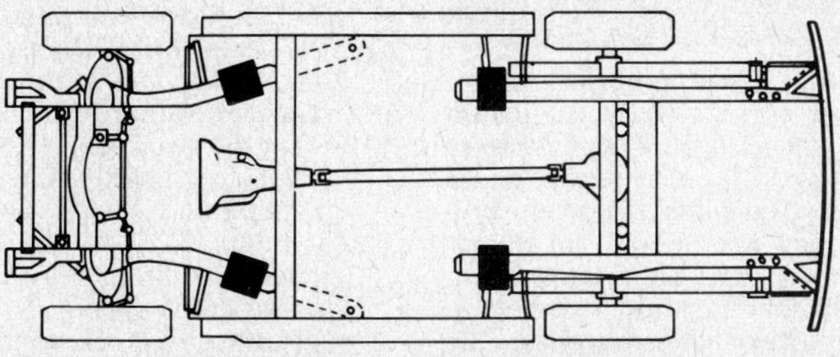

Positioning lift adapter (© Chrysler Corp)

FRONT SUSPENSION

All Chrysler vehicles utilize a torsion bar type front suspension. The front torsion bar attachments are part of the lower control arms; the rear fastenings are incorporated into the engine rear support crossmember. Compression type lower ball joints are located in the steering arms. When servicing the front suspension, it should be kept in mind that rubber bushings must not be lubricated at any time. In addition, any front suspension adjustments or servicing that is required on any part that contains rubber should be tightened with the suspension at the proper height and with full vehicle weight on the point in question.

Lubrication

Balloon-type and semi-permanently lubricated steering linkage and front suspension ball joints are used. Relubrication at these points is required at about 36,000 miles, or three year periods (whichever comes first.) However, the balloon seals should be inspected for leaks, or other damage, two or three times a year.

When lubricating these points, use only multi-mileage long-life chassis grease. Remove the threaded plug from each joint to be lubricated, and temporarily install lube fittings. Inject lubricant, while feeling the seal with the fingers. Stop just before the seal starts to balloon. Remove lube fittings and reinstall plugs.

Front Shock Absorber Removal and Replacement

1. Remove the washer and nut from shock absorber upper end. Be sure to note the positions of all small parts.
2. Jack the vehicle until the wheels clear the floor. Remove the shock absorber lower attaching bolt. Allow the control arm mounting bracket to lower itself.
3. Fully compress the shock absorber by pushing upward. Pull the shock firmly and remove it from the vehicle.
4. Fully compress the new shock absorber. Insert the mount through the upper bushing and install the retainer and nut. Torque to specifications. Be sure that all the retainers are installed with the concave side in contact with rubber.
5. Position and align the lower mount of shock absorber. Install the bolt (on some models it must be installed from the rear) with nut and finger-tighten it. Lower the vehicle and torque to specifications with the full weight of the vehicle on the wheels.

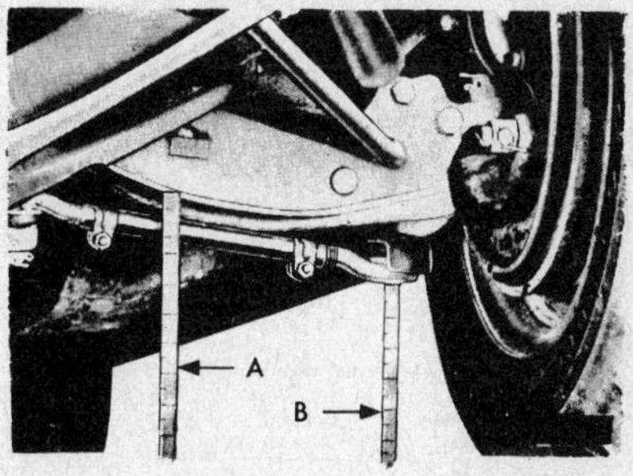
A
B

Front suspension height
(© Chrysler Corp)

Front Height Adjustment

1. Jounce the car and measure from the lower ball joint to the floor (measurement B).
2. Measure from the control arm torsion bar spring anchor housing to the floor (measurement A).
3. Subtract A from B. This is the front end height.
4. Measure the other side in the same way. Compare figures obtained with figure given in the wheel alignment specifications table in the front of this section.
5. Adjust, if necessary, by turning the torsion bar adjusting bolt, in to raise; out to lower.

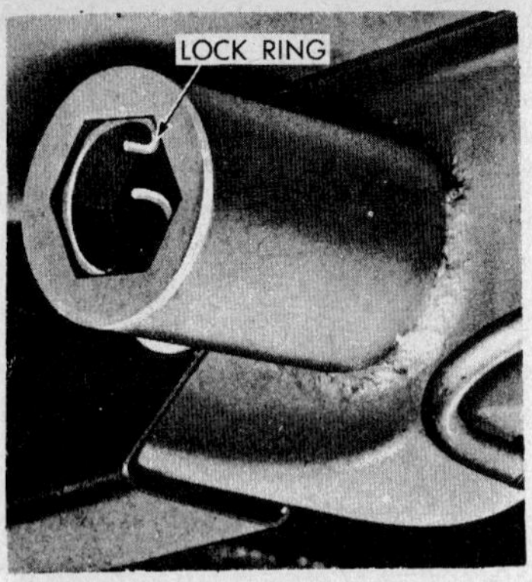
LOCK RING

Torsion bar rear anchor lock ring
(© Chrysler Corp)

Torsion Bars

Contrary to appearance, the torsion bars are not interchangeable from right to left. They are marked with an R or an L, according to their location.

Removal

1. Lift the car, by the body, high enough to free the front suspension of all load. If the car is to be raised with jacks, place jack under center of K-member and raise until suspension is free of all load.
2. Release load from torsion bar by backing off anchor adjusting nuts. Remove the adjusting nut and swivel bolt.
3. Remove the lower control arm strut, if necessary.
4. Remove the lock spring from the rear of torsion bar rear anchor.
5. Install tool or clamp, and remove torsion bar rearward by striking the clamping tool with a hammer.

NOTE: do not apply heat to the front or rear anchors. Do not scratch or otherwise mar the skin of the torsion bar during removal or installation.

6. Remove the clamping tool and slide the rear anchor balloon seal off the front end of the bar.
7. Remove torsion bar by sliding the bar rearward and out through the rear anchor.

Installation

1. Clean the hex openings of both front and rear anchors, also clean the male ends of the torsion bar.
2. Feed the torsion bar through the rear anchor.
3. Slide the balloon-type seal over the torsion bar, with the large cupped side of the seal facing the rear.
4. Coat both ends of the torsion bar with multi-purpose grease.
5. When starting the bar into the anchor in the lower control arm, position the adjusting arm about 60° below the horizontal plane. This will permit windup for future adjustment.
6. Position the lock-ring into the rear anchor, then move torsion bar rearward until the bar contacts the lock-ring.
7. Position swivel bolt on the control arm and hold in place while installing the adjusting nut and seat. Tighten the adjustment about ten turns before lowering car to the floor.
8. Pack the annular opening in the rear anchor with multi-purpose grease. Slide the rear anchor balloon type seal into position over the rear anchor until the lip of the seal fits in the groove.
9. Install lower control arm strut.
10. Lower car to the floor and adjust front suspension height.

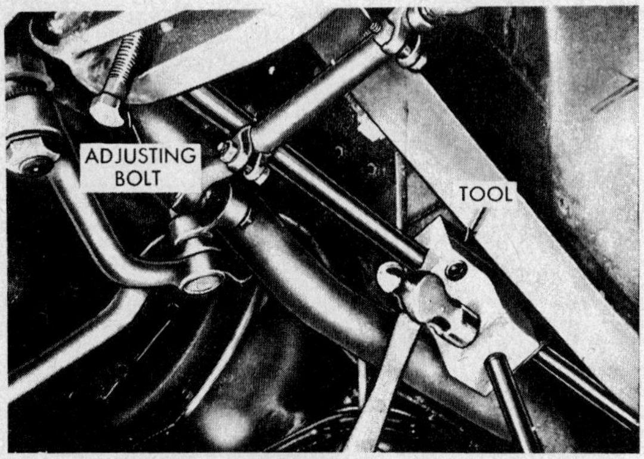
ADJUSTING BOLT
TOOL

Removing torsion bar
(© Chrysler Corp)

Upper and Lower Ball Joints

See Dodge-Plymouth section.

REAR SUSPENSION

All Dodge and Plymouth models utilize rear springs of the semi-elliptical leaf type. They are engineered to operate with little or no camber under conditions of small or no load. Heavy-duty springs are offered as an option on all models. They serve to increase the stability of the vehicle under conditions of heavy load. All vehicles with leaf springs are constructed with zinc interleaves between the normal leaves. They have the purpose of reducing spring corrosion and lengthening spring life.

Shock absorbers used on Chrysler vehicles are not utilized to support vehicle load. Their sole purpose is to control ride motion.

Chrysler shock absorbers have a built-in fluid weep. This is usually evident only during cold weather. Consequently, a slight fluid weep is not reason to replace a shock absorber.

Rear Shock Absorbers

Removal and Installation

1. Jack the vehicle under the axle assembly in such a manner as to relieve load from the shock absorbers.
2. Remove the nut attaching the shock to the spring mounting plate stud and withdraw the bolt.
3. At the upper mount, remove the shock attaching bolt and the shock.
4. To install the shock, position it so the upper bolt may be inserted. Hand-tighten only.
5. Align the shock with the spring mounting plate stud and install the bolt and nut. Hand-tighten only.
6. Lower the vehicle and tighten the shock absorber mounting bolts.

Rear Springs

Removal and Installation

1. Jack the vehicle and remove the wheels. Position jack stands under the axle in such a manner so as to relieve weight from the rear springs.
2. Disconnect the rear shock absorbers at the bottom attaching bolts. Lower the axle assembly to allow the rear springs to hang free.
3. Remove U-bolt nuts and withdraw bolts and spring plates. Remove the nuts securing the front spring hanger to the body mounting bracket.
4. Remove the rear spring hanger bolts and allow the spring to drop enough to allow the front spring hanger bolts to be removed.
5. Remove the front pivot bolt from the front spring hanger.
6. Remove the shackle nuts and shackle from the rear spring.
7. To begin installation, assemble the shackle and bushings in the rear of the spring and hanger. Start the shackle bolt nut. Do not lubricate rubber bushings to ease installation. Do not tighten the bolt nut.
8. Install the front spring hanger to the front spring eye and insert the pivot bolt and nut. Do not tighten them.

9. Install the rear spring hanger-to-body bracket and torque the bolts to 35–40 ft lbs.
10. With the aid of a helper, raise the spring and insert the bolts in the spring hanger mounting bracket holes. Install the nuts and torque them to 30 ft lbs.
11. Position the axle assembly so it is correctly aligned with the spring center bolt.
12. Position the center bolt over the lower spring plate. Insert the U-bolt and nut. Connect the rear shock absorbers.
13. Lower the vehicle. Torque the pivot bolts to 85 ft lbs and tighten the shackle nuts.

BRAKES

Beginning in 1967, disc brakes were offered as an option on the front wheels. In addition, 1967 marked the initial use of dual (tandem) master cylinders. In operation, this type master cylinder provides braking even if one section of the system should develop a leak.

Both drum and disc type brake systems are hydraulically operated. Power assist is offered as an option.

With the exception of heavy-duty units, brakes are self-adjusting.

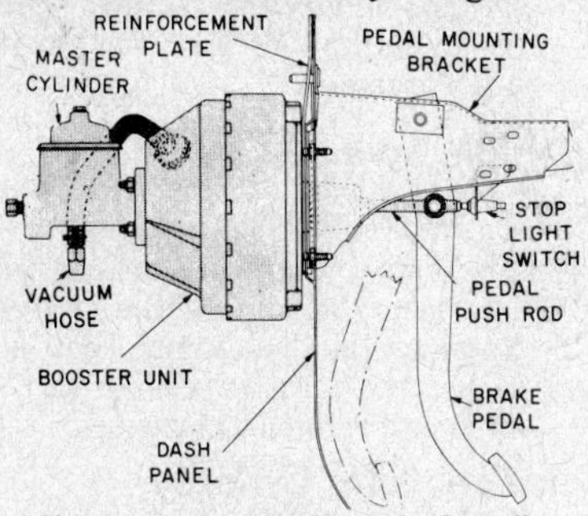
REINFORCEMENT PLATE
MASTER CYLINDER
PEDAL MOUNTING BRACKET
STOP LIGHT SWITCH
VACUUM HOSE
PEDAL PUSH ROD
BOOSTER UNIT
BRAKE PEDAL
DASH PANEL

Vacuum-suspended power brake unit (© Chrysler Corp)

In 1973, disc brakes are standard on all models with the exception of six-cylinder Valiants and Darts.

Master Cylinder R&R

1. Disconnect the brake line/s from the master clyinder. If equipped with disc brakes, plug the rear brake line outlet to prevent fluid loss.
2. Remove the nuts that attach the master clyinder to the cowl panel or brake booster.
3. On models with standard brakes, it is not necessary to disconnect the master cylinder pushrod from the brake pedal.
4. Slide the master cylinder straight out and off the cowl panel or brake booster.
5. Reverse above procedure to install and bleed brake system.

Power Brake Booster R&R

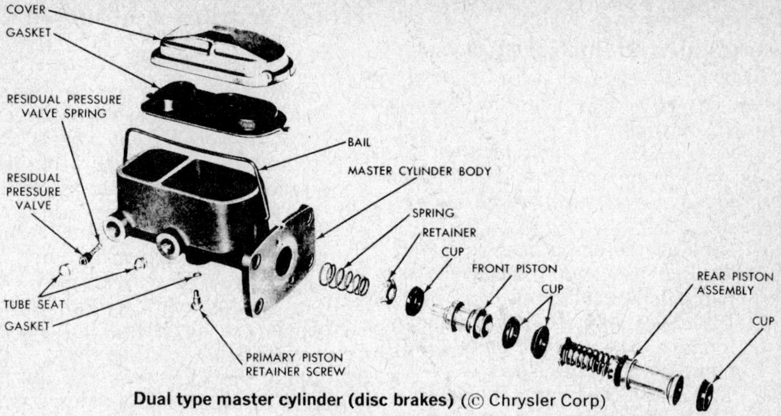
COVER
GASKET
RESIDUAL PRESSURE VALVE SPRING
BAIL
MASTER CYLINDER BODY
RESIDUAL PRESSURE VALVE
SPRING
RETAINER
CUP
FRONT PISTON
CUP
REAR PISTON ASSEMBLY
CUP
TUBE SEAT
GASKET
PRIMARY PISTON RETAINER SCREW

Dual type master cylinder (disc brakes) (© Chrysler Corp)

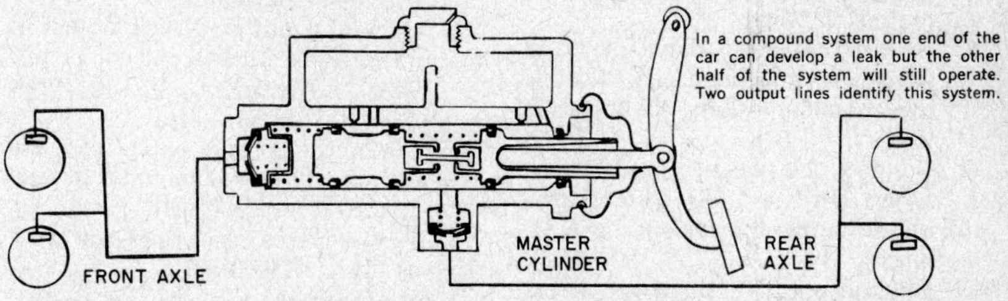
In a compound system one end of the car can develop a leak but the other half of the system will still operate. Two output lines identify this system.
FRONT AXLE
MASTER CYLINDER
REAR AXLE

Dual type master cylinder (© Chrysler Corp)

1. Remove the nuts that attach the master cylinder to the brake booster and position the master cylinder out of the way without disconnecting the lines. Use care not to kink the brake lines.
2. Disconnect the vacuum hose from the brake booster.
3. Working under the dash, remove the nut and bolt that attaches the brake booster pushrod to the brake pedal. On linkage type brake boosters, remove the lower pivot retaining bolt.
4. Remove the four brake booster attaching nuts and washers.
5. Remove booster assembly from the vehicle.
6. Reverse above procedure to install.

Parking Brake Adjustment

1. Release the parking brake lever and clean and lubricate the parking brake cable adjusting nut and threads. Loosen the cable adjusting nut.
2. Tighten the cable adjusting nut until a slight drag is felt in the rear wheels when the rear wheels are rotated. Loosen the cable adjusting nut until the rear wheels can be rotated freely. Back off the cable adjusting nut two additional turns.
3. Apply and release the parking brake several times and check to verify that the rear wheels rotate freely, without any brake drag.

STEERING

A worm and recirculating ball type steering gear is used with the manual steering system.

The worm shaft is supported at each end by ball-type thrust bearings.

The sector shaft includes an integral sector gear which meshes with helical grooves on the worm shaft ball nut.

The sector shaft is supported, and rotates, in two needle bearings in the housing and one in the housing cover.

Constant-Control power steering is an option on all models. Hydraulic power is provided by a vane type, belt-driven pump. A double-groove pump pulley is used.

Over the years, Chrysler Corporation has utilized four different power steering pumps in 0.94, 0.96, 1.02, and 1.06 cu in. displacement models. Usage varies with vehicle, engine, and rear axle combination. The 0.96 cu in. pump may be identified by the plain end of the pump driveshaft while the 1.02 cu in. pump may be identified by the hexagonal hole in the driveshaft pulley end. The 0.94 and 1.06 cu in. pumps may be identified by the differences in the filler tube shape (the 0.94 pump has an oval-shaped filler tube and the 1.06 pump has a round filler tube). The 0.96 and 1.02 cu in. pumps were last installed on production vehicles in 1968. After that date, only the 0.94 and 1.06 cu in. pumps were used.

Some power steering pumps were equipped from the factory with oil coolers. These were used on vehicles with high-performance engines and/or special axle ratios.

Up to and including 1968, most power steering pumps used an oil filter screen located in the oil return tube inside the reservoir. These only require service when completely clogged or when the pump is disassembled. Servicing is by replacement only.

Power Steering Pump Removal and Installation

NOTE: Before beginning removal, take careful note of exact hose routine. Hoses must be routed and installed in the exact same manner as they were removed. Read the entire procedure before beginning pump service.

1. Back off the pump mounting and locking bolts, and remove the pump drive belt.
2. Disconnect all hoses at the pump.
3. Remove the pump bolts and pump with the bracket.
4. To install the pump, place the pump in position and install the mounting bolts.
5. Install the pump drive belt and adjust to specifications. Torque the mounting bolts to 25–30 ft lbs.
6. Connect the pressure and return hoses. On the 1.06 cu in. pump, install a new pressure hose O-ring.
7. Fill the pump with power steering fluid.
8. Turn the vehicle on and rotate the steering wheel from stop to stop at least 10 times. This will tend to bleed the system. Check the pump oil level and fill as required.
9. The pump end hose fitting torque is 24 ft lbs. The gear end fitting torque is 160 in. lbs. Be certain the hoses are at least 2 in. from the exhaust manifolds and are not kinked or twisted.

Steering Wheel Removal

1. Disconnect the negative battery cable.
2. Remove the horn ring ornament assembly.
3. Disconnect the wire from the horn switch. Remove the screws that attach the horn ring and switch to the steering wheel and remove the ring and switch.
4. Remove the steering wheel attaching nut and washer and, using a puller, remove the steering wheel from the steering shaft. On models equipped with a collapsible steering column cylinder, remove the cylinder attaching nut and remove the cylinder from the column.

Turn Signal Switch

1. Disconnect the battery and remove the steering wheel.
2. Disconnect the horn and turn signal wires.
3. Tie a piece of string to the turn signal wires. Remove the turn signal switch screws while holding the other end of the string to prevent the wires from falling inside the steering column.
4. Remove the turn signal switch retainer ring and extract the switch.
5. To install the turn signal switch, reverse the removal procedure.

Wheel Bearing Adjustment

1967-69

1. Raise the front of the car and remove the hub caps and grease caps from the front wheels. Remove the cotter pin from the spindle and remove the adjusting nut lock.
2. The wheel must be rotated while the bearing adjusting nut is tightened. For all Dart and Valiant models and 1967-69 Barracudas the adjusting nut should be tightened to 70 in. lbs.
3. Place the lock over the nut so that one pair of slots aligns with the cotter pin hole.
4. Back the nut and lock assembly off one slot. Install the cotter pin. This adjustment should yield 0.0–0.003 in. end-play.
5. Clean the grease cap. Coat, but do not fill, the cap with grease. Install it on the hub.
6. Lower the car and road-test it.

1970-74

1. Jack up or hoist the car, so that the front wheels are off the floor.
2. Remove the hub caps, grease cup, cotter pin and nut lock.
3. Back off on the adjusting nut.
4. Check for free wheel rotation. If binding is present, repair the threads as required.
5. While rotating the wheel, tighten the wheel bearing adjustment nut to 240–300 in. lbs.
6. Release the torque. Retighten the nut so that it is finger tight.
7. Position the nut lock so that one pair of slots is in line with the cotter pin hole and install the cotter pin.
8. Install the rest of the items removed. Repeat the procedure for the other wheel and lower the car.

INSTRUMENT PANEL

Headlight Switch R&R

1967-69 All Models and 1970-74 Valiant and Dart

1. Remove the fuse box attaching screw and position the fuse box out of the way.
2. Press the release button on the body of the headlight switch and pull the control knob and shaft from the switch.
3. Disconnect the multiple connector from the rear of the headlight switch.
4. Remove the bezel nut that attaches the headlight switch to the dash and remove the switch.
5. Reverse above procedure to install.

1970-74 Barracuda and Challenger

1. Disconnect the negative battery cable.
2. Remove the six lamp panel mounting screws and carefully slide the lamp panel out of the dash and lay it on top of the instrument panel. It is not necessary to disconnect the wiring harness.
3. Remove the four switch bezel mounting screws. Carefully slide the switch bezel out and to the right, overlapping the center instrument cluster, then lower it until it is free of the instrument panel and disconnect the wiring harness.
4. Remove the two headlight switch mounting screws and remove the switch from the bezel assembly.

Ignition Switch R&R

1967-69 All Models

1. Disconnect the multiple connector from the rear of the switch.
2. Remove the bezel nut that attaches the ignition switch to the dash and remove the switch.

Ignition Lock Cylinder Replacement

1967-69

1. Insert the ignition key into the lock cylinder.
2. Insert a piece of stiff wire into the small hole in the front face of the cylinder and apply pressure to the wire.
3. Turn the ignition key counterclockwise toward the "acc" position.

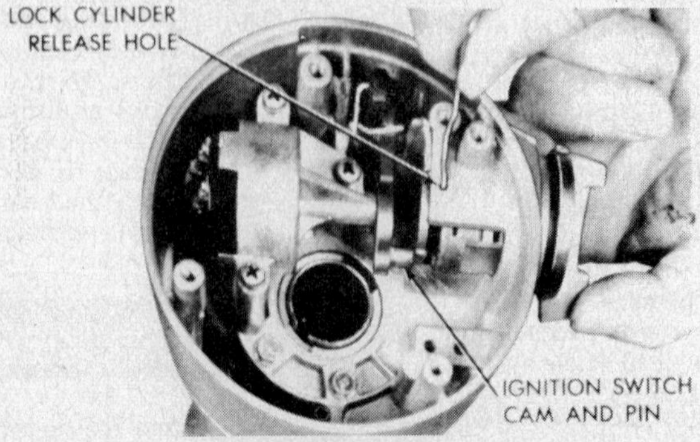
LOCK CYLINDER
RELEASE HOLE
IGNITION SWITCH
CAM AND PIN

Lock cylinder removal
(© Chrysler Corp)

4. Pull the lock cylinder and key from the instrument panel.
5. Insert a new lock cylinder into the instrument panel and it will lock itself in place.

Ignition Switch and/or Ignition Lock Cylinder Replacement

1970-74 Standard Steering Column

1. Disconnect the negative battery cable. Remove the steering wheel.
2. Remove the screw that attaches the turn signal lever to the steering column.
3. Remove the three screws that attach the upper bearing retainer to the turn signal switch.
4. Pull the turn signal switch as far upward as possible.
5. Using snap-ring pliers, remove the upper bearing housing snap-ring from the steering shaft.
6. Remove the screw that attaches the ignition key light assembly to the upper bearing housing.
7. Using care not to damage any components, pry the upper bearing housing off the steering shaft by lifting upward on alternate sides of the bearing housing with screwdrivers.
8. Lift upward as far as possible on the steering shaft lockplate and place a screwdriver or other object under it to hold it in the raised position. If this operation does not provide adequate working room under the lockplate, it will be necessary to press out the pin that attaches the lockplate to the steering shaft and remove the lockplate from the steering shaft. If the ignition switch is being replaced, the lockplate must be removed.
9. Using an offset screwdriver, remove the two screws that attach the lock lever guide plate to the steering column.
10. With the ignition lock cylinder in the "lock" position and the ignition key removed, insert a stiff wire into the lock cylinder release hole in the steering column. Push in on the wire to release the spring-loaded lock retainer and pull the lock cylinder out of the steering column.
11. If the ignition switch is being replaced, remove the two screws that attach the ignition key buzzer switch to the steering column and the three screws that attach the ignition switch to the steering column. Lift the ignition switch out of the housing.
12. Reverse the above procedure for installation.

1970-74 Tilt Steering Column

1. Disconnect the negative battery cable.
2. Remove the steering wheel.
3. Remove the three attaching screws and the shaft lock cover.
4. Remove the screws that attach the tilt control lever and the turn signal lever to the steering column and remove the levers.
5. Push the hazard warning knob in and unscrew the knob from the turn signal switch. Remove the ignition key lamp assembly.
6. Using a suitable tool, depress the lockplate to gain access to the lockplate retaining snap-ring. Remove the snap-ring from the steering shaft.
7. Remove the lockplate, cancelling cam, and spring.
8. Remove the three turn signal switch attaching screws, place the shift lever in the low (1) position, and pull the switch and wires as far upward as possible.
9. With the ignition lock cylinder in the "lock" position, insert a small screwdriver into the lock release slot in the housing cover.
10. Press down with the screwdriver to release the spring latch at bottom of the slot and pull the lock cylinder from the housing. The following steps are for ignition switch replacement only.
11. Remove the three screws that attach the upper steering column housing to the steering column and remove the housing.
12. Install the column tilt control lever and move the column to the full "up" position.
13. Insert a screwdriver into the slot in the spring retainer and press the retainer in approximately 3/16 in. Turn the retainer approximately 1/8 turn to the left until the ears align with the grooves in the housing. Remove the spring retainer, spring, and guide.
14. Push the steering shaft inward to enable removal of the inner race and seat. Remove the race and seat.
15. Make sure the ignition switch is in the "lock" position, then remove the wire connector from the ignition switch and remove the screws that attach the ignition switch to the outside of the steering column.
16. Lift the ignition switch from the column and twist it to disengage the switch actuating rod from the rack. Remove the switch.
17. To install the ignition lock cylinder, insert the cylinder into the housing with the cylinder in the lock position and the key removed.
18. Move the cylinder into the housing until it contacts the switch actuator. Move the switch actuator rod up and down to align the parts. When the parts are aligned the cylinder will move inward and lock into place. The following steps are for ignition switch installation only.
19. With the ignition switch in the "lock" position, insert the actuating rod into the steering column.
20. Twist the switch and rod assembly as required to engage the actuating rod with the rack. Make sure the ignition lock cylinder is in the "lock" position.
21. Install the ignition switch mounting screws but do not tighten them.
22. Move the ignition switch downward away from the steering wheel and tighten the switch mounting screws. Make sure the ignition switch has not moved out of the lock detent.
23. Attach the switch wiring connector.

WINDSHIELD WIPERS

Motor Removal

1967-74 Valiant and Dart and 1967-69 Barracuda

1. Disconnect battery.
2. Disconnect wiper motor wiring harness.
3. Remove three wiper motor mounting nuts. On vehicles without air conditioning it is easier to remove crank arm nut and crank arm from under instrument panel first and omit steps 4 and 5. On 1967–68 models, disconnect the drive link from the left wiper pivot.
4. Work motor off mounting studs far enough to gain access to crank arm mounting nuts.

CAUTION: do not force or pry motor from mounting studs as drive link can be easily distorted.

5. Using 1/2 in. open end wrench, remove motor crank arm nut. Carefully pry arm off shaft.
6. Remove wiper motor.

1970-74 Barracuda and Challenger

1. Disconnect battery.
2. Carefully remove wiper arm and blade assemblies.
3. Remove left cowl screen.
4. Remove drive crank arm retaining nut and drive crank. Disconnect wiring to motor.
5. Remove three wiper motor mounting nuts and remove motor.

Linkage Removal

1967-74 Valiant, Dart, and 1967-69 Barracuda

1. Disconnect battery.
2. If air conditioning equipped, remove duct supplying left spot cooler to provide easier access to left wiper pivot. Insert wide

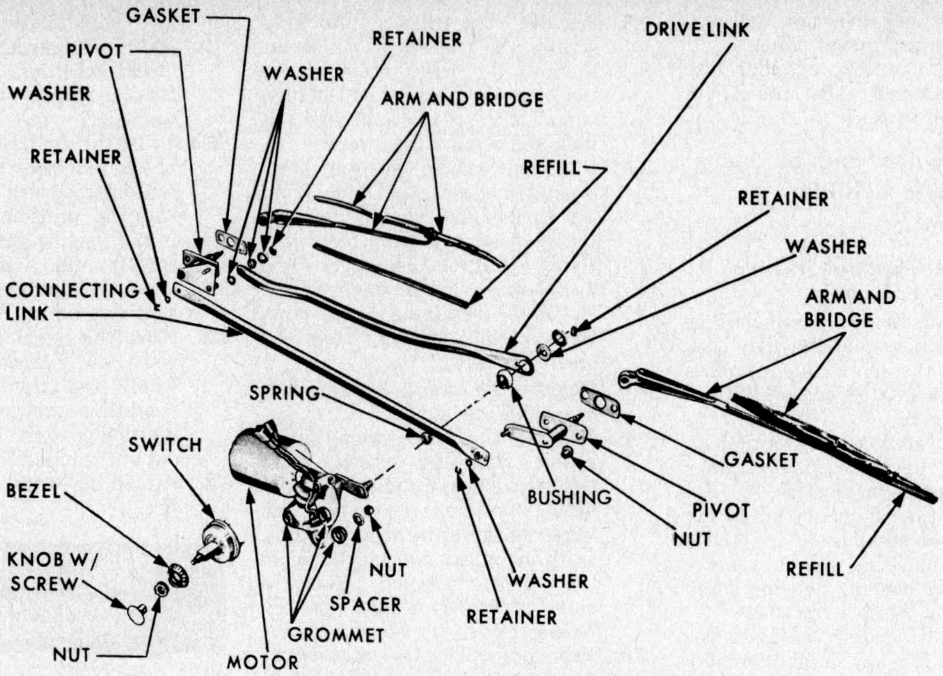
GASKET
PIVOT
WASHER
RETAINER
WASHER
ARM AND BRIDGE
RETAINER
DRIVE LINK
REFILL
RETAINER
WASHER
CONNECTING
LINK
ARM AND
BRIDGE
SPRING
SWITCH
BEZEL
KNOB W/
SCREW
NUT
MOTOR
GROMMET
SPACER
NUT
RETAINER
WASHER
BUSHING
NUT
PIVOT
GASKET
REFILL

Single speed windshield wiper (© Chrysler Corp)

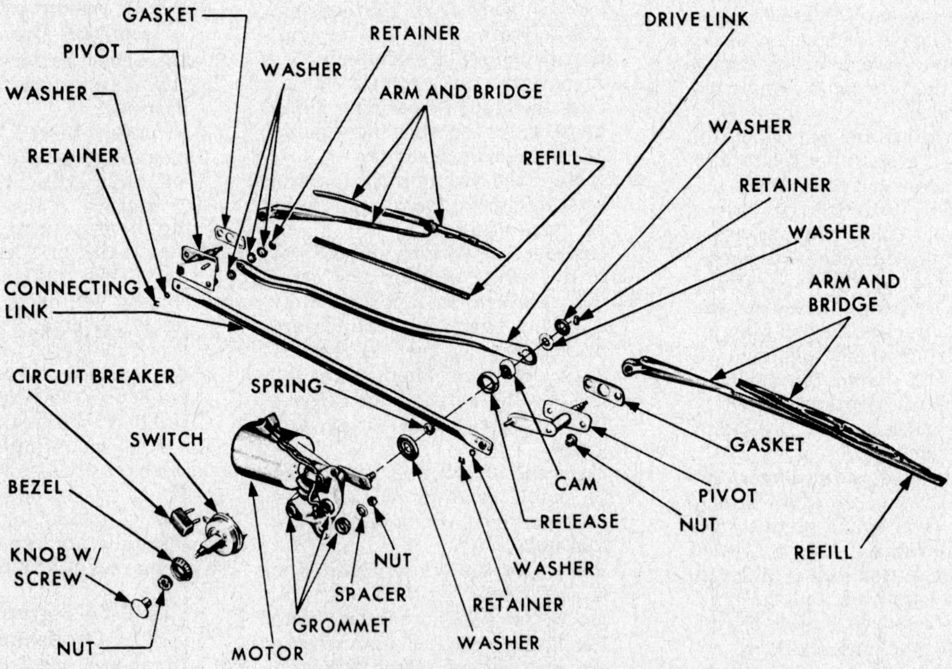
GASKET
PIVOT
WASHER
RETAINER
WASHER
RETAINER
ARM AND BRIDGE
REFILL
DRIVE LINK
WASHER
RETAINER
WASHER
CONNECTING
LINK
ARM AND
BRIDGE
CIRCUIT BREAKER
SPRING
SWITCH
BEZEL
KNOB W/
SCREW
NUT
MOTOR
GROMMET
SPACER
NUT
WASHER
RETAINER
WASHER
RELEASE
CAM
NUT
PIVOT
GASKET
REFILL

Variable speed windshield wiper (© Chrysler Corp)

blade screwdriver between plastic link bushing and pivot crank arm. Gently twist screwdriver to force bushing and link from pivot pin. Remove three motor mounting nuts, pull motor away from bulkhead and remove motor crank arm retaining nut. Hold the motor crank when removing the nut to prevent stressing the gears. After crank arm is removed from motor shaft, remove drive link assembly from under left side of panel. Remove motor drive crank arm retaining nut and pry crank arm off motor shaft. Gently pry drive link and bushing from left pivot crank arm pin and withdraw assembly from under panel. Remove motor drive crank arm from drive link after removal of assembly from vehicle.

3. To remove connecting link from pivots, remove glove box. Reaching through glove box opening, gently pry bushing and link from right pivot pin. Lift link from pivot crank arm pin and repeat operation at left pivot. Withdraw from under left side of panel.

1970-74 Barracuda and Challenger

1. Remove wiper arm and blade assemblies.
2. Remove left cowl screen for access to linkage.
3. Disconnect battery.
4. Remove crank arm nut and crank from motor shaft.
5. Remove bolts mounting left and right pivots to body.
6. Remove links and pivots through cowl top opening.

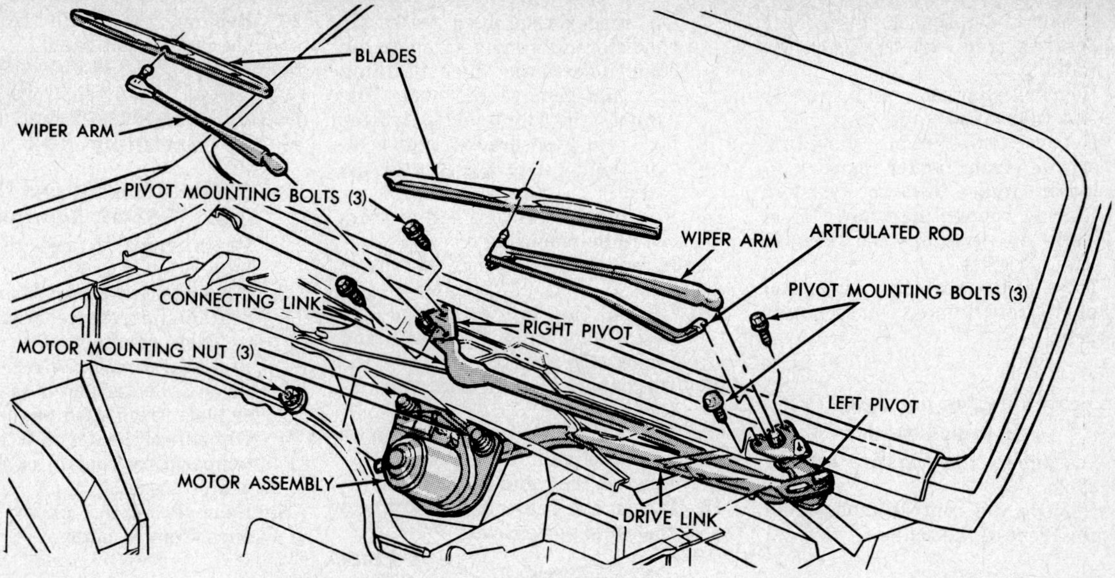
BLADES
WIPER ARM
PIVOT MOUNTING BOLTS (3)
CONNECTING LINK
MOTOR MOUNTING NUT (3)
MOTOR ASSEMBLY
WIPER ARM
ARTICULATED ROD
PIVOT MOUNTING BOLTS (3)
RIGHT PIVOT
LEFT PIVOT
DRIVE LINK

Barracuda and Challenger windshield wiper linkage (© Chrysler Corp)

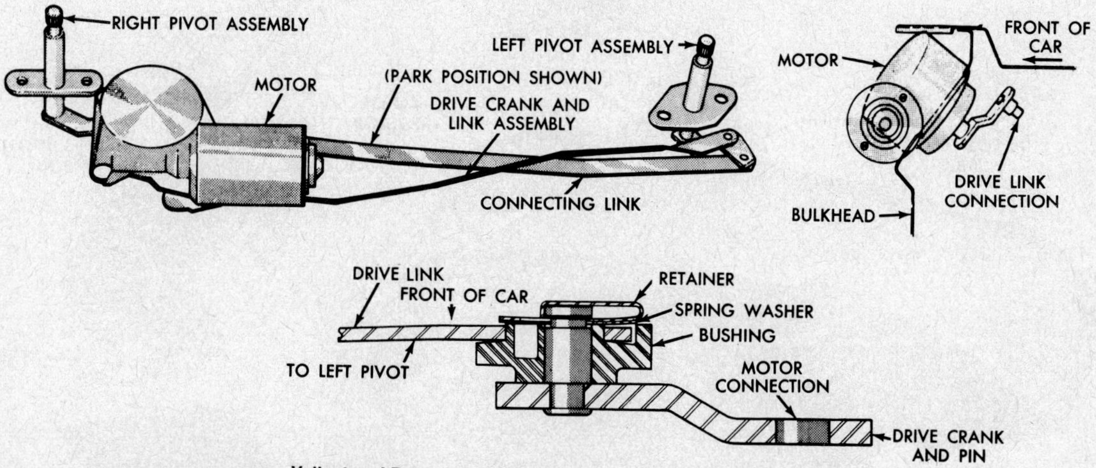
RIGHT PIVOT ASSEMBLY
MOTOR
LEFT PIVOT ASSEMBLY
(PARK POSITION SHOWN)
DRIVE CRANK AND
LINK ASSEMBLY
CONNECTING LINK
MOTOR
FRONT OF
CAR
DRIVE LINK
CONNECTION
BULKHEAD
DRIVE LINK
FRONT OF CAR
TO LEFT PIVOT
RETAINER
SPRING WASHER
BUSHING
MOTOR
CONNECTION
DRIVE CRANK
AND PIN

Valiant and Dart windshield wiper linkage (© Chrysler Corp)

RADIO

Removal

1967-68 Valiant and Barracuda

1. Disconnect battery.
2. Remove control knobs from front of radio.
3. From under instrument panel disconnect radio feed wire at connector. On air-conditioned models, remove the outlet duct, the right defroster hose, and the hose bracket from the radio back.
4. Remove bottom screw from radio mounting bracket.
5. Remove left defroster tube.
6. Loosen top screw on radio mounting bracket and remove bracket.
7. Disconnect antenna and speaker leads.
8. Remove mounting nuts from front of radio and remove radio bezel.
9. Remove radio from below instrument panel.

1967 Dart

1. Disconnect battery.
2. Remove radio control knobs and mounting nuts.
3. On air conditioned vehicles remove two outlet duct retaining bolts and remove duct. Remove right defroster hose and hose bracket.
4. From under instrument panel, remove radio support bracket lower screw and upper stud nut. Remove bracket.
5. Lower radio to position under panel and disconnect feed and speaker wires and antenna cable.
6. Remove radio.

1968 Dart

1. Disconnect battery.
2. Remove instrument cluster.
3. Remove six glove box mounting screws, collapse glove box, and remove box from panel.
4. Remove temperature control knobs.
5. Working through cluster and glove box openings, remove two heater or air conditioning mounting stud nuts and move controls out of way.
6. Remove center bezel seven mounting screws and remove center bezel.
7. Remove radio mounting bracket.
8. Disconnect speaker and antenna leads.
9. Remove ashtray by removing four mounting screws.
10. Remove two radio mounting screws.
11. Remove radio from under instrument panel.

1969 Valiant, Dart, and Barracuda

1. Disconnect battery.
2. From under panel disconnect speaker and wiring leads at radio.
3. Remove two radio mounting nuts from radio mounting bracket.
4. Move radio down and out from under instrument panel.

1970-74 Valiant, Dart, Barracuda, and Challenger

1. Disconnect battery.

2. From under panel, disconnect speaker and wiring leads at radio.
3. Remove channel selector shaft and knobs if so equipped.
4. Remove two radio mounting screws from under panel and loosen radio to lower support bracket mounting nut. Hold radio in position and remove radio bracket.
5. Move radio rearward, down, and out from under instrument panel.

1970-71 Dart and Valiant with Rallye Dash

1. Disconnect the negative battery cable.
2. Remove the control knobs from the front of the radio.
3. On models equipped with air conditioning, remove the two air conditioner outlet duct retaining nuts and remove the duct. Disconnect the right-side defroster hose and hose bracket and position them out of the way of the radio.
4. Remove the bottom screw from the radio mounting bracket.
5. Remove the left-side defroster hose.
6. Loosen the top screw on the radio mounting bracket and remove the bracket.
7. Disconnect the speaker and antenna leads.
8. Remove the radio mounting nuts from the front of the radio.
9. Remove the radio bezel.
10. Lower the radio and disconnect the radio power lead.
11. Remove the radio from under the instrument panel.

HEATER

Heater Assembly R&R

1967-74 Valiant and Dart and 1967-69 Barracuda

1. Drain radiator and disconnect battery.
2. Disconnect heater hoses from heater and remove heater hoses to dash retainer plate. Disconnect heater motor wires.
3. Remove heater motor seal retainer plate from dash panel.
4. Disconnect heater-defroster and temperature control cables from heater assembly.
5. Remove heater motor resistor wire from resistor.

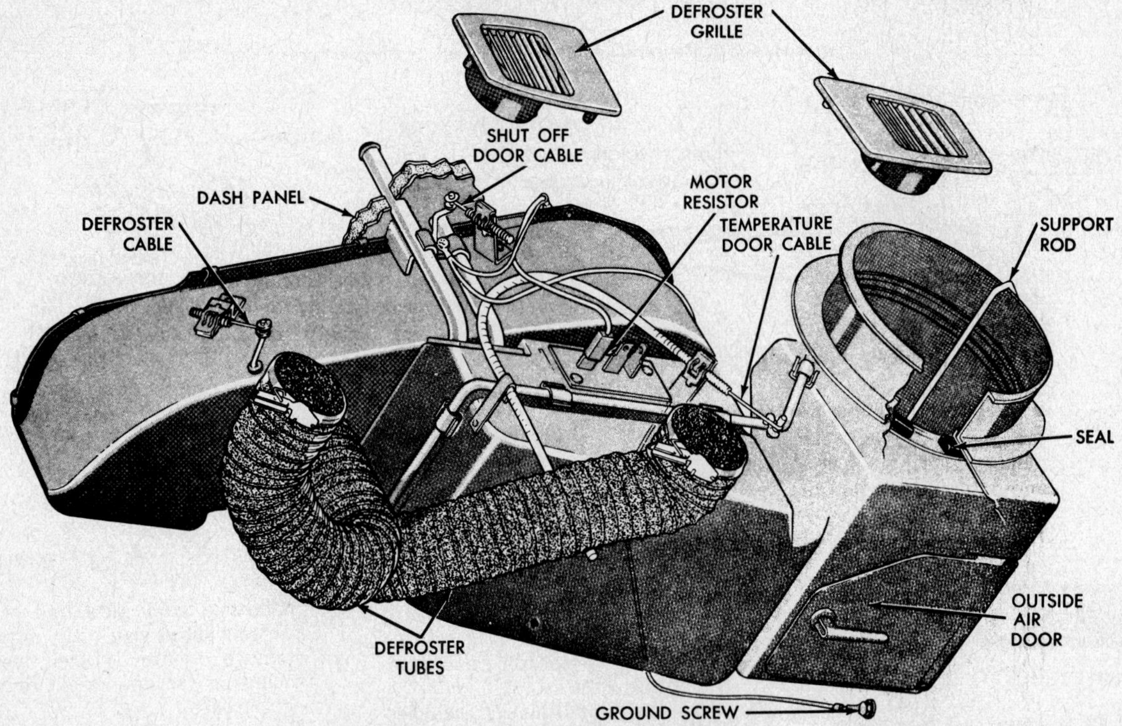
DEFROSTER GRILLE
SHUT OFF DOOR CABLE
DASH PANEL
DEFROSTER CABLE
MOTOR RESISTOR
TEMPERATURE DOOR CABLE
SUPPORT ROD
SEAL
OUTSIDE AIR DOOR
DEFROSTER TUBES
GROUND SCREW
Valiant-Dart heater assembly (© Chrysler Corp)

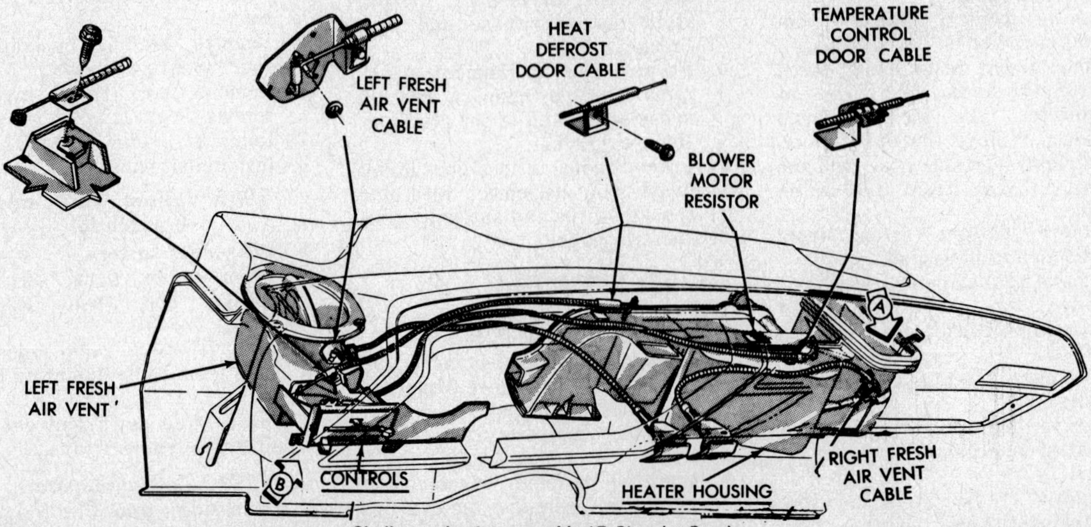
LEFT FRESH AIR VENT CABLE
HEAT DEFROST DOOR CABLE
TEMPERATURE CONTROL DOOR CABLE
BLOWER MOTOR RESISTOR
A
LEFT FRESH AIR VENT
B
CONTROLS
HEATER HOUSING
RIGHT FRESH AIR VENT CABLE
Challenger heater assembly (© Chrysler Corp)

6. Remove defroster tubes from heater assembly.
7. Disconnect heater housing support rod from fresh air duct.
8. Remove heater assembly.

1970-74 Barracuda and Challenger

1. Disconnect battery.
2. Drain coolant.
3. Disconnect heater hoses from core tubes at dash panel. Plug core tubes to prevent spilling coolant on interior of car.
4. Remove three mounting nuts from studs around blower motor and remove flange and air seal.
5. Unplug antenna from radio and place wire to one side.
6. Remove screw from housing to plenum support rod on right side of housing above fresh air opening.
7. Disconnect three air door cables.
8. Disconnect wires from blower motor resistor.
9. Tip unit down and out from under instrument panel.

Heater Blower Motor R&R —Except Air-Conditioned Cars

1967-74 Valiant and Dart and 1967-69 Barracuda

1. Remove the heater assembly.
2. Remove the seal from around the heater blower motor mounting studs.
3. Remove the spring clips that retain the spacers and the blower motor to the heater housing.
4. Remove the blower motor from the heater housing.

1970-74 Barracuda and Challenger

1. Remove heater assembly from car.
2. Disconnect blower motor lead from resistor block and ground wire from mounting plate.
3. Remove six sheet metal screws and six retaining clips holding blower motor assembly from housing.
4. Remove blower wheel from motor shaft.
5. Remove two retaining nuts and separate motor from mounting plate.

Heater Core R & R—Except Air-Conditioned Cars

1967-74 Valiant and Dart and 1967-69 Barracuda

1. Remove the heater assembly and the heater blower motor as outlined above.
2. Remove the fresh air door seal from either the inner or outer heating housing half only.
3. Remove the clips that retain the heater housing halves together.
4. Separate the heater housing halves.
5. Remove the screw that attaches the seal retainer and seal around the heater core tubes.
6. Remove the heater core tube support clamp.
7. Remove the screws that attach the heater core to the heater housing and remove the heater core.
8. Reverse above procedure to install.

1970-74 Barracuda and Challenger

1. Remove the heater assembly.
2. Remove the nine spring clips and four screws that hold the front cover to the heater housing.
3. Cut the sponge rubber plenum-to-heater housing air seal in two places where the front cover separates the cover from the housing.
4. Remove the core tube retaining screw from behind the housing, between the core tubes.
5. Remove the two sponge rubber gaskets from the heater core tubes and remove the core from the heater housing.

Heater Core R & R Air-Conditioned Cars

1967-74 Dart and Valiant, 1967-69 Barracuda

1. The core and cover are serviced as an assembly. They are located just forward of the instrument panel.
2. Disconnect the battery and remove the air cleaner. Remove glove box, the air outlet assembly, and the right defroster tube.
3. Drain the cooling system and remove the heater hoses at the core.
4. Disconnect the vacuum hoses from the fresh air recirculating actuator, the electrical wires from the resistor block, the temperature control cable, the evaporator temperature control switch control cable, and the ground wire from the heater core.

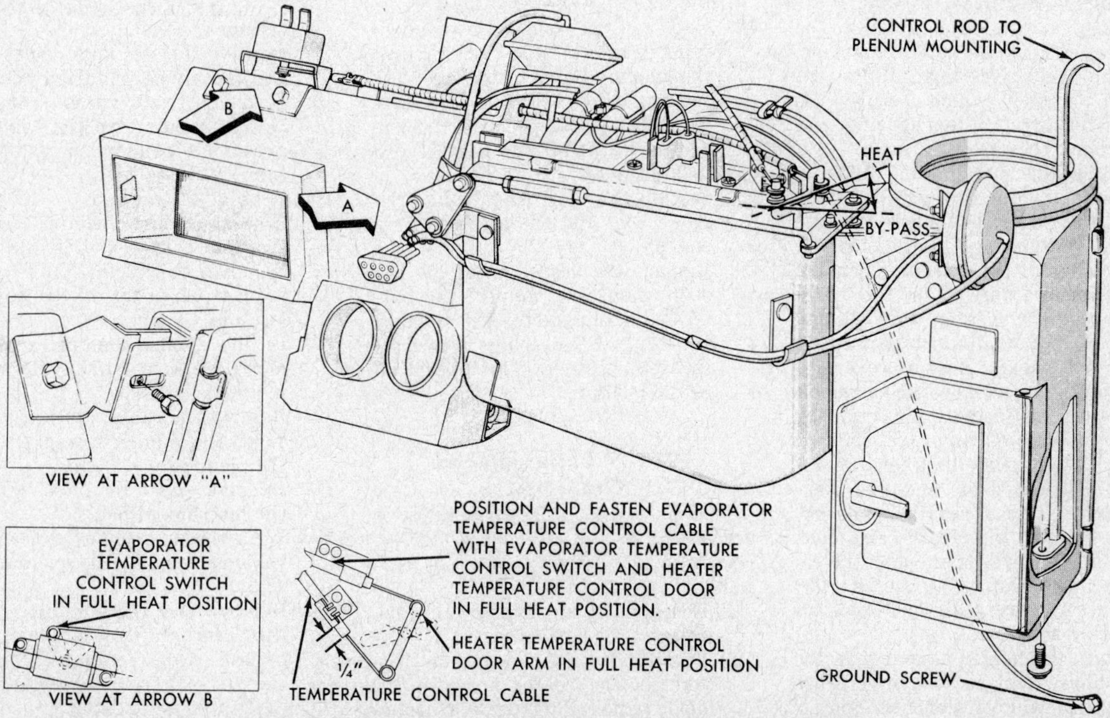
CONTROL ROD TO
PLENUM MOUNTING
HEAT
BY-PASS
B
A
VIEW AT ARROW "A"
EVAPORATOR
TEMPERATURE
CONTROL SWITCH
IN FULL HEAT POSITION
VIEW AT ARROW B
POSITION AND FASTEN EVAPORATOR TEMPERATURE CONTROL CABLE WITH EVAPORATOR TEMPERATURE CONTROL SWITCH AND HEATER TEMPERATURE CONTROL DOOR IN FULL HEAT POSITION.
1/4"
HEATER TEMPERATURE CONTROL DOOR ARM IN FULL HEAT POSITION
TEMPERATURE CONTROL CABLE
GROUND SCREW

Front view of Dart and Valiant heater/evaporator assembly (© Chrysler Corp)

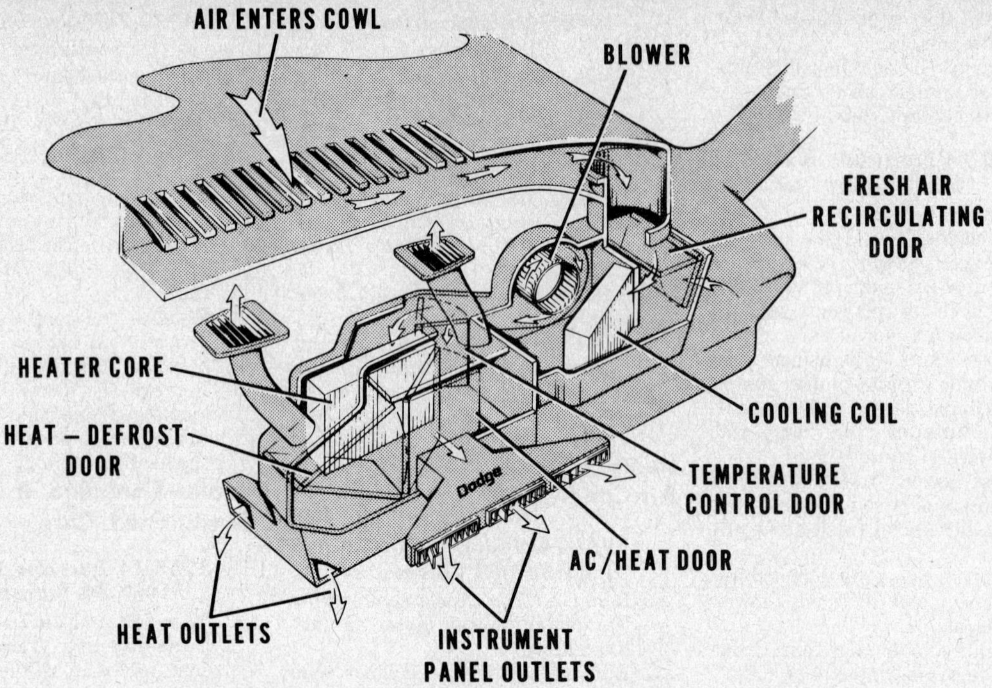
AIR ENTERS COWL
BLOWER
FRESH AIR RECIRCULATING DOOR
HEATER CORE
HEAT – DEFROST DOOR
COOLING COIL
TEMPERATURE CONTROL DOOR
Dodge
AC/HEAT DOOR
HEAT OUTLETS
INSTRUMENT PANEL OUTLETS

1973 Dart and Valiant heater and air conditioner assembly (© Chrysler Corp)

5. Extract the screws holding the heater to the evaporator assemblies. Disconnect the heater housing support rod from its position at the fresh air duct.
6. Take out the entire heater assembly.
7. Remove the fresh air recirculating door actuator.
8. Remove the operating link between the recirculating door and the bellcrank.
9. Remove the fresh air intake seal from either the front or rear heater housing halves only.
10. Remove the clips holding the heater housing halves together. Pull the halves apart. Take out the screws which secure the heater core to the housing and remove the core.
11. To begin installation, place a small amount of sealer into the heater housing flange. Replace the heater core in the housing and install the attaching screws.
12. Place weatherseal on the inner lip of the heater core flange. Squeeze a small amount of sealer onto the heater housing cover.
13. Install the two housing halves together and install their retaining clips. Wipe off any excess sealer.
14. Install the link between the recirculating door and the bellcrank. It may require some adjustment; the fresh air door should be fully open when the recirculating door is closed. Replace the fresh air door recirculating actuator.
15. Place the heater assembly in the vehicle. Replace the temperature control cable on the outer operating arm; position it so that it is in the full heat position with the end of the cable housing ¼ in. beyond the edge of the retainer clip.
16. Replace the evaporator temperature control switch cable on the inner operating arm. In the full heat position, the end of the cable housing should be ¼ in. beyond the edge of the cable clip.
17. Install the heater assembly on the dash panel. Replace the heater support rod to the fresh air duct and install the evaporator assembly screw.
18. Replace the electrical connections to the resistor block. Install the vacuum hoses to the fresh air recirculating actuator. Be certain the red stripe is facing the rod side. Install the heater core ground wire.
19. Install the defroster tube, the glove box, and the air outlet assembly.
20. Replace the heater hoses, fill the cooling system, connect the battery and replace the air cleaner.
21. Start engine and bring to operating temperature. Test operation of the heater.

1970-74 Barracuda and Challenger

NOTE: This procedure requires evacuation of the air conditioner refrigerant, use proper safety precautions.

1. Remove the air cleaner and disconnect the battery.
2. Drain the cooling system. Disconnect the heater hoses at the dash panel. Plug the core tubes to prevent spillage.
3. Discharge refrigerant from the system.
4. Disconnect the refrigerant lines at the dash panel (use two wrenches for this procedure). Leave the expansion valve attached to the line. Plug all refrigerant openings.
5. Disconnect the blower motor electrical connections. Remove the motor cooling tube and remove the blower motor.
6. Remove the glove box assembly.
7. Remove the appearance shield from the lower edge of the instrument panel.
8. Remove the left spot cooler duct and the air distribution housing.
9. Disconnect all wires from the blower motor resistor, and the antenna wire from the radio bottom.
10. Remove the radio.
11. Disconnect the vacuum harness from the control switch rear.
12. Remove the water valve cable from the bracket on the housing left end.
13. In the engine compartment, remove the nuts from the housing mounting studs.
14. Remove the rubber drain tube.
15. Take the support bracket from the plenum-to-housing panel.
16. Remove the unit from beneath the instrument panel.
17. With the unit removed from the vehicle, remove the plenum air seal.
18. Remove the vacuum hose from the fresh air door actuator and bypass door actuator. Remove the air seal from the evaporator core tubes and heater.
19. Remove the 18 screws securing

the front and rear covers, extract one screw from between the evaporator core tubes. Pull the housings apart.

20. Extract the three screws from the evaporator core access plate and remove the plate. With access now clear to the 2 evaporator core mounting screws, remove them. In addition, remove the four screws securing the evaporator core to the front cover and remove the core.
21. Carefully lift the left housing half seal from the rear cover. Do not remove the entire seal; the lower portion acts as a water seal.
22. Remove the two core retaining screws from the mounting plate. From the back of the rear cover, remove one screw from between the core tubes. Lift the heater core from the housing.
23. To begin assembly and installation, place the heat door in the "up" position. Place the heater core into the rear cover. Install its retaining screws.
24. Apply rubber cement to the bottom of the raised portion of the housing seal; carefully replace it in its original position over the heater core.
25. Insert the evaporator core into the front cover and replace its four securing screws.
26. Place the front and rear covers together. Make sure the cover seal is seated properly. Replace the 18 securing screws (and the screw between the evaporator core tubes at the back of the rear cover).
27. Replace the air seal over the heater and evaporator core tubes.
28. Connect all vacuum hoses to their respective actuators. Connect the hose with the red tracer to the actuator rod side.
29. Install the evaporator core access cover plate to the housing front and replace its three sheet metal screws.
30. Apply rubber cement to the plenum air seal and install it in position.
31. Position the housing up under the instrument panel. Connect the housing-to-plenum support bracket.
32. In the engine compartment, install four retaining nuts on the housing mounting studs; torque them to 24 in. lbs.
33. Install the vacuum harness to the rear of the control switch. Install the water valve control cable in its retaining bracket.
34. Install the radio.
35. Install all blower motor resistor wiring. Plug the antenna lead into the radio bottom.
36. Replace the center outlet air distribution housing. Replace the left spot cooler duct.
37. Replace the appearance shield at the instrument panel bottom.
38. Replace the glove box.
39. Replace the blower motor and connect its wiring. Install the blower motor cooling tube and replace the evaporator drain tube.
40. Connect the refrigerant lines to the evaporator core tubes. Freely lubricate the fittings and O-rings with refrigerant oil. Use two wrenches to avoid twisting the tubes.
41. Connect the heater hoses to the core tubes. Fill the cooling system.
42. Sweep the system. Evacuate the system. Charge the system and check for leaks.

Blower Motor Removal

1967-74 All Models

1. Working inside the engine compartment, disconnect the feed wire and ground wire. Remove the air tube (if so equipped).
2. Remove the mounting screws located on the outer surface of the mounting plate.
3. Remove the mounting plate, blower motor, and fan as an assembly.
4. To install the motor, if the motor was removed from its mounting plate, be sure its mounting grommets are installed at the attaching bolts. In addition, be sure the blower wheel is free and does not rub.
5. Install the blower motor assembly to the evaporator casing with the air tube opening toward the bottom. Install its retaining screws.
6. Install the air tube, ground, and feed wires.
7. Check operation of the blower motor.

SEAT BELTS

Seat Belt/Starter Interlock System

All 1974 models are equipped with Chrysler Corporation's seat belt/starter interlock sytem, which prevents starting of the car engine until front seat belts are fastened. For full information on this system, refer to the Dodge/Plymouth and Chrysler/Imperial car sections.

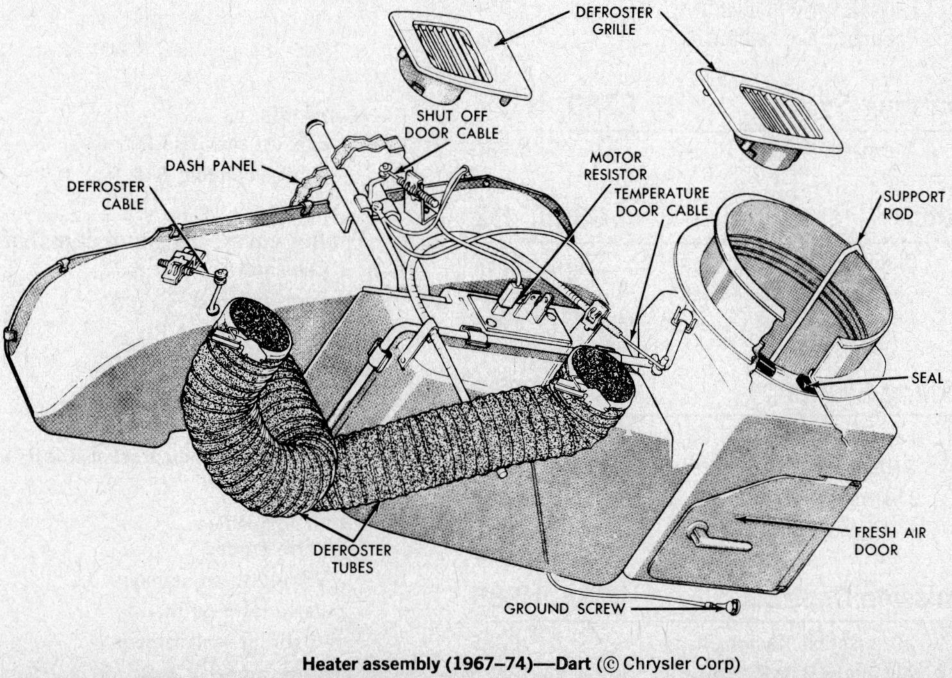
DEFROSTER GRILLE
SHUT OFF DOOR CABLE
DASH PANEL
DEFROSTER CABLE
MOTOR RESISTOR
TEMPERATURE DOOR CABLE
SUPPORT ROD
SEAL
FRESH AIR DOOR
DEFROSTER TUBES
GROUND SCREW

Heater assembly (1967–74)—Dart (© Chrysler Corp)

Vega

YEAR IDENTIFICATION

1971-72 Vega

1973 Vega

1974 Vega

FIRING ORDER

Model Identification

The vehicle serial number plate is found on top of the instrument panel and is visible through the left side of the windshield. The body number, trim code and paint number are located on the upper right side of the dash panel. Interpretation of the serial number is as follows:

Engine Identification Number

The engine identification number is located on a machined pad, on the right side of the cylinder block, above the starter motor.

Body Style

11 .... 2 dr., 4 passenger notchback coupe
77 .... 2 dr., 4 passenger hatchback coupe
15 .... 2 dr., 4 passenger station wagon
05 .... 2 dr., panel delivery

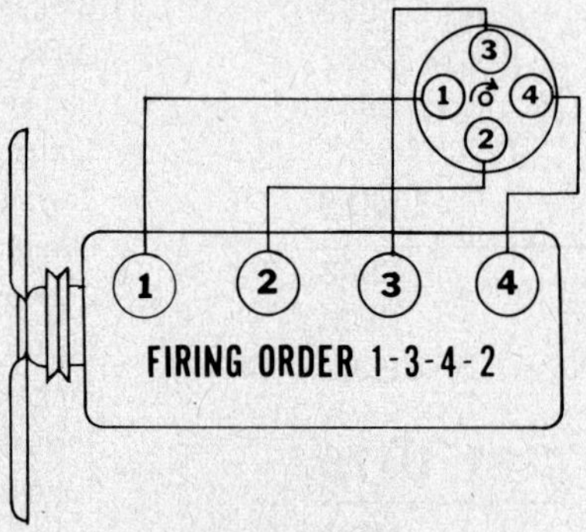
3
1
4
2
1
2
3
4
FIRING ORDER 1-3-4-2

Vega firing order
(© Chevrolet Div., G.M. Corp)

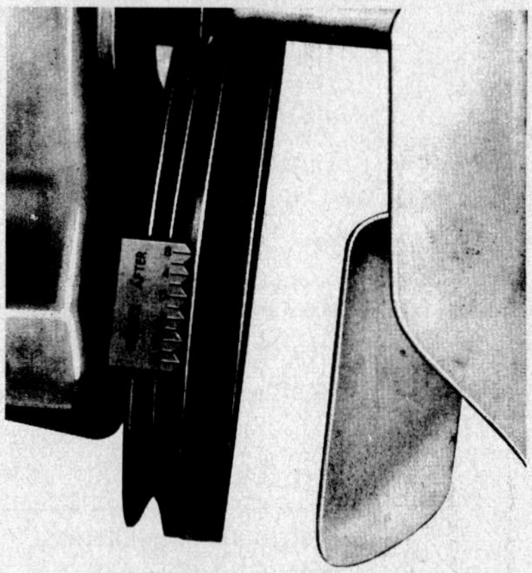

Timing mark location
(© Chevrolet Div., G.M. Corp)

1971

Manufacturer's Identity①	Body Style②	Model Year③	Assembly Plant④	Unit Number⑤
1	4111	1	U	100025

① Chevrolet
② See Model Identification
③ Last digit of model year (1971)
④ Lordstown
⑤ Unit numbering to begin with 100001

1972

Manufacturer's Identity①	Series Code Letter②	Body Style③	Engine Code④	Model Year⑤	Assembly Plant⑥	Unit Number⑦
1	V	77	B	2	U	100025

① Chevrolet
② Vega
③ See Model Identification
④ B, 140 cu in. 4 cylinder eng.
⑤ Last digit of model year (1972)
⑥ Lordstown
⑦ Unit numbering to begin with 100001

1973-74

Manufacturer's Identity①	Body Code Letter②	Series Code Letter③	Body Style④	Model Year⑤	Assembly Plant⑥	Unit Number⑦
1	H	V	77	3	U	100025

① Chevrolet
② Vega body
③ Vega
④ See Model Identification
⑤ Last digit of model year (1973)
⑥ Lordstown
⑦ Unit numbering to begin with 100001

GENERAL ENGINE SPECIFICATIONS

Year	Engine No. Cyl. Cu. In. Displacement	Carburetor Type	Advertised Horsepower @ rpm ■	Advertised Torque @ rpm (ft lbs) ■	Bore and Stroke (in.)	Advertised Compression Ratio	Oil Pressure @ 2050 rpm
'71	4-140	1 bbl	90 @ 4600	136 @ 2400	3.501 x 3.625	8.00:1	40
	4-140	2 bbl	110 @ 4800	138 @ 3200	3.50 x 3.625	8.00:1	40
'72	4-140	1 bbl	80 @ 4400	121 @ 2800	3.50 x 3.625	8.00:1	40
	4-140	2 bbl	90 @ 4800	121 @ 3200	3.50 x 3.625	8.00:1	40
'73	4-140	1 bbl	72 @ 4400	100 @ 2000	3.50 x 3.625	8.00:1	40
	4-140	2 bbl	85 @ 4800	115 @ 2400	3.50 x 3.625	8.00:1	40
'74	4-140	1 bbl	75 @ 4400	115 @ 2400	3.50 x 3.625	8.00:1	40
	4-140	2 bbl	85 @ 4400	122 @ 2400	3.50 x 3.625	8.00:1	40
	4-122	①	N.A.	N.A.	3.50 x 3.160	8.50:1	40

■ Beginning 1972, horsepower and torque are SAE net figures. They are measured at the rear of the transmission with all accessories installed and operating. Since the figures vary when a given engine is installed in different models, some are representative rather than exact.

N.A. Not Available

① Electronic fuel injection

TUNE-UP SPECIFICATIONS

When analyzing compression test results, look for uniformity among cylinders rather than specific pressures.

	ENGINE		SPARK PLUGS		DISTRIBUTOR		IGNITION TIMING (deg) ▲		VALVES	Fuel	IDLE SPEED (rpm) ▲ *	
Year	No. Cyl Displacement (cu in.)	hp	Type §	Gap (in.)	Point Dwell (deg)	Point Gap (in.)	Man Trans	Auto Trans	Intake Opens ■ (deg) ●	Pump Pressure (psi)	Man Trans	Auto Trans
'71	4-140①	90	R42TS	.035	31-34	.019	6B	6B	22	—	850/700	650/550
	4-140①	110	R42TS	.035	31-34	.019	6B	10B	25	—	1200/700	650/550
'72	4-140①	80	R42TS	.035	31-34	.019	6B	6B(4B)	22(28)	3-4½	700	700②/550
	4-140①	90	R42TS	.035	31-34	.019	8B	8B	28	3-4½	700	700②/550
'73	4-140①	72	R42TS	.035	31-34	.019	8B	8B	22	3-4½	1000/450	750/450
	4-140①	85	R42TS	.035	31-34	.019	10B	12B	28	3-4½	1200/450	750②/450
'74	4-140①	75	R42TS	.035	31-34	.019	10B(8B)	12B(8B)	22	3-4½	700/450	750/450
	4-140①	85	R42TS	.035	31-34	.019	10B(8B)	12B(8B)	28	3-4½	700/450	750②/450
	4-122	N.A.	R43LTS	.035	31-34	.019	N.A.	—	33	3-4½③	1000	—

▲ See text for procedure

● Figure in parentheses indicates California engine

■ All figures Before Top Dead Center

* Where two figures are separated by a slash, the first figure is for idle speed with solenoid connected, while the second is for idle speed with solenoid disconnected

§ All spark plug listings are A.C. original equipment numbers

① Adjust mechanical valve lifter clearance to .015 inch for intake with engine cold, and to .030 inch for exhaust with engine cold

② For air-conditioned vehicles, adjust idle speed to 800 rpm with A/C on

③ Inline pump 40 psi

B Before Top Dead Center

— Not applicable

CAPACITIES

Year	ENGINE No. Cyl. Displacement (Cu. In.)	Engine Crankcase Add 1 Qt For New Filter	TRANSMISSION Pts To Refill After Draining: Manual 3-Speed	Manual 4-Speed	Automatic ●	Drive Axle (pts)	Gasoline Tank (gals)	COOLING SYSTEM (qts) With Heater	With A/C
'71	4-140	3	2.4	3	6	2.3	11	6.5	6.5
'72	4-140	3	2.4	3	6①	2.8	11	6.5	6.5
'73	4-140	3	3	3	6②	2.8	11	8.6	9.0
'74	4-140, 4-122	3	3	3	8	2.8	16	8.6	9.0

● Specifications do not include torque converter

① 5 pts with Turbo Hydra-Matic

② 8 pts with Turbo Hydra-Matic

VALVE SPECIFICATIONS

Year	Engine No. Cyl. Displacement (cu in.)	Seat Angle (deg)	Face Angle (deg)	Spring Test Pressure (lbs @ in.)	Spring Installed Height (in.)	STEM TO GUIDE Clearance (in.)		STEM Diameter (in.)	
						Intake	Exhaust	Intake	Exhaust
'71	4-140	46	45	75 @ 1.75	1 3/4	.0010-.0027	.0010-.0027	.3414	.3414
'72	4-140	46	45	75 @ 1.75	1 3/4	.0010-.0027	.0010-.0027	.3414	.3414
'73	4-140	46	45	75 @ 1.75	1 3/4	.0010-.0027	.0010-.0027	.3414	.3414
'74	4-140	46	45	75 @ 1.75	1 3/4	.0010-.0027	.0010-.0027	.3414	.3414
	4-122	46	45	45 @ 1.30①	1 19/64②	.0010-.0027	.0010-.0027	.2790	.2790

① Outer spring, inner spring 30 @ 1.25
② Outer spring, inner spring 1 1/4

CRANKSHAFT AND CONNECTING ROD SPECIFICATIONS

All measurements are given in in.

Year	Engine No. Cyl. Displacement (cu in.)	CRANKSHAFT				CONNECTING ROD		
		Main Brg. Journal Dia	Main Brg. Oil Clearance	Shaft End-Play	Thrust on No.	Journal Diameter	Oil Clearance	Side Clearance
'71-'72	140	2.2983-2.2993	.0029-.0003	.002-.008	4	1.999-2.000	.0007-.0027①	.0085-.0135
'73	140	2.2983-2.2993	.0003-.0020②	.002-.007	4	1.999-2.000	.0007-.0038①	.0085-.0135
'74	140	2.3004	.0003-.0029	.002-.008	4	1.999-2.000	.0007-.0027	.0009-.0013
	122	2.3011	.0008-.0034	.002-.008	4	1.999-2.000	.0007-.0027	.0009-.0013

① Maximum service clearance = .004 in.
② No. 1, .0003-.0027 for No. 2, 3, 4, 5

TORQUE SPECIFICATIONS

All readings in ft lbs

Year	Engine No. Cyl. Displacement (cu in.)	Cylinder Head Bolts	Rod Bearing Bolts	Main Bearing Bolts	Crankshaft Pulley Bolt	Flywheel to Crankshaft Bolts	MANIFOLD	
							Intake	Exhaust
'71-'74	140	60	35	65	80	60	30	30

ALTERNATOR AND REGULATOR SPECIFICATIONS

Year	ALTERNATOR			REGULATOR						
					Field Relay			Regulator		
	Part No. or Manufacturer	Field Current @ 12 V	Output (amps)	Part No. or Manufacturer	Air Gap (in.)	Point Gap (in.)	Volts to Close	Air Gap (in.)	Point Gap (in.)	Volts @ 75°
'71-'74	1100545	4-4.5	32	—	Integral	—	—	—	—	13.8-14.8
	1100559	4-4.5	32	—	Integral	—	—	—	—	13.8-14.8
	1100546	4-4.5	55	—	Integral	—	—	—	—	13.8-14.8
	1100560	4-4.5	55	—	Integral	—	—	—	—	13.8-14.8
	1100950	4-4.5	42	—	Integral	—	—	—	—	13.8-14.8

— Not applicable

BATTERY AND STARTER SPECIFICATIONS

Year	Engine Displacement (cu in.)	Battery: Ampere Hour Capacity	Battery: Volts	Battery: Terminal Grounded	Starter Lock Test: Amps	Starter Lock Test: Volts	Starter Lock Test: Torque (ft lbs)	Starter No-Load Test: Amps	Starter No-Load Test: Volts	Starter No-Load Test: RPM	Brush Spring Tension (oz)
'71-'74	140	45	12	Neg.	Not Recommended			50-75	9	6,500-10,000	—

BRAKE SPECIFICATIONS

All measurements given in in.

Year	Model	Master Cylinder: Disc	Master Cylinder: Drum	Wheel Cylinder Front: Disc	Wheel Cylinder Front: Drum	Wheel Cylinder: Rear	Brake Disc or Drum Diameter Front: Disc	Brake Disc or Drum Diameter Front: Drum	Brake Disc or Drum Diameter: Rear
'71-'74	All	.75	—	1.875	—	.75	9.88	—	9.0

— Not applicable

WHEEL ALIGNMENT SPECIFICATIONS

Year	Model	Caster: Range (deg)	Caster: Pref Setting (deg)	Camber: Range (deg)	Camber: Pref Setting (deg)	Toe-in (in.)	Steering Axis Inclin.	Wheel Pivot Ratio (deg): Inner Wheel	Wheel Pivot Ratio (deg): Wheel Outer
'71-'74	All	1¼N to ¼N	¾N	¼N to ¾P	¼P	3/16 to 5/16	8.55	N.A.	N.A.

RING GAP

All measurements are given in inches

Year	Engine	Top Compression	Bottom Compression
'71-'74	All	.015-.025	.009-.019

Year	Engine	Oil Control
'71-'74	All	.010-.030

RING SIDE CLEARANCE

All measurements are given in inches

Year	Engine	Top Compression	Bottom Compression
'71-'74	All	.0012-.0027	.0012-.0027

Year	Engine	Oil Control
'71-'74	All	.000-.005

PISTON CLEARANCE

Year	Engine	Piston to Bore Clearance (in.)
'71-'74	4-140	.0018-.0028
'74	4-122	.0020-.0030

CHARGING SYSTEM

A 10-SI Series Delcotron alternator is used. This unit features a non-adjustable, integral solid-state regulator mounted inside the slip-ring end frame. Testing and overhaul procedures for the integrated charging system are found in the Unit Repair Section.

Caution Observe the following precautions when servicing a Delcotron:

1. When installing a battery, be certain that the ground polarity of the battery and the generator and regulator are matched correctly.
2. Make sure that the correct terminals are connected when jumping the battery.
3. When charging the battery, make sure that the correct leads are connected to the battery terminals.
4. Never operate the generator on an open circuit. Be sure all connections in the circuit are tight.
5. Do not short across or ground any of the terminals on the generator or regulator.
6. Never polarize an AC system.
7. Do not use test lamps of more than 12 V for checking diode continuity.
8. Avoid long soldering times when replacing diodes or transistors; prolonged heat will damage them.
9. Always disconnect the battery ground terminal when servicing an AC system. This will prevent accidentally reversing polarity.

Alternator R & R

1. Disconnect the battery.
2. Disconnect the alternator wiring.
3. Remove the alternator brace bolt and V-belt.
4. Remove the pivot mount bolt and the alternator.
5. Installation is the reverse of the removal procedure. Adjust the belt tension.

STARTING SYSTEM

A 45 amp./hr., 54 plate battery is standard equipment on all Vega models. Vehicles being shipped by the Verti-Pak method (on end in railway cars) use a special battery having side terminals and filler caps along the edge. These batteries require terminal adapters to facilitate charging.

The starter is a solenoid actuated Delco-Remy unit similar to other Chevrolet starters used in the past. See the Unit Repair Section for testing and overhaul procedures.

Starter R & R

1. Disconnect the battery ground cable and all wiring at the solenoid terminals. Install each nut on the terminal from which it was removed, as these nuts are not interchangeable.
2. Loosen the front starter bracket and remove the two mounting bolts.
3. Remove the front bracket bolt and rotate the bracket out of the way.

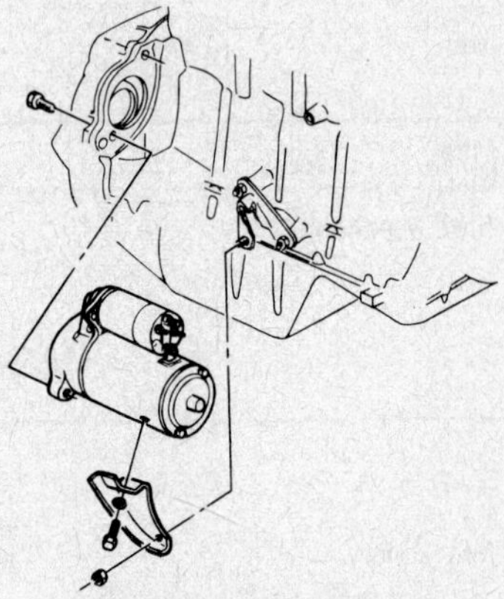

Starter motor installation
(© Chevrolet Div., G.M. Corp)

4. Remove the starter from the car, lowering the front end first.
5. To install, reverse the removal procedure. Tighten the mounting bolts, and then install the brace.

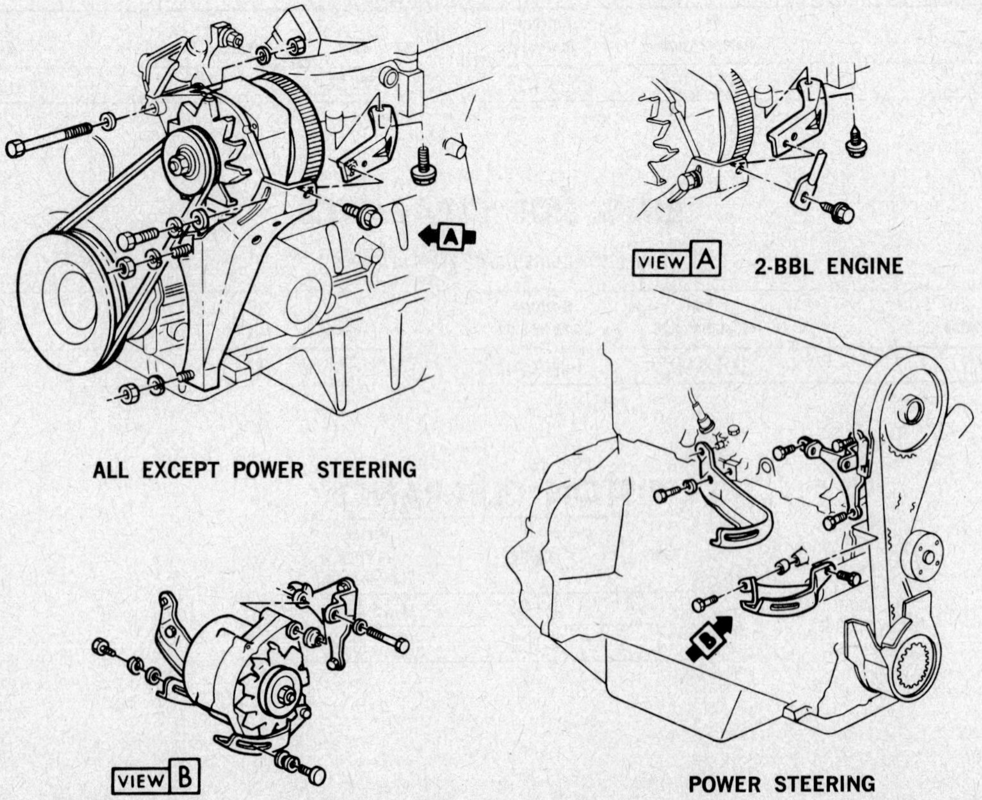
A
ALL EXCEPT POWER STEERING
VIEW A
2-BBL ENGINE
B
VIEW B
POWER STEERING

Alternator mounting (© Chevrolet Div., G.M. Corp)

IGNITION SYSTEM

The 140 cu in. distributor is mounted in the cylinder head at the rear of the engine and is driven by the camshaft. An unusual feature of this unit is a cup, mounted at the lower end of the driveshaft. This cup is under full engine oil pressure when the engine is running, acting as a vibration damper to reduce driveshaft oscillations. If this cup is not installed after the distributor has been disassembled, engine oil pressure will be lost.

A replaceable cam lubricator is installed, which should be changed each time the points are replaced.

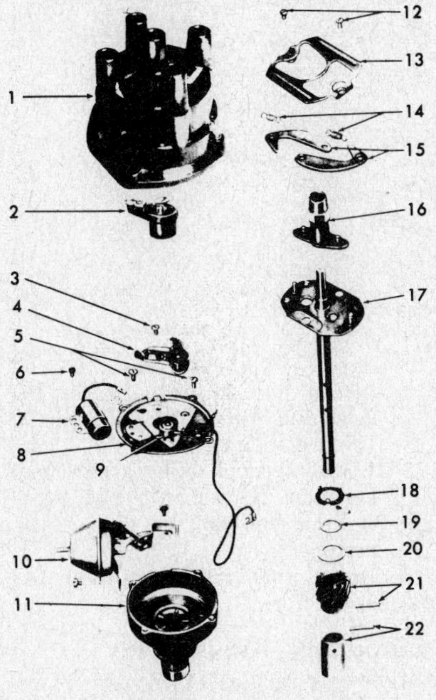

Distributor—exploded view
(© Chevrolet Div., G.M. Corp)

1 Distributor cap
2 Rotor
3 Contact point attaching screw
4 Contact point assembly
5 Breaker plate attaching screws
6 Condenser attaching screws
7 Condenser
8 Breaker plate assembly
9 Cam lubricator
10 Vacuum advance control assembly
11 Distributor housing
12 Weight cover attaching screws
13 Weight cover
14 Weight springs
15 Advance weights
16 Cam assembly
17 Distributor main shaft
18 Tanged washer
19 Flat washer
20 Shim (as required)
21 Drive gear and roll pin
22 Damper and roll pin

The Cosworth-Vega distributor is mounted in its own housing which is bolted to the right side of the cylinder head directly behind the belt cover. The distributor is a magnetic pulse unit without conventional breaker points. Switching is controlled by an external, transistorized pulse amplifier. Operation and troubleshooting for this unit can be found in the Electronic Ignition chapter of the Unit Repair section.

A short belt driven off the right camshaft gear turns a shaft which drives the distributor through gears. The distributor additionally functions as an engine speed sensor for input to the electronic fuel injection.

Distributor Removal

1. Release the cap hold-down screws and remove the cap.
2. Disconnect the vacuum line and the primary lead.

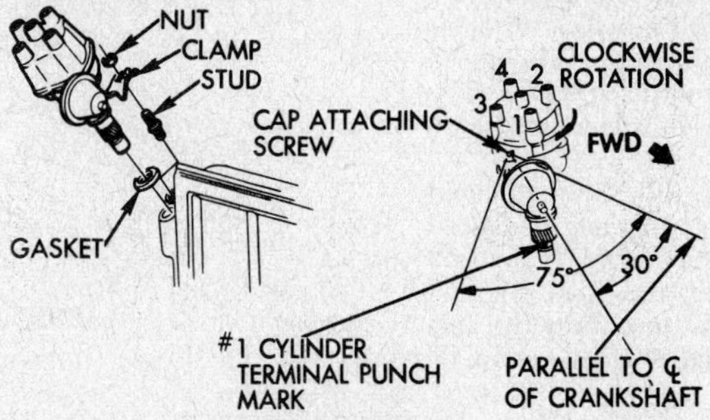
NUT
CLAMP
STUD
GASKET
CAP ATTACHING SCREW
CLOCKWISE ROTATION
4 2
3 1
FWD
75°
30°
#1 CYLINDER TERMINAL PUNCH MARK
PARALLEL TO ℄ OF CRANKSHAFT

Distributor alignment
(© Chevrolet Div., G.M. Corp)

3. Mark the distributor housing and the engine in line with the rotor centerline with chalk.
4. Remove the hold-down clamp and distributor.

NOTE: avoid turning the engine while the distributor is removed.

Distributor Installation

1. Turn the rotor approximately 1/8 turn clockwise past the alignment mark.
2. Push the distributor into position, moving the rotor to mesh the gears.
3. Install the clamp bolt.
4. Connect the vacuum line and the primary lead.
5. Install the cap and, if necessary, adjust the timing.

Installation—Engine Disturbed

1. Remove No. 1 spark plug and place a finger over the plug hole. Remove the center coil wire and crank the engine until compression is felt in No. 1 cylinder. Rotate the engine until the timing pointer is aligned with the 8° ATDC mark.
2. Install the distributor with the vacuum advance pointing toward the front of the engine and the punchmarks on the drive gear in line with the No. 1 cap tower.
3. Install the hold-down clamp and rotate the distributor slightly so that the points are just open. Tighten the clamp bolt.
4. Install the rotor, cap and vacuum line.
5. Connect the primary lead.
6. Check and adjust the ignition timing.

Point Adjustment

Inspect the points for alignment and pitting. If necessary, clean the points with a point file. All the roughness need not be removed. To set the gap, rotate the crankshaft until one of the distributor cam lobes is directly opposite the rubbing block of the point arm (gap at maximum separation). Measure the gap, and if it is not within specifications, loosen the contact point assembly attaching screw and move the assembly to obtain the specified gap. This is done by inserting a screwdriver in the slot

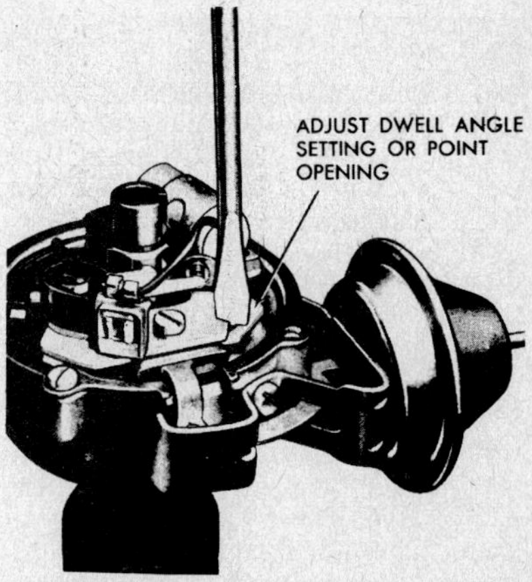
ADJUST DWELL ANGLE SETTING OR POINT OPENING

Point adjustment
(© Chevrolet Div., G.M. Corp)

formed by the contact points and the breaker plate and levering the points as required. Tighten the attaching screw.

Check the dwell angle. Check the ignition timing, adjusting it if necessary.

Ignition Timing

The timing marks are on a plate mounted on the front of the block and the timing notch is on the crankshaft pulley.

Timing is set as follows:

1. Bring the engine to normal operating temperature, shut the engine off, and connect a timing light to no. 1 spark plug. Clean the timing plate and mark the notch in the pulley with chalk.
2. Disconnect and plug the vacuum line to the distributor.

3. Disconnect the fuel tank line from the evaporative emission canister.
4. Disconnect the electrical lead from the idle stop solenoid on the carburetor.
5. Start the engine and adjust the carburetor idle screw for an idle speed of 700 rpm or less for 1971-72 models, 1000 rpm or less for 1973 models.

NOTE: The idle solenoid is turned to adjust the idle speed on single barrel carburetor models.

6. Aim the timing light at the timing marks. If the notch does not align with the correct value on the scale, loosen the distributor clamp locknut and slowly turn the distributor to adjust.
7. Tighten the clamp locknut. Adjust the carburetor idle speed screw to give the specified idle speed with the solenoid disconnected.
8. Reconnect the idle stop solenoid lead. Increase the engine speed to allow the solenoid to extend and then adjust the solenoid plunger screw to obtain the idle speed specified with the solenoid connected.
9. Shut the engine off and connect the vacuum and evaporative emission line.

FUEL SYSTEM

Two types of carburetors are used through 1972. Base engines are equipped with a Rochester MV one barrel carburetor. The optional engine is equipped with a Rochester 2GV two barrel carburetor. The MV one barrel continues to be used on the base engine for 1973, but the optional engine is equipped with a Holley 5210-C two barrel. 1973-74 carburetors are all equipped with a tube takeoff for vacuum supply to the EGR valve. There are variations on each carburetor for manual and automatic transmission applications. Each has an integral fuel filter.

The electrical fuel pump is an integral part of the fuel tank unit assembly, which includes the fuel gauge metering unit. The fuel pump is energized by the ignition switch when the key is in the start or on position. After the engine starts, the pump receives current through the oil pressure safety switch as long as there is approximately 2 psi oil pressure.

The Cosworth-Vega is equipped with electronic fuel injection. An additional inline electric fuel pump is used on the Cosworth-Vega.

Fuel Pump R & R

1. Disconnect the battery ground cable and siphon the fuel from the tank.
2. Disconnect the gauge sending-unit and pump wires at the rear harness connector.
3. Raise the car. Disconnect the fuel line at the gauge connection.
4. On 1971 models, disconnect the tank vent lines to the vapor separator, which is mounted on the top of the tank. On later models, disconnect the tank vent line to the vapor separator, which is mounted in the tank.
5. Disconnect the gauge wire ground screw from the floorpan.
6. Remove the tank strap bolts and, very carefully, lower the tank.
7. Use the special wrench, or a suitable substitute, to unscrew the retaining cam ring. Do not strike any part of the tank with a metal tool, such as a hammer; there is a danger of explosion from sparks.

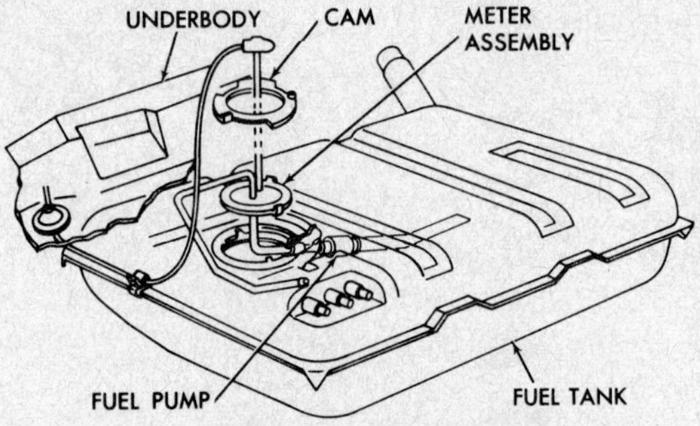

UNDERBODY
CAM
METER ASSEMBLY
FUEL PUMP
FUEL TANK

Fuel pump installation
(© Chevrolet Div., G.M. Corp)

8. Remove the gauge sending-unit and fuel pump assembly.
9. Remove the flat wire conductor from the plastic clip on the fuel tube.
10. While squeezing the clamp, pull the pump straight back ½ in. for access to the terminals. Remove the two nuts, lockwashers, and wires from the pump.
11. Squeeze the clamp and pull the pump straight back to completely remove it from the sending unit.

Caution Be careful not to bend the circular support bracket.

12. Slide the replacement pump through the circular support bracket until it rests against the rubber coupling. Be sure that the rubber isolator and saran strainer, supplied in the service package, are attached to the pump.
13. Attach the two pump terminals, using lockwashers and nuts. Be sure that the flat conductor is attached to the terminal farthest away from the float arm.
14. Squeeze the clamp and push the pump into the rubber coupling.
15. Replace the flat wire conductor in the plastic clip on the fuel tube.
16. Install the pump and gauge unit into the tank opening. Tighten the cam ring.
17. Install the fuel tank using a reverse of the removal procedure.

Fuel Filter R & R

Both paper and bronze filters are used. The Cosworth-Vega uses an in-line filter located in the engine compartment.

1. Disconnect the fuel line at the intake fuel filter nut on the carburetor.
2. Remove the intake fuel filter nut.
3. Remove the filter element and spring.
4. Replace the filter element every 12,000 miles or 12 months, whichever comes first. Inspect the filter element to determine its serviceability.
5. Install the element spring and element. Bronze filters are installed with the conical section facing out and with a gasket between the filter element and the fuel intake nut.
6. Install the nut using a new gasket and tighten. Do not overtighten this nut, as it is easily stripped.
7. Install fuel line and tighten the connector.

Carburetor Adjustments

The only carburetor adjustment required is for idle speed. The idle mixture screw(s) is equipped with a sealed limiter cap(s). Mixture should not be adjusted, except after carburetor overhaul or repair, since it is factory-set to ensure the lowest possible level of exhaust emissions.

1971-72

1. The engine must be at normal operating temperature and the air cleaner in place. Air conditioning should be on in 1971 models; off in later models.
2. Detach the fuel tank line from the top of the evaporative emission canister.
3. Disconnect the distributor vacuum line and plug the carburetor hose.
4. Disconnect the electrical connector at the idle stop solenoid on the carburetor.
5. Start the engine and adjust the carburetor idle speed screw to obtain the idle speed specified in the "Tune-Up Specifications

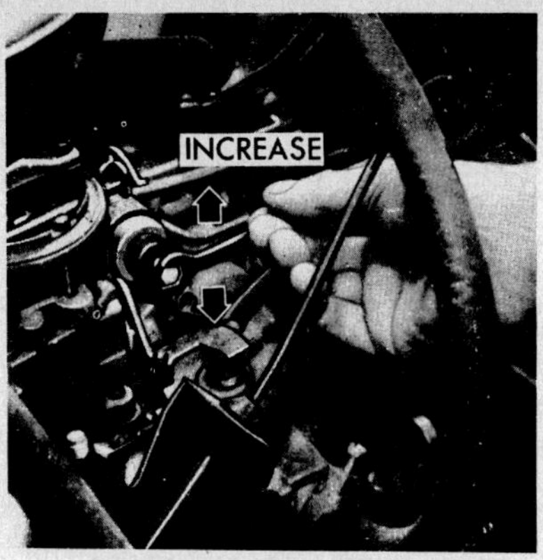
INCREASE

Idle stop solenoid adjustment
(© Chevrolet Div., G.M. Corp)

Chart" (for speed with the solenoid disconnected).

6. Reconnect the idle stop solenoid electrical lead. Speed up the engine to allow the solenoid plunger to extend, then adjust the solenoid plunger screw to obtain the idle speed specified in the "Tune-Up Specifications Chart" (for speed with the solenoid connected).
7. Stop the engine and reconnect the vacuum line and the evaporative emission canister line.

1973-74

Follow steps 1 through 4 of the 1971-72 procedure, then proceed as follows.

Rochester MV 1-bbl

1. Start the engine and, using a 1/8 in. allen wrench, adjust the idle speed to the figure given in the "Tune-Up Specifications Chart" (for speed with the solenoid disconnected).
2. Check the dwell and ignition timing. Check the idle speed again.
3. Reconnect the electrical wire to the solenoid.
4. Adjust the idle speed (for speed with solenoid connected) by turning the body of the solenoid itself.

Holley 5210-C 2-bbl

1. Start the engine and adjust the idle speed screw for the speed listed in the "Tune-Up Specifications Chart" (speed with solenoid disconnected).
2. Check the dwell and ignition timing. Check the idle speed again.
3. Reconnect the electrical wire to the solenoid.
4. Adjust the screw on the throttle lever (not the same screw as step 1). Set the idle speed to the figure given in the "Tune-Up Specifications Chart" (for speed with the solenoid connected).

Throttle Linkage Adjustment

The Vega throttle linkage is the cable type, and is not adjustable. The throttle linkage should be checked for correct operation and binding. Have an assistant hold the accelerator pedal to the floor and check to see that the throttle valves are wide-open.

COOLING SYSTEM

Vega engine cooling is of conventional design and utilizes an impeller type water pump to circulate the coolant. The system is pressurized and utilizes a thermostat to maintain operating temperature. The intake manifold is water heated to provide an even intake temperature. Only early 1971 models have an engine block drain plug. All 1971 models and 1973 models built after March have a radiator drain petcock. The 1972 models have neither a block drain plug nor a radiator petcock. To drain the cooling system on these models, either the lower radiator hose must be removed or the coolant must be siphoned out.

There are two radiators: a standard type and a larger heavy duty radiator equipped with a fan shroud.

Radiator R & R

1. Drain the radiator.
2. On models with the heavy duty radiator, remove the fan shroud as described below.
3. Disconnect the intake and outlet hoses.
4. Remove the two screws which secure the fan guard to the radiator support, then remove the support and the two radiator pads.

NOTE: on vehicles with the heavy duty radiator, remove the two upper brackets (instead of the single support).

5. Lift the radiator up and out of the lower brackets.
6. To install, reverse the removal procedure.

Fan Shroud R & R

1. Remove the two screws which secure the shroud to the upper radiator brackets.
2. Remove the screw which holds the two halves of the shroud together at the lower left-hand corner.
3. Remove the left and right sections of the shroud from the clips at the bottom of the radiator.
4. To install, reverse the above procedure.

Water Pump R & R

The water pump is located on the front of the engine block immediately above the crankshaft pulley. The pump bearings are permanently lubricated during manufacture and do not require periodic maintenance other than keeping the air vent (top of housing) and drain holes (bottom of housing) free of dirt and grease.

The pump components cannot be serviced separately and, in the event of pump failure, the complete assembly must be replaced as a unit, as follows:

1. Raise the hood and install a bolt through the hood hold-open link. ~~tightening the bolts to 20 ft. lbs.~~
2. Disconnect the battery negative cable.
3. Remove the fan and spacer.

Caution No attempt should be made to repair a bent or damaged fan. The fan assembly must be in proper balance and an improperly balanced fan may cause extensive damage.

4. Loosen, but do not remove, the two lower timing belt cover retaining screws. The holes in the cover are slotted so that the cover is easily removed.
5. Remove the two upper timing belt cover retaining screws and remove the cover.
6. Drain the coolant.
7. Loosen the water pump bolts to relieve the tension on the timing belt.
8. Remove the hoses from the water pump.
9. Remove the water pump bolts, pump and gasket.
10. Thoroughly clean the old gasket material from the pump and block.
11. To install, position the water pump on the block using a new gasket and loosely install the water pump bolts. Make sure that the V grooves of the belt are aligned with the grooves in the water pump.

NOTE: use an anti-seize compound on the water pump bolt threads.

12. A special tool is available to adjust the timing belt. It fits into the round hole in the square lug to the upper right (facing) of the water pump and bears against the pump housing midway between the bolt holes. If this tool is available, apply 15 ft lbs of torque against the water pump (and belt). If the tool is not available, apply a force to the pump in a similar manner. Tighten the pump bolts to 15 ft lbs.
13. Install the radiator and heater hoses to the pump.
14. Install the timing belt cover, lowering the cover lower screw slots over the screws. Loosely tighten the screws against the cover.
15. Install the two upper timing cover screws, then tighten the upper and lower screws to 50 in. lbs.

16. Install the fan spacer and fan, tightening the bolts to 20 ft lbs.
17. Fill the cooling system, connect the battery negative cable, start the engine and check for leaks
18. Remove the bolt from the hood hold-open link and close the hood.

Thermostat R & R

The thermostat is located in a housing at the cylinder head water outlet adjacent to the intake manifold.

1. Drain the cooling system.
2. Disconnect the upper radiator hose at the engine.
3. If the alternator is attached to the water outlet, loosen the swivel bolt attachment and move it out of the way.
4. Unbolt the housing and remove the housing, gasket, and thermostat.
5. Replace the thermostat and housing, using a new gasket.
6. Install the alternator and adjust the drive belt. The adjustment procedure is outlined further on in this section.
7. Replace the radiator hose, fill the cooling system, start the engine, and check for leaks.

EMISSION CONTROLS

Positive Crankcase Ventilation

All models use the Positive Crankcase Ventilation System (PCV).

Some unburned fuel and combustion products leak past the rings during combustion. These gases travel into the crankcase where, if they are not removed, they will combine with the oil to form sludge and also build excessive pressure inside the crankcase. The PCV system removes these gases from the crankcase and routes them to the intake manifold where they are combined with the raw air fuel mixture and reburned in the combustion chamber.

The crankcase gases are drawn from the crankcase by intake manifold vacuum. There is a PCV valve in the line between the crankcase and the intake manifold which regulates the flow of the gases.

Evaporative Emission Control

The Evaporative Emission Control system (EEC) is used on all 1971–74 models. This system limits the amount of gasoline vapor discharged into the air from the gas tank and carburetor. The fuel tank has a non-vented cap. As vapors are generated in the fuel tank, they flow through a liquid vapor separator to a canister where they are stored. Vapors generated by the carburetor after the engine is turned off are also routed to this canister. From the canister, the vapors are routed back to the carburetor where they are burned when the engine is started.

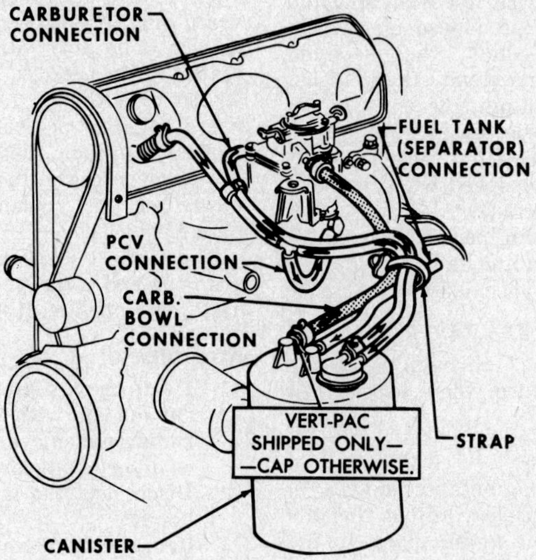
CARBURETOR CONNECTION
FUEL TANK (SEPARATOR) CONNECTION
PCV CONNECTION
CARB. BOWL CONNECTION
VERT-PAC SHIPPED ONLY— —CAP OTHERWISE.
STRAP
CANISTER

1971-72 Evaporation control system canister and hoses
(© Chevrolet Div., G.M. Corp)

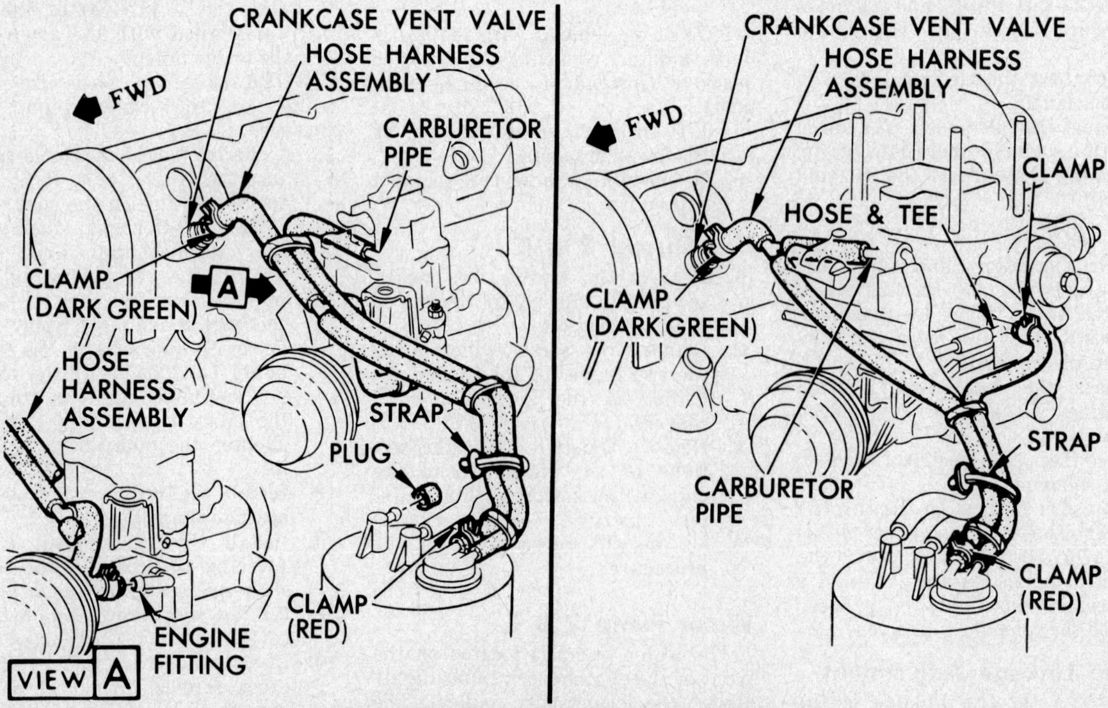
CRANKCASE VENT VALVE
HOSE HARNESS ASSEMBLY
FWD
CARBURETOR PIPE
CLAMP (DARK GREEN)
A
HOSE HARNESS ASSEMBLY
STRAP
PLUG
CLAMP (RED)
ENGINE FITTING
VIEW A
CRANKCASE VENT VALVE
HOSE HARNESS ASSEMBLY
FWD
CLAMP
HOSE & TEE
CLAMP (DARK GREEN)
STRAP
CARBURETOR PIPE
CLAMP (RED)

1973-74 Evaporation Control System canister and hoses—1-bbl engine (left) and 2-bbl engine (right) (© Chevrolet Div., G.M. Corp)

Controlled Combustion System

The Controlled Combustion System (CCS) is used on all 1971-74 models. Essentially the CCS increases combustion efficiency through carburetor and distributor calibrations and by increasing engine operating temperatures.

Carburetors are calibrated leaner and initial ignition timing is retarded. The vacuum advance curve is also altered to decrease emissions.

The CCS also incorporates a higher engine operation temperature. A 195° thermostat is used. Engines that run hotter provide more complete vaporation of fuel and reduce quench area in the combustion chamber. Quench area is the relatively cool area near the cylinder wall and combustion chamber surfaces. Fuel in these areas does not burn properly because of the lower temperatures. This incomplete burning increases emissions.

The CCS uses a thermostatically controlled air cleaner called the Auto-Therm air cleaner. It is designed to keep the temperature of the air entering the carburetor at approximately 100°F. This allows the lean carburetor to work properly, minimizes carburetor icing, and improves engine warm-up characteristics. A sensor unit located on the clean air side of the air filter senses the temperature of the air passing over it and regulates the vacuum supplied to a vacuum diaphragm in the inlet tube of the air cleaner. The colder the air, the greater the amount of vacuum supplied to the vacuum diaphragm. The vacuum diaphragm, depending on the vacuum supplied to it, opens or closes a damper door in the inlet tube of the air cleaner. If the door is open it allows air from the engine compartment to go to the carburetor. If the door is closed, air flows from the heat stove located on the exhaust manifold into the carburetor. In this way, heated air is supplied to the carburetor during cold days and when first starting the engine and warming it up.

Air Injection Reactor System

AIR is used on all 1972 models except non-California cars with single-barrel carburetors.

The Air Injection Reactor (AIR) system was used to treat exhaust emissions. It consists of an air pump, a diverter valve, and tubes and hoses used to inject the air into the exhaust manifolds. The pump, driven by the engine, compresses air which is routed to the exhaust port of each cylinder. The air provides oxygen to further burn any unburned gases that are left over from the combustion process.

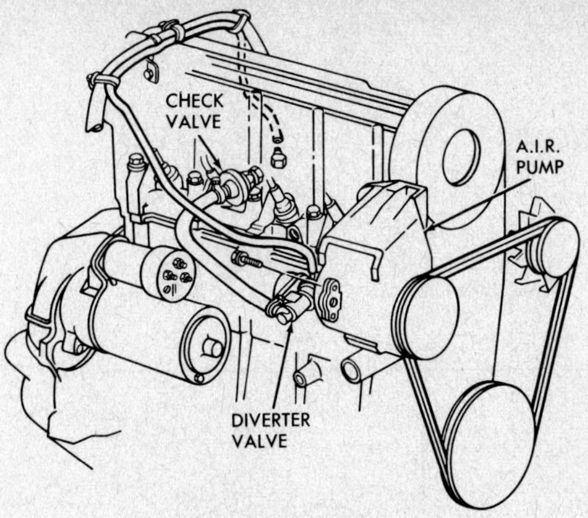
CHECK VALVE
A.I.R. PUMP
DIVERTER VALVE

AIR system components
(© Chevrolet Div., G.M. Corp)

The diverter valve closes during engine overrun and deceleration and dumps the output from the air pump to the atmosphere. This prevents backfire due to air being injected when an overly rich mixture is present in the exhaust port.

Air Pump R & R

1. Disconnect the output hose.
2. Hold the pump from turning by squeezing the drive belt.
3. Loosen the pulley bolts.
4. Loosen the alternator so the belt can be removed.
5. Remove the pulley.
6. Remove the pump mounting bolts and the pump.
7. Install the pump with the mounting bolts hand-tight.
8. Install the pulley and tighten the bolts hand-tight.
9. Install and adjust the drive belt as outlined in the "Engine" portion of this section.
10. Squeeze the drive belt to prevent the pump from turning.
11. Torque the pulley bolts to 25 ft lbs. Tighten the pump mountings.
12. Check and adjust the belt tension again, if necessary.
13. Reconnect the hose.

Transmission Controlled Spark System

The Transmission Controlled Spark (TCS) is used on all 1971–72 models and on all 1973 85 hp engines with manual transmissions. It is also used on all 1973 cars built for California with manual transmissions and the Cosworth-Vega.

The TCS system is used to prevent vacuum advances when the transmission is in low forward gear. The TCS system consists of a temperature-sensing switch, a transmission switch, an idle stop solenoid, and a vacuum advance solenoid.

On 1971–72 cars, the vacuum advance solenoid is normally open, providing full vacuum to the distributor. When the vacuum advance solenoid is energized, the vacuum to the distributor is turned off and the advance unit is vented to the atmosphere.

The transmission switch is located on the transmission and senses when the transmission is in one of the lower gears. When in a lower gear, the switch activates the vacuum advance solenoid, shutting off vacuum advance. There is also an engine-temperature-sensing switch which overrides the transmission switch. It will allow vacuum advance in the lower gears when engine temperature is below 82° F. There is always vacuum advance in high gear and reverse.

On 1972 California models equipped with an automatic transmission, the transmission switch is a dummy switch and will not energize the solenoid. These engines have vacuum advance only when engine temperature is below 82° F.

An idle stop solenoid is used to prevent afterrun when the ignition is turned off. Afterrun is caused by the higher operating temperatures of today's engines and the wider throttle plate openings necessary for emission controls. The loss of spark from turning off the ignition is usually sufficient to stop the engine. However, if the engine has high enough cylinder temperatures, enough air-fuel mixture can pass the wide throttle plate opening and be ignited without the spark plug and the engine will continue to run even after the key is turned off. The idle solenoid is attached to the carburetor to solve this problem. The solenoid has an adjustable plunger and is electrically operated. When the ignition is turned on, the plunger is extended and contacts the carburetor throttle lever, opening the throttle plate wide enough for the engine to idle properly. When the ignition is turned off, the plunger retracts and the throttle lever falls back on the lever stop. When the throttle lever is on its stop the throttle plate opening is very small and will not allow enough air-fuel mix-

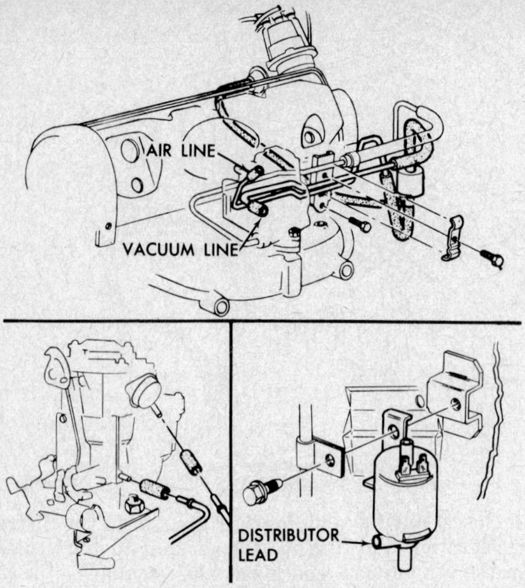
AIR LINE
VACUUM LINE
DISTRIBUTOR LEAD
1971-72 TCS vacuum components
(© Chevrolet Div., G.M. Corp)

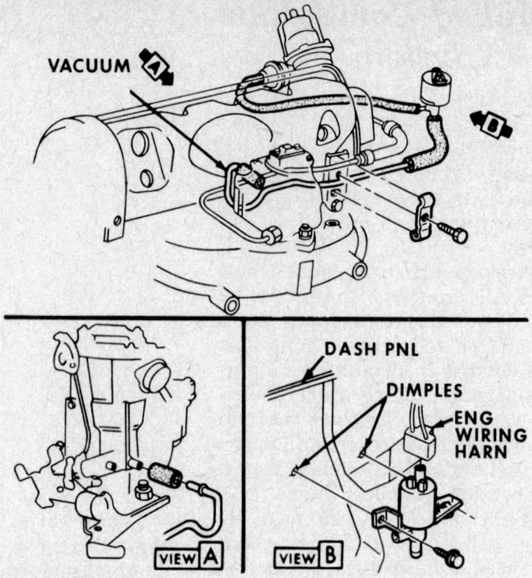
VACUUM
A
B
DASH PNL
DIMPLES
ENG WIRING HARN
VIEW A
VIEW B
1973-74 TCS vacuum components

ture to pass to run the engine with the ignition off.

On 1973 cars, the vacuum advance solenoid is normally closed, when (de-energized), venting the vacuum advance circuit to the atmosphere and shutting off vacuum to the distributor advance unit.

When the key is turned on the idle stop solenoid is energized, the plunger extends to touch the throttle lever and maintains idle speed. As long as the engine temperature remains below 93°F, the vacuum advance solenoid is energized and the distributor receives a vacuum supply.

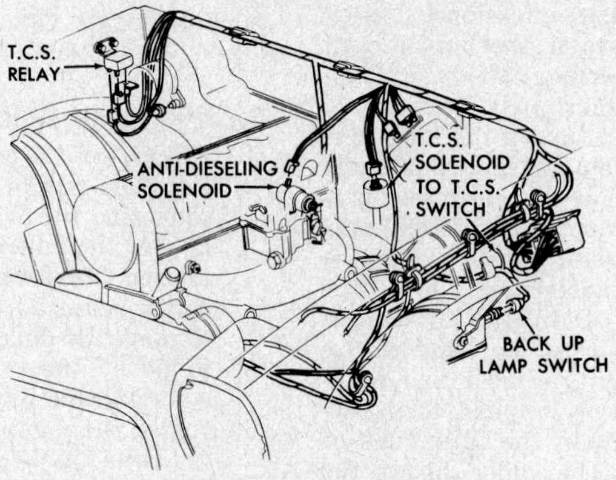
T.C.S. RELAY
ANTI-DIESELING SOLENOID
T.C.S. SOLENOID
TO T.C.S. SWITCH
BACK UP LAMP SWITCH
1971-72 TCS electrical components
(© Chevrolet Div., G.M. Corp)

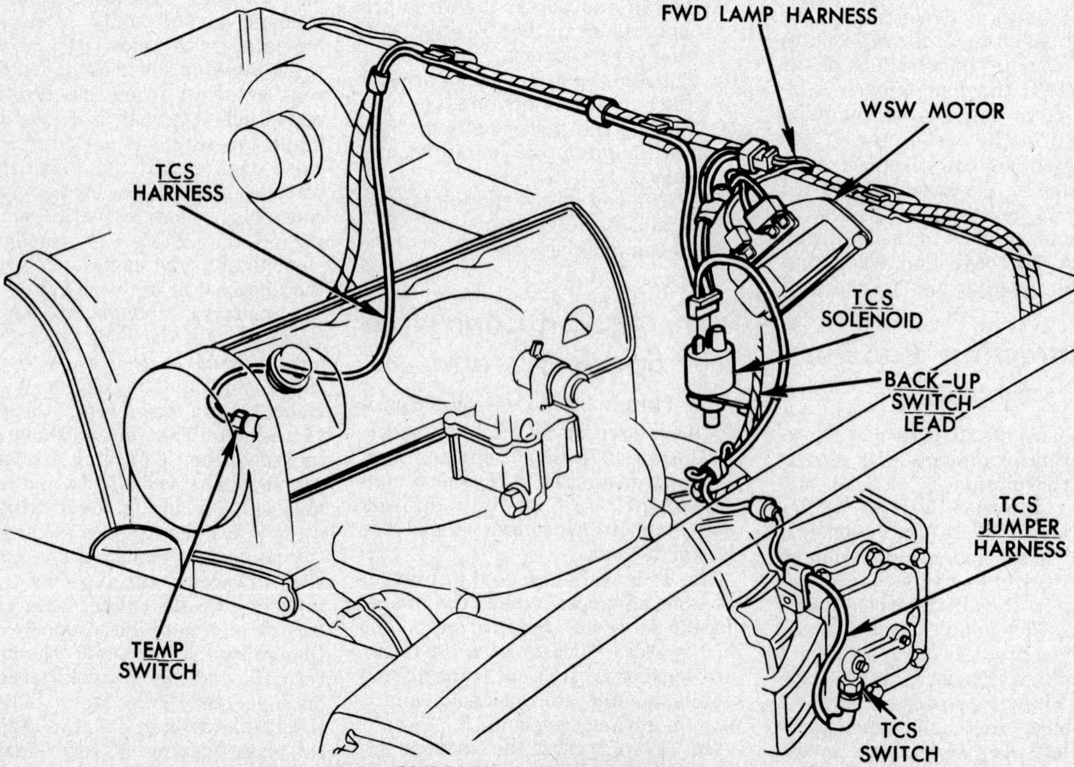
FWD LAMP HARNESS
WSW MOTOR
TCS HARNESS
TCS SOLENOID
BACK-UP SWITCH LEAD
TCS JUMPER HARNESS
TEMP SWITCH
TCS SWITCH
1973-74 TCS electrical components

The vacuum advance unit functions to give good start-up and drive-away characteristics. When the engine temperature reaches approximately 93°F, the temperature switch breaks the circuit, causing the vacuum advance solenoid to de-energize and cut off the vacuum supply. When the engine overheats, the temperature switch completes the circuit to activate the instrument panel warning lamp. Under normal driving conditions, the transmission switch controls the vacuum advance solenoid. In the lower gears, the switch is open and the solenoid de-energized. In high gear, the switch is closed and energizes the solenoid to open the vacuum port to the distributor and permits the advance unit to function. The idle stop solenoid operates as before.

Exhaust Gas Recirculation

Exhaust Gas Recirculation (EGR) was introduced in 1973 on all models, except the Cosworth-Vega.

EGR is used to reduce oxides of nitrogen (NO_x) that are formed at high operating temperatures.

EGR operates by introducing small amounts of relatively inert exhaust gas into the intake manifold, lowering the peak combustion temperature. The amount of exhaust gas introduced is regulated by the EGR valve. The EGR valve is vacuum modulated. The vacuum to operate the valve is supplied by an orifice just above the throttle valve in the carburetor.

When there is a high vacuum during heavy cruising speeds, the valve opens to allow exhaust gas into the intake manifold. At idle or heavy acceleration the valve is closed and no exhaust gas is introduced into the intake manifold.

EGR Valve R & R

1. Disconnect the vacuum line at the top of the valve.
2. Remove the valve-to-manifold retaining bolts.
3. Remove the EGR valve from the manifold.
4. Reinstall the EGR valve on the manifold.
5. Tighten the clamp bolt to 25 ft lb. Bend the lock tab over the bolt head.
6. Reconnect the vacuum line to the valve.

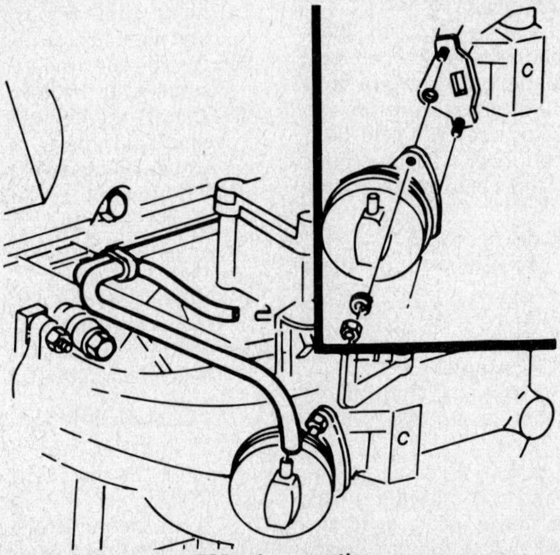

EGR valve mounting

ENGINE

The Vega engine is a single overhead camshaft, four-cylinder design using a die cast aluminum cylinder block and a cast iron cylinder head. The iron-plated aluminum pistons ride directly on honed and electrochemically treated aluminum bores. The cylinder block is cast of an alloy containing silicon which, after suitable etching, provides a proper bore surface for the pistons and rings.

The valve train is completely contained in the head, with a straight-line vertical valve configuration. The camshaft is driven by a timing belt which in turn is driven from a front crankshaft pulley.

The 140 cu in. engine is available in the base single-barrel and an optional version with a two-barrel carburetor and high-performance camshaft.

The limited production Cosworth-Vega uses the basic Vega engine block with a shorter stroke, forged steel crankshaft. Unlike the standard cast iron head, the Cosworth cylinder head is cast aluminum. The dual overhead cams, water pump, and fan are belt driven in a similar manner to the standard engine. The cylinder head is a crossflow design with intake and exhaust manifolds on opposite sides of the head. Each cylinder is serviced by two intake and two exhaust valves.

Engine R & R

1. Raise the hood and install a bolt in the hold-open link.
2. Disconnect the battery cables.
3. Drain the cooling system and disconnect the hoses at the radiator.
4. Disconnect the heater hoses at the water pump and at the heater inlet (bottom hose).
5. Disconnect the following emission hoses:
   a. PCV at the cam cover.
   b. The canister vacuum hose at the carburetor.
   c. PCV vacuum hose at the intake manifold.
   d. Bowl vent at the carburetor.
6. Remove the radiator, fan, fan spacer and air cleaner.
7. Disconnect the following electrical leads:
   a. Alternator.
   b. Ignition coil.
   c. Starter solenoid.
   d. Oil pressure sending unit.
   e. Temperature sending unit.
   f. TCS switch at the transmission.
   g. TCS solenoid on the firewall.
   h. Ground strap at the firewall.
8. Disconnect:
   a. Powerglide throttle valve linkage or Turbo Hydra-Matic detent cable.
   b. Fuel line at the rubber hose, rearward of the carburetor.
   c. Automatic transmission vacuum modulator and air conditioning vacuum line at the intake manifold.
   d. Throttle cable at the manifold bellcrank.
9. On cars with air conditioning, disconnect the compressor at the front support, rear support, rear lower bracket and remove the drive belt from the compressor.

NOTE: Do not disconnect any air conditioning lines or fittings.

10. Being careful not to crimp or bend the hoses, move the compressor slightly forward, allowing the front of the compressor to rest on the frame forward brace. Secure the rear of the compressor to the engine compartment so that it does not interfere with the engine removal.
11. If so equipped, disconnect the power steering pump and position it out of the way.
12. Raise the car on a hoist.
13. Disconnect the exhaust pipe at the exhaust manifold.
14. Remove the engine flywheel lower cover or the torque converter underpan.
15. On vehicles equipped with automatic transmission:
    a. Mark the converter-to-flywheel relationship for reassembly.
    b. Remove the converter to flywheel retaining bolts and install a coverter safety strap, to keep the converter from falling out.

c. Remove the converter housing to engine retaining bolts.
d. Loosen the engine front mount retaining bolts at the frame attachment and lower the vehicle on the hoist.
e. Install a floor jack under the transmission and an engine lifting adapter to raise the engine slightly from its mounts.
f. Remove the engine front mount retaining bolts.
g. Remove the engine from the vehicle. Pull the engine forward enough to clear the transmission while slowly lifting the engine.

16. On vehicles with manual transmission:
    a. Remove the flywheel housing to engine retaining bolts.
    b. Proceed with Step 15 above, parts d, e, f, and g.

To install engine:

17. Install two guide pins into the upper bolt holes in the engine block. Guide pins can be fabricated by cutting the heads off two bolts and sawing screwdriver slots into them.
18. Lower the engine into place, aligning the engine with the transmission.
19. Install the front mount bolts hand-tight.
20. Install the converter or clutch housing-to-engine bolts, replacing the guide pins. Remove the torque converter retaining strap, if one was used.
21. Torque the clutch housing-to-engine bolts to 25 ft lbs and the converter housing-to-engine bolts to 35 ft lbs.
22. After checking to make sure that the front engine mounts are aligned and not making metal-to-metal contact, tighten them to 20 ft lbs.
23. Align the previously made converter and flywheel marks, and torque the bolts to 35 ft lbs.
24. Install the flywheel dust cover or torque converter underpan.
25. Connect the exhaust pipe at the manifold.
26. If so equipped, install the air conditioning compressor and power steering pump. Adjust the alternator belt.
27. Reconnect:
    a. the accelerator cable,
    b. the automatic transmission vacuum modulator line and the air conditioning vacuum line,
    c. the fuel line, and
    d. the Powerglide transmission throttle valve linkage or the Turbo Hydra-Matic detent cable.
28. Attach the following electrical connections:
    a. alternator
    b. coil
    c. starter solenoid
    d. oil pressure switch
    e. temperature switch
    f. TCS transmission switch
    g. TCS solenoid
    h. engine ground strap
29. Replace the air cleaner and install these hoses:
    a. vent tube at the air cleaner base
    b. carburetor bowl vent
    c. PCV vacuum line
    d. vacuum canister hose
30. Install the radiator, radiator panel or shroud, spacer, and fan.
31. Connect the heater and radiator hoses. Fill the cooling system.
32. Connect the battery cables. Start the engine and check for leaks. Remember to remove the bolt from the hood hold-open link.

Manifolds

Intake Manifold R & R

1. Raise the hood and install a bolt through the hold-open link.
2. Disconnect the negative battery cable.
3. Drain the cooling system.
4. Remove the EGR tube retaining clamps from both the intake and exhaust manifolds. Remove the EGR tube by carefully driving it off.
5. Disconnect the heater hose at the fitting on the intake manifold.
6. Disconnect the vent tube at the base of the air cleaner, then remove the air cleaner.
7. Remove the air cleaner silencer.
8. Disconnect:
    a. The choke rod at the carburetor.
    b. PCV valve at the cam cover.
    c. Fuel line at the carburetor.
    d. The carburetor bowl vent line at the carburetor.
    e. Throttle linkage and the transmission throttle valve linkage.
    f. Power steering pump brace at the manifold.
9. Remove the alternator to thermostat housing through-bolt and loosen the alternator swivel bolt. Move the alternator aside to gain access to the manifold bolt.
10. Remove the four intake manifold bolts and remove the manifold.
11. Remove from the manifold:
    a. The carburetor and carburetor linkage.
    b. Pipe plug.
    c. Vacuum fittings.
    d. Hot water nipple.
12. Install the items removed in Step 10 above to the new manifold.
13. Clean the gasket surfaces on the manifold and the cylinder head.
14. Position a new gasket over the dowels on the cylinder head, then carefully install the manifold. Make sure that the gasket remains in place.
15. Install the manifold bolts, tightening to 30 ft. lbs. The stud goes in the hole nearest No. 3 intake port.
16. Connect the power steering pump brace to the manifold.
17. Install the alternator to thermostat housing through bolt and adjust the belt tension.
18. Connect:
    a. The choke rod at the carburetor.
    b. The PCV valve at the cam cover.
    c. Fuel line at the carburetor.
    d. Carburetor bowl vent line at the carburetor.
    e. The throttle and transmission throttle valve linkage.
    f. Vacuum connections at the carburetor.
19. Install the air cleaner silencer and secure it to the heat stove tube.
20. Install the air cleaner. Connect the vent tube at the base of the air cleaner.
21. Connect the heater hose to the intake manifold fitting and fill the cooling system.
22. Raise the car. Install the EGR tube on the intake and exhaust manifolds.
23. Install the EGR tube retaining clamps. Lower the car.
24. Connect the negative battery cable and start the engine. Check for leaks and adjust the carburetor.

Exhaust Manifold R & R

Standard Engine

1. From under the car, disconnect the exhaust pipe from the manifold.
2. Remove the intake manifold as described above.
3. Disconnect the oil dipstick bracket at the exhaust manifold.
4. Remove the exhaust manifold bolts, then remove the manifold and carburetor heater assembly.
5. Install the carburetor heater assembly on the new manifold.
6. Install the exhaust manifold and manifold bolts (loosely). The upper bolts are shorter.
7. Tighten the manifold bolts to 30 ft. lbs.
8. Connect the exhaust pipe to the manifold.
9. Connect the oil dipstick bracket to the exhaust manifold.
10. Install the intake manifold as described above.

Cosworth-Vega engine

1. Disconnect the exhaust pipe from the manifold.
2. Disconnect the oil dipstick tube from the manifold.
3. Remove the retaining bolts and

remove the manifold, being careful not to damage the temperature sensor or its wiring.

4. Install the exhaust manifold bolts hand tight. Gradually tighten the bolts from the inside out.
5. Connect the exhaust pipe to the manifold.
6. Install the oil dipstick tube on the manifold.

Valve System

The Vega valve system consists of an overhead camshaft operating directly on mechanical tappets which open and close the valves.

and four spark plug wires on the side of the distributor with chalk. (Refer to the firing order illustration.)

2. Remove the distributor cap, air cleaner, and valve cover.
3. Turn the engine until the rotor points to the No. one position and the points are open. The No. one intake and exhaust, No. two intake and No. three exhaust valves are adjusted at this position.
4. Insert the correct size feeler gauge between the camshaft lobe and the valve tappet. If the clearance is between 0.014 and 0.017 in. for intakes or 0.029 and

by pressing down on the tappet while adjusting.

7. Turn the engine so that the rotor points to no. four. Adjust no. two exhaust, no. three intake, and no. four intake and exhaust valves in this position.
8. Replace the valve cover, air cleaner, and distributor cap.

Valve Stem Oil Seal and/or Valve Spring Replacement

1. Remove the valve tappet, and leave the tappet compressing tool in place.
2. Remove the spark plug at the cylinder to be serviced.
3. With the crankshaft position 90°

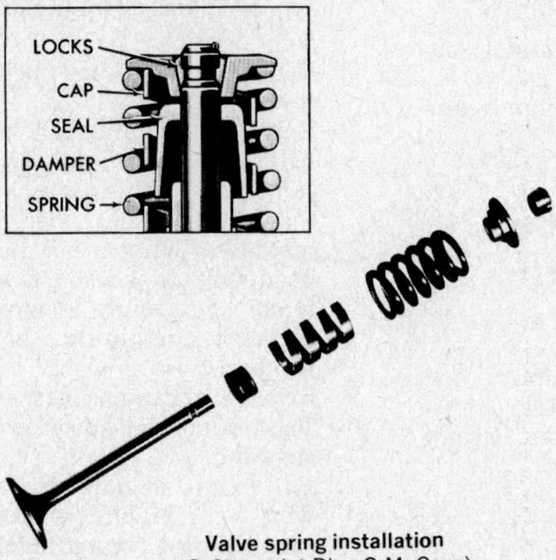
LOCKS
CAP
SEAL
DAMPER
SPRING
Valve spring installation
(© Chevrolet Div., G.M. Corp)

J-23587
Valve tappet and adjusting screw assembly
(© Chevrolet Div., G.M. Corp)

Valve Tappet R & R

NOTE: the tappet adjusting screw may be replaced without removing the tappet from the engine.

1. Remove the camshaft as described in this section. A special tool is necessary for this job.
2. Release the tension on the tappet depressing levers and slide the levers to one side.
3. Remove the tappet and adjusting screw assembly. Identify each tappet so that it may be installed in its original position.
4. Remove the adjusting screw from the tappet.

NOTE: identify each adjusting screw and the tappet from which it was removed. Tappet adjusting screws may be standard, or one of two undersizes.

5. Install the adjusting screw in the tappet (hole nearer the top of the tappet).
6. With the flat side of the adjusting screw facing down, install the tappet in its original bore.
7. Depress the tappet with the camshaft removal tool and install the camshaft as outlined later in this section.
8. Adjust the valve lash as described below.

Valve Lash Adjustment

1. Mark the locations of No. one

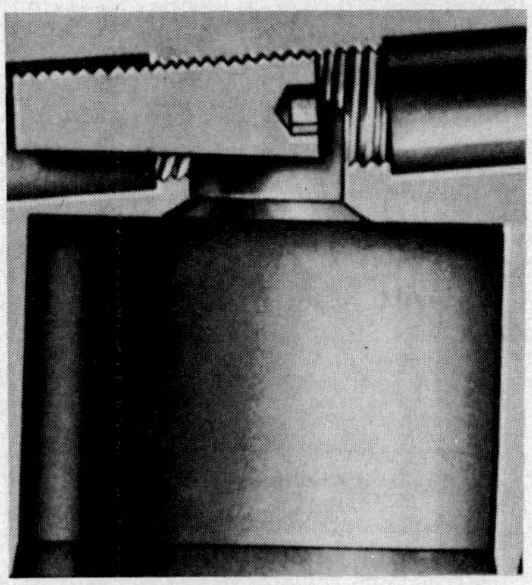
Adjusting valve lash
(© Chevrolet Div., G.M. Corp)

0.032 in. for exhausts, no adjustment is necessary. This is due to the fact that the adjusting mechanism only allows adjustments in increments of 0.003 in.

5. If lash is 0.003 in. or more out of adjustment, insert a 1/8 in. allen wrench into the tappet adjusting screw and turn it one full turn. Turning clockwise tightens; turning counterclockwise loosens.
6. Check the lash again and adjust further if necessary. Always turn the adjuster screw one full turn. You can feel the flat spot

from top dead center, install an air line adapter in the spark plug hole and apply air pressure to hold the valves in place.

4. Compress the valve spring, then remove the valve keepers.
5. Remove the valve cap, valve spring and damper assembly and the valve stem oil seal.
6. Install a new valve stem oil seal over the valve guide.
7. Install the valve spring and damper assembly and the valve cap over the valve stem.
8. Compress the valve spring and install the keepers. Grease will hold the keepers in place while releasing the spring.
9. Remove the air line adapter tool and install the spark plug.
10. Install the valve tappet.
11. Adjust the tappets.
12. Install all of the components which were removed. See Camshaft Installation.

Valve Guides

Valves with oversize stems are available in three sizes: 0.003 in. o/s, 0.015 in. o/s and 0.030 in. o/s. Remove the cylinder head and remove the camshaft from the head. Remove the valves. Ream the valve guides with an appropriate oversize reamer.

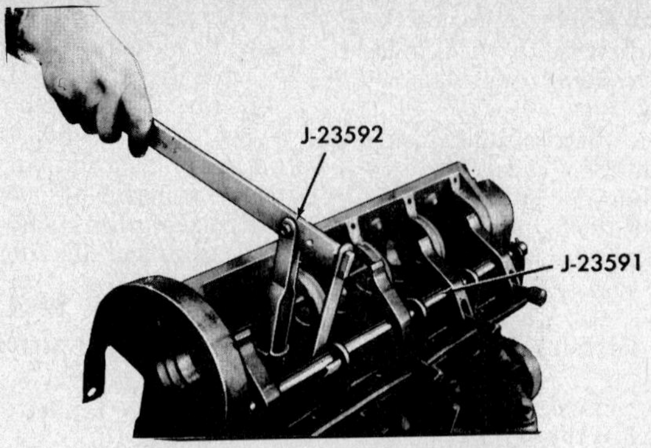
J-23592
J-23591

Compressing valve springs
(© Chevrolet Div., G.M. Corp)

Cylinder Head

Cylinder Head R & R

NOTE: Cylinder head gasket R&R does not require separating the intake and exhaust manifolds from the cylinder head.

1. Remove the timing belt cover and camshaft cover. Drain the cooling system.
2. Remove the timing belt and camshaft sprocket.
3. Remove the intake and exhaust manifolds.
4. Disconnect the water hose at the thermostat housing (outlet).
5. Remove the cylinder head bolts, then the head and gasket.

NOTE: If the head sticks, bump the starter a few times to loosen it with compression. Do not insert any tools between the head and block to pry them apart.

6. Using a new gasket (smooth side up), carefully position the cylinder head on the block.
7. Install the cylinder head bolts finger-tight. Use an anti-seize compound on the threads. Install the lifting bracket under the second head bolt from the front on the spark plug side. The 6-3/8 in. bolts are installed on the manifold side and the 5-5/8 in. bolts are installed on the spark plug side.
8. Tighten the head bolts to 60 ft. lbs. (in steps), using the illustration.
9. Connect the water hose to the thermostat housing.
10. Install the intake and exhaust manifolds.
11. Install the timing bolt and sprocket.
12. Install the front cover and camshaft cover.

Timing Cover, Belt, and Camshaft

Front Cover R & R

1. Raise the hood and install a bolt in the hood hold-open link.
2. Disconnect the negative battery cable.
3. Remove the fan and spacer.
4. Loosen the two lower cover retaining screws.
5. Remove the two top cover retaining screws and remove the cover, lifting it until the slots clear the lower screws.
6. To install, position the cover, lowering it until the slots are over the lower screws. Loosely tighten the lower screws.
7. Install the upper screws, then tighten all four screws to 50 in. lbs.
8. Install the spacer and fan, tightening the bolts to 20 ft. lbs.
9. Connect the battery cable and remove the bolt from the hood hold-open link.

Timing Belt and Sprocket R & R

1. Raise the hood and install a bolt in the hood hold-open link.
2. Disconnect the negative battery cable.
3. Loosen the air conditioner and alternator as necessary and remove the drive belts.
4. Remove the crankshaft pulley and four pulley-to-sprocket bolts. Remove the pulley and damper or washer as applicable.

NOTE: it is not necessary to remove the pulley if only the camshaft sprocket is being removed.

5. Drain the engine coolant and loosen the water pump bolts to relieve the tension on the timing belt.
6. Remove the timing belt lower cover.
7. Remove the timing belt.
8. Align one of the holes in the camshaft timing sprocket with the head bolt behind the sprocket. Using a socket on the head bolt to keep the sprocket from rotating, remove the sprocket retaining bolt and washer.
9. Remove the camshaft sprocket.
10. The crankshaft sprocket may be removed.
11. Pull the crankshaft sprocket with an installation tool. Make sure that the timing mark is facing out and that the key is installed.
12. To install the camshaft sprocket, align the dowel in the camshaft with the locating hole in the end of the camshaft.
13. Install the sprocket retaining bolt, tightening to 80 ft. lbs.
14. Align the timing mark on the camshaft sprocket with the notch on the timing belt upper cover and the crankshaft sprocket timing mark with the cast rib on the oil pump cover.
15. Install the timing belt on the crankshaft sprocket, then with the back of the belt positioned in

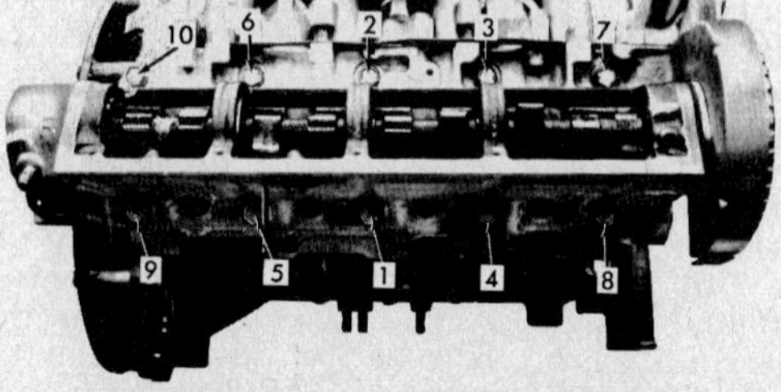
FRONT
10
6
2
3
7
9
5
1
4
8

Vega cylinder head torque sequence (all engines)
(© Chevrolet Div., G.M. Corp)

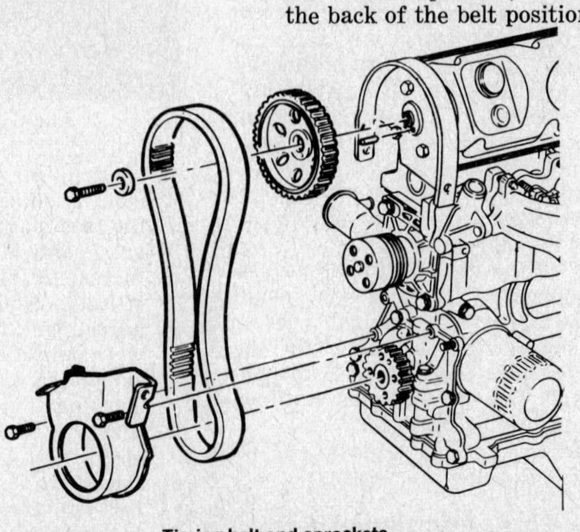

Timing belt and sprockets
(© Chevrolet Div., G.M. Corp)

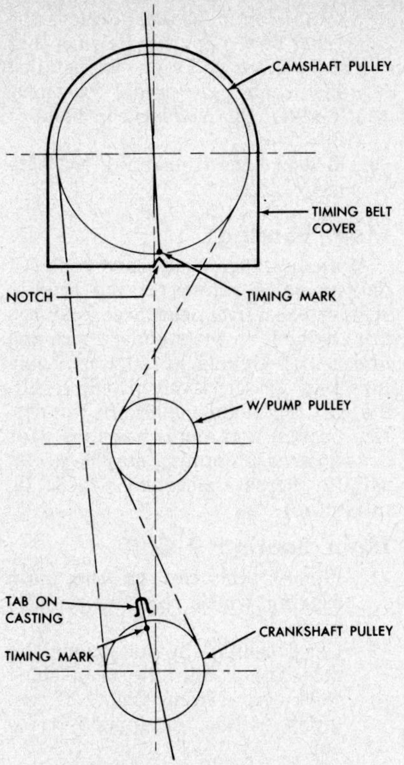
CAMSHAFT PULLEY
TIMING BELT COVER
NOTCH
TIMING MARK
W/PUMP PULLEY
TAB ON CASTING
CRANKSHAFT PULLEY
TIMING MARK

Timing sprocket alignment marks
(© Chevrolet Div., G.M. Corp)

the water pump track, install the belt on the camshaft sprocket. Make sure that both sprockets maintain their indexed positions.

16. Install the lower timing belt cover, using anti-seize compound on the threads of the bolts and tightening them to 50 in. lbs.
17. Adjust the timing belt tension as described under Water Pump R&R above, Steps 11 and 12.
18. Fill the cooling system.
19. Install the accessory drive pulley to the crankshaft sprocket, aligning the tang on the pulley with the keyway on the crankshaft. Install the damper locating dowel in the locating hole of the sprocket.
20. Loosely install the four sprocket bolts, then install the crankshaft (center) bolt. Tighten the crankshaft bolt to 80 ft. lbs. and the four sprocket bolts to 15 ft. lbs.
21. Install the alternator and air conditioning compressor as applicable and adjust the belts.
22. Install the engine front cover, fan and fan spacer.
23. Connect the battery cable and remove the bolt from the hood hold-open link.

Camshaft Cover R & R

1. Raise the hood and install a bolt in the hood hold-open link.
2. Disconnect the negative battery cable.
3. Remove the air cleaner and the vent tube (at cam cover).
4. Remove the PCV valve from the cam cover.
5. Remove the cam cover screws and the cover.
6. To install, reverse the above procedure. The gasket is reusable. The oil filler cap is at the forward end of the cover. Tighten the cam cover screws to 35 in. lbs.

Camshaft R & R

NOTE: A special valve tappet depressing tool is necessary for camshaft removal. This tool is only available through Chevrolet.

1. Remove the hood.
2. Remove the camshaft timing sprocket.
3. Remove the three screws securing the camshaft seal and retainer assembly and timing cover to the cylinder head.
4. Inspect the seal, prying it out and replacing it if necessary.
5. Remove the camshaft cover.
6. Disconnect the fuel line at the carburetor.
7. Remove:
   a. Idle solenoid from its bracket.
   b. The choke coil, cover and rod assembly.
   c. Ignition distributor.
8. Raise the vehicle on a hoist, disconnect the front engine mounts at the body attachment, raise the front of the engine and install wood blocks, about 1-½ in. thick, between the engine mounts and the body.
9. Install camshaft removal tool on the cylinder head to hold down the lifters so that the camshaft may be removed.
   a. Position the tool so that the attaching holes are aligned with the lower cam cover bolt holes and the tappet levers of the tool are aligned to depress both valves of each cylinder.
   b. Back off the bolts in the bottom of the tool so that they are not contacting the bosses beneath the tool.
   c. Install the tool attaching bolts, tightening them securely.
   d. Tighten the bolts in the bottom of the tool until they just touch the bosses of the cylinder head. Before depressing the tappets, rotate the crankshaft pulley timing mark 90° clockwise from the timing mark on the tab. This assures that the pistons are not at TDC and will prevent valve-to-piston contact.
   e. Grease the ball end of the lever depressing bolts and tighten the bolts to depress the tappets.

NOTE: torque the lever bolts to 10 ft. lbs. If more tightening is required, check to see that the tool is properly installed, then proceed cautiously to prevent damaging the depressing lever.

10. Slide the camshaft forward until it clears the head.

NOTE: the camshaft bearings may be removed. It is not necessary to remove the camshaft end plug. Gently tap out the bearings, starting at the forward end. Tap out the rear bearing slowly into the distributor housing, being careful not to unseat the end plug. Crush the rear bearing to remove it from the distributor housing. Install, starting with the rear bearing. The oil holes in the bearings must align with the oil holes in the case. On the first two bearings the oil holes are at 11 o'clock (as

J-23591

Installing camshaft removing tool
(© Chevrolet Div., G.M. Corp)

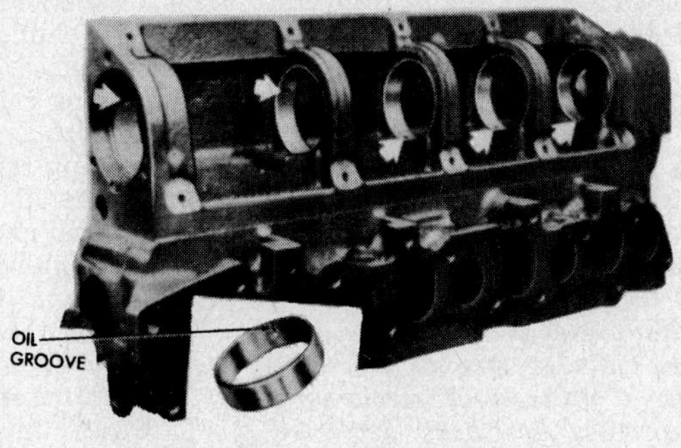
OIL GROOVE

Camshaft bearing alignment
(© Chevrolet Div., G.M. Corp)

seen from the front of the engine) and the oil groove in the number one bearing toward the front of the engine.

11. Install the camshaft with the journals seated in the bores.
12. With the car up on a hoist, raise the front of the engine and remove the wood blocks from the engine mounts.
13. Install the front engine mounts, then lower the vehicle.
14. Using a new gasket, install the timing belt upper cover and retainer plate and seal assembly. Tighten the retaining bolts to 15 ft. lbs.
15. Using a dial indicator, measure the camshaft end-play. If it is not 0.004-0.012 in., select a camshaft retainer (according to cam locator thickness) which will provide more or less end-play as required.
16. Remove the tappet depressing tool by first releasing the tappet depressing lever bolts, and then removing the tool attaching bolts.
17. Install:
    a. Camshaft timing sprocket.
    b. The timing belt.
    c. Front engine cover.
    d. Distributor.
    e. Vehicle hood.
18. Adjust the valve tappets.
19. Install the camshaft cover.
20. Install and adjust the carburetor choke coil, cover and rod assembly.
21. Connect the carburetor fuel line.
22. Install the idle solenoid to the bracket.
23. Check and adjust the ignition timing.

Piston & Rod R & R

1. Remove the intake and exhaust manifolds, cylinder head, oil pan and baffle.
2. Check the connecting rods and caps for cylinder number identification and, if necessary, mark them.
3. Using a ridge reamer, remove any ridge or deposits from the upper end of the cylinder bore.
4. Remove the connecting rod cap and install protective tubes on the studs. Push the piston and connecting rod assembly out the top of the block.
5. The piston and wrist pin are a matched set and not serviced separately.

NOTE: Oversize pistons were not supplied initially, since there was no mechanical means available for duplicating the cylinder bore electrochemical etching process. A mechanical honing process has been perfected and oversize pistons are now available.

6. Select the piston rings comparable in size to the piston being used. Measure the ring gap with the ring squarely in the cylinder bore. If the gap is not within specifications, select the ring to fit. Install the rings on the piston in the following order, making sure that the gaps are positioned as illustrated:
    a. Install the oil spacer.
    b. Holding the oil spacer ends butted, install the lower oil ring rail.
    c. Install the upper steel oil ring rail.
    d. Install the second compression ring.
    e. Install the first compression ring.

    Check the ring side clearance, dressing the groove with a cut file if necessary.
7. Clean the cylinder bores thoroughly and wipe with a light engine oil.
8. If required, install new bearing inserts in the rod cap. The F on the piston must face towards the front of the engine. Be sure that the pistons and rods are installed in their original locations. Tighten the bearing cap bolts to 35 ft. lbs.
9. Measure the connecting rod side clearance.

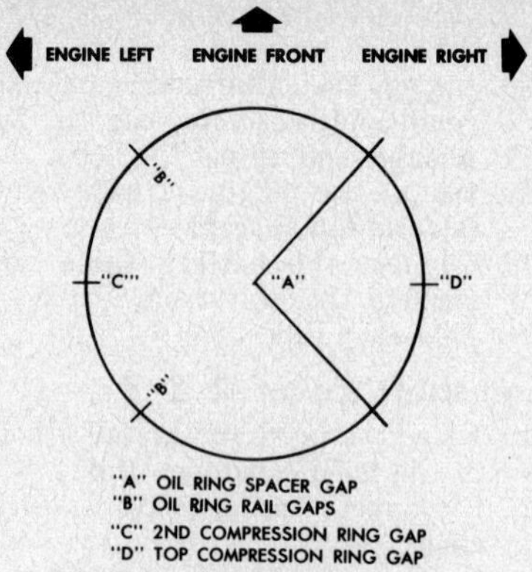
ENGINE LEFT
ENGINE FRONT
ENGINE RIGHT
"A"
"B"
"B"
"C"
"D"
"A" OIL RING SPACER GAP
"B" OIL RING RAIL GAPS
"C" 2ND COMPRESSION RING GAP
"D" TOP COMPRESSION RING GAP

Ring gap locations
(© Chevrolet Div., G.M. Corp)

F

Piston marking
(© Chevrolet Div., G.M. Corp)

Main Bearings

Main bearing inserts are replaced only in pairs. Shims are not used to remove excessive clearance. Bearings are available in the standard size and undersizes. During production, bearings may be selectively fitted, resulting in occasional 0.001 in. undersize bearings. If main bearings caps are replaced, shimming may be necessary to increase clearance (0.001 in. minimum).

Main Bearing R & R

1. Remove the cap on the main bearing which requires replacement.
2. Use a rollpin in the journal oil hole and rotate the crankshaft clockwise (from front of engine), rolling the upper bearing out.
3. Oil the new selected upper bearing and insert the plain (unnotched) end between the crankshaft and the indented or notched side of the block.
4. Rotate the bearing into place and remove the rollpin from the oil hole in the journal.
5. Oil the lower bearing and install it in the bearing cap.
6. Install the bearing cap with the F toward the front of the engine and install the bearing cap bolts, tightening to 65 ft. lbs.

Lubrication

The oil pump is crankshaft driven, externally mounted on the front of the engine, and is an eccentric gear type. Oil flow from the pump is at 40-45 psi and leads directly to the oil filter. There are two main oil galleries: the crankcase main gallery and the cylinder head main gallery. The main and rod bearings are lubricated from the crankcase gallery. The cylinder head gallery is supplied with oil from the front main bearing, which acts as a metering device, through a vertical passage in the block. The head gallery has five passages to the cam bearings, from which all valve train components are lubricated. At the rear end of the head gallery there is a short passage which supplies oil pressure for the distributor damper.

Oil Pan and Baffle R & R

1. Raise the vehicle and drain the engine oil. Raise the front of the engine, being careful not to distort the pan.
2. Support the engine with a jack

and remove the frame crossmember and both front crossmember braces.
3. Disconnect the steering idler arm at the frame side rail. On vehicles with air conditioning, disconnect the idler arm at the relay rod.
4. Mark the position of the steering linkage pitman arm to the steering gear pitman shaft and remove the pitman arm.

NOTE: do not rotate the steering gear pitman shaft while the linkage is disconnected, because the steering wheel alignment will be changed.

5. Remove the flywheel cover or converter underpan.
6. Remove the oil pan bolts, tap the oil pan to break the seal, then remove the pan.
7. Remove the pick-up screen-to-support retaining bolt and the pick-up screen-to-baffle support bolts, then remove the support from the baffle.
8. Remove the bolt which secures the oil drain back tube to the baffle, then rotate the baffle 90° toward the left side of the car and remove the baffle from the pick-up screen.
9. The oil pump screen and pick up tube may be removed as follows:
   a. Remove the two self-locking mounting bolts (in block).
   b. Lightly tap on the U section of the pick-up tube to remove the tube from the casting.
   c. If damaged, the tube and screen assembly are replaced as a unit.
   d. Apply sealing compound to the pick-up tube sealing surface.
   e. Install the tube into its bore, using an open end wrench on the tube boss, tapping the wrench with a mallet. Make sure that the retaining brackets are aligned with the bolt holes.
   f. Using anti-seize compound on the threads, install the retaining bolts. Tighten the bolts to 25 ft. lbs.
10. Install the oil pan and baffle in the reverse order of removal. Use sealing compound on the oil pump gasket surface. Tighten the oil pan bolts to 15 ft. lbs. See Steering Linkage R&R for correct pitman arm and idler arm installation procedure. Tighten frame crossmember and brace bolts to 35 ft. lbs.

Oil Pump R & R

1. Remove:
   a. Front engine cover.
   b. Accessory drive pulley.
   c. Timing belt.
   d. Timing belt lower cover.
   e. Crankshaft sprocket.
2. Raise the vehicle on a hoist and drain the engine oil.
3. Remove the oil pan and baffle.
4. Remove the oil pump bolts and the pump.
5. Inspect the oil pump for wear. The pump gears and body are not serviced separately. Replacement of the entire oil pump is required. Check the pressure regulator for free operation.

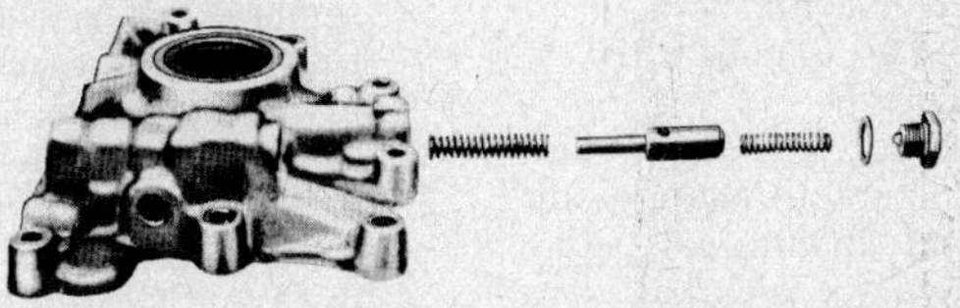

Oil pump pressure regulator
(© Chevrolet Div., G.M. Corp)

6. When installing, clean all gasket surfaces. Be sure that the pump drive key is installed properly. Use anti-seize compound on the threads of the pump mounting bolts, tightening them to 15 ft. lbs. The stud is installed in the upper right (facing pump) and tightened to 30 ft. lbs. Install the oil pan before tightening the timing cover bolts.

Oil Pump (Front Cover) Seal R & R

1. Remove the following:
   a. Engine front cover.
   b. Accessory drive pulley.
   c. Timing belt.
   d. Timing belt lower cover.
   e. Crankshaft timing sprocket.
2. Pry out the old seal, being careful not to damage the housing seal surfaces.
3. Coat the lips of the new seal with oil and apply sealing compound to the outside diameter of the seal.
4. Install the seal with the closed end outward.
5. Install all components removed in Step 1 above.

Rear Main Oil Seal R & R

NOTE: This repair can be made without removing the engine, but the transmission must be removed so that the crankshaft can be lowered.

1. Remove the oil pan and baffle.
2. Remove the rear main bearing cap and discard the lower seal.
3. Loosen the remaining bearing caps to allow the crankshaft to be lowered.
4. Push the upper seal on one end enough so that the other end can be grasped with pliers. Pull out the upper seal.
5. Cut and form a new braided fabric upper seal in the bearing cap. Taper the end of the seal and insert a piece of soft wire through the seal about ¼ in. from the end. Wrap the wire around the seal to form a secure attachment.
6. Thread the wire through the upper seal groove, then start the seal and pull it into position.
7. Tighten all the bearing caps except the rear cap to 65 ft. lbs.
8. Cut the seal flush to 1/64 in. below the bearing edge, making a clean cut and leaving no raveled edges.
9. Install and cut a seal in the rear main bearing cap.

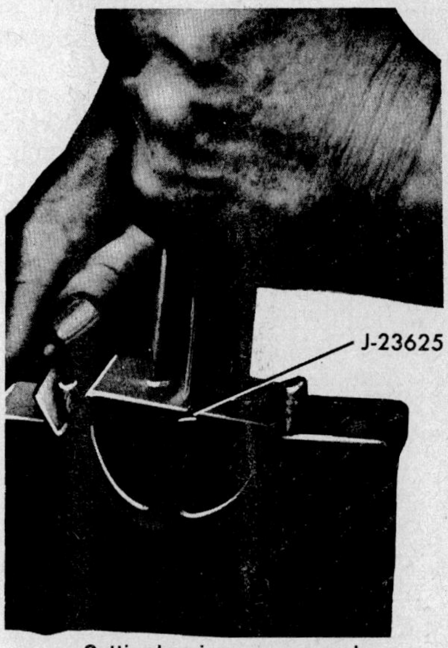
J-23625

Cutting bearing cap rope seal
(© Chevrolet Div., G.M. Corp)

10. Install the rear main bearing cap and measure the clearance with Plastigage, tightening the cap bolts to 65 ft. lbs. If the bearing clearance is within specifications, the seal is properly seated.
11. Install the bearing cap, tightening to 65 ft. lbs.
12. Install rear main bearing cap side sealant. This is available in a kit, complete with plunger applicator, from Chevrolet. Force the compound firmly into place to ensure that there are no air bubbles.
13. Install the oil pan and baffle.

CLUTCH

The Vega clutch is a diaphragm spring type, actuated by a cable and pulley arrangement. The clutch disc is pressed against the flywheel by the spring-loaded clutch cover. The clutch release fingers are depressed by a ball bearing type release bearing. The release fork pivots on an adjustable ball stud which is located on the right side of the bell housing. The clutch is actuated by a cable.

Clutch Pedal Free Travel Adjustment

Adjustment for normal clutch wear is accomplished by turning the clutch fork ball stud counterclockwise to give .90 ± .25 in. lash at clutch pedal.

1. Remove ball stud cap and loosen locknut on ball stud end located to the right of the transmission on the clutch housing.
2. Adjust ball stud to obtain .90 ± .25 in. free travel.
3. Tighten locknut to 25 ft lbs. being careful not to change adjustment and install ball stud cap.
4. Check operation of clutch.

Clutch Cable Replacement

1. Remove clutch fork cover at side of housing.
2. Disconnect return spring and clutch cable at clutch shift fork.
3. Remove clip and pin retaining cable to pedal arm.
4. Pull cable assembly through reinforcement and disengage from fender skirt reinforcement.
5. Push new cable through body reinforcement and around pulley. Secure cable end to pedal arm with pin, washer and clip.

NOTE: lubricate retaining pin with graphite type grease.

6. Route cable over fender skirt reinforcement and down to the clutch fork lever. Install cable end in fork lever as previously outlined under adjustment procedures.
7. Install clutch fork cover and tighten retaining screws to 80 in. lbs.

Clutch Disc R & R

1. Raise vehicle on hoist.
2. Remove transmission as outlined in this section.
3. Remove clutch fork cover then disconnect clutch return spring and control cable from clutch fork.
4. Remove main drive gear oil seal from clutch release bearing sleeve.
5. Remove flywheel housing lower cover.
6. Remove flywheel housing from engine.
7. To remove the release bearing from clutch fork and sleeve, slide lever off ball stud against spring action. If necessary to replace ball stud, remove cap, locknut and stud from housing.
8. If assembly marks on clutch assembly and flywheel are not distinguishable, remark with paint or center-punch.
9. Loosen clutch cover to flywheel, attaching bolts one turn at a time until spring pressure is released, to avoid bending clutch cover flange.
10. Support the pressure plate and cover assembly then remove the bolts and clutch assembly.

Caution Do not disassemble the clutch cover, spring and pressure plate for repair. If defective replace complete assembly.

11. Index alignment marks on clutch assembly and flywheel. Place driven plate on pressure plate with long end of splined end facing forward, damper springs inside pressure plate, and insert a dummy clutch gear shaft through the cover and driven plate.
12. Position the complete assembly against the flywheel and insert the dummy shaft into the pilot bearing in the crankshaft.
13. Index the alignment marks and install clutch cover to flywheel bolts finger-tight.

Caution Tighten all bolts evenly and gradually until tight to avoid possible clutch distortion. Torque bolts 18 ft. bs. and remove dummy shaft.

14. Lubricate the clutch fork ball socket and the fingers at the release bearing with a high melting point grease such as graphite grease.
15. Lubricate the recess on the inside of the throwout bearing collar and the fork groove with a light coat of graphite grease. Install fork in housing but not on stud.
16. Install bearing on sleeve, then position clutch fork over bearing in housing and slide fork onto ball stud.
17. Install flywheel housing and lower cover. Tighten bolts to 25 ft. lbs.
18. Install transmission as outlined previously.
19. Adjust clutch as previously outlined.
20. Lower and remove vehicle from hoist.

MANUAL TRANSMISSION

The 1971-72 three and four-speed manual transmissions available on the Vega are both fully synchronized in all forward gears and have floor mounted shift controls. The three-speed transmission first-reverse synchronizer sleeve has gear teeth on the outside diameter which enable it to function as a reverse gear when engaged with the reverse idler gear. The reverse gear on the four-speed transmission is similar to that of the three-speed except that the reverse teeth are on the first-second synchronizer. The control lever on this transmission has a reverse lockout feature.

The Opel-made transmissions used in 1971-72 were replaced with Saginaw three and four-speed units in 1973. These are fully synchronized and are similar to those used throughout the Chevrolet line. The Cosworth-Vega is equipped with a Muncie four-speed.

Shift Mechanism Adjustment

1971-72 Four-Speed

The reverse gearshift blocker adjustment can only be made on the four-speed transmission. This adjustment is made at the selector shaft on the left side of the transmission.

1. Shift into second gear.
2. Adjust the selector ring so that

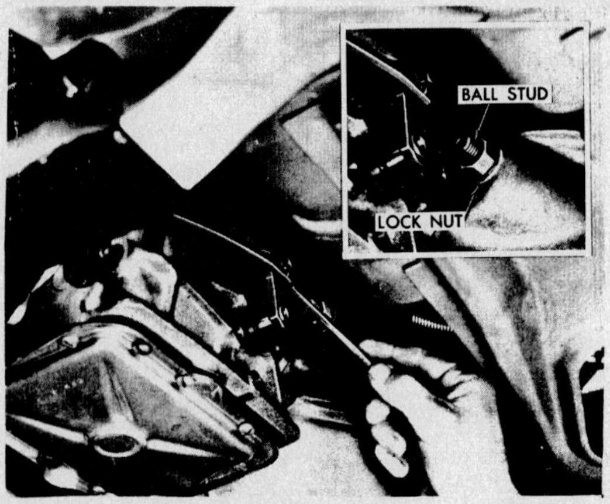
BALL STUD
LOCK NUT

Clutch ball stud adjustment
(© Chevrolet Div., G.M. Corp)

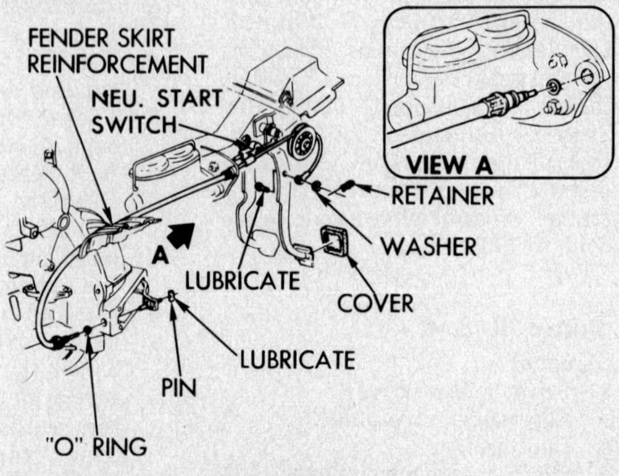
FENDER SKIRT REINFORCEMENT
NEU. START SWITCH
VIEW A
RETAINER
WASHER
A
LUBRICATE
COVER
LUBRICATE
PIN
"O" RING

Clutch control cable
(© Chevrolet Div., G.M. Corp)

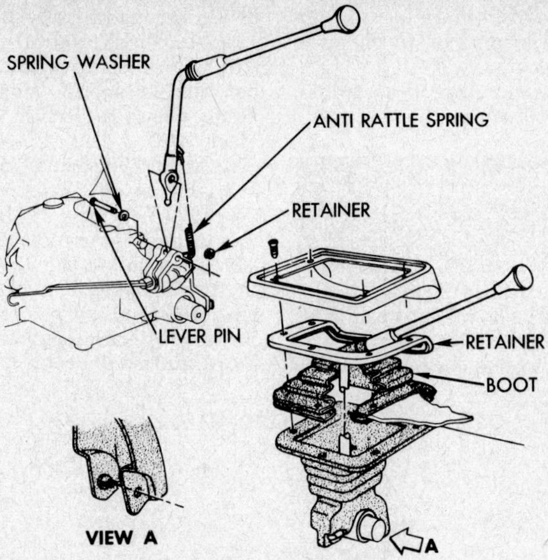
SPRING WASHER
ANTI RATTLE SPRING
RETAINER
LEVER PIN
RETAINER
BOOT
VIEW A
A

1971-72 shift control lever installation
(© Chevrolet Div., G.M. Corp)

the shift lever finger ball has equal clearance on both sides in the intermediate lever hole.
3. Back off the selector ring a quarter turn and tighten the locknut.

Linkage Adjustment

1973-74 Three and Four-Speed

1. Turn the ignition switch to "Off" and place the shift lever in neutral.
2. Raise the car.
3. Loosen the lock nuts on the control rods. Position the transmission side cover levers in their neutral detents.
4. With the floor shift lever in neutral, align the shifter levers and insert a gauge pin into the levers and bracket.
5. Tighten the First/Reverse (First/Second on four-speed) control rod lock nut against its swivel.
6. Tighten the Second/Third (Third/Fourth on four-speed) control rod lock nut against its swivel.
7. On four-speeds, tighten the Reverse control rod lock nut against its swivel.

NOTE: All lock nuts are tightened to 120 in. lbs.

8. Remove the gauge pin and check shifter operation.

Gearshift Lever Control Wire Replacement

1971-72 Four-Speed

1. Remove gearshift lever from vehicle.
2. Carefully remove gearshift lever knob (by pulling) and loosen set screw.
3. Drive out spiral pins.
4. Take off shift finger and pull Bowden control wire out of gearshift lever. Thrust spring may also be removed at this time.

NOTE: before installation, oil sliding surface of stop sleeve on shift finger tube.

5. Install new control wire through gearshift lever and fasten new control wire with clamp sleeve so that the cutout of the stop sleeve shows toward the left. Insert spiral pin (long pin).

NOTE: spiral pin must not protrude on either side.

6. With set screw, clamp Bowden control wire tight so that pull ring is positioned on gearshift lever tube and clamping block on pull ring.

NOTE: do not put tension on Bowden cable. Pull knob should have approximately 1/16 in. free travel.

7. With short spiral pin, attach shift finger.
8. Install gearshift lever knob and adhere to a distance of .30 in.

Transmission R & R

1971-72

1. Place transmission shift lever in neutral and pull the boot up.
2. Unhook the antirattle coil spring. Remove the shift finger (lower end of the lever) pin retaining clip and pin. Remove shift lever.
3. Raise the vehicle and drain the lubricant from transmission.
4. Remove driveshaft assembly.
5. Disconnect the speedometer cable, TCS switch and back-up lamp switch.
6. Remove crossmember-to-transmission mount bolts.
7. Support engine with an appropriate jack stand and remove crossmember-to-frame bolts. Remove crossmember from vehicle.
8. Remove transmission to clutch housing upper retaining bolts and install guide pins in holes.
9. Remove lower bolts, then slide transmission rearward and remove from vehicle.

NOTE: inspect throwout bearing support gasket located beneath lip of support. If defective, replace gasket before installing transmission.

10. Lightly lubricate inside diameter of clutch drive gear seal and install seal on drive gear.
11. Position new gasket to face of clutch housing. The gasket can be temporarily retained by a small amount of grease.
12. Position transmission to clutch housing and slide forward, piloting clutch gear in to pilot bearing.

NOTE: make certain main drive gear splines are clean and dry.

13. Install transmission-to-clutch housing retaining bolts and lockwashers.
14. Position crossmember to frame and loosely install retaining bolts. Install crossmember-to-transmission mount bolts. Tighten all retaining bolts to specifications. Remove engine support.

Caution Check position of engine in front mounts and align as required.

15. Connect speedometer cable, back-up lamp switch and TCS switch.
16. Install driveshaft assembly.
17. Fill transmission to proper level. Lower vehicle.
18. Lubricate shift finger bolt and spherical end of shaft. Install shift lever in shift housing and install bolt. Secure with retaining clip.
19. Install shift lever spring. Position shift lever boot and bezel to floor pan. Install retaining screws.
20. Check operation of transmission.

1973-74

1. Raise the car and drain the transmission.
2. Remove the driveshaft.
3. Disconnect the speedometer cable, TCS switch, and the back-up light switch.
4. Detach the control rods and levers from the transmission, tie them together, and position them out of the way.
5. Remove the crossmember-to-transmission mounting bolts.
6. Support the engine and remove the crossmember-to-frame bolts. Remove the crossmember.
7. Remove the top transmission-to-clutch housing bolts and install guide pins in the holes.
8. Remove the lower bolts and pull the transmission back and out of the car.
9. Guide the input shaft through the throwout bearing and into the pilot bearing.

10. Install the transmission retaining bolts and lockwashers. Tighten the bolts to 40 ft lbs.
11. Position the crossmember on the frame and install the retaining bolts hand-tight.
12. Install the crossmember-to-transmission bolts and then tighten all bolts to 28 ft lbs.
13. Remove the engine support.
14. Install the transmission control rods to the shifter. Adjust the linkage as previously outlined.
15. Connect the speedometer cable, TCS switch, and back-up light switch.
16. Install the driveshaft.
17. Fill the transmission to the level of the filler plug.
18. Lower the car and check transmission operation.

AUTOMATIC TRANSMISSION

Several automatic transmissions have been available on the Vega. The aluminum Powerglide consists of a three-element torque converter which drives through a two-speed planetary gear-set. The Torque Drive transmission is essentially a Powerglide without the automatic shifting mechanisms. Torque Drive was dropped after 1972. A three-speed Turbo Hydra-Matic 350 transmission became available in 1972. Beginning February 1973, a Turbo Hydra-Matic 250 was introduced to replace the 350. The 250 is similar to the 350, except that the intermediate clutch assembly has been replaced by an externally adjustable intermediate band assembly. Powerglide was dropped in mid-1973.

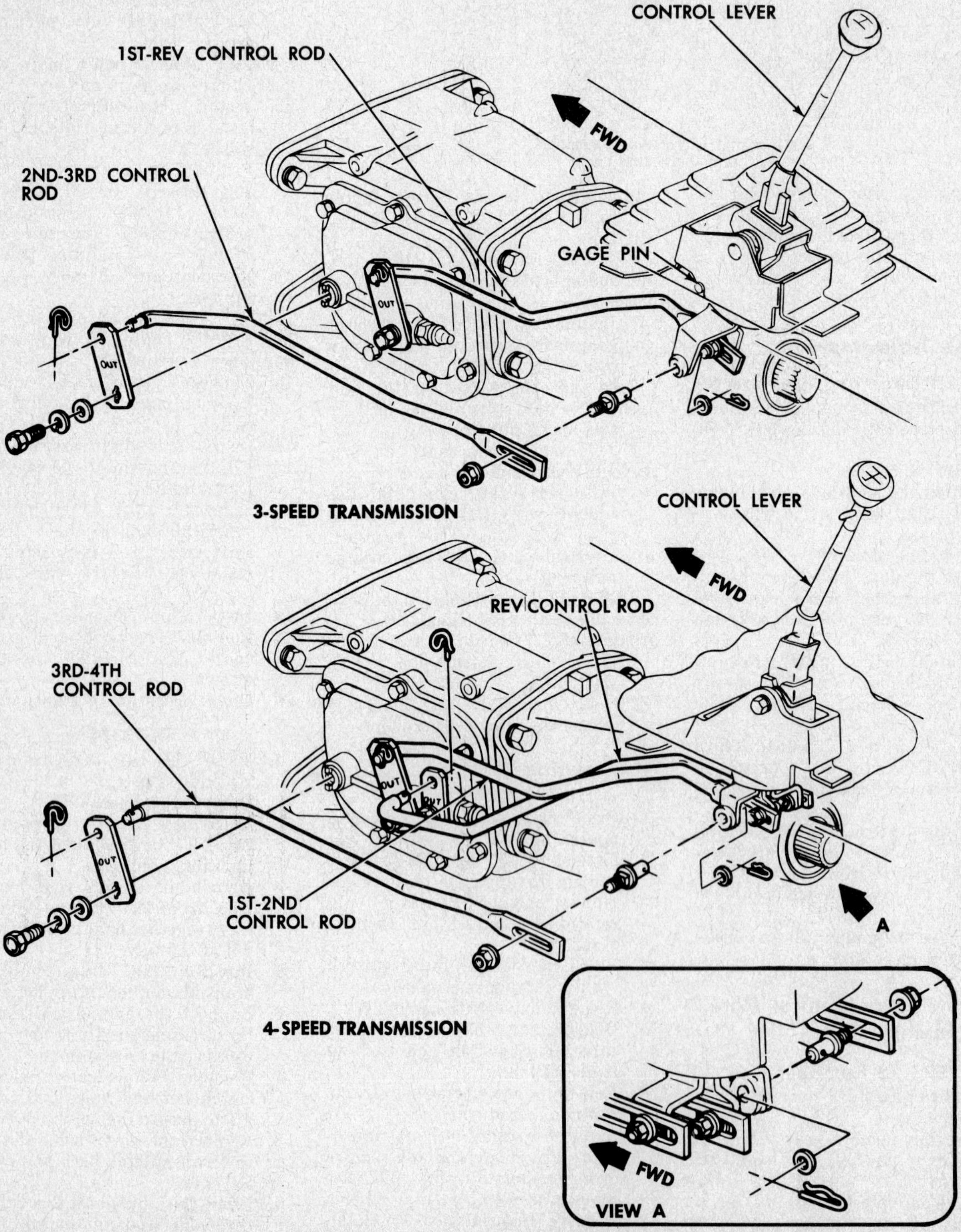
CONTROL LEVER
1ST-REV CONTROL ROD
FWD
2ND-3RD CONTROL ROD
GAGE PIN
OUT
3-SPEED TRANSMISSION
CONTROL LEVER
FWD
REV CONTROL ROD
3RD-4TH CONTROL ROD
OUT
1ST-2ND CONTROL ROD
A
4-SPEED TRANSMISSION
FWD
VIEW A

1973-74 three and four-speed linkage

Neutral Safety Switch Adjustment

1. Remove four screws securing floor console.
2. Disconnect the electrical plugs on the back-up, neutral start, and seat belt buzzer (1973-74) contacts of the neutral safety switch.
3. Place shift lever in Neutral.
4. Remove two screws securing shift indicator plate.
5. Remove two screws securing shift lever curved cover.
6. Remove two screws securing neutral start switch to lever assembly.

NOTE: screws are hidden beneath lever cover.

7. Tilt switch assembly to right as you lift switch out of lever hole.
8. Make sure shift lever is in Neutral before installing switch assembly.
9. Assemble switch assembly to control lever bracket by inserting drive tang into hole in neutral start switch lever.

NOTE: When installing the same neutral switch, align the contact support slot with the service adjustment hole in the switch and insert a 3/32 in. drill to hold the switch in neutral. Remove the drill after the switch is fastened to the shift lever mounting bracket.

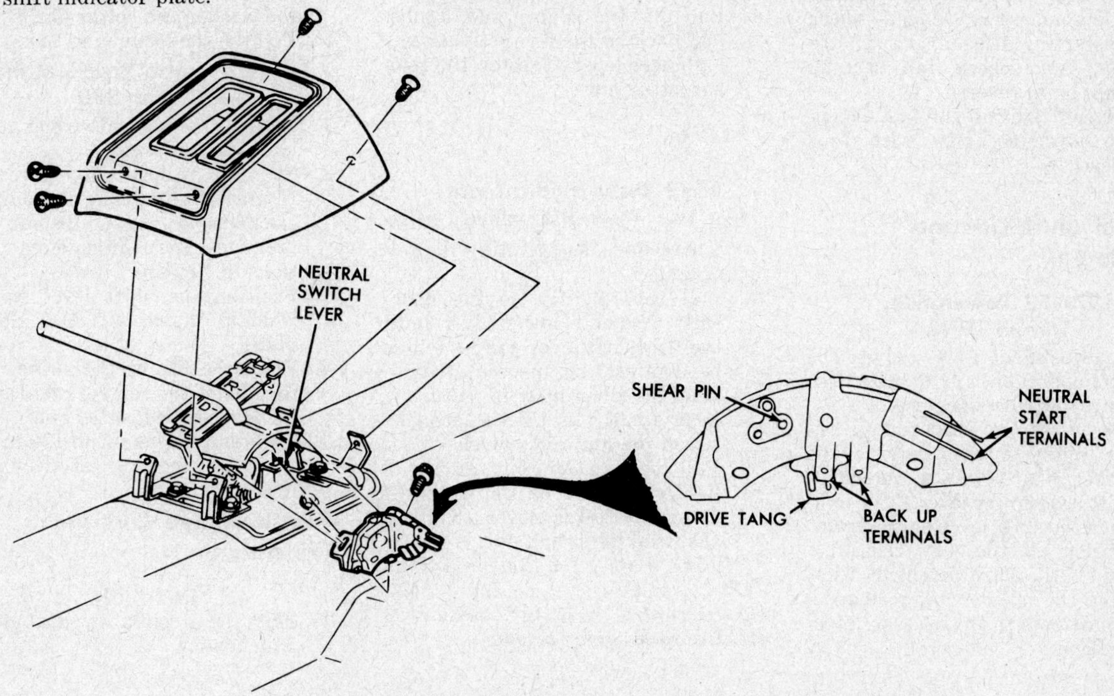
NEUTRAL SWITCH LEVER
SHEAR PIN
NEUTRAL START TERMINALS
DRIVE TANG
BACK UP TERMINALS

1971-72 neutral safety switch adjustment—1973-74 switch has two additional terminals for seat belt alarm (© Chevrolet Div., G.M. Corp)

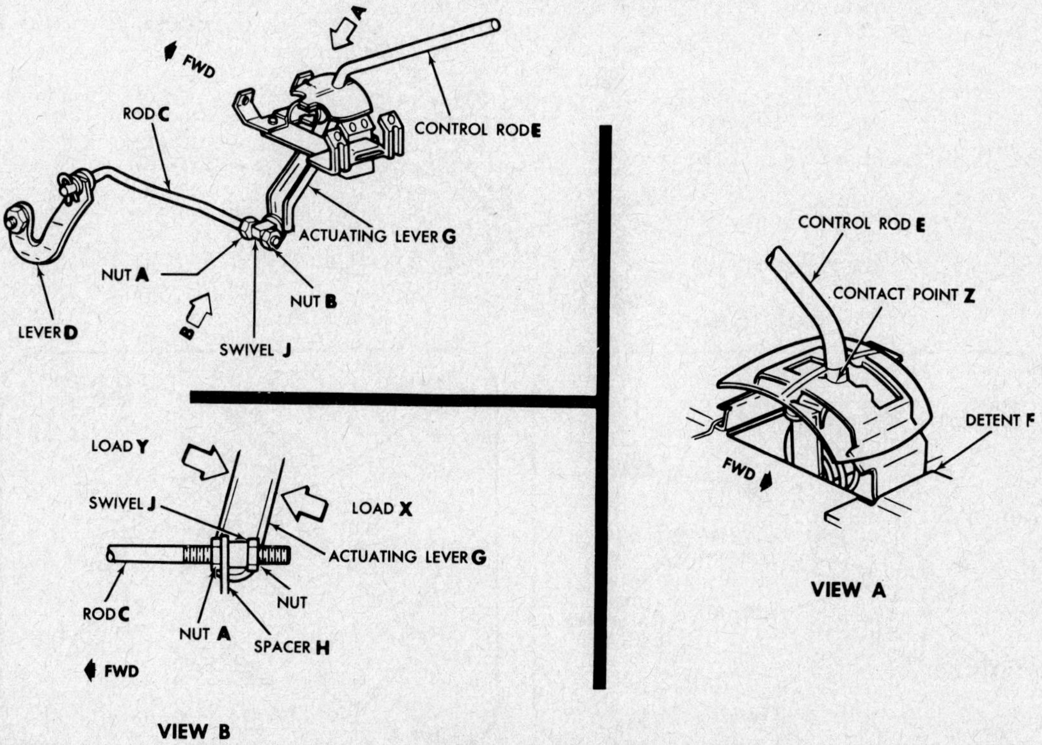
A
FWD
ROD C
CONTROL ROD E
ACTUATING LEVER G
NUT A
NUT B
LEVER D
B
SWIVEL J
CONTROL ROD E
CONTACT POINT Z
DETENT F
FWD
VIEW A
LOAD Y
SWIVEL J
LOAD X
ACTUATING LEVER G
ROD C
NUT
NUT A
SPACER H
FWD
VIEW B

1971-72 Powerglide linkage adjustment (© Chevrolet Div., G.M. Corp)

10. Tighten two mounting screws securing switch assembly to lever bracket.
11. Install curved shift lever cover and secure with two screws.
12. Install shift indicator plate and attach with two screws.
13. Moving control lever out of Neutral will shear the switch plastic locating pin.
14. Plug electrical connectors into switch assembly; apply parking brake and start vehicle—check for starting in Neutral and Park only. Also check for back-up lamps on in reverse.
15. Turn off ignition and install console cover securing with four screws.

Manual Shift Linkage Adjustment

1971-72 Powerglide, Torque Drive

This adjustment gives about 0.05 in. overtravel in each gear shift position to provide full engagement.

1. Loosen the two shift rod adjusting nuts at the swivel. The swivel is attached to the floorshift lever lower lever.
2. Turn the shift lever on the transmission all the way clockwise. This is the Park detent position. Turn the lever counterclockwise two detents to the neutral detent position.
3. Make sure that the floorshift is in the neutral position.
4. Push forward lightly on the floorshift assembly lower lever until the floorshift lever can be felt against its neutral detent. Hold the lower lever in place.
5. Hold a 0.073 in. thick spacer in front of the swivel. Tighten the front adjusting nut to clamp the spacer between the nut and swivel.
6. Pull out the spacer and lightly pull back on the floorshift assembly lower lever. Tighten the rear adjusting nut.

1972 Turbo Hydra-Matic

Use the Powerglide and Torque Drive procedure, substituting the following steps:

4. Pull back lightly on the floorshift assembly lower lever until the floorshift lever can be felt to be against its neutral detent. Hold the lower lever in place.
5. Hold a 0.073 in. thick spacer between the nut and swivel.
6. Pull the spacer out and pull lightly forward on the floorshift assembly lower lever. Tighten the front adjusting nut.

NOTE: Late 1972 models and all 1973-74 models are equipped with slotted control rods. Adjustment of this linkage is given below.

1973 Powerglide

1. Loosen the nut and swivel at the shifter.
2. Set the transmission lever in Neutral by moving the lever clockwise to the Park detent and then counterclockwise two detents to Neutral.
3. Position the shift lever in the Neutral notch of the detent plate.
4. Place the flat of the swivel into the slot of the control rod. Install the washer and cotter pin.
5. Tighten the locknut to 120 in lbs.

1973-74 Turbo Hydra-Matic 250 and 350

1. Loosen the nut and swivel at the transmission lever.
2. Set the transmission lever in Neutral by moving it counterclockwise to the L1 detent and then clockwise three detent positions to Neutral.
3. Position the shift lever in the Neutral notch of the detent plate.
4. Place the flat of the swivel into the slot of the control rod. Install the washer and cotter pin.
5. Tighten the locknut to 120 in lbs. Adjust the neutral safety switch, if necessary.

Throttle Valve Linkage Adjustment

Powerglide

1. Hold the accelerator pedal all the way down.

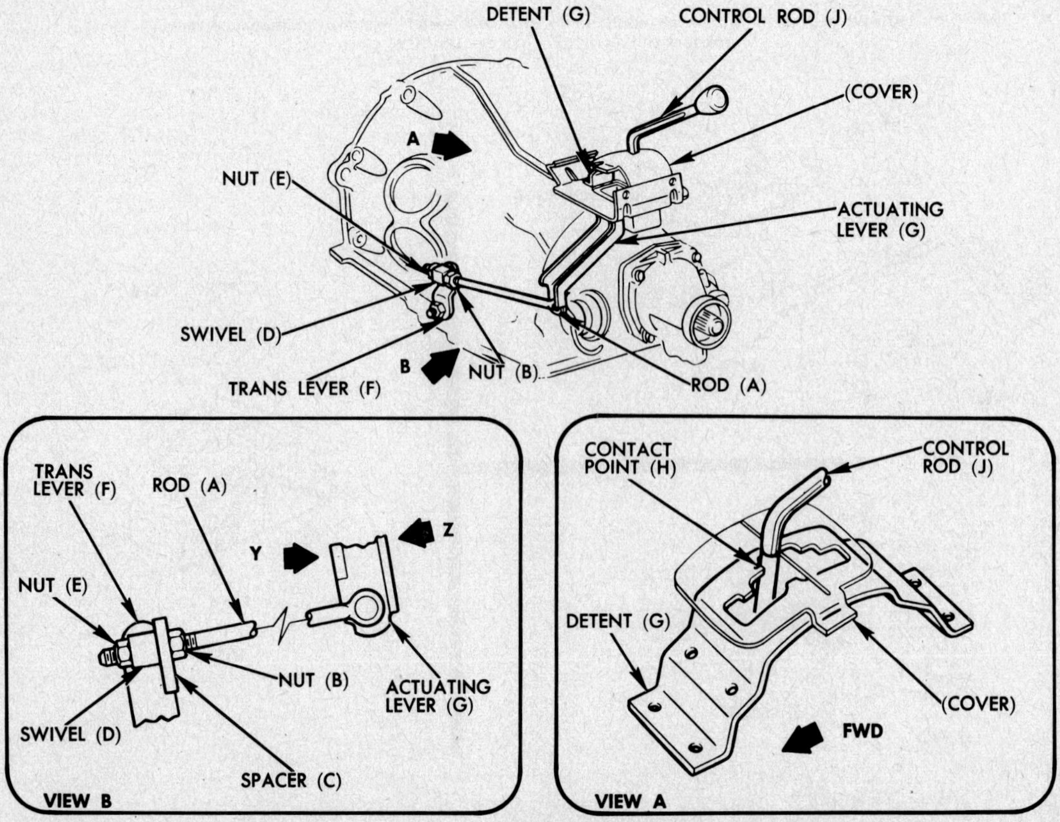
DETENT (G)
CONTROL ROD (J)
(COVER)
A
NUT (E)
ACTUATING LEVER (G)
SWIVEL (D)
B
NUT (B)
TRANS LEVER (F)
ROD (A)
TRANS LEVER (F)
ROD (A)
Z
Y
NUT (E)
NUT (B)
ACTUATING LEVER (G)
SWIVEL (D)
SPACER (C)
VIEW B
CONTACT POINT (H)
CONTROL ROD (J)
DETENT (G)
(COVER)
FWD
VIEW A

1972 Turbo Hydra-Matic 350 linkage adjustment (© Chevrolet Div., G.M. Corp)

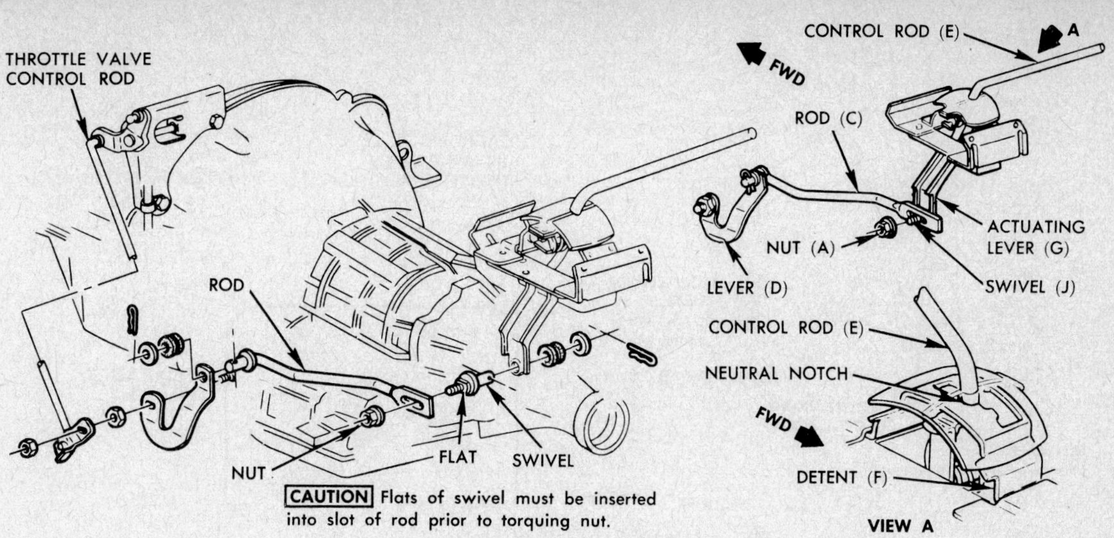
THROTTLE VALVE CONTROL ROD
ROD
NUT
FLAT
SWIVEL
CAUTION Flats of swivel must be inserted into slot of rod prior to torquing nut.
CONTROL ROD (E)
A
FWD
ROD (C)
ACTUATING LEVER (G)
NUT (A)
LEVER (D)
SWIVEL (J)
CONTROL ROD (E)
NEUTRAL NOTCH
FWD
DETENT (F)
VIEW A

1973 Powerglide linkage

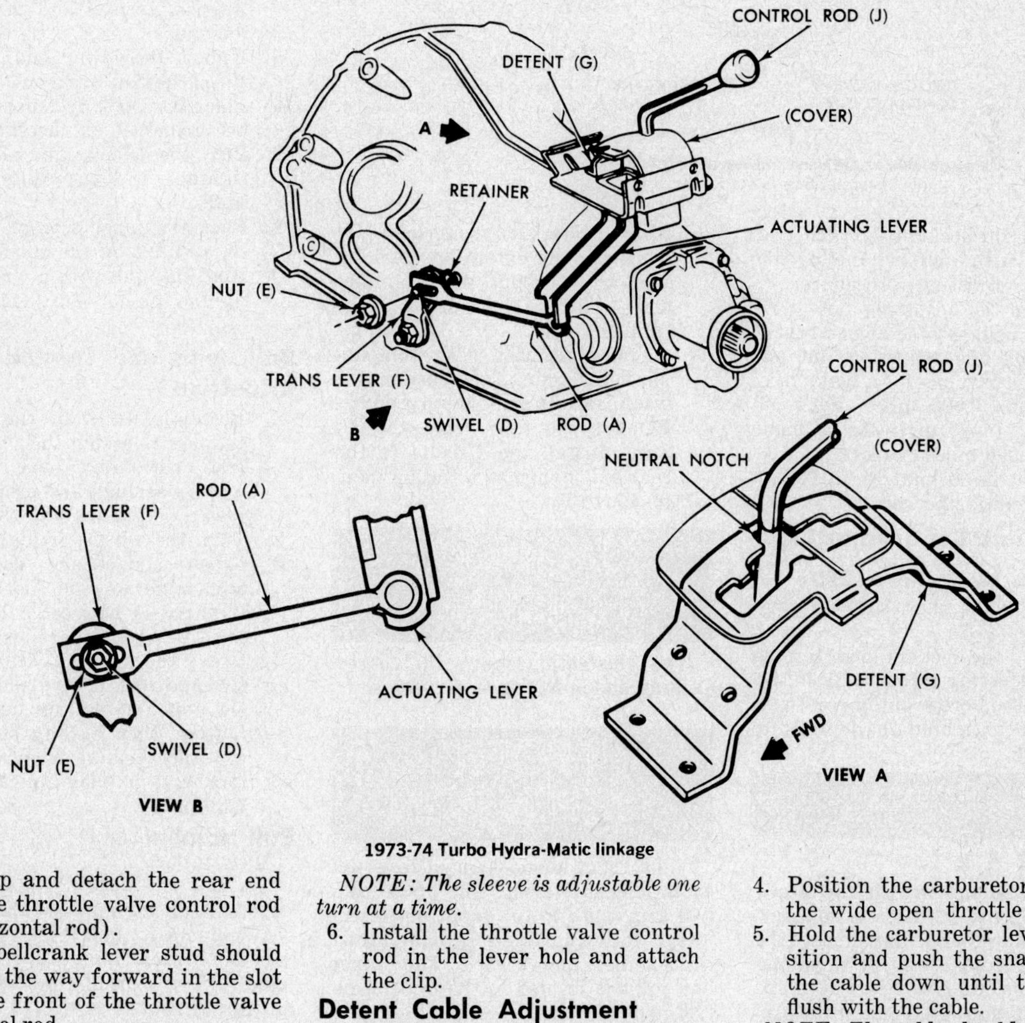
CONTROL ROD (J)
DETENT (G)
(COVER)
A
RETAINER
ACTUATING LEVER
NUT (E)
TRANS LEVER (F)
B
SWIVEL (D)
ROD (A)
CONTROL ROD (J)
(COVER)
NEUTRAL NOTCH
ROD (A)
TRANS LEVER (F)
ACTUATING LEVER
NUT (E)
SWIVEL (D)
VIEW B
DETENT (G)
FWD
VIEW A

1973-74 Turbo Hydra-Matic linkage

2. Unclip and detach the rear end of the throttle valve control rod (horizontal rod).
3. The bellcrank lever stud should be all the way forward in the slot at the front of the throttle valve control rod.
4. Hold the lever at the transmission against its internal stop.
5. If the rear end of the throttle valve control rod does not align with the hole in the lever, pull out the retaining clip from the sleeve in the center of the rod. Adjust the sleeve to lengthen or shorten the rod.

NOTE: The sleeve is adjustable one turn at a time.

6. Install the throttle valve control rod in the lever hole and attach the clip.

Detent Cable Adjustment

Turbo Hydra-Matic 250 and 350

1. Remove the air cleaner.
2. Insert a screwdriver on each side of the snap-lock on the bracket at the front of the transmission and pry up to release the lock.
3. Compress the lock tabs and disconnect the snap-lock assembly from the bracket.
4. Position the carburetor lever in the wide open throttle position.
5. Hold the carburetor lever in position and push the snap-lock on the cable down until the top is flush with the cable.

NOTE: The cable should not be lubricated.

6. Install the air cleaner.

Low Band Adjustment

Powerglide, Torque Drive

1. Position the shift lever in neutral.
2. Remove the protective cap from the adjusting screw.

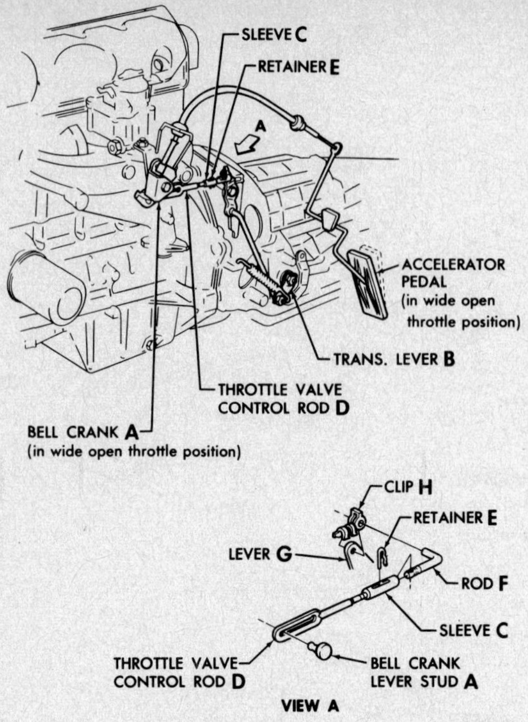
SLEEVE C
RETAINER E
A
ACCELERATOR
PEDAL
(in wide open
throttle position)
TRANS. LEVER B
THROTTLE VALVE
CONTROL ROD D
BELL CRANK A
(in wide open throttle position)
CLIP H
RETAINER E
LEVER G
ROD F
SLEEVE C
THROTTLE VALVE
CONTROL ROD D
BELL CRANK
LEVER STUD A
VIEW A

Powerglide throttle valve linkage adjustment
(© Chevrolet Div., G.M. Corp)

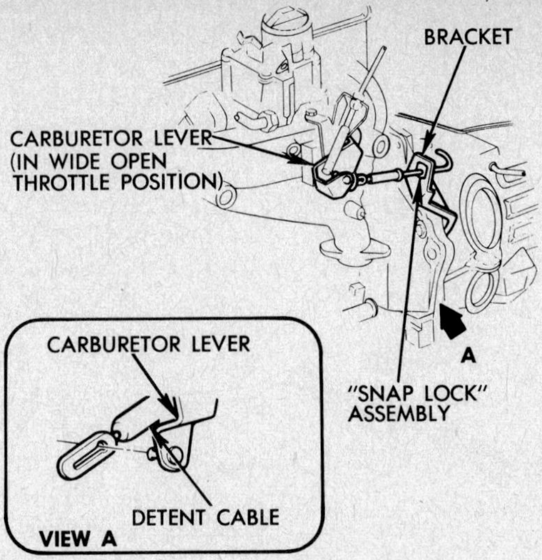
BRACKET
CARBURETOR LEVER
(IN WIDE OPEN
THROTTLE POSITION)
CARBURETOR LEVER
DETENT CABLE
VIEW A
A
"SNAP LOCK"
ASSEMBLY

Turbo Hydra-Matic 350 and 250 detent cable adjustment
(© Chevrolet Div., G.M. Corp)

3. Loosen the locknut 1/4 turn and hold it with a wrench during the entire adjusting procedure.
4. Tighten the adjusting nut to 70 in. lbs, using a 7/32 allen wrench.
5. Back off the adjusting nut exactly three turns for a band used less than 6,000 miles. Back off exactly four turns for a band used 6,000 miles or more.
6. Torque the locknut to 15 ft lbs. and replace the cap.

Intermediate Band Adjustment

Turbo Hydra-Matic 250

1. Position the shift lever in Neutral.
2. Loosen the locknut and tighten the adjusting screw to 30 in lbs.
3. Back the screw out three turns and then tighten the locknut to 15 ft lbs.

U-JOINTS

U-Joint R & R

1. Raise and support the car. Mark relationship of shaft to companion flange and disconnect the rear universal joint by removing trunnion bearing U-bolts. Tape bearing cups to trunnion to prevent losing the bearing rollers.
2. Withdraw driveshaft front yoke from transmission by moving shaft rearward and passing it under the axle housing. Cover the transmission opening to prevent fluid or oil loss.
3. Inspect yoke seal in the transmission extension, replace if necessary.
4. Insert driveshaft front yoke into transmission extention, making sure that output shaft splines mate with driveshaft yoke splines.
5. Align driveshaft with companion flange using reference marks established in removal procedure. Remove the tape from the U-joint, install the U-bolts to the rear axle flange, and torque them to 15 ft lbs.

JACKING, HOISTING

The illustration shows the correct jacking and hoist lifting positions.

FRONT SUSPENSION

Vega front suspension utilizes unequal length A-arms. The lower control arm bolts to the front end sheet metal with cam bolts which adjust the camber and caster. The upper ball joint is riveted to the upper control arm and the lower ball joint is pressed into the lower control arm.

Shock Absorber R & R

1. Pry out the access plug in the engine compartment so that the upper mount is visible.
2. Raise the front of the car and safely support it.
3. Turn the wheels for clearance.
4. Hold the upper shock stud with a wrench. Loosen and remove the locknut.
5. Unbolt the lower end and pull the shock down and out.
6. Place the lower retainer and rubber grommet on the shock stud.
7. Put the shock in place and tighten the lower bolts. Torque to 20 ft lbs.
8. Place the upper grommet, retainer, and nut on the shock stud.
9. Hold the stud with a wrench and tighten the nut. Torque to 120 in. lbs.

Ball Joint and Tie-Rod End Inspection

1. Raise the front of the car and support it under the lower control arm. Make sure that the wheel bearings are properly adjusted before making this check.
2. Turn the wheels straight ahead.
3. Grasp and shake the wheel from side to side, horizontally. If there is noticeable looseness, the tie-rod ends are worn.
4. Grasp the top and bottom of the tire and rock it by pushing in on the top and pulling out on the bottom, then pulling out on the top and pushing in on the bottom. A 1/4 in. play indicates worn ball joints.

Ball Joint R & R

Upper

1. Jack up the front of the car and support it under the crossmember braces. Remove the wheel.
2. Place a hydraulic jack under the lower control arm.
3. Remove the cotter pin from the ball joint stud. Loosen, but do not remove the nut.
4. The stud may now be pressed out upward. There is a special tool available to do this.
5. Remove the ball joint by grinding off the rivets, or removing the heads of the rivets with a cold chisel.

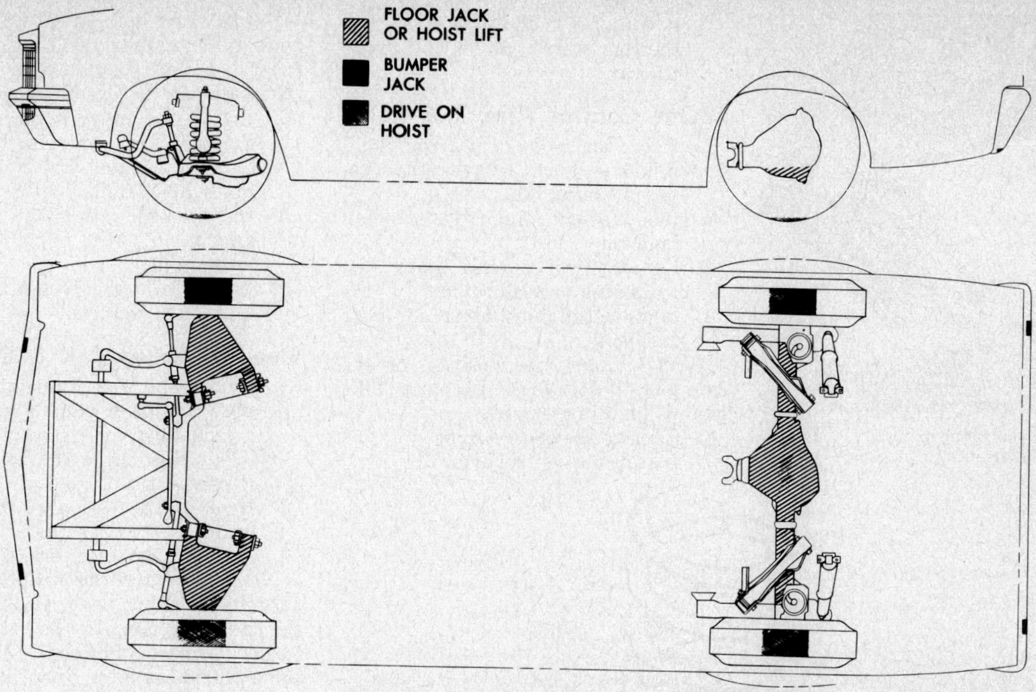
FLOOR JACK
OR HOIST LIFT
BUMPER
JACK
DRIVE ON
HOIST

Vega lift points (© Chevrolet Div., G.M. Corp)

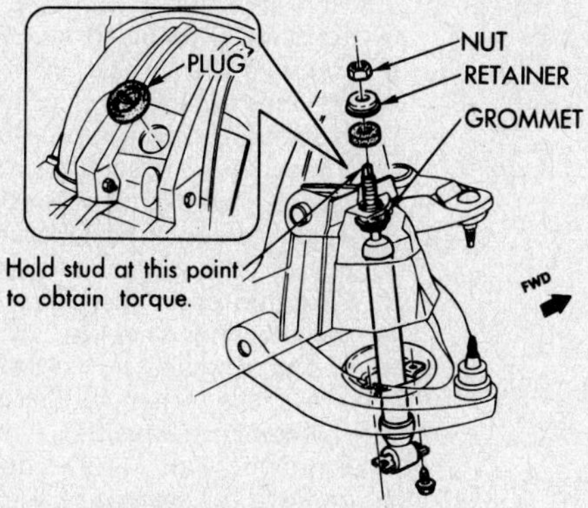
NUT
RETAINER
GROMMET
PLUG
Hold stud at this point
to obtain torque.
FWD

Front shock absorber mounting
(© Chevrolet Div., G.M. Corp)

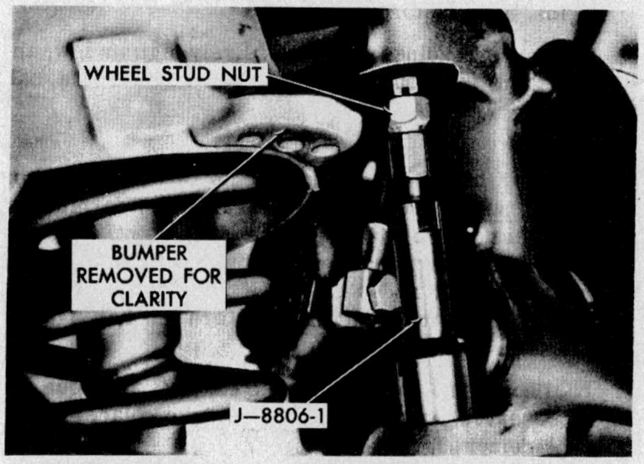
WHEEL STUD NUT
BUMPER
REMOVED FOR
CLARITY
J—8806-1

Removing ball joint stud from steering knuckle
(© Chevrolet Div., G.M. Corp)

6. Bolt the new ball joint on, using the nuts and bolts supplied with the replacement joint.
7. Install the stud to the steering knuckle and torque the nut to 30 ft lbs. If the cotter pin hole does not align, tighten the nut ½ of a turn further to line it up. Install a new cotter pin.
8. Install the wheel and lower the car.

Lower

1. Repeat steps one through four of the upper ball joint procedure.
2. The stud may now be pressed out downward. A special tool is available for this purpose.
3. The old joint must be pressed out of the control arm. A tool is available for this operation.
4. Press in the new joint, positioning it so that the grease bleed vent in the rubber boot is facing inward.
5. Install a lubrication fitting in the new joint.
6. Install the stud to the steering knuckle and torque the nut to 60 ft lbs. If the cotter pin hole does not align, tighten it 1/6 of a turn further. Do not loosen the nut to install the cotter pin.
7. Install the wheel and lower the car.

Spring R & R

1. Raise the front of the car and support it with jackstands placed under the front cross-member braces.
2. Remove the wheel, shock absorbers, and stabilizer bar.
3. Support the lower control arm outer end with a hydraulic floor jack and a block of wood.
4. Securely fasten the spring to the lower control arm with a heavy chain.
5. To detach the tie rod, remove the cotter pin and nut, and tap on the steering arm (not the tie-rod end) with a hammer. Hold another hammer behind the steering arm to take the force of the tapping. The tie rod should then fall free.
6. Remove the lower ball joint stud from the steering knuckle as described in the "Lower Ball Joint R&R" procedure.
7. Very cautiously lower the jack until the spring is fully expanded.
8. Place the spring in its pads on the lower control arm and shock tower. Secure it with a chain as in step four.
9. Carefully raise the jack.
10. Place the lower ball joint stud in the steering knuckle. Torque the stud nut to 60 ft lbs. If the cotter pin does not align, tighten it further 1/6 of a turn and insert a new cotter pin.
11. Install the tie-rod end to the steering arm. Torque the nut to 35 ft lbs. If the cotter pin hole does not align, tighten further up to a maximum of 50 ft lbs. Insert a new cotter pin.

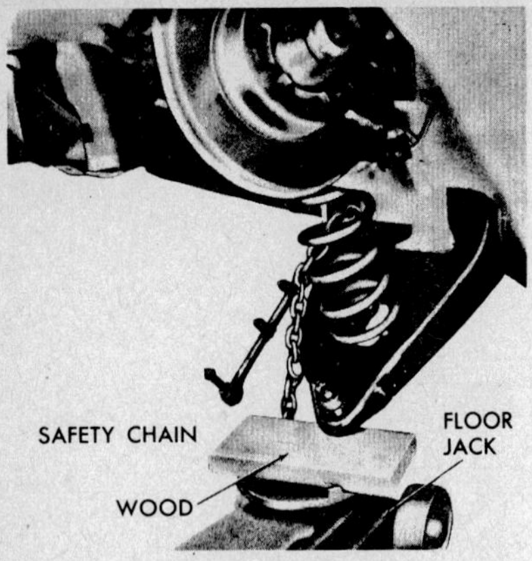
SAFETY CHAIN
FLOOR JACK
WOOD

Front spring removal
(© Chevrolet Div., G.M. Corp)

12. Replace the shock absorber as described in "Shock Absorber R&R." Do not attach the top end of the shock at this point.
13. Install the stabilizer bar. Tighten the bracket bolts to 30 ft lbs and the control arm bolts to 10 ft lbs.
14. Replace the wheel and lower the car. Install the upper end of the shock absorber.

Wheel Bearing Adjustment

1. Jack up the front of the car and support it with jackstands.
2. Remove the dust cap with a pair of slip-joint pliers.
3. Remove and discard the cotter pin. Loosen the spindle nut. Tighten it snugly to seat the bearings, and then loosen the nut again.
4. Rotate the wheel and tighten the spindle nut to 12 ft lbs. which is roughly equivalent to finger tightness.
5. Back the nut off one flat and insert a new cotter pin. If the hole does not line up, back the nut off ½ flat or less to align the hole.
6. Check that the wheel turns freely, and then lock the cotter pin.
7. Bearing end-play should be between 0.001 and 0.008 in. Tap the dust cap back on and lower the car.

Lower Control Arm R & R

1. Raise the front of the car.
2. Remove shock absorber as previously outlined.
3. Remove ball stud from steering knuckle.
4. Remove coil spring using the preceding procedure.
5. Remove the inner pivot cam nuts and bolts.

NOTE: mark the position of the cam bolts before loosening nuts. This step will aid in assembly.

6. Remove the control arm.
7. Install the control arm.

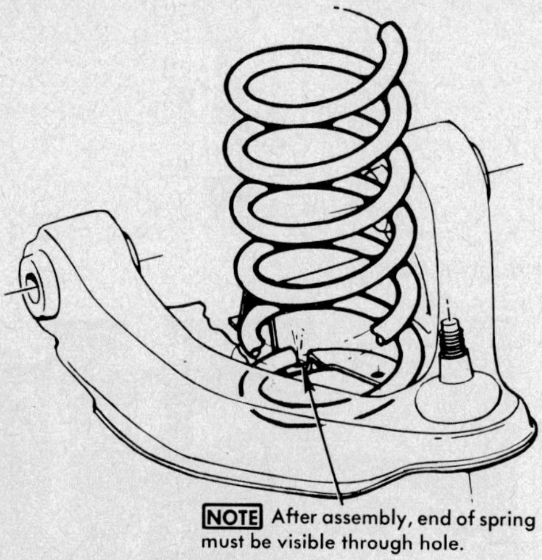
NOTE After assembly, end of spring must be visible through hole.

Front spring positioning
(© Chevrolet Div., G.M. Corp)

NOTE: be sure that the control arm bushings have the metal caps installed.

8. Install the cam bolts through the control arm bushings.

NOTE: the front cam bolt (camber) must be installed with the head toward the front of the vehicle and the rear cam bolt (caster) must be installed with the head toward the rear of the vehicle.

9. Install the inner cams to the cam bolt.
10. Install the lockwasher and nut.
11. Align the cam bolts with the marks made before removal.
12. Install the coil spring.
13. Install the shock absorber.
14. Lower vehicle to the floor.
15. Check front alignment.

Upper Control Arm R & R

1. Raise vehicle on a hoist and remove the wheel.
2. Support the lower control arm with a floor jack.
3. Remove upper ball stud nut and remove ball stud from steering knuckle.
4. Remove control arm pivot bolts and remove control arm from vehicle.
5. Install upper control arm to vehicle at inner pivot.

NOTE: the inner pivot bolts must be installed with the bolt heads to the front (on the front bushing) and to the rear, (on the rear bushing).

6. Install the inner pivot nuts.
7. Position the control arm in a horizontal plane and tighten the inner pivot nuts.
8. Install ball stud to steering knuckle. Tighten nut and install cotter pin.
9. Install tire and wheel assembly and lower vehicle.

Steering Knuckle R & R

1. Raise vehicle on a hoist and support the lower control arm with a jackstand.

NOTE: this keeps the coil spring compressed.

2. Remove the tire and wheel assembly.
3. Remove the disc brake caliper.

NOTE: secure the caliper to the suspension using wire. Do not allow the caliper to hang by the brake hose. Insert a piece of wood (about the same thickness as a brake disc) between the shoes to hold the piston in the caliper bore.

4. Remove the hub and disc.
5. Remove the splash shield.
6. Remove the tie rod end from the steering knuckle.
7. Remove the cotter pins from the upper and lower ball studs and loosen the ball stud nuts.
8. Install a spare wheel stud nut on either the upper or lower ball stud and press the ball stud from the steering knuckle.
9. Using a spare nut as in Step 8 press the other ball stud from the steering knuckle.
10. Remove ball stud nuts and remove the steering knuckle.
11. Place steering knuckle in position and insert the upper and lower ball studs into knuckle bosses.
12. Install ball stud nuts and tighten to 60 ft. lbs. Install cotter pin.

NOTE: if necessary, tighten to the next slot to insert cotter pin. Never back off on a ball stud nut to align cotter pin.

13. Install splash shield to the steering knuckle.
14. Install the tie rod end to the steering knuckle. Torque to 35 ft lbs.
15. Install the hub and disc, bearings and nut. Install cotter pin.
16. Install the brake caliper.
17. Install the wheels, remove the jackstand and lower the car.

REAR SUSPENSION

Shock Absorber R & R

1. Raise the vehicle and support the rear axle.
2. Remove upper attaching bolts

and lower attaching nut, retainer, and cushion on early 1971 models or the through-bolt on later models.
3. Remove the shock absorber.
4. Install retainer and rubber grommet onto shock.
5. Place shock absorber into installed position and install upper retaining bolts. Torque to 18 ft. lbs.
6. On early models, install cushion, retainer and nut onto lower shock absorber attachment. Torque to 80 in. lbs.
7. On later models, install the through bolt and a rubber grommet on each side of the shock eye. Torque the nut to 80 ft lbs.
8. Lower the car.

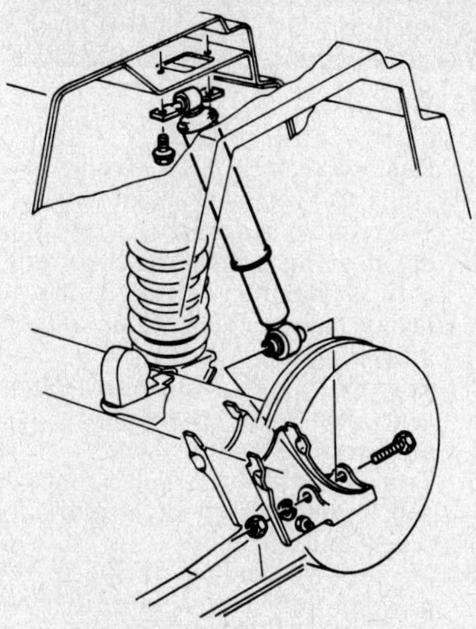

Rear shock absorber mounting
(© Chevrolet Div., G.M. Corp)

Rear Spring R & R

1. Raise vehicle and support the rear axle, with a hydraulic jack.
2. Disconnect both shock absorbers from lower brackets.
3. Lower axle and remove springs and spring insulators.

NOTE: one or both springs may be removed at this point.

Caution When lowering axle do not stretch brake hose running from frame to axle.

4. Install insulators on top and bottom of springs and position on axle.
5. Raise axle and reconnect shock absorbers. Torque the bottom stud or bolt nuts to 80 in. lbs.
6. Lower the vehicle.

Upper Control Arm R & R

Caution If both control arms are to be replaced, remove and replace one control arm at a time to prevent the axle from rolling or slipping sideways.

1. Raise vehicle on hoist and support the rear axle.
2. Remove control arm front and rear bolts and remove arm.
3. Press out the bushing.
4. Before bushing installation, observe that holes in control arm have different diameters.
5. Install small end of bushing in largest hole.
6. Press bushing into control until bushing flange seats on control arm.
7. Install control arm front and rear attaching bolts. Torque to 60 ft. lbs.

NOTE: car must be at curb height when tightening pivot bolts.

8. Remove support from axle.
9. Lower vehicle and remove from hoist.

Lower Control Arm R & R

Caution If both control arms are to be replaced, remove and replace one control arm at a time to prevent the axle from rolling or slipping sideways.

1. Raise vehicle on hoist.
2. Support rear axle.
3. Disconnect stabilizer bar if so equipped. On Cosworth Vega, detach the restraint cable from the control arm.
4. Remove control arm front and rear attaching bolts and remove control arm.
5. Replacement of these bushings is the same procedure as that described for the Upper Control Arm above.
6. Place control arm into position and install front and rear bolts. Torque to 80 ft. lbs.
7. Attach stabilizer bar and restraint cable, if so equipped.
8. Remove support from axle.
9. Lower vehicle.

BRAKES

Front disc brakes are standard equipment on all models. The disc is 10 in. in diameter and 0.5 in. thick. Hub and disc are one-piece and the assembly is mounted to a one-piece steering knuckle and steering arm. The disc caliper design is similar to the single-piston Delco-Moraine disc brake used on other Chevrolet vehicles.

Rear brakes are drum-type, 9 in. in diameter. Unlike most other brake designs, the rear brakes are not automatically adjusted when the brakes are applied, but are adjusted when the parking brake is applied. For this reason, consistent parking in gear without using the parking brake is not recommended.

The tandem master cylinder pushrod is not adjustable, thus eliminating a pedal free travel adjustment.

Both front and rear hydraulic systems are routed to and from a distribution valve. Any significant change in the pressure difference between the front and rear systems moves a piston which activates a warning light switch, indicating pressure failure in one of the systems.

Master Cylinder R & R

1. Disconnect the master cylinder from the brake pedal by detaching the clip and pin.
2. Disconnect the two hydraulic lines at the master cylinder, plugging or covering the ends of the lines.
3. Remove master cylinder attaching nuts and remove the master cylinder.
4. Reverse the removal procedure to install. Torque the mounting nuts to 24 ft lbs.
5. Bleed the hydraulic system.

Front Disc Brake Caliper R & R

1. Raise the front of the vehicle and remove the front wheel.
2. Remove and discard the two mounting pin stamped nuts.

NOTE: it is not necessary to disconnect the hydraulic line when removing the caliper. Do not let the weight of the caliper assembly hang on the hydraulic line.

3. Remove the two caliper mounting pins.
4. Lift the caliper off the disc.
5. Remove the shoes (pads) by sliding them to the mounting sleeve opening.
6. The mounting sleeves and bushing assemblies may be removed for inspection.

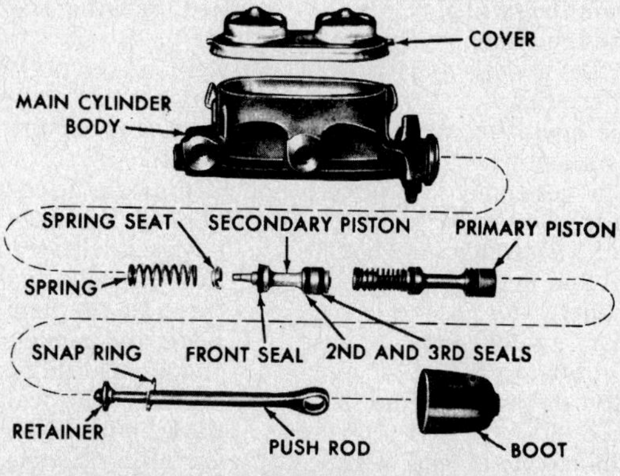
COVER
MAIN CYLINDER BODY
SPRING SEAT
SECONDARY PISTON
PRIMARY PISTON
SPRING
SNAP RING
FRONT SEAL
2ND AND 3RD SEALS
RETAINER
PUSH ROD
BOOT

Brake master cylinder
(© Chevrolet Div., G.M. Corp)

7. To install, position the sleeves with bushings into the caliper grooves with the shouldered end toward the outside.
8. Install the inner shoe and slide the shoe ears over the sleeve, then install the outer shoe in the same manner.
9. Position the caliper on the vehicle.

NOTE: if new shoes are being installed, remove half of the brake fluid in the master cylinder.

10. Install the mounting pins, head end to the outside.
11. Install new stamped retaining nuts with a socket that just seats on the outer edge of the nut.
12. Install the front wheels and lower the vehicle.

Brake Disc R & R

1. Raise the vehicle and remove the wheel and caliper as described above.
2. Remove the dust cap with pliers.
3. Remove the cotter pin and nut from the spindle.
4. Pull on the disc to loosen the outer bearing, then remove the outer bearing.
5. Remove the disc and clean the spindle.
6. The inner bearing may be knocked out (use a brass drift or wooden hammer handle) for inspection or replacement.
7. Clean the bearings and bearing surfaces.
8. Grease the bearings, using a disc brake wheel bearing lubricant.
9. Install the inner bearing and a new dust seal, tapping them carefully into the disc.
10. Install the brake disc onto the spindle and insert the outer bearing and washer.
11. Adjust the wheel bearings as outlined under "Wheel Bearing Adjustment."
12. Replace the dust cap and brake caliper.

Brake Distribution and Switch Assembly R & R

1. Disconnect the battery cable and the lead from the switch.
2. Disconnect the four hydraulic lines from the switch and cover the ends of the lines.
3. Remove the mounting screw and the switch assembly.
4. The switch assembly may be cleaned with denatured alcohol.
5. The switch assembly is non-serviceable and must be replaced as a unit if defective.
6. Install the switch with the mounting screw.
7. Connect the hydraulic lines to the switch.
8. Connect the electrical lead to the switch and the battery cable.
9. Bleed the hydraulic system.

Brake Warning Light Checking

1. Disconnect the wire from the switch and use a jumper to make a good ground.
2. Turn the ignition to ON. The warning light should come on. If it does not, check the circuit or change the bulb as required.
3. Turn the ignition off and connect the wire to the switch.
4. To check the switch mechanism turn the ignition to ON, remove a rear wheel, install a bleeder hose and momentarily open the bleeder valve while heavy pressure is being applied to the brake pedal. Close the bleeder valve before the pedal is released.
5. The warning light should have come on.
6. Repeat Step 4 above for one of the front brakes.
7. If the warning light did not come on during either Step 4 or Step 6, replace the defective switch as a unit.

Parking Brake Adjustment

1. Raise and support the rear of the car.
2. Apply the parking brake one notch from the fully released position.
3. Loosen the adjusting locknut and tighten the adjusting nut until a slight drag is felt when the rear wheels are rotated.
4. Tighten the locknut securely.
5. The rear wheels should rotate freely when the parking brake is fully released.
6. Lower the vehicle.

Parking Brake Cable R & R

1. Raise and support the car.
2. Disconnect the equalizer from the cables.
3. Free the cable from the underbody tabs and remove the cable retainers (two per cable).
4. Remove the rear wheels and drums.
5. Remove the parking brake cable from the parking brake lever.

NOTE: do not let the lever swing forward, causing the brakes to self-adjust.

6. Remove the pull-back spring and remove the brake shoes with the strut and adjuster assembly attached.
7. Compress the conduit locking fingers at the backing plate entry hole and withdraw the cable.
8. To install, push the cable through the hole in the backing plate and make sure the locking fingers are fully expanded.
9. Connect the cable end to the parking brake lever.
10. Install both shoes on the backing plate with the lower spring under the shoe anchor, guiding the adjusting lever and assembly into position.
11. Engage the leading and trailing shoes with the wheel cylinder links and the parking brake lever with the leading shoe.
12. Install the pull back spring on the leading shoe.
13. Install the drums and wheels.
14. Route the cable through the underbody retainers and tabs, bending the tabs to secure the cable in position.
15. Install the equalizer to the cables and to the parking brake lever rod. Install the adjusting nut and locknut.
16. Adjust the parking brake as described above.
17. Lower the vehicle.

STEERING

Tie Rod R & R

1. Place vehicle on hoist.
2. Remove cotter pins from ball studs and remove special nuts.
3. To remove outer ball stud, tap on steering arm at tie rod end with a hammer while using a heavy hammer or similar tool as a backing.
4. Remove inner ball stud from relay rod using same procedure as described in Step 3.
5. To remove tie rod ends from tie rod, loosen clamp bolts and unscrew end assemblies.
6. If the tie rod ends were removed, lubricate the tie rod threads with chassis lube and install ends on tie rod making sure both ends are threaded an equal distance from the tie rod.
7. Make sure that threads on ball studs and in ball stud nuts are perfectly clean and smooth. Check condition of ball stud seals; replace if necessary.

NOTE: if threads are not clean and smooth, ball studs may turn in tie rod ends when attempting to tighten nut.

8. Install ball studs in steering arms and relay rod.
9. Install ball stud nut, tighten and install new cotter pins. Lubricate tie rod ends.
10. Remove vehicle from hoist.
11. Adjust toe-in.

Caution Before tightening the tie rod adjusting sleeve clamp bolts, be sure that the following conditions have been met:

a. The sleeve clamps must be positioned between the locating dimples at either end of the sleeve.
b. The clamps must be positioned within the angular travel as illustrated.
c. The relationship of the clamp slot with the slit in the sleeve should be maintained as shown.
d. Both inner and outer tie rod

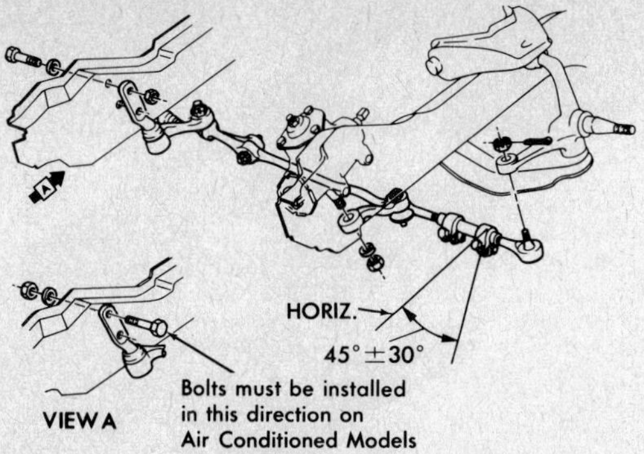
HORIZ.
45° ± 30°
VIEW A
Bolts must be installed
in this direction on
Air Conditioned Models

Steering linkage
(© Chevrolet Div., G.M. Corp)

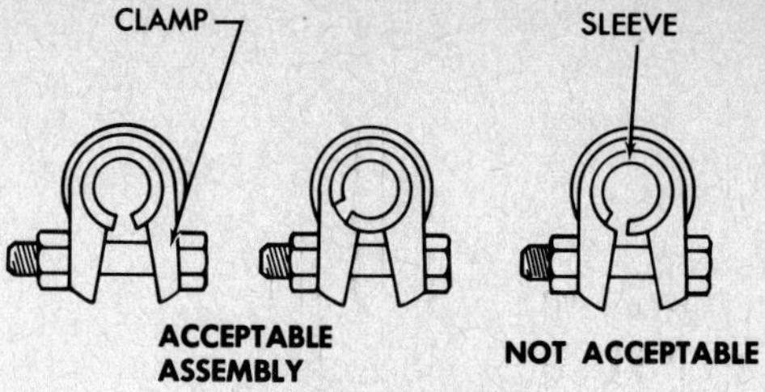
CLAMP
SLEEVE
ACCEPTABLE
ASSEMBLY
NOT ACCEPTABLE

Tie rod clamp installation
(© Chevrolet Div., G.M. Corp)

ends must rotate for full travel in the same direction. The position of each tie rod end must be maintained as the clamps are tightened to ensure free movement of each joint.

e. All procedures for alignment, adjustment and assembly of tie rods applies to each side.

Relay Rod R & R

1. Raise the front of the car and support with jackstands.
2. Remove inner ends of the tie rods from relay rod.
3. Remove the cotter pins from the pitman and idler arm ball studs at the relay rod. Remove the nuts.
4. Remove the relay rod from the pitman and idler arms by tapping on the relay rod ball stud bosses with a hammer, while using a heavy hammer as a backing.
5. Remove the relay rod from the vehicle.
6. Make sure that threads on the ball studs and in the ball stud nuts are perfectly clean and smooth. Check condition of ball stud seals; replace if necessary.

NOTE: if threads are not clean and smooth, ball studs may turn in sockets when attempting to tighten nut.

7. Install the relay rod to the idler arm and pitman arm ball studs, making certain the seals are in place. Install and torque the nut and then install the cotter pin. Tighten nut to 35 ft. lbs.
8. Install the tie rods to the relay rod. Lubricate the tie rod ends.
9. Remove the vehicle from the hoist.
10. Adjust toe-in and align steering wheel.

Idler Arm R & R

1. Place vehicle on a hoist.
2. Remove the cotter pin and special nut from ball stud at the relay rod. Remove the ball stud from the relay rod by tapping on the relay rod boss with a hammer, while using a heavy hammer as a backing.
3. Remove the idler arm to frame bolts and remove the idler arm assembly.
4. Position the idler arm on the frame and install the mounting bolts (special plain washers under bolt heads). Torque the nuts to 30 ft. lbs.
5. Make sure that the threads on the ball stud and in the ball stud nut are perfectly clean and smooth. Check condition of ball stud seal; replace if necessary.

NOTE: if threads are not clean and smooth, ball stud may turn in the socket when attempting to tighten nut.

6. Install the idler arm ball stud in the relay rod, making certain the seal is positioned properly; install the nut and cotter pin, tightening to 35 ft. lbs.
7. Lower the car.

Pitman Arm R & R

1. Raise the front of the car and support it with jackstands.
2. Remove the cotter pin and special nut from ball stud at the relay rod. Remove the ball stud from the relay rod by tapping on the relay rod boss with a hammer, while using a heavy hammer as a backing.
3. Remove the pitman arm to pitman shaft nut. Mark relationship of the arm to the shaft and then remove the pitman arm.
4. Install the pitman arm on the pitman shaft, aligning the marks made during removal. Install and torque the nut.
5. Make sure that the threads on the ball stud and in the ball stud [illegible]tly clean and smooth. Check co[illegible]ition of ball stud seal; replace if necessary.

NOTE: if threads are not clean and smooth, ball stud may turn in the socket when attempting to tighten nut.

6. Install the pitman arm ball stud to the relay rod, making certain the seal is positioned properly. Install the nut and cotter pin.
7. Lower the car.

Pitman Shaft Seal Replacement

A faulty seal may be replaced without removal of steering gear from car by removing pitman arm and proceeding as follows:

1. Rotate the steering wheel from stop to stop, counting the total number of turns. Then turn back exactly half-way, placing the gear on center (the wormshaft flat should be at the 12 o'clock position).
2. Remove the three self-locking bolts attaching side cover to the housing and lift the pitman shaft and side cover assembly from the housing.
3. Pry the pitman shaft seal from the gear housing using a screwdriver and being careful not to damage the housing bore.

Caution Inspect the lubricant in the gear for contamination. If the lubricant is contaminated in any way, the gear must be removed from the vehicle and completely overhauled as outlined in the Unit Repair Section of this manual.

4. Coat the new pitman shaft seal with steering gear lubricant. Position the seal in the pitman shaft bore and tap into position using a suitable size socket.
5. Remove the lash adjuster locknut. Remove the side cover from the pitman shaft assembly by turning the lash adjuster screw clockwise.
6. Place the pitman shaft in the steering gear such that the center tooth of the pitman shaft sector enters the center tooth space of the ball nut.
7. Fill the steering gear housing with 9 oz. of steering gear lubricant.
8. Install a new side cover gasket on the gear housing.
9. Install the side cover onto the lash adjuster screw by reaching through the threaded hole in the side cover with a small screwdriver and turning the lash adjuster screw counter-clockwise.
10. Install the side cover bolts and torque to 18 ft. lbs.
11. Install the lash adjuster screw locknut, perform steering gear adjustment and install the pitman arm.

Steering Wheel R & R

Standard Wheel

1. Disconnect the battery ground cable.

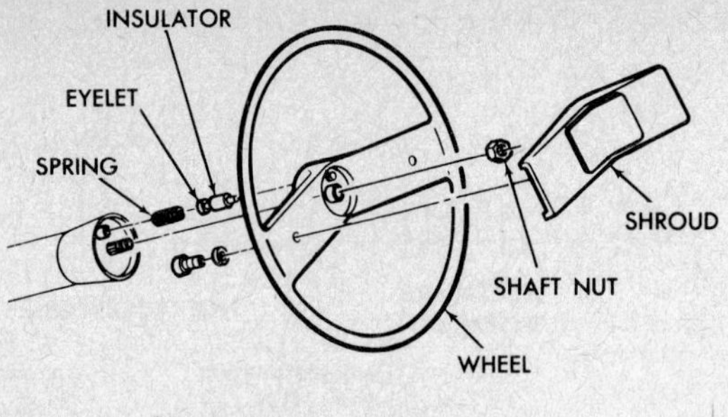
INSULATOR
EYELET
SPRING
SHROUD
SHAFT NUT
WHEEL

Standard steering wheel assembly
(© Chevrolet Div., G.M. Corp)

2. Remove the two screws from the back of the wheel, allowing the shroud (horn actuator bar) to be removed.
3. Set the wheel straight ahead. Mark the relationship of the wheel to the shaft and remove the nut.
4. Remove the steering wheel with a puller, using the two threaded holes in the wheel.
5. Install the wheel, aligning the previously made marks. Make sure that the turn signal switch is in the neutral position. Torque the nut to 30 ft lbs.
6. Make sure that the lower horn insulator, eyelet, and spring are in place.
7. Position the shroud, seating the pin on the right side of the wheel in the hole in the shroud.
8. Replace the two screws in the rear of the wheel. Connect the battery cable.

GT and Sport Wheel

1. Disconnect the battery ground cable.
2. Pry off the horn button. Set the wheel in the straight ahead position.
3. Mark the relationship of the wheel to the shaft.
4. Remove the three screws and the upper horn insulator, receiver, and round belleville spring.
5. Remove the steering wheel with a puller, utilizing the two threaded holes in the wheel.
6. Replace the wheel, aligning the marks previously made. Make sure that the turn signal switch is in the neutral position. Torque the nut to 30 ft lbs.
7. Make sure that the lower horn insulator, eyelet, and spring are in place.
8. Install the belleville spring, receiver, upper horn insulator, and the three screws.
9. Install the horn button and connect the battery cable.

Turn Signal Switch R & R

1. Remove the steering wheel as outlined above.
2. Loosen the three captive screws and lift the cover off the shaft.
3. The lockplate must be depressed with a special tool. Depress the lockplate and remove the wire snap-ring from the shaft.

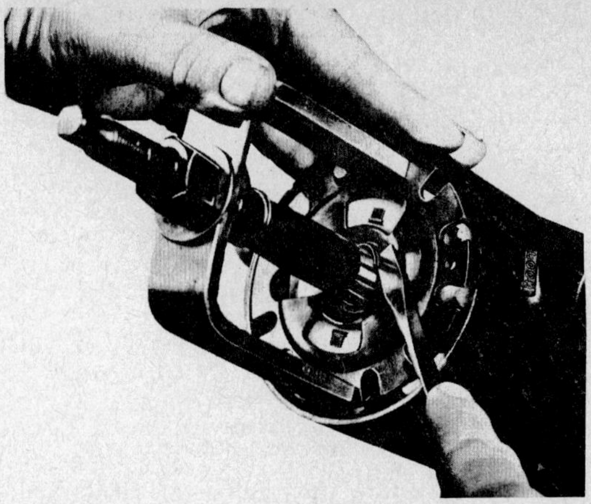

Removing lockplate retaining ring from steering column assembly
(© Chevrolet Div., G.M. Corp)

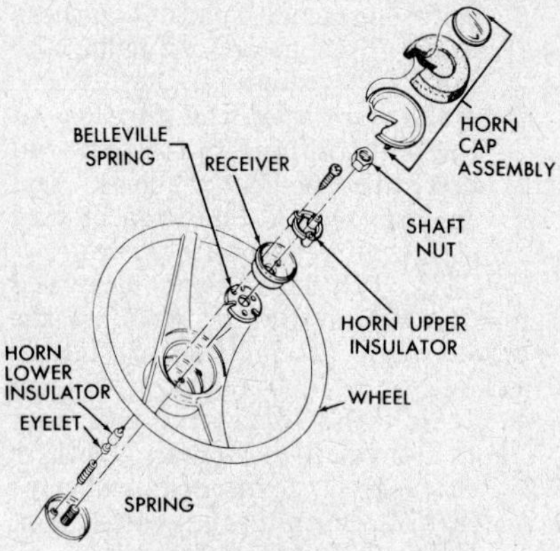
HORN CAP ASSEMBLY
BELLEVILLE SPRING
RECEIVER
SHAFT NUT
HORN UPPER INSULATOR
HORN LOWER INSULATOR
WHEEL
EYELET
SPRING

Optional steering wheel assembly
(© Chevrolet Div., G.M. Corp)

4. Remove the cancelling cam, upper bearing pre-load spring, and thrust washer from the shaft.
5. Remove the turn signal lever screw and the lever.
6. Push the hazard knob in and unscrew it.
7. Unplug the switch connector from the column and wrap the upper part of the connector with tape.
8. Remove the three switch mounting screws and pull the switch straight up. Guide the wiring connector through the column.
9. Tape the new switch connector. Feed the connector down through [illegible] and under the mounting bracket.
10. Install the three switch mounting screws.
11. Replace the hazard flasher knob and the turn signal lever. The turn signal switch should be in neutral and the hazard flasher knob out.
12. Place the thrust washer, upper bearing preload spring, and cancelling cam on the shaft.
13. Place the lockplate and a new snap-ring on the shaft. Press the lockplate down as in step three and install the new snap-ring.
14. Replace the cover and its three screws.
15. Install the steering wheel.

Power Steering Pump R & R

1. Disconnect the pressure and return hoses at the pump. Cap the ends to prevent leakage and contamination.
2. Remove the drive belt.
3. Unbolt and remove the pump.
4. Reverse the removal procedure to install the pump.
5. Fill the reservoir. Turn the pulley counterclockwise to bleed the pump until no more bubbles appear in the reservoir.
6. Install the drive belt and adjust its tension.

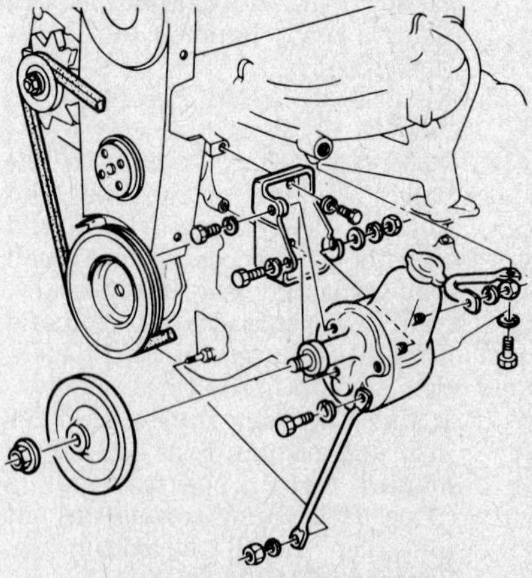

Power steering pump mounting
(© Chevrolet Div., G.M. Corp)

INSTRUMENT PANEL

There are two basic instrument panel designs used on Vega models. The standard cluster consists of a full-panel-width speedometer with fuel gauge, clock and indicator lights. The optional GT model has a separate 7,000 rpm tachometer and 130 mph speedometer units, surrounded by a fuel gauge, clock, water temperature gauge and ammeter.

The speedometer cable and instruments are removed from the front of the panel. All indicator bulbs are ¼ turn twist-in type and are removed from the rear.

Descriptive and diagnostic information on dash gauges and indicators is contained in the "Unit Repair Section."

Ignition Switch R & R

The ignition switch is mounted on top of the column jacket under the dashboard, completely inaccessible unless the steering column is lowered. The energy-absorbing column is fragile when disconnected and should not be subjected to any shock or excess pressure. Since the column will distort under its own weight, make sure that it is fully supported along its entire length while it is disconnected from the dashboard.

1. Disconnect the battery ground cable.
2. Remove the steering wheel.
3. On manual steering columns, remove the pot joint coupling clamp bolt.
4. On power steering columns, remove the flexible coupling pinch bolt.
5. Move the front seat back out of the way.
6. Remove the three floor pan bracket screws.
7. Remove the two column-to-instrument panel nuts and carefully lower the column far enough to allow the harness plugs to be disconnected.
8. Disconnect the turn signal and ignition switch harnesses.
9. Place the ignition switch in LOCK position.
10. Remove the two switch screws and the switch assembly.
11. When installing, make sure that the switch is in LOCK position.
12. Install the rod to the switch and the switch to the column. Do not use mounting screws longer than the original ones because they could interfere with the ability of the column to collapse.

NOTE: the following is a mandatory column installation procedure, and must be followed exactly to prevent severe column damage.

13. On power steering models, place the pot joint clamp over the lower end of the pot joint and assemble the intermediate shaft assembly (pot joint, intermediate shaft and flex coupling) to the steering gear stub shaft, aligning the flat on the stub shaft with the flat in the pot joint.
14. Position the column in the vehicle.
15. On manual steering models, place the pot joint clamp over the lower end of the pot joint and assemble the pot joint to the steering gear wormshaft with the flat in the pot joint. On power steering models, align the steering shaft flat with the flat in the flex coupling. When the shaft is bottomed against the coupling reinforcement, install and tighten bolt to 30 ft lbs.
16. Connect the turn signal and ignition switch wiring harnesses.
17. Loosely install the steering column bracket to instrument panel stud nuts.
18. Align the pot joint clamp with the groove across the end of the pot joint. Install bolt and nut, tightening nut to 55 ft. lbs.

NOTE: bolt must pass through the shaft undercut.

19. With the vehicle on the ground, tighten instrument panel nuts to 19 ft lbs.
20. Slide the toe plate down the column to the floorboard and install the three screws.

NOTE: on power steering models, alignment flange on the toe plate must be engaged with the front of the toe pan before driving screws. On manual steering models, no side load is allowed during installation of the attaching screws. A side load could cause misalignment.

21. On manual steering models: remove the alignment spacers. The minimum allowable clearance between the O.D. of the steering shaft and the I.D. of the column jacket lower plastic bushing after installation is 0.18 in.
22. Install the steering wheel.
23. Connect the battery ground cable.

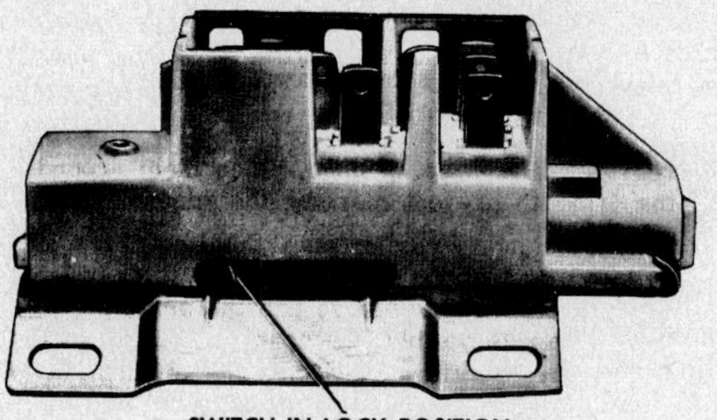
SWITCH IN LOCK POSITION

Ignition switch in lock
(© Chevrolet Div., G.M. Corp)

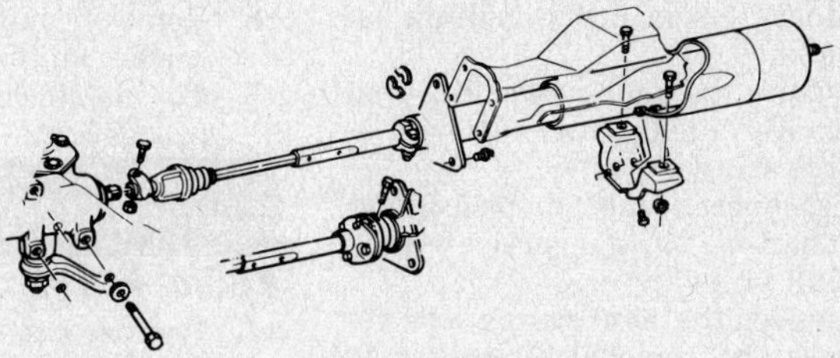

Steering column installation
(© Chevrolet Div., G.M. Corp)

Ignition Lock Cylinder R & R

1. Place the lock cylinder in the "On" position.
2. Remove the turn signal switch as previously described.
3. Insert a thin-bladed screwdriver into the rectangular slot inside the column housing. Keep the screwdriver to the right side of the slot and break the housing casting flash loose. Depress the spring latch at the lower end of the lock cylinder. The lock cylinder can be removed with the latch depressed.
4. Place the key part way into the new lock cylinder assembly. If the key is in all the way, the sleeve assembly cannot be installed. Place the wave washer and antitheft ring onto the cylinder.
5. Make sure that the plastic keeper in the sleeve assembly is protruding. Align the lock cylinder lock bolt, the antitheft ring tab, and the slot in the sleeve.
6. Push the sleeve onto the cylinder. Push the key all the way in and rotate the cylinder clockwise.
7. Clamp the tabs of the lock in a padded vise.
8. Place the adaptor ring on the cylinder with the serrations out. The adaptor ring tab should be against the step in the sleeve. The key must be free to rotate 120°.
9. Tap the adaptor into place so that the cylinder extends through it about 1/16 in.
10. Use a small, flat-tipped punch, at least ⅛ in. in diameter, to stake the cylinder over the adaptor ring in four places just outside the four dimples.
11. Check the lock for proper operation.
12. Hold the sleeve and turn the tabs clockwise against the stop. Insert the assembly into the housing, aligning the key on the sleeve with the slot in the housing bore.
13. Hold a 0.070 in. drill bit between the lock rim and the housing. Turn the cylinder counterclockwise while pushing in lightly.

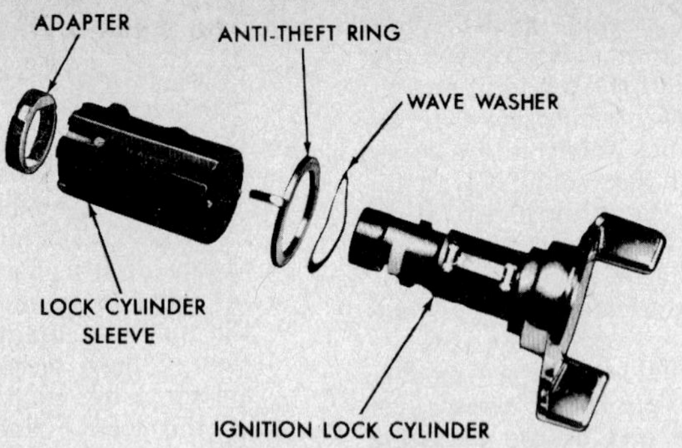
ADAPTER
ANTI-THEFT RING
WAVE WASHER
LOCK CYLINDER
SLEEVE
IGNITION LOCK CYLINDER

Ignition lock assembly
(© Chevrolet Div., G.M. Corp)

14. When the cylinder is felt to go into place, push the cylinder in until the retainer pops into place, securing the cylinder.
15. Remove the drill. Check the operation of the lock.
16. Install the turn signal switch and the steering wheel.

Headlight Switch R & R

1. Disconnect the battery ground cable.
2. Pull the light switch to ON position.
3. Reach up under the instrument panel and depress the switch retainer button while pulling on the knob.
4. Remove the knob and shaft, then remove the ferrule nut with a large screwdriver.
5. Disconnect the multi-contact connector, prying gently with a small screwdriver.
6. Connect the new switch and reverse the removal procedure to complete the replacement.

WINDSHIELD WIPERS

Motor R & R

1. Raise hood.
2. Reaching through cowl opening, loosen the two transmission drive link attaching nuts to motor crankarm.
3. Remove transmission drive link from motor crankarm.
4. Disconnect wiring.
5. Remove three motor attaching screws.
6. Remove motor while guiding crankarm through hole.
7. To install, reverse the removal procedure.

RADIO

Radio R & R

1. Remove battery ground cable.
2. Remove knobs, controls, washers and nuts from radio bushings.
3. Disconnect antenna lead, power connector, and speaker connectors from rear of receiver.
4. Remove two screws securing radio mounting bracket to instrument panel lower reinforcement and lift out radio receiver.
5. To install, reverse the removal procedure.

HEATER

Blower Motor R & R

1. Disconnect the battery ground cable.
2. Disconnect the blower motor lead wire. Disconnect the motor cooling tube on air-conditioned models.
3. Scribe the blower motor flange to case position.
4. Remove the blower to case attaching screws and remove the blower wheel and motor assembly. Pry the flange gently if the sealer is retaining the assembly.
5. Remove the blower wheel retaining nut and separate the motor and wheel.
6. To install, reverse Steps 1-5, lining up the match-marks on the motor flange and case which were made at removal.

NOTE: assemble the blower wheel to the motor with the open end of the blower away from the motor. Reseal the motor flange, if necessary.

Heater Core R & R

W/O Air Conditioning

1. Disconnect the battery ground cable.
2. Disconnect the blower motor lead wire.
3. Place a pan under the vehicle. Disconnect the heater hoses at

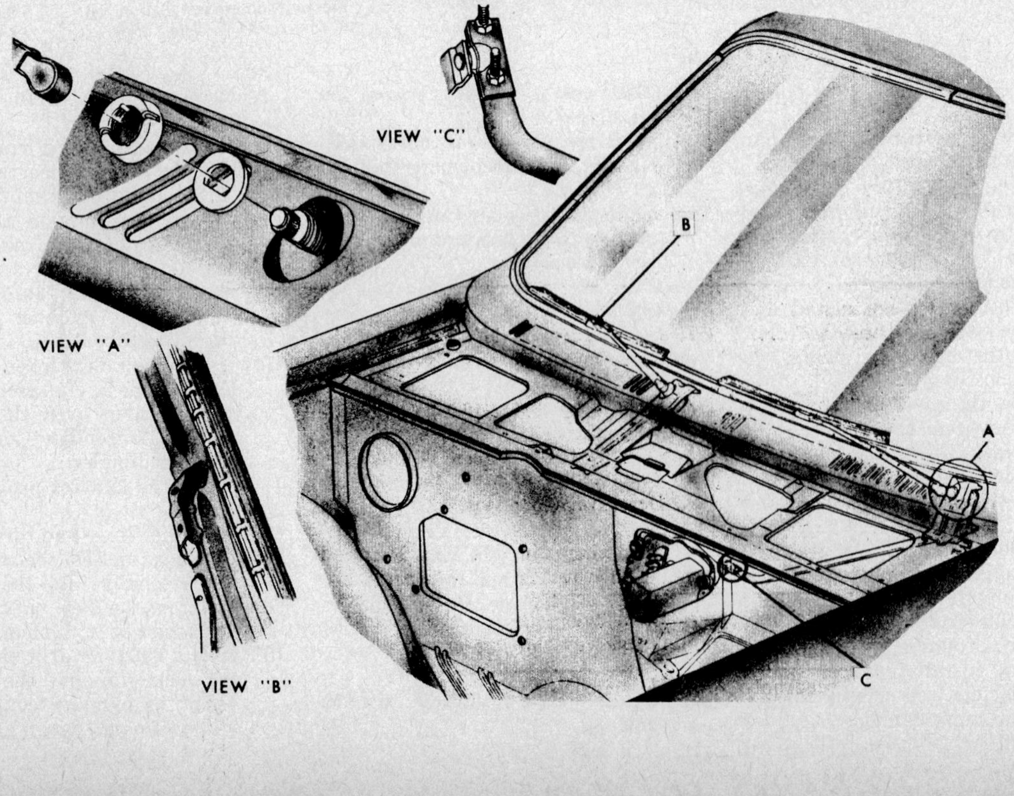
VIEW "C"
B
VIEW "A"
A
VIEW "B"
C

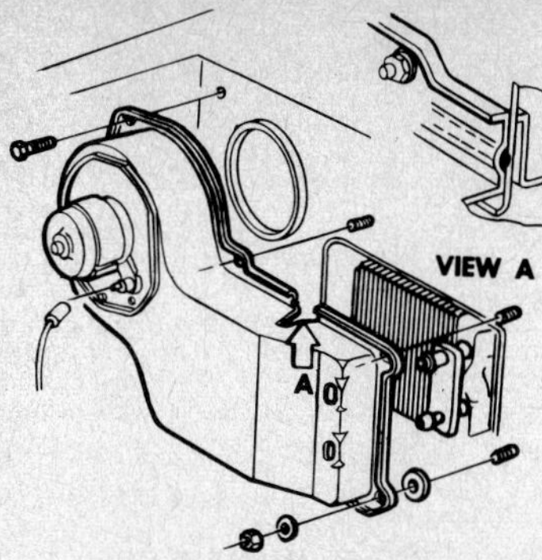
VIEW A
A

Heater installation
(© Chevrolet Div., G.M. Corp)

the core connections and secure the ends of the hoses in a raised position.

4. Remove the coil bracket to dash panel stud nut and move the coil out of the way.
5. Remove the blower intake to dash panel screws and nuts and remove the blower intake, blower motor and wheel as an assembly.
6. Remove the core retaining strap screws and remove the core from the vehicle.
7. To install, reverse Steps 1-6.

NOTE: be sure that the blower intake sealer is intact, replace if necessary.

Air Conditioned Models

1. Disconnect the battery ground cable.
2. Disconnect the heater hoses at the core and plug them.
3. Remove the firewall selector stud nuts.
4. Disconnect the left-side flexible dash outlet hose from the center distributor duct.
5. Remove the right-side dash outlet assembly.
6. Remove the instrument bezel and center outlet as an assembly.
7. Remove the ash tray and retainer.
8. Remove the radio as previously outlined.
9. Remove the control-to-dash screws and lower the control assembly.
10. Remove the cigarette lighter. Remove the screw retaining the right side of the dash reinforcement.
11. Pry out the center duct-to-dash clip. Remove the center duct-to-selector duct screws and remove the center duct. Turn the duct clockwise and pull down and to the left to remove.
12. Remove the defroster duct-to-selector duct screw. Remove the remaining selector duct-to-dash screws and pull the duct back far enough to allow the electrical and vacuum lines to be disconnected.
13. Disconnect the lines and the control cable and remove the selector duct assembly.

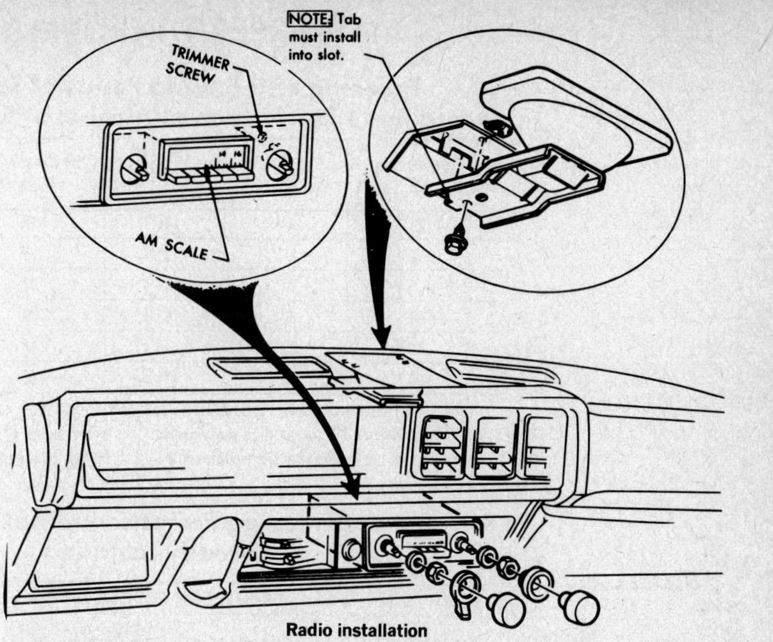
NOTE: Tab must install into slot.
TRIMMER SCREW
AM SCALE

Radio installation
(© Chevrolet Div., G.M. Corp)

14. Pry off the temperature door bellcrank, being careful not to bend the arm or damage the selector case.
15. Remove the temperature door. Remove the backing plate and temperature door cable retainer screws.
16. Remove the heater core and backing plate as an assembly. Remove the core retaining straps and withdraw the core.
17. Reverse the removal procedure to install the core.

SEAT BELTS

Warning System

1972-73

The seat belt warning system consists of lap belt retractor switches, a pressure-sensitive switch underneath the right-hand front passenger's seat, a warning lamp and a buzzer.

On manual transmission-equipped cars, the circuit is wired through the ignition switch, the parking brake warning light switch, and a relay, which is located between the instrument cluster wiring and the switch on the parking brake. A diode is used to prevent feedback into the parking brake warning circuit.

On cars having automatic transmissions, the seat belt warning circuit is wired through the ignition switch and the combination back-up lamp/neutral safety switch.

With the ignition key in the "RUN" position, on the driver's side and/or a weight of 40-50 lbs on the passenger's seat (pressure-sensitive switch), energizes the circuit when the parking brake is released (M/T) or the gear selector placed in a forward drive range (A/T).

A warning light will glow and a buzzer will sound with the circuit energized, unless the seat belts are withdrawn from the retractors and fastened over the laps of the two outboard front seat occupants.

Seat Belt/Starter Interlock System

1974

As required by law, all 1974 Chevrolet passenger cars cannot be started until the front seat occupants are seated, then fasten their seat belts. If the proper sequence is not followed, e.g., the occupants fasten their seat belts and then sit on them, the car cannot be started.

If, after the car is started, the seat belts are unfastened, a warning buzzer and light are activated in a similar manner to that described above for 1972-73 models.

The shoulder harness and lap belt are permanently fastened together, so that they both must be worn. The shoulder harness uses an inertia-lock reel to allow freedom of movement under normal driving conditions.

NOTE: This type of reel locks up when the car decelerates rapidly, as during a crash.

The lap belts use the same ratchet-type retractors that the 1972-73 models use.

The switches for the interlock system have been removed from the lap belt retractors and placed in the belt buckles. The seat sensors remain the same as those used in 1972-73.

For ease of service, the car may be started from outside, by reaching in and turning the key, but without depressing the seat sensors.

In case of system failure, an override switch is located under the hood. This is a "one start" switch and it must be reset each time it is used.

ANTI-FREEZE INFORMATION

Freezing and Boiling Points of Solutions According to Percentage of Alcohol or Ethylene Glycol

Freezing Point of Solution	Alcohol Volume %	Alcohol Solution Boils at	Ethylene Glycol Volume %	Ethylene Glycol Solution Boils at
20°F.	12	196°F.	16	216°F.
10°F.	20	189°F.	25	218°F.
0°F.	27	184°F.	33	220°F.
−10°F.	32	181°F.	39	222°F.
−20°F.	38	178°F.	44	224°F.
−30°F.	42	176°F.	48	225°F.

Note: above boiling points are at sea level. For every 1,000 feet of altitude, boiling points are approximately 2°F. lower than those shown. For every pound of pressure exerted by the pressure cap, the boiling points are approximately 3°F. higher than those shown.

To Increase the Freezing Protection of Anti-Freeze Solutions Already Installed

Cooling System Capacity Quarts	Number of Quarts of **ETHYLENE GLYCOL** Anti-Freeze Required to Increase Protection													
	From +20°F. to					From +10°F. to					From 0°F. to			
	0°	−10°	−20°	−30°	−40°	0°	−10°	−20°	−30°	−40°	−10°	−20°	−30°	−40°
10	1 3/4	2 1/4	3	3 1/2	3 3/4	3/4	1 1/2	2 1/4	2 3/4	3 1/4	3/4	1 1/2	2	2 1/2
12	2	2 3/4	3 1/2	4	4 1/2	1	1 3/4	2 1/2	3 1/4	3 3/4	1	1 3/4	2 1/2	3 1/4
14	2 1/4	3 1/4	4	4 3/4	5 1/2	1 1/4	2	3	3 3/4	4 1/2	1	2	3	3 1/2
16	2 1/2	3 1/2	4 1/2	5 1/4	6	1 1/4	2 1/2	3 1/2	4 1/4	5 1/4	1 1/4	2 1/4	3 1/4	4
18	3	4	5	6	7	1 1/2	2 3/4	4	5	5 3/4	1 1/2	2 1/2	3 3/4	4 3/4
20	3 1/4	4 1/2	5 3/4	6 3/4	7 1/2	1 3/4	3	4 1/4	5 1/2	6 1/2	1 1/2	2 3/4	4 1/4	5 1/4
22	3 1/2	5	6 1/4	7 1/4	8 1/4	1 3/4	3 1/4	4 3/4	6	7 1/4	1 3/4	3 1/4	4 1/2	5 1/2
24	4	5 1/2	7	8	9	2	3 1/2	5	6 1/2	7 1/2	1 3/4	3 1/2	5	6
26	4 1/4	6	7 1/2	8 3/4	10	2	4	5 1/2	7	8 1/4	2	3 3/4	5 1/2	6 3/4
28	4 1/2	6 1/4	8	9 1/2	10 1/2	2 1/4	4 1/4	6	7 1/2	9	2	4	5 3/4	7 1/4
30	5	6 3/4	8 1/2	10	11 1/2	2 1/2	4 1/2	6 1/2	8	9 1/2	2 1/4	4 1/4	6 1/4	7 3/4

Test radiator solution with proper hydrometer. Determine from the table the number of quarts of solution to be drawn off from a full cooling system and replace with undiluted anti-freeze, to give the desired increased protection. For example, to increase protection of a 22-quart cooling system containing Ethylene Glycol (permanent type) anti-freeze, from +20°F. to −20°F. will require the replacement of 6 1/4 quarts of solution with undiluted anti-freeze.

ANTI-FREEZE CHART

Temperatures Shown in Degrees Fahrenheit +32 is Freezing

Cooling System Capacity Quarts	Quarts of **ETHYLENE GLYCOL** Needed for Protection to Temperatures Shown Below													
	1	2	3	4	5	6	7	8	9	10	11	12	13	14
10	+24°	+16°	+ 4°	−12°	−34°	−62°								
11	+25	+18	+ 8	− 6	−23	−47								
12	+26	+19	+10	0	−15	−34	−57°							
13	+27	+21	+13	+ 3	− 9	−25	−45							
14			+15	+ 6	− 5	−18	−34							
15			+16	+ 8	0	−12	−26							
16			+17	+10	+ 2	− 8	−19	−34	−52°					
17			+18	+12	+ 5	− 4	−14	−27	−42					
18			+19	+14	+ 7	0	−10	−21	−34	−50°				
19			+20	+15	+ 9	+ 2	− 7	−16	−28	−42				
20				+16	+10	+ 4	− 3	−12	−22	−34	−48°			
21				+17	+12	+ 6	0	− 9	−17	−28	−41			
22				+18	+13	+ 8	+ 2	− 6	−14	−23	−34	−47°		
23				+19	+14	+ 9	+ 4	− 3	−10	−19	−29	−40		
24				+19	+15	+10	+ 5	0	− 8	−15	−23	−34	−46°	
25				+20	+16	+12	+ 7	+ 1	− 5	−12	−20	−29	−40	−50°
26					+17	+13	+ 8	+ 3	− 3	− 9	−16	−25	−34	−44
27					+18	+14	+ 9	+ 5	− 1	− 7	−13	−21	−29	−39
28					+18	+15	+10	+ 6	+ 1	− 5	−11	−18	−25	−34
29					+19	+16	+12	+ 7	+ 2	− 3	− 8	−15	−22	−29
30					+20	+17	+13	+ 8	+ 4	− 1	− 6	−12	−18	−25

For capacities over 30 quarts divide true capacity by 3. Find quarts Anti-Freeze for the 1/3 and multiply by 3 for quarts to add.

Conversion—Common Fractions to Decimals and Millimeters

INCHES			INCHES			INCHES		
Common Fractions	*Decimal Fractions*	*Millimeters (approx.)*	*Common Fractions*	*Decimal Fractions*	*Millimeters (approx.)*	*Common Fractions*	*Decimal Fractions*	*Millimeters (approx.)*
1/128	.008	0.20	11/32	.344	8.73	43/64	.672	17.07
1/64	.016	0.40	23/64	.359	9.13	11/16	.688	17.46
1/32	.031	0.79	3/8	.375	9.53	45/64	.703	17.86
3/64	.047	1.19	25/64	.391	9.92	23/32	.719	18.26
1/16	.063	1.59	13/32	.406	10.32	47/64	.734	18.65
5/64	.078	1.98	27/64	.422	10.72	3/4	.750	19.05
3/32	.094	2.38	7/16	.438	11.11	49/64	.766	19.45
7/64	.109	2.78	29/64	.453	11.51	25/32	.781	19.84
1/8	.125	3.18	15/32	.469	11.91	51/64	.797	20.24
9/64	.141	3.57	31/64	.484	12.30	13/16	.813	20.64
5/32	.156	3.97	1/2	.500	12.70	53/64	.828	21.03
11/64	.172	4.37	33/64	.516	13.10	27/32	.844	21.43
3/16	.188	4.76	17/32	.531	13.49	55/64	.859	21.83
13/64	.203	5.16	35/64	.547	13.89	7/8	.875	22.23
7/32	.219	5.56	9/16	.563	14.29	57/64	.891	22.62
15/64	.234	5.95	37/64	.578	14.68	29/32	.906	23.02
1/4	.250	6.35	19/32	.594	15.08	59/64	.922	23.42
17/64	.266	6.75	39/64	.609	15.48	15/16	.938	23.81
9/32	.281	7.14	5/8	.625	15.88	61/64	.953	24.21
19/64	.297	7.54	41/64	.641	16.27	31/32	.969	24.61
5/16	.313	7.94	21/32	.656	16.67	63/64	.984	25.00
21/64	.328	8.33						

Conversion—Millimeters to Decimal Inches

mm	*inches*	*mm*	*inches*	*mm*	*inches*	*mm*	*inches*	*mm*	*inches*
1	.039 370	31	1.220 470	61	2.401 570	91	3.582 670	210	8.267 700
2	.078 740	32	1.259 840	62	2.440 940	92	3.622 040	220	8.661 400
3	.118 110	33	1.299 210	63	2.480 310	93	3.661 410	230	9.055 100
4	.157 480	34	1.338 580	64	2.519 680	94	3.700 780	240	9.448 800
5	.196 850	35	1.377 949	65	2.559 050	95	3.740 150	250	9.842 500
6	.236 220	36	1.417 319	66	2.598 420	96	3.779 520	260	10.236 200
7	.275 590	37	1.456 689	67	2.637 790	97	3.818 890	270	10.629 900
8	.314 960	38	1.496 050	68	2.677 160	98	3.858 260	280	11.032 600
9	.354 330	39	1.535 430	69	2.716 530	99	3.897 630	290	11.417 300
10	.393 700	40	1.574 800	70	2.755 900	100	3.937 000	300	11.811 000
11	.433 070	41	1.614 170	71	2.795 270	105	4.133 848	310	12.204 700
12	.472 440	42	1.653 540	72	2.834 640	110	4.330 700	320	12.598 400
13	.511 810	43	1.692 910	73	2.874 010	115	4.527 550	330	12.992 100
14	.551 180	44	1.732 280	74	2.913 380	120	4.724 400	340	13.385 800
15	.590 550	45	1.771 650	75	2.952 750	125	4.921 250	350	13.779 500
16	.629 920	46	1.811 020	76	2.992 120	130	5.118 100	360	14.173 200
17	.669 290	47	1.850 390	77	3.031 490	135	5.314 950	370	14.566 900
18	.708 660	48	1.889 760	78	3.070 860	140	5.511 800	380	14.960 600
19	.748 030	49	1.929 130	79	3.110 230	145	5.708 650	390	15.354 300
20	.787 400	50	1.968 500	80	3.149 600	150	5.905 500	400	15.748 000
21	.826 770	51	2.007 870	81	3.188 970	155	6.102 350	500	19.685 000
22	.866 140	52	2.047 240	82	3.228 340	160	6.299 200	600	23.622 000
23	.905 510	53	2.086 610	83	3.267 710	165	6.496 050	700	27.559 000
24	.944 880	54	2.125 980	84	3.307 080	170	6.692 900	800	31.496 000
25	.984 250	55	2.165 350	85	3.346 450	175	6.889 750	900	35.433 000
26	1.023 620	56	2.204 720	86	3.385 820	180	7.086 600	1000	39.370 000
27	1.062 990	57	2.244 090	87	3.425 190	185	7.283 450	2000	78.740 000
28	1.102 360	58	2.283 460	88	3.464 560	190	7.480 300	3000	118.110 000
29	1.141 730	59	2.322 830	89	3.503 903	195	7.677 150	4000	157.480 000
30	1.181 100	60	2.362 200	90	3.543 300	200	7.874 000	5000	196.850 000

To change decimal millimeters to decimal inches, position the decimal point where desired on either side of the millimeter measurement shown and reset the inches decimal by the same number of digits in the same direction. For example, to convert .001 mm into decimal inches, reset the decimal behind the 1 mm (shown on the chart) to .001; change the decimal inch equivalent (.039" shown) to .00039").

TOWING CARS WITH AUTOMATIC TRANSMISSIONS

When towing a disabled car, care must be used to avoid damage to the automatic transmission. None of the automatic transmission cars covered in this book can be push started. If it becomes necessary to tow one of these cars, the following chart should be used for reference.

Transmission	Towing: Maximum Speed	Towing: Maximum Distance (Miles)
Flash-o-Matic, Shift Command 1967-71	35	50
Torque-Command	30	①
Torqueflite	30	①
Ford FMX/MX	30	15
Ford C4	30	15
Ford C6	30	15
Ford C4S	30	15
Powerglide	35	50
Torque Drive	35	50
G.M. Type 300	35	50
G.M. Type 250, 350	35	50
G.M. Type 375, 400	35	50

①—Do not tow extended distances without disconnecting driveshaft or raising rear wheels.

MECHANICS' DATA

Tap Drill Sizes

National Coarse or U.S.S.

Screw & Tap Size	Threads Per Inch	Use Drill Number
No. 5	40	39
No. 6	32	36
No. 8	32	29
No. 10	24	25
No. 12	24	17
1/4	20	8
5/16	18	F
3/8	16	5/16
7/16	14	U
1/2	13	27/64
9/16	12	31/64
5/8	11	17/32
3/4	10	21/32
7/8	9	49/64
1	8	7/8
1 1/8	7	63/64
1 1/4	7	1 7/64
1 1/2	6	1 11/32

National Fine or S.A.E.

Screw & Tap Size	Threads Per Inch	Use Drill Number
No. 5	44	37
No. 6	40	33
No. 8	36	29
No. 10	32	21
No. 12	28	15
1/4	28	3
5/16	24	1
3/8	24	Q
7/16	20	W
1/2	20	29/64
9/16	18	33/64
5/8	18	37/64
3/4	16	11/16
7/8	14	13/16
1 1/8	12	1 3/64
1 1/4	12	1 11/64
1 1/2	12	1 27/64

Decimal Equivalent Size of the Number Drills

Drill No.	Decimal Equivalent	Drill No.	Decimal Equivalent	Drill No.	Decimal Equivalent
80	.0135	53	.0595	26	.1470
79	.0145	52	.0635	25	.1495
78	.0160	51	.0670	24	.1520
77	.0180	50	.0700	23	.1540
76	.0200	49	.0730	22	.1570
75	.0210	48	.0760	21	.1590
74	.0225	47	.0785	20	.1610
73	.0240	46	.0810	19	.1660
72	.0250	45	.0820	18	.1695
71	.0260	44	.0860	17	.1730
70	.0280	43	.0890	16	.1770
69	.0292	42	.0935	15	.1800
68	.0310	41	.0960	14	.1820
67	.0320	40	.0980	13	.1850
66	.0330	39	.0995	12	.1890
65	.0350	38	.1015	11	.1910
64	.0360	37	.1040	10	.1935
63	.0370	36	.1065	9	.1960
62	.0380	35	.1100	8	.1990
61	.0390	34	.1110	7	.2010
60	.0400	33	.1130	6	.2040
59	.0410	32	.1160	5	.2055
58	.0420	31	.1200	4	.2090
57	.0430	30	.1285	3	.2130
56	.0465	29	.1360	2	.2210
55	.0520	28	.1405	1	.2280
54	.0550	27	.1440		

Decimal Equivalent Size of the Letter Drills

Letter Drill	Decimal Equivalent	Letter Drill	Decimal Equivalent	Letter Drill	Decimal Equivalent
A	.234	J	.277	S	.348
B	.238	K	.281	T	.358
C	.242	L	.290	U	.368
D	.246	M	.295	V	.377
E	.250	N	.302	W	.386
F	.257	O	.316	X	.397
G	.261	P	.323	Y	.404
H	.266	Q	.332	Z	.413
I	.272	R	.339		

Decimal Equivalents of the Common Fractions

Fraction	Decimal
1/64	.0156
1/32	.0313
3/64	.0469
1/16	.0625
5/64	.0781
3/32	.0938
7/64	.1094
1/8	.1250
9/64	.1406
5/32	.1563
11/64	.1719
3/16	.1875
13/64	.2031
7/32	.2188
15/64	.2344
1/4	.2500
17/64	.2656
9/32	.2813
19/64	.2969
5/16	.3125
21/64	.3281
11/32	.3438
23/64	.3594
3/8	.3750
25/64	.3906
13/32	.4063
27/64	.4219
7/16	.4375
29/64	.4531
15/32	.4688
31/64	.4844
1/2	.5000
33/64	.5156
17/32	.5313
35/64	.5469
9/16	.5625
37/64	.5781
19/32	.5938
39/64	.6094
5/8	.6250
41/64	.6406
21/32	.6563
43/64	.6719
11/16	.6875
45/64	.7031
23/32	.7188
47/64	.7344
3/4	.7500
49/64	.7656
25/32	.7813
51/64	.7969
13/16	.8125
53/64	.8281
27/32	.8438
55/64	.8594
7/8	.8750
57/64	.8906
29/32	.9063
59/64	.9219
15/16	.9375
61/64	.9531
31/32	.9688
63/64	.9844

CHILTON'S AUTOMOTIVE TECHNICAL / ENGINEERING BOOKS

AUTOMATIC TRANSMISSIONS
by Walter B. Larew
The author employs elementary algebra in this discussion of the principles and factors of automotive automatic transmissions. He gives methods of computing the torque and speed multiplication factors of fluid clutches and torque converters, and their effects on the performance of automobiles.
$7.95

Automatic transmissions

CARBURETORS & CARBURETION
by Walter B. Larew
This in-depth study is based solidly on principles underlying the various design-uses—gives explanations of cause and effect in carburetor functions, and suggests methods of solving carburetion problems brought about by engines operating under varying loads and climatic conditions. It covers fluids, carburetion systems and devices, and the many varying kinds of carburetors. There is a section on aircraft manifold-injection, and another on intake manifolds. Appendices supply information on pressures, heads, air-weight densities, and symbols. It is illustrated with charts, graphs, and line drawings.
$7.95

FLUID CLUTCHES AND TORQUE CONVERTERS
by Walter B. Larew
Drive-line specialists and students will find this a valuable discussion of the principles, functions, and problems of fluid clutches and torque converters. In four parts, it covers from an introduction to units of measurement to multi-element converters.
$9.95

IGNITION SYSTEMS
by Walter B. Larew
Designed for engine specialists and advanced students, this book provides analysis and discussion of the principles, problems, and systems involved in the ignition of fuel-air mixtures in gasoline engines.
$7.95

IGNITION SYSTEMS

AUTOMOBILE ENGINEERING DRAWING FOR TECHNICAL STUDENTS
by E. B. Weston
This comprehensive textbook covers the drawing of gears, transmission assemblies, steering and suspension components, braking systems, and much more. Test questions and exercises make it suitable for schools and colleges.
$6.50

Automobile Engineering Drawing for Technical Students

CHILTON'S NEW RECREATIONAL GUIDES

Repair and Tune-Up Guide for the SNOWMOBILE
This book covers Arctic Cat, Evinrude/Johnson, Mercury, Polaris, Rupp, and Yamaha models through 1972. Up-to-date information; step-by-step maintenance and repair procedures; disassembly, servicing, troubleshooting, and reassembly of major components and all specification tables for each model are included.
Cloth $6.95; Paper $4.95

Repair and Tune-Up Guide for OUTBOARD MOTORS (30 Horsepower & Over)

Repair and Tune-Up Guide for OUTBOARD MOTORS (Less Than 30 Horsepower)

Both the above books cover Chrysler, Evinrude, Johnson, and Mercury models from 1966 through 1972 in complete up-to-date manuals with the necessary propeller selection; hull design; and troubleshooting charts; are heavily illustrated including diagrams and exploded views of assemblies. All specification tables necessary for each model are also included.
Both titles: Cloth $6.95; Paper $4.95

CHILTON'S
OUTBOARD MOTOR
REPAIR & TUNE-UP GUIDE

Repair & Tune-Up Guide for INBOARD/OUTDRIVES
This guide covers Mercury, Chrysler/Volvo Penta, and OMC (Evinrude and Johnson) 1968-1972. Detailed procedures for routine maintenance, tune-up, and servicing of the engine's electrical, mechanical, and fuel systems, and the outdrive water pump. A special chapter on troubleshooting, plus, information on propeller selection, winterizing, safety and emergency procedures. Profusely illustrated with tables, photos, drawings and diagrams.
Cloth $6.95; Paper $4.95